SCOTT

# 2024 STANDARD POSTAGE STAMP CATALOGUE

**ONE HUNDRED AND EIGHTIETH EDITION IN SIX VOLUMES**

## Volume 2A

### C-Cur

| | |
|---|---|
| EDITOR-IN-CHIEF | Jay Bigalke |
| EDITOR-AT-LARGE | Donna Houseman |
| CONTRIBUTING EDITOR | Charles Snee |
| EDITOR EMERITUS | James E. Kloetzel |
| SENIOR EDITOR /NEW ISSUES AND VALUING | Martin J. Frankevicz |
| ADMINISTRATIVE ASSISTANT/CATALOGUE LAYOUT | Eric Wiessinger |
| PRINTING AND IMAGE COORDINATOR | Stacey Mahan |
| SENIOR GRAPHIC DESIGNER | Cinda McAlexander |
| SALES DIRECTOR | David Pistello |
| SALES DIRECTOR | Eric Roth |
| SALES DIRECTOR | Brenda Wyen |
| SALES REPRESENTATIVE | Julie Dahlstrom |

Released May 2023
Includes New Stamp Listings through the March 2023 *Linn's Stamp News Monthly* Catalogue Update



AMOS MEDIA
1660 Campbell Road, Suite A, Sidney, OH 45365
Publishers of *Linn's Stamp News, Linn's Stamp News Monthly, Coin World* and *Coin World Monthly.*

# Table of contents



See the following volumes for other country listings:
Volume 1A: United States, United Nations, Abu Dhabi-Australia; Volume 1B: Austria-B
Volume 2B: Cyp-F
Volume 3A: G; Volume 3B: H-I
Volume 4A: J-L; Volume 4B: M
Volume 5A: N-Phil; Volume 5B: Pit-Sam
Volume 6A: San-Tete; Volume 6B: Thai-Z

**Scott Catalogue Mission Statement**

The Scott Catalogue Team exists to serve the recreational, educational and commercial hobby needs of stamp collectors and dealers.

We strive to set the industry standard for philatelic information and products by developing and providing goods that help collectors identify, value, organize and present their collections.

Quality customer service is, and will continue to be, our highest priority. We aspire toward achieving total customer satisfaction.

# Copyright Notice



# Trademark Notice



ISBN 978-0-89487-695-0

Library of Congress Card No. 2-3301

# What's new for 2024 Scott Standard Volume 2

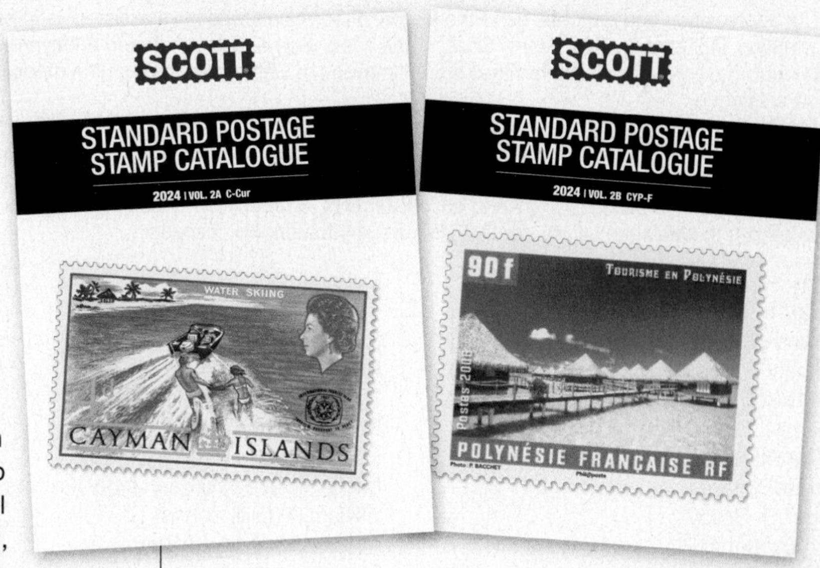


Another catalog season is upon us as we continue the journey of the 155-year history of the Scott catalogs. The 2024 volumes are the 180th edition of the Scott *Standard Postage Stamp Catalogue*. Volume 2A includes listings for countries of the world Cambodia through Curacao. Listings for Cyprus through F countries of the world can be found in Vol. 2B. Because Vol. 2B is a continuation of the first part of the Vol. 2 catalog, the introduction pages are not repeated in each volume this year.

This year's covers feature the Cayman Islands 1967 4-penny Water Skiing stamp (Scott 193) from the four-stamp International Tourist Year set that also depicts skin diving, sports fishing and sailing on the Vol. 2A catalog and the French Polynesia 2006 90-franc Stilt Houses stamp (930b) from a booklet pane of six stamps on Vol. 2B.

Our review of Canada revealed that auction realizations for quality used stamps remained fairly stable, but auction realizations for stamps of extraordinary quality were extremely strong (though not necessarily affecting the values in the catalog). Overall there was a mix of increases and decreases, with more than 400 value changes made.

One increase of note was the 1855 6-penny brownish gray Prince Albert stamp (Scott 5a), which moved from $45,000 to $47,500 in unused condition.

Canadian Provinces were also examined, and value changes were minimal. A typical example of a value change was for the Nova Scotia 3p dark blue Crown of Great Britain and Heraldic Flowers of the Empire stamp (Scott 3). It is now valued at $325 in used condition, an increase from the previous value of $300.

China, the Republic of China (Taiwan) and the People's Republic of China were reviewed closely.

China stamps issued through 1949 showed very little auction activity for those in the Scott catalog benchmark grade of very fine, and most of the post-1920s stamps are appearing largely in collections and not individually. Approximately 250 value changes were made for China, all reflecting increases. For example, the 1883 3¢ Imperial Dragon stamp (Scott 8) in used condition moved from $400 to $450.

A review of Taiwan resulted in almost 500 value changes. One of the changes was for the 1961 Ancient Chinese Art Treasures set of six stamps (Scott 1290-1295), which doubled from $20.05 in unused condition to $40.10.

People's Republic of China stamps received a thorough review, and more than 1,300 value changes were made, almost all of which were increases. There is some extreme volatility for this country's stamps, and the Scott catalog editors have placed values in italics for issues beginning with the 1960 Goldfish stamps (Scott 506-517) and continuing through the last stamp issue of 1980, the two Dolphins stamps (1645-1646).

Values of People's Republic of China stamps listed in footnotes were scrutinized. The imperforate 1963 Children's Day set of 12 footnoted under Scott 684-695 jumped from $450 in unused condition to $600.

Costa Rica was extensively reviewed for the Vol. 2 catalog, and nearly 2,700 value changes were made. Here increases were more prevalent. One of the increases was for the 2017 America Issue pair (Scott 690) that moved from $3.75 to $5.75 in unused condition and from $3.75 to $4.50 used.

Cape Verde and Chile also received more substantial reviews.

Many other countries received less extensive reviews that are not noted in this letter. We encourage you to pay special attention to the Number Additions, Deletions and Changes listing in this volume. We also suggest reading the catalog introduction, which includes an abundance of useful information.

A digital subscription is also available for the Scott catalogs, and information about the subscription can be found online at www.amosadvantage.com. Approximately 700 images of stamps not pictured in the Vol. 2 print edition were added to this year's Vol. 2 digital catalog.

Best wishes in your collecting pursuits!

Jay Bigalke, Scott catalog editor-in-chief

# Acknowledgments

Our appreciation and gratitude go to the following individuals who have assisted us in preparing information included in this year's Scott catalogues. Some helpers prefer anonymity. These individuals have generously shared their stamp knowledge with others through the medium of the Scott catalogue.

Those who follow provided information that is in addition to the hundreds of dealer price lists and advertisements and scores of auction catalogues and realizations that were used in producing the catalogue values. It is from those noted here that we have been able to obtain information on items not normally seen in published lists and advertisements. Support from these people goes beyond data leading to catalogue values, for they also are key to editorial changes.

A special acknowledgment to Liane and Sergio Sismondo of The Classic Collector for their assistance and knowledge sharing that have aided in the preparation of this year's Standard and Classic Specialized Catalogues.

Clifford J. Alexander (Carriers and Locals Society)
Roland Austin
Michael & Cecilia Ball (A To Z Stamps)
Jim Bardo (Bardo Stamps)
Brian M. Bleckwenn (The Philatelic Foundation)
Les Bootman
Roger S. Brody
Tom Brougham (Canal Zone Study Group)
Paul and Josh Buchsbayew (Cherrystone Auctions, Inc.)
Timothy Bryan Burgess
Tina and John Carlson (JET Stamps)
Jay T. Carrigan
Carlson Chambliss
Bob Coale
Tony L. Crumbley (Carolina Coin and Stamp, Inc.)
Christopher Dahle
Charles Deaton
Bob and Rita Dumaine (Sam Houston Duck Co.)
Charles Epting (H.R. Harmer)
Mike Farrell
David Feldman International Auctioneers
Robert A. Fisher
Jeffrey M. Forster
Robert S. Freeman
Henry L. Gitner (Henry Gitner Philatelists, Inc.)
Stan Goldfarb
Marc E. Gonzales
Daniel E. Grau
Bruce Hecht (Bruce L. Hecht Co.)
Eric Jackson
Michael Jaffe (Michael Jaffe Stamps, Inc.)
William A. (Bill) Jones
Allan Katz (Ventura Stamp Co.)
Patricia A. Kaufmann (Civil War Philatelic Society)
Jon Kawaguchi (Ryukyu Philatelic Specialist Society)
Han Ki Kim
Ingert Kuzych
Ulf Lindahl (Ethiopian Philatelic Society)
Ignacio Llach (Filatelia Llach, S.L.)
William K. McDaniel
Pat McElroy
Brian Metz
Mark S. Miller (India Study Circle)
Gary Morris (Pacific Midwest Co.)
Peter Mosiondz Jr.
Bruce M. Moyer (Moyer Stamps & Collectables)
Scott Murphy (Professional Stamp Experts)
Dr. Tiong Tak Ngo
Nik and Lisa Oquist
Don Peterson (International Philippine Philatelic Society)
Todor Drumev Popov
Dr. Charles Posner
Peter W. W. Powell
Ed Reiser (Century Stamp Co.)
Ghassan D. Riachi
Robert G. Rufe
Theodosios D. Sampson Ph.D.
Dennis W. Schmidt
Joyce and Chuck Schmidt
Guy Shaw (Mexico-Elmhurst Philatelic Society International)
J. Randall Shoemaker (Philatelic Stamp Authentication and Grading, Inc.)
Sergio and Liane Sismondo (The Classic Collector)
Jay Smith
Telah Smith
Mark Stelmacovich
Scott R. Trepel (Robert A. Siegel Auction Galleries)
Dan Undersander
Steven Unkrich
Herbert R. Volin
Val Zabijaka (Zabijaka Auctions)

# Addresses, telephone numbers, web sites, email addresses of general and specialized philatelic societies

Collectors can contact the following groups for information about the philately of the areas within the scope of these societies, or inquire about membership in these groups. Aside from the general societies, we limit this list to groups that specialize in particular fields of philately, particular areas covered by the Scott *Standard Postage Stamp Catalogue*, and topical groups. Many more specialized philatelic society exist than those listed below. These addresses are updated yearly, and they are, to the best of our knowledge, correct and current. Groups should inform the editors of address changes whenever they occur. The editors also want to hear from other such specialized groups not listed.

Unless otherwise noted all website addresses begin with http://

## General Societies

**American Philatelic Society,** 100 Match Factory Place, Bellefonte, PA 16823-1367; (814) 933-3803; https://stamps.org; apsinfo@stamps.org

**International Society of Worldwide Stamp Collectors,** Joanne Murphy, M.D., P.O. Box 19006, Sacramento, CA 95819; www.iswsc.org; executivedirector@iswsc.org

**Royal Philatelic Society of Canada,** P.O. Box 69080, St. Clair Post Office, Toronto, ON M4T 3A1 Canada; (888) 285-4143; www.rpsc.org; info@rpsc.org

**Royal Philatelic Society London,** 15 Abchurch Lane, London EX4N 7BW, United Kingdom; +44 (0) 20 7486 1044; www.rpsl.org.uk; secretary@rpsl.org.uk

## Libraries, Museums, and Research Groups

**American Philatelic Research Library,** 100 Match Factory Place, Bellefonte, PA 16823; (814) 933-3803; www.stamplibrary.org; library@stamps.org.

**V. G. Greene Philatelic Research Foundation,** P.O. Box 69100, St. Clair Post Office, Toronto, ON M4T 3A1, Canada; (416) 921-2073; info@greenefoundation.ca

### Aero/Astro Philately

**American Air Mail Society,** Stephen Reinhard, P.O. Box 110, Mineola, NY 11501; www.americanairmailsociety.org; sreinhard1@optonline.net

## Postal History

**Auxiliary Markings Club,** Jerry Johnson, 6621 W. Victoria Ave., Kennewick, WA 99336; www.postal-markings.org; membership-2010@postal-markings.org

**Postage Due Mail Study Group,** Bob Medland, Camway Cottage, Nanny Hurn's Lane, Cameley, Bristol BS39 5AJ, United Kingdom; 01761 45959; www.postageduemail.org.uk; secretary.pdmsg@gmail.com

**Postal History Society,** Yamil Kouri, 405 Waltham St. #347, Lexington, MA 02421; www.postalhistorysociety.org; yhkouri@massmed.org

**Post Mark Collectors Club,** Bob Milligan, 7014 Woodland Oaks Drive, Magnolia, TX 77354; (281) 259-2735; www.postmarks.org; bob.milligan0@gmail.com

**U.S. Cancellation Club,** Roger Curran, 18 Tressler Blvd., Lewisburg, PA 17837; rdcnrc@ptd.net

### Revenues and Cinderellas

**American Revenue Association,** Lyman Hensley, 473 E. Elm St., Sycamore, IL 60178-1934; www.revenuer.org; ilrno2@netzero.net

**Christmas Seal and Charity Stamp Society,** John Denune Jr., 234 E. Broadway, Granville, OH 43023; (740) 814-6031; www.seal-society.org

**National Duck Stamp Collectors Society,** Anthony J. Monico, P.O. Box 43, Harleysville, PA 19438-0043; www.ndscs.org; ndscs@ndscs.org

**State Revenue Society,** Kent Gray, P.O. Box 67842, Albuquerque, NM 87193; www.staterevenue.org; srssecretary@comcast.net

## Thematic Philately

**Americana Unit,** Dennis Dengel, 17 Peckham Road, Poughkeepsie, NY 12603-2018; www.americanaunit.org; ddengel@americanaunit.org

**American Topical Association,** Jennifer Miller, P.O. Box 2143, Greer, SC 29652-2143; (618) 985-5100; americantopical.org; ata@americantopical.org

**Astronomy Study Unit,** Leonard Zehr, 1411 Chateau Ave., Windsor, ON N8P 1M2, Canada; (416) 833-9317; www.astronomystudyunit.net; lenzehr@gmail.com

**Bicycle Stamps Club,** Corey Hjalseth, 1102 Broadway, Suite 200, Tacoma, WA 98402; (253) 318-6222; www.bicyclestampsclub.org; coreyh@evergreenhomeloans.com

**Biology Unit,** Chris Dahle, 1401 Linmar Drive NE, Cedar Rapids, IA 52402-3724; www.biophilately.org; chris-dahle@biophilately.org

**Bird Stamp Society,** Mr. S. A. H. (Tony) Statham, Ashlyns Lodge, Chesham Road, Berkhamsted, Herts HP4 2ST United Kingdom; www.bird-stamps.org/bss; tony.statham@sky.com

**Captain Cook Society,** Jerry Yucht, 8427 Leale Ave., Stockton, CA 95212, www.captaincooksociety.com; us@captaincooksociety.com

**The CartoPhilatelic Society,** Marybeth Sulkowski, 2885 Sanford Ave., SW, #32361, Grandville, MI 49418-1342; www.mapsonstamps.org; secretary@mapsonstamps.org

**Casey Jones Railroad Unit,** Jeff Lough, 2612 Redbud Land, Apt. C, Lawrence, KS 66046; www.uqp.de/cjr; jeffydplaugh@gmail.com

**Cats on Stamps Study Unit,** Robert D. Jarvis, 2731 Teton Lane, Fairfield, CA 94533; www.catstamps.info; catmews1@yahoo.com

**Chemistry and Physics on Stamps Study Unit,** Dr. Roland Hirsch, 13830 Metcalf Ave., Apt. 15218, Overland Park, KS 66223-8017; (301) 792-6296; www.cpossu.org; rfhirsch@cpossu.org

**Chess on Stamps Study Unit,** Barry Keith, 511 First St. N., Apt. 106; Charlottesville, VA 22902; www.chessonstamps.org; keithfam@embarqmail.com

**Cricket Philatelic Society,** A. Melville-Brown, 11 Weppons, Ravens Road, Shorham-by-Sea, West Sussex BN43 5AW, United Kingdom; www.cricketstamp.net; mel.cricket.100@googlemail.com

**Earth's Physical Features Study Group,** Fred Klein, 515 Magdalena Ave., Los Altos, CA 94024; http://epfsu.jeffhayward.com; epfsu@jeffhayward.com

**Ebony Society of Philatelic Events and Reflections (ESPER),** Don Neal, P.O. Box 5245, Somerset, NJ 08875-5245; www.esperstamps.org; esperdon@verizon.net

**Europa Study Unit,** Tonny E. Van Loij, 3002 S. Xanthia St.; Denver, CO 80231-4237; (303) 752-0189; www.europastudyunit.org; tvanloij@gmail.com

**Fire Service in Philately,** John Zaranek, 81 Hillpine Road, Cheektowaga, NY 14227-2259; (716) 668-3352; jczaranek@roadrunner.com

**Gastronomy on Stamps Study Unit,** David Wolfersburger, 5062 NW 35th Lane Road, Ocala, FL 34482; (314) 494-3795; www.gastronomystamps.org

**Gay and Lesbian History on Stamps Club,** Joe Petronie, P.O. Box 190842, Dallas, TX 75219-0842; www.glhsonline.org; glhsc@aol.com

**Gems, Minerals and Jewelry Study Unit,** Fred Haynes, 10 Country Club Drive, Rochester, NY 14618-3720; fredmhaynes55@gmail.com

**Graphics Philately Association,** Larry Rosenblum. 1030 E. El Camino Real, PMB 107, Sunnyvale, CA 94087-3759; www.graphics-stamps.org; larry@graphics-stamps.org

**Journalists, Authors and Poets on Stamps,** Christopher D. Cook, 7222 Hollywood Road, Berrien Springs, MI 49103; cdcook2@gmail.com

**Lighthouse Stamp Society,** www.lighthousestampsociety.org

**Lions International Stamp Club,** David McKirdy, s-Gravenwetering 248, 3062 SJ Rotterdam, Netherlands; 31(0) 10 212 0313; www.lisc.nl; davidmckirdy@aol.com

**Masonic Study Unit,** Gene Fricks, 25 Murray Way, Blackwood, NJ 08012-4400; genefricks@comcast.net

**Medical Subjects Unit,** Dr. Frederick C. Skvara, P.O. Box 6228, Bridgewater, NJ 08807; fcskvara@optonline.net

**Napoleonic Age Philatelists,** Ken Berry, 4117 NW 146th St., Oklahoma City, OK 73134-1746; (405) 748-8646; www.nap-stamps.org; krb4117@att.net

**Old World Archaeological Study Unit,** Caroline Scannell, 14 Dawn Drive, Smithtown, NY 11787-176; www.owasu.org; editor@owasu.org

**Petroleum Philatelic Society International,** Feitze Papa, 922 Meander Drive, Walnut Creek, CA 94598-4239; www.ppsi.org.uk; oildad@astound.net

**Rotary on Stamps Fellowship,** Gerald L. Fitzsimmons, 105 Calle Ricardo, Victoria, TX 77904; www.rotaryonstamps.org; glfitz@suddenlink.net

**Scouts on Stamps Society International,** Woodrow (Woody) Brooks, 498 Baldwin Road, Akron, OH 44312; (330) 612-1294; www.sossi.org; secretary@sossi.org

**Ships on Stamps Unit,** Erik Th. Matzinger, Voorste Havervelden 30, 4822 AL Breda, Netherlands; www.shipsonstamps.org; erikships@gmail.com

**Space Topic Study Unit,** David Blog, P.O. Box 174, Bergenfield, NJ 07621; www.space-unit.com; davidblognj@gmail.com

**Stamps on Stamps Collectors Club,** Michael Merritt, 73 Mountainside Road, Mendham, NJ 07945; www.stampsonstamps.org; michael@mischu.me

**Windmill Study Unit,** Walter J. Hallien, 607 N. Porter St., Watkins Glenn, NY 14891-1345; (607) 229-3541; www.windmillworld.com

**Wine On Stamps Study Unit,** David Wolfersburger, 5062 NW 35th Lane Road, Ocala, FL 34482; (314) 494-3795; www.wine-on-stamps.org;

## United States

**American Air Mail Society,** Stephen Reinhard, P.O. Box 110, Mineola, NY 11501; www.americanairmailsociety.org; sreinhard1@optonline.net

**American First Day Cover Society,** P.O. Box 246, Colonial Beach VA 22443-0246; (520) 321-0880; www.afdcs.org; afdcs@afdcs.org

**Auxiliary Markings Club,** Jerry Johnson, 6621 W. Victoria Ave., Kennewick, WA 99336; www.postal-markings.org; membership-2010@postal-markings.org

**American Plate Number Single Society,** Rick Burdsall, APNSS Secretary, P.O. BOX 1023, Palatine, IL 60078-1023; www.apnss.org; apnss.sec@gmail.com

**American Revenue Association,** Lyman Hensley, 473 E. Elm St., Sycamore, IL 60178-1934; www.revenuer.org; ilrno2@netzero.net

**American Society for Philatelic Pages and Panels,** Ron Walenciak, P.O. Box 1042, Washington Township, NJ 07676; www.asppp.org; ron.walenciak@asppp.org

**Canal Zone Study Group,** Mike Drabik, P.O. Box 281, Bolton, MA 01740, www.canalzonestudygroup.com; czsgsecretary@gmail.com

**Carriers and Locals Society,** John Bowman, 14409 Pentridge Drive, Corpus Christi, TX 78410; (361) 933-0757; www.pennypost.org; jbowman@stx.rr.com

**Christmas Seal & Charity Stamp Society,** John Denune Jr., 234 E. Broadway, Granville, OH 43023; (740) 814-6031; www.seal-society.org; john@christmasseals.net

**Civil War Philatelic Society,** Patricia A. Kaufmann, 10194 N. Old State Road, Lincoln, DE 19960-3644; (302) 422-2656; www.civilwarphilatelicsociety.org; trishkauf@comcast.net

**Error, Freaks, and Oddities Collectors Club,** Scott Shaulis, P.O. Box 549, Murrysville, PA 15668-0549; (724) 733-4134; www.efocc.org; scott@shaulisstamps.com

**National Duck Stamp Collectors Society,** Anthony J. Monico, P.O. Box 43, Harleysville, PA 19438-0043; www.ndscs.org; ndscs@ndscs.org

**Plate Number Coil Collectors Club (PNC3),** Gene Trinks, 16415 W. Desert Wren Court, Surprise, AZ 85374; (623) 322-4619; www.pnc3.org; gctrinks@cox.net

**Post Mark Collectors Club,** Bob Milligan, 7014 Woodland Oaks Drive, Magnolia, TX 77354; (281) 259-2735; www.postmarks.org; bob.milligan0@gmail.com

**Souvenir Card Collectors Society,** William V. Kriebel, www.souvenircards.org; kriebewv@drexel.edu

**United Postal Stationery Society,** Dave Kandziolka, 404 Sundown Drive, Knoxville, TN 37934; www.upss.org; membership@upss.org

**U.S. Cancellation Club,** Roger Curran, 18 Tressler Blvd., Lewisburg, PA 17837; rdcnrc@ptd.net

**U.S. Philatelic Classics Society,** Rob Lund, 2913 Fulton St., Everett, WA 98201-3733; www.uspcs.org; membershipchairman@uspcs.org

**US Possessions Philatelic Society,** Daniel F. Ring, P.O. Box 113, Woodstock, IL 60098; http://uspps.tripod.com; danielfring@hotmail.com

**United States Stamp Society,** Rod Juell, P.O. Box 3508, Joliet, IL 60434-3508; www.usstamps.org; execsecretary@usstamps.org

## Africa

**Bechuanalands and Botswana Society,** Otto Peetoom, Roos, East Yorkshire HU12 0LD, United Kingdom; 44(0)1964 670239; www.bechuanalandphilately.com; info@bechuanalandphilately.com

**Egypt Study Circle,** Mike Murphy, 11 Waterbank Road, Bellingham, London SE6 3DJ United Kingdom; (44) 0203 6737051; www.egyptstudycircle.org.uk; secretary@egyptstudycircle.org.uk

**Ethiopian Philatelic Society,** Ulf Lindahl, 21 Westview Place, Riverside, CT 06878; (203) 722-0769; https://ethiopianphilatelicsociety.weebly.com; ulindahl@optonline.net

**Liberian Philatelic Society,** P.O. Box 1570, Parker, CO 80134; www.liberiastamps.org; liberiastamps@comcast.net

**Orange Free State Study Circle,** J. R. Stroud, RDPSA, 24 Hooper Close, Burnham-on-sea, Somerset TA8 1JQ United Kingdom; 44 1278 782235; www.orangefreestatephilately.org.uk; richard@richardstroud.plus.com

**Philatelic Society for Greater Southern Africa,** David McNamee, 15 Woodland Drive, Alamo, CA 94507; www.psgsa.org; alan.hanks@sympatico.ca

**Rhodesian Study Circle,** William R. Wallace, P.O. Box 16381, San Francisco, CA 94116; (415) 564-6069; www.rhodesianstudycircle.org.uk; bwall8rscr@earthlink.net

**Society for Moroccan and Tunisian Philately,** S.P.L.M., 206, Bld Pereire, 75017 Paris, France; http://splm-philatelie.org; splm206@aol.com

**South Sudan Philatelic Society,** William Barclay, 1370 Spring Hill Road, South Londonderry, VT 05155; barclayphilatelics@gmail.com

**Sudan Study Group,** Andy Neal, Bank House, Coedway, Shrewsbury SY5 9AR United Kingdom; www.sudanstamps.org; andywneal@gmail.com

**Transvaal Study Circle,** c/o 9 Meadow Road, Gravesend, Kent DA11 7LR United Kingdom; www.transvaalstamps.org.uk; transvaalstudycircle@aol.co.uk

**West Africa Study Circle,** Martin Bratzel, 1233 Virginia Ave., Windsor, ON N8S 2Z1 Canada; www.wasc.org.uk; marty_bratzel@yahoo.ca

## Asia

**Aden & Somaliland Study Group,** Malcom Lacey, 108 Dalestorth Road, Sutton-in-Ashfield, Nottinghamshire NG17 3AA, United Kingdom; www.stampdomain.com/aden; neil53williams@yahoo.co.uk

**Burma (Myanmar) Philatelic Study Circle,** Michael Whittaker, 1, Ecton Leys, Hillside, Rugby, Warwickshire CV22 5SL United Kingdom; https://burmamyanmarphilately.wordpress.com/burma-myanmar-philatelic-study-circle; manningham8@mypostoffice.co.uk

**Ceylon Study Circle,** Rodney W. P. Frost, 42 Lonsdale Road, Cannington, Bridgwater, Somerset TA5 2JS United Kingdom; 01278 652592; www.ceylonsc.org; rodney.frost@tiscali.co.uk

**China Stamp Society,** H. James Maxwell, 1050 W. Blue Ridge Blvd., Kansas City, MO 64145-1216; www.chinastampsociety.org; president@chinastampsociety.org

**Hong Kong Philatelic Society,** John Tang, G.P.O. Box 446, Hong Kong; www.hkpsociety.com; hkpsociety@outlook.com

**Hong Kong Study Circle,** Robert Newton, www.hongkongstudycircle.com/index.html; newtons100@gmail.com

**India Study Circle,** John Warren, P.O. Box 7326, Washington, DC 20044; (202) 488-7443; https://indiastudycircle.org; jw-kbw@earthlink.net

**International Philippine Philatelic Society,** James R. Larot, Jr., 4990 Bayleaf Court, Martinez, CA 94553; (925) 260-5425; www.theipps.info; jlarot@ccwater.com

**International Society for Japanese Philately,** P.O. Box 1283, Haddonfield NJ 08033; www.isjp.org; secretary@isjp.org

**Iran Philatelic Study Circle,** Nigel Gooch, Marchwood, 56, Wickham Ave., Bexhill-on-Sea, East Sussex TN39 3ER United Kingdom; www.iranphilately.org; nigelmgooch@gmail.com

**Korea Stamp Society,** Peter Corson, 1109 Gunnison Place, Raleigh, NC 27609; (919) 787-7611; koreastampsociety.org; pbcorson@aol.com

**Nepal & Tibet Philatelic Study Circle,** Colin Hepper, 12 Charnwood Close, Peterborough, Cambs PE2 9BZ United Kingdom; http://fuchs-online.com/ntpsc; ntpsc@fuchs-online.com

**Pakistan Philatelic Study Circle,** Jeff Siddiqui, P.O. Box 7002, Lynnwood, WA 98046; jeffsiddiqui@msn.com

**Society of Indo-China Philatelists,** Ron Bentley, 2600 N. 24th St., Arlington, VA 22207; (703) 524-1652; www.sicp-online.org; ron.bentley@verizon.net

**Society of Israel Philatelists, Inc.,** Sarah Berezenko, 100 Match Factory Place, Bellefonte, PA 16823-1367; (814) 933-3803 ext. 212; www.israelstamps.com; israelstamps@gmail.com

## Australasia and Oceania

**Australian States Study Circle of the Royal Sydney Philatelic Club,** Ben Palmer, G.P.O. 1751, Sydney, NSW 2001 Australia; http://club.philas.org.au/states

**Fellowship of Samoa Specialists,** Trevor Shimell, 18 Aspen Drive, Newton Abbot, Devon TQ12 4TN United Kingdom; www.samoaexpress.org; trevor.shimell@gmail.com

**Malaya Study Group,** Michael Waugh, 151 Roker Lane, Pudsey, Leeds LS28 9ND United Kingdom; http://malayastudygroup.com; mawpud43@gmail.com

**New Zealand Society of Great Britain,** Michael Wilkinson, 121 London Road, Sevenoaks, Kent TN13 1BH United Kingdom; 01732 456997; www.nzsgb.org.uk; mwilkin799@aol.com

**Pacific Islands Study Circle,** John Ray, 24 Woodvale Ave., London SE25 4AE United Kingdom; www.pisc.org.uk; secretary@pisc.org.uk

**Papuan Philatelic Society,** Steven Zirinsky, P.O. Box 49, Ansonia Station, New York, NY 10023; (718) 706-0616; www.papuanphilatelicsociety.com; szirinsky@cs.com

**Pitcairn Islands Study Group,** Dr. Everett L. Parker, 207 Corinth Road, Hudson, ME 04449-3057; (207) 573-1686; www.pisg.net; eparker@hughes.net

**Ryukyu Philatelic Specialist Society,** Laura Edmonds, P.O. Box 240177, Charlotte, NC 28224-0177; (336) 509-3739; www.ryukyustamps.org; secretary@ryukyustamps.org

**Society of Australasian Specialists / Oceania,** Steve Zirinsky, P.O. Box 230049, New York, NY 10023-0049; www.sasoceania.org; president@sosoceania.org

**Sarawak Specialists' Society,** Stephen Schumann, 2417 Cabrallo Drive, Hayward, CA 94545; (510) 785-4794; www.britborneostamps.org.uk; vpnam@s-s-s.org.uk

**Western Australia Study Group,** Brian Pope, P.O. Box 423, Claremont, WA 6910 Australia; (61) 419 843 943; www.wastudygroup.com; wastudygroup@hotmail.com

## Europe

**American Helvetia Philatelic Society,** Richard T. Hall, P.O. Box 15053, Asheville, NC 28813-0053; www.swiss-stamps.org; secretary2@swiss-stamps.org

**American Society for Netherlands Philately,** Hans Kremer, 50 Rockport Court, Danville, CA 94526; (925) 820-5841; www.asnp1975.com; hkremer@usa.net

**Andorran Philatelic Study Circle,** David Hope, 17 Hawthorn Drive, Stalybridge, Cheshire SK15 1UE United Kingdom; www.andorranpsc.org.uk; andorranpsc@btinternet.com

**Austria Philatelic Society,** Ralph Schneider, P.O. Box 978, Iowa Park, TX 76376; (940) 213-5004; www.austriaphilatelicsociety.com; rschneiderstamps@gmail.com

**Channel Islands Specialists Society,** Richard Flemming, Burbage, 64 Falconers Green, Hinckley, Leicestershire, LE102SX, United Kingdom; www.ciss.uk; secretary@ciss.uk

**Cyprus Study Circle,** Rob Wheeler, 47 Drayton Ave., London W13 0LE United Kingdom; www.cyprusstudycircle.org; robwheeler47@aol.com

**Danish West Indies Study Unit of Scandinavian Collectors Club,** Arnold Sorensen, 7666 Edgedale Drive, Newburgh, IN 47630; (812) 480-6532; www.scc-online.org; valbydwi@hotmail.com

**Eire Philatelic Association,** John B. Sharkey, 1559 Grouse Lane, Mountainside, NJ 07092-1340; www.eirephilatelicassoc.org; jsharkeyepa@me.com

**Faroe Islands Study Circle,** Norman Hudson, 40 Queen's Road, Vicar's Cross, Chester CH3 5HB United Kingdom; www.faroeislandssc.org; jntropics@hotmail.com

**France & Colonies Philatelic Society,** Edward Grabowski, 111 Prospect St., 4C, Westfield, NJ 07090; (908) 233-9318; www.franceandcolsps.org; edjjg@alum.mit.edu

**Germany Philatelic Society,** P.O. Box 6547, Chesterfield, MO 63006-6547; www.germanyphilatelicusa.org; info@germanyphilatelicsocietyusa.org

**Gibraltar Study Circle,** Susan Dare, 22, Byways Park, Strode Road, Clevedon, North Somerset BS21 6UR United Kingdom; www.gibraltarstudycircle.wordpress.com; smldare@yahoo.co.uk

**International Society for Portuguese Philately,** Clyde Homen, 1491 Bonnie View Road, Hollister, CA 95023-5117; www.portugalstamps.com; ispp1962@sbcglobal.net

**Italy and Colonies Study Circle,** Richard Harlow, 7 Duncombe House, 8 Manor Road, Teddington, Middlesex TW118BE United Kingdom; 44 208 977 8737; www.icsc-uk.com; richardharlow@outlook.com

**Liechtenstudy USA,** Paul Tremaine, 410 SW Ninth St., Dundee, OR 97115-9731; (503) 538-4500; www.liechtenstudy.org; tremaine@liechtenstudy.org

**Lithuania Philatelic Society,** Audrius Brazdeikis, 9915 Murray Landing, Missouri City, TX 77459; (281) 450-6224; www.lithuanianphilately.com/lps; audrius@lithuanianphilately.com

**Luxembourg Collectors Club,** Gary B. Little, 7319 Beau Road, Sechelt, BC V0N 3A8 Canada; (604) 885-7241; http://lcc.luxcentral.com; gary@luxcentral.com

**Plebiscite-Memel-Saar Study Group of the German Philatelic Society,** Clayton Wallace, 100 Lark Court, Alamo, CA 94507; claytonwallace@comcast.net

**Polonus Polish Philatelic Society,** Daniel Lubelski, P.O. Box 2212, Benicia, CA 94510; (419) 410-9115; www.polonus.org; info@polonus.org

**Rossica Society of Russian Philately,** Alexander Kolchinsky, 1506 Country Lake Drive, Champaign, IL 61821-6428; www.rossica.org; alexander.kolchinsky@rossica.org

**Scandinavian Collectors Club,** Alan Warren, Scandinavian Collectors Club, P.O. Box 39, Exton PA 19341-0039; (612) 810-8640; www.scc-online.org; alanwar@att.net

**Society for Czechoslovak Philately,** Tom Cossaboom, P.O. Box 4124, Prescott, AZ 86302; (928) 771-9097; www.csphilately.org; klfck1@aol.com

**Society for Hungarian Philately,** Alan Bauer, P.O. Box 4028, Vineyard Haven, MA 02568; (617) 645-4045; www.hungarianphilately.org; alan@hungarianstamps.com

**Spanish Study Circle,** Edith Knight, www.spaincircle.wixsite.com/spainstudycircle; spaincircle@gmail.com

**Ukrainian Philatelic & Numismatic Society,** Martin B. Tatuch, 5117 8th Road N., Arlington, VA 22205-1201; www.upns.org; treasurer@upns.org

**Vatican Philatelic Society,** Dennis Brady, 4897 Ledyard Drive, Manlius NY 13104-1514; www.vaticanphilately.org; dbrady7534@gmail.com

**Yugoslavia Study Group,** Michael Chant, 1514 N. Third Ave., Wausau, WI 54401; 208-748-9919; www.yugosg.org; membership@yugosg.org

## Interregional Societies

**American Society of Polar Philatelists,** Alan Warren, P.O. Box 39, Exton, PA 19341-0039; (610) 321-0740; www.polarphilatelists.org; alanwar@att.net

**First Issues Collector's Club,** Kurt Streepy, 3128 E. Mattatha Drive, Bloomington, IN 47401; www.firstissues.org; secretary@firstissues.org

**Former French Colonies Specialist Society,** Col.fra, BP 628, 75367 Paris, France; www.colfra.org; postmaster@colfra.org

**France & Colonies Philatelic Society,** Edward Grabowski, 111 Prospect St., 4C, Westfield, NJ 07090; (908) 233-9318, www.franceandcolsps.org; edjjg@alum.mit.edu

**Joint Stamp Issues Society,** Richard Zimmermann, 29A, Rue Des Eviats, 67220 Lalaye, France; www.philarz.net; richard.zimmermann@club-internet.fr

**The King George VI Collectors Society,** Brian Livingstone, 21 York Mansions, Prince of Wales Drive, London SW11 4DL United Kingdom; www.kg6.info; livingstone484@btinternet.com

**International Society of Reply Coupon Collectors,** Peter Robin, P.O. Box 353, Bala Cynwyd, PA 19004; peterrobin@verizon.net

**Italy and Colonies Study Circle,** Richard Harlow, 7 Duncombe House, 8 Manor Road, Teddington, Middlesex TW118BE United Kingdom; 44 208 977 8737; www.icsc-uk.com; richardharlow@outlook.com

**St. Helena, Ascension & Tristan Da Cunha Philatelic Society,** Dr. Everett L. Parker, 207 Corinth Road, Hudson, ME 04449-3057; (207) 573-1686; www.shatps.org; eparker@hughes.net

**United Nations Philatelists,** Blanton Clement, Jr., P.O. Box 146, Morrisville, PA 19067-0146; www.unpi.com; bclemjunior@gmail.com

## Latin America

**Asociación Filatélica de Panamá,** Edward D. Vianna B. ASOFILPA, 0819-03400, El Dorado, Panama; http://asociacionfilatelicadepanama.blogspot.com; asofilpa@gmail.com

**Asociacion Mexicana de Filatelia (AMEXFIL),** Alejandro Grossmann, Jose Maria Rico, 129, Col. Del Valle, 3100 Mexico City, DF Mexico; www.amexfil.mx; amexfil@gmail.com

**Associated Collectors of El Salvador,** Pierre Cahen, Vipsal 1342, P.O. Box 02-5364, Miami FL 33102; www.elsalvadorphilately.org; sfes-aces@elsalvadorphilately.org

**Association Filatelic de Costa Rica,** Giana Wayman (McCarty), #SJO 4935, P.O. Box 025723, Miami, FL 33102-5723; 011-506-2-228-1947; scotland@racsa.co.cr

**Brazil Philatelic Association,** William V. Kriebel, www.brazilphilatelic.org, info@brazilphilatelic.org

**Canal Zone Study Group,** Mike Drabik, P.O. Box 281, Bolton, MA 01740; www.canalzonestudygroup.com; czsgsecretary@gmail.com

**Colombia-Panama Philatelic Study Group,** Allan Harris, 26997 Hemmingway Ct, Hayward CA 94542-2349; www.copaphil.org; copaphilusa@aol.com

**Falkland Islands Philatelic Study Groups,** Morva White, 42 Colton Road, Shrivenham, Swindon SN6 8AZ United Kingdom; 44(0) 1793 783245; www.fipsg.org.uk; morawhite@supanet.com

**Federacion Filatelica de la Republica de Honduras,** Mauricio Mejia, Apartado Postal 1465, Tegucigalpa, D.C. Honduras; 504 3399-7227; www.facebook.com/filateliadehonduras; ffrh@hotmail.com

**International Cuban Philatelic Society (ICPS),** Ernesto Cuesta, P.O. Box 34434, Bethesda, MD 20827; (301) 564-3099; www.cubafil.org; ecuesta@philat.com

**International Society of Guatemala Collectors,** Jaime Marckwordt, 449 St. Francis Blvd., Daly City, CA 94015-2136; (415) 997-0295; www.guatemalastamps.com; president@guatamalastamps.com

**Mexico-Elmhurst Philatelic Society International,** Eric Stovner, P.O. Box 10097, Santa Ana, CA 92711-0097; www.mepsi.org; treasurer@mepsi.org

**Nicaragua Study Group,** Erick Rodriguez, 11817 S. W. 11th St., Miami, FL 33184-2501; nsgsec@yahoo.com

## North America (excluding United States)

**British Caribbean Philatelic Study Group,** Bob Stewart, 7 West Dune Lane, Long Beach Township, NJ 08008; (941) 379-4108; www.bcpsg.com; bcpsg@comcast.net

**British North America Philatelic Society,** Andy Ellwood, 10 Doris Ave., Gloucester, ON K1T 3W8 Canada; www.bnaps.org; secretary@bnaps.org

**British West Indies Study Circle,** Steve Jarvis, 5 Redbridge Drive, Andover, Hants SP10 2LF United Kingdom; 01264 358065; www.bwisc.org; info@bwisc.org

**Bermuda Collectors Society,** John Pare, 405 Perimeter St., Mount Horeb, WI 53572; (608) 852-7358; www.bermudacollectorssociety.com; pare16@mhtc.net

**Haiti Philatelic Society,** Ubaldo Del Toro, 5709 Marble Archway, Alexandria, VA 22315; www.haitiphilately.org; u007ubi@aol.com

**Hawaiian Philatelic Society,** Gannon Sugimura, P.O. Box 10115, Honolulu, HI 96816-0115, www.hpshawaii.com; hiphilsoc@gmail.com

## Stamp Dealer Associations

**American Stamp Dealers Association, Inc.,** P.O. Box 513, Centre Hall PA 16828; (800) 369-8207; www.americanstampdealer.com; asda@americanstampdealer.com

**National Stamp Dealers Association,** Sheldon Ruckens, President, 3643 Private Road 18, Pinckneyville, IL 62274-3426; (618) 357-5497; www.nsdainc.org; nsda@nsdainc.org

## Youth Philately

**Young Stamp Collectors of America,** 100 Match Factory Place, Bellefonte, PA 16823; (814) 933-3803; https://stamps.org/learn/youth-in-philately; ysca@stamps.org

# Expertizing services

The following organizations will, for a fee, provide expert opinions about stamps submitted to them. Collectors should contact these organizations to find out about their fees and requirements before submitting philatelic material to them. The listing of these groups here is not intended as an endorsement by Amos Media Co.

## General Expertizing Services

**American Philatelic Expertizing Service (a service of the American Philatelic Society)**
100 Match Factory Place
Bellefonte PA 16823-1367
(814) 237-3803
www.stamps.org/stamp-authentication
apex@stamps.org
Areas of Expertise: Worldwide

**BPA Expertising, Ltd.**
P.O. Box 1141
Guildford, Surrey, GU5 OWR
United Kingdom
www.bpaexpertising.com
sec@bpaexpertising.org
Areas of Expertise: British Commonwealth, Great Britain, Classics of Europe, South America and the Far East

**Philatelic Foundation**
353 Lexington Avenue, Suite 804
New York NY 10016
(212) 221-6555
www.philatelicfoundation.org
philatelicfoundation@verizon.net
Areas of Expertise: U.S. & Worldwide

**Philatelic Stamp Authentication and Grading, Inc.**
P.O. Box 41-0880
Melbourne FL 32941-0880
(305) 345-9864
www.psaginc.com
info@psaginc.com
Areas of Expertise: U.S., Canal Zone, Hawaii, Philippines, Canada & Provinces

**Professional Stamp Experts**
P.O. Box 539309
Henderson NV 89053-9309
(702) 776-6522
www.gradingmatters.com
www.psestamp.com
info@gradingmatters.com
Areas of Expertise: Stamps and Covers of U.S., U.S. Possessions, British Commonwealth

**Royal Philatelic Society London Expert Committee**
15 Abchurch Lane
London, EX4N 7BW
United Kingdom
www.rpsl.limited/experts.aspx
experts@rpsl.limited
Areas of Expertise: Worldwide

Expertizing Services Covering Specific Fields or Countries

**China Stamp Society Expertizing Service**
1050 W. Blue Ridge Blvd.
Kansas City MO 64145
(816) 942-6300
hjmesq@aol.com
Areas of Expertise: China

**Civil War Philatelic Society Authentication Service**
C/O Stefan T. Jaronski
P.O. Box 232
Sidney, MT 59270-0232
www.civilwarphilatelicsociety.org/authentication/
authentication@civilwarphilatelicsociety.org
Areas of Expertise: Confederate stamps and postal history

**Errors, Freaks and Oddities Collectors Club Expertizing Service**
138 East Lakemont Drive
Kingsland GA 31548
(912) 729-1573
Areas of Expertise: U.S. errors, freaks and oddities

**Hawaiian Philatelic Society Expertizing Service**
P.O. Box 10115
Honolulu HI 96816-0115
www.stampshows.com/hps.html
hiphilsoc@gmail.com
Areas of Expertise: Hawaii

**Hong Kong Stamp Society Expertizing Service**
P.O. Box 206
Glenside PA 19038
Areas of Expertise: Hong Kong

**International Association of Philatelic Experts United States Associate members:**

Paul Buchsbayew
300 Frank W. Burr Blvd. - Second Floor
Box 35
Teaneck, NJ 07666.
(212) 977-7734
Areas of Expertise: Russia, Soviet Union

William T. Crowe
P.O. Box 2090
Danbury CT 06813-2090
wtcrowe@aol.com
Areas of Expertise: United States

Sergio Sismondo
The Regency Tower, Suite 1109
770 James St.
Syracuse NY 13203
(315) 422-2331
Areas of Expertise: British East Africa, Camerouns, Cape of Good Hope, Canada, British North America

**International Society for Japanese Philately Expertizing Committee**
132 North Pine Terrace
Staten Island NY 10312-4052
(718) 227-5229
Areas of Expertise: Japan and related areas, except WWII Japanese Occupation issues

**International Society for Portuguese Philately Expertizing Service**
P.O. Box 43146
Philadelphia PA 19129-3146
(215) 843-2106
s.s.washburne@worldnet.att.net
Areas of Expertise: Portugal and Colonies

**Mexico-Elmhurst Philatelic Society International Expert Committee**
Expert Committee Administrator
Marc E. Gonzales
P.O. Box 29040
Denver CO 80229-0040
www.mepsi.org/expert_committeee.htm
expertizations@mepsi.org
Areas of Expertise: Mexico

**Ukrainian Philatelic & Numismatic Society Expertizing Service**
30552 Dell Lane
Warren MI 48092-1862
Areas of Expertise: Ukraine, Western Ukraine

**V. G. Greene Philatelic Research Foundation**
P.O. Box 69100
St. Clair Post Office
Toronto, ON M4T 3A1
Canada
(416) 921-2073
www.greenefoundation.ca
info@greenefoundation.ca
Areas of Expertise: British North America

# Information on catalogue values, grade and condition

## Catalogue value

The Scott Catalogue value is a retail value; that is, an amount you could expect to pay for a stamp in the grade of Very Fine with no faults. Any exceptions to the grade valued will be noted in the text. The general introduction on the following pages and the individual section introductions further explain the type of material that is valued. The value listed for any given stamp is a reference that reflects recent actual dealer selling prices for that item.

Dealer retail price lists, public auction results, published prices in advertising and individual solicitation of retail prices from dealers, collectors and specialty organizations have been used in establishing the values found in this catalogue. Amos Media Co. values stamps, but Amos Media is not a company engaged in the business of buying and selling stamps as a dealer.

Use this catalogue as a guide for buying and selling. The actual price you pay for a stamp may be higher or lower than the catalogue value because of many different factors, including the amount of personal service a dealer offers, or increased or decreased interest in the country or topic represented by a stamp or set. An item may occasionally be offered at a lower price as a "loss leader," or as part of a special sale. You also may obtain an item inexpensively at public auction because of little interest at that time or as part of a large lot.

Stamps that are of a lesser grade than Very Fine, or those with condition problems, generally trade at lower prices than those given in this catalogue. Stamps of exceptional quality in both grade and condition often command higher prices than those listed.

Values for pre-1900 unused issues are for stamps with approximately half or more of their original gum. Stamps with most or all of their original gum may be expected to sell for more, and stamps with less than half of their original gum may be expected to sell for somewhat less than the values listed. On rarer stamps, it may be expected that the original gum will be somewhat more disturbed than it will be on more common issues. Post-1900 unused issues are assumed to have full original gum. From breakpoints in most countries' listings, stamps are valued as never hinged, due to the wide availability of stamps in that condition. These notations are prominently placed in the listings and in the country information preceding the listings. Some countries also feature listings with dual values for hinged and never-hinged stamps.

## Grade

A stamp's grade and condition are crucial to its value. The accompanying illustrations show examples of Very Fine stamps from different time periods, along with examples of stamps in Fine to Very Fine and Extremely Fine grades as points of reference. When a stamp seller offers a stamp in any grade from fine to superb without further qualifying statements, that stamp should not only have the centering grade as defined, but it also should be free of faults or other condition problems.

**FINE** stamps (illustrations not shown) have designs that are quite off center, with the perforations on one or two sides very close to the design but not quite touching it. There is white space between the perforations and the design that is minimal but evident to the unaided eye. Imperforate stamps may have small margins, and earlier issues may show the design just touching one edge of the stamp design. Very early perforated issues normally will have the perforations slightly cutting into the design. Used stamps may have heavier than usual cancellations.

**FINE-VERY FINE** stamps will be somewhat off center on one side, or slightly off center on two sides. Imperforate stamps will have two margins of at least normal size, and the design will not touch any edge. For perforated stamps, the perfs are well clear of the design, but are still noticeably off center. *However, early issues of a country may be printed in such a way that the design naturally is very close to the edges. In these cases, the perforations may cut into the design very slightly.* Used stamps will not have a cancellation that detracts from the design.

**VERY FINE** stamps will be just slightly off center on one or two sides, but the design will be well clear of the edge. The stamp will present a nice, balanced appearance. Imperforate stamps will be well centered within normal-sized margins. *However, early issues of many countries may be printed in such a way that the perforations may touch the design on one or more sides. Where this is the case, a boxed note will be found defining the centering and margins of the stamps being valued.* Used stamps will have light or otherwise neat cancellations. This is the grade used to establish Scott Catalogue values.

**EXTREMELY FINE** stamps are close to being perfectly centered. Imperforate stamps will have even margins that are slightly larger than normal. Even the earliest perforated issues will have perforations clear of the design on all sides.

**Amos Media Co. recognizes that there is no formally enforced grading scheme for postage stamps, and that the final price you pay or obtain for a stamp will be determined by individual agreement at the time of transaction.**

## Condition

*Grade addresses* only centering and (for used stamps) cancellation. *Condition* refers to factors other than grade that affect a stamp's desirability.

Factors that can increase the value of a stamp include exceptionally wide margins, particularly fresh color, the presence of selvage, and plate or die varieties. Unusual cancels on used stamps (particularly those of the 19th century) can greatly enhance their value as well.

Factors other than faults that decrease the value of a stamp include loss of original gum, regumming, a hinge remnant or foreign object adhering to the gum, natural inclusions, straight edges, and markings or notations applied by collectors or dealers.

Faults include missing pieces, tears, pin or other holes, surface scuffs, thin spots, creases, toning, short or pulled perforations, clipped perforations, oxidation or other forms of color changelings, soiling, stains, and such man-made changes as reperforations or the chemical removal or lightening of a cancellation.

## Grading illustrations

On the following two pages are illustrations of various stamps from countries appearing in this volume. These stamps are arranged by country, and they represent early or important issues that are often found in widely different grades in the marketplace. The editors believe the illustrations will prove useful in showing the margin size and centering that will be seen on the various issues.

In addition to the matters of margin size and centering, collectors are reminded that the very fine stamps valued in the Scott catalogues also will possess fresh color and intact perforations, and they will be free from defects.

Examples shown are computer-manipulated images made from single digitized master illustrations.

## Stamp illustrations used in the catalogue

It is important to note that the stamp images used for identification purposes in this catalogue may not be indicative of the grade of stamp being valued. Refer to the written discussion of grades on this page and to the grading illustrations on the following two pages for grading information.

Fine-Very Fine

SCOTT CATALOGUES VALUE STAMPS IN THIS GRADE

Very Fine

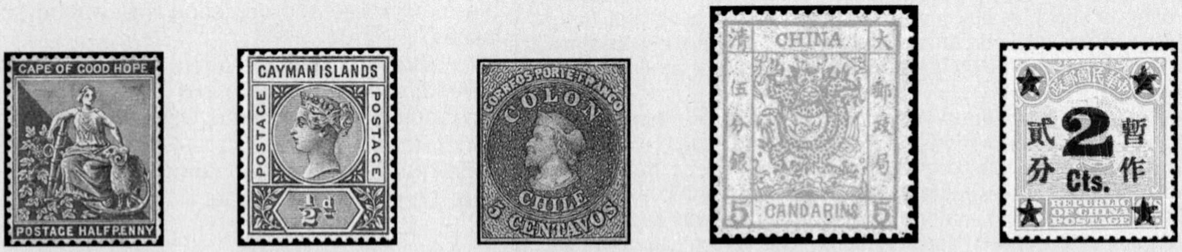

Extremely Fine

Fine-Very Fine

SCOTT CATALOGUES VALUE STAMPS IN THIS GRADE

Very Fine

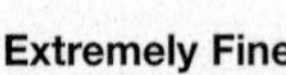

Fine-Very Fine

**SCOTT CATALOGUES VALUE STAMPS IN THIS GRADE**

Very Fine

Extremely Fine

Fine-Very Fine

**SCOTT CATALOGUES VALUE STAMPS IN THIS GRADE**

Very Fine

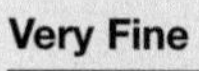

Extremely Fine

## Gum Conditions

For purposes of helping to determine the gum condition and value of an unused stamp, Scott presents the following chart which details different gum conditions and indicates how the conditions correlate with the Scott values for unused stamps. Used together, the Illustrated Grading Chart on the previous pages and this Illustrated Gum Chart should allow catalogue users to better understand the grade and gum condition of stamps valued in the Scott catalogues.

**Never Hinged (NH; ★★):** A never-hinged stamp will have full original gum that will have no hinge mark or disturbance. The presence of an expertizer's mark does not disqualify a stamp from this designation.

**Original Gum (OG; ★):** Pre-1900 stamps should have approximately half or more of their original gum. On rarer stamps, it may be expected that the original gum will be somewhat more disturbed than it will be on more common issues. Post-1900 stamps should have full original gum. Original gum will show some disturbance caused by a previous hinge(s) which may be present or entirely removed. The actual value of a post-1900 stamp will be affected by the degree of hinging of the full original gum.

**Disturbed Original Gum:** Gum showing noticeable effects of humidity, climate or hinging over more than half of the gum. The significance of gum disturbance in valuing a stamp in any of the Original Gum categories depends on the degree of disturbance, the rarity and normal gum condition of the issue and other variables affecting quality.

**Regummed (RG; (★))**: A regummed stamp is a stamp without gum that has had some type of gum privately applied at a time after it was issued. This normally is done to deceive collectors and/or dealers into thinking that the stamp has original gum and therefore has a higher value. A regummed stamp is considered the same as a stamp with none of its original gum for purposes of grading.

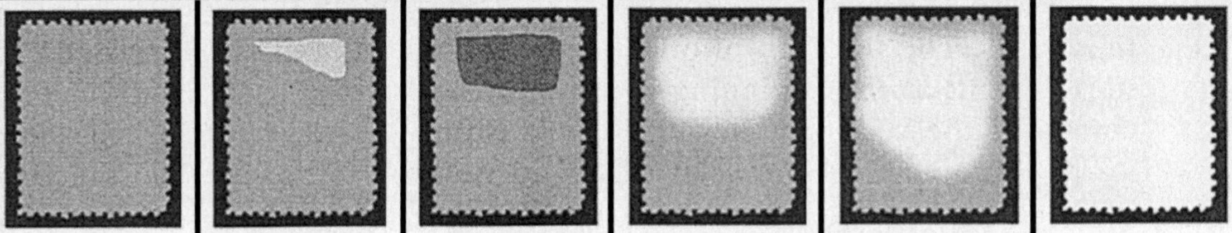

| **Gum Categories:** | **MINT N.H.** | **ORIGINAL GUM (O.G.)** | | | | **NO GUM** |
|---|---|---|---|---|---|---|
| | **Mint Never Hinged** *Free from any disturbance* | **Lightly Hinged** *Faint impression of a removed hinge over a small area* | **Hinge Mark or Remnant** *Prominent hinged spot with part or all of the hinge remaining* | **Large part o.g.** *Approximately half or more of the gum intact* | **Small part o.g.** Approximately less than half of the gum intact | **No gum** *Only if issued with gum* |
| **Commonly Used Symbol:** | ★★ | ★ | ★ | ★ | ★ | (★) |
| Pre-1900 Issues (Pre-1881 for U.S.) | *Very fine pre-1900 stamps in these categories trade at a premium over Scott value* | | | Scott Value for "Unused" | | Scott "No Gum" listings for selected unused classic stamps |
| From 1900 to breakpoints for listings of never-hinged stamps | Scott "Never Hinged" listings for selected unused stamps | Scott Value for "Unused" (Actual value will be affected by the degree of hinging of the full o.g.) | | | | |
| *From breakpoints noted for many countries* | Scott Value for "Unused" | | | | | |

# Catalogue listing policy

It is the intent of Amos Media Co. to list all postage stamps of the world in the Scott *Standard Postage Stamp Catalogue*. The only strict criteria for listing is that stamps be decreed legal for postage by the issuing country and that the issuing country actually have an operating postal system. Whether the primary intent of issuing a given stamp or set was for sale to postal patrons or to stamp collectors is not part of our listing criteria. Scott's role is to provide basic comprehensive postage stamp information. It is up to each stamp collector to choose which items to include in a collection.

It is Scott's objective to seek reasons why a stamp should be listed, rather than why it should not. Nevertheless, there are certain types of items that will not be listed. These include the following:

1. Unissued items that are not officially distributed or released by the issuing postal authority. If such items are officially issued at a later date by the country, they will be listed. Unissued items consist of those that have been printed and then held from sale for reasons such as change in government, errors found on stamps or something deemed objectionable about a stamp subject or design.

2. Stamps "issued" by non-existent postal entities or fantasy countries, such as Nagaland, Occusi-Ambeno, Staffa, Sedang, Torres Straits and others. Also, stamps "issued" in the names of legitimate, stamp-issuing countries that are not authorized by those countries.

3. Semi-official or unofficial items not required for postage. Examples include items issued by private agencies for their own express services. When such items are required for delivery, or are valid as prepayment of postage, they are listed.

4. Local stamps issued for local use only. Postage stamps issued by governments specifically for "domestic" use, such as Haiti Scott 219-228, or the United States nondenominated stamps, are not considered to be locals, since they are valid for postage throughout the country of origin.

5. Items not valid for postal use. For example, a few countries have issued souvenir sheets that are not valid for postage. This area also includes a number of worldwide charity labels (some denominated) that do not pay postage.

6. Egregiously exploitative issues such as stamps sold for far more than face value, stamps purposefully issued in artificially small quantities or only against advance orders, stamps awarded only to a selected audience such as a philatelic bureau's standing order customers, or stamps sold only in conjunction with other products. All of these kinds of items are usually controlled issues and/or are intended for speculation. These items normally will be included in a footnote.

7. Items distributed by the issuing government only to a limited group, club, philatelic exhibition or a single stamp dealer or other private company. These items normally will be included in a footnote.

8. Stamps not available to collectors. These generally are rare items, all of which are held by public institutions such as museums. The existence of such items often will be cited in footnotes.

The fact that a stamp has been used successfully as postage, even on international mail, is not in itself sufficient proof that it was legitimately issued. Numerous examples of so-called stamps from non-existent countries are known to have been used to post letters that have successfully passed through the international mail system.

There are certain items that are subject to interpretation. When a stamp falls outside our specifications, it may be listed along with a cautionary footnote.

A number of factors are considered in our approach to analyzing how a stamp is listed. The following list of factors is presented to share with you, the catalogue user, the complexity of the listing process.

**Additional printings** — "Additional printings" of a previously issued stamp may range from an item that is totally different to cases where it is impossible to differentiate from the original. At least a minor number (a small-letter suffix) is assigned if there is a distinct change in stamp shade, noticeably redrawn design, or a significantly different perforation measurement. A major number (numeral or numeral and capital-letter combination) is assigned if the editors feel the "additional printing" is sufficiently different from the original that it constitutes a different issue.

**Commemoratives** — Where practical, commemoratives with the same theme are placed in a set. For example, the U.S. Civil War Centennial set of 1961-65 and the Constitution Bicentennial series of 1989-90 appear as sets. Countries such as Japan and Korea issue such material on a regular basis, with an announced, or at least predictable, number of stamps known in advance. Occasionally, however, stamp sets that were released over a period of years have been separated. Appropriately placed footnotes will guide you to each set's continuation.

**Definitive sets** — Blocks of numbers generally have been reserved for definitive sets, based on previous experience with any given country. If a few more stamps were issued in a set than originally expected, they often have been inserted into the original set with a capital-letter suffix, such as U.S. Scott 1059A. If it appears that many more stamps than the originally allotted block will be released before the set is completed, a new block of numbers will be reserved, with the original one being closed off. In some cases, such as the U.S. Transportation and Great Americans series, several blocks of numbers exist. Appropriately placed footnotes will guide you to each set's continuation.

**New country** — Membership in the Universal Postal Union is not a consideration for listing status or order of placement within the catalogue. The index will tell you in what volume or page number the listings begin.

**"No release date" items** — The amount of information available for any given stamp issue varies greatly from country to country and even from time to time. Extremely comprehensive information about new stamps is available from some countries well before the stamps are released. By contrast some countries do not provide information about stamps or release dates. Most countries, however, fall between these extremes. A country may provide denominations or subjects of stamps from upcoming issues that are not issued as planned. Sometimes, philatelic agencies, those private firms hired to represent countries, add these later-issued items to sets well after the formal release date. This time period can range from weeks to years. If these items were officially released by the country, they will be added to the appropriate spot in the set. In many cases, the specific release date of a stamp or set of stamps may never be known.

**Overprints** — The color of an overprint is always noted if it is other than black. Where more than one color of ink has been used on overprints of a single set, the color used is noted. Early overprint and surcharge illustrations were altered to prevent their use by forgers.

**Personalized Stamps** — Since 1999, the special service of personalizing stamp vignettes, or labels attached to stamps, has been offered to customers by postal administrations of many countries. Sheets of these stamps are sold, singly or in quantity, only through special orders made by mail, in person, or through a sale on a computer website with the postal administrations or their agents for which an extra fee is charged, though some countries offer to collectors at face value personalized stamps having generic images in the vignettes or on the attached labels. It is impossible for any catalogue to know what images have been chosen by customers. Images can be 1) owned or created by the customer, 2) a generic image, or 3) an image pulled from a library of stock images on the stamp creation website. It is also impossible to know the quantity printed for any stamp having a particular image. So from a valuing standpoint, any image is equivalent to any other image for any personalized stamp having the same catalogue number. Illustrations of personalized stamps in the catalogue are not always those of stamps having generic images.

Personalized items are listed with some exceptions. These include:

1. Stamps or sheets that have attached labels that the customer cannot personalize, but which are nonetheless marketed as "personalized," and are sold for far more than the franking value.

2. Stamps or sheets that can be personalized by the customer, but where a portion of the print run must be ceded to the issuing country for sale to other customers.

3. Stamps or sheets that are created exclusively for a particular commercial client, or clients, including stamps that differ from any similar stamp that has been made available to the public.

4. Stamps or sheets that are deliberately conceived by the issuing authority that have been, or are likely to be, created with an excessive number of different face values, sizes, or other features that are changeable.

5. Stamps or sheets that are created by postal administrations using the same system of stamp personalization that has been put in place for use by the public that are printed in limited quantities and sold above face value.

6. Stamps or sheets that are created by licensees not directly affiliated or controlled by a postal administration.

Excluded items may or may not be footnoted.

**Se-tenants** — Connected stamps of differing features (se-tenants) will be listed in the format most commonly collected. This includes pairs, blocks or larger multiples. Se-tenant units are not always symmetrical. An example is Australia Scott 508, which is a block of seven stamps. If the stamps are primarily collected as a unit, the major number may be assigned to the multiple, with minors going to each component stamp. In cases where continuous-design or other unit se-tenants will receive significant postal use, each stamp is given a major Scott number listing. This includes issues from the United States, Canada, Germany and Great Britain, for example.

# Understanding the listings

On the opposite page is an enlarged "typical" listing from this catalogue. Below are detailed explanations of each of the highlighted parts of the listing.

**1 Scott number** — Scott catalogue numbers are used to identify specific items when buying, selling or trading stamps. Each listed postage stamp from every country has a unique Scott catalogue number. Therefore, Germany Scott 99, for example, can only refer to a single stamp. Although the Scott catalogue usually lists stamps in chronological order by date of issue, there are exceptions. When a country has issued a set of stamps over a period of time, those stamps within the set are kept together without regard to date of issue. This follows the normal collecting approach of keeping stamps in their natural sets.

When a country issues a set of stamps over a period of time, a group of consecutive catalogue numbers is reserved for the stamps in that set, as issued. If that group of numbers proves to be too few, capital-letter suffixes, such as "A" or "B," may be added to existing numbers to create enough catalogue numbers to cover all items in the set. A capital-letter suffix indicates a major Scott catalogue number listing. Scott generally uses a suffix letter only once. Therefore, a catalogue number listing with a capital-letter suffix will seldom be found with the same letter (lower case) used as a minor-letter listing. If there is a Scott 16A in a set, for example, there will seldom be a Scott 16a. However, a minor-letter "a" listing may be added to a major number containing an "A" suffix (Scott 16Aa, for example).

Suffix letters are cumulative. A minor "b" variety of Scott 16A would be Scott 16Ab, not Scott 16b.

There are times when a reserved block of Scott catalogue numbers is too large for a set, leaving some numbers unused. Such gaps in the numbering sequence also occur when the catalogue editors move an item's listing elsewhere or have removed it entirely from the catalogue. Scott does not attempt to account for every possible number, but rather attempts to assure that each stamp is assigned its own number.

Scott numbers designating regular postage normally are only numerals. Scott numbers for other types of stamps, such as air post, semi-postal, postal tax, postage due, occupation and others have a prefix consisting of one or more capital letters or a combination of numerals and capital letters.

**2 Illustration number** — Illustration or design-type numbers are used to identify each catalogue illustration. For most sets, the lowest face-value stamp is shown. It then serves as an example of the basic design approach for other stamps not illustrated. Where more than one stamp use the same illustration number, but have differences in design, the design paragraph or the description line clearly indicates the design on each stamp not illustrated. Where there are both vertical and horizontal designs in a set, a single illustration may be used, with the exceptions noted in the design paragraph or description line.

When an illustration is followed by a lower-case letter in parentheses, such as "A2(b)," the trailing letter indicates which overprint or surcharge illustration applies.

Illustrations normally are 70 percent of the original size of the stamp. Oversized stamps, blocks and souvenir sheets are reduced even more. Overprints and surcharges are shown at 100 percent of their original size if shown alone, but are 70 percent of original size if shown on stamps. In some cases, the illustration will be placed above the set, between listings or omitted completely. Overprint and surcharge illustrations are not placed in this catalogue for purposes of expertizing stamps.

**3 Paper color** — The color of a stamp's paper is noted in italic type when the paper used is not white.

**4 Listing styles** — There are two principal types of catalogue listings: major and minor.

Major listings are in a larger type style than minor listings. The catalogue number is a numeral that can be found with or without a capital-letter suffix, and with or without a prefix.

Minor listings are in a smaller type style and have a small-letter suffix or (if the listing immediately follows that of the major number) may show only the letter. These listings identify a variety of the major item. Examples include perforation and shade differences, multiples (some souvenir sheets, booklet panes and se-tenant combinations), and singles of multiples.

Examples of major number listings include 16, 28A, B97, C13A, 10N5, and 10N6A. Examples of minor numbers are 16a and C13Ab.

**5 Basic information about a stamp or set** — Introducing each stamp issue is a small section (usually a line listing) of basic information about a stamp or set. This section normally includes the date of issue, method of printing, perforation, watermark and, sometimes, some additional information of note. *Printing method, perforation and watermark apply to the following sets until a change is noted.* Stamps created by overprinting or surcharging previous issues are assumed to have the same perforation, watermark, printing method and other production characteristics as the original. Dates of issue are as precise as Scott is able to confirm and often reflect the dates on first-day covers, rather than the actual date of release.

**6 Denomination** — This normally refers to the face value of the stamp; that is, the cost of the unused stamp at the post office at the time of issue. When a denomination is shown in parentheses, it does not appear on the stamp. This includes the nondenominated stamps of the United States, Brazil and Great Britain, for example.

**7 Color or other description** — This area provides information to solidify identification of a stamp. In many recent cases, a description of the stamp design appears in this space, rather than a listing of colors.

**8 Year of issue** — In stamp sets that have been released in a period that spans more than a year, the number shown in parentheses is the year that stamp first appeared. Stamps without a date appeared during the first year of the issue. Dates are not always given for minor varieties.

**9 Value unused and Value used** — The Scott catalogue values are based on stamps that are in a grade of Very Fine unless stated otherwise. Unused values refer to items that have not seen postal, revenue or any other duty for which they were intended. Pre-1900 unused stamps that were issued with gum must have at least most of their original gum. Later issues are assumed to have full original gum. From breakpoints specified in most countries' listings, stamps are valued as never hinged. Stamps issued without gum are noted. Modern issues with PVA or other synthetic adhesives may appear ungummed. Unused self-adhesive stamps are valued as appearing undisturbed on their original backing paper. Values for used self-adhesive stamps are for examples either on piece or off piece. For a more detailed explanation of these values, please see the "Catalogue Value," "Condition" and "Understanding Valuing Notations" sections elsewhere in this introduction.

In some cases, where used stamps are more valuable than unused stamps, the value is for an example with a contemporaneous cancel, rather than a modern cancel or a smudge or other unclear marking. For those stamps that were released for postal and fiscal purposes, the used value represents a postally used stamp. Stamps with revenue cancels generally sell for less.

Stamps separated from a complete se-tenant multiple usually will be worth less than a pro-rated portion of the se-tenant multiple, and stamps lacking the attached labels that are noted in the listings will be worth less than the values shown.

**10 Changes in basic set information** — Bold type is used to show any changes in the basic data given for a set of stamps. These basic data categories include perforation gauge measurement, paper type, printing method and watermark.

**11 Total value of a set** — The total value of sets of three or more stamps issued after 1900 are shown. The set line also notes the range of Scott numbers and total number of stamps included in the grouping. The actual value of a set consisting predominantly of stamps having the minimum value of 25 cents may be less than the total value shown. Similarly, the actual value or catalogue value of se-tenant pairs or of blocks consisting of stamps having the minimum value of 25 cents may be less than the catalogue values of the component parts.

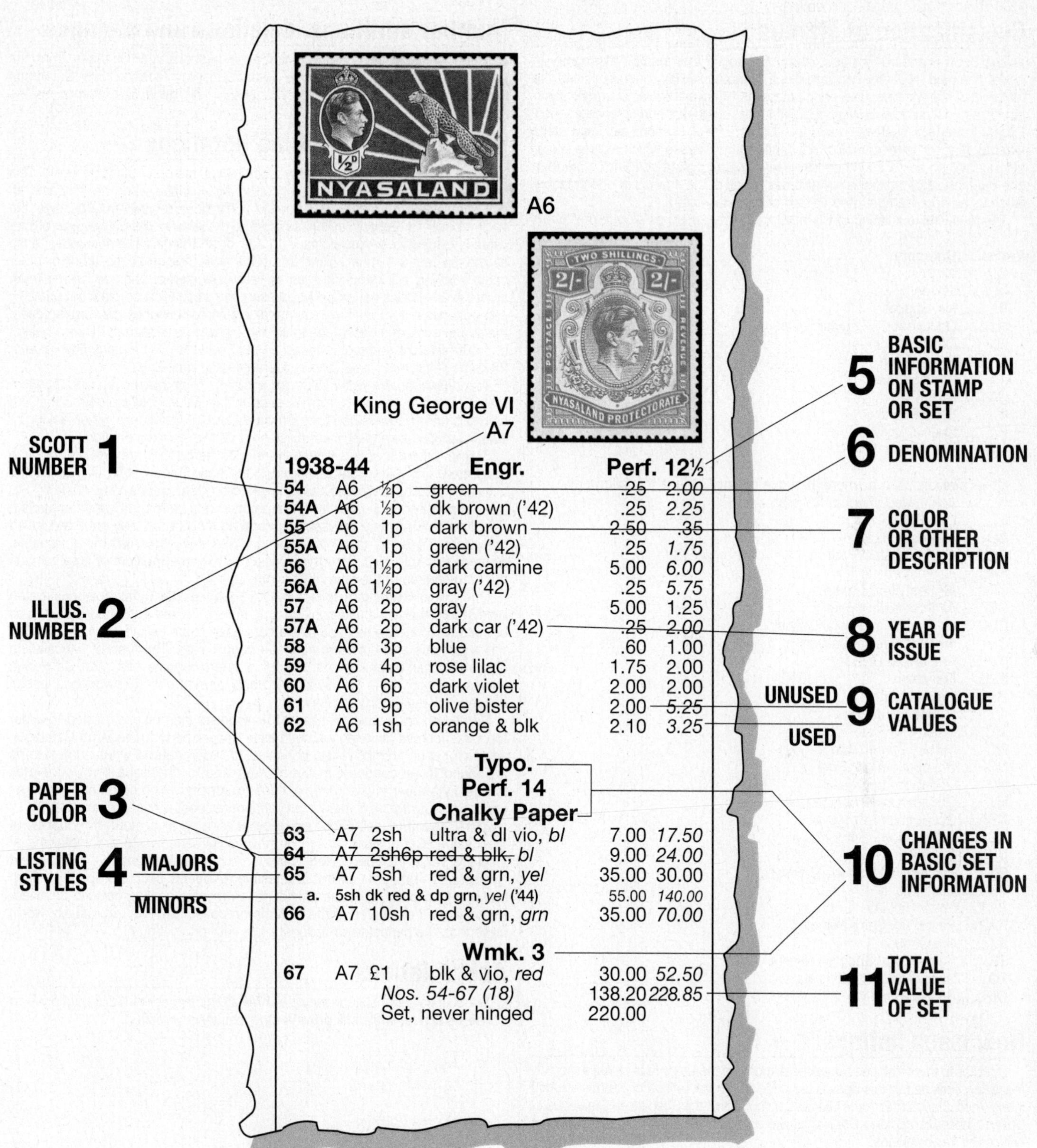
NYASALAND
A6
TWO SHILLINGS
2/-
POSTAGE
REVENUE
NYASALAND PROTECTORATE
King George VI
A7
1938-44 Engr. Perf. 12½
54 A6 ½p green .25 2.00
54A A6 ½p dk brown ('42) .25 2.25
55 A6 1p dark brown 2.50 .35
55A A6 1p green ('42) .25 1.75
56 A6 1½p dark carmine 5.00 6.00
56A A6 1½p gray ('42) .25 5.75
57 A6 2p gray 5.00 1.25
57A A6 2p dark car ('42) .25 2.00
58 A6 3p blue .60 1.00
59 A6 4p rose lilac 1.75 2.00
60 A6 6p dark violet 2.00 2.00
61 A6 9p olive bister 2.00 5.25
62 A6 1sh orange & blk 2.10 3.25
Typo.
Perf. 14
Chalky Paper
63 A7 2sh ultra & dl vio, bl 7.00 17.50
64 A7 2sh6p red & blk, bl 9.00 24.00
65 A7 5sh red & grn, yel 35.00 30.00
a. 5sh dk red & dp grn, yel ('44) 55.00 140.00
66 A7 10sh red & grn, grn 35.00 70.00
Wmk. 3
67 A7 £1 blk & vio, red 30.00 52.50
Nos. 54-67 (18) 138.20 228.85
Set, never hinged 220.00
SCOTT NUMBER 1
ILLUS. NUMBER 2
PAPER COLOR 3
LISTING STYLES 4 MAJORS
MINORS
5 BASIC INFORMATION ON STAMP OR SET
6 DENOMINATION
7 COLOR OR OTHER DESCRIPTION
8 YEAR OF ISSUE
UNUSED
9 CATALOGUE VALUES
USED
10 CHANGES IN BASIC SET INFORMATION
11 TOTAL VALUE OF SET

# Special notices

## Classification of stamps

The Scott Standard Postage Stamp Catalogue lists stamps by country of issue. The next level of organization is a listing by section on the basis of the function of the stamps. The principal sections cover regular postage, semi-postal, air post, special delivery, registration, postage due and other categories. Except for regular postage, catalogue numbers for all sections include a prefix letter (or number-letter combination) denoting the class to which a given stamp belongs. When some countries issue sets containing stamps from more than one category, the catalogue will at times list all of the stamps in one category (such as air post stamps listed as part of a postage set).

The following is a listing of the most commonly used catalogue prefixes.

**Prefix.......Category**
C..........Air Post
M.........Military
P..........Newspaper
N..........Occupation - Regular Issues
O..........Official
Q..........Parcel Post
J..........Postage Due
RA.......Postal Tax
B..........Semi-Postal
E..........Special Delivery
MR.......War Tax

Other prefixes used by more than one country include the following:
H..........Acknowledgment of Receipt
I...........Late Fee
CO.......Air Post Official
CQ.......Air Post Parcel Post
RAC.....Air Post Postal Tax
CF........Air Post Registration
CB.......Air Post Semi-Postal
CBO....Air Post Semi-Postal Official
CE.......Air Post Special Delivery
EY........Authorized Delivery
S..........Franchise
G..........Insured Letter
GY.......Marine Insurance
MC.......Military Air Post
MQ......Military Parcel Post
NC.......Occupation - Air Post
NO.......Occupation - Official
NJ........Occupation - Postage Due
NRA.....Occupation - Postal Tax
NB.......Occupation - Semi-Postal
NE.......Occupation - Special Delivery
QY.......Parcel Post Authorized Delivery
AR.......Postal-fiscal
RAJ......Postal Tax Due
RAB.....Postal Tax Semi-Postal
F..........Registration
EB........Semi-Postal Special Delivery
EO.......Special Delivery Official
QE.......Special Handling

## New issue listings

Updates to this catalogue appear each month in the *Linn's Stamp News* monthly magazine. Included in this update are additions to the listings of countries found in the Scott *Standard Postage Stamp Catalogue* and the *Specialized Catalogue of United States Stamps and Covers,* as well as corrections and updates to current editions of this catalogue.

From time to time there will be changes in the final listings of stamps from the *Linn's Stamp News* magazine to the next edition of the catalogue. This occurs as more information about certain stamps or sets becomes available.

The catalogue update section of the *Linn's Stamp News* magazine is the most timely presentation of this material available. Annual subscriptions to *Linn's Stamp News* are available from Linn's Stamp News, Box 4129, Sidney, OH 45365-4129.

## Number additions, deletions and changes

A listing of catalogue number additions, deletions and changes from the previous edition of the catalogue appears in each volume. See Catalogue Number Additions, Deletions & Changes in the table of contents for the location of this list.

## Understanding valuing notations

The *minimum catalogue value* of an individual stamp or set is 25 cents. This represents a portion of the cost incurred by a dealer when he prepares an individual stamp for resale. As a point of philatelic-economic fact, the lower the value shown for an item in this catalogue, the greater the percentage of that value is attributed to dealer mark up and profit margin. In many cases, such as the 25-cent minimum value, that price does not cover the labor or other costs involved with stocking it as an individual stamp. The sum of minimum values in a set does not properly represent the value of a complete set primarily composed of a number of minimum-value stamps, nor does the sum represent the actual value of a packet made up of minimum-value stamps. Thus a packet of 1,000 different common stamps — each of which has a catalogue value of 25 cents — normally sells for considerably less than $250!

The *absence of a retail value* for a stamp does not necessarily suggest that a stamp is scarce or rare. A dash in the value column means that the stamp is known in a stated form or variety, but information is either lacking or insufficient for purposes of establishing a usable catalogue value.

Stamp values in *italics* generally refer to items that are difficult to value accurately. For expensive items, such as those priced at $1,000 or higher, a value in italics indicates that the affected item trades very seldom. For inexpensive items, a value in italics represents a warning. One example is a "blocked" issue where the issuing postal administration may have controlled one stamp in a set in an attempt to make the whole set more valuable. Another example is an item that sold at an extreme multiple of face value in the marketplace at the time of its issue.

One type of warning to collectors that appears in the catalogue is illustrated by a stamp that is valued considerably higher in used condition than it is as unused. In this case, collectors are cautioned to be certain the used version has a genuine and contemporaneous cancellation. The type of cancellation on a stamp can be an important factor in determining its sale price. Catalogue values do not apply to fiscal, telegraph or non-contemporaneous postal cancels, unless otherwise noted.

Some countries have released back issues of stamps in canceled-to-order form, sometimes covering as much as a 10-year period. The Scott Catalogue values for used stamps reflect canceled-to-order material when such stamps are found to predominate in the marketplace for the issue involved. Notes frequently appear in the stamp listings to specify which items are valued as canceled-to-order, or if there is a premium for postally used examples.

Many countries sell canceled-to-order stamps at a marked reduction of face value. Countries that sell or have sold canceled-to-order stamps at *full* face value include United Nations, Australia, Netherlands, France and Switzerland. It may be almost impossible to identify such stamps if the gum has been removed, because official government canceling devices are used. Postally used examples of these items on cover, however, are usually worth more than the canceled-to-order stamps with original gum.

## Abbreviations

Scott uses a consistent set of abbreviations throughout this catalogue to conserve space, while still providing necessary information.

**Color Abbreviations**

| | | | | | |
|---|---|---|---|---|---|
| amb | amber | crim | crimson | ol | olive |
| anil | aniline | cr | cream | olvn | olivine |
| ap | apple | dk | dark | org | orange |
| aqua | aquamarine | dl | dull | pck | peacock |
| az | azure | dp | deep | pnksh | pinkish |
| bis | bister | db | drab | Prus | Prussian |
| bl | blue | emer | emerald | pur | purple |
| bld | blood | gldn | golden | redsh | reddish |
| blk | black | grysh | grayish | res | reseda |
| bril | brilliant | grn | green | ros | rosine |
| brn | brown | grnsh | greenish | ryl | royal |
| brnsh | brownish | hel | heliotrope | sal | salmon |
| brnz | bronze | hn | henna | saph | sapphire |
| brt | bright | ind | indigo | scar | scarlet |
| brnt | burnt | int | intense | sep | sepia |
| car | carmine | lav | lavender | sien | sienna |
| cer | cerise | lem | lemon | sil | silver |
| chlky | chalky | lil | lilac | sl | slate |
| cham | chamois | lt | light | stl | steel |
| chnt | chestnut | mag | magenta | turq | turquoise |
| choc | chocolate | man | manila | ultra | ultramarine |
| chr | chrome | mar | maroon | Ven | Venetian |
| cit | citron | mv | mauve | ver | vermilion |
| cl | claret | multi | multicolored | vio | violet |
| cob | cobalt | mlky | milky | yel | yellow |
| cop | copper | myr | myrtle | yelsh | yellowish |

When no color is given for an overprint or surcharge, black is the color used. Abbreviations for colors used for overprints and surcharges include: "(B)" or "(Blk)," black; "(Bl)," blue; "(R)," red; and "(G)," green.

Additional abbreviations in this catalogue are shown below:

Adm. ............Administration
AFL ..............American Federation of Labor
Anniv. ............Anniversary
APS..............American Philatelic Society
Assoc.............Association
ASSR. ...........Autonomous Soviet Socialist Republic
b....................Born
BEP..............Bureau of Engraving and Printing
Bicent. ..........Bicentennial
Bklt. ..............Booklet
Brit. ...............British
btwn..............Between
Bur. ...............Bureau
c. or ca. ........Circa
Cat. ...............Catalogue
Cent. .............Centennial, century, centenary
CIO ...............Congress of Industrial Organizations
Conf. .............Conference
Cong. ............Congress
Cpl. ...............Corporal
CTO ..............Canceled to order
d....................Died
Dbl. ...............Double
EDU ..............Earliest documented use
Engr...............Engraved
Exhib.............Exhibition
Expo. ............Exposition
Fed................Federation
GB ................Great Britain
Gen...............General
GPO..............General post office
Horiz. ............Horizontal
Imperf. ..........Imperforate
Impt. .............Imprint
Intl.................International
Invtd.............Inverted
L....................Left
Lieut., lt.........Lieutenant
Litho..............Lithographed
LL..................Lower left
LR .................Lower right
mm ...............Millimeter
Ms.................Manuscript
Natl. ..............National
No. ................Number
NY.................New York
NYC ..............New York City
Ovpt. .............Overprint
Ovptd.............Overprinted
P ....................Plate number
Perf. ..............Perforated, perforation
Phil................Philatelic
Photo. ...........Photogravure
PO.................Post office
Pr. .................Pair
P.R. ...............Puerto Rico
Prec. .............Precancel, precanceled
Pres. .............President
PTT ...............Post, Telephone and Telegraph
R ...................Right
Rio ................Rio de Janeiro
Sgt. ...............Sergeant
Soc. ..............Society
Souv..............Souvenir
SSR...............Soviet Socialist Republic, see ASSR
St. .................Saint, street
Surch. ............Surcharge
Typo. .............Typographed
UL .................Upper left
Unwmkd. .......Unwatermarked
UPU ..............Universal Postal Union
UR.................Upper Right
US.................United States
USPOD .........United States Post Office Department
USSR.............Union of Soviet Socialist Republics
Vert. ..............Vertical
VP .................Vice president
Wmk. ............Watermark
Wmkd. ..........Watermarked
WWI .............World War I
WWII.............World War II

## Examination

Amos Media Co. will not comment upon the genuineness, grade or condition of stamps, because of the time and responsibility involved. Rather, there are several expertizing groups that undertake this work for both collectors and dealers. Neither will Amos Media Co. appraise or identify philatelic material. The company cannot take responsibility for unsolicited stamps or covers sent by individuals.

All letters, emails, etc. are read attentively, but they are not always answered because of time considerations.

## How to order from your dealer

When ordering stamps from a dealer, it is not necessary to write the full description of a stamp as listed in this catalogue. All you need is the name of the country, the Scott catalogue number and whether the desired item is unused or used. For example, "Japan Scott 422 unused" is sufficient to identify the unused stamp of Japan listed as "422 A206 5y brown."

# Basic stamp information

A stamp collector's knowledge of the combined elements that make a given stamp issue unique determines his or her ability to identify stamps. These elements include paper, watermark, method of separation, printing, design and gum. On the following pages each of these important areas is briefly described.

## Paper

Paper is an organic material composed of a compacted weave of cellulose fibers and generally formed into sheets. Paper used to print stamps may be manufactured in sheets, or it may have been part of a large roll (called a web) before being cut to size. The fibers most often used to create paper on which stamps are printed include bark, wood, straw and certain grasses. In many cases, linen or cotton rags have been added for greater strength and durability. Grinding, bleaching, cooking and rinsing these raw fibers reduces them to a slushy pulp, referred to by paper makers as "stuff." Sizing and, sometimes, coloring matter is added to the pulp to make different types of finished paper.

After the stuff is prepared, it is poured onto sieve-like frames that allow the water to run off, while retaining the matted pulp. As fibers fall onto the screen and are held by gravity, they form a natural weave that will later hold the paper together. If the screen has metal bits that are formed into letters or images attached, it leaves slightly thinned areas on the paper. These are called watermarks.

When the stuff is almost dry, it is passed under pressure through smooth or engraved rollers — dandy rolls — or placed between cloth in a press to be flattened and dried.

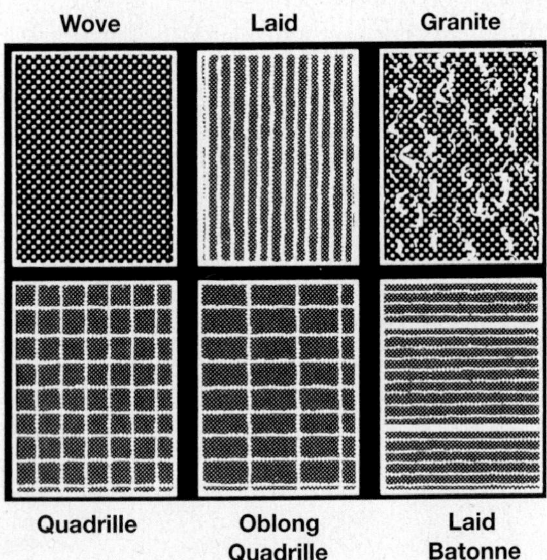


Stamp paper falls broadly into two types: wove and laid. The nature of the surface of the frame onto which the pulp is first deposited causes the differences in appearance between the two. If the surface is smooth and even, the paper will be of fairly uniform texture throughout. This is known as wove paper. Early papermaking machines poured the pulp onto a continuously circulating web of felt, but modern machines feed the pulp onto a cloth-like screen made of closely interwoven fine wires. This paper, when held to a light, will show little dots or points very close together. The proper name for this is "wire wove," but the type is still considered wove. Any U.S. or British stamp printed after 1880 will serve as an example of wire wove paper.

Closely spaced parallel wires, with cross wires at wider intervals, make up the frames used for what is known as laid paper. A greater thickness of the pulp will settle between the wires. The paper, when held to a light, will show alternate light and dark lines. The spacing and the thickness of the lines may vary, but on any one sheet of paper they are all alike. See Russia Scott 31-38 for examples of laid paper.

**Batonne,** from the French word meaning "a staff," is a term used if the lines in the paper are spaced quite far apart, like the printed ruling on a writing tablet. Batonne paper may be either wove or laid. If laid, fine laid lines can be seen between the batons.

**Quadrille** is the term used when the lines in the paper form little squares. Oblong quadrille is the term used when rectangles, rather than squares, are formed. Grid patterns vary from distinct to extremely faint. See Mexico-Guadalajara Scott 35-37 for examples of oblong quadrille paper.

Paper also is classified as thick or thin, hard or soft, and by color. Such colors may include yellowish, greenish, bluish and reddish.

Brief explanations of other types of paper used for printing stamps, as well as examples, follow.

**Colored** — Colored paper is created by the addition of dye in the paper-making process. Such colors may include shades of yellow, green, blue and red. Surface-colored papers, most commonly used for British colonial issues in 1913-14, are created when coloring is added only to the surface during the finishing process. Stamps printed on surface-colored paper have white or uncolored backs, while true colored papers are colored through. See Jamaica Scott 71-73.

**Pelure** — Pelure paper is a very thin, hard and often brittle paper that is sometimes bluish or grayish in appearance. See Serbia Scott 169-170.

**Native** — This is a term applied to handmade papers used to produce some of the early stamps of the Indian states. Stamps printed on native paper may be expected to display various natural inclusions that are normal and do not negatively affect value. Japanese paper, originally made of mulberry fibers and rice flour, is part of this group. See Japan Scott 1-18.

**Manila** — This type of paper is often used to make stamped envelopes and wrappers. It is a coarse-textured stock, usually smooth on one side and rough on the other. A variety of colors of manila paper exist, but the most common range is yellowish-brown.

**Silk** — Introduced by the British in 1847 as a safeguard against counterfeiting, silk paper contains bits of colored silk thread scattered throughout. The density of these fibers varies greatly and can include as few as one fiber per stamp or hundreds. U.S. revenue Scott R152 is a good example of an easy-to-identify silk paper stamp.

Silk-thread paper has uninterrupted threads of colored silk arranged so that one or more threads run through the stamp or postal stationery. See Great Britain Scott 5-6 and Switzerland Scott 14-19.

**Granite** — Filled with minute cloth or colored paper fibers of various colors and lengths, granite paper should not be confused with either type of silk paper. Austria Scott 172-175 and a number of Swiss stamps are examples of granite paper.

**Chalky** — A chalk-like substance coats the surface of chalky paper to discourage the cleaning and reuse of canceled stamps, as well as to provide a smoother, more acceptable printing surface. Because the designs of stamps printed on chalky paper are imprinted on what is often a water-soluble coating, any attempt to remove a cancellation will destroy the stamp. Do not soak these stamps in any fluid. To remove a stamp printed on chalky paper from an envelope, wet the paper from underneath the stamp until the gum dissolves enough to release the stamp from the paper. See St. Kitts-Nevis Scott 89-90 for examples of stamps printed on this type of chalky paper.

**India** — Another name for this paper, originally introduced from China about 1750, is "China Paper." It is a thin, opaque paper often used for plate and die proofs by many countries.

**Double** — In philately, the term double paper has two distinct meanings. The first is a two-ply paper, usually a combination of a thick and a thin sheet, joined during manufacture. This type was used experimentally as a means to discourage the reuse of stamps.

The design is printed on the thin paper. Any attempt to remove a cancellation would destroy the design. U.S. Scott 158 and other Banknote-era stamps exist on this form of double paper.

The second type of double paper occurs on a rotary press, when the end of one paper roll, or web, is affixed to the next roll to save time feeding the paper through the press. Stamp designs are printed over the joined paper and, if overlooked by inspectors, may get into post office stocks.

**Goldbeater's Skin** — This type of paper was used for the 1866 issue of Prussia, and was a tough, translucent paper. The design was printed in reverse on the back of the stamp, and the gum applied over the printing. It is impossible to remove stamps printed on this type of paper from the paper to which they are affixed without destroying the design.

**Ribbed** — Ribbed paper has an uneven, corrugated surface made by passing the paper through ridged rollers. This type exists on some copies of U.S. Scott 156-165.

Various other substances, or substrates, have been used for stamp manufacture, including wood, aluminum, copper, silver and gold foil, plastic, and silk and cotton fabrics.

## Watermarks

Watermarks are an integral part of some papers. They are formed in the process of paper manufacture. Watermarks consist of small designs, formed of wire or cut from metal and soldered to the surface of the mold or, sometimes, on the dandy roll. The designs may be in the form of crowns, stars, anchors, letters or other characters or symbols. These pieces of metal — known in the paper-making industry as "bits" — impress a design into the paper. The design sometimes may be seen by holding the stamp to the light. Some are more easily seen with a watermark detector. This important tool is a small black tray into which a stamp is placed face down and dampened with a fast-evaporating watermark detection fluid that brings up the watermark image in the form of dark lines against a lighter background. These dark lines are the thinner areas of the paper known as the watermark. Some watermarks are extremely difficult to locate, due to either a faint impression, watermark location or the color of the stamp. There also are electric watermark detectors that come with plastic filter disks of various colors. The disks neutralize the color of the stamp, permitting the watermark to be seen more easily.

Multiple watermarks of Crown Agents and Burma

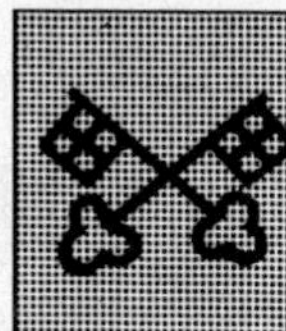

Watermarks of Uruguay, Vatican City and Jamaica

**WARNING: Some inks used in the photogravure process dissolve in watermark fluids (Please see the section on Soluble Printing Inks).** Also, see "chalky paper."

Watermarks may be found normal, reversed, inverted, reversed and inverted, sideways or diagonal, as seen from the back of the stamp. The relationship of watermark to stamp design depends on the position of the printing plates or how paper is fed through the press. On machine-made paper, watermarks normally are read from right to left. The design is repeated closely throughout the sheet in a "multiple-watermark design." In a "sheet watermark," the design appears only once on the sheet, but extends over many stamps. Individual stamps may carry only a small fraction or none of the watermark.

"Marginal watermarks" occur in the margins of sheets or panes of stamps. They occur on the outside border of paper (ostensibly outside the area where stamps are to be printed). A large row of letters may spell the name of the country or the manufacturer of the paper, or a border of lines may appear. Careless press feeding may cause parts of these letters and/or lines to show on stamps of the outer row of a pane.

## Soluble printing inks

**WARNING:** Most stamp colors are permanent; that is, they are not seriously affected by short-term exposure to light or water. Many colors, especially of modern inks, fade from excessive exposure to light. There are stamps printed with inks that dissolve easily in water or in fluids used to detect watermarks. Use of these inks was intentional to prevent the removal of cancellations. Water affects all aniline inks, those on so-called safety paper and some photogravure printings - all such inks are known as fugitive colors. Removal from paper of such stamps requires care and alternatives to traditional soaking.

## Separation

"Separation" is the general term used to describe methods used to separate stamps. The three standard forms currently in use are perforating, rouletting and die-cutting. These methods are done during the stamp production process, after printing. Sometimes these methods are done on-press or sometimes as a separate step. The earliest issues, such as the 1840 Penny Black of Great Britain (Scott 1), did not have any means provided for separation. It was expected the stamps would be cut apart with scissors or folded and torn. These are examples of imperforate stamps. Many stamps were first issued in imperforate formats and were later issued with perforations. Therefore, care must be observed in buying single imperforate stamps to be certain they were issued imperforate and are not perforated copies that have been altered by having the perforations trimmed away. Stamps issued imperforate usually are valued as singles. However, imperforate varieties of normally perforated stamps should be collected in pairs or larger pieces as indisputable evidence of their imperforate character.

### PERFORATION

The chief style of separation of stamps, and the one that is in almost universal use today, is perforating. By this process, paper between the stamps is cut away in a line of holes, usually round, leaving little bridges of paper between the stamps to hold them together. Some types of perforation, such as hyphen-hole perfs, can be confused with roulettes, but a close visual inspection reveals that paper has been removed. The little perforation bridges, which project from the stamp when it is torn from the pane, are called the teeth of the perforation.

As the size of the perforation is sometimes the only way to differentiate between two otherwise identical stamps, it is necessary to be able to accurately measure and describe them. This is done with a perforation gauge, usually a ruler-like device that has dots or graduated lines to show how many perforations may be counted in the space of two centimeters. Two centimeters is the space universally adopted in which to measure perforations.

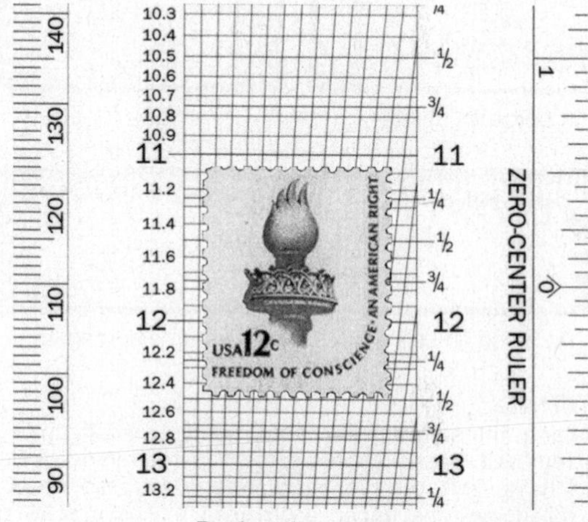


Perforation gauge

To measure a stamp, run it along the gauge until the dots on it fit exactly into the perforations of the stamp. If you are using a graduated-line perforation gauge, simply slide the stamp along the surface until the lines on the gauge perfectly project from the center of the bridges or holes. The number to the side of the line of dots or lines that fit the stamp's perforation is the measurement. For example, an "11" means that 11 perforations fit between two centimeters. The description of the stamp therefore is "perf. 11." If the gauge of the perforations on the top and bottom of a stamp differs from that on the sides, the result is what is known as compound perforations. In measuring compound perforations, the gauge at top and bottom is always given first, then the sides. Thus, a stamp that measures 11 at top and bottom and 10½ at the sides is "perf. 11 x 10½." See U.S. Scott 632-642 for examples of compound perforations.

Stamps also are known with perforations different on three or all four sides. Descriptions of such items are clockwise, beginning with the top of the stamp.

A perforation with small holes and teeth close together is a "fine perforation." One with large holes and teeth far apart is a "coarse perforation." Holes that are jagged, rather than clean-cut, are "rough perforations." *Blind perforations* are the slight impressions left by the perforating pins if they fail to puncture the paper. Multiples of stamps showing blind perforations may command a slight premium over normally perforated stamps.

The term *syncopated perfs* describes intentional irregularities in the perforations. The earliest form was used by the Netherlands from 1925-33, where holes were omitted to create distinctive patterns. Beginning in 1992, Great Britain has used an oval perforation to help prevent counterfeiting. Several other countries have started using the oval perfs or other syncopated perf patterns.

A new type of perforation, still primarily used for postal stationery, is known as microperfs. Microperfs are tiny perforations (in some cases hundreds of holes per two centimeters) that allows items to be intentionally separated very easily, while not accidentally breaking apart as easily as standard perforations. These are not currently measured or differentiated by size, as are standard perforations.

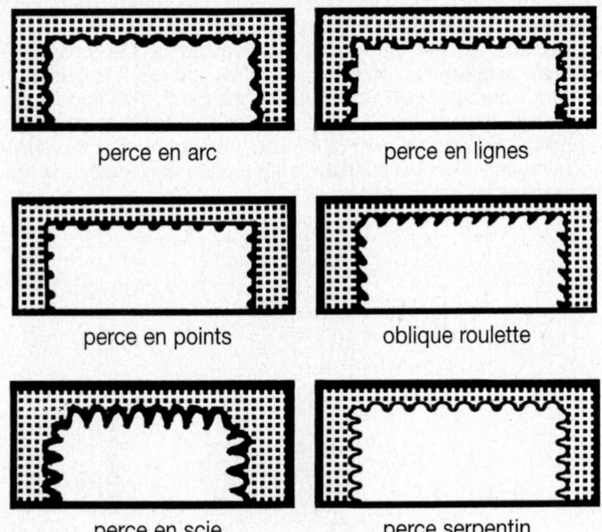


## ROULETTING

In rouletting, the stamp paper is cut partly or wholly through, with no paper removed. In perforating, some paper is removed. Rouletting derives its name from the French roulette, a spur-like wheel. As the wheel is rolled over the paper, each point makes a small cut. The number of cuts made in a two-centimeter space determines the gauge of the roulette, just as the number of perforations in two centimeters determines the gauge of the perforation.

The shape and arrangement of the teeth on the wheels varies. Various roulette types generally carry French names:

*Perce en lignes* — rouletted in lines. The paper receives short, straight cuts in lines. This is the most common type of rouletting. See Mexico Scott 500.

*Perce en points* — pin-rouletted or pin-perfed. This differs from a small perforation because no paper is removed, although round, equidistant holes are pricked through the paper. See Mexico Scott 242-256.

*Perce en arc and perce en scie* — pierced in an arc or saw-toothed designs, forming half circles or small triangles. See Hanover (German States) Scott 25-29.

*Perce en serpentin* — serpentine roulettes. The cuts form a serpentine or wavy line. See Brunswick (German States) Scott 13-18.

Once again, no paper is removed by these processes, leaving the stamps easily separated, but closely attached.

## DIE-CUTTING

The third major form of stamp separation is die-cutting. This is a method where a die in the pattern of separation is created that later cuts the stamp paper in a stroke motion. Although some standard stamps bear die-cut perforations, this process is primarily used for self-adhesive postage stamps. Die-cutting can appear in straight lines, such as U.S. Scott 2522, shapes, such as U.S. Scott 1551, or imitating the appearance of perforations, such as New Zealand Scott 935A and 935B.

# Printing processes

**ENGRAVING (Intaglio, Line-engraving, Etching)**

**Master die** — The initial operation in the process of line engraving is making the master die. The die is a small, flat block of softened steel upon which the stamp design is recess engraved in reverse.

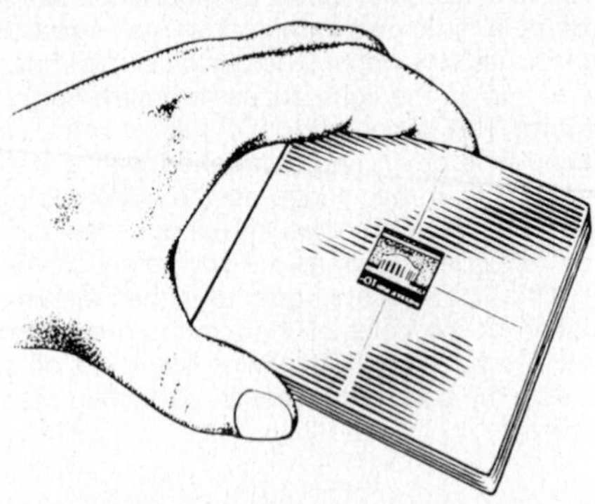

Photographic reduction of the original art is made to the appropriate size. It then serves as a tracing guide for the initial outline of the design. The engraver lightly traces the design on the steel with his graver, then slowly works the design until it is completed. At various points during the engraving process, the engraver hand-inks the die and makes an impression to check his progress. These are known as progressive die proofs. After completion of the engraving, the die is hardened to withstand the stress and pressures of later transfer operations.

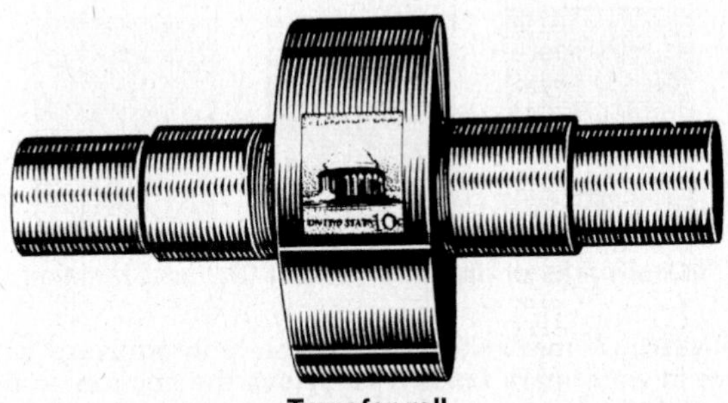

**Transfer roll**

**Transfer roll** — Next is production of the transfer roll that, as the name implies, is the medium used to transfer the subject from the master die to the printing plate. A blank roll of soft steel, mounted on a mandrel, is placed under the bearers of the transfer press to allow it to roll freely on its axis. The hardened die is placed on the bed of the press and the face of the transfer roll is applied to the die, under pressure. The bed or the roll is then rocked back and forth under increasing pressure, until the soft steel of the roll is forced into every engraved line of the die. The resulting impression on the roll is known as a "relief" or a "relief transfer." The engraved image is now positive in appearance and stands out from the steel. After the required number of reliefs are "rocked in," the soft steel transfer roll is hardened.

Different flaws may occur during the relief process. A defective relief may occur during the rocking in process because of a minute piece of foreign material lodging on the die, or some other cause. Imperfections in the steel of the transfer roll may result in a breaking away of parts of the design. This is known as a relief break, which will show up on finished stamps as small, unprinted areas. If a damaged relief remains in use, it will transfer a repeating defect to the plate. Deliberate alterations of reliefs sometimes occur. "Altered reliefs" designate these changed conditions.

**Plate** — The final step in pre-printing production is the making of the printing plate. A flat piece of soft steel replaces the die on the bed of the transfer press. One of the reliefs on the transfer roll is positioned over this soft steel. Position, or layout, dots determine the correct position on the plate. The dots have been lightly marked on the plate in advance. After the correct position of the relief is determined, the design is rocked in by following the same method used in making the transfer roll. The difference is that this time the image is being transferred from the transfer roll, rather than to it. Once the design is entered on the plate, it appears in reverse and is recessed. There are as many transfers entered on the plate as there are subjects printed on the sheet of stamps. It is during this process that double and shifted transfers occur, as well as re-entries. These are the result of improperly entered images that have not been properly burnished out prior to rocking in a new image.

Modern siderography processes, such as those used by the U.S. Bureau of Engraving and Printing, involve an automated form of rocking designs in on preformed cylindrical printing sleeves. The same process also allows for easier removal and re-entry of worn images right on the sleeve.

**Transferring the design to the plate**

Following the entering of the required transfers on the plate, the position dots, layout dots and lines, scratches and other markings generally are burnished out. Added at this time by the siderographer are any required guide lines, plate numbers or other marginal markings. The plate is then hand-inked and a proof impression is taken. This is known as a plate proof. If the impression is approved, the plate is machined for fitting onto the press, is hardened and sent to the plate vault ready for use.

On press, the plate is inked and the surface is automatically wiped clean, leaving ink only in the recessed lines. Paper is then forced under pressure into the engraved recessed lines, thereby receiving the ink. Thus, the ink lines on engraved stamps are slightly raised, and slight depressions (debossing) occur on the back of the stamp. Prior to the advent of modern high-speed presses and more advanced ink formulations, paper had to be dampened before receiving the ink. This sometimes led to uneven shrinkage by the time the stamps were perforated, resulting in improperly perforated stamps, or misperfs. Newer presses use drier paper, thus both *wet and dry printings* exist on some stamps.

**Rotary Press** — Until 1914, only flat plates were used to print engraved stamps. Rotary press printing was introduced in 1914, and slowly spread. Some countries still use flat-plate printing.

After approval of the plate proof, older rotary press plates require additional machining. They are curved to fit the press cylinder. "Gripper slots" are cut into the back of each plate to receive the "grippers," which hold the plate securely on the press. The plate is then hardened. Stamps printed from these bent rotary press plates are longer or wider than the same stamps printed from flat-plate presses. The stretching of the plate during the curving process is what causes this distortion.

**Re-entry** — To execute a re-entry on a flat plate, the transfer roll is re-applied to the plate, often at some time after its first use on the press. Worn-out designs can be resharpened by carefully burnishing out the original image and re-entering it from the transfer roll. If the original impression has not been sufficiently removed and the transfer roll is not precisely in line with the remaining impression, the resulting double transfer will make the re-entry obvious. If the registration is true, a re-entry may be difficult or impossible to distinguish. Sometimes a stamp printed from a successful re-entry is identified by having a much sharper and clearer impression than its neighbors. With the advent of rotary presses, post-press re-entries were not possible. After a plate was curved for the rotary press, it was impossible to make a re-entry. This is because the plate had already been bent once (with the design distorted).

However, with the introduction of the previously mentioned modern-style siderography machines, entries are made to the preformed cylindrical printing sleeve. Such sleeves are dechromed and softened. This allows individual images to be burnished out and re-entered on the curved sleeve. The sleeve is then rechromed, resulting in longer press life.

**Double Transfer** — This is a description of the condition of a transfer on a plate that shows evidence of a duplication of all, or a portion of the design. It usually is the result of the changing of the registration between the transfer roll and the plate during the rocking in of the original entry. Double transfers also occur when only a portion of the design has been rocked in and improper positioning is noted. If the worker elected not to burnish out the partial or completed design, a strong double transfer will occur for part or all of the design.

It sometimes is necessary to remove the original transfer from a plate and repeat the process a second time. If the finished re-worked image shows traces of the original impression, attributable to incomplete burnishing, the result is a partial double transfer.

With the modern automatic machines mentioned previously, double transfers are all but impossible to create. Those partially doubled images on stamps printed from such sleeves are more than likely re-entries, rather than true double transfers.

**Re-engraved** — Alterations to a stamp design are sometimes necessary after some stamps have been printed. In some cases, either the original die or the actual printing plate may have its "temper" drawn (softened), and the design will be re-cut. The resulting impressions from such a re-engraved die or plate may differ slightly from the original issue, and are known as "re-engraved." If the alteration was made to the master die, all future printings will be consistently different from the original. If alterations were made to the printing plate, each altered stamp on the plate will be slightly different from each other, allowing specialists to reconstruct a complete printing plate.

**Dropped Transfers** — If an impression from the transfer roll has not been properly placed, a dropped transfer may occur. The final stamp image will appear obviously out of line with its neighbors.

**Short Transfer** — Sometimes a transfer roll is not rocked its entire length when entering a transfer onto a plate. As a result, the finished transfer on the plate fails to show the complete design, and the finished stamp will have an incomplete design printed. This is known as a "short transfer." U.S. Scott No. 8 is a good example of a short transfer.

## TYPOGRAPHY (Letterpress, Surface Printing, Flexography, Dry Offset, High Etch)

Although the word "Typography" is obsolete as a term describing a printing method, it was the accepted term throughout the first century of postage stamps. Therefore, appropriate Scott listings in this catalogue refer to typographed stamps. The current term for this form of printing, however, is "letterpress."

As it relates to the production of postage stamps, letterpress printing is the reverse of engraving. Rather than having recessed areas trap the ink and deposit it on paper, only the raised areas of the design are inked. This is comparable to the type of printing seen by inking and using an ordinary rubber stamp. Letterpress includes all printing where the design is above the surface area, whether it is wood, metal or, in some instances, hardened rubber or polymer plastic.

For most letterpress-printed stamps, the engraved master is made in much the same manner as for engraved stamps. In this instance, however, an additional step is needed. The design is transferred to another surface before being transferred to the transfer roll. In this way, the transfer roll has a recessed stamp design, rather than one done in relief. This makes the printing areas on the final plate raised, or relief areas.

For less-detailed stamps of the 19th century, the area on the die not used as a printing surface was cut away, leaving the surface area raised. The original die was then reproduced by stereotyping or electrotyping. The resulting electrotypes were assembled in the required number and format of the desired sheet of stamps. The plate used in printing the stamps was an electroplate of these assembled electrotypes.

Once the final letterpress plates are created, ink is applied to the raised surface and the pressure of the press transfers the ink impression to the paper. In contrast to engraving, the fine lines of letterpress are impressed on the surface of the stamp, leaving a debossed surface. When viewed from the back (as on a typewritten page), the corresponding line work on the stamp will be raised slightly (embossed) above the surface.

## PHOTOGRAVURE (Gravure, Rotogravure, Heliogravure)

In this process, the basic principles of photography are applied to a chemically sensitized metal plate, rather than photographic paper. The design is transferred photographically to the plate through a halftone, or dot-matrix screen, breaking the reproduction into tiny dots. The plate is treated chemically and the dots form depressions, called cells, of varying depths and diameters, depending on the degrees of shade in the design. Then, like engraving, ink is applied to the plate and the surface is wiped clean. This leaves ink in the tiny cells that is lifted out and deposited on the paper when it is pressed against the plate.

Gravure is most often used for multicolored stamps, generally using the three primary colors (red, yellow and blue) and black. By varying the dot matrix pattern and density of these colors, virtually any color can be reproduced. A typical full-color gravure stamp will be created from four printing cylinders (one for each color). The original multicolored image will have been photographically separated into its component colors.

Modern gravure printing may use computer-generated dot-matrix screens, and modern plates may be of various types including metal-coated plastic. The catalogue designation of Photogravure (or "Photo") covers any of these older and more modern gravure methods of printing.

For examples of the first photogravure stamps printed (1914), see Bavaria Scott 94-114.

### LITHOGRAPHY (Offset Lithography, Stone Lithography, Dilitho, Planography, Collotype)

The principle that oil and water do not mix is the basis for lithography. The stamp design is drawn by hand or transferred from engraving to the surface of a lithographic stone or metal plate in a greasy (oily) substance. This oily substance holds the ink, which will later be transferred to the paper. The stone (or plate) is wet with an acid fluid, causing it to repel the printing ink in all areas not covered by the greasy substance.

Transfer paper is used to transfer the design from the original stone or plate. A series of duplicate transfers are grouped and, in turn, transferred to the final printing plate.

**Photolithography** — The application of photographic processes to lithography. This process allows greater flexibility of design, related to use of halftone screens combined with line work. Unlike photogravure or engraving, this process can allow large, solid areas to be printed.

**Offset** — A refinement of the lithographic process. A rubber-covered blanket cylinder takes the impression from the inked lithographic plate. From the "blanket" the impression is offset or transferred to the paper. Greater flexibility and speed are the principal reasons offset printing has largely displaced lithography. The term "lithography" covers both processes, and results are almost identical.

#### EMBOSSED (Relief) Printing

Embossing, not considered one of the four main printing types, is a method in which the design first is sunk into the metal of the die. Printing is done against a yielding platen, such as leather or linoleum. The platen is forced into the depression of the die, thus forming the design on the paper in relief. This process is often used for metallic inks.

Embossing may be done without color (see Sardinia Scott 4-6); with color printed around the embossed area (see Great Britain Scott 5 and most U.S. envelopes); and with color in exact registration with the embossed subject (see Canada Scott 656-657).

### HOLOGRAMS

For objects to appear as holograms on stamps, a model exactly the same size as it is to appear on the hologram must be created. Rather than using photographic film to capture the image, holography records an image on a photoresist material. In processing, chemicals eat away at certain exposed areas, leaving a pattern of constructive and destructive interference. When the photoresist is developed, the result is a pattern of uneven ridges that acts as a mold. This mold is then coated with metal, and the resulting form is used to press copies in much the same way phonograph records are produced.

A typical reflective hologram used for stamps consists of a reproduction of the uneven patterns on a plastic film that is applied to a reflective background, usually a silver or gold foil. Light is reflected off the background through the film, making the pattern present on the film visible. Because of the uneven pattern of the film, the viewer will perceive the objects in their proper three-dimensional relationships with appropriate brightness. The first hologram on a stamp was produced by Austria in 1988 (Scott 1441).

### FOIL APPLICATION

A modern technique of applying color to stamps involves the application of metallic foil to the stamp paper. A pattern of foil is applied to the stamp paper by use of a stamping die. The foil usually is flat, but it may be textured. Canada Scott 1735 has three different foil applications in pearl, bronze and gold. The gold foil was textured using a chemical-etch copper embossing die. The printing of this stamp also involved two-color offset lithography plus embossing.

### THERMOGRAPHY

In the 1990s stamps began to be enhanced with thermographic printing. In this process, a powdered polymer is applied over a sheet that has just been printed. The powder adheres to ink that lacks drying or hardening agents and does not adhere to areas where the ink has these agents. The excess powder is removed and the sheet is briefly heated to melt the powder. The melted powder solidifies after cooling, producing a raised, shiny effect on the stamps. See Scott New Caledonia C239-C240.

### COMBINATION PRINTINGS

Sometimes two or even three printing methods are combined in producing stamps. In these cases, such as Austria Scott 933 or Canada 1735 (described in the preceding paragraph), the multiple-printing technique can be determined by studying the individual characteristics of each printing type. A few stamps, such as Singapore Scott 684-684A, combine as many as three of the four major printing types (lithography, engraving and typography). When this is done it often indicates the incorporation of security devices against counterfeiting.

### INK COLORS

Inks or colored papers used in stamp printing often are of mineral origin, although there are numerous examples of organic-based pigments. As a general rule, organic-based pigments are far more subject to varieties and change than those of mineral-based origin.

The appearance of any given color on a stamp may be affected by many aspects, including printing variations, light, color of paper, aging and chemical alterations.

Numerous printing variations may be observed. Heavier pressure or inking will cause a more intense color, while slight interruptions in the ink feed or lighter impressions will cause a lighter appearance. Stamps printed in the same color by water-based and solvent-based inks can differ significantly in appearance. This affects several stamps in the U.S. Prominent Americans series. Hand-mixed ink formulas (primarily from the 19th century) produced under different conditions (humidity and temperature) account for notable color variations in early printings of the same stamp (see U.S. Scott 248-250, 279B, for example). Different sources of pigment can also result in significant differences in color.

Light exposure and aging are closely related in the way they affect stamp color. Both eventually break down the ink and fade colors, so that a carefully kept stamp may differ significantly in color from an identical copy that has been exposed to light. If stamps are exposed to light either intentionally or accidentally, their colors can be faded or completely changed in some cases.

Papers of different quality and consistency used for the same stamp printing may affect color appearance. Most pelure papers, for example, show a richer color when compared with wove or laid papers. See Russia Scott 181a, for an example of this effect.

The very nature of the printing processes can cause a variety of differences in shades or hues of the same stamp. Some of these shades are scarcer than others, and are of particular interest to the advanced collector.

## Luminescence

All forms of tagged stamps fall under the general category of luminescence. Within this broad category is fluorescence, dealing with forms of tagging visible under longwave ultraviolet light, and phosphorescence, which deals with tagging visible only under shortwave light. Phosphorescence leaves an afterglow and fluorescence does not. These treated stamps show up in a range of different colors when exposed to UV light. The differing wavelengths of the light activates the tagging material, making it glow in various colors that usually serve different mail processing purposes.

Intentional tagging is a post-World War II phenomenon, brought about by the increased literacy rate and rapidly growing mail volume. It was one of several answers to the problem of the need for more automated mail processes. Early tagged stamps served the purpose of triggering machines to separate different types of mail. A natural outgrowth was to also use the signal to trigger machines that faced all envelopes the same way and canceled them.

Tagged stamps come in many different forms. Some tagged stamps have luminescent shapes or images imprinted on them as a form of security device. Others have blocks (United States), stripes, frames (South Africa and Canada), overall coatings (United States), bars (Great Britain and Canada) and many other types. Some types of tagging are even mixed in with the pigmented printing ink (Australia Scott 366, Netherlands Scott 478 and U.S. Scott 1359 and 2443).

The means of applying taggant to stamps differs as much as the intended purposes for the stamps. The most common form of tagging is a coating applied to the surface of the printed stamp. Since the taggant ink is frequently invisible except under UV light, it does not interfere with the appearance of the stamp. Another common application is the use of phosphored papers. In this case the paper itself either has a coating of taggant applied before the stamp is printed, has taggant applied during the papermaking process (incorporating it into the fibers), or has the taggant mixed into the coating of the paper. The latter method, among others, is currently in use in the United States.

Many countries now use tagging in various forms to either expedite mail handling or to serve as a printing security device against counterfeiting. Following the introduction of tagged stamps for public use in 1959 by Great Britain, other countries have steadily joined the parade. Among those are Germany (1961); Canada and Denmark (1962); United States, Australia, France and Switzerland (1963); Belgium and Japan (1966); Sweden and Norway (1967); Italy (1968); and Russia (1969). Since then, many other countries have begun using forms of tagging, including Brazil, China, Czechoslovakia, Hong Kong, Guatemala, Indonesia, Israel, Lithuania, Luxembourg, Netherlands, Penrhyn Islands, Portugal, St. Vincent, Singapore, South Africa, Spain and Sweden to name a few.

In some cases, including United States, Canada, Great Britain and Switzerland, stamps were released both with and without tagging. Many of these were released during each country's experimental period. Tagged and untagged versions are listed for the aforementioned countries and are noted in some other countries' listings. For at least a few stamps, the experimentally tagged version is worth far more than its untagged counterpart, such as the 1963 experimental tagged version of France Scott 1024.

In some cases, luminescent varieties of stamps were inadvertently created. Several Russian stamps, for example, sport highly fluorescent ink that was not intended as a form of tagging. Older stamps, such as early U.S. postage dues, can be positively identified by the use of UV light, since the organic ink used has become slightly fluorescent over time. Other stamps, such as Austria Scott 70a-82a (varnish bars) and Obock Scott 46-64 (printed quadrille lines), have become fluorescent over time.

Various fluorescent substances have been added to paper to make it appear brighter. These optical brightners, as they are known, greatly affect the appearance of the stamp under UV light. The brightest of these is known as Hi-Brite paper. These paper varieties are beyond the scope of the Scott Catalogue.

Shortwave UV light also is used extensively in expertizing, since each form of paper has its own fluorescent characteristics that are impossible to perfectly match. It is therefore a simple matter to detect filled thins, added perforation teeth and other alterations that involve the addition of paper. UV light also is used to examine stamps that have had cancels chemically removed and for other purposes as well.

## Gum

The Illustrated Gum Chart in the first part of this introduction shows and defines various types of gum condition. Because gum condition has an important impact on the value of unused stamps, we recommend studying this chart and the accompanying text carefully.

The gum on the back of a stamp may be shiny, dull, smooth, rough, dark, white, colored or tinted. Most stamp gumming adhesives use gum arabic or dextrine as a base. Certain polymers such as polyvinyl alcohol (PVA) have been used extensively since World War II.

The *Scott Standard Postage Stamp Catalogue* does not list items by types of gum. The *Scott Specialized Catalogue of United States Stamps and Covers* does differentiate among some types of gum for certain issues.

Reprints of stamps may have gum differing from the original issues. In addition, some countries have used different gum formulas for different seasons. These adhesives have different properties that may become more apparent over time.

Many stamps have been issued without gum, and the catalogue will note this fact. See, for example, United States Scott 40-47. Sometimes, gum may have been removed to preserve the stamp. Germany Scott B68, for example, has a highly acidic gum that eventually destroys the stamps. This item is valued in the catalogue with gum removed.

## Reprints and reissues

These are impressions of stamps (usually obsolete) made from the original plates or stones. If they are valid for postage and reproduce obsolete issues (such as U.S. Scott 102-111), the stamps are reissues. If they are from current issues, they are designated as *second, third,* etc., *printing*. If designated for a particular purpose, they are called *special printings*.

When special printings are not valid for postage, but are made from original dies and plates by authorized persons, they are *official reprints*. *Private reprints* are made from the original plates and dies by private hands. An example of a private reprint is that of the 1871-1932 reprints made from the original die of the 1845 New Haven, Conn., postmaster's provisional. *Official reproductions* or imitations are made from new dies and plates by government authorization. Scott will list those reissues that are valid for postage if they differ significantly from the original printing.

The U.S. government made special printings of its first postage stamps in 1875. Produced were official imitations of the first two stamps (listed as Scott 3-4), reprints of the demonetized pre-1861 issues (Scott 40-47) and reissues of the 1861 stamps, the 1869 stamps and the then-current 1875 denominations. Even though the official imitations and the reprints were not valid for postage, Scott lists all of these U.S. special printings.

Most reprints or reissues differ slightly from the original stamp in some characteristic, such as gum, paper, perforation, color or watermark. Sometimes the details are followed so meticulously that only a student of that specific stamp is able to distinguish the reprint or reissue from the original.

## Remainders and canceled to order

Some countries sell their stock of old stamps when a new issue replaces them. To avoid postal use, the remainders usually are canceled with a punch hole, a heavy line or bar, or a more-or-less regular-looking cancellation. The most famous merchant of remainders was Nicholas F. Seebeck. In the 1880s and 1890s, he arranged printing contracts between the Hamilton Bank Note Co., of which he was a director, and several Central and South American countries. The contracts provided that the plates and all remainders of the yearly issues became the property of Hamilton. Seebeck saw to it that ample stock remained. The "Seebecks," both remainders and reprints, were standard packet fillers for decades.

Some countries also issue stamps *canceled-to-order (CTO)*, either in sheets with original gum or stuck onto pieces of paper or envelopes and canceled. Such CTO items generally are worth less than postally used stamps. In cases where the CTO material is far more prevalent in the marketplace than postally used examples, the catalogue value relates to the CTO examples, with postally used examples noted as premium items. Most CTOs can be detected by the presence of gum. However, as the CTO practice goes back at least to 1885, the gum inevitably has been soaked off some stamps so they could pass as postally used. The normally applied postmarks usually differ slightly from standard postmarks, and specialists are able to tell the difference. When applied individually to envelopes by philatelically minded persons, CTO material is known as *favor canceled* and generally sells at large discounts.

## Cinderellas and facsimiles

*Cinderella* is a catch-all term used by stamp collectors to describe phantoms, fantasies, bogus items, municipal issues, exhibition seals, local revenues, transportation stamps, labels, poster stamps and many other types of items. Some cinderella collectors include in their collections local postage issues, telegraph stamps, essays and proofs, forgeries and counterfeits.

A *fantasy* is an adhesive created for a nonexistent stamp-issuing authority. Fantasy items range from imaginary countries (Occusi-Ambeno, Kingdom of Sedang, Principality of Trinidad or Torres Straits), to non-existent locals (Winans City Post), or nonexistent transportation lines (McRobish & Co.'s Acapulco-San Francisco Line).

On the other hand, if the entity exists and could have issued stamps (but did not) or was known to have issued other stamps, the items are considered bogus stamps. These would include the Mormon postage stamps of Utah, S. Allan Taylor's Guatemala and Paraguay inventions, the propaganda issues for the South Moluccas and the adhesives of the Page & Keyes local post of Boston.

*Phantoms* is another term for both fantasy and bogus issues.

*Facsimiles* are copies or imitations made to represent original stamps, but which do not pretend to be originals. A catalogue illustration is such a facsimile. Illustrations from the Moens catalogue of the last century were occasionally colored and passed off as stamps. Since the beginning of stamp collecting, facsimiles have been made for collectors as space fillers or for reference. They often carry the word "facsimile," "falsch" (German), "sanko" or "mozo" (Japanese), or "faux" (French) overprinted on the face or stamped on the back. Unfortunately, over the years a number of these items have had fake cancels applied over the facsimile notation and have been passed off as genuine.

## Forgeries and counterfeits

Forgeries and counterfeits have been with philately virtually from the beginning of stamp production. Over time, the terminology for the two has been used interchangeably. Although both forgeries and counterfeits are reproductions of stamps, the purposes behind their creation differ considerably.

Among specialists there is an increasing movement to more specifically define such items. Although there is no universally accepted terminology, we feel the following definitions most closely mirror the items and their purposes as they are currently defined.

Forgeries (also often referred to as Counterfeits) are reproductions of genuine stamps that have been created to defraud collectors. Such spurious items first appeared on the market around 1860, and most old-time collections contain one or more. Many are crude and easily spotted, but some can deceive experts.

An important supplier of these early philatelic forgeries was the Hamburg printer Gebruder Spiro. Many others with reputations in this craft included S. Allan Taylor, George Hussey, James Chute, George Forune, Benjamin & Sarpy, Julius Goldner, E. Oneglia and L.H. Mercier. Among the noted 20th-century forgers were Francois Fournier, Jean Sperati and the prolific Raoul DeThuin.

Forgeries may be complete replications, or they may be genuine stamps altered to resemble a scarcer (and more valuable) type. Most forgeries, particularly those of rare stamps, are worth only a small fraction of the value of a genuine example, but a few types, created by some of the most notable forgers, such as Sperati, can be worth as much or more than the genuine. Fraudulently produced copies are known of most classic rarities and many medium-priced stamps.

In addition to rare stamps, large numbers of common 19th- and early 20th-century stamps were forged to supply stamps to the early packet trade. Many can still be easily found. Few new philatelic forgeries have appeared in recent decades. Successful imitation of well-engraved work is virtually impossible. It has proven far easier to produce a fake by altering a genuine stamp than to duplicate a stamp completely.

Counterfeit (also often referred to as Postal Counterfeit or Postal Forgery) is the term generally applied to reproductions of stamps that have been created to defraud the government of revenue. Such items usually are created at the time a stamp is current and, in some cases, are hard to detect. Because most counterfeits are seized when the perpetrator is captured, postal counterfeits, particularly used on cover, are usually worth much more than a genuine example to specialists. The first postal counterfeit was of Spain's 4-cuarto carmine of 1854 (the real one is Scott 25). Apparently, the counterfeiters were not satisfied with their first version, which is now very scarce, and they soon created an engraved counterfeit, which is common. Postal counterfeits quickly followed in Austria, Naples, Sardinia and the Roman States. They have since been created in many other countries as well, including the United States.

An infamous counterfeit to defraud the government is the 1-shilling Great Britain "Stock Exchange" forgery of 1872, used on telegraph forms at the exchange that year. The stamp escaped detection until a stamp dealer noticed it in 1898.

## Fakes

*Fakes* are genuine stamps altered in some way to make them more desirable. One student of this part of stamp collecting has estimated that by the 1950s more than 30,000 varieties of fakes were known. That number has grown greatly since then. The widespread existence of fakes makes it important for stamp collectors to study their philatelic holdings and use relevant literature. Likewise, collectors should buy from reputable dealers who guarantee their stamps and make full and prompt refunds should a purchased item be declared faked or altered by some mutually agreed-upon authority. Because fakes always have some genuine characteristics, it is not always possible to obtain unanimous agreement among experts regarding specific items. These students may change their opinions as philatelic knowledge increases. More than 80 percent of all fakes on the philatelic market today are regummed, reperforated (or perforated for the first time), or bear forged overprints, surcharges or cancellations.

Stamps can be chemically treated to alter or eliminate colors. For example, a pale rose stamp can be re-colored to resemble a blue shade of high market value. In other cases, treated stamps can be made to resemble missing color varieties. Designs may be changed by painting, or a stroke or a dot added or bleached out to turn an ordinary variety into a seemingly scarcer stamp. Part of a stamp can be bleached and reprinted in a different version, achieving an inverted center or frame. Margins can be added or repairs done so deceptively that the stamps move from the "repaired" into the "fake" category.

Fakers have not left the backs of the stamps untouched either. They may create false watermarks, add fake grills or press out genuine grills. A thin India paper proof may be glued onto a thicker backing to create the appearance an issued stamp, or a proof printed on cardboard may be shaved down and perforated to resemble a stamp. Silk threads are impressed into paper and stamps have been split so that a rare paper variety is added to an otherwise inexpensive stamp. The most common treatment to the back of a stamp, however, is regumming.

Some in the business of faking stamps have openly advertised fool-proof application of "original gum" to stamps that lack it, although most publications now ban such ads from their pages. It is believed that very few early stamps have survived without being hinged. The large number of never-hinged examples of such earlier material offered for sale thus suggests the widespread extent of regumming activity. Regumming also may be used to hide repairs or thin spots. Dipping the stamp into watermark fluid, or examining it under longwave ultraviolet light often will reveal these flaws.

Fakers also tamper with separations. Ingenious ways to add margins are known. Perforated wide-margin stamps may be falsely represented as imperforate when trimmed. Reperforating is commonly done to create scarce coil or perforation varieties, and to eliminate the naturally occurring straight-edge stamps found in sheet margin positions of many earlier issues. Custom has made straight-edged stamps less desirable. Fakers have obliged by perforating straight-edged stamps so that many are now uncommon, if not rare.

Another fertile field for the faker is that of overprints, surcharges and cancellations. The forging of rare surcharges or overprints began in the 1880s or 1890s. These forgeries are sometimes difficult to detect, but experts have identified almost all. Occasionally, overprints or cancellations are removed to create non-overprinted stamps or seemingly unused items. This is most commonly done by removing a manuscript cancel to make a stamp resemble an unused example. "SPECIMEN" overprints may be removed by scraping and repainting to create non-overprinted varieties. Fakers use inexpensive revenues or pen-canceled stamps to generate unused stamps for further faking by adding other markings. The quartz lamp or UV lamp and a high-powered magnifying glass help to easily detect removed cancellations.

The bigger problem, however, is the addition of overprints, surcharges or cancellations — many with such precision that they are very difficult to ascertain. Plating of the stamps or the overprint can be an important method of detection.

Fake postmarks may range from many spurious fancy cancellations to a host of markings applied to transatlantic covers, to adding normally appearing postmarks to definitives of some countries with stamps that are valued far higher used than unused. With the increased popularity of cover collecting, and the widespread interest in postal history, a fertile new field for fakers has come about. Some have tried to create entire covers. Others specialize in adding stamps, tied by fake cancellations, to genuine stampless covers, or replacing less expensive or damaged stamps with more valuable ones. Detailed study of postal rates in effect at the time a cover in question was mailed, including the analysis of each handstamp used during the period, ink analysis and similar techniques, usually will unmask the fraud.

## Restoration and repairs

Scott bases its catalogue values on stamps that are free of defects and otherwise meet the standards set forth earlier in this introduction. Most stamp collectors desire to have the finest copy of an item possible. Even within given grading categories there are variances. This leads to a controversial practice that is not defined in any universal manner: stamp *restoration*.

There are broad differences of opinion about what is permissible when it comes to restoration. Carefully applying a soft eraser to a stamp or cover to remove light soiling is one form of restoration, as is washing a stamp in mild soap and water to clean it. These are fairly accepted forms of restoration. More severe forms of restoration include pressing out creases or removing stains caused by tape. To what degree each of these is acceptable is dependent upon the individual situation. Further along the spectrum is the freshening of a stamp's color by removing oxide build-up or the effects of wax paper left next to stamps shipped to the tropics.

At some point in this spectrum the concept of *repair* replaces that of restoration. Repairs include filling thin spots, mending tears by reweaving or adding a missing perforation tooth. Regumming stamps may have been acceptable as a restoration or repair technique many decades ago, but today it is considered a form of fakery.

Restored stamps may or may not sell at a discount, and it is possible that the value of individual restored items may be enhanced over that of their pre-restoration state. Specific situations dictate the resultant value of such an item. Repaired stamps sell at substantial discounts from the value of sound stamps.

# Terminology

**Booklets** — Many countries have issued stamps in small booklets for the convenience of users. This idea continues to become increasingly popular in many countries. Booklets have been issued in many sizes and forms, often with advertising on the covers, the panes of stamps or on the interleaving.

The panes used in booklets may be printed from special plates or made from regular sheets. All panes from booklets issued by the United States and many from those of other countries contain stamps that are straight edged on the sides, but perforated between. Others are distinguished by orientation of watermark or other identifying features. Any stamp-like unit in the pane, either printed or blank, that is not a postage stamp, is considered to be a *label* in the catalogue listings.

Scott lists and values booklet panes. Modern complete booklets also are listed and valued. Individual booklet panes are listed only when they are not fashioned from existing sheet stamps and, therefore, are identifiable from their sheet stamp counterparts.

Panes usually do not have a used value assigned to them because there is little market activity for used booklet panes, even though many exist used and there is some demand for them.

**Cancellations** — The marks or obliterations put on stamps by postal authorities to show that they have performed service and to prevent their reuse are known as cancellations. If the marking is made with a pen, it is considered a "pen cancel." When the location of the post office appears in the marking, it is a "town cancellation." A "postmark" is technically any postal marking, but in practice the term generally is applied to a town cancellation with a date. When calling attention to a cause or celebration, the marking is known as a "slogan cancellation." Many other types and styles of cancellations exist, such as duplex, numerals, targets, fancy and others. See also "precancels," below.

**Coil Stamps** — These are stamps that are issued in rolls for use in dispensers, affixing and vending machines. Those coils of the United States, Canada, Sweden and some other countries are perforated horizontally or vertically only, with the outer edges imperforate. Coil stamps of some countries, such as Great Britain and Germany, are perforated on all four sides and may in some cases be distinguished from their sheet stamp counterparts by watermarks, counting numbers on the reverse or other means.

**Covers** — Entire envelopes, with or without adhesive postage stamps, that have passed through the mail and bear postal or other markings of philatelic interest are known as covers. Before the introduction of envelopes in about 1840, people folded letters and wrote the address on the outside. Some people covered their letters with an extra sheet of paper on the outside for the address, producing the term "cover." Used airletter sheets, stamped envelopes and other items of postal stationery also are considered covers.

**Errors** — Stamps that have some major, consistent, unintentional deviation from the normal are considered errors. Errors include, but are not limited to, missing or wrong colors, wrong paper, wrong watermarks, inverted centers or frames on multicolor printing, inverted or missing surcharges or overprints, double impressions, missing perforations, unintentionally omitted tagging and others. Factually wrong or misspelled information, if it appears on all examples of a stamp, are not considered errors in the true sense of the word. They are errors of design. Inconsistent or randomly appearing items, such as misperfs or color shifts, are classified as freaks.

**Color-Omitted Errors** — This term refers to stamps where a missing color is caused by the complete failure of the printing plate to deliver ink to the stamp paper or any other paper. Generally, this is caused by the printing plate not being engaged on the press or the ink station running dry of ink during printing.

**Color-Missing Errors** — This term refers to stamps where a color or colors were printed somewhere but do not appear on the finished stamp. There are four different classes of color-missing errors, and the catalog indicates with a two-letter code appended to each such listing what caused the color to be missing. These codes are used only for the United States' color-missing error listings.

**FO** = A *foldover* of the stamp sheet during printing may block ink from appearing on the face of a stamp. Instead, the color will appear on the back of the foldover (where it might fall on the back of the selvage or perhaps a bit on the back of the stamp or on the back of another stamp. FO also will be used in the case of foldunders, where the paper may fold underneath the other stamp paper and the color will print on the platen.

**EP** = When the extraneous paper is removed, an unprinted area of stamp paper remains and may show a color or colors to be totally missing on the finished stamp.

**CM** = A misregistration of the printing plates during printing will result in a *color misregistration*, and such a misregistraion may result in a color not appearing on the finished stamp.

**PS** = *A perforation shift* after printing may remove a color from the finished stamp. Normally, this will occur on a row of stamps at the edge of the stamp pane.

**Measurements** – When measurements are given in the Scott catalogues for stamp size, grill size or any other reason, the first measurement given is always for the top and bottom dimension, while the second measurement will be for the sides (just as perforation gauges are measured). Thus, a stamp size of 15mm x 21mm will indicate a vertically oriented stamp 15mm wide at top and bottom, and 21mm tall at the sides. The same principle holds for measuring or counting items such as U.S. grills. A grill count of 22x18 points (B grill) indicates that there are 22 grill points across by 18 grill points down.

**Overprints and Surcharges** — Overprinting involves applying wording or design elements over an already existing stamp. Overprints can be used to alter the place of use (such as "Canal Zone" on U.S. stamps), to adapt them for a special purpose ("Porto" on Denmark's 1913-20 regular issues for use as postage due stamps, Scott J1-J7) or to commemorate a special occasion (United States Scott 647-648).

A *surcharge* is a form of overprint that changes or restates the face value of a stamp or piece of postal stationery.

Surcharges and overprints may be handstamped, typeset or, occasionally, lithographed or engraved. A few hand-written overprints and surcharges are known.

**Personalized Stamps** — In 1999, Australia issued stamps with se-tenant labels that could be personalized with pictures of the customer's choice. Other countries quickly followed suit, with some offering to print the selected picture on the stamp itself within a frame that was used exclusively for personalized issues. As the picture used on these stamps or labels vary, listings for such stamps are for any picture within the common frame (or any picture on a se-tenant label), be it a "generic" image or one produced especially for a customer, almost invariably at a premium price.

**Precancels** — Stamps that are canceled before they are placed in the mail are known as precancels. Precanceling usually is done to expedite the handling of large mailings and generally allow the affected mail pieces to skip certain phases of mail handling.

In the United States, precancellations generally identified the point of origin; that is, the city and state. This information appeared across the face of the stamp, usually centered between parallel lines. More recently, bureau precancels retained the parallel lines, but the city and state designations were dropped. Recent coils have a service inscription that is present on the original printing plate. These show the mail service paid for by the stamp. Since these stamps are not intended to receive further cancellations when used as intended, they are considered precancels. Such items often do not have parallel lines as part of the precancellation.

In France, the abbreviation *Affranchts* in a semicircle together with the word *Postes* is the general form of precancel in use. Belgian precancellations usually appear in a box in which the name of the city appears. Netherlands precancels have the name of the city enclosed between concentric circles, sometimes called a "lifesaver." Precancellations of other countries usually follow these patterns, but may be any arrangement of bars, boxes and city names.

Precancels are listed in the Scott catalogues only if the precancel changes the denomination (Belgium Scott 477-478); if the precanceled stamp is different from the non-precanceled version (such as untagged U.S. precancels); or if the stamp exists only precanceled (France Scott 1096-1099, U.S. Scott 2265).

**Proofs and Essays** — Proofs are impressions taken from an approved die, plate or stone in which the design and color are the same as the stamp issued to the public. Trial color proofs are impressions taken from approved dies, plates or stones in colors that vary from the final version. An essay is the impression of a design that differs in some way from the issued stamp. "Progressive die proofs" generally are considered to be essays.

**Provisionals** — These are stamps that are issued on short notice and intended for temporary use pending the arrival of regular issues. They usually are issued to meet such contingencies as changes in government or currency, shortage of necessary postage values or military occupation.

During the 1840s, postmasters in certain American cities issued stamps that were valid only at specific post offices. In 1861, postmasters of the Confederate States also issued stamps with limited validity. Both of these examples are known as "postmaster's provisionals."

**Se-tenant** — This term refers to an unsevered pair, strip or block of stamps that differ in design, denomination or overprint.

Unless the se-tenant item has a continuous design (see U.S. Scott 1451a, 1694a) the stamps do not have to be in the same order as shown in the catalogue (see U.S. Scott 2158a).

**Specimens** — The Universal Postal Union required member nations to send samples of all stamps they released into service to the International Bureau in Switzerland. Member nations of the UPU received these specimens as samples of what stamps were valid for postage. Many are overprinted, handstamped or initial-perforated "Specimen," "Canceled" or "Muestra." Some are marked with bars across the denominations (China-Taiwan), punched holes (Czechoslovakia) or back inscriptions (Mongolia).

Stamps distributed to government officials or for publicity purposes, and stamps submitted by private security printers for official approval, also may receive such defacements.

The previously described defacement markings prevent postal use, and all such items generally are known as "specimens."

**Tete-Beche** — This term describes a pair of stamps in which one is upside down in relation to the other. Some of these are the result of intentional sheet arrangements, such as Morocco Scott B10-B11. Others occurred when one or more electrotypes accidentally were placed upside down on the plate, such as Colombia Scott 57a. Separation of the tete-beche stamps, of course, destroys the tete beche variety.

# Vols. 2A-2B number additions, deletions and changes

| Number in 2023 Catalogue | Number in 2024 Catalogue |
|---|---|
| **Canada** | |
| new | 537a |
| new | 764b |
| **Colombia - Cundinamarca** | |
| new | 14a |

# Currency conversion

| Country | Dollar | Pound | S Franc | Yen | HK $ | Euro | Cdn $ | Aus $ |
|---|---|---|---|---|---|---|---|---|
| Australia | 1.4850 | 1.7819 | 1.5872 | 0.0114 | 0.1901 | 1.5688 | 1.0867 | — |
| Canada | 1.3665 | 1.6397 | 1.4606 | 0.0105 | 0.1749 | 1.4436 | — | 0.9202 |
| European Union | 0.9466 | 1.1358 | 1.0118 | 0.0072 | 0.1212 | — | 0.6927 | 0.6374 |
| Hong Kong | 7.8130 | 9.3750 | 8.3508 | 0.0598 | — | 8.2538 | 5.7175 | 5.2613 |
| Japan | 130.67 | 156.79 | 139.66 | — | 16.725 | 138.04 | 95.624 | 87.993 |
| Switzerland | 0.9356 | 1.1226 | — | 0.0072 | 0.1197 | 0.9884 | 0.6847 | 0.6300 |
| United Kingdom | 0.8334 | — | 0.8908 | 0.0064 | 0.1067 | 0.8804 | 0.6099 | 0.5612 |
| United States | — | 1.1999 | 1.0688 | 0.0077 | 0.1280 | 1.0564 | 0.7318 | 0.6734 |

| Country | Currency | U.S. $ Equiv. |
|---|---|---|
| Cambodia | riel | .0002 |
| Cameroun | Community of French Africa (CFA) franc | .0016 |
| Canada | dollar | .7318 |
| Cape Verde | escudo | .0096 |
| Caribbean Netherlands | US dollar | 1.0000 |
| Cayman Islands | dollar | 1.2195 |
| Central African Republic | CFA franc | .0016 |
| Chad | CFA franc | .0016 |
| Chile | peso | .0012 |
| China (Taiwan) | dollar | .0326 |
| China (People's Republic) | yuan | .1448 |
| Christmas Island | Australian dollar | .6734 |
| Cocos Island | Australian dollar | .6734 |
| Colombia | peso | .0002 |
| Comoro Islands | franc | .0021 |
| Congo Republic | CFA franc | .0016 |
| Cook Islands | New Zealand dollar | .6246 |
| Costa Rica | colon | .0017 |
| Croatia | euro | 1.0564 |
| Curacao | guilder | .5587 |
| Cyprus | euro | 1.0564 |
| Czech Republic | koruna | .0438 |
| Denmark | krone | .1420 |
| Djibouti | franc | .0056 |
| Dominica | East Caribbean dollar | .3704 |
| Dominican Republic | peso | .0178 |
| Ecuador | US dollar | 1.0000 |
| Egypt | pound | .0404 |
| Equatorial Guinea | CFA franc | .0016 |
| Eritrea | nakfa | .0667 |
| Estonia | euro | 1.0564 |
| Ethiopia | birr | .0187 |
| Falkland Islands | pound | 1.1999 |
| Faroe Islands | krone | .1420 |
| Fiji | dollar | .4521 |
| Finland | euro | 1.0564 |
| Aland Islands | euro | 1.0564 |
| France | euro | 1.0564 |
| French Polynesia | Community of French Pacific (CFP) franc | .0089 |
| French So. & Antarctic Terr. | euro | 1.0564 |

*Source: xe.com Jan. 3, 2023. Figures reflect values as of Jan. 3, 2023.*

# British Commonwealth of Nations

## Dominions, Colonies, Territories, Offices and Independent Members

Comprising stamps of the British Commonwealth and associated nations.

A strict observance of technicalities would bar some or all of the stamps listed under Burma, Ireland, Kuwait, Nepal, New Republic, Orange Free State, Samoa, South Africa, South-West Africa, Stellaland, Sudan, Swaziland, the two Transvaal Republics and others but these are included for the convenience of collectors.

## 1. Great Britain

Great Britain: Including England, Scotland, Wales and Northern Ireland.

## 2. The Dominions, Present and Past

### AUSTRALIA

The Commonwealth of Australia was proclaimed on Jan. 1, 1901. It consists of six former colonies as follows:

New South Wales
Queensland
South Australia
Victoria
Tasmania
Western Australia

The following islands and territories are, or have been, administered by Australia: Australian Antarctic Territory, Christmas Island, Cocos (Keeling) Islands, Nauru, New Guinea, Norfolk Island, Papua.

### CANADA

The Dominion of Canada was created by the British North America Act in 1867. The following provinces were former separate colonies and issued postage stamps:

British Columbia and Vancouver Island
New Brunswick
Newfoundland
Nova Scotia
Prince Edward Island

### FIJI

The colony of Fiji became an independent nation with dominion status on Oct. 10, 1970.

### GHANA

This state came into existence March 6, 1957, with dominion status. It consists of the former colony of the Gold Coast and the Trusteeship Territory of Togoland. Ghana became a republic July 1, 1960.

### INDIA

The Republic of India was inaugurated on Jan. 26, 1950. It succeeded the Dominion of India which was proclaimed Aug. 15, 1947, when the former Empire of India was divided into Pakistan and the Union of India. The Republic is composed of about 40 predominantly Hindu states of three classes: governor's provinces, chief commissioner's provinces and princely states. India also has various territories, such as the Andaman and Nicobar Islands.

The old Empire of India was a federation of British India and the native states. The more important princely states were autonomous. Of the more than 700 Indian states, these 43 are familiar names to philatelists because of their postage stamps.

### CONVENTION STATES

Chamba
Faridkot
Gwalior
Jhind
Nabha
Patiala

### FEUDATORY STATES

Alwar
Bahawalpur
Bamra
Barwani
Bhopal
Bhor
Bijawar
Bundi
Bussahir
Charkhari
Cochin
Dhar
Dungarpur
Duttia
Faridkot (1879-85)
Hyderabad
Idar
Indore
Jaipur
Jammu
Jammu and Kashmir
Jasdan
Jhalawar
Jhind (1875-76)
Kashmir
Kishangarh
Kotah
Las Bela
Morvi
Nandgaon
Nowanuggur
Orchha
Poonch
Rajasthan
Rajpeepla
Sirmur
Soruth
Tonk
Travancore
Wadhwan

### NEW ZEALAND

Became a dominion on Sept. 26, 1907. The following islands and territories are, or have been, administered by New Zealand:

Aitutaki
Cook Islands (Rarotonga)
Niue
Penrhyn
Ross Dependency
Samoa (Western Samoa)
Tokelau Islands

### PAKISTAN

The Republic of Pakistan was proclaimed March 23, 1956. It succeeded the Dominion which was proclaimed Aug. 15, 1947. It is made up of all or part of several Moslem provinces and various districts of the former Empire of India, including Bahawalpur and Las Bela. Pakistan withdrew from the Commonwealth in 1972.

### SOUTH AFRICA

Under the terms of the South African Act (1909) the self-governing colonies of Cape of Good Hope, Natal, Orange River Colony and Transvaal united on May 31, 1910, to form the Union of South Africa. It became an independent republic May 3, 1961.

Under the terms of the Treaty of Versailles, South-West Africa, formerly German South-West Africa, was mandated to the Union of South Africa.

### SRI LANKA (CEYLON)

The Dominion of Ceylon was proclaimed Feb. 4, 1948. The island had been a Crown Colony from 1802 until then. On May 22, 1972, Ceylon became the Republic of Sri Lanka.

## 3. Colonies, Past and Present; Controlled Territory and Independent Members of the Commonwealth

Abu Dhabi
Aden
Aitutaki
Alderney
Anguilla
Antigua
Ascension
Australia
Bahamas
Bahrain
Bangladesh
Barbados
Barbuda
Basutoland
Batum
Bechuanaland
Bechuanaland Prot.
Belize
Bermuda
Botswana
British Antarctic Territory
British Central Africa
British Columbia and Vancouver Island

British East Africa
British Guiana
British Honduras
British Indian Ocean Territory
British New Guinea
British Solomon Islands
British Somaliland
Brunei
Burma
Bushire
Cameroons
Canada
Cape of Good Hope
Cayman Islands
Christmas Island
Cocos (Keeling) Islands
Cook Islands
Crete,
  British Administration
Cyprus
Dominica
East Africa & Uganda
  Protectorates
Egypt
Falkland Islands
Fiji
Gambia
German East Africa
Ghana
Gibraltar
Gilbert Islands
Gilbert & Ellice Islands
Gold Coast
Grenada
Griqualand West
Guernsey
Guyana
Heligoland
Hong Kong
Indian Native States
  (see India)
Ionian Islands
Jamaica
Jersey
Jordan
Kenya
Kenya, Uganda & Tanzania
Kiribati
Kuwait
Labuan
Lagos
Leeward Islands
Lesotho
Madagascar
Malawi
Malaya
  Federated Malay States
  Johore
  Kedah
  Kelantan
  Malacca
  Negri Sembilan
  Pahang
  Penang
  Perak
  Perlis
  Selangor
  Singapore
  Sungei Ujong
  Trengganu
Malaysia
Maldive Islands
Malta
Man, Isle of
Mauritius
Mesopotamia
Montserrat
Mozambique
Muscat
Namibia
Natal
Nauru
Nevis
New Britain
New Brunswick
Newfoundland
New Guinea
New Hebrides
New Republic
New South Wales
New Zealand
Niger Coast Protectorate
Nigeria
Niue
Norfolk Island
North Borneo
Northern Nigeria
Northern Rhodesia
North West Pacific Islands
Nova Scotia
Nyasaland Protectorate
Oman
Orange River Colony
Pakistan
Palestine
Papua New Guinea
Penrhyn Island
Pitcairn Islands
Prince Edward Island
Qatar
Queensland
Rhodesia
Rhodesia & Nyasaland
Ross Dependency
Rwanda
Sabah
St. Christopher
St. Helena
St. Kitts
St. Kitts-Nevis-Anguilla
St. Lucia
St. Vincent
Samoa
Sarawak
Seychelles
Sierra Leone
Singapore
Solomon Islands
Somaliland Protectorate
South Africa
South Arabia
South Australia
South Georgia
Southern Nigeria
Southern Rhodesia
South-West Africa
Sri Lanka
Stellaland
Straits Settlements
Sudan
Swaziland
Tanganyika
Tanzania
Tasmania
Tobago
Togo
Tokelau Islands
Tonga
Transvaal
Trinidad
Trinidad and Tobago
Tristan da Cunha
Trucial States
Turks and Caicos
Turks Islands
Tuvalu
Uganda
United Arab Emirates
Vanuatu
Victoria
Virgin Islands
Western Australia
Zambia
Zanzibar
Zimbabwe
Zululand

**POST OFFICES IN FOREIGN COUNTRIES**

Africa
  East Africa Forces
  Middle East Forces
Bangkok
China
Morocco
Turkish Empire

# Colonies, former colonies, offices, territories controlled by parent states

## Belgium

Belgian Congo
Ruanda-Urundi

## Denmark

Danish West Indies
Faroe Islands
Greenland
Iceland

## Finland

Aland Islands

## France

### COLONIES PAST AND PRESENT, CONTROLLED TERRITORIES

Afars & Issas, Territory of
Alaouites
Alexandretta
Algeria
Alsace & Lorraine
Anjouan
Annam & Tonkin
Benin
Cambodia (Khmer)
Cameroun
Castellorizo
Chad
Cilicia
Cochin China
Comoro Islands
Dahomey
Diego Suarez
Djibouti (Somali Coast)
Fezzan
French Congo
French Equatorial Africa
French Guiana
French Guinea
French India
French Morocco
French Polynesia (Oceania)
French Southern & Antarctic Territories
French Sudan
French West Africa
Gabon
Germany
Ghadames
Grand Comoro
Guadeloupe
Indo-China
Inini
Ivory Coast
Laos
Latakia
Lebanon
Madagascar
Martinique
Mauritania
Mayotte
Memel
Middle Congo
Moheli
New Caledonia
New Hebrides
Niger Territory
Nossi-Be
Obock
Reunion
Rouad, Ile
Ste.-Marie de Madagascar
St. Pierre & Miquelon
Senegal
Senegambia & Niger
Somali Coast
Syria
Tahiti
Togo
Tunisia
Ubangi-Shari
Upper Senegal & Niger
Upper Volta
Viet Nam
Wallis & Futuna Islands

### POST OFFICES IN FOREIGN COUNTRIES

China
Crete
Egypt
Turkish Empire
Zanzibar

## Germany

### EARLY STATES

Baden
Bavaria
Bergedorf
Bremen
Brunswick
Hamburg
Hanover
Lubeck
Mecklenburg-Schwerin
Mecklenburg-Strelitz
Oldenburg
Prussia
Saxony
Schleswig-Holstein
Wurttemberg

### FORMER COLONIES

Cameroun (Kamerun)
Caroline Islands
German East Africa
German New Guinea
German South-West Africa
Kiauchau
Mariana Islands
Marshall Islands
Samoa
Togo

## Italy

### EARLY STATES

Modena
Parma
Romagna
Roman States
Sardinia
Tuscany
Two Sicilies
  Naples
  Neapolitan Provinces
  Sicily

### FORMER COLONIES, CONTROLLED TERRITORIES, OCCUPATION AREAS

Aegean Islands
  Calimno (Calino)
  Caso
  Cos (Coo)
  Karki (Carchi)
  Leros (Lero)
  Lipso
  Nisiros (Nisiro)
  Patmos (Patmo)
  Piscopi
  Rodi (Rhodes)
  Scarpanto
  Simi
  Stampalia
Castellorizo
Corfu
Cyrenaica
Eritrea
Ethiopia (Abyssinia)
Fiume
Ionian Islands
  Cephalonia
  Ithaca
  Paxos
Italian East Africa
Libya
Oltre Giuba
Saseno
Somalia (Italian Somaliland)
Tripolitania

### POST OFFICES IN FOREIGN COUNTRIES

"ESTERO"*
Austria
China
  Peking
  Tientsin
Crete
Tripoli
Turkish Empire
  Constantinople
  Durazzo
  Janina
Jerusalem
Salonika
Scutari
Smyrna
Valona

**Stamps overprinted "ESTERO" were used in various parts of the world.*

## Netherlands

Aruba
Caribbean Netherlands
Curacao
Netherlands Antilles (Curacao)
Netherlands Indies
Netherlands New Guinea
St. Martin
Surinam (Dutch Guiana)

## Portugal

### COLONIES PAST AND PRESENT, CONTROLLED TERRITORIES

Angola
Angra
Azores
Cape Verde
Funchal
Horta
Inhambane
Kionga
Lourenco Marques
Macao
Madeira
Mozambique
Mozambique Co.
Nyassa
Ponta Delgada
Portuguese Africa
Portuguese Congo
Portuguese Guinea
Portuguese India
Quelimane
St. Thomas & Prince Islands
Tete
Timor
Zambezia

## Russia

### ALLIED TERRITORIES AND REPUBLICS, OCCUPATION AREAS

Armenia
Aunus (Olonets)
Azerbaijan
Batum
Estonia
Far Eastern Republic
Georgia
Karelia
Latvia
Lithuania
North Ingermanland
Ostland
Russian Turkestan
Siberia
South Russia
Tannu Tuva
Transcaucasian Fed. Republics
Ukraine
Wenden (Livonia)
Western Ukraine

## Spain

### COLONIES PAST AND PRESENT, CONTROLLED TERRITORIES

Aguera, La
Cape Juby
Cuba
Elobey, Annobon & Corisco
Fernando Po
Ifni
Mariana Islands
Philippines
Puerto Rico
Rio de Oro
Rio Muni
Spanish Guinea
Spanish Morocco
Spanish Sahara
Spanish West Africa

### POST OFFICES IN FOREIGN COUNTRIES

Morocco
Tangier
Tetuan

# Dies of British colonial stamps

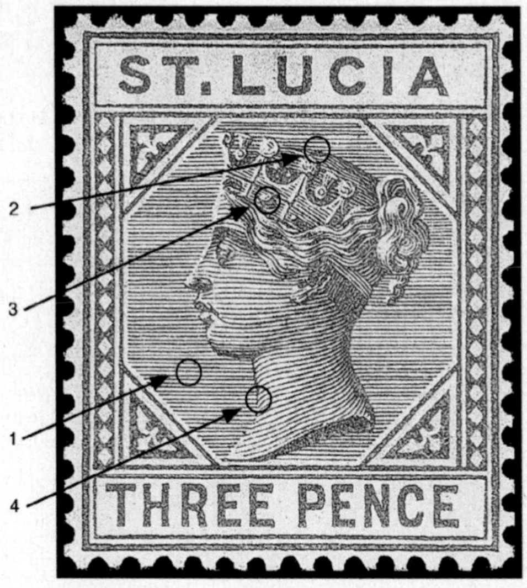


**DIE A:**

**1.** The lines in the groundwork vary in thickness and are not uniformly straight.

**2.** The seventh and eighth lines from the top, in the groundwork, converge where they meet the head.

**3.** There is a small dash in the upper part of the second jewel in the band of the crown.

**4.** The vertical color line in front of the throat stops at the sixth line of shading on the neck.

**DIE B:**

**1.** The lines in the groundwork are all thin and straight.

**2.** All the lines of the background are parallel.

3. There is no dash in the upper part of the second jewel in the band of the crown.

**4.** The vertical color line in front of the throat stops at the eighth line of shading on the neck.

**DIE I:**

**1.** The base of the crown is well below the level of the inner white line around the vignette.

**2.** The labels inscribed “POSTAGE” and “REVENUE” are cut square at the top.

**3.** There is a white “bud” on the outer side of the main stem of the curved ornaments in each lower corner.

**4.** The second (thick) line below the country name has the ends next to the crown cut diagonally.

| DIE Ia. | DIE Ib. |
|---|---|
| 1 as die II. | 1 and 3 as die II. |
| 2 and 3 as die I. | 2 as die I. |

**DIE II:**

**1.** The base of the crown is aligned with the underside of the white line around the vignette.

**2.** The labels curve inward at the top inner corners.

**3.** The “bud” has been removed from the outer curve of the ornaments in each corner.

**4.** The second line below the country name has the ends next to the crown cut vertically.

Wmk. 1
Crown and C C

Wmk. 2
Crown and C A

Wmk. 3
Multiple Crown and C A

Wmk. 4
Multiple Crown and Script C A

Wmk. 4a

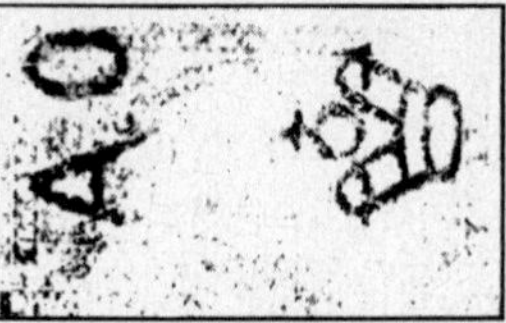
Wmk. 46

Wmk. 314
St. Edward's Crown and C A Multiple

Wmk. 373

Wmk. 384

Wmk. 406

# British Colonial and Crown Agents watermarks

Watermarks 1 to 4, 314, 373, 384 and 406, common to many British territories, are illustrated here to avoid duplication.

The letters "CC" of Wmk. 1 identify the paper as having been made for the use of the Crown Colonies, while the letters "CA" of the others stand for "Crown Agents." Both Wmks. 1 and 2 were used on stamps printed by De La Rue & Co.

Wmk. 3 was adopted in 1904; Wmk. 4 in 1921; Wmk. 46 in 1879; Wmk. 314 in 1957; Wmk. 373 in 1974; Wmk. 384 in 1985; Wmk 406 in 2008.

In Wmk. 4a, a non-matching crown of the general St. Edwards type (bulging on both sides at top) was substituted for one of the Wmk. 4 crowns which fell off the dandy roll. The non-matching crown occurs in 1950-52 printings in a horizontal row of crowns on certain regular stamps of Johore and Seychelles, and on various postage due stamps of Barbados, Basutoland, British Guiana, Gold Coast, Grenada, Northern Rhodesia, St. Lucia, Swaziland and Trinidad and Tobago. A variation of Wmk. 4a, with the non-matching crown in a horizontal row of crown-CA-crown, occurs on regular stamps of Bahamas, St. Kitts-Nevis and Singapore.

Wmk. 314 was intentionally used sideways, starting in 1966. When a stamp was issued with Wmk. 314 both upright and sideways, the sideways varieties usually are listed also — with minor numbers. In many of the later issues, Wmk. 314 is slightly visible.

Wmk. 373 is usually only faintly visible.

# CAMBODIA

kam-ˈbō-dē-ə

(Kampuchea)

(Khmer Republic)

LOCATION — Southern Indo-China
GOVT. — Republic
AREA — 69,898 sq. mi.
POP. — 11,626,520 (1999 est.)
CAPITAL — Phnom Penh

Before 1951, Cambodia used stamps of Indo-China. In October, 1970, the Kingdom of Cambodia became the Khmer Republic.

From 1978 to 1980 money was abolished.

100 Cents = 1 Piaster
100 Cents = 1 Riel (1955)

Imperforates

Most Cambodia stamps exist imperforate in issued and trial colors, and also in small presentation sheets in issued colors.

**Catalogue values for all unused stamps in this country are for Never Hinged items.**

Apsaras — A1

Enthronement Hall — A2

King Norodom Sihanouk — A3

**1951-52 Unwmk. Engr. *Perf. 13***

| No. | Type | Description | Unused | Used |
|---|---|---|---|---|
| 1 | A1 | 10c dk blue green | .90 | *3.00* |
| 2 | A1 | 20c red & org brn | .60 | *1.25* |
| 3 | A1 | 30c vio & indigo | .60 | .50 |
| 4 | A1 | 40c blue & bl grn | .80 | .80 |
| 5 | A2 | 50c Pruss blue & dk ol grn | .70 | .70 |
| 6 | A3 | 80c blksh grn & bl grn | 1.50 | *2.50* |
| 7 | A2 | 1pi indigo & dk pur | 1.40 | 1.00 |
| 8 | A3 | 1.10pi dp car & red | 1.75 | *2.50* |
| 9 | A3 | 1.50pi blk brn & red brn ('51) | 1.75 | 1.25 |
| 10 | A1 | 1.50pi dp car & cerise | 1.75 | 1.75 |
| 11 | A2 | 1.50pi indigo & dp ultra | 1.75 | 1.25 |
| 12 | A3 | 1.90pi indigo & dull bl | 3.50 | *5.75* |
| 13 | A2 | 2pi dp car & redsh brn | 2.50 | 1.00 |
| 14 | A3 | 3pi car & lake brn | 3.75 | 2.00 |
| 15 | A1 | 5pi indigo & purple | 12.00 | 6.50 |
| *a.* | | Souvenir sheet of 1 | 52.50 | |
| 16 | A2 | 10pi redsh vio & indigo | 14.00 | 11.00 |
| *a.* | | Souvenir sheet of 1 | 52.50 | |
| 17 | A3 | 15pi blk vio & pur | 32.50 | 22.50 |
| *a.* | | Souvenir sheet of 1 | 52.50 | |
| | | *Nos. 1-17 (17)* | 81.75 | 65.25 |

Nos. 15a, 16a, 17a sold in a booklet. Value, $300.

Stamps with completely white gum and no toning sell for a premium.

For surcharges see Nos. B1-B4.

Phnom Daun Penh — A4

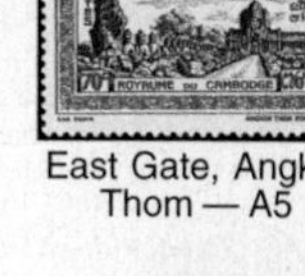
East Gate, Angkor Thom — A5

Arms of Cambodia A6

Methods of Mail Transport A7

**1954-55 Unwmk. *Perf. 13***

| No. | Type | Description | Unused | Used |
|---|---|---|---|---|
| 18 | A4 | 10c rose carmine | 1.25 | *1.75* |
| *a.* | | Souvenir sheet of 5 ('55) | 45.00 | 45.00 |
| 19 | A4 | 20c dark green | 1.50 | .45 |
| 20 | A4 | 30c indigo | 1.40 | *2.10* |
| 21 | A4 | 40c dark purple | 1.60 | .70 |
| 22 | A4 | 50c dk violet brn | 1.50 | .30 |
| 23 | A5 | 70c chocolate | 2.00 | *3.00* |
| *a.* | | Souvenir sheet of 5 ('55) | 45.00 | 45.00 |
| 24 | A5 | 1pi red violet | 2.00 | 1.60 |
| 25 | A5 | 1.50pi red | 2.00 | .50 |
| 26 | A6 | 2pi rose red | 2.00 | .40 |
| *a.* | | Souvenir sheet of 5 ('55) | 45.00 | 45.00 |
| 27 | A6 | 2.50pi green | 2.00 | .55 |
| 28 | A7 | 2.50pi blue green | 2.00 | .50 |
| *a.* | | Souvenir sheet of 5 ('55) | 45.00 | 45.00 |
| 29 | A6 | 3pi ultra | 2.10 | 1.50 |
| 30 | A7 | 4pi black brown | 3.00 | 2.75 |
| 31 | A6 | 4.50pi purple | 2.75 | 2.75 |
| 32 | A7 | 5pi rose red | 3.50 | 1.60 |
| 33 | A6 | 6pi chocolate | 3.00 | 2.25 |
| 34 | A7 | 10pi purple | 3.75 | 2.50 |
| 35 | A7 | 15pi deep blue | 4.50 | 4.50 |
| 36 | A5 | 20pi ultra | 10.00 | 4.75 |
| 37 | A5 | 30pi blue green | 16.00 | 7.50 |
| | | *Nos. 18-37 (20)* | 67.85 | 41.95 |
| | | Nos. 18a//28a, Set of 4 | 160.00 | |

The 4 souvenir sheets each contain 5 stamps: No. 18a (10c, 20c, 30c, 40c, 50c); #23a (70c, 1pi, 1.50pi, 20pi, 30pi); No. 26a (2pi, 2.50pi green, 3pi, 4.50pi, 6pi); No. 28a (2.50pi blue green, 4pi, 5pi. 10pi, 15pi). Size of No. 18a, 26a and 28a: 120x120mm. Size of No. 23a: 160x92mm. Values are for very fine, unblemished sheets. Examples with toning and/or gum bends sell for less.

For overprints see Nos. 99-100.

King Norodom Suramarit A8

King Norodom Suramarit and Queen Kossamak Nearirat Serey Vathana A9

Portraits: 50c (No. 39), 2.50r, 4r, 6r, 15r, Queen Kossamak Nearirat Serey Vathana.

***Perf. 14x13(A8), 13(A9)***

**1955, Nov. 24 Engr. Unwmk.**

| No. | Type | Description | Unused | Used |
|---|---|---|---|---|
| 38 | A8 | 50c violet | .40 | .40 |
| 39 | A8 | 50c indigo | .40 | .40 |
| 40 | A8 | 1r car lake | .50 | .45 |
| 41 | A9 | 1.50r dk brown | .80 | .50 |
| 42 | A9 | 2r black & indigo | .70 | .45 |
| 43 | A8 | 2r dp ultra | .80 | .60 |
| 44 | A8 | 2.50r dk vio brn | 1.10 | .60 |
| 45 | A9 | 3r brn org & car | 1.00 | .60 |
| 46 | A8 | 4r dark green | 1.40 | .90 |
| 47 | A9 | 5r blk & dk grn | 1.50 | 1.10 |
| 48 | A8 | 6r deep plum | 1.75 | 1.10 |
| 49 | A8 | 7r dark brown | 2.00 | 1.10 |
| 50 | A9 | 10r brn car & vio | 2.50 | 1.25 |
| 51 | A8 | 15r purple | 3.00 | 2.00 |
| 52 | A8 | 20r deep green | 4.75 | 2.75 |
| | | *Nos. 38-52 (15)* | 22.60 | 14.20 |

Coronation of King Norodom Suramarit and Queen Kossamak Nearirat Serey Vathana.

See Nos. 74-75. For surcharge see No. 122.

Queen Kossamak Nearirat Serey Vathana — A10

Portrait: 2r, 10r, 30r, King Norodom Suramarit.

**1956, Mar. 8 *Perf. 13***

| No. | Type | Description | Unused | Used |
|---|---|---|---|---|
| 53 | A10 | 2r dark red | 2.25 | 2.00 |
| 54 | A10 | 3r dark blue | 3.25 | 2.75 |
| 55 | A10 | 5r yellow green | 4.50 | 3.75 |
| 56 | A10 | 10r dark green | 9.00 | 7.50 |
| 57 | A10 | 30r dark violet | 19.00 | 15.00 |
| 58 | A10 | 50r rose lilac | 35.00 | 35.00 |
| | | *Nos. 53-58 (6)* | 73.00 | 66.00 |

Coronation of King Norodom Suramarit and Queen Kossamak Nearirat Serey Vathana.

Prince Sihanouk, Globe and Flags — A11

**1957, Mar. 1**

| No. | Type | Description | Unused | Used |
|---|---|---|---|---|
| 59 | A11 | 2r grn, ultra & car | 1.50 | 1.10 |
| 60 | A11 | 4.50r ultra | 1.50 | 1.10 |
| 61 | A11 | 8.50r carmine | 1.50 | 1.10 |
| | | *Nos. 59-61 (3)* | 4.50 | 3.30 |

Admission to the UN, 1st anniv. (in 1956).

**Type of Semi-Postal Stamps, 1957**

**1957, May 12 Unwmk. *Perf. 13***

| No. | Type | Description | Unused | Used |
|---|---|---|---|---|
| 62 | SP1 | 1.50r vermilion | 1.00 | 1.00 |
| 63 | SP1 | 6.50r bluish violet | 1.25 | 1.25 |
| 64 | SP1 | 8r dark green | 1.50 | 1.50 |
| | | *Nos. 62-64 (3)* | 3.75 | 3.75 |

2500th anniv. of the birth of Buddha.

King Ang Duong — A12

**1958, Mar. 4**

| No. | Type | Description | Unused | Used |
|---|---|---|---|---|
| 65 | A12 | 1.50r purple & brown | .60 | .60 |
| 66 | A12 | 5r olive gray & olive | .80 | .80 |
| 67 | A12 | 10r claret & dull brn | 1.50 | 1.50 |
| *a.* | | Souvenir sheet of 3, #65-67 | 6.50 | 6.00 |
| | | *Nos. 65-67 (3)* | 2.90 | 2.90 |

King Ang Duong (1795-1860).

No. 67a sold for 25r.

King Norodom I — A13

**1958-59 Engr. *Perf. 12½x13***

| No. | Type | Description | Unused | Used |
|---|---|---|---|---|
| 68 | A13 | 2r ultra & olive | .70 | .50 |
| 69 | A13 | 6r orange & sl grn | 1.00 | .70 |
| 70 | A13 | 15r green & ol gray | 2.00 | 1.40 |
| *a.* | | Souv. sheet of 3, #68-70 ('59) | 6.50 | 6.00 |
| | | *Nos. 68-70 (3)* | 3.70 | 2.60 |

King Norodom I (1835-1904).

No. 70a sold for 32r.

Issued: Nos. 68-70, 11/3/58; No. 70a, 1/31/59.

For surcharge see No. 184.

Children of the World — A14

**1959, Dec. 9 Unwmk. *Perf. 13***

| No. | Type | Description | Unused | Used |
|---|---|---|---|---|
| 71 | A14 | 20c rose violet | .30 | .30 |
| 72 | A14 | 50c blue | .55 | .55 |
| 73 | A14 | 80c rose carmine | 1.10 | 1.10 |
| | | *Nos. 71-73 (3)* | 1.95 | 1.95 |

Issued to promote friendship among the children of the world.

For surcharges see Nos. 115, B8-B10.

Nos. 49 and 52 with Black Border

**1960 *Perf. 14x13***

| No. | Type | Description | Unused | Used |
|---|---|---|---|---|
| 74 | A8 | 7r dk brown & blk | 4.50 | 4.50 |
| 75 | A8 | 20r dp green & blk | 4.50 | 4.50 |

Death of King Norodom Suramarit.

Port of Sihanoukville, Prince Sihanouk and Serpent Naga — A15

20r (double size)

**1960, Apr. *Perf. 13x12½***

| No. | Type | Description | Unused | Used |
|---|---|---|---|---|
| 76 | A15 | 2r carmine & sepia | .65 | .65 |
| *a.* | | Cambodian 20r | 3.50 | 3.50 |
| 77 | A15 | 5r ultra & dp brown | .65 | .65 |
| *a.* | | Cambodian 20r | 4.00 | 4.00 |
| 78 | A15 | 20r lilac & dk blue | 2.40 | 2.40 |
| | | *Nos. 76-78 (3)* | 3.70 | 3.70 |

Opening of the port of Sihanoukville. By error the denomination in Cambodian on the 2r and 5r was engraved as 20r; it was corrected later.

Ceremonial Plow — A16

**1960 *Perf. 12***

| No. | Type | Description | Unused | Used |
|---|---|---|---|---|
| 79 | A16 | 1r magenta | .65 | .65 |
| 80 | A16 | 2r brown | .90 | .90 |
| 81 | A16 | 3r bluish green | 1.25 | 1.25 |
| | | *Nos. 79-81 (3)* | 2.80 | 2.80 |

Feast of the Sacred Furrow.

Fight Against Illiteracy — A17

Water Conservation, Dam at Chhouksar A18

Dove, Factory and Books A19

Buddhist Ceremony — A20

Works of Sangkum: 6r, Workman and house. 10r, Woman in rice field.

**1960, Sept. 1 Engr. *Perf. 13***

**82** A17 2r dk grn, brn & dk bl .65 .40
*a.* Souvenir sheet of 3 8.00 8.00
**83** A18 3r brown & green .80 .40
*a.* Souvenir sheet of 3 8.00 8.00
**84** A19 4r rose car, vio & grn .80 .55
**85** A17 6r brown, org & grn .90 .70
**86** A17 10r ultra, grn & bis 2.25 1.40
**87** A20 25r dk car, red & mag 4.50 2.75
*Nos. 82-87 (6)* 9.90 6.20

No. 82a contains one each of Nos. 82, 85 and 87, and sold for 42r. No. 83a contains one each of Nos. 83, 84 and 86, and sold for 23r. Nos. 82a-83a were issued Dec. 5, 1960.

Cambodian Flag and Dove — A21

**1960, Dec. 24 Engr. *Perf. 13***

**Flag in Ultramarine and Red**

**88** A21 1.50r brown & green .40 .25
**89** A21 5r orange red .60 .35
**90** A21 7r green & ultra 1.25 1.00
*a.* Souvenir sheet of 3, #88-90 14.00 14.00
*b.* Souv. sheet of 3 (colors changed) 9.50 9.50
*Nos. 88-90 (3)* 2.25 1.60

Peace propaganda. No. 90a sold for 16r. No. 90b contains one of each denomination with colors changed to: 1.50r orange red, 5r green & ultramarine, 7r brown & green and sold for 20r.

Frangipani — A22

**1961, July 1 Unwmk. *Perf. 13***

**91** A22 2r shown .65 .65
**92** A22 5r Oleander 1.10 1.10
**93** A22 10r Amaryllis 2.75 2.75
*a.* Souvenir sheet of 3, #91-93 8.50 8.50
*Nos. 91-93 (3)* 4.50 4.50

No. 93a sold for 20r.

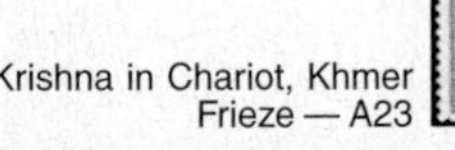

Krishna in Chariot, Khmer Frieze — A23

**1961-63 Typo. *Perf. 14x13½***

**94** A23 1r lilac .40 .25
**94A** A23 2r blue ('63) 3.25 1.60
**95** A23 3r emerald .90 .40
**96** A23 6r orange .90 .40
*a.* Souvenir sheet of 3 6.50 6.50
*Nos. 94-96 (4)* 5.45 2.65

Issued to honor Cambodian armed forces.
No. 94A issued in coils. No. 96a contains one each of Nos. 94, 95, 96. Sold for 12r.

Independence Monument — A24

**1961, Nov. 9 Engr. *Perf. 13x12½***

**97** A24 2r green .50 .50
**98** A24 4r gray brown .50 .50
*a.* Souvenir sheet of 2, #97-98 5.00 5.00
*Nos. 97-98,C15-C17 (5)* 9.40 7.05

10th anniv. of Independence.
For surcharge see No. 116.

Nos. 27 and 31 Overprinted in Red

**1961, Nov. 11 *Perf. 13***

**99** A6 2.50pi green 1.10 .65
**100** A6 4.50pi purple 1.75 1.00

Sixth World Conference of Buddhism.

Highway (American Aid) — A25

Foreign Aid: 2r, Power station (Czech aid). 4r, Textile factory (Chinese aid). 5r, Hospital (Russian aid). 6r, Airport (French aid).

**1961, Dec. Engr. *Perf. 13***

**101** A25 2r org & rose car .45 .30
**102** A25 3r bl, grn & org brn .45 .30
**103** A25 4r dl bl, org brn & mag .45 .40
**104** A25 5r dl grn & lil rose .65 .40
**105** A25 6r dk bl & org brn 1.25 .55
*a.* Souvenir sheet of 5, #101-105 7.00 7.00
*Nos. 101-105 (5)* 3.25 1.95

Malaria Eradication Emblem — A26

**1962, Apr. 7 Unwmk. *Perf. 13***

**106** A26 2r magenta & brown .50 .40
**107** A26 4r green & dk brown .50 .40
**108** A26 6r violet & olive bister .75 .45
*Nos. 106-108 (3)* 1.75 1.25

WHO drive to eradicate malaria.
For surcharges see Nos. B11-B12.

Fruits — A27

**1962, June 4 Engr.**

**109** A27 2r Cardamom .60 .45
**110** A27 4r Sugar apple 1.10 .75
**111** A27 6r Mangosteens 1.10 .75
*a.* Souvenir sheet of 3, #109-111 5.50 5.50
*Nos. 109-111 (3)* 2.80 1.95

Nos. 111a sold for 15r.

Pineapples — A28

**1962 Unwmk. *Perf. 13***

**112** A28 2r shown .80 .50
**113** A28 5r Sugar cane 1.25 .75
**114** A28 9r Sugar palms 1.50 .70
*Nos. 112-114 (3)* 3.55 1.95

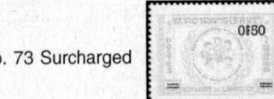

No. 73 Surcharged

**1962, Nov. 9 *Perf. 13***

**115** A14 50c on 80c rose car .70 .40

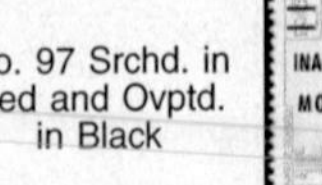

No. 97 Srchd. in Red and Ovptd. in Black

**1962**

**116** A24 3r on 2r green 1.00 .40

Dedication of Independence Monument. See No. C18.

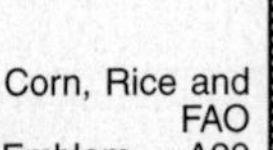

Corn, Rice and FAO Emblem — A29

**1963, Mar. 21 Engr. *Perf. 13***

**117** A29 3r multicolored .70 .55
**118** A29 6r org red, vio bl & ocher .70 .55

FAO "Freedom from Hunger" campaign.

Preah Vihear, Ancient Temple — A30

**1963, June 15 *Perf. 12½x13***

**119** A30 3r clar, brn & sl grn .45 .40
**120** A30 6r org, sl grn & grnsh blk .80 .65
**121** A30 15r blue, choc & green 1.25 1.10
*Nos. 119-121 (3)* 2.50 2.15

Return by Thailand of Preah Vihear on the Mekong River.
For overprint see No. 176.

No. 44 Surcharged

**1963 Engr. *Perf. 14x13***

**122** A8 3r on 2½r dk violet brn .90 .55

Tonsay Lake — A31

7r, Popokvil Falls. 20r, Beach, horiz.

***Perf. 12x12½, 12½x12***

**1963, Aug. 1 Photo.**

**123** A31 3r multicolored .50 .50
**124** A31 7r multicolored .80 .70
**125** A31 20r multicolored 2.50 1.10
*Nos. 123-125 (3)* 3.80 2.30

UNESCO Emblem, Scales and Globe — A32

**1963, Dec. 10 Engr. *Perf. 13***

**126** A32 1r vio bl, rose cl & grn .50 .50
**127** A32 3r yel grn, vio bl & rose cl .90 .90
**128** A32 12r rose cl, yel grn & vio bl 1.60 1.60
*Nos. 126-128 (3)* 3.00 3.00

15th anniversary of the Universal Declaration of Human Rights.
For surcharge see No. 183.

Kouprey — A33

**1964, Mar. 3 Unwmk. *Perf. 13***

**129** A33 50c grn, dk brn & org brn .95 .55
**130** A33 3r org, brn, dk brn & grn 1.40 .70
**131** A33 6r blue, dk brn & grn 2.10 1.40
*Nos. 129-131 (3)* 4.45 2.65

Black-billed Magpie — A34

**1964, May 2 Engr. *Perf. 13***

**132** A34 3r shown 1.40 .65
**133** A34 6r Kingfisher 2.10 1.00
**134** A34 12r Gray heron 3.75 2.00
*Nos. 132-134 (3)* 7.25 3.65

For overprint & surcharge see Nos. 303, B16.

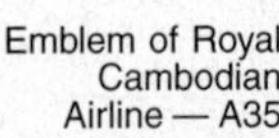

Emblem of Royal Cambodian Airline — A35

**1964 Unwmk. *Perf. 13x12½***

**135** A35 1.50r rose car & purple .40 .25
**136** A35 3r ver & dk blue .55 .40
**137** A35 7.50r ultra & car 1.25 .60
*Nos. 135-137 (3)* 2.20 1.25

8th anniv. of the Royal Cambodian Airline.

Prince Norodom Sihanouk — A36

**1964 Engr. *Perf. 12½x13***

**138** A36 2r purple .50 .40
**139** A36 3r red brown .70 .50
**140** A36 10r dark blue 1.35 .90
*Nos. 138-140 (3)* 2.55 1.80

10th anniv. of the Sangkum (political party).
For overprints see Nos. 144-145.

A set of three stamps, imperf, showing clasped hands, was prepared for International Cooperation Year but were never issued. Value, $200.

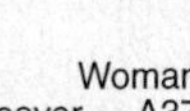

Woman Weaver — A37

Khmer Handicrafts: 3r, Metal worker. 5r, Basket maker.

**1965, Feb. 1 *Perf. 13x12½***

**141** A37 1r multicolored .40 .40
**142** A37 3r red lil, red brn & gray ol .65 .40
**143** A37 5r green, dk brn & car 1.10 .85
*Nos. 141-143 (3)* 2.15 1.65

Nos. 139-140 Overprinted in Black or Red

**1965, Mar. 1 *Perf. 12½x13***

**144** A36 3r red brown .70 .40
**145** A36 10r dark blue (R) 1.00 .55

Conference of the people of Indo-China.

ITU Emblem, Old and New Communication Equipment — A38

**1965, May 17 Engr. *Perf. 13***

146 A38 3r green & olive bister .40 .30
147 A38 4r red & blue .70 .40
148 A38 10r violet & rose lilac 1.00 .70
*Nos. 146-148 (3)* 2.10 1.40

Centenary of the ITU.

Cotton Plant — A39

3r, Peanut plant. 7.50r, Coconut palm.

**1965, Aug. 2 *Perf. 12½x13***

149 A39 1.50r org, sl grn & pur .50 .40
150 A39 3r blue, yel, grn & brn .80 .60
151 A39 7.50r org brn & sl grn 1.35 1.00
*Nos. 149-151 (3)* 2.65 2.00

Preah Ko Temple, Rolouoh A40

Temples at Angkor: 5r, Baksei Chamkrong, Rolouoh. 7r, Banteay Srei (Citadel of Women). 9r, Angkor Wat. 12r, Bayon, Angkor Thom.

**1966, Feb. 1 Engr. *Perf. 13***

152 A40 3r gray ol, sal & dl grn 1.25 .80
153 A40 5r lil, dk grn & redsh brn 1.50 .85
154 A40 7r dk grn, redsh brn & bis 1.75 1.60
155 A40 9r vio bl, pur & dk grn 2.50 2.10
156 A40 12r dk grn, rose car & ver 3.00 2.75
*Nos. 152-156 (5)* 10.00 8.10

For overprints see Nos. 172-175, 177.

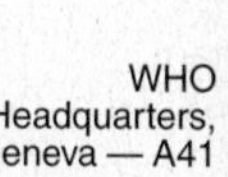

WHO Headquarters, Geneva — A41

**1966, July 1 Photo. *Perf. 12½x13***
**WHO Emblem in Blue and Yellow**

157 A41 2r black & pale rose .40 .25
158 A41 3r black & yel grn .50 .40
159 A41 5r black & lt bl .80 .55
*Nos. 157-159 (3)* 1.70 1.20

Inauguration of WHO Headquarters, Geneva.

Tree Planting — A42

**1966, July 22 Engr. *Perf. 12½x13***

160 A42 1r brn, dull brn & brt grn .30 .25
161 A42 3r org, dull brn & brt grn .55 .30
162 A42 7r gray, dull brn & brt grn .85 .40
*Nos. 160-162 (3)* 1.70 .95

Issued for Arbor Day.

UNESCO Emblem — A43

**1966 Photo. *Perf. 13***

163 A43 3r multicolored .50 .40
164 A43 7r multicolored .75 .55

20th anniv. of UNESCO.

Wrestlers and Games' Emblem — A44

GANEFO Games (Games Emblem and): 3r, Stadium, Phnom Penh. 7r, Swordsmen. 10r, Indian club swingers. Bas-reliefs from Angkor Wat.

**1966, Nov. 25 Engr. *Perf. 13***

165 A44 3r violet blue .40 .25
166 A44 4r green .45 .30
167 A44 7r dk car rose .70 .50
168 A44 10r dark brown 1.10 .65
*Nos. 165-168 (4)* 2.65 1.70

Indian Wild Boar — A45

***Perf. 13x12½, 12½x13***
**1967, Feb. 20 Engr.**

169 A45 3r shown 1.40 .40
170 A45 5r Muntjac, vert. 1.75 .65
171 A45 7r Elephant 2.40 .95
*Nos. 169-171 (3)* 5.55 2.00

**Nos. 152-153, 155-156 and 121 Overprinted in Red**

**1967, Apr. 27 Engr. *Perf. 13***

172 A40 3r multicolored .75 .75
173 A40 5r multicolored .80 .75
174 A40 9r multicolored 1.25 1.25
175 A40 12r multicolored 1.50 1.50
176 A30 15r multicolored 1.75 1.75
*Nos. 172-176 (5)* 6.05 6.00

International Tourist Year, 1967.

**No. 154 Overprinted in Red**

**1967, Apr. 27**

177 A40 7r multicolored 1.50 .60

Banteay Srei Temple at Angkor, millennium.

Royal Ballet Dancer — A46

Various Dancers

**1967, June Engr. *Perf. 13***

178 A46 1r orange .40 .40
179 A46 3r Prus blue .75 .60
180 A46 5r ultra 1.25 .55
181 A46 7r carmine rose 1.50 .80
182 A46 10r multicolored 1.75 1.00
*Nos. 178-182 (5)* 5.65 3.35

Cambodian Royal Ballet.

Nos. 128 and 70 Srchd. in Red

**1967, Sept. 8 Engr.**

183 A32 6r on 12r multi 1.00 .50
184 A13 7r on 15r grn & olive gray 1.25 .70

Intl. Literacy Day, Sept. 8. The surcharge on No. 184 is adapted to fit the shape of the stamp.

Symbolic Water Cycle — A47

**1967, Nov. 1 Typo. *Perf. 13x14***

185 A47 1r black, bl & org .30 .25
186 A47 6r lilac, lt bl & org .60 .30
187 A47 10r dk blue, emer & org .90 .50
*Nos. 185-187 (3)* 1.80 1.05

Hydrological Decade (UNESCO), 1965-74.

Royal University, Kompong Cham — A48

6r, Engineering School, Phnom Penh. 9r, University Center, Sangkum Reastr Niyum.

**1968, Mar. 1 Engr. *Perf. 13***

188 A48 4r violet bl & multi .50 .40
189 A48 6r slate & multi .65 .40
190 A48 9r Prus blue & multi .90 .55
*Nos. 188-190 (3)* 2.05 1.35

Vaccination and WHO Emblem — A49

WHO, 20th Anniv.: 7r, Malaria control and WHO emblem (man spraying DDT).

**1968, July 8 Engr. *Perf. 13***

191 A49 3r ultramarine .60 .40
192 A49 7r deep blue .90 .55

Stadium, Mexico City — A50

**1968, Oct. 12 Engr. *Perf. 13***

193 A50 1r shown .55 .55
194 A50 2r Wrestling .70 .55
195 A50 3r Bicycling .75 .55
196 A50 5r Boxing, vert. .95 .55
197 A50 7.50r Torch bearer, vert. 1.25 .75
*Nos. 193-197 (5)* 4.20 2.95

19th Olympic Games, Mexico City, 12/12-27.

Red Cross Team — A51

**1968, Nov. 1 Engr. *Perf. 13***

198 A51 3r Prus bl, grn & red 1.50 .50

Issued to honor the Cambodian Red Cross.

Prince Norodom Sihanouk — A52

8r, Soldiers wading through swamp.

**1968, Nov. 9**

199 A52 7r emer, ultra & pur .50 .40
200 A52 8r bl, grn & dp brn .75 .55

15th anniversary of independence.

Human Rights Flame and Prince Sihanouk — A53

**1968, Dec. 10 Engr. *Perf. 13***

201 A53 3r blue .45 .25
202 A53 5r bright plum .80 .35
203 A53 7r multicolored 1.10 .55
*Nos. 201-203 (3)* 2.35 1.15

International Human Rights Year.

ILO Emblem — A54

**1969, May 1 Engr. *Perf. 13***

204 A54 3r ultra .50 .25
205 A54 6r dp carmine .70 .40
206 A54 9r blue green 1.00 .55
*Nos. 204-206 (3)* 2.20 1.20

ILO, 50th anniversary.

Globe, Red Cross, Crescent, Lion and Sun Emblems — A55

**1969, May 8**

207 A55 1r blue, red & yel .40 .25
208 A55 3r sl grn, red & vio brn .65 .40
209 A55 10r brt lil, red & brn 1.40 .60
*Nos. 207-209 (3)* 2.45 1.25

50th anniv. of the League of Red Cross Societies.

Papilio Oeacus — A56

Butterflies: 4r, Papilio agamenon. 8r, Danaus plexippus.

**1969, Oct. 10 Engr. *Perf. 13***

210 A56 3r lilac, blk & yel 3.25 1.00
211 A56 4r ver, blk & grn 4.00 2.00
212 A56 8r yel grn, dk brn & org 5.75 3.00
*Nos. 210-212 (3)* 13.00 6.00

Map of Cambodia and Diesel Engine — A57

Various railroad stations and trains.

**1969, Nov. 27 Engr. *Perf. 13***

213 A57 3r multicolored 1.00 .75
214 A57 6r slate grn & lt brn 2.00 1.50
215 A57 8r black 3.25 2.25
216 A57 9r dk green & blue 3.75 2.40
*Nos. 213-216 (4)* 10.00 6.90

Issued to publicize the new rail link between Phnom Penh and Sihanoukville.

Fish — A58

**1970, Jan. 29 Photo. *Perf. 13***

217 A58 3r Tripletail 1.75 .90
218 A58 7r Sleeper goby 3.75 1.50
219 A58 9r Snakehead 5.50 2.00
*Nos. 217-219 (3)* 11.00 4.40

Wat Maniratanaram A59

Monasteries: 2r, Wat Tepthidaram, vert. 6r, Wat Patumavati. 8r, Wat Unnalom.

**1970, Apr. 29 Photo. *Perf. 13***

| | | | | |
|---|---|---|---|---|
| **220** | A59 | 2r multicolored | .35 | .40 |
| **221** | A59 | 3r multicolored | .40 | .40 |
| **222** | A59 | 6r multicolored | .85 | .40 |
| **223** | A59 | 8r multicolored | 1.60 | .55 |
| | | *Nos. 220-223 (4)* | 3.20 | 1.75 |

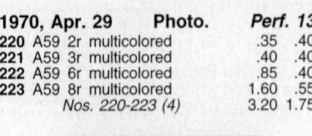

UPU Headquarters and Monument, Bern — A60

**1970, May 20**

| | | | | |
|---|---|---|---|---|
| **224** | A60 | 1r green & multi | .35 | .25 |
| **225** | A60 | 3r scarlet & multi | .50 | .30 |
| **226** | A60 | 4r dp blue & multi | .65 | .30 |
| **227** | A60 | 10r brown & multi | 1.00 | .60 |
| | | *Nos. 224-227 (4)* | 2.50 | 1.45 |

New UPU Headquarters in Bern.

Open Book and Satellite Earth Receiving Station — A61

**1970, May 17 Photo. *Perf. 13***

| | | | | |
|---|---|---|---|---|
| **228** | A61 | 3r dk vio bl & multi | .30 | .25 |
| **229** | A61 | 4r sl grn & multi | .40 | .25 |
| **230** | A61 | 9r brn ol & multi | .85 | .35 |
| | | *Nos. 228-230 (3)* | 1.55 | .85 |

World Telecommunications Day.

Nelumbium Speciosum A62

Flowers: 4r, Eichhornia crassipes. 13r, Nymphea lotus.

**1970, Aug. 17 Photo. *Perf. 13***

| | | | | |
|---|---|---|---|---|
| **231** | A62 | 3r multicolored | .70 | .30 |
| *a.* | | Cambodian and Arabic 3's transposed | 35.00 | 35.00 |
| **232** | A62 | 4r multicolored | 1.40 | .45 |
| **233** | A62 | 13r multicolored | 3.00 | .70 |
| | | *Nos. 231-233 (3)* | 5.10 | 1.45 |

Elephant God, Bas relief at Banteay Srei — A63

**1970, Sept. 21 Engr. *Perf. 13***

| | | | | |
|---|---|---|---|---|
| **234** | A63 | 3r lil rose & dp grn | .35 | .25 |
| **235** | A63 | 4r bl grn, grn & lil rose | .55 | .25 |
| **236** | A63 | 7r bl grn, dk brn & grn | .85 | .40 |
| | | *Nos. 234-236 (3)* | 1.75 | .90 |

Issued for World Meteorological Day.

### Khmer Republic

Globe, Rocket, Dove and UN Emblem — A64

**1970, Nov. 9 Photo. *Perf. 12½x12***

| | | | | |
|---|---|---|---|---|
| **237** | A64 | 3r black & multi | .30 | .25 |
| **238** | A64 | 5r brown red & multi | .45 | .25 |
| **239** | A64 | 10r dp violet & multi | .90 | .50 |
| | | *Nos. 237-239 (3)* | 1.65 | 1.00 |

25th anniversary of the United Nations.

Education Year Emblem — A65

**1970, Nov. 9 Engr. *Perf. 13x12½***

| | | | | |
|---|---|---|---|---|
| **240** | A65 | 1r blue | .25 | .25 |
| **241** | A65 | 3r brt rose lilac | .35 | .25 |
| **242** | A65 | 8r blue green | .75 | .45 |
| | | *Nos. 240-242 (3)* | 1.35 | .95 |

Issued for International Education Year.

Chuon-Nath A66

**1971, Jan. 27 Photo. *Perf. 13***

| | | | | |
|---|---|---|---|---|
| **243** | A66 | 3r ol grn & multi | .35 | .25 |
| **244** | A66 | 8r purple & multi | .75 | .35 |
| **245** | A66 | 9r violet & multi | 1.00 | .55 |
| | | *Nos. 243-245 (3)* | 2.10 | 1.15 |

In memory of Chuon-Nath (1883-1969), Cambodian language expert.

For surcharge see No. 322.

Soldiers in Battle — A67

**1971, Mar. 18 Photo. *Perf. 13***

| | | | | |
|---|---|---|---|---|
| **246** | A67 | 1r gray & multi | .35 | .25 |
| **247** | A67 | 3r bister & multi | .55 | .40 |
| **248** | A67 | 10r blue & multi | 1.40 | .75 |
| | | *Nos. 246-248 (3)* | 2.30 | 1.40 |

National territorial defense.

For overprint see No. 321.

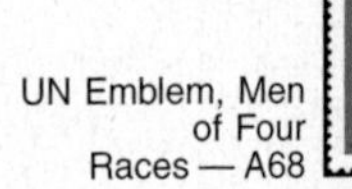

UN Emblem, Men of Four Races — A68

**1971, Mar. 21**

| | | | | |
|---|---|---|---|---|
| **249** | A68 | 3r blue & multi | .65 | .25 |
| **250** | A68 | 7r green & multi | 1.25 | .40 |
| **251** | A68 | 8r brt rose & multi | 2.00 | .55 |
| | | *Nos. 249-251 (3)* | 3.90 | 1.20 |

Intl. year against racial discrimination.

General Post Office, Phnom Penh — A69

**1971, Apr. 19**

| | | | | |
|---|---|---|---|---|
| **252** | A69 | 3r blue & multi | .35 | .25 |
| **253** | A69 | 9r lilac rose & multi | .65 | .35 |
| **254** | A69 | 10r black & multi | 1.05 | .40 |
| | | *Nos. 252-254 (3)* | 2.05 | 1.00 |

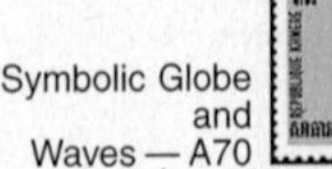

Symbolic Globe and Waves — A70

Design: 7r, 8r, ITU emblem and waves.

**1971, May 17 Photo. *Perf. 13***

| | | | | |
|---|---|---|---|---|
| **255** | A70 | 3r green, blk & bl | .25 | .25 |
| **256** | A70 | 4r yellow & multi | .40 | .25 |
| **257** | A70 | 7r lilac, blk & red | .50 | .25 |
| **258** | A70 | 8r sal pink, blk & red | .60 | .30 |
| | | *Nos. 255-258 (4)* | 1.75 | 1.05 |

3rd World Telecommunications Day.

Erythrina Indica — A71

Wild Flowers: 3r, Bauhinia variegata. 6r, Butea frondosa. 10r, Lagerstroemia floribunda, vert.

**1971, July 5 *Perf. 13x12½, 12½x13***

| | | | | |
|---|---|---|---|---|
| **259** | A71 | 2r lt ultra & multi | .55 | .45 |
| **260** | A71 | 3r yel grn & multi | .65 | .55 |
| **261** | A71 | 6r blue & multi | 1.40 | 1.10 |
| **262** | A71 | 10r brown & multi | 1.75 | 1.40 |
| | | *Nos. 259-262 (4)* | 4.35 | 3.50 |

Khmer Coat of Arms A72

Flag and Square of the Republic A73

**1971, Oct. 9 Engr. *Perf. 13***

| | | | | |
|---|---|---|---|---|
| **263** | A72 | 3r brt grn & bis | .25 | .25 |
| **264** | A73 | 3r purple & multi | .30 | .25 |
| **265** | A73 | 4r dp claret & multi | .40 | .25 |
| **266** | A72 | 8r orange & bis | .50 | .25 |
| **267** | A72 | 10r lt brn & bis | .80 | .30 |
| *a.* | | Souv. sheet of 3, #263, 266-267 | 3.25 | 3.25 |
| **268** | A73 | 10r slate grn & multi | .80 | .35 |
| *a.* | | Souv. sheet of 3, #264-265, 268 | 3.25 | 3.25 |
| | | *Nos. 263-268 (6)* | 3.05 | 1.65 |

Republic, 1st anniv.

No. 267a sold for 25r, No. 268a for 20r.

For overprints and surcharges see Nos. 301-302, B13-B14.

UNICEF Emblem — A74

**1971, Dec. 11**

| | | | | |
|---|---|---|---|---|
| **269** | A74 | 3r black brown | .35 | .25 |
| **270** | A74 | 5r ultra | .50 | .25 |
| **271** | A74 | 9r dk pur & brn red | 1.00 | .45 |
| | | *Nos. 269-271 (3)* | 1.85 | .95 |

25th anniv. of UNICEF.

This set and others exist with overprint "RPK," both with and without frame. Status has not been determined.

Book Year Emblem — A75

**1972, Feb. 7**

| | | | | |
|---|---|---|---|---|
| **272** | A75 | 3r blue, grn & vio | .40 | .25 |
| **273** | A75 | 8r violet, grn & bl | .60 | .30 |
| **274** | A75 | 9r emerald & multi | 1.00 | .50 |
| *a.* | | Souvenir sheet of 3, #272-274 | 3.00 | 3.00 |
| | | *Nos. 272-274 (3)* | 2.00 | 1.05 |

Intl. Book Year. No. 274a sold for 23r.

Lion of St. Mark — A76

Designs: 5r, Waves engulfing St. Mark's Basilica. 10r, Bridge of Sighs, vert.

**1972, Feb. 7 Engr. *Perf. 13***

| | | | | |
|---|---|---|---|---|
| **275** | A76 | 3r lil rose & org brn | .50 | .25 |
| **276** | A76 | 5r yel grn & org brn | 1.00 | .40 |
| **277** | A76 | 10r org brn, bl & yel grn | 1.25 | .50 |
| *a.* | | Souvenir sheet of 3, #275-277 | 3.00 | 3.00 |
| | | *Nos. 275-277 (3)* | 2.75 | 1.15 |

UNESCO campaign to save Venice. No. 277a sold for 23r.

UN Emblem — A77

**1972, Mar. 28**

| | | | | |
|---|---|---|---|---|
| **278** | A77 | 3r deep carmine | .50 | .25 |
| **279** | A77 | 6r deep blue | .75 | .35 |
| **280** | A77 | 9r deep orange | .90 | .50 |
| *a.* | | Souvenir sheet of 3, #278-280 | 2.75 | 2.75 |
| | | *Nos. 278-280 (3)* | 2.15 | 1.10 |

25th anniv. UN Economic Commission for Asia and the Far East (ECAFE). No. 280a sold for 23r.

Dancing Apsarases — A78

**1972, May 5 Engr. *Perf. 13***

| | | | | |
|---|---|---|---|---|
| **281** | A78 | 1r golden brn | .25 | .25 |
| **282** | A78 | 3r violet | .30 | .25 |
| **283** | A78 | 7r rose claret | .40 | .30 |
| **284** | A78 | 8r olive brn | .55 | .30 |
| **285** | A78 | 9r blue grn | .60 | .30 |
| **286** | A78 | 10r ultra | .90 | .30 |
| **287** | A78 | 12r purple | 1.00 | .30 |
| **288** | A78 | 14r Prus blue | 1.25 | .45 |
| | | *Nos. 281-288 (8)* | 5.25 | 2.45 |

"UIT" — A79

**1972, May 17 Litho.**

| | | | | |
|---|---|---|---|---|
| **289** | A79 | 3r blk, yel & grnsh bl | .40 | .25 |
| **290** | A79 | 9r blk, dp lil rose & bl grn | .75 | .30 |
| **291** | A79 | 14r blk, brn & bl grn | 1.10 | .45 |
| | | *Nos. 289-291 (3)* | 2.25 | 1.00 |

4th World Telecommunications Day.

"Human Environment" — A80

**1972, June 5 Engr.**

| | | | | |
|---|---|---|---|---|
| **292** | A80 | 3r org, plum & grn | .50 | .25 |
| **293** | A80 | 12r brt grn & plum | .75 | .30 |
| **294** | A80 | 15r plum & brt grn | 1.25 | .50 |
| *a.* | | Souvenir sheet of 3, #292-294 | 3.00 | 3.00 |
| | | *Nos. 292-294 (3)* | 2.50 | 1.05 |

UN Conf. on Human Environment, Stockholm, June 5-16. No. 294a sold for 35r.

For overprints and surcharges see Nos. 304-305, B15, B17.

Javan Rhinoceros A81

**1972, Aug. 1 Engr. *Perf. 13***

| | | | | |
|---|---|---|---|---|
| **295** | A81 | 3r shown | .55 | .25 |
| **296** | A81 | 4r Serow | .65 | .25 |
| **297** | A81 | 6r Malayan sambar | 1.25 | .30 |
| **298** | A81 | 7r Banteng | 1.75 | .30 |
| **299** | A81 | 8r Water buffalo | 2.00 | .50 |
| **300** | A81 | 10r Gaur | 2.25 | .60 |
| | | *Nos. 295-300 (6)* | 8.45 | 2.20 |

Nos. 263, 267, 134, 293, 294 Overprinted in Red

**1972, Sept. 9 Engr. *Perf. 13***

| | | | | |
|---|---|---|---|---|
| **301** | A72 | 3r brt grn & bister | .60 | .30 |
| **302** | A72 | 10r orange & bister | 1.20 | .65 |
| **303** | A34 | 12r multicolored | 1.20 | .80 |
| **304** | A80 | 12r brt grn & plum | 1.30 | .80 |
| **305** | A80 | 15r plum & brt grn | 1.75 | 1.00 |
| | | *Nos. 301-305 (5)* | 6.05 | 3.55 |

20th Olympic Games, Munich, 8/26-9/11.

Raising Khmer Flag — A82

**1972, Oct. 9 Photo. *Perf. 12½x13***

| | | | | |
|---|---|---|---|---|
| **306** | A82 | 3r multicolored | .25 | .25 |
| **307** | A82 | 5r brt rose & multi | .40 | .30 |
| **308** | A82 | 9r yel grn & multi | .90 | .50 |
| | | *Nos. 306-308 (3)* | 1.55 | 1.05 |

2nd anniversary of the establishment of the Khmer Republic.
For surcharge see No. 323.

Stupa and Crest — A83

**1973, May 12 Engr. *Perf. 13***

| | | | | |
|---|---|---|---|---|
| **309** | A83 | 3r ocher & multi | .45 | .25 |
| **310** | A83 | 12r yel grn & multi | .45 | .25 |
| **311** | A83 | 14r blue & multi | .75 | .50 |
| *a.* | | Souvenir sheet of 3, #309-311 | 3.25 | 3.25 |
| | | *Nos. 309-311 (3)* | 1.65 | 1.00 |

New Constitution. No. 311a sold for 34r.

Apsaras — A84

Sculptures from Angkor Wat: 8r, 10r, Devata, diff.

**1973, July 23 Engr. *Perf. 13***

| | | | | |
|---|---|---|---|---|
| **312** | A84 | 3r brown black | .50 | .25 |
| **313** | A84 | 8r Prus green | .65 | .30 |
| **314** | A84 | 10r olive bister | 1.60 | .50 |
| *a.* | | Souvenir sheet of 3, #312-314 | 3.00 | 3.00 |
| | | *Nos. 312-314 (3)* | 2.75 | 1.05 |

No. 314a sold for 25r.

INTERPOL Emblem — A85

**1973, Oct. 2 Engr. *Perf. 13***

| | | | | |
|---|---|---|---|---|
| **315** | A85 | 3r green & multi | .45 | .25 |
| **316** | A85 | 7r red brn & multi | .55 | .30 |
| **317** | A85 | 10r olive & multi | .75 | .45 |
| *a.* | | Souvenir sheet of 3, #315-317 | 4.50 | 4.50 |
| | | *Nos. 315-317 (3)* | 1.75 | 1.00 |

50th anniv. of the Intl. Criminal Police Org. No. 317a sold for 30r.

Marshal Lon Nol — A86

**1973, Oct. 9**

| | | | | |
|---|---|---|---|---|
| **318** | A86 | 3r lt grn, blk & brn | .40 | .25 |
| **319** | A86 | 8r brown, ol & blk | .60 | .30 |
| **320** | A86 | 14r black & brn | 1.00 | .40 |
| *a.* | | Souvenir sheet of 3 | 5.00 | 5.00 |
| | | *Nos. 318-320 (3)* | 2.00 | .95 |

Marshal Lon Nol, 1st pres. of the Republic. No. 320a contains stamps similar to Nos. 318-320 in changed colors. Sold for 50r.

Nos. 248, 243 and 307 Srchd. & Ovptd. in Red or Silver

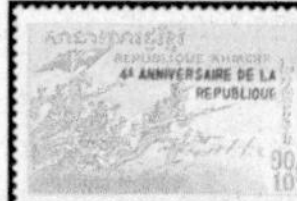

**1974 Photo. *Perf. 13, 12½x13***

| | | | | |
|---|---|---|---|---|
| **321** | A67 | 10r multi (R) | *4.50* | 2.50 |
| **322** | A66 | 50r on 3r multi | *9.50* | 4.00 |
| **323** | A82 | 100r on 5r multi | *22.50* | 6.50 |
| | | *Nos. 321-323 (3)* | *36.50* | 13.00 |

4th anniversary of the Republic.

Copernicus and "Nerva" — A87

Copernicus, various spacecraft and events: 5r, Mariner II. 10r, Apollo. 25r, Telstar. 50r, Space walk. 100r, Moon landing. 150r, Separation of spaceship and module.

**1974, Sept. 10 Litho. *Perf. 13***

| | | | | |
|---|---|---|---|---|
| **324** | A87 | 1r shown | .35 | .30 |
| **325** | A87 | 5r multicolored | .40 | .30 |
| **326** | A87 | 10r multicolored | .65 | .40 |
| **327** | A87 | 25r multicolored | 1.50 | .75 |
| **328** | A87 | 50r multicolored | 2.50 | 1.50 |
| **329** | A87 | 100r multicolored | 6.00 | 3.75 |
| **330** | A87 | 150r multicolored | 8.00 | 5.50 |
| | | *Nos. 324-330 (7)* | 19.40 | 12.50 |
| | | *Nos. 324-330,C46-C47 (9)* | 44.40 | 28.00 |

500th anniversary of the birth of Nicolaus Copernicus (1473-1543), Polish astronomer.

Carrier Pigeon and UPU Emblem A88

Design: 60r, Sailing ship and UPU emblem.

**1974, Nov. 2**

| | | | | |
|---|---|---|---|---|
| **331** | A88 | 10r multicolored | *1.50* | *1.50* |
| **332** | A88 | 60r multicolored | *4.50* | *4.50* |
| | | *Nos. 331-332,C50 (3)* | *17.50* | *17.50* |

Cent. of UPU. Souvenir sheets of one exist, both imperf. and simulated perfs for Nos. 331 and 332. Value, set of 3, $30 each. Also, set of 2 souvenirs sheets of one each No. 332 and No. C50 with silver borders, perf. and imperf. (simulated perfs.) Value, set $9 perf., $40 imperf.

A set of 8 stamps picturing musical instruments, overprinted and surcharged for use by the Khmer Republic just before the fall of the government in Apr. 1975, exists. Value, $1,100. Value for same set without surcharge, $500.

A89

1976 Summer Olympic Games, Montreal A90

1r, 18th cent. swordsmen. 5r, Modern fencers. 10r, Ancient Olympic runner. 25r, Modern runner. 50r, Ancient rowers. 100r, Modern kayakers. 150r, Ancient horseman. 200r, Modern equestrian competitor. 250r, Buildings, Olympic flame. No. 345, Buildings, runner.

**1975, Jan. 2 Litho. *Perf. 13½***

| | | | | |
|---|---|---|---|---|
| **333-341** | A89 | Set of 9 | 11.00 | |

**Litho. & Embossed**

| | | | | |
|---|---|---|---|---|
| **342** | A90 | 1200r gold & multi | *20.00* | |

**Souvenir Sheets**

| | | | | |
|---|---|---|---|---|
| **343** | A89 | 200r silver & multi | *9.00* | |
| **344** | A89 | 250r silver & multi | *9.00* | |
| **345** | A90 | 1,200r gold & multi | *20.00* | |

Nos. 337-345 are airmail.
Nos. 333-341 exist imperf. Value, set $47.50. Nos. 333-341 exist in souvenir sheets of one.
Nos. 342-345 exist imperf. Value, set $175.

A91

1974 World Cup Soccer Championships A92

Soccer players and arms of: 1r, Hamburg. 5r, Gelsenkirchen. 10r, Dortmund. 25r, Stuttgart. 50r, Dusseldorf. 100r, Hannover. 150r, Frankfurt. 200r, Munich. 250r, Berlin.

**Litho. (#346-354, 356-357)**
**Litho. & Embossed (#355, 358)**

**1975, Feb. 13**

| | | | | |
|---|---|---|---|---|
| **346-354** | A91 | Set of 9 | 12.00 | |
| **355** | A92 | 1200r gold & multi | *16.00* | |

**Souvenir Sheets**

| | | | | |
|---|---|---|---|---|
| **356** | A91 | 200r gold & multi | *6.50* | |
| **357** | A91 | 250r gold & multi | *6.50* | |
| **358** | A92 | 1200r gold & multi | *14.00* | |

Nos. 350-358 are airmail. Nos. 346-354 exist in imperforate souvenir sheets.

UPU, Cent. A93

Designs: 15r, Letter carrier, pack mule. 20r, Biplane. 70r, Post coach. 160r, Biplane, Concorde. 180r, Steam-powered wagon. 235r, Postrider, tail of mailplane. 500r, Railway mail car. 1000r, Airship. 2000r, Caravel.

**1975, Apr. 12**

| | | | | |
|---|---|---|---|---|
| **359-367** | A93 | Set of 9 | 9.00 | |
| *366a* | | Souvenir sheet of 1 | *4.75* | |
| *367a* | | Souvenir sheet of 1 | *4.75* | |

Nos. 365-367 are airmail. Nos. 366a and 367a exist imperf. Values, each $25.
Nos. 359-367 exist in imperf souvenir sheets of 1 with simulated perforations. Value, set of 9 sheets $22.50.

## People's Republic of Kampuchea

Soldiers — A94

Designs, horiz.: 20c, People, flag. 50c, Fishermen. 1r, Soldiers passing flag.

**1980, Apr. 10 Litho. *Perf. 11***

| | | | | |
|---|---|---|---|---|
| **368-371** | A94 | Set of 4 | *57.50* | *57.50* |

Soviet Union, 60th Anniv. — A95

Designs: 50c, Globe, Kremlin. 1r, Buildings, map of USSR.

**1982, Dec. 30 *Perf. 12x12½***

| | | | | |
|---|---|---|---|---|
| **372-373** | A95 | Set of 2 | 1.60 | .55 |

People's Republic of Kampuchea, 4th Anniv. — A96

Designs: 50c, Natl. arms, vert. 1r, shown. 3r, Map, stylized figures, vert. 6r, Temple, vert.

**1983, Jan. 7 Litho. *Perf. 13***

| | | | | |
|---|---|---|---|---|
| **374-376** | A96 | Set of 3 | 4.75 | 1.25 |

**Souvenir Sheet**

| | | | | |
|---|---|---|---|---|
| **377** | A96 | 6r multicolored | 6.00 | 2.25 |

1984 Summer Olympic Games, Los Angeles — A97

Designs: 20c, Runner with torch. 50c, Javelin. 80c, Pole vault. 1r, Discus. 1.50r, Relay race. 2r, Swimming. 3r, Basketball.
20c-1r, 3r are vert.

**1983, Jan. 20 Litho. *Perf. 13***

| | | | | |
|---|---|---|---|---|
| **378-384** | A97 | Set of 7 | 7.00 | 1.50 |

**Souvenir Sheet**

| | | | | |
|---|---|---|---|---|
| **385** | A97 | 6r Soccer | 5.75 | 3.25 |

No. 385 contains one 32x40mm stamp.

Butterflies A98

20c, Salatura genutia. 50c, Euploea althaea. 80c, Byasa polyeuctes. 1r, Stichophthalma howqua. 1.50r, Kallima inachus. 2r, Precis orithya. 3r, Catopsilia pomona.
20c, 50c, 1.50r, 2r, 3r are vert.

**1983, Feb. 18 Litho. *Perf. 13***

| | | | | |
|---|---|---|---|---|
| **386-392** | A98 | Set of 7 | 8.50 | 2.00 |

Khmer Culture — A99

Designs: 20c, Ruins, Srah Srang. 50c, Temple, Bakong. 80c, Ta Son. 1r, North Gate, Angkor Thom. 1.50r, Two winged figures. 2r, Apsara, Angkor. 3r, Statue of Banteai Srei.
80c-3r are vert.

**1983, Mar. 15**

| | | | | |
|---|---|---|---|---|
| **393-399** | A99 | Set of 7 | 6.00 | 1.75 |

Folk Dances — A100

Various dances. Denominations 50c, 1r, 3r.

**1983, Apr. 17 Litho. *Perf. 13***
**400-402** A100 Set of 3 4.00 1.25

**Souvenir Sheet**

**403** A100 6r Native, "buffalo" 6.50 1.40

No. 403 contains one 32x40mm stamp.

Raphael (1483-1520) A101

Parnassus (details): No. 404, 20c, Dante, Ennius, Homer. No. 406, 80c, Horace, Ovid, others. No. 409, 2r, The Muses. No. 410, 3r, Alcaeus, Petrarch, others.
School at Athens (details): No. 407, 1r, Euclid, disciples. No. 408, 1.50r, Telange, Pythagoras.
Details from: No. 405, 50c, Mass of Bolsena). 6r, Angels from Dispute of the Holy Sacrament, horiz.

**1983, May 10 Litho. *Perf. 12½x13***
**404-410** A101 Set of 7 6.00 2.25

**Souvenir Sheet**

***Perf. 13***

**411** A101 6r multicolored 7.25 2.75

No. 411 contains one 40x32mm stamp.

1st Hot Air Balloon Ascension, Bicent. — A102

Designs: 20c, Montgolfier. 30c, Ville d'Orleans. 50c, Hydrogen balloon. 1r, Blanchard & Jeffries, 1785. 1.50r, Ascension in Arctic. 2r, Stratosphere balloon. 3r, Balloon race. 6r, Balloons over town.

**1983, June 3 *Perf. 12½***
**412-418** A102 Set of 7 6.00 2.00

**Souvenir Sheet**

***Perf. 13***

**419** A102 6r multicolored 7.25 1.75

Reptiles A103

Designs: 20c, Iguana. 30c, Cobra. 80c, Trionyx turtle. 1r, Chameleon. 1.50r, Boa constrictor. 2r, Crocodile. 3r, Turtle.
30c, 1r, 1.50r are vert.

**1983, June 28**
**420-426** A103 Set of 7 8.00 2.50

Birds — A104

Designs: 20c, Lorikeet. 50c, Swallow. 80c, Eagle. 1r, Vulture. 1.50r, Turtle dove. 2r, Magpie. 3r, Hornbill.
20c-50c, 2r-3r are vert.

**1983, Sept. 20**
**427-433** A104 Set of 7 11.00 3.00

Flowers — A105

20c, Sunflower. 50c, Caprifoliacae. 80c, Bougainvillea. 1r, Renonculacae. 1.50r, Nyctaginaceae. 2r, Cockscomb. 3r, Roses.

**1983, Oct. 18 *Perf. 13***
**434-440** A105 Set of 7 6.00 1.75

1984 Winter Olympic Games, Sarajevo A106

Designs: 1r, Luge. 2r, Biathlon. 4r, Ski jumping. 5r, Two-man bobsled. 7r, Hockey.
6r, Cross-country skiing.

**1983, Nov. 10 *Perf. 12½***
**441-445** A106 Set of 5 14.00 2.75

**Souvenir Sheet**

**446** A106 6r multicolored 5.50 3.25

No. 446 contains one 40x32mm stamp.

Fish — A107

20c, 1.50r, 2r, 3r, Various Cyprinidae. 50c, Trout. 80c, Catfish. 1r, Moray eel.

**1983, Nov. 16 *Perf. 13***
**447-453** A107 Set of 7 8.00 2.00

Festival of Rebirth A108

50c, Factory. 1r, Bull, tractor. 3r, Bridge, ship, train. 6r, Radio antenna. 50c, 3r, 6r vert.

***Perf. 12½x13, 13x12½***

**1983, Dec. 2 Litho.**
**454-456** A108 Set of 3 3.50 1.00

**Souvenir Sheet**

**457** A108 6r multicolored 6.50 1.75

No. 457 contains one 32x40mm stamp.

People's Republic of Kampuchea, 5th Anniv. — A109

Designs: 50c, Red Cross. 1r, Soldiers. 3r, People celebrating. 6r, Man carrying water.

**1984, Jan. 7 Litho. *Perf. 13***
**458-460** A109 Set of 3 3.75 1.25

**Souvenir Sheet**

**461** A109 6r multicolored 6.50 1.75

No. 461 contains one 32x40mm stamp.
For surcharges see No. 776.

1984 Winter Olympics, Sarajevo — A110

Designs: 20c, Speed skating. 50c, Hockey. 80c, Slalom skiing. 1r, Ski jumping. 1.50r, Biathlon. 2r, Cross-country skiing. 3r, Pairs figure skating. 6r, Women's figure skating.

**1984, Jan. 6 Litho. *Perf. 13***
**462-468** A110 Set of 7 6.50 2.50

**Souvenir Sheet**

**469** A110 6r multicolored 5.00 3.00

No. 469 contains one 32x40mm stamp.
For surcharges see No. 775.

Birds — A111

Designs: 10c, Bubulcus ibis. 40c, Lanius schach. 80c, Psittacula himalayana. 1r, Chloropsis aurifrons. 1.20r, Clamator coromandus. 2r, Motacilla cinerea. 2.50r, Dendronanthus indicus.

**1984, Feb. 2**
**470-476** A111 Set of 7 15.00 4.00

Intl. Peace in Southeast Asia Forum — A112

Background color: 50c, Green. 1r, Blue. 3r, Violet.

**1984, Feb. 25 *Perf. 13x12½***
**477-479** A112 Set of 3 3.75 1.00

Space Exploration A113

Designs: 10c, Luna 1. 40c, Luna 2. 80c, Luna 3. 1r, Soyuz 6. 1.20r, Soyuz 7. 2r, Soyuz 8. 2.50r, Book, rocket, S.P. Koralev. 6r, Salyut space station.
1r-2.50r are vert.

**1984, Mar. 8 *Perf. 12½***
**480-486** A113 Set of 7 6.00 2.00

**Souvenir Sheet**

**487** A113 6r multicolored 6.50 1.75

No. 487 contains one 40x32mm stamp.

1984 Summer Olympic Games, Los Angeles — A114

Designs: 20c, Discus. 50c, Long jump. 80c, Hurdles. 1r, Relay race. 1.50r, Pole vault. 2r, Javelin. 3r, High jump. 6r, Sprint race.

**1984, Apr. 20 *Perf. 13***
**488-494** A114 Set of 7 7.00 2.50

**Souvenir Sheet**

**495** A114 6r multicolored 5.00 2.50

No. 495 contains one 32x40mm stamp.

Souvenir Sheet

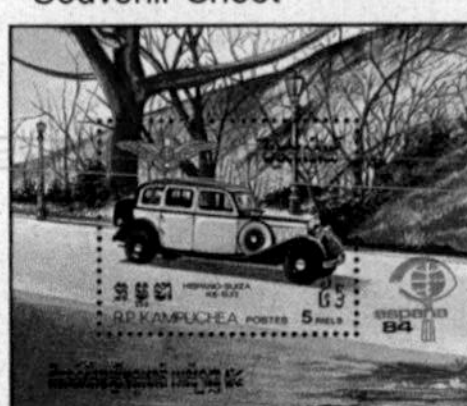

ESPAÑA '84, Madrid A115

5r, 1933 Hispano-Suiza K6.

**1984, Apr. 24 *Perf. 12½***
**496** A115 5r multicolored 5.75 2.25

Wild Animals A116

Designs: 10c, Canis latrans. 40c, Canis dingo. 80c, Lycaon pictus. 1r, Canis aureus. 1.20r, Vulpes vulpes. 2r, Chrysocyon brachyurus, vert. 2.50r, Canis lupus.

**1984, May 5 *Perf. 13***
**497-503** A116 Set of 7 9.00 1.75

Locomotives A117

Designs: 10c, BB-1002, France, 1966. 40c, BB-1052, France, 1966. 80c, Franco-Belgian, 1945. 1r, #231-505, Franco-Belgian, 1929. 1.20r, #803, Germany, 1968. 2r, BDE-405, France, 1957. 2.50r, DS-01, France, 1979.

**1984, June 15 Litho. *Perf. 12½***
**504-510** A117 Set of 7 7.75 1.75

Flowers — A118

Designs: 10c, Magnolia. 40c, Plumeria. 80c, Himenoballis. 1r, Peltophorum roxburghii. 1.20r, Couroupita guianensis. 2r, Lagerstroemia. 2.50r, Thevetia perubiana.

**1984, July 10 Litho. *Perf. 13***
**511-517** A118 Set of 7 6.00 2.25

Classic Automobiles A119

Designs: 20c, Mercedes-Benz. 50c, Bugatti. 80c, Alfa Romeo. 1r, Franklin. 1.50r, Hispano-Suiza. 2r, Rolls Royce. 3r, Tatra. 6r, Mercedes Benz, diff.

**1984, Sept. 15 *Perf. 13x12½***
**518-524** A119 Set of 7 6.00 2.00

**Souvenir Sheet**

***Perf. 12½***

**525** A119 6r multicolored 5.00 1.75

No. 525 contains one 40x32mm stamp.

Musical Instruments A120

Designs: 10c, Sra Lai. 40c, Skor drum. 80c, Skor thom. 1r, Thro khmer. 1.20r, Raneat ek. 2r, Raneat kong. 2.50r, Thro khe.
10c, 80c are vert.

**1984, Oct. 10 *Perf. 13***
**526-532** A120 Set of 7 5.00 1.75

Wild Animals A121

Designs: 10c, Gazelle. 40c, Capreolus capreolus. 80c, Lepus. 1r, Cervus elaphus. 1.20r, Elephas maximus. 2r, Genet. 2.50r, Bibos sauveli.
10c-40c, 1r-1.20r are vert.

**1984, Nov. 11** ***Perf. 13***
**533-539** A121 Set of 7 7.50 1.75

Correggio (1489-1534) A122

Details from paintings: 20c, Rest on Flight into Egypt. 50c, Martyrdom of the Four Saints. 80c, Mystic Marriage of St. Catherine with Saints Francis and Dominic. 1r, Madonna & Child with Saints John the Baptist, Geminian, Peter Martyr and George. 1.50r, Mystic Marriage of St. Catherine. 2r, The Deposition. 2.50r, The Deposition, diff. 6r, Virgin Crowned by Christ.

**1984, Dec. 10** ***Perf. 12½x13***
**540-546** A122 Set of 7 4.25 1.00

**Souvenir Sheet**

***Perf. 12½***

**547** A122 6r multicolored 5.00 1.00

No. 547 contains one 40x32mm stamp.

Natl. Festival A123

50c, Oxcart. 1r, Horse-drawn cart. 3r, Elephants. 6r, Oxcart with passengers, vert.

**1985, Jan. 5** ***Perf. 12½x12***
**548-550** A123 Set of 3 4.00 1.00

**Souvenir Sheet**

***Perf. 12½***

**551** A123 6r multicolored 6.00 1.00

No. 551 contains one 32x40mm stamp.

1986 World Cup Soccer Championships, Mexico — A124

Various soccer players; 20c, vert. 50c, vert. 80c, vert. 1r. 1.50r. 2r, vert. 3r, vert.

**1985, Feb. 4** ***Perf. 13***
**552-558** A124 Set of 7 4.50 1.25

**Souvenir Sheet**

**559** A124 6r multicolored 5.50 1.00

No. 559 contains one 40x32mm stamp.

Motorcycles A125

20c, 1939 Eska-Mofa. 50c, 1939 Wanderer. 80c, 1929 Premier. 1r, 1939 Ardie. 1.50r, 1932 Jawa. 2r, 1983 Simson. 3r, 1984 CZ-125.

**1985, Mar. 8** **Litho.** ***Perf. 13***
**560-566** A125 Set of 7 5.00 1.75

**Souvenir Sheet**

**567** A125 6r 1984 MBA 6.00 1.50

No. 567 contains one 40x32mm stamp.

Mushrooms A126

Designs: 20c, Gymnopilus spectabilis. 50c, Coprinus micaceus. 80c, Amanita panterina. 1r, Hebelona crustuliniforme. 1.50r, Amanita muscaria. 2r, Coprinus comatus. 3r, Amanita caesarea.
Nos. 569-574 are vert.

**1985, Apr. 4** ***Perf. 13***
**568-574** A126 Set of 7 6.00 1.40

Soviet Space Achievements A127

Designs: 20c, Sputnik. 50c, Yuri Gagarin, rocket. 80c, Valentina Tereshkova, Vostok 6. 1r, Cosmonaut walking in space. 1.50r, Soyuz 4 docked with Soyuz 5. 2r, Lunar rover. 3r, Apollo-Soyuz mission. 6r, Soyuz capsule.

**1985, Apr. 12** ***Perf. 13***
**575-581** A127 Set of 7 4.50 1.25

**Souvenir Sheet**

**582** A127 6r multicolored 5.00 1.00

No. 582 contains one 40x32mm stamp.

Traditional Dances A128

Designs: 50c, Four dancers. 1r, Three dancers. 3r, One dancer, vert.

**1985, Apr. 13** **Litho.** ***Perf. 12½***
**583-585** A128 Set of 3 3.00 1.25

End of World War II, 40th Anniv. — A129

Designs: 50c, Soldiers celebrating. 1r, Victory parade, Moscow. 3r, Tank battle.

**1985, May 9** **Litho.** ***Perf. 12x12½***
**586-588** A129 Set of 3 4.25 1.50

Cats — A130

Various cats: 20c, 50c, 80c, 1r, 1.50r, 2r, 3r.

**1985, May 16** **Litho.** ***Perf. 12x12½***
**589-595** A130 Set of 7 5.50 2.50

Flowers — A131

20c, Lilium Black Dragon. 50c, Iris delavayi. 80c, Crocus aureus. 1r, Cyclamen persicum, wild form. 1.50r, Primula malacoides. 2r, Viola tricolor. 3r, Crocus purpureus.

**1985, June 5** **Litho.** ***Perf. 13***
**596-602** A131 Set of 7 4.75 1.25

Intl. Music Year — A132

Paintings: 20c, Mezzetin, by Watteau. 50c, St. Cecilia and the Angel, by Saraceni. 80c, Still Life with Violin, Flute and Guitar, by Oudry, horiz. 1r, Three Musicians, by F. Leger. 1.50r, Opera Orchestra, by Degas. 2r, St. Cecilia, by Schedoni. 3r, Young Harlequin with Violin, by Caillard. 6r, The Fifer, by Manet.

**1985, June 13** ***Perf. 13***
**603-609** A132 Set of 7 4.00 1.25

**Souvenir Sheet**

**610** A132 6r multicolored 4.00 1.25

No. 610 contains one 32x40mm stamp.

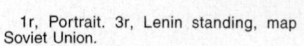

Lenin (1870-1924) — A133

1r, Portrait. 3r, Lenin standing, map of Soviet Union.

**1985, June 20** **Litho.** ***Perf. 13***
**611-612** A133 Set of 2 3.25 1.00

ARGENTINA '85 — A134

Birds: 20c, Xanthopsar flavus. 50c, Sicalis flaveola. 80c, Thraupis bonariensis. 1r, Amblyramphus holosericeus. 1.50r, Chiloroceryle amazona. 2r, Ramphastos toco. 3r, Turdus rufiventris.
20c-80c, 1.50r-2r are vert.

**1985, July 5** **Litho.** ***Perf. 12½***
**613-619** A134 Set of 7 8.50 2.00

Ships — A135

Designs: 10c, River boat, 1942. 40c, River boat, 1948. 80c, Tugboat, Japan, 1913. 1r, Dredge. 1.20r, Tugboat, US. 2r, Freighter. 2.50r, Tanker, Panama.

**1985, Aug. 8**
**620-626** A135 Set of 7 4.00 1.40

ITALIA 85 — A136

Paintings: 20c, The Flood, by Michelangelo. 50c, Virgin & St. Margaret, by Il Parmigianino (Filippo Mazzola). 80c, Martyrdom of St. Peter Martyr, by Domenichino. 1r, Spring, by Botticelli. 1.50r, Sacrifice of Abraham, by Veronese. 2r, Meeting of St. Joachim and St. Anne, by Giotto. 3r, Bacchus, by Caravaggio.
6r, Early train.

**1985, Oct. 25**
**627-633** A136 Set of 7 5.00 1.10

**Souvenir Sheet**

**634** A136 6r multicolored 4.00 1.25

No. 634 contains one 32x40mm stamp.

Son Ngoc Minh — A137

**1985, Dec. 2** **Litho.** ***Perf. 12x12½***
**635-637** A137 Set of 3, 50c, 1r, 3r 2.50 1.25

Fish — A138

20c, Barbus tetrazona. 50c, Ophiocephalus micropeltes. 80c, Carassius auratus. 1r, Trichogaster leeri. 1.50r, Puntius hexazona. 2r, Betta splendens. 3r, Datnioides microlepis.

**1985, Dec. 28** **Litho.** ***Perf. 13***
**638-644** A138 Set of 7 5.50 1.50

1986 World Cup Soccer Championships, Mexico — A139

Various soccer players: 20c, 50c, 80c, 1r, 1.50r, 2r, 3r.

**1986, Jan. 29**
**645-651** A139 Set of 7 4.25 1.25

**Souvenir Sheet**

**652** A139 6r multicolored 4.50 2.50

No. 652 contains one 32x40mm stamp.

Horses — A140

Designs: 20c, Cob. 50c, Arabian. 80c, Australian pony. 1r, Appaloosa. 1.50r, Quarter horse. 2r, Vladimir heavy draft. 3r, Andalusian.

**1986, Feb. 15**
**653-659** A140 Set of 7 5.00 1.50

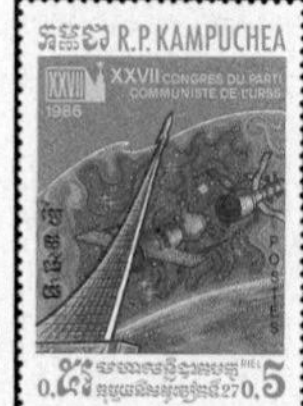

27th Soviet Communist Party Congress — A141

Designs: 50c, Space capsules. 1r, Lenin. 5r, Statue, rocket lift-off.

**1986, Feb. 25** ***Perf. 12x12½***
**660-662** A141 Set of 3 4.25 1.25

Prehistoric Animals — A142

Designs: 20c, Edaphosaurus, horiz. 50c, Sauroctonus, horiz. 80c, Mastodonsaurus, horiz. 1r, Rhamphorhynchus. 1.50r, Brachiosaurus. 2r, Tarbosaurus. 3r, Indricotherium.

**1986, Mar. 20** *Perf. 12½*
**663-669** A142 Set of 7 9.00 3.00

Manned Space Flight, 25th Anniv. A143

10c, Luna 16. 40c, Luna 3. 80c, Vostok. 1r, Alexei Leonov walking in space. 1.20r, Apollo-Soyuz mission. 2r, Soyuz capsule docking with Salyut station. 2.50r, Yuri Gagarin.

**1986, Apr. 12** *Perf. 12½*
**670-676** A143 Set of 7 5.75 1.50

Khmer Culture — A144

20c, Temple. 50c, Head of Buddha. 80c, Temple entrance. 1r, 1.50r, 2r, 3r, Various fans.

**1986, Apr. 12** *Perf. 13*
**677-683** A144 Set of 7 4.00 1.60

Mercedes-Benz Automobiles — A145

20c, 1885 3-wheel. 50c, 1935 sedan. 80c, 1907 open touring car. 1r, 1920 convertible. 1.50r, 1932 cabriolet. 2r, 1938 2-door. 3r, 1985 sedan.

**1986, May 14** *Perf. 13x12½*
**684-690** A145 Set of 7 4.25 1.50

Butterflies — A146

Designs: 20c, Danaus genutia. 50c, Graphium amtiphates. 80c, Papilio demoleus. 1r, Danaus sita. 1.50r, Idea blanchardi. 2r, Papilio polytes. 3r, Dabasa payeni.

**1986, June 19** *Perf. 13*
**691-697** A146 Set of 7 5.50 1.75

Ships — A147

20c, English cog. 50c, Cog. 80c, Nile barge. 1r, Galley. 1.50r, Viking long ship. 2r, Two-masted lateen-rigged ship. 3r, Cog, diff.

**1986, July 7** *Perf. 13*
**698-704** A147 Set of 7 4.25 1.50

Halley's Comet — A148

Designs: 10c, Solar system, Copernicus, Galileo, Brahe. 20c, Comet above Adoration of the Magi in painting by Giotto. 50c, Comet, observatory. 80c, Edmond Halley. 1.20r, Giotto probe. 1.50r, Vega probe. 2r, Computer-enhanced images of comet. 6r, Vega probe, diff.

**1986, July 21** **Litho.** *Perf. 12x12½*
**705-711** A148 Set of 7 3.25 1.40

**Souvenir Sheet**

*Perf. 13*

**712** A148 6r multicolored 4.25 1.25

No. 712 contains one 32x40mm stamp.

STOCKHOLMIA 86 — A149

Chess masters: 20c, Ruy Lopez. 50c, Francois Philador. 80c, Adolph Anderssen. 1r, Wilhelm Steinetz. 1.50r, Emanuel Lasker. 2r, José Capablanca. 3r, Alexander Alekhine.
6r, Chess pieces.

**1986, Aug. 28** **Litho.** *Perf. 12½*
**713-719** A149 Set of 7 5.00 1.60

**Souvenir Sheet**

*Perf. 13*

**720** A149 6r multicolored 6.00 1.60

No. 720 contains one 40x32mm stamp.

Cactus — A150

20c, Parodia maasii. 50c, Rebutia marsoneri. 80c, Melocactus evae. 1r, Gymnocalycium valnicekianum. 1.50r, Discocactus silichromus. 2r, Neochilenia simulans. 3r, Weingartia chiqichuquensis.

**1986, Sept. 25** *Perf. 13*
**721-727** A150 Set of 7 4.25 1.40

Fruit — A151

Designs: 10c, Bananas. 40c, Papayas. 80c, Mangos. 1r, Breadfruit. 1.20r, Litchi. 2r, Pineapple. 2.50r, Grapefruit, horiz.

**1986, Oct. 4** *Perf. 12½*
**728-734** A151 Set of 7 3.00 1.50

Aircraft A152

20c, Concorde. 50c, DC-10. 80c, 747. 1r, IL-62. 1.50r, IL-86. 2r, AN-124. 3r, A-300.

**1986, Nov. 21**
**735-741** A152 Set of 7 4.25 1.60

Silverware A153

Designs: 50c, Elephant, containers. 1r, Covered bowl. 3r, Serving dish.

**1986, Dec. 2** *Perf. 13*
**742-744** A153 Set of 3 3.75 1.40

World Wildlife Fund — A154

Designs: No. 745, 20c, Kouprey. No. 746, 20c, Gaur. 80c, Banteng. 1.50r, Buffalo.

**1986, Dec. 30** **Litho.** *Perf. 13*
**745-748** A154 Set of 4 *14.00* 4.00

Tou Samouth — A155

Denominations and background colors: 50c, green. 1r, blue, 3r, yellow.

**1987, Jan. 7** **Litho.** *Perf. 13*
**749-751** A155 Set of 3 2.75 1.00

1988 Winter Olympic Games, Calgary A156

Designs: 20c, Biathlon. 50c, Women's figure skating. 80c, Speed skating. 1r, Hockey. 1.50r, Luge. 2r, Two-man bobsled. 3r, Cross-country skiing. 6r, Slalom skiing.

**1987, Jan. 14** *Perf. 13x12½*
**752-758** A156 Set of 7 4.25 1.25

**Souvenir Sheet**

*Perf. 12½*

**759** A156 6r multicolored 4.25 1.10

No. 759 contains one 40x32mm stamp.

1988 Summer Olympic Games, Seoul A157

Designs: 20c, Weight lifting, vert. 50c, Archery. 80c, Fencing. 1r, Gymnastics, vert. 1.50r, Discus. 2r, Javelin, vert. 3r, Hurdles. 6r, Wrestling.

**1987, Feb. 2** *Perf. 12½x13, 13x12½*
**760-766** A157 Set of 7 4.25 1.25

**Souvenir Sheet**

*Perf. 13*

**767** A157 6r multicolored 4.25 1.25

No. 767 contains one 40x32mm stamp.

Dogs — A158

Designs: 20c, shown. 50c, Greyhound. 80c, Great Dane. 1r, Doberman pinscher. 1.50r, Samoyed. 2r, Borzoi. 3r, Collie.

**1987, Mar. 3** *Perf. 13*
**768-774** A158 Set of 7 6.50 1.50

**Nos. 458, 463 Surcharged**

**1987, Mar.** **Litho.** *Perf. 13*
**775** A110 35r on 50c #463 5.00
**776** A109 50r on 50c #458 5.00

Soviet Spacecraft — A159

Designs: 20c, Sputnik. 50c, Weather satellite. 80c, Proton. 1r, Vostok 1. 1.50r, Electron-2. 2r, Kosmos. 3r, Luna 2. 6r, Electron-4.

**1987, Apr. 12** **Litho.** *Perf. 13*
**777-783** A159 Set of 7 4.25 1.60

**Souvenir Sheet**

**784** A159 6r multicolored 4.25 1.25

No. 784 contains one 40x32mm stamp.

Silverware — A159a

Designs: 50c, Long-necked pot, vert. 1r, Box. 1.50r, Tea set. 3r, Sword.

**1987, Apr. 13** *Perf. 13*
**785-788** A159a Set of 4 3.00 1.00

CAPEX 87 — A160

Birds: 20c, Merops nubicus. 50c, Upupa epops. 80c, Balearica pavonina. 1r, Tyto alba. 1.50r, Halcyon leucocephala. 2r, Pycnonotus jocosus. 3r, Ardea purpurea. 6r, Terpsiphone paradisi.
50c-1.50r, 3r are vert.

**1987, May 5** *Perf. 13*
**789-795** A160 Set of 7 4.75 1.25

**Souvenir Sheet**

**796** A160 6r multicolored 5.25 2.50

No. 796 contains one 32x40mm stamp.

Early Aircraft Designs A161

Designs by: 20c, Horatio F. Phillips, 1893. 50c, John Stringfellow, 1848. 80c, Thomas Moy, 1875. 1r, Leonardo da Vinci, 1490. 1.50r, Sir George Cayley, 1840. 2r, Sir Hiram Maxim, 1894. 3r, William S. Henson, 1842. 6r, Da Vinci, diff.

**1987, Aug. 7** ***Perf. 13***
**797-803** A161 Set of 7 5.25 1.40

**Souvenir Sheet**

***Perf. 12½***

**804** A161 6r multicolored 5.00 1.00

No. 804 contains one 32x40mm stamp.

Reptiles — A162

Designs: 20c, Testudo gigantea. 50c, Uromastix acanthinuros. 80c, Cyclura macleayi. 1r, Phrynosoma coronatum. 1.50r, Sauromalus obesus. 2r, Ophisaurus apodus. 3r, Thamnophis sirtalis.

**1987, Sept. 9** ***Perf. 13***
**805-811** A162 Set of 7 4.75 1.75

HAFNIA 87 — A163

Helicopters: 20c, Kamov KA-15. 50c, Kamov KA-18. 80c, Westland Lynx WG-13. 1r, Sud Aviation Gazelle. 1.50r, Sud Aviation Puma. 2r, Boeing CH-47 Chinook. 3r, Boeing UTTAS. 6r, Fairey Rotodyne.

**1987, Oct. 16** ***Perf. 12½x12***
**812-818** A163 Set of 7 4.00 1.40

**Souvenir Sheet**

***Perf. 13***

**819** A163 6r multicolored 4.25 1.50

No. 819 contains one 40x32mm stamp.

Russian October Revolution, 70th Anniv. A164

**1987** **Litho.** ***Perf. 12x12¼***
**820** A164 2r Soldiers, horse 1.25 .30
**821** A164 3r Soldiers 1.75 .50
**822** A164 5r Lenin, aides 3.50 .80

Two additional stamps were issued in this set. The editors would like to examine them.

Fire Trucks — A165

**1987, Nov. 24** **Litho.** ***Perf. 13***
**823-829** A165 20c, 50c, 80c, 1r, 1.50r, 2r, 3r, set of 7 5.50 2.25

Telecommunications — A166

50c, Dish antenna, vert. 1r, Broadcast center, vert. 3r, Dish antenna, broadcast center.

***Perf. 13x12½, 12x12½, 12½x12***

**1987, Dec. 2**
**830-832** A166 Set of 3 3.00 1.10

No. 830 is 29x40mm. No. 831 is 28x44mm. No. 832 printed with se-tenant label.

1988 Winter Olympic Games, Calgary — A167

Designs: 20c, Speed skating. 50c, Hockey. 80c, Downhill skiing. 1r, Ski jumping. 1.50r, Biathlon. 2r, Pairs figure skating. 3r, Cross-country skiing. 6r, Four-man bobsled.

**1988, Jan. 7** ***Perf. 12½***
**833-839** A167 Set of 7 4.00 1.00

**Souvenir Sheet**

***Perf. 13***

**840** A167 6r multicolored 2.75 1.10

No. 840 contains one 32x40mm stamp.

Water Projects A168

Designs: 50c, Canal. 1r, Dam under construction. 3r, Dam, bridge.

**1988, Jan. 7** **Litho.** ***Perf. 13***
**841-843** A168 Set of 3 3.00 1.25

1988 Summer Olympic Games, Seoul A169

Designs: 20c, Balance beam, vert. 50c, Uneven bars. 80c, Rhythmic gymnastics ribbon, vert. 1r, Rhythmic gymnastics hoop, vert. 1.50r, Rhythmic gymnastics clubs, vert. 2r, Rhythmic gymnastics ball. 3r, Floor exercise. 6r, Rhythmic gymnastics, diff.

***Perf. 12½x13, 13x12½***

**1988, Feb. 2** **Litho.**
**844-850** A169 Set of 7 4.00 1.50

**Souvenir Sheet**

***Perf. 12½***

**851** A169 6r multicolored 5.00 2.50

No. 851 contains one 32x40mm stamp.

JUVALUX 88 — A170

Various cats. Denominations: 20c, 50c, 80c, 1r, 1.50r, 2r, 3r. Nos. 853-854, 856-858 are vert.

**1988, Mar. 15** ***Perf. 12½***
**852-858** A170 Set of 7 4.75 1.25

**Souvenir Sheet**

***Perf. 13***

**859** A170 6r multicolored 5.25 2.50

No. 859 contains one 40x32mm stamp.

ESSEN 88 A171

Ships: 20c, Passenger liner. 50c, Passenger liner, diff. 80c, Research ship. 1r, Communications ship. 1.50r, Tanker. 2r, Hydrofoil. 3r, Hovercraft.

**1988, Apr. 14** **Litho.** ***Perf. 12½***
**860-866** A171 Set of 7 4.00 1.50

**Souvenir Sheet**

***Perf. 13***

**867** A171 6r Hydrofoil 3.25 1.10

Satellites A172

Various satellites. Denominations: 20c, 50c, 80c, 1r, 1.50r, 2r, 3r. Nos. 868-870 are vert.

**1988, Apr. 24** ***Perf. 12½x13, 13x12½***
**868-874** A172 Set of 7 4.00 1.50

**Souvenir Sheet**

***Perf. 13***

**875** A172 6r multicolored 4.75 1.50

No. 875 contains one 40x32mm stamp.

FINLANDIA 88 — A173

Fish: 20c, Xiphophorus helleri. 50c, Hemigrammus ocellifer. 80c, Macropodus opercularis. 1r, Carassius auratus. 1.50r, Hyphessobrycon inesi. 2r, Corynopoma riisei. 3r, Mollienisia latipinna. 6r, Pterophyllum scalare.

**1988, Jun 10** **Litho.** ***Perf. 13x12½***
**876-882** A173 Set of 7 5.75 1.50

**Souvenir Sheet**

***Perf. 12½***

**883** A173 6r multicolored 5.00 1.50

No. 883 contains one 32x40mm stamp.

Shells — A174

Designs: 20c, Helicostyla florida. 50c, Helicostyla marinduquensis. 80c, Helicostyla fulgens. 1r, Helicostyla woodiana. 1.50r, Chloraea sirena. 2r, Helicostyla mirabilis. 3r, Helicostyla limansauensis.

**1988, Aug. 5** **Litho.** ***Perf. 13x12½***
**884-890** A174 Set of 7 5.25 1.50

Insects A175

Designs: 20c, Coccinellidae. 50c, Zonabride geminata. 80c, Carabus auronitens. 1r, Apis mellifera. 1.50r, Praying mantis. 2r, Odonata. 3r, Malachius aeneus.

**1988, Sept. 6** ***Perf. 13x12½***
**891-897** A175 Set of 7 6.00 1.50

Orchids — A176

Designs: 20c, Cattleya aclandiae. 50c, Odontoglossum Royal Sovereign. 80c, Cattleya labiata. 1r, Ophrys apifera. 1.50r, Laelia anceps. 2r, Laelia pumila. 3r, Stanhopea tigrina, horiz.

**1988, Oct. 10** ***Perf. 12½x13, 13x12½***
**898-904** A176 Set of 7 5.00 2.00

Reptiles A177

Designs: 20c, Naja haje, vert. 50c, Iguana iguana, vert. 80c, Dryophis nasuta. 1r, Terrapene carolina. 1.50r, Cyclura macleayi. 2r, Bothrops bicolor. 3r, Naja naja, with hood spread, vert.

**1988, Nov. 7** ***Perf. 12x12½, 12½x12***
**905-911** A177 Set of 7 6.00 1.75

Dance of the Peacock A178

50c, Trott dance (3 dancers), vert. 1r, Paons dance. 3r, Kantere dance (2 dancers).

**1988, Dec. 2** ***Perf. 13***
**912-914** A178 Set of 3 3.50 1.25

For surcharges see Nos. 1195-1196.

Bridges A179

Various Bridges. Denominations: 50c, 1r, 3r.

**1989** ***Perf. 13x12½***
**915-917** A179 Set of 3 3.25 1.40

Decade of Progress A180

3r, Telecommunications station. 12r, Central Electrical Plant No. 4. 30r, Cement plant, vert.

**1989**
**918-920** A180 Set of 3 2.75 1.50

1990 World Cup Soccer Championships, Italy — A181

Various soccer players. Denominations: 2r, 3r, 5r, 10r, 15r, 20r, 35r.

**1989** ***Perf. 12½x13***
**921-927** A181 Set of 7 5.50 1.50

**Souvenir Sheet**

***Perf. 13***

**928** A181 45r multicolored 4.00 2.00

No. 928 contains one 32x40mm stamp.

Trains — A182

Various locomotives. Denominations: 2r, 3r, 5r, 10r, 15r, 20r, 35r.

**1989** ***Perf. 13***
**929-935** A182 Set of 7 5.75 1.50

**Souvenir Sheet**

***Perf. 12½***

**936** A182 45r multicolored 5.00 2.00

No. 936 contains one 40x32mm stamp.

A183

**1989** ***Perf. 13***
**937** A183 12r red & black 1.10 .55

Cuban Revolution, 30th anniv.

Birds — A184

20c, Ara macao. 80c, Kakatoe galerita. 3r, Psittacula krameri. 6r, Ara ararauna. 10r, Poicephalus robustus. 15r, Amazona aestiva. 25r, Pionus senilis, horiz.
45r, Cyanoramphus novaezelandiae.

**1989**
**938-944** A184 Set of 7 6.25 1.25

**Souvenir Sheet**

***Perf. 12½***

**945** A184 45r multicolored 5.25 2.00

No. 945 contains one 40x32mm stamp.

1992 Winter Olympic Games, Albertville — A185

2r, Slalom skiing. 3r, Biathlon. 5r, Cross-country skiing. 10r, Ski jumping. 15r, Speed skating. 20r, Hockey. 35r, Bobsled.
45r, Pairs figure skating.

**1989, Mar. 30** ***Perf. 13***
**946-952** A185 Set of 7 5.50 1.50

**Souvenir Sheet**

***Perf. 12½***

**953** A185 45r multicolored 5.00 2.00

No. 953 contains one 32x40mm stamp.

Water Lilies — A186

20c, Nymphaea capensis (pink). 80c, Nymphaea capensis (purple). 3r, Nymphaea lotus. 6r, Nymphaea Dir. Geo. T. Moore. 10r, Nymphaea Sunrise. 15r, Nymphaea Escarboncie. 25r, Nymphaea Cladstoniana.
45r, Nymphaea Paul Hariot.

**1989** ***Perf. 12½x13***
**954-960** A186 Set of 7 4.25 1.25

**Souvenir Sheet**

***Perf. 12½***

**961** A186 45r multicolored 4.00 2.00

No. 961 contains one 32x40mm stamp.

1992 Summer Olympic Games, Barcelona A187

Designs: 2r, Wrestling. 3r, Pommel horse, vert. 5r, Shot put. 10r, Running, vert. 15r, Fencing. 20r, Canoeing, vert. 35r, Steeple-chase, vert.
45r, Weight lifting, vert.

**1989** ***Perf. 13***
**962-968** A187 Set of 7 5.50 1.50

**Souvenir Sheet**

***Perf. 12½***

**969** A187 45r multicolored 5.00 2.50

No. 969 contains one 32x40mm stamp.

Mushrooms — A188

Designs: 20c, Xerocomus subtomentosus. 80c, Inocybe patouillardii. 3r, Armillaria mellea. 6r, Agaricus campestris. 10r, Paxillus involutus. 15r, Coprinus comatus. 25r, Lepiota procera.

**1989** ***Perf. 12½x13***
**970-976** A188 Set of 7 4.50 2.50

Horses A189

Designs: 2r, Shire. 3r, Brabant. 5r, Bolounais. 10r, Breton. 15r, Vladimir heavy draft. 20r, Italian heavy draft. 35r, Freiberger.
45r, Horse-drawn cart.

**1989** ***Perf. 12½***
**977-983** A189 Set of 7 4.50 1.50

**Souvenir Sheet**

**984** A189 45r multicolored 4.50 2.50

Nos. 977-983 printed with se-tenant label. No. 984 contains one 40x32mm stamp.

Angkor Wat — A190

Denominations: 35r, 50r, 80r, 100r.

**1989, May 15** **Litho.** ***Perf. 13¼***
**985-988** A190 Set of 4 *175.00 175.00*

**Cambodia**

PHILEXFRANCE 89 — A191

Mail coaches: 2r, 17th cent. 3r, Paris-Lyon, 1720. 5r, 1793. 10r, 1805. 15r, Royal Mail. 20r, 1843. 35r, Paris-Lille, 1837, vert.
45r, 1815, vert.

**1989** **Litho.** ***Perf. 13***
**989-995** A191 Set of 7 4.75 1.50

**Souvenir Sheet**

***Perf. 12½***

**996** A191 45r multicolored 4.00 2.50

No. 996 contains one 23x40mm stamp.

BRASILIANA 89 — A192

Butterflies: 2r, Papilio zagreus. 3r, Morpho catenarius. 5r, Morpho aega. 10r, Callithea sapphira. 15r, Catagramma sorana. 20r, Pierella nereis. 35r, Papilio brasiliensis.
45r, Thacia marsyas, horiz.

**1989** ***Perf. 13***
**997-1003** A192 Set of 7 8.00 1.50

**Souvenir Sheet**

**1004** A192 45r multicolored 7.00 2.00

No. 1004 contains one 40x32mm stamp.

Khmer Boats — A193

Various pirogues. Denominations: 3r, 12r, 30r.

**1989, Dec. 2** **Litho.** ***Perf. 12½***
**1005-1007** A193 Set of 3 3.00 1.25

Natl. Organizations A194

3r, Youth, vert. 12r, Labor. 30r, Natl. Front.

**1990, Jan. 7** **Litho.** ***Perf. 13***
**1008-1010** A194 Set of 3 3.50 1.25

1990 World Cup Soccer Championships, Italy — A195

Various soccer players. Denominations: 2r, 3r, 5r, 10r, 15r, 20r, 35r.

**1990, Jan. 5** **Litho.** ***Perf. 13***
**1011-1017** A195 Set of 7 4.00 1.50

**Souvenir Sheet**

**1018** A195 45r multicolored 3.00 2.00

No. 1018 contains one 32x40mm stamp.
For surcharges see Nos. 1072-1076A.

STAMPWORLD LONDON 90 — A196

Various mail coaches. Denominations: 2r, 3r, 5r, 10r, 15r, 20r, 35r.
45r, Single horse van for rural deliveries.

**1990** ***Perf. 12½x12***
**1019-1025** A196 Set of 7 4.00 1.25

**Souvenir Sheet**

***Perf. 13***

**1026** A196 45r multicolored 4.25 1.50

Nos. 1019-1025 are printed with se-tenant label. No. 1026 contains one 40x32mm stamp.

Rice — A197

Designs: 3r, Woman, rice. 12r, People hauling rice, horiz. 30r, Women threshing rice.

**1990, June 19** **Litho.** ***Perf. 13***
**1027-1029** A197 Set of 3 3.25 1.25

1992 Winter Olympic Games, Albertville — A198

2r, 4-man bobsled. 3r, Speed skating. 5r, Pairs figure skating. 10r, Hockey. 15r, Biathlon. 20r, Luge. 35r, Ski jumping.
45r, Hockey goalie.

**1990** **Litho.** ***Perf. 13***
**1030-1036** A198 Set of 7 4.50 1.50

**Souvenir Sheet**

**1037** A198 45r multicolored 3.25 1.50

No. 1037 contains one 32x40mm stamp.

1992 Summer Olympic Games, Barcelona — A199

Designs: 2r, Shooting. 3r, Shot put. 5r, Weight lifting. 10r, Boxing. 15r, Pole vault. 20r, Basketball. 35r, Fencing.
45r, Rhythmic gymnastics.

**1990**
**1038-1044** A199 Set of 7 4.50 1.50

**Souvenir Sheet**

**1045** A199 45r multicolored 3.00 1.50

No. 1045 contains one 32x40mm stamp.

Khmer Culture — A200

Designs: 3r, Facade, Bantey Srei. 12r, Relief. 30r, Ruins, Banon.

***Perf. 12½, 12½x13 (#1048)***

**1990, Dec. 2** **Litho.**
**1046-1048** A200 Set of 3 3.25 1.25

No. 1048 is 36x21mm.

Dogs — A201

20c, Poodle. 80c, Shetland. 3r, Samoyed. 6r, Springer spaniel. 10r, Fox terrier. 15r, Afghan. 25r, Dalmatian.
45r, Bernese.

**1990** **Litho.** ***Perf. 13***
**1049-1055** A201 Set of 7 5.25 1.25

**Souvenir Sheet**

**1056** A201 45r multicolored 4.00 1.50

No. 1056 contains one 40x32mm stamp.

Cacti — A202

Designs: 20c, Cereus hexagonus. 80c, Arthrocereus rondonianus. 3r, Matucana multicolor. 6r, Hildewintera aureispina. 10r, Opuntia retrosa. 15r, Erdisia tenuicula. 25r, Mamillaria yaquensis.

**1990**
**1057-1063** A202 Set of 7 4.50 1.50

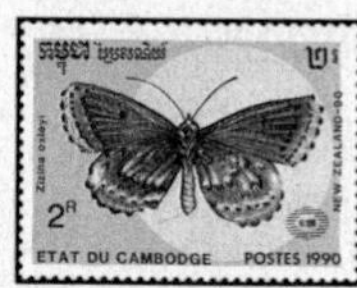
NEW ZEALAND 90 — A203

Butterflies: 2r, Zizina oxleyi. 3r, Cupha prosope. 5r, Heteronympha merope. 10r, Dodonidia helmsi. 15r, Argiropheng a antipodum. 20r, Tysonotis danis. 35r, Pyrameis gonnarilla.
45r, Pyrameis itea.

**1990** ***Perf. 13***
**1064-1070** A203 Set of 7 8.00 1.50

**Souvenir Sheet**
***Perf. 12½***
**1071** A203 45r multicolored 5.50 1.25
No. 1071 contains one 40x32mm stamp.

Nos. 1012-1017 Surcharged in Red

**1990** **Litho.** ***Perf. 13***
**1072** A195 200r on 3r #1012
**1073** A195 300r on 5r #1013
**1074** A195 500r on 10r #1014
**1075** A195 800r on 15r #1015
**1076** A195 1000r on 20r #1016
**1076A** A195 2000r on 35r #1017

Intl. Literacy Year — A204

Denominations: 3r, 12r, 30r.

**1990** **Litho.** ***Perf. 13***
**1077-1079** A204 Set of 3 4.25 1.50

Ships — A205

Designs: 20c, English, 1200. 80c, Spanish galleon, 16th cent. 3r, Dutch ship, 1627. 6r, La Couronne, 1638. 10r, L'Astrolabe, 1826. 15r, French packet, Louisiana, 1864. 25r, Clipper ship, 1900, vert.
45r, Merchant ship, 1800.

**1990** **Litho.** ***Perf. 13***
**1080-1086** A205 Set of 7 6.00 1.50

**Souvenir Sheet**
***Perf. 12½***
**1087** A205 45r multicolored 3.50 1.50
No. 1087 contains one 32x40mm stamp.

Natl. Building Campaign A206

3r, Railroad. 12r, Cargo ship, Kampong Som. 30r, Fishing boats, Kampong Som.

**1990** **Litho.** ***Perf. 13***
**1088-1090** A206 Set of 3 4.50 1.25

PARIS 90 — A207

Chess pieces and: 2r, Sacré Coeur. 3r, Equestrian statue. 5r, Winged Victory of Samothrace. 10r, Chateau, Azay le Riddeau. 15r, Sculpture, "The Dance." 20r, Eiffel Tower. 35r, Arc de Triomphe.
45r, Chess pieces, horiz.

**1990, Nov. 15** **Litho.** ***Perf. 13***
**1091-1097** A207 Set of 7 5.75 2.00

**Souvenir Sheet**
**1098** A207 45r multicolored 4.75 1.50
No. 1098 contains one 40x32mm stamp.

Space Day — A208

Designs: 2r, Vostok. 3r, Soyuz. 5r, Artificial satellite. 10r, Luna 10. 15r, Mars 1. 20r, Venera 3. 35r, Mir.
45r, Energia, Buran.

**1990** **Litho.** ***Perf. 13***
**1099-1105** A208 Set of 7 5.00 1.50

**Souvenir Sheet**
**1106** A208 45r multicolored 3.50 1.50
No. 1106 contains one 32x40mm stamp.
For surcharges see Nos. 1145-1151.

Discovery of America, 500th Anniv. (in 1992) — A209

Designs: 2r, Columbus. 3r, Queen Isabella's jewelry chest. 5r, Queen Isabella. 10r, Santa Maria. 15r, Juan de la Cosa. 20r, Columbus Monument. 35r, Pyramid, Yucatan.
45r, Columbus, diff.

**1990, Oct. 12** **Litho.** ***Perf. 13***
**1107-1113** A209 Set of 7 6.75 2.00

**Souvenir Sheet**
**1114** A209 45r multicolored 4.00 1.25
No. 1114 contains one 32x40mm stamp.

Natl. Festival — A210

Designs: 100r, Tire production. 300r, Rural infirmary. 500r, Fisherman, vert.

***Perf. 12½, 13 (#1117)***
**1991, Jan. 7** **Litho.**
**1115-1117** A210 Set of 3 4.00 1.75
No. 1117 is 28x40mm.

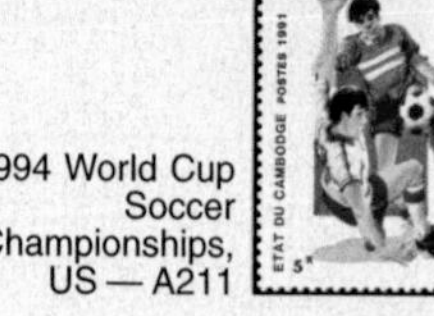
1994 World Cup Soccer Championships, US — A211

Various soccer players. Denominations: 5r, 25r, 70r, 100r, 200r, 400r, 1000r.

**1991, Feb. 15** **Litho.** ***Perf. 13***
**1118-1124** A211 Set of 7 5.00 1.75

**Souvenir Sheet**
**1125** A211 900r multicolored 2.75 1.25
No. 1125 contains one 32x40mm stamp.

1992 Winter Olympic Games, Albertville — A212

Designs: 5r, Speed skating. 25r, Slalom skiing. 70r, Hockey. 100r, Bobsled. 200r, Freestyle skiing. 400r, Pairs figure skating. 1000r, Downhill skiing.
900r, Ski jumping.

**1991, Mar. 30** **Litho.** ***Perf. 12½***
**1126-1132** A212 Set of 7 5.00 2.00

**Souvenir Sheet**
***Perf. 13***
**1133** A212 900r multicolored 4.25 1.25
No. 1133 contains one 32x40mm stamp.

Khmer Culture — A213

Statues: 100r, Garuda, 10th cent. 300r, Torso of Vishnu reclining, 11th cent. 500r, Reclining Nandin, 7th cent.

**1991, Apr. 13** **Litho.** ***Perf. 12½***
**1134-1136** A213 Set of 3 3.25 2.00

1992 Summer Olympic Games, Barcelona A214

Designs: 5r, Pole vault. 25r, Table tennis. 70r, Women's running. 100r, Wrestling. 200r, Women's gymnastics. 400r, Tennis. 1000r, Boxing.
900r, Balance beam.

**1991, Apr. 25** **Litho.** ***Perf. 12½x13***
**1137-1143** A214 Set of 7 4.75 1.50

**Souvenir Sheet**
***Perf. 13***
**1144** A214 900r multicolored 3.25 1.25
No. 1144 contains one 32x40mm stamp.

**Nos. 1099-1105 Surcharged in Red**

**1991** **Litho.** ***Perf. 13***
**1145** A208 100r on 2r #1099 —
**1146** A208 150r on 3r #1100 *75.00*
**1147** A208 200r on 5r #1101 *75.00*
**1148** A208 300r on 10r #1102 *75.00*
**1149** A208 500r on 15r #1103 *75.00*
**1150** A208 1500r on 20r #1104 — —
**1151** A208 2000r on 35r #1105 *75.00*

Aircraft A215

Designs: 5r, DC-10-30. 25r, MD-11. 70r, IL-96-300. 100r, A-310. 200r, YAK-42. 400r, TU-154. 1000r, DC-9

**1991, June 15** **Litho.** ***Perf. 13x12½***
**1152-1158** A215 Set of 7 5.00 1.75

ESPAMER 91 — A216

Pre-Columbian pottery: 5r, Catamarca. 25r, Catamarca, vert. 70r, Tucuman, vert. 100r, Santiago del Estero. 200r, Santiago del Estero, diff. 400r, Tucuman, diff., vert. 1000r, Catamarca, diff.
900r, Catamarca, diff.

**1991, July 10** ***Perf. 13***
**1159-1165** A216 Set of 7 5.50 2.00

**Souvenir Sheet**
***Perf. 12½***
**1166** A216 900r multicolored 3.75 1.25
No. 1166 contains one 40x32mm stamp.

Discovery of America, 500th Anniv. (in 1992) A217

Designs: 5r, Pinta, vert. 25r, Niña, vert. 70r, Santa Maria, vert. 100r, Landing of Columbus. 200r, Encountering new cultures. 400r, First European settlement in Americas. 1000r, Native village.
900r, Columbus.

**1991, Oct. 12** ***Perf. 12½x13, 13x12½***
**1167-1173** A217 Set of 7 6.00 2.00

**Souvenir Sheet**
***Perf. 12½***
**1174** A217 900r multicolored 3.25 1.10
No. 1174 contains one 40x32mm stamp.

PHILANIPPON 91 — A218

Butterflies: 5r, Neptis pryeri. 25r, Papilio xuthus. 70r, Cyrestis thyodamas. 100r, Argynnis anadiomene. 200r, Lethe marginalis. 400r, Artopoetes pryeri. 1000r, Danaus chrysippus.
900r, Ochlodes subhyalina.

**1991, Nov. 16** ***Perf. 13***
**1175-1181** A218 Set of 7 7.50 2.00

**Souvenir Sheet**
***Perf. 12½***
**1182** A218 900r multicolored 6.00 2.50
No. 1182 contains one 40x32mm stamp.

Natl. Building Campaign A219

Designs: 100r, Fishing port. 300r, Preparing palm sugar, vert. 500r, Harvesting peppers.

**1991, Dec. 2** **Litho.** ***Perf. 12½***
**1183-1185** A219 Set of 3 4.25 2.40

Natl. Festival — A220

Traditional costumes: 150r, Chakdomuk. 350r, Longvek. 1000r, Angkor.

**1992, Jan. 7** ***Perf. 13***
**1186-1188** A220 Set of 3 3.50 1.25

1992 Summer Olympic Games, Barcelona — A221

5r, Wrestling. 15r, Soccer. 80r, Weight lifting. 400r, Archery. 1500r, Balance beam.
1000r, Equestrian.

**1992, Jan. Litho.** ***Perf. 13***
**1189-1193** A221 Set of 5 3.50 1.25

**Souvenir Sheet**

***Perf. 12½***

**1194** A221 1000r multicolored 3.25 1.25

No. 1194 contains one 32x40mm stamp.

**Nos. 913-914 Surcharged in Red**

**1992, Jan. Litho.** ***Perf. 13***
**1195** A178 200r on 3r #914
**1196** A178 300r on 1r #913

Fish — A222

Designs: 5r, Hyphessobrycon innesi. 15r, Betta splendens. 80r, Nematobrycon palmen. 400r, Colisa lalia. 1500r, Hoplosternum thoracatum.
1000r, Pterophyllum scalare.

**1992, Feb. 8 Litho.** ***Perf. 12½***
**1197-1201** A222 Set of 5 5.00 1.50

**Souvenir Sheet**

**1202** A222 1000r multicolored 3.75 1.25

No. 1202 contains one 40x32mm stamp.

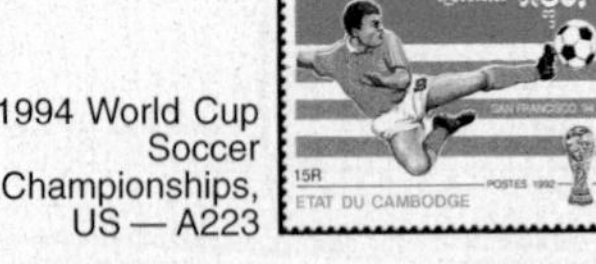

1994 World Cup Soccer Championships, US — A223

Various soccer plays. Denominations: 5r, 15r, 80r, 400r, 1500r. Nos. 1203, 1205-1207 are vert.

**1992, Mar. 6 Litho.** ***Perf. 12½***
**1203-1207** A223 Set of 5 3.75 1.50

**Souvenir Sheet**

**1208** A223 1000r multicolored 2.75 1.25

No. 1208 contains one 40x32mm stamp.

Khmer Culture — A224

19th cent. structures: 150r, Monument. 350r, Stupa. 1000r, Library of Mandapa.

**1992, Apr. 13 Litho.** ***Perf. 12½***
**1209-1211** A224 Set of 3 4.75 2.75

Leonardo da Vinci (1452-1519) — A225

Designs: 5r, Automobile. 15r, Container ship. 80r, Helicopter. 400r, Scuba gear. 1500r, Parachute, vert.
1000r, Portrait.

**1992, Apr. 15 Litho.** ***Perf. 12x12½***
**1212-1216** A225 Set of 5 7.00 1.50

**Souvenir Sheet**

***Perf. 13***

**1217** A225 1000r multicolored 4.25 1.25

Nos. 1212-1216 each printed with se-tenant labels showing Da Vinci's conceptions of the items shown on the stamps. No. 1217 contains one 32x40mm stamp.

EXPO 92, Seville — A226

Inventors, builders: 5r, De la Cierva, autogyro. 15r, Edison, electric light bulb. 80r, Morse, telegraph. 400r, Monturiol, submarine. No. 1222, 1500r, Bell, telephone.
No. 1223, 1500r, Fulton, steamship.

**1992, Apr. 23** ***Perf. 12½***
**1218-1222** A226 Set of 5 4.75 1.25

**Souvenir Sheet**

***Perf. 13***

**1223** A226 1000r pink & black 3.25 1.25

No. 1223 contains one 32x40mm stamp.

1992 Summer Olympic Games, Barcelona A227

Designs: 5r, Weight lifting. 15r, Boxing. 80r, Basketball. 400r, Sprints. 1500r, Water polo.
1000r, Women's gymnastics.

**1992, May 15** ***Perf. 13***
**1224-1228** A227 Set of 5 7.00 1.50

**Souvenir Sheet**

***Perf. 12½***

**1229** A227 1000r multicolored 4.50 1.25

No. 1229 contains one 40x32mm stamp.

Environmental Protection A228

Designs: 5r, Women filling water jars. 15r, Pagoda. 80r, Palm trees. 400r, Boy riding water buffalo. 1500r, Lake, swimmers.
1000r, Angkor Wat.

**1992, June 16 Litho.** ***Perf. 12½***
**1230-1234** A228 Set of 5 5.00 1.75

**Souvenir Sheet**

***Perf. 13***

**1235** A228 1000r multicolored 3.75 1.25

No. 1235 contains one 42x32mm stamp.

GENOA 92 — A229

Explorers, ship: 5r, Bougainville, Boudeuse. 15r, Cook, Endeavour. 80r, Darwin, Beagle. 400r, Cousteau, Calypso. 1500r, Heyerdahl, Kon Tiki.
1000r, Columbus.

**1992, Aug. 1 Litho.** ***Perf. 12x12½***
**1236-1240** A229 Set of 5 4.25 1.50

**Souvenir Sheet**

***Perf. 12½***

**1241** A229 1000r multicolored 3.00 1.25

No. 1241 contains one 32x40mm stamp.

Mushrooms — A230

Designs: 5r, Albatrellus confluens. 15r, Boletus calopus. 80r, Stropharia aeruginosa. 400r, Telamonia armillata. 1500r, Cortinarius traganus.

**1992, Sept. 25** ***Perf. 13***
**1242-1246** A230 Set of 5 4.50 1.50

Seaplanes A231

Designs: 5r, Bellanca Pacemaker, 1930. 15r, Canadair CL-215, 1965. 80r, G-21A Goose, 1937. 400r, Sealand SA-6, 1947. 1500r, Short S-23, 1936.
1000r, G-44 Widgeon, 1940.

**1992, Oct. 16** ***Perf. 12½x12***
**1247-1251** A231 Set of 5 4.00 1.25

**Souvenir Sheet**

***Perf. 13***

**1252** A231 1000r multicolored 3.00 1.25

No. 1252 contains one 32x40mm stamp.

Natl. Development — A232

Designs: 150r, Dish antenna. 350r, Dish antenna, flags. 1000r, Hotel Cambodiana.

**1992, Dec. 2 Litho.** ***Perf. 12½***
**1253-1255** A232 Set of 3 4.25 1.25

Natl. Festival — A233

Designs: 50r, Sociological Institute. 450r, Motel Cambodiana. 1000r, Theater.

**1993, Jan. 7 Litho.** ***Perf. 12½***
**1256-1258** A233 Set of 3 4.25 1.25

Dolphin, Bathyscaph A234

Fauna, machine: 150r, shown. 200r, Falcon, jet fighter. 250r, Beaver, dam. 500r, Bat, satellite. 900r, Hummingbird, helicopter.

**1993, Feb. 5 Litho.** ***Perf. 13***

**Without Gum**

**1259-1263** A234 Set of 5 4.50 1.25

Flowers — A235

Designs: 150r, Datura suaveolens. 200r, Convolvulus tricolor. 250r, Hippeastrum hybrid. 500r, Camellia hybrid. 900r, Lilium speciosum.
1000r, Datura suaveolens, camellia, lilium speciosum.

**1993, Mar. 15** ***Perf. 13***

**Without Gum**

**1264-1268** A235 Set of 5 5.75 1.25

**Souvenir Sheet**

***Perf. 12½***

**1269** A235 1000r multicolored 3.75 1.25

No. 1269 contains one 40x32mm stamp.

Khmer Culture — A236

Designs: 50r, Statue of a Nandin. 450r, Temple Vihear. 1000r, Man with offerings.

**1993, Apr. 13 Litho.** ***Perf. 12½***
**1270-1272** A236 Set of 3 5.00 2.75

Wildlife A237

150r, Cynocephalus volans. 200r, Petuarista petuarista. 250r, Ptychozoon homalocephalum. 500r, Rhacophorus nigropalmatus. 900r, Draco volans.

**1993, May 4 Litho.** ***Perf. 12½x12***

**Without Gum**

**1273-1277** A237 Set of 5 4.50 1.50

BRASILIANA 93 — A238

Butterflies: 250r, Symbrenthia hypselis. 350r, Sithon nedymond. 600r, Geitoneura minyas. 800r, Argyreus hyperbius. 1000r, Argyrophenga antipodum.
1500r, Pararge schakra.

**1993, June 15** ***Perf. 12½x12***

**Without Gum**

**1278-1282** A238 Set of 5 8.25 1.50

**Souvenir Sheet**

***Perf. 12½***

**1283** A238 1500r multicolored 5.00 2.50

No. 1283 contains one 40x32mm stamp.

UN Transitional Authority in Cambodia (UNTAC) Pacification Program — A239

150r, Cambodian soldiers approaching UN base. 200r, Cambodians entering camp. 250r, Cambodians surrendering weapons to UN. 500r, Vocational training. 900r, Cambodians re-entering society.
1000r, Returning to homes and family.

**1993, Aug. 4 Litho. *Perf. 12½***

**1284-1288** A239 Set of 5 5.00 1.50

**Souvenir Sheet**

***Perf. 13***

**1289** A239 1000r blue & black 4.50 2.00

No. 1289 contains one 32x40mm stamp.

Ships — A240

150r, Venetian caravel. 200r, Phoenician galley. 250r, Egyptian merchantman. 500r, Genoese merchantman. 900r, English merchantman.

**1993, Aug. 27 Litho. *Perf. 13***

**Without Gum**

**1290-1294** A240 Set of 5 4.00 1.25

Alberto Santos-Dumont (1873-1932) A241

Designs: 150r, Portrait, Balloon, Eiffel Tower, vert. 200r, 14-bis, 1906. 250r, Demoiselle. 500r, EMB-201A. 900r, EMB-111.

**1993, Sept. 10 *Perf. 13***

**Without Gum**

**1295-1299** A241 Set of 5 4.00 1.25

1994 World Cup Soccer Championships, US — A242

Various soccer plays. Denominations: 250r, 350r, 600r, 800r, 1000r, vert.

**1993, Sept. 23 Litho. *Perf. 12½***

**1300-1304** A242 Set of 5 5.00 1.75

**Souvenir Sheet**

**1305** A242 1500r multicolored 4.00 1.50

No. 1305 contains one 40x32mm stamp.

BANGKOK 93 — A243

Ducks: 250r, Anas penelope. 350r, Anas formosa. 600r, Aix galericulata. 800r, Aix sponsa. 1000r, Histrionicus histrionicus.
1500r, Head of Air galericulata.

**1993, Oct. 1 Litho. *Perf. 13***

**Without Gum**

**1306-1310** A243 Set of 5 5.00 1.75

**Souvenir Sheet**

**1311** A243 1500r multicolored 5.00 2.50

No. 1311 contains one 40x32mm stamp.

Vertical Take-Off Aircraft A244

Designs: 150r, First helicopter model, France, 1784, vert. 200r, Steam helicopter model, 1863, vert. 250r, New York-Atlanta-Miami autogyro flight, 1927. 500r, Sikorsky helicopter, 1943. 900r, French VTOL jet.
1000r, Juan de la Cierva's autogyro C-4, 1923.

***Perf. 12x12½, 12½x12***

**1993, Nov. 6 Without Gum**

**1312-1316** A244 Set of 5 4.00 1.25

**Souvenir Sheet**

***Perf. 12½***

**1317** A244 1000r multicolored 3.00 1.25

No. 1317 contains one 40x32mm stamp.

Insects — A245

Designs: 50r, Cnaphalocrosis medinalis. 450r, Cicadelle brune. 500r, Scirpophaga incertulas. No. 1321, 1000r, Diopsis macrophthlalma.
No. 1322, Leptocorisa oratorius.

**1993, Dec. 2 *Perf. 13***

**1318-1321** A245 Set of 4 5.00 1.25

**Souvenir Sheet**

***Perf. 12½***

**1322** A245 1000r multicolored 4.00 1.25

Issued without gum.
No. 1322 contains one 32x40mm stamp.

Independence, 40th Anniv. — A246

Designs: 300r, Ministry of Posts and Telecommunications. 500r, Independence Monument, 1953, vert. 700r, Natl. flag.

**1993 Litho. *Perf. 12½***

**1323-1325** A246 Set of 3 5.25 2.00

Hummel Figurines — A247

Designs: 50r, Boy riding pony. 100r, Girl with baby carriage. 150r, Girl bathing doll. 200r, Girl holding doll. 250r, Boys playing. 300r, Girls pulling boy in cart. 350r, Girls playing ring-around-the-rosie. 600r, Boys with stick and drum.

**1993 Litho. *Perf. 12½***

**1326-1333** A247 Set of 8 6.25 1.75

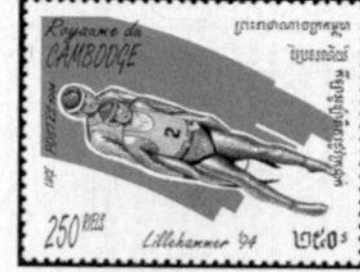

1994 Winter Olympic Games, Lillehammer A248

150r, Women's figure skating, vert. 250r, Two-man luge. 400r, Downhill skiing. 700r, Biathlon. 1000r, Speed skating, vert.
1500r, Curling, vert.

**1994, Jan. 23 *Perf. 13***

**1334-1338** A248 Set of 5 5.00 1.50

**Souvenir Sheet**

**1339** A248 1500r multicolored 3.25 1.25

No. 1339 contains one 32x40mm stamp.

Classic Automobiles A249

Designs: 150r, 1924 Opel. 200r, 1901 Mercedes. 250r, 1927 Model T Ford. 500r, 1907 Rolls Royce. 900r, 1908 Hutton.
1000r, 1931 Duesenberg.

**1994, Feb. 20 *Perf. 13***

**1340-1344** A249 Set of 5 5.00 1.25

**Souvenir Sheet**

**1345** A249 1000r multicolored 4.00 1.25

No. 1345 contains one 32x40mm stamp.

1996 Summer Olympic Games, Atlanta — A250

Designs: 150r, Women's gymnastics. 200r, Soccer. 250r, Javelin. 300r, Canoeing. 600r, Running. 1000r, Diving, horiz.
1500r, Equestrian.

**1994, Mar. 20 *Perf. 13***

**1346-1351** A250 Set of 6 4.50 1.50

**Souvenir Sheet**

**1352** A250 1500r multicolored 4.00 1.25

No. 1352 contains one 32x40mm stamp.

Khmer Statues — A251

Designs: 300r, Siva and Uma. 500r, Vishnu. 700r, King Jayavarman VII.

**1994, Apr. 13**

**1353-1355** A251 Set of 3 5.00 2.75

Intl. Olympic Committee, Cent. — A252

Designs: 100r, Olympic Flag. 300r, Flag, Torch. 600r, Flag, Baron de Coubertin.

**1994, Apr. 23 *Perf. 12½***

**1356-1358** A252 Set of 3 3.25 1.40

Prehistoric Animals A253

150r, Mesonyx. 250r, Doedicurus. 400r, Mylodon. 700r, Uintatherium. 1000r, Hyrachyus.

**1994, May 10 *Perf. 12½***

**1359-1363** A253 Set of 5 6.00 2.00

1994 World Cup Soccer Championships, U.S. — A254

Various soccer plays. Denominations: 150r, 250r, 400r, 700r, 1000r.
1500r, Player in long sleeved green shirt and black shorts with "1" holding ball.

**1994, June 17 *Perf. 12½***

**1364-1368** A254 Set of 5 5.00 1.50

**Souvenir Sheet**

**1369** A254 1500r multicolored 4.00 1.25

No. 1369 contains one 32x40mm stamp.

Statues A255

Designs: 300r, shown. 500r, Soldiers in combat, vert. 700r, Lions, vert.

**1994 *Perf. 13***

**1370-1372** A255 Set of 3 4.50 2.75

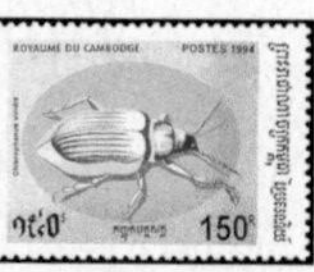

Beetles — A256

Designs: 150r, Chlorophanus viridis. 200r, Chrysochroa fulgidissima. 250r, Lytta vesicatoria. 500r, Purpuricenus kaehleri. 900r, Dynastes hercules.
1000r, Timarcha tenebricosa.

**1994, July 7 *Perf. 12½***

**1373-1377** A256 Set of 5 5.50 1.50

**Souvenir Sheet**

**1378** A256 1000r multicolored 3.75 1.00

No. 1378 contains one 40x32mm stamp.

Submarines A257

Designs: 150r, Halley's diving bell, 1690, vert. 200r, Gimnote, 1886. 250r, Peral, 1888. 500r, Nuclear-powered Nautilus, 1954. 900r, Bathyscaphe Trieste, 1953.
1000r, Ictineo, 1885.

**1994, Aug. 12 *Perf. 13***

**1379-1383** A257 Set of 5 5.25 1.50

**Souvenir Sheet**

***Perf. 12½***

**1384** A257 1000r multicolored 3.75 1.00

No. 1384 contains one 40x32mm stamp.

Chess Champions A258

Designs: 150r, Francois-André Philador, 1795. 200r, Louis de la Bourdonnais, 1821. 250r, Adolph Anderssen, 1851. 500r, Paul Morphy, 1858. 900r, Wilhelm Steinitz, 1866.
1000r, Emanuel Lasker, 1894.

**1994, Sept. 20 *Perf. 13***

**1385-1389** A258 Set of 5 4.75 1.50

**Souvenir Sheet**

**1390** A258 1000r multicolored 3.00 1.00

No. 1390 contains one 32x40mm stamp.

Aircraft — A259

Designs: 150r, Sikorsky S-42 flying boat. 200r, Vought-Sikorsky VS-300A helicopter. 250r, Sikorsky S-37 biplane. 500r, Sikorsky S-35 biplane. 900r, Sikorsky S-43 amphibian.
1000r, 1st 4-engine bomber, Ilya Mourometz.

**1994, Oct. 6 *Perf. 13***

**1391-1395** A259 Set of 5 4.25 1.50

**Souvenir Sheet**

***Perf. 12½***

**1396** A259 1000r multicolored 3.25 1.00

No. 1396 contains one 40x32mm stamp.

Birds — A260

Designs: 150r, Remiz pendulinus, vert. 250r, Panurus biarmicus. 400r, Emberiza rustica. 700r, Emberiza schoeniclus. 1000r, Regulus regulus.
1500r, Pitta angolensis.

**1994, Nov. 20** ***Perf. 12½***
**1397-1401** A260 Set of 5 5.50 1.50

**Souvenir Sheet**
***Perf. 13***

**1402** A260 1500r multicolored 4.00 1.40

No. 1402 contains one 32x40mm stamp.

Independence Festival — A261

Designs: 300r, Postal Service float. 500r, Soldiers marching. 700r, Army unit marching.

**1994, Dec. 9** ***Perf. 13***
**1403-1405** A261 Set of 3 4.50 1.75

Natl. Development A262

Designs: 300r, Chruoi Changwar Bridge. 500r, Olympic Commercial Center. 700r, Sakamony Chedei Temple.

**1994, Dec. 10**
**1406-1408** A262 Set of 3 4.50 1.50

Prehistoric Animals A263

100r, Psittacosaurus. 200r, Protoceratops. 300r, Montanoceraptors. 400r, Centrosaurus. 700r, Styracosaurus. 800r, Triceratops.

**1995, Jan. 10**
**1409-1414** A263 Set of 6 6.50 1.50

Butterflies — A264

100r, Anthocharis cardamines. 200r, Iphiclides podalirius. 300r, Mesoacidalia aglaja. 600r, Vanessa atalanta. 800r, Inachis io.

**1995, Feb. 12**
**1415-1419** A264 Set of 5 7.00 1.50

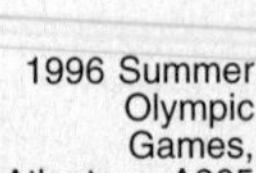

1996 Summer Olympic Games, Atlanta — A265

Designs: 100r, Swimming. 200r, Rhythmic gymnastics. 400r, Basketball. 800r, Soccer. 1000r, Cycling. 1500r, Running.
200r-1500r are vert.

**1995, Mar. 9**
**1420-1424** A265 Set of 5 5.50 1.50

**Souvenir Sheet**

**1425** A265 1500r multicolored 3.50 1.25

No. 1425 contains one 32x40mm stamp.

Mushrooms — A266

Designs: 100r, Amanita phalloides. 200r, Cantharellus cibarius. 300r, Armillaria mellea. 600r, Agaricus campestris. 800r, Amanita muscaria.

**1995, Mar. 23**
**1426-1430** A266 Set of 5 5.25 1.50

Statues — A267

Designs: 300r, Kneeling ascetic. 500r, Parasurama. 700r, Siva.

**1995, Apr. 13** ***Perf. 12½***
**1431-1433** A267 Set of 3 4.00 1.40

Protected Wildlife — A268

Designs: 300r, Bos gaurus. 500r, Bos sauveli, vert. 700r, Grus antigone, vert.

**1995, May 5** ***Perf. 13***
**1434-1436** A268 Set of 3 4.00 1.25

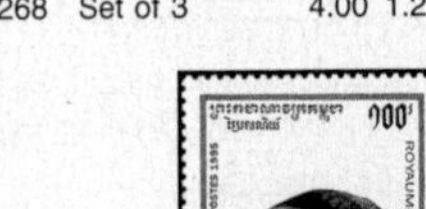
Parrots — A269

Designs: 100r, Lorus lory. 200r, Polytelis alexandrae. 400r, Eclectus voratus. 800r, Ara macao. 1000r, Melopsittacus undulatus.
1500r, Amazona ochrocephala.

**1995, May 23** ***Perf. 13***
**1437-1441** A269 Set of 5 6.50 1.50

**Souvenir Sheet**
***Perf. 12½***

**1442** A269 1500r multicolored 5.00 2.50

No. 1442 contains one 32x40mm stamp.

Tourism — A270

Public gardens: 300r, Sculpture of Garuda. 500r, Fountain. 700r, Sculpture of mythological figures.

**1995, July 15** ***Perf. 12½***
**1443-1445** A270 Set of 3 4.00 1.50

Locomotives A271

100r, Richard Trevithick's steam locomotive, 1804. 200r, George Stephenson's Rocket, 1830. 300r, Stephenson's Locomotion, 1825. 600r, Lafayette, 1837. 800r, Best Friend of Charleston, 1830.
1000r, Stephenson, vert.

**1995, Aug. 17**
**1446-1450** A271 Set of 5 4.50 1.50

**Souvenir Sheet**

**1451** A271 1000r multicolored 3.50 1.25

No. 1451 contains one 32x40mm stamp.

World War II Aircraft A272

100r, Bristol Blenheim II, vert. 200r, North American B-25. 300r, Avro Anson. 600r, Avro Manchester. 800r, Consolidated B-24.
1000r, Boeing B-17E.

***Perf. 12x12½, 12½x12***

**1995, Sept. 15**
**1452-1456** A272 Set of 5 4.50 1.50

**Souvenir Sheet**
***Perf. 12½***

**1457** A272 1000r multicolored 3.25 1.25

No. 1457 contains one 32x40mm stamp.

FAO, 50th Anniv. — A273

Designs: 300r, Separating rice plants. 500r, Transplanting rice. 700r, Model rice farm.

**1995, Oct. 24** ***Perf. 13***
**1458-1460** A273 Set of 3 3.50 1.00

UN, 50th Anniv. — A274

Designs: 300r, Bridge. 500r, People on bridge. 700r, Central spans of bridge.

**1995, Oct. 24** ***Perf. 12½***
**1461-1463** A274 Set of 3 4.00 1.50

Queen Monineath A275

700r, shown. 800r, King Norodom Sihanouk.

**1995, Nov. 9** ***Perf. 12½x13***
**1464-1465** A275 Set of 2 4.75 1.50

Fish — A276

100r, Heniochus acuminatus. 200r, Chelmon rostratus. 400r, Amphiprion percula. 800r, Paracanthurus hepatus. 1000r, Holocanthus ciliaris.
1500r, Coris angulata, vert.

**1995, Nov. 19** ***Perf. 12½***
**1466-1470** A276 Set of 5 5.75 1.50

**Souvenir Sheet**

**1471** A276 1500r multicolored 4.75 1.25

Main Post Office, Cent. — A277

Denominations: 300r, 500r, 700r.

**1995, Dec. 2** ***Perf. 12½***
**1472-1474** A277 Set of 3 5.50 1.40

Admission to UN, 40th Anniv. — A278

300r, Independence Monument. 400r, Angkor Wat. 800r, Natl. flag, vert.

***Perf. 12½x13, 13x12½***

**1995, Dec. 14** **Litho.**
**1475-1477** A278 Set of 3 5.50 1.25

1996 Summer Olympic Games, Atlanta — A279

Designs: 100r, Tennis. 200r, Volleyball. 300r, Soccer. No. 1480A, 500r, Running. 900r, Baseball. 1000r, Basketball.
1500r, Windsurfing.

**1996, Jan. 10** **Litho.** ***Perf. 12½x13***
**1478-1482** A279 Set of 6 5.50 1.50

**Souvenir Sheet**
***Perf. 12½***

**1483** A279 1500r multicolored 3.50 1.25

No. 1483 contains one 32x40mm stamp.

Tourism — A280

50r, Kep State Chalet. 100r, Power station. 200r, Wheelchair. 500r, Wheelchair basketball. 800r, Making crutches, vert. 1000r, Kep beach. 1500r, Serpent Island.

**1996, Jan. 30** ***Perf. 12½***

| | | | | |
|---|---|---|---|---|
| **1484** | A280 | 50r multi | .25 | .25 |
| **1485** | A280 | 100r multi | .25 | .25 |
| **1486** | A280 | 200r multi | .25 | .25 |
| **1487** | A280 | 500r multi | .55 | .25 |
| **1488** | A280 | 800r multi | .90 | .25 |
| **1489** | A280 | 1000r multi | 1.25 | .35 |
| **1490** | A280 | 1500r multi | 1.75 | .45 |
| | | *Nos. 1484-1490 (7)* | 5.20 | 2.05 |

Wild Cats — A281

100r, Felis libyca, vert. 200r, Felis silvestris. 300r, Felis caracal. 500r, Felis geoffroyi. 900r, Felis nigripes. 1000r, Felis planiceps.

**1996, Feb. 8** ***Perf. 13***
**1491-1496** A281 Set of 6 5.75 2.00

1998 World Cup Soccer Championships, France — A282

Various soccer players. Denominations: 100r, 200r, 300r, 500r, 900r, 1000r. No. 1502 is horiz.

**1996, Mar. 15** *Perf. 13*

**1497-1502** A282 Set of 6 5.50 1.50

**Souvenir Sheet**

**1503** A282 1500r multicolored 3.50 1.25

No. 1503 contains one 32x40mm stamp.

Khmer Culture — A283

100r, Tusmukh. 500r, Ream Iso. 900r, Isei.

**1996, Apr. 13 Litho.** *Perf. 12½x13*

**1504-1506** A283 Set of 3 3.75 1.50

Locomotives A284

100r, Pacific Type. 200r, Unidentified, 1902. 300r, Unidentified, 1930. 500r, Unidentified, 1914. 900r, LMS #6202, 1930. 1000r, Snake, 1864.
1500r, Canadian Pacific.

**1996, Apr. 20**

**1507-1512** A284 Set of 6 4.25 1.50

**Souvenir Sheet**

**1513** A284 1500r multicolored 2.75 1.25

No. 1513 contains one 40x32mm stamp.
CAPEX 96 (No. 1513).

Birds — A285

Designs: 100r, Kittacinela malabarica, vert. 200r, Leiothrix lutea. 300r, Parus varius, vert. 500r, Oriolus chinensis. 900r, Cettia diphone. 1000r, Cyanoptila cyanomelana, vert.

**1996, May 7**

**1514-1519** A285 Set of 6 5.00 1.50

Olymphilex '96 — A286

Designs: 100r, Rhythmic gymnastics. 200r, Judo. 300r, High jump. 500r, Wrestling. 900r, Weight lifting. 1000r, Soccer.
1500r, Diving.

**1996, June 14 Litho.** *Perf. 13x12½*

**1520-1525** A286 Set of 6 5.00 1.25

**Souvenir Sheet**

*Perf. 12½*

**1526** A286 1500r multicolored 4.00 1.25

No. 1526 contains one 32x40mm stamp.

Early Aircraft A287

100r, Douglas M-2, 1926. 200r, Pitcairn PA-5 Mailwing, 1928. 300r, Boeing 40 B, 1928. 500r, Potez 25, 1925. 900r, Stearman C-3MB, 1927. 1000r, De Havilland DH4, 1918.
1500r, Standard JR-1B, 1918.

**1996, July 5** *Perf. 12½x12*

**1527-1532** A287 Set of 6 4.25 1.50

**Souvenir Sheet**

*Perf. 13*

**1533** A287 1500r multicolored 3.00 1.00

No. 1533 contains one 40x32mm stamp.

Historic Sites — A288

50r, 100r, 200r, Diff. Apsaras, Tonle Bati. No. 1537, Statue, Angkor Wat. No. 1538, Statue of a Goddess. 500r, Carved wall, Tonle Bati. No. 1540, 1000r, No. 1543, Various structures, Tonle Bati. No. 1541, No. 1544, 1700r, 2500r, 3000r, Various views of Angkor Wat.
Nos. 1539, 1543, 1545-1547 are horiz.

**1996-97 Litho.** *Perf. 12½*

| | | | | |
|---|---|---|---|---|
| **1534** | A288 | 50r blk & yel org | .25 | .25 |
| **1535** | A288 | 100r black & blue | .25 | .25 |
| **1536** | A288 | 200r black & tan | .40 | .25 |
| **1537** | A288 | 300r blk & light bl | .30 | .25 |
| **1538** | A288 | 300r black & red | .30 | .25 |
| **1539** | A288 | 500r blk & bright bl | .80 | .25 |
| **1540** | A288 | 800r blk & yel grn | 1.00 | .25 |
| **1541** | A288 | 800r blk & yel grn | .60 | .25 |
| **1542** | A288 | 1000r black & green | 1.10 | .40 |
| **1543** | A288 | 1500r black & bister | 1.40 | .50 |
| **1544** | A288 | 1500r black & brown | 1.40 | .25 |
| **1545** | A288 | 1700r black & org brn | 1.50 | .30 |
| **1546** | A288 | 2500r black & blue | 2.00 | .40 |
| **1547** | A288 | 3000r black & dk grn | 3.50 | .50 |
| | | *Nos. 1534-1547 (14)* | 14.80 | 4.35 |

Issued: 50r, 100r, 200r, 500r, No. 1540, 1000r, No. 1543, 7/30/96; others, 3/26/97.
See Nos. 1686-1692, 1846-1852.

Dinosaurs A289

No. 1548: a, 50r, Coelophysis. b, 100r, Euparkeria. c, 150r, Plateosaurus. d, 200r, Herrerasaurus.
No. 1549: a, 250r, Dilophosaurus. b, 300r, Tuojiangosaurus. c, 350r, Camarasaurs. d, 400r, Ceratosaurus.
No. 1550: a, 500r, Spinosaurus. b, 700r, Ouranosaurus. c, 800r, Avimimus. d, 1200r, Deinonychus.

**1996, Aug. 8 Litho.** *Perf. 13*

| | | | | |
|---|---|---|---|---|
| **1548** | A289 | Sheet of 4, #a.-d. | 1.00 | .25 |
| **1549** | A289 | Sheet of 4, #a.-d. | 2.75 | .60 |
| **1550** | A289 | Sheet of 4, #a.-d. | 6.25 | 1.50 |

Chess Champions — A290

100r, José Raul Capablanca. 200r, Alexander Alekhine. 300r, Vassily Smyslov. 500r, Mikhail Tal. 900r, Bobby Fischer. 1000r, Anatoly Karpov.
1500r, Garry Kasparov.

**1996, Sept. 10** *Perf. 13*

**1551-1556** A290 Set of 6 4.50 1.50

**Souvenir Sheet**

*Perf. 12½*

**1557** A290 1500r multicolored 3.00 1.25

No. 1557 contains one 32x40mm stamp.

Wild Animals A291

Designs: 100r, Ursus arctos. 200r, Panthera leo. 300r, Tapirus indicus. 500r, Camelus ferus. 900r, Capra ibex. 1000r, Zalophus californianus.

**1996, Oct. 3** *Perf. 13x12½*

**1558-1563** A291 Set of 6 4.50 1.25

Dogs — A292

Designs: 200r, Collie. 300r, Labrador retriever. 500r, Doberman pinscher. 900r, German shepherd. 1000r, Boxer.

**1996, Nov. 8** *Perf. 12½x13*

**1564-1568** A292 Set of 5 4.75 1.25

Independence A293

100, 500, 900r, Various water treatment plants.

**1996, Nov. 9** *Perf. 13*

**1569-1571** A293 Set of 3 3.00 1.50

Ships — A294

Designs: 200r, Chinese junk. 300r, Galley. 500r, Roman galley. 900r, Clipper ship, 19th cent. 1000r, Paddle steamer Sirius, 1838.
1500r, Great Eastern, 1858.

**1996, Dec. 15** *Perf. 12½x13*

**1572-1576** A294 Set of 5 4.00 1.25

**Souvenir Sheet**

*Perf. 12½*

**1577** A294 1500r multicolored 2.75 1.00

No. 1577 contains one 40x32mm stamp.

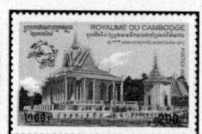

Cambodia's Admission to UPU, 45th Anniv. A295

Denominations: 200r, 400r, 900r.

**1996, Dec. 21** *Perf. 12½*

**1578-1580** A295 Set of 3 3.50 1.50

New Year 1997 (Year of the Ox) — A296

Paintings of oxen, attributed to Han Huang 723-87): a, Facing left. b, Looking right. c, Brown & white spotted. d, Facing left, head down.

**1996, Dec. 28** *Perf. 13x12½*

**1581** A296 500r Strip of 4, #a.-d. + label 3.00 1.00

UN Intl. Day of Volunteers A297

Designs: 100r, Phnom Kaun Sat Dam. 900r, Chrey Krem Dam. 1500r, Angkrung Canal.

**1996, Dec. 30**

**1582-1584** A297 Set of 3 3.50 1.50

Greenpeace, 25th Anniv. — A298

Helicopter: 200r, Hovering over cargo. 300r, Hovering over ship. 500r, On helipad. 900r, Lifting cargo.
1000r, Close-up of helicopter.

**1996, Dec. 30** *Perf. 12½x13*

**1585-1588** A298 Set of 4 5.00 1.75

**Souvenir Sheet**

*Perf. 12½*

**1589** A298 1000r multicolored 5.25 1.00

No. 1589 contains one 32x40mm stamp.

1998 World Cup Soccer Championships, France — A299

Various soccer plays. Denominations: 100r, 200r, 300r, 500r, 900r, 1000r.

**1997, Jan. 6 Litho.** *Perf. 12½x13*

**1590-1595** A299 Set of 6 4.25 1.50

**Souvenir Sheet**

*Perf. 13*

**1596** A299 2000r multicolored 2.75 1.25

No. 1596 contains one 40x32mm stamp.

Elephas Maximus — A300

World Wildlife Fund: a, 300r, Two walking. b, 500r, Three standing. c, 900r, Two fighting. d, 1000r, Adult, calf.

**1997, Feb. 12** *Perf. 12½x12*

**1597** A300 Strip of 4, #a.-d. 7.00 3.00

Birds — A301

600r, Bombycilla garrulus. 900r, Lanius excubitor. 1000r, Passer montanus. 2000r, Phoenicurus phoenicurus. 2500r, Emberiza schoeniclus. 3000r, Emberiza hortulana.

**1997, Feb. 20** *Perf. 13x12½*

**1598-1603** A301 Set of 6 13.00 4.50

Express mail service.

Fire Fighting Vehicles A302

Designs: 200r, English, 1731. 500r, Putnam, 1863. 900r, Merryweather, 1894. 1000r,

Shand Mason Co., 1901. 1500r, Maxim Motor Co., Ford, 1949. 4000r, Merryweather, 1950. 5400r, Mack Truck Co., 1953.

**1997, Mar. 11** ***Perf. 12½x13***

**1604-1609** A302 Set of 6 7.00 1.50

**Souvenir Sheet**

***Perf. 13***

**1610** A302 5400r multicolored 4.75 1.25

No. 1610 contains one 40x32mm stamp.

Ducks — A303

Designs: 200r, Polystieta stelleri. 500r, Alopochen aegyptiacus. 900r, Anas americana. 1000r, Anas falcata. 1500r, Melanitta perspicillata. 4000r, Anas discors.
5400r, Anas formosa, vert.

**1997, Apr. 7** ***Perf. 12½x13***

**1611-1616** A303 Set of 6 4.50 1.50

**Souvenir Sheet**

***Perf. 12½***

**1617** A303 5400r multicolored 3.25 1.75

No. 1617 contains one 32x40mm stamp.

Heinrich Von Stephan (1831-1897), Founder of UPU — A304

Denominations: 500r, 1500r, 2000r.

**1997, Apr. 8** ***Perf. 12½x13***

**1618-1620** A304 Set of 3 3.00 1.00

Khmer Culture — A305

Various views of Bantea Srei Temple. Denominations: 500r, 1500r, 2000r.

**1997, Apr. 13** ***Perf. 13x12½***

**1621-1623** A305 Set of 3 3.50 1.00

Cats — A306

Designs: 200r, Birman. 500r, Exotic short-hair. 900r, Persian. 1000r, Turkish. 1500r, American short-hair. 4000r, Scottish fold.
5400r, Sphinx.

**1997, May 8** ***Perf. 13x12½***

**1624-1629** A306 Set of 6 9.00 1.75

**Souvenir Sheet**

***Perf. 13***

**1630** A306 5400r multicolored 4.00 1.25

No. 1630 contains one 32x40mm stamp.

Trains — A307

200r, 4-4-2T, #488. 500r, Frederick Smith 4-6-0. 900r, 0-8-0, #3131. 1000r, Transport #1, London #L44, 0-4-4. 1500r, 0-6-2, #1711. 4000r, 4-6-2, #60523.
5400r, North Yorkshire Moor (K1), 2-6-0, #2005.

**1997, Jun 9** ***Perf. 12½x12***

**1631-1636** A307 Set of 6 4.25 1.50

**Souvenir Sheet**

***Perf. 13***

**1637** A307 5400r multicolored 3.25 1.75

No. 1637 contains one 40x32mm stamp.

Dogs — A308

Designs: 200r, Shar-pei. 500r, Tchin-tchin. 900r, Pekinese. 1000r, Chow-chow, vert. 1500r, Pug, vert. 4000r, Akita, vert.
5400r, Tufted Chinese, vert.

**1997, July 4** ***Perf. 12½x13, 13x12½***

**1638-1643** A308 Set of 6 4.25 1.50

**Souvenir Sheet**

***Perf. 12½***

**1644** A308 5400r multicolored 3.00 1.50

No. 1644 contains one 32x40mm stamp.

ASEAN, 30th Anniv. — A309

Designs: 500r, Dunalom Wat. 1500r, Royal Palace. 2000r, Natl. Museum.

**1997, Aug. 5** ***Perf. 12½x13***

**1645-1647** A309 Set of 3 4.00 1.00

Ships — A310

Designs: 200r, Caravelle, 15th cent. 500r, Spanish galleon, 16th cent. 900r, Galleon "Great Harry," 16th cent. 1000r, Galleon "Le Couronne," 17th cent. 1500r, Cargo ship, 18th cent. 4000r, Clipper ship, 19th cent.
5400r, HMS Victory.

**1997, Sept. 10** ***Perf. 12½x12***

**1648-1653** A310 Set of 6 5.50 1.50

**Souvenir Sheet**

***Perf. 13***

**1654** A310 5400r multicolored 4.00 1.10

No. 1654 contains one 40x32mm stamp.

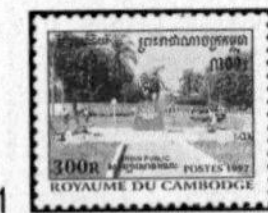

A311

Nos. 1655-1658, Various public gardens. Nos. 1659-1661, Various dams. No. 1657 is vert.

**1997, Sept. 30** ***Perf. 12½***

| | | | | |
|---|---|---|---|---|
| **1655** | A311 | 300r black & yel grn | .25 | .25 |
| **1656** | A311 | 300r black & red | .25 | .25 |
| **1657** | A311 | 800r black & citron | .50 | .25 |
| **1658** | A311 | 1500r black & org brn | .95 | .30 |
| **1659** | A311 | 1700r blk & red brn | 1.05 | .35 |
| **1660** | A311 | 2500r blk & grn bl | 1.20 | .50 |
| **1661** | A311 | 3000r black & blue | 1.50 | .65 |
| | | *Nos. 1655-1661 (7)* | 5.70 | 2.55 |

Mushrooms — A312

Designs: 200r, Boletus satanas. 500r, Amanita regalis. 900r, Morchella semilibera. 1000r, Gomphus clavatus. 1500r, Hygrophorus hypothejus. 4000r, Albatrellus confluens.
5400r, Boletus chrysenteron.

**1997, Oct. 5** ***Perf. 12½x13***

**1662-1667** A312 Set of 6 6.00 1.50

**Souvenir Sheet**

***Perf. 12½***

**1668** A312 5400r multicolored 4.00 1.25

No. 1668 contains one 32x40mm stamp.

Fish — A313

200r, Betta imbellis. 500r, Colisa fasciata. 900r, Puntius conchonius. 1000r, Macropodus concolor. 1500r, Epalzeorhynchos frenatus. 4000r, Capoeta tetrazona.
5400r, Rasbora heteromorpha.

**1997, Nov. 8** ***Perf. 12½x13***

**1669-1674** A313 Set of 6 5.25 1.50

**Souvenir Sheet**

***Perf. 13***

**1675** A313 5400r multicolored 3.50 1.25

No. 1675 contains one 40x32mm stamp.

Independence, 44th Anniv. — A314

Post Offices: 1000r, Kampot. 3000r, Prey Veng.

**1997, Nov. 9** ***Perf. 13***

**1676-1677** A314 Set of 2 2.75 1.00

Orchids — A315

200r, Orchis milicaris. 500r, Orchiaceras bivonae. 900r, Orchiaceras spuria. 1000r, Gymnadenia conopsea. 1500r, Serapias neglecta. 4000r, Pseudorhiza bruniana.
5400r, Dactylodenia wintonii.

**1997, Dec. 12** ***Perf. 13***

**1678-1683** A315 Set of 6 9.00 1.75

**Souvenir Sheet**

**1684** A315 5400r multicolored 6.75 1.10

No. 1684 contains one 32x40mm stamp.

Princess Diana (1961-97) — A316

Designs: a, 100r, In dark blue jacket. b, 200r, In black dress. c, 300r, Holding hand to throat. d, 500r, Wearing face shield. e, 1000r, Watching mine clearing operation. f, 1500r, With Elizabeth Dole. g, 2000r, Holding land mine. h, 2500r, With members of Mother Teresa's Order.

**1997, Dec. 30** ***Perf. 12x12½***

**1685** A316 Sheet of 8, #a.-h. + label 6.00 1.75

**Historic Sites Type of 1996-97**

Temples: 300r, Prasat Suorprat. 500r, Preah Kumlung, horiz. 1200r, Prasat Bapuon, horiz. 1500r, Palilai. 1700r, Prasat Prerup, horiz. 2000r, Prasat Preah Khan, horiz. 3000r, Prasat Bayon.

**1998** **Litho.** ***Perf. 12½***

| | | | | |
|---|---|---|---|---|
| **1686** | A288 | 300r black & orange | .25 | .25 |
| **1687** | A288 | 500r black & pink | .30 | .25 |
| **1688** | A288 | 1200r black & buff | .70 | .25 |
| **1689** | A288 | 1500r black & buff | .90 | .30 |
| **1690** | A288 | 1700r black & blue | 1.00 | .35 |
| **1691** | A288 | 2000r black & green | 1.25 | .45 |
| **1692** | A288 | 3000r black & violet | 1.75 | .65 |
| | | *Nos. 1686-1692 (7)* | 6.15 | 2.50 |

New Year 1998 (Year of the Tiger) — A317

Various pictures of panthera tigris: 200r, vert., 500r, vert., 900r, vert., 1000r, 1500r, 4000r.
5400r, Tiger, vert.

**1998** ***Perf. 13***

**1693-1698** A317 Set of 6 4.75 1.50

**Souvenir Sheet**

***Perf. 12½***

**1699** A317 5400r multicolored 4.00 1.50

No. 1699 contains one 32x40mm stamp.

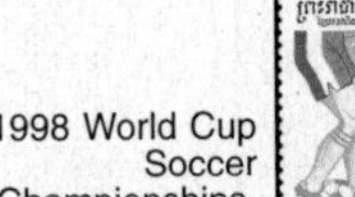

1998 World Cup Soccer Championships, France — A318

Designs showing portion of soccer player at left, various plays at right, stadium: 200r, 500r, 900r, 1000r, 1500r, 4000r.
5400r, Two players kicking ball.

**1998** ***Perf. 13***

**1700-1705** A318 Set of 6 4.25 1.50

**Souvenir Sheet**

**1706** A318 5400r multicolored 3.00 1.50

No. 1706 contains one 40x32mm stamp.

Domestic Cats — A319

Designs: 200r, Scottish fold. 500r, Ragdoll. 900r, Welsh. 1000r, Devon rex. 1500r, American curl. 4000r, Sphinx.
5400r, Japanese bobtail.

**1998**

**1707-1712** A319 Set of 6 4.00 1.50

**Souvenir Sheet**

**1713** A319 5400r multi 3.00 1.50

No. 1713 contains one 40x32mm stamp.

Italia '98, Intl. Philatelic Exhibition — A320

Paintings: 200r, Baptism of Christ from triptych, Jean de Trompes, by Gerard David. 500r, The Virgin of Martin van Niuwenhoven, by Hans Memling. 900r, Baptism of Christ, by Hendrich Goltzius. 1000r, Christ Carrying the Cross, by Luis de Morales. 1500r, Angel in the Desert, by Dirk Bouts. 4000r, The Virgin, by Petrus Christus.
5400r, The Immaculate Conception, by Bartolomé Esteban Murillo.

**1998** **Litho.** ***Perf. 12½x13***

**1714-1719** A320 Set of 6 5.00 1.50

**Souvenir Sheet**

*Perf. 12½*

**1720** A320 5400r multicolored 4.00 1.50

No. 1720 contains one 40x32mm stamp.

Butterflies A321

200r, Phyciodes tharos. 500r, Pararge mergera. 900r, Danaus plexippus. 1000r, Parnassius apollo. 1500r, Papilio machaon. 4000r, Eumenis semele.
5400r, Morpho rhetenor.

**1998** *Perf. 12½*

**1721-1726** A321 Set of 6 5.25 1.50

**Souvenir Sheet**

**1727** A321 5400r multicolored 5.25 1.50

No. 1727 contains one 40x32mm stamp.

Mail Boxes — A322

Designs: 1000r, 1997. 3000r, 1951.

**1998 Litho.** *Perf. 13*

**1728-1729** A322 Set of 2 2.25 1.00

Trains A323

No. 1730a, 200r, Oakland, Antioch & Eastern. No. 1730b, 500r, New York, Westchester & Boston. No. 1731a, 900r, Spokane & Inland. No. 1731b, 1000r, International Railway. No. 1732a, 1500r, British columbia Electric Railway. No. 1732b, 4000r, Southern Pacific.
5400r, Storage battery locomotive.

**1998, Mar. 2 Litho.** *Perf. 12½*

**Pairs, #a.-b.**

**1730-1732** A323 Set of 3 5.00 1.50

**Souvenir Sheet**

**1733** A323 5400r multicolored 4.00 1.50

Dogs — A324

200r, Rottweiler. 500r, Beauceron. 900r, Boxer. 1000r, Siberian husky. 1500r, Welsh corgi (Pembroke). 4000r, Basset hound.
5400r, Schnauzer.

**1998, Mar. 30 Litho.** *Perf. 12¼*

**1734-1739** A324 Set of 6 4.75 1.50

**Souvenir Sheet**

*Perf. 12½*

**1740** A324 5400r multicolored 3.25 1.50

Insects — A325

200r, Lucanus cervus. 500r, Carabus auronitens. 900r, Rosalia alpina. 1000r, Geotrupes. 1500r, Megasoma elephas. 4000r, Chalcosoma.
5400r, Leptura rubra.

**1998, Apr. 10 Litho.** *Perf. 12½*

**1741-1746** A325 Set of 6 5.00 1.50

**Souvenir Sheet**

**1747** A325 5400r multicolored 4.00 1.75

Khmer Culture — A326

Designs: 500r, Prasat Prerup. 1500r, Prasat Bayon. 2000r, Angkor Wat.

**1998, Apr. 13 Litho.** *Perf. 12¾*

**1748-1750** A326 Set of 3 3.25 1.10

Historic Ships — A327

200r, Cutter. 500r, Steamship "Britannia." 900r, Viking ship. 1000r, Steamship "Great Britain." 1500r, Coaster. 4000r, Frigate.
5400r, Tartan.

**1998, May 7 Litho.** *Perf. 12¾*

**1751-1756** A327 Set of 6 5.75 1.50

**Souvenir Sheet**

*Perf. 13*

**1757** A327 5400r multicolored 3.50 1.75

No. 1757 contains one 40x32mm stamp.

Flowers — A328

200r, Petasites japonica. 500r, Gentiana triflora. 900r, Doronicum cordatum. 1000r, Scabiosa japonica. 1500r, Magnolia sieboldii. 4000r, Erythronium japonica.
5400r, Callistephus chinensis.

**1998 Litho.** *Perf. 12¾*

**1758-1763** A328 Set of 6 4.75 1.50

**Souvenir Sheet**

*Perf. 13*

**1764** A328 5400r multicolored 3.25 1.50

No. 1764 contains one 32x40mm stamp.

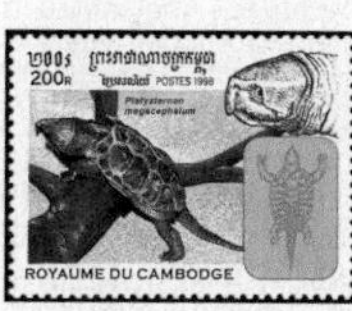

Turtles — A329

200r, Platysternon megacephalum. 500r, Chelonia mydas. 900r, Trionyx spiniferus. 1000r, Eretmochelys imbricata. 1500r, Megalochelys gigantea. 4000r, Dermochelys coriacea.
5400r, Chelus fimbriatus.

**1998, Nov. 8 Litho.** *Perf. 12¾*

**1765-1770** A329 Set of 6 5.00 1.50

**Souvenir Sheet**

*Perf. 13x13¼*

**1771** A329 5400r multi 4.75 1.50

No. 1771 contains one 40x32mm stamp.

Independence, 45th Anniv. — A330

Various dancers: 500r, 1500r, 2000r.

**1998, Nov. 9 Litho.** *Perf. 12½x12¼*

**1772-1774** A330 Set of 3 2.50 1.00

Gemstones — A331

Designs: 200r, Aquamarine. 500r, Cat's eye. 900r, Malachite. 1000r, Emerald. 1500r, Turquoise. 4000r, Ruby.
5400r, Diamond, horiz.

**1998, Dec. 28 Litho.** *Perf. 12¾*

**1775-1780** A331 Set of 6 4.50 1.50

**Souvenir Sheet**

*Perf. 13*

**1781** A331 5400r multi 3.50 1.50

No. 1781 contains one 40x32mm stamp.

Wild Cats — A332

Designs: 200r, Acinonyx juabatus. 500r, Panthera uncia. 900r, Felis pardalis. 1000r, Panthera pardus. 1500r, Felis serval. 4000r, Panthera onca.
5400r, Panthera tigris.

**1998 Litho.** *Perf. 12½x12¼*

**1782-1787** A332 Set of 6 5.00 1.50

**Souvenir Sheet**

*Perf. 13*

**1788** A332 5400r multi 4.00 1.50

No. 1788 contains one 32x40mm stamp.

New Year 1999 (Year of the Rabbit) — A333

Various rabbits: 200r, 500r, 900r, 1000r, 1500r, 4000r. 4000r is vert.

**1999, Jan. 5 Litho.** *Perf. 12¾*

**1790-1795** A333 Set of 6 6.75 1.50

**Souvenir Sheet**

*Perf. 13*

**1796** A333 5400r Rabbit, diff. 5.00 1.50

No. 1796 contains one 40x32mm stamp.

Trains A334

Designs: 200r, Stourbridge Lion. 500r, Atlantic. 900r, 035. 100r, Iron Duke. 1500r, 4-6-0. 4000r, 4-4-2.

*Perf. 12½x12¼*

**1999, Nov. 20 Litho.**

**1797-1802** A334 Set of 6 5.25 1.50

**Souvenir Sheet**

*Perf. 12½*

**1803** A334 5400r Firefly 3.25 1.50

No. 1803 contains one 40x32mm stamp.

Dogs — A335

Designs: 200r, Shiba inu, vert. 500r, Shih tzu. 900r, Tibetan spaniel. 1000r, Ainu, vert. 1500r, Lhasa apso. 4000r, Tibetan terrier.

*Perf. 12¼x12½ (200, 1000r), 12¾*

**1999, Feb. 3 Litho.**

**1804-1809** A335 Set of 6 5.00 1.50

**Souvenir Sheet**

*Perf. 12½*

**1810** A335 5400r Tosa inu, vert. 3.00 1.50

Size of Nos. 1804, 1807: 48x30mm. No. 1810 contains one 32x40mm stamp.

Antique Automobiles A336

Designs: 200r, 1881 La Rapide. 500r, 1895 Duryea. 900r, 1898 Barbarou. 1000r, 1898 Panhard. 1500r, 1901 Mercedes-Benz. 4000r, 1915 Ford.
5400r, 1875 Siegfried Marcus.

**1999, Mar. 5 Litho.** *Perf. 13x12¾*

**1811-1816** A336 Set of 6 4.75 1.50

**Souvenir Sheet**

*Perf. 13*

**1817** A336 5400r multi 3.75 1.50

No. 1817 contains one 40x32mm stamp.

Cats — A337

Designs: 200r, Ragdoll. 500r, Russian blue. 900r, Bombay. 1000r, Snowshoe. 1500r, Oriental. 4000r, Somali.

**1999, Mar. 30 Litho.** *Perf. 13*

**1818-1823** A337 Set of 6 5.25 1.50

**Souvenir Sheet**

**1824** A337 5400r Egyptian mau 3.00 1.50

No. 1824 contains one 32x40mm stamp.

Butterflies — A338

Designs: 200r, Araschnia levana. 500r, Vanessa cardui, horiz. 900r, Clossiana euphrosyne. 1000r, Coenonympha hero. 1500r, Parnassius apollo, horiz. 4000r, Plebejus argus.
5400r, Palaeochrysophanus hippothoe.

**1999, Apr. 25** *Perf. 12¾*

**1825-1830** A338 Set of 6 6.00 1.50

**Souvenir Sheet**

*Perf. 12½*

**1831** A338 5400r multi 4.00 2.00

No. 1831 contains one 32x40mm stamp.

Dinosaurs A339

Designs: 200r, Saurornitholestes. 500r, Prenocephalus. 900r, Wuerhosaurus. 1000r, Muttaburrasaurus. 1500r, Shantungosaurus. 4000r, Microceratops.
5400r, Daspletosaurus.

**1999, May 10 Litho.** *Perf. 12¾*

**1832-1837** A339 Set of 6 4.75 1.50

**Souvenir Sheet**

*Perf. 13*

**1838** A339 5400r multi 3.25 1.50

No. 1838 contains one 40x32mm stamp.

Molluscs — A340

Designs: 200r, Flabellina affinis. 500r, Octopus macropus. 900r, Helix hortensis. 1000r, Lima hians. 1500r, Arion empiricorum. 4000r, Anodonta cygnaea.
5400r, Eledone aldrovandii.

**1999, May 31** **Litho.** ***Perf. 12¾***
**1839-1844** A340 Set of 6 5.00 1.50

**Souvenir Sheet**

***Perf. 12½***

**1845** A340 5400r multi 3.50 1.00

No. 1845 contains one 32x40mm stamp.

**Historic Sites Type of 1996-97**

Designs: 100r, Prasat Neak Poan, horiz. 300r, Statue, Prasat Neak Poan, horiz. 500r, Prasat Banteay Srey. 1400r, Prasat Banteay Samré, horiz. 1600r, Prasat Banteay Srey, horiz. 1800r, Bas-relief, Angkor Wat. 1900r, Prasat Takeo, horiz.

**1999** **Litho.** ***Perf. 12½***

**Vignette Colors**

**1846** A288 100r blue .30 .25
**1847** A288 300r red .30 .25
**1848** A288 500r olive green .40 .25
**1849** A288 1400r bright green 1.00 .30
**1850** A288 1600r pink 1.10 .30
**1851** A288 1800r violet 1.25 .35
**1852** A288 1900r brown 1.50 .45
*Nos. 1846-1852 (7)* 5.85 2.15

Khmer Culture — A341

Designs: 500r, Dragon Bridge. 1500r, Temple with 100 columns, Kratie. 2000r, Krapum Chhouk stupa, Kratie.

**1999, Apr. 13** ***Perf. 13***
**1853-1855** A341 Set of 3 3.00 .85

UPU, 125th Anniv. A342

**1999** **Litho.** ***Perf. 12½x12¼***
**1856** A342 1600r multi 1.50 .85

Independence A343

People and: 500r, Map. 1500r, Ship, airplane, dove, public works. 2000r, Buildings.

**1999, Nov. 9** ***Perf. 12½***
**1857-1859** A343 Set of 3 2.75 1.00

Snakes — A344

Designs: 200r, Aspidelaps lubricus. 500r, Epicrates cenchria. 900r, Eunectes notaeus. 1000r, Diadophus punctatus. 1500r, Micrurus fulvius. 4000r, Telescopus semiannulatus.
5400r, Chondropython viridis.

**1999, Dec. 6** ***Perf. 12¾***
**1860-1865** A344 Set of 6 5.75 1.50

**Souvenir Sheet**

***Perf. 13***

**1866** A344 5400r multi 3.25 1.50

No. 1866 contains one 39x31mm stamp.

Birds of Prey — A345

Designs: 200r, Harpia harpyja. 500r, Terthopius ecaudatus, vert. 900r, Neophron pernopterus, vert. 1000r, Falco peregrinus, vert. 1500r, Buteo jamaicensis, vert. 4000r, Haliaetus leucocephalus.
5400r, Milvus milvus.

**1999, Oct. 5** **Litho.** ***Perf. 12¾***
**1867-1872** A345 Set of 6 6.00 1.50

**Souvenir Sheet**

***Perf. 12½***

**1873** A345 5400r multi 3.75 1.50

No. 1873 contains one 31x39mm stamp.

Philex France 99 — A346

Still life paintings by: 200r, Henri Fantin-Latour. 500r, Paul Cézanne. 900r, André Derain. 1000r, Henri Matisse. 1500r, Othon Friesz. 4000r, Matisse, diff.
5400r, Cézanne, diff.

**1999, June 10** **Litho.** ***Perf. 12½***
**1874-1879** A346 Set of 6 6.00 1.50

**Souvenir Sheet**

***Perf. 13***

**1880** A346 5400r multi 5.00 2.50

Souvenir Sheet

China 1999 World Philatelic Exhibition — A347

Pagodas: a, 200r, Tongzhou. b, 500r, Tianing Temple. c, 900r, Summer Palace. d, 900r, Temple of the Clouds. e, 1000r, Bei Hai. f, 1000r, Perfumed Hill. g, 1500r, Yunju. h, 4000r, Miaoying Temple.

***Perf. 12¼x12½***

**1999, Aug. 12** **Litho.**
**1881** A347 Sheet of 8, #a-h, + label 6.25 3.00

Orchids — A348

Designs: 200r, Cymbidium insigne. 500r, Papillonanthe teres. 900r, Panisea uniflora. 1000r, Euanthe sanderiana. 1500r, Dendrobium trigonopus. 4000r, Vanda coerulea.
5400r, Paphiopedilum callosum.

**1999, Aug. 5** **Litho.** ***Perf. 12¾***
**1889-1894** A348 Set of 6 5.75 1.50

**Souvenir Sheet**

***Perf. 12½***

**1895** A348 5400r multi 5.50 2.00

No. 1895 contains one 32x40mm stamp.

Birds — A349

Designs: 200r, Pyrrhula pyrrhula. 500r, Coccothraustes coccothraustes. 900r, Carduelis chloris. 1000r, Dendroica petechia. 1500r, Lanius excubitor. 4000r, Parus caeruleus.
5400r, Erithacus rubecula.

**1999, Sept. 5** **Litho.** ***Perf. 12¾***
**1896-1901** A349 Set of 6 6.00 1.50

**Souvenir Sheet**

***Perf. 13***

**1902** A349 5400r multi 5.00 2.50

No. 1902 contains one 40x32mm stamp.

Fish — A350

Designs: 200r, Capoeta tetrazona. 500r, Epalzeorhynchus frenatus. 900r, Rasbora kalochroma. 1000r, Etroplus maculatus. 1500r, Betta imbellis. 4000r, Colisa sota.
5400r, Tetraodon biocellatus.

***Perf. 12½x12¼***

**1999, Sept. 20** **Litho.**
**1903-1908** A350 Set of 6 6.00 1.50

**Souvenir Sheet**

***Perf. 13***

**1909** A350 5400r multi 5.00 2.00

No. 1909 contains one 40x32mm stamp.

Wildlife — A351

Designs: 200r, Ailuropada melanoleuca. 500r, Bos mutus. 900r, Hydropotes inermis. 1000r, Neomys fodiens, horiz. 1500r, Lutra lutra, horiz. 4000r, Panthera tigris, horiz.
5400r, Elaphurus davidianus, vert.

**1999, Nov. 20** **Litho.** ***Perf. 12¾***
**1910-1915** A351 Set of 6 6.00 1.50

**Souvenir Sheet**

***Perf. 12½***

**1916** A351 5400r multi 5.00 2.50

No. 1916 contains one 32x40mm stamp.

Bangkok 2000 Stamp Exhibition A352

Turtle-shaped objects and turtles: 200r, Cuora amboinensis, vert. 500r, Cuora flavomarginata, vert. 900r, Geoemyda spengleri. 1000r, Manouria impressa. 1500r, Chinemys reevesi. 4000r, Heosemys spinosa.
4500r, Hieremys annandalei.

**2000, Feb. 27** ***Perf. 12¾***
**1917-1922** A352 Set of 6 7.00 1.50

**Souvenir Sheet**

***Perf. 13***

**1923** A352 4500r multi 5.00 2.00

No. 1923 contains one 40x32mm stamp.

Dinosaurs — A353

Designs: 200r, Iguanodon. 500r, Euoplocephalus. 900r, Dilophosaurus. 1000r, Diplodocus. 1500r, Stegoceras. 4000r, Stegosaurus.
4500r, Brachiosaurus, vert.

**2000, Jan. 30** **Litho.** ***Perf. 12½x12¼***
**1924-1929** A353 Set of 6 4.50 1.50

**Souvenir Sheet**

***Perf. 12½***

**1930** A353 4500r multi 3.00 1.50

No. 1930 contains one 32x40mm stamp.

Beetles A354

Designs: 200r, Calosoma sycophanta. 500r, Oryctes nasicornis. 900r, Diochrysa fastuosa. 1000r, Blaps gigas. 1500r, Cincindela campestris. 4000r, Cissistes cephalotes.
4500r, Scarabeus aegyptiorum.

**2000, Feb. 5** **Litho.** ***Perf. 12¾***
**1931-1936** A354 Set of 6 5.50 1.50

**Souvenir Sheet**

***Perf. 13***

**1937** A354 4500r multi 2.75 1.50

No. 1937 contains one 40x32mm stamp.

New Year 2000 (Year of the Dragon) — A355

Various dragons. Denominations: 200r, 500r, 900r, 1000r, 1500r, 4000r.

**2000, Jan. 20** **Litho.** ***Perf. 12¼x12½***
**1938-1943** A355 Set of 6 6.00 1.50

**Souvenir Sheet**

***Perf. 13***

**1944** A355 4500r multi 3.25 1.50

No. 1944 contains one 32x40mm stamp.

Bettas A356

Designs: 200r, Unimaculata, Pugnax. 500r, Macrostoma, Taeniata. 900r, Foerschi, Imbellis. 1000r, Tessyae, Picta. 1500r, Edithae, Belica. 4000r, Smaragdina.
4500r, Splendens.

**2000, Apr. 10** **Litho.** ***Perf. 12½x12¼***
**1945-1950** A356 Set of 6 4.00 1.50

**Souvenir Sheet**

***Perf. 13***

**1951** A356 4500r multi 3.25 1.50

No. 1951 contains one 40x32mm stamp.

Mushrooms — A357

Designs: 200r, Amanita muscaria. 500r, Amanita pantherina. 900r, Clitocybe oleana.

1000r, Lactarius scrobiculatus. 1500r, Scleroderma vulgare. 4000r, Amanita verna.
4500r, Amanita phalloides.

**2000, Mar. 20 Litho. *Perf. 12¾***
**1952-1957** A357 Set of 6 4.50 1.50

**Souvenir Sheet**
***Perf. 13***

**1958** A357 4500r multi 2.75 1.50

No. 1958 contains one 32x40mm stamp.

Khmer Culture — A358

Designs: 500r, Srei Snam. 1500r, Srei Snam, diff. 2000r, Srei Krub Lakhna,

**2000, Apr. 13 Litho. *Perf. 13***
**1959-1961** A358 Set of 3 2.75 1.10

Growing Rice — A359

Designs: 100r, Transporting seedlings. 300r, Harrowing. 500r, Threshing. 1400r, Winnowing. 1600r, Transplanting. 1900r, Plowing. 2200r, Harvesting.

**2000, Mar. 1 *Perf. 12¼x12½***
**Vignette Color**

**1962** A359 100r brt yel grn .25 .25
**1963** A359 300r brt blue .25 .25
**1964** A359 500r brt pink .35 .25
**1965** A359 1400r brn orange .95 .25
**1966** A359 1600r dull blue 1.05 .30
**1967** A359 1900r bister brn 1.30 .35
**1968** A359 2200r red 1.50 .40
*Nos. 1962-1968 (7)* 5.65 2.05

Locomotives A360

Designs: 200r, Jules Petiet. 500r, Longue Chaudiere. 900r, Les Grand Chocolats. 1000r, Glehn du Bousquet. 1500r, Le Pendule Français. 4000r, TGV 001.
4500r, Le Shuttle.

**2000, Mar. 5 Litho. *Perf. 12½x12¼***
**1969-1974** A360 Set of 6 6.75 1.50

**Souvenir Sheet**
***Perf. 13***

**1975** A360 4500r multi 3.00 1.50

WIPA 2000 Philatelic Exhibition, Vienna (No. 1975). No. 1975 contains one 80x32mm stamp.

Birds — A361

Designs: 200r, Diomedea irrorata. 500r, Charadrius alexandrinus, vert. 900r, Sula nebouxii. 1000r, Sterna hirundo. 1500r, Larus argentatus, vert. 4000r, Chlidonia hybrida.
4500r, Sula bassana.

**2000, May 8 *Perf. 12¾***
**1976-1981** A361 Set of 6 5.00 1.50

**Souvenir Sheet**
***Perf. 13***

**1982** A361 4500r multi 3.00 1.50

No. 1982 contains one 40x32mm stamp.

Orchids — A362

Designs: 200r, Cypripedium macranthum. 500r, Vandopsis gigantea. 900r, Calypso bulbosa. 1000r, Vanda luzonica. 1500r, Paphiopedilum villosum. 4000r, Vanda merrillii.
4500r, Paphiopedilum victoria.

**2000, May 30 *Perf. 12¾***
**1983-1988** A362 Set of 6 6.00 1.50

**Souvenir Sheet**
***Perf. 13***

**1989** A362 4500r multi 4.00 1.50

No. 1989 contains one 32x40mm stamp.

Children's Stories — A363

Designs: 200r, The Courageous Little Tailor, vert. 500r, Tom Thumb, vert. 900r, Thumbelina, vert. 1000r, Pinocchio. 1500r, The Crayfish. 4000r, Peter Pan.
4500r, The Pied Piper, vert.

**2000, Nov. 20 Litho. *Perf. 12¾***
**1990-1995** A363 Set of 6 4.75 4.00

**Souvenir Sheet**
***Perf. 12½***

**1996** A363 4500r multi 3.00 3.00

No. 1996 contains one 32x40mm stamp.

Water Festival and Tourism A364

Designs: 500r, Men rowing canoe. 1500r, Men at canoe prow. 2000r, Temples, elephant, woman.

**2000, June 1 Litho. *Perf. 13***
**1997-1999** A364 Set of 3 4.25 2.75

Fire Trucks — A365

Designs: 200r, Metz DLK 23-6. 500r, Iveco-Magirus SLF24/100. 900r, Metz SLF 7000 WS. 1000r, Iveco-Magirus TLF 24/50. 1500r, Saval-Kronenburg RFF 11000. 4000r, Metz TLF 24/50.
4500r, Metz TLF 16/25.

**2000, July 30 *Perf. 12¾***
**2000-2005** A365 Set of 6 5.25 5.25

**Souvenir Sheet**
***Perf. 13***

**2006** A365 4500r multi 3.50 3.50

No. 2006 contains one 40x32mm stamp.

Independence, 47th Anniv. — A366

Flag, temple and: 500r, Flowers. 1500r, Dove. 2000r, People carrying torch.

**2000, Oct. 9 *Perf. 12¾***
**2007-2009** A366 Set of 3 4.25 2.75

Antique Automobiles A367

Designs: 200r, 1912 Rover 12C. 500r, 1907, Austin 30CV. 900r, 1909 Rolls-Royce Silver Ghost. 1000r, 1929 Graham Paige Phaeton DC. 1500r, 1937 Austin 12. 4000r, 1957 Mercedes-Benz 300SL.
4500r, 1936 MG.

**2000, Sept. 30 *Perf. 12¾***
**2010-2015** A367 Set of 6 5.00 2.50

**Souvenir Sheet**
***Perf. 13***

**2016** A367 4500r multi 3.50 2.00

España 2000 Intl. Philatelic Exhibition (No. 2016). No. 2016 contains one 40x32mm stamp.

Dachshunds A368

Designs: 200r, Smooth-haired dachshund. 500r, Wire-haired dachshund. 900r, Long-haired dachshund. 1000r, Two dachshunds. 1500r, Dachshund with pups. 4000r, Dachshunds resting.
4500r, Wire-haired dachshund, vert.

**2000, Aug. 30 *Perf. 13***
**2017-2022** A368 Set of 6 5.75 2.50

**Souvenir Sheet**
***Perf. 12½***

**2023** A368 4500r multi 2.75 2.00

No. 2023 contains one 32x40mm stamp.

Cats and Art — A369

Cat or cats and: 200r, Korean silk painting, 18th cent. 500r, Portuguese tile, 18th cent. 900r, Japanese ceramic cat. 1000r, Egyptian metallic cat. 1500r, Scandinavian engraving. 4000r, Japanese painting.
4500r, Cat on hind legs.

**2000, Oct. 5 *Perf. 12½x12¼***
**2024-2029** A369 Set of 6 5.75 2.50

**Souvenir Sheet**
***Perf. 13x13¼***

**2030** A369 4500r multi 3.00 1.50

No. 2030 contains one 40x32mm stamp.

Birds — A370

Designs: 200r, Creatophora cinerea. 500r, Sturnus vulgaris. 900r, Leiothrix lutea. 1000r, Rupicola rupicola. 1500r, Prunella collaris. 4000r, Panurus biarnicus.
4500r, Muscicapula pallipes, vert.

**2000, Dec. 10 *Perf. 13***
**2031-2036** A370 Set of 6 5.00 3.50

**Souvenir Sheet**

**2037** A370 4500r multi 3.25 2.00

No. 2037 contains one 32x40mm stamp.

Sports — A371

Designs: 200r, Weight lifting. 500r, Rhythmic gymnastics. 900r, Baseball. 1000r, Women's tennis. 1500r, Basketball. 4000r, Women's high jump.

***Perf. 12¾, 12½ (#2044)***
**2000, June 30 Litho.**
**2038-2043** A371 Set of 6 5.75 2.75

**Souvenir Sheet**

**2044** A371 4500r Runners 2.75 1.75

No. 2044 contains one 32x40mm stamp.

New Year 2001 (Year of the Snake) — A372

Various stylized snakes with background colors of: 200r, Beige. 500r, Dull bister. 900r, Light blue. 1000r, Greenish blue. 1500r, Dull green. 4000r, Blue.
5400r, Blue, horiz.

**2001, Jan. 15 Litho. *Perf. 12¼x12½***
**2045-2050** A372 Set of 6 5.25 3.50

**Souvenir Sheet**
***Perf. 13x13¼***

**2051** A372 5400r multi 4.00 2.75

No. 2051 contains one 40x32mm stamp.

Millennium A373

Designs: 200r, Johannes Gutenberg, printers. 500r, Michael Faraday, electric motor. 900r, Samuel F. B. Morse, telegraph. 1000r, Alexander Graham Bell, telephone. 1500r, Enrico Fermi, nuclear energy. 4000r, Edward Roberts, computer.
No. 2058: a, Christopher Columbus, ships. b, Neil Armstrong, lunar module.

**2001, Jan. 5 Litho. *Perf. 12¾***
**2052-2057** A373 Set of 6 7.00 4.00

**Souvenir Sheet**
***Perf. 12½***

**2058** A373 5400r Sheet of 2, #a-b + label 8.00 8.00

No. 2058 contains two 40x32mm stamps.

Fire and Rescue Equipment A374

Designs: 200r, 1910 Sandou ladder wagon. 500r, 1899 Gallo cart. 900r, Merryweather pumper, 1950s. 1000r, 1940 Merryweather ambulance. 1500r, 1972 Man-Metz pumper. 4000r, Roman Diesel pumper, 1970s.
5400r, 1898 Metropolitan steam pumper.

**2001, Feb. 5 *Perf. 12¾***
**2059-2064** A374 Set of 6 7.00 4.00

**Souvenir Sheet**
***Perf. 13x13¼***

**2065** A374 5400r multi 4.00 4.00

No. 2065 contains one 40x32mm stamp.

Mushrooms A375

Designs: 200r, Lycoperdon perlatum. 500r, Trametes versicolor. 900r, Hipholoma sublateritium. 1000r, Amanita muscaria. 1500r, Lycoperdon umbrinum. 4000r, Cortinarius orellanus.
5400r Amanita phalloides, vert.

**2001, Feb. 25 *Perf. 12¾***
**2066-2071** A375 Set of 6 6.00 4.00

**Souvenir Sheet**

*Perf. 12½*

**2072** A375 5400r multi 4.00 4.00

No. 2072 contains one 32x40mm stamp.

Belgica 2001 Intl. Stamp Exhibition, Brussels A376

Butterflies: 200r, Nymphalis polychloros. 500r, Cethosia hypsea. 900r, Papilio palinurus. 1000r, Apatura ilia. 1500r, Parthenos sylvia. 4000r, Morpho grandensis.
5400r, Heliconius melpomene.

**2001, Apr. 5** *Perf. 12¾*

**2073-2078** A376 Set of 6 6.25 4.00

**Souvenir Sheet**

*Perf. 13x13¼*

**2079** A376 5400r multi 4.00 2.50

Film Personalities — A377

Designs: 200r, Gary Cooper. 500r, Marlene Dietrich. 900r, Walt Disney. 1000r, Clark Gable. 1500r, Jeanette MacDonald. 4000r, Melvyn Douglas.
No. 2086: a, Rudolph Valentino. b, Marilyn Monroe.

**2001, Apr. 25** **Litho.** *Perf. 12¾*

**2080** A377 200r multi .25 .25
**2081** A377 500r multi .50 .30
**2082** A377 900r multi .70 .40
**2083** A377 1000r multi .90 .50
**2084** A377 1500r multi 1.25 .75
**2085** A377 4000r multi 3.25 1.75
*Nos. 2080-2085 (6)* 6.85 3.95

**Souvenir Sheet**

*Perf. 13*

**2086** A377 5400r Sheet of 2, #a-b 9.00 7.00

Natl. Culture Day — A378

Sculptures: 500r, Angkor. 1500r, Bayon. 2000r, Bayon, diff.

**2001, Apr. 3** **Litho.** *Perf. 12¾*

**2087-2089** A378 Set of 3 3.50 2.00

Temples — A379

Designs: 200r, Preah Vihear. 300r, Thonmanom. 600r, Tasom. 1000r, Kravan. 1500r, Takeo. 1700r, Mebon. 2200r, Banteay Kdei.

**2001, Mar. 15** *Perf. 12¼x12½*

**2090-2096** A379 Set of 7 6.00 3.50

Automobiles A380

Designs: 200r, 1972 TVR Series M. 500r, 1958 Ferrari 410. 900r, 1995 Peugeot 405. 1000r, 1953 Fiat 8VZ. 1500r, 1997 Citroen Xsara. 4000r, 1997 Renault Espace.
5400r, 1963 Ferrari 250 GT SWB.

**2001, June 5** **Litho.** *Perf. 12¾*

**2097-2102** A380 Set of 6 7.00 4.00

**Souvenir Sheet**

*Perf. 13x13¼*

**2103** A380 5400r multi 3.50 2.50

No. 2103 contains one 40x32mm stamp.

Tourism A381

Designs: 500r, Sourire de Bayon. 1500r, Bayon. 2000r, Bayon, diff.

**2001, June 5** *Perf. 12¾*

**2104-2106** A381 Set of 3 3.25 2.50

Philanippon '01 — A382

Locomotives: 200r, 4-6-0. 500r, 4-6-4. 900r, 4-4-0. 1000r, 4-6-4, diff. 1500r, 4-6-2. 4000r, 4-8-2.
5400r, Undescribed locomotive.

**2001, July 5** *Perf. 12½x12¼*

**2107-2112** A382 Set of 6 7.50 5.00

**Souvenir Sheet**

*Perf. 13x13¼*

**2113** A382 5400r multi 5.50 4.50

No. 2113 contains one 40x32mm stamp.

Penguins — A383

Designs: 200r, Aptenodytes forsteri. 500r, Spheniscus demersus. 900r, Spheniscus humboldti. 1000r, Eudypes cristatus. 1500r, Aptenodytes patagonica. 4000r, Pygoscelis antarctica.
5400r, Pygoscelis papua.

**2001, Aug. 5** *Perf. 12¾*

**2114-2119** A383 Set of 6 8.00 5.50

**Souvenir Sheet**

*Perf. 13x13¼*

**2120** A383 5400r multi 5.00 5.00

No. 2120 contains one 40x32mm stamp.

Cats — A384

Designs: 200r, Singapura. 500r, Cymric. 900r, Exotic shorthair. 1000r, Ragdoll. 1500r, Manx. 4000r, Somali.
5400r, Egyptian Mau.

**2001, Aug. 25** *Perf. 12½x12¼*

**2121-2126** A384 Set of 6 7.00 5.00

**Souvenir Sheet**

*Perf. 13x13¼*

**2127** A384 5400r multi 5.75 4.75

No. 2127 contains one 40x32mm stamp.

Kites — A385

Designs: 300r, Khleng Chak. 500r, Khleng Kanton. 1000r, Khleng Phnong. 1500r, Khleng Kaun Morn. 3000r, Khleng Me Ambao.

**2001, Sept. 7** *Perf. 12¾*

**2128-2132** A385 Set of 5 6.50 5.50

Cacti — A386

Designs: 200r, Parodia cintiensis. 500r, Astrophytum astenas. 900r, Parodia faustiana. 1000r, Coryphantha sulcolanata. 1500r, Neochilenia hankena. 4000r, Mammilaria boolii.
5400r, Mammilaria swinglei.

**2001, Sept. 15** *Perf. 12¾*

**2133-2138** A386 Set of 6 7.00 5.00

**Souvenir Sheet**

*Perf. 12½*

**2139** A386 5400r multi 6.25 5.00

No. 2139 contains one 32x40mm stamp.

Khmer Culture — A387

Designs: 500r, Fish Dance. 1500r, Red Fish Ballet. 2000r, Apsara Ballet.

**2001, Oct. 9** *Perf. 12¾*

**2140-2142** A387 Set of 3 4.25 3.50

Wolves and Foxes — A388

Designs: 200r, Canis lupus occidentalis. 500r, Canis lupus tundrorum, vert. 900r, Vulpes fulvas. 1000r, Canis latrans. 1500r, Vulpes zerda, vert. 4000r, Alopex lagopus.
5400r, Canis lupus signatus, vert.

**2001, Oct. 15** *Perf. 12¾*

**2143-2148** A388 Set of 6 7.00 5.00

**Souvenir Sheet**

*Perf. 12½*

**2149** A388 5400r multi 3.00 3.00

No. 2103 contains one 32x40mm stamp.

Human Evolution A389

Designs: 100r, Australopithecus anamensis. 200r, Australopithecus afarensis. 300r, Australopithecus africanus. No. 2153, 500r, Australopithecus rudolfensis. No. 2154, 500r, Australopithecus boisei. 1000r, Homo habilis. 1500r, Homo erectus. 4000r, Homo sapiens neanderthalensis.
5400r, Homo sapiens sapiens.

**2001, Oct. 25** *Perf. 13*

**2150-2157** A389 Set of 8 9.50 6.00

**Souvenir Sheet**

**2158** A389 5400r multi 6.50 5.00

No. 2158 contains one 40x32mm stamp.

King Norodom Sihanouk, 80th Birthday (in 2002) A389a

Various photos: 100r, 200r, 300r, 400r, 500r, 600r, 700r, 800r, 900r, 1000r, 1500r, 2000r, 3000r.

**2001, Oct. 31** **Litho.** *Perf. 13*

**2158A-2158M** A389a Set of 13 *17.00 10.00*

Chess — A390

Designs: 200r, Rook. 500r, Pawn. 900r, King. 1000r, Bishop. 1500r, Queen. 4000r, Knight.
5400r, Pieces of Oriental chess-like game.

**2001, Dec. 25** *Perf. 12¾*

**2159-2164** A390 Set of 6 7.00 6.00

**Souvenir Sheet**

*Perf. 13*

**2165** A390 5400r multi 5.50 4.00

No. 2165 contains one 40x32mm stamp.

Italian Soccer — A391

Designs: 200r, 1934 World Cup championship team. 500r, 1938 World Cup championship team. 900r, 1968 European Cup championship team. 1000r, 1982 World Cup championship team. 1500r, 2002 World Cup team. 4000r, Italian soccer federation emblem.

**2001** *Perf. 12¾*

**2166-2171** A391 Set of 6 7.00 7.00

ASEAN Post, 10th Anniv — A392

Temples: 500r, Prasat Preah Vihear. 1000r, Prasat Preah Ko. 1500r, Prasat Banteay Srei. 2500r, Prasat Bayon. 3500r, Prasat Angkor Wat.

**2002, July 9** *Perf. 13*

**2172-2176** A392 Set of 5 11.00 10.00

Sugar Palm — A393

Designs: 300r, Tree. 500r, Female flower. 700r, Male flower. 1500r, Fruit.

**2003, June 20** **Litho.**

**2177-2180** A393 Set of 4 7.50 7.00

Japanese Grant Aid — A394

Designs: 100r, Drawing of Bridge No. 26, Highway 6A. 200r, Bridge No. 26, Highway 6A. 400r, Chroy Changvar Bridge. 800r, Kizuna Bridge. 3500r, Monument, vert.

**2003, Apr. 25**

**2181-2185** A394 Set of 5 7.50 6.00

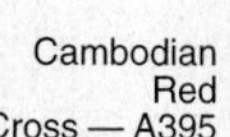

Cambodian Red Cross — A395

Designs: 100r, Ox cart. 200r, Woman carrying rice bag, vert. 300r, Queen with Red Cross volunteers. 400r, Queen and women. 500r, Queen and elderly people. 700r, Queen and women, diff. 800r, Queen and Prime Minister's wife giving items to people. 1000r, Like 800r, diff. 1900r, Like 800r, diff., vert. 2100r, Like 800r, diff., vert. 4000r, Queen and Prime Minister's wife with baby.

**2003, May 8**
**2186-2196** A395 Set of 11 12.00 12.00

Cambodia/People's Republic of China Diplomatic Relations, 50th Anniv. — A396

No. 2197: a, Angkor Wat. b, Great Wall of China.

**2003, July 19** *Perf. 12¼x12*
**2197** A396 2000r Horiz. pair, #a-b 5.00 4.00

Association of South East Asian Nations, 36th Anniv. — A397

Designs: 400r, Conference emblem. 500r, Apsara dancer. 600r, Apsara dancer, diff. 1600r, Apsara dancers. 1900r, Temonorom dancers.

**2003, Aug. 8** *Perf. 13*
**2198-2202** A397 Set of 5 8.00 6.50

King Norodom Sihanouk A398

Designs: 200r, Pointing at map. 400r, Meeting rural Cambodians, vert. 500r, Sitting in forest, vert. 800r, Pointing in forest, vert. 1000r, Saluting, vert. 2000r, Saluting, with flag and Independence Monument, vert. 5000r, With handicapped people.

**2003, Nov. 9**
**2203-2209** A398 Set of 7 10.00 7.00

Khmer Culture — A399

Sculptures: 100r, Bayon. 200r, Banteay Srei. 400r, Banteay Srei, diff. 800r, Bayon, vert. 3500r, Banteay Srei, vert.
2000r, Unattributed sculpture, vert.

**2004, Apr. 3**
**2210-2214** A399 Set of 5 5.00 4.00

**Souvenir Sheet**

**2215** A399 2000r multi 3.25 2.00

Rural Areas — A400

Designs: 600r, Mill. 900r, House, field and cattle. 2000r, House and trees.
2000r, Ox cart and driver.

**2004, Apr. 13**
**2216-2218** A400 Set of 3 6.00 4.00

**Souvenir Sheet**

**2219** A400 2000r multi 3.00 2.25

Tepmonorum Dancers — A401

Dancers with: 400r, Yellow costumes. 1000r, Blue costumes. 2100r, Blue and yellow costumes.
2100r, Blue and yellow costumes, diff.

**2004, May 5**
**2220-2222** A401 Set of 3 5.00 4.00

**Souvenir Sheet**

**2223** A401 2000r multi 3.00 2.50

Flowers — A402

Designs: 600r, Cassia fistula. 700r, Butea monosperma. 900r, Couroupita quianensis. 1000r, Delonix regia, horiz. 1800r, Lagerstroemia floribunda.
2000r, Lagerstroemia floribunda, horiz.

**2004, Aug. 25** **Litho.** *Perf. 13*
**2224-2228** A402 Set of 5 5.50 4.00

**Souvenir Sheet**

**2229** A402 2000r multi 3.25 1.75

Tourism A403

Designs: 200r, Prasat Preah Khan. 500r, Prasat Preup. 600r, PrasatBanteay Samre. 1600r, Prasat Bayon. 1900r, Angkor Wat.
2000r, Prasat Bayon, vert.

**2004, Sept. 27** **Litho.** *Perf. 13*
**2230-2234** A403 Set of 5 5.00 3.50

**Souvenir Sheet**

**2235** A403 2000r multi 3.25 2.00

Coronation of King Norodom Shiamoni — A404

Various photos: 100r, 400r, 500r, 600r, 700r, 900r, 2100r, 2200r, 4000r. 700r-4000r are horiz.

**2004, Oct. 29**
**2236-2244** A404 Set of 9 8.00 8.00

Ancient Fishing Tools — A405

Various scoops and baskets: 100r, 200r, 800r, 1700r, 2200r. 1700r and 2200r are vert.
2000r, Child with basket, vert.

**2004, Dec. 5**
**2245-2249** A405 Set of 5 5.50 4.00

**Souvenir Sheet**

**2250** A405 2000r multi 4.25 2.50

Cambodian Red Cross, 50th Anniv. — A406

Designs: 400r, Emblem. 700r, Volunteers, horiz. 800r, Volunteers, diff., horiz. 1900r, Volunteers, diff., horiz. 2100r, Volunteers, diff. horiz. 2200r, Royalty on dais, horiz.

**2005, Feb. 18**
**2251-2256** A406 Set of 6 7.25 7.25

Apsaras Dance — A407

Dancer with background color of: 800r, Pink. 900r, Light blue. 1400r, Green. 1600r, Rose. 2000r, Blue.
4000r, Brown.

**2005, Apr. 12**
**2257-2261** A407 Set of 5 6.50 5.00

**Souvenir Sheet**

**2262** A407 4000r multi 4.25 3.00

Khmer Culture A408

Designs: 500r, Banteay Kdei. 700r, Elephant Terrace. 1000r, Thommanon. 2000r, Ta Prohm. 2500r, Angkor Wat.
4000r, Ta Reach, vert.

**2005, May 16**
**2263-2267** A408 Set of 5 6.25 5.00

**Souvenir Sheet**

**2268** A408 4000r multi 4.25 3.00

Flowers — A409

Nymphaea lotus in: 100r, Purple. 500r, White. 1200r, Blue. 2000r, Yellow. 2500r, Red.
4000r, Red flowers in canoe, horiz.

**2005, July 25** **Litho.** *Perf. 13*
**2269-2273** A409 Set of 5 6.00 4.50

**Souvenir Sheet**

**2274** A409 4000r multi 4.25 3.00

Fish — A410

Designs: 700r, Pangasionodon gigas. 800r, Catlocarpio siamensis. 1000r, Mekongina erythrospila. 1900r, Probarbus labeaminor, vert. 2200r, Wallago leeri, vert.
4000r, Scleropages formosus.

**2005, Sept. 5** *Perf. 13*
**2275-2279** A410 Set of 5 6.25 5.50

**Souvenir Sheet**

**2280** A410 4000r multi 4.25 3.75

Coronation of King Norodom Sihamoni, 1st Anniv. — A411

Frame colors: 500r, Green. 1500r, Blue. 2200r, Red.

**2005, Oct. 29** **Litho.** *Perf. 13*
**2281-2283** A411 Set of 3 3.25 3.25

**Miniature Sheet**

Birds A412

No. 2284: a, 200r, Great egret. b, 400r, Great-billed heron. c, 1000r, Painted stork. d, 1200r, Spot-billed pelican. e, 1800r, Sarus crane, horiz. f, 3500r, Greater adjutant, horiz.

**2005, Dec. 5**
**2284** A412 Sheet of 6, #a-f 8.00 8.00

Khmer Culture A413

Women at work: 100r, Scooping dyes. 800r, Washing clothes. 1500r, Weaving. 2200r, Spinning thread. 3500r, Weaving, diff.
5400r, Weaving, diff.

**2006, Jan. 26**
**2285-2289** A413 Set of 5 6.75 6.00

**Souvenir Sheet**

**2290** A413 5400r multi 4.00 3.00

Marine Mammals A414

Designs: 500r, Sousa chinensis. 900r, Neophocaena phocaenoides. 1400r, Dolphinus capensis tropicalis. 2100r, Stenella longirostris roseinventris. 3500r, Tursiops aduncus.
5400r, Neophocaena phocaenoides and boat.

**2006, Mar. 9**
**2291-2295** A414 Set of 5 7.50 6.50

**Souvenir Sheet**

**2296** A414 5400r multi 4.00 3.00

Reamker Legend A415

Designs: 1000r, Jup Leak and Ream Leak. 1400r, Preah Ream, vert. 1600r, Neang Seda, vert. 1900r, Krong Reap, vert. 2100r, Hanuman, vert.
5400r, Two characters in water.

**2006, Apr. 13**
**2297-2301** A415 Set of 5 6.50 5.50

**Souvenir Sheet**

**2302** A415 5400r multi 4.25 3.25

Elephants A416

Designs: 400r, Adult and juvenile elephant. 700r, Elephants in water. 1600r, Elephant, vert. 2200r, Elephant facing right. 3500r, Elephant facing left.
5400r, Elephants in water, diff.

**2006, June 15 Litho. *Perf. 13***
**2303-2307** A416 Set of 5 7.00 5.50

**Souvenir Sheet**

**2308** A416 5400r multi 4.25 3.50

Dances A417

Designs: 600r, Chhai Yaim dance. 1900r, Sacrifice of Buffalo dance. 2200r, Mouth Organ dance. 3500r, Rice Harvest dance.

**2006, Aug. 17**
**2309-2312** A417 Set of 4 6.50 5.50

Birds — A418

Designs: 600r, Threskionis melanocephalus. 800r, Plegadis facinellus. 1500r, Houbaropsis bengalensis. 2100r, Pseudibis gigantea. 3500r, Pseudibis davisoni.
5400r, Pseudibis gigantea, vert.

**2006, Nov. 8 Litho. *Perf. 13***
**2313-2317** A418 Set of 5 7.50 6.00

**Souvenir Sheet**

**2318** A418 5400r multi 7.00 5.50

Condom Use Program A419

Designs: 300r, Man, woman, program emblem. 500r, Man, motorcycle, program emblem. 2200r, Men on boat, flag with program emblem.

**2006, Dec. 1 Litho. *Perf. 13***
**2319-2321** A419 Set of 3 2.25 2.25

World AIDS Day.

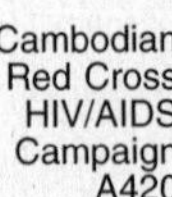

Cambodian Red Cross HIV/AIDS Campaign A420

Campaign leader Bun Rany, wife of Prime Minister Hun Sen and captions: 1500r, Caring. 1900r, Stop discrimination, vert. 2000r, Give hope to families. 2100r, National and Asia-Pacific Leadership Forum Champion. 2200r, National and Asia-Pacific Leadership Forum Champion, diff.

**2007 Litho. *Perf. 13***
**2322-2326** A420 Set of 5 6.50 6.50

Sculpture A421

Flags of Viet Nam and Cambodia A422

**2007, June 24**
**2327** A421 500r shown .45 .45
**2328** A421 800r Sculpture, diff. .65 .65
**2329** A421 1000r Sculpture, diff. .75 .75
**2330** A421 1500r Sculpture, diff. 1.25 1.25
**2331** A422 1900r shown 1.50 1.50
*Nos. 2327-2331 (5)* 4.60 4.60

Diplomatic relations between Cambodia and Viet Nam, 40th anniv.

Handicap International, 25th Anniv. — A423

Denominations: 1000r, 1500r.

**2007, July 25**
**2332-2333** A423 Set of 2 2.00 2.00

Dancers A424

Architecture — A425

Various dancers with denominations of: 800r, 900r, 1400r, 1600r, 2000r.
No. 2339: a, Secretariat Building, Bandar Seri Begawan, Brunei. b, National Museum of Cambodia. c, Fatahillah Museum, Jakarta, Indonesia. d, Typical house, Laos. e, Malayan Railway Headquarters Building, Kuala Lumpur, Malaysia. f, Yangon Post Office, Myanmar (Burma). g, Malacañang Palace, Philippines. h, National Museum of Singapore. i, Vimanmek Mansion, Bangkok, Thailand. j, Presidential Palace, Hanoi, Viet Nam.

**2007, Aug. 8**
**2334-2338** A424 Set of 5 5.00 5.00
**2339** A425 1000r Sheet of 10, #a-j 10.00 10.00

Association of South East Asian Nations (ASEAN), 40th anniv. See Brunei Nos. 607, Burma No. 370, Indonesia Nos. 2120-2121, Laos Nos. 1717-1718, Malaysia No. 1170, Philippines Nos. 3103-3105, Singapore No. 1265, Thailand No. 2315, and Viet Nam Nos. 3302-3311.

Flowers — A426

Designs: 100r, Monochoria vaginalis. 600r, Alternanthera sessilis. 1900r, Nymphoides hydrophylla. 2000r, Limnophila geoffrayi. 2200r, Xyris indica.
6000r, Eichhornia crassipes.

**2008, June 30 Litho. *Perf. 13***
**2340-2344** A426 Set of 5 — —

**Souvenir Sheet**
***Perf. 13¾x13½***

**2345** A426 6000r multi — —

No. 2345 contains one 32x43mm stamp.

Friendship Between Cambodia and People's Republic of China, 50th Anniv. — A427

No. 2346: a, Tian An Men Rostrum, flag of People's Republic of China. b, Royal Palace, flag of Cambodia.

**2008, July 25 Litho. *Perf. 12***
**2346** A427 2000r Horiz. pair, #a-b 2.00 2.00

Best Wishes Dancers — A428

Various dancers with background color of: 600r, Yellow green. 1000r, Lilac. 1700r, Green. 1800r, Dark blue. 1900r, Dark blue.
6000r, Best Wishes dancer with temple in background.

**2008, Aug. 8 Litho. *Perf. 13***
**2347** A428 600r multi — —
**2348** A428 1000r multi — —
**2349** A428 1700r multi — —
**2350** A428 1800r multi — —
**2351** A428 1900r multi — —

**Souvenir Sheet**
***Perf. 13¾x13½***

**2352** A428 6000r multi — —

No. 2352 contains one 32x43mm stamp.

Addition of Preah Vihear to UNESCO World Heritage List — A429

Designs: 600r, Gopura I. 700r, Gopura II. 1000r, Gopura III. 2000r, Gopura IV. 3000r, Gopura V.
6000r, Temple of Preah Vihear.

**2008, Nov. 9 Litho. *Perf. 13***
**2353** A429 600r multi — —
**2354** A429 700r multi — —
**2355** A429 1000r multi — —
**2356** A429 2000r multi — —
**2357** A429 3000r multi — —

**Souvenir Sheet**
***Perf. 13½x13¾***

**2358** A429 6000r multi — —

No. 2358 contains one 43x32mm stamp.

A430

Pottery Making A431

Various women making pottery: 100r, 700r, 1900r, 2000r, 2200r.
6000r, Oxcart with pottery.

**2008, Dec. 5 Litho. *Perf. 13***
**2359-2363** A430 Set of 5 3.50 3.50

**Souvenir Sheet**
***Perf. 13¾x13½***

**2364** A431 6000r multi 3.00 3.00

Buildings, School Children, Athletes — A432

30th Anniversary Emblem — A432a

Designs: 200r, Agriculture. 1500r, Factory, power line towers, dam. 2200r, Mail truck and telecommunications. 2500r, Trucks, bridge and cranes at port. 2800r, Temple, dancers, elephant and boats.

**2009, Jan. 7 Litho. *Perf. 13***
**2365-2370** A432 Set of 6 — —
**2371** A432a 3000r multi — —

Victory Day, 30th anniv.

Preah Vihear as UNESCO World Heritage Site, 1st Anniv. — A433

UNESCO World Heritage emblem and various sites at Preah Vihear: 300r, 800r, 1600r, 1800r, 2800r.

**2009, July 7 Litho. *Perf. 13***
**2372-2376** A433 Set of 5 — —

Ancient Agricultural Tools — A434

Designs: 300r, Plow. 1200r, Harrow. 1700r, Spiked roller. 1800r, Water wheel. 2800r, Cart.
6000r, Farmer operating water wheel, vert.

**2010, Mar. 30 Litho. *Perf. 13***
**2377-2381** A434 Set of 5 3.75 3.75

**Souvenir Sheet**
***Perf. 13¾x13½***

**2382** A434 6000r multi 3.00 3.00

Environmental Protection — A435

Designs: 200r, Filled trash can, face on Earth. 800r, Watering can pouring water on Earth, cars in flood. 1400r, Tree inside split Earth. 1700r, Buildings in hourglass. 3000r, Tree in hands.
6000r, Cars in flood, palm trees.

**2010, May 25 Litho. *Perf. 13***
**2383-2387** A435 Set of 5 3.50 3.50

**Souvenir Sheet**
***Perf. 13¾x13½***

**2388** A435 6000r multi 3.00 3.00

Diplomatic Relations Between Cambodia and the United States, 60th Anniv. — A436

**2010, July 11 Litho. *Perf. 13***
**2389** A436 2800r multi 1.40 1.40

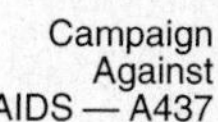

Campaign Against AIDS — A437

Red AIDS ribbon and: 1000r, Wrapped and unwrapped condoms, condom with face. 1500r, Man, woman and child. 2800r, Men and woman at night club. 4000r, Two birds.

**2011, June 29 Litho. *Perf. 13***
**2390-2393** A437 Set of 4 4.75 4.75

First day cancels show a June 5 date, but the stamps were not sold until June 29.

Fish — A438

Designs: 500r, Barbonymus schwanenfeldii. 1500r, Hypsibarbus lagleri. 2800r, Puntioplites falcifer. 3000r, Osteochilus melanopleurus. 3500r, Hampala macrolepidota.
6000r, Fish, fishermen and nets.

**2011, Aug. 8 Litho. *Perf. 13***
**2394-2398** A438 Set of 5 5.25 5.25

**Souvenir Sheet**

***Perf. 13½x13¾***

**2399** A438 6000r multi 3.00 3.00

A439

King Norodom Sihanouk (1922-2012) — A440

**2011, Nov. 14 Litho. *Perf. 13***
**2400** A439 2800r multi — —
**2401** A440 3000r multi — —

Return of King Norodom Sihanouk to Cambodia, 20th anniv.

Temples — A441

Designs: 500r, Prasat Ta Moan Thom. 2800r, Prasat Nokor Bachey. 3500r, Prasat Ta Krabey. 5000r, Prasat Ta Moan Thom, horiz.
6000r, Prasat Phnom Banan.

**2012, July 27 Litho. *Perf. 13***
**2402** A441 500r multi — —
**2403** A441 2800r multi — —
**2404** A441 3500r multi — —
**2405** A441 5000r multi — —

**Souvenir Sheet**

***Perf. 13¾x13½***

**2406** A441 6000r multi — —

Banteay Srei Temple Statues — A442

Statue of: 2000r, Ascetic. 2500r, Apsara. 2800r, Apsara, diff. 3000r, Apsara, diff.
6000r, Dancer.

**2012, Sept. 18 Litho. *Perf. 13***
**2407-2410** A442 Set of 4 — —

**Souvenir Sheet**

***Perf. 13¾x13½***

**2411** A442 6000r multi — —

60th Birthday of King Norodom Sihamoni — A443

**2013, May 14 Litho. *Perf. 13***
**2412** A443 5000r multi 6.25 6.25

Banteay Srei Temple — A444

Various temple details.

**2013, July 17 Litho. *Perf. 13***
**2413** A444 1500r multi 1.90 1.90
**2414** A444 2500r multi 3.25 3.25
**2415** A444 2800r multi 3.50 3.50
**2416** A444 3000r multi 3.75 3.75
*Nos. 2413-2416 (4)* 12.40 12.40

Nos. 2413-2416 exist in perforated and imperforate sheets of 4. Value, $16 and $42.50, respectively.

Rice Growing — A445

Designs: 1800r, Three planters in paddy. 2200r, Four transplanters in paddy. 3000r, Farmer and oxen plowing in paddy. 3500r, Farmers and oxen in paddy.
6000r, Farmers harvesting crops.

**2013, Sept. 19 Litho. *Perf. 13***
**2417-2420** A445 Set of 4 13.00 13.00

**Souvenir Sheet**

***Perf. 13¾x13½***

**2421** A445 6000r multi 8.75 8.75

Nos. 2417-2420 exist in perforated and imperforate sheets of 4. Value, $16 and $42.50, respectively.

Friendship Between Cambodia and People's Republic of China, 55th Anniv. (in 2013) — A446

No. 2422: a, Wat Phnom, Phnom Penh, Cambodia. b, Kaiyuan Temple, Quanzhou, People's Republic of China.

**2014, May 14 Litho. *Perf. 12***
**2422** A446 3000r Horiz. pair, #a-b 7.75 7.75
*c.* Souvenir sheet of 2, #2422a-2422b 8.75 8.75

Dated 2013.

Traditional Dances — A447

Various dancers: 1000r, 2000r, 3000r, 3500r.
6000r, Dancers, diff.

**2014, Oct. 10 Litho. *Perf. 13***
**2423-2426** A447 Set of 4 11.00 11.00

**Souvenir Sheet**

***Perf. 13x13¼***

**2427** A447 6000r multi 8.25 8.25

No. 2427 contains one 31x46mm stamp.
Nos. 2423-2426 exist in perforated and imperforate sheets of 4. Value, $16 and $42.50, respectively.

Flags and Emblem of Association of Southeast Asian Nations — A448

**2015, Aug. 8 Litho. *Perf. 13½***
**2428** A448 1200r multi 1.60 1.60

See Brunei No. 656, Burma Nos. 417-418, Indonesia No. 2428, Laos No. 1906, Malaysia No. 1562, Philippines No. 3619, Singapore No. 1742, Thailand No. 2875, Viet Nam No. 3529.

Banteay Chhmar — A449

Various views of Banteay Chhmar: 500r, 2000r, 2800r, 3000r.
6000r, Banteay Chhmar, vert.

**2015, Oct. 9 Litho. *Perf. 13***
**2429-2432** A449 Set of 4 9.25 9.25

**Souvenir Sheet**

**2433** A449 6000r multi 13.00 13.00

No. 2433 contains one 31x46mm stamp.
Nos. 2429-2432 exist in perforated and imperforate sheets of 4. Value, $16 and $42.50, respectively.

United Nations Mine Sweeping — A450

Various soldiers sweeping for mines: 2000r, 3000r, 3500r.
6000r, Soldier sweeping for mines, diff.

**2016, Aug. 8 Litho. *Perf. 13***
**2434-2436** A450 Set of 3 9.25 9.25

**Souvenir Sheet**

**2437** A450 6000r multi 7.75 7.75

No. 2437 contains one 31x46mm stamp.
Nos. 2434-2436 exist in perforated and imperforate sheets of 3. Value, $16 and $42.50, respectively.

Statues — A451

Designs: 500r, Tevi. 2000r, Buddha. 2500r, Harihara. 3000r, Vishnu, facing left. 3500r, Vishnu, facing forward.
6000r, Shiva statues.

**2016, Nov. 11 Litho. *Perf. 13***
**2438-2442** A451 Set of 5 12.50 12.50
*2442a* Souvenir sheet of 5, #2438-2442, + label *21.00 21.00*

**Souvenir Sheet**

**2443** A451 6000r multi 7.75 7.75

No. 2442a exists imperforate. Value, $45. No. 2443 contains one 31x46mm stamp.

Rumdul — A452

**2017, Aug. 8 Litho. *Perf. 13***
**2444** A452 3000r multi 3.25 3.25

**Souvenir Sheet**

**2445** A452 6000r Rumdul, vert. 15.00 15.00

Association of Southeast Asian Nations, 50th anniv. No. 2445 contains one 31x41mm stamp.

International Year of Sustainable Tourism for Development A453

Tourist attractions: 500r, Koh Rong Sanloem. 1000r, Ream National Park. 2000r, Wat Phnom. 3000r, Angkor Wat at sunset. 4000r, Angkor Wat and 3 men.
6000r, Angkor Wat, vert.

**2017, Sept. 19 Litho. *Perf. 13***
**2446-2450** A453 Set of 5 11.00 11.00

**Souvenir Sheet**

**2451** A453 6000r multi 22.00 22.00

No. 2451 contains one 31x46mm stamp.

Lighthouses — A454

Designs: 500r, Chong Khneas Lighthouse. 800r, Croachamar Lighthouse. 2100r, Chhlong Lighthouse. 3000r, Koh Dach Lighthouse. 4000r, Kohrongsamloem Lighthouse.
6000r, Kampong Cham Lighthouse.

**2017, Oct. 10 Litho. *Perf. 13***
**2452-2456** A454 Set of 5 11.00 11.00
*2456a* Souvenir sheet of 5, #2452-2456, perf. 13¾ *27.50 27.50*

**Souvenir Sheet**

**2457** A454 6000r multi 11.00 11.00

No. 2456a exists imperforate. Value, $40. No. 2457 contains one 31x46mm stamp.

Friendship Between Cambodia and People's Republic of China — A455

Designs: No. 2458, 3000r, Iron Lion of Cangzhou, People's Republic of China. No. 2459, 3000r, Stone Lion, Temple Phnom Bakheng, Cambodia, vert.

**2017, Nov. 16 Litho. *Perf. 13***
**2458-2459** A455 Set of 2 6.75 6.75

See People's Republic of China Nos. 4496-4497.

Sculptures of Apsaras — A456

Various sculptures of Apsaras: 500r, 800r, 2000r, 3000r, 4000r.
6000r, Apsaras, diff.

**2017, Dec. 12 Litho. *Perf. 13***
**2460-2464** A456 Set of 5 11.50 11.50

**Souvenir Sheet**

**2465** A456 6000r multi 22.00 22.00

No. 2465 contains one 46x31mm stamp.

Soccer — A457

Soccer Federation of Cambodia emblem and: 500r, Cambodian flag, crowd at soccer match. 900r, Three soccer players. 2000r, Six soccer players. 3000r, Four soccer players, vert. 4000r, Crowd at soccer match, vert.
6000r, Emblem and Phnom Penh Olympic Stadium, vert.

**2018, June 14 Litho. *Perf. 13***
**2466-2470** A457 Set of 5 11.00 11.00

**Souvenir Sheet**

**2471** A457 6000r multi 13.50 13.50

No. 2471 contains one 31x46mm stamp.
No. 2471 exists imperforate. Value, $16.50.

A458

Baha'i House of Worship, Battambang — A459

**2018, June 22 Litho. *Perf. 13***
**2472** A458 2000r multi 2.75 2.75
**2473** A459 2100r multi 2.75 2.75

Bahá'u'lláh (1817-92), founder of Baha'i Faith.

Sambor Prei Kuk Temple — A460

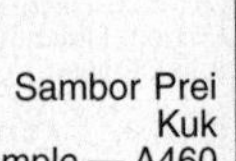

Various sculptures and buildings: 2000r, 3000r, 4000r.
6000r, Temple, vert.

**2018, July 8 Litho. *Perf. 13***
**2474-2476** A460 Set of 3 12.00 12.00

**Souvenir Sheet**

**2477** A460 6000r multi 13.50 13.50

No. 2477 contains one 31x46mm stamp.

Carved Stone Heads of Angkor Wat — A461

Stamps with white frames depicting various heads: 500r, 1200r, 2100r, 3000r, 4000r.
No. 2483: a, Head, small area of blue sky at UR, denomination below chin. b, Head, diff, larger area of blue sky at UR, denomination touching chin.

**2018, Aug. 13 Litho. *Perf. 13***
**2478-2482** A461 Set of 5 12.00 12.00

**Souvenir Sheet**

**2483** A461 3000r Sheet of 2, #a-b 14.50 14.50

No. 2483 contains two 31x46mm stamps.
No. 2483 exists imperforate. Value, $15.

National Museum — A462

Designs: 500r, Vessel for Prahok fermented fish. 800r, Statue of King Jayavarman VII. 2000r, Statue of Buddhist Trial. No. 2487, 3000r, Kinnari box, horiz. 4000r, Statue of reclining Vishnu, horiz.
No. 2489, 3000r, National Museum, vert.

**2018, Sept. 7 Litho. *Perf. 13***
**2484-2488** A462 Set of 5 11.00 11.00

**Souvenir Sheet**

**2489** A462 3000r multi 6.75 6.75

No. 2489 contains one 31x46mm stamp.
No. 2489 exists imperforate. Value, $8.75.

Birds — A463

Designs: 500r, Giant ibis. 900r, Red-headed vulture. 2000r, White-shouldered ibis. 3000r, Sarus crane, vert. 4000r, Greater adjutant, vert.
6000r, Juvenile painted stork, (Mycteria leucocephala), vert.

**2018, Nov. 16 Litho. *Perf. 13***
**2490-2494** A463 Set of 5 11.00 11.00

**Souvenir Sheet**

**2495** A463 6000r multi 13.50 13.50

No. 2495 contains one 31x46mm stamp.

A464

Prionailurus Viverrinus — A465

Various depictions of Prionailurus viverrinus: 500r, 900r, 1000r, 2000r, 2500r, 3000r, 4000r. 3000r and 4000r are vert.
6000r, Prionailurus viverrinus, vert.

**2019, Feb. 22 Litho. *Perf. 13***
**2496-2502** A464 Set of 7 15.50 15.50

**Souvenir Sheet**

**2503** A465 6000r multi 13.50 13.50

An imperforate 6000r souvenir sheet with a different illustration was produced in limited quantities. Value, $15.
Nos. 2496-2502 were issued individually in sheets of 10 with a gutter between two rows of five stamps.

Angkor Wat — A466

Various sites at Angkor Wat: 500r, 900r, 1400r, 3000r, 4000r,
6000r, Stupa.

**2019, Mar. 13 Litho. *Perf. 13***
**2504-2508** A466 Set of 5 10.50 10.50

**Souvenir Sheet**

**2509** A466 6000r multi 14.00 14.00

No. 2509 contains one 46x31mm stamp.
No. 2509 exists imperforate. Value, $14.
Nos. 2404-2508 were issued individually in sheets of 10 with a gutter between two rows of five stamps.

New Year 2019 (Year of the Pig) — A467

**2019, Mar. 13 Litho. *Perf. 13***
**2510** A467 3000r multi 4.00 4.00

No. 2510 was issued in sheets of 10: two vertical strips of five with a gutter.

Tonle Sap — A468

Designs: 500r, Shelter with thatched roof. 900r, Birds. 1000r, Houses on stilts above water, boats. 1200r, Aerial view of village and boats. 2000r, Water level view of village and boats. 3000r, Fisherman casting net. 3500r, Boat near jungle.
6000r, Bird facing left.

**2019, Apr. 24 Litho. *Perf. 13***
**2511-2517** A468 Set of 7 13.50 13.50

**Souvenir Sheet**

**2518** A468 6000r multi 14.00 14.00

No. 2518 contains one 46x31mm stamp. An imperforate 6000r souvenir sheet with a different bird illustration was produced in limited quantities. Value, $14.
Nos. 2511-2517 were issued individually in sheets of 10 with a gutter between two rows of five stamps.

Angkor Era Gold Jewelry — A469

Various pieces of jewelry: 500r, 800r, 2000r, 3000r, 4000r.
6000r, Statue with jewelry, vert.

**2019, May 15 Litho. *Perf. 13***
**2519-2523** A469 Set of 5 11.00 11.00

**Souvenir Sheet**

**2524** A469 6000r multi 8.75 8.75

No. 2524 contains one 31x46mm stamp.
No. 2524 exists imperforate. Value, $14.
Nos. 2519-2523 were issued individually in sheets of 10 with a gutter between two rows of five stamps.

Traditional Costumes for Cambodian Men and Women — A470

**2019, Aug. 8 Litho. *Perf. 13***
**2525** A470 3000r multi 2.75 2.75

No. 2525 was issued in sheets of 10: two vertical strips of five with a gutter.

Treasures of Cambodia A471

Map and flag of Cambodia, unpolished and polished gemstones and items made of: 3000k, Blue zircon. 4000k, Blue sapphire. 5000k, Ruby.
6000k, Unpolished yellow zircon.

**2020, Dec. 15 Litho. *Perf. 13***
**2526-2528** A471 Set of 3 6.00 6.00

**Souvenir Sheet**

**2529** A471 6000k multi 3.00 3.00

No. 2529 contains one 47x31mm stamp.

People and Ancient Coins of the Khmer Angkor Period (c. 802-1431) A472

Various coins and people, with denominations of: 700k, 800k, 3000k, 4000k, 5000k.
6000k, Ancient coin, vert.

**2020, Dec. 15 Litho. *Perf. 13***
**2530-2534** A472 Set of 5 6.75 5.75

**Souvenir Sheet**

**2535** A472 6000k multi 3.00 3.00

No. 2535 contains one 31x47mm stamp. An additional stamp was issued in this set. The editors would like to examine any example of it.

Birds — A473

Designs: 500k, Treron phayrei. 800k, Grus virgo. 2000k, Orthotomus chaktomuk. 3000k, Athene brama. 4000k, Aythya fuligula.
6000k, Platalea minor.

**2020, Dec. 15 Litho. *Perf. 13***
**2537-2541** A473 Set of 5 5.25 5.25

**Souvenir Sheet**

**2542** A473 6000k multi 3.00 3.00

No. 2542 contains one 47x31mm stamp. An additional stamp was issued in this set. The editors would like to examine any example of it.

Reptiles — A474

Designs: No. 2544, 900k, Snake. No. 2545, 900k, Turtle. No. 2546, 2000k, Python. No. 2547, 2000k, Turtle diff. No. 2548, 3000k, Python, diff. No. 2549, 3000k, Turtle, diff.
No. 2550, 6000k, Snake, diff.

**2020, Dec. 15 Litho. *Perf. 13***
**2544-2549** A474 Set of 6 6.00 6.00

**Souvenir Sheet**

**2550** A474 6000k multi 3.00 3.00

No. 2550 contains one 31x47mm stamp. An additional stamp was issued in this set. The editors would like to examine any example of it.

Angkor Wat at Night — A475

Various photographs of Angkor Wat at night: 900k, 1000k, 2000k, 3000k, 4000k.
No. 2557, vert.: a, 3000k, Temple lit with blue light. b, 6000k, Temple lit with white light. c, Temple lit with white light with entranceway with pink border at bottom.

**2020, Dec. 15 Litho. *Perf. 13***
**2552-2556** A475 Set of 6 5.50 5.50

**Souvenir Sheet**

***Perf. 13 (3000k), Imperf. (6000k)***

**2557** A475 Sheet of 3, #a-c 7.50 7.50

No. 2557 contains one 31x47mm perforated stamp. An additional souvenir sheet was issued in this set. The editors would like to examine any example of it.

Bayon Temple — A476

**2020, Dec. 15 Litho. *Perf. 13***

| | | | | |
|---|---|---|---|---|
| **2559** | A476 | 15,000k multi | 7.50 | 7.50 |
| **2560** | A476 | 20,000k multi | 10.00 | 10.00 |
| **2561** | A476 | 50,000k multi | 25.00 | 25.00 |
| | | *Nos. 2559-2561 (3)* | 42.50 | 42.50 |

Scenes of the Reamker Epic — A477

Various scenes: 2000k, 2500k, 3000k, 4000k.
6000k, The Reamker.

**2020, Dec. 15 Litho. *Perf. 13***

**2562-2565** A477 Set of 4 5.75 5.75

**Souvenir Sheet**

**2566** A477 6000k multi 3.00 3.00

No. 2566 contains one 47x31mm stamp. An additional stamp was issued in this set. The editors would like to examine any example of it.

Angkor Wat — A478

Various photographs: 1900k, 2000k, 3000k, 4000k, 5000k.

**2020 Litho. *Perf. 13***

**2568-2572** A478 Set of 5 8.00 8.00

New Year 2020 (Year of the Rat) — A479

**2020, Dec. 15 Litho. *Perf. 13***

**2573** A479 3000k multi 1.50 1.50

New Year 2021 (Year of the Ox) — A480

**2021, Dec. 28 Litho. *Perf. 13***

**2574** A480 3000k multi 1.50 1.50

Flowers — A481

Designs: 1900k, Kabah. 2000k, Clitiria ternatea. 3000k, White gardenias. 4000k, Cheung ko. 5000k, Nyctaginaceae.

**2021, Dec. 28 Litho. *Perf. 13***

**2575-2579** A481 Set of 5 8.00 8.00

Repatriated Khmer Artifacts — A482

Statue of: 500k, Female God of Knowledge, late 12th cent. 1000k, Male God, late 11th cent. 2000k, Lord Shiva and Uma, 10th cent. 3000k, Lord Shiva and Skanda Kumra, first half of 10th cent. 4000k, Garuca figurehead of a boat, late 12th cent.
6000k, Buddha.

**2021, Dec. 28 Litho. *Perf. 13***

**2580-2584** A482 Set of 5 5.25 5.25

**Souvenir Sheet**

**2585** A482 6000k multi 3.00 3.00

No. 2585 contains one 31x46mm stamp.

Landscapes A483

Designs: 700k, People in roçe paddy. 800k, House near river. 3000k, Tatal Waterfall. 4000k, Phnom Kulen Waterfall. 5000k, Bou Sra Waterfall.
6000k, Oxcarts.

**2021, Dec. 28 Litho. *Perf. 13***

**2586-2590** A483 Set of 5 6.75 6.75

**Souvenir Sheet**

**2591** A483 6000k multi 3.00 3.00

No. 2591 contains one 47x31mm stamp.

Kun Khmer (Free Boxing) — A484

Scenes from various matches: 2000k, 3000k, 4000k, 5000k.
6000k, Kun Khmer match, diff.

**2021, Dec. 28 Litho. *Perf. 13***

**2592-2595** A484 Set of 4 7.00 7.00

**Souvenir Sheet**

**2596** A484 6000k multi 3.00 3.00

No. 2596 contains one 31x46mm stamp.

Salt Harvesting A485

Various salt harvesters: 1600k, 2000k, 3000k.
6000k, Salt havester, vert.

**2021, Dec. 28 Litho. *Perf. 13***

| | | | | |
|---|---|---|---|---|
| **2599** | A485 | 1600k multi | .80 | .80 |
| **2600** | A485 | 2000k multi | 1.00 | 1.00 |
| **2601** | A485 | 3000k multi | 1.50 | 1.50 |

**Souvenir Sheet**

**2602** A485 6000k multi 3.00 3.00

Two additional stamps were issued in this set. The editors would like to examine any examples.

Fish — A486

Designs: 500r, Pufferfish. 800r, Orange-cheeked parrotfish. 2000r, Ocellaris clownfish. 3000r, Broadbarred firefish. 4000r, Giant moray eel.
No. 2608, Whale shark. No. 2609, Sharp-nose pufferfish.

**2021, Dec. 28 Litho. *Perf. 13***

**2603-2607** A486 Set of 5 5.25 5.25

**Souvenir Sheet**

**2608** A486 6000r multi 3.00 3.00

***Imperf***

**Size:120x80mm**

**2609** A486 6000r multi — —

No. 2608 contains one 46x31mm stamp.

Spiders — A487

Designs: 2000r, Cyriopagopus lividus. 2500r, Cyriopagopus albostriatus. 3000r, Cyriopagopus lividus, diff. 4000r, Phidippus regius.
6000r, Golden silk spider.

**2021, Dec. 28 Litho. *Perf. 13***

**2610-2613** A487 Set of 4 5.75 5.75

**Souvenir Sheet**

**2614** A487 6000r multi 3.00 3.00

No. 2614 contains one 46x31mm stamp. An additional stamp was issued in this set. The editors would like to examine any example of it.

Diplomatic Relations Between Cambodia and Viet Nam, 55th Anniv. — A488

Designs: 500r, National flags and flowers of Cambodia and Viet Nam, "55." 700r, Sign on Phnom Penh-Hanoi Boulevard, horiz. 900r, Building and automobiles, horiz. 2000r, Monument, horiz. 3000r, Traditional and modern buildings, horiz.

**2022, June 24 Litho. *Perf. 13***

**2616-2620** A488 Set of 5 3.50 3.50
*2620a* Souvenir sheet of 5, #2616-2620, perf. 13½ 3.50 3.50

2022 International Forum for Tiger Population Preservation, Vladivostok, Russia — A489

Designs: 4000r, Tiger standing. 6000r, Tiger drinking, horiz.

**2022, Sept. 22 Litho. *Perf. 13***

**2621** A489 4000r multi 2.00 2.00

**Souvenir Sheet**

**2622** A489 6000r multi 3.00 3.00

World Post Day — A490

**2022, Oct. 9 Litho. *Perf. 13***

**2623** A490 4000r multi 2.00 2.00

## SEMI-POSTAL STAMPS

Nos. 8, 12, 14 and 15 Surcharged in Black

**1952, Oct. 20 Unwmk. *Perf. 13***

| | | | | |
|---|---|---|---|---|
| **B1** | A3 | 1.10pi + 40c | 4.25 | *8.50* |
| **B2** | A3 | 1.90pi + 60c | 4.25 | *8.50* |
| **B3** | A3 | 3pi + 1pi | 4.25 | *8.50* |
| **B4** | A1 | 5pi + 2pi | 4.25 | *8.50* |
| | | *Nos. B1-B4 (4)* | 17.00 | *34.00* |

For students assistance.

Preah Stupa — SP1

**1957, Mar. 15 Engr. *Perf. 13***

| | | | | |
|---|---|---|---|---|
| **B5** | SP1 | 1.50r + 50c ind, ol & red | 2.00 | 2.00 |
| **B6** | SP1 | 6.50r + 1.50r red lil, ol & red | 3.00 | 3.00 |
| **B7** | SP1 | 8r + 2r bl, ol & red | 5.00 | 5.00 |
| | | *Nos. B5-B7 (3)* | 10.00 | 10.00 |

Birth of Buddha, 2,500th anniv. See #62-64.

Regular Issue, 1959, with Red Typographed Surcharge

**1959, Dec. 9**

| | | | | |
|---|---|---|---|---|
| **B8** | A14 | 20c + 20c rose vio | .50 | .50 |
| **B9** | A14 | 50c + 30c blue | .80 | .80 |
| **B10** | A14 | 80c + 50c rose car | 1.75 | 1.75 |
| | | *Nos. B8-B10 (3)* | 3.05 | 3.05 |

The surtax was for the Red Cross.

Nos. 107-108 Surcharged and Overprinted in Red

**1963, Oct. 1 Unwmk. *Perf. 13***

| | | | | |
|---|---|---|---|---|
| **B11** | A26 | 4r + 40c grn & dk brn | 1.00 | 1.00 |
| **B12** | A26 | 6r + 60c vio & ol bis | 1.50 | 1.50 |

Centenary of International Red Cross.

Nos. 263, 267, 293-294, 134 Surcharged in Red

**1972, Nov. 15 Engr. *Perf. 13***

| | | | | |
|---|---|---|---|---|
| **B13** | A72 | 3r + 2r multi | .60 | .40 |
| **B14** | A72 | 10r + 6r multi | .90 | .80 |
| **B15** | A80 | 12r + 7r multi | 1.00 | .90 |
| **B16** | A34 | 12r + 7r multi | 1.00 | .90 |
| **B17** | A80 | 15r + 8r multi | 1.50 | 1.50 |
| | | *Nos. B13-B17 (5)* | 5.00 | 4.50 |

Surtax was for war victims. Surcharge arranged differently on Nos. B15-B17.

## AIR POST STAMPS

Kinnari — AP1

**Unwmk.**

**1953, Apr. 16 Engr. *Perf. 13***

| | | | | |
|---|---|---|---|---|
| **C1** | AP1 | 50c deep green | 2.00 | 1.00 |
| *a.* | | Souv. sheet of 4, #C1, C3, C5, C9 | 75.00 | 75.00 |
| **C2** | AP1 | 3pi red brown | 2.00 | 1.25 |
| *a.* | | Souv. sheet of 3, #C2, C4, C8 | 75.00 | 75.00 |
| **C3** | AP1 | 3.30pi rose violet | 3.00 | 2.00 |
| **C4** | AP1 | 4pi dk brn & dp bl | 2.00 | 2.00 |
| **C5** | AP1 | 5.10pi brn, red & org | 3.75 | 3.00 |
| **C6** | AP1 | 6.50pi dk brn & lil rose | 3.75 | 3.25 |
| *a.* | | Souv. sheet of 2, #C6-C7 | 75.00 | 75.00 |
| **C7** | AP1 | 9pi lil rose & dp grn | 4.50 | 5.00 |
| **C8** | AP1 | 11.50pi multi | 9.00 | 7.00 |

**C9** AP1 30pi dk brn, bl grn & org 17.50 12.00
*Nos. C1-C9 (9)* 47.50 36.50

No. C1a sold for 50pi, No. C2a for 25pi, No. C6a for 20pi.

Souvenir sheets with completely white gum, no toning and no gum bends sell for a premium.

AP2

**1957, Dec. 11**
**C10** AP2 50c maroon .40 .25
**C11** AP2 1r emerald .70 .25
**C12** AP2 4r ultra 2.25 .75
**C13** AP2 50r carmine rose 8.75 4.00
**C14** AP2 100r grn, bl & car 16.00 6.00
*a.* Souv. sheet of 5, #C10-C14 32.50 32.50
*Nos. C10-C14 (5)* 28.10 11.25

No. C14a sold for 160r.
See note after No. C9.

### Independence Type of 1961

**1961, Nov. 9** ***Perf. 13x12½***
**C15** A24 7r multicolored .90 .80
**C16** A24 30r grn, car & ultra 3.00 2.25
**C17** A24 50r ind, grn & ol 4.50 3.00
*a.* Souv. sheet of 3, #C15-C17 11.00 11.00
*Nos. C15-C17 (3)* 7.55 7.55

No. C15 Srchd. in Red and Ovptd. in Black

**1962, Nov. 9**
**C18** A24 12r on 7r multi 2.25 1.25

Dedication of Independence Monument.

Hanuman, Monkey God — AP3

**1964, Sept. 1** **Engr.** ***Perf. 13***
**C19** AP3 5r multicolored 1.00 .50
**C20** AP3 10r ol bis, lil rose & grn 1.50 .60
**C21** AP3 20r vio, bl & ol bis 2.25 1.25
**C22** AP3 40r bl, ol bis & dk bl 5.50 2.00
**C23** AP3 80r multicolored 9.50 5.50
*Nos. C19-C23 (5)* 19.75 9.85

Nos. C19-C22 Surcharged in Red

**1964, Oct.**
**C24** AP3 3r on 5r multi .90 .55
**C25** AP3 6r on 10r multi 1.40 .85
**C26** AP3 9r on 20r multi 1.75 1.10
**C27** AP3 12r on 40r multi 3.50 2.00
*Nos. C24-C27 (4)* 7.55 4.50

18th Olympic Games, Tokyo, Oct. 10-25.

1972 Summer Olympic Games, Munich AP4

Designs: No. C28, shown. No. C29, Munich churches, Olympic emblem, vert.

### Litho. & Embossed

**1972, Sept. 28** ***Perf. 13½***
**C28** AP4 900r gold & multi *42.50 42.50*
**C29** AP4 900r gold & multi *42.50 42.50*
*a.* Souvenir sheet of 2, #C28-C29 *80.00*

No. C29a exists imperf. Value, $110.

Apollo 16 — AP5

Designs: No. C30, Astronauts in Lunar Rover. No. C31, Astronaut walking on moon.

**1972, Sept. 28**
**C30** AP5 900r gold & multi *45.00 45.00*
**C31** AP5 900r gold & multi *45.00 45.00*
*a.* Souvenir sheet of 2, #C30-C31 *70.00*

No. C31a exists imperf. Value, $130.

AP6

Nixon, Mao Zedong: No. C32, Large portraits (shown). No. C33, Small portraits.

**1972, Sept. 28** ***Perf. 12½***
**C32** AP6 900r gold & multi *80.00 80.00*
**C33** AP6 900r gold & multi *80.00 80.00*

Pres. Nixon's visit to the People's Republic of China.

Garuda, 12th Century, Angkor Thom — AP7

**1973, Jan. 18** **Engr.** ***Perf. 13***
**C34** AP7 3r carmine .35 .25
**C35** AP7 30r violet blue 2.00 1.00
**C36** AP7 50r dull purple 3.75 2.00
**C37** AP7 100r dull green 5.25 3.00
*Nos. C34-C37 (4)* 11.35 6.25

1972 Summer Olympic Games, Munich — AP8

Gold medalists: No. C38, Heide Rosendahl. No. C39, Mark Spitz.

### Litho. & Embossed

**1973, May 18** ***Perf. 13½***
**C38** AP8 900r gold & multi *35.00 35.00*
**C39** AP8 900r gold & multi *35.00 35.00*
*a.* Souvenir sheet, #C38-C39 *60.00*

No. C39a exists imperf. Value $100.

### Nos. C38-C39 Overprinted

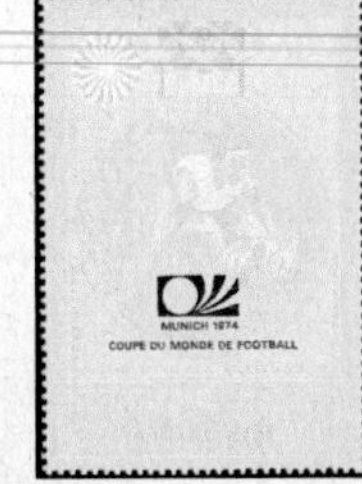


**1973, Nov. 19**
**C40** AP8 900r on C38 *40.00 40.00*
**C41** AP8 900r on C39 *40.00 40.00*
*a.* Souvenir sheet, #C40-C41 *80.00*

No. C41a exists imperf. Value, $160.

1974 World Cup Soccer Championships, Munich — AP9

Designs: No. C42, Trophy, players. No. C43, Trophy, players, vert.

**1973, Nov. 19** **Litho. & Embossed**
**C42** AP9 900r gold & multi *35.00 35.00*
**C43** AP9 900r gold & multi *35.00 35.00*
*a.* Souvenir sheet, #C42-C43 *55.00*

No. C43a exists imperf. Value, $100.

John F. Kennedy, Apollo 11 AP10

No. C44, shown. No. C45, Kennedy, Apollo 17.

**1974, Feb. 18**
**C44** AP10 1100r gold & multi *95.00 95.00*
**C45** AP10 1100r gold & multi *95.00 95.00*
*a.* Souv. sheet of 2, #C44-C45 *200.00*

Nos. C44-C45a exist imperf. Values slightly higher.

### Copernicus Type of 1974 and

Copernicus, Sun — AP11

200r, Copernicus and Skylab III. 250r, Copernicus, Concorde and solar eclipse. No. C48, shown. No. C49, Moon, Skylab, hand holding symbol of sun.

**1974, Sept. 10** **Litho.** ***Perf. 13***
**C46** A87 200r multi 10.00 5.50
**C47** A87 250r multi 15.00 10.00

### Litho. & Engraved
***Perf. 13½***
**C48** AP11 1200r gold & multi *30.00 30.00*

### Souvenir Sheet of 1
**C49** AP11 1200r gold & multi *30.00 30.00*

Nos. C46-C47 exist in perf or imperf souvenir sheets of 1. Values, $25 perf., $50 imperf. Nos. C48-C49 exist imperf. Values, each $55.

### UPU Type of 1974 and

AP12

700r, Rocket, globe and UPU emblem. No. C51, UPU Headquarters. No. C52, US #1434-1435.

**1974, Nov. 2** **Litho.** ***Perf. 13***
**C50** A88 700r gold & multi *11.50 11.50*

### Litho. & Embossed
***Perf. 13½***
**C51** AP12 1200r gold & multi *20.00 20.00*

### Souvenir Sheet
**C52** AP12 1200r gold & multi *30.00*

Nos. C50-C51 exist in souvenir sheets of one. Nos. C51-C52 exist imperf.

UPU, Cent. (in 1974) — AP13

UPU emblem and: No. C53, Biplane, train. No. C54, Satellite, sailboat.

### Litho. & Embossed

**1975, Apr. 12** ***Perf. 13¼***
**C53** AP13 2000r gold & multi *13.50* —

### Souvenir Sheet
**C54** AP13 2000r gold & multi *40.00* —

No. C53 exists in a souvenir sheet of 1.

Post Aerienne at Right — AP14

Denominations: 5r, 10r, 15r, 25r.

**1984, Feb. 1** **Litho.** ***Perf. 12x12½***
**C55-C58** AP14 Set of 4 45.00 8.50

Post Aerienne at Left — AP15

Denominations: 5r, 10r, 15r, 25r.

**1986, Mar. 4** **Litho.** ***Perf. 12x12½***
**C59-C62** AP15 Set of 4 40.00 8.00

---

## POSTAGE DUE STAMPS

D1

**1957** **Unwmk.** **Typo.** ***Perf. 13½***
### Denomination in Black
**J1** D1 10c ver & pale blue .30 .30
**J2** D1 50c ver & pale blue .55 .55
**J3** D1 1r ver & pale blue .85 .85
**J4** D1 3r ver & pale blue 1.25 1.25
**J5** D1 5r ver & pale blue 2.00 2.00
*Nos. J1-J5 (5)* 4.95 4.95

Frieze, Angkor Wat — D2

**1974, Feb. 18 Engr. *Perf. 12½x13***

**J6** D2 2r ocher .30 .30
**J7** D2 6r green .45 .45
**J8** D2 8r deep carmine .70 .70
**J9** D2 10r violet blue 1.00 1.00
*Nos. J6-J9 (4)* 2.45 2.45

## CAMEROONS

ˌka-mə-ˈrüns

LOCATION — West coast of Africa, north of equator
GOVT. — British Trust Territory
AREA — 34,081 sq. mi.
POP. — 868,637 (estimated)
CAPITAL — Buea

Prior to World War I, Cameroons (Kamerun) was a German Protectorate. It was occupied during the War by Great Britain and France and in 1922 was mandated to these countries by the League of Nations. Stamps of Nigeria were used in the British part until 1960. The northern section of the British Cameroons became part of the independent state of Nigeria in 1960, and the southern section became a United Kingdom Trust Territory. After a referendum, this U.K.T.T. joined the independent State of Cameroun to form the Federal Republic of Cameroun, Oct. 1, 1961.

Stamps of the German Protectorate, the French Mandate, the independent state and the Cameroun Federal Republic are listed under Cameroun.

**Catalogue values for unused stamps in this country are for Never Hinged items.**

**United Kingdom Trust Territory**

Stamps and Type of Nigeria, 1953, Ovptd. in Red

***Perf. 13½, 14***
**1960, Oct. 1 Wmk. 4 Engr.**

**Size: 35½x22½mm**

**66** A17 ½p red org & black .25 1.75
**67** A17 1p ol gray & black .25 .60
**68** A17 1½p blue green .25 .25
**69** A17 2p gray .65 2.00
**70** A17 3p purple & black .25 .25
**71** A17 4p ultra & black .25 2.25
**72** A18 6p blk & org brn, perf. 14 .40 .25
*a.* Perf. 13x13½ ('61) .35 2.25
**73** A17 1sh brown vio & blk .35 .25

**Size: 40½x24½mm**

**74** A17 2sh6p green & black 2.00 .80
**75** A17 5sh ver & black 3.00 3.00
**76** A17 10sh red brn & blk 3.75 6.50

**Size: 42x31½mm**

**77** A17 £1 violet & black 18.50 27.50
*Nos. 66-77 (12)* 29.90 45.40

Nos. 66-77 were withdrawn in Northern Cameroons on May 31, 1961, when that territory joined Nigeria and in Southern Cameroons Sept. 30, 1961, when that territory joined the Cameroun Federal Republic.

## CAMEROUN

ˌka-mə-ˈrün

(Kamerun)

LOCATION — On the west coast of Africa, north of the equator
GOVT. — Republic
AREA — 183,520 sq. mi.
POP. — 15,456,092 (1999 est.)
CAPITAL — Yaounde

Before World War I, Cameroun (Kamerun) was a German Protectorate. It was occupied during the war by Great Britain and France and in 1922 was mandated to these countries by the League of Nations. The French-mandated part became the independent State of Cameroun on January 1, 1960. The Southern Cameroons, a United Kingdom Trust Territory, joined this state to form the Federal Republic of Cameroun on October 1, 1961. The name was changed to United Republic of Cameroon on May 20, 1972.

Stamps of Southern Cameroons are listed under Cameroons.

100 Pfennig = 1 Mark
12 Pence = 1 Shilling
100 Centimes = 1 Franc

**Catalogue values for unused stamps in this country are for Never Hinged items, beginning with Scott 296 in the regular postage section, Scott B29 in the semi-postal section, Scott C8 in the air-post section, Scott J24 in the postage due section, and Scott M1 in the military stamp section.**

**Watermark**

Wmk. 125 — Lozenges

Wmk. 385

**Issued under German Dominion**

Stamps of Germany Overprinted in Black

**1897 Unwmk. *Perf. 13½x14½***

**1** A9 3pf yel brn 11.00 15.00
*a.* 3pf red brown 55.00 200.00
*b.* 3pf dark brown 15.00 37.50
*c.* 3pf olive brown 8.75 37.50
**2** A9 5pf green 7.00 7.00
**3** A10 10pf carmine 5.00 4.50
**4** A10 20pf ultra 5.00 7.00
*a.* Diagonal half used as 10pf on cover 18,750.
**5** A10 25pf orange 20.00 37.50
**6** A10 50pf red brn 15.00 24.00
*Nos. 1-6 (6)* 63.00 95.00

A3

Kaiser's Yacht "Hohenzollern"
A4

**1900 Unwmk. Typo. *Perf. 14***

**7** A3 3pf brown 1.25 1.50
**8** A3 5pf green 10.50 1.20
**9** A3 10pf carmine 35.00 1.25
**10** A3 20pf ultra 22.50 1.75
*a.* Vertical half used as 10pf on cover (Longii, '11) 6,750.
**11** A3 25pf org & blk, *yel* 1.50 5.00
**12** A3 30pf org & blk, *sal* 2.00 4.00
**13** A3 40pf lake & blk 2.00 4.00
**14** A3 50pf pur & blk, *sal* 2.00 6.00
**15** A3 80pf lake & blk, *rose* 2.25 10.00

**Engr. *Perf. 14½x14***

**16** A4 1m carmine 67.50 67.50
**17** A4 2m blue 5.25 65.00
**18** A4 3m blk vio 5.25 105.00
**19** A4 5m slate & car 150.00 450.00
*Nos. 7-19 (13)* 307.00 722.20

**1905-18 Wmk. 125 Typo.**

**20** A3 3pf brown ('18) .70
**21** A3 5pf green .70 1.60
*a.* Bklt. pane of 6 15.00
*b.* Bklt. pane of 6, 2 #21 + 4 #22 62.50
*c.* Booklet pane of 5 + label 375.00
**22** A3 10pf carmine ('06) 2.25 1.50
*a.* Bklt pane of 6 17.50
*b.* Booklet pane of 5 + label 500.00
**23** A3 20pf ultra ('14) 3.50 125.00
**24** A4 1m carmine ('15) 12.00
**25** A4 5m slate & car ('13) 40.00 4,000.
*Nos. 20-25 (6)* 68.35

The 3pf and 1m were not placed in use.
Nos. 21a, 22a were made from sheet stamps.

**Issued under British Occupation**

Stamps of German Cameroun Surcharged

No. 53 No. 62

**Wmk. Lozenges (125) (#54-56, 65); Unwmk. (Other Values)**
**1915 *Perf. 14, 14½***

**Blue Surcharge**

**53** A3 ½p on 3pf brn 15.00 60.00
**54** A3 ½p on 5pf grn 7.75 11.00
*a.* Double surcharge 1,100.
*b.* Black surcharge —
**55** A3 1p on 10pf car 1.45 11.00
*a.* "1" with thin serifs 15.00 75.00
*b.* Double surcharge 475.00
*c.* Black surcharge 18.00 65.00
*d.* As "c," "1" with thin serifs 300.00

**Black Surcharge**

**56** A3 2p on 20pf ultra 4.00 24.00
**57** A3 2½p on 25pf org & blk, *yel* 21.00 60.00
*a.* Double surcharge 15,000.
**58** A3 3p on 30pf org & blk, *sal* 15.00 65.00
**59** A3 4p on 40pf lake & blk 15.00 65.00
**60** A3 6p on 50pf pur & blk, *sal* 15.00 65.00
**61** A3 8p on 80pf lake & blk, *rose* 15.00 65.00
**62** A4 1sh on 1m car 220.00 1,000.
*a.* "S" inverted 1,100. 4,000.
**63** A4 2sh on 2m bl 250.00 1,050.
*a.* "S" inverted 1,100. 4,000.
**64** A4 3sh on 3m blk vio 250.00 1,050.
*a.* "S" inverted 1,100. 4,400.
*b.* Double surcharge 16,500.
**65** A4 5sh on 5m sl & car 300.00 1,100.
*a.* "S" inverted 1,425. 4,750.
*Nos. 53-65 (13)* 1,129. 4,626.

The letters "C. E. F." are the initials of "Cameroons Expeditionary Force."
Numerous overprint varieties exist for Nos. 53-65.
Counterfeits exist of Nos. 54a, 54b.

See Cameroons for Nos. 66-77.

**Issued under French Occupation**

Gabon Nos. 37, 49-52, 54, 57-58, 60, 62-64, 66, 69-70 Overprinted

**1915 Unwmk. *Perf. 13½x14***
**Inscribed "Congo Français"**

**101** A10 10c red & car 32.50 24.00

**Inscribed "Afrique Equatoriale"**

**102** A10 1c choc & org 110.00 47.50
**103** A10 2c blk & choc 200.00 150.00
**104** A10 4c vio & dp bl 200.00 150.00
**105** A10 5c ol gray & grn 40.00 24.00
**105A** A10 10c red & car 21,500. 24,000.
**106** A10 20c ol brn & dk vio 210.00 210.00
**107** A11 25c dp bl & choc 60.00 47.50
**108** A11 30c gray blk & red 200.00 200.00
**109** A11 35c dk vio & grn 67.50 45.00
*a.* Double overprint 1,900.
**110** A11 40c choc & ultra 200.00 200.00
**111** A11 45c car & vio 225.00 225.00
**112** A11 50c bl grn & gray 225.00 225.00
**113** A11 75c org & choc 275.00 225.00
**114** A12 1fr dk brn & bis 260.00 225.00
**115** A12 2fr car & brn 300.00 260.00
*Nos. 101-105,106-115 (15)* 2,605. 2,258.

The overprint is vertical, reading up, on Nos. 101-106, 114-115, and horizontal on Nos. 107-113.

Stamps of Middle Congo, Issue of 1907, Overprinted

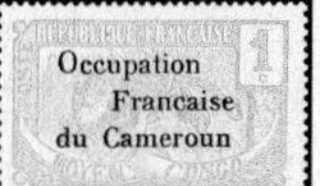


**1916 Unwmk.**

**116** A1 1c ol gray & brn 110.00 110.00
**117** A1 2c violet & brn 110.00 110.00
**118** A1 4c blue & brown 120.00 120.00
**119** A1 5c dk green & blue 32.50 32.50
**120** A2 35c violet brn & bl 110.00 75.00
**121** A2 45c violet & red 87.50 75.00

The overprint is vert., reading down, on Nos. 120-121.

**Same Overprint On Stamps of French Congo, 1900**

**Wmk. Branch of Thistle (122)**

**122** A4 15c dull vio & ol grn 120.00 120.00
*a.* Inverted overprint 200.00 180.00

**Wmk. Branch of Rose Tree (123)**

**123** A5 20c yellow grn & org 140.00 92.50
**124** A5 30c car rose & org 110.00 87.50
**125** A5 40c org brn & brt grn 105.00 80.00
**126** A5 50c gray vio & lil 110.00 87.50
**127** A5 75c red vio & org 110.00 85.00

**Wmk. Branch of Olive (124)**

**128** A6 1fr gray lilac & ol 125.00 120.00
**129** A6 2fr carmine & brn 160.00 120.00
*Nos. 116-129 (14)* 1,550. 1,315.

The overprint is horiz. on No. 122. The overprint is vert., reading down or up, on Nos. 123-129. Values are for the cheaper variety. See the *Scott Classic Specialized Catalogue of Stamps & Covers* for detailed listings.

Values are for stamps centered in the grade of fine.
Counterfeits exist of Nos. 101-129.

Stamps of Middle Congo, Issue of 1907 Overprinted

**1916-17 Unwmk.**

**130** A1 1c ol gray & brn .40 .40
**131** A1 2c violet & brn .50 .50
**132** A1 4c blue & brn .75 .75
**133** A1 5c dk green & bl .50 .40
**134** A1 10c carmine & bl 1.10 .80
**135** A1 15c brn vio & rose ('17) 2.00 .80
**136** A1 20c brown & bl .80 .80
**137** A2 25c blue & grn .80 .80
*a.* Triple overprint 550.00 700.00
**138** A2 30c scarlet & grn 1.25 .80
*a.* Double overprint 400.00 575.00
**139** A2 35c vio brn & bl .80 .80
**140** A2 40c dull grn & brn 2.40 1.60
**141** A2 45c violet & red 2.40 1.60
**142** A2 50c blue grn & red 2.40 1.60
**143** A2 75c brown & blue 2.40 1.60
**144** A3 1fr dp grn & vio 2.00 1.60
**145** A3 2fr vio & gray grn 8.00 6.75
**146** A3 5fr blue & rose 13.50 11.00
*Nos. 130-146 (17)* 42.00 32.60

Nos. 130-146 exist on ordinary paper and, with the exception of No. 135, on chalk surfaced paper. Nos. 137-146 are known with inverted 'S' in 'Francaise' and without period after 'Francaise.' See the *Scott Classic Specialized Catalogue of Stamps & Covers* for detailed listings.

On Nos. 137-146 there is 7mm between "Cameroun" and "Occupation."

**Provisional French Mandate**

Types of Middle Congo, 1907, Overprinted

**1921**

**147** A1 1c ol grn & org .35 .30
**148** A1 2c brown & rose .35 .30
**149** A1 4c gray & lt grn .55 .55
**150** A1 5c dl red & org .55 .55
*a.* Double overprint 1,200.
**151** A1 10c bl grn & lt grn 1.25 .90
**152** A1 15c blue & org .55 .55
**153** A1 20c red brn & ol .80 .80
**154** A2 25c slate & org 1.20 .80
**155** A2 30c rose & ver 1.25 .80
**156** A2 35c gray & ultra .80 .80
**157** A2 40c ol grn & org 1.25 .80
**158** A2 45c brown & rose .80 .80
**159** A2 50c blue & ultra 1.25 .80
**160** A2 75c red brn & lt grn 1.25 .80
**161** A3 1fr slate & org 2.40 2.40
**162** A3 2fr ol grn & rose 6.50 5.50
**163** A3 5fr dull red & gray 9.50 8.00
*Nos. 147-163 (17)* 30.60 25.45

The 1c, 2c, 4c, 15c, 20c, 25c and 50c exist with overprint omitted. For listings, see the *Scott Specialized Catalogue of Stamps & Covers.*

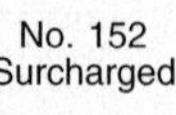

No. 152 Surcharged

Nos. 162-163 Surcharged

Nos. 158, 160 Surcharged

**1924-25**

**164** A1 25c on 15c bl & org ('25) 1.25 1.25
**165** A3 25c on 2fr ol grn & rose 1.25 1.60
**166** A3 25c on 5fr red & gray 1.25 1.60
*a.* Pair, one without new value and bars
**167** A2 65c on 45c brn & rose ('25) 2.00 2.00
**168** A2 85c on 75c red brn & lt grn ('25) 2.40 2.40
*Nos. 164-168 (5)* 8.15 8.85

**French Mandate**

Herder and Cattle Crossing Sanaga River — A5

Tapping Rubber Tree — A6

Rope Suspension Bridge — A7

**1925-38 Typo. *Perf. 14x13½***

**170** A5 1c ol grn & brn vio, *lav* .25 .25
**171** A5 2c rose & grn, *grnsh* .25 .25
**172** A5 4c blue & blk .25 .25
**173** A5 5c org & red vio, *lav* .25 .25
**174** A5 10c red brn & org, *yel* .45 .40
**175** A5 15c sl grn & grn .45 .40
**176** A5 15c lilac & red ('27) 1.00 .80

***Perf. 13½x14***

**177** A6 20c ol brn & red brn .70 .40
**178** A6 20c green ('26) .65 .50
**179** A6 20c brn red & ol brn ('27) .65 .65
**180** A6 25c lt green & blk .95 .50
**181** A6 30c bluish grn & ver .50 .30
**182** A6 30c dk grn & grn ('27) .90 .65
**183** A6 35c brown & black 1.10 .50
**184** A6 35c dl grn & grn ('38) 1.90 1.20
**185** A6 40c orange & vio 2.00 1.20
**186** A6 45c dp rose & cer .80 .50
**187** A6 45c vio & org brn ('27) 2.25 1.60

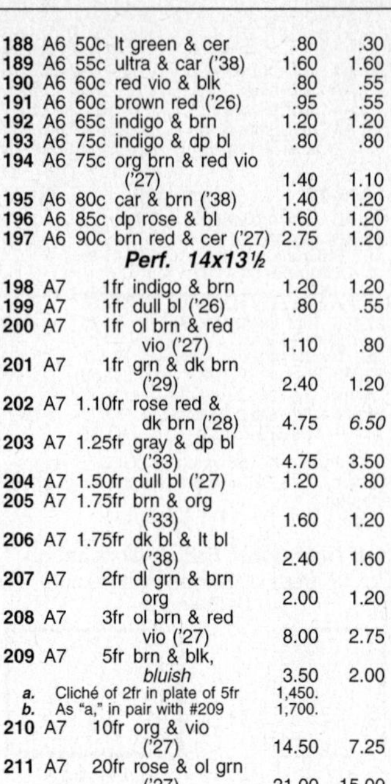

**188** A6 50c lt green & cer .80 .30
**189** A6 55c ultra & car ('38) 1.60 1.60
**190** A6 60c red vio & blk .80 .55
**191** A6 60c brown red ('26) .95 .55
**192** A6 65c indigo & brn 1.20 1.20
**193** A6 75c indigo & dp bl .80 .80
**194** A6 75c org brn & red vio ('27) 1.40 1.10
**195** A6 80c car & brn ('38) 1.40 1.20
**196** A6 85c dp rose & bl 1.60 1.20
**197** A6 90c brn red & cer ('27) 2.75 1.20

***Perf. 14x13½***

**198** A7 1fr indigo & brn 1.20 1.20
**199** A7 1fr dull bl ('26) .80 .55
**200** A7 1fr ol brn & red vio ('27) 1.10 .80
**201** A7 1fr grn & dk brn ('29) 2.40 1.20
**202** A7 1.10fr rose red & dk brn ('28) 4.75 *6.50*
**203** A7 1.25fr gray & dp bl ('33) 4.75 3.50
**204** A7 1.50fr dull bl ('27) 1.20 .80
**205** A7 1.75fr brn & org ('33) 1.60 1.20
**206** A7 1.75fr dk bl & lt bl ('38) 2.40 1.60
**207** A7 2fr dl grn & brn org 2.00 1.20
**208** A7 3fr ol brn & red vio ('27) 8.00 2.75
**209** A7 5fr brn & blk, *bluish* 3.50 2.00
*a.* Cliché of 2fr in plate of 5fr 1,450.
*b.* As "a," in pair with #209 1,700.
**210** A7 10fr org & vio ('27) 14.50 7.25
**211** A7 20fr rose & ol grn ('27) 21.00 15.00
*Nos. 170-211 (42)* 97.80 65.85

Shades exist for several values.
For overprints and surcharge see Nos. 212, 264, 276, 278, 279, B7-B9, B21.

**No. 199 Surcharged in Red**

**1926**

**212** A7 1.25fr on 1fr dull blue 1.20 .80

Common Design Types pictured following the introduction.

**Colonial Exposition Issue**
Common Design Types
Name of Country in Black

**1931 Engr. *Perf. 12½***

**213** CD70 40c deep green 5.50 4.00
**214** CD71 50c violet 5.50 4.75
**215** CD72 90c red orange 5.50 4.75
**216** CD73 1.50fr dull blue 6.50 4.75
*Nos. 213-216 (4)* 23.00 18.25

**Paris International Exposition Issue**
Common Design Types

**1937 *Perf. 13***

**217** CD74 20c deep violet 1.75 1.75
**218** CD75 30c dark green 1.75 1.75
**219** CD76 40c car rose 1.75 1.75
**220** CD77 50c dark brown 1.75 1.75
**221** CD78 90c red 1.90 1.90
**222** CD79 1.50fr ultramarine 1.90 1.90
*Nos. 217-222 (6)* 10.80 10.80

**French Colonial Art Exhibition**
Common Design Type
Souvenir Sheet

**1937 *Imperf.***

**222A** CD77 3fr org red & blk 8.00 *9.50*

**New York World's Fair Issue**
Common Design Type

**1939 *Perf. 12½x12***

**223** CD82 1.25fr carmine lake 1.40 1.20
**224** CD82 2.25fr ultra 1.40 1.20

For overprints and surcharges see Nos. 280-281, B14-B17, B23, B25.

Mandara Woman A19

Falls on M'bam River near Banyo A20

Elephants — A21

Man in Yaré — A22

**1939-40 Engr. *Perf. 13***

**225** A19 2c black brn .25 .25
**226** A19 3c magenta ('40) .25 .25
**227** A19 4c deep ultra .25 .25
**228** A19 5c red brown .25 .25
**229** A19 10c dp bl grn .25 .25
**230** A19 15c rose red .30 .30
**231** A19 20c plum .30 .30
**232** A20 25c black brn .65 .65
**233** A20 30c dk red .80 .70
**234** A20 40c ultra ('40) .80 .80
**235** A20 45c sl grn ('40) 2.60 2.25
**236** A20 50c brown car .90 .70
**237** A20 60c pck blue ('40) .75 .65
**238** A20 70c plum ('40) 3.25 2.90
**239** A21 80c Prus blue 2.60 2.10
**240** A21 90c Prus blue .95 .75
**241** A21 1fr car rose 1.90 .95
**242** A21 1fr choc ('40) 1.40 .80
**243** A21 1.25fr car rose 4.00 3.25
**244** A21 1.40fr org red ('40) 1.25 .95
**245** A21 1.50fr chocolate 1.20 .95
**246** A21 1.60fr black brn ('40) 2.50 2.25
**247** A21 1.75fr dk blue 1.40 .95
**248** A21 2fr dk green .90 .90
**249** A21 2.25fr dk blue 1.40 .90
**250** A21 2.50fr brt red vio ('40) 1.20 1.00
**251** A21 3fr dk violet 1.40 .80
**252** A22 5fr black brn 1.40 .95
**253** A22 10fr brt red vio 2.00 1.60
**254** A22 20fr dk green 4.00 3.25
*Nos. 225-254 (30)* 41.10 32.85

For overprints and surcharges see Nos. 255-263, 265-275, 277, 278A, 279A, B10-B13, B22, B24.

Stamps of 1925-40 Overprinted in Black or Orange

**1940 *Perf. 14x13½, 13½x14, 13***

**255** A19 2c blk brn (O) 1.60 1.60
**256** A19 3c magenta 2.40 2.40
**257** A19 4c dp ultra (O) 1.60 1.60
**258** A19 5c red brn 5.50 5.50
**259** A19 10c dp bl grn (O) 1.60 1.60
**260** A19 15c rose red 2.40 2.40
**260A** A19 20c plum (O) 13.50 13.50
**261** A20 25c blk brn 1.60 1.60
*b.* Inverted overprint 260.00 260.00
**261A** A20 30c dk red 14.50 14.50
**262** A20 40c ultra 5.50 5.50
**263** A20 45c slate green 4.00 4.00
**264** A6 50c lt grn & cer 2.40 1.60
*a.* Inverted overprint 225.00
**265** A20 60c pck bl 6.50 6.50
**266** A20 70c plum 3.25 3.25
**267** A21 80c Prus bl (O) 5.50 5.50
**268** A21 90c Prus bl (O) 1.60 1.60
**269** A21 1.25fr car rose 1.60 1.60
**270** A21 1.40fr org red 4.75 4.75
**271** A21 1.50fr chocolate 1.60 1.60
**272** A21 1.60fr blk brn (O) 3.25 3.25
**273** A21 1.75fr dk bl (O) 2.40 2.40
**274** A21 2.25fr dk bl (O) 1.60 1.60
**275** A21 2.50fr brt red vio 1.60 1.60
**276** A7 5fr brn & blk, *bluish* 24.00 24.00
**277** A22 5fr black brn 24.00 16.00
**278** A7 10fr org & vio 32.50 32.50
**278A** A22 10fr brt red vio 65.00 45.00
**279** A7 20fr rose & ol grn 55.00 55.00
**279A** A22 20fr dk green 190.00 190.00

**Overprint on Stamps of 1939**

***Perf. 12½x12***

**280** CD82 1.25fr car lake 12.00 12.00
**281** CD82 2.25fr ultra 12.00 12.00
*Nos. 255-281 (31)* 504.75 475.95

Issued to note Cameroun's affiliation with General de Gaulle's "Free France" movement.
Numerous overprint varieties exist.

Cattle Fording Sanaga River and Marshal Petain — A22a

**1941 Engr. *Perf. 12½x12***

**281A** A22a 1fr green .40
**281B** A22a 2.50fr dark blue .40
Set, never hinged 1.60

Nos. 281A-281B were issued by the Vichy government in France, but were not placed on sale in Cameroun.
For surcharges, see Nos. B25A-B25B.

Lorraine Cross and Joan of Arc Shield — A23

**1941 Photo. *Perf. 14x14½***

**282** A23 5c brown .25 .25
**283** A23 10c dk blue .25 .25
**284** A23 25c emerald .25 .25
**285** A23 30c dp orange .25 .25
**286** A23 40c dk slate green .25 .25
**287** A23 80c red brown .50 .25
**288** A23 1fr dp red lilac .50 .50
**289** A23 1.50fr brt red .50 .50
**290** A23 2fr gray black .75 .50
**291** A23 2.50fr brt ultra .80 .50
**292** A23 4fr dull violet .90 .75
**293** A23 5fr bister .95 .90
**294** A23 10fr dp brown .95 .90
**295** A23 20fr dp green 1.90 1.40
*Nos. 282-295 (14)* 9.00 7.45

For surcharges see Nos. 297A-303.

**Catalogue values for unused stamps in this section, from this point to the end of the section, are for Never Hinged items.**

**Eboue Issue**
Common Design Type

**1945 Unwmk. Engr. *Perf. 13***

**296** CD91 2fr black .80 .55
**297** CD91 25fr Prus green 1.60 1.40

**Nos. 282, 284, 291 Surcharged with New Values and Bars in Red, Carmine or Black**

**1946 *Perf. 14x14½***

**297A** A23 50c on 5c (R) .65 .50
**298** A23 60c on 5c (R) .75 .55
*a.* Inverted surcharge 200.00
**299** A23 70c on 5c (R) 1.00 .75
**300** A23 1.20fr on 5c (C) 1.00 .75
**301** A23 2.40fr on 25c .95 .75
**302** A23 3fr on 25c 1.40 1.00
**302A** A23 4.50fr on 25c 1.90 1.40
**303** A23 15fr on 2.50fr (C) 2.00 1.50
*Nos. 297A-303 (8)* 9.65 7.20

Zebu and Herder A25

Tikar Women A26

Porters Carrying Bananas A27

Bowman A28

Lamido Horsemen A29

Farmer A30

**1946 Engr. *Perf. 12½x12, 12x12½***

**304** A25 10c blue grn .50 .30
**305** A25 30c brown org .50 .30
**306** A25 40c brt ultra .50 .30
**307** A26 50c olive brn .50 .30
**308** A26 60c dp plum .65 .30
**309** A26 80c chnt brn .80 .50
**310** A27 1fr org red .50 .25
**311** A27 1.20fr dp green .90 .50
**312** A27 1.50fr dk car 2.25 1.40
**313** A28 2fr black .50 .25
**314** A28 3fr dk carmine .65 .30
**314A** A28 3.60fr red brn 1.60 1.10
**315** A28 4fr dp blue .90 .40
**316** A29 5fr brown car 1.00 .65
**317** A29 6fr ultra 1.00 .55
**318** A29 10fr slate green 1.75 .50
**319** A30 15fr grnsh blue 2.40 .90
**320** A30 20fr dk green 3.25 .90
**321** A30 25fr black 3.25 1.40
*Nos. 304-321 (19)* 23.40 11.10

Shades exist for most values.
For surcharges see Nos. 343-344, 346.

Imperforates

Most Cameroun stamps from 1952 onward exist imperforate in issued and trial colors, and also in small presentation sheets in issued colors.

**Military Medal Issue**
Common Design Type
**Engraved and Typographed**

**1952 Unwmk. *Perf. 13***

**322** CD101 15fr multicolored 7.25 3.25

Porters Carrying Bananas A32

Picking Coffee Beans A33

**1954 Engr.**

**323** A32 8fr red vio, org brn & vio bl 1.20 .80
**324** A32 15fr brn red, yel & blk brn 1.60 .80
**325** A33 40fr blk brn, org brn & lil rose 2.00 .80
*Nos. 323-325 (3)* 4.80 2.40

**FIDES Issue**
Common Design Type

Designs: 5fr, Plowmen. 15fr, Wouri bridge. 20fr, Technical instruction. 25fr, Mobile medical station.

**1956 Unwmk. *Perf. 13***

**326** CD103 5fr org brn & dk brn 1.20 .50
**327** CD103 15fr aqua, slate & blk 1.60 .80
**328** CD103 20fr grnsh bl & dp ultra 1.60 .80
**329** CD103 25fr dp ultra 2.50 1.10
*Nos. 326-329 (4)* 6.90 3.20

For surcharges see Nos. 345, 347.

**Coffee Issue**

Coffee — A35

**1956 Engr. *Perf. 13***

**330** A35 15fr car & brt red 1.60 .80

For surcharge see No. 348.

**Autonomous Government**

Flag and Woman Holding Child — A36

**1958**

**331** A36 20fr multicolored 1.60 .80

Anniv. of the installation of the 1st autonomous government of Cameroun.

Men Looking to the Sun — A37

**1958**

**332** A37 20fr sepia & brn red 1.60 .80

10th anniv. of the signing of the Universal Declaration of Human Rights.

**Flower Issue**
Common Design Type

Design: 20fr, Randia malleifera.

**1959 Photo. *Perf. 12½x12***

**333** CD104 20fr dp grn, yel & rose 1.60 .80

Loading Bananas A38

Harvesting Bananas A39

**1959 Engr. *Perf. 13***

**334** A38 20fr dk grn & org 1.20 .40
**335** A39 25fr maroon & slate grn 1.60 .80

For surcharge see No. 349.

**Independent State**

Map and Flag of Cameroun A40

Prime Minister Ahmadou Ahidjo A41

**1960 Unwmk. Engr. *Perf. 13***

**336** A40 20fr multicolored .80 .25
**337** A41 25fr blk, grn & pale lem .85 .25

Declaration of independence, Jan. 1, 1960.
For surcharge see No. 350.

Uprooted Oak Emblem — A42

**1960**

**338** A42 30fr red brn, ultra & yel grn 1.10 .45

World Refugee Year, 7/1/59-6/30/60.
For surcharge see No. 351.

**C.C.T.A. Issue**
Common Design Type

**1960**

**339** CD106 50fr dull claret & slate 1.60 .75

UN Headquarters, NYC, and Flag — A43

**1961, May 20 *Perf. 13***
**Flag in Green, Red and Yellow**

**340** A43 15fr grn, dk bl & brn .60 .30
**341** A43 25fr dk blue & grn .75 .30
**342** A43 85fr red, dk bl & vio brn 2.40 1.20
*Nos. 340-342 (3)* 3.75 1.80

Cameroun's admission to the UN, Sept. 20, 1960.

**Federal Republic**

Stamps of 1946-60 Surcharged in Red or Black

Type I

Type II

Two types of 2sh6p:
I — Large figures. "2/6" measures 8x3¾mm.
II — Small figures. "2/6" measures 6x2½mm.

***Perf. 12x12½, 13***

**1961, Oct. 1 Engr.**

**343** A27 ½p on 1fr (#310) .35 .25
**344** A28 1p on 2fr (#313) .45 .30
**345** CD103 1½p on 5fr (#326) .55 .35
**346** A29 2p on 10fr (#318) 1.00 .45
**347** CD103 3p on 15fr (#327) 1.40 .60
**348** A35 4p on 15fr (Bk) (#330) 1.10 .70
**349** A38 6p on 20fr (#334) 2.40 1.00
**350** A41 1sh on 25fr (#337) 2.75 1.50
**351** A42 2sh6p on 30fr (#338) (I) 5.00 5.00
*a.* Type II 21.00 21.00
*Nos. 343-351 (9)* 15.00 10.15

Issued for use in the former United Kingdom Trust Territory of Southern Cameroons.

The "Republique Federale" overprint is in one line on Nos. 345, 347-349, in two vertical lines on No. 350. See Nos. C38-C40.

President Ahidjo and Prime Minister Foncha — A45

**Unwmk.**
**1962, Jan. 1 Engr. *Perf. 13***

**352** A45 20fr vio & choc 8.00 7.00
**353** A45 25fr dk grn & brn 14.00 11.00
**354** A45 60fr car & dl grn 40.00 32.50
*Nos. 352-354 (3)* 62.00 50.50

Surcharged for Use in Southern Cameroons

**355** A45 3p on 20fr 175.00 160.00
**356** A45 6p on 25fr 175.00 160.00
**357** A45 2sh6p on 60fr 175.00 160.00
*Nos. 355-357 (3)* 525.00 480.00

Reunification of the former French and British Sections of Cameroun. It is reported that Nos. 352-357 were withdrawn after a few days and destroyed.

Mustache Monkey — A46

Designs: 1fr, 4fr, Elephant, Ntem Falls. 1.50fr, 3fr, Buffon's kob, Dschang. 2fr, 5fr, Hippopotamus. 6fr, 15fr, Mustache monkey. 8fr, 30fr, Manatee, Lake Ossa. 10fr, 25fr, Buffalo, Batouri. 20fr, 40fr, Giraffes, Waza Reservation, vert.

**1962 Unwmk. Engr. *Perf. 12***

**358** A46 50c brn, brt grn & bl .25 .25
**359** A46 1fr gray brn, bl grn & org .25 .25
**360** A46 1.50fr brn, lt grn & sl grn .25 .25
**361** A46 2fr dk gray, grnsh bl & grn .25 .25
**362** A46 3fr brn, org & lil rose .25 .25
**363** A46 4fr brn, yel grn & bl grn .25 .25
**364** A46 5fr gray brn, grn & sal .25 .25
**365** A46 6fr brn, yel & bl .45 .25
**366** A46 8fr dk bl, red & grn .90 .50
**367** A46 10fr ol blk, org & brt bl .75 .25
**368** A46 15fr brn, Prus bl & bl 1.00 .40
**369** A46 20fr brn & gray 1.25 .40
**370** A46 25fr red brn, grn & yel 3.25 1.00
**371** A46 30fr blk, org & bl 4.50 1.10
**372** A46 40fr dp cl, yel grn & blk 7.50 1.50
*Nos. 358-372 (15)* 21.35 7.15

See Nos. 396-397.

**African and Malagasy Union Issue**
Common Design Type

**1962, Sept. 8 Photo. *Perf. 12½x12***

**373** CD110 30fr multicolored 2.00 .75

Village and Map of Cameroun — A48

Designs: 20fr, 25fr, Sun rising over city. 50fr, Hands holding scroll.

**1962, Oct. 1 Engr. *Perf. 13***

**374** A48 9fr pur, olive & dk brn .40 .25
**375** A48 18fr grn, org brn & dk bl .50 .25
**376** A48 20fr lil rose, ol bis & ind .50 .25
**377** A48 25fr bl, red org & sep .60 .25
**378** A48 50fr dk red, sepia & bl 1.75 .50
*Nos. 374-378 (5)* 3.75 1.50

1st anniv. of the reunification of Cameroun.

"School under the Trees" — A49

**1962, Nov. 5 Photo. *Perf. 12x12½***

**379** A49 20fr ver, emerald & yel 1.00 .35

Literacy and popular education campaign.

Telstar and Globe — A50

**1963, Feb. 9 Engr. *Perf. 13***
**Size: 36x22mm**

**380** A50 1fr dk bl, olive & pur .25 .25
**381** A50 2fr dk bl, claret & grn .25 .25
**382** A50 3fr dk grn, ol & dp cl .25 .25
**383** A50 25fr grn, dp cl & brt bl .75 .40
*Nos. 380-383,C45 (5)* 4.00 1.80

1st TV connection of the US and Europe through the Telstar satellite, July 11-12, 1962.

High Frequency Transmission Station, Mt. Bankolo — A51

Design: 20fr, Station and wiring plan.

**1963, May 18 Photo. *Perf. 12x12½***

**384** A51 15fr multicolored .45 .25
**385** A51 20fr multicolored .60 .25
*Nos. 384-385,C46 (3)* 3.55 1.15

Issued to publicize the high frequency telegraph connection Douala-Yaounde.

"Yaoundé-Regional Center of Textbook Production" — A52

**1963, Aug. 10 Unwmk. *Perf. 12½***

**386** A52 20fr emer, blk & red .45 .25
**387** A52 25fr org, blk & red .55 .25
**388** A52 100fr gold, blk & red 2.10 .60
*Nos. 386-388 (3)* 3.10 1.10

UNESCO regional center for the production of school books at Yaounde.

Pres. Ahmadou Ahidjo and Flag — A53

Design: 18fr, Flag and map of Cameroun.

**1963, Oct. 1 *Perf. 12x12½***
**Flag in Green, Red and Yellow**

**389** A53 9fr grn, bl & dk brn .45 .25
**390** A53 18fr grn, bl & lil .65 .25
**391** A53 20fr grn, blk & yel grn .70 .25
*Nos. 389-391 (3)* 1.80 .75

Second anniversary of reunification.

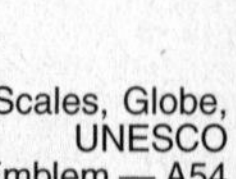

Scales, Globe, UNESCO Emblem — A54

**1963, Dec. 10 Photo. *Perf. 12½x12***

**392** A54 9fr ultra, blk & sal .40 .25
**393** A54 18fr brt yel grn, blk & rose red .50 .25
**394** A54 25fr rose red, blk & brt yel grn .70 .25
**395** A54 75fr yel, blk & ultra 2.00 .50
*Nos. 392-395 (4)* 3.60 1.25

Universal Declaration of Human Rights, 15th anniv.

**Animal Type of 1962**

Design: 10fr, 25fr, Lion, Waza National Park, North Cameroun.

**1964, June 20 Engr. *Perf. 13***

**396** A46 10fr red brn, bis & grn 1.25 .40
**397** A46 25fr green & bister 3.00 1.25

Soccer Game in Stadium — A55

18fr, Pile of sports equipment. 30fr, Stadium (outside), flags and map of Africa.

**1964, July 11 Engr. *Perf. 13***

**398** A55 10fr grn, bl & red brn .50 .25
**399** A55 18fr car, grn & vio .60 .35
**400** A55 30fr blk, dk bl & org brn 1.00 .50
*Nos. 398-400 (3)* 2.10 1.10

Tropics Cup Games, Yaounde, July 11-19.

**Europafrica Issue**
Common Design Type and

Palace of Justice, Yaounde A56

40fr, Emblems of Science, Agriculture, Industry and Education and two sunbursts.

**1964, July 20 Photo. *Perf. 12x13***

**401** A56 15fr multicolored 1.25 .25
**402** CD116 40fr multicolored 2.25 .60

1st anniv. of the economic agreement between the European Economic Community and the African and Malgache Union.

Hurdling and Olympic Flame A57

Design: 10fr, Runners, vert.

**1964, Oct. 10 Engr. *Perf. 13***

**403** A57 9fr red, yel grn & blk 1.50 .40
**404** A57 10fr red, vio & ol gray 2.25 .40
*Nos. 403-404,C49 (3)* 11.25 2.80

18th Olympic Games, Tokyo, Oct. 10-25.

Bamileke Dance Dress A58

Ntem Falls, Ebolowa Region A59

Designs: 18fr, Dance mask, Bamenda region. 25fr, Fulani horseman, North Cameroun, horiz.

**1964 Unwmk. *Perf. 13***

**405** A58 9fr red, yel grn & bl .55 .25
**406** A58 18fr bl, red & brn .70 .25
**407** A59 20fr dk car, grn & brn ol .90 .25
**408** A58 25fr dk brn, org & car 1.40 .25
*Nos. 405-408,C50 (5)* 4.55 1.35

**Cooperation Issue**
Common Design Type

**1964, Nov. 7 Engr.**

**409** CD119 18fr dk bl, yel grn & dk brn 1.00 .25
**410** CD119 30fr red brn, bl grn & dk brn 1.50 .25

Memorial Stone — A60

**1965, Jan. 1 Engr. *Perf. 13***

**411** A60 12fr bl, indigo & grn 1.00 .25

Diesel Train — A61

**Typo. *Perf. 14x13***

**412** A61 20fr rose car, yel & grn 2.50 .25

Laying of the 1st rail of the Mbanga-Kumba Railroad, Mar. 28, 1964.

Red Cross Station and Ambulance A62

50fr, Red Cross nurse and infant, vert.

**1965, May 8 Engr. *Perf. 13***

**413** A62 25fr car, slate grn & ocher .95 .25
**414** A62 50fr gray, red & red brn 2.25 .30

Issued for the Cameroun Red Cross.

Coins Inserted in Map of Cameroun, and Bankbook A63

Savings Bank Building A64

Design: 20fr, Bankbook and coins inserted in cacao pod-shaped bank, vert.

**1965, June 10 Size: 22x37mm**

**415** A63 9fr grn, red & org .45 .25

**Size: 48x27mm, 27x48mm**

**416** A64 15fr choc, ultra & grn .55 .25
**417** A63 20fr ocher, brt grn & brn .65 .25
*Nos. 415-417 (3)* 1.65 .75

Federal Postal Savings Banks.

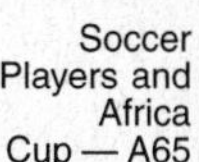

Soccer Players and Africa Cup — A65

**Unwmk.**
**1965, June 26 Engr. *Perf. 13***

**418** A65 9fr car, brn & yel .55 .25
**419** A65 20fr car, slate bl & yel 1.40 .25

Cameroun Oryx Club, winner of the club champions' Africa Cup, February 1965.

Symbolic Map of Europe and Africa — A66

40fr, Delegates around conference table.

**1965, July 20 Photo. *Perf. 12x12½***

**420** A66 5fr car, blk & lilac .30 .25
**421** A66 40fr brn, buff, grn & ultra 1.50 .35

2nd. anniv. of the economic agreement between the European Economic Community and the African and Malgache Union.

UPU Monument, Bern — A67

**1965, July 26 Engr. *Perf. 13***

**422** A67 30fr black & red .80 .25

Cameroun's admission to the UPU, 5th anniv.

ICY Emblem A68

**1965, Sept. 11 Unwmk. *Perf. 13***

**423** A68 10fr dk bl & car rose .45 .25

Issued for the International Cooperation Year, 1964-65. See No. C57.

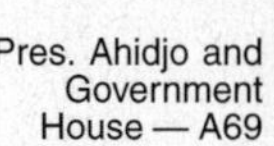

Pres. Ahidjo and Government House — A69

Design: 9fr, 20fr, Pres. Ahidjo and Government House, vert.

***Perf. 12x12½, 12½x12***
**1965, Oct. 1 Photo. Unwmk.**

**424** A69 9fr multicolored .25 .25
**425** A69 18fr multicolored .55 .25
**426** A69 20fr multicolored .65 .25
**427** A69 25fr multicolored .80 .25
*Nos. 424-427 (4)* 2.25 1.00

Reelection of Pres. Ahmadou Ahidjo.

National Tourist Office, Yaoundé — A70

Designs: 9fr, Pouss Musgum houses. 18fr, Great Calao's dance (North Cameroun). 20fr, Gate of Sultan's Palace, Foumban, vert.

**1965 Engr. *Perf. 13***

**428** A70 9fr brn, rose red & grn .45 .25
**429** A70 18fr brt bl, brn & grn .65 .25
**430** A70 20fr bl, brn & choc 1.00 .25
**431** A70 25fr mar, emer & gray .90 .25
*Nos. 428-431 (4)* 3.00 1.00

See No. C58.

Mountain Hotel, Buea — A71

Designs: 20fr, Hotel of the Deputies, Yaoundé. 35fr, Dschang Health Center.

**1966**

**432** A71 9fr sl grn, rose cl & brn .35 .25
**433** A71 20fr brt bl, sl grn & blk .45 .25
**434** A71 35fr brn, sl grn & car .80 .30
*Nos. 432-434,C63-C69 (10)* 15.10 4.90

Bas-relief, Foumban — A72

Designs: 18fr, Ekoi mask, vert. 20fr, Mother and child, carving, Bamiléké, vert. 25fr, Ceremonial stool, Bamoun.

**1966, Apr. 15 Unwmk.**

**435** A72 9fr red & blk .60 .25
**436** A72 18fr brt grn, org brn & choc .75 .25
**437** A72 20fr brt bl, red brn & pur 1.15 .25
**438** A72 25fr pur & dk brn 1.25 .25
*Nos. 435-438 (4)* 3.75 1.00

Intl. Negro Arts Festival, Dakar, Senegal, 4/1-24.

New WHO Headquarters, Geneva — A73

**1966, May 3 Photo. *Perf. 12½x13***

**439** A73 50fr ultra, red brn & yel 1.25 .50

ITU Headquarters, Geneva — A74

**1966, May 3 Photo. *Perf. 12½x13***

**440** A74 50fr ultra & yellow 1.25 .50

Phaeomeria Magnifica — A75

Flowers: 18fr, Hibiscus (rose of China). 20fr, Mountain rose.

**1966, May 20 *Perf. 12x12½***

**Flowers in Natural Colors**

**Size: 22x36mm**

**441** A75 9fr red brown .55 .25
**442** A75 18fr green .70 .25
**443** A75 20fr dark green .70 .25
*Nos. 441-443,C70-C72 (6)* 7.55 1.50

See No. 469.

"6" and Men Dancing around UN Emblem — A76

Design: 50fr, UN General Assembly, horiz.

**1966, Sept. 20 Engr. *Perf. 13***

**444** A76 50fr ultra, grn & vio brn .90 .25
**445** A76 100fr red brn, grn & ultra 2.00 .50

6th anniv. of Cameroun's admission to the UN.

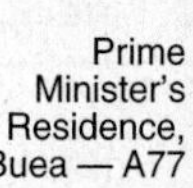

Prime Minister's Residence, Buea — A77

Designs (Prime Minister's Residences): 18fr, at Yaoundé, front view. 20fr, at Yaoundé, side view. 25fr, at Buea, front view.

**1966, Oct. 1 Photo.**

**446** A77 9fr multicolored .45 .25
**447** A77 18fr multicolored .65 .25
**448** A77 20fr multicolored .60 .35
**449** A77 25fr multicolored .80 .35
*Nos. 446-449 (4)* 2.50 1.20

5th anniversary of re-unification.

Learning to Write and UNESCO Emblem — A78

No. 451, Children's heads & UNICEF emblem.

**1966, Nov. 24 Engr. *Perf. 13***

**450** A78 50fr red lil, bl & brn 1.40 .30
**451** A78 50fr red lil, blk & brt bl 1.40 .30

20th anniv. of UNESCO, 20th anniv. of UNICEF.

Independence Proclamation A79

**1967, Jan. 1 Engr. *Perf. 13***

**452** A79 20fr grn, red & yel 2.25 .60

7th anniversary of independence.

Map of Africa and Madagascar, Railroad Tracks and Symbols — A80

25fr, Map of Africa and Madagascar and train.

**1967, Feb. 21 Photo. *Perf. 13***

**453** A80 20fr multicolored 3.50 1.50
**454** A80 25fr multicolored 5.00 2.00

5th Conf. of African and Madagascan Railroad Technicians.

Lions Emblem and Forest A81

Design: 100fr, Lions emblem and palms.

**1967, Mar. 3**

**455** A81 50fr multicolored .90 .35
**456** A81 100fr multicolored 2.10 .65

Lions International, 50th anniversary.

Jet and I.C.A.O. Emblem A82

Dove and I.A.E.A. Emblem A83

***Perf. 13x12½, 12½x13***

**1967, Mar. 15 Photo.**

**457** A82 50fr ultra, lt bl, brn & gold 1.40 .35
**458** A83 50fr ultra & emer 1.40 .35

UN agencies: No. 457, the ICAO; No. 458, the Intl. Atomic Energy Agency.

Rotary International Emblem — A84

**1967, Apr. 17 Photo. *Perf. 12½***

**459** A84 25fr crim, vio bl & gold 1.25 .25

10th anniversary of the Douala, Cameroun, branch of Rotary International.

Grapefruit — A85

**1967, May 10 Photo. *Perf. 12x12½***

**460** A85 1fr shown .25 .25
**461** A85 2fr Papaya .25 .25
**462** A85 3fr Custard apple .25 .25
**463** A85 4fr Breadfruit .25 .25
**464** A85 5fr Coconut .35 .25
**465** A85 6fr Mango .45 .25
**466** A85 8fr Avacado .90 .25
**467** A85 10fr Pineapple 1.40 .25
**468** A85 30fr Bananas 3.50 .25
*Nos. 460-468 (9)* 7.60 2.25

For surcharges see Nos. 550, 593.

Bird of Paradise Flower — A86

**1967, June 22 Photo. *Perf. 12x12½***

**Size: 22x36mm**

**469** A86 15fr lt blue & multi .90 .25

Sanaga Falls and ITY Emblem — A87

**1967, Aug. 14 Photo. *Perf. 13x12½***

**470** A87 30fr multicolored .85 .25

Issued for International Tourist Year 1967.

Art of Cameroun: Coconut Harvest — A88

Carved Bas-relief: 20fr, Lion hunt. 30fr, Women carrying baskets. 100fr, Carved chest.

**1967, Sept. 22 *Perf. 12½x13***

**471** A88 10fr brn, bl & car .35 .25
**472** A88 20fr brn, yel & grn .55 .25
**473** A88 30fr emer, brn & car .90 .25
**474** A88 100fr red org, brn & emer 2.25 .40
*Nos. 471-474 (4)* 4.05 1.15

Coat of Arms — A89

**1968, Jan. 1 Litho. *Perf. 12½x13***

**475** A89 30fr gold & multi 1.00 .25

Spiny Lobster — A90

Designs (Fish and Crustaceans): 10fr, River crayfish. 15fr, Nile mouth-breeder. 20fr, Sole. 25fr, Common pike. 30fr, Crab. 40fr, Spadefish, vert. 50fr, Shrimp, vert. 55fr, African snakehead. 60fr, Threadfin.

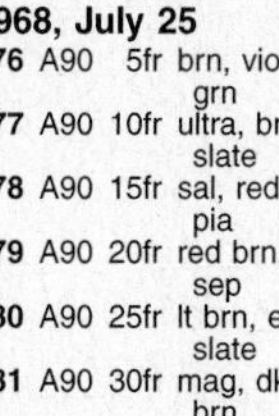

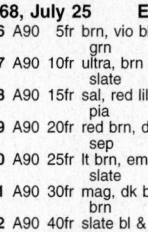

**1968, July 25 Engr. *Perf. 13***

**476** A90 5fr brn, vio bl & dl grn .30 .25
**477** A90 10fr ultra, brn ol & slate .30 .25
**478** A90 15fr sal, red lil & sepia .85 .25
**479** A90 20fr red brn, dp bl & sep 1.00 .25
**480** A90 25fr lt brn, emer & slate 1.10 .25
**481** A90 30fr mag, dk bl & dk brn 1.50 .25
**482** A90 40fr slate bl & org 2.25 .25
**483** A90 50fr emer, gray & rose car 3.00 .25
**484** A90 55fr lt brn, Prus bl & dk brn 4.50 .25
**485** A90 60fr brn, bl grn & indigo 6.75 .35
*Nos. 476-485 (10)* 21.55 2.60

Tanker, Refinery and Map of Area Served A91

**1968, July 30 Photo. *Perf. 12½***

**486** A91 30fr multicolored 1.60 .25

Port Gentil (Gabon) Refinery opening, 6/12/68.

Human Rights Flame — A92

**1968, Sept. 14 Photo. *Perf. 12½x13***

**487** A92 15fr blue & salmon .65 .25

Intl. Human Rights Year. See No. C110.

Pres. Ahmadou Ahidjo — A93

**1969, Apr. 10 Photo. *Perf. 12½x12***

**488** A93 30fr carmine & multi .80 .25

Chocolate Vat — A94

Designs: 30fr, Chocolate factory. 50fr, Candy making, vert.

**1969, Apr. 24 Engr. *Perf. 13***

**489** A94 15fr red brn, ind & choc .50 .25
**490** A94 30fr grn, blk & red brn .80 .25
**491** A94 50fr brown & multi 1.10 .25
*Nos. 489-491 (3)* 2.40 .75

Cameroun chocolate industry.

Fertility Symbol, Abbia — A95

Art and Folklore from Abbia: 10fr, Two toucans, horiz. 15fr, Forest symbol. 30fr, Vulture attacking monkey, horiz. 70fr, Oliphant player.

**1969, May 30 Engr. *Perf. 13***

**492** A95 5fr ultra, Prus bl & brt rose lil .25 .25
**493** A95 10fr bl, ol gray & org .35 .25
**494** A95 15fr ultra, dk red & blk .50 .25
**495** A95 30fr brt bl, lem & grn .90 .25
**496** A95 70fr brt bl, dk grn & ver 1.90 .50
*Nos. 492-496 (5)* 3.90 1.50

Diesel Train on Bridge — A96

Design: 30fr, Kumba Railroad station, horiz.

*Perf. 12½x13, 13x12½*

**1969, July 11** **Photo.**

**497** A96 30fr blue & multi 1.25 .30
**498** A96 50fr black & multi 3.25 .60

Opening of Mbanga-Kumba Railroad.

### Development Bank Issue
Common Design Type

**1969, Sept. 10** **Engr.** ***Perf. 13***

**499** CD130 30fr vio bl, grn & ocher .80 .25

African Development Bank, 5th anniv.

### ASECNA Issue
Common Design Type

**1969, Dec. 12** **Engr.** ***Perf. 13***

**500** CD132 100fr slate green 2.00 .60

Red Sage — A99

Design: 30fr, Passionflower.

**1970, Mar. 24** **Photo.** ***Perf. 12x12½***
**Size: 22x36½mm**

**501** A99 15fr yel grn & multi .45 .25
**502** A99 30fr multicolored 1.00 .25
*Nos. 501-502,C140-C141 (4)* 5.60 1.75

### UPU Headquarters Issue
Common Design Type

**1970, May 20** **Engr.** ***Perf. 13***

**503** CD133 30fr blue, pur & grn 1.00 .25
**504** CD133 50fr gray, red & bl 1.60 .30

Brewery — A100

Design: 30fr, Cellar with barrels.

**1970, July 9** **Engr.** ***Perf. 13***

**505** A100 15fr brn, gray & dk grn .50 .25
**506** A100 30fr bl grn, dk brn & brn red 1.00 .30

Cameroun brewing industry.

Ozila Dancers — A101

Design: 50fr, Ozila dancer and drummer.

**1970, Oct. 19** **Engr.** ***Perf. 13***

**507** A101 30fr multicolored 1.00 .35
**508** A101 50fr red & multi 1.25 .75

Cameroun Doll — A102

Designs: 15fr, Doll in short skirt. 30fr, Doll with basket on back.

**1970, Nov. 2**

**509** A102 10fr car & multi .60 .25
**510** A102 15fr dk grn & multi .70 .25
**511** A102 30fr brn red & multi 1.90 .30
*Nos. 509-511 (3)* 3.20 .80

Cogwheels and Grain — A103

**1970, Feb. 9** **Photo.** ***Perf. 13***

**512** A103 30fr multicolored .85 .25

Europafrica Economic Conference.

Federal University, Yaoundé — A104

**1971, Jan. 19** **Engr.**

**513** A104 50fr multicolored 1.00 .25

Inauguration of Federal University at Yaoundé.

Presidents Ahidjo and Pompidou, Flags of Cameroun and France A105

**1971, Feb. 9** **Photo.** ***Perf. 13***

**514** A105 30fr multicolored 1.50 .35

Visit of Georges Pompidou, Pres. of France.

Young People, Globe, Map of Cameroun A106

**1971, Feb. 11**

**515** A106 30fr blue & multi .90 .30

Fifth National Youth Festival, Feb. 11.

Gerbera Hybrida — A107

Designs: 40fr, Opuntia polyantha (cactus). 50fr, Hemerocallis hybrida (lily).

**1971, Mar. 14** **Photo.**

**516** A107 20fr multicolored .60 .25
**517** A107 40fr green & multi 1.50 .25
**518** A107 50fr blue & multi 2.10 .25
*Nos. 516-518 (3)* 4.20 .75

Men of Four Races — A108

Design: 30fr, Hands and globe.

**1971, Mar. 21** ***Perf. 13x12½***

**519** A108 20fr green & multi .55 .25
**520** A108 30fr ultra & multi .75 .25

Intl. year against racial discrimination.

Crowned Cranes at Waza Camp — A109

20fr, Canoe on Sanaga River. 30fr, Sanaga River.

**1971, Apr. 9.** **Engr.** ***Perf. 13***

**521** A109 10fr red, grn & blk 1.50 .25
**522** A109 20fr dk grn, brn & red 1.00 .25
**523** A109 30fr red, dk grn & brt bl 1.50 .25
*Nos. 521-523 (3)* 4.00 .75

International Court, The Hague — A110

**1971, June 14** **Engr.** ***Perf. 13***

**524** A110 50fr ultra, org brn & sl grn 1.25 .35

25th anniversary of the International Court in The Hague, Netherlands.

Liana Bridge A111

Local Market A112

**1971, Aug. 16** **Photo.** ***Perf. 13***

**525** A111 40fr multicolored 1.60 .25
**526** A112 45fr multicolored 1.60 .25

Bamoun Horseman — A113

African Art: 15fr, Animal fetish statuette.

**1971, Sept. 18**

**527** A113 10fr brown & yellow .50 .50
**528** A113 15fr dp brn & org yel .50 .50

Communications Satellite and Globe — A114

**1971, Oct. 14** ***Perf. 13x12½***

**529** A114 40fr Prus bl, sl grn & org .80 .25

Pan-African telecommunications system.

UNICEF Emblem — A115

50fr, UNICEF emblem and grain, vert.

**1971, Dec. 11** **Engr.** ***Perf. 13***

**530** A115 40fr sl grn, bl grn & plum .95 .25
**531** A115 50fr dp bl, dk red & lt grn 1.25 .25

25th anniv. of UNICEF.

Houses from South-Central Region — A116

Design: 15fr, Adamaua round houses.

**1972, Jan. 15** **Photo.** ***Perf. 13***

**532** A116 10fr dk blue & multi .25 .25
**533** A116 15fr black & multi .55 .25

Giraffe — A117

Designs: 5fr, Home industries. 10fr, Smith, horiz. 15fr, Women carrying burdens.

***Perf. 13x13½, 13½x13***

**1972, Feb. 18** **Litho.**

**534** A117 2fr multicolored .30 .25
**535** A117 5fr black, org & red .30 .25
**536** A117 10fr multicolored .30 .25
**537** A117 15fr multicolored .30 .25
*Nos. 534-537 (4)* 1.20 1.00

Youth Day 1972.

Soccer Players and Field — A118

Designs: 20fr, African Soccer Cup, vert. 45fr, Team captains shaking hands, vert.

**1972, Feb. 22** ***Perf. 13½***

**538** A118 20fr gray & multi .55 .25
**539** A118 40fr gray & multi .95 .25
**540** A118 45fr yellow & multi 1.50 .25
*Nos. 538-540 (3)* 3.00 .75

African Soccer Cup, Yaoundé, 2/23-3/5.

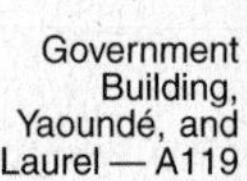
Government Building, Yaoundé, and Laurel — A119

**1972, Apr. 6** **Photo.** ***Perf. 12½x12***

**541** A119 40fr multicolored .80 .25

110th session of Inter-Parliamentary Council, Yaoundé, Apr. 1972.

"Fantasia," North Cameroun A120

Bororo Woman A121

40fr, Boat on Wouri River & Mt. Cameroun.

**1972, Apr. 24** ***Perf. 13x12½, 12½x13***

**542** A120 15fr dk vio & multi .35 .25
**543** A121 20fr multicolored .45 .25
**544** A120 40fr multicolored 1.50 .25
*Nos. 542-544 (3)* 2.30 .75

Chemical Apparatus A122

**1972, May 15** **Engr.** ***Perf. 13***

**545** A122 40fr lilac, red & green .80 .25

President Ahmadou Ahidjo Prize.

### United Republic

Solanum Macranthum — A123

Design: 45fr, Wax plant.

**1972, July 20 Photo. *Perf. 13***

**546** A123 40fr multicolored .95 .25
**547** A123 45fr yellow & multi 1.25 .25

Charaxes Ameliae — A124

Design: 45fr, Papilio tynderaeus.

**1972, Aug. 20 Photo. *Perf. 13***

**548** A124 40fr bl, dk bl & gold 4.00 .40
**549** A124 45fr lt grn, blk & gold 5.50 .60

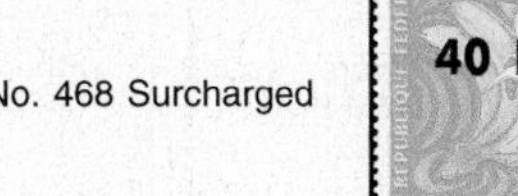

No. 468 Surcharged

**1972, Aug. 30 Photo. *Perf. 12x12½***

**550** A85 40fr on 30fr multicolored 1.00 .25

Resurrection Lily — A125

Flowers: 45fr, Candlestick cassia. 50fr, Amaryllis.

**1972, Sept. 16 *Perf. 13***

**551** A125 40fr lt green & multi 1.00 .25
**552** A125 45fr multicolored 1.25 .25
**553** A125 50fr lt blue & multi 1.50 .35
*Nos. 551-553 (3)* 3.75 .85

Great Blue Touraco — A126

Design: 45fr, Red-faced lovebirds, horiz.

***Perf. 12½x13, 13x12½***

**1972, Nov. 20 Litho.**

**554** A126 10fr yellow & multi 1.75 .25
**555** A126 45fr yellow & multi 3.75 .25

Cotton (North) — A127

10fr, Cacao (south central). 15fr, Logging (southeast & southern coast). 20fr, Coffee (west). 45fr, Tea (northwest & southwest).

**1973, Mar. 26 Photo. *Perf. 12½x13***

**556** A127 5fr black & multi .25 .25
**557** A127 10fr black & multi .25 .25
**558** A127 15fr black & multi .75 .25
**559** A127 20fr black & multi 1.50 .25
**560** A127 45fr black & multi 2.50 .40
*Nos. 556-560 (5)* 5.25 1.40

Third 5-Year Plan.
For surcharge see No. 568.

Flag and Map of Cameroun, Pres. Ahidjo and No. 331 — A128

Design: 20fr, Proclamation of independence, Pres. Ahidjo and No. 336.

**1973, May 20 Engr. *Perf. 13***

**561** A128 10fr ultra & multi .65 .25
**562** A128 20fr multicolored 1.00 .25
*Nos. 561-562,C200-C201 (4)* 3.45 1.15

United Republic of Cameroun, 1st anniv.

Bamoun Mask — A129

Designs: Various Bamoun masks.

**1973, July 10 Engr. *Perf. 13***

**563** A129 5fr green, brn & blk .25 .25
**564** A129 10fr lilac, brn & blk .25 .25
**565** A129 45fr red, brn & blk .75 .25
**566** A129 100fr ultra, brn & blk 2.00 .40
*Nos. 563-566 (4)* 3.25 1.15

Dr. Hansen — A130

**1973, July 25 Engr. *Perf. 13***

**567** A130 45fr multicolored 2.00 .25

Centenary of the discovery by Dr. Armauer G. Hansen of the Hansen bacillus, the cause of leprosy.

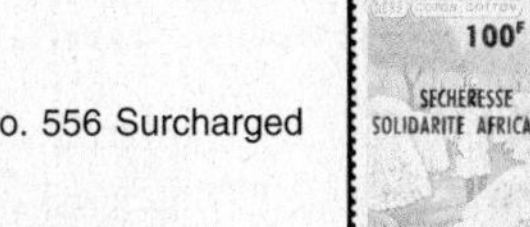

No. 556 Surcharged

**1973, Aug. 16 Photo. *Perf. 12½x13***

**568** A127 100fr on 5fr 1.75 .40

African solidarity in drought emergency.

Dancers, South West Africa — A131

Designs: Southwest African dances.

**1973, Aug. 17 *Perf. 13***

**569** A131 10fr multicolored .25 .25
**570** A131 25fr multicolored .55 .25
**571** A131 45fr multicolored 1.10 .25
*Nos. 569-571 (3)* 1.90 .75

WMO Emblem — A132

**1973, Sept. 1 Engr. *Perf. 13***

**572** A132 45fr green & ultra 1.60 .25

Cent. of intl. meteorological cooperation.

Garoua Party Headquarters — A133

**1973, Sept. 1 Photo.**

**573** A133 40fr multicolored .80 .25

7th anniv. of Cameroun National Union.

**African Postal Union Issue, 1973**
Common Design Type

**1973, Sept. 12 Engr.**

**574** CD137 100fr brt bl, bl & sl grn 1.75 .40

Avocados — A135

**1973, Sept. 20**

**575** A135 10fr shown .70 .25
**576** A135 20fr Mangos .80 .25
**577** A135 45fr Plums 2.00 .25
**578** A135 50fr Custard apple 2.50 .25
*Nos. 575-578 (4)* 6.00 1.00

Kirdi Village — A136

45fr, Mabas village. 50fr, Fishing village.

**1973, Oct. 25 Engr. *Perf. 13***

**579** A136 15fr black, bis & grn .25 .25
**580** A136 45fr mag, brn & org .90 .25
**581** A136 50fr green, blk & org 1.25 .25
*Nos. 579-581 (3)* 2.40 .75

Handshake on Map of Africa — A137

**1974, May 15 Engr. *Perf. 12½x13***

**582** A137 40fr carmine & multi .55 .25
**583** A137 45fr indigo & multi .70 .25

Organization for African Unity, 10th anniv.

Spinning Mill — A138

**1974, May 25 Engr. *Perf. 13x12½***

**584** A138 45fr multicolored .80 .25

CICAM Industrial Complex.

Carved Panel from Bilinga — A139

Cameroun Art (Carvings): 40fr, Detail from Bubinga chair. 45fr, Detail Acajou Ngollon panel.

**1974, May 30**

**585** A139 10fr brt grn & ocher .25 .25
**586** A139 40fr red & brown .80 .25
**587** A139 45fr blue & rose brn 1.10 .25
*Nos. 585-587 (3)* 2.15 .75

Zebu — A140

**1974, June 1 *Perf. 13½***

**588** A140 40fr multicolored 1.40 .25

North Cameroun cattle raising. See No. C210.

Laying Rail Section — A141

Designs: 5fr, Map showing line Yaoundé to Ngaoundéré, vert. 40fr, Welding rail joint, vert. 100fr, Train on Djerem River Bridge.

***Perf. 12½x13, 13x12½***

**1974, June 10 Engr.**

**589** A141 5fr multicolored .65 .25
**590** A141 20fr multicolored 1.25 .30
**591** A141 40fr multicolored 2.00 .60
**592** A141 100fr multicolored 3.25 .90
*Nos. 589-592 (4)* 7.15 2.05

Opening of Yaoundé-Ngaoundéré railroad line.
For surcharge see No. 596.

No. 466 Surcharged

**1974, June 1 Photo. *Perf. 12x12½***

**593** A85 40fr on 8fr multi .80 .25

UPU Emblem, Hands Holding Letters — A142

**1974, Oct. 8 Engr. *Perf. 13***

**594** A142 40fr multicolored .90 .25
*Nos. 594,C218-C219 (3)* 5.90 1.75

Cent. of the UPU.

A143

Design: Presidents and flags of Cameroun, CAR, Congo, Gabon and meeting center.

**1974, Dec. 8 Photo. *Perf. 13***

**595** A143 40fr gold & multi 1.50 .25

10th anniversary of Central African Customs and Economic Union (Union Douanière et Economique de l'Afrique Centrale, UDEAC). See No. C223.

No. 589 Surcharged in Violet Blue

**1974, Dec. 10 Engr. *Perf. 12½x13***

**596** A141 100fr on 5fr multi 2.50 .85

Virgin of Autun, 15th Century Sculpture — A144

Christmas: 45fr, Virgin and Child, by Luis de Morales (c. 1509-1586).

**1974, Dec. 20 Photo. *Perf. 13***

| | | | | |
|---|---|---|---|---|
| **597** | A144 | 40fr gold & multi | .95 | .25 |
| **598** | A144 | 45fr gold & multi | 1.25 | .25 |

Tropical Plants — A145

5fr, Cockscomb. 40fr, Costus spectabilis. 45fr, Mussaenda erythrophylla.

**1975, Mar. 10 Photo. *Perf. 13***

| | | | | |
|---|---|---|---|---|
| **599** | A145 | 5fr multicolored | .30 | .25 |
| **600** | A145 | 40fr multicolored | 1.50 | .25 |
| **601** | A145 | 45fr multicolored | 1.90 | .35 |
| | | *Nos. 599-601 (3)* | 3.70 | .85 |

Fishing by Night A146

**1975, Apr. 1 Engr. *Perf. 13***

| | | | | |
|---|---|---|---|---|
| **602** | A146 | 40fr shown | 1.75 | .40 |
| **603** | A146 | 45fr Fishing by day | 1.75 | .40 |

Afo Akom Statue and Chief's Stool — A147

**1975, Apr. 1 Photo.**

| | | | | |
|---|---|---|---|---|
| **604** | A147 | 40fr multicolored | .65 | .25 |
| **605** | A147 | 45fr multicolored | .85 | .25 |
| **606** | A147 | 200fr multicolored | 2.50 | .75 |
| | | *Nos. 604-606 (3)* | 4.00 | 1.25 |

Tree Fungus — A148

**1975, Apr. 14**

| | | | | |
|---|---|---|---|---|
| **607** | A148 | 15fr shown | *125.00* | 2.00 |
| **608** | A148 | 40fr Chrysalis | *85.00* | 1.00 |

Ministry of Posts and Telecommunications — A149

**1975, July 21 Engr. *Perf. 13***

| | | | | |
|---|---|---|---|---|
| **609** | A149 | 40fr brn, grn & Prus bl | .65 | .25 |
| **610** | A149 | 45fr Prus bl, brn & grn | .90 | .25 |

Presbyterian Church, Elat — A150

Designs: No. 612, Foumban Mosque. 45fr, Catholic Church, Ngaoundere.

**1975, Aug. 20 Engr. *Perf. 13***

| | | | | |
|---|---|---|---|---|
| **611** | A150 | 40fr multicolored | .45 | .25 |
| **612** | A150 | 40fr multicolored | .45 | .25 |
| **613** | A150 | 45fr multicolored | .65 | .25 |
| | | *Nos. 611-613 (3)* | 1.55 | .75 |

Plowing — A151

Design: No. 615, Corn harvest, vert.

***Perf. 13x12½, 12½x13***

**1975, Dec. 15 Photo.**

| | | | | |
|---|---|---|---|---|
| **614** | A151 | 40fr deep grn & multi | .70 | .25 |
| **615** | A151 | 40fr deep grn & multi | .70 | .25 |

Green revolution.

Zamengoe Satellite Monitoring Station A152

**1976, May 20 Litho. *Perf. 13***

| | | | | |
|---|---|---|---|---|
| **616** | A152 | 40fr shown | .50 | .25 |
| **617** | A152 | 100fr Radar, vert. | 1.25 | .40 |

Porcelain Rose — A153

Design: 50fr, Flower of North Cameroun.

**1976, July 20 Litho. *Perf. 12½***

| | | | | |
|---|---|---|---|---|
| **618** | A153 | 40fr multicolored | 1.00 | .25 |
| **619** | A153 | 50fr multicolored | 1.40 | .35 |

Leopard Dance — A154

**1976, Sept. 15 Litho. *Perf. 12***

| | | | | |
|---|---|---|---|---|
| **620** | A154 | 40fr gray & multi | .80 | .25 |
| | | *Nos. 620,C233-C234 (3)* | 2.55 | .85 |

Telephone Exchange — A155

**1976, Oct. 5 *Perf. 13***

| | | | | |
|---|---|---|---|---|
| **621** | A155 | 50fr multicolored | .80 | .25 |

Centenary of first telephone call by Alexander Graham Bell, Mar. 10, 1876.

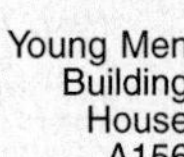

Young Men Building House A156

Design: 45fr, Young women working in field.

**1976, Oct. 10 Litho. *Perf. 12***

| | | | | |
|---|---|---|---|---|
| **622** | A156 | 40fr multicolored | .35 | .25 |
| **623** | A156 | 45fr multicolored | .60 | .25 |

10th National Youth Day.

Konrad Adenauer (1876-1967), German Chancellor, Cologne Cathedral — A157

**1976, Oct. 20**

| | | | | |
|---|---|---|---|---|
| **624** | A157 | 100fr multicolored | .95 | .40 |

Party Headquarters, Douala — A158

No. 626, Party Headquarters, Yaoundé.

**1976, Dec. 28 Litho. *Perf. 12***

| | | | | |
|---|---|---|---|---|
| **625** | A158 | 50fr orange & multi | .45 | .25 |
| **626** | A158 | 50fr blue & multi | .45 | .25 |

10th anniv. of the Cameroun National Union.

Bamoun Copper Pipe — A159

**1977, Feb. 4 Litho. *Perf. 12½***

| | | | | |
|---|---|---|---|---|
| **627** | A159 | 50fr multicolored | .70 | .25 |

2nd World Black and African Festival, Lagos, Nigeria, 1/15-2/12. See No. C239.

Ostrich — A160

**1977, Mar. 20 Litho. *Perf. 12***

| | | | | |
|---|---|---|---|---|
| **628** | A160 | 30fr shown | 2.50 | .40 |
| **629** | A160 | 50fr Crowned cranes | 3.00 | .75 |

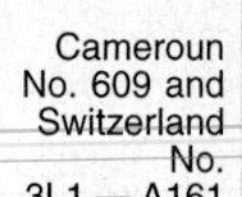

Cameroun No. 609 and Switzerland No. 3L1 — A161

**1977, June 5 Litho. *Perf. 12***

| | | | | |
|---|---|---|---|---|
| **630** | A161 | 50fr multicolored | 1.00 | .30 |
| | | *Nos. 630,C252-C253 (3)* | 4.35 | 1.25 |

Jufilex Philatelic Exhibition, Bern, Switzerland. See Nos. C252-C253.

---

Winter Olympics 1976, set of five, 40, 50fr, airmail 140, 200, 350fr, and airmail souv. sheet, 500fr, issued Aug. 10, 1977. Nos. 7701-7706. Value, set $7.50, souvenir sheet $5.

---

Apollo-Soyuz A163

Designs: 40fr, Astronaut Thomas P. Stafford, Apollo lifting off. 60fr, Cosmonaut Alexei Leonov, Soyuz lifting off.

**1977, Aug. 10 Litho. *Perf. 14x13½***

| | | | | |
|---|---|---|---|---|
| **633** | A163 | 40fr multicolored | *.45* | *.25* |
| **634** | A163 | 60fr multicolored | *.70* | *.50* |
| | | *Nos. 633-634,C256-C258 (5)* | *7.55* | *2.60* |

No. 617 Overprinted in French and English

**1977, Aug. 22 Litho. *Perf. 13***

| | | | | |
|---|---|---|---|---|
| **635** | A152 | 100fr multicolored | .90 | .40 |

Palestinian fighters and their families.

Chairman Mao and Great Wall — A164

**1977, Sept. 9 Engr. *Perf. 13***

| | | | | |
|---|---|---|---|---|
| **636** | A164 | 100fr olive & brown | 4.25 | .55 |

Mao Tse-tung (1893-1976), Chinese communist leader, first death anniversary.

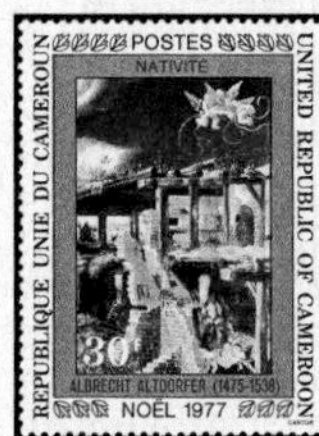

Nativity, by Albrecht Altdorfer — A165

50fr, Madonna of the Grand Duke, by Raphael.

**1977, Dec. 15 Litho. *Perf. 12½x12***

| | | | | |
|---|---|---|---|---|
| **637** | A165 | 30fr multicolored | .55 | .25 |
| **638** | A165 | 50fr multicolored | 1.10 | .25 |
| | | *Nos. 637-638,C264-C265 (4)* | 7.65 | 2.50 |

Christmas 1977.

Gazelle and Rotary Emblem — A166

**1978, Feb. 11 Litho. *Perf. 12***

| | | | | |
|---|---|---|---|---|
| **639** | A166 | 50fr orange & multi | .70 | .25 |

Rotary Club of Yaounde, 20th anniversary.

Pres. Ahidjo, Flag and Map of Cameroun — A167

**1978, Apr. 3** **Litho.** ***Perf. 12½***
**640** A167 50fr multicolored .90 .25

New flag of Cameroun. See No. C266.

Cardioglossa Escalerae A168

Design: 60fr, Cardioglossa elegans.

**1978, Apr. 5**
**641** A168 50fr multicolored 1.75 .25
**642** A168 60fr multicolored 3.00 .25
*Nos. 641-642,C267 (3)* 8.50 1.25

Jules Verne and "From Earth to Moon" — A169

**1978, Oct. 10** **Litho.** ***Perf. 12***
**643** A169 250fr multicolored 2.25 1.40

Jules Verne (1828-1905), science fiction writer, birth sesquicentennial. See No. C276.

Hypolimnas Salmacis Drury A170

Butterflies: 25fr, Euxanthe trajanus ward. 30fr, Euphaedra cyparissa cramer.

**1978, Oct. 15**
**644** A170 20fr multicolored 2.00 .60
**645** A170 25fr multicolored 2.25 .60
**646** A170 30fr multicolored 3.75 .60
*Nos. 644-646 (3)* 8.00 1.80

Men Planting Seedlings — A171

**1978, Oct. 30** ***Perf. 12½***
**647** A171 10fr multicolored .25 .25
**648** A171 15fr multicolored .35 .25

Green barrier against the desert.

Carved Bamun Drum — A172

60fr, String instrument (Gueguerou), horiz.

**1978, Nov. 20** **Litho.** ***Perf. 12½***
**649** A172 50fr multicolored .45 .25
**650** A172 60fr multicolored .90 .25
*Nos. 649-650,C277 (3)* 2.60 .90

Pres. Ahidjo, Giscard D'Estaing, Flags of Cameroun and France A173

**1979, Feb. 8** **Photo.** ***Perf. 13***
**651** A173 60fr multicolored 1.50 .60

Visit of Pres. Valery Giscard D'Estaing of France to Cameroun.

Human Rights Emblem, Globe, Scroll and African A174

**1979, Feb. 11** **Litho.** ***Perf. 12x12½***
**652** A174 5fr multicolored .25 .25

Universal Declaration of Human Rights, 30th anniversary (in 1978).
See Nos. 803, C278.

Boy and Girl Greeting Sun — A175

**1979, Aug. 15** **Litho.** ***Perf. 12***
**653** A175 50fr multicolored .80 .25

International Year of the Child.

Protected Animals — A176

Nos. 655, 658 vert.

**1979, Sept. 20** ***Perf. 12½***
**654** A176 50fr Rhinoceros 1.40 .30
**655** A176 60fr Giraffe 1.90 .40
**656** A176 60fr Gorilla 1.90 .40
**657** A176 100fr Leopard 2.90 .60
**658** A176 100fr Elephant 2.90 .60
*Nos. 654-658 (5)* 11.00 2.30

Eugene Jamot, Map of Cameroun, Tsetse Fly — A177

**1979, Nov. 5** **Engr.** ***Perf. 13***
**659** A177 50fr multicolored 3.00 .40

Eugene Jamot (1879-1937), discoverer of sleeping sickness cure.

Annunciation, by Fra Filippo Lippi — A178

Paintings; 50fr, Rest During the Flight to Egypt, c. 1620. No. 662, Flight into Egypt, by Jan Joest, No. 663, Nativity, by Joest. 100fr, Nativity, by Botticelli.

**1979, Dec. 6** **Litho.** ***Perf. 12½x12***
**660** A178 10fr multicolored .25 .25
**661** A178 50fr multicolored .60 .25
**662** A178 60fr multicolored .75 .30
**663** A178 60fr multicolored .75 .30
*a.* Pair, #662-663 1.50 1.50
**664** A178 100fr multicolored 1.50 .40
*Nos. 660-664 (5)* 3.85 1.50

Christmas 1979.

Piper Capense — A179

Medicinal Plants: 60fr, Bracken fern.

**1979, Dec. 15** **Litho.** ***Perf. 12½***
**665** A179 50fr multicolored 1.25 .30
**666** A179 60fr multicolored 1.50 .40

Pres. Ahidjo, Cameroun Map, Arms and No. 331 — A180

**1980, Feb. 12** **Litho.** ***Perf. 12½***
**667** A180 50fr multicolored .65 .25

Independence, 20th anniversary.

Congress Building, Bafoussam A181

**1980, Feb. 12**
**668** A181 50fr multicolored .65 .25

Cameroun National Union, 3rd Ordinary Congress, Bafoussam, Feb. 12-17.

Rotary Emblem, Map of Cameroun — A182

Rotary Intl., 75th Anniv.: No. 670, Anniv. emblem.

**1980, Mar. 15** **Litho.** ***Perf. 12½***
**669** A182 200fr multicolored 2.00 .80
**670** A182 200fr multicolored 2.00 .80
*a.* Souvenir sheet of 2, #669-670 5.25 4.00

Voacanga Medicinal Beans — A183

60fr, Voacanga tree, vert. 100fr, Voacanga flower, vert.

**1980, Dec. 3** **Litho.** ***Perf. 12½***
**671** A183 50fr shown 1.00 .25
**672** A183 60fr multicolored 1.25 .25
**673** A183 100fr multicolored 1.75 .40
*Nos. 671-673 (3)* 4.00 .90

Violet Mellowstone — A184

60fr, Patula. 100fr, Cashmere bouquet.

**1980, Dec. 5**
**674** A184 50fr shown .70 .25
**675** A184 60fr multicolored 1.00 .25
**676** A184 100fr multicolored 1.60 .40
*Nos. 674-676 (3)* 3.30 .90

Occupation of Mecca by Mohammed, 1350th Anniversary A185

**1980, Dec. 9**
**677** A185 50fr multicolored 1.00 .30

African Slender-snouted Crocodile (Endangered Species) — A186

300fr, Buffon's antelope, vert.

**1980, Dec. 24**
**678** A186 200fr shown 3.25 .80
**679** A186 300fr multicolored 4.00 1.20

See Nos. 888-889.

Bororo Girls and Roumsiki Peaks A187

60fr, Dschang tourist center.

**1980, Dec. 29**
**680** A187 50fr shown .55 .25
**681** A187 60fr multicolored .55 .25

Banana Tree — A188

**1981, Feb. 5**
**682** A188 50fr shown .65 .30
**683** A188 60fr Cattle, vert. .80 .40

Girl on Crutches — A189

150fr, Boy in motorized wheelchair.

**1981, Feb. 20** **Litho.** ***Perf. 12½***
**684** A189 60fr shown .55 .25
**685** A189 150fr multicolored 1.25 .65

International Year of the Disabled.

Air Terminal, Douala Airport A190

200fr, Boeing 747. 300fr, Douala Intl. Airport.

**1981, Apr. 4** **Litho.** ***Perf. 12½***
**686** A190 100fr shown 1.00 .55
**687** A190 200fr multi 2.00 1.10
**688** A190 300fr multi 3.00 1.60
*Nos. 686-688 (3)* 6.00 3.25

Cameroun Airlines, 10th anniv.

Pres. Ahidjo Presenting Trophy to Canon Soccer Team — A191

No. 690, Union team captain.

**1981, Apr. 20**

**689** A191 60fr shown .90 .40
**690** A191 60fr multicolored .90 .40

1979 African Soccer Cup champions.

Scaly Anteater — A192

Designs: Endangered species.

**1981, July 20 Litho. *Perf. 12½***

**691** A192 50fr Moutourou 1.50 .25
**692** A192 50fr Tortoise 1.50 .25
**693** A192 100fr shown 3.25 .40
*Nos. 691-693 (3)* 6.25 .90

Prince Charles and Lady Diana, St. Paul's Cathedral — A193

No. 695, Couple, royal coach.

**1981, July 29 Litho. *Perf. 12½***

**694** A193 500fr shown 4.50 2.00
**695** A193 500fr multicolored 4.50 2.00
*a.* Souvenir sheet of 2, #694-695 10.00 4.00

Royal wedding.

Bafoussam-Bamenda Highway — A194

**1981, Sept. 10 Litho. *Perf. 12½***

**696** A194 50fr multicolored .55 .25

Freighter Cam Iroko (Cameroun Shipping Line) — A195

**1981, Sept. 25**

**697** A195 60fr multicolored 1.00 .40

20th Anniv. of Reunification A196

**1981, Oct. 10 *Perf. 12½x13***

**698** A196 50fr multicolored .70 .25

Medicinal Plants — A197

60fr, Voacanga thouarsii. 70fr, Cassia alata.

**1981, Dec. 31 Litho. *Perf. 12½***

**699** A197 60fr multicolored 1.10 .30
**700** A197 70fr multicolored 1.40 .40

Easter 1982 A198

Paintings: 100fr, Christ in the Garden of Olives, by Delacroix. 200fr, Descent from the Cross, by Giotto. 250fr, Pieta in the Countryside, by Bellini.

**1982, Apr. 10 Litho. *Perf. 13***

**701** A198 100fr multicolored .90 .35
**702** A198 200fr multicolored 1.75 .65
**703** A198 250fr multicolored 2.25 .90
*Nos. 701-703 (3)* 4.90 1.90

PHILEXFRANCE '82 Stamp Exhibition, Paris, June 11-21 — A199

**1982, Apr. 25 *Perf. 12***

**704** A199 90fr multicolored 1.90 .40

Snakeskin Handbag — A200

**1982, Apr. 30 *Perf. 12½***

**705** A200 60fr shown .70 .25
**706** A200 70fr Clay water jug .80 .35

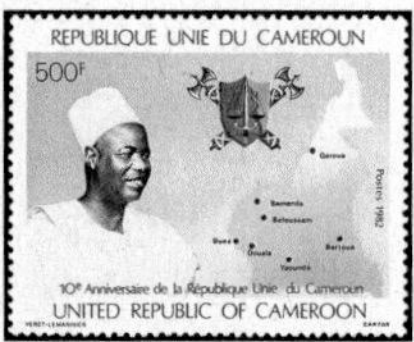

10th Anniv. of Republic A201

**1982, May 20 *Perf. 13***

**707** A201 500fr multicolored 4.50 2.00

Town Hall, Douala A202

**1982, June 15 Litho. *Perf. 12½***

**708** A202 40fr shown .45 .25
**709** A202 60fr Yaounde .65 .25

See Nos. 730-731, 757-758, 790-791, 867.

1982 World Cup A203

100fr, National team. 200fr, Semi-finalists. 300fr, Players, vert. 400fr, National team 2nd lineup.

**1982, July 10 *Perf. 13***

**710** A203 100fr multi 1.40 .40
**711** A203 200fr multi 2.75 .75
**712** A203 300fr multi 4.50 1.25
**713** A203 400fr multi 5.75 1.60
*a.* Souvenir sheet of 2, #713 14.50 3.50
*Nos. 710-713 (4)* 14.40 4.00

Partridge — A204

Bongo Antelope — A204a

15fr, Turtle dove. 20fr, Swallow. 300fr, Black colobus.

**1982 *Perf. 12½x13***

**714** A204 10fr shown 2.50 .40
**715** A204 15fr multi 3.00 .85
**716** A204 20fr multi 5.50 1.10
**717** A204a 200fr shown 3.00 .80
**718** A204a 300fr multi 4.00 1.25
*Nos. 714-718 (5)* 18.00 4.40

Issued: 200fr, 300fr, July 20; others Aug. 10.
See No. 804.

Scouting Year — A205

**1982, Sept. 30 Litho. *Perf. 13x12½***

**719** A205 200fr Campfire 2.50 .80
**720** A205 400fr Baden-Powell 4.50 1.60

25th Anniv. of the Presbyterian Church in Cameroun A206

45fr, Buea Chapel. 60fr, Nyasoso Chapel, vert.

**1982, Oct. 30 *Perf. 13x12½, 12½x13***

**721** A206 45fr multi .55 .25
**722** A206 60fr multi .65 .25

ITU Plenipotentiaries Conference, Nairobi, Sept. — A207

**1982, Oct. 5 Litho. *Perf. 12½x13***

**723** A207 70fr multicolored .70 .25

Italy's Victory in 1982 World Cup A208

**1982, Nov. *Perf. 13***

**724** A208 500fr multicolored 5.50 2.00
**725** A208 1000fr multicolored 10.50 4.00

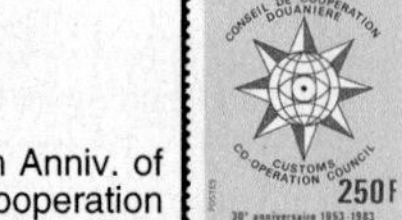

30th Anniv. of Customs Cooperation Council — A209

No. 726, Emblem. No. 727, Headquarters, Brussels.

**1983, Jan. 10 *Perf. 12½x13***

**726** A209 250fr multicolored 2.25 .80
**727** A209 250fr multicolored 2.25 .80

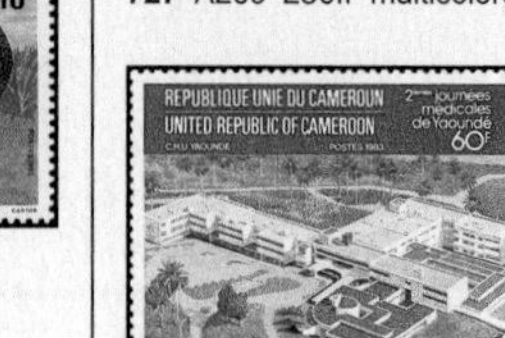

2nd Yaoundé Medical Conference A210

**1983, Jan. 23 Litho. *Perf. 13***

**728** A210 60fr grn & multi .70 .25
**729** A210 70fr brn & multi .90 .25

**City Hall Type of 1982**

**1983, Feb. 25 Litho. *Perf. 12½***

**730** A202 60fr Bafoussam .60 .25
**731** A202 70fr Garoua .70 .30

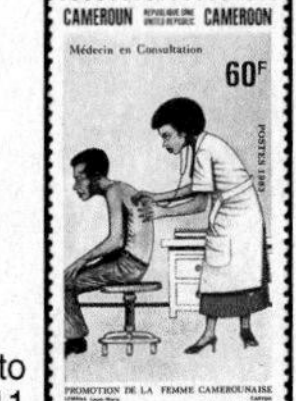

Homage to Women — A211

**1983, Apr. 25 Litho. *Perf. 12½***

**733** A211 60fr Nurse .75 .25
**734** A211 70fr Lawyer .75 .25

11th Anniv. of Independence — A212

Flag and Pres. Paul Biya.

**1983, May 18 Litho. *Perf. 13***

**735** A212 60fr dk grn & multi .55 .25
**736** A212 70fr dk bl & multi .70 .30

25th Anniv. of Intl. Maritime Org. — A213

**1983, May 23 *Perf. 13x12½***

**737** A213 500fr multicolored 5.50 1.50

Eagle — A214

**1983, June 15 Litho. *Perf. 12½x13***

**738** A214 25fr shown 1.50 .40
**739** A214 30fr Sparrowhawk 2.50 .75
**740** A214 50fr Purple heron 4.50 1.00
*Nos. 738-740 (3)* 8.50 2.15

See Nos. 798-800, 873, 882, 886.

A215

60fr, Pearl mask, by Wery-Nwen-Nto, 1899. 70fr, Basket with lid.

**1983, July 25 Litho. *Perf. 12***
**741** A215 60fr multicolored .70 .25
**742** A215 70fr multicolored .90 .30

A216

90fr, Mobile Post Office, horiz. 150fr, Telegraph Operator. 250fr, Tom-tom.

**1983, Aug. 20 Litho. *Perf. 12***
**743** A216 90fr multicolored .90 .25
**744** A216 150fr multicolored 1.40 .35
**745** A216 250fr multicolored 2.75 .55
*Nos. 743-745 (3)* 5.05 1.15

World Communications Year.

Endangered Species A217

**1983, Sept. 22 *Perf. 12***
**746** A217 200fr Civet Cat 2.75 .50
**747** A217 200fr Gorilla, vert 2.75 .50
**748** A217 350fr Cobaya, vert 4.50 1.25
*Nos. 746-748 (3)* 10.00 2.25

See No. 887.

Lake Tizon A218

**1983, Nov. 25 Litho. *Perf. 13***
**749** A218 60fr shown .55 .25
**750** A218 70fr Mt. Cameroon .70 .25

Human Rights Declaration, 35th Anniv — A219

**1983, Dec. 20 Litho. *Perf. 12½x13***
**751** A219 60fr multicolored .55 .25
**752** A219 70fr multicolored .70 .25

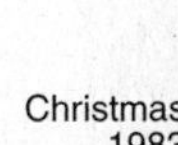

Christmas 1983 A220

60fr, Christmas tree. 200fr, Stained glass window, Yaoundé Cathedral. No. 755, Rest during Flight into Egypt, by Philipp Otto Runge. No. 756, Angel of the Annunciation. 60fr, 200fr, No. 756 vert.

**1983, Dec. 20 Litho. *Perf. 12½***
**753** A220 60fr multicolored .45 .25
**754** A220 200fr multicolored 1.75 .50
**755** A220 500fr multicolored 4.50 1.25
**756** A220 500fr multicolored 4.50 1.25
*a.* Souvenir sheet of 3, #754-756 12.50 12.50
*Nos. 753-756 (4)* 11.20 3.25

### City Hall Type of 1982

**1984, Apr. 20 Litho. *Perf. 12½***
**757** A202 60fr Bamenda .55 .25
**758** A202 70fr Mbalmayo .70 .25

Catholic Church, Zoetele A221

70fr, Protestant Church, Yaounde.

**1984, July 25 Litho. *Perf. 13***
**759** A221 60fr shown .55 .25
**760** A221 70fr multicolored .70 .25

Endangered Species — A222

**1984, Aug. 15**
**761** A222 250fr Wild pig 3.50 .75
**762** A222 250fr Deer 3.50 .75

**1984, Oct. 10 Litho. *Perf. 13½***
**763** A222 60fr Nightingale 4.50 1.00
**764** A222 60fr Vultures 4.50 1.00

See No. 883.

Bamenda Farming Fair — A223

**1984, Dec. 10 Litho. *Perf. 13***
**765** A223 60fr Corn .60 .25
**766** A223 70fr Cattle .90 .25
**767** A223 300fr Potatoes 3.50 .90
*Nos. 765-767 (3)* 5.00 1.40

International Civil Aviation Organization, 40th Anniv. — A224

No. 768, Icarus. No. 769, ICAO emblem, vert. No. 770, Boeing 747. No. 771, Solar Princess painting.

**1984, Dec. 20 Litho. *Perf. 12½***
**768** A224 200fr multi 1.75 .60
**769** A224 200fr multi 1.75 .60
**770** A224 300fr multi 2.75 .90
**771** A224 300fr multi 3.25 .90
*Nos. 768-771 (4)* 9.50 3.00

Olymphilex '85, Lausanne A225

150fr, Wrestlers, exhibition emblem.

**Wmk. 385**

**1985, Apr. 5 Photo. *Perf. 13***
**772** A225 150fr multicolored 1.50 .40

Domestic Musical Instruments — A226

60fr, Balafons (xylophone). 70fr, Guitar. 100fr, Flute.

**1985, Apr. 23 *Perf. 13½***
**773** A226 60fr multicolored .65 .25
**774** A226 70fr multicolored .80 .25
**775** A226 100fr multicolored 1.10 .30
*Nos. 773-775 (3)* 2.55 .80

INTELSAT Org., 20th Anniv. A227

125fr, Intelsat V. 200fr, Intelcam, Yaounde.

**1985, May 8 *Perf. 13***
**776** A227 125fr multicolored 1.60 .35
**777** A227 200fr multicolored 2.10 .60

New York Headquarters A228

**1985, May 30**
**778** A228 250fr multicolored 2.40 1.10
**779** A228 500fr multicolored 4.50 2.25

UN, 40th anniv.

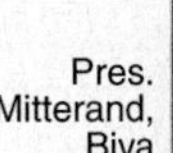

Pres. Mitterand, Biya A229

**1985, June 20**
**780** A229 60fr multicolored 2.25 .25
**781** A229 70fr multicolored 2.50 .25

Visit of Pres. Mitterand of France.

UNICEF — A230

UN Infant Survival Campaign A231

**1985, July 15**
**782** A230 60fr multicolored .55 .25
**783** A231 300fr multicolored 2.75 1.00

Visit of Pope John Paul II, Aug. 10-14 — A232

60fr, Pope, papal arms. 70fr, Pope, crosier. 200fr, Pres. Biya, John Paul II.

**1985, Aug. 9 *Perf. 13x12½***
**784** A232 60fr multi 1.10 .40
**785** A232 70fr multi 1.25 .55

**Size: 55x38mm**

**786** A232 200fr multi 4.00 2.25
*a.* Souv. sheet of 3, #784-786 8.00 8.00
*Nos. 784-786 (3)* 6.35 3.20

Landscapes A233

60fr, Lake Barumbi, Kumba. 70fr, Bonando Pygmy Village, Doume. 150fr, Cameroun River.

**1985, July 25 Litho. *Perf. 12½***
**787** A233 60fr multicolored .70 .25
**788** A233 70fr multicolored .70 .25
**789** A233 150fr multicolored 1.40 .40
*Nos. 787-789 (3)* 2.80 .90

### City Hall Type of 1982

**1985, July 30**
**790** A202 60fr Ngaoundere .55 .25
**791** A202 60fr D'Ebolowa .55 .25

Wildlife — A234

**1985, Aug. 20 *Perf. 13½***
**792** A234 125fr Porcupine 1.50 .40
**793** A234 200fr Squirrel 2.50 .60
**794** A234 350fr Hedgehog 4.00 1.10
*Nos. 792-794 (3)* 8.00 2.10

Wood Sculptures — A235

60fr, Mask. 70fr, Mask, diff. 100fr, Wood bas-relief, horiz.

**1985, Sept. 15**
**795** A235 60fr multicolored .65 .25
**796** A235 70fr multicolored .90 .25
**797** A235 100fr multicolored 1.25 .30
*Nos. 795-797 (3)* 2.80 .80

### Bird Type of 1983 Redrawn

140fr, Toucans. 150fr, Rooster. 200fr, Red-throated bee-eater.

**1985, Nov. 10**
**798** A214 140fr multicolored 2.25 .50
**799** A214 150fr multicolored 2.25 .55
**800** A214 200fr multicolored 3.25 .70
*Nos. 798-800 (3)* 7.75 1.75

Nos. 798-800 inscribed "Republic of Cameroon".

See No. 873. For surcharge see No. 871.

American Peace Corps in Cameroun, 25th Anniv. A237

**1986, Jan. 1 Litho. *Perf. 12½***
**801** A237 70fr multicolored .70 .25
**802** A237 100fr multicolored 1.00 .30

### Stamps of 1979-1982 Redrawn

**1986, Mar. *Perf. 13, 13½***
**803** A174 5fr multicolored .35 .35
**804** A204 10fr multicolored .35 .35

Nos. 803-804 inscribed "Republic of Cameroon" instead of "United Republic of Cameroon."

Easter — A238

Paintings: 210fr, Head of the Virgin, by Pierre-Paul Prud'Hon (1758-1823). 350fr, The Stoning of St. Steven, by Van Scorel (1495-1562).

**1986, Apr. 15** *Perf. 13½*

| | | | | |
|---|---|---|---|---|
| **805** | A238 | 210fr multicolored | 1.75 | .60 |
| **806** | A238 | 350fr multicolored | 3.00 | 1.00 |

Insects — A239

**1986, Apr. 20**

| | | | | |
|---|---|---|---|---|
| **807** | A239 | 70fr Honeybee | 1.75 | .40 |
| **808** | A239 | 70fr Dragonfly | 1.75 | .40 |
| **809** | A239 | 100fr Grasshopper | 2.50 | .65 |
| | | *Nos. 807-809 (3)* | 6.00 | 1.45 |

Nos. 808-809 horiz.

Flags, Conference Center A240

**1986, Apr. 25** **Litho.** *Perf. 13*

| | | | | |
|---|---|---|---|---|
| **810** | A240 | 100fr Map, vert. | 1.00 | .30 |
| **811** | A240 | 175fr shown | 2.00 | .60 |

Conference of Ministers of the Economic Commission for Africa, Apr. 9-29.

Statues — A241

70fr, Bronze earth mother. 100fr, Wood funerary figure. 130fr, Wood equestrian figure.

**1986, July 5** **Litho.** *Perf. 13½*

| | | | | |
|---|---|---|---|---|
| **812** | A241 | 70fr multicolored | .85 | .25 |
| **813** | A241 | 100fr multicolored | .95 | .30 |
| **814** | A241 | 130fr multicolored | 1.60 | .40 |
| | | *Nos. 812-814 (3)* | 3.40 | .95 |

Queen Elizabeth II, 60th Birthday A242

100fr, Elizabeth. 175fr, Elizabeth, Pres. Biya. 210fr, Elizabeth, diff.

**1986, July 15** **Litho.** *Perf. 13*

| | | | | |
|---|---|---|---|---|
| **815** | A242 | 100fr multicolored | 1.00 | .40 |
| **816** | A242 | 175fr multicolored | 1.40 | .60 |
| **817** | A242 | 210fr multicolored | 2.00 | .75 |
| | | *Nos. 815-817 (3)* | 4.40 | 1.75 |

Natl. Democratic Party, 1st Anniv. A243

No. 818, Party headquarters, Bamenda. No. 819, Pres. Biya, vert. No. 820, Presidential address, vert.

**1986, July 25** *Perf. 12½*

| | | | | |
|---|---|---|---|---|
| **818** | A243 | 70fr multicolored | .70 | .25 |
| **819** | A243 | 70fr multicolored | .70 | .25 |
| **820** | A243 | 100fr multicolored | 1.00 | .35 |
| | | *Nos. 818-820 (3)* | 2.40 | .85 |

Kwem Mask Dancers of the Northeast — A244

**1986, Aug. 1** *Perf. 13½*

| | | | | |
|---|---|---|---|---|
| **821** | A244 | 100fr multicolored | 1.00 | .35 |
| **822** | A244 | 130fr multicolored | 1.25 | .45 |

Endangered Species — A245

**1986, Aug. 20**

| | | | | |
|---|---|---|---|---|
| **823** | | 300fr Varanus niloticus | 3.50 | 1.00 |
| **824** | | 300fr Panthera pardus | 3.50 | 1.00 |

For surcharge see No. 872.

A246

Intl. Peace Year: 175fr, 200fr, Desmond Tutu, South Africa, Nobel Peace Prize winner. 250fr, UN and IPY emblems.

**1986, Sept. 7** **Litho.** *Perf. 13½*

| | | | | |
|---|---|---|---|---|
| **825** | A246 | 175fr multicolored | 1.75 | 1.10 |
| **826** | A246 | 200fr multicolored | 2.00 | 1.25 |
| **827** | A246 | 250fr multicolored | 2.50 | 1.50 |
| | | *Nos. 825-827 (3)* | 6.25 | 3.85 |

A247

**1986, Oct. 30** **Litho.** *Perf. 13½*

| | | | | |
|---|---|---|---|---|
| **828** | A247 | 70fr multicolored | .65 | .25 |

Natl. Fed. of Associations for the Handicapped.

African Vaccination Year — A248

70fr, Family under umbrella. 100fr, Child immunization.

**1986, Nov. 9**

| | | | | |
|---|---|---|---|---|
| **829** | A248 | 70fr multicolored | .90 | .25 |
| **830** | A248 | 100fr multicolored | 1.10 | .35 |

Arbor Day — A249

70fr, Afforestation map. 100fr, Hands, seedling.

**1986, Dec. 20** **Litho.** *Perf. 13½*

| | | | | |
|---|---|---|---|---|
| **831** | A249 | 70fr multicolored | .90 | .25 |
| **832** | A249 | 100fr multicolored | 1.10 | .35 |

Agricultural Development A250

No. 833, ONCPB seminar. No. 834, Coconut farming, Dibombari. No. 835, Pineapple farm.

**1986, Dec. 24**

| | | | | |
|---|---|---|---|---|
| **833** | A250 | 70fr multicolored | .75 | .40 |
| **834** | A250 | 70fr multicolored | .75 | .40 |
| **835** | A250 | 200fr multicolored | 2.00 | 1.10 |
| | | *Nos. 833-835 (3)* | 3.50 | 1.90 |

Insects Destructive to Agriculture A251

70fr, Antestiopsis lineaticollis intricata. 100fr, Distantiella theobroma.

**1987, Sept. 25** **Litho.** *Perf. 13½*

| | | | | |
|---|---|---|---|---|
| **836** | A251 | 70fr multicolored | 1.50 | .50 |
| **837** | A251 | 100fr multicolored | 2.00 | .70 |

4th African Games, Nairobi A252

**1987, Oct. 1** *Perf. 12½*

| | | | | |
|---|---|---|---|---|
| **838** | A252 | 100fr Shot put | .90 | .70 |
| **839** | A252 | 140fr Pole vault | 1.25 | 1.00 |

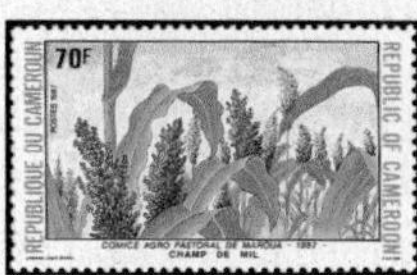

Maroua Agricultural Show A253

**1988, Jan. 6**

| | | | | |
|---|---|---|---|---|
| **840** | A253 | 70fr Millet field | .90 | .50 |
| **841** | A253 | 100fr Cotton | 1.10 | .70 |
| **842** | A253 | 150fr Cattle | 1.60 | 1.10 |
| | | *Nos. 840-842 (3)* | 3.60 | 2.30 |

World Wildlife Fund A254

Baboons, Papio leucophaeus: 30fr, Adult. 40fr, Adult grooming young. 70fr, Baboon on branch. 100fr, Adult carrying young.

**1988, Apr. 25** **Litho.** *Perf. 13*

| | | | | |
|---|---|---|---|---|
| **843** | A254 | 30fr multicolored | 1.75 | .75 |
| **844** | A254 | 40fr multicolored | 2.25 | .75 |
| **845** | A254 | 70fr multicolored | 3.50 | 1.25 |
| **846** | A254 | 100fr multicolored | 6.00 | 1.75 |
| | | *Nos. 843-846 (4)* | 13.50 | 4.50 |

Interparliamentary Union, Cent. — A255

**1989** **Litho.** *Perf. 13½*

| | | | | |
|---|---|---|---|---|
| **847** | A255 | 50fr Natl. Assembly | .60 | .30 |

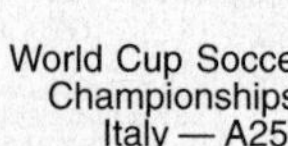

World Cup Soccer Championships, Italy — A256

No. 849, Players, diff. No. 850, Goalkeeper, flags. No. 851, Team.

**1990, Oct. 27** **Litho.** *Perf. 11½*

**Granite Paper**

| | | | | |
|---|---|---|---|---|
| **848** | A256 | 200fr shown | 1.75 | 1.00 |
| **849** | A256 | 250fr multicolored | 2.25 | 1.25 |
| **850** | A256 | 250fr multicolored | 2.25 | 1.25 |
| **851** | A256 | 300fr multicolored | 3.00 | 1.50 |
| *a.* | | Souv. sheet of 4, #848-851 | 9.00 | 6.50 |
| | | *Nos. 848-851 (4)* | 9.25 | 5.00 |

Roger Milla, World Cup Soccer Player — A257

**1990, July 4** **Litho.** *Perf. 11½*

**Granite Paper**

| | | | | |
|---|---|---|---|---|
| **852** | A257 | 500fr multicolored | 6.50 | 3.50 |
| *a.* | | Souv. sheet of 1 | 9.00 | 6.00 |

Agriculture A258

70fr, Treating cacao plants. 100fr, Sheep.

**1990, Dec. 1** **Litho.** *Perf. 13½*

| | | | | |
|---|---|---|---|---|
| **853** | A258 | 70fr multicolored | 1.25 | .55 |
| **854** | A258 | 100fr multicolored | 1.75 | .80 |
| *a.* | | Sheet of 2, #853-854, perf. 12½ | 8.00 | 8.00 |

For surcharges see Nos. 894-895.

UN Development Program, 40th Anniv. — A259

**1990, Dec. 31** **Litho.** *Perf. 13½*

| | | | | |
|---|---|---|---|---|
| **855** | A259 | 50fr multicolored | .60 | .40 |

Intl. Literacy Year — A260

**1990, Dec. 31**

| | | | | |
|---|---|---|---|---|
| **856** | A260 | 200fr bl, blk, & lt bl | 2.00 | .75 |

Independence, 30th Anniv. — A261

1000fr, Flag, Palace, #336.

**1991, Jan. 1** *Perf. 13*

| | | | | |
|---|---|---|---|---|
| **857** | A261 | 150fr shown | 1.75 | 1.25 |
| **858** | A261 | 1000fr multi | 9.00 | 8.00 |
| *a.* | | Souv. sheet. of 2, #857-858 | 12.50 | 12.50 |

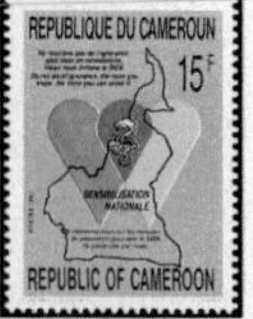

A262

Fight Against AIDS — A262a

**1991, Jan. 15**

**859** A262 15fr Hearts, map, vert. .25 .25
**860** A262a25fr shown .35 .25

See Nos. 884-885.

Birds — A263

Designs: Nos. 861, 864, Pie grieche, vert. Nos. 862, 863, Picathartes chauve.

**1991, May 3** **Litho.** ***Perf. 13½***

**861** A263 70fr grn & multi .75 .35
**862** A263 70fr bl & multi .75 .40
**863** A263 300fr blk & multi 3.25 2.00
**864** A263 350fr blk & multi 3.50 2.25
*a.* Souv. sheet of 2, #863-864 9.00 5.50
*Nos. 861-864 (4)* 8.25 5.00

Wild Animals — A264

**1991, May 8** ***Perf. 13½***

**865** A264 125fr Elephant 1.60 1.00
**866** A264 250fr Water buffalo 3.00 2.00
*a.* Souvenir sheet of 2, #865-866, perf. 12½ 9.00 3.50

**City Hall Type of 1982 Redrawn**

**1991** ***Perf. 13***

**867** A202 40fr multicolored .60 .25

No. 867 inscribed "Republic of Cameroon" instead of "United Republic of Cameroon."

Cameroun Catholic Church, Cent. (in 1990) — A265

125fr, Mvolye church. 250fr, Akono church.

**1991, Dec. 8** **Litho.** ***Perf. 13½***

**868** A265 125fr multicolored 1.25 .75
*a.* Booklet pane of 4 7.00 —
Complete booklet, #868a 7.00
**869** A265 250fr multicolored 2.25 1.75
*a.* Souvenir sheet of 2, #868-869 perf. 12½x13 4.00 3.00
*b.* Booklet pane of 4 10.00 —
Complete booklet, #869a 10.00

Issued: Nos. 868a, 869b, 1993.

Intl. Savings Banks Institute, 7th Meeting of the African Group — A266

**1991, Dec. 9**

**870** A266 250fr multicolored 2.40 1.60
*a.* Souv. sheet of 1, perf. 12½x13 3.00 2.00

No. 799 Surcharged

No. 824 Surcharged

**1992** ***Perf. 13½***

**871** A214 20fr on 150fr #799 1.75 .25
**872** A245 70fr on 300fr #824 5.75 .55

**Bird Type of 1983**

**1992** **Litho.** ***Perf. 13½***

**873** A214 125fr like #800 1.50 .95

Dated 1985.

Cameroun Soccer League — A267

125fr, Mbappe Mbappe Samuel (1936-85), soccer player, vert. 250fr, Linafoote League emblem, vert. 400fr, Linafoote emblem, diff. 500fr, Stadium.

**1992, Aug.** ***Perf. 11½***

**874** A267 125fr multicolored 1.25 .75
**875** A267 250fr multicolored 2.40 1.75
**876** A267 400fr multicolored 3.50 2.75
**877** A267 500fr multicolored 5.50 3.50
*Nos. 874-877 (4)* 12.65 8.75

See Nos. 896-896B.

Discovery of America, 500th Anniv. — A268

Columbus and: 125fr, Fleet of ships. 250fr, Landing in New World. 400fr, Meeting with natives. 500fr, Map, ships.

**1992, Aug.**

**878** A268 125fr multicolored 1.40 .75
**879** A268 250fr multicolored 2.10 1.75
**880** A268 400fr multicolored 3.50 2.75
**881** A268 500fr multicolored 5.00 3.50
*Nos. 878-881 (4)* 12.00 8.75

**Types of 1983-84 Redrawn**

**1992** **Litho.** ***Perf. 13½***

**882** A214 200fr like #739 2.25 1.40
*a.* Booklet pane of 5
Complete booklet, #882a
**883** A222 350fr like #763 3.75 2.50

Nos. 882-883 inscribed "Republic of Cameroon".

**AIDS Type of 1991**

**1993** **Litho.** ***Perf. 13½***

**884** A262 100fr like #859 1.10 .70
**885** A262 175fr like #860 1.90 1.25

**Types of 1983 Redrawn**

**886** A214 370fr like #738 3.50 2.50

***Perf. 13***

**887** A217 410fr like #746 4.50 2.90

Nos. 886-887 inscribed "Republic of Cameroon".

**Wild Animal Type of 1980 Redrawn**

125fr, Crocodile. 250fr, Buffon's antelope, vert.

**1993** **Litho.** ***Serpentine Die Cut 9½***
**Booklet Stamps**
**Self-Adhesive**

**888** A186 125fr multicolored 1.40 .65
*a.* Booklet pane of 4 5.75
**889** A186 250fr multicolored 2.75 1.25
*a.* Booklet pane of 4 11.50

Nos. 888-889 inscribed "Republic of Cameroon".

By their nature, Nos. 888a, 889a are complete booklets. The peelable backing serves as a booklet cover.

1994 World Cup Soccer Championships, US — A270

Designs: 125fr, Pres. Paul Biya holding soccer ball, lion. 250fr, Logo, lion, player, map. 450fr, Players, globe, World Cup, flag. 500fr, US eagle, Cameroun lion, soccer ball.

**1994, Mar. 28** **Litho.** ***Perf. 13***

**890** A270 125fr multicolored .75 .40
**891** A270 250fr multicolored 1.50 .75
**892** A270 450fr multicolored 2.75 1.50
**893** A270 500fr multicolored 3.00 1.75
*a.* Min. sheet of 4, #890-893 55.00 40.00
*Nos. 890-893 (4)* 8.00 4.40

Nos. 853-854 Srchd. in Gold and Black

**1993** **Litho.** ***Perf. 13½***

**894** A258 125fr on 70fr #853 — 6.00
**895** A258 125fr on 100fr #854 — —
*a.* With gold obliterator, new denomination in black omitted 65.00 —

**Cameroun Soccer League Type of 1992**

**1992-93** **Litho.** ***Perf. 11½***

**896** A267 10fr like #876 — —
**896A** A267 25fr like #875 — —
**896B** A267 50fr like #874 — —

Nos. 896-896A dated 1993.
Issued: 50fr, 8/1/92; others, 1993.

Psittacus Erithacus — A271

**1995** **Litho.** ***Perf. 11½***
**Granite Paper**

**897** A271 125fr multicolored 3.00 1.00

Visit of Pope John Paul II — A272

125fr, Pope, open text, cross.

**1995, Sept. 14** ***Perf. 12½***

**898** A272 55fr shown .35 .25
*a.* Souvenir sheet of 1 — —
**899** A272 125fr multicolored .95 .50
*a.* Souvenir sheet of 1 — —

UN, 50th Anniv. — A273

**1995, Oct. 24** ***Perf. 11½***

**900** A273 200fr shown 1.25 .60
**901** A273 250fr "50," people 1.50 .80

Conf. of Heads of State & Govt., Yaounde — A274

***Perf. 12½, 14¾x14 (200fr, 250fr)***

**1996-97** **Litho.**

**902** A274 125fr blue & multi 1.00 .50
*c.* A274 125fr Perf. 14¾x14 — .75
**902A** A274 200fr lt grn & multi ('97) 1.50 .75
**902B** A274 250fr yel & multi ('97) 2.00 1.00
**903** A274 410fr pink & multi, vert. 3.00 2.00

No. 902c is dated "1997."

World Records Set at 1996 Summer Olympic Games, Atlanta — A275

125fr, Baily, M. Johnson. 250fr, Harrison, Galfione, Perec, vert.

**1996** ***Perf. 11½***

**904** A275 125fr multi — 1.50
**905** A275 250fr multi — 2.00

Universal Declaration of Human Rights, 50th Anniv. — A279

**1998** **Litho.** ***Perf. 14x14¾***

**918** A279 370fr multicolored 6.00 2.00

1998 World Cup Soccer Championships, France — A280

Design: 125fr, Flag of Cameroun, World Cup trophy, vert.

**1998** **Litho.** ***Perf. 13***

**922** A280 125fr multicolored — 2.00
**923** A280 250fr multicolored 7.00 2.50

Shrike — A281

**1998** **Litho.** ***Perf. 13x13½***

**926** A281 125fr multicolored 22.50 2.00

Economic and Monetary Community of Central Africa Week — A281a

Design: 125fr, Flags surrounding map of Africa. 225fr, Flags above map of Africa.

**1999** **Litho.** ***Perf. 14½***

**927** A281a 125fr multi — —
**928** A281a 225fr multi — —

Flora & Fauna — A282

**2000** **Litho.** ***Perf. 14x14½***

**929** A282 100fr Pineapple 11.00 2.00
**930** A282 125fr Pineapple — 2.00
**930A** A282 150fr Coffee beans 12.00 3.00
**930B** A282 175fr Crowned crane — —
**931** A282 200fr Baboon 20.00 2.00
**932** A282 250fr Coffee beans 12.00 2.00
**934** A282 410fr Crowned crane 20.00 2.00

Dated 1998.

Peace, Work, Country A283

Map and Scenes A284

Airplane and Wildlife — A285

**2000 Litho. *Perf. 11¾***

**935** A283 125fr multi *20.00 2.00*
**936** A284 200fr multi *20.00 2.00*
**937** A285 250fr multi *20.00 2.00*

Palais des Congrés, Yaounde — A286

***Perf. 11¾x11½***

**2001, Mar. 26 Litho.**

**938** A286 125fr multi — —

Cooperation between Cameroun and People's Republic of China, 30th anniv.

Campaign Against AIDS — A287

Design: 125fr, Woman vaccinating child, Chantal Biya Foundation emblem. 250fr, Chantal Biya Foundation emblem, globe, ribbon, woman with fetus.

**2001 Litho. *Perf. 13¼x13***

**939** A287 125fr multi *12.50 4.00*
**941** A287 250fr multi *12.50 4.00*
*a.* Souvenir sheet, #939, 941 *150.00* —

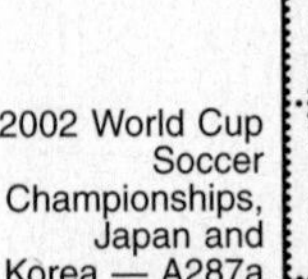

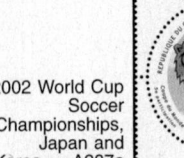

2002 World Cup Soccer Championships, Japan and Korea — A287a

Indomitable Lions Soccer Team, 20th Anniv. of Success — A288

**2002, June 20 Litho. *Perf. 13¾***

**943** A287a 125fr multi *50.00 3.00*

***Perf. 13x13¼***

**944** A288 250fr multi *50.00 3.00*

**Souvenir Sheet**

**945** Sheet of 2, #943, 945a *100.00* —
*a.* As #944, 40x44mm, perf. 13½ — —

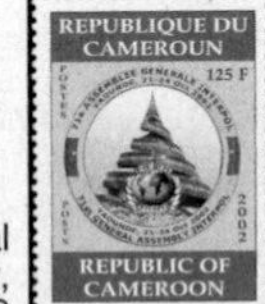

71st Interpol General Assembly, Yaounde — A289

**2002 Litho. *Perf. 13¼x13***

**946** A289 125fr multi *11.00* —
*a.* Souvenir sheet of 1 *27.50* —

Cooperation Between Cameroun and Japan A290

**2005 Litho. *Perf. 13***

**948** A290 100fr multi *20.00 1.50*
*a.* "Postes 2005" *12.00 1.00*
**949** A290 125fr multi *20.00 1.50*
*a.* "Postes 2005" *12.00 1.00*
**950** A290 200fr multi *20.00 1.50*
*a.* "Postes 2005" *12.00 1.00*
**951** A290 250fr multi *15.00 1.50*
*a.* "Postes 2005" *12.00 1.00*
**952** A290 370fr multi — —
**953** A290 410fr multi *12.00 2.00*
**954** A290 500fr multi *21.00 3.50*
*a.* "Postes 2005" *12.00 2.00*
**955** A290 1000fr multi *28.00 6.50*
*a.* "Postes 2005" *12.00 4.00*

---

Cameroun postal officials have declared as illegal a stamp inscribed "Republic of Cameroun" dated "2005" marking the 70th birthday of Elvis Presley.

---

Postal Savings Bank — A291

**2006 Litho. *Perf. 15x14***

**956** A291 500fr multi — —

No. 956 was issued in 1997 as a stamp to pay fees for opening an account with the Postal Savings Bank. It was made available for postal use in 2006.

Visit of Pope Benedict XVI to Cameroun A292

Flags of Vatican City and Cameroun, Pope Benedict XVI, Pres. Paul Biya and background color of: 200fr, Yellow. 250fr, Bright pink.

**2009 Litho. *Perf. 13x13¼***

**957-958** A292 Set of 2 6.00 3.00

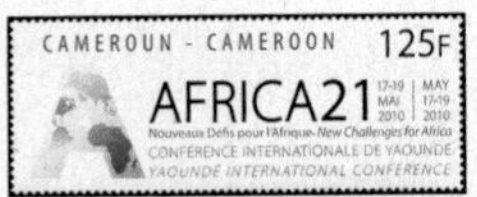

New Challenges for Africa Conference, Yaounde — A293

Colors: 125fr, Black & gray. 250fr, Multicolored.

**2010 Litho. *Perf. 13½***

**959-960** A293 Set of 2 *5.75* —

Reunification and Independence, 50th Anniv. — A294

Designs: 125fr, Cameroun flag shown rotated 90 degrees clockwise. 200fr, 50th anniversary emblem. 250fr, Arms of Cameroun. 500fr, Pres. Paul Biya in black. 1000fr, Pres. Biya in color.

**2010**

**961-964** A294 Set of 4 *20.00 9.00*
*964a* Horiz. strip of 4, #961-964 *20.00* —
*964b* Booklet pane of 8, 2 each #961-964 *40.00* —
Complete booklet, #964b *40.00*

**Souvenir Sheet**

**965** A294 1000fr multi *20.00* —

No. 965 sold for 1500fr.

A295

Designs: 125fr, Workers digging trenches for optical fibers. 200fr, Gynecological, Obstetrics and Pediatric Hospital, Yaounde. 250fr, Multi-purpose Sports Complex, Yaounde. 500fr, Cameroun Pres. Paul Biya and Chinese Pres. Hu Jintao shaking hands.

**2011, Mar. 26 *Perf. 12***

**966-969** A295 Set of 4 *20.00 8.00*
*968a* Souvenir sheet of 3, #966-968 *15.00* —

Diplomatic Relations Between Cameroun and People's Republic of China, 25th Anniv. See Nos. 975-976.

First Douala-Paris Camair-Co Flight — A296

**Litho. & Embossed**

**2011, Mar. 28 *Perf. 13x13¼***

**Denomination Color**

**970** A296 250fr green *8.00 3.00*
**971** A296 500fr white *8.00 3.00*
*a.* Souvenir sheet of 2, #970-971 *20.00* —

Discovery of AIDS and HIV, 30th Anniv. — A297

Designs: 100fr, Emblem of Cameroun National Committee for the Campaign Against AIDS. 250fr, AIDS ribbon, map of Africa. 500fr, Chantal Biya, First Lady of Cameroun and founder of Synergies Africaines charity.

**2011, June 3 Litho.**

**972-974** A297 Set of 3 *11.00 6.00*

**Diplomatic Relations Type of 2011**

Souvenir Sheets

Design as before.

**2011, Sept. 14 Litho. *Perf. 12***

**975** A295 500fr multi *15.00* —

**Litho. With Three-Dimensional Plastic Affixed**

**Without Gum**

**976** A295 500fr multi *30.00* —

No. 975 contains one 60x40mm stamp. No. 976 contains one 76x50mm stamp.

E-Post Data Center — A298

**2014, July 21 Litho. *Perf. 13x13¼***

**Panel Color**

**977** A298 70fr yellow *1.50 1.50*
**978** A298 250fr black *1.50 1.50*

EMS Emblem, Sprinter, Cameroun Post Office, Pyramid, Eiffel Tower and Statue of Liberty — A299

**2014, Aug. 18 Litho. *Perf. 13x13¼***

**Panel Color**

**979** A299 50fr white *1.50 1.50*
**980** A299 200fr dark blue *1.50 1.50*

A300

Reunification Monument, Buéa — A301

**2015 Litho. *Perf. 13***

**981** A300 100fr multi *6.00 3.00*

***Perf. 13x13¼***

**982** A301 125fr multi *6.00 3.00*

Values for No. 981 are for stamps with surrounding selvage.

Deep Water Port, Kribi — A302

**2015 Litho. *Perf. 13¼x13***

**983** A302 500fr multi *6.00 3.00*

---

## SEMI-POSTAL STAMPS

**Curie Issue**

Common Design Type

**1938 Unwmk. *Perf. 13***

**B1** CD80 1.75fr + 50c brt ultra 10.00 10.00

**French Revolution Issue**

Common Design Type

**Photogravure; Name and Value Typographed in Black**

**1939**

**B2** CD83 45c + 25c green 11.50 11.50
**B3** CD83 70c + 30c brown 11.50 11.50
**B4** CD83 90c + 35c red org 11.50 11.50
**B5** CD83 1.25fr + 1fr rose pink 11.50 11.50
**B6** CD83 2.25fr + 2fr blue 14.00 14.00
*Nos. B2-B6 (5)* 60.00 60.00

Stamps of 1925-33 Srchd. in Black

**1940 *Perf. 14x13½***

**B7** A7 1.25fr + 2fr gray & dp bl 32.50 24.00
**B8** A7 1.75fr + 3fr brn & org 32.50 24.00
**B9** A7 2fr + 5fr dl grn & brn org 32.50 24.00
*Nos. B7-B9 (3)* 97.50 72.00

The surtax was used for war relief work.

Regular Stamps of 1939 Surcharged in Black

**1940 *Perf. 13***

**B10** A20 25c + 5fr blk brn 130.00 110.00
**B11** A20 45c + 5fr slate grn 130.00 110.00
**B12** A20 60c + 5fr peacock bl 130.00 120.00
**B13** A20 70c + 5fr plum 130.00 120.00
*Nos. B10-B13 (4)* 520.00 460.00

The surtax was used to purchase Spitfire planes for the Free French army.

**Common Design Type and**

Military Doctor SP2

Cameroun Militiaman SP4

**1941 Photo. *Perf. 13½***

**B13A** SP2 1fr + 1fr red 1.60
**B13B** CD86 1.50fr + 3fr maroon 1.60
**B13C** SP4 2.50fr + 1fr dk bl 1.60
*Nos. B13A-B13C (3)* 4.80

Nos. B13A-B13C were issued by the Vichy government in France, but were not placed on sale in Cameroun.

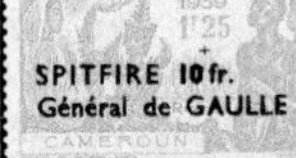

Nos. 223-224 Surcharged in Black or Blue

**1941** ***Perf. 12½x12***

**B14** CD82 1.25fr + 10fr car lake 120.00 120.00
**B15** CD82 2.25fr + 10fr ultra 120.00 120.00

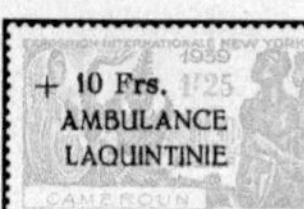


Nos. 223-224 Surcharged in Black or Blue

**1941**

**B16** CD82 1.25fr + 10fr car lake (Bl) 40.00 40.00
**B17** CD82 2.25fr + 10fr ultra (Bk) 40.00 40.00

The surtax was used to purchase ambulances for the Free French army.

Regular Stamps of 1933-39 Surcharged in Black

**1943** ***Perf. 14x13½, 13, 12½x12***

**B21** A7 1.25fr + 100 gray & dp bl 27.50 27.50
**B22** A21 1.25fr + 100fr car rose 27.50 27.50
**B23** CD82 1.25fr + 100fr car lake 27.50 27.50
**B24** A21 1.50fr + 100fr choc 27.50 27.50
**B25** CD82 2.25fr + 100fr ultra 27.50 27.50
*Nos. B21-B25 (5)* 137.50 137.50

Nos. 281A-281B Surcharged in Black or Red

**1944** **Engr.** ***Perf. 12½x12***

**B25A** 50c + 1.50fr on 2.50fr deep blue (R) .40
**B25B** + 2.50fr on 1fr green .40

Colonial Development Fund.

Nos. B25A-B25B were issued by the Vichy government in France, but were not placed on sale in Cameroun.

## Red Cross Issue

Common Design Type

**1944** **Photo.** ***Perf. 14½x14***

**B28** CD90 5fr + 20fr rose 2.00 1.60

The surtax was for the French Red Cross and national relief.

**Catalogue values for unused stamps in this section, from this point to the end of the section, are for Never Hinged items.**

## Tropical Medicine Issue

Common Design Type

**1950** **Engr.** ***Perf. 13***

**B29** CD100 10fr + 2fr dk bl grn & dk grn 7.25 5.50

The surtax was for charitable work.

## Independent State

Map and Flag — SP7

**Unwmk.**

**1961, Mar. 25** **Engr.** ***Perf. 13***

**B30** SP7 20fr + 5fr grn, car & yel 1.10 1.00
**B31** SP7 25fr + 10fr multi 1.40 1.25
**B32** SP7 30fr + 15fr car, yel & grn 2.00 1.75
*Nos. B30-B32 (3)* 4.50 4.00

The surtax was for the Red Cross.

## Federal Republic

Map of Cameroun, Lions Emblem and Physician Helping Leper — SP8

**1962, Jan. 28**

**B33** SP8 20fr + 5fr multi .70 .40
**B34** SP8 25fr + 10fr multi .90 .50
**B35** SP8 50fr + 15fr multi 1.75 .85
*Nos. B33-B35 (3)* 3.35 1.75

Issued for leprosy relief work.

## Anti-Malaria Issue

Common Design Type

**1962, Apr. 7** ***Perf. 12½x12***

**B36** CD108 25fr + 5fr rose lilac 1.00 .45

WHO drive to eradicate malaria.

## Freedom from Hunger Issue

Common Design Type

**1963, Mar. 21** **Engr.** ***Perf. 13***

**B37** CD112 18fr + 5fr multi 1.00 .35
**B38** CD112 25fr + 5fr multi 1.25 .40

Antelopes SP9

Designs: 125fr+10fr, Ourebia ourebi. 250fr+20fr, Kobus defassa.

**1991, Apr. 30** **Litho.** ***Perf. 13½x13***

**B39** SP9 125fr + 10fr multi 2.00 1.10
**B40** SP9 250fr + 20fr multi 3.00 2.25
*a.* Souvenir sheet of 2, #B39-B40, perf. 12½ 8.00 8.00

---

## AIR POST STAMPS

### Common Design Type

**1942** **Unwmk.** **Photo.** ***Perf. 14½x14***

**C1** CD87 1fr dk orange .30 .30
**C2** CD87 1.50fr brt red .30 .30
**C3** CD87 5fr brown red .65 .65
**C4** CD87 10fr black .80 .80
**C5** CD87 25fr ultra 1.10 1.10
**C6** CD87 50fr dk green 1.40 1.40
**C7** CD87 100fr plum 1.75 1.75
*Nos. C1-C7 (7)* 6.30 6.30

### Types AP9 and AP10 without "RF" and

Plane Over Coast — AP3

**1943-44** **Photo.** ***Perf. 13, 13½***

**C7A** AP9 25c brown red .25
**C7B** AP9 50c green .25
**C7C** AP9 1fr brt violet .30
**C7D** AP10 5fr red brown .55
**C7E** AP10 10fr black .65
**C7F** AP10 12fr orange .70
**C7G** AP10 20fr crimson .95
**C7H** AP10 50fr blue 1.10
**C7I** AP3 100fr lilac brown 1.25
*Nos. C7A-C7I (9)* 6.00

Nos. C7A to C7I were issued by the Vichy Government in France, but were not placed on sale in Cameroun.

For Types AP9 and AP10 inscribed RF, see Nos. C15-C24.

**Catalogue values for unused stamps in this section, from this point to the end of the section, are for Never Hinged items.**

## Victory Issue

Common Design Type

**1946, May 8** **Engr.** ***Perf. 12½***

**C8** CD92 8fr dk violet brn 1.60 1.20

European victory of the Allied Nations in WWII.

## Chad to Rhine Issue

Common Design Types

**1946, June 6**

**C9** CD93 5fr dk blue grn 1.60 1.25
**C10** CD94 10fr dk rose vio 1.60 1.25
**C11** CD95 15fr red 2.00 1.60
**C12** CD96 20fr brt blue 2.00 1.60
**C13** CD97 25fr orange red 2.10 1.75
**C14** CD98 50fr gray 2.75 2.25
*Nos. C9-C14 (6)* 12.05 9.70

Plane and Map AP9

Seaplane Alighting AP10

Plane and Freighters AP11

**1946** **Photo.** ***Perf. 13, 13½***

**C15** AP9 25c brown red .40 .25
**C16** AP9 50c green .40 .25
**C17** AP9 1fr brt violet .50 .30
**C18** AP10 2fr olive grn .65 .50
**C19** AP10 3fr chocolate .65 .50
**C20** AP10 4fr deep ultra .65 .50
**C21** AP10 6fr blue grn .65 .50
**C22** AP10 7fr brt violet 1.10 .80
**C23** AP10 12fr orange 5.50 3.50
**C24** AP10 20fr crimson 1.90 1.40
**C25** AP11 50fr dk ultra 2.75 1.90
*Nos. C15-C25 (11)* 15.15 10.40

Nos. C15 to C25 were issued in 1941 in France by the Vichy Government, but were not sold in Cameroun until 1946.

See Nos. C7A-C7H for stamps without "RF."

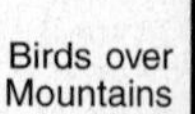


Birds over Mountains AP12

Cavalry and Plane AP13

Warrior, Dance Mask and Nose of Plane — AP14

***Perf. 12½***

**1947, Feb. 10** **Unwmk.** **Engr.**

**C26** AP12 50fr dk green 3.25 1.20
**C27** AP13 100fr brn red 4.75 1.20
**C28** AP14 200fr black 7.25 2.40
*Nos. C26-C28 (3)* 15.25 4.80

## UPU Issue

Common Design Type

**1949, July** ***Perf. 13***

**C29** CD99 25fr multicolored 8.00 4.75

Rhumsiki Peak — AP16

**1953, Feb. 16**

**C30** AP16 500fr grnsh blk, dk vio & vio bl 26.00 4.00

For surcharge see No. C40.

Edéa Dam and Sacred Ibis — AP17

**1953, Nov. 18**

**C31** AP17 15fr choc, brn lake & ultra 5.50 1.60

Dedication of Edea Dam on the Sanaga River.

## Liberation Issue

Common Design Type

**1954, June 6**

**C32** CD102 15fr dk grnsh bl & bl grn 7.25 4.75

Dr. Eugene Jamot, Research Laboratory and Tsetse Flies AP19

**1954, Nov. 29**

**C33** AP19 15fr dk grn, ind & dk brn 4.75 2.75

75th anniv. of the birth of Dr. Eugene Jamot.

Logging AP20

100fr, Giraffes. 200fr, Port of Douala.

**1955, Jan. 24**

**C34** AP20 50fr ol grn, brn & vio brn 4.00 .80
**C35** AP20 100fr grnsh bl, brn & dk brn 8.00 1.60
**C36** AP20 200fr dk grn, choc & dp ultra 10.50 2.40
*Nos. C34-C36 (3)* 22.50 4.80

For surcharges see Nos. C38-C39.

## Federal Republic

Air Afrique Issue

Common Design Type

**Unwmk.**

**1962, Feb. 17** **Engr.** ***Perf. 13***

**C37** CD107 25fr mar, pur & lt grn 1.00 .50

### Nos. C35-C36 and C30 Surcharged in Red

Type I

Type II

Two types of 5sh:
I — "5/-" measures 6½x4mm.
II — "5/" measures 3¾x3mm, No dash after diagonal line.

Three types of 10sh:
I — "10/-" measures 9x3¾mm.
II — "10/-" measures 7x2½-3mm.
III — "1" of "10/" vertically in line with last "E" of "FEDERALE".

Two types of £1:
I — "REPUBLIQUE / FEDERALE" 17¼mm wide.
II — "REPUBLIQUE / FEDERALE" 22mm wide.

**1961, Oct. 1 Engr. *Perf. 13***

**C38** AP20 5sh on 100fr (I) 10.00 6.00
*a.* Type II 32.50 18.00
**C39** AP20 10sh on 200fr (I) 22.00 13.00
*a.* Type II 77.50 42.50
*b.* Type III 32.50 30.00
**C40** AP16 £1 on 500fr (I) 35.00 22.00
*a.* Type II 60.00 35.00
*Nos. C38-C40 (3)* 67.00 41.00

Issued for use in the former United Kingdom Trust Territory of Southern Cameroons.

Kapsikis Mokolo AP21

Designs: 50fr, Cocotieres Hotel, Douala. 100fr, Cymothoe sangaris butterflies. 200fr, Ostriches, Waza Reservation.

**1962, June 15**

**C41** AP21 50fr sl grn, bl & dl red .90 .25
**C42** AP21 100fr multicolored 5.75 .60
**C43** AP21 200fr dk grn, blk & bis 8.00 1.40
**C44** AP21 500fr vio brn, bl & ocher 9.00 2.25
*Nos. C41-C44 (4)* 23.65 4.50

**Telstar Type of Regular Issue**

**1963, Feb. 9 Size: 48x27mm**

**C45** A50 100fr dk grn & red brn 2.50 .65

Edéa Relay Station — AP22

**1963, May 18 Photo. *Perf. 12x12½***

**C46** AP22 100fr multicolored 2.50 .65

Issued to publicize the high frequency telegraph connection Douala-Yaoundé.

**African Postal Union Issue**
Common Design Type

**1963, Sept. 8 Unwmk. *Perf. 12½***

**C47** CD114 85fr ultra, ocher & red 2.25 1.00

**Air Afrique Issue, 1963**
Common Design Type

**1963, Nov. 19 *Perf. 13x12***

**C48** CD115 50fr pink, gray, blk & grn 1.25 .40

**Olympic Games Type of 1964**

300fr, Greco-Roman wrestlers (ancient).

**1964, Oct. 10 Engr. *Perf. 13***

**C49** A57 300fr red, dk brn & dl grn 7.50 2.00
*a.* Sheet of 3, #403-404, C49 13.50 4.25

Kribi Port — AP25

**1964, Oct. 26 Unwmk. *Perf. 13***

**C50** AP25 50fr red brn, ultra & grn 1.00 .35

Black Rhinoceros AP26

**1964, Dec. 15 Engr. *Perf. 13***

**C51** AP26 250fr brn red, grn & dk brn 10.00 3.00

Pres. John F. Kennedy AP27

**1964, Dec. 8 Photo. *Perf. 12½***

**C52** AP27 100fr grn, yel grn & brn 2.50 1.10
*a.* Souvenir sheet of 4 10.00 4.50

Pres. John F. Kennedy (1917-63).

Abraham Lincoln AP28

**1965, Apr. 20 Unwmk. *Perf. 13***

**C53** AP28 100fr multicolored 2.50 .80

Abraham Lincoln, death centenary.

Syncom Satellite and ITU Emblem AP29

**1965, May 17 Engr.**

**C54** AP29 70fr red, dk bl, & blk 1.60 .60

Cent. of the ITU.

Sir Winston Spencer Churchill, Statesman and World War II Leader — AP30

Designs: 12fr, Churchill giving V sign. 18fr, Churchill, battleship and oak leaves with acorns.

***Perf. 13x12½***

**1965, May 28 Photo. Unwmk.**

**C55** 12fr multicolored 1.00 .50
**C56** 18fr multicolored 1.00 .50
*a.* AP40 Strip of 2, #C55-C56 + label 2.75 1.40

**ICY Type of Regular Issue**

**1965, Sept. 11 Engr. *Perf. 13***

**C57** A68 100fr dk red & dk bl 2.25 .70

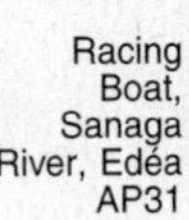

Racing Boat, Sanaga River, Edéa AP31

**1965, Oct. 27 Unwmk. *Perf. 13***

**C58** AP31 50fr brn, dk grn & sl 2.25 .35

Edward H. White Floating in Space and Gemini IV — AP32

Designs: 50fr, Vostok 6. 200fr, Gemini V and REP (rendezvous evaluation pod). 500fr, Gemini VI & VII rendezvous.

**1966, Mar. 30 Engr. *Perf. 13***

**C59** AP32 50fr car rose & dk sl grn .90 .35
**C60** AP32 100fr red lil & vio bl 2.10 .65
**C61** AP32 200fr ultra & dk pur 3.75 1.40
**C62** AP32 500fr brt bl & indigo 9.00 3.00
*Nos. C59-C62 (4)* 15.75 5.40

Man's conquest of space.

**Hotel Type of Regular Issue**

18fr, Mountain Hotel, Buea. 25fr, Hotel Akwa Palace, Douala. 50fr, Terminus Hotel, Yaoundé. 60fr, Imperial Hotel, Yaoundé. 85fr, Independence Hotel, Yaoundé. 100fr, Hunting Lodge, Mora, vert. 150fr, Boukarous (round huts), Waza Camp.

**1966**

**C63** A71 18fr sl grn, brt bl & blk .45 .25
**C64** A71 25fr car, ultra & sl .65 .25
**C65** A71 50fr choc, grn & ocher 2.50 .90
**C66** A71 60fr choc, grn & brt bl 1.50 .50
**C67** A71 85fr dk car rose, dl bl & grn 1.90 .60
**C68** A71 100fr brn, grn & sl 2.75 .70
**C69** A71 150fr brn, dl bl & ocher 3.75 .90
*Nos. C63-C69 (7)* 13.50 4.05

Issued: Nos. C63-C64, 4/6; Nos. C65-C69, 6/4.

**Flower Type of Regular Issue**

Flowers: 25fr, Hibiscus mutabilis. 50fr, Delonix regia. 100fr, Bougainvillea.

**1966, May 20 Photo. *Perf. 12½***
**Flowers in Natural Colors**
**Size: 26x45mm**

**C70** A75 25fr slate green .75 .25
**C71** A75 50fr brt grnsh bl 1.60 .25
**C72** A75 100fr gold 3.25 .25
*Nos. C70-C72 (3)* 5.60 .65

Military Police AP33

25fr, "Army," soldier, tanks & parachutes. 60fr, "Navy," & "Vigilante." 100fr, "Air Force," plane.

**1966, June 21 Engr. *Perf. 13***

**C73** AP33 20fr vio bl, org brn & dl pur .55 .25
**C74** AP33 25fr dk grn, dl pur & brn .55 .25
**C75** AP33 60fr bl grn, bl & ind 1.60 .30
**C76** AP33 100fr brn, Prus bl & car rose 2.75 .65
*Nos. C73-C76 (4)* 5.45 1.45

Issued to honor Cameroun's armed forces.

Wembley Stadium, London AP34

**1966, July 20**

**C77** AP34 50fr shown 1.40 .25
**C78** AP34 200fr Soccer 4.75 1.10

8th World Cup Soccer Championship, Wembley, England, July 11-30.

**Air Afrique Issue, 1966**
Common Design Type

**1966, Aug. 31 Photo. *Perf. 13***

**C79** CD123 25fr red lil, blk & gray .80 .25

Yaoundé Cathedral AP35

18fr, Buea Cathedral. 30fr, Orthodox Church, Yaoundé. 60fr, Mosque, Garoua.

**1966, Dec. 19 Engr. *Perf. 13***

**C80** AP35 18fr choc, bl & grn .45 .25
**C81** AP35 25fr brn, grn & brt vio .55 .25
**C82** AP35 30fr lil, grn & dl red .70 .25
**C83** AP35 60fr mar, brt grn & grn 1.40 .35
*Nos. C80-C83 (4)* 3.10 1.10

Pioneer A and Moon AP36

**1967, Apr. 30 Engr. *Perf. 13***

**C84** AP36 25fr shown .50 .25
**C85** AP36 50fr Ranger 6 .90 .35
**C86** AP36 100fr Luna 9 2.25 .65
**C87** AP36 250fr Luna 10 4.75 2.00
*Nos. C84-C87 (4)* 8.40 3.25

"Conquest of the Moon."

**Flower Type of Regular Issue**

200fr, Thevetia Peruviana. 250fr, Amaryllis.

**1967, June 22 Photo. *Perf. 12½***
**Size: 26x46mm**

**C88** A86 200fr multi 4.50 .90
**C89** A86 250fr multi 5.50 1.10

**African Postal Union Issue, 1967**
Common Design Type

**1967, Sept. 9 Engr. *Perf. 13***

**C90** CD124 100fr red brn, Prus bl & brt lil 2.40 .65

Skis, Ice Skates, Olympic Flame and Emblem — AP38

**1967, Oct. 11 Engr. *Perf. 13***

**C91** AP38 30fr ultra & sepia 1.60 .25

Issued to publicize the 10th Winter Olympic Games, Grenoble, Feb. 6-8, 1968.

Cameroun Exhibit, EXPO '67 — AP39

100fr, Bangwa house poles carved with ancestor figures. 200fr, Canadian Pavilions.

**1967, Oct. 18**

**C92** AP39 50fr mag, ol & mar 1.00 .25
**C93** AP39 100fr dk grn, mar & dk brn 3.25 .70
**C94** AP39 200fr brn, lil rose & sl grn 4.25 1.25
*Nos. C92-C94 (3)* 8.50 2.20

EXPO '67, International Exhibition, Montreal, Apr. 28-Oct. 27, 1967.

See note after No. C116 regarding 1969 moon overprint.

Konrad Adenauer (1876-1967), Chancellor of West Germany (1949-63) and Cologne Cathedral — AP40

70fr, Adenauer and Chancellery, Bonn.

**1967, Dec. 1 Photo. *Perf. 12½***

**C95** AP40 30fr multi .90 .25
**C96** AP40 70fr multi 1.50 .40
*a.* Pair, #C95-C96 + label 3.50 2.50

Pres. Ahidjo, King Faisal and View of Mecca AP41

60fr, Pres. Ahidjo, Pope Paul VI & view of Rome.

**1968, Feb. 18 Photo. *Perf. 12½***

C97 AP41 30fr multi .90 .25
C98 AP41 60fr multi 2.10 .30

Issued to commemorate President Ahidjo's Pilgrimage to Mecca and visit to Rome.

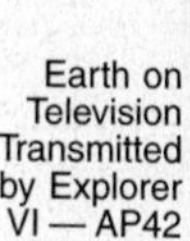

Earth on Television Transmitted by Explorer VI — AP42

30fr, Molniya spacecraft. 40fr, Earth on television screen transmitted by Molniya.

**1968, Apr. 20 Engr. *Perf. 13***

C99 AP42 20fr multi .55 .25
C100 AP42 30fr multi .80 .25
C101 AP42 40fr multi 1.10 .25
*Nos. C99-C101 (3)* 2.45 .75

Telecommunication by satellite.

Forge — AP43

No. C103, Tea harvest. No. C104, Trans-Cameroun railroad (diesel train emerging from tunnel). 40fr, Rubber harvest. 60fr, Douala Harbor, horiz.

**1968, June 5 Engr. *Perf. 13***

C102 AP43 20fr red brn, dk grn & ind .60 .25
C103 AP43 30fr dk brn, grn & ultra 1.10 .35
C104 AP43 30fr ind, sl grn & bis brn 7.50 2.50
C105 AP43 40fr ol bis, dk grn & bl grn 1.10 .35
C106 AP43 60fr ultra, dk brn & sl 3.00 1.00
*Nos. C102-C106 (5)* 13.30 4.45

Second Economic Development Five-Year Plan.

Boxing — AP44

50fr, Long jump. 60fr, Athlete on rings.

**1968, Aug. 19 Engr. *Perf. 13***

C107 AP44 30fr brt grn, dk grn & choc .65 .25
C108 AP44 50fr brt grn, brn red & choc 1.25 .30
C109 AP44 60fr brt grn, ultra & choc 1.50 .35
a. Min. sheet of 3, #C107-C109 4.00 4.00
*Nos. C107-C109 (3)* 3.40 .90

19th Olympic Games, Mexico City, 10/12-27.

**Human Rights Type of Regular Issue**

**1968, Sept. 14 Photo. *Perf. 12½x13***

C110 A92 30fr grn & brt pink .80 .25

Martin Luther King, Jr. — AP45

Portraits: No. C112, Mahatma Gandhi and map of India. 40fr, John F. Kennedy. 60fr, Robert F. Kennedy. No. C115, Rev. Martin Luther King, Jr. No. C116, Mahatma Gandhi.

**1968, Dec. 5 Photo. *Perf. 12½***

C111 AP45 30fr bl & blk .60 .25
C112 AP45 30fr multi .60 .25
C113 AP45 40fr pink & blk 1.00 .50
C114 AP45 60fr bluish lil & blk 1.25 .50
C115 AP45 70fr yel grn & blk 1.40 .60
a. Souvenir sheet of 4, #C112-C115 8.00 8.00
C116 AP45 70fr multi 1.40 .60
*Nos. C111-C116 (6)* 6.25 2.70

Issued to honor exponents of non-violence. The 2 King stamps (Nos. C111 and C115), the 2 Gandhi stamps (Nos. C112 and C116) and the 2 Kennedy stamps (Nos. C113-C114) are each printed as triptychs with a descriptive label between.

---

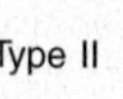

Type II

In 1969 Nos. C111-C116 and C94 were overprinted in carmine capitals: "Premier Homme / sur la Lune / 20 Juillet 1969" and "First Man / Landing on Moon / 20 July 1969".

Two types of overprints were used:

Type I — English and French text 25mm apart.

Type II — English and French text close together.

Values: on No. C94, $50; on Nos. C111-C116, $325; on No. C115a (2 different souvenir sheets, with both overprint types on different stamps), each $300.

---

**PHILEXAFRIQUE Issue**

The Letter, by Armand Cambon — AP46

**1968, Dec. 10**

C117 AP46 100fr multi 3.25 1.25

PHILEXAFRIQUE, Philatelic Exhibition in Abidjan, Feb. 14-23, 1969. Printed with alternating light green label.

**2nd PHILEXAFRIQUE Issue**

Common Design Type

Design: Cameroun #199 and Wouri Bridge.

**1969, Feb. 14 Engr. *Perf. 13***

C118 CD128 50fr multi 3.25 1.25

Caladium Bicolor — AP47

Flowers: 50fr, Aristolochia elegans. 100fr, Gloriosa simplex.

**1969, May 14 Photo. *Perf. 12½***

C119 AP47 30fr lil & multi .75 .25
C120 AP47 50fr grn & multi 1.50 .40
C121 AP47 100fr brn & multi 3.50 1.00
*Nos. C119-C121 (3)* 5.75 1.65

3rd Intl. Flower Show, Paris, Apr. 23-Oct. 5.

Douala Post Office AP48

50fr, Buèa P.O. 100fr, Bafoussam P.O.

**1969, June 19 Engr. *Perf. 13***

C122 AP48 30fr grn, vio bl & brn .55 .25
C123 AP48 50fr sl, emer & red brn .90 .25
C124 AP48 100fr dk brn, brt grn & brn 1.75 .50
*Nos. C122-C124 (3)* 3.20 1.00

Coronation of Napoleon I, by Jacques Louis David AP49

Napoleon Crossing Saint Bernard, after J. L. David AP50

**1969, July 4 Photo. *Perf. 12x12½***

C125 AP49 30fr vio bl & multi 1.00 .40

***Die-cut Perf. 10***

**Embossed on Gold Foil**

C126 AP50 1000fr gold 45.00 45.00

Bicentenary of birth of Napoleon I.

William E. B. Du Bois (1868-1963), American Writer — AP51

15fr, Dr. Price Mars, Haiti (1876-1969). No. C128, Aimé Cesaire, Martinique (1913- ). No. C130, Langston Hughes, US (1902-67). No. C131, Marcus Garvey, Jamaica (1887-1940). 100fr, René Maran, Martinique (1887-1960).

**1969, Sept. 25 Photo. *Perf. 12½***

C127 AP51 15fr lt bl & blk .45 .25
C128 AP51 30fr lem & blk .55 .25
C129 AP51 30fr rose brn & blk .55 .25
C130 AP51 50fr gray & blk .80 .25
C131 AP51 50fr emer & blk .80 .25
C132 AP51 100fr yel & blk 2.00 .60
a. Min. sheet of 6, #C127-C132 6.75 4.50
*Nos. C127-C132 (6)* 5.15 1.85

Issued to honor Negro writers.

ILO Emblem AP52

**1969, Oct. 29 Photo. *Perf. 13***

C133 AP52 30fr blk, bl grn & gray .80 .25
C134 AP52 50fr blk, dp lil rose & gray 1.40 .35

50th anniv. of the ILO.

Armstrong, Collins and Aldrin Splashdown in the Pacific AP53

Design: 500fr, Landing module and Nell A. Armstrong's first step on moon.

**1969, Nov. 29 Photo. *Perf. 12½***

C135 AP53 200fr multi 5.00 1.25
C136 AP53 500fr multi 12.00 3.00

See note after Algeria No. 427.

Pres. Ahidjo, Arms and Map of Cameroun — AP54

**Embossed on Gold Foil**

**1970, Jan. 1 *Die-cut Perf. 10***

C137 AP54 1000fr gold & multi 26.00 25.00

10th anniversary of independence.

Hotel Mont Fébé, Yaoundé AP55

**1970, Jan. 15 Engr. *Perf. 13***

C138 AP55 30fr lt brn, sl grn & gray .80 .25

Lenin — AP56

**1970, Jan. 25 Photo. *Perf. 12½***

C139 AP56 50fr org & blk 2.00 .55

**Plant Type of Regular Issue**

Designs: 50fr, Cleome speciosa (caper). 100fr, Mussaenda erythrophylla (madder).

**1970, Mar. 24 Photo. *Perf. 12½***

**Size: 26x46mm**

C140 A99 50fr blk & multi 1.40 .35
C141 A99 100fr multi 2.75 .90

Map of Africa and Lions Emblem Pinpointing Yaoundé AP57

**1970, May 2 Photo. *Perf. 12½***

C142 AP57 100fr multi 2.25 .75

13th Lions International Congress of District 13, Yaoundé, May 2, 1970.

UN Emblem and Doves AP58

Design: 50fr, UN emblem and dove, vert.

**1970, June 26 Engr. *Perf. 13***

**C143** AP58 30fr brn & org 1.00 .25
**C144** AP58 50fr Prus bl & sl bl 1.25 .40

25th anniversary of the United Nations.

Japanese Pavilion and EXPO Emblem AP59

Designs (EXPO Emblem and): 100fr, Map of Japan, vert. 150fr, Australian pavilion.

**1970, Aug. 1 Engr. *Perf. 13***

**C145** AP59 50fr ind, lt grn & ver .90 .30
**C146** AP59 100fr bl, lt grn & red 2.00 .55
**C147** AP59 150fr choc, bl & gray 3.25 .65
*Nos. C145-C147 (3)* 6.15 1.50

EXPO '70 International Exhibition, Osaka, Japan, Mar. 15-Sept. 13.

Charles de Gaulle AP60

Design: 200fr, de Gaulle in unifrom.

**1970, Aug. 27**

**C148** 100fr grn, vio bl & ol brn 2.25 .80
**C149** 200fr ol brn, vio bl & grn 4.50 1.40
*a.* AP60 Pair, #C148-C149 + label 8.00 8.00

Rallying of the Free French, 30th anniv. For overprints see Nos. C159-C160.

Pelé and Team — AP61

Designs: 50fr, Aztec Stadium, Mexico City, horiz. 100fr, Mexican soccer team, horiz.

**1970, Oct. 14 Photo. *Perf. 12½***

**C150** AP61 50fr multi .90 .30
**C151** AP61 100fr multi 2.00 .65
**C152** AP61 200fr multi 3.50 1.00
*Nos. C150-C152 (3)* 6.40 1.95

9th World Soccer Championships for the Jules Rimet Cup, Mexico City, May 30-June 21, and the final victory of Brazil over Italy.

Ludwig van Beethoven (1770-1827), Composer — AP62

**1970, Nov. 23 Engr. *Perf. 13***

**C153** AP62 250fr multi 5.75 1.75

Christ at Emmaus, by Rembrandt AP63

150fr, The Anatomy Lesson, by Rembrandt.

**1970, Dec. 5 Photo. *Perf. 12x12½***

**C154** AP63 70fr grn & multi 1.40 .35
**C155** AP63 150fr multi 2.75 .75

Charles Dickens — AP64

Designs: 50fr, Scenes from David Copperfield. 100fr, Dickens holding quill.

**1970, Dec. 22 *Perf. 13***

**C156** AP64 40fr blk & rose .95 .25
**C157** AP64 50fr bis & multi 1.00 .30
**C158** AP64 100fr rose & multi 2.00 .65
*a.* Strip of 3, #C156-C158 5.00 2.00

Charles Dickens (1812-1870), English novelist.

**De Gaulle Type of 1970 Overprinted**

**1971, Jan. 15 Engr. *Perf. 13***

**C159** 100fr vio bl, emer & brn red 2.75 .75
**C160** 200fr brn red, emer & vio bl 5.00 1.25
*a.* AP60 Pair, #C159-C160 + label 8.00 8.00

In memory of Gen. Charles de Gaulle (1890-1970), President of France.

Timber Storage, Douala AP65

Industrialization: 70fr, ALUCAM aluminum plant, Edea, vert. 100fr, Mbakaou Dam.

**1971, Feb. 14 Engr. *Perf. 13***

**C161** AP65 40fr dk red, bl grn & ol brn .55 .25
**C162** AP65 70fr ol brn, sl grn & brt bl 1.10 .30
**C163** AP65 100fr Prus bl, yel grn & red brn 1.75 .40
*Nos. C161-C163 (3)* 3.40 .95

Relay Race AP66

50fr, Torch bearer, vert. 100fr, Discus.

**1971, Apr. 24 Engr. *Perf. 13***

**C164** AP66 30fr dk brn, ver & ind .65 .25
**C165** AP66 50fr blk, bl & choc .80 .25
**C166** AP66 100fr multi 1.75 .40
*Nos. C164-C166 (3)* 3.20 .90

75th anniv. of revival of Olympic Games.

Fishing Trawler AP67

Designs: 40fr, Local fishermen, Northern Cameroun. 70fr, Fishing harbor, Douala. 150fr, Shrimp boats, Douala.

**1971, May 14 Engr. *Perf. 13***

**C167** AP67 30fr lt brn, bl & grn .70 .30
**C168** AP67 40fr sl grn, bl & dk brn .90 .30
**C169** AP67 70fr dk brn, bl & red org 2.00 .40
**C170** AP67 150fr multi 4.25 1.00
*Nos. C167-C170 (4)* 7.85 2.00

Cameroun fishing industry.

Cameroun No. 123 and War Memorial, Yaoundé AP68

Designs (Cameroun Stamps): 25fr, No. C33 and Jamot memorial. 40fr, No. 431 and government buildings, Yaoundé. 50fr, No. 19 and Imperial German postal emblem. 100fr, No. 101 and World War II memorial.

**1971, Aug. 1 Engr. *Perf. 13***

**C171** AP68 20fr grn, ocher & dk brn .45 .25
**C172** AP68 25fr dk brn, vio bl & sl grn .65 .25
**C173** AP68 40fr grn, mar & sl .80 .25
**C174** AP68 50fr dk brn, blk & ver 1.25 .25
**C175** AP68 100fr mar, sl grn & org 1.75 .50
*Nos. C171-C175 (5)* 4.90 1.50

PHILATECAM 1971 Philatelic Exhibition.

Cameroun Flag, Pres. Ahidjo and Reunification Highway — AP69

**Typographed, Silk Screen, Embossed**

**1971, Oct. 1 *Perf. 12½***

**C176** AP69 250fr gold & multi 6.00 4.50

PHILATECAM Philatelic Exhibition, Yaoundé-Douala.

**African Postal Union Issue, 1971**

Common Design Type

**1971, Nov. 13 Photo. *Perf. 13x13½***

**C177** CD135 100fr bl & multi 2.00 .50

Annunciation, by Fra Angelico — AP71

Christmmas (Paintings): 45fr, Virgin and Child, by Andrea del Sarto. 150fr, Christ Child with Lamb, detail from Holy Family, by Raphael, vert.

**1971, Dec. 19 *Perf. 13x13½, 13½x13***

**C178** AP71 40fr multi .55 .25
**C179** AP71 45fr multi .70 .25
**C180** AP71 150fr multi 3.25 .75
*Nos. C178-C180 (3)* 4.50 1.25

Cameroun Airlines Emblem — AP72

**1972, Feb. 2 Photo. *Perf. 12½x12***

**C181** AP72 50fr lt bl & multi .80 .25

Inauguration of Cameroun Airlines.

Doge's Palace, by Ippolito Caffi — AP73

100fr, 200fr, Details from "Regatta on the Grand Canal," by School of Canaletto.

**1972, Mar. 19 Photo. *Perf. 13***

**C182** AP73 40fr gold & multi .70 .25
**C183** AP73 100fr gold & multi 1.75 .40
**C184** AP73 200fr gold & multi 4.00 .80
*Nos. C182-C184 (3)* 6.45 1.45

UNESCO campaign to save Venice.

Cosmonauts Patsayev, Dobrovolsky and Volkov AP74

**1972, May 1 Photo. *Perf. 13x13½***

**C185** AP74 50fr multi 1.00 .30

Salute-Soyuz 11 space mission, and in memory of the Russian cosmonauts Victor I. Patsayev, Georgi T. Dobrovolsky and Vladislav N. Volkov, who died during Soyuz 11 space mission, June 6-30, 1971.

UN Headquarters, Chinese Flag and Gate of Heavenly Peace — AP75

**1972, May 19 *Perf. 13***

**C186** AP75 50fr blk, scar & gold 3.25 .35

Admission of People's Republic of China to UN.

**United Republic**

Olympic Rings, Swimming AP76

Designs (Olympic Rings and): No. C188, Boxing, vert. 200fr, Equestrian.

**1972, Aug. 1 Engr. *Perf. 13***

**C187** AP76 50fr lake & slate grn .90 .25
**C188** AP76 50fr choc & slate .90 .25
**C189** AP76 200fr cl, gray & dk brn 3.50 1.00
*a.* Min. sheet of 3 5.75 5.75
*Nos. C187-C189 (3)* 5.30 1.50

20th Olympic Games, Munich, Aug. 26-Sept. 11. No. C189a contains stamps similar to Nos. C187-C189, but in changed colors. The 50fr (swimming) is Prussian blue, violet & brown; the 50c (boxing) lilac, Prussian blue & brown; the 200fr, Prussian blue & brown.

**Nos. C187-C189 Overprinted in Red or Black**

a

b

c

**1972, Oct. 23 Engr. *Perf. 13***

**C190** AP76(a) 50fr (R) .90 .25
**C191** AP76(b) 50fr .90 .25
**C192** AP76(c) 200fr 3.50 1.00
*Nos. C190-C192 (3)* 5.30 1.50

Gold Medal Winners in 20th Olympic Games: Mark Spitz, US, swimming (No. C190); Dieter Kottysch, West Germany, light middleweight boxing (No. C191); Richard Meade, Great Britain, 3-day equestrian (No. C192).

Madonna with Angels, by Cimabue — AP77

Christmas: 140fr, Madonna of the Rose Arbor, by Stefan Lochner.

**1972, Dec. 21 Photo. *Perf. 13***

**C193** AP77 45fr gold & multi 1.00 .25
**C194** AP77 140fr gold & multi 2.75 1.00

St. Teresa, the Little Flower — AP78

100fr, Lisieux Cathedral and St. Teresa.

**1973, Jan. 2 Engr.**

**C195** AP78 45fr vio bl, pur & mar .70 .25
**C196** AP78 100fr mag, ultra & brn 1.75 .40

Centenary of the birth of St. Teresa of Lisieux (1873-1897), Carmelite nun.

AP79

Design: African unity hall, Addis Ababa and Emperor Haile Selassie.

**1973, Mar. 14 Photo. *Perf. 13***

**C197** AP79 45fr yellow & multi 1.00 .25

80th birthday of Emperor Haile Selassie of Ethiopia.

Corn, Grain, Healthy and Starving People AP80

**1973, Apr. 10 Typo. *Perf. 13***

**C198** AP80 45fr multi .80 .25

World Food Program, 10th anniversary.

Hearts and Blood Vessels — AP81

**1973, May 5 Engr.**

**C199** AP81 50fr dk car rose & dk vio bl 1.00 .25

"Your Heart is Your Health" and for the 25th anniv. of the WHO.

**Type of Regular Issue**

Designs: 45fr, Map of Cameroun, Pres. Ahidjo and No. C176. 70fr, National colors and commemorative inscriptions.

**1973, May 20 Engr. *Perf. 13***

**C200** A128 45fr grn & multi .80 .25
**C201** A128 70fr red & multi 1.00 .40

Scout Emblem and Flags — AP82

**1973, July 31 Typo. *Perf. 13***

**C202** AP82 40fr multi 1.00 .25
**C203** AP82 45fr multi 1.25 .35
**C204** AP82 100fr multi 3.25 .60
*Nos. C202-C204 (3)* 5.50 1.20

Cameroun's admission to the World Scout Conference, Mar. 26, 1971.

**African Weeks Issue**

Head and City Hall, Brussels — AP83

**1973, Sept. 17 Engr. *Perf. 13***

**C205** AP83 40fr dp brn & rose claret .80 .25

African Weeks, Brussels, Sept. 15-30.

Map of Africa with Cameroun AP84

**1973, Sept. 29 Engr. *Perf. 13***

**C206** AP84 40fr blk, red & grn .80 .25

Help for handicapped children.

Zamengoe Radar Station — AP85

**1973, Dec. 8 Engr. *Perf. 13***

**C207** AP85 100fr bl, lt brn & grn 1.50 .45

Chancellor Rolin Madonna, by Van Eyck — AP86

Christmas: 140fr, Nativity, by Federigo Barocei.

**1973, Dec. 11 Photo. *Perf. 13***

**C208** AP86 45fr gold & multi 1.00 .30
**C209** AP86 140fr gold & multi 2.75 1.00

**Zebu Type of 1974**

**1974, June 1 Litho. *Perf. 13***

**C210** A140 45fr Zebu herd 1.40 .35

Churchill and Union Jack — AP87

**1974, July 10 Engr. *Perf. 13***

**C211** AP87 100fr blk, bl & red 1.60 .45

Winston Churchill (1874-1965).

Soccer, Arms of Frankfurt, Dortmund, Gelsenkirchen and Stuttgart — AP88

100fr, Soccer & arms of Berlin, Hamburg, Hanover & Düsseldorf. 200fr, Soccer cup & game.

**1974, Aug. 5 Photo. *Perf. 13***

**C212** AP88 45fr gray, sl & org .70 .25
**C213** AP88 100fr gray, sl & org 1.25 .40
**C214** AP88 200fr org, slate & bl 2.75 1.00
*a.* Strip of 3, Nos. C212-C214 5.00 5.00

World Cup Soccer Championship, Munich, June 13-July 7.

**Nos. C212-C214 Overprinted in Dark Blue**

**1974, Sept. 16 Photo. *Perf. 13***

**C215** AP88 45fr multi .65 .25
**C216** AP88 100fr multi 1.25 .40
**C217** AP88 200fr multi 2.40 1.00
*a.* Strip of 3, Nos. C215-C217 5.00 5.00

World Cup Soccer Championship, 1974, victory of German Federal Republic.

**UPU Type of 1974**

100fr, Cameroun #503. 200fr, Cameroun #C29.

**1974, Oct. 8 Engr. *Perf. 13***

**C218** A142 100fr blue & multi 1.75 .50
**C219** A142 200fr red & multi 3.25 1.00

Copernicus and Planets Circling Sun — AP89

**1974, Oct. 15 Engr. *Perf. 13***

**C220** AP89 250fr multi 3.50 1.25

500th anniversary of the birth of Nicolaus Copernicus (1473-1543), Polish astronomer.

21st Chess Olympiad, Nice, France, June 6-30 — AP90

**1974, Nov. 3 Photo. *Perf. 13x12½***

**C221** AP90 100fr Chess pieces 5.25 1.00

Mask and ARPHILA Emblem AP91

**1974, Nov. 30 Engr. *Perf. 13***

**C222** AP91 50fr choc & magenta .80 .25

ARPHILA 75, Paris, June 6-16, 1975.

Presidents and Flags of Cameroun, CAR, Gabon and Congo AP92

**1974, Dec. 8 Photo.**

**C223** AP92 100fr gold & multi 2.25 .45

See note after No. 595.

Man Landing on Moon AP93

**1974, Dec. 15 Engr.**

**C224** AP93 200fr brn, bl & car 3.25 1.00

5th anniv. of man's 1st landing on the moon.

Charles de Gaulle and Félix Eboué AP94

**1975, Feb. 24 Typo. *Perf. 13***

**C225** AP94 45fr multi 1.50 .35
**C226** AP94 200fr multi 5.00 1.50

Felix A. Eboué (1884-1944), Governor of Chad, first colonial governor to join Free French in WWII, 30th death anniversary.

Marquis de Lafayette — AP95

American Bicentennial: 140fr, Washington and soldiers. 500fr, Franklin and Independence Hall.

**1975, Oct. 20 Engr. *Perf. 13***

**C227** AP95 100fr vio bl & multi 2.25 .60
**C228** AP95 140fr brn & multi 2.40 .65
**C229** AP95 500fr grn & multi 7.25 2.00
*Nos. C227-C229 (3)* 11.90 3.25

The Burning Bush, by Nicolas Froment — AP96

Painting: 500fr, Adoration of the Kings, by Gentile da Fabriano, horiz.

**1975, Dec. 25 Photo. *Perf. 13***

**C230** AP96 50fr gold & multi .90 .30
**C231** AP96 500fr gold & multi 7.25 3.00

Christmas 1975.

Concorde and Route: Paris-Dakar-Rio de Janeiro — AP97

**1976, July 20 Litho. *Perf. 13***

| | | | | |
|---|---|---|---|---|
| **C232** | AP97 500fr lt bl & multi | | 6.50 | 1.60 |
| *a.* | Souvenir sheet of 1 | | 9.00 | 9.00 |

1st commercial flight of supersonic jet Concorde from Paris to Rio de Janeiro, Jan. 21. No. C232a sold for 600fr.

For overprint see No. C263.

### Dance Type of 1976

50fr, Dancers & drummer. 100fr, Woman dancer.

**1976, Sept. 15 Litho. *Perf. 12***

| | | | |
|---|---|---|---|
| **C233** | A154 50fr gray & multi | .65 | .25 |
| **C234** | A154 100fr gray & multi | 1.10 | .35 |

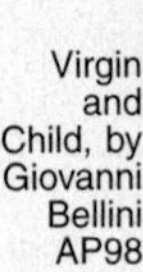

Virgin and Child, by Giovanni Bellini AP98

Paintings: 30fr, Adoration of the Shepherds, by Le Brun. 60fr, Adoration of the Kings, by Rubens. 500fr, The Newborn, by Georges de la Tour.

**1976, Dec. 15 Litho. *Perf. 12½***

| | | | |
|---|---|---|---|
| **C235** | AP98 30fr gold & multi | .70 | .25 |
| **C236** | AP98 60fr gold & multi | .90 | .25 |
| **C237** | AP98 70fr gold & multi | 1.25 | .35 |
| **C238** | AP98 500fr gold & multi | 9.00 | 3.00 |
| *a.* | Souv. sheet of 4, #C235-C238 | 12.50 | 12.00 |
| | *Nos. C235-C238 (4)* | 11.85 | 3.85 |

Christmas 1976.

### Festival Type of 1977

Traditional Chief on his throne, sculpture.

**1977, Feb. 4 Litho. *Perf. 12½***

| | | | |
|---|---|---|---|
| **C239** | A159 60fr multi | 1.10 | .25 |

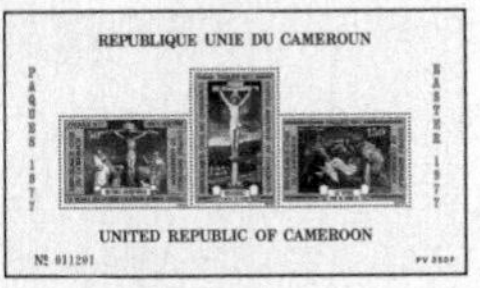


Easter AP99

75fr, Crucifixion, by Matthias Grunewald. 125fr, Christ on the Cross, by Velazquez, vert. 150fr, The Deposition, by Titian.

**1977, Apr. 2 Litho. *Perf. 12½***

| | | | |
|---|---|---|---|
| **C240** | 50fr gold & multi | .90 | .25 |
| **C241** | 125fr gold & multi | 1.75 | .45 |
| **C242** | 150fr gold & multi | 2.50 | .65 |
| *a.* | AP99 Souv. sheet of 3, #C240-C242, perf. 12 | 6.75 | 1.75 |
| | *Nos. C240-C242 (3)* | 5.15 | 1.35 |

No. C242a sold for 350fr.

Lions Emblem, Map of Africa — AP100

**1977, Apr. 29 Litho. *Perf. 12½***

| | | | |
|---|---|---|---|
| **C243** | AP100 250fr multi | 3.00 | 1.00 |

Lions Club of Douala, 19th Cong., 4/29-30.

Rotary Emblem — AP101

**1977, May 18**

| | | | |
|---|---|---|---|
| **C244** | AP101 60fr multi | .70 | .25 |

Rotary Club of Douala, 20th anniversary.

Antoine de Saint-Exupéry AP102

Charles Lindbergh and Spirit of St. Louis AP103

Designs: 50fr, Jean Mermoz and his plane. 80fr, Maryse Bastié and her plane. 100fr, Sikorsky S-43. 300fr, Concorde.

**1977, May 20 Engr. *Perf. 13***

| | | | |
|---|---|---|---|
| **C245** | AP103 50fr org & bl | .90 | .25 |
| **C246** | AP102 60fr dp car & org | .95 | .25 |
| **C247** | AP103 80fr mag & bl | 1.25 | .30 |
| *a.* | Souv. sheet, #C245-C247 | 3.25 | 3.25 |
| **C248** | AP103 100fr grn & yel | 1.50 | .40 |
| **C249** | AP103 300fr multi | 5.50 | 1.25 |
| **C250** | AP103 500fr multi | 8.00 | 2.50 |
| *a.* | Souv. sheet, #C248-C250 | 14.50 | 14.50 |
| | *Nos. C245-C250 (6)* | 18.10 | 4.95 |

Aviation pioneers and events. No. C247a sold for 200fr. No. C250a sold for 1000fr.

For overprint see No. C262.

Sassenage Castle, Grenoble — AP104

**1977, May 21 Litho. *Perf. 12½***

| | | | |
|---|---|---|---|
| **C251** | AP104 70fr multi | 1.60 | 1.00 |

10th anniv. of Intl. French Language Council.

### Jufilex Type of 1977

Designs: 70fr, Switzerland (Zurich) No. 1L1 and Cameroun No. 16. 100fr, Switzerland (Geneva) No. 2L1 and Cameroun No. 254.

**1977, June 5 Litho. *Perf. 12***

| | | | |
|---|---|---|---|
| **C252** | A161 70fr multi | 1.25 | .35 |
| **C253** | A161 100fr multi | 2.10 | .60 |

### Apollo-Soyuz Type

100fr, Astronaut Vance Brand, Apollo in orbit. 250fr, Apollo and Soyuz docking. 350fr, Cosmonaut Valery Kubasov, Soyuz in orbit.

500fr, Astronaut Donald Slayton, handshake.

**1977, Aug. 10 Litho. *Perf. 14x13½***

| | | | |
|---|---|---|---|
| **C256** | A163 100fr multicolored | .90 | .25 |
| **C257** | A163 250fr multicolored | 2.25 | .60 |
| **C258** | A163 350fr multicolored | 3.25 | 1.00 |
| | *Nos. C256-C258 (3)* | 6.40 | 5.85 |

### Souvenir Sheet

| | | | |
|---|---|---|---|
| **C259** | A163 500fr multicolored | 5.00 | 5.00 |

Diseased Knee, WHO Emblem — AP105

**1977, Oct. 15 Engr. *Perf. 13***

| | | | |
|---|---|---|---|
| **C260** | AP105 70fr multi | .70 | .25 |

World Rheumatism Year.

### Nos. C249 and C232 Overprinted in Red

### Engraved, Lithographed

**1977, Nov. 22 *Perf. 13***

| | | | |
|---|---|---|---|
| **C262** | AP103 300fr multi | 3.25 | 1.25 |
| **C263** | AP97 500fr multi | 5.00 | 2.00 |

Concorde, 1st commercial flight Paris to NY.

### Christmas Type of 1977

Paintings: 60fr, Virgin and Child with 4 Saints, by Bellini, horiz. 400fr, Adoration of the Shepherds, by George de la Tour, horiz.

**1977, Dec. 15 Litho. *Perf. 12x12½***

| | | | |
|---|---|---|---|
| **C264** | A165 60fr multi | 1.00 | .25 |
| **C265** | A165 400fr multi | 5.00 | 1.75 |

### Flag Type of 1978

60fr, New flag, Pres. Ahidjo and spear.

**1978, Apr. 3 Litho. *Perf. 12½***

| | | | |
|---|---|---|---|
| **C266** | A167 60fr multi | .55 | .25 |

### Frog Type of 1978

Design: 100fr, Cardioglossa trifasciata.

**1978, Apr. 5**

| | | | |
|---|---|---|---|
| **C267** | A168 100fr multi | 3.75 | .75 |

L'Arlesienne, by Van Gogh — AP106

No. C269, Burial of Christ, by Albrecht Dürer.

**1978, May 15 Litho. *Perf. 12½***

| | | | |
|---|---|---|---|
| **C268** | AP106 200fr multi | 4.25 | 1.10 |
| **C269** | AP106 200fr multi | 5.75 | 1.10 |

Leprosy Distribution on World Map, Raoul Follereau AP107

**1978, June 6 Litho. *Perf. 12***

| | | | |
|---|---|---|---|
| **C270** | AP107 100fr multi | 1.10 | .55 |

25th World Leprosy Day.

Capt. Cook and Siege of Quebec AP108

Design: 250fr, Capt. Cook, Adventure and Resolution, map of voyages.

**1978, July 26 Engr. *Perf. 13***

| | | | |
|---|---|---|---|
| **C271** | AP108 100fr multi | 2.10 | .55 |
| **C272** | AP108 250fr multi | 5.00 | 1.40 |

Capt. James Cook (1728-1779), explorer.

Argentine Soccer Team, Coat of Arms and Rimet Cup — AP109

200fr, Two soccer players, vert. 1000fr, Soccer ball illuminating world map, vert.

**1978, Sept. 1 Litho. *Perf. 13***

| | | | |
|---|---|---|---|
| **C273** | AP109 100fr multi | 1.00 | .55 |
| **C274** | AP109 200fr multi | 1.75 | 1.10 |
| **C275** | AP109 1000fr multi | 10.00 | 5.50 |
| | *Nos. C273-C275 (3)* | 12.75 | 7.15 |

11th World Cup Soccer Championship, Argentina, June 1-25.

### Jules Verne Type of 1978

Design: 400fr, Jules Verne and "20,000 Leagues Under the Sea," horiz.

**1978, Oct. 10 Litho. *Perf. 12***

| | | | |
|---|---|---|---|
| **C276** | A169 400fr multi | 4.00 | 2.00 |

### Musical Instrument Type of 1978

Design: 100fr, Man playing Mvet zither.

**1978, Nov. 20 Litho. *Perf. 12½***

| | | | |
|---|---|---|---|
| **C277** | A172 100fr multi | 1.25 | .40 |

### Human Rights Type of 1979

**1979, Feb. 11 Litho. *Perf. 12x12½***

| | | | |
|---|---|---|---|
| **C278** | A174 500fr multi | 5.50 | 2.50 |

Lions Emblem, Map of District 403 — AP110

**1979, Apr. 26 Litho. *Perf. 12½***

| | | | |
|---|---|---|---|
| **C279** | AP110 60fr multi | .70 | .25 |

21st Congress of Lions Club of Yaoundé.

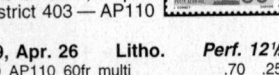

Penny Black, Hill, Cameroun No. 9 AP111

**1979, Oct. 10 Engr. *Perf. 13***

| | | | |
|---|---|---|---|
| **C280** | AP111 100fr multi | 1.00 | .40 |

Sir Rowland Hill (1795-1879), originator of penny postage.

"TELECOM 79" — AP112

**1979, Sept. 26 Litho. *Perf. 13x12½***

| | | | |
|---|---|---|---|
| **C281** | AP112 100fr multi | 1.10 | .40 |

3rd World Telecommunications Exhibition, Geneva, Sept. 20-26.

Pope Paul VI — AP113

**1979, Oct. 23 Engr. *Perf. 12½x13***

| | | | |
|---|---|---|---|
| **C282** | AP113 100fr shown | 2.25 | .50 |
| **C283** | AP113 100fr John Paul I | 2.25 | .50 |
| **C284** | AP113 100fr John Paul II | 2.25 | .50 |
| | *Nos. C282-C284 (3)* | 6.75 | 1.50 |

"Double Eagle" over French Coastline AP114

Design: No. C286, Balloonists and balloon.

**1979, Dec. 15 Litho. *Perf. 12½***

| | | | |
|---|---|---|---|
| **C285** | AP114 500fr multi | 5.00 | 2.25 |
| **C286** | AP114 500fr multi | 5.00 | 2.25 |

First Transatlantic balloon crossing.

100-Meter Race — AP115

Designs: 150fr, Figure skating pairs. 200fr, Javelin. 300fr, Wrestling.

**1980, Dec. 18 Litho. *Perf. 12½***

| | | | | |
|---|---|---|---|---|
| **C287** | AP115 100fr yel brn & brn | .90 | .50 |
| **C288** | AP115 150fr bl & brn | 1.25 | .70 |
| **C289** | AP115 200fr grn & brn | 1.75 | 1.00 |
| **C290** | AP115 300fr red & brn | 2.50 | 1.40 |
| | *Nos. C287-C290 (4)* | 6.40 | 3.60 |

22nd Summer Olympic Games, Moscow, July 19-Aug. 3; 13th Winter Olympic Games, Lake Placid, Feb. 12-24 (150fr).

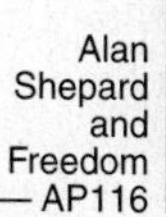

Alan Shepard and Freedom 7 — AP116

No. C292, Yuri Gagarin, Vostok I.

**1981, Sept. 15 Litho. *Perf. 12½***

| | | | |
|---|---|---|---|
| **C291** | AP116 500fr shown | 5.00 | 2.25 |
| **C292** | AP116 500fr multi | 5.00 | 2.25 |

Manned space flight, 20th anniv.

4th African Scouting Conference, Abidjan, June — AP117

100fr, Emblem, salute, badge. 500fr, Scout saluting.

**1981, Oct. 5**

| | | | |
|---|---|---|---|
| **C293** | AP117 100fr multi | .70 | .40 |
| **C294** | AP117 500fr multi | 4.50 | 2.00 |

Guernica (detail), by Pablo Picasso (1881-1973) AP118

No. C296, Landscape, by Paul Cezanne (1839-1906).

**1981, Nov. 10 Litho. *Perf. 12½***

| | | | |
|---|---|---|---|
| **C295** | AP118 500fr multi | 6.00 | 2.00 |
| **C296** | AP118 500fr multi | 6.00 | 2.00 |

Christmas 1981 AP119

Designs: 50fr, Virgin and Child, by Froment, vert. 60f, San Zeno Altarpiece, by Mantegna, vert. 400fr, Flight into Egypt, by Giotto.

**1981, Dec. 1 Litho. *Perf. 12½***

| | | | |
|---|---|---|---|
| **C297** | AP119 50fr multi | .45 | .25 |
| **C298** | AP119 60fr multi | .65 | .30 |
| **C299** | AP119 400fr multi | 3.50 | 2.00 |
| *a.* | Souv. sheet of 3, #C297-C299, perf. 13x13½ | 9.00 | 9.00 |
| | *Nos. C297-C299 (3)* | 4.60 | 2.55 |

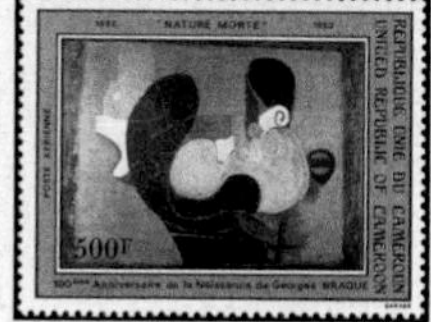

Still Life, by Georges Braque (1882-1963) AP120

Paintings: No. C301, Olympia, by Edouard Manet (1832-1883).

**1982, Dec. 5 Litho. *Perf. 13***

| | | | |
|---|---|---|---|
| **C300** | AP120 500fr multi | 5.00 | 2.00 |
| **C301** | AP120 500fr multi | 5.00 | 2.00 |

Pres. John F. Kennedy (1917-63) — AP121

**1983, Mar. 15 Litho. *Perf. 13***

| | | | |
|---|---|---|---|
| **C302** | AP121 500fr multi | 4.50 | 2.00 |

Lions District 403 (Douala), 2nd Convention, May — AP122

**1983, May 5 Litho. *Perf. 12½***

| | | | |
|---|---|---|---|
| **C303** | AP122 70fr multi | .55 | .30 |
| **C304** | AP122 150fr multi | 1.25 | .65 |

Jeanne of Aragon by Raphael AP123

No. C306, Massacre of Scio by Delacroix.

**1983, Oct. 15 Litho. *Perf. 13***

| | | | |
|---|---|---|---|
| **C305** | AP123 500fr multi | 5.00 | 1.00 |
| **C306** | AP123 500fr multi | 5.00 | 1.00 |

Easter 1984 AP124

200fr, Pieta, by G. Hernandez. 500fr, Martyrdom of St. John the Evangelist, by C. Le Brun.

**1984, Mar. 30 Litho. *Perf. 13***

| | | | |
|---|---|---|---|
| **C307** | AP124 200fr multi | 1.75 | .50 |
| **C308** | AP124 500fr multi | 4.50 | 1.40 |
| *a.* | Souv. sheet of 2, #C307-C308 | 7.25 | 7.25 |

1984 Summer Olympics — AP125

**1984, Apr. 30 *Perf. 12½***

| | | | |
|---|---|---|---|
| **C309** | AP125 100fr High jump | .90 | .25 |
| **C310** | AP125 150fr Volleyball | 1.25 | .35 |
| **C311** | AP125 250fr Handball | 2.25 | .55 |
| **C312** | AP125 500fr Bicycling | 4.50 | 1.10 |
| | *Nos. C309-C312 (4)* | 8.90 | 2.25 |

See Nos. C321-C324.

European Soccer Championship, June 12-27 — AP126

No. C313, Player in red shorts. No. C314, Yellow shorts. No. C315, Players.

**1984, June 5 Litho. *Perf. 12½***

| | | | |
|---|---|---|---|
| **C313** | AP126 250fr multicolored | 2.25 | .65 |
| **C314** | AP126 250fr multicolored | 2.25 | .65 |
| **C315** | AP126 500fr multicolored | 4.50 | 1.25 |
| *a.* | Souvenir sheet of 3 | 10.00 | 10.00 |
| | *Nos. C313-C315 (3)* | 9.00 | 2.55 |

No. C315a contains Nos. C313-C315 in changed panel colors.

Presidential Oath AP127

**1984 Litho. *Perf. 13***

| | | | |
|---|---|---|---|
| **C316** | AP127 60fr French inscription | .55 | .25 |
| *a.* | English inscription | .55 | .25 |
| **C317** | AP127 70fr French inscription | .55 | .25 |
| *a.* | English inscription | .55 | .25 |
| **C318** | AP127 200fr French inscription | 1.75 | .40 |
| *a.* | English inscription | 1.75 | .40 |
| | *Nos. C316-C318 (3)* | 2.85 | .90 |

Issue dates: French, Sept. 15; English, Nov.

Paintings AP128

No. C319, Diana in the Bath, by Watteau (1684-1721). No. C320, Portrait of Diderot (1713-1784).

**1984, Sept. 20 Litho. *Perf. 13***

| | | | |
|---|---|---|---|
| **C319** | AP128 500fr Watteau | 5.00 | 1.00 |
| **C320** | AP128 500fr Diderot, vert. | 5.00 | 1.00 |

**Nos. C309-C312 in Changed Colors with Added Inscriptions**

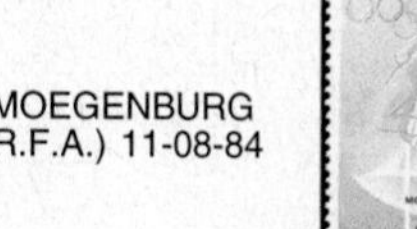

MOEGENBURG (R.F.A.) 11-08-84

U.S.A. 11-08-84

YOUGOSLAVIE 9-08-84

GORSKI (U.S.A.) 3-08-84

**1984, Sept. 25 Litho. *Perf. 12½***

| | | | |
|---|---|---|---|
| **C321** | AP125 100fr multi | .90 | .25 |
| **C322** | AP125 150fr multi | 1.25 | .30 |
| **C323** | AP125 250fr multi | 2.25 | .50 |
| **C324** | AP125 500fr multi | 4.50 | 1.00 |
| | *Nos. C321-C324 (4)* | 8.90 | 2.05 |

Moon Landing, 15th Anniv. — AP129

No. C325, Neil Armstrong. No. C326, Apollo 12 launching.

**1984, Nov. 15 Litho. *Perf. 12½***

| | | | |
|---|---|---|---|
| **C325** | AP129 500fr multi | 4.50 | 1.50 |
| **C326** | AP129 500fr multi | 4.50 | 1.50 |

Louis Pasteur (1822-1895), Chemist, Microbiologist AP130

No. C328, Mourning Woman (detail), Mausoleum of Henri Claude d'Harcourt, by sculptor Jean Baptiste Pigalle (1714-1785).

**1985, Oct. 10 Litho. *Perf. 13***

| | | | |
|---|---|---|---|
| **C327** | AP130 500fr multi | 6.00 | 1.75 |
| **C328** | AP130 500fr multi | 6.00 | 1.75 |

Christmas AP131

250fr, Children's gifts. 300fr, Akono Church. 400fr, Holy Family & drummer boy. 500fr, The Virgin with the Blue Diadem, by Raphael.

**1985, Dec. 20 Litho. *Perf. 13***

| | | | |
|---|---|---|---|
| **C329** | AP131 250fr multi | 2.25 | .90 |
| **C330** | AP131 300fr multi | 2.50 | 1.10 |
| **C331** | AP131 400fr multi | 3.25 | 1.50 |
| **C332** | AP131 500fr multi | 5.00 | 2.00 |
| | *Nos. C329-C332 (4)* | 13.00 | 5.50 |

1986 World Cup Soccer Championships, Mexico — AP132

250fr, Argentina, winner. 300fr, Stadium. 400fr, Mexican team.

**1986** *Perf. 13½*

| | | | | |
|---|---|---|---|---|
| **C333** | AP132 | 250fr multi | 2.75 | 1.40 |
| **C334** | AP132 | 300fr multi | 2.75 | 1.60 |
| **C335** | AP132 | 400fr multi | 3.50 | 2.25 |
| | | *Nos. C333-C335 (3)* | 9.00 | 5.25 |

Issued: 300fr, 400fr, 5/15; 250fr, 7/26.

Famous Men AP133

No. C336, Pierre Curie (1859-1906), chemist, atom, and elements. No. C337, Jean Mermoz (1901-1936), aviator, and aircraft.

**1986, Sept. 10** **Litho.** *Perf. 12½*

| | | | | |
|---|---|---|---|---|
| **C336** | AP133 | 500fr multi | 6.25 | 2.00 |
| **C337** | AP133 | 500fr multi | 6.25 | 2.00 |

## AIR POST SEMI-POSTAL STAMPS

Doctor Examining Child — SPAP1

**Unwmk.**

**1942, June 22** **Engr.** *Perf. 13*

| | | | |
|---|---|---|---|
| **CB1** | SPAP1 | 1.50fr + 50c green | 1.00 |
| **CB2** | SPAP1 | 2fr + 6fr brn & red brn | 1.00 |

Native children's welfare fund.

Nos. CB1-CB2 were issued by the Vichy government in France, but were not placed on sale in Cameroun.

**Colonial Education Fund**

Common Design Type

**1942, June 22**

| | | | |
|---|---|---|---|
| **CB3** | CD86a | 1.20fr + 1.80fr blue & red | 1.10 |

No. CB3 was issued by the Vichy government in France, but was not placed on sale in Cameroun.

## POSTAGE DUE STAMPS

Man Felling Tree — D1

*Perf. 14x13½*

**1925-27** **Unwmk.** **Typo.**

| | | | | |
|---|---|---|---|---|
| **J1** | D1 | 2c lt bl & blk | .30 | .50 |
| **J2** | D1 | 4c ol bis & red vio | .30 | .50 |
| **J3** | D1 | 5c vio & blk | .65 | .80 |
| **J4** | D1 | 10c red & blk | .65 | .80 |
| **J5** | D1 | 15c gray & blk | .75 | .95 |
| **J6** | D1 | 20c olive grn & blk | .75 | .95 |
| **J7** | D1 | 25c yel & blk | 1.40 | 1.60 |
| **J8** | D1 | 30c blue & org | 1.60 | 1.90 |
| **J9** | D1 | 50c brn & blk | 2.00 | 2.40 |
| **J10** | D1 | 60c bl grn & rose red | 2.00 | 2.40 |
| **J11** | D1 | 1fr dl red & grn, *grnsh* | 2.40 | 3.25 |
| **J12** | D1 | 2fr red & vio ('27) | 4.75 | 5.50 |
| **J13** | D1 | 3fr org brn & ultra ('27) | 7.25 | 8.00 |
| | | *Nos. J1-J13 (13)* | 24.80 | 29.55 |

Shades occur for several values.

Carved Figures — D2

**1939** **Engr.** *Perf. 14x13*

| | | | | |
|---|---|---|---|---|
| **J14** | D2 | 5c brt red vio | .25 | .80 |
| **J15** | D2 | 10c Prus blue | .75 | .90 |
| **J16** | D2 | 15c car rose | .25 | .40 |
| **J17** | D2 | 20c blk brn | .25 | .40 |
| **J18** | D2 | 30c ultra | .50 | .65 |
| **J19** | D2 | 50c dk grn | .50 | .65 |
| **J20** | D2 | 60c brn vio | .85 | 1.00 |
| **J21** | D2 | 1fr dk vio | 1.10 | 1.20 |
| **J22** | D2 | 2fr org red | 1.60 | 1.60 |
| **J23** | D2 | 3fr dark blue | 2.25 | 2.40 |
| | | *Nos. J14-J23 (10)* | 8.30 | 10.00 |

**1944** **Type D2 without "RF"**

| | | | |
|---|---|---|---|
| **J23A** | D2 | 10c Prussian blue | .80 |

No. J23A was issued by the Vichy government in France, but was not placed on sale in Cameroun.

**Catalogue values for unused stamps in this section, from this point to the end of the section, are for Never Hinged items.**

D3

**1947** **Unwmk.** *Perf. 13*

| | | | | |
|---|---|---|---|---|
| **J24** | D3 | 10c dark red | .40 | .30 |
| **J25** | D3 | 30c dp org | .40 | .30 |
| **J26** | D3 | 50c grnsh blk | .40 | .30 |
| **J27** | D3 | 1fr dark car | .50 | .40 |
| **J28** | D3 | 2fr dp yel grn | .65 | .55 |
| **J29** | D3 | 3fr dp red lil | .65 | .55 |
| **J30** | D3 | 4fr dp ultra | .90 | .70 |
| **J31** | D3 | 5fr red brn | 1.00 | .90 |
| **J32** | D3 | 10fr peacock bl | 1.90 | 1.60 |
| **J33** | D3 | 20fr sepia | 2.75 | 2.25 |
| | | *Nos. J24-J33 (10)* | 9.55 | 7.85 |

**Federal Republic**

Hibiscus D4

Flowers: No. J35, Erythrina. No. J36, Plumeria lutea. No. J37, Ipomoea. No. J38, Hoodia gordonii. No. J39, Crinum. No. J40, Ochna. No. J41, Gloriosa. No. J42, Costus spectabilis. No. J43, Bougainvillea spectabilis. No. J44, Delonix regia. No. J45, Haemanthus. No. J46, Ophthalmophyllum. No. J47, Titanopsis. No. J48, Amorphophallus. No. J49, Zingiberacee.

**Unwmk.**

**1963, Apr. 10** **Engr.** *Perf. 11*

| | | | | |
|---|---|---|---|---|
| **J34** | D4 | 50c car, bl, grn & yel | .25 | .25 |
| **J35** | D4 | 50c car, bl, grn & yel | .25 | .25 |
| *a.* | | Pair, #J34-J35 | .55 | .45 |
| **J36** | D4 | 1fr mag, grn & yel | .25 | .25 |
| **J37** | D4 | 1fr mag, grn & yel | .25 | .25 |
| *a.* | | Pair, #J36-J37 | .55 | .45 |
| **J38** | D4 | 1.50fr dk grn, lil & yel | .25 | .25 |
| **J39** | D4 | 1.50fr dk grn, lil & yel | .25 | .25 |
| *a.* | | Pair, #J38-J39 | .55 | .45 |
| **J40** | D4 | 2fr org ver, yel & grn | .25 | .25 |
| **J41** | D4 | 2fr org ver, yel & grn | .25 | .25 |
| *a.* | | Pair, #J40-J41 | .55 | .45 |
| **J42** | D4 | 5fr mag, grn & yel | .25 | .25 |
| **J43** | D4 | 5fr mag, grn & yel | .25 | .25 |
| *a.* | | Pair, #J42-J43 | .55 | .45 |
| **J44** | D4 | 10fr crim, grn & yel | .50 | .25 |
| **J45** | D4 | 10fr crim, grn & yel | .50 | .25 |
| *a.* | | Pair, #J44-J45 | 1.20 | .45 |
| **J46** | D4 | 20fr grn, yel & lil | 1.10 | .45 |
| **J47** | D4 | 20fr grn, yel & lil | 1.10 | .45 |
| *a.* | | Pair, #J46-J47 | 2.40 | 1.00 |
| **J48** | D4 | 40fr lilac & yel | 2.00 | .80 |
| **J49** | D4 | 40fr lilac & yel | 2.00 | .80 |
| *a.* | | Pair, #J48-J49 | 4.25 | 1.75 |
| | | *Nos. J34-J49 (16)* | 9.70 | 5.50 |

The pairs are se-tenant at the base.

## MILITARY STAMPS

**Catalogue values for unused stamps in this section are for Never Hinged items.**

M1

**Unwmk.**

**1963, July 1** **Typo.** *Perf. 13*

| | | | | |
|---|---|---|---|---|
| **M1** | M1 | rose claret | 3.00 | 3.00 |

**Type of 1963 Inscribed "REPUBLIC UNIE DU CAMEROUN / UNITED REPUBLIC OF CAMEROUN"**

**1976?** **Litho.** *Perf. 13x13½*

| | | |
|---|---|---|
| **M2** | M1 | rose claret |

# CANADIAN PROVINCES

# BRITISH COLUMBIA & VANCOUVER IS.

'bri-tish kə-'ləm-bē-ə

and van-'kü-vər 'ī-lənd

LOCATION — On the northwest coast of North America

GOVT. — British Colony

AREA — 355,900 sq. mi.

POP. — 36,247 (1871)

In 1871 the colony became a part of the Canadian Confederation and the postage stamps of Canada have since been used.

12 Pence = 1 Shilling

20 Shillings = 1 Pound

100 Cents = 1 Dollar (1865)

Values for unused stamps are for examples with original gum as defined in the catalogue introduction. Very fine examples of Nos. 2 and 5-18 will have perforations touching the design on at least one side due to the narrow spacing of the stamps on the plates. Stamps with perfs clear of the design on all four sides are extremely scarce and will command much higher prices.

Queen Victoria — A1

**1860** **Unwmk.** **Typo.** *Imperf.*

| | | | |
|---|---|---|---|
| **1** | A1 | 2½p dull rose | *27,500.* |

No. 1 was not placed in use and may be a proof or reprint. Most examples are without gum. Value without gum, $18,000.

*Perf. 14*

| | | | | |
|---|---|---|---|---|
| **2** | A1 | 2½p dull rose | *475.* | 240. |

## VANCOUVER ISLAND

A2

A3

**1865** **Wmk. 1** *Imperf.*

| | | | | |
|---|---|---|---|---|
| **3** | A2 | 5c rose | *70,000.* | *11,000.* |
| | | No gum | *40,000.* | |
| **4** | A3 | 10c blue | 3,500. | 1,200. |

*Perf. 14*

| | | | | |
|---|---|---|---|---|
| **5** | A2 | 5c rose | 500. | 300. |
| **6** | A3 | 10c blue | 500. | 300. |

## BRITISH COLUMBIA

Seal of British Columbia — A4

**1865, Nov. 1**

| | | | | |
|---|---|---|---|---|
| **7** | A4 | 3p blue | 250.00 | 110.00 |

**Type A4 of 1865 Surcharged in Various Colors**

**1867-69** *Perf. 14*

| | | | |
|---|---|---|---|
| **8** | 2c on 3p brown (Bk) | 160.00 | 150.00 |
| **9** | 5c on 3p brt red (Bk) ('69) | 300.00 | 250.00 |
| **10** | 10c on 3p lilac rose (Bl) | 2,400. | |
| **11** | 25c on 3p orange (V) ('69) | 400.00 | 325.00 |
| **12** | 50c on 3p violet (R) | 1,000. | *1,050.* |
| **13** | $1 on 3p green (G) | 2,000. | |

Nos. 10 and 13 were not placed in use.

**1869** *Perf. 12½*

| | | | |
|---|---|---|---|
| **14** | 5c on 3p brt red (Bk) | 2,500. | 1,400. |
| **15** | 10c on 3p lilac rose (Bl) | 1,500. | 1,100. |
| **16** | 25c on 3p orange (V) | 1,200. | 850. |
| **17** | 50c on 3p violet (R) | 1,600. | 1,000. |
| **18** | $1 on 3p green (G) | 2,000. | 1,750. |

## NEW BRUNSWICK

'nü 'brənz-ˌwik

LOCATION — Eastern Canada, bordering on the Bay of Fundy and the Gulf of St. Lawrence.
GOVT. — British Province
AREA — 27,985 sq. mi.
POP. — 285,594 (1871)
CAPITAL — Fredericton

At one time a part of Nova Scotia, New Brunswick became a separate province in 1784. Upon joining the Canadian Confederation in 1867 its postage stamps were superseded by those of Canada.

12 Pence = 1 Shilling
100 Cents = 1 Dollar (1860)

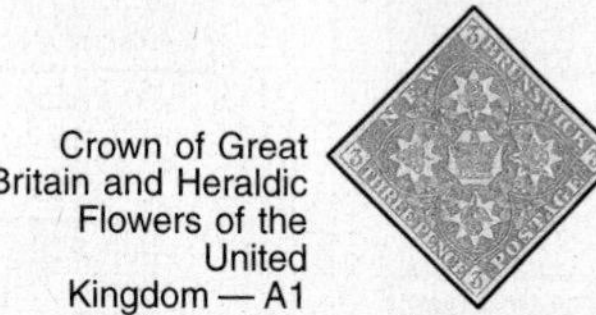

Crown of Great Britain and Heraldic Flowers of the United Kingdom — A1

**1851 Unwmk. Engr. *Imperf.***
**Blue Paper**

| | | | | |
|---|---|---|---|---|
| 1 | A1 | 3p red | 5,500. | 575. |
| *a.* | | 3p dark red | 5,750. | 625. |
| *b.* | | Half used as 1½p on cover | | 4,750. |
| 2 | A1 | 6p olive yellow | 7,500. | 1,200. |
| *a.* | | 6p orange yellow | 7,500. | 1,200. |
| *b.* | | Half used as 3p on cover | | 3,000. |
| *c.* | | Quarter used as 1½p on cover | | *35,000.* |
| *d.* | | 6p mustard yellow | 10,000. | 1,400. |
| 3 | A1 | 1sh brt red violet | *35,000.* | *6,250.* |
| *a.* | | Half used as 6p on cover | | *22,500.* |
| *b.* | | Quarter used as 3p on cover | | *45,000.* |
| 4 | A1 | 1sh dull violet | 40,000. | *9,000.* |
| *a.* | | Half used as 6p on cover | | *22,500.* |
| *b.* | | Quarter used as 3p on cover | | *45,000.* |

*The reprints are on stout white paper. The 3p is printed in orange and the 6p and 1sh in violet black. Value about $275 per set of 3.*

Charles Connell — A2

**1860 *Perf. 12***

| | | | | |
|---|---|---|---|---|
| 5 | A2 | 5c brown | *14,000.* | |

No. 5 was prepared for use but not issued.
Most examples of No. 5 have creases or other faults. Value of an average example is about half that shown here.

Locomotive A3

Victoria A4

A5

A6

Steam and Sailing Ship A7

Edward VII as Prince of Wales A8

**1860-63 White Paper *Perf. 12***

| | | | | |
|---|---|---|---|---|
| 6 | A3 | 1c red lilac | 42.50 | 37.50 |
| *a.* | | 1c brown violet | 90.00 | 70.00 |
| *b.* | | Horiz. pair, imperf. vert., no gum | 800.00 | |
| 7 | A4 | 2c orange ('63) | 32.50 | 17.50 |
| *a.* | | Vertical pair, imperf. horiz., no gum | 775.00 | |
| 8 | A5 | 5c yellow green | 30.00 | 22.50 |
| *a.* | | 5c blue green | 35.00 | 22.50 |
| *b.* | | 5c olive green | 175.00 | 37.50 |
| 9 | A6 | 10c vermilion | 55.00 | 47.50 |
| *a.* | | Half used as 5c on cover | | 1,100. |
| *b.* | | Double impression | — | *850.00* |
| 10 | A7 | 12½c blue | 90.00 | 75.00 |
| 11 | A8 | 17c black | 55.00 | *65.00* |
| | | *Nos. 6-11 (6)* | 305.00 | 265.00 |
| | | Set, never hinged | 645.00 | |

## NEWFOUNDLAND

'nü-fən,dˌ-lənd

LOCATION — Island in the Atlantic Ocean off the coast of Canada, and Labrador, a part of the mainland
GOVT. — British Dominion
AREA — 42,734 sq. mi.
POP. — 321,177 (1945)
CAPITAL — St. John's

Newfoundland was a self-governing Dominion of the British Empire from 1855 to 1933, when it became a Crown Colony. In 1949 it united with Canada.

12 Pence = 1 Shilling
100 Cents = 1 Dollar (1866)

Values for unused stamps are for examples with original gum as defined in the catalogue introduction. However, very fine examples of Nos. 2-7, 9, 11, 12, 13 and 15 without gum are often traded at values very close to those for examples with original gum.

**Watermark**

Wmk. 224 Coat of Arms

As the watermark 224 does not show on every stamp in the sheet, pairs are found one with and one without watermark. This applies to all stamps with watermark 224.

Crown of Great Britain and Heraldic Flowers of the United Kingdom A1

Rose, Thistle and Shamrock A3

A2 A4

A5

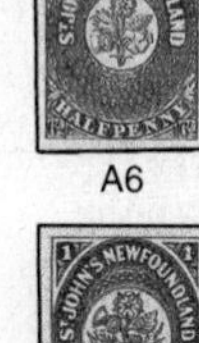

A6

A7

A8

**1857 Unwmk. Engr. *Imperf.***
**Thick Porous Wove Paper with Mesh**

| | | | | |
|---|---|---|---|---|
| 1 | A1 | 1p brn vio | 125.00 | *250.00* |
| *a.* | | Half used as ½p on cover | | *37,500.* |
| 2 | A2 | 2p scar ver | *30,000.* | 7,000. |
| *a.* | | Vert. half used as 1p on cover | | *22,500.* |
| 3 | A3 | 3p green | 1,000. | 575.00 |
| 4 | A4 | 4p scar ver | *22,500.* | 4,500. |
| *a.* | | Half used as 2p on cover | | *22,500.* |
| 5 | A1 | 5p brn vio | 325.00 | *450.00* |
| 6 | A5 | 6p scar ver | *42,500.* | 5,000. |
| 7 | A6 | 6½p scar ver | 8,500. | *4,000.* |
| 8 | A7 | 8p scar ver | 400.00 | *600.00* |
| *a.* | | Half used as 4p on cover | | 4,250. |
| 9 | A8 | 1sh scar ver | *60,000.* | *9,500.* |
| *a.* | | Half used as 6p on cover | | *20,000.* |

**1860**
**Thin to Thick Wove Paper, No Mesh**

| | | | | |
|---|---|---|---|---|
| 11 | A2 | 2p orange | 500.00 | *450.00* |
| 11A | A3 | 3p green | 85.00 | *115.00* |
| 12 | A4 | 4p orange | 5,500. | 1,350. |
| *b.* | | Half used as 2p on cover | | *22,500.* |
| 12A | A1 | 5p vio brown | 85.00 | *150.00* |
| 13 | A5 | 6p orange | 6,000. | 1,100. |
| 15 | A8 | 1sh orange | *50,000.* | 12,000. |
| *b.* | | Half used as 6p on cover | | *37,500.* |

A 6½p orange exists as a souvenir item.
A 1sh exists in orange on horizontally or vertically laid paper. Most authorities consider these to be proofs. Value, $27,500.

**1861-62**

| | | | | |
|---|---|---|---|---|
| 15A | A1 | 1p vio brown | 150.00 | *225.00* |
| 16 | A1 | 1p reddish brown | *22,500.* | |
| 17 | A2 | 2p rose | 150.00 | *150.00* |
| 18 | A4 | 4p rose | 37.50 | *70.00* |
| *a.* | | Half used as 2p on cover | | *45,000.* |
| 19 | A1 | 5p reddish brown | 75.00 | *77.50* |
| 20 | A5 | 6p rose | 22.50 | *62.50* |
| *a.* | | Half used as 3p on cover | | *15,000.* |
| 21 | A6 | 6½p rose | 85.00 | *150.00* |
| 22 | A7 | 8p rose | 85.00 | *300.00* |
| 23 | A8 | 1sh rose | 42.50 | *110.00* |
| *a.* | | Half used as 6p on cover | | *22,500.* |

Some sheets of Nos. 11-23 are known with the papermaker's watermark "STACEY WISE 1858" in large capitals. Values unused and used about 25% more than values shown, except about 50% more for unused Nos. 12 and 13, and 75% more for unused No. 16.
No. 16 was prepared but not issued.
False cancellations are found on Nos. 1, 3, 5, 8, 11, 11A, 12A and 17-23.
Forgeries exist of most or all of Nos. 1-23.

Codfish — A9

Harp Seal — A10

Prince Albert A11

Victoria A12

Fishing Ship A13

Victoria A14

**1865-94 *Perf. 12***
**White Paper(#24, 27, 28)**
**Thin Yellowish Paper (#25-26, 29-31)**

| | | | | |
|---|---|---|---|---|
| 24 | A9 | 2c green | 150.00 | 35.00 |
| *a.* | | Thin yellowish paper | 250.00 | 70.00 |
| *b.* | | Half used as 1c on cover | | *8,000.* |
| 25 | A10 | 5c brown | 750.00 | 450.00 |
| *a.* | | Half used as 2c on cover | | *10,000.* |
| 26 | A10 | 5c black ('68) | 750.00 | 275.00 |
| *a.* | | Half used as 2c on cover | | *6,000.* |
| 27 | A11 | 10c black | 600.00 | 50.00 |
| *a.* | | Thin yellowish paper | 725.00 | 90.00 |
| *b.* | | Half used as 5c on cover | | *9,000.* |
| 28 | A12 | 12c pale red brn | 85.00 | 47.50 |
| *a.* | | Thin yellowish paper | 850.00 | 190.00 |
| *b.* | | Half used as 6c on cover | | *4,500.* |
| 29 | A12 | 12c brn, *white* ('94) | 70.00 | 45.00 |
| 30 | A13 | 13c orange | 250.00 | 115.00 |
| 31 | A14 | 24c blue, thin transluscent paper | 75.00 | 35.00 |
| *a.* | | Thicker white paper ('70) | 375.00 | 300.00 |

See Nos. 38, 40.

Edward VII as Prince of Wales A15

Queen Victoria A16

**1868-94**

| | | | | |
|---|---|---|---|---|
| 32 | A15 | 1c violet | 175.00 | 60.00 |
| 32A | A15 | 1c brn lil (re-engr. '71) | 200.00 | 75.00 |
| 33 | A16 | 3c ver ('70) | 900.00 | 190.00 |
| 34 | A16 | 3c blue ('73) | 700.00 | 75.00 |
| 35 | A16 | 6c dull rose ('70) | 37.50 | 17.50 |
| 36 | A16 | 6c car lake ('94) | 50.00 | 22.50 |
| | | *Nos. 32-36 (6)* | 2,063. | 440.00 |

In the re-engraved 1c the top of the letters "N" and "F" are about ½mm from the ribbon with "ONE CENT." In No. 32 they are fully 1mm away. There are many small differences in the engraving.

**1876-79** ***Rouletted***

**37** A15 1c brn lilac ('77) 150.00 52.50
**38** A9 2c green ('79) 200.00 52.50
**39** A16 3c blue ('77) 425.00 15.00
**40** A10 5c blue 275.00 15.00
*Nos. 37-40 (4)* 1,050. 135.00

A17

A19

A18

A20

**1880-96** ***Perf. 12***

**41** A17 1c violet brown 60.00 11.50
**42** A17 1c gray brown 60.00 11.50
**43** A17 1c brown ('96) 130.00 70.00
**44** A17 1c deep green ('87) 30.00 4.25
**45** A17 1c green ('97) 30.00 4.25
**46** A19 2c yellow green 75.00 14.00
**47** A19 2c green ('96) 125.00 27.50
**48** A19 2c red org ('87) 37.50 9.50
*a.* Imperf., pair, no gum 300.00
*c.* Half used as 1c on cover *450.00*
**49** A18 3c blue ('96) 70.00 7.00
**51** A18 3c umber brn ('87) 80.00 4.75
**52** A18 3c vio brown ('96) 120.00 90.00
**53** A20 5c pale blue 425.00 14.00
**54** A20 5c dark blue ('87) 225.00 10.00
**55** A20 5c bright bl ('94) 75.00 6.50
*Nos. 41-55 (14)* 1,543. 284.75

Newfoundland Dog — A21

Schooner — A22

**1887-96**

**56** A21 ½c rose red 12.50 7.50
**57** A21 ½c org red ('96) 80.00 45.00
**58** A21 ½c black ('94) 14.00 7.25
**59** A22 10c black 145.00 60.00
*Nos. 56-59 (4)* 251.50 119.75
Set, never hinged 505.00

Queen Victoria — A23

**1890**

**60** A23 3c slate 30.00 1.25
*a.* 3c gray lilac 30.00 1.60
*b.* 3c brown lilac 50.00 1.60
*c.* 3c lilac 35.00 1.60
*d.* 3c slate violet 70.00 3.00
*e.* Vert. pair, imperf. horiz. 750.00

For surcharges see Nos. 75-77.

Victoria A24

Cabot (John?) A25

Cape Bonavista A26

Caribou Hunting A27

Mining A28

Logging A29

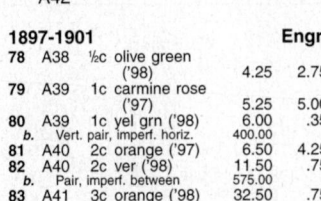

Fishing A30

Cabot's Ship "Matthew" A31

Willow Ptarmigan A32

Seals A33

Salmon Fishing A34

Colony Seal A35

Iceberg off St. John's A36

Henry VII A37

**1897, June 24**

**61** A24 1c deep green 1.60 1.75
**62** A25 2c carmine lake 2.10 1.40
**63** A26 3c ultramarine 4.25 1.40
**64** A27 4c olive green 6.00 2.75
**65** A28 5c violet 11.00 2.75
**66** A29 6c red brown 5.50 3.25
**67** A30 8c red orange 22.50 15.00
**68** A31 10c black brown 22.50 7.50
**69** A32 12c dark blue 25.00 15.00
**70** A33 15c scarlet 20.00 13.00
**71** A34 24c gray violet 25.00 12.00
**72** A35 30c slate 60.00 55.00
**73** A36 35c red 110.00 60.00
**74** A37 60c black 16.00 11.50
*Nos. 61-74 (14)* 331.45 202.30
Set, never hinged 662.50

400th anniv. of John Cabot's discovery of Newfoundland; 60th year of Victoria's reign. The ship on the 10c was previously used by the American Bank Note Co. as the "Flagship of Columbus" on US No. 232. The portrait on the 2c, intended to be of John Cabot, is said to be a Holbein painting of his son, Sebastian.

For surcharges and overprints see Nos. 127-130, C2-C4.

**No. 60a Surcharged**

No. 75

No. 76

No. 77

**Available Oct. 19 through Dec. 3, 1897**

**75** A23 1c on 3c gray lil 85.00 50.00
*a.* Dbl. surch., one diagonal *2,000.*
*b.* Vert. pair, "ONE CENT" and lower bar omitted on bottom stamp *4,250.*
**76** A23 1c on 3c gray lil 275.00 225.00
**77** A23 1c on 3c gray lil 900.00 850.00
*Nos. 75-77 (3)* 1,260. 1,125.
Set, never hinged 3,065.

Most examples of Nos. 75-77 are poorly centered. Fine examples sell for about 60% of the values given. No. 75b is valued in the grade of fine.

Trial surcharges of Nos. 75-77 exist with red surcharge and with double surcharge, one in red and one in black, but these were not issued.

Edward VIII as a Child A38

Victoria A39

Edward VII as Prince of Wales A40

Queen Alexandra as Princess of Wales A41

Queen Mary as Duchess of York A42

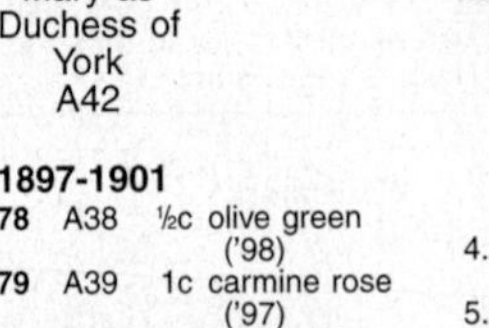

George V as Duke of York A43

**1897-1901** **Engr.**

**78** A38 ½c olive green ('98) 4.25 2.75
**79** A39 1c carmine rose ('97) 5.25 5.00
**80** A39 1c yel grn ('98) 6.00 .35
*b.* Vert. pair, imperf. horiz. 400.00
**81** A40 2c orange ('97) 6.50 4.25
**82** A40 2c ver ('98) 11.50 .75
*b.* Pair, imperf. between 575.00
**83** A41 3c orange ('98) 32.50 .75
*a.* Vert. pair, imperf. horiz. 400.00
**84** A42 4c violet ('01) 45.00 4.50
**85** A43 5c blue ('99) 45.00 3.00
*Nos. 78-85 (8)* 156.00 21.35
Set, never hinged 312.00

No. 80b is valued in the grade of fine.

**Imperf., Pairs**

*78a* A38 ½c 600.00 *400.00*
*81a* A40 2c *450.00*
*82a* A40 2c 400.00 *950.00*
*83b* A41 3c 425.00
*84a* A42 4c 650.00

No. 82a used is valued on cover. Three such covers are recorded.

---

Imperf., Pairs

Newfoundland imperforates virtually always are proofs on stamp paper or "postmaster's perquisites." Most part-perforate varieties also are "postmaster's perquisites." These items were not regularly issued, but rather were sold or given to favored persons.

---

Map of Newfoundland — A44

**1908, Sept.**

**86** A44 2c rose carmine 60.00 3.50
Never hinged 120.00

**Guy Issue**

James I — A45

Arms of the London and Bristol Co. — A46

John Guy A47

Guy's Ship, the "Endeavour" A48

View of Cupids A49

Lord Bacon A50

View of Mosquito A51

Logging Camp A52

Paper Mills — A53

Edward VII — A54

George V — A55

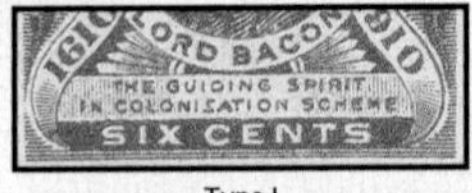



Type I

Type II

SIX CENT TYPES
I — "Z" of "COLONIZATION" reversed.
II — "Z" of normal.

**1910, Aug. 15** **Litho.** ***Perf. 12***

**87** A45 1c deep green, perf. 12x11 2.00 1.10
*a.* Perf. 12 4.25 1.90
*b.* Perf. 12x14 7.00 2.25
*c.* Horiz. pair, imperf. btwn. 400.00 —
*d.* Vert. pair, imperf. btwn. 450.00
*h.* Perf. 12x12x12x11 —
**88** A46 2c carmine 11.00 1.15
*a.* Perf. 12x14 7.50 .85
*b.* As "a," horiz. pair, imperf. between 750.00
*c.* Perf. 12x11 ½ 900.00 325.00
**89** A47 3c brown olive 27.50 14.00
**90** A48 4c dull violet 25.00 14.00
**91** A49 5c ultramarine, perf. 14x12 27.50 4.50
*a.* Perf. 12 32.50 7.50
**92** A50 6c claret, type I 97.50 70.00
**92A** A50 6c claret, type II 55.00 37.50
*b.* Imperf., pair 450.00
**93** A51 8c pale brown 75.00 55.00
**94** A52 9c olive green 75.00 55.00
**95** A53 10c vio black 75.00 55.00
**96** A54 12c lilac brown 75.00 55.00
*a.* Imperf., pair 425.00
**97** A55 15c gray black 75.00 65.00
*Nos. 87-97 (12)* 620.50 427.25
Set, never hinged 1,500.

Tercentenary of the Colonization of Newfoundland.

On No. 87 printing flaws such as "NFW," "JAMRS" and "JANES" exist.

A vertical bisect on cover is known for No. 90.

**1911** **Engr.** ***Perf. 14***

**98** A50 6c brown vio 42.50 25.00
*b.* Horiz. pair, imperf. btwn. *1,150.*
**99** A51 8c bister brn 75.00 67.50
*b.* Horiz. pair, imperf. btwn. *1,150.*
**100** A52 9c olive grn 70.00 60.00
*b.* Horiz. pair, imperf. btwn. *1,150.*

| | | | | |
|---|---|---|---|---|
| **101** | A53 | 10c violet blk | 95.00 | 90.00 |
| *b.* | | Horiz. pair, imperf. btwn. | *1,150.* | |
| **102** | A54 | 12c red brown | 70.00 | 70.00 |
| *b.* | | Horiz. pair, imperf. btwn. | *1,150.* | |
| **103** | A55 | 15c slate grn | 70.00 | 70.00 |
| *b.* | | Horiz. pair, imperf. btwn. | *1,150.* | |
| | | *Nos. 98-103 (6)* | 422.50 | *382.50* |
| | | Set, never hinged | 812.50 | |

Nos. 100 and 103 are known with papermaker's watermark "E. TOWGOOD FINE." Values, unused or used: No. 100, $800; No. 103, $1,000.

### Imperf., Pairs

| | | | |
|---|---|---|---|
| *98a* | A50 | 6c | 325.00 |
| *99a* | A51 | 8c | 325.00 |
| *100a* | A52 | 9c | 325.00 |
| *101a* | A53 | 10c | 325.00 |
| *102a* | A54 | 12c | 325.00 |
| *103a* | A55 | 15c | 325.00 |

Nos. 98a-103a were made with and without gum. Values the same.

### Royal Family Issue

Queen Mary A56

George V A57

Prince of Wales (Edward VIII) A58

Prince Albert (George VI) A59

Princess Mary A60

Prince Henry A61

Prince George A62

Prince John A63

Queen Alexandra A64

Duke of Connaught A65

Seal of Colony — A66

| **1911, June 19** | | | | *Perf. 13½x14, 14* |
|---|---|---|---|---|
| **104** | A56 | 1c yellow grn | 3.00 | .25 |
| **105** | A57 | 2c carmine | 2.75 | 1.00 |
| **106** | A58 | 3c red brown | 35.00 | 19.00 |
| **107** | A59 | 4c violet | 35.00 | 13.50 |
| **108** | A60 | 5c ultra | 22.50 | 1.90 |
| **109** | A61 | 6c black | 32.50 | 22.50 |
| **110** | A62 | 8c blue (paper colored through) | 80.00 | 65.00 |
| *a.* | | 8c peacock blue | 90.00 | 70.00 |
| **111** | A63 | 9c bl violet | 35.00 | 20.00 |
| **112** | A64 | 10c dark green | 50.00 | 37.50 |
| **113** | A65 | 12c plum | 40.00 | 37.50 |
| **114** | A66 | 15c magenta | 32.50 | *37.50* |
| | | *Nos. 104-114 (11)* | 368.25 | 255.65 |
| | | Set, never hinged | 744.00 | |

Coronation of King George V.

### Imperf., Pairs
### Without Gum

| | | | |
|---|---|---|---|
| *104a* | A56 | 1c | 325.00 |
| *105a* | A57 | 2c | 325.00 |
| *108a* | A60 | 5c | 325.00 |
| *113a* | A65 | 12c | 425.00 |
| *114a* | A66 | 15c | 140.00 |

### Trail of the Caribou Issue

Caribou
A67 A68

| **1919, Jan. 2** | | | | *Perf. 14* |
|---|---|---|---|---|
| **115** | A67 | 1c green | 2.75 | .35 |
| **116** | A68 | 2c scarlet | 3.00 | .50 |
| **117** | A67 | 3c red brown | 3.50 | .30 |
| **118** | A67 | 4c violet | 5.00 | 1.40 |
| **119** | A68 | 5c ultramarine | 9.00 | 1.40 |
| **120** | A67 | 6c gray | 22.50 | 22.50 |
| **121** | A68 | 8c magenta | 25.00 | 19.00 |
| **122** | A67 | 10c dark green | 22.50 | 5.50 |
| **123** | A68 | 12c orange | 75.00 | 45.00 |
| **124** | A67 | 15c dark blue | 42.50 | 42.50 |
| **125** | A67 | 24c bister | 45.00 | 42.50 |
| **126** | A67 | 36c olive green | 37.50 | 35.00 |
| | | *Nos. 115-126 (12)* | 293.25 | 215.95 |
| | | Set, never hinged | 616.50 | |

Services of the Newfoundland contingent in WWI.

Each denomination of type A67 is inscribed with the name of a different action in which Newfoundland troops took part.

For overprint and surcharge see Nos. C1, C5.

A shipment delay of the Trail of the Caribou issue led to trial surcharges of No. 74 reading "TWO / 2 / CENTS" in red. Fifty stamps were so surcharged, including examples with double surcharge. Value, $1,000.

### Imperf., Pairs
### Without Gum

| | | | |
|---|---|---|---|
| *115a* | A67 | 1c | 290.00 |
| *116a* | A68 | 2c | 290.00 |
| *117a* | A67 | 3c red brown | 290.00 |
| *118a* | A67 | 4c | 290.00 |
| *119a* | A68 | 5c | 290.00 |
| *120a* | A67 | 6c | 290.00 |
| *121a* | A68 | 8c | 290.00 |
| *122a* | A67 | 10c | 290.00 |
| *123a* | A68 | 12c | 290.00 |
| *124a* | A67 | 15c | 290.00 |
| *125a* | A67 | 24c | 290.00 |
| *126a* | A67 | 36c | 290.00 |

No. 72 Surcharged in Black

### Available Sept. 24 through Sept. 27, 1920

| | | | | |
|---|---|---|---|---|
| **127** | A35 | 2c on 30c slate | 5.25 | 5.50 |
| | | Never hinged | 8.00 | |
| *a.* | | Inverted surcharge | 1,250. | |

No. 127 with red surcharge is an unissued color trial. 25 examples are known. Value, $1,250.

Nos. 70 and 73 Surcharged in Black

THREE CENTS
Type I — Bars 10½mm apart.
Type II — Bars 13½mm apart.

### Available Sept. 13 through Oct. 3, 1920

| | | | | |
|---|---|---|---|---|
| **128** | A33 | 3c on 15c scar (I) | 220.00 | 240.00 |
| | | Never hinged | 350.00 | |
| *a.* | | Inverted surcharge | *3,000.* | |
| **129** | A33 | 3c on 15c scar (II) | 17.50 | 11.00 |
| | | Never hinged | 35.00 | |
| **130** | A36 | 3c on 35c red | 11.00 | 9.50 |
| | | Never hinged | 20.00 | |
| *a.* | | Lower bar omitted | 140.00 | 140.00 |

Trial surcharges of "THREE CENTS" between bars on No. 66 in red or brown are known. Twenty-five of each were produced, Value, $700.

Twin Hills, Tor's Cove A70

South West Arm, Trinity A71

War Memorial, St. John's A72

Humber River A73

Coast of Trinity A74

Upper Steadies, Humber River A75

Quidi Vidi, near St. John's A76

Caribou Crossing Lake A77

Humber River Canyon A78

Shell Bird Island A79

Mt. Moriah, Bay of Islands A80

Humber River near Little Rapids A81

Placentia, from Mt. Pleasant A82

Topsail Falls near St. John's A83

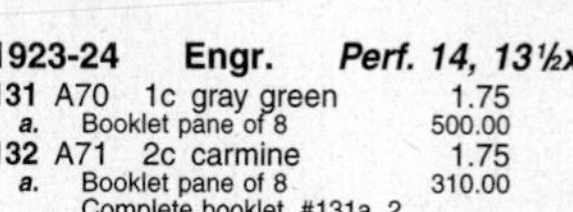

| **1923-24** | | **Engr.** | *Perf. 14, 13½x14* | |
|---|---|---|---|---|
| **131** | A70 | 1c gray green | 1.75 | .30 |
| *a.* | | Booklet pane of 8 | 500.00 | |
| **132** | A71 | 2c carmine | 1.75 | .30 |
| *a.* | | Booklet pane of 8 | 310.00 | |
| | | Complete booklet, #131a, 2 #132a | *2,750.* | |
| **133** | A72 | 3c brown | 2.25 | .30 |
| **134** | A73 | 4c brn violet | 2.60 | 1.80 |
| **135** | A74 | 5c ultramarine | 6.50 | 2.25 |
| **136** | A75 | 6c gray black | 6.50 | 6.00 |
| **137** | A76 | 8c dull violet | 4.75 | 4.50 |
| **138** | A77 | 9c slate green | 42.50 | 27.50 |
| **139** | A78 | 10c dark violet | 4.25 | 2.50 |
| **140** | A79 | 11c olive green | 7.00 | 7.00 |
| **141** | A80 | 12c lake | 7.00 | 7.50 |
| **142** | A81 | 15c deep blue | 8.50 | 8.00 |
| **143** | A82 | 20c red brn ('24) | 12.00 | 7.50 |
| **144** | A83 | 24c blk brn ('24) | 80.00 | 50.00 |
| | | *Nos. 131-144 (14)* | 187.35 | 125.45 |
| | | Set, never hinged | 315.50 | |

For surcharge see No. 160.

### Imperf., Pairs

| | | | |
|---|---|---|---|
| *131b* | A70 | 1c | 200.00 |
| *132b* | A71 | 2c | 200.00 |
| *133a* | A72 | 3c | 475.00 |
| *134a* | A73 | 4c | 250.00 |
| *135a* | A74 | 5c | 250.00 |
| *136a* | A75 | 6c | 250.00 |
| *137a* | A76 | 8c | 250.00 |
| *138a* | A77 | 9c | 250.00 |
| *139a* | A78 | 10c | 250.00 |
| *140a* | A79 | 11c | 250.00 |
| *141a* | A80 | 12c | 250.00 |
| *142a* | A81 | 15c | 185.00 |

Nos. 133a-139a, 141a-142a are without gum. Others are either with or without gum; values about the same.

Map of New-foundland A84

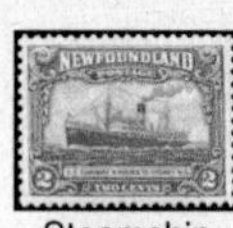

Steamship "Caribou" A85

Queen Mary, George V A86

Prince of Wales A87

Express Train — A88

Newfoundland Hotel, St. John's — A89

Heart's Content A90

Cabot Tower, St. John's A91

War Memorial, St. John's A92

GPO, St. John's A93

First Nonstop Transatlantic Flight, 1919 — A94

Colonial Building, St. John's A95

Grand Falls, Labrador A96

### *Perf. 14, 13½x13, 13x13½*

| **1928, Jan. 3** | | | | |
|---|---|---|---|---|
| **145** | A84 | 1c deep green | 1.85 | .75 |
| **146** | A85 | 2c deep carmine | 2.50 | .70 |
| *a.* | | Imperf., pair | 300.00 | |
| **147** | A86 | 3c brown | 2.75 | .50 |
| **148** | A87 | 4c lilac rose | 3.50 | 1.80 |
| **149** | A88 | 5c slate green | 10.00 | 4.25 |
| **150** | A89 | 6c ultramarine | 5.75 | 5.00 |
| **151** | A90 | 8c lt red brown | 7.25 | 4.50 |
| **152** | A91 | 9c myrtle green | 7.00 | 7.00 |
| **153** | A92 | 10c dark violet | 9.00 | 4.25 |
| **154** | A93 | 12c brn carmine | 5.50 | 5.00 |
| **155** | A91 | 14c red brown | 10.50 | 7.00 |
| **156** | A94 | 15c dark blue | 9.25 | 7.00 |
| **157** | A95 | 20c gray black | 12.50 | 6.50 |
| **158** | A93 | 28c gray green | 35.00 | 27.50 |
| **159** | A96 | 30c olive brown | 17.50 | 7.50 |
| | | *Nos. 145-159 (15)* | 139.85 | 89.25 |
| | | Set, never hinged | 280.25 | |

See Nos. 163-182.

No. 136 Surcharged in Red or Black

Type I — 5mm between "CENTS" and bar.
Type II — 3mm between "CENTS" and bar.

### Available Aug. 23-Aug. 30, 1929

| | | | |
|---|---|---|---|
| **160** A75 3c on 6c gray black (II) (R) | 4.25 | *5.50* |
| Never hinged | 6.75 | |
| *a.* Inverted surcharge (II) | 1,250. | |

The stamps with black surcharge, type I and II, were trial surcharges, and were not issued. There were 50 examples of each. Value, each $1,250.

### Types of 1928 Issue Re-engraved

**1c** — On No. 145 the lines of the engraving are thinner and the impression is clearer than on No. 163. On the former "C. BAULD" is above "C. NORMAN." On the latter these words are transposed.

**2c** — On the 1928 stamp the "D" of "NEWFOUNDLAND" is 1mm from the scroll at the right; the flag at the stern is lower than the top of the boat davit. On the 1929 stamp the "D" is ½mm from the scroll and the flag rises above the davits.

**3c** — On the 1928 stamp the pearls at the top of the crown, the jewels of the tiara and the pillars flanking the portraits are all unshaded. On the reengraved stamp there are small curved lines inside the pearls, the jewels of the tiara are in solid color, and the pillars have vertical shading lines. On the 1928 stamps the tablets with "THREE" and "CENTS" have a background of crossed lines (vertical and horizontal). On the 1929 stamp the background is of horizontal lines only.

**4c** — On the 1928 stamp the figures "4" have shading of horizontal and diagonal crossed lines. There are six circles at each side of the portrait.

On the 1929 stamp the "4s" have shading of horizontal lines only. There are five roses at each side of the portrait.

**5c** — The crossbars of the telegraph pole touch the frame at the left on the 1929 stamp but just clear it on the 1928 stamp. In the 1928 issue the foliate ornaments beside and below the figures "5" end in small scrolls and a small spur. These spurs are omitted on the 1929 stamp.

**6c** — On the re-engraved stamp the columns at right and left of the picture have heavy wavy outlines on the inner sides. There is no period after "JOHNS." The numerals in the lower corners are 1½mm wide instead of 1¼mm.

**8c** — The impression of the 1928 stamp is clear, that of 1931 is slightly blurred. The 1928 stamp has three horizontal lines above "EIGHT CENTS" and four berries on the laurel branch at the right side. On the 1931 stamp there are two horizontal lines and three berries.

**10c** — On the re-engraved stamp there is no period after "ST. JOHN'S." The letters of "TEN CENTS" are slightly larger and the numerals "10" slightly smaller than in 1928. Inside the "0" of "10" at the right there are two vertical lines instead of three. The clouds are fainter in 1929 and the cross upheld by the figure on the monument is more distinct. On the 1928 stamp the torch at the left side terminates in a single tongue of flame. On the 1929-30 stamp it terminates in two tongues.

**15c** — On the 1928 stamp the "N" of "NEWFOUNDLAND" is 1½mm from the left frame, the "L" of "LEAVING" is under the first "A" of "AIRPLANE" and the apostrophe in "JOHN'S" breaks the first line above it.

On the 1929 stamp the "N" of "NEWFOUNDLAND" is 1mm from the left frame, the "L" of "LEAVING" is below the "T" of "FIRST" and the apostrophe in "JOHN'S" does not touch the line above it.

**20c** — On the 1928 stamp the points of the "W" of "NEWFOUNDLAND" are truncated. The "O" is wide and nearly round. The columns that form the sides of the frame have a shading of evenly spaced horizontal lines at their inner sides.

On the 1929-31 stamp the points of the "W" form sharp angles. The "O" is narrow and has a small opening. Many lines have been added to the shading on the inner sides of the columns, making it almost solid.

**30c** — 1928 stamp. Size: 19¼x24½mm. At the outer side of the right column there are three strong and two faint vertical lines. Faint period after "FALLS."

1931 stamp. Size: 19x25mm. At the outer side of the right column there are two strong vertical lines and a fragment of the lower end of a faint one. Clear period after "FALLS." A great many of the small lines of the design have been deepened making the whole stamp appear darker.

### 1929-31 Unwmk. *Perf. 13½ to 14*

| | | |
|---|---|---|
| **163** A84 1c green | 2.00 | .65 |
| *a.* Double impression | *425.00* | |
| *b.* Vert. pair, imperf. btwn. | 210.00 | |
| **164** A85 2c deep carmine | 2.00 | .70 |
| **165** A86 3c dp red brown | 2.00 | .70 |
| **166** A87 4c magenta | 3.50 | 1.25 |
| **167** A88 5c slate green | 7.00 | 2.50 |
| **168** A89 6c ultramarine | 9.00 | 9.00 |
| **169** A92 10c dark violet | 8.00 | 2.25 |
| **170** A94 15c deep blue ('30) | 45.00 | 37.50 |
| **171** A95 20c gray blk ('31) | 70.00 | 27.50 |
| *Nos. 163-171 (9)* | 148.50 | 82.05 |
| Set, never hinged | 297.00 | |

### Imperf., Pairs

| | | | |
|---|---|---|---|
| *163c* | A84 | 1c | 120.00 |
| *164a* | A85 | 2c pale carmine, *cream* | 145.00 |
| *b.* | | 2c dark carmine | 145.00 |
| *165a* | A86 | 3c | 145.00 |
| *166a* | A87 | 4c | 160.00 |

No. 164b is without gum, others with gum.

### Types of 1928 Issue Re-engraved

### 1931 Wmk. 224 *Perf. 13½x14*

| | | |
|---|---|---|
| **172** A84 1c green, perf. 13½ | 2.25 | 1.30 |
| *a.* Horiz. pair, imperf. btwn. | 450.00 | |
| **173** A85 2c red | 7.00 | 1.30 |
| **174** A86 3c red brown | 3.50 | 1.30 |
| **175** A87 4c rose | 4.25 | 2.75 |
| **176** A88 5c grnsh gray | 12.50 | 7.00 |
| **177** A89 6c ultramarine | 17.50 | 17.50 |
| **178** A90 8c lt red brn | 22.50 | 17.50 |
| **179** A92 10c dk violet | 15.00 | 9.00 |
| **180** A94 15c deep blue | 45.00 | 27.50 |
| **181** A95 20c gray black | 55.00 | 17.50 |
| **182** A96 30c olive brown | 45.00 | 25.00 |
| *Nos. 172-182 (11)* | 229.50 | 127.65 |
| Set, never hinged | 459.00 | |

Codfish A97

George V A98

Queen Mary A99

Prince of Wales A100

Caribou A101

Princess Elizabeth A102

Salmon Leaping Falls — A103

Newfoundland Dog — A104

Harp Seal Pup — A105

Cape Race — A106

Sealing Fleet A107

Fishing Fleet Leaving for "The Banks" A108

Type I

Type II

FIVE CENT
Die I — Antlers even, or equal in height.
Die II — Antler under "T" higher.

### 1932-38 Engr. *Perf. 13½, 14*

| | | |
|---|---|---|
| **183** A97 1c green | 2.75 | .50 |
| *a.* Booklet pane of 4, perf. 13 | 75.00 | |
| *c.* Vert. pair, imperf. btwn. | 200.00 | |
| **184** A97 1c gray black | .60 | .25 |
| *a.* Bklt. pane of 4, perf. 13½ | 57.50 | |
| *b.* Booklet pane of 4, perf. 14 | 72.50 | |
| **185** A98 2c rose | 2.25 | .35 |
| *a.* Booklet pane of 4, perf. 13½ | 35.00 | |
| *b.* Booklet pane of 4, perf. 13 | 47.50 | |
| **186** A98 2c green | 1.10 | .25 |
| *a.* Bklt. pane of 4, perf. 13½ | 25.00 | |
| *b.* Booklet pane of 4, perf. 14 | 35.00 | |
| *d.* Horiz. pair, imperf. btwn. | 150.00 | |
| **187** A99 3c orange brn | 1.10 | .35 |
| *a.* Bklt. pane of 4, perf. 13½ | 55.00 | |
| Complete booklet, #184a, 3 #186a, #187a | *525.00* | |
| *b.* Booklet pane of 4, perf. 14 | 67.50 | |
| Complete booklet, #184b, 3 #186b, #187b | *575.00* | |
| *c.* Booklet pane of 4, perf. 13 | 75.00 | |
| Complete booklet, #183a, 3 #185b, #187c | *900.00* | |
| Complete booklet, #183a, 3 #185a, #187c | *900.00* | |
| *e.* Vert. pair, imperf. btwn. | 300.00 | |
| **188** A100 4c deep violet | 7.00 | 2.00 |
| **189** A100 4c rose lake | .75 | .50 |
| *b.* Vert. pair, imperf. btwn. | 120.00 | |
| *c.* Horiz. pair, imperf. btwn. | 120.00 | |
| **190** A101 5c vio brn, perf. 13½ (Die I) | 9.50 | 2.00 |
| **191** A101 5c dp vio, perf. 13½ (Die II) | 1.10 | .40 |
| *a.* 5c dp vio, perf. 13½ (Die I) | 14.00 | 1.25 |
| *c.* Horiz. pair, imperf. btwn. (I) | 240.00 | |
| *g.* Horiz. pair, imperf. btwn. (II) | 240.00 | |
| **192** A102 6c dull blue | 10.00 | 11.00 |
| **193** A103 10c olive black | 1.40 | .85 |
| **194** A104 14c int black | 3.25 | 2.75 |
| **195** A105 15c magenta | 2.50 | 2.25 |
| **196** A106 20c gray green | 2.50 | 1.00 |
| **197** A107 25c gray | 2.75 | 2.00 |
| *b.* Horiz. pair, imperf. btwn. | 500.00 | |
| *c.* Vert. pair, imperf. btwn. | 500.00 | |
| **198** A108 30c ultra | 32.50 | 24.00 |
| *b.* Vert. pair, imperf. btwn. | 1,000. | |
| **199** A108 48c red brn ('38) | 10.00 | 5.25 |
| *Nos. 183-199 (17)* | 91.05 | 55.70 |
| Set, never hinged | 133.05 | |

Two dies were used for 2c green, one for 2c rose.

See Nos. 253-266.

### Imperf., Pairs

| | | | |
|---|---|---|---|
| *183b* | A97 | 1c | 240.00 |
| *184c* | A97 | 1c | 47.50 |
| *185c* | A98 | 2c | 250.00 |
| *186c* | A98 | 2c | 47.50 |
| *187d* | A99 | 3c | 95.00 |
| *189a* | A100 | 4c | 60.00 |
| *190a* | A101 | 5c | 200.00 |
| *191b* | A101 | 5c (II) | 75.00 |
| *191d* | A101 | 5c (I) | 100.00 |
| *192a* | A102 | 6c | 175.00 |
| *193a* | A103 | 10c | 110.00 |
| *194a* | A103 | 14c | 130.00 |
| *195a* | A103 | 15c | 130.00 |
| *196a* | A106 | 20c | 225.00 |
| *197a* | A107 | 25c | 225.00 |
| *198a* | A108 | 30c | 800.00 |
| *199a* | A108 | 48c | 125.00 |

All with gum. Nos. 186c, 187d, 192a, 193a and 196a also made without gum; values about 10% less.

Queen Elizabeth when Duchess of York A109

Corner Brook Paper Mills A110

Loading Iron Ore at Bell Island — A111

### 1932

| | | |
|---|---|---|
| **208** A109 7c red brown | 1.40 | 1.25 |
| *a.* Imperf., pair | 160.00 | |
| *b.* Horiz. pair, imperf. between | 550.00 | |
| **209** A110 8c orange red | 1.40 | 1.10 |
| *a.* Imperf., pair | 140.00 | |
| **210** A111 24c light blue | 2.75 | 2.75 |
| *a.* Imperf., pair | 200.00 | |
| *b.* Double impression | 1,900. | |
| *Nos. 208-210 (3)* | 5.55 | 5.10 |
| Set, never hinged | 7.75 | |

No. 208a was made both with and without gum. Values about the same.

See Nos. 259, 264.

No. C9 Overprinted Bars and

### 1933, Feb. 9 Wmk. 224 *Perf. 14*

| | | |
|---|---|---|
| **211** AP6 15c brown | 11.00 | 9.50 |
| Never hinged | 17.00 | |
| *a.* Vert. pair, one without overprint | 8,000. | |
| *b.* Overprint reading up | 6,000. | |

The end of the period of use and availability of No. 211 is unknown.

"L. & S." stands for "Land and Sea."

### Sir Humphrey Gilbert Issue

Sir Humphrey Gilbert A112

Compton Castle, Home of the Gilbert Family A113

Gilbert Coat of Arms A114

Eton College A115

Token from Queen Elizabeth I — A116

Sir Humphrey Receiving Royal Patents for Colonization A117

Sir Humphrey's Ships Leaving Plymouth, 1583 A118

The Ships Arriving at St. John's — A119

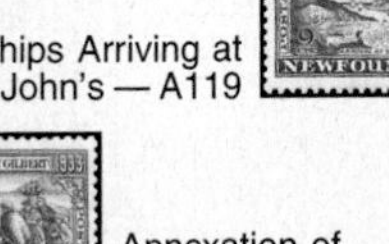

Annexation of Newfoundland, Aug. 5, 1583 — A120

Coat of Arms of England A121

Sir Humphrey on the Deck of the "Squirrel" A122

Capt. John Mason's Map of Newfoundland, 1626 — A123

Queen Elizabeth I A124

Gilbert Statue at Truro A125

**Wmk. 224**

**1933, Aug. 3 Engr. *Perf. 13½***

| No. | Type | Description | Unused | Used |
|---|---|---|---|---|
| **212** | A112 | 1c gray black | 1.30 | .75 |
| **213** | A113 | 2c green | 1.30 | .75 |
| *b.* | | Double impression | *600.00* | |
| **214** | A114 | 3c yellow brn | 2.75 | .75 |
| **215** | A115 | 4c carmine | 2.00 | .75 |
| **216** | A116 | 5c dull violet | 3.25 | 1.10 |
| **217** | A117 | 7c blue | 17.50 | 12.50 |
| **218** | A118 | 8c orange red | 8.50 | 7.00 |
| **219** | A119 | 9c ultramarine | 10.00 | 7.50 |
| **220** | A120 | 10c red brown | 8.50 | 6.25 |
| **221** | A121 | 14c black | 17.50 | 15.00 |
| **222** | A122 | 15c claret | 17.50 | 15.00 |
| **223** | A123 | 20c deep green | 15.00 | 10.00 |
| **224** | A124 | 24c vio brown | 27.50 | 22.50 |
| **225** | A125 | 32c gray | 27.50 | 22.50 |
| | | *Nos. 212-225 (14)* | 160.10 | 122.35 |
| | | Set, never hinged | 229.90 | |

350th anniv. of annexation of Newfoundland to England, Aug. 5, 1583, by authority of Letters Patent issued by Queen Elizabeth I to Sir Humphrey Gilbert.

**Imperf., Pairs**

| No. | Type | Value | Unused |
|---|---|---|---|
| *212a* | A112 | 1c | 45.00 |
| *213a* | A113 | 2c | 45.00 |
| *214a* | A114 | 3c | 375.00 |
| *215a* | A115 | 4c | 50.00 |
| *216a* | A116 | 5c | 375.00 |
| *219a* | A119 | 9c | 500.00 |
| *220a* | A120 | 10c | 500.00 |
| *221a* | A120 | 14c | 400.00 |
| *222a* | A120 | 15c | 240.00 |
| *224a* | A124 | 24c | 225.00 |

No. 212a was made both with and without gum. Value of pair without gum about 10% less.

Common Design Types pictured following the introduction.

**Silver Jubilee Issue**
Common Design Type

**1935, May 6 Wmk. 4 *Perf. 11x12***

| No. | Type | Description | Unused | Used |
|---|---|---|---|---|
| **226** | CD301 | 4c bright rose | 2.25 | .70 |
| **227** | CD301 | 5c violet | 2.25 | .85 |
| **228** | CD301 | 7c dark blue | 4.00 | 3.50 |
| **229** | CD301 | 24c olive brown | 9.00 | 7.00 |
| | | *Nos. 226-229 (4)* | 17.50 | 12.05 |
| | | Set, never hinged | 25.35 | |

**Coronation Issue**
Common Design Type

**1937, May 12 *Perf. 11x11½***

| No. | Type | Description | Unused | Used |
|---|---|---|---|---|
| **230** | CD302 | 2c deep green | 1.75 | .70 |
| **231** | CD302 | 4c carmine rose | 1.75 | .70 |
| **232** | CD302 | 5c dark violet | 3.50 | 1.40 |
| | | *Nos. 230-232 (3)* | 7.00 | 2.80 |
| | | Set, never hinged | 9.80 | |

Codfish — A126

Map of Newfoundland A127

Caribou — A128

Corner Brook Paper Mills — A129

Salmon — A130

Newfoundland Dog — A131

Harp Seal Pup — A132

Cape Race — A133

Loading Iron Ore at Bell Island — A134

Sealing Fleet — A135

Fishing Fleet Leaving for "The Banks" — A136

Type I

Type II

Two types of the 3c
Type I — Fine impression; no lines on bridge of nose.
Type II — Coarse impression; lines on bridge of nose.

***Perf. 13½, 14 (#234-235)***

**1937, May 12 Wmk. 224**

| No. | Type | Description | Unused | Used |
|---|---|---|---|---|
| **233** | A126 | 1c gray black | .65 | .30 |
| **234** | A127 | 3c org brn, die I | 2.75 | 1.10 |
| *a.* | | Die II | 2.25 | 1.10 |
| *b.* | | Vert. pair, imperf. btwn. (I) | 850.00 | |
| *c.* | | Vert. pair, imperf. btwn. (II) | 850.00 | |
| *d.* | | Horiz. pair, imperf. btwn. (I) | 575.00 | |
| *e.* | | Horiz. pair, imperf. btwn. (II) | 575.00 | |
| *f.* | | Imperf., pair (II) | 240.00 | |
| *i.* | | Horiz. pair, imperf. vert., never hinged | *1,600.* | |
| *j.* | | Imperf., pair (I) | *750.00* | |
| **235** | A128 | 7c blue | 3.00 | 2.50 |
| **236** | A129 | 8c vermilion | 3.00 | 2.50 |
| *a.* | | Imperf., pair | 450.00 | |
| *b.* | | Vert. pair, imperf. between | 1,500. | |
| *c.* | | Horiz. pair, imperf. vert. | *1,900.* | |
| **237** | A130 | 10c brn blk | 4.25 | 4.25 |
| *a.* | | Double impression | 280.00 | |
| **238** | A131 | 14c black | 4.25 | 3.50 |
| *a.* | | Imperf., pair | 400.00 | |
| **239** | A132 | 15c rose lake | 4.25 | 3.50 |
| *a.* | | Vert. pair, imperf. between | 1,500. | |
| **240** | A133 | 20c green | 4.25 | 2.25 |
| *a.* | | Vert. pair, imperf. between | 2,500. | |
| **241** | A134 | 24c turq blue | 4.25 | 3.25 |
| *a.* | | Vert. pair, imperf. between | 3,500. | |
| **242** | A135 | 25c gray | 4.25 | 3.25 |
| *a.* | | Imperf., pair | 250.00 | |
| **243** | A136 | 48c plum | 7.00 | 4.00 |
| *a.* | | Vert. pair, imperf. between | 3,000. | |
| *b.* | | Imperf., pair | 275.00 | |
| | | *Nos. 233-243 (11)* | 41.90 | 30.40 |
| | | Set, never hinged | 64.50 | |

Imperfs are with gum. No. 238a, 242a issued without gum. No. 234f and 243b also made without gum; value the same.

Princess Elizabeth — A139

Designs: 2c, King George VI. 3c, Queen Elizabeth. 7c, Queen Mother Mary.

**1938, May 12 *Perf. 13½***

| No. | Type | Description | Unused | Used |
|---|---|---|---|---|
| **245** | A139 | 2c green | 1.75 | .25 |
| **246** | A139 | 3c dark carmine | 1.75 | .25 |
| **247** | A139 | 4c light blue | 2.30 | .25 |
| **248** | A139 | 7c dark ultra | 1.60 | 1.10 |
| *b.* | | Vert. pair, imperf. between | *1,500.* | |
| | | *Nos. 245-248 (4)* | 7.40 | 1.85 |
| | | Set, never hinged | 9.40 | |

See Nos. 254-256, 258, 269.

**Imperf., Pairs**

| No. | Type | Value | Unused |
|---|---|---|---|
| *245a* | A139 | 2c | 120.00 |
| *246a* | A139 | 3c | 120.00 |
| *247a* | A139 | 4c | 120.00 |
| *248a* | A139 | 7c | 120.00 |
| | | Set, never hinged | 700.00 |

Nos. 245a-248a issued with or without gum; values the same.

George VI and Queen Elizabeth — A141

**1939, June 17 Unwmk.**

| No. | Type | Description | Unused | Used |
|---|---|---|---|---|
| **249** | A141 | 5c violet blue | 1.25 | 1.10 |
| | | Never hinged | 1.75 | |

Visit of King George and Queen Elizabeth.

No. 249 Surcharged in Brown or Red

**Available Nov. 21 and exhausted by Dec. 16, 1939**

| No. | Type | Description | Unused | Used |
|---|---|---|---|---|
| **250** | A141 | 2c on 5c vio blue (Br) | 1.40 | 1.00 |
| **251** | A141 | 4c on 5c vio blue (R) | 1.00 | 1.00 |
| | | Set, never hinged | 3.20 | |

There are many varieties of broken letters and figures in the settings of the surcharges.

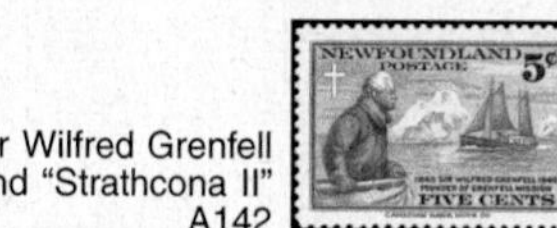

Sir Wilfred Grenfell and "Strathcona II" A142

**1941, Dec. 1 *Perf. 12***

| No. | Type | Description | Unused | Used |
|---|---|---|---|---|
| **252** | A142 | 5c dull blue | .40 | .30 |
| | | Never hinged | .50 | |

Grenfell Mission, 50th anniv.

**Types of 1931-38**

**1941-43 Wmk. 224 *Perf. 12½***

| No. | Type | Description | Unused | Used |
|---|---|---|---|---|
| **253** | A97 | 1c dark gray ('42) | .35 | .25 |
| *a.* | | Imperf., pair | 140.00 | |
| **254** | A139 | 2c deep green | .35 | .25 |
| **255** | A139 | 3c rose carmine | .50 | .25 |
| *a.* | | Imperf., pair | 275.00 | |
| **256** | A139 | 4c blue | .70 | .30 |
| **257** | A101 | 5c violet (Die I) | 1.00 | .25 |
| *a.* | | Imperf., pair | 180.00 | |
| *b.* | | Horiz. pair, imperf. vert. | 450.00 | |
| *c.* | | Double impression | 400.00 | |
| **258** | A139 | 7c vio blue ('42) | 1.20 | 1.00 |
| **259** | A110 | 8c red ('42) | 1.40 | .65 |
| **260** | A103 | 10c brownish blk | 1.40 | .60 |
| **261** | A104 | 14c black ('43) | 2.00 | 1.75 |
| *a.* | | Imperf., pair | 240.00 | |
| *c.* | | Vert. pair, imperf. horiz. | 500.00 | |
| **262** | A105 | 15c pale rose vio ('43) | 2.00 | 1.40 |
| **263** | A106 | 20c green ('43) | 2.00 | 1.10 |
| **264** | A111 | 24c deep blue ('43) | 2.25 | 2.00 |
| **265** | A107 | 25c slate ('43) | 2.25 | 2.00 |
| **266** | A108 | 48c red brown ('43) | 3.25 | 1.75 |
| | | *Nos. 253-266 (14)* | 20.65 | 13.55 |
| | | Set, never hinged | 26.35 | |

Nos. 254 and 255 are re-engraved.

Memorial University College — A143

**1943, Jan. 2 Unwmk. *Perf. 12***

| No. | Type | Description | Unused | Used |
|---|---|---|---|---|
| **267** | A143 | 30c carmine | 1.40 | 1.00 |
| | | Never hinged | 1.85 | |

No. 267 Surcharged in Black

**Available Mar. 21 through April 1, 1946**

| No. | Type | Description | Unused | Used |
|---|---|---|---|---|
| **268** | A143 | 2c on 30c carmine | .30 | .30 |
| | | Never hinged | .40 | |

Princess Elizabeth — A144

**Wmk. 224**

**1947, Apr. 21 Engr. *Perf. 12½***

| No. | Type | Description | Unused | Used |
|---|---|---|---|---|
| **269** | A144 | 4c light blue | .30 | .25 |
| | | Never hinged | .40 | |
| *a.* | | Imperf., pair | 150.00 | |
| *b.* | | Horiz. pair, imperf. vert. | 400.00 | |

Princess Elizabeth's 21st birthday.

Deck of the Matthew — A145

**1947, June 24**

| No. | Type | Description | Unused | Used |
|---|---|---|---|---|
| **270** | A145 | 5c rose violet | .30 | .25 |
| | | Never hinged | .40 | |
| *a.* | | Horiz. pair, imperf. between | 1,350. | |
| *b.* | | Imperf., pair | 240.00 | |

Cabot's arrival off Cape Bonavista, 450th anniv.

## AIR POST STAMPS

No. 117 Overprinted in Black

Manuscript "Aerial Atlantic Mail JAR"

**1919, Apr. 12 Unwmk. *Perf. 14***

| No. | Type | Description | Unused | Used |
|---|---|---|---|---|
| **C1** | A67 | 3c red brown | *25,000.* | *15,000.* |
| | | Never hinged | *40,000.* | |
| *a.* | | Manuscript "Aerial Atlantic Mail JAR" | *75,000.* | *25,000.* |

No. 70 Surcharged in Black on Block of 25 with Selvage Removed

**1919, June 9 *Perf. 12***

| No. | Type | Description | Unused | Used |
|---|---|---|---|---|
| **C2** | A33 | $1 on 15c scarlet | 210.00 | 210.00 |
| | | Never hinged | 300.00 | |
| *a.* | | Without comma after "Post" | 240.00 | *275.00* |
| *b.* | | As "a," without period after "1919" | 450.00 | 450.00 |

No. 73 Overprinted in Black on Block of 25 with Selvage Removed

**1921, Nov. 7**

| No. | Type | Description | Unused | Used |
|---|---|---|---|---|
| **C3** | A36 | 35c red, 2½mm between "AIR" and "MAIL" | 140.00 | *190.00* |
| *a.* | | Inverted overprint | 5,750. | |
| *b.* | | With period after "1921" | 160.00 | *200.00* |
| *c.* | | As "b," inverted overprint | *6,500.* | |

No. 74 Overprinted in Red on Block of 50 with Selvage

**1927, May 21**

| No. | Type | Description | Unused | Used |
|---|---|---|---|---|
| **C4** | A37 | 60c black | *45,000.* | *17,500.* |
| | | Never hinged | *60,000.* | |

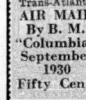

No. 126 Surcharged in Black on Block of 4

**1930, Sept. 25** *Perf. 14*

**C5** A67 50c on 36c ol grn 9,000. 9,000.
Never hinged 13,000.

Dog Sled and Airplane — AP6

First Transatlantic Mail Airplane and Packet Ship — AP7

Routes of Historic Transatlantic Flights AP8

**1931, Jan. 2** **Engr.** **Unwmk.**

**C6** AP6 15c chocolate 10.00 7.00
- *a.* Horiz. pair, imperf. between 950.00
- *b.* Vert. pair, imperf. between 1,050.
- *c.* Imperf., pair 625.00

**C7** AP7 50c green 32.50 25.00
- *a.* Horiz. pair, imperf. between 1,250. 750.00
- *b.* Vert. pair, imperf. between 1,350. 850.00
- *c.* Imperf., pair 725.00

**C8** AP8 $1 blue 70.00 55.00
- *a.* Horiz. pair, imperf. between 1,200.
- *b.* Vert. pair, imperf. between 1,200.
- *c.* Imperf., pair 725.00

*Nos. C6-C8 (3)* 112.50 87.00
Set, never hinged 190.00

**1931** **Wmk. 224 Sideways**

**C9** AP6 15c brown 10.00 7.00
- *a.* Horiz. pair, imperf. between 1,000.
- *b.* Vert. pair, imperf. between 1,300.
- *c.* Imperf., pair 600.00

**C10** AP7 50c green 35.00 35.00
- *a.* Horiz. pair, imperf. between 1,100.
- *b.* Vert. pair, imperf. between 1,250.
- *c.* Horiz. pair, Imperf. vert. 950.00

**C11** AP8 $1 blue 95.00 90.00
- *a.* Vert. pair, imperf. between 1,200.
- *c.* Horiz. pair, imperf. between 1,200.
- *d.* Vert. pair, imperf. horiz. 1,100.
- *e.* Imperf., pair 700.00

*Nos. C9-C11 (3)* 140.00 132.00
Set, never hinged 260.00

As the watermark 224 does not show on every stamp in the sheet, pairs are found one with and one without watermark.

For overprint and surcharge see Nos. 211, C12.

### No. C11 Surcharged in Red on Block of 4

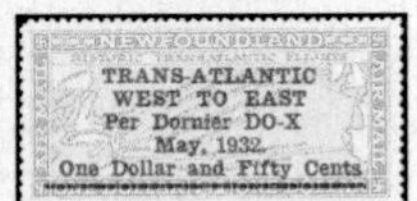


**1932, May 19**

**C12** AP8 $1.50 on $1 blue 275.00 275.00
Never hinged 350.00
- *a.* Inverted surcharge 20,000.
  Never hinged 25,000.

A stamp of this design was produced in the US in 1932 by a private company under contract with Newfoundland authorities. The government canceled the contract and the stamp was not valid for prepayment of postage. Value, $35.

"Put to Flight" — AP9

"Land of Heart's Delight" — AP10

"Spotting the Herd" — AP11

"News from Home" — AP12

"Labrador, The Land of Gold" — AP13

***Perf. 11½ (10, 60c), 14 (5, 30, 75c)***

**1933, June 9** **Engr.**

**C13** AP9 5c lt brown 9.50 11.00
- *b.* Horiz. pair, imperf. between 1,100.
- *c.* Vert. pair, imperf. between 1,250.

**C14** AP10 10c yellow 17.00 17.50
**C15** AP11 30c blue 29.00 30.00
**C16** AP12 60c green 62.50 57.50
**C17** AP13 75c bister, perf. 14.3 57.50 57.50
- *b.* Horiz. pair, imperf. between 3,500.
- *c.* Vert. pair, imperf. between 3,500.

*Nos. C13-C17 (5)* 175.50 173.50
Set, never hinged 270.00

Beware of clever forgeries of Nos. C13b, C13c, C17b and C17c. Certificates of authenticity are highly recommended.

**Imperf., Pairs**

| | | | |
|---|---|---|---|
| *C13a* | AP9 | 5c | 250.00 |
| *C14a* | AP10 | 10c | 180.00 |
| *C15a* | AP11 | 30c | 700.00 |
| *C16a* | AP12 | 60c | 700.00 |
| *C17a* | AP13 | 75c | 700.00 |
| Set, never hinged | | | 3,150. |

No. C17 Surcharged in Black

**1933, July 24** *Perf. 14.3*

**C18** AP13 $4.50 on 75c bister 325.00 350.00
Never hinged 475.00
- *a.* Inverted surcharge 120,000.
  Never hinged 150,000.

On return from the Chicago World Fair "Century of Progress" with his "armada" of 24 seaplanes, Gen. Italo Balbo made a stopover in Shoal Harbour and accepted mail to Italy of about 1,150 covers.

No. C18a was not regularly issued.

The $4.50 on No. C14, 10c yellow, is a proof. Value, $62,500.

View of St. John's — AP14

**1943, June 1** **Unwmk.** *Perf. 12*

**C19** AP14 7c bright ultra .35 .30
Never hinged .45

## POSTAGE DUE STAMPS

D1

***Perf. 10-10½, Compound***

**1939-49** **Litho.** **Unwmk.**

**J1** D1 1c yellow green, perf. 11 ('49) 4.25 5.50
- *a.* Perf. 10-10½ 7.00 5.50

**J2** D1 2c vermilion 7.00 5.50
- *a.* Perf. 11x9 ('46) 7.00 5.50

**J3** D1 3c ultramarine 7.00 5.50
- *a.* Perf. 11x9 ('49) 7.50 7.50
- *b.* Perf. 9 3,750.

**J4** D1 4c yel org, perf. 11x9 ('49) 9.50 9.50
- *a.* Perf 10-10½ 15.00 15.00

**J5** D1 5c pale brown 15.00 4.25
**J6** D1 10c dark violet 7.00 6.50

*Nos. J1-J6 (6)* 49.75 36.75
Set, never hinged 78.75

**1949** **Wmk. 224** *Perf. 11*

**J7** D1 10c dark violet 10.00 15.00
Never hinged 17.50
- *a.* Vert. pair, imperf. between 1,000.

For used examples of Nos. J1-J7 with dated cancels from 1939-49, triple the values shown.

# NOVA SCOTIA

ˌnō-və-ˈskō-shə

LOCATION — Eastern coast of Canada between the Gulf of St. Lawrence and the Atlantic Ocean
GOVT. — British Crown Colony
AREA — 21,428 sq. mi.
POP. — 386,500 (1871)
CAPITAL — Halifax

Nova Scotia joined the Canadian Confederation in 1867 and is now a province of the Dominion. Postage stamps of Canada are used.

12 Pence = 1 Shilling
100 Cents = 1 Dollar (1860)

Values for unused stamps are for examples with original gum as defined in the catalogue introduction except for Nos. 4-7, which are rarely found with any remaining original gum.

Queen Victoria A1

Crown of Great Britain and Heraldic Flowers of the Empire A2

**Blue Paper**

**1851-57** **Unwmk.** **Engr.** ***Imperf.***

**1** A1 1p red brown ('53) 4,000. 500.
- *a.* Half used as ½p on cover —

**2** A2 3p bright blue 1,750. 225.
- *a.* Half used as 1½p on cover 3,750.
- *b.* 3p pale blue ('57) 1,750. 275.
- *c.* As "b," half used as 1½p on cover 3,750.

**3** A2 3p dark blue 2,250. 325.
- *a.* Half used as 1½p on cover 4,500.

**4** A2 6p yellow green 5,000. 825.
- *a.* Half used as 3p on cover 4,000.

**5** A2 6p dark green ('57) 10,000. 2,750.
- *a.* Half used as 3p on cover 4,500.
- *b.* Quarter used as 1½p on cover 47,500.

**6** A2 1sh reddish pur ('57) 22,500. 5,000.
- *a.* Half used as 6p on cover 35,000.
- *b.* 1sh deep purple 25,000. 6,000.
- *c.* As "6," quarter used as 3p on cover 90,000.

**7** A2 1sh dull violet 27,500. 6,000.
- *a.* Half used as 6p on cover 47,500.

Reprints are on thin hard white paper. 1p in brown, 3p in blue, 6p dark green. 1sh violet black. Value about $300 per set.

No. 6 was reproduced by the collotype process in a souvenir sheet distributed at the London International Stamp Exhibition 1950.

Queen Victoria — A3

A5

A6

**White or Yellowish Paper**

**1860-63** *Perf. 12*

**8** A3 1c black 15.00 7.50
- *a.* White paper 15.00 7.50
- *b.* Half used as ½c on cover 8,500.
- *c.* Horiz. pair, imperf. vert. 350.00

**9** A3 2c lilac 15.00 12.50
- *a.* Yellowish paper 15.00 12.50
- *b.* Half used as 1c on cover 3,500.

**10** A3 5c blue 425.00 12.00
- *a.* Yellowish paper 425.00 12.00
- *b.* Half used as 2½c on cover 5,000.

**11** A5 8½c green 15.00 22.00
- *a.* White paper 15.00 22.00

**12** A5 10c vermilion 15.00 12.00
- *a.* Yellowish paper 15.00 12.00
- *b.* Half used as 5c on cover 1,200.

**13** A6 12½c black 42.50 37.50
- *a.* White paper 42.50 37.50

*Nos. 8-13 (6)* 527.50 103.50
Set, never hinged 1,460.

The stamps of Nova Scotia were replaced by those of Canada.

## PRINCE EDWARD ISLAND

ˈprin͵t͵s ˈed-wərd ˈī-lənd

LOCATION — In the Gulf of St. Lawrence, opposite the provinces of New Brunswick and Nova Scotia
GOVT. — British Crown Colony
AREA — 2,184 sq. mi.
POP. — 92,000 (estimated)
CAPITAL — Charlottetown

Originally annexed to Nova Scotia, Prince Edward Island was a separate colony from 1769 to 1873, when it became a part of the Canadian Confederation. Postage stamps of Canada are now used.

12 Pence = 1 Shilling
100 Cents = 1 Dollar (1872)

A1

A2

Queen Victoria — A3

**1861, Jan. 1 Unwmk. Typo. *Perf. 9***

1 A1 2p dull rose 1,400. 350.
- a. 2p deep rose 1,750. 375.
- b. Rouletted 27,500.
- c. Horiz. pair, imperf. between 6,750.
- d. Diagonal half used as 1p on cover 7,000.

2 A2 3p blue 2,500. 750.
- a. Diagonal half used as 1½p on cover 7,500.
- b. Double impression 4,750.

No. 2b is valued with very small faults.

3 A3 6p yellow green 3,250. 1,250.

A4

A5

**White or Yellowish Paper**

**1862-65** ***Perf. 11½-12***

4 A4 1p yellow orange 42.50 35.00
- a. 1p brown orange, perf. 11 50.00 35.00
- b. Imperf., pair 200.00
- c. Half used as ½p on cover 3,500.

5 A1 2p rose 8.50 7.50
- a. Yellowish paper 22.50 7.50
- b. Imperf., pair 100.00
- c. Horiz. pair, imperf. vert. 275.00
- d. Vert. pair, imperf. horiz. 400.00
- e. Diagonal half used as 1p on cover 2,750.
- f. "TWC" for "TWO" 75.00 60.00

6 A2 3p blue 16.00 15.00
- a. Yellowish paper 35.00 15.00
- b. Imperf., pair 150.00
- c. Vert. pair, imperf. horiz. 400.00
- d. Horiz. pair, imperf. vert. 400.00
- e. Diagonal half used as 1½p on cover 250.00
- g. Imperf. pair with gutter btwn. 950.00
- h. Imperf. tete-beche pair with gutter btwn. 3,000.

7 A3 6p yellow green 125.00 95.00
- a. 6p blue green 125.00 95.00
- c. Diagonal half used as 3p on cover 5,500.

8 A5 9p mauve 95.00 80.00
- a. Imperf., pair 375.00
- b. Horiz. pair, imperf. vert. 450.00
- c. Diagonal half used as 4½p on cover 4,250.

*Nos. 4-8 (5)* 287.00 232.50
Set, never hinged 465.00

Queen Victoria — A6

**1868**

9 A6 4p black 9.00 19.00
- a. Yellowish paper 15.00 20.00
- b. Horiz. pair, imperf. vert. 190.00
- c. Diagonal half used as 2p on cover 2,250.
- d. Imperf., pair 140.00
- e. Horiz. pair, imperf. between 160.00
- g. Horiz. strip of 3, imperf. btwn. 1,100.

Queen Victoria — A7

**1870, June 1 Engr. *Perf. 12***

10 A7 4½p brown 90.00 75.00

A8

A9

A10

A11

A12

A13

**1872, Jan. 1 Typo. *Perf. 12, 12½***

11 A8 1c brown orange 7.00 7.50
- a. Imperf., pair 240.00

12 A9 2c ultra 35.00 42.50
- a. Imperf., pair 450.00
- b. Diagonal half used as 1c on cover 3,250.

13 A10 3c rose 32.50 22.50
- a. Imperf., pair 475.00
- b. Diagonal half used as 1½c on cover —
- c. Horiz. or vert. pair, imperf. between 275.00

14 A11 4c green 11.50 16.00
- a. Imperf., pair 475.00
- b. Diagonal half used as 2c on cover 5,500.

15 A12 6c black 7.50 13.00
- a. Horiz. pair, imperf. btwn. 250.00
- b. Half used as 3c on cover 1,750.

16 A13 12c violet 7.50 30.00
- a. Imperf., pair 450.00
- b. Half used as 6c on cover —

*Nos. 11-16 (6)* 101.00 131.50
Set, never hinged 138.50

Scott 14b is unique and used in combination with No. 11.

## CANADA

ˈka-nə-də

LOCATION — Northern part of North American continent, except for Alaska
GOVT. — Self-governing dominion in the British Commonwealth of Nations
AREA — 3,851,809 sq. mi.
POP. — 28,846,761 (1996)
CAPITAL — Ottawa

Included in the dominion are British Columbia, Vancouver Island, Prince Edward Island, Nova Scotia, New Brunswick and Newfoundland, all of which formerly issued stamps.

12 Pence = 1 Shilling
100 Cents = 1 Dollar (1859)

**Catalogue values for unused stamps in this country are for Never Hinged items, beginning with Scott 268 in the regular postage section, Scott B1 in the semi-postal section, Scott C9 in the air post section, Scott CE3 in the air post special delivery section, Scott CO1 in the air post official section, Scott E11 in the special delivery section, Scott EO1 in the special delivery official section, Scott J15 in the postage due section, and Scott O1 in the official section.**

Values for unused stamps of Nos. 1-33 are for examples with partial original gum. Stamps without gum often trade at prices very close to those of stamps with partial gum. Examples with full original gum and lightly hinged are extremely scarce and generally sell for substantially more than the values listed.

Very fine examples of the perforated issues between Nos. 11-20 will have perforations touching the design or frameline on at least one side due to the narrow spacing of the stamps on the plates. Stamps with perfs clear of the designs on all four sides are extremely scarce and will command much higher prices.

**Province of Canada**

Beaver
A1

Prince Albert
A2

Queen Victoria — A3

**1851 Unwmk. Engr. *Imperf.***
**Laid Paper**

1 A1 3p red 45,000. 1,200.
2 A2 6p slate violet 45,000. 1,500.
- a. Diagonal half used as 3p on cover 35,000.

3 A3 12p black 175,000. 145,000.

On some stamps the laid lines of Nos. 1-3 are practically invisible.

**1852-57** **Wove Paper**

4 A1 3p red 2,500. 200.
- a. 3p brown red ('53) 2,750. 250.
- b. Diagonal half used as 1½p on cover 35,000.
- c. Ribbed paper 7,500. 525.
- d. Thin paper 2,500. 225.

5 A2 6p slate gray ('55) 45,000. 1,150.
- a. 6p brownish gray 47,500. 1,700.
- b. 6p greenish gray 45,000. 1,150.
- c. Diagonal half used as 3p on cover 20,000.
- d. Thick hard paper (gray vio) ('57) 32,500. 2,750.

Re-entries of the 3p are numerous. The main re-entry is distinguishable most easily by the line through "EE" and "PEN".

Most authorities believe the 12p black does not exist on wove paper.

Jacques Cartier — A4

**1855**

7 A4 10p blue 15,000. 1,500.
*a.* Thick paper 9,500. 2,000.

Queen Victoria
A5 A6

**1857**

8 A5 ½p rose 2,000. 700.
*a.* Horizontally ribbed paper 12,500. 2,500.
*b.* Vertically ribbed paper 15,000. 3,750.
9 A6 7½p green 15,000. 3,000.

**Very Thick Soft Wove Paper**

10 A2 6p reddish pur 35,000. 6,750.
*a.* Half used as 3p on cover *30,000.*

**1858-59 Wove Paper *Perf. 12***

11 A5 ½p rose 5,000. 1,500.
12 A1 3p red 20,000. 1,400.
13 A2 6p brown vio ('59) 30,000. 7,500.
*a.* 6p gray violet 30,000. 7,500.
*b.* Diagonal half used as 3p on cover *20,000.*

Nos. 11-13 values are for examples with perfs touching the design.

A7

A8

A9

A10

A11

**1859**

14 A7 1c rose 750.00 90.00
*a.* Imperf., pair 5,500.
*b.* 1c deep rose 975.00 150.00
15 A8 5c ver 800.00 37.50
On cover 30.00
*a.* Imperf., pair *17,500.* —
*b.* Diagonal half used as 2½c on cover *6,500.*
*c.* 5c brick red 2,000. 42.50
16 A9 10c blk brn, perf. 11¾ 30,000. 6,000.
*a.* Half used as 5c on cover *12,500.*
17 A9 10c red lil 2,000. 175.00
*a.* 10c violet 2,200. 200.00
*b.* 10c brown 2,000. 140.00
*c.* Imperf., pair 15,000.
*d.* Diagonal half used as 5c on cover *7,000.*
*e.* 10c deep red purple 4,250. 900.00
18 A10 12½c yel grn 2,000. 150.00
*a.* 12½c blue green 2,250. 135.00
*b.* Imperf., pair 6,500.
19 A11 17c blue 3,000. 225.00
*a.* 17c slate blue 3,250. 250.00
*b.* Imperf., pair 6,000.

Values for Nos. 14-19 are for examples with perfs touching the design.

No. 15b was used with a 10c for a 12½c rate.

No. 16 should be accompanied by a certificate of authenticity issued by a recognized expertizing authority. Less expensive dark brown shades of the 10c often are offered as the rare black brown.

Imperfs. are without gum.

Re-entries of the 5c are numerous. Many of them are slight and have only small premium value. The major re-entry has many lines of the design double, especially the outlines of the ovals and frame at left. Value, used, about $800.

A12

**1864**

20 A12 2c rose 1,250. 350.00
*a.* 2c deep claret rose 1,300. 400.00
*b.* Imperf., pair 3,500.

Imperfs. are without gum.

Values are for examples with perfs touching the design.

## Dominion of Canada

Queen Victoria
A13 A14

A15

A16

A17

A18

A19

A20

**1868-76 *Perf. 12, 11½x12 (5c)***

21 A13 ½c black 250.00 80.00
*a.* Perf. 11½x12 ('73) 350.00 90.00
*b.* Watermarked *25,000.* *11,000.*
*c.* Thin paper 350.00 80.00
22 A14 1c brn red 1,200. 150.00
*a.* Watermarked *4,000.* 500.00
*b.* Thin paper 1,500. 150.00
23 A14 1c yell org 2,750. 180.00
*a.* 1c deep orange 4,000. 275.00
24 A15 2c green 1,500. 100.00
*a.* Watermarked 4,500. 400.00
*b.* Thin paper 1,500. 100.00
*c.* Diagonal half used as 1c on cover *4,000.*
25 A16 3c red 3,000. 40.00
*a.* Watermarked 6,000. 500.00
*b.* Thin paper 3,250. 55.00
26 A17 5c ol grn ('75) 3,000. 225.00
*a.* Perf. 12 *8,000.* 1,000.
*b.* Imperf., pair *32,500.*
27 A18 6c dk brn 3,000. 140.00
*a.* 6c yellow brown 2,250. 125.00
*b.* Watermarked *22,500.* *2,500.*
*c.* Thin paper 2,500. 160.00
*d.* Diagonal half used as 3c on cover *3,000.*
*e.* Vert. half used as 3c on cover *3,500.*
*f.* 6c black brown, thin paper (Mar. '68, 1st printing) 3,500. 225.00
28 A19 12½c blue 1,750. 125.00
*a.* Watermarked *7,000.* 450.00
*b.* Thin paper 1,500. 150.00
*c.* Horiz. pair, imperf. vert. —
*d.* Vert. pair, imperf. horiz. *16,000.*
29 A20 15c gray vio 125.00 60.00
*a.* Perf. 11½x12 ('74) 2,500. 500.00
*b.* 15c red lilac 1,250. 110.00
*c.* Watermarked *12,500.* 1,200.
*d.* Imperf., pair 1,500.
*e.* Thin paper 1,250. 120.00
30 A20 15c gray 125.00 60.00
*a.* Perf. 11½x12 ('73) 2,500. 500.00
*b.* 15c blue gray ('75) 135.00 75.00
*c.* Very thick paper (dp vio) *7,500.* 1,200.
*d.* Script wmk., Perf. 11½x12, ('76) *30,000.* *7,500.*
*e.* 15c deep blue 2,500. 450.00

The watermark on Nos. 21b, 22a, 24a, 25a, 27b, 28a and 29c consists of double-lined letters reading: "E. & G. BOTHWELL CLUTHA MILLS." The script watermark on No. 30d reads in full: "Alexr. Pirie & Sons." Values for all these watermarked stamps are for fine examples. Very fine examples are rare, seldom traded, and generally command premiums of about 100% over the values listed.

No. 21b unused and used, and Nos. 26a and 26b unused are valued in the grade of fine. No. 26b is a unique pair.

The existence of No. 28c has been questioned.

**1868 Laid Paper**

31 A14 1c brown red *55,000.* *9,000.*
32 A15 2c green *250,000.*
33 A16 3c bright red *35,000.* 2,400.

Only three examples of No. 32 are recorded, none being very fine.

## Montreal and Ottawa Printings

A21

A22

A23

A24

A25

A26

A27

**1870-89 Wove Paper *Perf. 12***

34 A21 ½c black ('82) 22.50 10.00
*a.* Imperf., pair 600.00 400.00
*b.* Horiz. pair, imperf. between 1,000.
35 A22 1c yellow 45.00 1.25
*a.* 1c orange ('70) 300.00 11.00
*b.* Imperf., pair 425.00
*c.* Diagonal half used as ½c on circular 4,250.
36 A23 2c green ('72) 70.00 2.50
*a.* Imperf., pair 650.00
*b.* Diagonal half used as 1c on cover 2,100.
*c.* Vertical half used as 1c on cover 2,100.
*d.* 2c blue green ('89) 110.00 5.00
*f.* Double impression *5,500.* *4,000.*
37 A24 3c org red ('73) 175.00 1.50
*a.* 3c rose ('71) 625.00 17.50
*b.* 3c copper red ('70) 1,750. 65.00
*c.* 3c dull red ('72) 175.00 3.25
38 A25 5c sl green ('76) 725.00 27.50
39 A26 6c yel brn ('72) 600.00 27.50
*a.* Diagonal half used as 3c on cover 3,500.
*c.* Imperf., pair 3,500.
40 A27 10c dull rose lil ('77) 1,250. 90.00
*a.* 10c magenta ('80) 1,275. 90.00
*b.* 10c deep lilac rose 1,600. 90.00

No. 34a was made with and without gum; values the same.

Examples of Nos. 36b and 36c postmarked "Halifax" are a private speculation.

No. 39c is unique and in the form of a strip of three.

**1870 *Perf. 12½***

*37d* A24 3c copper red (Ottawa) 11,000. 1,500.

**1873-79 *Perf. 11½x12***

*35d* A22 1c orange 450.00 20.00
*36e* A23 2c green 750.00 22.50
*37e* A24 3c red 575.00 10.00
*38a* A25 5c slate green 1,250. 52.50
*39b* A26 6c yellow brown 900.00 60.00
*40c* A27 10c dull rose lilac 1,750. 325.00

The gum on Nos. 35d-40c is always dull and usually blotchy or streaky. It is distinct from the earlier clear, smooth gum and from the bright shiny gums of the later periods.

Nos. 38 and 40 were printed at Montreal. Printings of Nos. 34 to 37, and 39 were made at Ottawa or Montreal and can be separated only by differences in paper and gum.

## Ottawa Printing

A28

A29

**1888-97 *Perf. 12***

41 A24 3c brt vermilion 65.00 .80
*a.* 3c rose carmine 525.00 16.00
42 A25 5c gray 210.00 5.00
43 A26 6c red brown 225.00 12.50
*a.* 6c chocolate ('90) 600.00 37.50
44 A28 8c viol blk ('93) 260.00 7.00
*a.* 8c blue gray 425.00 8.50
*b.* 8c slate 300.00 7.00
*c.* 8c gray 300.00 7.00
45 A27 10c brn red ('97) 675.00 65.00
*a.* 10c dull rose 600.00 55.00
*b.* 10c pink 725.00 65.00
46 A29 20c ver ('93) 400.00 110.00
47 A29 50c dp blue ('93) 400.00 75.00

Stamps of the 1870-93 issues are found on paper varying from very thin to thick, also occasionally on paper showing a distinctly ribbed surface.

The gum on Nos. 41-47 appears bright and shiny, often with a yellowish tint.

**Imperf., Pairs**

| | | | |
|---|---|---|---|
| *41b* | A24 | 3c | 450. |
| *42a* | A25 | 5c | 675. |
| *43b* | A26 | 6c | 550. |
| *44d* | A28 | 8c | 725. |
| *45c* | A27 | 10c | 550. |
| *46a* | A29 | 20c | 1,350. |
| *47a* | A29 | 50c | 1,350. |

Nos. 41b-45c made with and without gum. Without gum sell for the same as the unused hinged price.

### Imperforates and Part-Perforates

From 1859 through 1943 (Nos. 14a/262a), imperforate stamps were printed. The earliest imperforates through perhaps 1917 most likely were from imprimatur sheets (i.e. the first sheets from the approved plates, normally kept in government files) or proof sheets on stamp paper that once were in the post office archives. The imperforates from approximately 1927 to 1943 (often made both with and without gum) were specially created and traded for classic stamps needed for the post office museum, given as gifts to governmental or other dignitaries, or sold or given to favored persons.

The only imperforates from this entire period that were issued to the public were Nos. 90A and 136-138.

Similarly, almost all stamps that are known part-perforate (i.e., horizontal pairs imperforate vertically and vertical pairs imperforate horizontally) were specially made for trading purposes or as presentation items to be given to favored persons. These part-perforates are not listed here, but they are listed in *Scott Classic Specialized Catalogue of Stamps & Covers.* Part-perforate error stamps that are believed to have been actually issued to the public are listed in this catalogue.

See the similar imperforates in the air post, Nos. CE1a and CE2a, special delivery, No. F2c (but not No. F1c which was an issued error), postage dues, and Nos. MR4b and MR4c.

## Jubilee Issue

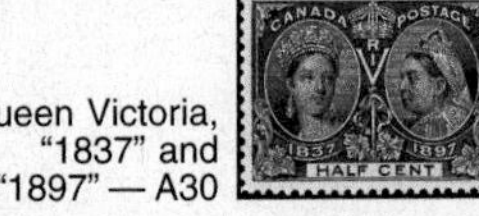

Queen Victoria, "1837" and "1897" — A30

**1897, June 19 Unwmk. *Perf. 12***

50 A30 ½c black 110.00 110.00
Never hinged 275.00
51 A30 1c orange 30.00 8.00
Never hinged 75.00
52 A30 2c green 37.50 15.00
Never hinged 92.50
53 A30 3c bright rose 30.00 2.50
Never hinged 75.00
54 A30 5c deep blue 70.00 45.00
Never hinged 200.00
55 A30 6c yell brn 220.00 175.00
Never hinged 625.00
56 A30 8c dark violet 130.00 70.00
Never hinged 300.00
57 A30 10c brown violet 175.00 120.00
Never hinged 450.00
58 A30 15c steel blue 300.00 190.00
Never hinged 750.00
59 A30 20c vermilion 300.00 190.00
Never hinged 750.00
60 A30 50c ultra 375.00 190.00
Never hinged 775.00
61 A30 $1 lake 750.00 750.00
Never hinged 1,900.
62 A30 $2 dk purple 1,300. 550.00
Never hinged 3,750.
63 A30 $3 yel bister 1,300. 1,000.
Never hinged 3,750.
64 A30 $4 purple 1,300. 1,000.
Never hinged 3,750.

# Canadian Philately at its Best!

Our award-winning auction catalogues regularly feature the best that Canadian philately has to offer.

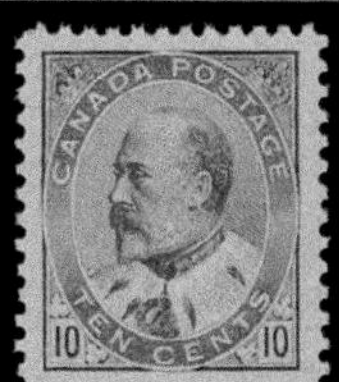


10c Brown Lilac
May 2021; Lot 537
Realized $6,220

½c Leaf progressive die
October 2020; Lot 666
Realized $27,255

25c London to London Flight
November 2021; Lot 306
Realized $47,400

2c laid paper, used CDS,
the finest of three known.
October 2014; Lot 1193
Realized $247,250

2p scarlet vermilion, used
February 2019; Lot 108
Realized $17,775

1sh dull violet, unused
June 2019; Lot 39
Realized $53,325

12p black, a superlative mint
example, widely regarded as
the finest in existence

*ex. Duveen, Dale-Lichtenstein*
February 2013; Lot 353
Realized $224,250

1897 $1 Lake, XF NH
November 2021; Lot 695
Realized $6,515

Hawker Flight, mint NH
February 2019; Lot 208
Realized $44,435

1875 registered cover to Norway with three examples of the 10c pale milky rose lilac shade
November 2018; Lot 887 – Realized $33,180

3c Dark Yellowish Brown
November 2021; Lot 780
Realized $1,480

## Canada's Most Trusted Auction House

Our expertise combined with meticulous research and descriptions have been fundamental in achieving highly successful results for our consignors. For over 40 years, the offering of numerous rarities, proofs, high-quality stamps and postal history has been the delight of serious collectors around the world. We look forward to working with you!

# Eastern Auctions Ltd.

P.O. Box 250 - Bathurst - New Brunswick - E2A -3Z2 - Canada
Tel: 1(506) 548-8986 - Fax 1(506) 546-6627
Toll Free Tel: 1(800) 667-8267 - Fax 1(888) 867-8268 *(North America only)*
Email: contact@easternauctions.com - Website: www.easternauctions.com

**65** A30 $5 olive green 1,300. 1,000.
Never hinged 4,250.
*Nos. 50-60 (11)* 1,778. 1,116.
Set, never hinged 3,317.50

60th year of Queen Victoria's reign.

**Roller and smudged cancels on Nos. 61-65 sell for less.**

A31

**1897-98**

**66** A31 ½c black 15.00 8.50
Never hinged 37.50
**67** A31 1c blue green 55.00 2.00
Never hinged 140.00
**68** A31 2c purple 55.00 2.25
Never hinged 125.00
**69** A31 3c car ('98) 95.00 2.00
Never hinged 250.00
**70** A31 5c dk bl, *bluish* 175.00 10.00
Never hinged 500.00
**71** A31 6c brown 140.00 45.00
Never hinged 350.00
**72** A31 8c orange 325.00 21.00
Never hinged 850.00
**73** A31 10c brn vio ('98) 600.00 100.00
Never hinged 1,500.
*Nos. 66-73 (8)* 1,460. 190.75
Set, never hinged 3,752.50

For surcharge see No. 87.

### Imperf., Pairs

*66a* A31 ½c 500.
Never hinged 950.
*67a* A31 1c 500.
Never hinged 950.
*68a* A31 2c 500.
Never hinged 950.
*69a* A31 3c 800.
Never hinged 1,450.
*70a* A31 5c 525.
Never hinged 800.
*71a* A31 6c 700.
Never hinged 1,300.
*72a* A31 8c 700.
Never hinged 1,300.
*73a* A31 10c 700.
Never hinged 1,300.

Nos. 66a, 67a, 68a and 70a made with and without gum. Specialists can distinguish printings made with and without gum by shade and paper quality. Without gum sell for about 80% of the unused hinged price.

A32

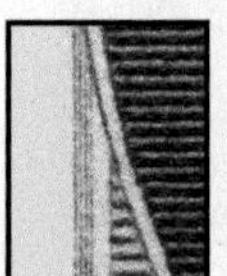
Type I

Type II

TWO CENTS:
Type I — Frame of four very thin lines.
Type II — Frame of a thick line between two thin ones.

**1898-1902**

**74** A32 ½c black 12.50 2.75
Never hinged 25.00
**75** A32 1c gray green 50.00 .75
Never hinged 100.00
**76** A32 2c purple (I) 50.00 .75
Never hinged 100.00
*a.* Thick paper ('99) 175.00 15.00
Never hinged 350.00
**77** A32 2c car (I) ('99) 55.00 .75
Never hinged 110.00
*a.* 2c carmine (II) ('99) 70.00 .60
Never hinged 140.00
*b.* Booklet pane of 6 (II) ('00) 1,600. —
Never hinged 3,000.
Complete booklet, 2 #77b *3,250.*
**78** A32 3c carmine 110.00 1.10
Never hinged 250.00
**79** A32 5c blue, *bluish* ('99) 250.00 3.00
Never hinged 500.00
**80** A32 6c brown 200.00 57.50
Never hinged 400.00
**81** A32 7c ol yel ('02) 140.00 22.50
Never hinged 300.00
**82** A32 8c orange 350.00 27.50
Never hinged 700.00
**83** A32 10c brown vio 450.00 30.00
Never hinged 900.00
**84** A32 20c ol grn ('00) 650.00 110.00
Never hinged 1,300.
*Nos. 74-84 (11)* 2,318. 256.60
Set, never hinged 4,685.

For surcharges see Nos. 88-88C.

### Imperf., Pairs

*74a* A32 ½c 500.
Never hinged 800.
*75a* A32 1c 1,100.
Never hinged 2,100.
*77c* A32 2c (I) 550.
Never hinged 875.
*77d* A32 2c (II) *1,150.*
*e.* As No. 77b, imperf., 2 panes tete beche ('00) *15,000.*
*79a* A32 5c 1,100.
Never hinged 1,750.
*80a* A32 6c 1,100.
Never hinged 1,750.
*81a* A32 7c 600.
*82a* A32 8c 1,100.
Never hinged 2,000.
*83a* A32 10c 1,100.
Never hinged 2,000.
*84a* A32 20c 5,500.

Nos. 77d, 77e, 81a and 84a were made only without gum. No. 80a was made only with gum. Others either with or without gum and of these those without gum sell for about ⅔ of the values shown for unused hinged. Specialists can distinguish printings made with and without gum by shade and paper quality.

Values for complete booklets from No. 77b to No. 306b are for booklets with uncreased and very fine covers containing never-hinged panes with normal centering, which is fine. Booklets with very fine panes will sell for more. Booklet values from No. 325a to the present are for booklets with panes that are very fine. Values are for the most common booklet covers; other cover types exist for some booklets from No. 104a to 341a, and these may sell for more.

### Imperial Penny Postage Issue

Map of British Empire on Mercator Projection — A33

No. 86

**1898, Dec. 7** **Engr. & Typo.**

**85** A33 2c black, lav & car 40.00 9.00
Never hinged 100.00
*a.* Imperf., pair 450.00
**86** A33 2c black, bl & car 40.00 9.00
Never hinged 100.00
*a.* Imperf., pair 450.00

Imperfs. are without gum.

Nos. 69 and 78 Surcharged in Black

**1899, July**

**87** A31 2c on 3c carmine 17.50 7.50
Never hinged 45.00
**88** A32 2c on 3c carmine 32.50 6.00
Never hinged 82.50

### No. 78 Surcharged in Blue or Violet

A32a A32b

**1899, Jan. 5**

**88B** A32a 1(c) on ⅓ of 3c, on cover (Bl) *7,500.*
**88C** A32b 2(c) on ⅔ of 3c, on cover (V) *7,000.*

Nos. 88B-88C were prepared and used on Jan. 5 only at Port Hood, Nova Scotia, without official authorization.

Nos. 88B-88C must be accompanied by certificates from recognized expertizing organizations. Covers reported to date were backdated and never saw postal use.

King Edward VII — A34

Type I

Type II

Two types of 2c carmine.
Type I — Has breaks in the upper left shading lines above "DA" in Canada.
Type II — Has solid lines, no breaks.

**1903-08** **Engr.**

**89** A34 1c green 50.00 .40
Never hinged 140.00
**90** A34 2c carmine, type II 60.00 .40
Never hinged 190.00
*b.* Booklet pane of 6 1,600. *1,100.*
Never hinged *2,750.*
Complete booklet, 2 #90b *3,500.*
*e.* 2c carmine, type I 150.00 2.00
Never hinged 375.00
*f.* Vert. pair, imperf. btwn and at either top or bottom *4,000.*
**91** A34 5c blue, *blue* 250.00 5.75
Never hinged 800.00
**92** A34 7c olive bister 225.00 6.25
Never hinged 750.00
**93** A34 10c brown lilac 400.00 15.00
Never hinged 1,250.
**94** A34 20c ol grn ('04) 750.00 50.00
Never hinged 2,500.
**95** A34 50c purple ('08) 850.00 175.00
Never hinged 2,750.
*Nos. 89-95 (7)* 2,585. 252.80
Set, never hinged 8,320.

Values for Nos. 94 and 95 used are for examples with contemporaneous circular datestamps. Stamps with heavy cancellations or parcel cancellations sell for much less.

Issued: 1c-10c, 7/1/03; 20c, 9/27/04; 50c, 11/19/08.

### Imperf., Type II

**90A** A34 2c carmine 40.00 40.00
Never hinged 80.00

No. 90A is the only imperforate Canada stamp besides Nos. 136-138 regularly issued to the public. 100,000 were issued.

### Imperf., Pairs, Without Gum

*89a* A34 1c 675.00
*90c* A34 2c Type I 825.00
*d.* As No. 90c, imperf, 2 panes tete beche *20,000.*
*91a* A34 5c 1,100.
*92a* A34 7c 750.
*93a* A34 10c 1,100.

### Quebec Tercentenary Issue

Prince and Princess of Wales, 1908 A35

Jacques Cartier and Samuel de Champlain A36

Queen Alexandra and King Edward — A37

Champlain's Home in Quebec — A38

Generals Montcalm and Wolfe — A39

View of Quebec in 1700 — A40

Champlain's Departure for the West — A41

Arrival of Cartier at Quebec — A42

**1908, July 16** ***Perf. 12***

**96** A35 ½c black brown 8.00 5.00
Never hinged 19.00
**97** A36 1c blue green 30.00 6.00
Never hinged 75.00
**98** A37 2c carmine 40.00 3.00
Never hinged 100.00
**99** A38 5c dark blue 85.00 70.00
Never hinged 210.00
**100** A39 7c olive green 140.00 100.00
Never hinged 350.00
**101** A40 10c dark violet 200.00 125.00
Never hinged 500.00
**102** A41 15c red orange 225.00 160.00
Never hinged 550.00
**103** A42 20c yellow brown 250.00 225.00
Never hinged 625.00
*Nos. 96-103 (8)* 978.00 694.00
Set, never hinged 2,429.

### Imperf., Pairs

*96a* A35 ½c 750.
Never hinged 1,400.
*97a* A36 1c 750.
Never hinged 1,400.
*98a* A37 2c 750.
Never hinged 1,400.
*99a* A38 5c 750.
Never hinged 1,400.
*100a* A39 7c 750.
Never hinged 1,400.
*101a* A40 10c 750.
Never hinged 1,400.
*102a* A41 15c 750.
Never hinged 1,400.
*103a* A42 20c 750.
Never hinged 1,400.

100 pairs of imperfs made, 50 with gum and 50 without. Due to demand, pairs without gum generally sell for 90-95% of the unused hinged price.

King George V — A43

Type I

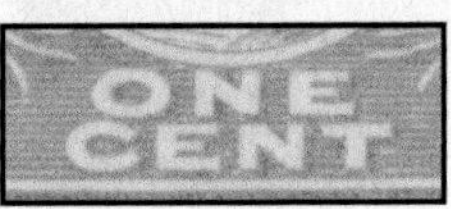
Type II

Two types of 1c.
Type I — The "N" of "ONE" is separated from the oval above it.
Type II — The "N" of "ONE" almost touches the oval above it.

Type I

Type II

Two types of 3c carmine.
Type I — The "R" of "THREE" is separated from the oval above it. The bottom line of the vignette does not touch the heavy diagonal stroke at right.
Type II — The "R" of "THREE" almost touches the oval above it. The bottom horizontal line of the vignette touches the heavy diagonal stroke at right.

Note that the values for Nos. 104-122 are for sheet stamps with perforations on four sides. Single stamps from booklet panes Nos. 104a, 105a, 105b, 106a, 106d, 107b, 107c, 108a and 109a all have natural straight edges on one or two sides, and (except for No. 107d singles) they are worth much less than the listed sheet stamps.

See note on booklet panes and complete booklets after Nos. 74-84. Values for listed booklet panes throughout this catalog are for very fine panes.

**1911-25**

**104** A43 1c dark green 30.00 .25
Never hinged 65.00
*a.* As "b," booklet pane of 6 30.00 30.00
Never hinged 70.00
Complete booklet, 4 #104a 200.00
*b.* 1c blue green 45.00 .25
Never hinged 100.00
*c.* 1c deep blue green 60.00 .25
Never hinged 120.00
*d.* As "c," booklet pane of 6 180.00 180.00
Never hinged 325.00
Complete booklet, 4 #104d *875.00*
*e.* 1c yellow green 30.00 .25
Never hinged 65.00
*f.* As "e," booklet pane of 6 35.00 35.00
Never hinged 70.00
Complete booklet, 4 #104f 180.00

**105** A43 1c org yell (I) ('22) 30.00 .25
Never hinged 65.00
*a.* Booklet pane of 4 + 2 labels 60.00 55.00
Never hinged 110.00
*b.* Booklet pane of 6 65.00 62.50
Never hinged 125.00
Complete booklet, 4 #105b *375.00*
*d.* 1c org yellow (II) 20.00 .25
Never hinged 50.00
**106** A43 2c carmine 30.00 .25
Never hinged 65.00
*a.* Booklet pane of 6 35.00 35.00
Never hinged 70.00
Complete booklet, 2 #106a 90.00
*b.* 2c pink 150.00 18.00
Never hinged 350.00
*c.* 2c rose carmine 30.00 .25
Never hinged 75.00
*d.* As "c," booklet pane of 6 160.00 160.00
Never hinged 320.00
*e.* 2c deep rose red 30.00 .25
**107** A43 2c yel grn ('22) 35.00 .25
Never hinged 90.00
*a.* Thin paper ('24) 20.00 2.50
Never hinged 50.00
*b.* Booklet pane of 4 + 2 labels ('22) 70.00 *80.00*
Never hinged 140.00
*c.* Booklet pane of 6 ('22) 325.00 *325.00*
Never hinged 650.00
Complete booklet, 2 #107c 800.00
**108** A43 3c brown ('18) 35.00 .40
Never hinged 65.00
*a.* Booklet pane of 4 + 2 labels 90.00 *95.00*
Never hinged 180.00
Complete booklet, 2 #108a 550.00
Complete booklet, #105a, 107b, 108a *475.00*
**109** A43 3c car (I) ('23) 20.00 .25
Never hinged 47.50
*a.* Booklet pane of 4 + 2 labels 70.00 *75.00*
Never hinged 140.00
Complete booklet, 2 #109a 325.00
Complete booklet, #105a, 107b, 109a *350.00*
*c.* Die II ('24) 50.00 .50
Never hinged 150.00
**110** A43 4c ol bis ('22) 60.00 4.50
Never hinged 125.00
**111** A43 5c dark blue ('12) 225.00 1.75
Never hinged 500.00
**112** A43 5c violet ('22) 40.00 1.00
Never hinged 110.00
*a.* Thin paper ('24) 35.00 7.50
Never hinged 87.50
**113** A43 7c yel ocher ('12) 60.00 3.50
Never hinged 130.00
**114** A43 7c red brn ('24) 25.00 10.00
Never hinged 65.00
**115** A43 8c blue ('25) 40.00 10.00
Never hinged 100.00
**116** A43 10c plum ('12) 275.00 4.00
Never hinged 700.00
**117** A43 10c blue ('22) 60.00 2.00
Never hinged 150.00
**118** A43 10c bis brn ('25) 40.00 2.00
Never hinged 120.00
**119** A43 20c ol grn ('25) 110.00 1.75
Never hinged 290.00
**120** A43 50c blk brn ('25) 70.00 3.75
Never hinged 200.00
*a.* 50c black ('12) 375.00 12.00
Never hinged 775.00
**122** A43 $1 orange ('23) 85.00 10.00
Never hinged 215.00
*Nos. 104-122 (18)* 1,270. 55.90
Set, never hinged 2,965.

For type A43 perforated 12x8 see No. 184.
For surcharges see Nos. 139-140.
Issued: Nos. 104, 106, 12/22/11; No. 105, 6/7/22; No. 108, 8/6/18; No. 109, 12/18/23; 4c, 7/7/22; No. 111, 1/17/12; No. 112, 2/2/22; Nos. 113, 116, 1/12/12; No. 114, 12/12/24; 8c, 9/1/25; No. 117, 2/20/22; No. 118, 8/1/25; 20c, 1/23/12; 50c, 1/26/12; $1, 7/22/23.

### Imperf., Panes

*105c* As No. 105b, imperf, 2 panes tete beche *15,000.*
*107d* As No. 107c, imperf, 2 panes tete beche *15,000.*
*109b* As No. 109a, imperf, 2 panes tete beche *15,000.*

### Imperf., Pairs

*110a* A43 4c 2,250.
Never hinged 4,250.
*112b* A43 5c 2,250.
Never hinged 4,250.
*114a* A43 7c 2,250.
Never hinged 4,250.
*115a* A43 8c 2,250.
Never hinged 4,250.
*118a* A43 10c 2,250.
Never hinged 4,250.
*119a* A43 20c 2,250.
Never hinged 4,250.
*120b* A43 50c 2,750.
Never hinged 5,500.
*122a* A43 $1 2,250.
Never hinged 4,250.

Nos. 105c and 109b made without gum, others with gum. About half of the No. 120b pairs have creases; value thus $500.

## Coil Stamps

**1913** ***Perf. 8 Horizontally***

**123** A43 1c dark green 110.00 65.00
Never hinged 275.00
**124** A43 2c carmine 110.00 65.00
Never hinged 275.00

**1912-24** ***Perf. 8 Vertically***

**125** A43 1c green 30.00 2.00
Never hinged 75.00
**126** A43 1c org yell (II) ('23) 11.00 7.50
Never hinged 30.00
*a.* As #126, block of 4 (II) 55.00 55.00
Never hinged 110.00
*b.* 1c org yellow (I) 30.00 11.00
Never hinged 90.00
*c.* As "b," block of 4 (I) 700.00
Never hinged 2,250.
**127** A43 2c carmine 42.50 2.00
Never hinged 100.00
**128** A43 2c green ('22) 30.00 1.10
Never hinged 75.00
*a.* Block of 4 55.00 55.00
Never hinged 85.00
**129** A43 3c brown ('18) 30.00 1.30
Never hinged 75.00
**130** A43 3c carmine (I) ('24) 60.00 9.00
Never hinged 175.00
*a.* Block of 4 (I) 1,050. 625.00
Never hinged 2,750.
*b.* Die II 90.00 10.00
Never hinged 225.00
*Nos. 125-130 (6)* 203.50 22.90
Set, never hinged 530.00

Nos. 126a and 128a were issued to the public. Nos. 126c and 130a were issued "by favor" as were the various other imperf and part-perfs of this era.

Beware of fakes of No. 130a made from No. 138.

**1915-24** ***Perf. 12 Horizontally***

**131** A43 1c dark green 7.00 6.50
Never hinged 17.50
**132** A43 2c carmine 40.00 9.00
Never hinged 100.00
**133** A43 2c yell grn ('24) 85.00 70.00
Never hinged 210.00
**134** A43 3c brown ('21) 12.50 9.00
Never hinged 30.00
*Nos. 131-134 (4)* 144.50 94.50
Set, never hinged 340.00

"The Fathers of Confederation" A44

**1917, Sept. 15** ***Perf. 12***

**135** A44 3c brown 47.50 2.25
Never hinged 135.00
*a.* Imperf., pair 500.00

50th anniv. of the Canadian Confederation. Imperfs. are without gum.

**1924** ***Imperf.***

**136** A43 1c orange yellow (I) 35.00 35.00
Never hinged 70.00
Pair 70.00 70.00
Never hinged 140.00
**137** A43 2c green 35.00 35.00
Never hinged 70.00
Pair 70.00 70.00
Never hinged 140.00
**138** A43 3c carmine (I) 17.50 17.50
Never hinged 35.00
Pair 35.00 35.00
Never hinged 70.00
*Nos. 136-138 (3)* 87.50 87.50
Set, never hinged 175.00

### No. 109 Surcharged

a

b

**1926** ***Perf. 12***

**139** A43(a) 2c on 3c carmine (I) 55.00 55.00
Never hinged 135.00
*a.* Pair, one without surcharge 700.00
Never hinged 1,400.
*b.* Double surcharge 275.00
Never hinged 575.00
*c.* Die II 850.00
Never hinged 2,125.
**140** A43(b) 2c on 3c carmine 25.00 25.00
Never hinged 62.50
*a.* Double surcharge 250.00 *250.00*
Never hinged 500.00
*b.* Triple surcharge 350.00 *250.00*
Never hinged 700.00
*c.* Double surch., one invtd. 525.00
Never hinged 1,050.

Sir John A. Macdonald A45

Sir Wilfrid Laurier A48

"The Fathers of Confederation" A46

Parliament Building at Ottawa A47

Map of Canada — A49

**1927, June 29**

**141** A45 1c orange 2.75 1.30
Never hinged 5.00
**142** A46 2c green 2.00 .25
Never hinged 3.75
**143** A47 3c brown carmine 8.50 4.25
Never hinged 15.00
**144** A48 5c violet 4.25 2.10
Never hinged 8.00
**145** A49 12c dark blue 22.50 5.75
Never hinged 40.00
*Nos. 141-145 (5)* 40.00 13.65
Set, never hinged 71.75

60th year of the Canadian Confederation.
Nos. 141-145 exist partly perforated.

### Imperf., Pairs

*141a* A45 1c 120.00
Never hinged 180.00
*142a* A46 2c 120.00
Never hinged 180.00
*143a* A47 3c 120.00
Never hinged 180.00
*144a* A48 5c 120.00
Never hinged 180.00
*145a* A49 12c 120.00
Never hinged 180.00

Thomas d'Arcy McGee A50

Laurier and Macdonald A51

Robert Baldwin and Sir Louis Hypolyte Lafontaine — A52

**1927, June 29**

**146** A50 5c violet 4.00 3.00
Never hinged 7.25
**147** A51 12c green 10.00 5.50
Never hinged 18.00
**148** A52 20c brown carmine 27.50 6.50
Never hinged 50.00
*Nos. 146-148 (3)* 41.50 15.00
Set, never hinged 75.25

Nos. 146-148 were to have been issued in July, 1926, as a commemorative series, but were withheld and issued June 29, 1927.

### Imperf., Pairs

*146a* A50 5c 120.00
Never hinged 180.00
*147a* A51 12c 120.00
Never hinged 180.00
*148a* A52 20c 120.00
Never hinged 180.00

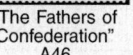

King George V — A53

Mt. Hurd from Bell-Smith's Painting "The Ice-crowned Monarch of the Rockies" — A54

Quebec Bridge — A55

Harvesting Wheat — A56

Schooner "Bluenose" — A57

Parliament Building — A58

**1928-29**

| No. | Type | Description | Unused | Used |
|---|---|---|---|---|
| 149 | A53 | 1c orange | 3.25 | .30 |
| | | Never hinged | 6.00 | |
| *a.* | | Booklet pane of 6 | 27.50 | 20.00 |
| | | Never hinged | 40.00 | |
| | | Complete booklet, 4 #149a | 140.00 | |
| 150 | A53 | 2c green | 1.90 | .25 |
| | | Never hinged | 3.50 | |
| *a.* | | Booklet pane of 6 | 27.50 | 20.00 |
| | | Never hinged | 40.00 | |
| | | Complete booklet, 2 #150a | 85.00 | |
| 151 | A53 | 3c dk carmine | 27.50 | 12.50 |
| | | Never hinged | 50.00 | |
| 152 | A53 | 4c bister ('29) | 22.50 | 5.00 |
| | | Never hinged | 40.00 | |
| 153 | A53 | 5c dp violet | 15.00 | 2.50 |
| | | Never hinged | 30.00 | |
| *a.* | | Booklet pane of 6 | 220.00 | 220.00 |
| | | Never hinged | 300.00 | |
| | | Complete booklet, 3 #149a, 2 #150a, 1 #153a | *600.00* | |
| 154 | A53 | 8c blue | 18.00 | 9.00 |
| | | Never hinged | 32.50 | |
| 155 | A54 | 10c green | 20.00 | 2.50 |
| | | Never hinged | 37.50 | |
| 156 | A55 | 12c gray ('29) | 45.00 | 8.00 |
| | | Never hinged | 85.00 | |
| 157 | A56 | 20c dk car ('29) | 65.00 | 11.00 |
| | | Never hinged | 120.00 | |
| 158 | A57 | 50c dk blue ('29) | 225.00 | 65.00 |
| | | Never hinged | 425.00 | |
| 159 | A58 | $1 ol grn ('29) | 300.00 | 80.00 |
| | | Never hinged | 575.00 | |
| | | *Nos. 149-159 (11)* | 743.15 | 196.05 |
| | | Set, never hinged | 1,405. | |

**Imperf., Panes**

| | | |
|---|---|---|
| *149c* | As No. 149a, imperf, 2 panes tete beche | 950. |
| | Never hinged | 1,750. |
| *150c* | As No. 150a, imperf, 2 panes tete beche | 950. |
| | Never hinged | 1,750. |
| *153c* | As No. 153a, imperf, 2 panes tete beche | 950. |
| | Never hinged | 1,750. |

**Imperf., Pairs**

| No. | Type | Description | Value |
|---|---|---|---|
| *149b* | A53 | 1c | 90.00 |
| | | Never hinged | 125.00 |
| *150b* | A53 | 2c | 90.00 |
| | | Never hinged | 125.00 |
| *151a* | A53 | 3c | 110.00 |
| | | Never hinged | 160.00 |
| *152a* | A53 | 4c | 110.00 |
| | | Never hinged | 160.00 |
| *153b* | A53 | 5c | 110.00 |
| | | Never hinged | 160.00 |
| *154a* | A53 | 8c | 110.00 |
| | | Never hinged | 160.00 |
| *155a* | A54 | 10c | 180.00 |
| | | Never hinged | 270.00 |
| *156a* | A55 | 12c | 180.00 |
| | | Never hinged | 270.00 |
| *157a* | A56 | 20c | 180.00 |
| | | Never hinged | 270.00 |
| *158a* | A57 | 50c | 750.00 |
| | | Never hinged | 1,125. |
| *159a* | A58 | $1 | 675.00 |
| | | Never hinged | 975.00 |

**Coil Stamps**

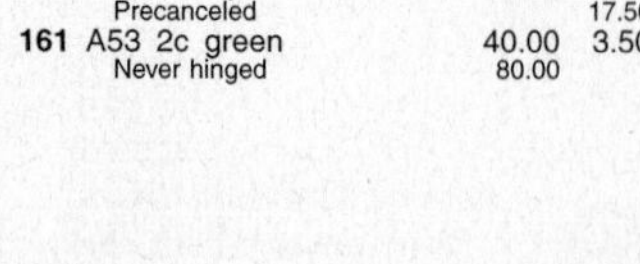

**1929** *Perf. 8 Vertically*

| No. | Type | Description | Unused | Used |
|---|---|---|---|---|
| 160 | A53 | 1c orange | 40.00 | 22.50 |
| | | Never hinged | 80.00 | |
| | | Precanceled | | 17.50 |
| 161 | A53 | 2c green | 40.00 | 3.50 |
| | | Never hinged | 80.00 | |

King George V A59

Library of Parliament A60

The Citadel at Quebec — A61

Harvesting Wheat — A62

Museum at Grand Pré and Monument to Evangeline — A63

Mt. Edith Cavell — A64

Type I

Type II

Two types of 1c.

Type I — Three thick and one thin colored lines between "P" at right and ornament above it.

Type II — Four thick colored lines. Curved line in ball of ornament at right is longer than in die I.

Type I

Type II

Two types of 2c.

Type I — The top of the letter "P" encloses a tiny dot of color.

Type II — The top of the "P" encloses a larger spot of color than in die I. The "P" appears almost like a "D."

**1930-31** *Perf. 11*

| No. | Type | Description | Unused | Used |
|---|---|---|---|---|
| 162 | A59 | 1c orange | 1.25 | .70 |
| | | Never hinged | 2.50 | |
| 163 | A59 | 1c dp grn (II) | 2.00 | .25 |
| | | Never hinged | 4.00 | |
| *a.* | | Booklet pane of 4 + 2 labels (II) | 120.00 | 100.00 |
| | | Never hinged | 180.00 | |
| *b.* | | Die I | 2.00 | .25 |
| | | Never hinged | 4.00 | |
| *c.* | | Booklet pane of 6 (I) | 22.50 | 20.00 |
| | | Never hinged | 35.00 | |
| | | Complete booklet, 4 #163c | 180.00 | |
| 164 | A59 | 2c dull green (I) | 1.75 | .25 |
| | | Never hinged | 3.50 | |
| *a.* | | Booklet pane of 6 | 32.50 | 32.50 |
| | | Never hinged | 47.50 | |
| | | Complete booklet, 2 #164a | 170.00 | |
| 165 | A59 | 2c deep red (I) | 1.75 | .30 |
| | | Never hinged | 3.50 | |
| *a.* | | Die II | 1.90 | .25 |
| | | Never hinged | 3.75 | |
| *b.* | | Booklet pane of 6 (I) | 25.00 | 22.50 |
| | | Never hinged | 37.50 | |
| | | Complete booklet, 2 #165b | 80.00 | |
| 166 | A59 | 2c dk brn (II) ('31) | 1.75 | .25 |
| | | Never hinged | 3.50 | |
| *a.* | | Booklet pane of 4 + 2 labels (II) | 130.00 | 115.00 |
| | | Never hinged | 200.00 | |
| *b.* | | Die I | 5.00 | 4.00 |
| | | Never hinged | 10.00 | |
| *c.* | | Booklet pane of 6 (I) | 57.50 | 57.50 |
| | | Never hinged | 87.50 | |
| | | Complete booklet, 2 #166c | 225.00 | |
| 167 | A59 | 3c deep red ('31) | 2.75 | .25 |
| | | Never hinged | 5.50 | |
| *a.* | | Booklet pane of 4 + 2 labels | 40.00 | 32.50 |
| | | Never hinged | 60.00 | |
| | | Complete booklet, 2 #167a | 110.00 | |
| | | Complete booklet, #163a, 166a, 167a | *450.00* | |
| 168 | A59 | 4c yel bister | 15.00 | 6.00 |
| | | Never hinged | 30.00 | |
| 169 | A59 | 5c dull violet | 7.00 | 5.00 |
| | | Never hinged | 14.00 | |
| 170 | A59 | 5c dull blue | 8.50 | 1.25 |
| | | Never hinged | 17.00 | |
| 171 | A59 | 8c dark blue | 20.00 | 13.50 |
| | | Never hinged | 55.00 | |
| 172 | A59 | 8c red orange | 8.50 | 5.50 |
| | | Never hinged | 17.00 | |
| 173 | A60 | 10c olive green | 10.00 | 1.30 |
| | | Never hinged | 20.00 | |
| 174 | A61 | 12c gray black | 25.00 | 4.50 |
| | | Never hinged | 50.00 | |
| 175 | A62 | 20c brown red | 47.50 | 1.40 |
| | | Never hinged | 95.00 | |
| 176 | A63 | 50c dull blue | 175.00 | 14.00 |
| | | Never hinged | 350.00 | |
| 177 | A64 | $1 dk ol green | 175.00 | 27.50 |
| | | Never hinged | 350.00 | |
| | | *Nos. 162-177 (16)* | 502.75 | 81.95 |
| | | Set, never hinged | 1,020.50 | |

See No. 201. For surcharge see No. 191. For overprint see No. 203.

**Imperf., Pairs**

| No. | Type | Description | Value |
|---|---|---|---|
| *163d* | A59 | 1c (II) | 1,500. |
| | | Never hinged | 2,500. |
| *173a* | A60 | 10c | 1,500. |
| | | Never hinged | 2,500. |
| *174a* | A61 | 12c | 875. |
| | | Never hinged | 1,450. |
| *175a* | A62 | 20c | 875. |
| | | Never hinged | 1,450. |
| *176a* | A63 | 50c | 875. |
| | | Never hinged | 1,450. |
| *177a* | A64 | $1 | 875. |
| | | Never hinged | 1,450. |

**Coil Stamps**

**1930-31** *Perf. 8½ Vertically*

| No. | Type | Description | Unused | Used |
|---|---|---|---|---|
| 178 | A59 | 1c orange | 12.50 | 8.00 |
| | | Never hinged | 25.00 | |
| 179 | A59 | 1c deep green | 9.00 | 5.25 |
| | | Never hinged | 18.00 | |
| 180 | A59 | 2c dull green | 5.00 | 2.50 |
| | | Never hinged | 10.00 | |
| 181 | A59 | 2c deep red | 20.00 | 2.00 |
| | | Never hinged | 40.00 | |
| 182 | A59 | 2c dark brown ('31) | 12.50 | .65 |
| | | Never hinged | 25.00 | |
| 183 | A59 | 3c deep red ('31) | 18.00 | .65 |
| | | Never hinged | 36.00 | |
| | | *Nos. 178-183 (6)* | 77.00 | 19.05 |
| | | Set, never hinged | 154.00 | |

**George V Type of 1912-25**

**1931, June 24** *Perf. 12x8*

| No. | Type | Description | Unused | Used |
|---|---|---|---|---|
| 184 | A43 | 3c carmine | 8.00 | 4.00 |
| | | Never hinged | 24.00 | |

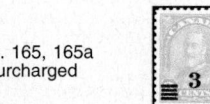

Sir Georges Etienne Cartier — A65

**1931, Sept. 30** *Perf. 11*

| No. | Type | Description | Unused | Used |
|---|---|---|---|---|
| 190 | A65 | 10c deep olive | 12.50 | .25 |
| | | Never hinged | 35.00 | |
| *a.* | | Imperf., pair | 375.00 | |
| | | Never hinged | 750.00 | |

Nos. 165, 165a Surcharged

**1932, June 21**

| No. | Type | Description | Unused | Used |
|---|---|---|---|---|
| 191 | A59 | 3c on 2c dp red (II) | 1.25 | .25 |
| | | Never hinged | 2.00 | |
| *a.* | | Die I | 3.00 | 1.90 |
| | | Never hinged | 4.50 | |

King George V A66

Edward, Prince of Wales A67

Allegory of British Empire — A68

**1932, July 12**

| No. | Type | Description | Unused | Used |
|---|---|---|---|---|
| 192 | A66 | 3c deep red | 1.25 | .25 |
| | | Never hinged | 2.50 | |
| 193 | A67 | 5c dull blue | 7.00 | 2.50 |
| | | Never hinged | 14.00 | |
| 194 | A68 | 13c deep green | 9.00 | 6.00 |
| | | Never hinged | 18.00 | |
| | | *Nos. 192-194 (3)* | 17.25 | 8.75 |
| | | Set, never hinged | 34.50 | |

Imperial Economic Conference, Ottawa.

**Type of 1930 and**

King George V — A69

Type I

Type II

Two types of 3c.

Type I — Upper left tip of "3" level with horizontal line to its left.

Type II — Raised "3"; upper left tip of "3" is above horizontal line.

**1932, Dec. 1**

| No. | Type | Description | Unused | Used |
|---|---|---|---|---|
| 195 | A69 | 1c dk green | 1.25 | .25 |
| | | Never hinged | 2.25 | |
| *a.* | | Booklet pane of 4 + 2 labels ('33) | 90.00 | 85.00 |
| | | Never hinged | 135.00 | |
| *b.* | | Booklet pane of 6 ('33) | 50.00 | 47.50 |
| | | Never hinged | 75.00 | |
| | | Complete booklet, 4 #195b | 225.00 | |
| 196 | A69 | 2c black brown | 1.30 | .25 |
| | | Never hinged | 2.50 | |
| *a.* | | Booklet pane of 4 + 2 labels ('33) | 120.00 | 110.00 |
| | | Never hinged | 180.00 | |
| *b.* | | Booklet pane of 6 ('33) | 90.00 | 70.00 |
| | | Never hinged | 135.00 | |
| | | Complete booklet, 2 #196b | *375.00* | |
| *d.* | | Rotary press dry printing, perf. 11¼x12 | *37.50* | *5.50* |
| 197 | A69 | 3c deep red (I) | 1.40 | .25 |
| | | Never hinged | 2.75 | |
| *c.* | | Die II | 1.40 | .25 |
| | | Never hinged | 2.75 | |
| *d.* | | Booklet pane of 4 + 2 labels, die II ('33) | 42.50 | 37.50 |
| | | Never hinged | 85.00 | |
| | | Complete booklet, 2 #197d | 125.00 | |
| | | Complete booklet, #195a, 196a, 197d | 250.00 | |
| 198 | A69 | 4c ocher | 50.00 | 7.00 |
| | | Never hinged | 95.00 | |
| 199 | A69 | 5c dark blue | 12.00 | .50 |
| | | Never hinged | 21.00 | |
| *a.* | | Horiz. pair, imperf. vert. | 1,350. | |
| | | Never hinged | 1,900. | |
| 200 | A69 | 8c red orange | 35.00 | 3.50 |
| | | Never hinged | 65.00 | |
| 201 | A61 | 13c dull violet | 40.00 | 3.50 |
| | | Never hinged | 75.00 | |
| | | *Nos. 195-201 (7)* | 140.95 | 15.25 |
| | | Set, never hinged | 263.50 | |

Type A66 has at the foot of the stamp "OTTAWA-CONFERENCE 1932". This inscription does not appear on the stamps of type A69.

**Imperf., Pairs**

| No. | Type | Description | Value |
|---|---|---|---|
| *195c* | A69 | 1c | 225.00 |
| | | Never hinged | 375.00 |
| *196c* | A69 | 2c | 225.00 |
| | | Never hinged | 375.00 |
| *197b* | A69 | 3c (I) | 225.00 |
| | | Never hinged | 375.00 |
| *197e* | A69 | 3c (II) | *3,500.* |
| *198a* | A69 | 4c | 225.00 |
| | | Never hinged | 375.00 |
| *199b* | A69 | 5c | 225.00 |
| | | Never hinged | 375.00 |
| *200a* | A69 | 8c | 225.00 |
| | | Never hinged | 375.00 |
| *201a* | A69 | 13c | 750.00 |
| | | Never hinged | 1,200. |

No. 197e exists as one unused block of 4.

Government Buildings, Ottawa — A70

**1933, May 18** *Perf. 11*

| No. | Type | Description | Unused | Used |
|---|---|---|---|---|
| 202 | A70 | 5c dark blue | 10.00 | 3.00 |
| | | Never hinged | 18.50 | |
| *a.* | | Imperf., pair | 575.00 | |
| | | Never hinged | 950.00 | |

Meeting of the Executive Committee of the UPU at Ottawa, May and June, 1933.

No. 175 Overprinted in Blue

**1933, July 24**

| | | | |
|---|---|---|---|
| **203** | A62 20c brown red | 40.00 | 14.00 |
| | Never hinged | 70.00 | |
| *a.* | Imperf., pair | 575.00 | |
| | Never hinged | 950.00 | |

World's Grain Exhibition and Conference at Regina.

Steamship Royal William — A71

**1933, Aug. 17**

| | | | |
|---|---|---|---|
| **204** | A71 5c dark blue | 11.00 | 3.75 |
| | Never hinged | 20.00 | |
| *a.* | Imperf., pair | 575.00 | |
| | Never hinged | 950.00 | |

Centenary of the linking by steam of the Dominion, then a colony, with Great Britain, the mother country. The Royal William's 1833 voyage was the first Trans-Atlantic passage under steam all the way.

**George V Type of 1932**
**Coil Stamps**

**1933** ***Perf. 8½ Vertically***

| | | | |
|---|---|---|---|
| **205** | A69 1c dark green | 12.50 | 2.50 |
| | Never hinged | 20.00 | |
| **206** | A69 2c black brown | 17.50 | 1.10 |
| | Never hinged | 27.50 | |
| **207** | A69 3c deep red | 17.50 | .40 |
| | Never hinged | 29.00 | |
| | *Nos. 205-207 (3)* | 47.50 | 4.00 |
| | Set, never hinged | 76.50 | |

Cartier's Arrival at Quebec — A72

**1934, July 1** ***Perf. 11***

| | | | |
|---|---|---|---|
| **208** | A72 3c blue | 4.00 | 1.40 |
| | Never hinged | 8.00 | |
| *a.* | Imperf., pair | 575.00 | |
| | Never hinged | 1,150. | |
| *1.* | "Burr on shoulder" variety | 110.00 | 65.00 |

Landing of Jacques Cartier, 400th anniv.

Group from Loyalists Monument, Hamilton, Ontario — A73

**1934, July 1**

| | | | |
|---|---|---|---|
| **209** | A73 10c olive green | 28.00 | 7.50 |
| | Never hinged | 52.50 | |
| *a.* | Imperf., pair | 1,400. | |
| | Never hinged | 2,250. | |

Emigration of the United Empire Loyalists from the US to Canada, 150th anniv.

Seal of New Brunswick — A74

**1934, Aug. 16**

| | | | |
|---|---|---|---|
| **210** | A74 2c red brown | 2.50 | 2.00 |
| | Never hinged | 5.00 | |
| *a.* | Imperf., pair | 600.00 | |
| | Never hinged | 1,050. | |

150th anniv. of the founding of the Province of New Brunswick.

Princess Elizabeth A75

Duke of York A76

King George V and Queen Mary A77

Prince of Wales A78

Windsor Castle — A79

Royal Yacht Britannia — A80

**1935, May 4** ***Perf. 12***

| | | | |
|---|---|---|---|
| **211** | A75 1c green | .65 | .35 |
| | Never hinged | 1.00 | |
| **212** | A76 2c brown | .70 | .25 |
| | Never hinged | 1.10 | |
| **213** | A77 3c carmine | 2.00 | .25 |
| | Never hinged | 3.00 | |
| **214** | A78 5c blue | 4.00 | 3.00 |
| | Never hinged | 6.00 | |
| **215** | A79 10c green | 8.00 | 3.00 |
| | Never hinged | 12.75 | |
| **216** | A80 13c dark blue | 8.50 | 6.50 |
| | Never hinged | 13.25 | |
| | *Nos. 211-216 (6)* | 23.85 | 13.35 |
| | Set, never hinged | 37.10 | |

25th anniv. of the accession to the throne of George V.

**Imperf., Pairs**

| | | |
|---|---|---|
| *211a* | A75 1c | 275.00 |
| | Never hinged | 425.00 |
| *212a* | A76 2c | 275.00 |
| | Never hinged | 425.00 |
| *213a* | A77 3c | 275.00 |
| | Never hinged | 425.00 |
| *214a* | A78 5c | 275.00 |
| | Never hinged | 425.00 |
| *215a* | A79 10c | 275.00 |
| | Never hinged | 425.00 |
| *216b* | A80 13c | 275.00 |
| | Never hinged | 425.00 |

King George V — A81

Royal Canadian Mounted Police — A82

Confederation Conference at Charlottetown, 1864 — A83

Niagara Falls — A84

Parliament Buildings, Victoria, B.C. — A85

Champlain Monument, Quebec — A86

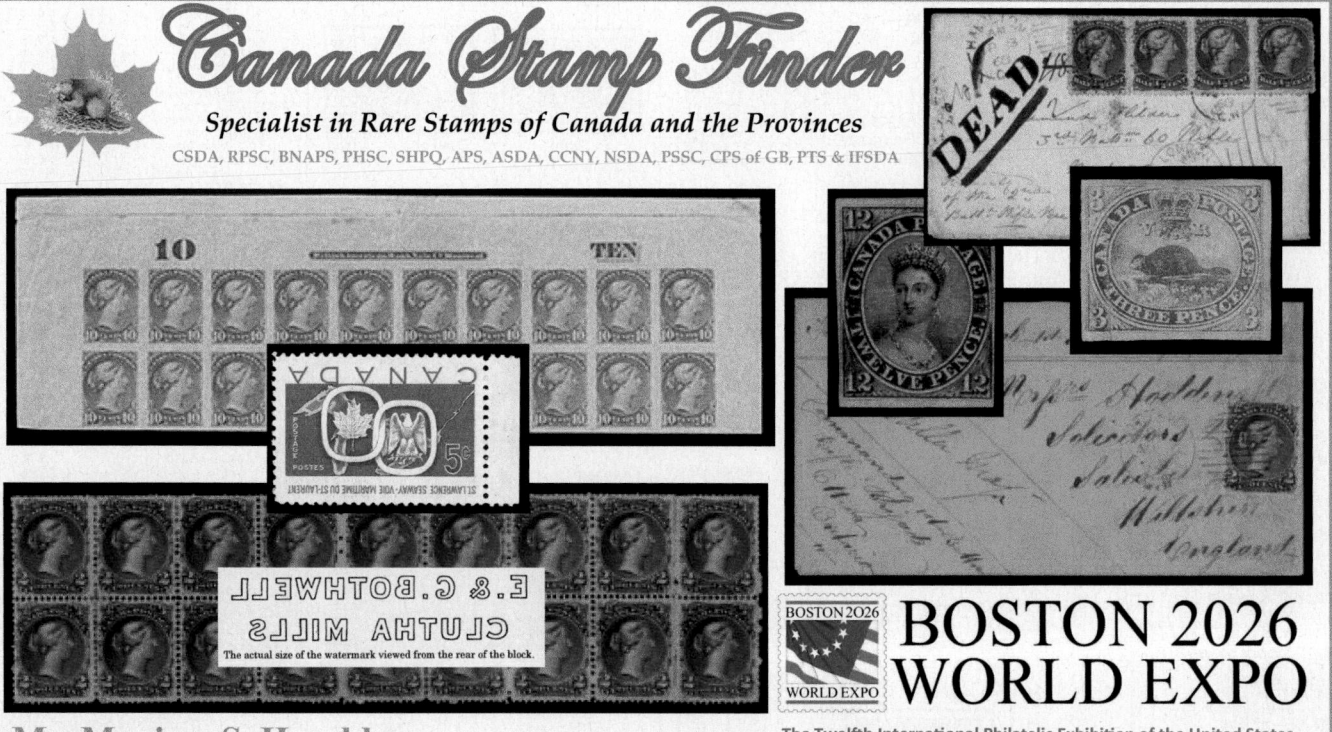

**1935, June 1** ***Perf. 12***

217 A81 1c green .30 .25
Never hinged .45
a. Bklt. pane of 4 + 2 labels 70.00 70.00
Never hinged 105.00
b. Booklet pane of 6 50.00 50.00
Never hinged 80.00
Complete booklet, 4 #217b 125.00
218 A81 2c brown .30 .25
Never hinged .45
a. Bklt. pane of 4 + 2 labels 70.00 70.00
Never hinged 105.00
b. Booklet pane of 6 60.00 60.00
Never hinged 75.00
Complete booklet, 2 #218b 130.00
219 A81 3c dk carmine .65 .25
Never hinged .90
a. Bklt. pane of 4 + 2 labels 40.00 40.00
Never hinged 60.00
Complete booklet, 2 #219a 100.00
Complete booklet, #217a, 218a, 219a 225.00
c. Printed on gummed side 550.00
220 A81 4c yellowish org 2.50 .55
Never hinged 3.75
221 A81 5c blue 3.25 .35
Never hinged 5.00
a. Horiz. pair, imperf. vert. 200.00
Never hinged 300.00
222 A81 8c dp orange 2.50 2.25
Never hinged 3.75
223 A82 10c car rose 8.00 .25
Never hinged 12.50
224 A83 13c violet 8.00 .75
Never hinged 12.50
225 A84 20c deep olive 14.00 .75
Never hinged 21.00
226 A85 50c dull violet 25.00 6.00
Never hinged 37.50
227 A86 $1 deep blue 55.00 11.00
Never hinged 82.50
*Nos. 217-227 (11)* 119.50 22.65
Set, never hinged 180.30

No. 219c is valued in the grade of fine. Very fine examples are rare and sell for much more.

**Imperf., Pairs**

217c A81 1c 250.00
Never hinged 375.00
218c A81 2c 250.00
Never hinged 375.00
219b A81 3c 250.00
Never hinged 375.00
220a A81 4c 250.00
Never hinged 375.00
221b A81 5c 250.00
Never hinged 375.00
222a A81 8c 250.00
Never hinged 375.00
223a A82 10c 250.00
Never hinged 375.00
224a A83 13c 250.00
Never hinged 375.00
225a A84 20c 250.00
Never hinged 375.00
226a A85 50c 250.00
Never hinged 375.00
227a A86 $1 325.00
Never hinged 475.00

**Coil Stamps**

**1935** ***Perf. 8 Vertically***

228 A81 1c green 12.50 3.00
Never hinged 19.00
229 A81 2c brown 17.50 1.00
Never hinged 26.00
230 A81 3c dark carmine 12.50 .60
Never hinged 19.00
*Nos. 228-230 (3)* 42.50 4.60
Set, never hinged 64.00

George VI — A87

**1937** ***Perf. 12***

231 A87 1c green .30 .25
Never hinged .45
a. Booklet pane of 4 + 2 labels 15.00 *22.50*
Never hinged 22.50
b. Booklet pane of 6 7.50 *20.00*
Never hinged 11.50
Complete booklet, 4 #231b *37.50*
232 A87 2c brown .65 .25
Never hinged 1.00
a. Booklet pane of 4 + 2 labels 20.00 *22.50*
Never hinged 30.00
b. Booklet pane of 6 12.00 *16.00*
Never hinged 18.00
Complete booklet, 2 #232b *40.00*
233 A87 3c carmine .65 .25
Never hinged 1.00
a. Booklet pane of 4 + 2 labels 7.00 *12.50*
Never hinged 10.50
Complete booklet, 2 #233a *17.50*
Complete booklet, #231a, 232a, 233a *47.50*
234 A87 4c yellow 2.75 .25
Never hinged 4.00
235 A87 5c blue 3.50 .25
Never hinged 5.00
236 A87 8c orange 2.75 .45
Never hinged 4.00
*Nos. 231-236 (6)* 10.60 1.70
Set, never hinged 15.45

**Imperf., Pairs**

231c A87 1c 300.00
Never hinged 425.00
232c A87 2c 300.00
Never hinged 425.00
233b A87 3c 300.00
Never hinged 425.00

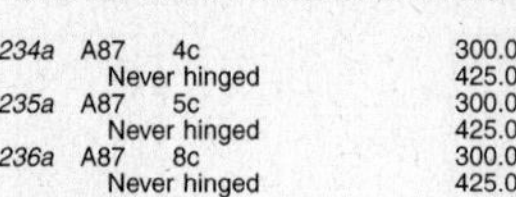

234a A87 4c 300.00
Never hinged 425.00
235a A87 5c 300.00
Never hinged 425.00
236a A87 8c 300.00
Never hinged 425.00

George VI and Queen Elizabeth — A88

**1937, May 10**

237 A88 3c carmine .35 .25
Never hinged .40
a. Imperf., pair 550.00
Never hinged 800.00

Coronation of King George VI and Queen Elizabeth.

**George VI Types of 1937**
**Coil Stamps**

**1937** ***Perf. 8 Vertically***

238 A87 1c green 2.75 1.00
Never hinged 4.00
239 A87 2c brown 5.00 .35
Never hinged 7.50
240 A87 3c carmine 8.00 .25
Never hinged 12.00
*Nos. 238-240 (3)* 15.75 1.60
Set, never hinged 23.50

Memorial Chamber, Parliament Building, Ottawa A89

Entrance to Halifax Harbor A90

Fort Garry Gate, Winnipeg — A91

Vancouver Harbor — A92

Chateau de Ramezay, Montreal — A93

**1938** ***Perf. 12***

241 A89 10c dk carmine 10.00 .25
Never hinged 13.00
a. 10c carmine rose 7.00 .25
Never hinged 10.50
242 A90 13c deep blue 12.00 .60
Never hinged 18.00
243 A91 20c red brown 16.00 .45
Never hinged 24.00
244 A92 50c green 35.00 6.00
Never hinged 50.00
245 A93 $1 dull violet 70.00 7.00
Never hinged 110.00
a. Vert. pair, imperf., horiz. *4,250.*
Never hinged *6,500.*
*Nos. 241-245 (5)* 143.00 14.30
Set, never hinged 215.00

**Imperf., Pairs**

241b A89 10c dark carmine 500.00
Never hinged 750.00
241c A89 10c carmine rose 500.00
Never hinged 750.00
242a A90 13c 500.00
Never hinged 750.00
243a A91 20c 500.00
Never hinged 750.00
244a A92 50c 500.00
Never hinged 750.00
245b A93 $1 675.00
Never hinged 1,000.

Princess Elizabeth and Princess Margaret Rose A94

War Memorial, Ottawa A95

King George VI and Queen Elizabeth — A96

**Unwmk.**

**1939, May 15** **Engr.** ***Perf. 12***

246 A94 1c green & black .35 .25
Never hinged .40
247 A95 2c brown & black .35 .25
Never hinged .40
248 A96 3c dk car & black .35 .25
Never hinged .40
*Nos. 246-248 (3)* 1.05 .75
Set, never hinged 1.20

Visit of George VI and Queen Elizabeth to Canada and the US.

**Imperf., Pairs**

246a A94 1c 500.00
Never hinged 725.00
247a A95 2c 500.00
Never hinged 725.00
248a A96 3c 500.00
Never hinged 725.00

A97

A98

King George VI A99

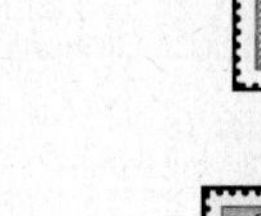

Grain Elevators A100

Farm Scene A101

Parliament Buildings A102

"Ram" Tank — A103

Corvette — A104

Munitions Factory — A105

Destroyer — A106

**1942-43** **Engr.** ***Perf. 12***

249 A97 1c green .35 .25
Never hinged .45
a. Booklet pane of 4 + 2 labels 3.50 *3.50*
Never hinged 5.25
b. Booklet pane of 6 5.00 *5.00*
Never hinged 7.50
Complete booklet, 4 #249b *21.00*
c. Booklet pane of 3 ('43) 2.50 *5.00*
Never hinged 3.75
250 A98 2c brown .40 .25
Never hinged .60
a. Booklet pane of 4 + 2 labels ('43) 7.00 *7.00*
Never hinged 10.50
b. Booklet pane of 6 10.50 *11.50*
Never hinged 16.00
Complete booklet, 2 #250b *32.50*
d. Vert. strip of 3, imperf. horiz. *5,500.*
251 A99 3c dk carmine .60 .25
Never hinged .90
a. Booklet pane of 4 + 2 labels 4.25 *5.25*
Never hinged 6.50
Complete booklet, 2 #251a *10.00*
Complete booklet, #249a, 250a, 251a *22.50*
252 A99 3c rose violet ('43) .50 .25
Never hinged .70
a. Booklet pane of 4 + 2 labels 3.25 4.50
Never hinged 5.00
Complete booklet, 2 #252a *5.50*
b. Booklet pane of 3 3.25 *4.50*
Never hinged 4.75
c. Booklet pane of 6 ('47) 3.75 *3.75*
Never hinged 5.50
253 A100 4c greenish black 1.25 .60
Never hinged 1.90
254 A98 4c dk car ('43) .65 .25
Never hinged .95
a. Booklet pane of 6 5.25 *10.50*
Never hinged 8.00
Complete booklet, #254a *6.50*
Complete booklet, #252c, 254a, 2 #C9a *30.00*
b. Booklet pane of 3 3.25 *4.50*
Never hinged 4.75
Complete booklet, #249c, 252b, 254b *11.25*
255 A97 5c deep blue 1.20 .25
Never hinged 1.80
256 A101 8c red brown 1.60 .50
Never hinged 2.40
257 A102 10c brown 4.75 .25
Never hinged 7.00
258 A103 13c dull green 4.75 3.60
Never hinged 7.00
259 A103 14c dull grn ('43) 7.50 .35
Never hinged 11.25
260 A104 20c chocolate 9.00 .25
Never hinged 13.50
261 A105 50c violet 27.50 1.75
Never hinged 40.00
262 A106 $1 deep blue 55.00 7.50
Never hinged 85.00
*Nos. 249-262 (14)* 115.05 16.30
Set, never hinged 173.45

Canada's contribution to the war effort of the Allied Nations.

No. 250d totally imperf horiz. is unique and is valued in the grade of fine. Beware of strips with blind perfs; these sell for much less.

For overprints see Nos. O1-O4.

For valuing information concerning complete booklets, see lined note before No. 85.

**Imperf., Pairs**

249d A97 1c 275.00
Never hinged 400.00
250c A98 2c 275.00
Never hinged 400.00
251b A99 3c 275.00
Never hinged 400.00
252d A99 3c 275.00
Never hinged 400.00
253a A100 4c 275.00
Never hinged 400.00
254c A98 4c 275.00
Never hinged 400.00
255a A97 5c 275.00
Never hinged 400.00
256a A100 8c 275.00
Never hinged 400.00
257a A102 10c 400.00
Never hinged 600.00
258a A103 13c 400.00
Never hinged 600.00
259a A103 14c 400.00
Never hinged 600.00
260a A104 20c 400.00
Never hinged 600.00
261a A105 50c 400.00
Never hinged 600.00
262a A106 $1 575.00
Never hinged 850.00

**Types of 1942**
**Coil Stamps**

**1942-43** ***Perf. 8 Vertically***

263 A97 1c green ('43) 1.40 .55
Never hinged 2.25
264 A98 2c brown 2.10 1.10
Never hinged 3.00
265 A99 3c dark carmine 2.10 1.10
Never hinged 3.00
266 A99 3c rose violet ('43) 4.25 .35
Never hinged 6.00
267 A98 4c dk carmine ('43) 7.00 .30
Never hinged 9.00
*Nos. 263-267 (5)* 16.85 3.40
Set, never hinged 23.25

See Nos. 278-281.

**Catalogue values for unused stamps in this section, from this point to the end of the section, are for Never Hinged items.**

Farm Scene, Ontario A107

Great Bear Lake, Mackenzie A108

Hydroelectric Station, Saint Maurice River — A109

Combine — A110

Logging, British Columbia — A111

Train Ferry, Prince Edward Island — A112

**1946, Sept. 16 Engr. *Perf. 12***

**268** A107 8c red brown 3.00 .70
**269** A108 10c olive 4.75 .25
**270** A109 14c black brown 6.00 .25
**271** A110 20c slate black 7.50 .25
**272** A111 50c dk blue green 20.00 1.75
**273** A112 $1 red violet 47.50 3.00
*Nos. 268-273 (6)* 88.75 6.20

For overprints see Nos. O6-O10, O21-O23, O25.

Alexander Graham Bell — A113

**1947, Mar. 3**

**274** A113 4c deep blue .30 .25

Birth centenary of Alexander Graham Bell.

Citizen of Canada — A114

**1947, July 1**

**275** A114 4c deep blue .30 .25

Issued on the 80th anniv. of the Canadian Confederation, to mark the advent of Canadian Citizenship.

Princess Elizabeth — A115

**1948, Feb. 16**

**276** A115 4c deep blue .30 .25

Marriage of Princess Elizabeth to Lieut. Philip Mountbatten, R. N., on Nov. 20, 1947.

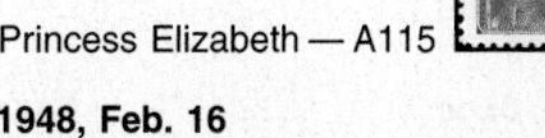

Parliament Buildings Ottawa — A116

**1948, Oct. 1**

**277** A116 4c dk gray bl .30 .25

Centenary of Responsible Government.

**George VI Types of 1942**
**Coil Stamps**

**1948 *Perf. 9½ Vertically***

**278** A97 1c green 6.50 2.25
**279** A98 2c brown 21.00 8.50
**280** A99 3c rose violet 15.00 2.25
**281** A98 4c dark carmine 21.00 2.50
*Nos. 278-281 (4)* 63.50 15.50

John Cabot's Ship "Matthew" — A117

**1949, Apr. 1 Engr. *Perf. 12***

**282** A117 4c blue green .30 .25

Entry of Newfoundland into confederation with Canada.

"Founding of Halifax, 1749" — A118

**1949, June 21 Unwmk.**

**283** A118 4c purple .30 .25

200th anniv. of the founding of Halifax, Nova Scotia.

A119

A120

A121

A122

A123

**1949, Nov. 15**

**284** A119 1c green .30 .25
*a.* Booklet pane of 3 ('50) .75 *3.00*
**285** A120 2c sepia .30 .25
**286** A121 3c rose violet .35 .25
*a.* Booklet pane of 3 ('50) 2.50 *6.50*
*b.* Booklet pane of 4 + 2 labels ('50) 3.25 *3.75*
Complete booklet, 2 #286b *7.00*
**287** A122 4c dk carmine .55 .25
*a.* Booklet pane of 3 ('50) 12.50 12.50
Complete booklet, #284a, 286a, 287a *21.00*
*b.* Booklet pane of 6 ('50) 18.00 18.00
Complete booklet, #287b *22.50*
**288** A123 5c deep blue 1.25 .65
*Nos. 284-288 (5)* 2.75 1.65

Stamps from booklet panes of 3 are imperf. on 2 or 3 sides.

**"POSTES POSTAGE" Omitted**

**1950, Jan. 19**

**289** A119 1c green .30 .25
**290** A120 2c sepia .35 .25
**291** A121 3c rose violet .35 .25
**292** A122 4c dark carmine .35 .25
**293** A123 5c deep blue 1.25 1.00
*Nos. 289-293 (5)* 2.60 2.00

See Nos. 295-300, 305-306, 309-310. For overprints see Nos. O12-O20.

Oil Wells, Alberta — A124

**1950, Mar. 1 Engr. *Perf. 12***

**294** A124 50c blue green 7.00 1.30

Development of oil wells in Canada. For overprints see Nos. O11, O24.

**Types of 1949**
**"POSTES POSTAGE" Omitted**
**Coil Stamps**

**1950 *Perf. 9½ Vertically***

**295** A119 1c green .75 .30
**296** A121 3c rose violet 1.10 .55

**With "POSTES POSTAGE"**
***Perf. 9½ Vertically***

**297** A119 1c green .40 .25
**298** A120 2c sepia 3.50 1.50
**299** A121 3c rose violet 2.10 .25
**300** A122 4c dark carmine 19.00 .75
*Nos. 297-300 (4)* 25.00 2.75

Indians Drying Skins on Stretchers — A125

**1950, Oct. 2 *Perf. 12***

**301** A125 10c black brown .90 .25

Canada's fur resources. For overprint see No. O26.

Fishing — A126

**1951, Feb. 1 Unwmk.**

**302** A126 $1 bright ultra 35.00 10.00

Canada's fish resources. For overprint see No. O27.

Sir Robert Laird Borden A127

William L. Mackenzie King A128

**1951, June 25 *Perf. 12***

**303** A127 3c dp turq green .30 .25
**304** A128 4c rose pink .30 .25

**George VI Types of 1949**

**1951 *Perf. 12***

**305** A120 2c olive green .30 .25
**306** A122 4c orange vermilion .35 .25
*a.* Booklet pane of 3 5.25 2.75
Complete booklet, #284a, 286a, 306a *13.00*
*b.* Booklet pane of 6 5.00 5.00
Complete booklet, #306b *6.75*

For overprints see Nos. O28-O29.

**Coil Stamps**
***Perf. 9½ Vertically***

**309** A120 2c olive green 1.40 .60
**310** A122 4c orange vermilion 2.75 .70

Trains of 1851 and 1951 A129

"Threepenny Beaver" of 1851 A130

Designs: 5c, Steamships City of Toronto and Prince George. 7c, Stagecoach and Plane.

**1951, Sept. 24 Unwmk. *Perf. 12***

**311** A129 4c dark gray .60 .25
**312** A129 5c purple 1.80 1.25
**313** A129 7c deep blue 1.10 .30
**314** A130 15c bright red 1.20 .30
*Nos. 311-314 (4)* 4.70 2.10

Centenary of British North American postal administration.

Princess Elizabeth and Duke of Edinburgh — A131

**1951, Oct. 26** **Engr.**
**315** A131 4c violet .30 .25

Visit of Princess Elizabeth, Duchess of Edinburgh and the Duke of Edinburgh to Canada and the US.

Symbols of Newsprint Paper Production — A132

**1952, Apr. 1** **Unwmk.** ***Perf. 12***
**316** A132 20c gray 1.50 .25

Canada's paper production. For overprint see No. O30.

Red Cross on Sun — A133

**1952, July 26** **Engr. and Litho.**
**317** A133 4c blue & red .30 .25

18th Intl. Red Cross Conf., Toronto, July 1952.

Sir John J. C. Abbott A134

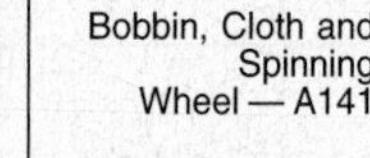

Alexander Mackenzie A135

**1952, Nov. 3** **Engr.**
**318** A134 3c rose lilac .30 .25
**319** A135 4c orange vermilion .30 .25

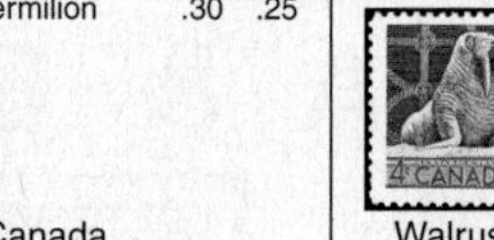

Canada Goose — A136

**1952, Nov. 3**
**320** A136 7c blue .40 .25

For overprint see No. O31.

Pacific Coast Indian House and Totem Pole — A137

**1953, Feb. 2**
**321** A137 $1 gray 5.75 .90

For overprint see No. O32.

Natl. Wildlife Week — A138

**1953, Apr. 1**
**322** A138 2c Polar bear .30 .25
**323** A138 3c Moose .30 .25
**324** A138 4c Bighorn sheep .30 .25
*Nos. 322-324 (3)* .90 .75

Elizabeth II — A139

**1953, May 1**
**325** A139 1c violet brown .30 .25
*a.* Booklet pane of 3 1.40 1.40
**326** A139 2c green .30 .25
**327** A139 3c carmine rose .30 .25
*a.* Booklet pane of 3 1.90 1.40
*b.* Booklet pane of 4 + 2 labels 1.30 *1.75*
Complete booklet, 2 #327b 3.00
**328** A139 4c violet .30 .25
*a.* Booklet pane of 3 1.90 1.75
Complete booklet, #325a, 327a, 328a 9.00
*b.* Booklet pane of 6 1.40 1.40
Complete booklet, #328b 2.00
**329** A139 5c ultramarine .35 .25
*Nos. 325-329 (5)* 1.55 1.25

Stamps from booklet panes of 3 are imperf. on 2 or 3 sides.

See Nos. 331-333. For overprints see Nos. O33-O37.

### Coronation Issue

Queen Elizabeth II — A140

**1953, June 1**
**330** A140 4c violet .30 .25

### Coil Stamps

**1953** ***Perf. 9½ Vertically***
**331** A139 2c green 1.50 1.00
**332** A139 3c carmine rose 1.50 1.00
**333** A139 4c violet 3.50 1.50
*Nos. 331-333 (3)* 6.50 3.50

See note after No. 329.
Issued: 2c, 7/30; 3c, 7/27; 4c, 9/3.

Bobbin, Cloth and Spinning Wheel — A141

**1953, Nov. 2** ***Perf. 12***
**334** A141 50c light green 2.75 .25

For overprint see No. O38.

Walrus A142

Beaver A143

**1954, Apr. 1**
**335** A142 4c gray .30 .25
**336** A143 5c ultramarine .35 .25
*a.* Booklet pane of 5 + label 1.75 1.40
Complete booklet, #336a 2.25

National Wildlife Week, 1954.

Elizabeth II A144

Gannet A145

**1954-61**
**337** A144 1c violet brn .30 .25
*a.* Booklet pane of 5 + label ('56) 1.10 1.10
**338** A144 2c green .30 .25
*a.* Pane of 25 ('61) 3.75 3.75
*b.* Vert. pair, imperf. between, 5 pairs in a block of 10 *25,000.*
**339** A144 3c carmine rose .30 .25
*a.* Horiz. pair, imperf. vert. *1,400.*
**340** A144 4c violet .30 .25
*a.* Booklet pane of 5 + label ('56) 1.40 1.40
Complete booklet, #337a, 340a 3.00
*b.* Booklet pane of 6 ('55) 3.00 3.00
Complete booklet, #340b 3.50
**341** A144 5c bright blue .30 .25
*a.* Booklet pane of 5 + label 1.10 1.10
Complete booklet, #341a 2.00
*b.* Pane of 20 (5 x 4) ('61) 6.50 6.50
*c.* Horiz. pair, imperf. vert. *5,500.*
**342** A144 6c orange .50 .25
**343** A145 15c gray 1.50 .25
*Nos. 337-343 (7)* 3.50 1.75

Panes of 20 and 25 are imperf. on 4 sides.
Issued: 5c, 15c, 4/1; others, 6/10.
At this time, No. 338b is known only as a unique block of 10, as listed.

For overprints see Nos. O40-O44.

---

Luminescence

The overprinting of regular stamps with vertical luminescent bands began experimentally in 1962 when Nos. 337p-341p were released at Winnipeg. The bands are of varying number, position and chemical content.

Tagged varieties of stamps which were issued both untagged and with luminescent overprint are listed with suffix letter "p".

---

**1962, Jan. 13** **Tagged**
*337p* A144 1c violet brown 1.30 .95
*338p* A144 2c green 1.30 .95
*339p* A144 3c carmine rose 1.30 .95
*340p* A144 4c violet 3.75 3.25
*341p* A144 5c bright blue 4.00 2.25
*Nos. 337p-341p (5)* 11.65 8.35

### Coil Stamps

**1954** ***Perf. 9½ Vertically***
**345** A144 2c green .55 .25
**347** A144 4c violet 1.50 .25
**348** A144 5c bright blue 2.25 .25
*Nos. 345-348 (3)* 4.30 .75

Issued: 2c, 9/9; 3c, 8/23; 4c, 7/6.

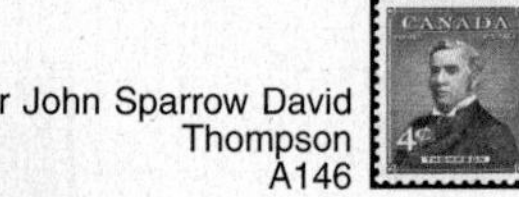


Sir John Sparrow David Thompson A146

Sir Mackenzie Bowell A147

**1954, Nov. 1** ***Perf. 12***
**349** A146 4c violet .35 .25
**350** A147 5c bright blue .35 .25

Eskimo and Kayak — A148

**1955, Feb. 21**
**351** A148 10c violet brown .40 .25

For overprint see No. O39.

Musk Ox A149

Whooping Cranes A150

**1955, Apr. 4**
**352** A149 4c purple .35 .25
**353** A150 5c blue .40 .25

National Wildlife Week, April 10-16.

Torch, Dove and Maple Leaves — A151

**1955, June 1** **Unwmk.**
**354** A151 5c brt blue & dk blue .40 .25

ICAO, 10th anniversary.

Pioneer Settlers — A152

**1955, June 30** ***Perf. 12***
**355** A152 5c ultramarine .40 .25

50th anniv. of the founding of the provinces of Alberta and Saskatchewan.

Globe and Scout Emblem — A153

**1955, Aug. 20** **Engr.**
**356** A153 5c green & org brown .40 .25

8th Boy Scout World Jamboree, Niagara-on-the-Lake, Ont.

Richard Bedford Bennett A154

Sir Charles Tupper A155

**1955, Nov. 8**
**357** A154 4c violet .35 .25
**358** A155 5c ultramarine .35 .25

Ice Hockey Players — A156

**1956, Jan. 23**
**359** A156 5c ultramarine .35 .25

Issued to publicize Canada's most popular winter sport.

Caribou A157

Mountain Goat A158

**1956, Apr. 12**
**360** A157 4c violet .40 .25
**361** A158 5c ultramarine .40 .25

National Wildlife Week, 1956.

"Paper Industry" A159

"Chemical Industry" A160

**1956, June 7** **Engr.**
**362** A159 20c green 1.50 .25
**363** A160 25c red 1.60 .25

For overprint see No. O45.

House on Fire — A161

**1956, Oct. 9** **Unwmk.** ***Perf. 12***
**364** A161 5c gray & red .35 .25

Issued to emphasize the needless waste caused by preventable fires.

Canada's Outdoor Recreation Facilities — A162

No. 365, Fishing. No. 366, Swimming. No. 367, Hunter and dog. No. 368, Skiing.

**1957, Mar. 7**

**365** A162 5c blue .40 .25
**366** A162 5c blue .40 .25
**367** A162 5c blue .40 .25
**368** A162 5c blue .40 .25
*a.* Block of 4, #365-368 1.60 1.10

All four designs are printed alternating in sheet of 50, with various combinations possible.

Loon — A163

**1957, Apr. 10** ***Perf. 12***

**369** A163 5c black .35 .25

David Thompson and Map of Western Canada — A164

**1957, June 5** **Unwmk.**

**370** A164 5c ultramarine .35 .25

David Thompson (1770-1857), explorer and geographer.

Parliament Building, Ottawa A165

Post Horn and Globe A166

**1957, Aug. 14** ***Perf. 12***

**371** A165 5c deep dull blue .35 .25
**372** A166 15c deep dull blue 2.25 2.00

UPU, 14th Congress, Ottawa, Aug. 1957.

Miner With Pneumatic Drill — A167

**1957, Sept. 5**

**373** A167 5c black .30 .25

Canada's mining industry; 6th Commonwealth Mining and Metallurgical Congress, Vancouver, Sept. 8-Oct. 8.

Elizabeth II and Prince Philip — A168

**1957, Oct. 10** **Unwmk.**

**374** A168 5c black .30 .25

Visit of Queen Elizabeth II and Prince Philip to Canada, Oct. 12-16.

Newspapers and Symbols of Industry — A169

**1958, Jan. 22** **Engr.**

**375** A169 5c black .35 .25

Canadian press; the importance of a free press.

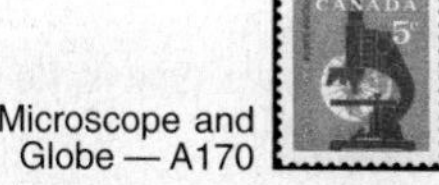


Microscope and Globe — A170

**1958, Mar. 5** ***Perf. 12***

**376** A170 5c blue .35 .25

Intl. Geophysical Year, 1957-1958.

Miner Panning Gold — A171

**1958, May 8**

**377** A171 5c bluish green .35 .25

Province of British Columbia, cent.

La Verendrye — A172

**1958, June 4**

**378** A172 5c bright ultra .35 .25

Pierre Gaultier de Varenne, Sieur de la Verendrye, 18th century French explorer of Western Canada.

Champlain and View of Quebec — A173

**1958, June 26**

**379** A173 5c dk green & bis brn .35 .25

Founding of Quebec, 350th anniv.

Nurse — A174

**1958, July 30** **Engr.**

**380** A174 5c rose lilac .35 .25

Importance of health, both to the individual and to the nation.

Kerosene Lamp and Refinery — A175

**1958, Sept. 10** ***Perf. 12***

**381** A175 5c olive & red .35 .25

Centennial of Canada's oil industry.

Speaker's Chair and Mace — A176

**1958, Oct. 2**

**382** A176 5c slate blue .35 .25

Bicentennial of the meeting of the first House of Representatives in Canada, Halifax, Oct. 2, 1758.

"Silver Dart" and Delta Wing Planes — A177

**1959, Feb. 23**

**383** A177 5c blue & black .35 .25

50th anniv. of the 1st airplane flight in Canada near Baddeck, N. S., with J. A. D. McCurdy as pilot.

Globe and Dove — A178

**1959, Apr. 2**

**384** A178 5c violet blue .35 .25

NATO, 10th anniversary.

Woman Tending Tree — A179

**1959, May 13**

**385** A179 5c olive yell & blk .35 .25

Associated Country Women of the World.

Elizabeth II — A180

**1959, June 18**

**386** A180 5c dark carmine .35 .25

Visit of Queen Elizabeth and Prince Philip to Canada, June 18-Aug. 1.

Great Lakes, Maple Leaf and Eagle Emblems — A181

**1959, June 26** **Engr.**

**387** A181 5c red & blue .35 .25
*a.* Center inverted *9,000. 7,500.*

Opening of the St. Lawrence Seaway, June 26, 1959.

See United States No. 1131.

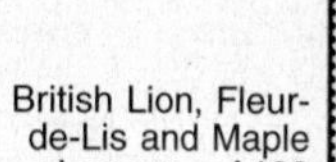

British Lion, Fleur-de-Lis and Maple Leaves — A182

**1959, Sept. 10** ***Perf. 12***

**388** A182 5c crim rose & dk green .35 .25

Bicentenary of the Battle of the Plains of Abraham.

Girl Guide Emblem — A183

**1960, Apr. 20** **Unwmk.**

**389** A183 5c brn org & dp blue .35 .25

Canadian Girl Guides Assoc., 50th anniv.

Dollard des Ormeaux and Battle Scene — A184

**1960, May 19**

**390** A184 5c ultra & bis brown .35 .25

Battle of the Long Sault, 300th anniv.

Compass Rose, Earth Mover and Surveyor — A185

**1961, Feb. 8** **Engr.**

**391** A185 5c green & vermilion .35 .25

Development of Canada's Northland.

Emily Pauline Johnson — A186

**1961, Mar. 10**

**392** A186 5c green & red .35 .25

Emily Pauline Johnson (1861-1913), Mohawk princess and poet.

Arthur Meighen — A187

**1961, Apr. 19**

**393** A187 5c ultramarine .35 .25

Arthur Meighen, Prime Minister of Canada, (1920-21, 1926).

Power Plant and Men Holding Blueprint — A188

**1961, June 28** **Unwmk.**

**394** A188 5c lt red brn & blue .35 .25

10th anniv. of the Colombo Plan, initiated to assist underdeveloped countries by providing trained manpower and resources.

Natural Resources and Hands Holding Cogwheel — A189

**1961, Oct. 12** **Engr.**

**395** A189 5c brown & blue grn .35 .25

Canada's "Resources for Tomorrow Program" and to publicize the close link between industry and the country's renewable natural resources.

Young Adults and Education Symbols — A190

**1962, Feb. 28**

**396** A190 5c black & lt red brn .35 .25

Issued to stimulate public awareness of the importance of education.

Scottish Settler and Lord Selkirk — A191

**1962, May 3**

**397** A191 5c lt green & vio brn .35 .25

150th anniv. of the Red River Settlement in Western Canada (Prairie Provinces).

Jean Talon Presenting Gifts to Young Farm Couple — A192

**1962, June 13** **Unwmk.**

**398** A192 5c dark blue .35 .25

Jean Talon, administrator of New France (Canada), 1665-1668.

British Columbia Legislative Building and Stamp of 1860 — A193

**1962, Aug. 22** **Engr.**

**399** A193 5c black & reddish org .35 .25

Centenary of Victoria as incorporated city.

---

In middle to late 1962, Canadian Bank Note Co. changed their perforation equipment from a gauge of 11.95 to gauge 11.85. The gauge 11.85 perforation holes are slightly larger than those of the 11.95 gauge.

This change affected some of the reprintings of then-current low- and medium-value Wilding definitives (including Nos. 320, 321, 334, 338, 340, 343, 351, 362, 363, 411), at least one commemorative (No. 399), low-value Cameo definitives (Nos. 401a, 402a, 404a, 405b, 405p), a low-value Centennial booklet (No. 458a) and several postage dues (Nos. J15-J20). Other issues may be affected and the editors would like to hear of any new discoveries.

---

Arms of the Provinces — A194

**1962, Aug. 31**

**400** A194 5c brown orange & black .35 .25

Official opening of the Trans-Canada Highway, Rogers Pass, Glacier National Park, Sept. 4.

Queen Elizabeth II and Wheat — A195

Designs (Symbol in upper left corner): 1c, Mineral crystals. 2c, Tree. 3c, Fish. 4c, Electric high tension tower.

**1962-63** **Engr.** ***Perf. 12***

**401** A195 1c dp brn ('63) .30 .25
- *a.* Booklet pane of 5 + label ('63) 3.00 3.00

**402** A195 2c green ('63) .30 .25
- *a.* Pane of 25 ('63) 7.50 7.50

**403** A195 3c purple ('63) .30 .25

**404** A195 4c carmine ('63) .30 .25
- *a.* Booklet pane of 5 + label ('63) 3.00 3.00
- Complete booklet, #401a, 404a 6.75
- *b.* Pane of 25 ('63) 11.00 11.00

**405** A195 5c violet blue .30 .25
- *a.* Booklet pane of 5 + label ('63) 3.00 3.00
- Complete booklet, #405a 3.75
- *b.* Pane of 20 ('63) 13.00 13.00
- *c.* Imperf., pair (#405b) *4,500.*
- *d.* Vert. pair, imperf. horiz. *4,250.* *575.00*

*Nos. 401-405 (5)* 1.50 1.25

Nos. 402a, 404b, and 405b are imperf. on four sides.

Used examples of No. 405d are canceled "Gonor, MB." Beware of examples with traces of blind perfs; a certificate of authenticity is recommended.

Issued: 5c, 10/3; 1c, 4c, 2/4/63; 2c, 3c, 5/2/63.

For overprints see Nos. O46-O49.

**1963** **Tagged**

| | | | | |
|---|---|---|---|---|
| *401p* | A195 | 1c deep brown | .30 | .25 |
| *402p* | A195 | 2c green | .30 | .25 |
| *403p* | A195 | 3c purple | .30 | .25 |
| *404p* | A195 | 4c carmine | .75 | .50 |
| *405p* | A195 | 5c violet blue | .45 | .25 |
| *q.* | | Pane of 20 | 42.50 | 42.50 |
| | | *Nos. 401p-405p (5)* | 2.10 | 1.50 |

See note after No. 343.

### Coil Stamps

**1962-63** ***Perf. 9½ Horiz.***

**406** A195 2c green 4.75 2.25

**407** A195 3c purple 3.50 1.75

**408** A195 4c carmine 4.75 2.25
- *a.* Pair, imperf between *3,000.*

**409** A195 5c violet blue 4.75 1.00

*Nos. 406-409 (4)* 17.75 7.25

No. 408a is valued in the grade of fine. Beware of dangerous fakes; a certificate of authenticity is necessary.

Issued: 5c, 10/3; 4c, 2/4/63; 2c, 3c, 5/2/63.

Sir Casimir Stanislaus Gzowski (1813-98), Engineer, Soldier and Educator — A196

**1963, Mar. 5** **Unwmk.** ***Perf. 12***

**410** A196 5c rose lilac .30 .25

Export Crate and Mercator Map — A197

**1963, June 14**

**411** A197 $1 rose carmine 8.00 2.25

Sir Martin Frobisher (1535-1594), Explorer and Discoverer of Frobisher Bay — A198

**1963, Aug. 21**

**412** A198 5c ultramarine .30 .25

Postrider and First Land Mail Routes — A199

**1963, Sept. 25**

**413** A199 5c green & red brn .30 .25

Bicentennial of the 1st regular postal service between Quebec, Three Rivers & Montreal.

Jet at Ottawa Airport A200

Canada Geese A201

**1963-64**

**414** A200 7c blue ('64) .50 .40

**415** A201 15c deep ultra 1.80 .25

See No. 436. For surcharge see No. 430.

"Peace on Earth" — A202

**1964, Apr. 8** **Engr. & Litho.**

**416** A202 5c blue grn, Prus bl & ocher .30 .25

Issued to promote world peace.

Three-Maple-Leaf Emblem (Canadian Unity) — A203

White Trillium and Arms of Ontario — A204

No. 419, White garden lily and arms of Quebec. No. 420, Mayflower (trailing arbutus) and arms of Nova Scotia. No. 421, Purple violet and arms of New Brunswick. No. 422, Prairie crocus and arms of Manitoba. No. 423, Dogwood and arms of British Columbia. No. 424, Lady's slipper and arms of Prince Edward Island. No. 425, Prairie lily and arms of Saskatchewan. No. 426, Wild rose and arms of Alberta. No. 427, Pitcher plant and arms of Newfoundland. No. 428, Fireweed and arms of Yukon. No. 429, Mountain avens and arms of Northwest Territories. No. 429A, Maple leaf and arms of Canada.

**1964-66** **Engr. & Litho.** ***Perf. 12***

| | | | | |
|---|---|---|---|---|
| **417** | A203 | 5c lt blue & dk car | .30 | .25 |
| **418** | A204 | 5c red brn, buff & green | .30 | .25 |
| **419** | A204 | 5c grn, yel & org | .30 | .25 |
| **420** | A204 | 5c blue, pink & grn | .30 | .25 |
| **421** | A204 | 5c car, green & vio | .30 | .25 |
| **422** | A204 | 5c red brn, lil & dl grn | .30 | .25 |
| **423** | A204 | 5c lilac, grn & bis | .30 | .25 |
| **424** | A204 | 5c vio, grn & dp rose | .30 | .25 |
| **425** | A204 | 5c sepia, org & grn | .30 | .25 |
| **426** | A204 | 5c dl grn, yel & car | .30 | .25 |
| **427** | A204 | 5c black, grn & car | .30 | .25 |
| **428** | A204 | 5c dk bl, rose & grn | .30 | .25 |
| **429** | A204 | 5c ol, yel & green | .30 | .25 |
| **429A** | A204 | 5c dk blue & dp red | .30 | .25 |
| | | *Nos. 417-429A (14)* | 4.20 | 3.50 |

Issued: No. 417, 5/14/64; Nos. 418-419, 6/30/64; Nos. 420-421, 2/3/65; Nos. 422-423, 4/28/65; No. 424, 7/21/65; Nos. 425-426, 1/19/66; No. 427, 2/23/66; Nos. 428-429, 3/23/66; No. 429A, 6/30/66.

No. 414 Surcharged

**1964, July 15** **Engr.**

**430** A200 8c on 7c blue .45 .25
- *a.* Pair, one without surcharge *11,500.*
- *b.* Surcharge on reverse, inverted *3,750.*

Nos. 430a and 430b are each unique.

Fathers of Confederation Memorial, Charlottetown A205

**1964, July 29**

**431** A205 5c black .30 .25

Centenary of the Charlottetown, P.E.I., Conference, Sept. 1-9, 1864, which led to the creation of the Canadian nation in 1867.

Maple Leaf and Hand Holding Quill Pen — A206

**1964, Sept. 9**

**432** A206 5c dark brown & rose .30 .25

Centenary of the Quebec Conference, Oct. 10-27, 1864, which led to the creation of the Canadian nation.

Elizabeth II — A207

**1964, Oct. 5**

**433** A207 5c claret .30 .25

Queen Elizabeth's visit, Oct. 6-13.

Family and Star of Bethlehem — A208

**1964, Oct. 14** ***Perf. 12***

**434** A208 3c red .30 .25
- *a.* Pane of 25 7.50 7.50
- *p.* Tagged .65 .35
- *q.* As "a," tagged 11.00 11.00

**435** A208 5c blue .30 .25
- *p.* Tagged 1.10 .35

Panes of 25 are imperf. on four sides.

### Jet Type of 1964

**1964, Nov. 18** **Unwmk.**

**436** A200 8c blue .40 .25

Maple Leaf and ICY Emblem — A209

**1965, Mar. 3**

| | | | | |
|---|---|---|---|---|
| **437** | A209 | 5c slate green | .30 | .25 |

International Cooperation Year.

Sir Wilfred Grenfell at Wheel of Hospital Ship Strathcona II A210

**1965, June 9**

| | | | | |
|---|---|---|---|---|
| **438** | A210 | 5c Prussian blue | .30 | .25 |

Sir Wilfred Grenfell, author, medical missionary and founder of the Grenfell Mission, birth cent.

Canada's Maple Leaf Flag, 1965 — A211

**1965, June 30**

| | | | | |
|---|---|---|---|---|
| **439** | A211 | 5c blue & red | .30 | .25 |

Winston Churchill — A212

**1965, Aug. 12** **Litho.** ***Perf. 12***

| | | | | |
|---|---|---|---|---|
| **440** | A212 | 5c brown | .30 | .25 |

Sir Winston Spencer Churchill (1874-1965).

Peace Tower, Ottawa — A213

**1965, Sept. 8** **Engr.**

| | | | | |
|---|---|---|---|---|
| **441** | A213 | 5c slate green | .30 | .25 |

Meeting of the Inter-Parliamentary Union, Ottawa, Sept. 8-17.

Parliament and Ottawa River — A214

**1965, Sept. 8**

| | | | | |
|---|---|---|---|---|
| **442** | A214 | 5c brown | .30 | .25 |

Centenary of the final selection of Ottawa as national capital.

Gifts of the Wise Men — A215

**1965, Oct. 13**

| | | | | |
|---|---|---|---|---|
| **443** | A215 | 3c olive | .30 | .25 |
| *a.* | | Pane of 25 | 6.25 | 6.25 |
| *p.* | | Tagged | .30 | .25 |
| *q.* | | As "a," tagged | 8.50 | 8.50 |
| **444** | A215 | 5c violet blue | .30 | .25 |
| *p.* | | Tagged | .35 | .25 |

Christmas. Panes of 25 are imperf. on four sides.

Alouette II Orbiting Globe — A216

**1966, Jan. 5**

| | | | | |
|---|---|---|---|---|
| **445** | A216 | 5c dark violet blue | .30 | .25 |

Launching (in California) of the Canadian satellite Alouette II, Nov. 28, 1965, as part of the Canadian-American program of space research.

La Salle, Map of 17th Century Canada, Ship, Canoe, Spyglass and Compass — A217

**1966, Apr. 13**

| | | | | |
|---|---|---|---|---|
| **446** | A217 | 5c blue green | .30 | .25 |

Tercentenary of the arrival in Canada of Rene Robert Cavelier, Sieur de La Salle (1643-1687).

Traffic Signs — A218

**1966, May 2**

| | | | | |
|---|---|---|---|---|
| **447** | A218 | 5c black, lt blue & yel | .30 | .25 |

Issued to publicize traffic safety.

House of Commons, Thames River and Canadian Delegates — A219

**1966, May 26**

| | | | | |
|---|---|---|---|---|
| **448** | A219 | 5c brown | .30 | .25 |

Centenary of the London Conf., Dec. 4, 1866, which resulted in the British North America Act.

Atomic Reactor, Heavy Water Atom Symbol and Microscope A220

**1966, July 27**

| | | | | |
|---|---|---|---|---|
| **449** | A220 | 5c deep ultra | .30 | .25 |

Peaceful uses of atomic power. The design shows a stylized view of the Douglas Point Nuclear Power Station, Lake Huron, Ontario.

Parliamentary Library, Ottawa — A221

**1966, Sept. 8**

| | | | | |
|---|---|---|---|---|
| **450** | A221 | 5c plum | .30 | .25 |

12th General Conf. of the Commonwealth Parliamentary Assoc., Ottawa, Sept. 8-Oct. 5.

Praying Hands, by Albrecht Dürer — A222

**1966, Oct. 12**

| | | | | |
|---|---|---|---|---|
| **451** | A222 | 3c carmine rose | .25 | .25 |
| *a.* | | Pane of 25 | 3.75 | 3.75 |
| *p.* | | Tagged | .30 | .25 |
| *q.* | | As "a," tagged | 5.00 | 5.00 |
| **452** | A222 | 5c orange | .30 | .25 |
| *p.* | | Tagged | .45 | .25 |

Christmas. Panes of 25 are imperf. on four sides.

Canadian Flag over Globe and Centennial Emblem — A223

**1967, Jan. 11**

| | | | | |
|---|---|---|---|---|
| **453** | A223 | 5c blue & red | .30 | .25 |
| *p.* | | Tagged | .40 | .30 |

Canada's centenary as a nation.

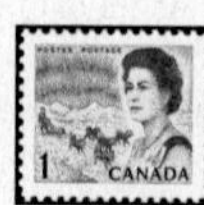

Northern Lights and Dog Team A224

"Alaska Highway" by A. Y. Jackson A225

**Two Types of 6c Black**

Type I

Type II

Designs: 2c, Totem pole (Pacific Area). 3c, Combine and oil rig (Prairie Region). 4c, Ship in lock (Central Canada). 5c, Lobster traps and boat (Atlantic Provinces). 6c, Transportation means. 10c, "The Jack Pine" by Tom Thomson. 15c, "Bylot Island" by Lawren Harris. 20c, "The Ferry, Quebec" by James Wilson Morrice. 25c, "The Solemn Land" by J. E. H. MacDonald. 50c, "Summer's Stores" by John Ensor (grain elevators). $1, Oilfield near Edmonton, by H. G. Glyde.

**1967-72** **Engr.** ***Perf. 12***

| | | | | |
|---|---|---|---|---|
| **454** | A224 | 1c brown | .30 | .25 |
| *a.* | | Booklet pane of 5 + label | .45 | .35 |
| *b.* | | Bklt. pane, 1 #454d, 4 #459 + label, perf. 10 ('68) | 3.00 | 2.50 |
| *c.* | | Bklt. pane, 5 #454d + 5 #457d, perf. 10 ('68) | 1.40 | 1.40 |
| *d.* | | Perf. 10 ('68) | .30 | .25 |
| *e.* | | Perf. 12½x12 ('71) | .30 | .25 |
| *f.* | | Printed on gummed side | *1,000.* | |
| **455** | A224 | 2c green | .30 | .25 |
| *a.* | | Bklt. pane, 4 #455, 4 #456 with gutter btwn. ('70) | 1.50 | 1.50 |
| **456** | A224 | 3c dull purple | .30 | .25 |
| *a.* | | Perf. 12½x12 ('71) | .75 | .30 |
| **457** | A224 | 4c car rose | .30 | .25 |
| *a.* | | Booklet pane of 5 + label | 1.25 | 1.25 |
| *b.* | | Pane of 25 (5x5) | 25.00 | 20.00 |
| *c.* | | Booklet pane of 25 + 2 labels, perf. 10 ('68) | 7.50 | 7.00 |
| *d.* | | Perf. 10 | .50 | .25 |
| **458** | A224 | 5c blue | .30 | .25 |
| *a.* | | Booklet pane of 5 + label | 5.25 | 5.25 |
| *b.* | | Pane of 20 | 30.00 | 27.50 |
| *c.* | | Bklt. pane of 20, perf. 10 ('68) | 7.50 | 7.50 |
| *d.* | | Perf. 10 | .60 | .25 |
| **459** | A224 | 6c org, perf. 10 | .30 | .25 |
| *a.* | | Bklt. pane of 25 + 2 labels, perf. 10 ('68) | 7.50 | 7.50 |
| *b.* | | Perf. 12½x12 ('69) | .30 | .25 |
| **460** | A224 | 6c black (I), perf. 12½x12 | .30 | .25 |
| *a.* | | Bklt. pane of 25 + 2 labels (I), perf. 10 ('70) | 11.00 | 7.50 |
| *b.* | | As "a," perf. 12½x12 | 15.00 | 13.00 |
| *c.* | | Type II, perf. 12½x12 | .30 | .25 |
| *d.* | | As "c," booklet pane of 4 | 3.50 | 3.25 |
| *e.* | | As "d," perf. 10 ('70) | 10.00 | 6.00 |
| *f.* | | Type II, perf. 12 ('72) | .35 | .25 |
| *g.* | | Type I, perf. 10 | 1.50 | .30 |
| *h.* | | Type II, perf. 10 | 2.00 | .65 |
| *i.* | | As "f," printed on gummed side | 18.00 | |
| **461** | A225 | 8c violet brown | .30 | .25 |
| **462** | A225 | 10c olive green | .30 | .25 |
| **463** | A225 | 15c dull purple | .45 | .25 |
| **464** | A225 | 20c dark blue | .55 | .25 |
| **465** | A225 | 25c slate green | 1.50 | .25 |
| **465A** | A225 | 50c brown org | 3.75 | .25 |
| **465B** | A225 | $1 carmine rose | 6.00 | .75 |
| | | *Nos. 454-465B (14)* | 14.95 | 4.00 |

Nos. 454d, 454e, 456a, 457d, 458d, 460c, 460g and 460h are from booklet panes.

Issued: No. 459, 11/1/68; No. 460, 1/7/70; others, 2/8/67.

See Nos. 543-544, 549-550.

**Tagged**

| | | | | |
|---|---|---|---|---|
| *454p* | A224 | 1c brown | .30 | .25 |
| *ep.* | | Perf. 12½x12 ('71) | .30 | .25 |
| *455p* | A224 | 2c green | .30 | .25 |
| *456p* | A224 | 3c dull purple | .30 | .25 |
| *457p* | A224 | 4c car rose | .60 | .25 |
| *458p* | A224 | 5c blue | .60 | .25 |
| *bp.* | | Pane of 20 | 55.00 | 47.50 |
| *459p* | A224 | 6c org, perf. 10 | .70 | .25 |
| *bp.* | | Perf. 12½x12 ('69) | .75 | .30 |
| *460p* | A224 | 6c black (I), perf. 12½x12 | .35 | .25 |
| *cp.* | | Type II ('70) | .45 | .50 |
| *fp.* | | As "cp," perf. 12 ('72) | .30 | .25 |
| *462p* | A225 | 10c olive green | .90 | .35 |
| *463p* | A225 | 15c dull purple | .90 | .35 |
| *464p* | A225 | 20c dark blue | 1.50 | .55 |
| *465p* | A225 | 25c slate green | 7.50 | 2.25 |
| | | *Nos. 454p-465p (11)* | 13.95 | 5.25 |

Nos. 454ep and 460cp are from booklet panes Nos. 544q-544s.

Issued: 1c-5c, 2/8/67; No. 459p, 11/1/68; No. 460p, 1/7/70; others, 12/9/69.

See note after No. 343.

**Coil Stamps**

**1967-70** ***Perf. 9½ Horiz.***

| | | | | |
|---|---|---|---|---|
| **466** | A224 | 3c dull purple | 3.75 | .85 |
| **467** | A224 | 4c carmine rose | 1.10 | .50 |
| **468** | A224 | 5c blue | 2.25 | .65 |

***Perf. 10 Horiz.***

| | | | | |
|---|---|---|---|---|
| **468A** | A224 | 6c orange | .45 | .25 |
| *c.* | | Imperf., pair | 275.00 | |
| **468B** | A224 | 6c black, die II | .35 | .25 |
| *d.* | | Imperf., pair | 2,500. | |
| | | *Nos. 466-468B (5)* | 7.90 | 2.50 |

Horizontal pairs or blocks of Nos. 468A and 468B may be found with a fine vertical score line between the stamps. These sell for little more than vertical pairs or strips.

Issued: No. 468A, 1/69; No. 468B, 8/70; others, 2/8/67.

EXPO '67 Emblem and Canadian Pavilion — A226

**1967, Apr. 28** **Engr.** ***Perf. 12***

| | | | | |
|---|---|---|---|---|
| **469** | A226 | 5c blue & red | .30 | .25 |

EXPO '67, Intl. Exhib., Montreal, Apr. 28-Oct. 27.

Symbolic Woman and Ballot — A227

**1967, May 24** **Litho.**

| | | | | |
|---|---|---|---|---|
| **470** | A227 | 5c black & rose lilac | .30 | .25 |

50th anniversary of woman suffrage.

Elizabeth II — A228

**1967, June 30** **Engr.**

| | | | | |
|---|---|---|---|---|
| **471** | A228 | 5c deep org & purple | .30 | .25 |

Centennial Year visit of Queen Elizabeth II and the Duke of Edinburgh.

Runner — A229

**1967, July 19**

| | | | | |
|---|---|---|---|---|
| **472** | A229 | 5c red | .30 | .25 |

Pan-American Games, Winnipeg, Manitoba, July 22-Aug. 7.

Globe and Flash — A230

**1967, Aug. 31**

| | | | | |
|---|---|---|---|---|
| **473** | A230 | 5c deep ultra | .30 | .25 |

50th anniv. of the Canadian Press, news gathering and distributing service.

Georges Philias Vanier — A231

**1967, Sept. 15 Engr. & Litho.**
**474** A231 5c black .30 .25

Georges Philias Vanier (1888-1967), Governor General of Canada, 1959-1967.

Toronto in 1967 and Citizens of 1867 — A232

**1967, Sept. 28**
**475** A232 5c sl grn & sal pink .30 .25

Centenary of Toronto as capital of Ontario.

Singing Children and Peace Tower, Ottawa — A233

**1967, Oct. 11**
**476** A233 3c carmine .30 .25
*a.* Pane of 25 3.25 3.25
*p.* Tagged .30 .25
*q.* As "a" tagged 4.50 4.50
**477** A233 5c green .30 .25
*p.* Tagged .30 .25

Christmas. Panes of 25 are imperf. on four sides.

Gray Jays — A234

**1968, Feb. 15 Litho.**
**478** A234 5c grn, blk & pink .45 .25

Weather Map and Composite of Instruments A235

**1968, Mar. 13** ***Perf. 11***
**479** A235 5c dk & lt blue, yel & red .30 .25

200th anniv. of Canada's first long-term fixed point weather observations at Fort Prince of Wales, Churchill, by William Wales and Joseph Dymond.

Male Narwhal — A236

**1968, Apr. 10**
**480** A236 5c multicolored .30 .25

Weighing Rain Gauge, World Map and Maple Leaf — A237

**1968, May 8**
**481** A237 5c multicolored .30 .25

Intl. Hydrological Decade, 1965-74.

The Nonsuch — A238

**Photo. & Engr.**
**1968, June 5** ***Perf. 10***
**482** A238 5c dk blue & multi .30 .25

300th anniv. of the voyage of the Nonsuch which opened the way to Canada's West through the fur trade.

Contemporary and Indian Lacrosse Players — A239

**1968, July 3**
**483** A239 5c yel, black & red .30 .25

A240

Design: George Brown, "Globe" Front Page and Legislature, Prince Edward Island.

**1968, Aug. 21**
**484** A240 5c multicolored .30 .25

George Brown (1818-1880), founder of Toronto "Globe" and political leader.

Henri Bourassa and Newspaper Page — A241

**Litho. & Engr.**
**1968, Sept. 4** ***Perf. 12***
**485** A241 5c ver, buff & black .30 .25

Henri Bourassa (1868-1952), jounalist and statesman.

Canadian Memorial, Near Vimy, France — A242

**1968, Oct. 15 Engr.**
**486** A242 15c slate 2.00 1.25

50th anniv. of the Armistice which ended WWI. The stamp shows "The Defenders and the Breaking of the Sword," a detail from the memorial designed by W. S. Allward.

John McCrae and "Flanders Fields" — A243

**1968, Oct. 15 Litho. & Engr.**
**487** A243 5c multicolored .30 .25

50th death anniv. of Lt. Col. John McCrae (1872-1918), author of "In Flanders Fields."

Eskimo Family, Carving — A244

Eskimo soapstone carving: 6c, Mother and infant, by Munamee of Cape Dorset.

**1968, Nov. Photo.**
**488** A244 5c brt blue & black .30 .25
*a.* Booklet pane of 10 3.00 3.00
*p.* Tagged .30 .25
*q.* As "a," tagged 3.75 3.75
**489** A244 6c dp bister & black .30 .25
*p.* Tagged .30 .25

Christmas. Issued: 5c, Nov. 1; 6c, Nov. 15.

Curling — A245

**Photo. & Engr.**
**1969, Jan. 15** ***Perf. 10***
**490** A245 6c black, brt blue & car .30 .25

Vincent Massey — A246

**Litho. & Engr.**
**1969, Feb. 20** ***Perf. 12***
**491** A246 6c yel olive & dk brn .30 .25

Vincent Massey (1887-1967), 1st Canadian-born Gov. General of Canada, 1952-59.

Return from the Harvest Field, by Aurele de Foy Suzor-Cote A247

**1969, Mar. 14 Photo.**
**492** A247 50c multicolored 3.50 2.50

Aurele de Foy Suzor-Cote (1869-1937), painter.

Globe and Tools of Various Trades — A248

**1969, May 21 Engr.** ***Perf. 12x12½***
**493** A248 6c dk olive green .30 .25

50th anniv. of the ILO.

Vickers Vimy, 1919, and Map of the Atlantic — A249

**1969, June 13 Photo. and Engr.**
**494** A249 15c red brn, yel grn & lt ultra 1.90 1.50

50th anniv. of the first non-stop Atlantic flight from Newfoundland to Ireland of Capt. John Alcock and Lt. Arthur Whitten Brown.

Sir William Osler — A250

**1969, June 23** ***Perf. 12½x12***
**495** A250 6c dk blue & lt red brn .30 .25

Osler (1849-1919), physician, professor of physiology and pathology in Canada, US and England.

Ipswich Sparrow — A251

Birds: 6c, White-throated sparrows, vert. 25c, Hermit thrush.

**1969, July 23 Litho.** ***Perf. 12***
**496** A251 6c multicolored .35 .25
**497** A251 10c ultra & multi .75 .40
**498** A251 25c black & multi 1.90 1.50
*Nos. 496-498 (3)* 3.00 2.15

Map of Prince Edward Island — A252

**Photo. & Engr.**
**1969, Aug. 15** ***Perf. 12x12½***
**499** A252 6c ultra, org brn & black .30 .25

Bicentenary of Charlottetown as capital of Prince Edward Island.

Flags of Summer and Winter Canada Games — A253

**Litho. & Engr.**
**1969, Aug. 15** ***Perf. 12***
**500** A253 6c ultra, brt green & red .30 .25

1st Canada Summer Games, Halifax and Dartmouth, N.S., Aug. 16-24.

Sir Isaac Brock and Memorial Queenston Heights — A254

**1969, Sept. 12**
**501** A254 6c pale yel, brn & pale sal .30 .25

Major General Sir Isaac Brock (1769-1812), administrator of Upper Canada and leader in the war of 1812.

Children of Various Races — A255

**1969, Oct. 8 Litho.**
**502** A255 5c blue & multi .30 .25
*a.* Booklet pane of 10 3.00 3.00
*p.* Tagged .30 .25
*q.* As "a" tagged 3.75 3.75
**503** A255 6c red & multi .30 .25
*a.* Black (inscriptions & frame line) omitted 1,500. 1,500.
*p.* Tagged .30 .25

Christmas.

Stephen Leacock, Comedy Mask and Mariposa View — A256

**Photo. & Engr.**
**1969, Nov. 12** ***Perf. 12x12½***
**504** A256 6c multicolored .30 .25

Stephen Butler Leacock (1869-1944), humorist, historian and economist.

Manitoba, Crossroads of Canada — A257

**1970, Jan. 27 Litho.** ***Perf. 12***
**505** A257 6c blue, yel & red .30 .25
*p.* Tagged .30 .25

Centenary of the province of Manitoba.

Enchanted Owl, by Kenojuak — A258

**1970, Jan. 27** **Engr.**

**506** A258 6c dark red & black .30 .25

Centenary of Nortwest Territories.

Microscopic View of Inside of Leaf — A259

**1970, Feb. 18** **Photo. & Engr.**

**507** A259 6c green, lt org & blue .30 .25

Canada's participation in the Intl. Biological Program, 1967-1972.

Emblems of EXPO '67 and '70 — A260

EXPO '70 Emblem and Dogwood, British Columbia — A261

Designs: No. 510, EXPO '70 emblem and white garden lily, Quebec. No. 511, EXPO '70 emblem and white trillium, Ontario.

**1970, Mar. 18** **Litho.**

**508** A260 25c red emblem 2.00 2.00
*p.* Tagged 2.50 2.50
**509** A261 25c violet emblem 2.00 2.00
*p.* Tagged 2.50 2.50
**510** A261 25c green emblem 2.00 2.00
*p.* Tagged 2.50 2.50
**511** A261 25c blue emblem 2.00 2.00
*p.* Tagged 2.50 2.50
*a.* Block of 4, #508-511 8.00 8.00
*b.* As "a," tagged 10.00 10.00
*Nos. 508-511 (4)* 8.00 8.00

EXPO '70 Intl. Exhibition, Osaka, Japan, Mar. 15-Sept. 13. Nos. 508-511 printed se-tenant in panes of 50 (5x10), with various combinations possible.

Henry Kelsey — A262

**Photo. & Engr.**

**1970, Apr. 15** ***Perf. 12x12½***

**512** A262 6c multicolored .30 .25

300th birth anniv. of Henry Kelsey, explorer of Canada's western plains.

"A Divided World, with Energy Focused on Unification..." A263

**1970, May 13** **Litho.** ***Perf. 11***

**513** A263 10c blue .75 .60
*p.* Tagged .95 .95
**514** A263 15c lilac & dk red 1.20 .75
*p.* Tagged 1.60 1.60

25th anniversary of the United Nations.

Louis Riel — A264

**1970, June 19** **Photo.** ***Perf. 12½x12***

**515** A264 6c red & brt blue .30 .25

Louis Riel (1844-1885), Metis leader who became president of the Council of Assiniboin in 1870.

Mackenzie Rock, Dean Channel — A265

**1970, June 25** **Engr.** ***Perf. 12***

**516** A265 6c brown .30 .25

Sir Alexander Mackenzie (1764-1820), Scottish explorer who in 1793 completed the first crossing of the North American continent north of Mexico.

Sir Oliver Mowat and Parliament, Ottawa — A266

**Photo. & Engr.**

**1970, Aug. 12** ***Perf. 12x12½***

**517** A266 6c red & black .30 .25

Sir Oliver Mowat (1820-1903), government leader and a Father of Confederation.

Isle of Spruce, by Arthur Lismer — A267

**1970, Sept. 18** **Litho.** ***Perf. 11***

**518** A267 6c multicolored .30 .25

50th anniv. of "The Group of Seven," Canadian landscape artists.

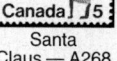

Santa Claus — A268

Christ Child — A269

Child in the Manger and Star-studded Sky — A270

Christmas, Designs by Canadian School Children: No. 519, 527 Santa Claus. No. 520, Horse-drawn Sleigh. No. 521, Nativity. No. 522, Children Skiing. No. 523, Snowmen and Christmas Tree. No. 524, 529 Christ Child. No. 525, Christmas Tree and Children. No. 526, Toy Store. . No. 528, Church. No. 530, Snowmobile and Trees.

**1970, Oct. 7** **Litho.** ***Perf. 12***

**519** A268 5c multicolored .30 .25
**520** A268 5c multicolored .30 .25
**521** A268 5c multicolored .30 .25
**522** A268 5c multicolored .30 .25
**523** A268 5c multicolored .30 .25
*a.* Strip of 5, #519-523 2.75 2.25
*b.* As "a," triple impression of black 550.00
**524** A269 6c multicolored .35 .25
**525** A269 6c multicolored .35 .25
**526** A269 6c multicolored .35 .25
**527** A269 6c multicolored .35 .25
**528** A269 6c multicolored .35 .25
*a.* Strip of 5, #524-528 3.00 2.50
**529** A270 10c multicolored .40 .35
**530** A270 15c multicolored .90 .90
*Nos. 519-530 (12)* 4.55 3.75

**Tagged**

*519p* A268 5c multicolored .35 .25
*520p* A268 5c multicolored .35 .25
*521p* A268 5c multicolored .35 .25
*522p* A268 5c multicolored .35 .25
*523p* A268 5c multicolored .35 .25
*ap.* Strip of 5, #519p-523p 3.25 2.75
*524p* A269 6c multicolored .40 .25
*525p* A269 6c multicolored .40 .25
*526p* A269 6c multicolored .40 .25
*527p* A269 6c multicolored .40 .25
*528p* A269 6c multicolored .40 .25
*ap.* Strip of 5, #524p-528p 4.50 3.00
*529p* A270 10c multicolored .50 .50
*530p* A270 15c multicolored 1.10 1.10
*Nos. 519p-530p (12)* 5.35 4.10

Christmas.

The sheets of 100 of both 5c and 6c contain all 5 designs, generally alternating, and arranged to permit vertical and horizontal pairs of each design in the two center vertical and horizontal rows. The center block of 4 is entirely of No. 522 (5c) and 525 (6c). The sheet may also be broken to provide 20 strips of 5, each stamp of different design.

Sir Donald Alexander Smith — A271

**1970, Nov. 4**

**531** A271 6c dk grn, yel & black .30 .25

Smith (1820-1914), railroad builder and Canadian High Commissioner, 1896-1914.

Big Raven, by Emily Carr — A272

**1971, Feb. 12**

**532** A272 6c multicolored .30 .25

Emily Carr (1871-1945), painter and writer.

Laboratory Equipment Used for Insulin Discovery — A273

**1971, Mar. 3** ***Perf. 11***

**533** A273 6c multicolored .30 .25

Discovery of insulin by Dr. Frederick G. Banting and Dr. Charles H. Best, 50th anniversary.

A274

**1971, Mar. 24**

**534** A274 6c red, org & black .30 .25

Sir Ernest Rutherford (1871-1937), physicist, developer of theory of spontaneous disintegration of the atom.

Spring, Winged Maple Seed — A275

**1971**

**535** A275 6c shown .30 .25
*a.* Imperf., pair *800.00* *1,400.*
**536** A275 6c Summer .30 .25
**537** A275 7c Autumn .30 .25
*a.* Grey inscription omitted 800.00
**538** A275 7c Winter .30 .25
*Nos. 535-538 (4)* 1.20 1.00

Issue dates: No. 535, Apr. 14; No. 536, June 16; No. 537, Sept. 3; No. 538, Nov. 19.

Louis Joseph Papineau — A276

**Litho. & Engr.**

**1971, May 7** ***Perf. 12½x12***

**539** A276 6c multicolored .30 .25

Louis Joseph Papineau (1786-1871), member of Legislative Assembly and leader of French Canadian Patriote party.

Map of Copper Mine River Basin — A277

**1971, May 7** ***Perf. 12x12½***

**540** A277 6c buff, red & brown .30 .25

Bicentenary of Samuel Hearne's expedition to the Copper Mine River.

Maple Leaves — A278

**1971, June 1**

**541** A278 15c blk, red org & yel 1.75 1.10
*p.* Tagged 2.50 2.25

Inauguration of new transmitters for Radio Canada International.

Computer Tape and Reels — A279

**1971, June 1**

**542** A279 6c black, ultra & red .30 .25

Centenary of measured progress through census.

---

Migrating Phosphor

Canada's "Ottawa/General" tagging of engraved stamps printed March-October, 1972, used a phosphor which migrates onto or through other stamps, booklet covers and album pages. It fluoresces yellow under ultraviolet light.

This bleeding, contaminating "OP4" phosphor can be somewhat contained in mounts or envelopes of acetate, glassine or polyethylene, but it may leak or penetrate.

The migrating phosphor is found on all examples of Nos. 560p-561p, and on some of Nos. 544p, 544q, 544r, 544s, 562p-565p and 594-598.

---

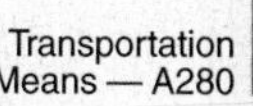

Transportation Means — A280

Design: 8c, Library of Parliament.

**1971-72** **Engr.** ***Perf. 12½x12***

**543** A280 7c slate green .35 .25
*a.* Booklet pane of 5 + label (#454e, #456a + 3#543) 7.50 4.50
*b.* Booklet pane of 20 (4 #454e, 4 #456a, 12 #543) 8.00 6.50
*p.* Tagged .60 .25
**544** A280 8c slate .30 .25
*a.* Booklet pane of 6 (3 #454e, 1 #460c, 2 #544) 3.50 1.75
*b.* Booklet pane of 18 (6 #454e, 1 #460c, 11 #544) 5.25 3.00
*c.* Booklet pane of 10 (4 #454e, 1 #460c, 5 #544 ('72) 2.25 2.25
*p.* Tagged .30 .25
*q.* As "a," tagged 1.75 1.75
*r.* As "b," tagged 3.25 3.25
*s.* As "c," tagged 2.00 2.00

**Coil Stamps**

**1971** ***Perf. 10 Horiz.***

**549** A280 7c slate green .40 .25
*a.* Imperf, pair 1,050.
**550** A280 8c slate .30 .25
*a.* Imperf, pair 600.00
*p.* Tagged .30 .25
*q.* As "p," imperf, pair 850.00

See note below No. 468B.
Issued: 7c, 6/30/71; 8c, 12/30/71.

Abstract "BC" — A282

**1971, July 20** **Litho.** ***Perf. 12***

**552** A282 7c multicolored .30 .25

Centenary of British Columbia's entry into Canadian Confederation.

Indian Encampment on Lake Huron, by Kane — A283

**1971, Aug. 11** *Perf. 12½*

**553** A283 7c multicolored .40 .25

Paul Kane (1810-1871), painter.

Snowflake — A284

**1971, Oct. 6** **Engr.** *Perf. 12*

**Size: 24x30mm**

**554** A284 6c dark blue .30 .25

*p.* Tagged .30 .25

*a.* All color omitted (from foldover) *1,750.*

*b.* Printed on gummed side (from foldover) *1,000.*

**555** A284 7c bright green .30 .25

*p.* Tagged .30 .25

**Litho. and Engr.**

**Size: 30x30mm**

**556** A284 10c dp car & silver .35 .30

*p.* Tagged .45 .30

**557** A284 15c lt ultra, dp car & silver .70 .65

*p.* Tagged .90 .75

*Nos. 554-557 (4)* 1.65 1.45

Christmas.

Pierre Laporte — A285

**1971, Oct. 20** *Perf. 12½x12*

**558** A285 7c black .30 .25

Pierre Laporte (1921-1970), Minister of Labor, kidnapped and killed.

Figure Skating — A286

**1972, Mar. 1** **Litho.** *Perf. 12*

**559** A286 8c deep red lilac .30 .25

World Figure Skating Championships, Calgary, Alberta, Mar. 6-12.

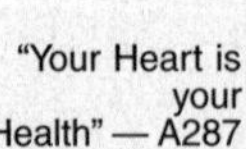

"Your Heart is your Health" — A287

**1972, Apr. 7** **Engr.** *Perf. 12x12½*

**560** A287 8c red .30 .25

*p.* Tagged .55 .35

World Health Day, Apr. 7.

Frontenac, by Philippe Hébert and Fort Saint Louis, Quebec — A288

**1972, May 17** **Photo. and Engr.**

**561** A288 8c red brown & multi .30 .25

*p.* Tagged .75 .75

Tercentenary of the appointment of Louis de Buade, Count of Frontenac and Palluau (1622-1698), as Governor of New France.

## Indians of Canada

Buffalo Chase, by George Catlin A289

Thunderbird, Assiniboin Pattern A290

No. 563, Plains Indian artifacts. No. 565, Ceremonial sun dance costume.

In Nos. 562-581, the first two and last two stamps of each annual set are printed checkerwise in same sheet of 50.

**1972** **Litho.** *Perf. 12x12½*

**562** A289 8c shown .40 .25

*p.* Tagged .55 .30

**563** A289 8c multicolored .40 .25

*p.* Tagged .55 .30

*a.* Pair, #562-563 .80 .50

*b.* As "a," tagged 1.10 .75

*Perf. 12½x12*

**Photo. & Engr.**

**564** A290 8c shown .35 .25

*p.* Tagged .55 .30

**565** A290 8c multicolored .35 .25

*p.* Tagged .55 .30

*a.* Pair, #564-565 .70 .50

*b.* As "a," tagged 1.10 .75

Plains Indians of Canada.

Issued: Nos. 562-563, 7/6; Nos. 564-565, 10/4.

**Tagged (Nos. 566-581)**

No. 566, Algonkian artifacts. No. 567, "Micmac Indians." No. 568, Thunderbird and belt. No. 569, Algonkian man and woman.

**1973** **Litho.** *Perf. 12x12½*

**566** A289 8c multicolored .35 .25

**567** A289 8c multicolored .35 .25

*a.* Pair, #566-567 .70 .50

*Perf. 12½x12*

**Photo. & Engr.**

**568** A290 8c multicolored .30 .25

**569** A290 8c multicolored .30 .25

*a.* Pair, #568-569 .60 .50

Algonkian-speaking Indians of Canada (Malecite, Micmac, Montagnais, Algonquin and Ojibwa).

Issued: Nos. 566-567, 2/21; Nos. 568-569, 11/28.

**1974** **Litho.** *Perf. 12x12½*

No. 570, Nootka Sound, house, inside. No. 571, Artifacts. No. 572, Chief wearing Chilkat blanket. No. 573, Thunderbird from Kwakiutl house.

**570** A289 8c multicolored .30 .25

**571** A289 8c multicolored .30 .25

*a.* Pair, #570-571 .60 .50

*Perf. 12½x12*

**Photo. & Engr.**

**572** A290 8c multicolored .30 .25

**573** A290 8c multicolored .30 .25

*a.* Pair, #572-573 .60 .50

Pacific Coast Indians of Canada (Haida, Salish, Tsimshian, Chilkat and Kwakiutl).

Issued: Nos. 570-571, 1/16; Nos. 572-573, 2/22.

**1975, Apr. 4** **Litho.** *Perf. 13½*

No. 574, Montagnais-Naskapi artifacts. No. 575, Dance of the Kutcha-Kutchin. No. 576, Kutchin ceremonial costume. No. 577, Ojibwa thunderbird and Naskapi pattern.

**574** A289 8c multicolored .30 .25

**575** A289 8c multicolored .30 .25

*a.* Pair, #574-575 .50 .50

*Perf. 12½*

**576** A290 8c multicolored .30 .25

**Litho. and Embossed**

**577** A290 8c multicolored .30 .25

*a.* Pair, #576-577 .50 .50

Subarctic Indians.

**1976, Sept. 17** **Litho.** *Perf. 13½*

No. 578, Cornhusk mask, artifacts. No. 579, Iroquoian Encampment, by George Heriot. No. 580, Iroquoian thunderbird. No. 581, Iroquoian man, woman.

**578** A289 10c multicolored .30 .25

**579** A289 10c multicolored .30 .25

*a.* Pair, #578-579 .50 .50

*Perf. 12½*

**Litho. & Embossed**

**580** A290 10c multicolored .30 .25

**Litho.**

**581** A290 10c multicolored .30 .25

*a.* Pair, #580-581 .50 .50

*Nos. 562-581 (20)* 6.40 5.00

Iroquois (Mohawk, Cayuga, Seneca, Oneida, Onondaga and Tuscarora).

Geological Fault — A291

No. 583, Bird's eye view of town. No. 584, Aerial map photography. No. 585, Contour lines.

**1972, Aug. 2** *Perf. 12*

**582** A291 15c shown 1.50 1.10

*p.* Tagged 2.00 1.50

**583** A291 15c multicolored 1.50 1.10

*p.* Tagged 2.00 1.50

**584** A291 15c multicolored 1.50 1.10

*p.* Tagged 2.00 1.50

**585** A291 15c multicolored 1.50 1.10

*p.* Tagged 2.00 1.50

*a.* Block of 4, #582-585 6.00 5.50

*b.* As "a," tagged 8.00 *11.00*

*Nos. 582-585 (4)* 6.00 4.40

Earth sciences: 24th Intl. Geological Cong. (No. 582); 22nd Intl. Geographical Cong. (No. 583); 12th Cong. of Intl. Soc. of Photogrammetry (No. 584); 6th Cong. of Intl. Cartographic Assoc. (No. 585).

Sir John A. Macdonald A292

Elizabeth II A292a

Forest, Central Canada A293

Vancouver, B.C. A294

Designs: 2c, Sir Wilfrid Laurier. 3c, Sir Robert L. Borden. 4c, William Lyon Mackenzie King. 5c Richard Bedford Bennett. 6c, Lester B. Pearson. 7c, Louis St. Laurent. 15c, Mountain sheep, Western Canada. 20c, Grain fields, Prairie. 25c, Polar bears, North. 50c, Seashore. $2, Quebec.

**1972-76** **Engr.** *Perf. 12x12½*

**Tagged**

**586** A292 1c orange ('73) .30 .25

*a.* Booklet pane, 3 #586, 1 #591, 2 #593 ('74) 1.25 1.10

*b.* Bklt. pane, 6 #586, 1 #591, 11 #593 ('75) 1.50 1.50

*c.* Bklt. pane, 2 #586, 4 #587, 4 #593Ac ('76) 1.25 1.10

*d.* Printed on gummed side 850.00

**587** A292 2c green ('73) .30 .25

**588** A292 3c brown ('73) .30 .25

**589** A292 4c black ('73) .30 .25

**590** A292 5c lilac ('73) .30 .25

**591** A292 6c dk red ('73) .30 .25

*a.* Printed on gummed side 180.00

**592** A292 7c dk brn ('74) .30 .25

**593** A292a 8c ultra ('73) .30 .25

*b.* Perf. 13x13½ ('76) .75 .25

*Perf. 13x13½*

**593A** A292a 10c dk car ('76) .30 .25

*c.* Perf. 12x12½ .35 .25

*Perf. 12½x12*

**Photo. & Engr.**

**594** A293 10c multicolored .30 .25

**595** A293 15c multicolored .50 .25

**596** A293 20c multicolored .50 .25

**597** A293 25c multicolored .55 .25

**598** A293 50c multicolored 1.20 .25

**599** A294 $1 multi ('73) 2.50 .50

*Perf. 11*

**Litho. & Engraved**

**600** A294 $1 multicolored 6.00 1.60

**601** A294 $2 multicolored 4.50 2.25

*Nos. 586-601 (17)* 18.75 7.85

No. 599 has engraved shading added in some areas.

Plates 1 and 2 of the scenic 10c differ in impression and colors. Plate 1 has distinct crosshatching of "Canada" background. On plate 2, released in 1974, this area appears solidly inked.

A 1976 printing of the 15c shows the blue trees on the hillside as solid color, while the 1972 printing shows clear detail on the trees.

A 1974 printing of the 50c has darker shading and a deeper tone for the dark blue areas of the photogravure impression.

Nos. 600 and 601 are untagged.

**1976-77** **Photo. & Engr.** *Perf. 13½*

*594a* A293 10c multicolored .30 .25

*595a* A293 15c multicolored .45 .25

*596a* A293 20c multicolored .60 .25

*597a* A293 25c multicolored .65 .25

*598a* A293 50c multicolored 1.75 .25

*599a* A294 $1 multi ('77) 2.50 .30

*Nos. 594a-599a (6)* 6.25 1.55

**Coil Stamps**

**1974-76** **Engr.** *Perf. 10 Vert.*

**604** A292a 8c ultramarine .30 .25

*a.* Imperf., horiz. pair 150.00

**605** A292a 10c dk carmine ('76) .30 .25

*a.* Imperf., horiz. pair 160.00

See note below No. 468B. No. 604 also exists in vertical multiples without score line.

Candles A295

Candles and Fruit A296

Christmas: 8c, Like 6c. 15c, Candles, 15th century prayer book, boxes and brass vase.

**1972, Nov. 1** **Litho.** *Perf. 12½x12*

**606** A295 6c red & multi .30 .25

*p.* Tagged .30 .25

**607** A295 8c vio blue & multi .30 .25

*p.* Tagged .35 .25

*Perf. 11*

**608** A296 10c green & multi .45 .35

*p.* Tagged .65 .55

**609** A296 15c yel bister & multi .75 .75

*p.* Tagged 1.25 1.20

*Nos. 606-609 (4)* 1.80 1.60

"The Blacksmith's Shop," by Krieghoff — A297

**1972, Nov. 29** *Perf. 12½*

**610** A297 8c multicolored .30 .25

*p.* Tagged .35 .25

Cornelius Krieghoff (1815-1872), painter.

**Tagged**

From No. 611 onward, all stamps are tagged unless otherwise noted.

Monsignor de Laval — A298

**1973, Jan. 31** *Perf. 11*

**611** A298 8c silver, ultra & gold .30 .25

Francois-Xavier de Montmorency-Laval de Montigny (1623-1708), 1st Bishop of Quebec and founder of many educational institutions; one of the builders of New France.

Commissioner G. A. French and Map of 1874 Trek — A299

10c, Spectrograph. 15c, R.C.M.P. Musical Ride.

**1973, Mar. 9**

612 A299 8c dk brn, org & red .30 .25
613 A299 10c dk blue & multi .35 .30
614 A299 15c yel grn & multi .75 .50
a. Imperf., pair 375.00
*Nos. 612-614 (3)* 1.40 1.05

Royal Canadian Mounted Police, cent.
Imperfs of No. 614 with a double impression and examples with 15c printed on 10c are from printer's waste.

Jeanne Mance — A300

**1973, Apr. 18**

615 A300 8c multicolored .30 .25
a. Printed on gummed side 750.00

Jeanne Mance (1606-1673), first secular nurse in North America and founder of first hospital, the Hôtel-Dieu in Montreal settlement.

Joseph Howe — A301

**1973, May 16**

616 A301 8c gold & black .30 .25

Joseph Howe (1804-1873), journalist, poet and Lieutenant-Governor of Nova Scotia.

Mist Fantasy, by James MacDonald — A302

**1973, June 8** ***Perf. 12½***

617 A302 15c multicolored .60 .50

Centenary of the birth of James E. H. MacDonald (1873-1932), painter.

Oaks on Shore — A303

**Photo. & Engr.**

**1973, June 22** ***Perf. 12x12½***

618 A303 8c orange & red brn .30 .25

Centenary of Prince Edward Island's entry into Confederation.

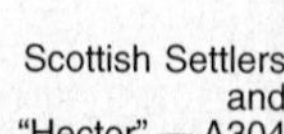

Scottish Settlers and "Hector" — A304

**1973, July 20**

619 A304 8c multicolored .30 .25

Bicentenary of arrival of Scottish settlers at Pictou, N.S.
No. 619 exists on yellow paper.

Queen Elizabeth II — A305

**1973, Aug. 2** **Photo. and Engr.**

620 A305 8c silver & multi .30 .25
621 A305 15c gold & multi .70 .60

Visit to Ottawa of Elizabeth II and the Duke of Edinburgh, July 31-Aug. 4, and meeting of Commonwealth Heads of Government, Ottawa, Aug. 2-10.

Nellie McClung — A306

**1973, Aug. 29 Litho.** ***Perf. 10½x11***

622 A306 8c multicolored .30 .25

Nellie McClung (1873-1951), leader of women's suffrage movement, social reformer and writer.

Montreal Olympic Games — A307

**1973, Sept. 20** ***Perf. 12x12½***

**Size: 26x44mm**

623 A307 8c silver & multi .30 .25
624 A307 15c gold & multi .60 .50

21st Olympic Games, Montreal, 1976.
See Nos. B1-B3.

Ice Skate A308

Santa Claus A309

8c, Dove. 15c, Shepherd and star.

**1973, Nov. 7** ***Perf. 12½x12***

625 A308 6c multicolored .30 .25
a. Double impression of black 100.00
626 A308 8c multicolored .30 .25

***Perf. 10½***

627 A309 10c multicolored .30 .30
628 A309 15c multicolored .60 .60
*Nos. 625-628 (4)* 1.50 1.40

Christmas.

Children Diving from Dock — A310

**1974, Mar. 22 Engr.** ***Perf. 12***

629 A310 8c shown .35 .25
630 A310 8c Joggers .35 .25
631 A310 8c Bicycling family .35 .25
632 A310 8c Hikers .35 .25
a. Block of 4, #629-632 1.40 1.00

"Keep Fit." 21st Summer Olympic Games, Montreal, 1976. When stamps are observed at an angle the Montreal Olympic Games' emblem can be seen.

Main St. and Portage Ave., Winnipeg, 1872 — A311

**Litho. & Engr.**

**1974, May 3** ***Perf. 12x12½***

633 A311 8c multicolored .30 .25

Winnipeg's incorporation as a city, cent.

Postmaster — A312

No. 635, Mail collector and truck. No. 636, Mail handler. No. 637, Mail sorters. No. 638, Mailman. No. 639, Rural mail delivery.

**1974, June 11 Litho.** ***Perf. 13½x13***

634 A312 8c shown .35 .30
635 A312 8c multicolored .35 .30
636 A312 8c multicolored .35 .30
637 A312 8c multicolored .35 .30
638 A312 8c multicolored .35 .30
639 A312 8c multicolored .35 .30
a. Block of 6, #634-639 2.25 2.25

Centenary of letter carrier delivery service. Printed in sheets of 50 (5x10).

Agricultural Education — A313

**1974, July 12** ***Perf. 12½x12***

640 A313 8c multicolored .30 .25

Ontario Agricultural College centenary.

Pedestal, Gallows Frame and Contempra Telephones A314

**1974, July 26** ***Perf. 12½***

641 A314 8c multicolored .30 .25
a. Imperf., pair 1,000.

Centenary of the idea for the telephone by Alexander Graham Bell while visiting Brantford, Canada.

Bicycle Wheel and Cycling Emblem — A315

**Photo. & Engr.**

**1974, Aug. 7** ***Perf. 12x12½***

642 A315 8c black, red & silver .30 .25

World Cycling Championships, Montreal, Aug. 14-25.

Mennonite Settlers — A316

**1974, Aug. 28 Litho.** ***Perf. 12x12½***

643 A316 8c multicolored .30 .25

Centenary of arrival of Mennonite settlers in Manitoba.

Snowshoeing A317

**1974, Sept. 23 Engr.** ***Perf. 13½***

644 A317 8c shown .35 .25
645 A317 8c Skiing .35 .25
646 A317 8c Skating .35 .25
647 A317 8c Curling .35 .25
a. Block of 4, #644-647 1.40 1.40
b. Block or strip of 4, printed on gummed side 3,000.

"Keep Fit." 1976 Winter Olympic Games. When the stamps are observed at an angle the Montreal Olympic Games' emblem can be seen.
Warning: No. 647b must show each design; blocks exist that contain 2 No. 645 but no example of No. 647. Value thus, $1,500.

Mercury with Winged Horses, UPU Emblem — A318

**Photo. & Engr.**

**1974, Oct. 9** ***Perf. 12x12½***

648 A318 8c violet, red & blue .30 .25
649 A318 15c violet, red & blue .90 .75

Centenary of Universal Postal Union.

Nativity, by Jean Paul Lemieux A319

Skaters at Hull, by Henri Masson A320

Christmas (Paintings): 10c, The Ice Cone, Montmorency Falls, by Robert C. Todd. 15c, Village in the Laurentian Mountains, by Clarence A. Gagnon.

**1974, Nov. 1 Litho.** ***Perf. 13½***

650 A319 6c multicolored .30 .25
651 A320 8c multicolored .30 .25
652 A319 10c multicolored .35 .30
653 A319 15c multicolored .60 .55
*Nos. 650-653 (4)* 1.55 1.35

Marconi and St. John's, Newfoundland, from Signal Hill — A321

**1974, Nov. 15** ***Perf. 13***

654 A321 8c multicolored .30 .25

Guglielmo Marconi (1874-1937), Italian electrical engineer and inventor.

Merritt and Welland Canal — A322

**Litho. & Engr.**

**1974, Nov. 29** ***Perf. 13x13½***

655 A322 8c multicolored .30 .25

Sesquicentennial of the start of construction of the Welland Canal between Lakes Ontario and Erie, a project conceived and supervised by William Hamilton Merritt (1793-1862). Portrait by Robert Whale.

The Sprinter A323

The Plunger — A324

Designs: Sculptures by Robert Tait McKenzie, M.D. (1867-1938), and Montreal Olympic Games' emblem.

*Perf. 12½x12, 12x12½*

**1975, Mar. 14 Litho.; Embossed**

| | | | | |
|---|---|---|---|---|
| **656** | A323 | $1 multicolored | 2.25 | 2.25 |
| **657** | A324 | $2 multicolored | 4.50 | 4.50 |

21st Olympic Games, Montreal, July 17-Aug. 1, 1976.

A325

No. 658, Anne of Green Gables. No. 659, Maria Chapdelaine.

**1975, May 15 Litho. *Perf. 13***

| | | | |
|---|---|---|---|
| **658** | 8c blue & multi | .30 | .25 |
| **659** | 8c brown & multi | .30 | .25 |
| *a.* | A325 Pair, #658-659 | .50 | .50 |

Birth centenary of Lucy Maud Montgomery (1874-1942), writer and author of "Anne of Green Gables"; Louis Hémon (1880-1913), writer and author of "Maria Chapdelaine." Nos. 658-659 printed checkerwise.

Marguerite Bourgeoys
A327

Alphonse Desjardins
A328

**1975, May 30 Litho. *Perf. 12½x12***

| | | | | |
|---|---|---|---|---|
| **660** | A327 | 8c red & multi | .30 | .25 |
| **661** | A328 | 8c red & multi | .30 | .25 |

Marguerite Bourgeoys (1620-1700), founder of the Congrégation de Notre-Dame, Montreal, first girls' school in New France; Alphonse Desjardins (1854-1920), journalist, founder of first credit union in North America.

A329

No. 662, Samuel Dwight Chown (1853-1933), Methodist minister, leader of temperance movement, founder of United Church. No. 663, Dr. John Cook (1805-92), 1st Moderator of the United Presbyterian Church in Canada.

Nos. 662-663 printed checkerwise.

**Photo. & Engr.**

**1975, May 30 *Perf. 12x12½***

| | | | |
|---|---|---|---|
| **662** | 8c dk brown, yel & buff | .30 | .25 |
| **663** | 8c dk brown, buff & yel | .30 | .25 |
| *a.* | A329 Pair, #662-663 | .50 | .50 |

Pole Vaulting
A331

Hurdling
A332

Design: 25c, Marathon running and Montreal Olympic Games' emblem.

**1975, June 11 Litho. *Perf. 12x12½***

| | | | | |
|---|---|---|---|---|
| **664** | A331 | 20c dk blue & multi | .60 | .45 |
| **665** | A331 | 25c maroon & multi | .75 | .50 |
| **666** | A332 | 50c green & multi | 1.50 | 1.00 |
| | | *Nos. 664-666 (3)* | 2.85 | 1.95 |

21st Olympic Games, Montreal, July 17-Aug. 1, 1976.

"Untamed" (Wild Horse Race) — A333

**1975, July 3**

| | | | | |
|---|---|---|---|---|
| **667** | A333 | 8c gray & multi | .30 | .25 |

Centenary of the founding of Calgary.

Female Symbol — A334

**Photo. & Engr.**

**1975, July 14 *Perf. 13***

| | | | | |
|---|---|---|---|---|
| **668** | A334 | 8c dp yel, gray & black | .30 | .25 |

International Women's Year.

"Justice," by Walter S. Allward — A335

**1975, Sept. 2 Litho. *Perf. 12½***

| | | | | |
|---|---|---|---|---|
| **669** | A335 | 8c multicolored | .30 | .25 |

Supreme Court of Canada, centenary.

"Wm. D. Lawrence" A336

**Photo. & Engr.**

**1975, Sept. 24 *Perf. 13***

| | | | | |
|---|---|---|---|---|
| **670** | A336 | 8c shown | .35 | .30 |
| **671** | A336 | 8c "Beaver" | .35 | .30 |
| **672** | A336 | 8c "Neptune" | .35 | .30 |
| **673** | A336 | 8c "Quadra" | .35 | .30 |
| *a.* | | Block of 4, #670-673 | 1.40 | 1.40 |

Coastal ships.

Santa Claus — A337

Child — A338

Trees — A339

Designs by Canadian School Children: "What Christmas Means to Me" — No. 675, Skater. No. 677, Family and Christmas tree. No. 678, Gift box.

**1975, Oct. 22 Litho. *Perf. 13½***

| | | | | |
|---|---|---|---|---|
| **674** | A337 | 6c shown | .30 | .25 |
| **675** | A337 | 6c multicolored | .30 | .25 |
| *a.* | | Pair, #674-675 | .50 | .50 |
| **676** | A338 | 8c shown | .30 | .25 |
| **677** | A338 | 8c multicolored | .30 | .25 |
| *a.* | | Pair, #676-677 | .50 | .50 |
| *b.* | | Double impression of black | 90.00 | |
| *c.* | | As "a," triple impression of black | 300.00 | |
| **678** | A338 | 10c multicolored | .30 | .25 |
| **679** | A339 | 15c shown | .45 | .45 |
| | | *Nos. 674-679 (6)* | 1.95 | 1.70 |

Christmas. Stamps of same denomination printed checkerwise.

Legion Emblem and Bugle — A340

**Photo. & Engr.**

**1975, Nov. 10 *Perf. 13***

| | | | | |
|---|---|---|---|---|
| **680** | A340 | 8c gray & multi | .30 | .25 |

Royal Canadian Legion, 50th anniversary.

Olympic Torch Ignited by Satellite in Canada — A341

Montreal Olympic Games' Emblem and: 20c, Canadian athletes carrying Olympic flag. 25c, Women athletes receiving Olympic medals.

**1976, June 18 Litho. *Perf. 13***

| | | | | |
|---|---|---|---|---|
| **681** | A341 | 8c black & multi | .30 | .25 |
| **682** | A341 | 20c black & multi | .70 | .55 |
| **683** | A341 | 25c black & multi | .90 | .60 |
| | | *Nos. 681-683 (3)* | 1.90 | 1.40 |

1976 Olympic Games ceremonies.

Communication Arts — A342

25c, Handicraft tools. 50c, Performing arts.

**1976, Feb. 6 Photo. *Perf. 12x12½***

| | | | | |
|---|---|---|---|---|
| **684** | A342 | 20c gray & multi | 1.25 | .60 |
| **685** | A342 | 25c ocher & multi | 1.50 | .75 |
| **686** | A342 | 50c blue & multi | 2.50 | 1.25 |
| | | *Nos. 684-686 (3)* | 5.25 | 2.60 |

Olympic Fine Arts and Cultural Program.

High-rise Tower, Notre Dame Church, Montreal, and Games' Emblem
A343

Design: $2, Olympic Stadium, Velodrome, flags and emblem.

**Photo. & Engr.**

**1976, Mar. 12 *Perf. 13***

| | | | | |
|---|---|---|---|---|
| **687** | A343 | $1 silver & multi | 3.25 | 2.25 |
| **688** | A343 | $2 gold & multi | 5.25 | 4.50 |

Nos. 681-688 were issued in commemoration of, or in connection with the 21st Olympic Games, Montreal, July 17-Aug. 1. Nos. 687-688 were issued in panes of 8.

Snowflake, Winter Olympics' Emblem — A344

**Photo. and Embossed**

**1976, Feb. 6 *Perf. 12½***

| | | | | |
|---|---|---|---|---|
| **689** | A344 | 20c multicolored | .90 | .65 |

12th Winter Olympic Games, Innsbruck, Austria, Feb. 4-15.

Flower Growing from City — A345

**1976, May 12 Litho. *Perf. 12x12½***

| | | | | |
|---|---|---|---|---|
| **690** | A345 | 20c multicolored | .60 | .45 |

Habitat, UN Conference on Human Settlements, Vancouver, May 31-June 11.

Franklin and Map of North America, 1776 — A346

**Litho. & Engr.**

**1976, June 1 *Perf. 13***

| | | | | |
|---|---|---|---|---|
| **691** | A346 | 10c multicolored | .35 | .25 |

American Bicentennial; Benjamin Franklin (1706-1790), deputy postmaster general for the colonies (1753-1774).

See US No. 1690.

Royal Military College, Kingston, Ont., Cent. — A347

No. 692, Color Parade, Memorial Arch. No. 693, Wing Parade, Mackenzie Building.

**1976, June 1 Litho. *Perf. 12***

| | | | |
|---|---|---|---|
| **692** | 8c red & multi | .30 | .25 |
| **693** | 8c red & multi | .30 | .25 |
| *a.* | A347 Pair, #692-693 | .50 | .50 |
| *b.* | As "a," imperf., untagged | *1,700.* | |
| *c.* | Block of 4, imperf. horiz. | *650.00* | |
| *d.* | As "a," double impression | *3,250.* | |

A few used singles exist of Nos. 692-693 with double impression. Very rare.

Archer in Wheelchair
A349

**1976, Aug. 3 *Perf. 12x12½***

| | | | | |
|---|---|---|---|---|
| **694** | A349 | 20c green & multi | .60 | .50 |

Olympiad for the Physically Disabled (25th Stoke Mandeville Games), Toronto, Aug. 3-11.

A350

No. 695, The Cremation of Sam McGee. No. 696, The Outlander.

**1976, Aug. 17 *Perf. 13½***

| | | | |
|---|---|---|---|
| **695** | 8c multicolored | .30 | .25 |
| **696** | 8c multicolored | .30 | .25 |
| *a.* | A350 Pair, #695-696 | .50 | .50 |

Robert W. Service (1874-1958), author of poem "The Cremation of Sam McGee"; Germaine Guevremont, author of "Le Survenant" (The Outlander).

Nativity, St. Michael's, Toronto — A352

Stained-glass windows: 10c, Nativity, St. Jude, London, Ontario. 20c, Nativity, by Yvonne Williams.

**1976, Nov. 3** *Perf. 13½*

**697** A352 8c multicolored .30 .25
**698** A352 10c multicolored .30 .25
**699** A352 20c multicolored .40 .40
*Nos. 697-699 (3)* 1.00 .90

Christmas.

Inland Vessels — A353

**Litho. & Engr.**

**1976, Nov. 19** *Perf. 12*

**700** A353 10c Northcote .35 .30
**701** A353 10c Passport .35 .30
*a.* Double impression of purple 275.00
**702** A353 10c Chicora .35 .30
*a.* Double impression of blue 275.00
**703** A353 10c Athabasca .35 .30
*a.* Block of 4, #700-703 1.40 1.25

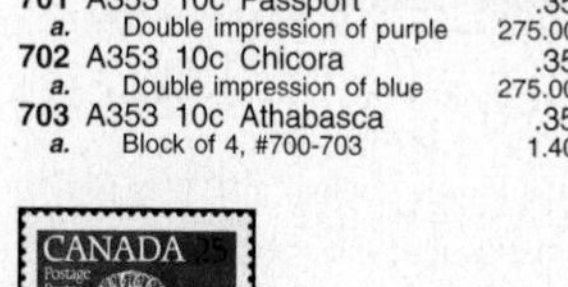

Elizabeth II — A354

**Litho. and Typo.**

**1977, Feb. 4** *Perf. 12½x12*

**704** A354 25c silver & multi .70 .50
*a.* Silver omitted *1,000.*

25th anniv. of the reign of Elizabeth II.
Authentication strongly recommended for No. 704a. Fakes exist.

Bottle Gentian A355

Elizabeth II A356

Parliament, Ottawa A357

Trembling Aspen A358

Main Street, Prairie Town — A359

Fundy National Park — A359a

Designs: 2c, Western columbine. 3c, Canada lily. 4c, Hepatica. 5c, Shooting star. 10c, Franklin's lady's-slipper. No. 712, Jewelweed. No. 715, Parliament, Ottawa. No. 716, Queen Elizabeth II. 20c, Douglas fir. 25c, Maple. 30c, Red oak. 35c, White pine. 60c, Street scene, Ontario City. 75c, Old houses, eastern City Street. 80c, Street leading to the sea, Eastern Maritime Provinces. $2 Kluane National Park.

**Litho. & Engr.**

**1977-82** *Perf. 12x12½*

**705** A355 1c multicolored .30 .25
*a.* Printed on gummed side, precanceled 1,200.
**707** A355 2c multicolored .30 .25
*a.* Printed on gummed side 850.00
**708** A355 3c multicolored .30 .25
**709** A355 4c multicolored .30 .25
*a.* Printed on gummed side 275.00
**710** A355 5c multicolored .30 .25
**711** A355 10c multicolored .30 .25
*a.* Perf. 13x13½ ('78) .30 .25

**Photo. & Engr.**

*Perf. 13x13½*

**712** A355 12c multi ('78) .30 .25
**713** A356 12c blue & multi .30 .25
*a.* Perf. 12x12½ .30 .25

**Engraved**

*Perf. 13x13½*

**714** A357 12c blue .30 .25
*a.* Printed on gummed side 300.00
**715** A357 14c red ('78) .30 .25
*a.* Printed on gummed side 37.50
*b.* All color omitted 375.00

**Photo. & Engr.**

*Perf. 13x13½*

**716** A356 14c red & blk ('78) .30 .25
*a.* Perf. 12x12½ .50 .25
*b.* As "a," booklet pane of 25 + 2 labels ('78) 5.50 6.00
*c.* Red omitted *1,000.*

*Perf. 13½*

**717** A358 15c multi .50 .25
**718** A358 20c multi .35 .25
*a.* Black (denomination) omitted *750.00*
**719** A358 25c multi .50 .25
**720** A358 30c multi ('78) .60 .25
**721** A358 35c multi ('79) .60 .25
**723** A359 50c multi ('78) 1.10 .25
**723A** A359 50c multi, litho. & engr. ('78) .90 .25
*b.* Dark brown (engr., all inscriptions, etc.) omitted *1,800.*
*c.* Magenta (litho.) and dark brown (engr.) missing (from foldover) *15,000.*
**723C** A359 60c multi, litho. ('82) 1.25 .25
**724** A359 75c multi ('78) 1.30 .30
**725** A359 80c multi ('78) 1.50 .35

**Lithographed and Engraved**

**726** A359a $1 multi ('79) 1.50 .55
*a.* Untagged 2.50 .70
*b.* As "a," blk inscriptions omitted 500.00 500.00
**727** A359a $2 multi ('79) 3.60 1.40
*a.* Silver inscriptions omitted 300.00
*b.* Double impression of silver inscriptions *750.00*
*Nos. 705-727 (23)* 17.00 7.35

All known pairs of No. 705a are precanceled.

On No. 715b, a strong embossed impression from the plate, without color, is evident.

On No. 723A license plate on yellow car reads "1978."

No. 723Ac is unique.

Certificate of authenticity recommended for No. 727b. "Kiss prints" also exist that are not true double impressions.

See Nos. 781-806, 934-937, 1084.

**Coil Stamps**

**1977-78** **Engr.** *Perf. 10 Vert.*

**729** A357 12c blue .30 .25
*a.* Imperf., pair 140.00
**730** A357 14c red ('78) .30 .25
*a.* Imperf., pair 160.00

See note below No. 468B.

Eastern Cougar — A360

**1977, Mar. 30** **Litho.** *Perf. 12½*

**732** A360 12c multicolored .30 .25

Wildlife protection.

April in Algonquin Park, by Thomson — A361

No. 734, Autumn Birches, by Tom Thomson.

**1977, May 26** *Perf. 12*

**733** A361 12c black & multi .30 .25
**734** A361 12c ocher & multi .30 .25
*a.* Pair, #733-734 .50 .50

Tom Thomson (1877-1917), landscape painter, birth centenary. Nos. 733-734 printed checkerwise.

Names of Governors General and Standard — A362

**1977, June 30** *Perf. 12½*

**735** A362 12c vio blue & multi .30 .25

Honoring Canadian-born Governors General: Vincent Massey, Georges Philias Vanier, Daniel Roland Michener and Jules Léger.

Order of Canada — A363

**Litho. & Embossed**

**1977, June 30**

**736** A363 12c multicolored .30 .25

Order of Canada, 10th anniversary.

Peace Bridge, Canadian, US and UN Flags — A364

**1977, Aug. 4** **Litho.**

**737** A364 12c blue & multi .30 .25

50th anniversary of the Peace Bridge, connecting Fort Erie, Ontario, with Buffalo, N.Y.

Joseph E. Bernier, CGS Arctic — A365

Sandford Fleming, Railroad Bridge — A366

**1977, Sept. 16** **Engr.** *Perf. 13*

**738** A365 12c dark blue .30 .25
**739** A366 12c brown .30 .25
*a.* Pair, #738-739 .50 .50

Joseph-Elzéar Bernier (1852-1934), explorer; Sandford Fleming (1827-1915), mapped route for Intercolonial Railway and designed Canada's first stamp.

Nos. 738-739 printed checkerwise.

Peace Tower, Parliament, Ottawa — A367

**1977, Sept. 19** **Litho.** *Perf. 12½*

**740** A367 25c multicolored .75 .65

23rd Commonwealth Parliamentary Conference, Ottawa, Sept. 19-25.

Hunters Following Star — A368

Christmas: 12c, Angelic choir in northern light. 25c, Christ Child in Ring of Glory blessing chiefs from afar. Illustrations for Canada's first Christmas carol, written by Father Brébeuf, 1649.

**1977, Oct. 26** *Perf. 13½*

**741** A368 10c multicolored .30 .25
*a.* Horiz. pair, imperf between *1,000.*
*b.* Printed on gummed side 700.00
*c.* Imperf., pair *1,000.*
**742** A368 12c multicolored .30 .25
*a.* Left margin block of 4, left vert. pair imperf, right pair part perf *1,750.*
*b.* Double impression of purple, blue, green; quadruple impression of black (inscriptions) 650.00
**743** A368 25c multicolored .45 .35
*Nos. 741-743 (3)* 1.05 .85

Pinky — A369

Canadian sailing ships — No. 745, Tern schooner. No. 746, 5-masted schooner. No. 747, Mackinaw boat.

**Litho. and Engr.**

**1977, Nov. 18** *Perf. 12x12½*

**744** A369 12c shown .30 .25
**745** A369 12c multicolored .30 .25
**746** A369 12c multicolored .30 .25
**747** A369 12c multicolored .30 .25
*a.* Block of 4, #744-747 1.00 1.00
*b.* As "a," #745, 747 imperf; #744, 746 part perf *3,000.*

See Nos. 776-779.

Seal Hunter, Soapstone Sculpture A370

Disguised Caribou Hunter, Print A371

Inuit Art: No. 749, Spear fishing. No. 751, Walrus hunt. Nos. 749-751 are after stonecut prints.

**1977, Nov. 18** **Litho.**

**748** A370 12c multicolored .30 .25
**749** A371 12c multicolored .30 .25
*a.* Pair, #748-749 .50 .50
*b.* As "a," gray (inscriptions) omitted on No. 749 *2,250.*
**750** A371 12c multicolored .30 .25
**751** A371 12c multicolored .30 .25
*a.* Pair, #750-751 .50 .50
*Nos. 748-751 (4)* 1.20 1.00

Inuit hunting. Nos. 748-749 and Nos. 750-751 printed se-tenant checkerwise.

Peregrine Falcon — A372

**1978, Jan. 18**

**752** A372 12c multicolored .30 .25

Endangered wildlife.

Canada No. 3, 1851 — A373

**1978** **Photo. & Engr.** *Perf. 13½*

**753** A373 12c shown .30 .25
**754** A373 14c No. 7 .30 .25
**755** A373 30c No. 8 .55 .30
**756** A373 $1.25 No. 2 2.00 1.00
*a.* Souvenir sheet of 3 3.25 3.25
*Nos. 753-756 (4)* 3.15 1.80

CAPEX '78, Canadian Intl. Phil. Exhib., Toronto, June 9-18 (cent. of Canada's admission to UPU).

No. 756a contains one each of Nos. 754-756 ($1.25 untagged). Value of No. 756 untagged, $2.75.

Issue dates: 12c, Jan. 18; others, June 10.

Games' Emblem — A374

Design: 30c, Badminton.

**1978, Mar. 31** **Litho.** *Perf. 12½*

**757** A374 14c silver & multi .30 .25
**758** A374 30c silver & multi .55 .45

Stadium — A375

No. 760, Running. No. 761, Alberta Legislature building, Edmonton. No. 762, Lawn bowling.

**1978, Aug. 3**

**759** A375 14c silver & multi .30 .25
**760** A375 14c silver & multi .30 .25
*a.* Pair, #759-760 .60 .50
*b.* Imperf., pair *650.00*
**761** A375 30c silver & multi .55 .50
**762** A375 30c silver & multi .55 .50
*a.* Pair, #761-762 1.10 1.00
*Nos. 759-762 (4)* 1.70 1.50

Nos. 757-762 commemorate 11th Commonwealth Games, Edmonton, Aug. 3-12.

Nos. 760a, 762a printed checkerwise.

All known examples of No. 760b have slight wrinkling from mishandling. Value is for a pair with only minimal wrinkling.

A376

No. 763, Capt. Cook, by Nathaniel Dance. No. 764, Nootka Sound, by John Webber.

**1978, Apr. 26** *Perf. 13*
**763** 14c multicolored .30 .25
**764** 14c multicolored .30 .25
*a.* A376 Pair, #763-764 .60 .50
*b.* Imperf., untagged 750.00

Capt. James Cook (1728-1779), explorer of Canada's East and West Coasts and bicentenary of his anchorage near Anchorage, June 1, 1778. Nos. 763-764 printed checkerwise.

Silver Mine, Cobalt Lake — A378

Stripmining, Athabasca Tar Sands — A379

**1978, May 19** *Perf. 12½*
**765** A378 14c multicolored .30 .25
**766** A379 14c multicolored .30 .25
*a.* Pair, #765-766 .50 .50
*b.* As "a," No. 766 with double impression of brown (inscriptions) 600.00

Development of national resources. Nos. 765-766 printed checkerwise.

Prince's Gate — A380

**1978, Aug. 16**
**767** A380 14c multicolored .30 .25

Canadian National Exhibition, centenary.

Mère d'Youville and Miracle of Food — A381

**1978, Sept. 21** *Perf. 13x13½*
**768** A381 14c multicolored .30 .25

Marguerite d'Youville (1701-1771), founder of the Gray Nuns, beatified 1959.

Woman Walking, by Pitseolak — A382

Migration, Soapstone by Joe Talurinili — A383

Works by Eskimo Artists: No. 771, Plane over village, stonecut and stencil print by Pudlo. No. 772, Dogteam and sled, ivory sculpture by Abraham Kingmeatook.

**1978, Sept. 27** *Perf. 13½*
**769** A382 14c multicolored .30 .25
**770** A383 14c multicolored .30 .25
*a.* Pair, #769-770 .50 .50
**771** A382 14c multicolored .30 .25
**772** A383 14c multicolored .30 .25
*a.* Pair, #771-772 .50 .50
*Nos. 769-772 (4)* 1.20 1.00

Travels of the Inuit. Printed checkerwise.

Madonna of the Flowering Pea, Cologne School — A384

Renaissance Paintings in National Gallery of Canada: 14c, Virgin and Child, by Hans Memling. 30c, Virgin and Child, by Jacopo Di Cione.

**1978, Oct. 20** *Perf. 12½*
**773** A384 12c multicolored .30 .25
**774** A384 14c multicolored .30 .25
*a.* Black omitted 1,000.
**775** A384 30c multicolored .55 .25
*Nos. 773-775 (3)* 1.15 .75

Christmas.

**Sailing Ships Type of 1977**

No. 776, "Chief Justice Robinson," 1842. No. 777, "St. Roch," 1928. No. 778, "Northern Light," 1928. No. 779, "Labrador," 1954.

**Litho. & Engr.**

**1978, Nov. 15** *Perf. 13*
**776** A369 14c multicolored .30 .25
**777** A369 14c multicolored .30 .25
**778** A369 14c multicolored .30 .25
**779** A369 14c multicolored .30 .25
*a.* Block of 4, #776-779 1.25 1.10

Ice vessels.

Quebec Carnival — A386

**1979, Feb. 1** **Litho.** *Perf. 13½*
**780** A386 14c multicolored .30 .25

**Flower, Queen & Parliament Types**

1c, Bottle gentian. 2c, Western columbine. 3c, Canada lily. 4c, Hepatica. 5c, Shooting star. 10c, Franklin's lady's-slipper. 15c, Canada violet. No. 789, Elizabeth II. No. 790, Parliament, Ottawa.

**Photo. & Engr., Engr. (#790)**

**1977-83** *Perf. 13x13½*
**781** A355 1c multi ('79) .30 .25
*a.* Perf. 12x12½ ('77) .30 .25
*b.* Bklt. pane, 2 #781a, 4 #713a 1.00 1.00
**782** A355 2c multi ('79) .30 .25
*a.* Bklt. pane, 4 #782b, 3 #716a + label 1.00 1.00
*b.* Perf. 12x12½ ('78) .30 .25
**783** A355 3c multi ('79) .30 .25
**784** A355 4c multi ('79) .30 .25
**785** A355 5c multi ('79) .30 .25
**786** A355 10c multi ('79) .30 .25
**787** A355 15c multi ('79) .30 .25
**789** A356 17c green & blk ('79) .30 .25
*a.* Perf. 12x12½ .35 .25
*b.* Bklt. pane of 25 #789a + 2 labels 6.50 *7.50*
*c.* Horiz. pair, imperf. btwn. and at left and bottom *1,800.*
*d.* Black inscriptions omitted *750.00*
**790** A357 17c slate green ('79) .30 .25
*a.* Printed on gummed side 37.50
**791** A356 30c multi ('82) .45 .25
*a.* Black (engr.) omitted *2,250.*
**792** A356 32c multi ('83) .50 .25
*Nos. 781-792 (11)* 3.65 2.75

Nos. 781a, 782b, 789a are from booklet panes. No. 782b has one straight edge, others one or two.

Beware of examples purported to be No. 791a that actually have tiny amounts of black present. Only two examples have been confirmed with 100% omission. Certification strongly recommended.

No. 789d also shows the horiz. perfs. shifted.

No. 790 exists with double tagging. Value, *$110.*

**Parliament Type of 1977**
**Booklet Stamps**

**1979, Mar. 28** **Engr.** *Perf. 12x12½*
**797** A357 1c slate blue .40 .25
*a.* Bklt. pane, 1 #797, 3 #800, 2 #789a 1.40
**800** A357 5c violet brown .30 .25

No. 797 has one straight edge, No. 800 has one or two.

**Coil Stamps**

**1979, Mar. 8** *Perf. 10 Vert.*
**806** A357 17c slate green .30 .25
*a.* Imperf., pair 150.00

Endangered Wildlife — A392

**1979, Apr. 10** **Litho.** *Perf. 12½*
**813** A392 17c Soft-shelled turtle .30 .25
**814** A392 35c Bowhead whale .75 .40

Ribbon Around Woman's Finger — A393

No. 816, String around man's finger.

**1979, Apr. 10**
**815** A393 17c multicolored .30 .25
**816** A393 17c multicolored .30 .25
*a.* Pair, #815-816 .50 .50
*b.* As "a," double impression of black 110.00
*c.* As "a," triple impression of black 225.00
*d.* As "a," double impression of red 110.00

Use postal code. Printed checkerwise.

Fruits of the Earth, by F. P. Grove — A394

The Golden Vessel, by Emile Nelligan — A395

**1979, May 3** *Perf. 13x13½*
**817** A394 17c multicolored .30 .25
*a.* Double impression of brown 375.00
**818** A395 17c multicolored .30 .25
*a.* Double impression of blue 375.00
*b.* Pair, #817-818 .50 .55
*c.* As "b," left margin block of 4, left vert. pair imperf, right pair part perf *1,500.*

Frederick Philip Grove (1879-1948), teacher and writer; Emile Nelligan (1879-1941), French-Canadian poet. Nos. 817-818 printed checkerwise.

Warning: horizontal pairs exist of No. 818a that appear to be imperforate. These actually are pairs made from No. 818c with normal perforations trimmed off the right edge.

A396

**1979, May 11** *Perf. 13½*
**819** 17c De Salaberry .30 .25
**820** 17c John By .30 .25
*a.* A396 Pair, #819-820 .50 .50

Charles-Michel d'Irumberry de Salaberry (1778-1829), and John By (1779-1836), Canadian colonels. Printed checkerwise.

Flag of Ontario — A398

Provincial and Territorial flags: No. 822, Quebec. No. 823, Nova Scotia. No. 824, New Brunswick. No. 825, Manitoba. No. 826, British Columbia. No. 827, Prince Edward Island. No. 828, Saskatchewan. No. 829, Alberta. No. 830, Newfoundland. No. 831, Northwest Territories. No. 832, Yukon Territory.

**1979, June 15** *Perf. 13½*
**821** A398 17c shown .30 .25
**822** A398 17c multicolored .30 .25
**823** A398 17c multicolored .30 .25
**824** A398 17c multicolored .30 .25
**825** A398 17c multicolored .30 .25
**826** A398 17c multicolored .30 .25
**827** A398 17c multicolored .30 .25
**828** A398 17c multicolored .30 .25
**829** A398 17c multicolored .30 .25
**830** A398 17c multicolored .30 .25
**831** A398 17c multicolored .30 .25
**832** A398 17c multicolored .30 .25
*a.* Pane of 12, #821-832 4.00 3.75

White Water Kayak Race — A399

**1979, July 3** *Perf. 12½*
**833** A399 17c multicolored .30 .25

Canoe-Kayak (Slalom and Wild Water) World Championships, Jonquière and Desbiens, Quebec, June 30-July 8.

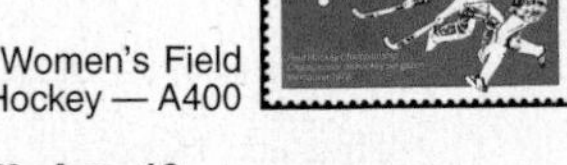
Women's Field Hockey — A400

**1979, Aug. 16**
**834** A400 17c multicolored .30 .25

Women's Field Hockey Championship, Vancouver, B.C., Aug. 16-30.

Summer Tent, Print by Kiakshuk A401

Eskimos Building Igloo, by Abraham of Povungnituk A402

Works by Eskimo Artists: No. 837, The Dance, print by Kalvak of Holman Island. No. 838, Two soapstone figures from Repulse Bay, by Madeleine Isserkut and Jean Mapsalak.

**1979, Sept. 13** *Perf. 13½*
**835** A401 17c multicolored .30 .25
**836** A402 17c multicolored .30 .25
*a.* Pair, #835-836 .50 .50
**837** A401 17c multicolored .30 .25
**838** A402 17c multicolored .30 .25
*a.* Pair, #837-838 .50 .50
*Nos. 835-838 (4)* 1.20 1.00

Inuit shelters and community. Printed checkerwise.

Painted Wooden Train — A403

Antique Toys: 17c, Horse, pull toy. 35c, Knitted doll, vert.

**1979, Oct. 17** *Perf. 13*
**839** A403 15c multicolored .30 .25
**840** A403 17c multicolored .30 .25
**841** A403 35c multicolored .60 .30
*a.* Gold (and tagging) omitted *1,000.* *700.00*
*Nos. 839-841 (3)* 1.20 .80

Christmas.

Girl Watering Tree of Life — A404

**1979, Oct. 24**
**842** A404 17c multicolored .30 .25

International Year of the Child.

Curtiss HS-2L — A405

No. 844, Canadair CL-215. No. 845, Vickers Vedette. No. 846, Consolidated Canso.

**1979, Nov. 15** *Perf. 12½*

**843** A405 17c shown .30 .25
**844** A405 17c multicolored .30 .25
*a.* Pair, #843-844 .65 .55
**845** A405 35c multicolored .65 .50
**846** A405 35c multicolored .65 .50
*a.* Pair, #845-846 1.30 1.25
*Nos. 843-846 (4)* 1.90 1.50

Map of Canada Showing Arctic Islands — A406

**1980, Jan. 23** *Perf. 13½*

**847** A406 17c multicolored .30 .25

Acquisition of the Arctic Islands, centenary.

Downhill Skiing — A407

**1980, Jan. 23**

**848** A407 35c multicolored .65 .45

13th Winter Olympic Games, Lake Placid, NY, Feb. 12-24.

Meeting of the School Trustees, by Robert Harris — A408

Royal Canadian Academy of Arts Centenary: No. 850, Inspiration, bronze sculpture, by Louis-Philippe Hebert (1850-1917). No. 851, Parliament Buildings, by Thomas Fuller (1822-1919). No. 852, Sunrise on the Saguenay, by Lucius O'Brien (1832-99).

**1980, Mar. 6**

**849** A408 17c multicolored .30 .25
**850** A408 17c multicolored .30 .25
*a.* Pair, #849-850 .60 .55
**851** A408 35c multicolored .65 .50
**852** A408 35c multicolored .65 .50
*a.* Pair, #851-852 1.30 1.25
*Nos. 849-852 (4)* 1.90 1.50

Printed checkerwise.

Atlantic Whitefish — A409

Endangered wildlife. No. 854, Greater prairie chicken.

**1980, May 6** *Perf. 12½*

**853** A409 17c multicolored .35 .25
**854** A409 17c multicolored .35 .25

Garden — A410

**1980, May 29** *Perf. 13½*

**855** A410 17c multicolored .30 .25

Intl. Flower Show, Montreal, May 17-Sept. 1.

Helping Hands — A411

**Litho. & Embossed**

**1980, May 29** *Perf. 12½*

**856** A411 17c ultra & gold .30 .25

14th World Congress of Rehabilitation International, Winnipeg, June 22-27.

"O Canada" Opening Bars — A412

Composers Lavallee, Routhier, Weir — A413

**1980, June 6** **Litho.**

**857** A412 17c multicolored .30 .25
**858** A413 17c multicolored .30 .25
*a.* Pair, #857-858 .50 .50

"O Canada" centenary. Printed checkerwise in sheets of 16.

John George Diefenbaker (1895-1979), Prime Minister, 1956-63 — A414

**1980, June 20** **Engr.** *Perf. 13½*

**859** A414 17c dark blue .30 .25

Emma Albani (1847-1930), Soprano — A415

No. 861, Healey Willan (1880-1968), organist, composer. Printed checkerwise.

**1980, July 4** **Litho.**

**860** A415 17c multicolored .30 .25
**861** A415 17c multicolored .30 .25
*a.* Pair, #860-861 .50 .50

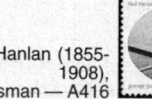

Ned Hanlan (1855-1908), Oarsman — A416

**1980, July 4**

**862** A416 17c multicolored .30 .25

Wheat Fields, Saskatchewan A417

No. 864, Strip farming and town, Alberta.

**1980, Aug. 27**

**863** A417 17c multicolored .30 .25
**864** A417 17c multicolored .30 .25

75th anniversary of Saskatchewan's and Alberta's creation as Provinces.

Uraninite Molecular Structure — A418

**1980, Sept. 3**

**865** A418 35c multicolored .65 .50
*a.* Printed on gummed side 950.00

Discovery of uranium in Canada, 80th anniversary.

Sedna, by Ashoona Kiawak A419

Return of the Sun, Print by Kenojouak A420

Works by Eskimo Artists: No. 868, Bird Spirit, by Doris Hagiolok. No. 869, Shaman, print by Simon Tookoome.

**1980, Sept. 25**

**866** A419 17c multicolored .30 .25
**867** A420 17c multicolored .30 .25
*a.* Pair, #866-867 .50 .50
**868** A419 35c multicolored .55 .55
**869** A420 35c multicolored .55 .55
*a.* Pair, #868-869 1.10 1.10
*b.* As No. 869, double impression of gray 625.00
*Nos. 866-869 (4)* 1.70 1.60

Inuit spirits. Printed checkerwise.

Christmas Morning, by Frank Charles Hennessey — A421

Christmas (Greeting Cards, 1931): 17c, Sleigh Ride, by Joseph Sydney Hallam. 35c, McGill Cab Stand, by Kathleen Morris.

**1980, Oct. 22** *Perf. 12½x12*

**870** A421 15c multicolored .30 .25
**871** A421 17c multicolored .30 .25
**872** A421 35c multicolored .55 .45
*Nos. 870-872 (3)* 1.15 .95

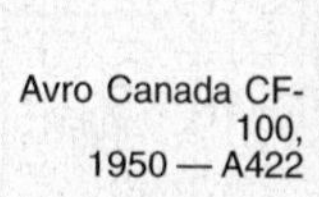

Avro Canada CF-100, 1950 — A422

Military Aircraft: No. 874, Avro Lancaster, 1941. No. 875, Curtiss JN-4 Canuck. No. 876, Hawker Hurricane, 1935.

**1980, Nov. 10** *Perf. 13x13½*

**873** A422 17c multicolored .30 .25
**874** A422 17c multicolored .30 .25
*a.* Pair, #873-874 .60 .55
**875** A422 35c multicolored .65 .55
**876** A422 35c multicolored .65 .55
*a.* Pair, #875-876 1.30 1.25
*Nos. 873-876 (4)* 1.90 1.60

Printed checkerwise.

Emmanuel-Persillier Lachapelle, Caduceus — A423

**1980, Dec. 5** *Perf. 13½*

**877** A423 17c multicolored .30 .25

Lachapelle (1845-1918), physician, founded Notre Dame Hospital, Montreal, 1880.

Mandora, 18th Century — A424

**1981, Jan. 19** *Perf. 12½*

**878** A424 17c multicolored .30 .25

"The Look of Music" rare musical instrument exhibition, Vancouver, Nov. 2, 1980-Apr. 5, 1981.

No. 878 exists printed on gummed side with gold color and tagging omitted, from printer's waste.

Emily Stowe (1831-1903) and Toronto General Hospital — A425

Designs: No. 880, Louise McKinney, (1868-1931) Alberta legislative building. No. 881, Idola Saint-Jean, (1875-1945) Quebec legislative building. No. 882, Henrietta Edwards, (1849-1931) clubwomen.

**1981, Mar. 4** *Perf. 13x13½*

**879** A425 17c multicolored .35 .25
**880** A425 17c multicolored .35 .25
**881** A425 17c multicolored .35 .25
**882** A425 17c multicolored .35 .25
*a.* Block of 4, #879-882 1.40 1.25

Vancouver Island Marmot, by Michael Dumas — A426

Endangered Wildlife: 35c, Wood bison, by Robert Bateman.

**1981, Apr. 6**

**883** A426 17c multicolored .30 .25
**884** A426 35c multicolored .70 .60

Kateri Tekakwitha ("Lily of the Mohawks"), by Emile Brunet — A427

Brunet Sculpture: No. 886, Marie de L'Incarnation.

**1981, Apr. 24** *Perf. 12½*

**885** A427 17c brown & pale grn .30 .25
**886** A427 17c dark blue & lt blue .30 .25
*a.* Pair, #885-886 .50 .50

Beatification of Kateri Tekakwitha (1656-1680), first North American Indian saint, and Marie De L'Incarnation (1599-1672), founder of Ursuline Order.

At Baie Saint-Paul, by Marc-Aurele Fortin (1888-1970) A428

Paintings: No. 888, Self-portrait, by Frederick H. Varley (1881-1969). 35c, Untitled No. 6, by Paul-Emile Borduas (1905-60).

**1981, May 22**

**887** A428 17c multi .30 .25
**888** A428 17c multi, vert. .30 .25
*a.* Imperf, pair *1,500.*

**Photo.**

*Perf. 13*

**889** A428 35c multi, vert. .60 .60
*Nos. 887-889 (3)* 1.20 1.10

Map of Canada Showing Provincial Boundaries, 1867 — A429

**1981, June 30** **Litho.** *Perf. 13½*

**890** A429 17c shown .30 .25
**891** A429 17c 1873 .30 .25
**892** A429 17c 1905 .30 .25
**893** A429 17c 1949 .30 .25
*a.* Strip of 4, #890-893 1.20 1.20

Canada Day.

Frere Marie-Victorin (1885-1944) Botanist — A430

Botanists: No. 895, John Macoun (1831-1920).

**1981, July 22** *Perf. 12½*

**894** A430 17c multicolored .30 .25
**895** A430 17c multicolored .30 .25
*a.* Pair, #894-895 .50 .50

Montreal Rose — A431

**1981, July 22** *Perf. 13½*
**896** A431 17c multicolored .30 .25

A432

**1981, July 31** **Photo. & Engr.**
**897** A432 17c multicolored .30 .25

Niagara-on-the-Lake (1st capital of Upper Canada).

A433

**1981, Aug. 14** **Litho.**
**898** A433 17c multicolored .30 .25

Acadian Congress centenary.

A434

**1981, Sept. 8**
**899** A434 17c multicolored .30 .25

Aaron Mosher (1881-1959), Labor Congress founder.

A435

**1981, Nov. 16** **Litho.**
**900** A435 15c 1781 .30 .25
**901** A435 15c 1881 .30 .25
**902** A435 15c 1981 .30 .25
*Nos. 900-902 (3)* .90 .75

Christmas; bicentenary of 1st illuminated Christmas tree in Canada.

Canadair CL-41 Tutor — A436

No. 904, de Havilland Tiger Moth. No. 905, Avro Canada C-102. No. 906, de Havilland Canada Dash-7.

**1981, Nov. 24** *Perf. 12½*
**903** A436 17c shown .30 .25
**904** A436 17c multicolored .30 .25
*a.* Pair, #903-904 .60 .55
**905** A436 35c multicolored .60 .55
**906** A436 35c multicolored .60 .55
*a.* Pair, #905-906 1.20 1.10
*Nos. 903-906 (4)* 1.80 1.60

A437

**1981, Dec. 29** **Engr.** *Perf. 13x13½*
**907** A437 (30c) red .90 .25
*a.* Printed on gummed side *750.00*

**Coil Stamp**
***Perf. 10 Vert.***
**908** A437 (30c) red .75 .25
*a.* Imperf., pair *275.00 225.00*

See Nos. 923-924, 940, 943-946, 950-951.

CANADA '82 Intl. Philatelic Youth Exhibition, Toronto, May 20-24 — A438

**1982** **Litho.** *Perf. 13½*
**909** A438 30c No. 1 .50 .25
**910** A438 30c No. 102 .50 .25
**911** A438 35c No. 223 .60 .50
**912** A438 35c No. 155 .60 .50
**913** A438 60c No. 158 1.20 .75
*a.* Souvenir sheet of 5, #909-913 3.75 3.75
*b.* As No. 913, triple impression of reddish brown *1,400.*
*Nos. 909-913 (5)* 3.40 2.25

Issued: Nos. 909, 911, 3/11; others, 5/20.

Jules Leger (1913-1980), 26th Governor General — A439

**1982, Apr. 2**
**914** A439 30c multicolored .45 .25

Terry Fox (1958-1981), Marathon of Hope — A440

**1982, Apr. 13** *Perf. 12½*
**915** A440 30c multicolored .50 .25

1982 Constitution — A441

**1982, Apr. 16** *Perf. 12x12½*
**916** A441 30c multicolored .50 .25

**Types of 1979-81 and**

18th-19th Cent. Artifacts A442

Parliament (Library) A443

Parliament (West Block) A444

Parliament (East Block) A445

Elizabeth II — A446

Designs: 1c, Duck decoy. 2c, Fishing spear. 3c, Stable lantern. 5c, Bucket. 10c, Weather-cock. 20c, Ice skates. 37c, Wooden plow. 39c, Settle-bed. 48c, Cradle. 50c, Sleigh. 64c, Wood stove. 68c, Spinning wheel. $1, Glacier National Park. $1.50, Waterton Lakes National Park. $2, Moraine Lake, Banff National Park. $5, Point Pelee National Park.

**1982-87** **Litho.** *Perf. 14x13½*
**917** A442 1c multicolored .30 .25
*a.* Perf. 13x13½ ('85) .30 .25
**918** A442 2c multicolored .30 .25
*a.* Perf. 13x13½ ('84) .30 .25
*b.* Bottom margin block of 4, bottom pair imperf, top pair part perf *1,750.*
*c.* As "a," printed on gummed side 50.00
**919** A442 3c multicolored .30 .25
*a.* Perf. 13x13½ ('85) .30 .25
**920** A442 5c multicolored .30 .25
*a.* Perf. 13x13½ ('84) .30 .25
**921** A442 10c multicolored .30 .25
*a.* Perf. 13x13½ ('85) .30 .25
**922** A442 20c multicolored .30 .25

The previously listed No. 922 variety with "brown omitted" has been determined to be a normal No. 922 with a color shade or a color changeling.

**Photo. & Engr.**
***Perf. 13x13½***
**923** A437 30c lt blue, bl, & red .50 .25
*a.* Bklt. pane of 20, perf. 12x12½ 10.00
*b.* Perf. 12x12½ 1.40 .45
**924** A437 32c beige, red & brn .50 .25
*a.* Bklt. pane of 25, perf. 12x12½ 12.50 *13.50*
*b.* Perf. 12x12½ 1.00 .70
*c.* As #924, beige (and tagging) omitted 900.00

**Litho.**
***Perf. 13½x13***
**925** A443 34c multicolored .55 .25
*a.* Booklet pane of 25 13.75
*b.* Perf. 13½x14 ('86) .75 .25
*c.* Bklt. pane of 25, perf. 13½x14 14.00 *16.50*

**Photo. & Engr.**
***Perf. 13x13½***
**926** A446 34c lt bl & int bl .55 .25
**926A** A446 36c plum 3.00 2.25

***Perf. 13½x13***
**926B** A443 36c multicolored .55 .25
*c.* Booklet pane of 10 #926Be 5.00
*d.* Booklet pane of 25 #926Be 12.50
*e.* Perf. 13½x14 ('87) .70 .25
*f.* Left margin block of 4, left vert. pair imperf, right pair part perf *1,400.*
*g.* Imperf., horiz. pair *525.00*
*h.* All color missing *1,400.*

No. 926Bh was caused by an extraneous piece of paper overlaying the pane during printing. Two such panes are recorded, one with two color-missing stamps and the other with 16 color-missing stamps. All adjoining stamps have some to most color missing, and if the panes are broken, the color-missing variety must be left se-tenant with a partially printed stamp.

**Litho.** *Perf. 12x12½*
**Size A442: 26x20mm**
**927** A442 37c multi .55 .25
**928** A442 39c multi .65 .25
**929** A442 48c multi .75 .30
**930** A442 50c multi .75 .25
**932** A442 64c multi .95 .35
**933** A442 68c multi 1.10 .35

**Litho. & Engr.**
***Perf. 13½***
**934** A359a $1 multi 1.60 .50
*a.* Blue inscriptions omitted *750.00*
*b.* Imperf., pair *3,000.*
**935** A359a $1.50 multi 3.25 .55
*a.* Black omitted *4,750.*
**936** A359a $2 multi 3.25 1.10
*a.* Bluish green inscriptions omitted *1,000.*
**937** A359a $5 multi 9.00 2.00
*Nos. 917-937 (22)* 29.30 10.90

Issued:1c-20c, 10/19; 30c, 5/11; $1.50, 6/18; $5, 1/10/83; 32c, 2/10/83; 37c, 48c, 64c, 4/8/83; $1, 8/15/84; No. 925, $2, 6/21/85; No. 926, 7/12/85; 39c, 50c, 68c, 8/1/85; No. 926B, 3/30/87; No. 926A, 10/1/87.

For former No. 931, see new No. 723C.

**Booklet Stamps**
***Perf. 12x12½ (A437), 12½x12***
**Engr.**
**938** A445 1c sage green ('87) .30 .25
**939** A444 2c myrtle grn ('85) .30 .25
*a.* 2c slate green ('89) .30 .25
**940** A437 5c deep claret .30 .25
**941** A445 5c dp brown ('85) .30 .25
**942** A444 6c henna brn ('87) .30 .25
**943** A437 8c dk blue ('83) .30 .25
**944** A437 10c dark green .45 .25
**945** A437 30c red .75 .30
*a.* Bklt. pane of 4 + 2 labels (2 #940, 944, 945) 1.20 *1.40*
**946** A437 32c brown ('83) .60 .25
*b.* Bklt. pane of 4 + 2 labels (2 #940, 943, 946) 1.10 *1.30*
**947** A443 34c dp slate bl ('85) 1.15 .70
*a.* Bklt. pane of 6 (3 #939, 2 #941, #947) 1.70 *1.25*
**948** A443 36c dark lil rose ('87) 1.35 .70
*a.* Bklt. pane of 5 + label (2 #938, 2 #942, #948) 2.25 *1.40*

Issued: No. 940, 10c, 30c, 3/1; 8c, 32c, 2/15/83; No. 941, 30c, 6/21/85; 1c, 6c, 36c, 3/30/87.

**Coil Stamps**
**Engr.** *Perf. 10 Vert.*
**950** A437 30c red .90 .25
*a.* Imperf., pair 325.00
**951** A437 32c brown ('83) .75 .25
*a.* Imperf., pair 160.00

***Perf. 10 Horiz.***
**952** A443 34c dull red brn ('85) .75 .25
*a.* Imperf., pair 135.00
**953** A443 36c dark red ('87) .75 .25
*a.* Imperf., pair 250.00

Issued: 30c, 5/11; 32c, 2/10/83; 34c, 8/1/85; 36c, 5/19/87.

See Nos. 1080-1083, 1186-1188, 1194-1194A.

Centenary of Salvation Army in Canada — A457

**1982, June 25** **Litho.** *Perf. 13*
**954** A457 30c multicolored .50 .25

Canada Day — A458

Paintings: No. 955, The Highway near Kluana Lake, by A.Y. Jackson. No. 956, Montreal Street Scene, by Adrien Hebert. No. 957, Breakwater, by Christopher Pratt. No. 958, Along Great Slave Lake, by Rene Richard. No. 959, Tea Hill, by Molly Lamb. No. 960, Family and Rainstorm, by Alex Colville. No. 961, Brown Shadows, by Dorothy Knowles. No. 962, The Red Brick House, by David Milne. No. 963, Campus Gates, by Bruno Bobak. No. 964, Prairie Town—Early Morning, by Illingworth Kerr. No. 965, Totems at Ninstints, by Joe Plaskett. No. 966, Doc Snider's House, by Lionel LeMoine FitzGerald.

**1982, June 30** *Perf. 12½x12*
**955** A458 30c multicolored .65 .65
**956** A458 30c multicolored .65 .65
**957** A458 30c multicolored .65 .65
**958** A458 30c multicolored .65 .65
**959** A458 30c multicolored .65 .65
**960** A458 30c multicolored .65 .65
**961** A458 30c multicolored .65 .65
**962** A458 30c multicolored .65 .65
**963** A458 30c multicolored .65 .65
**964** A458 30c multicolored .65 .65
**965** A458 30c multicolored .65 .65
**966** A458 30c multicolored .65 .65
*a.* Min. pane of 12, #955-966 8.00 8.00

Regina Centenary A459

**1982, Aug. 3** *Perf. 13½x13*
**967** A459 30c multicolored .50 .25

A460

Design: Centenary of Royal Canadian Henley Regatta, St. Catharines, Aug. 4-8.

**1982, Aug. 4**
**968** A460 30c multicolored .50 .25

Fairchild FC-2W1 — A461

No. 970, De Havilland Canada Beaver. No. 971, Noorduyn Norseman. No. 972, Fokker Super Universal.

**1982, Oct. 5 Litho. *Perf. 12½***

**969** A461 30c shown .75 .25
**970** A461 30c multicolored .75 .25
*a.* Pair, #969-970 1.50 1.10
**971** A461 60c multicolored 1.10 .75
**972** A461 60c multicolored 1.10 .75
*a.* Pair, #971-972 2.20 1.75
*Nos. 969-972 (4)* 3.70 2.00

Christmas — A462

Designs: Creche figures.

**1982, Nov. 3 *Perf. 13½***

**973** A462 30c Holy Family .45 .25
*a.* All colors except black omitted *11,000.*
*b.* Printed on gummed side, black omitted *11,000.*
**974** A462 35c Shepherds .55 .45
**975** A462 60c Three Kings .90 .75
*Nos. 973-975 (3)* 1.90 1.45

Nos. 973a and 973b were caused by a paper foldover.

World Communications Year — A463

**1983, Mar. 10 Litho. *Perf. 12x12½***

**976** A463 32c multicolored .50 .25
*a.* Double impression of central multicolored globe 750.00

Commonwealth Day — A464

**1983, Mar. 14**

**977** A464 $2 multicolored 9.00 3.75

Scene from Angeline de Montbrun, by Laure Conan (1845-1924), Painted by Rene Milot — A465

Design: No. 979, Sea Gulls, by Edwin John Pratt (1882-1966), woodcut by Claire Pratt.

**1983, Apr. 22 Litho. *Perf. 13½***

**978** A465 32c multicolored .50 .25
**979** A465 32c multicolored .50 .25
*a.* Pair, #978-979 1.00 .90
*b.* As "a," all color missing *7,500.*

No. 979b resulted from an extraneous piece of paper receiving the colors. After removal, the issued pane shows two horizontal pairs without color plus six other stamps with only partial color.

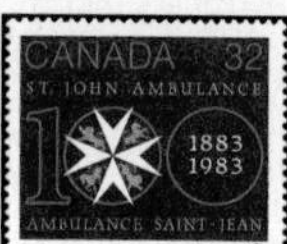

St. John Ambulance Centenary — A466

**1983, June 3 *Perf. 13½***

**980** A466 32c Emblem .50 .25

World University Games, Edmonton, July 1-11 — A467

**1983, June 28 *Perf. 13½***

**981** A467 32c multicolored .50 .25
*a.* Printed on gummed side 900.00
**982** A467 64c multicolored 1.10 .75

Canada Day — A468

No. 983, Fort Henry, Ontario. No. 984, Fort William, Ontario. No. 985, Fort Rodd Hill, British Columbia. No. 986, Fort Wellington, Ontario. No. 987, Fort Prince of Wales, Manitoba. No. 988, Halifax Citadel, Nova Scotia. No. 989, Fort Chambly, Quebec. No. 990, Fort No. 1, Point Levis, Quebec. No. 991, Fort at Coteau-du-Lac, Quebec. No. 992, Fort Beausejour, New Brunswick. Sizes: Nos. 983, 988: 44x22mm; Nos. 984-985, 989-990, 36x22mm; Nos. 986-987, 991-992, 28x22mm.

### Booklet Stamps

**1983, June 30 *Perf. 12½x13***

**983** A468 32c multicolored .75 .75
**984** A468 32c multicolored .75 .75
**985** A468 32c multicolored .75 .75
**986** A468 32c multicolored .75 .75
**987** A468 32c multicolored .75 .75
**988** A468 32c multicolored .75 .75
**989** A468 32c multicolored .75 .75
**990** A468 32c multicolored .75 .75
**991** A468 32c multicolored .75 .75
**992** A468 32c multicolored .75 .75
*a.* Booklet pane of 10, #983-992 7.50 7.50

Scouting Year — A469

**1983, July 6 *Perf. 13½***

**993** A469 32c multicolored .50 .25
*a.* Red omitted —

Church Council Emblem — A470

**1983, July 22 Litho.**

**994** A470 32c tan & green .50 .25

6th World Council of Churches Assembly, Vancouver, July 24-Aug. 10.

Humphrey Gilbert — A471

**1983, Aug. 3 Litho.**

**995** A471 32c multicolored .50 .25

400th anniv. of discovery of Newfoundland by Sir Humphrey Gilbert (1537-1583).

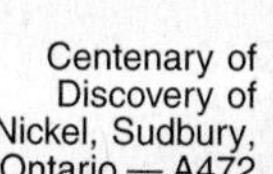

Centenary of Discovery of Nickel, Sudbury, Ontario — A472

**Litho. & Typo.**

**1983, Aug. 12 *Perf. 13***

**996** A472 32c multicolored .55 .25
*a.* Silver (and tagging) omitted *625.00*

Beware of forgeries of No. 996a. A certificate of authenticity is mandatory.

Josiah Henson (1789-1883), Preacher — A473

**1983, Sept. 16 Litho. *Perf. 13x13½***

**997** A473 32c multicolored .50 .25

Antoine Labelle (1833-1891), Deputy Minister for Settlement — A474

**1983, Sept. 16 *Perf. 13½***

**998** A474 32c multicolored .50 .25

Locomotives A475

No. 999, Toronto 4-4-0, 1853. No. 1000, Dorchester 0-4-0, 1836. No. 1001, Samson 0-6-0, 1838. No. 1002, Adam Brown 4-4-0, 1860.

**1983, Oct. 3 *Perf. 12½x13***

**999** A475 32c multicolored .50 .25
**1000** A475 32c multicolored .50 .25
*a.* Pair, #999-1000 1.00 .90
**1001** A475 37c multicolored .60 .60
**1002** A475 64c multicolored 1.10 .90
*Nos. 999-1002 (4)* 2.70 2.00

Dalhousie Law School Centenary A476

**1983, Oct. 28 *Perf. 13***

**1003** A476 32c Arms .50 .25

Christmas — A477

32c, Urban church. 37c, Family going to church. 64c, Rural church.

**1983, Nov. 3 *Perf. 13½***

**1004** A477 32c multicolored .50 .25
**1005** A477 37c multicolored .55 .45
**1006** A477 64c multicolored 1.00 .75
*Nos. 1004-1006 (3)* 2.05 1.45

Army Regiments, Centenaries — A478

19th Cent. Uniforms: No. 1007, Royal Canadian Regiment, British Columbia Regiment. No. 1008, Royal Winnipeg Rifles, Royal Canadian Dragoons.

**1983, Nov. 10 *Perf. 13½x13***

**1007** A478 32c shown .50 .25
**1008** A478 32c multicolored .50 .25
*a.* Pair, #1007-1008 1.00 .90

Yellowknife, 50th Anniv. — A479

**1984, Mar. 15 *Perf. 13½***

**1009** A479 32c Gold mine .50 .25

50th Anniv. of Montreal Symphony Orchestra — A480

**1984, Mar. 24 *Perf. 12½***

**1010** A480 32c multicolored .50 .25

450th Anniv. of Cartier's Landing in Quebec — A481

**1984, Apr. 20 Photo. & Engr.**

**1011** A481 32c multicolored .50 .25

See France No. 1923.

Voyage of Tall Ships, Saint-Malo, France, to Quebec City — A482

**1984, May 18 Litho. *Perf. 12x12½***

**1012** A482 32c multicolored .50 .25

450th anniv. of Cartier's landing in Quebec.

Canadian Red Cross Society, 75th Anniv. — A483

32c, Meritorious Service Medal.

**1984, May 28 *Perf. 13***

**1013** A483 32c multicolored .50 .25

New Brunswick, Bicentenary — A484

**1984, June 18 Photo. & Engr.**

**1014** A484 32c Galleys .50 .25

St. Lawrence Seaway, 25th Anniv. A485

32c, Seaway, Lake Superior.

**1984, June 26 Litho.**

**1015** A485 32c multicolored .50 .25

Canada Day — A486

Provincial Landscapes by Jean Paul Lemieux (b. 1904): No. 1016, New Brunswick. No. 1017, British Columbia. No. 1018, Yukon Territory. No. 1019, Quebec. No. 1020, Manitoba. No. 1021, Alberta. No. 1022, Prince Edward Island. No. 1023, Saskatchewan. No. 1024, Nova Scotia, vert. No. 1025, Northwest Territories. No. 1026, Newfoundland. No. 1027, Ontario, vert.

**1984, June 29**

**1016** A486 32c multicolored .55 .40
**1017** A486 32c multicolored .55 .40
**1018** A486 32c multicolored .55 .40
**1019** A486 32c multicolored .55 .40
**1020** A486 32c multicolored .55 .40
**1021** A486 32c multicolored .55 .40
**1022** A486 32c multicolored .55 .40
**1023** A486 32c multicolored .55 .40

**1024** A486 32c multicolored .55 .40
**1025** A486 32c multicolored .55 .40
**1026** A486 32c multicolored .55 .40
**1027** A486 32c multicolored .55 .40
*a.* Min. pane of 12, #1016-1027 6.75 6.25

Nos. 1018 and 1025 incorrectly inscribed. No. 1018 shows Northwest Territories landscape; No. 1025, Yukon Territory church.

Loyalists, British Flag (1606-1801) A487

**1984, July 3**
**1028** A487 32c multicolored .50 .25

United Empire Loyalists, American colonists who remained loyal to British throne and immigrated to Canada during American Revolution.

Roman Catholic Church in Newfoundland — A488

32c, St. John's Basilica.

**1984, Aug. 17** ***Perf. 13½***
**1029** A488 32c multicolored .50 .25

Papal Visit — A489

**1984, Aug. 31** ***Perf. 12½***
**1030** A489 32c multicolored .50 .25
**1031** A489 64c multicolored 1.10 .65

Lighthouses A490

No. 1032, Louisbourg, 1734. No. 1033, Fisgard, 1860. No. 1034, Ile Verte, 1809. No. 1035, Gibraltar Point, 1808.

**1984, Sept. 21**
**1032** A490 32c multicolored .55 .25
**1033** A490 32c multicolored .55 .25
**1034** A490 32c multicolored .55 .25
**1035** A490 32c multicolored .55 .25
*a.* Block of 4, #1032-1035 2.20 1.20

Steam Locomotives — A491

No. 1036, Scotia. No. 1037, Countess of Dufferin. No. 1038, Grand Trunk Class E3. No. 1039, Canadian Pacific D10a.

**1984, Oct. 25** ***Perf. 12½x13***
**1036** A491 32c multicolored .50 .25
**1037** A491 32c multicolored .50 .25
*a.* Pair, #1036-1037 1.00 .90
**1038** A491 37c multicolored .75 .65
**1039** A491 64c multicolored 1.30 .90
*a.* Souvenir sheet 3.00 3.00
*Nos. 1036-1039 (4)* 3.05 2.05

No. 1039a contains Nos. 1036-1039 in changed colors.
See Nos. 1071-1074, 1118-1121.

Christmas — A492

Paintings: 32c, The Annunciation, by Jean Dallaire. 37c, The Three Kings, by Simone Mary Bouchard. 64c, Snow in Bethlehem, by David Milne.

**1984, Nov. 2** ***Perf. 13***
**1040** A492 32c multicolored .50 .25
**1041** A492 37c multicolored .55 .55
**1042** A492 64c multicolored 1.00 .75
*Nos. 1040-1042 (3)* 2.05 1.55

Royal Canadian Air Force — A493

**1984, Nov. 9** ***Perf. 12x12½***
**1043** A493 32c Pilots .50 .25

Cent. of La Presse — A494

32c, Treffle Berthiaume.

**1984, Nov. 16** ***Perf. 13x13½***
**1044** A494 32c multicolored .50 .25

Heart, Arrow, Jeans — A495

**1985, Feb. 8** ***Perf. 12½***
**1045** A495 32c multicolored .50 .25

International Youth Year.

Canadians in Space — A496

**1985, Mar. 15** ***Perf. 13½***
**1046** A496 32c Astronaut .55 .25

Therese Casgrain (1896-1981), Suffragist A497

Emily Murphy (1868-1933), Writer A498

**1985, Apr. 17**
**1047** A497 32c multicolored .50 .25
**1048** A498 32c multicolored .50 .25
*a.* Pair, #1047-1048 1.00 .90

Gabriel Dumont (1837-1906), Metis Leader — A499

**1985, May 6** ***Perf. 13***
**1049** A499 32c multicolored .50 .25

Centenary of the Northwest Rebellion.

Canada Day — A500

No. 1050, Lower Ft. Garry, Manitoba. No. 1051, Ft. Anne, Nova Scotia. No. 1052, Ft. York, Ontario. No. 1053, Castle Hill, Newfoundland. No. 1054, Ft. Whoop Up, Alberta. No. 1055, Ft. Erie, Ontario. No. 1056, Ft. Walsh, Saskatchewan. No. 1057, Ft. Lennox, Quebec. No. 1058, York Redoubt, Nova Scotia. No. 1059, Ft. Frederick, Ontario.

Sizes: Nos. 1050, 1055: 48x26mm. Nos. 1051-1052, 1056-1057: 40x26mm. Nos. 1053-1054, 1058-1059, 32x26mm.

### Booklet Stamps

**1985, June 28** ***Perf. 12½x13***
**1050** A500 34c multicolored .95 .65
**1051** A500 34c multicolored .95 .65
**1052** A500 34c multicolored .95 .65
**1053** A500 34c multicolored .95 .65
**1054** A500 34c multicolored .95 .65
**1055** A500 34c multicolored .95 .65
**1056** A500 34c multicolored .95 .65
**1057** A500 34c multicolored .95 .65
**1058** A500 34c multicolored .95 .65
**1059** A500 34c multicolored .95 .65
*a.* Bklt. pane of 10, #1050-1059 9.50 *12.50*

Intl. Pharmaceutical Federation Congress — A501

Design: Louis Hebert (1575-1627), 1st French Apothecary in North America.

**1985, Aug. 30** ***Perf. 12½***
**1060** A501 34c multicolored .55 .25

Interparliamentary Union '85, Ottawa — A502

**1985, Sept. 3** ***Perf. 13½***
**1061** A502 34c multicolored .55 .25

Guide, Brownie Saluting — A503

**1985, Sept. 12 Photo.** ***Perf. 13½x13***
**1062** A503 34c multicolored .55 .25

Natl. Girl Guides movement, cent.

Lighthouses A504

**1985, Oct. 3 Litho.** ***Perf. 13½***
**1063** A504 34c Sisters Islets .75 .25
**1064** A504 34c Pelee Passage .75 .25
**1065** A504 34c Haut-fond Prince .75 .25
**1066** A504 34c Rose Blanche .75 .25
*a.* Block of 4, #1063-1066 3.00 2.50
*b.* Souv. sheet of 4, #1063-1066 4.75 4.75

Santa Claus Parade — A505

Paintings by Barbara Carroll: 34c, Santa Claus. 39c, Horse-drawn coach. 68c, Christmas tree. No. 1070, 32c, Polar float.

**1985, Oct. 23**
**1067** A505 34c multicolored .55 .25
**1068** A505 39c multicolored .65 .55
**1069** A505 68c multicolored 1.25 .90

***Perf. 13½ on 3 Sides***

**1070** A505 32c multicolored 1.10 .50
*a.* Booklet pane of 10 11.00 10.00
*Nos. 1067-1070 (4)* 3.55 2.20

No. 1070 printed in booklets only.

### Locomotives Type of 1984

No. 1071, Grand Trunk K2. No. 1072, Canadian Pacific P2a. No. 1073, Canadian Northern O10a. No. 1074, Canadian Govt. Railways H4D.

**1985, Nov. 7** ***Perf. 12½x13***
**1071** A491 34c multicolored .75 .25
**1072** A491 34c multicolored .75 .25
*a.* Pair, #1071-1072 1.50 1.10
**1073** A491 39c multicolored .75 .70
**1074** A491 68c multicolored 1.30 1.00
*Nos. 1071-1074 (4)* 3.55 2.20

1910 Gunner's Mate, World War II Officer, 1985 Woman Recruit — A507

**1985, Nov. 8** ***Perf. 13½x13***
**1075** A507 34c multicolored .55 .25

Royal Canadian Navy, 75th anniv.

A508

Design: 34c, Old Holton House, Sherbrooke Street, Montreal, by James Wilson Morrice (1865-1924).

**1985, Nov. 15** ***Perf. 13½***
**1076** A508 34c multicolored .55 .25

Montreal Museum of Fine Arts, 120th anniv.

Southwestern Alberta, Computer Design Map — A509

**1986, Feb. 13 Litho.** ***Perf. 12½x13***
**1077** A509 34c multicolored .55 .25

1988 Winter Olympics, Calgary, Alberta, Feb. 13-28.

EXPO '86, Vancouver, May 2-Oct. 13 — A510

**1986, Mar. 7** **Photo. & Engr.**
**1078** A510 34c Canada Pavilion .55 .25
**1079** A510 39c Communications .65 .55

### Artifacts Type of 1982

Designs: 25c Butter stamp. 42c, Linen chest. 55c, Iron kettle. 72c, Hand-drawn cart.

**1987, May 6 Litho.** ***Perf. 14x13½***
**1080** A442 25c multicolored .55 .30

**Size: 20x26mm**

***Perf. 12x12½***

**1081** A442 42c multicolored 1.10 .25
**1082** A442 55c multicolored 1.40 .30
**1083** A442 72c multicolored 1.75 .35
*a.* Imperf., pair 800.00
*Nos. 1080-1083 (4)* 4.80 1.20

### Park Type of 1979

Design: La Mauricie National Park.

**Litho. & Engr.**

**1986, Mar. 14** ***Perf. 13½***
**1084** A359a $5 multi 9.00 2.00
*a.* Dark blue inscriptions omitted *2,500. 1,500.*

No. 1084a is valued in the grade of fine as all known examples are centered thus.

Philippe Aubert de Gaspe (1786-1871), Novelist A511

Molly Brant (1736-1796), Iroquois Leader and Loyalist A512

**1986, Apr. 14 Litho. *Perf. 12½***

**1090** A511 34c multicolored .55 .25

***Perf. 13½***

**1091** A512 34c multicolored .55 .25

EXPO '86 — A513

34c, Expo Center, Vancouver. 68c, Transportation, horiz.

**Photo. & Engr.**

**1986, Apr. 28 *Perf. 13x13½***

**1092** A513 34c multicolored .55 .25
**1093** A513 68c multicolored 1.10 .70

Canadian Forces Postal Service, 75th Anniv. — A514

**1986, May 9 Litho. *Perf. 13½***

**1094** A514 34c multicolored .55 .25

Indigenous Birds — A515

**1986, May 22**

**1095** A515 34c Great blue heron .70 .30
**1096** A515 34c Snow goose .70 .30
**1097** A515 34c Great horned owl .70 .30
**1098** A515 34c Spruce grouse .70 .30
*a.* Block of 4, #1095-1098 2.80 2.50

19th Intl. Ornithological Congress, Ottawa, June 22-29.

Canada Day — A516

Invention blueprints: No. 1099, Rotary snowplow, 1869. No. 1100, Canadarm, 1986. No. 1101, Anti-gravity flight suit, 1938. No. 1102, Variable pitch propeller, 1923.

**1986, June 27**

**1099** A516 34c multicolored .75 .25
**1100** A516 34c multicolored .75 .25
**1101** A516 34c multicolored .75 .25
**1102** A516 34c multicolored .75 .25
*a.* Block of 4, #1099-1102 3.00 2.50

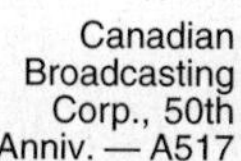

Canadian Broadcasting Corp., 50th Anniv. — A517

**1986, July 23 *Perf. 12½***

**1103** A517 34c Emblem, map .55 .25

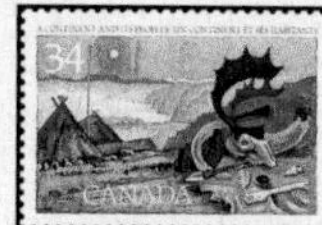

Exploration of Canada — A518

No. 1104, Siberian Indians discover and inhabit America, 10,000 B.C. No. 1105, Viking settlement, A.D. 1000. No. 1106, John Cabot lands, 1498. No. 1107, Henry Hudson pioneers Hudson Strait and Bay, 1610.

**1986, Aug. 29 *Perf. 12½x13***

**1104** A518 34c multicolored .55 .30
**1105** A518 34c multicolored .55 .30
**1106** A518 34c multicolored .55 .30
**1107** A518 34c multicolored .55 .30
*a.* Block of 4, #1104-1107 2.20 2.00
*b.* Souv. sheet of 4, #1104-1107 3.00 2.50

No. 1107b issued Oct. 1 for CAPEX '87.

See Nos. 1126-1129, 1199-1202, 1233-1236.

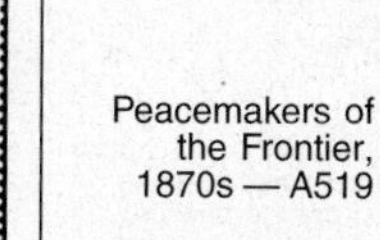

Peacemakers of the Frontier, 1870s — A519

Designs: No. 1108, Crowfoot (1830-1890), Blackfoot Indian chief. No. 1109, James F. Macleod (1836-1894), asst. commissioner of Northwest Mounted Police.

**1986, Sept. 5 *Perf. 13x13½***

**1108** A519 34c scar, gray & ind .55 .25
**1109** A519 34c ind, gray & scar .55 .25
*a.* Pair, #1108-1109 1.10 .90

Intl. Peace Year — A520

**Litho. & Embossed**

**1986, Sept. 16 *Perf. 13½***

**1110** A520 34c multicolored .55 .25

1988 Calgary Winter Olympics — A521

**1986, Oct. 15 *Perf. 13½x13***

**1111** A521 34c Ice hockey .55 .25
**1112** A521 34c Biathlon .55 .25
*a.* Pair, #1111-1112 1.10 .90

See Nos. 1130-1131, 1152-1153, 1195-1198.

Christmas Angels — A522

**1986, Oct. 29 *Perf. 12½***

**1113** A522 34c multicolored .55 .25
**1114** A522 39c multicolored .65 .55
**1115** A522 68c multicolored 1.10 .80

**Booklet Stamps**

**Size: 72x26mm**

***Perf. 13½ Horiz.***

**1116** A522 29c multicolored 1.40 1.10
*a.* Booklet pane of 10 14.00 13.00
*b.* Perf. 12½ horiz. 6.00 2.25
*c.* Bklt. pane of 10, #1116b 60.00 52.50
*Nos. 1113-1116 (4)* 3.70 2.70

No. 1116 has bar code at left, for use on covers with printed postal code matrix.

John Molson (1763-1836), Entrepreneur A523

**1986, Nov. 4**

**1117** A523 34c multicolored .55 .25

**Locomotives Type of 1984**

Locomotives, 1925-1945.

**1986, Nov. 21 *Perf. 12½x13***

**1118** A491 34c CN V1a .75 .30
**1119** A491 34c CP T1a .75 .30
*a.* Pair, #1118-1119 1.50 1.10
**1120** A491 39c CN U2a .90 .75
**1121** A491 68c CP H1c 1.30 1.10
*Nos. 1118-1121 (4)* 3.70 2.45

CAPEX '87 — A524

34c, 1st Toronto P.O. 36c, Nelson-Miramichi P.O. 42c, Saint Ours P.O. 72c, Battleford P.O.

**1987 Litho. & Engr. *Perf. 13x13½***

**1122** A524 34c multicolored .55 .25
**1123** A524 36c multicolored .60 .25
**1124** A524 42c multicolored .75 .65
**1125** A524 72c multicolored 1.30 1.10
*Nos. 1122-1125 (4)* 3.20 2.25

**Souvenir Sheet**

**Yellow Green Inscription**

**1125A** Sheet of 4 3.25 3.25
*b.* A524 36c like #1122 .65 .65
*c.* A524 36c like #1123 .65 .65
*d.* A524 42c like #1124 .75 .75
*e.* A524 72c like #1125 1.20 1.20

Issue dates: 34c, Feb. 16; others, June 12.

**Exploration Type of 1986**

Pioneers of New France: No. 1126, Etienne Brule (c. 1592-1633), 1st European to see the Great Lakes. No. 1127, Pierre Esprit Radisson (c. 1636-1710) & Medard Chouart des Groseilliers 1625-98), British expedition to Hudson Bay, 1668. No. 1128, Louis Jolliet (1645-1700) & Fr. Jacques Marquette (1637-75) discovering the Mississippi River, 1673. No. 1129, Recollet wilderness mission, 1615.

**1987, Mar. 13 Litho. *Perf. 12½x13***

**1126** A518 34c multicolored .55 .30
**1127** A518 34c multicolored .55 .30
**1128** A518 34c multicolored .55 .30
**1129** A518 34c multicolored .55 .30
*a.* Block of 4, #1126-1129 2.20 2.00

**Olympics Type of 1986**

**1987, Apr. 3 *Perf. 13½x13***

**1130** A521 36c Speed skating .60 .25
**1131** A521 42c Bobsledding .75 .65

Volunteers Week — A525

**1987, Apr. 13 *Perf. 12½x13***

**1132** A525 36c multicolored .60 .25

Law Day — A526

**1987, Apr. 15 *Perf. 14x13½***

**1133** A526 36c Coat of arms .60 .25
*a.* Imperf, pair *1,350.*

Canadian Charter of Rights and Freedoms, 5th anniv.

Engineering Institute of Canada, Cent. — A527

**1987, May 19 *Perf. 12½x13***

**1134** A527 36c multicolored .60 .25

Canada Day — A528

Inventors & communications innovations: No. 1135, Reginald Aubrey Fessenden (1866-1932), AM radio, 1900. No. 1136, Charles Fenerty, newsprint, 1838. No. 1137, Georges-Edouard Desbarats and William Leggo, half-tone engraving, 1869. No. 1138, Frederick Newton Gisborne, No. America's 1st undersea cable, 1852, New Brunswick-Prince Edward Island.

**1987, June 25 *Perf. 13½***

**1135** A528 36c multicolored .65 .30
**1136** A528 36c multicolored .65 .30
**1137** A528 36c multicolored .65 .30
**1138** A528 36c multicolored .65 .30
*a.* Block of 4, #1135-1138 2.60 2.40

Steamships A529

No. 1139, Segwun, 1887. No. 1140, Princess Marguerite, 1948.

**1987, July 20 *Perf. 13½x13***

**1139** A529 36c multicolored .60 .30

**51x22mm**

**1140** A529 36c multicolored .60 .30
*a.* Pair, #1139-1140 1.20 1.00

Shipwrecks A530

No. 1141, Hamilton & Scourge, 1813. No. 1142, San Juan, 1565. No. 1143, Breadalbane, 1853. No. 1144, Ericsson, 1892.

**1987, Aug. 7**

**1141** A530 36c multicolored .60 .30
**1142** A530 36c multicolored .60 .30
**1143** A530 36c multicolored .60 .30
**1144** A530 36c multicolored .60 .30
*a.* Block of 4, #1141-1144 2.40 2.20

Air Canada, 50th Anniv. — A531

**1987, Sept. 1 *Perf. 13½***

**1145** A531 36c multicolored .60 .25

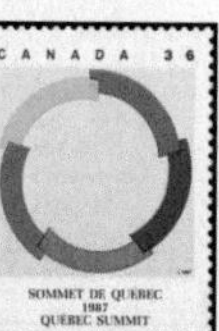

2nd Intl. Francophone Summit, Quebec, 9/2-4 — A532

**1987, Sept. 2 *Perf. 13x12½***

**1146** A532 36c multicolored .60 .25

9th Commonwealth Meeting, Vancouver, Oct. 13-17 — A533

**1987, Oct. 13**

**1147** A533 36c multicolored .60 .25

Christmas — A534

36c, Poinsettia. 42c, Holly wreath. 72c, Mistletoe, Christmas tree. 31c, Gifts, Christmas tree.

**1987, Nov. 2 Litho. *Perf. 13½***

**1148** A534 36c multicolored .65 .25
**1149** A534 42c multicolored .75 .65
**1150** A534 72c multicolored 1.20 .90

**Size: 39x25mm**

**1151** A534 31c multicolored .75 .75
*a.* Booklet pane of 10 7.50 *10.00*
*b.* Imperf. btwn., pair, from miscut bklt. pane *2,500.*
*Nos. 1148-1151 (4)* 3.35 2.55

No. 1151 has bar code at left, for use on covers with printed postal code matrix. Issued in booklets only.

**Olympics Type of 1986**

No. 1152, Cross-country skiing. No. 1153, Ski jumping.

**1987, Nov. 13 *Perf. 13½x13***

**1152** A521 36c multicolored .60 .25
**1153** A521 36c multicolored .60 .25
*a.* Pair, #1152-1153 1.20 .90

75th Grey Cup, Vancouver, Nov. 29 — A535

**1987, Nov. 20 *Perf. 12½***

**1154** A535 36c multicolored .60 .25

**Types of 1982 and**

Queen Elizabeth II A536

Mammals A538

Parliament (Center Block)
A537 A539

Architecture A540

Flag and Clouds A541

Flag A542

Natl. Flag, Deciduous Forest A543



Flag and Mountains — A544

Designs: No. 1155, Flying squirrel. 2c, Prickly porcupine. 3c, Muskrat. No. 1158, Varying hare. No. 1159, Red fox. 10c, Skunk. 25c, Beaver. 43c, Lynx. 44c, Walrus. 45c, Pronghorn. 46c, Wolverine. 57c, Killer whale. 59c, Musk-ox. 61c, Timber wolf. 63c, Harbor porpoise. 74c, Wapiti. 76c, Grizzly bear. 78c, Beluga whale. 80c, Peary caribou. $1, Runnymede Library, Toronto. $2, McAdam Railway Station, New Brunswick. $5, Bonsecours Market, Montreal. No. 1192, Flag and field. No. 1193, Flag and seacoast.

**Sizes Vary on A536, A538**

**1987-91 Litho. *Perf. 13x13½***

**1155** A538 1c multicolored .30 .25
*a.* Perf. 13x12½ *4.00* .85
*b.* Imperf, pair *700.00*
**1156** A538 2c multicolored .30 .25
*a.* Imperf, pair *700.00*
**1157** A538 3c multicolored .30 .25
*a.* Imperf, pair *850.00*
**1158** A538 5c multicolored .30 .25
*a.* Imperf, pair *1,500.*
**1159** A538 6c multicolored .30 .25
*a.* Horiz. pair, imperf *2,250.*
**1160** A538 10c multicolored .30 .25
*a.* Perf. 13x12½ 6.00 .40
*b.* Imperf., pair *700.00*
**1161** A538 25c multicolored .40 .25

***Perf. 13½x13***

**1162** A536 37c multicolored .75 .25
**1163** A537 37c multicolored .75 .25
*a.* Bklt. pane of 10, #1163c 7.50 7.50
*b.* Bklt. pane of 25, #1163c 19.00 17.50
*c.* Perf. 13½x14 1.40 .40

***Perf. 13x12½***

**1164** A536 38c multicolored .75 .25
*a.* Perf. 13x13½ .75 .35
*b.* As "a," bklt. pane of 10 + 2 labels 7.50 7.00
*c.* Vert. block of 10, middle pair imperf, 2nd and 4th pairs part perf *900.00*
*d.* As "a," horiz. pair, imperf btwn. *850.00*
*e.* Bottom margin horiz. pair, imperf —

***Perf. 13x13½ on 3 or 4 Sides***

**1165** A539 38c multicolored .75 .25
*a.* Bklt. pane of 10 + 2 labels 5.50 7.50
*b.* Bklt. pane of 25 + 2 labels 12.50 19.00
*c.* Printed on gummed side 90.00
*d.* Double impression of all litho colors except black 225.00

***Perf. 13½x13***

**1166** A541 39c multicolored .75 .25
*a.* Bklt. pane of 10 + 2 labels 7.50
*b.* Bklt. pane of 25 + 2 labels 19.00
*c.* Perf. 12½x13 18.00 .75
*d.* Imperf, pair *525.00*

***Perf. 13x13½***

**1167** A536 39c multicolored .75 .25
*a.* Bklt. pane of 10 + 2 labels 7.50 7.50
*b.* Perf. 13 15.00 .85
*c.* Imperf, pair *500.00*
*d.* Horiz. pair, imperf btwn. *325.00*
**1168** A536 40c multicolored .75 .25
*a.* Bklt. pane of 10 + 2 labels 7.50 7.00

***Perf. 13½x13***

**1169** A544 40c multicolored .75 .25
*a.* Bklt. pane of 25 + 2 labels 25.00
*b.* Bklt. pane of 10 + 2 labels 7.50

***Perf. 12x12½***

**1170** A538 43c multicolored 1.10 .40

***Perf. 14½x14***

**1171** A538 44c multicolored 1.40 .25
*a.* Perf. 12½x13 2.75 1.75
*b.* As "a," bklt. pane of 5 + label 12.50 11.50
*c.* Perf. 13½x13 400.00 400.00
**1172** A538 45c multicolored .90 .25
*b.* As "f," bklt. pane of 5 + label 10.00 9.00
*d.* Perf. 13 20.00 1.20
*f.* Perf. 12½x13 2.60 .50
*h.* Imperf., pair *750.00*

***Perf. 13***

**1172A** A538 46c multicolored .90 .25
*c.* Perf. 12½x13 1.25 .50
*e.* As "c," bklt. pane of 5 + label 5.50 5.00
*g.* Perf. 14½x14 5.25 .40

***Perf. 12x12½***

**1173** A538 57c multicolored 1.10 .35

***Perf. 14½x14***

**1174** A538 59c multicolored 1.20 .30
*a.* Perf. 13 10.00 2.50
**1175** A538 61c multicolored 1.20 .35
*a.* Perf. 13 80.00 6.50
**1176** A538 63c multicolored 3.00 .40
*a.* Perf. 13 6.50 3.00

***Perf. 12x12½***

**1177** A538 74c multicolored 1.90 .75

***Perf. 14½x14***

**1178** A538 76c multicolored 1.90 .75
*a.* Perf. 12½x13 3.00 2.50
*b.* As "a," bklt. pane of 5 + label 15.00 15.00
*c.* Perf. 13 37.50 14.00
**1179** A538 78c multicolored 2.20 .75
*a.* As "c," bklt. pane of 5 15.00 15.00
*b.* Perf. 13 30.00 6.00
*c.* Perf. 12½x13 3.00 2.00
*d.* Imperf, pair *850.00*

***Perf. 13***

**1180** A538 80c multicolored 1.80 .75
*a.* Perf. 12½x13 3.00 1.10
*b.* As "a," bklt. pane of 5 + label 15.00 15.00
*c.* Perf. 14½x14 5.50 2.25
*d.* Imperf, pair *1,100.*

***Perf. 13½***

**Litho. & Engr.**

**1181** A540 $1 multicolored 1.50 .55
*a.* Engr. inscriptions inverted *12,000.*
*b.* Imperf, pair *1,100.*
*c.* "CANADA $1" inscription omitted *1,750.*
*d.* Vert. block of 6, top pair imperf., middle pair perf. at bottom, bottom pair normal *2,750.*
**1182** A540 $2 multicolored 3.75 1.00
*a.* Imperf., pair *850.00*
*b.* Vert. strip of 5, stamps 3 and 4 imperf vert., horiz. imperf btwn. stamps 2 and 3, and btwn. stamps 3 and 4 *1,500.*
**1183** A540 $5 multicolored 7.50 2.25
*a.* Vert. strip of 5, top stamp imperf on 3 sides, stamp 4 imperf at top and sides *2,600.*
*Nos. 1155-1183 (30)* 39.55 13.10

A later printing of No. 1182 has more intense and clearly defined green shading on the roofline and the deep orange background extends closer to the roofline.

Imperfs exist of Nos. 1155-1157 and 1160, from printer's waste.

Issued: 1c, 2c, 3c, 5c, 6c, 10c, 25c, 10/3/88; 37c, 12/30/87; 38c, 12/29/88; 43c, 57c, 74c, 1/18/88; 44c, 59c, 76c, 1/18/89; $1, $2, 5/5/89; No. 1166, 12/28/89; 45c, 61c, 78c, No. 1167, 1/12/90; $5, 5/28/90; 40c, 46c, 63c, 80c, 12/28/90.

**Booklet Stamps**

***Perf. 13½x14 on 3 Sides***

**Litho.**

**1184** A542 1c multicolored .30 .25
*a.* Perf. 12½x13 11.00 11.00
**1185** A542 5c multicolored .30 .25
*a.* Perf. 12½x13 7.50 7.50

***Perf. 12½x12 on 2 or 3 sides***

**Engr.**

**1186** A445 6c dark purple .70 .30
**1187** A443 37c dark blue .90 .70
*a.* Bklt. pane of 4 + 2 labels (#938, 2 #942, #1187) 1.40 1.40
**1188** A443 38c dark blue .90 .40
*a.* Bklt. pane of 5 (3 #939a, #1186, #1188) 1.40 1.40

***Perf. 13½x14 on 3 Sides***

**Litho.**

**1189** A542 39c multicolored .90 .40
*a.* Bklt. pane of 4 (#1184, 2 #1185, #1189) 1.65 .65
*b.* Perf. 12½x13 12.00 12.00
*c.* Bklt. pane of 4 (#1184a, 2 #1185a, 1189b) 37.50 37.50
**1190** A542 40c multicolored 1.50 .55
*a.* Bklt. pane of 4 (2 #1184, #1185, #1190) 2.40 1.20
*b.* As "a," imperf *1,350.*

Nos. 1190a, 1190c sold for 50c.

Issued: No. 1187, 2/3/88; No. 1188, 1/18/89; No. 1186, 1989; Nos. 1184-1185, 1189, 1/12/90; No. 1190, 12/28/90.

**Self-Adhesives**

***Die Cut***

**Booklet Stamps**

**1191** A543 38c multicolored 1.50 .75
*a.* Booklet of 12 15.00
*b.* Blue omitted *1,750.*
*c.* Yellow omitted *900.00*
**1192** A543 39c multicolored 1.40 .75
*a.* Booklet of 12 15.25
**1193** A543 40c multicolored 1.40 .75
*a.* Booklet of 12 17.00

Issued: 38c, 6/30/89; 39c, 2/8/90; 40c, 1/11/91.

Issued on peelable paper backing serving as booklet cover. Nos. 1191a, 1192a sold for $5, No. 1193a for $5.25.

**Coil Stamps**

***Perf. 10 Horiz.***

**Engr.**

**1194** A443 37c dark blue .75 .25
*d.* Imperf., pair 170.00
**1194A** A443 38c dark green 1.10 .25
*e.* Imperf., pair 375.00
**1194B** A542 39c violet .75 .25
*f.* Imperf., pair 150.00
**1194C** A542 40c blue gray .75 .25
*g.* Imperf., pair 275.00
*h.* All color omitted (tagged) 375.00

Issued: 37c, 2/22/88; 38c, 2/1/89; 39c, 2/8/90; 40c, 12/28/90.

No. 1194Ch must be collected in a pair with normal or misperfed stamp or (more often) in a strip of four with a pair of normal (or misperfed) stamps and a pair of the color-omitted stamps.

See Nos. 1356-1362, 1375-1376, 1388, 1394-1396, 1682-1683, 1687, 1695, 1698.

**Olympics Type of 1986**

**1988, Feb. 12 Litho. *Perf. 12x12½***

**1195** A521 37c Alpine skiing .60 .25
**1196** A521 37c Curling .60 .25
*a.* Pair, #1195-1196 1.20 .90
**1197** A521 43c Figure skating .70 .70
**1198** A521 74c Luge 1.20 .90
*Nos. 1195-1198 (4)* 3.10 2.10

**Exploration Type of 1986**

18th Cent. explorers of the western territories: No. 1199, Anthony Henday, who traveled the Prairies in 1754 from the Hayes River to Red Deer, Alberta. No. 1200, George Vancouver (1757-1798), who circumnavigated Vancouver Is. and explored the Pacific Coast, 1792-94. No. 1201, Simon Fraser (1776-1862), fur trader who discovered and navigated the Fraser River. No. 1202, John Palliser (1807-1887), geographer who determined the topographical boundary between Canada and the US from Lake Superior to the Pacific Coast.

**1988, Mar. 17 Litho. *Perf. 12½x13***

**1199** A518 37c multicolored .60 .35
**1200** A518 37c multicolored .60 .35
**1201** A518 37c multicolored .60 .35
**1202** A518 37c multicolored .60 .35
*a.* Block of 4, #1199-1202 2.40 2.00

The Young Reader, by Ozias Leduc — A546

**Photo. & Engr. with Foil Application**

**1988, May 20 *Perf. 13x13½***

**1203** A546 50c multicolored 1.10 .90

Masterpieces of Canadian art. Printed in sheets of 16.

See Nos. 1241, 1271, 1310, 1419, 1466, 1516, 1545, 1602, 1635, 1754, 1800, 1863, 1916, 1945.

Wildlife and Habitat Conservation — A547

**1988, June 1 Litho. *Perf. 13x13½***

**1204** A547 37c Duck landing .60 .35
**1205** A547 37c Moose at water hole .60 .35
*a.* Pair, #1204-1205 1.20 .90

Grey Owl, born Archibald Belaney, (b. 1888), conservationist; Ducks Unlimited Canada, 50th anniv.

Science and Technology — A548

Inventions: No. 1206, Kerosene, invented by Abraham Gesner (1797-1864), patented in 1854. No. 1207, Marquis wheat, developed in 1908 by Charles Saunders. No. 1208, Electron microscope, developed in 1938 at the University of Toronto by James Hillier and Albert Prebus under the supervision of Eli Burton. No. 1209, Cobalt cancer therapy, introduced by Dr. Harold Johns and Atomic Energy of Canada, Ltd., in 1951.

**1988, June 17 *Perf. 12½x13***

**1206** A548 37c multicolored .60 .30
**1207** A548 37c multicolored .60 .30
**1208** A548 37c multicolored .60 .30
**1209** A548 37c multicolored .60 .30
*a.* Block of 4, #1206-1209 2.40 2.00

Intl. Entomology Congress, Vancouver — A549

No. 1210, Short-tailed swallowtail. No. 1211, Northern blue. No. 1212, Macoun's Arctic. No. 1213, Canadian tiger swallowtail.

**1988, July 4** *Perf. 12*
**1210** A549 37c multicolored .60 .35
**1211** A549 37c multicolored .60 .35
**1212** A549 37c multicolored .60 .35
**1213** A549 37c multicolored .60 .35
*a.* Block of 4, #1210-1213 2.40 2.10

St. John's, Newfoundland, Cent. of Incorporation A550

37c, Harbor entrance, skyline.

**1988, July 22** *Perf. 13½x13*
**1214** A550 37c multicolored .60 .25

Canadian 4-H Council, 75th Anniv. — A551

37c, Motto, farm, young scientists.

**1988, Aug. 5**
**1215** A551 37c multicolored .60 .25

Les Forges Du St. Maurice (1738-1883), Canada's 1st Industrial Complex — A552

**Litho. & Engr.**

**1988, Aug. 19** *Perf. 13½*
**1216** A552 37c multicolored .60 .25

Canadian Kennel Club, Cent. — A553

No. 1217, Tahltan bear dog. No. 1218, Nova Scotia duck-tolling retriever. No. 1219, Canadian Eskimo dog. No. 1220, Newfoundland.

**1988, Aug. 26** *Perf. 12½x12*
**1217** A553 37c multicolored .90 .40
**1218** A553 37c multicolored .90 .40
**1219** A553 37c multicolored .90 .40
**1220** A553 37c multicolored .90 .40
*a.* Block of 4, #1217-1220 3.60 2.75

A554

**1988, Sept. 14** **Litho.** *Perf. 13½x13*
**1221** A554 37c multicolored .60 .25

Sesquicentennial of the 1st baseball game played in Canada, June 4, 1838 at Beachville, Upper Canada.

A555

Christmas (Icons of the Eastern Church): 32c, Nativity. 37c, Conception. 43c, Virgin and Child. 74c, Virgin and Child, diff.

**1988, Oct. 27** *Perf. 13½*
**1222** A555 37c multicolored .60 .25
**1223** A555 43c multicolored .75 .65
**1224** A555 74c multicolored 1.50 .90

**Booklet Stamp**
**Size: 35½x21mm**
*Perf. 12½x13½*

**1225** A555 32c multicolored .90 .75
*a.* Booklet pane of 10 9.00 9.00
*Nos. 1222-1225 (4)* 3.75 2.55

Millennium of Christianity in the Ukraine. No. 1225 has bar code at left; for use on covers with printed postal code matrix.

Inglis and Anglican Church — A556

**1988, Nov. 1** *Perf. 12½x12*
**1226** A556 37c multicolored .60 .25

Charles Inglis (1734-1816), Canada's 1st Anglican bishop and founder of the Kings-Edgehill School, Nova Scotia, and the University of King's College at Halifax, bicent.

Hopkins and *Canoe Manned by Voyageurs* A557

**1988, Nov. 18** *Perf. 13½x13*
**1227** A557 37c multicolored .60 .25

Frances Ann Hopkins (1838-1918), painter.

The Bluenose and Capt. Walters — A558

**1988, Nov. 18** *Perf. 13½*
**1228** A558 37c multicolored .60 .25

Angus Walters (1882-1968), mariner.

Small Craft — A559

**1989, Feb. 1** *Perf. 13½x13*
**1229** A559 38c Chipewyan canoe .60 .35
**1230** A559 38c Haida canoe .60 .35
**1231** A559 38c Inuit kayak .60 .35
**1232** A559 38c Micmac canoe .60 .35
*a.* Block of 4, #1229-1232 2.40 2.20

See Nos. 1266-1269, 1317-1320.

**Exploration Type of 1986**

Explorers of the North: No. 1233, Matonabbee (c. 1737-1782), Indian guide who led 1st overland European expedition to the Arctic Ocean. No. 1234, Relics of expedition led by Sir John Franklin (1786-1847) that proved the existence of the Northwest Passage. No. 1235, Relics of the discovery of the Alberta fossil bed by geologist Joseph Burr Tyrrell (1858-1957). No. 1236, Vilhjalmur Stefansson (1879-1962), American ethnologist who discovered the last uncharted islands in the Arctic Archipelago.

**1989, Mar. 22** *Perf. 12½x13*
**1233** A518 38c multicolored .60 .35
**1234** A518 38c multicolored .60 .35
**1235** A518 38c multicolored .60 .35
**1236** A518 38c multicolored .60 .35
*a.* Block of 4, #1233-1236 2.40 2.20

Photography in Canada, Sesquicentennial A560

Photographers and their work: No. 1237, William Notman (1826-1891). No. 1238, W. Hanson Boorne (1859-1945). No. 1239, Alexander Henderson (1831-1913). No. 1240, Jules-Ernest Livernois (1851-1933).

**1989, June 23** *Perf. 12½x12*
**1237** A560 38c multicolored .60 .35
**1238** A560 38c multicolored .60 .35
**1239** A560 38c multicolored .60 .35
**1240** A560 38c multicolored .60 .35
*a.* Block of 4, #1237-1240 2.40 2.20

**Art Type of 1988**

Design: Ceremonial Frontlet (headpiece) Worn by Tsimshian Indian Chiefs, Early 20th Cent.

**Litho. with Foil Application**

**1989, June 29** *Perf. 12½x13*
**1241** A546 50c multicolored 1.10 .90

Masterpieces of Canadian Art and opening of the Museum of Civilization.

Poets — A562

No. 1243, Louis Frechette (1839-1908). No. 1244, Archibald Lampman (1861-1899).

**1989, July 7** **Litho.** *Perf. 13½*
**1243** A562 38c multicolored .60 .35
**1244** A562 38c multicolored .60 .35
*a.* Pair, #1243-1244 1.20 .90

Mushrooms — A563

No. 1245, Clavulinopsis fusiformis. No. 1246, Boletus mirabilis. No. 1247, Cantharellus cinnabarinus. No. 1248, Morchella esculenta.

**1989, Aug. 4**
**1245** A563 38c multicolored .60 .35
**1246** A563 38c multicolored .60 .35
**1247** A563 38c multicolored .60 .35
**1248** A563 38c multicolored .60 .35
*a.* Block of 4, #1245-1248 2.40 2.20

Infantry Regiments, 75th Annivs. — A564

No. 1249, Princess Patricia's Canadian Light Infantry. No. 1250, Royal 22nd Regiment.

**Litho. & Engr.**

**1989, Sept. 8** *Perf. 13*
**1249** A564 38c multicolored .75 .40
**1250** A564 38c multicolored .75 .40
*a.* Pair, #1249-1250 1.50 1.25

Intl. Trade — A565

**1989, Oct. 2** **Litho.** *Perf. 13½x13*
**1251** A565 38c multicolored .60 .25

Performing Arts — A566

No. 1252, Dancers. No. 1253, Musicians. No. 1254, Camera, director. No. 1255, Youth and adult entertainers.

**1989, Oct. 4** *Perf. 13x13½*
**1252** A566 38c multicolored .60 .35
**1253** A566 38c multicolored .60 .35
**1254** A566 38c multicolored .60 .35
**1255** A566 38c multicolored .60 .35
*a.* Block of 4, #1252-1255 2.40 2.00

Royal Winnipeg Ballet 50th anniv. (No. 1252), Vancouver Opera 30th anniv. (No. 1253), Natl. Film Board 50th anniv. (No. 1254), and Confederation Center of the Arts, Charlottetown, P.E.I., 25th anniv. (No. 1255).

A566a

A567

Winter landscapes: 33c, *Champ-de-Mars, Winter,* 1892, by William Brymner (1855-1925). 38c, *Bend in the Gosselin River, Arthabaska,* c. 1906, by Marc-Aurele de Foy Suzor-Cote (1869-1937). 44c, *Snow II,* 1915, by Lawren S. Harris (1885-1970). 76c, *Ste. Agnes,* c. 1925-30, by Albert H. Robinson (1881-1956). Nos. 1256-1258 vert.

**1989, Oct. 26**
**Size of 44c, 76c: 25x31mm**

**1256** A566a 38c multi .60 .25
*a.* Bklt. pane of 10, #1256b 40.00 40.00
*b.* Perf. 13x12½ 4.50 4.50

*Perf. 13½*

**1257** A566a 44c multi .75 .60
*a.* Booklet pane of 5 + label 15.00 15.00
**1258** A566a 76c multi 1.30 .90
*a.* Booklet pane of 5 + label 27.50 27.50

**Booklet Stamp**
**Size: 35x21mm**
*Perf. 12½x13½*

**1259** A567 33c shown 1.50 1.50
*a.* Booklet pane of 10 10.00
*b.* Horiz. pair, imperf btwn. *2,000.*
*c.* As "a," imperf. vert. between *11,000.*
*Nos. 1256-1259 (4)* 4.15 3.25

Christmas. No. 1259 has bar code at left; for use on covers with printed postal code matrix. Booklet panes separate easily.

Declaration of War, 1939 — A568

Political and military actions taken by Canada at the outbreak of World War II: No. 1261, Army mobilization. No. 1262, Navy convoy system. No. 1263, Commonwealth Air Training Plan.

**1989, Nov. 10** *Perf. 13½*
**1260** A568 38c shown .75 .55
**1261** A568 38c multicolored .75 .55
**1262** A568 38c multicolored .75 .55
**1263** A568 38c multicolored .75 .55
*a.* Block of 4, #1260-1263 3.00 2.50

See Nos. 1298-1301, 1345-1348, 1448-1451, 1503-1506, 1537-1544.

Norman Bethune (1890-1939), Surgeon — A569

**Litho. & Engr.**

**1990, Mar. 2** *Perf. 13x13½*
**1264** A569 39c In Canada .90 .40
**1265** A569 39c In China .90 .40
*a.* Pair, #1264-1265 1.80 1.10

See People's Republic of China Nos. 2263-2264.

**Small Craft Type of 1989**

**1990, Mar. 15** **Litho.** *Perf. 13½x13*
**1266** A559 39c Dory .70 .35
**1267** A559 39c Pointer .70 .35
**1268** A559 39c York boat .70 .35
**1269** A559 39c North canoe .70 .35
*a.* Block of 4, #1266-1269 2.80 2.40

Multicultural Heritage of Canada — A570

### Litho. & Engr.

**1990, Apr. 5** *Perf. 13*
**1270** A570 39c multicolored .60 .25
*a.* Black (inscriptions) omitted *1,000.*

### Art Type of 1988

Painting: *The West Wind,* by Tom Thomson.

### Litho. with Foil Application

**1990, May 3** *Perf. 12½x13*
**1271** A546 50c multicolored 1.10 .90

Masterpieces of Canadian Art.

Mail Trucks
A571 A572

**1990, May 3 Litho.** *Perf. 13½*

### Booklet Stamps

**1272** A571 39c multicolored .75 .55
**1273** A572 39c multicolored .75 .55
*a.* Bklt. pane of 8+printed margin (4 each #1272-1273) 6.00 6.00
*b.* Bklt. pane of 9+3 labels, printed margin (5 #1272, 4 #1273) 11.50 11.50

Dolls — A573

**1990, June 8** *Perf. 12½x12*
**1274** A573 39c Native .65 .35
**1275** A573 39c Settlers .65 .35
**1276** A573 39c 4 Commercial .65 .35
**1277** A573 39c 5 Commercial .65 .35
*a.* Block of 4, #1274-1277 2.60 2.40

Natl. Flag, 25th Anniv. — A574

39c, Flag, fireworks.

**1990, June 29** *Perf. 13x12½*
**1278** A574 39c multicolored .65 .25
*a.* Silver (inscriptions) omitted *2,000.*

Printed in sheets of 16.

Prehistoric Life — A575

### Litho. & Engr.

**1990, July 12** *Perf. 13x13½*
**1279** A575 39c Trilobite .65 .35
**1280** A575 39c Sea scorpion .65 .35
**1281** A575 39c Fossil algae .65 .35
**1282** A575 39c Soft invertebrate .65 .35
*a.* Block of 4, #1279-1282 2.60 2.20

See Nos. 1306-1309.

Canadian Forests — A576

No. 1283, Acadian. No. 1284, Great Lakes-St. Lawrence. No. 1285, Coast. No. 1286, Boreal.

**1990, Aug. 7 Litho.** *Perf. 12½x13*
**1283** A576 39c multicolored .65 .30
*a.* Pane of 4 9.00 7.50
**1284** A576 39c multicolored .65 .30
*a.* Pane of 4 9.00 7.50
**1285** A576 39c multicolored .65 .30
*a.* Pane of 4 9.00 7.50
**1286** A576 39c multicolored .65 .30
*a.* Block of 4, #1283-1286 2.60 2.20
*b.* Pane of 4 9.00 7.50

Panes of four sold for $1 each through Petro-Canada gas stations, and for full face value through the philatelic bureau. Issue date: Sept. 7.

Weather Observations in Canada, 150th Anniv. — A577

**1990, Sept. 5** *Perf. 12½x13½*
**1287** A577 39c multicolored .60 .25

The left and right margin singles of No. 1287 differ slightly in design from stamps from columns 2-4, due to the nature of the continuous cloud design across the pane.

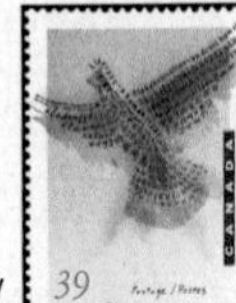

Intl. Literacy Year — A578

**1990, Sept. 7** *Perf. 13½x13*
**1288** A578 39c multicolored .60 .25

Legendary Creatures A579

**1990, Oct. 1** *Perf. 12½x13½*
**1289** A579 39c Sasquatch .75 .75
**1290** A579 39c Kraken .75 .75
**1291** A579 39c Werewolf .75 .75
**1292** A579 39c Ogopogo .75 .75
*a.* Block of 4, #1289-1292 3.00 3.00
*b.* As "a," imperf. *1,250.*

*Perf. 12½x12*

*1289a* A579 39c 11.00 3.75
*1290a* A579 39c 11.00 3.75
*1291a* A579 39c 11.00 3.75
*1292c* A579 39c 11.00 3.75
*d.* Block of 4, #1289a-1292c 45.00 32.50

Agnes Campbell Macphail (1890-1954), First Woman Member of Parliament — A580

**1990, Oct. 9** *Perf. 13x13½*
**1293** A580 39c multicolored .60 .25

Virgin Mary with Christ Child and St. John the Baptist by Norval Morrisseau A581

Rebirth by Jackson Beardy A582

Indian Art: 45c, Sculpture of Mother and Child by an Inuit artist. 78c, Children of the Raven by Bill Reid.

**1990, Oct. 25** *Perf. 13½*
**1294** A581 39c multicolored .75 .25
*a.* Booklet pane of 10 7.50 *9.00*
**1295** A581 45c multicolored .75 .65
*a.* Bklt. pane of 5 + label 3.75 4.00
**1296** A581 78c multicolored 1.50 1.10
*a.* Bklt. pane of 5 + label 7.50 6.50

### Booklet Stamp

*Perf. 12½x13 on 2 or 3 Sides*

**1297** A582 34c multicolored .85 .30
*a.* Booklet pane of 10 8.50 *10.00*
*Nos. 1294-1297 (4)* 3.85 2.30

Christmas. No. 1297 has bar code at left; for use on covers with printed postal code matrix.

### World War II Type of 1989

No. 1298, Home front. No. 1299, Communal war efforts. No. 1300, Food production. No. 1301, Science and war.

**1990, Nov. 9** *Perf. 12½x12*
**1298** A568 39c multicolored .75 .60
**1299** A568 39c multicolored .75 .60
**1300** A568 39c multicolored .75 .60
**1301** A568 39c multicolored .75 .60
*a.* Block of 4, #1298-1301 3.00 3.00

A583

Physicians: No. 1302, Jennie Trout (1841-1921), first licensed Canadian woman physician. No. 1303, Wilder Penfield (1891-1976), neurosurgeon. No. 1304, Sir Frederick Banting (1891-1941), discoverer of insulin. No. 1305, Harold Griffith (1894-1985), anesthesiologist.

**1991, Mar. 15** *Perf. 13½*
**1302** A583 40c multicolored .65 .35
**1303** A583 40c multicolored .65 .35
**1304** A583 40c multicolored .65 .35
**1305** A583 40c multicolored .65 .35
*a.* Block of 4, #1302-1305 2.60 2.20

### Prehistoric Life Type of 1990

**1991, Apr. 5** *Perf. 12½x13½*
**1306** A575 40c Microfossils .65 .35
**1307** A575 40c Early tree .65 .35
**1308** A575 40c Early fish .65 .35
**1309** A575 40c Land reptile .65 .35
*a.* Block of 4, #1306-1309 2.60 2.20

### Art Type of 1988

Design: Forest, British Columbia by Emily Carr.

### Litho. with Foil Application

**1991, May 7** *Perf. 12½x13*
**1310** A546 50c multicolored 1.10 .90

Masterpieces of Canadian Art.

A584

Public Gardens: No. 1311, Butchart Gardens, Victoria, B.C. No. 1312, Intl. Peace Garden, Boissevain, Manitoba. No. 1313, Royal Botanical Gardens, Hamilton, Ontario. No. 1314, Montreal Botanical Gardens. No. 1315, Halifax Public Gardens, Nova Scotia.

### Booklet Stamps

**1991, May 22 Litho.** *Perf. 13x12½*
**1311** A584 40c multicolored .75 .40
**1312** A584 40c multicolored .75 .40
**1313** A584 40c multicolored .75 .40
**1314** A584 40c multicolored .75 .40
**1315** A584 40c multicolored .75 .40
*a.* Strip of 5, #1311-1315 3.75 2.75
*b.* Bklt. pane, 2 each #1311-1315 7.50 7.00

Canada Day — A585

**1991, June 28** *Perf. 13½x13*
**1316** A585 40c multicolored .75 .25

### Small Craft Type of 1989

**1991, July 18**
**1317** A559 40c Verchere rowboat .65 .35
**1318** A559 40c Touring kayak .65 .35
**1319** A559 40c Sailing dinghy .65 .35
**1320** A559 40c Cedar strip canoe .65 .35
*a.* Block of 4, #1317-1320 2.60 2.25

Canadian Rivers — A586

No. 1321, South Nahanni. No. 1322, Athabasca. No. 1323, Boundary Waters-Voyageur Waterway. No. 1324, Jacques Cartier. No. 1325, Main.

### Booklet Stamps

**1991, Aug. 20** *Perf. 13x12½*
**1321** A586 40c multicolored .75 .40
**1322** A586 40c multicolored .75 .40
**1323** A586 40c multicolored .75 .40
**1324** A586 40c multicolored .75 .40
**1325** A586 40c multicolored .75 .40
*a.* Strip of 5, #1321-1325 3.75 3.25
*b.* Bklt. pane, 2 each #1321-1325 7.50 6.75

See Nos. 1408-1412, 1485-1489, 1511-1515.

Arrival of Ukrainians, Cent. — A587

Paintings by William Kurelek: No. 1326, Leaving homeland. No. 1327, Winter in Canada. No. 1328, Clearing land. No. 1329, Growing wheat.

**1991, Aug. 29** *Perf. 13½x13*
**1326** A587 40c multicolored .65 .35
**1327** A587 40c multicolored .65 .35
**1328** A587 40c multicolored .65 .35
**1329** A587 40c multicolored .65 .35
*a.* Block of 4, #1326-1329 2.60 2.20

Dangerous Public Service Occupations — A588

**1991, Sept. 23** *Perf. 13½*
**1330** A588 40c Ski Patrol 1.10 .35
**1331** A588 40c Police 1.10 .35
**1332** A588 40c Fire fighters 1.10 .35
**1333** A588 40c Search & Rescue 1.10 .35
*a.* Block of 4, #1330-1333 4.40 2.60

Folktales — A589

**1991, Oct. 1 Litho.** *Perf. 13½x12½*
**1334** A589 40c Witched Canoe .75 .30
**1335** A589 40c Orphan Boy .75 .30
**1336** A589 40c Chinook Wind .75 .30
**1337** A589 40c Buried Treasure .75 .30
*a.* Block of 4, #1334-1337 3.00 2.50

Queen's University, Kingston, Ont., Sesqui. — A590

**1991, Oct. 16**
**1338** A590 40c multicolored .75 .55
*a.* Bklt. pane of 10 + 2 labels 7.50 6.00

A591

Santa Claus — A592

**1991, Oct. 23** ***Perf. 13½***

**1339** A591 40c At fireplace .75 .25
*a.* Booklet pane of 10 7.50 6.00
**1340** A591 46c With white horse, tree .75 .50
*a.* Bklt. pane of 5 + label 3.75 3.00
**1341** A591 80c Sinterklaas, girl 1.30 .90
*a.* Bklt. pane of 5 + label 6.50 6.00
*b.* Imperf., pair *750.00*

### Booklet Stamp

***Perf. 12½x13 on 2 or 3 Sides***

**1342** A592 35c With punchbowl .75 .25
*a.* Booklet pane of 10 7.50 4.50
*Nos. 1339-1342 (4)* 3.55 1.90

Christmas. No. 1342 has bar code at left; for use on covers with printed postal code matrix.

Basketball, Cent. — A593

**1991, Oct. 25** ***Perf. 13x13½***

**1343** A593 40c multicolored .75 .25

### Souvenir Sheet

**1344** Pane of 3 5.00 5.00
*a.* A593 40c like #1343 1.10 1.10
*b.* A593 46c Player shooting, diff. 1.50 1.50
*c.* A593 80c Player dribbling 2.20 2.20

No. 1344a has 3-line inscription.

### World War II Type of 1989

No. 1345, Women's Armed Forces. No. 1346, War industry. No. 1347, Cadets and veterans. No. 1348, Defense of Hong Kong.

**1991, Nov. 8** ***Perf. 13½***

**1345** A568 40c multicolored .75 .55
**1346** A568 40c multicolored .75 .55
**1347** A568 40c multicolored .75 .55
**1348** A568 40c multicolored .75 .55
*a.* Block or strip of 4, #1345-1348 3.00 2.50

### Types of 1987-91 and

Edible Berries A594

Flag and Hills A595

Flag and Prairie A596

Flag and Building A597

Trees — A598

Designs: 1c, Blueberry. 2c, Wild strawberry. 3c, Black crowberry. 5c, Rose hip. 6c, Black raspberry. 10c, Kinnikinnick. 25c, Saskatoon berry. 48c, McIntosh apple. 49c, Delicious apple. 50c, Snow apple. 52c, Gravenstein apple. 65c, Black walnut. 67c, Beaked hazelnut. 69c, Shagbark hickory. 71c, American chestnut. 84c, Stanley plum. 86c, Bartlett pear. 88c, Westcot apricot. 90c, Elberta peach. $1, Court House, Yorkton, Saskatchewan. $2, Provincial Normal School, Truro, Nova Scotia. $5, Carnegie Public Library, Victoria, British Columbia. No. 1388, Flag and mountains. No. 1389, Flag and estuary shore.

**1991-98** **Litho.** ***Perf. 13x13½***

**1349** A594 1c multicolored .30 .25
*a.* Imperf., pair *650.00*
**1350** A594 2c multicolored .30 .25
*a.* Imperf., pair *650.00*
**1351** A594 3c multicolored .30 .25
*a.* Imperf., pair *650.00*
**1352** A594 5c multicolored .30 .25
*a.* Imperf., pair *650.00*
**1353** A594 6c multicolored .30 .25
*a.* Imperf., pair *650.00*
**1354** A594 10c multicolored .30 .25
*a.* Horiz. pair, imperf at sides and bottom *1,000.*
*b.* Imperf., pair *650.00*
**1355** A594 25c multicolored .75 .25
*a.* Imperf., pair *650.00*

***Perf. 13½x13***

**1356** A595 42c multicolored .80 .25
*a.* Booklet pane of 10 7.50 5.75
*b.* Bklt. pane of 50 + 2 labels 90.00 75.00
*c.* Bklt. pane of 25 + 2 labels 17.50 12.50
*d.* Vert. pair, imperf between *700.00*
*e.* Imperf., pair *700.00*

***Perf. 13x13½***

**1357** A536 42c multicolored .75 .25
*a.* Booklet pane of 10 7.50 6.00
*b.* Imperf., pair *575.00*
**1358** A536 43c multicolored .90 .25
*a.* Booklet pane of 10 9.00 8.50
*b.* Imperf., pair 900.00

***Perf. 13½x13***

**1359** A596 43c multicolored .90 .25
*a.* Booklet pane of 10 7.00 5.50
*b.* Bklt. pane of 25 + 2 labels 20.00 17.50
*c.* Perf. 14½ 1.10 .25
*d.* As "c," bklt. pane of 10 9.00 7.50
*e.* As "c," bklt. pane of 25 + 2 labels 25.00 21.00
*f.* Vert. pair, imperf between (from #1359e) 700.00
*g.* Imperf., pair 650.00

***Perf. 13x13½***

**1360** A536 45c multicolored .75 .25
*a.* Booklet pane of 10 7.50 6.00
Complete booklet, #1360a 7.50

***Perf. 14½***

**1361** A597 45c multicolored .75 .25
*a.* Booklet pane of 10 7.50 7.00
Complete booklet, #1361a 7.50
*b.* Bklt. pane of 25 + 2 labels 27.50 22.50
Complete booklet, #1361b 27.50
*c.* Perf. 13½x13 .75 .25
*d.* As "c," bklt. pane of 10 7.50 6.75
Complete booklet, #1361d 7.50
*e.* As "c," bklt. pane of 25 + 2 labels 19.00
Complete booklet, #1361e 19.00

***Perf. 13x13½***

### Size: 16x20mm

**1362** A597 45c multicolored .70 .25
*a.* Booklet pane of 10 7.00 *8.25*
Complete booklet, #1362a 7.00
*b.* Booklet pane of 30 24.00 24.00
Complete booklet, #1362b 24.00
*c.* Imperf, pair *450.00*

No. 1361 is 17x21mm.

***Perf. 13***

**1363** A598 48c multicolored 1.00 .25
*a.* Perf. 14½x14 on 3 sides 1.50 .40
*b.* As "a," bklt. pane of 5 + label 7.50 5.75
*c.* Imperf., pair *850.00*
**1364** A598 49c multicolored .90 .25
*a.* Perf. 14½x14 2.60 .35
*b.* As "a," bklt. pane of 5 + 1 label 13.00 6.00
*c.* Booklet pane of 5 + label 12.00 9.50
**1365** A598 50c multicolored .90 .30
*a.* Booklet pane of 5 + label 6.50 5.00
*b.* Perf. 14½x14 2.25 .45
*c.* As "b," bklt. pane of 5 + label 13.00 11.50
**1366** A598 52c multicolored 1.50 .40
*a.* Booklet pane of 5 + label 7.50 6.00
Complete booklet, #1366a 8.00
*b.* Perf. 14½x14 2.25 .55
*c.* As "b," bklt. pane of 5 + label 11.50 10.00
Complete booklet, #1366c 12.00
**1367** A598 65c multicolored 1.10 .40
*a.* Imperf., pair *1,100.*
**1368** A598 67c multicolored 1.10 .40
*a.* Imperf., pair *1,400.*
**1369** A598 69c multicolored 1.10 .35
**1370** A598 71c multicolored 1.10 .35
*a.* Perf. 14½x14 75.00 12.50
**1371** A598 84c multicolored 1.50 .40
*a.* Perf. 14½x14 on 3 sides 2.25 .60
*b.* As "a," bklt. pane of 5 + label 11.50 9.00
*c.* Imperf., pair *1,350.*
**1372** A598 86c multicolored 1.80 .55
*a.* Perf. 14½x14 3.00 1.50
*b.* As "a," bklt. pane of 5 + 1 label 15.00 12.50
*c.* Booklet pane of 5 + label 17.00 15.00
**1373** A598 88c multicolored 1.50 .50
*a.* Booklet pane of 5 + label 11.00 7.50
*b.* Perf. 14½x14 4.00 2.25
*c.* As "b," bklt. pane of 5 + label 20.00 15.00
**1374** A598 90c multicolored 1.80 .45
*a.* Booklet pane of 5 + label 10.00 8.00
Complete booklet, #1374a 10.50
*b.* Perf. 14½x14 3.75 1.50
*c.* As "b," bklt. pane of 5+label 19.00 13.00
Complete booklet, #1374c 20.00

### Size: 48x40mm

### Litho. & Engr.

***Perf. 14½x14***

**1375** A540 $1 multicolored 1.80 .55
*a.* Dk bl (inscriptions) omitted *1,250.*
*b.* Perf 13½x13 1.80 .55
*c.* As "b," dk bl (inscriptions) omitted *1,250.*
**1376** A540 $2 multicolored 3.75 1.00
*a.* Dk grn (inscriptions) omitted *950.00*
*b.* Engr. inscriptions inverted *8,000.*
*c.* Perf. 13½x13 3.75 1.10
*d.* As "c," dk grn (inscriptions) omitted *1,500.*

***Perf. 13½x13***

**1378** A540 $5 multicolored 7.50 2.20
*Nos. 1349-1378 (29)* 36.45 11.85

### Self-Adhesive

***Die Cut***

***Imperf***

### Booklet Stamps

**1388** A543 42c multicolored 1.10 .75
*a.* Booklet of 12 13.50
**1389** A543 43c multicolored 1.10 .75
*a.* Booklet pane of 12 13.50

Nos. 1388a, 1389a issued on peelable paper backing serving as booklet cover and sold for $5.25.

### Coil Stamps

***Perf. 10 Horiz.***

### Engr.

**1394** A542 42c red .75 .25
*a.* Imperf., pair 150.00
**1395** A542 43c olive green .75 .25
*a.* Imperf., pair 125.00
**1396** A542 45c blue green .75 .25
*a.* Imperf., pair 125.00
*Nos. 1394-1396 (3)* 2.25 .75

Nos. 1349-1363 are known imperf from printer's waste. Items exist imperf in wrong colors and with wrong denominations. These may be essays or printer's waste.

Issued: 1c-25c, 8/5/92; Nos. 1356-1357, 1394, 48c, 65c, 84c, 12/27/91; No. 1388, 1/28/92; Nos. 1358-1359, 1364, 1368, 1372, 1395, 12/30/92; No. 1389, 2/15/93; Nos. 1359c-1359e, 1/18/94; Nos. 1364c, 1372c, 1/7/94; 50c, 69c, 88c, 2/25/94; $1, $2, 2/21/94; NOs. 1375b, 1376c, 2/20/95; Nos. 1365c, 1373c, 3/27/95; Nos. 1360-1361, 1396, 52c, 71c, 90c, 7/31/95; $5, 2/29/96; No. 1362, 2/2/98.

1992 Winter Olympics, Albertville — A601

No. 1399, Ski jumping. No. 1400, Pairs figure skating. No. 1401, Hockey. No. 1402, Bobsledding. No. 1403, Alpine skiing.

### Booklet Stamps

**1992, Feb. 7** **Litho.** ***Perf. 12½x13***

**1399** A601 42c multicolored .75 .40
**1400** A601 42c multicolored .75 .40
**1401** A601 42c multicolored .75 .40
**1402** A601 42c multicolored .75 .40
**1403** A601 42c multicolored .75 .40
*a.* Strip of 5, #1399-1403 3.75 3.00
*b.* Bklt. pane, 2 each #1399-1403 7.50 7.50
Complete booklet, #1403b 8.50

See Nos. 1414-1418.

City of Montreal, 350th Anniv. — A602

Designs: No. 1404, City of Montreal, modern times. No. 1405, Early settlement of Montreal (Ville-Marie). 48c, Jacques Cartier's chart of Canada, snowshoe, ship's mast. 84c, World map, nocturnal and Aztec calendar stone.

**1992, Mar. 25** ***Perf. 13½***

**1404** A602 42c multicolored .65 .30
**1405** A602 42c multicolored .65 .30
*a.* Pair, #1404-1405 1.30 .75
**1406** A602 48c multicolored .75 .70
**1407** A602 84c multicolored 1.35 .90
*a.* Souvenir sheet of 4, #1404-1407 4.00 4.00
*Nos. 1404-1407 (4)* 3.40 2.20

Discovery of America, 500th anniv. (No. 1407).

Nos. 1404-1405 printed checkerwise. No. 1407a with engraved signatures in margin was produced in limited quantities for World Philatelic Youth Exhibition catalogue which sold for $12.

### Canadian Rivers Type of 1991

No. 1408, Margaree. No. 1409, West (Eliot). No. 1410, Ottawa. No. 1411, Niagara. No. 1412, South Saskatchewan.

### Booklet Stamps

**1992, Apr. 22** ***Perf. 12½***

**1408** A586 42c multicolored .75 .40
**1409** A586 42c multicolored .75 .40
**1410** A586 42c multicolored .75 .40
**1411** A586 42c multicolored .75 .40
**1412** A586 42c multicolored .75 .40
*a.* Strip of 5, #1408-1412 3.75 3.25
*b.* Bklt. pane, 2 each #1408-1412 7.50
Complete booklet, #1412b 8.50

Nos. 1408-1412 are horiz.

Alaska Highway, 50th Anniv. — A603

**1992, May 15** ***Perf. 13½***

**1413** A603 42c multicolored .65 .25

### 1992 Olympic Games Type

**1992, June 15** ***Perf. 12½x13***

**1414** A601 42c Gymnastics .75 .40
**1415** A601 42c Running .75 .40
**1416** A601 42c Diving .75 .40
**1417** A601 42c Cycling .75 .40
**1418** A601 42c Swimming .75 .40
*a.* Strip of 5, #1414-1418 3.75 3.75
*b.* Bklt. pane, 2 each #1414-1418 7.50 7.50
Complete booklet, #1418b 8.50

1992 Summer Olympics, Barcelona.

Stamps in bottom row of No. 1418b are in different sequence than those in No. 1418a.

### Art Type of 1988

Painting: Red Nasturtiums, by David Milne.

### Litho. with Foil Application

**1992, June 29**

**1419** A546 50c multicolored .90 .75

Masterpieces in Canadian Art.

### Miniature Sheet

Canada Day — A604

No. 1420, Nova Scotia. No. 1421, Ontario. No. 1422, Prince Edward Island. No. 1423, New Brunswick. No. 1424, Quebec. No. 1425, Saskatchewan. No. 1426, Manitoba. No. 1427, Northwest Territories. No. 1428, Alberta. No. 1429, British Columbia. No. 1430, Yukon. No. 1431, Newfoundland.

**1992, June 29**

**1420** A604 42c multicolored 1.50 1.50
**1421** A604 42c multicolored 1.50 1.50
**1422** A604 42c multicolored 1.50 1.50
**1423** A604 42c multicolored 1.50 1.50
**1424** A604 42c multicolored 1.50 1.50
**1425** A604 42c multicolored 1.50 1.50
**1426** A604 42c multicolored 1.50 1.50
**1427** A604 42c multicolored 1.50 1.50
**1428** A604 42c multicolored 1.50 1.50
**1429** A604 42c multicolored 1.50 1.50
**1430** A604 42c multicolored 1.50 1.50
**1431** A604 42c multicolored 1.50 1.50
*a.* Pane of 12, #1420-1431 + 13 labels 18.00 18.00

Canadian Folklore — A605

Legendary heroes: No. 1432, Jerry Potts, guide, interpreter. No. 1433, Captain William Jackman, rescuer. No. 1434, Laura Secord, patriot. No. 1435, Jos Monferrand, lumberjack.

**1992, Sept. 8** *Perf. 12½*

**1432** A605 42c multicolored .75 .35
**1433** A605 42c multicolored .75 .35
**1434** A605 42c multicolored .75 .35
**1435** A605 42c multicolored .75 .35
*a.* Block of 4, #1432-1435 3.00 2.50

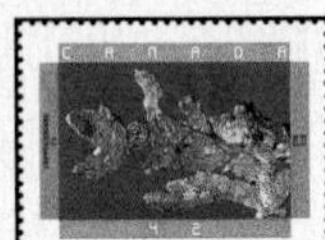

Minerals — A606

**1992, Sept. 21**

**1436** A606 42c Copper .90 .40
**1437** A606 42c Sodalite .90 .40
**1438** A606 42c Gold .90 .40
**1439** A606 42c Galena .90 .40
**1440** A606 42c Grossular .90 .40
*a.* Strip of 5, #1436-1440 4.50 4.50
*b.* Bklt. pane, 2 each #1436-1440 9.00 9.00
Complete booklet, #1440b 8.50

Canada in Space — A607

No. 1441, Anik E2 satellite. No. 1442, Earth, space shuttle.

**1992, Oct. 1** *Perf. 13*

**1441** A607 42c multicolored .75 .80
*a.* Silver omitted *2,500. 2,000.*

**Size: 32x26mm**

**1442** A607 42c multicolored 1.10 1.10
*a.* Pair, #1441-1442 1.80 *1.80*
*b.* As "a," hologram omitted on #1442 *1,300. 1,200.*

No. 1442 has a holographic image. Soaking in water may affect the hologram.

Natl. Hockey League, 75th Anniv. — A608

Designs: No. 1443, Skates, stick, puck, photograph from the early years (1917-1942). No. 1444, Photograph, team emblems from the six-team years (1942-1967). No. 1445, Goalie's mask, gloves, photograph from the expansion years (1967-1992).

**Booklet Stamps**

**1992, Oct. 9** *Perf. 13x12½*

**1443** A608 42c multicolored .75 .25
*a.* Bklt. pane of 8 + 4 labels 6.00 5.00
**1444** A608 42c multicolored .75 .25
*a.* Bklt. pane of 8 + 4 labels 6.00 5.00
**1445** A608 42c multicolored .75 .25
*a.* Bklt. pane of 9 + 3 labels 6.75 5.75
Complete booklet, #1443a, 1444a, 1445a 21.00
*Nos. 1443-1445 (3)* 2.25 .75

A609

No. 1446, Order of Canada, 25th anniv. No. 1447, Daniel Roland Michener (1900-1991), Governor General.

**1992, Oct. 21** *Perf. 12½*

**1446** 42c multicolored .65 .25
**1447** 42c multicolored .65 .30
*a.* A609 Pair, #1446-1447 1.30 1.10

Nos. 1446-1447 printed in panes of 25 containing 16 No. 1446 and 9 No. 1447.

**World War II Type of 1989**

No. 1448, War reporting. No. 1449, Newfoundland air bases. No. 1450, Raid on Dieppe. No. 1451, U-boats offshore.

**1992, Nov. 10** *Perf. 13½*

**1448** A568 42c multicolored .75 .45
**1449** A568 42c multicolored .75 .45
**1450** A568 42c multicolored .75 .45
**1451** A568 42c multicolored .75 .45
*a.* Block or strip of 4, #1448-1451 3.00 2.50

A611

Santa Claus — A612

**1992, Nov. 13** *Perf. 12½*

**1452** A611 42c Jouluvana .65 .25
*a.* Perf. 13½ .90 .25
*b.* As "a," booklet pane of 10 9.00 5.00
Complete booklet, #1452b 10.00

***Perf. 13½***

**1453** A611 48c La Befana 1.10 .75
*a.* Booklet pane of 5 + label 5.50 4.75
Complete booklet, #1453a 6.00
**1454** A611 84c Weihnachtsmann 1.50 .75
*a.* Booklet pane of 5 + label 7.50 6.00
Complete booklet, #1454a 8.50

**Booklet Stamp**

***Perf. 12½x13***

**1455** A612 37c Santa Claus .75 .75
*a.* Booklet pane of 10 7.50
Complete booklet, #1455a 8.50
*Nos. 1452-1455 (4)* 4.00 2.50

Christmas. No. 1455 has bar code at left; for use on covers with printed postal code matrix.

A613

Canadian Women: No. 1456, Adelaide Sophia Hoodless (1857-1910), founder of Victorian Order of Nurses. No. 1457, Marie-Josephine Gerin-Lajoie (1890-1971), founder of Notre-Dame du Bon Conseil Institute. No. 1458, Pitseolak Ashoona (c. 1904-83), Inuit graphic artist. No. 1459, Helen Alice Kinnear (1894-1970), first woman appointed King's Counsel and first federally appointed woman judge.

**1993, Mar. 8** *Perf. 12½*

**1456** A613 43c multicolored .65 .30
**1457** A613 43c multicolored .65 .30
**1458** A613 43c multicolored .65 .30
**1459** A613 43c multicolored .65 .30
*a.* Block or strip of 4, #1456-1459 2.60 2.25

Natl. Council of Women of Canada (NCWC), and Natl. office of YWCA, cent.

Stanley Cup, Cent. — A614

**1993, Apr. 16** *Perf. 13½*

**1460** A614 43c multicolored .75 .25

Handcrafted Textiles — A615

No. 1461, Coverlet, New Brunswick. No. 1462, Pieced quilt, Ontario. No. 1463, Doukhobor bedcover, Saskatchewan. No. 1464, Kwakwaka'wakw ceremonial robe, British Columbia. No. 1465, Boutonne coverlet, Quebec.

**Booklet Stamps**

***Perf. 13x12½ on 3 Sides***

**1993, Apr. 30**

**1461** A615 43c multicolored .75 .40
**1462** A615 43c multicolored .75 .40
**1463** A615 43c multicolored .75 .40
**1464** A615 43c multicolored .75 .40
**1465** A615 43c multicolored .75 .40
*a.* Strip of 5, #1461-1465 3.75 3.00
*b.* Bklt. pane, 2 ea #1461-1465 7.50
Complete booklet, #1465b 8.50

Stamps in bottom row of No. 1465b are in different sequence than those in No. 1465a.

**Art Type of 1988**

Painting: Drawing for The Owl, by Kenojuak Ashevak.

**Litho. with Foil Application**

**1993, May 17** *Perf. 12½x13½*

**1466** A546 86c multicolored 1.50 1.10

Intl. Year of Indigenous People.

Historic Canadian Pacific Railway Hotels — A616

No. 1467, Empress, Victoria, B.C. No. 1468, Banff Springs, Banff, Alberta. No. 1469, Royal York, Toronto, Ont. No. 1470, Chateau Frontenac, Quebec. No. 1471, Algonquin, St. Andrews, N.B.

**Booklet Stamps**

**1993, June 14** *Perf. 13½ on 3 Sides*

**1467** A616 43c multicolored .90 .60
**1468** A616 43c multicolored .90 .65
**1469** A616 43c multicolored .90 .60
**1470** A616 43c multicolored .90 .60
**1471** A616 43c multicolored .90 .60
*a.* Strip of 5, #1467-1471 4.50 3.50
*b.* Booklet pane, 2 #1471a 9.00
Complete booklet, #1471b 10.00

Opening of Chateau Frontenac, cent.

Miniature Sheet

Canada Day — A617

Provincial and Territorial Parks: No. 1472, Algonquin, Ontario. No. 1473, De la Gaspesie, Quebec. No. 1474, Cedar Dunes, Prince Edward Island. No. 1475, Cape St. Mary's Seabird Ecological Reserve, Newfoundland. No. 1476, Mount Robson, British Columbia. No. 1477, Writing-On-Stone, Alberta. No. 1478, Spruce Woods, Manitoba. No. 1479, Herschel Island, Yukon. No. 1480, Cypress Hills, Saskatchewan. No. 1481, The Rocks, New Brunswick, No. 1482, Blomidon, Nova Scotia. No. 1483, Katannilik, Northwest Territories.

**1993, June 30** *Perf. 13*

**1472** A617 43c multicolored 1.00 1.00
**1473** A617 43c multicolored 1.00 1.00
**1474** A617 43c multicolored 1.00 1.00
**1475** A617 43c multicolored 1.00 1.00
**1476** A617 43c multicolored 1.00 1.00
**1477** A617 43c multicolored 1.00 1.00
**1478** A617 43c multicolored 1.00 1.00
**1479** A617 43c multicolored 1.00 1.00
**1480** A617 43c multicolored 1.00 1.00
**1481** A617 43c multicolored 1.00 1.00
**1482** A617 43c multicolored 1.00 1.00
**1483** A617 43c multicolored 1.00 1.00
*a.* Pane of 12, #1472-1483 12.00 12.00

Algonquin Park, centennial.

City of Toronto, Bicent. — A618

**1993, Aug. 6** *Perf. 13½x13*

**1484** A618 43c multicolored .75 .25

**Canadian Rivers Type of 1991**
**Booklet Stamps**

**1993, Aug. 10** *Perf. 13x12½*

**1485** A586 43c Fraser .75 .40
**1486** A586 43c Yukon .75 .40
**1487** A586 43c Red .75 .40
**1488** A586 43c St. Lawrence .75 .40
**1489** A586 43c St. John .75 .40
*a.* Strip of 5, #1485-1489 3.75 3.50
*b.* Bklt. pane, 2 each #1485-1489 7.50
Complete booklet, #1489b 8.50
*c.* As "a," imperf *2,500.*

Miniature Sheet

Historic Automobiles — A619

a, 1867 H.S. Taylor Steam Buggy. b, 1908 Russell Model L Touring Car. c, 1914 Ford Model T Open Touring Car. d, 1950 Studebaker Champion Deluxe Starlight Coupe. e, 1928 McLaughlin-Buick Model 28-496 Special Car. f, 1923-24 Gray-Dort 25-SM Luxury Sedan.

**1993, Aug. 23** *Perf. 12½x13*

**1490** A619 Pane of 6 7.50 7.50
*a.-b.* 43c any single, 35x22mm .75 .75
*c.-d.* 49c any single, 43x22mm .90 .90
*e.-f.* 86c any single, 51x22mm 1.50 1.40

See Nos. 1527, 1552, 1604-1605.

Folk Songs — A620

Designs: No. 1491, The Alberta Homesteader, Alberta. No. 1492, Les Raftmans, Quebec. No. 1493, I'se the B'y That Builds the Boat, Newfoundland. No. 1494, Onkwa:ri tenhanonniahkwe, Kanien'kehaka (Mohawk).

**1993, Sept. 7** *Perf. 12½*

**1491** A620 43c multicolored .65 .30
**1492** A620 43c multicolored .65 .30
**1493** A620 43c multicolored .65 .30
**1494** A620 43c multicolored .65 .30
*a.* Block of 4, #1491-1494 2.60 2.20

Dinosaurs A621

No. 1495, Massospondylus. No. 1496, Styracosaurus. No. 1497, Albertosaurus. No. 1498, Platecarpus.

**1993, Oct. 1** *Perf. 13½*

**1495** A621 43c multicolored .65 .30
**1496** A621 43c multicolored .65 .30
**1497** A621 43c multicolored .65 .30
**1498** A621 43c multicolored .65 .30
*a.* Block or strip of 4, #1495-1498 2.60 2.20
*b.* As "a," imperf. *2,500.*

See Nos. 1529-1532.

A622

Santa Claus — A623

43c, Swiety Mikolaj. 49c, Ded Moroz. 86c, Father Christmas, Australia. No. 1502, 38c, Santa Claus.

**1993, Nov. 4**

**1499** A622 43c multicolored .65 .25
*a.* Booklet pane of 10 6.50 5.00
Complete booklet, #1499a 7.50
*b.* Horiz. pair, imperf between *1,000.*
**1500** A622 49c multicolored .75 .45
*a.* Booklet pane of 5 + label 3.75 3.25
Complete booklet, #1500a 4.75
**1501** A622 86c multicolored 1.50 .55
*a.* Booklet pane of 5 + label 7.50 6.50
Complete booklet, #1501a 8.50

### Booklet Stamp

***Perf. 13***

**1502** A623 38c multicolored .75 .60
*a.* Booklet pane of 10 7.50 7.00
Complete booklet, #1502a 8.50
*Nos. 1499-1502 (4)* 3.65 1.85

Christmas. No. 1502 has bar code at left; for use on covers with printed postal code matrix.

### World War II Type of 1989

No. 1503, Aid to Allies. No. 1504, Bomber forces. No. 1505, Battle of the Atlantic. No. 1506, Italian campaign.

**1993, Nov. 8** ***Perf. 13½***
**1503** A568 43c ol grn & blk .75 .45
**1504** A568 43c dp turq grn & blk .75 .45
**1505** A568 43c blue & black .75 .45
**1506** A568 43c org brn & blk .75 .45
*a.* Block or strip of 4, #1503-1506 3.00 2.50

Greetings A624

Design: No. 1508, "Canada" at right.

**1994, Jan. 28** ***Die Cut***

**Self-Adhesive**

**1507** A624 43c multicolored .90 .70
**1508** A624 43c multicolored .90 .70
*a.* Bklt. pane of 10, 5 each #1507-1508 9.00

No. 1508a also contains 35 self-adhesive greetings labels in seven designs that complete the design when placed in the central circle of Nos. 1507-1508.

See Nos. 1568-1569, 1600-1601.

Jeanne Sauve (1922-93), Governor General A625

**1994, Mar. 8** ***Perf. 12½x13***
**1509** A625 43c + label, multi .75 .30
*a.* Block or horiz. strip of 4 + 4 labels 3.00 2.25

No. 1509 issued se-tenant with label in sheets of 20 + 20 labels in four designs. In alternating rows, labels appear on left or right side of stamp.

T. Eaton Company, 125th Anniv. — A626

**1994, Mar. 17** ***Perf. 13½x13***
**1510** A626 43c multicolored .75 .30
*a.* Booklet pane of 10 + 2 labels 7.50 6.25
Complete booklet, #1510a 8.50

### Canadian Rivers Type of 1991

### Booklet Stamps

**1994, Apr. 22** ***Perf. 13½***
**1511** A586 43c Saguenay .90 .45
**1512** A586 43c French .90 .45
**1513** A586 43c Mackenzie .90 .45
**1514** A586 43c Churchill .90 .45
**1515** A586 43c Columbia .90 .45
*a.* Strip of 5, #1511-1515 4.50 3.50
*b.* Bklt. pane, 2 ea #1511-1515 9.00 9.00
Complete booklet, #1515b 10.00

### Art Type of 1988

Design: Vera, by Frederick H. Varley (1881-1969).

### Litho. with Foil Application

**1994, May 6** ***Perf. 14x14½***
**1516** A546 88c multicolored 1.50 1.10

XV Commonwealth Games, Victoria, BC — A627

No. 1517, Lawn bowls. No. 1518, Lacrosse. No. 1519, Wheelchair marathon. No. 1520, High jump. No. 1521, Diving. No. 1522, Cycling.

**1994** **Litho.** ***Perf. 14***
**1517** A627 43c multicolored .75 .25
**1518** A627 43c multicolored .75 .25
*a.* Pair, #1517-1518 1.50 1.10
**1519** A627 43c multicolored .75 .25
**1520** A627 43c multicolored .75 .25
*a.* Pair, #1519-1520 1.50 1.10
**1521** A627 50c multicolored .90 .75
*a.* Gold ("CANADA 50") omitted *1,300.*
**1522** A627 88c multicolored 1.50 .90
*a.* Gold ("CANADA 88") omitted *1,600.*
*Nos. 1517-1522 (6)* 5.40 2.65

Certificates of authenticity recommended for Nos. 1521a and 1522a.

Issued: Nos. 1517-1518, 5/20; Nos. 1519-1522, 8/5.

Souvenir Sheet

Intl. Year of the Family A628

Designs: a, Mother and infant. b, Adults, children playing. c, Elderly woman, child. d, Adults, children in class. e, Judge, health care worker, child.

**1994, June 2**
**1523** A628 Pane of 5 3.75 3.75
*a.-e.* 43c any single .75 .75

Canada Day — A629

Maple trees: a, Big leaf. b, Sugar. c, Silver. d, Striped. e, Norway. f, Manitoba. g, Black. h, Douglas. i, Mountain. j, Vine. k, Hedge. l, Red.

**1994, June 30** ***Perf. 13x13½***
**1524** A629 Pane of 12 9.00 9.00
*a.-l.* 43c any single .75 .75

A630

No. 1525, Billy Bishop (1894-1956), Fighter Ace. No. 1526, Mary Travers, "La Bolduc" (1894-1941), folk singer.

**1994, Aug. 12** ***Perf. 13***
**1525** 43c multicolored .65 .30
**1526** 43c multicolored .65 .30
*a.* A630 Pair, #1525-1526 1.30 .90

### Historic Vehicles Type of 1993

Miniature Sheet

Designs: a, 1942 Ford F60L-AMB military ambulance. b, 1925 REO Speed Wagon Police Wagon. c, 1927 Sicard Snow Remover/Snowblower. d, 1936 Bickle Chieftain Fire Engine. e, 1894 Ottawa Car Company Streetcar. f, 1950 Motor Coach Industries Courier 50 Skyview bus.

**1994, Aug. 19** ***Perf. 12½x13***
**1527** Pane of 6 6.75 6.75
*a.-b.* A619 43c any single .75 .75
*c.-d.* A619 50c any single .90 .90
*e.-f.* A619 88c any single 1.70 1.60

ICAO, 50th Anniv. — A632

**1994, Sept. 16** ***Perf. 13***
**1528** A632 43c multicolored 1.10 .25

### Dinosaur Type of 1993

Prehistoric animals: No. 1529, Coryphodon. No. 1530, Megacerops. No. 1531, Short-faced bear. No. 1532, Woolly mammoth.

**1994, Sept. 26**
**1529** A621 43c multicolored .65 .30
**1530** A621 43c multicolored .65 .30
**1531** A621 43c multicolored .65 .30
**1532** A621 43c multicolored .65 .30
*a.* Block or strip of 4, #1529-1532 2.60 2.20

Family Singing Carols — A633 Soloist — A634

**1994, Nov. 3** ***Perf. 13½***
**1533** A633 43c multicolored .65 .25
*a.* Booklet pane of 10 6.50 6.50
Complete booklet, #1533a 7.00
**1534** A633 50c Choir, vert. .75 .55
*a.* Booklet pane of 5 + label 5.00 4.00
Complete booklet, #1534a 5.50
**1535** A633 88c Caroling, vert. 1.50 .90
*a.* Booklet pane of 5 + label 7.50 7.00
Complete booklet, #1535a 8.00

### Booklet Stamp

***Perf. 13***

**1536** A634 38c multicolored .75 .55
*a.* Booklet pane of 10 7.50 6.00
Complete booklet, #1536a 8.00
*Nos. 1533-1536 (4)* 3.65 2.25

Christmas. No. 1536 has bar code at left; for use on covers with printed postal code matrix.

Examples exist of 52c and 90c denominations with the same designs as Nos. 1534 (52c) and 1535 (90c). These were prepared in advance in anticipation of a rate increase that was not approved. Virtually all were destroyed, but a small quantity are known in private hands. None were regularly issued or sold at post offices. Values: 52c, $150; 90c, $425.

### World War II Type of 1989

No. 1537, D-Day beachhead. No. 1538, Artillery-Normandy. No. 1539, Tactical Air Forces. No. 1540, Walcheren and the Scheldt.

**1994, Nov. 7** ***Perf. 13½***
**1537** A568 43c multicolored .90 .35
**1538** A568 43c multicolored .90 .35
**1539** A568 43c multicolored .90 .35
**1540** A568 43c multicolored .90 .35
*a.* Block or strip of 4, #1537-1540 3.60 2.20

### World War II Type of 1989

No. 1541, Veterans return home. No. 1542, Freeing the POW. No. 1543, Liberation of civilians. No. 1544, Crossing the Rhine.

**1995, Mar. 20**
**1541** A568 43c multicolored .90 .35
**1542** A568 43c multicolored .90 .35
**1543** A568 43c multicolored .90 .35
**1544** A568 43c multicolored .90 .35
*a.* Block or strip of 4, #1541-1544 3.60 3.00

### Art Type of 1988

Painting: Floraison, by Alfred Pellan (1906-88).

### Litho. with Foil Application

**1995, Apr. 21** ***Perf. 13***
**1545** A546 88c multicolored 1.70 1.10
*a.* Gold foil omitted *1,400.*

Flag Over Lake — A635

**1995, May 1** **Litho.** ***Perf. 13½x13***
**1546** A635 (43c) multicolored .90 .25

No. 1546 was valued at the first class domestic letter rate on day of issue.

Fortress of Louisbourg, 275th Anniv. A636

No. 1547, Louisbourg Harbor, ships near Dauphin Gate. No. 1548, Walls, streets, buildings of Louisbourg. No. 1549, Museum behind King's Bastion. No. 1550, Drawing of King's Garden, Convent, Hospital and barracks. No. 1551, Partially eroded fortifications.

**1995, May 5** ***Perf. 12½x13***
**1547** A636 (43c) 48x32mm .75 .40
**1548** A636 (43c) 32x32mm .75 .40
**1549** A636 (43c) 40x32mm .75 .40
**1550** A636 (43c) 56x32mm .75 .40
**1551** A636 (43c) 48x32mm .75 .40
*a.* Strip of 5, #1547-1551 3.75 3.25
*b.* Booklet pane, 2 #1551a 7.50 6.75
Complete booklet, #1551b 7.75

Nos. 1547-1551 were valued at the first class domestic letter rate on day of issue. No. 1551a is a continuous design.

### Historic Vehicles Type of 1993

Miniature Sheet

Farm, frontier vehicles: a, 1950 Cockshutt "30" farm tractor. b, 1970 Bombardier Ski-Doo Olympique 335 snowmobile. c, 1948 Bombardier B-12 CS multi-passenger snowmobile. d, 1924 Gotfredson model 20 farm truck. e, 1962 Robin-Nodwell RN 110 tracked carrier. f, 1942 Massey-Harris No. 21 self-propelled combine.

**1995, May 26**
**1552** Pane of 6 7.00 7.00
*a.-b.* A619 43c any single, 35x22mm .75 .75
*c.-d.* A619 50c any single, 43x22mm .95 .95
*e.-f.* A619 88c any single, 43x22mm 1.80 1.80

Golf in Canada — A637

Designs: No. 1553, Banff Springs Golf Club. No. 1554, Riverside Country Club. No. 1555, Glen Abbey Golf Club. No. 1556, Victoria Golf Club. No. 1557, Royal Montreal Golf Club.

### Booklet Stamps

***Perf. 13½x13 on 3 Sides***

**1995, June 6**
**1553** A637 43c multicolored .90 .40
**1554** A637 43c multicolored .90 .40
**1555** A637 43c multicolored .90 .40
**1556** A637 43c multicolored .90 .40
**1557** A637 43c multicolored .90 .40
*a.* Strip of 5, #1553-1557 4.50 3.75
*b.* Booklet pane, 2 #1557a 9.00 8.00
Complete booklet, #1557b 9.50

Nat. Golf Week. Canadian Amateur Golf Championship, cent. Royal Canadian Golf Assoc., cent.

Lunenburg Academy, Cent. — A638

**1995, June 29** ***Perf. 13***
**1558** A638 43c multicolored .65 .25

Souvenir Sheets

Group of Seven A639

Painting, original members: No. 1559a, October Gold, by Franklin Carmichael. b, From the North Shore, Lake Superior, by Lawren Harris. c, Evening, Les Eboulements, Quebec, by A.Y. Jackson.

No. 1560a, Serenity, Lake of the Woods, by Frank H. Johnston. b, A September Gale, Georgian Bay, by Arthur Lismer. c, Falls, Montreal River, by J.E.H. MacDonald. d, Open Window, by Frederick Horsman Varley.

Painting, new members: No. 1561a, Mill Houses, by Alfred J. Casson. b, Pembina Valley, by Lionel LeMoine FitzGerald. c, The Lumberjack, by Edwin Headley Holgate.

**1995, June 29**
**1559** A639 Pane of 3 2.75 2.75
*a.-c.* 43c any single .90 .90
**1560** A639 Pane of 4 3.60 3.60
*a.-d.* 43c any single .90 .90
**1561** A639 Pane of 3 2.75 2.75
*a.-c.* 43c any single .90 .90

Manitoba's Entry Into Confederation, 125th Anniv. — A640

**1995, July 14** *Perf. 13½x13*
**1562** A640 43c multicolored .65 .30

Migratory Wildlife — A641

No. 1563, Monarch butterfly. No. 1564, Belted kingfisher. No. 1565, Northern pintail. No. 1566, Hoary bat.

**1995, Aug. 15** *Perf. 13x12½*
**1563** A641 45c multicolored .75 .25
**1564** A641 45c multicolored .75 .40
**1565** A641 45c multicolored .75 .25
**1566** A641 45c multicolored .75 .25
*a.* Block or strip of 4, #1563-1566 3.00 2.50

### No. 1564 with Revised Inscription

**1995, Sept. 26**
**1567** A641 45c like #1564 .90 .75
*a.* Block or strip of 4, #1563, 1565-1567 3.60 3.60

No. 1564 inscribed "aune," No. 1567 "Faune." See Mexico No. 1924.

### Greetings Type of 1994

Designs: No. 1568, "Canada" at left. No. 1569, "Canada" at right.

### Self-Adhesive
### Size: 46x22mm

**1995, Sept. 1** *Die Cut*
**1568** A624 45c green & multi .90 .75
**1569** A624 45c green & multi .90 .75
*a.* Bklt. pane, 5 ea #1568-1569 9.00

By its nature, No. 1569a is a complete booklet. The peelable backing serves as a booklet cover.

No. 1569a also contains 15 self-adhesive greetings labels in four designs that complete the design when placed in the central circle of Nos. 1568-1569.

No. 1569a exists with special cover and labels commemorating the Canadian Memorial Chiropractic College, Toronto, 50th anniv.

Bridges — A642

No. 1570, Quebec Bridge, Quebec. No. 1571, Highway 403-401-410 interchange, Ontario. No. 1572, Hartland Covered Wooden Bridge, New Brunswick. No. 1573, Alex Fraser Bridge, British Columbia.

**1995, Sept. 1** *Perf. 12½x13*
**1570** A642 45c multicolored .75 .30
**1571** A642 45c multicolored .75 .30
**1572** A642 45c multicolored .75 .30
**1573** A642 45c multicolored .75 .30
*a.* Block or strip of 4, #1570-1573 3.00 2.50

Canadian Arctic — A643

No. 1574, Polar bear, caribou. No. 1575, Arctic poppy, cargo canoe. No. 1576, Inuk man, igloo, sled dogs. No. 1577, Dog-sled team, ski plane. No. 1578, Children.

### Booklet Stamps

**1995, Sept. 15** *Perf. 13x12½*
**1574** A643 45c multicolored .75 .30
**1575** A643 45c multicolored .75 .30
**1576** A643 45c multicolored .75 .30
**1577** A643 45c multicolored .75 .30
**1578** A643 45c multicolored .75 .30
*a.* Strip of 5, #1574-1578 3.75 3.25
*b.* Bklt. pane, 2 #1578a 7.50 7.50
Complete booklet, #1578b 8.00

Stamps in bottom row of No. 1578b are in different sequence.

Comic Book Characters — A644

No. 1579, Superman. No. 1580, Johnny Canuck. No. 1581, Nelvana. No. 1582, Captain Canuck. No. 1583, Fleur de Lys.

### Booklet Stamps

**1995, Oct. 2** *Perf. 13x12½*
**1579** A644 45c multi 1.10 .40
**1580** A644 45c multi 1.10 .40
**1581** A644 45c multi 1.10 .40
**1582** A644 45c multi 1.10 .40
**1583** A644 45c multi 1.10 .40
*a.* Strip of 5, #1579-1583 5.50 5.00
*b.* Booklet pane, 2 #1583a 11.00 11.00
Complete booklet, #1583b 11.50

Stamps in the bottom row of No. 1583b are in different sequence.

UN, 50th Anniv. — A645

**1995, Oct. 24** *Perf. 13½*
**1584** A645 45c blue & multi 1.20 .25

No. 1584 printed in panes of 10 with top label equal to 10 stamps. Label shows details of Canadian participation in UN activities. UN emblem on No. 1584 is stamped in blue foil.

Capital Sculptures, by Emile Brunet (1893-1977), Sainte-Anne-de-Deaupre Basilica — A646

Holly — A647

45c, The Nativity. 52c, The Annunciation. 90c, Flight to Egypt.

**1995, Nov. 2**
**1585** A646 45c multicolored .70 .25
*a.* Booklet pane of 10 7.00 5.50
Complete booklet, #1585a 7.50
**1586** A646 52c multicolored .85 .50
*a.* Booklet pane of 5 + label 4.25 4.25
Complete booklet, #1586a 4.50
**1587** A646 90c multicolored 1.40 .60
*a.* Booklet pane of 5 + label 7.00 7.00
Complete booklet, #1587a 7.50

### Booklet Stamp
### *Perf. 12½x13*

**1588** A647 40c multicolored .75 .75
*a.* Booklet pane of 10 7.50 *10.00*
Complete booklet, #1588a 7.75
*Nos. 1585-1588 (4)* 3.70 2.10

Christmas. No. 1588 has bar code at left; for use on covers with printed postal code matrix.

La Francophonie's Agency for Cultural and Technical Cooperation, 25th Anniv. — A648

**1995, Nov. 6** *Perf. 13x13½*
**1589** A648 45c multicolored .70 .25

End of the Holocaust, 50th Anniv. A649

**1995, Nov. 9** *Perf. 12½x13*
**1590** A649 45c multicolored .70 .25

Birds — A650

No. 1591, American kestrel. No. 1592, Atlantic puffin. No. 1593, Pileated woodpecker. No. 1594, Ruby-throated hummingbird.

**1996, Jan. 9** *Perf. 13½*
**1591** A650 45c multicolored .75 .30
**1592** A650 45c multicolored .75 .30
**1593** A650 45c multicolored .75 .30
**1594** A650 45c multicolored .75 .30
*a.* Strip of 4, Nos. 1591-1594 3.00 2.75

Issued in panes of 12 stamps, printed checkerwise, and in uncut sheets of 5 panes.

See Nos. 1631-1634, 1710-1713, 1770-1777, 1839-1846, 1886-1893.

High Technology Industries A651

Designs: No. 1595, Ocean technology. No. 1596, Aerospace technology. No. 1597, Information technology. No. 1598, Biotechnology.

### Booklet Stamps

**1996, Feb. 15** *Perf. 13½ on 3 Sides*
**1595** A651 45c multicolored .90 .35
**1596** A651 45c multicolored .90 .35
**1597** A651 45c multicolored .90 .35
**1598** A651 45c multicolored .90 .35
*a.* Booklet pane of 12, 3 each Nos. 1595-1598 11.00 7.50
Complete booklet, No. 1598a 11.50
*Nos. 1595-1598 (4)* 3.60 1.40

### Greetings Type of 1994

"Canada": No. 1600, at L. No. 1601, at R.

### Self-Adhesive
### Size: 51x25mm

**1996, Jan. 15** *Die Cut*
**1600** A624 45c green & multi 1.50 1.20
**1601** A624 45c green & multi 1.50 1.20
*a.* Booklet pane, 5 ea #1600-1601 15.00
*b.* As "a," die cutting omitted *3,250.*
*c.* Imperf., pair *650.00*

By its nature No. 1601a is a complete booklet. The peelable backing serves as a booklet cover.

No. 1601a also contains 35 self-adhesive greetings labels in seven designs that complete the design when placed in the central circle of Nos. 1600-1601.

### Art Type of 1988

Sculpture: The Spirit of Haida Gwaii, by Bill Reid.

### Litho. with Foil Application

**1996, Apr. 30** *Perf. 12½x13*
**1602** A546 90c multicolored 1.50 1.00

AIDS Awareness A652

**1996, May 8** **Litho.** *Perf. 13½*
**1603** A652 45c multicolored .70 .25

### Historic Vehicles Type of 1993

No. 1604: a, 1899 Still Motor Co. Ltd. Electric Van. b. 1914 Waterous Engine Works Road Roller. c, 1938 International D-35 Delivery Truck. d, 1936 Champion Road Grader. e, 1947 White Model WA 122 Tractor Trailer. f, 1975 Hayes HDX 45-115 Logging Truck.

No. 1605: a, like #1490a. b, like #1490b. c, like 1527a. d, like #1527b. e, like #1552b. f, like #1604a. g, like #1604b, h, like #1552a. i, like #1604c. j, like 1604d. k, like #1527e. l, like #1527f. m, like #1604e. n, like #1604f. o, like #1490c. p, like #1490d. q, like #1527d. r, like #1490e. s, like #1490f. t, like #1527c. u, like #1552c. v, like #1552d. w, like #1552e. x, like #1552f. y, 1975 Bricklin SV-1 Sports car.

**1996** *Perf. 12½x13*
**1604** A619 Pane of 6 6.25 6.25
*a.-b.* 45c any single .80 .80
*c.-d.* 52c any single .90 .90
*e.-f.* 90c any single 1.60 1.60
**1605** A619 Pane of 25 7.00 7.00
*a.-j.* 5c any single .25 .25
*k.-n.* 10c any single .30 .30
*o.-x.* 20c any single .45 .45
*y.* 45c multicolored 1.00 1.00

Nos. 1604e-1604f, 1605k-1605n, 1605y are 51x22mm. Nos. 1605o-1605x are 43x21mm.

Yukon Gold Rush, Cent. — A653

Designs: a, "Skookum" Jim Mason's discovery on Rabbit (Bonanza) Creek, 1896. b, Miners trekking to gold fields, boats on Lake Laberge. c, Supr. Sam Steele, North West Mounted Police, Alaska-Yukon border. d, Dawson, boom town, city of entertainment. e, Klondike gold fields.

**1996, June 13** *Perf. 13½*
**1606** A653 Strip of 5 5.50 4.75
*a.-e.* 45c any single 1.10 .60

CAPEX '96. No. 1606 was issued in panes of 10 stamps.

Canada Day — A654

### Self-Adhesive

**1996, June 28** *Die Cut*
**1607** A654 45c multicolored .75 .25
*a.* Pane of 12 9.00 4.00

Canadian Olympic Gold Medalists — A655

No. 1608, Ethel Catherwood, high jump, 1928. No. 1609, Etienne Desmarteau, 56 lb. weight throw, 1904. No. 1610, Fanny Rosenfeld, 100m, 400m relay, 1928. No. 1611, Gerald Ouellette, smallbore rifle, prone, 1956. No. 1612, Percy Williams, 100m, 200m, 1928.

### Booklet Stamps
### Litho. & Typo.

**1996, July 8** *Perf. 13x12½*
**1608** A655 45c multicolored 1.10 .60
**1609** A655 45c multicolored 1.10 .60
**1610** A655 45c multicolored 1.10 .60
**1611** A655 45c multicolored 1.10 .60
**1612** A655 45c multicolored 1.10 .60
*a.* Strip of 5, #1608-1612 5.50 4.00
*b.* Booklet pane, 2 #1612a 11.00
Complete booklet, #1612b 11.50

British Columbia's Entry Into Confederation, 125th Anniv. — A656

**1996, July 19**
**1613** A656 45c multicolored .70 .25

Canadian Heraldry — A657

**1996, Aug. 19 Litho.** ***Perf. 12½x12***

**1614** A657 45c multicolored .70 .25

Motion Pictures, Cent. — A658

Film strips from motion pictures: No. 1615a, L'arrivée d'un train en gare, Lumière cinematography, 1896. b, Back to God's Country, Nell & Ernest Shipman, 1919. c, Hen Hop, Norman McLaren, 1942. d, Pour la suite du monde, Pierre Perrault, Michel Brault, 1963. e, Goin' Down the Road, Don Shebib, 1970.

No. 1616a, Mon oncle Antoine, Claude Jutra, 1971. b, The Apprenticeship of Duddy Kravitz, Ted Kotcheff, 1974. c, Les Ordres, Michel Brault, 1974. d, Les Bons Débarras, Francis Mankiewiez, 1980. e, The Grey Fox, Philip Borsos, 1982.

### Self-Adhesive

**1996, Aug. 22** ***Die Cut***

**1615** Pane of 5 3.50 3.50
*a.-e.* A658 45c Any single .70 .70
**1616** Pane of 5 3.50 3.50
*a.-e.* A658 45c Any single .70 .70

Edouard Montpetit (1881-1954), Educator — A659

**1996, Sept. 26** ***Perf. 12½***

**1617** A659 45c multicolored .70 .25

Winnie the Pooh — A660

Designs: No. 1618, Winnie, Lt. Colebourne, 1914. No. 1619, Winnie, Christopher Robin, 1925. No. 1620, Milne and Shepard's Winnie the Pooh, 1926. No. 1621, Winnie the Pooh at Walt Disney World, 1996.

**1996, Oct. 1** ***Perf. 12½x13***

**1618** A660 45c multicolored .75 .40
**1619** A660 45c multicolored .75 .40
**1620** A660 45c multicolored .75 .40
**1621** A660 45c multicolored .75 .40
*a.* Block of 4, #1618-1621 3.00 2.50
*b.* Souv. sheet of 4, #1618-1621 7.50 7.50
*c.* Booklet pane of 16, 4 each #1618-1621 12.00 12.00
Complete booklet, #1621c 12.50

No. 1621c was issued with the halves of the booklet pane printed tete-beche. The booklet pane of 16 was used as a cover for a souvenir story booklet.

Walt Disney World, 25th anniv.

Authors — A661

No. 1622, Margaret Laurence (1926-87). No. 1623, Donald G. Creighton (1902-79). No. 1624, Gabrielle Roy (1909-83). No. 1625, Felix-Antoine Savard (1896-1982). No. 1626, Thomas C. Haliburton (1796-1865).

### Booklet Stamps

***Perf. 13½x13 on 3 Sides***

**1996, Oct. 10 Litho. & Engr.**

**1622** A661 45c multicolored 1.10 .40
**1623** A661 45c multicolored 1.10 .40
**1624** A661 45c multicolored 1.10 .40
**1625** A661 45c multicolored 1.10 .40
**1626** A661 45c multicolored 1.10 .40
*a.* Strip of 5, #1622-1626 5.50 5.00
*b.* Booklet pane, 2 #1626a 11.00 12.00
Complete booklet, #1626b 11.50

A662

Christmas: 45c, Children on snowshoes, sled. 52c, Santa Claus skiing. 90c, Children skating.

***Perf. 13½ (#1627, 1629a), 12¾x12¼ (#1628, 1629), 13½x13 (#1627a, 1628a)***

**1996, Nov. 1 Litho.**

**1627** A662 45c multicolored .70 .25
*a.* Booklet pane of 10 7.00 7.00
Complete booklet, #1627a 7.50
**1628** A662 52c multicolored .85 .25
*a.* Booklet pane of 5 + label 4.25 4.75
Complete booklet, #1628a 4.50
**1629** A662 90c multicolored 1.40 .50
*a.* Booklet pane of 5 + label 7.00 7.00
Complete booklet, #1629a 7.50

UNICEF, 50th anniv.

New Year 1997 (Year of the Ox) — A663

**1997, Jan. 7** ***Perf. 13x12½***

**1630** A663 45c multicolored .90 .25
*a.* Souvenir sheet of 2 2.60 2.60
*b.* As No. 1630, gold omitted *3,250.*
*c.* As "a," gold omitted *8,000.*

No. 1630a is fan shaped.

No. 1630a with Hong Kong 97 overprint was sold as a limited edition only at the show. Value $7.50.

### Bird Type of 1996

No. 1631, Mountain bluebird. No. 1632, Western grebe. No. 1633, Northern gannet. No. 1634, Scarlet tanager.

**1997, Jan. 10** ***Perf. 12½x13***

**1631** A650 45c multicolored .75 .25
**1632** A650 45c multicolored .75 .25
**1633** A650 45c multicolored .75 .25
**1634** A650 45c multicolored .75 .25
*a.* Block or strip of 4, #1631-1634 3.00 2.50

Nos. 1631-1634 were issued in panes of 20, 5 each, printed checkerwise to contain 4 complete blocks or 5 strips.

### Art Type of 1988

Painting: York Boat on Lake Winnipeg, by Walter J. Phillips.

### Litho. with Foil Application

**1997, Feb. 17**

**1635** A546 90c gold & multi 1.80 1.10

Canadian Tire, 75th Anniv. — A664

**1997, Mar. 3 Litho.** ***Perf. 13x13½***

**1636** A664 45c multicolored .75 .25

Father Charles-Emile Gadbois (1906-81), Musicologist — A665

**1997, Mar. 20** ***Perf. 13½x13***

**1637** A665 45c multicolored .75 .25

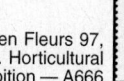

Québec en Fleurs 97, Intl. Horticultural Exhibition — A666

### Booklet Stamps

***Perf. 13x12½ on 3 Sides***

**1997, Apr. 4**

**1638** A666 45c Blue poppy .75 .25
*a.* Booklet pane of 12 9.00 10.00
Complete booklet, #1638a 9.50

Victorian Order of Nurses for Canada, Cent. — A667

**1997, May 12** ***Perf. 12½x13***

**1639** A667 45c multicolored .75 .25

Law Society of Upper Canada, Bicent. — A668

**1997, May 23** ***Perf. 13½x13***

**1640** A668 45c multicolored .75 .25

Salt Water Fish — A669

No. 1641, Great white shark. No. 1642, Pacific halibut. No. 1643, Atlantic sturgeon. No. 1644, Bluefin tuna.

**1997, May 30** ***Perf. 12½x13***

**1641** A669 45c multicolored .70 .25
**1642** A669 45c multicolored .70 .25
**1643** A669 45c multicolored .70 .25
**1644** A669 45c multicolored .70 .25
*a.* Block or strip of 4, #1641-1644 2.80 2.20

Opening of the Confederation Bridge A670

No. 1645, Lighthouse, bridge. No. 1646, Bridge, bird.

**1997, May 31**

**1645** A670 45c multicolored .70 .25
**1646** A670 45c multicolored .70 .25
*a.* Pair, #1645-1646 + label 1.40 1.10

Gilles Villeneuve (1950-82), Formula One Race Car Driver — A671

45c, Villeneuve winning race in Ferrari T-4. 90c, Close-up, racing in Number 12 Ferrari T-3.

**1997, June 12**

**1647** A671 45c multicolored .75 .25
**1648** A671 90c multicolored 1.50 .90
*a.* Pair, #1647-1648 2.25 2.25
*b.* Pane of 4 #1648a 9.00 9.00

A672

**1997, June 24**

**1649** A672 45c multicolored .75 .25

John Cabot's Voyage to Canada, 500th Anniv.

Joint issue between Canada and Italy. See Italy No. 2162.

Scenic Canadian Highways — A673

Designs: No. 1650, Sea to Sky Highway, British Columbia. No. 1651, The Cabot Trail, Nova Scotia. No. 1652, The Wine Route, starting in Ontario. No. 1653, The Big Muddy, Saskatchewan.

**1997, June 30**

**1650** A673 45c multicolored .70 .40
**1651** A673 45c multicolored .70 .40
**1652** A673 45c multicolored .70 .40
**1653** A673 45c multicolored .70 .40
*a.* Block or strip of 4, #1650-1653 2.80 2.25

See Nos. 1739-1742, 1780-1783.

Canadian Industrial Design A674

**1997, July 23**

**1654** A674 45c multicolored .70 .25

No. 1654 was issued with se-tenant label in panes of 24 + 24 labels. The 12 different labels each appear twice in different colors. In alternating rows, labels appear on left or right side of stamp.

Association of Canadian Industrial Designers, 50th anniv. and 20th Intl. Congress of Intl. Council of Societies of Industrial Design.

Highland Games, Maxville, Ontario A675

**1997, Aug. 1**

**1655** A675 45c multicolored .70 .25

Knights of Columbus in Canada, Cent. — A676

**1997, Aug. 5** ***Perf. 13***

**1656** A676 45c multicolored .70 .25

28th World Congress of Postal, Telegraph and Telephone Intl. Labor Union, Montreal — A677

**1997, Aug. 18**

**1657** A677 45c multicolored .70 .25

Asia Pacific Year — A678

**1997, Aug. 25** ***Perf. 13½***

**1658** A678 45c multicolored .70 .25

Canada-USSR Ice Hockey "Series of the Century," 25th Anniv. — A679

Designs: No. 1659, Canadian players, Paul Henderson, Yvan Cournoyer (No. 12), after scoring winning goal in final game. No. 1660, Canadian team members celebrating victory.

### Booklet Stamps

**1997, Sept. 20** *Perf. 14x13*

**1659** A679 45c multicolored .75 .30
**1660** A679 45c multicolored .75 .30
*a.* Bklt. pane, 5 ea #1659-1660 7.50 8.00
Complete booklet, #1660a 8.00

Famous Politicians — A680

No. 1661, Martha Black (1866-1957). No. 1662, Lionel Chevrier (1903-87). No. 1663, Judy LaMarsh (1924-80). No. 1664, Réal Caouette (1917-76).

**1997, Sept. 26** *Perf. 13½x13*

**1661** A680 45c multicolored .70 .35
**1662** A680 45c multicolored .70 .35
**1663** A680 45c multicolored .70 .35
*a.* Double impression of "Canada 45" 55.00
*b.* Quadruple impression of "Canada 45" 300.00
**1664** A680 45c multicolored .70 .35
*a.* Quintuple impression of "Canada 45" 375.00
*b.* Block or strip of 4, #1661-1664 2.80 2.25

Supernatural — A681

**1997, Oct. 1** *Perf. 13x12½*

**1665** A681 45c Vampire .70 .35
**1666** A681 45c Werewolf .70 .35
**1667** A681 45c Ghost .70 .35
**1668** A681 45c Goblin .70 .35
*a.* Block of 4, #1665-1668 2.80 2.25

Christmas A682

Stained glass windows: 45c, "Our Lady of the Rosary," Holy Rosary Cathedral, Vancouver. 52c, "Nativity Scene," United Church, Leith, Ontario. 90c, Madonna and Child, St. Stephen's Ukrainian Byzantine Rite Roman Catholic Church, Calgary.

**1997, Nov. 3** *Perf. 12½x13*

**1669** A682 45c multicolored .70 .25
*a.* Booklet pane of 10 7.00 7.00
Complete booklet, #1669a 7.50
**1670** A682 52c multicolored .80 .35
*a.* Booklet pane of 5 4.00 4.00
Complete booklet, #1670a 4.25
**1671** A682 90c multicolored 1.40 .55
*a.* Booklet pane of 5 7.00 7.00
Complete booklet, #1671a 7.50
*Nos. 1669-1671 (3)* 2.90 1.15

75th Royal Agriculture Winter Fair, Toronto — A683

**1997, Nov. 6**

**1672** A683 45c multicolored .70 .25

### Types of 1987-98 and

Traditional Handiwork A684

Maple Leaf A685

Loon — A686

Moose A687

Flag and Inukshuk — A688

Designs: 1c, Bookbinding. 2c, Ironwork. 3c, Glass blowing. 4c, Oyster farmer. 5c, Weaving. 9c, Quilting. 10c, Artistic woodworking. 25c, Leatherwork. Nos. 1682, 1698, Flag over icebergs. No. 1688, White-tailed deer. No. 1689, Atlantic walrus. No. 1690, Polar bear. No. 1691, Peregrine falcon. No. 1692, Sable Island horses. $8, Grizzly bear.

**1997-2005** **Litho.** *Perf. 13¼*

**1673** A684 1c multicolored .30 .25
*a.* Gray (in numeral "1") omitted 300.00 —
**1674** A684 2c multicolored .30 .25
**1675** A684 3c multicolored .30 .25
**1676** A684 4c multicolored .30 .25
*a.* Imperf., pair 800.00
**1677** A684 5c multicolored .30 .25
**1678** A684 9c multicolored .30 .25
**1679** A684 10c multicolored .30 .25
*a.* Imperf, single *450.00*
*b.* Block of 4, top two stamps imperf (cut between) —
*c.* Imperf., vert. pair *750.00*
**1680** A684 25c multicolored .40 .25

*Perf. 13¼x13*

**1681** A536 46c multicolored .75 .25

*Perf. 13x13¼*

**1682** A541 46c multicolored .75 .25
*a.* Booklet pane of 10 7.50 *11.00*
Complete booklet, #1682a 8.00

*Perf. 13¼x13*

**1683** A536 47c multicolored .75 .25
*a.* Imperf, pair *600.00*
*b.* Block of 4, bottom pair imperf., top pair part perf. *750.00*

*Perf. 13x13¼*

**1684** A685 55c multicolored .90 .25
*a.* Booklet pane of 5 + label 4.50 3.75
Complete booklet, #1684a 4.75
**1685** A685 73c multicolored 1.15 .40
**1686** A685 95c multicolored 1.70 .50
*a.* Booklet pane of 5 + label 8.50 8.00
Complete booklet, #1686a 9.00

**Litho. & Engr.**

*Perf. 13¼x13*

**1687** A686 $1 multicolored 1.60 .55

*Perf. 12½x13*

**1688** A686 $1 multicolored 1.60 .55
**1689** A686 $1 multicolored 1.60 .55
*a.* Pair, #1688-1689 3.20 2.50
*b.* Souvenir sheet, 2 each #1688-1689 7.50 7.50

*Perf. 13¼x13*

**1690** A686 $2 multicolored 3.25 1.00

*Perf. 12½x13*

**1691** A686 $2 multicolored 3.25 1.00
**1692** A686 $2 multicolored 3.25 1.00
*a.* Pair, #1691-1692 6.50 4.75
*b.* Souvenir sheet, 2 each #1691-1692 15.00 15.00

**Size 63x48mm**

**1693** A687 $5 multicolored 8.00 2.00
*a.* Engraved colors (Moose, etc.) omitted *5,500.*
**1694** A687 $8 multicolored 12.50 4.50
*Nos. 1673-1694 (22)* 43.55 15.05

**Coil Stamp**

**Engr.**

*Perf. 10 Horiz.*

**1695** A542 46c red .75 .25
*a.* Imperf, pair 150.00

**Photo.**

**Booklet Stamp**

**Self-Adhesive**

*Die Cut*

**1696** A685 45c multicolored 1.30 *2.00*
*a.* Booklet pane of 18 25.00

**Typo. & Embossed**

*Die Cut Perf. 13*

**Coil Stamp**

**1697** A685 45c multicolored 1.10 .75

**Litho.**

**Booklet Stamps**

*Die Cut*

**1698** A541 46c multicolored .90 .25
*a.* Booklet pane of 30 22.50
*b.* Imperf, pair *300.00*
*c.* Vert. strip of 3, die cutting omitted between bottom pair 100.00

**Photo.**

**1699** A685 46c multicolored 2.75 2.75
*a.* Booklet pane of 18 50.00

**Litho.**

**1700** A688 47c multicolored .75 .25
*a.* Booklet of 10 7.50
*b.* Booklet of 30 22.50
*c.* All colors omitted 225.00
*d.* As "a," all colors omitted 2,250.
*e.* As "a," die cutting omitted 1,750.

Nos. 1696a, 1698a-1699a are complete booklets. The peelable backing serves as a booklet cover.

Issued: Nos. 1681, 1682, 1684-1686, 1695, 1698-1700, 12/28/98; No. 1693, 12/19/03; No. 1694, 10/15; No. 1696, 4/14/98. No. 1697, 9/30/98; Nos. 1687, 1690, 10/27/98; Nos. 1673-1680, 4/29/99; No. 1683, 12/28/00; Nos. 1688-1689, 10/20/05; Nos. 1691-1692, 12/19/05.

No. 1697 does not have the "POSTAGE / POSTES" and copyright inscriptions found in No. 1696. The gold on No. 1697 is embossed and brighter than that on No. 1696.

On Nos. 1700c and 1700d, the booklet cover on the reverse side is properly printed, and the tagging is printed as normal.

See Nos. 1928-1930.

New Year 1998 (Year of the Tiger) — A690

**1998, Jan. 8** **Litho.** *Perf. 13x12½*

**1708** A690 45c multicolored .75 .25
*a.* Souvenir sheet of 2 1.60 1.40

No. 1708a overprinted exists. Value $3.

Provincial Leaders — A691

Designs: a, John P. Robarts (1917-82), Ontario. b, Jean Lesage (1912-80), Quebec. c, John B. McNair (1889-1968), New Brunswick. d, Tommy Douglas (1904-86), Saskatchewan. e, Joseph R. Smallwood (1900-91), Newfoundland. f, Angus L. MacDonald (1890-1954), Nova Scotia. g, W.A.C. Bennett (1900-79), British Columbia. h, Ernest C. Manning (1908-95), Alberta. i, John Bracken (1883-1969), Manitoba. j, J. Walter Jones (1878-1954), Prince Edward Island.

**1998, Feb. 18** *Perf. 13½*

**1709** A691 Sheet of 10 11.00 9.00
*a.-j.* 45c any single 1.10 .75

### Bird Type of 1996

No. 1710, Hairy woodpecker. No. 1711, Great crested flycatcher. No. 1712, Eastern screech owl. No. 1713, Gray-crowned rosy-finch.

**1998, Mar. 13** *Perf. 13x13½*

**1710** A650 45c multicolored .75 .30
**1711** A650 45c multicolored .75 .30
**1712** A650 45c multicolored .75 .30
**1713** A650 45c multicolored .75 .30
*a.* Block or strip of 4, #1710-1713 3.00 2.25

Nos. 1710-1713 were issued in panes of 20, 5 each, printed checkerwise to contain 4 complete blocks or 5 strips.

Fly Fishing in Canada A693

Lure, type of fish: No. 1715, Coquihalla orange, steelhead trout. No. 1716, Steelhead bee, steelhead trout. No. 1717, Dark Montreal, brook trout. No. 1718, Lady Amherst, Atlantic salmon. No. 1719, Coho blue, coho salmon. No. 1720, Cosseboom special, Atlantic salmon.

**1998, Apr. 16** *Perf. 12½x13*

**1715** A693 45c multicolored .90 .45
**1716** A693 45c multicolored .90 .45
**1717** A693 45c multicolored .90 .45
**1718** A693 45c multicolored .90 .45
**1719** A693 45c multicolored .90 .45
**1720** A693 45c multicolored .90 .45
*a.* Vertical strip of 6, #1715-1720 5.50 4.50
*b.* Bklt. pane, 2 ea #1715-1720 11.00
Complete booklet, #1720a 11.50

Canadian Institute of Mining, Metallurgy and Petroleum, Cent. — A694

**1998, May 4** *Perf. 12½*

**1721** A694 45c multicolored .75 .25

Imperial Penny Post, Cent. — A695

St. Edward's Crown, #86, Sir William Mulock.

**1998, May 29** *Perf. 12½x13*

**1722** A695 45c multicolored .75 .25

No. 1722 was issued in panes of 14 + 1 label.

Sumo Wrestling Tournament, Vancouver A696

Rising sun, mapleleaf and: No. 1723, Two wrestlers. No. 1724, Sumo champion performing bow twirling ceremony.

**1998, June 5** **Litho. & Embossed**

**1723** A696 45c multicolored .75 .25
**1724** A696 45c multicolored .75 .25
*a.* Horiz. or Vert. Pair, #1723-1724 + 4 labels 1.50 1.50
*b.* Souvenir sheet, #1723-1724 3.75 3.75

Nos. 1723-1724 were printed checkerwise in panes of 20, 10 each + 40 labels.

Canals of Canada — A697

No. 1725, St. Peters Canal, Nova Scotia. No. 1726, St. Ours Canal, Quebec. No. 1727, Port Carling Lock, Ontario. No. 1728, Locks, Rideau Canal, Ontario. No. 1729, Peterborough lift lock, Trent-Severn Waterway, Ontario. No. 1730, Chambly Canal, Quebec. No. 1731, Lachine Canal, Quebec. No. 1732, Ice skating on Rideau Canal, Ottawa. No. 1733, Boat on Big Chute Marine Railway, Trent-Severn Waterway. No. 1734, Sault Ste. Marie Canal, Ontario.

### Booklet Stamps

**1998, June 17** **Litho.** *Perf. 12½*

**1725** A697 45c multicolored 1.10 .75
**1726** A697 45c multicolored 1.10 .75
**1727** A697 45c multicolored 1.10 .75
**1728** A697 45c multicolored 1.10 .75
**1729** A697 45c multicolored 1.10 .75
**1730** A697 45c multicolored 1.10 .75
**1731** A697 45c multicolored 1.10 .75
**1732** A697 45c multicolored 1.10 .75
**1733** A697 45c multicolored 1.10 .75
**1734** A697 45c multicolored 1.10 .75
*a.* Bklt. pane, #1725-1734 + 10 labels 14.00
Complete booklet, #1734a 15.00

Health Professionals — A698

**Litho. & Embossed with Foil Application**

| **1998, June 25** | | | |
|---|---|---|---|
| **1735** | A698 45c multicolored | .70 | .25 |

Royal Canadian Mounted Police, 125th Anniv. A699

No. 1736, Male mountie, native, horse. No. 1737, Female mountie, helicopter, cityscape.

| **1998, July 3** | ***Perf. 12½x13*** | | |
|---|---|---|---|
| **1736** | A699 45c multicolored | .70 | .25 |
| **1737** | A699 45c multicolored | .70 | .25 |
| *a.* | Pair, #1736-1737 + 2 labels | 1.40 | 1.10 |
| *b.* | Souvenir sheet, #1736-1737 + 1 label | 1.50 | 1.50 |
| *c.* | As "b," with signature | 3.00 | 3.00 |
| *d.* | As "b," with Portugal 98 emblem | 4.50 | 4.50 |
| *e.* | As "b," with Italia 98 emblem | 4.50 | 4.50 |
| *f.* | As "d," gold embossed emblem omitted | *750.00* | |

Nos. 1737c-1737e have added inscriptions in gold. Issued: No. 1737c, 7/3; No. 1737d, 9/4; No. 1737e, 10/23.

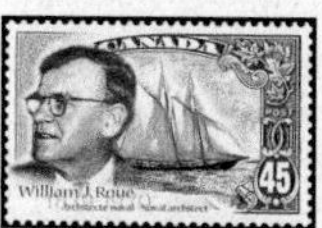

William James Roué (1879-1970), Naval Architect — A700

**Litho. & Engr.**

| **1998, July 24** | ***Perf. 13*** | | |
|---|---|---|---|
| **1738** | A700 45c multicolored | .75 | .25 |

**Scenic Highway Type of 1997**

Designs: No. 1739, Dempster Highway, Yukon. No. 1740, Dinosaur Trail, Alberta. No. 1741, River Valley Scenic Drive, New Brunswick. No. 1742, Blue Heron Route, Prince Edward Island.

| **1998, July 28** | **Litho.** ***Perf. 12½x13*** | | |
|---|---|---|---|
| **1739** | A673 45c multicolored | .70 | .35 |
| **1740** | A673 45c multicolored | .70 | .35 |
| **1741** | A673 45c multicolored | .70 | .35 |
| **1742** | A673 45c multicolored | .70 | .35 |
| *a.* | Block or strip of 4, #1739-1742 | 2.80 | 2.30 |

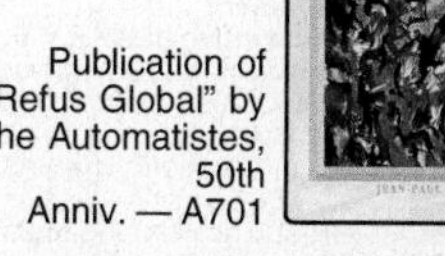

Publication of "Refus Global" by The Automatistes, 50th Anniv. — A701

Painting, artist: No. 1743, "Peinture," Jean-Paul Riopelle. No. 1744, "La dernière campagne de Napoléon," Fernand Leduc. No. 1745, "Jet fuligineux sur noir torturé," Jean-Paul Mousseau. No. 1746, "Le fond du garde-robe," Pierre Gauvreau. No. 1747, "Joie lacustre," Paul-Emile Borduas. No. 1748, "Syndicat des gens de mer," Marcelle Ferron. No. 1749, "Le tumulte á la machoire crispée," Marcel Barbeau.

**Self-Adhesive Booklet Stamps**

| **1998, Aug. 7** | ***Die Cut*** | | |
|---|---|---|---|
| **1743** | A701 45c multicolored | 1.10 | 1.10 |
| **1744** | A701 45c multicolored | 1.10 | 1.10 |
| **1745** | A701 45c multicolored | 1.10 | 1.10 |
| **1746** | A701 45c multicolored | 1.10 | 1.10 |
| **1747** | A701 45c multicolored | 1.10 | 1.10 |
| **1748** | A701 45c multicolored | 1.10 | 1.10 |
| **1749** | A701 45c multicolored | 1.10 | 1.10 |
| *a.* | Booklet pane, #1743-1749 | 7.75 | |

No. 1746 is 34x48mm. No. 1749a is a complete booklet. The peelable paper backing serves as a booklet cover.

Legendary Canadians — A702

No. 1750, Napoléon-Alexandre Comeau (1848-1923), outdoorsman, "King of the North Shore." No. 1751, Phyllis Munday (1894-1990), mountaineer, community service worker. No. 1752, Bill Mason (1929-88), film maker, canoe enthusiast. No. 1753, Harry "Red" Foster (1905-1985), founder of Canadian Special Olympics, sports enthusiast.

| **1998, Aug. 15** | ***Perf. 13½*** | | |
|---|---|---|---|
| **1750** | A702 45c multicolored | .70 | .25 |
| **1751** | A702 45c multicolored | .70 | .25 |
| **1752** | A702 45c multicolored | .70 | .25 |
| **1753** | A702 45c multicolored | .70 | .25 |
| *a.* | Block or strip of 4, #1750-1753 | 2.80 | 2.30 |

**Art Type of 1988**

Painting: The Farmer's Family (detail), by Bruno Bobak.

**Litho. with Foil Application**

| **1998, Sept. 8** | ***Perf. 12½x13*** | | |
|---|---|---|---|
| **1754** | A546 90c gold & multi | 1.50 | .90 |

Housing in Canada — A703

a, Native peoples. b, Settler. c, Regional. d, Heritage preservation. e, Multiple unit. f, Prefabricated. g, Veterans. h, Planned community. i, Innovative.

| **1998, Sept. 23** | **Litho.** | | |
|---|---|---|---|
| **1755** | Pane of 9 | 10.00 | 10.00 |
| *a.-i.* | A703 45c Any single | 1.10 | 1.10 |

University of Ottawa, 150th Anniv. — A704

| **1998, Sept. 25** | ***Perf. 13*** | | |
|---|---|---|---|
| **1756** | A704 45c multicolored | .70 | .25 |

The Circus — A705

Various circus clowns and: No. 1757, Elephant, bear performing tricks. No. 1758, Woman standing on horse, aerial act. No. 1759, Lion tamer. No. 1760, Contortionists, acrobats.

**Booklet Stamps**

| **1998, Oct. 1** | ***Perf. 13 on 3 Sides*** | | |
|---|---|---|---|
| **1757** | A705 45c multicolored | .70 | .30 |
| **1758** | A705 45c multicolored | .70 | .30 |
| **1759** | A705 45c multicolored | .70 | .30 |
| **1760** | A705 45c multicolored | .70 | .30 |
| *a.* | Bklt. pane, 3 ea #1757-1760 | 7.00 | 7.00 |
| | Complete booklet, #1760a | 7.50 | |
| *b.* | Souvenir sheet, #1757-1760 | 4.50 | 3.75 |

Stamps in No. 1760b are perforated on all four sides.

John Peters Humphrey (1905-95), Author of Universal Declaration of Human Rights — A706

| **1998, Oct. 7** | ***Perf. 13*** | | |
|---|---|---|---|
| **1761** | A706 45c multicolored | .70 | .25 |

Canadian Naval Reserve, 75th Anniv. A707

No. 1762, HMCS Sackville. No. 1763, HMCS Shawinigan.

| **1998, Nov. 4** | ***Perf. 12½x13*** | | |
|---|---|---|---|
| **1762** | A707 45c multicolored | .75 | .25 |
| **1763** | A707 45c multicolored | .75 | .25 |
| *a.* | Pair, #1762-1763 | 1.50 | 1.40 |

Christmas — A708

Sculpted wooden angels: 45c, "Angel of Last Judgment" blowing trumpet. 52c, "Adoring Angel" raising hand. 90c, "Adoring Angel, Kneeling," by Thomas Baillairgé.

| **1998, Nov. 6** | ***Perf. 13*** | | |
|---|---|---|---|
| **1764** | A708 45c multicolored | .75 | .25 |
| *a.* | Booklet pane of 10 | 32.50 | 32.50 |
| | Complete booklet, #1764a | 35.00 | |
| *b.* | Perf 13x13½ | 375.00 | 16.00 |
| *c.* | As "b," booklet pane of 10 | 15.00 | 13.50 |
| | Complete booklet, #1764c | 16.00 | |

The values for No. 1764b are for singles perfed on all four sides from sheet format. These are extremely scarce. Single stamps from booklet pane No. 1764c have a straight edge on one side. Value, booklet single, unused $1.50, used $.30.

***Perf. 13x13½***

| | | | |
|---|---|---|---|
| **1765** | A708 52c multicolored | .85 | .40 |
| *a.* | Booklet pane of 5 + label | 22.50 | 22.50 |
| | Complete booklet, #1765a | 23.50 | |
| *b.* | Perf 13 | 1.10 | .60 |
| *c.* | As "b," booklet pane of 5 + label | 5.50 | 5.00 |
| | Complete booklet, #1765c | 6.00 | |
| **1766** | A708 90c multicolored | 1.50 | .75 |
| *a.* | Booklet pane of 5 + label | 37.50 | 37.50 |
| | Complete booklet, #1766a | 40.00 | |
| *b.* | Perf 13 | 1.50 | .75 |
| *c.* | As "b," booklet pane of 5 + label | 7.50 | 6.75 |
| | Complete booklet, #1766c | 8.00 | |
| | *Nos. 1764-1766 (3)* | 3.10 | 1.40 |

New Year 1999 (Year of the Rabbit) — A709

| **1999, Jan. 8** | ***Perf. 13½*** | | |
|---|---|---|---|
| **1767** | A709 46c multicolored | .75 | .25 |
| *a.* | Red and tagging omitted | *850.00* | |

**Souvenir Sheet**

***Perf. 12½x13***

| | | | |
|---|---|---|---|
| **1768** | A709 95c Pane of 1 | 2.25 | 2.00 |
| *a.* | Single stamp | 1.50 | 1.25 |
| *b.* | Red and tagging omitted | *850.00* | |

No. 1768 with China 99 overprint was sold only at the show. Value same as unoverprinted pane. Also known with red and tagging omitted. Value $1,750.

Le Theatre du Rideau Vert, 50th Anniv. — A710

| **1999, Feb. 17** | ***Perf. 13x12½*** | | |
|---|---|---|---|
| **1769** | A710 46c multicolored | .75 | .25 |

**Bird Type of 1996**

Designs: No. 1770, Northern goshawk. No. 1771, Red-winged blackbird. No. 1772, American goldfinch. No. 1773, Sandhill crane.

| **1999, Feb. 24** | ***Perf. 12½x13*** | | |
|---|---|---|---|
| **1770** | A650 46c multicolored | .75 | .30 |
| **1771** | A650 46c multicolored | .75 | .30 |
| **1772** | A650 46c multicolored | .75 | .30 |
| **1773** | A650 46c multicolored | .75 | .30 |
| *a.* | Block or strip of 4, #1770-1773 | 3.00 | 1.50 |

**Booklet Stamps**

**Self-Adhesive**

***Die Cut Perf. 11½***

| | | | |
|---|---|---|---|
| **1774** | A650 46c like #1770 | .90 | .35 |
| **1775** | A650 46c like #1771 | .90 | .35 |
| **1776** | A650 46c like #1772 | .90 | .35 |
| **1777** | A650 46c like #1773 | .90 | .35 |
| *a.* | Booklet pane, 2 each #1774-1775, 1 each #1776-1777 | 5.50 | |
| *b.* | Booklet pane, 2 each #1776-1777, 1 each #1774-1775 | 5.50 | |
| | Complete booklet, #1777a, #1777b | 11.00 | |

Nos. 1770-1773 were issued in panes of 20, 5 each, printed checkerwise to contain 4 complete blocks or strips.

The peelable paper backing of Nos. 1777a, 1777b serves as the booklet cover.

Univ. of British Columbia's Museum of Anthropology, 50th Anniv. A711

| **1999, Mar. 9** | ***Perf. 13½*** | | |
|---|---|---|---|
| **1778** | A711 46c multicolored | .75 | .25 |

Sailing Ship Marco Polo — A712

| **1999, Mar. 19** | ***Perf. 13x12½*** | | |
|---|---|---|---|
| **1779** | A712 46c multicolored | .75 | .25 |
| *a.* | Pane of 2, #1779b, Australia #1631 perf. 13½ | 2.75 | 2.75 |
| *b.* | Perf 13 (from No. 1779a) | 1.80 | 1.80 |

Australia '99 World Stamp Expo. See Australia No. 1631a.

**Scenic Highway Type of 1997**

No. 1780, Gaspé Peninsula, Highway 132, Quebec. No. 1781, Yellowhead Highway (PTH 16), Manitoba. No. 1782, Dempster Highway 8, Northwest Territories. No. 1783, Discovery Trail, Route 230N, Newfoundland.

| **1999, Mar. 31** | ***Perf. 12½x13*** | | |
|---|---|---|---|
| **1780** | A673 46c multicolored | .75 | .35 |
| **1781** | A673 46c multicolored | .75 | .35 |
| **1782** | A673 46c multicolored | .75 | .35 |
| **1783** | A673 46c multicolored | .75 | .35 |
| *a.* | Block or strip of 4, #1780-1783 | 3.00 | 2.50 |

Creation of the Nunavut Territory A713

| **1999, Apr. 1** | | | |
|---|---|---|---|
| **1784** | A713 46c multicolored | .75 | .25 |

Intl. Year of Older Persons A714

| **1999, Apr. 12** | ***Perf. 13½*** | | |
|---|---|---|---|
| **1785** | A714 46c multicolored | .75 | .25 |

A715

**1999, Apr. 19** ***Perf. 13***

**1786** A715 46c multicolored 1.80 .40

Baisakhi, Religious Holiday of Sikh Canadians, 300th Anniv.

A716

Paintings (Canadian Orchids): No. 1787, Arethusa bulbosa, by Poon-Kuen Chow. No. 1788, Amerorchis rotundifolia, by Yakman Lai. No. 1789, Platanthera psycodes, by Lai. No. 1790, Cypripedium pubescens, by Chow.

### Booklet Stamps

**1999, Apr. 27** ***Perf. 13x12½***

**1787** A716 46c multicolored .90 .30
**1788** A716 46c multicolored .90 .30
**1789** A716 46c multicolored .90 .30
**1790** A716 46c multicolored .90 .30
*a.* Bklt. pane, 3 ea #1787-1790 11.00
Complete booklet, #1790a 11.50
*b.* Souvenir sheet, #1787-1790 3.75 3.75

China '99 World Philatelic Exhibition, Beijing. Designs of some stamps contained in No. 1790a extend into selvage of booklet pane.

Issued: No. 1790b, 8/21/99.

Horses — A717

No. 1791, Northern Dancer, thoroughbred race horse. No. 1792, Kingsway Skoal, bucking horse. No. 1793, Big Ben, show horse. No. 1794, Armbro Flight, harness race horse.

**1999, June 2** ***Perf. 13x13½***

**1791** A717 46c multicolored .90 .40
**1792** A717 46c multicolored .90 .40
**1793** A717 46c multicolored .90 .40
**1794** A717 46c multicolored .90 .40
*a.* Block or strip of 4, #1791-1794 3.60 3.00

### Booklet Stamps
### Self-Adhesive
***Serpentine Die Cut 11½***

**1795** A717 46c like #1791 1.10 .30
**1796** A717 46c like #1792 1.10 .30
**1797** A717 46c like #1793 1.10 .30
**1798** A717 46c like #1794 1.10 .30
*a.* Block of 4, #1795-1798 4.40
*b.* Complete booklet, 3 each #1795-1798 13.25

Nos. 1791-1794 were issued in panes of 16, 4 each, printed checkerwise to contain 4 complete blocks or strips.

Quebec Bar Assoc., 150th Anniv. — A718

**1999, June 3** ***Perf. 13½***

**1799** A718 46c multicolored .70 .25

### Art Type of 1988

Design: Coq Licorne, by Jean Dallaire (1916-65).

### Litho. with Foil Application

**1999, July 3** ***Perf. 12½x13¼***

**1800** A546 95c Rose gold & multi 1.50 1.10
*a.* Silver omitted *1,250.*

1999 Pan American Games, Winnipeg — A719

Designs: No. 1801, Track & field. No. 1802, Cycling, weight lifting, gymnastics. No. 1803, Swimming, sailboarding, kayaking. No. 1804, Soccer, tennis, medal winners.

**1999, July 12** **Litho.** ***Perf. 13¼***

**1801** A719 46c multicolored .75 .35
**1802** A719 46c multicolored .75 .35
**1803** A719 46c multicolored .75 .35
**1804** A719 46c multicolored .75 .35
*a.* Block of 4, #1801-1804 3.00 2.50

Issued in panes of 16 stamps.

23rd World Rowing Championships, St. Catharines, Ont. — A720

**1999, Aug. 22** ***Perf. 12½x13***

**1805** A720 46c multicolored .75 .25

UPU, 125th Anniv. A721

**1999, Aug. 26**

**1806** A721 46c multicolored .75 .25

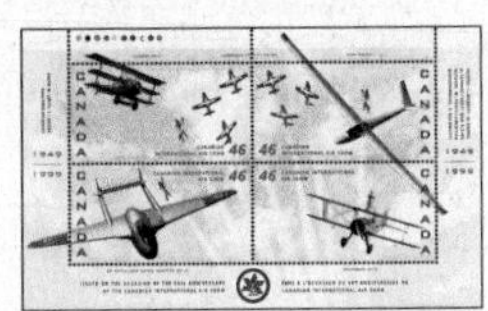

Airplanes — A722

No. 1807: a, Fokker DR-1, CT-114 Tutors. b, Tutors, H101 Salto sailplane. c, De Havilland DH100 Vampire MKIII. d, Stearman A-75.

No. 1808: a, De Havilland Mosquito FBVI. b, Sopwith F1 Camel. c, De Havilland Canada DHC-3 Otter. d, De Havilland Canada CC-108 Caribou. e, Canadair CL-28 Argus MK 2. f, North American F-86 Sabre 6. g, McDonnell Douglas CF-18 Hornet. h, Sopwith SF-1 Dolphin. i, Armstrong Whitworth Siskin IIIA. j, Canadian Vickers (Northrop) Delta II. k, Sikorsky CH-124A Sea King helicopter. l, Vickers-Armstrong Wellington MKII. m, Avro Anson MKI. n, Canadair (Lockheed) CF-104G Starfighter. o, Burgess-Dunne seaplane. p, Avro 504K.

**1999, Sept. 4**

**1807** A722 Pane of 4 4.40 4.40
*a.-d.* 46c any single 1.10 .90
**1808** A722 Pane of 16 18.00 18.00
*a.-p.* 46c any single 1.00 1.00

Canadian Intl. Air Show, 50th anniv. (No. 1807). Royal Canadian Air Force, 75th anniv. (No. 1808). Nos. 1808a-1808p are each 56x28mm.

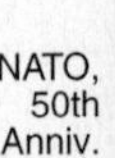

NATO, 50th Anniv. A723

**1999, Sept. 21**

**1809** A723 46c multicolored .75 .25

Frontier College, 100th Anniv. — A724

**1999, Sept. 24** ***Perf. 13x13½***

**1810** A724 46c multicolored .75 .25

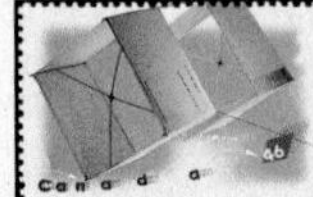

Kites — A725

Designs: a, Master Control, sport kite by Lam Hoac (triagular). b, Indian Garden Flying Carpet, edo kite by Skye Morrison (trapezoidal). c, Gibson Girl, manufactured box kite (rectangular). d, Dragon centipede kite by Zhang tian Wei (oval).

***Die cut in various patterns***

**1999, Oct. 1** **Self-Adhesive**

**1811** Complete booklet, 2 each #a.-d. 8.00
*a.-d.* A725 46c any single 1.00 .35

A726

A727

Millennium A728

### Self-Adhesive (46c)

**1999, Oct. 12** **Holography** ***Die Cut***

**1812** A726 46c silver 1.00 .40
Pane of 4 4.75 4.75

### Litho.
***Perf. 13¼***

**1813** A727 55c multicolored 1.00 .80
Pane of 4 4.75 4.75

### Engr.
***Perf. 12¾***

**1814** A728 95c brown 1.70 1.50
Pane of 4 7.00 7.00
*Nos. 1812-1814 (3)* 3.70 2.70

Nos. 1812-1814 each exist in souvenir sheets of 1 with decorative border.

Christmas — A729

**1999, Nov. 4** **Litho.** ***Perf. 13¼***

**1815** A729 46c Angel, drum .75 .25
*a.* Booklet pane of 10 7.50 *8.00*
Complete booklet 8.00
*b.* Horiz. pair, imperf. btwn. *1,750.*
**1816** A729 55c Angel, toys .85 .35
*a.* Booklet pane of 5 + label 4.25 *7.50*
Complete booklet 4.50
**1817** A729 95c Angel, candle 1.50 .75
*a.* Booklet pane of 5 + label 8.00 *10.00*
Complete booklet 8.50
*b.* Horiz. pair, imperf. btwn. *1,000.*
*Nos. 1815-1817 (3)* 3.10 1.35

### Souvenir Sheets

Millennium — A730

No. 1818 — Media Technologies: a, IMAX movies. b, Softimage animation software. c, Ted Rogers, Sr. (1900-39) and radio tube. d, Invention of radio facsimile device for transmission of photographs for publishing by Sir William Stephenson (1896-1989).

No. 1819 — Canadian Entertainment: a, Calgary Stampede. b, Performers from Cirque du Soleil. c, Hockey Night in Canada. d, La Soiree du Hockey.

No. 1820 — Entertainers: a, Portia White (1911-68), singer. b, Glenn Gould (1932-82), pianist. c, Guy Lombardo (1902-77), band leader. d, Félix Leclerc (1914-88), singer, guitarist.

No. 1821 — Fostering Canadian Talent: a, Royal Canadian Academy of Arts (men viewing painting). b, Canada Council (sky, musical staff, "A"). c, National Film Board of Canada. d, Canadian Broadcasting Corporation.

No. 1822 — Medical Innovators: a, Sir Frederick Banting (1891-1941), co-discoverer of insulin, syringe and dog. b, Dr. Armand Frappier (1904-91), microbiologist, holding flask. c, Dr. Hans Selye (1907-82), endocrinologist, and molecular diagram. d, Maude Abbott (1869-1940), pathologist, and roses.

No. 1823 — Social Progress: a, Nun, doctor, hospital. b, Statue of woman holding decree. c, Alphonse Desjardins (1854-1920) and wife Dorimène (1858-1932), credit union founders, and credit union emblem. d, Father Moses Coady (1882-1959), educator of adults.

No. 1824 — Charity: a, Canadian International Development Agency (hands and tools). b, Dr. Lucille Teasdale (1929-96), hospital administrator in Uganda. c, Marathon of Hope inspired by Terry Fox (1958-81). d, Meals on Wheels program.

No. 1825 — Humanitarians and Peacekeepers: a, Raoul Dandurand (1861-1942), b, Pauline Vanier (1898-1991), Red Cross volunteer, and Elizabeth Smellie (1884-1968), head of various nursing services. c, Lester B. Pearson (1897-1972), prime minister, and Nobel Peace Prize winner, and dove. d, Amputee and shadow (Ottawa Convention on Land Mines).

No. 1826 — Canada's First People: a, Chief Pontiac (c. 1720-69). b, Tom Longboat (1887-1949), marathon runner. c, Inuit sculpture of shaman. d, Medicine man.

No. 1827 — Canada's Cultural Fabric: a, Norse boat, L'Anse aux Meadows. b, Immigrants on Halifax's Pier 21. c, Neptune Theater, Halifax (head of Neptune). d, Stratford Festival (actor and theater).

No. 1828 — Literary Legends: a, W. O. Mitchell (1914-98), novelist, and prairie scene. b, Gratien Gélinas (1909-99), actor and playwright, and stars. c, Le Cercle du Livre de France book club. d, Harlequin paperback books.

No. 1829 — Great Thinkers: a, Marshall McLuhan (1911-80), philosopher, and television set. b, Northrop Frye (1912-91), literary critic, and word "code." c, Roger Lemelin (1919-92), novelist, and cast of "The Plouffe Family" TV series. d, Hilda Marion Neatby (1904-75), historian, and farm scene.

No. 1830 — A Tradition of Generosity: a, Hart Massey (1823-96), Hart House, University of Toronto. b, Dorothy (1899-1965) and Izaak Killam (1885-1955), philantropists, and molecular model. c, Eric Lafferty Harvie (1892-1975), philantropist, and mountain scene. d, Macdonald Stewart Foundation.

No. 1831 — Engineering and Technological Marvels: a, Map of Rogers Pass, locomotive, tunnel diggers. b, Manic Dams. c, Canadian satellites, Remote Manipulator Arm. d, CN Tower.

No. 1832 — Fathers of Invention: a, George Klein (1904-92), gearwheels. b, Abraham Gesner (1797-1864), beaker of kerosene and lamp. c, Alexander Graham Bell (1847-1922), passenger-carrying kite, hydrofoil. d, Joseph-Armand Bombardier (1907-64), snowmobile.

No. 1833 — Food: a, Sir Charles Saunders (1867-1937), Marquis wheat. b, Pablum. c, Dr. Archibald Gowanlock Huntsman (1883-1973), marketer of frozen fish. d, Products of McCain Foods, Ltd., tractor.

No. 1834 — Enterprising Giants: a, Hudson's Bay Company (Colonist, Indian, canoe). b, Bell Canada Enterprises (earth, satellite, string of binary digits). c, Vachon Co. snack cakes. d, George Weston Limited (Baked goods, eggs).

**1999-2000 Litho. *Perf. 13¼***

| | | | | |
|---|---|---|---|---|
| **1818** | A730 | Pane of 4 | 6.50 | 6.50 |
| *a.-d.* | | 46c any single | 1.60 | 1.25 |
| **1819** | A730 | Pane of 4 | 6.50 | 6.50 |
| *a.-d.* | | 46c any single | 1.60 | 1.25 |
| **1820** | A730 | Pane of 4 | 6.50 | 6.50 |
| *a.-d.* | | 46c any single | 1.60 | 1.25 |
| **1821** | A730 | Pane of 4 | 6.50 | 6.50 |
| *a.-d.* | | 46c any single | 1.60 | 1.25 |
| **1822** | A730 | Pane of 4 | 6.50 | 6.50 |
| *a.-d.* | | 46c any single | 1.60 | 1.25 |
| **1823** | A730 | Pane of 4 | 6.50 | 6.50 |
| *a.-d.* | | 46c any single | 1.60 | 1.25 |
| **1824** | A730 | Pane of 4 | 6.50 | 6.50 |
| *a.-d.* | | 46c any single | 1.60 | 1.25 |
| **1825** | A730 | Pane of 4 | 6.50 | 6.50 |
| *a.-d.* | | 46c any single | 1.60 | 1.25 |
| **1826** | A730 | Pane of 4 | 6.50 | 6.50 |
| *a.-d.* | | 46c any single | 1.60 | 1.25 |
| **1827** | A730 | Pane of 4 | 6.50 | 6.50 |
| *a.-d.* | | 46c any single | 1.60 | 1.25 |
| **1828** | A730 | Pane of 4 | 6.50 | 6.50 |
| *a.-d.* | | 46c any single | 1.60 | 1.25 |
| **1829** | A730 | Pane of 4 | 6.50 | 6.50 |
| *a.-d.* | | 46c any single | 1.60 | 1.25 |
| **1830** | A730 | Pane of 4 | 6.50 | 6.50 |
| *a.-d.* | | 46c any single | 1.60 | 1.25 |
| **1831** | A730 | Pane of 4 | 6.50 | 6.50 |
| *a.-d.* | | 46c any single | 1.60 | 1.25 |
| **1832** | A730 | Pane of 4 | 6.50 | 6.50 |
| *a.-d.* | | 46c any single | 1.60 | 1.25 |
| **1833** | A730 | Pane of 4 | 6.50 | 6.50 |
| *a.-d.* | | 46c any single | 1.60 | 1.25 |
| **1834** | A730 | Pane of 4 | 6.50 | 6.50 |
| *a.-d.* | | 46c any single | 1.60 | 1.25 |
| | | *Nos. 1818-1834 (17)* | 110.50 | 110.50 |

Issued: Nos. 1818-1821, 12/17; Nos. 1822-1825, 1/17/00; Nos. 1826-1830, 2/17/00; Nos. 1831-1834, 3/17/00.

Stamps similar to these were printed in a hardcover book produced by Canada Post Sept. 15, 1999 that sold for $59.99. Stamps from souvenir panes show a distinct upward turn of the tails of the nines in the small 1999 date at upper left. The tails of the nines on stamps from the book are flat.

Millennium — A731

**2000, Jan. 1 *Perf. 13x12½***

**1835** A731 46c multicolored .75 .25

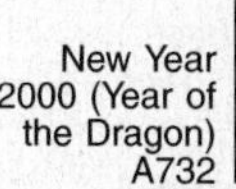

New Year 2000 (Year of the Dragon) A732

**Litho. & Embossed**

**2000, Jan. 5 *Perf. 12½x12¾***

**1836** A732 46c multicolored .75 .25
*a.* Red and tagging omitted 1,100.

**Souvenir Sheet**

***Perf. 13¾x13¼***

**1837** A732 95c multicolored 1.70 1.70
*a.* Orange and tagging omitted *1,500.*

No. 1837 has rounded corners and contains one 56x29mm stamp.

50th National Hockey League All-Star Game — A733

Famous NHL players: a, Wayne Gretzky (Oilers jersey No. 99). b, Gordie Howe (Red Wings jersey No. 9). c, Maurice Richard (red, white and blue Canadiens jersey No. 9). d, Doug Harvey (Canadiens jersey No. 2). e, Bobby Orr (Bruins jersey No. 4). f, Jacques Plante (Canadiens jersey No. 1).

**2000, Feb. 5 Litho. *Perf. 12¾***

**1838** Pane of 6 4.50 4.50
*a.-f.* A733 46c any single .75 .60

**Bird Type of 1996**

Designs: Nos. 1839, 1843, Canada warbler. Nos. 1840, 1844, Osprey. Nos. 1841, 1845, Pacific loon. Nos. 1842, 1846, Blue jay.

**2000, Mar. 1 Litho. *Perf. 12½x13¼***

**1839** A650 46c multi .90 .30
**1840** A650 46c multi .90 .30
**1841** A650 46c multi .90 .30
**1842** A650 46c multi .90 .30
*a.* Block or strip of 4 3.60 2.50

**Booklet Stamps**

**Self-Adhesive**

***Die Cut 11½x11¼***

**1843** A650 46c multi .90 .30
**1844** A650 46c multi .90 .30
**1845** A650 46c multi .90 .30
**1846** A650 46c multi .90 .30
*a.* Booklet pane, 2 each #1843-1844, 1 each #1845-1846 5.50
*b.* Booklet pane, 2 each #1845-1846, 1 each #1843-1844 5.50
Complete bklt., #1846a, 1846b 11.00

Nos. 1839-1842 were issued in panes of 20, 5 each printed checkerwise to contain 4 complete blocks or strips.

Supreme Court, 125th Anniv. — A734

**2000, Apr. 10 *Perf. 12½x13¼***

**1847** A734 46c multi .75 .25

Ritual of the Calling of an Engineer, 75th Anniv. — A735

**2000, Apr. 25**

**1848** A735 46c multi .75 .25
*a.* Tete-beche pair 1.50 1.10
*b.* Silver ("CANADA 46") omitted *2,250.*

Decorated Rural Mailboxes A736

Mailboxes with: No. 1849, Ship, fish, house designs. No. 1850, Flower, cow and church designs. No. 1851, Tractor design. No. 1852, Goose head, house designs.

**Booklet Stamps**

***Perf. 12½x13¼ on 3 sides***

**2000, Apr. 28**

**1849** A736 46c multi .90 .40
**1850** A736 46c multi .90 .40
**1851** A736 46c multi .90 .40
**1852** A736 46c multi .90 .40
*a.* Block of 4, #1849-1852 3.60 2.75
*b.* Bklt. pane, 3 ea #1849-1852 11.00
Complete booklet, #1852a 11.50

Picture Frame — A737

**Self-Adhesive**

***Serpentine Die Cut 11½***

**2000, Apr. 28**

**1853** A737 46c multi .90 .60
*a.* Booklet pane of 5 + 5 different labels 4.50
Complete booklet, #1853a 5.00
*b.* Pane of 25 + stickers *100.00*

No. 1853b sold for $24.95 each for one or two panes, and $22.95 for three to ten panes. Twenty-five self-adhesive, die cut address labels and reproductions of a photo sent in by the customer are on the reverse of No. 1853b. These panes were not available at post offices or through the philatelic bureau, but special orders from the printer, Ashton-Potter. The front cover of the booklet containing No. 1853a served as the order blank for No. 1853b.

See Nos. 1872, 1882.

A738

A739

A740

A741

A742

A743

A744

A745

A746

Fresh Waters A747

**Self-Adhesive**

***Serpentine Die Cut 2½ Horiz.***

**2000, Feb. 23**

**1854** Complete booklet, #a.-e. 7.50
*a.* A738 55c multi 1.50 .90
*b.* A739 55c multi 1.50 .90
*c.* A740 55c multi 1.50 .90
*d.* A741 55c multi 1.50 .90
*e.* A742 55c multi 1.50 .90
**1855** Complete booklet, #a.-e. 9.50
*a.* A743 95c multi 1.90 1.50
*b.* A744 95c multi 1.90 1.50
*c.* A745 95c multi 1.90 1.50
*d.* A746 95c multi 1.90 1.50
*e.* A747 95c multi 1.90 1.50

Queen Mother (b. 1900) — A748

**2000, May 23 *Perf. 13x13¼***

**1856** A748 95c multi 1.50 .90
*a.* Imperf., pair *750.00*

Boys and Girls Clubs of Canada, Cent. — A749

**2000, June 1 *Perf. 13***

**1857** A749 46c multi .75 .25

World Session of Seventh Day Adventist Church, Toronto — A750

**2000, June 29 *Perf. 13½x13¼***

**1858** A750 46c multi .90 .25

Stampin' the Future Children's Stamp Design Contest Winners — A751

Designs: No. 1859, Rainbow, space vehicle, astronauts, flag, by Rosalie Anne Nardelli. No. 1860, Three children in space vehicle, three children on ground, by Sarah Lutgen. No. 1861, Children and map of Canada, by Christine Weera. No. 1862, Two astronauts in space vehicle, planets, by Andrew Wright.

**2000, July 1 *Perf. 13¼***

**1859** A751 46c multi .75 .35
**1860** A751 46c multi .75 .35
**1861** A751 46c multi .75 .35
**1862** A751 46c multi .75 .35
*a.* Block or strip, #1859-1862 3.00 2.50
*b.* Souvenir sheet, #1859-1862 4.75 3.25

**Art Type of 1988**

Design: The Artist at Niagara, by Cornelius Krieghoff.

**Litho. with Foil Application**

**2000, July 7 *Perf. 12½x13¼***

**1863** A546 95c multi 1.40 .90

Tall Ships in Halifax Harbor A752

Various ships: No. 1864, Denomination at L. No. 1865, Denomination at R.

**Self-Adhesive**

**Booklet Stamps**

***Serpentine Die Cut 4¾x5***

**2000, July 19 Litho.**

**1864** A752 46c multicolored .90 .40
**1865** A752 46c multicolored .90 .40
*a.* Pair, #1864-1865 1.80
*b.* Booklet, 5 #1864a 9.00

Dept. of Labor, Cent. — A753

**2000, Sept. 1 *Perf. 12½x13¼***

**1866** A753 46c multi .75 .25

Petro-Canada, 25th Anniv. — A754

**Self-Adhesive**

**Booklet Stamp**

**2000, Sept. 13 *Die Cut***

**1867** A754 46c multi .90 .40
*a.* Booklet pane of 12 11.00
Booklet, #1867a 11.50
*b.* Die cutting inverted (2 points jut at T, L) 7.50 7.50

No. 1867a is the cover of an informational booket about Petro-Canada. No. 1867b was issued in collector packs.

Cetaceans A755

No. 1868, Monodon monoceros. No. 1869, Balaenoptera musculus. No. 1870, Balaena mysticetus. No. 1871, Delphinapterus leucas.

**2000, Oct. 2** ***Perf. 12½x13***

**1868** A755 46c multi .75 .30
**1869** A755 46c multi .75 .30
**1870** A755 46c multi .75 .30
**1871** A755 46c multi .75 .30
*a.* Block of 4, #1868-1871 3.00 2.25

Christmas — A756

**Self-Adhesive**
**Booklet Stamp**
***Serpentine Die Cut 11¾***

**2000, Oct. 5**

**1872** A756 46c multi .90 .80
*a.* Booklet pane of 5 + 5 labels 4.50
Booklet, #1872a 5.00
*b.* Pane of 25 + stickers 100.00

See No. 1882f.

Christmas — A757

Designs: 46c, Adoration of the shepherds. 55c, Creche. 95c Flight into Egypt.

**2000, Nov. 3** ***Perf. 13¼***

**1873** A757 46c multi .75 .25
*a.* Booklet pane of 10 7.50 *9.00*
Booklet, #1873a 8.00
**1874** A757 55c multi .90 .35
*a.* Booklet pane of 6 5.50 *6.50*
Booklet, #1874a 6.00
**1875** A757 95c multi 1.50 .65
*a.* Booklet pane of 6 9.00 *10.50*
Booklet, #1875a 9.50
*Nos. 1873-1875 (3)* 3.15 1.25

Regiments — A758

No. 1876, Lord Strathcona's Horse Regiment. No. 1877, Les Voltigeurs de Quebec.

**2000, Nov. 11** ***Perf. 13¼x13***

**1876** A758 46c multi .75 .30
**1877** A758 46c multi .75 .30
*a.* Pair, #1876-1877 1.50 .90

Maple Leaves A759

Animals A760

Designs: 60c, Red fox. 75c, Gray wolf. $1.05, White-tailed deer.

**Coil Stamps**
***Serpentine Die Cut 8½ Horiz.***

**2000, Dec. 28** **Self-Adhesive**

**1878** A759 47c multi .75 .25
*a.* Blue inscriptions omitted *600.00*
**1879** A760 60c multi 1.00 .35
*a.* Booklet pane of 6 10.00
**1880** A760 75c multi 1.20 .45
**1881** A760 $1.05 multi 1.70 .75
*a.* Booklet pane of 6 11.00
*Nos. 1878-1881 (4)* 4.65 1.80

Nos. 1879a and 1881a are complete booklets. See No. 1927.

**Frame Type of 2000**

No. 1882: a, Silver. b, Like #1853. c, Mahogany. d, Love (roses). e, Christmas.

**Booklet Stamps**
***Serpentine Die Cut 11¾***

**2000, Dec. 28** **Self-Adhesive**

**1882** Bklt. pane of 5 + 5 labels 4.50
*a.-e.* A737 47c Any single .90 .90
Booklet, #1882 5.00
*f.* Pane of 25 + stickers 125.00

No. 1882f was available only by special order.

New Year 2001 (Year of the Snake) — A761

**Litho. & Embossed**

**2001, Jan. 5** ***Perf. 13¼***

**1883** A761 47c green & multi .75 .25
*a.* Gold omitted 1,250.

**Souvenir Sheet**

**1884** A761 $1.05 brown & multi 2.25 2.25

National Hockey League Stars — A762

No. 1885: a, Jean Beliveau (Montreal Canadiens jersey No. 4). b, Terry Sawchuk (goalie in Detroit Red Wings uniform). c, Eddie Shore (Boston Bruins jersey No. 2). d, Denis Potvin (Islanders jersey No. 5). e, Bobby Hull (Chicago Black Hawks jersey No. 9). f, Syl Apps, Sr. (Toronto Maple Leafs jersey).

***Perf. 12½x13 on 3 sides***

**2001, Jan. 18** **Litho.**

**1885** Sheet of 6 + 3 labels 4.50 4.50
*a.-f.* A762 47c Any single .75 .45
*g.* Strip of 3 (#1885a, 1885c, 1885e), blue circle and text omitted *5,500.*

**Bird Type of 1996**

Designs: Nos. 1886, 1890, Golden eagle. Nos. 1887, 1891, Arctic tern. Nos. 1888, 1892, Rock ptarmigan. Nos. 1889, 1893, Lapland longspur.

**2001, Feb. 1** ***Perf. 12½x13***

**1886** A650 47c multi .75 .30
**1887** A650 47c multi .75 .30
**1888** A650 47c multi .75 .30
**1889** A650 47c multi .75 .30
*a.* Block or strip of 4, #1886-1889 3.00 2.25

**Booklet Stamps**
**Self-Adhesive**
***Die Cut Perf 11½x11¼***

**1890** A650 47c multi .90 .35
**1891** A650 47c multi .90 .35
**1892** A650 47c multi .90 .35
**1893** A650 47c multi .90 .35
*a.* Booklet pane, 2 each #1890-1891, 1 each #1892-1893 5.50
*b.* Booklet pane, 2 each #1892-1893, 1 each #1890-1891 5.50
Booklet, #1893a, 1893b 11.00

Nos. 1886-1889 were issued in panes of 20, 5 each printed checkerwise to contain 4 complete blocks or strips.

Games of La Francophonie, Ottawa and Hull — A763

**2001, Feb. 28** ***Perf. 13¼***

**1894** 47c High jumper .75 .25
**1895** 47c Dancer .75 .25
*a.* A763 Horiz. pair, #1894-1895 1.50 .90

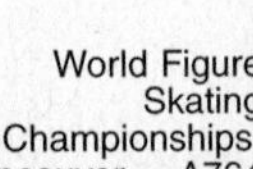

World Figure Skating Championships, Vancouver — A764

Designs: No. 1896, Pairs. No. 1897, Ice dancing. No. 1898, Men's singles. No. 1899, Women's singles.

**2001, Mar. 19** ***Perf. 13x12½***

**1896** A764 47c shown .75 .30
**1897** A764 47c multi .75 .30
**1898** A764 47c multi .75 .30
**1899** A764 47c multi .75 .30
*a.* Block of 4, #1896-1899 3.00 2.25

First Canadian Postage Stamps, 150th Anniv. — A765

**Litho. & Engr.**

**2001, Apr. 6** ***Perf. 13***

**1900** A765 47c multi .75 .25

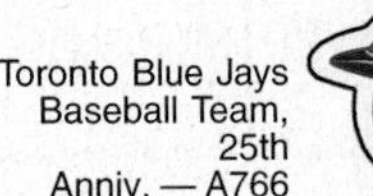

Toronto Blue Jays Baseball Team, 25th Anniv. — A766

**Self-Adhesive**

**2001, Apr. 9** **Litho.** ***Die Cut***

**1901** A766 47c multi .90 .25
*a.* Booklet pane of 8 7.25

No. 1901a is a complete booklet.

Summit of the Americas, Quebec — A767

**2001, Apr. 20** ***Perf. 13¼x13***

**1902** A767 47c multi .75 .25

Tourist Attractions A768

No. 1903: a, Butchart Gardens, British Columbia. b, Apple Blossom Festival, Nova Scotia. c, White Pass and Yukon Route. d, Sugar bushes, Quebec. e, Niagara-on-the-Lake, Ontario.

No. 1904: a, The Forks, Manitoba. b, Barkerville, British Columbia. c, Canadian Tulip Festival, Ontario. d, Auyuittuq National Park, Nunavut. e, Signal Hill National Historic Site, Newfoundland.

**Self-Adhesive**

**2001, May 11** ***Die Cut Perf. 11x11¼***

**1903** Booklet of 5 4.50
*a.-e.* A768 60c Any single .90 .75
**1904** Booklet of 5 8.50
*a.-e.* A768 $1.05 Any single 1.70 1.10

See Nos. 1952-1953, 1989-1990, 2019-2023.

Armenian Church, 1,700th Anniv. — A769

**2001, May 16** ***Perf. 13x12½***

**1905** A769 47c multi .75 .25

Royal Military College of Canada, 125th Anniv. A770

**2001, June 1** ***Perf. 12½x13***

**1906** A770 47c multi .75 .25

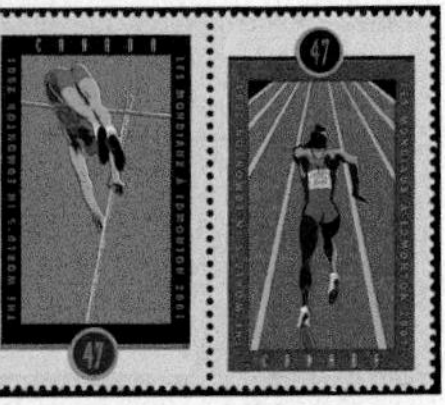

Eighth Intl. Amateur Athletic Federation World Championships, Edmonton — A771

**2001, June 25** ***Perf. 12¾x12½***

**1907** 47c Pole vault .75 .25
**1908** 47c Runner .75 .25
*a.* A771 Pair, #1907-1908 1.50 .90

Pierre Elliott Trudeau (1919-2000), Prime Minister — A772

**2001, July 1** ***Perf. 13x12½***

**1909** A772 47c multi .75 .25
*a.* Souvenir sheet of 4 3.25 3.25

Roses A773

Designs: Nos. 1910a, 1911, Morden Centennial. Nos. 1910b, 1912, Agnes. Nos. 1910c, 1913, Champlain. Nos. 1910d, 1914, Canadian White Star.

**Souvenir Sheet**

**2001, Aug. 1** ***Perf. 12½x13***

**1910** Pane of 4 4.40 4.40
*a.-d.* A773 47c Any single 1.10 1.10

**Booklet Stamps**
***Die Cut***

**1911** A773 47c multi .75 .30
**1912** A773 47c multi .75 .30
**1913** A773 47c multi .75 .30
**1914** A773 47c multi .75 .30
*a.* Booklet pane, #1911-1914 3.00
Booklet, 3 #1914a 9.00

Phila Nippon '01, Japan (No. 1910). Die cutting on Nos. 1911-1914 has "thorn" at the center of each side, pointing outward at top and left and toward the design at bottom and right.

Great Peace of Montreal, 300th Anniv. A774

**2001, Aug. 3** ***Perf. 12½x13***

**1915** A774 47c multi .75 .25

**Art Type of 1988**

Design: The Space Between Columns #21 (Italian), by Jack Shadbolt.

**Litho. with Foil Application**

**2001, Aug. 24** ***Perf. 13x13¼***

**1916** A546 $1.05 multi 1.70 .90

Shriners — A775

**2001, Sept. 19 Litho.** ***Perf. 13¼x13***
**1917** A775 47c multi .75 .25

**Frame Type of 2000 Inscribed "Domestic Lettermail / Poste-lettres du régime intérieur"**

No. 1918: a, Like #1882a. b, Like #1882b. c, Baby toys and flowers. d, Like #1882d. e, Like #1882e.

***Serpentine Die Cut 11¾***

**2001, Sept. 21** **Self-Adhesive**
**1918** Bklt. pane of 5 + 5 labels 5.00
*a.-e.* A737 (47c) Any single .90 .90
Booklet, #1918 5.00
*f.* Pane of 25 + stickers 125.00
*g.* Pane of 10 + stickers 100.00

Nos. 1918f and 1918g were available only by special order.

Theater Anniversaries A776

Designs: No. 1919, Théatre du Nouveau Monde, Montreal, 50th anniv. No. 1920, Grand Theater, London, Ont., cent.

**2001, Sept. 28** ***Perf. 12½x12¾***
**1919** A776 47c multi .70 .25
**1920** A776 47c multi .70 .25
*a.* Horiz. pair, #1919-1920 1.40 .90

Hot Air Balloons — A777

Background colors: a, Green. b, Blue violet. c, Red violet. d, Olive.

**Self-Adhesive**

**2001, Oct. 1** ***Die Cut***
**1921** Booklet, 2 each #a-d 7.25
*a.-d.* A777 47c Any single .90 .40

Christmas A778

Illuminated trees and: 47c, Horse-drawn sleigh. 60c, Skaters. $1.05, Children making snowman.

**2001, Nov. 1** ***Perf. 12½x13¼***
**1922** A778 47c multi .75 .25
*a.* Booklet pane of 10 7.50 7.50
Booklet, #1922a 8.00
**1923** A778 60c multi .95 .40
*a.* Booklet pane of 6 5.75 5.50
Booklet, #1923a 6.25
**1924** A778 $1.05 multi 1.65 .60
*a.* Booklet pane of 6 10.00 10.00
Booklet, #1924a 10.50

YMCA in Canada, 150th Anniv. — A779

**2001, Nov. 8** ***Perf. 13¼***
**1925** A779 47c multi .75 .25

Royal Canadian Legion, 75th Anniv. A780

**2001, Nov. 11** ***Perf. 12½x13***
**1926** A780 47c multi .75 .25

**Maple Leaves Type of 2000, Traditional Handiwork Type of 1999 and**

Flag and Canada Post Headquarters, Ottawa — A781

Designs: 65c, Jewelry making, horiz. 77c, Basket weaving, horiz. $1.25, Sculpture, horiz.

**Self-Adhesive**
**Coil Stamps**

***Serpentine Die Cut 8½ Horiz.***

**2002, Jan. 2**
**1927** A759 48c multi .75 .25
**1928** A684 65c multi 1.00 .30
*a.* Booklet of 6 6.00
**1929** A684 77c multi 1.10 .40
**1930** A684 $1.25 multi 1.80 .65
*a.* Booklet of 6 11.00

**Booklet Stamp**

***Serpentine Die Cut 8½***

**1931** A781 48c multi .75 .25
*a.* Booklet of 10 7.50
*b.* Booklet of 30 22.50
*c.* Blue omitted 350.00
*Nos. 1927-1931 (5)* 5.40 1.85

By separating the booklet along the columns of rouletting, No. 1931b could be broken up into three separately obtainable examples of No. 1931a. See No. 1991.

Reign of Queen Elizabeth II, 50th Anniv. — A782

**2002, Jan. 2** ***Perf. 13¼x12½***
**1932** A782 48c multi .70 .25
*a.* Imperf, pair *1,100.*
*b.* Gold omitted 1,300.

See No. 1987.

New Year 2002 (Year of the Horse) — A783

Horse and: 48c, Bamboo leaves. $1.25, Peach blossoms.

**Litho. & Embossed With Foil Application**

**2002, Jan. 3** ***Perf. 13¼***
**1933** A783 48c multi .75 .25
*a.* Foil (horse) omitted *1,200.*

**Souvenir Sheet**

**1934** A783 $1.25 multi 2.25 2.25

National Hockey League Stars — A784

No. 1935: a, Tim Horton (Toronto Maple Leafs jersey No. 7). b, Guy Lafleur (Montreal Canadiens jersey No. 10). c, Howie Morenz (Canadiens jersey, with brown gloves). d, Glenn Hall (Chicago Black Hawks jersey No. 1). e, Red Kelly (Maple Leafs jersey No. 4). f, Phil Esposito (Boston Bruins jersey no. 7).

***Perf. 12½x13 on 3 Sides***

**2002, Jan. 12**
**1935** Pane of 6 + 3 labels 5.00 5.00
*a.-f.* A784 48c Any single .80 .60

2002 Winter Olympics, Salt Lake City — A785

Designs: No. 1936, Short track speed skating. No. 1937, Curling. No. 1938, Freestyle aerial skiing. No. 1939, Women's hockey.

**2002, Jan. 25** ***Perf. 13¼x13***
**1936** A785 48c multi .75 .35
**1937** A785 48c multi .75 .35
**1938** A785 48c multi .75 .35
**1939** A785 48c multi .75 .35
*a.* Block or strip of 4, #1936-1939 3.00 2.50

Appointment of First Canadian Governor General, 50th Anniv. — A786

**2002, Feb. 1** ***Perf. 13¼x12½***
**1940** A786 48c multi .75 .25

Universities A787

Design: No. 1941, University of Manitoba, 125th anniv. No. 1942, Laval University, 150th anniv. No. 1943, University of Trinity College, 150th anniv. No. 1944, Saint Mary's University, Halifax, 200th anniv.

**2002** **Booklet Stamp** ***Perf. 13½***
**1941** A787 48c multi .75 .25
*a.* Booklet pane of 8 6.00 6.00
Booklet, #1941a 6.50
**1942** A787 48c multi .75 .25
*a.* Booklet pane of 8 6.00 6.00
Booklet, #1942a 6.50
**1943** A787 48c multi .75 .25
*a.* Booklet pane of 8 6.00 6.00
Booklet, #1943a 6.50
**1944** A787 48c multi .75 .25
*a.* Booklet pane of 8 6.00 6.00
Booklet, #1944a 6.50
*Nos. 1941-1944 (4)* 3.00 1.00

Issued: No. 1941, 2/28. No. 1942, 4/4. No. 1943, 4/30. No. 1944, 5/27.

**Art Type of 1988**

Design: Church and Horse, by Alex Colville.

**Litho. with Foil Application**

**2002, Mar. 22** ***Perf. 12½x13***
**1945** A546 $1.25 multi 2.00 1.10
*a.* Foil only (all other colors and tagging omitted) *1,400.*
*b.* Imperf, pair *1,250.*

Tulips — A788

Tulip varieties: a, City of Vancouver. b, Monte Carlo. c, Ottawa. d, The Bishop.

No. 1947: a, Like #1946a. b, Like #1946b. c, Like #1946c. d, Like #1946d.

**Self-Adhesive**

**2002, May 3** **Litho.** ***Die Cut***
**1946** Booklet pane of 4 3.00
*a.-d.* A788 48c Any single .75 .30
Booklet, 2 #1946 6.00

**Souvenir Sheet**

***Perf. 13x12½***

**1947** Pane of 4 3.00 3.00
*a.-d.* A788 48c Any single .75 .75

Issued: No. 1946, 5/3; No. 1947, 8/30.

Dendronepthea Gigantea and Dendronepthea Corals — A789

Tubastrea and Echinogorgia Corals A790

North Atlantic Pink Tree, Pacific Orange Cup and North Pacific Horn Corals A791

North Atlantic Giant Orange Tree and Black Corals A792

**2002, May 19** ***Perf. 12½x13***
**1948** A789 48c multi .75 .30
**1949** A790 48c multi .75 .30
**1950** A791 48c multi .75 .30
**1951** A792 48c multi .75 .30
*a.* Block of 4, #1948-1951 3.00 2.00
*b.* Souvenir sheet, #1948-1951, perf. 13¼x13 3.75 3.75

See Hong Kong Nos. 979-982.

**Tourist Attractions Type of 2001**

No. 1952: a, Yukon Quest, Yukon Territory. b, Icefields Parkway, Alberta. c, Agawa Canyon, Ontario. d, Old Port of Montreal, Quebec. e, Kings Landing, New Brunswick.

No. 1953: a, Northern Lights, Northwest Territories. b, Stanley Park, Vancouver, British Columbia. c, Head-Smashed-In Buffalo Jump, Alberta. d, Saguenay Fjord, Quebec. e, Peggy's Cove, Nova Scotia.

**Self-Adhesive**

**2002, June 1** ***Die Cut Perf. 11x11¼***
**1952** Booklet of 5 5.50
*a.-e.* A768 65c Any single 1.10 .75
**1953** Booklet of 5 10.00
*a.-e.* A768 $1.25 Any single 2.00 1.10

Sculpture A793

Designs: No. 1954, Embacle, by Charles Daudelin. No. 1955, Lumberjacks, by Leo Mol.

**2002, June 10** ***Perf. 13¼***
**1954** A793 48c multi .75 .25
**1955** A793 48c multi .75 .25
*a.* Horiz. or vert. pair, #1954-1955 1.50 .90

Canadian Postmasters and Assistants Association, Cent. A794

**2002, July 5** ***Perf. 13¼x12½***
**1956** A794 48c multi .75 .25

Printed in panes of 16 stamps + 12 labels.

17th World Youth Day, Toronto — A795

**Self-Adhesive**
**Booklet Stamp**

**2002, July 23** ***Die Cut***

**1957** A795 48c multi .75 .30
*a.* Booklet of 8 6.00

Public Services International World Congress, Ottawa — A796

**2002, Sept. 4** ***Perf. 12½x13***

**1958** A796 48c multi .75 .25

Public Pensions, 75th Anniv. — A797

**2002, Sept. 10** ***Perf. 13¼***

**1959** A797 48c multi .75 .25

Souvenir Sheet

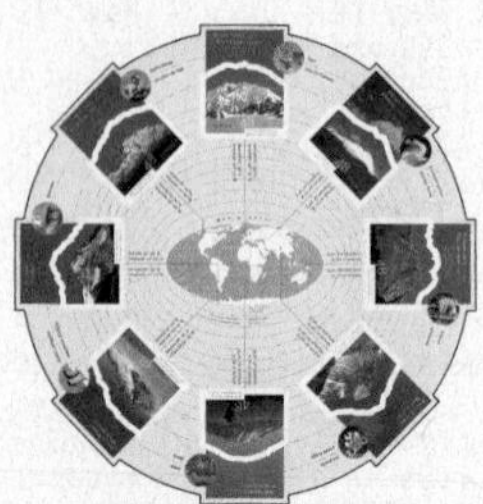

Intl. Year of Mountains — A798

No. 1960: a, Mt. Logan, Canada. b, Mt. Elbrus, Russia. c, Puncak Jaya, Indonesia. d, Mt. Everest, Nepal and China. e, Mt. Kilimanjaro, Tanzania. f, Vinson Massif, Antarctica. g, Mt. Aconcagua, Argentina. h, Mt. McKinley, Alaska.

**Self-Adhesive**

**2002, Oct. 1** ***Die Cut***

**1960** A798 Pane of 8 + 8 labels 7.25
*a.-h.* 48c Any single .90 *1.10*

World Teachers' Day — A799

**2002, Oct. 4** ***Perf. 12½x13***

**1961** A799 48c multi .75 .25

Toronto Stock Exchange, 150th Anniv. A800

**2002, Oct. 24**

**1962** A800 48c multi .75 .25

Communication Technology Centenaries — A801

Part of map of North America and: No. 1963, Sir Sandford Fleming (1827-1915), cable-laying ship. No. 1964, Guglielmo Marconi (1874-1937), radio and transmission towers.

**2002, Oct. 31** ***Perf. 13x12½***

**1963** 48c multi .75 .25
**1964** 48c multi .75 .25
*a.* A801 Horiz. pair, #1963-1964 1.50 1.10

Cent. of first telegraph message sent over transpacific cable (No. 1963); first transatlantic radio message (No. 1964).

Christmas — A802

Art by aboriginals: 48c, Genesis, by Daphne Odjig. 65c, Winter Travel, by Cecil Youngfox. $1.25, Mary and Child, sculpture by Irene Katak Angutitaq.

**2002, Nov. 4** ***Perf. 12½x13***

**1965** A802 48c multi .75 .25
*a.* Booklet pane of 10 7.50 7.50
Booklet, #1965a 8.00
**1966** A802 65c multi 1.00 .40
*a.* Booklet pane of 6 6.00 6.00
Booklet, #1966a 6.50
**1967** A802 $1.25 multi 2.00 .75
*a.* Booklet pane of 6 12.00 12.00
Booklet, #1967a 12.50
*Nos. 1965-1967 (3)* 3.75 1.40

Quebec Symphony Orchestra, Cent. — A803

**2002, Nov. 7**

**1968** A803 48c multi .80 .30

New Year 2003 (Year of the Ram) — A804

**Litho. & Embossed with Foil Application**

**2003, Jan. 3** ***Perf. 13***

**1969** A804 48c shown .75 .25
*a.* Gold omitted *400.00*
*b.* Imperf, pair *1,750.*

**Souvenir Sheet**

***Perf. 13¼***

**1970** A804 $1.25 Ram, diff. 2.50 2.50

No. 1970 contains one 33x58mm stamp. Slits replace perforations on the vertical sides of the stamps between the point of the acute angle made with the curving perforations and the point perpendicular to where the perforations on the opposite side form the obtuse angle with the curving perforations.

National Hockey League Stars — A805

Designs: Nos. 1971a, 1972a, Frank Mahovlich (orange panel). Nos. 1971b, 1972b, Raymond Bourque (lilac panel). Nos. 1971c, 1972c, Serge Savard (blue panel). Nos. 1971d, 1972d, Stan Mikita (red violet panel). Nos. 1971e, 1972e, Mike Bossy (bright pink panel). Nos. 1971f, 1972f, Bill Durnan (green panel).

***Perf. 12½x13¼ on 3 Sides***

**2003, Jan. 18**

**1971** Pane of 6 + 3 labels 14.00 —
*a.-f.* A805 48c Any single 2.25 1.50

**Self-Adhseive**

***Die Cut***

**1972** Pane of 6 60.00 —
*a.-f.* A805 48c Any single 6.50 1.50

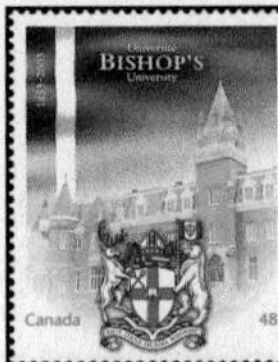


Universities — A806

Design: No. 1973, Bishop's University, Lennoxville, Quebec, 150th anniv. No. 1974, University of Western Ontario, London, Ont., 125th anniv. No. 1975, St. Francis Xavier University, Antigonish, N. S., 150th Anniv. No. 1976, Macdonald Institute, Guelph, Ont., cent. No. 1977, University of Montreal, 125th anniv.

**Booklet Stamps**

**2003** ***Perf. 13¼x13½***

**1973** A806 48c multi .75 .25
*a.* Booklet pane of 8 6.00 6.00
Booklet, #1973a 6.50
**1974** A806 48c multi .75 .25
*a.* Booklet pane of 8 6.00 6.00
Booklet, #1974a 6.50
**1975** A806 48c multi .75 .25
*a.* Booklet pane of 8 6.00 6.00
Complete booklet, #1975a 6.50
**1976** A806 48c multi .75 .25
*a.* Booklet pane of 8 6.00 6.00
Complete booklet, #1976a 6.50
**1977** A806 48c multi .75 .25
*a.* Booklet pane of 8 6.00 6.00
Complete booklet, #1977a 6.50

Issued: No. 1973, 1/28. No. 1975, 4/4. No. 1976, 6/20. No. 1977, 9/4. No. 1974, 3/19.

See Nos. 2033-2034, 2089, 2172, 2209-2210.

Bird Paintings by John James Audubon A807

Designs: No. 1979, Leach's storm petrel. No. 1980, Brant. No. 1981, Great cormorant. No. 1982, Common murre. 65c, Gyrfalcon, vert.

**2003, Feb. 21** ***Perf. 13¼x12½***

**1979** A807 48c multi .75 .35
**1980** A807 48c multi .75 .35
**1981** A807 48c multi .75 .35
**1982** A807 48c multi .75 .35
*a.* Block of 4, #1979-1982 3.00 2.25

**Booklet Stamp**

**Self-Adhesive**

***Die Cut***

**1983** A807 65c multi 1.10 .75
*a.* Booklet pane of 6 6.75
*Nos. 1979-1983 (5)* 4.10 2.15

Canadian Rangers A808

**2003, Mar. 3** ***Perf. 12½x13¼***

**1984** A808 48c multi .75 .25

American Hellenic Educational Progressive Association In Canada, 75th Anniv. — A809

**2003, Mar. 25**

**1985** A809 48c multi .75 .25

Volunteer Firefighters A810

**2003, May 30** ***Perf. 13¼***

**1986** A810 48c multi .75 .25

Coronation of Queen Elizabeth II, 50th Anniv. — A811

**2003, June 2** ***Perf. 13x12½***

**1987** A811 48c multi .75 .25

See No. 1932.

Quebec City, Seal of Sovereign Council of New France, Signature of Pedro da Silva A812

**2003, June 6** ***Perf. 13***

**1988** A812 48c multi .75 .25

Pedro da Silva, first courier in New France, 50th anniv. of Portuguese immigration to Canada.

**Tourist Attractions Type of 2001**

No. 1989: a, Wilberforce Falls, Nunavut. b, Inside Passage, B. C. c, Royal Canadian Mounted Police Depot Division, Regina, Sask. d, Casa Loma, Toronto, Ont. e, Gatineau Park, Que.

No. 1990: a, Dragon boat races, Vancouver, B. C. b, Polar bear watching, Man. c, Niagara Falls, Ont. d, Magdalen Islands, Que. e, Charlottestown, P. E. I.

**Self-Adhesive**

**2003, June 12** ***Die Cut Perf. 11¼***

**1989** Booklet of 5 5.50
*a.-e.* A768 65c Any single 1.10 .75
**1990** Booklet of 5 10.00
*a.-e.* A768 $1.25 Any single 2.00 1.10

"Vancouver 2010" Added in Red

**Self-Adhesive**
**Booklet Stamp**

***Serpentine Die Cut 8½***

**2003, July 11** **Litho.**

**1991** A781 48c multi 1.50 1.20
*a.* Booklet of 10 15.00
*b.* Booklet of 30 45.00
*e.* Die cutting omitted, pair *750.00*

Selection of Vancouver as site of 2010 Winter Olympics. By separating the booklet along the columns of rouletting, No. 1991b could be broken up into three separately obtainable examples of No. 1991a.

Canada-Alaska Cruise Scenes — A813

Mountains and: No. 1991C, Totem pole. No. 1991D, Whale's tail.

**Self-Adhesive**

**2003, July 19** ***Die Cut***

**1991C** A813 ($1.25) multi 7.50 7.50
**1991D** A813 ($1.25) multi 7.50 7.50
*e.* Horiz. pair, #19901C-1991D 15.00

Nos. 1991C-1991D were printed in panes of 10 containing five of each stamp. The blank spaces in each stamp and the three stamp-like vignettes at the left of the pane that lack die cutting and "Postage Paid / Port Payé" inscription could be personalized on cruise ships. Personalized panes sold for $19.95 in US currency, while unpersonalized panes sold for $12.50. Value, unpersonalized complete pane $85.

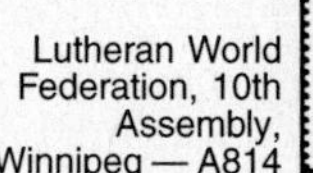

Lutheran World Federation, 10th Assembly, Winnipeg — A814

**2003, July 21** *Perf. 12½x13*

**1992** A814 48c multi .75 .25

Korean War Armistice Agreement, 50th Anniv. — A815

**2003, July 25** *Perf. 12¾*

**1993** A815 48c multi .75 .25

Authors — A816

Designs: No. 1994, Anne Hébert (1916-2000). No. 1995, Hector de Saint-Denys Garneau (1912-43). No. 1996, Morley Callaghan (1903-90). No. 1997, Susanna Moodie (1803-85), and Catharine Parr Traill (1802-99).

### Booklet Stamps

**2003, Sept. 8** *Perf. 13¼x12½*

**1994** A816 48c multi .75 .35
**1995** A816 48c multi .75 .35
**1996** A816 48c multi .75 .35
**1997** A816 48c multi .75 .35
*a.* Block of 4, #1994-1997 3.00 2.25
*b.* Booklet pane, 2 #1997a 6.00 —
Complete booklet, #1997b 6.50

2003 Road Cycling World Championships, Hamilton, Ont. — A817

### Booklet Stamp

**2003, Sept. 10** *Perf. 12½x13*

**1998** A817 48c multi .75 .55
*a.* Booklet pane of 8 6.00 —
Complete booklet, #1998a 6.50

Canadian Astronauts A818

No. 1999: a, Marc Garneau. b, Roberta Bondar. c, Steve MacLean. d, Chris Hadfield. e, Robert Thirsk. f, Bjarni Tryggvason. g, Dave Williams. h, Julie Payette.

### Self-Adhesive

### Litho. With Foil Application

**2003, Oct. 1** *Die Cut*

**1999** Pane of 8 8.00
*a.-h.* A818 48c Any single .90 .90

Trees of Canada and Thailand — A819

Designs: No. 2000, Acer saccharum leaves (Canada). No. 2001, Cassia fistula (Thailand).

**2003, Oct. 4 Litho.** *Perf. 12¾x12½*

**2000** A819 48c multi .75 .25
**2001** A819 48c multi .75 .25
*a.* Pair, #2000-2001 1.50 1.10
*b.* Souvenir sheet, #2000-2001 7.50 4.00
*c.* As "a," imperf *900.00*
*d.* As "b," imperf *1,250.*

Bangkok 2003 Intl. Philatelic Exhibition (No. 2001b).
See Thailand No. 2090.

L'Hommage à Rosa Luxemburg, by Jean-Paul Riopelle — A820

Painting details — No. 2002; a, Red and blue dots between birds at LR. b, Bird with yellow beak at center. c, Three birds in circle at R. d, Sun at UR. e, Birds with purple outlines at L. f, Bird with red outline in circle at R. $1.25, Pink bird in red circle at R.

**2003, Oct. 7** *Perf. 12½x13*

**2002** A820 Pane of 6 7.50 7.50
*a.-f.* 48c Any single 1.25 1.25

### Souvenir Sheet

*Perf. 12¾*

**2003** A820 $1.25 multi 3.00 3.00

Christmas — A821

Gift boxes and: 48c, Ice skates. 65c, Teddy bear. $1.25, Toy duck.

### Self-Adhesive Booklet Stamps

**2003, Nov. 4** *Die Cut*

**2004** A821 48c multi .75 .25
*a.* Booklet pane of 6 4.50
Complete booklet, 2 #2004a 9.00
*b.* Pair, die cutting omitted 375.00
**2005** A821 65c multi 1.00 .60
*a.* Booklet pane of 6 6.00
*b.* As "a," die cutting omitted 1,500.
*c.* Die cutting omitted, pair *450.00*
**2006** A821 $1.25 multi 2.00 1.00
*a.* Booklet pane of 6 12.00
*b.* Die cutting omitted, pair 450.00
*Nos. 2004-2006 (3)* 3.75 1.85

Maple Leaf and Samara A822

Maple Leaf on Twig A823

Flag Over Edmonton, Alberta A824

Queen Elizabeth II A825

### Coil Stamps

*Serpentine Die Cut 8½ Horiz.*

**2003, Dec. 19** **Self-Adhesive**

**2008** A822 49c multi .75 .25
*a.* Die cutting omitted, pair 150.00

*Serpentine Die Cut 8½ Vert.*

**2009** A823 80c red & multi 1.20 .40
**2010** A823 $1.40 grn & multi 3.00 .55

### Booklet Stamps

*Die Cut*

**2011** A824 49c multi .75 .25
*a.* Booklet pane of 10 7.50
*b.* Die cutting omitted, pair 150.00
*c.* As "a," die cutting omitted *750.00*
**2012** A825 49c multi .80 .25
*a.* Booklet pane of 10 8.00
**2013** A823 80c red & multi 1.50 .40
*a.* Booklet pane of 6 9.00
**2014** A823 $1.40 grn & multi 2.25 .75
*a.* Booklet pane of 6 13.50
*Nos. 2008-2014 (7)* 10.25 2.85

See Nos. 2053-2055, 2075.

New Year 2004 (Year of the Monkey) — A826

Scenes from Chinese story *Journey to the West*: 49c, Monkey King. $1.40, Monkey King, Xuan Zang, Sandy, Pigsy and horse.

### Litho. & Embossed with Foil Application

**2004, Jan. 8** *Perf. 13x12½*

**2015** A826 49c multi .80 .25

### Souvenir Sheet

**2016** A826 $1.40 multi 3.00 3.00
*a.* As No. 2016, with 2004 Hong Kong Stamp Expo ovpt. in margin 3.75 3.75

No. 2016 has rouletted tab at right showing bar code.

National Hockey League Stars — A827

Designs: Nos. 2017a, 2018a, Larry Robinson (blue background). Nos. 2017b, 2018b, Marcel Dionne (orange background). Nos. 2017c, 2018c, Ted Lindsay (red background). Nos. 2017d, 2018d, Johnny Bower (green background). Nos. 2017e, 2018e, Brad Park (brown background). Nos. 2017f, 2018f, Milt Schmidt (purple background).

*Perf. 12½x13¼ on 3 Sides*

**2004, Jan. 24** **Litho.**

**2017** Pane of 6 + 3 labels 6.00 6.00
*a.-f.* A827 49c Any single .75 .60

### Self-Adhesive

*Die Cut*

**2018** Pane of 6 6.00
*a.-f.* A827 49c Any single .75 .55

### Tourist Attractions Type of 2001

Design: No. 2019, Quebec Winter Carnival; No. 2020, St. Joseph's Oratory, Montreal, Quebec; No. 2021, International Jazz Festival, Montreal. No. 2022, Traversée Internationale du Lac St. Jean Swimming Marathon, Quebec; No. 2023, Canadian National Exhibition, Toronto.

### Self-Adhesive Booklet Stamp

**2004, Jan. 29** *Die Cut*

**2019** A768 49c multi .75 .35
*a.* Booklet of 6 4.50
**2020** A768 49c multi .75 .35
*a.* Booklet of 6 4.50
**2021** A768 49c multi .75 .35
*a.* Booklet of 6 4.50
**2022** A768 49c multi .75 .35
*a.* Booklet of 6 4.50
**2023** A768 49c multi .75 .35
*a.* Booklet of 6 4.50

Issued: No. 2019, 1/29; No. 2020, 4/2; No. 2021, 6/1; No. 2022, 6/18; No. 2023, 7/19.

Governor General Ramon John Hnatyshyn (1934-2002) — A828

**2004, Mar. 16** *Perf. 12½x13*

**2024** A828 49c multi .75 .25

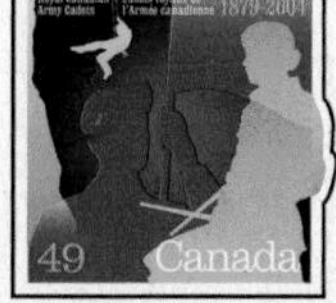

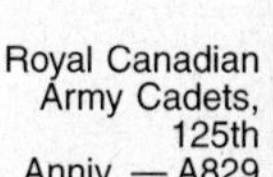

Royal Canadian Army Cadets, 125th Anniv. — A829

### Self-Adhesive Booklet Stamp

**2004, Mar. 26** *Die Cut*

**2025** A829 49c multi .75 .30
*a.* Booklet pane of 4 3.00
Complete booklet, 2 #2025a 6.00

The Fram, Ship of Otto Sverdrup (1854-1930), Arctic Explorer — A830

### Litho. & Engr.

**2004, Mar. 26** *Perf. 13¼*

**2026** A830 49c multi .75 .25

### Souvenir Sheet

**2027** A830 $1.40 multi + 2 labels 3.00 3.00

See Greenland No. 426, Norway Nos. 1398-1399.

Urban Transit and Light Rail Systems A831

Train cars, station names and system emblems of: No. 2028, Toronto Transit Commission. No. 2029, TransLink SkyTrain, Vancouver. No. 2030, Société de Transport de Montreal. No. 2031, Calgary Transit Light Rail.

**2004, Mar. 30 Litho.** *Perf. 12½x13*

**2028** A831 49c multi .75 .30
**2029** A831 49c multi .75 .30
**2030** A831 49c multi .75 .30
**2031** A831 49c multi .75 .30
*a.* Vert. strip of 4, #2028-2031 3.00 2.75

Home Hardware, 40th Anniv. — A832

### Self-Adhesive Booklet Stamp

**2004, Apr. 19** *Die Cut Perf. 11*

**2032** A832 49c multi .75 .30
*a.* Booklet pane of 10 + label 7.50
Complete booklet, #2032a 8.00

No. 2032a is the inside front cover of the complete booklet. Fifteen self-adhesive seals are on the inside back cover of the complete booklet.

### Universities Type of 2003

Designs: No. 2033, Sherbrooke University, Sherbrooke, Quebec, 50th anniv. No. 2034, University of Prince Edward Island, Charlottetown, bicent.

### Booklet Stamps

**2004** *Perf. 13¼x13½*

**2033** A806 49c multi .75 .30
*a.* Booklet pane of 8 6.00 6.50
Complete booklet, #2033a 6.50
**2034** A806 49c multi .75 .30
*a.* Booklet pane of 8 6.00 6.50
Complete booklet, #2034a 6.50

Issued: No. 2033, 5/4; No. 2034, 5/8.

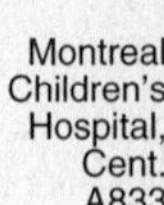

Montreal Children's Hospital, Cent. A833

**Self-Adhesive**
**Booklet Stamp**

**2004, May 6** ***Die Cut Perf. 9½x10¾***

| | | | |
|---|---|---|---|
| **2035** | A833 49c multi | .75 | .30 |
| *a.* | Booklet pane of 4 | 3.00 | |
| | Complete booklet, 2 #2035a | 6.00 | |

Bird Paintings by John James Audubon — A834

Designs: No. 2036, Ruby-crowned kinglet. No. 2037, White-winged crossbill. No. 2038, Bohemian waxwing. No. 2039, Boreal chickadee. 80c, Lincoln's sparrow.

**2004, May 14** ***Perf. 12½x13***

| | | | |
|---|---|---|---|
| **2036** | A834 49c multi | .75 | .35 |
| **2037** | A834 49c multi | .75 | .35 |
| **2038** | A834 49c multi | .75 | .35 |
| **2039** | A834 49c multi | .75 | .35 |
| *a.* | Block of 4, #2036-2039 | 3.00 | 2.75 |

**Self-Adhesive**
**Booklet Stamp**
***Die Cut***

| | | | |
|---|---|---|---|
| **2040** | A834 80c multi | 1.20 | .75 |
| *a.* | Booklet pane of 6 | 7.25 | |
| | *Nos. 2036-2040 (5)* | 4.20 | 2.15 |

Pioneers of Transatlantic Mail Service — A835

Designs: No. 2041, Sir Samuel Cunard (1787-1865). No. 2042, Sir Hugh Allan (1810-82).

**Self-Adhesive**

**2004, May 28** ***Perf. 13¼x12½***

| | | | |
|---|---|---|---|
| **2041** | 49c multi | .75 | .30 |
| **2042** | 49c multi | .75 | .30 |
| *a.* | A835 Horiz. pair, #2041-2042 | 1.50 | 1.10 |

D-Day, 60th Anniv. — A836

**2004, June 6** ***Perf. 13x12½***

| | | | |
|---|---|---|---|
| **2043** | A836 49c multi | .75 | .30 |

Pierre Dugua de Mons, Leader of First French Settlement in Acadia, and Ship — A837

**2004, June 26** **Litho. & Engr.**

| | | | |
|---|---|---|---|
| **2044** | A837 49c multi | .75 | .30 |

See France No. 3032.

Butterfly and Flower — A838

Children on Beach — A839

Rose — A840

Dog — A841

**Self-Adhesive**
**Booklet Stamps**

***Serpentine Die Cut 11¾***

**2004, June** **Litho.**

| | | | |
|---|---|---|---|
| **2045** | A838 (49c) multi | 22.50 | *13.00* |
| *a.* | Booklet pane of 2 | 55.00 | |
| | Complete booklet, #2045a + phonecard in greeting card | 60.00 | |
| **2046** | A839 (49c) multi | 9.00 | *13.00* |
| *a.* | Booklet pane of 2 | 18.00 | |
| | Complete booklet, #2046a + phonecard in greeting card | 24.00 | |
| **2047** | A840 (49c) multi | 9.00 | *13.00* |
| *a.* | Booklet pane of 2 | 18.00 | |
| | Complete booklet, #2047a + phonecard in greeting card | 24.00 | |
| **2048** | A841 (49c) multi | 9.00 | *13.00* |
| *a.* | Booklet pane of 2 | 18.00 | |
| | Complete booklet, #2048a + phonecard in greeting card | 24.00 | |
| | *Nos. 2045-2048 (4)* | 49.50 | 52.00 |

Nos. 2045-2048, have a frame like No. 1918a, and are similarly inscribed "Domestic Lettermail" and "Poste-lettres du régime intérieur," but Nos. 2045-2048 have the vignettes printed on the stamps, while any vignettes found on No. 1918a are affixed stickers. Nos. 2045a-2048a are affixed to the insides of greeting cards that contain detachable phonecards valid for 15 minutes calling time on any touchtone phone in Canada or the United States. The stamps were available only in the greeting card, which sold for $5.99 along with a blank envelope for sending the greeting card.

2004 Summer Olympics, Athens A842

Olympic rings and: No. 2049, Spyros Louis, 1896 Marathon gold medalist, diagram of track, "Athens" in Greek, and stylized runner. No. 2050, Soccer net inscribed "Canada," girls playing soccer.

**2004, July 28** ***Perf. 12½x13¼***

| | | | |
|---|---|---|---|
| **2049** | A842 49c multi | .75 | .30 |
| **2050** | A842 49c multi | .75 | .30 |
| *a.* | Horiz. pair, #2049-2050 | 1.50 | 1.10 |

Canadian Open Golf Championship, Cent. — A843

Crowd, trophy and golfer: No. 2051, Finishing swing. No. 2052, Ready to putt.

**Self-Adhesive**

**Litho. & Embossed With Foil Application**

**2004, Aug. 12** ***Serpentine Die Cut***

| | | | |
|---|---|---|---|
| **2051** | A843 49c multi | .75 | .30 |
| **2052** | A843 49c multi | .75 | .30 |
| *a.* | Horiz. pair, #2051-2052, silver omitted on both stamps | *2,750.* | |

Nos. 2051-2052 were issued in a sheet containing four of each stamp.

**Maple Leaf Types of 2003**
**Self-Adhesive Coil Stamps**

**2004, Aug. 18** **Litho.** ***Die Cut***

| | | | |
|---|---|---|---|
| **2053** | A822 49c multi | .75 | .25 |
| *a.* | Die cutting omitted, pair | 170.00 | |

***Serpentine Die Cut 8¼ Horiz.***

| | | | |
|---|---|---|---|
| **2054** | A823 80c red & multi | 2.00 | .50 |
| **2055** | A823 $1.40 grn & multi | 3.75 | .90 |
| *a.* | Die cutting omitted, pair | — | |
| | *Nos. 2053-2055 (3)* | 6.50 | 1.65 |

Die cut gauges on Nos. 2054-2055 vary widely within the roll, from 8¼-8¾. Gauge 8¼ is the most common.

Montreal Heart Institute, 50th Anniv. — A844

**Self-Adhesive**
**Booklet Stamp**

**2004, Sept. 15** ***Die Cut Perf. 13½***

| | | | |
|---|---|---|---|
| **2056** | A844 49c multi | .75 | .30 |
| *a.* | Booklet pane of 4 | 3.00 | |
| | Complete booklet, 2 #2056 | 6.00 | |

Pets — A845

**Self-Adhesive**
**Booklet Stamps**

**2004, Oct. 1** ***Die Cut***

| | | | |
|---|---|---|---|
| **2057** | A845 49c Fish | .75 | .35 |
| **2058** | A845 49c Cats | .75 | .35 |
| **2059** | A845 49c Rabbit | .75 | .35 |
| **2060** | A845 49c Dog | .75 | .35 |
| *a.* | Booklet pane, #2057-2060 | 3.00 | |
| | Complete booklet, 2 #2060a | 6.00 | |

Nobel Laureates in Chemistry A846

Designs: No. 2061, Gerhard Herzberg, 1971 laureate, and molecular structures. No. 2062, Michael Smith, 1993 laureate, and DNA double helix.

**2004, Oct. 4** ***Perf. 12½x13***

| | | | |
|---|---|---|---|
| **2061** | A846 49c multi | .75 | .30 |
| **2062** | A846 49c multi | .75 | .30 |
| *a.* | Pair, #2061-2062 | 1.50 | 1.10 |

Ribbon Frame — A847

Picture Album Frame — A848

***Serpentine Die Cut 12¾x13***

**2004, Oct. 8** **Self-Adhesive**

| | | | |
|---|---|---|---|
| **2063** | A847 (49c) multi | 1.50 | 1.25 |
| **2064** | A848 (49c) multi | 1.50 | 1.25 |

Nos. 2063 and 2064 were each printed in panes of 21 that sold for $9.80. These panes were split by a row of rouletting in the center, with 20 stamps on one side and one on the other side. Panes of 21 with vignettes that could be personalized by the customer were available for $24.95. Panes of 40 stamps with personalized vignettes were also available for $39.95.

Victoria Cross, 150th Anniv. — A849

Designs: No. 2065, Victoria Cross. No. 2066, Design for Canadian Victoria Cross, approved with Queen Elizabeth II's signature.

**Litho. & Embossed**

**2004, Oct. 21** ***Perf. 13x12½***

| | | | |
|---|---|---|---|
| **2065** | A849 49c multi | .75 | .30 |

**Litho.**

| | | | |
|---|---|---|---|
| **2066** | A849 49c multi | .75 | .30 |
| *a.* | Pair, #2065-2066 | 1.50 | 1.20 |

Paintings by Jean Paul Lemieux — A850

Designs: 49c, Self-portrait. 80c, A June Wedding, horiz. (53x35mm). $1.40, Summer, horiz. (64x31mm).

**2004, Oct. 22** ***Perf. 13x13¼***

| | | | |
|---|---|---|---|
| **2067** | A850 49c multi | .75 | .30 |
| *a.* | Perf. 13 | 1.50 | 1.50 |

**Souvenir Sheet**
***Perf. 13***

| | | | |
|---|---|---|---|
| **2068** | Sheet, #2067a, 2068a, 2068b | 5.25 | 5.25 |
| *a.* | A850 80c multi | 1.50 | 1.50 |
| *b.* | A850 $1.40 multi | 2.25 | 2.25 |

Christmas A851

Santa Claus and: 49c, Sleigh. 80c, Automobile. $1.40, Train.

**Booklet Stamps**

***Serpentine Die Cut 7¼ Horiz.***

**2004, Nov. 2** **Self-Adhesive**

| | | | |
|---|---|---|---|
| **2069** | A851 49c multi | .75 | .25 |
| *a.* | Booklet pane of 6 | 4.50 | |
| | Complete booklet, 2 #2069a | 9.00 | |
| *b.* | Printed on gummed side | 11.00 | |
| *c.* | As "a," printed on gummed side | 150.00 | |
| **2070** | A851 80c multi | 1.25 | .45 |
| *a.* | Booklet pane of 6 | 7.50 | |
| *b.* | Printed on gummed side | — | |
| *c.* | Imperf, pair | *1,100.* | |
| **2071** | A851 $1.40 multi | 2.25 | .75 |
| *a.* | Booklet pane of 6 | 13.50 | |
| *b.* | Printed on gummed side | 45.00 | |
| *c.* | As "a," printed on gummed side | *750.00* | |

**Queen Type of 2003 and**

Red Calla Lilies A852

Flag and Saskatoon, Saskatchewan A853

Flag and Durrell, Newfoundland A854

Flag and Shannon Falls, British Columbia A855

Flag and Mont-Saint-Hilaire, Quebec — A856

Flag and Toronto — A857

Designs: 85c, Yellow calla lily. $1.45, Dutch iris.

### Coil Stamps

***Serpentine Die Cut 6½-8¾ Horiz.***

**2004-05** **Self-Adhesive**

**2072** A852 50c multi .75 .25
*a.* Serpentine die cut 6¾ horiz. ('05) .75 .25
*b.* Die cutting omitted, pair 75.00
**2073** A852 85c multi 1.30 .25
*a.* Serpentine die cut 6¾ horiz. ('05) 1.50 .25
**2074** A852 $1.45 multi 2.25 .60
*a.* Serpentine die cut 6¾ horiz. ('05) 5.50 2.20

The die cutting gauge on Nos. 2072-2074a will vary between stamps on a roll and between stamps on one roll and other rolls.

Issued: Nos. 2072, 2073, 2074, 12/20/04. Nos. 2072a, 2073a, 2074a, 2/2005. Die cuttings on these issues are variable.

### Booklet Stamps

***Die Cut***

**2075** A825 50c multi .75 .25
*a.* Booklet pane of 10 7.50
**2076** A853 50c multi .75 .25
**2077** A854 50c multi .75 .25
**2078** A855 50c multi .75 .25
**2079** A856 50c multi .75 .25
**2080** A857 50c multi .75 .25
*a.* Booklet pane, 2 each #2076-2080 7.50
*b.* As "a," printed on gummed side 75.00
**2081** A852 85c multi 1.40 .40
*a.* Booklet pane of 6 8.50
*b.* As "a," black inscriptions omitted *4,000.*
**2082** A852 $1.45 multi 2.20 .60
*a.* Booklet pane of 6 13.25
*Nos. 2072-2082 (11)* 12.40 3.60

New Year 2005 (Year of the Cock) — A858

Rooster with: 50c, Red tail feathers. $1.45, Gold tail feathers.

### Litho. & Embossed with Foil Application

**2005, Jan. 7** ***Perf. 13¼***

**2083** A858 50c multi .75 .30
*a.* Red omitted *1,350.*

### Souvenir Sheet

***Perf. 12½x13***

**2084** A858 $1.45 multi 2.20 2.20
*a.* With dates, Canadian and Chinese flags added in sheet margin 3.20 3.20

Canada — People's Republic of China diplomatic relations, 35th anniv. (No. 2084a). No. 2084 contains one 40x40mm stamp.

National Hockey League Stars — A859

Designs: Nos. 2085a, 2086a, Henri Richard (blue background). Nos. 2085b, 2086b, Grant Fuhr (orange background). Nos. 2085c, 2086c, Allan Stanley (red background). Nos. 2085d, 2086d, Pierre Pilote (green background). Nos. 2085e, 2086e, Bryan Trottier (purple background). Nos. 2085f, 2086f, John Bucyk (yellow background).

***Perf. 12½x13¼ on 3 Sides***

**2005, Jan. 29** **Litho.**

**2085** Pane of 6 + 3 labels 4.50 4.50
*a.-f.* A859 50c Any single .75 .55

### Self-Adhesive

***Die Cut***

**2086** Pane of 6 4.50
*a.-f.* A859 50c Any single .75 .55

Fishing Flies A860

Designs: Nos. 2087a, 2088a, Alevin. Nos. 2087b, 2088b, Jock Scott. Nos. 2087c, 2088d, P. E. I. Fly. Nos. 2087d, 2088c, Mickey Finn.

**2005, Feb. 4** ***Perf. 12½x13¼***

**2087** A860 Pane of 4 7.50 5.50
*a.-d.* 50c Any single 1.90 1.10

### Self-Adhesive

***Serpentine Die Cut 10 Syncopated***

**2088** A860 Booklet pane of 4 3.60
*a.-d.* 50c Any single .90 .35
Complete booklet, 2 #2088 7.25

### Universities Type of 2003

Design: Nova Scotia Agricultural College, cent.

### Booklet Stamp

***Die Cut Perf. 12¾x13¼***

**2005, Feb. 14** **Self-Adhesive**

**2089** A806 50c multi .75 .30
*a.* Booklet pane of 4 3.00
Complete booklet, 2 #2089a 6.00

Expo 2005, Aichi, Japan — A861

**2005, Mar. 4** ***Perf. 13½***

**2090** A861 50c multi .75 .30

Daffodils — A862

Designs: Nos. 2091a, 2092, Yellow daffodils, green and yellow background. Nos. 2091b, 2093, White daffodils, red orange and yellow background.

### Souvenir Sheet

**2005, Mar. 10** ***Perf. 13x13¼***

**2091** Pane of 2 2.20 2.20
*a.-b.* A862 50c Either single 1.10 .75

### Booklet Stamps

### Self-Adhesive

***Die Cut Perf. 10***

**2092** A862 50c multi .75 .30
**2093** A862 50c multi .75 .30
*a.* Booklet pane, 5 each #2092-2093 + 10 stickers 7.50

Pacific Explore 2005 World Stamp Expo, Sydney, Australia (No. 2091).

TD Bank Financial Group, 150th Anniv. — A863

### Self-Adhesive

### Booklet Stamp

**2005, Mar. 18** ***Die Cut Perf. 11¼***

**2094** A863 50c multi .75 .35
*a.* Booklet pane of 10 7.50
Complete booklet, #2094a 10.00

The booklet pane of 10 is the inside front cover of the booklet. Fifteen stickers are on inside back cover.

Bird Paintings by John James Audubon A864

Designs: No. 2095, Horned lark. No. 2096, Piping plover. No. 2097, Stilt sandpiper. No. 2098, Willow ptarmigan. 85c, Double-crested cormorant.

**2005, Mar. 23** ***Perf. 12½x13¼***

**2095** A864 50c multi .75 .40
**2096** A864 50c multi .75 .40
**2097** A864 50c multi .75 .40
**2098** A864 50c multi .75 .40
*a.* Block of 4, #2095-2098 3.00 2.50

### Booklet Stamp

### Self-Adhesive

### Size: 48x39mm

***Die Cut***

**2099** A864 85c multi 1.20 .45
*a.* Booklet pane of 6 7.25

Bridges A865

Designs: No. 2100, Jacques Cartier Bridge, Quebec. No. 2101, Souris Swinging Bridge, Manitoba. No. 2102, Angus L. Macdonald Bridge, Nova Scotia. No. 2103, Canso Causeway, Nova Scotia.

### Self-Adhesive

**2005, Apr. 2** ***Perf. 12½x13***

**2100** A865 50c multi .75 .45
**2101** A865 50c multi .75 .45
**2102** A865 50c multi .75 .45
**2103** A865 50c multi .75 .45
*a.* Block or strip of 4, #2100-2103 3.00 2.75
*b.* As "a," imperf. 1,500.

Maclean's Magazine, Cent. — A866

**2005, Apr. 12**

**2104** A866 50c multi .75 .30

Biosphere Reserves in Canada and Ireland A867

Designs: No. 2105, Saskatoon berries, Waterton Lakes National Park, Canada. No. 2106, Deer, Killarney National Park, Ireland.

**2005, Apr. 22**

**2105** A867 50c multi .75 .30
**2106** A867 50c multi .75 .30
*a.* Pair, #2105-2106 1.50 1.10
*b.* Souvenir sheet, #2105-2106 2.00 2.00

See Ireland Nos. 1611-1612.

Battle of the Atlantic, World War II — A868

**2005, Apr. 29**

**2107** A868 50c multi .75 .30

Opening of Canadian War Museum, Ottawa A869

### Booklet Stamp

***Serpentine Die Cut 8x8½ Syncopated***

**2005, May 6** **Self-Adhesive**

**2108** A869 50c multi .75 .30
*a.* Booklet pane of 4 3.00
Complete booklet, 2 #2108a 6.00

Paintings by Homer Watson (1855-1936) A870

Designs: 50c, Down in the Laurentides. 85c, The Flood Gate (54x40mm)

**2005, May 27** ***Perf. 13¼x13***

**2109** A870 50c multi .75 .30
*a.* Perf. 13½x13 1.50 1.50

### Souvenir Sheet

***Perf. 13½x13***

**2110** Pane of 2, Nos. 2109a, 2110a 4.50 4.50
*a.* A870 85c multi 3.00 3.00

### Miniature Sheet

Search and Rescue A871

No. 2111: a, Rescuer and dog at plane crash. b, Rescuers at shipwreck. c, Helicopter, airplane and rescuers. d, Mountainside rescuers.

**2005, June 13** ***Perf. 13x13¼***

**2111** A871 Pane of 8, 2 each #a-d 6.00 6.00
*a.-d.* 50c Any single .75 .55

No. 2111 contains two horizontal strips, one of which is inverted, so that a tete-beche pair of No. 2111c and two tete-beche pairs containing Nos. 2111b and 2111d can be created.

Ellen Fairclough (1905-2004), First Female Cabinet Minister — A872

**2005, June 21** ***Perf. 13x12½***

**2112** A872 50c multi .75 .30

Diver A873

Swimmer A874

**2005, July 5** ***Perf. 13¼***

**2113** A873 50c multi .75 .45
**2114** A874 50c multi .75 .45
*a.* Horiz. pair, #2113-2114 1.50 1.00

9th FINA World Championships, Montreal. In No. 2114a, the denomination for one stamp is on the opposite side of the pair from that of the other stamp.

Founding of Port-Royal, Nova Scotia, 400th Anniv. — A875

### Litho. & Engr.

**2005, July 16** ***Perf. 13x12½***

**2115** A875 50c multi .75 .30

Province of Alberta, Cent. — A876

**Self-Adhesive**

**2005, July 21 Litho.** ***Perf. 12½x13***
**2116** A876 50c multi .75 .30

Printed in panes of 8 with each stamp having a different design on the backing.

Province of Saskatchewan, Cent. — A877

**2005, Aug. 2** ***Perf. 13x12½***
**2117** A877 50c multi .75 .30

Oscar Peterson, Pianist, 80th Birthday — A878

**2005, Aug. 15**
**2118** A878 50c multi .75 .30
*a.* Souvenir sheet of 4 3.00 3.00

No. 176 and Acadian Flag — A879

**2005, Aug. 15**
**2119** A879 50c multi .75 .30

Acadian Deportation, 250th anniv.

Children Playing and Leg Braces A880

**2005, Sept. 2** ***Perf. 12½x13***
**2120** A880 50c multi .75 .30

Mass polio vaccinations in Canada, 50th anniv.

Youth Sports — A881

No. 2121: a, Wall climbing. b, Skateboarding. c, Mountain biking. d, Snowboarding.

**Self-Adhesive**

**2005, Oct. 1** ***Die Cut***
**2121** Complete booket, 2 each #a-d 6.00
*a.-d.* A881 50c Any single .75 .35

Wild Cats — A882

Designs: No. 2122, Puma concolor. No. 2123, Panthera pardus orientalis.

***Perf. 13½x13¼ Syncopated***

**2005, Oct. 13**
**2122** 50c multi .75 .35
**2123** 50c multi .75 .35
*a.* A882 Horiz. pair, #2122-2123 1.50 .90
*b.* Souvenir sheet, #2123a 1.70 1.90

Diplomatic relations with People's Republic of China, 35th anniv. (No. 2123b). The perforation column between the two stamps, which gauges perf. 13½, has a maple leaf shaped syncopation.

See People's Republic of China Nos. 3458-3459.

Snowman — A883

**Self-Adhesive**

**Litho. with Hologram Applied**
***Serpentine Die Cut 8¼ Horiz.***

**2005, Nov. 2** **Booklet Stamp**
**2124** A883 50c multi .75 .30
*a.* Booklet pane of 6 4.50
Complete booklet, 2 #2124a 9.00

A884 A885

Creche Figures, St. Joseph's Oratory, Montreal — A886

**Self-Adhesive**

***Serpentine Die Cut 6¾ Horiz.***

**2005, Nov. 2** **Booklet Stamps**
**2125** A884 50c multi .75 .30
*a.* Booklet pane of 6 4.50
Complete booklet, 2 #2125a 9.00

***Serpentine Die Cut 6½ Horiz.***

**2126** A885 85c multi 1.25 .60
*a.* Booklet pane of 6 7.50

***Serpentine Die Cut 6¾ Horiz.***

**2127** A886 $1.45 multi 2.25 1.10
*a.* Booklet pane of 6 13.50

Flowers — A887

Designs: 51c, Red bergamot. 89c, Yellow lady's slipper. $1.05, Pink fairy slipper. $1.49, Himalayan blue poppy.

**Coil Stamps**

***Serpentine Die Cut 7 to 9¼ Horiz.***

**2005, Dec. 19** **Self-Adhesive**
**2128** A887 51c multi .75 .25
**2129** A887 89c multi 1.40 .45
**2130** A887 $1.05 multi 1.70 .60
**2131** A887 $1.49 multi 2.20 .90

**Booklet Stamps**

***Die Cut***

**2132** A887 89c multi 1.40 .40
*a.* Booklet pane of 6 8.50
**2133** A887 $1.05 multi 1.70 .65
*a.* Booklet pane of 6 10.25
**2134** A887 $1.49 multi 2.20 1.00
*a.* Booklet pane of 6 13.00
*Nos. 2128-2134 (7)* 11.35 4.25

Flag and Houses, New Glasgow, Prince Edward Island A888

Flag and Bridge, Bouctouche, New Brunswick A889

Flag and Windmills, Pincher Creek, Alberta A890

Flag and Lower Fort Garry, Manitoba A891

Flag and Dogsled, Yukon Territory — A892

**Self-Adhesive**
**Booklet Stamps**

**2005, Dec. 19** ***Die Cut***
**2135** A888 51c multi .75 .25
**2136** A889 51c multi .75 .25
**2137** A890 51c multi .75 .25
**2138** A891 51c multi .75 .25
**2139** A892 51c multi .75 .25
*a.* Booklet pane, 2 each #2135-2139 7.50
*b.* As "a," die cutting omitted *1,500.*
*Nos. 2135-2139 (5)* 3.75 1.25

New Year 2006 (Year of the Dog) — A893

**Litho. & Embossed With Foil Application**

**2006, Jan. 6** ***Perf. 13¼***
**2140** A893 51c shown .75 .30

**Souvenir Sheet**

**2141** A893 $1.49 Dog and pup 2.25 2.25

Queen Elizabeth II, 80th Birthday — A894

**Self-Adhesive**
**Booklet Stamp**

***Serpentine Die Cut 10***

**2006, Jan. 12** **Litho.**
**2142** A894 51c multi .75 .30
*a.* Booklet pane of 10 7.50
*b.* Die cutting omitted, pair 250.00

See No. 2150.

2006 Winter Olympics, Turin, Italy — A895

Designs: No. 2143, Team pursuit speed skating. No. 2144, Skeleton.

**2006, Feb. 3** ***Perf. 12½x13***
**2143** A895 51c multi .75 .30
**2144** A895 51c multi .75 .30
*a.* Horiz. pair, #2143-2144 1.50 1.00

Gardens — A896

No. 2145: a, Shade garden and black-throated blue warbler. b, Flower garden and American painted lady butterfly. c, Water garden and green darner dragonfly. d, Rock garden and blue-spotted salamander.

**Self-Adhesive**

**2006, Mar. 8** ***Serpentine Die Cut 10***
**2145** Complete booklet, 2 each #a-d 6.00
*a.-d.* A896 51c Any single .75 .45

Party Balloons — A897

**Booklet Stamp**

***Serpentine Die Cut 6¾ Horiz.***

**2006, Apr. 3** **Self-Adhesive**
**2146** A897 51c multi .75 .30
*a.* Booklet pane of 6 6.00

Paintings by Dorothy Knowles A898

Designs: 51c, The Field of Rapeseed. 89c, North Saskatchewan River, vert. (42x51mm).

**2006, Apr. 7** ***Perf. 13¼x12½***
**2147** A898 51c multi .75 .30
*a.* Perf. 12¾x12½ 1.50 1.50

**Souvenir Sheet**

***Perf. 13***

**2148** Pane, Nos. 2147a, 2148a 3.75 3.75
*a.* A898 89c multi 2.20 2.20

Canadian Labor Congress, 50th Anniv. — A899

**2006, Apr. 20** ***Perf. 13½x13¼***
**2149** A899 51c multi .75 .30

**Queen Elizabeth II, 80th Birthday Type of 2006**
**Souvenir Sheet**

**2006, Apr. 21** ***Perf. 12½x13***
**2150** Pane of 2, No. 2150a 4.50 4.50
*a.* A894 149c multi, 36x28mm 2.40 2.40

McClelland & Stewart Publishing House, Cent. — A900

**Self-Adhesive**
**Booklet Stamp**

**2006, Apr. 26** ***Die Cut Perf. 11¼x11***
**2151** A900 51c slate grn & sil .75 .30
*a.* Booklet pane of 4 + 4 stickers 3.00
Complete booklet, 2 #2151a 6.00

Northwest Coast Transformation Mask and Northwest Coast Exhibit — A901

**Booklet Stamp**

***Serpentine Die Cut 8 Horiz. Syncopated***

**2006, May 11** **Self-Adhesive**
**2152** A901 89c multi 1.40 .80
*a.* Booklet pane of 4 3.60
Complete booklet, 2 #2152a 7.50
*b.* Die cutting omitted, pair *700.00*

Canadian Museum of Civilization, 150th anniv.

Canadians in Hollywood — A903

Actors and actresses: Nos. 2153a, 2154a, John Candy (1950-94). Nos. 2153b, 2154c, Fay Wray (1907-2004). Nos. 2153c, 2154d, Lorne Greene (1915-87). Nos. 2153d, 2154b, Mary Pickford (1893-1979).

**2006, May 26** ***Perf. 13x12½***
**2153** Souvenir sheet of 4 4.50 4.50
*a.-d.* A903 51c Any single 1.10 1.10

**Self-Adhesive**

***Serpentine Die Cut 9¾x10***

**2154** Booklet pane of 4 + 4 stickers 3.25
*a.-d.* A903 51c Any single .75 .45
Complete booklet, 2 #2154 6.00

Complete booklets were issued with four different covers depicting the featured actors or actresses.

See Nos. 2279-2280.

A904

Exploration of Eastern Coast by Samuel de Champlain, 400th Anniv. — A905

**Litho. & Engr.**

**2006, May 28** ***Perf. 13x12½***
**2155** A904 51c multi .75 .30

**Souvenir Sheet**

***Perf. 11***

**2156** A905 Pane of 2 #2156a, 2 US #4074a 7.50 7.00
*a.* A904 51c multi 1.50 1.10

Washington 2006 World Philatelic Exhibition (No. 2156). No. 2156, sold only by Canada Post for $2, has bar code in pane margin at lower left. United States No. 4074, sold only by the United States Postal Service, lacks this bar code.

Vancouver Aquarium, 50th Anniv. A906

**Self-Adhesive**

**Booklet Stamp**

***Serpentine Die Cut 9½***

**2006, June 15** **Litho.**
**2157** A906 51c multi .75 .30
*a.* Booklet pane of 5 3.75
Complete booklet, 2 #2157a 7.50

Canadian Forces Snowbirds Aerobatics Team — A907

Designs: No. 2158, Pilot in cockpit, two airplanes. No. 2159, Three airplanes, Snowbirds emblem.

**2006, June 28** ***Perf. 12½x13¼***
**2158** A907 51c multi .75 .30
**2159** A907 51c multi .75 .30
*a.* Horiz. pair, #2158-2159 1.50 1.10
*b.* Souvenir sheet, #2159a 2.25 2.25

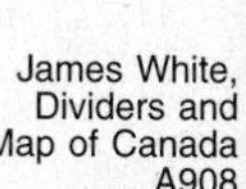

James White, Dividers and Map of Canada A908

**2006, June 30** ***Perf. 13¼x12½***
**2160** A908 51c multi .75 .30

Atlas of Canada, cent. Printed in panes of 16 + 4 labels.

World Lacrosse Championships, London, Ontario — A909

**Booklet Stamp**

***Serpentine Die Cut 11¾ Horiz.***

**2006, July 6** **Self-Adhesive**
**2161** A909 51c multi .75 .30
*a.* Booklet pane of 8 6.00

Alpine Club of Canada, Cent. — A910

**Self-Adhesive**

**Booklet Stamp**

**2006, July 19** ***Die Cut Perf. 12½x13***
**2162** A910 51c multi .75 .30
*a.* Booklet pane of 8 6.00

Ducks and Duck Decoys — A911

Designs: No. 2163, Barrow's goldeneyes. No. 2164, Mallards. No. 2165, American black ducks. No. 2166, Redbreasted mergansers.

**2006, Aug. 3** ***Perf. 13¼x12½***
**2163** A911 51c blue & multi .75 .45
**2164** A911 51c yel & multi .75 .45
**2165** A911 51c red & multi .75 .45
**2166** A911 51c grn & multi .75 .45
*a.* Block of 4, #2163-2166 3.00 2.20
*b.* Souvenir sheet, #2163-2166 3.75 3.75

Society of Graphic Designers of Canada, 50th Anniv. — A912

**2006, Aug. 16** ***Perf. 12½x13***
**2167** A912 51c multi .75 .30

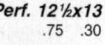

Canadian Wines — A913

Canadian Cheeses — A914

Designs: No. 2168, Three glasses of wine. No. 2169, Wine taster, barrels. No. 2170, Various cheeses. No. 2171, Woman with tray of cheeses and fruit.

**Self-Adhesive**

**Booklet Stamps**

**2006, Aug. 23** ***Die Cut***
**2168** A913 51c multi .75 .45
**2169** A913 51c multi .75 .45
**2170** A914 51c multi .75 .45
**2171** A914 51c multi .75 .45
*a.* Booklet pane, 2 each #2168-2171 6.00
*Nos. 2168-2171 (4)* 3.00 1.80

**Universities Type of 2003**

Design: Macdonald College, Sainte-Anne-de-Bellevue, Quebec, cent.

**Booklet Stamp**

***Die Cut Perf. 12¾x13¼***

**2006, Sept. 26** **Self-Adhesive**
**2172** A806 51c multi .75 .30
*a.* Booklet pane of 4 3.00
Complete booklet, 2 #2172a 6.00

Endangered Animals A915

Designs: Nos. 2173a, 2174, Newfoundland marten. Nos. 2173b, 2175, Blotched tiger salamander. Nos. 2173c, 2176, Blue racer snake. Nos. 2173d, 2177, Swift fox.

**2006, Sept. 29** ***Perf. 13¼***
**2173** Pane of 4 + 4 labels 4.50 4.00
*a.-d.* A915 51c Any single 1.10 .90

**Booklet Stamps**

**Self-Adhesive**

**Size: 47x24mm**

***Die Cut***

**2174** A915 51c multi .75 .45
**2175** A915 51c multi .75 .45
**2176** A915 51c multi .75 .45
**2177** A915 51c multi .75 .45
*a.* Block of 4, #2174-2177 3.00
*b.* Booklet pane, 2, #2177a 6.00

See Nos. 2229-2233, 2285-2289.

Opera Singers A916

Designs: No. 2178, Maureen Forrester. No. 2179, Raoul Jobin (1906-74). No. 2180, Léopold Simoneau (1916-2006) and Pierrette Alarie. No. 2181, Jon Vickers. No. 2182, Edward Johnson (1878-1959).

**2006, Oct. 17** ***Perf. 13½x13***
**2178** A916 51c multi .75 .45
**2179** A916 51c multi .75 .45
**2180** A916 51c multi .75 .45
**2181** A916 51c multi .75 .45
**2182** A916 51c multi .75 .45
*a.* Vert. strip of 5, #2178-2182 3.75 3.75

Madonna and Child, by Antoine-Sébastien Falardeau A917

Christmas Card Art A918

Designs: No. 2184, Snowman, by Yvonne McKague Housser. 89c, Winter Joys, by J. E. Sampson. $1.49, Contemplation, by Edwin Holgate.

**Self-Adhesive**

**Booklet Stamp**

**2006, Nov. 1** ***Die Cut***
**2183** A917 51c multi .75 .25
*a.* Booklet pane of 12 9.00

***Serpentine Die Cut 13¼ Horiz.***

**2184** A918 51c multi .75 .25
*a.* Booklet pane of 12 9.00
**2185** A918 89c multi 1.35 .55
*a.* Booklet pane of 6 8.00
**2186** A918 $1.49 multi 2.25 .90
*a.* Booklet pane of 6 13.50
*Nos. 2183-2186 (4)* 5.10 1.95

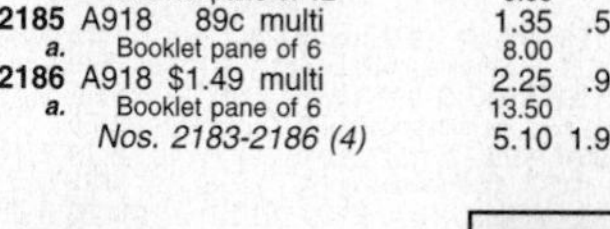

Spotted Coralroot A919

Queen Elizabeth II A920

Flag and Sirmilik Natl. Park, Nunavut A921

Flag and Cliff Near Chemainus, British Columbia A922

Flag and Polar Bears Near Churchill, Manitoba A923

Flag and Bras d'Or Lake, Nova Scotia A924

Flag and Tuktut Nogait Natl. Park, Northwest Territories — A925

**Self-Adhesive**

**Coil Stamp**

***Serpentine Die Cut 7½-9 Horiz.***

**2006, Nov. 16** **Litho.**
**2187** A919 P multi 1.25 .25

**Booklet Stamps**

***Die Cut***

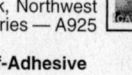

**2188** A920 P multi 1.30 .25
*a.* Booklet pane of 10 13.00
*b.* As "a," die cutting omitted *900.00*
**2189** A921 P multi 1.30 .25
**2190** A922 P multi 1.30 .25
**2191** A923 P multi 1.30 .25
**2192** A924 P multi 1.30 .25
**2193** A925 P multi 1.30 .25
*a.* Booklet pane, 2 each #2189-2193 13.00
*b.* Booklet pane, 6 each #2189-2193 39.00
*Nos. 2187-2193 (7)* 9.05 1.75

Nos. 2187-2193 each sold for 51c on day of issue. On Nos. 2188a, 2193a and 2193b, adjacent stamps that are on both sides of the booklet fold have rouletting rather than die cutting between them. No. 2193b is sold folded into thirds. Each of the thirds has selvage surrounding the ten stamps on it, unlike No. 2193a. Beware of fake examples of No. 2139b

that have been found hand cut from printer's waste.
See No. 2194a.

**Spotted Coralroot Type of 2006 and**

Flat-leaved Bladderwort — A926

Designs: $1.10, Marsh skullcap. $1.55, Little larkspur.

**2006, Dec. 19** ***Perf. 13¼x13***
2194 Souvenir sheet of 4 7.25 7.25
a. A919 P multi 1.30 .75
b. A926 93c multi 1.40 1.10
c. A926 $1.10 multi 1.65 1.25
d. A926 $1.55 multi 2.30 1.90

**Self-Adhesive**
**Coil Stamps**
***Serpentine Die Cut 7½-9 Horiz.***

2195 A926 93c multi 1.40 .40
2196 A926 $1.10 multi 1.65 .60
2197 A926 $1.55 multi 2.30 .60

**Booklet Stamps**
***Die Cut***

2198 A926 93c multi 1.40 .60
a. Booklet pane of 6 8.50
2199 A926 $1.10 multi 1.65 .75
a. Booklet pane of 6 10.00
2200 A926 $1.55 multi 2.30 1.10
a. Booklet pane of 6 13.75
*Nos. 2195-2200 (6)* 10.70 4.05

No. 2194a sold for 51c on day of issue.
See Nos. 2243, 2245-2247, 2254-2256.

New Year 2007 (Year of the Pig) — A927

Pig facing: 52c, Left. $1.55, Right.

**Litho. & Embossed with Foil Application**

**2007, Jan. 5** ***Perf. 13½x13***
2201 A927 52c red & multi .80 .30
a. Gold foil omitted 75.00

**Souvenir Sheet**

2202 A927 $1.55 grn & multi 2.25 2.25

Confetti and Streamers — A928

**Self-Adhesive**
**Booklet Stamp**
***Serpentine Die Cut 6¾ Horiz.***

**2007, Jan. 15** **Litho.**
2203 A928 52c multi .80 .30
a. Booklet pane of 6 4.75

International Polar Year — A929

Designs: No. 2204, Somateria spectabilis. No. 2205, Crossota millsaeare.

***Perf. 13½ Syncopated***

**2007, Feb. 12**
2204 52c multi .80 .30
2205 52c multi .80 .30
a. A929 Horiz. pair, #2204-2205 1.60 .90
b. Souvenir sheet, #2205a 2.25 2.25

Lilacs A930

Color of lilacs: Nos. 2206a, 2207, White. Nos. 2206b, 2208, Purple.

**Souvenir Sheet**

**2007, Mar. 1** ***Perf. 12¾***
2206 A930 Pane of 2 2.20 2.20
a.-b. 52c Either single 1.10 .75
c. Imperf., pane of 2 *2,000.*

**Booklet Stamps**
**Self-Adhesive**
***Die Cut***

2207 A930 52c multi .80 .30
2208 A930 52c multi .80 .30
a. Booklet pane of 10, 5 each #2207-2208 8.00

**Universities Type of 2003**

Design: No. 2209, HEC Montreal, cent. No. 2210, University of Saskatchewan, cent.

**Self-Adhesive**
**Booklet Stamp**

**2007** ***Die Cut Perf. 12¾x13¼***
2209 A806 52c multi .80 .30
a. Booklet pane of 4 3.25
Complete booklet, 2 #2209a 6.50
2210 A806 52c multi .80 .30
a. Booklet pane of 4 3.25
Complete booklet, 2 #2210a 6.50

Issued: No. 2209, 3/12. No. 2210, 4/3.

Art by Mary Pratt — A931

Designs: 52c, Jelly Shelf. $1.55 Iceberg in the North Atlantic (58x36mm).

**2007, Mar. 15** ***Perf. 13x12½***
2211 A931 52c multi .80 .30

**Souvenir Sheet**

2212 Pane, #2211, 2212a 3.10 3.10
a. A931 $1.55 multi 2.30 2.50

Selection of Ottawa as National Capital, 150th Anniv. A932

**Litho., Litho & Embossed with Foil Application (#2213b)**

**2007, May 3** ***Perf. 13¼***
2213 Pane of 2, #2213a, 2213b 3.50 3.50
a. A932 52c multi 1.10 1.10
b. A932 $1.55 multi 2.30 2.30

**Booklet Stamp**
**Self-Adhesive**
***Serpentine Die Cut 7¼ Horiz.***

2214 A932 52c multi .80 .30
a. Booklet pane of 4 3.25
Complete booklet, 2 #2214a 6.50

Royal Architectural Institute of Canada, Cent. — A933

Buildings: No. 2215, University of Lethbridge, by Arthur Erickson. No. 2216, St. Mary's Church, by Douglas Cardinal. No. 2217, Ontario Science Centre, by Raymond Moriyama. No. 2218, National Gallery of Canada, by Moshe Safdie.

**2007, May 9** **Litho.** ***Perf. 13***
2215 A933 52c multi + label .80 .45
2216 A933 52c multi + label .80 .45
2217 A933 52c multi + label .80 .45
2218 A933 52c multi + label .80 .45
a. Vert. strip of 4, #2215-2218, + 4 labels 3.25 2.50

Nos. 2215-2218 were printed in panes containing two of each stamp. Labels flank the stamps, with labels on the left showing drawings of the buildings and the labels on the right showing the architect.

Capt. George Vancouver (1757-98), Explorer — A934

**Litho. & Embossed**

**2007, June 22** ***Perf. 13x12½***
2219 A934 $1.55 multi 2.25 1.00
a. Souvenir sheet of 1, perf. 13 2.25 2.25

FIFA Under-20 World Soccer Championships, Canada — A935

**2007, June 26** **Litho.** ***Perf. 12½x13***
2220 A935 52c multi .80 .30
a. Imperf., pair *950.00*

Popular Singers A936

Designs: Nos. 2221a, 2222a, Gordon Lightfoot. Nos. 2221b, 2222b, Joni Mitchell. Nos. 2221c, 2222c, Anne Murray. Nos. 2221d, 2222d, Paul Anka.

**2007, June 29** ***Perf. 12½x13***
2221 A936 Pane of 4 3.25 3.25
a.-d. 52c Any single .80 .80

**Self-Adhesive**
***Serpentine Die Cut 13½***

2222 A936 Booklet pane of 4 3.25
a.-d. 52c Any single .80 .40
Complete booklet, 2 #2222 6.50

Complete booklets were issued with four different covers depicting the featured singers.

National Parks — A937

Designs: No. 2223, Terra Nova National Park, Newfoundland, 50th anniv. No. 2224, Jasper National Park, Alberta, cent.

**Self-Adhesive**
**Booklet Stamps**

**2007** ***Serpentine Die Cut 13½***
2223 A937 52c multi .80 .30
a. Booklet pane of 5 4.00
Complete booklet, 2 #2223a 8.00
2224 A937 52c multi .80 .30
a. Booklet pane of 5 4.00
Complete booklet, 2 #2224a 8.00
b. Gutter pane, 5 each #2223-2224 11.00

Issued: No. 2223, 7/6; No. 2224, 7/20.

Scouting, Cent. — A938

**Self-Adhesive**
**Booklet Stamp**

**2007, July 25**
2225 A938 52c multi .80 .30
a. Booklet pane of 4 + 4 labels 3.25
Complete booklet, 2 #2225a 6.50

Henri Membertou, Grand Chief of Mi'kmaq Tribe — A939

**2007, June 26** **Engr.** ***Perf. 13x12½***
2226 A939 52c multi .80 .30

Law Society of Saskatchewan, Cent. — A940

**2007, Sept. 13** **Litho.** ***Perf. 13***
2227 A940 52c multi 1.50 .75

Printed in panes of 8 + 8 labels.

Law Society of Alberta, Cent. — A941

**2007, Sept. 13** ***Perf. 12½x13***
2228 A941 52c multi .80 .30

**Endangered Animals Type of 2006**

Designs: Nos. 2229a, 2230, North Atlantic right whale. Nos. 2229b, 2231, Northern cricket frog. Nos. 2229c, 2232, White sturgeon. Nos. 2229d, 2233, Leatherback turtle.

**2007, Oct. 1** ***Perf. 13¼***
2229 Pane of 4 + 4 labels 3.50 3.50
a.-d. A915 52c Any single .85 .85

**Booklet Stamps**
**Self-Adhesive**
**Size: 47x24mm**
***Die Cut***

2230 A915 52c multi .80 .30
2231 A915 52c multi .80 .30
2232 A915 52c multi .80 .30
2233 A915 52c multi .80 .30
a. Block of 4, #2230-2233 3.25
b. Booklet pane, 2 #2233a 6.50

Beneficial Insects — A942

No. 2235

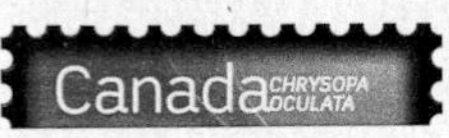

No. 2235a

Designs: 1c, Convergent lady beetle (Hippodamia convergens). 3c, Golden-eyed lacewing (Chrysopa oculata). 5c, Northern bumblebee (Bombus polaris). 10c, Canada darner (Aeshna canadensis). 25c, Cecropia moth (Hyalophora cecropia).

**2007, Oct. 12** ***Perf. 13¼x13***
2234 A942 1c multi .30 .25
2235 A942 3c multi .30 .25
a. "Canada" shifted to right, touching "Oculata" (pos. 11-14) .40 .25
b. Dated "2012," with added microprinting and small design features (#2409b) .30 .25
2236 A942 5c multi .30 .25
2237 A942 10c multi .30 .25
2238 A942 25c multi .40 .25
a. Souvenir sheet, #2234-2238 1.10 1.00
*Nos. 2234-2238 (5)* 1.60 1.25

No. 2235a occurs four times on each pane of 50. Panes printed in 2010 correct the errors.
See Nos. 2328, 2406-2410, 2708.
Issued: No. 2235b, 10/16/12.

Christmas
A943 A944

Designs: No. 2239, Reindeer and snowflakes. No. 2240, Holy Family. 93c, Angel over town. $1.55, Dove.

**Booklet Stamps**
**Litho. With Hologram Affixed**
***Serpentine Die Cut 8¼ Horiz.***

**2007, Nov. 1 Self-Adhesive**

**2239** A943 (52c) multi 1.35 .25
*a.* Booklet pane of 6 8.00
Complete booklet, 2 #2239a 16.00
*b.* Die cutting omitted, pair 400.00

**Litho.**
***Serpentine Die Cut 13½***

**2240** A944 (52c) multi 1.35 .25
*a.* Booklet pane of 6 8.00
Complete booklet, 2 #2240a 16.00
**2241** A944 93c multi 1.40 .40
*a.* Booklet pane of 6 8.50
**2242** A944 $1.55 multi 2.25 .60
*a.* Booklet pane of 6 13.50
*b.* Die cutting omitted, pair 550.00
*Nos. 2239-2242 (4)* 6.35 1.50

**Flowers Type of 2006 and**

Odontioda Island Red Orchid
A945

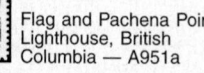

Queen Elizabeth II
A946

Flag and Sambro Island Lighthouse, Nova Scotia
A947

Flag and Point Clark Lighthouse, Ontario
A948

Flag and Cap-des-Rosiers Lighthouse, Quebec — A949

Flag and Warren Landing Lighthouse, Manitoba
A950

Flag and Pachena Point Lighthouse, British Columbia
A951

Flag and Pachena Point Lighthouse, British Columbia — A951a

Designs: 96c, Potinara Janet Elizabeth "Fire Dancer" orchid. $1.15, Laeliocattleya Memoria Evelyn Light orchid. $1.60, Masdevallia Kaleidoscope "Conni" orchid.

**2007, Dec. 27 Litho. *Perf. 13¼x13***

**2243** Pane of 4 7.00 7.00
*a.* A945 P multi 1.30 .85
*b.* A926 96c multi 1.40 1.20
*c.* A926 $1.15 multi 1.70 1.30
*d.* A926 $1.60 multi 2.40 1.80

**Self-Adhesive**
**Coil Stamps**
***Serpentine Die Cut 8-9½ Horiz.***

**2244** A945 P multi 1.30 .25

***Serpentine Die Cut 9.2 Horiz.***

**2244A** A945 P multi 1.45 1.45

***Serpentine Die Cut 8-9½***

**2245** A926 96c multi 1.45 .30
**2246** A926 $1.15 multi 1.70 .45
**2247** A926 $1.60 multi 2.40 .60
*Nos. 2244-2247 (5)* 8.30 3.05

Die cutting is irregular across the stamp (saw tooth tips) on Nos. 2244 and 2245-2247 compared to being consistent across the stamp (rounded tips) on No. 2244A. On No. 2244, stamps are vertically contiguous on the backing paper, while on No. 2244A the stamps are separated on horizontal backing paper that is taller than the stamp.

**Booklet Stamps**
***Serpentine Die Cut 13¼***

**2248** A946 P multi 1.30 .25
*a.* Booklet pane of 10 13.00
**2249** A947 P multi 1.30 .25
**2250** A948 P multi 1.30 .25
**2251** A949 P multi 1.30 .25
**2252** A950 P multi 1.30 .25
**2253** A951 P multi 1.30 .25
*a.* Booklet pane of 10, 2 each #2249-2253 13.00

***Serpentine Die Cut 13¼***

**2253B** A951a P multi 1.30 .25
*c.* Booklet pane of 10, 2 each #2249-2252, 2253B 13.00
*d.* Booklet pane of 30, 6 each #2249-2252, 2253B 39.00

***Die Cut***

**2254** A926 96c multi 1.45 .25
*a.* Booklet pane of 6 8.75
**2255** A926 $1.15 multi 1.70 .40
*a.* Booklet pane of 6 10.25
**2256** A926 $1.60 multi 2.40 .60
*a.* Booklet pane of 6 14.50
*Nos. 2248-2256 (10)* 14.65 3.00

Nos. 2243a, 2244, 2248-2253 each sold for 52c on day of issue.

No. 2244A issued 2/21/08.

No. 2253B issued 5/1/08. No. 2253Bd was separated into thirds by two rows of rouletting. The separated thirds of this booklet have the same contents as No. 2253Bc, but have different selvage markings.

New Year 2008 (Year of the Rat) — A952

Designs: 52c, Rat with umbrella. $1.60, Rat with fan.

**Litho. & Embossed With Foil Application**

**2008, Jan. 8 *Perf. 13***

**2257** A952 52c multi .80 .30

**Souvenir Sheet**

**2258** A952 $1.60 multi 3.00 3.00

No. 2257 printed in panes of 25 + 20 labels.

Fireworks — A953

**Self-Adhesive**
**Booklet Stamp**
***Serpentine Die Cut 13½ Horiz.***

**2008, Jan. 15 Litho.**

**2259** A953 P multi 1.30 .30
*a.* Booklet pane of 6 7.75

No. 2259 sold for 52c on day of issue.

Peonies — A954

Peony color: Nos. 2260a, 2261, Pink. Nos. 2260b, 2262, Red.

**2008, Mar. 3 Litho. *Perf. 13¼***

**2260** Pane of 2 2.20 2.20
*a.-b.* A954 52c Either single 1.10 .75

**Booklet Stamps**
**Self-Adhesive**
***Serpentine Die Cut 13¼***

**2261** A954 52c multi .80 .30
**2262** A954 52c multi .80 .30
*a.* Pair, #2261-2262 1.60
*b.* Booklet pane, 5 each #2261-2262, + 10 stickers 8.50
*c.* Die cutting omitted, pair 375.00

The country name and denomination are closer to the flowers on Nos. 2261-2262 than on Nos. 2260a-2260b.

Universities — A955

Designs: No. 2263, University of Alberta, cent. No. 2264, University of British Columbia, cent.

**Self-Adhesive**
***Serpentine Die Cut 13¼***

**2008, Mar. 7 Booklet Stamps**

**2263** A955 52c multi .80 .25
*a.* Booklet pane of 8 6.50
*b.* Die cutting omitted, pair 325.00
**2264** A955 52c multi .80 .25
*a.* Booklet pane of 8 6.50
*b.* Gutter pane, 4 each #2263-2264 11.00

2008 Intl. Ice Hockey Federation Championships, Halifax and Quebec — A956

**Self-Adhesive**
***Serpentine Die Cut 13½***

**2008, Apr. 3 Booklet Stamp**

**2265** A956 52c multi .80 .25
*a.* Booklet pane of 10 8.00
*b.* Die cutting omitted, pair 300.00

No. 2265a was printed with two different booklet covers.

Guide Dog — A957

**Self-Adhesive**
**Booklet Stamp**
***Serpentine Die Cut 13½x13***

**2008, Apr. 21 Litho. & Embossed**

**2266** A957 52c multi .80 .25
*a.* Booklet pane of 10 8.00

Montreal Association for the Blind, cent.

Oil and Gas Anniversaries
A958

Designs: No. 2267, Welder welding Trans-Canada Pipeline. No. 2268, James M. Williams, Charles Tripp, Oil Springs, Ontario oil field.

**Self-Adhesive**
**Booklet Stamps**
***Serpentine Die Cut 13¼***

**2008, May 2 Litho.**

**2267** A958 52c multi .80 .25
*a.* Die cutting omitted, pair 750.00
**2268** A958 52c multi .80 .25
*a.* Die cutting omitted, pair 750.00
*b.* Booklet pane of 10, 5 each #2267-2268 8.00

Trans-Canada Pipeline, 50th anniv., First commercial oil well in Canada, 150th anniv.

Quebec City, 400th Anniv. — A959

**Litho. & Engr.**

**2008, May 16 *Perf. 13x12½***

**2269** A959 52c multi .80 .30

See France No. 3437. A souvenir sheet containing No. 2269 and France No. 3437 sold for $4.99.

Photographic Portraits by Yousuf Karsh (1908-2008) — A960

Designs: 52c, Self-portrait, 1952. 96c, Audrey Hepburn, 1956. $1.60, Sir Winston Churchill, 1941.

**2008, May 21 Litho. *Perf. 13x12½***

**2270** A960 52c multi .80 .30

**Souvenir Sheet**

**2271** Pane of 3, #2270, 2271a, 2271b 4.75 4.75
*a.* A960 96c multi 1.45 1.10
*b.* A960 $1.60 multi 2.40 2.25

**Booklet Stamps**
**Self-Adhesive**

**2272** A960 96c multi 1.45 .60
*a.* Booklet pane of 4 5.75
Complete booklet, 2 #2272a 11.50
**2273** A960 $1.60 multi 2.40 .90
*a.* Booklet pane of 4 9.50
Complete booklet, 2 #2273a 19.00
*b.* Gutter pane, #2272a, 2273a 16.00

No. 2270 printed in panes of 16 + 4 labels.

1908 Fifty-cent Coin — A961

**Litho. & Embossed**

**2008, June 4 *Perf. 13x13¼***

**2274** A961 52c multi .80 .30

Royal Canadian Mint, cent. Printed in panes of 16 + 4 labels.

Canadian Nurses Association, Cent. — A962

**Self-Adhesive**
**Booklet Stamp**
***Serpentine Die Cut 13¼***

**2008, June 16 Litho.**

**2275** A962 52c multi .80 .30
*a.* Booklet pane of 10 8.00

Publication of *Anne of Green Gables*, by Lucy Maud Montgomery, Cent. — A963

Designs: Nos. 2276a, 2277, Anne holding buttercups. Nos. 2276b, 2278, Green Gables House.

***Perf. 13½ Syncopated***

**2008, June 20**

**Souvenir Sheet**

**2276** A963 Pane of 2 2.20 2.20
*a.-b.* 52c Either single 1.10 .90

**Booklet Stamps**

**Self-Adhesive**

***Serpentine Die Cut 13¼x13***

**2277** A963 52c multi .80 .30
**2278** A963 52c multi .80 .30
*a.* Booklet pane of 10, 5 each #2277-2278 + 10 stickers 8.00
*b.* Die cutting omitted, pair (#2277-2278) *375.00*

See Japan No. 3028.

**Canadians in Hollywood Type of 2006**

Actors and actresses: Nos. 2279a, 2280c, Norma Shearer (1902?-83). Nos. 2279b, 2280b, Chief Dan George (1899-1981). Nos. 2279c, 2280a, Marie Dressler (1868-1934). Nos. 2279d, 2280d, Raymond Burr (1917-93).

**2008, June 30** ***Perf. 13x12½***

**2279** Souvenir sheet of 4 4.40 4.40
*a.-d.* A903 52c Any single 1.10 .90

**Self-Adhesive**

***Serpentine Die Cut 13½x13¼***

**2280** Booklet pane of 4 + 4 stickers 3.25
*a.-d.* A903 52c Any single .80 .30
Complete booklet, 2 #2280 6.50

Complete booklets were issued with four different covers depicting the featured actors or actresses. The order of the stamps and labels in the booklet pane differed in the four booklets.

2008 Summer Olympics, Beijing — A964

**Self-Adhesive**

***Serpentine Die Cut 13½***

**2008, July 18** **Booklet Stamp**

**2281** A964 52c multi .80 .30
*a.* Booklet pane of 10 8.00
*b.* Die cutting omitted, strip of 3 900.00

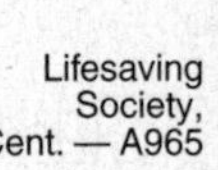

Lifesaving Society, Cent. — A965

**Self-Adhesive**

***Serpentine Die Cut 13¼x12¾***

**2008, July 25** **Booklet Stamp**

**2282** A965 52c multi .80 .25
*a.* Booklet pane of 10 8.00

British Columbia, 150th Anniv. A966

**Self-Adhesive**

**2008, Aug. 1** ***Perf. 12½x13***

**2283** A966 52c multi .80 .30

R. Samuel McLaughlin (1871-1972), Automobile Manufacturer, and Buick Automobile A967

**2008, Sept. 8** ***Perf. 12½x13***

**2284** A967 52c multi .80 .30

**Endangered Animals Type of 2006**

Designs: Nos. 2285a, 2286, Prothonotary warbler. Nos. 2285b, 2287, Taylor's checkerspot butterfly. Nos. 2285c, 2288, Roseate tern. Nos. 2285d, 2289, Burrowing owl.

**2008, Oct. 1** ***Perf. 13¼***

**2285** Pane of 4 + 4 labels 3.25 3.25
*a.-d.* A915 52c Any single .80 .85

**Booklet Stamps**

**Self-Adhesive**

**Size: 48x24mm**

***Die Cut***

**2286** A915 52c multi .80 .30
**2287** A915 52c multi .80 .30
**2288** A915 52c multi .80 .30
**2289** A915 52c multi .80 .30
*a.* Block of 4, #2286-2289 3.20
*b.* Booklet pane, 2 #2289a 6.40

12th Francophone Summit, Quebec — A968

**2008, Oct. 15** ***Perf. 12½x13¼***

**2290** A968 52c multi .80 .30

A969

Christmas — A970

Child: Nos. 2291a, 2293, Making snow angel. Nos. 2291b, 2294, Skiing. Nos. 2291c, 2295, Tobogganing.

**Souvenir Sheet**

**2008, Nov. 3** ***Perf. 13½***

**2291** Pane of 3 5.25 5.25
*a.* A969 P multi 1.30 1.00
*b.* A969 96c multi 1.45 1.45
*c.* A969 $1.60 multi 2.40 2.40

**Booklet Stamps**

**Self-Adhesive**

***Serpentine Die Cut 13¼***

**2292** A970 P multi 1.30 .25
*a.* Booklet pane of 6 7.75
Complete booklet, 2 #2292a 15.50
*b.* Die cutting omitted, pair 600.00

***Serpentine Die Cut 13¾***

**2293** A969 P multi 1.30 .25
*a.* Booklet pane of 6 7.75
Complete booklet, 2 #2293a 15.50
**2294** A969 96c multi 1.45 .60
*a.* Booklet pane of 6 8.75
**2295** A969 $1.60 multi 2.40 .90
*a.* Booklet pane of 6 14.50
*b.* Gutter pane, #2294a, 2295a 26.00
*Nos. 2292-2295 (4)* 6.45 2.00

Nos. 2291a, 2292 and 2293 each sold for 52c on day of issue.

See No. 2343a.

A971

New Year 2009 (Year of the Ox) — A972

**Litho. & Embossed With Foil Application**

**2009, Jan. 8** ***Perf. 12½***

**2296** A971 P multi 1.30 .25

**Souvenir Sheet**

**2297** A972 $1.65 multi 2.50 2.50
*a.* With China 2009 emblem overprinted in gold in pane margin 3.40 3.40

No. 2296 sold for 54c on day of issue. See Nos. 3259b, 3260b, 3262.

Queen Elizabeth II — A973

**Self-Adhesive**

**Booklet Stamp**

***Serpentine Die Cut 13½x13¼***

**2009, Jan. 12** **Litho.**

**2298** A973 P multi 1.30 .25
*a.* Booklet pane of 10 13.00

No. 2298 sold for 54c on day of issue.

Sports of the Winter Olympics and Paralympics
A974 A975

Designs: Nos. 2299a, 2303, Curling. Nos. 2299b, 2302, Bobsledding. Nos. 2299c, 2304, Snowboarding. Nos. 2299d, 2300, Freestyle skiing. Nos. 2299e, 2301, Ice-sled hockey.

**2009, Jan. 12** ***Perf. 13¼x13***

**2299** Pane of 5 6.50 6.50
*a.-d.* A974 P Any single 1.30 1.10
*e.* A975 P multi 1.30 1.10
*f.* As No. 2299, with "Vancouver / 2010" overprinted in sheet margin in silver 17.50 17.50

No. 2299f exists with the overprint in gold. Value, *$1,500.*

**Booklet Stamps**

**Self-Adhesive**

***Serpentine Die Cut 13¼x13½***

**2300** A974 P multi 1.30 .25
**2301** A975 P multi 1.30 .25
**2302** A974 P multi 1.30 .25
**2303** A974 P multi 1.30 .25
**2304** A974 P multi 1.30 .25
*a.* Booklet pane of 10, 2 each #2300-2304 13.00
*b.* Booklet pane of 30, 6 each #2300-2304 39.00

On day of issue, Nos. 2299a-2299e, 2300-2304 each sold for 54c.

No. 2299f was originally sold with a set of coins in 2009. It was made available in 2010 in a set of 3 sheets, Nos. 2299f, 2305f, and 2366c that sold for $8.73.

2010 Vancouver Winter Olympics Emblem A976

2010 Vancouver Winter Paralympics Emblem A977

Miga, Winter Olympics Mascot A978

Sumi, Paralympics Mascot A979

Quatchi, Winter Olympics Mascot — A980

**2009** ***Perf. 13¼x13***

**2305** Pane of 5 8.25 8.25
*a.* A976 P multi 1.30 1.10
*b.* A977 P multi 1.30 1.10
*c.* A978 98c multi 1.45 1.55
*d.* A979 $1.18 multi 1.75 1.90
*e.* A980 $1.65 multi 2.45 2.65
*f.* As No. 2305, with "Vancouver / 2010" overprinted in sheet margin in bronze 19.00 19.00

No. 2305f exists imperf. Value, *$3,675.*

**Self-Adhesive**

**Coil Stamps**

***Serpentine Die Cut 9¼ (Rounded Tips)***

**2306** A976 P multi 1.30 1.30
**2307** A977 P multi 1.30 1.30

***Serpentine Die Cut 7¾-9½ (Sawtooth Tips)***

**2307A** A976 P multi 1.30 .25
**2307B** A977 P multi 1.30 .25
*c.* Vert. pair, #2307A-2307B 2.60
**2308** A978 98c multi 1.45 .35
**2309** A979 $1.18 multi 1.75 .55
**2310** A980 $1.65 multi 2.45 .75

**Booklet Stamps**

***Serpentine Die Cut 9¼ (Rounded Tips)***

**2311** A978 98c multi 1.40 .25
*a.* Booklet pane of 6 8.50
**2312** A979 $1.18 multi 1.80 .40
*a.* Booklet pane of 6 11.00
**2313** A980 $1.65 multi 2.40 .55
*a.* Booklet pane of 6 14.50
*Nos. 2306-2313 (10)* 16.45 5.95

Issued: Nos. 2305, 2309, 2312, 2/12; Nos. 2306-2308, 2310-2311, 2313, 1/12. On day of issue, Nos. 2305a, 2305b, 2306-2307B each sold for 54c. Rolls of Nos. 2306 and 2307 have horizontal pairs of the same stamp that do not abut each other. Stamps from rolls containing Nos. 2307A and 2307B have pairs of different stamps that abut each other vertically.

No. 2305f was originally sold with a set of coins in 2009. It was made available in 2010 in a set of 3 sheets, Nos. 2299f, 2305f, and 2366c that sold for $8.73.

Celebration — A981

**Self-Adhesive**

***Serpentine Die Cut 13½ Horiz.***

**2009, Feb. 2** **Booklet Stamp**

**2314** A981 P multi 1.30 .30
*a.* Booklet pane of 6 7.75

No. 2314 sold for 54c on day of issue.

Rosemary Brown (1930-2003) A982

Abraham Doras Shadd (1801-82) — A983

**2009, Feb. 2** *Perf. 13x12½*

**2315** A982 54c multi .80 .30
**2316** A983 54c multi .80 .30
*a.* Pair, #2315-2316 1.60 1.10

Black History Month. Brown and Shadd were the first black woman and man elected to public office in Canada.

First Airplane Flight in Canada, Cent. A984

**Self-Adhesive**

**2009, Feb. 23** *Perf. 12½x13*

**2317** A984 P multi 1.30 .30

No. 2317 sold for 54c on day of issue.

Rhododendrons — A985

Color of rhododendrons: Nos. 2318a, 2319, White and pink. Nos. 2318b, 2320, Pink.

**2009, Mar. 13** *Perf. 13¼*

**2318** A985 Pane of 2 2.20 2.20
*a.-b.* 54c Either single 1.10 .85

**Booklet Stamps**

**Self-Adhesive**

***Serpentine Die Cut 13½x12¾***

**2319** A985 54c multi .80 .30
**2320** A985 54c multi .80 .30
*a.* Booklet pane of 10, 5 each #2319-2320 8.00
*b.* Die cutting omitted, pair 525.00

Paintings by Jack Bush (1909-77) — A986

Designs: 54c, Striped Column. $1.65, Chopsticks, horiz. (57x23mm).

**2009, Mar. 20** *Perf. 13x13¼*

**2321** A986 54c multi .80 .30
*a.* Perf. 12½x13¼ 1.10 1.10

**Souvenir Sheet**

***Perf. 12½x13¼***

**2322** Pane, #2321a, 2322a 3.75 3.75
*a.* A986 $1.65 multi 2.25 2.25

Souvenir Sheet

Intl. Year of Astronomy — A987

Designs: Nos. 2323a, 2324, Dominion Astrophysical Observatory, Saanich, British Columbia, and Horsehead Nebula. Nos. 2323b, 2325, Canada-France-Hawaii Telescope, Hawaii, and Eagle Nebula.

**2009, Apr. 2** *Perf. 13¼x13*

**2323** A987 Pane of 2 2.20 2.20
*a.-b.* 54c Either single 1.10 .75
*c.* As #2323, with buff background behind product code 3.75 3.75

**Booklet Stamps**

**Size: 24x34mm**

**Self-Adhesive**

***Serpentine Die Cut 13½***

**2324** A987 54c multi .80 .30
**2325** A987 54c multi .80 .30
*a.* Booklet pane, 5 each #2324-2325 8.00

The product code on No. 2323 is "063491072031," and on No. 2323c, "063491072024." The background behind the product code on No. 2323 is white. No. 2323c also has a fluorescent overprint in the margin, not found on No. 2323. Nos. 2323a and 2323b are 27x36mm.

Preservation of Polar Regions and Glaciers — A988

**2009, Apr. 9** *Perf. 13x12¾*

**2326** A988 54c Polar bear .80 .30
**2327** A988 54c Arctic tern .80 .30
*a.* Pair, #2326-2327 1.60 .90
*b.* Souvenir sheet, #2326-2327 1.90 1.90

**Beneficial Insects Type of 2007**

Design: Danaus plexippus caterpillar.

**2009, Apr. 22** *Perf. 13¼x13*

**2328** A942 2c multi .30 .25

Horses — A989

Designs: No. 2329, Canadian horse. No. 2330, Newfoundland pony.

**Self-Adhesive**

***Serpentine Die Cut 13¼***

**2009, May 15** **Booklet Stamps**

**2329** A989 54c multi .80 .30
**2330** A989 54c multi .80 .30
*a.* Booklet pane of 10, 5 each #2329-2330 8.00

Department of Foreign Affairs and International Trade, Cent. — A990

**2009, June 1** *Perf. 13¼x13*

**2331** A990 54c multi .80 .30

Boundary Waters Treaty, Cent. — A991

**2009, June 12** *Perf. 13¼*

**2332** A991 54c multi .80 .30

Popular Singers A992

Designs: Nos. 2333a, 2334d, Robert Charlebois. Nos. 2333b, 2334c, Edith Butler. Nos. 2333c, 2334b, Stompin' Tom Connors. Nos. 2333d, 2334a, Bryan Adams.

**2009, July 2** *Perf. 12½x13*

**2333** A992 Pane of 4 3.25 3.25
*a.-d.* 54c Any single .80 .80

**Self-Adhesive**

***Serpentine Die Cut 13½***

**2334** A992 Booklet pane of 4 3.25
*a.-d.* 54c Any single .80 .40
Complete booklet, 2 #2334 6.50

Complete booklets were issued with four different covers depicting the featured singers. The order of the stamps is different in each booklet.

Roadside Attractions — A993

Designs: Nos. 2335a, 2336a, Mr. PG, Prince George, British Columbia. Nos. 2335b, 2336b, Sign Post Forest, Watson Lake, Yukon Territory. Nos. 2335c, 2336c, Inukshuk, Hay River, Northwest Territories. Nos. 2335d, 2336d, Pysanka, Vegreville, Alberta.

**2009, July 6** *Perf. 13*

**2335** A993 Pane of 4 3.25 3.25
*a.-d.* 54c Any single .80 .80

**Self-Adhesive**

***Serpentine Die Cut 13½***

**2336** A993 Booklet pane of 4 3.25
*a.-d.* 54c Any single .80 .40
Complete booklet, 2 #2336 6.50

Captain Robert Abram Bartlett (1875-1946), Arctic Explorer — A994

**2009, July 10** *Perf. 13*

**2337** A994 54c multi .80 .30

Sports Invented By Canadians — A995

No. 2338: a, Five-pin bowling. b, Ringette. c, Lacrosse. d, Basketball.

***Serpentine Die Cut 13¼***

**2009, Aug. 10**

**2338** Booklet pane of 4 3.25
*a.-d.* A995 54c Any single .80 .40
Complete booklet, 2 #2338 6.50

Montreal Canadiens Hockey Jersey — A996

500-Goal Scorers of the Montreal Canadiens — A997

No. 2340 — 500th goal of: a, Maurice Richard. b, Jean Béliveau. c, Guy Lafleur.

**Self-Adhesive**

***Serpentine Die Cut 13½x13¼***

**2009, Oct. 17** **Booklet Stamp**

**2339** A996 P multi 1.30 .30
*a.* Booklet pane of 10 13.00

**Souvenir Sheet**

**Litho. With Three-Dimensional Plastic Affixed**

***Serpentine Die Cut 13x13¼***

**Self-Adhesive**

**2340** A997 Pane of 3 13.50 13.50
*a.-c.* $3 Any single 4.50 4.50
*d.* Die cutting omitted, pane of 3 *1,800.*

Montreal Canadiens hockey team, cent. No. 2339 sold for 54c on day of issue.

Soaking of No. 2340 may cause the stamps to separate into layers. Soaking of used examples also may cause the cancellations to dissolve.

National War Memorial, Ottawa, and Poppy — A998

**2009, Oct. 19** **Litho.** *Perf. 12½*

**2341** A998 P multi 1.30 1.10
*a.* Souvenir sheet of 2 2.60 2.60

**Booklet Stamp**

**Self-Adhesive**

***Serpentine Die Cut 13¼***

**2342** A998 P multi 1.30 .30
*a.* Booklet pane of 10 13.00

End of World War I, 91st anniv. On day of issue, Nos. 2341-2342 each sold for 54c. No. 2341 was issued only in the souvenir sheet of 2.

**Christmas Type of 2008 and**

Christmas
A999 A1000

Designs: Nos. 2343b, 2345, Madonna and child. 98c, Magus. $1.65, Shepherd and lamb.

**2009, Nov. 2** *Perf. 13x12½*

**2343** Pane of 4 + 6 labels 6.50 6.50
*a.* A970 P multi 1.30 1.10
*b.* A999 P multi 1.30 1.10
*c.* A999 98c multi 1.45 1.50
*d.* A999 $1.65 multi 2.45 2.65

**Booklet Stamps**

**Self-Adhesive**

**Litho. With Hologram Affixed**

***Serpentine Die Cut 8¼ Horiz.***

**2344** A1000 P multi 1.30 .25
*a.* Booklet pane of 6 7.75
Complete booklet, 2 #2344a 15.50

**Litho.**

***Serpentine Die Cut 13½***

**2345** A999 P multi 1.30 .25
*a.* Booklet pane of 6 7.75
Complete booklet, 2 #2345 15.50
**2346** A999 98c multi 1.45 .60
*a.* Booklet pane of 6 8.75
**2347** A999 $1.65 multi 2.45 .90
*a.* Booklet pane of 6 14.75
*b.* Booklet pane of 12, 6 each #2346-2347 24.00
*Nos. 2344-2347 (4)* 6.50 2.00

On day of issue, Nos. 2343a, 2343b, 2344, and 2345 each sold for 54c. No. 2347b is Nos. 2346a and 2347a unseparated but with horizontal slits cut in margin between the panes.

New Year 2010 (Year of the Tiger) — A1001

Designs: P, Seal impression of tiger in circle. $1.70, Sculpted tiger seal.

### Litho. & Embossed With Foil Application

**2010, Jan. 8** *Perf. 12½*

**2348** A1001 P multi 1.30 .45

### Souvenir Sheet

**2349** A1001 $1.70 multi 2.50 2.50

No. 2348 sold for 57c on day of issue. See Nos. 3259c, 3260c, 3263.

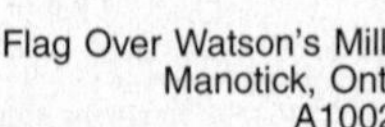

Flag Over Watson's Mill, Manotick, Ont. A1002

Flag Over Keremeos Grist Mill, Keremeos, B.C. A1003

Flag Over Old Stone Mill Natl. Historic Site, Delta, Ont. A1004

Flag Over Riordon Grist Mill, Caraquet, N. B. A1005

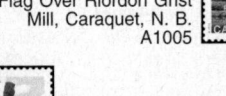

Flag Over Cornell Mill, Stanbridge East, Que. — A1006

**2010, Jan. 11** **Litho.** *Perf. 13x13¼*

**2350** Souvenir sheet of 5 6.50 6.50
- *a.* A1002 P multi 1.30 1.10
- *b.* A1003 P multi 1.30 1.10
- *c.* A1004 P multi 1.30 1.10
- *d.* A1005 P multi 1.30 1.10
- *e.* A1006 P multi 1.30 1.10

### Booklet Stamps
### Self-Adhesive
*Serpentine Die Cut 13¼*

**2351** A1002 P multi 1.30 .25
**2352** A1003 P multi 1.30 .25
**2353** A1004 P multi 1.30 .25
**2354** A1005 P multi 1.30 .25
**2355** A1006 P multi 1.30 .25
- *a.* Booklet pane of 10, 2 each #2351-2355 13.00
- *b.* Booklet pane of 30, 6 each #2351-2355 39.00

*Nos. 2351-2355 (5)* 6.50 1.25

On day of issue, Nos. 2350a-2350e and 2351-2355 each sold for 57c.

Striped Coralroot Orchid A1007

Giant Helleborine Orchid A1008

Rose Pogonia Orchid A1009

Grass Pink Orchid A1010

**2010, Jan. 11** *Perf. 13¼x13*

**2356** Souvenir sheet of 4 7.00 7.00
- *a.* A1007 P multi 1.30 1.10
- *b.* A1008 $1 multi 1.50 1.25
- *c.* A1009 $1.22 multi 1.80 1.50
- *d.* A1010 $1.70 multi 2.50 2.00

### Coil Stamps
### Self-Adhesive
*Serpentine Die Cut 8 to 9½ (Saw-tooth Tips)*

**2357** A1007 P multi 1.30 .25
**2358** A1008 $1 multi 1.50 .30
**2359** A1009 $1.22 multi 1.80 .50
**2360** A1010 $1.70 multi 2.50 .75

Horiz. pairs, imperf. between, of No. 2357 are from uncut press panels of 100. Value unused, $4.

*Serpentine Die Cut 9¼ (Rounded Tips)*

**2361** A1007 P multi 1.50 1.50

*Nos. 2357-2361 (5)* 8.60 3.30

### Booklet Stamps

**2362** A1008 $1 multi 1.50 .35
- *a.* Booklet pane of 6 9.00

**2363** A1009 $1.22 multi 1.80 .50
- *a.* Booklet pane of 6 10.75

**2364** A1010 $1.70 multi 2.50 .75
- *a.* Booklet pane of 6 15.00

*Nos. 2362-2364 (3)* 5.80 1.60

On day of issue, Nos. 2356a and 2357 each sold for 57c. No. 2357 was printed in vertical rolls with stamps that are adjacent. No. 2361 was printed in horizontal rolls with stamps that are separated.

Queen Elizabeth II — A1011

### Self-Adhesive
*Serpentine Die Cut 13¼*

**2010, Jan. 11** **Booklet Stamp**

**2365** A1011 P multi 1.30 .25
- *a.* Booklet pane of 10 13.00

No. 2365 sold for 57c on day of issue.

Venues of the 2010 Winter Olympics A1012

Designs: Nos. 2366a, 2367, Whistler, B.C. Nos. 2366b, 2368, Vancouver.

**2010, Jan. 12** *Perf. 13½x13¼*

**2366** A1012 Souvenir sheet of 2 2.20 2.20
- *a.-b.* 57c Either single 1.10 .75
- *c.* As No. 2366, with "Vancouver / 2010" overprinted in sheet margin in gold 12.00 12.00

### Booklet Stamps
### Self-Adhesive
*Serpentine Die Cut 13¼*

**2367** A1012 57c multi .85 .30
**2368** A1012 57c multi .85 .30
- *a.* Booklet pane of 10, 5 each #2367-2368, + 10 stickers 8.50

No. 2366c was sold in a package of 3 sheets that also contained Nos. 2299f and 2305f.

William Hall (1827-1904), First Black Recipient of Victoria Cross — A1013

**2010, Feb. 1** *Perf. 12¾x12½*

**2369** A1013 57c multi .85 .30

Roméo LeBlanc (1927-2009), Governor-General A1014

**2010, Feb. 8** *Perf. 12½*

**2370** A1014 57c multi .85 .30

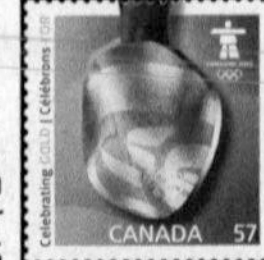

Gold Medal From Vancouver Winter Olympics — A1015

**2010, Feb. 15** *Perf. 12½*

**2371** Sheet of 2 #2371a 2.20 2.20
- *a.* A1015 57c Single stamp 1.10 .75

First day cancels have a Feb. 14 date, which was the date on which the first gold medal was awarded to a Canadian athlete on home soil, but which also was a Sunday. Post offices in Vancouver had the stamp available for sale on Feb. 15.

### Booklet Stamp
### Self-Adhesive
*Serpentine Die Cut 13½*

**2372** A1015 57c multi .85 .30
- *a.* Booklet pane of 10 8.50

Awarding of first gold medal to a Canadian on home soil.

Spirit of the Winter Olympics A1016

Winter Olympic athletes and: Nos. 2373a, 2374, Woman with painted face at left. Nos. 2373b, 2375, Woman with painted face at right.

**2010, Feb. 22** *Perf. 13*

**2373** A1016 Souvenir sheet of 2 2.20 2.20
- *a.-b.* 57c Either single 1.10 .75

### Booklet Stamps
### Self-Adhesive
*Serpentine Die Cut 13¼*

**2374** A1016 57c multi .85 .30
**2375** A1016 57c multi .85 .30
- *a.* Booklet pane of 10, 5 each #2374-2375 8.50

African Violet Hybrids A1017

Flower colors: Nos. 2376a, 2377, Red (Descelles' Avalanche). Nos. 2376b, 2378, Purple (Picasso).

**2010, Mar. 3** **Litho.** *Perf. 13*

**2376** A1017 Souvenir sheet of 2 2.60 2.60
- *a.-b.* P Either single 1.30 1.10

### Booklet Stamps
### Self-Adhesive
*Serpentine Die Cut 13½*

**2377** A1017 P multi 1.30 .30
**2378** A1017 P multi 1.30 .30
- *a.* Booklet pane of 10, 5 each #2377-2378 13.00
- *b.* Imperf., pair —
- *c.* As "a," imperf. —

On day of issue, Nos. 2376a, 2376b, 2377 and 2378 each sold for 57c.

Friendship Between Canada and Israel, 60th Anniv. — A1018

### Booklet Stamp
### Self-Adhesive
*Serpentine Die Cut 13¼*

**2010, Apr. 14** **Litho.**

**2379** A1018 $1.70 multi 2.60 1.10
- *a.* Booklet pane of 3 + label 7.75
- Complete booklet, 2 #2379a 15.50

See Israel No. 1812.

Indian Kings — A1019

Portraits by John Verelst of: No. 2380, Tee Yee Neen Ho Ga Row. No. 2381, Sa Ga Yeath Qua Pieth Tow. No. 2382, Ho Nee Yeath Taw No Row. No. 2383, Etow Oh Koam.

**2010, Apr. 19** **Litho.** *Perf. 12½*

**2380** A1019 57c multi .85 .40
**2381** A1019 57c multi .85 .40
**2382** A1019 57c multi .85 .40
**2383** A1019 57c multi .85 .40
- *a.* Block or strip of 4, #2380-2383 3.40 3.40
- *b.* Souvenir sheet of 4, #2380-2383 3.75 3.75
- *c.* As "b," with London 2010 emblem on sheet margin 5.50 5.50

*Nos. 2380-2383 (4)* 3.40 1.60

Meeting of the four Indian Kings and Queen Anne in London, 300th anniv.

Canadian Navy, Cent. — A1020

Designs: Nos. 2384a, 2385, Male sailor, HMCS Niobe. Nos. 2384b, 2386, Female sailor, HMCS Halifax.

**2010, May 4** **Litho.** *Perf. 12½*

**2384** A1020 Sheet of 2 2.20 2.20
- *a.-b.* 57c Either single 1.10 .75

### Booklet Stamps
### Self-Adhesive
*Serpentine Die Cut 13¼x13½*

**2385** A1020 57c multi .85 .30
**2386** A1020 57c multi .85
- *a.* Booklet pane of 10, 5 each #2385-2386 8.50

Sea Mammals — A1021

Designs: No. 2387a, Harbor porpoise. No. 2387b, Sea otter.

*Perf. 13x12¼x13x13 Syncopated (#2387a), 13x13x13x12¼ Syncopated (#2387b)*

**2010, May 13** **Litho. & Engr.**

**2387** A1021 Sheet of 2 2.20 2.20
- *a.-b.* 57c Either single 1.10 .90
- *c.* As "a," perf. 13x12¾ syncopated .75 .35
- *d.* As "b," perf. 13x12¾ syncopated .75 .35
- *e.* Booklet pane of 8, 4 each #2387c-2387d 6.00 6.00
- Complete booklet, #2387e 7.00

Nos. 2387a and 2387b have syncopation on left and right side, with the syncopation between the stamps in the shape of a maple leaf. Nos. 2387c and 2387d have syncopation on one side only, with the syncopation between pairs of stamps in the shape of conjoined ovals.

See Sweden No. 2638.

*Canadian Geographic's* Wildlife Photography of the Year — A1022

Designs: Nos. 2388a, 2393, Ardia herodias, by Martin Cooper. Nos. 2388b, 2392, Vulpes vulpes, by Ben Boulter. Nos. 2388c, 2391, Tettigoniidae, by Julie Bazinet. Nos. 2388d, 2390, Tachycineta bicolor, by Mark Bradley. Nos. 2388e, 2389, Selasphorus rufus, by Wing Yan Tam.

**2010, May 22** **Litho.** *Perf. 12½x13*

**2388** A1022 Sheet of 5 5.00 5.00
- *a.-e.* 57c Any single .85 .85

### Booklet Stamps
### Self-Adhesive
*Serpentine Die Cut 13¼*

**2389** A1022 57c multi .85 .30
**2390** A1022 57c multi .85 .30
**2391** A1022 57c multi .85 .30
**2392** A1022 57c multi .85 .30
**2393** A1022 57c multi .85 .30
- *a.* Booklet pane of 10, 2 each #2389-2393 8.50

*Nos. 2389-2393 (5)* 4.25 1.50

Rotary International in Canada, Cent. — A1023

**Self-Adhesive**

**Booklet Stamp**

***Serpentine Die Cut 13½x12¾***

**2010, June 18** **Litho.**

**2394** A1023 57c multi .85 .30
*a.* Booklet pane of 8 6.75

Paintings by Prudence Heward (1896-1947) A1024

Designs: 57c, Rollande. $1.70, At the Theatre, horiz. (42x40mm).

**2010, July 2** ***Perf. 13¼x13***

**2395** A1024 57c multi .85 .30

**Souvenir Sheet**

**2396** Sheet of 2, #2395, 2396a 3.75 3.75
*a.* A1024 $1.70 multi 2.60 2.60

Roadside Attractions — A1025

Designs: Nos. 2397a, 2398, Coffee Pot, Davidson, Saskatchewan. Nos. 2397b, 2399, Happy Rock, Gladstone, Manitoba. Nos. 2397c, 2400, Wawa Goose, Wawa, Ontario. Nos. 2397d, 2401, Puffin, Longue-Pointe-de-Mingan, Quebec.

**2010, July 5** ***Perf. 13***

**2397** A1025 Sheet of 4 5.25 5.25
*a.-d.* P Any single 1.30 1.10

**Booklet Stamps**

**Self-Adhesive**

***Serpentine Die Cut 13½***

**2398** A1025 P multi 1.30 .40
**2399** A1025 P multi 1.30 .40
**2400** A1025 P multi 1.30 .40
**2401** A1025 P multi 1.30 .40
*a.* Booklet pane of 4, #2398-2401 5.25
Complete booklet, 2 #2401a 10.50

On day of issue, Nos. 2397a-2397d, 2398-2401 each sold for 57c.

Girl Guides, Cent. — A1026

**Self-Adhesive**

***Serpentine Die Cut 13¾***

**2010, July 8** **Booklet Stamp**

**2402** A1026 P multi 1.30 .30
*a.* Booklet pane of 10 13.00

No. 2402 sold for 57c on day of issue.

Founding of Cupids, Newfoundland Settlement, 400th Anniv. — A1027

**2010, Aug. 17** ***Perf. 12½***

**2403** A1027 57c multi .85 .35

Year of British Home Children — A1028

**2010, Sept. 1**

**2404** A1028 57c multi .85 .35

Blue Whale A1029

**Litho., Engr. & Silk-screened**

**2010, Oct. 4** ***Perf. 12½x13***

**2405** A1029 $10 multi 15.00 5.50

Printed in sheets of 2.

**Beneficial Insects Type of 2007**

Designs: 4c, Paper wasp (Polistes fuscatus). 6c, Assassin bug (Zelus luridus). 7c, Large milkweed bug (Oncopeltus fasciatus). 8c, Margined leatherwing (Chauliognathus marginatus). 9c, Dogbane beetle (Chrysochus auratus).

**2010, Oct. 19** **Litho.** ***Perf. 13¼x13***

**2406** A942 4c multi .30 .25
*a.* With added microprinting and small design features (#2409b) .30 .25
**2407** A942 6c multi .30 .25
**2408** A942 7c multi .30 .25
**2409** A942 8c multi .30 .25
*a.* With added microprinting and small design features (#2409b) .30 .25
*b.* Souvenir sheet of 3, #2235b, 2406a, 2409a .30 .25
**2410** A942 9c multi .30 .25
*a.* Souvenir sheet, #2406-2410 2.20 .40
*Nos. 2406-2410 (5)* 1.50 1.25

Issued: Nos. 2406a, 2409a, 2409b, 10/16/12.

Christmas Ornaments A1030

Madonna and Child, Sculpture by Antonio Caruso A1031

Designs: Nos. 2411a, 2413, Three red ornaments, greenish blue background. $1, Two blue ornaments, purple background. $1.70, Three red ornaments, dull blue background.

**2010, Nov. 1** **Litho.** ***Perf. 12½***

**2411** Souvenir sheet of 3 5.50 5.50
*a.* A1030 P multi 1.30 1.10
*b.* A1030 $1 multi 1.50 1.50
*c.* A1030 $1.70 multi 2.60 2.60

**Booklet Stamps**

**Self-Adhesive**

***Serpentine Die Cut 13¼***

**2412** A1031 P multi 1.30 .25
*a.* Booklet pane of 6 7.75
Complete booklet, 2 #2412a 15.00

***Serpentine Die Cut 13½***

**2413** A1030 P multi 1.30 .25
*a.* Booklet pane of 6 7.75
Complete booklet, 2 #2413a 15.50
**2414** A1030 $1 multi 1.50 .60
*a.* Booklet pane of 6 9.00
**2415** A1030 $1.70 multi 2.60 1.10
*a.* Booklet pane of 6 15.50
*b.* Gutter pane, #2414a, 2415a 27.50
*Nos. 2412-2415 (4)* 6.70 2.20

Nos. 2411a, 2412 and 2413 each sold for 57c on day of issue.

New Year 2011 (Year of the Rabbit) — A1032

Design: $1.75, Two rabbits in circle.

**Litho. & Embossed With Foil Application**

**2011, Jan. 7** ***Perf. 12½***

**2416** A1032 P gold & multi 1.30 .40

**Souvenir Sheet**

**2417** A1032 $1.75 multi 2.60 2.60

No. 2416 sold for 59c on day of issue. See Nos. 3259d, 3260d, 3264.

Canadian Flag on Soldier's Uniform A1033

Canadian Flag on Hot-air Balloon A1034

Canadian Flag on Search and Rescue Team's Uniform A1035

Canadian Flag on Canadarm A1036

Canadian Flag on Backpack — A1037

**2011, Jan. 17** **Litho.** ***Perf. 13x13¼***

**2418** Sheet of 5 6.50 6.50
*a.* A1033 P multi 1.30 1.10
*b.* A1034 P multi 1.30 1.10
*c.* A1035 P multi 1.30 1.10
*d.* A1036 P multi 1.30 1.10
*e.* A1037 P multi 1.30 1.10

**Booklet Stamps**

**Self-Adhesive**

***Serpentine Die Cut 13¼***

**2419** A1033 P multi 1.30 .25
**2420** A1034 P multi 1.30 .25
**2421** A1035 P multi 1.30 .25
**2422** A1036 P multi 1.30 .25
**2423** A1037 P multi 1.30 .25
*a.* Booklet pane of 10, 2 each #2419-2423 13.00
*b.* Booklet pane of 30, 6 each #2419-2423 39.00
*Nos. 2419-2423 (5)* 6.25 3.00

On day of issue, Nos. 2418a-2418e, 2419-2423 each sold for 59c.

Juvenile Wildlife — A1038

Designs: P, Arctic hare leverets. $1.03, Red fox kit in hollow log. $1.25, Canada goslings. $1.75, Polar bear cub.

**2011, Jan. 17** ***Perf. 13¼x13***

**2424** Sheet of 4 7.25 7.25
*a.* A1038 P multi 1.30 1.10
*b.* A1038 $1.03 multi 1.50 1.30
*c.* A1038 $1.25 multi 1.90 1.65
*d.* A1038 $1.75 multi 2.60 2.40

**Coil Stamps**

**Self-Adhesive**

***Serpentine Die Cut 9¼ Horiz.***

**2425** A1038 P multi 1.50 1.50

***Serpentine Die Cut 8¼ Horiz.***

**2426** A1038 P multi 1.30 .25
**2427** A1038 $1.03 multi 1.55 .30

Horiz. pairs, imperf. between, of No. 2426 are from uncut press panels of 100. Value unused, $3.25.

***Serpentine Die Cut 8½ Horiz.***

**2428** A1038 $1.25 multi 1.90 .55

***Serpentine Die Cut 8¼ Horiz.***

**2429** A1038 $1.75 multi 2.60 .75

**Booklet Stamps**

***Serpentine Die Cut 9¼ Horiz.***

**2430** A1038 $1.03 multi 1.55 .30
*a.* Booklet pane of 6 9.25
**2431** A1038 $1.25 multi 1.90 .55
*a.* Booklet pane of 6 11.50
**2432** A1038 $1.75 multi 2.60 .75
*a.* Booklet pane of 6 15.50
*Nos. 2425-2432 (8)* 18.70 9.40

On day of issue, Nos. 2424a, 2425 and 2426 each sold for 59c. On rolls of No. 2425, stamps do not touch each other and pairs are horizontal. On rolls of No. 2426, stamps touch each other and pairs are vertical.

See Nos. 2504-2512, 2602-2610, 2692, 2692A, 2709-2717.

Black History Month — A1039

Order of Canada recipients: No. 2433, Carrie Best (1903-2001), journalist. No. 2434, Ferguson Jenkins, baseball player.

**Self-Adhesive**

***Serpentine Die Cut 13½x13¾***

**2011, Feb. 1** **Booklet Stamps**

**2433** A1039 59c multi .90 .30
*a.* Booklet pane of 10 9.00
**2434** A1039 59c multi .90 .30
*a.* Booklet pane of 10 9.00

Gift Box — A1040

**Self-Adhesive**

***Serpentine Die Cut 13½ Horiz.***

**2011, Feb. 7** **Booklet Stamp**

**2435** A1040 P multi 1.30 .30
*a.* Booklet pane of 6 7.75

No. 2435 sold for 59c on day of issue.

Paintings of Daphne Odjig — A1041

Paintings: 59c, Pow-wow Dancer. $1.03, Pow-wow (32x39mm). $1.75, Spiritual Renewal (56x39mm).

**2011, Feb. 21** ***Perf. 12½***

**2436** A1041 59c multi .90 .30

**Souvenir Sheet**

**2437** Sheet of 3, #2436, 2437a-2437b 4.00 4.00
*a.* A1041 $1.03 multi 1.50 1.50
*b.* A1041 $1.75 multi 2.60 2.60

**Booklet Stamps**

**Self-Adhesive**

***Serpentine Die Cut 13½x13¼***

**2438** A1041 $1.03 multi 1.55 .65
*a.* Booklet pane of 6 9.25
**2439** A1041 $1.75 multi 2.60 1.10
*a.* Booklet pane of 6 15.50

Sunflower
A1042 A1043

Sunflower varieties: Nos. 2440a, 2441, 2443, Prado Red. Nos. 2440b, 2442, 2444, Sunbright (yellow flower).

**2011, Mar. 3** **Litho.** ***Perf. 13¼***

**Souvenir Sheet**

**2440** Sheet of 2 2.60 2.60
*a.-b.* A1042 P Either single 1.30 1.10

**Coil Stamps**

**Self-Adhesive**

***Serpentine Die Cut 8¼ Horiz.***

**2441** A1043 P multi 1.30 .40
**2442** A1043 P multi 1.30 .40
*a.* Vert. pair, #2441-2442 2.60

### Booklet Stamps

*Serpentine Die Cut 13½*

**2443** A1042 P multi 1.30 .30
**2444** A1042 P multi 1.30 .30
*a.* Booklet pane of 10, 5 each #2443-2444 13.00

On day of issue, Nos. 2440a-2440b, 2441-2444 each sold for 59c.

Signs of the Zodiac — A1044

No. 2445: a, Aries. b, Taurus. c, Gemini. d, Cancer. No. 2446: a, Leo. b, Virgo. c, Libra. d, Scorpio. No. 2447: a, Sagittarius. b, Capricorn. c, Aquarius. d, Pisces.

No. 2448: a, Aries. b, Taurus. c, Gemini. d, Cancer. e, Leo. f, Virgo. g, Libra. h, Scorpio. i, Sagittarius. j, Capricorn. k, Aquarius. l, Pisces.

No. 2449, Aries. No. 2450, Taurus. No. 2451, Gemini. No. 2452, Cancer. No. 2453, Leo. No. 2454, Virgo. No. 2455, Libra. No. 2456, Scorpio. No. 2457, Sagittarius. No. 2458, Capricorn. No. 2459, Aquarius. No. 2460, Pisces.

**2011-13** **Litho.** ***Perf. 12½***

**2445** Sheet of 4 5.25 5.25
*a.-d.* A1044 P Any single 1.30 1.10
**2446** Sheet of 4 5.25 5.25
*a.-d.* A1044 P Any single 1.30 1.10
**2447** Sheet of 4 5.25 5.25
*a.-d.* A1044 P Any single 1.30 1.10

***Perf. 12½x13***

**2448** Sheet of 12 18.00 18.00
*a.-l* A1044 P Any single 1.50 1.50

### Booklet Stamps
### Self-Adhesive

*Serpentine Die Cut 13½*

**2449** A1044 P multi 1.30 .30
*a.* Booklet pane of 10 13.00
**2450** A1044 P multi 1.30 .30
*a.* Booklet pane of 10 12.00
*b.* Gutter pane of 12, 6 each #2449-2450 15.00
**2451** A1044 P multi 1.30 .30
*a.* Booklet pane of 10 13.00
**2452** A1044 P multi 1.30 .30
*a.* Booklet pane of 10 13.00
*b.* Gutter pane of 12, 6 each #2451-2452 15.00
**2453** A1044 P multi 1.30 .30
*a.* Booklet pane of 10 13.00
**2454** A1044 P multi 1.30 .30
*a.* Booklet pane of 10 13.00
**2455** A1044 P multi 1.30 .30
*a.* Booklet pane of 10 13.00
**2456** A1044 P multi 1.30 .30
*a.* Booklet pane of 10 13.00
*b.* Gutter pane of 24, 6 each #2453-2456 30.00
**2457** A1044 P multi 1.30 .30
*a.* Booklet pane of 10 13.00
**2458** A1044 P multi 1.30 .30
*a.* Booklet pane of 10 13.00
**2459** A1044 P multi 1.30 .30
*a.* Booklet pane of 10 13.00
**2460** A1044 P multi 1.30 .30
*a.* Booklet pane of 10 13.00
*b.* Gutter pane of 24, 6 each #2457-2460 30.00
*Nos. 2449-2460 (12)* 15.60 3.60

Issued: No. 2449, 3/21; Nos. 2450, 2450b, 4/21; No. 2451, 5/20; Nos. 2445, 2452, 2452b, 6/22, Nos. 2446, 2453-2456, 2456b, 7/23/12. Nos. 2447-2448, 2457-2460, 2460b, 2/20/13. Nos. 2445a-2445d, 2449-2452 each sold for 59c on day of issue. Nos. 2446a-2446d, 2453-2456 each sold for 61c on day of issue. Nos. 2447a-2447d, 2448a-2448l, 2457-2460 each sold for 63c on day of issue.

Intl. Year of Forests A1045

Designs: Nos. 2461a, 2462, Tree. Nos. 2461b, 2463, Mushrooms and plants on forest floor.

**2011, Apr. 21** **Litho.** ***Perf. 13½x13***

**2461** A1045 Sheet of 2 2.60 2.60
*a.-b.* P Either single 1.30 1.10

### Booklet Stamps
### Self-Adhesive

*Serpentine Die Cut 13x13¼*

**2462** A1045 P multi 1.30 .30
**2463** A1045 P multi 1.30 .30
*a.* Booklet pane of 8, 4 each #2462-2463 10.50

On day of issue, Nos. 2461a-2461b, 2462-2463 each sold for 59c.

Wedding of Prince William and Catherine Middleton — A1046

Couple with Prince William at: P, Right. $1.75, Left.

**2011, Apr. 29** ***Perf. 12¾x13¼***

**2464** A1046 P multi 1.30 .30
**2465** A1046 $1.75 multi 2.60 1.10
*a.* Horiz. pair, #2464-2465 4.00 3.00
*b.* Souvenir sheet, #2464-2465 4.00 4.00
*c.* As "b," with arms of Prince William overprinted in sheet margin in gold 4.50 4.50

### Booklet Stamps
### Self-Adhesive

*Serpentine Die Cut 13¼*

**2466** A1046 P multi 1.30 .30
*a.* Booklet pane of 10 13.00
**2467** A1046 $1.75 multi 2.60 1.10
*a.* Booklet pane of 10 26.00
*b.* Gutter pane, 6 #2466, 4 #2467 55.00

On day of issue, Nos. 2464 and 2468 each sold for 59c.

Methods of Mail Delivery — A1047

Designs: No. 2468, Ponchon. No. 2469, Dog sled.

**2011, May 13** ***Perf. 12½***

**2468** 59c multi .85 .30
**2469** 59c multi .85 .30
*a.* A1047 Horiz. pair, #2468-2469 1.70 1.10

Parks Canada, Cent. — A1048

### Self-Adhesive

*Serpentine Die Cut 13½*

**2011, May 19** **Booklet Stamp**

**2470** A1048 59c multi .85 .30
*a.* Booklet pane of 10 8.50

Details of Art Deco Structures — A1049

Designs: Nos. 2471a, 2472, Burrard Bridge, Vancouver. Nos. 2471b, 2473, Cormier House, Montreal. Nos. 2471c, 2474, R. C. Harris Water Treatment Plant, Toronto. Nos. 2471d, 2475, Supreme Court of Canada, Ottawa. Nos. 2471e, 2476, Dominion Building, Regina, Saskatchewan.

**2011, June 9** **Litho.** ***Perf. 13x12½***

**2471** A1049 Sheet of 5 + 5 labels 6.50 6.50
*a.-e.* P Any single 1.30 1.10

### Booklet Stamps
### Self-Adhesive

*Serpentine Die Cut 13¼x13½*

**2472** A1049 P multi 1.30 .30
**2473** A1049 P multi 1.30 .30
**2474** A1049 P multi 1.30 .30
**2475** A1049 P multi 1.30 .30
**2476** A1049 P multi 1.30 .30
*a.* Booklet pane of 10, 2 each #2472-2476 13.00
*Nos. 2472-2476 (5)* 6.50 1.50

On day of issue, Nos. 2471a-2471e, 2472-2476 each sold for 59c.

Duke and Duchess of Cambridge on Their Wedding Day — A1050

**2011, June 22** ***Perf. 12¾x13¼***

**2477** Sheet of 2 #2477a 3.00 2.60
*a.* A1050 P multi 1.50 .90
*b.* Sheet similar to #2477, with Royal Tour emblem overprinted in gold in sheet margin 3.75 2.60

### Booklet Stamp
### Self-Adhesive

*Serpentine Die Cut 13¼*

**2478** A1050 P multi 1.30 .30
*a.* Booklet pane of 10 13.00

On day of issue, Nos. 2477a and 2478 each sold for 59c. Margin of No. 2477 depicts Westminster Abbey, and that of No. 2477b depicts the Canadian Parliament.

Popular Singers — A1051

Designs: Nos. 2479, 2483c, Ginette Reno. Nos. 2480, 2483a, Bruce Cockburn. Nos. 2481, 2483d, Robbie Robertson. Nos. 2482, 2483b, Kate and Anna McGarrigle.

**2011** ***Perf. 12½***

**2479** A1051 P multi 1.80 1.80
*a.* Perf. 12½x13 1.30 1.10
**2480** A1051 P multi 1.80 1.80
*a.* Perf. 12½x13 1.30 1.10
**2481** A1051 P multi 1.80 1.80
*a.* Perf. 12½x13 1.30 1.10
**2482** A1051 P multi 1.80 1.80
*a.* Perf. 12½x13 1.30 1.10
*b.* Souvenir sheet of 4, #2479a-2482a 5.25 3.50
*Nos. 2479-2482 (4)* 7.20 7.20

### Self-Adhesive

*Serpentine Die Cut 13½*

**2483** Booklet pane of 4 5.25
*a.-d.* A1051 P Any single 1.30 .45
Complete booklet, 2 #2483 10.50

Issued: Nos. 2479-2482, 7/30; Nos. 2479a-2482a, 2482b, 2483, 6/30. On day of issue, Nos. 2479a2482, 2479a-2482a and 2483a-2483d each sold for 59c.

Complete booklets were issued with four different covers depicting the featured singers. The order of the stamps is different in each booklet.

Roadside Attractions — A1052

Designs: Nos. 2484a, 2485a, World's Largest Lobster, Shediac, New Brunswick. Nos. 2484b, 2485b, Wild Blueberry, Oxford, Nova Scotia. Nos. 2484c, 2485c, Big Potato, O'Leary, Prince Edward Island. Nos. 2484d, 2485d, Giant Squid, Glover's Harbour, Newfoundland.

**2011, July 7** ***Perf. 12¾***

**2484** A1052 Sheet of 4 5.25 5.25
*a.-d.* P Any single 1.30 1.10

### Self-Adhesive

*Serpentine Die Cut13½*

**2485** A1052 Booklet pane of 4 5.25
*a.-d.* P Any single 1.30 .45
Complete booklet, 2 #2485 10.50

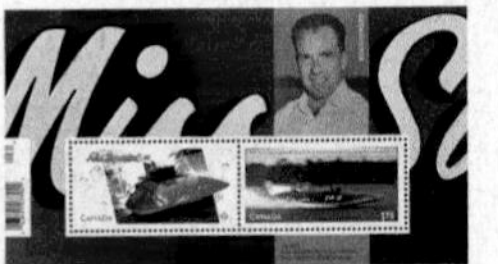

Third Consecutive Victory of Intl. Harmsworth Trophy by Miss Supertest III Hydroplane — A1053

Designs: P, Miss Supertest III. $1.75, Miss Supertest III, diff.

**2011, Aug. 8** **Litho.** ***Perf. 13¼***

**2486** A1053 Sheet of 2 4.00 4.00
*a.* P multi 1.30 1.10
*b.* $1.75 multi 2.60 2.40

### Booklet Stamp
### Self-Adhesive

*Serpentine Die Cut 13¼ Horiz.*

**2487** A1053 P multi 1.20 .30
*a.* Booklet pane of 10 13.00

Nos. 2486a and 2487 each sold for 59c on day of issue.

Canadian Inventions — A1054

No. 2488: a, Pacemaker, developed by Dr. John Hopps. b, BlackBerry, developed by Research in Motion. c, Electric oven, developed by Thomas Ahearn. d, Electric wheelchair, developed by George J. Klein.

*Serpentine Die Cut 13¼*

**2011, Aug. 17** **Self-Adhesive**

**2488** Booklet pane of 4 3.60
*a.-d.* A1054 59c Any single .90 .45
Complete booklet, 2 #2488 7.25

Dr. John Charles Polanyi, Winner of 1986 Nobel Prize for Chemistry — A1055

### Self-Adhesive
### Booklet Stamp

*Serpentine Die Cut 13½*

**2011, Oct. 3** **Litho.**

**2489** A1055 P multi 1.20 .30
*a.* Booklet pane of 10 13.00

Intl. Year of Chemistry. No. 2489 sold for 59c on day of issue.

Christmas
A1056 A1057

Stained-glass windows, Cathedral of Saint Mary of the Immaculate Conception, Kingston, Ontario: Nos. 2490a, 2492, Angel. $1.03, Nativity. $1.75, Epiphany.

**2011, Nov. 1** **Litho.** ***Perf. 13x12½***

**2490** Sheet of 3 5.50 5.50
*a.* A1056 P multi 1.30 1.10
*b.* A1056 $1.03 multi 1.50 1.40
*c.* A1056 $1.75 multi 2.60 2.50

### Booklet Stamps
### Self-Adhesive

**Litho. With Hologram Affixed**

*Serpentine Die Cut 8¼ Horiz.*

**2491** A1057 P multi 1.20 .25
*a.* Booklet pane of 6 7.75
Complete booklet, 2 #2491a 15.50

**Litho.**

***Serpentine Die Cut 13¼***

**2492** A1056 P multi 1.30 .25
*a.* Booklet pane of 6 7.75
Complete booklet, 2 #2492a 15.50
**2493** A1056 $1.03 multi 1.55 .60
*a.* Booklet pane of 6 9.25
**2494** A1056 $1.75 multi 2.60 1.10
*a.* Booklet pane of 6 15.50
*b.* Gutter pane, #2493a, 2494a 26.00
*Nos. 2491-2494 (4)* 6.65 2.20

On day of issue, Nos. 2490a, 2491 and 2492 each sold for 59c.

New Year 2012 (Year of the Dragon) — A1058

Design: $1.80, Dragon's head.

**Litho. & Embossed With Foil Application**

**2012, Jan. 10** ***Perf. 12½***
**2495** A1058 P gold & multi 1.30 .40

**Souvenir Sheet**

**2496** A1058 $1.80 multi 2.70 2.70
*a.* Souvenir sheet of 2, #2417, 2496 5.25 5.25

**Booklet Stamp**
**Self-Adhesive**
**Litho.**

***Serpentine Die Cut 13½***

**2497** A1058 $1.80 multi 2.70 1.10
*a.* Booklet pane of 6 16.25

No. 2495 sold for 61c on day of issue. See Nos. 3259e, 3260e, 3265.

Flag on Coast Guard Ship A1059

Flag in Van Window A1060

Olympic Athlete Carrying Flag A1061

Flag on Bobsled A1062

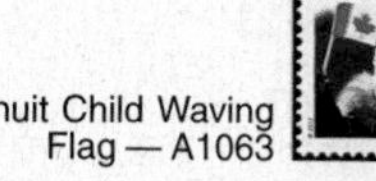

Inuit Child Waving Flag — A1063

**2012, Jan. 16** **Litho.** ***Perf. 13x13¼***
**2498** Souvenir sheet of 5 6.50 6.50
*a.* A1059 P multi 1.30 1.10
*b.* A1060 P multi 1.30 1.10
*c.* A1061 P multi 1.30 1.10
*d.* A1062 P multi 1.30 1.10
*e.* A1063 P multi 1.30 1.10

**Booklet Stamps**
**Self-Adhesive**

***Serpentine Die Cut 13¼***

**2499** A1059 P multi 1.30 .25
*a.* With "Canada" visible on reverse of stamp 2.25 .35
**2500** A1060 P multi 1.30 .25
*a.* With "Canada" visible on reverse of stamp 2.25 .35
**2501** A1061 P multi 1.30 .25
*a.* With "Canada" visible on reverse of stamp 2.25 .35
**2502** A1062 P multi 1.30 .25
*a.* Microprinting with corrected spelling "Lueders" 1.50 .25
*b.* As "a," with "Canada" visible on reverse of stamp 2.25 .35
**2503** A1063 P multi 1.30 .25
*a.* Booklet pane of 10, 2 each #2499-2503 13.00
*b.* Booklet pane of 30, 6 each #2499-2503 39.00
*c.* Booklet pane of 10, 2 each #2499-2502, 2502a, 2503 19.00
*d.* With "Canada" visible on reverse of stamp 2.25 .35
*e.* Booklet pane of 10, 2 each #2499a, 2500a, 2501a, 2502b, 2503d 26.00
*Nos. 2499-2503 (5)* 6.50 1.25

On day of issue, Nos. 2498a-2498e, 2499-2503 each sold for 61c. The printing on the backing paper on No. 2503a differs from that on the backing paper of any of the component thirds of No. 2503b.

Issued: Nos. 2502a, 2503c, 9/28/12; Nos. 2499a, 2500a, 2501a, 2502b, 2503d, 2013. Nos. 2498d and 2502 have incorrect spelling in microprinting of "Leuders."

**Juvenile Wildlife Type of 2011**

Designs: P, Three raccoon kits. $1.05, Two caribou calves. $1.29, Adult loon and two chicks. $1.80, Moose calves.

**2012, Jan. 16** ***Perf. 13¼x13***
**2504** Souvenir sheet of 4 8.00 6.50
*a.* A1038 P multi 1.30 1.10
*b.* A1038 $1.05 multi 1.60 1.20
*c.* A1038 $1.29 multi 1.90 1.50
*d.* A1038 $1.80 multi 2.70 2.40

**Self-Adhesive**
**Coil Stamps**

***Serpentine Die Cut 9¼ Horiz.***

**2505** A1038 P multi 1.50 1.50

***Serpentine Die Cut 8¼ Horiz.***

**2506** A1038 P multi 1.30 .25
**2507** A1038 $1.05 multi 1.60 .30
**2508** A1038 $1.29 multi 1.90 .75
**2509** A1038 $1.80 multi 2.70 .90
*Nos. 2505-2509 (5)* 9.00 3.70

**Booklet Stamps**

***Serpentine Die Cut 9¼ Horiz.***

**2510** A1038 $1.05 multi 1.60 .30
*a.* Booklet pane of 6 9.50
**2511** A1038 $1.29 multi 1.90 .55
*a.* Booklet pane of 6 11.50
**2512** A1038 $1.80 multi 2.70 .90
*a.* Booklet pane of 6 16.25
*Nos. 2510-2512 (3)* 6.20 1.75

On day of issue, Nos. 2504a, 2505 and 2506 each sold for 61c. On rolls of No. 2505, stamps do not touch each other and pairs are horizontal. On rolls of No. 2506, stamps touch each other and pairs are vertical.

A1064

Reign of Queen Elizabeth II, 60th Anniv. — A1065

Designs: No. 2513, Crown, Canada #330. No. 2514, Map of Canada, Canada #471. No. 2515, Document, pen, Canada #704. No. 2516, Jubilee bouquet, Canada #1168. No. 2517, Tiara details, Canada #1932. Nos. 2518, 2519, Queen Elizabeth II wearing robe and tiara.

**2012** **Litho.** ***Perf. 13¼***
**2513** A1064 P multi 1.30 1.00
**2514** A1064 P multi 1.30 1.00
**2515** A1064 P multi 1.30 1.00
**2516** A1064 P multi 1.30 1.00
**2517** A1064 P multi 1.30 1.00

***Perf. 13¼x12½***

**2518** A1065 P multi 1.30 1.10

**Booklet Stamp**
**Self-Adhesive**

**2519** A1065 P multi 1.30 .30
*a.* Booklet pane of 10 13.00

Issued: Nos. 2513, 2519, 1/16; No. 2514, 2/6; No. 2515, 3/6; No. 2516, 4/10; No. 2517, 5/7; No. 2518, 6/1. On day of issue, Nos. 2513-2519 each sold for 61c. Nos. 2513-2518 each were printed in sheets of 4.

Black History Month — A1066

Designs: No. 2520, John Ware (c. 1845-1905), cattle driver and rancher. No. 2521, Viola Desmond (1914-65), civil rights activist.

**Self-Adhesive**
**Booklet Stamps**

***Serpentine Die Cut 13½***

**2012, Feb. 1** **Litho.**
**2520** A1066 P multi 1.30 .30
*a.* Booklet pane of 10 13.00
**2521** A1066 P multi 1.30 .30
*a.* Booklet pane of 10 13.00
*b.* Gutter pane of 12, 6 each #2520-2521 15.00

On day of issue, Nos. 2520-2521 each sold for 61c.

Sculptures by Joe Fafard — A1067

Designs: P, Smoothly She Shifted. $1.05, Dear Vincent, vert. (32x40mm). $1.80, Capillery, horiz. (64x32mm).

**2012, Feb. 23** ***Perf. 12½***
**2522** A1067 P multi 1.30 .30

**Souvenir Sheet**

**2523** Sheet of 3, #2522, 2523a, 2523b 5.00 5.00
*a.* A1067 $1.05 multi 1.60 1.60
*b.* A1067 $1.80 multi 1.90 1.90

**Booklet Stamps**
**Self-Adhesive**

***Serpentine Die Cut 13½***

**2524** A1067 $1.05 multi 1.60 .65
*a.* Booklet pane of 6 9.50

***Serpentine Die Cut 13¼***

**2525** A1067 $1.80 multi 2.60 1.10
*a.* Booklet pane of 6 15.75
*b.* Gutter pane of 6, 3 each #2524-2525 15.00

No. 2522 sold for 61c on day of issue.

A1068

Daylilies — A1069

Color of daylily: Nos. 2526a, 2527, 2529, Orange. Nos. 2526b, 2528, 2530, Purple.

**2012, Mar. 1** ***Perf. 13¼***

**Souvenir Sheet**

**2526** Sheet of 2 2.60 2.60
*a.-b.* A1068 P Either single 1.30 1.10

**Coil Stamps**
**Self-Adhesive**

***Serpentine Die Cut 8¼ Horiz.***

**2527** A1069 P multi 1.30 .40
**2528** A1069 P multi 1.30 .40
*a.* Vert. pair, #2527-2528 2.60

**Booklet Stamps**

***Serpentine Die Cut 13½***

**2529** A1068 P multi 1.30 .30
**2530** A1068 P multi 1.30 .30
*a.* Booklet pane of 10, 5 each #2529-2530 13.00

On day of issue, Nos. 2526a, 2526b, 2527-2530 each sold for 61c.

A1070

Sinking of the Titanic, Cent. A1071

Flag of the White Star Line and: Nos. 2531, 2536, Bow of Titanic, map showing Halifax, Nova Scotia. Nos. 2532, 2537, Bow of Titanic, map showing Southampton, England. No. 2533, Propellers of Titanic, three men. No. 2534, Propellers of Titanic, six men.

$1.80, Titanic, map of North Atlantic, flag of the White Star Line.

**2012, Apr. 5** **Litho.** ***Perf. 12½***
**2531** A1070 P multi 1.30 .45
**2532** A1070 P multi 1.30 .45
**2533** A1070 P multi 1.30 .45
**2534** A1070 P multi 1.30 .45
*a.* Block of 4, #2531-2534 5.25 2.60
*Nos. 2531-2534 (4)* 5.20 1.80

**Souvenir Sheet**

***Perf. 13***

**2535** A1071 $1.80 multi 2.60 2.60

**Booklet Stamps**
**Self-Adhesive**

***Serpentine Die Cut 13½***

**2536** A1070 P multi 1.30 .30
**2537** A1070 P multi 1.30 .30
*a.* Booklet pane of 10, 5 each #2536-2537 13.00
**2538** A1071 $1.80 multi 2.60 1.50
*a.* Booklet pane of 6 15.75
*Nos. 2536-2538 (3)* 5.20 2.10

On day of issue, Nos. 2531-2534, 2536-2537 each sold for 61c.

Thomas Douglas, 5th Earl of Selkirk (1771-1820), Founder of Red River Settlement, and Settlers A1072

**2012, May 3** **Litho.** ***Perf. 13¼***
**2539** A1072 P multi 1.30 .30

Red River Settlement, bicent. No. 2539 sold for 61c on day of issue.

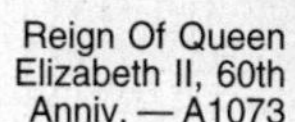

Reign Of Queen Elizabeth II, 60th Anniv. — A1073

**2012, May 7** **Engr.** ***Perf. 11½***
**2540** A1073 $2 purple 3.00 1.50
*a.* Souvenir sheet of 1 3.75 3.75

Franklin the Turtle, Children's Book Character by Paulette Bourgeois — A1074

Designs: Nos. 2541a, 2542, Franklin, beaver and teddy bear. Nos. 2541b, 2543, Franklin helping young turtle to read book. Nos. 2541c, 2544, Franklin and snail. Nos. 2541d, 2545, Franklin watching bear feed fish in bowl.

**2012, May 11** ***Perf. 13x12½***
**2541** Miniature sheet of 4 5.25 5.25
*a.-d.* A1074 P Any single 1.30 1.10

**Booklet Stamps**
**Self-Adhesive**

***Serpentine Die Cut 13¼***

**2542** A1074 P multi 1.30 .40
**2543** A1074 P multi 1.30 .40
**2544** A1074 P multi 1.30 .40

**2545** A1074 P multi 1.30 .40
 *a.* Booklet pane of 12, 3 each #2542-2545 15.50
 *Nos. 2542-2545 (4)* 5.20 1.60

Nos. 2541a-2541d, 2542-2545 each sold for 61c on day of issue.

Calgary Stampede, Cent. — A1075

Designs: P, Saddle on rodeo horse. $1.05, Commemorative belt buckle.

**2012, May 17** ***Perf. 13x13¼***

**2546** Souvenir sheet of 2 3.00 3.00
 *a.* A1075 P multi 1.30 1.10
 *b.* A1075 $1.05 multi 1.60 1.60

**Booklet Stamps**
**Self-Adhesive**
***Serpentine Die Cut 13¼x13***

**2547** A1075 P multi 1.30 .30
 *a.* Booklet pane of 10 13.00
**2548** A1075 $1.05 multi 1.60 .65
 *a.* Booklet pane of 10 16.00
 *b.* Gutter pane of 10, 6 #2547, 4 #2548 15.00

Nos. 2546a and 2547 each sold for 61c on day of issue.

Order of Canada Recipients — A1076

Designs: Nos. 2549a, 2550, Louise Arbour, president of International Crisis Group. Nos. 2549b, 2551, Rick Hansen, founder of Rick Hansen Foundation (spinal cord injury research). Nos. 2549c, 2552, Sheila Watt-Cloutier, Inuit rights activist. Nos. 2549d, 2553, Michael J. Fox, actor, founder of Michael J. Fox Foundation for Parkinson's Research.

**2012, May 22** **Litho.** ***Perf. 12½***

**2549** Miniature sheet of 4 5.25 5.25
 *a.-d.* A1076 P Any single 1.30 1.10

**Booklet Stamps**
**Self-Adhesive**
***Serpentine Die Cut 13½***

**2550** A1076 P multi 1.30 .30
 *a.* Booklet pane of 10 13.00
**2551** A1076 P multi 1.30 .30
 *a.* Booklet pane of 10 13.00
**2552** A1076 P multi 1.30 .30
 *a.* Booklet pane of 10 13.00
**2553** A1076 P multi 1.30 .30
 *a.* Booklet pane of 10 13.00
 *Nos. 2550-2553 (4)* 5.20 1.20

On day of issue Nos. 2549a-2549d, 2550-2553 each sold for 61c.

War of 1812, Bicent. — A1077

Designs: No. 2554, Sir Isaac Brock (1769-1812), British Major General. No. 2555, Tecumseh (1768-1813), leader of Indian confederacy.

**2012, June 15** ***Perf. 13¼x12½***

**2554** P multi 1.30 .30
**2555** P multi 1.30 .30
 *a.* A1077 Horiz. pair, #2554-2555 2.60 1.10

On day of issue, Nos. 2554-2555 each sold for 61c. See Guernsey No. 1172.

2012 Summer Olympics, London — A1078

**Self-Adhesive**
**Booklet Stamp**

**2012, June 27** ***Serpentine Die Cut 8***

**2556** A1078 P multi 1.30 .35
 *a.* Booklet pane of 10 13.00

No. 2556 sold for 61c on day of issue.

Tommy Douglas (1904-86), Politician A1079

**2012, June 29** ***Perf. 12½***

**2557** A1079 P multi 1.30 .30

Passage of Saskatchewan's Medical Care Insurance Act, 50th anniv. (start of socialized medicine in Canada). No. 2557 sold for 61c on day of issue.

Canadian Football League Team Emblems — A1080

Designs: Nos. 2558a, 2559, British Columbia Lions. Nos. 2558b, 2560, Edmonton Eskimos. Nos. 2558c, 2561, Calgary Stampeders. Nos. 2558d, 2562, Saskatchewan Roughriders. Nos. 2558e, 2563, Winnipeg Blue Bombers. Nos. 2558f, 2564, Hamilton Tiger-Cats. Nos. 2558g, 2565, Toronto Argonauts. Nos. 2558h, 2566, Montreal Alouettes.

**2012, June 29** ***Perf. 13¼x13***

**2558** A1080 Sheet of 8 10.50 10.50
 *a.-h.* P Any single 1.30 1.30

**Coil Stamps**
**Self-Adhesive**
***Serpentine Die Cut 8¼ Horiz.***

**2559** A1080 P multi 1.30 .45
**2560** A1080 P multi 1.30 .45
**2561** A1080 P multi 1.30 .45
**2562** A1080 P multi 1.30 .45
**2563** A1080 P multi 1.30 .45
**2564** A1080 P multi 1.30 .45
**2565** A1080 P multi 1.30 .45
**2566** A1080 P multi 1.30 .45
 *Nos. 2559-2566 (8)* 10.40 3.60

On day of issue, Nos. 2558a-2558h, 2559-2566 each sold for 61c. See No. 2754.

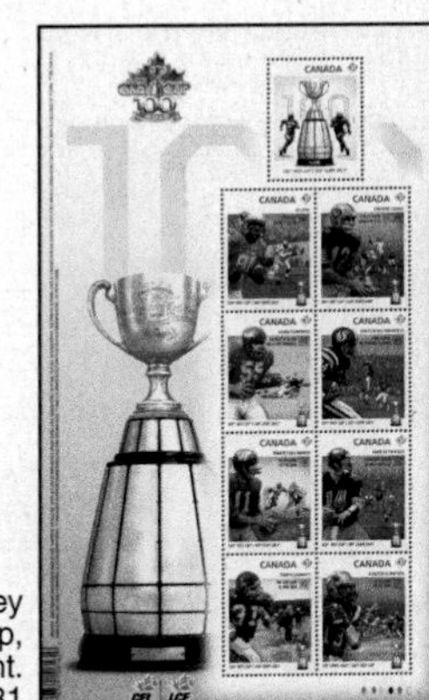


Grey Cup, Cent. A1081

Grey Cup and: Nos. 2567a, 2568, Two football players, "100." Nos. 2567b, 2569, British Columbia Lions player Geroy Simon, kicker and holder in 1994 game. Nos. 2567c, 2570, Edmonton Eskimos player Tom Wilkinson, quarterback ready to throw pass. Nos. 2567d, 2571, Calgary Stampeders player "Thumper" Wayne Harris, running back and tacklers from 1948 game. Nos. 2567e, 2572, Saskatchewan Roughriders player George Reed, players celebrating in 1989 game. Nos. 2567f, 2573, Winnipeg Blue Bombers player Ken Pipen, players in fog in 1962 game. Nos. 2567g, 2574, Hamilton Tiger-Cats player Danny Mcmanus, player catching ball in 1972 game. Nos. 2567h, 2575, Toronto Argonauts player Michael "Pinball" Clemons, players on muddy field in 1950 game. Nos. 2567i, 2576, Montreal Alouettes player Anthony Calvillo, players at line of scrimmage in 1977 game.

**Litho. & Embossed**

**2012, Aug. 16** ***Perf. 12½***

**2567** A1081 Sheet of 9 11.75 11.75
 *a.-i.* P Any single 1.30 1.00

**Litho.**
**Booklet Stamps**
**Self-Adhesive**
***Serpentine Die Cut 13¼***

**2568** A1081 P multi 1.30 .30
 *a.* Booklet pane of 10 13.00
**2569** A1081 P multi 1.30 .30
 *a.* Booklet pane of 10 13.00
**2570** A1081 P multi 1.30 .30
 *a.* Booklet pane of 10 13.00
**2571** A1081 P multi 1.30 .30
 *a.* Booklet pane of 10 13.00
**2572** A1081 P multi 1.30 .30
 *a.* Booklet pane of 10 13.00
**2573** A1081 P multi 1.30 .30
 *a.* Booklet pane of 10 13.00
**2574** A1081 P multi 1.30 .30
 *a.* Booklet pane of 10 13.00
**2575** A1081 P multi 1.30 .30
 *a.* Booklet pane of 10 13.00
**2576** A1081 P multi 1.30 .30
 *a.* Booklet pane of 10 13.00
 *Nos. 2568-2576 (9)* 11.70 2.70

Nos. 2567a-2567i, 2568-2576 each sold for 61c on day of issue. For overprint, see No. 2598.

Military Regiments, 150th Anniv. — A1082

Uniforms of: Nos. 2577a, 2578, Black Watch (Royal Highland) Regiment of Canada. Nos. 2577b, 2579, Royal Hamilton Light Infantry (Wentworth Regiment). Nos. 2577c, 2580, Royal Regiment of Canada

**2012, Oct. 11** **Litho.** ***Perf. 13x13½***

**2577** Souvenir sheet of 3 4.00 4.00
 *a.-c.* A1082 P Any single 1.30 1.10

**Booklet Stamps**
**Self-Adhesive**
***Serpentine Die Cut 13¼x13***

**2578** A1082 P multi 1.30 .45
 *a.* Booklet pane of 10 13.00
**2579** A1082 P multi 1.30 .45
 *a.* Booklet pane of 10 13.00
**2580** A1082 P multi 1.30 .45
 *a.* Booklet pane of 10 13.00
 *Nos. 2578-2580 (3)* 3.90 1.35

On day of issue, Nos. 2577a-2577c, 2578-2580 each sold for 61c.

Gingerbread Cookies A1083

Stained Glass Window From St. Mary's of the Immaculate Conception Cathedral, Kingsoton, Ontario A1084

Ribbons on Christmas cookies shaped as: P, Man and woman. $1.05, Five-pointed star. $1.80, Snowflake.

**Souvenir Sheet**

**2012, Oct. 15** ***Perf. 13¾x13¼***

**2581** Sheet of 3 5.50 5.50
 *a.* A1083 P multi 1.30 1.10
 *b.* A1083 $1.05 multi 1.60 1.50
 *c.* A1083 $1.80 multi 2.70 2.70

**Booklet Stamps**
**Self-Adhesive**
***Serpentine Die Cut 13¼***

**2582** A1084 P multi 1.30 .25
 *a.* Booklet pane of 12 15.50

***Serpentine Die Cut 13¼x13***

**2583** A1083 P multi 1.30 .25
 *a.* Booklet pane of 12 13.00
**2584** A1083 $1.05 multi 1.60 .60
 *a.* Booklet pane of 6 9.50
**2585** A1083 $1.80 multi 2.70 1.00
 *a.* Booklet pane of 6 16.25
 *Nos. 2582-2585 (4)* 6.90 2.10

Christmas. On day of issue, Nos. 2581a, 2582 and 2583 each sold for 61c.

Dots A1085

Frame A1086

Hearts A1087

Creatures A1088

Butterflies A1089

Maple Leaves A1090

Flowers A1091

Snowflakes A1092

Wedding Bells A1093

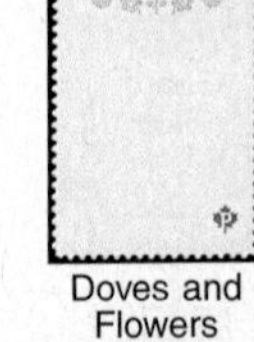


Doves and Flowers A1094

Balloons, Stars, Party Hat A1095

Holly A1096

***Serpentine Die Cut 13¼***

**2012, Nov.** **Self-Adhesive** **Litho.**

**2586** A1085 P gray 2.25 2.25
 *a.* Personalized version, any denomination or orientation — —
**2587** A1086 P gray 2.25 2.25
 *a.* Personalized version, any denomination or orientation — —
**2588** A1087 P gray & red 2.25 2.25
 *a.* Personalized version, any denomination or orientation — —
**2589** A1088 P multi 2.25 2.25
 *a.* Personalized version, any denomination or orientation — —
**2590** A1089 P multi 2.25 2.25
 *a.* Personalized version, any denomination or orientation — —
**2591** A1090 P multi 2.25 2.25
 *a.* Personalized version, any denomination or orientation — —
**2592** A1091 P multi 2.25 2.25
 *a.* Personalized version, any denomination or orientation — —
**2593** A1092 P multi 2.25 2.25
 *a.* Personalized version, any denomination or orientation — —

**2594** A1093 P gray & black 2.25 2.25
*a.* Personalized version, any denomination or orientation — —
**2595** A1094 P gray 2.25 2.25
*a.* Personalized version, any denomination or orientation — —
**2596** A1095 P multi 2.25 2.25
*a.* Personalized version, any denomination or orientation — —
**2597** A1096 P multi 2.25 2.25
*a.* Personalized version, any denomination or orientation — —
*Nos. 2586-2597 (12)* 27.00 27.00

Nos. 2586-2597 had a franking value on the day of issue of 61c, and were sold together in a package of single stamps that sold for $7.32. Each vertically-oriented stamp in the package had a gray image area. Horizontally-oriented stamps were not made available in these packages. First day covers of Nos. 2586-2597 are dated 11/5.

Nos. 2586a-2597a have personalized photographs in the image area, and were available with vertical or horizontal orientations and in various denominations. On Nov. 16-24 personalized stamps were offered for sale on iPad and iPhone apps at the P rate (with a franking value of 61c), $1.05, $1.29 and $1.80. It is not known if any personalized stamps of the $1.05, $1.29 and $1.80 denominations were created for customers through these apps during this brief period. On Nov. 24 stamps at the P rate (with a franking value of 61c), $1.10, $1.34 and $1.85 were offered to customers through the Picture Postage page of the Canada Post website, as well as through the apps. Additional stamps with different denominations may be offered for sale later. A $1.29 stamp featuring the image of a Turtle was made available on Nov. 1. It was only available affixed to packages containing a box of Nestle's Turtles candy. A box of candy and affixed stamp sold at post offices for $4.99, and the package could only be sent to Canadian addresses.

Except for the stamp with the turtle's image, the stamps of the various denominations were each made available in sheets of 26, sheets of 50 and booklet panes of 12 (a minimum of three booklet panes needed to be ordered). The selling prices of the personalized sheets and booklets were substantially higher than the face value of the stamps within them.

Vertically oriented stamps have the denomination in the lower right corner of the stamp, with the "C" of "Canada" at the upper left of the stamp, as shown in the illustrations. Horizontally oriented stamps have the denomination in the lower right corner of the stamp, with the "C" of "Canada" at the lower left corner. The dots, frame, hearts, creatures and butterflies images on horizontally-oriented stamps differ from those shown on the vertically-oriented stamps.

No. 2568 Overprinted in Dark Blue, Light Blue, Black and Silver

### Booklet Stamp

***Serpentine Die Cut 13¼***

**2012, Nov. 28** **Litho.**

**Self-Adhesive**

**2598** A1081 P multi 1.30 .50
*a.* Booklet pane of 10 13.00

Grey Cup victory of Toronto Argonauts. No. 2598 sold for 61c on day of issue.

New Year 2013 (Year of the Snake) — A1097

Design: $1.85, Snake's head.

**Litho. & Embossed**

**2013, Jan. 8** ***Perf. 12½***

**2599** A1097 P shown 1.30 .40

### Souvenir Sheet

**Litho. & Embossed With Foil Application**

**2600** A1097 $1.85 multi 3.00 3.00
*a.* Souvenir sheet of 2, #2496, 2600 5.50 4.75

### Booklet Stamp
### Self-Adhesive

**Litho.**

***Serpentine Die Cut 13½***

**2601** A1097 $1.85 multi 3.00 1.20
*a.* Booklet pane of 6 18.00

No. 2599 sold for 63c on day of issue. See Nos. 2700a, 3259f, 3260f, 3266.

### Juvenile Wildlife Type of 2011

Designs: P, Four woodchuck pups. $1.10, Porcupette. $1.34, Fawn. $1.85, Bear cub.

**2013, Jan. 14** ***Perf. 13¼x13***

**2602** Souvenir sheet of 4 7.75 7.75
*a.* A1038 P multi 1.30 1.10
*b.* A1038 $1.10 multi 1.65 1.25
*c.* A1038 $1.34 multi 2.00 1.60
*d.* A1038 $1.85 multi 2.80 2.60

### Self-Adhesive
### Coil Stamps

***Serpentine Die Cut 9¼ Horiz.***

**2603** A1038 P multi 1.50 1.50

***Serpentine Die Cut 8¼ Horiz.***

**2604** A1038 P multi 1.30 .25
**2605** A1038 $1.10 multi 1.65 .35
**2606** A1038 $1.34 multi 2.00 .55
**2607** A1038 $1.85 multi 2.80 1.00

### Booklet Stamps

***Serpentine Die Cut 9¼ Horiz.***

**2608** A1038 $1.10 multi 1.65 .35
*a.* Booklet pane of 6 10.00
**2609** A1038 $1.34 multi 2.00 .55
*a.* Booklet pane of 6 12.00
**2610** A1038 $1.85 multi 2.80 .90
*a.* Booklet pane of 6 16.75
*Nos. 2603-2610 (8)* 15.70 5.45

On day of issue, Nos. 2602a, 2603 and 2604 each sold for 63c. On rolls of No. 2603, stamps do not touch each other and pairs are horizontal. On rolls of No. 2604, stamps touch each other and pairs are vertical.

See No. 2692.

Flag Design on Chairs A1098

Flag on Hay Roll A1099

Flag Design on Spinnaker A1100

Flag in Flower Bed A1101

Flag Design on Hut — A1102

**2013, Jan. 14** **Litho.** ***Perf. 13x13¼***

**2611** Souvenir sheet of 5 6.50 6.50
*a.* A1098 P multi 1.30 1.10
*b.* A1099 P multi 1.30 1.10
*c.* A1100 P multi 1.30 1.10
*d.* A1101 P multi 1.30 1.10
*e.* A1102 P multi 1.30 1.10

### Booklet Stamps
### Self-Adhesive

***Serpentine Die Cut 13¼***

**2612** A1098 P multi 1.30 .25
*a.* With "Canada" visible on reverse of stamp 1.30 .25
**2613** A1099 P multi 1.30 .25
*a.* With "Canada" visible on reverse of stamp 1.30 .25
**2614** A1100 P multi 1.30 .25
*a.* With "Canada" visible on reverse of stamp 1.30 .25
**2615** A1101 P multi 1.30 .25
*a.* With "Canada" visible on reverse of stamp 1.30 .25
**2616** A1102 P multi 1.30 .25
*a.* With "Canada" visible on reverse of stamp 1.30 .25
*b.* Booklet pane of 10, 2 each #2612-2616 13.00
*c.* Booklet pane of 10, 2 each #2612a-2616a 13.00
*d.* Booklet pane of 30, 6 each #2612-2616 39.00
*e.* Booklet pane of 30, 6 each #2612a-2616a 39.00
*Nos. 2612-2616 (5)* 6.50 1.25

On day of issue, Nos. 2611a-2611e, 2612-2616, 2612a-2616a each sold for 63c. The printing on the backing paper on Nos. 2616b and 2616c differs from that on the backing paper of any of the component thirds of Nos. 2616d and 2616e.

See Nos. 2693-2697.

Queen Elizabeth II — A1103

### Booklet Stamp

***Serpentine Die Cut 13¼***

**2013, Jan. 14** **Self-Adhesive**

**2617** A1103 P multi 1.30 .25
*a.* Booklet pane of 10 13.00
*b.* As #2617,with "Canada" visible on reverse of stamp 1.30 .25
*c.* Booklet pane of 10 #2617b 13.00

No. 2617 sold for 63c on day of issue. Issued: Nos. 2617b, 2617c, 6/1.

See No. 2698.

A1104

185c, Raoul Wallenberg (1912-47), Swedish Diplomat Who Rescued Jews During World War II.

### Booklet Stamp

***Serpentine Die Cut 13¼***

**2013, Jan. 17** **Self-Adhesive**

**2618** A1104 185c multi 2.80 1.50
*a.* Booklet pane of 6 16.75

Oliver Jones, Jazz Musician A1105

Joe Fortes (1863-1922), First Official Lifeguard of Vancouver A1106

### Booklet Stamps

***Serpentine Die Cut 13¼***

**2013, Feb. 1** **Self-Adhesive**

**2619** A1105 P multi 1.30 .35
*a.* Booklet pane of 10 13.00
**2620** A1106 P multi 1.30 .35
*a.* Booklet pane of 10 13.00

On day of issue, Nos. 2619-2620 each sold for 63c.

Magnolias

A1107 A1108

Magnolia varieties: Nos. 2621a, 2622, 2624, Yellow Bird (yellow flower). Nos. 2621b, 2623, 2625, Eskimo (lilac and white flower).

**2013, Mar. 4** **Litho.** ***Perf. 13¼***

### Souvenir Sheet

**2621** Sheet of 2 2.60 2.60
*a.-b.* A1107 P Either single 1.30 1.10

### Coil Stamps
### Self-Adhesive

***Serpentine Die Cut 8¼ Horiz.***

**2622** A1108 P multi 1.30 .40
**2623** A1108 P multi 1.30 .40
*a.* Vert. pair, #2622-2623 2.60

### Booklet Stamps

***Serpentine Die Cut 13½***

**2624** A1107 P multi 1.30 .35
**2625** A1107 P multi 1.30 .35
*a.* Booklet pane of 10, 5 each #2624-2625 13.00

On day of issue, Nos. 2621a-2621b, 2622-2625 each sold for 63c.

Photography — A1109

Designs: Nos. 2626a, 2629, Louis-Joseph Papineau, by Thomas Coffin Doane, 1852. Nos. 2626b, 2630, The Kitchen Sink, by Margaret Watkins, 1919. Nos. 2626c, 2632, Koo-tuck-tuck, by Geraldine Moodie, 1903-05. Nos. 2627a, 2628, Hot Properties #1, by Jim Breukelman, 1987, horiz. Nos. 2627b, 2631, Andor Pasztor, by Gabor Szilasi, 1978, horiz. $1.10, Basement Camera Shop circa 1937, by Rodney Graham, 2011, horiz. $1.85, Yousuf Karsh, by Arnaud Maggs, 1981, horiz.

**2013, Mar. 22** ***Perf. 13¼***

**2626** A1109 Sheet of 3 4.00 4.00
*a.-c.* P Any single 1.30 1.10
**2627** A1109 Sheet of 4 7.00 7.00
*a.-b.* P Any single 1.30 1.10
*c.* $1.10 multi 1.65 1.50
*d.* $1.85 multi 2.80 2.60

### Booklet Stamps
### Self-Adhesive

***Serpentine Die Cut 13½***

**2628** A1109 P multi 1.30 .35
**2629** A1109 P multi 1.30 .35
**2630** A1109 P multi 1.30 .35
**2631** A1109 P multi 1.30 .35
**2632** A1109 P multi 1.30 .35
*a.* Booklet pane of 10, 2 each #2628-2632 13.00
**2633** A1109 $1.10 multi 1.65 .80
*a.* Booklet pane of 6 10.00
**2634** A1109 $1.85 multi 2.80 1.40
*a.* Booklet pane of 6 16.75
*Nos. 2628-2634 (7)* 10.95 3.95

On day of issue, Nos. 2626a-2626c, 2627a, 2627b, 2628-2632 each sold for 63c.

See Nos. 2756-2764, 2814-2822, 2902-2910, 3010-3016.

The Prince of Wales' Own Regiment, 150th Anniv. — A1110

***Serpentine Die Cut 13¼x13***

**2013, Apr. 9** **Self-Adhesive**

### Booklet Stamp

**2635** A1110 P multi 1.30 .35
*a.* Booklet pane of 10 13.00

No. 2635 sold for 63c on day of issue.

Pet Adoption A1111

Designs: Nos. 2636a, 2637, Cat with bird on branch in background (24x32mm). Nos. 2636b, 2638, Parrot on perch (24x24mm). Nos. 2636c, 2639, Dog with squirrel, butterfly, flower and ball in background (24x40mm). Nos. 2636d, 2640, Dog with fireplace, dog bed and bone in background (40x40mm). Nos. 2636e, 2641, Cat with cat toys in background (24x32mm).

***Perf. 12½ (#2636a, 2636e), 13¼ (#2636b), 12½x13¼***

**2013, Apr. 22**

**2636** A1111 Sheet of 5 8.00 5.00
*a.-e.* P Any single 1.30 .45

### Booklet Stamps
### Self-Adhesive

***Serpentine Die Cut 13x13¼***

**2637** A1111 P multi 1.30 .45

***Serpentine Die Cut 13***

**2638** A1111 P multi 1.30 .45

***Serpentine Die Cut 13½***

**2639** A1111 P multi 1.30 .45
**2640** A1111 P multi 1.30 .45

***Serpentine Die Cut 13x13¼***

**2641** A1111 P multi 1.30 .45
*a.* Booklet pane of 10, 2 each #2637-2641 13.00
*Nos. 2637-2641 (5)* 6.50 2.25

On day of issue, Nos. 2636a-2636e, 2637-2641 each sold for 63c.

Chinatown Gates — A1112

Gates in: Nos. 2642a, 2643a, Toronto. Nos. 2642b, 2643b, Montreal. Nos. 2642c, 2643c, Winnipeg. Nos. 2642d, 2643e, Edmonton. Nos. 2642e, 2643d, Vancouver. Nos. 2642f, 2643f, Ottawa. Nos. 2642g, 2643g, Mississauga, Ontario. Nos. 2642h, 2643h, Victoria.

**Litho. With Foil Application**

**2013, May 1** *Perf. 12½*

**2642** A1112 Miniature sheet of 8 + central label 10.50 10.50
*a.-h.* P Any single 1.30 1.10

An imperf. pane of 8 exists of No. 2642. Sold only in a "Gates of Chinatown Collection," along with a normal No. 2642 and two coins, for $88.88. Value of imperf. pane, $140.

**Litho.**

**Booklet Stamps Self-Adhesive**

***Serpentine Die Cut 13½***

**2643** A1112 Booklet pane of 8 10.50
*a.-h.* P Any single 1.30 .35

On day of issue Nos. 2642a-2642h, 2643a-2643h each sold for 63c. Label on No. 2642 has a die cut square opening in center.

Coronation of Queen Elizabeth II, 60th Anniv. — A1113

***Serpentine Die Cut 13¼***

**2013, May 8** **Litho.**

**Booklet Stamp Self-Adhesive**

**2644** A1113 P multi 1.30 .35
*a.* Booklet pane of 10 13.00

No. 2644 sold for 63c on day of issue.

Big Brothers Big Sisters of Canada, Cent. — A1114

***Serpentine Die Cut 13x13½***

**2013, May 14** **Litho.**

**Booklet Stamp Self-Adhesive**

**2645** A1114 P multi 1.30 .35
*a.* Booklet pane of 10 13.00

No. 2645 sold for 63c on day of issue.

Motorcycles — A1115

Designs: Nos. 2646a, 2647, 1908 CCM. Nos. 2646b, 2648, 1914 Indian.

**2013, June 5** *Perf. 12½x13*

**Souvenir Sheet**

**2646** A1115 Sheet of 2 2.60 2.60
*a.-b.* P Either single 1.30 1.10

**Booklet Stamps Self-Adhesive**

***Serpentine Die Cut 13¼***

**2647** A1115 P multi 1.30 .35
**2648** A1115 P multi 1.30 .35
*a.* Booklet pane of 10, 5 each #2647-2648 13.00

On day of issue, Nos. 2646a-2646b, 2647-2648 each sold for 63c.

A1116

Design: Quebec Harbor Scene and Benjamin Franklin (1706-90), British North America Deputy Postmaster.

**Booklet Stamp**

***Serpentine Die Cut 13½***

**2013, June 10** **Self-Adhesive**

**2649** A1116 P multi 1.30 .35
*a.* Booklet pane of 10 13.00

Mail packet service from Montreal to New York, 250th anniv. No. 2649 sold for 63c on day of issue.

War of 1812 A1117

Heroic figures of War of 1812: No. 2650, Lieutenant Colonel Charles de Salaberry (1778-1829). No. 2651, Laura Secord (1775-1868).

**2013, June 20** *Perf. 13x12½*

**2650** P multi 1.30 .35
**2651** P multi 1.30 .35
*a.* A1117 Horiz. pair, #2650-2651 2.60 1.10

On day of issue, Nos. 2650-2651 each sold for 63c.

Children's Literature — A1118

Characters from series of *Stella* books, by Marie-Louise Gay: Nos. 2652a, 2653, Stella hanging by legs from tree. Nos. 2652b, 2654, Stella, brother Sam, and dog, Fred.

**2013, July 5** *Perf. 12½*

**Souvenir Sheet**

**2652** A1118 Sheet of 2 2.60 2.60
*a.-b.* P Either single 1.30 1.10

**Booklet Stamps Self-Adhesive**

***Serpentine Die Cut 13¼***

**2653** A1118 P multi 1.30 .35
**2654** A1118 P multi 1.30 .35
*a.* Booklet pane of 10, 5 each #2653-2654 13.00

On day of issue, Nos. 2652a-2652b, 2653-2654 each sold for 63c.

Canadian Bands — A1119

Designs: Nos. 2655a, 2656, The Tragically Hip (36x28mm). Nos. 2655b, 2657, Rush (28x28mm). Nos. 2655c, 2658, Beau Dommage (36x28mm). Nos. 2655d, 2659, The Guess Who (28x28mm).

**2013, July 19** *Perf. 12½*

**Souvenir Sheet**

**2655** A1119 Sheet of 4 5.25 5.25
*a.-d.* P Any single 1.30 1.10

**Booklet Stamps Self-Adhesive**

***Serpentine Die Cut 13½***

**2656** A1119 P multi 1.30 .35
*a.* Booklet pane of 10 13.00
**2657** A1119 P multi 1.30 .35
*a.* Booklet pane of 10 13.00
**2658** A1119 P multi 1.30 .35
*a.* Booklet pane of 10 13.00
**2659** A1119 P multi 1.30 .35
*a.* Booklet pane of 10 13.00
*Nos. 2656-2659 (4)* 5.20 1.40

On day of issue, Nos. 2655a-2655d, 2656-2659 each sold for 63c.

Robertson Davies (1913-95), Writer — A1120

**Booklet Stamp**

***Serpentine Die Cut 13¼***

**2013, Aug. 28** **Self-Adhesive**

**2660** A1120 63c multi .95 .35
*a.* Booklet pane of 10 9.50

Pucks With Emblems of Canadian National Hockey League Teams — A1121

Pucks with emblem of: Nos. 2661a, 2662, Vancouver Canucks. Nos. 2661b, 2663, Edmonton Oilers. Nos. 2661c, 2664, Toronto Maple Leafs. Nos. 2661d, 2665, Montreal Canadiens. Nos. 2661e, 2666, Calgary Flames. Nos. 2661f, 2667, Winnipeg Jets. Nos. 2661g, 2668, Ottawa Senators.

**2013, Sept. 3** **Litho.** *Perf. 13¼x13*

**2661** A1121 Sheet of 7 6.60 6.60
*a.-g.* 63c Any single .95 .75

**Coil Stamps Self-Adhesive**

***Serpentine Die Cut 8¼ Horiz.***

**2662** A1121 63c multi .95 .40
**2663** A1121 63c multi .95 .40
**2664** A1121 63c multi .95 .40
**2665** A1121 63c multi .95 .40
**2666** A1121 63c multi .95 .40
**2667** A1121 63c multi .95 .40
**2668** A1121 63c multi .95 .40
*Nos. 2662-2668 (7)* 6.65 2.80

Player and Fans Wearing Home and Away Jerseys — A1122

Uniforms of Canadian National Hockey League Teams: Nos. 2669a, 2670, Vancouver Canucks. Nos. 2669b, 2671, Montreal Canadiens. Nos. 2669c, 2672, Edmonton Oilers. Nos. 2669d, 2673, Ottawa Senators. Nos. 2669e, 2674, Calgary Flames. Nos. 2669f, 2675, Winnipeg Jets. Nos. 2669g, 2676, Toronto Maple Leafs.

***Serpentine Die Cut 13¼x13½***

**2013, Sept. 3** **Litho. & Embossed**

**2669** Sheet of 7 + 2 labels 6.60 6.60
*a.-g.* A1122 63c Any single .95 .75

**Litho.**

**Booklet Stamps Self-Adhesive**

**2670** A1122 63c multi .95 .35
*a.* Booklet pane of 10 9.50
**2671** A1122 63c multi .95 .35
*a.* Booklet pane of 10 9.50
**2672** A1122 63c multi .95 .35
*a.* Booklet pane of 10 9.50
**2673** A1122 63c multi .95 .35
*a.* Booklet pane of 10 9.50
**2674** A1122 63c multi .95 .35
*a.* Booklet pane of 10 9.50
**2675** A1122 63c multi .95 .35
*a.* Booklet pane of 10 9.50
**2676** A1122 63c multi .95 .35
*a.* Booklet pane of 10 9.50
*Nos. 2670-2676 (7)* 6.65 2.45

A1123 A1124

A1125 A1126

A1127

Superman Comics, 75th Anniv. — A1128

**2013, Sept. 10** *Perf. 12½*

**2677** Sheet of 5 6.50 6.50
*a.* A1123 P multi 1.30 1.10
*b.* A1124 P multi 1.30 1.10
*c.* A1125 P multi 1.30 1.10
*d.* A1126 P multi 1.30 1.10
*e.* A1127 P multi 1.30 1.10

**Coil Stamp Self-Adhesive**

***Die Cut Perf. 13½***

**2678** A1128 P multi 1.30 .50

**Booklet Stamps**

***Serpentine Die Cut 13½x13¼***

**2679** A1123 P multi 1.30 .45
**2680** A1124 P multi 1.30 .45
**2681** A1125 P multi 1.30 .45
**2682** A1126 P multi 1.30 .45
**2683** A1127 P multi 1.30 .45
*a.* Booklet pane of 10, 2 each #2679-2683 13.00
*Nos. 2678-2683 (6)* 7.80 2.75

Nos. 2677a-2677e, 2678-2683 each sold for 63c on day of issue.

Hastings and Prince Edward Regiment, 150th Anniv. — A1129

***Serpentine Die Cut 13¼x13***

**2013, Oct. 18** **Litho.**

**Booklet Stamp Self-Adhesive**

**2684** A1129 P multi 1.30 .35
*a.* Booklet pane of 10 13.00

No. 2684 sold for 63c on day of issue.

Birth of Prince George of Cambridge — A1130

**2013, Oct. 22** **Litho.** *Perf. 12½*

**2685** Sheet of 2 #2685a 2.60 2.60
*a.* A1130 P Single stamp 1.30 1.10

**Booklet Stamp Self-Adhesive**

***Serpentine Die Cut 13½***

**2686** A1130 P multi 1.30 .35
*a.* Booklet pane of 10 13.00

On day of issue, Nos. 2685a and 2686 each sold for 63c.

Christmas
A1131 A1132

Designs: Nos. 2687a, 2689, Cross-stitched horn. $1.10, Cross-stitched reindeer. $1.85, Cross-stitched Christmas tree. No. 2688, St. Anne with the Christ Child, by Georges de La Tour.

**2013, Oct. 22 Litho.** ***Perf. 13½x13¼***

**2687** Sheet of 3 5.50 5.50
*a.* A1131 63c multi .95 .95
*b.* A1131 $1.10 multi 1.65 1.60
*c.* A1131 $1.85 multi 2.80 2.60

**Booklet Stamps**
**Self-Adhesive**

***Serpentine Die Cut 13½***

**2688** A1132 63c multi 1.00 .25
*a.* Booklet pane of 12 12.00

***Serpentine Die Cut 13¼x13***

**2689** A1131 63c multi .95 .25
*a.* Booklet pane of 12 11.50
**2690** A1131 $1.10 multi 1.65 .60
*a.* Booklet pane of 6 10.00
**2691** A1131 $1.85 multi 2.80 .90
*a.* Booklet pane of 6 17.00
*Nos. 2688-2691 (4)* 6.40 2.00

**Juvenile Wildlife Type of 2011**

Design: 63c, Four woodchuck pups.

***Serpentine Die Cut 9¼ Horiz.***

**2013, Dec. 11 Litho.**

**Coil Stamps**
**Self-Adhesive**

**2692** A1038 63c multi .95 .25
*b.* Without repeating "Canada" underprint on reverse *75.00 7.50*

***Serpentine Die Cut 8¼ Horiz.***

**2692A** A1038 63c multi 1.10 1.10

Coils containing No. 2692A are adjacent in vertical strips. Coils containing No. 2692 are in horizontal strips with stamps separated.

**Flag Types of 2013**

***Serpentine Die Cut 13¼***

**2013, Dec. 11 Litho.**

**Booklet Stamps**
**Self-Adhesive**

**2693** A1098 63c multi .95 .25
**2694** A1099 63c multi .95 .25
**2695** A1100 63c multi .95 .25
**2696** A1101 63c multi .95 .25
**2697** A1102 63c multi .95 .25
*a.* Booklet pane of 10, 2 each #2693-2697 9.50
*Nos. 2693-2697 (5)* 4.75 1.25

**Queen Elizabeth II Type of 2013**

***Serpentine Die Cut 13¼***

**2013, Dec. 11 Litho.**

**Booklet Stamp**
**Self-Adhesive**

**2698** A1103 63c multi .95 .25
*a.* Booklet pane of 10 9.50

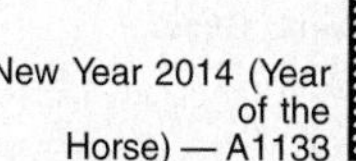

New Year 2014 (Year of the Horse) — A1133

Design: $1.85, Horse, diff.

**Litho. & Embossed**

**2014, Jan. 13** ***Perf. 12½***

**2699** A1133 63c multi .95 .30

**Litho. & Embossed With Foil Application**

**Souvenir Sheet**

**2700** A1133 $1.85 multi 2.75 2.75
*a.* Souvenir sheet of 2, #2600, 2700 5.50 5.50

**Litho. With Foil Application**

**Booklet Stamp**
**Self-Adhesive**

***Serpentine Die Cut 13½***

**2701** A1133 $1.85 multi 2.80 1.70
*a.* Booklet pane of 6 16.75

See Nos. 3259g, 3260g, 3267.

African-Canadian Neighborhoods A1134

Residents and buildings of: No. 2702, Africville, neighborhood of Halifax, Nova Scotia. No. 2703, Hogan's Alley, neighborhood of Vancouver, British Columbia.

***Serpentine Die Cut 13¼***

**2014, Jan. 30 Litho.**

**Booklet Stamps**
**Self-Adhesive**

**2702** A1134 63c multi .95 .35
*a.* Booklet pane of 10 9.50
**2703** A1134 63c multi .95 .35
*a.* Booklet pane of 10 9.50

Female Athletes — A1135

Designs: Nos. 2704a, 2705, Barbara Ann Scott (1928-2012), figure skater. Nos. 2704b, 2706, Sandra Schmirler (1963-2000), curler. Nos. 2704c, 2707, Sarah Burke (1982-2012), freestyle skier.

**2014, Feb. 3 Litho.** ***Perf. 13***

**Souvenir Sheet**

**2704** Sheet of 3 2.90 2.90
*a.-c.* A1135 63c Any single .95 .95

**Booklet Stamps**
**Self-Adhesive**

***Serpentine Die Cut 13¼***

**2705** A1135 63c multi .95 .35
*a.* Booklet pane of 10 9.50
**2706** A1135 63c multi .95 .35
*a.* Booklet pane of 10 9.50
**2707** A1135 63c multi .95 .35
*a.* Booklet pane of 10 9.50
*Nos. 2705-2707 (3)* 2.85 1.05

**Beneficial Insects Type of 2007**

Design: 22c, Monarch butterfly.

**2014, Mar. 31 Litho.** ***Perf. 13¼x13***

**2708** A942 22c multi .30 .25

**Juvenile Wildlife Type of 2011**

Designs: P, Beaver kits. $1, Burrowing owl chicks. $1.20, Mountain goat kid. $1.80, Puffin chicks. $2.50, Newborn wapiti.

**2014, Mar. 31 Litho.** ***Perf. 13¼x13***

**2709** Souvenir sheet of 5 11.00 11.00
*a.* A1038 P multi 1.30 1.10
*b.* A1038 $1 multi 1.50 1.50
*c.* A1038 $1.20 multi 1.80 1.80
*d.* A1038 $1.80 multi 2.70 2.60
*e.* A1038 $2.50 multi 3.75 3.75

**Coil Stamps**
**Self-Adhesive**

***Die Cut Perf. 13½***

**2710** A1038 $1 multi 1.50 .25
*b.* "CANADA $1" inscription omitted *500.00*

***Serpentine Die Cut 9¼ Horiz.***

**2710A** A1038 P multi 1.50 1.50

***Serpentine Die Cut 8¼ Horiz.***

**2711** A1038 P multi 1.30 .25
**2712** A1038 $1.20 multi 1.80 .35
**2713** A1038 $1.80 multi 2.70 .60
**2714** A1038 $2.50 multi 3.75 1.10
*Nos. 2710-2714 (5)* 11.05 2.55

**Booklet Stamps**

***Serpentine Die Cut 9¼ Horiz.***

**2715** A1038 $1.20 multi 1.80 .35
*a.* Booklet pane of 6 10.75
**2716** A1038 $1.80 multi 2.70 .60
*a.* Booklet pane of 6 16.25
**2717** A1038 $2.50 multi 3.75 1.10
*a.* Booklet pane of 6 22.50
*Nos. 2715-2717 (3)* 8.25 2.05

On day of issue, Nos. 2709a, 2710A, 2711 each sold for 85c. On rolls of No. 2710A, stamps do not touch each other and pairs are horizontal. On rolls of No. 2711, stamps touch each other and pairs are vertical.

Gros Morne National Park, Newfoundland and Labrador A1136

Joggins Fossil Cliffs, Nova Scotia A1137

Canadian Rocky Mountain Parks, Alberta and British Columbia A1138

Nahinni National Park, Northwest Territories A1139

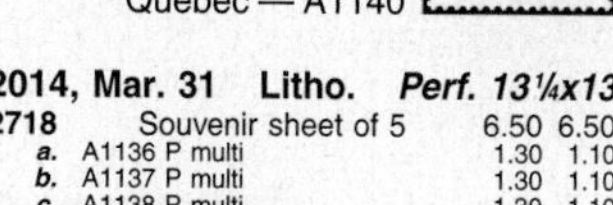

Miguasha National Park, Quebec — A1140

**2014, Mar. 31 Litho.** ***Perf. 13¼x13***

**2718** Souvenir sheet of 5 6.50 6.50
*a.* A1136 P multi 1.30 1.10
*b.* A1137 P multi 1.30 1.10
*c.* A1138 P multi 1.30 1.10
*d.* A1139 P multi 1.30 1.10
*e.* A1140 P multi 1.30 1.10

**Booklet Stamps**
**Self-Adhesive**

***Serpentine Die Cut 13¼***

**2719** A1136 P multi 1.30 .25
**2720** A1139 P multi 1.30 .25
**2721** A1137 P multi 1.30 .25
**2722** A1140 P multi *1.30* .25
**2723** A1138 P multi 1.30 .25
*a.* Booklet pane of 10, 2 each #2719-2723 13.00
*b.* Booklet pane of 30, 6 each #2719-2723 37.50
*Nos. 2719-2723 (5)* 6.50 1.25

UNESCO World Heritage Sites. On day of issue, Nos. 2718a-2718f, 2719-2723 each sold for 85c.

Shiva Natajara Sculpture, Mummified Cat and Bison A1141

Hadrasaur Skeleton and Luohan Chinese Sculpture A1142

**2014, Apr. 14 Litho.** ***Perf. 12½***

**2724** Souvenir sheet of 2 2.60 2.60
*a.* A1141 P multi 1.30 1.10
*b.* A1142 P multi 1.30 1.10

**Booklet Stamps**
**Self-Adhesive**

***Serpentine Die Cut 13½x13¼***

**2725** A1141 P multi 1.30 .35
**2726** A1142 P multi 1.30 .35
*a.* Booklet pane of 10, 5 each #2725-2726 13.00

Royal Ontario Museum, cent. On day of issue, Nos. 2724a-2724b, 2725-2726 each sold for 85c.

Roses
A1143 A1144

Rose varieties: Nos. 2727a, 2729, 2730, Konrad Henkel (red) rose. Nos. 2727b, 2728, 2731, Maid of Honor (white) rose.

**2014, Apr. 23 Litho.** ***Perf. 13***

**Souvenir Sheet**

**2727** Sheet of 2 2.60 2.60
*a.-b.* A1143 P Either single 1.30 1.10

**Coil Stamps**
**Self-Adhesive**

***Serpentine Die Cut 8¼ Horiz.***

**2728** A1144 P multi 1.30 .35
**2729** A1144 P multi 1.30 .35
*a.* Vert. pair, #2728-2729 2.60

**Booklet Stamps**

***Serpentine Die Cut 13¼***

**2730** A1143 P multi 1.30 .35
**2731** A1143 P multi 1.30 .35
*a.* Booklet pane of 10, 5 each #2730-2731 13.00
*Nos. 2728-2731 (4)* 5.20 1.40

On day of issue, Nos. 2727a-2727b, 2728-2731 each sold for 85c.

Komagata Maru Incident, Cent. — A1145

***Serpentine Die Cut 13x12¾***

**2014, May 1 Litho.**

**Booklet Stamp**
**Self-Adhesive**

**2732** A1145 $2.50 multi 3.75 1.90
*a.* Booklet pane of 6 22.50

National Film Board, 75th Anniv. A1146

Scenes from Canadian films: Nos. 2733a, 2734, *Flamenco at 5:15,* 1983. Nos. 2733b, 2735, *The Railrodder,* 1965. Nos. 2733c, 2736, *Mon Oncle Antoine,* 1971. Nos. 2733d, 2737, *Log Driver's Waltz,* 1979. Nos. 2733e, 2738, *Neighbours,* 1952.

**2014, May 2 Litho.** ***Perf. 13¼x12½***

**2733** A1146 Sheet of 5 + label 6.50 6.50
*a.-e.* P Any single 1.30 1.10

**Booklet Stamps**
**Self-Adhesive**

***Serpentine Die Cut 13¼***

**2734** A1146 P multi 1.30 .35
**2735** A1146 P multi 1.30 .35
**2736** A1146 P multi 1.30 .35
**2737** A1146 P multi 1.30 .35
**2738** A1146 P multi 1.30 .35
*a.* Booklet pane of 10, 2 each #2734-2738 13.00
*Nos. 2734-2738 (5)* 6.50 1.75

On day of issue, Nos. 2733a-2733e and 2734-2738 each sold for 85c.

UNESCO World Heritage Sites — A1147

Designs: Nos. 2739a, 2741, Head-Smashed-In Buffalo Jump, Alberta. Nos. 2739b, 2740, Old Town Lunenburg, Nova Scotia. Nos. 2739c, 2742, Landscape of Grand Pré, Nova Scotia. Nos. 2739d, 2743, SGang Gwaay, British Columbia. Nos. 2739e, 2744, Rideau Canal, Ontario.

**2014, May 16 Litho.** ***Perf. 12½***

**Miniature Sheet**

**2739** A1147 Sheet of 5 13.00 13.00
*a.-c.* $1.20 Any single 1.80 1.50
*d.-e.* $2.50 Either single 3.75 3.50

**Booklet Stamps**
**Self-Adhesive**

***Serpentine Die Cut 13¼x13½***

**2740** A1147 $1.20 multi 1.80 1.10
**2741** A1147 $1.20 multi 1.80 1.10
**2742** A1147 $1.20 multi 1.80 1.10
*a.* Booklet pane of 6, 2 each #2740-2742 10.75

**2743** A1147 $2.50 multi 3.75 2.30
**2744** A1147 $2.50 multi 3.75 2.30
*a.* Booklet pane of 6, 3 each #2743-2744 22.50
*Nos. 2740-2744 (5)* 12.90 7.90

Sinking of the RMS Empress of Ireland, Cent. — A1148

Designs: P, Empress of Ireland facing right. $2.50, Empress of Ireland facing left, horiz.

**2014, May 29 Litho. *Perf. 12½***
**2745** A1148 P multi 1.30 .60

**Souvenir Sheet**
***Perf. 12¾***
**2746** A1148 $2.50 multi 3.75 3.50

**Booklet Stamp**
**Self-Adhesive**
***Serpentine Die Cut 13½***
**2747** A1148 P multi 1.30 .35
*a.* Booklet pane of 10 13.00

On day of issue, Nos. 2745 and 2747 each sold for 85c. No. 2745 was printed in sheets of 16 + 4 labels. No. 2746 contains one 80x32mm stamp.

Haunted Canada — A1149

Designs: Nos. 2748a, 2749, Ghost bride, Banff Springs, Alberta. Nos. 2748b, 2751, Ghost train, St. Louis, Saskatchewan. Nos. 2748c, 2753, Apparitions of Fort George, Ontario. Nos. 2748d, 2752, Count of Frontenac Apparition, Château Frontenac Hotel, Quebec. Nos. 2748e, 2750, Phantom ship off Nova Scotia and Prince Edward Island.

**2014, June 13 Litho. *Perf. 12½***
**2748** Sheet of 5 6.50 6.50
*a.-e.* A1149 P Any single 1.30 1.10

**Booklet Stamps**
**Self-Adhesive**
***Serpentine Die Cut 13¼***
**2749** A1149 P multi 1.30 .45
**2750** A1149 P multi 1.30 .45
**2751** A1149 P multi 1.30 .45
**2752** A1149 P multi 1.30 .45
**2753** A1149 P multi 1.30 .45
*a.* Booklet pane of 10, 2 each #2749-2753 13.00
*Nos. 2749-2753 (5)* 6.50 2.25

On day of issue, Nos. 2748a-2748e, 2749-2753 each sold for 85c.

**Canadian Football League Team Emblems Type of 2012 and**

Russ Jackson in Ottawa Rough Riders Uniform, TD Place Stadium, Ottawa Redblacks Emblem — A1150

Design: No. 2754, Ottawa Redblacks emblem.

***Serpentine Die Cut 8¼ Horiz.***
**2014, June 19 Litho.**

**Coil Stamp**
**Self-Adhesive**
**2754** A1080 P multi 1.30 .45

**Booklet Stamp**
**2755** A1150 P multi 1.30 .35
*a.* Booklet pane of 10 13.00

On day of issue, Nos. 2754 and 2755 each sold for 85c.

**Photography Type of 2013**

Designs: Nos. 2756a, 2762, Unidentified Chinese Man, by C. D. Hoy, c. 1912. Nos. 2756b, 2759, St. Joseph's Convent School, by Michel Lambeth, 1960. Nos. 2756c, 2763, Sitting Bull and Buffalo Bill, Montreal, by William Notman, 1885. Nos. 2757a, 2761, Untitled, by Lynne Cohen, 1970, horiz. Nos. 2757b, 2760, La Ville de Québec en Hiver (Quebec City in Winter), by Louis-Prudent Vallée, 1894, horiz. Nos. 2757c, 2758, Bogner's Grocery, by Fred Herzog, 1960, horiz. Nos. 2757d, 2764, Railcuts: #1, by Edward Burtynsky, 1985, horiz.

**2014, July 7 Litho. *Perf. 13¼***
**2756** Sheet of 3 4.40 4.40
*a.-b.* A1109 P Either single 1.30 1.10
*c.* A1109 $1.20 multi 1.80 1.65
**2757** Sheet of 4 7.75 7.75
*a.-c.* A1109 P Any single 1.30 1.10
*d.* A1109 $2.50 multi 3.75 4.00

**Booklet Stamps**
**Self-Adhesive**
***Serpentine Die Cut 13¼***
**2758** A1109 P multi 1.30 .45
**2759** A1109 P multi 1.30 .45
**2760** A1109 P multi 1.30 .45
**2761** A1109 P multi 1.30 .45
**2762** A1109 P multi 1.30 .45
*a.* Booklet pane of 10, 2 each #2758-2762 13.00
**2763** A1109 $1.20 multi 1.80 .90
*a.* Booklet pane of 6 10.75
**2764** A1109 $2.50 multi 3.75 2.00
*a.* Booklet pane of 6 22.50
*Nos. 2758-2764 (7)* 12.05 5.15

On day of issue, Nos. 2756a-2756b, 2757a-2757c, 2758-2762 each sold for 85c.

Hank Snow (1914-99), Country Music Recording Artist — A1151

Renée Martel, Country Music Recording Artist — A1152

Shania Twain, Country Music Recording Artist — A1153

Tommy Hunter, Country Music Recording Artist — A1154

K. D. Lang, Country Music Recording Artist — A1155

**2014, July 31 Litho. *Perf. 12½***
**2765** Sheet of 5 6.50 6.50
*a.* A1151 P multi 1.30 1.10
*b.* A1152 P multi 1.30 1.10
*c.* A1153 P multi 1.30 1.10
*d.* A1154 P multi 1.30 1.10
*e.* A1155 P multi 1.30 1.10

**Booklet Stamps**
**Self-Adhesive**
***Serpentine Die Cut 13¼***
**2766** A1151 P multi 1.30 .35
*a.* Booklet pane of 10 13.00
**2767** A1152 P multi 1.30 .35
*a.* Booklet pane of 10 13.00
**2768** A1153 P multi 1.30 .35
*a.* Booklet pane of 10 13.00
**2769** A1154 P multi 1.30 .35
*a.* Booklet pane of 10 13.00
**2770** A1155 P multi 1.30 .35
*a.* Booklet pane of 10 13.00
*Nos. 2766-2770 (5)* 6.50 1.75

On day of issue, Nos. 2765a-2765e, 2766-2770 each sold for 85c.

Canadian Museum for Human Rights, Winnipeg A1156

***Serpentine Die Cut 13¼***
**2014, Aug. 20 Litho.**

**Booklet Stamp**
**Self-Adhesive**
**2771** A1156 P multi 1.30 .35
*a.* Booklet pane of 10 13.00

No. 2771 sold for 85c on day of issue.

Comedians A1157

Designs: Nos. 2772a, 2773, Mike Myers. Nos. 2772b, 2774, Martin Short. Nos. 2772c, 2775, Catherine O'Hara. Nos. 2772d, 2776, Olivier Guimond (1914-71). Nos. 2772e, 2777, Jim Carrey.

**2014, Aug. 29 Litho. *Perf. 12½x13***
**2772** Sheet of 5 + label 6.50 6.50
*a.-e.* A1157 P Any single 1.30 1.10

**Booklet Stamps**
**Self-Adhesive**
***Serpentine Die Cut 13¼***
**2773** A1157 P multi 1.30 .35
*a.* Booklet pane of 10, #2774-2777, 6#2773 13.00
**2774** A1157 P multi 1.30 .35
*a.* Booklet pane of 10, #2773, 2775-2777, 6#2774 13.00
**2775** A1157 P multi 1.30 .35
*a.* Booklet pane of 10, #2773-2774, 2776-2777, 6#2775 13.00
**2776** A1157 P multi 1.30 .35
*a.* Booklet pane of 10, #2773-2775, 2777, 6#2776 13.00
**2777** A1157 P multi 1.30 .35
*a.* Booklet pane of 10, #2773-2776, 6#2777 13.00
*Nos. 2773-2777 (5)* 6.50 1.75

On day of issue, Nos. 2772a-2772e, 2773-2777 each sold for 85c.

Zamboni With Canadian National Hockey League Team Emblems — A1158

Zamboni with emblem of: Nos. 2778a, 2779, Winnipeg Jets. Nos. 2778b, 2780, Ottawa Senators. Nos. 2778c, 2781, Toronto Maple Leafs. Nos. 2778d, 2782, Montreal Canadiens. Nos. 2778e, 2783, Vancouver Canucks. Nos. 2778f, 2784, Calgary Flames. Nos. 2778g, 2785, Edmonton Oilers.

**2014, Oct. 3 Litho. *Perf. 13¼x13***
**Miniature Sheet**
**2778** Sheet of 7 9.00 9.00
*a.-g.* A1158 P Any single 1.30 1.10

**Coil Stamps**
**Self-Adhesive**
***Serpentine Die Cut 8¼ Horiz.***
**2779** A1158 P multi 1.30 .55
**2780** A1158 P multi 1.30 .55
**2781** A1158 P multi 1.30 .55
**2782** A1158 P multi 1.30 .55
**2783** A1158 P multi 1.30 .55
**2784** A1158 P multi 1.30 .55
**2785** A1158 P multi 1.30 .55
*Nos. 2779-2785 (7)* 9.10 3.85

On day of issue, Nos. 2778a-2778g, 2779-2785 each sold for 85c.

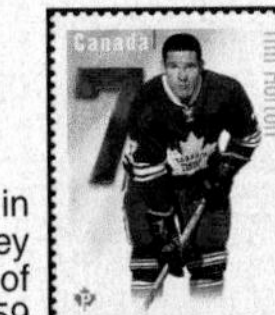


Defensemen in National Hockey League Hall of Fame — A1159

Designs: Nos. 2786a, 2787a, 2788, Tim Horton (1930-74). Nos. 2786b, 2787b, 2789, Doug Harvey. Nos. 2786c, 2787c, 2790, Bobby Orr. Nos. 2786d, 2787d, 2791, Harry Howell. Nos. 2786e, 2787e, 2792, Pierre Pilote. Nos. 2786f, 2787f, 2793, Red Kelly.

**Litho., Sheet Margin Litho. & Embossed With Foil Application**
**2014, Oct. 3 *Perf. 12½x13***
**Miniature Sheet**
**2786** Sheet of 6 7.75 7.75
*a.-f.* A1159 P Any single 1.30 1.10

**Litho.**
**Booklet Stamps**
**Self-Adhesive**
***Serpentine Die Cut 13¼x13½***
**2787** Booklet pane of 6 8.00
*a.-f.* A1159 P Any single 1.35 .30

**Souvenir Sheets**
***Serpentine Die Cut 13½x13¼***
**2788** A1159 $2.50 multi 3.75 3.00
**2789** A1159 $2.50 multi 3.75 3.00
**2790** A1159 $2.50 multi 3.75 3.00
**2791** A1159 $2.50 multi 3.75 3.00
**2792** A1159 $2.50 multi 3.75 3.00
**2793** A1159 $2.50 multi 3.75 3.00
*Nos. 2788-2793 (6)* 22.50 18.00

Nos. 2786a-2786f, 2787a-2787f each sold for 85c on day of issue. Nos. 2788-2793 each contain one 52x78mm stamp. Nos, 2788-2793 were sold together in a sealed opaque plastic package. One of every 50 packages contained a souvenir sheet that was autographed by one of the 5 living players depicted.

"Wait for Me Daddy," Photograph by Claude P. Dettloff — A1160

**2014, Oct. 4 Litho. *Perf. 13½x13¼***
**2794** A1160 P multi 1.30 .75

**Booklet Stamp**
**Self-Adhesive**
***Serpentine Die Cut 13¼x13½***
**2795** A1160 P multi 1.30 .35
*a.* Booklet pane of 10 13.00

Dedication of statue depicting photograph in New Westminster, British Columbia. Nos. 2794 and 2795 each sold for 85c on day of issue. No. 2794 was printed in sheets of 5.

Santa Claus A1161

The Virgin and Child with St. John the Baptist, by Abraham Janssens van Nuyssen A1162

Santa Claus: P, Writing letter. $1.20, Carrying sack. $2.50, With dove.

**2014, Oct. 23 Litho. *Perf. 13½x13¼***
**Souvenir Sheet**
**2796** Sheet of 3 7.00 7.00
*a.* A1161 P multi 1.30 1.10
*b.* A1161 $1.20 multi 1.80 1.50
*c.* A1161 $2.50 multi 3.75 3.25

**Booklet Stamps**
**Self-Adhesive**
***Serpentine Die Cut 13½***
**2797** A1162 P multi 1.30 .25
*a.* Booklet pane of 12 15.50

***Serpentine Die Cut 13¼x13***
**2798** A1161 P multi 1.30 .25
*a.* Booklet pane of 12 15.50
**2799** A1161 $1.20 multi 1.80 .75
*a.* Booklet pane of 6 10.75
**2800** A1161 $2.50 multi 3.75 1.30
*a.* Booklet pane of 6 22.50
*Nos. 2797-2800 (4)* 8.15 2.55

Christmas. Nos. 2796a, 2797 and 2798 each sold for 85c on day of issue.

New Year 2015 (Year of the Ram) — A1163

Design: $2.50, Ram facing left.

**Litho. & Embossed With Foil Application**

**2015, Jan. 8** *Perf. 12½*

**2801** A1163 P multi 1.30 .55

**Souvenir Sheet**

**2802** A1163 $2.50 multi 3.75 3.75
*a.* Souvenir sheet of 2, #2700, 2802 6.50 6.50
*b.* Perf. 13¼ (#2885a) 3.75 3.75

**Litho. With Foil Application**

**Booklet Stamp**
**Self-Adhesive**

***Serpentine Die Cut 13½***

**2803** A1163 $2.50 multi 3.75 2.00
*a.* Booklet pane of 6 22.50

No. 2801 sold for 85c on day of issue.
Issued: No. 2802b, 2/1/16.
See Nos. 3259h, 3260h, 3268.

Sir John A. Macdonald (1815-91), First Prime Minister of Canada — A1164

***Serpentine Die Cut 13¼***

**2015, Jan. 11** **Litho.**

**Self-Adhesive**
**Booklet Stamp**

**2804** A1164 P multi 1.30 .35
*a.* Booklet pane of 10 13.00

No. 2804 sold for 85c on day of issue.

Nelson Mandela (1918-2013), President of South Africa — A1165

**2015, Jan. 30** **Litho.** *Perf. 12½x13*

**Souvenir Sheet**

**2805** A1165 $2.50 multi 3.75 3.50

**Booklet Stamp**
**Self-Adhesive**
**Size: 33x33mm**

***Serpentine Die Cut 13¼***

**2806** A1165 P multi 1.30 .35
*a.* Booklet pane of 10 13.00

No. 2806 sold for 85c on day of issue.

A1166

Canadian Flag, 50th Anniv. — A1167

***Serpentine Die Cut 13¼x13½***

**2015, Feb. 15** **Litho.**

**Booklet Stamp**
**Self-Adhesive**

**2807** A1166 P multi 1.30 .35
*a.* Booklet pane of 10 13.00

**Souvenir Sheet**
**On Rayon Fabric**

***Serpentine Die Cut 9½***

**2808** A1167 $5 multi 7.50 7.50

No. 2807 sold for 85c on day of issue.

A1168

Pansies — A1169

Designs: Nos. 2809a, 2810, 2812, Delta Premium Pure Light Blue pansy (blue and yellow flower). No. 2809b, 2811, 2813, Midnight Glow pansy (purple and yellow flower).

**2015, Mar. 2** **Litho.** *Perf. 13x13¼*

**Souvenir Sheet**

**2809** Sheet of 2 2.60 2.60
*a.-b.* A1168 P Either single 1.30 1.10

**Coil Stamps**
**Self-Adhesive**

***Serpentine Die Cut 8¼ Horiz.***

**2810** A1169 P multi 1.30 .45
**2811** A1169 P multi 1.30 .45
*a.* Vert. pair, #2810-2811 2.60

**Booklet Stamps**

***Serpentine Die Cut 13½***

**2812** A1168 P multi 1.30 .35
**2813** A1168 P multi 1.30 .35
*a.* Booklet pane of 10, 5 each #2812-2813 13.00

On day of issue Nos. 2809a-2809b, 2810-2813 each sold for 85c.

**Photography Type of 2013**

Designs: Nos. 2814a, 2820, Shoeshine Stand, by Nina Raginsky, 1974. Nos. 2814b, 2817, Southan Sisters, Montreal, by Harold Mortimer-Lamb, c. 1915-19, horiz. Nos. 2814c, 2822, La Voie Lactée, by Geneviève Cadieux, 1992, horiz. Nos. 2815a, 2816, Angels, Saint-Jean-Baptiste Day, by Sam Tata, 1962, horiz. Nos. 2815b, 2819, Isaac's First Swim, Lambton County, Ontario, Canada, by Larry Towell, 1996, horiz. Nos. 2815c, 2818, Friends and Family and Trips. In Front of Simpsons, by Conrad Poirier, 1936, horiz. Nos. 2815d, 2821, Alex Colville on the Tantramar Marshes, by Geoffrey James, c. 1970, horiz.

**2015, Apr. 8** **Litho.** *Perf. 12¾*

**2814** A1109 Sheet of 3 6.25 6.25
*a.-b.* P Either single 1.30 1.10
*c.* $2.50 multi 3.75 3.75
**2815** A1109 Sheet of 4 5.75 5.75
*a.-c.* P Any single 1.30 1.10
*d.* $1.20 multi 1.80 1.50

**Booklet Stamps**
**Self-Adhesive**

***Serpentine Die Cut 13¼***

**2816** A1109 P multi 1.30 .55
**2817** A1109 P multi 1.30 .55
**2818** A1109 P multi 1.30 .55
**2819** A1109 P multi 1.30 .55
**2820** A1109 P multi 1.30 .55
*a.* Booklet pane of 10, 2 each #2816-2820 13.00
**2821** A1109 $1.20 multi 1.80 1.10
*a.* Booklet pane of 6 11.00
**2822** A1109 $2.50 multi 3.75 2.25
*a.* Booklet pane of 6 22.50
*Nos. 2816-2822 (7)* 12.05 6.10

On day of issue, Nos. 2814a-2814b, 2815a-2815c, 2816-2820 each sold for 85c.

Dinosaurs — A1170

Designs: Nos. 2823a, 2827, Euplocephalus tutus (33x28mm). Nos. 2823b, 2826, Chasmosaurus belli (28x28mm). Nos. 2823c, 2824, Tyrannosaurus rex. Nos. 2823d, 2828, Ornithomimus edmontonicus. Nos. 2823e, 2825, Tylosaurus pembinensis.

**Litho. & Embossed With Foil Application**

***Serpentine Die Cut 13¼***

**2015, Apr. 3** **Self-Adhesive**

**2823** Sheet of 5 6.50 6.50
*a.-e.* A1170 P Any single 1.30 1.10

**Booklet Stamps**

**Litho. With Foil Application**

**2824** A1170 P multi 1.30 .55
**2825** A1170 P multi 1.30 .55
**2826** A1170 P multi 1.30 .55
**2827** A1170 P multi 1.30 .55
**2828** A1170 P multi 1.30 .55
*a.* Booklet pane of 10, 2 each #2824-2828 13.00

On day of issue, Nos. 2823a-2823e, 2824-2828 each sold for 85c.

Love Your Pet — A1171

Designs: Nos. 2829a, 2830, Cat in head cone sniffing flowers. Nos. 2829b, 2831, Dog chasing snowball. Nos. 2829c, 2832, Veterinarian examining cat. Nos. 2829d, 2834, Dog drinking water from bowl. Nos. 2829e, 2833, Cat on leash wearing identification tags.

**2015, May 2** **Litho.** *Perf. 13*

**2829** Sheet of 5 6.50 6.50
*a.-e.* A1171 P Any single 1.30 1.10

**Booklet Stamps**
**Self-Adhesive**

***Serpentine Die Cut 13¼***

**2830** A1171 P multi 1.30 .55
**2831** A1171 P multi 1.30 .55
**2832** A1171 P multi 1.30 .55
**2833** A1171 P multi 1.30 .55
**2834** A1171 P multi 1.30 .55
*a.* Booklet pane of 10, 2 each #2830-2834 13.00
*Nos. 2830-2834 (5)* 6.50 2.75

On day of issue, Nos. 2829a-2829e, 2830-2834 each sold for 85c.

*In Flanders Fields*, Poem by John McCrae, Cent. — A1172

**2015, May 3** **Litho.** *Perf. 12½*

**2835** A1172 P multi 1.30 .75

**Booklet Stamp**
**Self-Adhesive**

***Serpentine Die Cut 13¼x13½***

**2836** A1172 P multi 1.30 .35
*a.* Booklet pane of 10 13.00

On day of issue, Nos. 2835-2836 each sold for 85c. No. 2835 was printed in sheets of 5.

2015 Women's World Cup Soccer Championships, Canada — A1173

***Serpentine Die Cut 13¼x13½***

**2015, May 6** **Litho.**

**Booklet Stamp**
**Self-Adhesive**

**2837** A1173 P multi 1.30 .35
*a.* Booklet pane of 10 13.00

No. 2837 sold for 85c on day of issue.

Weather Phenomena — A1174

Designs: Nos. 2838a, 2839, Lightning. Nos. 2838b, 2842, Double rainbow. Nos. 2838c, 2843, Sun dog over Iqaluit, Nunavut. Nos. 2838d, 2841, Fog near Cape Spear Lighthouse. Nos. 2838e, 2840, Hoar frost on tree.

*Perf. 12½x13¼*

**2015, June 18** **Litho.**

**2838** A1174 Sheet of 5 + label 6.50 6.50
*a.-e.* P Any single 1.30 1.10

**Booklet Stamps**
**Self-Adhesive**

***Serpentine Die Cut 13¼***

**2839** A1174 P multi 1.30 .55
**2840** A1174 P multi 1.30 .55
**2841** A1174 P multi 1.30 .55
**2842** A1174 P multi 1.30 .55
**2843** A1174 P multi 1.30 .55
*a.* Booklet pane of 10, 2 each #2839-2843 13.00

Nos. 2838a-2838e, 2839-2843 each sold for 85c on day of issue.

Hoodoos, Alberta — A1175

Wood Buffalo National Park, Alberta and Northwest Territories A1176

Red Bay Basque Whaling Station, Newfoundland and Labrador A1177

Waterton Glacier International Peace Park, Alberta and Montana A1178

Kluane National Park, Yukon, Wrangell-St. Elias and Glacier Bay National Parks, Alaska, Tatshenshini-Alsek Park, British Columbia — A1179

**2015, July 3** **Litho.** *Perf. 12½*

**2844** Sheet of 5 *75.00 75.00*
*a.* A1175 $1.20 multi *60.00 30.00*
*b.* A1176 $1.20 multi 1.80 1.25
*c.* A1177 $1.20 multi 1.80 1.50
*d.* A1178 $2.50 multi 3.75 3.00
*e.* A1179 $2.50 multi 3.75 3.00

**Booklet Stamps**
**Self-Adhesive**

***Serpentine Die Cut 13¼***

**2845** A1175 $1.20 multi *22.50 19.00*
**2846** A1177 $1.20 multi 1.80 1.50
**2847** A1176 $1.20 multi 1.80 1.50
*a.* Booklet pane of 6, 2 each #2845-2847 *55.00*
**2848** A1178 $2.50 multi 3.75 2.10
**2849** A1179 $2.50 multi 3.75 2.10
*a.* Booklet pane of 6, 3 each #2848-2849 22.50

UNESCO World Heritage Sites. Nos. 2844 and 2847a were withdrawn from sale on July 6 after it was discovered that illustration A1175 shows hoodoos not located in Dinosaur Provincial Park in Alberta. See Nos. 2857-2858.

Alice Munro, 2013 Nobel Literature Laureate — A1180

***Serpentine Die Cut 13¾***

**2015, July 10** **Litho.**

**Booklet Stamp**
**Self-Adhesive**

**2850** A1180 P multi 1.30 .35
*a.* Booklet pane of 10 13.00

No. 2850 sold for 85c on day of issue.

HMS Erebus Trapped in Ice A1181

Map of Northern Canadian Islands A1182

Wreckage and Diagram of HMS Erebus — A1183

**Litho & Embossed, Litho (A1183)**

**2015, Aug. 6** *Perf. 12½*

**2851** A1181 P multi 1.30 .60
**2852** A1182 P multi 1.30 .60
*a.* Horiz. pair, #2851-2852 2.60 1.25

**Souvenir Sheet**

*Perf. 13¼*

**2853** A1183 $2.50 multi 3.75 3.75

**Booklet Stamps Self-Adhesive**

*Serpentine Die Cut 13½x13¼*

**2854** A1181 P multi 1.30 .35
**2855** A1182 P multi 1.30 .35
*a.* Booklet pane of 10, 5 each #2854-2855 13.00

*Serpentine Die Cut 13¼x13¾*

**2856** A1183 $2.50 multi 3.75 2.00
*a.* Booklet pane of 6 22.50
*Nos. 2854-2856 (3)* 6.35 2.70

Discovery of wreckage of HMS Erebus, 1st anniv. Nos. 2851-2852, 2854-2855 each sold for 85c on day of issue.

Dinosaur Provincial Park, Alberta — A1184

**2015, Aug. 21 Litho.** *Perf. 12½*

**2857** Sheet of 5, #2844b-2844e, 2857a 13.00 13.00
*a.* A1184 $1.20 multi 1.80 .95

**Booklet Stamp Self-Adhesive**

**2858** A1184 $1.20 multi 1.80 1.10
*a.* Booklet pane of 6, 2 each #2846, 2847, 2858 11.00

UNESCO World Heritage Sites. Nos. 2857a and 2858 show correct images of landscapes in Dinosaur Provincial Park.

Queen Elizabeth II, Longest-Reigning British Monarch A1185

*Serpentine Die Cut 13¼*

**2015, Sept. 9 Litho.**

**Booklet Stamp Self-Adhesive**

**2859** A1185 P multi 1.30 .35
*a.* Booklet pane of 10 13.00

No. 2859 sold for 85c on day of issue.

Haunted Canada A1186

Designs: Nos. 2860a, 2861, Brakeman ghost, Vancouver, British Columbia. Nos. 2860b, 2864, Red River Trail Oxcart, Winnipeg, Manitoba. Nos. 2860c, 2863, Gray Lady of the Citadel, Halifax, Nova Scotia. Nos. 2860d, 2862, Ghost of Marie-Josephte Corriveau, Lévis, Quebec. Nos. 2860e, 2865, Ghost of Caribou Hotel, Carcross, Yukon.

**Litho. With Holographic Foil**

**2015, Sept. 14** *Perf. 12½x13*

**2860** A1186 Sheet of 5 6.50 6.50
*a.-e.* P Any single 1.30 1.10

**Booklet Stamps Self-Adhesive**

*Serpentine Die Cut 13¼*

**2861** A1186 P multi 1.30 .55
**2862** A1186 P multi 1.30 .55
**2863** A1186 P multi 1.30 .55
**2864** A1186 P multi 1.30 .55
**2865** A1186 P multi 1.30 .55
*a.* Booklet pane of 10, 2 each #2861-2865 13.00
*Nos. 2861-2865 (5)* 6.50 2.75

On day of issue, Nos. 2860a-2860e, 2861-2865 each sold for 85c.

A1187

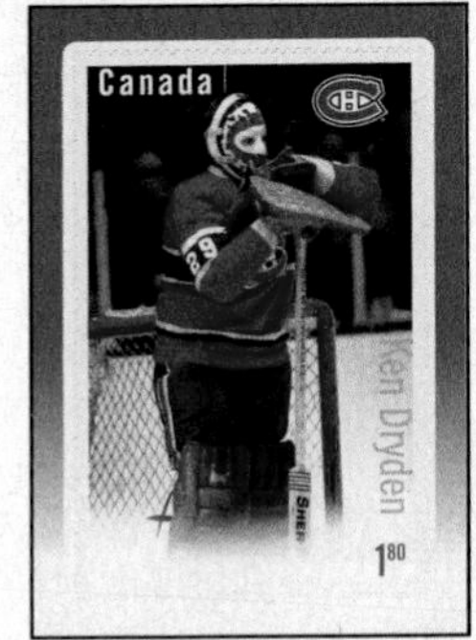

Hockey Goaltenders — A1188

Designs: Nos. 2866a, 2867, 2873, Ken Dryden. Nos. 2866b, 2868, 2874, Tony Esposito. Nos. 2866c, 2869, 2875, Johnny Bower. Nos. 2866d, 2870, 2876, Gump Worsley (1929-2007). Nos. 2866e, 2871, 2877, Bernie Parent. Nos. 2866f, 2872, 2878, Martin Brodeur.

**Litho., Sheet Margin Litho. & Embossed With Foil Application**

**2015, Oct. 2** *Perf. 12½*

**2866** Sheet of 6 + 3 labels 7.75 7.75
*a.-f.* A1187 P Any single 1.30 1.10

**Booklet Stamps Self-Adhesive Litho.**

*Serpentine Die Cut 13¼x13½*

**2867** A1187 P multi 1.30 .55
**2868** A1187 P multi 1.30 .55
**2869** A1187 P multi 1.30 .55
**2870** A1187 P multi 1.30 .55
**2871** A1187 P multi 1.30 .55
**2872** A1187 P multi 1.30 .55
*a.* Booklet pane of 6, #2867-2872 7.75
*Nos. 2867-2872 (6)* 7.80 3.30

**Souvenir Sheets**

*Serpentine Die Cut 13½x13¼*

**2873** A1188 $1.80 multi 2.70 2.25
**2874** A1188 $1.80 multi 2.70 2.25
**2875** A1188 $1.80 multi 2.70 2.25
**2876** A1188 $1.80 multi 2.70 2.25
**2877** A1188 $1.80 multi 2.70 2.25
**2878** A1188 $1.80 multi 2.70 2.25
*Nos. 2873-2878 (6)* 16.20 13.50

Nos. 2866a-2866f, 2867-2872 each sold for 85c on day of issue. Nos. 2873-2878 each contain one 52x78mm stamp. Nos. 2873-2878 were sold together in a sealed opaque plastic package. One of every 40 packages contained a souvenir sheet signed by Esposito, Bower, Parent or Brodeur.

Christmas — A1190

A1189

Designs: Nos. 2879a, 2881, Moose. Nos. 2879b, 2882, Beaver. Nos. 2879c, 2883, Polar bear. No. 2880, Adoration of the Magi, by Adriaen Isenbrandt.

**2015, Nov. 2 Litho.** *Perf. 13¾x13¼*

**2879** A1189 Sheet of 3 6.75 6.75
*a.* P multi 1.30 1.10
*b.* $1.20 multi 1.80 1.60
*c.* $2.50 multi 3.75 3.25

**Booklet Stamps Self-Adhesive**

*Serpentine Die Cut 13¼x13½*

**2880** A1190 P multi 1.30 .25
*a.* Booklet pane of 12 15.50

*Serpentine Die Cut 13¼x13*

**2881** A1189 P multi 1.30 .25
*a.* Booklet pane of 12 15.50
**2882** A1189 $1.20 multi 1.80 .95
*a.* Booklet pane of 6 11.00
**2883** A1189 $2.50 multi 3.75 1.50
*a.* Booklet pane of 6 22.50
*Nos. 2880-2883 (4)* 8.15 2.95

Nos. 2879a, 2880 and 2881 each sold for 85c on day of issue.

New Year 2016 (Year of the Monkey) — A1191

Design: $2.50, Monkey's head.

**Litho. & Embossed With Foil Application**

**2016** *Perf. 13¼*

**2884** A1191 P multi 1.30 .55

**Souvenir Sheet**

**2885** A1191 $2.50 multi 3.75 3.75
*a.* Souvenir sheet of 2, #2802b, 2885 7.50 7.50
*b.* Perf. 12½ (#2960a) 3.75 3.50

**Litho.**

**Booklet Stamps Self-Adhesive**

*Serpentine Die Cut 13½*

**2886** A1191 P multi 1.30 .45
*a.* Booklet pane of 10 13.00
**2887** A1191 $2.50 multi 3.75 2.25
*a.* Booklet pane of 6 22.50

Issued: Nos. 2884, 2886, 1/11; Nos. 2885, 2887, 2/1. No. 2885a, 1/9/17. No. 2885b, 1/9/17. Nos. 2884 and 2886 each sold for 85c on day of issue.

See Nos. 3259i, 3260i, 3269.

Queen Elizabeth II — A1192

*Serpentine Die Cut 13½x13¾*

**2016, Jan. 11 Litho.**

**Booklet Stamp Self-Adhesive**

**2888** A1192 P multi 1.30 .25
*a.* Booklet pane of 10 13.00

No. 2888 sold for 85c on day of issue.

Landscape of Grand Pré, Nova Scotia A1193

Rideau Canal, Ontario A1194

SGang Gwaay, British Columbia — A1195

Head-Smashed-In Buffalo Jump, Alberta — A1196

Old Town Lunenburg, Nova Scotia — A1197

**2016, Jan. 11 Litho.** *Perf. 13¼x13*

**Souvenir Sheet**

**2889** Sheet of 5 6.50 6.50
*a.* A1193 P multi 1.30 1.10
*b.* A1194 P multi 1.30 1.10
*c.* A1195 P multi 1.30 1.10
*d.* A1196 P multi 1.30 1.10
*e.* A1197 P multi 1.30 1.10

**Booklet Stamps Self-Adhesive**

*Serpentine Die Cut 13¾x13½*

**2890** A1193 P multi 1.30 .25
**2891** A1195 P multi 1.30 .25
**2892** A1197 P multi 1.30 .25
**2893** A1194 P multi 1.30 .25
**2894** A1196 P multi 1.30 .25
*a.* Booklet pane of 10, 2 each #2890-2894 13.00
*b.* Booklet pane of 30, 6 each #2890-2894 37.50

UNESCO World Heritage Sites. On day of issue, Nos. 2889a-2889e, 2890-2894 each sold for 85c.

Organization of No. 2 Construction Battalion (First Black Battalion), Cent. — A1198

*Serpentine Die Cut 13½*

**2016, Feb. 1 Litho.**

**Booklet Stamp Self-Adhesive**

**2895** A1198 P multi 1.30 .50
*a.* Booklet pane of 10 13.00

No. 2895 sold for 85c on day of issue.

A1199

Hydrangeas — A1200

Designs: Nos. 2896a, 2897, 2899, Hydrangea macrophylla. Nos. 2896b, 2898, 2900, Hydrangea arborescens.

**2016, Mar. 1 Litho.** *Perf. 13*

**Souvenir Sheet**

**2896** Sheet of 2 2.60 2.60
*a.-b.* A1199 P Either single 1.30 1.10

**Coil Stamps Self-Adhesive**

*Serpentine Die Cut 8¼ Vert.*

**2897** A1200 P multi 1.30 .45
**2898** A1200 P multi 1.30 .45
*a.* Horiz. pair, #2897-2898 2.60

**Booklet Stamps**

*Serpentine Die Cut 13¼*

**2899** A1199 P multi 1.30 .45
**2900** A1199 P multi 1.30 .45
*a.* Booklet pane of 10, 5 each #2899-2900 13.00
*Nos. 2897-2900 (4)* 5.20 1.80

On day of issue, Nos. 2896a-2896b, 2897-2900 each sold for 85c.

Woman Suffrage, Cent. — A1201

***Serpentine Die Cut 13½x13¾***

**2016, Mar. 8 Self-Adhesive Litho.**

**Booklet Stamp**

**2901** A1201 P gold & black 1.30 .45
*a.* Booklet pane of 10 13.00

No. 2901 sold for 85c on day of issue.

**Photography Type of 2013**

Designs: Nos. 2902a, 2904, Toronto, by Lutz Dille, 1960, horiz. Nos. 2902b, 2905, Window, by Angela Grauerholz, 1988, horiz. Nos. 2902c, 2907, Victoria Bridge, Grand Trunk Railway, by Alexander Henderson, c. 1878, horiz. Nos. 2902d, 2906, Freighter's Boat on the Banks of the Red River, Manitoba, by Humphrey Lloyd Hime, 1858, horiz. Nos. 2903a, 2908, Sans Titre 0310/La Chambre Noire, by Michel Campeau, 2005-10, vert. Nos. 2903b, 2909, Climbing Mt. Habel, by Byron Harmon, c. 1909, horiz. Nos. 2903c, 2910, Grey Owl, by Yousuf Karsh, 1936, vert.

**2016, Apr. 13 Litho. *Perf. 12¾***

**2902** A1109 Sheet of 4 5.25 5.25
*a.-d.* P Any single 1.30 1.30
**2903** A1109 Sheet of 3 7.00 7.00
*a.* P multi 1.30 1.10
*b.* $1.20 multi 1.80 1.50
*c.* $2.50 multi 3.75 3.00

**Booklet Stamps Self-Adhesive**

***Serpentine Die Cut 13¼***

**2904** A1109 P sil & multi 1.30 .55
**2905** A1109 P sil & multi 1.30 .55
**2906** A1109 P sil & multi 1.30 .55
**2907** A1109 P sil & multi 1.30 .55
**2908** A1109 P sil & multi 1.30 .55
*a.* Booklet pane of 10, 2 each #2904-2908 13.00
**2909** A1109 $1.20 sil & multi 1.80 1.10
*a.* Booklet pane of 6 10.75
**2910** A1109 $2.50 sil & multi 3.75 2.25
*a.* Booklet pane of 6 22.50
*Nos. 2904-2910 (7)* 12.05 6.10

On day of issue, Nos. 2902a-2902d, 2903a, 2904-2908 each sold for 85c.

U.S.S. Enterprise NCC-1701 A1202

Klingon Battle Cruiser A1203

Captain James T. Kirk — A1204

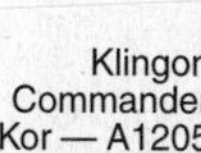

Klingon Commander Kor — A1205

Dr. Leonard "Bones" McCoy A1206

Lieutenant Commander Montgomery "Scotty" Scott — A1207

Commander Spock — A1208

Characters From *Star Trek* Television Series — A1209

No. 2922: a, McCoy, Kirk, Spock and Scott in transporter room. b, Spock, Kirk and planet.

**2016, May 5 Litho. *Perf. 13¼x13***

**2911** Sheet of 2 2.60 2.60
*a.* A1202 P multi 1.30 1.10
*b.* A1203 P multi 1.30 1.10

***Perf. 13¼***

**2912** Sheet of 5 11.00 11.00
*a.* A1204 P multi 1.30 1.10
*b.* A1205 $1 multi 1.50 1.30
*c.* A1206 $1.20 multi 1.80 1.60
*d.* A1207 $1.80 multi 2.70 2.40
*e.* A1208 $2.50 multi 3.75 3.50
*f.* Booklet pane of 4 #2912a 5.25 5.25
*g.* Booklet pane of 3, #2912c, 2912d, 2912e 8.25 8.25
*h.* Booklet pane of 1 #2912b 1.50 1.30
*i.* Booklet pane of 5, #2912a-2912e 11.00 11.00

**Coil Stamps Self-Adhesive**

***Serpentine Die Cut 8¼ Horiz.***

**2913** A1202 P multi 1.30 .55
**2914** A1203 P multi 1.30 .55
*a.* Vert. pair, #2913-2914 2.60

**Booklet Stamps**

***Serpentine Die Cut 13¾***

**2915** A1202 P multi 3.00 3.00
**2916** A1203 P multi 3.00 3.00
*a.* Booklet pane of 2, #2915-2916 6.00
Complete booklet, #2912f, 2912g, 2912h, 2912i, 2916a 30.00

***Serpentine Die Cut 13¼x13¼***

**2917** A1204 P multi 1.30 .55
**2918** A1207 P multi 1.30 .55
**2919** A1205 P multi 1.30 .55
**2920** A1208 P multi 1.30 .55
**2921** A1206 P multi 1.30 .55
*a.* Booklet pane of 10, 2 each #2917-2921 13.00
*Nos. 2915-2921 (7)* 12.50 8.75

**Souvenir Sheet**

**Litho. With Three-Dimensional Plastic Affixed**

***Perf. 14¾***

**2922** A1209 Sheet of 2 15.00 15.00
*a.-b.* $5 Either single 7.50 7.50

*Star Trek* television series, 50th anniv. Nos. 2911a, 2911b, 2912a, 2913, 2914, 2917-2921 each sold for 85c on day of issue. Complete booklet sold for $19.95. Nos. 2915-2916 each had a franking value of 85c on day of issue.

Dinosaurs A1210

Designs: Nos. 2923a, 2924, Troodon inequalis. Nos. 2923b, 2926, Dimetrodon borealis. Nos. 2923c, 2928, Comox Valley elasmosaur. Nos. 2923d, 2925, Cypretherium coarctatum. Nos. 2923e, 2927, Acrotholus audeti.

**2016, May 26 Litho. *Perf. 13***

**2923** Sheet of 5 6.50 6.50
*a.-e.* A1210 P Any single 1.30 1.10

**Booklet Stamps Self-Adhesive**

***Serpentine Die Cut 13¼***

**2924** A1210 P multi 1.30 .55
**2925** A1210 P multi 1.30 .55
**2926** A1210 P multi 1.30 .55
**2927** A1210 P multi 1.30 .55
**2928** A1210 P multi 1.30 .55
*a.* Booklet pane of 10, 2 each #2924-2928 13.00
*Nos. 2924-2928 (5)* 6.50 2.75

On day of issue, Nos. 2923a-2923e, 2924-2928 each sold for 85c.

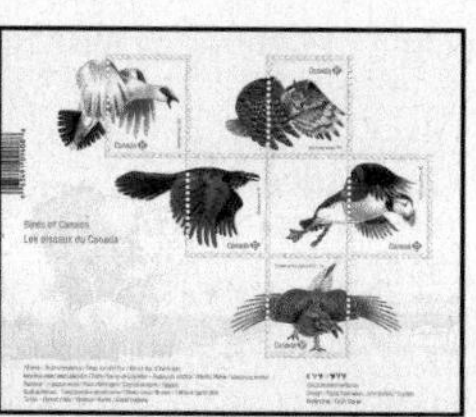

Birds A1211

Designs: Nos. 2929a, 2934, Lagopus muta. Nos. 2929b, 2931, Bubo virginianus. Nos. 2929c, 2933, Corvus corax. Nos. 2929d, 2932, Fratercula arctica. Nos. 2929e, 2930, Tympanuchus phasianellus.

**2016, July 12 Litho. *Perf. 13x13¼***

**2929** A1211 Sheet of 5 + label 6.50 6.50
*a.-e.* P Any single 1.30 1.10

**Booklet Stamps Self-Adhesive**

***Serpentine Die Cut 13½x13¾***

**2930** A1211 P multi 1.30 .55
**2931** A1211 P multi 1.30 .55
**2932** A1211 P multi 1.30 .55
**2933** A1211 P multi 1.30 .55
**2934** A1211 P multi 1.30 .55
*a.* Booklet pane of 10, 2 each #2930-2934 13.00
*Nos. 2930-2934 (5)* 6.50 2.75

On day of issue, Nos. 2929a-2929e, 2930-2934 each sold for 85c.

Haunted Canada A1212

Designs: Nos. 2935a, 2936, Bell Island Hag, Newfoundland and Labrador. Nos. 2935b, 2937, Dungarvon Whooper, New Brunswick. Nos. 2935c, 2939, Ghost of the Winter Garden Theater, Toronto, Ontario. Nos. 2935d, 2938, Lady in White of Montmorency Falls, Quebec. Nos. 2935e, 2940, Phantom Bell Ringers of the Kirk of St. James, Charlottetown, Prince Edward Island.

**Litho. With Holographic Foil**

**2016, Sept. 8 *Perf. 13***

**2935** A1212 Sheet of 5 6.50 6.50
*a.-e.* P Any single 1.30 1.10

**Booklet Stamps Self-Adhesive**

***Serpentine Die Cut 13½***

**2936** A1212 P multi 1.30 .55
**2937** A1212 P multi 1.30 .55
**2938** A1212 P multi 1.30 .55
**2939** A1212 P multi 1.30 .55
**2940** A1212 P multi 1.30 .55
*a.* Booklet pane of 10, 2 each #2936-2940 13.00
*Nos. 2936-2940 (5)* 6.50 2.75

On day of issue, Nos. 2935a-2935e, 2936-2940 each sold for 85c.

A1213

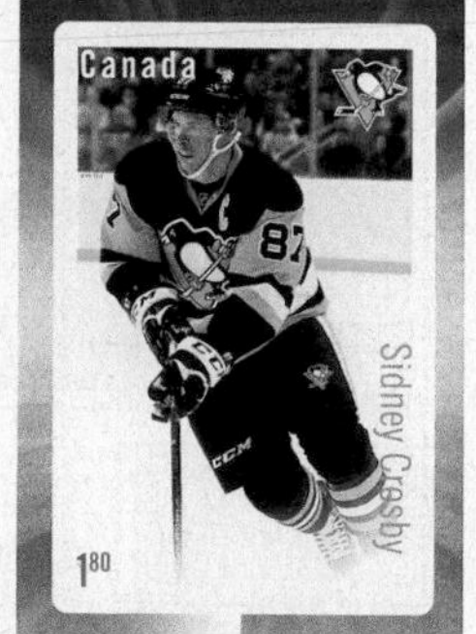


Hockey Forwards A1214

Designs: Nos. 2941a, 2942, 2948, Sidney Crosby. Nos. 2941b, 2943, 2949, Phil Esposito. Nos. 2941c, 2944, 2950, Guy Lafleur. Nos. 2941d, 2945, 2951, Steve Yzerman. Nos. 2941e, 2946, 2952, Mark Messier. Nos. 2941f, 2947, 2953, Darryl Sittler.

**Litho., Sheet Margin Litho. & Embossed With Foil Application**

**2016, Sept. 23 *Perf. 12½x13***

**2941** Sheet of 6 + 3 labels 7.75 7.75
*a.-f.* A1213 P Any single 1.30 1.10

**Booklet Stamps Self-Adhesive**

**Litho.**

***Serpentine Die Cut 13¼x13½***

**2942** A1213 P multi 1.30 .55
**2943** A1213 P multi 1.30 .55
**2944** A1213 P multi 1.30 .55
**2945** A1213 P multi 1.30 .55
**2946** A1213 P multi 1.30 .55
**2947** A1213 P multi 1.30 .55
*a.* Booklet pane of 6, #2942-2947 7.75
*Nos. 2942-2947 (6)* 7.80 3.30

**Souvenir Sheets**

***Serpentine Die Cut 13½x13¼***

**2948** A1214 $1.80 multi 2.70 2.40
**2949** A1214 $1.80 multi 2.70 2.40
**2950** A1214 $1.80 multi 2.70 2.40
**2951** A1214 $1.80 multi 2.70 2.40
**2952** A1214 $1.80 multi 2.70 2.40
**2953** A1214 $1.80 multi 2.70 2.40
*Nos. 2948-2953 (6)* 16.20 14.40

Nos. 2941a-2941f, 2942-2947 each sold for 85c on day of issue. Nos. 2948-2953 each contain one 52x78mm stamp. Nos. 2873-2878 were sold together in a sealed opaque plastic package. One of every 40 packages contained a souvenir sheet signed by Crosby, Esposito, Lafleur, Yzerman, Messier or Sittler.

A1215

Christmas — A1216

Designs: Nos. 2954a, 2956, Santa Claus and Christmas tree. Nos. 2954b, 2957, Stocking cap on Christmas tree. Nos. 2954c, 2958, Dove and Christmas tree. No. 2955, Virgin and Child, by Master of the Castello Nativity.

**2016, Nov. 1 Litho. *Perf. 12¾x12½***

**2954** Sheet of 3 6.75 6.75
*a.* A1215 P multi 1.30 1.10
*b.* A1215 $1.20 multi 1.80 1.60
*c.* A1215 $2.50 multi 3.75 3.50

**Booklet Stamps Self-Adhesive**

***Serpentine Die Cut 13¼x13½***

**2955** A1216 P multi 1.30 .25
*a.* Booklet pane of 12 15.50

***Serpentine Die Cut 13***

**2956** A1215 P multi 1.30 .25
*a.* Booklet pane of 12 15.50
**2957** A1215 $1.20 multi 1.80 .90
*a.* Booklet pane of 6 10.75
**2958** A1215 $2.50 multi 3.75 1.90
*a.* Booklet pane of 6 22.50
*Nos. 2955-2958 (4)* 8.15 3.30

Nos. 2954a, 2955 and 2956 each sold for 85c on day of issue.

New Year 2017 (Year of the Rooster) — A1217

Designs: P, Rooster. $2.50, Head of rooster.

**Litho. With Foil Application, Litho. (#2961)**

**2017, Jan. 9 *Perf. 12½x13¼***

**2959** A1217 P gold & multi 1.30 .55
*a.* Perf. 13¼x12½ 1.30 .55
*b.* Pair, #2959, 2959a 2.60 1.90

**Souvenir Sheet**

***Perf. 12½***

**2960** A1217 $2.50 gold & multi 3.75 3.75
*a.* Souvenir sheet of 2, #2885b, 2960 7.50 7.50

**Booklet Stamps Self-Adhesive**

***Serpentine Die Cut 13½***

**2961** A1217 P multi 1.30 .55
*a.* Booklet pane of 10 13.00
**2962** A1217 $2.50 gold & multi 3.75 2.25
*a.* Booklet pane of 6 22.50

Nos. 2959 and 2961 each sold for 85c on day of issue. On No. 2959b, one stamp of the pair is rotated 90 degrees in relation to the other stamp. Blocks of four contain stamps with four different orientations.

See Nos. 3259j, 3260j, 3270.

---

The tagging for all Canada stamps issued in 2017 will include the text "Canada 150."

Dinosaur Provincial Park, Alberta A1218

Mistaken Point, Newfoundland and Labrador A1219

Historic District of Old Quebec A1220

L'Anse aux Meadows National Historic Site, Newfoundland and Labrador A1221

Red Bay Basque Whaling Station, Newfoundland and Labrador — A1222

**2017, Jan. 16 Litho. *Perf. 13¼x13***

**2963** Sheet of 5 6.50 6.50
a. A1218 P multi 1.30 1.10
b. A1219 P multi 1.30 1.10
c. A1220 P multi 1.30 1.10
d. A1221 P multi 1.30 1.10
e. A1222 P multi 1.30 1.10

**Booklet Stamps**
**Self-Adhesive**
***Serpentine Die Cut 13***

**2964** A1218 P multi 1.30 .25
**2965** A1220 P multi 1.30 .25
**2966** A1222 P multi 1.30 .25
**2967** A1219 P multi 1.30 .25
**2968** A1221 P multi 1.30 .25
a. Booklet pane of 10, 2 each #2964-2968 13.00
b. Booklet pane of 30, 6 each #2964-2968 39.00
*Nos. 2964-2968 (5)* 6.50 1.25

UNESCO World Heritage Sites. Nos. 2963a-2963e, 2964-2968 each sold for 85c on day of issue.

A1223

Design: No. 2969, Mathieu Da Costa, First Recorded Person of African Descent in Canada.

***Serpentine Die Cut 13½***
**2017, Feb. 1 Self-Adhesive Litho.**
**Booklet Stamp**

**2969** A1223 P multi 1.30 .45
a. Booklet pane of 10 13.00

No. 2969 sold for 85c on day of issue.

Canadian Opera — A1224

Designs: Nos. 2970a, 2971, *Filumena*, by John Estacio and John Murrell. Nos. 2970b, 2972, Gerald Finley, baritone singer. Nos. 2970c, 2973, Adrianne Pieczonka, soprano singer. Nos. 2970d, 2974, Irving Guttman (1928-2014), operatic director. Nos. 2970e, 2975, *Louis Riel*, by Harry Somers, Mavor Moore and Jacques Languirand.

**2017, Feb. 4 Litho. *Perf. 13¼***

**2970** A1224 Sheet of 5 6.50 6.50
a.-e. P Any single 1.30 1.10

**Booklet Stamps**
**Self-Adhesive**
***Serpentine Die Cut 13½***

**2971** A1224 P multi 1.30 .55
**2972** A1224 P multi 1.30 .55
**2973** A1224 P multi 1.30 .55
**2974** A1224 P multi 1.30 .55
**2975** A1224 P multi 1.30 .55
a. Booklet pane of 10, 2 each #2971-2975 13.00
*Nos. 2971-2975 (5)* 6.50 2.75

On day of issue, Nos. 2970a-2970e, 2971-2975 each sold for 85c.

Daisies
A1225 A1226

Designs: Nos. 2976a, 2977, 2979, Erigeron speciosus (purple petals). Nos. 2976b, 2978, 2980, Tetraneuris herbacea (yellow petals).

**2017, Mar. 1 Litho. *Perf. 13***
**Souvenir Sheet**

**2976** Sheet of 2 2.60 2.60
a.-b. A1225 P Either single 1.30 1.10

**Self-Adhesive**
**Coil Stamps**
***Serpentine Die Cut 8 Vert.***

**2977** A1226 P multi 1.30 .55
**2978** A1226 P multi 1.30 .55
a. Horiz. pair, #2977-2978 2.60

**Booklet Stamps**
***Serpentine Die Cut 13½***

**2979** A1225 P multi 1.30 .45
**2980** A1225 P multi 1.30 .45
a. Booklet pane of 10, 5 each #2979-2980 + 10 stickers 13.00

On day of issue, Nos. 2976a-2976b, 2977-2980 each sold for 85c.

A1227

Battle of Vimy Ridge, Cent. — A1228

No. 2981: a, Pillars and statue. b, Statue of weeping woman.

**Litho. & Engr.**
**2017, Apr. 8 *Perf. 13¼***

**2981** A1227 Sheet of 2 7.50 7.50
a.-b. $2.50 Either single 3.75 3.50

**Litho.**
**Booklet Stamp**
**Self-Adhesive**
***Serpentine Die Cut 13½***

**2982** A1228 P multi 1.30 .45
a. Booklet pane of 10 13.00

No. 2982 sold for 85c on day of issue. See France No. 5216.

Admiral James T. Kirk — A1229

Captain Jonathan Archer A1230

Captain Kathryn Janeway A1231

Captain Benjamin Sisko — A1232

Captain Jean-Luc Picard A1233

Borg Cube A1234

Galileo Shuttle — A1235

**Litho., Litho & Embossed With Foil Application (#2983)**
**2017, Apr. 27 *Perf. 13¼***

**2983** Miniature sheet of 5 11.00 11.00
a. A1229 P multi 1.30 1.10
b. A1230 $1 multi 1.50 1.30
c. A1231 $1.20 multi 1.80 1.50
d. A1232 $1.80 multi 2.70 2.40
e. A1233 $2.50 multi 3.75 3.50
f. Booklet pane of 3 #2983a 3.90 —
g. Booklet pane of 4, #2983b-2983e 9.75 —
h. Booklet pane of 5, #2983a-2983e 11.25 —

**Booklet Stamp**
***Perf. 13¼ on 2 Sides, 13 on 4 Sides***

**2984** A1234 $5 blk & silver 7.50 7.50
a. Booklet pane of 1 7.50 —

**Coil Stamp**
**Self-Adhesive**
***Serpentine Die Cut 8 Horiz.***

**2985** A1235 P multi 1.30 .55

**Booklet Stamps**
***Serpentine Die Cut 13¼x13¾***

**2986** A1229 P multi 1.30 .55
**2987** A1233 P multi 1.30 .55
**2988** A1232 P multi 1.30 .55
**2989** A1231 P multi 1.30 .55
**2990** A1230 P multi 1.30 .55
a. Booklet pane of 10, 2 each #2986-2990 13.00

***Serpentine Die Cut 13¾***

**2991** A1235 P multi 3.75 3.75
a. Booklet pane of 1 3.75 —
Complete booklet, #2983f, 2983g,2983h, 2984a, 2991a 35.00
*Nos. 2986-2991 (6)* 10.25 6.50

Lead characters of various *Star Trek* television series. On day of issue, Nos. 2983a, 2985-2991 each sold for 85c. Complete booklet sold for $21.95.

Formula 1 Race Car Drivers A1236

Race car, checkered flag and: Nos. 2992a, 2993, Sir Jackie Stewart, flag of Great Britain. Nos. 2992b, 2994, Gilles Villeneuve (1950-82), flag of Canada. Nos. 2992c, 2995, Ayrton Senna (1960-94), flag of Brazil. Nos. 2992d, 2996, Michael Schumacher, flag of Germany. Nos. 2992e, 2997, Lewis Hamilton, flag of Great Britain.

**2017, May 16 Litho. *Perf. 13***

**2992** A1236 Sheet of 5 6.50 6.50
a.-e. P Any single 1.30 1.10

**Booklet Stamps**
**Self-Adhesive**
***Serpentine Die Cut 16½***

**2993** A1236 P multi 1.30 .55
**2994** A1236 P multi 1.30 .55
**2995** A1236 P multi 1.30 .55
**2996** A1236 P multi 1.30 .55
**2997** A1236 P multi 1.30 .55
a. Booklet pane of 10, 2 each #2993-2997 13.00
*Nos. 2993-2997 (5)* 6.50 2.75

Canadian Formula 1 Grand Prix, 50th anniv. On day of issue, Nos. 2992a-2992e, 2993-2997 each sold for 85c.

Eid — A1237

***Serpentine Die Cut 13½x13¼***
**2017, May 24 Litho.**
**Booklet Stamp**
**Self-Adhesive**

**2998** A1237 P multi 1.30 .45
a. Booklet pane of 10 13.00

No. 2998 sold for 85c on day of issue.

A1238

Canadian Confederation, 150th Anniv. — A1239

Designs: Nos. 2999a, 3000, Habitat 67 at Expo 67, Montreal, 1967. Nos. 2999b, 3001, Route marker on completed Trans-Canada Highway, 1971. Nos. 2999c, 3002, Summit Series, 1972. Nos. 2999d, 3003, Terry Fox running Marathon of Hope, 1980. Nos. 2999e, 3004, Canadarm in space, 1981. Nos. 2999f, 3005, Canadian Constitution and Charter of Rights and Freedoms, 1982. Nos. 2999g, 3006, Woman from Nunavut, 1999. Nos. 2999h, 3007, Rainbow flag (marriage equality), 2005. Nos. 2999i, 3008, Canadian Olympic athlete (Olympic Games in Canada), 1976, 1988, 2010. Nos. 2999j, 3009, Paralympic skiier (Paralympic Games in Canada), 1976, 2010.

**2017, June 1 Litho. *Perf.***

**2999** Sheet of 10 + 2 labels 13.00 13.00
a.-j. A1238 P Any single 1.30 1.10

**Booklet Stamps**
**Self-Adhesive**
***Die Cut***

**3000** A1239 P multi 1.30 .45
**3001** A1239 P multi 1.30 .45
**3002** A1239 P multi 1.30 .45
**3003** A1239 P multi 1.30 .45
**3004** A1239 P multi 1.30 .45
**3005** A1239 P multi 1.30 .45
**3006** A1239 P multi 1.30 .45
a. Booklet pane of 8 10.50
**3007** A1239 P multi 1.30 .45
a. Booklet pane of 8 10.50
**3008** A1239 P multi 1.30 .45
**3009** A1239 P multi 1.30 .45
a. Booklet pane of 10, #3000-3009 13.00
*Nos. 3000-3009 (10)* 13.00 4.50

On day of issue, Nos. 2999a-2999j, 3000-3009 each sold for 85c.

**Photography Type of 2013**

Designs: Nos. 3010a, 3013, Enlacées, by Gilbert Duclos, 1994. Nos. 3010b, 3016, Sir John A. Macdonald, by William James Topley, c. 1883. Nos. 3011a, 3014, Ontario, Canada, by Robert Bourdeau, 1989, horiz. Nos. 3011b, 3015, Construction of the Parliament Buildings, by Samuel McLaughlin, c. 1862, horiz. Nos. 3011c, 3012, Ti-Noir Lajeunesse, the Blind Violinist, Disraeli, Quebec, by Claire Beaugrand-Champagne, 1972, horiz.

**2017, July 4 Litho. *Perf. 12¾***

**3010** A1109 Sheet of 2 2.60 2.60
a.-b. P Either single 1.30 1.10
**3011** A1109 Sheet of 3 4.00 4.00
a.-b. P Any single 1.30 1.10

**Booklet Stamps**
**Self-Adhesive**
***Serpentine Die Cut 13¼***

**3012** A1109 P multi 1.30 .45
**3013** A1109 P multi 1.30 .45
**3014** A1109 P multi 1.30 .45
**3015** A1109 P multi 1.30 .45

**3016** A1109 P multi 1.30 .45
*a.* Booklet pane of 10, 2 each #3012-3016 13.00

On day of issue, Nos. 3010a-3010b, 3011a-3011b, 3012-3016 each sold for 85c.

Birds A1240

Designs: Nos. 3017a, 3020, Cyanocitta cristata. Nos. 3017b, 3019, Falco rusticolus. Nos. 3017c, 3021, Strix nebulosa. Nos. 3017d, 3018, Pandion haliaetus. Nos. 3017e, 3022, Gavia immer.

**2017, Aug. 1 Litho. *Perf. 13x13¼***

**3017** A1240 Sheet of 5 + label 6.50 6.50
*a.-e.* P Any single 1.30 1.10

**Booklet Stamps**
**Self-Adhesive**
***Serpentine Die Cut 13***

**3018** A1240 P multi 1.30 .55
**3019** A1240 P multi 1.30 .55
**3020** A1240 P multi 1.30 .55
**3021** A1240 P multi 1.30 .55
**3022** A1240 P multi 1.30 .55
*a.* Booklet pane of 10, 2 each #3018-3022 13.00
*Nos. 3018-3022 (5)* 6.50 2.75

On day of issue, Nos. 3017a-3017e, 3018-3022 each sold for 85c.

A1241

Diwali — A1242

**2017, Sept. 21 Litho. *Perf. 13¼***
**Souvenir Sheet**

**3023** Souvenir sheet of 2, #3023a and Indian stamp 4.50 4.50
*a.* A1241 $2.50 multi 3.75 3.25

**Booklet Stamps**
**Self-Adhesive**
***Serpentine Die Cut 13¾x13½***

**3024** A1241 P multi 1.30 .55
**3025** A1242 P multi 1.30 .55
*a.* Booklet pane of 10, 5 each #3024-3025 13.00

On day of issue, Nos. 3024-3025 each sold for 85c. No. 3023 sold for $3, and contains one 25r Indian stamp similar to type A1242. See India Nos. 2961-2962.

A1243

National Hockey League, Cent. A1244

French and English versions of National Hockey League emblem and famous players: Nos. 3026a, 3027, 3033, Maurice Richard (1921-2000). Nos. 3026b, 3028, 3034, Jean Béliveau (1931-2014). Nos. 3026c, 3029, 3035, Gordie Howe (1928-2016). Nos. 3026d, 3030, 3036, Bobby Orr. Nos. 3026e, 3031, 3037, Mario Lemieux. Nos. 3026f, 3032, 3038, Wayne Gretzky.

**Litho., Sheet Margin Litho. & Embossed With Foil Application**

**2017, Sept. 28 *Perf. 12½x13***

**3026** Sheet of 6 7.75 7.75
*a.-f.* A1243 P Any single 1.30 .55

**Booklet Stamps**
**Self-Adhesive**
**Litho.**
***Serpentine Die Cut 13¼x13½***

**3027** A1243 P multi 1.30 .55
**3028** A1243 P multi 1.30 .55
**3029** A1243 P multi 1.30 .55
**3030** A1243 P multi 1.30 .55
**3031** A1243 P multi 1.30 .55
**3032** A1243 P multi 1.30 .55
*a.* Booklet pane of 6, #3027-3032 7.75
*Nos. 3027-3032 (6)* 7.80 3.30

**Souvenir Sheets**
***Serpentine Die Cut 13½x13¼***

**3033** A1244 $1.80 multi 2.70 2.40
**3034** A1244 $1.80 multi 2.70 2.40
**3035** A1244 $1.80 multi 2.70 2.40
**3036** A1244 $1.80 multi 2.70 2.40
**3037** A1244 $1.80 multi 2.70 2.40
**3038** A1244 $1.80 multi 2.70 2.40
*Nos. 3033-3038 (6)* 16.20 14.40

Nos. 3026a-3026f, 3027-3032 each sold for 85c on day of issue. Nos. 3033-3038 each contain one 52x78mm stamp. Nos. 3033-3038 were sold together in a sealed opaque plastic package. One of every 40 packages contained a souvenir sheet signed by Orr or Lemieux.

Ice Hockey Player Wearing Helmet and Protective Gear A1245

Ice Hockey Player Wearing Hat and Scarf A1246

**2017, Oct. 20 Litho. *Perf. 13***
**Souvenir Sheet**

**3039** Sheet of 2 2.60 2.60
*a.* A1245 P multi 1.30 1.10
*b.* A1246 P multi 1.30 1.10

**Booklet Stamps**
**Self-Adhesive**

**3040** A1245 P multi 1.30 .45
**3041** A1246 P multi 1.30 .45
*a.* Booklet pane of 10, 5 each #3040-3041 13.00

History of ice hockey. On day of issue, Nos. 3039a-3039b, 3040-3041 each sold for 85c. See United States Nos. 5252-5253.

Emblem of Toronto Maple Leafs on Jersey A1247

Emblem of Toronto Maple Leafs on Hockey Puck — A1248

Maple Leaf and "100" — A1249

**Litho. With Cloth Patch Affixed**

**2017, Oct. 24 *Perf. 13x13¼***
**Souvenir Sheet**

**3042** A1247 $5 multi 7.50 7.50

**Coil Stamp**
**Self-Adhesive**
***Die Cut***

**3043** A1248 P multi 1.30 .60

**Booklet Stamp**
***Serpentine Die Cut 13¼x13½***

**3044** A1249 P multi 1.30 .45
*a.* Booklet pane of 10 13.00

Toronto Maple Leafs hockey team, cent. On day of issue, Nos. 3043-3044 each sold for 85c.

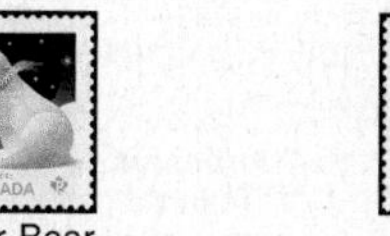

Polar Bear A1250

Cardinal A1251

Caribou A1252

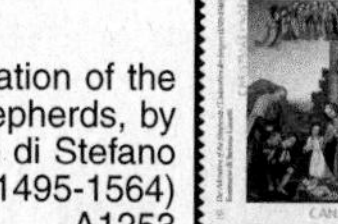

The Adoration of the Shepherds, by Tommaso di Stefano Lunetti (c. 1495-1564) A1253

**2017, Nov. 3 Litho. *Perf. 13½x13¼***
**Souvenir Sheet**

**3045** Sheet of 3 6.75 6.75
*a.* A1250 P multi 1.30 1.10
*b.* A1251 $1.20 multi 1.50 .95
*c.* A1252 $2.50 multi 3.75 3.50

**Booklet Stamps**
**Self-Adhesive**
**Litho. With Foil Application**
***Serpentine Die Cut 13½***

**3046** A1253 P multi 1.30 .25
*a.* Booklet pane of 12 15.50

**Litho.**
***Serpentine Die Cut 13¼x13***

**3047** A1250 P multi 1.30 .25
*a.* Booklet pane of 12 15.00
**3048** A1251 $1.20 multi 1.80 .90
*a.* Booklet pane of 6 11.00
**3049** A1252 $2.50 multi 3.75 3.50
*a.* Booklet pane of 6 24.00
*Nos. 3046-3049 (4)* 8.15 4.90

Christmas. On day of issue, Nos. 3045a, 3046 and 3047 each sold for 85c.

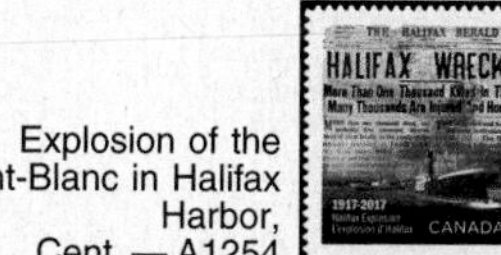


Explosion of the Mont-Blanc in Halifax Harbor, Cent. — A1254

***Serpentine Die Cut 13¼x13½***
**2017, Nov. 6 Litho.**

**Booklet Stamp**
**Self-Adhesive**

**3050** A1254 P multi 1.30 .45
*a.* Booklet pane of 10 13.00

On day of issue, No. 3050 sold for 85c.

Hanukkah — A1255

***Serpentine Die Cut 13¼x13½***
**2017, Nov. 14 Litho.**

**Booklet Stamp**
**Self-Adhesive**

**3051** A1255 P multi 1.30 .45
*a.* Booklet pane of 10 13.00

On day of issue, No. 3051 sold for 85c.

New Year 2018 (Year of the Dog) — A1256

Dog on Chinese lantern: P, Small dog with bushy tail. $2.50, Large dog with curled tail.

**Litho. & Embossed With Foil Application**

**2018, Jan. 15 *Perf. 12½***

**3052** A1256 P gold & multi 1.30 .55

**Souvenir Sheet**

**3053** A1256 $2.50 gold & multi 3.25 3.75
*a.* Souvenir sheet of 2, #2960, 3053 7.50 7.50
*b.* Perf. 13¼ (#3162a) 4.00 4.00

**Booklet Stamps**
**Self-Adhesive**
**Litho.**
***Serpentine Die Cut 13½***

**3054** A1256 P multi 1.30 .55
*a.* Booklet pane of 10 13.00

**Litho. With Foil Application**

**3055** A1256 $2.50 gold & multi 3.75 2.25
*a.* Booklet pane of 6 222.50

Nos. 3052 and 3054 each sold for 85c on day of issue. Issued: No. 3053b, 1/18/19. See Nos. 3259k, 3260k, 3271.

St. John's, Newfoundland and Labrador A1257

Hopewell Rocks, New Brunswick A1258

MacMillan Provincial Park, British Columbia A1259

Covehead Harbor Lighthouse, Prince Edward Island National Park A1260

Ile-Bonaventure-et-du-Rocher-Percé National Park, Quebec — A1261

Pisew Falls Provincial Park, Manitoba A1262

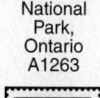

Point Pelee National Park, Ontario A1263

Nááts'jhch'oh National Park Reserve, Northwest Territories A1264

Arctic Bay, Nunavut A1265

**2018, Jan. 15 Litho. *Perf. 13¼x13***

**3056** Sheet of 9 16.00 16.00
*a.* A1257 P multi 1.30 1.10
*b.* A1258 P multi 1.30 1.10
*c.* A1259 P multi 1.30 1.10
*d.* A1260 P multi 1.30 1.10
*e.* A1261 P multi 1.30 1.10
*f.* A1262 $1 multi 1.50 1.30
*g.* A1263 $1.20 multi 1.80 1.30
*h.* A1264 $1.80 multi 2.70 1.70
*i.* A1265 $2.50 multi 3.75 2.40

### Coil Stamps
### Self-Adhesive

*Serpentine Die Cut 9¼ Horiz.*

**3057** A1257 P multi 1.50 1.50
**3058** A1258 P multi 1.50 1.50
**3059** A1259 P multi 1.50 1.50
**3060** A1261 P multi 1.50 1.50
**3061** A1260 P multi 1.50 1.50
*a.* Horiz. strip of 5, #3057-3061 7.50

*Serpentine Die Cut 8¼ Horiz.*

**3062** A1257 P multi 1.30 .25
**3063** A1258 P multi 1.30 .25
**3064** A1259 P multi 1.30 .25
**3065** A1261 P multi 1.30 .25
**3066** A1260 P multi 1.30 .25
*a.* Vert. strip of 5, #3062-3066 6.50
**3067** A1263 $1.20 multi 1.80 .35
**3068** A1264 $1.80 multi 2.70 .65
**3069** A1265 $2.50 multi 3.75 .95

*Die Cut Perf. 13¼x13*

**3070** A1262 $1 multi 1.50 .25
*Nos. 3057-3070 (14)* 23.75 10.95

### Booklet Stamps

*Serpentine Die Cut 13¼x13½*

**3071** A1257 P multi 1.30 .25
**3072** A1259 P multi 1.30 .25
**3073** A1260 P multi 1.30 .25
**3074** A1258 P multi 1.30 .25
**3075** A1261 P multi 1.30 .25
*a.* Booklet pane of 10, 2 each #3071-3075 13.00
*b.* Booklet pane of 30, 6 each #3071-3075 39.00

*Serpentine Die Cut 9¼ Horiz.*

**3076** A1263 $1.20 multi 1.80 .35
*a.* Booklet pane of 6 10.75
**3077** A1264 $1.80 multi 2.70 .65
*a.* Booklet pane of 6 16.25
**3078** A1265 $2.50 multi 3.75 .95
*a.* Booklet pane of 6 22.50
*Nos. 3071-3078 (8)* 14.75 3.20

On day of issue, Nos. 3056a-3056e, 3057-3066, 3071-3075 each sold for 85c.

Women in Winter Sports — A1266

Designs: Nos. 3079a, 3080, Nancy Greene, alpine skier. Nos. 3079b, 3081, Sharon and Shirley Firth, cross-country skiers. Nos. 3079c, 3082, Danielle Goyette, ice hockey player. Nos. 3079d, 3083, Clara Hughes, speed skater. Nos. 3079e, 3084, Sonja Gaudet, wheelchair curler.

**2018, Jan. 24 Litho.** ***Perf. 13x13¼***

**3079** Sheet of 5 6.50 6.50
*a.-e.* A1266 P Any single 1.30 1.10

### Booklet Stamps
### Self-Adhesive

*Serpentine Die Cut 13¼x13¾*

**3080** A1266 P multi 1.30 .55
**3081** A1266 P multi 1.30 .55
**3082** A1266 P multi 1.30 .55
**3083** A1266 P multi 1.30 .55
**3084** A1266 P multi 1.30 .55
*a.* Booklet pane of 10, 2 each #3080-3084 13.00
*Nos. 3080-3084 (5)* 6.50 2.75

On day of issue, Nos. 3079a-3079e, 3080-3084 each sold for 85c.

Black History Month — A1267

Designs: No. 3085, Kay Livingstone (1918-75), founder of Canadian Negro Women's Association. No. 3086, Lincoln M. Alexander (1922-2012), first Black elected to House of Commons.

*Serpentine Die Cut 13½x13¼*

**2018, Feb. 1 Self-Adhesive Litho.**

### Booklet Stamps

**3085** A1267 P multi 1.30 .45
*a.* Booklet pane of 10 13.00
**3086** A1267 P multi 1.30 .45
*a.* Booklet pane of 10 13.00

On day of issue, Nos. 3085 and 3086 each sold for 85c.

Lotus Flowers
A1268 A1269

Designs: Nos. 3087a, 3088, 3090, Nelumbo nucifera (pink petals). Nos. 3087b, 3089, 3091, Nelumbo lutea (yellow petals).

**2018, Mar. 1 Litho.** ***Perf. 13***

### Souvenir Sheet

**3087** Sheet of 2 2.60 2.60
*a.-b.* A1268 P Either single 1.30 1.10

### Self-Adhesive
### Coil Stamps

*Serpentine Die Cut 8 Vert.*

**3088** A1269 P multi 1.30 .55
**3089** A1269 P multi 1.30 .55
*a.* Horiz. pair, #3088-3089 2.60

### Booklet Stamps

*Serpentine Die Cut 13½*

**3090** A1268 P multi 1.30 .45
**3091** A1268 P multi 1.30 .45
*a.* Booklet pane of 10, 5 each #3090-3091 + 10 stickers 13.00

On day of issue, Nos. 3087a-3087b, 3088-3091 each sold for 85c.

Illustrations — A1270

Designs: Nos. 3092a, 3093, *Best Friends,* by Anita Kunz (32x40mm). Nos. 3092b, 3096, *Untitled,* by Will Davies (1924-2016) (32x40mm). Nos. 3092c, 3094, *Stage Fright,* by Blair Drawson (32x40mm). Nos. 3092d, 3097, *It's Not a Stream of Consciousness,* by Gérard DuBois (32x32mm). Nos. 3092e, 3095, *Untitled,* by James Hill (1930-2004) (32x32mm).

**2018, Apr. 5 Litho.** ***Perf. 12½***

**3092** A1270 Sheet of 5 + label 6.50 6.50
*a.-e.* P Any single 1.30 1.10

### Booklet Stamps
### Self-Adhesive

*Serpentine Die Cut 13½x13¼*

**3093** A1270 P multi 1.30 .55
**3094** A1270 P multi 1.30 .55
**3095** A1270 P multi 1.30 .55
**3096** A1270 P multi 1.30 .55
**3097** A1270 P multi 1.30 .55
*a.* Booklet pane of 10, 2 each #3093-3097 13.00
*Nos. 3093-3097 (5)* 6.50 2.75

On day of issue, Nos. 3092a-3092e, 3093-3097 each sold for 85c.

Queen Elizabeth II, 65th Anniv. of Coronation — A1271

*Serpentine Die Cut 13¼*

**2018, Apr. 20 Litho.**

### Booklet Stamp
### Self-Adhesive

**3098** A1271 P gold & multi 1.30 .45
*a.* Booklet pane of 10 13.00

No. 3098 sold for 85c on day of issue.

Bees — A1272

Designs: No. 3099, Bombus affinis. No. 3100, Agapostemon virescens.

*Serpentine Die Cut 13*

**2018, May 1 Litho.**

### Booklet Stamp
### Self-Adhesive

**3099** A1272 P multi 1.30 .45
**3100** A1272 P multi 1.30 .45
*a.* Booklet pane of 10, 5 each #3099-3100 13.00

Nos. 3099-3100 each sold for 85c on day of issue.

100th Presentation of the Memorial Cup — A1273

*Serpentine Die Cut 13¼x13¾*

**2018, May 18 Litho.**

### Booklet Stamp
### Self-Adhesive

**3101** A1273 P sil & multi 1.30 .45
*a.* Booklet pane of 10 13.00

No. 3101 sold for 85c on day of issue.

Astronomy — A1274

Designs: Nos. 3102a, 3103, Milky Way. No. 3102b, 3104, Northern lights.

**2018, June 29 Litho.** ***Perf. 13¼***

**3102** A1274 Sheet of 2 2.60 2.60
*a.-b.* P Either single 1.30 1.10

### Booklet Stamps
### Self-Adhesive

*Serpentine Die Cut 14x14½*

**3103** A1274 P multi 1.30 .45
**3104** A1274 P multi 1.30 .45
*a.* Booklet pane of 10, 5 each #3103-3104 13.00

On day of issue, Nos. 3102a-3102b, 3103-3104 each sold for 85c.

Sharks A1275

Designs: Nos. 3105a, 3110, Isurus oxyrinchus. Nos. 3105b, 3107, Cetorhinus maximus. Nos. 3105c, 3106, Carcharodon carcharias. Nos. 3105d, 3108, Somniosus microcephalus. Nos. 3105e, 3109, Prionace glauca.

**2018, July 13 Litho.** ***Perf. 12½***

**3105** A1275 Sheet of 5 6.50 6.50
*a.-e.* P Any single 1.30 1.10

### Booklet Stamps
### Self-Adhesive

*Serpentine Die Cut 13½*

**3106** A1275 P multi 1.30 .55
**3107** A1275 P multi 1.30 .55
**3108** A1275 P multi 1.30 .55
**3109** A1275 P multi 1.30 .55
**3110** A1275 P multi 1.30 .55
*a.* Booklet pane of 10, 2 each #3106-3110 13.00
*Nos. 3106-3110 (5)* 6.50 2.75

On day of issue, Nos. 3105a-3105e, 3106-3110 each sold for 85c.

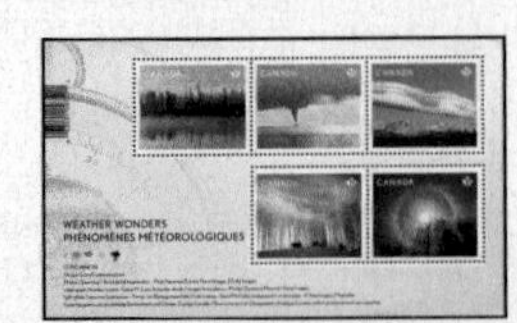

Meteorological Phenomena — A1276

Designs: Nos. 3111a, 3112, Steam fog. Nos. 3111b, 3113, Waterspout. Nos. 3111c, 3114, Lenticular clouds. Nos. 3111d, 3115, Light pillars. Nos. 3111e, 3116, Moon halo.

**2018, July 26 Litho.** ***Perf. 12½***

**3111** A1276 Sheet of 5 6.50 6.50
*a.-e.* P Any single 1.30 1.10

### Booklet Stamps
### Self-Adhesive

*Serpentine Die Cut 13¼x13½*

**3112** A1276 P multi 1.30 .55
**3113** A1276 P multi 1.30 .55
**3114** A1276 P multi 1.30 .55
**3115** A1276 P multi 1.30 .55
**3116** A1276 P multi 1.30 .55
*a.* Booklet pane of 10, 2 each #3112-3116 13.00
*Nos. 3112-3116 (5)* 6.50 2.75

On day of issue, Nos. 3111a-3111e, 3112-3116 each sold for 85c.

Birds A1277

Designs: Nos. 3117a, 3118, Poecile atricapillus. Nos. 3117b, 3121, Bubo scandiacus. Nos. 3117c, 3122, Cyanocitta stelleri. Nos. 3117d, 3120, Branta canadensis. Nos. 3117e, 3119, Grus americana.

**2018, Aug. 20 Litho.** ***Perf. 13x13¼***

**3117** A1277 Sheet of 5 + label 7.00 7.00
*a.-e.* P Any single 1.40 .70
*f.* As No. 3117, with 2018 International Ornithological Congress emblem added in sheet margin 7.00 7.00

### Booklet Stamps
### Self-Adhesive

*Serpentine Die Cut 13*

**3118** A1277 P multi 1.40 .70
**3119** A1277 P multi 1.40 .70
**3120** A1277 P multi 1.40 .70
**3121** A1277 P multi 1.40 .70
**3122** A1277 P multi 1.40 .70
*a.* Booklet pane of 10, 2 each #3118-3122 14.00
*Nos. 3118-3122 (5)* 7.00 3.50

On day of issue, Nos. 3117a-3117e, 3118-3122 each sold for 85c.

Emergency Responders — A1278

Designs: Nos. 3123a, 3124, Members of Canadian Armed Forces and raft. Nos. 3123b, 3126, Paramedics, ambulance and helicopter. Nos. 3123c, 3125, Firefighters and fire. Nos. 3123d, 3127, Police officers, police car and city skyline. Nos. 3123e, 3128, Search and rescue crew members and helicopter in mountains.

**2018, Sept. 14 Litho.** ***Perf. 13¼x13***

**3123** A1278 Sheet of 5 + label 7.00 7.00
*a.-e.* P Any single 1.40 .70

### Booklet Stamps
### Self-Adhesive

*Serpentine Die Cut 13¾x13½*

**3124** A1278 P multi 1.40 .70
**3125** A1278 P multi 1.40 .70
**3126** A1278 P multi 1.40 .70
**3127** A1278 P multi 1.40 .70
**3128** A1278 P multi 1.40 .70
*a.* Booklet pane of 10, 2 each #3124-3128 14.00
*Nos. 3124-3128 (5)* 7.00 3.50

On day of issue, Nos. 3123a-3123e, 3124-3128 each sold for 85c.

Rocky Mountain Bighorn Sheep A1279

**Litho. & Engr.**

**2018, Oct. 10** *Perf. 12½x13*

**3129** A1279 $4 multi 6.25 3.25

No. 3129 was printed in sheets of 4.

World War I Armistice, Cent. — A1280

**2018, Oct. 24 Litho.** *Perf. 13¼x13*

**3130** A1280 P multi 1.40 .70

**Booklet Stamp**
**Self-Adhesive**

*Serpentine Die Cut 13¾x14*

**3131** A1280 P multi 1.40 .70
*a.* Booklet pane of 10 14.00

On day of issue, Nos. 3130 and 3131 each sold for 85c. No. 3130 was printed in sheets of 5.

Socks A1281

Cap A1282

Mittens A1283

Nativity Scene A1284

**2018, Nov. 2 Litho.** *Perf. 13½x13¼*

**3132** Sheet of 3 7.50 7.50
*a.* A1281 P multi 1.40 .70
*b.* A1282 $1.20 multi 1.90 .95
*c.* A1283 $2.50 multi 4.00 2.00

**Booklet Stamps**
**Self-Adhesive**

*Serpentine Die Cut 13¼x13*

**3133** A1284 P multi 1.40 .70
*a.* Booklet pane of 12 14.00
**3134** A1281 P multi 1.40 .70
*a.* Booklet pane of 12 14.00
**3135** A1282 $1.20 multi 1.90 .95
*a.* Booklet pane of 6 11.50
**3136** A1283 $2.50 multi 4.00 2.00
*a.* Booklet pane of 6 24.00
*Nos. 3133-3136 (4)* 8.70 4.35

Christmas. On day of issue, Nos. 3132a, 3133, and 3134 each sold for 85c.

Queen Elizabeth II — A1285

*Serpentine Die Cut 13¾x13½*

**2019, Jan. 14 Litho.**

**Booklet Stamp**
**Self-Adhesive**

**3137** A1285 P multi 1.40 .70
*a.* Booklet pane of 10 14.00

No. 3137 sold for 90c on day of issue.

Tombstone Territorial Park, Yukon A1286

Athabasca Falls, Jasper National Park, Alberta A1287

Quttinirpaaq National Park, Nunavut A1288

Mahone Bay, Nova Scotia A1289

Little Limestone Lake Provincial Park, Manitoba A1290

Castle Butte, Big Muddy Badlands, Saskatchewan A1291

Algonquin Provincial Park, Ontario A1292

Mingan Archipelago National Park Reserve, Quebec A1293

Iceberg Alley Near Ferryland, Newfoundland and Labrador — A1294

**2019, Jan. 14 Litho.** *Perf. 13¼x13*

**3138** Sheet of 9 17.50 17.50
*a.* A1286 P multi 1.40 .70
*b.* A1287 P multi 1.40 .70
*c.* A1288 P multi 1.40 .70
*d.* A1289 P multi 1.40 .70
*e.* A1290 P multi 1.40 .70
*f.* A1291 $1.05 multi 1.60 .80
*g.* A1292 $1.27 multi 1.90 .95
*h.* A1293 $1.90 multi 3.00 1.50
*i.* A1294 $2.65 multi 4.00 2.00

**Coil Stamps**
**Self-Adhesive**

*Serpentine Die Cut 9 Horiz.*

**3139** A1286 P multi 1.40 .70
**3140** A1287 P multi 1.40 .70
**3141** A1288 P multi 1.40 .70
**3142** A1289 P multi 1.40 .70
**3143** A1290 P multi 1.40 .70
*a.* Horiz. strip of 5, #3139-3143 7.00

*Serpentine Die Cut 8 Horiz.*

**3144** A1286 P multi 1.40 .70
**3145** A1287 P multi 1.40 .70
**3146** A1288 P multi 1.40 .70
**3147** A1289 P multi 1.40 .70
**3148** A1290 P multi 1.40 .70
*a.* Vert. strip of 5, #3144-3148 7.00

*Serpentine Die Cut 13¼*

**3149** A1291 $1.05 multi 1.60 .80

*Serpentine Die Cut 8¼ Horiz.*

**3150** A1292 $1.27 multi 1.90 .95
**3151** A1293 $1.90 multi 3.00 1.50
**3152** A1294 $2.65 multi 4.00 2.00
*Nos. 3139-3152 (14)* 24.50 12.25

**Booklet Stamps**

*Serpentine Die Cut 13¾x13½*

**3153** A1286 P multi 1.40 .70
**3154** A1288 P multi 1.40 .70
**3155** A1290 P multi 1.40 .70
**3156** A1287 P multi 1.40 .70
**3157** A1289 P multi 1.40 .70
*a.* Booklet pane of 10, 2 each #3153-3157 14.00

*Serpentine Die Cut 9¼ Horiz.*

**3158** A1292 $1.27 multi 1.90 .95
*a.* Booklet pane of 6 11.50
**3159** A1293 $1.90 multi 3.00 1.50
*a.* Booklet pane of 6 18.00
**3160** A1294 $2.65 multi 4.00 2.00
*a.* Booklet pane of 6 24.00
*Nos. 3153-3160 (8)* 15.90 7.95

On day of issue, Nos. 3138a-3138e, 3139-3148, and 3153-3157 each sold for 90c.

New Year 2019 (Year of the Pig) — A1295

Rake and pig in: P, Armor. $2.65, Robe.

**Litho. & Embossed With Foil Application**

**2019, Jan. 18** *Perf. 13¼*

**3161** A1295 P multi 1.40 .70

**Souvenir Sheet**

**3162** A1295 $2.65 multi 4.00 4.00
*a.* Souvenir sheet of 2, #3053b, 3162 8.00 8.00
*b.* Perf. 13 (3230a) 4.00 4.00

**Booklet Stamps**
**Self-Adhesive**
**Litho.**

*Serpentine Die Cut 13½*

**3163** A1295 P multi 1.40 .70
*a.* Booklet pane of 10 14.00

**Litho. With Foil Application**

**3164** A1295 $2.65 multi 4.00 2.00
*a.* Booklet pane of 6 24.00

On day of issue, Nos. 3161 and 3163 each sold for 90c. Issued: No. 3162b, 1/17/20.

See Nos. 3259l, 3260lk, 3272.

Albert Jackson (c. 1856-1918), First Black Letter Carrier in Canada — A1296

*Serpentine Die Cut 13½x13*

**2019, Jan. 25** **Litho.**

**Booklet Stamp**
**Self-Adhesive**

**3165** A1296 P multi 1.40 .70
*a.* Booklet pane of 10 14.00

No. 3165 sold for 90c on day of issue.

Gardenia Jasminoides
A1297 A1298

Gardenia with background color of: Nos. 3166a, 3167, 3169, Orange brown. Nos. 3166b, 3168, 3170, Blue green.

**2019, Feb. 14 Litho.** *Perf. 13*

**Souvenir Sheet**

**3166** Sheet of 2 2.80 2.80
*a.-b.* A1297 P Either single 1.40 .70

**Self-Adhesive**
**Coil Stamps**

*Serpentine Die Cut 8 Vert.*

**3167** A1298 P multi 1.40 .70
**3168** A1298 P multi 1.40 .70
*a.* Horiz. pair, #3167-3168 2.80

**Booklet Stamps**

*Serpentine Die Cut 13½*

**3169** A1297 P multi 1.40 .70
**3170** A1297 P multi 1.40 .70
*a.* Booklet pane of 10, 5 each #3169-3170 + 10 stickers 14.00

On day of issue, Nos. 3166a-3166b, 3167-3170 each sold for 90c.

Aviation Pioneers and Airplanes A1299

Designs: Nos. 3171a, 3172, Elizabeth "Elsie" MacGill (1905-80), first female aeronautical engineer. Nos. 3171b, 3176, Ultraflight Lazair ultralight aircraft. Nos. 3171c, 3175, Avro CF-105 Arrow. Nos. 3171d, 3174, C. H. "Punch" Dickins (1899-1995), bush pilot. Nos. 3171e, 3173, William George Barker (1894-1930), World War I flying ace.

**2019, Mar. 27 Litho.** *Perf. 12½*

**3171** A1299 Sheet of 5 + label 7.00 7.00
*a.-e.* P Any single 1.40 .70

**Booklet Stamps**
**Self-Adhesive**

*Serpentine Die Cut 13¼x13½*

**3172** A1299 P multi 1.40 .70
**3173** A1299 P multi 1.40 .70
**3174** A1299 P multi 1.40 .70
**3175** A1299 P multi 1.40 .70
**3176** A1299 P multi 1.40 .70
*a.* Booklet pane of 10, 2 each #3172-3176 14.00

On day of issue, Nos. 3171a-3171e, 3172-3176 each sold for 90c.

Sweet Foods A1300

No. 3177: a, Sugar pie (35x32mm). b, Butter tart (33mm diameter). c, Saskatoon berry pie (43x30mm). d, Nanaimo bar (36x33mm). e, Blueberry grunt (46x26mm).

*Serpentine Die Cut 13½*

**2019, Apr. 17** **Litho.**

**Self-Adhesive**

**3177** A1300 Sheet of 5 7.00
*a.-e.* P Any single 1.40 .70
*f.* Booklet pane of 10, 2 each #3177a-3177e 14.00

Nos. 3177a-3177e each sold for 90c on day of issue.

1940 Vancouver Asahi Baseball Team — A1301

**2019, Apr. 25 Litho.** *Die Cut*

**Booklet Stamp**
**Self-Adhesive**

**3178** A1301 P multi 1.40 .70
*a.* Booklet pane of 10 14.00

No. 3178 sold for 90c on day of issue.

Endangered Turtles — A1302

No. 3179: a, Clemmys guttata (36x33mm). b, Emydoidea blandingii (36x35mm).

*Serpentine Die Cut 13½*

**2019, May 23** **Litho.**

**Self-Adhesive**

**3179** A1302 Sheet of 2 2.80
*a.-b.* P Either single 1.40 .70
*c.* Booklet pane of 10, 5 each #3179a-3179b 14.00

Nos. 3179a-3179b each sold for 90c on day of issue.

Covered Bridges A1303

Designs: Nos. 3180a, 3181, Hartland Covered Bridge, New Brunswick. Nos. 3180b, 3182, Powerscourt Covered Bridge, Quebec. Nos. 3180c, 3183, Félix-Gabriel-Marchand Covered Bridge, Quebec. Nos. 3180d, 3184, West Montrose Covered Bridge, Ontario. Nos.

3180e, 3185, Ashnola No. 1 Covered Bridge, British Columbia.

**2019, June 17 Litho. *Perf. 12¾***

**3180** A1303 Sheet of 5 7.00 7.00
*a.-e.* P Any single 1.40 .70

**Booklet Stamps**
**Self-Adhesive**
***Serpentine Die Cut 12¾***

**3181** A1303 P multi 1.40 .70
**3182** A1303 P multi 1.40 .70
**3183** A1303 P multi 1.40 .70
**3184** A1303 P multi 1.40 .70
**3185** A1303 P multi 1.40 .70
*a.* Booklet pane of 10, 2 each #3181-3185 14.00
*Nos. 3181-3185 (5)* 7.00 3.50

Nos. 3180a-3180e, 3181-3185 each sold for 90c on day of issue.

Flight of Apollo 11, 50th Anniv. — A1304

Designs: Nos. 3186, 3188, Command and Service Modules, Earth. Nos. 3187, 3189, Lunar Module and Moon.

**2019, June 27 Litho. *Perf. 13¼***

**3186** A1304 P multi 1.40 .70
**3187** A1304 P multi 1.40 .70
*a.* Vert. pair, #3186-3187 2.80 1.40

**Booklet Stamps**
**Self-Adhesive**
***Serpentine Die Cut 13½***

**3188** A1304 P multi 1.40 .70
**3189** A1304 P multi 1.40 .70
*a.* Booklet pane of 10, 5 each #3188-3189 14.00

Nos. 3186-3189 each sold for 90c on day of issue. Nos. 3186-3187 were printed in sheets containing three pairs.

Bears
A1305

Designs: Nos. 3190a, 3194, Ursus arctos (grizzly bear). Nos. 3190b, 3192, Ursus maritimus (polar bear). Nos. 3190c, 3191, Ursus americanus with black fur (American black bear). Nos. 3190d, 3193, Ursus americanus with white fur (Kermode bear).

**2019, July 24 Litho. *Perf. 13¼***

**3190** A1305 Sheet of 4 5.60 5.60
*a.-d.* P Any single 1.40 .70

**Booklet Stamps**
**Self-Adhesive**
***Serpentine Die Cut 13½***

**3191** A1305 P multi 1.40 .70
**3192** A1305 P multi 1.40 .70
**3193** A1305 P multi 1.40 .70
**3194** A1305 P multi 1.40 .70
*a.* Booklet pane of 8, 2 each #3191-3194 11.50
*Nos. 3191-3194 (4)* 5.60 2.80

On day of issue, Nos. 3190a-3019d, 3191-3194 each sold for 90c.

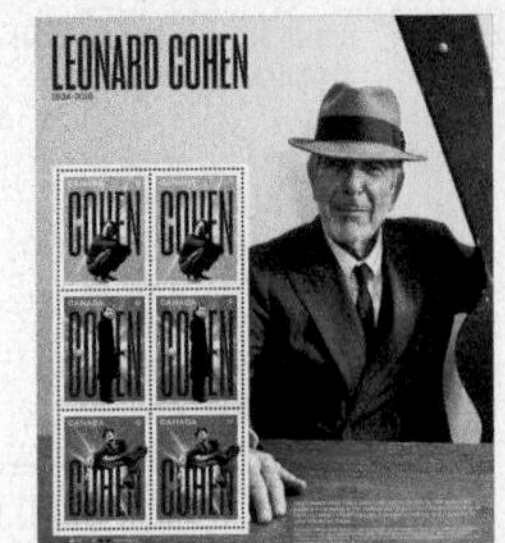


Leonard Cohen (1934-2016), Poet and Singer — A1306

Cohen: Nos. 3195a, 3195d, 3196, Squatting. Nos. 3195b, 3195e, 3197, Standing. Nos. 3195c, 3195f, 3198, Sitting and holding eyeglasses.

**2019, Sept. 21 Litho. *Perf. 12½***

**3195** A1306 Sheet of 6 13.50 13.50
*a.-c.* P Any single 1.40 .70
*d.* $1.27 multi 1.90 .95
*e.* $1.90 multi 3.00 1.50
*f.* $2.65 multi 4.00 2.00

**Booklet Stamps**
**Self-Adhesive**
***Serpentine Die Cut 13½x13¼***

**3196** A1306 P multi 1.40 .70
**3197** A1306 P multi 1.40 .70
**3198** A1306 P multi 1.40 .70
*a.* Booklet pane of 9, 3 each #3196-3198 13.00
*Nos. 3196-3198 (3)* 4.20 2.10

On day of issue, Nos. 3195a-3195c, 3196-3198 each sold for 90c.

Christmas
A1307 A1308

Designs: Nos. 3199a, 3201, Reindeer. Nos. 3199b, 3202, Dancers. Nos. 3199c, 3203, Partridge and pears. No. 3200, Magi on camels.

**2019, Nov. 4 Litho. *Perf. 13x12½***

**3199** Sheet of 3 7.50 7.50
*a.* A1307 P multi 1.40 .70
*b.* A1307 $1.27 multi 2.00 1.00
*c.* A1307 $2.65 multi 4.00 2.00

**Booklet Stamps**
**Self-Adhesive**
***Serpentine Die Cut 13¾***

**3200** A1308 P gold & multi 1.40 .70
*a.* Booklet pane of 12 17.00

***Serpentine Die Cut 13¼x13***

**3201** A1307 P multi 1.40 .70
*a.* Booklet pane of 12 17.00
**3202** A1307 $1.27 multi 2.00 1.00
*a.* Booklet pane of 6 12.00
**3203** A1307 $2.65 multi 4.00 2.00
*a.* Booklet pane of 6 24.00
*Nos. 3200-3203 (4)* 8.80 4.40

On day of issue, Nos. 3199a, 3200 and 3201 each sold for 90c.

Fort Garry and Métis Provisional Government Members — A1309

***Serpentine Die Cut 13½***
**2019, Nov. 6 Litho.**

**Booklet Stamp**
**Self-Adhesive**

**3204** A1309 P multi 1.40 .70
*a.* Booklet pane of 10 14.00

Red River Resistance, 150th anniv. No. 3204 sold for 90c on day of issue.

Hanukkah — A1310

***Serpentine Die Cut 13¼x13½***
**2019, Nov. 14 Litho.**

**Booklet Stamp**
**Self-Adhesive**

**3205** A1310 P multi 1.40 .70
*a.* Booklet pane of 10 14.00

No. 3205 sold for 90c on day of issue.

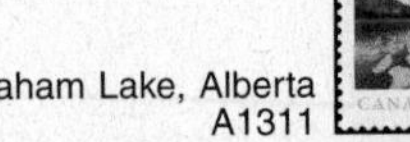

Abraham Lake, Alberta
A1311

Athabaska Sand Dunes Provincial Park, Saskatchewan
A1312

Herschel Island-Qikiqtaruk Territorial Park, Yukon — A1313

French River, Prince Edward Island
A1314

Magdalen Islands, Quebec
A1315

Carcajou Falls, Northwest Territories
A1316

Kootenay National Park, British Columbia
A1317

Swallowtail Lighthouse, Grand Manan Island, New Brunswick
A1318

Cabot Trail, Cape Breton Island, Nova Scotia
A1319

**2020, Jan. 13 Litho. *Perf. 13¼x13***

**3206** Sheet of 9 18.00 18.00
*a.* A1311 P multi 1.40 .70
*b.* A1312 P multi 1.40 .70
*c.* A1313 P multi 1.40 .70
*d.* A1314 P multi 1.40 .70
*e.* A1315 P multi 1.40 .70
*f.* A1316 $1.07 multi 1.60 .80
*g.* A1317 $1.30 multi 2.00 1.00
*h.* A1318 $1.94 multi 3.00 1.50
*i.* A1319 $2.71 multi 4.25 1.10

**Coil Stamps**
**Self-Adhesive**
***Serpentine Die Cut 9¼ Horiz.***

**3207** A1311 P multi 1.40 .70
**3208** A1312 P multi 1.40 .70
**3209** A1313 P multi 1.40 .70
**3210** A1314 P multi 1.40 .70
**3211** A1315 P multi 1.40 .70
*a.* Horiz. strip of 5, #3207-3211 7.00

***Serpentine Die Cut 8½ Horiz.***

**3212** A1311 P multi 1.40 .70
**3213** A1312 P multi 1.40 .70
**3214** A1313 P multi 1.40 .70
**3215** A1314 P multi 1.40 .70
**3216** A1315 P multi 1.40 .70
*a.* Vert. strip of 5, #3212-3216 7.00

***Serpentine Die Cut 8¼ Horiz.***

**3217** A1317 $1.30 multi 2.00 1.00
**3218** A1318 $1.94 multi 3.00 1.50
**3219** A1319 $2.71 multi 4.25 2.10

***Die Cut Perf. 13¼***

**3220** A1316 $1.07 multi 1.60 .80
*Nos. 3207-3220 (14)* 24.85 12.40

**Booklet Stamps**
***Serpentine Die Cut 13¾x13½***

**3221** A1311 P multi 1.40 .70
**3222** A1313 P multi 1.40 .70
**3223** A1315 P multi 1.40 .70
**3224** A1312 P multi 1.40 .70
**3225** A1314 P multi 1.40 .70
*a.* Booklet pane of 10, 2 each #3221-3225 14.00

***Serpentine Die Cut 9¼ Horiz.***

**3226** A1317 $1.30 multi 2.00 1.00
*a.* Booklet pane of 6 12.00
**3227** A1318 $1.94 multi 3.00 1.50
*a.* Booklet pane of 6 18.00
**3228** A1319 $2.71 multi 4.25 2.10
*a.* Booklet pane of 6 25.50
*Nos. 3221-3228 (8)* 16.25 8.10

On day of issue, Nos. 3206a-3206e, 3207-3216, and 3221-3225 each sold for 92c.

New Year 2020 (Year of the Rat) — A1320

Designs: P, Rats carrying rat in palinquin. $2.71, Two rats wearing Chinese robes.

**Litho. & Embossed With Foil Application**

**2020, Jan. 17 *Perf. 13***

**3229** A1320 P gold & multi 1.40 .70

**Souvenir Sheet**

**3230** A1320 $2.71 gold & multi 4.25 4.25
*a.* Souvenir sheet of 2, #3162b, 3230 8.25 8.25

**Booklet Stamps**
**Self-Adhesive**
**Litho.**
***Serpentine Die Cut 13½***

**3231** A1320 P multi 1.40 .70
*a.* Booklet pane of 10 14.00

**Litho. With Foil Application**

**3232** A1320 $2.71 gold & multi 4.25 4.25
*a.* Booklet pane of 6 25.50

On day of issue, Nos. 3229 and 3231 each sold for 92c. See Nos. 3259a, 3260a, 3261.

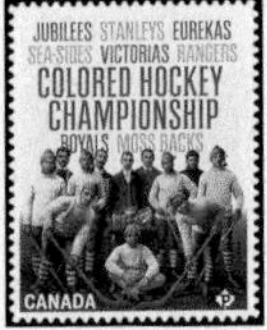


African-Canadian Ice Hockey Players From the Halifax Eurekas 1904 Champions of the Colored Hockey League — A1321

***Serpentine Die Cut 13½x13¼***
**2020, Jan. 24 Litho.**

**Booklet Stamp**
**Self-Adhesive**

**3233** A1321 P multi 1.40 .70
*a.* Booklet pane of 10 14.00

No. 3233 sold for 92c on day of issue.

Dahlias
A1322 A1323

Designs: Nos. 3234a, 3235, 3237, Dahlia without background. Nos. 3234b, 3236, 3238, Dahlias, turquoise green background.

**2020, Mar. 2 Litho. *Perf. 12¼x12½***

**Souvenir Sheet**

**3234** Sheet of 2 2.80 2.80
*a.-b.* A1322 P Either single 1.40 .70

**Self-Adhesive**
**Coil Stamps**
***Serpentine Die Cut 8 Vert.***

**3235** A1323 P multi 1.40 .70
**3236** A1323 P multi 1.40 .70
*a.* Horiz. pair, #3235-3236 2.80

**Booklet Stamps**
***Serpentine Die Cut 13½***

**3237** A1322 P multi 1.40 .70
**3238** A1322 P multi 1.40 .70
*a.* Booklet pane of 10, 5 each #3237-3238 + 10 stickers 14.00

On day of issue, Nos. 3234a-3234b, 3235-3238 each sold for 92c.

Eid Ul-Fitr — A1324

*Serpentine Die Cut 13¼x13½*

**2020, Apr. 24 Litho.**

**Booklet Stamp**
**Self-Adhesive**

**3239** A1324 P multi 1.40 .70
*a.* Booklet pane of 10 14.00

No. 3239 sold for 92c on day of issue.

Léo Major (1921-2008), Recipient of Distinguished Conduct Medal in World War II and Korean War — A1325

Veronica Foster (1922-2000), Worker on Machine Gun Assembly Line in World War II Popularized on Propaganda Posters — A1326

*Serpentine Die Cut 13¼x13½*

**2020, Apr. 29 Litho.**

**Booklet Stamps**
**Self-Adhesive**

**3240** A1325 P gold & multi 1.40 .70
**3241** A1326 P gold & multi 1.40 .70
*a.* Booklet pane of 10, 5 each #3240-3241 14.00

V-E (Victory in Europe) Day, 75th anniv. Nos. 3240-3241 each sold for 92c on day of issue.

Paintings by Group of Seven Artists A1327

Designs: Nos. 3242a, 3243a, In the Nickel Belt, by Franklin Carmichael (1890-1945). Nos. 3242b, 3243b, Miners' Houses, Glace Bay, by Lawren S. Harris (1887-1970). Nos. 3242c, 3243c, Labrador Coast, by A. Y. Jackson (1882-1974). Nos. 3242d, 3243d, Fire-swept Algoma, by Frank H. Johnston (1888-1949). Nos. 3242e, 3243e, Quebec Village, by Arthur Lismer (1885-1969). Nos. 3242f, 3243f, Church by the Sea, by J. E. H. Macdonald (1873-1932). Nos. 3242g, 3243g, Stormy Weather, Georgian Bay, by Frederick H. Varley (1881-1969).

**2020, May 7 Litho. *Perf. 13x13¼***

**3242** A1327 Sheet of 7 10.00 10.00
*a.-g.* P Any single 1.40 .70

**Booklet Stamps**
**Self-Adhesive**

*Serpentine Die Cut13¼x13½*

**3243** A1327 Booklet pane of 7 10.00 10.00
*a.-g.* P Any single 1.40 .70

Nos. 3242a-3242g, 3243a-3243g each sold for 92c on day of issue.

Microphone of Radio Station XWA and Headphones A1328

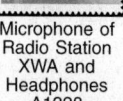

Radio Receiver, Speaker and Vacuum Tubes A1329

*Serpentine Die Cut 13¼x13½*

**2020, May 20 Litho.**

**Booklet Stamps**
**Self-Adhesive**

**3244** A1328 P multi 1.40 .70
**3245** A1329 P multi 1.40 .70
*a.* Booklet pane of 10, 5 each #3244-3245 14.00

First radio broadcast in Canada, cent. Nos. 3244-3245 each sold for 92c on day of issue.

Medical Researchers A1330

Designs: No. 3246, Dr. James Till and Dr. Ernest McCulloch (1926-2011), stem cell researchers. No. 3247, Dr. M. Vera Peters (1911-93), oncologist. No. 3248, Dr. Julio Montaner, HIV and AIDS researcher. No. 3249, Dr. Balfour Mount, palliative care physician. No. 3250, Dr. Bruce Chown (1893-1986), Rhesus disease researcher.

*Serpentine Die Cut 13½*

**2020, Sept. 10 Litho.**

**Booklet Stamps**
**Self-Adhesive**

**3246** A1330 P multi 1.40 .70
**3247** A1330 P multi 1.40 .70
**3248** A1330 P multi 1.40 .70
**3249** A1330 P multi 1.40 .70
**3250** A1330 P multi 1.40 .70
*a.* Booklet pane of 10, 2 each #3246-3250 14.00
*Nos. 3246-3250 (5)* 7.00 3.50

On day of issue, Nos. 3246-3250 each sold for 92c.

Diwali — A1331

*Serpentine Die Cut 15¼x15*

**2020, Oct. 15 Litho.**

**Booklet Stamp**
**Self-Adhesive**

**3251** A1331 P multi 1.40 .70
*a.* Booklet pane of 10 14.00

No. 3251 sold for 92c on day of issue. No. 3251 was sent to some standing order customers at least ten days in advance of official first day of issue.

Trenches on the Somme, Painting by Mary Riter Hamilton (1867-1954) A1332

*Serpentine Die Cut 13*

**2020, Oct. 28 Litho.**

**Booklet Stamp**
**Self-Adhesive**

**3252** A1332 P multi 1.40 .70
*a.* Booklet pane of 10 14.00

No. 3252 sold for 92c on day of issue.

Winter Sleigh Ride, Painting by Maud Lewis (1901-70) A1333

Team of Oxen in Winter, Painting by Lewis A1334

Family and Sled, Painting by Lewis A1335

Holy Family, Ox and Donkey A1336

**2020, Nov. 2 Litho. *Perf. 13½x13¼***

**3253** Souvenir sheet of 3 7.75 7.75
*a.* A1333 P multi 1.40 .70
*b.* A1334 $1.30 multi 2.00 1.00
*c.* A1335 $2.71 multi 4.25 2.10

**Booklet Stamps**
**Self-Adhesive**

*Serpentine Die Cut 13½*

**3254** A1336 P multi 1.40 .70
*a.* Booklet pane of 12 17.00

*Serpentine Die Cut 13¾x13½*

**3255** A1333 P multi 1.40 .70
*a.* Booklet pane of 12 17.00
**3256** A1334 $1.30 multi 2.00 1.00
*a.* Booklet pane of 6 12.00
**3257** A1335 $2.71 multi 4.25 2.10
*a.* Booklet pane of 6 25.50
*Nos. 3254-3257 (4)* 9.05 4.50

Christmas. On day of issue, Nos. 3253a, 3254 and 3255 each sold for 92c.

Menorah — A1337

*Serpentine Die Cut 15½x15¼*

**2020, Nov. 5 Litho.**

**Booklet Stamp**
**Self-Adhesive**

**3258** A1337 P multi 1.40 .70
*a.* Booklet pane of 10 14.00

Hanukkah. No. 3258 sold for 92c on day of issue.

**New Year Types of 2009-20 Redrawn With 2021 Date**

**Litho. & Embossed With Foil Application (#3259a-3259e, 3259h-3259i, 3259k-3259l, 3260a-3260i, 3260k-3260l), Litho. With Foil Application (#3259f-3259g, 3260j), Litho. & Embossed (#3259j)**

**2021, Jan. 15 *Perf. 12½***

**3259** Sheet of 12 18.00 18.00
*a.* A1320 P Like #3229 (Rats) 1.50 .75
*b.* A971 P Like #2296 (Ox) 1.50 .75
*c.* A1001 P Like #2348 (Tiger) 1.50 .75
*d.* A1032 P Like #2416 (Rabbits) 1.50 .75
*e.* A1055 P Like #2495 (Dragon) 1.50 .75
*f.* A1097 P Like #2599 (Snake) 1.50 .75
*g.* A1133 P Like #2699 (Horse) 1.50 .75
*h.* A1163 P Like #2801 (Ram) 1.50 .75
*i.* A1191 P Like #2884 (Monkey) 1.50 .75
*j.* A1217 P Like #2959 (Rooster) 1.50 .75
*k.* A1256 P Like #3052 (Dog) 1.50 .75
*l.* A1295 P Like #3161 (Pig) 1.50 .75
**3260** Sheet of 12 51.00 51.00
*a.* A1320 $2.71 Like #3230 (Rats) 4.25 4.25
*b.* A972 $2.71 Like #2297 (Ox) 4.25 4.25
*c.* A1001 $2.71 Like #2349 (Tiger) 4.25 4.25
*d.* A1032 $2.71 Like #2417 (Rabbits) 4.25 4.25
*e.* A1058 $2.71 Like #2496 (Dragon) 4.25 4.25
*f.* A1097 $2.71 Like #2600 (Snake) 4.25 4.25
*g.* A1133 $2.71 Like #2700 (Horse) 4.25 4.25
*h.* A1163 $2.71 Like #2802 (Ram) 4.25 4.25
*i.* A1191 $2.71 Like #2885 (Monkey) 4.25 4.25
*j.* A1217 $2.71 Like #2960 (Rooster) 4.25 4.25
*k.* A1256 $2.71 Like #3053 (Dog) 4.25 4.25
*l.* A1295 $2.71 Like #3162 (Pig) 4.25 4.25

**Booklet Stamps**
**Self-Adhesive**
**Litho.**

*Serpentine Die Cut 13½*

**3261** A1320 P Like #3232 (Rats) 1.50 .75
**3262** A972 P Like #2297 (Ox) 1.50 .75
**3263** A1001 P Like #2349 (Tiger) 1.50 .75
**3264** A1032 P Like #2417 (Rabbits) 1.50 .75
**3265** A1058 P Like #2497 (Dragon) 1.50 .75
**3266** A1097 P Like #2601 (Snake) 1.50 .75
**3267** A1133 P Like #2701 (Horse) 1.50 .75
**3268** A1163 P Like #2803 (Ram) 1.50 .75
**3269** A1191 P Like #2887 (Monkey) 1.50 .75
**3270** A1217 P Like #2962 (Rooster) 1.50 .75
**3271** A1256 P Like #3055 (Dog) 1.50 .75
**3272** A1295 P Like #3154 (Pig) 1.50 .75
*a.* Booklet pane of 12, #3261-3272 18.00
*Nos. 3261-3272 (12)* 18.00 9.00

Nos. 3259a-3259l, 3261-3272 each sold for 92c on day of issue.

Location of 2021 date: No. 3259a, LL in frame. No. 3259b, On hind leg of ox. No. 3259c, At LL. No. 3259d, At right, below rabbit's lower leg. No. 3259e, At LL above panel. No. 3259f, On red line of snake's bottom coil. No. 3259g, On hoof of hind leg of horse. No. 3259h, At right, above ram. No. 3259i, At LR. No. 3259j, Below tail and above leg. No. 3259k, On left side of bottom ring of lantern. No. 3259l, LL in frame.

Nos. 3260a, 3261, LL in frame. Nos. 3260b, 3262, At right above jar handle. Nos. 3260c, 3263, To right of denomination. Nos. 3260d, 3264, Below bottom rabbit's hind leg. Nos. 3260e, 3265, At UR. Nos. 3260f, 3266, At top, to left of snake. Nos. 3260g, 3267, At right of lower hoof. Nos. 3260h, 3268, On hind leg of ram. Nos. 3260i, 3269, On blue ornament to left of top central red circle. Nos. 3260j, 3270, Below rooster's wattle. Nos. 3260k, 3271, On left side of bottom ring of lantern. Nos. 3260l, 3272, LL in frame.

Black Settlers of Amber Valley, Alberta — A1338

Black Settlers of Willow Grove, New Brunswick A1339

*Serpentine Die Cut 13¼x13½*

**2021, Jan. 22 Litho.**

**Booklet Stamps**
**Self-Adhesive**

**3273** A1338 P multi 1.50 .75
**3274** A1339 P multi 1.50 .75
*a.* Booklet pane of 10, 5 each #3273-3274 15.00

On day of issue, Nos. 3273-3274 each sold for 92c.

Mammals in Winter — A1340

Designs: No. 3275a, 3278, Peary caribou. Nos. 3275b, 3276, Ermine. Nos. 3275c, 3277, Snowshoe hare. Nos. 3275d, 3280, Northern collared lemming, horiz. Nos. 3275e, 3279, Arctic fox, horiz.

**2021, Feb. 16 Litho. *Perf. 12¼***

**3275** A1340 Sheet of 5 7.50 7.50
*a.-e.* P Any single 1.50 .75

**Booklet Stamps**
**Self-Adhesive**

*Serpentine Die Cut 12½x13, 13x12½*

**3276** A1340 P multi 1.50 .75
**3277** A1340 P multi 1.50 .75
**3278** A1340 P multi 1.50 .75
**3279** A1340 P multi 1.50 .75
**3280** A1340 P multi 1.50 .75
*a.* Booklet pane of 10, 2 each #3276-3280 15.00
*Nos. 3276-3280 (5)* 7.50 3.75

On day of issue, Nos. 3275a-3275e, 3276-3280 each sold for 92c.

Crabapple Blossoms
A1341 A1342

Designs: Nos. 3281a, 3282, 3285, Malus "Maybride" (white blossoms). Nos. 3281b, 3283, 3284, Malus "Rosseau" (pink blossoms).

**2021, Mar. 1 Litho. *Perf. 12¼x12½***

**Souvenir Sheet**

3281 Sheet of 2 3.00 3.00
a.-b. A1341 P Either single 1.50 .75

**Self-Adhesive**
**Coil Stamps**

***Serpentine Die Cut 8¼ Vert.***

3282 A1342 P multi 1.50 .75
3283 A1342 P multi 1.50 .75
a. Horiz. pair, #3282-3283 3.00

**Booklet Stamps**

***Serpentine Die Cut 13½***

3284 A1341 P multi 1.50 .75
3285 A1341 P multi 1.50 .75
a. Booklet pane of 10, 5 each #3284-3285 + 10 stickers 15.00

On day of issue, Nos. 3281a-3281b, 3282-3285 each sold for 92c.

Juno Awards, 50th Anniv. — A1343

***Serpentine Die Cut 14x13¾***

**2021, Apr. 8 Litho.**

**Booklet Stamp**
**Self-Adhesive**

3286 A1343 P multi 1.50 .75
a. Booklet pane of 5 7.50

No. 3286 sold for 92c on day of issue.

Insulin, Cent. — A1344

***Serpentine Die Cut 13¼***

**2021, Apr. 15 Litho.**

**Booklet Stamp**
**Self-Adhesive**

3287 A1344 P multi 1.50 .75
a. Booklet pane of 10 15.00

No. 3287 sold for 92c on day of issue.

Eid — A1345

***Serpentine Die Cut 13¼x13½***

**2021, Apr. 22 Litho.**

**Booklet Stamp**
**Self-Adhesive**

3288 A1345 P multi 1.50 .75
a. Booklet pane of 10 15.00

No. 3288 sold for 92c on day of issue.

Ballet Dancers
A1346

Designs: Nos. 3289a, 3290, Fernand Nault (1920-2006). Nos. 3289b, 3291, Karen Kain.

**2021, Apr. 29 Litho. *Perf. 13***

3289 A1346 Sheet of 2 3.00 3.00
a.-b. P Either single 1.50 .75

**Booklet Stamps**
**Self-Adhesive**

***Serpentine Die Cut 13¼***

3290 A1346 P multi 1.50 .75
a. Booklet pane of 6 9.00
3291 A1346 P multi 1.50 .75
a. Booklet pane of 6 9.00

On day of issue, Nos. 3289a-3289b, 3290-3291 each sold for 92c.

John Turner (1929-2020), 17th Prime Minister of Canada — A1347

***Serpentine Die Cut 13¼x14***

**2021, June 7 Litho.**

**Booklet Stamp**
**Self-Adhesive**

3292 A1347 P multi 1.50 .75
a. Booklet pane of 10 15.00

No. 3292 sold for 92c on day of issue.

Schooner Bluenose, Cent. — A1348

Designs: Nos. 3293a, 3294, Bluenose and fishermen in fishing boat. Nos. 3293b, 3295, Bluenose racing another schooner.

**2021, June 29 Litho. *Perf. 13***

3293 A1348 Souvenir sheet of 2 3.00 3.00
a.-b. P Either single 1.50 .75
c. As #3293, with CAPEX 22 emblem added to sheet margin 3.00 3.00

**Booklet Stamps**
**Self-Adhesive**

***Serpentine Die Cut 13¼x13½***

3294 A1348 P multi 1.50 .75
3295 A1348 P multi 1.50 .75
a. Booklet pane of 10, 5 each #3294-3295 15.00

On day of issue, Nos. 3293a-3293b, 3294 and 3295 each sold for 92c.

Stan Rogers (1949-83), Folksinger — A1349

***Serpentine Die Cut 13½x13¼***

**2021, July 21 Litho.**

**Booklet Stamp**
**Self-Adhesive**

3296 A1349 P multi 1.50 .75
a. Booklet pane of 10 15.00

No. 3296 sold for 92c on day of issue.

Editorial Cartoon by Brian Gable — A1350

Editorial Cartoon by Terry Mosher — A1351

Editorial Cartoon by Duncan Macpherson (1924-93) A1352

Editorial Cartoon by Serge Chapleau A1353

Editorial Cartoon by Bruce MacKinnon A1354

***Serpentine Die Cut 13***

**2021, Oct. 8 Litho.**

**Booklet Stamps**
**Self-Adhesive**

3297 A1350 P multi 1.50 .75
3298 A1351 P multi 1.50 .75
3299 A1352 P multi 1.50 .75
3300 A1353 P multi 1.50 .75
3301 A1354 P multi 1.50 .75
a. Booklet pane of 10, 2 each #3297-3301 15.00
*Nos. 3297-3301 (5)* 7.50 3.75

On day of issue, Nos. 3297-3301 each sold for 92c.

Christopher Plummer (1929-2021), Actor — A1355

**2021, Oct. 14 Litho. *Perf. 13***

3302 A1355 P multi 1.50 .75

**Booklet Stamp**
**Self-Adhesive**

***Serpentine Die Cut 13¼x13½***

3303 A1355 P multi 1.50 .75
a. Booklet pane of 10 15.00

On day of issue, Nos. 3302-3303 each sold for 92c.

Diwali — A1356

***Serpentine Die Cut 13¼x13½***

**2021, Oct. 19 Litho.**

**Booklet Stamp**
**Self-Adhesive**

3304 A1356 P multi 1.50 .75
a. Booklet pane of 10 15.00

No. 3304 sold for 92c on day of issue.

Victoria Cross Recipients — A1357

**2021, Oct. 21 Litho. *Perf. 13¼x13½***

3305 A1357 P multi 1.50 .75

**Booklet Stamp**
**Self-Adhesive**

***Serpentine Die Cut 13¾x13¼***

3306 A1357 P multi 1.50 .75
a. Booklet pane of 10 15.00

Lionel Clark (1892-1916), Robert Shankland (1887-1968), and Frederick William Hall (1885-1915), World War I recipients of Victoria Cross, who at one time lived on Pine Street (later renamed Valour Road) in Winnipeg, Manitoba. On day of issue, Nos. 3305-3306 each sold for 92c.

Royal Canadian Legion Remembrance Poppy — A1358

***Serpentine Die Cut 13¼***

**2021, Oct. 29 Litho.**

**Booklet Stamp**
**Self-Adhesive**

3307 A1358 P multi 1.50 .75
a. Booklet pane of 10 15.00

No. 3307 sold for 92c on day of issue.

A1359

Christmas — A1360

Designs: Nos. 3308a, 3310, Santa Claus. Nos. 3308b, 3311, Reindeer. Nos. 3308c, 3312, Elf.

**2021, Nov. 1 Litho. *Perf. 13¼***

**Souvenir Sheet**

3308 Sheet of 3 8.25 8.25
a. A1359 P multi 1.50 .75
b. A1359 $1.30 multi 2.10 1.10
c. A1359 $2.71 multi 4.50 2.25

**Booklet Stamps**
**Self-Adhesive**

***Serpentine Die Cut 13½x13¼***

3309 A1360 P gold & sil 1.50 .75
a. Booklet pane of 12 18.00

***Serpentine Die Cut 13***

3310 A1359 P multi 1.50 .75
a. Booklet pane of 12 18.00
3311 A1359 $1.30 multi 2.10 1.10
a. Booklet pane of 6 13.00
3312 A1359 $2.71 multi 4.50 2.25
a. Booklet pane of 6 27.00
*Nos. 3309-3312 (4)* 9.60 4.85

On day of issue, Nos. 3308a, 3309 and 3310 each sold for 92c.

Hanukkah — A1361

***Serpentine Die Cut 13¼x13½***

**2021, Nov. 8 Litho.**

**Booklet Stamp**
**Self-Adhesive**

3313 A1361 P multi 1.50 .75
a. Booklet pane of 10 15.00

No. 3313 sold for 92c on day of issue.

Buffy Sainte-Marie, Singer — A1362

***Serpentine Die Cut 13¼x13½***

**2021, Nov. 19 Litho.**

**Booklet Stamp**
**Self-Adhesive**

3314 A1362 P multi 1.50 .75
a. Booklet pane of 10 15.00

No. 3314 sold for 92c on day of issue.

Margaret Atwood, Writer — A1363

***Serpentine Die Cut 13¾x13¼***

**2021, Nov. 25 Litho.**

**Booklet Stamp**
**Self-Adhesive**

**3315** A1363 P multi 1.50 .75
*a.* Booklet pane of 10 15.00

No. 3315 sold for 92c on day of issue.

Eleanor Collins, Jazz Singer and Television Host — A1364

***Serpentine Die Cut 13¾x13¼***

**2022, Jan. 21 Litho.**

**Booklet Stamp**
**Self-Adhesive**

**3316** A1364 P multi 1.50 .75
*a.* Booklet pane of 6 9.00

No. 3316 sold for 92c on day of issue.

Reign of Queen Elizabeth II, 70th Anniv. — A1365

**2022, Feb. 7 Litho. *Perf. 12½x13***

**3317** A1365 P silver & black 1.50 .75

**Booklet Stamp**
**Self-Adhesive**

***Serpentine Die Cut 13¼x13½***

**3318** A1365 P silver & black 1.50 .75
*a.* Booklet pane of 10 15.00

On day of issue Nos. 3317 and 3318 each sold for 92c.

A1366

Calla Lilies — A1367

Color of lily: Nos. 3319a, 3321, 3322, White. Nos. 3319b, 3320, 3323, Pink.

**2022, Mar. 1 Litho. *Perf. 13***

**Souvenir Sheet**

**3319** Sheet of 2 3.00 3.00
*a.-b.* A1366 P Either single 1.50 .75
*c.* As #3319, with CAPEX 22 emblem in sheet margin 3.00 3.00

**Self-Adhesive**
**Coil Stamps**

***Serpentine Die Cut 8¼ Vert.***

**3320** A1367 P multi 1.50 .75
**3321** A1367 P multi 1.50 .75
*a.* Horiz. pair, #3320-3321 3.00

**Booklet Stamps**

***Serpentine Die Cut 13½***

**3322** A1366 P multi 1.50 .75
**3323** A1366 P multi 1.50 .75
*a.* Booklet pane of 10, 5 each #3322-3323 + 10 stickers 15.00

On day of issue, Nos. 3319a-3319b, 3320-3323 each sold for 92c.

Organ and Tissue Donation — A1368

***Serpentine Die Cut 13½***

**2022, Apr. 7 Litho.**

**Booklet Stamp**
**Self-Adhesive**

**3324** A1368 P multi 1.50 .75
*a.* Booklet pane of 10 15.00

No. 3324 sold for 92c on day of issue.

Copper Lantern — A1369

***Serpentine Die Cut 13¾***

**2022, Apr. 12 Litho.**

**Booklet Stamp**
**Self-Adhesive**

**3325** A1369 P multi 1.50 .75
*a.* Booklet pane of 6 9.00

Eid. No. 3325 sold for 92c on day of issue.

Salome Bey (1933-2020), Blues Singer and Actress — A1370

***Serpentine Die Cut 14x13¾***

**2022, Apr. 22 Litho.**

**Booklet Stamp**
**Self-Adhesive**

**3326** A1370 P multi 1.50 .75
*a.* Booklet pane of 6 9.00

No. 3326 sold for 92c on day of issue.

Endangered Whales — A1371

Designs: Nos. 3327a, 3329, Orcinus orca. Nos. 3327b, 3328, Delphinapterus leucas, Nos. 3327c, 3331, Balaenoptera musculus. Nos. 3327d, 3332, Hyperoodon ampullatus. Nos. 3327e, 3330, Eubalaena glacialis.

**2022, May 20 Litho. *Perf. 13¾x14***

**3327** A1371 Sheet of 5 7.50 7.50
*a.-e.* P Any single 1.50 .75

**Booklet Stamps**
**Self-Adhesive**

***Serpentine Die Cut 13½x13¾***

**3328** A1371 P multi 1.50 .75
**3329** A1371 P multi 1.50 .75
**3330** A1371 P multi 1.50 .75
**3331** A1371 P multi 1.50 .75
**3332** A1371 P multi 1.50 .75
*a.* Booklet pane of 10, 2 each #3328-3332 15.00
*Nos. 3328-3332 (5)* 7.50 3.75

On day of issue, Nos. 3327a-3327e, 3328-3332 each sold for 92c.

Vintage Travel Posters A1372

Poster: Nos. 3333a, 3334, Mont Tremblant Resort, Quebec, by Herbert Bayer, 1939. Nos. 3333b, 3335, The Royal York Hotel, Toronto, Ontario, by Norman Fraser, c. 1935. Nos. 3333c, 3337, Cruise the Great Lakes, after the work of Tom Purvis, c. 1937. Nos. 3333d, 3336, Travel the Canadian, by Roger Couillard, 1955. Nos. 3333e, 3338, Canada's Picturesque East Coast, by Peter Ewart, c. 1950.

**2022, June 9 Litho. *Perf. 12½***

**3333** A1372 Sheet of 5 7.50 7.50
*a.-e.* P Any single 1.50 .75
*f.* As No. 3333, with CAPEX22 emblem in sheet margin 7.50 7.50

**Booklet Stamps**
**Self-Adhesive**

***Serpentine Die Cut 13½x13¼***

**3334** A1372 P multi 1.50 .75
**3335** A1372 P multi 1.50 .75
**3336** A1372 P multi 1.50 .75
**3337** A1372 P multi 1.50 .75
**3338** A1372 P multi 1.50 .75
*a.* Booklet pane of 10, 2 each #3334-3338 15.00
*Nos. 3334-3338 (5)* 7.50 3.75

CAPEX22 International Philatelic Exhibition, Toronto (No. 3333f). On day of issue, Nos. 3333a-3333e, 3334-3338 each sold for 92c.

Indigenous Leaders — A1373

Designs: Nos. 3339a, 3340, Marie-Anne Day Walker-Pelletier, Chief of Okanese First Nation. Nos. 3339b, 3341, Jose Kusugak (1950-2011), Inuk politician, horiz. Nos. 3339c, 3342, Harry Daniels (1940-2004), Métis politician and president of Congress of Aboriginal Peoples, horiz.

**2022, June 21 Litho. *Perf. 12½***

**3339** A1373 Sheet of 3 4.50 4.50
*a.-c.* P Any single 1.50 .75

**Booklet Stamps**
**Self-Adhesive**

***Serpentine Die Cut 13¼x13½***

**3340** A1373 P multi 1.50 .75
*a.* Booklet pane of 6 9.00

***Serpentine Die Cut 13½x13¼***

**3341** A1373 P multi 1.50 .75
*a.* Booklet pane of 6 9.00
**3342** A1373 P multi 1.50 .75
*a.* Booklet pane of 6 9.00
*Nos. 3340-3342 (3)* 4.50 2.25

On day of issue, Nos. 3339a-3339c, 3340-3342 each sold for 92c.

Miniature Sheet

Carousel Animals A1374

Designs: Nos. 3343a, 3344, Horse, Rosneath Fairgrounds, Rosneath, Ontario. Nos. 3343b, 3345, Horse, La Ronde, Montreal, Quebec. Nos. 3343c, 3346, Lion, Lakeside Park, St. Catherines, Ontario. Nos. 3343d, 3347, Horse, Heritage Park Historical Village, Calgary, Alberta. Nos. 3343e, 3348, Horse, Burnaby Village Museum, Burnaby, British Columbia.

**2022, July 21 Litho. *Perf. 14 Vert.***

**3343** A1374 Sheet of 5 + central label 7.50 7.50
*a.-e.* P Any single 1.50 .75

**Booklet Stamps**
**Self-Adhesive**

***Serpentine Die Cut 13½ Vert.***

**3344** A1374 P multi 1.50 .75
**3345** A1374 P multi 1.50 .75
**3346** A1374 P multi 1.50 .75
**3347** A1374 P multi 1.50 .75
**3348** A1374 P multi 1.50 .75
*a.* Booklet pane of 10, 2 each #3344-3348 15.00
*Nos. 3344-3348 (5)* 7.50 3.75

On day of issue, Nos. 3343a-3343e, 3344-3348 each sold for 92c.

A1375

***Serpentine Die Cut 13½x13¼***

**2022, Sept. 21 Litho.**

**Booklet Stamp**
**Self-Adhesive**

**3349** A1375 P multi 1.40 .70
*a.* Booklet pane of 10 14.00

Summit series victory of Canadian ice hockey team against Soviet Union team, 50th anniv.

No. 3349 sold for 92c on day of issue.

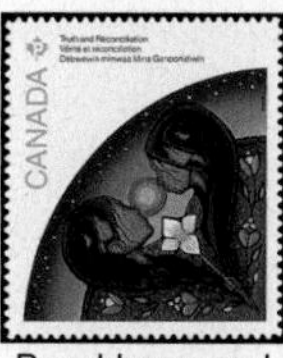


Bunchberry and Faces — A1376

Woman Lighting Inuit Stone Lamp — A1377

Hands and Tears — A1378

Beaded Flowers Over Map — A1379

***Serpentine Die Cut 13½x13¼***

**2022, Sept. 29 Litho.**

**Booklet Stamps**
**Self-Adhesive**

**3350** A1376 P multi 1.40 .70
**3351** A1377 P multi 1.40 .70
**3352** A1378 P multi 1.40 .70
**3353** A1379 P multi 1.40 .70
*a.* Booklet pane of 8, 2 each #3350-3353 11.50
*Nos. 3350-3353 (4)* 5.60 2.80

National Day for Truth and Reconciliation. On day of issue, Nos. 3350-3353 each sold for 92c.

Diwali — A1380

***Serpentine Die Cut 13½x13¼***

**2022, Oct. 6 Litho.**

**Booklet Stamp**
**Self-Adhesive**

**3354** A1380 P multi 1.40 .70
*a.* Booklet pane of 6 8.50

No. 3354 sold for 92c on day of issue.

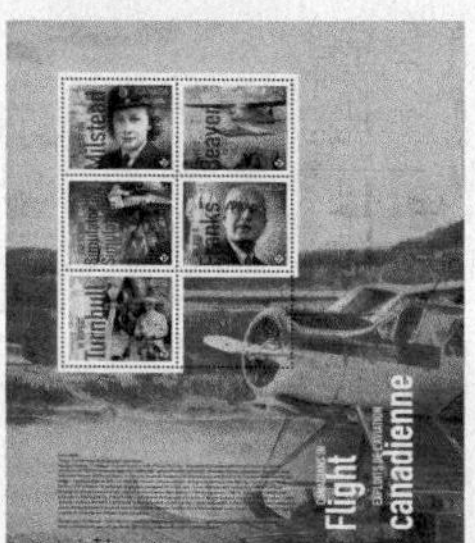


Canadians in Flight — A1381

Designs: Nos. 3355a, 3356, Violet Milstead (1919-2014), member of British Air Transport Auxiliary and bush pilot. Nos. 3355b, 3359, De Havilland Canada DHC-2 Beaver airplane. Nos. 3355c, 3360, CAE flight simulator. Nos. 3355d, 3357, Dr. Wilbur R. Franks (1901-86), developer of anti-gravity flight suit. Nos. 3355e, 3358, W. Rupert Turnbull (1870-1954), aeronautical engineer.

**2022, Oct. 17 Litho. *Perf. 12½***

**3355** A1381 Sheet of 5 + label 7.00 7.00
*a.-e.* P Any single 1.40 .70

**Booklet Stamps**
**Self-Adhesive**
***Serpentine Die Cut 13¼x13½***

**3356** A1381 P multi 1.40 .70
**3357** A1381 P multi 1.40 .70
**3358** A1381 P multi 1.40 .70
**3359** A1381 P multi 1.40 .70
**3360** A1381 P multi 1.40 .70
*a.* Booklet pane of 10, 2 each #3356-3360 14.00
*Nos. 3356-3360 (5)* 7.00 3.50

On day of issue, Nos. 3355a-3355e, 3356-3360 each sold for 92c.

Tommy Prince (1915-77), Military Hero and Vice-President of Manitoba Indian Association — A1382

**2022, Oct. 28 Litho. *Perf. 12½***

**3361** A1382 P multi 1.40 .70

**Booklet Stamp**
**Self-Adhesive**
***Serpentine Die Cut 13½***

**3362** A1382 P multi 1.40 .70
*a.* Booklet pane of 10 14.00

On day of issue, Nos. 3361 and 3362 each sold for 92c.

Christmas
A1383 A1384

Designs: Nos. 3363a, 3365, Cardinal. Nos. 3363b, 3366, Blue jay. Nos. 3363c, 3367, Grosbeak. No. 3364, Star and manger.

**2022, Nov. 1 Litho. *Perf. 13½x13¼***

**3363** Sheet of 3 7.50 7.50
*a.* A1383 P multi 1.40 .70
*b.* A1383 $1.30 multi 1.90 .95
*c.* A1383 $2.71 multi 4.00 2.00

**Booklet Stamps**
**Self-Adhesive**
***Serpentine Die Cut 13¾x13½***

**3364** A1384 P multi 1.40 .70
*a.* Booklet pane of 12 17.00

***Serpentine Die Cut 13¼x13***

**3365** A1383 P multi 1.40 .70
*a.* Booklet pane of 12 17.00
**3366** A1383 $1.30 multi 1.90 .95
*a.* Booklet pane of 6 11.50
**3367** A1383 $2.71 multi 4.00 2.00
*a.* Booklet pane of 6 24.00
*Nos. 3364-3367 (4)* 8.70 4.35

On day of issue, Nos. 3363a, 3364 and 3365 each sold for 92c.

Hanukkah A1385

***Serpentine Die Cut 13¾x14***

**2022, Nov. 7 Litho.**

**Booklet Stamp**
**Self-Adhesive**

**3368** A1385 P multi 1.40 .70
*a.* Booklet pane of 6 8.50

No. 3368 sold for 92c on day of issue.

Monique Mercure (1930-2020), Actress — A1386

***Perf. 13¼x13½***

**2022, Nov. 14 Litho.**

**3369** A1386 P multi 1.40 .70

**Booklet Stamp**
**Self-Adhesive**
***Serpentine Die Cut 13½x13¼***

**3370** A1386 P multi 1.40 .70
*a.* Booklet pane of 6 8.50

On day of issue, Nos. 3369 and 3370 each sold for 92c.

Chloe Cooley, Woman Enslaved in Ontario Forcibly Transported and Sold to Slaveholder in New York in 1793 — A1387

***Serpentine Die Cut 13¼x13½***

**2023, Jan. 30 Litho.**

**Booklet Stamp**
**Self-Adhesive**

**3371** A1387 P multi 1.40 .70
*a.* Booklet pane of 6 8.50

No. 3371 sold for 92c on day of issue.

---

## SEMI-POSTAL STAMPS

**Catalogue values for unused stamps in this section are for Never Hinged items.**

**Olympic Type of 1973**
**Size: 20x36mm**

**1974, Apr. 17 Litho. *Perf. 12½***

**B1** A307 8c + 2c multi .35 .35
**B2** A307 10c + 5c multi .55 .55
**B3** A307 15c + 5c multi .75 .75
*Nos. B1-B3 (3)* 1.65 1.65

SP1

**1975, Feb. 5 *Perf. 13***

**B4** SP1 8c + 2c Swimming .35 .35
**B5** SP1 10c + 5c Rowing .60 .60
**B6** SP1 15c + 5c Sailing .75 .75
*Nos. B4-B6 (3)* 1.70 1.70

SP2

**1975, Aug. 6**

**B7** SP2 8c + 2c Fencing .35 .35
**B8** SP2 10c + 5c Boxing .60 .60
**B9** SP2 15c + 5c Judo .75 .75
*Nos. B7-B9 (3)* 1.70 1.70

**1976, Jan. 7**

**B10** SP2 8c + 2c Basketball .35 .35
**B11** SP2 10c + 5c Vaulting .60 .60
**B12** SP2 20c + 5c Soccer .90 .90
*Nos. B10-B12 (3)* 1.85 1.85

21st Olympic Games, Montreal, July 17-Aug. 1. The surtax was for the Canadian Olympic Committee.

Literacy — SP3

**1996, Sept. 9 Litho. *Perf. 13x12½***

**B13** SP3 45c +5c multi 1.00 .60
*a.* Booklet pane of 10 10.00
Complete booklet 11.50

No. B13 has die cut opening in center to represent missing puzzle piece.

Surcharge donated to ABC CANADA literacy organization.

Mental Health — SP4

**Self-Adhesive**
**Booklet Stamp**
***Serpentine Die Cut 13¼***

**2008, Oct. 6 Litho.**

**B14** SP4 P +10c multi 1.40 .75
*a.* Booklet pane of 10 14.00

No. B14 had a franking value of 52c on day of issue. Surtax for Canada Post Foundation for Mental Health.

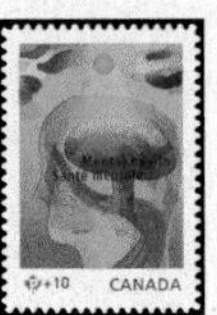

Mental Health — SP5

**Self-Adhesive**
**Booklet Stamp**
***Serpentine Die Cut 13¼***

**2009, Sept. 14 Litho.**

**B15** SP5 P +10c multi 1.40 .75
*a.* Booklet pane of 10 14.00

No. B15 had a franking value of 54c on day of issue. Surtax for Canada Post Foundation for Mental Health.

Mental Health — SP6

**Self-Adhesive**
**Booklet Stamp**
***Serpentine Die Cut 13¼***

**2010, Sept. 7 Litho.**

**B16** SP6 P + 10c multi 1.10 .75
*a.* Booklet pane of 10 11.00

No. B16 had a franking value of 57c on day of issue. Surtax for Canada Post Foundation for Mental Health.

Mental Health — SP7

**2011, Sept. 6 Litho. *Perf. 12¾x13¼***

**B17** Souvenir sheet of 2 #B17a 3.00 3.00
*a.* SP7 P+10c multi 1.50 1.25

**Booklet Stamp**
**Self-Adhesive**
***Serpentine Die Cut 13¼***

**B18** SP7 P+10c multi 1.35 .45
*a.* Booklet pane of 10 13.50

Nos. B17a and B18 each had a franking value of 59c on day of issue. Surtax was for Canada Post Foundation for Mental Health.

Hands and Heart — SP8

**Self-Adhesive**
***Serpentine Die Cut13x13¼***

**2012, Sept. 17 Litho.**

**Booklet Stamp**

**B19** SP8 P +10c multi 1.35 .75
*a.* Booklet pane of 10 13.50

No. B19 had a franking value of 61c on day of issue. Surtax for Canada Post Community Foundation.

Floating Abroad, Children's Art by Ezra Peters — SP9

***Serpentine Die Cut 13x12½***

**2013, Sept. 30 Booklet Stamp**
**Self-Adhesive**

**B20** SP9 63c+10c multi 1.10 .75
*a.* Booklet pane of 10 11.00

Surtax for Canada Post Community Foundation.

Children in Paper Sailboat — SP10

***Serpentine Die Cut 13½***

**2014, Sept. 29 Litho.**

**Booklet Stamp**
**Self-Adhesive**

**B21** SP10 P+10c multi 1.35 .75
*a.* Booklet pane of 10 13.50

No. B21 had a franking value of 85c. Surtax for Canada Post Community Foundation.

Children Reading Story Under Tented Bedsheet — SP11

***Serpentine Die Cut 13x12½***

**2015, Sept. 28 Litho.**

**Booklet Stamp**
**Self-Adhesive**

**B22** SP11 P+10c multi 1.35 .75
*a.* Booklet pane of 10 13.50

No. B22 had a franking value of 85c on day of issue. Surtax for Canada Post Community Foundation.

Stylized Bird — SP12

***Serpentine Die Cut 13½***

**2016, Sept. 26 Litho.**

**Booklet Stamps**
**Self-Adhesive**

**B23** SP12 P+10c blue & multi 1.35 .75
**B24** SP12 P+10c apple grn & multi 1.35 .75
*a.* Booklet pane of 10, 5 each #B23-B24 13.50

Nos. B23-B24 each had a franking value of 85c on day of issue. Surtax for Canada Post Community Foundation.

Stylized Cats — SP13

*Serpentine Die Cut 13½*

**2017, Sept. 25** **Litho.**

**Booklet Stamps**
**Self-Adhesive**

**B25** SP13 P+10c red violet & multi 1.35 .75
**B26** SP13 P+10c brt grn & multi 1.35 .75
*a.* Booklet pane of 10, 5 each #B25-B26 13.50

Nos. B25-B26 each had a franking value of 85c on day of issue. Surtax for Canada Post Community Foundation.

Child on Hill Looking at Clouds Shaped Like Animals — SP14

*Serpentine Die Cut 13¾x13½*

**2018, Sept. 24** **Litho.**

**Booklet Stamp**
**Self-Adhesive**

**B27** SP14 P+10c multi 1.50 1.50
*a.* Booklet pane of 10 15.00

No. B27 had a franking value of 85c on day of issue. Surtax for Canada Post Community Foundation.

Walking Ice Cream Cones and Ice Pops — SP15

Designs: No. B28, Cone with red ice cream, green pop. No. B29, Cone with blue ice cream, purple pop.

*Serpentine Die Cut 13½*

**2019, Sept. 23** **Litho.**

**Booklet Stamps**
**Self-Adhesive**

**B28** SP15 P+10c multi 1.50 1.50
**B29** SP15 P+10c multi 1.50 1.50
*a.* Booklet pane of 10, 5 each #B28-B29 15.00

Nos. B28-B28 both had a franking value of 90c on day of issue. Surtax for Canada Post Community Foundation.

Tree and Wildlife — SP16

*Serpentine Die Cut 13x13¼*

**2020, Sept. 21** **Litho.**

**Booklet Stamp**
**Self-Adhesive**

**B30** SP16 P+10c multi 1.60 1.60
*a.* Booklet pane of 10 16.00

No. B30 had a franking value of 92c on day of issue. Surtax for Canada Post Community Foundation.

Fireflies — SP17

*Serpentine Die Cut 13*

**2021, Sept. 20** **Litho.**

**Booklet Stamp**
**Self-Adhesive**

**B31** SP17 P+10c multi 1.60 1.60
*a.* Booklet pane of 10 16.00

No. B31 had a franking value of 92c on day of issue. Surtax for Canada Post Community Foundation.

Sunflower — SP18

*Serpentine Die Cut 13½*

**2022, July 7** **Litho.**

**Booklet Stamp**
**Self-Adhesive**

**B32** SP18 P+10c multi 1.60 1.60
*a.* Booklet pane of 10 16.00

No. B32 had a franking value of 92c on day of issue. Surtax for Canada-Ukraine Foundation.

Treehouses — SP19

*Serpentine Die Cut 13½*

**2022, Sept. 19** **Litho.**

**Booklet Stamp**
**Self-Adhesive**

**B33** SP19 P+10c multi 1.50 1.50
*a.* Booklet pane of 10 15.00

No. B33 had a franking value of 92c on day of issue. Surtax for Canada Post Community Foundation.

## AIR POST STAMPS

Allegory of Flight — AP1

**Unwmk.**

**1928, Sept. 21** **Engr.** ***Perf. 12***

**C1** AP1 5c brown 14.00 5.50
Never hinged 25.00
*a.* Imperf., pair 260.00
Never hinged 390.00

No. C1 is known imperforate horizontally and imperforate vertically.
For surcharge see No. C3.

For information on imperforate and part-perforate varieties, see note following No. 47a.

Allegory-Air Mail Circles Globe — AP2

**1930, Dec. 4** ***Perf. 11***

**C2** AP2 5c dark brown 45.00 24.00
Never hinged 90.00

For surcharge see No. C4.

No. C1 Surcharged

**1932, Feb. 22** ***Perf. 12***

**C3** AP1 6c on 5c brown 9.00 4.00
Never hinged 20.00
*a.* Inverted surcharge 225.00
Never hinged 325.00
*b.* Double surcharge 650.00
Never hinged 925.00
*c.* Triple surcharge 400.00
Never hinged 525.00
*d.* Pair, one without surcharge 950.00
Never hinged 1,350.

Counterfeit surcharges exist.
No. C3b is valued in the grade of fine.

**No. C2 Surcharged in Dark Blue**

**1932, July 12** ***Perf. 11***

**C4** AP2 6c on 5c dk brown 32.50 14.00
Never hinged 65.00

Daedalus — AP3

**1935, June 1** ***Perf. 12***

**C5** AP3 6c red brown 4.25 1.25
Never hinged 6.00
*a.* Horiz. pair, imperf. vert. *10,000.*
*b.* Imperf., pair 600.00
Never hinged 900.00

No. C5a is unique and is the result of a pre-perforating paper foldover.

Mackenzie River Steamer and Seaplane — AP4

**1938, June 15**

**C6** AP4 6c blue 3.75 .40
Never hinged 5.25
*a.* Imperf., pair 575.00
Never hinged 850.00

Planes and Student Flyers — AP5

**1942-43**

**C7** AP5 6c deep blue 5.50 1.30
Never hinged 7.50
*a.* Imperf., pair 575.00
Never hinged 850.00
**C8** AP5 7c deep blue ('43) 1.10 .25
Never hinged 1.60
*a.* Imperf., pair 575.00
Never hinged 850.00

Canada's contribution to the war effort of the Allied Nations.

**Catalogue values for unused stamps in this section, from this point to the end of the section, are for Never Hinged items.**

Canada Geese in Flight — AP6

**1946, Sept. 16**

**C9** AP6 7c deep blue 1.25 .25
*a.* Booklet pane of 4 2.50 2.50

For overprints see Nos. CO1, CO2.
For listing of complete booklet containing No. C9a, see No. 254a.

## AIR POST SPECIAL DELIVERY STAMPS

Trans-Canada Airplane and Aerial View of a City — APSD1

**1942-43** **Unwmk.** **Engr.** ***Perf. 12***

**CE1** APSD1 16c bright ultra 2.50 2.00
Never hinged 3.50
*a.* Imperf., pair 575.00
Never hinged 850.00
**CE2** APSD1 17c brt ultra ('43) 3.25 3.00
Never hinged 4.75
*a.* Imperf., pair 575.00
Never hinged 850.00

Canada's contribution to the war effort of the Allied Nations.

**Catalogue values for unused stamps in this section, from this point to the end of the section, are for Never Hinged items.**

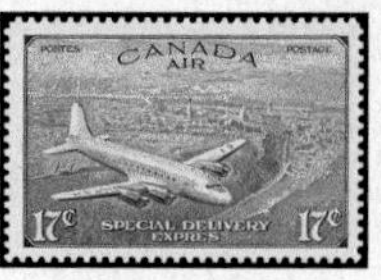
DC-4 Transatlantic Mail Plane Over Quebec APSD2

**1946, Sept. 16**

**CE3** APSD2 17c bright ultra 7.50 4.75

Circumflex accent on second "E" of "EXPRES."

**1946, Dec. 3** **Corrected Die**

**CE4** APSD2 17c bright ultra 7.50 6.00

Grave accent on the 2nd "E" of "EXPRES."

## AIR POST OFFICIAL STAMPS

**Catalogue values for unused stamps in this section are for Never Hinged items.**

No. C9 Overprinted in Black

**1949** **Unwmk.** ***Perf. 12***

**CO1** AP6 7c deep blue 11.00 4.75
*a.* No period after "S" 150.00 60.00

Same Overprinted

**1950**

**CO2** AP6 7c deep blue 17.50 13.50

## SPECIAL DELIVERY STAMPS

SD1

**Unwmk.**

**1898, June 28** **Engr.** ***Perf. 12***

**E1** SD1 10c blue green 170.00 11.00
Never hinged 675.00

SD2

**1922, Aug. 21**

**E2** SD2 20c carmine 100.00 9.00
Never hinged 300.00

Five Stages of Mail Transportation — SD3

**1927, June 29**

E3 SD3 20c orange 35.00 22.50
Never hinged 52.50
a. Imperf., pair 190.00
Never hinged 380.00

No. E3 forms part of the Confederation Commemorative issue. It is known imperforate vertically and imperforate horizontally.

SD4

**1930, Sept. 2** *Perf. 11*

E4 SD4 20c henna brown 65.00 17.50
Never hinged 125.00

SD5

**1932, Dec. 24**

E5 SD5 20c henna brown 60.00 17.50
Never hinged 115.00
a. Imperf., pair 600.00
Never hinged 1,200.

Allegory of Progress SD6

**1935, June 1** *Perf. 12*

E6 SD6 20c dark carmine 11.00 7.50
Never hinged 19.25
a. Imperf., pair 575.00
Never hinged 1,000.

Arms of Canada SD7

**1938-39**

E7 SD7 10c dk green (4/1/39) 9.00 3.50
Never hinged 15.00
a. Imperf., pair 575.00
Never hinged 1,000.
E8 SD7 20c dark carmine (6/15/38) 32.50 31.00
Never hinged 56.00
a. Imperf., pair 575.00
Never hinged 1,000.

**No. E8 Surcharged in Black**

**1939, Mar. 1**

E9 SD7 10c on 20c dk car 8.00 6.50
Never hinged 14.00

Coat of Arms and Flags — SD8

**1942, July 1**

E10 SD8 10c green 4.00 2.00
Never hinged 6.00
a. Imperf., pair 575.00
Never hinged 850.00

Canada's contribution to the war effort of the Allied Nations.

**Catalogue values for unused stamps in this section, from this point to the end of the section, are for Never Hinged items.**

Arms of Canada SD9

**1946, Sept. 16**

E11 SD9 10c green 7.00 1.25

The laurel and olive branches symbolize Victory and Peace.
For overprints see Nos. EO1, EO2.

## SPECIAL DELIVERY OFFICIAL STAMPS

**Catalogue values for unused stamps in this section are for Never Hinged items.**

**No. E11 Overprinted in Black**

**1950** **Unwmk.** *Perf. 12*

EO1 SD9 10c green 17.50 12.50

**Same Overprinted**

EO2 SD9 10c green 27.00 17.50

## REGISTRATION STAMPS

R1

**1875-88 Unwmk. Engr.** *Perf. 12*

F1 R1 2c orange 110.00 6.00
Never hinged 330.00
a. 2c vermilion 185.00 17.50
Never hinged 550.00
b. 2c rose carmine 370.00 110.00
Never hinged 1,100.
c. As "a," imperf., pair *3,000.*
d. Perf. 12x11½ 600.00 110.00
Never hinged 1,750.
F2 R1 5c dark green 140.00 5.50
Never hinged 280.00
a. 5c blue green ('88) 155.00 5.50
Never hinged 465.00
b. 5c yellow green 280.00 7.00
Never hinged 840.00
c. Imperf., pair 1,100.
Never hinged *2,200.*
d. Perf. 12x11½ 2,750. 300.00
Never hinged *7,500.*
F3 R1 8c dull blue ('76) 675.00 330.00
Never hinged 4,000.
*Nos. F1-F3 (3)* 925.00 341.50

The used No. F1c is unique (fine centering).

## POSTAGE DUE STAMPS

D1

**1906-28 Unwmk. Engr.** *Perf. 12*

J1 D1 1c violet 25.00 4.75
Never hinged 50.00
a. Thin paper ('24) 52.50 7.50
Never hinged 105.00
b. Imperf., pair 350.00
J2 D1 2c violet 25.00 1.00
Never hinged 50.00
a. Thin paper ('24) 52.50 11.00
Never hinged 105.00
b. Imperf., pair 350.00
J3 D1 4c violet ('28) 70.00 22.50
Never hinged 140.00
J4 D1 5c violet 25.00 2.00
Never hinged 50.00
a. As "c," thin paper 35.00 7.50
Never hinged 70.00
b. Imperf., pair 350.00
c. 5c reddish violet ('28) 25.00 2.00
Never hinged 50.00
J5 D1 10c violet ('28) 100.00 13.00
Never hinged 200.00
*Nos. J1-J5 (5)* 245.00 43.25
Set, never hinged 490.00

In 1924 there was a printing of Nos. J1, J2 and J4 on thin semi-transparent paper. Imperf pairs are without gum.

D2

**1930-32** *Perf. 11*

J6 D2 1c dark violet 12.50 4.25
Never hinged 25.00
J7 D2 2c dark violet 7.00 1.10
Never hinged 14.00
J8 D2 4c dark violet 15.00 5.50
Never hinged 30.00
J9 D2 5c dark violet 22.50 6.50
Never hinged 45.00
J10 D2 10c dark violet ('32) 110.00 10.00
Never hinged 220.00
a. Vert. pair, imperf. horiz. 1,850. —
Never hinged 3,700.
*Nos. J6-J10 (5)* 167.00 27.35
Set, never hinged 334.00

No. J10a is valued in the grade of fine.

D3

**1933-34**

J11 D3 1c dark violet ('34) 17.50 6.50
Never hinged 35.00
a. Imperf., pair 375.00
Never hinged 750.00
J12 D3 2c dark violet 9.00 1.25
Never hinged 18.00
J13 D3 4c dark violet 17.50 8.00
Never hinged 35.00
J14 D3 10c dark violet 35.00 7.25
Never hinged 70.00
*Nos. J11-J14 (4)* 79.00 23.00
Set, never hinged 158.00

**Catalogue values for unused stamps in this section, from this point to the end of the section, are for Never Hinged items.**

D4

**1935-65** *Perf. 12*

J15 D4 1c dark violet .40 .25
a. Imperf., pair 325.00
J16 D4 2c dark violet .40 .25
a. Imperf., pair 325.00
J16B D4 3c dark vio ('65) 2.50 1.50
J17 D4 4c dark violet .50 .25
a. Imperf., pair 325.00
J18 D4 5c dark vio ('48) .55 .35
J19 D4 6c dark vio ('57) 2.75 1.75
J20 D4 10c dark violet .55 .25
a. Imperf., pair 325.00
*Nos. J15-J20 (7)* 7.65 4.60

D5

**Size: 20x17mm**

**1967, Feb. 8 Litho.** *Perf. 12*

J21 D5 1c carmine rose .30 .25
J22 D5 2c carmine rose .30 .25
J23 D5 3c carmine rose .30 .25
J24 D5 4c carmine rose .30 .25
J25 D5 5c carmine rose 1.50 1.50
J26 D5 6c carmine rose .30 .25
J27 D5 10c carmine rose .40 .30
*Nos. J21-J27 (7)* 3.40 3.05

**Size: 20x15¾mm**

**1969-78** *Perf. 12*

J28 D5 1c car rose ('70) .45 .30
a. Perf. 12½x12 ('77) .30 .25
J29 D5 2c car rose ('72) .30 .25
J30 D5 3c car rose ('74) .30 .25
J31 D5 4c carmine rose .40 .30
a. Perf. 12½x12 ('77) .30 .25
b. Printed on gummed side *1,400.*
J32 D5 5c car rose, perf. 12½x12 ('77) .30 .25
a. Perf. 12 16.00 12.50
J33 D5 6c car rose ('72) .30 .25
J34 D5 8c carmine rose .30 .25
a. Perf. 12½x12 ('78) .40 .30
J35 D5 10c carmine rose .55 .25
a. Perf. 12½x12 ('77) .30 .25
J36 D5 12c carmine rose .75 .60
a. Perf. 12½x12 ('77) 1.50 .70
J37 D5 16c carmine rose ('74) .40 .25

*Perf. 12½x12*

J38 D5 20c carmine rose ('77) .55 .40
J39 D5 24c carmine rose ('77) .65 .40
J40 D5 50c carmine rose ('77) 1.00 .75
*Nos. J28-J40 (13)* 6.25 4.50

## WAR TAX STAMPS

WT1

**Unwmk.**

**1915, Mar. 25 Engr.** *Perf. 12*

MR1 WT1 1c green 27.50 .35
Never hinged 82.50
MR2 WT1 2c carmine 27.50 .40
Never hinged 82.50

In 1915 postage stamps of 5, 20 and 50 cents were overprinted "WAR TAX" in two lines. These stamps were intended for fiscal use, the war tax on postal matter being 1 cent. A few of these stamps were used to pay postage.

WT2

Type I

Type II

TWO TYPES:
Type I — There is a colored line between two white lines below the large letter "T."
Type II — The right half of the colored line is replaced by two short diagonal lines and five small dots.

**1916**

MR3 WT2 2c + 1c car (I) 40.00 .25
Never hinged 120.00
a. 2c + 1c carmine (II) 275.00 4.50
Never hinged 825.00
b. 2c + 1c rose red (I) 52.50 .40
Never hinged 157.50
MR4 WT2 2c + 1c brn (II) 27.50 .25
Never hinged 82.50
a. 2c + 1c brown (I) 975.00 10.00
Never hinged 2,925.
b. Imperf., pair (I) 200.00
c. Imperf., pair (II) 2,250.

Nos. MR4b and MR4c were made without gum.

*Perf. 12x8*

MR5 WT2 2c + 1c car (I) 52.50 30.00
Never hinged 172.50

### Coil Stamps

*Perf. 8 Vertically*

**MR6** WT2 2c + 1c car (I) 150.00 10.00
Never hinged 450.00
**MR7** WT2 2c + 1c brn (II) 50.00 2.25
Never hinged 150.00
*a.* 2c + 1c brown (I) 180.00 7.50
Never hinged 540.00

### OVERPRINTED OFFICIAL STAMPS

**Catalogue values for unused stamps in this section are for Never Hinged items.**

With Perforated Initials O H M S

On March 28, 1939 the Treasury Board ruled that on and after June 30, 1939 all stamps used by government departments throughout the country should be perforated O H M S (On His Majesty's Service) and that "the Post Office Department is to make arrangements required to provide that all stamps sold to Government Departments are perforated with the letters O H M S." The sale of such perforated stamps was discontinued in 1948.

For listings see the *Scott Classic Specialized Catalogue.*

Nos. 249, 250, 252 and 254 Overprinted in Black

**1949-50** **Unwmk.** ***Perf. 12***

**O1** A97 1c green 3.25 1.75
*a.* No period after "S" 210.00 110.00
**O2** A98 2c brown 10.00 10.00
*a.* No period after "S" 325.00 170.00
**O3** A99 3c rose violet 3.25 1.25
**O4** A98 4c dark carmine 4.50 .75

Nos. 269 to 273 Overprinted in Black

**O6** A108 10c olive 6.50 .60
*a.* No period after "S" 110.00 67.50
**O7** A109 14c black brown 11.00 2.25
*a.* No period after "S" 165.00 85.00
**O8** A110 20c slate black 27.00 3.00
*a.* No period after "S" 180.00 75.00
**O9** A111 50c dk blue grn 245.00 110.00
*a.* No period after "S" 1,000. 550.00
**O10** A112 $1 red violet 87.50 42.50
*a.* No period after "S" *6,750.* *3,750.*
*Nos. O1-O4,O6-O10 (9)* 398.00 172.10

It is recommended that a certificate of authenticity be acquired for No. O10a.

**Same Overprint on No. 294**

**1950**

**O11** A124 50c dull green 45.00 15.00

Nos. 284 to 288 Overprinted in Black

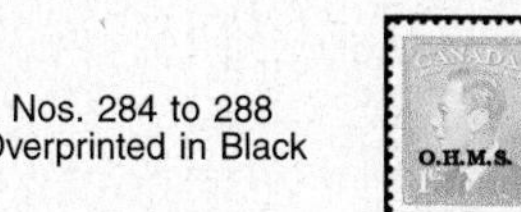


**1950**

**O12** A119 1c green .85 .35
**O13** A120 2c sepia 1.65 .80
**O14** A121 3c rose violet 1.65 .50
**O15** A122 4c dark carmine 1.65 .25
*b.* No period after "S" 650.00 290.00
**O15A** A123 5c deep blue 2.75 1.50
*c.* No period after "S" 110.00 60.00
*Nos. O12-O15A (5)* 8.55 3.40

It is recommended that a certificate of authenticity be acquired for No. O15b.

**Stamps of 1946-50 Overprinted in Black**

a

b

**1950**

**O16** A119(a) 1c grn (#284) 1.10 .25
**O17** A120(a) 2c sep (#285) 2.20 .90
**O18** A121(a) 3c rose vio (#286) 2.20 .25
**O19** A122(a) 4c dk car (#287) 2.20 .25
**O20** A123(a) 5c dp bl (#288) 3.25 .90
**O21** A108(b) 10c olive 6.50 .50
**O22** A109(b) 14c black brn 15.00 1.80
**O23** A110(b) 20c slate blk 22.50 1.00
**O24** A124(b) 50c dull green 13.50 5.25
**O25** A112(b) $1 red violet 90.00 75.00
*Nos. O16-O25 (10)* 158.45 86.10

Nos. 301-302 Ovptd.

**1950-51**

**O26** A125 10c black brown 2.25 .25
*a.* Pair, one without "G" 950.00 550.00
**O27** A126 $1 brt ultra ('51) 85.00 57.50

It is recommended that a certificate of authenticity be acquired for No. O26a.

Nos. 305-306 Overprinted

**1951-52** **Unwmk.** ***Perf. 12***

**O28** A120 2c olive green .75 .25
**O29** A122 4c orange ver ('52) 1.10 .25

No. 316 Ovptd.

**1952**

**O30** A132 20c gray 4.50 .25

Nos. 320-321 Ovptd.

**1952-53**

**O31** A136 7c blue 4.75 1.25
**O32** A137 $1 gray ('53) 13.50 7.50

Nos. 325-329, 334 Overprinted

**1953-61**

**O33** A139(a) 1c violet brown .40 .25
**O34** A139(a) 2c green .40 .25
**O35** A139(a) 3c carmine rose .40 .25
**O36** A139(a) 4c violet .45 .25
**O37** A139(a) 5c ultramarine .45 .25
**O38** A141(b) 50c light green 5.00 1.20
*a.* Overprinted type "c" ('61) 5.00 2.00
*Nos. O33-O38 (6)* 7.10 2.45

**No. 351 Overprinted**

No. O39 No. O39a

**1955-62**

**O39** A148 10c violet brown 1.00 .25
*a.* Overprinted type "c" ('62) 1.90 1.25

Nos. 337-338, 340-341 Ovptd.

**1955-56**

**O40** A144 1c vio brown ('56) .40 .30
**O41** A144 2c green ('56) .40 .25
**O43** A144 4c violet ('56) 1.20 .25
**O44** A144 5c bright blue .75 .25
*Nos. O40-O44 (4)* 2.75 1.05

**No. 362 Overprinted**

No. O45

No. O45a

**1956-62**

**O45** A159 20c green 1.75 .25
*a.* Overprinted type "c" ('62) 7.00 .50

Nos. 401-402, 404-405 Overprinted

**1963, May 15** **Engr.** ***Perf. 12***

**O46** A195 1c deep brown .75 .70
*a.* Double overprint 750.00
**O47** A195 2c green .75 .70
*a.* Pair, one without "G" 1,000.
**O48** A195 4c carmine .80 .70
**O49** A195 5c violet blue .70 .50
*Nos. O46-O49 (4)* 3.00 2.60

## CAPE JUBY

ˈkāp ˈjü-bē

LOCATION — Northwest coast of Africa in Spanish Sahara
GOVT. — Spanish administration
AREA — 12,700 sq. mi.
POP. — 9,836
CAPITAL — Villa Bens (Cape Juby)

By agreement with France, Spain's Sahara possessions were extended to include Cape Juby and in 1916 Spanish troops occupied the territory. It was attached for administrative purposes to Spanish Sahara.

100 Centimos = 1 Peseta

Stamps of Rio de Oro, 1914 Surcharged in Violet, Red, Green or Blue

**1916** **Unwmk.** ***Perf. 13***

**1** A6 5c on 4p rose (V) 200.00 19.00
*a.* Inverted surcharge 250.00 30.00
*d.* Double surcharge 325.00 50.00
**2** A6 10c on 10p dl vio (R) 50.00 19.00
*a.* Inverted surcharge 55.00 30.00
*d.* Double surcharge 75.00 50.00
**2E** A6 10c on 10p dl vio (V) 100.00 72.50
*f.* Double surcharge (R, V) 150.00 90.00
**2G** A6 10c on 10p dl vio (B) 100.00 72.50
**3** A6 15c on 50c dk brn (G) 52.50 30.00
*a.* Inverted surcharge 57.50 30.00
**4** A6 15c on 50c dk brn (R) 50.00 19.00
*a.* Inverted surcharge 55.00 30.00
**5** A6 40c on 1p red vio (G) 87.50 35.00
*a.* Inverted surcharge 75.00 37.50
**6** A6 40c on 1p red vio (R) 75.00 26.00
*a.* Inverted surcharge 75.00 42.50
*Nos. 1-6 (8)* 715.00 293.00
Set, never hinged 1,150.

Very fine examples of Nos. 1-6 will be somewhat off center. Well centered examples are uncommon and will sell for more.

Stamps of Spain, 1876-1917, Overprinted in Red or Black

**1919** ***Imperf.***

**7** A21 ¼c bl grn (R) .30 .30

*Perf. 13x12½, 14*

**8** A46 2c dk brn (Bk) .30 .30
*a.* Double overprint 50.00 *60.00*
*b.* Double overprint (Bk + R) 110.00 110.00
**9** A46 5c grn (R) .85 .75
*a.* Double overprint 50.00 *50.00*
*b.* Inverted overprint 47.50 *60.00*
**10** A46 10c car (Bk) 1.00 .70
*a.* Double overprint (Bk + R) 110.00 80.00
*b.* Double overprint (Bk) 40.00 *50.00*
**11** A46 15c ocher (Bk) 3.50 3.00
*b.* Double overprint 50.00 *50.00*
*c.* Red control # 6.50 3.75
*d.* As "c," inverted overprint 45.00 45.00
**12** A46 20c ol grn (R) 24.00 14.00
**13** A46 25c dp bl (R) 3.50 2.50
*a.* Double overprint 50.00 *52.50*
**14** A46 30c bl grn (R) 3.50 3.25
**15** A46 40c rose (Bk) 3.50 3.25
**16** A46 50c sl bl (R) 4.00 4.00
**17** A46 1p lake (Bk) 11.50 9.50
**18** A46 4p dp vio (R) 52.50 47.50
**19** A46 10p org (Bk) 70.00 65.00
*Nos. 7-19 (13)* 178.45 154.05
Set, never hinged 355.00

Nos. 8-19 have blue control number on back. For imperfs, see the *Scott Classic Catalogue.*

**Same on Stamps of Spain, 1920-21**

**1922** ***Imperf.***

**20** A47 1c blue green (R) 25.00 14.00
Never hinged 45.00

**Engr.** ***Perf. 13x12½***

**Blue Control Number on Back**

**23** A46 20c violet 145.00 42.50

A 2c and a 15c exist, values $400 and $10, respectively, for unused, hinged examples, $600 and $15 for never hinged. Overprint on 2c privately applied.

**Same on Stamps of Spain, 1922-23**

**1925** ***Perf. 13½x13***

**25** A49 5c red vio 5.25 3.50
**26** A49 10c bl grn 13.00 3.50
**28** A49 20c violet 27.50 10.00
*Nos. 25-28 (3)* 45.75 17.00
Set, never hinged 72.50

Exists on Spain No. 331, 2c olive green. Value $425 unused hinged and $650 never hinged. Overprint was privately applied.

**Seville-Barcelona Exposition Issue**

Stamps of Spain, 1929, Overprinted in Red or Blue

**1929** ***Perf. 11***

**29** A52 5c rose lake (Bl) .35 .35
**30** A53 10c green (R) .35 .35
**31** A50 15c Prus bl (R) .35 .35
**32** A51 20c pur (R) .35 .35
**33** A50 25c brt rose (Bl) .35 .35
**34** A52 30c blk brn (Bl) .35 .35
**35** A53 40c dk bl (R) .35 .35
**36** A51 50c dp org (Bl) .55 .55
**37** A52 1p bl blk (R) 11.00 11.00
**38** A53 4p dp rose (Bl) 13.00 13.00
**39** A53 10p brn (Bl) 13.00 13.00
*Nos. 29-39 (11)* 40.00 40.00
Set, never hinged 80.00

Stamps of Spanish Morocco, 1928-33, Overprinted in Black or Red

**1934** ***Perf. 14***

**40** A7 1c brt rose (Bk) .55 .55
**41** A2 2c dk vio (R) 5.00 5.00
**42** A2 5c dp bl (R) 5.75 5.75
**43** A2 10c dk grn (Bk) 14.00 11.50
**43A** A10 10c dk grn (R) 3.50 3.50
**44** A2 15c org brn (Bk) 32.50 29.00
**45** A7 20c sl grn (R) 13.00 10.00
**46** A3 25c cop red (Bk) 6.00 5.50
**47** A10 30c red brn (Bk) 11.00 10.00
**48** A13 40c dp bl (R) 40.00 37.50
**49** A13 50c red org (Bk) 80.00 70.00
**50** A4 1p yel grn (Bk) 57.50 57.50
**51** A5 2.50p red vio (Bk) 120.00 115.00
**52** A6 4p ultra (R) 160.00 145.00

No. 43A and 1c, 20c, 30c, 40c, 50c, with control numbers.

### Same Overprint in Black on Stamp of Spanish Morocco, 1932

| No. | Type | Description | Unused | Used |
|---|---|---|---|---|
| 53 | A2 | 1c car rose ("Ct") | 2.40 | 2.40 |
| | | *Nos. 40-53 (15)* | 551.20 | 508.20 |
| | | Set, never hinged | 900.00 | |

Stamps of Spanish Morocco, 1933-35, Overprinted in Black, Blue or Red

**1935-36**

| No. | Type | Description | Unused | Used |
|---|---|---|---|---|
| 54 | A8 | 2c grn (R) | 1.25 | 1.00 |
| 55 | A9 | 5c mag (Bk) | 3.50 | 3.50 |
| 55A | A10 | 10c dk grn (R) ('36) | 21.00 | 21.00 |
| 56 | A11 | 15c yel (Bl) | 8.00 | 8.00 |
| 57 | A12 | 25c crim (Bk) | 100.00 | 85.00 |
| 58 | A8 | 1p sl blk (R) | 13.50 | 12.50 |
| 59 | A9 | 2.50p brn (Bl) | 60.00 | 47.50 |
| 60 | A11 | 4p yel grn (R) | 100.00 | 85.00 |
| 61 | A12 | 5p blk (R) | 85.00 | 65.00 |
| | | *Nos. 54-61 (9)* | 392.25 | 328.50 |
| | | Set, never hinged | 750.00 | |

### Same Overprint in Black or Red on Stamps of Spanish Morocco, 1935

**1935** ***Perf. 13½***

| No. | Type | Description | Unused | Used |
|---|---|---|---|---|
| 62 | A14 | 25c vio (R) | 4.00 | 4.00 |
| 63 | A15 | 30c crim (Bk) | 4.00 | 4.00 |
| 64 | A14 | 40c org (Bk) | 5.75 | 5.25 |
| 65 | A15 | 50c brt bl (R) | 15.00 | 11.00 |
| 66 | A14 | 60c dk bl grn (R) | 17.50 | 14.00 |
| 67 | A15 | 2p brn lake (Bk) | 95.00 | 75.00 |

### Same Overprint on Stamps of Spanish Morocco, 1933

***Perf. 13½, 14***

| No. | Type | Description | Unused | Used |
|---|---|---|---|---|
| 68 | A7 | 1c brt rose (Bk) | .30 | .30 |

***Perf. 14***

| No. | Type | Description | Unused | Used |
|---|---|---|---|---|
| 69 | A7 | 20c slate grn (R) | 6.75 | 6.75 |
| | | *Nos. 62-69 (8)* | 148.30 | 120.30 |
| | | Set, never hinged | 200.00 | |

### Same Overprint on Stamps of Spanish Morocco, 1937

**1937** ***Perf. 13½***

| No. | Type | Description | Unused | Used |
|---|---|---|---|---|
| 70 | A21 | 1c dk bl (Bk) | .50 | .50 |
| 71 | A21 | 2c org brn (Bk) | .50 | .50 |
| 72 | A21 | 5c cer (Bk) | .50 | .50 |
| 73 | A21 | 10c emer (Bk) | .50 | .50 |
| 74 | A21 | 15c brt bl (Bk) | .50 | .50 |
| 75 | A21 | 20c red brn (Bk) | .50 | .50 |
| 76 | A21 | 25c mag (Bk) | .50 | .50 |
| 77 | A21 | 30c red org (Bk) | .50 | .50 |
| 78 | A21 | 40c org (Bk) | 1.50 | 1.50 |
| 79 | A21 | 50c ultra (R) | 1.50 | 1.50 |
| 80 | A21 | 60c yel grn (Bk) | 1.50 | 1.50 |
| 81 | A21 | 1p bl vio (Bk) | 1.50 | 1.50 |
| 82 | A21 | 2p Prus bl (Bk) | 80.00 | 80.00 |
| 83 | A21 | 2.50p gray blk (R) | 80.00 | 80.00 |
| 84 | A21 | 4p dk brn (Bk) | 80.00 | 80.00 |
| 85 | A22 | 10p vio blk (R) | 80.00 | 80.00 |
| | | *Nos. 70-85 (16)* | 330.00 | 330.00 |
| | | Set, never hinged | 550.00 | |

1st Year of the Revolution.

### Same Overprint in Black on Types of Spanish Morocco, 1939

Designs: 5c, Spanish quarter. 10c, Moroccan quarter. 15c, Street scene, Larache. 20c, Tetuan.

**1939** **Photo.** ***Perf. 13½***

| No. | Type | Description | Unused | Used |
|---|---|---|---|---|
| 86 | A25 | 5c vermilion | .50 | .50 |
| 87 | A25 | 10c deep green | .50 | .50 |
| 88 | A25 | 15c brown lake | .50 | .50 |
| 89 | A25 | 20c bright blue | .50 | .50 |
| | | *Nos. 86-89 (4)* | 2.00 | 2.00 |
| | | Set, never hinged | 4.00 | |

### Same Overprint in Black or Red on Stamps of Spanish Morocco, 1940

**1940** ***Perf. 11½x11***

| No. | Type | Description | Unused | Used |
|---|---|---|---|---|
| 90 | A26 | 1c dk brn (Bk) | .25 | .25 |
| 91 | A27 | 2c ol grn (R) | .25 | .25 |
| 92 | A28 | 5c dk bl (R) | .25 | .25 |
| 93 | A29 | 10c dk red lil (Bk) | .25 | .25 |
| 94 | A30 | 15c dk grn (R) | .25 | .25 |
| 95 | A31 | 20c pur (R) | .30 | .30 |
| 96 | A32 | 25c blk brn (R) | .30 | .30 |
| 97 | A33 | 30c brt grn (Bk) | .35 | .35 |
| 98 | A34 | 40c slate grn (R) | .85 | .75 |
| 99 | A35 | 45c org ver (Bk) | .85 | .75 |
| 100 | A36 | 50c brn org (Bk) | .90 | .90 |
| 101 | A37 | 70c saph (R) | 2.40 | 2.25 |
| 102 | A38 | 1p dk bl & brn (Bk) | 5.00 | 5.00 |
| 103 | A39 | 2.50p choc & dk grn (Bk) | 14.00 | 12.50 |
| 104 | A40 | 5p dk cer & sep (Bk) | 14.00 | 13.00 |
| 105 | A41 | 10p dk ol grn & brn org (Bk) | 40.00 | 35.00 |
| | | *Nos. 90-105 (16)* | 80.20 | 72.35 |
| | | Set, never hinged | 150.00 | |

Imperfs exist. Value, set $300.

Stamps of Spanish Morocco, 1944. Overprinted in Black or Red

**1944, Oct. 2** **Unwmk.** ***Perf. 12½***

| No. | Type | Description | Unused | Used |
|---|---|---|---|---|
| 106 | A47 | 1c choc & lt bl | .25 | .25 |
| 107 | A48 | 2c slate grn & lt grn | .25 | .25 |
| 108 | A49 | 5c choc & grnsh blk (R) | .25 | .25 |
| 109 | A50 | 10c brt ultra & red org | .25 | .25 |
| 110 | A51 | 15c sl grn & lt grn | .25 | .25 |
| 111 | A52 | 20c dp cl & blk (R) | .25 | .25 |
| 112 | A53 | 25c lt bl & choc | .25 | .25 |
| 113 | A47 | 30c yel grn & brt ultra (R) | .25 | .25 |
| 114 | A48 | 40c choc & red vio | .25 | .25 |
| 115 | A49 | 50c brt ultra, & red brn | .25 | .25 |
| 116 | A50 | 75c yel grn & brt ultra (R) | 1.25 | 1.25 |
| 117 | A51 | 1p brt ultra & choc | 1.40 | 1.40 |
| 118 | A52 | 2.50p blk & brt ultra (R) | 3.25 | 3.25 |
| 119 | A53 | 10p sal & gray blk (R) | 25.00 | 25.00 |
| | | *Nos. 106-119 (14)* | 33.40 | 33.40 |
| | | Set, never hinged | 70.00 | |

Nos. 106-119 exist imperf. Value, set $300.

### Same Overprint on Stamps of Spanish Morocco, 1946

**1946, Mar.** ***Perf. 10½x10***

| No. | Type | Description | Unused | Used |
|---|---|---|---|---|
| 120 | A54 | 1c pur & brn | .25 | .25 |
| 121 | A55 | 2c dk Prus grn & vio blk (R) | .25 | .25 |
| 122 | A54 | 10c dp org vio bl | .25 | .25 |
| 123 | A55 | 15c dk bl & bl grn | .25 | .25 |
| 124 | A54 | 25c yel grn & ultra | .25 | .25 |
| 125 | A56 | 40c dk bl & brn (R) | .30 | .30 |
| 126 | A55 | 45c blk & rose | .45 | .45 |
| 127 | A57 | 1p dk Prus grn & dp bl | 1.60 | 1.60 |
| 128 | A58 | 2.50p dp org & grnsh gray (R) | 4.75 | 4.75 |
| 129 | A59 | 10p dk bl & gray (R) | 13.50 | 13.50 |
| | | *Nos. 120-129 (10)* | 21.85 | 21.85 |
| | | Set, never hinged | 40.00 | |

Nos. 120-129 exist imperf. Value, set $200.

### Same Overprint in Carmine, Black or Brown on Stamps of Spanish Morocco, 1948

**1948, Jan. 1** ***Perf. 10, 10x10½***

| No. | Type | Description | Unused | Used |
|---|---|---|---|---|
| 130 | A64 | 2c pur & brn | .40 | *1.00* |
| 131 | A65 | 5c dp claret & vio | .25 | .25 |
| 132 | A66 | 15c brt ultra & bl grn (Bk) | .25 | .25 |
| 133 | A67 | 25c blk & Prus grn | .25 | .25 |
| 134 | A65 | 35c brt ultra & gray blk | .25 | .25 |
| 135 | A68 | 50c red & vio (Br) | .25 | .25 |
| 136 | A66 | 70c dk gray grn & ultra (Bk) | .25 | .25 |
| 137 | A67 | 90c cer & dk gray grn (Bk) | .30 | .30 |
| 138 | A68 | 1p brt ultra & vio (Br) | .45 | .45 |
| 139 | A64 | 2.50p vio brn & sl grn | 1.60 | 1.60 |
| 140 | A69 | 10p blk & dp ultra | 3.00 | 3.00 |
| | | *Nos. 130-140 (11)* | 7.25 | 7.85 |
| | | Set, never hinged | 12.00 | |

Nos. 130-140 exist imperf. Value, set $200.

## SEMI-POSTAL STAMPS

Types of Semi-Postal Stamps of Spain, 1926, Overprinted

**1926** **Unwmk.** ***Perf. 12½, 13***

| No. | Type | Description | Unused | Used |
|---|---|---|---|---|
| B1 | SP1 | 1c orange | 11.50 | 11.50 |
| B2 | SP2 | 2c rose | 11.50 | 11.50 |
| B3 | SP3 | 5c blk brn | 3.00 | 3.00 |
| B4 | SP4 | 10c dk grn | 1.60 | 1.60 |
| B5 | SP1 | 15c dk vio | 1.10 | 1.10 |
| B6 | SP4 | 20c vio brn | 1.10 | 1.10 |
| B7 | SP5 | 25c dp car | 1.10 | 1.10 |
| B8 | SP1 | 30c ol grn | 1.10 | 1.10 |
| B9 | SP3 | 40c ultra | .45 | .45 |
| B10 | SP2 | 50c red brn | .45 | .45 |
| B11 | SP4 | 1p vermilion | .45 | .45 |
| B12 | SP3 | 4p bister | 2.00 | 2.00 |
| B13 | SP5 | 10p lt vio | 3.00 | 3.00 |
| | | *Nos. B1-B13 (13)* | 38.35 | 38.35 |
| | | Set, never hinged | 65.00 | |

Nos. B12-B13 surcharged "Alfonso XIII" and new value are listed as Spain Nos. B68-B69. See Spain No. B6a.

## AIR POST STAMPS

Spanish Morocco Nos. C1 to C10 Overprinted

**1938, June 1** **Unwmk.** ***Perf. 13½***

| No. | Type | Description | Unused | Used |
|---|---|---|---|---|
| C1 | AP1 | 5c lake brn | .25 | .25 |
| C2 | AP1 | 10c emerald | .25 | .25 |
| C3 | AP1 | 25c brt scarlet | .25 | .25 |
| C4 | AP1 | 40c light blue | 2.10 | 2.10 |
| C5 | AP2 | 50c brt mag | .25 | .25 |
| C6 | AP2 | 75c dk bl | .25 | .25 |
| C7 | AP1 | 1p blksh brn | .25 | .25 |
| C8 | AP1 | 1.50p dp vio | 1.90 | 1.90 |
| C9 | AP1 | 2p dp red brn | 2.75 | 2.75 |
| C10 | AP1 | 3p brn blk | 7.25 | 7.25 |
| | | *Nos. C1-C10 (10)* | 15.50 | 15.50 |
| | | Set, never hinged | 45.00 | |

Nos. C1-C10 exist imperf. Value, set $220.

Spanish Morocco Nos. C11 to C15 Overprinted

Moroccan Views: 5c, Ketama landscape. 10c, Mosque, Tangier. 15c, Velez. 90c, Sanjurjo. 5p, Strait of Gibraltar

**1942, Apr. 1** **Photo.** ***Perf. 12½***

| No. | Type | Description | Unused | Used |
|---|---|---|---|---|
| C11 | AP3 | 5c deep blue | .25 | .25 |
| C12 | AP3 | 10c org brn | .25 | .25 |
| C13 | AP3 | 15c grnsh blk | .25 | .25 |
| C14 | AP3 | 90c dk rose | .50 | .50 |
| C15 | AP3 | 5p black | 1.75 | 1.75 |
| | | *Nos. C11-C15 (5)* | 3.00 | 3.00 |
| | | Set, never hinged | 4.00 | |

Nos. C11-C15 exist imperf. Value, set $75.

## SPECIAL DELIVERY STAMPS

### Special Delivery Stamp of Spain Ovptd. "CABO JUBY" as on #7-28

**1919** **Unwmk.** ***Perf. 14***

| No. | Type | Description | Unused | Used |
|---|---|---|---|---|
| E1 | SD1 | 20c red (Bk) | 3.25 | 3.25 |
| *b.* | | Double overprint | 27.50 | 13.00 |

### Spanish Morocco #E4 Overprinted "CABO JUBY" as on #40-52 in Red

**1934**

| No. | Type | Description | Unused | Used |
|---|---|---|---|---|
| E2 | SD2 | 20c black | 10.00 | 10.00 |

### Spanish Morocco No. E5 Overprinted "CABO JUBY" as on Nos. 54-61

**1935**

| No. | Type | Description | Unused | Used |
|---|---|---|---|---|
| E3 | SD3 | 20c vermilion | 3.50 | 3.50 |

### Same Ovpt. on Spanish Morocco #E6

**1937** ***Perf. 13½***

| No. | Type | Description | Unused | Used |
|---|---|---|---|---|
| E4 | SD4 | 20c bright carmine | 1.10 | 1.10 |

1st Year of the Revolution.

### Same Ovpt. on Spanish Morocco #E8

**1940** ***Perf. 11½x11***

| No. | Type | Description | Unused | Used |
|---|---|---|---|---|
| E5 | SD5 | 25c scarlet | .65 | .65 |

## SEMI-POSTAL SPECIAL DELIVERY STAMP

### Type of Semi-Postal Special Delivery Stamp of Spain, 1926, Overprinted "CABO-JUBY" as on Nos. B1-B13

**1926** **Unwmk.** ***Perf. 12½, 13***

| No. | Type | Description | Unused | Used |
|---|---|---|---|---|
| EB1 | SPSD1 | 20c ultra & black | 3.50 | 3.50 |

# CAPE OF GOOD HOPE

'kāp əv 'gud 'hōp

LOCATION — In the extreme southern part of South Africa
GOVT. — Former British Colony
AREA — 276,995 sq mi. (1911)
POP. — 2,564,965 (1911)
CAPITAL — Cape Town

Cape of Good Hope joined with Natal, the Transvaal and the Orange River Colony in 1910, forming the Union of South Africa.

12 Pence = 1 Shilling

**Watermarks**

Wmk. 15 — Anchor

Wmk. 16 — Anchor

"Hope" Seated — A1

### Printed by Perkins, Bacon & Co.

**Wmk. 15**

**1853, Sept. 1** **Engr.** ***Imperf.***

| No. | Type | Description | Unused | Used |
|---|---|---|---|---|
| 1 | A1 | 1p brick red, bluish paper | 3,500. | 400.00 |
| *a.* | | 1p pale brick red, deeply blued paper | *4,500.* | 450.00 |
| *b.* | | 1p deep brick red, deeply blued paper | *10,500.* | 475.00 |
| 2 | A1 | 4p deep blue, lightly blued paper | 1,750. | 170.00 |
| *a.* | | 4p deep blue, deeply blued paper | 3,500. | 375.00 |
| *b.* | | 4p blue, bluish paper | 3,250. | 200.00 |

Counterfeits exist.

**1855-58** **White Paper**

| No. | Type | Description | Unused | Used |
|---|---|---|---|---|
| 3 | A1 | 1p rose ('57) | 850.00 | 325.00 |
| *a.* | | 1p dull red | 1,100. | 425.00 |
| *b.* | | 1p brick red | 6,000. | 1,050. |
| 4 | A1 | 4p blue | 1,000. | 85.00 |
| *a.* | | Half used as 2p on cover | | *35,000.* |
| *b.* | | 4p deep blue | 1,300. | 90.00 |
| *e.* | | 4p bright blue | 900.00 | 90.00 |
| 5 | A1 | 6p pale lilac ('58) | 1,200. | 300.00 |
| *a.* | | 6p rose lilac | 2,500. | 400.00 |
| *b.* | | 6p grayish lilac on bluish paper | 5,000. | 540.00 |
| *c.* | | 6p slate purple on bluish paper | 4,150. | 1,200. |
| *d.* | | Half used as 3p on cover | | — |
| 6 | A1 | 1sh yellow grn ('58) | *4,000.* | 300.00 |
| *a.* | | 1sh dark green | 450.00 | *600.00* |
| *b.* | | Half used as 6p on cover | | — |

Nos. 3-6 are known rouletted unofficially.
Counterfeits exist.

No. 4 was reproduced by the collotype process in an unwatermarked souvenir sheet distributed at the London Intl. Stamp Exhib. 1950.

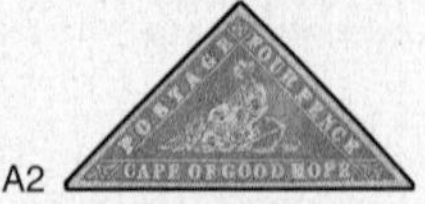


A2

### Printed by Saul Solomon & Co.

**1861 Laid Paper Unwmk. Typo.**

7 A2 1p vermilion 17,000. 2,750.
a. 1p carmine 42,500. 6,500.
b. 1p red 50,000. 7,500.
c. 1p milky blue (error) 200,000. 32,500.
d. 1p pale blue (error) 36,000.
9 A2 4p milky blue 40,000. 2,500.
a. 4p pale blue 42,000. 3,250.
b. 4p blue 45,000. 3,500.
c. 4p dark blue 120,000. 5,750.
d. As #9, right corner retouched 7,750.
e. As #9a, right corner retouched 7,750.
f. 4p vermilion (error) 200,000. 65,000.
g. 4p carmine (error) 112,500.

Nos. 7 and 9 are usually called Wood Blocks. The plates were made locally and composed of clichés mounted on wood. The errors were caused by a cliché of each value being mounted in the plate of the other value.

In 1883 plate proofs of both values on white paper, usually called "reprints," were made. The 1p is in dull orange red; the 4p in dark blue. These are known canceled, as a few were misused as stamps. The proofs do not include the errors.

Counterfeits exist.

### Printed by De La Rue & Co.

**1863-64 Wmk. 15 Engr.**

12 A1 1p dark carmine 350.00 *350.00*
a. 1p reddish brown 650.00 375.00
b. 1p brownish red 650.00 375.00
13 A1 4p dark blue 325.00 135.00
a. 4p slate blue 2,500. 600.00
14 A1 6p purple 450.00 *500.00*
15 A1 1sh emerald 675.00 *725.00*
a. 1sh pale emerald 1,400. —

Nos. 12-15 can be distinguished from Nos. 3-6 not only by colors but because Nos. 12-15 often appear in a granular ink or with the background lightly printed in whole or part.

No. 12a, Wmk. 1, is believed to be a proof. Value, $29,000.

Counterfeits exist.

"Hope" and Symbols of Colony — A3

**Frame Line Around Stamp**

**1864-77 Typo. Wmk. 1 *Perf. 14***

16 A3 1p rose ('65) 130.00 42.50
17 A3 4p blue ('65) 210.00 4.50
a. 4p pale blue 210.00 4.50
b. 4p dull ultramarine 350.00 50.00
c. 4p deep blue ('72) 275.00 4.50
18 A3 6p bright vio ('77) 235.00 1.50
a. 6p dull violet 375.00 8.25
b. 6p pale lilac 225.00 28.00
19 A3 1sh yellow green 225.00 4.75
a. 1sh blue green 250.00 6.00
*Nos. 16-19 (4)* 800.00 53.25

Imperf. stamps are believed to be proofs.

For surcharges see Nos. 20-21, N3.

For types A3 and A6 with manuscript surcharge of 1d or overprints "G. W." or "G," see Griqualand West listings.

**Stamps of 1864 Surcharged in Red or Black**

a

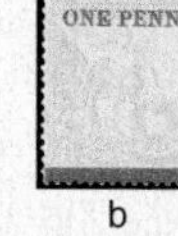


b

**1868-74 Red Surcharge**

20 A3(a) 4p on 6p 575.00 17.50
a. "Peuce" for "Pence" 2,400. 750.00
b. "Fonr" for "Four" 775.00
21 A3(b) 1p on 6p ('74) 850.00 140.00
a. "E" of "PENNY" omitted 1,800.

Space between words and bars varies from 12½-16mm on No. 20, and 16½-18mm on No. 21.

**1876 Black Surcharge**

22 A3 (b) 1p on 1sh green 150.00 75.00

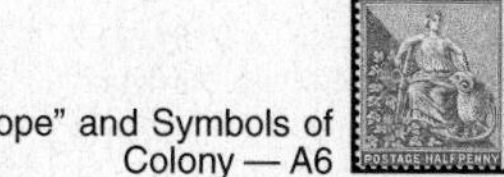

"Hope" and Symbols of Colony — A6

**Without Frame Line Around Stamp**

**1871-81 *Perf. 14***

23 A6 ½p gray black ('75) 37.50 17.50
24 A6 1p rose ('72) 55.00 1.25
25 A6 3p lilac rose ('80) 350.00 42.50
26 A6 3p claret ('81) 240.00 4.50
27 A6 4p blue ('76) 210.00 .90
a. 4p ultramarine 350.00 57.50
28 A6 5sh orange 650.00 25.00
*Nos. 23-28 (6)* 1,543. 91.65

For surcharges see Nos. 29-32, 39, 55.

No. 27 Surcharged in Red

**1879**

29 A6 3p on 4p blue 200.00 2.50
a. "THE.EE" 3,750. 300.00
b. "PENCB" 3,250. 250.00
c. Double surcharge 12,000. 4,250.
d. As "a," double surcharge — —

Type of 1871 Surcharged in Black

**1880**

30 A6 3p on 4p lilac rose 145.00 3.25

**No. 25 Surcharged in Black**

e

f

31 A6(e) 3p on 3p lilac rose 400.00 12.00
a. Inverted surcharge 12,500. 1,550.
32 A6(f) 3p on 3p lilac rose 130.00 2.25
a. Inverted surcharge 1,600. 47.50

**1882-83 Wmk. 2**

33 A6 ½p gray black 42.50 3.25
34 A6 1p rose 85.00 2.50
35 A6 2p bister 140.00 1.75
36 A6 3p claret 12.50 1.75
37 A3 6p bright violet 160.00 1.00
38 A6 5sh orange ('83) 925.00 300.00

For overprint see Rhodesia No. 49.

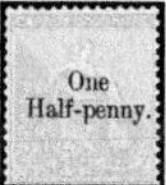


Nos. 26 and 36 Surcharged in Black

**1882 Wmk. 1**

39 A6 ½p on 3p claret 4,750. 180.00
a. Hyphen omitted 3,750.

**Wmk. 2**

40 A6 ½p on 3p claret 60.00 8.00
a. "ENNY" 2,300. 775.00
b. "PENN" 1,900. 750.00
c. Hyphen omitted 850.00 400.00

**1884-98 Wmk. 16**

41 A6 ½p gray black ('86) 12.00 .25
42 A6 ½p yel green ('96) 1.80 .75
43 A6 1p rose ('85) 15.00 .25
44 A6 2p bister 15.00 .25
45 A6 2p choc brown ('97) 4.75 3.50
46 A6 3p red violet ('98) 25.00 1.40
47 A6 4p blue ('90) 26.00 1.50
48 A6 4p pale ol grn ('97) 12.00 4.25
49 A3 6p violet 22.00 .50
50 A3 1sh dull bluish grn ('89) 180.00 1.25
51 A6 1sh blue grn ('94) 110.00 8.50
52 A6 1sh yel buff ('96) 19.00 3.25
53 A6 5sh orange ('87) 160.00 9.50
54 A6 5sh brown org ('96) 140.00 5.00
*Nos. 41-54 (14)* 742.55 40.15

For surcharges see Nos. 58, 162, 165-166. For overprints see Rhodesia Nos. 43, 45-48.

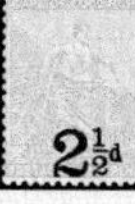


Type of 1871 Surcharged in Black

**1891, Mar.**

55 A6 2½p on 3p deep magenta 8.50 .25
a. "1" of "½" has straight serif 95.00 37.50

Hope Seated — A13

**1892-96**

56 A13 2½p sage green 26.00 .25
57 A13 2½p ultra ('96) 14.00 .25

For surcharge see No. N4. For overprint see Orange River Colony No. 55.

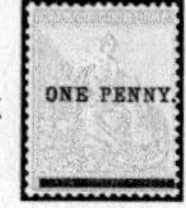


No. 44 Surcharged in Black

**1893, Mar.**

58 A6 1p on 2p bister 6.00 .60
a. Double surcharge 600.00
b. No period after "PENNY" 100.00 25.00

Hope Standing — A15

**1893-1902**

59 A15 ½p green ('98) 11.00 .25
60 A15 1p carmine 4.00 .25
61 A15 3p red violet ('02) 8.00 3.50
*Nos. 59-61 (3)* 23.00 4.00

For surcharges see Nos. 163-164, N2. For overprints see Orange River Colony Nos. 54, 56, Rhodesia No. 44, Transvaal Nos. 236-236A.

Table Mountain and Bay; Coat of Arms — A16

**1900, Jan.**

62 A16 1p carmine rose 8.50 .25

King Edward VII — A17

Various frames.

**1902-04 Wmk. 16**

63 A17 ½p emerald 4.00 .25
64 A17 1p car rose 3.50 .25
65 A17 2p brown ('04) 24.00 .95
66 A17 2½p ultra ('04) 5.75 *13.00*
67 A17 3p red violet ('03) 18.50 1.40
68 A17 4p ol green ('03) 20.00 .80
69 A17 6p violet ('03) 30.00 .60
70 A17 1sh bister 20.00 1.25
71 A17 5sh brown org ('03) 160.00 27.50
*Nos. 63-71 (9)* 285.75 46.00

Imperf. stamps are proofs.

Cape of Good Hope stamps were replaced by those of Union of South Africa.

---

### ISSUED IN MAFEKING

Excellent forgeries of Nos. 162-179 are known.

Stamps of Cape of Good Hope Surcharged

**1900, Mar. 24**

162 A6 1p on ½p grn 325.00 85.00
163 A15 1p on ½p grn 375.00 125.00
164 A15 3p on 1p rose 325.00 65.00
165 A6 6p on 3p red vio 45,000. 350.00
166 A6 1sh on 4p pale ol grn 8,000. 425.00

Stamps of Bechuanaland Protectorate Surcharged

**1900 Wmk. 30**

167 A54 1p on ½p ver 325.00 85.00
a. Inverted surcharge — 8,000.
b. Vert. pair, surcharge tête bêche *40,000.*
168 A40 3p on 1p lilac 1,000. 155.00
a. Double surcharge *37,500.*
169 A56 6p on 2p grn & car 3,000. 125.00
170 A58 6p on 3p vio, *yel* 7,500. 425.00
a. Inverted surcharge *42,500.*
b. Double surcharge — —

The lettering of "Mafeking Besieged" shows varying breaks in various letters, and may have either a period or no punctuation after "Mafeking."

**On Stamps of Bechuanaland**

**Wmk. 29**

171 A1 6p on 3p vio & blk 550.00 95.00

**Wmk. 30**

172 A59 1sh on 4p brn & grn 1,650. 110.00
a. Double surch., one inverted — *30,000.*
b. Triple surcharge — *30,000.*
c. Inverted surcharge — —
d. Double surcharge — *30,000.*
172E A59 2sh on 4p brn & grn *39,000.*

Stamps of Bechuanaland Protectorate Surcharged

173 A40 3p on 1p lil 1,100. 100.00
a. Double surcharge — *11,000.*
174 A56 6p on 2p grn & car 1,600. 100.00
175 A62 1sh on 6p vio, *rose* 7,500. 130.00

**On Stamps of Bechuanaland**

176 A62 1sh on 6p vio, *rose* 32,500. 850.00
177 A65 2sh on 1sh green 14,000. 650.00

Sgt. Major Goodyear M1

Gen. Robert S. S. Baden-Powell M2

**Wmk. OCEANA FINE Photographic Print**

**1900, Apr. *Perf. 12***

**Laid Paper**

178 M1 1p blue, *blue* 1,200. 425.00
a. Imperf, pair 25,000.
179 M2 3p blue, *blue,* 18½mm wide 1,750. 450.00
a. Horiz. pair, imperf. between — *100,000.*
b. Double impression — *25,000.*
c. Reversed design *100,000.* *55,000.*
180 M2 3p blue, *blue,* 21mm wide 12,000. 1,350.
a. 3p deep blue 13,500. 1,350.
On cover *16,500.*

The color of the paper varies from pale to deep blue.

OCEANA FINE is a sheet watermark and does not appear on every stamp.

Imperfs of No. 178 are proofs.

There is one used pair of No. 179a privately owned. A single used, partially imperf. example of No. 179 exists. Value, *$45,000.* There are four used examples of No. 179b reported. There are 2 unused and 6 used examples of No. 179c privately owned.

Issued: No. 179, Apr. 6; Nos. 178 and 180, Apr. 10.

---

### ISSUED IN VRYBURG

**Under Boer Occupation**

Cape of Good Hope Stamps of 1884-96 Surcharged

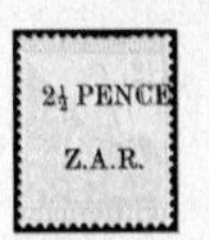

Type 1

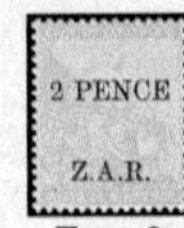

Type 2

Two Types of Surcharge:
Type I — Surcharge 10mm high. Space between lines 5½mm.
Type II — Surcharge 12mm high. Space between lines 7½mm.

**1899, Nov. Wmk. 16 *Perf. 14***

| No. | Type | Description | Unused | Used |
|---|---|---|---|---|
| N1 | A6 | ½p on ½p emer (I) | 240. | 95. |
| a. | | Type II | 2,250. | 825. |
| N2 | A15 | 1p on 1p rose (I) | 275. | 120. |
| a. | | Double surcharge | — | — |
| b. | | Type II | 2,500. | 950. |
| N3 | A3 | 2p on 6p vio (II) | 2,250. | 750. |
| N4 | A13 | 2½p on 2½p ultra (I) | 1,800. | 450. |
| a. | | Type II | *15,000.* | *4,500.* |

**Under British Occupation**

Transvaal Stamps of 1895-96 Handstamped

**1900 Unwmk. *Perf. 12½***

| No. | Type | Description | Unused | Used |
|---|---|---|---|---|
| N5 | A13 | ½p green | — | *3,500.* |
| N6 | A13 | 1p rose & grn | *14,000.* | *6,000.* |
| N7 | A13 | 2p brown & grn | — | *45,000.* |
| N8 | A13 | 2½p ultra & grn | — | *45,000.* |

## CAPE VERDE

ˈkāp ˈvərd

LOCATION — A group of 10 islands and five islets in the Atlantic Ocean, about 500 miles due west of Senegal.
GOVT. — Republic
AREA — 1,557 sq. mi.
POP. — 405,748 (1999 est.)
CAPITAL — Praia

The Portuguese territory of Cape Verde became independent on July 5, 1975.

1000 Reis = 1 Milreis
100 Centavos = 1 Escudo (1913)

**Catalogue values for unused stamps in this country are for Never Hinged items, beginning with Scott 268 in the regular postage section, Scott J31 in the postage due section, and Scott RA6 in the postal tax section.**

Crown of Portugal — A1

**1877 Unwmk. Typo. *Perf. 12½***

| No. | Type | Description | Unused | Used |
|---|---|---|---|---|
| 1 | A1 | 5r black | 4.25 | 2.50 |
| 2 | A1 | 10r yellow | 27.50 | 12.75 |
| 3 | A1 | 20r bister | 3.00 | 2.00 |
| 4 | A1 | 25r rose | 3.00 | 2.00 |
| 5 | A1 | 40r blue | 105.00 | 75.00 |
| b. | | Cliche of Mozambique in Cape Verde plate, in pair with #5 | *2,500.* | *2,500.* |
| 6 | A1 | 50r green | 170.00 | 90.00 |
| 7 | A1 | 100r lilac | 10.00 | 4.25 |
| 8 | A1 | 200r orange | 6.00 | 4.25 |
| 9 | A1 | 300r brown | 7.00 | 5.50 |
| | | *Nos. 1-9 (9)* | 335.75 | 198.25 |

For expanded treatment of Nos. 1-9, see the *Scott Classic Catalogue.*

**1881-85 *Perf. 12½***

| No. | Type | Description | Unused | Used |
|---|---|---|---|---|
| 10 | A1 | 10r green | 3.50 | 2.40 |
| 11 | A1 | 20r carmine ('85) | 6.00 | 4.50 |
| 12 | A1 | 25r violet ('85) | 5.00 | 4.00 |
| 13 | A1 | 40r yellow buff | 2.75 | 1.90 |
| a. | | Imperf. | 40.00 | |
| b. | | Cliche of Mozambique in Cape Verde plate, in pair with #13 | *150.00* | *140.00* |
| c. | | As "b," imperf. | — | |
| 14 | A1 | 50r blue | 8.00 | 5.00 |
| | | *Nos. 10-14 (5)* | 25.25 | 17.80 |

Reprints of the 1877-85 issues are on smooth white chalky paper, ungummed, and on thin white paper with shiny white gum. They are perf 13½.

For expanded treatment of nos. 10-14, see the *Scott Classic Catalogue.*

King Luiz — A2

**1886 Embossed *Perf. 12½, 13½***
**Chalk-Surfaced Paper**

| No. | Type | Description | Unused | Used |
|---|---|---|---|---|
| 15 | A2 | 5r black | 5.25 | 3.50 |
| 16 | A2 | 10r green | 6.00 | 3.50 |
| 17 | A2 | 20r carmine | 9.00 | 5.25 |
| 18 | A2 | 25r violet | 10.00 | 6.00 |
| 19 | A2 | 40r chocolate | 10.00 | 3.75 |
| 20 | A2 | 50r blue | 10.00 | 3.75 |
| 21 | A2 | 100r yel brown | 10.00 | 5.00 |
| 22 | A2 | 200r gray lilac | 21.00 | 12.50 |
| 23 | A2 | 300r orange | 24.00 | 6.00 |
| | | *Nos. 15-23 (9)* | 105.25 | 49.25 |

*The 25r, 50r and 100r have been reprinted in aniline colors with clean-cut Perf. 13½.*

For expanded treatment of nos. 15-19, see the *Scott Classic Catalogue.*

For surcharges see Nos. 59-67, 184-187.

King Carlos — A3

**1894-95 Typo. *Perf. 11½, 12½, 13½***

| No. | Type | Description | Unused | Used |
|---|---|---|---|---|
| 24 | A3 | 5r orange | 2.25 | 1.50 |
| 25 | A3 | 10r redsh violet | 2.25 | 1.50 |
| 26 | A3 | 15r chocolate | 4.75 | 3.25 |
| a. | | Perf. 12½ | 175.00 | 135.00 |
| 27 | A3 | 20r lavender | 4.50 | 3.25 |
| 28 | A3 | 25r dp green | 4.00 | 2.75 |
| a. | | Perf. 12½ | 4.00 | 3.25 |
| 29 | A3 | 50r lt blue | 4.00 | 2.75 |
| a. | | Perf. 13 1/2 | 15.00 | 5.00 |
| 30 | A3 | 75r carmine ('95) | 12.75 | 6.75 |
| a. | | Perf. 13½ | 65.00 | 50.00 |
| 31 | A3 | 80r yel grn ('95) | 27.00 | 20.00 |
| a. | | Perf. 13½ | 50.00 | 40.00 |
| 32 | A3 | 100r brn, *buff* ('95) | 11.00 | 6.00 |
| a. | | Perf. 12½ | 135.00 | 60.00 |
| 33 | A3 | 150r car, *rose* ('95) | 40.00 | 30.00 |
| a. | | Perf. 12½ | 525.00 | 475.00 |
| b. | | Perf. 11½ | 80.00 | 62.50 |
| 34 | A3 | 200r dk blue, *lt blue* ('95) | 40.00 | 30.00 |
| a. | | Perf. 12½ | 175.00 | 135.00 |
| 35 | A3 | 300r dk blue, *sal* ('95) | 42.00 | 21.00 |
| | | *Nos. 24-35 (12)* | 194.50 | 128.75 |

For surcharges see Nos. 68-78, 137, 189-193, 201-205.

King Carlos — A4

**1898-1903 *Perf. 11½***
**Name and Value in Black except 500r**

| No. | Type | Description | Unused | Used |
|---|---|---|---|---|
| 36 | A4 | 2½r gray | .40 | .30 |
| 37 | A4 | 5r orange | .50 | .30 |
| 38 | A4 | 10r lt green | .55 | .30 |
| 39 | A4 | 15r brown | 6.50 | 2.40 |
| 40 | A4 | 15r gray grn ('03) | 2.50 | 1.70 |
| 41 | A4 | 20r gray violet | 1.90 | 1.20 |
| 42 | A4 | 25r sea green | 4.00 | 1.50 |
| a. | | Perf 12½ | *375.00* | *220.00* |
| 43 | A4 | 25r carmine ('03) | 1.40 | .60 |
| 44 | A4 | 50r dark blue | 4.00 | 1.80 |
| 45 | A4 | 50r brown ('03) | 5.00 | 3.25 |
| 46 | A4 | 65r slate blue ('03) | 39.00 | *29.00* |
| 47 | A4 | 75r rose | 10.00 | 4.00 |
| 48 | A4 | 75r lilac ('03) | 4.00 | 3.00 |
| 49 | A4 | 80r violet | 9.25 | 4.00 |
| 50 | A4 | 100r dk blue, *blue* | 4.00 | 2.25 |
| 51 | A4 | 115r org brn, *pink* ('03) | 20.00 | *17.00* |
| 52 | A4 | 130r brown, *straw* ('03) | 20.00 | *17.00* |
| 53 | A4 | 150r brown, *straw* | 10.00 | 7.00 |
| 54 | A4 | 200r red vio, *pnksh* | 4.50 | 3.50 |
| 55 | A4 | 300r dk blue, *rose* | 10.75 | 5.75 |
| 56 | A4 | 400r dull blue, *straw* ('03) | 21.00 | 14.00 |
| 57 | A4 | 500r blk & red, *blue* ('01) | 11.75 | 6.00 |
| 58 | A4 | 700r violet, *yelsh* ('01) | 32.00 | 21.00 |
| | | *Nos. 36-58 (23)* | 223.00 | 146.85 |

For overprints and suecharges see Nos. 80-99, 139, 200.

Regular Issues Surcharged in Red or Black

Two spacing types of surcharge. See note above Angola No. 61.

**On Issue of 1886**

**1902, Dec. 1 *Perf. 12½, 13½***

| No. | Type | Description | Unused | Used |
|---|---|---|---|---|
| 59 | A2 | 65r on 5r black (R) | 7.00 | 4.75 |
| 60 | A2 | 65r on 200r gray lil | 7.00 | 4.75 |
| 61 | A2 | 65r on 300r orange | 7.00 | 4.75 |
| 62 | A2 | 115r on 10r green | 7.00 | 4.75 |
| 63 | A2 | 115r on 20r rose | 7.00 | 4.75 |
| a. | | Perf 13½ | 60.00 | 40.00 |
| 64 | A2 | 130r on 50r blue | 6.50 | 4.75 |
| 65 | A2 | 130r on 100r brown | 6.50 | 4.75 |
| 66 | A2 | 400r on 25r violet | 3.75 | 3.00 |
| 67 | A2 | 400r on 40r choc | 6.50 | 4.50 |
| a. | | Perf 13½ | 50.00 | 40.00 |

**On Issue of 1894**

***Perf. 11½, 12½, 13½***

| No. | Type | Description | Unused | Used |
|---|---|---|---|---|
| 68 | A3 | 65r on 10r red vio | 7.00 | 3.75 |
| 69 | A3 | 65r on 20r lavender | 7.00 | 3.75 |
| 70 | A3 | 65r on 100r brn, *buff* | 8.50 | 6.00 |
| a. | | Perf 12½ | 31.00 | 27.00 |
| 71 | A3 | 115r on 5r orange | 5.00 | 3.75 |
| a. | | Inverted surcharge | 60.00 | 60.00 |
| 72 | A3 | 115r on 25r blue grn | 4.00 | 2.50 |
| a. | | Perf 11½ | 67.50 | 55.00 |
| 73 | A3 | 115r on 150r car, *rose* | 9.00 | 7.50 |
| a. | | Perf 13½ | 45.00 | 28.00 |
| 74 | A3 | 130r on 75r car | 5.00 | 3.50 |
| a. | | Perf 13½ | *250.00* | *225.00* |
| 75 | A3 | 130r on 80r yel grn | 4.00 | 3.25 |
| 76 | A3 | 130r on 200r dk blue, *blue* | 4.00 | 3.25 |
| 77 | A3 | 400r on 50r lt blue | 6.50 | 3.75 |
| a. | | Inverted surcharge | 65.00 | 55.00 |
| b. | | Perf 13½ | *375.00* | *375.00* |
| 78 | A3 | 400r on 300r dk blue, *sal* | 3.50 | 2.20 |

**On Newspaper Stamp of 1893**

| No. | Type | Description | Unused | Used |
|---|---|---|---|---|
| 79 | N1 | 400r on 2½r brown | 1.75 | 1.75 |
| a. | | Inverted surcharge | 30.00 | |
| b. | | Perf 12½ | *250.00* | *225.00* |
| | | *Nos. 59-79 (21)* | 123.50 | 85.70 |

*Reprints of Nos. 59, 66, 67, and 77 have shiny white gum and clean-cut perforation 13½.*

For overprint and surcharge see Nos. 137, 205-206.

Overprinted in Black On Nos. 39, 42, 44, 47

**1902-03 *Perf. 11½***

| No. | Type | Description | Unused | Used |
|---|---|---|---|---|
| 80 | A4 | 15r brown | 2.00 | 1.50 |
| 81 | A4 | 25r sea green | 2.00 | 1.50 |
| 82 | A4 | 50r blue ('03) | 2.00 | 1.50 |
| 83 | A4 | 75r rose ('03) | 4.00 | 3.25 |
| a. | | Inverted overprint | 42.50 | 42.50 |
| | | *Nos. 80-83 (4)* | 10.00 | 7.75 |

For overprint see No. 139.

No. 46 Surcharged in Black

**1905, July 1**

| No. | Type | Description | Unused | Used |
|---|---|---|---|---|
| 84 | A4 | 50r on 65r slate blue | 5.00 | 4.00 |

Stamps of 1898-1903 Overprinted in Carmine or Green

**1911, Aug. 20**

| No. | Type | Description | Unused | Used |
|---|---|---|---|---|
| 85 | A4 | 2½r gray | .45 | .35 |
| 86 | A4 | 5r orange | .45 | .35 |
| 87 | A4 | 10r lt green | 1.40 | 1.10 |
| 88 | A4 | 15r gray green | 1.20 | .60 |
| 89 | A4 | 20r gray violet | 1.90 | 1.10 |
| 90 | A4 | 25r carmine (G) | 1.20 | .60 |
| 91 | A4 | 50r brown | 10.75 | 7.50 |
| 92 | A4 | 75r red lilac | 1.90 | 1.10 |
| 93 | A4 | 100r dk blue, *blue* | 1.90 | 1.10 |
| 94 | A4 | 115r org brn, *pink* | 1.90 | 1.10 |
| 95 | A4 | 130r brown, *straw* | 1.90 | 1.10 |
| 96 | A4 | 200r red vio, *pnksh* | 8.50 | 5.25 |
| 97 | A4 | 400r dull bl, *straw* | 4.50 | 1.60 |
| 98 | A4 | 500r blk & red, *bl* | 4.50 | 1.60 |
| 99 | A4 | 700r violet, *straw* | 4.50 | 1.60 |
| | | *Nos. 85-99 (15)* | 46.95 | 26.05 |

King Manuel II — A5

**Overprinted in Carmine or Green**

**1912 *Perf. 11½x12***

| No. | Type | Description | Unused | Used |
|---|---|---|---|---|
| 100 | A5 | 2½r violet | .30 | .30 |
| 101 | A5 | 5r black | .30 | .30 |
| 102 | A5 | 10r gray grn | .60 | .55 |
| 103 | A5 | 20r carmine (G) | 3.25 | 1.90 |
| 104 | A5 | 25r vio brown | .60 | .35 |
| 105 | A5 | 50r dk blue | 6.50 | 4.75 |
| 106 | A5 | 75r bister brn | 1.50 | 1.40 |
| 107 | A5 | 100r brown, *lt grn* | 1.50 | 1.40 |
| 108 | A5 | 200r dk green, *sal* | 2.25 | 1.50 |
| 109 | A5 | 300r black, *azure* | 2.25 | 1.50 |

***Perf. 14½x15***

| No. | Type | Description | Unused | Used |
|---|---|---|---|---|
| 110 | A5 | 400r black & blue | 5.00 | 4.00 |
| 111 | A5 | 500r ol grn & vio brn | 5.00 | 4.00 |
| | | *Nos. 100-111 (12)* | 29.05 | 21.95 |

Common Design Types pictured following the introduction.

**Vasco da Gama Issue of Various Portuguese Colonies**

Common Design Types CD20-CD27 Surcharged

**On Stamps of Macao**

**1913, Feb. 13 *Perf. 12½ to 16***

| No. | Description | Unused | Used |
|---|---|---|---|
| 112 | ¼c on ½a blue grn | 2.00 | 1.20 |
| 113 | ½c on 1a red | 2.00 | 1.20 |
| 114 | 1c on 2a red violet | 2.00 | 1.20 |
| 115 | 2½c on 4a yel grn | 2.00 | 1.20 |
| 116 | 5c on 8a dk blue | 9.00 | 7.75 |
| 117 | 7½c on 12a vio brn | 7.50 | 3.75 |
| 118 | 10c on 16a bister brn | 2.90 | 2.20 |
| 119 | 15c on 24a bister | 7.50 | 4.75 |
| | *Nos. 112-119 (8)* | 34.90 | 23.25 |

**On Stamps of Portuguese Africa**

***Perf. 14 to 15***

| No. | Description | Unused | Used |
|---|---|---|---|
| 120 | ¼c on 2½r bl grn | 2.20 | .95 |
| 121 | ½c on 5r red | 2.20 | .95 |
| 122 | 1c on 10r red vio | 2.20 | .95 |
| 123 | 2½c on 25r yel grn | 2.20 | .95 |
| 124 | 5c on 50r dk blue | 2.60 | 2.00 |
| 125 | 7½c on 75r vio brn | 5.00 | 4.00 |
| 126 | 10c on 100r bis brn | 2.60 | 2.50 |
| 127 | 15c on 150r bister | 3.40 | 3.40 |
| | *Nos. 120-127 (8)* | 22.40 | 15.70 |

**On Stamps of Timor**

| No. | Description | Unused | Used |
|---|---|---|---|
| 128 | ¼c on ½a bl grn | 2.20 | 1.15 |
| 129 | ½c on 1a red | 2.20 | 1.15 |
| 130 | 1c on 2a red vio | 2.20 | 1.15 |
| 131 | 2½c on 4a yel grn | 2.20 | 1.15 |
| 132 | 5c on 8a dk blue | 9.00 | 7.25 |
| 133 | 7½c On 12a vio brn | 7.25 | 4.25 |
| 134 | 10c on 16a bis brn | 3.00 | 2.50 |
| 135 | 15c on 24a bister | 6.00 | 3.25 |
| | *Nos. 128-135 (8)* | 34.05 | 21.85 |
| | *Nos. 112-135 (24)* | *91.35* | *60.80* |

For surcharges see Nos. 197-198.

No. 75 Overprinted in Red

**1913 *Perf. 11½, 12½, 13½***

| No. | Type | Description | Unused | Used |
|---|---|---|---|---|
| 137 | A3 | 130r on 80r yel grn | 6.75 | 5.00 |

Nos. 73 and 76 overprinted but not issued. Values, $20, $25.

**Same Overprint on No. 83 in Green**

**1914** ***Perf. 12***
**139** A4 75r rose 7.50 5.00
*a.* "PROVISORIO" double (G and R) 110.00 75.00

Ceres — A6

**1914 Typo. *Perf. 15x14***
**Name and Value in Black**
**Chalky Paper**
**144** A6 ¼c olive brn .85 .65
**145** A6 ½c black .85 .65
**146** A6 1c blue grn .85 .65
**147** A6 1½c lilac brown .85 .65
**148** A6 2c carmine 1.40 .80
**149** A6 2½c lt violet .70 .60
**150** A6 5c deep blue 1.15 .95
**151** A6 7½c yel brn 1.40 .80
**152** A6 8c slate 1.40 .85
**153** A6 10c orange brn 2.25 1.05
**154** A6 15c brn rose ('22) 10.75 6.50
**155** A6 20c yel grn 2.25 1.05
**156** A6 30c brown, *grn* 5.75 3.50
**157** A6 40c brown, *pink* 3.50 2.90
**158** A6 50c orange, *sal* 4.00 2.90
**159** A6 1e green, *blue* 4.00 3.50
*Nos. 144-159 (16)* 41.95 28.00

**1916**
**Enamel-Surfaced Paper**
**160** A6 ¼c olive brn .60 .45
**161** A6 5c deep blue 1.15 .85

**Ordinary Paper**
**162** A6 ¼c olive brn .35 .30
**163** A6 ½c black .35 .30
**164** A6 1c blue grn 6.25 4.75
**165** A6 1c yel grn ('22) .30 .30
**166** A6 1½c lilac brown .45 .30
**167** A6 2c carmine .45 .30
**168** A6 2½c lt violet .35 .30
**169** A6 3c org ('22) .45 .30
**170** A6 4c rose ('22) .45 *.30*
**171** A6 12c blue grn ('22) 1.00 .70
**172** A6 15c plum 3.25 2.00
*Nos. 162-172 (11)* 13.65 9.85

**1920-26** ***Perf. 12x11½***
**173** A6 ¼c olive brn .35 .30
**174** A6 ½c black .35 .30
**175** A6 1c yel grn ('22) .35 .30
**176** A6 1½c lilac brown .35 .30
**177** A6 2c carmine .35 .30
**178** A6 2c gray ('26) .35 .30
**179** A6 2½c lt violet .45 .35
**180** A6 3c org ('22) 3.50 3.25
**181** A6 4c rose ('22) .50 *.60*
**182** A6 4½c gray ('22) .50 *.60*
**183** A6 5c brt blue ('22) .50 .60
**183A** A6 6c lilac ('22) .50 .60
**183B** A6 7c ultra ('22) .50 *.60*
**183C** A6 7½c yel brn .50 *.60*
**183D** A6 8c slate .85 .70
**183E** A6 10c orange brn .45 .45
**183F** A6 12c blue grn ('22) 1.00 .80
**183G** A6 15c plum .45 .50
**183H** A6 20c yel grn .45 .50
**183I** A6 24c ultra ('26) 1.80 1.40
**183J** A6 25c choc ('26) 1.80 1.40
**183K** A6 30c gray grn ('26) .85 .55
**183L** A6 40c turq blue ('22) .85 .55
**183M** A6 50c violet ('26) 1.35 .95
**183N** A6 60c dk blue ('22) 2.00 1.15
**183O** A6 60c rose ('26) 2.25 1.10
**183P** A6 80c brt rose ('22) 5.25 1.75
*Nos. 173-183P (27)* 28.40 20.80

For surcharge see No. 214.

**Glazed Paper**
**183Q** A6 1e rose ('22) 6.50 3.50
**183R** A6 1e dp blue ('26) 7.00 4.25
**183S** A6 2e dk violet ('22) 6.50 4.00
**183T** A6 5e buff ('26) 13.50 8.00
**183U** A6 10e pink ('26) 80.00 45.00
**183V** A6 20e pale turq ('26) 115.00 70.00
*Nos. 183Q-183V (6)* 228.50 134.75

Provisional Issue of 1902 Overprinted in Carmine

**1915** ***Perf. 11½, 12½, 13½***
**184** A2 115r on 10r green (11½) 3.50 2.40
*a.* Perf. 13½ *160.00 160.00*
**185** A2 115r on 20r rose (12½) 3.75 2.40
*a.* Perf. 13½ 42.00 42.00
**186** A2 130r on 50r blue (12½) 3.50 1.90
**187** A2 130r on 100r brown (12½) 2.10 1.40
**188** A3 115r on 5r org (11½) 1.90 1.10
*a.* Inverted overprint 57.50 52.50
**189** A3 115r on 25r blue grn (12½) 3.40 2.20
*a.* Perf. 11½ *95.00 75.00*
**190** A3 115r on 150r car, *rose* (11½) 1.40 .75
**191** A3 130r on 75r car (12½) 3.50 1.40
**192** A3 130r on 80r yel grn (11½) 3.50 1.40
*a.* Inverted overprint 60.00 50.00
**193** A3 130r on 200r bl, *bl* (13½) 2.30 1.40
*a.* Perf. 12½ *145.00 135.00*
*Nos. 184-193 (10)* 28.85 16.35

War Tax Stamps of Portuguese Africa Srchd.

**1921, Feb. 3** ***Perf. 15x14***
**194** WT1 ¼c on 1c green .75 .55
**195** WT1 ½c on 1c green .85 .70
*a.* "1/2" instead of "½" as shown 17.50 15.00
**196** WT1 1c green .85 .70

***Perf. 12x11½***
**194B** WT1 ¼c on 1c green 1.40 1.20
**195B** WT1 ½c on 1c green 1.40 1.20
*a.* "1/2" instead of "½" as shown 25.00 19.00
**196B** WT1 1c green 1.30 1.10

Nos. 194B-196B also exist on enameled paper. The values are the same.

Nos. 127 and 126 Surcharged

***Perf. 14 to 15***
**197** CD27 2c on 15c on 150r 2.90 2.00
**198** CD26 4c on 10c on 100r 3.75 3.50
*a.* On No. 118 (error) 300.00 240.00

The 4c surcharge also exists on No. 134. Value, $500.

No. 50 Surcharged

***Perf. 12***
**200** A4 6c on 100r dk bl, *bl* 3.75 2.90
*a.* No accent on "U" of surcharge 17.50 15.00
*Nos. 194-200 (6)* 12.85 10.35

No. 200 has an accent on the "U" of the surcharge.

Stamps of 1913-15 Surcharged

**1922, Apr.** ***Perf. 11½, 12½, 13½***
**On No. 137**
**201** A3 4c on 130r on 80r 1.70 1.50

**On Nos. 191-193**
**202** A3 4c on 130r on 75r 2.20 1.40
**203** A3 4c on 130r on 80r 1.70 1.40
**204** A3 4c on 130r on 200r 1.40 1.20
*a.* Perf. 12½ 23.00 20.00
*Nos. 201-204 (4)* 7.00 5.50

Surcharge of Nos. 201-204 with smaller $ occurs once in sheet of 28. Value eight times normal.

Nos. 78-79 Surcharged

**1925** ***Perf. 13½, 11½***
**205** A3 40c on 400r on 300r 1.50 1.20
**206** N1 40c on 400r on 2½r 1.50 1.20

No. 176 Surcharged

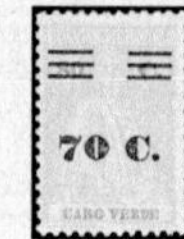

**1931, Nov.** ***Perf. 12x11½***
**214** A6 70c on 80c brt rose 32.50 12.00

Ceres — A7

**1934, May 1** **Wmk. 232**
**215** A7 1c bister .35 *.35*
**216** A7 5c olive brown .35 .35
**217** A7 10c violet .35 .35
**218** A7 15c black .35 .35
**219** A7 20c gray .35 .35
**220** A7 30c dk green .35 .35
**221** A7 40c red org .35 .35
**222** A7 45c brt blue 1.90 .95
**223** A7 50c brown 1.00 .60
**224** A7 60c olive grn 1.00 .60
**225** A7 70c brown org 1.00 .60
**226** A7 80c emerald 1.00 .60
**227** A7 85c deep rose 4.50 2.75
**228** A7 1e maroon 3.00 .55
**229** A7 1.40e dk blue 3.75 3.50
**230** A7 2e dk violet 5.25 2.75
**231** A7 5e apple green 22.50 6.00
**232** A7 10e olive bister 37.75 20.00
**233** A7 20e orange 60.00 27.00
*Nos. 215-233 (19)* 145.10 68.35

For surcharge see No. 256.

**Vasco da Gama Issue**
Common Design Types
**1938 Unwmk. *Perf. 13½x13***
**Name and Value in Black**
**234** CD34 1c gray green .35 .35
**235** CD34 5c orange brn .35 .35
**236** CD34 10c dk carmine .35 .35
**237** CD34 15c dk vio brn 1.05 1.00
**238** CD34 20c slate .50 .35
**239** CD35 30c rose vio .50 .35
**240** CD35 35c brt green .50 .35
**241** CD35 40c brown .50 .35
**242** CD35 50c brt red vio .50 .35
**243** CD36 60c gray blk .50 .35
**244** CD36 70c brown vio .50 .35
**245** CD36 80c orange .50 .35
**246** CD36 1e red .70 .35
**247** CD37 1.75e blue 1.95 .85
**248** CD37 2e dk blue grn 3.50 2.50
**249** CD37 5e ol grn 8.50 1.75
**250** CD38 10e blue vio 14.00 2.00
**251** CD38 20e red brown 45.00 6.25
*Nos. 234-251 (18)* 79.75 18.55

For surcharges see Nos. 255, 271-276, 288-292.

Outline Map of Africa — A8

**1939, June 23 Litho. *Perf. 11½x12***
**252** A8 80c vio, *pale rose* 6.75 3.25
**253** A8 1.75e blue, *pale bl* 48.50 32.50
**254** A8 20e brown, *buff* 105.00 39.00
*Nos. 252-254 (3)* 160.25 74.75

Visit of the President of Portugal in 1939.

**Nos. 239 and 221 Surcharged with New Value and Bars in Black**

**1948 Unwmk. *Perf. 13½x13***
**255** CD35 10c on 30c rose violet 2.90 1.70

***Perf. 12x11½***
**Wmk. 232**
**256** A7 25c on 40c red orange 2.90 1.70

Machado Pt., Sao Vicente
A9

Brava Creek, Sao Nicoláo
A10

Designs: 10c, Ribeira Grande. 1e, Harbor, Sao Vicente. 1.75e, Mindelo, distant view. 2e, Joao de Evora Beach. 5e, Mindelo. 10e, Volcano, Fire Island. 20e, Mt. Paul.

***Perf. 14½***
**1948, Oct. 1 Litho. Unwmk.**
**257** A9 5c vio brn & bis .35 .40
**258** A9 10c ol grn & pale grn .35 .40
**259** A10 50c mag & lil rose .65 .40
**260** A10 1e brn vio & rose lil 2.00 1.60
**261** A10 1.75e ultra & grnsh bl 3.00 2.90
**262** A10 2e dk brn & buff 6.00 2.50
**263** A10 5e ol grn & yel 12.00 6.25
**264** A10 10e red & cream 22.50 20.00
**265** A10 20e dk vio & bis 50.00 40.00
*Nos. 257-265 (9)* 96.85 74.45

**Lady of Fatima Issue**
Common Design Type
**1948, Dec.**
**266** CD40 50c dark blue 8.50 9.00

UPU Symbols — A10a

**1949, Oct.** ***Perf. 14***
**267** A10a 1e red vio & pink 7.00 5.50

UPU, 75th anniversary.

**Catalogue values for unused stamps in this section, from this point to the end of the section, are for Never Hinged items.**

**Holy Year Issue**
Common Design Types
**1950, May** ***Perf. 13x13½***
**268** CD41 1e orange brown 1.60 1.00
**269** CD42 2e slate 5.75 3.75

**Holy Year Conclusion Issue**
Common Design Type
**1951, Oct. Unwmk. *Perf. 14***
**270** CD43 2e pur & lil + label 1.75 1.25

Stamps without labels sell for less.

**Nos. 240, 244-245, 247, 250 Surcharged with New Value and Bars**
***Perf. 13½x13***
**1951, May 21** **Unwmk.**
**271** CD35 10c on 35c .85 .70
**272** CD36 20c on 70c 1.10 .70
**273** CD36 40c on 70c 1.40 .80
**274** CD36 50c on 80c 1.40 .80
**275** CD37 1e on 1.75e 1.50 .80
**276** CD38 2e on 10e 6.00 2.50
*a.* 1e on 10e 170.00 95.00
*Nos. 271-276 (6)* 12.25 6.30

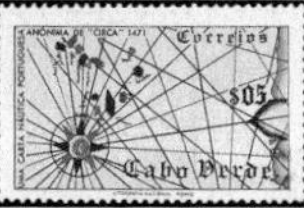
Map of Cape Verde Islands, 1502 — A11

Vicente Dias and Gonçalo de Cintra — A12

Portraits: 30c, Diogo Alfonso and Alvaro Fernandes. 50c, Lançarote and Soeiro da Costa. 1e, Diogo Gomes and Antonio da Nola. 2e, Prince Fernando and Prince Henry the Navigator. 3e, Antao Gonçalves and Dinis

Dias. 5e, Alfonso Goncalves Baldaia and Joao Fernandes. 10e, Dinis Eanes da Gra and Alvaro de Freitas. 20e, Map of Cape Verde Islands, 1502.

**1952, Feb. 24** ***Perf. 14***

| No. | Type | Description | Unused | Used |
|---|---|---|---|---|
| **277** | A11 | 5c multicolored | .30 | .30 |
| **278** | A12 | 10c multicolored | .30 | .30 |
| **279** | A12 | 30c multicolored | .30 | .30 |
| **280** | A12 | 50c multicolored | .30 | .30 |
| **281** | A12 | 1e multicolored | .30 | .30 |
| **282** | A12 | 2e multicolored | 1.70 | .30 |
| **283** | A12 | 3e multicolored | 13.00 | 2.00 |
| **284** | A12 | 5e multicolored | 4.50 | .95 |
| **285** | A12 | 10e multicolored | 9.00 | 2.40 |
| **286** | A11 | 20e multicolored | 15.50 | 3.50 |
| | | *Nos. 277-286 (10)* | 45.20 | 10.65 |

### Medical Congress Issue
Common Design Type

Design: Hypodermic Injection.

**1952, June** ***Perf. 13½***

| No. | Type | Description | Unused | Used |
|---|---|---|---|---|
| **287** | CD44 | 20c ol grn & dk brn | .95 | .75 |

### No. 247 Surcharged with New Values and "X" in Black

**1952, Jan. 25** ***Perf. 13½x13***

| No. | Type | Description | Unused | Used |
|---|---|---|---|---|
| **288** | CD37 | 10c on 1.75e | 1.70 | 1.50 |
| **289** | CD37 | 20c on 1.75e | 1.70 | 1.50 |
| **290** | CD37 | 50c on 1.75e | 7.75 | 6.75 |
| **291** | CD37 | 1e on 1.75e | .95 | .25 |
| **292** | CD37 | 1.50e on 1.75e | .95 | .25 |
| | | *Nos. 288-292 (5)* | 13.05 | 10.25 |

Facade of Jeronymos Convent — A13

***Perf. 13½***

**1953, Jan.** **Unwmk.** **Litho.**

| No. | Type | Description | Unused | Used |
|---|---|---|---|---|
| **293** | A13 | 10c brown & pale olive | .30 | .30 |
| **294** | A13 | 50c purple & fawn | 1.05 | .50 |
| **295** | A13 | 1e dark green & fawn | 2.40 | 1.35 |
| | | *Nos. 293-295 (3)* | 3.75 | 2.15 |

Exhibition of Sacred Missionary Art held at Lisbon in 1951.

Stamp of Portugal and Arms of Colonies — A13a

**1953** **Photo.**

| No. | Type | Description | Unused | Used |
|---|---|---|---|---|
| **296** | A13a | 50c multicolored | 2.25 | 1.50 |

Centenary of Portuguese stamps.

### Sao Paulo Issue
Common Design Type

**1954** **Litho.** ***Perf. 13½***

| No. | Type | Description | Unused | Used |
|---|---|---|---|---|
| **297** | CD46 | 1e green, cream & gray | .95 | .80 |

Belem Tower, Lisbon, and Colonial Arms — A14

**1955, May 15** **Litho.** ***Perf. 13½***

| No. | Type | Description | Unused | Used |
|---|---|---|---|---|
| **298** | A14 | 1e multicolored | .70 | .50 |
| **299** | A14 | 1.60e buff & multi | .95 | .80 |

Visit of Pres. Francisco H. C. Lopes.

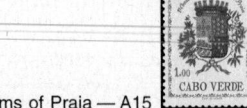

Arms of Praia — A15

**1958, June 14** ***Perf. 12x11½***

| No. | Type | Description | Unused | Used |
|---|---|---|---|---|
| **300** | A15 | 1e multicolored | .85 | .65 |
| **301** | A15 | 2.50e pink & multi | 1.45 | 1.25 |

Centenary of city of Praia.

Fair Emblem, Globe and Arms — A15a

**1958** ***Perf. 12x11½***

| No. | Type | Description | Unused | Used |
|---|---|---|---|---|
| **302** | A15a | 2e multicolored | 1.15 | .55 |

World's Fair, Brussels, Apr. 17-Oct. 19.

### Tropical Medicine Congress Issue
Common Design Type

**1958, Sept. 5** ***Perf. 13½***

| No. | Type | Description | Unused | Used |
|---|---|---|---|---|
| **303** | CD47 | 3e Aloe vera | 6.75 | 3.25 |

Prince Henry — A16

**1960, June 25** **Litho.** ***Perf. 13½***

| No. | Type | Description | Unused | Used |
|---|---|---|---|---|
| **304** | A16 | 2e multicolored | .70 | .35 |

500th anniv. of the death of Prince Henry the Navigator.

Antonio da Nola — A17

Design: 2.50e, Diogo Gomes.

**1960, Oct.** **Unwmk.** ***Perf. 14½***

| No. | Type | Description | Unused | Used |
|---|---|---|---|---|
| **305** | A17 | 1e multicolored | 1.10 | .65 |
| **306** | A17 | 2.50e multicolored | 2.90 | 1.40 |

Discovery of Cape Verde, 500th anniv.

School Children — A18

**1960**

| No. | Type | Description | Unused | Used |
|---|---|---|---|---|
| **307** | A18 | 2.50e multicolored | 1.70 | .95 |

10th anniv. of the Commission for Technical Cooperation in Africa South of the Sahara (C.C.T.A.).

Arms of Praia — A19

Arms of various cities & towns of Cape Verde.

**1961, July** **Litho.** ***Perf. 13½***

| No. | Type | Description | Unused | Used |
|---|---|---|---|---|
| **308** | A19 | 5c shown | .30 | .30 |
| **309** | A19 | 15c Nova Sintra | .30 | .30 |
| **310** | A19 | 20c Ribeira Brava | .30 | .30 |
| **311** | A19 | 30c Assomada | .30 | .30 |
| **312** | A19 | 1e Maio | .65 | .30 |
| **313** | A19 | 2e Mindelo | .65 | .30 |
| **314** | A19 | 2.50e Santa Maria | 1.00 | .30 |
| **315** | A19 | 3e Pombas | 2.00 | .65 |
| **316** | A19 | 5e Sal-Rei | 2.00 | .65 |
| **317** | A19 | 7.50e Tarrafal | 3.00 | 1.20 |
| **318** | A19 | 15e Maria Pia | 5.00 | 1.20 |
| **319** | A19 | 30e San Felipe | 9.00 | 3.25 |
| | | *Nos. 308-319 (12)* | 24.50 | 9.05 |

### Sports Issue
Common Design Type

Sports: 50c, Javelin. 1e, Discus. 1.50e, Cricket. 2.50e, Boxing. 4.50e, Hurdling. 12.50e, Golf.

**1962, Jan. 18** ***Perf. 13½***

| No. | Type | Description | Unused | Used |
|---|---|---|---|---|
| **320** | CD48 | 50c lt brown | .30 | .30 |
| **321** | CD48 | 1e lt green | .80 | .30 |
| **322** | CD48 | 1.50e lt blue grn | 10.50 | 2.90 |
| **323** | CD48 | 2.50e pale vio bl | .80 | .50 |
| **324** | CD48 | 4.50e orange | 1.15 | 1.10 |
| **325** | CD48 | 12.50e beige | 2.50 | 2.30 |
| | | *Nos. 320-325 (6)* | 16.05 | 7.40 |

### Anti-Malaria Issue
Common Design Type

Design: Anopheles pretoriensis.

**1962** **Litho.** ***Perf. 13½***

| No. | Type | Description | Unused | Used |
|---|---|---|---|---|
| **326** | CD49 | 2.50e multicolored | 1.90 | 1.60 |

### Airline Anniversary Issue
Common Design Type

**1963, Oct.** **Unwmk.** ***Perf. 14½***

| No. | Type | Description | Unused | Used |
|---|---|---|---|---|
| **327** | CD50 | 2.50e gray & multi | 1.50 | 1.10 |

### National Overseas Bank Issue
Common Design Type

Design: 1.50e, Jose da Silva Mendes Leal.

**1964, May 16** ***Perf. 13½***

| No. | Type | Description | Unused | Used |
|---|---|---|---|---|
| **328** | CD51 | 1.50e multicolored | 1.50 | 1.30 |

### ITU Issue
Common Design Type

**1965, May 17** **Litho.** ***Perf. 14½***

| No. | Type | Description | Unused | Used |
|---|---|---|---|---|
| **329** | CD52 | 2.50e buff & multi | 2.90 | 2.25 |

Militia Drummer, 1806 — A20

Designs: 1e, Soldier, Militia, 1806. 1.50e, Grenadier officer, 1833. 2.50e, Grenadier, 1833. 3e, Cavalry officer, 1834. 4e, Grenadier, 1835. 5e, Artillery officer, 1848. 10e, Drum major, infantry, 1856.

**1965, Dec. 1** **Litho.** ***Perf. 14½***

| No. | Type | Description | Unused | Used |
|---|---|---|---|---|
| **330** | A20 | 50c multicolored | .30 | .30 |
| **331** | A20 | 1e multicolored | .55 | .30 |
| **332** | A20 | 1.50e multicolored | .55 | .50 |
| **333** | A20 | 2.50e multicolored | 1.50 | .45 |
| **334** | A20 | 3e multicolored | 3.00 | .45 |
| **335** | A20 | 4e multicolored | 1.30 | .65 |
| **336** | A20 | 5e multicolored | 1.50 | .65 |
| **337** | A20 | 10e multicolored | 3.25 | 2.25 |
| | | *Nos. 330-337 (8)* | 11.95 | 5.55 |

### National Revolution Issue
Common Design Type

1e, Dr. Adriano Moreira School & Health Center.

**1966, May 28** **Litho.** ***Perf. 12***

| No. | Type | Description | Unused | Used |
|---|---|---|---|---|
| **338** | CD53 | 1e multicolored | .85 | .75 |

### Navy Club Issue
Common Design Type

Designs: 1e, Capt. Fontoura da Costa and gunboat Mandovy. 1.50e, Capt. Carvalho Araujo and minesweeper Augusto Castilho.

**1967, Jan. 31** **Litho.** ***Perf. 13***

| No. | Type | Description | Unused | Used |
|---|---|---|---|---|
| **339** | CD54 | 1e multicolored | 1.10 | .90 |
| **340** | CD54 | 1.50e multicolored | 1.60 | 1.40 |

Virgin Mary Statue — A21

**1967, May 13** **Litho.** ***Perf. 12½x13***

| No. | Type | Description | Unused | Used |
|---|---|---|---|---|
| **341** | A21 | 1e multicolored | .65 | .40 |

50th anniv. of the apparition of the Virgin Mary to 3 shepherd children at Fatima.

Pres. Rodrigues Thomaz — A22

**1968, Feb. 9** **Litho.** ***Perf. 13½***

| No. | Type | Description | Unused | Used |
|---|---|---|---|---|
| **342** | A22 | 1e multicolored | .65 | .40 |

Issued to commemorate the 1968 visit of Pres. Americo de Deus Rodrigues Thomaz.

### Cabral Issue

Pedro Alvares Cabral — A23

1e, Cantino's world map, 1502, horiz.

**1968, Apr. 22** **Litho.** ***Perf. 14***

| No. | Type | Description | Unused | Used |
|---|---|---|---|---|
| **343** | A23 | 1e multicolored | 1.20 | 1.00 |
| **344** | A23 | 1.50e multicolored | 1.80 | 1.10 |

See note after Angola No. 545.
For overprint see No. 365.

Sao Vicente Harbor — A24

Physic Nut — A25

Designs: 1.50e, Peanut plant. 2.50e, Castor-oil plant. 3.50e, Yams. 4e, Date palm. 4.50e, Guavas. 5e, Tamarind. 10e, Bitter cassava. 30e, Woman carrying fruit baskets.

**1968, Oct. 15** **Litho.** ***Perf. 14***

| No. | Type | Description | Unused | Used |
|---|---|---|---|---|
| **345** | A24 | 50c multicolored | .30 | .25 |
| **346** | A25 | 1e multicolored | .50 | .25 |
| **347** | A25 | 1.50e multicolored | .50 | .25 |
| **348** | A25 | 2.50e multicolored | .50 | .25 |
| **349** | A25 | 3.50e multicolored | .50 | .25 |
| **350** | A25 | 4e multicolored | .50 | .25 |
| **351** | A25 | 4.50e multicolored | 1.00 | .25 |
| **352** | A25 | 5 multicolored | 2.00 | .30 |
| **353** | A25 | 10e multicolored | 2.00 | .60 |
| **354** | A25 | 30e multicolored | 4.00 | 2.50 |
| | | *Nos. 345-354 (10)* | 11.80 | 5.15 |

For overprint see No. 372.

### Admiral Coutinho Issue
Common Design Type

Adm. Coutinho & map showing route of 1st flight from Lisbon to Rio de Janeiro.

**1969, Feb. 17** **Litho.** ***Perf. 14***

| No. | Type | Description | Unused | Used |
|---|---|---|---|---|
| **355** | CD55 | 30c multi, vert. | .60 | .25 |

For surcharge see No. 388.

### Vasco da Gama Issue

Vasco da Gama — A26

**1969, Aug. 29** **Litho.** ***Perf. 14***

| No. | Type | Description | Unused | Used |
|---|---|---|---|---|
| **356** | A26 | 1.50e multicolored | .65 | .40 |

Vasco da Gama (1469-1524), navigator.

### Administration Reform Issue
Common Design Type

**1969, Sept. 25** **Litho.** ***Perf. 14***

| No. | Type | Description | Unused | Used |
|---|---|---|---|---|
| **357** | CD56 | 2e multicolored | .65 | .40 |

### King Manuel I Issue

King Manuel I — A27

**1969, Dec. 1** **Litho.** ***Perf. 14***

| No. | Type | Description | Unused | Used |
|---|---|---|---|---|
| **358** | A27 | 3e multicolored | .65 | .50 |

500th anniv. of the birth of King Manuel I.

### Marshal Carmona Issue
Common Design Type

Design: 2.50e, Antonio Oscar Carmona in marshal's uniform.

**1970, Nov. 15** **Litho.** ***Perf. 14***

| No. | Type | Description | Unused | Used |
|---|---|---|---|---|
| **359** | CD57 | 2.50e multi | .70 | .50 |

Galleons on Sanaga River — A28

**1972, May 25 Litho. *Perf. 13***
**360** A28 5e lilac rose & multi 1.60 1.20

4th centenary of the publication of The Lusiads by Luiz Camoens.

**Olympic Games Issue**
Common Design Type

4e, Basketball & boxing, Olympic emblem.

**1972, June 20 *Perf. 14x13½***
**361** CD59 4e multicolored .85 .40

For surcharge see No. 371.

**Lisbon-Rio de Janeiro Flight Issue**
Common Design Type

Design: "Lusitania" landing at San Vicente.

**1972, Sept. 20 Litho. *Perf. 13½***
**362** CD60 3.50e multi .85 .40

**WMO Centenary Issue**
Common Design Type

**1973, Dec. 15 Litho. *Perf. 13***
**363** CD61 2.50e ultra & multi .85 .40

For overprint see No. 387.

Mindelo Desalination Plant — A29

**1974 Litho. *Perf. 13½***
**364** A29 4e multicolored 1.25 .85

Opening of the Mindelo desalination plant.
For surcharge see No. 371A.

**Republic**

No. 343 Overprinted

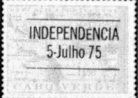

**1975, Dec. 19 Litho. *Perf. 14***
**365** A23 1e multicolored .35 .25

Proclamation of Independence.

Amilcar Cabral, Flag and Crowd — A30

**1976, Jan. 20**
**366** A30 5e multicolored .55 .25

3rd anniv. of the assassination of Amilcar Cabral (1924-73), revolutionary leader.

Rising Sun, Coat of Arms, Liberated People A31

**1976, July 5 Litho. *Perf. 14***

| | | | | |
|---|---|---|---|---|
| **367** | A31 | 50c multicolored | .30 | .25 |
| **368** | A31 | 3e multicolored | .90 | .25 |
| **369** | A31 | 15e multicolored | 2.00 | .35 |
| **370** | A31 | 50e multicolored | 6.25 | 1.25 |
| *a.* | | Miniature sheet, #367-370 | *15.00* | *15.00* |
| | | *Nos. 367-370 (4)* | 9.45 | 2.10 |

First anniversary of independence.

Nos. 351, 361, 364 Overprinted

**1976 Litho. *Perf. 14***

| | | | | |
|---|---|---|---|---|
| **371** | CD59 | 4e multi | *1,150.* | — |
| **371A** | A29 | 4e multi | *50.00* | *27.50* |
| **372** | A25 | 4.50e multi | 4.25 | 2.25 |

Amilcar Cabral, Map and Flag of Cape Verde — A32

**1976, Sept. 19 *Perf. 14***
**373** A32 1e multicolored .45 .25

Party of Intl. Action (PAICC), 20th anniv.

Electronic Tree and ITU Emblem — A33

**1977, May 17 Litho. *Perf. 13½x13***
**374** A33 5.50e multi .45 .25

World Telecommunications Day.

Ashtray — A34

Carved Coconut Shells: 30c, Bell on stand. 50c, Lamp with Adam and Eve. 1e, Hollow shell with Nativity. 1.50e, Desk lamp. 5e, Jar. 10e, Jar with hinged cover. 20e, Tobacco jar with palms. 30e, Stringed instrument.

**1977, July 5 Litho. *Perf. 14***

| | | | | |
|---|---|---|---|---|
| **375** | A34 | 20c lilac & multi | .30 | .25 |
| **376** | A34 | 30c rose & multi | .30 | .25 |
| **377** | A34 | 50c salmon & multi | .30 | .25 |
| **378** | A34 | 1e lt green & multi | .35 | .25 |
| **379** | A34 | 1.50e orange yel & multi | .35 | .25 |
| **380** | A34 | 5e gray & multi | .75 | .35 |
| **381** | A34 | 10e lt blue & multi | 1.25 | .55 |
| **382** | A34 | 20e yellow & multi | 2.00 | 1.25 |
| **383** | A34 | 30e rose lilac & multi | 3.25 | 1.40 |
| | | *Nos. 375-383 (9)* | 8.85 | 4.80 |

Cape Verde No. 1 and Coat of Arms — A35

**1977, Sept. 12 Litho. *Perf. 13½***
**384** A35 4e blue & multi .40 .25
**385** A35 8e lilac & multi .80 .35

Centenary of Cape Verde stamps.

Congress Emblem — A36

**1977, Nov. 15 *Perf. 14***
**386** A36 3.50e multi .60 .25

African Party of Independence of Guinea-Bissau and Cape Verde (PAIGC), 3rd cong., Nov. 15-20.

No. 363 Overprinted

**1978, May 1 *Perf. 12***
**387** CD61 2.50e ultra & multi .60 .25

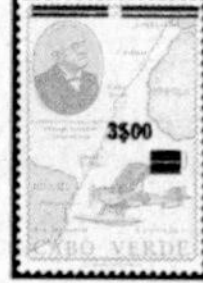

No. 355 Surcharged

**1978, May 1 *Perf. 14***
**388** CD55 3e on 30c multi 2.25 .35

Antenna and ITU Emblem A37

**1978, May 17 Litho. *Perf. 14***
**389** A37 3.50e silver & multi .55 .25

10th World Telecommunications Day.

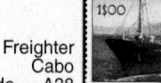

Freighter Cabo Verde — A38

**1978, June 25 Litho. *Perf. 14***
**391** A38 1e multicolored .70 .25

First ship of Cape Verde merchant marine.

Map of Africa and Equality Emblem — A39

**1978, June 21**
**392** A39 4.50e multicolored .75 .25

Anti-Apartheid Year.

Human Rights Emblem — A40

**1978, Dec. 10 Litho. *Perf. 14***
**393** A40 1.50e multicolored .35 .25
**394** A40 2e multicolored .55 .35

Universal Declaration of Human Rights, 30th anniversary.

Children and Balloons, IYC Emblem A41

IYC Emblem and Child's Drawing: 3.50e, Children and flowers.

**1979, June 1 Litho. *Perf. 14***
**395** A41 1.50e multi .65 .25
**396** A41 3.50e multi 1.10 .35

International Year of the Child.

Pindjiguiti Massacre Monument — A42

**1979, Aug. 3 *Perf. 13***
**397** A42 4.50e multi 3.00 .25

Massacre of Pindjiguiti, 20th anniversary.

Natl. Youth Week — A42a

**1979, Sept. 1 Litho. *Perf. 14***
**397A** A42a 3.50e Poster 1.25 .25

Centenary of Mindelo A43

**1980, Apr. 23 Litho. *Perf. 12½***
**398** A43 4e multicolored .70 .25

Flag of Cape Verde A44

Stylized Bird, "V" A45

**1980 Litho. *Perf. 12½***

| | | | | |
|---|---|---|---|---|
| **399** | A44 | 4e multicolored | 1.25 | .25 |
| **400** | A45 | 4e multicolored | .45 | .25 |
| **401** | A45 | 7e multicolored | .80 | .35 |
| **402** | A45 | 11e multicolored | 1.10 | .45 |
| | | *Nos. 399-402 (4)* | 3.60 | 1.30 |

5th anniversary of independence.
Issued: No. 399, June 1; others July 5.

A45a

**1980, May 13**
**402A** A45a 3.50e multi .55 .25
**402B** A45a 4.50e multi .70 .25

1980 Natl. census.

A46

**1980, June 6**

| | | | | |
|---|---|---|---|---|
| **403** | A46 | 1e Running | .30 | .25 |
| **404** | A46 | 2.50e Boxing | .30 | .25 |
| **405** | A46 | 3e Basketball | .35 | .25 |
| **406** | A46 | 4e Volleyball | .50 | .30 |
| **407** | A46 | 20e Swimming | 1.40 | .90 |
| **408** | A46 | 50e Tennis | 4.00 | 1.75 |
| | | *Nos. 403-408 (6)* | 6.85 | 3.70 |

### Souvenir Sheet

*Perf. 13*

**409** A46 30e Soccer, horiz. *18.00 18.00*

22nd Summer Olympic Games, Moscow, July 19-Aug. 3.

Thunnus Alalunga — A47

4.50e, Trachurus trachurus. 8e, Muraena helena. 10e, Corvina nigra. 12e, Katsuwonus pelamis. 50e, Prionace glauca.

**1980, Nov. 11 Litho. *Perf. 13***

**410** A47 50c shown .30 .25
**411** A47 4.50e multicolored .50 .25
**412** A47 8e multicolored .90 .25
**413** A47 10e multicolored 1.50 .35
**414** A47 12e multicolored 2.00 .60
**415** A47 50e multicolored 5.00 1.90
*Nos. 410-415 (6)* 10.20 3.60

Lochnera Rosea — A48

4.50e, Poinciana regia-bojer. 8e, Mirabilis jalapa. 10e, Nerium oleander. 12e, Bougainvillia litoralis. 30e, Hibiscus.

**1980, Dec. 29**

**416** A48 50c shown .30 .25
**417** A48 4.50e multicolored .30 .25
**418** A48 8e multicolored .75 .35
**419** A48 10e multicolored .95 .45
**420** A48 12e multicolored 1.10 .55
**421** A48 30e multicolored 2.60 1.50
*Nos. 416-421 (6)* 6.00 3.35

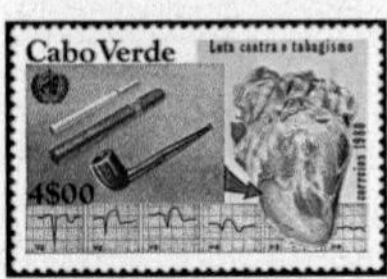

WHO Anti-smoking Campaign — A48a

**1980, Sept. 19 *Perf. 12½***

**421A** A48a 4e multicolored .50 .25
**421B** A48a 7e multicolored 1.10 .35

Arca Verde — A49

**1980, Nov. 30 Litho. *Perf. 12½x12***

**422** A49 3e shown .30 .25
**423** A49 5.50e Ilha do Maio .50 .25
**424** A49 7.50e Ilha de Komo .95 .55
**425** A49 9e Boa Vista 1.25 .75
**426** A49 12e Santo Antao 1.40 .55
**427** A49 30e Santiago 3.25 1.40
*Nos. 422-427 (6)* 7.65 3.75

Hand-woven Bag, Map — A49a

Various hand-woven articles. 10e, vert.

**1978, May 21 Litho. *Perf. 14***

**427A** A49a 50c multi .30 .25
**427B** A49a 1.50e multi .30 .25
**427C** A49a 2e multi .55 .25
**427D** A49a 3e multi .55 .30
**427E** A49a 10e multi 1.40 .70
*Nos. 427A-427E (5)* 3.10 1.75

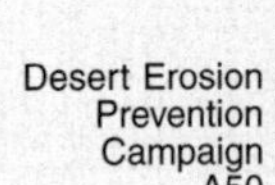

Desert Erosion Prevention Campaign A50

**1981, Mar. 30 Litho. *Perf. 13***

**428** A50 4.50e multi .60 .25
**429** A50 10.50e multi 1.25 .50

6th Anniv. of Constitution — A51

**1981, Apr. 15**

**430** A51 4.50e multicolored .60 .25

### Souvenir Sheet

Austria No. B336 — A52

**1981, May 18**

**431** A52 50e multicolored 6.50 6.50

WIPA '81 Philatelic Exhibition, Vienna, Austria, May 22-31.

Antenna — A53

**1981, Aug. 25 Litho. *Perf. 12½***

**432** A53 4.50e shown .65 .25
**433** A53 8e Dish antenna .95 .40
**434** A53 20e Dish antenna, diff. 2.00 .95
*Nos. 432-434 (3)* 3.60 1.60

Intl. Year of the Disabled — A54

**1981, Dec. 25 Litho. *Perf. 12½***

**435** A54 4.50e multicolored .65 .35

Purple Gallinule — A55

**1981, Dec. 30**

**436** A55 1e Egret, vert. .60 .25
**437** A55 4.50e Barn owl, vert. 1.25 .40
**438** A55 8e Passerine, vert. 2.75 .55
**439** A55 10e shown 3.00 .65
**440** A55 12e Guinea fowl 3.75 .75
*Nos. 436-440 (5)* 11.35 2.60

### Souvenir Sheet

*Perf. 13*

**441** A55 50e Razo Isld. lark 9.50 9.50

No. 441 contains 31x39mm one stamp.

CILSS Congress, Praia, Jan. 17 — A56

**1982, Jan. 17 *Perf. 13x12½***

**442** A56 11.50e multicolored 1.40 .65

Amilcar Cabral Soccer Championship — A57

Designs: Soccer players and flags.

**1982, Feb. 10 Litho. *Perf. 12½***

**443** A57 4.50e multicolored .55 .25
**444** A57 7.50e multicolored .85 .40
**445** A57 11.50e multicolored 1.40 .70
*Nos. 443-445 (3)* 2.80 1.35

1982 World Cup — A58

Designs: Soccer players and ball.

**1982, Apr. 25**

**446** A58 1.50e multi .30 .25
**447** A58 4.50e multi .50 .25
**448** A58 8e multi .85 .35
**449** A58 10.50e multi 1.00 .45
**450** A58 12e multi 1.25 .55
**451** A58 20e multi 2.25 .90
*Nos. 446-451 (6)* 6.15 2.75

### Souvenir Sheet

**452** A58 50e multi 6.25 6.25

First Anniv. of Women's Organization A59

**1982, Apr. 15 Litho. *Perf. 12½x12***

**453** A59 4.50e Marching .55 .25
**454** A59 8e Farming 1.10 .40
**455** A59 12e Child care 1.60 .70
*Nos. 453-455 (3)* 3.25 1.35

Estaleiros Navais Port, St. Vincent A59a

**1982, July 5 Litho. *Perf. 13x12½***

**455A** A59a 10.50e multi 1.75 .60

Natl. independence, 7th anniv.

Return of Barque Morrissey-Ernestina — A60

**1982, July 5 Litho. *Perf. 13***

**456** A60 12e multi 2.00 .80

Butterflies A61

2e, Hypolimnas misippus. 4.50e, Melanitis lede. 8e, Catopsilia florella. 10.50e, Colias electo. 11.50e, Danaus chrysippus. 12e, Papilio demodecus.

**1982, July 27 Litho.**

**457** A61 2e multicolored .35 .25
**458** A61 4.50e multicolored .70 .25
**459** A61 8e multicolored 1.10 .25
**460** A61 10.50e multicolored 1.50 .40
**461** A61 11.50e multicolored 1.60 .60
**462** A61 12e multicolored 2.75 .70
*Nos. 457-462 (6)* 8.00 2.45

Francisco Xavier da Cruz (1905-1958), Composer A62

14e, Eugenio Tavares (1867-1930), poet.

**1983, Feb. 20 Litho. *Perf. 13***

**463** A62 7e multicolored .45 .30
**464** A62 14e multicolored 1.90 .80

World Communications Year — A63

**1983, Oct. 10 Litho.**

**465** A63 13e multicolored 1.60 .80

Local Seashells — A64

**1983, Nov. 30 *Perf. 13½***

**466** A64 50c Conus ateralbus .30 .25
**467** A64 1e Conus decoratus .30 .25
**468** A64 3e Conus salreiensis .35 .25
**469** A64 10e Conus verdensis 1.50 .55
**470** A64 50e Conus cuneolus 5.00 2.75
*Nos. 466-470 (5)* 7.45 4.05

40th Anniv. of Intl. Civil Aviation Org. — A65

Airplanes: 50c, Ogma-Auster D5/160, 1966. 2e, De Havilland DH-104 Dove, 1945. 10e, Hawker Siddeley 748-200, 1972. 13e, De Havilland Dragon Rapide, 1945. 20e, De Havilland Twin Otter, 1977. 50e, Britten-Norman Islander, 1971.

**1984, Feb. 15 Litho.**

**471** A65 50c multicolored .30 .25
**472** A65 2e multicolored .30 .25
**473** A65 10e multicolored 1.10 .50
**474** A65 13e multicolored 1.25 .85
**475** A65 20e multicolored 1.90 1.25
**476** A65 50e multicolored 4.50 2.50
*Nos. 471-476 (6)* 9.35 5.60

Amilcar Cabral — A66

**1983, Jan. 17 Litho. *Perf. 14½***

**477** A66 7e multi 1.00 .50
**478** A66 10.50e multi 1.50 .90
*a.* Souvenir sheet of 2, #477-478 30.00 30.00

Amilcar Cabral Symposium, Jan. 17-20. No. 478a sold for 30e.

Cross Over Islands — A67

**1983, Dec. 10 Photo. *Perf. 14½***
479 A67 7e multicolored 1.10 .50

Christianity in Cape Verde, 450th anniv.

Natl. Solidarity Campaign — A68

**1984, Sept. 12 *Perf. 13½***
480 A68 6.50e multicolored 1.10 .25
481 A68 13.50e multicolored 2.10 .85

2nd Conference of Natl. Women's Orgs., Mar. 23-27 — A69

**1985, Mar. 27 Litho. *Perf. 13½***
482 A69 8e multicolored *3.00* 1.50

**Miniature Sheet**
483 A69 30e multicolored *100.00 100.00*

Natl. Independence, 10th Anniv. — A70

**1985, July 5 Litho. *Perf. 14***
484 A70 8c multicolored 1.25 .55
485 A70 12e multicolored 1.90 .80

Intl. Youth Year — A71

**1985, Sept. 12 Litho. *Perf. 14***
486 A71 12e multicolored 2.50 .90

Vapor, by Hundertwasser A72

**Photogravure and Engraved**
**1986, Apr. 25 *Perf. 14***
**Black Surcharge**
487 A72 30e on 10e multi 30.00 4.00

**Souvenir Sheets**
**Background Color**
488 Sheet of 4 150.00
a. A72 50e yellow & multi 17.50 17.50
489 Sheet of 4 150.00
a. A72 50e red & multi 17.50 17.50
490 Sheet of 4 150.00
a. A72 50e green & multi 17.50 17.50

No. 487 exists without surcharge.

World Wildlife Fund — A73

8e, Mabuya vaillanti. 10e, Tarentola gigas brancoensis. 15e, Tarentola gigas gigas. 30e, Hemidactylus bouvieri.
No. 495a, Mabuya vaillanti. No. 495b, Hemidactylus bouvieri.

***Perf. 13½x14½***
**1986, June 15 Litho.**
491 A73 8e multicolored 6.50 2.50
492 A73 10e multicolored 8.00 3.25
493 A73 15e multicolored 12.00 4.00
494 A73 30e multicolored 24.00 5.00
*Nos. 491-494 (4)* 50.50 14.75

**Souvenir Sheet**
495 Sheet of 2 30.00 22.50
a. A73 50e multi 14.00 10.00
b. A73 50e multi 14.00 10.00

No. 495 printed with center label picturing progress union emblem. Nos. 495a-495b printed without WWF emblem.

World Food Day — A74

**1986, June 20 *Perf. 14***
496 A74 8e Cauldron .50 .25
497 A74 12e Mortar & pestle .80 .35
498 A74 15e Quern stone 1.40 .50
*Nos. 496-498 (3)* 2.70 1.10

Intl. Peace Year — A75

**1986, Dec. 24 Litho. *Perf. 14***
499 A75 12e multicolored .60 .25
500 A75 30e multicolored 2.10 1.40

Natl. Child Survival Campaign — A76

**1987, Mar. 27 Litho. *Perf. 14***
501 A76 8e multicolored .45 .25
502 A76 10e multicolored .55 .25
503 A76 12e multicolored .65 .35
504 A76 16e multicolored .95 .50
505 A76 100e multicolored 4.50 2.75
*Nos. 501-505 (5)* 7.10 4.10

Tourism — A77

**1987, May 17**
506 A77 1e Bay, Mindelo .30 .25
507 A77 2.50e Hill country .30 .25
508 A77 5e Mountain peak .30 .25
509 A77 8e Monument .45 .25
510 A77 10e Mountain peaks 1.00 .30
511 A77 12e Beached boats 1.00 .40
512 A77 100e Harbor 5.25 3.00
*Nos. 506-512 (7)* 8.60 4.70

For surcharge see No. 710.

Ships — A78

**1987, Aug. 3 *Perf. 13½x14½***
513 A78 12e Carvalho, 1937 .75 .25
514 A78 16e Nauta, 1943 1.25 .25
515 A78 50e Maria Sony, 1911 3.75 1.25
*Nos. 513-515 (3)* 5.75 1.75

**Souvenir Sheet**
516 Sheet of 2 10.00 10.00
a. A78 60e Madalan, 1928 4.00 4.00

Crop Protection A80

50c, Identification of insect plague. 2e, Use of insecticides. 9e, Import of parasites. 13e, Import of predators. 16e, Locust. 19e, Estimation of crop loss.
50e, Agricultural Research Institute.

**1988, May 9 Litho. *Perf. 13½***
518 A80 50c multicolored .30 .25
519 A80 2e multicolored .30 .25
520 A80 9e multicolored .55 .25
521 A80 13e multicolored .65 .25
522 A80 16e multicolored 1.10 .40
523 A80 19e multicolored 1.40 .60
*Nos. 518-523 (6)* 4.30 2.00

**Souvenir Sheet**
524 A80 50e multicolored 5.50 5.50

Maps A81

1e, Dutch, 17th cent. 2.50e, Belgian, 18th cent. 4.50e, French, 18th cent. 9.50e, English, 18th cent. 19.50e, English, 19th cent. 20e, French, 18th cent., vert.

**1988, July 5 Litho. *Perf. 14***
525 A81 1e multicolored .30 .25
526 A81 2.50e multicolored .30 .25
527 A81 4.50e multicolored .30 .25
528 A81 9.50e multicolored .60 .25
529 A81 19.50e multicolored 1.25 .55
530 A81 20e multicolored 1.40 .65
*Nos. 525-530 (6)* 4.15 2.20

Churches — A82

5e, St. Amaro Abade, Tarrafal, Santiago Is. 8e, Our Lady of the Light, Maio Is. 10e, Nazarene, Praia, Santiago Is. 12e, Our Lady of Rosa'rio, Sao Nicolau Is. 15e, Nazarene, Mindelo, Sao Vicente Is. 20e, Our Lady of Grace, Praia, Santiago Is.

**1988, Aug. 15 *Perf. 13½x14½***
531 A82 5e multicolored .30 .25
532 A82 8e multicolored .45 .25
533 A82 10e multicolored .55 .25
534 A82 12e multicolored .60 .25
535 A82 15e multicolored .85 .35
536 A82 20e multicolored 1.25 .45
*Nos. 531-536 (6)* 4.00 1.80

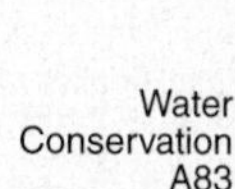

Water Conservation A83

**1988, Sept. 26 Litho. *Perf. 14***
537 A83 12e multicolored .75 .35

Intl. Red Cross, 125th Anniv. — A84

**1988, Oct. 20**
538 A84 7e multi .60 .25

3rd Communist Party (PAICV) Congress — A85

Portrait of Pres. Pereira, PAICV secretary-general, and: 7e, S. Jorginho Vocational Training Center. 10.50e, UN Secretary-General Perez de Cuellar. 30e, 100e, Star and text.

***Perf. 14½x13½***
**1988, Nov. 25 Litho.**
539 A85 7e multi .40 .25
540 A85 10.50e multi .60 .25
541 A85 30e multi 1.75 .75
*Nos. 539-541 (3)* 2.75 1.25

**Souvenir Sheet**
542 A85 100e multi 6.25 6.25

1988 Summer Olympics, Seoul — A86

**1988, Dec. 26**
543 A86 12e shown .60 .25
544 A86 15e Tennis .90 .35
545 A86 20e Soccer 1.25 .50
546 A86 30e Boxing 1.75 .90
*Nos. 543-546 (4)* 4.50 2.00

**Souvenir Sheet**
547 A86 50e Long jump 4.00 4.00

Roberto Duarte Silva (1837-89), Chemist — A86a

**1989, May 2 Litho. *Perf. 14¼x14***
547A A86a 12.50e multi .45 .25

2nd JAAC-CV Congress, Sept. 7-12 — A87

**1989, Apr. 7 Litho. *Perf. 14***
548 A87 30e Hot air balloon 1.25 .75

Liberty Guiding the People A88

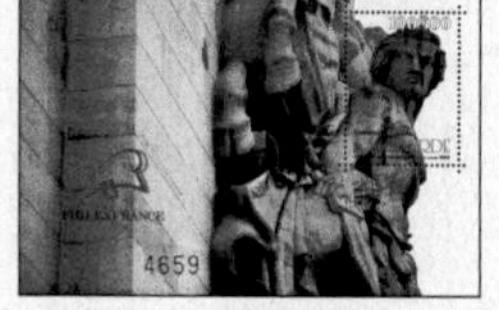
Relief, Arc de Triomphe — A89

**1989, July 7 Litho. *Perf. 14***
549 A88 20e multicolored .85 .45
550 A88 24e multicolored 1.10 .55
551 A88 25e multicolored 1.25 .65
*Nos. 549-551 (3)* 3.20 1.65

**Souvenir Sheet**
***Perf. 14½x13½***
552 A89 100e multicolored 5.50 5.50

French revolution, bicent.

Interparliamentary Union, Cent. — A90

**1989, Sept. 18 Litho. *Perf. 14***

**553** A90 2e shown .30 .25
**554** A90 4e Dove .30 .25
**555** A90 13e Natl. Assembly Bldg. .45 .25
*Nos. 553-555 (3)* 1.05 .75

Traditional Ceramics — A91

**1989, Nov. 13 Litho. *Perf. 13½***

**Panel Colors**

**556** A91 13e lilac .50 .25
**557** A91 20e red, vert. .70 .40
**558** A91 24e brown .90 .50
**559** A91 25e orange, vert. 1.00 .55
*Nos. 556-559 (4)* 3.10 1.70

Outdoor Toys — A92

**1989, Dec. 23**

**560** A92 1e Yellow truck .30 .25
**561** A92 6e Car .30 .25
**562** A92 8e White truck .35 .25
**563** A92 11.50e Trucks .45 .25
**564** A92 18e Scooter .75 .45
**565** A92 100e Boat 4.00 2.25
*Nos. 560-565 (6)* 6.15 3.70

Visit of Pope John Paul II — A93

**1990, Jan. 25**

**566** A93 13e blue & multi .50 .25
**567** A93 20e purple & multi 1.00 .40

**Souvenir Sheet**

**568** A93 200e multi, diff. 10.00 10.00

Turtles — A94

50c, Chelonia mydas. 1e, Dermochelys coriacea. 5e, Lepidochelys olivacea. 10e, Caretta caretta. 42e, Eretmochelys imbricata.

**1990, May 17 Litho. *Perf. 13½***

**569** A94 50c multicolored .50 .25
**570** A94 1e multicolored .50 .25
**571** A94 5e multicolored .75 .25
**572** A94 10e multicolored 1.00 .25
**573** A94 42e multicolored 4.00 .90
*Nos. 569-573 (5)* 6.75 1.90

Women's Congress — A95

**1990, Aug. 13**

**574** A95 9e multicolored .50 .25

A96

Various drawings of soccer players in action.

**1990, Aug. 7**

**575** A96 4e multicolored .30 .25
**576** A96 7.50e multicolored .30 .25
**577** A96 8e multicolored .30 .25
**578** A96 100e multicolored 3.50 2.10
*Nos. 575-578 (4)* 4.40 2.85

**Souvenir Sheet**

**579** A96 100e multi, diff. 4.50 4.50

World Cup Soccer Championships, Italy.
For surcharges see Nos. 711-712.

A97

Vaccinations: 5e, Emile Roux (1853-1933), diphtheria. 13e, Robert Koch (1843-1910), tuberculosis. 20e, Gaston Ramon (1886-1963), tetanus. 24e, Jonas Salk (1914-95), polio.

**Granite Paper**

**1990, Oct. 15 *Perf. 11½***

**580** A97 5e multicolored .35 .25
**581** A97 13e multicolored 1.00 .25
**582** A97 20e multicolored 1.40 .40
**583** A97 24e multicolored 1.75 .50
*Nos. 580-583 (4)* 4.50 1.40

Intl. Literacy Year — A98

Designs: 3e, Adult literacy class. 15e, Teacher holding flash card, children. 19e, Teacher, student at blackboard.

**1990, Sept. 28 Granite Paper**

**584** A98 2e shown .50 .25
**585** A98 3e multicolored .50 .25
**586** A98 15e multicolored .75 .25
**587** A98 19e multicolored 1.00 .30
*Nos. 584-587 (4)* 2.75 1.05

Traditional Fairy Tales — A99

2.50e, Man catching mermaid. 12e, Woman, snake. 25e, Man, eggs, woman.

**1990, Dec. 20 Litho. *Perf. 12½***

**588** A99 50c shown .30 .25
**589** A99 2.50e multicolored .30 .25
**590** A99 12e multicolored .50 .45
**591** A99 25e multicolored 1.00 .40
*Nos. 588-591 (4)* 2.10 1.35

Fight Against AIDS — A100

**1991, Feb. 20 Litho. *Perf. 14***

**Granite Paper**

**592** A100 13e multicolored *.75* .30
**593** A100 24e multi, diff. *1.25* .75

Fishing — A101

24e, Man removing hook from fish. 25e, Fishing boats. 50e, Two men long-line fishing.

**1991, Apr. 23 Litho. *Perf. 11½***

**594** A101 10e multicolored .35 .25
**595** A101 24e multicolored 1.10 .60
**596** A101 25e multicolored 1.25 .65
**597** A101 50e multicolored 2.40 1.50
*Nos. 594-597 (4)* 5.10 3.00

Medicinal Plants — A102

10e, Lavandula rotundifolia. 15e, Micromeria forbesii. 21e, Sarcostemma daltonii. 24e, Periploca chevalieri. 30e, Echium hypertropicum. 35e, Erysimum caboverdeanum.

**1991, July 5 Litho. *Perf. 11½***

**598** A102 10e multicolored .30 .25
**599** A102 15e multicolored .55 .25
**600** A102 21e multicolored 1.00 .30
**601** A102 24e multicolored 1.25 .35
**602** A102 30e multicolored 2.00 .45
**603** A102 35e multicolored 3.00 .55
*Nos. 598-603 (6)* 8.10 2.15

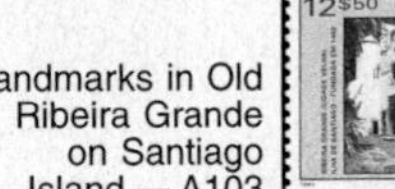

Landmarks in Old Ribeira Grande on Santiago Island — A103

12.50e, Church of Our Lady of the Rosary, 1495. 15e, Ruins of the Cathedral, 1556. 20e, Fortress of San Felipe, 1587. 30e, Ruins of the Convent of St. Francis, 1642. 100e, Pillory, 1520, vert.

**1991, June 25 Litho. *Perf. 11½***

**604** A103 12.50e multicolored .45 .25
**605** A103 15e multicolored .55 .25
**606** A103 20e multicolored .75 .45
**607** A103 30e multicolored 1.10 .75
*Nos. 604-607 (4)* 2.85 1.70

**Souvenir Sheet**

**608** A103 100e multicolored 4.00 4.00

Musical Instruments — A104

**1991, Oct. 9 Litho. *Perf. 11½***

**609** A104 10e 6-string guitar .35 .25
**610** A104 20e Violin .85 .55
**611** A104 29e 5-string guitar 1.40 .65
**612** A104 47e Cimba 2.00 1.25
*Nos. 609-612 (4)* 4.60 2.70

**Souvenir Sheet**

**613** A104 60e Accordion, horiz. 3.00 3.00

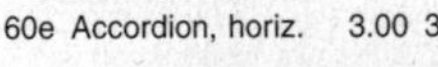

Christmas A105

**1991, Dec. 20 Litho. *Perf. 11½***

**614** A105 31e Nativity scene 1.10 .50
**615** A105 50e Nativity scene, diff. 1.75 .90

Discovery of America, 500th Anniv. — A106

**1992, Mar. 31 Litho. *Perf. 11½***

**616** A106 40e shown 2.50 1.10
**617** A106 40e Columbus on ship 2.50 1.10
*a.* Pair, #616-617 6.00 6.00

**Souvenir Sheet**

**618** A106 Sheet of 2 9.00 9.00

Stamps in No. 618 are smaller, without white border and "Luis Duran" and "Courvoisier" inscriptions. No. 618 was printed in continuous design and sold for 150e.

Souvenir Sheet

Granada '92 A107

**1992, Apr.24 *Perf. 11½***

**619** A107 50e multicolored 8.00 8.00

No. 619 sold for 150e.

Tropical Fruits — A108

16e, Syzygium jambos. 25e, Mangifera indica. 31e, Anacardium occidentale. 32e, Persea americana.

**1992, Feb. 29 *Perf. 12x11½***

**620** A108 16e multicolored .65 .30
**621** A108 25e multicolored 1.10 .50
**622** A108 31e multicolored 1.40 .65
**623** A108 32e multicolored 1.60 .75
*Nos. 620-623 (4)* 4.75 2.20

1992 Summer Olympics, Barcelona — A109

16e, Women's javelin. 20e, Weight lifting. 32e, Women's pole vault. 40e, Women's shot put.
100e, Women's gymnastics.

**1992, June 30 Litho. *Perf. 13½***

**624** A109 16e multicolored .60 .25
**625** A109 20e multicolored .75 .30
**626** A109 32e multicolored 1.40 .65
**627** A109 40e multicolored 1.60 .85
*Nos. 624-627 (4)* 4.35 2.05

**Souvenir Sheet**

**628** A109 100e multicolored 4.25 4.25

Sugar Cane Production A110

Designs: 19e, Oxen, sugar cane. 20e, Oxen yoked to press. 37e, Man placing cane inside press. 38e, Refining process.

**1992, Nov. Litho. *Perf. 11***

**629** A110 19e multicolored .65 .30
**630** A110 20e multicolored .65 .30
**631** A110 37e multicolored 1.25 .60
**632** A110 38e multicolored 1.40 .60
*Nos. 629-632 (4)* 3.95 1.80

Domestic Animals — A111

**1992, Nov. *Perf. 13½***

**633** A111 16e Cat .75 .40
**634** A111 31e Chickens 1.40 .80
**635** A111 32e Dog, vert. 1.50 .90
**636** A111 50e Horse 2.50 1.25
*Nos. 633-636 (4)* 6.15 3.35

Corals — A112

5e, Tubastrea aurea. 31e, Corallium rubrum. 37e, Porites porites. 50e, Millepora alcicornis.

**1993, Apr. 29 Litho. *Perf. 11½***
**637** A112 5e multicolored .30 .25
**638** A112 31e multicolored 1.25 .80
**639** A112 37e multicolored 1.50 1.00
**640** A112 50e multicolored 2.00 1.25
*Nos. 637-640 (4)* 5.05 3.30

Treaty of Tordesillas, 500th Anniv. (in 1994) — A113

Designs: No. 641, King Ferdinand, Queen Isabella of Spain, Pope Alexander VI. No. 642, Pope Julius II, King John II of Portugal. No. 643, Astrolabe, treaty signing. No. 644, Compass rose, map.

**1993, Aug. 1 Litho. *Perf. 12x11½***
**641** 37e multicolored 1.50 .65
**642** 37e multicolored 1.50 .65
*a.* A113 Pair, #641-642 3.50 3.25
**643** 38e multicolored 1.50 .65
**644** 38e multicolored 1.50 .65
*a.* A113 Pair, #643-644 3.50 3.25
*Nos. 641-644 (4)* 6.00 2.60

Souvenir Sheet

Santiago Island, 1806 — A114

**1993, July 30 *Perf. 13½***
**645** A114 100e multicolored 5.00 5.00

Brasiliana '93.

Lobsters — A115

2e, Palinurus charlestoni. 10e, Panulirus echinatus. 17e, Panulirus regius. 38e, Scyllarides latus.
100e, Panulirus regius, diff.

**1993, Sept. 29 Litho. *Perf. 11½***
**646** A115 2e multicolored .35 .25
**647** A115 10e multicolored .75 .25
**648** A115 17e multicolored 1.40 .50
**649** A115 38e multicolored 2.90 1.00
*Nos. 646-649 (4)* 5.40 2.00

**Souvenir Sheet**

**650** A115 100e multicolored 7.50 7.50

No. 650 contains one 51x36mm stamp.

Birds — A116

10e, Calonectris edwardsii. 30e, Sula leucogaster. 40e, Fregata magnificens. 41e, Phaeton aethereus.

**1993, Oct. 29 Litho. *Perf. 12x11½***
**651** A116 10e multicolored .75 .25
**652** A116 30e multicolored 3.00 .85
**653** A116 40e multicolored 4.00 1.10
*a.* Souvenir sheet of 1 12.00 11.00
**654** A116 41e multicolored 4.00 1.10
*Nos. 651-654 (4)* 11.75 3.30

Hong Kong '94 (No. 653a).
No. 653a sold for 150e.

Flowers — A117

**1993, Dec. 16 Litho. *Perf. 12x11½***
**655** A117 5e Rosa alexandra .30 .25
**656** A117 30e Strelitzia reginae 1.10 .80
**657** A117 37e Dianthus barbatus 1.60 1.00
*a.* Souvenir sheet of 1 7.50 7.50
**658** A117 50e Dahlia 2.00 1.25
*Nos. 655-658 (4)* 5.00 3.30

Singapore '95 (No. 657a). Issued 9/1/95. No. 657a sold for 150e.

1994 World Cup Soccer Championships, US — A118

Players, US flag, and: 1e, Giant's Stadium, New Jersey. 20e, Rose Bowl Stadium, Pasadena. 37e, Foxboro Stadium, Boston. 38e, Silverdome, Pontiac. 100e, RFK Stadium, Washington DC.

**1994, May 31 Litho. *Perf. 11½***
**659** A118 1e multicolored .30 .25
**660** A118 20e multicolored .85 .50
**661** A118 37e multicolored 1.50 1.00
**662** A118 38e multicolored 1.60 1.10
*Nos. 659-662 (4)* 4.25 2.85

**Souvenir Sheet**

**663** A118 100e multicolored 5.50 5.50

Prince Henry the Navigator (1394-1460) — A119

**1994, Mar. 4 Litho. *Perf. 12***
**664** A119 37e multicolored 3.00 1.00

See Brazil No. 2463, Macao No. 719, Portugal No. 1987.

Sharks — A120

21e, Eugomphodus taurus. 27e, Carcharhinus limbatus. 37e, Rhiniodon typus. 38e, Etmopterus spinax.

**1994, June 27 Litho. *Perf. 12x11½***
**665** A120 21e multicolored 1.00 .60
**666** A120 27e multicolored 1.25 .75
**667** A120 37e multicolored 1.75 1.25
**668** A120 38e multicolored 2.00 1.40
*Nos. 665-668 (4)* 6.00 4.00

Bananas — A121

**1994, Aug. 16 Litho. *Perf. 11½***
**669** A121 12e Prata, vert. .50 .25
**670** A121 16e Pao .75 .40
**671** A121 30e Ana roberta, vert. 1.50 .85
**672** A121 40e Roxa, vert. 2.00 1.10
*Nos. 669-672 (4)* 4.75 2.60

**Souvenir Sheet**

**673** A121 100e Prata, diff., vert. 9.00 9.00

PHILAKOREA '94, SINGPEX '94 (No. 673). No. 673 sold for 150e.

Lighthouses — A122

2e, Fontes Pereira de Melo. 37e, Morro Negro. 38e, Amelia, vert. 50e, Maria Pia, vert.

**1994, Oct. 17 *Perf. 12***
**674** A122 2e multicolored .30 .25
**675** A122 37e multicolored 1.75 1.00
**676** A122 38e multicolored 1.75 1.10
**677** A122 50e multicolored 2.25 1.40
*Nos. 674-677 (4)* 6.05 3.75

Wilhelm Roentgen (1845-1923), Discovery of the X-Ray, Cent. — A123

**1995, Mar. 31 Litho. *Perf. 12***
**678** A123 20e yellow & multi .80 .50
**679** A123 37e blue & multi 1.50 1.00
*a.* Souvenir sheet of 2, #678-679 4.50 4.50

No. 679a sold for 100e.

A124

FAO, 50th Anniv. — A125

**1995, May 17 Litho. *Perf. 12***
**680** A124 37e multicolored 1.50 .90
**681** A125 38e multicolored 1.50 .90

Dogs — A126

Dog, scene depicting story of dogs: 1e, Fox terrier, Two foxhounds and fox terrier, by John Emms. 10e, Cavalier King Charles, Shooting over Dogs, by Richard Ansdell. 40e, Rough collie, German shepherd. 50e, Braco, Hounds at Full Cry, by Thomas Blinks.

**1995, June 16 Litho. *Perf. 12x11½***
**682** A126 1e multicolored .30 .25
**683** A126 10e multicolored .55 .25
**684** A126 40e multicolored 2.25 1.25
**685** A126 50e multicolored 2.75 1.10
*Nos. 682-685 (4)* 5.85 2.85

Independence, 20th Anniv. — A127

**1995, July 20 Litho. *Perf. 12***
**686** A127 37e multicolored 1.90 1.25

Traditional Festival — A128

Designs: 2e, Horse race. 10e, Horseman leading parade. 37e, People singing, playing drums. 40e, Playing game on horseback.

**1995, Oct. 9 *Perf. 12x11½***
**687** A128 2e multicolored .30 .25
**688** A128 10e multicolored .45 .25
**689** A128 37e multicolored 1.50 .85
**690** A128 40e multicolored 1.75 1.00
*Nos. 687-690 (4)* 4.00 2.35

Children's Stories — A130

Designs: 10e, The cicadas making music, ants. 25e, Cicada being exposed to light. 38e, Cicada with guitar, ants working. 45e, Ants at table making fun of cicada.

**1995, Dec. 15 Litho. *Perf. 11½***
**692** A130 10e multicolored .40 .55
**693** A130 25e multicolored .85 .85
**694** A130 38e multicolored 1.40 1.10
**695** A130 45e multicolored 1.60 1.00
*Nos. 692-695 (4)* 4.25 3.50

Endangered Plants — A131

20e, Sonchus daltonii. 37e, Echium vulcanorum. 38e, Nauplius smithii. 50e, Campanula jacobaea.

**1996, Apr. 24 Litho. *Perf. 11½***
**696** A131 20e multicolored .65 .40
**697** A131 37e multicolored 1.20 .75
**698** A131 38e multicolored 1.20 .75
**699** A131 50e multicolored 1.60 1.10
*Nos. 696-699 (4)* 4.65 3.00

1996 Summer Olympic Games, Atlanta — A132

**1996, June 30 Litho. *Perf. 11½***
**700** A132 1e Tennis .30 .25
**701** A132 37e Gymnastics 1.10 .75
**702** A132 100e Athletics 3.25 2.10
*Nos. 700-702 (3)* 4.65 3.10

UNICEF, 50th Anniv. — A133

**1996, Aug. 1 Litho. *Perf. 12***
**703** A133 20e Young girl .90 .40
**704** A133 40e Mother, child 1.75 .85

Water Sports — A134

Designs: 2.50e, Fishing. 10e, Windsurfing. 22e, Jet skiing. No. 708, Surfing, horiz. No. 709, Diver's hand, pufferfish, horiz.

**1996, Oct. 9 Litho. *Perf. 12***
**705** A134 2.50e multicolored .30 .25
**706** A134 10e multicolored .35 .25
**707** A134 22e multicolored .70 .45
**708** A134 100e multicolored 3.25 2.10
*Nos. 705-708 (4)* 4.60 3.05

**Souvenir Sheet**

**709** A134 100e multicolored 4.50 4.50

No. 709 contains one 80x61mm stamp.

**Nos. 507, 575-576 Surcharged**

a

b

**1997 Litho. *Perf. 14***
**710** A77(a) 3e on 2.50e #507 .30 .25

***Perf. 13½***

**711** A96(b) 37e on 4e #575 3.00 .75
**712** A96(a) 38e on 7.50e #576 3.00 .75
*Nos. 710-712 (3)* 6.30 1.75

Natl. Symbols — A135

**1997** *Perf. 12*
**713** A135 25e Arms .80 .50
**714** A135 37e Anthem 1.10 .75
**715** A135 50e Flag 1.60 1.00
*Nos. 713-715 (3)* 3.50 2.25

World Wildlife Fund — A136

Pristis pectinata: a, On seabed. b, Swimming, school of small fish. c, Swimming along seabed, small fish. d, Two near seabed.

**1997** **Litho.** *Perf. 11½*
**716** A136 15e Strip of 4, #a.-d. 10.00 10.00

Legends of the Sea — A137

a, Fish, dolphins. b, Merman, mermaid. c, Fish swimming through portal, moray eel.

**1997** **Litho.** *Perf. 11½*
**717** A137 45e Strip of 3, #a.-c. 5.00 5.00

Fish — A138

Designs: 13e, Thunnus albacares. 21e, Thunnus obesus. 41e, Euthynnus alletteratus. 45e, Katsuwonus pelamis.

**1997** **Litho.** *Perf. 12*
**718** A138 13e multicolored .50 .30
**719** A138 21e multicolored 1.00 .60
**720** A138 41e multicolored 1.75 1.25
**721** A138 45e multicolored 2.00 1.50
*Nos. 718-721 (4)* 5.25 3.65

1998 World Cup Soccer Championships, France — A139

Designs: 30e, Soccer ball in net, vert. 45e, Soccer player, ball, vert. 50e, Globe, ball, World Cup trophy, fans in stadium.

**1998** **Litho.** *Perf. 12x11½, 11½x12*
**722** A139 10e shown .40 .25
**723** A139 30e multicolored 1.00 .80
**724** A139 45e multicolored 1.60 1.25
**725** A139 50e multicolored 2.00 1.40
*Nos. 722-725 (4)* 5.00 3.70

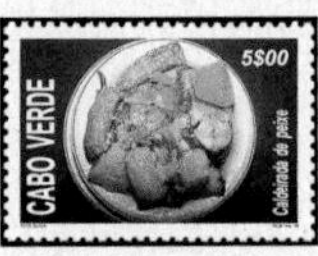


Traditional Cuisine — A140

5e, Boiled fish. 25e, Xerém com friginato. 35e, Cachupa. 40e, Molho de Saint-Nicholas.

**1998** **Litho.** *Perf. 12x11½*
**726** A140 5e multicolored .30 .25
**727** A140 25e multicolored .65 .65
**728** A140 35e multicolored 1.00 1.00
**729** A140 40e multicolored 1.10 1.10
*Nos. 726-729 (4)* 3.05 3.00

Early Exploration — A141

a, Quotation from Lusiadas, two men looking at maps. b, Man with sword, man & woman. c, Compass, map, sailing ship, buildings on cliff.

**1998** *Perf. 11½*
**730** A141 50e Strip of 3, #a.-c. 6.00 6.00

Women's Traditional Costumes — A142

**1998** **Litho.** *Perf. 12*
**731** A142 10e Brava .30 .25
**732** A142 18e Fogo .60 .50
**733** A142 30e Boa Vista .95 .80
**734** A142 50e Santiago 1.60 1.40
*Nos. 731-734 (4)* 3.45 2.95

Butterflies and Moths — A143

Designs: 5e, Byblia ilithyia. 10e, Aganais speciosa. 20e, Utetheisia pulchella. 30e, Vanessa cardui. 50e, Trichoplusia ni. 100e, Grammodes congenita.

**1999, Mar. 16** **Litho.** *Perf. 11¾*
**735** A143 5e multi .30 .25
**736** A143 10e multi .30 .25
**737** A143 20e multi .50 .50
**738** A143 30e multi .80 .80
*a.* Souvenir sheet, #737-738 4.00 4.00
**739** A143 50e multi 1.25 1.25
**740** A143 100e multi 2.60 2.60
*Nos. 735-740 (6)* 5.75 5.65

No. 738a sold for 100e.

First Concorde Flight, 30th Anniv. — A144

Concorde: 30e, In flight. 50e, On ground.

**1999, June 14** **Litho.** *Perf. 12*
**741-742** A144 Set of 2 2.75 2.75

Famous People A145

Design: 30e, Alain Gerbault (1893-1941), sailor, boats at dock. 50e, Roberto Duarte Silva (1837-89), chemist, Eiffel Tower.

**1999, July 2** **Litho.** *Perf. 14½*
**743** A145 30e multi 2.00 2.00
**744** A145 50e multi 3.25 3.25
*a.* Souvenir sheet, #743-744 6.50 6.50

Philex France 99 (No. 744a).

A146

UPU, 125th Anniv. — A147

**1999, Sept. 15** *Perf. 12x11¾*
**745** A146 30e shown 20.00 20.00
**746** A147 50e shown 20.00 20.00

**With Country Name Added**

No. 747

No. 748

**747** A146 30e multi .65 .65
**748** A147 50e multi 1.10 1.10
*Nos. 745-748 (4)* 41.75 41.75

Dance — A148

Designs: 10e, Colá Sanjon, vert. 30e, Contradança, vert. 50e, Desfile de tabanca. 100e, Batuque.

*Perf. 11¾x12, 12x11¾*

**1999, Nov. 5** **Litho.**
**749-752** A148 Set of 4 5.00 5.00

A149

Millennium — A149a

Designs: 40e, Globe, hourglass and open antique book inscribed "2000," vert. 50e, "2000 Milénio."

**2000, Jan. 31** **Litho.** *Perf. 11¾x11½*
**753** A149 40e multicolored 1.75 1.50
**754** A149a 50e multicolored 2.00 1.75

SOS Children's Villages — A150

Emblem and child: 50e, Seated, vert. 100e, With arms outstretched.

*Perf. 11¾x12, 12x11¾*

**2000, Apr. 28** **Litho.**
**755-756** A150 Set of 2 5.00 5.00

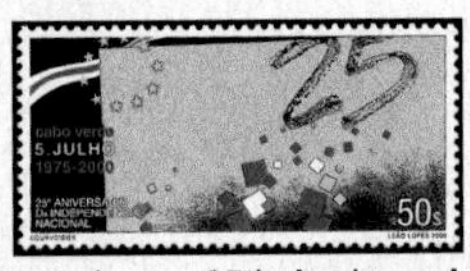


Independence, 25th Anniv. — A151

**2000, July 5** *Perf. 11¾*
**757** A151 50e multi 4.00 1.25

2000 Summer Olympics, Sydney — A152

Designs: 10e, Women's gymnastics. 40e, Taekwondo. 50e, Women's hurdles.

**2000, Sept. 15** **Litho.** *Perf. 11¾*
**758-760** A152 Set of 3 3.50 2.60
*760a* Souvenir sheet of 3, #758-760 4.00 2.75

Dragoeiro Tree — A153

**2000, Oct. 9** **Litho.** *Perf. 11¾x11½*
**761** A153 5e green .30 .25
**762** A153 40e red 1.00 1.00
**763** A153 60e brown 1.60 1.60

Sao Nicolau Seminary and School — A154

No. 764: a, Seminarians and students (denomination at LR, 27x26mm). b, Seminarians and students (denomination at LL, 29x26mm). c, José Alves Feijo, Dr. Julio Dias and Canon António Bouças (56x26mm).

**2000, Dec. 15** **Litho.** *Perf. 14½*
**764** A154 60e Horiz. strip of 3, #a-c 7.50 7.50

Fish — A155

Designs: 10e, Diplodus sargus lineatus. 22e, Diplodus prayensis. 28e, Lithognathus mormyrus. 48e, Diplodus fasciatus. 60e, Diplodus puntazzo.

**2001, Apr. 24** *Perf. 12x11¾*
**765-769** A155 Set of 5 6.50 6.50

Spiders — A156

Designs: 13e, Thomisus onustus. 16e, Scytodes velutina. 40e, Hersiliola simoni. 100e, Loxosceles rufescens.

**2001, May 28**
**770-773** A156 Set of 4 7.50 7.50

Trees — A156a

Designs: 50e, Acacia albida. 60e, Ficus sycomorus.

**2001, June 9** **Litho.** *Perf. 11¾x11½*
**773A-773B** A156a Set of 2 4.00 4.00

**Souvenir Sheet**

Belgica 2001 Intl. Stamp Exhibition, Brussels — A157

*Perf. 11¾x11½*

**2001, June 9** **Photo.**
**774** A157 100e multi 4.00 4.00

Medicinal Plants — A157a

Designs: 20e, Artimisia gorgonum. 27e, Globularia amygdalifolia. 47.50e, Sidereoxylon marginata, horiz. 50e, Umbilicus schmidtii, horiz. 60e, Verbascum cystolithicum. 100e, Limonium lobinii.

*Perf. 11¾x12, 12x11¾*

**2001, Sept. 27** **Litho.**
**774A-774F** A157a Set of 6 10.00 10.00

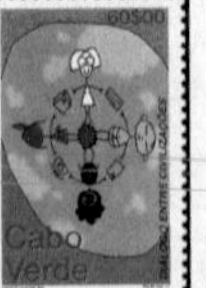


Year of Dialogue Among Civilizations — A158

**2001, Oct. 9** **Litho.** *Perf. 11¾x12*
**775** A158 60e multi 1.60 1.60

António Aurélio Gonçalves (1901-84), Writer — A159

**2001, Dec. 20** ***Perf. 12¼***
**776** A159 100e multi 2.75 2.75

Medicinal Plants — A160

Designs: 10e, Euphorbia tuckeyna. 50e, Limonium sunding, vert. 60e, Aeonium gorgoneum, vert. 100e, Polycarpaea gayi, vert.

***Perf. 12x11¾, 11¾x12***

**2002, Apr. 26** **Litho.**
**777-780** A160 Set of 4 5.75 5.75

2002 World Cup Soccer Championships, Japan and Korea — A161

Designs: 60e, Player heading ball towards goal. 100e, Player kicking ball towards goal.

**2002, July 22** ***Perf. 12x11¾***
**781-782** A161 Set of 2 6.00 4.00

Caretta Caretta — A162

Designs: 10e, Pair mating. 20e, Female laying eggs, vert. 30e, Eggs hatching. 60e, Hatchlings heading for sea, vert. No. 787, 100e, Turtle swimming underwater.
No. 788, 100e, Turtle on beach.

**2002, Sept. 9** ***Perf. 12x11¾, 11¾x12***
**783-787** A162 Set of 5 10.00 10.00

**Souvenir Sheet**

**788** A162 100e multi 5.00 5.00

No. 788 contains one 80x60mm stamp.

Basketry — A163

Baskets and basket weavers from: 20e, Sao Nicolau Island. 33e, Santo Antao Island. 60e, Santiago Island, 100e, Boa Vista Island.

**2002, Oct. 29** ***Perf. 12x11¾***
**789-792** A163 Set of 4 7.50 7.50

Composers and Poets — A164

Designs: 12e, Katchás (1951-88), composer. 20e, Jorge Monteiro (1913-98), composer. 32e, Luis Rendall (1898-1986), composer. 47.50e, Jorge Barbosa (1902-71), poet. 60e, Januário Leite (1865-1930), poet. 100e, José Lopes (1872-1962), poet.

**2003, Feb. 24**
**793-798** A164 Set of 6 9.00 9.00

Birds — A165

Designs: 10e, Ardea bournei. 27e, Ardea cinerea. 42e, Bubulcus ibis. 60e, Egretta garzeta.

**2003, July 9** ***Perf. 14x13¾***
**799-802** A165 Set of 4 6.00 6.00

Cesaria Evora, Singer — A166

Designs: 60e, Evora at left. 100e, Evora at right.
200e, Feet of Evora.

**2003, May 26** ***Perf. 13¾x14***
**803-804** A166 Set of 2 6.00 6.00

**Souvenir Sheet**

***Perf. 12¼x12***

**805** A166 200e multi + label 7.50 7.50

No. 805 contains one 50x38mm stamp.

Scouting in Cape Verde — A167

Emblem and scout of: 60e, Scouts Association of Cape Verde. 100e, Cape Verde Scouts Corps.

**2003, Oct. 24** **Litho.** ***Perf. 13¾x14***
**806-807** A167 Set of 2 7.50 7.50

Whales — A168

Designs: 10e, Balaenoptera musculus. 20e, Physeter macrocephalus. 50e, Megaptera novaeangliae. 60e, Globicephala macrorhynchus.

**2003, Nov. 25** ***Perf. 12***
**808-811** A168 Set of 4 12.00 12.00

First Dakar — Praia Seaplane Flight of Europe — Africa — South America Airmail Service, 75th Anniv. A169

Seaplane and: 10e, Crew. 42e, Pilot Paulin Paris, map of South America — Africa route. 60e, Map of entire route.
100e, Like 10e.

**2003, Dec. 11** ***Perf. 14***
**812-814** A169 Set of 3 4.00 4.00

**Souvenir Sheet**

**815** A169 100e multi 4.00 4.00

Election of Pope John Paul II, 25th Anniv. — A170

Pope John Paul II and: 30e, Girl. 60e, Boats, horiz.
100e, Censer and crucifix.

**2003, Dec. 29** ***Perf. 14x13¾, 13¾x14***
**816-817** A170 Set of 2 3.50 3.50

**Souvenir Sheet**

**818** A170 100e multi 5.00 5.00

Trees — A171

Designs: 20e, Khaya senegalensis. 27e, Acacia nilotica. 60e, Ceiba pentandra. 100e, Phoenix atlantica.

**2004, Jan. 25** ***Perf. 14x13¾***
**819-822** A171 Set of 4 7.50 7.50

Windmill — A172

Colors: 20e, Blue. 60e, Red. 100e, Green.

**2004, June 3** ***Perf. 13¼x13***
**823-825** A172 Set of 3 9.00 9.00

2004 Summer Olympics, Athens — A173

Designs: 10e, Taekwondo. 60e, Rhythmic gymnastics. 100e, Boxing, horiz.

***Perf. 13¼x13, 13x13¼***

**2004, Aug. 13** **Litho.**
**826-828** A173 Set of 3 6.00 6.00

Lighthouses — A174

Designs: 10e, Ponta do Barril Lighthouse, Sao Nicolau Island. 30e, Ponta Jalunga Lighthouse, Brava Island. 40e, D. Luis Lighthouse, Passaros Islands, horiz. 50e, Ponta Preta Lighthouse, Santiago Island, horiz.

**2004, Sept. 7**
**829-832** A174 Set of 4 6.50 6.50

Houses on Fogo Island — A175

Various houses: 20e, 40e, 50e, 60e.

**2004, Oct. 9** ***Perf. 13x13¼***
**833-836** A175 Set of 4 7.00 7.00

Telephones A176

Old telephones and: 10e, Switchboard. 40e, Operator. 60e, Telephone directory. 100e, Truck and telephone poles.

**2004, Nov. 12**
**837-840** A176 Set of 4 8.00 8.00

Oral Stories and Legends — A177

Designs: 10e, Stória Stória. 20e, Era um Vez! 30e, Sapatinha Ribera Baxu. 60e, Quem ki Sabi Mas, Conta Midjor!, vert.

***Perf. 13x13¼, 13¼x13***

**2005, Feb. 21** **Litho.**
**841-844** A177 Set of 4 6.00 6.00

Amilcar Cabral (1924-73), Revolutionary Leader — A178

**2005, June 30** **Litho.** ***Perf. 13¼x13***
**845** A178 60e multicolored 3.00 3.00

Independence, 30th anniv.

Shells — A179

Designs: 30e, Conus evorai. 40e, Harpa doris. 50e, Strombus lotus. 60e, Phyllonotus duplex.

**2005, July 18** ***Perf. 13x13¼***
**846-849** A179 Set of 4 7.50 7.50

Birds — A180

Designs: 19e, Passer iagoensis. 42e, Estrilda astrild. 44e, Passer domesticus. 55e, Acrocephalus brevipennis.

**2005, Aug. 8** ***Perf. 13¼x13***
**850-853** A180 Set of 4 6.50 6.50

World Summit on the Information Society, Tunis — A181

**2005, Nov. 16** **Litho.** ***Perf. 13x13¼***
**854** A181 60e multi 4.00 4.00

Artifacts of the Slave Trade — A182

Designs: 5e, Pipe. 10e, Telescope. 30e, Cannon. 60e, Nautical instrument.
100e, Shackles.

**2006, Jan. 31**
**855-858** A182 Set of 4 6.00 6.00

**Souvenir Sheet**

**859** A182 100e multi 6.00 6.00

No. 859 contains one 80x60mm stamp.

Whaling — A183

Designs: 10e, Ship and map. 20e, Whalers in ship and longboat chasing whales off shore. 40e, Ship, longboat and whale. 60e, Crew on whaling ship.

**2006, May 18 Litho.** ***Perf. 13¼x13½***
**Granite Paper**

**860-863** A183 Set of 4 *10.00 10.00*

2006 World Cup Soccer Championships, Germany — A184

Designs: 30e, Emblem and soccer players. 40e, Emblem, vert. 60e, World Cup trophy and soccer players.

***Perf. 13x13¼, 13¼x13***
**2006, Oct. 18 Litho.**
**Granite Paper**

**864-866** A184 Set of 3 *6.50 6.50*

Ribeira Grande and the International Slave Route — A185

Designs: 24e, Ship and buildings. 36e, Ship, slaves, map of Africa, North America and South America. 50e, Ship, slaves, map of Europe, North America, South America and Africa. 60e, Ship, small boat and buildings.

**2006, Oct. 30 Litho.** ***Perf. 13x13¼***
**Granite Paper**

**867-870** A185 Set of 4 *7.50 7.50*

An additional stamp was issued in this set. The editors would like to examine any example of it.

Community of Portuguese-Speaking Nations, 10th Anniv. — A186

**2006, Nov. 2**

**872** A186 60e multi *3.50 3.50*

Sir Francis Drake (c. 1540-96), Explorer — A187

Drake and: 5e, Sextant. 16e, Ship, map of Cape Verde, compass wheel, horiz. 44e, Ships, horiz. 60e, Old map of Atlantic Ocean, horiz.

**2006, Nov. 27** ***Perf. 13¼x13***
**Granite Paper (5e, 16e, 60e)**

**873** A187 5e multi — —
**874** A187 16e multi — —
**875** A187 44e multi — —
**876** A187 60e multi — —

Aeronautics A188

Designs: 10e, Map of Rome-Rio de Janeiro flight via Ilha do Sal, airplane and hangar on Ilha do Sal. 20e, Seaplane, map of Portugal-Brazil flight, monument. 40e, Zeppelin in flight over town. 50e, Ferdinand von Zeppelin, Zeppelins in flight. 60e, Graf Zeppelin in flight, Cape Verde newspaper article.

**2006, Dec. 15 Litho.** ***Perf. 13x13¼***
**Granite Paper**

**877-881** A188 Set of 5 *9.00 9.00*

Writers A189

Designs: No. 882, 60e, Manuel Lopes (1907-2005). No. 883, 60e, Baltasar Lopes da Silva (Osvaldo Alcantara) (1907-89).

**2007** ***Perf. 13¼***

**882-883** A189 Set of 2 *6.50 6.50*

Pico do Fogo Volcano — A190

Various depictions of erupting volcano: 10e, 50e, 55e, 60e. 50e and 55e are vert.

**2007** ***Perf. 13x13¼, 13¼x13***

**884-887** A190 Set of 4 *9.00 9.00*

Luis de Cadamosto (1432-88), Discoverer of Cape Verde Islands — A191

Designs: 16e, Cadamosto and ship. 44e, Ship and compass rose. 60e, Cadamosto. 100e, Cadamosto, ship and astrolabe.

**2007** ***Perf. 13¼x13***

**888** A191 16e multi — —
**889** A191 44e multi — —
**890** A191 60e multi — —
**891** A191 100e multi — —

Whaling — A192

Designs: 20e, Whale, map of Cape Verde and world showing whale reproduction sites. 30e, Crew on whaling ship stripping whale. 40e, Whale and ship near shore. 60e, Whale breaching near ship.

**2007, June 14 Litho.** ***Perf. 13x13¼***
**Granite Paper**

**892-895** A192 Set of 4 *10.00 10.00*

Aviation — A193

Designs: 10e, Airplane, map of South America, Cape Verde, and Africa. 50e, Concorde. 60e, Airplane, map of Africa and Asia. 100e, Airplane over airport.

**2007** ***Perf. 13x13¼***

**896-899** A193 Set of 4 7.50 7.50

Local Cuisine — A194

Designs: 10e, Cozido (stew). 20e, Cuscus com mel (couscous with honey), vert. 60e, Trotxida. 100e, Xerem (cornmeal puree).

**2008** ***Perf. 13x13¼, 13¼x13***

**900-903** A194 Set of 4 *12.00 12.00*

Occupations — A195

Designs: 30e, Engraxador (shoe polisher). 40e, Vendedeira de pao (bread seller). 50e, Vendedeira de leite (milk seller), horiz. 100e, Vendedeira de peixe (fish seller).

**2008** ***Perf. 13¼x13, 13x13¼***

**904-907** A195 Set of 4 *13.00 13.00*

Souvenir Sheet

Praia, 150th Anniv. A196

**2008** ***Perf. 13¼x13***

**908** A196 200e multi 12.00 12.00

Peace Corps in Cape Verde, 20th Anniv. — A197

**2008**

**909** A197 60e multi *4.00 4.00*

Birds of Prey — A198

Designs: 5e, Buteo bannermani. 20e, Falco tinnunculus. 40e, Pandion haliaetus. 60e, Falco peregrinus madeus.

**2008**

**910-913** A198 Set of 4 6.50 6.50

Louis Braille (1809-52), Educator of the Blind — A199

Designs: No. 914, 60e, Hands reading Braille text. No. 915, 60e, Blind man with cane. No. 916, 60e, Blind children. No. 917, 60e, Blind man with seeing-eye dog, vert.

**2009** ***Perf. 13x13¼, 13¼x13***
**Granite Paper**

**914-917** A199 Set of 4 9.00 9.00

Charles Darwin (1809-82), Naturalist — A200

No. 918 — Map of Darwin's voyages and: a, Darwin, skulls. b, Skull, ship, Darwin's legs. c, Darwin and octopus.

**2009** ***Perf. 13½x13¼***

**918** A200 Horiz. strip of 3 10.00 10.00
***a.-c.*** 60e Any single 3.00 3.00

Red Cross, 150th Anniv. — A201

**2009 Litho.** ***Perf. 13x13¼***
**Granite Paper**

**919** A201 100e multi 3.50 3.50

Flora and Fauna — A202

Designs: 5e, Chioninia delalandii. 10e, Tornabenea annua. 20e, Tarentola darwini. 30e, Satureja forbesii, vert. 40e, Campylnatus glaber glaber, vert. 60e, Chioninia vailanti.

**2009** ***Perf. 13x13¼, 13¼x13***
**Granite Paper**

**920-925** A202 Set of 6 6.00 6.00

Souvenir Sheet

Serra Malagueta Protected Areas — A203

No. 926 — Various views of Serra Malagueta: a, 50e. b, 100e.

**2009 Granite Paper** ***Perf. 13¼***

**926** A203 Sheet of 2, #a-b 6.00 6.00

Discovery of Cape Verde Islands, 550th Anniv. — A204

No. 927: a, Two ships. b, Map of Cape Verde and Africa, compass rose, birds, "14." c, Ship, rowboat, map of Africa and Asia, compass rose, "60."

**2010 Granite Paper** ***Perf. 13½x13¼***

**927** A204 Horiz. strip of 3 6.00 6.00
***a.-c.*** 60e Any single 1.75 1.75

Monte Gordo Protected Areas — A205

Flora and birds of Monte Gordo Protected Areas: 5e, Diplotaxis gracilis. 20e, Theresia. 30e, Verbascum capitis-viridis. 40e, Coturnix coturnix, horiz. 50e, Corvus ruficollis, horiz. 60e, Columba livia, horiz.
100e, Monte Gordo, horiz.

**2010** ***Perf. 13¼x13, 13x13¼***

**928-933** A205 Set of 6 7.50 7.50

Souvenir Sheet

**934** A205 100e multi 3.50 3.50

2010 World Cup Soccer Championships, South Africa — A206

Designs: 40e, Mascot, silhouettes of players. 50e, Emblem, players, vert. 60e, Mascot, players. 100e, World Cup, silhouettes of players.

**2010** ***Perf. 13x13¼, 13¼x13***

**935-938** A206 Set of 4 7.50 7.50

Independence, 35th Anniv. — A207

**2010, July 5 Litho. *Perf. 13¼***
**939** A207 100e multi *6.00 6.00*

Campaigns Against Chronic Diseases — A208

Campaign against: 10e, Alcoholism. 20e, Alcoholism, diff. 30e, Diabetes. 40e, Diabetes, diff. 50e, Tuberculosis. 60e, Tuberculosis, diff.

**2010, Aug. 12 *Perf. 13x13¼***
**940-945** A208 Set of 6 *12.00 12.00*

Assoc. of Postal and Telecommunications Operators of Portuguese-Speaking Countries and Territories, 20th Anniv. — A209

**2010**
**946** A209 100e multi *6.50 6.50*

Rebellions A210

Rebellions at: 40e, Mindelo, 1934. 50e, Paul, 1894. 60e, Rubon Manel, 1910.

**2010 *Perf. 13½***
**947-949** A210 Set of 3 *9.00 9.00*

Heart Health — A211

Designs: 20e, Hearts, electrocardiogram waves, mother lifting child. 40e, Heart and stethoscope. 60e, Family, hearts, electrocardiogram waves. 100e, Heart and arteries.

**2011 *Perf. 13x13¼***
**950-953** A211 Set of 4 7.50 7.50

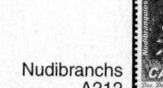

Nudibranchs A212

Designs: 5e, Flabellina arveloi. 10e, Flabellina bulbosa. 20e, Aplysia dactylomela. 40e, Pleurobranchus garciagomezi. 60e, Hypselodoris sp., vert.

**2011 *Perf. 13x13¼, 13¼x13***
**954-958** A212 Set of 5 5.00 5.00

Flora and Fauna of Cha das Caldeiras Protected Area — A213

Designs: 5e, Halcion leucocephala. 10e, Verbascum cystolithicum. 20e, Acrocephalus brevipennis. 40e, Echium vulcanorum. 60e, Pterodroma feae. 100e, Erisimum caboverdeanum.
150e, Halcion leucocephala, Acrocephalus brevipennis, horiz.

**2011 *Perf. 13¼x13***
**959-964** A213 Set of 6 9.00 9.00

**Souvenir Sheet**
***Perf. 13x13¼***
**965** A213 150e multi 6.00 6.00

Baltazar Lopes da Silva (1907-89), Writer — A214

**2012 *Perf. 13x13¼***
**966** A214 100e multi 4.00 4.00

Old Household Objects — A215

Designs: No. 967, 60e, Oil burner (Fogao a petróleo). No. 968, 60e, Oil lamp (Conddeeiro a petróleo). No. 969, 60e, Washbasin (Lavatório). No. 970, 60e, Iron (Ferro de engomar a carvao), horiz.

**2012 *Perf. 13¼x13, 13x13¼***
**967-970** A215 Set of 4 9.00 9.00

Emigration — A216

Designs: 30e, Compass rose, man on boat waving to family on dock. 50e, Man writing on envelope. 60e, Agricultural worker, hand picking cacao pod. 100e, Man wheeling suitcase, world map, horiz.

**2012 *Perf. 13¼x13, 13x13¼***
**971-974** A216 Set of 4 9.00 9.00

Composers and Musicians A217

Designs: 10e, Ano Nobu (1933-2004), composer. 20e, Ildo Lobo (1953-2004), singer. 30e, Renato Cardoso (1951-89), composer. 40e, Manuel d'Novas (1938-2009), composer. 50e, Codé di Dona (1940-2010), composer. 60e, Orlando Pantera (1967-2001), composer.

**2012 Litho. *Perf. 13¼***
**975-980** A217 Set of 6 7.50 7.50

Cape Verde National Soccer Team — A218

Designs: 40e, Team emblem. 60e, Team jersey, vert.
100e, Like 40e.

**2012 *Perf. 13x13¼, 13¼x13***
**981-982** A218 Set of 2 3.50 3.50

**Souvenir Sheet**
**983** A218 100e multi 3.50 3.50

Flora and Fauna of Santo Antao Proctected Area — A219

Designs: 10e, Buteo bannermani. 20e, Pterodroma feae. 30e, Sideroxylon marginata. 40e, Carex antolensis, horiz. 50e, Tarentola caboverdiana caboverdiana, horiz. 60e, Papaver gorgoneum, horiz.
100e, Birds in flight over Coza Natural Park, horiz.

**2012 *Perf. 13¼x13, 13x13¼***
**984-989** A219 Set of 6 7.50 7.50

**Souvenir Sheet**
**990** A219 100e multi 3.50 3.50

Brasiliana 2013 Intl. Philatelic Exhibition, Rio de Janeiro — A220

Brasiliana 2013 emblem, Brazil Nos. 1, 2 and 3, and: 60e, Map of Brazil and circle indicating location of Cape Verde. 150e, Cape Verde #1, map of Cape Verde, label without denomination similar to 60e.

**2013 Litho. *Perf. 13½***
**991** A220 60e multi 2.25 2.25

**Size: 145x81mm**
***Imperf***
**992** A220 150e multi + label 5.00 5.00

African Union, 50th Anniv. A221

**2013 Litho. *Perf. 13½***
**993** A221 60e multi 2.00 2.00

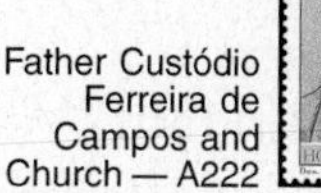
Father Custódio Ferreira de Campos and Church — A222

**2013, Oct. 9 Litho. *Perf. 13x13¼***
**994** A222 60e multi 2.00 2.00

Carnaval A223

Carnaval participants and animators: No. 995, 60e, Capote (1916-85). No. 996, 60e, Artur Boxe (1910-2004). No. 997, 60e, Negro Sarafe (1924-92).

**2014, Feb. 28 Litho. *Perf. 13½***
**995-997** A223 Set of 3 6.00 6.00

Portuguese Language, 800th Anniv. — A224

**2014, May 5 Litho. *Perf. 12x12½***
**998** A224 60e multi 2.00 2.00

A225

Intl. Children's Day — A226

**2014, June 1 Litho. *Perf. 13x13½***
**999** A225 60e multi 2.00 2.00
**1000** A226 60e multi 2.00 2.00

A227

A228

Corn Processing A229

**2014, Oct. 9 Litho. *Perf. 13x13½***
**1001** A227 60e multi 3.00 3.00
**1002** A228 60e multi 3.00 3.00
**1003** A229 60e multi 3.00 3.00
*Nos. 1001-1003 (3)* 9.00 9.00

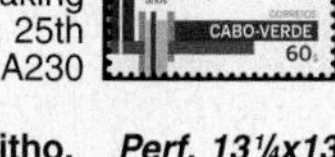
Intl. Association of Portuguese-Speaking Countries, 25th Anniv. — A230

**2015, Apr. 27 Litho. *Perf. 13¼x13***
**1004** A230 60e multi 1.50 1.50

See Angola No. , Brazil No. 3300, Guinea-Bissau No. , Macao No. 1440, Mozambique No. , Portugal Nos. 3694-3695, St. Thomas & Prince Islands No. 2954, and Timor No.

Independence, 40th Anniv. — A231

***Perf. 14½x14¼***
**2015, June 23 Litho.**
**1005** A231 60e multi 1.50 1.50

Economic Community of West African States, 40th Anniv. — A232

**2015, July Litho. *Perf. 13x13¼***
**1006** A232 60e multi 1.50 1.50

Admission to United Nations, 40th Anniv. — A233

**2015, Oct. 6 Litho. *Perf. 13x13¼***
**1007** A233 60e multi 1.50 1.50

United Nations Food and Agriculture Organization, 70th Anniv. — A234

Designs: No. 1008, 60e, Seeds and peas. No. 1009, 60e, Terraced farmland. No. 1010, 60e, Plate of food.

**2015, Oct. 16 Litho. Perf. 13¼**
**Stamp + Label**

1008-1010 A234 Set of 3 5.00 5.00

Kriol Jazz Festival, Praia — A235

**2016, Apr. 8 Litho. Perf. 13¼**

1011 A235 60e multi 1.50 1.50

Emblem of Atlantic Music Expo A236

**2016, Apr. 12 Litho. Perf. 13½**

1012 A236 60e multi 1.50 1.50

Values are for stamps with surrounding selvage.

Kavala Fresk Festival A237

**2016, July 9 Litho. Perf. 14¼x14½**

1013 A237 60e multi 1.50 1.50

Prionace Glauca A238

No. 1014 — WWF emblem, QR code and: a, Shark swimming left. b, Shark chasing squid. c, Shark swimming right, d, Two sharks, map.

**2016, Nov. 15 Litho. Perf. 13¼**

1014 Horiz. strip of 4 6.00 6.00
*a.-d.* A238 60e Any single 1.25 1.25

Worldwide Fund for Nature (WWF).

Cesária Evora (1941-2011), Singer — A239

**Litho. With Foil Application**

**2016, Nov. 16 Perf. 13¾**

1015 A239 60e multi 1.50 1.50

**Souvenir Sheet**

1016 A239 150e multi 3.50 3.50

Bataclan Terrorist Attack, Paris, 1st anniv. (No. 1016).

National Communications Authority, 10th Anniv. — A240

**2016, Nov. 25 Litho. Perf. 14¼**

1017 A240 60e multi 1.50 1.50

National Day Against Sexual Abuse and Exploitation of Minors — A241

**2017, Nov. 20 Litho. Perf. 13¼**

1018 A241 60e multi 1.60 1.60

Inforpress (Cape Verdean News Agency), 30th Anniv. — A242

Denominations: 40e, 60e.
100e, Graduates, airplane, map of Cape Verde, crane, bar graph, globe and 30th anniv. emblem.

**2018 Litho. Perf. 13½**

1019-1020 A242 Set of 2 2.10 2.10

**Size:183x110mm**
***Imperf***

1021 A242 100e multi + label 2.10 2.10

2019 African Beach Games, Sal Island — A243

Denominations: 40e, 60e.
150e, Children playing soccer, map of Sal Island, volleyball players, ships and turtle mascot.

**2019, June 13 Litho. Perf. 13½**

1022-1023 A243 Set of 2 2.10 2.10

**Souvenir Sheet**
**Size: 141x78mm**
***Imperf***

1024 A243 150e multi 3.25 3.25

A244

Intl. Association of Portuguese-Speaking Countries, 30th Anniv. — A245

**2020, Nov. 23 Litho. Perf. 13x13¼**

1025 A244 60e multi 1.30 1.30

***Imperf***

1026 A245 150e multi 3.25 3.25

See Portugal No. 4221.

Eugénio Tavares (1867-1930), Poet — A246

Denominations: 40e, 60e.

**2020, Oct. 18 Litho. Perf. 12¼x12½**

1027-1028 A246 Set of 2 2.10 2.10

Cape Verdean Association in Portugal, 50th anniv. See Portugal No. 4272.

A247

2021 Men's World Handball Championships, Egypt — A248

Denominations: 40e, 60e.

**2021, Feb. 15 Litho. Perf. 13½**

1029-1030 A247 Set of 2 2.25 2.25

**Size: 141x80mm**
***Imperf***

1031 A248 150e multi 3.25 3.25

A249

Campaign Against Alcoholism, 5th Anniv. — A250

Denominations: 40e, 60e.

**2021, Sept. 18 Litho. Perf. 13**

1032-1033 A249 Set of 2 2.10 2.10

**Size: 104x80mm**
***Perf. 13x13¼***

1034 A250 150e multi + label 3.25 3.25

A251

Chartering of City of Sao Felipe, Cent. — A252

**2022 Litho. Perf. 13x13¼**

1035 A251 40e multi .75 .75

***Perf. 13¼x13***

1036 A252 60e multi 1.10 1.10

A souvenir sheet containing No. 1036 sold for 200e.

## AIR POST STAMPS

**Common Design Type**
Name and Value in Black
***Perf. 13½x13***

**1938, July 26 Unwmk.**

| | | | | |
|---|---|---|---|---|
| **C1** | CD39 | 10c red orange | .85 | .65 |
| **C2** | CD39 | 20c purple | .85 | .65 |
| **C3** | CD39 | 50c orange | .85 | .65 |
| **C4** | CD39 | 1e ultra | .85 | .65 |
| **C5** | CD39 | 2e lilac brown | 2.00 | 1.05 |
| **C6** | CD39 | 3e dk green | 2.50 | 1.85 |
| **C7** | CD39 | 5e red brown | 7.75 | 2.75 |
| **C8** | CD39 | 9e rose carmine | 13.00 | 5.00 |
| **C9** | CD39 | 10e magenta | 14.00 | 6.50 |
| | | *Nos. C1-C9 (9)* | 42.65 | 19.75 |
| | | Set, never hinged | 70.00 | |

No. C7 exists with overprint "Exposicao Internacional de Nova York, 1939-1940" and Trylon and Perisphere. Value $200.

## POSTAGE DUE STAMPS

D1

**1904 Unwmk. Typo. Perf. 12**

| | | | | |
|---|---|---|---|---|
| **J1** | D1 | 5r yellow grn | .70 | *.45* |
| **J2** | D1 | 10r slate | .70 | *.45* |
| **J3** | D1 | 20r yellow brn | .70 | *.60* |
| **J4** | D1 | 30r red orange | 1.90 | *.60* |
| **J5** | D1 | 50r gray brown | .70 | *.55* |
| **J6** | D1 | 60r red brown | 14.50 | *6.00* |
| **J7** | D1 | 100r lilac | 3.00 | 1.90 |
| **J8** | D1 | 130r dull blue | 3.00 | 1.90 |
| **J9** | D1 | 200r carmine | 2.75 | 2.40 |
| **J10** | D1 | 500r dull violet | 8.00 | *4.75* |
| | | *Nos. J1-J10 (10)* | 35.95 | *19.60* |

Overprinted in Carmine or Green

**1911**

| | | | | |
|---|---|---|---|---|
| **J11** | D1 | 5r yellow grn | .50 | .40 |
| **J12** | D1 | 10r slate | .50 | .40 |
| **J13** | D1 | 20r yellow brn | .50 | .40 |
| **J14** | D1 | 30r orange | .50 | .40 |
| **J15** | D1 | 50r gray brown | .95 | .60 |
| **J16** | D1 | 60r red brown | .95 | .60 |
| **J17** | D1 | 100r lilac | .95 | .60 |
| **J18** | D1 | 130r dull blue | 1.10 | 1.00 |
| **J19** | D1 | 200r carmine (G) | 3.25 | 2.20 |
| **J20** | D1 | 500r dull violet | 4.00 | 3.50 |
| | | *Nos. J11-J20 (10)* | 13.20 | 10.10 |

D2

**1921 Perf. 11½**

| | | | | |
|---|---|---|---|---|
| **J21** | D2 | ½c yellow grn | .50 | .40 |
| **J22** | D2 | 1c slate | .50 | .40 |
| **J23** | D2 | 2c red brown | .50 | .40 |
| **J24** | D2 | 3c orange | .50 | .40 |
| **J25** | D2 | 5c gray brown | .50 | .40 |
| **J26** | D2 | 6c lt brown | .50 | .40 |
| **J27** | D2 | 10c red violet | .50 | .40 |
| **J28** | D2 | 13c dull blue | .90 | *.80* |
| **J29** | D2 | 20c carmine | 1.00 | *.90* |
| **J30** | D2 | 50c gray | 2.25 | *1.70* |
| | | *Nos. J21-J30 (10)* | 7.65 | *6.20* |

**Catalogue values for unused stamps in this section, from this point to the end of the section, are for Never Hinged items.**

Common Design Type

**Photogravure and Typographed**

**1952 Unwmk. Perf. 14**

**Numeral in Red, Frame Multicolored**

| | | | | |
|---|---|---|---|---|
| **J31** | CD45 | 10c chocolate | .30 | .25 |
| **J32** | CD45 | 30c black brown | .30 | .25 |
| **J33** | CD45 | 50c dark blue | .30 | .25 |
| **J34** | CD45 | 1e dark blue | .40 | .25 |
| **J35** | CD45 | 2e red brown | .40 | .30 |
| **J36** | CD45 | 5e olive green | 1.10 | 1.00 |
| | | *Nos. J31-J36 (6)* | 2.80 | 2.30 |

### NEWSPAPER STAMP

N1

**1893 Typo. Unwmk. *Perf. 11½***
**P1** N1 2½r chocolate 1.75 .90
*a.* Perf. 12½ 3.25 1.75
*b.* Perf. 13½ 9.00 3.25

For surcharges see Nos. 79, 206.

### POSTAL TAX STAMPS

**Pombal Issue**
Common Design Types

**1925 Unwmk. Engr. *Perf. 12½***
**RA1** CD28 15c dull vio & blk 1.60 1.60
**RA2** CD29 15c dull vio & blk 1.60 1.60
**RA3** CD30 15c dull vio & blk 1.60 1.60
*Nos. RA1-RA3 (3)* 4.80 4.80

St. Isabel — PT1

**1948 Litho. *Perf. 11***
**RA4** PT1 50c dark green 3.75 2.40
**RA5** PT1 1e henna brown 7.50 3.00

**Catalogue values for unused stamps in this section, from this point to the end of the section, are for Never Hinged items.**

**No. RA5 Surcharged with New Value and Bars**

**1959**
**RA6** PT1 50c on 1e henna brown 1.75 1.45

***Perf. 14***
**RA7** PT1 50c carmine rose 3.60 1.50
**RA8** PT1 1e blue 2.60 1.50

**St. Isabel Type Redrawn**

**1967-73 Litho. *Perf. 14***
**RA9** PT1 30c (blue panel) .50 .50
**RA9A** PT1 30c (orange panel) .50 .50
**RA10** PT1 50c (lilac rose panel) 1.10 .90
**RA11** PT1 50c (red panel) ('72) *.90 .90*
**RA12** PT1 1e (brn panel) 1.25 1.25
**RA13** PT1 1e (red lilac panel) ('72) *1.25 1.25*
*Nos. RA9-RA13 (6)* *5.50 5.30*

Nos. RA9-RA13 are inscribed "ASSISTENCIA" in large letters in bottom panel and "PORTUGAL" and "CABO VERDE" in small letters in upper left corner.

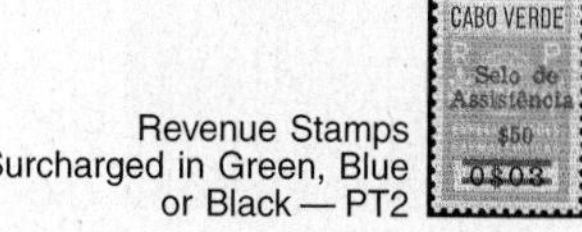
Revenue Stamps Surcharged in Green, Blue or Black — PT2

**Black "CABO VERDE" & Value**
**Pale Green Burelage**

**1967-72 Typo. *Perf. 12***
**RA14** PT2 50c on 1c org (Bl) ('71) 1.80 1.40
*a.* Black surcharge ('68?) *19.00 18.00*
**RA15** PT2 50c on 2c org (Bk) ('69) *19.00 18.00*
*c.* Inverted surcharge *47.50 42.50*
**RA16** PT2 50c on 3c org (G) ('72) 1.50 .80
**RA17** PT2 50c on 5c org (G) ('72) 1.50 .80
**RA18** PT2 50c on 10c org (G) ('71) 1.70 1.40
**RA19** PT2 1e on 1c org (Bk) 3.40 2.60
**RA20** PT2 1e on 2c org (G) ('71) 2.40 2.40
*a.* Blue surcharge ('71) 2.60 2.10
*b.* Black surcharge 3.25 2.50
*Nos. RA14-RA20 (7)* *31.30 27.40*

### POSTAL TAX DUE STAMPS

**Pombal Issue**
Common Design Types

**1925 Unwmk. *Perf. 12½***
**RAJ1** CD28 30c dull vio & blk 1.00 .95
**RAJ2** CD29 30c dull vio & blk 1.00 .95
**RAJ3** CD30 30c dull vio & blk 1.00 .95
*Nos. RAJ1-RAJ3 (3)* 3.00 2.85

## CARIBBEAN NETHERLANDS

'kar-ē-bbe-ə-n 'ne-thər-lən,dz

LOCATION — The islands of Bonaire (north of Venezuela), Saint Eustatius and Saba (south of Anguilla)
AREA — 125 sq. mi.
POP. — 18,012 (2010)
CAPITAL — Kralendijk, Bonaire; Oranjestad, Saint Eustatius; The Bottom, Saba

On Oct. 10, 2010, Caribbean Netherlands, formerly part of Netherlands Antilles, became special municipalities within the Kingdom of the Netherlands.

100 Cents = 1 Gulden
100 Cents = 1 Dollar (2011)

**Catalogue values for all unused stamps in this country are for Never Hinged items.**

Map of Islands and West Indies, Arms, Queen Beatrix — A1

***Perf. 13¾***
**2010, Oct. 10 Litho. Unwmk.**
**1** A1 111c multicolored 1.50 1.50

New Constitutional Status — A2

Designs: 63c, Triangle with flags of Bonaire, Saint Eustatius and Saba, Acropora palmata. 81c, Three Glassy sweepers with elements of flags of Bonaire, Saint Eustatius and Saba. 93c, Two Yellowcheek wrasses with elements of Bonaire flag. 96c, Parrotfish with elements of Saint Eustatius flag. 159c, Blue tang surgeonfish with elements of Saba flag.

**2011, June 1 *Perf. 13¼x13***
**2-6** A2 Set of 5 10.00 10.00

Greetings — A3

Inscriptions: 33c, Thinking of you. 63c, Always in my prayers. 93c, Celebrate another year. 159c, Love U so much. 226c, For you my cup of tea.

**2011, July 11 *Perf. 13x13¼***
**7-11** A3 Set of 5 10.00 10.00

Corals — A4

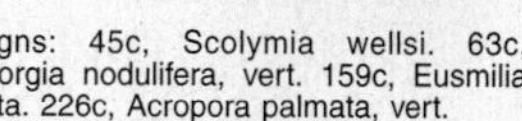

Designs: 45c, Scolymia wellsi. 63c, Diodogorgia nodulifera, vert. 159c, Eusmilia fastigiata. 226c, Acropora palmata, vert.

***Perf. 13¼x13, 13x13¼***
**2011, Sept. 11**
**12-15** A4 Set of 4 8.00 7.00

Visit of Queen Beatrix — A5

Queen Beatrix: 81c, Without hat. 159c, Wearing hat.
250c, Queen Beatrix in coach, horiz.

**2011, Nov. 4 *Perf. 14***
**16-17** A5 Set of 2 4.50 4.50

**Souvenir Sheet**
**18** A5 250c multi 5.00 5.00

Holiday Light Decorations — A6

Designs: 63c, Snowflakes. 81c, Reindeer. 93c, Flowers. 159c, Bells.

**2011, Nov. 11 *Perf. 13½x12¾***
**19-22** A6 Set of 4 8.00 8.00

Sailboats — A7

Designs: 66c, Catamaran. 99c, Optimist. 101c, Sunfish. 168c, Laser, vert.

***Perf. 13½x12¾, 12¾x13½***
**2012, Feb. 1**
**23-26** A7 Set of 4 8.50 8.50

Parrots — A8

Designs: 100c, Ara chloropterus. 150c, Aratinga pertinax. 200c, Amazona ochrocephala ochrocephala. 250c, Anodorhynchus hyacinthinus.

**2012, June 1 *Perf. 12¾x13½***
**27-30** A8 Set of 4 14.00 14.00

Rafflesia Flower — A9

Mandala A10

**2012, June 18 *Perf. 13½x12¾***
**31** A9 10c multicolored .25 .25

**Souvenir Sheet**
***Perf.***
**32** A10 200c multicolored 4.00 4.00

Indoensia 2012 World Stamp Exhibition, Jakarta.

**Miniature Sheet**

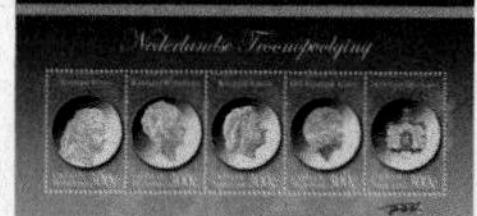
Dutch Queens and Heraldry A11

No. 33: a, Queen Emma. b, Queen Wilhelmina. c, Queen Juliana. d, Queen Beatrix. e, Royal arms.

**Litho. & Embossed**
**2012, Sept. 3 *Perf. 12¾x13½***
**33** A11 300c Sheet of 5, #a-e 30.00 30.00

Arms and Christmas Ornaments — A12

Designs: 66c, Arms of Saba, ornament in shape of Saba, ornament with Saba flag elements. 99c, Arms of St. Eustatius, ornament in shape of St. Eustatius, ornament with St. Eustatius flag elements. 101c, Arms of Bonaire, ornament in shape of Bonaire, ornament with Bonaire flag elements. 168c, Arms of Netherlands, ornaments with flag elements of Saba, St. Eustatius and Bonaire.

**2012, Nov. 1 Litho. *Perf. 13¼x13***
**34-37** A12 Set of 4 8.25 8.25

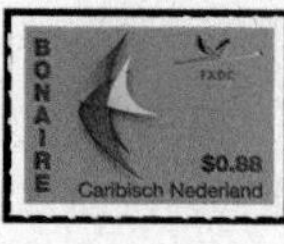
Emblem and Flamingo — A13

No. 38 — Inscribed: a, Bonaire. b, Saba. c, St, Eustatius. d, Bonaire. e, Saba. f, St. Eustatius.

**2014, Oct. 10 Litho. *Rouletted 6½***
**38** Horiz. strip of 6 11.50 11.50
*a.-c.* A13 88c Any single 1.75 1.75
*d.-f.* A13 99c Any single 2.00 2.00

**Miniature Sheets**

Flamingos — A14

Pelicans A15

Hummingbirds — A16

Various birds, as shown.

***Perf. 13¼x13½***
**2014, Nov. 10 Litho.**

**Inscribed "Bonaire"**
**39** A14 99c Sheet of 5, #a-e 10.00 10.00

**Inscribed "Saba"**
**40** A15 99c Sheet of 5, #a-e 10.00 10.00

**Inscribed "St. Eustatius"**
**41** A16 99c Sheet of 5, #a-e 10.00 10.00
*Nos. 39-41 (3)* 30.00 30.00

Personalized Stamp — A17

***Serpentine Die Cut 14¼***

**2014, Nov. 10 Litho.**

**Self-Adhesive**

**42** A17 99c multi + label 2.00 2.00

No. 42 was printed in sheets of 10 + 10 labels. The label shown is a generic label. Two other generic labels, depicting scenes of Saba and St. Eustatius were created. Labels could also be personalized. Sheets containing personalized labels sold for $15.

Miniature Sheet

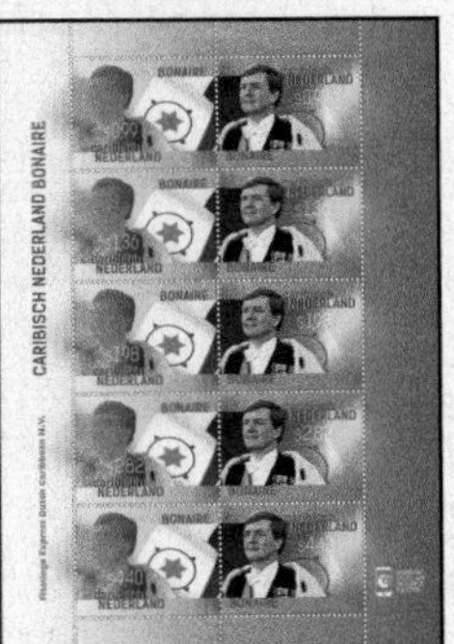


Flag and King Willem-Alexander — A18

Flag of Bonaire (No. 43), Saba (No. 44) or St. Eustatius (No. 45) with King Willem-Alexander in: a, 99c, Sepia. b, 99c, Full color. c, $1.36, Sepia. d, $1.36, Full color. e, $1.98, Sepia, f, $1.98, Full color. g, $2.82, Sepia, h, $2.82, Full color. i, $4.40, Sepia. j, $4.40, Full color.

**2015, Apr. 30 Litho. *Perf. 14x13½***

**Inscribed "Bonaire"**

**43** A18 Sheet of 10, #a-j 45.00 45.00

**Inscribed "Saba"**

**44** A18 Sheet of 10, #a-j 45.00 45.00

**Inscribed "St. Eustatius"**

**45** A18 Sheet of 10, #a-j 45.00 45.00
*Nos. 43-45 (3)* 135.00 135.00

A19

A20

A21

Personalized Stamps — A22

**2016, Jan. 15 Litho. *Perf. 13¼x14***

**Inscribed "Bonaire"**

**46** A19 88c multi 1.90 1.90
**47** A20 88c multi 1.90 1.90
**48** A21 88c multi 1.90 1.90
**49** A22 88c multi 1.90 1.90

**Inscribed "Saba"**

**50** A19 88c multi 1.90 1.90
**51** A20 88c multi 1.90 1.90
**52** A21 88c multi 1.90 1.90
**53** A22 88c multi 1.90 1.90

**Inscribed "St. Eustatius"**

**54** A19 88c multi 1.90 1.90
**55** A20 88c multi 1.90 1.90
**56** A21 88c multi 1.90 1.90

**Inscribed "Sint Eustatius"**

**57** A22 88c multi 1.90 1.90
*Nos. 46-57 (12)* 22.80 22.80

Vignette portions of stamps could be personalized. The vignettes shown for types A19-A22 are generic images. Different generic images were created for Nos. 50-57, with colors differing from types A19-A22 being used for frames on these stamps.

Kingdom of the Netherlands, 200th Anniv. — A23

**2016, Mar. 30 Litho. *Perf. 14½***

**Inscribed "Bonaire"**

**58** A23 99c purple & pink 2.00 2.00
**59** A23 99c deep red & red 2.00 2.00
**60** A23 99c grn & pale blue 2.00 2.00

**Inscribed "Saba"**

**61** A23 99c purple & pink 2.00 2.00
*a.* Souvenir sheet of 2, #60, 61, + central label 4.00 4.00
**62** A23 99c deep red & red 2.00 2.00
*a.* Souvenir sheet of 2, #58, 62, + central label 4.00 4.00
**63** A23 99c grn & pale blue 2.00 2.00

**Inscribed "St. Eustatius"**

**64** A23 99c purple & pink 2.00 2.00
*a.* Souvenir sheet of 2, #59, 64, + central label 4.00 4.00
*b.* Souvenir sheet of 2, #63, 64, + central label 4.00 4.00
**65** A23 99c deep red & red 2.00 2.00
*a.* Souvenir sheet of 2, #61, 65, + central label 4.00 4.00
**66** A23 99c grn & pale blue 2.00 2.00
*a.* Souvenir sheet of 2, #58, 66, + central label 4.00 4.00
*Nos. 58-66 (9)* 18.00 18.00

**Souvenir Sheets**

**Inscribed "Bonaire"**

**67** Sheet of 2 + central label 11.50 11.50
*a.* A23 282c green & pale blue 5.75 5.75
*b.* A23 282c orange red & orange 5.75 5.75

**Inscribed "Saba"**

**68** Sheet of 2 + central label 11.50 11.50
*a.* A23 282c green & pale blue 5.75 5.75
*b.* A23 282c purple & blue 5.75 5.75

**Inscribed "St. Eustatius"**

**69** Sheet of 2 + central label 11.50 11.50
*a.* A23 282c green & pale blue 5.75 5.75
*b.* A23 282c ol bister & yellow 5.75 5.75
*Nos. 67-69 (3)* 34.50 34.50

Souvenir Sheets

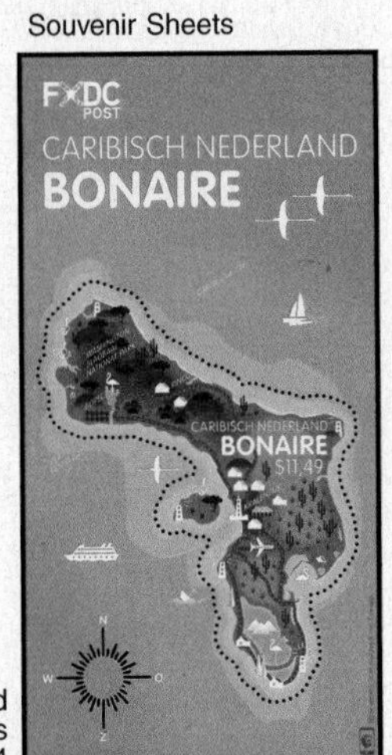


Island Maps A24

Map of: No. 70, Bonaire. No. 71, Saba. No. 72, St. Eustatius.

**2016, Oct. 10 Litho. *Perf.***

**Inscribed "Bonaire"**

**70** A24 $11.49 multi 23.00 23.00

**Inscribed "Saba"**

**71** A24 $11.49 multi 23.00 23.00

**Inscribed "St. Eustatius"**

**72** A24 $11.49 multi 23.00 23.00
*Nos. 70-72 (3)* 69.00 69.00

No. 70 contains one 68x87mm stamp. No. 71 contains one 68x60mm stamp. No. 72 contains one 68x76mm stamp.

A25

A26

A27

Personalized Stamps — A28

**2017, Mar. 3 Litho. *Perf. 13¼x13***

**Inscribed "Bonaire"**

**73** A25 99c multi 2.00 2.00
**74** A26 99c multi 2.00 2.00
**75** A27 99c multi 2.00 2.00
**76** A28 99c multi 2.00 2.00

**Inscribed "Saba"**

**77** A25 99c multi 2.00 2.00
**78** A26 99c multi 2.00 2.00
**79** A27 99c multi 2.00 2.00
**80** A28 99c multi 2.00 2.00

**Inscribed "St. Eustatius"**

**81** A25 99c multi 2.00 2.00
**82** A26 99c multi 2.00 2.00
**83** A27 99c multi 2.00 2.00
**84** A28 99c multi 2.00 2.00
*Nos. 73-84 (12)* 24.00 24.00

Vignette portions of stamps could be personalized. The vignettes shown for types A25-A28 are generic images. Different generic images were created for Nos. 77-84, with colors differing from types A27-A28 being used for frames on these stamps.

Miniature Sheets

A29

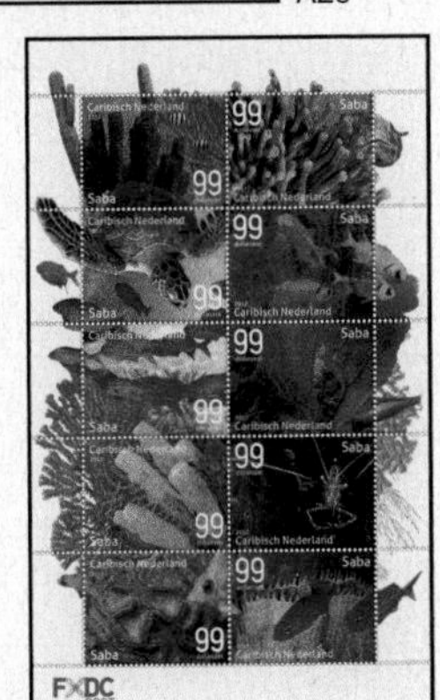


A30

Coral Reef Life A31

Various marine life, as shown.

**2017, July 31 Litho. *Perf. 14x13½***

**Inscribed "Bonaire"**

**85** A29 99c Sheet of 10, #a-j 20.00 20.00

**Inscribed "Saba"**

**86** A30 99c Sheet of 10, #a-j 20.00 20.00

**Inscribed "Sint Eustatius"**

**87** A31 99c Sheet of 10, #a-j 20.00 20.00
*Nos. 85-87 (3)* 60.00 60.00

Souvenir Sheets

Endangered Animals — A32

Designs: No. 88, Amazona barbadensis. No. 89, Epinephelus striatus. No. 90, Iguana delicatissima.

**2017, Nov. 27 Litho. *Perf.***

**Inscribed "Bonaire"**

**88** A32 $11.49 multi 20.00 20.00

**Inscribed "Saba"**

**89** A32 $11.49 multi 20.00 20.00

**Inscribed "Sint Eustatius"**

**90** A32 $11.49 multi 20.00 20.00
*Nos. 88-90 (3)* 60.00 60.00

Miniature Sheets

Cactus Forest A33

Cloud Forest A34

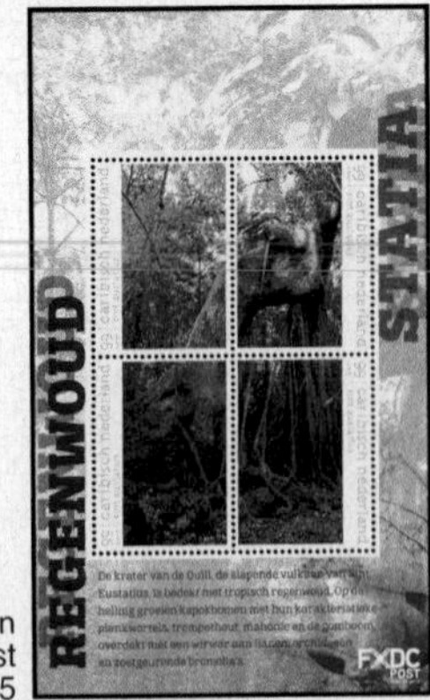


Rain Forest A35

Various plants, as shown.

**2018, Apr. 3 Litho. *Perf. 13½x14***

**Inscribed "Bonaire"**

**91** A33 99c Sheet of 4, #a-d 8.00 8.00

**Inscribed "Saba"**

**92** A34 99c Sheet of 4, #a-d 8.00 8.00

**Inscribed "Sint Eustatius"**

**93** A35 99c Sheet of 4, #a-d 8.00 8.00
*Nos. 91-93 (3)* 24.00 24.00

Miniature Sheets

Shells A36

No. 94: a, Nautilus pompilius. b, Strombus gigas. c, Trochus niloticus. d, Phyllonotus erythrostomus.

No. 95: a, Cymatium parthenopeum. b, Cypraea tigris. c, Trochus niloticus, diff. d, Melongena melongena.

No. 96: a, Tonna galea. b, Voluta ebraea. c, Cassis cornuta. d, Mitra papalis.

**2018, Apr. 3 Litho. *Perf. 13½x14***

**Inscribed "Bonaire"**

**94** A36 99c Sheet of 4, #a-d 8.00 8.00

**Inscribed "Saba"**

**95** A36 99c Sheet of 4, #a-d 8.00 8.00

**Inscribed "Sint Eustatius"**

**96** A36 99c Sheet of 4, #a-d 8.00 8.00
*Nos. 94-96 (3)* 24.00 24.00

Miniature Sheets

A37

A38

Shells A39

No. 97: a, Two shells, large shell on top. b, Four shells. c, Three shells. d, Two shells, large shell on bottom.

No. 98: a, Four shells, two on third row. b, Four shells in zigzag pattern. c, Two small shells. d, Two large shells.

No. 99: a, Two shells, large shell on top. b, Three shells. c, Two similarly-sized shells. d, Two shells, large shell on bottom.

**2018, Apr. 3 Litho. *Perf. 13¼***

**Inscribed "Bonaire"**

**97** A37 99c Sheet of 4, #a-d 8.00 8.00

**Inscribed "Saba"**

**98** A38 99c Sheet of 4, #a-d 8.00 8.00

**Inscribed "Sint Eustatius"**

**99** A39 99c Sheet of 4, #a-d 8.00 8.00
*Nos. 97-99 (3)* 24.00 24.00

Miniature Sheets

Marine Life A40

No. 100 — Inscriptions: a, Slablad Naaktslak op Sterkoraal. b, Boogkrab op Vaasspons. c, Caraibische Poetsvis in Paarse Buisspons. d, Gewone Koraalduivel.

No. 101 — Inscriptions: a, Lucifer-anemoon. b, Kaapersgarnaal op Azuurblauwe Vaasspons. c, Geelneus Koraalgrondel op Steenkoraal. d, Kerstboomworm op Sterkoraal.

No. 102 — Inscriptions: a, Tandbaars in Azuurblauwe Vaasspons. b, Hersenkoraal. c, Hoornkoraal. d, Poetsgarnaal op Een Zeeanemoon.

**2018, Apr. 3 Litho. *Perf. 13¼x14***

**Inscribed "Bonaire"**

**100** A40 99c Sheet of 4, #a-d 8.00 8.00

**Inscribed "Saba"**

**101** A40 99c Sheet of 4, #a-d 8.00 8.00

**Inscribed "St. Eustatius"**

**102** A40 99c Sheet of 4, #a-d 8.00 8.00
*Nos. 100-102 (3)* 24.00 24.00

Miniature Sheets

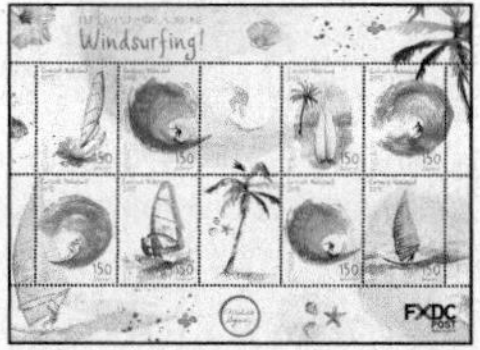


Surfing and Windsurfing — A41

Butterflies and Flowers — A42

Hummingbirds — A43

No. 103: a, Windsurfer to right of sail. b, Surfer, dark blue wave breaking at right. c, Palm tree and surfboards. d, Surfer on white surfboard, wave breaking at left. e, Surfer with white trunks on yellow surfboard, wave breaking at left. f, Windsurfer to left of sail. g, Surfer on white surfboard, wave breaking at right. h, Windsurfer in front of sail.

No. 104: a, Butterfly in flight. b, Six orange flowers. c, Striped butterfly on flower. d, Yellow and red orchids. e, Three pink orchids. f, Monarch butterfly on flower. g, Pink flower. h, Blue butterfly on foliage.

No. 105: a, Pink hummingbird with bill pointing to UR. b, Green hummingbird with red throat with bill pointing to UL. c, Green hummingbird with bill pointing to UR. d, Hummingbird with red head with bill pointing to LL. e, Hummingbird with orange tail feathers on branch. f, Hummingbird with purple breast with bill pointing to left. g, Hummingbird with red head and wings with bill pointing to LR. h, Blue and black hummingbird with bill pointing to UL.

**2018, July 20 Litho. *Perf. 13½x14***

**Inscribed "Bonaire"**

**103** A41 150c Sheet of 8, #a-h, + 2 labels 24.00 24.00

**Inscribed "Saba"**

**104** A42 150c Sheet of 8, #a-h, + 2 labels 24.00 24.00

**Inscribed "Sint Eustatius"**

**105** A43 150c Sheet of 8, #a-h, + 2 labels 24.00 24.00
*Nos. 103-105 (3)* 72.00 72.00

Miniature Sheet

The Night Watch, by Rembrandt (1606-69) — A44

No. 106 — Painting details: a, Head of woman at left, and head of arquebusier. b, Captain Frans Bannink Cocq and man behind him. c, Lieutenant Willem van Ruytenburch. d, Man with gun. e, Leg of Captain Bannink Cocq at LR. f. Legs of Captain Bannink Cocq. g, Legs of van Ruytenburch. h, Legs of man with gun. i, Man in red with gun. j, Head of woman. k, Gun barrel, extended arm. l, Three men. m, Legs of man in red with gun. n, Stock of gun, chicken, women's legs. o, Back of dog. p, Drum.

**2019, Jan. 21 Litho. *Perf. 13½x14***

**Stamps Inscribed "Bonaire"**

**106** A44 99c Sheet of 16, #a-p 32.00 32.00

Miniature Sheet

New Year 2019 (Year of the Pig) A45

No. 107 — Pig, Chinese lanterns with Chinese inscription and "2019" at: a, LR. b, LL. c, UR. d, UL.

**2019, Feb. 5 Litho. *Perf. 13½x14***

**Stamps Inscribed "Bonaire"**

**107** A45 99c Sheet of 4, #a-d 8.00 8.00

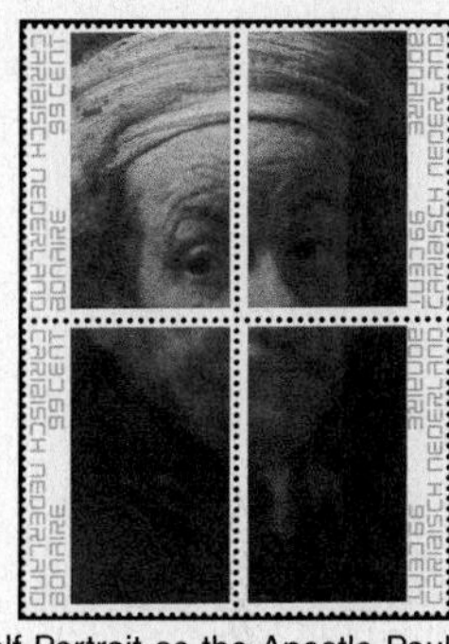

Self-Portrait as the Apostle Paul, by Rembrandt (1606-69) — A46

No. 108: a, Headdress and eye, inscriptions at left. b, Headdress, eye and nose, inscriptions at right. c, Cheek, inscriptions at left. d, Cheek, inscriptions at right.

**2019, Mar. 18 Litho. *Perf. 13½x14***

**Stamps Inscribed "Bonaire"**

**108** A46 99c Block of 4, #a-d 8.00 8.00

No. 108 was printed in sheets containing four blocks.

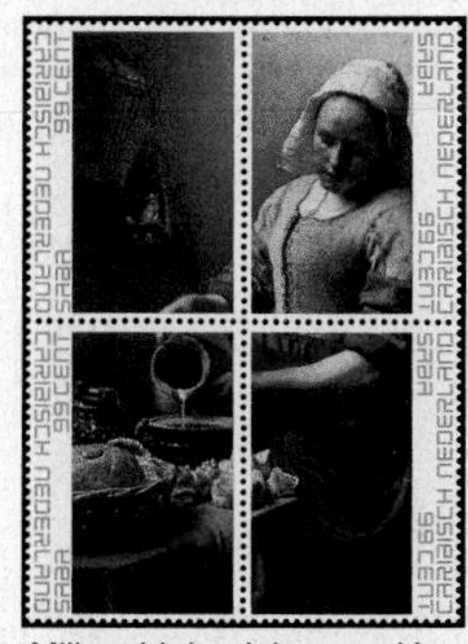

The Milkmaid, by Johannes Vermeer (1632-75) — A47

No. 109: a, Baskets on wall, hand of milkmaid, inscriptions at left. b, Head of milkmaid, inscriptions at right. c, Bread basket, milk being poured, inscriptions at left. d, Milkmaid's arm and corner of table, inscriptions at right.

**2019, June 24 Litho. *Perf. 13½x14***

**Stamps Inscribed "Saba"**

**109** A47 99c Block of 4, #a-d 8.00 8.00

No. 109 was printed in sheets containing four blocks.

---

A gold $50 stamp issued July 4, 2019, depicting Rembrandt van Rijn and inscribed "Bonaire" was produced in limited quantities.

---

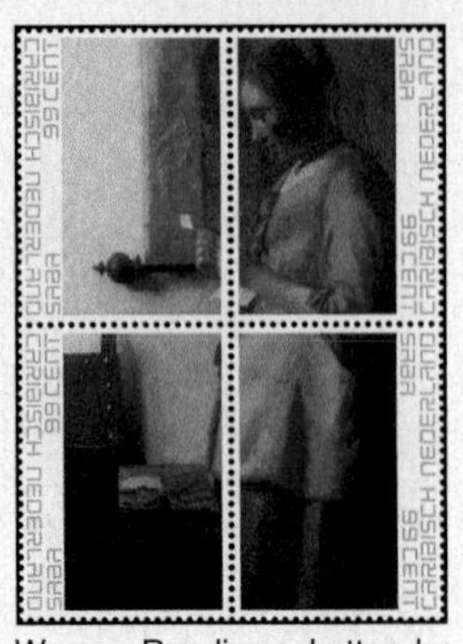

Woman Reading a Letter, by Johannes Vermeer (1632-75) — A48

No. 110 — Painting details: a, Side of window shade. b, Woman. c, Chair and desk. d, Legs of woman.

**2019, Aug. 20 Litho. *Perf. 13½x14***
**Stamps Inscribed "Saba"**

**110** A48 99c Block of 4, #a-d 8.00 8.00

No. 110 was printed in sheets containing four blocks.

Miniature Sheet

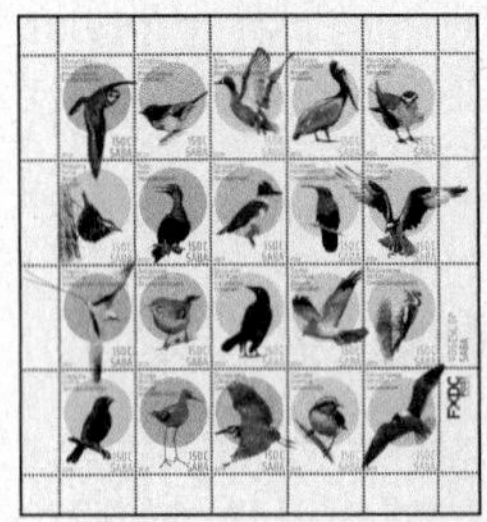

Birds A49

No. 111: a, Charadrius semipalmatus. b, Setophaga ruticilla. c, Anas discors. d, Pelegasnus occidentalis. e, Onychoprion anaethetus. f, Mniotilta varia. g, Sula sula. h, Megaceryle alcyon. i, Eulampis holosericeus. j, Pandion haliaetus. k, Phaethon lepturus. l, Setophaga americana. m, Quiscalus lugubris. n, Circus cyaneus. o, Sphyrapicus varius. p, Loxigilla noctis. q, Tringa flavipes. r, Nyctanassa violacea. s, Coereba flaveola. t, Leucophaeus atricilla.

**2019, Oct. 4 Litho. *Perf. 13½x14***
**Stamps Inscribed "Saba" Without "Caribisch Nederland" Inscription**

**111** A49 150c Sheet of 20, #a-t 60.00 60.00

Miniature Sheet

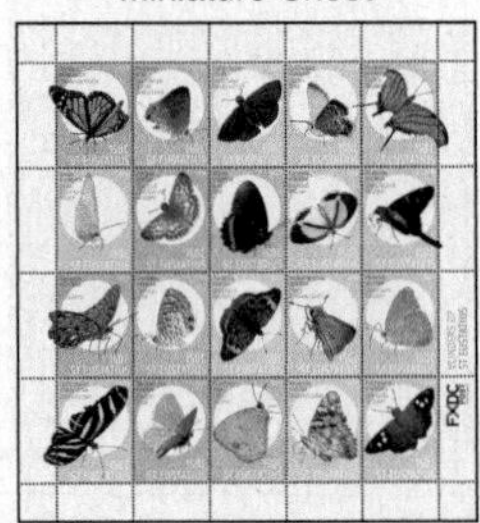

Butterflies — A50

No. 112: a, Danaus plexippus. b, Strymon acis. c, Ephyriades arcas. d, Cyclargus thomasi. e, Marpesia petreus. f, Ascia monuste. g, Pyrgus oileus. h, Biblis hyperia. i, Eurmea elathea. j, Urbanus proteus. k, Agraulis vanillae. l, Leptotes cassius. m, Junonia coenia. n, Wallengrenia ophites. o, Pheobis sennae. p, Heliconius charitonia. q, Hemiargus hanno. r, Eurema lisa. s, Vanessa cardui. t, Polygonus manueli.

**2019, Oct. 4 Litho. *Perf. 13½x14***
**Stamps Inscribed "St. Eustatius" Without "Caribisch Nederland" Inscription**

**112** A50 150c Sheet of 20, #a-t 60.00 60.00

Miniature Sheet

De Magere Compagnie (The Meagre Company), by Frans Hals (c. 1582-1666) — A51

No. 113 — Painting details: a, Flag bearer Nicolaes van Bambeeck. b, Captain Reinier Reael, Lieutenant Cornelis Michielsz Blaeuw and seated man. c, Four men. d, Man with mustache. e, Legs of Bambeeck. f, Shaft of halbard and legs of three men. g, Hand and shaft of halbard. h, Legs of man with mustache. i, Two men, one wearing hat with feather. j, Two men without hats, and arm of third man, two halbard shafts in background. k, Two men without hats. l, Two men, one with hat, two halbard shafts in background. m, Legs of men, one man wearing white stockings. n, Legs of men. o, Legs, two feet pointing in opposite directions. p, Legs of men, diff.

**2019, Oct. 21 Litho. *Perf. 13½x14***
**Stamps Inscribed "St. Eustatius"**

**113** A51 99c Sheet of 16, #a-p 32.00 32.00

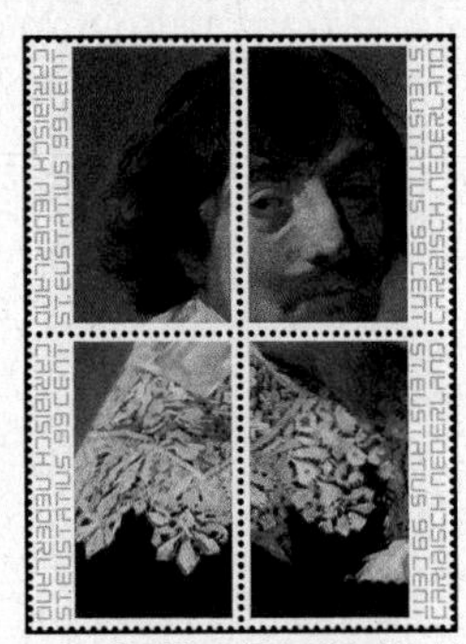

Portrait of a Man, Possibly Nicolaes Hasselaer, by Frans Hals (c. 1582-1666) — A52

No. 114 — Painting details: a, Hair. b, Face. c, Shoulder. d, Chin and chest.

**2019, Dec. 16 Litho. *Perf. 13½x14***
**Stamps Inscribed "St. Eustatius"**

**114** A52 99c Block of 4, #a-d 8.00 8.00

No. 114 was printed in sheets containing four blocks.

Dutch Royalty A53

No. 115: a, King Willem-Alexander, hands visible. b, Close-up of Queen Máxima. c, Queen Máxima, arms visible. d, Close-up of King Willem-Alexander.

**2020, Apr. 7 Litho. *Perf. 13¼x14***

**115** A53 99c Block of 4, #a-d 8.00 8.00

Birds — A54

No. 116: a, Coerba flaveola. b, Mimus gilvus. c, Quisculus lugubris. d, Eupsittula pertinax. e, Icterus icterus.
No. 117: a, Pelecanus occidentalis. b, Ongchoprion anaethetus. c, Oriolus xanthornus. d, Anous stolidu. e, Pandion haliaetus.
No. 118: a, Pluvialis dominica. b, Numenius phaeopus. c, Chrysolampis mosquitus. d, Caracara. e, Coccyzus americanus.

**2020, July 1 Litho. *Perf. 13¼x14***
**Inscribed "Bonaire"**

**116** Horiz. strip of 5 7.50 7.50
***a.-e.*** A54 75c Any single 1.50 1.50

**Inscribed "Saba"**

**117** Horiz. strip of 5 7.50 7.50
***a.-e.*** A54 75c Any single 1.50 1.50

**Inscribed "St. Eustatius"**

**118** Horiz. strip of 5 7.50 7.50
***a.-e.*** A54 75c Any single 1.50 1.50
*Nos. 116-118 (3)* 22.50 22.50

Vignette portions of St. Eustatius stamps of type A54 can be personalized. The editors would like to receive more information about personalization of Bonaire and Saba stamps of type A54, as well as types A55-A57 stamps from all islands.

Butterflies — A55

No. 119: a, Vanessa cardui. b, Danaus plexippus. c, Zerene cesonia. d, Ochlodes sylvanus. e, Calpodes ethlius.
No. 120: a, Leptotes cassius. b, Strymon aciss. c, Ascia monuste. d, Eurema lisa. e, Heliconius charitonia.
No. 121: a, Urbanus dorantes. b, Pyrgus carthami. c, Angerona prunaria. d, Junonia evarete. e, Pyrgus oileus.

**2020, July 1 Litho. *Perf. 13¼x14***
**Inscribed "Bonaire"**

**119** Horiz. strip of 5 7.50 7.50
***a.-e.*** A55 75c Any single 1.50 1.50

**Inscribed "Saba"**

**120** Horiz. strip of 5 7.50 7.50
***a.-e.*** A55 75c Any single 1.50 1.50

**Inscribed "St. Eustatius"**

**121** Horiz. strip of 5 7.50 7.50
***a.-e.*** A55 75c Any single 1.50 1.50
*Nos. 119-121 (3)* 22.50 22.50

Marine Life — A56

No. 122: a, Lobatus gigas. b, Chelonia mydas. c, Pterois. d, Stenella longirostris. e, Scaridae.
No. 123: a, Acanthurus coeruleus. b, Panulirus argus. c, Pomacanthus paru. d, Carcharhinus amblyrhynchos. e, Dermochelys coriacea.
No. 124: a, Dasyatidae. b, Cephalopholis fulva. c, Sphyraena. d, Eretmochelys imbricata. e, Thunnus albacares.

**2020, July 1 Litho. *Perf. 13¼x14***
**Inscribed "Bonaire"**

**122** Horiz. strip of 5 7.50 7.50
***a.-e.*** A56 75c Any single 1.50 1.50

**Inscribed "Saba"**

**123** Horiz. strip of 5 7.50 7.50
***a.-e.*** A56 75c Any single 1.50 1.50

**Inscribed "St. Eustatius"**

**124** Horiz. strip of 5 7.50 7.50
***a.-e.*** A56 75c Any single 1.50 1.50
*Nos. 122-124 (3)* 22.50 22.50

Flowers and Plants — A57

No. 125: a, Agave americana. b, Bougainvillea glabra. c, Hibiscus. d, Tabebuia billbergii. e, Lantana camara.
No. 126: a, Tecoma stans. b, Hippeastrum striatum. c, Orchidacea. d, Rudbeckia hirta. e, Alpinia purpurata.
No. 127: a, Aloe vera. b, Anthurium andreanum. c, Nerium oleander. d, Onagraceae. e, Cattleya luteola.

**2020, July 1 Litho. *Perf. 13¼x14***
**Inscribed "Bonaire"**

**125** Horiz. strip of 5 7.50 7.50
***a.-e.*** A57 75c Any single 1.50 1.50

**Inscribed "Saba"**

**126** Horiz. strip of 5 7.50 7.50
***a.-e.*** A57 75c Any single 1.50 1.50

**Inscribed "St. Eustatius"**

**127** Horiz. strip of 5 7.50 7.50
***a.-e.*** A57 75c Any single 1.50 1.50
*Nos. 125-127 (3)* 22.50 22.50

Miniature Sheets

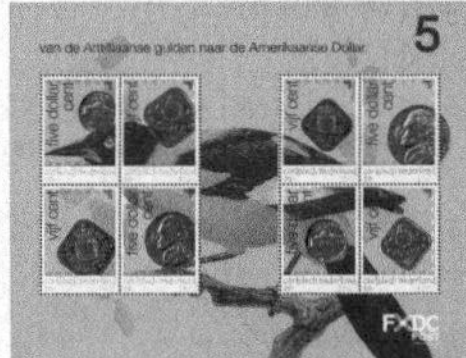

A58

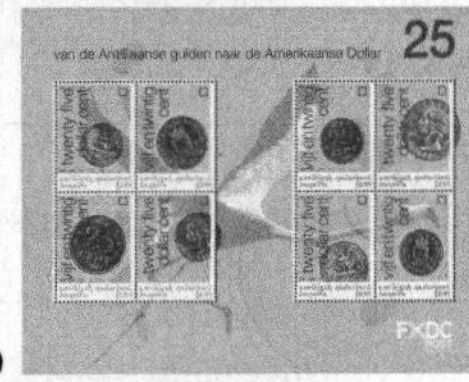

A59

A60

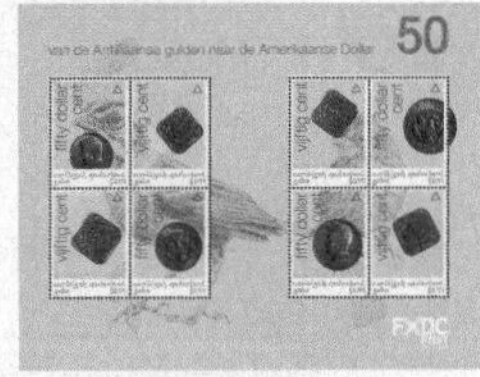

A61

Coins and Birds A62

No. 128 — Five-cent coin: a, Reverse, from United States, beak of bird. b, Reverse (numeral showing), from Netherlands Antilles, back of bird's head. c, Obverse (arms showing), from Netherlands Antilles, back of bird. d, Obverse, from United States, no part of bird. e, Obverse, from Netherlands Antilles, no part of bird. f, Obverse, from United States, breast of bird. g, Reverse, from United States, leg and tail feathers of bird. h, Reverse, from Netherlands Antilles, tail feathers of bird.
No. 129 — Twenty-five-cent coin: a, Reverse, from United States, wing tip of bird. b, Obverse, from Netherlands Antilles, part of wing of bird. c, Reverse, from Netherlands Antilles, part of wing of bird. d, Obverse, from United States, no part of bird. e, Reverse, from Netherlands Antilles, no part of bird. f,

Obverse, from United States, legs and breast of bird. g, Reverse, from United States, neck of bird. h, Obverse, from Netherlands Antilles, head of bird.

No. 130 — Ten-cent coin: a, Obverse, from United States, part of wing of bird at right. b, Obverse, from Netherlands Antilles, part of wing of bird. c, Obverse, from Netherlands Antilles, head of bird. d, Reverse, from United States, beak of bird. e, Reverse, from Netherlands Antilles, part of wing of bird at UR. f, Reverse, from United States, part of wing of bird. g, Obverse, from United States, part of wing of bird at bottom. h, Reverse, from Netherlands Antilles, part of wing of bird at bottom.

No. 131 — Fifty-cent coin: a, Obverse, from United States, head of bird. b, Reverse, from Netherlands Antilles, part of back of bird. c, Obverse (plant showing), from Netherlands Antilles, beak and eye of bird. d, Reverse, from United States, back of head of bird. e, Obverse, from Netherlands Antilles, breast of bird at UR. f, Reverse, from United States, leg and wing of bird. g, Obverse, from United States, part of breast and leg of bird. h, Reverse, from Netherlands Antilles, breast and leg of bird.

No. 132 — One-hundred-cent coin (dollar or gulden): a, Reverse (Statue of Liberty showing), from United States, beak of bird. b, Obverse (Queen showing), from Netherlands Antilles, head of bird. c, Obverse, from Netherlands Antilles, back of bird. d, Obverse (George Washington showing), from United States, tail feathers of bird. e, Reverse (arms showing), from Netherlands Antilles, no part of bird. f, Obverse, from United States, breast of bird. g, Reverse, from United States, part of breast and leg of bird. h, Reverse, from Netherlands Antilles, bird's perch.

**2020, Oct. 10 Litho. *Perf. 13¼x14***

**Inscribed "Bonaire"**

| No. | Type | Description | Unused | Used |
|---|---|---|---|---|
| **128** | A58 | 99c Sheet of 8, #a-h | 16.00 | 16.00 |
| **129** | A59 | 99c Sheet of 8, #a-h | 16.00 | 16.00 |

**Inscribed "Saba"**

| No. | Type | Description | Unused | Used |
|---|---|---|---|---|
| **130** | A60 | 99c Sheet of 8, #a-h | 16.00 | 16.00 |
| **131** | A61 | 99c Sheet of 8, #a-h | 16.00 | 16.00 |

**Inscribed "Sint Eustatius"**

| No. | Type | Description | Unused | Used |
|---|---|---|---|---|
| **132** | A62 | 99c Sheet of 8, #a-h | 16.00 | 16.00 |
| | | *Nos. 128-132 (5)* | 80.00 | 80.00 |

### SEMI-POSTAL STAMPS

Intl. Year of Cooperatives SP1

**2012, Oct. 9 Litho. *Perf. 13½x12¾***

| No. | Type | Description | Unused | Used |
|---|---|---|---|---|
| **B1** | SP1 | 99c+45c multi | 3.00 | 3.00 |

## CAROLINE ISLANDS

'kar-ə-ˌlīn 'ī-ləndz

LOCATION — A group of about 549 small islands in the West Pacific Ocean, north of the Equator.
GOVT. — German colony
AREA — 550 sq. mi.
POP. — 40,000 (approx. 1915)

100 Pfennig = 1 Mark

**Watermark**

Wmk. 125 — Lozenges

**Stamps of Germany 1889-90 Overprinted in Black**

Overprinted at 56 degree Angle

**1900 Unwmk. *Perf. 13½x14½***

| No. | Type | Description | Unused | Used |
|---|---|---|---|---|
| **1** | A9 | 3pf dk brown | 12.00 | 13.00 |
| **2** | A9 | 5pf green | 15.00 | 15.00 |
| **3** | A10 | 10pf carmine | 15.00 | 16.00 |
| **4** | A10 | 20pf ultra | 20.00 | 24.00 |
| **5** | A10 | 25pf orange | 45.00 | 55.00 |
| **6** | A10 | 50pf red brown | 45.00 | 55.00 |
| | | *Nos. 1-6 (6)* | 152.00 | 178.00 |

Overprinted at 48 degree Angle

**1899**

| No. | Type | Description | Unused | Used |
|---|---|---|---|---|
| *1a* | A9 | 3pf light brown | 575.00 | 650.00 |
| *2a* | A9 | 5pf green | 575.00 | 575.00 |
| *3a* | A10 | 10pf carmine | 60.00 | 125.00 |
| *4a* | A10 | 20pf ultra | 60.00 | 125.00 |
| *5a* | A10 | 25pf orange | 1,400. | 2,500. |
| *6a* | A10 | 50pf red brown | 600.00 | 1,400. |

A3

Kaiser's Yacht "Hohenzollern" A4

**1901, Jan. Typo. *Perf. 14***

| No. | Type | Description | Unused | Used |
|---|---|---|---|---|
| **7** | A3 | 3pf brown | .90 | 1.50 |
| **8** | A3 | 5pf green | .90 | 1.75 |
| **9** | A3 | 10pf carmine | .90 | 4.25 |
| *a.* | | Half used as 5pf on cover, back-stamped in Jaluit ('05) | | 120.00 |
| **10** | A3 | 20pf ultra | 1.10 | 7.50 |
| *a.* | | Half used as 10pf on cover ('10) | | 7,500. |
| **11** | A3 | 25pf org & blk, *yel* | 1.40 | 12.00 |
| **12** | A3 | 30pf org & blk, *sal* | 1.40 | 12.00 |
| **13** | A3 | 40pf lake & blk | 1.40 | 12.00 |
| **14** | A3 | 50pf pur & blk, *sal* | 1.75 | 19.00 |
| **15** | A3 | 80pf lake & blk, *rose* | 2.75 | 21.00 |

**Engr. *Perf. 14½x14***

| No. | Type | Description | Unused | Used |
|---|---|---|---|---|
| **16** | A4 | 1m carmine | 3.75 | 55.00 |
| **17** | A4 | 2m blue | 6.00 | 75.00 |
| **18** | A4 | 3m black violet | 9.00 | 130.00 |
| **19** | A4 | 5m slate & car | 160.00 | 450.00 |
| | | *Nos. 7-19 (13)* | 191.25 | 801.00 |

No. 9a is known as the "typhoon provisional" the stock of 5pf stamps having been destroyed during a typhoon. Covers (cards) without backstamp, value about $72.50.

Forged cancellations are found on #7-19.

No. 7 Handstamp Surcharged

**1910, July 12**

| No. | Type | Description | Unused | Used |
|---|---|---|---|---|
| **20** | A3 | 5pf on 3pf brown | | 4,500. |
| *a.* | | Inverted surcharge | | 7,750. |
| *b.* | | Double surcharge | | 11,000. |

Values are for stamps tied to cover. Stamps on piece sell for about 40% less.

**1915-19 Wmk. 125 Typo.**

| No. | Type | Description | Unused | Used |
|---|---|---|---|---|
| **21** | A3 | 3pf brown ('19) | .75 | |
| **22** | A3 | 5pf green | 10.50 | |

**Engr.**

| No. | Type | Description | Unused | Used |
|---|---|---|---|---|
| **23** | A4 | 5m slate & carmine | 35.00 | |
| | | *Nos. 21-23 (3)* | 46.25 | |

Nos. 21-23 were not placed in use.

## CARPATHO-UKRAINE

'kar-pā-thō-yü-'krān

LOCATION — Central Europe within the Czechoslovak Republic
GOVT. — Autonomous region 1938-1939
POP. — 814,000 (1938)
CAPITAL — Khust

An autonomous region established in December 1938 within the Second Czechoslovak Republic and proclaimed an independent republic in March 1939.

The Soviet National Council of Carpatho-Ukraine (NRZU) in Uzhhorod began issuing overprinted and surcharged Hungary stamps in February 1945; it also issued three sets of definitive stamps in May 1945. Carpatho-Ukraine was ceded to the Ukrainian Soviet Socialist Republic in 1946.

100 Fillér = 1 Pengö

**Catalogue values for unused stamps in this country are for Never Hinged items.**

Carpatho-Ukraine No. 1 was previously listed as Czechoslovakia No. 254B. The stamp was initially slated to be issued March 2, 1939, as a regional stamp, with 300,000 stamps sent to the province and more than 600,000 stamps retained in Prague for philatelic sales. The stamp's release was delayed. The Carpatho-Ukrainian diet declared its independence March 14, 1939, and decreed that No. 254B be its first postage stamp, placing it on sale the following day. Stocks in Prague also were placed on sale. It is unlikely that the stamp saw much, if any, postal use either in Carpatho-Ukraine or Czechoslovakia because Germany invaded Czechoslovakia on March 15, and Hungary invaded Carpatho-Ukraine March 16. A few covers, no doubt philatelic, are known from Carpatho-Ukraine.

View of Jasina — A1

***Perf. 12½***

**1939, Mar. 15 Engr. Unwmk.**

| No. | Type | Description | Unused | Used |
|---|---|---|---|---|
| **1** | A1 | 3k ultra, *yelsh* | 4.00 | 40.00 |

Inauguration of the Carpatho-Ukraine Diet, March 2, 1939.

Printed for use in the province of Carpatho-Ukraine but issued in Prague at the same time.

No. 1 was issued in sheets of 100 stamps with 12 blank labels. Values with attached labels: mint $12, used $80. Used value is for red commemorative cancel.

**Uzhhorod Provisional Overprints**

The basic Hungarian stamps used for overprinting were issued between 1939 and 1944. All were printed by photogravure. Various comb perforations were used, depending on the size of the stamps. Earlier issues were on paper with Wmk. 210, while later issues have Wmk. 266.

Stamps in used condition command a 50 percent to 100 percent premium, depending on the quality of the cancellation.

Hungary Churches Issue 1939, 1941 Ovptd. and Srchd.

**1945, Feb. 1**

| No. | Type | Description | Unused | Used |
|---|---|---|---|---|
| **2** | A75 | 60f on 3f dark brown | 90.00 | — |
| **3** | A75 | 60f on 16f rose violet | 90.00 | — |
| **4** | A76 | 60f on 24f brown lilac | 120.00 | — |
| **5** | A82 | 60f on 30f rose red | 125.00 | — |
| **6** | A79 | 60f on 40f gray black | 130.00 | — |
| **7** | A80 | 2p on 50f bright blue | 130.00 | — |
| **8** | A81 | 2p on 70f gray green | 140.00 | — |
| **9** | A78 | 2p on 80f bister brown | 175.00 | — |
| | | *Nos. 2-9 (8)* | 1,000. | |

A 40f-on-20f rose red stamp was prepared but not issued.

Nos. 2-5, and 9 exist with overprint and surcharge inverted.

Hungary Nos. 597-599 Ovptd. and Srchd. in Black

**1945, Feb.**

| No. | Type | Description | Unused | Used |
|---|---|---|---|---|
| **10** | A92 | 2p on 1p dk grn & buff | 120.00 | — |
| **11** | A92 | 4p on 2p dk brn & buff | 65.00 | — |
| **12** | A92 | 10p on 5p dk rose vio & buff | 225.00 | — |
| | | *Nos. 10-12 (3)* | 410.00 | |

No. 11 exists with surcharge and overprint inverted.

Varieties of Nos. 11 and 12 include sans-serif letters, broken and missing letters.

Hungary Nos. 570-572 also exist with the same overprints and surcharges. Scott editors are seeking additional information on these overprinted stamps.

Hungary Nos. 573-577 Ovptd. and Srchd. in Black

| No. | Type | Description | Unused | Used |
|---|---|---|---|---|
| **13** | A93 | 40f on 10f dk ol grn | 130.00 | — |
| **14** | A94 | 60f on 16f ol brn | 140.00 | — |
| **15** | A95 | 1p on 20f carmine | 130.00 | — |
| **16** | A96 | 1.40p on 32f red org | 130.00 | — |
| **17** | A97 | 2p on 40f ryl blue | 130.00 | — |
| | | *Nos. 13-17 (5)* | 660.00 | |

Hungary Nos. 601-616 Ovptd. and Srchd. in Black or Red

| No. | Type | Description | Unused | Used |
|---|---|---|---|---|
| **18** | A99 | 10f on 1f grnsh blk | 70.00 | — |
| **19** | A99 | 10f on 2f red org | 100.00 | — |
| **20** | A99 | 10f on 3f ultra (R) | 85.00 | — |
| **20A** | A99 | 10f on 3f ultra | — | — |
| **21** | A99 | 40f on 2f red org | 90.00 | — |
| **22** | A99 | 40f on 5f vermilion | 110.00 | — |
| **23** | A99 | 40f on 8f dk ol grn | 125.00 | — |
| **24** | A99 | 40f on 10f brown | 125.00 | — |
| **25** | A99 | 40f on 12f dp bl grn | 125.00 | — |
| **26** | A99 | 40f on 18f dk gray (R) | 150.00 | — |
| **27** | A109 | 40f on 20f chnt brn | 65.00 | — |
| **28** | A99 | 60f on 1f grysh blk | 10.00 | — |
| **29** | A99 | 60f on 2f red org | 15.00 | — |
| **30** | A99 | 60f on 3f ultra | 10.00 | — |
| **30A** | A99 | 60f on 3f ultra (R) | 500.00 | — |
| **31** | A99 | 60f on 4f brown | 10.00 | — |
| **32** | A99 | 60f on 5f vermilion | 25.00 | — |
| **33** | A99 | 60f on 6f slate blue | 10.00 | — |
| **34** | A99 | 60f on 8f dk ol grn | 20.00 | — |
| **35** | A99 | 60f on 10f brown | 5.00 | — |
| **36** | A99 | 60f on 12f dp bl grn | 20.00 | — |
| **37** | A99 | 60f on 18f dk gray (R) | 5.00 | — |
| **37A** | A99 | 60f on 18f blk & gray | 500.00 | — |
| **38** | A109 | 60f on 20f chnt brn | 10.00 | — |
| **39** | A99 | 60f on 24f rose vio | 35.00 | — |
| **40** | A109 | 60f on 30f brt car | 10.00 | — |
| **41** | A109 | 2p on 50f blue (R) | 40.00 | — |
| **41A** | A109 | 2p on 50f blue | — | — |
| **42** | A109 | 2p on 80f yel brn | 65.00 | — |
| **43** | A109 | 2p on 1p green | 25.00 | — |
| | | *Nos. 18-43 (30)* | 2,360. | |

No. 38 exists in vertical tete-beche pairs.

Varieties of Nos. 21, 23, 24 and 26 include sans-serif letters, broken and missing letters.

No. 41 is also known with offset of overprint on reverse.

Hungary Nos. B157-B165 Ovptd. and Srchd. in Black

| No. | Type | Description | Unused | Used |
|---|---|---|---|---|
| **44** | SP92 | 20f on 1f+1f dk gray | 55.00 | — |
| **45** | SP93 | 40f on 20f+2f dp claret | 125.00 | — |
| **46** | SP93 | 60f on 4f+1f lake | 55.00 | — |
| **47** | SP93 | 60f on 8f+2f green | 90.00 | — |
| **48** | SP93 | 60f on 12f+2f bis brn | 90.00 | — |
| **49** | SP93 | 60f on 40f+4f gray vio | 90.00 | — |
| **50** | SP93 | 1p on 50f+6f org brn | 100.00 | — |
| **51** | SP94 | 1.40p on 70f+8f sl bl | 100.00 | — |
| | | *Nos. 44-51 (8)* | 705.00 | |

Hungary Nos. 617-619 Ovptd. and Srchd. in Black

**52** A110 60f on 4f dark green *25.00* —
**53** A110 60f on 20f dark blue *35.00* —
**54** A110 60f on 30f brn org *40.00* —
*Nos. 52-54 (3)* *100.00*

Hungary No. 620 Ovptd. and Srchd. in Black

**55** A113 60f on 30f dp car *10.00* —

No. 55 exists in vertical tete-beche pair, and with overprint and surcharge inverted.
Varieties of No. 55 include sans-serif letters, and broken and missing letters.

Hungary Nos. B171-B174 Ovptd. and Srchd. in Black

**56** SP106 1p on 20f+20f brown *140.00* —
**57** SP106 1.40p on 30f+30f henna *160.00* —
**58** SP106 2p on 50f+50f brn vio *150.00* —
**59** SP106 4p on 70f+70f Prus blue *175.00* —
*Nos. 56-59 (4)* *550.00*

Hungary Nos. 621-624 Ovptd. and Srchd. in Black or Red

**60** A114 40f on 4f yel brn *65.00* —
**61** A115 40f on 30f hen brn *110.00* —
**62** A115 60f on 20f dk ol grn *70.00* —
**63** A117 1p on 50f slate bl *165.00* —
**64** A117 2p on 50f slate bl (R) *80.00* —
*Nos. 60-64 (5)* *490.00*

Nos. 60 and 63 exist with overprints and surcharges inverted. Varieties of both include sans-serif letters, and broken and missing letters.

Hungary Nos. 625-630 Ovptd. and Srchd. in Black or Red

**65** A118 40f on 20f brn olive *110.00* —
**66** A118 60f on 20f brn olive *30.00* —
**67** A118 60f on 24f rose vio *90.00* —
**68** A118 60f on 24f rose vio (R) *125.00* —
**69** A118 60f on 30f cop red *10.00* —
**70** A118 1p on 50f dk bl (R) *65.00* —
**71** A118 1.40p on 70f org red *100.00* —
**72** A118 2p on 50f dk bl (R) *75.00* —
**73** A118 2p on 70f org red *35.00* —
**74** A118 2p on 80f brn car *35.00* —
*Nos. 65-74 (10)* *675.00*

Nos. 65, 67, 69, 70, 71 and 74 exist with overprints and surcharges inverted.
Varieties of Nos. 66, 67, 68, 69, 70, 71 and 74 include sans-serif letters, and broken and missing letters.
A 2.40p-on-80f brown carmine stamp was prepared but not issued.

Hungary 1941, 1941-44 Postage Due Issues Surcharged

**75** D8 10f on 2f brown red *20.00* —
**76** D8 10f on 3f brown red *45.00* —
**77** D8 20f on 8f brown red *50.00* —
**78** D8 20f on 10f brown red *30.00* —
**79** D8 30f on 12f brown red *250.00* —
**80** D8 40f on 20f brown red *60.00* —
**81** D8 60f on 4f brown red *25.00* —
**82** D8 60f on 6f brown red *55.00* —
**83** D8 60f on 16f brown red *150.00* —
**84** D8 1p on 40f brown red *90.00* —
*Nos. 75-84 (10)* *775.00*

Nos. 77 and 79 exist with overprints and surcharges inverted.
Varieties of Nos. 75, 77, 78, 79, 80 and 84 include sans-serif letters, and broken and missing letters.
A 60f on 2f brown red stamp and 60f on 20f brown red stamp were prepared but not issued.

### Hungary 1944 Accounting Revenue Issue (Számolólap Illeték) Overprinted and Surcharged

A2

#### Surcharge at Left or Right

**85** A2 40f on 10f red org (L) *85.00* —
**86** A2 40f on 20f ultra (L) *175.00* —
**87** A2 60f on 50f dk bl grn (L) *250.00* —
*Nos. 85-87 (3)* *510.00*

A 60f-on-10f red orange was prepared but not issued.

Hungary 1944 Portraits Issue With Khust Overprint in Black or Red

**88** A99 60f on 1f grysh blk *100.00* —
**89** A99 60f on 2f red org *100.00* —
**90** A99 60f on 4f brown *100.00* —
**91** A99 60f on 8f dk ol grn *65.00* —
**92** A99 60f on 10f brown *65.00* —
**93** A99 60f on 12f dp bl grn *175.00* —
**94** A99 60f on 18f dk gray (R) *100.00* —
**95** A109 60f on 20f chnt brn *175.00* —
**96** A109 60f on 30f brt car *100.00* —
**97** A114 60f on 4f yel brn *190.00* —
**98** A114 60f on 30f copper red *175.00* —
**99** A118 2p on 70f orange red *175.00* —
*Nos. 88-99 (12)* *1,520.*

Nos. 88-99 exist with overprints and surcharges inverted.

### NRZU Issues

Three separate locally produced definitive stamp sets were issued by National Council of Carpatho-Ukraine (NRZU), all printed by offset lithography at Litografia Lam in Uzhhorod.
Shade varieties (from light to dark) are common, sometimes occurring within the same sheet.

#### First Definitive Issue

Red Banner, Red Army Soldier, Mountains of Carpatho-Ukraine — A3

Breaking Chain, Mountains — A4

Shackled Hand Breaking Free — A5

*Perf. 11½*

**1945, May 1** **Unwmk.** **Litho.**
**100** A3 60f red *5.00* —
**101** A4 100f dk vio blue *15.00* —
**102** A5 200f dark blue & red *20.00* —
*Nos. 100-102 (3)* *40.00*

Values for Nos. 100-102 are for examples with gum (applied by hand). Examples without gum are printer's waste.
Values are for well-centered stamps with intact perforations. Stamps of lesser quality are especially abundant and are often available at substantial discounts.
No. 100 exists in two types. In Type I, the "N" is directly above the "O," while in Type II, the "N" is shifted slightly to the right.

Nos. 100-102 exist imperforate. Value set, $90.

#### Second Definitive Issue

Star, Hammer and Sickle — A6

**1945, June**
**103** A6 10f bis yel *5.00* —
**104** A6 20f blusih gray *7.50* —
**105** A6 40f yellow green *5.00* —
**106** A6 60f dull ver *5.00* —
**107** A6 100f dk bl, lake brn *10.00* —
**108** A6 200f brown, red *12.50* —
*Nos. 103-108 (6)* *45.00*

Nos. 103-108 exist imperforate. Value set, $90.

#### Third Definitive Issue

Star, Hammer, Sickle, Year Date — A7

**1945, Aug.**
**109** A7 10f dull yellow *15.00* —
**110** A7 20f gray *15.00* —

The addition of the year "19 45" beside the denomination lozenge distinquishes this issue from the second definitive issue.
Nos. 109-110 exist imperforate. Value, $30 each.

# CASTELLORIZO

ˌkäs-tə-ˈlor-ə-ˌzō

(Castelrosso)

LOCATION — A Mediterranean island in the Dodecanese group lying close to the coast of Asia Minor and about 60 miles east of Rhodes.
GOVT. — Former Italian Colony
AREA — 4 sq. mi.
POP. — 2,238 (1936)

Formerly a Turkish possession, Castellorizo was occupied by the French in 1915 and ceded to Italy after World War I. In 1945 it became part of Greece.

25 Centimes = 1 Piaster
100 Centimes = 1 Franc

**Used values in italics are for postally used copies. Stamps with CTO cancels sell for about the same as hinged, unused stamps.**

### Issued under French Occupation

Stamps of French Offices in Turkey Overprinted

**1920** **Unwmk.** ***Perf. 14x13½***
**1** A2 1c gray 45.00 *65.00*
*a.* Inverted overprint 175.00 *250.00*
*b.* Double overprint 175.00 *350.00*
**2** A2 2c vio brn 50.00 *70.00*
*a.* Double overprint 225.00 *300.00*
**3** A2 3c red org 45.00 *65.00*
*a.* Inverted overprint 175.00 *250.00*
**4** A2 5c green 75.00 *90.00*
*a.* Inverted overprint 225.00 *300.00*
**5** A3 10c rose 90.00 *125.00*
**6** A3 15c pale red 115.00 *150.00*
*a.* Inverted overprint 450.00 *625.00*
**7** A3 20c brn vio 125.00 *150.00*
**8** A5 1pi on 25c blue 115.00 125.00
*a.* Pair, one without overprint 1,150. 800.00
**9** A3 30c lilac 125.00 *150.00*
**10** A4 40c red & pale bl (down) 200.00 *250.00*
*a.* Inverted ovpt (reading up) 875.00 950.00
**11** A6 2pi on 50c bis brn & lav (down) 225.00 *275.00*
*a.* Inverted ovpt (reading up) 900.00 1,000.
*b.* Double overprint 1,250. 1,300.
**12** A6 4pi on 1fr cl & ol grn (down) 275.00 *350.00*
*a.* Double overprint 1,300. 1,350.
*b.* Inverted ovpt (reading up) 1,050. 1,100.
**13** A6 20pi on 5fr dk bl & buff 625.00 *800.00*
*a.* Double overprint 1,850. *2,000.*
*Nos. 1-13 (13)* 2,110. 2,665.
Set, never hinged 4,500.

No. 1-9 were overprinted in blocks of 25. Position 4 had "CASTELLORIZO" inverted and Positions 8 and 18 had "CASTELLORISO." The later variety also occurred in the setting of the form for Nos. 10-13.
"B. N. F." are the initials of "Base Navale Francaise".

Overprinted in Black or Red

**1920**
#### On Stamps of French Offices in Turkey

**14** A2 1c gray 34.00 *40.00*
**15** A2 2c vio brn 37.50 *50.00*
**16** A2 3c red org 67.50 *80.00*
**17** A2 5c green (R) 32.50 *37.50*
**19** A3 10c rose 40.00 *47.50*
**20** A3 15c pale red 70.00 *80.00*
**21** A3 20c brn vio 105.00 *110.00*
**22** A5 1pi on 25c bl (R) 67.50 *70.00*
**23** A3 30c lilac (R) 77.50 *85.00*
**24** A4 40c red & pale bl 75.00 *75.00*
**25** A6 2pi on 50c bis brn & lav 72.50 *80.00*
**26** A6 4pi on 1fr claret & ol grn 115.00 *140.00*
**28** A6 20pi on 5fr dk bl & buff 400.00 450.00
*Nos. 14-28 (13)* 1,194. 1,345.

On Nos. 25, 26 and 28 the two lines of the overprint are set wider apart than on the lower values.
"O.N.F." are the initials of "Occupation Navale Francaise."
"Casetllorizo" and "astellorizo" varieties are known on Nos. 14-23.
Overprint on 5c in black and on 8pi on 2fr (#37) were prepared but not issued. Values: 5c, $1,300; 8pi on 2fr, $1,450.

#### On Stamps of France

**30** A22 10c red 50.00 *65.00*
*a.* Inverted overprint 200.00 *250.00*
**31** A22 25c blue (R) 50.00 *65.00*
*a.* Inverted overprint 200.00 *250.00*

This overprint exists on 8 other 1900-1907 denominations of France (5c, 15c, 20c, 30c, 40c, 50c, 1fr, 5fr). These are believed not to have been issued or postally used. Values: 5c, $750; 15c, $750; 20c, $800; 30c, $1,300; 40c, $1,300; 50c, $1,300; 1fr, $1,400; 5fr, $12,500.

Stamps of France, 1900-1907, Handstamped in Black or Violet

**1920**
**33** A22 5c green 175.00 *200.00*
*a.* Overprint inverted (reading up) 1,300.
*b.* Double overprint 1,000.
**34** A22 10c red 175.00 *200.00*
**35** A22 20c vio brn 175.00 *200.00*
*a.* Overprint inverted (reading up) *1,500.*
*b.* Double overprint *1,000.*
**36** A22 25c blue 175.00 *200.00*
**37** A18 50c bis brn & lav 1,000. *1,200.*
*a.* Double overprint *1,700.*
**38** A18 1fr cl & ol grn (V) 1,000. 1,200.
*Nos. 33-38 (6)* 2,700. 3,200.
Set, never hinged 5,400.

French Offices in Turkey Nos. 25//38 were handstamped as Nos. 33-38 locally by the officers in charge of the French Navy postal facilities but were not issued. Values: 5c, 10c, 15c, 20c, 1pi on 25c, each $1,000; 40c, 2pi on 50c, each $2,000; 4pi on 1fr, $2,350; 20pi on 5fr, $10,000.
**Covers:** Values for covers are for commercial items. Philatelic covers sell for less.
Forgeries of overprints on Nos. 1-38 exist. They abound of Nos. 33-38.

**Issued under Italian Dominion**

100 Centesimi = 1 Lira

Italian Stamps of 1906-20 Overprinted

**1922, July 22 Wmk. 140 *Perf. 14***

| | | | | |
|---|---|---|---|---|
| **51** | A48 | 5c green | 5.00 | *30.00* |
| **52** | A48 | 10c claret | 3.50 | *30.00* |
| **53** | A48 | 15c slate | 3.50 | *30.00* |
| **54** | A50 | 20c brn org | 3.50 | *30.00* |
| *a.* | | Double overprint | 500.00 | |
| *b.* | | Vertical pair, one without overprint | 2,250. | |
| **55** | A49 | 25c blue | 3.50 | *30.00* |
| **56** | A49 | 40c brown | 48.00 | 35.00 |
| **57** | A49 | 50c violet | 50.00 | 37.50 |
| **58** | A49 | 60c carmine | 50.00 | 57.50 |
| *a.* | | Diagonal overprint | | 800.00 |
| **59** | A49 | 85c chocolate | 5.50 | *65.00* |
| | | *Nos. 51-59 (9)* | 172.50 | *345.00* |
| | | Set, never hinged | 450.00 | |

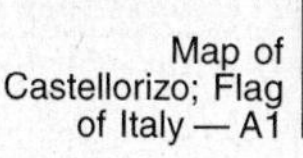

Map of Castellorizo; Flag of Italy — A1

**1923, Jan.**

| | | | | |
|---|---|---|---|---|
| **60** | A1 | 5c gray green | 7.00 | *40.00* |
| **61** | A1 | 10c dull rose | 7.00 | *40.00* |
| **62** | A1 | 25c dull blue | 7.00 | *40.00* |
| **63** | A1 | 50c gray lilac | 7.00 | *40.00* |
| **64** | A1 | 1 l brown | 7.00 | *40.00* |
| | | *Nos. 60-64 (5)* | 35.00 | *200.00* |
| | | Set, never hinged | 65.00 | |

Italian Stamps of 1901-20 Overprinted

**1924, March**

| | | | | |
|---|---|---|---|---|
| **65** | A48 | 5c green | 2.50 | *30.00* |
| **66** | A48 | 10c claret | 2.50 | *30.00* |
| **67** | A48 | 15c slate | 2.50 | *40.00* |
| **68** | A50 | 20c brn orange | 2.50 | *40.00* |
| *a.* | | Double overprint | 150.00 | |
| **69** | A49 | 25c blue | 2.50 | *30.00* |
| **70** | A49 | 40c brown | 2.50 | *30.00* |
| **71** | A49 | 50c violet | 2.50 | *40.00* |
| **72** | A49 | 60c carmine | 2.50 | *50.00* |
| *a.* | | Double overprint | 475.00 | |
| **73** | A49 | 85c red brown | 2.50 | *60.00* |
| **74** | A46 | 1 l brn & green | 2.50 | *60.00* |
| | | *Nos. 65-74 (10)* | 25.00 | *410.00* |
| | | Set, never hinged | 55.00 | |

**Ferrucci Issue**

Italian Stamps of 1930, Ovptd. in Red or Blue

**1930, Oct. 20 Wmk. Crowns (140)**

| | | | | |
|---|---|---|---|---|
| **75** | A102 | 20c violet | 10.00 | 6.00 |
| **76** | A103 | 25c dark green | 10.00 | *25.00* |
| **77** | A103 | 50c black | 10.00 | 6.00 |
| **78** | A103 | 1.25 l deep blue | 10.00 | *25.00* |
| **79** | A104 | 5 l + 2 l dp car (Bl) | 10.00 | *77.50* |
| | | *Nos. 75-79 (5)* | 50.00 | *139.50* |
| | | Set, never hinged | 150.00 | |

**Garibaldi Issue**

Types of Italian Stamps of 1932, Overprinted like Nos. 75-79 in Red or Blue

**1932, Aug. 28**

| | | | | |
|---|---|---|---|---|
| **80** | A138 | 10c brown | 20.00 | *25.00* |
| **81** | A138 | 20c red brn (Bl) | 20.00 | *25.00* |
| **82** | A138 | 25c dp grn | 20.00 | *25.00* |
| **83** | A138 | 30c bluish slate | 20.00 | *25.00* |
| **84** | A138 | 50c red vio (Bl) | 20.00 | *25.00* |
| **85** | A141 | 75c cop red (Bl) | 20.00 | *25.00* |
| **86** | A141 | 1.25 l dull blue | 20.00 | *25.00* |
| **87** | A141 | 1.75 l + 25c brn | 20.00 | *25.00* |
| **88** | A144 | 2.55 l + 50c org (Bl) | 20.00 | *25.00* |
| **89** | A145 | 5 l + 1 l dl vio | 20.00 | *25.00* |
| | | *Nos. 80-89 (10)* | 200.00 | *250.00* |
| | | Set, never hinged | 625.00 | |

## CAYMAN ISLANDS

ˌkā-ˈman ˈī-lənds

LOCATION — Three islands in the Caribbean Sea, about 200 miles northwest of Jamaica
GOVT. — British Crown Colony, formerly a dependency of Jamaica
AREA — 100 sq. mi.
POP. — 39,335 (1999 est.)
CAPITAL — George Town, located on Grand Cayman

12 Pence = 1 Shilling
20 Shilling = 1 Pound
100 Cents = 1 Dollar (1969)

**Catalogue values for unused stamps in this country are for Never Hinged items, beginning with Scott 112.**

Victoria — A1

**1900 Typo. Wmk. 2 Perf. 14**
1 A1 ½p pale green 15.00 *24.00*
2 A1 1p carmine rose 17.50 5.00

Edward VII — A2

**1901-03**
3 A2 ½p green ('02) 6.50 *30.00*
4 A2 1p car rose ('03) 12.00 *12.00*
5 A2 2½p ultramarine 12.00 *21.00*
6 A2 6p chocolate 35.00 *70.00*
7 A2 1sh brown orange 67.50 *125.00*
*Nos. 3-7 (5)* 133.00 *258.00*

**1905 Wmk. 3**
8 A2 ½p green 12.00 *19.00*
9 A2 1p carmine rose 24.00 *20.00*
10 A2 2½p ultramarine 12.50 6.00
11 A2 6p chocolate 19.00 *45.00*
12 A2 1sh brown orange 35.00 *55.00*
*Nos. 8-12 (5)* 102.50 *145.00*

For surcharge see No. 17.

**1907, Mar. 13**
13 A2 4p brown & blue 40.00 *67.50*
14 A2 6p ol green & rose 50.00 *80.00*
15 A2 1sh violet & green 65.00 *95.00*
16 A2 5sh ver & green 225.00 *350.00*
*Nos. 13-16 (4)* 380.00 *592.50*

Numerals of 4p, 1sh and 5sh of type A2 are in color on colorless tablet.
For surcharges see Nos. 18-20.

**Nos. 9, 16, 13 Handstamped**

No. 17

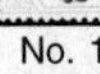
No. 18

No. 19

No. 20

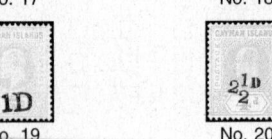

**1907-08**
17 A2 ½p on 1p 60.00 *92.50*
18 A2 ½p on 5sh 325.00 *525.00*
*a.* Inverted surcharge *100,000.*
*b.* Double surcharge *12,750.* *12,750.*
*c.* Double surcharge, one inverted
*d.* Pair, one without surcharge *100,000.*
19 A2 1p on 5sh 350.00 *525.00*
*a.* Double surcharge *22,500.* *20,000.*
*b.* Inverted surcharge *150,000.*
20 A2 2½p on 4p ('08) 2,000. *3,750.*
*a.* Double surcharge *60,000.* *30,000.*

No. 19b is unique. It exists on the upper left stamp in an upper left corner margin plate no. 1 block of four that is lightly hinged in the top margin only.

The 1p on 4p is a revenue stamp not authorized for postal use, although postally used examples exist. Value for unused is about $300.

A3

**1907-09 Perf. 14**
21 A3 ½p green 5.25 *5.50*
22 A3 1p carmine rose 2.10 1.10
23 A3 2½p ultramarine 7.50 3.00

**Chalky Paper**
24 A3 3p violet, *yellow* 4.50 *3.75*
25 A3 4p blk & red, *yel* 67.50 *100.00*
26 A3 6p purple & br pur 27.50 *40.00*
27 A3 1sh black, *grn* 11.00 *30.00*
28 A3 5sh grn & red, *yel* 60.00 *90.00*
*Nos. 21-28 (8)* 185.35 *273.35*

Issued: ½p, 1p, 12/27/07; 2½p, 3p, 4p, 5sh, 3/30/08; 6d, 10/2/08; 1sh, 4/5/09.
Forged cancellations are found on No. 28.

**1908, Mar. 30 Wmk. 2**
29 A3 1sh black, *green* 80.00 *125.00*
30 A3 10sh grn & red, *grn* 210.00 *350.00*

Numerals of 3p, 4p, 1sh and 5sh of type A3 are in color on plain tablet.
Forged cancellations are found on No. 30.

A4

**1908 Wmk. 3 Ordinary Paper**
31 A4 ¼p brown 6.00 1.00

King George V — A5

**1912-20**
32 A5 ¼p brown ('13) 1.25 .50
33 A5 ½p green 3.25 *6.00*
34 A5 1p carmine ('13) 4.00 3.00
35 A5 2p gray 1.25 *12.50*
36 A5 2½p ultra ('14) 8.50 *13.50*

**Chalky Paper**
37 A5 3p vio, *yel* ('13) 3.00 *22.50*
38 A5 4p blk & red, *yel* ('13) 1.25 *12.50*
39 A5 6p vio & red vio ('13) 5.50 *9.00*
40 A5 1sh blk, *grn* ('13) 4.25 *32.50*
41 A5 2sh vio & ultra, *bl* 16.00 *65.00*
42 A5 3sh green & vio 22.50 *77.50*
43 A5 5sh grn & red, *yel* ('14) 90.00 *190.00*
44 A5 10sh grn & red, *bl grn, olive back* ('18) 125.00 *250.00*
*a.* 10sh green & red, *grn* ('14) 150.00 *250.00*
*Nos. 32-44 (13)* 285.75 *694.50*

The first printings of the 3p, 1sh and 10sh have a white back.
For surcharges, see Nos. MR1-MR7.

**1913, Nov. 19**
**Surface-colored Paper**
45 A5 3p violet, *yel* 4.25 *9.50*
46 A5 1sh black, *green* 4.25 *4.25*
47 A5 10sh grn & red, *grn* 130.00 *200.00*
*Nos. 45-47 (3)* 138.50 *213.75*

Numeral of ¼p, 2p, 3p, 4p, 1sh, 2sh, 3sh and 5sh of type A5 are in color on plain tablet.

King George V — A6

**1921-26 Wmk. 4 Perf. 14**
50 A6 ¼p yel brown .60 *1.75*
51 A6 ½p gray green .60 .35
52 A6 1p rose red 1.75 1.00
53 A6 1½p orange brn 2.10 .35
54 A6 2p gray 2.10 *4.75*
55 A6 2½p ultramarine ('22) .60 .60
56 A6 3p violet, *yel* 3.25 *5.25*
57 A6 4½p olive grn 4.00 3.75
58 A6 6p claret 6.50 *37.50*
59 A6 1sh black, *grn* ('25) 11.50 *37.50*
60 A6 2sh violet, *blue* 17.00 *32.50*
61 A6 3sh violet 27.50 19.00
62 A6 5sh green, *yel* 30.00 *55.00*
63 A6 10sh car, *green* 72.50 *100.00*
*Nos. 50-63 (14)* 180.00 *299.30*

Issued: 1½p, 4/4/21; ¼p, ½p, 1p, 2p, 2½p, 6p, 2sh, 3sh, 4/1/22; 3p, 4½p, 6/29/23; 5sh, 2/15/25; 1sh, 5/15/25; 10sh, 9/5/26.

**1921-22 Wmk. 3**
64 A6 3p violet, *org* 1.75 *9.50*
65 A6 4p red, *yel* 1.25 *6.50*
66 A6 1sh black, *green* 1.75 *11.00*
67 A6 5sh green, *yel* 19.00 *80.00*
*a.* 5sh deep green, *pale yellow* 110.00 *170.00*
68 A6 10sh car, *green* 75.00 *125.00*
*Nos. 64-68 (5)* 98.75 *232.00*

Issued: 4p, 4/1/22; others, 4/4/21.

King William IV, King George V — A7

**Perf. 12½**
**1932, Dec. 5 Wmk. 4 Engr.**
69 A7 ¼p brown 1.90 1.40
70 A7 ½p green 3.25 *11.00*
71 A7 1p carmine 3.25 *15.00*
72 A7 1½p orange 3.25 3.75
73 A7 2p gray 3.25 *4.50*
74 A7 2½p ultramarine 3.25 2.00
75 A7 3p olive green 8.50 *6.75*
76 A7 6p red violet 13.00 *28.00*
77 A7 1sh brn & black 20.00 *40.00*
78 A7 2sh ultra & blk 55.00 *100.00*
79 A7 5sh green & blk 100.00 *160.00*
80 A7 10sh car & black 350.00 *475.00*
*Nos. 69-80 (12)* 564.65 *847.40*
Set, never hinged 1,250.

Centenary of the formation of the Cayman Islands Assembly.

Common Design Types pictured following the introduction.

**Silver Jubilee Issue**
Common Design Type
**1935, May 6 Perf. 13½x14**
81 CD301 ½p green & black .35 *1.50*
82 CD301 2½p blue & brown 6.50 *1.50*
83 CD301 6p ol grn & lt bl 1.75 *10.00*
84 CD301 1sh brt vio & ind 13.00 11.50
*Nos. 81-84 (4)* 21.60 *24.50*
Set, never hinged 26.00

King George V — A8

Catboat — A9

Red-footed Boobies — A10

Conches and Coconut Palms — A11

Hawksbill Turtles — A12

**1935-36 Perf. 12½**
85 A8 ¼p brown & blk .60 *1.25*
86 A9 ½p yel grn & ultra 1.25 *1.25*
87 A10 1p car & blue 5.00 3.00
88 A11 1½p org & black 1.75 *2.25*
89 A9 2p brown vio & ultra 4.50 1.40
90 A12 2½p blue & blk 4.00 1.50
91 A8 3p ol grn & blk 3.00 *3.75*
92 A12 6p red vio & blk 8.50 5.25
93 A9 1sh org & ultra 7.00 *8.00*
94 A10 2sh black & ultra 55.00 45.00
95 A12 5sh green & blk 65.00 65.00
96 A11 10sh car & black 100.00 *110.00*
*Nos. 85-96 (12)* 255.60 247.65
Set, never hinged 500.00

Issued: No. 86, 2½p, 6p, 1sh, 1/1/36; others, 5/1/35.

**Coronation Issue**
Common Design Type
**1937, May 13 Perf. 11x11½**
97 CD302 ½p deep green .25 *1.90*
98 CD302 1p dark carmine .30 .25
99 CD302 2½p deep ultra .55 .55
*Nos. 97-99 (3)* 1.10 2.70
Set, never hinged 2.25

Beach View, Grand Cayman — A13

Dolphin — A14

Map of the Islands A15

Hawksbill Turtles A16

Cayman Schooner — A17

**Perf. 12½; 11½x13 or 13x11½ (A14, #111); 14 (#104, 107)**
**1938-43 Engr.**
100 A13 ¼p red orange .45 *.75*
*a.* Perf. 13½x12½ ('43) .25 *1.00*
101 A14 ½p yel green .75 .75
*a.* Perf. 14 ('43) 1.50 *1.75*
102 A15 1p carmine .25 *1.00*
103 A13 1½p black .25 .25
104 A16 2p dp violet ('43) .40 .35
*a.* Perf. 11½x13 2.00 .40
105 A17 2½p ultra .25 .25
106 A15 3p orange .25 .25
107 A16 6p dk ol grn ('43) 2.10 1.75
*a.* Perf. 11½x13 9.00 5.25
108 A14 1sh reddish brown 4.00 2.00
*a.* Perf. 14 ('43) 4.25 2.50
109 A13 2sh green 17.50 12.00
110 A17 5sh deep rose 24.50 17.00
111 A16 10sh dark brown 20.00 11.00
*a.* Perf. 14 ('43) 20.00 11.00
*Nos. 100-111 (12)* 70.70 47.35
Set, never hinged 125.00

See Nos. 114-115.

**Catalogue values for unused stamps in this section, from this point to the end of the section, are for Never Hinged items.**

**Peace Issue**
Common Design Type
**1946, Aug. 26 Wmk. 4 Perf. 13½**
112 CD303 1½p black .40 .40
113 CD303 3p orange .40 .40

**Types of 1938**
**1947, Aug. 25 Perf. 12½**
114 A17 2½p orange 3.50 .65
115 A15 3p ultramarine 3.50 .45

**Silver Wedding Issue**
Common Design Types
**1948, Nov. 29 Photo. Perf. 14x14½**
116 CD304 ½p dark green .25 *1.00*
**Perf. 11½x11**
**Engr.; Name Typo.**
117 CD305 10sh blue violet 25.00 *32.50*

**UPU Issue**
Common Design Types
**Engr.; Name Typo. on #119, 120**
**1949, Oct. 10 *Perf. 13½, 11x11½***
**118** CD306 2½p orange .35 1.25
**119** CD307 3p indigo 1.75 2.75
**120** CD308 6p olive .75 2.75
**121** CD309 1sh red brown .75 .50
*Nos. 118-121 (4)* 3.60 7.25

Catboat — A18

Designs: ½p, Coconut grove. 1p, Green turtle. 1½p, Thatch rope industry. 2p, Caymanian seamen. 2½p, Map. 3p, Parrot fish. 6p, Bluff, Cayman Brac. 9p, George Town harbor. 1sh, Turtle "crawl". 2sh, Cayman schooner. 5sh, Boat-building. 10sh, Government offices.

***Perf. 11½x11***
**1950, Oct. 2 Wmk. 4 Engr.**
**122** A18 ¼p rose red & blue .25 .70
**123** A18 ½p bl grn & red vio .25 1.50
**124** A18 1p dp blue & olive .65 .90
**125** A18 1½p choc & bl grn .40 .90
**126** A18 2p rose car & vio 1.60 1.75
**127** A18 2½p sepia & aqua 1.90 .75
**128** A18 3p bl & blue grn 2.90 1.75
**129** A18 6p dp bl & org brn 2.25 1.50
**130** A18 9p dk grn & rose red 11.00 2.25
**131** A18 1sh red org & brn 4.00 3.25
**132** A18 2sh red vio & vio 11.50 13.00
**133** A18 5sh vio & olive 20.00 8.50
**134** A18 10sh rose red & blk 24.50 22.50
*Nos. 122-134 (13)* 81.20 59.25

**Types of 1950 with Portrait of Queen Elizabeth II and**

Lighthouse, South Sound A20

Elizabeth II and Turtles A21

***Perf. 11½x11, 11x11½***
**1953-59 Engr.**
**135** A18 ¼p rose red & bl 1.40 .70
**136** A18 ½p bl grn & red vio 1.10 .65
**137** A18 1p dp bl & olive 1.00 .60
**138** A18 1½p choc & bl grn .75 .30
**139** A18 2p rose car & vio 3.50 1.25
**140** A18 2½p black & aqua 4.25 1.10
**141** A18 3p blue & bl grn 5.25 .90
**142** A20 4p dp blue & blk 2.50 .60
**143** A18 6p dp bl & red brn 2.10 .30
**144** A18 9p dk grn & rose red 8.50 .40
**145** A18 1sh red org & brn 4.75 .40
**146** A18 2sh red vio & vio 16.00 10.50
**147** A18 5sh violet & olive 17.50 10.00
**148** A18 10sh rose red & blk 19.00 10.50
**149** A21 £1 bright blue 37.50 15.00
*Nos. 135-149 (15)* 125.10 53.20

Issued: 4p, 3/2; 2p, 2½p, 9p, 6/2/54; ½p, 1p, 1½p, 6p, 7/7/54; ¼p, 3p, 1sh-10sh, 2/21/55; £1, 1/6/59.

**Coronation Issue**
Common Design Type
**1953, June 2 *Perf. 13½x13***
**150** CD312 1p brt green & black .40 1.75

Arms of Cayman Islands — A22

***Perf. 12***
**1959, July 4 Wmk. 4 Photo.**
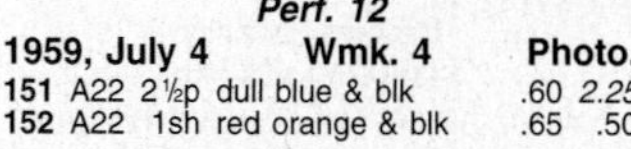
**151** A22 2½p dull blue & blk .60 2.25
**152** A22 1sh red orange & blk .65 .50

Granting of a new constitution.

Cayman Parrot A23

Catboat A24

1½p, Orchid. 2p, Map of Islands. 2½p, Fisherman casting net. 3p, West Bay Beach. 4p, Green turtle. 6p, Cayman schooner. 9p, Angler with kingfish. 1sh, Iguana. 1sh3p, Swimming pool, Cayman Brac. 1sh9p, Girl and sailboat. 5sh, Fort George. 10sh, Coat of Arms. £1, Queen Elizabeth II.

***Perf. 11x11½, 11½x11***
**1962, Nov. 28 Wmk. 314 Engr.**
**153** A23 ¼p rose red & emer 1.10 1.60
**154** A24 1p olive & black .95 .40
**155** A24 1½p purple & yel 3.75 1.00
**156** A24 2p sepia & blue 1.20 .50
**157** A24 2½p green & vio .95 1.25
**158** A24 3p car & blue .45 .40
**159** A24 4p pur & green 1.50 .75
**160** A24 6p sepia & green 3.50 .45
**161** A23 9p pur & vio bl 3.00 .65
**162** A24 1sh rose & sepia .95 .25
**163** A24 1sh3p brn org & lt grn 4.00 3.50
**164** A24 1sh9p vio & bl grn 16.50 1.75
**165** A24 5sh grn & dl pur 13.00 14.00
**166** A23 10sh blue & olive 20.00 14.00
**167** A23 £1 blk & car rose 20.00 27.50
Revenue cancel .80
*Nos. 153-167 (15)* 90.85 68.00

**Freedom from Hunger Issue**
Common Design Type
**1963, June 4 Photo. *Perf. 14x14½***
**168** CD314 1sh9p car rose .55 .30

**Red Cross Centenary Issue**
Common Design Type
**Wmk. 314**
**1963, Sept. 2 Litho. *Perf. 13***
**169** CD315 1p black & red .30 1.25
**170** CD315 1sh9p ultra & red .80 1.75

**Shakespeare Issue**
Common Design Type
**1964, Apr. 23 Photo. *Perf. 14x14½***
**171** CD316 6p deep lilac rose .35 .30

**ITU Issue**
Common Design Type
**1965, May 17 Litho. Wmk. 314**
**172** CD317 1p ultra & red lil .25 .25
**173** CD317 1sh3p rose lil & grn .75 .60

**Intl. Cooperation Year Issue**
Common Design Type
**1965, Oct. 25 Wmk. 314 *Perf. 14½***
**174** CD318 1p blue grn & claret .30 .25
**175** CD318 1sh lt vio & green .70 .50

**Churchill Memorial Issue**
Common Design Type
**1966, Jan. 24 Photo. *Perf. 14***
**Design in Black, Gold and Carmine Rose**
**176** CD319 ¼p bright blue .25 2.00
**177** CD319 1p green .45 .40
**178** CD319 1sh brown .80 .40
**179** CD319 1sh9p violet 1.60 .85
*Nos. 176-179 (4)* 3.10 3.65

**Royal Visit Issue**
Common Design Type
**1966, Feb. 4 Litho. *Perf. 11x12***
**180** CD320 1p violet blue .70 .30
**181** CD320 1sh9p dk car rose 2.75 1.50

**World Cup Soccer Issue**
Common Design Type
**1966, July 1 Litho. *Perf. 14***
**182** CD321 1½p multicolored .25 .25
**183** CD321 1sh9p multicolored .50 .40

**WHO Headquarters Issue**
Common Design Type
**1966, Sept. 20 Litho. *Perf. 14***
**184** CD322 2p multicolored .65 .30
**185** CD322 1sh3p multicolored 1.60 .90

**UNESCO Anniversary Issue**
Common Design Type
**1966, Dec. 1 Litho. *Perf. 14***
**186** CD323 1p "Education" .25 .25
**187** CD323 1sh9p "Science" .75 .35
**188** CD323 5sh "Culture" 1.50 .90
*Nos. 186-188 (3)* 2.50 1.50

Telephone and Map of Caymans A25

***Perf. 14½x14***
**1966, Dec. 5 Litho. Wmk. 314**
**189** A25 4p multicolored .25 .25
**190** A25 9p multicolored .30 .30

Linking of the Cayman telephone system with the intl. system.

BAC 1-11 Jet Liner over Schooner A26

**1966, Dec. 17**
**191** A26 1sh blue, ol & black .40 .35
**192** A26 1sh9p ultra, grn & sepia .70 .50

Opening of the Grand Cayman Airport jet service.

Water Skiing and ITY Emblem — A27

ITY Emblem and: 6p, Skin diving. 1sh, Sport fishing. 1sh9p, Sailing.

***Perf. 14½x14***
**1967, Dec. 1 Photo. Wmk. 314**
**193** A27 4p multi & gold .35 .25
*a.* Gold omitted 375.00 325.00
**194** A27 6p multi & gold .35 .25
**195** A27 1sh multi & gold .35 .35
**196** A27 1sh9p multi & gold .50 .75
*Nos. 193-196 (4)* 1.55 1.60

International Tourist Year.

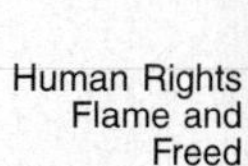

Human Rights Flame and Freed Slaves — A28

**1968, June 3 Photo. Wmk. 314**
**197** A28 3p slate bl, grn & gold .25 .25
**198** A28 9p lt brn, grn & gold .25 .25
**199** A28 5sh ultra, grn & gold .50 .80
*Nos. 197-199 (3)* 1.00 1.30

International Human Rights Year.

Long Jump — A29

1sh3p, High jump. 2sh, Pole vault, vert.

**1968, Oct. 1 Litho. *Perf. 13½***
**200** A29 1sh multicolored .25 .25
**201** A29 1sh3p multicolored .25 .25
**202** A29 2sh yellow & multi .30 .75
*Nos. 200-202 (3)* .80 1.25

19th Olympic Games, Mexico City, 10/12-27.

Adoration of Shepherds, by Carel Fabritius — A30

Christmas: 1p, 8p, 2sh, Adoration of the Shepherds, by Rembrandt.

***Perf. 14x14½***
**1968, Nov. 18 Photo. Wmk. 314**
**203** A30 ¼p brown & multi .25 .25
*a.* Gold omitted 275.00
**204** A30 1p violet & multi .25 .25
**205** A30 6p multicolored .25 .25
**206** A30 8p car & multi .25 .25
**207** A30 1sh3p multicolored .25 .30
**208** A30 2sh gray & multi .25 .30
*Nos. 203-208 (6)* 1.50 1.60

**1969, Jan. 8 Unwmk.**
**209** A30 ¼p red lilac & multi .75 .30

Grand Cayman Thrush — A31

1p, Brahman cattle. 2p, Blowholes on coast. 2½p, Map of Grand Cayman. 3p, Town scene in George Town. 4p, Royal poinciana. 6p, Map of Cayman Brac and Little Cayman. 8p, Motor vessels at berth. 1sh, Basket making. 1sh3p, Beach scene. 1sh6p, Rope making. 2sh, Barracudas. 4sh, Government House. 10sh, Coat of arms. £1, Queen Elizabeth II.

**Unwmk.**
**1969, June 5 Litho. *Perf. 14***
**210** A31 ¼p multi .25 .85
**211** A31 1p multi .25 .25
**212** A31 2p multi .25 .25
**213** A31 2½p multi .25 .25
**214** A31 3p multi .25 .25
**215** A31 4p multi .25 .25
**216** A31 6p multi .25 .25
**217** A31 8p multi .25 .25
**218** A31 1sh multi .25 .25
**219** A31 1sh3p multi .30 1.60
**220** A31 1sh6p multi .35 1.60
**221** A31 2sh multi 1.25 1.25
**222** A31 4sh multi .60 1.25
**223** A31 10sh multi, vert. 1.25 2.10
**224** A31 £1 multi, vert. 3.00 3.00
*Nos. 210-224 (15)* 9.00 13.65

See Nos. 262-276. For surcharges see Nos. 227-241.

**1969, Aug. 11 Wmk. 314 Sideways**
**225** A31 ¼p multicolored .70 .70

**Type of 1969 Surcharged**

**1969, Sept. 8 Wmk. 314 *Perf. 14***
**227** A31 ¼c on ¼p multi .25 .85
**228** A31 1c on 1p multi .25 .25
**229** A31 2c on 2p multi .25 .25
**230** A31 3c on 4p multi .25 .25
**231** A31 4c on 2½p multi .25 .25
**232** A31 5c on 6p multi .25 .25
**233** A31 7c on 8p multi .25 .25
**234** A31 8c on 3p multi .25 .25
**235** A31 10c on 1s multi .35 .25
**236** A31 12c on 1sh3p multi .45 1.90
**237** A31 15c on 1sh6p multi .55 1.50
**238** A31 20c on 2sh multi 2.00 1.90
**239** A31 40c on 4sh multi .55 1.10
**240** A31 $1 on 10sh multi 1.45 3.25
**241** A31 $2 on £1 multi 2.25 4.00
*Nos. 227-241 (15)* 9.60 16.50

The surcharge is arranged differently on various denominations.

Madonna and Child, by Alvise Vivarini — A32

Christmas: 1c, 7c, 20c, The Adoration of the Kings, by Jan Gossaert.

**1969, Nov. 4 Photo. *Perf. 14***
**242** A32 ¼c blue & multi .25 .25
**243** A32 ¼c emer & multi .25 .25
**244** A32 ¼c red org & multi .25 .25
**245** A32 ¼c brt pink & multi .25 .25
**246** A32 1c vio blue & multi .25 .25
**247** A32 5c red org & multi .25 .25
**248** A32 7c dk green & multi .25 .25

**249** A32 12c emer & multi .25 .25
**250** A32 20c multicolored .25 .25
*Nos. 242-250 (9)* 2.25 2.25

"Noli me Tangere," by Titian — A33

**1970, Mar. 23 Litho. Unwmk.**

**251** A33 ¼c dull grn & multi .25 .25
**252** A33 ¼c dk car & multi .25 .25
**253** A33 ¼c violet & multi .25 .25
**254** A33 ¼c bister & multi .25 .25
**255** A33 10c vio blue & multi .25 .25
**256** A33 12c red brn & multi .25 .25
**257** A33 40c brn vio & multi .50 *.60*
*Nos. 251-257 (7)* 2.00 2.10

Easter.

Barnaby from "Barnaby Rudge" by Dickens (1812-70), English Novelist — A34

Characters from Charles Dickens: 12c, Sairey Gamp, from "Martin Chuzzlewit." 20c, Mr. Micawber and David, from "David Copperfield." 40c, The Marchioness from "The Old Curiosity Shop."

**1970, June 17 Photo. *Perf. 14½x14***

**258** A34 1c ol green, yel & blk .25 .25
**259** A34 12c red brn, brick red & black .25 .25
**260** A34 20c dk ol bis, gold & black .35 .35
**261** A34 40c dp ultra, lt bl & blk .50 .40
*Nos. 258-261 (4)* 1.35 1.25

### Type of Regular Issue 1969 Values in Cents and Dollars

Designs: ¼c, Grand Cayman thrush. 1c, Brahman cattle. 2c, Blowholes on coast. 3c, Royal poinciana. 4c, Map of Grand Cayman. 5c, Map of Cayman Brac and Little Cayman. 7c, Motor vessels at berth. 8c, Town scene in George Town. 10c, Basket making. 12c, Beach scene. 15c, Rope making. 20c, Barracudas. 40c, Government House. $1, Coat of arms, vert. $2, Queen Elizabeth II, vert.

**Wmk. 314**

**1970, Sept. 8 Litho. *Perf. 14***

**262** A31 ¼c multicolored .60 .30
**263** A31 1c multicolored .25 .25
**264** A31 2c multicolored .25 .25
**265** A31 3c multicolored .25 .25
**266** A31 4c multicolored .25 .25
**267** A31 5c multicolored .45 .25
**268** A31 7c multicolored .40 .25
**269** A31 8c multicolored .40 .25
**270** A31 10c multicolored .40 .25
**271** A31 12c multicolored 1.00 *1.10*
**272** A31 15c multicolored 1.25 *4.00*
**273** A31 20c multicolored 3.25 1.75
**274** A31 40c multicolored .85 .85
**275** A31 $1 multicolored 1.25 *5.75*
**276** A31 $2 multicolored 2.00 *5.75*
*Nos. 262-276 (15)* 12.85 21.50

The Three Wise Men — A35

Christmas: 1c, 10c, 20c, Nativity and globe.

**1970, Oct. 8 Litho. *Perf. 14***

**277** A35 ¼c brt grn & yel grn .25 .25
**278** A35 1c bl grn, yel grn & blk .25 .25
**279** A35 5c dp claret & org .25 .25
**280** A35 10c red org, yel & blk .25 .25
**281** A35 12c ultra & lt grnsh bl .25 .25
**282** A35 20c grn, yel grn & blk .25 .25
*Nos. 277-282 (6)* 1.50 1.50

Grand Cayman Terrapin — A36

Cayman Islands Turtles: 7c, Green turtle. 12c, Hawksbill turtle. 20c, Turtle farm.

**1971, Jan. 28 *Perf. 14x14½***

**283** A36 5c multicolored .70 .40
**284** A36 7c multicolored .85 .40
**285** A36 12c multicolored 1.75 .50
**286** A36 20c multicolored 3.00 2.00
*Nos. 283-286 (4)* 6.30 3.30

Dendrophylax Fawcetii — A37

Wild Orchids of West Indies: 2c, Schomburgkia thomsoniana. 10c, Vanilla claviculata. 40c, Oncidium variegatum.

**1971, Apr. 7 Wmk. 314 *Perf. 14***

**287** A37 ¼c brown & multi .35 *1.40*
**288** A37 2c ol green & multi 1.00 *1.10*
**289** A37 10c gray bl & multi 3.25 .65
**290** A37 40c lt violet & multi 4.75 4.00
*Nos. 287-290 (4)* 9.35 7.15

Adoration of the Kings, 15th Century — A38

Christmas: 1c, 15c, Nativity (detail), Paris, 14th cent. 5c, 20c, Adoration of the Kings (detail), Burgundian, 15th cent.

**1971, Sept. 27 *Perf. 14***

**291** A38 ¼c gold & multi .25 .25
**292** A38 1c gold & multi .25 .25
**293** A38 5c gold & multi .25 .25
**294** A38 12c gold & multi .25 .25
**295** A38 15c gold & multi .25 .25
**296** A38 20c gold & multi .35 .35
*a.* Souvenir sheet of 6, #291-296 4.25 4.25
*Nos. 291-296 (6)* 1.60 1.60

Underwater Cable, Turtle and Telephone A39

**1972, Jan. 10**

**297** A39 2c multicolored .25 .25
**298** A39 10c multicolored .25 .25
**299** A39 40c multicolored .75 .75
*Nos. 297-299 (3)* 1.25 1.25

Coaxial cable for world communications.

Courthouse A40

Designs: 15c, 40c, Legislative Assembly Building, George Town.

**1972, Aug. 15 *Perf. 13½x14***

**300** A40 5c dp car & multi .25 .25
**301** A40 15c lilac rose & multi .25 .25
**302** A40 25c dull grn & multi .25 .25
**303** A40 40c dk blue & multi .25 *.40*
*a.* Souvenir sheet of 4, #300-303 .90 *2.00*
*Nos. 300-303 (4)* 1.00 1.15

New Cayman Islands government buildings.

### Silver Wedding Issue, 1972
Common Design Type

Design: Queen Elizabeth II, Prince Philip, hawksbill turtle and conch.

**1972, Nov. 20 Photo. *Perf. 14x14½***

**304** CD324 12c vio black & multi .25 .25
**305** CD324 30c olive & multi .50 .50

$1 Note and 1c Coin — A41

6c, $5 note and 5c coin. 15c, $10 note and 10c coin. 25c, $25 note and 25c coin.

**1973, Jan. 15**

**306** A41 3c emerald & multi .25 .25
**307** A41 6c yellow & multi .30 .60
**308** A41 15c lilac & multi .65 .50
**309** A41 25c orange & multi 1.25 .90
*a.* Souvenir sheet of 4, #306-309 4.00 4.00
*Nos. 306-309 (4)* 2.45 2.25

First Cayman Islands coinage and bank notes, May 1, 1972.

Last Supper — A42

Stained Glass Windows: 10c, Christ Carrying Cross, vert. 12c, Resurrection, vert. 30c, Crucifixion.

***Perf. 14½x14, 14x14½***

**1973, Apr. 11 Litho.**

**310** A42 10c pink & multi .25 .25
**311** A42 12c yel green & multi .25 .25
**312** A42 20c lt blue & multi .30 .30
**313** A42 30c yellow & multi .40 .40
*a.* Souvenir sheet of 4 1.25 *1.60*
*Nos. 310-313 (4)* 1.20 1.20

Easter. No. 313a contains 4 stamps similar to Nos. 310-313 with simulated perforations.

Nativity — A43

Christmas: 5c, 12c, 25c, Adoration of the Magi, from Breviary of Queen Isabella. 9c, 15c, Like 3c, Nativity from Sforza Book of Hours.

**1973, Oct. 2 *Perf. 14½***

**314** A43 3c dull green & multi .25 .25
**315** A43 5c dull pur & multi .25 .25
**316** A43 9c sepia & multi .25 .25
**317** A43 12c dk blue & multi .25 .25
**318** A43 15c dp rose & multi .25 .25
**319** A43 25c black & multi .25 .25
*Nos. 314-319 (6)* 1.50 1.50

### Princess Anne's Wedding Issue
Common Design Type

**1973, Nov. 14 Wmk. 314 *Perf. 14***

**320** CD325 10c brt green & multi .25 .25
**321** CD325 30c lilac & multi .25 .25

White-winged Dove — A44

10c, Vitelline warblers. 12c, Greater Antillean grackles. 20c, West Indian red-bellied woodpecker. 30c, Stripe-headed tanagers. 50c, Yucatan vireos.

**1974, Jan. 2 Litho. *Perf. 14x14½***

**322** A44 3c shown 2.50 .40
**323** A44 10c multicolored 3.25 .40
**324** A44 12c multicolored 3.25 .40
**325** A44 20c multicolored 5.25 1.00
**326** A44 30c multicolored 6.50 2.00
**327** A44 50c multicolored 8.75 6.00
*Nos. 322-327 (6)* 29.50 10.20

See Nos. 354-359.

One-room Schoolhouse A45

Designs: 20c, New comprehensive school. 30c, Creative Arts Center, Mona, Jamaica.

**1974, May 1 *Perf. 14***

**328** A45 12c multicolored .25 .25
**329** A45 20c multicolored .25 .25
**330** A45 30c multicolored .35 *.60*
*Nos. 328-330 (3)* .85 1.10

25th anniv. of the University College of the West Indies.

Hermit Crab and Pirate Gold (#346) — A46

Coat of Arms (#344) — A47

Elizabeth II (#348) — A48

Designs: 3c, Pirate, treasure chest and lion's paw. 4c, Spotted scorpionfish and crown. 5c, Flint-lock pistol and brain coral. 6c, Blackbeard on Grand Cayman and green turtle. 8c, 9c, Jeweled pomander and porkfish. 10c, Spiny lobster and gold coins. 12c, Jeweled sword, dagger and sea fan. 15c, Cabrit's murex and jeweled necklace. 20c, Queen conch, pistol and gold cup. 25c, Hogfish and pirate chest. 40c, Gold chalice and sea whip.

### Wmk. 314 Upright, Sideways (#331-332, 336, 344-345)

**1974-75 Litho. *Perf. 14***

**Size: 41x26.5mm**

**331** A46 1c multi ('75) 4.25 1.75
*a.* Wmk. upright 3.75 1.25
**332** A46 3c multicolored 4.25 1.75
*a.* Wmk. upright 3.75 .70
**333** A46 4c multicolored .70 *.95*
**334** A46 5c multicolored 3.50 1.00
**335** A46 6c multicolored .50 *2.75*
**336** A46 8c multicolored 3.00 *9.50*
**337** A46 9c multicolored 5.00 *12.50*
**338** A46 10c multicolored 5.50 1.10
**339** A46 12c multicolored .50 *2.25*
**340** A46 15c multicolored .55 *1.75*
**341** A46 20c multicolored 5.00 4.00
**342** A46 25c multicolored .60 *.85*
**343** A46 40c multicolored 5.00 1.50
**344** A47 $1 multicolored 3.25 *3.50*
**345** A48 $2 multicolored 9.50 *10.00*
*Nos. 331-345 (15)* 51.10 *55.15*

Issued: No. 332, 11/12; 8c, 12/16; No. 331, 9/29; others, 8/1.

**1976-77 Wmk. 373**

*332b* A46 3c multicolored 1.00 *4.50*
*333a* A46 4c multi ('77) 1.50 *5.00*
*334a* A46 5c multi ('77) 7.50 7.50
*336b* A46 8c multicolored 8.50 6.25
*338b* A46 10c multicolored 3.75 *5.00*
*341b* A46 20c multicolored 4.25 3.50
*344a* A47 $1 multi ('77) 7.50 *11.00*
*345b* A48 $2 multicolored 8.50 9.25
*Nos. 332b-345b (8)* 42.50 *52.00*

Issued: 3c, 8c, 10c, 20c, $2, 9/3; 4c, 5c, $1, 10/19.

### Design Smaller
Size: 39.5x25mm

### Wmk. 373 (Sideways on 1c-40c)

**1978-80**

**346** A46 1c multicolored 1.25 *1.75*
**346A** A46 3c multicolored 1.00 .75
**346B** A46 5c multi ('79) 2.75 *3.00*
**347** A46 10c multicolored 2.00 1.00
**347A** A46 20c multicolored 4.00 1.75
**347B** A46 40c multi ('79) 15.00 22.50

**347C** A47 $1 multi ('80) 22.50 7.00
**348** A48 $2 multi ('80) 6.50 *25.00*
*Nos. 346-348 (8)* 55.00 *62.75*

Issued: 1c, 3c, 3/16; 10c, 20c, 5/25; 5c, 12/11; $2, 4/3; $1, 7/30.

Sea Captain and Ship — A49

**1974, Oct. 7 Wmk. 314 *Perf. 14***

**349** A49 8c shown .25 .25
**350** A49 12c Thatch weaver .25 .25
**351** A49 20c Farmer .50 .50
*a.* Miniature sheet of 3, #349-351 1.75 *3.00*
*Nos. 349-351 (3)* 1.00 1.00

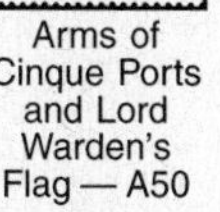

Arms of Cinque Ports and Lord Warden's Flag — A50

Churchill Coat of Arms — A51

**1974, Nov. 30**

**352** A50 12c multicolored .25 .25
**353** A51 50c multicolored .45 .70
*a.* Souvenir sheet of 2, #352-353 .95 *1.50*

Sir Winston Churchill (1874-1965).

### Bird Type of 1974

3c, Yellow-shafted flicker. 10c, West Indian tree duck. 12c, Yellow warblers. 20c, White-bellied dove. 30c, Magnificent frigate bird. 50c, Cayman amazon.

**Wmk. 314**

**1975, Jan. 1 Litho. *Perf. 14***

**354** A44 3c multicolored .70 .45
**355** A44 10c multicolored 1.25 .45
**356** A44 12c multicolored 1.60 .70
**357** A44 20c multicolored 2.50 2.00
**358** A44 30c multicolored 3.75 *4.25*
**359** A44 50c multicolored 4.50 *12.00*
*a.* Wmk. 362 (Lesotho) *1,000.*
*Nos. 354-359 (6)* 14.30 *19.85*

Ivory Crosier with Crucifixion — A52

Design: 35c, Crucifixion, ivory and gilt. Designs show heads of 14th century French pastoral staffs.

**Wmk. 314**

**1975, Mar. 24 Litho. *Perf. 14***

**360** A52 15c plum & multi .25 .25
**361** A52 35c gray & multi .40 *.55*
*a.* Souvenir sheet of 2, #360-361 1.10 *2.50*

Easter. No. 361a exists imperf.
See Nos. 366-367.

Israel Hands — A53

Designs: Pirates and various scenes.

**1975, July 25 Wmk. 314**

**362** A53 10c shown .50 .25
**363** A53 12c John Fenn .50 .25
**364** A53 20c Thomas Anstis .85 .50
**365** A53 30c Edward Low 1.10 *1.50*
*Nos. 362-365 (4)* 2.95 2.50

### Easter Type of 1975

Designs after ivory carved pastoral staffs showing Virgin and Child with angels, French, 14th century.

**Wmk. 373**

**1975, Oct. 31 Litho. *Perf. 14***

**366** A52 12c dk green & multi .25 .25
**367** A52 50c multicolored .70 .70
*a.* Souvenir sheet of 2, #366-367 1.50 *2.75*

Christmas.

A54

Cayman Islands 1st postage stamps, 75th anniv.: 10, Registered Letter with Nos. 1-2; Cayman Brac Government House and Sub Post Office. 20c, Cayman Islands #1 and cancelation used 1890-94; 30c, #2, 20; 50c, #1-2.

**1976, Mar. 12 Litho. *Perf. 13½x14***

**368** A54 10c lt blue & multi .25 .25
**369** A54 20c pink & multi .25 .25
**370** A54 30c multicolored .35 .35
**371** A54 50c yellow & multi .55 *.65*
*a.* Souvenir sheet of 4, #368-371 3.50 3.50
*Nos. 368-371 (4)* 1.40 1.50

Seals of Georgia, Delaware and New Hampshire — A55

15c, Seals of SC, NJ, MD. 20c, Seals of VA, RI, MA. 25c, Seals of NY, CT, NC. 30c, Seal of PA, Liberty Bell and Great Seal of the US.

**Wmk. 373**

**1976, May 29 Litho. *Perf. 14***

**372** A55 10c olive & multi .35 .25
**373** A55 15c blue & multi .45 .25
**374** A55 20c multicolored .60 .30
**375** A55 25c blue grn & multi .90 .60
**376** A55 30c red brn & multi 1.10 .85
*a.* Souvenir sheet of 5 + label 5.25 *8.00*
*Nos. 372-376 (5)* 3.40 2.25

American Bicentennial. Nos. 372-376 printed in sheets of 5. No. 376a contains one each of Nos. 372-376 and corner label inscribed "USA 200."

French Class 470 Racing Dinghies — A56

Design: 50c, One racing dinghy.

**1976, Aug. 16 Litho. *Perf. 14***

**377** A56 20c multicolored .60 .45
**378** A56 50c multicolored 1.10 1.10

21st Olympic Games, Montreal, Canada, July 17-Aug. 1.

Queen Elizabeth II — A57

8c, Prince Charles, 1973 visit. 50c, Preparation for anointing ceremony, horiz.

***Perf. 14x13½, 13½x14***

**1977, Feb. 7 Litho. Wmk. 373**

**379** A57 8c multicolored .25 .25
**380** A57 30c multicolored .25 .25
**381** A57 50c multicolored .25 .25
*Nos. 379-381 (3)* .75 .75

25th anniv. of the reign of Elizabeth II.

Scuba Diving — A58

10c, Divers examining underwater wreck. 20c, Fairy basslets (fish). 25c, Sergeant majors (fish).

**1977, July 25 *Perf. 13½***

**382** A58 5c multicolored .25 .25
**383** A58 10c multicolored .25 .25
**384** A58 20c multicolored .45 .45
**385** A58 25c multicolored .60 .60
*a.* Souvenir sheet of 4 3.00 *4.00*
*Nos. 382-385 (4)* 1.55 1.55

Tourist publicity. No. 385a contains one each of Nos. 382-385, perf. 14½.

Composia Fidelissima A59

Butterflies: 8c, Heliconius charitonius. 10c, Danaus gilippus. 15c, Agraulis vanillae. 20c, Junonia evarete. 30c, Anartia jatrophae.

**1977, Dec. 2 Wmk. 373 *Perf. 14x13***

**386** A59 5c multicolored 1.10 .25
**387** A59 8c multicolored 1.25 .30
**388** A59 10c multicolored 1.35 .35
**389** A59 15c multicolored 1.60 .55
**390** A59 20c multicolored 1.75 .60
**391** A59 30c multicolored 2.00 1.10
*Nos. 386-391 (6)* 9.05 3.15

Cruise Ship "Southward" — A60

Designs: 5c, "Renaissance." 30c, New harbor, vert. 50c, "Daphne," vert.

**1978, Jan. 23 Litho. *Perf. 14***

**392** A60 3c multicolored .45 .25
**393** A60 5c multicolored .45 .25
**394** A60 30c multicolored 1.25 .40
**395** A60 50c multicolored 1.50 .75
*Nos. 392-395 (4)* 3.65 1.65

New harbor and cruise ships.

Crucifixion, by Dürer — A61

Etchings by Dürer: 15c, Christ at Emmaus. 20c, Entry into Jerusalem. 30c, Christ washing Peter's feet.

**1978, Mar. 20 Litho. *Perf. 12***

**396** A61 10c multicolored .30 .25
**397** A61 15c multicolored .45 .30
**398** A61 20c multicolored .55 .40
**399** A61 30c multicolored .65 .55
*a.* Souvenir sheet of 4, #396-399 6.50 6.50
*Nos. 396-399 (4)* 1.95 1.50

Easter; Albrecht Dürer (1471-1528). Nos. 396-399 issued in sheets of 6.

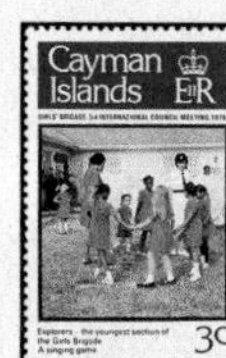

Explorers, Singing Game — A62

10c, Girls' Brigade presenting flag. 20c, Guides studying Bible, playing guitar, tennis and volleyball. 50c, Guides setting table.

**1978, Apr. 25 Litho. *Perf. 14***

**400** A62 3c multicolored .25 .25
**401** A62 10c multicolored .35 .35
**402** A62 20c multicolored .60 .60
**403** A62 50c multicolored 1.25 1.25
*Nos. 400-403 (4)* 2.45 2.45

3rd Intl. Council Meeting of Girls' Brigade.

### Elizabeth II Coronation Anniversary Issue

Common Design Types
Souvenir Sheet

**1978, June 2 Unwmk. *Perf. 15***

**404** Sheet of 6 2.00 2.00
*a.* CD326 30c Yale of Beaufort .30 .30
*b.* CD327 30c Elizabeth II .30 .30
*c.* CD328 30c Screech owl .30 .30

No. 404 contains 2 se-tenant strips of Nos. 404a-404c, separated by horizontal gutter with commemorative and descriptive inscriptions.

A63

A63a

A63: 1c, Trumpetfish. 3c, Nassau grouper. 5c, French angelfish. 10c, Schoolmaster snappers. 20c, Banded butterflyfish. 50c, Black-bar soldierfish.

A63a: 3c, Four-eyed butterflyfish. 5c, Grey angel fish. 10c, Squirrelfish. 15c, Parrotfish. 20c, Spanish hogfish. 30c, Queen angelfish.

**1978-79 Wmk. 373 Litho. *Perf. 14***

**405** A63 1c multicolored .25 .25
**406** A63 3c multicolored .35 .25
**407** A63a 3c multicolored .30 .25
**408** A63a 5c multicolored .35 .25
**409** A63 5c multicolored .30 .25
**412** A63a 10c multicolored .55 .25
**413** A63 10c multicolored .55 .25
**414** A63a 15c multicolored .60 .35
**415** A63a 20c multicolored .75 .45
**416** A63 20c multicolored .95 .45
**417** A63a 30c multicolored 1.50 .70
**418** A63 50c multicolored 2.25 1.10
*Nos. 405-418 (12)* 8.70 4.80

Issued: design A63, 4/20/79; design A63a, 8/28/78.

Lockheed Lodestar — A64

Aircraft: 5c, Consolidated PBY. 10c, Vickers Viking. 15c, BAC1-11. 20c, Piper Cheyenne, HS 125 and Bell 47. 30c, BAC1-11.

**1979, Feb. 5 *Perf. 14½***

**420** A64 3c multicolored .40 .25
**421** A64 5c multicolored .40 .25
**422** A64 10c multicolored .45 .25
**423** A64 15c multicolored .75 .40
**424** A64 20c multicolored .95 .45
**425** A64 30c multicolored 1.10 .55
*Nos. 420-425 (6)* 4.05 2.15

Opening of Owen Roberts Airport, 25th anniv.

Rowland Hill and No. 2 — A65

Sir Rowland Hill (1795-1879), originator of penny postage, and: 10c, Great Britain #132. 20c, Cayman Islands #149. 50c,Cayman Islands #20.

***Perf. 13½x14½***

**1979, Aug. 15 Litho.**

**426** A65 5c multicolored .25 .25
**427** A65 10c multicolored .25 .25
**428** A65 20c multicolored .50 .50
*Nos. 426-428 (3)* 1.00 1.00

**Souvenir Sheet**

**429** A65 50c multicolored 1.40 1.40

Flight into Egypt — A66

Christmas: 20c, Shepherds, Star of Bethlehem. 30c, Nativity. 40c, Three Kings, Star of Bethlehem.

**1979, Nov. 20 Litho. *Perf. 13½***
**430** A66 10c multicolored .25 .25
**431** A66 20c multicolored .25 .25
**432** A66 30c multicolored .35 .25
**433** A66 40c multicolored .55 .30
*Nos. 430-433 (4)* 1.40 1.05

Bonaventure House, Rotary Emblem A67

30c, Paul P. Harris, vert. 50c, Anniversary emblem, vert.

***Perf. 14x13½, 13½x14***
**1980, Feb. 14 Litho. Wmk. 373**
**434** A67 20c shown .25 .25
**435** A67 30c multicolored .45 .25
**436** A67 50c multicolored .70 .50
*Nos. 434-436 (3)* 1.40 1.00

Rotary International, 75th anniversary.

Mailman, London 1980 Emblem — A68

**1980, May 6 Litho. *Perf. 14***
**437** A68 5c shown .25 .25
**438** A68 10c Cat boat .25 .25
**439** A68 15c Mounted mailman .25 .25
**440** A68 30c Mail wagon .40 .35
**441** A68 40c Mailman on bicycle .50 .45
**442** A68 $1 Mail truck .70 .70
*Nos. 437-442 (6)* 2.35 2.25

London '80 Intl. Stamp Exhib., May 6-14.

**Queen Mother Elizabeth Birthday Issue**
Common Design Type

**1980, Aug. 4 Litho. *Perf. 14***
**443** CD330 20c multicolored .40 .40

Spondylus Americanus — A69

10c, Murex brevifrons. 30c, Cymatium femorale. 50c, Vasum muricatum.

**1980, Aug. 12 *Perf. 14½x14***
**444** A69 5c shown .80 .25
**445** A69 10c multicolored .80 .30
**446** A69 30c multicolored 1.60 .65
**447** A69 50c multicolored 1.75 1.25
*Nos. 444-447 (4)* 4.95 2.45

See Nos. 502-505, 518-521.

Lantana A70

**1980, Oct. 21 Litho. *Perf. 14***
**448** A70 5c shown .25 .25
**449** A70 15c Bauhinia .30 .25
**450** A70 30c Hibiscus .55 .30
**451** A70 $1 Milk and wine lily 1.45 1.40
*Nos. 448-451 (4)* 2.55 2.20

See Nos. 478-481.

Juvenile Tarpon and Fire Sponges — A71

5c, Mangrove root oysters. 10c, Mangrove crab. 15c, Lizard, crescent spot butterfly. 20c, Tricolored heron. 30c, Red mangrove flower. 40c, Red mangrove seeds. 50c, Waterhouse's leaf-nosed bat. $1, Black-crowned night heron. $2, Cayman Islands arms. $4, Queen Elizabeth II.

**1980, Dec. 9 Litho. *Perf. 13½x13***
**Without Imprint**
**452** A71 3c shown 1.10 *2.25*
**453** A71 5c multicolored 1.25 *1.10*
*d.* Wmk. 384 8.00 8.00
*e.* Wmk. 384, perf. 14 6.75 7.00
**454** A71 10c multicolored .65 *1.10*
*d.* Wmk. 384, perf. 14 10.00 9.75
**455** A71 15c multicolored 1.10 *2.25*
**456** A71 20c multicolored 1.50 *2.75*
**457** A71 30c multicolored .90 *1.40*
**458** A71 40c multicolored .95 *1.25*
**459** A71 50c multicolored 1.50 *1.75*
**460** A71 $1 multicolored 6.00 *5.50*
**461** A71 $2 multicolored 2.25 *3.75*
**462** A71 $4 multicolored 4.25 4.25
*Nos. 452-462 (11)* 21.45 *27.35*

Nos. 453d, 453e and 454d inscribed "1986" below design. Issued: No. 453d, 4/86; Nos. 453e, 454fa, 6/86.

**1982, June 14 Inscribed "1982"**
*452a* A71 3c shown 5.00 *4.00*
*453a* A71 5c multicolored 1.25 *.90*
*454a* A71 10c multicolored 1.25 *.90*
*455a* A71 15c multicolored 4.50 *2.00*
*456a* A71 20c multicolored 2.50 *2.25*
*457a* A71 30c multicolored 1.50 *1.50*
*458a* A71 40c multicolored 1.50 *1.50*
*459a* A71 50c multicolored 2.00 *2.00*
*460a* A71 $1 multicolored 6.00 *5.00*
*461a* A71 $2 multicolored 4.00 *4.00*
*462a* A71 $4 multicolored 9.00 *11.00*
*Nos. 452a-462a (11)* 38.50 *35.05*

Issued: No. 453a, 4/86; No. 454a, 6/86.

**1984 Inscribed "1984"**
*453b* A71 5c multicolored 2.50 *2.50*

Issued: No. 453b, 6/86.

**1985 Inscribed "1985"**
*453c* A71 5c multicolored 1.25 *1.25*
*454c* A71 10c multicolored 1.25 *1.25*
*455c* A71 15c multicolored 4.50 *4.50*
*456c* A71 20c multicolored 2.50 *2.50*
*457c* A71 30c multicolored 1.50 *1.50*
*458c* A71 40c multicolored 1.50 *1.50*
*459c* A71 50c multicolored 2.00 *2.00*
*460c* A71 $1 multicolored 6.00 *5.00*
*461c* A71 $2 multicolored 5.00 *5.00*
*Nos. 453c-461c (9)* 25.50 *24.50*

Bread and Wine — A72

**1981, Mar. 17 Wmk. 373 *Perf. 14***
**463** A72 3c shown .25 .25
**464** A72 10c Crown of thorns .25 .25
**465** A72 20c Crucifix .25 .25
**466** A72 $1 Christ .50 *.90*
*Nos. 463-466 (4)* 1.25 1.65

Easter.

Wood Slave — A73

**1981, June 16 Litho. *Perf. 13½***
**467** A73 20c shown .40 .40
**468** A73 30c Cayman iguana .60 .60
**469** A73 40c Lion lizard .80 .80
**470** A73 50c Freshwater turtle .95 .95
*Nos. 467-470 (4)* 2.75 2.75

**Royal Wedding Issue**
Common Design Type

**1981, July 22 Litho. *Perf. 14***
**471** CD331 20c Bouquet .25 .25
**472** CD331 30c Charles .30 .30
**473** CD331 $1 Couple .65 *.75*
*Nos. 471-473 (3)* 1.20 1.30

Intl. Year of the Disabled — A74

5c, Scuba divers. 15c, Old School for Handicapped. 20c, New School for Handicapped. $1, Beach scene.

**1981, Sept. 29 Litho. *Perf. 14***
**474** A74 5c multicolored .25 .25
**475** A74 15c multicolored .25 .25
**476** A74 20c multicolored .35 .35
**477** A74 $1 multicolored 1.40 1.40
*Nos. 474-477 (4)* 2.25 2.25

**Flower Type of 1980**

**1981, Oct. 20 Litho. *Perf. 14***
**478** A70 3c Bougainvillea .25 .25
**479** A70 10c Morning glory .25 .25
**480** A70 20c Wild amaryllis .55 .55
**481** A70 $1 Cordia 2.25 2.25
*Nos. 478-481 (4)* 3.30 3.30

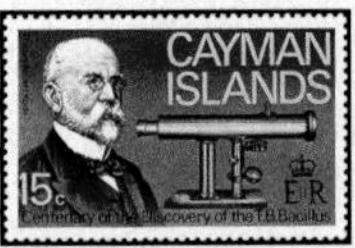


TB Bacillus Centenary A75

15c, Koch, horizontal microscope. 30c, Koch, vert. 40c, Microscope, vert. 50c, Koch, diff., vert.

**1982, Mar. 24 Litho. *Perf. 14½***
**482** A75 15c multicolored .30 .30
**483** A75 30c multicolored .65 .65
**484** A75 40c multicolored .80 .80
**485** A75 50c multicolored 1.10 1.10
*Nos. 482-485 (4)* 2.85 2.85

**Princess Diana Issue**
Common Design Type

**1982, July 1 Litho. *Perf. 13***
**486** CD333 20c Arms *.45* *.40*
**487** CD333 30c Diana *.80* *.55*
**488** CD333 40c Wedding *.90* *.75*
**489** CD333 50c Portrait *2.60* *1.00*
*Nos. 486-489 (4)* *4.75* *2.70*

Scouting Year — A76

**1982, Aug. 24 Wmk. 373 *Perf. 14***
**490** A76 3c Pitching tent .30 .25
**491** A76 20c Cooking .65 .65
**492** A76 30c Troop 1.10 1.10
**493** A76 50c Boating skills 1.50 1.50
*Nos. 490-493 (4)* 3.55 3.50

Christmas 1982 — A77

Virgin and Child Paintings by Raphael.

**1982, Oct. 26 *Perf. 14½***
**494** A77 3c multicolored .25 .25
**495** A77 10c multicolored .30 .30
**496** A77 20c multicolored .60 .60
**497** A77 30c multicolored .85 .85
*Nos. 494-497 (4)* 2.00 2.00

Representative Govt. Sesquicentennial — A78

3c, Mace. 10c, Old Courthouse. 20c, Commonwealth Parliamentary Assoc. arms. 30c, Legislative Assembley building.

**1982, Nov. 9 Litho. Wmk. 373**
**498** A78 3c multicolored .25 .25
**499** A78 10c multicolored .25 .25
**500** A78 20c multicolored .40 .40
**501** A78 30c multicolored .60 .60
*Nos. 498-501 (4)* 1.50 1.50

**Shell Type of 1980**

5c, Natica canrena. 10c, Cassis tuberosa. 20c, Strombus gallus. $1, Cypraecassis testiculus.

**1983, Jan. 11 Litho. *Perf. 13½***
**502** A69 5c multicolored .25 .25
**503** A69 10c multicolored .40 .40
**504** A69 20c multicolored .85 .85
**505** A69 $1 multicolored 3.50 *4.00*
*Nos. 502-505 (4)* 5.00 5.50

Visit of Queen Elizabeth II and Prince Philip — A79

20c, Legislative Building, Cayman Brac. 30c, Leg. Bldg., Grand Cayman. 50c, Prince Philip. $1, Queen Elizabeth II.

**1983, Feb. 15 Litho. *Perf. 14***
**506** A79 20c multicolored .50 .50
**507** A79 30c multicolored .85 .75
**508** A79 50c multicolored 1.50 1.25
**509** A79 $1 multicolored 2.50 2.50
*a.* Souvenir sheet of 4, #506-509 7.50 7.50
*Nos. 506-509 (4)* 5.35 5.00

A80

**1983, Mar. 14**
**510** A80 3c Globe .30 .25
**511** A80 15c Flags .65 .60
**512** A80 20c Fisherman .70 .70
**513** A80 40c Elizabeth II 1.10 .95
*Nos. 510-513 (4)* 2.75 2.50

Commonwealth Day.

Manned Flight Bicentenary and Mosquito Research and Control Unit — A81

Airplanes: 3c, MRCU Cessna. 10c, Consolidated Catalina PBY. 20c, Boeing 727. 40c, Hawker Siddeley HS-748.

**1983, Oct. 10 Litho. *Perf. 14½***
**514** A81 3c multicolored .95 .70
**515** A81 10c multicolored 1.10 .70
**516** A81 20c multicolored 1.90 1.90
**517** A81 40c multicolored 2.50 *3.75*
*Nos. 514-517 (4)* 6.45 7.05

**Shell Type of 1980**

3c, Natica floridana. 10c, Conus austini. 30c, Colubraria obscura. 50c, Turbo cailletii.

**1984, Jan. 18 *Perf. 14x14½***
**518** A69 3c multicolored 1.25 .40
**519** A69 10c multicolored 1.60 .40
**520** A69 30c multicolored 4.50 4.50
**521** A69 50c multicolored 4.75 4.75
*Nos. 518-521 (4)* 12.10 10.05

**Lloyd's List Issue**
Common Design Type

**1984, May 16 Litho. *Perf. 14***
**522** CD335 5c Cruise ship .65 .25
**523** CD335 10c Old Harbor .75 .30
**524** CD335 25c Ridgefield 1.40 1.40
**525** CD335 50c Goldfield 3.00 3.00
*Nos. 522-525 (4)* 5.80 4.95

**Souvenir Sheet**

**526** CD335 $1 Goldfield, diff. 3.50 3.50

No. 525 Overprinted

**1984, June 18**

| | | | | |
|---|---|---|---|---|
| 527 | CD335 | 50c multicolored | 1.60 | 2.00 |

Local Birds — A82

*Perf. 14x14½*

**1984, Aug. 15 Litho. Wmk. 373**

| | | | | |
|---|---|---|---|---|
| 528 | A82 | 5c Snowy egret | 1.25 | .65 |
| 529 | A82 | 10c Bananaquit | 1.25 | .65 |
| 530 | A82 | 35c Kingfisher | 4.00 | 2.50 |
| 531 | A82 | $1 Brown booby | 7.50 | 11.00 |
| | | Nos. 528-531 (4) | 14.00 | 14.80 |

Christmas — A83

Nos. 532a-532d, evening beach scenes. Nos. 533a-533d, daytime boating and beach scenes.

**1984, Oct. 17 Litho. *Perf. 14***

| | | | | |
|---|---|---|---|---|
| 532 | A83 | Strip of 4 | 5.00 | 5.50 |
| a.-d. | | 5c Any single | 1.25 | 1.35 |
| 533 | A83 | Strip of 4 | 6.00 | 5.50 |
| a.-d. | | 25c Any single | 1.50 | 1.35 |

**Souvenir Sheet**

| | | | | |
|---|---|---|---|---|
| 534 | A83 | $1 Bonfire, diff. | 6.25 | 6.25 |

No. 534 contains one stamp 29x48mm.

Orchids — A84

5c, Schomburgkia thomsoniana var. 10c, Schomburgkia thomsoniana. 25c, Encyclia plicata. 50c, Dendrophylax fawcetti.

**1985, Mar. 13 Litho. *Perf. 14x13½***

| | | | | |
|---|---|---|---|---|
| 535 | A84 | 5c multicolored | 1.50 | .55 |
| 536 | A84 | 10c multicolored | 1.50 | .55 |
| 537 | A84 | 25c multicolored | 3.75 | 1.25 |
| 538 | A84 | 50c multicolored | 4.75 | 3.50 |
| | | Nos. 535-538 (4) | 11.50 | 5.85 |

Shipwrecks — A85

Unspecified shipwrecks found in Cayman waters.

**1985, May 22 *Perf. 14***

| | | | | |
|---|---|---|---|---|
| 539 | A85 | 5c multicolored | 1.25 | .55 |
| 540 | A85 | 25c multicolored | 4.00 | 1.50 |
| 541 | A85 | 35c multicolored | 4.25 | 2.75 |
| 542 | A85 | 40c multicolored | 4.50 | 3.75 |
| | | Nos. 539-542 (4) | 14.00 | 8.55 |

Intl. Youth Year — A86

5c, Natl. Athletic Assoc. track competition. 15c, High school students studying in Grand Cayman Campus Library. 25c, Amateur League Competition Football. 50c, Natl. Netball Assoc. competition.

**1985, Aug. 14 *Perf. 14½***

| | | | | |
|---|---|---|---|---|
| 543 | A86 | 5c multicolored | .30 | .25 |
| 544 | A86 | 15c multicolored | .50 | .40 |
| 545 | A86 | 25c multicolored | 1.05 | .85 |
| 546 | A86 | 50c multicolored | 2.10 | 3.25 |
| | | Nos. 543-546 (4) | 3.95 | 4.75 |

Telecommunications, 50th Anniv. — A87

Designs: 5c, Morse Code transmitter, 1935. 10c, Hand-cranked telephone, 1935. 25c, Tropospheric scatter dish, 1966. 50c, Earth dish receiver, 1979.

**1985, Oct. 25 *Perf. 14***

| | | | | |
|---|---|---|---|---|
| 547 | A87 | 5c multicolored | .55 | .70 |
| 548 | A87 | 10c multicolored | .60 | .70 |
| 549 | A87 | 25c multicolored | 1.75 | 1.10 |
| 550 | A87 | 50c multicolored | 3.00 | 4.50 |
| | | Nos. 547-550 (4) | 5.90 | 7.00 |

Birds — A88

10c, Magnificent frigatebird. 25c, West Indian whistling duck. 35c, La Sagra's flycatcher. 40c, Yellow-faced grassquit.

**1986, Mar. 20 Litho. Wmk. 384**

| | | | | |
|---|---|---|---|---|
| 551 | A88 | 10c multicolored | 2.25 | 1.00 |
| 552 | A88 | 25c multicolored | 3.00 | 1.60 |
| 553 | A88 | 35c multicolored | 3.50 | 3.50 |
| 554 | A88 | 40c multicolored | 4.00 | 5.00 |
| | | Nos. 551-554 (4) | 12.75 | 11.10 |

Nos. 552-553 vert.

**Queen Elizabeth II 60th Birthday**

Common Design Type

Designs: 5c, As bridesmaid at wedding of Lady Mary Cambridge, 1931. 10c, Royal visit to Norway, 1955. 25c, Inspecting West Indian troop, royal tour, 1985. 50c, Gulf tour, 1979. $1, Visiting Crown Agents' offices, 1983.

**1986, Apr. 21 *Perf. 14x14½***

| | | | | |
|---|---|---|---|---|
| 555 | CD337 | 5c scar, blk & sil | .25 | .25 |
| 556 | CD337 | 10c ultra, blk & sil | .25 | .25 |
| 557 | CD337 | 25c grn & multi | 1.75 | .85 |
| 558 | CD337 | 50c vio & multi | .90 | 1.75 |
| 559 | CD337 | $1 rose vio & multi | 1.40 | 2.50 |
| | | Nos. 555-559 (5) | 4.55 | 5.60 |

**Royal Wedding Issue, 1986**

Common Design Type

Designs: 5c, Informal portrait. 50c, Andrew in uniform, helicopter.

*Perf. 14½x14*

**1986, July 23 Litho. Wmk. 384**

| | | | | |
|---|---|---|---|---|
| 560 | CD338 | 5c multicolored | .30 | .25 |
| 561 | CD338 | 50c multicolored | 1.40 | 2.10 |

Marine Life — A89

5c, Rhynchocinetes rigeus. 10c, Nemaster rubiginosa. 15c, Calcinus tibicen. 20c, Rhodactis sanctithomae. 25c, Spirobranchus gigantea. 35c, Diodon holacanthus. 50c, Pseudocorynactis aribbeorum. 60c, Astrophyton muricatum. 75c, Cyphoma gibbosum. $1, Conolylactis gigantea. $2, Malacoctenus boehlkei. $4, Lima scabra.

*Perf. 13½x13*

**1986, Sept. 15 Wmk. 373**

**Inscribed "1986"**

| | | | | |
|---|---|---|---|---|
| 562 | A89 | 5c multicolored | .80 | 1.00 |
| 563 | A89 | 10c multicolored | .80 | .65 |
| c. | | Wmk. 384, inscribed "1990" | 2.75 | 3.00 |
| 564 | A89 | 15c multicolored | .70 | .75 |
| 565 | A89 | 20c multicolored | .70 | .95 |
| 566 | A89 | 25c multicolored | .45 | 3.00 |
| 567 | A89 | 35c multicolored | .70 | 3.25 |
| 568 | A89 | 50c multicolored | .80 | 5.00 |
| 569 | A89 | 60c multicolored | 3.50 | 11.00 |
| 570 | A89 | 75c multicolored | 9.50 | 13.00 |
| 571 | A89 | $1 multicolored | 2.25 | 2.75 |
| 572 | A89 | $2 multicolored | 5.00 | 5.25 |
| 573 | A89 | $4 multicolored | 10.00 | 7.75 |
| | | Nos. 562-573 (12) | 35.20 | 54.35 |

**1987 Inscribed "1987"**

| | | | | |
|---|---|---|---|---|
| 562a | A89 | 5c multicolored | .80 | 1.60 |
| 563a | A89 | 10c multicolored | .80 | 1.25 |
| 564a | A89 | 15c multicolored | .70 | 1.50 |
| 565a | A89 | 20c multicolored | .70 | 2.00 |
| 571a | A89 | $1 multicolored | 2.25 | 6.50 |
| 572a | A89 | $2 multicolored | 5.00 | 10.50 |
| 573a | A89 | $4 multicolored | 10.00 | 17.50 |
| | | Nos. 562a-573a (7) | 20.25 | 40.85 |

**1990 Inscribed "1990"**

| | | | | |
|---|---|---|---|---|
| 562b | A89 | 5c multicolored | 2.75 | 5.00 |
| 563b | A89 | 10c multicolored | 2.75 | 4.00 |
| 564b | A89 | 15c multicolored | 2.50 | 5.00 |
| 565b | A89 | 20c multicolored | 2.50 | 7.00 |
| 566b | A89 | 25c multicolored | 1.50 | 10.00 |
| 567b | A89 | 35c multicolored | | — |
| 568b | A89 | 50c multicolored | | — |
| 571b | A89 | $1 multicolored | 8.00 | 10.00 |
| 572b | A89 | $2 multicolored | 17.50 | 17.50 |
| | | Nos. 562b-572b (7) | 37.50 | 58.50 |

Tourism — A90

*Perf. 13x13½*

**1987, Jan. 26 Wmk. 384**

| | | | | |
|---|---|---|---|---|
| 574 | A90 | 10c Golfing | 2.50 | 1.00 |
| 575 | A90 | 15c Sailing | 2.60 | 1.00 |
| 576 | A90 | 25c Snorkeling | 2.60 | 1.50 |
| 577 | A90 | 35c Parasailing | 2.60 | 2.00 |
| 578 | A90 | $1 Fishing | 5.75 | 11.00 |
| | | Nos. 574-578 (5) | 16.05 | 16.50 |

Fruit — A91

**1987, May 20 *Perf. 14½***

| | | | | |
|---|---|---|---|---|
| 579 | A91 | 5c Akee | 1.00 | 1.25 |
| 580 | A91 | 25c Breadfruit | 2.25 | .75 |
| 581 | A91 | 35c Papaya | 2.25 | 1.00 |
| 582 | A91 | $1 Soursop | 6.00 | 8.50 |
| | | Nos. 579-582 (4) | 11.50 | 11.50 |

Lizards — A92

**1987, Aug. 26 Litho. *Perf. 14***

| | | | | |
|---|---|---|---|---|
| 583 | A92 | 10c Lion lizard | 2.25 | 1.00 |
| 584 | A92 | 50c Iguana | 5.75 | 4.50 |
| 585 | A92 | $1 Anole | 6.75 | 8.75 |
| | | Nos. 583-585 (3) | 14.75 | 14.25 |

Flowers — A93

**1987, Nov. 18 *Perf. 14½x14***

| | | | | |
|---|---|---|---|---|
| 586 | A93 | 5c Poinsettia | 1.25 | .55 |
| 587 | A93 | 25c Periwinkle | 3.00 | .90 |
| 588 | A93 | 35c Yellow allamanda | 3.00 | 1.25 |
| 589 | A93 | 75c Blood lily | 5.25 | 6.00 |
| | | Nos. 586-589 (4) | 12.50 | 8.70 |

Butterflies — A94

Designs: 5c, Hemiargus ammon erembis and Strymon martialis. 25c, Phocides pigmalion batabano. 50c, Anaea troglodyta cubana. $1, Papilio andraemon andraemon.

**1988, Mar. 29 Wmk. 384 *Perf. 14***

| | | | | |
|---|---|---|---|---|
| 590 | A94 | 5c multicolored | 1.60 | .65 |
| 591 | A94 | 25c multicolored | 3.50 | 1.40 |
| 592 | A94 | 50c multicolored | 5.25 | 5.25 |
| 593 | A94 | $1 multicolored | 6.75 | 6.75 |
| | | Nos. 590-593 (4) | 17.10 | 14.05 |

Herons — A95

5c, Butorides striatus. 25c, Egretta tricolor. 50c, Nycticorax violaceus. $1, Egretta caerulea.

**1988, Jan. 26 Litho. *Perf. 14***

| | | | | |
|---|---|---|---|---|
| 594 | A95 | 5c multicolored | 2.40 | .65 |
| 595 | A95 | 25c multicolored | 4.50 | .90 |
| 596 | A95 | 50c multicolored | 5.50 | 5.25 |
| 597 | A95 | $1 multicolored | 6.00 | 5.50 |
| | | Nos. 594-597 (4) | 18.40 | 12.30 |

1988 Summer Olympics, Seoul — A96

10c, Cycling. 50c, Natl. team, passenger jet. $1, Yachting.

No. 601, Tennis.

**1988, Sept. 21 *Perf. 14½***

| | | | | |
|---|---|---|---|---|
| 598 | A96 | 10c multicolored | 2.25 | .90 |
| 599 | A96 | 50c multicolored | 3.75 | 3.00 |
| 600 | A96 | $1 multicolored | 4.00 | 4.00 |
| | | Nos. 598-600 (3) | 10.00 | 7.90 |

**Souvenir Sheet**

**Wmk. 373**

| | | | | |
|---|---|---|---|---|
| 601 | A96 | $1 multicolored | 5.75 | 5.75 |

No. 601 commemorates the 75th anniv. of the Intl. Tennis Federation.

Visit of Princess Alexandra — A97

**1988, Nov. 1 Wmk. 373 *Perf. 15***

| | | | | |
|---|---|---|---|---|
| 602 | A97 | 5c Portrait | 2.50 | 1.25 |
| 603 | A97 | $1 Seated in garden | 9.00 | 7.00 |

Cayman Islands P.O., Cent. — A98

Designs: 5c, P.O., Georgetown, 1889, and Jamaica #24, canceled. 25c, S.S. Orinoco and Cayman Isls. #1. 35c, Grand Cayman G.P.O. and #442. $1, Cayman Airways mail plane and #191.

**1989, Apr. 12 Wmk. 384 *Perf. 14½***

| | | | | |
|---|---|---|---|---|
| 604 | A98 | 5c multicolored | 1.10 | 1.25 |
| 605 | A98 | 25c multicolored | 2.50 | 1.50 |
| 606 | A98 | 35c multicolored | 2.75 | 1.75 |
| 607 | A98 | $1 multicolored | 10.00 | 11.00 |
| | | Nos. 604-607 (4) | 16.35 | 15.50 |

A99

Mutiny on the Bounty: a, Capt. Bligh. b, HMS Providence, two crewmen. c, HMS Assistant, transplanted breadfruit. d, Moving breadfruit on land, in longboat. e, Midshipman among casks and crates.

**1989, May 24 *Perf. 14***

| | | | | |
|---|---|---|---|---|
| 608 | | Strip of 5 | 30.00 | 30.00 |
| a.-e. | | A99 50c any single | 6.00 | 6.00 |

A100

5c, Panton House. 10c, Town Hall. 25c, Old Courts House. 35c, Elmslie Memorial Church. $1, Post office.

**Perf. 14½x14**

**1989, Oct. 18 Litho. Wmk. 373**

**609** A100 5c multicolored .90 *1.00*
**610** A100 10c multicolored .90 *1.00*
**611** A100 25c multicolored 2.00 .80
**612** A100 35c multicolored 2.00 1.25
**613** A100 $1 multicolored 5.00 *6.25*
*Nos. 609-613 (5)* 10.80 *10.30*

Natl. Trust emblem & architecture, George Town.

Island Surveys — A101

Maps or survey ships: 5c, Navigational instruments and George Gauld's map of 1773. 25c, Instruments and map created by surveyors aboard HMS *Vidal*, 1956. 50c, *Mutine*, 1914. $1, HMS *Vidal*.

**1989, Nov. 15**

**614** A101 5c multicolored 1.75 1.50
**615** A101 25c multicolored 4.50 1.75
**616** A101 50c multicolored 7.00 5.50
**617** A101 $1 multicolored 11.00 11.00
*Nos. 614-617 (4)* 24.25 19.75

Angelfish A102

**1990, Apr. 25 Wmk. 384 Perf. 14**

**618** A102 10c French 1.60 .65
**619** A102 25c Gray 3.00 1.40
**620** A102 50c Queen 4.50 1.00
**621** A102 $1 Rock beauty 7.25 8.00
*Nos. 618-621 (4)* 16.35 11.05

**Queen Mother, 90th Birthday**

Common Design Types

50c, King, Queen Elizabeth, 1948. $1, King, Queen with Churchill, 1940.

**1990, Aug. 4 Wmk. 384 Perf. 14x15**

**622** CD343 50c multicolored 1.25 *2.00*

**Perf. 14½**

**623** CD344 $1 multicolored 2.75 *3.50*

Butterflies — A103

5c, Soldier. 25c, Pygmy blue. 35c, Cayman crescent spot. $1, Gulf fritillary.

**1990, Oct. 24 Perf. 14½x14**

**624** A103 5c multicolored 1.25 1.10
**625** A103 25c multicolored 2.75 2.25
**626** A103 35c multicolored 3.25 2.50
**627** A103 $1 multicolored 7.75 *9.00*
*Nos. 624-627 (4)* 15.00 14.85

Expo '90, International Garden and Greenery Exposition, Osaka, Japan.

Hurricane Awareness A104

Designs: 5c, Goes weather satellite. 30c, Meteorologist tracks storm. 40c, Hurricane damage. $1, Lockheed WP-3D Orion flying in hurricane's eye.

**1991, Aug. 8 Perf. 14**

**628** A104 5c multicolored 1.40 1.40
**629** A104 30c multicolored 3.25 1.75
**630** A104 40c multicolored 3.50 2.10
**631** A104 $1 multicolored 8.50 8.50
*Nos. 628-631 (4)* 16.65 13.75

Christmas A105

Local flowers and Christmas scenes: 5c, Angel's trumpet, angels with trumpets. 30c, Golden trumpet, Mary on donkey led by Joseph. 40c, Christmas flower, Adoration of the Magi. 60c, Tree of life, nativity scene.

**1991, Nov. 6 Wmk. 373**

**632** A105 5c multicolored 1.00 1.00
**633** A105 30c multicolored 3.00 .85
**634** A105 40c multicolored 3.25 1.40
**635** A105 60c multicolored 3.75 *6.50*
*Nos. 632-635 (4)* 11.00 9.75

Island Scenes — A106

5c, Coconut tree, vert. 15c, Beach scene. 20c, Poincianas in bloom. 30c, Blowholes. 40c, Police band. 50c, Downtown scene, vert. 60c, The Bluff, Cayman Brac. 80c, Coat of arms, vert. 90c, View of Hell. $1, Sportfishing. $2, Harbor scene, vert. $8, Queen Elizabeth II, vert.

**Perf. 12½x13, 13x12½**

**1991, Dec. 11 Litho. Wmk. 373**

**636** A106 5c multicolored .65 .50
*a.* Inscribed "1994" 1.00 .75
**637** A106 15c multicolored 1.45 .50
**638** A106 20c multicolored .75 .60
**639** A106 30c multicolored 2.00 .80
**640** A106 40c multicolored 3.25 2.00
**641** A106 50c multicolored 2.75 2.00
**642** A106 60c multicolored 2.25 3.25
**643** A106 80c multicolored 2.00 3.25
**644** A106 90c multicolored 2.00 3.25
**645** A106 $1 multicolored 4.00 3.25
**646** A106 $2 multicolored 8.50 8.00
**647** A106 $8 multicolored 20.00 22.50
*Nos. 636-647 (12)* 49.60 49.90

**Queen Elizabeth II's Accession to the Throne, 40th Anniv.**

Common Design Type

**Wmk. 373, 384 (40c)**

**1992, Feb. 6 Litho. Perf. 14**

**648** CD349 5c multicolored .45 .45
**649** CD349 20c multicolored 1.40 .50
**650** CD349 30c multicolored 1.50 .75
**651** CD349 40c multicolored 1.50 1.40
**652** CD349 $1 multicolored 2.75 *3.50*
*Nos. 648-652 (5)* 7.60 6.60

1992 Summer Olympics, Barcelona A107

15c, Cyclist. 40c, Two cyclists. 60c, Feet, pedals. $1, Two cyclists, diff.

**1992, Aug. 5 Wmk. 373**

**653** A107 15c multicolored 2.00 .55
**654** A107 40c multicolored 3.50 1.50
**655** A107 60c multicolored 4.00 4.00
**656** A107 $1 multicolored 5.00 5.00
*Nos. 653-656 (4)* 14.50 11.05

Island Heritage — A108

5c, Lady with donkey. 30c, Making fish nets. 40c, Maypole dancing. 60c, Basket making. $1, Cooking on caboose.

**1992, Oct. 21**

**657** A108 5c multicolored .60 *.70*
**658** A108 30c multicolored 1.60 .95
**659** A108 40c multicolored 2.75 1.40
**660** A108 60c multicolored 3.25 *3.50*
**661** A108 $1 multicolored 3.75 *5.00*
*Nos. 657-661 (5)* 11.95 *11.55*

Rays — A109

5c, Yellow stingray. 30c, Southern stingray. 40c, Spotted eagle ray. $1, Manta ray.

**Perf. 13½x14**

**1993, June 16 Litho. Wmk. 373**

**662** A109 5c multicolored .95 .75
**663** A109 30c multicolored 2.40 1.50
**664** A109 40c multicolored 2.75 1.75
**665** A109 $1 multicolored 6.25 5.75
*Nos. 662-665 (4)* 12.35 9.75

A110

Tourism: No. 666a, Turtle, sailboats. b, Diver, coral, boats. c, Golf. d, Beach, tennis. e, Pirates, sailing ship.

No. 667: a, Cruise ship, boat, sailboat. b, City street scene. c, Submarines. d, Cyclist, scooters. e, Jet planes.

**Perf. 14x13½**

**1993, Sept. 30 Litho. Wmk. 373**

**666** A110 15c Strip of 5, #a.-e. 11.50 11.50
**667** A110 30c Strip of 5, #a.-e. 12.50 12.50
*f.* Booklet pane of 10, #666-667 35.00

A111

Various views of Grand Cayman Parrot.

**1993, Oct. 29 Perf. 14**

**668** A111 5c green & multi 1.25 1.25
**669** A111 5c red & multi 1.25 1.25
**670** A111 30c yellow & multi 3.00 3.00
**671** A111 30c blue & multi 3.00 3.00
*Nos. 668-671 (4)* 8.50 8.50

Christmas — A112

Christmas scenes, orchids: 5c, Manger, Ionopsis utricularioides. 40c, Shepherd, lamb, Encyclia cochleata. 60c, Magi, Vanilla pompona. $1, Virgin in prayer, Oncidium caymanense.

**Perf. 13½x14**

**1993, Dec. 6 Litho. Wmk. 384**

**672** A112 5c multicolored 1.40 .75
**673** A112 40c multicolored 3.75 .95
**674** A112 60c multicolored 4.75 4.50
**675** A112 $1 multicolored 6.25 *7.00*
*Nos. 672-675 (4)* 16.15 13.20

Souvenir Sheet

Reef Life — A113

Designs: a, Holocanthus ciliaris. b, Bodianus pulchellus, anisotremus virginicus. c, Holocanthus tricolor, gramma loreto. d, Pomacanthus paru, chaeton striatus.

**Perf. 14½x13**

**1994, Feb. 18 Litho. Wmk. 373**

**676** A113 60c Sheet of 4, #a.-d. 13.50 13.50

Hong Kong '94.

Royal Visit — A114

Designs: 5c, Cayman Islands, United Kingdom flags. 15c, Royal yacht Britannia. 30c, Queen Elizabeth II. $2, Queen, Prince Philip.

**1994, Feb. 22 Perf. 14½**

**677** A114 5c multicolored 2.00 1.10
**678** A114 15c multicolored 3.75 1.25
**679** A114 30c multicolored 3.75 1.50
**680** A114 $2 multicolored 10.50 *12.00*
*Nos. 677-680 (4)* 20.00 15.85

West Indian Whistling Duck — A115

5c, One standing. 15c, Landing in water. 20c, Four ducks, various activities. 80c, One raising wings. $1, Adult, chick.

**Wmk. 373**

**1994, Apr. 21 Litho. Perf. 14**

**681** A115 5c multi, vert. 1.75 .90
**682** A115 15c multi 2.50 .95
**683** A115 20c multi 2.50 1.00
**684** A115 80c multi, vert. 5.50 6.00
**685** A115 $1 multi, vert. 6.25 6.50
*a.* Souvenir sheet of 1 12.00 12.00
*Nos. 681-685 (5)* 18.50 15.35

No. 685a has a continuous design and contains Cayman Islands Natl. Trust emblem.

Butterflies — A116

No. 686: a, Fulvous hairstreak. b, Atala butterfly.

No. 687: a, Barred sulphur. b, Dorantes skipper.

**Wmk. 373**

**1994, Aug. 16 Litho. Perf. 13½**

**686** A116 10c Pair, #a.-b. 2.75 2.75
**687** A116 $1 Pair, #a.-b. 13.00 13.00

Wreck of the Ten Sail, Bicent. — A117

**Perf. 13½x14**

**1994, Oct. 12 Litho. Wmk. 373**

**688** A117 10c shown .65 .65
**689** A117 10c multicolored .65 .65
**690** A117 15c multicolored 1.10 .55
**691** A117 20c multicolored 1.25 .65
**692** A117 $2 multicolored 6.75 *7.50*
*Nos. 688-692 (5)* 10.40 10.00

Sea Turtles — A118

**Wmk. 384**

**1995, Feb. 28 Litho. Perf. 14**

**693** A118 10c Green .75 .45
**694** A118 20c Kemp's ridley 1.10 .55
**695** A118 25c Hawksbill 1.25 .65
**696** A118 30c Leatherback 1.45 .75
**697** A118 $1.30 Loggerhead 5.25 5.25
**698** A118 $2 Pacific ridley 6.50 6.50
*a.* Souvenir sheet, #693-698 16.50 16.50
*Nos. 693-698 (6)* 16.30 14.15

1995 CARIFTA & IAAF Games — A119

**1995, Apr. 15** **Litho.** ***Perf. 14***

**699** A119 10c Running .90 .50
**700** A119 20c Pole vault 1.25 1.00
**701** A119 30c Javelin 1.90 1.10
**702** A119 $1.30 Sailing 6.50 6.50
*Nos. 699-702 (4)* 10.55 9.10

**Souvenir Sheet**

**703** A119 $2 Medal winners 9.00 9.00

**End of World War II, 50th Anniv.**

Common Design Type

10c, Two soldiers, Cayman Home Guard. 25c, Freighter Comayagua torpedoed off Caymans, 5/14/42. 40c, Type IXc U-Boat U-125. $1, Navy airship L-3 used for U-boat patrol. $1.30, Reverse of War Medal 1939-45.

**Wmk. 373**

**1995, May 8** **Litho.** ***Perf. 13½***

**704** CD351 10c multicolored 1.40 .55
**705** CD351 25c multicolored 2.75 .90
**706** CD351 40c multicolored 3.25 2.25
**707** CD351 $1 multicolored 5.75 5.75
*Nos. 704-707 (4)* 13.15 9.45

**Souvenir Sheet**

***Perf. 14***

**708** CD352 $1.30 multicolored 4.50 4.50

Souvenir Sheet

Queen Mother, 95th Birthday A120

**1995, Aug. 25** ***Perf. 14½***

**709** A120 $4 multicolored 11.50 11.50

Singapore '95.

Wild Fruit — A122

Animals of the Nativity.

A121

**1995, Nov. 1** ***Perf. 14***

**710** A121 10c Ox .90 .30
**711** A121 20c Sheep, lamb 1.40 .50
**712** A121 30c Donkey 2.25 .60
**713** A121 $2 Camels 8.50 *10.00*
*a.* Souvenir sheet of 4, #710-713 14.00 14.00
*Nos. 710-713 (4)* 13.05 11.40

10c, Sea grape. 25c, Guava. 40c, West Indian cherry. $1, Tamarind.

**Wmk. 384**

**1996, Mar. 21** **Litho.** ***Perf. 14***

**714** A122 10c multicolored .60 .50
**715** A122 25c multicolored 1.25 .60
**716** A122 40c multicolored 2.00 1.00
**717** A122 $1 multicolored 4.00 *5.00*
*Nos. 714-717 (4)* 7.85 7.10

Modern Olympic Games, Cent. — A123

***Perf. 14x13½***

**1996, June 19** **Litho.** **Wmk. 384**

**718** A123 10c Sailing .65 .45
**719** A123 20c Sailboarding 1.25 .55
**720** A123 30c Sailing, diff. 1.60 .80
**721** A123 $2 Running 6.00 *7.00*
*Nos. 718-721 (4)* 9.50 8.80

Symbols of National Identity — A124

Designs: 10c, Guitar, music, natl. song. 20c, Boeing 737. 25c, Queen Elizabeth II opening Legislative Assembly. 30c, Seven Mile Beach. 40c, Scuba diver, stingrays. 60c, School children, Cayman Turtle Farm. 80c, Cayman parrot, natl. bird. 90c, Silver thatch palm, natl. tree. $1, Natl. flag. $2, Wild banana orchid, natl. flower. $4, Natl. arms. $6, Natl. currency.

**Wmk. 373**

**1996, Sept. 26** **Litho.** ***Perf. 14***

**Inscribed "1996"**

**722** A124 10c multicolored .50 .45
Complete booklet, 10 #722 5.25
*a.* Inscribed "1997" .50 .45
**723** A124 20c multicolored 1.10 .85
**724** A124 25c multicolored 1.25 .80
**725** A124 30c multicolored 1.25 .80
Complete booklet, 10 #725 13.00
**726** A124 40c multicolored 1.60 1.25
Complete booklet, 10 #726 17.00
**727** A124 60c multicolored 2.25 1.60
**728** A124 80c multicolored 3.75 3.00
*a.* Souvenir sheet of 1 4.25 4.25
**729** A124 90c multicolored 2.50 3.00
**730** A124 $1 multicolored 4.00 3.25
**731** A124 $2 multicolored 7.25 7.00
**732** A124 $4 multicolored 13.00 16.00
**733** A124 $6 multicolored 17.00 20.00
*Nos. 722-733 (12)* 55.45 58.00

No. 728a for Hong Kong '97. Issued 2/3/97.

**1999, Feb. 5** **Wmk. 373 Sideways**

*723a* A124 20c multicolored 1.10 .85
*725a* A124 30c multicolored 1.25 .80
*727a* A124 60c multicolored 2.25 1.60
*Nos. 723a-727a (3)* 4.60 3.25

Christmas — A125

Designs: 10c, Christmas time on North Church Street. 25c, Santa "Gone Fishing." 30c, "Claus Encounters." $2, "Caymanian Christmas."

**Wmk. 373**

**1996, Nov. 12** **Litho.** ***Perf. 14***

**734** A125 10c multicolored .65 .35
**735** A125 25c multicolored 1.60 .90
**736** A125 30c multicolored 2.00 1.25
**737** A125 $2 multicolored 4.00 6.00
*Nos. 734-737 (4)* 8.25 8.50

Queen Elizabeth II and Prince Philip, 50th Wedding Anniv. — A126

No. 738, Queen. No. 739, Royal Guard. No. 740, Young Prince riding horse. No. 741, Queen in blue, Prince in military attire in open carriage. No. 742 Prince holding horse's reins. No. 743, Queen looking at horses.

$1, Queen, Prince in open carriage.

***Perf. 14x13½***

**1997, July 10** **Litho.** **Wmk. 373**

**738** A126 10c multicolored 1.00 1.00
**739** A126 10c multicolored 1.00 1.00
*a.* Pair, #738-739 2.00 2.00
**740** A126 30c multicolored 1.60 1.60
**741** A126 30c multicolored 1.60 1.60
*a.* Pair, #740-741 3.25 3.25
**742** A126 40c multicolored 2.00 2.00
**743** A126 40c multicolored 2.00 2.00
*a.* Pair, #742-743 4.00 4.00
*Nos. 738-743 (6)* 9.20 9.20

**Souvenir Sheet**

**744** A126 $1 multicolored 6.25 6.25

Telecommunications — A127

Designs: 10c, Children using the Internet. 25c, Cable and wireless ship. 30c, Children wearing numbers of new area code, "345." 60c, Cable and wireless satellite communications.

***Perf. 14x14½***

**1997, Oct. 10** **Litho.** **Wmk. 384**

**745** A127 10c multicolored .45 .30
**746** A127 25c multicolored 1.25 .60
**747** A127 30c multicolored 1.40 .75
**748** A127 60c multicolored 1.90 *2.50*
*Nos. 745-748 (4)* 5.00 4.15

Christmas — A128

Santa Claus: 10c, Relaxing in hammock, Little Cayman. 30c, With children on bluff, Cayman Brac. 40c, Playing golf. $1, Diving with stingrays.

**Wmk. 373**

**1997, Dec. 3** **Litho.** ***Perf. 13***

**749** A128 10c multicolored .35 .25
**750** A128 30c multicolored .80 .45
**751** A128 40c multicolored 1.75 .80
**752** A128 $1 multicolored 2.75 *3.50*
*Nos. 749-752 (4)* 5.65 5.00

**Diana, Princess of Wales (1961-97)**

Common Design Type

Portraits: a, 10c. b, 20c. c, 40c. d, $1.

***Perf. 14½x14***

**1998** **Litho.** **Wmk. 373**

**752A** CD355 10c Like #753a .65 .65
**752B** CD355 20c Like #753b 1.25 1.25

**Sheet of 4**

**753** CD355 #a.-d. 5.50 5.50

No. 753 sold for $1.70 + 30c, with surtax from international sales being donated to the Princess Diana Memorial Fund and surtax from national sales being donated to designated local charity.

**Royal Air Force, 80th Anniv.**

Common Design Type of 1993 Re-Inscribed

Designs: 10c, Hawker Horsley. 20c, Fairey Hendon. 25c, Hawker Siddeley Gnat. 30c, Hawker Siddeley Dominie.

No. 758: a, 40c, Airco DH-9. b, 60c, Spad 13 Scout. c, 80c, Airspeed Oxford. d, $1, Martin Baltimore.

**Wmk. 373**

**1998, Apr. 1** **Litho.** ***Perf. 14***

**754** CD350 10c multicolored 1.00 1.00
**755** CD350 20c multicolored 1.25 1.25
**756** CD350 25c multicolored 1.60 1.60
**757** CD350 30c multicolored 1.90 1.90
*Nos. 754-757 (4)* 5.75 5.75

**Souvenir Sheet**

**758** CD350 Sheet of 4, #a.-d. 9.50 9.50

Birds — A129

Designs: 10c, West Indian whistling duck. 20c, Magnificent frigatebird. 60c, Red footed booby. $1, Grand Cayman parrot.

**1998** **Litho.** **Wmk. 373** ***Perf. 13½***

**759** A129 10c multicolored 1.10 .60
**760** A129 20c multicolored 2.00 .60
**761** A129 60c multicolored 3.50 3.50
**762** A129 $1 multicolored 4.25 4.25
*Nos. 759-762 (4)* 10.85 8.95

Christmas — A130

Santa at various island locations: 10c, At Blowholes. 30c, Diving on wreck of MV Capt. Keith Tibbetts. 40c, Visiting Pedro Castle. 60c, Arriving at Little Cayman.

**1998** ***Perf. 14x14½***

**763** A130 10c multicolored .40 .40
**764** A130 30c multicolored 1.10 .85
**765** A130 40c multicolored 1.50 1.10
**766** A130 60c multicolored 2.50 2.50
*Nos. 763-766 (4)* 5.50 4.85

Easter — A131

Artworks by Miss Lassie (Gladwyn Bush): 10c, "They Rolled the Stone Away." 20c, "Ascension," vert. 30c, "The World Praying for Peace." 40c, "Calvary," vert.

**Wmk. 373**

**1999, Mar. 26** **Litho.** ***Perf. 13***

**767** A131 10c multicolored .50 .50
**768** A131 20c multicolored .85 .85
**769** A131 30c multicolored 1.30 1.30
**770** A131 40c multicolored 1.40 1.40
*Nos. 767-770 (4)* 4.05 4.05

Vision 2008 — A132

Children's drawings: 10c, "Cayman House." 30c, "Coral Reef." 40c, "Fisherman on North Sound." $2, "Three Fish and A Turtle."

**1999, June** ***Perf. 13½***

**771** A132 10c multicolored .30 .30
**772** A132 30c multicolored 1.10 1.10
**773** A132 40c multicolored 1.25 1.25
**774** A132 $2 multicolored 6.50 6.50
*Nos. 771-774 (4)* 9.15 9.15

**Wedding of Prince Edward and Sophie Rhys-Jones**

Common Design Type

***Perf. 13¾x14***

**1999, June 16** **Litho.** **Wmk. 384**

**775** CD356 10c Separate portraits .45 .45
**776** CD356 $2 Couple 4.50 4.50

**1st Manned Moon Landing, 30th Anniv.**

Common Design Type

Designs: 10c, Coast Guard during launch. 25c, 3rd stage fires and puts rocket in orbit. 30c, Aldrin descends to lunar surface. 60c, Lander module sent back to moon.

$1.50, Looking at earth from moon.

**1999, July 20** ***Perf. 14x13¾***

**777** CD357 10c multicolored .40 .40
**778** CD357 25c multicolored 1.00 1.00
**779** CD357 30c multicolored 1.10 1.10
**780** CD357 60c multicolored 2.25 2.25
*Nos. 777-780 (4)* 4.75 4.75

**Souvenir Sheet**

***Perf. 14***

**781** CD357 $1.50 multicolored 4.50 4.50

No. 781 contains one circular stamp 40mm in diameter.

**Queen Mother's Century**

Common Design Type

Queen Mother: 10c, Looking at London's defenses, 1940. 20c, At Clarence House, 94th birthday. 30c, With Princes Charles and William. 40c, Reviewing the Chelsea Pensioners, 1986.

$1.50, At her wedding.

**Wmk. 384**

**1999, Aug. 18 Litho. *Perf. 13¼***

| | | | | |
|---|---|---|---|---|
| **782** | CD358 | 10c multicolored | .40 | .40 |
| **783** | CD358 | 20c multicolored | .70 | .70 |
| **784** | CD358 | 30c multicolored | 1.25 | 1.25 |
| **785** | CD358 | 40c multicolored | 1.50 | 1.50 |
| | | *Nos. 782-785 (4)* | 3.85 | 3.85 |

**Souvenir Sheet**

**786** CD358 $1.50 multicolored 4.50 4.50

Christmas A133

**Wmk. 373**

**1999, Nov. 17 Litho. *Perf. 13¼***

| | | | | |
|---|---|---|---|---|
| **787** | A133 | 10c #242, vert. | .35 | .35 |
| **788** | A133 | 30c #532d, vert. | 1.00 | .90 |
| **789** | A133 | 40c #749, vert. | 1.40 | 1.25 |
| **790** | A133 | $1 #431 | 2.75 | 2.75 |
| *a.* | | Souv. sheet, #787-790, perf. 12 | 5.25 | 5.25 |
| | | *Nos. 787-790 (4)* | 5.50 | 5.25 |

British Monarchs — A134

No. 792: a, Henry VIII. b, Mary I. c, Charles II. d, Anne. e, George IV. f, George V.

**Wmk. 373**

**2000, Feb. 29 Litho. *Perf. 14***

**791** A134 10c Henry VII .70 .70

**Sheet of 6**

**792** A134 40c #a.-f. 9.50 9.50

The Stamp Show 2000, London.

Sesame Street — A135

Designs: 10c, Ernie. 30c, Big Bird.

No. 795: a, Grover. b, Zoe. c, Oscar the Grouch. d, The Count. e, Like 30c. f, Cookie Monster. g, Like 10c. h, Bert. i, Elmo in pond.

No. 796, Elmo collecting stamps.

***Perf. 14½x14¾***

**2000, Mar. 15 Litho. Wmk. 373**

| | | | | |
|---|---|---|---|---|
| **793** | A135 | 10c multi | .35 | .35 |
| **794** | A135 | 30c multi | 1.00 | 1.00 |
| **795** | A135 | 20c Sheet of 9, #a-i | 5.50 | 5.50 |

**Souvenir Sheet**

**796** A135 20c multi 1.60 1.60

**Prince William, 18th Birthday**

Common Design Type

10c, In checked shirt and in sweater and checked shirt. 20c, In white shirt and black bow tie. 30c, In blue casual shirt, vert. 40c, As child, with beret, vert. $1, As infant.

***Perf. 14¼x13¾, 13¾x14¼***

**2000, June 21 Litho. Wmk. 373**

**Stamps With White Border**

| | | | | |
|---|---|---|---|---|
| **797** | CD359 | 10c multi | .50 | .40 |
| **798** | CD359 | 20c multi | .80 | .75 |
| **799** | CD359 | 30c multi | 1.10 | 1.00 |
| **800** | CD359 | 40c multi | 1.50 | 1.50 |
| | | *Nos. 797-800 (4)* | 3.90 | 3.65 |

**Souvenir Sheet**

**Stamps Without White Border**

***Perf. 14¼***

| | | | | |
|---|---|---|---|---|
| **801** | | Sheet of 5 | 7.25 | 7.25 |
| *a.* | CD359 | 10c multi | .30 | .30 |
| *b.* | CD359 | 20c multi | .65 | .65 |
| *c.* | CD359 | 30c multi | .90 | .90 |
| *d.* | CD359 | 40c multi | 1.25 | 1.25 |
| *e.* | CD359 | $1 multi | 3.50 | 3.50 |

Marine Life — A136

10c, Green turtle. 20c, Queen angelfish. 30c, Parrotfish. $1, Green moray eel.

**Wmk. 384**

**2000, Aug. 25 Litho. *Perf. 14***

**802-805** A136 Set of 4 7.75 7.75

National Drug Council — A137

Various children's drawings. Denominations, 10c, 15c, 30c, $2.

**2000, Aug. 25**

**806-809** A137 Set of 4 10.00 10.00

Christmas — A138

10c, Backing sand. 30c, Christmas dinner. 40c, Yard dance. 60c, Conch shell border.

***Perf. 14½x14¼***

**2000, Nov. 14 Wmk. 373**

**810-813** A138 Set of 4 9.50 9.50

UN Women's Human Rights Campaign — A139

**Wmk. 373**

**2001, Mar. 8 Litho. *Perf. 14***

**814** A139 10c multi .80 .80

Cayman Brac — A140

Designs: 15c, Red mangrove. 20c, Peter's Cave, vert. 25c, Bight Road stairway, vert. 30c, Westerly Pond. 40c, Aerial view. 60c, Marshes.

**2001, Apr. 21**

**815-820** A140 Set of 6 11.00 11.00

Non-profit Organizations A141

Designs: Nos. 821, 826a, 15c, National Council of Voluntary Organizations. Nos. 822, 826b, 20c, Cayman Humane Society. Nos. 823, 826c, 25c, Red Cross/Red Crescent. Nos. 824, 826d, 30c, Cayman Islands Cancer Society, vert. Nos. 825, 826e, 40c, Lions Club of Tropical Gardens, vert.

**Wmk. 373**

**2001, Aug. 15 Litho. *Perf. 14***

**Stamps With White Margins**

**821-825** A141 Set of 5 11.00 11.00

**Souvenir Sheet**

**Stamps With Pink Margins**

**826** A141 Sheet of 5, #a-e 11.00 11.00

No. 826 sold for $1.80, 50c of which went to the various organizations honored.

Transportation A142

Designs: No. 827, Walking home. No. 828, Boy on donkey. 20c, Bananas by canoe. 25c, Horse and buggy. 30c, Catboats. 40c, Schooner. 60c, Police bicycle, vert. 80c, Lady drivers. 90c, Launcing Cimboco, vert. $1, Seaplane. $4, Freighter. $10, Boeing 767.

***Perf. 14¼x14½, 14½x14¼***

**2001, Sept. 29 Litho. Wmk. 373**

| | | | | |
|---|---|---|---|---|
| **827** | A142 | 15c multi | .45 | .45 |
| **828** | A142 | 15c multi | .45 | .45 |
| **829** | A142 | 20c multi | .60 | .60 |
| **830** | A142 | 25c multi | .80 | .80 |
| **831** | A142 | 30c multi | .90 | .90 |
| **832** | A142 | 40c multi | 1.25 | 1.25 |
| **833** | A142 | 60c multi | 1.75 | 1.75 |
| **834** | A142 | 80c multi | 2.60 | 2.60 |
| **835** | A142 | 90c multi | 2.75 | 2.75 |
| **836** | A142 | $1 multi | 3.00 | 3.00 |
| **837** | A142 | $4 multi | 12.50 | 12.50 |
| **838** | A142 | $10 multi | 29.00 | 29.00 |
| | | *Nos. 827-838 (12)* | 56.05 | 56.05 |

Christmas — A143

Santa Claus: 15c, With children on dock. 30c, On eagle ray. 40c, In catboat. 60c, Parasailing.

***Perf. 14¼x14½***

**2001, Nov. 21 Litho. Wmk. 373**

**839-842** A143 Set of 4 7.50 7.50

In Remembrance of Sept. 11, 2001 Terrorist Attacks A144

***Perf. 14x14¾***

**2002, Jan. 22 Litho. Wmk. 373**

**843** A144 $1 multi 3.75 3.75

**Reign Of Queen Elizabeth II, 50th Anniv. Issue**

Common Design Type

Designs: Nos. 844, 848a, 15c, Princess Elizabeth as child. Nos. 845, 848b, 20c, In 1976. Nos. 846, 848c, 30c, With Princess Margaret, 1942. Nos. 847, 848d, 80c, In 1996. No. 848e, $1, 1955 portrait by Annigoni (38x50mm).

***Perf. 14¼x14½, 13¾ (#848e)***

**2002, Feb. 6 Litho. Wmk. 373**

**With Gold Frames**

| | | | | |
|---|---|---|---|---|
| **844** | CD360 | 15c multicolored | .45 | .45 |
| **845** | CD360 | 20c multicolored | .65 | .65 |
| **846** | CD360 | 30c multicolored | .90 | .90 |
| **847** | CD360 | 80c multicolored | 2.25 | 2.25 |
| | | *Nos. 844-847 (4)* | 4.25 | 4.25 |

**Souvenir Sheet**

**Without Gold Frames**

**848** CD360 Sheet of 5, #a-e 9.00 9.00

Peanuts Comic Strip Characters A145

Designs: 15c, Snoopy painting Woodstock at Cayman Brac Bluff. 20c, Charlie Brown and Sally at Hell Post Office. 25c, Peppermint Patty and Marcie at Little Cayman beach. 30c, Snoopy and Boeing 737-200. 40c, Linus and Snoopy at Point of Sand. 60c, Charlie Brown at Links Golf Course.

**Wmk. 373**

**2002, Mar. 9 Litho. *Perf. 14***

**849-854** A145 Set of 6 8.50 8.50

*854a* Souvenir sheet, #849-854 8.50 8.50

2002 World Cup Soccer Championships, Japan and Korea — A146

Denominations: 30c, 40c.

**2002, Apr. 30 *Perf. 13¾***

**855-856** A146 Set of 2 4.00 4.00

**Queen Mother Elizabeth (1900-2002)**

Common Design Type

Designs: 15c, Wearing hat (sepia photograph). 30c, Wearing dark blue hat. Nos. 859, 861a, 40c, Wearing hat (black and white photograph). Nos. 860, 861b, $1, Wearing tiara.

***Perf. 13¾x14¼, 14¼ (#859-860)***

**2002, Aug. 5 Litho. Wmk. 373**

**With Purple Frames**

| | | | | |
|---|---|---|---|---|
| **857** | CD361 | 15c multicolored | .65 | .65 |
| **858** | CD361 | 30c multicolored | 1.25 | 1.25 |
| **859** | CD361 | 40c multicolored | 1.60 | 1.60 |
| **860** | CD361 | $1 multicolored | 4.00 | 4.00 |
| | | *Nos. 857-860 (4)* | 7.50 | 7.50 |

**Souvenir Sheet**

**Without Purple Frames**

***Perf. 14½x14¼***

**861** CD361 Sheet of 2, #a-b 7.50 7.50

Christmas A147

Designs: 15c, Hail Mary. 20c, Journey to Bethlehem. 30c, Her firstborn Son. 40c, I bring good tidings. 60c Star in the east.

**Wmk. 373**

**2002, Oct. 18 Litho. *Perf. 14***

**Stamps + labels**

**862-866** A147 Set of 5 5.50 5.50

*866a* Souvenir sheet of 5, #862-866 + 5 labels 6.50 6.50

Aviation in the Cayman Islands, 50th Anniv. — A148

Designs: 15c, PBY Catalina Flying Boat. 20c, First landing at Grand Cayman Airport, 1952. 25c, Cayman Brac Airways AC 50. 30c, Cayman Airways B-737. 40c, Concorde at original airport, 1984. $1.30, Island Air DHC6.

**2002, Nov. 8**

**867-872** A148 Set of 6 15.00 15.00

Children's Games — A149

Designs: 15c, Rope skipping. 20c, Maypole dancing. 25c, Gig. 30c, Hopscotch. $1, Marbles.

**Wmk. 373**

**2003, May 27 Litho. *Perf. 13¾***

**873-877** A149 Set of 5 7.50 7.50

**Head of Queen Elizabeth II**
Common Design Type

**Wmk. 373**

**2003, June 2 Litho. *Perf. 13¾***
**878** CD362 $4 multi 14.00 14.00

**Coronation of Queen Elizabeth II, 50th Anniv.**
Common Design Type

Designs: Nos. 879, 15c, 881a, 20c, Queen wearing crown. Nos. 880, $2, 881b, $4, Queen holding symbols of office.

***Perf. 14¼x14½***

**2003, June 2 Litho. Wmk. 373**
**Vignettes Framed, Red Background**
**879** CD363 15c multicolored .50 .50
**880** CD363 $2 multicolored 6.75 6.75

**Souvenir Sheet**
**Vignettes Without Frame, Purple Panel**
**881** CD363 Sheet of 2, #a-b 12.00 12.00

**Prince William, 21st Birthday**
Common Design Type

Color photographs: 15c, William with backpack at right. 40c, William in suit and tie at left
No. 884: a, William with hand on chin at right. b, William with white bow tie at left.

**Wmk. 373**

**2003, June 21 Litho. *Perf. 14¼***
**882** CD364 15c multi .45 .45
**883** CD364 40c multi 1.25 1.25
**884** Horiz. pair 5.25 5.25
*a.* CD364 80c multi 2.25 2.25
*b.* CD364 $1 multi 3.00 3.00
*Nos. 882-884 (3)* 6.95 6.95

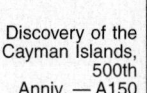

Discovery of the Cayman Islands, 500th Anniv. — A150

Designs: 15c, Turtle hatchlings. No. 886, 20c, Old waterfront. No. 887, 20c, Turtle and ship of Christopher Columbus. 25c, Nassau grouper. 30c, Cayman Brac schooner "Kirk-B." 40c, George Town harbor. 60c, Musical instruments. 80c, Smokewood tree. 90c, Little Cayman Baptist Church. $1, Thatch rope. $1.30, Children's dance troupe. $2, Parliament in session.

**Wmk. 373**

**2003, July 24 Litho. *Perf. 13¾***
**885-896** A150 Set of 12 27.50 27.50
*896a* Souvenir sheet, #885-896 29.00 29.00

Holiday Greetings — A151

Various Christmas decorations and inscriptions of: 15c, Merry Christmas. 20c, Celebrate With Family. 30c, Happy New Year. 40c, Happy Holidays. 60c, Seasons Greetings.

**Wmk. 373**

**2003, Nov. 4 Litho. *Perf. 13¼***
**897-901** A151 Set of 5 8.00 8.00

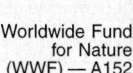

Worldwide Fund for Nature (WWF) — A152

Short-finned pilot whale: 15c, Adult and calf. 20c, Pod of four whales. 30c, Two whales at surface. 40c, One adult.

**2003, Nov. 26 *Perf. 14***
**902-905** A152 Set of 4 8.00 8.00
*905a* Sheet, 4 each #902-905 35.00 35.00

Shipping Registry, Cent. — A153

Ships: 15c, Lady Slater. 20c, Seanostrum. 30c, Kirk Pride. $1, Boadicea.

***Perf. 14x14¾***

**2004, Jan. 29 Litho. Wmk. 373**
**906-909** A153 Set of 4 11.00 11.00

Easter — A154

Designs: 15c, Jesus Carrying His Cross. 30c, The Ascension.

**2004, Mar. 16 *Perf. 14¾x14***
**910-911** A154 Set of 2 3.25 3.25

2004 Summer Olympics, Athens — A155

Designs: 15c, Swimmer. 40c, Runner. 60c, Long jumper. 80c, Swimmers.

***Perf. 13½x13¼***

**2004, Aug. 23 Litho. Wmk. 373**
**912-915** A155 Set of 4 6.25 6.25

Blue Iguana — A156

Designs: 15c, Adult on rocks. 20c, Eggs. 25c, Four juveniles. 30c, Juvenile on finger. 40c, Adult with open mouth. 90c, Eye.
No. 922: a, 60c, On rock facing right. b, 80c, On rock facing left.

**2004, Oct. 26 Litho. *Perf. 13¾***
**916-921** A156 Set of 6 8.50 8.50

**Souvenir Sheet**
**922** A156 Sheet of 2, #a-b 6.75 6.75
No. 922 sold for $1.90.

Battle of Trafalgar, Bicent. A157

Designs: 15c, HMS Victory. 20c, HMS Tonnant tangles into the bow of the Algesiras. 25c, Flint cannon lock and linstock. No. 926, 60c, Royal Navy boatswain's mate. $1, Adm. Horatio Nelson, vert. No. 928, $2, HMS Orion in action against the Intrepide.
No. 929, vert.: a, 60c, French gunship Pluton. b, $2, HMS Tonnant.

**Wmk. 373, Unwmkd. (15c)**

**2005, June 8 Litho. *Perf. 13¼***
**923-928** A157 Set of 6 14.50 14.50

**Souvenir Sheet**
**929** A157 Sheet of 2, #a-b 8.00 8.00

No. 923 has particles of wood from the HMS Victory embedded in the areas covered by a thermographic process that produces a raised, shiny effect.

Rotary International, Cent. — A158

Designs: 15c, Centennial emblem. 30c, PolioPlus emblem.

**2005, June 30 Wmk. 373 *Perf. 13¾***
**930-931** A158 Set of 2 2.50 2.50

Orchids — A159

Designs: 15c, Myrmecophila albopurpurea. 20c, Prosthechea boothiana. 30c, Tolumnia calochila, vert. 40c, Encyclia phoenicia. 80c, Prosthechea cochleata, vert.
$1.50, Encyclia kingsii.

**2005, July 28 *Perf. 14***
**932-936** A159 Set of 5 7.75 7.75

**Souvenir Sheet**
**937** A159 $1.50 multi 6.50 6.50

Pope John Paul II (1920-2005) — A160

**2005, Aug. 18**
**938** A160 30c multi 1.90 1.90

A161

Butterflies — A162

Designs: 15c, Queen. 20c, Mexican fritillary. 25c, Malachite. 30c, Cayman crescent spot. 40c, Cloudless sulphur. 90c, Swallowtail.

**Wmk. 373**

**2005, Sept. 21 Litho. *Perf. 14***
**939** A161 15c multi .65 .65
**940** A161 20c multi .85 .85
**941** A161 25c multi .95 .95
**942** A161 30c multi 1.20 1.20
**943** A161 40c multi 1.75 1.75
**944** A161 90c multi 3.50 3.50
*Nos. 939-944 (6)* 8.90 8.90

**Booklet Stamps**
**Self-Adhesive**
**Unwmk.**
***Serpentine Die Cut 9½x9***
**945** A162 15c multi .80 .80
*a.* Booklet pane of 10 8.00
**946** A162 20c multi 1.00 1.00
*a.* Booklet pane of 6 6.00
**947** A162 30c multi 1.35 1.35
*a.* Booklet pane of 10 13.50
*Nos. 945-947 (3)* 3.15 3.15

Christmas — A163

Designs: 15c, Angels. 30c, Magi, horiz. 40c, Holy Family. 60c, Shepherds, horiz.

***Perf. 14x14¾, 14¾x14***

**2005, Oct. 26 Wmk. 373**
**948-951** A163 Set of 4 5.50 5.50
*951a* Souvenir sheet, #948-951, perf. 14¾ 5.50 5.50

Trees and Blossoms — A164

Designs: 15c, Wash wood. 20c, Red mangrove. 30c, Ironwood. 60c, West Indian cedar. $2, Spanish elm.

**Wmk. 373**

**2006, Feb. 23 Litho. *Perf. 13¼***
**Stamp + Label**
**952-956** A164 Set of 5 12.00 12.00

Queen Elizabeth II, 80th Birthday — A165

Designs: 15c, As child. 40c, Wearing uniform and cap. $1, Wearing tiara. $2, Wearing sunglasses.
No. 961: a, 40c, Like #958. b, $1, Like #959.

**2006, Apr. 21 *Perf. 14***
**With White Frames**
**957-960** A165 Set of 4 11.00 11.00

**Souvenir Sheet**
**Without White Frames**
**961** A165 Sheet of 2, #a-b 11.00 11.00

A166

Marine Life — A167

Designs: Nos. 962, 967a, 968, Hawksbill turtle. Nos. 963, 967b, 969, Gray angelfish. Nos. 964, 967c, 970, Queen angelfish. Nos. 965, 967c, 971, Diamond blenny. Nos. 966, 967e, Juvenile spotted drum, vert. Nos. 964 and 967c are vert.

**Wmk. 373**

**2006, July 18 Litho. *Perf. 14***
**With White Margins**
**962** A166 25c multi 1.00 1.00
**963** A166 25c multi 1.00 1.00
**964** A166 60c multi 2.50 2.50
**965** A166 75c multi 3.25 3.25
**966** A166 $1 multi 4.25 4.25
*Nos. 962-966 (5)* 12.00 12.00

**Souvenir Sheet**
**Without White Margin**
**967** A166 Sheet of 5, #a-e 12.00 12.00

**Booklet Stamps**
**Self-Adhesive**
***Serpentine Die Cut 9½x9***
**Unwmk.**
**968** A167 25c multi .70 .70
*a.* Booklet pane of 10 7.00
**969** A167 25c multi .70 .70
*a.* Booklet pane of 10 7.00
**970** A167 60c multi 1.75 1.75
*a.* Booklet pane of 10 17.50
**971** A167 75c multi 2.00 2.00
*a.* Booklet pane of 10 20.00
*Nos. 968-971 (4)* 5.15 5.15

Birds — A168

Designs: 25c, Bananaquit. 50c, Vitelline warbler. 75c, Grand Cayman parrot. 80c, Caribbean dove. $1, Caribbean elaenia. $1.50, West Indian woodpecker. $1.60, Thick-billed vireo. $2, Northern flicker. $4, Cuban bullfinch. $5, Western spindalis. $10, Loggerhead kingbird. $20, Red-legged thrush.

*Perf. 13½x13¾*

**2006, Oct. 9 Litho. Wmk. 373**

**972** A168 25c multi .60 .60
**973** A168 50c multi 1.25 1.25
**974** A168 75c multi 1.90 1.90
**975** A168 80c multi 2.00 2.00
**976** A168 $1 multi 2.50 2.50
**977** A168 $1.50 multi 3.75 3.75
**978** A168 $1.60 multi 4.00 4.00
**979** A168 $2 multi 5.00 5.00
**980** A168 $4 multi 9.75 9.75
**981** A168 $5 multi 12.00 12.00
**982** A168 $10 multi 24.00 24.00
**983** A168 $20 multi 50.00 50.00
*Nos. 972-983 (12)* 116.75 116.75

**Booklet Stamps**

**Self-Adhesive**

**Unwmk.**

***Serpentine Die Cut 10x9½***

**Size:29x24mm**

**983A** A168 25c multi .85 .85
*d.* Booklet pane of 10 8.50
**983B** A168 75c multi 2.75 2.75
*e.* Booklet pane of 10 27.50
**983C** A168 80c multi 2.75 2.75
*f.* Booklet pane of 10 27.50
*Nos. 983A-983C (3)* 6.35 6.35

Christmas — A169

Designs: 25c, "Faith," Magi. 75c, "Hope," Prophet with scroll. 80c, "Joy," angel. $1, "Love," Madonna and Child.

*Perf. 12½x13¼*

**2006, Oct. 26 Litho. Wmk. 373**

**984-987** A169 Set of 4 12.00 12.00

Island Scenes — A170

Designs: 20c, Brac Reed dock. 25c, Waterfront buildings, Hog Sty Bay. 30c, East End blowholes, vert. 40c, Man in hammock, vert. 75c, Poinciana blooms. $1, Driftwood on Little Cayman.

**Wmk. 373**

**2007, June 26 Litho. *Perf. 13¾***

**988-993** A170 Set of 6 10.00 10.00

Scouting, Cent. — A171

Designs: 25c, Wolf Cubs and leaders, hands lashing rope. 75c, Cub Scouts and leaders, hands with trumpet. 80c, Scouts camping, hand with compass. $1, Scout Drill Team, poppies.

No. 998, vert.: a, 50c, Scouts marching. b, $1.50, Lord Robert Baden-Powell and dog.

**2007, July 9**

**994-997** A171 Set of 4 9.00 9.00

**Souvenir Sheet**

**998** A171 Sheet of 2, #a-b 5.50 5.50

Wedding of Queen Elizabeth II and Prince Philip, 60th Anniv. — A172

Designs: 50c, Couple and wedding coach. 75c, Elizabeth wearing bridal veil. 80c, Princess Elizabeth, Philip, Queen Mother Elizabeth, King George VI, Princess Margaret. $1, Wedding procession, Westminster Abbey.

$2, Couple.

**Wmk. 373**

**2007, Sept. 12 Litho. *Perf. 13¾***

**999-1002** A172 Set of 4 10.50 10.50

**Souvenir Sheet**

***Perf. 14***

**1003** A172 $2 multi 7.50 7.50

No. 1003 contains one 42x57mm stamp.

Christmas — A173

Stained-glass windows from local churches: 25c, Nativity, Wesleyan Holiness Church. 50c, Jesus Praying, Elmslie Memorial Church. 75c, Jesus Calling First Disciples, St. George's Anglican Church. 80c, Dove, East End Adventist Church. $1, Orb, First Baptist Church of Grand Cayman. $1.50, Shepherd, Frank Sound Church of God.

**2007, Oct. 22 *Perf. 15x14***

**1004-1009** A173 Set of 6 16.50 16.50

A174

Greetings — A175

Nos. 1010-1015: a, Hello. b, Good Luck. c, Congratulations. d, You're Invited. e, Best Wishes. f, Love.

No. 1016, Hello. No. 1017, Congratulations. No. 1018, You're Invited. No. 1019, Love.

**Wmk. 373**

**2008, Feb. 5 Litho. *Perf. 14¼***

**1010** A174 20c Sheet of 6, #a-f 3.00 3.00
**1011** A174 25c Sheet of 6, #a-f 3.75 3.75
**1012** A174 50c Sheet of 6, #a-f 7.50 7.50
**1013** A174 75c Sheet of 6, #a-f 11.00 11.00
**1014** A174 80c Sheet of 6, #a-f 12.00 12.00
**1015** A174 $1 Sheet of 6, #a-f 15.00 15.00
*Nos. 1010-1015 (6)* 52.25 52.25

**Booklet Stamps**

**Self-Adhesive**

***Serpentine Die Cut 9½x9***

**Unwmk.**

**1016** A175 20c multi .85 .85
*a.* Booklet pane of 10 8.50
**1017** A175 25c multi 1.00 1.00
*a.* Booklet pane of 10 10.00
**1018** A175 25c multi .85 .85
*a.* Booklet pane of 10 8.50
**1019** A175 25c multi 1.00 1.00
*a.* Booklet pane of 10 10.00
*Nos. 1016-1019 (4)* 3.70 3.70

Darwin Initiative — A176

Fauna: 20c, Land crab. 25c, Needlecase. 75c, Little Cayman green anole, vert. 80c, Cayman Brac ground boa. $1, White-shouldered bat.

$2, Caribbean reef squid, vert.

**Wmk. 373**

**2008, July 9 Litho. *Perf. 14***

**1020-1024** A176 Set of 5 11.00 11.00

**Souvenir Sheet**

**1025** A176 $2 multi 7.00 7.00

2008 Olympic Games, Beijing — A177

Designs: 20c, Lanterns, swimming. 25c, Fish, swimming. 50c, Bamboo, running. 75c, Dragon, hurdles.

**Wmk. 373**

**2008. Aug. 8 Litho. *Perf. 13¼***

**1026-1029** A177 Set of 4 7.00 7.00

Water Authority, 25th Anniv. — A178

Children's art: 25c, Stop Water Pollution. 75c, Water droplets. $2, Splash of Life.

**Wmk. 373**

**2008, Oct. 16 Litho. *Perf. 13¼***

**1030-1032** A178 Set of 3 11.00 11.00

Christmas — A179

Santa Claus and: 25c, Ship. 75c, Horse-drawn carriage. 80c, Helicopter. $1, Race car.

**2008, Nov. 12 *Perf. 13¾***

**1033-1036** A179 Set of 4 11.00 11.00

A180

No. 1037: a, Silver thatch plant. b, People making rope strands. c, Man cobbing rope. d, Thatch products. e, Traditional home.

**Wmk. 406**

**2009, Jan. 28 Litho. *Perf. 13¾***

**1037** A180 Horiz. strip of 5 5.00 5.00
*a.-e.* 25c Any single 1.00 1.00
Complete booklet, 2 #1037 10.00

Island Scenes — A181

Island Scenes — A181a

Designs: 20c, Hammock, palm trees, boat. 25c, House. 75c, Hammock under shelter at beach, palm trees, vert. 80c, Three cruise liners. $1, Direction signs near bus depot, vert. $1.50, Limestone pinnacles, Hell.

$2, Iguana.

**2009, Apr. 9 *Perf. 12½***

**1038-1043** A181 Set of 6 14.00 14.00

**Souvenir Sheet**

***Perf. 13***

**1044** A181 $2 multi 6.25 6.25

**Booklet Stamps**

**Self-Adhesive**

***Serpentine Die Cut 10x9½***

**1044A** A181a 20c multi .50 .50
*c.* Booklet pane of 10 5.00
**1044B** A181a 25c multi .60 .60
*d.* Booklet pane of 10 6.00

Space Exploration — A182

Designs: 20c, Mars Rover, 2004. 25c, Space Shuttle STS-71 launch, 1995. 75c, Hubble Space Telescope. $1, Apollo 11 launch, 1969. $1.50, International Space Station.

$2, Lunar Rover on Moon, painting by Capt. Alan Bean, vert.

**Wmk. 406**

**2009, July 20 Litho. *Perf. 13¼***

**1045-1049** A182 Set of 5 11.00 11.00

**Souvenir Sheet**

***Perf. 13x13¼***

**1050** A182 $2 multi 6.25 6.25

No. 1050 contains one 40x60mm stamp. Nos. 1045-1049 each were printed in sheets of 6.

Equality Through Democracy — A183

Designs: No. 1051, 25c, Hands holding pens signing voting rolls. No. 1052, 25c, George Town Town Hall. 50c, Woman casting ballot.

**Wmk. 406**

**2009, Sept. 23 Litho. *Perf. 13¾***

**1051-1053** A183 Set of 3 3.75 3.75
*1053a* Sheet of 3, #1051-1053 3.75 3.75

Woman suffrage and Cayman Islands constitution, 50th anniv.

Christmas — A184

Images of Christmas stamps of 1997: 25c, Cayman Islands #749. 75c, Cayman Islands #750. 80c, Cayman Islands #751. $1, Cayman Islands #752.

**Wmk. 406**

**2009, Oct. 22 Litho. *Perf. 14***

**1054-1057** A184 Set of 4 8.00 8.00

Shells — A185

Designs: 20c, Hawk-wing conch. 25c, Ornate scallop. 60c, Chestnut turban. 75c Beautiful mitre. 80c, Four-toothed nerite. $1.60, White-spotted marginella.

$3, Queen conch.

**Wmk. 406**

**2010, June 30 Litho. *Perf. 13¼***

**1058-1063** A185 Set of 6 13.50 13.50

**Souvenir Sheet**

**1064** A185 $3 multi 10.50 10.50

Shells — A186

Designs: 25c, Ornate scallop. 75c, Beautiful mitre.

***Serpentine Die Cut 9½x9***

**2010, June 30 Unwmk.**

**Booklet Stamps**

**Self-Adhesive**

**1065** A186 25c multi *1.75 1.75*
*a.* Booklet pane of 10 *17.50*
**1066** A186 75c multi *4.25 4.25*
*a.* Booklet pane of 10 *42.50*

Girld Guides, Cent. — A187

Girl Guides: 20c Uniforms. 25c, Camping. 50c, Parade. 80c, Badges.

**Wmk. 406**

**2010, Dec. 17 Litho. *Perf. 12½***
**1067-1070** A187 Set of 4 6.00 6.00

Wedding of Prince William and Catherine Middleton — A188

Designs: 25c, Couple kissing. 75c, Couple in carriage waving, horiz. 80c, Couple holding hands. $2, Couple and father of the bride, horiz.

**2011, Aug. 4 *Perf. 14***
**1071-1074** A188 Set of 4 8.50 8.50

Catboats A189

Designs: No. 1075, 20c, Men in catboats catching turtles. Nos. 1076, 1081, 25c, Men building catboat. No. 1077, 25c, Catboat sailing around Cayman Brac's Bluff. No. 1078, 50c, Catboats racing regatta style. No. 1079, $1.60, Catboats unloading cargo. No. 1080, $2, Women sewing catboat sail.

**2011, Aug. 31 Wmk. 406 *Perf. 14***
**1075-1080** A189 Set of 6 12.00 12.00

**Booklet Stamp**
**Self-Adhesive**
**Size:30x25mm**
***Serpentine Die Cut 9½x9***
**Unwmk.**

**1081** A189 25c multi *1.25 1.25*
*a.* Booklet pane of 10 *12.50*

Christmas — A190

Designs: 25c, Frontispiece for 1611 edition of the King James Bible. 75c, King James I. 80c, William Tyndale, Bible tanslator. $1, Printers printing the King James Bible. $1.60, Translators in the Jerusalem Chamber.

**2011, Nov. 8 Wmk. 406 *Perf. 12½***
**1082-1086** A190 Set of 5 12.50 12.50

King James Bible, 400th anniv.

Famous Cayman Islanders A191

Designs: 20c, Almerian Labertha McLaughlin Tomlinson (1882-1974), midwife. 25c, Captain Royal Brazley Bodden (1885-1976), shipwright and builder. 75c, Irskie Leila Yates (1899-1996), maternity nurse. $1.50, Major Joseph Rodriguez Watler (1890-1965), police inspector.

***Perf. 13¼x13¾***

**2011, Nov. 11 Wmk. 406**
**1087** A191 20c multi .65 .65
*a.* Booklet pane of 6 3.90 —
Complete booklet, #1087a 3.90
**1088** A191 25c multi .75 .75
*a.* Booklet pane of 6 4.50 —
Complete booklet, #1088a 4.50
**1089** A191 75c multi 2.25 2.25
*a.* Booklet pane of 6 13.50 —
Complete booklet, #1089a 13.50
**1090** A191 $1.50 multi 4.50 4.50
*a.* Booklet pane of 6 27.00 —
Complete booklet, #1090a 27.00
*Nos. 1087-1090 (4)* 8.15 8.15

A192

Reign of Queen Elizabeth II, 60th Anniv. — A193

Various photographs of Queen Elizabeth II: 25c, 80c, $1, $1.50.

**2012, June 12 Wmk. 406 *Perf. 14***
**1091-1094** A192 Set of 4 10.00 10.00

**Booklet Stamp**
**Self-Adhesive**
***Serpentine Die Cut 9½x9***
**Unwmk.**

**1095** A193 25c multi *1.50 1.50*
*a.* Booklet pane of 10 *15.00*

2012 Summer Olympics, London — A194

Designs: 25c, Runner. 50c, Hurdler. 75c, Swimmer. 80c, Two runners. $1.60, Swimmer, diff.

**Wmk. 406**

**2012, Aug. 2 Litho. *Perf. 13¼***
**1096-1100** A194 Set of 5 10.50 10.50

A195

A195a

Emergency Services: 20c, Patrol boats. 25c, Ambulance service. 75c, Fire department. $1.50, 911 public safety communications. $2, Police helicopter.

**2012, Aug. 30 Wmk. 406 *Perf. 14***
**1101-1105** A195 Set of 5 12.00 12.00
*1101a* Dated "2013" .50 .50

**Booklet Stamps**
**Self-Adhesive**
**Unwmk.**
***Serpentine Die Cut 9½x9***

**1105A** A195a 25c multi .75 .75
*c.* Booklet pane of 10 7.50
**1105B** A195a 75c multi 2.10 2.10
*d.* Booklet pane of 10 21.00

A196

A197

Marine Life: 25c, Stoplight parrotfish. 50c, Green sea turtle. 75c, Common sea fan, Yellow tube sponge. 80c, Upside-down jellyfish. $1, Juvenile yellowtail damselfish. $1.50, Spotted trunkfish. $1.60, Caribbean spiny lobster. $2, Giant barrel sponge. $4, Caribbean reef shark. $5, Great barracuda. $10, Southern stingray.$20, West Indian spider crab.

**2012, Oct. 9 Wmk. 406 *Perf. 14***
**1106** A196 25c multi .60 .60
**1107** A196 50c multi 1.25 1.25
**1108** A196 75c multi 1.90 1.90
**1109** A196 80c multi 2.00 2.00
**1110** A196 $1 multi 2.50 2.50
*a.* Souvenir sheet of 4 10.00 10.00
**1111** A196 $1.50 multi 3.75 3.75
**1112** A196 $1.60 multi 4.00 4.00
**1113** A196 $2 multi 5.00 5.00
**1114** A196 $4 multi 9.75 9.75
**1115** A196 $5 multi 12.50 12.50
**1116** A196 $10 multi 22.50 22.50
**1117** A196 $20 multi 45.00 45.00
*Nos. 1106-1117 (12)* 110.75 110.75

**Booklet Stamps**
**Self-Adhesive**
***Die Cut Perf. 14x15¼***
**Unwmk.**

**1118** A197 25c multi .60 .60
*a.* Booklet pane of 10 6.00
**1119** A197 75c multi 1.90 1.90
*a.* Booklet pane of 10 19.00
**1120** A197 80c multi 2.00 2.00
*a.* Booklet pane of 10 20.00
*Nos. 1118-1120 (3)* 4.50 4.50

Christmas A198

Paintings by Gladwyn K. Bush: 25c, Mary and Jesus. 75c, His Name is Jesus. 80c, Every Knee Shall Bow. $1, Nativity.

**2012, Dec. 6 Wmk. 406 *Perf. 14***
**Stamps + Label**
**1121-1124** A198 Set of 4 6.50 6.50

A199

Shipwrecks and Anchors — A200

Shipwreck: 20c, Mathusalem. Nos. 1126, 1130, 25c, Inga. No. 1127, 25c, Topsy. $1.50, Tofa. $2, Glamis.

**Wmk. 406**

**2013, Aug. 2 Litho. *Perf. 14***
**1125-1129** A199 Set of 5 10.50 10.50

**Booklet Stamp**
**Self-Adhesive**
***Die Cut Perf. 14x15¼***
**Unwmk.**

**1130** A200 25c multi .60 .60
*a.* Booklet pane of 10 6.00

Birth of Prince George of Cambridge — A201

Designs: 20c, Prince George. 25c, Duchess of Cambridge holding Prince George. 80c, Duke of Cambridge holding Prince George. $2, Duke and Duchess of Cambridge, Prince George.

**Wmk. 406**

**2013, Oct. 31 Litho. *Perf. 12½***
**1131-1134** A201 Set of 4 7.75 7.75

Christmas A202

Santa Claus and: 25c, Old Government House. 75c, Old Homestead. 80c, Bodden Town Mission House. $1, Old District Administration Building.

**Wmk. 406**

**2013, Nov. 5 Litho. *Perf. 13***
**1135-1138** A202 Set of 4 6.75 6.75

Houses on Little Cayman and Cayman Brac — A203

Designs: 20c, Captain Theo's Villa, Little Cayman. 25c, Carter's House, Cayman Brac. 75c, Captain Charlie's House, Cayman Brac. $1, Foster's House, Cayman Brac.

**Wmk. 406**

**2014, June 10 Litho. *Perf. 13***
**1139-1142** A203 Set of 4 5.50 5.50

A204

20th Commonwealth Games, Glasgow, Scotland — A205

Scottish flag and: 20c, Cycling. 25c, Swimming. 55c, Boxing. 80c, Squash. $1, Shooting. $1.60, Gymnastics. $2, Javelin.

***Perf. 13¼x13***

**2014, Oct. 3 Litho. Wmk. 406**
**1143-1149** A204 Set of 7 16.00 16.00

**Booklet Stamp**
**Self-Adhesive**
***Serpentine Die Cut 13¾x14***
**Unwmk.**

**1150** A205 25c multi .60 .60
*a.* Booklet pane of 10 6.00

A206

Christmas — A207

Christmas ornaments, poinsettia and: Nos. 1151, 1154, 25c, Little Cayman Baptist Church. Nos. 1152, 1155, 25c, South Sound United Church. Nos. 1153, 1156, 25c, Stake Bay Baptist Church.

**Wmk. 406**

**2014, Nov. 15 Litho. *Perf. 13¾***
**1151-1153** A206 Set of 3 1.90 1.90

**Booklet Stamps**
**Self-Adhesive**
***Die Cut Perf. 14x15¼***
**Unwmk.**

**1154-1156** A207 Set of 3 1.90 1.90
*1156a* Booklet pane of 12, 4 each #1154-1156 7.75

**Famous Cayman Islanders Type of 2011**

Designs: 25c, Timothy E. McField (1928-95), educator. 50c, Annie Huldah Bodden (1908-89), politician. 80c, Ormond L. Panton (1920-92), politician. $1, Captain Keith P. Tibbetts, Sr. (1916-96), politician.

***Perf. 13¼x13¾***

**2015, May 20 Litho. Wmk. 406**
**1157** A191 25c multi .60 .60
*a.* Booklet pane of 6 3.75 —
Complete booklet, #1157a 3.75
**1158** A191 50c multi 1.25 1.25
*a.* Booklet pane of 6 7.50 —
Complete booklet, #1158a 7.50
**1159** A191 80c multi 2.00 2.00
*a.* Booklet pane of 6 12.00 —
Complete booklet, #1159a 12.00
**1160** A191 $1 multi 2.50 2.50
*a.* Booklet pane of 6 15.00 —
Complete booklet, #1160a 15.00
*Nos. 1157-1160 (4)* 6.35 6.35

A208

Christmas — A209

Winning designs in children's Christmas stamp design contest depicting: 20c, Christmas tree, presents and crab, by Arianna Anglin. Nos. 1162, 1165, 25c, Parrot, by Clementine Bonnie Lumsden. 75c, Turtle, by Zara Garofolo. 80c, Sun, sailboat, Christmas stockings, by Cerys Martin.

**Wmk. 406**

**2015, Dec. 2 Litho. *Perf. 13***

**1161-1164** A208 Set of 4 5.00 5.00

**Booklet Stamp**
**Self-Adhesive**

***Serpentine Die Cut 13¾x14***

**Unwmk.**

**1165** A209 25c multi .60 .60
*a.* Booklet pane of 10 6.00

Cayman Islands National Museum, 25th Anniv. — A210

Designs: No. 1166, 25c, Ship's sextant, 1960s. No. 1167, 25c, Caymanian Woman, wood carving by Clarice Carter, 1960s. 75c, Coffee grinder, early 1900s. $1.60, Monkey jar, early 1900s.

**Wmk. 406**

**2015, Dec. 3 Litho. *Perf. 14***

**1166-1169** A210 Set of 4 7.00 7.00

Ships — A211

Designs: 25c, Kirk B. 80c, Nunoca. $1, Rembro. $2, Clara C. Scott.
$4, HMS Dragon.

**Wmk. 406**

**2016, May 16 Litho. *Perf. 13***

**1170-1173** A211 Set of 4 10.00 10.00

**Souvenir Sheet**

**1174** A211 $4 multi 9.75 9.75

Queen Elizabeth II, 90th Birthday — A212

Various photographs of Queen Elizabeth II: 20c, 25c, 75c, 80c.

**2016, Nov. 9 Litho. *Perf. 13½x13¼***

**1175-1178** A212 Set of 4 5.00 5.00

Agriculture, 50th Anniv. — A213

Designs: 20c, Boer goat. 25c, Fruits and vegetables. 50c, Mixed-breed cow. $2, Peppers. No. 1183 — Farmers: a, Kent Rankin (1946-2016). b, John Bothwell (1920-2006). c, Mercherito Chantilope (1937-2014).

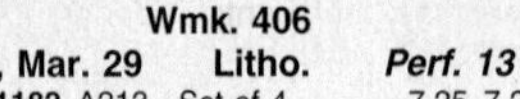

**Wmk. 406**

**2017, Mar. 29 Litho. *Perf. 13¼***

**1179-1182** A213 Set of 4 7.25 7.25

**Souvenir Sheet**

**1183** Sheet of 3 7.75 7.75
*a.* A213 75c multi 1.90 1.90
*b.* A213 80c multi 2.00 2.00
*c.* A213 $1.50 multi 3.75 3.75

Astronomy — A214

Designs: 25c, Moon. 50c, Saturn. 75c, Solar flares. $1.60, Jupiter.

**Wmk. 406**

**2017, June 2 Litho. *Perf. 13¼***

**1184-1187** A214 Set of 4 7.75 7.75

Moths — A215

Designs: 20c, Faithful beauty moth. 25c, Cayman clearwing wasp moth. $1.60, White-lined sphinx moth. $2, Gaudy sphinx moth.

**Wmk. 406**

**2017, Oct. 12 Litho. *Perf. 13¾***

**1188-1191** A215 Set of 4 10.00 10.00

Christmas A216

Christmas decorations at local homes: Nos. 1192, 1196, 25c, Bodden family's nativity scene. 75c, Crighton family's display of Santa Claus and Christmas trees. 80c, Bodden family's carolers. $1, Crighton family's display of Santa Claus and elves.

***Perf. 12½x13***

**2017, Nov. 2 Litho. Wmk. 406**

**1192-1195** A216 Set of 4 7.00 7.00

**Booklet Stamp**
**Self-Adhesive**

***Serpentine Die Cut 13¼x13½***

**Unwmk.**

**1196** A216 25c multi .60 .60
*a.* Booklet pane of 10 6.00

70th Wedding Anniversary of Queen Elizabeth II and Prince Philip — A217

Map of Cayman Islands and: 20c, Engagement photograph. 25c, Wedding photograph. 75c, Photograph from 1982. 80c, Photograph from 2016.

***Perf. 14¼x14½***

**2017, Dec. Litho. Wmk. 406**

**1197-1200** A217 Set of 4 5.00 5.00

Nos. 1197-1200 were each printed in sheets of 7 + label.

Wedding of Prince Harry and Meghan Markle — A218

Various photographs of couple: 25c, 75c, 80c, $1.

***Perf. 13x13¼***

**2018, July 18 Litho. Wmk. 406**

**1201-1204** A218 Set of 4 7.00 7.00

Cayman Airways, 50th Anniv. — A219

Designs: Nos. 1205, 1210, 25c, Boeing 737-300. 80c, Boeing 737-800. $1, DeHavilland DHC-6 Twin Otter. $1.50, Saab 340B+.
$2, 50th anniversary emblem, vert.

**Wmk. 406**

**2018, Aug. 17 Litho. *Perf. 13½***

**1205-1208** A219 Set of 4 8.75 8.75

**Souvenir Sheet**

***Perf. 14***

**1209** A219 $2 multi 5.00 5.00

**Booklet Stamp**
**Self-Adhesive**
**Size:39x24mm**

***Serpentine Die Cut 12¾x13***

**Unwmk.**

**1210** A219 25c multi .60 .60
*a.* Booklet pane of 10 6.00

No. 1209 contains one 33x45mm stamp.

Cayman Islands Coat of Arms, 60th Anniv. — A220

**Wmk. 406**

**2018, Oct. 19 Litho. *Perf. 12½***

**1211** A220 $2 multi 5.00 5.00
*a.* Souvenir sheet of 1 5.00 5.00

A221

Christmas — A222

Carols: 25c, "We Three Kings of Orient Are." 80c, "O Holy Night." $1.50, "Away in a Manger." $2, "Joy to the World."

**Wmk. 406**

**2018, Nov. 23 Litho. *Perf. 14***

**1212-1215** A221 Set of 4 11.00 11.00

**Booklet Stamp**
**Self-Adhesive**

**Unwmk.**

***Serpentine Die Cut 10x9¾***

**1216** A222 25c multi .60 .60
*a.* Booklet pane of 10 6.00

A223

Christmas — A224

Designs: 25c, Santa Claus playing guitar, reindeer playing drum. 75c, Santa Claus playing guitar in hammock, reindeer playing washboard, iguana playing drum. 80c, Santa Claus playing violin in sailboat, reindeer playing drum. $2, Santa Claus and reindeer playing guitars, parrot singing.

**Wmk. 406**

**2019, Nov. 15 Litho. *Perf. 14***

**1217-1220** A223 Set of 4 9.25 9.25

**Booklet Stamp**
**Self-Adhesive**

***Serpentine Die Cut 10x9¾***

**Unwmk.**

**1221** A224 25c multi .60 .60
*a.* Booklet pane of 10 6.00

First Man on the Moon, 500th Anniv. — A225

Designs: 20c, Astronaut's footprint on Moon. 25c, Moon. 75c, Astronaut and U.S. flag on Moon. $1.60, Rocket launch.

**Wmk. 406**

**2019, Dec. 13 Litho. *Perf. 14¼***

**1222-1225** A225 Set of 4 7.00 7.00

A226

Queen Elizabeth II Botanic Park — A226a

Designs: 25c, Water lily. 50c, Lakeview. 75c, Whistling ducks. 80c, Orchids. $1, Park entrance. $1.50, Heritage Garden. $1.60, Prince Charles touching Peter, the blue iguana. No. 1233, Queen Elizabeth II at Botanic Park. $4, Trail entrance. $5, Visitor's Center. $10, Fountain. $20, Cayman Julia butterfly.
No. 1238, Palm trees.

**Wmk. 406**

**2020, Nov. 18 Litho. *Perf. 14¼***

| | | | | |
|---|---|---|---|---|
| **1226** | A226 | 25c multi | .60 | .60 |
| **1227** | A226 | 50c multi | 1.25 | 1.25 |
| **1228** | A226 | 75c multi | 1.90 | 1.90 |
| **1229** | A226 | 80c multi | 2.00 | 2.00 |
| **1230** | A226 | $1 multi | 2.50 | 2.50 |
| **1231** | A226 | $1.50 multi | 3.75 | 3.75 |
| **1232** | A226 | $1.60 multi | 4.00 | 4.00 |
| **1233** | A226 | $2 multi | 5.00 | 5.00 |
| **1234** | A226 | $4 multi | 9.75 | 9.75 |
| **1235** | A226 | $5 multi | 12.50 | 12.50 |
| **1236** | A226 | $10 multi | 24.50 | 24.50 |
| **1237** | A226 | $20 multi | 49.00 | 49.00 |
| | *Nos. 1226-1237 (12)* | | 116.75 | 116.75 |

**Souvenir Sheet**

**1238** A226 $2 multi 5.00 5.00

**Booklet Stamps**
**Self-Adhesive**

***Serpentine Die Cut 10x9¾***

**Unwmk.**

| | | | | |
|---|---|---|---|---|
| **1238A** | A226a | 25c multi | .60 | .60 |
| *d.* | | Booklet pane of 10 | 6.00 | |
| **1238B** | A226a | 75c multi | 1.90 | 1.90 |
| *e.* | | Booklet pane of 10 | 19.00 | |
| **1238C** | A226a | 80c multi | 2.00 | 2.00 |
| *f.* | | Booklet pane of 10 | 20.00 | |
| | *Nos. 1238A-1238C (3)* | | 4.50 | 4.50 |

Cayman Islands Cancer Society, 25th Anniv. — A227

***Perf. 14¼x14***

**2021, Sept. 16 Litho. Wmk. 406**

**1239** A227 25c multi .60 .60

International College of the Cayman Islands, 50th Anniv. — A228

***Perf. 14x14¼***

**2021, Oct. 8 Litho. Wmk. 406**

**1240** A228 25c multi .60 .60

Prince Philip (1921-2021) — A229

Prince Philip: 20c, Wearing military uniform. 25c, Wearing suit and tie. $1, With Princess Elizabeth at their wedding. $1.60, In carriage with his wife, Queen Elizabeth II.
$2, Prince Philip and Queen Elizabeth II standing.

**Wmk. 406**

**2021, Dec. 16 Litho. *Perf. 14¼***
**1241-1244** A229 Set of 4 7.50 7.50

**Souvenir Sheet**

**1245** A229 $2 multi 5.00 5.00

Queen Elizabeth II, 95th Birthday — A230

Queen Elizabeth II: 25c, Wearing tiara. 30c, Wearing green hat. 80c, Wearing dark blue hat. $1.50, Wearing tiara, diff.
$2, Queen Elizabeth II wearing tiara and blue sash.

**Wmk. 406**

**2021, Dec. 16 Litho. *Perf. 14¼***
**1246-1249** A230 Set of 4 7.00 7.00

**Souvenir Sheet**

**1250** A230 $2 multi 5.00 5.00

Christmas A231

Santa Claus, palm tree and: 25c, Old Government House. 75c, Old Homestead. 80c, Bodden Town Mission House. $1.50, Old District Administration Building.

***Perf. 14¼x14***

**2021, Dec. 16 Litho. Wmk. 406**
**1251-1254** A231 Set of 4 8.00 8.00

Wellesley Howell (1915-2021), Oldest Cayman Islander — A232

Howell: 25c, At his shoe repair shop. $2, Playing saxophone.

***Perf. 14¼x14***

**2022, Apr. 21 Litho. Wmk. 406**
**1255-1256** A232 Set of 2 5.50 5.50

Reign of Queen Elizabeth II (1926-2022), 70th Anniv. — A233

Various photographs of Queen Elizabeth II: 25c, 80c, $1.50, $1.60.

**Wmk. 406**

**2022, June 30 Litho. *Perf. 14¼***
**1257-1260** A233 Set of 4 10.00 10.00

## WAR TAX STAMPS

**No. 36 Surcharged**

a b

**1917, Feb. 26 Wmk. 3 *Perf. 14***
**MR1** A5(a) 1½p on 2½p 20.00 *26.00*
*a.* Fraction bar omitted 275.00 *300.00*
*b.* Period missing after "STAMP" 900.00
**MR2** A5(b) 1½p on 2½p 2.10 *7.25*
*a.* Fraction bar omitted 85.00 *150.00*

On No. 1 the distance between "WAR STAMP" and "1½" varies.

Surcharged

**1917, Sept. 4**
**MR3** A5 1½p on 2½p ultra 850.00 *2,500.*

Surcharged

**1917, Sept. 4**
**MR4** A5 1½p on 2½p ultra .30 *.65*

No. 33 Overprinted

**1919, Feb. 4**
**MR5** A5 ½p green .70 *3.00*

The "brownish paper" variety comes from the interleaving used for shipment from England.

Type of 1912-16 Surcharged

**1919, Feb. 4**
**MR6** A5 1½p on 2½p orange 1.00 *2.00*

No. 35 Surcharged

**1920, Mar. 10**
**MR7** A5 1½p on 2p gray 5.50 *9.50*

The "rose-tinted paper" variety comes from the interleaving used for shipment from England.
A surcharge in red was not issued.

# CENTRAL AFRICAN REPUBLIC

ˈsen-trəl ˈa-fri-kən ri-ˈpə-blik

LOCATION — Western Africa, north of equator
GOVT. — Republic
AREA — 241,243 sq. mi.
POP. — 3,444,951 (1999 est.)
CAPITAL — Bangui

The former French colony of Ubangi-Shari, a unit in French Equatorial Africa, proclaimed itself the Central African Republic Dec. 1, 1958. It became the Central African Empire Dec. 4, 1976. It became the Central African Republic again in 1979.

100 Centimes = 1 Franc

**Catalogue values for all unused stamps in this country are for Never Hinged items.**

**Watermark**

Wmk. 385

Premier Barthélemy Boganda and Flag — A1

Design: 25fr, Boganda and flag, horiz.

**Unwmk.**

**1959, Dec. 1 Engr. *Perf. 13***
**1** A1 15fr multi .40 .30
**2** A1 25fr multi .60 .30

1st anniv. of the Republic and honoring Premier Barthélemy Boganda (1910-59).
For overprints & surcharge see Nos. 12, 59, M1-M2.

Imperforates

Many stamps of Central African Republic exist imperforate in issued and trial colors, and also in small presentation sheets in issued colors.

Common Design Types pictured following the introduction.

**C.C.T.A. Issue**
Common Design Type

**1960, May 21 Unwmk. *Perf. 13***
**3** CD106 50fr lt grn & dk bl 1.60 .75

Dactyloceras Widenmanni A2

Designs: Various butterflies.

**1960-61**
**4** A2 50c bl grn & dk red .25 .25
**5** A2 1fr multi .25 .25
**6** A2 2fr dk grn & brn .25 .30
**7** A2 3fr yel grn & dk red .30 .30
**8** A2 5fr multi .35 .30
**9** A2 10fr multi .85 .45
**10** A2 20fr multi 1.75 .60
**11** A2 85fr multi 7.00 1.60
*Nos. 4-11 (8)* 11.00 4.05

Issued: 50c-3fr, 6/10/61; others, 9/3/60.

No. 2 Overprinted

**1960, Dec. 1**
**12** A1 25fr multi 1.60 1.60

National Holiday, Dec. 1, 1960.

Louis Pasteur and Pasteur Institute, Bangui — A3

**1961, Feb. 25 Unwmk. *Perf. 13***
**13** A3 20fr multi 1.25 .70

Opening of Pasteur Institute at Bangui.

Flag, Map, and UN Emblem — A4

**1961, Mar. 4 Engr.**
**14** A4 15fr multi .45 .30
**15** A4 25fr multi .45 .30
**16** A4 85fr multi 1.50 1.00
*Nos. 14-16 (3)* 2.40 1.60

Admission to the UN.

No. 15 Overprinted in Green

**1961, Dec. 1**
**17** A4 25fr multi 2.00 2.00

National Holiday, Dec. 1.

No. 16 Srchd. in Red Brown

**1962, Mar. 25**
**18** A4 50fr on 85fr multi 1.90 1.90

Conf. of the African and Malgache Union at Bangui, Mar. 25-27.

**Abidjan Games Issue**
Common Design Type

**1962, July 21 Photo. *Perf. 12½x12***
**19** CD109 20fr Hurdling .45 .30
**20** CD109 50fr Bicycling 1.20 .80
*Nos. 19-20,C6 (3)* 4.15 2.85

**African-Malgache Union Issue**
Common Design Type

**1962, Sept. 8 Unwmk.**
**21** CD110 30fr multi 1.25 .75

African and Malgache Union, 1st anniv.

Pres. David Dacko — A5

**1962 *Perf. 12***
**22** A5 20fr multi .40 .25
**23** A5 25fr multi .60 .30

For surcharge see No. 60.

Soldiers with Flag — A6

**1963, Aug. 13 Photo.**
**24** A6 20fr blk & multi .75 .45

National Army, third anniversary.

Designs: 40fr, Elegant galago. 100fr, Calabar potto, horiz. 150fr, Bosman's potto, horiz. 200fr, Oustalet's colobo, horiz.

**1971, Oct. 25 Photo. *Perf. 13***

**142** A49 30fr pink & multi .70 .45
**143** A49 40fr lt bl & multi .90 .60
**144** A49 100fr multi 2.75 1.40
**145** A49 150fr multi 4.75 2.25
**146** A49 200fr multi 5.75 2.75
*Nos. 142-146 (5)* 14.85 7.45

Alan B. Shepard A50

No. 148, Yuri Gagarin. No. 149, Edwin E. Aldrin, Jr. No. 150, Alexei Leonov. No. 151, Neil A. Armstrong on moon. No. 152, Lunokhod I on moon.

**1971, Nov. 19 Litho. *Perf. 14***

**147** A50 40fr vio & multi .45 .30
**148** A50 40fr vio & multi .45 .30
**149** A50 100fr multi 1.15 .45
**150** A50 100fr multi 1.15 .45
**151** A50 200fr red & multi 2.25 1.10
**152** A50 200fr red & multi 2.25 1.10
*Nos. 147-152 (6)* 7.70 3.70

Space achievements of US and Russia.

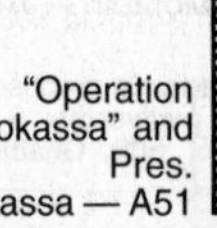

"Operation Bokassa" and Pres. Bokassa — A51

**1971, Dec. 1 Photo. *Perf. 13***

**153** A51 40fr red & multi .85 .40

12th anniversary of independence.

Racial Equality Emblem — A52

**1971, Dec. 6 Litho.**

**154** A52 50fr multi .90 .45

Intl. Year Against Racial Discrimination.

Bokassa School Emblem and Cadets — A53

**1972, Jan. 1 Photo.**

**155** A53 30fr gold & multi .90 .45

J. B. Bokassa Military School.

Book Year Emblem — A54

**1972, Mar. 11 Photo. *Perf. 12½x13***

**156** A54 100fr red brn, gold & org 3.00 1.25

International Book Year 1972.

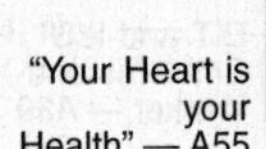

"Your Heart is your Health" — A55

**1972, Apr. 7 Photo. *Perf. 13x12½***

**157** A55 100fr yel, blk & car 1.75 .90

World Health Day.

Red Cross Workers in Village — A56

**1972, May 8 *Perf. 13***

**158** A56 150fr multi 3.00 1.40

25th World Red Cross Day.

Globe — A57

**1972, May 17 Litho.**

**159** A57 50fr yel, blk & dp org .90 .55

4th World Telecommunications Day.

Pres. and Mrs. Bokassa and Family — A58

**1972, May 28 *Perf. 14***

**160** A58 30fr yel & multi .70 .40

Mother's Day. Mothers' gold medal awarded to Catherine Bokassa.

Pres. Bokassa Planting Cotton, Map of Africa — A59

**1972, June 5 Photo. *Perf. 13***

**161** A59 40fr yel & multi .90 .45

Operation Bokassa, a natl. development plan.

Postal Checking and Savings Center — A60

**1972, June 21**

**162** A60 30fr yel org & multi .70 .35

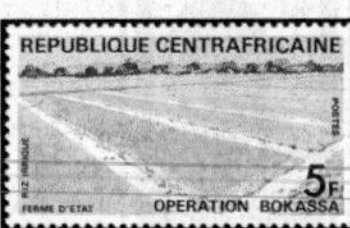


Irrigated Rice Fields — A61

"Le Pacifique" Apartment House — A62

25fr, Plowing rice field. No. 166, Swimming pool, Hotel St. Sylvestre. No. 167, Entrance, Hotel St. Sylvestre. No. 168, J. B. Bokassa University.

**1972 Litho. *Perf. 13x13½***

**163** A61 5fr multi 1.25 .25
**164** A61 25fr multi 2.10 .30

**Engr. *Perf. 13***

**165** A62 30fr multi .40 .25
**166** A62 30fr multi .50 .30
**167** A62 40fr multi .60 .40
**168** A62 40fr multi .65 .40
*Nos. 163-168 (6)* 5.50 1.90

Operation Bokassa. Issued: 5fr, 25fr, 11/10; No. 165, 6/27; Nos. 166-167, 12/9; No. 168, 8/26.

Bull Chasing Woman on Clock Face — A63

Scenes Painted on Clock Faces: 10fr, Men & open cooking fire. 20fr, Fishermen. 30fr, Palms, monkeys & giraffe. 40fr, Warriors.

**1972, July 31 Photo. *Perf. 12½***

**169** A63 5fr dk red & multi .30 .30
**170** A63 10fr brt bl & multi .30 .30
**171** A63 20fr grn & multi .60 .30
**172** A63 30fr yel & multi .85 .50
**173** A63 40fr vio & multi 1.25 .65
*Nos. 169-173 (5)* 3.30 2.05

HORCEN Central African clock and watch factory.

Protestant Youth Center A64

10fr, Postal runner carrying mail in cleft stick.

**1972, Aug. 12 *Perf. 13***

**174** A64 10fr multi, vert. .30 .30
**175** A64 20fr multi .50 .30
*Nos. 174-175,C95-C98 (6)* 8.35 5.10

Centraphilex 1972, Central African Philatelic Exhibition, Bangui.

Mail Truck — A65

**1972, Oct. 23 Photo. *Perf. 13***

**176** A65 100fr ocher & multi 2.00 .80

Universal Postal Union Day.

Mother Teaching Child to Write — A66

Central African Mothers: 10fr, Caring for infant. 15fr, Combing child's hair. 20fr, Teaching to read. 180fr, Nursing. 190fr, Teaching to walk.

**1972, Dec. 27 *Perf. 13½x13***

**177** A66 5fr multi .25 .25
**178** A66 10fr lil & multi .30 .25
**179** A66 15fr dl org & multi .30 .25
**180** A66 20fr yel grn & multi .50 .25
**181** A66 180fr multi 2.75 1.25
**182** A66 190fr pink & multi 2.75 1.25
*Nos. 177-182 (6)* 6.85 3.50

Farmer Carrying Sheaf — A67

**1973, May 30 Photo. *Perf. 13***

**183** A67 50fr vio bl & multi .90 .45

10th anniv. of the World Food Program.

Garcinia Punctata — A68

African Flora: 20fr, Bertiera racemosa. 30fr, Corynanthe pachyceras. 40fr, Combretodendron africanum. 50fr, Xylopia Villosa, vert.

**1973, June 8**

**184** A68 10fr pale bl & multi .50 .25
**185** A68 20fr multi .85 .30
**186** A68 30fr lt gray & multi 1.00 .45
**187** A68 40fr multi 1.60 .60
**188** A68 50fr multi 2.00 .80
*Nos. 184-188 (5)* 5.95 2.40

For surcharge see No. 193.

Pygmy Chameleon A69

**1973, June 26 Photo. *Perf. 13***

**189** A69 15fr multi 2.25 .40

Caterpillar A70

Designs: Various caterpillars.

**1973, Aug. 6 Photo. *Perf. 13***

**190** A70 3fr multi 1.25 .30
**191** A70 5fr multi 2.00 .40
**192** A70 25fr multi 4.00 .80
*Nos. 190-192 (3)* 7.25 1.50

For surcharge see No. 259.

No. 184 Srchd. and Ovptd. in Red

**1973, Aug. 16**

**193** A68 100fr on 10fr multi 1.75 1.00

African solidarity in drought emergency.

**African Postal Union Issue**

Common Design Type

**1973, Sept. 12 Engr. *Perf. 13***

**194** CD137 100fr dk brn, red org & ol 1.25 .75

Pres. Bokassa and CAR Flag — A71

**1973, Nov. 30 Photo. *Perf. 12½***

**195** A71 1fr brn & multi .25 .25
**196** A71 2fr pur & multi .25 .25
**197** A71 3fr vio bl & multi .25 .25
**198** A71 5fr ocher & multi .25 .25
**199** A71 10fr multi .40 .25
**200** A71 15fr org & multi .40 .25
**201** A71 20fr multi .50 .25
**202** A71 30fr dk grn & multi .50 .30
**203** A71 40fr dk brn & multi .65 .40
*Nos. 195-203,C117-C118 (11)* 5.60 3.55

INTERPOL Emblem — A72

**1973, Dec. 20 *Perf. 13x12½***

**204** A72 50fr yellow & multi 1.00 .60

Intl. Criminal Police Organization, 50th anniv.

Catherine Bokassa Center — A73

40fr, Ambulance in front of Catherine Bokassa Center.

**1974, Jan. 24 Engr. *Perf. 13***
**205** A73 30fr multi .40 .25
**206** A73 40fr multi .55 .35

Catherine Bokassa Center for Mothers and Children.

Cigarette-making Machine — A74

10fr, Cigarette in ashtray, & factory. 30fr, Hand lighting cigarette, & Administration Building.

**1974, Jan. 29**
**207** A74 5fr slate grn & multi .25 .25
**208** A74 10fr slate grn & multi .40 .25
**209** A74 30fr slate grn & multi .50 .25
*Nos. 207-209 (3)* 1.15 .75

Publicity for Centra cigarettes.

"Communications" A75

**1974, June 8 Photo. *Perf. 12½x13***
**210** A75 100fr multi 1.75 .90

World Telecommunications Day.
For surcharge see No. 280.

People and WPY Emblem — A76

**1974, June 20 Engr. *Perf. 13***
**211** A76 100fr red, slate grn & brn 1.25 .70

World Population Year.
For surcharge see No. 281.

Mother, Child, WHO Emblem — A77

**1974, July 10**
**212** A77 100fr multi 1.75 .70

26th anniv. of WHO.
For surcharge see No. 282.

Hoeing — A78

Veterans' activities: 10fr, Battle scene ("yesterday"). 15fr, Pastoral scene ("today"). 20fr, Rice planting. 25fr, Storehouse. 40fr, Veterans Headquarters. Borders show tanks and tractors.

**1974, Nov. 15 Litho. *Perf. 13***
**213** A78 10fr multi .25 .25
**214** A78 15fr multi .25 .25
**215** A78 20fr multi .25 .25
**216** A78 25fr multi .35 .25
**217** A78 30fr multi .35 .25
**218** A78 40fr multi .55 .25
*Nos. 213-218 (6)* 2.00 1.50

For surcharges see Nos. 260, 265, 267.

Presidents and Flags of Cameroun, CAR, Congo, Gabon and Meeting Center
A79

**1974, Dec. 8 Photo. *Perf. 13***
**219** A79 40fr gold & multi .70 .40

See No. C126 and note after Cameroun No. 595.
For surcharge see No. 272.

House in OCAM City — A80

Scenes in housing development, OCAM City.

**1975, Feb. 1 Photo. *Perf. 13***
**220** A80 30fr multi .35 .25
**221** A80 40fr multi .40 .30
**222** A80 50fr multi .50 .30
**223** A80 100fr multi .75 .55
*Nos. 220-223 (4)* 2.00 1.40

For surcharges see Nos. 269, 273.

**1975, Feb. 22**

Cottage scenes in J. B. Bokassa "pilot village."

**224** A80 25fr multi .30 .25
**225** A80 30fr multi .40 .25
**226** A80 40fr multi .50 .40
*Nos. 224-226 (3)* 1.20 .90

For surcharges see Nos. 268, 270, 274.

Foreign Ministry — A81

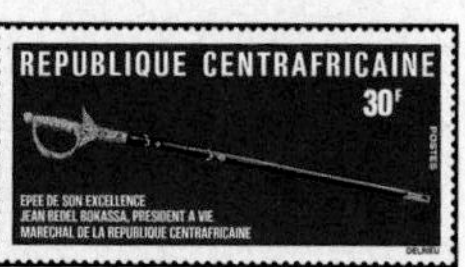


Television Station — A82

**1975, Feb. 28 *Perf. 13x12½***
**227** A81 40fr multi .75 .40

***Perf. 13***
**228** A82 40fr multi .75 .40

Public buildings, Bangui.
For surcharges see Nos. 275-276.

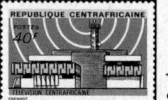

Bokassa's Saber — A83

Design: 40fr, Bokassa's baton.

**1975, Feb. 22 Photo. *Perf. 13***
**229** A83 30fr dp bl & multi .55 .30
**230** A83 40fr vio bl & multi .75 .30

Jean Bedel Bokassa, President for Life and Marshal of the Republic. See Nos. C127-C128. For surcharge see No. 286.

Traffic Signs — A84

**1975, Mar. 20**
**231** A84 5fr Do Not Enter .25 .25
**232** A84 10fr Stop .25 .25
**233** A84 20fr No parking .40 .25
**234** A84 30fr School .60 .25
**235** A84 40fr Intersection .85 .30
*Nos. 231-235 (5)* 2.35 1.30

For surcharges see Nos. 261, 277.

Buffon's Kob — A85

**1975, June 24 Photo. *Perf. 13***
**236** A85 10fr shown .50 .25
**237** A85 15fr Wart hog 1.25 .35
**238** A85 20fr Waterbuck 1.75 .35
**239** A85 30fr Lion 1.75 .50
*Nos. 236-239 (4)* 5.25 1.45

For surcharges see Nos. 262-263, 266, 271.

Crane Lifting Log onto Truck — A86

Designs: 10fr, Forest, vert. 15fr, Tree felling, vert. 100fr, Log pile. 150fr, Logs transported by raft. 200fr, Lumberyard.

**1975, Nov. 28 Engr. *Perf. 13***
**240** A86 10fr multi .25 .25
**241** A86 15fr multi .30 .25
**242** A86 50fr multi .55 .25
**243** A86 100fr multi 1.50 .55
**244** A86 150fr multi 1.75 1.00
**245** A86 200fr multi 2.25 1.40
*Nos. 240-245 (6)* 6.60 3.70

Promotion of Central African wood.
For surcharges see Nos. 264, 279.

Women's Heads and Various Occupations A87

**1975, Dec. 10 Photo.**
**246** A87 40fr multi .50 .25
**247** A87 100fr multi 1.40 .60

International Women's Year 1975.

---

This stamp, lacking the word 'Postes,' was prepared for use in 1976. It is known canceled on unaddressed first day covers, and off cover with a cancel different from that found on the first day cancel, but this stamp is not one of the many stamps of the same period that were overprinted in 1977. The editors would like to examine any contemporaneous commercial cover bearing this stamp and receive any other pertinent information concerning the issuance of this stamp.

---

Alexander Graham Bell — A88

**1976, Mar. 25 Litho. *Perf. 12½x13***
**248** A88 100fr yel & blk 2.25 1.00

Centenary of first telephone call by Alexander Graham Bell, Mar. 10, 1876.
For surcharge see No. 283.

Satellite and ITU Emblem A89

No. 250, UPU emblem, various forms of mail transport.

**1976 Engr. *Perf. 13***
**249** A89 100fr vio bl, claret & grn 1.90 1.10
**250** A89 100fr car, grn & ocher 1.60 .90

World Telecommunications Day (No. 249); Universal Postal Union Day (No. 250).
For surcharges see Nos. 284-285.

Soyuz on Launching Pad — A90

Design: 50fr, Apollo rocket.

**1976, June 14 Litho. *Perf. 14x13½***
**251** A90 40fr multi .55 .25
**252** A90 50fr multi 1.00 .25
*Nos. 251-252,C135-C137 (5)* 6.65 2.25

Apollo Soyuz space test project, Russo-American cooperation, launched July 15, link-up July 17, 1975.
For surcharges see Nos. 287, 290, C161, C168, C173, C177.

Drurya Antimachus A91

Butterfly: 40fr, Argema mittrei, vert.

**1976, Sept. 20 Litho. *Perf. 12½***
**253** A91 30fr ocher & multi 7.00 1.10
**254** A91 40fr ultra & multi 9.00 1.10
*Nos. 253-254,C145-C146 (4)* 31.00 5.70

For surcharge see No. 278.

Slalom, Piero Gros — A92

60fr, Karl Schnabel and Toni Innauer.

**1976, Sept. 23 *Perf. 13½***
**255** A92 40fr multi .65 .25
**256** A92 60fr multi 1.00 .35
*Nos. 255-256,C147-C149 (5)* 7.15 2.75

12th Winter Olympic Games winners, Innsbruck.
For surcharges see Nos. 288, 291, C164, C170, C174, C178.

Viking Components A93

Design: 60fr, Viking take-off.

**1976, Dec.**
**257** A93 40fr multi .65 .25
**258** A93 60fr multi 1.00 .35
*Nos. 257-258,C151-C153 (5)* 7.20 2.75

Viking Mars project.
For surcharges and overprints see Nos. 289, 292, 391-392, C165, C171, C175, C179.

## Central African Empire

Stamps of 1973-76 Overprinted in Black, Green, Violet Blue, Silver, Carmine, Brown or Red

Nos. 259, 278, 283

Nos. 260, 265, 267, 269, 273, 276, 279

Nos. 261, 277

Nos. 262-263, 266, 271

Nos. 264, 282

Nos. 268, 270, 274, 280, 284-285

Nos. 272, 275

No. 281

### Printing and Perforations as Before

**1977, Mar.**

| | | | | | |
|---|---|---|---|---|---|
| **259** | A70 | 3fr | (#190; B) | .50 | .45 |
| **260** | A78 | 10fr | (#213;B) | .35 | .35 |
| **261** | A84 | 10fr | (#232;VB) | .35 | .35 |
| **262** | A85 | 10fr | (#236;C) | .50 | .50 |
| **263** | A85 | 15fr | (#237;C) | .85 | .85 |
| **264** | A86 | 15fr | (#241;B) | .35 | .35 |
| **265** | A78 | 20fr | (#215;B) | .50 | .50 |
| **266** | A85 | 20fr | (#238;C) | .50 | .50 |
| **267** | A78 | 25fr | (#216;B) | .40 | .40 |
| **268** | A80 | 25fr | (#224;B) | .40 | .40 |
| **269** | A80 | 30fr | (#220;VB) | .50 | .50 |
| **270** | A80 | 30fr | (#225;B) | .50 | .50 |
| **271** | A85 | 30fr | (#239;C) | .60 | .60 |
| **272** | A79 | 40fr | (#219;B) | .50 | .50 |
| **273** | A80 | 40fr | (#221;VB) | .50 | .50 |
| **274** | A80 | 40fr | (#226;B) | .50 | .50 |
| **275** | A81 | 40fr | (#227;B & S) | .70 | .70 |
| **276** | A82 | 40fr | (#228;B) | .75 | .75 |
| **277** | A84 | 40fr | (#235;VB) | .75 | .75 |
| **278** | A91 | 40fr | (#254;B) | 1.00 | 1.00 |
| **279** | A86 | 50fr | (#242;Br) | 1.00 | 1.00 |
| **280** | A75 | 100fr | (#210;B) | 1.90 | 1.90 |
| **281** | A76 | 100fr | (#211;B) | 1.90 | 1.90 |
| **282** | A77 | 100fr | (#212;G) | 2.25 | 2.25 |
| **283** | A88 | 100fr | (#248;R) | 1.90 | 1.90 |
| **284** | A89 | 100fr | (#249;B) | 2.25 | 2.25 |
| **285** | A89 | 100fr | (#250;B) | 2.50 | 2.50 |
| | | | *Nos. 259-285 (27)* | 24.70 | 24.65 |

### Stamps of 1975-76 Overprinted in Black on Silver Panel

**1977, Apr. 1**

| | | | | |
|---|---|---|---|---|
| **286** | A83 | 40fr multi (#230) | .90 | .90 |
| **287** | A90 | 40fr multi (#251) | .70 | .70 |
| **288** | A92 | 40fr multi (#255) | .70 | .70 |
| **289** | A93 | 40fr multi (#257) | .70 | .70 |
| **290** | A90 | 50fr multi (#252) | 1.00 | 1.00 |
| **291** | A92 | 60fr multi (#256) | .90 | .90 |
| **292** | A93 | 60fr multi (#258) | .90 | .90 |
| | | *Nos. 286-292 (7)* | 5.80 | 5.80 |

Pierre and Marie Curie — A94

Design: 60fr, Wilhelm C. Roentgen.

**1977, Apr. 1 Litho. *Perf. 13½***

| | | | | |
|---|---|---|---|---|
| **293** | A94 | 40fr multi | 1.25 | .40 |
| **294** | A94 | 60fr multi | 1.00 | .40 |
| | | *Nos. 293-294,C180-C182 (5)* | 13.25 | 2.85 |

Nobel Prize winners.

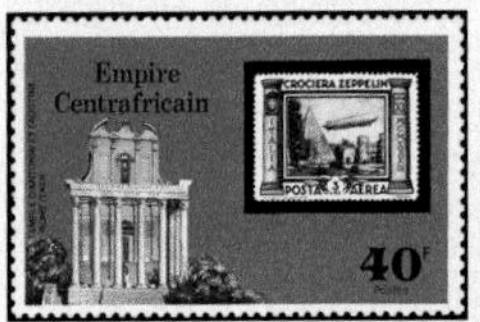

Italy No. C42 and Faustine Temple, Rome A95

60fr, Russia #C12 & St. Basil's Cathedral, Moscow.

**1977, Apr. 11 Litho. *Perf. 11***

| | | | | |
|---|---|---|---|---|
| **295** | A95 | 40fr multi | 1.00 | .25 |
| **296** | A95 | 60fr multi | 1.10 | .40 |
| | | *Nos. 295-296,C184-C186 (5)* | 8.70 | 2.65 |

75th anniversary of the Zeppelin.

Lindbergh over Paris — A96

Designs: 60fr, Santos Dumont and "14 bis." 100fr, Bleriot and monoplane. 200fr, Roald Amundsen and "N24." 300fr, Concorde. 500fr, Lindbergh and Spirit of St. Louis.

**1977, Sept. 30 Litho. *Perf. 13½***

| | | | | |
|---|---|---|---|---|
| **297** | A96 | 50fr multi | .60 | .25 |
| **298** | A96 | 60fr multi | .80 | .25 |
| **299** | A96 | 100fr multi | 1.60 | .50 |
| **300** | A96 | 200fr multi | 2.50 | .65 |
| **301** | A96 | 300fr multi | 5.00 | 1.25 |
| | | *Nos. 297-301 (5)* | 10.50 | 2.90 |

#### Souvenir Sheet

| | | | | |
|---|---|---|---|---|
| **302** | A96 | 500fr multi | 6.00 | 2.00 |

History of aviation, famous fliers.

Shot on Goal — A97

Designs: 60fr, Heading ball in net. 100fr, Backfield defense. 200fr, Argentina '78 poster. 300fr, Mario Zagalo and stadium. 500fr, Ferenc Puskas.

**1977, Nov. 18 Litho. *Perf. 13½***

| | | | | |
|---|---|---|---|---|
| **303** | A97 | 50fr multi | .50 | .25 |
| **304** | A97 | 60fr multi | .65 | .25 |
| **305** | A97 | 100fr multi | 1.25 | .30 |
| **306** | A97 | 200fr multi | 2.10 | .55 |
| **307** | A97 | 300fr multi | 3.50 | .90 |
| | | *Nos. 303-307 (5)* | 8.00 | 2.25 |

#### Souvenir Sheet

| | | | | |
|---|---|---|---|---|
| **308** | A97 | 500fr multi | 5.50 | 2.00 |

World Soccer Championships, Argentina, June 1-25, 1978.

For overprints see Nos. 370-375.

Emperor Bokassa I, Central African Flag — A98

**1977, Dec. 4 Litho. *Perf. 13½***

| | | | | |
|---|---|---|---|---|
| **309** | A98 | 40fr multi | .40 | .25 |
| **310** | A98 | 60fr multi | .55 | .25 |
| **311** | A98 | 100fr multi | 1.00 | .55 |
| **312** | A98 | 150fr multi | 1.40 | .70 |
| | | *Nos. 309-312,C188-C189 (6)* | 7.60 | 3.80 |

Coronation of Emperor Bokassa I, Dec. 4.

Lilium — A99

**1977 Litho. *Perf. 13½x14***

| | | | | |
|---|---|---|---|---|
| **313** | A99 | 5fr shown | .55 | .30 |
| **314** | A99 | 10fr Hibiscus | 1.10 | .65 |

For overprints see Nos. 408-409.

Electronic Tree, ITU Emblem — A100

**1977**

| | | | | |
|---|---|---|---|---|
| **315** | A100 | 100fr blk, org & brn | 3.00 | 2.00 |

World Telecommunications Day.

Bible and People — A101

**1977 Litho. *Perf. 14x13½***

| | | | | |
|---|---|---|---|---|
| **316** | A101 | 40fr multi | 8.00 | 1.25 |

Bible Week.

People and Rotary Emblem — A102

**1977**

| | | | | |
|---|---|---|---|---|
| **317** | A102 | 60fr multi | 4.25 | 2.00 |

Rotary Club of Bangui, 20th anniversary.

Holy Family, by Rubens — A103

Rubens Paintings: 150fr, Marie de Medicis. 200fr, Son of artist. 300fr, Neptune. 500fr, Marie de Medicis, diff.

**1978, Jan. 26**

| | | | | |
|---|---|---|---|---|
| **318** | A103 | 60fr multi | .60 | .25 |
| **319** | A103 | 150fr multi | 1.50 | .40 |
| **320** | A103 | 200fr multi | 2.40 | .60 |
| **321** | A103 | 300fr multi | 3.50 | .80 |
| | | *Nos. 318-321 (4)* | 8.00 | 2.05 |

#### Souvenir Sheet

| | | | | |
|---|---|---|---|---|
| **322** | A103 | 500fr gold & multi | 6.00 | 2.00 |

Peter Paul Rubens (1577-1640).

Rhinoceros A104

Endangered Animals and Wildlife Fund Emblem: 50fr, Slender-nosed crocodile. 60fr, Leopard, vert. 100fr, Giraffe, vert. 200fr, Elephant. 300fr, Gorilla, vert.

**1978, Feb. 21 Litho. *Perf. 13½***

| | | | | |
|---|---|---|---|---|
| **323** | A104 | 40fr multi | *1.60* | .30 |
| **324** | A104 | 50fr multi | *2.25* | .35 |
| **325** | A104 | 60fr multi | *2.50* | .55 |
| **326** | A104 | 100fr multi | *4.25* | .90 |
| **327** | A104 | 200fr multi | *11.00* | 1.25 |
| **328** | A104 | 300fr multi | *12.50* | 2.00 |
| | | *Nos. 323-328 (6)* | *34.10* | 5.35 |

Bokassa Sports Palace — A105

Design: 60fr, Sports Palace, side view.

**1978 *Perf. 14***

| | | | | |
|---|---|---|---|---|
| **329** | A105 | 40fr multi | .50 | .25 |
| **330** | A105 | 60fr multi | .65 | .40 |

Automatic Telephone Exchange, Bangui — A106

**1978**

| | | | | |
|---|---|---|---|---|
| **331** | A106 | 40fr multi | .50 | .25 |
| **332** | A106 | 60fr multi | .70 | .40 |

Diligence and Satellite A107

Designs (UPU Emblem and): 50fr, Steam locomotive and communications via satellite. 60fr, Paddle-wheel steamer and ship-to-shore communication via satellite. 80fr, Old mail truck and satellite.

**1978, May 17 *Perf. 13½***

| | | | | |
|---|---|---|---|---|
| **333** | A107 | 40fr multi | .50 | .25 |
| **334** | A107 | 50fr multi | 1.50 | .65 |
| **335** | A107 | 60fr multi | .70 | .30 |
| **336** | A107 | 80fr multi | .80 | .30 |
| | | *Nos. 333-336,C191-C192 (6)* | 5.70 | 2.40 |

Posts and telecommunications, cent. of progress.

Mask — A108

Designs: 30fr, Mask. 60fr, Women dancers, horiz. 100fr, Men dancers, horiz.

***Perf. 13½x14, 14x13½***

**1978, July 11 Litho.**

| | | | | |
|---|---|---|---|---|
| **337** | A108 | 20fr blk & yel | .65 | .30 |
| **338** | A108 | 30fr blk & brt bl | .65 | .30 |
| **339** | A108 | 60fr blk & multi | 1.60 | .70 |
| **340** | A108 | 100fr blk & multi | 3.00 | .95 |
| | | *Nos. 337-340 (4)* | 5.90 | 2.25 |

Black-African World Arts Festival, Lagos.

For overprints see Nos. 411-412.

Capt. Cook on "Endeavour" — A109

60fr, Resolution off Hawaii. 200fr, Hawaiians welcoming Capt. Cook. 350fr, Masked rowers in Hawaiian boat.

**1978, Aug. 30** *Perf. 14½*

**341** A109 60fr multi, horiz. .60 .25
**342** A109 80fr multi 1.00 .35
**343** A109 200fr multi, horiz. 2.00 .70
**344** A109 350fr multi, horiz. 3.50 1.25
*Nos. 341-344 (4)* 7.10 2.55

Capt. James Cook (1728-1779), explorer.

Dürer, Self-portrait A110

Dürer Paintings: 80fr, The Four Apostles. 200fr, Virgin and Child. 350fr, Emperor Maximilian I.

**1978, Oct. 24** **Litho.** *Perf. 13½*

**345** A110 60fr multi .60 .25
**346** A110 80fr multi 1.00 .25
**347** A110 200fr multi 2.25 .85
**348** A110 350fr multi 4.25 1.60
*Nos. 345-348 (4)* 8.10 2.95

Albrecht Dürer (1471-1528), German painter.

Tutankhamen's Gold Mask — A111

Treasures of Tutankhamen: 60fr, King and Queen, gold back panel of throne. 80fr, Gilt folding chair. 100fr, King wearing crowns of Upper and Lower Egypt, painted wood sculpture. 120fr, Lion's head. 150fr, Tutankhamen, wood stature. 180fr, Gold throne. 250fr, Gold miniature coffin.

**1978, Nov. 22**

**349** A111 40fr multi .65 .30
**350** A111 60fr multi .75 .40
**351** A111 80fr multi 1.25 .55
**352** A111 100fr multi 1.40 .55
**353** A111 120fr multi 2.00 .60
**354** A111 150fr multi 2.25 .70
**355** A111 180fr multi 2.50 .90
**356** A111 250fr multi 3.50 1.25
*Nos. 349-356 (8)* 14.30 5.25

Tutankhamen, c. 1358 B.C., King of Egypt.

Lenin at Smolny Institute — A112

Soviet Union, 60th anniv.: 60fr, 200fr, 300fr, Various Lenin portraits. 100fr, Ulyanov family, horiz. 150fr, Lenin, Cruiser "Aurora" and flag, horiz. 500fr, "Aurora" and star.

**1978, Nov.** *Perf. 14*

**357** A112 40fr multi .50 .30
**358** A112 60fr multi .60 .40
**359** A112 100fr blk & gold 1.00 .45
**360** A112 150fr blk, gold & red 1.90 .70
**361** A112 200fr multi 3.00 1.00
**362** A112 300fr multi 4.00 1.40
*Nos. 357-362 (6)* 11.00 4.25

**Souvenir Sheet**

**363** A112 500fr multi 6.00 4.00

Catherine Bokassa — A113

Design: 60fr, Emperor Bokassa.

**1978, Dec. 4** **Litho.** *Perf. 13*

**364** A113 40fr multi .65 .25
**365** A113 60fr multi .90 .30

1st anniv. of coronation. See No. C202.

Rowland Hill, Letter Scale and G.B. No. 1 — A114

Rowland Hill and: 50fr, US No. 1, mailman on bicycle. 60fr, Austria No. P4, 19th cent. mailman. 80fr, Switzerland No. 2L1, postilion and mailcoach.

**1978, Dec. 9** **Litho.** *Perf. 13½*

**366** A114 40fr multi .65 .30
**367** A114 50fr multi .65 .30
**368** A114 60fr multi .90 .40
**369** A114 80fr multi 1.00 .50
*Nos. 366-369,C203-C204 (6)* 7.20 2.80

Sir Rowland Hill (1795-1879), originator of penny postage.

**Nos. 303-307 Overprinted in Silver**

**1978, Dec. 27**

**370** A97 50fr multi .70 .25
**371** A97 60fr multi .85 .30
**372** A97 100fr multi 1.25 .55
**373** A97 200fr multi 3.00 1.00
**374** A97 300fr multi 4.25 1.40
*Nos. 370-374 (5)* 10.05 3.50

**Souvenir Sheet**
**No. 308 Overprinted in Silver**

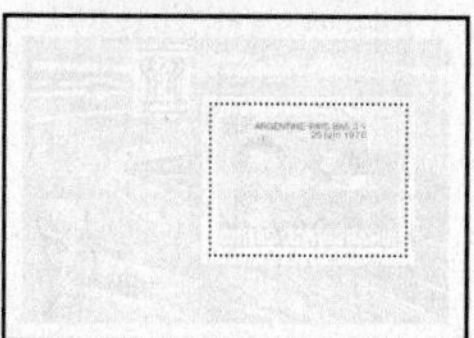

**375** A97 500fr multi 5.00 5.00

Argentina's victory in World Cup Soccer Championship 1978.

Balambo Chair — A114a

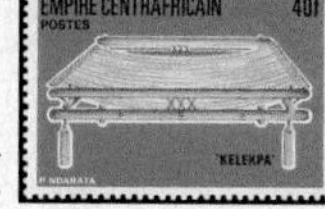

Kelekpa Table — A114b

**1978 ?** **Litho.** *Perf. 14x13¼*

**375A** A114a 20fr multi — —
**375B** A114b 40fr multi — —

See No. C205A. For overprint, see No. 410.

Children Painting and Dutch Portrait A115

UNICEF, Eagle Emblems and: 50fr, Eskimo children skiing, ski jump. 60fr, Children with toy racing car, Carl Benz with early car model. 80fr, Children launching rocket, Mariner 5.

**1979, Mar. 6** **Litho.** *Perf. 13½*

**376** A115 40fr multi .65 .25
**377** A115 50fr multi .75 .25
**378** A115 60fr multi .90 .25
**379** A115 80fr multi 1.25 .30
*Nos. 376-379,C206-C207 (6)* 7.30 2.25

International Year of the Child.

High Jump, Moscow '80 Emblem and "M" — A116

Designs (Moscow '80 Emblem, Various Sports and): 50fr, Bicycling and "O." 60fr, Weight lifting and "C." 80fr, Judo and "K."

**1979, Mar. 16** **Litho.** *Perf. 13*

**380** A116 40fr multi .55 .25
**381** A116 50fr multi .65 .25
**382** A116 60fr multi .75 .25
**383** A116 80fr multi 1.10 .30
*Nos. 380-383,C209-C210 (6)* 6.25 2.10

22nd Olympic Games, Moscow, July 19-Aug. 3, 1980. Background letters on Nos. 380-383, C209-C210 spell "Mockba." A 1500fr gold embossed stamp showing emblems and Discobolus exists.

Memorial, Bangui, Butterfly, Hibiscus A117

Design: 150fr, Canoe, truck and letters.

**1979, June 8** **Litho.** *Perf. 12x12½*

**384** A117 60fr multi 2.75 1.25
**385** A117 150fr multi 5.00 2.50

Philexafrique II, Libreville, Gabon, June 8-17. Nos. 384, 385 each printed in sheets of 10 with 5 labels showing exhibition emblem.

Schoolgirl A118

**1979, July 25** **Litho.** *Perf. 12½x12*

**386** A118 70fr multi .95 .50

Intl. Bureau of Education, Geneva, 50th anniv.

Chicken — A119

**1979, Aug.** *Perf. 13*

**387** A119 10fr shown 1.75 1.10
**388** A119 20fr Bull 1.75 1.10
**389** A119 40fr Sheep 3.75 2.10
*Nos. 387-389,C211 (4)* 12.50 6.30

National Husbandry Assoc.

**Souvenir Sheet**

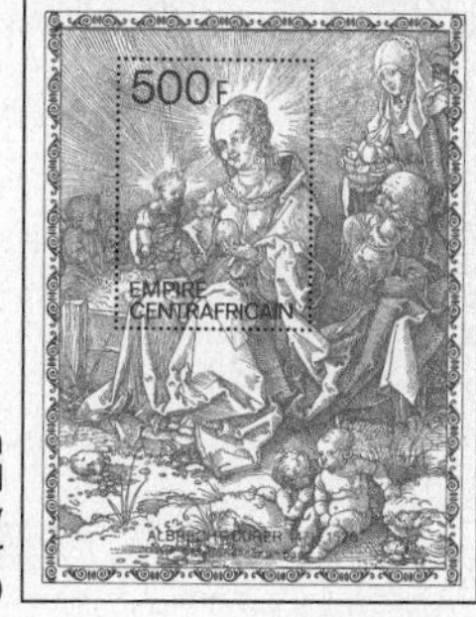

Virgin and Child, by Dürer A120

**1979, Aug.** *Perf. 13½*

**390** A120 500fr lt grn & dl red 5.25 1.75

Albrecht Dürer (1471-1528), German engraver and printer.

**Central African Republic**

Nos. 257-258 Overprinted

**1979, Nov. 11** **Litho.** *Perf. 13½*

**391** A93 40fr multi .65 .30
**392** A93 60fr multi .75 .40
*Nos. 391-392,C212-C214 (5)* 6.25 3.35

Apollo 11 moon landing, 10th anniversary.

Girl and Rose — A121

30fr, Butterfly and girl, vert. 60fr, Hansel and Gretel, vert. 200fr, The Little Match Girl. 250fr, Mermaid, vert.

**1979, Dec. 15**

**393** A121 30fr multicolored .30 .25
**394** A121 40fr shown .50 .25
**395** A121 60fr multicolored .55 .25
**396** A121 200fr multicolored 2.00 .70
**397** A121 250fr multicolored 2.50 .80
*Nos. 393-397 (5)* 5.85 2.25

International Year of the Child.

Locomotive, U.S. Type A27, Hill — A122

Locomotives, Hill and Stamps: 100fr, France No. 1. 150fr, Germany type A11. 250fr, Great Britain No. 32. 500fr, CAR No. 2.

**1979, Dec. 20**

**398** A122 60fr multi .55 .25
**399** A122 100fr multi 1.10 .30
**400** A122 150fr multi 1.75 .50
**401** A122 250fr multi 3.00 1.10
*Nos. 398-401 (4)* 6.40 2.15

**Souvenir Sheet**

**402** A122 500fr multi 5.75 2.25

Sir Rowland Hill (1795-1879), originator of penny postage.

Basketball, Moscow '80 Emblem — A123

Pre-Olympic Year: Men's or women's basketball.

**1979, Dec. 28** **Litho.** ***Perf. 14½***

**403** A123 50fr multi .45 .25
**404** A123 125fr multi 1.00 .40
**405** A123 200fr multi 1.75 .65
**406** A123 300fr multi 3.00 .90
**407** A123 500fr multi 4.50 1.60
*Nos. 403-407 (5)* 10.70 3.80

For overprints see Nos. 425-429.

Nos. 313-314 Overprinted in Black on Silver Panel

and

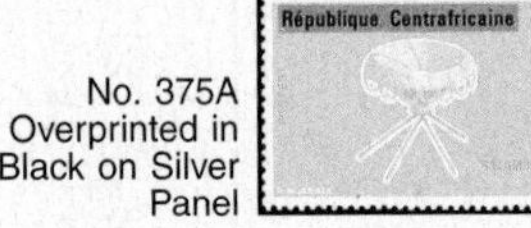


No. 375A Overprinted in Black on Silver Panel

and

Nos. 337-338 Overprinted in Black on Silver Panel

***Perf. 13½x14, 14x13½***

**1980, Mar. 20** **Litho.**

**408** A99 5fr multi .40 .30
**409** A99 10fr multi .40 .30
**410** A114a 20fr multi .30 .25
**411** A108 20fr multi .30 .25
**412** A108 30fr multi .50 .25
*Nos. 408-412 (5)* 1.90 1.35

Apollo-Soyuz A125

40fr, Viking Satellite. 50fr, Apollo-Soyuz. 60fr, Voyager. 100fr, European Space Agency emblem, flags.

**1980, Apr. 8** ***Perf. 13½***

**413** A125 40fr multicolored .55 .25
**414** A125 50fr multicolored .65 .25
**415** A125 60fr multicolored .75 .40
**416** A125 100fr multicolored 1.25 .60
*Nos. 413-416,C221-C222 (6)* 6.35 2.60

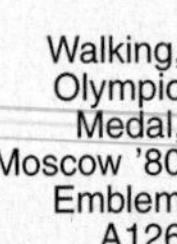

Walking, Olympic Medal, Moscow '80 Emblem A126

**1980, July 25** **Litho.** ***Perf. 13½***

**417** A126 30fr shown .50 .25
**418** A126 40fr Relay race .55 .25
**419** A126 70fr Running .75 .25
**420** A126 80fr High jump .90 .25
*Nos. 417-420,C231-C232 (6)* 5.30 1.65

For overprints see Nos. 462-465, C248-C250.

Fruit — A126a

**1980, Aug. 1** **Litho.** ***Perf. 13½***

**420A** A126a 40fr multicolored — —
**420B** A126a 70fr green & multi — —

Agricultural Development A127

40fr, Telecommunications. 70fr, Engineering. 100fr, Civil engineering.

**1980, Nov. 4** **Litho.** ***Perf. 13½***

**421** A127 30fr shown .30 .25
**422** A127 40fr multicolored .50 .25
**423** A127 70fr multicolored .90 .25
**424** A127 100fr multicolored 1.40 .40
*Nos. 421-424,C234-C235 (6)* 6.50 2.25

Europe-Africa cooperation.

Nos. 403-407 Overprinted in Black

**1980, Nov. 12** ***Perf. 14½***

**425** A123 50fr multi .55 .25
**426** A123 125fr multi 1.10 .40
**427** A123 200fr multi 1.90 .65
**428** A123 300fr multi 3.60 1.10
**429** A123 500fr multi 5.00 1.75
*Nos. 425-429 (5)* 12.15 4.15

Virgin and Child, by Raphael — A128

Christmas: Paintings by Raphael.

**1980, Dec. 20** ***Perf. 12½***

**430** A128 60fr multi .65 .25
**431** A128 150fr multi 1.60 .60
**432** A128 250fr multi 3.00 1.25
*Nos. 430-432 (3)* 5.25 2.10

African Postal Union, 5th Anniversary — A129

**1980, Dec. 24** **Photo.** ***Perf. 13½***

**433** A129 70fr multi .90 .45

Peruvian Soccer Team, Soccer Cup — A130

**1981, Jan. 13** **Litho.** ***Perf. 13½***

**434** A130 10fr shown .25 .25
**435** A130 15fr Scotland .35 .25
**436** A130 20fr Mexico .35 .25
**437** A130 25fr Sweden .35 .25
**438** A130 30fr Austria .50 .25
**439** A130 40fr Poland .50 .25
**440** A130 50fr France .90 .25
**441** A130 60fr Italy .90 .25
**442** A130 70fr Germany 1.00 .30
**443** A130 80fr Brazil 1.00 .35
*Nos. 434-443,C237-C238 (12)* 8.85 3.45

ESPANA '82 World Cup Soccer Championship.

13th World Telecommunications Day — A131

**1981, May 17** **Litho.** ***Perf. 12½***

**444** A131 150fr multi 1.40 .70

Apollo 15 Crew on Moon A132

Space Exploration: Columbia space shuttle.

**1981, June 10** **Litho.** ***Perf. 14***

**445** A132 100fr multi .80 .30
**446** A132 150fr multi 1.35 .40
**447** A132 200fr multi 1.90 .60
**448** A132 300fr multi 3.25 1.00
*Nos. 445-448 (4)* 7.30 2.30

### Souvenir Sheet

**449** A132 500fr multi 5.00 1.75

Family of Acrobats with Monkey, by Picasso — A133

Picasso Birth Cent.: 50fr, The Balcony. 80fr, The Artist's Son as Pierrot. 100fr, The Three Dancers.

**1981, June 30** ***Perf. 13½***

**450** A133 40fr multi .60 .25
**451** A133 50fr multi .75 .25
**452** A133 80fr multi 1.30 .40
**453** A133 100fr multi 1.75 .40
*Nos. 450-453,C245-C246 (6)* 9.15 2.40

First Anniv. of Zimbabwe's Independence — A134

**1981, July 9** **Litho.** ***Perf. 12½***

**454** A134 100fr multi 1.10 .45
**455** A134 150fr multi 1.50 .55
**456** A134 200fr multi 2.25 .80
*Nos. 454-456 (3)* 4.85 1.80

Royal Wedding — A135

75fr, Charles. 100fr, Diana. 150fr, St. Paul's Cathedral. 175fr, Prince Charles and Lady Diana.

500fr, Couple.

**1981, July, 24** ***Perf. 14***

**457** A135 75fr multicolored .50 .25
**458** A135 100fr multicolored .70 .25
**459** A135 150fr multicolored 1.20 .50
**460** A135 175fr multicolored 1.50 .50
*Nos. 457-460 (4)* 3.90 1.50

### Souvenir Sheet

**461** A135 500fr multicolored 5.00 1.75

For overprints see Nos. 529-533.

### Nos. 417-420 Overprinted in Gold

**1981** **Litho.** ***Perf. 13½***

**462** A126 30fr multi .35 .25
**463** A126 40fr multi .50 .25
**464** A126 70fr multi .90 .35
**465** A126 80fr multi .90 .50
*Nos. 462-465,C248-C249 (6)* 5.05 2.00

Prince Charles and Lady Diana A136

50fr, Crowned Prince of Wales. 80fr, Diana. 100fr, Naval training.

**1981, Aug. 20** **Litho.** ***Perf. 13½***

**466** A136 40fr shown .45 .25
**467** A136 50fr multicolored .45 .25
**468** A136 80fr multicolored .75 .30
**469** A136 100fr multicolored 1.00 .40
*Nos. 466-469,C251-C252 (6)* 6.35 2.15

Royal wedding.

1906 Renault A137

40fr, Mercedes-Benz, 1937. 50fr, Matra-Ford, 1969. 110fr, Tazio Nuvolari, 1927. 150fr, Jackie Stewart, 1965.

450fr, Finish line, 1914.

**1981, Sept. 22** **Litho.** ***Perf. 12½***

**470** A137 20fr shown .30 .25
**471** A137 40fr multicolored .55 .25
**472** A137 50fr multicolored .65 .25
**473** A137 110fr multicolored 1.30 .40
**474** A137 150fr multicolored 1.90 .70
*Nos. 470-474 (5)* 4.70 1.85

### Souvenir Sheet

***Perf. 10***

**475** A137 450fr multicolored 5.00 5.00

Grand Prix of France, 75th anniv.

World Food Day — A138

**1981, Oct. 16**

**476** A138 90fr multi .95 .30
**477** A138 110fr multi 1.10 .50

Navigators and their Ships A139

**1981, Sept. 4 Litho. *Perf. 13½***

| | | | | |
|---|---|---|---|---|
| **478** | A139 | 40fr C.V. Rietschoten | .50 | .30 |
| **479** | A139 | 50fr M. Pajot | .55 | .45 |
| **480** | A139 | 60fr K. Jaworski | .75 | .55 |
| **481** | A139 | 80fr M. Birch | 1.00 | .60 |
| | | *Nos. 478-481,C254-C255 (6)* | 6.30 | 4.00 |

Downfall of Empire — A140

5fr, Bayonet through crown. 25fr, Victory holding map. 90fr, Toppled Bokassa statue.

**1981, Oct. 6**

| | | | | |
|---|---|---|---|---|
| **482** | A140 | 5fr multicolored | .25 | .25 |
| **483** | A140 | 10fr like #482 | .25 | .25 |
| **484** | A140 | 25fr multicolored | .30 | .25 |
| **485** | A140 | 60fr like #484 | .65 | .25 |
| **486** | A140 | 90fr multicolored | 1.00 | .60 |
| **487** | A140 | 500fr like #486 | 4.25 | 2.00 |
| | | *Nos. 482-487 (6)* | 6.70 | 3.60 |

Komba — A141

**1981, Nov. 17**

| | | | | |
|---|---|---|---|---|
| **488** | A141 | 50fr shown | .90 | .25 |
| **489** | A141 | 90fr Dodoro, horiz. | 1.75 | .30 |
| **490** | A141 | 140fr Kaya, horiz. | 3.00 | .40 |
| | | *Nos. 488-490 (3)* | 5.65 | .95 |

Central African States Bank — A142

**1981, Dec. 12 Litho. *Perf. 12½x13***

| | | | | |
|---|---|---|---|---|
| **491** | A142 | 90fr multi | .90 | .30 |
| **492** | A142 | 110fr multi | 1.00 | .60 |

Christmas 1981 — A143

Virgin and Child Paintings: 50fr, Fra Angelico, 1430. 60fr, Cosimo Tura, 1484. 90fr, Bramantino. 110fr, Memling.

**1981, Dec. 24**

| | | | | |
|---|---|---|---|---|
| **493** | A143 | 50fr multicolored | .85 | .30 |
| **494** | A143 | 60fr multicolored | .95 | .40 |
| **495** | A143 | 90fr multicolored | 1.50 | .55 |
| **496** | A143 | 110fr multicolored | 1.90 | .80 |
| | | *Nos. 493-496,C260-C261 (6)* | 12.20 | 3.20 |

Scouting Year A144

100fr, Hiking. 150fr, Scouts, horiz. 200fr, Leaning against railing. 300fr, Salute, flag, vert.
500fr, Scout, Baden-Powell, vert.

**1982, Jan. 13 *Perf. 12½***

| | | | | |
|---|---|---|---|---|
| **497** | A144 | 100fr multicolored | 1.00 | .40 |
| **498** | A144 | 150fr multicolored | 1.50 | .55 |
| **499** | A144 | 200fr multicolored | 2.25 | .80 |
| **500** | A144 | 300fr multicolored | 3.00 | 1.25 |
| | | *Nos. 497-500 (4)* | 7.75 | 3.00 |

**Souvenir Sheet**

***Perf. 13***

| | | | | |
|---|---|---|---|---|
| **501** | A144 | 500fr multicolored | 5.75 | 1.60 |

Elephant — A145

**1982, Jan. 22 *Perf. 13½***

| | | | | |
|---|---|---|---|---|
| **502** | A145 | 60fr shown | .90 | .25 |
| **503** | A145 | 90fr Giraffes | 1.10 | .30 |
| **504** | A145 | 100fr Addaxes | 1.25 | .35 |
| **505** | A145 | 110fr Okapi | 1.50 | .50 |
| | | *Nos. 502-505,C263-C264 (6)* | 13.50 | 3.45 |

Norman Rockwell Illustrations A146

30fr, Grandfather snowman. 60fr, Croquet players. 110fr, Women talking. 150fr, Searching.

**1982, Feb. 17 *Perf. 13½x14***

| | | | | |
|---|---|---|---|---|
| **506** | A146 | 30fr multicolored | .30 | .25 |
| **507** | A146 | 60fr multicolored | .75 | .30 |
| **508** | A146 | 110fr multicolored | 1.25 | .40 |
| **509** | A146 | 150fr multicolored | 1.75 | .55 |
| | | *Nos. 506-509 (4)* | 4.05 | 1.50 |

AT 16 Dirigible A147

10fr, Beyer-Garrat locomotive. 20fr, Bugatti 24 "Royale," 1924. 110fr, Vickers "Valentia," 1928.

**1982, Feb. 27 Litho. *Perf. 13½***

| | | | | |
|---|---|---|---|---|
| **510** | A147 | 5fr shown | .25 | .25 |
| **511** | A147 | 10fr multicolored | .25 | .25 |
| **512** | A147 | 20fr multicolored | .30 | .25 |
| **513** | A147 | 110fr multicolored | 1.40 | .40 |
| | | *Nos. 510-513,C266-C267 (6)* | 11.45 | 3.20 |

Bellvue Garden, by Edouard Manet A148

Anniversaries: 400fr, Goethe, vert. Nos. 519-520, Princess Diana, 21st birthday, July 1, vert. 300fr, George Washington, vert.

**1982, Apr. 6 Litho. *Perf. 13***

| | | | | |
|---|---|---|---|---|
| **517** | A148 | 200fr multi | 3.00 | 1.00 |
| **517A** | A148 | 300fr multi | 2.75 | 1.00 |
| **518** | A148 | 400fr multi | 3.50 | 1.25 |
| **519** | A148 | 500fr multi | 4.50 | 2.00 |
| | | *Nos. 517-519 (4)* | 13.75 | 5.25 |

**Souvenir Sheet**

| | | | | |
|---|---|---|---|---|
| **520** | A148 | 500fr multi | 5.50 | 1.60 |

23rd Olympic Games, Los Angeles, 1984 A149

**1982, July 24 Litho. *Perf. 13½***

| | | | | |
|---|---|---|---|---|
| **521** | A149 | 5fr Soccer | .25 | .25 |
| **522** | A149 | 10fr Boxing | .25 | .25 |
| **523** | A149 | 20fr Running | .30 | .25 |
| **524** | A149 | 110fr Long jump | .90 | .30 |
| | | *Nos. 521-524,C269-C270 (6)* | 9.70 | 3.25 |

21st Birthday of Princess Diana A150

Portraits.

**1982, July 20 Litho. *Perf. 13½***

| | | | | |
|---|---|---|---|---|
| **525** | A150 | 5fr multi | .25 | .25 |
| **526** | A150 | 10fr multi | .25 | .25 |
| **527** | A150 | 20fr multi | .30 | .25 |
| **528** | A150 | 110fr multi | .90 | .30 |
| | | *Nos. 525-528,C272-C273 (6)* | 10.45 | 3.25 |

Nos. 457-461 Overprinted in Blue

**1982, Aug. 20 *Perf. 14***

| | | | | |
|---|---|---|---|---|
| **529** | A135 | 75fr multi | .55 | .25 |
| **530** | A135 | 110fr multi | .75 | .40 |
| **531** | A135 | 150fr multi | 1.40 | .55 |
| **532** | A135 | 175fr multi | 2.25 | .80 |
| | | *Nos. 529-532 (4)* | 4.95 | 2.00 |

**Souvenir Sheet**

| | | | | |
|---|---|---|---|---|
| **533** | A135 | 500fr multi | 5.50 | 3.50 |

Birth of Prince William of Wales, June 21.

2nd UN Conference on Peaceful Uses of Outer Space, Vienna, Aug. 9-21 — A151

Various satellites and space scenes.

**1982, Aug. 15 Litho. *Perf. 13½***

| | | | | |
|---|---|---|---|---|
| **534** | A151 | 5fr multi | .25 | .25 |
| **535** | A151 | 10fr multi | .25 | .25 |
| **536** | A151 | 20fr multi | .30 | .25 |
| **537** | A151 | 110fr multi | .90 | .30 |
| | | *Nos. 534-537,C277-C278 (6)* | 9.70 | 3.25 |

Sakpa Basket — A152

Baskets and bowls: 25fr, Ngbenda gourd, vert. 120fr, Ta ti ngou jugs. 175fr, Kangu bowls. 300fr, Kolongo bowls, vert.

**1982, Sept. 2 *Perf. 13***

| | | | | |
|---|---|---|---|---|
| **538** | A152 | 5fr shown | .25 | .25 |
| **539** | A152 | 10fr like 5fr | .25 | .25 |
| **540** | A152 | 25fr multicolored | .30 | .25 |
| **541** | A152 | 60fr like 25fr | .75 | .25 |
| **542** | A152 | 120fr multicolored | 1.60 | .40 |
| **543** | A152 | 175fr multicolored | 1.75 | .60 |
| **544** | A152 | 300fr multicolored | 3.50 | 1.25 |
| | | *Nos. 538-544 (7)* | 8.40 | 3.25 |

For surcharges see Nos. 792A-792B.

1982 World Cup Soccer Championships, Spain — A152a

Various soccer plays.

**1982, Sept. Litho. *Perf. 13½x13***

**Overprinted in Silver or Gold**

| | | | | |
|---|---|---|---|---|
| **545** | A152a | 60fr Italy, 1st, 2nd | .90 | .25 |
| **546** | A152a | 150fr Poland, 3rd | 1.75 | .55 |
| **547** | A152a | 300fr France, 4th | 3.50 | 1.25 |
| | | *Nos. 545-547 (3)* | 6.15 | 2.05 |

**Souvenir Sheet**

| | | | | |
|---|---|---|---|---|
| **548** | A152a | 500fr Italy, 1st (G) | 5.00 | 1.60 |

Not issued without overprint.

13th World UPU Day — A153

**1982, Oct. 9**

| | | | | |
|---|---|---|---|---|
| **549** | A153 | 60fr multi | .55 | .35 |
| **550** | A153 | 120fr multi | 1.20 | .55 |

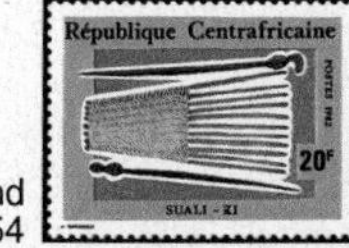

Comb and Hairpins — A154

**1982, Oct. 20 *Perf. 13x12½***

| | | | | |
|---|---|---|---|---|
| **551** | A154 | 20fr multi | .25 | .25 |
| **552** | A154 | 30fr multi | .40 | .25 |
| **553** | A154 | 60fr multi | .75 | .30 |
| **554** | A154 | 80fr multi | 1.10 | .40 |
| **555** | A154 | 120fr multi | 1.50 | .45 |
| | | *Nos. 551-555 (5)* | 4.00 | 1.65 |

Artist Pierre Ndarata and No.69 — A155

**1982, Oct. *Perf. 13***

| | | | | |
|---|---|---|---|---|
| **556** | A155 | 40fr Jean Tubind at easel, vert. | .30 | .25 |
| **557** | A155 | 70fr shown | .55 | .25 |
| **558** | A155 | 90fr like 70fr | .65 | .40 |
| **559** | A155 | 140fr like 40fr | 1.25 | .50 |
| | | *Nos. 556-559 (4)* | 2.75 | 1.40 |

TB Bacillus Centenary — A156

**1982, Nov. 30 *Perf. 13½x13***

| | | | | |
|---|---|---|---|---|
| **560** | A156 | 100fr vio & blk | 1.25 | .30 |
| **561** | A156 | 120fr red org & blk | 1.40 | .45 |
| **562** | A156 | 175fr bl & blk | 2.00 | .90 |
| | | *Nos. 560-562 (3)* | 4.65 | 1.65 |

10th Anniv. of UN Conference on Human Environment A157

**1982, Dec. 8**

| | | | | |
|---|---|---|---|---|
| **563** | A157 | 120fr multi | 1.20 | .40 |
| **564** | A157 | 150fr multi | 1.30 | .55 |
| **565** | A157 | 300fr multi | 2.50 | 1.10 |
| | | *Nos. 563-565 (3)* | 5.00 | 2.05 |

Granary — A158

**1982, Dec. 15 *Perf. 13***

| | | | | |
|---|---|---|---|---|
| **566** | A158 | 60fr multi | .55 | .25 |
| **567** | A158 | 80fr multi | .85 | .40 |
| **568** | A158 | 120fr multi | 1.20 | .60 |
| **569** | A158 | 200fr multi | 2.00 | 1.20 |
| | | *Nos. 566-569 (4)* | 4.60 | 2.45 |

A159

**1982, Dec.**

570 A159 100fr multi 1.00 .40
571 A159 120fr multi 1.25 .50

ITU Plenipotentiaries Conf., Nairobi, Sept.

A160

5fr, Modes of communication. 120fr, Map, jet.

**1983, Jan. 31 Litho. *Perf. 13½x13***

572 A160 5fr multicolored .25 .25
573 A160 60fr like 5fr .65 .30
574 A160 120fr multicolored 1.25 .40
575 A160 175fr like 120fr 1.50 .55
*Nos. 572-575 (4)* 3.65 1.50

UN Decade for African Transportation and Communication, 1978-88.

Chess Champions A161

Men and Chess Pieces: 5fr, Steinitz, first world champion, 1886. 10fr, Aaron Niemzovitch, castle. 20fr, Alexander Alekhine, knights. 110fr, Botvinnik. 300fr, Boris Spassky, glass pieces. 500fr, Bobby Fischer, king, knight. 600fr, Korchnoi, Karpov, pawn. No. 582A, Bobby Fischer. No. 582B, Reti, Larsen, Petrossian, and Mecking, horiz.

**1983, Jan. 15**

576 A161 5fr multi .25 .25
577 A161 10fr multi .25 .25
578 A161 20fr multi .35 .25
579 A161 110fr multi 1.10 .25
580 A161 300fr multi 3.00 .75
581 A161 500fr multi 4.25 1.40
*Nos. 576-581 (6)* 9.20 3.15

**Souvenir Sheet**

582 A161 600fr multi 5.75 2.00

**Litho. & Embossed**

***Perf. 13½***

**Size: 35x60mm**

582A A161 1500fr gold & multi 25.00 3.50

**Souvenir Sheet**

582B A161 1500fr gold & multi 10.00 10.00

No. 582 contains one 56x33mm stamp, No. 582B one 35x60mm stamp. 300fr, 500fr, 600fr, Nos. 582A and 582B are airmail.

Marshal Tito (1892-1980) — A162

20fr, George Washington.

**1983, Jan. 22**

583 A162 20fr multicolored .25 .25
a. Souvenir sheet 5.50 —
584 A162 110fr shown 1.25 .30
a. Souvenir sheet 5.50 —

1982 World Cup Soccer Championships, Spain — A162a

Trophy, flags, scores, players: 5fr, Hamilton, Pezzey. 10fr, Borovski, Boniek. 20fr, Littbarski, Zamora. 110fr, Zico, Passarella. 300fr, Rossi, Smolarek. 500fr, Rummenigge, Giresse. 600fr, Rossi, Rummenigge. No. 584I, Platini. No. 584J, Rossi.

**1983, Feb. 8 Litho. *Perf. 13½***

584B A162a 5fr multi .25 .25
584C A162a 10fr multi .25 .25
584D A162a 20fr multi .40 .25
584E A162a 110fr multi 1.30 .30
584F A162a 300fr multi 2.75 .70
584G A162a 500fr multi 4.75 1.40
*Nos. 584B-584G (6)* 9.70 3.15

**Souvenir Sheet**

584H A162a 600fr multi 5.50 4.25

**Litho. & Embossed**

584I A162a 1500fr gold & multi 21.00 5.50

**Souvenir Sheet**

584J A162a 1500fr gold & multi 10.00 10.00

Nos. 584F-584J are airmail.

Easter 1983 — A163

Rembrandt Paintings: 100fr, Entombment. 300fr, Crucifixion. 400fr, Descent from the Cross.

**1983, Apr. 16**

585 A163 100fr multicolored .90 .40
586 A163 300fr multicolored 2.75 1.25
587 A163 400fr multicolored 3.50 1.75
*Nos. 585-587 (3)* 7.15 3.40

Vintage Cars and their Makers — A164

A164a

Designs: 10fr, Emile Levassor, Rene Panhard, 1895 car. 20fr, Henry Ford, 1896 car. 30fr, Louis Renault, 1899 car. 80fr, Ettore Bugatti, type 37, 1925. 400fr, Enzo Ferrari, 815 sport, 1940. 500fr, Ferdinand Porsche, 356 coupe, 1951. 600fr, Karl Benz, velocipede, 1886. No. 594A, F.H. Royce and C.S. Rolls, 1911 Rolls-Royce Silver Ghost. No. 594B, G. Daimler, 1900 Mercedes 35CV.

**1983, June 3 Litho. *Perf. 13½***

588 A164 10fr multi .25 .25
589 A164 20fr multi .25 .25
590 A164 30fr multi .30 .25
591 A164 80fr multi .85 .30
592 A164 400fr multi 4.00 1.10
593 A164 500fr multi 4.75 1.40
*Nos. 588-593 (6)* 10.40 3.55

**Souvenir Sheet**

594 A164 600fr multi 5.75 1.60

**Litho. & Embossed**

594A A164a 1500fr gold & multi 20.00 4.00

**Souvenir Sheet**

594B A164a 1500fr gold & multi 8.00 6.00

Nos. 592-594B are airmail.

25th Anniv. of Intl. Maritime Org. — A165

**1983, July 8 Litho. *Perf. 12½x13***

595 A165 40fr multi .50 .25
596 A165 100fr multi 1.00 .40

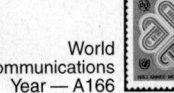

World Communications Year — A166

**1983, July 22**

597 A166 50fr multi .45 .25
598 A166 130fr multi 1.25 .45

Pre-Olympics, Los Angeles — A167

1984 Summer Olympics, Los Angeles A167a

5fr, Gymnast. 40fr, Javelin throwing. 60fr, Pole vault. 120fr, Fencing. 200fr, Cycling. 300fr, Sailing.
600fr, Handball. No. 605A, 1500fr, Shot put. No. 605B, 1500fr, Dressage, horiz.

**1983, Aug. 3 Litho. *Perf. 13***

599 A167 5fr multi .25 .25
600 A167 40fr multi .40 .25
601 A167 60fr multi .65 .25
602 A167 120fr multi 1.40 .30
603 A167 200fr multi 2.25 .40
604 A167 300fr multi 3.25 .80
*Nos. 599-604 (6)* 8.20 2.25

**Souvenir Sheet**

605 A167 600fr multi 5.00 1.60

**Litho. & Embossed**

***Perf. 13½***

605A A167a 1500fr multi 25.00 3.50

**Souvenir Sheet**

605B A167a 1500fr multi 9.00 9.00

Nos. 603-605B are airmail.

Namibia Day — A168

**1983, Sept. 16 Litho. *Perf. 13***

606 A168 100fr multi 1.00 .50
607 A168 200fr multi 1.75 .80

Manned Flight Bicentenary A169

A169a

Designs: 50fr, J. Montgolfier and his balloon, 1783. 100fr, J.P. Blanchard, English Channel crossing, 1785. 200fr, L.-J. Gay-Lussac, 4000-meter balloon ascent, 1804. 300fr, Giffard and his dirigible, 1852. 400fr, Santos Dumont, dirigible, Eiffel Tower. 500fr, A. Laquot, captive observation balloon, 1914. 600fr, J.A. Charles, first gas balloon; G. Tissandier, dirigible, 1883. No. 614, Marquis d'Arlandes and Jean Francois Pilatre de Rozier, Montgolfier balloon. No. 614B, Ferdinand von Zeppelin, Graf Zeppelin, horiz.

**1983, Sept. 30 Litho. *Perf. 13½***

608 A169 50fr multi .40 .25
609 A169 100fr multi .90 .40
610 A169 200fr multi 2.00 .80
611 A169 300fr multi 2.60 1.10
612 A169 400fr multi 3.50 1.50
613 A169 500fr multi 4.50 1.90
*Nos. 608-613 (6)* 13.90 5.95

**Souvenir Sheet**

614 A169 600fr multi 5.50 1.40

**Litho. & Embossed**

614A A169a 1500fr gold & multi 25.00 4.00

**Souvenir Sheet**

614B A169a 1500fr gold & multi 9.00 9.00

Nos. 612-614B are airmail.

Black Rhinoceros and World Wildlife Emblem A170

Various black rhinoceroses.

**1983, Nov. 14**

615 A170 10fr multi 1.00 .40
616 A170 40fr multi 1.20 .60
617 A170 70fr multi 1.75 .80
618 A170 180fr multi 5.25 1.60
*Nos. 615-618 (4)* 9.20 3.40

Nos. 615-618 were issued in support of the World Wildlife Fund.
See Nos. C291A-C293.

UPU Day, World Communications Year — A171

**1983, Nov. 2 Litho. *Perf. 13***

619 A171 205fr multi 2.00 .90

2nd Anniv. of the Natl. Military Committee A172

Gen. Andre Kolingba, head of state.

**1983, Sept. 1 *Perf. 12½***

620 A172 65fr sil & multi .55 .25
621 A172 130fr gold & multi 1.40 .55

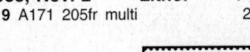

Earth Satellite Receiving Station, Bangui M'Poko — A173

**1983** *Perf. 13*

| | | | | |
|---|---|---|---|---|
| **622** | A173 130fr multi | | 1.40 | .55 |

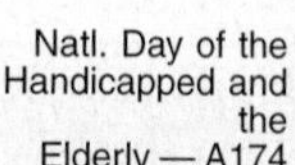

Natl. Day of the Handicapped and the Elderly — A174

**1983, Dec. 20** **Engr.** *Perf. 13x12½*

| | | | |
|---|---|---|---|
| **623** | A174 65fr vio & org | .55 | .30 |
| **624** | A174 130fr ultra & org | 1.10 | .55 |
| **625** | A174 205fr dk grn & org | 1.75 | .80 |
| | *Nos. 623-625 (3)* | 3.40 | 1.65 |

Fishing Resources A175

**1983, Dec. 31** **Litho.** *Perf. 12½*

| | | | |
|---|---|---|---|
| **626** | A175 25fr Breeding tank | .25 | .25 |
| **627** | A175 65fr Net fishing | .95 | .25 |
| **628** | A175 100fr Dam fishing | 1.05 | .40 |
| **629** | A175 130fr Still life with fish | 2.10 | .70 |
| **630** | A175 205fr Basket trap | 2.40 | .70 |
| | *Nos. 626-630 (5)* | 6.75 | 2.30 |

Wildlife Protection A176

**1984, Jan. 25** *Perf. 13*

| | | | |
|---|---|---|---|
| **631** | A176 30fr Forest fire | 3.25 | .40 |
| **632** | A176 130fr Hunters | 4.50 | 1.10 |

CC-1500 Locomotive A177

110fr, CC-1500 locomotive. 240fr, PLM series 210, 1868. 350fr, 231-726 locomotive, 1937. 440fr, Pacific S3/6, 1908. 500fr, Henschel 151 series 45, 1937.

**1984, July 16** **Litho.** *Perf. 12½*

| | | | |
|---|---|---|---|
| **633** | A177 110fr multicolored | 1.10 | .30 |
| **634** | A177 240fr multicolored | 2.40 | .85 |
| **635** | A177 350fr multicolored | 3.50 | 1.10 |
| **636** | A177 440fr multicolored | 4.50 | 1.25 |
| **637** | A177 500fr multicolored | 5.50 | 1.60 |
| | *Nos. 633-637 (5)* | 17.00 | 5.10 |

For overprints see Nos. 702, 704.

Packet Ship Pericles — A177a

120fr, Three-master Pereire. 250fr, Admella. 400fr, Royal William. 500fr, Great Britain.

**1984, July 23** **Litho.** *Perf. 12½*

| | | | |
|---|---|---|---|
| **638** | A177a 65fr shown | .70 | .30 |
| **639** | A177a 120fr multicolored | 1.10 | .55 |
| **640** | A177a 250fr multicolored | 2.40 | 1.10 |
| **641** | A177a 400fr multicolored | 4.50 | 1.90 |
| **642** | A177a 500fr multicolored | 5.00 | 2.40 |
| | *Nos. 638-642 (5)* | 13.70 | 6.25 |

For overprints see Nos. 701, 703.

J. W. Goethe, Scene from Faust — A178

Designs: 100fr, Henri Dunant, Red Cross Founder, Battle of Solferino, 125th anniv. 200fr, Alfred Nobel, Nobel Foundation headquarters. 300fr, Lord Baden-Powell, World Scouting Jamboree, Alberta, 1983. 400fr, John F. Kennedy, first man on the Moon, 1969. 500fr, 600fr, wedding of Prince and Princess of Wales.

**1984, Feb. 25** **Litho.** *Perf. 13½*

| | | | |
|---|---|---|---|
| **643** | A178 50fr multi | .45 | .25 |
| **644** | A178 100fr multi | .90 | .40 |
| **645** | A178 200fr multi | 2.00 | .55 |
| **646** | A178 300fr multi | 2.60 | 1.10 |
| **647** | A178 400fr multi | 3.50 | 1.10 |
| **648** | A178 500fr multi | 4.50 | 1.10 |
| | *Nos. 643-648 (6)* | 13.95 | 4.50 |

**Souvenir Sheet**

| | | | |
|---|---|---|---|
| **649** | A178 600fr multi | 4.00 | 1.40 |

Nos. 647-649 are airmail.

Old Masters — A179

Paintings: 50fr, Madonna and Child, by Raphael. 100fr, Madonna with Pear, by Durer. 200fr, Aldobrandini Madonna, by Raphael. 300fr, Madonna with Carnation, by Durer. 400fr, Virgin and Child, by Correggio. 500fr, La Bohemienne, by Modigliani. 600fr, Madonna and Child on the Throne, by Raphael.

**1984, Mar. 30** **Litho.** *Perf. 13½*

| | | | |
|---|---|---|---|
| **650** | A179 50fr multi | .50 | .25 |
| **651** | A179 100fr multi | .90 | .25 |
| **652** | A179 200fr multi | 2.00 | .45 |
| **653** | A179 300fr multi | 2.75 | .85 |
| **654** | A179 400fr multi | 3.75 | 1.90 |
| **655** | A179 500fr multi | 4.75 | 2.50 |
| | *Nos. 650-655 (6)* | 14.65 | 6.20 |

**Miniature Sheet**

| | | | |
|---|---|---|---|
| **656** | A179 600fr multi | 4.50 | 1.40 |

No. 656 contains 1 stamp, size 30x59mm. Nos. 654-656 are airmail.

Space — A180

20fr, Galileo, Ariane rocket. 70fr, Piccard, X-15, balloon. 150fr, Oberth, satellite. 205fr, Einstein, satellites. 300fr, Curie, Viking vehicle. 500fr, Merbold, Spacelab.

600fr, Armstrong, Apollo 11, horiz.

**1984, Aug. 6** **Litho.** *Perf. 13½*

| | | | |
|---|---|---|---|
| **657** | A180 20fr multicolored | .30 | .25 |
| **658** | A180 70fr multicolored | .75 | .25 |
| **659** | A180 150fr multicolored | 1.50 | .45 |
| **660** | A180 205fr multicolored | 2.25 | .55 |
| **661** | A180 300fr multicolored | 3.50 | .80 |
| **662** | A180 500fr multicolored | 5.00 | 1.00 |
| | *Nos. 657-662 (6)* | 13.30 | 3.30 |

**Miniature Sheet**

| | | | |
|---|---|---|---|
| **663** | A180 600fr multicolored | 5.00 | 1.50 |

No. 663 contains 1 stamp, size: 42x36mm. 300fr, 500fr and 600fr are airmail.

Forestry Resources — A181

**1984, Oct. 9** **Litho.** *Perf. 13x12½*

| | | | |
|---|---|---|---|
| **664** | A181 70fr Forest | .90 | .30 |
| **665** | A181 130fr Logging | 1.75 | .55 |

UNICEF — A182

**1984, Oct. 27** **Litho.** *Perf. 13x12½*

| | | | |
|---|---|---|---|
| **666** | A182 10fr Weighing child | .25 | .25 |
| **667** | A182 30fr Vaccinating child | .50 | .30 |
| **668** | A182 65fr Giving liquids | .60 | .40 |
| **669** | A182 100fr Balancing diet | 1.25 | .55 |
| | *Nos. 666-669 (4)* | 2.60 | 1.50 |

Fishing Traps — A183

**1984, Nov. 6** **Litho.** *Perf. 13*

| | | | |
|---|---|---|---|
| **670** | A183 50fr Bangui-Kette | .75 | .30 |
| **671** | A183 80fr Mbres | 1.00 | .55 |
| **672** | A183 150fr Bangui-Kette | 2.25 | .90 |
| | *Nos. 670-672 (3)* | 4.00 | 1.75 |

Mushrooms — A184

5fr, Leptoporus lignosus. 10fr, Phlebopus sudanicus. 40fr, Termitomyces letestui. 130fr, Lepiota esculenta. 300fr, Termitomyces aurantiacus. 500fr, Termitomyces robustus.

600fr, Tricholoma- lobayensis.

**1984, Nov. 15** **Litho.** *Perf. 13½*

| | | | |
|---|---|---|---|
| **673** | A184 5fr multicolored | .25 | .25 |
| **674** | A184 10fr multicolored | .25 | .25 |
| **675** | A184 40fr multicolored | .65 | .30 |
| **676** | A184 130fr multicolored | 2.00 | .30 |
| **677** | A184 300fr multicolored | 3.25 | .80 |
| **678** | A184 500fr multicolored | 5.75 | 1.25 |
| | *Nos. 673-678 (6)* | 12.15 | 3.15 |

**Souvenir Sheet**

| | | | |
|---|---|---|---|
| **679** | A184 600fr multicolored | 6.00 | 2.00 |

Nos. 677-679 are airmail.

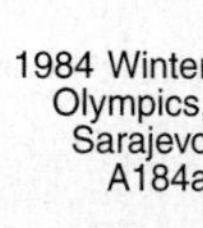

1984 Winter Olympics, Sarajevo A184a

Gold medalists, communications satellite and events: 30fr, Gaetan Boucher, Canada, 1000 and 1500-meter speed skating. 90fr, W. Hoppe, R. Wetzig, D. Schauerhammer and A. Kirchner, German Democratic Republic, 4-man bobsled. 140fr, Paoletta Magoni, Italy, women's slalom. 200fr, Jayne Torvill and Christopher Dean, Great Britain, ice dancing. 400fr, Matti Nykaenen, Finland, 90-meter ski jumping. 500fr, USSR, ice hockey. 600fr, Bill Johnson, US, men's downhill.

**1984, Nov. 30** **Litho.** *Perf. 13½*

| | | | |
|---|---|---|---|
| **679A** | A184a 30fr multi | .30 | .25 |
| **679B** | A184a 90fr multi | .90 | .30 |
| **679C** | A184a 140fr multi | 1.35 | .40 |
| **679D** | A184a 200fr multi | 2.00 | .55 |
| **679E** | A184a 400fr multi | 3.50 | 1.00 |
| **679F** | A184a 500fr multi | 4.75 | 1.25 |
| | *Nos. 679A-679F (6)* | 12.80 | 3.75 |

**Souvenir Sheet**

| | | | |
|---|---|---|---|
| **679G** | A184a 600fr multi | 5.00 | 1.60 |

Nos. 679E-679G are airmail.

Flowers — A185

65fr, Hibiscus. 130fr, Canna Indica. 205fr, Eichlornia Crassipes.

**1984, Nov. 22** **Litho.** *Perf. 13½*

| | | | |
|---|---|---|---|
| **680** | A185 65fr multicolored | 1.00 | .40 |
| **681** | A185 130fr multicolored | 1.75 | .50 |
| **682** | A185 205fr multicolored | 2.75 | 1.00 |
| | *Nos. 680-682 (3)* | 5.50 | 1.90 |

Economic Campaign A186

25fr, Cotton planting. 40fr, Selling cotton crop. 130fr, Cotton market.

**1984, Dec. 3** **Litho.** *Perf. 13½*

| | | | |
|---|---|---|---|
| **683** | A186 25fr multicolored | .40 | .25 |
| **684** | A186 40fr multicolored | .65 | .40 |
| **685** | A186 130fr multicolored | 1.70 | .55 |
| | *Nos. 683-685 (3)* | 2.75 | 1.20 |

World Food Day — A187

**1984, Dec. 10** **Litho.** *Perf. 13½*

| | | | |
|---|---|---|---|
| **686** | A187 205fr Picking corn | 2.25 | .90 |

OLYMPHILEX '85 — A188

Publicity posters from previous Games and host city landmarks: 5fr, Stockholm, 1912. 10fr, Paris, 1924. 20fr, London, 1948. 100fr, Tokyo, 1964. 400fr, Mexico. 500fr, Munich, 1972.

600fr, Athens, 1896, Baron Pierre de Coubertin.

**1985, Mar 18** **Litho.** *Perf. 13½*

| | | | |
|---|---|---|---|
| **687** | A188 5fr multicolored | .25 | .25 |
| **688** | A188 10fr multicolored | .25 | .25 |
| **689** | A188 20fr multicolored | .30 | .25 |
| **690** | A188 100fr multicolored | 4.75 | 1.00 |
| **691** | A188 400fr multicolored | 2.00 | .45 |
| **692** | A188 500fr multicolored | 2.50 | .55 |
| | *Nos. 687-692 (6)* | 10.05 | 2.75 |

**Souvenir Sheet**

| | | | |
|---|---|---|---|
| **693** | A188 600fr multicolored | 5.00 | 1.50 |

Nos. 691-693 are airmail. No. 693 contains one 60x30mm stamp.

Anniversaries and Events — A189

Famous men: 50fr, Abraham Lincoln, American Civil War soldiers. 90fr, Auguste Piccard (1884-1962), inventor, bathyscaphe Trieste. 120fr, Gottlieb Daimler (1834-1900), 1938 Mercedes Type 540. 200fr, Louis Bleriot (1872-1936), inventor, plane. 350fr, Anatoly Karpov, world chess champion. 400fr, Jean Henri Dunant (1828-1910), Red Cross founder, worker caring for wounded soldier.

**1984, Dec. 22** **Litho.** *Perf. 13½*

| | | | |
|---|---|---|---|
| **694** | A189 50fr multi | .50 | .25 |
| **695** | A189 90fr multi | .90 | .30 |
| **696** | A189 120fr multi | 1.40 | .40 |
| **697** | A189 200fr multi | 2.00 | .55 |
| **698** | A189 350fr multi | 3.50 | .80 |
| **698A** | A189 400fr multi | 3.50 | .90 |
| | *Nos. 694-698A (6)* | 11.80 | 3.20 |

Nos. 698-698A are airmail.

Souvenir Sheet

Queen Mother, 85th Birthday — A189a

| 1984 | Litho. | *Perf. 13½* |
|---|---|---|
| **698B** A189a 600fr multi | 5.00 | 1.60 |

Bangui Rotary Club and Water — A190

| 1984, Dec. 29 | | |
|---|---|---|
| **699** A190 130fr multi | 1.60 | .45 |
| **700** A190 205fr multi | 2.50 | .80 |

**Nos. 635//641, C302A Overprinted with Exhibitions in Red**

| 1985, Mar. 13 | Litho. | *Perf. 12½* |
|---|---|---|
| **701** A177 250fr Argentina '85, Buenos Aires (#640) | 2.50 | 1.25 |
| **702** A177a 350fr Tsukuba Expo '85 (#635) | 3.25 | 1.60 |
| **703** A177 400fr Italia '85, Rome (#641) | 4.50 | 2.25 |
| **704** A177a 440fr Mophila '85, Hamburg (#636) | 5.00 | 2.40 |
| *Nos. 701-704 (4)* | 15.25 | 7.50 |

**Souvenir Sheet**

***Perf. 13½x13***

| **705** AP89 500fr Olymphilex '85, Lausanne | 5.00 | 5.00 |
|---|---|---|

500fr airmail.

Beetles — A191

15fr, Chelorrhina polyphemus. 20fr, Fornasinius russus. 25fr, Goliathus giganteus. 65fr, Goliathus meleagris.

| 1985, Mar. | Litho. | *Perf. 13½* |
|---|---|---|
| **706** A191 15fr multicolored | *.65* | *.25* |
| **707** A191 20fr multicolored | *1.20* | *.30* |
| **708** A191 25fr multicolored | *1.75* | *.50* |
| **709** A191 65fr multicolored | *4.00* | *1.00* |
| *Nos. 706-709 (4)* | *7.60* | *2.05* |

Audubon Birth Bicentenary A192

Illustrations of North American bird species by John Audubon: 40fr, Cyanocitta cristata. 80fr, Caprimulgus carolinensis. 130fr, Campephilus principales. 250fr, Calocitta formosa. 300fr, Coccizus minor, horiz. 500fr, Hirundo rustica, horiz.

600fr, Dryocopus pileatus, horiz.

| 1985, Mar. 25 | Litho. | *Perf. 13½* |
|---|---|---|
| **710** A192 40fr multicolored | .75 | .25 |
| **711** A192 80fr multicolored | 1.00 | .25 |
| **712** A192 130fr multicolored | 1.90 | .25 |
| **713** A192 250fr multicolored | 2.60 | .55 |
| **714** A192 300fr multicolored | 2.75 | .60 |
| **715** A192 500fr multicolored | 4.75 | 1.10 |
| *Nos. 710-715 (6)* | 13.75 | 3.00 |

**Souvenir Sheet**

| **716** A192 600fr multicolored | 7.00 | 2.50 |
|---|---|---|

Nos. 714-716 are airmail.

Intl. Youth Year — A193

Famous children's book authors and scenes from their best-known novels: 100fr, The Jungle Book, 1894, by Kipling, vert. 200fr, Les Cavaliers, 1967, by Joseph Kessel (1898-1979). 300fr, Twenty-Thousand Leagues Under the Sea, 1873, by Verne. 400fr, The Adventures of Tom Sawyer, 1876, by Twain.

| 1985, Apr. | Litho. | *Perf. 13* |
|---|---|---|
| **718** A193 100fr multi | 1.40 | .45 |
| **719** A193 200fr multi | 2.50 | .85 |
| **720** A193 300fr multi | 3.00 | 1.25 |
| **721** A193 400fr multi | 4.50 | 2.10 |
| *Nos. 718-721 (4)* | 11.40 | 4.65 |

Philexafrica '85, Lome A194

No. 722, UPU emblem, Postmen unloading parcel post van. No. 723, Exhibition emblem, scout troop.

| 1985, May 15 | | *Perf. 13x12½* |
|---|---|---|
| **722** A194 200fr multi | 2.25 | .90 |
| **723** A194 200fr multi | 2.25 | .90 |
| ***a.*** Pair, #722-723 + label | 5.50 | 4.50 |

Rabies Vaccine Cent., Louis Pasteur (1822-95), Chemist, Microbiologist A195

Anniversaries and events: 200fr, Battle of Solferino, founding of the Red Cross, 125th Anniv., founder Jean-Henri Dunant (1828-1910), horiz. 300fr, Girl Guides, 75th anniv. 450fr, Elizabeth, the Queen Mother, 85th birthday. 500fr, Statue of Liberty, cent.

| 1985, June | | *Perf. 13* |
|---|---|---|
| **724** A195 150fr multi | 2.25 | .50 |
| **725** A195 200fr multi | 2.75 | .60 |
| **726** A195 300fr multi | 2.25 | .90 |
| **727** A195 450fr multi | 4.00 | 1.50 |
| **728** A195 500fr multi | 5.00 | 1.75 |
| *Nos. 724-728 (5)* | 16.25 | 5.25 |

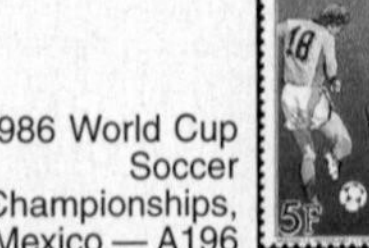

1986 World Cup Soccer Championships, Mexico — A196

Famous soccer players and match scenes: 5fr, Pele. 10fr, Tony Schumacher. 20fr, Paolo Rossi. 350fr, Kevin Keegan. 400fr, Michel Platini. 500fr, Karl Heinz Rummenigge.

600fr, Diego Armando Maradona.

| 1985, July 24 | Litho. | *Perf. 13½* |
|---|---|---|
| **730** A196 5fr multicolored | .25 | .25 |
| **731** A196 10fr multicolored | .25 | .25 |
| **732** A196 20fr multicolored | .25 | .25 |
| **733** A196 350fr multicolored | 3.25 | .90 |
| **734** A196 400fr multicolored | 3.75 | .90 |
| **735** A196 500fr multicolored | 4.75 | 1.10 |
| *Nos. 730-735 (6)* | 12.50 | 3.65 |

**Souvenir Sheet**

| **736** A196 600fr multicolored | 5.00 | 1.40 |
|---|---|---|

Nos. 734-736 are airmail.

Kotto Waterfalls — A197

| 1985, July 27 | Litho. | *Perf. 13½* |
|---|---|---|
| **737** A197 65fr multi | 1.00 | .30 |
| **738** A197 90fr multi | 1.10 | .40 |
| **739** A197 130fr multi | 1.75 | .60 |
| *Nos. 737-739 (3)* | 3.85 | 1.30 |

State Visit of Pope John Paul II — A198

Portraits.

| 1985, Aug. 14 | | |
|---|---|---|
| **740** A198 65fr multi | 1.25 | .40 |
| **741** A198 130fr multi | 2.50 | .80 |

Natl. Economic Development Campaign — A199

Designs: 5fr, Troops plowing. 60fr, Soldier preparing field for planting, vert. 130fr, Planting cotton seeds, vert.

| 1985, Sept. 1 | | *Perf. 13* |
|---|---|---|
| **742** A199 5fr multi | .25 | .25 |
| **743** A199 60fr multi | .75 | .30 |
| **744** A199 130fr multi | 1.50 | .45 |
| *Nos. 742-744 (3)* | 2.50 | 1.00 |

Queen Mother, 85th Birthday A200

100fr, Age 4, with brother. 200fr, Duchess of York, 1923. 300fr, Reviewing Irish Guards, 1928. 350fr, Family portrait, 1936. 400fr, George VI coronation, 1937. 500fr, Wedding anniv., 1948.

600fr, Christening Prince Charles, 1948.

| 1985, Sept. 16 | Litho. | *Perf. 13½* |
|---|---|---|
| **745** A200 100fr multicolored | .80 | .25 |
| **746** A200 200fr multicolored | 1.90 | .35 |
| **747** A200 300fr multicolored | 3.00 | .70 |
| **748** A200 350fr multicolored | 3.25 | .75 |
| **749** A200 400fr multicolored | 4.00 | .90 |
| **750** A200 500fr multicolored | 5.00 | 1.00 |
| *Nos. 745-750 (6)* | 17.95 | 3.95 |

**Souvenir Sheet**

| **751** A200 600fr multicolored | 4.50 | 1.40 |
|---|---|---|

Nos. 749-751 are airmail.

Dr. Rene Labusquiere (1919-1977), Promoter of Preventive Medicine — A201

| 1985, Sept. 22 | Litho. | *Perf. 13½* |
|---|---|---|
| **752** A201 10fr multi | .25 | .25 |
| **753** A201 45fr multi | .50 | .25 |
| **754** A201 110fr multi | .75 | .45 |
| *Nos. 752-754 (3)* | 1.50 | .95 |

Natl. Postal Service A202

15fr, Loading mail van. 60fr, Bangui P.O., van. 150fr, Hdqtrs, Bangui, and vans.

| 1985, Oct. 9 | | *Perf. 12½* |
|---|---|---|
| **755** A202 15fr multicolored | .25 | .25 |
| **756** A202 60fr multicolored | .65 | .25 |
| **757** A202 150fr multicolored | 1.60 | .80 |
| *Nos. 755-757 (3)* | 2.50 | 1.30 |

Space Research A203

Designs: 40fr, Yuri Gagarin, Soviet cosmonaut, and Sergei Korolev, rocket engineer. 110fr, Nicolaus Copernicus, Cassini probe. 240fr, Galileo, Viking orbiter. 300fr, Theodor von Karman (1881-1963), American aeronautical engineer, and space shuttle recovering Palapa B satellite. 450fr, Percival Lowell (1855-1916), American astronomer, and Viking probe. 500fr, Dr. U. Merbold and orbiting space station project Colombo. 600fr, Apollo 11 Project, first step on Moon by Neil Armstrong.

| 1985, Oct. 31 | Litho. | *Perf. 13½* |
|---|---|---|
| **758** A203 40fr multi | .25 | .25 |
| **759** A203 110fr multi | 1.00 | .30 |
| **760** A203 240fr multi | 2.75 | .55 |
| **761** A203 300fr multi | 3.50 | .80 |
| **762** A203 450fr multi | 5.50 | 1.00 |
| **763** A203 500fr multi | 6.00 | 1.10 |
| *Nos. 758-763 (6)* | 19.00 | 4.00 |

**Souvenir Sheet**

***Imperf***

| **764** A203 600fr multi | 5.00 | 1.40 |
|---|---|---|

Nos. 762-764 are airmail.

Solar Energy Apparatus, Damara — A204

| 1985, Nov. 4 | Litho. | *Perf. 13½* |
|---|---|---|
| **765** A204 65fr multi | .70 | .30 |
| **766** A204 130fr multi | 1.40 | .60 |

Girl Guides Nature Study A205

No. 768, Quaka Sugar Refinery.

| 1985, Nov. 16 | | *Perf. 13* |
|---|---|---|
| **767** A205 250fr shown | 4.00 | 1.75 |
| **768** A205 250fr multicolored | 4.00 | 1.75 |
| ***a.*** Pair, #767-768 + label | 11.50 | 6.50 |

PHILEXAFRICA '85, Lome, Togo, 11/16-24.

State Visit of Pres. Mitterand of France, Dec. 12-13 A206

| 1985-86 | Litho. | *Perf. 13x12½* |
|---|---|---|
| **769** A206 65fr multi | .75 | .25 |
| **770** A206 130fr multi | 1.50 | .55 |
| **770A** A206 160fr multi ('86) | 2.10 | .80 |
| *Nos. 769-770A (3)* | 4.35 | 1.60 |

Issued: Nos. 769-770, Dec. 12.

UN 40th Anniv., Central Africa Admission, 25th Anniv. — A207

**1985, Dec. 18** ***Perf. 13½***

| | | | | |
|---|---|---|---|---|
| **771** | A207 | 140fr multi | 1.40 | .55 |

Intl. Youth Year — A208

Designs: 40fr, David, by Andrea del Verrocchio; Madonna with the Carnation, 1470, by Leonardo da Vinci. 80fr, Johann Sebastian Bach. 100fr, St. John at Patmos, 1619, by Velazquez. 250fr, The Erl King score, by Franz Schubert. 400fr, Portrait of Vicente Osorio de Moscoso, by Goya. 500fr, The Young Mozart Playing in Paris, 1764. 600fr, Woman in a Plumed Hat, 1901, by Picasso.

**1985, Dec. 28**

| | | | | |
|---|---|---|---|---|
| **772** | A208 | 40fr multi | .40 | .25 |
| **773** | A208 | 80fr multi | .90 | .25 |
| **774** | A208 | 100fr multi | 1.25 | .25 |
| **775** | A208 | 250fr multi | 2.50 | .55 |
| **776** | A208 | 400fr multi | 4.50 | .90 |
| **777** | A208 | 500fr multi | 5.00 | 1.10 |
| | | *Nos. 772-777 (6)* | 14.55 | 3.30 |

**Souvenir Sheet**

| | | | | |
|---|---|---|---|---|
| **778** | A208 | 600fr multi | 5.25 | 1.40 |

Nos. 776-778 are airmail.

Halley's Comet — A209

100fr, Edmond Halley, British astronomer. 200fr, Sir Isaac Newton's telescope & comet sighting. 300fr, Halley & Newton observing comet. 350fr, US probe. 400fr, Soviet probe plotting comet's perihelion. 500fr, Isodensity photograph of comet. 600fr, Comet, Earth, Sun & probe.

**1985, Dec. 31**

| | | | | |
|---|---|---|---|---|
| **779** | A209 | 100fr multi | .80 | .30 |
| **780** | A209 | 200fr multi | 1.75 | .45 |
| **781** | A209 | 300fr multi | 2.75 | .90 |
| **782** | A209 | 350fr multi | 3.25 | 1.10 |
| **783** | A209 | 400fr multi | 3.75 | 1.00 |
| **784** | A209 | 500fr multi | 4.75 | 1.25 |
| | | *Nos. 779-784 (6)* | 17.05 | 5.00 |

**Souvenir Sheet**

| | | | | |
|---|---|---|---|---|
| **785** | A209 | 600fr multi | 5.25 | 1.75 |

Nos. 783-785 are airmail.

Christopher Columbus A210

Various events leading to the discovery of America and beyond: 90fr, Plotting course. 110fr, Receiving blessing. 240fr, Fleet in port. 300fr, Trade with natives. 400fr, Storm at sea. 500fr, Fleet at sea.
600fr, Portrait.

**1986**

| | | | | |
|---|---|---|---|---|
| **786** | A210 | 90fr multicolored | .90 | .30 |
| **787** | A210 | 110fr multicolored | 1.25 | .45 |
| **788** | A210 | 240fr multicolored | 2.50 | .60 |
| **789** | A210 | 300fr multicolored | 3.25 | .90 |
| **790** | A210 | 400fr multicolored | 4.25 | 1.00 |
| **791** | A210 | 500fr multicolored | 5.00 | 2.40 |
| | | *Nos. 786-791 (6)* | 17.15 | 5.65 |

**Souvenir Sheet**

| | | | | |
|---|---|---|---|---|
| **792** | A210 | 600fr multicolored | 5.75 | 1.75 |

Nos. 790-792 are airmail.

Nos. 543-544 Surcharged

No. 792A, Kangu bowls. No. 792B, Kolongo bowls.

**1986, Apr. 1** **Litho.** ***Perf. 13***

| | | |
|---|---|---|
| **792A** | A152 | 30fr on 175fr |
| **792B** | A152 | 65fr on 300fr |

Hairstyles — A211

**1986, May 21** **Litho.** ***Perf. 12½***

| | | | | |
|---|---|---|---|---|
| **793** | A211 | 20fr multi | .40 | .25 |
| **794** | A211 | 30fr multi | .50 | .25 |
| **795** | A211 | 65fr multi | .70 | .40 |
| **796** | A211 | 160fr multi | 2.50 | .70 |
| | | *Nos. 793-796 (4)* | 4.10 | 1.60 |

France - Central Africa Week — A212

**1986, May 26**

| | | | | |
|---|---|---|---|---|
| **797** | A212 | 40fr Communications, horiz. | .45 | .25 |
| **798** | A212 | 60fr Youth, horiz. | .60 | .30 |
| **799** | A212 | 100fr Basket maker | 1.25 | .45 |
| **800** | A212 | 130fr Bicycling | 1.75 | .60 |
| | | *Nos. 797-800 (4)* | 4.05 | 1.60 |

Centrapalm Palm Oil — A213

25fr, 65fr, Refinery, Bossongo, and palm tree. 120fr, 160fr, Refinery and palm tree.

**1986, Aug. 12** **Litho.** ***Perf. 13½***

| | | | | |
|---|---|---|---|---|
| **801** | A213 | 25fr multi | .30 | .25 |
| **802** | A213 | 65fr multi | .70 | .40 |
| **803** | A213 | 120fr multi, vert. | 1.25 | .80 |
| **804** | A213 | 160fr multi, vert. | 1.75 | .60 |
| | | *Nos. 801-804 (4)* | 4.00 | 2.05 |

Dogs and Cats — A214

10fr, Pointer. 20fr, Egyptian mau. 200fr, Newfoundland. 300fr, Borzoi. 400fr, Persian red.
500fr, Spaniel, Burmese-Malayan.

**1986, Sept. 9**

| | | | | |
|---|---|---|---|---|
| **805** | A214 | 10fr multicolored | .25 | .25 |
| **806** | A214 | 20fr multicolored | .45 | .25 |
| **807** | A214 | 200fr multicolored | 2.75 | .55 |
| **808** | A214 | 300fr multicolored | 3.50 | .60 |
| **809** | A214 | 400fr multicolored | 5.00 | .85 |
| | | *Nos. 805-809 (5)* | 11.95 | 2.50 |

**Souvenir Sheet**

| | | | | |
|---|---|---|---|---|
| **810** | A214 | 500fr multicolored | 6.25 | 1.75 |

Nos. 808-810 are airmail.

African Coffee Producers Organization, 25th Anniv. — A215

**1986, Sept. 25** **Litho.** ***Perf. 13***

| | | | | |
|---|---|---|---|---|
| **811** | A215 | 160fr multi | 1.60 | .60 |

1986 World Cup Soccer Championships, Mexico — A216

Satellites, final scores, World Cup and athletes: 30fr, Muller, Socrates. 110fr, Scifo, Ceulemans. 160fr, Stopyra, Platini. 350fr, Brehme, Schumacher. 450fr, Maradona. 500fr, Schumacher, Burruchaga.

**1986, Nov. 12** ***Perf. 13½***

| | | | | |
|---|---|---|---|---|
| **812** | A216 | 30fr multi | .30 | .25 |
| **813** | A216 | 110fr multi | 1.00 | .25 |
| **814** | A216 | 160fr multi | 1.40 | .30 |
| **815** | A216 | 350fr multi | 3.25 | .80 |
| **816** | A216 | 450fr multi | 4.50 | 1.10 |
| | | *Nos. 812-816 (5)* | 10.45 | 2.70 |

**Souvenir Sheet**

| | | | | |
|---|---|---|---|---|
| **817** | A216 | 500fr multi | 5.50 | 1.40 |

Nos. 816-817 are airmail.

US Anniversaries and Events — A217

15fr, Judith Resnik. 25fr, Frederic Auguste Bartholdi. 70fr, Elvis Presley. 300fr, Ronald McNair. 450fr, Christa McAuliffe. 500fr, Challenger Astronauts: McAuliffe, Scobee, Smith, Resnik, Onizuka, McNair, Jarvis.

**1986, Nov. 19**

| | | | | |
|---|---|---|---|---|
| **818** | A217 | 15fr multi | .25 | .25 |
| **819** | A217 | 25fr multi | .40 | .25 |
| **820** | A217 | 70fr multi | 1.90 | .25 |
| **821** | A217 | 300fr multi | 3.00 | .60 |
| **822** | A217 | 450fr multi | 4.50 | 1.10 |
| | | *Nos. 818-822 (5)* | 10.05 | 2.45 |

**Souvenir Sheet**

| | | | | |
|---|---|---|---|---|
| **823** | A217 | 500fr multi | 5.75 | 1.50 |

US space shuttle Challenger explosion; Statue of Liberty, cent. Nos. 822-823 are airmail.

For surcharges & overprint see Nos. 851-851B.

Flora and Fauna — A218

25fr, Allamanda neriifolia. 65fr, Taurotragus eurycerus. 160fr, Plumieria acuminata. 300fr, Acinonyx jubatus. 400fr, Eulophia erthoplata. 500fr, Leopard.
600fr, Derby's eland, eulophia cucullata.

**1986, May 30** **Litho.** ***Perf. 13½***

| | | | | |
|---|---|---|---|---|
| **824** | A218 | 25fr multicolored | .25 | .25 |
| **825** | A218 | 65fr multicolored | .90 | .25 |
| **826** | A218 | 160fr multicolored | 2.10 | .30 |
| **827** | A218 | 300fr multicolored | 4.50 | .80 |

| | | | | |
|---|---|---|---|---|
| **828** | A218 | 400fr multicolored | 4.75 | .90 |
| **829** | A218 | 500fr multicolored | 6.50 | 1.10 |
| | | *Nos. 824-829 (6)* | 19.00 | 3.60 |

**Souvenir Sheet**

| | | | | |
|---|---|---|---|---|
| **830** | A218 | 600fr multicolored | 5.25 | 1.75 |

Nos. 824, 826, 828 vert. Nos. 828-830 are airmail. No. 830 contains one 51x30mm stamp.

Intl. Peace Year — A219

**1986, Nov. 29**

| | | | | |
|---|---|---|---|---|
| **831** | A219 | 160fr multi | 1.75 | .75 |

Air Africa, 25th Anniv. — A220

**1986, Dec. 15**

| | | | | |
|---|---|---|---|---|
| **832** | A220 | 200fr multi | 1.75 | .80 |

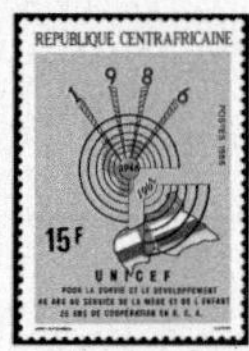


UNICEF, 40th Anniv. — A221

130fr, Child immunization. 160fr, Youth, food, map.

**1986, Dec. 24**

| | | | | |
|---|---|---|---|---|
| **833** | A221 | 15fr shown | .25 | .25 |
| **834** | A221 | 130fr multicolored | 1.35 | .55 |
| **835** | A221 | 160fr multicolored | 1.60 | .70 |
| | | *Nos. 833-835 (3)* | 3.20 | 1.50 |

German Railways Sesquicentenary — A222

Inventors and locomotives: 40fr, Alfred de Glehn, Prussian Railways DH2 Green Elephant. 70fr, Rudolf Diesel, S3/6 No. 1829 Rheingold. 160fr, Carl Golsdorf, Trans-Europe Express train Type 103. 300fr, Wilhelm Schmidt, Beyer Garratt locomotive. 400fr, Monsieur Du Bousquet, Series 3500 compound locomotive. 500fr, Werner von Siemens, 1980s electric locomotive.

**1986, Dec. 31**

| | | | | |
|---|---|---|---|---|
| **836** | A222 | 40fr multi | .45 | .25 |
| **837** | A222 | 70fr multi | .80 | .25 |
| **838** | A222 | 160fr multi | 1.75 | .40 |
| **839** | A222 | 300fr multi | 3.00 | .60 |
| **840** | A222 | 400fr multi | 3.75 | 1.10 |
| | | *Nos. 836-840 (5)* | 9.75 | 2.60 |

**Souvenir Sheet**

| | | | | |
|---|---|---|---|---|
| **841** | A222 | 500fr multi | 5.00 | 1.40 |

Nos. 840-841 are airmail. No. 841 contains one 42x36mm stamp.

Agriculture Radio Project — A223

265fr, Satellite communication.

**1986, Dec. 27 Litho. *Perf. 13½***

| | | | | |
|---|---|---|---|---|
| **842** | A223 | 170fr shown | 2.25 | .90 |
| **843** | A223 | 265fr multicolored | 3.25 | 1.40 |

Pan-African Telecommunications Union congress, Dec. 7, 1986.
No. 842 exists in souvenir sheet of one.

Space — A224

Scientists and inventions: 25fr, Sir William Herschel (1738-1822), British astronomer, and Mariner Mark II. 65fr, Wernher von Braun (1912-1977), American engineer, and Mars rover. 160fr, Rudolf Hanel, Mariner Mark II and Titan. 300fr, Patrick Baudry, Hermes shuttle and Eureka platform. 400fr, U. Keller, Halley's Comet and Giotto probe. 500fr, Wubbo Ockels, Ulf Merbold and Columbus European Space Station. 600fr, Wilhelm Obers (1758-1840) and Mariner Mark II surveying asteroids. No. 850 horiz.

**1987, Jan. 27**

| | | | | |
|---|---|---|---|---|
| **844** | A224 | 25fr multi | .35 | .25 |
| **845** | A224 | 65fr multi | .65 | .25 |
| **846** | A224 | 160fr multi | 1.60 | .30 |
| **847** | A224 | 300fr multi | 2.75 | .75 |
| **848** | A224 | 400fr multi | 3.00 | .90 |
| **849** | A224 | 500fr multi | 3.50 | 1.25 |
| | | *Nos. 844-849 (6)* | 11.85 | 3.70 |

**Souvenir Sheet**

| | | | | |
|---|---|---|---|---|
| **850** | A224 | 600fr multi | 5.75 | 1.75 |

Nos. 848-850 are airmail.

No. 820 Surcharged

**1987, Feb. 20 Litho. *Perf. 13½***

| | | | | |
|---|---|---|---|---|
| **851** | A217 | 485fr on 70fr Elvis Presley | 7.75 | 2.00 |

Nos. 820 and 851 Overprinted in Black

**1987, Feb. 20 Litho. *Perf. 13½***

| | | | | |
|---|---|---|---|---|
| **851A** | A217 | 70fr multi | 1.40 | .40 |
| **851B** | A217 | 485fr on 70fr multi | 6.50 | 2.00 |

Overprint in red exists.

1992 Barcelona Olympics — A225

Athletes and landmarks or sights: 30fr, Soccer player, Lady with Umbrella fountain. 150fr, Judo, Barcelona Cathedral. 265fr, Cyclist, Church of the Holy Family, by Gaudi. 350fr, Gymnast, Tomb of Columbus. 495fr, Runner, human tower. 500fr, Swimmer, Statue of Columbus.

**1987, June 4**

| | | | | |
|---|---|---|---|---|
| **852** | A225 | 30fr multi | .40 | .25 |
| **853** | A225 | 150fr multi | 1.40 | .45 |
| **854** | A225 | 265fr multi | 2.50 | .80 |
| **855** | A225 | 350fr multi | 3.50 | 1.00 |
| **856** | A225 | 495fr multi | 5.50 | 1.40 |
| | | *Nos. 852-856 (5)* | 13.30 | 3.90 |

**Souvenir Sheet**

| | | | | |
|---|---|---|---|---|
| **857** | A225 | 500fr multi | 4.50 | 1.40 |

Nos. 855-857 are airmail.

A226

1988 Winter Olympics, Calgary — A227

20fr, Two-man luge. 140fr, Cross-country skiing. 250fr, Women's figure skating. 300fr, Hockey. 400fr, Men's slalom.
500fr, Downhill skiing.

**1987, June 26**

| | | | | |
|---|---|---|---|---|
| **858** | A226 | 20fr multicolored | .30 | .25 |
| **859** | A226 | 140fr multicolored | 1.25 | .45 |
| **860** | A226 | 250fr multicolored | 2.00 | .80 |
| **861** | A226 | 300fr multicolored | 2.75 | .90 |
| **862** | A226 | 400fr multicolored | 3.50 | 1.10 |
| | | *Nos. 858-862 (5)* | 9.80 | 3.50 |

**Souvenir Sheet**

| | | | | |
|---|---|---|---|---|
| **863** | A227 | 500fr multicolored | 4.50 | 1.40 |

Nos. 861-863 are airmail.

Intl. Peace Year — A228

**1987, July 20**

| | | | | |
|---|---|---|---|---|
| **864** | A228 | 50fr dull ultra, sepia & blk | .50 | .25 |
| **865** | A228 | 160fr lt ol grn, sep & blk | 1.40 | .60 |

Intl. Decade of Drinkable Water — A228a

Designs: 5fr, Woman at village pump; 10fr, Two women at village pump; 200fr, Three women at village pump.

**1987, Sept. 22 Litho. *Perf. 13½***

| | | | | |
|---|---|---|---|---|
| **865A** | A228a | 5fr multi | *30.00* | — |
| **865B** | A228a | 10fr multi | *30.00* | — |
| **865C** | A228a | 200fr multi | *35.00* | — |
| | | *Nos. 865A-865C (3)* | *95.00* | |

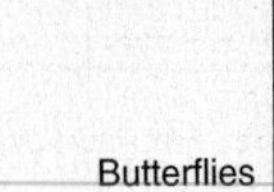

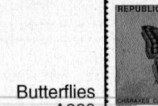

Butterflies A229

100fr, Charaxes candiope. 120fr, Graphium leonidas. 130fr, Charaxes brutus. 160fr, Salamis aetiops.

**1987, Oct. 5 Litho. *Perf. 13½***

| | | | | |
|---|---|---|---|---|
| **866** | A229 | 100fr multicolored | 2.00 | .85 |
| **867** | A229 | 120fr multicolored | 2.75 | .90 |
| **868** | A229 | 130fr multicolored | 3.00 | .90 |
| **869** | A229 | 160fr multicolored | 3.25 | 1.10 |
| | | *Nos. 866-869 (4)* | 11.00 | 3.75 |

Pygmy Soccer Team from Nola A230

**1987, Nov. 30 Litho. *Perf. 13***

| | | | | |
|---|---|---|---|---|
| **870** | A230 | 90fr multi | 1.35 | .75 |
| **871** | A230 | 160fr multi | 2.00 | 1.25 |

Integration of the pygmy people into Central African society.

Dinosaurs A231

50fr, Brontosaurus. 65fr, Triceratops. 100fr, Ankylosaurus. 160fr, Stegosaurus. 200fr, Tyrannosaurus rex. 240fr, Corythosaurus. 300fr, Allosaurus. 350fr, Brachiosaurus.

***Perf. 14x13½, 13½x14***

**1988, Mar. 19 Litho.**

| | | | | |
|---|---|---|---|---|
| **872** | A231 | 50fr multicolored | .40 | .25 |
| **873** | A231 | 65fr multicolored | .70 | .25 |
| **874** | A231 | 100fr multicolored | 1.00 | .40 |
| **875** | A231 | 160fr multicolored | 1.75 | .60 |
| **876** | A231 | 200fr multicolored | 1.75 | .80 |
| **877** | A231 | 240fr multicolored | 2.75 | .90 |
| **878** | A231 | 300fr multicolored | 3.25 | 1.25 |
| **879** | A231 | 350fr multicolored | 3.75 | 1.50 |
| | | *Nos. 872-879 (8)* | 15.35 | 5.95 |

Nos. 876-879 vert.

Anniversaries and Events — A232

Designs: 40fr, Pres. James Madison and "We the People..." from the US Constitution. 160fr, Elizabeth II and Duke of Edinburgh. 200fr, Steffi Graf, tennis champion. 300fr, Garri Kasparov of Russia, 1985 world chess champion. 400fr, Boris Becker, 1985-86 Wimbledon champion. 500fr, Christoph Willibald Gluck (1714-87), composer. Nos. 880-884 vert.

**1988, Feb. 15 *Perf. 13½***

| | | | | |
|---|---|---|---|---|
| **880** | A232 | 40fr multi | .40 | .25 |
| **881** | A232 | 160fr multi | 1.50 | .25 |
| **882** | A232 | 200fr multi | 1.90 | .45 |
| **883** | A232 | 300fr multi | 3.00 | .80 |
| **884** | A232 | 400fr multi | 3.50 | 1.25 |
| | | *Nos. 880-884 (5)* | 10.30 | 3.00 |

**Souvenir Sheet**

| | | | | |
|---|---|---|---|---|
| **885** | A232 | 500fr multi | 6.25 | 1.75 |

US Constitution bicentennial (40fr); 40th wedding anniv. of Elizabeth II and Prince Philip (160fr). Nos. 883-885 are airmail.

World Health Organization, 40th Anniv. — A233

**1988, Apr. 7 Litho. *Perf. 13½***

| | | | | |
|---|---|---|---|---|
| **886** | A233 | 70fr multi | .65 | .40 |
| **887** | A233 | 120fr multi | 1.00 | .55 |

Scout Ornithological Activities — A234

Scouts and: 25fr, *Merops nubicus*. 170fr, *Euplectes hordeacea*. 300fr, *Ceryle rudis*. 400fr, *Estrilda bengala*. 450fr, *Kaupifalco monogrammicus*. 500fr, *Lamprotornis splendidus*.

**1988, July 1 Litho. *Perf. 13½***

| | | | | |
|---|---|---|---|---|
| **888** | A234 | 25fr multi | .25 | .25 |
| **889** | A234 | 170fr multi | 1.50 | .70 |
| **890** | A234 | 300fr multi | 3.00 | 2.00 |
| **891** | A234 | 400fr multi | 4.25 | 2.00 |
| **892** | A234 | 450fr multi | 5.00 | 2.40 |
| | | *Nos. 888-892 (5)* | 14.00 | 7.35 |

**Souvenir Sheet**

| | | | | |
|---|---|---|---|---|
| **893** | A234 | 500fr multi | 6.00 | 1.75 |

Nos. 891-893 are airmail.
For surcharges see Nos. 921-924.

1988 Summer Olympics, Seoul — A235

**1988, Sept. 30**

| | | | | |
|---|---|---|---|---|
| **894** | A235 | 150fr Running, vert. | 1.25 | .25 |
| **895** | A235 | 300fr Judo, vert. | 2.75 | .70 |
| **896** | A235 | 400fr Soccer, vert. | 3.00 | 1.00 |
| **897** | A235 | 450fr Tennis, vert. | 3.50 | 1.10 |
| | | *Nos. 894-897 (4)* | 10.50 | 3.05 |

**Souvenir Sheet**

| | | | | |
|---|---|---|---|---|
| **898** | A235 | 500fr Boxing | 5.00 | 1.50 |

Nos. 896-898 are airmail.

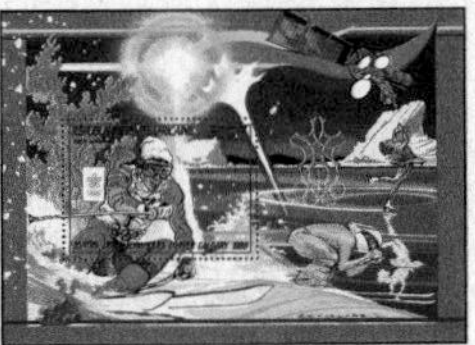
1988 Winter Olympics, Calgary — A236

170fr, Cross-country skiing. 350fr, Ice hockey. 400fr, Downhill skiing. 450fr, Freestyle.

**1988, Sept. 30 Litho. *Perf. 13½***

| | | | | |
|---|---|---|---|---|
| **899** | A236 | 170fr multicolored | 1.40 | .30 |
| **900** | A236 | 350fr multicolored | 2.25 | .60 |
| **901** | A236 | 400fr multicolored | 3.00 | .90 |
| **902** | A236 | 450fr multicolored | 3.25 | 1.00 |
| | | *Nos. 899-902 (4)* | 9.90 | 2.80 |

**Souvenir Sheet**

| | | | | |
|---|---|---|---|---|
| **903** | A236 | 500fr shown | 5.50 | 1.50 |

Nos. 899-902 vert. Nos. 901-903 are airmail.

Natl. Arbor Day — A237

50fr, Students planting trees. 130fr, Forest (before and after).

**1988, July 16 Litho. *Perf. 13½***

| | | | | |
|---|---|---|---|---|
| **904** | A237 | 50fr multicolored | .50 | .25 |
| **905** | A237 | 100fr like 50fr | 1.00 | .55 |
| **906** | A237 | 130fr multicolored | 1.40 | .70 |
| | | *Nos. 904-906 (3)* | 2.90 | 1.50 |

L'Amitie Hospital, 1st Anniv. — A238

**1988, Nov. 30**

| | | | | |
|---|---|---|---|---|
| **907** | A238 | 5fr shown | .25 | .25 |
| **908** | A238 | 60fr Aerial view | .65 | .40 |
| **909** | A238 | 160fr Front gate | 1.40 | .80 |
| | | *Nos. 907-909 (3)* | 2.30 | 1.45 |

Proclamation of Central African Republic, 30th Anniv. A238a

Design: 65fr, 160fr, Dove, map, flag, people. 240fr, Government buildings, horiz.

**1988 (?) Litho. *Perf. 13½***

**909A** A238a 65fr multi *47.50* —
**909B** A238b 160fr multi *47.50* —
**909C** A238a 240fr multi *47.50* —

A239

Olympic Medalists, Seoul, 1988: 150fr, Kristine Otto, DDR, swimming. 240fr, Matt Biondi, US, swimming. 300fr, Florence Griffith-Joyner, US, running. 450fr, Pierre Durand, France, equestrian. 600fr, Carl Lewis, US, running.

**1989, Apr. 1**

**910** A239 150fr multi 2.00 .55
**911** A239 240fr multi 3.25 .80
**912** A239 300fr multi 4.00 1.10
**913** A239 450fr multi 6.75 1.75
*a.* Souv. sheet of 4, #910-913 16.00
*Nos. 910-913 (4)* 16.00 4.20

**Souvenir Sheet**

**914** A239 600fr multi 5.25 2.00

Nos. 913-914 airmail. No. 914 contains one 37x43mm stamp.

A240

Transportation Innovations, Inventors: 20fr, Hebmuller and 1953 Volkswagen Beetle. 205fr, Werner von Siemens (1816-1892) and 1879 Locomotive B. 300fr, Dennis Conner, skipper of *Stars and Stripes,* winner of the 1988 America's Cup. 400fr, Andre Citroen (1878-1935) and 1955 Citroen-15 SIX. 450fr, Marc Seguin (1786-1875) and 1895 Decauville-Mallet 020-020. 750fr, Frederick S. Duesenberg (1876-1932), brother August, US flag and 1929 J Phaeton.

**1989, Apr. 10 Litho. *Perf. 13½***

**915** A240 20fr multi .25 .25
**916** A240 205fr multi 1.75 .55
**917** A240 300fr multi 2.25 .60
**918** A240 400fr multi 3.25 1.10
**919** A240 450fr multi 4.00 1.25
*Nos. 915-919 (5)* 11.50 3.75

**Souvenir Sheet**

**920** A240 750fr multi 5.75 1.50

Nos. 919-920 airmail. No. 920 contains one 43x37mm stamp.
Nos. 915-919 exist in souvenir sheets of 1.

**Nos. 889-892 Surcharged in Black or Silver**

**1988, Oct. 7 Litho. *Perf. 13½***

**921** A234 30fr on 170fr (B) .40 .25
**922** A234 70fr on 300fr 1.10 .55
**923** A234 160fr on 400fr 1.90 .85
**924** A234 200fr on 450fr 2.50 1.10
*Nos. 921-924 (4)* 5.90 2.75

Nos. 923-924 are airmail.

PHILEXFRANCE '89, French Revolution Bicent. — A241

Designs: 200fr, Allegory in Honor of Liberty. 300fr, Declaration of Human Rights and Citizenship. 500fr, The Bastille, horiz.

**1989, July 7 Litho. *Perf. 13***

**925** A241 200fr multi 1.75 .80
**926** A241 300fr multi 3.75 1.25
*a.* Pair, #925-926 + label 6.50 6.50

**Souvenir Sheet**

**927** A241 500fr multi 5.75 3.75

**Souvenir Sheet**

Statue of Liberty — A242

Designs: a, Crown and torch observatories lit at night. b, Working on statue's coiffure. c, Face and scaffolding. d, Workman sanding copper sheeting around the crown observatory. e, Re-opening ceremony, 1986. f, Crown observatory at night.

**Wmk. 385**

**1989, July Litho. *Perf. 13***

**928** A242 Sheet of 6 11.00 11.00
*a.-c.* 150fr any single 1.60 .60
*d.-f.* 200fr any single 1.75 1.00

Statue of Liberty cent. (in 1986). Photograph of the statue is reversed.

M. Champagnat (1789-1840), Founder of the Marist Order — A243

15fr, Madonna and child, map. 50fr, Cross, Earth.

**1989 Litho. Unwmk. *Perf. 13½***

**929** A243 15fr multicolored .25 .25
**930** A243 50fr multicolored .40 .25
**931** A243 160fr shown 1.60 1.25
*Nos. 929-931 (3)* 2.25 1.75

Nos. 929-930 vert.

Harvest Feast, Bambari — A244

**1989, Oct. 15**

**932** A244 100fr Produce 1.15 .60
**933** A244 160fr Ox plow 1.60 .80

World Food Day — A245

60fr, Domestic animals. 240fr, Arresting ivory poachers.

**1989, Oct. 16**

**934** A245 60fr multicolored .60 .40
**935** A245 240fr multicolored 2.50 1.20

French Revolution, Bicent. — A246

Battle scenes and leaders: 160fr, Brig.-Gen. Francois-Christophe Kellermann (1735-1820), Battle of Valmy, Sept. 22, 1792. 200fr, Minister of War Charles-Francois du Perier Dumouriez (1739-1823), Battle of Jemappes, Nov. 7, 1792. 500fr, Gen. Jean-Charles Pichegru (1761-1804), capture of the Dutch fleet, Jan. 22, 1795. 600fr, Gen. Louis-Lazare Hoche (1768-97), Battle of Quiberon Bay, July 21, 1795. 1000fr, Napoleon at the Battle of Rivoli Veronese, Jan. 15, 1797. 1500fr, General Jean-Baptiste Jourdan.

**1989, Dec. 5 Litho. *Perf. 13½***

**936** A246 160fr multicolored 1.40 .40
**937** A246 200fr multicolored 1.75 .55
**938** A246 500fr multicolored 5.50 1.10
**939** A246 600fr multicolored 5.00 1.00
*a.* Souvenir sheet of 4, #936-939 15.00 15.00
*Nos. 936-939 (4)* 13.65 3.05

**Souvenir Sheet**

**940** A246 1000fr multicolored 10.00 3.00

**Litho. & Embossed**

**940A** A246 1500fr gold & multi — —

PHILEXFRANCE '89. Nos. 938-940A are airmail.
No. 936 is incorrectly inscribed "Francois-Etienne." Jemappes is incorrectly spelled on No. 937. No. 940 is incorrectly inscribed "January 14."

1990 World Cup Soccer Championships, Italy — A247

Various athletes and Italian landmarks: 20fr, Bell tower, Palermo Cathedral. 120fr, Trinity of the Mount, Rome. 160fr, St. Francis Church apse, Bologna. 200fr, Palace, Florence. 1000fr, Milan Cathedral.

**1989, Dec. 23**

**941** A247 20fr multicolored .25 .25
**942** A247 120fr multicolored 1.25 .40
**943** A247 160fr multicolored 1.40 .40
**944** A247 200fr multicolored 1.60 .55
*Nos. 941-944 (4)* 4.50 1.60

**Souvenir Sheet**

**945** A247 1000fr multicolored 9.25 2.00

Nos. 942 and 945 are airmail.

Save the Forests — A247a

**1989 Litho. *Perf. 13½***

**945A** A247a 160fr multicolored 2.00 .75

Town of Bangui, Cent. — A247b

Designs: 100fr, Governor's Palace, 1906. 160fr, Outpost. 200fr, A. Dolisie, founder of Bangui, vert. 1000fr, Signing of peace treaty between Michel Dolisie and Chief Gbembo, 1889, vert.

**1989 Litho. *Perf. 13½***

**945B** A247b 100fr multi 1.25 .40
**945C** A247b 160fr multi 1.75 1.00
**945D** A247b 200fr multi 2.50 .95
**945E** A247b 1000fr multi 10.50 4.25
*Nos. 945B-945E (4)* 16.00 6.60

Championship Team from Central Africa, 1987 — A248

**1990, Feb. 23 Litho. *Perf. 13½***

**946** A248 160fr Flag, players, trophy 1.60 .75
**947** A248 240fr shown 2.25 1.00
**948** A248 500fr like 160fr 5.50 2.25
*Nos. 946-948 (3)* 9.35 4.00

African Basketball Championships. Dated 1988. Nos. 946 and 948 vert.

A249

**1990, Feb. 23 Litho. *Perf. 13½***

**949** A249 100fr multicolored 1.00 .40
**950** A249 130fr multicolored 1.10 .55

Central Africa, winner of the 1987 African Basketball Cup Championships, Tunis. Dated 1989.

A250

1992 Winter Olympics, Albertville: 10fr, Speed skating. 60fr, Cross-country skiing. 500fr, Slalom. 750fr, Figure skating.
1000fr, Downhill skiing. No. 955A, Slalom skier. No. 955B, Pairs figure skating.

**1990, Mar. 12 Litho. *Perf. 13½***

**951** A250 10fr multi .25 .25
**952** A250 60fr multi .55 .25
**953** A250 500fr multi 4.50 1.00
**954** A250 750fr multi 6.25 1.40
*Nos. 951-954 (4)* 11.55 2.90

**Souvenir Sheet**

**955** A250 1000fr multi 8.75 2.00

**Litho. & Embossed**

**955A** A250 1500fr gold & multi 12.00 3.50

**Souvenir Sheet**

**955B** A250 1500fr gold & multi 25.00 25.00

Nos. 953-955B are airmail. No. 955 contains one 36x42mm stamp. Nos. 951-954 exist in souvenir sheets of one.

Scout, *Euphaera eusemoides* A251

Boy scouts and butterflies: 65fr, *Cymothoe beckeri.* 160fr, *Pseudacraea clarki.* 250fr, *Charaxes castor.*300fr, *Euphaedra gausape.* 500fr, *Graphium ridleyanus.* 1000fr, *Euphaedra edwardsi.* No. 962A, Antanartia delius. No. 962B, Spotted flycatcher. No. 962C, Cymothoe sangaris.

**1990, Mar. 26**

**956** A251 25fr multicolored .30 .25
**957** A251 65fr multicolored .65 .35
**958** A251 160fr multicolored 1.60 .45
**959** A251 250fr multicolored 2.75 .75
**960** A251 300fr multicolored 3.00 .90
**961** A251 500fr multicolored 5.25 1.25
*Nos. 956-961 (6)* 13.55 3.95

**Souvenir Sheet**

**962** A251 1000fr multicolored 11.00 2.25

**Litho. & Embossed**

***Perf. 12½***

**962A** A251 1500fr gold & multi 15.00 5.00

***Perf. 13½***

**962B** A251 1500fr gold & multi 45.00 4.00

**Souvenir Sheet**

**962C** A251 1500fr gold & multi 12.00 12.00

Nos. 962A-962C are airmail. No. 962A exists in a souvenir sheet of 1.

1992 Summer Olympics, Barcelona A252

**1990, Apr. 1 Litho. *Perf. 13½***

| | | | | |
|---|---|---|---|---|
| **963** | A252 | 10fr Javelin | .25 | .25 |
| **964** | A252 | 40fr Runner | .40 | .25 |
| **965** | A252 | 130fr Tennis | 1.25 | .45 |
| **966** | A252 | 240fr Hurdles | 2.50 | .55 |
| **967** | A252 | 400fr Yachting | 4.00 | 1.00 |
| **968** | A252 | 500fr Soccer | 5.25 | 1.25 |
| | | *Nos. 963-968 (6)* | 13.65 | 3.75 |

**Souvenir Sheet**

| | | | | |
|---|---|---|---|---|
| **969** | A252 | 1000fr Boxing | 10.00 | 2.25 |

Nos. 963-965 vert. Nos. 967-969 are airmail.

Pres. Gorbachev, Pres. Bush A253

Pres. Gorbachev, Pope John Paul II — A254

**1990, July 27 Litho. *Perf. 13½***

| | | | | |
|---|---|---|---|---|
| **970** | A253 | 120fr multicolored | 1.00 | .30 |
| **971** | A254 | 200fr multicolored | 2.00 | .45 |

Pope John Paul II-Gorbachev meeting Dec. 2, 1989. Bush-Gorbachev Summit Meeting Dec. 3, 1989. Nos. 970-971 exist in souvenir sheets of 1. Value, each $20.

Great Britain No. 1, Sir Rowland Hill (1795-1879) A255

**1990, July 27**

| | | | | |
|---|---|---|---|---|
| **972** | A255 | 130fr multicolored | 1.40 | .30 |

No. 972 exists in a souvenir sheet of 1.

Events and Anniversaries — A256

Designs: 160fr, Galileo Probe to Jupiter. 240fr, Neil Armstrong, 1st man on moon. 250fr, Concorde, rapid-transit train, Rotary Intl. emblem.

**1990, July 27 Litho. *Perf. 13½***

| | | | | |
|---|---|---|---|---|
| **973** | A256 | 160fr multicolored | 1.50 | .40 |
| **974** | A256 | 240fr multicolored | 2.40 | .50 |
| **975** | A256 | 250fr multicolored | 2.75 | .75 |
| | | *Nos. 973-975 (3)* | 6.65 | 1.65 |

A258

Wildlife Protection — A258a

100fr, Declining elephant population.

**1991, Jan. 25 Litho. *Perf. 13½***

| | | | | |
|---|---|---|---|---|
| **976** | A258 | 15fr gold & multi | .75 | .25 |
| **977** | A258 | 60fr multicolored | 2.40 | .40 |
| **978** | A258a | 100fr multicolored | 3.25 | .55 |
| | | *Nos. 976-978 (3)* | 6.40 | 1.20 |

Eutropius A259

Design: 240fr, Distichodus.

**1991, Jan. 26**

| | | | | |
|---|---|---|---|---|
| **979** | A259 | 50fr multicolored | 1.25 | .25 |
| **980** | A259 | 160fr gold & multi | 2.75 | .75 |
| **981** | A259 | 240fr multicolored | 3.50 | .50 |
| | | *Nos. 979-981 (3)* | 7.50 | 1.50 |

Fight Against AIDS — A260

Design: 120fr, Class speaker, vert.

**1991, Jan. 24**

| | | | | |
|---|---|---|---|---|
| **982** | A260 | 5fr gold & multi | .90 | .25 |
| **983** | A260 | 70fr multicolored | 2.75 | .55 |
| **984** | A260 | 120fr multicolored | 3.50 | .80 |
| | | *Nos. 982-984 (3)* | 7.15 | 1.60 |

Central African Diamonds A260a

Designs: 65fr, Woman polishing diamond, 160fr, Map, diamond.

**1991, Feb. 14 Litho. *Perf. 11½***

**Granite Paper**

| | | | |
|---|---|---|---|
| **984A** | A260a | 65fr multicolored | — |
| **984B** | A260a | 160fr multicolored | — |

Assumption of Power by Pres. Andre Kolingba, 10th Anniv. (in 1991) — A261

**1992, Sept. 1 Litho. *Perf. 13x13½***

| | | | | |
|---|---|---|---|---|
| **985** | A261 | 160fr multicolored | 3.00 | .60 |

Anniversaries and Events — A262

Designs: 80fr, Maybach Zeppelin, zeppelin airship, Count Ferdinand Zeppelin. 140fr, Child being comforted, Jean-Henri Dunant. 160fr, Benetton-Ford B 192, Michael Schumacher. 350fr, Konrad Adenauer signing Constitution of German Republic. 500fr, Pope John Paul II, mother and child, map. 600fr, Wolfgang Amadeus Mozart. 1000fr, Columbus at La Rabida, sailing ship, and building in Seville, Spain.

**1992, Sept. 22 Litho. *Perf. 13½***

| | | | | |
|---|---|---|---|---|
| **986** | A262 | 80fr multicolored | 1.00 | .25 |
| **987** | A262 | 140fr multicolored | 1.60 | .50 |
| **988** | A262 | 160fr multicolored | 2.00 | .75 |
| **989** | A262 | 350fr multicolored | 4.50 | 1.00 |
| **990** | A262 | 500fr multicolored | 6.25 | 1.40 |
| **991** | A262 | 600fr multicolored | 8.25 | 1.50 |
| | | *Nos. 986-991 (6)* | 23.60 | 5.50 |

**Souvenir Sheet**

| | | | | |
|---|---|---|---|---|
| **992** | A262 | 1000fr multicolored | 10.00 | 2.00 |

Count Zeppelin, 75th anniv. of death (No. 986). Jean-Henri Dunant, first recipient of Nobel Peace Prize, 90th anniv. (in 1991) (No. 987). Grand Prix of Monaco (No. 988). Brandenburg Gate, bicent (No. 989). Visit of Pope John Paul II to Africa (No. 990). Wolfgang Amadeus Mozart, bicent. of death (in 1991) (No. 991). Discovery of America, 500th anniv. and Expo '92, Seville (No. 992).

Nos. 990-992 are airmail. Nos. 986-991 exist in souvenir sheets of 1.

For overprint see No. 1073.

A264

Elvis Presley (1935-1977) — A264a

Portrait of Presley, song or movie: 200fr, Heartbreak Hotel, 1956. 300fr, Love Me Tender, 1957. 400fr, Jailhouse Rock, 1957. 600fr, Harem Scarum, 1965.

1000fr, With guitar, at microphone.

No. 1001A, Holding microphone. No. 1001B, Playing guitar.

**1993, July 12 Litho. *Perf. 13½***

| | | | | |
|---|---|---|---|---|
| **997** | A264 | 200fr multi | 2.40 | .25 |
| **998** | A264 | 300fr multi | 3.50 | .50 |
| **999** | A264 | 400fr multi | 4.25 | .60 |
| **1000** | A264 | 600fr multi | 6.00 | 1.00 |
| | | *Nos. 997-1000 (4)* | 16.15 | 2.35 |

**Souvenir Sheet**

| | | | | |
|---|---|---|---|---|
| **1001** | A264 | 1000fr multi | 9.50 | 2.40 |

**Litho. & Embossed**

| | | | | |
|---|---|---|---|---|
| **1001A** | A264a | 1500fr gold & multi | 20.00 | 7.50 |

**Souvenir Sheet**

| | | | | |
|---|---|---|---|---|
| **1001B** | A264a | 1500fr gold & multi | 13.00 | 8.00 |

Nos. 1000-1001B are airmail. Nos. 997-1000, 1001A exist imperf. and in souvenir sheets of one. Nos. 1001, 1001B exist imperf.

A265

Wedding of Japan's Crown Prince Naruhito and Masako Owada — A265a

Designs: 50fr, Princess Masako, parents. 65fr, Crown Prince Naruhito, parents. 160fr, Princess Masako, Harvard University 450fr, Crown Prince Naruhito, Oxford University. 750fr, Crown Prince, Princess.

**1993, July 12 Litho. *Perf. 13½***

| | | | | |
|---|---|---|---|---|
| **1002** | A265 | 50fr multi | .40 | .25 |
| **1003** | A265 | 65fr multi | .65 | .25 |
| **1004** | A265 | 160fr multi | 1.75 | .25 |
| **1005** | A265 | 450fr multi | 4.50 | 1.00 |
| | | *Nos. 1002-1005 (4)* | 7.30 | 1.75 |

**Souvenir Sheet**

| | | | | |
|---|---|---|---|---|
| **1006** | A265 | 750fr multi | 7.75 | 3.00 |

**Litho. & Embossed**

| | | | | |
|---|---|---|---|---|
| **1006A** | A265a | 1500fr gold & multi | 26.00 | 4.00 |

Nos. 1005-1006A are airmail. Nos. 1002-1005, 1006A exist imperf. and in souvenir sheets of one. No. 1006 exists imperf.

A266

1994 World Cup Soccer Championships, US — A266a

Designs show winning team, scenes from: 40fr, Amsterdam, 1928; Montevideo, 1930. 50fr, Rome, 1934; Paris, 1938. 60fr, Rio, 1950; Berne, 1954. 80fr, Stockholm, 1958; Santiago, 1962. 160fr, London, 1966; Mexico City, 1970. 200fr, Munich, 1974; Buenos Aires, 1978. 400fr, Madrid, 1982; Mexico City, 1986. 500fr, Rome, 1990; emblem for US competition, 1994.

1000fr, 1990 German team; 1994 US team.

No. 1015A, Pele, Brazil. No. 1015B, Gerd Muller, Germany.

**1993, Oct. 9 Litho. *Perf. 13½***

| | | | | |
|---|---|---|---|---|
| **1007** | A266 | 40fr multi | .40 | .25 |
| **1008** | A266 | 50fr multi | .40 | .25 |
| **1009** | A266 | 60fr multi | .50 | .25 |
| **1010** | A266 | 80fr multi | .65 | .25 |
| **1011** | A266 | 160fr multi | 1.40 | .40 |
| **1012** | A266 | 200fr multi | 1.90 | .70 |
| **1013** | A266 | 400fr multi | 3.50 | .70 |
| **1014** | A266 | 500fr multi | 5.00 | 1.00 |
| | | *Nos. 1007-1014 (8)* | 13.75 | 3.80 |

**Souvenir Sheet**

| | | | | |
|---|---|---|---|---|
| **1015** | A266 | 1000fr multi | 10.00 | 2.75 |

**Litho. & Embossed**

| | | | | |
|---|---|---|---|---|
| **1015A** | A266a | 1500fr gold & multi | 26.00 | |

**Souvenir Sheet**

| | | | | |
|---|---|---|---|---|
| **1015B** | A266a | 1500fr gold & multi | 13.50 | |

No. 1015 contains one 60x30mm stamp. No. 1007-1014 exist in souvenir sheets of one. Nos. 1015A-1015B are airmail.

Miniature Sheets

Modern Olympic Games, Cent. (in 1996) A267

No. 1016: a, Ancient olympian. b, Baron de Coubertin, 1896. c, Charles Bennett, 1900. d, Etienne Desmarteau, 1904. e, Harry Porter, 1908. f, Patrick MacDonald, 1912. g, No games, 1916. h, Frank Loomis, 1920. i, Albert White, 1924.

No. 1017: a, El Ouafi, 1928. b, Eddie Tolan, 1932. c, Jesse Owens, 1936. d, No games, 1940. e, No games, 1944. f, Tapio Rautavaara, 1948. g, Jean Boiteux, 1952. h, Petrus Kasterman, 1956. i, Sante Gaiardoni, 1960.

No. 1018: a, Anton Geesink, 1964. b, Bob Beamon, 1968. c, Mark Spitz, 1972. d, Nadia Comaneci, 1976. e, Aleksandre Dityatin, 1980. f, J.F. Lamour, 1984. g, Pierre Durand, 1988. h, Michael Jordan, 1992. i, Soccer player, 1996.

**1993 Litho. *Perf. 13½***

| | | | | |
|---|---|---|---|---|
| **1016** | A267 | 90fr Sheet of 9, #a.-i. | 7.50 | 3.25 |
| **1017** | A267 | 100fr Sheet of 9, #a.-i. | 9.00 | 3.75 |
| **1018** | A267 | 160fr Sheet of 9, #a.-i. | 15.00 | 5.75 |

Miniature Sheet

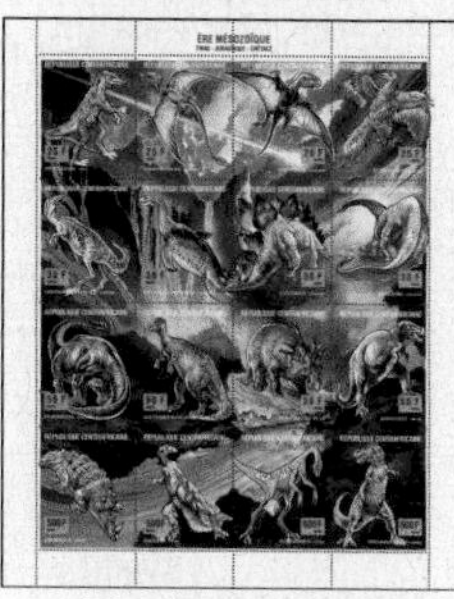

Dinosaurs — A268

Designs: No. 1019a, 25fr, Saltoposuchus. b, 25fr, Rhamphorhynchus. c, 25fr, Dimorphodon. d, 25fr, Archaeopteryx. e, 30fr, Compsognathus longipes. f, 30fr, Cryptocleidus oxoniensis. g, 30fr, Stegosaurus. h, 30fr, Cetiosaurus. i, 50fr, Brontosaurus. j, 50fr, Corythosaurus casuarius. k, 50fr, Styracosaurus. l, 50fr, Gorgosaurus. m, 500fr, Scolosaurus. n, 500fr, Trachodon. o, 500fr, Struthiomimus. p, 500fr, Tarbosaurus.

No. 1020, Tylosaur.

**1993, Dec. 3**

**1019** A268 Sheet of 16, #a.-p. 25.00 25.00

**Souvenir Sheet**

**1020** A268 1000fr multicolored 10.50 2.75

No. 1020 is airmail and contains one 51x60mm stamp.

Biodiversity — A269

Various fauna surrounding: 100fr, Man planting tree. 130fr, Man with local fauna, vert.

**1993, Oct. 20 Litho. *Perf. 13½***

**1021** A269 100fr multicolored 3.75 .75
**1022** A269 130fr multicolored 5.50 1.00

M'Bali Dam — A270

200fr, Women, men with fish.

**1993, Jan. 14 Litho. *Perf. 13***

**1023** A270 160fr shown 1.75 .65
**1024** A270 200fr multi 2.40 .90

Cooperation Council, 40th Anniv. — A271

**1993, Jan. 26**

**1025** A271 240fr multicolored 2.75 1.25

Intl. Conference on Nutrition, Rome — A272

**1993, Apr. 1**

**1026** A272 90fr shown .90 .45
**1027** A272 140fr Fresh foods 1.40 .75

University of Bangui — A273

**1993, Apr. 8**

**1028** A273 100fr multicolored 1.10 .45

Dated 1992.

Environmental Development — A274

Designs: 160fr, Woman with vegetables, fruit. 240fr, Woman cooking food.

**1993, Oct. 27 Litho. *Perf. 13½***

**1029** A274 160fr multicolored 1.75 .80
**1030** A274 240fr multicolored 2.60 1.40

Miniature Sheets

1994 Winter Olympics, Lillehammer — A275

Past Winter Olympic champions: 1031a, Th. Haug, Nordic combined skiing, Chamonix, 1924. b, J. Heaton, 1-man sled, St. Moritz, 1928. c, B. Ruud, ski jumping, Lake Placid, 1932. d, I. Ballangrud, speed skating, Garmisch-Partenkirchen, 1936. e, G. Fraser, women's slalom skiing, St. Moritz, 1948. f, German 4-man bobsled, Oslo, 1952. g, USSR hockey team, Cortina D'Ampezzo, 1956. h, J. Vuarnet, downhill skiing, Squaw Valley, 1960.

No. 1032a, M. Goitschel, giant slalom, Innsbruck, 1964. b, Jean-Claude Killy, slalom skiing, Grenoble, 1968. c, U. Wehling, Nordic combined, Sapporo, 1972. d, Rodnina & Zaitsev, pairs figure skating, Innsbruck, 1976. e, E. Heiden, speed skating, Lake Placid, 1980. f, K. Witt, figure skating, Sarajevo, 1984. g, J. Mueller, luge, Calgary, 1988. h, E. Grospiron, freestyle skiing, Albertville, 1992. i, Speed skiing, Lillehammer, 1994.

**1994, Jan. 14 Litho. *Perf. 13½***

**1031** A275 100fr Sheet of 8, #a.-h. + label 9.00 9.00
**1032** A275 200fr Sheet of 9, #a.-i. 15.00 15.00

1994 Winter Olympics, Lillehammer A276

Design: 1500fr, Women figure skaters.

**1994 Litho. & Embossed *Perf. 13½***

**1033** A276 1500fr gold & multi 15.00 5.00

No. 1033 is airmail & exists in a souvenir sheet of 1. Value $24.

Flowers, Vegetables, Fruit, & Mushrooms — A277

Flowers: No. 1034a, 25fr, Ansellia africana. b, 60fr, Polystachia bella. c, 90fr, Aerangis rhodosticta. d, 500fr, Angraecum eburneum.

Vegetables: No. 1035a, 30r, Yams. b, 65fr, Manioc. c, 100fr, Corn. d, 400fr, Sweet potato.

Fruits: No. 1036a, 40fr, Orange. b, 70fr, Banana. c, 160fr, Mango. d, 300fr, Coffee.

Mushrooms: No. 1037a, 50fr, Termitomyces schimperi. b, 80fr, Sympodia arborescens. c, 200fr, Phlebopus sudanicus. d, 600fr, Leucocoprinus africanus.

**1994, Jan. 21 Litho. *Perf. 13½***

**1034** A277 Strip of 4, #a.-d. 5.50 2.50
**1035** A277 Strip of 4, #a.-d. 5.00 2.25
**1036** A277 Strip of 4, #a.-d. 4.50 2.00
**1037** A277 Strip of 4, #a.-d. 8.75 3.75
*e.* Sheet of 16, #1034-1037 26.00 12.00

Catholic Church in Africa, Cent. — A278

Designs: 130fr, Monsignor Augouard, founder of mission, St. Paul of the Rapids. 160fr, Monsignor Grandin, Abbe Boganda, first sacred ordainment, 1938. 240fr, Father Louis Godart, House of Charity, Bangui.

**1994, June 2 Litho. *Perf. 13½***

**1038** A278 130fr multicolored .65 .45
**1039** A278 160fr multicolored .80 .45
**1040** A278 240fr multicolored 1.40 .60
*Nos. 1038-1040 (3)* 2.85 1.50

Relics from Early Civilizations, Landmarks — A279

Designs: 10fr, Cabin-shaped cinerary urn, Rome. 25fr, Face of the secret denunciation, Venice, vert. 30fr, Statue of the Tetrarchs, Venice, vert. 50fr, Little cube-shaped building, Palermo, vert. 65fr, Frieze, The Alhambra, Granada, vert. 90fr, Grand Chateau, Belinzona. 100fr, Museum D'Orsay, Paris, vert. 130fr, Granary, Galicia. 140fr, Mural, by Diego Rivera, Mexico, vert. 160fr, Guacamaya mask, Mexico, vert. 200fr, Ivory mask, Western Africa, vert. 240fr, La Sagrada Familia, Barcelona, vert. 260fr, Casbah of Amerhidil. 300fr, Gold aureus of Sulla, Rome, 82 BC. 400fr, Chimborazo volcano.

**1994, June 2 *Perf. 13***

**1041-1055** A279 Set of 15 12.50 4.50

D-Day, 50th Anniv. — A280

Pegasus Bridge, June 6: No. 1056a, British troops crossing bridge, piper. b, Glider, British and German soldiers. c, German soldiers.

Operation COBRA, July 24: a, Tank, monument, soldiers. b, Bombers, soldiers, gun barrel. c, Tank, soldiers up close.

**1994, Oct. 25 Litho. *Perf. 13½***

**1056** A280 600fr Strip of 3, #a.-c. 11.00 4.00
**1057** A280 600fr Strip of 3, #a.-c. 11.00 4.00

Nos. 1056b, 1057b are 30x46mm. Nos. 1056-1057 are continuous designs. See No. C359.

Anniversaries & Events — A281

No. 1058, 600fr — Characters from "Star Wars:" a, Han Solo, Chewbaca. b, Darth Vader, Princess Leia, Luke Skywalker, R2D2, C3PO. c, Obi Wan Kenobi.

No. 1059 — First manned moon landing, 25th anniv.: a, 400fr, Buzz Aldrin. b, 500fr, Neil Armstrong, Apollo 11 liftoff. c, 600fr, Michael Collins.

No. 1060: a, 400fr, Theodor von Karman. b, 500fr, Apollo 11 command module, Wernher von Braun. c, 600fr, Hermes Rocket, Hermann Oberth.

**1994, Oct. 25 Litho. *Perf. 13½***

**1058** A281 Strip of 3, #a.-c. 9.50 4.00
**1059** A281 Strip of 3, #a.-c. 8.00 3.50
**1060** A281 Strip of 3, #a.-c. 7.50 3.00

Motion Pictures, cent. (No. 1058).

Nos. 1058b, 1059b, 1060b are 60x51mm. Nos. 1058-1060 are continuous design and exist in a souvenir sheet of 1.

Natl. Assembly A282

**1994, Dec. 8**

**1061** A282 65fr blue & multi .35 .25
**1062** A282 430fr yel brn & multi 1.90 .90

Antoine de Saint-Exupery (1900-44), Aviator, Author — A283

**1994, Dec 16**

**1063** A283 80fr Airplane .60 .30
**1064** A283 235fr Portrait, vert. 1.10 .55

Inauguration of Pres. Ange-Felix Patasse, 1st Anniv. — A284

**1994, Oct. 22**

**1065** A284 65fr blue & multi .40 .25
**1066** A284 300fr yellow & multi 1.60 .60
**1067** A284 385fr green & multi 2.00 .75
*Nos. 1065-1067 (3)* 4.00 1.60

A285

Intl. Olympic Committee, Cent. — A286

**1994, Oct. 25**

**1068** A285 60fr bl grn & multi .35 .25
**1069** A285 405fr yel grn & multi 1.75 .80

**Souvenir Sheet**

**1070** A286 675fr Pierre de Coubertin 3.00 1.40

No. 1070 is airmail.

**Nos. 1031-1032 Ovptd. with Medalist & Country Name in Gold**

Overprints on No. 1031: No. 1071a, "F.B. LUNDBERG / NORVEGE." b, "G. HACKL / ALLEMAGNE." c, "B. DAEHLIE / NORVEGE." d, "J.O. KOSS / NORVEGE." e, "V. SCHNEIDER / SUISSE." f, "MEDAILLE D'OR / ALLEMAGNE." g, "MEDAILLE D'OR / SUEDE." h, "T. MOE / U.S.A."

Overprints on No. 1032: No. 1072a, "M. WASMEIER / ALLEMAGNE." b, "T. STANGASSINGER / AUTRICHE." c, "MEDAILLE D'OR / PAR EQUIPES / JAPON." d, "Y.

GORDEYEVA / S. GRINKOV / RUSSIE." e, "D. JANSEN / U.S.A." f, "O. BAYUL / UKRAINE." g, "G. HACKL / ALLEMAGNE." h, "J.-L. BRASSARO / CANADA." i, "K. SEIZINGER / ALLEMAGNE."

**1994**

**1071** A275 100fr Sheet of 8, #a.-h. + label 7.00 3.00
**1072** A275 200fr Sheet of 9, #a.-i. 16.00 7.00

**No. 988 Overprinted in Silver**

**1994, Dec. 28 Litho. *Perf. 13½***

**1073** A262 160fr multicolored 10.00 4.50

No. 1073 also exists in souvenir sheet of 1.

1995 Boy Scout Jamboree, Holland — A287

Scout with mushrooms or butterflies: 300fr, Armillariela mellea. 385fr, Charaxes pleione. 405fr, Charaxes candiope. 430fr, Charaxes pollux. 500fr, Volvaria esculenta. 1000fr, Cortinarius.

2000fr, Euphaedra medon.

**1995, May 24**

**1074-1079** A287 Set of 6 15.00 7.00
*1077a* Sheet, #1075-1077 10.00 2.75
*1079a* Sheet, #1074, #1078-1079 14.50 4.00

**Souvenir Sheet**

**1080** A287 2000fr multicolored 18.00 4.25

Nos. 1074-1079 exist in souvenir sheets of 1. No. 1080 is airmail and contains one 39x57mm stamp.

1994 World Cup Soccer Championships, US — A288

Stadium: 300fr, Citrus Bowl, Orlando. 385fr, RFK Stadium, Washington, DC. 405fr, Soldier Field, Chicago. 430fr, Cotton Bowl, Dallas. 500fr, Giants Stadium, East Rutherford, NJ. 1000fr, Foxboro Stadium, Foxboro, MA.

2000fr, Rose Bowl, vert.

**1995, July 14 Litho. *Perf. 13½***

**1081-1086** A288 Set of 6 14.00 6.50

**Souvenir Sheet**

**1087** A288 2000fr multicolored 12.50 5.75

No. 1087 is airmail.

African Development Bank, 30th Anniv. — A289

**1995, June 29**

**1088** A289 70fr multicolored .35 .25
**1089** A289 200fr multicolored 1.10 .50

Nos. 1088-1089 also exist in souvenir sheet of 1.

Fish — A290

Designs, 25fr, 300fr, Auchenoglanis. 30fr, 50fr, Chrisicntys.

**1995, June 22**

**1090-1093** A290 Set of 4 2.75 .90

Entertainers A291

Designs: 300fr, Freddie Mercury (Queen). 385fr, Jimi Hendrix. 430fr, Marilyn Monroe. 500fr, Michael Jackson. 600fr, Jerry Garcia (Grateful Dead). 800fr, Elvis Presley.

1500fr, Charlton Heston in "Planet of the Apes." 2000fr, Marilyn Monroe, diff.

**1995, July 21**

**1094-1099** A291 Set of 6 15.00 6.50

**Souvenir Sheets**

**1099B** A291 1500fr multicolored 8.25 3.25
**1100** A291 2000fr multicolored 10.50 4.25

Nos. 1094-1099 exist in souvenir sheets of 1. No. 1100 is airmail. No. 1099B contains one 51x60mm airmail stamp.

Volleyball, Cent. — A292

**1995, Oct. 3 Litho. *Perf. 13½***

**1101** A292 300fr multicolored 1.50 .65

No. 1101 exists in a souvenir sheet of 1. Value $10.

Sports Figures — A293

400fr, Andre Agassi, tennis. 500fr, Boris Becker, tennis. 700fr, Ayrton Senna (1960-94) race car driver. 800fr, Michael Schumacher, F-1 world driving champion.

2000fr, Michael Schumacher, diff.

**1996, June 20 Litho. *Perf. 13½***

**1102-1105** A293 Set of 4 12.00 5.50

**Souvenir Sheet**

**1106** A293 2000fr multicolored 10.00 4.50

No. 1102-1105 exist in souvenir sheets of 1. Value $30.

1996 Summer Olympic Games, Atlanta — A294

Olympic athletes, sites in Atlanta: 170fr, Atlanta-Fulton County Stadium. 300fr, Martin Luther King Memorial. 350fr, Alexander H. Stephens Monument. 600fr, High Museum of Art.

2000fr, Pierre de Coubertin, runner.

**1996, June 20**

**1107-1110** A294 Set of 4 7.50 3.25

**Souvenir Sheet**

**1110A** A294 2000fr multicolored 9.50 4.00

No. 1110A contains one 42x51mm stamp.

UN, 50th Anniv. (in 1995) — A295

**1996, July 15 *Perf. 14***

**1111** A295 5fr "50," emblem, vert. .25 .25
**1112** A295 430fr shown 2.25 .90

Nos. 1111-1112 each exist in souvenir sheets of 1. Value, set of two sheets $2.75.

1996 Summer Olympic Games, Atlanta — A296

1900 Summer Olympics, Paris: 235fr, Alvin Kraenzlein, vert. 300fr, Paris Stadium. 385fr, Irving Baxter. 430fr, British soccer team.

Past Olympic medalists: No. 1117a, Miruts Yifter, 5,000-meters, 1980. b, Germany, team dressage, 1976. c, Bruce Jenner, decathlon, 1976. d, Mark Gorski, 1000-meter match sprint, 1984. e, Randy Williams, long jump, 1972. f, Shinodu Sekine, judo, 1972. g, Kiyomi Kato, wrestling, 1972. h, Mitsuo Tsukahama, gymnastics, 1976. i, Hartwig Steenken, Germany, 1972.

Each 1000fr: No. 1118, Betty Cuthbert, 100-meters, 1956. No. 1119, Gerhard Stock, javelin, 1936.

**1996, July 19**

**1113-1116** A296 Set of 4 6.00 2.75
**1117** A296 200fr Sheet of 9, #a.-i. 8.00 3.50

**Souvenir Sheets**

**1118-1119** A296 Set of 2 8.75 4.00

Olymphilex '96 (Nos. 1113-1116, 1118-1119).

Francophonie, 25th Anniv. (in 1995) — A297

300fr, "25 ANS" surrounded by "1970-1995."

**1996, July 22**

**1120** A297 235fr multicolored 1.00 .50
**1121** A297 300fr multicolored 1.50 .60

Nos. 1120-1121 each exist in souvenir sheets of 1. Value, set of two sheets $7.50.

FAO, 50th Anniv. (in 1995) — A298

Designs: 10fr, Fish being lifted in net, vert. 385fr, Boy drinking water.

**1996**

**1122** A298 10fr multicolored .25 .25
**1123** A298 385fr multicolored 2.00 .75

Nos. 1122-1123 each exist in souvenir sheets of 1. Value, set of two sheets $2.75.

Queen Elizabeth II, 70th Birthday — A299

a, Formal portrait. b, In blue suit. c, In red hat.

1000fr, Balmoral Castle.

**1996, July 24 *Perf. 13½x14***

**1124** A299 300fr Strip of 3, #a.-c. 3.75 1.75

**Souvenir Sheet**

**1125** A299 1000fr multicolored 4.50 2.00

Nos. 1124 was issued in sheets of 9 stamps.

Pets — A300

**1996 Litho. *Perf. 13½***

**1126** A300 250fr Dog 1.25 .60
**1127** A300 600fr Cat 3.00 1.40

Nos. 1126-1127 exist in souvenir sheets of 1.

1998 World Cup Soccer Championships, France — A301

Winning country, year, player: No. 1128a, Uruguay 1930, Pedro Cea (Argentina), Italy 1934. b, Italy 1938, Piola (Italy), Uruguay 1950. c, Germany 1954, Brazil 1958, Walter, (Germany). d, Amarildo, (Brazil), Brazil 1962, England 1966.

No. 1129: a, Brazil 1970, Pele (Brazil), Germany 1974. b, Kempes (Argentina), Argentina 1978, Italy 1982. c, Argentina 1986, Mattaus (Germany), Germany 1990. d, Platini (France), Brazil 1994.

**1996 Litho. *Perf. 13½***

**1128** A301 375fr Sheet of 4, #a.-d. 7.25 3.25
**1129** A301 425fr Sheet of 4, #a.-d. 8.25 3.75

Dinosaur Eggs — A302

Denomination at: a, LR. b, LL.

**1996, Apr. 28**

**1130** A302 140fr Pair, #a.-b. 2.10 .65
*c.* Souv. Sheet, #1130a-1130b 3.00 .65

CHINA '96 (No. 1130c).

Scouting — A303

Raptors, butterflies, mushrooms: 175fr, Buzzard. 200fr, H. misippus. 300fr, Lepiota aspera. 350fr, Raptor with feathers ruffled. 450fr, Amanita caesarea. 500fr, Morpho portis-nymphalidae.

**1996 Litho. *Perf. 13½***

**1131-1136** A303 Set of 6 10.00 4.50

Nos. 1132-1133, 1135-1136 exist in souvenir sheets of 1.

Horses — A304

No. 1137, 235fr: a, Appaloosa. b, Arabian. c, Quarter horse. d, Belgian. e, Pure blood English. f, Mustang. g, Haflinger. h, Welsh pony.

No. 1138, 235fr: a, Pinto. b, Palomino. c, Welara. d, Morgan. e, Standard American. f, Norwegian fjord. g, Shetland. h, Shire.

1000fr, Saddlebred.

**1996, Nov. 20** *Perf. 14*

**Sheets of 8, #a-h**

**1137-1138** A304 235fr Set of 2 16.00 7.50

**Souvenir Sheet**

**1139** A304 1000fr multicolored 4.50 2.25

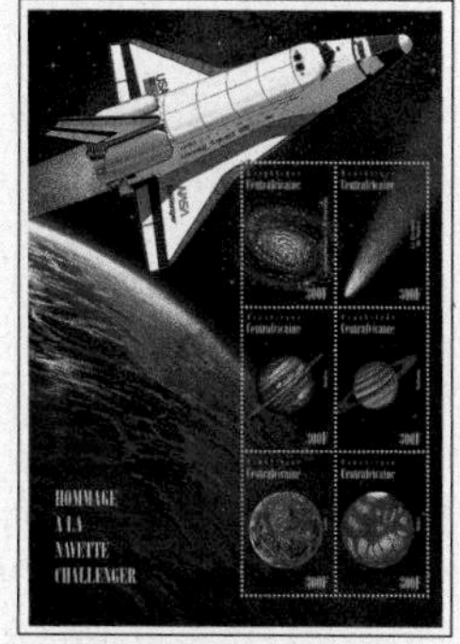

Great Nebula, Andromeda — A305

Designs: b, Halley's Comet. c, Jupiter. d, Saturn. e, Moon. f, Mars.

**1996, Nov. 22**

**1140** A305 300fr Sheet of 6, #a.-f. 8.00 3.50

Wildlife — A306

Flowers: a, Bomax costatum. b, Clappertonia flcifolia. c, Canarina abyssinica. d, Kigelia africana. e, Adenium obesum. f, Oncoba spinosa. g, Orinum ornatum. h, Gloriosa simplex. i, Strophanthus gratus.

Bird: 1500fr, Sagittarius serpentarius.

**1997, Feb. 6** **Litho.** *Perf. 14*

**1141** A306 205fr Sheet of 9, #a.-i. 8.25 3.75

**Souvenir Sheet**

**1142** A306 1500fr multicolored 8.25 3.00

Intl. Express Mail Service — A307

300fr, Globe, international express mail routes. 405fr, Emblem of hand holding letter.

**1996** **Litho.** *Perf. 13½*

**1143** A307 300fr multicolored 1.40 .65

**1144** A307 405fr multicolored 1.90 .90

No. 1144 exists in a souvenir sheet of 1.

Human Rights Advocates — A308

Designs: a, Dalai Lama. b, Martin Luther King. c, John F. Kennedy. d, Nelson Mandela. e, Mother Teresa. f, Mahatma Gandhi.

**1996**

**1145** A308 175fr Sheet of 6, #a.-f. + 2 labels 5.00 2.25

Red Cross and Red Crescent Societies A309

Designs: a, Doctor with patient. b, Man sifting grain. c, Using stethoscope on patient. d, Wounded man. e, Bandaging patient. f, Aiding infant.

**1996**

**1146** A309 250fr Sheet of 6, #a.-f. + 2 labels 7.25 3.25

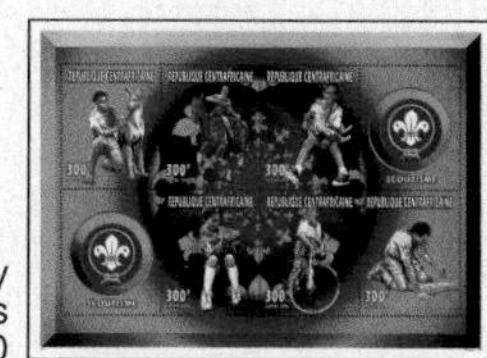

Boy Scouts A310

Boy scout: a, With dog. b, Riding horse. c, Holding cat. d, Holding butterfly. e, On bicycle. f, Playing game.

Butterfly: 2000fr, Saturnidae, horiz.

**1996** **Litho.** *Perf. 13½*

**1147** A310 300fr Sheet of 6, #a.-f. + 2 labels 9.00 4.00

**Souvenir Sheet**

**1148** A310 2000fr multicolored 10.00 4.50

No. 1148 contains one 42x36mm stamp.

Lions Intl., Rotary Intl. — A311

Designs: a, Child drinking from cup. b, Child carrying sack. c, Girl holding sheaves of grain. d, Man breaking bread. e, Woman cooking over fire. f, Boy, corn stalk.

**1996**

**1149** A311 500fr Sheet of 6, #a.-f. + 2 labels 14.00 6.50

Flora and Fauna — A312

15fr, Cucumis sativus, vert. 20fr, Phyllochistis citrella. 40fr, Cetonia aurata. 65fr, Nomadacris septemfasciata. 100fr, Crocodilus vulgaris. 140fr, Athyrium filix, vert. 405fr, Rhopalo ceres.

**1996**

**1150-1156** A312 Set of 7 5.00 1.75

Nos. 1151, 1156 exist in sourvenir sheets of 1.

UN, UNICEF, 50th Anniv. A313

Designs: a, Futuristic space vehicle. b, MIR space station. c, US space shuttle, space station. d, Woman carrying food. e, Child receiving vaccination. f, Baby being weighed.

**1996**

**1157** A313 350fr Sheet of 6, #a.-f. + 2 labels 10.00 4.50

Elizabeth Taylor, Actress A314

Princess Diana A315

Various portraits.

**1997, Apr. 10** **Litho.** *Perf. 14*

**1158** A314 300fr Sheet of 6, #a.-f. 8.00 3.50

**1159** A315 300fr Sheet of 6, #a.-f. 8.00 3.50

**Souvenir Sheets**

**1160** A314 1500fr multicolored 6.50 3.00

**1161** A315 1500fr multicolored 6.50 3.00

For overprints see Nos. 1181-1182.

UNESCO, 50th Anniv. — A316

No. 1162, 235fr: a, Fortress ruins, Ethiopia. b, Victoria Falls, Zambia. c, River during dry season, Zimbabwe. d, Nature Reserve, Niger. e, Pelican, Natl. Park, Mauritania. f, Native huts in village, Niokolo-Kobo Natl. Park, Senegal. g, M'Zab Valley, Algeria. h, Mosque, Morocco.

No. 1163, 235fr: a, c, Ruins of Roman Amphitheater, France. b, Split, Croatia. d, e, Quedlinberg, Germany. f, h, Tower of London, England. g, Olympic Natl. Park, US.

No. 1164, 235fr: a, Horyu-Ji, Japan. b, Waterfalls, Amazon River, Los Katios Natl. Park, Colombia. c, Abu Mena Church, Egypt. d, Boat on river, Fortress of Suomenlinna, Finland. e, Venice, Italy. f, Mural, Potala Palace, Lhasa, Tibet, China. g, Cathedral, town of Olinda, Brazil. h, Monastery, Mystras, Greece.

No. 1165, 1000fr, Jiuzhaigou Valley, China. No. 1166, 1000fr, Interior, Pilgrimage Church of Wies, Germany. No. 1167, 1000fr Ruins of Fountains Abbey, Studley Park, England.

**1997, Apr. 30** *Perf. 13½x14*

**Sheets of 8, #a-h + Label**

**1162-1164** A316 Set of 3 25.00 12.00

**Souvenir Sheets**

**1165-1167** A316 Set of 3 13.00 6.00

UNICEF, 50th Anniv. — A317

No. 1168: a, 200fr, UN headquarters building. b, 250fr, Baby. c, 500fr, Danny Kaye seated inside vehicle.

1500fr, Child.

**1997, Apr. 30** *Perf. 14*

**1168** A317 Sheet of 3, #a.-c. 4.00 1.90

**Souvenir Sheet**

**1169** A317 1500fr multicolored 6.50 3.00

US Pres. Bill Clinton and His Cat, "Socks" A318

Designs: a, b, c, e, g, h, i, Socks in various poses. d, f, Clinton, Socks.

**1996**

**1170** A318 200fr Sheet of 9, #a.-i. 9.00 3.75

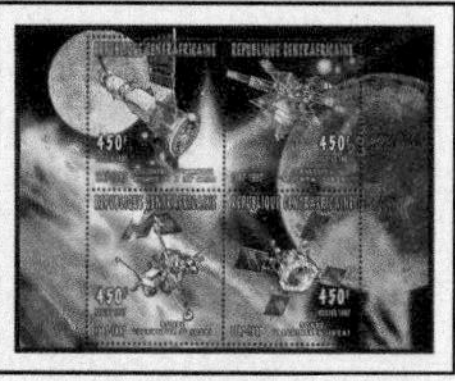

Conquest of Space — A319

Events in 1977: No. 1171: a, Voyager 1, US. b, Space Shuttle Enterprise, US. c, Meteosat 1, US. d, Salyut 6 Space Station, USSR.

Events in 1982: No. 1172: a, Salyut 7 Space Station, USSR. b, Landsat 4 Satellite, US. c, Venera 13, USSR. d, IRAS Infrared Telescope, US.

Events of 1967: No. 1173: a, Cosmos 186 & 188. b, Molniya satellite. c, Surveyor 3. d, Mariner 5.

Events in 1972: No. 1174: a, Copernicus probe, US. b, Pioneer 10, US. c, Apollo 16, US. d, Apollo 17, John F. Kennedy.

Events of 1962: No. 1175: a, Mariner 2, US. b, OSO 1, US. c, John Glenn. d, Mars 1, USSR.

Events of 1957: No. 1176: a, Vostok 1, Yuri Gagarin, USSR. b, Sputnik 2, USSR. c, Sputnik 1, USSR. d, Bell X15, US.

2000fr, Voyager, Pioneer 10, Apollo 11, US.

**1997** *Perf. 13½*

**1171** A319 250fr Sheet of 4, #a.-d. 5.00 2.00

**1172** A319 350fr Sheet of 4, #a.-d. 6.50 3.00

**1173** A319 450fr Sheet of 4, #a.-d. 9.00 3.75

**1174** A319 500fr Sheet of 4, #a.-d. 10.00 4.00

**1175** A319 600fr Sheet of 4, #a.-d. 11.00 5.00

**1176** A319 800fr Sheet of 4, #a.-d. 14.50 6.50

**Souvenir Sheet**

**1177** A319 2000fr multicolored 10.00 4.00

No. 1177 contains one 60x30mm stamp.

No. 1173 exists imperf.

Marilyn Monroe (1926-62) — A320

Various portraits.

**1997**

**1178** A320 375fr Sheet of 9, #a.-i. 16.00 6.50

John F. Kennedy (1917-63) — A321

Various portraits.

**1997**

**1179** A321 300fr Sheet of 9, #a.-i. 13.00 5.00

Bruce Lee (1940-73), Actor — A322

Various portraits.

**1997 Litho. *Perf. 13½***

**1180** A322 200fr Sheet of 9, #a.-i. 9.00 3.25

### Nos. 1159, 1161 Ovptd. "In Memoriam"

**1997 *Perf. 14***

**1181** A315 300fr Sheet of 6, #a.-f. 8.00 3.50

**Souvenir Sheet**

**1182** A315 1500fr multicolored 7.50 3.00

Nos. 1181-1182 each contain "Diana, Princess of Wales (1961-1997) IN MEMORIAM" in sheet margin and on each stamp in No. 1181.

Dogs & Cats A323

Dogs: No. 1183: a, Chinese crested. b, King Charles spaniel. c, Dachshund. d, Borzoi. e, Chow chow. f, Welsh springer. g, Rottweiler. h, Keeshond.

Cats: No. 1184: a, Birman. b, Black and white Persian. c, Siamese kitten. d, Red and black. e, American curl. f, Cornish rex. g, Silver shaded. h, White-footed cat.

1500fr, Pekingese. 2000fr, Somali.

**1997 Litho. *Perf. 13½***

**1183** A323 175fr Sheet of 8, #a.-h. 6.50 2.50
**1184** A323 250fr Sheet of 8, #a.-h. 9.00 3.75

**Souvenir Sheets**

**1185** A323 1500fr multicolored 7.50 2.75
**1186** A323 2000fr multicolored 10.00 3.75

Nos. 1185-1186 each contain one 42x51mm stamp.

Return of Hong Kong to China — A324

No. 1187: a, Tung Chee-Hwa, taking down British flag. b, Raising Chinese flag, Chris Patten, British flag. c, Jiang Zemin, skyline at night. d, City lights, Queen Elizabeth II.

600fr, Tung Chee-Hwa.

**1997**

**1187** A324 175fr Sheet of 4, #a.-d. 3.25 1.50

**Souvenir Sheet**

**1188** A324 600fr multicolored 3.25 1.25

No. 1188 contains one 38x42mm stamp.

Paintings by Hiroshige (1797-1858) A325

No. 1189: a, Minami-Shinagawa and Samezu Coast. b, Plum Garden, Kamata. c, The Kawaguchi Ferry and Zenkoji Temple. d, Armor-Hanging Pine, Hakkeizaka. e, Robe-Hanging Pine, Senzoku Pond. f, Benten Shrine, Inokashira Pond.

No. 1190: a, A Little Brown Owl on a Pine Branch with a Crescent Moon Behind. b, Sparrows and Camellia in snow. c, Three Wild Geese Flying Downward across the Moon. d, A Blue Bird on a Yellow-flowered Hibiscus. e, Five Swallows in flight.

No. 1191: a, Sparrows and Wild Rose. b, Peonies. c, Morning Glory and Cricket. d, Blossoming Plum Tree. e, Kingfisher above a Yellow-flowered Water Plant.

No. 1192, 1500fr, Haneda Ferry and Benten Shrine. No. 1193, 1500fr, A Bird Clinging to a Tendril of Wisteria. No. 1194, 1500fr, Butterfly and Peony.

**1998, Feb. 20 Litho. *Perf. 14***

**1189** A325 300fr Sheet of 6, #a.-f. 9.00 3.00
**1190** A325 430fr Sheet of 5, #a.-e. 11.00 3.75
**1191** A325 500fr Sheet of 5, #a.-e. 9.25 4.25

**Souvenir Sheets**

**1192-1194** A325 Set of 3 18.00 7.50

Nos. 1190-1191 each contain five 26x72mm stamps. Nos. 1192-1194 each contain one 26x72mm stamp.

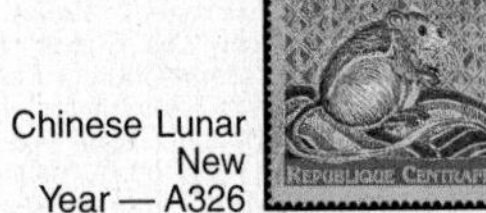

Chinese Lunar New Year — A326

Animals representing lunar year: a, Rat. b, Ox. c, Tiger. d, Hare. e, Dragon. f, Snake. g, Horse. h, Sheep. i, Monkey. j, Rooster. k, Dog. l, Boar.

1000fr, Tiger, diff.

**1998 Litho. & Typo. *Perf. 14***

**1195** A326 150fr Sheet of 12, #a.-l. 8.00 3.75

**Souvenir Sheet**

**1196** A326 1000fr gold & multi 3.75 1.75

Intl. Scouting, 90th Anniv. — A327

Insects: No. 1196A: b, Apis mellifica. c, Lucanus cervus. d, Oryctes nasicornis. e, Pseudacraea boisduvalii. f, Helictopleurus quadripunctatus, euchroea spininasuta. g, Bombus terrestris. h, Charaxes smaragdalis. i, Euchroea coelestis, mantis religiosa.

Wildlife — No. 1197: a, Coracias caudata, Otocyon megalotis. b, Gnu. c, Milvus aegyptus, pelecanus onocrotalus. d, Panthera leo. e, Loxondonta africana. f, Buffalo. g, Hippopotamus amphibius. h, Acinonyx jubatus.

Raptors — No. 1198: a, Buteo rufinus. b, Circus aeruginosus. c, Aquila verreauxii. d, Circaetus gallicus. e, Terathopius ecaudatus. f, Haliaeetus vocifer. g, Milvus milvus. h, Accipiter badius.

**1997(?) Litho. *Perf. 13***

**1196A** A327 200fr Sheet of 8, #b.-i. 7.00 3.00
**1197** A327 300fr Sheet of 8, #a.-h. 10.00 4.50
**1198** A327 350fr Sheet of 8, #a.-h. 13.00 5.25

1998 World Cup Soccer Championships, France — A328

Player, country, vert: No. 1199, 300fr, Moore, England. No. 1200, 300fr, Rahn, Germany. No. 1201, 300fr, Paulao, Angola. No. 1202, 300fr, Shearer, England.

No. 1203: a, Seaman, England. b, Schillaci, Italy. c, Romario, Brazil. d, McCoist, Scotland. e, Makanaky, Angola. f, Moore, England. g, Muller, Germany. h, Schmeichel, Denmark.

No. 1204, 1500fr, Moore, England, diff. No. 1205, 1500fr, Pele, Brazil.

**1998, June 2 *Perf. 13½x14, 14x13½***

**1199-1202** A328 Set of 4 4.50 2.00
**1203** A328 205fr Sheet of 8, #a-h, + label 7.00 7.00

**Souvenir Sheets**

**1204-1205** A328 Set of 2 12.00 12.00

Diana, Princess of Wales (1961-97) — A329

Various portraits.

**1998 *Perf. 13½***

**1206** A329 200fr Sheet of 9, #a.-i. 8.00 3.50
**1207** A329 250fr Sheet of 9, #a.-i. 10.00 4.50

Diana, Princess of Wales (1961-97) — A330

Diana wearing gowns in one of four seasons: No. 1208, White gown, spring. No. 1209, Blue gown, summer. No. 1210, Bridal gown, fall. No. 1211, High-collared white gown, winter.

**1998 Litho. *Perf. 13½***

**Souvenir Sheets**

**1208** A330 1500fr multicolored 7.50 2.50
**1209** A330 1500fr multicolored 7.50 2.50
**1210** A330 2000fr multicolored 9.00 3.50
**1211** A330 2000fr multicolored 9.00 3.50

Nos. 1208-1211 each contain one 50x60mm stamp.

Jacqueline Kennedy Onassis (1929-94) A331

Various portraits.

**1997 Litho. *Perf. 13½***

**1212** A331 250fr Sheet of 9, #a.-i. 10.50 4.25

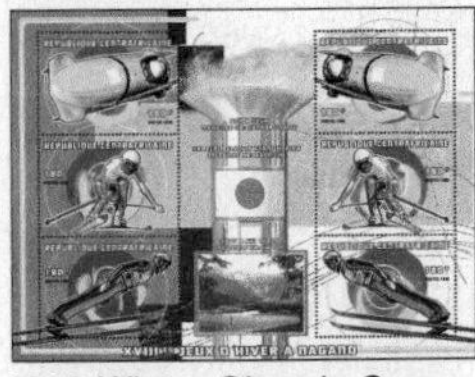

1998 Winter Olympic Games, Nagano — A332

Mirror images of vignette with different backgrounds, denomination at — No. 1213: a, Bobsled, LR. b, Slalom skier, CL. c, Ski jumper, CL. d, Bobsled, LL. e, Slalom skier, CR. f, Ski jumper, CR.

No. 1214: a, Ice hockey, LR. b, Cross-country skier, CR. c, Speed skater, LR. d, Ice hockey, LL. e, Cross-country skier, CL. f, Speed skater, LL.

No. 1215: a, Snow boarding, UR. b, Downhill skier, CR. c, Pairs figure skating, CR. d, Snow boarding, UL. e, Downhill skier, CL. f, Pairs figure skating, CL.

No. 1216, Cross-country, freestyle skiers.

**1998**

**1213** A332 180fr Sheet of 6, #a.-f. 4.00 1.75
**1214** A332 300fr Sheet of 6, #a.-f. 7.00 3.00
**1215** A332 350fr Sheet of 6, #a.-f. 8.25 3.75

**Souvenir Sheet**

**1216** A332 2000fr multicolored 9.25 3.50

Sports — A333

No. 1217 — Cyclists: a, Woman wearing helmet. b, Woman in pink, white & black outfit. c, Man in black & white outfit. d, Man in yellow & black outfit.

No. 1218 — Female tennis players: a, Holding racket above head. b, Wearing black head band. c, Wearing white head band. d, Wearing dreadlocks.

No. 1219 — Male tennis players: a, Holding racket with his right hand. b, In blue shirt, shorts. c, Holding racket behind head. d, Wearing cap backwards.

No. 1220 — Golfers: a, Completing swing. b, Hitting ball in sand trap. c, In orange knickers, argyle socks. d, Lining up putt.

**1998 Litho. *Perf. 13½***

**1217** A333 350fr Sheet of 4, #a.-d. 6.50 3.00
**1218** A333 375fr Sheet of 4, #a.-d. 7.50 3.50
**1219** A333 450fr Sheet of 4, #a.-d. 8.50 3.50
**1220** A333 500fr Sheet of 4, #a.-d. 9.00 3.50

Mickey Mouse, 70th Birthday — A334

Scenes from various Disney films drawn by Floyd Gottfredson.
No. 1221: a, 10/78. b, 11/78. c, 3/79. d, 7/79. e, 9/79.
No. 1222: a, 10/79. b, 2/80. c, 4/80. d, 6/80. e, 7/80.
No. 1223: a, 11/80. b, 3/81. c, 6/81. d, 9/81. e, 3/82.
No. 1224: a, 5/82. b, 7/82. c, 10/82. d, 3/83. e, 5/83.
No. 1225, 1500fr, Mickey with camera, flashlight. No. 1226, 1500fr, Mickey with pearl in box. No. 1227, 2000fr, Mickey and magic lamp. No. 1228, 2000fr, Floyd Gottfredson.

***Perf. 13½x14, 14x13½***

**1999, Feb. 10** **Litho.**

**1221** A334 280fr Sheet of 5, #a.-e., + label 7.00 3.00
**1222** A334 365fr Sheet of 5, #a.-e., + label 9.00 3.50
**1223** A334 390fr Sheet of 5, #a.-e., + label 10.00 4.00
**1224** A334 440fr Sheet of 5, #a.-e., + label 11.00 4.00

**Souvenir Sheets**

**1225-1226** A334 1500fr Set of 2 15.00 5.00
**1227-1228** A334 2000fr Set of 2 20.00 6.50

Birds of Africa — A335

Designs: No. 1229, 500fr, Pandion haliaetus. No. 1230, 500fr,Chaetops frenatus. No. 1231, 500fr, Tachymarptis melba. No. 1232, 500fr, Ceratogymna bucinator. No. 1233, 500fr, Laniarius atrococcineus. No. 1234, 500fr, Coturnix coturnix.
No. 1235: a, Lamprotornis superbus. b, Agapornis personatus. c, Coracias spatulata. d, Euplectes jacksoni. e, Nectarinia violacea. f, Emberiza schoeniclus. g, Pica pica. h, Tauraco erythrolophus. i, Sitta europaea.
No. 1236: a, Merops apiaster. b, Coracias garrulus. c, Cuculus canorus. d, Hirundo rustica. e, Motacilla flava. f, Ardea cinerea. g, Falco tinnunculus. h, Tyto alba. i, Charadrius hiaticula.
1500fr, Eremophila alpestris. 2000fr, Delichon urbica.

**1999, Mar. 10** **Litho.** ***Perf. 14***

**1229-1234** A335 Set of 6 11.00 5.00
**1235** A335 280fr Sheet of 9, #a.-i. 9.25 4.25
**1236** A335 490fr Sheet of 9, #a.-i. 16.00 7.50

**Souvenir Sheets**

**1237** A335 1500fr multicolored 5.50 2.50
**1238** A335 2000fr multicolored 7.50 3.50

World Wildlife Fund — A336

Balaeniceps rex: a, Eating fish. b, Up close. c, Standing. d, One in flight, one up close.

**1999**

**1239** A336 200fr Strip of 4, #a.-d. 5.00 4.00

No. 1239 was issued in sheets of 16 stamps.

Trains — A337

No. 1240: a, 40fr, 2-4-0 Steam locomotive. b, 50fr, German Mallat. c, 60fr, Shunting locomotive. d, 260fr, Rhodesian 14A 2-6-2+2-6-2 Garrat. e, 280fr, Steam train. f, 390fr, Engine No. 7, 0-6-0 Baldwin, 1920. g, 440fr, Amtrak passenger train. h, 460fr, German TEE diesel. i, 490fr, "Sir Nigel Gresley."
No. 1241: a, 40fr, Steam train. b, 50fr, 4-4-0, LNWR, 1897. c, 60fr, 2-4-0 locomotive, Midland. d, 260fr, Class XC. e, 280fr, 2-6-0T Sernada and Aveiro, 1910. f, 390fr, East Daggafontein Mines train, Great Britain. g, 440fr, Union Pacific. h, 460fr, Engine No. 6, Baldwin. i, 490fr, 4-4-2 aerodynamic train, Belgium, 1939.
No. 1242, 2000fr, Fairlie, Snake and Auckland, New Zealand, 1874. No. 1243, 2000fr, Steam train arriving at the London-Brighton Depot.

**1999, Mar. 11** **Sheets of 9**

**1240-1241** A337 Set of 2 25.00 10.00

**Souvenir Sheets**

**1242-1243** A337 Set of 2 18.00 6.50

Prehistoric Animals — A338

No. 1244: a, Archaeopteryx. b, Stegosaurus. c, Placerias. d, Rutiodon. e, Tyrannosaurus rex. f, Lystrosaurus.
No. 1245: a, Spinosaurus. b, Cynognathus. c, Kuehneosaurus. d, Compsognathus. e, Triceratops. f, Euoplocephalus.
2000fr, Desmatosuchus.

**1998** **Litho.** ***Perf. 13½***

**1244** A338 250fr Sheet of 6, #a.-f. 7.50 2.75
**1245** A338 300fr Sheet of 6, #a.-f. 8.50 3.25

**Souvenir Sheet**

**1246** A338 2000fr multicolored 9.00 3.75

No. 1246 contains one 51x36mm stamp.

Transportation — A339

No. 1247 — Antique automobiles: a, 1899 Fiat. b, First Chevrolet. c, Serpolet steam carriage. d, 130HP Fiat.
No. 1248 — Cyclists: a, Swiss rider. b, US rider. c, Miguel Indurain (riding to right). d, Jan. Ullrich (riding to left).
No. 1249 — Sports cars: a, Porsche Boxster. b, Corvette. c, Jaguar S-type. d, Maserati 3200 GT.
No. 1250 — High-speed trains: a, TGV Atlantique. b, Shin Kansen. c, ETR X-500. d, Advanced passenger train.
No. 1251 — Trains: a, Cornish Riviera Express. b, Lancashire and Yorkshire Railway. c, Type 230. d, Pacific Mallard.
No. 1252 — Fire trucks: a, 1916 Seagrave. b, 1927 Ahrens-Fox Model JS-2. c, 1992 Diesel. d, 1958 Mack Bulldog, Type B-95.
No. 1253 — Space flight of John Glenn: a, Portrait in business suit. b, In Project Mercury spacesuit. c, In shuttle launch suit, 1998. d, Orbiting earth, Space Shuttle.
No. 1254 — Supersonic airplanes: a, Boeing 2707. b, Transatmospheric prototype. c, Tupolev 144. d, Project of European Supersonic ESRP.

**1998**

**1247** A339 300fr Sheet of 4, #a.-d. 6.00 3.00
**1248** A339 350fr Sheet of 4, #a.-d. 6.50 2.50
**1249** A339 400fr Sheet of 4, #a.-d. 8.00 3.00
**1250** A339 450fr Sheet of 4, #a.-d. 9.00 3.50
**1251** A339 500fr Sheet of 4, #a.-d. 9.00 3.75
**1252** A339 600fr Sheet of 4, #a.-d. 11.00 4.50
**1253** A339 800fr Sheet of 4, #a.-d. 15.00 6.00
**1254** A339 1000fr Sheet of 4, #a.-d. 20.00 7.50

Scouting — A340

No. 1255 — Scouts with flowers: a, Vanilla planifolia. b, Flamboyant. c, Angraecum sesquipedale.
No. 1256 — Scouts with butterflies or bird: a, Hesperie a bande. b, Philepitte souimanga. c, Dryope.
No. 1257 — Scouts with dogs, cats, and their young: a, Basenji. b, Egyptian mau cat. c, White dog.
No. 1258 — Scouts with minerals: a, Tourmaline. b, Jasper. c, Madgascar corundum.
No. 1259 — Scouts administrering Red Cross aid: a, Girl Scout wiping child's tears. b, Scout bandaging child. c, Scout kneeling to help child.
No. 1260 — Scouts in leisure activities: a, Playing table tennis. b, Playing chess. c, Riding horse.

**1998** **Litho.** ***Perf. 13½***

**1255** A340 400fr Sheet of 3, #a.-c. 6.00 2.25
**1256** A340 475fr Sheet of 3, #a.-c. 7.00 2.50
**1257** A340 500fr Sheet of 3, #a.-c. 8.00 2.75
**1258** A340 600fr Sheet of 3, #a.-c. 9.00 3.25
**1259** A340 700fr Sheet of 3, #a.-c. 10.00 3.75
**1260** A340 800fr Sheet of 3, #a.-c. 10.00 4.50

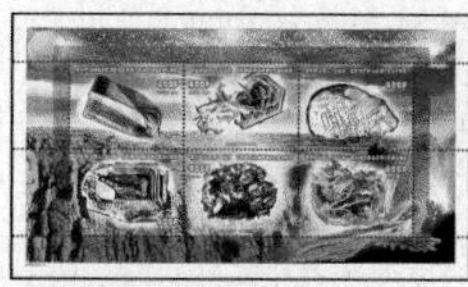
Minerals — A341

No. 1261: a, Hematite (red). b, Challophyllite. c, Fer natif. d, Sylvanite. e. Hematite (specularite). f, Spodumene.
No. 1262: a, Amber. b, Opal. c, Struvite. d, Rhodochrosite. e, Polybasite. f, Silver.

**1998** **Litho.** ***Perf. 13½***

**1261** A341 400fr Sheet of 6, #a.-f. 12.00 4.50
**1262** A341 600fr Sheet of 6, #a.-f. 17.00 6.75

A number has been reserved for a souvenir sheet to go with this set.

Mushrooms — A342

40fr, Jelly babies. 50fr, Herald of winter. 65fr, Dentate elf cup. 280fr, Pink wax cap. 345fr, Tripe fungus. 465fr, Funnel tooth. 485fr, Common white saddle. 600fr, False morel.
No. 1272: a, Parrot wax cap. b, Orange naval cap. c, Amethyst deceiver. d, Plums and custard. e, Blue legs. f, Tawny funnel cap. g, Goblet. h, Spindle-shank. i, Buttery tough shank.
No. 1273: a, Fetid mummy cap. b, Stainer. c, Lilac bonnet. d, Firm-fleshed brittle gill. e, Fly agaric. f, Arched bonnet. g, King bolete. h, Orange birch bolete. i, Dog stinkhorn.
1500fr, Hedgehog puffball. 2000fr, Striated earth star.

**1999, June 11** **Litho.** ***Perf. 14***

**1264-1271** A342 Set of 8 9.50 4.25
**1272** A342 390fr Sheet of 9, #a.-i. 15.00 6.50
**1273** A342 440fr Sheet of 9, #a.-i. 20.00 6.75

**Souvenir Sheets**

**1274** A342 1500fr multicolored 9.00 4.00
**1275** A342 2000fr multicolored 11.00 5.00

Birds — A343

No. 1276: a, Psittacula himalayama. b, Anodorhynchus hyacinthinus. c, Trichoglossus haematodus. d, Xipholena punicea. e, Chloebia gouldiae. f, Ramphastos tucanus.
No. 1277: a, Falco sparverius. b, Polyborus plancus. c, Terathopius ecaudatus. d, Tyto alba. e, Glaucidium passerinum. f, Speotyto cunicularia.

**1999** **Litho.** ***Perf. 13½***

**1276** A343 350fr Sheet of 6, #a.-f. 12.00 5.00
**1277** A343 500fr Sheet of 6, #a.-f. 17.50 7.00

Dogs, Cats, & Horses — A344

Designs: 60fr, Doberman, vert. 280fr, Domestic cat, vert. No. 1280, 390fr, Korat, vert. No. 1281, 390fr, Hanoverian, vert. 440fr, Ardennais. 490fr, Lhasa apso.
Dogs — No. 1284: a, Alaskan malamute. b, Musterlander. c, German shepherd. d, Borzoi. e, Afghan hound. f, Irish terrier. g, Komondor. h, Finnish spitz.
Cats — No. 1285: a, American bobtail. b, American curl. c, Singapura. d, Burmese. e, Tortoise shell. f, Scottish fold. g, British shorthair blue. h, Turkish van.
Horses — No. 1286: a, Shire. b, Clydesdale. c, Arabian. d, Soviet work horse. e, Finnish work horse. f, Percheron. g, Draco. h, North Swedish.
No. 1287, 2000fr, Beagle. No. 1288, 2000fr, Havana. No. 1289, 2000fr, Hanoverian.

**1999, July 9** **Litho.** ***Perf. 14***

**1278-1283** A344 Set of 6 9.50 5.00
**1284** A344 465fr Sheet of 8, #a.-h. 16.00 9.00
**1285** A344 485fr Sheet of 8, #a.-h. 16.00 8.00
**1286** A344 515fr Sheet of 8, #a.-h. 16.00 9.00

**Souvenir Sheets**

**1287-1289** A344 Set of 3 24.00 10.50

Nos. 1287-1289 each contain one 44x56mm stamp.

Butterflies A345

Designs: 40fr, Heliconius melpomene. 65fr, Large oak blue. 280fr, Danaus chrysippus. 345fr, Aricia agestis. 485fr, Danis danis. 600fr, Plebejus argus.
No. 1296: a, Delias mysis. b, Ornithoptera priamus. c, Phoebis philea. d, Heliconius doris. e, Thecla coronata f, Lycaena dispar. g, Bematistes aganise. h, Pereute leucodrosime.
No. 1297: a, Colotis danae. b, Eueides isabella. c, Papilio cresphontes. d, Mimacraea marshalli. e, Parathyma nefte. f, Appias nero. g, Uraneis ucubis. h, Eurema brigitta.
No. 1298: a, Heliconius melpomene, diff. b, Mylothris chloris. c, Catopsilia florella. d, Hebomoia glaucippe. e, Palla ussheri. f, Papilio glaucus. g, Colias erytheme. h, Euploea corus.
No. 1299, 1500fr, Unnamed. No. 1300, 1500fr, Papilio, glaucus, vert.

**1999, Dec.** **Litho.** ***Perf. 14***

**1290-1295** A345 Set of 6 9.00 3.25
**1296** A345 280fr Sheet of 8, #a.-h. 12.50 5.00
**1297** A345 390fr Sheet of 8, #a.-h. 16.00 6.00
**1298** A345 465fr Sheet of 8, #a.-h. 19.00 6.50

**Souvenir Sheets**

**1299-1300** A345 Set of 2 15.00 6.00

Trains — A346

Designs: No. 1301, 280fr, Le Capitole, France. No. 1302, 390fr, Montreaux-Bern Line, Switzerland. No. 1303, 485fr, Zugspitzbahn, Switzerland. No. 1304, 485fr, Rhatische Bahn, Swizerland.

No. 1305: a, Schwebebahn, Germany. b, Reichsbahn Class 44, Germany. c, Rembrandt, Germany. d, Trans-Europe Express, Germany. e, Inter-city, Germany. f, Steam locomotive, Germany.

No. 1306: a, ETR300, Italy. b, Mistral, France. c, ER200, Russia. d, Pendoline, Italy. e, Class 1100, Netherlands. f, Rheingold Express, Germany.

No. 1307, 1500fr, TGV, France. No. 1308, 1500fr, Austrian train.

**2000, Jan. 25**

| | | | | |
|---|---|---|---|---|
| **1301-1304** | A346 | Set of 4 | 8.50 | 3.00 |
| **1305** | A346 | 280fr Sheet of 6, #a.-f. | 9.00 | 3.00 |
| **1306** | A346 | 390fr Sheet of 6, #a.-f. | 12.00 | 4.25 |

**Souvenir Sheets**

| | | | | |
|---|---|---|---|---|
| **1307-1308** | A346 | Set of 2 | 17.50 | 5.00 |

Flowers — A347

No. 1309: a, Orchid, b, Water crinum. c, Flame lily. d, Narcissus poeticus. e, Belladonna lily. f, Table Mountain orchid. g, Upland cotton. h, Narcissus jonquilla.

No. 1310: a, Moore's crinum. b, Cyrtanthus brachyscyphus. c, Namaqualand daisy. d, "Narcissus poeticus," diff. e, Painted homeria. f, Helen O'Connor. g, Pink oxalis. h, Pink oxalis and pink arum.

No. 1311: a, Yellow wild iris. b, White arum lily (mountains in background). c, Blue tulip. d, Osteospermum. e, Table Mountain orchid, diff. f, White arum lily (with stems and leaves). g, Daisy. h, Meadow saffron.

No. 1312, 1500fr, Amaryllis belladonna, horiz. No. 1313, 1500fr, African tulip tree, horiz. No. 1314, 1500fr, Bird of paradise, horiz.

**2000, Feb. 24**

| | | | | |
|---|---|---|---|---|
| **1309** | A347 | 280fr Sheet of 8, #a.-h. | 12.00 | 3.50 |
| **1310** | A347 | 390fr Sheet of 8, #a.-h. | 16.00 | 4.75 |
| **1311** | A347 | 515fr Sheet of 8, #a.-h. | 20.00 | 6.00 |

**Souvenir Sheets**

| | | | | |
|---|---|---|---|---|
| **1312-1314** | A347 | Set of 3 | 22.50 | 8.00 |

Inscription on No. 1310d is incorrect.

Birds — A348

Designs: 100fr, Dendrocygna bicolor, vert. 150fr, Tockis flavirostris, vert. 200fr, Treron calva. 300fr, Ardeola ralloides. 450fr, Passer melanus, vert. 750fr, Sturnus vulgaris, vert.

No. 1321, vert.: a, Trachyphonus vaillantii. b, Polyhierax semitorquatus. c, Tockus nasutus. d, Estrilda astrild. e, Merops persicus. f, Amandava subflava. g, Guttera pucherani. h, Oriolus oriolus. i, Bycanistes brevis.

No. 1322: a, Butoides striatus. b, Limnocorax flavirostra. c, Terathopius ecaudatus. d, Mycteria ibis. e, Actophilornis africanus. f, Poicephalus rueppellii. g, Alopochen aegyptiacus. h, Morus capensis. i, Sagittarius serpentarius.

No. 1323: a, Gyps africanus. b, Tyto alba. c, Pelecanus onocrotalus. d, Ephippiorhynchus senegalensis. e, Ardea goliath. f, Sylvia communis. g, Buteo rufofuscus. h, Parus caeruleus. i, Dromas ardeola.

No. 1324, 2000fr, Buphagus africanus. No. 1325, 2000fr, Haliaeetus vocifer. No. 1326, 2000fr, Erythropgia coryphaeus, vert.

**2000, Feb. 25**

| | | | | |
|---|---|---|---|---|
| **1315-1320** | A348 | Set of 6 | 8.50 | 3.00 |
| **1321** | A348 | 390fr Sheet of 9, #a.-i. | 16.00 | 5.25 |
| **1322** | A348 | 440fr Sheet of 9, #a.-i. | 18.00 | 6.00 |
| **1323** | A348 | 485fr Sheet of 9, #a.-i. | 18.00 | 6.50 |

**Souvenir Sheets**

| | | | | |
|---|---|---|---|---|
| **1324-1326** | A348 | Set of 3 | 27.50 | 10.00 |

Aviation — A349

Designs: 280fr, Spirit of St. Louis. 345fr, Hindenburg. 465fr, Flight at Kitty Hawk. 485fr, AH-1 Cobra.

No. 1331: a, Fokker triplane. b, Spad XIII. c, Blériot XI. d, Nieuport 12. e, Sopwith Camel. f, 1920s US Mail plane. g, Otto Lilienthal's hang glider. h, Hydrogen-filled balloon of J. A. C. Charles.

No. 1332: a, Mitchell-B25. b, P-38E Lightning. c, Vought F-4U Corsair. d, Mitsubishi Zero. e, B-17 Flying Fortress. f, P-51 Mustang. g, Flying Tiger plane. h, Messerschmitt Bf-109.

No. 1333: a, X-1. b, B-52C. c, Boeing 707. d, F-16C. e, Sabre jet. f, MiG-15. g, F-4 Phantom. h, F-117A Stealth.

No. 1334, 1500fr, Concorde. No. 1335, 1500fr, Space shuttle "Enterprise."

**2000, Feb. 28**

| | | | | |
|---|---|---|---|---|
| **1327-1330** | A349 | Set of 4 | 7.50 | 2.40 |
| **1331** | A349 | 345fr Sheet of 8, #a.-h. | 13.00 | 4.25 |
| **1332** | A349 | 390fr Sheet of 8, #a.-h. | 14.50 | 4.75 |
| **1333** | A349 | 515fr Sheet of 8, #a.-h. | 19.00 | 6.25 |

**Souvenir Sheets**

| | | | | |
|---|---|---|---|---|
| **1334-1335** | A349 | 1500fr Set of 2 | 13.00 | 5.00 |

Chess Players A350

No. 1336, 280fr: a, Otto IV of Brandenburg. b, Mme. de Verzu and Chevalier de Bourgogne. c, Chess Players by Estienne Porcher. d, Fresco by F. Pella.

No. 1337, 300fr: a, Two Nobles. b, Depiction from book of Jean Wauquelin. c, Girolamo de Cremona. d, Ashtapada.

No. 1338, 390fr: a, Ulysses and Palamedes. b, Christian cavalier and Muslim. c, Two Moorish women. d, Burzurgmikhr and Kannuja.

No. 1339, 465fr: a, Two men, 18th Cent. b, Napoleon and Cornwallis. c, Adolf Anderssen and Wilhelm Steinitz. d, Queen Victoria.

No. 1340, 485fr: a, Two women. b, Chess on an enlarged board. c, Xerxes. d, King Evil-Merodach.

No. 1341, 515fr: a, King Henry VIII of England. b, Queen Elizabeth I of England. c, King Charles I of England. d, Russian czarevitch.

**1999 Litho. *Perf. 13½***
**Sheets of 4, #a-d**

| | | | | |
|---|---|---|---|---|
| **1336-1341** | A350 | Set of 6 | 45.00 | 18.00 |

Cosmonauts and Astronauts — A351

No. 1342, 485fr: a, Vladimir Soloviev. b, Georgi Beregovoy. c, Alexei Leonov. d, Pavel Popovich. e, Yuri Gagarin. f, Valentina Tereshkova. g, Helena Kondakova. h, Gherman Titov. i, Alexander Volkov.

No. 1343, 515fr: a, Neil Armstrong. b, Edwin Aldrin. c, Michael Collins. d, Alan Bean. e, James Lovell. f, Alan Shepard. g, David Scott. h, John Young. i, Eugene Cernan.

2000fr, Armstrong and Gagarin, horiz.

**1999 Sheets of 9, #a-i**

| | | | | |
|---|---|---|---|---|
| **1342-1343** | A351 | Set of 2 | 35.00 | 14.00 |

**Souvenir Sheet**

| | | | | |
|---|---|---|---|---|
| **1344** | A351 | 2000fr multi | 9.00 | 3.25 |

No. 1344 contains one 60x51mm stamp.

Millennium A352

**2000, Mar. 31 *Perf. 14***

| | | | | |
|---|---|---|---|---|
| **1345** | A352 | 515fr multicolored | 2.50 | 1.00 |

Issued in sheets of six.

2000 Summer Olympics, Sydney — A353

No. 1346, 300fr: a, Individual dressage. b, Rhythmic gymnastics. c, Women's 100-meter hurdles. d, Cycling.

No. 1347, 485fr: a, Tennis. b, Diving. c, Soccer. d, Pole vault.

No. 1348, 750fr: a, Long jump. b, Judo. c, Basketball. d, Show jumping.

No. 1349, 800fr: a, Boxing. b, Table tennis. c, Women's 200-meter sprint. d, Individual three-day equestrian event.

**2000 *Perf. 13½***
**Sheets of 4, #a-d**

| | | | | |
|---|---|---|---|---|
| **1346-1349** | A353 | Set of 4 | 40.00 | 15.00 |

2002 Winter Olympics, Salt Lake City — A354

No. 1350, 280fr: a, Freestyle skiing. b, Cross-country skiing. c, Bobsled. d, Men's slalom.

No. 1351, 390fr: a, Luge. b, Women's ski relay. c, Downhill skiing. d, Short track skating.

No. 1352, 465fr: a, Women's figure skating. b, Hockey. c, Ski jumping. d, Biathlon.

No. 1353, 515fr, a, Pairs figure skating. b, Women's giant slalom. c, Speed skating. d, Nordic combined.

**2000 Sheets of 4, #a-d**

| | | | | |
|---|---|---|---|---|
| **1350-1353** | A354 | Set of 4 | 30.00 | 12.00 |

UPU, 125th Anniv. A355

UPU emblem and various men: 280fr, 300fr, 390fr, 465fr, 485fr, 515fr, 750fr, 800fr.

**2000, Sept. 8 Litho. *Perf. 13¼***

| | | | | |
|---|---|---|---|---|
| **1354-1361** | A355 | Set of 8 | 18.00 | 6.50 |

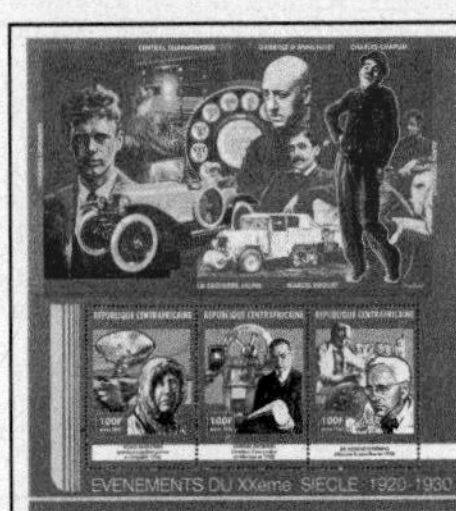

Millennium — A356

No. 1362: a, Roald Amundsen, first polar exploration by dirigible, 1926. b, Vladimir Zworykin, inventor of television camera, 1928. c, Sir Alexander Fleming, discoverer of penicillin, 1928.

No. 1363: a, Henri Dunant, 1901 Nobel Peace prize winner. b, Wilbur and Orville Wright, first airplane, 1903. c, Enrico Caruso, opera singer.

No. 1364: a, Theodore Roosevelt, opening of Panama Canal, 1914. b, Albert Einstein, theory of general relativity, 1916. c, Battle of Verdun, 1916.

No. 1365: a, Auguste Piccard, flight to stratosphere in balloon, 1931. b, Robert Goddard, rocketry pioneer, 1935. c, Ferdinand von Zeppelin and Graf Zeppelin, 1928-37.

No. 1366: a, Felix Eboue, governor of Chad, 1940. b, Mahatma Gandhi, independence of India, 1947. c, Marilyn Monroe (1926-62), actress.

No. 1367: a, Juan Manuel Fangio, race car driver. b, James Dean (1931-55), actor. c, Sputnik 1, 1957.

No. 1368: a, Charles De Gaulle (1890-1970), French general and political leader. b, Yuri Gagarin (1934-68), Soviet Cosmonaut. c, Neil Armstrong (1930-), American Astronaut.

No. 1369: a, Apollo-Soyuz. b, Elvis Presley (1935-77), American entertainer. b, Muhammad Ali (1942-), American boxer.

No. 1370: a, John Young, Space Shuttle, 1981. b, Mikhail Gorbachev, fall of the Berlin Wall, 1989. c, Dalai Lama, 1989 Nobel Peace prize winner.

No. 1371: a, Nelson Mandela, 1993 Nobel Peace prize winner. b, Galileo probe reaches Jupiter, 1995. c, Mars Pathfinder, 1998.

**2000, Sept. 28 *Perf. 13¼***

| | | | | |
|---|---|---|---|---|
| **1362** | A356 | 100fr Sheet of 3, #a-c | 1.50 | .75 |
| **1363** | A356 | 280fr Sheet of 3, #a-c | 4.00 | 1.50 |
| **1364** | A356 | 300fr Sheet of 3, #a-c | 4.50 | 2.25 |
| **1365** | A356 | 390fr Sheet of 3, #a-c | 6.00 | 2.25 |
| **1366** | A356 | 465fr Sheet of 3, #a-c | 7.50 | 3.00 |
| **1367** | A356 | 485fr Sheet of 3, #a-c | 7.50 | 3.00 |
| **1368** | A356 | 515fr Sheet of 3, #a-c | 7.50 | 3.00 |
| **1369** | A356 | 750fr Sheet of 3, #a-c | 9.00 | 4.50 |
| **1370** | A356 | 800fr Sheet of 3, #a-c | 12.00 | 4.50 |
| **1371** | A356 | 1000fr Sheet of 3, #a-c | 15.00 | 6.50 |
| | | *Nos. 1362-1371 (10)* | 74.50 | 31.25 |

Flora, Dinosaurs and Mushrooms — A357

No. 1372 — Buttlerflies: a, Cymothoe lurida. b, Charaxes lasti. c, Charaxes lactetinctus. d, Charaxes opinatus. e, Charaxes subornatus. f, Coelides hanno.

No. 1373 — Butterflies: a, Charaxes cithaeron. b, Charaxes anticlea. c, Bebearia plistonax. d, Charaxes jahlusa. e, Charaxes acraeoides. f, Bebearia oxione.

No. 1374 — Dinosaurs: a, Compsognathus. b, Kritosaurus. c, Nodosaurus. d, Tuojiangosaurus. e, Homalocephalus. f, Tsintaosaurus.

No. 1375 — Birds: a, Veuve royale. b, Travailleur cardinal. c, Gonolek a ventre rouge.

d, Touraco de Schalow. e, Touraco Pauline. f, Souimanga orange.

No. 1376 — Dinosaurs: a, Monoclonius. b, Dryosaurus. c, Anatosaurus. d, Styracosaurus. e, Pinacosaurus. f, Kentrosaurus.

No. 1377 — Birds: a, Bateleur de savanes. b, Corbeau a nuque blanche. c, Corvinelle pie. d, Cordon-bleu violace. e, Fauvette passerinette. f, Crombec a face rousse.

No. 1378 — Mushrooms: a, Lentinus sajor-caju. b, Lentinus velutinus. c, Pleurotus luteoalbus. d, Pluteus congolensis. e, Lentinus crinitus. f, Leucoagaricus ferruginosus.

No. 1379 — Mushrooms: a, Lentinus squarrosulus. b, Phlebopus colossus. c, Lentinus tuberregium. d, Phlebopus sudanicus. e, Phlebopus silvaticus. f, Volvariella congolensis.

No. 1380 — Dogs: a, Briard. b, Pyrenees shepherd. c, Chow chow. d, Cocker spaniel. e, Puli. f, Yorkshire terrier.

No. 1381 — Cats: a, American wirehair. b, California spangled cat. c, Chinchilla. d, Exotic shorthair. e, Selkirk Rex. f, Oriental.

No. 1382 — Dogs: a, Greenland dog. b, Alaskan malamute. c, Samoyed. d, Siberian husky.

**2001, May 28 Litho.** ***Perf. 13¼***

**1372** A357 280fr Sheet of 6, #a-f 7.25 3.00
**1373** A357 300fr Sheet of 6, #a-f 7.75 3.00
**1374** A357 300fr Sheet of 6, #a-f 7.75 3.00
**1375** A357 350fr Sheet of 6, #a-f 9.50 3.50
**1376** A357 390fr Sheet of 6, #a-f 9.50 4.00
**1377** A357 390fr Sheet of 6, #a-f 9.50 4.00
**1378** A357 390fr Sheet of 6, #a-f 9.50 4.00
**1379** A357 465fr Sheet of 6, #a-f 11.50 4.50
**1380** A357 465fr Sheet of 6, #a-f 11.00 4.50
**1381** A357 485fr Sheet of 6, #a-f 12.00 4.50
**1382** A357 600fr Sheet of 4, #a-d 10.00 4.00
*Nos. 1372-1382 (11)* 105.25 42.00

Fauna and Fish — A358

Designs: 280fr, Salamandra salamandra. No. 1384, 300fr, Epiplatys annualatus. No. 1385, 350fr, Pseudotropheus zebra. 400fr, Trichechus senegalensis. 450fr, Pelomedusa subrufa. 500fr, Xenomystus nigri.

No. 1389, vert.: a, Damaliscus dorcas. b, Manis temmincki. c, Hyaena brunnea. d, Lycaon pictus. e, Diceros bicornis. f, Osteolaemis tetraspis. g, Cercocebus torquatus. h, Bunologus monticularis. i, Myosciurus pumilia.

No. 1390: a, Plotosus lineatus. b, Protopterus dolloi. c, Calamoichthys calabaricus. d, Malapterurus electricus. e, Discoglossus pictus. f, Dugong dugon.

No. 1391, 1500fr, Julidochromis ornatus, vert. No. 1392, 1500fr, Hippopotamus amphibius, vert. No. 1393, 1500fr, Afropavo congensis, vert.

***Perf. 13¼x13½, 13½x13¼***

**2001, July 12**

**1383-1388** A358 Set of 6 10.00 3.00
**1389** A358 300fr Sheet of 9, #a-i 12.50 3.50
**1390** A358 350fr Sheet of 6, #a-f 9.50 2.75

**Souvenir Sheets**

**1391-1393** A358 Set of 3 21.00 7.50

Reptiles and Amphibians — A359

No. 1394, 350fr: a, Boa arc-en-ciel. b, Crapaud marine. c, Basilic vert. d, Grenouille taureau. e, Tortue happante. f, Pseudoeurycea leprosa.

No. 1395, 350fr: a, Trionix epinelix. b, Iguane rhinoceros. c, Boa constrictor. d, Boa canin. e, Tortue d'etang. f, Dermophis mexicanus.

No. 1396, 1500fr, Serpent des arbres. No. 1397, 1500fr, Grenouille poison.

**2001, July 12** ***Perf. 13¼x13½***

**Sheets of 6, #a-f**

**1394-1395** A359 Set of 2 20.00 5.50

**Souvenir Sheets**

**1396-1397** A359 Set of 2 14.00 6.00

Butterflies — A360

No. 1398, 350fr, vert.: a, Papilio garamus. b, Eunica orphise. c, Parides lysander. d, Julia dryas iulia. e, Adelpha mythra. f, Thecla coronata.

No. 1399, 350fr, vert.: a, Battus polydamas. b, Mesene phareus. c, Anartia jatrophae. d, Siproeta epaphus. e, Uraneis ucubis. f, Pereute leucodrosime.

No. 1400, 1500fr, Prepona meander. No. 1401, 1500fr, Morpho peleides. No. 1402, 1500fr, Pieris rapae. No. 1403, 1500fr, Heliconius melpomene.

**2001, July 12** ***Perf. 13½x13¼***

**Sheets of 6, #a-f**

**1398-1399** A360 Set of 2 20.00 6.00

**Souvenir Sheets**

**1400-1403** A360 Set of 4 27.50 10.00

Nos. 1398-1399 each contain six 28x42mm stamps.

A361

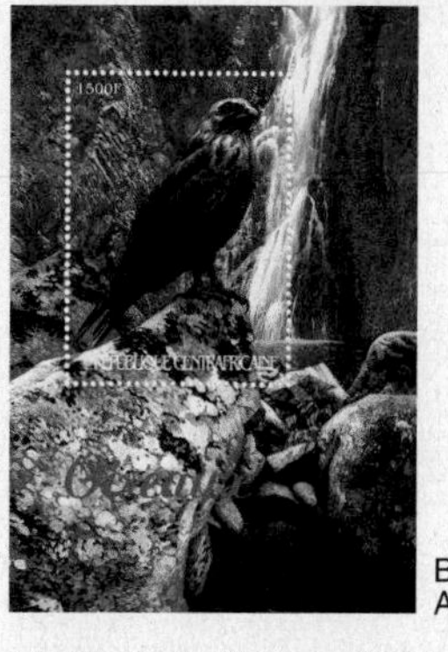

Birds A362

Designs: 50fr, Macareux moine. 75fr, Harfang des neiges, vert. 100fr, Manchots, vert. 150fr, Fou à pieds bleus, vert.

No. 1408, 325fr: a, Perruche soleil. b, Toucan de cuviée. c, Colibri. d, Ara hyacinthe. e, Pione à tete bleue. f, Perruche flavéolée. g, Pelican. h, Flamant rose. i, Toucan toco.

No. 1409, 325fr: a, Touraco à gros bec. b, Martin-chaseur à poitrine bleue. c, Faucon lanier. d, Inséparable masqué. e, Loriquet à tete bleue. f, Perroquet jaco. g, Perenoptere d'Egypte. h, Grue grise couronnée. i, Marabou.

No. 1410, 350fr, vert.: a, Colibri caraibe. b, Jaseur des cèdres. c, Colibri d'abeille. d, Bruant indigo. e, Tourterelle pleureuse. f, Talève pourprée.

No. 1411, 350fr: a, Gros-bec bleu. b, Fauvette à gorge orangée. c, Pic flamboyant. d, Passerin nonpareil. e, Fauvette à capuchon. f, Bananaquit.

No. 1412, 1500fr, Cygne, vert. No. 1413, 1500fr, Pygargue à tete blanche, vert.

No. 1414, 1500fr, shown. No. 1415, 1500fr, Balbuzard, vert.

***Perf. 13¼x13½, 13½x13¼***

**2001, July 19**

**1404-1407** A361 Set of 4 3.75 1.50

**Sheets of 9, #a-i**

**1408-1409** A361 Set of 2 26.50 8.25

**Sheets of 6, #a-f**

***Perf. 13¼x13, 13x13¼***

**1410-1411** A362 Set of 2 20.00 6.00

**Souvenir Sheets**

***Perf. 13½x13¼***

**1412-1413** A361 Set of 2 14.00 5.00

***Perf. 13¼***

**1414-1415** A362 Set of 2 14.00 5.00

No. 1410 contains six 30x40mm stamps; No. 1411 contains six 40x30mm stamps.

Mushrooms — A363

Designs: 550fr, Coltricia montagnei. 600fr, Inocybe fuscodisca. 650fr, Hydnum imbricatum. 700fr, Hygrophorus miniatus.

No. 1420: a, Coprinus picaceus. b, Crinipellis zonata. c, Naematoloma fasciculare. d, Cortinarius caerulescens. e, Amanita muscaria. f, Cortinarius obtusus. g, Entoloma serrulatum. h, Strobilomyces floccopus.

1500fr, Sarcosphaera crassa, horiz.

***Perf. 13½x13¼, 13¼x13½***

**2001, July 26**

**1416-1419** A363 Set of 4 12.00 3.50
**1420** A363 350fr Sheet of 8, #a-h 13.00 4.00

**Souvenir Sheet**

**1421** A363 1500fr multi 7.00 2.50

Prehistoric Animals — A364

Designs: 50fr, Anatasaurus. 100fr, Apatosaurus. 150fr, Allosaurus. 200fr, Velociraptor.

No. 1426, 240fr: a, Rhamphorhynchus. b, Pteranodon. c, Tyrannosaurus rex. d, Deinonychus antirrhopus. e, Parasaurolophus. f, Corythosaurus. g, Patagosaurus. h, Triceratops. i, Brachylophosaurus. j, Europlocephalus. k, Dimetrodon. l, Leptoceratops.

No. 1427, 240fr: a, Perosaur. b, Albertosaurus. c, Dryptosaurus. d, Archaeopteryx. e, Ouranosaurus. f, Myahuera. g, Camptosaurus. h, Ichthyosaurus. i, Geosaurus. j, Trilobita. k, Plesiosaurus. l, Lewisiceras.

No. 1428, 1500fr, Herrerasaurus. No. 1429, 1500fr, Stegosaurus.

**2001, July 31** ***Perf. 12½***

**1422-1425** A364 Set of 4 2.50 .70

**Sheets of 12, #a-l, + 8 labels**

**1426-1427** A364 Set of 2 27.50 8.25

**Souvenir Sheets**

**1428-1429** A364 Set of 2 14.00 4.25

Dinosaurs A365

Designs: 250fr, Apatosaurus. 300fr, Baryonyx. 325fr, Albertosaurus. 375fr, Dimetrodon.

No. 1434, 350fr: a, Triceratops. b, Ornithocherius. c, Brachiosaurus. d, Utahraptor. e, Tyrannosaurus rex. f, Stegosaurus.

No. 1435, 350fr: a, Diplodicus. b, Pachycephalosaurus. c, Archaeopteryx. d, Pteranodon. e, Herrerasaurus. f, Struthiomimus.

No. 1436, 1500fr, Rhamphorhynchus. No. 1437, 1500fr, Proleratops and Deinonychus.

**2001, July 31** ***Perf. 13¼x13½***

**1430-1433** A365 Set of 4 6.00 1.75

**Sheets of 6, #a-f**

**1434-1435** A365 Set of 2 20.00 6.00

**Souvenir Sheets**

**1436-1437** A365 Set of 2 12.00 5.00

Belgica 2001 Intl. Stamp Exhibition, Brussels (Nos. 1434-1437).

2001 Catastrophes — A366

No. 1438: a, Jan. 26 earthquake, India. b, Sept. 11 terrorist attacks, US. c, Dec. 26 fires, Australia. d, Hurricane Michelle, Cuba, Oct. 27. e, July 4 tornado, Canada. f, July 24 eruption of Mt. Etna, Italy.

**2002, July 23** ***Perf. 13¼***

**1438** A366 390fr Sheet of 6, #a-f 9.00 4.00

Each stamp in sheet exists in a souvenir sheet of 1.

Painters and Paintings A367

No. 1439, 390fr: a, Claude Monet. b, Woman with an Umbrella, by Monet. c, Argenteuil, by Edouard Manet. d, Manet. e, Joseph Mallord William Turner. f, Mornings Amongst the Conniston Falls, Cumberland, by Turner.

No. 1440, 390fr: a, Girl with a Mandolin, by Pablo Picasso. b, Picasso. c, Georges Braque. d, The Musician, by Braque. e, Woman in Blue, by Fernand Leger. f, Leger.

**2002, July 23** **Sheets of 6, #a-f**

**1439-1440** A367 Set of 2 17.00 7.00

Chess A368

No. 1441: a, Board from match between Garry Kasparov and Viswantathan Anand. b, Kasparov. c, Anand. d, Board from match between Anand and Shirov. e, Board from match between Ruslan Ponomariov and Vassily Ivanchuk. f, Ponomariov.

**2002, July 23**

**1441** A368 605fr Sheet of 6, #a-f 13.00 5.50

Each horizontal pair in the sheet exists in a souvenir sheet of 2 stamps.

Cosmonauts — A369

No. 1442: a, Yuri Gagarin, Vostok 1. b, Pavel Vinogradov, Mir 24. c, Valentina Tereshkova, Vostok 6. d, Valeri Kubasov, Apollo-Soyuz. e, Alexei Leonov, Voskhod 2. f, Sergei Treschev, Intl. Space Station.

**2002, July 23**

**1442** A369 605fr Sheet of 6, #a-f 13.00 5.50

Zeppelin NT and Concorde — A370

No. 1443: a, Zeppelin NT over Friedrichshafen, Germany. b, Concorde over Rio de Janeiro. c, Concorde over Alaska. d, Zeppelin NT over Lake Constance. e, Zeppelin NT over Orly Airport, Paris. f, Concorde over New York.

**2002, July 23**

**1443** A370 665fr Sheet of 6, #a-f 15.00 6.00

Each stamp in sheet exists in a souvenir sheet of 1.

Famous People A371

No. 1444: a, Paul Harris, founder of Rotary International. b, Princess Diana, Intl. Red Cross Ambassador against land mines. c, Pope John Paul II. d, Sir Alexander Fleming. e, Mother Teresa. f, Melvin Jones, founder of Lions Club International.

**2002, July 23**

**1444** A371 665fr Sheet of 6, #a-f 15.00 6.00

Each stamp in sheet exists in a souvenir sheet of 1.

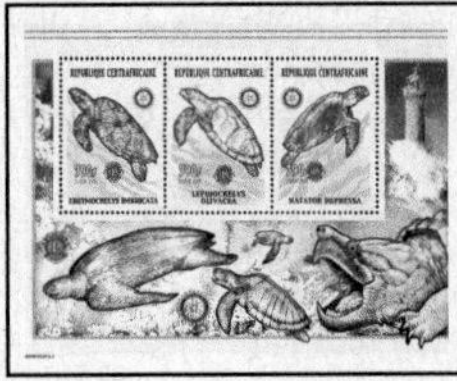

Rotary and Lions Emblems and Animals A372

No. 1445, 390fr — Turtles: a, Eretmochelys imbricata. b, Lepidochelys olivacea. c, Natator depressa.

No. 1446, 600fr — Dinosaurs: a, Sauropelta. b, Chasmosaurus. c, Herrerasaurus.

**2002, Dec. 23** **Sheets of 3, #a-c**

**1445-1446** A372 Set of 2 11.00 4.75

Scouts A373

No. 1447, 605fr — Orchids: a, Dactylorhiza markusii. b, Cephalanthera rubra. c, Neotinea maculata.

No. 1448, 665fr — Mushrooms: a, Agaricus ostreatus. b, Russula virescens. c, Lactarius deliciosus.

No. 1449, 815fr — Dinosaurs: a, Brachiosaurus. b, Sarcosuchus. c, Gigantosaurus carolinii.

No. 1450, 840fr — Minerals: a, Guilleminite. b, Torbernite. c, Bornite.

Nos. 1451-1452A (each 3000fr), Scout playing: Nos. 1451, 1451A, Chess. Nos. 1452, 1452A, Table tennis.

**2002, Dec. 23** **Sheets of 3, #a-c**

**1447-1450** A373 Set of 4 32.50 14.00

A373a

**Litho. & Embossed**

***Perf. 13½***

**1451** A373a gold & multi 9.50 9.50
**1451A** A373a sil & multi 9.50 9.50
**1452** A373a gold & multi 9.50 9.50
**1452A** A373a sil & multi 9.50 9.50
*Nos. 1451-1452A (4)* 38.00 38.00

Each stamp in each sheet and Nos. 4151-4152A exists in a souvenir sheet of 1.

Famous People — A374

Designs: No. 1453, 485fr, Christopher Columbus (1450-1506), explorer. No. 1454, 485fr, Admiral Horatio Nelson (1758-1805). No. 1455, 605fr, Jacques Cartier (1491-1557), explorer. No. 1456, 605fr, Vladimir Yourkevitch (1885-1964), naval designer. No. 1457, 665fr, Columbus, diff. No. 1458, 665fr, Sir Francis Drake (1540-96), explorer. No. 1459, 815fr, Jean-François Champollion (1790-1832), Egyptologist. No. 1460, 815fr, Queen Mother Elizabeth of England (1900-2002). No. 1461, 840fr, Marilyn Monroe (1926-62), actress. No. 1462, 840fr, Elvis Presley (1935-77), singer. No. 1463, 1000fr, Pres. John F. Kennedy (1917-63). No. 1464, 1000fr, French President Charles de Gaulle (1890-1970).

**2003, May 15** **Litho.** ***Perf. 13½***

**1453-1464** A374 Set of 12 40.00 16.00

Dated 2002. Each stamp also exists in souvenir sheet of 1.

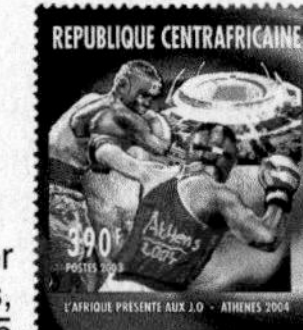


2004 Summer Olympics, Athens — A375

Designs: 390fr, Boxing. 485fr, Basketball. 605fr, Equestrian. 655fr, Tennis. 815fr, Table tennis.

**2004, Mar. 3** **Litho.** ***Perf. 13½***

**1465-1469** A375 Set of 5 14.00 5.75

Dated 2003. Each stamp also exists in souvenir sheet of 1.

2006 World Cup Soccer Championships, Germany — A376

Various soccer players and stadia: 160fr, 390fr, 485fr, 605fr, 815fr.

**2004, Mar. 3** **Litho.** ***Perf. 13½***

**1470-1474** A376 Set of 5 9.25 9.25
*1474a* Horiz. strip of 5, #1470-1474 9.25 9.25

Each stamp also exists in a souvenir sheet of 1.

2004 Summer Olympics, Athens — A376a

Designs: Nos. 1475, 1476, Table tennis. Nos. 1477, 1478, Tennis.

**Litho. & Embossed**

**2004, Mar. 3** ***Perf. 13½***

**1475** A376a 3000fr gold & multi 11.00 11.00
**1476** A376a 3000fr sil & multi 11.00 11.00
**1477** A376a 3000fr gold & multi 11.00 11.00
**1478** A376a 3000fr sil & multi 11.00 11.00
*Nos. 1475-1478 (4)* 44.00 44.00

Europa Stamps, 50th Anniv. (in 2006) — A377

Top stamp: 5fr, Netherlands #387. 20fr, Italy #810. 100fr, San Marino #1065. 150fr, Greece #718. 300fr, Italy #1039. 390fr, Italy #916. 465fr, Liechtenstein #368. 485fr, Germany #996. 515fr, Spain #941. 750fr, Finland #419. 800fr, Italy #979. 1500fr, Belgium #840.

**2005, Apr. 10** **Litho.** ***Perf. 13½***

**1479-1490** A377 Set of 12 22.00 22.00

Gen. François Bozizé, President of Central Africa — A378

**2005 ?** **Litho.** ***Perf. 13¼***

**Frame Color**

**1491** A378 5fr olive green — —
**1492** A378 10fr reddish purple — —
**1493** A378 15fr purple — —
**1494** A378 20fr brt blue — —
**1495** A378 40fr green — —
**1497** A378 65fr olive yellow — —
**1498** A378 100fr blue — —
**1499** A378 150fr lake brown — —
**1501** A378 300fr red —
**1502** A378 390fr yellow green — —
**1503** A378 485fr green —
**1504** A378 515fr bister —

Nos. 1498, 1501, 1503 and 1504 are dated 2004. Nos. 1491, 1492, 1493, 1494, 1495, 1497, 1499, 1502 are dated 2006. Two additional stamps were issued in this set. The editors would like to examine any examples.

Pope John Paul II (1920-2005) A379

Various portraits of Pope John Paul II: 280fr, 1000fr.

**2007, Aug. 24** **Litho.** ***Perf. 13¼***

**1505-1506** A379 Set of 2 6.00 3.00

Each stamp also exists in a souvenir sheet of 1.

2008 Summer Olympics, Beijing A380

Designs: 300fr, Chinese female athlete, swimmer. 390fr, Chinese soccer players, stadium. 1000fr, Chinese table tennis players, building.

**2007, Apr. 24**

**1507-1509** A380 Set of 3 7.00 3.50

Each stamp also exists in a souvenir sheet of 1.

Princess Diana (1961-97) A381

Princess Diana with: No. 1510, 390fr, Mother Teresa. No. 1511, 390fr, Pope John Paul II.

**2007, Aug. 24** **Litho.** ***Perf. 13¼***

**1510-1511** A381 Set of 2 3.50 3.50

Nos. 1510 and 1511 each exist in souvenir sheets of 1.

Worldwide Fund For Nature (WWF) A382

Civettictis civetta: 390fr, Standing in grass. 485fr, Adult and juvenile at den. 515fr, Head. 750fr, On branch.

**2007, Aug. 24**

**1512-1515** A382 Set of 4 9.00 9.00

Nos. 1512-1515 exist with printer's inscription at lower left in a souvenir sheet of four. Value, $30.

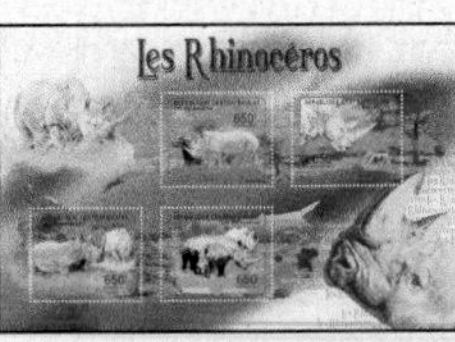


A386

No. 1522, 650fr — Rhinoceroses: a, Two rhinocersoses facing left. b, Head of rhinoceros facing right, rhinoceros walking left. c, Two rhinoceroses, one facing right, one facing forward. d, Three rhinoceroses.

No. 1523, 650fr — Gorillas: a, Gorilla beringei, adult and juvenile at left, large gorilla at right. b, Gorilla beringei, gorilla in foliage at left, large gorilla at right. c, Gorilla gorilla, large gorilla at left. d, Gorilla beringei, adult and juvenile at left, large gorilla showing teeth at right.

No. 1524, 650fr — Bats: a, Two Rousettus lanosus. b, Three Rousettus lanosus. c, Two

Megaloglossus woermanni. d, Two Hipposideros abae.

No. 1525, 650fr — Lions: a, Male and female. b, Two females in tree. c, Three cubs, two playing, one front paws on rock. d, Head of male, cub chewing on stick.

No. 1526, 650fr — Wild cats: a, Felis margarita. b, Pardofelis temminckii. c, Felis silvestris lybica. d, Caracal aurata.

No. 1527, 650fr — Dogs: a, Dogues de Bordeaux. b, Irish terriers. c, Basenjis. d, Boerboels.

No. 1528, 650fr — Elephants: a, Two Loxondonta africana, grass in foreground. b, Two Loxodonta cyclotis, grass in foreground. c, Two Loxodonta africana, elephant with raised trunk at left. d, Loxodonta cyclotis, elephant eating at right..

No. 1529, 650fr — Horses: a, Horse leaping in background. b, Horse running left in background. c, Light brown horses. d, White horse at left, brown horse in background.

No. 1530, 650fr — Dolphins: a, Sousa teuszii, Tursiops truncatus. b,Two Tursiops truncatus, Latin name at LR. c, Two Sousa teuszii. d, Two Tursiops truncatus, latin name at LL.

No. 1531, 650fr — Whales: a, Balaenoptera acutorostrata, Latin name at LL. b, Eubalaena australis. c, Balaenoptera acutorostrata, Latin name at center left. d, Megaptera novaeangliae.

No. 1532, 650fr — Birds of prey: a, Aquila rapax rapax. b, Terathopius ecaudatus. c, Buteo augur. d, Haliaeetus vocifer.

No. 1533, 650fr — Parrots: a, Poicephalus senegalus, Latin name in white. b, Poicephalus rueppellii. c, Psittacus erithacus. d, Poicephalus senegalus, Latin name in black.

No. 1534, 650fr — Peacocks (Afropavo congensis) with Latin name at: a, UR, denomination at LL. b, LL, denomination at top center. c, UR, denomination at right center. d, LR, denomination at UL.

No. 1535, 650fr — Kingfishers: a, Ceryle rudis, Latin name at top. b, Merops apiaster. c, Megaceryle maxima. d, Ceryle rudis, Latin name at right.

No. 1536, 650fr — Owls: a, Asio madagascariensis. b, Asio capensis. c, Bubo africanus. d, Asio flammeus.

No. 1537, 650fr — Owls: a, Scotopelia peli. b, Strix aluco yamadae. c, Scotopelia peli, Strix aluco aluco. d, Strix aluco aluco, denomination at LL.

No. 1538, 650fr — Bees: a, Apis mellifera scutellata and Jean-Henri Fabre (1823-1915), entomologist. b, Apis mellifera monticola and Charles Valentine Riley (1843-95), entomologist. c, Apis mellifera scutellata and Pierre André Latreille (1762-1833), zoologist. d, Apis mellifera scutellata and Léon Provancher (1820-92), naturalist.

No. 1539, 650fr — Beetles: a, Chrysocarabus auronitens, Cleridae. b, Cortodera humeralis, Goliathus goliathus. c, Cleridae. d, Ips typographus, Stictoleptura tripartita.

No. 1540, 650fr — Butterflies: a, Papilio demodocus. b, Phalanta phalantha, Latin name at top center. c, Tarucus thespis. d, Phalanta phalantha, Latin name at left center.

No. 1541, 650fr — Butterflies: a, Tarucus theophrastus, Melanitis leda. b, Catopsilia florella. c, Colotis danae. d, Junonia hierta.

No. 1542, 650fr — Fish: a, Sphyraena barracuda. b, Balistes vetula. c, Pomacanthus imperator. d, Naso elegans.

No. 1543, 650fr — Marine life (Homarus gammarus) and: a, Ostreidae. b, Pecten maximus. c, Tripneustes ventricosus. d, Sepia officinalis.

No. 1544, 650fr — Cacti: a, Opuntia ficus-indica, denomination at UR. b, Opuntia ficus-indica, denomination at LR. c, Brachycereus nesioticus, Rhipsalis baccifera. d, Euphorbia lactea.

No. 1545, 650fr — Orchids: a, Spathoglottis kimballiana and Pierre Marie Auguste Broussonet (1761-1807), naturalist. b, Spathoglottis plicata and Jean-Baptiste de Lamarck (1744-1829), naturalist. c, Eurychone galeandrae and Antoine Gouan (1733-1821), naturalist. d, Eulophia alta and Joseph Pitton de Tournefort (1656-1708), botanist.

No. 1546, 650fr — Minerals: a, Hématite and rutile. b, Limonite, denomination at LL. c, Limonite, denomination at LR. d, Gold.

No. 1547, 650fr — Worldwide Fund for Nature stamps of other countries: a, Botswana #915. b, Niue #730. c, Sierra Leone #588. d, British Antarctic Territory #192.

No. 1548, 2400fr, Two rhinoceroses, diff. No. 1549, 2400fr, Gorilla gorilla and Dian Fossey (1932-85), primatologist. No. 1550, 2400fr, Epomops franqueti. No. 1551, 2400fr, Two male lions. No. 1552, 2400fr, Profelis aurata. No. 1553, 2400fr, Azawakhs. No. 1554, 2400fr, Two elephants, diff. No. 1555, 2400fr, Horse and man. No. 1556, 2400fr, Cephalorhynchus heavisidii. No. 1557, 2400fr, Caperea marginata, Balaenoptera acutorostrata. No. 1558, 2400fr, Aquila nipalensis, Aquila rapax. No. 1559, 2400fr, Poicephalus senegalus, Poicephalus gulielmi. No. 1560, 2400fr, Two Afropavo congensis, diff. No. 1561, 2400fr, Megaceryle maxima, diff. No. 1562, 2400fr, Asio capensis, diff. No. 1563, 2400fr, Strix butleri, Scotopelia peli. No. 1564, 2400fr, Apis mellifera scutellata and Fabre, diff. No. 1565, 2400fr, Phchynoteus, Goliathus goliathus. No. 1566, 2400fr, Belenois aurota and boy with butterfly net. No. 1567, 2400fr, Leptotes pirithous, Eurema hecabe. No. 1568, 2400fr, Ctenochaetus hawaiiensis. No. 1569, 2400fr, Homarus, Venerupis decussata. No. 1570, 2400fr, Opuntia ficus-indica and bat. No. 1571, 2400fr, Eulophia alta and Jean Jules Linden (1817-98), botanist. No. 1572, 2400fr, Quartz and boy. No. 1573, 2400fr, Slovenia #247c.

**2011, Dec. 20 Litho. *Perf. 13¼***

**Sheets of 4, #a-d**

**1522-1547** A386 Set of 26 275.00 275.00

**Souvenir Sheets**

**1548-1573** A386 Set of 26 250.00 250.00

A387

No. 1574, 1000fr — Wedding of Prince William and Catherine Middleton: a, Couple. b, Couple and archbishop. c, Couple, vert.

No. 1575, 1000fr — Princess Diana (1961-97): a, Visiting child in Japanese hospital, 1995. b, Visiting child at Mother Teresa Hospice, 1995. c, Holding Camila Fiocco at Northwick Park Hospital, 1997, vert.

No. 1576, 1000fr — Mohandas K. Gandhi (1869-1948), Indian nationalist: a, Leading march, 1931. b, Addressing crowd in Calcutta, 1919. c, With Sarojini Naidu in Salt March, 1930, vert.

No. 1577, 1000fr — Pope John Paul II (1920-2005), papal arms and: a, African animals. b, Map of Africa. c, Tree, vert.

No. 1578, 1000fr — Yuri Gagarin (1934-68), first man in space, and: a, MiG-15. b, His children, monument to Gagarin in Moscow. c, Vostok 1 lifting off, vert.

No. 1579, 1000fr — Marilyn Monroe (1926-62), actress: a, With camera and flag in background. b, With flag stripes in background. c, With mouth open, vert.

No. 1580, 1000fr — Brigitte Bardot, actress, and scene from: a, Viva Maria!, 1965. b, Don Juan, 1973. c, Shalako, 1968, vert.

No. 1581, 1000fr — Romy Schneider (1938-82), actress, and scene from: a, Max and the Junkmen, 1971. b, 10:30 P.M. Summer, 1966. c, Otley, 1968, vert.

No. 1582, 1000fr — Elvis Presley (1935-77), playing guitar, and: a, Denomination at UL. b, Wife, Priscilla, and daughter, Lisa Marie. c, White star in background, vert.

No. 1583, 1000fr — Composers: a, Felix Mendelssohn (1809-47). b, Johann Sebastian Bach (1685-1750). c, Johannes Brahms (1833-97), vert.

No. 1584, 1000fr — Presidents of France: a, Charles de Gaulle (1890-1970). b, Jacques Chirac and Nicolas Sarkozy. c, Georges Pompidou (1911-74), vert.

No. 1585, 1000fr — Nobel Prize winners: a, Ada Yonath, 2009 Chemistry laureate, and ribosome. b, Andre Geim, 2010 Physics laureate, and graphene lattice. c, Elizabeth Blackburn, 2009 Physiology or Medicine laureate, and telomerase, vert.

No. 1586, 1000fr — Impressionist painters and their paintings: a, View of Pontoise: Quai du Pothuis, by Camille Pissarro (1830-1903). b, Flood at Port Marly, by Alfred Sisley (1839-99). c, The Absinthe Drinker, by Edgar Degas (1834-1917), vert.

No. 1587, 1000fr — Entomologists: a, Andrey Avinoff (1884-1949), and Daphnis nerii. b, Eleanor Anne Ormerod (1828-1901), and Junonia orithya. c, Jean-Henri Fabre (1823-1915), and Graphium agamemnon, vert.

No. 1588, 1000fr — Mycologists: a, William Murrill (1869-1957), and Cantharellus aurantiacus. b, Fred Jay Seaver (1877-1970), and Stropharia viridula. c, Arthur Henry Reginald Buller (1874-1944), and Amanita mappa, vert.

No. 1589, 1000fr — Mineralogists: a, Florence Bascom (1862-1945), and kyanite. b, Otto Wilhelm Herrmann von Abich (1806-86), and abichite. c, Auguste Michel-Lévy (1844-1911), and calcaires, vert.

No. 1590, 1000fr — Sports of 2012 Summer Olympics, London: a, Taekwondo. b, Boxing. c, Archery, vert.

No. 1591, 1000fr — Table tennis players: a, Timo Boll. b, Wang Liqin. c, Liu Shiwen, vert.

No. 1592, 1000fr — World chess champions: a, Paul Morphy (1837-84). b, Mikhail Botvinnik (1911-95). c, Alexander Alekhine (1892-1946), vert.

No. 1593, 1000fr — Scouts: a, Five Boy Scouts. b, Boy Scout bugler, Boy Scout with pigeons. c, Boy Scouts adjusting tent, Olave Baden-Powell (1889-1977), vert.

No. 1594, 1000fr — Survivors of the sinking of the Titanic: a, Eva Hart (1905-96). b, Dorothy Gibson (1889-1946). c, Ruth Elizabeth Becker (1899-1990), vert.

No. 1595, 1000fr — New Year 2012 (Year of the Dragon): a, Dragon, denomination at UL. b, Dragon, denomination at UR. c, Dragon, vert.

No. 1596, 1000fr — Indonesia 2012 Intl. Philatelic Exhibition emblem and: a, Rinjani Volcano, Panthera tigris sumatrae. b, Ijen volcanic crater, Pongo abelii, vert. c, Krakatoa Volcano, Elephas maximus borneensis, vert.

No. 1597, 2700fr, Prince William and Catherine Middleton, diff. No. 1598, 2700fr, Princess Diana with child at Hindu temple, London. No. 1599, 2700fr, Gandhi and young girl. No. 1600, 2700fr, Pope John Paul II kissing ground at Bangui Airport. No. 1601, 2700fr, Gagarin and Vostok 1 lifting off, diff. No. 1602, 2700fr, Monroe, diff. No. 1603, 2700fr, Bardot, diff. No. 1604, 2700fr, Schneider, scene from Adorable Sinner, 1959. No. 1605, 2700fr, Presley, diff. No. 1606, 2700fr, Wolfgang Amadeus Mozart (1756-91), composer. No. 1607, 2700fr, French President Nicolas Sarkozy, U.S. President Barack Obama. No. 1608, 2700fr, Robert G. Edwards, 2010 Physiology and Medicine Nobel laureate and in-vitro fertilization. No. 1609, 2700fr, Impression, Soleil Levant, by Clause Monet (1840-1926). No. 1610, 2700fr, Evelyn Cheesman (1881-1969), entomologist, and Phalacrognathus muelleri. No. 1611, 2700fr, Elsie Maud Wakefield (1886-1972), mycologist, and Lactaria vellerea. No. 1612, 2700fr, Ignacy Domeyko (1802-89), mineralogist, and domeykite. No. 1613, 2700fr, Dressage. No. 1614, 2700fr, Table tennis player Ding Ning. No. 1615, 2700fr, World chess champion Anatoly Karpov. No. 1616, 2700fr, Boy Scouts and Lord Robert Baden-Powell (1857-1941). No. 1617, 2700fr, Lolo and Edmond Navratil, survivors of sinking of the Titanic. No. 1618, 2700fr, Dragon, diff. No. 1619, 2700fr, Indonesia 2012 Intl. Philatelic Exhibition emblem and Varanus komodoensis, vert.

**2011, Dec. 27 Litho. *Perf. 13¼***

**Sheets of 3, #a-c**

**1574-1596** A387 Set of 23 275.00 275.00

**Souvenir Sheets**

**1597-1619** A387 Set of 23 250.00 250.00

A388

A389

Art A390

No. 1620, 400fr — Inscriptions: a, Adam et Eve. b, Marie-Madeleine Pénitente. c, La Vierge à L'Enfant.

No. 1621, 400fr — Inscriptions: a, Venus en Devant le Miroir. b, La Flore. c, Le Suicide de Lucrèce.

No. 1622, 400fr — Inscriptions: a, Noli Me Tangere. b, Mater Dolorosa. c, Marie avec L'Enfant et des Saintes.

No. 1623, 400fr, horiz. — Inscriptions: a, La Venus d'Urbino (woman in background). b, La Venus d'Urbino (no woman in background). c, Danaé avec Nourrice.

No. 1624, 3200fr, Like #1620a. No. 1625, 3200fr, Like #1620b. No. 1626, 3200fr, Like #1620c. No. 1627, 3200fr, Like #1621a. No. 1628, 3200fr, Like #1621b. No. 1629, 3200fr, Like #1621c. No. 1630, 3200fr, Like #1622a. No. 1631, 3200fr, Like #1622b. No. 1632, 3200fr, Like #1622c, horiz. No. 1633, 3200fr, Like #1623a (image flipped). No. 1634, 3200fr, Like #1623b. No. 1635, 3200fr, Like #1623c.

No. 1636, 4000fr, Venus et Adonis.

No. 1637, 400fr — Inscriptions: a, La Toilette de Venus. b, Hercule et Omfala. c, Marquise de Pompadour.

No. 1638, 400fr — Inscriptions: a, Venus Consoler Amour. b, Jeune Femme avec un Bouquet de Roses. c, Venus Fin Cupidon.

No. 1639, 400fr — Inscriptions: a, Portrait d'une Femme. b, Putti avec des Oiseaux. c, Diana au Bain.

No. 1640, 400fr, horiz. — Inscriptions: a, Portrait de Marie-Louise O'Murphy. b, L'Odalisque. c, Léda et la Cygne.

No. 1641, 3200fr, Like #1637a. No. 1642, 3200fr, Like #1637b. No. 1643, 3200fr, Like #1637c. No. 1644, 3200fr, Like #1638a. No. 1645, 3200fr, Like #1638b. No. 1646, 3200fr, Like #1638c. No. 1647, 3200fr, Like #1639a. No. 1648, 3200fr, Like #1639b. No. 1649, 3200fr, Like #1639c, horiz. No. 1650, 3200fr, Like #1640a. No. 1651, 3200fr, Like #1640b. No. 1652, 3200fr, Like #1640c.

No. 1653, 4000fr, Renaud et Armide.

No. 1654, 400fr — Inscriptions: a, Portrait de Victor Jaquemont. b, Déjeuner sur l'Herbe de l'Etude. c, Peupliers le Long du Fleuve Epte.

No. 1655, 400fr — Inscriptions: a, Camille avec un Petit Chien. b, Camille Monet en Costume Japonais. c, Femme à l'Ombrelle.

No. 1656, 400fr — Inscriptions: a, Femme à l'Ombrelle Tournée vers la Droite. b, Poly, Pêcheur de Belle-Ile. c, Le Déjeuner.

No. 1657, 400fr, horiz. — Inscriptions: a, Le Pont sur la Seine. b, Le Pont, D'Amsterdam. c, Chambres du Parlement, Coucher de Soleil.

No. 1658, 3200fr, Like #1654a. No. 1659, 3200fr, Like #1654b. No. 1660, 3200fr, Like #1654c. No. 1661, 3200fr, Like #1655a. No. 1662, 3200fr, Like #1655b. No. 1663, 3200fr, Like #1655c. No. 1664, 3200fr, Like #1656a. No. 1665, 3200fr, Like #1656b. No. 1666, 3200fr, Like #1656c. No. 1667, 3200fr, Like #1657a. No. 1668, 3200fr, Like #1657b. No. 1669, 3200fr, Like #1657c.

No. 1670, 4000fr, Camille Monet et un Enfant dans le Jardin de l'Artiste à Argenteuil.

No. 1671, 400fr — Inscriptions: a, Sainte-Anne avec la Vierge et l'Enfant. b, Portrait d'une Jeune Femme Vénitienne. c, Christ comme l'Homme des Douleurs. d, Portrait de Maximilien I. e, Portrait d'Elsbeth Tucher. f, Portrait de Oswolt Krel.

No. 1672, 400fr — Inscriptions: a, Madone et l'Enfant. b, Adam et Eve. c, Lamentations sur le Christ Mort. d, Vierge et l'Enfant avant d'une Arcade. e, Le Vol à Destination de l'Egypte Résineux. f, Jérôme Pénitent.

No. 1673, 3200fr, Like #1671a. No. 1674, 3200fr, Like #1671b. No. 1675, 3200fr, Like #1671c. No. 1676, 3200fr, Like #1671d. No. 1677, 3200fr, Like #1671e. No. 1678, 3200fr, Like #1671f. No. 1679, 3200fr, Like #1672a. No. 1680, 3200fr, Like #1672b. No. 1681, 3200fr, Like #1672c. No. 1682, 3200fr, Like #1672d. No. 1683, 3200fr, Like #1672e. No. 1684, 3200fr, Like #1672f.

No. 1685, 4000fr, Bacchanales avec Silene.

No. 1686, 400fr — Inscriptions: a, David (statue). b, La Pietà (statue). c, Jugement Dernier Christ Juge. d, Le Prophète Zacharie. e, Le Prophète Jérémie. f, La Sibylle de Cumes.

No. 1687, 400fr — Inscriptions: a, Le Prophète Joel. b, Le Prophète Jessaja. c, Le Prophète Ezéchiel. d, La Sibylle d'Erythrée. e, La Sibylle de Delphes. f, La Sibylle de Libye.

No. 1688, 3200fr, Like #1686a. No. 1689, 3200fr, Like #1686b. No. 1690, 3200fr, Like #1686c. No. 1691, 3200fr, Like #1686d. No. 1692, 3200fr, Like #1686e. No. 1693, 3200fr, Like #1686f. No. 1694, 3200fr, Like #1687a. No. 1695, 3200fr, Like #1687b. No. 1696, 3200fr, Like #1687c. No. 1697, 3200fr, Like #1687d. No. 1698, 3200fr, Like #1687e. No. 1699, 3200fr, Like #1687f.

No. 1700, 4000fr, La Chapelle Sixtine.

No. 1701, 400fr — Inscriptions: a, Le Christ Bénissant. b, La Vierge Colonna. c, Saint-George aux Prises avec les Dragons. d, Madone du Chardonneret. e, La Vierge Garvagh. f, La Madone Sixtine.

No. 1702, 400fr — Inscriptions: a, Saint-Michel. b, Le Portrait d'une Jeune Femme. c, Sainte-Catherine d'Alexandrie. d, Madonna del Baldacchio. e, La Sainte Famille avec les Saints Elizabeth et John. f, La Vierge de la Maison d'Orléans.

No. 1703, 3200fr, Like #1701a. No. 1704, 3200fr, Like #1701b. No. 1705, 3200fr, Like #1701c. No. 1706, 3200fr, Like #1701d. No. 1707, 3200fr, Like #1701e. No. 1708, 3200fr, Like #1701f. No. 1709, 3200fr, Like #1702a.

No. 1710, 3200fr, Like #1702b. No. 1711, 3200fr, Like #1702c. No. 1712, 3200fr, Like #1702d. No. 1713, 3200fr, Like #1702e. No. 1714, 3200fr, Like #1702f.

No. 1715, 4000fr, La Dispute du Saint Sacrement.

No. 1716, 400fr — Inscriptions: a, Alexandre et de Roxane. b, Viol des Filles de Leucippe. c, Le Débarquement de Marie de Médicis à Marseille. d, Bethsabée à la Fontaine. e, Persée Libératrice Andromède. f, Diane et ses Nymphes Surpris par les Faunes.

No. 1717, 400fr — Inscriptions: a, L'Union de la Terre et de l'Eau. b, Bacchus. c,Vénus à un Miroir. d, Les Trois Grâces. e, Isabelle, Gouverneur des Pays Bas. f, Erection de la Croix.

No. 1718, 3200fr, Like #1716a. No. 1719, 3200fr, Like #1716b. No. 1720, 3200fr, Like #1716c. No. 1721, 3200fr, Like #1716d. No. 1722, 3200fr, Like #1716e. No. 1723, 3200fr, Like #1716f. No. 1724, 3200fr, Like #1717a. No. 1725, 3200fr, Like #1717b. No. 1726, 3200fr, Like #1717c. No. 1727, 3200fr, Like #1717d. No. 1728, 3200fr, Like #1717e. No. 1729, 3200fr, Like #1717f.

No. 1730, 4000fr, Ixion.

No. 1731, 400fr — Inscriptions: a, Philadelphie et Elisabeth Cary. b, Marchesa Durazzo. c, Saint-Pierre. d, Susanna & Aînés. e, Saint Jean le Baptiste dans le Desert. f, St. Rosalie Intercédant pour les Pestiférés de Palerme.

No. 1732, 400fr — Inscriptions: a, Charles Ier de Chasse. b, Golgotha. c, Silène Ivre. d, L'Homme en Armure avec Foulard Rouge. e, Portrait de Famille. f, Tête d'une Jeune Femme.

No. 1733, 3200fr, Like #1731a. No. 1734, 3200fr, Like #1731b. No. 1735, 3200fr, Like #1731c. No. 1736, 3200fr, Like #1731d. No. 1737, 3200fr, Like #1731e. No. 1738, 3200fr, Like #1731f. No. 1739, 3200fr, Like #1732a. No. 1740, 3200fr, Like #1732b. No. 1741, 3200fr, Like #1732c. No. 1742, 3200fr, Like #1732d. No. 1743, 3200fr, Like #1732e. No. 1744, 3200fr, Like #1732f.

No. 1745, 4000fr, Déploration du Christ.

No. 1746, 400fr — Inscriptions: a, Saskia en Flore. b, Artemis. c, Une Jeune Femme qui Tente sur Boucles d'Oreilles. d, David et Jonathan. e, La Sainte Famille (Jesus in cradle). f, La Sainte Famille (Mary holding Jesus).

No. 1747, 400fr — Inscriptions: a, Abraham le Sacrifice. b, Balaam Ass. c, Tobie Accusant Anna de Voler le Kid. d, La Fête de la Musique. e, Christ dans la Tempête sur le Lac de Galilée. f, Enlèvement de Ganymède.

No. 1748, 3200fr, Like #1746a. No. 1749, 3200fr, Like #1746b. No. 1750, 3200fr, Like #1746c. No. 1751, 3200fr, Like #1746d. No. 1752, 3200fr, Like #1746e. No. 1753, 3200fr, Like #1746f. No. 1754, 3200fr, Like #1747a. No. 1755, 3200fr, Like #1747b. No. 1756, 3200fr, Like #1747c. No. 1757, 3200fr, Like #1747d. No. 1758, 3200fr, Like #1747e. No. 1759, 3200fr, Like #1747f.

No. 1760, 4000fr, La Scène de l'Enfant Prodigue dans la Taverne.

No. 1761, 400fr — Inscriptions: a, Baigneuse Arrangeant ses Cheveux. b, Femme Endormie. c, Baigneuse aux Cheveux Longs. d, La Promenade. e, Une Femme Jouant de la Guitare. f, Femme Arranger ses Cheveux.

No. 1762, 400fr — Inscriptions: a, Femme de Baignade. b, Jeanne Samary. c, Junge Badende. d, La Loge. e, Gabrielle à la Rose. f, Deux Soeurs sur la Terrasse.

No. 1763, 3200fr, Like #1761a. No. 1764, 3200fr, Like #1761b. No. 1765, 3200fr, Like #1761c. No. 1766, 3200fr, Like #1761d. No. 1767, 3200fr, Like #1761e. No. 1768, 3200fr, Like #1761f. No. 1769, 3200fr, Like #1762a. No. 1770, 3200fr, Like #1762b. No. 1771, 3200fr, Like #1762c. No. 1772, 3200fr, Like #1762d. No. 1773, 3200fr, Like #1762e. No. 1774, 3200fr, Like #1762f.

No. 1775, 4000fr, Oarsmen at Chatou.

No. 1776, 400fr — Inscriptions: a, Après le Bain (woman kneeling, striped floral wallpaper in background). b, Les Buveurs d'Absinthe. c, Après le Bain (woman standing with leg lifted). d, La Ballerine. e, Après le Bain (woman kneeling, plain background). f, Petit-Déjeuner Après un Bain.

No. 1777, 400fr — Inscriptions: a, Danseuse Assise. b, Inclinaison Dancer. c, Mademoiselle Malo. d, Femme se Coiffant Devant un Miroir. e, Musiciens de l'Orchestre. f, Six Amis de l'Artiste.

No. 1778, 3200fr, Like #1776a. No. 1779, 3200fr, Like #1776b. No. 1780, 3200fr, Like #1776c. No. 1781, 3200fr, Like #1776d. No. 1782, 3200fr, Like #1776e. No. 1783, 3200fr, Like #1776f. No. 1784, 3200fr, Like #1777a. No. 1785, 3200fr, Like #1777b. No. 1786, 3200fr, Like #1777c. No. 1787, 3200fr, Like #1777d. No. 1788, 3200fr, Like #1777e. No. 1789, 3200fr, Like #1777f.

No. 1790, 4000fr, Filles Spartiates Difficile Garçons.

Illustrations on Nos. 1776a-1776f, 1777a-1777f are flipped in comparison to Nos. 1778-1789.

No. 1791, 400fr — Inscriptions: a, Ange. b, Chef de une Vielle Femme dans un Bonnet Blanc. c, Portrait de Camille Roulin. d, Joseph Etienne Roulin. e, Chef de une Vielle Femme dans un Bonnet Blanc (woman with hand touching her face). f, Le Zouave Assis.

No. 1792, 400fr — Inscriptions: a, Vase avec Douze Tournesols. b, Irisews (Irises). c, Portrait du Père Tanguy. d, Chef de une Paysanne avec un Bonnet de Dentelles Verdatre. e, Van Gogh Chair. f, Berceuse.

No. 1793, 3200fr, Like #1791a. No. 1794, 3200fr, Like #1791b. No. 1795, 3200fr, Like #1791c. No. 1796, 3200fr, Like #1791d. No. 1797, 3200fr, Like #1791e. No. 1798, 3200fr, Like #1791f. No. 1799, 3200fr, Like #1792a. No. 1800, 3200fr, Like #1792b. No. 1801, 3200fr, Like #1792c. No. 1802, 3200fr, Like #1792d. No. 1803, 3200fr, Like #1792e. No. 1804, 3200fr, Like #1792f.

No. 1805, 4000fr, Village de Rue et Escalier avec Chiffres.

No. 1806, 400fr — Inscriptions: a, Nu Assis (blue area at LL). b, Jeanne Hebuterne (head). c, Portrait de Madame Kisling. d, Nu Assise sur un Canapé. e, Portrait de Chaim Soutner. f, Portrait de Celso Lagar.

No. 1807, 400fr — Inscriptions: a, Femme nue. b, Jeanne Hebuterne (seated). c, Nu Assis (seated, dark blue background). d, Nu Assis (seated, blue green background). e, Madame Pompadour. f, Jeune Fille Assise.

No. 1808, 3200fr, Like #1806a. No. 1809, 3200fr, Like #1806b. No. 1810, 3200fr, Like #1806c. No. 1811, 3200fr, Like #1806d. No. 1812, 3200fr, Like #1806e. No. 1813, 3200fr, Like #1806f. No. 1814, 3200fr, Like #1807a. No. 1815, 3200fr, Like #1807b. No. 1816, 3200fr, Like #1807c. No. 1817, 3200fr, Like #1807d. No. 1818, 3200fr, Like #1807e. No. 1819, 3200fr, Like #1807f.

No. 1820, 4000fr, Nu Couché.

No. 1821, 400fr — Inscriptions: a, A. S. Pouchkine. b, Bateau à Voile. c, Mer (Etude). d, Tapez Leandrovoy Tour à Constantinople. e, Navire dans la Mer Orageuse. f, Acropole d'Athènes. g, Portrait de l'Epouse de l'Artiste.

No. 1822, 400fr, horiz. — Inscriptions: a, Brigue "Mercury" Attaque par Deux Navires Turcs. b, L'Arrivée de Flotille Colomb. c, La Bataille dans la Manche Chios. d, Examen de la Flotte de la Mer Noire en 1849. e, Bataille Navale Russo-Turque de Sinop. f, La Bataille de Navarin. g, Bataille près de Sinop.

No. 1823, 400fr, horiz. — Inscriptions: a, Paysage Italien. b, Napoléon. c, La Flotte de la Mer Noire à Feodosiya. d, Vue de Saint-Pétersbourg. e, Vue de Kertch. f, Pêcheurs sur Littoral. g, Pouchkine.

No. 1824, 400fr, horiz — Inscriptions: a, Un Naufrage près du Mont Athos. b, La Tempête. c, Tempête sur la Mer. d, Sur l'Île de Crète. e, La Neuvième Vague. f, Signal de la Tempête. g, Le Bulow

No. 1825, 4000fr, Tempête.

**Works of Titian (Tiziano Vecelli)**

**2011, Dec. 29 Litho. *Perf. 13¾***
**Sheets of 3, #a-c, + label**

**1620-1623** A388 Set of 4 19.50 19.50

**Souvenir Sheets**
***Perf. 13x13¼, 13¼x13***

**1624-1635** A389 Set of 12 155.00 155.00
**1636** A390 4000fr multi 16.00 16.00

**Works of François Boucher**
**Sheets of 3, #a-c, + label**
***Perf. 13¾***

**1637-1640** A388 Set of 4 19.50 19.50

**Souvenir Sheets**
***Perf. 13x13¼, 13¼x13***

**1641-1652** A389 Set of 12 155.00 155.00
**1653** A390 4000fr multi 16.00 16.00

**Works of Claude Monet**
**Sheets of 3, #a-c, + label**
***Perf. 13¾***

**1654-1657** A388 Set of 4 19.50 19.50

**Souvenir Sheets**
***Perf. 13x13¼, 13¼x13***

**1658-1669** A389 Set of 12 155.00 155.00
**1670** A390 4000fr multi 16.00 16.00

**Works of Albrecht Dürer**
**Sheets of 6, #a-f, + 2 labels**
***Perf. 13¾***

**1671-1672** A388 Set of 2 19.50 19.50

**Souvenir Sheets**
***Perf. 13x13¼***

**1673-1684** A389 Set of 12 155.00 155.00
**1685** A390 4000fr multi 16.00 16.00

**Works of Michelangelo**
**Sheets of 6, #a-f, + 2 labels**
***Perf. 13¾***

**1686-1687** A388 Set of 2 19.50 19.50

**Souvenir Sheets**
***Perf. 13x13¼***

**1688-1699** A389 Set of 12 155.00 155.00
**1700** A390 4000fr multi 16.00 16.00

**Works of Raphael (Raffaello Sanzio)**
**Sheets of 6, #a-f, + 2 labels**
***Perf. 13¾***

**1701-1702** A388 Set of 2 19.50 19.50

**Souvenir Sheets**
***Perf. 13x13¼***

**1703-1714** A389 Set of 12 155.00 155.00
**1715** A390 4000fr multi 16.00 16.00

**Works of Peter Paul Rubens**
**Sheets of 6, #a-f, + 2 labels**
***Perf. 13¾***

**1716-1717** A388 Set of 2 19.50 19.50

**Souvenir Sheets**
***Perf. 13x13¼***

**1718-1729** A389 Set of 12 155.00 155.00
**1730** A390 4000fr multi 16.00 16.00

**Works of Anthony van Dyck**
**Sheets of 6, #a-f, + 2 labels**
***Perf. 13¾***

**1731-1732** A388 Set of 2 19.50 19.50

**Souvenir Sheets**
***Perf. 13x13¼***

**1733-1744** A389 Set of 12 155.00 155.00
**1745** A390 4000fr multi 16.00 16.00

**Works of Rembrandt van Rijn**
**Sheets of 6, #a-f, + 2 labels**
***Perf. 13¾***

**1746-1747** A388 Set of 2 19.50 19.50

**Souvenir Sheets**
***Perf. 13x13¼***

**1748-1759** A389 Set of 12 155.00 155.00
**1760** A390 4000fr multi 16.00 16.00

**Works of Pierre-Auguste Renoir**
**Sheets of 6, #a-f, + 2 labels**
***Perf. 13¾***

**1761-1762** A388 Set of 2 19.50 19.50

**Souvenir Sheets**
***Perf. 13x13¼***

**1763-1774** A389 Set of 12 155.00 155.00
**1775** A390 4000fr multi 16.00 16.00

**Works of Edgar Degas**
**Sheets of 6, #a-f, + 2 labels**
***Perf. 13¾***

**1776-1777** A388 Set of 2 19.50 19.50

**Souvenir Sheets**
***Perf. 13x13¼***

**1778-1789** A389 Set of 12 155.00 155.00
**1790** A390 4000fr multi 16.00 16.00

**Works of Vincent van Gogh**
**Sheets of 6, #a-f, + 2 labels**
***Perf. 13¾***

**1791-1792** A388 Set of 2 19.50 19.50

**Souvenir Sheets**
***Perf. 13x13¼***

**1793-1804** A389 Set of 12 155.00 155.00
**1805** A390 4000fr multi 16.00 16.00

**Works of Amedeo Modigliani**
**Sheets of 6, #a-f, + 2 labels**
***Perf. 13¾***

**1806-1807** A388 Set of 2 19.50 19.50

**Souvenir Sheets**
***Perf. 13x13¼***

**1808-1819** A389 Set of 12 155.00 155.00
**1820** A390 4000fr multi 16.00 16.00

**Works of Ivan Aivazovsky**
**Sheets of 7, #a-g, + label**
***Perf. 13¾***

**1821-1824** A388 Set of 4 45.00 45.00

**Souvenir Sheets**
***Perf. 13x13¼***

**1825** A390 4000fr multi 16.00 16.00

## SEMI-POSTAL STAMPS

**Anti-Malaria Issue**
Common Design Type
***Perf. 12½x12***

**1962, Apr. 7 Engr. Unwmk.**

**B1** CD108 25fr + 5fr slate 1.40 1.40

WHO drive to eradicate malaria.

**Freedom from Hunger Issue**
Common Design Type

**1963, Mar. 21 *Perf. 13***

**B2** CD112 25fr + 5fr multi 1.25 1.25

Guinea Fowl and Partridge — SP1

Designs: 10fr+5fr, Yellow-backed duiker and snail. 20fr+5fr, Elephant, tortoise and hippopotamus playing tug-of-war. 30fr+10fr, Cuckoo and tortoise. 50fr+20fr, Patas monkey and leopard.

**1971, Feb. 9 Photo. *Perf. 12½x12***

**B3** SP1 5fr + 5fr multi 5.25 2.00
**B4** SP1 10fr + 5fr multi 6.75 2.50
**B5** SP1 20fr + 5fr multi 8.75 2.75
**B6** SP1 30fr + 10fr multi 11.50 7.00
**B7** SP1 50fr + 20fr multi 18.50 12.00
*Nos. B3-B7 (5)* 50.75 26.25

Lengué Dancer — SP2

Dancers: 40fr+10fr, Le Lengué. 100fr+40fr, Teke. 140fr+40fr, Englabolo.

**1971 Litho. *Perf. 13***

**B8** SP2 20fr + 5fr multi .80 .25
**B9** SP2 40fr + 10fr multi 1.40 .40
**B10** SP2 100fr + 40fr multi 3.25 1.25
**B11** SP2 140fr + 40fr multi 4.25 1.50
*Nos. B8-B11 (4)* 9.70 3.40

## AIR POST STAMPS

Abyssinian Roller AP1

Birds: 200fr, Gold Coast touraco. 500fr, African fish eagle.

**Unwmk.**

**1960, Sept. 3 Engr. *Perf. 13***

**C1** AP1 100fr vio bl, org brn & emer 2.25 .80
**C2** AP1 200fr multi 4.25 2.25
**C3** AP1 500fr Prus bl, emer & red brn 13.50 5.25
*Nos. C1-C3 (3)* 20.00 8.30

**French Equatorial Africa No. C37 Surcharged in Red**

**1960, Dec. 15 *Perf. 13***

**C4** AP8 250fr on 500fr grnsh blk, blk & slate 9.00 8.25

17th Olympic Games, Rome, 8/25-9/11.

**Air Afrique Issue**
Common Design Type

**1962, Feb. 17 Unwmk. *Perf. 13***

**C5** CD107 50fr vio, lt grn & red brn 1.00 .65

Founding of Air Afrique airline.

Pole Vault — AP1a

**1962, July 21 Photo. *Perf. 12x12½***
**C6** AP1a 100fr grn, yel, brn & blk 2.50 1.75

Abidjan games.

Red-faced Lovebirds AP2

**1962-63 Engr. *Perf. 13***
**C7** AP2 50fr Great blue touraco 2.50 .55
**C8** AP2 250fr shown ('63) 7.50 2.50

Issued: 50fr, Nov. 15; 250fr, Mar. 11, 1963.

Runner with Torch and Palm Branch — AP3

**1962, Dec. 24**
**C9** AP3 100fr gray grn, brn & car 2.50 1.50

Tropics Cup Games, Bangui, Dec. 24-31.

**African Postal Union Issue**
Common Design Type

**1963, Sept. 8 Photo. *Perf. 12½***
**C10** CD114 85fr emer, ocher & red 1.90 .90

Sun Shining on Africa AP4

**1963, Nov. 9 *Perf. 13x12***
**C11** AP4 25fr bl, yel & vio bl .75 .40

Issued for African unity.

**Europafrica Issue**
Common Design Type

**1963, Nov. 30 *Perf. 12x13***
**C12** CD116 50fr ultra, yel & dk brn 2.50 1.75

Diesel Engine AP5

Various Locomotives; 25fr, 50fr, vertical.

**1963, Dec. 1 Engr. *Perf. 13***
**C13** AP5 20fr brn, cl & dk grn .70 .70
**C14** AP5 25fr brn, bl & choc .80 .80
**C15** AP5 50r brn, red lil & vio 2.75 2.75
**C16** AP5 100fr brn, grn & dl red brn 3.75 3.75
*a.* Min. sheet of 4, #C13-C16 13.00 13.00
*Nos. C13-C16 (4)* 8.00 8.00

Bangui-Douala railroad project.

Bangui Cathedral AP6

**1964, Jan. 21 Unwmk. *Perf. 13***
**C17** AP6 100fr yel grn, org brn & bl 1.90 1.00

Radar Tracking Station and WMO Emblem AP7

**1964, Mar. 23 Engr. *Perf. 13***
**C18** AP7 50fr org brn, bl & pur 1.25 1.25

World Meteorological Day.

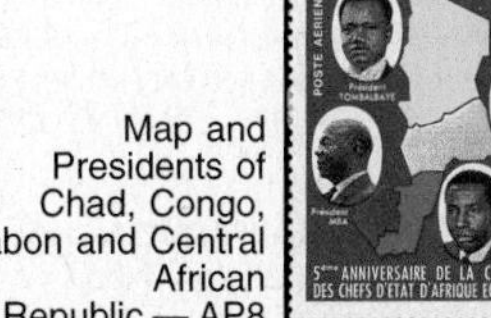

Map and Presidents of Chad, Congo, Gabon and Central African Republic — AP8

**1964, June 23 Photo. *Perf. 12½***
**C19** AP8 100fr multi 2.00 .90

5th anniversary of the Conference of Chiefs of State of Equatorial Africa.

Javelin Throwers AP9

Designs: 50fr, Basketball game. 100fr, Four runners. 250fr, Swimmers, one in water.

**1964, June 23 Engr. *Perf. 13***
**C20** AP9 25fr grn, dk brn & lt vio bl .50 .30
**C21** AP9 50fr blk, car & grn 1.00 .50
**C22** AP9 100fr grn, vio bl & dk brn 2.00 1.05
**C23** AP9 250fr grn, blk & car 5.50 2.75
*a.* Min. sheet of 4, #C20-C23 13.50 13.50
*Nos. C20-C23 (4)* 9.00 4.60

18th Olympic Games, Tokyo, 10/10-25/64.

John F. Kennedy — AP10

**1964, July 4 Photo. *Perf. 12½***
**C24** AP10 100fr lil, brn & blk 2.25 1.75
*a.* Min. sheet of 4 10.00 10.00

Industrial Symbols, Maps of Africa and Europe AP11

**1964, Dec. 19 Unwmk. *Perf. 13x12***
**C25** AP11 50fr yel, org & grn 1.35 .90

See note after Cameroun No. 402.

International Cooperation Year Emblem AP12

**1965, Jan. 2 *Perf. 13***
**C26** AP12 100fr red brn, yel & bl 1.60 .85

International Cooperation Year.

Nimbus Weather Satellite AP13

**1965, Mar. 23 Engr. *Perf. 13***
**C27** AP13 100fr org brn, ultra & blk 1.75 .90

Fifth World Meteorological Day.

Lincoln and Statue of Liberty AP14

**1965, Apr. 15 Photo. *Perf. 13***
**C28** AP14 100fr bluish grn, ind & bis 1.50 .85

Centenary of death of Abraham Lincoln.

ITU Emblem and Relay Satellite AP15

**1965, May 17 Engr. *Perf. 13***
**C29** AP15 100fr dk grn vio bl & brn 1.75 1.00

Centenary of the ITU.

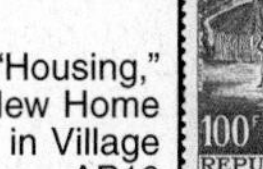

"Housing," New Home in Village AP16

**1965, June 10 Unwmk.**
**C30** AP16 100fr ultra, brn & sl grn 1.40 .80

See note after No. 52.

**Europafrica Issue**

Tractor, Cotton Picker, Cotton, Sun and Emblem — AP17

**1965, Nov. 7 Photo. *Perf. 12x13***
**C31** AP17 50fr multi 1.00 .70

See note after Chad No. C11.

Mercury by Antoine Coysevox — AP18

**1965, Dec. 5 Engr. *Perf. 13***
**C32** AP18 100fr red brn, bl & blk 1.75 1.00

5th anniv. of Central African Republic's admission to the UPU.

Father Holding Sick Child — AP19

Design: 100fr, Mother and child.

**1965, Dec. 12**
**C33** AP19 50fr dk bl, car & blk 1.10 .55
**C34** AP19 100fr red brn, red & brt grn 2.50 1.10

Issued to honor the Red Cross.

**Air Afrique Issue**
Common Design Type

**1966, Aug. 31 Photo. *Perf. 13***
**C35** CD123 25fr bl, blk & lem 1.00 .50

For surcharge see No. C43.

Surveyor Spacecraft on Moon AP20

Designs: No. C37, Luna 9 on Moon and Earth. 200fr, Rocket take-off, Jules Verne's "From the Earth to the Moon."

**1966, Oct. 24 Photo. *Perf. 12x12½***
**C36** AP20 130fr multi 1.45 1.00
**C37** AP20 130fr multi 1.45 1.00
**C38** AP20 200fr multi 2.75 1.90
*a.* Souv. sheet of 3, #C36-C38 8.50 8.50
*Nos. C36-C38 (3)* 5.65 3.90

Conquest of the Moon.
For surcharges see Nos. C58, C61.

Eugene A. Cernan, Gemini 9 and Agena Rocket — AP21

No. C40, Pavel R. Popovich and rocket.

**1966, Nov. 14 Photo. *Perf. 13***
**C39** AP21 50fr multi 1.10 .55
**C40** AP21 50fr multi 1.10 .55

American and Russian astronauts.

Diamant Rocket, D-1 Satellite and Globe with Map of Africa AP22

**1966, Nov. 14 Engr.**
**C41** AP22 100fr brt rose lil & brn 1.75 .90

Issued to commemorate the launching of France's first satellite, Nov. 26, 1965, and the launching of the D-1 satellite, Feb. 17, 1966.

Exchange of Agricultural and Industrial Products between Africa and Europe — AP23

**1966, Dec. 5 Photo. *Perf. 12x13***
**C42** AP23 50fr multi 1.25 .85

See note after Gabon No. C46.

**No. C35 Surcharged**

**1967, May 8** ***Perf. 13***
**C43** CD123 5fr on 25fr multi .55 .30

The surcharge obliterates the "2" of the original 25fr denomination.

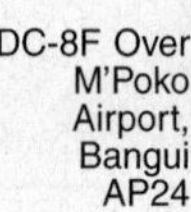

DC-8F Over M'Poko Airport, Bangui
AP24

**1967, July 3** **Engr.** ***Perf. 13***
**C44** AP24 100fr sl, dk grn & brn 2.25 1.10

View of EXPO '67, Montreal
AP25

**1967, July 17**
**C45** AP25 100fr vio bl, dk red brn & dk grn 2.25 .80

International Exposition. EXPO '67, Montreal, Apr. 28-Oct. 27.

**African Postal Union Issue, 1967**
Common Design Type

**1967, Sept. 9** **Engr.** ***Perf. 13***
**C46** CD124 100fr brt grn, dk car rose & plum 2.25 .85

Potez 25 TOE
AP26

**1967, Nov. 24** **Engr.** ***Perf. 13***
**C47** AP26 100fr shown 1.75 .80
**C48** AP26 200fr Junkers 52 4.50 1.75
**C49** AP26 500fr Caravelle 11R 13.50 4.25
*Nos. C47-C49 (3)* 19.75 6.80

For surcharges see Nos. C59-C60.

Presidents Boganda and Bokassa
AP27

**1967, Dec. 1** **Photo.** ***Perf. 12½***
**C50** AP27 130fr org, red, lt bl & blk 2.00 1.25

9th anniversary of the republic.

Pres. Jean Bedel Bokassa — AP28

**1968, Jan. 1** ***Perf. 12½x12***
**C51** AP28 30fr multi .85 .45

Human Rights Flame, Men and Globe
AP29

**1968, Mar. 26** **Photo.** ***Perf. 13***
**C52** AP29 200fr brt grn, vio & ver 3.50 1.50

International Human Rights Year.

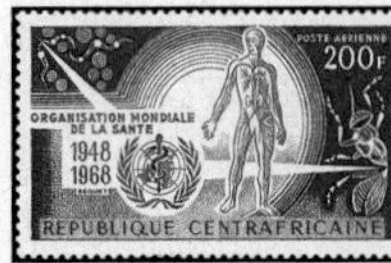


Man, WHO Emblem and Tsetse Fly — AP30

**1968, Apr. 8** **Engr.**
**C53** AP30 200fr multi 3.75 1.75

20th anniv. of WHO.

Javelin Thrower — AP31

**1968, Apr. 16** **Engr.** ***Perf. 13***
**C54** AP31 200fr shown 4.50 3.00
**C55** AP31 200fr Downhill skier 4.50 3.00

The 1968 Olympic Games.

Space Probe Landing on Venus — AP32

**1968, Apr. 23**
**C56** AP32 100fr ultra, dk & brt grn 1.75 .95

Venus exploration by Venera 4, 10/18/67.

Marie Curie and "Cancer Destroyed"
AP33

**1968, Apr. 30**
**C57** AP33 100fr vio, brt bl & brn 2.50 1.10

Marie Curie (1867-1934), scientist.

**Nos. C36-C37 and C47-C48 Surcharged with New Value**

**Photogravure; Engraved**

**1968, Sept. 16** ***Perf. 12x12½, 13***
**C58** AP20 5fr on 130fr multi .25 .25
**C59** AP26 10fr on 100fr multi .30 .25
**C60** AP26 20fr on 200fr multi .50 .30
**C61** AP20 50fr on 130fr multi 1.10 .55
*Nos. C58-C61 (4)* 2.15 1.35

On No. C58 the old denomination has been obliterated with "XIX," on No. C61 the obliteration is a rectangular bar. On Nos. C59-C60 the last zero of the old denomination has been obliterated with a black square.

**River Boat Type of Regular Issue**

Craft: 100fr, "Pie X," Bangui, 1894. 130fr, "Ballay," Bangui, 1891.

**1968, Dec. 10** **Engr.** ***Perf. 13***
**Size: 48x27mm**
**C62** A37 100fr bl, dk brn & ol 2.25 1.00
**C63** A37 130fr brt pink, sl grn & slate 2.75 1.25

**PHILEXAFRIQUE Issue**

Mme. de Sévigné, French School, 17th Century — AP34

**1968, Dec. 17** **Photo.** ***Perf. 12½***
**C64** AP34 100fr brn & multi 3.00 2.25

Issued to publicize PHILEXAFRIQUE, Philatelic Exhibition in Abidjan, Feb. 14-23. Printed with alternating brown label.

**2nd PHILEXAFRIQUE Issue**
Common Design Type

Design: 50fr, Ubangi-Shari No. J16, cotton field and Pres. Bokassa.

**1969, Feb. 14** **Engr.** ***Perf. 13***
**C65** CD128 50fr bis brn, blk & dk grn 1.75 1.75

Holocerina Angulata Aur.
AP35

Butterflies and Moths: 20fr, Nudaurelia dione fabr. 30fr, Eustera troglophylla hamp., vert. 50fr, Aurivillius aratus west. 100fr, Epiphora albida druce.

**1969, Feb. 25** **Photo.**
**C66** AP35 10fr yel & multi 1.10 .35
**C67** AP35 20fr vio & multi 1.60 .55
**C68** AP35 30fr multi 3.75 1.00
**C69** AP35 50fr multi 5.25 2.25
**C70** AP35 100fr multi 9.00 3.25
*Nos. C66-C70 (5)* 20.70 7.40

Boxing
AP36

**1969, Mar. 18** **Photo.** ***Perf. 13***
**C71** AP36 50fr shown 1.10 .35
**C72** AP36 100fr Basketball 2.10 .65

Apollo 8 over Moonscape
AP37

**1969, May 27** **Photo.** ***Perf. 13***
**C73** AP37 200fr dp bl, gray & yel 3.50 1.75

US Apollo 8 mission, the 1st men in orbit around the moon, Dec. 21-27, 1968.
For overprint see No. C81.

Market Cross, Nuremberg, and Toys
AP38

**1969, June 3**
**C74** AP38 100fr blk, brt rose lil & emer 2.10 1.10

Intl. Toy Fair in Nuremberg, Germany.

Napoleon as First Consul, by Anne-Louis Girodet-Trioson
AP39

Designs: 130fr, Napoleon meeting Emperor Francis II, by Antoine Jean Gros, horiz. 200fr, The Wedding of Napoleon and Marie-Louise, by Georges Rouget, horiz.

**1969, Nov. 4** **Photo.** ***Perf. 12½***
**C75** AP39 100fr multi 2.00 1.25
**C76** AP39 130fr brn & multi 3.00 1.50
**C77** AP39 200fr multi 5.00 2.75
*Nos. C75-C77 (3)* 10.00 5.50

Napoleon Bonaparte (1769-1821).

Pres. Bokassa, Map of Africa and Flag — AP40

**1970, Jan. 1** ***Die-cut; Perf. 10½***
**Embossed on Gold Foil**
**C78** AP40 2000fr gold *35.00 35.00*

Franklin Delano Roosevelt — AP41

**1970** **Litho.** ***Perf. 13½x14***
**C79** AP41 100fr shown 2.00 1.00
**C80** AP41 100fr Lenin 3.00 1.25

Roosevelt, 25th death anniv., Lenin, birth cent.
Issue dates: No. C79, Apr. 29; No. C80. Apr. 22.

**No. C73 Overprinted in Red**

**1970, June 1** **Photo.** ***Perf. 13***
**C81** AP37 200fr multi 13.50 9.00

Moon landing mission of Apollo 12, 11/14-24/69.

AP42

**1970, Sept. 15** **Litho.** ***Perf. 10***
**C82** AP42 Pair + label 4.00 2.75
*a.* 100fr Dancer 1.75 .65
*b.* 100fr Still life 1.75 .65

Knokphila 70, 6th Intl. Phil. Exhib. at Knokke, Belgium, July 4-10. Imperf. between stamps and label.

**Sericulture Type of Regular Issue**

**1970, Sept. 15** ***Perf. 10***
**C83** A45 140fr multi 4.00 1.25

C.A.R. Flag, EXPO Emblem and Pavilion — AP43

**1970, Dec. 18 Litho. *Perf. 13½x13***
**C84** AP43 200fr red & multi 3.00 1.50

Intl. Exposition EXPO '70, Osaka, Japan.

Soccer AP44

**1970, Dec. 8 *Perf. 13x13½***
**C85** AP44 200fr multi 3.50 1.50

World Soccer Championships, Mexico, May 30-June 21, 1970.

Dove AP45

**1970, Dec. 31**
**C86** AP45 200fr bl, yel & blk 3.50 1.50

25th anniversary of the United Nations.

Presidents Mobutu, Bokassa, and Tombalbaye AP46

**1971, Jan. 10**
**C87** AP46 140fr multi 2.75 .90

Return of Central African Republic to the United States of Central Africa which also includes Congo Democratic Republic and Chad.

Satellite over Globe AP47

**1971, May 17 Photo. *Perf. 12½***
**C88** AP47 100fr multi 2.25 .90

3rd World Telecommunications Day.

**African Postal Union Issue, 1971**
Common Design Type

Design: 100fr, Carved head and UAMPT building, Brazzaville, Congo.

**1971, Nov. 13 Photo. *Perf. 13x13½***
**C89** CD135 100fr bl & multi 2.25 .85

Child and Education Year Emblem AP48

**1971, Nov. 11 Litho. *Perf. 13x13½***
**C90** AP48 140fr multi 1.75 .70

25th anniv. of UNESCO.

Fight Against Cancer — AP49

**1971, Nov. 20 Photo. *Perf. 12½***
**C91** AP49 100fr grn & multi 2.75 1.10

Gamal Abdel Nasser — AP50

**1972, Jan. 15**
**C92** AP50 100fr dk red, blk & bister 2.10 .90

In memory of Gamal Abdel Nasser (1918-1970), president of Egypt.

Olympic Rings and Boxing AP51

No. C94, Long jumper and Olympic rings, vert.

**1972, May 26 Engr. *Perf. 13***
**C93** AP51 100fr brn org & sepia 1.50 1.10
**C94** AP51 100fr green & violet 1.50 1.10
*a.* Miniature sheet of 2 4.25 4.25

20th Olympic Games, Munich, Aug. 26-Sept. 10. No. C94a contains 2 stamps similar to Nos. C93-C94, but in changed colors. The boxing stamp is red lilac and green, the track stamp ocher and red lilac.

For overprints see Nos. C100-C101.

Tiling's Mail Rocket, 1931, and Mailman AP52

Designs: 50fr, DC-3 and mailman riding camel, vert. 150fr, Sirio satellite and rocket, vert. 200fr, Intelsat 4 and rocket.

**1972, Aug. 12**
**C95** AP52 40fr bl, org & indigo .65 .45
**C96** AP52 50fr bl, brn & org .90 .55
**C97** AP52 150fr brn, org & gray 2.50 1.25
**C98** AP52 200fr brn, bl & org 3.50 2.25
*a.* Souv. sheet of 4, #C95-C98 8.00 8.00
*Nos. C95-C98 (4)* 7.55 4.50

Centraphilex 1972, Central African Philatelic Exhibition, Bangui.

**Europafrica Issue**

Arrows with Symbols of Agriculture and Industry — AP53

**1972, Nov. 17 Litho. *Perf. 13***
**C99** AP53 100fr multi 1.75 .90

**Nos. C93-C94, C94a Overprinted**

(a)

(b)

**1972, Nov. 24 Engr.**
**C100** AP51 (a) 100fr 1.60 .95
**C101** AP51 (b) 100fr 1.60 .95
*a.* Miniature sheet of 2 3.75 3.75

Gold Medal Winners in 20th Olympic Games: Viatcheslav Lemechev, USSR, middleweight boxing; Randy Williams, US, broad jump.

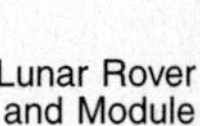

Lunar Rover and Module AP54

**1972, Dec. 18 Engr. *Perf. 13***
**C102** AP54 100fr slate grn, bl & gray 1.60 .90

Apollo 16 US moon mission, 4/15-27/72.

Virgin and Child, by Francesco Pesellino — AP55

Christmas: 150fr, Adoration of the Child with St. John the Baptist and St. Romuald, by Fra Filippo Lippi.

**1972, Dec. 25 Photo.**
**C103** AP55 100fr gold & multi 1.40 .90
**C104** AP55 150fr gold & multi 2.50 1.40

Parthenon, Athens, Spyridon Louis, Marathon, 1896 AP56

Olympic Rings and: 40fr, Arc de Triomphe, Paris, H. Barrelet, single scull, 1900. 50fr, Old Courthouse and Western Arch, St. Louis, Myer Prinstein, triple jump, 1904. 100fr, Tower, London, Henry Taylor, swimming, 1908. 150fr, City Hall, Stockholm, Greco-Roman wrestling, 1912.

**1972, Dec. 28 Engr.**
**C105** AP56 30fr brt grn, mag & brn .40 .25
**C106** AP56 40fr vio bl, emer & brn .50 .25
**C107** AP56 50fr car rose, vio bl & Prus bl .55 .40
**C108** AP56 100fr sl, red lil & brn 1.00 .50
**C109** AP56 150fr red lil, blk & Prus bl 1.60 1.20
*Nos. C105-C109 (5)* 4.05 2.60

Olympic Games 1896-1912.

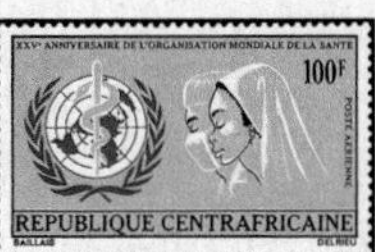

WHO Emblem, Surgeon and Nurse AP57

**1973, Apr. 7 Photo. *Perf. 13***
**C110** AP57 100fr multi 1.50 .85

WHO, 25th anniv.

World Map, Arrows, Waves — AP58

**1973, May 17 Litho. *Perf. 12½***
**C111** AP58 200fr multicolored 2.40 1.10

5th International Telecommunications Day.

AP58a

Head and City Hall, Brussels.

**1973, Sept. 17 Engr. *Perf. 13***
**C112** AP58a 100fr pur, ocher & brn 1.40 .80

African Weeks, Brussels, Sept. 15-30, 1973.

**Europafrica Issue**

Map of Central African Republic with Industry and Agriculture, Young Man AP59

**1973, Sept. 28 Engr. *Perf. 13***
**C113** AP59 100fr sepia, grn & org 1.60 .80

Carrier Pigeon with Letter and UPU Emblem AP60

**1973, Oct. 9 Photo.**
**C114** AP60 200fr multi 2.50 1.10

Universal Postal Union Day.

WMO Emblem, Weather Map AP61

**1973, Oct. 20 Engr. *Perf. 13***
**C115** AP61 150fr brt ultra & sl grn 2.50 1.00

Cent. of intl. meteorological cooperation.

Copernicus, Heliocentric System AP62

**1973, Nov. 2** **Photo.**
**C116** AP62 100fr gold & multi 3.00 1.75

Copernicus (1473-1543), Polish astronomer.

Pres. Bokassa AP63

Pres. Bokassa AP64

**1973, Nov. 30** **Photo.** ***Perf. 12½***
**C117** AP63 50fr multi .75 .40
**C118** AP64 100fr multi 1.40 .70

Rocket Launch and Apollo 17 Badge — AP65

65fr, Capsule over moonscape, horiz. 100fr, Moon landing, horiz. 150fr, Astronauts on moon. 200fr, Splashdown with parachutes and badge.

**1973, Dec. 15** **Engr.** ***Perf. 13***
**C119** AP65 50fr ver, gray grn & brn .50 .30
**C120** AP65 65fr dk brn, brn red & sl grn .65 .40
**C121** AP65 100fr ver, slate & choc 1.10 .60
**C122** AP65 150fr brn, ol & sl grn 1.75 .80
**C123** AP65 200fr red, bl & sl grn 2.00 1.10
*Nos. C119-C123 (5)* 6.00 3.20

Apollo 17 US moon mission, 12/7-19/72.

St. Teresa — AP66

**1973, Dec. 25**
**C124** AP66 500fr vio bl & grnsh bl 5.75 3.50

St. Teresa of the Infant Jesus, the Little Flower (1873-1897), Carmelite nun.

UPU Emblem, Letter — AP67

**1974, Oct. 9** **Engr.** ***Perf. 13***
**C125** AP67 500fr multi 6.75 4.00

Centenary of Universal Postal Union.
For surcharge see No. C159.

Presidents and Flags of Cameroun, CAR, Gabon and Congo AP68

**1974, Dec. 8** **Photo.** ***Perf. 13***
**C126** AP68 100fr gold & multi 1.40 .70

See note after Cameroun No. 595.
For surcharge see No. C155.

Marshal Bokassa — AP69

100fr, Bokassa in Marshal's uniform with cape.

**1975, Feb. 22** **Photo.** ***Perf. 13***
**C127** AP69 50fr tan & multi .65 .40
**C128** AP69 100fr tan & multi 1.40 .45

Jean Bedel Bokassa, President for Life and Marshal of the Republic.

Mask, Map of Africa, Arphila Emblem — AP70

**1975, Aug. 25** **Engr.** ***Perf. 13***
**C129** AP70 100fr brt bl, red brn & red 1.25 .65

ARPHILA 75 International Philatelic Exhibition, Paris, June 6-16.
For surcharge see No. C156.

Albert Schweitzer and Dugout, Lambarene — AP71

**1975, Sept. 30** **Engr.** ***Perf. 13***
**C130** AP71 200fr blk, ultra & ol 4.50 2.25

Dr. Albert Schweitzer (1875-1965), medical missionary and musician.
For surcharge see No. C158.

Pres. Bokassa's Houseboat, Bow AP72

40fr, Pres. Bokassa's houseboat, stern.

**1976, Feb. 22** **Litho.** ***Perf. 13***
**C131** AP72 30fr multi .60 .30
**C132** AP72 40fr multi .80 .55

Monument to Franco-CAR Cooperation AP73

Presidents and Flags of France and CAR — AP74

**1976, Mar. 5**
**C133** AP73 100fr multi 1.40 .90
**C134** AP74 200fr multi 2.50 1.35

Official visit of Pres. Valery Giscard d'Estaing to Central African Republic, 3/5-8.
For surcharge see No. C157.

### Apollo Soyuz Type, 1976

Designs: 100fr, Soyuz space ship. 200fr, Apollo space ship. 300fr, Astronauts and cosmonauts in cabin. 500fr, Apollo and Soyuz after link-up.

**1976, June 14** **Litho.** ***Perf. 14x13½***
**C135** A90 100fr multi .90 .25
**C136** A90 200fr multi 1.60 .55
**C137** A90 300fr multi 2.60 .95
*Nos. C135-C137 (3)* 6.45 1.75

**Souvenir Sheet**

**C138** A90 500fr multi 5.00 1.75

For surcharges see Nos. C161, C168, C173, C177.

French Hussar — AP75

Uniforms: 125fr, Scottish "Black Watch." 150fr, German dragoon. 200fr, British grenadier. 250fr, American ranger. 450fr, American dragoon.

**1976, July 4** ***Perf. 13½***
**C139** AP75 100fr multi .75 .30
**C140** AP75 125fr multi .80 .45
**C141** AP75 150fr multi 1.00 .45
**C142** AP75 200fr multi 1.50 .55
**C143** AP75 250fr multi 2.00 .95
*Nos. C139-C143 (5)* 6.05 2.70

**Souvenir Sheet**

**C144** AP75 450fr multi 6.75 2.50

American Bicentennial.
For surcharges see Nos. C162, C166-C167, C169, C172, C176.

Acherontia Atropos AP76

100fr, Papilio nireus & niocha marnois.

**1976, Sept. 20** **Litho.** ***Perf. 12½***
**C145** AP76 50fr multi 5.00 1.50
**C146** AP76 100fr multi 10.00 2.00

For surcharges see Nos. C160, C163.

### Olympic Winners Type, 1976

Designs: 100fr, Women's figure skating, Dorothy Hamill, vert. 200fr, Ice skating, Alexander Gorshkov and Ludmilla Pakhomova. 300fr, Men's figure skating, John Curry, vert. 500fr, Downhill skiing, Rosi Mittermaier, vert.

**1976, Sept. 23** **Litho.** ***Perf. 13½***
**C147** A92 100fr multi .65 .35
**C148** A92 200fr multi 2.10 .70
**C149** A92 300fr multi 2.75 1.10
*Nos. C147-C149 (3)* 5.50 2.15

**Souvenir Sheet**

**C150** A92 500fr multi 5.50 1.75

For surcharges see Nos. C164, C170, C174, C178.

### Viking Mars Type, 1976

Designs: 100fr, Phases of Mars landing. 200fr, Viking descending on Mars, horiz. 300fr, Viking probe. 500fr, Viking flight to Mars, horiz.

**1976, Dec.**
**C151** A93 100fr multi .85 .35
**C152** A93 200fr multi 2.10 .70
**C153** A93 300fr multi 2.60 1.10
*Nos. C151-C153 (3)* 5.55 2.15

**Souvenir Sheet**

**C154** A93 500fr multi 5.00 1.75

For surcharges and overprints see Nos. C165, C171, C175, C179, C212-C215.

### Central African Empire

Stamps of 1973-76 Overprinted in Black, Violet Blue or Gold

**Printing and Perforations as Before**

**1977, Mar.**
**C155** AP68 100fr (#C126;B) 1.30 1.30
**C156** AP70 100fr (#C129;VB) 1.30 1.30
**C157** AP73 100fr (#C133;G) 1.30 1.30
**C158** AP71 200fr (#C130;B) 4.00 4.00
**C159** AP67 500fr (#C125;B) 12.00 12.00
*Nos. C155-C159 (5)* 19.90 19.90

No bar on No. C159.

**Stamps of 1976 Overprinted in Black on Silver Panel**

**1977, Apr. 1**
**C160** AP76 50fr (#C145) .55 .55
**C161** A90 100fr (#C135) 1.10 1.10
**C162** AP75 100fr (#C139) 1.10 1.10
**C163** AP76 100fr (#C146) 1.10 1.10
**C164** A92 100fr (#C147) 1.10 1.10
**C165** A93 100fr (#C151) 1.10 1.10
**C166** AP75 125fr (#C140) 1.40 1.40
**C167** AP75 150fr (#C141) 1.60 1.60
**C168** A90 200fr (#C136) 2.75 2.75
**C169** AP75 200fr (#C142) 2.50 2.50
**C170** A92 200fr (#C148) 2.25 2.25
**C171** A93 200fr (#C152) 2.25 2.25
**C172** AP75 250fr (#C143) 2.75 2.75
**C173** A90 300fr (#C137) 3.50 3.50
**C174** A92 300fr (#C149) 3.50 3.50
**C175** A93 300fr (#C153) 3.50 3.50
*Nos. C160-C175 (16)* 32.05 32.05

**Souvenir Sheets**

**C176** AP75 450fr (#C144) 5.50 5.50
**C177** A90 500fr (#C138) 8.00 8.00
**C178** A92 500fr (#C150) 5.50 5.50
**C179** A93 500fr (#C154) 5.50 5.50

Overprint on type AP75 is in upper and lower case letters.

### Nobel Prize Type, 1977

Designs: 100fr, Rudyard Kipling. 200fr, Ernest Hemingway. 300fr, Luigi Pirandello. 500fr, Rabindranath Tagore.

**1977, Apr. 1** **Litho.** ***Perf. 13½***
**C180** A94 100fr multi 1.75 .40
**C181** A94 200fr multi 3.50 .70
**C182** A94 300fr multi 5.75 .95
*Nos. C180-C182 (3)* 11.00 2.05

**Souvenir Sheet**

**C183** A94 500fr multi 5.50 1.75

### Zeppelin Type of 1977

100fr, Germany No. C42 and North Pole. 200fr, Germany No. C44 and Science and Industry Building, Chicago. 300fr, Germany No. C35 and Brandenburg Gate, Berlin. 500fr, US No. C14 and US Capitol.

**1977, Apr. 11** **Litho.** ***Perf. 11***
**C184** A95 100fr multi 1.20 .35
**C185** A95 200fr multi 2.40 .65
**C186** A95 300fr multi 3.00 1.00
*Nos. C184-C186 (3)* 6.60 2.00

**Souvenir Sheet**

**C187** A95 500fr multi 5.50 2.00

75th anniversary of Zeppelin.

### Bokassa Type of 1977

**1977, Dec. 4 Litho. *Perf. 13½***
**C188** A98 200fr multi 1.75 .80
**C189** A98 300fr multi 2.50 1.25
*a.* Souvenir sheet, 500fr 5.50 2.50

Coronation of Emperor Bokassa I, Dec. 4. No. C189a contains a horizontal stamp in similar design. A 2500fr gold embossed horizontal stamp in similar design exists. Value $20.

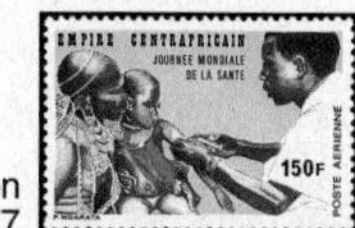

Vaccination
AP77

**1977 Litho. *Perf. 14x13½***
**C190** AP77 150fr multi 3.50 1.50

World Health Day.

### Communications Type of 1978

Designs: 100fr, Balloon and spaceships docking in space. 200fr, Hydrofoil and Concorde. 500fr, Tom-tom and Zeppelin. No. C193A, Early postman and rider, UPU emblem, Concorde. No. C193B, Mail coach, dove, satellites.

**1978, May 17 Litho. *Perf. 13½***
**C191** A107 100fr multi 1.10 .35
**C192** A107 200fr multi 1.10 .55

**Souvenir Sheet**

**C193** A107 500fr multi 5.75 2.25

Cent. of progress of posts and telecommunications. No. C193 contains one 53x35mm stamp.

**1978, Mar. 21 Litho. & Embossed**
**Size: 57x39mm**
**C193A** A107 1500fr gold & multi *30.00* 5.00

**Souvenir Sheet**

**C193B** A107 1500fr gold & multi 15.00 4.75

Nos. C193A-C193B exist imperf. No. C193A exists in a souvenir sheet of one. No. C193B contains one 57x39mm stamp.

Clement Ader and his Plane
AP78

Designs: 50fr, Wilbur and Orville Wright and plane. 60fr, John W. Alcock, Arthur W. Brown and plane. 100fr, Alan Cobham and plane 150fr, Claude Dornier and hydroplane. 500fr, Wilbur and Orville Wright and plane.

**1978, Sept. 19 *Perf. 14***
**C194** AP78 40fr multi .50 .25
**C195** AP78 50fr multi .50 .25
**C196** AP78 60fr multi .60 .35
**C197** AP78 100fr multi 1.15 .40
**C198** AP78 150fr multi 1.75 .65
*Nos. C194-C198 (5)* 4.50 1.90

**Souvenir Sheet**

**C199** AP78 500fr multi 5.50 1.75

History of aviation.

### Philexafrique II-Essen Issue
Common Design Types

No. C200, Crocodile, No. C3. No. C201, Birds, Mecklenburg-Schwerin No. 1.

**1978, Nov. 1 Litho. *Perf. 12½***
**C200** CD138 100fr multi 1.90 1.10
**C201** CD139 100fr multi 1.90 1.10
*a.* Pair, #C200-C201 + label 7.50 7.50

### Bokassa Type of 1978

150fr, Catherine & Jean Bedel Bokassa.

**1978, Dec. 4 Litho. *Perf. 13***
**C202** A113 150fr multi, horiz. 1.90 .70

First anniv. of coronation. A 1000fr gold embossed souvenir sheet showing Emperor Bokassa exists. Value $9.

### Rowland Hill Type of 1978

Designs (Rowland Hill and): 100fr, Mailman and Tuscany No. 23. 200fr, Balloon and France No. 1. 500fr, Central Africa Nos. 1-2.

**1978, Dec. 27**
**C203** A114 100fr multi 1.75 .60
**C204** A114 200fr multi 2.25 .70

**Souvenir Sheet**

**C205** A114 500fr multi 5.00 1.75

Sir Rowland Hill (1795-1879), originator of penny postage. No. C205 contains one 37½x39mm stamp.

A 1500fr gold embossed stamp and souvenir sheet exist. Value, set $27.50.

Rattan Table and Chair — AP76a

**1978 ? Litho. *Perf. 14x13¼***
**C205A** AP76a 60fr multi — —

### IYC Type of 1979

Designs (UNICEF, Eagle Emblems and): 100fr, Chinese girl flying kites and German Do-X flying boat, 1929. 200fr, Boys playing leapfrog, hurdler and Olympic emblem. 500fr, Child with abacus and Albert Einstein with his equation.

**1979, Mar. 6 *Perf. 13½***
**C206** A115 100fr multi 1.25 .40
**C207** A115 200fr multi 2.50 .80

**Souvenir Sheet**

**C208** A115 500fr multi 5.00 1.75

International Year of the Child. No. C208 contains one 56x33mm stamp.

A 1500fr gold embossed stamp and souvenir sheet exist. Value, set $27.50.

### Olympic Type of 1979

Moscow '80 Emblem, various sports and: 100fr, Hurdles & "B." 200fr, Broad jump & "A." 500fr, Pole vault, horiz.

**1979, Mar. 16 Litho. *Perf. 13***
**C209** A116 100fr multi 1.10 .40
**C210** A116 200fr multi 2.10 .65

**Souvenir Sheet**

**C210A** A116 500fr multi — —

22nd Olympic Games, Moscow, July 19-Aug. 3, 1980. No. C210A contains one 57x39mm stamp. A 1500fr gold embossed souvenir sheet exists showing diver, runner and javelin. Value, $12.50.

### National Husbandry Association Type

**1979, Aug. Litho. *Perf. 13***
**C211** A119 60fr Horse 5.25 2.00

### Central African Republic

Nos. C151-C154 Overprinted in Black or Silver

**1979, Oct. Litho. *Perf. 14x13½***
**C212** A93 100fr multi .85 .55
**C213** A93 200fr multi 1.60 .85
**C214** A93 300fr multi 2.40 1.25
*Nos. C212-C214 (3)* 4.85 2.65

**Souvenir Sheet**

**C215** A93 500fr multi (S) 5.00 5.00

Apollo 11 moon landing, 10th anniversary.

Ski Jump, Lake Placid '80 Emblem
AP79

**1979, Nov. 11 Litho. *Perf. 13½***
**C216** AP79 60fr shown .55 .25
**C217** AP79 100fr Downhill skiing .90 .40
**C218** AP79 200fr Hockey 1.90 .85
**C219** AP79 300fr Slalom 2.60 1.25
*Nos. C216-C219 (4)* 5.95 2.75

**Souvenir Sheet**

**C220** AP79 500fr Bobsledding 5.00 1.75

13th Winter Olympics Games, Lake Placid, NY, Feb. 12-24, 1980.

For overprints see Nos. C224-C228.

### Space Type of 1980

150fr, Early satellites. 200fr, Space shuttle. 500fr, Apollo 11, Armstrong. No. C223A, Armstrong, Apollo 11. No. C223B, Space shuttle, horiz.

**1980, Apr. 8 Litho. *Perf. 13½***
**C221** A125 150fr multi 1.40 .45
**C222** A125 200fr multi 1.75 .65

**Souvenir Sheet**

**C223** A125 500fr multi 5.50 1.40

**Litho. & Embossed**
**Size: 51x57mm**
**C223A** A125 1500fr multi *25.00* 5.00

**Souvenir Sheet**

**C223B** A125 1500fr multi 8.50

C223A-C223B exist imperf. No. C223A exists in a souvenir sheet of one. Value $40. No. C223B contains one 57x51mm stamp.

### Nos. C216-C220 Overprinted

a

b

c

d

e

**1980, May 12 Litho. *Perf. 13½***
**C224** AP79 (a) 60fr multi .45 .25
**C225** AP79 (b) 100fr multi .70 .40
**C226** AP79 (c) 200fr multi 1.75 .85
**C227** AP79 (d) 300fr multi 2.50 1.25
*Nos. C224-C227 (4)* 5.40 2.75

**Souvenir Sheet**

**C228** AP79 (e) 500fr multi 5.00 5.00

World Telecommunications Day — AP80

**1980, June 26 Litho. *Perf. 12½***
**C229** AP80 100fr multi 1.10 .55
**C230** AP80 150fr multi, vert. 1.40 .80

### Olympic Type of 1980

100fr, Boxing. 150fr, Hurdles.
250fr, Long jump. No. C233A, Relay race, diff. No. C233B, Basketball, vert.

**1980, July 25 Litho. *Perf. 13½***
**C231** A126 100fr multi 1.00 .25
**C232** A126 150fr multi 1.60 .40

**Souvenir Sheet**

**C233** A126 250fr multi 3.00 .65

**Litho. & Embossed**
**C233A** A126 1500fr multi 25.00 5.00

**Souvenir Sheet**

**C233B** A126 1500fr multi 11.00 4.75

22nd Summer Olympic Games, Moscow, July 19-Aug. 3. No. C233 contains one 39x36mm stamp.

For overprints see Nos. C248-C250B.

### Europe-Africa Type of 1980

150fr, Meteorology. 200fr, Aviation.
500fr, Concorde jet. No. C236A, Boy Scouts. No. C236B, Concorde.

**1980, Nov. 4 Litho. *Perf. 13½***
**C234** A127 150fr multi 1.50 .50
**C235** A127 200fr multi 1.90 .60

**Souvenir Sheet**

**C236** A127 500fr multi 5.50 1.60

No. C236 contains one 41½x29mm stamp.

**Litho. & Embossed**
**Size: 42x39mm**
**C236A** A127 1500fr multi 15.00 4.00

**Souvenir Sheet**

**C236B** A127 1500fr multi 12.00 4.75

Nos. C236A-C236B exist imperf. No. C236B contains one 42x39mm stamp.

No. C236A exists in a souvenir sheet of one. Value $30.

### Soccer Type of 1981

100fr, Netherlands. 200fr, Spain.
500fr, Argentina. No. C239A, Players, trophy. No. C239B, Players, trophy, diff.

**1981, Jan. 13 Litho. *Perf. 13½***
**C237** A130 100fr multi 1.00 .25
**C238** A130 200fr multi 1.75 .55

**Souvenir Sheet**

**C239** A130 500fr multi 6.25 1.75

**Litho. & Embossed**
**Size: 57x39mm**
**C239A** A130 1500fr multi 22.50 5.50

**Souvenir Sheet**

**C239B** A130 1500fr multi 10.00 4.00

No. C239A exists with tabs for either Philexafrique II or Essen 78.

Nos. C239A-C239B exist imperf. No. C239A exists in a souvenir sheet of one. Value $38. No. C239B contains one 36x60mm stamp.

Jacob Wrestling with the Angel, by Rembrandt
AP81

Rembrandt Paintings: 90fr, Christ during the Storm. 150fr, Jeremiah Mourning the Destruction of Jerusalem. 250fr, Tobit Accusing Anne of Theft of a Goat. 500fr, Belshazzar's Feast, horiz.

**1981, Feb. 20 *Perf. 12½***
**C240** AP81 60fr multi .55 .25
**C241** AP81 90fr multi 1.00 .25
**C242** AP81 150fr multi 1.75 .65
**C243** AP81 250fr multi 3.00 .80
*Nos. C240-C243 (4)* 6.30 1.95

**Souvenir Sheet**

**C244** AP81 500fr multi 5.50 1.75

### Picasso Type of 1981

Paintings: 150fr, Woman in Mirror with Self-portrait. 200fr, Woman Sleeping, The Dream. 500fr, Portrait of Maia (the Artist's Daughter). No. C247A, Two Women and Glasses,

Picasso. No. C247B, Woman with Handbag, statue of standing woman, vert.

**1981, June 30 Litho. *Perf. 13½***
**C245** A133 150fr multi 2.25 .45
**C246** A133 200fr multi 2.50 .65

**Souvenir Sheet**

**C247** A133 500fr multi 5.75 2.25

No. C247 contains one 42x46mm stamp.

**Litho. & Embossed**
**Size: 57x39mm**

**C247A** A133 1500fr gold & multi 17.50 6.00

**Souvenir Sheet**

**C247B** A133 1500fr gold & multi 12.00

Nos. C247A-C247B exist imperf. No. C247A exists in a souvenir sheet of one. Value $22.50. No. C247B contains one 39x58mm stamp.

### Nos. C231-C233B Overprinted in Gold

**1981 Litho. *Perf. 13½***
**C248** A126 100fr multi 1.00 .25
**C249** A126 150fr multi 1.40 .40

**Souvenir Sheet**

**C250** A126 250fr multi 3.00 .65

**Litho. & Embossed**

**C250A** A126 1500fr on #C233A 16.00 6.00

**Souvenir Sheet**

**C250B** A126 1500fr on #C233B 15.00

No. C250A exists in a souvenir sheet of 1. Value $35.

### Royal Wedding Type of 1981

150fr, Prince of Wales arms. 200fr, Palace. 500fr, St. Paul's Cathedral. No. C253A, Diana, Charles. No. C253B, Charles, Diana, ship.

**1981, Aug. 20 Litho. *Perf. 13½***
**C251** A136 150fr multi 1.60 .40
**C252** A136 200fr multi 2.10 .55

**Souvenir Sheet**

**C253** A136 500fr multi 4.75 1.40

No. C253 contains one 60x32mm stamp.

**Litho. & Embossed**
**Size: 51x42mm**

**C253A** A136 1500fr multi 15.00 4.00

**Souvenir Sheet**

**C253B** A136 1500fr multi 12.00

Nos. C253A-C253B exist imperf. No. C253A exists in a souvenir sheet of one. Value $21. No. C253B contains one 51x42mm stamp.

### Navigator Type of 1981

100fr, O. Kersauson. 200fr, Chichester. 500fr, A. Colas. No. C256A, Riguidel. No. C256B, Tabarly.

**1981, Sept. 4 Litho. *Perf. 13½***
**C254** A139 100fr multi 1.10 .70
**C255** A139 200fr multi 2.40 1.40

**Souvenir Sheet**

**C256** A139 500fr multi 6.50 1.40

**Litho. & Embossed**
**Size: 51x42mm**

**C256A** A139 1500fr multi 16.00 4.50

**Souvenir Sheet**

**C256B** A139 1500fr multi 13.00

Nos. C256A-C256B exist imperf. No. C256A exists in a souvenir sheet of one. Value $40. No. C256B contains one 51x42mm stamp.

Lizard — AP82

**1981, Oct. 30 *Perf. 12½x13***
**C257** AP82 30fr shown 1.00 .25
**C258** AP82 60fr Snake 1.25 .30
**C259** AP82 110fr Crocodile 2.50 .45
*Nos. C257-C259 (3)* 4.75 1.00

### Christmas Type of 1981

140fr, Correggio. 200fr, Gentileschi, 1610. 500fr, Holy Family, by Cranach. No. C262A, Hans Memling, c. 1470. No. C262B, Fra Angelico, 1438.

**1981, Dec. 24 *Perf. 13½***
**C260** A143 140fr multi 2.50 .45
**C261** A143 200fr multi 4.50 .70

**Souvenir Sheet**

**C262** A143 500fr multi 6.75 1.75

No. C262 contains one 41x50mm stamp.

**Litho. & Embossed**
**Size: 30x60mm**

**C262A** A143 1500fr multi 15.00 4.50

**Souvenir Sheet**

**C262B** A143 1500fr multi 11.00

Nos. C262A-C262B exist imperf. No. C262A exists in a souvenir sheet of one. Value $25. No. C262B contains one 30x60mm stamp.

### Animal Type of 1982

300fr, Mandrill. 500fr, Lion.
600fr, Nile crocodiles. No. C265A, Leopard, Rotary emblem. No. C265B, Emblem, eagle, horiz.

**1982, Jan. 22 Litho. *Perf. 13½***
**C263** A145 300fr multi 3.25 .65
**C264** A145 500fr multi 5.50 1.40

**Souvenir Sheet**

**C265** A145 600fr multi 6.75 1.60

No. C265 contains one 47x38mm stamp.

**Litho. & Embossed**
**Size: 51x57mm**

**C265A** A145 1500fr multi 15.00 4.00

**Souvenir Sheet**

**C265B** A145 1500fr multi 13.00

Nos. C265A-C265B exist imperf. No. C265A exists in a souvenir sheet of one. Value $42.50. No. C265B contains one 57x51mm stamp.

### Transportation Type of 1982 and

AP82a

Designs: 300fr, Savannah cargo ship. 500fr, Columbia space shuttle. 600fr, Spirit of Locomotion emblem. No. C268A, Space shuttle launch, horiz. No. C268B, Shuttle, space telescope.

**1982, Feb. 27 Litho. *Perf. 13½***
**C266** A147 300fr multi 3.75 .65
**C267** A147 500fr multi 5.50 1.40

**Souvenir Sheet**

**C268** A147 600fr multi 5.50 1.60

**Litho. & Embossed**

**C268A** AP82a 1500fr gold & multi 15.00 4.50

**Souvenir Sheet**

**C268B** AP82a 1500fr gold & multi 11.50

No. C268 contains one 39x43mm stamp. No. C268B contains one 51x42mm stamp.
No. C268A exists in a souvenir sheet of 1. Value $50.

### Olympic Type of 1982

**1982, July 24 Litho. *Perf. 13½***
**C269** A149 300fr Diving 3.00 .80
**C270** A149 500fr Equestrian 5.00 1.40

**Souvenir Sheet**

**C271** A149 600fr Basketball 5.50 1.60

No. C271 contains one 38x56mm stamp.

### Diana Type of 1982

**1982, July 20 Litho. *Perf. 13½***
**C272** A150 300fr multi 3.25 .80
**C273** A150 500fr multi 5.50 1.40

**Souvenir Sheet**

**C274** A150 600fr multi 5.75 1.60

No. C274 contains one 56x32mm stamp.

Christmas 1982 — AP83

Raphael Paintings: 150fr, Beautiful Gardener. 500fr, Holy Family.

**1982, Dec. *Perf. 13***
**C275** AP83 150fr multi 2.00 .50
**C276** AP83 500fr multi 5.50 1.40

### Space Type of 1982

Designs: Various satellites and space scenes. No. C279A, European communications satellite, controller. No. C279B, Viking on Mars, vert.

**1982, Aug. 15 Litho. *Perf. 13½***
**C277** A151 300fr multi 3.00 .80
**C278** A151 500fr multi 5.00 1.40

**Souvenir Sheet**

**C279** A151 600fr multi 5.00 1.60

**Litho. & Embossed**
**Size: 60x36mm**

**C279A** A151 1500fr gold & multi 15.00 4.50

**Souvenir Sheet**

**C279B** A151 1500fr gold & multi 12.00

Nos. C279A-C279B exist imperf. No. C279A exists in a souvenir sheet of one. Value $55. No. C279B contains one 36x60mm stamp.

Birth of Prince William of Wales, June 21, 1982 — AP84

500fr, Diana, William.
600fr, Family. No. C281A, Diana, William, Charles. No. 281B, Diana, William, vert.

**1983, Jan. 22**
**C280** AP84 500fr multi 5.50 1.40

**Souvenir Sheet**

**C281** AP84 600fr multi 5.50 4.00

**Litho. & Embossed**

**C281A** AP84 1500fr gold & multi 15.00 3.50

**Souvenir Sheet**

**C281B** AP84 1500fr gold & multi 10.00

No. C281A exists in a souvenir sheet of 1. Value $40.

Manned Flight Bicentenary AP85

65fr, Robert's & Hullin's balloon. 130fr, John Wise's, 1859. 350fr, Mail balloon, 1870. 400fr, Dirigible Underberg.
500fr, Montgolfiere, 1783.

**1983, Apr.**
**C282** AP85 65fr multicolored 1.00 .25
**C283** AP85 130fr multicolored 1.50 .35
**C284** AP85 350fr multicolored 3.25 1.00
**C285** AP85 400fr multicolored 4.25 1.25
*Nos. C282-C285 (4)* 10.00 2.85

**Souvenir Sheet**

**C286** AP85 500fr multicolored 5.75 1.75

Pre-Olympics — AP86

Various equestrian events.

**1983, July Litho. *Perf. 13***
**C287** AP86 100fr multi 1.00 .50
**C288** AP86 200fr multi 2.10 .70
**C289** AP86 300fr multi 2.75 .90
**C290** AP86 400fr multi 3.50 1.25
*Nos. C287-C290 (4)* 9.35 3.35

**Souvenir Sheet**

**C291** AP86 500fr multi 5.50 1.40

### Animal Type of 1983

Endangered Animals, Rotary Emblem: 400fr, Black rhinoceros, parrot, zebra, scouts. 500fr, Lions, parrot, antelope, elephant, flag, Rotary Int'l emblem. 600fr, Leopard.

**1983, Nov. 14 Litho. *Perf. 13½***
**C291A** A170 400fr multicolored 10.00 3.00
**C292** A170 500fr multicolored 12.00 3.50

**Souvenir Sheet**

**C293** A170 600fr multicolored 16.00 4.00

15th World Scout Jamboree, Alberta (400fr). No. C293 contains one 47x32mm stamp.

Christmas 1983 — AP88

Paintings: 130fr, Annunciation, by da Vinci. 205fr, Virgin of the Rocks, by da Vinci. 350fr, Adoration of the Shepherds, by Rubens. 500fr, Virgin and Child with Donor, by Rubens.

**1984, Jan. 3 Litho. *Perf. 13***
**C294** AP88 130fr multi 1.25 .40
**C295** AP88 205fr multi 2.00 .55
**C296** AP88 350fr multi 3.50 1.10
**C297** AP88 500fr multi 5.00 1.35
*Nos. C294-C297 (4)* 11.75 3.40

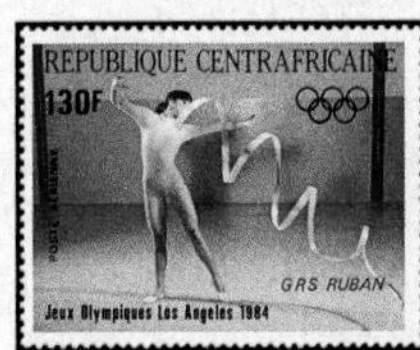


1984 Summer Olympics AP89

Various gymnastic and rhythmic gymnastic events. 65fr, 100fr, 205fr, 350fr vert.
500fr, Rhythmic formation.

**1984, Mar. 13 Litho. *Perf. 13***
**C298** AP89 65fr multi .55 .25
**C299** AP89 100fr multi 1.10 .25
**C300** AP89 130fr multi 1.40 .35
**C301** AP89 205fr multi 2.25 .65
**C302** AP89 350fr multi 4.00 1.10
*Nos. C298-C302 (5)* 9.30 2.60

**Souvenir Sheet**
***Perf. 13½x13***

**C302A** AP89 500fr multi 5.50 1.75

For overprint see No. 705.

Summer Olympics Winners — AP90

60fr, 400 meter relay. 140fr, 400 meter hurdles. 300fr, 5000 meter race. 440fr, Decathlon. 550fr, 800 meter race, horiz.

**1985, Jan. 7 Litho. *Perf. 14***

**C303** AP90 60fr multicolored .55 .25
**C304** AP90 140fr multicolored 1.75 .45
**C305** AP90 300fr multicolored 3.50 .90
**C306** AP90 440fr multicolored 4.50 1.20
*Nos. C303-C306 (4)* 10.30 2.80

**Souvenir Sheet**

**C307** AP90 500fr multicolored 5.50 1.75

Christmas 1984 AP91

Paintings by Titian: 130fr, Virgin and Infant Jesus. 350fr, Virgin with Rabbit. 400fr, Virgin and Child.

**1985, Jan. 17 Litho. *Perf. 13***

**C308** AP91 130fr multi 1.10 .55
**C309** AP91 350fr multi 2.50 1.25
**C310** AP91 400fr multi 3.50 1.60
*Nos. C308-C310 (3)* 7.10 3.40

Audubon Bicentenary AP92

60fr, Otus asio. 110fr, Coccizus minor, vert. 200fr, Zenaidura macroura, vert. 500fr, Aix sponsa.

**1985, Jan. 25 Litho. *Perf. 13***

**C311** AP92 60fr multicolored .80 .25
**C312** AP92 110fr multicolored 1.20 .45
**C313** AP92 200fr multicolored 2.00 1.00
**C314** AP92 500fr multicolored 5.00 2.50
*Nos. C311-C314 (4)* 9.00 4.20

Christmas 1985 — AP93

Religious paintings: 100fr, Virgin with Angels, by the Master of Burgo de Osma. 200fr, Nativity, by Louis Le Nain (1593-1648). 400fr, Virgin and Child with Dove, by Piero de Cosimo (1462-1521).

**1985, Dec. 24 Litho. *Perf. 13***

**C315** AP93 100fr multi 1.00 .45
**C316** AP93 200fr multi 2.25 .90
**C317** AP93 400fr multi 4.25 1.50
*Nos. C315-C317 (3)* 7.50 2.85

Halley's Comet AP94

110fr, Edmond Halley. 130fr, Giotto probe. 200fr, Comet, planet. 300fr, Vega probe. 400fr, Space shuttle.

**1986, Mar. 8**

**C318** AP94 110fr multicolored 1.00 .25
**C319** AP94 130fr multicolored 1.40 .25
**C320** AP94 200fr multicolored 2.25 .50
**C321** AP94 300fr multicolored 3.00 .75
**C322** AP94 400fr multicolored 4.50 1.00
*Nos. C318-C322 (5)* 12.15 2.75

Christmas AP95

Painting details: 250fr, Nativity, by Giotto. 440fr, Adoration of the Magi, by Botticelli, vert. 500fr, Nativity, by Giotto, diff.

**1986, Dec. 24 Litho. *Perf. 13½***

**C323** AP95 250fr multi 2.10 .90
**C324** AP95 440fr multi 3.75 1.35
**C325** AP95 500fr multi 4.50 1.90
*Nos. C323-C325 (3)* 10.35 4.15

Tennis at the 1988 Olympics AP96

Various plays.

**1986, Dec. 31 *Perf. 12½***

**C326** AP96 150fr multi 1.40 .60
**C327** AP96 250fr multi, vert. 2.75 .70
**C328** AP96 440fr multi, vert. 3.25 1.25
**C329** AP96 600fr multi 5.75 1.40
*Nos. C326-C329 (4)* 13.15 3.95

1988 Summer Olympics, Seoul AP97

100fr, Triple jump, vert. 200fr, High jump. 300fr, Long jump. 400fr, Pole vault, vert. 500fr, High jump, diff.

**1987, June 15 Litho. *Perf. 13***

**C330** AP97 100fr multicolored .80 .35
**C331** AP97 200fr multicolored 1.60 .65
**C332** AP97 300fr multicolored 2.40 .90
**C333** AP97 400fr multicolored 3.25 1.75
*Nos. C330-C333 (4)* 8.05 3.65

**Souvenir Sheet**

**C334** AP97 500fr multicolored 4.25 2.50

1988 Summer Olympics, Seoul AP98

Stamps on stamps and gymnasts: 90fr, No. C94, balance beam, vert. 200fr, No. C21, balance beam, diff. 300fr, No. C22, pommel horse. 400fr, No. C23, parallel bars. 500fr, No. C93, rings.

**1988, July 26 Litho. *Perf. 13***

**C335** AP98 90fr multi .80 .30
**C336** AP98 200fr multi 1.75 .50
**C337** AP98 300fr multi 2.75 .90
**C338** AP98 400fr multi 3.50 1.40
*Nos. C335-C338 (4)* 8.80 3.10

**Souvenir Sheet**

**C339** AP98 500fr multi 5.00 2.00

1st Moon Landing, 20th Anniv. — AP99

**1989, Aug. 4 Litho. *Perf. 13***

**C340** AP99 40fr Apollo 11 .30 .25
**C341** AP99 80fr Apollo 15 .65 .30
**C342** AP99 130fr Apollo 16 1.25 .75
**C343** AP99 1000fr Apollo 17 9.00 2.75
*Nos. C340-C343 (4)* 11.20 4.05

World Cup Soccer Championships, Italy — AP100

**1990, July 7 Litho. *Perf. 13***

**C344** AP100 5fr multicolored .25 .25
**C345** AP100 30fr multi, diff. .30 .25
**C346** AP100 500fr multi, diff. 4.50 1.10
**C347** AP100 1000fr multi, diff. 8.25 2.00
*Nos. C344-C347 (4)* 13.30 3.60

Charles de Gaulle (1890-1979) AP101

**1990, July 27 *Perf. 13½***

**C348** AP101 500fr multicolored 3.75 1.10

No. C348 exists in a souvenir sheet of 1.
For overprint see No. C360.

Don Mattingly, Baseball Player AP102

Saturn V Rocket, Apollo 11 Astronauts — AP103

Charles de Gaulle, Birth Cent. — AP104

No. C352, De Gaulle and Cross of Lorraine.

**1990, July 27 Litho. *Perf. 13½***

**C349** AP102 300fr multicolored 2.75 .80

**Souvenir Sheet**

**C350** AP103 1000fr multicolored 9.00 2.00

**Litho. & Embossed**

**C351** AP104 1500fr gold & multi 16.00 5.50

**Souvenir Sheet**

**C352** AP104 1500fr gold & multi 12.00

No. C351 exists in souvenir sheet of 1. Value $15. This souvenir sheet also exists imperf. and with an overprint in the sheet margin.
For overprints see Nos. C355-C356.

Visit of Pope John Paul II to Africa — AP105

Pope John Paul II and: No. C353, Mother Theresa, portrait. No. C354, Papal arms, globe.

**1993 Litho. & Embossed *Perf. 13½***

**C353** AP105 1500fr gold & multi 15.00 5.00

**Souvenir Sheet**

**C354** AP105 1500fr gold & multi 20.00

No. C353 exists in a souvenir sheet of 1. Value $20.

No. C351 Overprinted

**Litho. & Embossed**

**1994, June 6 *Perf. 13½***

**C355** AP104 1500fr gold & multi 15.00 5.00

**No. C352 Ovptd. in Silver in Sheet Margin**

**Souvenir Sheet**

**C356** AP104 1500fr gold & multi 15.00 5.00

Overprint on No. C356 contains map, soldiers and "50 eme ANNIVERSAIRE DU /DEBARQUEMENT."
No. C355 exists in souvenir sheet of 1. Value $15.

Souvenir Sheets

Japanese Exploration of Antarctica — AP106

No. C357, Nobu Shirase. No. C358, Schooner Kainman Maru, horiz.

**1994, Oct. 25**

**C357** AP106 1200fr multi 5.50 4.75
**C358** AP106 1200fr multi 5.50 4.75

D-Day, 50th Anniv. (in 1994) AP107

Designs: a, Gliders over Pegasus Bridge, Sword beach. b, Fighter planes over Juno, Gold and Omaha beaches. c, Planes over Utah beach, St. Mere Eglise.

**Litho. & Embossed**

**1995, Oct. 25 *Perf. 13½***

**C359** AP107 1000fr Strip of 3, #a.-c. 13.00 13.00

No. C359b is 60x45mm.

**Souvenir Sheet**
No. C348 Overprinted

**1995, Oct. 10 Litho. *Perf. 13½***

| | | | | |
|---|---|---|---|---|
| **C360** | AP101 | 500fr multicolored | 11.50 | 11.50 |

## AIR POST SEMI-POSTAL STAMPS

Isis of Kalabsha — SPAP1

**Unwmk.**
**1964, Mar. 7 Engr. *Perf. 13***

| | | | | |
|---|---|---|---|---|
| **CB1** | SPAP1 | 25fr + 10fr multi | 1.25 | 1.25 |
| **CB2** | SPAP1 | 50fr + 10fr multi | 2.00 | 2.00 |
| **CB3** | SPAP1 | 100fr + 10fr multi | 3.00 | 3.00 |
| | | *Nos. CB1-CB3 (3)* | 6.25 | 6.25 |

UNESCO world campaign to save historic monuments in Nubia.

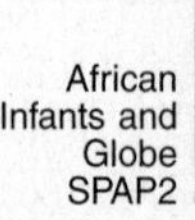

African Infants and Globe SPAP2

**1971, Dec. 11 Litho. *Perf. 13x13½***

| | | | | |
|---|---|---|---|---|
| **CB4** | SPAP2 | 140fr + 50fr multi | 3.25 | 1.75 |

25th anniv. of UNICEF, and Children's Day.

## POSTAGE DUE STAMPS

Sternotomis Virescens — D1

Beetles: No. J2, Sternotomis gama. No. J3, Augosoma centaurus. No. J4, Phosphorus virescens, ceroplesis carabarica. No. J5, Cetoine scaraboidae. No. J6, Ceroplesis S.P. No. J7, Macrorhina S.P. No. J8, Cetoine scaraboidae. No. J9, Phryneta leprosa. No. J10, Taurina longiceps. No. J11, Monohamus griseoplagiatus. No. J12, Jambonus trifasciatus.

**Unwmk.**
**1962, Oct. 15 Engr. *Perf. 11***

| | | | | |
|---|---|---|---|---|
| **J1** | D1 | 50c grn & dp org | .25 | .25 |
| **J2** | D1 | 50c grn & dp org | .25 | .25 |
| *a.* | | Pair, #J1-J2 | .45 | |
| **J3** | D1 | 1fr blk, brn & lt grn | .30 | .30 |
| **J4** | D1 | 1fr blk, brn & lt grn | .30 | .30 |
| *a.* | | Pair, #J3-J4 | .75 | |
| **J5** | D1 | 2fr blk, org & yel grn | .40 | .40 |
| **J6** | D1 | 2fr blk & red org | .40 | .40 |
| *a.* | | Pair, #J5-J6 | .85 | |
| **J7** | D1 | 5fr brn, org & grn | .55 | .55 |
| **J8** | D1 | 5fr brn, org, grn & red | .55 | .55 |
| *a.* | | Pair, #J7-J8 | 1.25 | |
| **J9** | D1 | 10fr blk, grn & brn | 1.00 | 1.00 |
| **J10** | D1 | 10fr blk, brn & grn | 1.00 | 1.00 |
| *a.* | | Pair, #J9-J10 | 2.25 | |
| **J11** | D1 | 25fr blk, bl grn & brn | 3.00 | 2.40 |
| **J12** | D1 | 25fr blk, brn & bl grn | 3.00 | 2.40 |
| *a.* | | Pair, #J11-J12 | 6.50 | |
| | | *Nos. J1-J12 (12)* | 11.00 | 9.80 |

Pairs se-tenant at the base.

Giant Anteater D2

**1985, Jan. 25 Litho. *Perf. 12½***

| | | | | |
|---|---|---|---|---|
| **J13** | D2 | 5fr multi | .50 | .50 |
| **J14** | D2 | 20fr multi | .90 | .90 |
| **J15** | D2 | 30fr multi | 1.10 | 1.10 |
| | | *Nos. J13-J15 (3)* | 2.50 | 2.50 |

## MILITARY STAMPS

No. 1 Overprinted

**Unwmk.**
**1962, Jan. 1 Engr. *Perf. 13***

| | | | | |
|---|---|---|---|---|
| **M1** | A1 | bl, car, grn & yel | 14.00 | — |

No. 1 Overprinted

**1963**

| | | | | |
|---|---|---|---|---|
| **M2** | A1 | bl, car, grn & yel | 15.00 | — |

## OFFICIAL STAMPS

Coat of Arms — O1

**Imprint: "d'après G. RICHER SO.GE.IM."**

***Perf. 13x12½***
**1965-69 Litho. Unwmk.**
**Arms in Original Colors**

| | | | | |
|---|---|---|---|---|
| **O1** | O1 | 1fr blk & brn org | .25 | .25 |
| **O2** | O1 | 2fr blk & violet | .25 | .25 |
| **O3** | O1 | 5fr blk & gray | .25 | .25 |
| **O4** | O1 | 10fr blk & green | .25 | .25 |
| **O5** | O1 | 20fr blk & red brn | .55 | .25 |
| **O6** | O1 | 30fr blk & emer ('69) | 1.00 | .55 |
| **O7** | O1 | 50fr blk & dk bl | 1.10 | .70 |
| **O8** | O1 | 100fr blk & bister | 2.60 | 1.10 |
| **O9** | O1 | 130fr blk & ver ('69) | 4.00 | 2.25 |
| **O10** | O1 | 200fr blk & claret | 5.75 | 2.75 |
| | | *Nos. O1-O10 (10)* | 16.00 | 8.60 |

**Redrawn**
Imprint: "d'après G. RICHER DELRIEU"

**1971 Photo. *Perf. 12x12½***
**Arms in Original Colors**

| | | | | |
|---|---|---|---|---|
| **O11** | O1 | 5fr blk & gray | .25 | .25 |
| **O12** | O1 | 30fr blk & emer | .50 | .25 |
| **O13** | O1 | 40fr blk & dp claret | .70 | .30 |
| **O14** | O1 | 100fr blk & bister | 1.60 | .55 |
| **O15** | O1 | 140fr blk & lt bl | 3.00 | .85 |
| **O16** | O1 | 200fr blk & claret | 3.75 | 1.40 |
| | | *Nos. O11-O16 (6)* | 9.80 | 3.60 |

**Empire**

Nos. O11, O13-O16 Overprinted in Black

**1977 Litho. *Perf. 12x12½***

| | | | | |
|---|---|---|---|---|
| **O17** | O1 | 5fr multi | .35 | .25 |
| **O18** | O1 | 40fr multi | .50 | .30 |
| **O19** | O1 | 100fr multi | 1.40 | .45 |
| **O20** | O1 | 140fr multi | 1.75 | .70 |
| **O21** | O1 | 200fr multi | 2.75 | 1.10 |
| | | *Nos. O17-O21 (5)* | 6.75 | 2.80 |

**Type of 1965 Inscribed: "EMPIRE CENTRAFRICAIN"**

**1978, July Litho. *Perf. 12½***

| | | | | |
|---|---|---|---|---|
| **O22** | O1 | 1fr multi | .25 | .25 |
| **O23** | O1 | 2fr multi | .25 | .25 |
| **O24** | O1 | 5fr multi | .25 | .25 |
| **O25** | O1 | 10fr multi | .25 | .25 |
| **O26** | O1 | 15fr multi | .25 | .25 |
| **O27** | O1 | 20fr multi | .25 | .25 |
| **O28** | O1 | 30fr multi | .30 | .25 |
| **O29** | O1 | 40fr multi | .40 | .25 |
| **O30** | O1 | 50fr multi | .55 | .30 |
| **O31** | O1 | 60fr multi | .75 | .40 |
| **O32** | O1 | 100fr multi | 1.00 | .55 |
| **O33** | O1 | 130fr multi | 1.60 | .95 |
| **O34** | O1 | 140fr multi | 1.75 | .95 |
| **O35** | O1 | 200fr multi | 3.50 | 1.60 |
| | | *Nos. O22-O35 (14)* | 11.35 | 6.75 |

# CENTRAL LITHUANIA

'sen-trəl ˌli-thə-'wā-nē-ə

LOCATION — North of Poland and east of Lithuania
CAPITAL — Vilnius

At one time Central Lithuania was a grand duchy of Lithuania but at the end of the 18th Century it fell under Russian rule. After World War I, Lithuania regained her sovereignty but certain areas were occupied by Poland. During the Russo-Polish war this territory was seized by Lithuania whose claim was promptly recognized by the Soviet Government. Under the leadership of the Polish General Zeligowski the territory was recaptured and it was during this occupation the stamps of Central Lithuania came into being. Subsequently the territory became a part of Poland.

100 Fennigi = 1 Markka

Coat of Arms — A1

***Perf. 11½, Imperf.***
**1920-21 Typo. Unwmk.**

| | | | | |
|---|---|---|---|---|
| **1** | A1 | 25f red | .40 | *.55* |
| **2** | A1 | 25f dark grn ('21) | .40 | *.55* |
| **3** | A1 | 1m blue | .40 | *.55* |
| **4** | A1 | 1m dark brn ('21) | .40 | *.55* |
| **5** | A1 | 2m violet | .40 | *.55* |
| **6** | A1 | 2m orange ('21) | .40 | *.55* |
| | | *Nos. 1-6 (6)* | 2.40 | *3.30* |

For surcharges see Nos. B1-B5.

Lithuanian Stamps of 1919 Surcharged in Blue or Black

***Perf. 11½x12, 12½x11½, 14***
**1920, Nov. 23 Wmk. 145**

| | | | | |
|---|---|---|---|---|
| **13** | A5 | 2m on 15sk lil | 47.50 | *55.00* |
| *a.* | | Inverted surcharge | *200.00* | *900.00* |
| **14** | A5 | 4m on 10sk red | 47.50 | *52.50* |
| *a.* | | Inverted surcharge | *150.00* | |
| **15** | A5 | 4m on 20sk dl bl (Bk) | 47.50 | *52.50* |
| *a.* | | Inverted surcharge | *150.00* | |
| **16** | A5 | 4m on 30sk buff | 75.00 | *52.50* |
| *a.* | | Inverted surcharge | *150.00* | |
| **17** | A6 | 6m on 50sk lt grn | 47.50 | *52.50* |
| *a.* | | 4m on 50sk (error) | *200.00* | |
| *b.* | | 10m on 50sk (error) | *200.00* | |
| *c.* | | Surcharge inverted | | — |
| **18** | A6 | 6m on 60sk vio & red | 47.50 | *52.50* |
| *a.* | | 4m on 60sk (error) | *200.00* | |
| *b.* | | 10m on 60sk (error) | *200.00* | |
| **19** | A6 | 6m on 75sk bis & red | 47.50 | *52.50* |
| *a.* | | 4m on 75sk (error) | *200.00* | |
| *b.* | | 10m on 75sk (error) | *200.00* | |
| **20** | A8 | 10m on 1auk gray & red | 95.00 | 110.00 |
| *a.* | | Inverted surcharge | *210.00* | |
| **21** | A8 | 10m on 3auk lt brn & red | *1,400.* | *1,800.* |
| **22** | A8 | 10m on 5auk bl grn & red | *1,400.* | *1,800.* |
| | | *Nos. 13-20 (8)* | 455.00 | *480.00* |
| | | *Nos. 13-22 (10)* | *3,255.* | *4,080.* |

The overprint on Nos. 17-19 is down-reading, i.e., the top of the overprint is at the right of the original design, the bottom at the left. The inverted overprint on No. 17c is up-reading.

*Reprints of Nos. 17a, 17b, 18a, 18b, 19a, 19b. Value, each $45.*

Counterfeits of Nos. 21-22 exist.

Lithuanian Girl — A2

Warrior A3

Holy Gate of Vilnius A4

Tower and Cathedral, Vilnius A5

Rector's Insignia A6

Gen. Lucien Zeligowski — A7

***Perf. 11½, Imperf.***
**1920 Litho. Unwmk.**

| | | | | |
|---|---|---|---|---|
| **23** | A2 | 25f gray | .25 | *.75* |
| **24** | A3 | 1m orange | .25 | *.75* |
| **25** | A4 | 2m claret | .45 | *1.00* |
| **26** | A5 | 4m gray grn & buff | .60 | *1.25* |
| **27** | A6 | 6m rose & gray | 2.00 | *2.75* |
| **28** | A7 | 10m brown & yellow | 3.00 | *4.00* |
| | | *Nos. 23-28 (6)* | 6.55 | *10.50* |

For surcharges see Nos. B13-B14, B17-B19.

St. Anne's Church, Vilnius A8

St. Stanislas Cathedral, Vilnius A9

White Eagle, White Knight Vytis A10

Queen Hedwig and King Ladislas II Jagello A11

Coat of Arms of Vilnius
A12

Poczobut Astronomical Observatory
A13

Union of Lithuania and Poland
A14

Tadeusz Kosciuszko and Adam Mickiewicz
A15

**1921** ***Perf. 14, Imperf.***

| No. | Type | Description | Unused | Used |
|---|---|---|---|---|
| **35** | A8 | 1m dk gray & yel | .60 | *1.10* |
| **36** | A9 | 2m rose & green | .60 | *1.10* |
| **37** | A10 | 3m dark green | .60 | *1.10* |
| **38** | A11 | 4m brown & buff | .60 | *1.10* |
| **39** | A12 | 5m red brown | .60 | *1.10* |
| **40** | A13 | 6m indigo, bl blk & buff | .60 | *1.40* |
| **41** | A14 | 10m red vio & buff | .85 | *2.25* |
| **42** | A15 | 20m choc & pink | .85 | *2.25* |
| | | *Nos. 35-42 (8)* | 5.30 | *11.40* |

Set, perf. 13½, $150.
Stamps perf. 11½ were privately produced.

Peasant Girl Sowing
A16

White Eagle and Vytis
A17

Great Theater at Vilnius
A18

Allegory: Peace and Industry
A19

Gen. Zeligowski Entering Vilnius
A20

Gen. Zeligowski
A21

**1921-22** ***Perf. 11½, Imperf.***

| No. | Type | Description | Unused | Used |
|---|---|---|---|---|
| **53** | A16 | 10m brown ('22) | 3.00 | *6.00* |
| **54** | A17 | 25m red & yel ('22) | 3.25 | *7.50* |
| **55** | A18 | 50m dk blue ('22) | 4.50 | *11.00* |
| **56** | A19 | 75m violet ('22) | 4.75 | *20.00* |
| **57** | A20 | 100m bl & bister | 2.00 | *5.25* |
| **58** | A21 | 150m ol grn & brn | 3.00 | *6.75* |
| | | *Nos. 53-58 (6)* | 20.50 | *56.50* |

Opening of the Natl. Parliament, Nos. 53-56; anniv. of the entry of General Zeligowski into Vilnius, Nos. 57-58.

## SEMI-POSTAL STAMPS

Nos. 1-6 Surcharged in Black or Red

**1921** **Unwmk.** ***Perf. 11½, Imperf.***

| No. | Type | Description | Unused | Used |
|---|---|---|---|---|
| **B1** | A1 | 25f + 2m red (Bk) | 1.00 | *1.75* |
| **B2** | A1 | 25f + 2m dk green | 1.00 | *1.75* |
| **B3** | A1 | 1m + 2m blue | 1.00 | *1.75* |
| **B4** | A1 | 1m + 2m dk brown | 1.00 | *1.75* |
| **B5** | A1 | 2m + 2m violet | 1.00 | *1.75* |
| **B6** | A1 | 2m + 2m orange | 1.00 | *1.75* |
| | | *Nos. B1-B6 (6)* | 6.00 | *10.50* |

The surcharge means "For Silesia 2 marks." The stamps were intended to provide a fund to assist the plebiscite in Upper Silesia.

### Nos. 25, 26 Surcharged

a

b

***Perf. 11½, Imperf.***

| No. | Type | Description | Unused | Used |
|---|---|---|---|---|
| **B13** | A4 (a) | 2m + 1(m) claret | 1.10 | *2.00* |
| **B14** | A5 (b) | 4m + 1m gray green & buff | 1.10 | *2.00* |
| *a.* | | Tête-beche pair | 25.00 | |

Nos. 25-26, 28 with inset

***Perf. 11½, Imperf.***

| No. | Type | Description | Unused | Used |
|---|---|---|---|---|
| **B17** | A4 | 2m + 1m claret | .85 | *1.25* |
| **B18** | A5 | 4m + 1m gray green & buff | .85 | *1.25* |
| **B19** | A7 | 10m + 2m brn & yel | 1.00 | *1.25* |
| | | *Nos. B13-B19 (5)* | 4.90 | *7.75* |

## POSTAGE DUE STAMPS

University, Vilnius
D1

Castle Hill, Vilnius
D2

Castle Ruins, Troki
D3

Holy Gate, Vilnius
D4

St. Stanislas Cathedral
D5

St. Anne's Church, Vilnius
D6

**1920-21** **Unwmk.** ***Perf. 11½, Imperf.***

| No. | Type | Description | Unused | Used |
|---|---|---|---|---|
| **J1** | D1 | 50f red violet | .40 | *1.25* |
| **J2** | D2 | 1m green | .40 | *1.25* |
| **J3** | D3 | 2m red violet | .50 | *1.25* |
| **J4** | D4 | 3m red violet | .85 | *1.60* |
| **J5** | D5 | 5m red violet | 1.00 | *2.50* |
| **J6** | D6 | 20m scarlet | 2.00 | *3.25* |
| | | *Nos. J1-J6 (6)* | 5.15 | *11.10* |

# CEYLON

si-'län

LOCATION — An island in the Indian Ocean separated from India by the Gulf of Manaar

GOVT. — Independent republic within the British Commonwealth

AREA — 25,332 sq. mi.

POP. — 12,670,000 (est. 1971)

CAPITAL — Colombo

Ceylon changed its name to Republic of Sri Lanka on May 22, 1972.

12 Pence = 1 Shilling
100 Cents = 1 Rupee (1872)

Values for unused stamps are for examples with original gum as defined in the catalogue introduction except for Nos. 2, 5, 8-9 which seldom have any remaining trace of their original gum. Many unused stamps of Ceylon, especially between Nos. 59 and 274, have toned gum or tropical stains. Values quoted are for stamps with fresh gum. Toned stamps have lower values, and common stamps with toned gum are worth very little.

Very fine examples of Nos. 1-15 will be cut square, will have small margins, but will show an intact design. Inferior examples with the design partly cut away will sell for much less, and examples with large margins will command higher prices. Very fine examples of Nos. 17-58b will have perforations just cutting into the design on one or more sides due to the narrow spacing of the stamps on the plates and to imperfect perforating methods. Stamps with perfs clear on all four sides are extremely scarce and will command substantially higher prices.

**Catalogue values for unused stamps in this country are for Never Hinged items, beginning with Scott 290 in the regular postage section and Scott B1 in the semi-postal section.**

### Watermarks

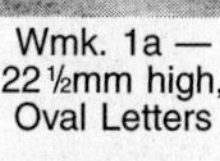
Wmk. 1a — 22½mm high, Oval Letters

Wmk. 1b — 21mm high, Round Letters

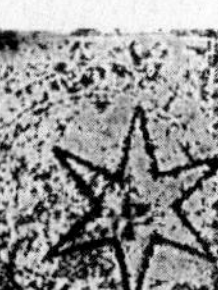
Wmk. 6 — Large Star

Wmk. 290 — Lotus and "Sri" Multiple

Queen Victoria
A1 A2

**1857** **Engr.** **Wmk. 6** ***Imperf.***
**Blued Paper**

| No. | Type | Description | Unused | Used |
|---|---|---|---|---|
| **1** | A1 | 1p blue | — | 500. |
| **2** | A1 | 6p plum | *12,000.* | 575. |

**1857-59** **White Paper**

| No. | Type | Description | Unused | Used |
|---|---|---|---|---|
| **3** | A1 | 1p dp turq | 1,100. | 45.00 |
| **4** | A1 | 2p deep grn | 210.00 | 65.00 |
| *a.* | | 2p yellow green | 575.00 | 105.00 |
| **5** | A2 | 4p dl rose ('59) | *75,000.* | 5,250. |
| **6** | A1 | 5p org brown | 1,750. | 175.00 |
| **6A** | A1 | 6p plum | *2,850.* | 170.00 |
| **7** | A1 | 6p brown | *10,500.* | 700.00 |
| **8** | A2 | 8p brown ('59) | *30,000.* | 1,750. |
| **9** | A2 | 9p lil brn ('59) | *62,500.* | 1,050. |
| **10** | A1 | 10p vermilion | 950.00 | 350.00 |
| **11** | A1 | 1sh violet | 5,750. | 260.00 |
| **12** | A2 | 1sh9p green ('59) | 1,000. | 925.00 |
| *a.* | | 1sh9p yellow green | 5,500. | 3,500. |
| **13** | A2 | 2sh blue ('59) | 6,750. | 1,400. |

Stamps of type A2 frequently have repaired corners.

Nos. 3-4 exist unofficially rouletted. See the *Scott Classic Specialized Catalogue of Stamps & Covers* for listings.

Beware of Nos. 17-57 trimmed to resemble Nos. 3-13. Values are for stamps with clear margins on all sides.

No. 5 was reproduced by the collotype process in a souvenir sheet distributed at the London International Stamp Exhibition 1950. The paper is unwatermarked.

A3

**1857-58** **Typo.** **Unwmk.**

| No. | Type | Description | Unused | Used |
|---|---|---|---|---|
| **14** | A3 | ½p lilac ('58) | 200. | *250.* |
| **15** | A3 | ½p lilac, *bluish* | 4,250. | 650. |

Values are for stamps without cracking of the surface, and examples showing cracking should be discounted.

***Clean-Cut Perf. 14 to 15½***

**1861** **Wmk. 6** **Engr.**

| No. | Type | Description | Unused | Used |
|---|---|---|---|---|
| **17** | A1 | 1p blue | 210.00 | 18.00 |
| **18** | A1 | 2p yel grn | 275.00 | 27.50 |
| *b.* | | Vert. pair, imperf between | | — |
| **19** | A2 | 4p dull rose | 2,300. | 325.00 |
| **20** | A1 | 5p org brown | 125.00 | 10.00 |
| **20A** | A1 | 6p brown | 3,200. | 190.00 |
| *b.* | | 6p bister brown | 2,250. | 290.00 |
| **21** | A2 | 8p brown | 2,600. | 575.00 |
| **22** | A2 | 9p lilac brown | 16,000. | 275.00 |
| **23** | A1 | 1sh violet | 145.00 | 17.50 |
| **24** | A2 | 2sh blue | 4,750. | 875.00 |

***Rough Perf. 14 to 15½***

| No. | Type | Description | Unused | Used |
|---|---|---|---|---|
| **25** | A1 | 1p blue | 170.00 | 12.50 |
| *b.* | | Blued paper | 850.00 | 27.50 |
| **26** | A1 | 2p yel green | 475.00 | 92.50 |
| **27** | A2 | 4p rose red | 600.00 | 130.00 |
| **28** | A1 | 6p olive brown | 1,250. | 120.00 |
| *a.* | | 6p deep brown | 1,350. | 130.00 |
| *b.* | | 6p bister brown | 2,300. | 200.00 |
| **29** | A2 | 8p brown | 1,775. | 675.00 |
| **30** | A2 | 8p yel brown | 1,800. | 425.00 |
| **31** | A2 | 9p olive brown | 875.00 | 85.00 |
| **32** | A2 | 9p deep brown | 160.00 | 120.00 |
| **33** | A1 | 10p vermilion | 325.00 | 30.00 |
| *a.* | | Imperf. vert., pair | | — |
| **34** | A1 | 1sh violet | 300.00 | 17.50 |
| **35** | A2 | 1sh9p green | 825.00 | |
| **36** | A2 | 2sh blue | 800.00 | 160.00 |

The 1sh9p green was never placed in use.

**1863** ***Perf. 12½***

| No. | Type | Description | Unused | Used |
|---|---|---|---|---|
| **37** | A1 | 10p vermilion | 340.00 | 22.50 |

**1864** **Typo.** **Unwmk.**

| No. | Type | Description | Unused | Used |
|---|---|---|---|---|
| **38** | A3 | ½p lilac | 225.00 | 175.00 |

See note following No. 15.

**1862** **Engr.** ***Perf. 13***

| No. | Type | Description | Unused | Used |
|---|---|---|---|---|
| **39** | A1 | 1p blue | 180.00 | 7.00 |
| **40** | A1 | 5p car brown | 1,850. | 175.00 |
| **41** | A1 | 6p deep brown | 210.00 | 30.00 |
| **42** | A2 | 9p brown | 1,400. | 120.00 |
| **43** | A1 | 1sh grayish violet | 2,100. | 95.00 |

Parts of the papermaker's sheet watermark, "T. H. SAUNDERS 1862," may be found on some examples of Nos. 39-43.

***Perf. 12***

| No. | Type | Description | Unused | Used |
|---|---|---|---|---|
| **44** | A1 | 1p blue | 1,900. | 150.00 |
| *a.* | | Horiz. pair, imperf. btwn. | | *18,000.* |

**Two Types of Watermark Crown and CC (1)**

**1863-67** **Typo.** **Wmk. 1a** ***Perf. 12½***

| No. | Type | Description | Unused | Used |
|---|---|---|---|---|
| **45** | A3 | ½p lilac | 80.00 | 50.00 |
| *a.* | | ½p reddish lilac | 90.00 | 65.00 |

### Engr.

**46** A1 1p blue 180.00 9.00
*a.* 1p dark blue 180.00 9.00
*c.* Perf. 11½ 3,400. 350.00
**47** A1 2p gray green 100.00 15.00
**48** A1 2p emerald 190.00 120.00
**48A** A1 2p yel green *10,000.* 475.00
**48B** A1 2p bottle green *4,250.*
**49** A1 2p olive 325.00 275.00
**50** A2 4p rose 550.00 130.00
*a.* 4p carmine rose 900.00 275.00
**51** A1 5p car brown 325.00 110.00
**52** A1 5p olive green 1,700. 350.00
*e.* 5p deep sage green 2,000. 425.00
**53** A1 6p choc brown 250.00 7.50
*a.* Perf. 13 2,750. 250.00
*b.* 6p black brown 300.00 11.50
*c.* As "b," double impression *4,500.*
*d.* 6p reddish brown 350.00 14.00
**54** A2 8p red brown 150.00 80.00
**55** A2 9p brown 360.00 52.50
*c.* Perf. 13 6,750. 1,100.
**56** A1 10p vermilion 5,000. 70.00
*a.* 10p orange 7,500. 500.00
**58** A2 2sh blue 375.00 45.00

The ½p, 1p blue, 2p olive, 4p and 5p green exist imperf.

### Wmk. 1b

*46d* A1 1p blue 325.00 17.50
*e.* 1p dark blue 275.00 16.00
*49d* A1 2p orange yellow 135.00 8.00
*e.* 2p olive yellow 175.00 14.00
*f.* 2p olive green 175.00 20.00
*50b* A2 4p rose 325.00 65.00
*c.* 4p carmine rose 80.00 30.00
*52b* A1 5p myrtle green 100.00 25.00
*c.* 5p olive green 150.00 27.50
*d.* 5p bronze green 60.00 *60.00*
*53e* A1 6p chocolate brown 140.00 11.00
*f.* 6p brown 190.00 9.00
*54a* A2 8p red brown 140.00 80.00
*55a* A2 9p dark brown 70.00 8.00
*b.* 9p bister brown 975.00 40.00
*56b* A1 10p orange 150.00 18.00
*c.* 10p orange red 90.00 18.00
*d.* 10p vermilion *5,600.* 170.00
**57** A1 1sh purple 150.00 12.00
*a.* 1sh reddish lilac 325.00 32.50
*58a* A2 2sh deep blue 160.00 17.50
*b.* 2sh indigo 300.00 22.50

The 1p blue and 6p brown exist imperf.
For overprints see Nos. O2, O4-O7.

A4

A5

**1866 Typo. Wmk. 1 Perf. 12½**
**59** A5 3p rose 275.00 105.00
*a.* Imperf., pair *1,000.*

For overprint see No. O3.

**1868 Perf. 14**
**61** A4 1p blue 30.00 12.00
*a.* Imperf., pair —
**62** A5 3p rose 95.00 52.50

For overprint see No. O1.

A6 A7

A8 A9

A10 A11

A12 A13

A14 A15

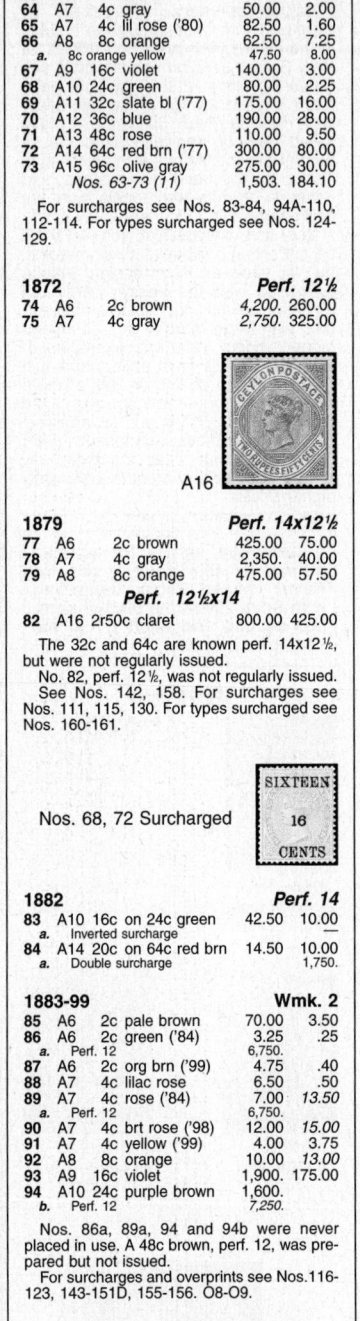

**1872-80 Perf. 14**
**63** A6 2c brown 37.50 4.50
**64** A7 4c gray 50.00 2.00
**65** A7 4c lil rose ('80) 82.50 1.60
**66** A8 8c orange 62.50 7.25
*a.* 8c orange yellow 47.50 8.00
**67** A9 16c violet 140.00 3.00
**68** A10 24c green 80.00 2.25
**69** A11 32c slate bl ('77) 175.00 16.00
**70** A12 36c blue 190.00 28.00
**71** A13 48c rose 110.00 9.50
**72** A14 64c red brn ('77) 300.00 80.00
**73** A15 96c olive gray 275.00 30.00
*Nos. 63-73 (11)* 1,503. 184.10

For surcharges see Nos. 83-84, 94A-110, 112-114. For types surcharged see Nos. 124-129.

**1872 Perf. 12½**
**74** A6 2c brown *4,200.* 260.00
**75** A7 4c gray *2,750.* 325.00

A16

**1879 Perf. 14x12½**
**77** A6 2c brown 425.00 75.00
**78** A7 4c gray 2,350. 40.00
**79** A8 8c orange 475.00 57.50

**Perf. 12½x14**
**82** A16 2r50c claret 800.00 425.00

The 32c and 64c are known perf. 14x12½, but were not regularly issued.
No. 82, perf. 12½, was not regularly issued.
See Nos. 142, 158. For surcharges see Nos. 111, 115, 130. For types surcharged see Nos. 160-161.

Nos. 68, 72 Surcharged

SIXTEEN 16 CENTS

**1882 Perf. 14**
**83** A10 16c on 24c green 42.50 10.00
*a.* Inverted surcharge —
**84** A14 20c on 64c red brn 14.50 10.00
*a.* Double surcharge 1,750.

**1883-99 Wmk. 2**
**85** A6 2c pale brown 70.00 3.50
**86** A6 2c green ('84) 3.25 .25
*a.* Perf. 12 6,750.
**87** A6 2c org brn ('99) 4.75 .40
**88** A7 4c lilac rose 6.50 .50
**89** A7 4c rose ('84) 7.00 *13.50*
*a.* Perf. 12 6,750.
**90** A7 4c brt rose ('98) 12.00 *15.00*
**91** A7 4c yellow ('99) 4.00 3.75
**92** A8 8c orange 10.00 *13.00*
**93** A9 16c violet 1,900. 175.00
**94** A10 24c purple brown 1,600.
*b.* Perf. 12 *7,250.*

Nos. 86a, 89a, 94 and 94b were never placed in use. A 48c brown, perf. 12, was prepared but not issued.
For surcharges and overprints see Nos.116-123, 143-151D, 155-156. O8-O9.

### Issues of 1872-82 Surcharged

Postage & FIVE CENTS Revenue
a

TEN CENTS
b

Twenty-five Cents
c

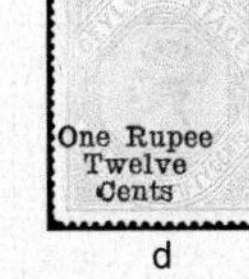
One Rupee Twelve Cents
d

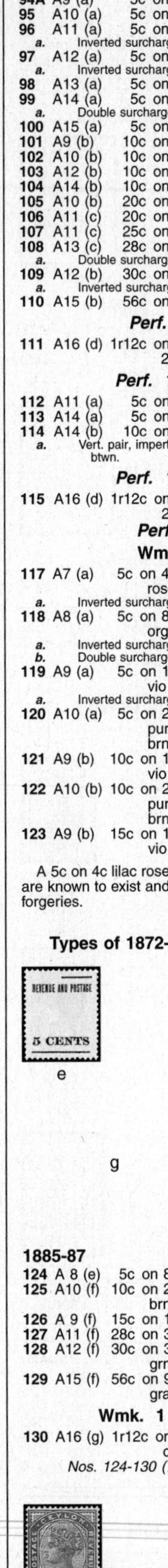

**1885 Wmk. 1 Perf. 14**
**94A** A9 (a) 5c on 16c *3,000.*
**95** A10 (a) 5c on 24c *6,000.* 100.00
**96** A11 (a) 5c on 32c 67.50 16.00
*a.* Inverted surcharge 2,700.
**97** A12 (a) 5c on 36c 275.00 13.50
*a.* Inverted surcharge *2,750.*
**98** A13 (a) 5c on 48c 2,300. 65.00
**99** A14 (a) 5c on 64c 135.00 12.50
*a.* Double surcharge 3,250.
**100** A15 (a) 5c on 96c 525.00 75.00
**101** A9 (b) 10c on 16c *11,000.* 3,000.
**102** A10 (b) 10c on 24c 475.00 130.00
**103** A12 (b) 10c on 36c 450.00 260.00
**104** A14 (b) 10c on 64c 425.00 240.00
**105** A10 (b) 20c on 24c 80.00 30.00
**106** A11 (c) 20c on 32c 87.50 75.00
**107** A11 (c) 25c on 32c 26.00 10.00
**108** A13 (c) 28c on 48c 40.00 11.50
*a.* Double surcharge 3,000.
**109** A12 (b) 30c on 36c 17.00 13.00
*a.* Inverted surcharge 300.00 140.00
**110** A15 (b) 56c on 96c 35.00 27.50

**Perf. 12½**
**111** A16 (d) 1r12c on 2r50c 700.00 110.00

**Perf. 14x12½**
**112** A11 (a) 5c on 32c 800.00 52.50
**113** A14 (a) 5c on 64c 900.00 52.50
**114** A14 (b) 10c on 64c 90.00 *160.00*
*a.* Vert. pair, imperf. btwn. 6,000.

**Perf. 12½x14**
**115** A16 (d) 1r12c on 2r50c 110.00 47.50

**Perf. 14**
**Wmk. 2**
**117** A7 (a) 5c on 4c rose 25.00 5.50
*a.* Inverted surcharge *325.00*
**118** A8 (a) 5c on 8c org 90.00 12.00
*a.* Inverted surcharge *4,250.*
*b.* Double surcharge *3,500.*
**119** A9 (a) 5c on 16c vio 175.00 18.00
*a.* Inverted surcharge *240.00*
**120** A10 (a) 5c on 24c pur brn — 540.00
**121** A9 (b) 10c on 16c vio 12,000. 1,650.
**122** A10 (b) 10c on 24c pur brn 18.00 11.00
**123** A9 (b) 15c on 16c vio 15.00 11.50

A 5c on 4c lilac rose and a 5c on 24c green are known to exist and are considered to be a forgeries.

### Types of 1872-80 Surcharged

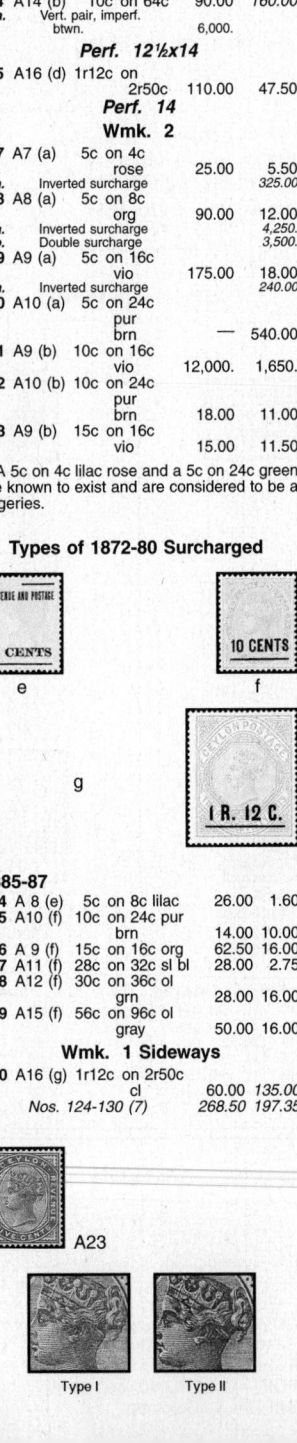

REVENUE AND POSTAGE 5 CENTS
e

10 CENTS
f

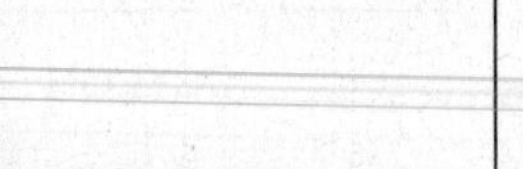
1 R. 12 C.
g

**1885-87**
**124** A 8 (e) 5c on 8c lilac 26.00 1.60
**125** A10 (f) 10c on 24c pur brn 14.00 10.00
**126** A 9 (f) 15c on 16c org 62.50 16.00
**127** A11 (f) 28c on 32c sl bl 28.00 2.75
**128** A12 (f) 30c on 36c ol grn 28.00 16.00
**129** A15 (f) 56c on 96c ol gray 50.00 16.00

**Wmk. 1 Sideways**
**130** A16 (g) 1r12c on 2r50c cl 60.00 *135.00*
*Nos. 124-130 (7)* 268.50 197.35

A23

Type I Type II

FIVE CENTS
Type I — Thin lines in background. Hair and curl clear.
Type II — Thicker lines in background. Heavier shading under chin.

**1886 Wmk. 2**
**131** A23 5c lilac, type I 3.75 .25
*a.* Type II 3.75 .25

For overprint see No. O12.

A24

**1886-1900**
**132** A24 3c org brn & green ('93) 6.50 .50
**133** A24 3c green ('00) 4.75 .60
**134** A24 6c rose & blk ('99) 3.00 .50
**135** A24 12c ol grn & car ('00) 5.50 *10.00*
**136** A24 15c olive green 10.00 2.40
**137** A24 15c ultra ('00) 8.00 1.50
**138** A24 25c yel brn 7.50 2.00
*a.* 25c yel brn, value in ol yel 155.00 90.00
**139** A24 28c slate 27.00 1.50
**140** A24 30c vio & org brown ('93) 4.75 3.50
**141** A24 75c blk & org brown ('00) 11.00 10.00
*Nos. 132-141 (10)* 88.00 *32.50*

Numeral tablet of 3c, 12c and 75c has lined background with colorless value and "c."
For surcharges & overprints see Nos. 152-154, 157, 159, O10-O11, O13-O17.

**1887 Wmk. 1**
**142** A16 1r12c claret 37.50 32.50

For overprint see No. O18.

Issue of 1883-84 Surcharged

TWO CENTS

**1888-90 Wmk. 2**
**143** A7 2c on 4c lilac rose 1.50 1.00
*a.* Inverted surcharge 25.00 24.00
*b.* Double surcharge, one invtd. 375.00
**144** A7 2c on 4c rose 2.75 .50
*a.* Inverted surcharge 20.00 *21.00*
*b.* Double surcharge 400.00

Surcharged

Two

**145** A7 2c on 4c lilac rose 1.10 .30
*a.* Inverted surcharge 42.50 *42.50*
*b.* Double surcharge 125.00 130.00
*c.* Double surcharge, one invtd. 92.50 95.00
**146** A7 2c on 4c rose 10.00 .25
*a.* Double surcharge, one invtd. 110.00 *135.00*
*b.* Double surcharge 110.00 *135.00*
*c.* Inverted surcharge 425.00

Surcharged

2 Cents

**147** A7 2c on 4c lilac rose 80.00 45.00
*a.* Inverted surcharge 175.00 47.50
*b.* Double surcharge, one inverted 240.00
**148** A7 2c on 4c rose 4.50 .80
*a.* Inverted surcharge 19.00 10.00
*b.* Double surcharge, one inverted 10.00 *15.00*
*c.* Double surcharge 210.00 160.00

Surcharged

Two Cents

**149** A7 2c on 4c lilac rose 67.50 30.00
*a.* Inverted surcharge 200.00 32.50
**150** A7 2c on 4c rose 3.00 1.25
*a.* Inverted surcharge 19.00 10.00
*b.* Double surcharge 160.00 150.00
*c.* Double surcharge, one inverted 20.00 12.50

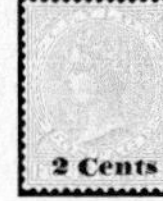


Surcharged

151 A7 2c on 4c rose 15.00 1.10
a. Inverted surcharge 25.00 10.00
b. Double surcharge 145.00 150.00
c. Double surch., one invtd. 27.50 13.50
i. "S" of "Cents" inverted 650.00 350.00
151D A7 2c on 4c lilac rose 67.50 37.50
e. Inverted surcharge 100.00 45.00
f. Double surcharge 425.00
g. Double surch., one invtd. 150.00 150.00
h. "S" of "Cents" inverted 725.00

Counterfeit errors of surcharges of Nos. 143 to 151D are prevalent.

No. 136 Surcharged

**1890**
152 A24 5c on 15c ol green 4.00 2.75
a. "FIve" instead of "Five" 135.00 95.00
b. "REVENUE" omitted 210.00 190.00
c. Inverted surcharge 62.50 *75.00*
d. Double surcharge 125.00 *145.00*
e. As "a," inverted surcharge — 1,800.
f. Inverted "s" in "Cents" 130.00 *105.00*
g. As "f," inverted surcharge 2,200.
h. As "b," invtd. "s" in "Cents" 1,700.

Nos. 138-139 Surcharged

**1891**
153 A24 15c on 25c brown 19.00 20.00
154 A24 15c on 28c slate 20.00 10.00

Nos. 88, 89 and 139 Surcharged

**1892**
155 A7 3c on 4c lilac rose 2.00 *3.50*
156 A7 3c on 4c rose 9.50 *13.50*
a. Double surcharge, one invtd.
157 A24 3c on 28c slate 6.75 6.25
a. Double surcharge 180.00
*Nos. 155-157 (3)* 18.25 *23.25*

### Type of 1879

**1898**
158 A16 2r50c violet, *red* 42.50 *65.00*

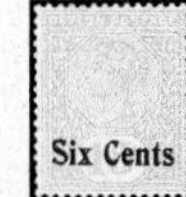


No. 136 Surcharged in Black

**1899**
159 A24 6c on 15c olive green 1.35 *.85*

### Surcharged Type "g" in Black

**1899 Wmk. 1**
160 A16 1r50c on 2r50c gray 22.50 *52.50*
161 A16 2r25c on 2r50c yel 47.50 *85.00*

A35

**1900 Wmk. 1**
162 A35 1r50c car rose 35.00 *52.50*
163 A35 2r25c dull blue 37.50 *52.50*

Nos. 166-292 exist in many different shades, representing different printings for each stamp.

King Edward VII
A36 A37

A38

A39

A40

**1903-05 Wmk. 2**
166 A36 2c org brown 2.10 .25
167 A37 3c green 2.10 1.10
168 A37 4c yel & blue 2.10 *5.50*
169 A38 5c dull lilac 3.00 .65
170 A39 6c car rose 10.00 1.60
171 A37 12c ol grn & car 5.50 *11.50*
172 A40 15c ultra 6.75 3.50
173 A40 25c bister 6.00 *11.00*
174 A40 30c vio & green 3.50 *4.25*
175 A37 75c bl & org ('05) 4.00 *24.00*
176 A40 1r50c gray ('04) 67.50 67.50
177 A40 2r25c brn & grn ('04) 90.00 65.00
*Nos. 166-177 (12)* 202.55 195.85
Set, never hinged 400.00

For overprints see Nos. O19-O24.

**1904-10 Wmk. 3**
178 A36 2c orange brown 2.50 .25
a. 2c orange 1.60 .55
179 A37 3c green 1.75 .25
180 A37 4c yel & blue 3.00 1.60
181 A38 5c dull lilac 3.50 1.30
a. Booklet pane of 12
b. 5c dull lilac, "chalky paper" 7.00 .75
182 A39 6c car rose 5.25 .25
183 A40 10c ol grn & vio ('10) 2.60 3.50
184 A37 12c ol grn & car 1.75 *1.90*
185 A40 15c ultra 3.50 .65
186 A40 25c bister ('05) 6.25 4.00
187 A40 25c slate ('10) 2.75 3.00
188 A40 30c vio & grn ('05) 2.75 *3.25*
189 A40 50c brown ('10) 4.25 *7.75*
190 A37 75c bl & org ('05) 5.50 *8.25*
191 A40 1r vio, *yel* ('10) 8.50 *12.50*
192 A40 1r50c gray ('05) 45.00 20.00
193 A40 2r scar, *yel* ('10) 16.00 *30.00*
194 A40 2r25c brn & grn 24.00 *32.50*
195 A40 5r blk, *grn* ('10) 47.50 *115.00*
196 A40 10r blk, *red* ('10) 135.00 *290.00*
*Nos. 178-196 (19)* 321.35 *535.95*
Set, never hinged 600.00

A41

A42

**1908**
197 A41 5c deep red violet 7.50 .25
a. Booklet pane of 12
198 A42 6c carmine rose 3.50 .25

**1911, July 5**
199 A40 3c green 1.10 .85

A44

King George V — A45

Type I

Type II

3 AND 6 CENTS
Type I — Small "c" after value, 2¼mm wide and 2mm high.
Type II — Large "c" after value, 2½mm wide and 2¼mm high.
1, 5 AND 9 CENTS are Type II, other denominations Type I.

For description of dies I and II see "Dies of British Colonial Stamps" in the Table of Contents.

**1912-25 Die I Wmk. 3**
200 A44 1c dp brn (Die Ib) ('20) 1.20 .25
201 A44 2c brown org .45 .30
202 A44 3c dp grn (Die Ia, type II) 5.25 .50
a. 3c deep green, die I, type I 6.75 2.40
203 A44 5c red violet 1.20 .70
a. 5c purple 12.00 3.00
204 A44 6c car (Die Ib, type II) 1.50 1.60
a. 6c carmine, die I, type I 20.00 1.30
b. As "a," bklt. pane of 6
205 A44 10c olive green 3.50 2.00
206 A44 15c ultra 3.00 1.50

### Chalky Paper

207 A44 25c yel & ultra 1.75 2.10
208 A44 30c green & vio 4.75 3.75
209 A44 50c black & scar 1.75 *2.10*
210 A44 1r violet, *yel* 6.00 4.25
211 A44 2r blk & red, *yel* 4.00 *15.00*
212 A44 5r blk, *green* 20.00 *47.50*
a. 5r black, *bl grn*, olive back 25.00 *50.00*
b. 5r blk, *emer* (Die II) ('20) 52.50 *120.00*
213 A44 10r vio & blk, *red* 85.00 *105.00*
a. Die II ('20) 95.00 *190.00*
214 A44 20r blk & red, *bl* 175.00 *170.00*
215 A45 50r dull violet 750.00 *1,500.*
216 A45 100r gray black 3,250.
217 A45 500r gray green *8,750.*
218 A45 1000r vio, *red* ('25) *37,500.*
*Nos. 200-214 (15)* 314.35 *356.55*
Set, never hinged 600.00

Although Nos. 217 and 218 were theoretically available for postage it is not probable that they were ever used for other than fiscal purposes.
The 1r through 100r with revenue cancellations sell for minimal prices.
For surcharge & overprints see Nos. 223, MR1-MR3.

### Die I

**1913-14 Surface-colored Paper**
220 A44 1r violet, *yellow* 6.50 *5.75*
221 A44 2r black & red, *yel* 4.25 *17.50*
222 A44 5r black, *green* 26.00 *42.50*
*Nos. 220-222 (3)* 36.75 *65.75*

No. 203 Surcharged

**1918**
223 A44 1c on 5c red violet 3.50 *3.50*
a. 1c on 5c purple .25 .30

For overprint see No. MR4.

### Die I

**1921-33 Wmk. 4 Ordinary Paper**
225 A44 1c dp brn (Die Ib) ('27) 1.20 .40
226 A44 2c brn org (Die II) .85 .30
227 A44 3c green (Die Ia, type II) 5.75 .90
228 A44 3c slate (Die Ia, type II) ('22) .90 .25
229 A44 5c red vio (Die I) .70 .25
230 A44 6c carmine (Die Ib, type II) 4.00 .90
231 A44 6c vio (Die Ib, type II) ('22) 3.00 .25
232 A44 9c red, *yel* (Die II) ('26) 3.25 .45
233 A44 10c olive green 1.60 .45
a. Die II 2.10 .70
234 A44 12c scarlet, Die II 1.20 *4.00*
a. Die I ('25) 10.00 *10.00*
235 A44 15c ultramarine 4.00 *22.50*
236 A44 15c green, *yel*, Die II 5.00 1.20
a. Die I ('22) 5.75 *3.00*
237 A44 20c ultra, Die II ('24) 4.25 .50
a. Die I ('22) 6.00 *7.25*
238 A44 25c yel & blue 3.25 2.25
a. Die II 5.75 1.50

For surcharges see Nos. 248-249.

### Chalky Paper

239 A44 30c green & violet 1.90 *6.75*
a. Die II 6.25 1.50
240 A44 50c blk & scar (Die II) 2.25 .95
a. Die I 65.00 *100.00*
241 A44 1r vio, *yel*, Die II 26.00 *42.50*
a. Die I 16.00 *52.50*
242 A44 2r blk & red, *yel* (Die II) 8.50 *15.00*
243 A44 5r blk, *emer*, (Die II) 52.50 *97.50*
244 A44 20r blk & red, *bl*, (Die II) 325.00 *425.00*
245 A45 50r dull vio 825.00 *1,500.*
246 A45 100r gray black 3,250.
247 A45 100r ultra & dl vio ('27) 2,750.
*Nos. 225-244 (20)* 455.10 622.30
Set, never hinged 725.00

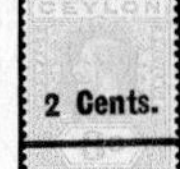


Nos. 228, 231 Surcharged

**1926**
248 A44 2c on 3c slate 3.50 1.20
a. Double surcharge 85.00
b. Bar omitted 90.00 *100.00*
249 A44 5c on 6c violet 1.25 .45
a. Double surcharge

A46

**1927-29 Chalky Paper Wmk. 4**
254 A46 1r red vio & dl vio ('28) 3.00 1.50
255 A46 2r car & green ('29) 4.50 3.25
256 A46 5r brn vio & grn ('28) 17.50 *30.00*
257 A46 10r org & green 75.00 *160.00*
258 A46 20r ultra & dl vio 325.00 *450.00*
*Nos. 254-258 (5)* 425.00 *644.75*
Set, never hinged 700.00

Nos. 256-258 are valued with postal cancellations. Revenue cancellations are more common.

Common Design Types pictured following the introduction.

### Silver Jubilee Issue
Common Design Type

**1935, May 6 Engr. *Perf. 13½x14***
260 CD301 6c gray blk & ultra .70 .35
261 CD301 9c indigo & green .70 2.50
262 CD301 20c blue & brown 4.00 2.75
263 CD301 50c brt vio & ind 5.00 16.00
*Nos. 260-263 (4)* 10.40 21.60
Set, never hinged 20.00

Tapping Rubber Tree A47

Colombo Harbor A49

Adam's Peak — A48

Picking Tea — A50

Coconut Palms A53

Rice Terraces A51

River Scene — A52

Temple of the Tooth, Kandy — A54

Ancient Reservoir — A55

Wild Elephants — A56

View of Trincomalee — A57

***Perf. 11x11½ (266, 267), 11½x11 (269, 269, 271, 272, 274), 11½x13 (264, 270), 13x11½ (265), 14 (273)***

**1935-36** **Wmk. 4**

**264** A47 2c car rose & blk .45 *.55*
*a.* Perf. 14 12.00 .55
**265** A48 3c olive & black 1.40 *.55*
*a.* Perf. 14 40.00 *.40*
**266** A49 6c blue & black .45 .40
**267** A50 9c org red & ol grn 1.50 .90
**268** A51 10c dk vio & blk 1.75 *3.25*
**269** A52 15c grn & org brn 2.25 .70
**270** A53 20c ultra & black 2.75 *3.50*
**271** A54 25c choc & dk ultra 2.00 1.75
**272** A55 30c green & lake 3.00 *3.75*
**273** A56 50c dk vio & blk 17.50 2.50
**274** A57 1r brown & vio 40.00 29.00
*Nos. 264-274 (11)* 73.05 46.85
Set, never hinged 220.00

Issued: 2c, 15c, 25c, 5/1/35; 10c, 6/1/35; 1r, 7/1/35; 30c, 8/1/35; 3c, 10/1/35; 6c, 9c, 20c, 50c, 1/1/36.

**Coronation Issue**
Common Design Type

**1937, May 12** ***Perf. 11x11½***

**275** CD302 6c dark carmine .75 1.10
*a.* Booklet pane of 10 25.00
**276** CD302 9c deep green 3.00 *4.75*
*a.* Booklet pane of 10 300.00
**277** CD302 20c deep ultra 4.50 *4.50*
*Nos. 275-277 (3)* 8.25 10.35
Set, never hinged 16.00

**Types of 1935 with "Postage & Revenue Removed" and Picturing George VI and**

Sigiriya (Lion Rock) A61

Ancient Guard Stone A68

George VI — A69

***Perf. 11x11½, 11½x11; 12 (#286)***

**1938-52** **Engr.** **Wmk. 4**

**278** A47 2c car rose & blk ('44) .45 *2.00*
*a.* Perf. 13½x13 ('38) 100.00 2.00
*b.* Perf. 13½ ('38) 2.00 .25
*c.* Perf. 12 ('49) 1.25 *5.75*
*d.* Perf. 11½x13 ('38) 10.00 3.75
**279** A48 3c dk grn & blk ('42) .50 .25
*a.* Perf. 13x13½ ('38) 225.00 17.50
*b.* Perf. 14 ('41) 100.00 1.10
*c.* Perf. 13½ ('38) 3.50 .25
*d.* Perf. 12 ('46) .70 *.95*
*e.* Perf. 13x11½ 8.00 3.75
**280** A49 6c blue & black .25 .25
**281** A61 10c blue & black 1.75 .25
**282** A52 15c red brn & grn 1.25 .25
**283** A50 20c dull bl & blk 2.25 .25
**284** A54 25c choc & dk ultra 3.25 .30
**285** A55 30c dk grn & rose car 8.00 3.75
**286** A56 50c dk vio & blk ('46) 2.75 .25
*a.* Perf. 14 ('42) 90.00 29.00
*b.* Perf. 13x11½ ('38) 150.00 52.50
*c.* Perf. 13x13½ ('38) 300.00 3.00
*d.* Perf. 13½ ('38) 15.00 1.00
*e.* Perf. 11½x11 ('42) 4.00 5.00
**287** A57 1r dk brn & bl ('46) 10.50 2.00
**288** A68 2r dark car & blk 9.25 5.00

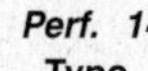

***Perf. 14***
**Typo.**

**289** A69 5r brn vio & grn 27.50 19.00
**289A** A69 10r yel org & dl grn ('52) 75.00 50.00
*Nos. 278-289A (13)* 142.70 83.55
Set, never hinged 265.00

No. 289A differs from type A69 in having "REVENUE" inscribed vertically at either side of the frame. This revenue 10r was valid for postage Dec. 1, 1952-Mar. 14, 1954.

Used examples of Nos. 278-289A are valued postally used.

See Nos. 292, 295. For surcharges see Nos. 290-291.

**Catalogue values for unused stamps in this section, from this point to the end of the section, are for Never Hinged items.**

No. 283 Surcharged in Black

**1940, Nov. 5** ***Perf. 11x11½***

**290** A50 3c on 20c dull bl & blk *4.50 4.50*

No. 280 Surcharged

**1941, May 10**

**291** A49 3c on 6c blue & black .65 *1.00*

Coconut Palms — A70

**1943-47** **Wmk. 4** **Engr.** ***Perf. 12***

**292** A70 5c red org & ol grn ('47) 2.10 .35
*a.* Perf. 13½ ('43) .35 .25

**Peace Issue**
Common Design Type

**1946, Dec. 10** ***Perf. 13½x14***

**293** CD303 6c deep blue .30 *.35*
**294** CD303 15c brown .30 *1.75*

**Guard Stone Type of 1938**

**1947, Mar. 15** ***Perf. 11x11½***

**295** A68 2r violet & black 2.75 *3.00*

Parliament Building, Colombo — A71

Adam's Peak — A72

Dagoba at Anuradhapura A74

Temple of the Tooth, Kandy A73

**1947, Nov. 25** ***Perf. 11x12, 12x11***

**296** A71 6c deep ultra & black .25 .25
**297** A72 10c car, orange & black .25 *.40*
**298** A73 15c red vio & grnsh blk .25 *.80*
**299** A74 25c brt green & bister .25 *1.75*
*Nos. 296-299 (4)* 1.00 3.20

New constitution of 1947.

National Flag A75

D. S. Senanayake A76

**Engr., Flag Typo. (A75); Engr. (A76)**
***Perf. 12½x12, 12x12½, 13x12½***

**1949** **Wmk. 4**

**300** A75 4c org brn, car & yel .25 .25
**301** A76 5c dark green & brn .25 .25

**Wmk. 290**

**302** A75 15c red org, car & yel 1.10 1.00
**303** A76 25c dp blue & brown .25 1.00
*Nos. 300-303 (4)* 1.85 2.50

Size of No. 302: 28x22¼mm.
1st anniv. of Ceylon's independence.
Issued: Nos. 300-301, Feb. 4; Nos. 302-303, Apr. 5.

A77

A77a

A78

**Wmk. 290**

**1949, Oct. 10** **Engr.** ***Perf. 12***

**304** A77 5c dk green & brown .85 .25
**305** A77a 15c dark car & black 1.25 *2.75*
**306** A78 25c ultra & black 1.25 1.25
*Nos. 304-306 (3)* 3.35 4.25

75th anniv. of the UPU.

Kandyan Dancer A79

Kiri Vehera, Polonnaruwa A80

Vesak Orchid A81

Sigiriya A82

Ratmalana, Plane A83

Vatadage Ruins at Madirigiriya A84

**1950, Feb. 4** ***Perf. 12x12½***

**307** A79 4c bright red & choc .25 .25
**308** A80 5c green .25 .25
**309** A81 15c pur & blue green 2.75 .50
**310** A82 30c carmine & yel .40 *.70*

***Perf. 11x11½, 11½x11***

**311** A83 75c red org & blue 8.75 .25
**312** A84 1r red brn & dp blue 2.50 .45
*Nos. 307-312 (6)* 14.90 2.40

See Nos. 340-345.

Coconut Palms A85

Star Orchid A86

**1951-52** **Unwmk.** **Photo.** ***Perf. 11½***

**313** A85 10c gray & dark green 1.25 .75
**314** A86 35c dk grn & rose brn ('52) 1.50 1.50
*a.* Corrected inscription ('54) 6.50 .70

On No. 314a a dot has been added above the third character in the second line of the Tamil inscription.

Issue dates: 10c, Aug. 1; 35c, Feb. 1.
See No. 351.

Mace and Symbols of Industry — A87

***Perf. 12½x14***

**1952, Feb. 23** **Wmk. 290**

**315** A87 5c green .25 .30
**316** A87 15c brt ultramarine .40 .60

Colombo Plan Exhibition, February 1952.

**Coronation Issue**

Queen Elizabeth II — A88

**1953, June 2** **Engr.** ***Perf. 12x12½***

**317** A88 5c green 1.40 .25

Royal Procession — A89

**1954, Apr. 10** ***Perf. 13x12½***

**318** A89 10c deep blue 1.00 .25

Visit of Queen Elizabeth II and the Duke of Edinburgh, 1954.

Sambar in Ruhuna National Park — A90

Rubber Trees — A91

Designs: 3c, Ancient guard stone. 6c and 10r, Harvesting rice. 25c, Sigiriya fresco. 50c, Outrigger fishing canoe. 85c, Tea Picker. 2r, Gal Oya dam. 5r, Bas-relief, "The Lovers."

**1954** **Unwmk.** **Photo.** ***Perf. 11½***

**Size: 21x25½mm**

**319** A90 2c green & brown .25 *1.25*
**320** A90 3c violet & black .25 *1.00*
**321** A90 6c yel grn & blk brn .25 *.30*
**322** A90 25c vio bl, bl & brn orange .25 .25

**Size: 25½x21mm**

**323** A91 40c black brown 5.50 1.25
**324** A91 50c indigo .45 .25

**Size: 23x32½mm, 32½x23mm**

**325** A90 85c dk grn & gray 1.50 .40
**326** A91 2r blue & blk brn 9.25 1.40
**327** A90 5r dp org & blk brn 8.00 1.50
**328** A90 10r brown 52.50 20.00
*Nos. 319-328 (10)* 78.20 27.60

See Nos. 346-356.
Issued: 25c, 50c, 5r, 10r, 3/15; others, 5/15.

Nos. 327-328 with revenue cancellations sell for minimal prices.

King Coconuts — A92

**1954, Dec. 1**
329 A92 10c brown & orange .30 .25
See No. 349.

Symbols of Agriculture — A93

*Perf. 14x14½*
**1955, Dec. 10 Wmk. 290**
330 A93 10c orange & brown .30 .25
Royal Agricultural and Food Exhibition.

House of Representatives A94

**1956, Mar. 26 Unwmk. *Perf. 11½***
**Granite Paper**
331 A94 10c deep green .25 .25
25th anniv. of Prime Minister Sir John Kotelawala's entry into the Ceylon Legislature.

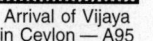

Arrival of Vijaya in Ceylon — A95

Dharmachakra Encircling Globe — A96

**1956, May 23 Granite Paper**
332 A95 3c dull vio gray & saph .50 .25
333 A96 15c ultramarine .25 .25
Birth of Buddha, 2500th anniv. See Nos. B1-B2.

Methods of Transportation — A97

35c, 85c, Ceylon's 1st stamp & coat of arms.

**1957, Apr. 1 Photo. *Perf. 12½x13***
334 A97 4c blue green & ver .70 .50
335 A97 10c blue & vermilion .70 .25

*Perf. 11½*
**Granite Paper**
336 A97 35c blue, yel & brown .40 *.40*
337 A97 85c dull grn, yel & brn .70 *1.25*
*Nos. 334-337 (4)* 2.50 2.40
Ceylon's 1st postage stamps, cent.

### Nos. B1-B2 Overprinted with Black Bars and Squares

**1958, Jan. 15 Unwmk.**
**Granite Paper**
338 SP1 4c dp blue & lt yel .25 .25
a. Inverted overprint 22.50 *37.50*
b. Double overprint 37.50 *50.00*
339 SP1 10c dk gray, yel & brt pink .25 .25
a. Inverted overprint 15.00 *20.00*
The overprint obliterates the surtax and inscription at right.

### Types of 1950-54 Redrawn

*Perf. 12x12½*
**1958-59 Engr. Wmk. 290**
340 A79 4c brt red & chocolate .25 .25
341 A80 5c green .25 *1.60*
342 A81 15c purple & blue grn 3.50 1.10
343 A82 30c car & yel ('59) .25 *1.50*

*Perf. 11½x11*
344 A83 75c red org & bl ('59) 9.50 5.75

*Perf. 11x11½*
345 A84 1r red brn & dp blue .65 .25
*Nos. 340-345 (6)* 14.40 10.45

Issued: 4c, 5/14; 5c, 15c, 1r, 10/1; 30c, 75c, 5/1.
For surcharge see No. 368.

No. 328

No. 356

**1958-59 Unwmk. Photo. *Perf. 11½***
**Granite Paper**
346 A90 2c green & brown .25 .50
347 A90 3c violet & black .25 .70
348 A90 6c yel grn & blk brn .25 .65
349 A92 10c brown & orange .25 .25
350 A90 25c vio bl, bl & brn orange .25 .25
351 A86 35c dk grn & rose brn 7.75 .40
352 A91 50c indigo .25 .25
353 A90 85c dark green & gray 4.50 8.50
354 A91 2r blue & blk brn 2.00 .30
355 A90 5r dp org & blk brn 10.00 .40
356 A90 10r brown 12.00 1.40
*Nos. 346-356 (11)* 37.75 13.60

Designs and sizes of Nos. 340-356 remain as before, but wording has been changed to be predominantly Singhalese. "Ceylon" appears in small letters only in English and Tamil.
Nos. 355-356 with revenue cancellations sell for minimal prices.
Issue dates: 35c, 50c, July 15; 10c, Oct. 1; 85c, May 1, 1959; others, May 14, 1958.
For surcharges, see Sri Lanka Nos. 1572, 1577.

Hands Reaching for UN Symbol — A98

*Perf. 13x12½*
**1958, Dec. 10 Photo. Unwmk.**
357 A98 10c red brown & red .25 .25
358 A98 85c Prus green & red .30 .30
10th anniv. of the signing of the Universal Declaration of Human Rights.

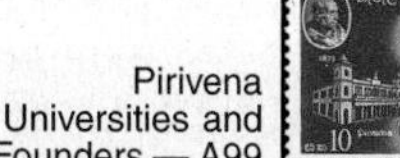
Pirivena Universities and Founders — A99

**1959, Dec. 31**
359 A99 10c brt ultra & dp org .25 .25
Institution of Pirivena Universities; founders Hikkaduwe Sri Sumangala Nayaka Thero and Ratmalane Sri Dharmaloka Nayake Thero.

Uprooted Oak Emblem — A100

**1960, Apr. 7 Photo. *Perf. 11½***
**Granite Paper**
360 A100 4c chocolate & gold .25 *.85*
361 A100 25c vio blue & gold .25 .25
World Refugee Year, 7/1/59-6/30/60.

Prime Minister Bandaranaike — A101

Type I Type II

Two types:
I — Gray hair at temple.
II — Dark hair at temple (redrawn).

**1961, Jan. 8 Granite Paper**
362 A101 10c vio bl & gray bl (I) .30 .25
a. Type II .40 .25
Solomon West Ridgeway Dias Bandaranaike, assassinated Sept. 26, 1959.

Badge of Singhalese Scouts — A102

**1962, Feb. 26 Unwmk. *Perf. 11½***
**Granite Paper**
363 A102 35c dark blue & ocher .35 .25
Boy Scouts of Ceylon, 50th anniv.

Malaria Eradication Emblem — A103

*Perf. 14½x14*
**1962, Apr. 7 Photo. Wmk. 290**
364 A103 25c lt sep, red org & brn .40 .40
WHO drive to eradicate malaria.

Monoplane 1938, and De Havilland Comet IV — A104

**1963, Feb. 28 Unwmk. *Perf. 11½***
**Granite Paper**
365 A104 50c lt grnsh blue & blk .60 .60
25th anniv. of Ceylonese airmail service.

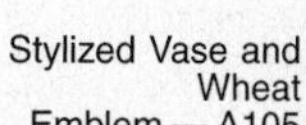

Stylized Vase and Wheat Emblem — A105

**1963, Mar. 21 Granite Paper**
366 A105 5c blue & orange ver 1.00 *2.50*
367 A105 25c olive & brown 3.00 .50
FAO "Freedom from Hunger" campaign.

No. 340 Surcharged

*Perf. 12x12½*
**1963, June 1 Engr. Wmk. 290**
368 A79 2c on 4c brt red & choc .40 .40
a. Inverted surcharge 20.00
b. Double surcharge 40.00

Rural Life — A106

**1963, July 5 Photo. *Perf. 14x14½***
369 A106 60c dull red & black 2.00 .75
50th anniv. of the Cooperative Movement.

Landscape and Elephant — A107

**1963, Dec. 2 Wmk. 290**
370 A107 5c blue & black .65 .45
National Conservation Week.

S.W.R.D. Bandaranaike — A108

*Perf. 11½*
**1963, Sept. 26 Unwmk. Engr.**
**Granite Paper**
371 A108 10c blue .25 .25

**Redrawn**
**Granite Paper**
**1964, July 1 Photo.**
372 A108 10c grnsh gray & bl vio .25 .25
Frame redrawn on No. 372; inscription in bottom panel replaced by ornament.
For surcharge see No. 389.

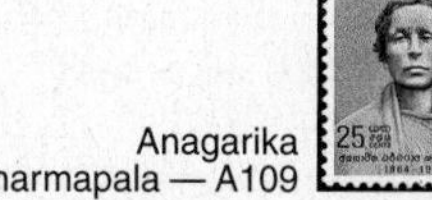
Anagarika Dharmapala — A109

**1964, Sept. 16 Unwmk. *Perf. 11½***
**Granite Paper**
373 A109 25c gray brn & dull yel .25 .25
Anagarika Dharmapala, Buddhist missionary, birth cent.

Ceylon Jungle Fowl A110

Tea Picker A112

Vatadage Ruins at Madirigiriya — A111

Designs: 5c, Hill myna. 15c, Blue peafowl. 75c, Asiatic black-headed oriole. 5r, Girls, working in rice field. 10r, Map of Ceylon on scroll, showing agricultural development stations.

**Wmk. 290, Unwmkd. (20c)**

**1964-69 Photo. *Perf. 14, 11½ (20c)***

**374** A110 5c brt bl, blk, yel & grn 2.00 1.40
**375** A110 15c yel, grn, blk, brt bl & rose 3.75 .30
**376** A111 20c dk red brn, *buff* .25 .25
**377** A110 60c yel & multi 4.50 1.10
*a.* Blue omitted 50.00
*b.* Red omitted 50.00
**378** A110 75c ol, blk, org & brn 3.00 .75
*a.* Souvenir sheet of 4 10.00 14.00
*b.* As "a," overprinted 10.00
**379** A112 1r brown & grn 1.00 .25
*c.* Brown omitted *1,500.*
**379A** A111 5r multicolored 9.50 9.50
**379B** A112 10r brown & multi 22.50 3.50
*Nos. 374-379B (8)* 46.50 17.05

No. 378a contains four imperf. stamps with simulated perforations similar to Nos. 374-375 and 377-378.

No. 378b is overprinted "First National Stamp Exhibition 1967" in two lines of black capitals.

No. 376 is on granite paper.

Issued: 20c, 1r, 10/1/; 5c, 15c, 60c, 75c, 2/5/66; 5r, 8/15/69; 10r, 10/1/69.

See No. 325.

Exhibition Buildings, Cogwheels A113

**"Industrial Exhibition" in Singhalese and English**

**1964, Dec. 1 Unwmk. *Perf. 11***
**380** A113 5c multicolored .25 *.75*

**"Industrial Exhibition" in Singhalese and Tamil**

**381** A113 5c multicolored .25 *.75*
*a.* Pair, #380-381 .35 *2.50*

1965 Industrial Exhibition.

Railroad Trains, 1864-1964 — A114

**"Railway Centenary" in Singhalese and English**

**Wmk. 290**

**1964, Dec. 21 Photo. *Perf. 14***
**382** A114 60c lil rose, bl & yel grn 3.25 .55

**"Railway Centenary" in Singhalese and Tamil**

**383** A114 60c lil rose, bl & yel grn 3.25 .55
*a.* Vertical pair, #382-383 7.75 7.75

Centenary of Ceylonese railroads.

ITU Emblem, Old and New Communication Equipment — A115

**1965, May 17 *Perf. 14***
**384** A115 2c ultra & red 1.60 1.40
**385** A115 30c brown & red 4.50 .55

ITU, centenary.

ICY Emblem — A116

**1965, June 26 Unwmk. *Perf. 11½***

**Granite Paper**

**386** A116 3c rose car & dk bl 1.50 1.25
**387** A116 50c gold, rose car & blk 4.00 .60

International Cooperation Year.

Municipal Council Building — A117

**1965, Oct. 29 Photo. *Perf. 11½***

**Granite Paper**

**388** A117 25c gray & green .30 .30

Centenary of Colombo Municipal Council.

No. 372 Surcharged

**1965, Dec. 18 Photo. *Perf. 11½***
**389** A108 5c on 10c .25 1.25

D. S. Senanayake — A118

**1966, Mar. 22 Unwmk. *Perf. 11½***

**Granite Paper**

**390** A118 10c bright green .80 .25

D. S. Senanayake, first prime minister of Ceylon, 14th death anniv. See No. 418.

View and Arms of Kandy — A119

***Perf. 14x13½***

**1966, June 15 Photo. Wmk. 290**
**391** A119 25c multicolored .25 .25

Centenary of Kandy Municipal Council.

Opening of WHO Headquarters, Geneva — A120

**Unwmk.**

**1966, Oct. 8 Litho. *Perf. 14***
**392** A120 4c multicolored 2.50 3.00
**393** A120 1r multicolored 8.00 1.60

Rice, Map of Ceylon, FAO Emblem — A121

Design: 30c, Rice and globe.

**1966, Oct. 25 Photo. *Perf. 11½***

**Granite Paper**

**394** A121 6c dk green, org & brn .25 *.75*
**395** A121 30c brt blue, org & brn .50 .25

Intl. Rice Year under sponsorship of the FAO.

UNESCO Emblem — A122

**1966, Nov. 3 Litho. *Perf. 12***
**396** A122 3c tan & multi 3.00 *3.50*
**397** A122 50c brt green & multi 7.75 .75

20th anniv. of UNESCO.
For surcharge, see Sri Lanka No. 1578.

Map of Ceylon and UNESCO Emblem — A123

**1966, Dec. 1 Unwmk. *Perf. 14***
**398** A123 2c yel brn, yel & blue .35 *1.00*
**399** A123 2r multicolored 1.50 *2.25*

Intl. Hydrological Decade (UNESCO), 1965-74.

Worshippers at Buddhist Shrine — A124

Designs: 20c, Muhintale Rock. 35c, Sacred Bo Tree. 60c, Adam's Peak.

**1967, Jan. 2 Photo. *Perf. 12***
**400** A124 5c multicolored .25 .25
**401** A124 20c multicolored .25 .25
**402** A124 35c multicolored .25 .25
**403** A124 60c multicolored .25 .25
*Nos. 400-403 (4)* 1.00 1.00

1st anniv. of the Poya Holiday System, Buddhist holiday replacing Sunday.
For surcharge, see Sri Lanka No. 1573.

Dutch Ramparts, Clock Tower and Arms of Galle — A125

**1967, Jan. 5 Litho. *Perf. 14x13½***
**404** A125 25c dk green & multi .80 .25

Centenary of Galle Municipal Council.

Tea Research A126

40c, Tea tasting (cup & loose tea). 50c, Tea picking. 1r, Tea export (crate & freighter).

**1967, Aug. 1 Unwmk. *Perf. 13½***
**405** A126 4c multicolored .60 .60
**406** A126 40c multicolored 1.75 1.60
**407** A126 50c multicolored 1.75 .40
**408** A126 1r multicolored 1.75 .25
*Nos. 405-408 (4)* 5.85 2.85

Centenary of the Ceylonese tea industry.

Elephant and ITY Emblem — A127

**1967, Aug. 15 Litho.**
**409** A127 45c multicolored 3.00 .85

Intl. Tourist Year.

Girl Guide, Jubilee Emblem and Flag — A128

**1967, Sept. 19 *Perf. 12x12½***
**410** A128 3c green & multi .60 .25
**411** A128 25c org yel & multi .90 .25

Ceylon Girl Guide Assoc., 50th anniv.

Henry S. Olcott and Buddhist Flag — A129

***Perf. 13½***

**1967, Dec. 12 Unwmk. Litho.**
**412** A129 15c multicolored .40 .25

Colonel Henry S. Olcott (1832-1907), an American who reorganized the Buddhist hierarchy and school system in Ceylon and was the first president of the Theosophical Society.

Independence Memorial, Colombo — A130

Design: 1r, Flag of Ceylon and mace.

**1968, Feb. 4 Wmk. 290 *Perf. 14***
**413** A130 5c multicolored .25 .45
**414** A130 1r multicolored .50 .25

20th anniversary of independence.

D. B. Jayatilaka — A131

**1968, Feb. 14 Photo.**
**415** A131 25c brown .25 .25

Sir Don Baron Jayatilaka (1868-1944), Buddhist leader and scholar.

Hygiene Institute, Kalutara — A132

***Perf. 11½x12***

**1968, Apr. 4 Litho. Wmk. 290**
**416** A132 50c multicolored .25 .25

WHO, 20th anniversary.

Jet over Colombo Terminal — A133

**1968, Aug. 5 *Perf. 13½***
**417** A133 60c org brn, dk bl & org .75 .25

Opening of Colombo Airport.

D. S. Senanayake — A134

**1968, Sept. 23 Photo. *Perf. 14***
**418** A134 10c deep green .25 .25

See No. 390.

Open Koran — A135

**1968, Oct. 14 Photo. *Perf. 14***
**419** A135 25c org brn, blk, blue & emerald .25 .25

1,400th anniversary of the Koran.

Human Rights Flame — A136

*Perf. 12½x13½*

**1968, Dec. 10** **Unwmk.**

**420** A136 2c multicolored .25 *.30*
**421** A136 20c multicolored .25 .25
**422** A136 40c multicolored .25 .25
**423** A136 2r multicolored .90 *4.00*
*Nos. 420-423 (4)* 1.65 4.80

International Human Rights Year.

Ceylon Buddhist Headquarters, Colombo — A137

**1968, Dec. 19** **Litho.** ***Perf. 13½***

**424** A137 5c multicolored .25 *.50*

All-Ceylon Buddhist Cong., 50th anniv.

A multicolored 50c showing the Sri Padmaya (Sacred Footprint) on Adam's Peak was prepared but the issuance order was countermanded on Dec. 18. Some were sold in ignorance of the withdrawal order. Value $65.

E. W. Perera — A138

**Wmk. 290**

**1969, Feb. 17** **Photo.** ***Perf. 14***

**425** A138 60c brown .25 *.30*

E. W. Perera, member of Legislative Council.

"Strength in Saving" — A139

**1969, Mar. 20**

**426** A139 3c blue, yel & black .25 *.30*

National Savings Movement, 25th anniv.

A140

4c, Seat of Enlightenment under Bodhi Tree. 6c, Buduresmala (disk symbolic of six-fold Buddha rays).

**Wmk. 290**

**1969, Apr. 10** **Litho.** ***Perf. 15***

**427** A140 4c orange & multi .25 *.40*
**428** A140 6c gold & multi .25 *.40*
**429** A140 35c scarlet & multi .25 .25
*Nos. 427-429 (3)* .75 1.05

Vesak Day, which commemorates the birth, enlightenment and death of Buddha.

For surcharges see Nos. 463, 466.

A141

**1969, Apr. 29** **Photo.** ***Perf. 14x14½***

**430** A141 15c org yel & multi .25 .25

Alexander Ekanayake Goonesingha (1891-1967), trade unionist, political leader and diplomat.

ILO, 50th Anniv. — A142

**1969, May 4** ***Perf. 14½x14***

**431** A142 5c grnsh bl & black .25 .25
**432** A142 25c car rose & black .25 .25

Convocation Hall, University of Ceylon A143

Elephant Lamp (Ath Pana) A144

35c, "Lamp of Education," globe & flags. 50c, Uranium atom diagram. 60c, Symbols of science education. 1r, Aerial view of Sigiriya rock fortress.

**Inscribed: "SIYAWASA"**

**Unwmk.**

**1969, Aug. 1** **Litho.** ***Perf. 14***

**433** A143 4c yellow & multi .25 *.80*
**434** A144 6c multicolored .30 *1.50*
**435** A143 35c multicolored .25 .25
**436** A144 50c red & multi .25 .25
**437** A143 60c blue & multi .30 .25
**438** A144 1r yel & multi .30 .25
*Nos. 433-438 (6)* 1.65 3.30

Centenary of public education and archaeological research.

For surcharges see Nos. 464-467.

Wild Water Buffalo — A145

15c, Slender loris. 50c, Axis deer. 1r, Leopard.

*Perf. 14x13½*

**1970, May 11** **Litho.** **Unwmk.**

**439** A145 5c lt blue & multi 1.20 *1.25*
**440** A145 15c buff & multi 2.00 1.00
**441** A145 50c salmon & multi 1.40 1.25
**442** A145 1r gray & multi 1.40 *1.75*
*Nos. 439-442 (4)* 6.00 5.25

Symbols of Agriculture and Industry — A146

**1970, June 17**

**443** A146 60c multicolored .25 .25

Asian Productivity Year.

Inauguration of UPU Headquarters, Bern — A147

**1970, Aug. 14** **Litho.** **Unwmk.**

**444** A147 50c org, black & blue .50 .25
**445** A147 1.10r red, black & blue 4.25 .40

Caduceus and Oil Lamp — A148

**1970, Sept. 1** ***Perf. 13½x14***

**446** A148 5c multicolored 1.00 *.75*
**447** A148 45c gray & multi 1.00 *.60*

Centenary of the Ceylon Medical School.

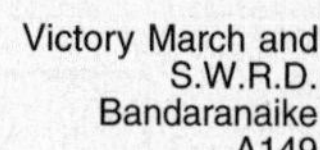

Victory March and S.W.R.D. Bandaranaike A149

**1970, Sept. 25** ***Perf. 14***

**448** A149 10c red & multi .25 .25

For surcharge see No. 465.

UN Emblem and Dove — A150

**1970, Oct. 24** **Photo.** ***Perf. 12½x14***

**449** A150 2r dp orange & multi 2.75 *3.50*

25th anniversary of the United Nations.

Keppetipola Dissawe — A151

**1970, Nov. 26** **Litho.** ***Perf. 14x14½***

**450** A151 25c multicolored .25 .25

The 152nd anniversary of the execution of Keppetipola Dissawe, leader of the Great Rebellion of 1817-18.

Ola Leaf Manuscript and Education Year Emblem A152

**1970, Dec. 21** **Photo.** ***Perf. 13***

**451** A152 15c brown & multi 2.75 1.50

International Education Year.

Charles Henry de Soysa — A153

**1971, Mar. 3** **Litho.** ***Perf. 14x13½***

**452** A153 20c orange & multi .30 .30

de Soysa (1836-90), philanthropist who founded hospitals and schools.

Edward Henry Pedris — A154

**1971, July 8** **Litho.** ***Perf. 14x14½***

**453** A154 25c blue & multi .30 .30

Edward Henry Pedris (1888-1925), patriot.

---

A 5c stamp for the 10th Conf. of World Fellowship of Buddhists, Ceylon, May 9-13, was supposedly not issued without "1972" overprint. See Sri Lanka No. 471.

---

Lenin (1870-1924) — A156

**1971, Aug. 31** ***Perf. 14½***

**455** A156 40c dp car & multi .55 .55

Cumaratunga Munidasa — A157

Poets and Philosophers: No. 457, Ananda Coomaraswamy (1887-1947). No. 458, Rev. S. Mahinda Thero (1905-51). No. 459, Ananda Rajakaruna (1885-1957). No. 460, Arumuga Navalar (1822-78).

**1971, Oct. 29** ***Perf. 14***

**456** A157 5c brown .25 .25
**457** A157 5c slate .25 .25
**458** A157 5c deep orange .25 .25
**459** A157 5c dp vio blue .25 .25
**460** A157 5c brown red .25 .25
*Nos. 456-460 (5)* 1.25 1.25

CARE Package — A158

**1971, Dec. 28** ***Perf. 14x13***

**461** A158 50c purple, blue & pink .55 .35

25th anniv. of CARE, a US-Canadian Co-operative for American Relief Everywhere.

Map of Ceylon, Colombo Plan Emblem — A159

**1971, Dec. 28** **Litho.** ***Perf. 14x14½***

**462** A159 20c multicolored .30 .30

20th anniversary of the Colombo Plan.

**Issues of 1969-70 Surcharged**

a

b

c

d

e

**Wmk. 290, Unwmkd.**

**1971, Dec. 5** ***Perf. 15, 14***

**463** A140 (a) 5c on 4c (#427) 6.00 2.50
**464** A143 (b) 5c on 4c (#433) .25 1.90
**465** A149 (c) 15c on 10c (#448) .25 .50
**466** A140 (d) 25c on 6c (#428) .65 .95
**467** A144 (e) 25c on 6c (#434) .65 *3.25*
*Nos. 463-467 (5)* 7.80 9.10

Nos. 463-466 exist with surcharge inverted.

WHO Emblem and Heart — A160

**1972, May 2 Unwmk. *Perf. 13x13½***

**468** A160 25c multicolored 2.75 .90

"Your heart is your health," World Health Day.

UN Emblem, Map Showing Asian Highway A161

**1972, May 2 *Perf. 13x12½***

**469** A161 85c lt blue & multi 5.25 3.25

Economic Commission for Asia and the Far East (ECAFE), 25th anniversary.

### SEMI-POSTAL STAMPS

**Catalogue values for unused stamps in this section are for Never Hinged items.**

Lamp and Dharmachakra — SP1

Design: 10c+5c, Hand of Peace.

***Perf. 11½***

**1956, May 10 Unwmk. Photo.**

**Granite Paper**

**B1** SP1 4c + 2c dp bl & lt yel .35 *.75*
**B2** SP1 10c + 5c dk gray, yel & brt pink .50 *1.00*

2500th anniv. of the birth of Buddha. The surtax went to the Buddha Jayanti Fund. For overprints, see Nos. 338-339.

### WAR TAX STAMPS

Nos. 201, 202, 202a and 203 Overprinted

**Die I**

**1918 Wmk. 3 *Perf. 14***

**MR1** A44 2c brown orange .25 *.45*
*a.* Double overprint 35.00 47.50
*b.* Inverted overprint 75.00 *85.00*
**MR2** A44 3c dp grn (Die Ia, type II) 4.00 .45
*a.* 3c dp green (Die I, type I) .25 *.60*
*b.* Double overprint (Die I) 110.00 *120.00*
*c.* 5c Double overprint (Die Ia, type II) 150.00
**MR3** A44 5c red violet 4.75 3.50
*a.* Double overprint 75.00 *75.00*
*b.* Inverted overprint 75.00
*c.* 5c purple .60 .35

No. 223 Overprinted in Black

**MR4** A44 1c on 5c red violet 3.50 *.45*
*a.* Double overprint 225.00
*b.* 1c on No. 223a .60 .45
*Nos. MR1-MR4 (4)* 12.50 4.85

### OFFICIAL STAMPS

Regular Issues Overprinted

**Black Overprint**

**1869 Wmk. 1 *Perf. 12½, 14***

**O1** A4 1p blue 97.50
**O2** A1 2p yellow 97.50
**O3** A5 3p rose 190.00
**O4** A2 8p red brown 97.50
**O5** A1 1sh gray lilac 220.00

**Red Overprint**

**O6** A1 6p brown 97.50
**O7** A2 2sh blue 160.00
*a.* Imperf. *1,250.*
*Nos. O1-O7 (7)* 960.00

Nos. O1-O7 were never placed in use.
The overprint measures 15mm on Nos. O1, O3.

Regular Issues Overprinted in Black or Red

**1895-1900 Wmk. 2 *Perf. 14***

**O8** A6 2c green 17.00 .75
**O9** A6 2c org brn ('00) 11.50 .65
**O10** A24 3c org brn & grn 11.50 2.50
**O11** A24 3c green ('00) 12.50 4.50
**O12** A23 5c lilac 5.25 .35
**O13** A24 15c olive green 24.00 .50
**O14** A24 15c ultra ('00) 25.00 .60
**O15** A24 25c brown 13.50 3.00
**O16** A24 30c vio & org brn 13.50 .65
**O17** A24 75c blk & org brn (R) ('99) 10.00 *8.50*

**Wmk. 1**

**O18** A16 1r12c claret 100.00 62.50
*Nos. O8-O18 (11)* 243.75 84.50

**1903-04 Wmk. 2**

**O19** A36 2c orange brown 24.00 1.75
**O20** A37 3c green 17.50 2.10
**O21** A38 5c dull lilac 32.50 1.60
**O22** A40 15c ultramarine 40.00 3.25
**O23** A40 25c bister 35.00 22.50
**O24** A40 30c violet & green 20.00 1.50
*Nos. O19-O24 (6)* 169.00 32.70

# CHAD

'chad

## (Tchad)

LOCATION — Central Africa, south of Libya
GOVT. — Republic
AREA — 495,572 sq. mi.
POP. — 7,557,436 (1999 est.)
CAPITAL — N'Djamena

A former dependency of Ubangi-Shari, Chad became a separate French colony in 1920. In 1934, the colonies of Chad, Gabon, Middle Congo and Ubangi-Shari were grouped in a single administrative unit known as French Equatorial Africa, with the capital at Brazzaville. The Republic of Chad was proclaimed November 28, 1958.

100 Centimes = 1 Franc

**Catalogue values for unused stamps in this country are for Never Hinged items, beginning with Scott 64 in the regular postage section, Scott B1 in the semi-postal section, Scott C1 in the air post section, Scott CB1 in the air post semi-postal section, Scott J23 in the postage due section, Scott M1 in the military stamp section, and Scott O1 in the officials section.**

See French Equatorial Africa No. 190 for stamp inscribed "Tchad."

Types of Middle Congo, 1907-17, Overprinted

***Perf. 14x13½, 13½x14***

**1922 Unwmk.**

**1** A1 1c red & violet .40 .55
*a.* Overprint omitted 225.00
**2** A1 2c ol brn & salmon .40 .80
*a.* Overprint omitted 260.00
**3** A1 4c ind & vio 1.20 1.60
**4** A1 5c choc & grn 1.25 1.60
**5** A1 10c dp grn & gray grn 2.40 2.75
**6** A1 15c vio & red 2.50 2.75
**7** A1 20c grn & vio 4.00 4.75
**8** A2 25c ol brn & brn 12.00 12.00
**9** A2 30c rose & pale rose 2.40 2.00
**10** A2 35c dl bl & dl rose 3.25 3.25
**11** A2 40c choc & grn 4.00 4.00
**12** A2 45c vio & grn 3.25 3.25
**13** A2 50c dk bl & pale bl 3.25 4.00
**14** A2 60c on 75c vio, *pnksh* 4.00 4.75
*a.* "TCHAD" omitted 300.00
*b.* "60" omitted 300.00
**15** A2 75c red & violet 4.00 4.00
**16** A3 1fr indigo & salmon 12.00 16.00
**17** A3 2fr indigo & violet 24.00 24.00
**18** A3 5fr ind & olive brn 24.00 24.00
*Nos. 1-18 (18)* 108.30 116.05

See Nos. 26a, 32a, 38a, 55a.

**Stamps of 1922 Overprinted in Various Colors**

Nos. 19-28

Nos. 29-50

**1924-33**

**19** A1 1c red & vio .40 .80
*a.* "TCHAD" omitted 225.00 *250.00*
*b.* Double overprint 300.00
*c.* Violet omitted 300.00
**20** A1 2c ol brn & sal .40 *.50*
*a.* "TCHAD" omitted 225.00
*b.* Double overprint 240.00
**21** A1 4c ind & vio .40 *.50*
*a.* "TCHAD" omitted 950.00
**22** A1 5c choc & grn (Bl) 1.60 *2.00*
*a.* "TCHAD" omitted 200.00 225.00
**23** A1 5c choc & grn .80 *.70*
*a.* "TCHAD" omitted 225.00
**24** A1 10c dp grn & gray grn (Bl) 1.60 1.40
**25** A1 10c dp grn & gray grn 1.60 1.40
**26** A1 10c red org & blk ('25) .60 .80
*a.* "Afrique Equatoriale Francaise" omitted 225.00 250.00
*b.* "TCHAD" omitted 240.00 260.00
**27** A1 15c vio & red .80 .85
**28** A1 20c grn & vio .80 .80
*a.* "TCHAD" omitted 225.00
*b.* "Afrique Equatoriale Francaise" doubled 340.00
**29** A2 25c ol brn & brn .80 .85
*a.* "Afrique Equatoriale Francaise" doubled 160.00
**30** A2 30c rose & pale rose .80 1.10
**31** A2 30c gray & bl (R) ('25) .40 .80
**32** A2 30c dk grn & grn ('27) 1.20 1.60
*a.* "Afrique Equatoriale Francaise" omitted 340.00
**33** A2 35c indigo & dl rose .80 .85
**34** A2 40c choc & grn 1.25 1.60
*a.* Double overprint (R + Bk) 275.00
**35** A2 45c vio & grn 1.20 1.40
*a.* Double overprint (R + Bk) 275.00
**36** A2 50c dk bl & pale bl (R) 2.40 1.90
*a.* Inverted overprint 160.00
**37** A2 50c grn & vio ('25) 2.40 2.00
**38** A2 65c org brn & bl ('28) 2.40 2.40
*a.* "Afrique Equatoriale Francaise" omitted 260.00
**39** A2 75c red & vio (Bl) 2.00 1.90
**40** A2 75c dp bl & lt bl (R) ('25) .80 1.20
*a.* "TCHAD" omitted 260.00
**41** A2 75c rose & dk brn ('28) 3.25 3.25
**42** A2 90c brn red & pink ('30) 8.00 12.00
**43** A3 1fr ind & salmon 2.40 2.50
**44** A3 1.10fr dl grn & bl ('28) 4.00 4.00
**45** A3 1.25fr org brn & lt bl ('33) 8.00 9.50
**46** A3 1.50fr ultra & bl ('30) 8.00 12.00
**47** A3 1.75fr ol brn & vio ('33) 40.00 45.00
**48** A3 2fr ind & vio 3.25 3.50
*a.* Double impression of frame 550.00
**49** A3 3fr red vio ('30) 12.00 16.00
**50** A3 5fr ind & ol brn 4.00 4.75
*Nos. 19-50 (32)* 118.35 139.85

See No. 58a.

**Types of 1922 Overprinted like Nos. 29-50 and Surcharged with New Values**

**1924-27**

**51** A2 60c on 75c dk vio, *pnksh* .80 1.20
*a.* "60" omitted 200.00
**52** A3 65c on 1fr brn & ol grn ('25) 2.50 2.00
**53** A3 85c on 1fr brn & ol grn ('25) 2.50 2.00
**54** A2 90c on 75c brn red & rose red ('27) 2.50 2.00
**55** A3 1.25fr on 1fr dk bl & ultra (R) ('26) 1.25 .80
*a.* "Afrique Equatoriale Francaise" omitted 175.00
**56** A3 1.50fr on 1fr ultra & bl ('27) 2.50 2.00
**57** A3 3fr on 5fr org brn & dl red ('27) 6.50 6.00
**58** A3 10fr on 5fr ol grn & cer ('27) 16.00 14.50
*a.* "10fr" omitted 400.00 400.00
**59** A3 20fr on 5fr vio & ver ('27) 20.00 21.00
*Nos. 51-59 (9)* 54.55 51.50

Common Design Types pictured following the introduction.

**Colonial Exposition Issue**
Common Design Types

**1931 Engr. *Perf. 12½***

**Name of Country in Black**

**60** CD70 40c deep green 5.50 5.50
**61** CD71 50c violet 5.50 5.50
**62** CD72 90c red orange 5.50 5.50
**63** CD73 1.50fr dull blue 5.50 5.50
*Nos. 60-63 (4)* 22.00 22.00

**Catalogue values for unused stamps in this section, from this point to the end of the section, are for Never Hinged items.**

### Republic

"Birth of the Republic" A1

"Solidarity of the Community" A2

**1959 Unwmk. Engr. *Perf. 13***

**64** A1 15fr ultra, grn & maroon .70 .25
**65** A2 25fr dk grn & dp claret .90 .25

1st anniv. of the proclamation of the Republic.

Imperforates
Most Chad stamps from 1959 onward exist imperforate in issued and trial colors, and also in small presentation sheets in issued colors.

**C.C.T.A. Issue**
Common Design Type

**1960**
**66** CD106 50fr rose lil & dk pur 1.75 .50

Flag and Map of Chad and UN Emblem — A3

**Unwmk.**
**1961, Jan. 11 Engr. *Perf. 13***
**Flag in blue, yellow and carmine**
**67** A3 15fr brn & dk bl .60 .25
**68** A3 25fr org brn & dk bl .90 .25
**69** A3 85fr slate grn & dk bl 2.50 .40
*Nos. 67-69 (3)* 4.00 .90

Admission of Chad to United Nations.

Chari Bridge and Hippopotamus A4

Abtouyoua Mountain and Ox — A5

Designs: 50c, Biltine and dorcas gazelle. 1fr, Logone and elephant. 2fr, Batha and lion. 3fr, Salamat and buffalo. 4fr, Ouaddai and Kudu. 15fr, Bessada and giant eland. 20fr, Tibesti mountains and mouflon. 25fr, Rocherg and antelope. 30fr, Kanem and cheetah. 60fr, Borkou and oryx. 85fr, Gorge of Archet and addax.

***Perf. 13½x14, 14x13½***
**1961-62 Typo.**
**70** A5 50c yel grn & dk grn ('62) .25 .25
**71** A5 1fr bl grn & dk bl grn ('62) .25 .25
**72** A5 2fr dk red brn & blk ('62) .25 .25
**73** A5 3fr ocher & dl grn ('62) .25 .25
**74** A5 4fr dk crim & blk ('62) .25 .25
**75** A4 5fr yellow & blk .25 .25
**76** A5 10fr pink & blk .35 .25
**77** A5 15fr lilac & blk ('62) .70 .25
**78** A5 20fr red & blk .85 .25
**79** A5 25fr blue & blk ('62) .90 .25
**80** A5 30fr ultra & blk ('62) 1.00 .25
**81** A5 60fr yel & ol grn ('62) 2.25 .25
**82** A5 85fr org & blk 2.75 .25
*Nos. 70-82 (13)* 10.30 3.25

First anniversary of Independence.
For overprint see No. M1.

**Abidjan Games Issue**
Common Design Type

**1962, July 21 Photo. *Perf. 12½x12***
**83** CD109 20fr Relay race .80 .25
**84** CD109 50fr High jump 2.00 .30
*Nos. 83-84,C8 (3)* 5.80 1.55

**African-Malgache Union Issue**
Common Design Type

**1962, Sept. 8 Unwmk.**
**85** CD110 30fr dk bl, bluish grn, red & gold 1.25 .25

Pres. Ngarta Tombalbaye — A7

**1963, Apr. 22 *Perf. 12x12½***
**86** A7 20fr multi .50 .25
**87** A7 85fr multi 1.40 .30

For surcharge, see No. 125.

**Space Communciations Issue**

Waves Around Globe — A8

Design: 100fr, Orbit patterns around globe.

***Perf. 12½***
**1963, Sept. 19 Unwmk. Photo.**
**88** A8 25fr grn & pur .75 .25
**89** A8 100fr pink & ultra 2.25 .60

Ancestral Mask — A9

Excavated Sao Art: 5fr, Clay weight in Pavia headform. 25fr, Ancestral clay statuette. 60fr, Gazelle, bronze. 80fr, Bronze pectoral.

**1963, Dec. 2 Engr. *Perf. 13***
**90** A9 5fr brt grn & red brn .25 .25
**91** A9 15fr gray, dl cl & red .25 .25
**92** A9 25fr dk bl & org brn .90 .25
**93** A9 60fr org brn & slate grn 2.25 .35
**94** A9 80fr org red & olive 2.50 .40
*Nos. 90-94 (5)* 6.15 1.50

UNESCO Emblem, Scales and Tree — A10

**1963, Dec. 10**
**95** A10 25fr green & maroon 1.00 .25

15th anniv. of the Universal Declaration of Human Rights.

Potter — A11

***Perf. 12½***
**1964, Feb. 5 Unwmk. Engr.**
**96** A11 10fr shown .30 .25
**97** A11 30fr Boatmaker .80 .25
**98** A11 50fr Weaver 1.35 .25
**99** A11 85fr Smiths 2.00 .35
*Nos. 96-99 (4)* 4.45 1.10

Barograph and WMO Emblem — A12

**1964, Mar. 23 *Perf. 13***
**100** A12 50fr mag, dk vio & ultra 1.40 .25

Fourth World Meteorological Day.

Cotton — A13

**1964, Apr. 6 Photo. *Perf. 12½x13***
**101** A13 20fr shown 1.40 .35
**102** A13 25fr Royal poinciana 1.60 .40

**Co-operation Issue**
Common Design Type

**1964, Nov. 7 Engr. *Perf. 13***
**103** CD119 25fr ver, dk bl & dk brn 1.00 .25

National Guard and Map of Chad — A14

Design: 25fr, Infantry, flag and map, vert.

***Perf. 12½x13, 13x12½***
**1964, Dec. 11 Photo.**
**104** A14 20fr multi .75 .25
**105** A14 25fr lt bl & multi .90 .25

Issued to honor the army of Chad.

Aoudad or Barbary Sheep — A15

10fr, Addax. 20fr, Oryx. 25fr, Derby's eland, vert. 30fr, Giraffe, buffalo & lion, Zakouma Park, vert. 85fr, Great kudu at water hole, vert.

***Perf. 12½x12, 12x12½***
**1965, Jan. 11 Unwmk.**
**106** A15 5fr dk brn, ultra & yel .50 .25
**107** A15 10fr ultra, org & blk .75 .25
**108** A15 20fr multi 1.50 .25
**109** A15 25fr multi 1.75 .25
**110** A15 30fr multi 2.50 .40
**111** A15 85fr multi 5.00 .75
*Nos. 106-111 (6)* 12.00 2.15

Olsen Perforator — A16

Designs: 60fr, Mildé telephone, vert. 100fr, Distributor of Baudot telegraph.

**1965, May 17 Engr. *Perf. 13***
**112** A16 30fr multi .65 .25
**113** A16 60fr multi 1.10 .45
**114** A16 100fr multi 1.80 .60
*Nos. 112-114 (3)* 3.55 1.30

Cent. of the ITU.

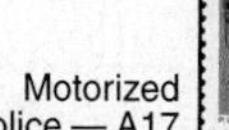

Motorized Police — A17

***Perf. 12½x12***
**1965, June 22 Photo. Unwmk.**
**115** A17 25fr ol, dk grn, gold & brn 1.00 .25

Issued to honor the national police.

Drum and stool — A18

Musical Instruments from National Museum: 2fr, Guitar. 3fr, Shoulder drums, vert. 15fr, Viol. 60fr, Harp, vert.

**1965, Oct. 26 Engr. *Perf. 13***
**Size: 22x36mm, 36x22mm**
**116** A18 1fr car, emer & brn .25 .25
**117** A18 2fr red, purple & brn .25 .25
**118** A18 3fr red, brn lake & sepia .25 .25
**119** A18 15fr red, ocher & sl grn .75 .25
**120** A18 60fr maroon & slate grn 1.75 .60
*Nos. 116-120,C23 (6)* 5.25 2.60

See No. C23.

Head and Bowl — A19

Sao Art: 20fr, Head. 60fr, Head with crown. 80fr, Circlet with human head. From excavations at Bouta Kebira and Gawi.

**1966, Apr. 1 Engr. *Perf. 13***
**121** A19 15fr ol, choc & ultra .40 .25
**122** A19 20fr dk red, brn & bl grn .75 .25
**123** A19 60fr brt bl, choc & ver 1.75 .50
**124** A19 80fr brn org, grn & pur 2.50 .60
*Nos. 121-124 (4)* 5.40 1.60

Issued to publicize the International Negro Arts Festival, Dakar, Senegal, Apr. 1-24.

No. 86 Surcharged in Orange

**1966, Apr. 15 Photo. *Perf. 12x12½***
**125** A7 25fr on 20fr multi 1.00 .30

WHO Headquarters, Geneva — A20

**1966, May 3**
**126** A20 25fr car, lt ultra & yel .80 .25
**127** A20 32fr emer, ultra & yel .90 .25

New WHO Headquarters, Geneva.

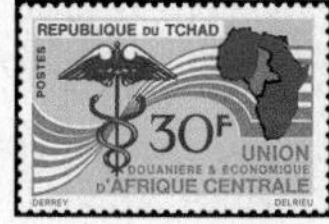

Staff of Mercury and Map of Africa — A21

**1966, May 24 *Perf. 12½x12***
**128** A21 30fr multi 1.00 .25

Central African Customs and Economic Union (Union Douaniere et Economique de l'Afrique Centrale, UDEAC).

Soccer Player — A22

Design: 60fr, Soccer player facing left.

**1966, July 12 Engr. *Perf. 13***
**129** A22 30fr grn, bl grn & mar .80 .25
**130** A22 60fr dk bl, gray & car 1.60 .40

8th World Cup Soccer Championship, Wembley, England, July 11-30.

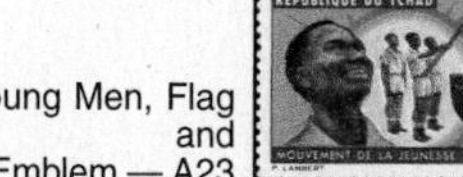

Young Men, Flag and Emblem — A23

**1966, Aug. 11 Photo. *Perf. 12½x13***
**131** A23 25fr dk bl & multi 1.00 .25

Chad Youth Movement.

Greek Columns and UNESCO Emblem — A24

**1966, Aug. 23 Engr. *Perf. 13***
**132** A24 32fr sl bl, vio & car rose 1.00 .25

20th anniv. of UNESCO.

Reconstructed Skull of Chadanthropus A25

**1966, Sept. 20 Engr. *Perf. 13***
133 A25 30fr gray, red & ocher 2.00 .50

Yves Coppens' discovery of Lake Chad man.

Stone Axe — A26

Prehistoric Tools: 30fr, Flint arrow head. 85fr, Bone harpoon. 100fr, Sandstone mill-stone with grinder.

**1966, Dec. 11 Engr. *Perf. 13***
134 A26 25fr dp bl, red & dk brn .70 .25
135 A26 30fr brn, dp bl & blk .80 .25
136 A26 85fr dk red, brt bl & brn 2.50 .50
137 A26 100fr Prus grn, dk brn & bis brn 2.75 .65
*a.* Miniature sheet of 4, #134-137 15.00 8.00
*Nos. 134-137 (4)* 6.75 1.65

Map of Chad and Various Sports — A27

**1967, Apr. 10 Photo. *Perf. 12x12½***
138 A27 25fr multi 1.00 .30

Issued for Sports Day, Apr. 10, 1967.

Colotis Protomedia A28

Various Butterflies.

**1967, May 23 Photo. *Perf. 12½x12***
139 A28 5fr blue & multi 2.00 .30
140 A28 10fr emerald & multi 4.25 .75
141 A28 20fr orange & multi 8.50 1.50
142 A28 130fr red & multi 17.50 2.50
*Nos. 139-142 (4)* 32.25 5.05

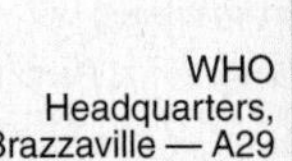

WHO Headquarters, Brazzaville — A29

**1967, Sept. 23 Photo. *Perf. 12½x13***
143 A29 30fr vio bl & multi 1.00 .25

Opening of the Regional Office of the WHO, Brazzaville.

Jamboree Emblem and Boy Scouts — A30

32fr, Jamboree emblem and Boy Scout.

**1967, Oct. 17 Photo. *Perf. 12½x13***
144 A30 25fr multi .90 .25
145 A30 32fr multi 1.00 .25

12th Boy Scout World Jamboree, Farragut State Park, Idaho, Aug. 1-9.

Great Mills of Chad — A31

30fr, Lake reclamation project, grain fields.

**1967, Nov. 14 Engr. *Perf. 13***
146 A31 25fr brt bl, ind & sep .90 .25
147 A31 30fr ultra, emer & ol brn 1.00 .25

Economic development of Chad.

Woman and Harp Player — A32

Rock Paintings: 30fr, Giraffes. 50fr, Camel rider hunting ostrich.

**1967, Dec. 19 Engr. *Perf. 13***
**Size: 36x22mm**
148 A32 15fr bl, sal & mar 1.00 .25
149 A32 30fr grnsh bl, sal & mar 2.00 .40
150 A32 50fr emer, sal & mar 2.75 .55
*Nos. 148-150,C38-C39 (5)* 14.25 3.65

Balloud expedition in the Ennedi Mountains. See Nos. 163-166.

Rotary Emblem — A33

**1968, Jan. 9 Photo. *Perf. 13x12½***
151 A33 50fr multi 1.80 .50

Rotary Club of Chad, 10th anniversary.

Map of Chad, WHO Emblem, Well, Physicians, Mother and Child — A34

**1968, Apr. 6 *Perf. 13x12½***
152 A34 25fr multi .75 .25
153 A34 32fr multi .90 .25

20th anniv. of WHO.

"Water" Aiding Agriculture and Industry — A35

**1968, Apr. 23 Engr. *Perf. 13***
154 A35 50fr grnsh bl, brn & brt grn 1.10 .25

Hydrological Decade (UNESCO), 1965-74.

National Administration School — A36

**1968, Aug. 20 Engr. *Perf. 13***
155 A36 25fr slate, brn red & rose vio 1.00 .25

Boy Learning to Write — A37

**1968, Sept. 10**
156 A37 60fr dk bl, dk brn & blk 2.00 .50

Issued for National Literacy Day.

Cotton Harvest A38

Loom, Fort Archambault Factory A39

**1968, Sept. 24 Engr. *Perf. 13***
157 A38 25fr Prus bl, choc & dk grn .90 .25
158 A39 30fr brt grn, ol & ultra 1.00 .25

Issued to publicize the cotton industry.

Tiger Moth — A40

Moths: 30fr, Owlet. 50fr, Saturnid (Gynanisa maja). 100fr, Saturnid (Epiphora bauhiniae).

**1968, Oct. 1 Photo.**
159 A40 25fr multi 5.25 .60
160 A40 30fr multi 6.25 .75
161 A40 50fr multi 9.50 .85
162 A40 100fr multi 11.00 1.50
*Nos. 159-162 (4)* 32.00 3.70

### Rock Paintings Type of 1967

Rock Paintings: 2fr, Archers. 10fr, Costumes (4 women, 1 man). 20fr, Funeral vigil. 25fr, Dispute.

**1968, Nov. 19 Engr. *Perf. 13***
**Size: 36x22mm**
163 A32 2fr scar, brn & dk brn .55 .25
164 A32 10fr pur, salmon & dk red 1.50 .25
165 A32 20fr grn, salmon & mar 1.90 .50
166 A32 25fr bl, salmon & maroon 3.25 .60
*Nos. 163-166 (4)* 7.20 1.60

Man and Human Rights Flame — A41

**1968, Dec. 10 Engr. *Perf. 13***
167 A41 32fr grn, brt bl & red 1.00 .25

International Human Rights Year.

St. Paul — A42

Apostles: 1fr, St. Peter. 2fr, St. Thomas. 5fr, St. John the Evangelist. 10fr, St. Bartholomew. 20fr, St. Matthew. 25fr, St. James the Less. 30fr, St. Andrew. 40fr, St. Jude. 50fr, St. James the Greater. 85fr, St. Philip. 100fr, St. Simon.

**1969, May 6 Litho. *Perf. 12½x13***
168 A42 50c multi .25 .25
169 A42 1fr multi .25 .25
170 A42 2fr multi .25 .25
171 A42 5fr multi .25 .25
172 A42 10fr multi .25 .25
173 A42 20fr multi .30 .25
174 A42 25fr multi .40 .25
175 A42 30fr multi .50 .25
176 A42 40fr multi .60 .25
177 A42 50fr multi .70 .25
178 A42 85fr multi 1.10 .40
179 A42 100fr multi 1.25 .40
*a.* Sheet of 12, #168-179 6.00 1.75

Jubilee Year of the Catholic Church in Chad.

Tractors and Trucks — A43

**1969, June 19 Engr. *Perf. 13***
180 A43 32fr grn, red brn & ind .75 .25

50th anniv. of the ILO.

Deborah Meyer, US, 200 Meter Freestyle — A44

Woman with Flowers, by Veneto — A45

Portrait of an African Woman, by Bezombes — A45a

Winners of 1968 Olympic Games: No. 182, Roland Matthes, East Germany, 100m backstroke. No. 183, Klaus DiBiasi, Italy, springboard diving. No. 184, Bruno Cipolla, Primo Baran and Renzo Sambo, Italy, pair with coxswain. No. 185, Annemarie Zimmermann and Rosewitha Esser, West Germany, women's kayak tandem. No. 186, Sailing, G.B. No. 187, Pierre Trentin, France, 1000 meter bicycling. No. 188, Pier Franco Vianelli, Italy, 196k bicycle road race. No. 189, Daniel Morelon and Pierre Trentin, France, tandem.

No. 190, Daniel R. Rebillard, France, 4000m pursuit (bicycle). No. 191, Ingrid Becker, West Germany, pentathlon. No. 192, Jean J. Guyon, France, equestrian. No. 193, Olympic dressage team, West Germany. No. 194, Bernd Klinger, West Germany, small bore rifle. No. 195, Manfred Wolke, East Germany, welterweight. No. 196, Randy Matson, US, shot put. No. 197, Colette Besson, France, 400m run. No. 198, Mohammed Gammoudi, Tunisia, 5,000m run. No. 199, Tommie Smith, US, 200m run.

No. 200, David Hemery, G.B., 200m hurdles. No. 201, Willie Davenport, US, 110m hurdles. No. 202, Bob Beamon, US, long jump. No. 203, Sawao Kato, Japan, all around gymnastics. No. 204, Dick Fosbury, US, high jump.

Paintings: No. 206, Holy Family, by Murillo, horiz. No. 207, Adoration of the Magi, by Rubens. No. 209, Three Black Men, by Rubens. No. 210, Mother and Child, by Gauguin.

**1969, June 30 Litho. *Perf. 12½x13***
181-204 A44 1fr set of 24 8.00 8.00
***Perf. 12½x13, 13x12½***
205 A45 1fr shown .35 .35
206 A45 1fr multi .35 .35
207 A45 1fr multi .35 .35
208 A45a 1fr shown .35 .35
209 A45 1fr multi .35 .35
210 A45 1fr multi .35 .35

Issued to stress the brotherhood of mankind.
For overprints see Nos. 244A-244F, 245A-245X.

Cochlospermum Tinctorium — A46

Flowers: 4fr, Parkia biglobosa. 10fr, Pancratium trianthum. 15fr, Morning glory.

**1969, July 8 Photo. *Perf. 12½x13***
211 A46 1fr pink, yel & blk .60 .25
212 A46 4fr dk grn, yel & red .90 .25
213 A46 10fr dk grn, yel & gray 1.10 .25
214 A46 15fr vio bl & multi 1.90 .25
*Nos. 211-214 (4)* 4.50 1.00

Meat Freezer, Farcha — A47

30fr, Cattle at Farcha slaughterhouse.

**1969, Aug. 19 Engr. *Perf. 13***

| | | | | |
|---|---|---|---|---|
| 215 | A47 | 25fr sl grn, ocher & red brn | .60 | .25 |
| 216 | A47 | 30fr red brn, sl grn & gray | .75 | .25 |

Economic development in Chad.

**Development Bank Issue**

Common Design Type

**1969, Sept. 10**

| | | | | |
|---|---|---|---|---|
| 217 | CD130 | 30fr dl red, grn & ocher | .90 | .25 |

Tilapia Nilotica — A48

Fish: 3fr, Citharinus latus. 5fr, Tetraodon fahaka strigosus. 20fr, Hydrocyon forskali.

**1969, Nov. 25 Engr. *Perf. 13***

| | | | | |
|---|---|---|---|---|
| 218 | A48 | 2fr choc, grn & gray | .40 | .25 |
| 219 | A48 | 3fr gray, red & bl | .90 | .25 |
| 220 | A48 | 5fr ocher, blk & yel | 1.40 | .25 |
| 221 | A48 | 20fr blk, red & grn | 3.75 | .60 |
| | | *Nos. 218-221 (4)* | 6.45 | 1.35 |

**ASECNA Issue**

Common Design Type

**1969, Dec. 12 Engr. *Perf. 13***

| | | | | |
|---|---|---|---|---|
| 222 | CD132 | 30fr orange | 1.00 | .25 |

Pres. François Tombalbaye — A49

**1970, Jan. 11 Litho. *Perf. 14***

| | | | | |
|---|---|---|---|---|
| 223 | A49 | 25fr multi | 1.00 | .25 |

Lenin — A50

**1970, Apr. 22 Photo. *Perf. 11½***

| | | | | |
|---|---|---|---|---|
| 224 | A50 | 150fr gold, blk & buff | 2.75 | 1.10 |

Lenin (1870-1924), Russian communist leader.

**UPU Headquarters Issue**

Common Design Type

**1970, May 20 Engr. *Perf. 13***

| | | | | |
|---|---|---|---|---|
| 225 | CD133 | 30fr dk red, pur & brn | 1.20 | .25 |

During the 1970-73 period three different agents had entered into contracts to produce stamps with various officials of the Chad government, apparently including Pres. Tombalbaye.

In June 1973, Tombalbaye declared that some of the stamps produced by these agents were not recognized by the Chad government but might be put on sale at a later date, and that other stamps produced and shipped to Chad were refused by the government.

In July 1973, the Chad government announced that the stamps that were not recognized would be put on sale by the end of the year. We have no evidence that this actually happened.

Apollo Program A50a

Designs: 15fr, Apollo 11 in Lunar orbit. 25fr, Apollo 12 astronaut deploying lunar research equipment. 40fr, Astronaut, lunar module on moon. 50fr, Astronauts Conrad and Bean in life raft after splashdown, horiz.

**1970, June 12 Litho. *Perf. 12x12½***

| | | | | |
|---|---|---|---|---|
| 225A | A50a | Strip of 3, #b-d | 6.00 | — |

**Souvenir Sheet**

***Perf. 13½x13***

| | | | | |
|---|---|---|---|---|
| 225E | A50a | 50fr multicolored | 10.00 | — |

No. 225E contains one 66x44mm stamp. 15fr, 25fr are airmail.

Expo '70, Japan — A50b

Japanese prints of women: 50c, by Kiyonaga. 1fr, by Utamaro. 2fr, from Heian period.

**1970, June 12 Litho. *Perf. 12x12½***

| | | | | |
|---|---|---|---|---|
| 225F | A50b | Strip of 3, #a-c | 13.50 | — |

For overprint see No. 239C.

Adult Education Class and UN Emblem — A52

**1970, June 16 Litho. *Perf. 14***

| | | | | |
|---|---|---|---|---|
| 226 | A52 | 100fr blue & multi | 1.75 | .60 |

International Education Year.

Bull's Head, Symbols of Weather and Agriculture — A53

**1970, July 22 Engr. *Perf. 13***

| | | | | |
|---|---|---|---|---|
| 227 | A53 | 50fr org, gray & grn | .90 | .25 |

Issued for World Meteorological Day.

1970 World Cup Soccer Championships, Mexico City — A53a

Designs: 1fr, Three players, Italian flag. 4fr, Franz Beckenbauer, German flag. Nos. 227C, 227E, English players receiving World Cup trophy, 1966. No. 227D, Three players, Brazilian flag. No. 227F, Four players, "1970."

**1970-71 Litho. *Perf. 12***

| | | | | |
|---|---|---|---|---|
| 227A | A53a | 1fr multicolored | | |
| 227B | A53a | 4fr multicolored | | |
| 227C | A53a | 5fr multicolored | | |
| 227D | A53a | 5fr multicolored | | |
| | | *Nos. 227A-227D (4)* | 3.75 | — |

**Embossed**

***Die Cut Perf 13***

| | | | | |
|---|---|---|---|---|
| 227E | A53a | 5fr gold | 17.50 | — |

**Souvenir Sheet**

**Litho.**

***Perf. 13½x13***

| | | | | |
|---|---|---|---|---|
| 227F | A53a | 15fr multicolored | 6.25 | — |

No. 227F contains one 66x44mm stamp. Nos. 227D, 227F are airmail.

Issued: Nos. 227A-227D, 227F, 7/2; No. 227E, 11/1/71.

For overprints see Nos. 267A-267E.

Christmas A53b

Virgin and Child by: 3fr, Solario. 25fr, Durer. 32fr, Fouquet.

**1970, Aug. 19 Litho. *Perf. 12x12½***

| | | | | |
|---|---|---|---|---|
| 227G | A53b | 3fr multicolored | | |
| 227H | A53b | 25fr multicolored | | |
| 227I | A53b | 32fr multicolored | | |
| | | *Nos. 227G-227I (3)* | 14.00 | — |

No. 227I is airmail.

Ahmed Mangue, Minister of Education — A54

**1970, Sept. 15 Litho. & Engr.**

| | | | | |
|---|---|---|---|---|
| 228 | A54 | 100fr gold, car & blk | 1.80 | .50 |

1972 Summer Olympics, Munich — A54a

Designs: No. 228A, 3fr, Horses pulling chariot. 8fr, Men running. 10fr, No. 228C, Woman hurdling. No. 228B, 20fr, Equestrian. 35fr, Woman diving. No. 228D, Woman diver in tuck position.

**1970 Litho. *Perf. 12½x12***

| | | | | |
|---|---|---|---|---|
| 228A | A54a | Strip of 3, #a-c | 4.00 | — |

***Perf. 12x12½***

| | | | | |
|---|---|---|---|---|
| 228B | A54a | Pair, #a-b + label | 4.00 | — |

**Embossed**

***Die Cut Perf 13***

| | | | | |
|---|---|---|---|---|
| 228C | A54a | 10fr gold | 17.50 | — |

**Souvenir Sheet**

**Litho.**

***Perf. 13½x13***

| | | | | |
|---|---|---|---|---|
| 228D | A54a | 40fr multicolored | 10.00 | — |

10fr, 35fr, Nos. 228C-228D are airmail. No. 228D contains one 66x43mm stamp.

Issued: Nos. 228A-228B, 228D, Sept; No. 228C, 10/14.

For overprints see Nos. 239D-239F.

Tanner — A55

Designs: 2fr, Cloth dyer, vert. 3fr, Camel turning oil press. 4fr, Water carrier, vert. 5fr, Copper worker.

**1970, Oct. 10 Engr. *Perf. 13***

| | | | | |
|---|---|---|---|---|
| 229 | A55 | 1fr ol brn, bl & brn | .25 | .25 |
| 229A | A55 | 2fr dk brn, ol & ind | .25 | .25 |
| 229B | A55 | 3fr pur, ol brn & rose car | .40 | .25 |
| 229C | A55 | 4fr choc, lem & bl grn | .50 | .25 |
| 229D | A55 | 5fr red, choc & sl grn | .50 | .25 |
| | | *Nos. 229-229D (5)* | 1.90 | 1.25 |

UN Emblem, Grain and Dove — A56

**1970, Oct. 24 Photo. *Perf. 12x12½***

| | | | | |
|---|---|---|---|---|
| 230 | A56 | 32fr dk bl & multi | 1.00 | .25 |

25th anniversary of United Nations.

OCAM Headquarters, Map of Africa, Stars — A57

**1971, Jan. 23 Photo. *Perf. 12½x12***

| | | | | |
|---|---|---|---|---|
| 231 | A57 | 30fr dk grn & multi | 1.00 | .25 |

OCAM (Organisation Commune Africaine, Malgache et Mauricienne) Summit Conference, N'djamena, Jan. 22-30.

Space Exploration — A57a

10fr, Apollo 11. 35fr, Soviet space station. 40fr, John F. Kennedy, Apollo spacecraft, vert.

**1971, Feb. 16 Litho. *Perf. 13x13½***

| | | | | |
|---|---|---|---|---|
| 231A | A57a | 8fr shown | .60 | — |
| 231B | A57a | 10fr multi | .90 | — |
| 231C | A57a | 35fr multi | 6.25 | — |
| | | *Nos. 231A-231C (3)* | 7.75 | |

**Embossed**

***Die Cut Perf 13***

| | | | | |
|---|---|---|---|---|
| 231D | A57a | 8fr gold, like #231A | 8.25 | — |
| *f.* | | Sheet of 1, Imperf. | | |

**Souvenir Sheet**

***Perf. 13½x13***

| | | | | |
|---|---|---|---|---|
| 231E | A57a | 40fr multi | 10.00 | — |

Nos. 231C, 231E are airmail. No. 231Df contains one 73x45mm stamp with same size design as No. 231D. No. 231E contains one 33x50mm stamp.

Nos. 231D, 231Df probably were not available in Chad.

1972 Winter Olympics, Sapporo — A57b

Paintings by Kiyonaga: 50c, Cherry Trees in Bloom, Tokyo. 1fr, Snowy Morning. 2fr, Sake Party.

**1971 Litho. *Perf. 12x12½***

**231G** A57b 50c multicolored .80
**231H** A57b 1fr multicolored 1.40
**231I** A57b 2fr multicolored 2.25
*Nos. 231G-231I (3)* 4.45

**Embossed**

***Die Cut Perf 13***

**231J** A57b 2fr gold, like #231I 17.50
*k.* Sheet of 1, Imperf. 35.00

Issued: Nos. 231G-231I, 2/16; Nos. 231J-231Jk, 11/1. No. 231Jk contains one 43x54mm stamp with same size design as No. 231I.

For overprints see Nos. 246A-246C.

Nos. 231J-231Jk probably were not available in Chad.

Portraits of French Royalty — A57c

Designs: No. 232A, 25fr, The Dauphin (Louis XVII), by J.M. Vien the Younger. 32fr, Marie Antoinette, by E. Vigee-Lebrun. 60fr, Louis XVI, by J.S. Duplessis.

No. 232B, 25fr, Comtesse du Barry, by E. Vigee-Lebrun. 40fr, Louis XV, by M.Q. Delatour.

No. 232C, 40fr, Marie Antoinette, by Charpentier. 50fr, Louis XVI (Dauphin), by Michel Van Loo.

No. 232D, 35fr, Madame de Pompadour (detail), by Delatour. 70fr, Louis XV by Delatour.

No. 232E, 30fr, Madame de Pompadour (entire), by Delatour. 60fr, Marie Leszczynska, by Jean Marc Nattier. 80fr, Louis XV, by Van Loo.

No. 232F, 40fr, Duc D'Orleans as Regent, by 19th cent. French school. 200fr, Louis XIV, by H. Rigaud.

No. 232G, 100fr, Madame de Montespan, by Henry Gascard. 100fr, Madame de Maintenon, by Pierre Mignard.

No. 232H, 50fr, Colbert, by Claude Lefebvre. 200fr, Louis XIV, by J. Garnier.

No. 232J, 50fr, Marie Therese, by Mignard. 200fr, Louis XIV, by Marot.

No. 232K, 50fr, Marie de la Valliere, by English school. 200fr, Louis XIV, by French school.

No. 232L, 100fr, Giulio Cardinal Mazarin, by Mignard. 100fr, Anne of Austria, by Rubens.

No. 232M, 50fr, Vicomte de Turenne, by Champaigne. 200fr, Louis XIV as a Boy, by Mignard.

No. 232N, 100fr, Marquis de Cinq-Mars, by M. le Nain. 150fr, Cardinal Richelieu, by Champaigne.

No. 232P, 150fr, Anne of Austria, by Rubens. 250fr, Louis XIII (detail), by Simon Vouet.

No. 232Q, 150fr, Marriage of Marie de Medicis (looking right), by Rubens. 150fr, Mirror image.

No. 232R, 150fr, Duke of Sully, by Quesnel. 150fr, Mirror image.

No. 232S, 150fr, Henry IV, by Rubens. 150fr, Marie de Medicis, by Rubens.

No. 232T, 200fr, Gabrielle d'Estrees, by unknown artist. 250fr, Henry IV, by French school, c. 1595.

No. 232U, 150fr, Jeanne d'Albret, by Francois Clouet. 200fr, Marie de Medicis as a Girl, by Angelo Bronzino.

No. 232V, 200fr, Henry III, by Clouet. 250fr, Ambroise Pare, by 16th century French school.

No. 232W, 150fr, Catherine de Medicis, by Clouet. 250fr, Henry II, by Clouet.

No. 233A, 200fr, Elizabeth of Austria, by Clouet. 250fr, Charles IX, by Clouet.

No. 233B, 200fr, Mary Stuart, by 16th cent. Scottish school. 300fr, Diane of Poitiers, by Fontainbleu school.

No. 233C, 200fr, Elizabeth of Valois, by Alonso S. Coello. 250fr, Francis, Duke of Alencon, by Clouet.

No. 233D, 150fr, Marguerite d'Angouleme, by Clouet. 300fr, Francis I, by Clouet.

No. 233E, 200fr, Francis I, by Titian. 300fr, Francis I as Dauphin, by Corneille of Lyon.

No. 233F, 100fr, Anne of Austria, by Coello. 250fr, Louis XIII, by Champaigne.

No. 233G, 200fr, Marie de Medicis, by Rubens. 200fr, Marie de Medicis, Louis XIII, by Rubens.

No. 233H, 150fr, The Exchange of Princess Elizabeth of France and Princess Anne of Austria on the Andaye River, by Rubens. 250fr, Louis XIII of France and Navarre, by Vouet.

No. 233J, 250fr, Marie de Medicis, by Rubens. 250fr, Henry IV, by Rubens.

No. 233K, Louis XV and the Dauphin at Battle of Fontenoy. No. 233L, The Grand Dauphin and his Family, by Mignard. No. 233M, Madame de Montespan, horiz. No. 233N, Madame de la Valliere and her Children. No. 233P, The Birth of Louis XIII at Fontainebleau, by Rubens. No. 233Q, Reconciliation of the Queen and Louis XIII, by Rubens. No. 233R, Henry IV Entrusting Regency to Marie de Medici, by Rubens. No. 233S, The Majority of Louis XIII, by Rubens. No. 233T, The Apotheosis of Henry IV and the Proclamation of Regency, by Rubens. No. 233U, Felicity of the Regency, by Rubens.

Small numbers appear at the lower right on Nos. 232A-233J. To ease identification, these numbers are shown in parentheses after each listing.

**1971-73 Litho. *Perf. 12½x13***

**232A** A57c Strip of 3, #aa-ac (58-60) 3.00
**232B** A57c Pair, #aa-ab (53-54) 2.00
**232C** A57c Pair, #aa-ab (56-57) 2.00
**232D** A57c Pair, #aa-ab (51-52) 2.00
**232E** A57c Strip of 3, #aa-ac (48-50) 4.00
**232F** A57c Pair, #aa-ab (45, 47) 4.00
**232G** A57c Pair, #aa-ab (44, 45B) 3.00
**232H** A57c Pair, #aa-ab (42-43) 4.00
**232J** A57c Pair, #aa-ab (40-41) 4.00
**232K** A57c Pair, #aa-ab (38-39) 4.00
**232L** A57c Pair, #aa-ab (36-37) 2.50
**232M** A57c Pair, #aa-ab (34-35) 4.00
**232N** A57c Pair, #aa-ab (32-33) 4.00
**232P** A57c Pair, #aa-ab (30-31) 6.00
**232Q** A57c Pair, #aa-ab (22-23) 4.00
**232R** A57c Pair, #aa-ab (22A-22B) 4.50
**232S** A57c Pair, #aa-ab (26, 27A) 4.50
**232T** A57c Pair, #aa-ab (18-19) 7.50
**232U** A57c Pair, #aa-ab (16-17) 5.50
**232V** A57c Pair, #aa-ab (16-16A) 7.50
**232W** A57c Pair, #aa-ab (14-15) 6.50
**233A** A57c Pair, #aa-ab (13-13A) 7.50
**233B** A57c Pair, #aa-ab (11-12) 8.00
**233C** A57c Pair, #aa-ab (10, 11A) 6.50
**233D** A57c Pair, #aa-ab (8-9) 7.50
**233E** A57c Pair, #aa-ab (7, 8A) 8.00
**233F** A57c Pair, #aa-ab (29, 32B) 6.00
**233G** A57c Pair, #aa-ab (24-25) 6.00
**233H** A57c Pair, #aa-ab (27-28) 6.00
**233J** A57c Pair, #aa-ab (20-21) 7.50
*Nos. 232A-233J (30)* 151.50

**Souvenir Sheets**

***Perf. 13x13½, 13½x13, 13½***

**233K** A57c 75fr multi 6.50
**233L** A57c 100fr multi 6.00
**233M** A57c 200fr multi 6.00
**233N** A57c 300fr multi 6.00
**233P** A57c 350fr multi 12.00
**233Q** A57c 400fr multi 16.00
**233R** A57c 400fr multi 10.00
**233S** A57c 400fr multi 10.00
**233T** A57c 400fr multi 6.00
**233U** A57c 500fr multi 13.50
*Nos. 233K-233U (10)* 92.00

Nos. 232A 60fr, 232B 40fr, 232C 50fr, 232D 70fr, 232E 80fr, 232F 200fr, 232G, 232H 200fr, 232J 200fr, 232K, 232L, 232M 200fr, 232N-233U are airmail.

Issued: 1971 — No. 232A, 2/24; No. 232B, 3/30; No. 232C, 3/4; Nos. 232D, 233K, 3/15; No. 232E, 4/12; Nos. 232F, 233L, 4/26; No. 232G, 8/10; No. 232H, 9/6; No. 232J, 9/23; No. 232K, 10/6; No. 232L, 10/26; No. 232M, 11/16; No. 232N, 11/20.

1972 — Nos. 232P, 233P, Jan.; Nos. 232Q, 233M-233N, Feb.; Nos. 233Q-233R, May; Nos. 232R, 233S, 6/15; Nos. 232S, 233T, 6/26; No. 232T, 8/8; No. 232U, 8/17; No. 232V, 8/30; Nos. 232W, 233U, 12/11; No. 233A, 12/18; No. 233B, 12/28.

1973 — Nos. 233C-233J.

Nos. 233K-233L, 233T-233U each contain one 37x62mm stamp. Nos. 233N, 233P each contain one 32x50mm stamp. No. 233M contains one 45x65mm stamp. Nos. 233Q-233R, 233U each contain one 65x45mm stamp.

Nos. 232Q-232V, 233G, 233J, 233R-233U and possibly 232P, 232W-233F, 233H probably were not available in Chad.

Symbolic Tree — A58

**1971, Mar. 21 Engr. *Perf. 13***

**236** A58 40fr bl grn, dk red & grn 1.00 .25

Intl. year against racial discrimination.

Paintings of Flowers — A58a

Designs: 1fr, The Three Graces (detail), by Rubens. 4fr, Imperial Bouquet, by Van Os. 5fr, Bouquet, by Jan Brueghel.

**1971, Apr. 28 Litho. *Perf. 12x12½***

**236A** A58a Strip of 3, #a-c 5.50 —

For overprint see No. 278A.

Summer Olympic Games A58b

15fr, Swimming. 20fr, Women's relay races. 25fr, Swimming, medals. 50fr, Running.

***Perf. 12x12½, 12½x12***

**1971, Apr. 28 Litho.**

**236B** A58b 15fr multi, vert. 1.60 —
**236C** A58b 20fr multi, vert. 2.50 —
**236D** A58b 25fr multi 3.00 —
*Nos. 236B-236D (3)* 7.10

**Embossed**

***Perf. 13***

**236E** A58b 25fr gold, like No. 236D 17.50

**Souvenir Sheet**

**Litho.**

***Die Cut Perf 13***

**236F** A58b 50fr multicolored 10.00

Nos. 236D-236F are airmail. No. 236F contains one 62x36mm stamp.

Issued: Nos. 236B-236D, 236F, 4/28; No. 236E, 11/1.

For overprints see Nos. 251A-251D.

No. 236E probably was not available in Chad.

Map of Africa, Radar Antenna — A59

Map of Africa and: 40fr, Communications tower. 50fr, Communications satellite.

**1971, May 17 Engr. *Perf. 13***

**237** A59 5fr ultra, org & dk red .25 .25
**238** A59 40fr pur, emer & brn .75 .25
**239** A59 50fr dk red, blk & brn 1.00 .25
*Nos. 237-239 (3)* 2.00 .75

3rd World Telecommunications Day.

Apollo 11 A59a

**1971, July 5 Embossed *Perf. 13***

**239A** A59a 10fr gold 22.50
*b.* Sheet of 1, Imperf. 40.00

No. 239Ab contains one 73x45mm stamp with same size design as No. 239A.

Nos. 239A-239Ab probably were not available in Chad.

No. 225F Overprinted in Gold

**1971, July 17 Litho. *Perf. 12x12½***

**239C** A50b Strip of 3, #a-c 4.75

1972 Winter Olympics, Sapporo.

**Nos. 228A-228B, 228D Ovptd. with "MUNICH 72" and Olympic Rings in Gold**

***Perf. 12½x12, 12x12½***

**1971, Nov. 1 Litho.**

**239D** A54a Strip of 3, #a-c 10.00
**239E** A54a Pair, #a-b + label 6.00

**Souvenir Sheet**

***Perf. 13½x13***

**239F** A54a 40fr on #228D 20.00

UNICEF Emblem and Children — A60

**1971, Dec. 11 Engr. *Perf. 13***

**240** A60 50fr Prus bl, emer & brt pink 2.00 .25

25th anniv. of UNICEF.

Gorane Nangara Dancers — A61

Dancers: 15fr, Girls' initiation dance, Yondo. 30fr, Women of M'Boum, vert. 40fr, Men of Sara Kaba, vert.

**1971, Dec. 18 Litho. *Perf. 13***

**241** A61 10fr blk & multi .75 .25
**242** A61 15fr brn org & multi 1.10 .25
**243** A61 30fr bl & multi 1.50 .25
**244** A61 40fr yel grn & multi 1.90 .25
*Nos. 241-244 (4)* 5.25 1.00

Nos. 205-210 Ovptd. in Gold

**1971 Litho. *Perf. 12½x13, 13x12½***

**244A-244F** A45 1fr on #205-210 4.50

Nos. 244A-244F probably were not available in Chad.

Presidents Pompidou and Tombalbaye, Map with Paris and Fort Lamy
A62

**1972, Jan. 25 Photo. *Perf. 13***
**245** A62 40fr blue & multi 1.60 .25

Visit of Pres. Georges Pompidou of France, Jan. 1972.

Nos. 181-204 Ovptd. in Gold

**1972, Feb. 7 Litho. *Perf. 12½x13***
**245A-245X** A44 1fr on #181-204 20.00

Nos. 245A-245X probably were not available in Chad.

**Nos. 231G-231I Ovptd. in Gold**

a

b

**1972, Feb. Litho. *Perf. 12x12½***
**246A** A57b 50c Pair, #d.-e. 1.50
**246B** A57b 1fr Pair, #f.-g. 2.25
**246C** A57b 2fr Pair, #h.-i. 2.75

Nos. 246A-246C probably were not available in Chad.

President Tombalbaye
A63

**1972, Apr. 13 Litho. *Perf. 13***
**247** A63 30fr multi .40 .25
**247A** A63 40fr multi .60 .25
*Nos. 247-247A,C112-C113 (4)* 2.65 1.15

Downhill Skiing
A64

75fr, Women's figure skating. 150fr, Luge.

**1972, Apr. 13 *Perf. 13½***
**248** A64 25fr multi .30 .25
**249** A64 75fr multi .75 .25
**250** A64 150fr multi 1.50 .45
*Nos. 248-250,C114-C115 (5)* 6.45 2.00

11th Winter Olympic Games, Sapporo, Japan.

Heart — A65

**1972, Apr. 25 Engr. *Perf. 13***
**251** A65 100fr purple, bl & car 1.60 .25

"Your heart is your health," World Health Month.

Nos. 236B-236D, 236F Ovptd. in Gold

**1972 Litho. *Perf. 12x12½, 12½x12***
**251A** A58b 15fr multicolored 3.25
**251B** A58b 20fr multicolored 5.00
**251C** A58b 25fr multicolored 7.75
*Nos. 251A-251C (3)* 16.00

**Souvenir Sheet**
***Die Cut Perf 13***

**251D** A58b 50fr multicolored 47.50

Nos. 251C-251D are airmail.

Gorrizia Dubiosa — A66

Insects and Spiders: 2fr, Spider (argiope sector). 3fr, Silk spider (nephila senegalense). 4fr, Beetle (oryctes boas). 5fr, Dragonfly (hemistigma albipunctata).

**1972, May 6 Photo.**
**252** A66 1fr green & multi 1.25 .25
**253** A66 2fr blue & multi 2.00 .25
**254** A66 3fr car rose & multi 2.25 .30
**255** A66 4fr yellow grn & multi 4.00 .40
**256** A66 5fr dp green & multi 4.50 .60
*Nos. 252-256 (5)* 14.00 1.80

Trains
A66a

10fr, Orient Express. 40fr, Osaka Express. 50fr, St. Germain. 150fr, Blue train. 200fr, Trans-Europe Express.
300fr, Rogers "Madison," 1855.

**1972 Litho. *Perf. 12***
**256A** A66a 10fr multi 1.00
**256B** A66a 40fr multi 2.25
**256C** A66a 50fr multi 2.50
**256D** A66a 150fr multi 5.00
**256E** A66a 200fr multi 9.25
*Nos. 256A-256E (5)* 20.00

**Souvenir Sheet**

**256F** A66a 300fr multi 14.00

No. 256F contains one 60x40mm stamp. See note before No. 225A.

Scout Greeting
A67

70fr, Mountain climbing. 80fr, Canoeing.

**1972, May 15 Photo.**
**257** A67 30fr multi .75 .25
**258** A67 70fr multi 1.40 .25
**259** A67 80fr multi 1.75 .25
*Nos. 257-259,C118-C119 (5)* 8.55 1.65

Scout Jamboree.

Hurdles, Motion and Olympic Emblems — A68

Motion and Olympic Emblems and: 130fr, Gymnast on rings. 150fr, Swimming. 300fr, Bicycling.

**1972, June 9 Litho. *Perf. 13½***
**260** A68 50fr blk & multi .75 .25
**261** A68 130fr blk & multi 1.90 .25
**262** A68 150fr blk & multi 2.25 .30
*Nos. 260-262 (3)* 4.90 .80

**Souvenir Sheet**

**263** A68 300fr blk & multi 5.00 2.00

20th Olympic Games, Munich, Aug. 26-Sept. 10.

Ski Jump, Kasaya, Japan
A69

Designs: 75fr, Cross-country skiing, P. Tyldum, Sweden. 100fr, Figure-skating, pairs, L. Rodnina and A. Ulanov, USSR. 130fr, Men's speed skating, A. Schenk, Netherlands.

**1972, June 15 *Perf. 14½***
**264** A69 25fr gold & multi .40 .25
**265** A69 75fr gold & multi 1.00 .25
**266** A69 100fr gold & multi 1.50 .40
**267** A69 130fr gold & multi 1.90 .50
*Nos. 264-267,C130-C131 (6)* 11.55 3.15

11th Winter Olympic Games, gold-medal winners. Nos. 264-267 exist se-tenant with label showing earth satellite.

**Nos. 227A-227D, 227F Ovptd. in Gold**

**1972 Litho. *Perf. 12***
**267A** A53a 1fr multicolored .95
**267B** A53a 4fr multicolored 1.20
**267C** A53a 5fr multicolored 1.90
**267D** A53a 5fr multicolored 1.90
*Nos. 267A-267D (4)* 5.95

**Souvenir Sheet**
***Perf. 13½x13***

**267E** A53a 15fr multicolored 9.00

Nos. 267D-267E are airmail.
Nos. 267A-267E probably were not available in Chad.

TV Tower and Weight-lifting — A70

Designs (TV Tower, Munich and): 40fr, Woman sprinter. 60fr, Soccer goalkeeper.

**1972, Aug. 15 Litho. *Perf. 14½***
**268** A70 20fr gold & multi .65 .25
**269** A70 40fr gold & multi .80 .25
**270** A70 60fr gold & multi 1.40 .25
*Nos. 268-270,C135-C137 (6)* 10.70 2.65

20th Summer Olympic Games, Munich. Nos. 268-270 exist se-tenant with label showing arms of Munich.
Nos. 268-270, C135-C137 exist in souvenir sheets of one. Value, set, $130.

Domestic Animals — A71

**1972, Aug. 29 Engr. *Perf. 13***
**271** A71 25fr Dromedary 1.40 .25
**272** A71 30fr Horse 1.75 .25
**273** A71 40fr Dog 2.75 .30
**274** A71 45fr Goat 3.00 .40
*Nos. 271-274 (4)* 8.90 1.20

For surcharge see No. 293.

Tobacco Cultivation — A72

**1972, Oct. 24 Engr. *Perf. 13***
**275** A72 40fr shown .75 .25
**276** A72 50fr Plowing 1.25 .25

Massa Warrior — A73

Design: 20fr, Moundang warrior.

**1972, Nov. 15 Photo. *Perf. 14x13***
**277** A73 15fr orange & multi .70 .25
**278** A73 20fr yellow & multi .90 .25

No. 236A Overprinted in Gold

**1972 Litho. *Perf. 12x12½***
**278A** A58a Strip of 3, #a-c 5.50

No. 278A probably was not available in Chad.

King Faisal and Pres. Tombalbaye
A74

**1972, Nov. 17 Litho. *Perf. 13***
**279** A74 100fr gold & multi 2.50 .75

Visit of King Faisal of Saudi Arabia. See No. C143.

Gen. Gowon and Pres. Tombalbaye
A75

**1972, Dec. 7**
**280** A75 70fr multi 1.00 .25

Visit of Gen. Yakubu Gowon of Nigeria.

Olympic Emblem and 100-meter Sprint, Valeri Borzov, USSR — A76

Designs (Olympic Emblem and): 20fr, Shotput, Komar, Poland. 40fr, Hammer throw, Bondartchuk, USSR. 60fr, Discus, Danek, Czechoslovakia.

**1972, Dec. 22** *Perf. 11*

| | | | | |
|---|---|---|---|---|
| **281** | A76 | 10fr multi | .55 | .25 |
| **282** | A76 | 20fr multi | .55 | .25 |
| **283** | A76 | 40fr multi | .70 | .25 |
| **284** | A76 | 60fr multi | 1.10 | .30 |
| | | *Nos. 281-284,C148-C149 (6)* | 10.15 | 2.40 |

20th Summer Olympic Games, winners.

Nos. 281-284, C148-C149 exist as souvenir sheets of one. Value, set, $150.

Olympic Emblem and Fencing, Woyda, Poland — A77

Olympic Emblem and: 30fr, 3-day equestrian event, Richard Meade, Gt. Britain. 50fr, Two-man sculls, Brietzke-Mager, East Germany.

**1972, Dec. 22**

| | | | | |
|---|---|---|---|---|
| **285** | A77 | 20fr gold & multi | .65 | .25 |
| **286** | A77 | 30fr gold & multi | .65 | .25 |
| **287** | A77 | 50fr gold & multi | 1.00 | .25 |
| | | *Nos. 285-287,C151-C152 (5)* | 10.55 | 2.50 |

20th Summer Olympic Games, winners.

1972 Summer Olympics Gold Medalists — A77a

20fr, Teofilo Stevenson, boxing, Cuba. 25fr, Yugoslavia, team handball. 30fr, M. Peters, pentathlon, Great Britain. 40fr, basketball, USSR. No. 287E, W. Ruska, judo, Netherlands. No. 287F, Women's gymnastics, Ludmila Tourischeva, USSR. 75fr, Men's volleyball, Japan. No. 287H, A. Scalzone, shooting, Italy. No. 287I, Soccer, Poland. 130fr, J. Williams, archery, US. No. 287K, A. Nakayama, men's rings, Japan. No. 287L, Field hockey, West Germany. 200fr, Vassily Alexeiev, weight lifting, USSR. 250fr, D. Morelon, cycling, France.

**1972, Dec. 22** **Litho.** *Perf. 11½*

| | | | |
|---|---|---|---|
| **287A** | A77a | 20fr multicolored | |
| **287B** | A77a | 25fr multicolored | |
| **287C** | A77a | 30fr multicolored | |
| **287D** | A77a | 40fr multicolored | |
| **287E** | A77a | 50fr multicolored | |
| **287F** | A77a | 50fr multicolored | |
| **287G** | A77a | 75fr multicolored | |
| **287H** | A77a | 100fr multicolored | |
| **287I** | A77a | 100fr multicolored | |
| **287J** | A77a | 130fr multicolored | |
| **287K** | A77a | 150fr multicolored | |
| **287L** | A77a | 150fr multicolored | |
| | | *Nos. 287A-287L (12)* | 18.00 |

**Souvenir Sheets**

***Perf. 15***

| | | | |
|---|---|---|---|
| **287M** | A77a | 200fr multicolored | 13.50 |
| **287N** | A77a | 250fr multicolored | 13.50 |

Nos. 287G-287N are airmail.

Soviet Flag and Shield — A78

**1972, Dec. 30** **Litho.** *Perf. 12*

| | | | | |
|---|---|---|---|---|
| **288** | A78 | 150fr red & multi | 1.90 | .40 |

50th anniversary of the Soviet Union.

High Jump — A79

Designs (Games Emblem and): 125fr, Running. 200fr, Shot put. 250fr, Discus.

**1973, Jan. 17** **Litho.** *Perf. 13½x13*

| | | | | |
|---|---|---|---|---|
| **289** | A79 | 50fr vio bl & multi | .75 | .25 |
| **290** | A79 | 125fr olive & multi | 1.60 | .40 |
| **291** | A79 | 200fr lilac & multi | 3.00 | .65 |
| | | *Nos. 289-291 (3)* | 5.35 | 1.30 |

**Souvenir Sheet**

| | | | | |
|---|---|---|---|---|
| **292** | A79 | 250fr brn & multi | 3.75 | 2.25 |

2nd African Games, Lagos, Nigeria, 1/7-18.

Paintings with Musical Instruments A79a

Details from Paintings: 30fr, Madeleine Playing her Lute, by unknown artist. 70fr, A Concert, by Lorenzo Costa. 100fr, Bass and Sheet Music, by Jean-Baptiste Oudry, horiz. 125fr, St. Cecilia and Angel, by Carlo Saraceni. 150fr, Woman Listening to Violinist, by Gabriel Metsu. 300fr, Still Life with Musical Instruments, by Pieter Claesz, horiz.

**1973, Apr.** **Litho.** *Perf. 11½*

| | | | |
|---|---|---|---|
| **292A** | A79a | 30fr multicolored | |
| **292B** | A79a | 70fr multicolored | |
| **292C** | A79a | 100fr multicolored | |
| **292D** | A79a | 125fr multicolored | |
| **292E** | A79a | 150fr multicolored | |
| | | *Nos. 292A-292E (5)* | 13.50 |

**Souvenir Sheet**

***Perf. 15***

| | | | |
|---|---|---|---|
| **292F** | A79a | 300fr multicolored | 13.50 |

Nos. 292D-292F are airmail.

No. 271 Srchd. and Ovptd. in Red

**1973, Aug. 16** **Engr.** *Perf. 13*

| | | | | |
|---|---|---|---|---|
| **293** | A71 | 100fr on 25fr multi | 2.25 | .50 |

African solidarity in drought emergency.

**African Postal Union Issue**

Common Design Type

**1973, Sept. 17** **Engr.** *Perf. 13*

| | | | | |
|---|---|---|---|---|
| **294** | CD137 | 100fr multicolored | 1.75 | .40 |

Easter — A79b

Details from paintings: 40fr, Christ on the Cross, by Lucas Cranach. 60fr, Supper in Emmaus, by Titian, horiz. 120fr, The Crucifixion, by Durer. 150fr, The Tribute, by Titian. 250fr, The Pieta, by Botticelli. 400fr, Entombment of Christ, by Gaspard Isenmann, horiz.

**1973** **Litho.** *Perf. 11½*

| | | | |
|---|---|---|---|
| **294A** | A79b | 40fr multicolored | |
| **294B** | A79b | 60fr multicolored | |
| **294C** | A79b | 120fr multicolored | |
| **294D** | A79b | 150fr multicolored | |
| **294E** | A79b | 250fr multicolored | |
| | | *Nos. 294A-294E (5)* | 13.50 |

**Souvenir Sheet**

***Perf. 15***

| | | | |
|---|---|---|---|
| **294F** | A79b | 400fr multicolored | 13.50 |

Nos. 294A, 294D-294F are airmail.

Animals — A79c

**1973** **Litho.** *Perf. 13½*

| | | | |
|---|---|---|---|
| **294G** | A79c | 20fr Sheep | |
| **294H** | A79c | 30fr Camels | |
| **294J** | A79c | 100fr Cats | |
| **294K** | A79c | 130fr Dogs | |
| **294L** | A79c | 150fr Horses | |
| | | *Nos. 294G-294L (5)* | 13.50 |

Nos. 294J-294L are airmail.

See note before No. 225A.

Christmas — A79d

30fr, The Virgin & Infant Surrounded by Saints, by Lorenzo Lotto. 40fr, Madonna and Child with St. Peter and a Martyred Saint, by Paolo Veronese (not Tintoretto), vert. 55fr, Nativity Scene, by Martin Schongauer, vert. 60fr, Nativity Scene, by Federico Barocci, vert. 250fr, Adoration of the Magi, by Stephan Lochner, vert. 400fr, Epiphany, by Hans Memling.

**1973** **Litho.** *Perf. 11½*

| | | | |
|---|---|---|---|
| **294M** | A79d | 30fr multicolored | |
| **294N** | A79d | 40fr multicolored | |
| **294P** | A79d | 55fr multicolored | |
| **294Q** | A79d | 60fr multicolored | |
| **294R** | A79d | 250fr multicolored | |
| | | *Nos. 294M-294R (5)* | 13.50 |

**Souvenir Sheet**

***Perf. 15***

| | | | |
|---|---|---|---|
| **294S** | A79d | 400fr multicolored | 13.50 |

Nos. 294Q-294S are airmail.

See note before No. 225A.

Insects — A80

No. 295, Dinothrombium Tinctorium. No. 296, Bupreste sternocera. No. 297, Diptere hyperechia. No. 298, Chrysis. No. 299, Longicorn beetle. No. 300, Spider.

**1974, Sept. 3** **Photo.** *Perf. 13*

| | | | | |
|---|---|---|---|---|
| **295** | A80 | 25fr multicolored | 1.50 | .25 |
| **296** | A80 | 30fr multicolored | 2.25 | .25 |
| **297** | A80 | 40fr multicolored | 2.75 | .25 |
| **298** | A80 | 50fr multicolored | 3.25 | .35 |
| **299** | A80 | 100fr multicolored | 4.75 | .65 |
| **300** | A80 | 130fr multicolored | 7.50 | .95 |
| | | *Nos. 295-300 (6)* | 22.00 | 2.70 |

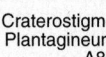

Rotary Emblem — A81

**1975, Apr. 11** **Typo.** *Perf. 13*

| | | | | |
|---|---|---|---|---|
| **301** | A81 | 50fr multi | 1.00 | .25 |

Rotary International, 70th anniversary.

Craterostigma Plantagineum A82

Flowers: 10fr, Tapinanthus globiferus. 15fr, Commelina forskalaei, vert. 20fr, Adenium obesum. 25fr, Yellow hibiscus. 30fr, Red hibiscus. 40fr, Kigelia africana.

**1975, Sept. 25** **Photo.** *Perf. 13*

| | | | | |
|---|---|---|---|---|
| **302** | A82 | 5fr org & multi | .40 | .25 |
| **303** | A82 | 10fr gray bl & multi | .60 | .25 |
| **304** | A82 | 15fr yel grn & multi | .75 | .25 |
| **305** | A82 | 20fr lt brn & multi | 1.00 | .25 |
| **306** | A82 | 25fr lil & multi | 1.75 | .25 |
| **307** | A82 | 30fr bis & multi | 1.90 | .35 |
| **308** | A82 | 40fr ultra & multi | 3.00 | .50 |
| | | *Nos. 302-308 (7)* | 9.40 | 2.10 |

A. G. Bell, Satellite and Waves — A83

**1976, June 10** **Litho.** *Perf. 12½*

| | | | | |
|---|---|---|---|---|
| **309** | A83 | 100fr bl, brn & ocher | 1.40 | .40 |
| **310** | A83 | 125fr lt grn, brn & ocher | 1.90 | .60 |

Centenary of first telephone call by Alexander Graham Bell, Mar. 10, 1876.



Ice Hockey, USSR A84

90fr, Ski jump, Karl Schnabl, Austria.

**1976, June 21** *Perf. 14*

| | | | | |
|---|---|---|---|---|
| **311** | A84 | 60fr multi | .75 | .25 |
| **312** | A84 | 90fr multi | 1.25 | .25 |
| | | *Nos. 311-312,C178-C179 (4)* | 8.25 | 2.10 |

12th Winter Olympic Games, winners. See No. C180.



High Hurdles — A85

**1976, July 12 Litho. *Perf. 13½***

313 A85 45fr multi .70 .25
*Nos. 313,C187-C189 (4)* 8.70 1.70

21st Summer Olympic Games, Montreal, Canada.

See No. C190.

Mars Landing and Viking Rocket — A86

Mars Landing and: 90fr, Viking trajectory, Earth to Mars.

**1976, July 23 *Perf. 14***

| | | | |
|---|---|---|---|
| **314** A86 45fr multi | .50 | .25 |
| **315** A86 90fr multi | 1.00 | .25 |
| *Nos. 314-315,C191-C193 (5)* | 7.35 | 2.10 |

Viking Mars project.

See Nos. C191-C193. For overprints see Nos. 379-380.

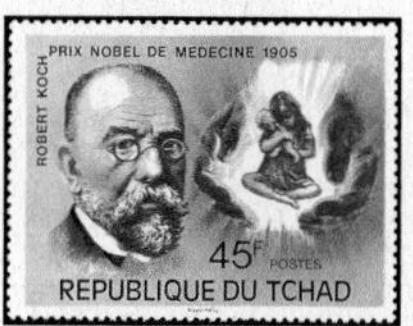
Robert Koch, Medicine A87

Design: 90fr, Anatole France, literature.

**1976, Dec. 15**

| | | |
|---|---|---|
| **316** A87 45fr multi | .75 | .25 |
| **317** A87 90fr multi | 1.50 | .25 |
| *Nos. 316-317,C196-C198 (5)* | 9.75 | 2.05 |

Nobel Prize winners.

Map and Flag of Chad, Clasped Hands — A88

120fr, Map of Chad, people & occupations.

**1976, Sept. 15 Litho. *Perf. 12½x13***

| | | |
|---|---|---|
| **318** A88 30fr multi | .60 | .25 |
| **319** A88 60fr orange & multi | 1.10 | .30 |
| **320** A88 120fr brown & multi | 2.25 | .50 |
| *Nos. 318-320 (3)* | 3.95 | 1.05 |

National reconciliation.

Freed Political Prisoners — A89

Designs: 60fr, Parade of cadets.

**1976, Sept. 25 Litho. *Perf. 12½***

| | | |
|---|---|---|
| **321** A89 30fr blue & multi | .30 | .25 |
| **322** A89 60fr black & multi | .75 | .25 |
| **323** A89 120fr red & multi | 1.40 | .25 |
| *Nos. 321-323 (3)* | 2.45 | .75 |

Revolution of Apr. 13, 1975, 1st anniv.

Decorated Calabashes A90

Designs: Various pyrographed calabashes.

**1976, Nov. Litho. *Perf. 12½x13***

| | | |
|---|---|---|
| **324** A90 30fr multi | .40 | .25 |
| **325** A90 60fr multi | .90 | .25 |
| **326** A90 120fr multi | 1.75 | .25 |
| *Nos. 324-326 (3)* | 3.05 | .75 |

Germany No. C57 and Friedrichshafen, Germany — A91

**1977, Mar. 30 *Perf. 14***

| | | |
|---|---|---|
| **327** A91 100fr multi | 1.40 | .25 |
| *Nos. 327,C206-C209 (5)* | 11.55 | 2.10 |

75th anniversary of the Zeppelin.

Elizabeth II in Coronation Regalia and Clergy — A92

Design: 450fr, Elizabeth II and Prince Philip.

**1977, June 15 Litho. *Perf. 14x13½***

**328** A92 250fr multi 3.25 .75

**Souvenir Sheet**

**329** A92 450fr multi 6.00 2.50

25th anniv. of the reign of Elizabeth II.

Nos. 328-329 exist imperf. For overprints see Nos. 347-348.

Simon Bolivar — A93

Famous Personalities: 175fr, Joseph J. Roberts. No. 332, Queen Wilhelmina of Netherlands. No. 333, Charles de Gaulle. 325fr, King Baudouin and Queen Fabiola of Belgium.

**1977, June 15 *Perf. 13½x14***

| | | |
|---|---|---|
| **330** A93 150fr multi | 1.50 | .30 |
| **331** A93 175fr multi | 2.25 | .45 |
| **332** A93 200fr multi | 3.00 | .65 |
| **333** A93 200fr multi | 3.00 | .75 |
| **334** A93 325fr multi | 4.00 | 1.00 |
| *Nos. 330-334 (5)* | 13.75 | 3.15 |

Post and Telecommunications Emblem — A94

Map of Chad and Waves A95

Society Emblem A96

**1977, Aug. 15 Litho. *Perf. 13***

**335** A94 30fr yel & blk .50 .25

***Perf. 12½***

**336** A95 60fr multi .75 .25

***Perf. 13½x13***

| | | |
|---|---|---|
| **337** A96 120fr multi | 1.60 | .50 |
| *Nos. 335-337 (3)* | 2.85 | 1.00 |

Telecommunications (30fr); Natl. Telecommunications School, 10th anniv. (60fr); Intl. Telecommunication Soc. of Chad (120fr).

WHO Emblem and Man (Back Pain) — A97

World Rheumatism Year (WHO Emblem and): 60fr, Woman's head (neck pain), horiz. 120fr, Leg (knee pain).

***Perf. 12½x13, 13x12½***

**1977, Nov. 10 Engr.**

| | | |
|---|---|---|
| **338** A97 30fr multi | .50 | .25 |
| **339** A97 60fr multi | 1.00 | .25 |
| **340** A97 120fr multi | 1.40 | .40 |
| *Nos. 338-340 (3)* | 2.90 | .90 |

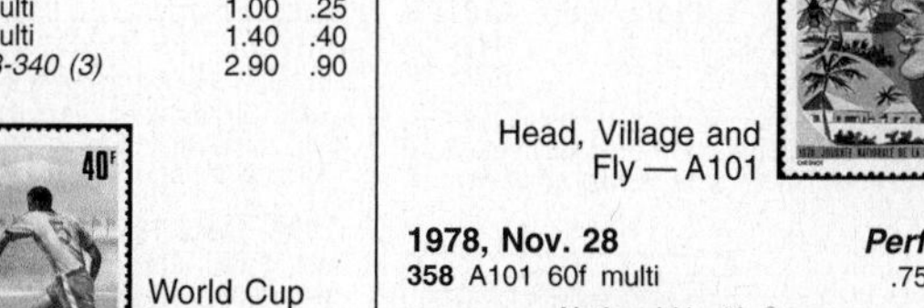
World Cup Emblems and Saving a Goal — A98

Designs (Argentina '78, World Cup Emblems and): 60fr, Heading the ball. 100fr, Referee whistling a goal. 200fr, World Cup poster. 300fr, Pelé. 500fr, Helmut Schoen and Munich stadium.

**1977, Nov. 25 Litho. *Perf. 13½***

| | | |
|---|---|---|
| **341** A98 40fr multi | .50 | .25 |
| **342** A98 60fr multi | .75 | .25 |
| **343** A98 100fr multi | 1.10 | .25 |
| **344** A98 200fr multi | 2.50 | .50 |
| **345** A98 300fr multi | 3.75 | .75 |
| *Nos. 341-345 (5)* | 8.60 | 2.00 |

**Souvenir Sheet**

**346** A98 500fr multi 5.75 3.00

World Cup Soccer Championship, Argentina '78.

For overprints see Nos. 359-364.

**Nos. 328-329 Overprinted in Silver**

**1978, Sept. 13 *Perf. 14x13½***

**347** A92 250fr multi 3.00 1.00

**Souvenir Sheet**

**348** A92 450fr multi 5.50 4.50

25th anniv. of coronation of Elizabeth II.

Abraham and Melchisedek, by Rubens A99

Rubens Paintings: 120fr, Helene Fourment, vert. 200fr, David and the Elders of Israel. 300fr, Anne of Austria, vert. 500fr, Marie de Medicis, vert.

**1978, Nov. 23 Litho. *Perf. 13½***

| | | |
|---|---|---|
| **349** A99 60fr multi | .75 | .25 |
| **350** A99 120fr multi | 1.75 | .35 |
| **351** A99 200fr multi | 3.00 | .75 |
| **352** A99 300fr multi | 4.50 | 1.25 |
| *Nos. 349-352 (4)* | 10.00 | 2.60 |

**Souvenir Sheet**

**353** A99 500fr multi 6.75 3.00

Peter Paul Rubens (1577-1640).

Dürer Portrait — A100

Dürer Paintings: 150fr, Jacob Muffel. 250fr, Young Woman. 350fr, Oswolt Krel.

**1978, Nov. 23**

| | | |
|---|---|---|
| **354** A100 60fr multi | .60 | .25 |
| **355** A100 150fr multi | 1.75 | .50 |
| **356** A100 250fr multi | 3.00 | .80 |
| **357** A100 350fr multi | 4.50 | 1.25 |
| *Nos. 354-357 (4)* | 9.85 | 2.80 |

Head, Village and Fly — A101

**1978, Nov. 28 *Perf. 13***

**358** A101 60f multi .75 .25

National Health Day.

**Nos. 341-346 Overprinted in Silver**

a

b

c

d

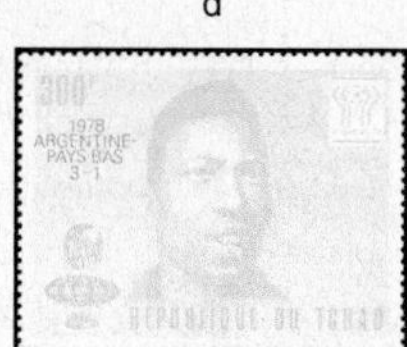
e

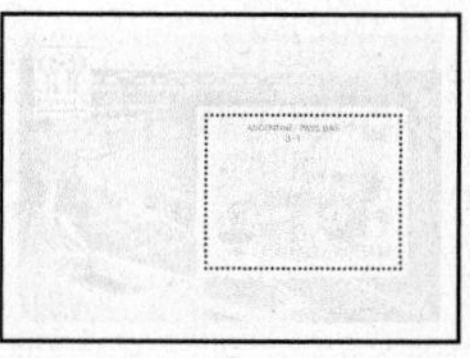
f

**1978, Dec. 30 Litho. *Perf. 13½***

**359** A98(a) 40fr multi .50 .25
**360** A98(b) 60fr multi .75 .25
**361** A98(c) 100fr multi 1.40 .40
**362** A98(d) 200fr multi 2.50 .75
**363** A98(e) 300fr multi 3.50 1.25
*Nos. 359-363 (5)* 8.65 2.90

**Souvenir Sheet**

**364** A98(f) 500fr multi 5.75 5.00

World Soccer Championship winners.

UPU Emblems, Camel Caravan, Satellites A102

Design: 150fr, Obus woman and houses, Massa Territory, hibiscus.

**1979, June 8 Litho. *Perf. 12x12½***

**365** A102 60fr multi 3.00 .25
**366** A102 150fr multi 5.00 .40

Philexafrique II, Libreville, Gabon, June 8-17. Nos. 365, 366 each printed in sheets of 10 with 5 labels showing exhibition emblem.

Wildlife Fund Emblem and Gazelle A103

Protected Animals.

**1979, Sept. 15 Litho. *Perf. 14½***

**367** A103 40fr shown 1.75 .30
**368** A103 50fr Addax 2.00 .50
**369** A103 60fr Oryx antelope 2.50 .75
**370** A103 100fr Cheetah 3.75 1.40
**371** A103 150fr Wild Ass 5.25 1.90
**372** A103 300fr Rhinoceros 10.00 3.00
*Nos. 367-372 (6)* 25.25 7.85

Souvenir Sheet

Holy Family, by Dürer A104

**1979, Sept. 1 *Perf. 13½***

**373** A104 500fr brown & dull red 6.75 2.50

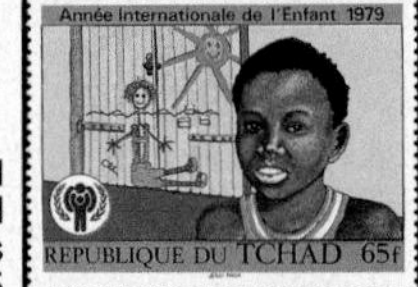


Boy and Handpainted Doors A105

IYC Emblem and: 75fr, Oriental girl. 100fr, Caucasian girl, doves. 150fr, African boys. 250fr, Pencil and outlines of child's hands.

**1979, Sept. 19 Litho. *Perf. 13½***

**374** A105 65fr multi .60 .25
**375** A105 75fr multi .75 .25
**376** A105 100fr multi 1.00 .25
**377** A105 150fr multi 1.50 .40
*Nos. 374-377 (4)* 3.85 1.15

**Souvenir Sheet**

**378** A105 250fr multi 3.00 1.50

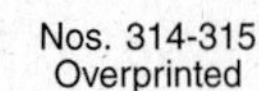

Nos. 314-315 Overprinted

**1979, Nov. 26 Litho. *Perf. 13½x14***

**379** A86 45fr multi .60 .25
**380** A86 90fr multi 1.00 .30
*Nos. 379-380,C240-C242 (5)* 7.45 2.55

Apollo 11 moon landing, 10th anniversary.

Ski Jump, Lake Placid '80 Emblem A106

Lake Placid '80 Emblem and: 20fr, Slalom, vert. 40fr, Biathlon, vert. 150fr, Women's slalom, vert. 350fr, Cross-country skiing. 500fr, Downhill skiing.

**1979, Dec. 18 *Perf. 14½***

**381** A106 20fr multi .30 .25
**382** A106 40fr multi .65 .25
**383** A106 60fr multi .80 .25
**384** A106 150fr multi 1.75 .50
**385** A106 350fr multi 3.00 1.40
**386** A106 500fr multi 4.50 1.90
*Nos. 381-386 (6)* 11.00 4.55

13th Winter Olympic Games, Lake Placid, NY, Feb. 12-24, 1980.

Jet over Map of Africa — A107

**1980, Feb. 20 Litho. *Perf. 12½***

**387** A107 15fr yellow & multi .25 .25
**388** A107 30fr blue & multi .40 .25
**389** A107 60fr red & multi .60 .25
*Nos. 387-389 (3)* 1.25 .75

ASECNA (Air Safety Board), 20th anniv.

---

A set of four stamps (50fr, 80fr, 100fr air post, 200fr air post) commemorating cooperation between Chad and Libya were prepared for use in 1981 but not issued. Value, $300.

---

1982 World Cup Soccer Championships, Spain — A108

**1982 Litho. *Perf. 13½***

**390** A108 30fr Hungary .30 .25
**391** A108 40fr Italy .40 .25
**392** A108 50fr Algeria .50 .25
**393** A108 60fr Argentina .60 .25
*Nos. 390-393,C258-C259 (6)* 5.80 1.75

21st Birthday of Princess Diana — A109

**1982, July 2 Litho. *Perf. 13½***

**395** A109 30fr 1961 .30 .25
**396** A109 40fr 1965 .40 .25
**397** A109 50fr 1967 .50 .25
**398** A109 60fr 1975 .60 .25
*Nos. 395-398,C260-C261 (6)* 5.80 2.20

For overprints see Nos. 413-419B.

A110

1984 Summer Olympics, Los Angeles A110a

No. 405A, Runner. No. 405B, Long jumper, vert.

**1982, Aug. 2 Litho. *Perf. 13½***

**399** A110 30fr Gymnast .30 .25
**400** A110 40fr Equestrian .40 .25
**401** A110 50fr Judo .50 .25
**402** A110 60fr High jump .60 .25
**403** A110 80fr Hurdles 1.00 .25
**404** A110 300fr Woman gymnast 3.00 .95
*Nos. 399-404 (6)* 5.80 2.20

**Souvenir Sheet**

**405** A110 500fr Relay race 4.75 1.50

For surcharge see No. C302.

**1982, July 31 Litho. & Embossed**

**405A** A110a 1500fr gold & multi 16.00

**Souvenir Sheet**

**405B** A110a 1500fr gold & multi 10.00

No. 405 contains one 56x39mm stamp. Nos. 403-405B airmail.

No. 405A exists in a souvenir sheet of 1. Value $47.50.

Scouting Year — A111

Boy Scouts, 75th Anniv. — A111a

Scouts from various countries. No. 412A, Lord Robert Baden-Powell. No. 412B, Scouts at campsite, Baden-Powell, horiz.

**1982, July 15**

**406** A111 30fr West Germany .30 .25
**407** A111 40fr Upper Volta .40 .25
**408** A111 50fr Mali .50 .25
**409** A111 60fr Scotland .60 .25
**410** A111 80fr Kuwait 1.00 .25
**411** A111 300fr Chad 3.00 .95
*Nos. 406-411 (6)* 5.80 2.20

**Souvenir Sheet**

**412** A111 500fr Chad, diff. 4.75 2.00

**Litho. & Embossed**

**412A** A111a 1500fr gold & multi 14.00

**Souvenir Sheet**

**412B** A111a 1500fr gold & multi 17.00

No. 412 contains one 53x35mm stamp. Nos. 410-412B airmail.

No. 412A exists in a souvenir sheet of 1. Value $40.

For overprints see Nos. 466-472B.

**Nos. 395-398, C260-C262B Overprinted "21 JUIN 1982 / WILLIAM ARTHUR PHILIP LOUIS/ PRINCE DE GALLES"**

**1982, Oct. 4 Litho. *Perf. 13½***

**413** A109 30fr multi .30 .25
**414** A109 40fr multi .40 .25
**415** A109 50fr multi .50 .25
**416** A109 60fr multi .60 .25
**417** A109 80fr multi 1.00 .25
**418** A109 300fr multi 3.00 .95
*Nos. 413-418 (6)* 5.80 2.20

**Souvenir Sheet**

**419** A109 500fr multi 5.50 1.60

**Litho. & Embossed**

**419A** AP71b 1500fr on #C262A 16.00

**Souvenir Sheet**

**419B** AP71b 1500fr on #C262B 10.00

Birth of Prince William of Wales, June 21. Nos. 417-419B airmail.

No. 419A exists in a souvenir sheet of 1. Value $42.50.

A112

1982 World Cup Soccer Championships, Spain — A112a

Various players and flags. No. 426A, Dino Zoff, Italy, holding World Cup trophy. No. 426B, Paolo Rossi, Italy, two players, trophy, horiz.

**1982, Nov. 30**

**420** A112 30fr multi .30 .25
**421** A112 40fr multi .40 .25
**422** A112 50fr multi .50 .25
**423** A112 60fr multi .60 .25
**424** A112 80fr multi 1.00 .25
**425** A112 300fr multi 3.00 .95
*Nos. 420-425 (6)* 5.80 2.20

**Souvenir Sheet**

**426** A112 500fr multi 4.75 2.00

**Litho. & Embossed**

**426A** A112a 1500fr gold & multi 16.00

**Souvenir Sheet**

**426B** A112a 1500fr gold & multi 16.00

No. 426 contains one 56x32mm stamp. Nos. 424-426B airmail.

No. 426A exists in a souvenir sheet of 1. Value $42.50.

For surcharge see No. C306.

A113

Chess Champions — A113a

30fr, Philidor. 40fr, Paul Morphy. 50fr, Howard Staunton. 60fr, Capablanca. 80fr, Boris Spassky. 300fr, Anatoly Karpov.

500fr, Victor Korchnoi. No. 433A, Bobby Fischer. No. 433B, William Steinitz.

**1982, Dec. 24**

**427** A113 30fr multi 1.00 .25
**428** A113 40fr multi 1.10 .25
**429** A113 50fr multi 1.25 .25
**430** A113 60fr multi 1.40 .25
**431** A113 80fr multi 2.10 .25
**432** A113 300fr multi 3.75 .75
*Nos. 427-432 (6)* 10.60 2.00

**Souvenir Sheet**

**433** A113 500fr multi 10.00 3.00

**Litho. & Embossed**

**433A** A113a 1500fr gold & multi 17.50

### Souvenir Sheet

**433B** A113a 1500fr gold & multi 12.00

No. 433 contains one 53x35mm stamp. Nos. 431-433B airmail.
No. 433A exists in a souvenir sheet of 1. Value $50.
For overprints see Nos. 459-465.

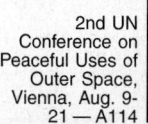

2nd UN Conference on Peaceful Uses of Outer Space, Vienna, Aug. 9-21 — A114

A114a

Inventors and Satellites: 30fr, K.E. Tsiolkovsky, Soyuz. 40fr, R.H. Goddard, space telescope design. 50fr, Korolev, ultraviolet telescope. 60fr, von Braun, Columbia space shuttle. 80fr, Esnault Pelterie, Ariana rocket. 300fr, H. Oberth, orbital space station. 500fr, Pres. Kennedy, Apollo 11 badge, lunar rover. No. 440A, Sir Bernard Lovell, Viking I & II. No. 440B, Sir Isaac Newton, satellite TDF 1.

**1983, Feb. 1 Litho. *Perf. 13½***

**434** A114 30fr multi .30 .25
**435** A114 40fr multi .40 .25
**436** A114 50fr multi .50 .25
**437** A114 60fr multi .60 .25
**438** A114 80fr multi 1.00 .25
**439** A114 300fr multi 3.00 .95
*Nos. 434-439 (6)* 5.80 2.20

### Souvenir Sheet

**440** A114 500fr multi 5.50 2.50

### Litho. & Embossed

**440A** A114a 1500fr gold & multi 16.00

### Souvenir Sheet

**440B** A114a 1500fr gold & multi 12.00

No. 440 contains one 42x50mm stamp. Nos. 438-440B airmail.
No. 440A exists in a souvenir sheet of 1. Value $50.

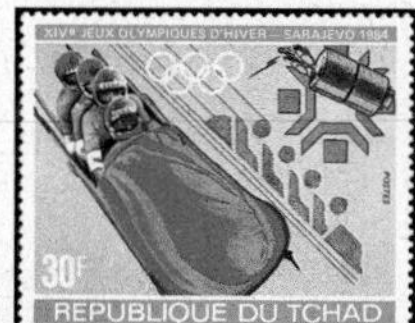

Bobsledding A115

Woman Figure Skater — A115a

40fr, Speed skating. 50fr, Cross-country skiing. 60fr, Hockey. 80fr, Ski jumping. 300fr, Downhill skiing.
500fr, Figure skating. No. 447B, Slalom skier, horiz.

**1983, Apr. 25 Litho. *Perf. 13½***

**441** A115 30fr shown .30 .25
**442** A115 40fr multi .40 .25
**443** A115 50fr multi .50 .25
**444** A115 60fr multi .60 .25
**445** A115 80fr multi 1.00 .30
**446** A115 300fr multi 3.00 1.10
*Nos. 441-446 (6)* 5.80 2.40

### Souvenir Sheet

**447** A115 500fr multi 5.50 1.60

### Litho. & Embossed

**447A** A115a 1500fr gold & multi 16.00

### Souvenir Sheet

**447B** A115a 1500fr gold & multi 12.00

14th Winter Olympic Games, Sarajevo, Yugoslavia, Feb. 8-19, 1984.
Nos. 445-447B airmail.
No. 447A exists in a souvenir sheet of 1. Value $45.
For surcharge see No. C298.

First Manned Balloon Flight, 200th Anniv. — A116

Designs: 25fr, Hot air balloon, Montgolfier Brothers. 45fr, Captive balloon, Pilatre De Rozier. 50fr, First parachute descent, Jacques Garnerin. 60fr, Chelsea balloon, J.P. Blanchard.

**1983, May 30 Litho. *Perf. 13½***

**448** A116 25fr multi .30 .25
**449** A116 45fr multi .40 .25
**450** A116 50fr multi .50 .25
**451** A116 60fr multi .60 .25
*Nos. 448-451,C268-C269 (6)* 5.80 1.65

Automobiles — A116a

Automobiles and their builders: 25fr, 1927 Mercedes Type S, Gottlieb Daimler and Karl Benz. 45fr, 1913 Torpedo Martini Type GC 32-2, 6L, Friedrich Martini. 50fr, 1926 Chrysler "70," Walter P. Chrysler. 60fr, 1929 Alfa Romeo 6C 1750 Grand Sport, Nicola Romeo. 80fr, 1934 Phantom II Continental, Stewart Rolls and Henry Royce. 250fr, 1948 Talbot Lago, Lord Shrewsbury and Talbot.

**1983, July 15 Litho. *Perf. 13½***

**451A** A116a 25fr multicolored
**451B** A116a 45fr multicolored
**451C** A116a 50fr multicolored
**451D** A116a 60fr multicolored
**451E** A116a 80fr multicolored
**451F** A116a 250fr multicolored
*Nos. 451A-451F (6)* 6.75 1.60

Nos. 451E-451F are airmail.

1984 Summer Olympics, Los Angeles — A117

A117a

**1983, Nov. 15 Litho. *Perf. 13½***

**452** A117 25fr Kayak .30 .25
**453** A117 45fr Long jump .60 .25
**454** A117 50fr Boxing .70 .25
**455** A117 60fr Discus .75 .25
**456** A117 80fr Running 1.00 .25
**457** A117 350fr Equestrian 3.50 .75
*Nos. 452-457 (6)* 6.85 2.00

### Souvenir Sheet

**458** A117 500fr Gymnastics 5.50 2.50

### Litho. & Embossed

**458A** A117a 1500fr Hurdles 16.00

### Souvenir Sheet

**458B** A117a 1500fr Equestrian, vert. 13.00

Nos. 456-458B are airmail.
No. 458A exists in a souvenir sheet of 1. Value $47.50.

Pres. Hissein Habre — A117b

Designs: Nos. 458D, 458H, Sources of food. Nos. 458E, 458I, Dove of peace, different tribal groups, country map.

**1983, Dec. 26 Litho. *Perf. 13½***

**458C** A117b 50fr multicolored .60 .25
**458D** A117b 50fr multicolored .60 .25
**458E** A117b 50fr multicolored .60 .25
**458F** A117b 60fr multicolored .70 .25
**458G** A117b 80fr multicolored .90 .25
**458H** A117b 80fr multicolored .90 .25
**458I** A117b 80fr multicolored .90 .25
**458J** A117b 100fr multicolored 1.10 .35

See Nos. C276-C279.

### Nos. 427-433 Overprinted: "60e ANNIVERSAIRE FEDERATION / MONDIALE D'ECHECS 1924-1984"

**1983, Dec. 27 Litho. *Perf. 13½***

**459** A113 30fr multi .90 .25
**460** A113 40fr multi 1.10 .25
**461** A113 50fr multi 1.40 .25
**462** A113 60fr multi 1.75 .25
**463** A113 80fr multi 2.25 .30
**464** A113 300fr multi 4.50 .75
*Nos. 459-464 (6)* 11.90 2.05

### Souvenir Sheet

**465** A113 500fr multi 4.50 2.50

World Chess Fedn., 60th anniv.

### Nos. 406-412B Ovptd. with Emblem for the 15th World Scout Jamboree, Alberta, Canada, 1983

**1983, Dec. 27 Litho. *Perf. 13½***

**466** A111 30fr multi .30 .25
**467** A111 40fr multi .40 .25
**468** A111 50fr multi .50 .25
**469** A111 60fr multi .60 .25
**470** A111 80fr multi .70 .25
**471** A111 300fr multi 3.00 .50
*Nos. 466-471 (6)* 5.50 1.75

### Souvenir Sheet

**472** A111 500fr multi 6.00 2.50

### Litho. & Embossed

**472A** A111a 1500fr on #412A 16.00

### Souvenir Sheet

**472B** A111a 1500fr on #412B 12.00

Locomotive "Lady," 1879 — A118

200fr, Sailboat, Lake Chad. 300fr, Graf Zeppelin. 350fr, Renault desert transport, 1930. 400fr, Bloch 120 monoplane. 500fr, Air Africa DC-8.
600fr, Intelsat V satellite.

**1984, Mar. 15**

**473** A118 50fr shown .60 .25
**474** A118 200fr multicolored 2.40 .60
**475** A118 300fr multicolored 3.25 .90
**476** A118 350fr multicolored 4.00 1.10
**477** A118 400fr multicolored 4.25 1.25
**478** A118 500fr multicolored 5.50 1.50
*Nos. 473-478 (6)* 20.00 5.60

### Souvenir Sheet

**479** A118 600fr multicolored 5.75 5.00

Nos. 477-479 airmail. For surcharge see No. 579.

Liberation, 2nd Anniv. — A119

**1984, June 6 *Perf. 12½***

**480** A119 50fr multi .60 .25

Pres. Hissein Habre — A120

**1984, June 18 *Perf. 12½x13***

**481** A120 125fr multi 1.50 .40

Anniversaries and Events — A121

Designs: 50fr, Pres. Habre, civil war martyrs. 200fr, Paul Harris, Rotary Intl. headquarters, Illinois. 300fr, Alfred Nobel, will establishing fund for Prizes. 350fr, Raphael, detail from Virgin with Child and St. John the Baptist. 400fr, Rembrandt, detail from The Holy Family. 500fr, J.W. Goethe, scene from Faust. 600fr, Rubens, detail from Helene Fourment and Her Two Children.

**1984, Jan. 16 Litho. *Perf. 13½***

**482** A121 50fr multi .50 .25
**483** A121 200fr multi 1.90 .30
**484** A121 300fr multi 3.00 .45
**485** A121 350fr multi 3.75 .55
**486** A121 400fr multi 4.50 .60
**487** A121 500fr multi 5.75 .70
*Nos. 482-487 (6)* 19.40 2.85

### Souvenir Sheet

**488** A121 600fr multi 6.75 2.50

Nos. 486-488 are airmail.

Homage to Our Martyred Dead — A122

**1984, Feb. 22 Litho. *Perf. 13½***

**500** A122 50fr multi .50 .25
**501** A122 80fr multi .75 .25
**502** A122 120fr multi 1.10 .25
**503** A122 200fr multi 1.90 .40
**504** A122 250fr multi 2.50 .50
*Nos. 500-504 (5)* 6.75 1.65

Nos. 503-504 are airmail. For surcharge see C303.

World Communications Year — A123

**1984, Feb. 29 Litho. *Perf. 13½***

**505** A123 50fr sil & multi .50 .25
**506** A123 60fr sil & multi .60 .25
**507** A123 70fr sil & multi .75 .25
**508** A123 125fr sil & multi 1.10 .25
**509** A123 250fr sil & multi 2.50 .50
*Nos. 505-509 (5)* 5.45 1.50

Nos. 508-509 are airmail. For surcharge see C304.

Anniversaries and Events — A123a

50fr, Durer, detail from Madonna of the Rosary. 200fr, Henri Dunant, Red Cross founder, Battle of Solferino. 300fr, Early telephone, Goonhilly Downs Satellite Station, Britain. 350fr, J.F. Kennedy, Neil Armstrong's 1st step on Moon, 1969. 400fr, Europe-Africa Satellite infrared photograph. 500fr, Prince Charles & Lady Diana. 600fr, Wedding photograph of Prince Charles & Lady Diana.

**1984**

510 A123a 50fr multi .50 .25
511 A123a 200fr multi 2.10 .30
512 A123a 300fr multi 3.00 .45
513 A123a 350fr multi 3.50 .50
514 A123a 400fr multi 3.75 .55
515 A123a 500fr multi 5.00 .80
*Nos. 510-515 (6)* 17.85 2.85

**Souvenir Sheet**

516 A121 600fr multicolored 5.25

A souvenir sheet of 6 containing Nos. 510-515 exists. Nos. 514-516 are airmail.
For surcharge see No. 578.

Development of Communications — A123b

Ships and locomotives: 90fr, Indiaman, East India Co. 100fr, Nord 701, 1885. 125fr, Vera Cruz. 150fr, Columbia, 1888. 200fr, Carlisle Castle. 250fr, Rete Mediterranea, 1900. 300fr, Britannia. 350fr, Mav 114.

**1984, Aug. 1 Litho. *Perf. 12½***

517 A123b 90fr multi 1.10 .25
518 A123b 100fr multi 1.10 .25
519 A123b 125fr multi 1.75 .25
520 A123b 150fr multi 1.75 .25
521 A123b 200fr multi 2.50 .25
522 A123b 250fr multi 3.00 .30
523 A123b 300fr multi 3.25 .35
524 A123b 350fr multi 3.75 .50
*Nos. 517-524 (8)* 18.20 2.40

Christmas — A124

**1984, Dec. 28 Litho. *Perf. 13***

525 A124 50fr lt bl & org brn .50 .25
526 A124 60fr ver & org brn .60 .25
527 A124 80fr emer & org brn .75 .25
528 A124 85fr rose lil & org brn .75 .25
529 A124 100fr org yel & org brn 1.00 .30
530 A124 135fr dp bl vio & org brn 1.25 .40
*Nos. 525-530 (6)* 4.85 1.70

European Music Year — A125

Instruments.

**1985, Apr. 30 Litho. *Perf. 12x12½***

531 A125 20fr Guitar .30 .25
532 A125 25fr Harp .35 .25
533 A125 30fr Xylophone .45 .25
534 A125 50fr Shoulder drum .55 .25
535 A125 70fr like #534 .80 .25
536 A125 80fr like #532 .85 .30
537 A125 100fr like #531 1.10 .40
538 A125 250fr like #533 2.75 .80
*Nos. 531-538 (8)* 7.15 2.75

Mushrooms — A126

25fr, Chlorophyllum molybdites. 30fr, Tulostoma volvulatum. 50fr, Lentinus tuber-regium. 80fr, Podaxis pistillaris.

**1985, May 15 Litho. *Perf. 12½***

539 A126 25fr multi .50 .25
540 A126 30fr multi .60 .25
541 A126 50fr multi .90 .25
542 A126 70fr like #541 1.25 .25
543 A126 80fr multi 1.40 .25
544 A126 100fr like #539 2.10 .35
*Nos. 539-544 (6)* 6.75 1.60

Anniversaries and Events — A127

25fr, Abraham Lincoln. 45fr, Henri Dunant, Geneva birthplace and red cross. 50fr, Gottlieb Daimler, 1887 Motor Carriage. 60fr, Louis Bleriot, Bleriot XI monoplane, 1909. 80fr, Paul Harris, Chicago site of Rotary Intl. founding. 350fr, Auguste Piccard, bathyscaphe Trieste, 1953.

600fr, Anatoly Karpov, 1981 world chess champion. 1500fr, Paul Harris on Medal.

**1985, May 25 Litho. *Perf. 13½***

545 A127 25fr multi .30 .25
546 A127 45fr multi .60 .25
547 A127 50fr multi .75 .25
548 A127 60fr multi 1.00 .25
549 A127 80fr multi 1.10 .35
550 A127 350fr multi 4.00 1.25
*Nos. 545-550 (6)* 7.75 2.60

**Souvenir Sheets**

551 A127 600fr multi 6.75 5.00

**Litho. & Embossed**

551A A127 1500fr multi 14.50

No. 551A contains one 130x90mm stamp. Nos. 548-551A are airmail.
Souvenir sheets of 1 exist for Nos. 545-551.

Intl. Youth Year — A128

70fr, Development levels. 200fr, Globe, horiz.

**1985, May 30 Litho. *Perf. 13***

552 A128 70fr multi .70 .25
553 A128 200fr multi 1.75 .50

A129 3rd Anniv. of the Republic — A130

***Perf. 13, 12½x13***

**1985, June 7 Litho.**

554 A129 70fr Hand, claw .70 .25
555 A129 70fr Hands, map .70 .25
556 A130 70fr Pres. Hissein Habre .70 .25
557 A129 110fr like #554 1.10 .40
558 A129 110fr like #555 1.25 .40
559 A130 110fr like #556 1.25 .40
*Nos. 554-559 (6)* 5.70 1.95

Audubon Birth Bicent. — A131

**1985, July 20 Engr. *Perf. 13***

560 A131 70fr Stork 1.10 .30
561 A131 110fr Ostrich 1.60 .40
562 A131 150fr Marabou 2.25 .65
563 A131 200fr Snake eagle 3.00 .90
*Nos. 560-563 (4)* 7.95 2.25

**Souvenir Sheet**

564 A131 500fr like 200fr 6.75 5.00

Mammals — A132

**1985, Aug. 25**

565 A132 50fr Waterbuck .75 .25
566 A132 70fr Kudus, horiz. 1.00 .40
567 A132 250fr Shaggy mouflon 3.25 1.25
*Nos. 565-567 (3)* 5.00 1.90

**Souvenir Sheet**

568 A132 500fr White rhinoceros 5.75 5.00

UN, 40th Anniv. A133

**1985, Nov. 24**

569 A133 200fr brt bl, red & brn 2.25 .75

Chad Admission to UN, 25th Anniv. — A134

**1985, Nov. 24**

570 A134 300fr red, brt bl & yel 3.25 1.00

President's Visit to the Nation's Interior — A135

**1986, June 7 Litho. *Perf. 12½x13***

571 A135 100fr multi 1.10 .25
572 A135 170fr multi 2.25 .35
573 A135 200fr multi 2.50 .45
*Nos. 571-573 (3)* 5.85 1.05

Lions Club Intl. — A135a

100fr, Sick child. 170fr, Three children, horiz. 200fr, Eye exam, horiz.

**1987 Litho. *Perf. 14***

573A A135a 30fr Like #573C 50.00 —
573C A135a 100fr multi
573E A135a 170fr multi
573F A135a 200fr multi

There are two additional stamps in this set. The editors would like to examine them.

World Wildlife Fund A136

Various mouflons, *Ammotragus lervia.*

**1988, Nov. 10 Litho. *Perf. 13***

574 A136 25fr shown 2.00 .50
575 A136 45fr Adult, young 2.50 .75
576 A136 70fr Two adults, diff. 3.50 1.25
577 A136 100fr Adults, young 4.75 1.75
*Nos. 574-577 (4)* 12.75 4.25

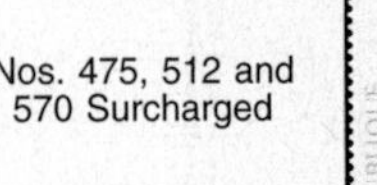

Nos. 475, 512 and 570 Surcharged

**Methods and Perfs. As Before**

**1987-89**

578 A123a 170fr on 300fr #512
578A A134 230fr on 300fr #570
579 A118 240fr on 300fr #475

At least eleven additional stamps were issued in this set. The editors would like to examine any examples.

Liberation — A137

**1989 *Perf. 11½x12***

580 A137 20fr multi .50 .30
581 A137 25fr multi .60 .30
582 A137 40fr multi 1.00 .50
583 A137 100fr multi 1.50 .75
584 A137 170fr multi 2.50 1.25
*Nos. 580-584 (5)* 6.10 3.10

World Post Day — A137a

**1989, Oct. 9 Photo. *Perf. 12***

**Granite Paper**

584A A137a 100fr grn bl & multi
584B A137a 120fr red & multi
584C A137a 170fr pur & multi
584D A137a 250fr ol & multi
*Nos. 584A-584D (4)* 160.00

Visit of Pope John Paul II — A138

Cathedral in Chad and: 20fr, 100fr, Pope holding crosier. 80fr, 170fr, Pope, diff.

**1989, Dec. 20 Litho. *Perf. 13***

585 A138 20fr multicolored .25 .25
586 A138 80fr multicolored 1.00 .40
587 A138 100fr multicolored 1.25 .50
588 A138 170fr multicolored 2.10 1.10
*Nos. 585-588 (4)* 4.60 2.25

Traditional Hair Styles — A139

**1989, Oct. 9 Photo. *Perf. 12***
**Granite Paper**

**589** A139 100fr apple grn & multi
**590** A139 120fr purple & multi
**591** A139 170fr pink & multi
**592** A139 250fr org yel & multi
*Nos. 589-592 (4)* 160.00

Vaccinations A140

**1991, Dec. 1 Photo. *Perf. 11½***
**Granite Paper**

**593** A140 30fr brown & multi .30 .25
**594** A140 100fr green & multi 1.00 .45
**595** A140 170fr vio & multi 1.60 .75
**596** A140 180fr blue & multi 1.75 .80
**597** A140 200fr red & multi 1.90 .90
*Nos. 593-597 (5)* 6.55 3.15

Liberty and Democracy Day — A141

**1991, Dec. 1 Litho.**

**598** A141 10fr green & multi .25 .25
**599** A141 20fr lilac & multi .25 .25
**600** A141 40fr yellow & multi .40 .25
**601** A141 70fr blue & multi .65 .30
**602** A141 130fr tan & multi 1.25 .75
**603** A141 200fr pink & multi 1.90 1.00
*Nos. 598-603 (6)* 4.70 2.80

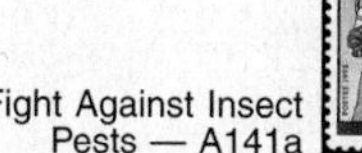

Fight Against Insect Pests — A141a

**1992, Sept. 1 Photo. *Perf. 12***

**603A** A141a 25fr multi 30.00 15.00
**603B** A141a 45fr multi 30.00 15.00
**603C** A141a 100fr multi 30.00 15.00
**603D** A141a 150fr multi 30.00 15.00
**603E** A141a 170fr multi 30.00 15.00
*Nos. 603A-603E (5)* 150.00 75.00

A142

**1992, Nov. 15 Litho. *Perf. 11½***

**604** A142 20fr bright yel & multi .25 .25
**605** A142 45fr golden yel & multi .40 .25
**606** A142 85fr pink & multi .75 .35
**607** A142 170fr blue & multi 1.50 .70
**608** A142 300fr gray & multi 3.00 1.40
*Nos. 604-608 (5)* 5.90 2.95

Doctors Without Borders, 20th anniv.

Campaign Against Illiteracy — A143

**1992, Nov. 30**

**609** A143 25fr yel grn & multi .25 .25
**610** A143 40fr golden yel & multi .40 .25
**611** A143 70fr pink & multi .60 .30
**612** A143 100fr lilac & multi .75 .40
**613** A143 180fr blue & multi 1.60 .60
**614** A143 200fr gray & multi 1.75 .70
*Nos. 609-614 (6)* 5.35 2.50

Intl. Conference on Nutrition, Rome — A144

**1992, Dec. 15**

**615** A144 10fr yellow & multi .25 .25
**616** A144 60fr pink & multi 1.00 .25
**617** A144 120fr yel grn & multi 1.75 .40
**618** A144 500fr blue & multi 4.50 1.60
*Nos. 615-618 (4)* 7.50 2.50

Palace of the People — A145

**1993, Apr. 15 Litho. *Perf. 11½***

**619** A145 80fr multi 40.00 5.00
**620** A145 100fr multi 40.00 5.00
**621** A145 130fr multi 40.00 5.00
**622** A145 400fr multi 40.00 5.00
*Nos. 619-622 (4)* 160.00 20.00

Natl. Conference — A146

**1993, Dec. 1 Litho. *Perf. 11¾***
**Granite paper**

**623** A146 55fr multi .80 .35
**624** A146 70fr multi 1.00 .45
**625** A146 110fr multi 1.40 .80
**626** A146 125fr multi 1.75 .90
*Nos. 623-626 (4)* 4.95 2.50

OAU, 30th Anniv. — A147

**1993, Dec. 4 Litho. *Perf. 11½x11¾***

**627** A147 15fr multi .25 .25
**628** A147 30fr multi .30 .25
**629** A147 110fr multi 1.10 .80
**630** A147 190fr multi 2.00 1.50
*Nos. 627-630 (4)* 3.65 2.80

Victor Schoelcher (1804-93), Abolitionist — A148

***Perf. 11¾x11½***
**1993, Dec. 26 Litho.**

**631** A148 55fr multi .40 .40
**632** A148 105fr multi 1.10 .75
**633** A148 125fr multi 1.40 1.10
**634** A148 300fr multi 2.75 2.00

Tourism — A149

***Perf. 11¾x11½***
**1993, Dec. 27 Litho.**

**635** A149 15fr multi *40.00 20.00*
**636** A149 95fr multi *40.00 20.00*
**637** A149 100fr multi *40.00 20.00*
**638** A149 190fr multi — —

Bank of Central African States — A150

**1994 Litho. *Perf. 11½***

**639** A150 20fr multicolored .25 .25
**640** A150 30fr pink & multi .40 .25
**641** A150 105fr blue & multi .90 .30
**642** A150 190fr lilac & multi 1.60 .90
*Nos. 639-642 (4)* 3.15 1.70

Huts for Storing Grain — A151

Designs: 75fr, Arabe, kim. 150fr, Sara, moundang. 300fr, Boulala, kotoko. 450fr, Ouaddai, kenga.

**1995, Oct. 15 Litho. *Perf. 14***

**643** A151 75fr multicolored .50 .25
**644** A151 150fr multicolored .90 .30
**645** A151 300fr multicolored 1.50 .75
**646** A151 450fr multicolored 2.50 1.00
*Nos. 643-646 (4)* 5.40 2.30

Souvenir Sheet

Chinese Post, Cent. — A151a

**1996 Litho. *Perf. 13¼***

**646A** A151a 270fr multi 2.25 2.00

1996 Olympic Games, Atlanta A151b

No. 646B: e, Tennis. f, Equestrian. g, Soccer. h, Boxing.
No. 646C: i, Judo. j, Running. k, Cycling. l, Table tennis.
1500fr, Hurdler.

**1996 Litho. *Perf. 13¼***

**646B** A151b 250fr Sheet of 4, #e-h 3.00 4.00
**646C** A151b 300fr Sheet of 4, #i-l 4.00 5.00

**Souvenir Sheet**

**646D** A151b 1500fr multi 5.50 5.50

No. 646D contains one 39x57mm stamp.

1995 Boy Scout Jamboree, Holland — A152

Mushrooms: 150fr, Amanita phalloides. 170fr, Phallus impudicus. 200fr, Lyloperdon perlatum. 350fr, Hydne commun. 450fr, Agaricus bisporus. 800fr, Cortinarius orellanus.
1500fr, Pleurotus ostreatus.

**1996, Apr. 15 Litho. *Perf. 13½***

**647-652** A152 Set of 6 8.00 4.75
*a.* Souvenir sheet, #647-652 9.25 4.75

**Souvenir Sheet**

**653** A152 1500fr multicolored 5.50 5.00

Nos. 647-652 exist in souvenir sheets of 1.

Butterflies, Mushrooms and Minerals A152a

No. 653A: g, Papilio zalmoxis. h, Anacridium melanorhodon. i, Otidea leporina. j, Haliaetus vocifer.
No. 653B: k, Amanita phalloides, Papilio dardanus. l, Papilio antimachus, Cortinarius praestans. m, Phallus impudicus, Chrysidia croesus. n, Papilio dardanus, Lycoperon perlatum.
No. 653C: o, Charaxes brutus. p, Epiphora albida. q, Euchloron megaera. r, Salamis duprei.
No. 653D: s, Disthene. t, Olivine. u, Sphene. v, Hemimorphite.
No. 653E, Argema mittrei. No. 653F, Zoisite.

**1996 Litho. *Perf. 13¼***

**653A** A152a 350fr Sheet of 4, #g-j 7.00 6.00
**653B** A152a 400fr Sheet of 4, #k-n 8.00 7.00
**653C** A152a 650fr Sheet of 4, #o-r 12.00 10.00
**653D** A152a 800fr Sheet of 4, #s-v 15.00 12.00
*Nos. 653A-653D (4)* 42.00 35.00

**Souvenir Sheets**

**653E** A152a 2000fr multi 7.50 7.50
**653F** A152a 2000fr multi 7.50 7.50

A number has been reserved for an additional sheet in this set. Nos. 653E-653F each contain one 42x36mm stamp.

Greenpeace, 25th Anniv. — A153

No. 654: a, 170fr, Green coral, school of small fish. b, 200fr, Yellow & orange coral. c, 300fr, Red orange coral. d, 350fr, White coral.
1500fr, Diver, coral, vert.

**1996, July 16**

**654** A153 Block of 4, #a.-d. 5.00 5.00

**Souvenir Sheet**

**655** A153 1500fr multicolored 9.50 9.50

Entertainers A154

Designs: No. 656, 170fr, Bob Marley. No. 657, 170fr, Marilyn Monroe. No. 658, 200fr, Elvis Presley. No. 659, 200fr, Monroe. No. 660, 300fr, Monroe. No. 661, 350fr, Stevie Wonder. No. 662, 350fr, Presley. No. 663, 400fr, John Lennon. No. 664, 500fr, Presley. No. 665, 600fr, Lennon. No. 666, 700fr, Madonna. No. 667, 800fr, Presley. No. 668, 1000fr, Monroe.
No. 669, 1500fr, Tina Turner. No. 670, 1500fr, Clint Eastwood. No. 670A, 1500fr, Presley.

**1996, May 15**

**656-668** A154 Set of 13 29.00 22.50
*665a* Sheet of 2, #663, 665 4.50 2.25
*667a* Sheet of 4, #658, 662, 664, 667 8.00 3.75
*668a* Sheet of 4, #657, 659-660, 668 7.00 3.50

**Souvenir Sheets**

**669-670A** A154 Set of 3 18.00 10.00

Nos. 656-668 exist in souvenir sheets of 1. No. 670A contains one 51x90mm stamp.
See No. 674.

A155

No. 671: a, Pres. Bill Clinton. b, Elvis Presley in white jumpsuit.
No. 672: a, Pres. Richard Nixon. b, Presley in white shirt, black jacket.

**1996, Dec. 17 Litho. *Perf. 13½***

| | | | | |
|---|---|---|---|---|
| **671** A155 | 1500fr Sheet of 2, #a.-b. | 14.00 | 14.00 |
| **672** A155 | 1500fr Sheet of 2, #a.-b. | 14.00 | 14.00 |

Giant Panda — A156

No. 673: a, Holding branch, left claw out. b, Holding branch. c, Lying on back. d, Holding branch in mouth.

**1996, Oct. 15**

**673** A156 100fr Sheet of 4, #a.-d. 2.25 2.25

### Entertainers Type of 1996

**1996 Litho. *Perf. 13½***

**674** A154 500fr Jerry Garcia 2.50 1.75

No. 674 exists in a souvenir sheet of 1.

1998 World Cup Soccer Championships, France — A157

1998 World Cup Soccer Championships, France — A157a

Unidentified players, stadium: No. 675, 150fr, The Beaujoire, Nantes. No. 676, 200fr, Lescure Park, Bordeaux. No. 676A, 300fr, Municipal Stadium, Toulouse. No. 676B, 600fr, Felix Bollaert, Lens.
No. 677A: b, Player in white shirt. c, Player in red shirt.

**1996, Dec. 17**

**675-676B** A157 Set of 4 5.00 4.00

### Souvenir Sheet

| | | | | |
|---|---|---|---|---|
| **677** | A157a | 1500fr George Weah | 7.50 | 5.00 |
| **677A** | A157a | 3000fr Sheet of 2, #b-c | 13.00 | 11.00 |

UNICEF, UN, 50th Anniv., Lions Intl. A159

No. 682 — UNICEF, 50th anniv.: a, 150fr, Girl, boy turtles. b, 400fr, Feeding small child.
No. 683 — UN, 50th anniv.: a, 170fr, Huygens probe, starving child. b, 500fr, Man with plant, Marsnet probe.
No. 684 — Lions Intl.: a, 200fr, Man carrying sack of grain. b, 800fr, Men examining plants, native man stirring kettle over fire.

**1996, Oct. 15 Litho. *Perf. 13½***

| | | | |
|---|---|---|---|
| **682** A159 | Pair, #a.-b. + label | 3.00 | 2.00 |
| **683** A159 | Pair, #a.-b. + label | 3.50 | 2.50 |
| **684** A159 | Pair, #a.-b. + label | 5.50 | 3.50 |

Nos. 682-684 exist as souvenir sheets with colored margins. Value, each $13.

No. 678 — Dinosaurs: a, Heterodontosaurus. b, Ornitholestes. c, Dromaeosaurus. d, Pinacosaurus.
No. 679 — Dinosaurs: a, Corythosaurus. b, Ankylosaurides. c, Ornithomimus. d, Styracosaurus.
No. 680 — Dogs & cats: a, Artois. b, Bengal. c, Persian. d, Vendeen.
No. 681 — Butterflies & insects: a, Euphaedra zaddachi. b, Pseudacraea dolomena. c, Cicindela barbara. d, Goliath.

**1996, Oct. 15**

| | | | |
|---|---|---|---|
| **678** A158 | 150fr Sheet of 4, #a.-d. | 3.00 | 3.00 |
| **679** A158 | 200fr Sheet of 4, #a.-d. | 3.75 | 3.75 |
| **680** A158 | 250fr Sheet of 4, #a.-d. | 5.00 | 5.00 |
| **681** A158 | 300fr Sheet of 4, #a.-d. | 6.00 | 4.00 |

### Ovptd. in Gold in Sheet Margin

**1997 Litho. *Perf. 13½***

| | | | |
|---|---|---|---|
| *678e* | Sheet of 4 | 3.00 | 3.00 |
| *679e* | Sheet of 4 | 3.75 | 3.75 |
| *680e* | Sheet of 4 | 5.00 | 5.00 |

Gold overprints on Nos. 678e-680e contain two-line inscription in Chinese and Hong Kong '97 exhibition emblem.

1996 European Soccer Championships — A160

No. 685: a, Oliver Bierhoff holding trophy. b, Two players. c, Two players, referee. d, Queen Elizabeth II, player holding trophy.

**1996, Dec. 17**

**685** A160 350fr Sheet of 4, #a.-d. 6.00 4.75

Michael Schumacher, 1995 World Driving Champion — A161

No. 686: a, Ferrari Formula-1 race car. b, Schumacher close-up. c, Schumacher in Benetton uniform. d, Benetton Formula-1 race car.
No. 687, Schumacher with arms raised. No. 687A, Winner of 1996 Italian Grand Prix.

**1997, June 16**

**686** A161 700fr Sheet of 4, #a.-d. 12.50 9.00

### Souvenir Sheets

| | | | |
|---|---|---|---|
| **687** A161 | 2000fr multicolored | 8.50 | 7.00 |
| **687A** A161 | 2000fr multicolored | 8.50 | 7.00 |

No. 687 contains one 36x51mm stamp.

1998 Winter Olympic Games, Nagano, Japan — A162

Designs: 100fr, Women's figure skating. 170fr, Hockey. 350fr, Downhill skiing. 750fr, Speed skating.
1500fr, Slalom skiing.

**1996, Dec. 17**

**688-691** A162 Set of 4 5.75 4.00

### Souvenir Sheet

**692** A162 1500fr multicolored 6.25 4.00

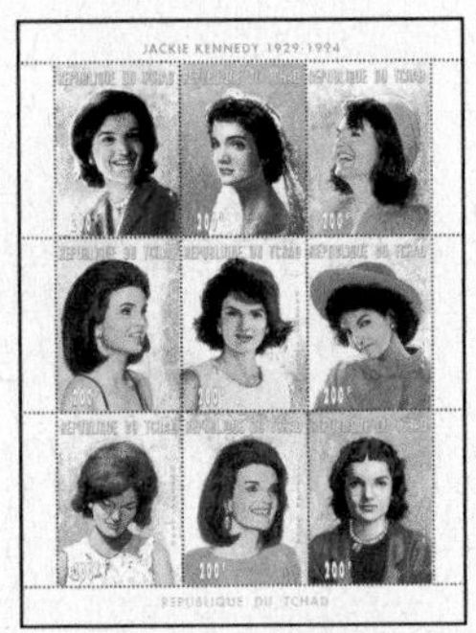

World Wildlife Fund — A163

No. 693 — Struthio camelus rothschildi: a, Female. b. Male. c, Chicks. d, Male, female up close.

**1996, Dec. 17 Litho. *Perf. 13½***

**693** A163 200fr Block of 4, #a.-d. 15.00 15.00

Jacqueline Kennedy Onassis (1929-94) — A164

Various portraits.

**1996, Dec. 17**

**694** A164 200fr Sheet of 9, #a.-i. 8.00 6.00

A165

No. 695 — Intl. Red Cross: a, 100fr, Woman, airplane. b, 350fr, Man, train.
No. 696 — Rotary Intl.: a, 300fr, Boy, water coming through pipes. b, 700fr, Native boy and man, volunteers.
No. 697 — Scouts: a, 250fr, Boy scout holding book, hyena. b, 1000fr, Garry Kasparov, chess player, scout.

**1996, Oct. 15 Litho. *Perf. 13½***

| | | | |
|---|---|---|---|
| **695** A165 | Pair, #a.-b. + label | 2.50 | 1.75 |
| **696** A165 | Pair, #a.-b. + label | 5.50 | 3.50 |
| **697** A165 | Pair, #a.-b. + label | 6.50 | 4.50 |

Nos. 695-697 exist in souvenir sheets with colored margins. Value, each $13.

Japanese Sumo Wrestling — A166

Various wrestlers in ring.

**1996, Dec. 17 Litho. *Perf. 13½***

**698** A166 400fr Sheet of 4, #a.-d. 7.00 5.00

China '96 — A168

Various paintings showing mountains and trees.

**1996**

**704** A168 100fr Sheet of 9, #a.-i. 4.50 3.50

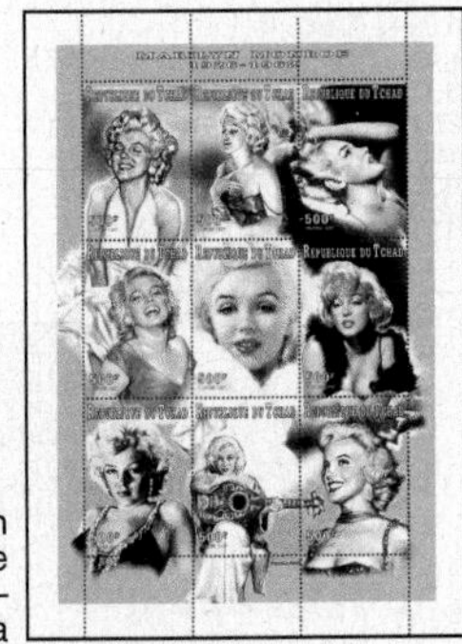

Marilyn Monroe — A168a

Various portraits.

**1997 Litho. *Perf. 13¼***

**704J** A168a 500fr Sheet of 9, #k-s 14.00 14.00

History of Space Travel A169

No. 705: a, Lunar N1 rocket, USSR, Saturn 1, US, Apollo 1 crew, Grissom, White, Chaffee. b, Launch of Soyuz, USSR, V.M. Komarov. c, US Lunar Orbiter 4. d, Neil Armstrong, US, Molniya 1, USSR. e, Venera 4, USSR, Mariner, US. f, Surveyor 3, US.
No. 706: a, Ariane 1, Landsat 4, US. b, Spacelab & space shuttle, NASA, ESA, Thomas Mattingly, US. c, L-Sat Telecom Satelite, ESA. d, J.L. Chretien, Soviet Salyut 7, US Space Shuttle. e, Venera 13, USSR. f, Intelsat 6, US.
No. 707: a, John Glenn, Atlas rocket, Mercury capsule. b, Mariner 2, US. c, Scott Carpenter, US. d, Telstar, Tiros 6, US. e, Vostok capsule, USSR, Bell X15 airplane, US. f, Mars 1, USSR.
No. 708: a, "Sounds of Earth" record, Voyager 1 & 2, US. b, Himawari 1, MU-3H, Japan, Atlas Centaur, US. c, Soviet Salyut 6, Proton rocket, Galileo (1564-1642). d, Meteosat, SMS Geos, Atlas EF, US. e, Boeing 747, space shuttle, US. f, ISEE, US.
No. 709: a, Saturn 5, US, OAO 3 Copernicus. b, Pioneer 10, US. c, Luna 20, USSR, John F. Kennedy. d, Landsat 1, US. e, Apollo 16, US astronauts Mattingly, Duke, Young. f,

Lunar Rover, US Apollo 17 astronauts Schmitt, Evans, Cernan.
No. 710: a, RD 107 rocket, USSR, Vanguard rocket, US, Vanguard I, US. b, Aerobee, Goddard rockets, Robert H. Goddard. c, Laika, 1st dog in space, USSR. d, Theodor von Karman, V2A, Gird 09 rockets, USSR. e, Sputnik 1, USSR, Korolev airplane. f, Sanger, Bell X1 airplanes, US, Eugene Sanger.
No. 711, US Astronauts, Neil Armstrong, Michael Collins, Edwin E. Aldrin, Jr., USSR animals in space, Laika, Felix the cat.
Illustration reduced.

**1997 Litho. *Perf. 13½***

**705** A169 150fr Sheet of 6, #a.-f. 3.25 3.25
**706** A169 250fr Sheet of 6, #a.-f. 4.75 4.75
**707** A169 300fr Sheet of 6, #a.-f. 6.00 6.00
**708** A169 450fr Sheet of 6, #a.-f. 7.25 7.25
**709** A169 475fr Sheet of 6, #a.-f. 9.25 9.25
**710** A169 800fr Sheet of 6, #a.-f. 14.50 14.50

**Souvenir Sheet**

**711** A169 2000fr multicolored 7.00 7.00

No. 711 contains one 80x85mm stamp.

Elvis Presley — A169a

Various portraits.

**1997 Litho. *Perf. 13¼***

**711A** A169a 300fr Sheet of 9, #b-j 9.50 9.50

Jacqueline Kennedy Onassis (1929-94) — A170

Various portraits.

**1997, July 15 Litho. *Perf. 13½***

**712** A170 150fr Sheet of 9, #a.-i. 5.00 2.75

Pres. John F. Kennedy — A170a

No. 712J: k, Standing, looking right. l, With family. m, Looking left. n, With statue of George Washington. o, Seated, with Great Seal of the United States. p, Facing forward, with stars and arrows. q, In chair. r, With statue of Lincoln. s, Behind podium, with flag and Capitol.

**1997 Litho. *Perf. 13¼***

**712J** A170a 250fr Sheet of 9, #k-s 7.00 7.00

Diana, Princess of Wales (1961-97) — A171

Various portraits.

**1997**

**713** A171 300fr Sheet of 9, #a.-i. 9.00 9.00
**714** A171 450fr Sheet of 9, #a.-i. 12.50 12.50

**Souvenir Sheet**

**715** A171 2000fr multicolored 7.00 6.25

No. 715 contains one 42x60mm stamp.

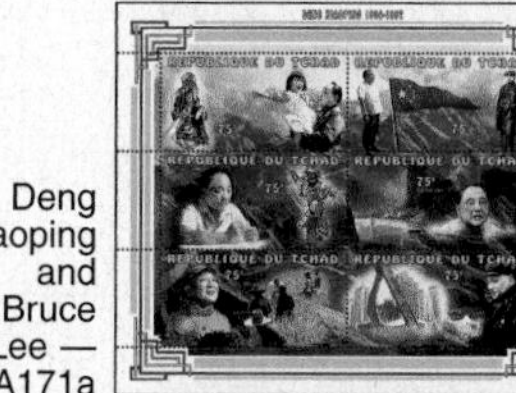

Deng Xiaoping and Bruce Lee — A171a

No. 715A — Deng and: c, Child. d, Chinese flag. e, Dancer. f, Boats in water. g, Farmers. h, Cityscape.
No. 715B — Lee and movie titles: i, Operation Dragon. j, La Fureur du Dragon. k, La Fureur de Vaincre. l, La Flute Silencieuse. m, Le Jeu de la Mort. n, Le Retour du Dragon.
1000fr, Deng and stars.

**1997 Litho. *Perf. 13¼***

**715A** A171a 75fr Sheet of 6, #c-h 1.75 1.75
**715B** A171a 125fr Sheet of 6, #i-n 3.00 3.00

**Souvenir Sheet**

**715O** A171a 1000fr multi — —

No. 715O contains one 36x41mm stamp.

Mahatma Gandhi (1869-1948), Mother Teresa (1910-97) — A172

No. 716: a, Gandhi seated, dendrobium speciosum. b, Mother Teresa with Indian people. c, Bulbophyllum umbellatum, Gandhi with 2 women.

**1998, Feb. 5 Litho. *Perf. 13½***

**716** A172 150fr Sheet of 3, #a.-c. 1.90 1.90

Famous Men — A173

Designs: 300fr, Nelson Mandela, Pres. of South Africa, diamond. 450fr, Albert Einstein (1879-1955), physicist, satellite. 800fr, Robert Barany (1876-1936), physician, Felix the space cat.
2000fr, Alfred Nobel (1833-96).

**1998, Feb. 5**

**717-719** A173 Set of 3 7.00 5.50

**Souvenir Sheet**

**720** A173 2000fr multicolored 8.25 7.50

Nos. 717-719 exist in souvenir sheets of 1. No. 720 contains one 41x60mm stamp.
See Nos. 729-734.

The Beatles — A174

No. 721: a-i, Various portraits of John Lennon.
No. 722 — The Beatles: a, Paul McCartney. b, Silhouettes. c, John Lennon. d, George Harrison, Lennon. e, Four faces. f, McCartney, Ringo Starr. g, Starr. h, Four in Sgt. Pepper's costumes. i, Harrison.
No. 723 — Life of John Lennon: a, Yoko Ono. b, With McCartney. c, In profile. d, Wearing suit. e, Wearing white shirt, tie. f, With mother. g, Wearing dark glasses. h, With guru. i, In white suit.
No. 724: Various portraits of Lennon, McCartney, Harrison, Starr.
No. 724J, Beatles in suits and ties. No. 724K, Beatles in Sgt. Pepper uniforms.

**1996 Litho. *Perf. 13½***

**721** A174 100fr Sheet of 9, #a-f 2.75 2.75
**722** A174 170fr Sheet of 9, #a.-i. 5.50 5.50
**723** A174 200fr Sheet of 9, #a.-i. 5.25 5.25
**724** A174 300fr Sheet of 9, #a.-i. 12.00 12.00

**Souvenir Sheets**

**724J** A174 1500fr multi 7.50 6.00
**724K** A174 1500fr multi 7.50 6.00

Antelopes — A175

Designs: a, 170fr, Damaliscus dorcas. b, 350fr, Oryx gazella. c, 500fr, Addax nasomaculatus. d, 600fr, Aepyceros melampus.

**1996, Dec. 17**

**725** A175 Block of 4, #a.-d. 6.00 6.00

Nos. 725a-725d exist in souvenir sheets of 1.

**No. 725 Overprinted in Gold**

**1996**

**726** A175 Block of 4, #a.-d. 7.00 7.00

Nos. 726a-726d exist in souvenir sheets of 1.

Marilyn Monroe (1926-1962) — A176

Various portraits.

**1996**

**727** A176 250fr Sheet of 9, #a.-i. 9.50 8.00

**Souvenir Sheet**

**728** A176 1500fr multicolored 5.00 5.00

No. 728 contains one 51x90mm stamp.

**Famous People Type of 1997**

Nobel Prize winners: 100fr, Mother Teresa (1910-97), humanitarian. 150fr, Martin Luther King, Jr. (1929-68), civil rights leader. 475fr, Otto Hahn (1879-1968), chemist, nuclear powered ship. 500fr, Ivan Pavlov (1849-1936), physiologist, Russian space dog, Laika. 600fr, Johannes van der Waals (1837-1923), physicist. 1000fr, Sir Edward Appleton (1892-1965), physicist, Concorde jet.

**1998, Feb. 5**

**729-734** A173 Set of 6 14.50 10.00

Nos. 729-734 exist in souvenir sheets of 1.

Scouting — A177

Wild animals: No. 735: a, Hyena. b, Mongoose.
No. 736: a, Wildcat. b, Addax nasomaculatus.
No. 737: a, Fennec. b, Hyena, diff.

**1998, Feb. 6**

**735** A177 150fr Pair, #a.-b. 1.75 1.75
**736** A177 550fr Pair, #a.-b. 5.25 5.25
**737** A177 600fr Pair, #a.-b. 6.25 6.25

Cats and Dogs A178

No. 738: a, Maine coon. b, Singapore.
No. 739: a, Siberian husky. b, Malamute.
No. 740: a, Spitz. b, Eskimo.
No. 741: a, Siamese. b, Common cat.
No. 742, 1500fr, Abyssinian. No. 743, 1500fr, Samoyed.

**1998, Feb. 6**

**738** A178 300fr Pair, #a.-b. 2.75 2.75
**739** A178 450fr Pair, #a.-b. 3.00 3.00
**740** A178 475fr Pair, #a.-b. 3.75 3.75
**741** A178 500fr Pair, #a.-b. 4.00 4.00

**Souvenir Sheets**

**742-743** A178 Set of 2 11.00 11.00

Nos. 742-743 each contain one 42x60mm stamp.

Airplanes, Ships, & Trains — A179

No. 743A — Early aircraft: b, Latecoere 28, France. c, D'Equeuilly, France. d, Liore et Olivier Leo-213, France. e, Louis Bleriot monoplane. f, Graf Zeppelin LZ 127. g, Caproni CA 133, Italy.

No. 744 — Airplanes: a, Sikorsky VS-44A. b, Short S25/V Sandringham 4. c, Bristol 167 Brabazon 1. d, Savoia S13 Bis. e, Curtiss CR-3. f, Curtiss R3C-2.

No. 745 — Ships: a, Normandy, 1935. b, Persia, 1856. c, Queen Elizabeth II, 1968. d, Christian Radich, 1937. e, Amerigo Vespucci, 1933. f, Tovarich, 1933.

No. 745G — Classic sports cars: h, 1963-65 Porsche 356 SC. i, 1961-66 AC Cobra. j, 1960-61 Maserati Tipo 63 Birdcage. k, 1962-63 Austin Healey 3000 MK11. l, 1959-62 Ferrari 250 GT Berlinetta SWB. m, 1958 Aston Martin DB4.

No. 746 — Trains: a, BRB cog steam train. b, AE 4/7 10969. c, Crocodile of Saint-Gothard BE 6/8 111. d, RAE 2/4 1001. e, Steam train, Spain. f, RE 6/6 11612 express.

No. 746G — High speed trains: h, ETR 470, Italy. i, TGV Metro, France. j, Hikari, Japan. k, TGV 001 turbotrain, France. l, Eurostar 3203/3204 Metro train, France, Germany, Great Britain. m, 990 ICE train, Germany.

1500fr, Steam locomotive, C5/6 2978. 2000fr, TGV, France.

**1998, Feb. 4**

**743A** A179 150fr Sheet of 6, #b.-g. 3.50 3.50
**744** A179 200fr Sheet of 6, #a.-f. 4.50 4.50
**745** A179 250fr Sheet of 6, #a.-f. 5.50 5.50
**745G** A179 300fr Sheet of 6, #h.-m. 6.75 6.75
**746** A179 350fr Sheet of 6, #a.-f. 8.00 8.00
**746G** A179 400fr Sheet of 6, #h.-m. 9.00 9.00

**Souvenir Sheets**

**747** A179 1500fr multicolored 5.50 5.50
**748** A179 2000fr multicolored 7.75 7.75

Nos. 747-748 contain one 36x42mm stamp.

Swiss rail service, 150th anniv. (Nos. 746-747).

Issued: No. 745G, 2/6.

See No. 758.

Diana, Princess of Wales (1961-97) — A180

Various portraits.
2000fr, Portrait wearing high lace collar.

**1997 Litho. *Perf. 13½***

**749** A180 250fr Sheet of 9, #a.-i. 8.00 8.00

**Souvenir Sheet**

**749J** A180 2000fr multicolored 7.75 7.75

Literacy Campaign — A181

**1997, June 16**

**750** A181 150fr olive & multi .80 .80
**751** A181 300fr buff & multi 1.75 1.60
**752** A181 475fr salmon & multi 2.50 2.50
*Nos. 750-752 (3)* 5.05 4.90

Kellou Dahalob — A182

**1998, Apr. 8**

**753** A182 50fr pink & multi .30 .30
**754** A182 100fr blue & multi .40 .40
**755** A182 150fr green & multi .65 .65
**756** A182 300fr lilac & multi 1.10 1.10
**757** A182 400fr yellow & multi 1.50 1.50
*Nos. 753-757 (5)* 3.95 3.95

**Transportation Type of 1997**

No. 758 — Modern aircraft: a, SAT, France, Germany. b, BAC/Aerospatiale Concorde. c, X001, Japan. d, Bell X-2, US. e, Douglas X-3, US. f, Aerospatiale STS 2000, France.

**1998, Feb. 4 Litho. *Perf. 13½***

**758** A179 475fr Sheet of 6, #a.-f. 12.00 12.00

Women — A183

Women: 50fr, 100fr, 150fr, Using grindstone. 300fr, 450fr, 500fr, Kneeling.

**1997, June 16**

**759** A183 50fr vio & multi, vert. .30 .30
**760** A183 100fr grn & multi, vert. .40 .40
**761** A183 150fr yel & multi, vert. .55 .55
**762** A183 300fr vio & multi 1.10 1.10
**763** A183 450fr grn & multi 1.75 1.75
**764** A183 500fr yel & multi 1.90 1.90
*Nos. 759-764 (6)* 6.00 6.00

Protect the Ozone Layer — A184

**1998 Litho. *Perf. 13½***

**765** A184 150fr blue & multi .60 .60
**766** A184 300fr green & multi 1.25 1.25
**767** A184 475fr pink & multi 1.90 1.60
**768** A184 500fr blue green & multi 1.90 1.90
*Nos. 765-768 (4)* 5.65 5.35

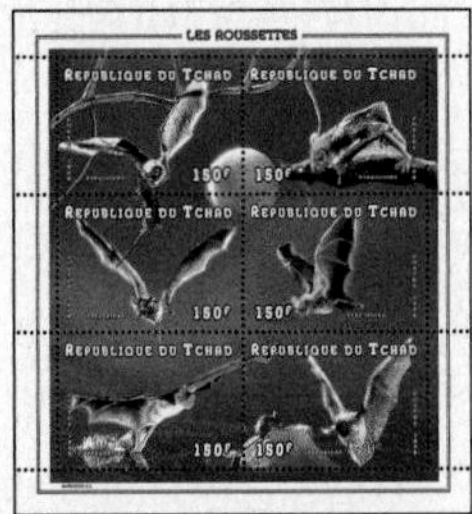


Fauna A185

No. 769 — Bats: a, Holding mouse, tree branch. b, Drinking. c, One in flight, bottom of mouse. d, One flying left. e, One flying right. f, Mouse on rock, bat landing.

No. 769G — Horses: h, Gray Arabian. i, Brown Arabian. j, Przewalski's. k, Australian brumbies. l, Camargue. m, Zebras.

No. 769N — Sea mammals: o-t, Various portraits of Trichechus senegalensis.

No. 770 — Gorillas & chimpanzees: a, Chimpanzee scratching head. b, Gorilla walking on all fours. c, Gorilla seated. d, Chimpanzee swinging from branch. e, Chimpanzee using stick. f, Two gorillas.

No. 771 — Raptors: a, Terathopius ecaudatus. b, Buteo buteo. c, Sagittarius serpentarius. d, Polemaetus belligosus. e, Circaetus allicus. f, Aquila chrysaetos.

No. 771G — Reptiles: h, Crocodylus niloticus. i, Drendroaspis angusticeps. j, Bitis nasicornis. k, Chamaeleo johnstoni. l, Naja nigricolis. m, Meroles cuneirostris.

No. 771N — Mushrooms: o, Coprinus atramentarius. p, Romaria botrytis. q, Aleuria aurantia. r, Amanita muscaria. s, Macrolepiota rhacodes. t, Helvella crispa.

No. 771U — Mushrooms: v, Morchella vulgaris. w, Tuber aestiuum. x, Tuber melanosporum. y, Mitrophora hybrida. z, Morchella conica. aa, Choeromyces meandriformis.

No. 772 — Butterflies: a, Charaxes jasius. b, Hamanumidia daedalus. c, Charaxes bohemani. d, Hallimoides rumia, denomination LL. e, Hallimoides rumia, denomination LR. f, Pseudacraea boisduuali.

1500fr, Coelogyne ovalis, palla ussheri. 2000fr, Baleniceps, Neurophyllum clauatum.

**1998, June 20**

**769** A185 150fr Sheet of 6, #a.-f. 5.00 5.00
**769G** A185 250fr Sheet of 6, #h.-m. 5.50 5.50
**769N** A185 300fr Sheet of 6, #o.-t. 6.50 6.50
**770** A185 300fr Sheet of 6, #a.-f. 8.00 8.00
**771** A185 350fr Sheet of 6, #a.-f. 10.00 10.00
**771G** A185 450fr Sheet of 6, #h.-m. 12.00 12.00
**771N** A185 475fr Sheet of 6, #o.-t. 10.50 10.50
**771U** A185 500fr Sheet of 6, #v.-aa. 12.00 12.00
**772** A185 600fr Sheet of 6, #a.-f. 16.00 8.00

**Souvenir Sheets**

**773** A185 1500fr multicolored 6.50 6.50
**773A** A185 2000fr multicolored 7.50 7.50

Nos. 773-773A contain one 51x42mm stamp.

Bela Lugosi as Dracula — A185a

Lugosi in various poses.

**1998, Dec. 11 Litho. *Perf. 13½***

**773B** A185a 250fr Sheet of 9, #d.-l. 7.50 7.50

**Souvenir Sheet**

**773C** A185a 1500fr multi, horiz. 5.00 5.00

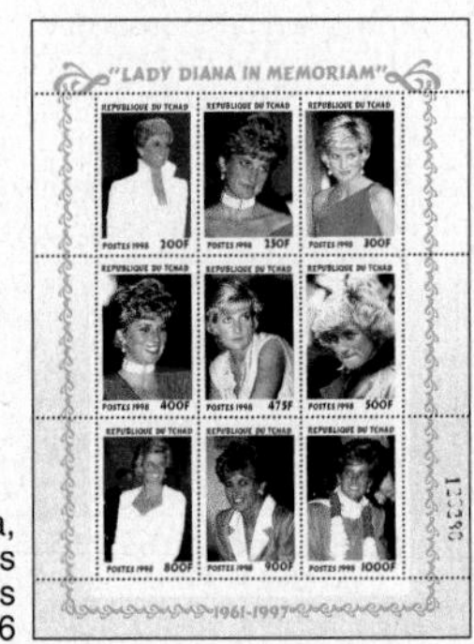


Diana, Princess of Wales A186

No. 774 — Various portraits: a, 200fr. b, 250fr. c, 300fr. d, 400fr. e, 475fr. f, 500fr. g, 800fr. h, 900fr. i, 1000fr.

**1999, Jan. 10 Litho. *Perf. 12½***

**774** A186 Sheet of 9, #a.-i. 18.00 18.00

Birds — A187

Designs: 75fr, Ibis ibis. 150fr, Ephippiorhynchus senegalensis. 200fr, Phoenicopterus ruber. 300fr, Leptoptilus crumeniferus. 400fr, Scopus umbretta. 475fr, Platalea alba.

1000fr, Balaeniceps rex.

**1999, Jan. 15 Litho. *Perf. 12¾***

**775-780** A187 Set of 6 5.75 5.75

**Souvenir Sheet**

**781** A187 1000fr multicolored 3.50 3.50

No. 781 contains one 32x40mm stamp.

Fire Trucks — A188

Designs: 50fr, 1840 model. 150fr, 1920 Fiat. 200fr, 1915 Mack. 300fr, 1930 Renault. 400fr, Pegaso M 1090. 500fr, 1960 Jet Fire Power.

700fr, 1720 King George III Fire Company.

**1998, Dec. 30**

**782-787** A188 Set of 6 5.75 5.75

**Souvenir Sheet**

**788** A188 700fr multicolored 2.50 2.50

No. 788 contains one 35x28mm stamp.

Minerals — A188a

No. 788A: a, Opal. b, Cyanite. c, Chalcopyrite. d, Apatite. e, Celestite. f, Scorodite.

No. 788B: a, Agate. b, Wulfenite. c, Barytine. d, Tanzanite. e, Amazonite. f, Malachite.

**1998 Litho. *Perf. 13½***

**788A** A188a 475fr Sheet of 6, #a.-f. 10.00 10.00
**788B** A188a 500f Sheet of 6, #a.-f. 10.50 10.50

Dinosaurs — A188b

No. 788C: a, Dilophosaurus. b, Argentinosaurus. c, Kritosaurus. d, Scutellosaurus. e, Ornithomimosaurus. f, Bactrosaurus.

No. 788D: a, Coelophysis. b, Kannemeyeria. c, Apatosaurus. d, Scipionyx. e, Lystrosaurus. f, Kentrosaurus.

No. 788E, Giganotosaurus, vert.

**1998, Nov. 12 Litho. *Perf. 13¼***

**Sheets of 6**

**788C** A188b 400fr #a.-f. 7.75 7.75
**788D** A188b 450fr #a.-f. 9.00 9.00

**Souvenir Sheet**

**788E** A188b 2000fr multi 6.50 6.50

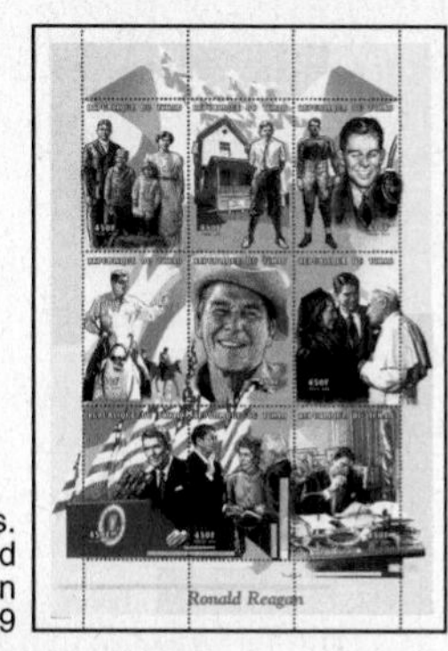
US Pres. Ronald Reagan A189

No. 789: a, Family portrait as young boy. b, In front of family home. c, In football uniform, as radio announcer. d, Riding horse. e, Up close portrait. f, With Nancy, greeting Pope John Paul II. g, Making speech at podium. h, Being sworn in as president. i, At desk in Oval Office.

2000fr, At desk, White House.

**1999, Feb. 2 Litho. *Perf. 13½***
**789** A189 450fr Sheet of 9, #a.-i. 14.00 14.00

**Souvenir Sheet**
**790** A189 2000fr multicolored 6.50 6.50

American Railroads — A190

No. 791 — Train, railroad pioneer: a, "Alco" Santa Fe, 1945, Cyrus Holliday. b, Rio Grande, 1961, J.F. Stevens. c, Amtrak, 1976, Thomas Dehone Judah. d, 250 Gobernador, 1884, Mark Hopkins. e, Meeting of Central Pacific and Union Pacific at Promontory Point, 1869, Leland Stanford, Thomas Durant. f, Great Northern W1, 1947, Jim Hill. g, Union Pacific Railroad, 1951, G.M. Dodge. h, Pennsylvania GG1, 1934, S.M. Vauclain. i, 151 Santa Fe U.P, 1917, S. Barstow Strong.

**1998, Dec. 11**
**791** A190 200fr Sheet of 9, #a.-i. 7.00 7.00

Fossils and Cave Paintings A191

No. 792: a, Harlania enigmatica. b, Spirophyton. c, Fossils, dunes of Djourab. d, Chain of people, oxen, Bardai. e, Man of Gonoa. f, Oxen, Kozen, Borkou.

**1998, Dec. 11**
**792** A191 150fr Sheet of 6, #a.-f. 4.00 4.00

Frank Sinatra — A191a

No. 792G — Sinatra with: h, Blonde actress. i, Green jacket. j, Ava Gardner. k, Striped suit. l, Actor. m, Gun. n, Dark green hat. o, Oscar statuette. p, Military cap.

**1998, Dec. 30 Litho. *Perf. 13½***
**792G** A191a 300fr Sheet of 9, #h.-p. 9.50 9.50

James Dean (1931-55), Actor — A192

Various portraits.

**1999, Feb. 2**
**793** A192 200fr Sheet of 9, #a.-i. 6.25 6.25

Pope John Paul II A193

Various portraits.

**1999, Feb. 2**
**794** A193 300fr Sheet of 9, #a.-i. 9.00 9.00

**Souvenir Sheet**
**795** A193 1500fr multicolored 5.50 5.00

No. 795 contains one 58x51mm stamp.

John Glenn's Return to Space A194

Various portraits.

**1999, Feb. 11 Litho. *Perf. 13½***
**796** A194 500fr Sheet of 9, #a.-i. 15.00 15.00

**Souvenir Sheet**
**797** A194 2000fr multicolored 6.50 6.50

No. 797 contains one 57x51mm stamp.

Kofi Annan, UN Secretary-General — A195

Various portraits.

**1998, Dec. 11**
**798** A195 150fr Sheet of 9, #a.-i. 4.75 4.75

Chess A196

No. 798J: k, Paul Morphy. l, Chess board, Morphy-Anderssen, 1858. m, Adolf Anderssen. n, Emanuel Lasker. o, Chess board, Lasker-Capablanca, 1914. p, José Raul Capablanca. q, David Bronstein. r, Chess board, Bronstein-Botvinnik, 1951. s, Mikhail Botvinnik.

a, Bobby Fischer. b, Chess board, Fischer-Tal, 1961. c, Mikhail Tal. d, Boris Spassky. e, Chess board, Spassky-Petrosian, 1969. f, Tigran Petrosian. g, Garry Kasparov. h, Chess board, Kasparov-Karpov, 1960. i, Anatoly Karpov.

No. 800, Margrave Othon IV of Brandenburg.

No. 800A, King Louis XVI playing chess, horiz.

**1999, Feb. 20**
**798J** A196 375fr Sheet of 9, #k.-s. 11.00 11.00
**799** A196 500fr Sheet of 9, #a.-i. 14.75 14.75

**Souvenir Sheets**
**800** A196 2000fr multi 6.75 6.75
**800A** A196 2000fr multi 6.75 6.75

Dated 1998. No. 800 contains one 58x51mm stamp. No. 800A contains one 58x51mm stamp. Sheets of 3 stamps, containing Nos. 798Jk-798Jm, 798Jn-798Jp, 798Jq-798Js, 799a-799c, 799d-799f, or 799g-799i exist.

Souvenir Sheets

France, 1998 World Cup Champions — A197

No. 801: a, Bikente Lizarazu. b, Christian Karembeu. c, Frank Leboeuf. d, Emmanuel Petit.

No. 802: a, Fabien Barthez. b, Marcel Desailly. c, Didier Deschamps. d, Christophe Dugarry.

No. 803: Youri Djorkaeff. b, Aime Jacquet. c, Lilian Thuram. d, Zinedine Zidane.

2000fr, Deschamps holding World Cup.

**1999, Feb. 20 Litho. *Perf. 13½***
**801** A197 300fr Sheet of 4, #a.-d. 4.00 4.00
**802** A197 400fr Sheet of 4, #a.-d. 5.75 5.75
**803** A197 500fr Sheet of 4, #a.-d. 7.25 7.25

***Perf. 13¼***
**804** A197 2000fr multicolored 7.00 7.00

No. 804 contains one 57x51mm stamp.

Hokusai Paintings — A198

Designs: a, Voyagers Crossing the Oi River. b, Bird. c, On Totomi Mountain. d, Evening at Ueno. e, Higashimachi-matsuri-yatai-tenjou. f, Evening shower at Yoshiwara. g, Woman with Umbrella. h, Cascade. i, Courtesan.

**1999, Sept. 10 Litho. *Perf. 13½***
**805** A198 475fr Sheet of 9, #a.-i. 17.50 17.50

Japex '99.

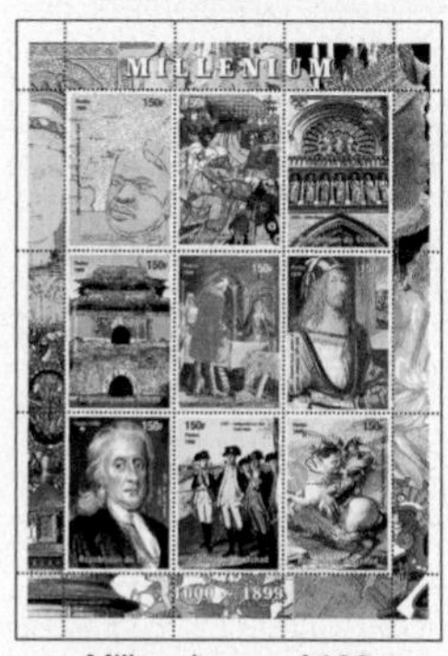

Millennium — A199

No. 806 — Highlights of 1000-1899: a, Commercial routes in West Africa. b, Crusades. c, Notre Dame Cathedral. d, Ming dynasty tombs. e, Discovery of America. f, Albrecht Dürer. g, Sir Isaac Newton. h, American Independence. i, Napoleon.

No. 807 — 1900-24: a, Return of Halley's Comet. b, Lord Baden-Powell founds Scouting movement. c, Sinking of the Titanic. d, 1st film in Technicolor. e, Marconi sends 1st message across Atlantic, birth of radio. f, Harry Houdini. g, Capablanca-Lasker chess matches. h, Pierre & Marie Curie win Nobel Prize. i, Theft of the Mona Lisa.

No. 808 — 1925-49: a, Birth of Marilyn Monroe. b, Discovery of Pluto. c, Laurel and Hardy. d, Independence of India. e, Alexander Fleming discovers penicillin. f, Introduction of Volkswagen Beetle & Vespa motor scooter. g, Opening of film "Dracula." h, World War II. i, Discovery of Lascaux cave drawings.

No. 809 — 1950-74: a, 1st flight of the Concorde, 7 original astronauts. b, Death of Buddy Holly. c, 1st Super Bowl. d, Death of Eva Peron. e, Art by Andy Warhol. f, The Beatles. g, Cultural Revolution in China. h, Assassination of Pres. John F. Kennedy. i, Cuban Revolution.

No. 810 — 1975-99: a, Death of Princess Diana. b, Death of Enzo Ferrari. c, Akira. d, Argentina, 1986 World Cup Soccer champions. e, B. Lara breaks cricket records. f, France, 1998 World Cup Soccer champions. g, Explosion of the Space Shuttle Challenger. h, Pope John Paul II meets Lech Walesa. i, Deaths of Frank Sinatra, Freddie Mercury.

**1999, Sept. 10**
**806** A199 150fr Sheet of 9, #a.-i. 5.25 5.25
**807** A199 300fr Sheet of 9, #a.-i. 10.00 10.00
**808** A199 450fr Sheet of 9, #a.-i. 15.00 15.00
**809** A199 475fr Sheet of 9, #a.-i. 16.00 16.00
**810** A199 500fr Sheet of 9, #a.-i. 16.00 16.00
*Nos. 806-810 (5)* 62.25 62.25

Souvenir Sheet

PhilexFrance '99 — A200

**1999, Sept. 10**

**811** A200 1500fr multi 6.00 6.00

I Love Lucy A201

No. 812: a, Lucy leaning against tree, Ricky. b, Lucy, Ricky kissing. c, Lucy pointing gun. d, Ricky falling to ground. e, Lucy in apartment. f, Ricky holding animal. g, Ricky drinking from canteen. h, Lucy, Ricky talking. i, Lucy behind bush.

No. 813, Lucy in grape vat. No. 814, Lucy, Ricky in bed.

**1999, Feb. 20 Litho.** ***Perf. 13¼***

**812** A201 450fr Sheet of 9, #a.-i. 17.00 17.00

**Souvenir Sheets**

**813** A201 1500fr multi 6.00 6.00
**814** A201 2000fr multi 8.00 8.00

Dated 1998.

See Nos. 865-867.

Betty Boop A202

No. 815: a, With cat and dog. b, In flowered dress. c, Looking back over shoulder. d, With hammer, dresser. e, As majorette. f, In red dress with fur collar. g, Holding paper. h, Holding blue dress. i, Holding telephone.

No. 816, With feathered hat. No. 817, In leopard-spotted blouse.

**1999, Feb. 20 Litho.** ***Perf. 13¼***

**815** A202 450fr Sheet of 9, #a.-i. 16.00 16.00

**Souvenir Sheets**

**816** A202 1500fr multi 5.00 5.00
**817** A202 2000fr multi 7.00 7.00

Dated 1998.

See Nos. 856-858.

Antique Automobiles A203

150fr, 1900 F.N. 300fr, 1906 Bianchi. 400fr, 1906 Renault. 500fr, 1919 Pierce-Arrow. 700fr, 1919 Citroen 5CV. 900fr, 1928 Ford. 1000fr, 1898 Renault.

**1999 Litho.** ***Perf. 13x12¾***

**818-823** A203 Set of 6 11.00 11.00

**Souvenir Sheet**

***Perf. 13x13¼***

**824** A203 1000fr multi 5.00 5.00

No. 824 contains one 40x31mm stamp.

Locomotives A204

Designs: 150fr, 0-4-4-0. 300fr, Red 0-4-0. 400fr, Green 0-6-0. 500fr, Brown 0-4-0. 700fr, Blue 0-4-0. 900fr, Blue 0-6-0.

1000fr, Electric locomotive.

**1999** ***Perf. 12¾***

**825-830** A204 Set of 6 11.00 11.00

**Souvenir Sheet**

***Perf. 13x13¼***

**831** A204 1000fr multi 5.00 5.00

No. 831 contains one 36x28mm stamp.

Wonders of Forgotten Cultures A205

Designs: 50fr, Easter Island. 150fr, Stonehenge. 300fr, Jericho. 400fr, Machu Picchu. 500fr, Valley of Statues. 700fr, Chichén Itzá. 900fr, Persepolis.

**1999** ***Perf. 12¾***

**832-838** A205 Set of 7 15.00 15.00

Chad postal officials have declared the following items to be "not authorized:"

Set of six stamps of various denominations: New Year 2000 (Year of the Dragon)

Sheet of nine stamps of various denominations: Orchids

Sheet of nine 150fr stamps: Spanish Impressionist paintings

Sheet of nine 300fr stamps: Millennium (Composers), Van Gogh paintings

Sheet of nine 450fr stamps: Millennium (Marilyn Monroe), French Impressionist paintings

Sheet of nine 475fr stamps: Impressionist paintings

Sheet of nine 500fr stamps: Renoir nudes, Elvis Presley, Olympics

Souvenir sheets of one: Millennium (three 300fr, two 450fr, one 475fr, three 500fr, one 1500fr), New Year 2000 (1000fr), Palace of Versailles (1500fr, 2000fr), Hiroshige paintings (1500fr, 2000fr).

Minerals A206

Designs: 150fr, Wulfenite. 200fr, Argentite. 400fr, Siderite. 500fr, Dolomite and quartz. 700fr, Azurite. 900fr, Spinel and calcite.

1000fr, Cassiterite.

**2000, Jan. 15 Litho.** ***Perf. 12¾***

**839-844** A206 Set of 6 14.00 14.00

**Souvenir Sheet**

**845** A206 1000fr multi 5.00 5.00

Dated 1999.

Dogs — A206a

Designs: 150fr, Caucasian Mountain dog (Berger caucasique). 300fr, Belgian shepherd (Berger Belgue). 400fr, Spanish mastiff (Mâtin Espagne). 500fr, Kuvasz. 700fr, Beauceron. 900fr, Rough collie.

**2000, Jan. 15 Litho.** ***Perf. 13***

**845A** A206a 150fr multi —
**845B** A206a 300fr multi —
**845C** A206a 400fr multi —
**845D** A206a 500fr multi —
**845E** A206a 700fr multi —
**845F** A206a 900fr multi —

Dated 1999.

Elvis Presley A207

No. 846: a, Playing guitar, wearing red jacket. b, Holding microphone and guitar, wearing red jacket. c, Holding guitar, wearing gold jacket. d, Playing guitar wearing black leather jacket. e, Playing guitar, wearing black jacket. f, Playing guitar, wearing blue jacket. g, Holding microphone, wearing blue shirt. h, Singing, wearing brown jacket. i, Holding microphone, wearing striped yellow jacket.

**2000, Mar. 10** ***Perf. 13¼***

**846** A207 300fr Sheet of 9, #a-i 10.00 10.00

Dated 1999.

Carl Benz and Mercedes-Benz Automobiles — A208

No. 847: a, 1934 W-25. b, 1934 500 K. c, 1964 230 SL. d, 1935 150. e, 1954 300 SL. f, 1971 280 SE.

2000fr, 1934 500 K, diff.

**2000, Mar. 10**

**847** A208 250fr Sheet of 6, #a-f 6.25 6.25

**Souvenir Sheet**

**848** A208 2000fr multi 8.00 8.00

No. 847 contains six 30x30mm stamps. Dated 1999.

Trains A209

No. 849: a, FES 3228, European Union flag. b, TGV Duplex, French flag. c, 500 Series Unit W1, Japanese flag. d, AVE Class 100, Spanish flag. e, ICE3, German flag. f, ETR 500, Italian flag.

2000fr, TGC 001 V56, TGV Duplex, Etienne Chambron.

**2000, Mar. 10**

**849** A209 600fr Sheet of 6, #a-f 10.00 10.00

**Souvenir Sheet**

**850** A209 2000fr multi 5.50 5.50

No. 849 contains six 30x30mm stamps. Dated 1999.

French Rulers A210

No. 851, 150fr: a, Charlemagne. b, King Charles VIII. c, King Francis I. d, King Henry II. e, Catherine de Medici. f, King Henry III.

No. 852, 200fr: a, King Louis XII. b, King Louis XIII. c, King Louis XIV. d, King Louis XV. e, King Louis XVI. f, King Louis XVIII.

No. 853, 300fr — Napoleon Bonaparte: a, Standing, wearing red cape. b, On horseback, wearing red cape. c, On horseback, with soldier at right. d, On horseback, with crowd at right. e, Standing with other people. f, On white horse, leading battle.

**2000, Mar. 10** **Sheets of 6, #a-f**

**851-853** A210 Set of 3 17.50 17.50

Dated 1999.

Pope John Paul II A211

No. 854 — Pope John Paul II and: a, Dalai Lama. b, Fidel Castro. c, King Hassan II of Morocco. d, Grand Rabbi Elio Toaff. e, Patriarch Bartholomew I. f, Mother Teresa.

**2000, Mar. 10**

**854** A211 475fr Sheet of 6, #a-f 11.00 11.00

Dated 1999.

Space A212

No. 855: a, Sputnik, dog Laika. b, Yuri Gagarin, Vostok 1. c, Konstantin Feoktistov, Vladimir Komarov, Boris Yegorov, Voskhod 1. d, Luna 1, chimpanzee Ham. e, Neil Armstrong, Michael Collins, Edwin Aldrin, Apollo 11. f, Aldrin, splashdown of capsule.

**2000, Mar. 10**

**855** A212 500fr Sheet of 6, #a-f 11.00 11.00

Dated 1999.

**Betty Boop Type of 1999**

No. 856: a, Wearing red and violet striped leotard, kicking leg up. b, As cheerleader. c, At football field, holding pennant. d, At ice cream shop. e, Wearing yellow and green striped leotard. f, Wearing baseball cap and orange shorts. g, Wearing baseball cap and checked shirt. h, Seated, drinking beverage. i, Wearing cut-off shorts.

No. 857, 1500fr, Riding bicycle. No. 858, 2000fr, Wearing glasses, elbow and knee pads.

**2000, Mar. 30**

**856** A202 250fr Sheet of 9, #a-i 8.50 8.50

**Souvenir Sheets**

**857-858** A202 Set of 2 12.50 12.50

The Three Stooges A213

No. 859, 250fr, horiz.: a, Larry, in surgeon's gown, and Curly. b, Curly, Moe, Larry around barrel. c, Moe, Larry and Curly on horse. d, Larry attacking man. e, Moe getting hair pulled. f, Moe with mallet. g, Curly, Moe and Larry in western outfits, outdoors. h, Larry, Curly and Moe in white doctor's jackets. i, Man looking at Moe.

No. 860, 300fr, horiz.: a, Larry grabbing Moe's chin. b, Moe and Larry holding scrolls. c, Moe, yellow background. d, Larry, blue background. e, Moe, Shemp and Larry. f, Shemp, blue background. g, Shemp, yellow background. h, Shemp pointing bellows at Larry. i, Moe and Larry in white.

No. 861, 1500fr, Moe in surgeon's gown. No. 862, 1500fr, Moe wearing hat. No. 863, 2000fr, Curly, Moe and Larry in western outfits, outdoors. No. 864, 2000fr, Larry with violin.

**2000 Sheets of 9, #a-i**

**859-860** A213 Set of 2 20.00 20.00

**Souvenir Sheets**

**861-864** A213 Set of 4 27.50 27.50

Issued: Nos. 859, 861, 863, 3/30; Nos. 860, 862, 864, 5/29.

**I Love Lucy Type of 1999**

No. 865: a, Lucy dancing, man in background. b, Lucy dancing, with knees bent and arms extended. c, Lucy in doorway. d, Lucy dancing behind sofa. e, Lucy kicking out leg. f, Lucy being caught by two men. g, Lucy with one arm extended. h, Lucy being sprayed with seltzer water. i, Lucy with leg on dance rail.

No. 866, 1500fr, Lucy looking at clock, horiz. No. 867, 2000fr, Lucy with clown costume and arms extended.

**2000, May 29**

**865** A201 225fr Sheet of 9, #a-i 8.00 8.00

**Souvenir Sheets**

**866-867** A201 Set of 2 14.50 14.50

N'Djamena, Cent. — A213a

Background colors: 150fr, Blue. 300fr, Red. 475fr, Green.

**2000, May 29 Litho. *Perf. 13¼***

**867A-867C** A213a Set of 3 — —

Chadian Political History A214

No. 868, 150fr: a, Louis Léon César Faidherbe. b, François Joseph Lamy. c, Henri Eugène Gouraud. d, Gustav Nachtigal. e, Head of Rabah on spike. f, Fernand Foureau.

No. 869, 300fr: a, Pierre Savorgnan de Brazza. b, Philippe Marie de Hautecloque Leclerc. c, Emile Gentil. d, Gabriel Lisette. e, Charles de Gaulle. f, Felix Eboué.

**2000, May 29 *Perf. 13½***

**Sheets of 6, #a-f**

**868-869** A214 Set of 2 16.00 16.00

Wildlife, Map of Chad, Scouting Emblem A215

No. 870, 150fr — Giraffa camelopardalis: a, Pair, one with head lowered. b, Pair, both with heads extended. c, Pair near forest. d, Trio.

No. 871, 200fr: a, Pair of Gazella granti in field. b, Gazella cuiveri. c, Gazella dorcas. d, Pair of Gazella granti at waterhole.

No. 872, 250fr — Addax nasomaculatus: a, View of head. b, Lying in grass. c, Standing. d, Grazing.

No. 873, 300fr — Ammotragus lervia: a, Pair. b, View of head. c, Standing on mountain ledge. d, Standing, with purple mountain in background

No. 874, 375fr — Diceros bicornis: a, View of head. b, Facing right, line of dark green foliage in background. c, Facing left. d, Facing right, with trees in background.

No. 875, 400fr — Panthera pardus: a, On tree branch. b, Lying in grass. c, Standing. d, View of head.

No. 876, 450fr: a, Head of Theropithecus gelada. b, Cercopithecus aethiops. c, Papio anubis. d, Adult and juvenile Thereopithecus gelada.

No. 877, 450fr — Hippopotamus amphibius: a, Pair laying in mud. b, With open mouth. c, Standing. d, Herd.

No. 878, 475fr — Oryx dammah: a, Facing right, green foliage in background. b, View of head. c, Pair. d, Grazing, mountain in background.

No. 879, 500fr — Panthera leo: a, Male on female. b, Females at waterhole. c, Female and cub. d, Female and male.

No. 880, 600fr — Loxodonta africana: a, With tree at right. b, Facing right. c, View of head. d, With tree and mountain in background.

No. 881, 750fr — Syncerus caffer: a, Juvenile, adult grazing. b, Adult in field. c, Pair lying on ground. d, With grass in mouth.

No. 882, 1000fr, Pair of Diceros bicornis. No. 883, 1000fr, Pair of Hippopotamus amphibius fighting. No. 884, 1500fr, Panthera leo with kill.

Illustration reduced.

**2000, Aug. 1 *Perf. 13¼***

**Horiz. Strips of 4, #a-d**

**870-881** A215 Set of 12 75.00 75.00

**Souvenir Sheets**

**882-884** A215 Set of 3 14.00 14.00

Nos. 882-884 each contain one 36x51mm stamp.

Miniature Sheet

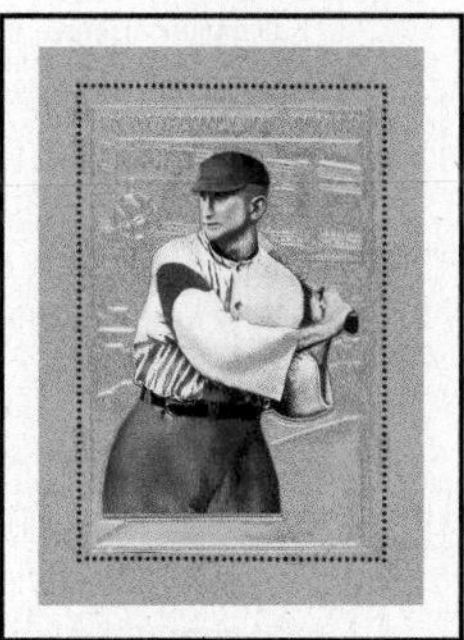

Baseball Player A216

**2000, Oct. 11 Litho. & Embossed**

**885** A216 3000fr gold & multi 10.00 10.00

Exists with silver background.

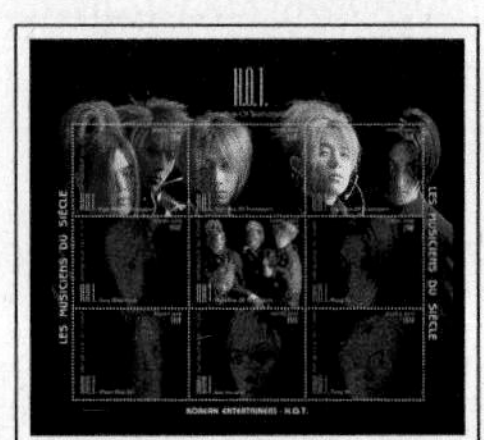

High-five of Teenagers — A217

No. 886: a, Moon Hee-jun and Lee Jae-won. b, Jang Woo-hyuk and ear of Tony An. c, Tony an and Kang Ta. d, Jang Woo-hyuk. e, Entire group. f, Kang Ta. g, Moon Hee-jun. h, Lee Jae-won. i, Tony An.

**2000 Litho.**

**886** A217 150fr Sheet of 9, #a-i 4.50 4.50

Sports and Chess A218

No. 887, 30fr — Dogs involved in sport activities: a, Sled dogs. b, Dog racing. c, Hunting dogs. d, Dogs and skier.

No. 888, 70fr — Various sports: a, Petanque. b, Rugby. c, Archery. d, Jai alai.

No. 889, 250fr — 2000 Summer Olympics, Sydney: a, Fencing. b, Judo. c, Tennis. d, Boxing.

No. 890, 300fr — 2000 Summer Olympics, Sydney: a, Cycling. b, Basketball. c, Beach volleyball. d, Baseball.

No. 891, 400fr — Soccer players: a, Zinedine Zidane. b, Lilian Thuram. c, Yuri Djorkaeff. d, Nicolas Anelka

No. 892, 475fr — 2000 Summer Olympics, Sydney: a, Table tennis. b, Equestrian. c, Swimming. d, Kayaking.

No. 893, 500fr — Golf: a, Man with white pants swinging club. b, Golfer analyzing putt. c, Man with black pants swinging club. d, Woman golfer.

No. 894, 750fr — Formula I race drivers: a, Michael Schumacher. b, Mikka Hakkinen. c, Ralf Schumacher. d, David Coulthard.

No. 895, 1000fr — Chess: a, Knight with shield. b, Knight on donkey. c, Knight with attendant. d, Horses and wheeled castle.

2000fr, Venus Williams.

**2001, Jan. 31 *Perf. 13¼***

**Sheets of 4, #a-d**

**887-895** A218 Set of 9 75.00 75.00

**Souvenir Sheet**

**896** A218 2000fr multi 9.00 9.00

2000 Summer Olympics, Sydney (No. 896). No. 896 contains one 36x51mm stamp.

Trains A219

No. 897, 200fr: a, Mallard, 1935. b, P8 Prussian, 1908. c, F2A, 1936. b, 240 P, 1940.

No. 898, 300fr: a, NSB No. 3641. b, New Zealand Railways Sereis EW. c, Series 277, Renfe. d, Series DF4 Vent d'Est IV Co-Co.

No. 899, 400fr: a, SNCF Series 9100 2-D-2, 1950. b, SNCF Series 72000 C-C, 1967. c, CC 21000, 1969. d, VL-80, 1963.

No. 900, 475fr: a, GNER Eurostar. b, Electric EMU ETR 500. c, DER OBB 1016 001. d, GNER train.

No. 901, 500fr: a, OL-49, 1951. b, Pacific Series 16E, 1935. c, Andaluces 030, 1877. d, Franco-Crosti Gr. 743, 1937.

No. 902, 500fr: a, JR West 8-car unit E4. b, TGV KTX. c, 300 Series unit J3. d, E3 Series unit R6.

No. 903, 600fr: a, 2D2 PO, 1926. b, Metropolitan BB Vickers, 1920. c, DB ET 491, 1935. d, Series D, 1925.

No. 904, 600fr: a, Electric EMU 490. b, Acela, 2001. c, CFF-FFS Electric EMU RABe 500. d, ICE-T Bavereihe 41.

No. 905, 750fr: a, Single Driver, 1870. b, Great Western Railway Castle, 1923. c, Schools Class, 1930. d, 230 Besa, 1905.

No. 906, 750fr: a, TGV Thalys. b, TGV Duplex. c, TGV La Poste. d, TGV Atlantique.

1500fr, SAR Series 26 2-D-2. 2000fr, TGV Sud-est.

**2001, June 22 Litho.**

**Sheets of 4, #a-d**

**897-906** A219 Set of 10 75.00 75.00

**Souvenir Sheets**

**907-908** A219 Set of 2 13.50 13.50

Nos. 907-908 each contain one 51x36mm stamp.

British Royalty A220

No. 909, 300fr — Queen Mother: a, With King George VI. b, With young daughter. c, With Prince Charles. d, Waving. e, Wearing tiara and yellow dress. f, Wearing pink dress and hat. g, Wearing green dress and hat. h, Holding flowers. i, With dogs.

No. 910, 300fr — Prince William wearing: a, Black suit with lapel handkerchief. b, Suit with red and blue vest. c, Suit with gold vest. d, Sweater, looking right. e, Black suit and dark blue tie. f, Sweater, facing forward. g, Blue shirt with button. h, Dark blue shirt without button. i, Light blue suit.

**2001, July 22 *Perf. 13¼***

**Sheets of 9, #a-i**

**909-910** A220 Set of 2 20.00 20.00

No. 910 contains nine 36x51mm stamps.

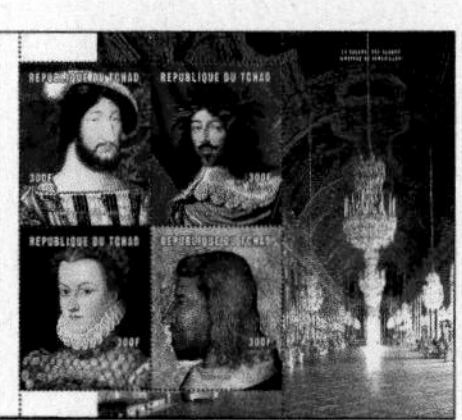

French Rulers A221

No. 911, 300fr: a, King Francis I. b, King Louis XIII. c, Elizabeth of Austria, consort of King Charles IX. d, King John II the Good.

No. 912, 375fr: a, King Louis XIV. b, King Francis I, diff. c, King Louis XVI. d, King Louis XVIII.

No. 913, 475fr: a, King Louis XV as child. b, King Louis XV as adult. c, Queen Marie Antoinette. d, King Charles VII.

No. 914, 500fr — Napoleon Bonaparte wearing: a, White tunic. b, Black jacket. c, Emperor's robes. d, Red tunic.

**2001, July 22 Sheets of 4, #a-d**

**911-914** A221 Set of 4 25.00 25.00

Stamps of Nos. 911-913 exist in souvenir sheets of 1. Value, set $70.

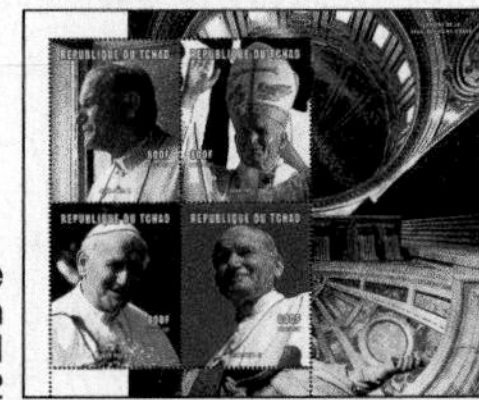

Pope John Paul II A222

No. 915, 800fr: a, Standing in room, looking left. b, Waving, c, Holding flowers. d, With blue sky background.

No. 916, 1000fr: a, Wearing red hat. b, Wearing miter, waving. c, Bending to kiss ground. d, Wearing miter, holding crucifix.

4000fr, Wearing zucchetto.

**2001 Litho. *Perf. 13¼***

**Sheets of 4, #a-d**

**915-916** A222 Set of 2 29.00 29.00

**Miniature Sheet**

**Litho. & Embossed**

**917** A222 4000fr gold & multi 22.50 22.50

Issued: Nos. 915-916, 7/22; No. 917, 7/23. No. 917 contains one 60x90mm stamp and exists with a silver background. Stamps of Nos. 915-916 exist in souvenir sheets of 1. Value, set $60.

Famous Men — A223

Designs: 200fr, Charles Darwin (1809-82), naturalist. 250fr, Christopher Columbus (1451-1506), explorer. 300fr, Jacques-Yves Cousteau (1910-97), marine scientist. 350fr, Albert Schweitzer (1875-1965), missionary. 400fr, Juan Manuel Fangio (1911-95), race car driver. 450fr, Nicolaus Copernicus (1473-1543), astronomer. 500fr, Robert Stephenson (1803-59), engineer. 550fr, Etienne Chambron, high speed rail pioneer. 600fr, Garry Kasparov, chess player. 750fr, Lord Robert Baden-Powell (1857-1941), founder of scouting. 800fr, Neil Armstrong, astronaut. 1000fr, Sir Alexander Fleming (1881-1955), bacteriologist.

**2001, Oct. 30** **Litho.**

**918-929** A223 Set of 12 25.00 25.00

Nos. 918-929 exist in souvenir sheets of 1. Value, set $115.

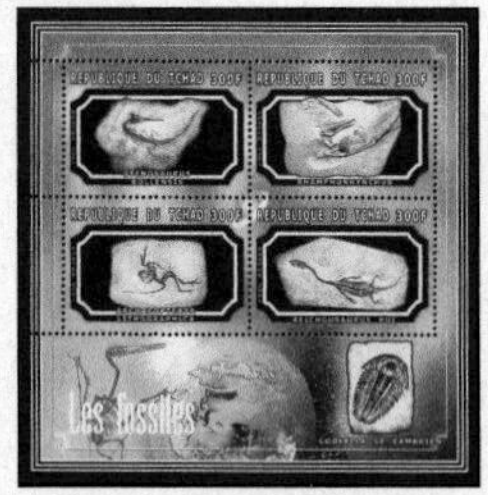

Fossils, Dinosaurs, Meteorites and Minerals — A224

No. 930, 300fr — Fossils: a, Stenosaurus bollensis. b, Rhamphorhynchus. c, Archaeopteryx lithographica. d, Keichousaurus hui.
No. 931, 375fr — Dinosaurs: a, Mesadactylus. b, Pteranodon. c, Tropeognathus. d, Quetzalcoatlus.
No. 932, 400fr — Meteorites found in: a, India. b, Nigeria. c, US. d, Australia.
No. 933, 500fr — Dinosaurs: a, Deinonychus. b, Seismosaurus. c, Pleurocoelus, Acrocanthosaur. d, Styracosaurus.
No. 934, 500fr — Minerals: a, Fluorite. b, Pyrite. c, Wulfenite. d, Merovingian scoria.
No. 935, 550fr — Meteorites found in: a, Antarctica. b, Libya. c, USSR. d, China.
No. 936, 600fr — Minerals: a, Magnetite. b, Kunzite. c, Apophyllite, Stilbite. d, Fluorite, diff.
No. 937, 750fr — Minerals: a, Quartz. b, Merovingian scoria, diff. c, Epidote. d, Amethyst, agate.
3000fr, Tyrannosaurus rex, vert.

**2001, Dec. 27** **Litho.**

**Sheets of 4, #a-d**

**930-937** A224 Set of 8 70.00 70.00

**Miniature Sheet**

**Litho. & Embossed**

**938** A224 3000fr gold & multi 17.00 17.00

No. 938 contains one 60x90mm stamp and exists with silver background.

French Kings A225

Designs: No. 939, 3000fr, Louis IX. No. 940, 3000fr, Francis I. No. 941, 3000fr, Henry IV. No. 942, 3000fr, Louis XIII. No. 943, 3000fr, Louis XV.

**2002, Apr. 10** **Litho. & Embossed**

**Gold & Multicolored**

**939-943** A225 Set of 5 50.00 50.00

Nos. 939-943 exist with silver background.

Egyptian Treasures A225a

Designs: No. 943A, 3000fr, Painted wooden box. No. 943B, 3000fr, Nekhbet vulture. No. 943C, 3000fr, Oushebti of Tutankhamen, vert. No. 943D, 3000fr, Pair of royal scepters, vert. No. 943E, 3000fr, Diadem, vert. No. 943F, 3000fr, Gold-plated throne, vert. No. 943G, 3000fr, Cynocephalic pectoral, vert. No. 943H, 3000fr, Coffin of Tutankhamen, vert. No. 943I, 3000fr, Statue of Ka, vert. No. 943J, 3000fr, Duck earring, vert. No. 943K, 3000fr, Lion-shaped vase, vert. No. 943L, 3000fr, Canopic dais and chapel, vert.

**Embossed on Gold Paper**

**2002, Apr. 10** ***Perf. 13¼***

**943A-943L** A225a Set of 12 140.00 140.00

Artists and Their Paintings A226

On Nos. 944-957, painting titles (in French) and artist's birth and death dates are in margins adjacent to each stamp. On Nos. 958-962 painting titles are not shown, but artist's name is in sheet margin

No. 944, 150fr: a, Berthe Morisot (1841-95). b, Cache-cache. c, Le Berceau. d, Au bal. e, Jeune femme se poudrant. f, Paule Gobillard peignant.
No. 945, 200fr: a, Marc Chagall (1887-1985). b, Nature morte. c, Le violoniste vert. d, La maison bleue. e, Mariage. f, Le soldat ivre.
No. 946, 250fr: a, Camille Pissarro (1830-1903). b, Les chataigniers a Osny. c, Le verger. d, Le repos des glaneuses. e, Jeune paysanne prenant son cafe. f, La bergére.
No. 947, 300fr: a, Alfred Sisley (1839-99). b, Le pont de Villeneuve la Garenne. c, Allee de jardin a Louveciennes. d, Meule de foin bord du Loing. e, Moret sur Loing. f, Moulin a Moret.
No. 948, 325fr: a, Paul Delvaux (1897-1994). b, La voix publique. c, Nocturnes. d, Balgnade des Nymphes. e, Pygmalion. f, Jeunes femmes revant.
No. 949, 350fr: a, Edouard Manet (1832-83). b, Le Déjeuner sur l'herbe. c, Olympia. d, Le fifre. e, La serveuse de bocks. f, Le balcon.
No. 950, 375fr: a, Vincent van Gogh (1853-90). b, Champ de blé avec cypres. c, Rue a Auvers. d, La sieste. e, Chambre jaune a Arles. f, Rue de village.
No. 951, 400fr: a, Salvador Dali (1904-89). b, Cannibalisme en automne. c, Corpus Hypercubicus. d, Le sommeil. e, Le tentation de St. Antoine. f, Meditation sur harpe.
No. 952, 425fr: a, Paul Cézanne (1839-1906). b, Les baigneurs. c, Les grandes baigneuses (light blue background). d, Les grandes baigneuses, diff. (dark blue background). e, Les baigneueses. f, Les baigneurs au repos.
No. 953, 450fr: a, Pablo Picasso (1881-1973). b, Les demoiselles d'Avignon. c, Femme a l'eventail. d, La danse. e, La vie. f, La mere et son fils.
No. 954, 475fr: a, Amadeo Modigliani (1884-1920). b, Nu souche sur un divan. c, Nu debout. d, Cariatide debout. e, Nu allongé. f, Nu assis de dos.
No. 955, 500fr: a, Auguste Renoir (1841-1919). b, Diane chasseresse. c, Nu allongé. d, Baigneuses. e, Baigneuse assise. f, Nymphe au printemps.
No. 956, 550fr: a, Edgar Degas (1834-1917). b, Femme se coiffant. c, Aprés le bain (view of front of seated woman). d, Femme se peignant. e, Aprés le bain (view of back of woman). f, Aprés le bain (woman dressing).
No. 957, 600fr: a, Henri Matisse (1869-1954). b, Le nu bleu. c, Le genou levé. d, Nu assis sur un fauteuil. e, Odalisques. f, Nu allongé.
No. 958, 1500fr, Gustave Caillebotte. No. 959, 1500fr, Picasso, diff. No. 960, 1500fr, Auguste Renoir, diff. No. 961, 2000fr, Pablo Picasso, diff. No. 962, 2000fr, Van Gogh, diff.

**2002, Apr. 10** ***Perf. 12¾x13¼***

**Sheets of 6, #a-f**

**944-957** A226 Set of 14 110.00 110.00

**Souvenir Sheets**

***Perf. 13¼x12¾***

**958-962** A226 Set of 5 27.50 27.50

Nos. 944a-955a and 957a exist in souvenir sheets of 1 that are perf. 13¼x12¾. Value, set $92.50.

Miniature Sheet

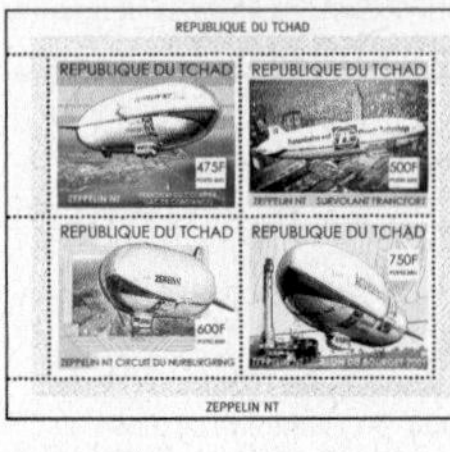


Zeppelin NT A227

No. 963: a, 475fr, Over Lake Constance. b, 500fr, Over Frankfurt. c, 600fr, Over Nürburgring, Germany. d, 750fr, At 2001 Salon du Bourget.

**2002, Oct. 30** ***Perf. 13¼***

**963** A227 Sheet of 4, #a-d 10.00 10.00

Nos. 963a-963d exist in souvenir sheets of 1. Value, set $45.

Fauna and Mushrooms — A228

No. 964, 150fr: a, Hemichromis lifalili. b, Trichechus senegalensis. c, Synodontis nigriventris. d, Gnathonemus petersii. e, Ctenopoma ansorgii. f, Pseudocrenilabrus multicolor.
No. 965, 300fr, vert.: a, Nectarina venusta. b, Lamprotornis splendidus. c, Poicephalus meyeri. d, Halcyon leucocephala. e, Quelea quelea. f, Merops pusillus.
No. 966, 350fr, vert.: a, Terathopius ecaudatus. b, Gymnogyps californianus. c, Buteo jamaicensis. d, Lophaetus occipitalis. e, Aquila rapax. f, Melierax metabates.
No. 967, 375fr, vert.: a, Elanus caeruleus. b, Harpia harpyja. c, Gyps rueppellii. d, Milvus migrans. e, Torgos tracheliotus. f, Aquila chrysaetos.
No. 968, 550fr: a, Kallimoides rumia. b, Zophopetes dysmephila. c, Megalopalpus zymna. d, Coeliades forestan. e, Catopsilia florella. f, Anaphaesis aurota.
No. 969, 600fr: a, Amanita muscaria. b, Amanita rubescens. c, Cortinarius orellanus. d, Hygrophorus hypothejus. e, Leccinum piceinum. f, Strobilomyces strobilaceus.

**2003, June 2** **Litho.**

**Sheets of 6, #a-f**

**964-969** A228 Set of 6 55.00 55.00

Stamps of Nos. 965-969 exist in a set of twelve souvenir sheets of two, with each souvenir sheet of two containing adjacent stamps found in the sheet of six. Value, set $160.

Chad — Taiwan Cooperation A229

Flags and: 50fr, Grain. 100fr, Surgeon's hands, Red Cross. 150fr, Bridge. 300fr, Handshake, maps.

**2003, Dec. 1**

| | | | |
|---|---|---|---|
| **970-973** A229 | Set of 4 | 2.50 | 2.50 |
| *973a* | Booklet pane, 2 each #970-973 | 5.00 | — |
| | Complete booklet, #973a | 5.00 | |
| *973b* | Souvenir sheet, #970-973 | 2.50 | 2.50 |

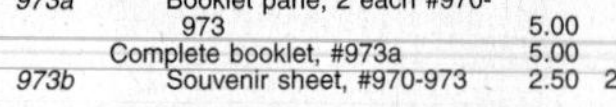

AIDS Prevention — A230

Red ribbon and: 50fr, People under umbrella. 100fr, Man and woman. 150fr, Doctor. 300fr, "Prudence, Abstinence, Fidelité."

**2004, July 7** **Litho.** ***Perf. 13x12¾***

**974-977** A230 Set of 4 2.50 2.50

Opening of Petroleum Refinery, 1st Anniv. — A231

Pres. Idriss Deby opening pipeline and: 150fr, Storage tank. 350fr, Storage tanks. 400fr, Refinery. 500fr, Tower, vert.

**2004, Oct. 10** ***Perf. 12¾x13, 13x12¾***

**978-981** A231 Set of 4 6.50 6.50

Women's Hairstyles — A232

Designs: 150fr, Figuerier. 350fr, Sakkindjala. 550fr, Kileskou. 575fr, Dabbou.

**2005, Mar. 8** ***Perf. 13***

**982-985** A232 Set of 4 8.00 8.00

Toumai Skull — A233

Color of skull: 25fr, Purple. 50fr, Green. 100fr, Gray. 150fr, Red. 1500fr, Gray.

**2005, July 19** **Litho.** ***Perf. 12¾x13***

**986-989** A233 Set of 4 1.40 1.40

**Souvenir Sheet**

**990** A233 1500fr multi 5.75 5.75

Campaign Against Trypanosomiasis, 10th Anniv. — A234

Tsetse fly and: 150fr, Trypanosomiasis protozoa, eradication campaign emblem. 300fr, Eradication campaign emblem, map of Africa. 350fr, Pan-African Postal Union emblem, eradication campaign emblem, map of Africa. 550fr, Trypanosomiasis protozoa, maps of Chad and Africa.

**2010** ***Perf. 12¾***

**991-994** A234 Set of 4 5.50 5.50

Independence, 50th Anniv. — A235

Emblem with denomination color of: 150fr, Red. 300fr, White. 350fr, Yellow. 550fr, Blue.

**2010**

**995-998** A235 Set of 4 5.50 5.50

A236

Designs: No. 999, 150fr, Cyphotilapia frontosa, Lysmata amboinensis. No. 1000, 150fr, Cyrtocara moorii, Potamonautes maculata. No. 1001, 150fr, Placidochromis milomo, Sesarma mederi. No. 1002, 150fr, Tropheus brichardi, Atyopsis gabonensis. No. 1003, 200fr, Phocidae, Swakopmund Lighthouse, Namibia. No. 1004, 200fr, Odobenus rosmarus, Nosy Iranja Lighthouse, Madagascar. No. 1005, 200fr, Lobodon carcinophaga, Pelican Point Lighthouse, Namibia. No. 1006, 200fr, Odobenus rosmarus, Katsepy Lighthouse, Madagascar. No. 1007, 300fr, Morus capensis, Pointe-Noire Lighthouse, Congo. No. 1008, 300fr, Phalacrocorax capensis, Slangkop Point Lighthouse, South Africa. No. 1009, 300fr, Fregata magnificens, Cap Agulhas Lighthouse, South Africa. No. 1010, 300fr, Phalacrocorax melanoleucos, Ngombe Lighthouse, Gabon. No. 1011, 300fr, Strombus gibberulus albus, Grand Bassam Lighthouse, Ivory Coast. No. 1012, 300fr, Argonauta cornuta, Cap Blanc Lighthouse, Mauritania. No. 1013, 300fr, Calpurnus verrucosus, Conakry Lighthouse, Guinea. No. 1014, 300fr, Haliotis queketti, Cap Miné Lighthouse, Madagascar. No. 1015, 350fr, Galeocerdo cuvier, Cherchell Lighthouse, Algeria. No. 1016, 350fr, Isurus paucus, l'ilot d'Arzew Lighthouse, Algeria. No. 1017, 350fr, Sphyrna mokarran, Amirauté Lighthouse, Algeria. No. 1018, 350fr, Carcharodon carcharias, Cap Ivi Lighthouse, Algeria. No. 1019, 500fr, Amanita jacksonii, Eugaster spinulosa. No. 1020, 500fr, Amanita caesarea, Zographus regalis. No. 1021, 500fr, Armillaria gallica, Megaponera foetens. No. 1022, 500fr, Sarcoscypha coccinea, Mylabris sp. No. 1023, 600fr, Cystodermella cinnabarina, Schistocerca gregaria. No. 1024, 600fr, Marasmius rotula, Palpopleura lucia. No. 1025, 600fr, Periphragmoides lysurus, Myrmeleontidae. No. 1026, 600fr, Boletus edulis, Trithemis kirbyi. No. 1027, 750fr, Fluorine. No. 1028, 750fr, Malachite. No. 1029, 750fr, Pyrite. No. 1030, 750fr, Vanadinite.

**2012, Sept. 4 Litho. *Perf. 13¼***
**999-1030** A236 Set of 32 50.00 50.00

Nos. 999-1030 each exist in souvenir sheets of 1.

## SEMI-POSTAL STAMPS

**Catalogue values for unused stamps in this section are for Never Hinged items.**

### Anti-Malaria Issue
Common Design Type
***Perf. 12½x12***

**1962, Apr. 7 Engr. Unwmk.**
**B1** CD108 25fr + 5fr orange 1.00 .50

### Freedom from Hunger Issue
Common Design Type

**1963, Mar. 21 *Perf. 13***
**B2** CD112 25fr + 5fr dk grn, dk bl & brn 1.10 .50

Red Cross, Mother and Children — SP1

**1974, Oct. 2 Photo. *Perf. 12½x13***
**B3** SP1 30fr + 10fr multi 1.25 .40

Red Cross of Chad, first anniversary.

## AIR POST STAMPS

**Catalogue values for unused stamps in this section are for Never Hinged items.**

### Olympic Games Issue
French Equatorial Africa No. C37 Surcharged in Red

**Unwmk.**

**1960, Dec. 15 Engr. *Perf. 13***
**C1** AP8 250fr on 500fr grnsh blk, blk & slate 10.00 6.00

17th Olympic Games, Rome, Aug. 25-Sept. 11. Surcharge 46mm wide.

Red Bishops — AP1

Birds in pairs: 100fr, Scarlet-chested sunbird. 200fr, African paradise flycatcher. 250fr, Malachite kingfisher. 500fr, Nubian carmine bee-eater.

**1961-63 Unwmk. Engr. *Perf. 13***
**C2** AP1 50fr dk grn, mag & blk 1.00 .35
**C3** AP1 100fr multi 3.25 1.25
**C4** AP1 200fr multi 5.75 1.90
**C5** AP1 250fr dk bl, grn & dp org ('63) 7.50 3.00
**C6** AP1 500fr multi 17.50 9.50
*Nos. C2-C6 (5)* 35.00 16.00

### Air Afrique Issue
Common Design Type

**1962, Feb. 17 Unwmk. *Perf. 13***
**C7** CD107 25fr lt bl, org brn & blk 1.00 .25

### Abidjan Games Issue

Discus Thrower — AP2

**1962, July 21 Photo. *Perf. 12x12½***
**C8** AP2 100fr brn, lt grn & blk 3.00 1.00

### African Postal Union Issue
Common Design Type

**1963, Sept. 8 Unwmk. *Perf. 12½***
**C9** CD114 85fr dk bl, ocher & red 1.80 .60

### Air Afrique Issue, 1963
Common Design Type

**1963, Nov. 19 *Perf. 13x12***
**C10** CD115 50fr multi 1.80 .60

### Europafrica Issue
Common Design Type

**1963, Nov. 30 Photo. *Perf. 12x13***
**C11** CD116 50fr dp grn, yel & dk brn 1.60 .50

Mail Truck and Broussard Plane AP4

**Unwmk.**

**1963, Dec. 16 Engr. *Perf. 13***
**C12** AP4 100fr sl grn, ultra & red brn 3.00 .90

### Chiefs of State Issue

Map and Presidents of Chad, Congo, Gabon and Central African Republic — AP4a

**1964, June 23 Photo. *Perf. 12½***
**C13** AP4a 100fr multi 1.70 .60

See note after Central African Republic No. C19.

### Europafrica Issue

Globe and Emblems of Industry and Agriculture AP5

**1964, July 20 *Perf. 13x12***
**C14** AP5 50fr brn, pur & dp org 1.60 .40

See note after Cameroun No. 402.

Soccer AP6

Designs: 50fr, Javelin throw, vert. 100fr, High jump, vert. 200fr, Runners.

**1964, Aug. 12 Engr. *Perf. 13***
**C15** AP6 25fr yel grn, sl grn & org brn .75 .30
**C16** AP6 50fr org brn, ind & brt bl 1.50 .60
**C17** AP6 100fr blk, red & brt grn 2.75 1.00
**C18** AP6 200fr bis, blk & car 4.75 2.00
*a.* Min. sheet of 4, #C15-C18 14.00 6.50
*Nos. C15-C18 (4)* 9.75 3.90

18th Olympic Games, Tokyo, 10/10-25/64.

Communications Symbols — AP7

**1964, Nov. 2 Litho. *Perf. 12½x13***
**C19** AP7 25fr lil, dk brn & lt red brn .80 .25

Pan-African and Malagasy Posts and Telecommunications Cong., Cairo, Oct. 24-Nov. 6.

President John F. Kennedy (1917-63) — AP8

**1964, Nov. 3 Photo. *Perf. 12½***
**C20** AP8 100fr multi 1.90 .75
*a.* Souvenir sheet of 4 12.00 6.00

ICY Emblem AP9

**1965, July 5 Photo. *Perf. 13***
**C21** AP9 100fr multi 1.80 .60

International Cooperation Year, 1965.

Abraham Lincoln AP10

**1965, Sept. 7 Unwmk. *Perf. 13***
**C22** AP10 100fr multi 2.00 .75

Centenary of death of Abraham Lincoln.

### Musical Instrument Type

Design: 100fr, Xylophone (marimba).

**1965, Oct. 26 Engr. *Perf. 13***
**Size: 48x27mm**
**C23** A18 100fr ocher, brt bl & vio bl 2.00 1.00

Sir Winston Spencer Churchill (1874-1965) — AP11

**1965, Nov. 23 Engr. *Perf. 13***
**C24** AP11 50fr dk grn & blk 1.50 .50

Dr. Albert Schweitzer and Outstretched Hands AP12

**1966, Feb. 15 Photo. *Perf. 12½***
**C25** AP12 100fr multi 2.75 .80

Dr. Albert Schweitzer (1875-1965), medical missionary, theologian and musician.

### Air Afrique Issue, 1966
Common Design Type

**1966, Aug. 31 Photo. *Perf. 13***
**C26** CD123 30fr yel grn, blk & gray .85 .25

White-throated Bee-eater — AP13

Birds: 50fr, Blue-eared glossy starling. 200fr, African pygmy kingfisher. 250fr, Red-throated bee-eater. 500fr, Little green bee-eater.

**1966-67 Photo. *Perf. 13x12½***
**C27** AP13 50fr gold & multi 1.20 .40
**C28** AP13 100fr bluish gray & multi 2.75 1.00
**C29** AP13 200fr grnsh gray & multi 5.25 1.75
**C30** AP13 250fr pale bl & multi 6.00 1.75
**C31** AP13 500fr pale sal & multi 11.00 3.25
*Nos. C27-C31 (5)* 26.20 8.15

Issued: 100fr, 200fr, 500fr, 8/18/66; others, 3/21/67.

For surcharges see Nos. C67-C69.

Congress Hall — AP14

**1967, Jan. 5 Photo. *Perf. 12½***
**C32** AP14 25fr multi .70 .25

Opening of the new Congress Hall.

Breguet 19 Biplane AP15

Planes: 30fr, Latécoère 631 hydroplane. 50fr, Douglas DC-3. 100fr, Piper Cherokee 6.

**1967, Aug. 1 Engr. *Perf. 13***

| | | | | |
|---|---|---|---|---|
| **C33** | AP15 | 25fr sky bl, sl grn & lt brn | .75 | .25 |
| **C34** | AP15 | 30fr sky bl, indigo & grn | 1.00 | .30 |
| **C35** | AP15 | 50fr sky bl, ol bis & sl grn | 1.75 | .60 |
| **C36** | AP15 | 100fr dk bl, sl grn & dk red | 3.50 | .90 |
| | | *Nos. C33-C36 (4)* | 7.00 | 2.05 |

First anniversary of Air Chad.

**African Postal Union Issue, 1967**

Common Design Type

**1967, Sept. 9 Engr. *Perf. 13***

| | | | | |
|---|---|---|---|---|
| **C37** | CD124 | 100fr ol, brt pink & red brn | 2.00 | .60 |

**Rock Painting Type of Regular Issue**

**1967, Dec. 19 Engr. *Perf. 13***

**Size: 48x27mm**

| | | | | |
|---|---|---|---|---|
| **C38** | A32 | 100fr Masked dancers | 4.00 | .95 |
| **C39** | A32 | 125fr Rabbit hunt | 4.50 | 1.50 |

Downhill Skiing AP16

**1968, Feb. 5 Engr. *Perf. 13***

| | | | | |
|---|---|---|---|---|
| **C40** | AP16 | 30fr shown | 1.25 | .30 |
| **C41** | AP16 | 100fr Ski jump, vert. | 3.25 | .90 |

10th Winter Olympic Games, Grenoble, France, Feb. 6-18.

Konrad Adenauer (1876-1967), Chancellor of West Germany (1949-63) — AP17

**1968, Mar. 19 Photo. *Perf. 12½***

| | | | | |
|---|---|---|---|---|
| **C42** | AP17 | 52fr grn, dk brn & lt lil | 1.30 | .50 |
| *a.* | | Souvenir sheet of 4 | 5.00 | 4.50 |

The Snake Charmer, by Henri Rousseau AP18

Design: 130fr, "War" by Henri Rousseau.

**1968, May 14 Photo. *Perf. 13½***

**Size: 41x41mm**

| | | | | |
|---|---|---|---|---|
| **C43** | AP18 | 100fr ultra & multi | 3.50 | 1.00 |

**Size: 48x35mm**

***Perf. 12½***

| | | | | |
|---|---|---|---|---|
| **C44** | AP18 | 130fr brn & multi | 5.50 | 1.50 |

Hurdlers AP19

**1968, Oct. 16 Engr. *Perf. 13***

| | | | | |
|---|---|---|---|---|
| **C45** | AP19 | 32fr shown | 1.00 | .40 |
| **C46** | AP19 | 80fr Relay race | 2.25 | .80 |

19th Olympic Games, Mexico City, 10/12-27.

**PHILEXAFRIQUE Issue**

The Actor Wolf (Bernard), by Jacques L. David — AP20

**1969, Jan. 15 Photo. *Perf. 12½***

| | | | | |
|---|---|---|---|---|
| **C47** | AP20 | 100fr multi | 2.90 | 1.75 |

PHILEXAFRIQUE, Philatelic Exhib. in Abidjan, Feb. 14-23. Printed with alternating label. Value is for stamp with label attached.

**2nd PHILEXAFRIQUE Issue**

Common Design Type

50fr, Chad #J12 and Moundang Dancers.

**1969, Feb. 14 Engr. *Perf. 13***

| | | | | |
|---|---|---|---|---|
| **C48** | CD128 | 50fr red, brt bl, brn & grn | 2.40 | 1.00 |

Gustav Nachtigal and Tibesti Gorge, 1869 AP21

No. C50, Heinrich Barth & Lake Chad, 1851.

**1969, Feb. 17**

| | | | | |
|---|---|---|---|---|
| **C49** | AP21 | 100fr vio bl, dk brn & brn | 2.40 | .60 |
| **C50** | AP21 | 100fr grn, pur & bl | 2.40 | .60 |

German explorers Gustav Nachtigal (1834-85) and Heinrich Barth (1821-65), and state visit of the Pres. of West Germany Heinrich Lubke.

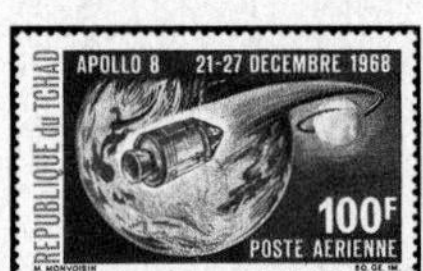

Apollo 8, Earth and Moon AP22

**1969, Apr. 10 Photo. *Perf. 13***

| | | | | |
|---|---|---|---|---|
| **C51** | AP22 | 100fr multi | 2.50 | .75 |

US Apollo 8 mission, the 1st men in orbit around the moon, Dec. 21-27, 1968.

Mahatma Gandhi — AP23

No. C53, John F. Kennedy. No. C54, Dr. Martin Luther King, Jr. No. C55, Robert F. Kennedy.

**1969, May 20 Photo. *Perf. 12½***

| | | | | |
|---|---|---|---|---|
| **C52** | AP23 | 50fr blk & lt grn | 1.25 | .40 |
| **C53** | AP23 | 50fr blk & tan | 1.25 | .40 |
| **C54** | AP23 | 50fr blk & pink | 1.25 | .40 |
| **C55** | AP23 | 50fr blk & lt vio bl | 1.25 | .40 |
| *a.* | | Souvenir sheet of 4, #C52-C55 | 6.00 | 6.00 |
| | | *Nos. C52-C55 (4)* | 5.00 | 1.60 |

Issued to honor exponents of non-violence.

Presidents Tombalbaye and Mobutu, Map and Flags of Chad and Congo AP24

**Embossed on Gold Foil**

**1969 *Die-cut Perf. 13½***

| | | | | |
|---|---|---|---|---|
| **C56** | AP24 | 1000fr gold, dk bl & red | 27.50 | 27.50 |

1st anniv. of the establishment of the Union of Central African States, comprising Chad, Congo Democratic Republic and Central African Republic.

Napoleon Visiting Hospital, by Alexandre Veron-Bellecourt — AP25

Paintings: 85fr, Battle of Wagram, by Horace Vernet. 130fr, Battle of Austerlitz, by Francois Pascal Gerard.

**1969, July 23 Photo. *Perf. 12x12½***

| | | | | |
|---|---|---|---|---|
| **C57** | AP25 | 30fr multi | 1.20 | .40 |
| **C58** | AP25 | 85fr multi | 2.50 | .75 |
| **C59** | AP25 | 130fr multi | 4.50 | 1.25 |
| | | *Nos. C57-C59 (3)* | 8.20 | 2.40 |

Bicentenary of birth of Napoleon I.

**Apollo 11 Issue**

Astronaut on Moon AP26

**Embossed on Gold Foil**

**1969, Oct. 17 *Die-cut Perf. 13½***

| | | | | |
|---|---|---|---|---|
| **C60** | AP26 | 1000fr gold | 27.50 | 27.50 |

See note after Algeria No. 427.

Village Life, by Goto Narcisse AP27

No. 62, Women at the Market, by Iba N'Diaye. No. 63, Woman with Flowers, by Iba N'Diaye, vert.

**1970 Photo. *Perf. 12x12½, 12½x12***

| | | | | |
|---|---|---|---|---|
| **C61** | AP27 | 100fr multi | 3.25 | .75 |
| **C62** | AP27 | 250fr grn & multi | 5.00 | 1.00 |
| **C63** | AP27 | 250fr brn & multi | 5.00 | 1.00 |
| | | *Nos. C61-C63 (3)* | 13.25 | 2.75 |

Issued: 100fr, Mar. 17; Nos. C62-C63, Aug. 28.

Napoleon — AP27a

Designs: Nos. C63A, C63E, Napoleon II, Duke of Reichstadt, vert.

No. C63B: g, 10fr, Crossing the Grand St. Bernard, by David. h, 25fr, Emperor Napoleon, by Gerard. i, 32fr, Marriage of Napoleon and Marie Louise, by Rouget.

40fr, Napoleon after return from Elba, vert.

***Perf. 12x12½, 12½x12***

**1970-71 Litho.**

| | | | | |
|---|---|---|---|---|
| **C63A** | AP27a | 10fr multicolored | 4.00 | — |
| **C63B** | AP27a | Strip of 3, #g.-i. | 14.00 | — |

**Embossed**

***Perf. 13***

| | | | | |
|---|---|---|---|---|
| **C63C** | AP27a | 10fr gold | 20.00 | — |
| *f.* | | Sheet of 1, Imperf. | 37.50 | — |

**Souvenir Sheets**

**Litho.**

***Perf. 13x13½***

| | | | | |
|---|---|---|---|---|
| **C63D** | AP27a | 40fr multicolored | 10.00 | — |

**Embossed**

***Imperf***

| | | | | |
|---|---|---|---|---|
| **C63E** | AP27a | 10fr gold, like #C63A | 37.50 | — |

No. C63A is printed se-tenant with label. No. C63D contains one 43x67mm stamp. No. C63Cf contains one 53x42mm stamp with same size design as No. C63Bg. No. C63E contains one 43x104mm stamp with same size design as No. C63A.

No. C63E probably was not available in Chad.

Issued: No. C63B, 6/12; Nos. C63A, C63D-C63E, 4/1971; No. C63C, 11/1/71.

EXPO Emblem and Osaka Print — AP28

EXPO Emblem and: 100fr, Tower of the Sun. 125fr, Osaka print, diff.

**1970, June 30 Engr. *Perf. 13***

| | | | | |
|---|---|---|---|---|
| **C64** | AP28 | 50fr bl, red brn & sl grn | .70 | .25 |
| **C65** | AP28 | 100fr red, yel grn & Prus bl | 1.40 | .40 |
| **C66** | AP28 | 125fr blk, dk red & bis | 1.90 | .60 |
| | | *Nos. C64-C66 (3)* | 4.00 | 1.25 |

Issued to publicize EXPO '70 International Exhibition, Osaka, Japan, Mar. 15-Sept. 13.

1968 Summer Olympics, 1970 World Cup Soccer Championships, Mexico AP28a

5fr, Flags, soccer players. 15fr, Olympic torch, soccer player.

**1970, July 1 Litho. *Perf. 12½x12***

| | | | | |
|---|---|---|---|---|
| **C66A** | AP28a | 5fr multicolored | 1.50 | |

**Souvenir Sheet**

***Perf. 13½x13***

| | | | | |
|---|---|---|---|---|
| **C66C** | AP28a | 15fr multicolored | 6.50 | |

No. C66A printed in sheets of 2 + 2 labels. No. C66C contains one 66x43mm stamp.

For overprints see Nos. C88A-C88B.

**Nos. C28-C30 Surcharged and Overprinted in Carmine**

a

b

c

**1970, July 9 Photo. *Perf. 13x12½***

| | | | | |
|---|---|---|---|---|
| **C67** | AP13 (a) | 50fr on 100fr | 1.70 | .25 |
| **C68** | AP13 (b) | 100fr on 200fr | 2.75 | .45 |
| **C69** | AP13 (c) | 125fr on 250fr | 4.00 | .55 |
| | | *Nos. C67-C69 (3)* | 8.45 | 1.25 |

Space missions of Apollo 11, 12 and 13.

DC-8 "Fort Lamy" over Airport
AP29

**1970, Aug. 5** ***Perf. 12½***
**C70** AP29 30fr dk sl grn & multi 1.30 .30

### Souvenir Sheet

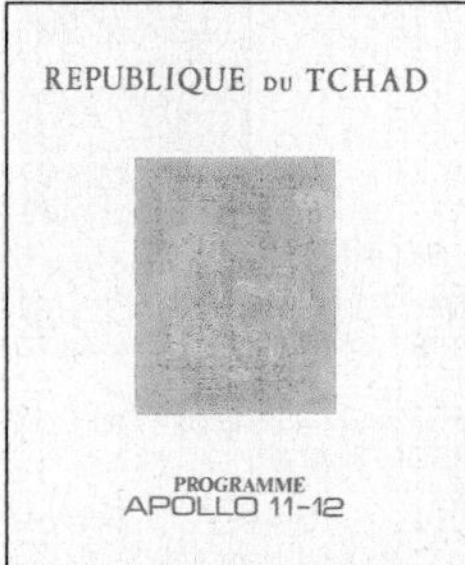


Apollo 12
AP29a

**1970, Sept.** **Embossed** ***Perf. 12¾***
**C70A** AP29a 25fr gold 18.00

No. C70A exists imperf. Value, $35.
No. C70A probably was not available in Chad.

The Visitation, Venetian School, 15th Century — AP30

Paintings, Venetian School: 25fr, Nativity, 15th century. 30fr, Virgin and Child, c. 1350.

**1970, Dec. 15** **Photo.** ***Perf. 12½x12***
**C71** AP30 20fr gold & multi .65 .25
**C72** AP30 25fr gold & multi .90 .25
**C73** AP30 30fr gold & multi 1.00 .25
*Nos. C71-C73 (3)* 2.55 .75

Christmas 1970. See Nos. C144-C147.

Post Office Mauritius and Emblem — AP31

**1971, Jan. 23** **Engr.** ***Perf. 13***
**C74** AP31 10fr shown .25 .25
**C75** AP31 20fr Tuscany #23 .40 .25
**C76** AP31 30fr France #8 .60 .25
**C77** AP31 60fr US #2 1.10 .30
**C78** AP31 80fr Japan #8 1.50 .60
**C79** AP31 100fr Saxony #1 1.90 .75
*a.* Souvenir sheet of 6, #C74-C79 8.00 5.00
*Nos. C74-C79 (6)* 5.75 2.40

Publicity for PHILEXOCAM, philatelic exhibition, Fort Lamy, Jan. 23-30.

Gamal Abdel Nasser — AP32

**1971, Feb. 16** **Photo.** ***Perf. 12½***
**C80** AP32 75fr multi 1.50 .50

In memory of Gamal Abdel Nasser (1918-1970), President of Egypt.

Presidents Mobutu, Bokassa and Tombalbaye
AP33

**1971, Apr. 28** **Photo.** ***Perf. 13***
**C81** AP33 100fr multi 1.50 .60

Return of Central African Republic to the United States of Central Africa which also includes Congo Democratic Republic and Chad.

Map of Africa, Communications Network and Symbols — AP34

**1971, May 17** **Engr.** ***Perf. 13***
**C82** AP34 125fr ultra, sl grn & brn red 3.00 .75

Pan-African telecommunications system.

Boys Around Campfire, Torii — AP35

**1971, Aug. 24** **Photo.** ***Perf. 12½***
**C83** AP35 250fr multi 1.50 .40

13th Boy Scout World Jamboree, Asagiri Plain, Japan, Aug. 2-10.

White Egret
AP36

**1971, Sept. 28** **Photo.** ***Perf. 13x12½***
**C84** AP36 1000fr blk, dk bl & ocher 60.00 12.50

Greek Marathon Runners
AP37

45fr, Ancient Olympic Stadium. 75fr, Greek wrestlers. 130fr, Olympic Stadium, Athens, 1896.

**1971, Oct. 5** ***Perf. 12½***
**C85** AP37 40fr multi .75 .25
**C86** AP37 45fr multi 1.00 .25
**C87** AP37 75fr multi 1.75 .40
**C88** AP37 130fr multi 2.00 .75
*Nos. C85-C88 (4)* 5.50 1.65

75th anniv. of modern Olympic Games.

### Nos. C66A, C66C Ovptd. in Gold

**1971** **Litho.** ***Perf. 12½x12***
**C88A** AP28a 5fr multi 2.50

### Souvenir Sheet

***Perf. 13½x13***

**C88B** AP28a 15fr multi 5.50

Overprint on No. C88B is 36mm long.

Duke Ellington — AP38

50fr, Sidney Bechet. 100fr, Louis Armstrong.

**1971, Oct. 20** **Litho.** ***Perf. 13***
**C89** AP38 50fr multi 2.00 .50
**C90** AP38 75fr lt bl & multi 3.00 .70
**C91** AP38 100fr multi 5.00 .85
*Nos. C89-C91 (3)* 10.00 2.05

Famous American jazz musicians.

Charles de Gaulle — AP39

Design: No. C93, Félix Eboué.

### Lithographed and Embossed

**1971, Nov. 9** ***Perf. 12½***
**C92** AP39 200fr grn, yel grn & gold 8.00 4.00
**C93** AP39 200fr bl, lt bl & gold 8.00 4.00
*a.* Souv. sheet, #C92-C93 + label 15.00 15.00

Charles de Gaulle (1890-1970), pres. of France.

### African Postal Union Issue, 1971
Common Design Type

Design: 100fr, Sao antelope head and UAMPT building, Brazzaville, Congo.

**1971, Nov. 13** **Photo.** ***Perf. 13x13½***
**C94** CD135 100fr bl & multi 1.50 .50

Apollo 15 Rocket — AP40

80fr, Apollo 15 capsule, horiz. 150fr, Lunar module on Moon, horiz. 250fr, Astronaut making tests. 300fr, Moon-buggy. No. C100, Successful splashdown, horiz. No. C101, Apollo 15 insignia.

**1972, Jan. 5** **Litho.** ***Perf. 13½***
**C95** AP40 40fr multi .50 .25
**C96** AP40 80fr multi .90 .25
**C97** AP40 150fr multi 1.50 .30
**C98** AP40 250fr multi 2.50 .45
**C99** AP40 300fr multi 3.00 .60
**C100** AP40 500fr multi 5.50 1.40
*Nos. C95-C100 (6)* 13.90 3.25

### Souvenir Sheet

**C101** AP40 500fr multi 8.00 2.50

Apollo 15 moon landing.

Soyuz 11 Link-up
AP41

Designs: 30fr, Soyuz 11 on launching pad, vert. 50fr, No. C108, Cosmonauts in uniform. 200fr, V. I. Patsayev. No. C106, V. N. Volkov. 400fr, G. L. Dobrovolsky. No. C109, Three cosmonauts.

**1972, Jan. 5** ***Perf. 13½x13***
**C102** AP41 30fr multi .25 .25
**C103** AP41 50fr multi .45 .25
**C104** AP41 100fr multi .80 .25
**C105** AP41 200fr multi 2.00 .50
**C106** AP41 300fr multi 3.25 .75
**C107** AP41 400fr multi 4.25 1.10
*Nos. C102-C107 (6)* 11.00 3.10

### Souvenir Sheets

**C108** AP41 300fr multi 3.50 1.25
**C109** AP41 400fr multi 4.00 1.50

Soyuz 11 link-up project.

Bobsledding
AP42

Design: 100fr, Slalom.

**1972, Feb. 24** **Engr.** ***Perf. 13***
**C110** AP42 50fr Prus bl & rose red .90 .30
**C111** AP42 100fr red lil & slate grn 1.70 .50

11th Winter Olympic Games, Sapporo, Japan, Feb. 3-13.

### Pres. Tombalbaye Type, 1972

**1972, Apr. 13** **Litho.** ***Perf. 13***
**C112** A63 70fr multi .75 .30
**C113** A63 80fr multi .90 .35

### 11th Winter Olympic Type, 1972

130fr, Speed skating. No. C115, Ice hockey. No. C116, Ski jumping. 250fr, 4-man bobsled.

**1972, Apr. 13** ***Perf. 13½***
**C114** A64 130fr multi 1.40 .45
**C115** A64 200fr multi 2.50 .60

### Souvenir Sheets

**C116** A64 200fr multi 3.50 1.25
**C117** A64 250fr multi 4.50 1.50

### Scout Jamboree Type, 1972

Designs: 100fr, Cooking preparation. 120fr, Lord Baden Powell. 250fr, Hiking.

**1972, May 15**
**C118** A67 100fr multi 2.25 .40
**C119** A67 120fr multi 2.40 .50

### Souvenir Sheet

**C120** A67 250fr multi 8.50 1.75

Zebras — AP43

African wild animals: 30fr, Mandrills. 100fr, African elephants. 130fr, Gazelles. 150fr, Hippopotamuses. 200fr, Lion cub.

**1972, May 15** **Litho.** ***Perf. 13***
**C121** AP43 20fr multi .35 .25
**C122** AP43 30fr multi .50 .25
**C123** AP43 100fr multi 1.40 .35
**C124** AP43 130fr multi 2.25 .50
**C125** AP43 150fr multi 3.50 .75
*Nos. C121-C125 (5)* 8.00 2.10

### Souvenir Sheet

**C126** AP43 200fr multi 15.00 10.00

View of Venice, by Caffi
AP44

Paintings by Ippolito Caffi: 40fr, Sailing ship and Doge's Palace, vert. 140fr, Grand Canal, vert.

**1972, May 23 — Photo.**

C127 AP44 40fr gold & multi 1.10 .25
C128 AP44 45fr gold & multi 1.90 .25
C129 AP44 140fr gold & multi 3.50 .60
*Nos. C127-C129 (3)* 6.50 1.10

UNESCO campaign to save Venice.

### 11th Winter Olympic Winners Type, 1972

Designs: 150fr, Slalom, B. Cochran, US. 200fr, Women's figure skating, B. Schuba, Austria. 250fr, Ice hockey, USSR. 300fr, 2-man bobsled, W. Zimmerer and P. Utzschneider, West Germany.

**1972, June 15 — *Perf. 14½***

C130 A69 150fr gold & multi 3.00 .75
C131 A69 200fr gold & multi 3.75 1.00

### Souvenir Sheets

C132 A69 250fr gold & multi 3.25 2.75
C133 A69 300fr gold & multi 3.75 3.00

Nos. C130-C131 exist se-tenant with label showing earth satellite.

Daudet, "Tartarin de Tarascon," Book Year Emblem AP45

**1972, July 22 — Engr. — *Perf. 13***

C134 AP45 100fr dk red, lil & dk brn 1.70 .60

Intl. Book Year, 1972, and to honor Alphonse Daudet (1840-1897), French writer.

### 20th Summer Olympics Type, 1972

Designs (TV Tower, Munich and): 100fr, Gymnast. 120fr, Pole vault. 150fr, Fencing. 250fr, Hammer throw. 300fr, Boxing.

**1972, Aug. 15 — *Perf. 14½***

C135 A70 100fr gold & multi 2.10 .50
C136 A70 120fr gold & multi 2.50 .60
C137 A70 150fr gold & multi 3.25 .80
*Nos. C135-C137 (3)* 7.85 1.90

### Souvenir Sheets

C138 A70 250fr gold & multi 3.50 2.75
C139 A70 300fr gold & multi 4.00 3.00

Nos. C135-C137 exist se-tenant with label showing arms of Munich.

Lunokhod on Moon AP46

Russian moon missions: 100fr, Luna 16 on moon and rocket in flight, vert.

**1972, Sept. 19 — *Perf. 13***

C140 AP46 100fr dk bl, pur & bis 1.50 .50
C141 AP46 150fr slate, brn & lil 2.00 .75

Farcha Laboratory, Cattle, Scientist AP47

**1972, Nov. 11 — Photo. — *Perf. 13***

C142 AP47 75fr yellow & multi 1.40 .30

20th anniversary of the Farcha Laboratory for veterinary research.

King Faisal and Holy Kaaba, Mecca AP48

**1972, Nov. 17**

C143 AP48 75fr multi 1.40 .40

Visit of King Faisal of Saudi Arabia.

### Christmas Type of 1970

Christmas: 40fr, Virgin and Child, by Giovanni Bellini. 75fr, Virgin and Child, by Dall'Occhio. 80fr, Nativity, by Fra Angelico, horiz. 95fr, Adoration of the Kings, by Il Perugino.

**1972, Dec. 15 — Photo. — *Perf. 13***

C144 AP30 40fr gold & multi .25 .25
C145 AP30 75fr gold & multi 1.75 .30
C146 AP30 80fr gold & multi 2.00 .40
C147 AP30 95fr gold & multi 2.00 .50
*Nos. C144-C147 (4)* 6.00 1.45

### Summer Olympic Winners Type, 1972

Olympic Emblems and: 150fr, Pole vault, Nordwig, East Germany. 250fr, Hurdles, Milburn, US. 300fr, Javelin, Wolfermann, West Germany.

**1972, Dec. 22 — *Perf. 11***

C148 A76 150fr multi 3.00 .60
C149 A76 250fr multi 4.25 .75

### Souvenir Sheet

C150 A76 300fr multi 12.00 3.00

### Summer Olympic Winners Type, 1972

Olympic Emblem and: 150fr, Dressage, Mancinelli, Italy. No. C152, Finn class sailing, Serge Maury, France. No. C153, Swimming, Mark Spitz.

**1972, Dec. 22 — Litho. — *Perf. 11***

C151 A77 150fr gold & multi 3.25 .75
C152 A77 250fr gold & multi 5.00 1.00

### Souvenir Sheet

C153 A77 250fr multi 15.00 3.00

Copernicus and Solar System AP49

**1973, Mar. 31 — Engr. — *Perf. 13***

C154 AP49 250fr gray, mag & brn 5.25 1.25

500th anniversary of the birth of Nicolaus Copernicus (1473-1543), Polish astronomer.

Horses AP49a

Details from paintings: 20fr, A Horse Frightened by Lightning, by Theordore Gericault. 60fr, The White Horse, by Paul Potter. 100fr, Mares and Foals, by George Stubbs. 150fr, Horse Head, by Theordore Gericault, vert. 500fr, The Carriage, by Vernet.

**1973 — Litho. — *Perf. 11½***

C154A AP49a 20fr multi
C154B AP49a 60fr multi
C154C AP49a 100fr multi
C154D AP49a 150fr multi
Nos. C154A-C154D (4) 14.00

### Souvenir Sheet

***Perf. 15***

C154E AP49a 500fr multi 15.00

See note before No. 225A.

Airplanes AP49b

5fr, Fokker F VII/3M. 25fr, DH 89A Rapide. 70fr, Viscount. 150fr, Boeing 747. 200fr, Concorde.
350fr, Concorde, diff.

**1973 — Litho. — *Perf. 12***

C154F AP49b 5fr multi
C154G AP49b 25fr multi
C154H AP49b 70fr multi
C154J AP49b 150fr multi
C154K AP49b 200fr multi
Nos. C154F-C154K (5) 14.00

### Souvenir Sheet

***Perf. 12***

C154L AP49b 350fr multi 14.00

Nos. C154L contains one 60x40mm stamp. See note before No. 225A.

Skylab over Africa AP50

**1974, Aug. 6 — Engr. — *Perf. 13***

C155 AP50 100fr shown 1.50 .25
C156 AP50 150fr Skylab 2.50 .60

Exploits of Skylab, US manned space station.

Soccer AP51

125fr, 150fr, Soccer players; 125fr, vert.

**1974, Oct. 22 — Engr. — *Perf. 13***

C157 AP51 50fr dl red & choc .75 .25
C158 AP51 125fr red & dp grn 1.75 .50
C159 AP51 150fr grn & rose red 2.50 .75
*Nos. C157-C159 (3)* 5.00 1.50

World Cup Soccer Championship, Munich, June 13-July 7.

Family and WPY Emblem — AP52

**1974, Nov. 11**

C160 AP52 250fr multi 4.00 1.25

World Population Year.

Mail Delivery by Canoe AP53

UPU Cent.: 40fr, Diesel train. 100fr, Jet. 150fr, Spacecraft.

**1974, Dec. 20 — Engr. — *Perf. 13***

C161 AP53 30fr car & multi .60 .25
C162 AP53 40fr ultra & blk 1.00 .25
C163 AP53 100fr brn, ultra & blk 1.90 .40
C164 AP53 150fr grn, lil & ol 2.40 .55
*Nos. C161-C164 (4)* 5.90 1.45

Women of Different Races, IWY Emblem AP54

**1975, June 25 — Photo. — *Perf. 13***

C165 AP54 250fr bl & multi 4.50 1.25

International Women's Year 1975.

Apollo and Soyuz Before Link-up AP55

130fr, Apollo and Soyuz after link-up.

**1975, July 15 — Engr. — *Perf. 13***

C166 AP55 100fr ultra, choc & grn 1.50 .40
C167 AP55 130fr vio bl, brn & grn 2.00 .50

Apollo Soyuz space test project (Russo-American space cooperation), launching 7/15; link-up 7/17.

For overprints see Nos. C171-C172.

Soccer Player, View of Montreal — AP56

Olympic Rings, Montreal Skyline: 100fr, Discus thrower. 125fr, Runner.

**1975, Oct. 14 — Engr. — *Perf. 13***

C168 AP56 75fr car & slate grn 1.00 .25
C169 AP56 100fr car, choc & bl grn 1.40 .40
C170 AP56 125fr brn, bl & car 1.90 .75
*Nos. C168-C170 (3)* 4.30 1.40

Pre-Olympic Year 1975.

### Nos. C166-C167 Overprinted: "JONCTION / 17 JUILLET 1975"

**1975, Nov. 4 — Engr. — *Perf. 13***

C171 AP55 100fr multi 1.75 .25
C172 AP55 130fr multi 2.10 .35

Apollo-Soyuz link-up in space, July 17.

Stylized British and American Flags, "200" AP57

**1975, Dec. 5 — Engr. — *Perf. 13***

C173 AP57 150fr vio bl, car & ol bis 2.25 .75

American Bicentennial.

Adoration of the Shepherds, by Murillo AP58

Christmas (Paintings): 75fr, Adoration of the Shepherds, by Georges de La Tour. 80fr, Virgin and Child with Bible, by Rogier van der Weyden, vert. 100fr, Holy Family, by Raphael, vert.

**1975, Dec. 15 — Litho. — *Perf. 13x12½***

C174 AP58 40fr yel & multi .75 .25
C175 AP58 75fr yel & multi 1.25 .35
C176 AP58 80fr yel & multi 1.75 .40
C177 AP58 100fr yel & multi 2.75 .75
*Nos. C174-C177 (4)* 6.50 1.75

### 12th Winter Olympic Winners Type, 1976

250fr, 4-man bobsled, West Germany. 300fr, Speed skating, J. E. Storholt, Norway. 500fr, Downhill skiing, F. Klammer, Austria.

**1976, June 21 — *Perf. 14***

C178 A84 250fr multi 2.75 .60
C179 A84 300fr multi 3.50 1.00

### Souvenir Sheet

C180 A84 500fr multi 6.00 3.00

Paul Revere's Ride and Portrait by Copley AP59

American Bicentennial: 125fr, Washington crossing Delaware. 150fr, Lafayette offering his services to America. 200fr, Rochambeau at Yorktown with Washington. 250fr, Franklin presenting Declaration of Independence. 400fr, Count de Grasse's victory at Cape Charles.

**1976, July 4 Litho. *Perf. 14***
**C181** AP59 100fr multi 1.10 .30
**C182** AP59 125fr multi 1.25 .35
**C183** AP59 150fr multi 1.90 .40
**C184** AP59 200fr multi 2.25 .50
**C185** AP59 250fr multi 3.00 .55
*Nos. C181-C185 (5)* 9.50 2.10

**Souvenir Sheet**

**C186** AP59 400fr multi 6.00 3.00

### Summer Olympics Type, 1976

**1976, July 12 *Perf. 13½***
**C187** A85 100fr Boxing 1.50 .30
**C188** A85 200fr Pole vault 2.50 .50
**C189** A85 300fr Shot put 4.00 .65
*Nos. C187-C189 (3)* 8.00 1.45

**Souvenir Sheet**

**C190** A85 500fr Sprint 6.00 3.00

### Viking Mars Project Type, 1976

Mars Lander and: 100fr, Viking landing on Mars. 200fr, Capsule over Mars. 250fr, Lander over Mars. 450fr, Lander and probe.

**1976, July 23 Litho. *Perf. 14***
**C191** A86 100fr multi 1.10 .30
**C192** A86 200fr multi 2.25 .55
**C193** A86 250fr multi 2.50 .75
*Nos. C191-C193 (3)* 5.85 1.60

**Souvenir Sheet**

**C194** A86 450fr multi 7.50 3.00

See Nos. 314-315. For overprints see Nos. C240-C243.

Concorde AP60

**1976, Oct. 15 Litho. *Perf. 12½***
**C195** AP60 250fr bl, blk & ver 6.00 1.75

First commercial flight of supersonic jet Concorde, Jan. 21.

### Nobel Prize Type, 1976

100fr, Albert Einstein, physics. 200fr, Dag Hammarskjold, peace. 300fr, Shinichiro Tomanaga, physics. 500fr, Alexander Fleming, medicine.

**1976, Dec. 15 *Perf. 14***
**C196** A87 100fr multi 1.50 .30
**C197** A87 200fr multi 2.50 .55
**C198** A87 300fr multi 3.50 .70
*Nos. C196-C198 (3)* 7.50 1.55

**Souvenir Sheet**

**C199** A87 500fr multi 8.00 3.50

Adoration of the Shepherds, by Gerard van Honthorst — AP61

Christmas (Paintings): 30fr, Nativity, by Albrecht Altdorfer, vert. 60fr, Nativity, by Hans Holbein, vert. 150fr, Adoration of the Kings, by Gerard David.

**1976, Dec. 22 Litho. *Perf. 12½***
**C200** AP61 30fr gold & multi .50 .25
**C201** AP61 60fr gold & multi .75 .25
**C202** AP61 120fr gold & blk 1.50 .50
**C203** AP61 150fr gold & blk 2.25 .75
*Nos. C200-C203 (4)* 5.00 1.75

Lesdiguières Bridge, by Jongkind AP62

Design: 120fr, Sailing Ship and Boats, by Johan Barthold Jongkind (1819-1891).

**1976, Dec. 27 Photo. *Perf. 13***
**C204** AP62 100fr multi 1.75 .55
**C205** AP62 120fr multi 2.25 .60

Centenary of impressionism.

### Zeppelin Type of 1977

125fr, Germany #C40, North Pole. 150fr, Germany #C45, Chicago department store. 175fr, Germany #C38 and scenes of NYC and London. 200fr, 500fr, US #C15, NYC.

**1977, Mar. 30 *Perf. 11***
**C206** A91 125fr multi 1.90 .35
**C207** A91 150fr multi 2.25 .40
**C208** A91 175fr multi 2.75 .50
**C209** A91 200fr multi 3.25 .60
*Nos. C206-C209 (4)* 10.15 1.85

**Souvenir Sheet**

**C210** A91 500fr multi 8.00 3.00

Sassenage Castle, Grenoble — AP63

**1977, May 21 Litho. *Perf. 12½***
**C211** AP63 100fr multi 1.00 .30

Intl. French Language Council, 10th Anniv.

Lafayette and Ships AP64

American Bicentennial: 120fr, Abraham Lincoln, eagle and flags, vert. 150fr, James Madison and family.

**1977, July 30 Engr. *Perf. 13***
**C212** AP64 100fr multi 1.40 .35
**C213** AP64 120fr multi 1.75 .40
**C214** AP64 150fr multi 2.25 .50
*Nos. C212-C214 (3)* 5.40 1.25

Lindbergh and Spirit of St. Louis AP65

100fr, Concorde. 150fr, 200fr, 300fr, Various Lindbergh portraits & Spirit of St. Louis.

**1977, Sept. 27**
**C215** AP65 100fr multi 1.25 .30
**C216** AP65 120fr multi 1.25 .40
**C217** AP65 150fr multi 1.40 .55
**C218** AP65 200fr multi 2.25 .65
**C219** AP65 300fr multi 3.00 .90
*Nos. C215-C219 (5)* 9.15 2.80

Charles A. Lindbergh's solo transatlantic flight from NY to Paris, 50th anniv., and 1st supersonic transatlantic flight of Concorde.
For overprint see No. C227.

Mariner 10 — AP66

Spacecraft: 200fr, Lunokhod on moon, Luna 21. 300fr, Viking on Mars.

**1977, Oct. 10 Engr. *Perf. 13***
**C220** AP66 100fr multi 1.25 .40
**C221** AP66 200fr multi 2.00 .70
**C222** AP66 300fr multi 2.75 .90
*Nos. C220-C222 (3)* 6.00 2.00

Running — AP67

**1977, Oct. 24 Engr. *Perf. 13***
**C223** AP67 30fr shown .40 .25
**C224** AP67 60fr Volleyball .85 .25
**C225** AP67 120fr Soccer 1.50 .45
**C226** AP67 125fr Basketball 1.25 .50
*Nos. C223-C226 (4)* 4.00 1.45

### No. C215 Overprinted: "PARIS NEW-YORK / 22.11.77"

**1977, Nov. 22**
**C227** AP65 100fr multi 3.25 .25

Concorde, 1st commercial flight Paris-NYC.

Virgin and Child, by Rubens — AP68

Rubens Paintings: 60fr, Virgin and Child and Two Donors. 100fr, Adoration of the Shepherds. 125fr, Adoration of the Kings.

**1977, Dec. 20 Litho. *Perf. 12½x12***
**C228** AP68 30fr multi .75 .25
**C229** AP68 60fr multi 1.10 .30
**C230** AP68 100fr multi 1.50 .40
**C231** AP68 125fr multi 1.90 .60
*Nos. C228-C231 (4)* 5.25 1.55

Christmas 1977.

Antoine de Saint-Exupéry — AP69

50fr, Wilbur & Orville Wright & Flyer. 80fr, Hugo Junkers & his plane. 100fr, Gen. Italo Balbo & his plane. 120fr, Concorde. 500fr, Wilbur & Orville Wright & Flyer.

**1978, Oct. 25 Litho. *Perf. 13½***
**C232** AP69 40fr multi .60 .25
**C233** AP69 50fr multi .75 .25
**C234** AP69 80fr multi 1.10 .30
**C235** AP69 100fr multi 1.50 .40
**C236** AP69 120fr multi 1.75 .50
*Nos. C232-C236 (5)* 5.70 1.70

**Souvenir Sheet**

**C237** AP69 500fr multi 6.75 2.00

History of aviation and 75th anniversary of 1st powered flight.

### Philexafrique II-Essen Issue
Common Design Types

No. C238, Rhinoceros & Chad #C6. No. C239, Kingfisher & Mecklenburg-Strelitz #1.

**1978, Nov. 1 *Perf. 12½***
**C238** CD138 100fr multi 3.00 1.00
**C239** CD139 100fr multi 3.00 1.00
*a.* Pair, #C238-C239 + label 7.50 4.00

### Nos. C191-C194 Overprinted "ALUNISSAGE/APOLLO XI/ JUILLET 1969"

**1979, Nov. 26 Litho. *Perf. 13½x14***
**C240** A86 100fr multi 1.10 .35
**C241** A86 200fr multi 2.25 .65
**C242** A86 250fr multi 2.50 1.00
*Nos. C240-C242 (3)* 5.85 2.00

**Souvenir Sheet**

**C243** A86 450fr multi 5.50 4.50

Apollo 11 moon landing, 10th anniversary.

Hurdles, Moscow '80 Emblem AP70

Emblem and: 30fr, Field hockey. 250fr, Swimming. 350fr, Running. 500fr, Yachting.

**1979, Nov. 30 *Perf. 13½***
**C244** AP70 15fr multi .25 .25
**C245** AP70 30fr multi .30 .25
**C246** AP70 250fr multi 1.90 .60
**C247** AP70 350fr multi 3.00 1.10
*Nos. C244-C247 (4)* 5.45 2.20

**Souvenir Sheet**

**C248** AP70 500fr multi 5.75 3.00

Pre-Olympic Year.
For overprints see Nos. C254-C255.

Austria Jubilee Issue of 1910, Canoe, Hill — AP71

Hill, Stamps & Vessels: 100fr, US design A97, dhow. 200fr, France #21, Sidewheeler. 300fr, Holstein #16, ocean liner. 500fr, Chad #J13, ocean liner.

**1979, Dec. 3 *Perf. 14x13½***
**C249** AP71 65fr multi .60 .25
**C250** AP71 100fr multi 1.40 .25
**C251** AP71 200fr multi 2.25 .45
**C252** AP71 300fr multi 2.75 .70
*Nos. C249-C252 (4)* 7.00 1.65

**Souvenir Sheet**

**C253** AP71 500fr multi 5.75 3.00

Sir Rowland Hill (1795-1879), originator of penny postage.
For overprints see Nos. C256-C257.

### Nos. C244-C245, C249-C250 Overprinted: "POSTES 1981" in Red or Overprinted and Surcharged Silver on Red

***Perf. 13½, 14x13½***
**1981, Nov. 15 Litho.**
**C254** AP70 30fr on 15fr multi 1.25 .40
**C255** AP70 30fr multi 1.25 .40
**C256** AP71 60fr on 65fr multi 2.25 .70
**C257** AP71 60fr on 100fr multi 2.25 .70
*Nos. C254-C257 (4)* 7.00 2.20

### Soccer Type of 1982 and

1982 World Cup Soccer Championships, Spain — AP71a

80fr, Brazil. 300fr, W. Germany.
No. C259C, Soccer players, ball, & trophy, vert.

**1982 Litho. *Perf. 13½***
**C258** A108 80fr multi 1.00 .25
**C259** A108 300fr multi 3.00 .50

**Souvenir Sheet**

**C259A** A108 500fr like 300fr 5.00 2.00

**Litho. & Embossed**

**C259B** AP71a 1500fr shown 16.00

**Souvenir Sheet**

**C259C** AP71a 1500fr gold & multi 11.50

No. C259A contains one 42x51mm stamp.
No. C259B exists in a souvenir sheet of 1. Value $42.50.
For surcharge see No. C305.

### Diana Type of 1982 and

Princess Diana, 21st Birthday — AP71b

Design: No. C262A, Portrait, horiz.

**1982, July 2 Litho. *Perf. 13½***
**C260** A109 80fr 1977 1.00 .25
**C261** A109 300fr 1980 3.00 .95

**Souvenir Sheet**

**C262** A109 500fr 1981 4.50 2.00

**Litho. & Embossed**

**C262A** AP71b 1500fr gold & multi 12.50

**Souvenir Sheet**

**C262B** AP71b 1500fr gold & multi 13.50

No. C262A exists in a souvenir sheet of 1. Value $42.50.
For overprints see Nos. 419A-419B.

Manned Flight Bicentenary AP72

Balloons: 100fr, Charles' & Roberts', 1783. 200fr, J.P. Blanchard, Berlin, 1788. 300fr, Charles Green, London, 1837. 400fr, Modern blimp. 500fr, Montgolfiere, 1783.

**1983, Apr. Litho. *Perf. 13***
**C263** AP72 100fr multi, vert. 1.25 .25
**C264** AP72 200fr multi, vert. 2.50 .40
**C265** AP72 300fr multi 3.50 .60
**C266** AP72 400fr multi 4.75 .75
*Nos. C263-C266 (4)* 12.00 2.00

**Souvenir Sheet**

**C267** AP72 500fr multi, vert. 5.75 2.50

### Balloon Type and

First Balloon Ascension, Bicent. AP72a

80fr, Steam Powered Airship, H. Giffard. 250fr, Graf Zeppelin; Airship L-1, 1st flight. 300fr, 1st Balloon Flight, Montgolfier & Rozier. No. C270A, Airship Hindenburg, Count Ferdinand von Zeppelin. No. C270B, Jean-Francois Pilatre de Rozier & Marquis d'Arlandes, 1st balloon ascension.

**1983, May 30 Litho. *Perf. 13½***
**C268** A116 80fr multi 1.00 .25
**C269** A116 250fr multi 3.00 .40

**Souvenir Sheet**

**C270** A116 300fr multi 3.75 2.50

**Litho. & Embossed**
***Perf. 13½***

**C270A** AP72a 1500fr gold & multi 16.00

**Souvenir Sheet**

**C270B** AP72a 1500fr gold & multi 12.00

No. C270A exists in a souvenir sheet of 1. Value $25.
For surcharge see No. C299.

1984 Summer Olympics AP73

Various kayak scenes.

**1984, Mar. 1 Litho. *Perf. 13***
**C271** AP73 100fr multi 1.00 .25
**C272** AP73 200fr multi 2.00 .25
**C273** AP73 300fr multi 3.00 .50
**C274** AP73 400fr multi 4.00 .60
*Nos. C271-C274 (4)* 10.00 1.60

**Souvenir Sheet**

**C275** AP73 500fr multi 5.00 3.50

Natl. Goals AP73a

Nos. C276, C278, Peace & reconciliation. Nos. C277, C279, Self-sufficiency in food production.

**1983, Dec. 26 Litho. *Perf. 13½***
**C276** AP73a 150fr multi 1.50 .40
**C277** AP73a 150fr multi 1.50 .40
**C278** AP73a 200fr multi 2.25 .55
**C279** AP73a 200fr multi 2.25 .55
*Nos. C276-C279 (4)* 7.50 1.90

For surcharges see Nos. C300-C301.

Souvenir Sheet

Paul P. Harris (1868-1947), Founder of Rotary Intl. — AP73b

**Litho. & Embossed**

**1984, Jan. 16 *Perf. 13½***
**C279B** AP73b 1500fr gold & multi 12.00

IYY, PHILEXAFRICA '85 — AP74

No. C280, Boy scout, tree. No. C281, Air Chad Fokker 27.

**1985, May 2 Litho. *Perf. 13***
**C280** AP74 200fr multicolored 3.00 1.50
**C281** AP74 200fr multicolored 3.00 1.50
*a.* Pair, #C280-C281 + label 6.75 5.00

### IYY, PHILEXAFRICA Type of 1985

No. C283, Girl, Scout ceremony. No. C284, Communications and transportation.

**1985, Nov. 1 Litho. *Perf. 13x12½***
**C283** AP74 250fr multicolored 3.00 1.50
**C284** AP74 250fr multicolored 3.00 1.50
*a.* Pair, #C283-C284 + label 6.75 5.00

ASCENA Airlines, 25th Anniv. AP75

**1985, Aug. 25 *Perf. 12½***
**C285** AP75 70fr bl & multi .60 .25
**C286** AP75 110fr org & multi 1.00 .25
**C287** AP75 250fr yel & multi 2.25 .80
*Nos. C285-C287 (3)* 3.85 1.30

Victor Hugo (1802-1885), French Novelist AP76

Scene from Les Miserables.

**1985, Nov. 24 Engr. *Perf. 13***
**C288** AP76 70fr org brn, chlky bl & dp brn .75 .25
**C289** AP76 110fr lake, dk brn & dk grn 1.00 .30
**C290** AP76 250fr brt org, blk & dk red 2.50 .80
**C291** AP76 300fr dk red, cl & sl bl 2.75 .90
*Nos. C288-C291 (4)* 7.00 2.25

Adoration of the Magi — AP77

**1985, Dec. 22 Litho. *Perf. 13½***
**C292** 250fr multicolored 2.25 .60

Christmas 1985.

1988 Summer Olympics, Seoul AP78

100fr, 400-Meter hurdles, vert. 170fr, 5000-Meter race. 200fr, Long jump. 600fr, Triple jump, vert.
750fr, 10,000-Meter race, vert.

**1988, June 1 Litho. *Perf. 13***
**C293** AP78 100fr multi 1.10 .30
**C294** AP78 170fr multi 1.75 .55
**C295** AP78 200fr multi 2.25 .65
**C296** AP78 600fr multi 5.75 2.00
*Nos. C293-C296 (4)* 10.85 3.50

**Souvenir Sheet**

**C297** AP78 750fr multi 8.00 6.00

### Stamps of 1982-84 Surcharged

**1989 *Perfs. as Before***
**C298** A115 100 on 300fr #446
**C299** A116 100 on 250fr #C269
**C300** AP73a 100 on 200fr #C278
**C301** AP73a 100 on 200fr #C279
**C302** A110 170 on 300fr #404
**C303** A122 170 on 200fr #503
**C304** A123 170 on 250fr #509
**C305** A108 170 on 300fr #C259
**C306** A112 240 on 300fr #425

---

## AIR POST SEMI-POSTAL STAMPS

**Catalogue values for unused stamps in this section are for Never Hinged items.**

Ramses II Battling the Hittites (from Abu Simbel) SPAP1

**Unwmk.**

**1964, Mar. 9 Engr. *Perf. 13***
**CB1** SPAP1 10fr + 5fr multi .75 .25
**CB2** SPAP1 25fr + 5fr multi 1.40 .40
**CB3** SPAP1 50fr + 5fr multi 2.75 .75
*Nos. CB1-CB3 (3)* 4.90 1.40

UNESCO world campaign to save historic monuments in Nubia.

Lions Emblem — SPAP2

**1967, July 5 Photo. *Perf. 13***
**CB4** SPAP2 50fr + 10fr multi 2.00 .25

50th anniv. of Lions Intl. and to publicize the Lions work for the blind.

---

## POSTAGE DUE STAMPS

Postage Due Stamps of France Overprinted

**1928 Unwmk. *Perf. 14x13½***
**J1** D2 5c light blue .70 1.20
**J2** D2 10c gray brown .70 1.20
**J3** D2 20c olive green .70 1.20
**J4** D2 25c bright rose 1.10 1.60
**J5** D2 30c light red 1.10 1.60
**J6** D2 45c blue green 1.45 2.00
**J7** D2 50c brown violet 2.25 2.40
**J8** D2 60c yellow brown 2.25 2.40
**J9** D2 1fr red brown 2.25 2.75
**J10** D2 2fr orange red 5.00 6.00
**J11** D2 3fr bright violet 4.25 5.50
*Nos. J1-J11 (11)* 21.75 27.85

Huts D3

Canoe D4

**1930 Typo. *Perf. 14x13½, 13½x14***
**J12** D3 5c dp bl & olive .40 .80
**J13** D3 10c dk red & brn .40 .80
**J14** D3 20c grn & brn 1.20 1.60
**J15** D3 25c lt bl & brn 1.20 2.40
**J16** D3 30c bis brn & Prus bl 1.60 2.00
**J17** D3 45c Prus bl & olive 2.40 2.75
**J18** D3 50c red vio & brn 2.40 4.00
**J19** D3 60c gray lil & bl blk 3.25 4.75
**J20** D4 1fr bis brn & bl blk 3.25 4.75
**J21** D4 2fr vio & brn 8.00 8.00
**J22** D4 3fr dp red & brn 35.00 40.00
*Nos. J12-J22 (11)* 59.10 71.85

In 1934 stamps of Chad were superseded by those of French Equatorial Africa.

**Catalogue values for unused stamps in this section, from this point to the end of the section, are for Never Hinged items.**

### Republic

Rhinoceros — D5

Tibesti Pictographs: #J24, Kudu. #J25, 2 antelopes. #J26, 3 antelopes. #J27, Ostrich. #J28, Horned bull. #J29, Bull. #J30, Wild swine. #J31, Elephant. #J32, Rhinoceros. #J33, Warrior with spear and shield. #J34, Masked archer.

**Unwmk.**

**1962, Apr. 20 Engr. *Perf. 13***
**J23** D5 50c olive bister .30 .25
**J24** D5 50c brown red .30 .25
*a.* Pair, #J23-J24 .55
**J25** D5 1fr blue .40 .25
**J26** D5 1fr green .40 .25
*a.* Pair, #J25-J26 .75
**J27** D5 2fr vermilion .50 .25
**J28** D5 2fr maroon .50 .25
*a.* Pair, #J27-J28 1.00

J29 D5 5fr slate green .75 .40
J30 D5 5fr violet blue .75 .40
a. Pair, #J29-J30 1.50
J31 D5 10fr brown 1.40 .75
J32 D5 10fr orange brown 1.40 .75
a. Pair, #J31-J32 2.75
J33 D5 25fr carmine rose 3.25 1.75
J34 D5 25fr violet 3.25 1.75
a. Pair, #J33-J34 6.50
*Nos. J23-J34 (12)* 13.20 7.30

Dolls — D6

**1969, Sept. 19 Engr. *Perf. 14x13***
J35 D6 1fr Kanem .25 .25
J36 D6 2fr Kotoko .25 .25
J37 D6 5fr Leather .40 .25
J38 D6 10fr Kotoko .50 .25
J39 D6 25fr Guera .60 .25
*Nos. J35-J39 (5)* 2.00 1.25

## MILITARY STAMPS

**Catalogue values for unused stamps in this section are for Never Hinged items.**

### No. 78 Overprinted "F.M."

**1965 Typo. *Perf. 14x13½***
M1 A5 20fr red & black 300.00 300.00

Flag Bearer and Map of Chad — M1

**1968 Unwmk. Litho. *Perf. 13x12½***
M2 M1 tan & multi 2.00 5.00

1st Regiment Emblem — M2

**1972, Jan. 21 Photo. *Perf. 13***
M3 M2 blue & multi 1.00 2.00

## OFFICIAL STAMPS

**Catalogue values for unused stamps in this section are for Never Hinged items.**

Flag and Map of Chad — O1

***Perf. 13½x14***
**1966-71 Typo. Unwmk.**
**Flag in blue, yellow and carmine**
O1 O1 1fr light blue .25 .25
O2 O1 2fr gray .25 .25
O3 O1 5fr black .25 .25
O4 O1 10fr violet blue .25 .25
O5 O1 25fr orange .30 .25
O6 O1 30fr bright green .50 .25
O7 O1 40fr carmine ('71) .75 .25
O8 O1 50fr red lilac .75 .25
O9 O1 85fr green 1.10 .30
O10 O1 100fr brown 1.75 .35
O11 O1 200fr red 3.00 .50
*Nos. O1-O11 (11)* 9.15 3.15

### Flag and Map Type of 1966-71 Redrawn with "N'Djamena" as Capital on Map

***Perf. 13½x13¼, 11¾ (100fr)***
**1993-2000 ? Litho.**
**Center Flag Stripe in Yellow**
**Frame Color**
O12 O1 30fr violet — —
O13 O1 100fr brown — —
O14 O1 200fr red — —

Nos. O13 and O14 have a large "F" in denomination, "POSTES" without serifs, and has printer's inscription of "COURVOISIER."

**Center Flag Stripe in Orange**
**Frame Color**
O17 O1 50fr green — —
O18 O1 85fr orange — —
O19 O1 100fr red orange — —
O20 O1 150fr blue green — —
O21 O1 200fr green — —
O22 O1 250fr lilac — —
O23 O1 300fr blue — —
O24 O1 500fr red — —
O25 O1 1000fr dark green — —

Additional stamps may have been issued in this set. The editors would like to examine any examples. Numbers may change.

# CHILE

'chi-lē

LOCATION — Southwest corner of South America
GOVT. — Republic
AREA — 284,520 sq. mi.
POP. — 14,973,843 (1999 est.)
CAPITAL — Santiago

100 Centavos = 1 Peso
1000 Milésimos = 100 Centésimos = 1 Escudo (1960)
100 Centavos = 1 Peso (1975)

**Catalogue values for unused stamps in this country are for Never Hinged items, beginning with Scott 257 in the regular postage section, Scott B3 in the semi-postal section, Scott C125 in the airpost section, Scott CB1 in the airpost semi-postal section, and Scott O60 in the officials section.**

## Issues of the Republic

Unused values for Nos. 1-14 are for stamps without gum. Examples with original gum are very scarce and are worth considerably more.

Pen cancellations are common on the 1862-67 issues. Such stamps sell for much less than the quoted values which are for those with handstamped postal cancellations.

### Watermarks

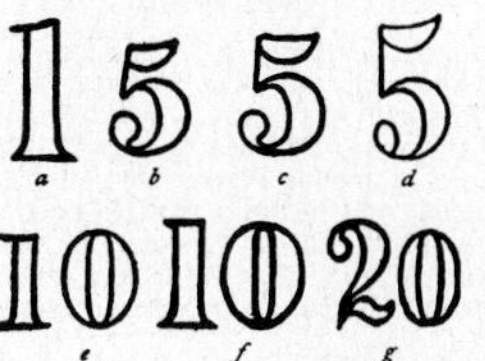


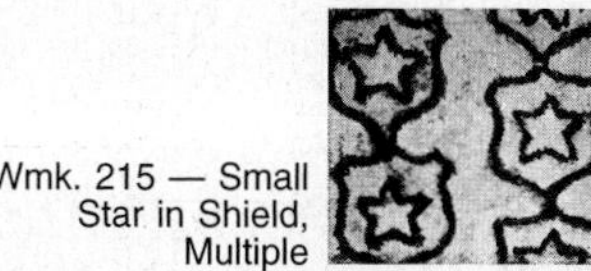


Wmk. 215 — Small Star in Shield, Multiple

Christopher Columbus — A1

**London Prints**
**1853 Wmk. b Engr. *Imperf.***
**Blued Paper**
1 A1 5c brown red 650.00 125.00
a. White paper 250.00

**Wmk. e**
**White Paper**
2 A1 10c dp brt bl 1,000. 150.00
a. Blued paper 225.00
b. Diag. half used as 5c on cover 800.00
c. Horiz. half used as 5c on cover 800.00
d. Vert. half used as 5c on cover 800.00

**Santiago Prints**
Impressions Fine and Clear
**1854 Wmk. b and e**
**White Paper**
3 A1 5c pale red brn 600.00 75.00
a. 5c deep red brown 650.00 75.00
b. 5c chestnut 1,000. 200.00
e. Double impression 275.00
4 A1 5c burnt sienna 1,800. 300.00
a. 5c dull chocolate 3,500. 2,000.
5 A1 10c deep blue 1,200. 275.00
a. 10c slate blue 275.00
b. 10c greenish blue *475.00*
d. Diag. half used as 5c on cover 450.00
e. Horiz. half used as 5c on cover 450.00
f. Vert. half used as 5c on cover 450.00
6 A1 10c lt dl bl 800.00 150.00
a. 10c pale blue 190.00
b. Diag. half used as 5c on cover 425.00
c. Horiz. half used as 5c on cover 425.00
d. Vert. half used as 5c on cover 425.00

**Litho.**
7 A1 5c pale brown *1,200.* 300.00

**London Print**
**1855 Blued Paper Wmk. c Engr.**
8 A1 5c brown red 220.00 16.00
Fiscal cancellation 2.75

**Santiago Prints**
Impressions Worn and Blurred
**1856-62 Wmk. b and e**
**White Paper**
9 A1 5c rose red ('58) 60.00 8.00
Fiscal cancellation 1.40
a. 5c carmine red ('62) 90.00 20.00
b. 5c orange red ('61) *225.00* 100.00
c. 5c dull redsh brn ('57) *250.00* 27.50
f. Printed on both sides *450.00* *250.00*
g. Double impression *450.00* 140.00
10 A1 10c sky blue ('57) 160.00 40.00
Fiscal cancellation 1.40
a. 10c deep blue *160.00* 40.00
b. 10c light blue ('59) *160.00* 40.00
c. 10c indigo blue ('60) *175.00* 50.00
k. Printed on both sides *350.00*
n. As "j," half used as 5c on cover 165.00
o. Any shade, horiz. half used as 5c on cover 200.00
p. Any shade, vert. half used as 5c on cover 200.00

**London Prints**
**1862 Wmk. a, f and g**
11 A1 1c lemon yellow 67.50 40.00
Fiscal cancellation 1.50
a. Double impression, one inverted *2,000.* *200.00*
12 A1 10c bright blue 40.00 15.00
Fiscally used 1.50
a. 10c deep blue 32.50 21.00
b. Blued paper — 17.50
c. Wmkd. "20" (error) *5,000.* *5,200.*
d. Diag. half used as 5c on cover 110.00
e. Horiz. half used as 5c on cover 125.00
f. Vert. half used as 5c on cover 125.00
13 A1 20c green 160.00 70.00
Fiscally used 6.75
*Nos. 11-13 (3)* 267.50 125.00

No. 11a is only known fiscally used.

**Santiago Print**
**1865 Wmk. d**
14 A1 5c rose red 80.00 20.00
Fiscally used 1.50
a. 5c carmine red 80.00 20.00
b. Printed on both sides *375.00* *200.00*
c. Laid paper — *90.00*
d. Double impression, entire stamp *825.00* *160.00*

The 5c rose red (shades) on unwatermaked paper, either wove or ribbed, and on paper watermarked Chilean arms in the sheet are reprints made about 1870.

*No. 13 has been reprinted in the color of issue and in fancy colors, both from the original engraved plate and from lithographic transfers. The reprints are on paper without watermark or with watermark CHILE and Star.*

A2

**1867 Unwmk. *Perf. 12***
15 A2 1c orange 70.00 15.00
Pen cancellation 1.25
16 A2 2c black 80.00 30.00
Pen cancellation 2.00
17 A2 5c red 60.00 2.00
Pen cancellation .40
18 A2 10c blue 80.00 6.00
Pen cancellation 1.25
19 A2 20c green 80.00 8.00
Pen cancellation 1.60
*Nos. 15-19 (5)* 370.00 61.00

Unused values for Nos. 15-19 are for stamps with original gum.

A3

**1877 *Rouletted***
20 A3 1c gray 10.00 3.00
Pen cancellation .60
21 A3 2c orange 30.00 3.00
Pen cancellation .60
22 A3 5c dull lake 24.00 2.00
Pen cancellation .40
23 A3 10c blue 18.00 2.75
a. Diagonal half used as 5c on cover —
24 A3 20c green 20.00 4.50
*Nos. 20-24 (5)* 102.00 15.25

The panel inscribed "CENTAVO" is straight on No. 22.

A4

A5

Columbus — A6

**1878-99 *Rouletted***
25 A4 1c green ('81) 1.10 .30
26 A4 2c rose ('81) 1.10 .30
27 A5 5c dull lake ('78) 9.00 1.10
28 A5 5c ultra ('83) 2.40 .30
29 A5 10c orange ('85) 3.50 .40
a. 10c yellow 10.00 1.90
30 A5 15c dk grn ('92) 3.50 .70
31 A5 20c gray ('86) 3.50 .70
32 A5 25c org brn ('92) 3.50 .70
33 A5 30c rose car ('99) 9.00 4.75
34 A5 50c lilac ('78) 55.00 35.00
35 A5 50c violet ('85) 3.50 2.40
36 A6 1p dk brn & blk ('92) 26.00 3.50
a. Imperf. horiz. or vert., pair 75.00
*Nos. 25-36 (12)* 121.10 50.15

On Nos. 25-26 there is a small colorless ornament at each side of the base of the numeral, above the "E" and "V" of "CENTAVO."

For surcharge and overprint see Nos. 50, O16.

Columbus — A7

No. 25

No. 37

No. 26

No. 38

| **1894** | | | | **Re-engraved** |
|---|---|---|---|---|
| **37** | A7 | 1c blue green | 1.10 | .40 |
| **38** | A7 | 2c carmine lake | 1.10 | .40 |

On Nos. 37-38 the ornaments on Nos. 25-26 are missing. On No. 37 the figure "1" is broader than on No. 25. On No. 38 the head of the figure "2" is formed by a curved line instead of a ball like on No. 26.

Columbus — A8

Type I Type II

Type I — There is a heavy shadow, or shading, below "Chile" and the adjacent ornaments.

Type II — There is practically no shading below "Chile" and the ornaments.

### Type I

| **1900-01** | | | | |
|---|---|---|---|---|
| **39** | A8 | 1c yel grn | .80 | .25 |
| **40** | A8 | 2c brn rose | 1.25 | .25 |
| **41** | A8 | 5c dp bl | 6.50 | .35 |
| **42** | A8 | 10c violet | 6.50 | .70 |
| **43** | A8 | 20c gray | 6.50 | 2.50 |
| **44** | A8 | 30c dp org ('01) | 6.50 | 2.50 |
| **45** | A8 | 50c red brn | 7.50 | 2.50 |
| | | *Nos. 39-45 (7)* | 35.55 | 9.05 |

### Type II

| | | | | |
|---|---|---|---|---|
| **46** | A8 | 1c yel grn ('01) | .85 | .30 |
| **47** | A8 | 2c rose ('01) | .85 | .35 |
| **48** | A8 | 5c dull blue ('01) | 5.00 | .30 |
| *a.* | | Printed on both sides | | — |
| **49** | A8 | 10c vio ('01) | 6.00 | 1.00 |
| | | *Nos. 46-49 (4)* | 12.70 | 1.95 |

For surcharge see No. 57.

No. 33 Surcharged in Black

| **1900** | | | | |
|---|---|---|---|---|
| **50** | A5 | 5c on 30c rose car | 1.25 | .75 |
| *a.* | | Inverted surcharge | 32.50 | 24.00 |
| *b.* | | Double surcharge | 90.00 | 60.00 |
| *c.* | | Double surcharge, both invtd. | 90.00 | 60.00 |
| *d.* | | Double surcharge, one invtd. | 90.00 | 60.00 |

Columbus — A10

| **1901-02** | | | | ***Perf. 12*** |
|---|---|---|---|---|
| **51** | A10 | 1c green | .50 | .30 |
| **52** | A10 | 2c carmine | .65 | .25 |
| **53** | A10 | 5c ultra | 1.50 | .25 |
| **54** | A10 | 10c red & blk | 2.25 | .35 |
| **55** | A10 | 30c vio & blk | 6.75 | .85 |
| **56** | A10 | 50c red org & blk | 7.25 | 2.25 |
| | | *Nos. 51-56 (6)* | 18.90 | 4.25 |

No. 44 Surcharged in Dark Blue

| **1903** | | | | ***Rouletted*** |
|---|---|---|---|---|
| **57** | A8 | 10c on 30c orange | 2.60 | .50 |
| *a.* | | Inverted surcharge | 18.00 | 12.00 |
| *b.* | | Double surcharge | 25.00 | 15.00 |
| *c.* | | Double surch., one inverted | 25.00 | 15.00 |
| *d.* | | Double surch., both invtd. | 25.00 | 15.00 |
| *e.* | | Stamp design printed on both sides | | |

### Telegraph Stamps Surcharged or Overprinted in Black

Pedro de Valdivia A11

Coat of Arms A12

A13

Type I

Type II

Type I — Animal at left has neither mane nor tail.

Type II — Animal at left has mane and tail.

| **1904** | | | | ***Perf. 12*** |
|---|---|---|---|---|
| **58** | A11 | 1c on 20c ultra | .50 | .40 |
| *a.* | | Imperf. horiz., pair | 40.00 | 40.00 |
| *b.* | | Inverted surcharge | 50.00 | 50.00 |
| **59** | A13 | 2c yel brn, I | .50 | .40 |
| *a.* | | Inverted overprint | 20.00 | 20.00 |
| *b.* | | Pair, one without overprint | 50.00 | 50.00 |
| **60** | A13 | 5c red, I | .60 | .40 |
| *a.* | | Inverted overprint | 20.00 | 20.00 |
| *c.* | | Pair, one without overprint | 50.00 | 50.00 |
| **61** | A13 | 10c ol grn, I | 2.25 | .60 |
| *a.* | | Inverted overprint | 50.00 | 50.00 |
| | | *Nos. 58-61 (4)* | 3.85 | 1.80 |

### *Perf. 12½ to 16*

| | | | | |
|---|---|---|---|---|
| **62** | A13 | 2c yel, brn, II | 7.00 | *4.50* |
| **63** | A11 | 3c on 5c brn red | 70.00 | 60.00 |
| *a.* | | Inverted surcharge | | |
| **64** | A12 | 3c on 1p brn, II | .70 | .40 |
| *a.* | | Double surcharge | 50.00 | 50.00 |
| **65** | A13 | 5c red, II | 11.00 | 5.50 |
| *a.* | | Inverted overprint | 30.00 | 20.00 |
| **66** | A13 | 10c ol grn, II | 25.00 | 10.00 |
| **67** | A11 | 12c on 5c brn red | 1.30 | .70 |
| *a.* | | No star at left of "Centavos" | 3.00 | 2.50 |
| *b.* | | Inverted surcharge | 40.00 | 40.00 |
| *c.* | | Double surcharge | 50.00 | 50.00 |
| | | *Nos. 62-67 (6)* | 115.00 | 81.10 |

Counterfeits exist of the overprint and surcharge varieties of Nos. 57-67.

For overprint see No. O12.

A14

A15

Columbus — A16

| **1905-09** | | | | ***Perf. 12*** |
|---|---|---|---|---|
| **68** | A14 | 1c green | .25 | .25 |
| **69** | A14 | 2c carmine | .30 | .25 |
| **70** | A14 | 3c yel brn | .65 | .30 |
| **71** | A14 | 5c ultra | .70 | .25 |
| **72** | A15 | 10c gray & blk | 1.10 | .25 |
| **73** | A15 | 12c lake & blk | 5.50 | 2.25 |
| **74** | A15 | 15c vio & blk | 1.25 | .25 |
| **75** | A15 | 20c org brn & blk | 2.25 | .25 |
| **76** | A15 | 30c bl grn & blk | 3.50 | .35 |
| **77** | A15 | 50c ultra & blk | 3.50 | .40 |
| **78** | A16 | 1p brnz, ol grn & gray ('08) | 16.00 | 11.00 |
| | | *Nos. 68-78 (11)* | 35.00 | 15.80 |

A 20c dull red and black, type A15, was prepared but not issued. Value $125. "Specimen" examples of Nos. 74, 76-78 exist, punched to prevent postal use.

For surcharges and overprints see Nos. 79-82, O9, O11-O15.

No. 78a lacks metallic gold sheen of No. 78.

Nos. 68-72 exist overprinted "Isla de Mas Afuera". Overprints were authorized for use only on Juan Fernandez Islands. Value, $125 each.

See Nos. O1A-O1C.

### Nos. 73, 78 Surcharged in Blue or Red

a

b

| **1910** | | | | |
|---|---|---|---|---|
| **79** | A15 (a) | 5c on 12c (Bl) | .50 | .25 |
| **80** | A16 (b) | 10c on 1p (R) | 1.10 | .30 |
| **81** | A16 (b) | 20c on 1p (R) | 1.60 | .60 |
| **82** | A16 (b) | 1p (R) | 3.00 | 1.10 |
| | | *Nos. 79-82 (4)* | 6.20 | 2.25 |

The 1p is overprinted "ISLAS DE JUAN FERNANDEZ" only. The use of these stamps throughout Chile was authorized.

### Independence Centenary Issue

Oath of Independence A17

Monument to O'Higgins A26

Adm. Lord Thomas Cochrane — A29

Designs: 2c, Battle of Chacabuco. 3c, Battle of Roble. 5c, Battle of Maipu. 10c, Naval Engagement of "Lautaro" and "Esmeralda." 12c, Capturing the "Maria Isabel." 15c, First Sortie of Liberating Forces. 20c, Abdication of O'Higgins. 25c, Chile's First Congress. 50c, Monument to José M. Carrera. 1p, Monument to San Martin. 2p, Gen. Manuel Blanco Encalada. 5p, Gen. José Ignacio Zenteno.

| **1910** | | | | **Center in Black** |
|---|---|---|---|---|
| **83** | A17 | 1c dk green | .25 | .25 |
| *a.* | | Center inverted | *50,000.* | *24,000.* |
| **84** | A17 | 2c lake | 1.10 | .75 |
| **85** | A17 | 3c red brown | .80 | .45 |
| **86** | A17 | 5c dp blue | .45 | .25 |
| **87** | A17 | 10c gray brn | 1.20 | .30 |
| **88** | A17 | 12c vermilion | 2.50 | 1.00 |
| **89** | A17 | 15c slate | 1.90 | .55 |
| **90** | A17 | 20c red orange | 2.50 | .85 |
| **91** | A17 | 25c ultra | 3.25 | 2.00 |
| **92** | A26 | 30c violet | 3.25 | 1.40 |
| **93** | A26 | 50c olive grn | 6.75 | 2.25 |
| **94** | A26 | 1p yel org | 14.00 | 5.25 |
| **95** | A29 | 2p red | 14.00 | 5.25 |

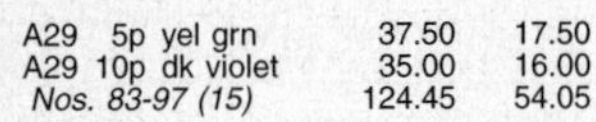

| | | | | |
|---|---|---|---|---|
| **96** | A29 | 5p yel grn | 37.50 | 17.50 |
| **97** | A29 | 10p dk violet | 35.00 | 16.00 |
| | | *Nos. 83-97 (15)* | 124.45 | 54.05 |

Nos. 83-93 exist overprinted "Isla de Mas Afuera". Overprints were authorized for use only on Juan Fernandez Islands. Value, $200 each.

Columbus A32

Pedro de Valdivia A33

Mateo de Toro Zambrano A34

Bernardo O'Higgins A35

Ramón Freire A36

F. A. Pinto A37

Joaquín Prieto A38

Manuel Bulnes A39

Manuel Montt A40

José Joaquín Pérez A41

Federico Errázuriz Zanartu A42

José de Balmaceda A43

Designs: 1p, Anibal Pinto, 2p, Domingo Santa María. 10p, Federico Errázuriz Echaurren.

### Outer backgrounds consist of horizontal and diagonal lines

| **1911** | | **Engr.** | | ***Perf. 12*** |
|---|---|---|---|---|
| **98** | A32 | 1c dp green | .25 | .25 |
| **99** | A33 | 2c scarlet | .25 | .25 |
| **100** | A34 | 3c sepia | .75 | .25 |
| **101** | A35 | 5c dk blue | .25 | .25 |
| **102** | A36 | 10c gray & blk | .75 | .25 |
| *a.* | | Center inverted | 1,800. | 1,250. |
| **103** | A37 | 12c carmine & blk | 1.00 | .25 |
| **104** | A38 | 15c reddsh pur & blk | .90 | .25 |
| *a.* | | Center inverted | *2,000.* | 25,000. |
| **105** | A39 | 20c org red & blk | 1.75 | .25 |
| *a.* | | Center inverted | 125.00 | 125.00 |
| **106** | A40 | 25c lt blue & blk | 2.75 | .60 |
| **107** | A41 | 30c bis brn & blk | 4.00 | .30 |
| **108** | A42 | 50c myr grn & blk | 5.00 | .30 |
| **109** | A43 | 1p green & blk | 11.00 | .40 |
| **110** | A43 | 2p ver & blk | 22.00 | 2.00 |
| **111** | A43 | 5p ol grn & blk | 70.00 | 11.00 |
| **112** | A43 | 10p org yel & blk | 60.00 | 9.00 |
| | | *Nos. 98-112 (15)* | 180.65 | 25.60 |

See Nos. 117, 121, 123, 127-128, 133-141, 143, 155A, 157-161, 165-169,171-172 and designs A47-A55, A57. For overprints see

Nos. C6, C6B-C6D, C7-C8, C10-C11, C13-C21, O19-O22, O24-O27, O30-O34, O40.

Columbus A47

Toro Zambrano A48

Freire A49

O'Higgins A50

**1912-13** **Engr.** ***Perf. 12***

| | | | | |
|---|---|---|---|---|
| **113** | A47 | 2c scarlet | .25 | .25 |
| **114** | A48 | 4c black brn | .30 | .25 |
| **115** | A49 | 8c gray | 1.00 | .25 |
| **116** | A50 | 10c blue & blk | 1.00 | .25 |
| *a.* | | Center inverted | 625.00 | 500.00 |
| *b.* | | Imperf. horiz. or vert., pair | 50.00 | |
| **117** | A37 | 14c car & blk | 1.50 | .25 |
| **121** | A38 | 40c violet & blk | 5.75 | .60 |
| **123** | A40 | 60c lt blue & blk | 14.00 | 1.75 |
| | | *Nos. 113-123 (7)* | 23.80 | 3.60 |

See Nos. 125-126, 131, 164, 170, 173. For overprints see Nos. C6E, O18, O23, O28, O29.

Cochrane — A52

**1915** **Engr.** ***Perf. 13½x14***

| | | | | |
|---|---|---|---|---|
| **124** | A52 | 5c slate blue | .60 | .40 |
| *a.* | | Imperf., pair | 11.50 | |

See Nos. 155, 162-163. For overprints see Nos. O17, O37.

**1918**

| | | | | |
|---|---|---|---|---|
| **125** | A49 | 8c slate | 17.50 | .80 |

No. 125 is from a plate made in Chile to resemble No. 115. The top of the head is further from the oval, the spots of color enclosed in the figures "8" are oval instead of round, and there are many small differences in the design.

**1921** **Worn Plate**

| | | | | |
|---|---|---|---|---|
| **126** | A49 | 8c gray | 20.00 | 5.00 |

No. 126 differs from No. 125 in not having diagonal lines in the frame and only a few diagonal lines above the shoulders (due to wear), while No. 125 has diagonal lines in the oval up to the level of the forehead.

Columbus — A53

**1915-25** **Typo.** ***Perf. 13½ to 14½***

| | | | | |
|---|---|---|---|---|
| **127** | A32 | 1c gray green | .25 | .25 |
| **128** | A33 | 2c red | .25 | .25 |
| **129** | A53 | 4c brown ('18) | .25 | .25 |

**Frame Litho.; Head Engr.**

| | | | | |
|---|---|---|---|---|
| **131** | A50 | 10c bl & blk | 1.25 | .25 |
| *a.* | | 10c dark blue & black | 1.25 | .25 |
| *b.* | | Imperf., pair | 110.00 | |
| *c.* | | Center inverted | 325.00 | |
| **133** | A38 | 15c vio & blk | .90 | .25 |
| **134** | A39 | 20c org red & blk | 1.40 | .25 |
| *a.* | | 20c brown orange & blk | 1.75 | .25 |
| **135** | A40 | 25c dl bl & blk | .55 | .25 |
| **136** | A41 | 30c bis brn & blk | 1.75 | .25 |
| **137** | A42 | 50c dp grn & blk | 1.75 | .25 |

***Perf. 14***

| | | | | |
|---|---|---|---|---|
| **138** | A43 | 1p grn & blk | 14.00 | .50 |
| **139** | A43 | 2p red & blk | 17.00 | .30 |
| *a.* | | 2p vermilion & black | 50.00 | 1.00 |
| **140** | A43 | 5p ol grn & blk ('20) | 40.00 | 1.00 |
| **141** | A43 | 10p org & blk ('25) | 40.00 | 2.50 |
| | | *Nos. 127-141 (13)* | 119.35 | 6.55 |

The frames have crosshatching on the 15c, 20c, 30c, 2p, 5p and 10p. They have no crosshatching on the 10c, 25c, 50c and 1p.

Nos. 131a and 134a are printed from new head plates which give blacker and heavier impressions. No. 131a exists with; (a) frame litho., head engr.; (b) frame typo., head engr.; (c) frame typo., head litho. No. 134a is with frame typo., head engr.

A 4c stamp with portrait of Balmaceda and a 14c with portrait of Manuel de Salas were prepared but not placed in use. Both stamps were sent to the paper mill at Puente Alto for destruction. They were not all destroyed as some were privately preserved and sold.

Columbus — A54

**Types of 1915-20 Redrawn**

**1918-20** ***Perf. 13½x14½***

| | | | | |
|---|---|---|---|---|
| **143** | A32 | 1c gray grn ('20) | .30 | .30 |
| **144** | A54 | 4c brown | .50 | .50 |

No. 143 has all the lines much finer and clearer than No. 127. The white shirt front is also much less shaded.

Manuel Rengifo — A55

**1921**

| | | | | |
|---|---|---|---|---|
| **145** | A55 | 40c dk vio & blk | 2.00 | .40 |

For overprints see Nos. C6A, C9.

Pan-American Congress Building — A56

**1923, Apr. 25** **Typo.** ***Perf. 14½x14***

| | | | | |
|---|---|---|---|---|
| **146** | A56 | 2c red | .25 | .25 |
| **147** | A56 | 4c brown | .25 | .25 |

**Typo.; Center Engr.**

| | | | | |
|---|---|---|---|---|
| **148** | A56 | 10c blue & blk | .25 | .25 |
| **149** | A56 | 20c orange & blk | .75 | .25 |
| **150** | A56 | 40c dl vio & blk | 1.00 | .30 |
| **151** | A56 | 1p green & blk | 1.25 | .50 |
| **152** | A56 | 2p red & blk | 5.00 | .60 |
| **153** | A56 | 5p dk grn & blk | 17.00 | 4.50 |
| | | *Nos. 146-153 (8)* | 25.75 | 6.90 |

Fifth Pan-American Congress.

Adm. Juan José Latorre — A57

**Typographed; Head Engraved**

**1927** ***Perf. 13½x14½***

| | | | | |
|---|---|---|---|---|
| **154** | A57 | 80c dk brn & blk | 2.00 | .60 |

**Types of 1915-25 Issues Inscribed: "Chile Correos"**

***Perf. 13½x14½***

**1928-31** **Engr.** **Wmk. 215**

| | | | | |
|---|---|---|---|---|
| **155** | A52 | 5c slate blue | 1.40 | .40 |

**Frame Typo.; Center Engr.**

| | | | | |
|---|---|---|---|---|
| **155A** | A38 | 15c violet & blk | | *2,200.* |
| **156** | A55 | 40c dk vio & blk | .60 | .40 |
| **157** | A42 | 50c dp grn & blk | 2.50 | .40 |

***Perf. 14***

| | | | | |
|---|---|---|---|---|
| **158** | A43 | 1p green & blk | 1.00 | .40 |
| **159** | A43 | 2p red & blk | 5.00 | .40 |
| **160** | A43 | 5p ol grn & blk | 9.75 | .45 |
| **161** | A43 | 10p orange & blk | 9.75 | 1.90 |
| | | *Nos. 155,156-161 (7)* | 30.00 | 4.35 |

Paper of Nos. 155-161 varies from thin to thick.

**Types of 1915-25 Issues Inscribed: "Correos de Chile"**

**1928** **Engr.** ***Perf. 13½x14½***

| | | | | |
|---|---|---|---|---|
| **162** | A52 | 5c deep blue | .40 | .40 |

**1929** **Litho.**

| | | | | |
|---|---|---|---|---|
| **163** | A52 | 5c light green | .50 | .40 |

**Frame Litho.; Center Engr.**

| | | | | |
|---|---|---|---|---|
| **164** | A50 | 10c blue & blk | 2.00 | .40 |
| **165** | A38 | 15c violet & blk | 2.50 | .40 |
| **166** | A39 | 20c org red & blk | 5.75 | .40 |
| **167** | A40 | 25c blue & blk | .95 | .40 |
| **168** | A41 | 30c brown & blk | .75 | .40 |
| **169** | A42 | 50c dp grn & blk | .65 | .40 |
| | | *Nos. 163-169 (7)* | 13.10 | 2.80 |

**Redrawn**

**1929** **Frame Typo.; Center Litho.**

| | | | | |
|---|---|---|---|---|
| **170** | A50 | 10c blue & blk | 3.00 | .40 |
| **171** | A38 | 15c violet & blk | 2.75 | .40 |
| **172** | A39 | 20c org red & blk | 4.25 | .40 |
| | | *Nos. 170-172 (3)* | 10.00 | 1.20 |

**1931** **Unwmk.**

| | | | | |
|---|---|---|---|---|
| **173** | A50 | 10c blue & blk | 1.50 | .40 |

In the redrawn stamps the lines behind the portraits are heavier and completely fill the ovals. There are strong diagonal lines above the shoulders. On No. 170 the head is larger than on Nos. 164, 173.

A58

Prosperity of Saltpeter Trade
A59 A60

***Perf. 13½x14***

**1930, July 21** **Litho.** **Wmk. 215**

**Size: 20x25mm**

| | | | | |
|---|---|---|---|---|
| **175** | A58 | 5c yellow grn | .60 | .40 |
| **176** | A58 | 10c red brown | .60 | .30 |
| **177** | A58 | 15c violet | .60 | .30 |
| **178** | A59 | 25c deep gray | 1.90 | .60 |
| **179** | A60 | 70c dark blue | 4.50 | 1.50 |

***Perf. 14***

**Size: 24½x30mm**

| | | | | |
|---|---|---|---|---|
| **180** | A60 | 1p dk gray grn | 3.75 | .75 |
| | | *Nos. 175-180 (6)* | 11.95 | 3.85 |

Cent. of the 1st shipment of saltpeter from Chile, July 21, 1830.

Manuel Bulnes — A61

**1931** ***Perf. 13½, 14***

| | | | | |
|---|---|---|---|---|
| **181** | A61 | 20c brown | 1.00 | .40 |

For overprints see Nos. O35, O39.

Bernardo O'Higgins — A62

**1932**

| | | | | |
|---|---|---|---|---|
| **182** | A62 | 10c deep blue | 1.50 | .40 |

For overprints see Nos. O36, O38.

Mariano Egana A63

Joaquin Tocornal A64

**1934** ***Perf. 13½x14***

| | | | | |
|---|---|---|---|---|
| **183** | A63 | 30c magenta | .65 | .40 |

***Perf. 14***

| | | | | |
|---|---|---|---|---|
| **184** | A64 | 1.20p bright blue | 1.10 | .40 |

Centenary of the constitution.

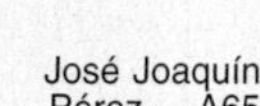

José Joaquín Pérez — A65

**1934** ***Perf. 13½x14***

| | | | | |
|---|---|---|---|---|
| **185** | A65 | 30c bright pink | 1.60 | .40 |

Atacama Desert — A66

Designs: 10c, Fishing boats. 20c, Coquito palms. 25c, Sheep. 30c, Mining. 40c, Lonquimay forest. 50c, Colliery at Port Lota. 1p, Shipping at Valparaiso. 1.20p, Puntiagudo volcano. 2p, Diego de Almagro. 5p, Cattle. 10p, Mining saltpeter.

**Wmk. 215**

**1936, Mar. 1** **Litho.** ***Perf. 14***

| | | | | |
|---|---|---|---|---|
| **186** | A66 | 5c vermilion | .60 | .40 |
| **187** | A66 | 10c violet | .30 | .40 |
| **188** | A66 | 20c magenta | .40 | .40 |
| **189** | A66 | 25c grnsh blue | 3.00 | 2.00 |
| **190** | A66 | 30c lt green | .40 | .40 |
| **191** | A66 | 40c blk, *cream* | 3.25 | 2.50 |
| **192** | A66 | 50c bl, *bluish* | 1.75 | .40 |

**Engr.**

| | | | | |
|---|---|---|---|---|
| **193** | A66 | 1p dk green | 1.75 | 2.00 |
| **194** | A66 | 1.20p dp blue | 2.00 | 2.50 |
| **195** | A66 | 2p dk brown | 2.50 | 2.50 |
| **196** | A66 | 5p copper red | 5.75 | 8.50 |
| **197** | A66 | 10p dk violet | 14.00 | 28.00 |
| | | *Nos. 186-197 (12)* | 35.70 | 50.00 |

400th anniv. of the discovery of Chile by Diego de Almagro.

Laja Waterfall A78

Fishing in Chiloé A84

Designs: 10c, Agriculture. 15c, Boldo tree. 20c, Nitrate Industry. 30c, Mineral spas. 40c, Copper mine. 50c, Mining. 1.80p, Osorno Volcano. 2p, Mercantile marine. 5p, Lake Villarrica. 10p, State railways.

***Perf. 13½x14***

**1938-40** **Litho.** **Wmk. 215**

| | | | | |
|---|---|---|---|---|
| **198** | A78 | 5c brn car ('39) | .40 | .40 |
| **199** | A78 | 10c sal pink ('39) | .40 | .40 |
| **200** | A78 | 15c brn org ('40) | .40 | .40 |
| **201** | A78 | 20c light blue | .40 | .40 |
| **202** | A78 | 30c brt pink | .40 | .40 |
| **203** | A78 | 40c lt grn ('39) | .40 | .40 |
| **204** | A78 | 50c violet | .40 | .40 |

**Engr.** ***Perf. 14***

| | | | | |
|---|---|---|---|---|
| **205** | A84 | 1p orange brn | .40 | .40 |
| **206** | A84 | 1.80p deep blue | .45 | .25 |
| **207** | A84 | 2p car lake ('39) | .40 | .40 |
| **208** | A84 | 5p dk slate grn ('39) | .40 | .40 |
| **209** | A84 | 10p dk purple ('40) | .90 | .25 |
| | | *Nos. 198-209 (12)* | 5.35 | 4.50 |

See Nos. 217-227. For surcharge and overprints see Nos. 253, O41-O66, O70-O71.

Map of the Americas — A89

**Unwmk.**

**1940, Sept. 11** **Litho.** ***Perf. 14***

| | | | | |
|---|---|---|---|---|
| **210** | A89 | 40c dl grn & yel grn | .60 | .40 |

Pan American Union, 50th anniversary.

Camilo Henríquez — A90

Founding of Santiago A93

Designs: 40c, Pedro de Valdivia. 1.10p, Benjamin Vicuna Mackenna. 3.60p, Diego Barros Arana.

*Perf. 14½x14, 14½*

**1941, Jan. 23 Engr. Wmk. 215**

**211** A90 10c carmine lake .40 .40
**212** A90 40c green .65 .40
**213** A90 1.10p red 2.25 .75
**214** A93 1.80p blue 2.25 .75
**215** A90 3.60p indigo 6.75 2.75
*Nos. 211-215 (5)* 12.30 5.05

400th anniversary of Santiago.

**Types of 1938**

*Perf. 13½x14*

**1942-46 Unwmk. Litho.**

**217** A78 10c sal pink ('43) .25 .40
**218** A78 15c brown org ('43) .25 .40
**219** A78 20c lt blue ('43) .25 .40
**220** A78 30c brt pink ('43) .25 .40
**221** A78 40c yellow grn .80 .40
**222** A78 50c violet ('43) .25 .40

**Engr.** ***Perf. 14***

**223** A84 1p brown orange 1.50 .40
**225** A84 2p car lake ('43) .25 .40
**226** A84 5p dk sl grn ('43) .50 .40
**227** A84 10p rose violet ('46) .90 .40
*Nos. 217-227 (10)* 5.20 4.00

Valentin Letelier A95

University of Chile A98

Designs: 40c, Andrés Bello. 90c, Manuel Bulnes. 1.80p, Manuel Montt.

**1942, Nov. 1** ***Perf. 14x14½, 14 (1p)***

**228** A95 30c rose red .25 .25
**229** A95 40c deep green .25 .25
**230** A95 90c rose violet 1.90 1.50
**231** A98 1p deep brown 1.10 .90
**232** A95 1.80p dark blue 3.50 3.00
*Nos. 228-232 (5)* 7.00 5.90

University of Chile cent. See No. C89.

Manuel Bulnes A100

Map Showing Strait of Magellan A104

Designs: 30c, Juan Williams Wilson. 40c, Diego Duble Almeida. 1p, José Mardones.

**1944, Mar. 2 Litho.** ***Perf. 14***

**233** A100 15c black .25 .25
**234** A100 30c deep rose .25 .25
**235** A100 40c yellow green .25 .25
**236** A100 1p brown carmine .95 .50
**237** A104 1.80p ultra 1.40 1.25
*Nos. 233-237 (5)* 3.10 2.50

100th anniversary of the occupation of the Strait of Magellan.

Red Cross and Lamp of Life — A105

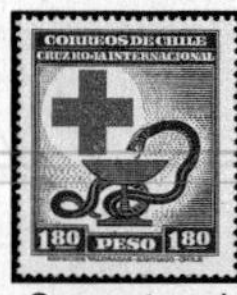

Serpent and Cup — A106

**1944, Oct. 18 Unwmk.**

**238** A105 40c green, red & blk .30 .30
**239** A106 1.80p ultra & red .90 .55

80th anniv. of the Intl. Red Cross Soc.

Bernardo O'Higgins A107

"Embrace of Maipú" (O'Higgins Joining San Martin) A108

Designs: 40c, Abdication of O'Higgins. 1.80p, Battle of Rancagua.

**1945 Engr.** ***Perf. 14 (15c), 14½***

**Center in Black**

**240** A107 15c carmine .30 .35
**241** A108 30c brown .30 .35
**242** A108 40c deep green .40 .35
**243** A108 1.80p dark blue 1.50 .95
*Nos. 240-243 (4)* 2.50 2.00

Death of Bernardo O'Higgins in 1842, cent.

A111

Proposed Columbus lighthouse.

**Wmk. 215**

**1945, Sept. 10 Litho.** ***Perf. 14***

**244** A111 40c light green .50 .40

Issued in honor of the discovery of America by Columbus and the Memorial Lighthouse to be erected in his memory.

A112

**1946 Engr.**

**245** A112 40c dark green .40 .40
**246** A112 1.80p dark blue .40 .40

80th anniv. of the death of Andrés Bello, poet and educator.

Map Showing Chile's Claims of Antarctic Territory — A113

**1947, May 12 Litho.** ***Perf. 14½***

**247** A113 40c carmine 1.00 .30
**248** A113 2.50p deep blue 2.00 .50

Eusebio Lillo and Ramon Carnicer A114

**1947, Sept. 18 Engr.**

**249** A114 40c dark green .40 .40

Centenary of national anthem.

Miguel de Cervantes Saavedra — A115

**1947, Oct. 11 Wmk. 215**

**250** A115 40c dk carmine .40 .40

400th anniv. of the birth of Cervantes, novelist, playwright and poet.

Arturo Prat Chacón and Iquique Naval Battle — A116

**1948, Dec. 24** ***Perf. 14½***

**251** A116 40c deep blue .40 .40

Centenary of the birth of Arturo Prat Chacon, Chilean naval hero.

Bernardo O'Higgins — A117

*Perf. 13½x14*

**1948 Wmk. 215 Litho.**

**252** A117 60c black .30 .40

See No. 262. For surcharges see Nos. 266-267.

No. 203 Surcharged in Black

**1948**

**253** A78 20c on 40c lt grn .40 .40

Chilean Pigeons — A118

FAUNA: a, Chilean Otter. b, tree. d, American skunk. f, Southern sea lions. g, Sugarcane borer moth. h, Emperor penguins. i, Bat. j, Chinchilla. k, Grant's stag beetle. l, Trevally (fish). m, Chilean slender lizard. o, Crested caracara. q, Red-gartered coot. r, Chilean guemal (deer). s, Spiny rock lobster. u, Tilefish. v, Praying mantis. x, Torrent duck. y, Red conger.

FLORA: b, Araucarian pine (monkey puzzle tree). e, Evening primrose. n, Chilean red bell flower. p, Loxodon (flower). t, Boldo tree. w, Coquito palm trees.

**Wmk. 215**

**1948, Dec. 6 Litho.** ***Perf. 14***

**254** 60c Block of 25 45.00 45.00
*a.-y.* A118 any single 1.00 .80
**255** 2.60p Block of 25 70.00 70.00
*a.-y.* A118 any single 1.75 1.25

Issued in panes of 100.

Cent. (in 1944) of the publication of the 1st volume of Claudio Gay's Natural History of Chile. See No. C124.

**Catalogue values for unused stamps in this section, from this point to the end of the section, are for Never Hinged items.**

Benjamin Vicuna Mackenna — A121

**1949, Mar. 22 Engr.** ***Perf. 13½x14***

**257** A121 60c deep blue .30 .25

See No. C126.

Symbols of Arts and Crafts Education — A122

Design: 2.60p, Badge and book.

**Unwmk.**

**1949, Nov. 11 Litho.** ***Perf. 14***

**258** A122 60c lilac rose .25 .25
**259** A122 2.60p violet blue .40 .30
*Nos. 258-259,C127-C128 (4)* 3.15 1.55

Cent. of the foundation of Chile's School of Arts and Crafts.

Heinrich von Stephan — A123

**1950, Jan. 6 Engr.**

**260** A123 60c deep carmine .25 .25
**261** A123 2.50p deep blue .75 .50
*Nos. 260-261,C129-C130 (4)* 3.00 2.15

UPU, 75th anniv.

**O'Higgins Type of 1948**

**1950 Litho.** ***Perf. 13x14***

**262** A117 60c black .40 .40

For surcharge see No. 266.

San Martín — A124

**Wmk. 215**

**1951, Mar. 16 Engr.** ***Perf. 14***

**263** A124 60c deep blue .40 .25

Cent. of the death of Gen. José de San Martin. See No. C165.

Isabella I — A125

**1952, Mar. 20**

**264** A125 60c brt blue .50 .25

500th anniv. of the birth of Queen Isabella I of Spain. See No. C166.

Bernardo O'Higgins — A126

**1952 Unwmk. Litho.** ***Perf. 13½x14***

**265** A126 1p dk blue grn .65 .40

See No. 275. For overprints see Nos. O67-O69.

No. 262 Surcharged in Red, Numbers & Letters Thicker

No. 252 Surcharged in Red, Numbers & Letters Thinner

**1952, Sept.**

| | | | |
|---|---|---|---|
| **266** | A117 | 40c on 60c black | .65 .40 |

**Wmk. 215**

| | | | |
|---|---|---|---|
| **267** | A117 | 40c on 60c black | .65 .40 |

Mateo de Toro Zambrano — A127

**1953, Mar. 13 Wmk. 215**

| | | | |
|---|---|---|---|
| **268** | A127 | 80c green | .65 .40 |

See No. 285.

Valdivia Arms — A128

Old Fort — A129

3p, Modern Valdivia. 5p, Street in ancient Valdivia.

**1953, May** ***Perf. 14***

| | | | | |
|---|---|---|---|---|
| **269** | A128 | 1p brt ultra | .65 | .30 |
| **270** | A129 | 2p dull rose vio | .65 | .30 |
| **271** | A129 | 3p blue green | .95 | .30 |
| **272** | A129 | 5p deep brown | .95 | .30 |
| | | *Nos. 269-272,C167 (5)* | 5.95 | 2.00 |

4th centenary of the founding of Valdivia, capital of Valdivia province.

José Toribio Medina (1852-1930), Historian and Bibliographer A130

**1953, June Engr.** ***Perf. 14½***

| | | | | |
|---|---|---|---|---|
| **273** | A130 | 1p brown | .50 | .40 |
| **274** | A130 | 2.50p deep blue | .70 | .40 |

**O'Higgins Type of 1952**

***Perf. 13½x14***

**1953, Oct. Wmk. 215 Litho.**

| | | | | |
|---|---|---|---|---|
| **275** | A126 | 1p dk blue green | .65 | .40 |

For overprint see No. O69.

Stamp of 1853 — A131

**1953, Oct. 15 Engr.** ***Perf. 14½***

| | | | | |
|---|---|---|---|---|
| **276** | A131 | 1p reddish brn | 1.00 | .30 |

Centenary of Chile's first postage stamps.
Souvenir sheet including No. 276 is noted below No. C168.

A132

Census chart and map.

**1953, Nov. 5 Litho.** ***Perf. 13½x14***

| | | | | |
|---|---|---|---|---|
| **277** | A132 | 1p blue green | .50 | .30 |
| **278** | A132 | 2.50p violet blue | .50 | .30 |
| **279** | A132 | 3p chocolate | .80 | .50 |
| **280** | A132 | 4p carmine | .80 | .50 |
| | | *Nos. 277-280 (4)* | 2.60 | 1.60 |

12th general census of population and housing.

Arms of Angol — A133

**1954, May 28 Unwmk.** ***Perf. 14***

| | | | | |
|---|---|---|---|---|
| **281** | A133 | 2p deep carmine | .65 | .40 |

400th anniversary of the founding of Angol, capital of Malleco province.

Ignacio Domeyko — A134

**1954, Aug. 16 Engr.** ***Perf. 13½x14***

| | | | | |
|---|---|---|---|---|
| **282** | A134 | 1p blue slate | .70 | .40 |

150th anniversary of the birth of Ignacio Domeyko (1802-89), mineralogist and educator. See No. C171.

Early Steam Locomotive A135

**1954, Sept. 10 Wmk. 215** ***Perf. 14½***

| | | | | |
|---|---|---|---|---|
| **283** | A135 | 1p red | .75 | .40 |

Centenary (in 1951) of the first South American railroad. See No. C172.

Adm. Arturo Prat Chacón — A136

**1954 Unwmk. Litho.** ***Perf. 14***

| | | | | |
|---|---|---|---|---|
| **284** | A136 | 2p dk violet blue | .65 | .40 |

75th anniv. of the naval Battle of Iquique.

**Toro Zambrano Type of 1953**

**1954, Nov. 6** ***Perf. 13½x14***

| | | | | |
|---|---|---|---|---|
| **285** | A127 | 80c green | .65 | .40 |

Arms of Viña del Mar — A137

Design: 2p, Arms of Valparaiso.

**1955, Mar. 5 Wmk. 215** ***Perf. 14***

| | | | | |
|---|---|---|---|---|
| **286** | A137 | 1p violet blue | .65 | .40 |
| **287** | A137 | 2p carmine | .65 | .40 |

1st Intl. Phil. Exhib., Valparaiso, Mar. 1955.

Dr. Alejandro del Rio — A138

**1955, May 24** ***Perf. 13½x14***

| | | | | |
|---|---|---|---|---|
| **288** | A138 | 2p violet blue | .65 | .40 |

14th Pan-American Sanitary Conference.

Christ of the Andes, Emblems of Chile, Argentina — A139

**1955, Aug. 31 Unwmk.** ***Perf. 14½***

| | | | | |
|---|---|---|---|---|
| **289** | A139 | 1p violet blue | .50 | .25 |

Reciprocal visits of Presidents Juan D. Peron and Carlos Ibanez del Campo. See No. C173.

Manuel Rengifo — A140

5p, Mariano Egana. 50p, Diego Portales.

**1955-56 Unwmk.** ***Perf. 14x14½***

| | | | | |
|---|---|---|---|---|
| **290** | A140 | 3p violet blue | .45 | .30 |
| **291** | A140 | 5p dk car rose | .45 | .30 |
| **292** | A140 | 50p rose lilac ('56) | 2.25 | .90 |
| | | *Nos. 290-292 (3)* | 3.15 | 1.50 |

Joaquin Prieto (1786-1854), soldier and political leader; president, 1831-41. See No. QRA1.

Jose M. Carrera A141

Ramón Freire A142

Portraits: 5p, Manuel Bulnes. 10p, Pres. Francisco A. Pinto. 50p, Manuel Montt.

***Perf. 14x14½***

**1956-58 Unwmk. Litho.**

| | | | | |
|---|---|---|---|---|
| **293** | A141 | 2p purple | .60 | .40 |
| **293A** | A142 | 3p lt violet blue | .50 | .40 |
| **294** | A141 | 5p redsh brn (19½x23mm) | .60 | .40 |
| *a.* | | Size 19x22mm | .60 | .40 |
| **295** | A142 | 10p vio (19x22¼mm) | .60 | .40 |
| *a.* | | Perf. 13½x14 (19¼x22½mm) ('58) | 1.00 | .40 |
| **296** | A141 | 50p rose red | 1.00 | .40 |
| | | *Nos. 293-296 (5)* | 3.30 | 2.00 |

**Wmk. 215**

| | | | | |
|---|---|---|---|---|
| **297** | A141 | 2p dull purple | .65 | .40 |
| **298** | A142 | 3p violet blue | .65 | .40 |

No. 294 has yellow gum; No. 294a, white gum.
For overprints see Nos. O72-O76.

Federico Santa Maria — A143

**Unwmk.**

**1957, Jan. 31 Engr.** ***Perf. 14***

| | | | | |
|---|---|---|---|---|
| **299** | A143 | 5p dk red brown | .40 | .25 |

25th anniv. of the Federico Santa Maria Technical University. See Nos. C190-C191.
Souvenir sheet including No. 299 is noted below No. C191.

Gabriela Mistral — A144

**1958, Jan. 10**

| | | | | |
|---|---|---|---|---|
| **300** | A144 | 10p red brown | .90 | .40 |

Issued in honor of Gabriela Mistral, poet and educator. See No. C192.

Arms of Osorno — A145

Design: 50p, Garcia Hdo. de Mendoza.

**1958, Mar. 23 Litho.** ***Perf. 14***

| | | | | |
|---|---|---|---|---|
| **301** | A145 | 10p carmine | .45 | .40 |

**Engr.**

| | | | | |
|---|---|---|---|---|
| **302** | A145 | 50p green | .80 | .40 |

400th anniversary of the founding of the city of Osorno, capital of Osorno province.
Souvenir sheet including No. 302 in red brown is noted below No. C193.

Arms of Santiago — A146

**1958, Oct. 18 Unwmk.** ***Perf. 14***

| | | | | |
|---|---|---|---|---|
| **303** | A146 | 10p dark violet | .50 | .30 |

Natl. Philatelic Exposition, Santiago, Oct. 18-26.
Souvenir sheet including No. 303 in deep red is noted below No. C194.

Symbolical Savings Bank — A147

**1958, Dec. 18**

| | | | | |
|---|---|---|---|---|
| **304** | A147 | 10p dark blue | .80 | .30 |

Savings Bank for Public Employees, cent.
Souvenir sheet including No. 304 in violet is noted below No. C195.

Modern Map of Antarctica — A148

**1958, Aug. 28 Unwmk.** ***Perf. 14***

| | | | | |
|---|---|---|---|---|
| **305** | A148 | 40p rose carmine | .80 | .60 |

IGY, 1957-1958. See No. C214.

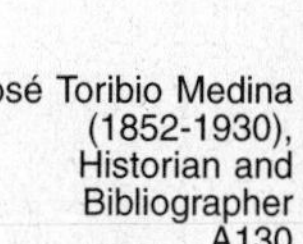


Antarctic Map and "La Araucana" A149

Map of Strait of Magellan, 1588 A150

**1958 Litho.** ***Perf. 14***

| | | | | |
|---|---|---|---|---|
| **310** | A149 | 10p violet blue | 1.10 | .25 |

**Engr.**

| | | | | |
|---|---|---|---|---|
| **311** | A150 | 200p dull purple | 3.25 | 1.75 |
| | | *Nos. 310-311,C199-C200 (4)* | 10.95 | 4.00 |

For overprint see No. O77.

Valdivia River Bridge — A153

**1959, Feb. 9 Engr.** ***Perf. 14***

| | | | | |
|---|---|---|---|---|
| **319** | A153 | 40p green | 1.10 | .50 |

Cent. of the German School in Valdivia and to publicize the Valdivia Phil. Exhib., 2/9-18.
Souvenir sheet including No. 319 is noted below No. C213.

Strait of Magellan, Map by Pedro Sarmiento de Gamboa, c. 1582 — A154

**1959, Aug. 27** **Litho.**
**320** A154 10p dull purple .65 .40

Juan Ladrillero expedition to explore the Strait of Magellan, 1557-58, 400th anniv. See No. C215.

Diego Barros Arana — A155

**1959, Aug. 27**
**321** A155 40p ultra .65 .40

50th anniv. of the death of Diego Barros Arana (1830-1907), historian. See No. C216.

Henri Dunant — A156

**1959, Oct. 6** **Unwmk.** ***Perf. 14***
**322** A156 20p red & red brn .65 .40

Cent. of the Red Cross idea. See No. C217.

Manuel Bulnes A157

Francisco A. Pinto A158

Choshuenco Volcano — A159

No. 326, Choshuenco volcano, redrawn. 5c, Manuel Montt. 10c, Maule River Valley. 20c, 1e, Inca Lake.

**1960-67** **Litho.** ***Perf. 13x14***
**323** A157 5m bluish grn .45 .40
**324** A158 1c carmine .45 .40

***Perf. 14***

**Size: 29x25mm**

**325** A159 2c ultra ('61) .45 .40

***Perf. 14x13***

**Size: 23½x18mm**

**326** A159 2c ultra ('62) .45 .40

***Perf. 13x14***

**327** A157 5c blue .45 .40

***Perf. 14***

**Size: 29x25mm**

**328** A159 10c green ('62) .45 .40
**329** A159 20c Prus blue ('62) .60 .40
**329A** A159 1e grnsh bl ('67) 1.10 .40
*Nos. 323-329A (8)* 4.40 3.20

On No. 325 "Volcan Choshuenco" is at upper left, below "Correos." On No. 326, it is at bottom, above "Centesimos."

For overprint and surcharge see Nos. B7, O79, RA1.

Refugee Family — A160

**1960, Apr. 7** ***Perf. 14½***
**330** A160 1c green .60 .40

WRY, July 1, 1959-June 30, 1960. A souvenir sheet is noted below No. C218.

**Type of Air Post Issue, 1962, and**

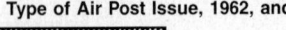

Arms of Chile — A161

José M. Carrera — A162

No. 332, Palace of Justice. 5c, Natl. Memorial. 10c, Manuel de Toro y Zambrano and Martinez de Rozas. 20c, Manuel de Salas and Juan Egana. 50c, Manuel Rodriguez and Juan Mackenna.

**Wmk. 215 (#331, 1e); Unwmk.**

**1960-65** **Engr.** ***Perf. 14½***
**331** A161 1c maroon & sepia .55 .30
**332** A161 1c brn & claret ('62) .55 .30
**333** A162 5c grn & Prus grn ('61) .55 .30
**334** AP54 10c brn & vio brn ('64) .90 .30
**334A** AP54 20c ind & bl grn ('65) .90 .30
**335** AP54 50c red brn & mar ('65) 1.40 .30
**336** A162 1e gray ol & brn 2.75 .50
*Nos. 331-336,C218A-C220D (14)* 13.60 4.60

150th anniv. of the formation of the 1st Natl. Government. A souvenir sheet is noted below No. C220B. See No. C285.

Family — A163

Design: 10c, Various buildings.

**Unwmk.**

**1960, Jan. 18** **Litho.** ***Perf. 14***
**337** A163 5c green .65 .40
**338** A163 10c brt violet .65 .40

13th population census (No. 337) and 2nd housing census (No. 338).

Chamber of Deputies A164

**1961, Aug. 14** **Unwmk.** ***Perf. 14½***
**339** A164 2c red brown .85 .25

150th anniv. of the 1st National Congress. See No. C245.

Soccer Players and Globe — A165

Design: 5c, Goalkeeper and stadium, vert.

**1962, May 30** **Engr.** ***Perf. 14½***
**340** A165 2c blue .75 .40
**341** A165 5c green 1.00 .40

World Soccer Championship, Chile, May 30-June 17. Note on souvenir sheet follows No. C247.

Mother and Child — A166

**1963, Mar. 21** **Litho.** ***Perf. 14***
**342** A166 3c maroon .70 .40

FAO "Freedom from Hunger" campaign. See No. C248.

Centenary Emblem — A167

**1963, Aug. 23** **Unwmk.** ***Perf. 14***
**343** A167 3c red & gray .70 .40

Cent. of the Intl. Red Cross. See No. C249.

Fireman Carrying Woman — A168

**1963, Dec. 20** **Unwmk.** ***Perf. 14***
**344** A168 3c violet .60 .40

Centenary of the Santiago Fire Brigade. See No. C250.

Enrique Molina — A169

Design: No. 346, Magr. Carlos Casanueva.

**1964, Nov. 14** **Litho.** ***Perf. 14***
**345** A169 4c bister brown .60 .40
**346** A169 4c rose claret .60 .40
*Nos. 345-346,C257-C258 (4)* 2.60 1.60

Enrique Molina, founder of the University of Concepcion, and Msgr. Carlos Casanueva, rector of the Catholic University, 1920-53.

Easter Island Statue A170

Copihue, National Flower A171

Design: 30c, Robinson Crusoe.

**1965-69** **Litho.** ***Perf. 14x14½***
**347** A170 6c rose lilac 1.75 .40
**347A** A170 10c rose pink ('68) .65 .40

***Perf. 14***

**348** A171 15c yel grn & rose red 1.25 .40
**348A** A171 20c yel grn & rose red ('69) .65 .40

***Perf. 14x14½***

**349** A170 30c rose claret .95 .40
*Nos. 347-349 (5)* 5.25 2.00

For surcharge see No. RA2.

Skier — A172

**1965, Aug. 30** ***Perf. 14***
**350** A172 4c blue green .65 .40

World Skiing Championships, Chile, 1966.

Lorenzo Sazie — A173

**1966, Feb. 9** **Litho.** ***Perf. 14x14½***
**351** A173 1e green 1.75 .40

Cent. of the death of Dr. Lorenzo Sazie, dean of the Faculty of Medicine, University of Santiago.

German Riesco, President in 1901-1906 — A174

Portrait: 30c, Jorge Montt (1847-1922), president in 1891-1896.

**1966** **Unwmk.** ***Perf. 13x14***
**354** A174 30c violet .60 .40
**355** A174 50c dull brown .70 .40

For surcharge see No. 450.

William Wheelwright and S.S. Chile — A175

**1966, Aug. 2** ***Perf. 14½***
**358** A175 10c ultra & lt bl .65 .40

125th anniv. (in 1965) of the arrival of the paddle steamers "Chile" and "Peru." See No. C268.

Learning to Read — A176

**1966, Aug. 13** **Litho.** ***Perf. 14***
**359** A176 10c red brown .65 .40

Literacy campaign.

UN and ICY Emblems A177

**1966, Oct. 28** **Unwmk.** ***Perf. 14½***
**360** A177 1e green & brown 1.75 .40

Intl. Cooperation Year, 1965. See No. C269.

Capt. Luis Pardo and Ship in Antarctica A178

**1967, Jan. Litho. *Perf. 14½***
**361** A178 20c turquoise blue 1.75 .40

Rescue of the Shackleton South Pole expedition by Capt. Luis Pardo of Chile, 50th anniv. See No. C271.

Family — A179

**1967, Apr. 13 Unwmk. *Perf. 14***
**362** A179 10c magenta & blk .65 .40

8th Intl. Conf. for Family Planning, Santiago, Apr. 1967. See No. C272.

Trees and Mountains — A180

**1967, June 9 Litho. *Perf. 14½***
**363** A180 10c blue grn & lt bl .95 .40

Reforestation Campaign. See No. C274.

Lions Emblem — A181

**1967, July 12 Litho. *Perf. 14***
**364** A181 20c Prus blue & yel .50 .40
*Nos. 364,C275-C276 (3)* 2.55 1.20

50th anniv. of Lions Intl.

Chilean Flag — A182

**1967, Oct. 20 Unwmk. *Perf. 14½***
**365** A182 80c crimson & ultra .90 .25

Natl, flag, 150th anniv. See No. C277.

José Maria Cardinal Caro — A183

**1967, Dec. 4 Engr. *Perf. 14½***
**366** A183 20c deep carmine .75 .40

Cent. of the birth of José Maria Cardinal Caro, the first Chilean cardinal. See No. C279.

San Martin and O'Higgins A184

**1968, Apr. 23 Litho. Unwmk.**
**367** A184 3e blue .90 .40

Sesquicentennial of the Battles of Chacabuco and Maipu. See No. C280.

Farm Couple — A185

**1968, June 18 *Perf. 14½***
**368** A185 20c black, org & grn 1.10 .40

Agrarian reforms. See No. C281.

Juan I. Molina — A186

**1968, Aug. 27 Litho. *Perf. 14½***
**369** A186 2e red lilac .90 .40

Issued to honor Juan I. Molina, educator and scientist. See No. C282.

Hand Holding Cogwheel — A187

**1968, Sept. *Perf. 14x14½***
**370** A187 30c deep carmine .65 .40

Fourth census of manufacturers.

Map of Chiloé Province, Sailing Ship and Coastal Vessel — A188

**1968, Oct. 7 *Perf. 14½***
**371** A188 30c ultra .70 .40

Anniversaries of the founding of five towns in Chiloé Province. See No. C283.

Automobile Club Emblem — A189

**1968, Nov. 10 Engr. *Perf. 14½x14***
**372** A189 1e carmine rose .65 .40

40th anniversary of the Automobile Club of Chile. See No. C284.

Francisco Garcia Huidobro A190

Design: 5e, King Philip V of Spain.

**1968, Dec. 31 Litho. *Perf. 14½***
**373** A190 2e pale rose & ultra .75 .40
**374** A190 5e brown & yel grn .75 .40
*Nos. 373-374,C288-C289 (4)* 2.60 1.60

225th anniv. of the founding of the State Mint (Casa de Moneda de Chile).

Satellite and Radar Station — A191

**1969, May 20 Litho. *Perf. 14½***
**375** A191 30c blue .65 .40

Inauguration of ENTEL-Chile, the 1st commercial satellite communications ground station, Longovilo.

See No. C290. For surcharges see Nos. 397, C308.

Red Cross, Crescent and Lion and Sun Emblems A192

**1969, Sept. Litho. *Perf. 14½***
**376** A192 2e violet blue & red .65 .40

50th anniversary of the League of Red Cross Societies. See No. C291.

Rapel Hydroelectric Plant — A193

**1969, Nov. 18 Litho. *Perf. 14½***
**377** A193 40c green .50 .40

See No. C292. For surcharge see No. B8.

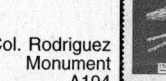

Col. Rodriguez Monument A194

**1969, Nov. 24**
**378** A194 2e rose claret .60 .40

150th anniversary of the death of Col. Manuel Rodriguez. See No. C293.

EXPO '70 Emblem — A195

**1969, Dec. 2 Litho. *Perf. 14***
**379** A195 3e blue .55 .25

EXPO '70 Intl. Exhibition, Osaka, Japan, Mar. 15-Sept. 13, 1970. See No. C294.

Open Book — A196

**1969, Dec. 3 *Perf. 14½***
**380** A196 40c red brown .65 .40

Translation of the Bible into Spanish by Casiodoro de Reina, 400th anniv. See No. C295. For surcharge see No. B10.

Globes and ILO Emblem — A197

**1969, Dec. 17 *Perf. 14½***
**381** A197 1e green & blk .70 .40

ILO, 50th anniv. See No. C296.

Human Rights Flame — A198

**1969, Dec. 18**
**382** A198 4e blue & red .85 .40

Human Rights Year, 1968. See No. C297.

Policarpo Toro and Easter Island — A199

**1970, Jan. 26 *Perf. 14½***
**383** A199 5e lilac 1.50 .45

80th anniversary of the acquisition of Easter Island. See No. C298.

Sailing Ship and Arms of Valdivia — A200

**1970, Feb. 4 Litho. *Perf. 14½***
**384** A200 40c dk carmine .70 .40

150th anniv. of the capture of Valdivia during Chile's war of independence by Thomas Cochrane (1775-1860), naval commander. See No. C299.

Paul Harris and Rotary Emblem — A201

**1970, Mar. 18 Litho. *Perf. 14***
**385** A201 10e violet blue .70 .40

Cent. of the birth of Paul Harris (1868-1947), founder of Rotary Intl. See No. C300.

Mahatma Gandhi — A202

**1970, Apr. 1 Litho. *Perf. 14½***
**386** A202 40c blue green 3.75 .40

Mohandas K. Gandhi (1869-1948), leader in India's fight for independence, birth cent. See No. C301. For surcharge see No. 449.

Santo Domingo Church, Santiago, Chile — A203

Designs: 2e, Casa de Moneda de Chile, horiz. 3e, Pedro de Valdivia. 5e, Bridge, horiz. 10e, Ambrosio O'Higgins.

**1970, Apr. 30 Engr.**
**387** A203 2e violet brown .75 .40
**388** A203 3e dark red .75 .40
**389** A203 4e dark blue .55 .40
**390** A203 5e brown .55 .40
**391** A203 10e green .55 .40
*Nos. 387-391 (5)* 3.15 2.00

Exploration and development of Chile by Spanish explorers.

A sheet containing imperf examples of Nos. 388, 390 and 391 exists. It was not valid for postage. Size:109x140mm, value $11.

Education Year Emblem — A204

**1970, July 17 Litho. *Perf. 14½***

**392** A204 2e claret .65 .40

International Education Year. See No. C302.

Virgin and Child — A205

**1970, July 28**

**393** A205 40c green .65 .40

O'Higgins National Shrine at Maipu. See No. C303. For surcharge see No. 454.

Torch and Snake — A206

**1970, Aug. 11**

**394** A206 40c claret & light blue .90 .40

International Cancer Congress, Houston, Texas, May 22-29. See No. C304.

Copper Symbol, Chile Arms — A207

**1970, Oct. 21 Litho. *Perf. 14½***

**395** A207 40c car & lt red brn .55 .40

Nationalization of the copper industry. See No. C305. For surcharges see Nos. 459, B9.

Dove and World Map — A208

**1970, Oct. 22**

**396** A208 3e rose mag & dp pur .65 .40

25th anniv. of the UN. See No. C306.

**No. 375 Surcharged in Red**

**1970, Dec. 24 Litho. *Perf. 14½***

**397** A191 52c on 30c blue .65 .40

Freighter and Ship's Wheel — A209

**1971, Jan. 18 Litho. *Perf. 14***

**398** A209 52c deep carmine .65 .40

Natl. Maritime Commission. See No. C307.

Bernardo O'Higgins and Ship — A210

**1971, Feb. 3 *Perf. 14½***

**399** A210 5e lt blue and blue grn 1.10 .40

150th anniv. of the expedition to liberate Peru from Spanish rule. See No. C309.

An imperforate souvenir sheet containing Nos. 399, C280, and C303 exists. Size: 120x150mm.

Youth, Girl and UN Emblem A211

**1971, Feb. 11 Litho. *Perf. 14½***

**400** A211 52c dk blue & brn .70 .40

1st meeting in Latin America of the Executive Council of UNICEF, Santiago, May 20-31, 1969. See No. C310.

Chilean Boy Scout Emblem — A212

**1971, Feb. 10 *Perf. 14***

**401** A212 1e green & brn .70 .40

Founding of Chilean Boy Scouts, 60th anniversary. See No. C311.

Satellite and Radar Station — A213

**1971, May 25 Litho. *Perf. 14½***

**402** A213 40c dull green .75 .65

First commercial Chilean satellite communications ground station, Longovilo. See No. C312.

Diver with Harpoon Gun — A214

**1971, Sept. 1**

**403** A214 1.15e lt & dk green 1.40 .40
**404** A214 2.35e vio bl & dp vio bl .60 .40

10th World Championship of Underwater Fishing.

Ferdinand Magellan and Sailing Ship — A215

**1971, Nov. 3**

**405** A215 35c lt vio & brn vio .65 .40

450th anniv. of 1st trip through and discovery of the Strait of Magellan, Oct. 21-Nov. 28, 1520.

Dagoberto Godoy and Plane over Andes — A216

**1971, Nov. 4**

**406** A216 1.15e blue & grn .65 .40

First trans-Andean flight, Dec. 12, 1918.

Virgin of San Cristobal A217

Chilean Flag and Congress Emblem A218

Congress Emblem and: 4.35e, Church of San Francisco. 9.35e, Central post office, horiz. 18.35e, La Posada (Inn) del Corregidor, horiz.

**1971**

**407** A217 1.15e dk blue .80 .40
**408** A218 2.35e ultra & car .80 .40
**409** A217 4.35e brown red .80 .40
**410** A217 9.35e violet .80 .40
**411** A217 18.35e lilac rose 1.50 .40
*Nos. 407-411 (5)* 4.70 2.00

10th Cong. of the Postal Union of the Americas and Spain, Santiago.

An imperf souvenir sheet containing Nos. 407-411 was not valid for postage. Value $11.50.

Issued: 2.35e, 4.35e, Nov. 5; 1.15e, Nov. 11; 9.35e, Nov. 18; 18.35e, Nov. 19.

Observation Dome, Cerro el Tololo Observatory A219

**1971, Dec. 18**

**412** A219 1.95e lt & dk blue .65 .40

Boeing 707 over Easter Island — A220

**1971, Dec. 18**

**413** A220 2.35e vio brn and ocher .70 .40

Inauguration of regular flights: Santiago, Easter Island, Tahiti.

Alonso de Ercilla y Zuniga — A221

**1972, Mar. 20 Engr. *Perf. 14***

**414** A221 1e dark red .85 .40

4th centenary (in 1969) of "La Araucana," by Alonso de Ercilla y Zuniga (1533-1596), Spanish author. See No. C313.

Map of Antarctica and Dog Sled — A222

**1972, Mar. 20 Litho. *Perf. 14½x15***

**415** A222 1.15e vio bl & blk .90 .40
**416** A222 3.50e blue grn & grn 1.40 .40

10th anniversary (in 1971) of the Antarctic Treaty pledging peaceful uses of and scientific cooperation in Antarctica.

For surcharge see No. 630.

"Your Heart is your Health" — A223

**1972, Apr. 2 Litho. *Perf. 14½***

**417** A223 1.15e black & car .65 .40

World Health Month.

For surcharge see No. 631.

People and Statement by Pres. Allende — A224

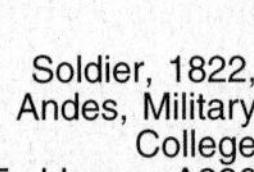

Conference Hall and UN Emblem A225

**1972, Apr. 13 Litho. *Perf. 14½***

**418** A224 35c dl grn & buff .50 .40
**419** A225 1.15e ultra & pur .60 .40
**420** A224 4e dk pur & pale rose .90 .40
**421** A225 6e orange & vio bl .75 .40
*Nos. 418-421 (4)* 2.75 1.60

3rd UN Conf. on Trade and Development (UNCTAD III), Santiago, Apr.-May 1972. Design A224 is perf. horiz. in the middle.

Soldier, 1822, Andes, Military College Emblem — A226

**1972, June 9**

**422** A226 1.15e blue & yel .65 .40

Sesquicentennial of Bernardo O'Higgins Military College.

Miner Holding Copper Ingot, Chilean Flag — A227

**1972, July 11 Litho. *Perf. 15x14½***

**423** A227 1.15e blue & rose red .60 .40
**424** A227 5e blue, blk & rose red .70 .40

Nationalization of copper industry.

An imperforate souvenir sheet exists of Nos. 423-424. Size:110x140mm. Value, $21.

Sailing Ship — A228

**1972, Aug. 4**

**425** A228 1.15e violet brown .80 .40

Arturo Pratt Naval Training School, sesqui.

Mt. Calan Observatory A229

**1972, Aug. 31 Litho. *Perf. 14½***
**426** A229 50c ultra .65 .40

University of Chile Mt. Calan Observatory.

Carrier Pigeon — A230

**1972, Oct. 9 Litho. *Perf. 14½***
**427** A230 1.15e red lilac & vio .65 .40

Intl. Letter Writing Week, Oct. 9-15.

René Schneider and Army Flag A231

**1972, Oct. 25 *Perf. 14***
**428** A231 2.30e multi .65 .40

2nd anniv. of the death of Gen. René Schneider. No. 428 is perforated vertically in the middle.

Book and Young People — A232

**1972, Oct. 31 *Perf. 14½***
**429** A232 50c black & dp org .65 .40

International Book Year 1972.

Guitar and Earthen Jar — A233

Designs: 2.65e, Fish and produce. 3.50e, Stove, pots and rug, vert.

**1972, Nov. 20 Litho. *Perf. 14½***
**430** A233 1.15e red & blk .70 .40
**431** A233 2.65e ultra & rose lake .85 .40
**432** A233 3.50e red & red brn .95 .40
*Nos. 430-432 (3)* 2.50 1.20

Tourism Year of the Americas.

José M. Carrera Before Execution — A234

**1973, Feb. 1 Litho. *Perf. 14½***
**433** A234 2.30e lt ultra .65 .40

Sesquicentennial of the death of José Miguel Carrera (1785-1821), Chilean revolutionist and dictator.

Map of Antarctica, Flag at Base — A235

**1973, Feb. 8**
**434** A235 10e ultra & red 1.75 .40

Bernardo O'Higgins Antarctic Base, 25th anniv.

Naval Air Service Emblem, Destroyer — A236

**1973, Mar. 16 Litho. *Perf. 14½***
**435** A236 20e brt bl & ocher .70 .40

Chilean Naval Aviation, 50th anniversary.

La Silla Observatory — A237

**1973, Apr. 25 Litho. *Perf. 14½***
**436** A237 2.30e ultra & blk .65 .40

INTERPOL Emblem — A238

Designs: 50e, Fingerprint over globe.

**1973, Sept. 23 Litho. *Perf. 14½***
**437** A238 30e bister & ultra 1.50 .75
**438** A238 50e black & red 1.20 .50

50th anniversary of International Criminal Police Organization.

Grapes — A239

Chilean wine export: 100e, Globe inscribed "Chile Exporta Vino."

**1973, Dec. 10 Litho. *Perf. 14½***
**439** A239 20e buff & lilac .90 .40
**440** A239 100e blue & claret 2.10 .40

UPU Headquarters, Bern — A240

**1974, Apr. 4**
**441** A240 500e on 45c green 1.00 .40

UPU cent. No. 441 was not issued without dark green surcharge and overprint.

No. 441 exists on an imperforate souvenir sheet. Size: 115x140mm. Value, $21.

Bernardo O'Higgins, Armed Forces Emblems A241

No. 443, Soldiers with mortar. No. 444, Navy anti-aircraft gunners. No. 445, Pilot in cockpit. No. 446, Mounted policeman.

**1974, Apr. 11 Litho. *Perf. 14½***
**442** A241 30e shown .65 .40
**443** A241 30e multicolored .65 .40
**444** A241 30e multicolored .65 .40
**445** A241 30e multicolored .65 .40
**446** A241 30e multicolored .65 .40
*Nos. 442-446 (5)* 3.25 2.00

Honoring the Armed Forces.

Soccer Ball and Globe — A242

1000e, Soccer ball and stadium, horiz.

**1974 Litho. *Perf. 14***
**447** A242 500e dk red & org .60 .40
**448** A242 1000e bl & indigo 1.75 .40

World Cup Soccer Championship, Munich, June 13-July 7.

A souvenir sheet contains 2 imperf. stamps similar to Nos. 447-448, with blue marginal inscription. Printed on thin card. Size: 90x119mm. Value, $15.

Nos. 386, 355 Surcharged

**1974, June Litho. *Perf. 14½***
**449** A202 100e on 40c bl grn .60 .40
***Perf. 13x14***
**450** A174 300e on 50c dl brn .70 .40

Traffic Police — A243

**1974, June 20 *Perf. 14½***
**451** A243 30e red brn & grn .65 .40

Traffic safety.

Santiago-Australia Air Service — A244

**1974, Sept. 5 Litho. *Perf. 14½x14***
**452** A244 Block of 4 7.00 4.00
*a.* 200e Easter Island turtle 1.00 .40
*b.* 200e Polynesian dancer 1.00 .40
*c.* 200e Map of Fiji Islands 1.00 .40
*d.* 200e Kangaroo 1.00 .40

Inauguration of air service by LAN (Chile's national airline) from Santiago to Easter Island, Tahiti, Fiji, Australia.

Globe Cut to Show Mantle and Core — A245

**1974, Sept. 9 *Perf. 14x14½***
**453** A245 500e red brn & org 1.75 1.50

International Volcanology Congress, Santiago, Sept. 9-14.

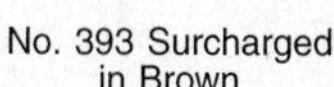

No. 393 Surcharged in Brown

**1974, Oct. 24 Litho. *Perf. 14½***
**454** A205 100e on 40c green .65 .40

Inauguration of the O'Higgins National Shrine at Maipu, Oct. 24, 1974.

Juan Fernandez Archipelago — A246

**1974, Nov. 22 Litho. *Perf. 14½x14***
**455** A246 Block of 4 9.00 3.00
*a.* 200e Robinson Crusoe Island 1.50 .40
*b.* 200e Chonta palms 1.50 .40
*c.* 200e Mountain goat 1.50 .40
*d.* 200e Spiny rock lobster 1.50 .40

400th anniversary of discovery of Juan Fernandez Archipelago.

O'Higgins and Bolivar — A247

**1974, Dec. 9 *Perf. 14½***
**456** A247 100e red brn & buff .65 .40

Sesquicentennial of the Battles of Junin and Ayacucho.

F. Vidal Gormaz and Institute Seal — A248

**1975, Jan. 22 Litho. *Perf. 14½***
**457** A248 100e rose claret & bl .65 .40

Centenary of the Naval Hydrographic Institute; F. Vidal Gormaz was first commandant.

Albert Schweitzer — A249

**1975, Apr. 7 Litho. *Perf. 14x14½***
**458** A249 500e yel & red brn .95 .40

Dr. Albert Schweitzer (1875-1965), medical missionary, birth centenary.

No. 395 Surcharged in Red

**1975, Apr. 7** ***Perf. 14½***

| | | | |
|---|---|---|---|
| **459** | A207 70e on 40c car & lt red brn | .65 | .40 |

Note: souvenir cards were issued by Chile starting in 1975 for various issues. They were printed on thin card. These are not souvenir sheets.

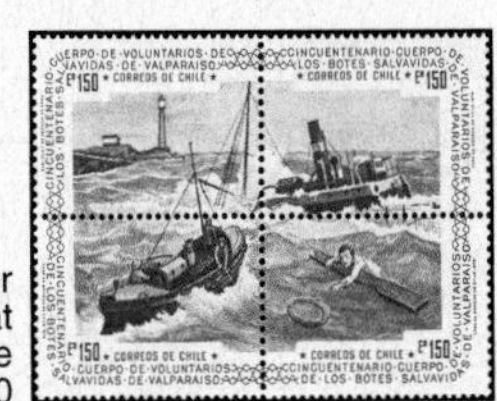

Volunteer Lifeboat Service A250

**1975, Apr. 15** **Litho.** ***Perf. 14½x14***

| | | | | |
|---|---|---|---|---|
| **460** | A250 | Block of 4 | 9.50 | 6.00 |
| *a.* | | 150e Lighthouse | 1.50 | .40 |
| *b.* | | 150e Shipwreck | 1.50 | .40 |
| *c.* | | 150e Lifeboat | 1.50 | .40 |
| *d.* | | 150e Sailor reaching for life preserver | 1.50 | .40 |

Valparaiso Volunteer Lifeboat service, 50th anniversary.

Frigate Lautaro — A251

No. 462, Corvette Baquedano. No. 463, Cruiser Chacabuco. No. 464, Brigantine Goleta Esmeralda.

**1975, May 21** **Photo. & Engr.**

| | | | | |
|---|---|---|---|---|
| **461** | A251 | 500e shown | .90 | .40 |
| **462** | A251 | 500e multi | .90 | .40 |
| **463** | A251 | 500e multi | .90 | .40 |
| **464** | A251 | 500e multi | .90 | .40 |
| *a.* | | Block of 4, #461-464 | 8.00 | 8.00 |
| **465** | A251 | 800e like #461 | 1.20 | .45 |
| **466** | A251 | 800e like #462 | 1.20 | .45 |
| **467** | A251 | 800e like #463 | 1.20 | .45 |
| **468** | A251 | 800e like #464 | 1.20 | .45 |
| *a.* | | Block of 4, #465-468 | 11.00 | 11.00 |
| **469** | A251 | 1000e like #461 | 1.75 | .60 |
| **470** | A251 | 1000e like #462 | 1.75 | .60 |
| **471** | A251 | 1000e like #463 | 1.75 | .60 |
| **472** | A251 | 1000e like #464 | 1.75 | .60 |
| *a.* | | Block of 4, #469-472 | 14.00 | 14.00 |
| | | *Nos. 461-472 (12)* | 15.40 | 5.80 |

Shipwreck of training frigate Lautaro, 30th anniversary. Se-tenant in sheets of 25 (5x5) with 7 Lautaro stamps and 6 each of the others.

Happy Mother, by Alfredo Valenzuela P. — A252

Paintings: No. 474, Young Girl, by Francisco Javier Mandiola. No. 475, Lucia Guzman, by Pedro Lira Rencoret. No. 476, Woman, by Magdalena Mira Mena.

**1975, Oct. 13** **Litho.** ***Perf. 14½***

| | | | |
|---|---|---|---|
| **473** | A252 50c multicolored | 1.10 | .40 |
| **474** | A252 50c multicolored | 1.10 | .40 |
| **475** | A252 50c multicolored | 1.10 | .40 |
| **476** | A252 50c multicolored | 1.10 | .40 |
| | *Nos. 473-476 (4)* | 4.40 | 1.60 |

International Women's Year 1975. Gray inscription on back, printed beneath gum, gives details about painting shown.

Diego Portales, Finance Minister — A253

**Inscribed: D. Portales**

**1975-78** **Litho.** ***Perf. 13½x14½***

| | | | | |
|---|---|---|---|---|
| **477** | A253 | 10c gray grn | .65 | .40 |
| **478** | A253 | 20c violet ('76) | .65 | .40 |
| **479** | A253 | 30c orange ('76) | .65 | .40 |
| **480** | A253 | 50c lt brown | .65 | .40 |
| **481** | A253 | 1p blue | .65 | .40 |
| **482** | A253 | 1.50p ocher ('76) | .65 | .40 |
| **483** | A253 | 2p gray ('77) | .65 | .40 |
| **483A** | A253 | 2.50p citron ('78) | .65 | .40 |
| **483B** | A253 | 3.50p pnksh rose ('78) | .75 | .40 |
| **484** | A253 | 5p rose claret | .75 | .40 |
| | | *Nos. 477-484 (10)* | 6.70 | 4.00 |

See Nos. 635-639. For surcharge see No. 533.

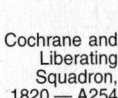

Cochrane and Liberating Squadron, 1820 — A254

No. 486, Capture of Valdivia, 1820. No. 487, Capture of Three-master Esmeralda, 1820. No. 488, Cruiser Cochrane, 1874. No. 489, Destroyer Cochrane, 1962.

**1976, Jan. 6** ***Perf. 14½***

| | | | |
|---|---|---|---|
| **485** | A254 1p multicolored | .85 | .40 |
| **486** | A254 1p multicolored | .85 | .40 |
| **487** | A254 1p multicolored | .85 | .40 |
| **488** | A254 1p multicolored | .85 | .40 |
| **489** | A254 1p multicolored | .85 | .40 |
| *a.* | Strip of 5, #485-489 | 5.25 | 5.25 |

Lord Thomas Cochrane, first commander of Chilean Navy, birth bicentenary.

Flags of Chile and Bolivia — A255

**1976, May 25** **Litho.** ***Perf. 14½***

| | | | |
|---|---|---|---|
| **490** | A255 1.50p multicolored | 2.50 | .50 |

Sesquicentennial of Bolivia's independence.

Lake of the Inca, OAS Emblem — A256

**1976, June 11**

| | | | |
|---|---|---|---|
| **491** | A256 1.50p multicolored | 1.60 | .40 |

6th General Assembly of the Organization of American States.

George Washington — A257

**1976, July 3**

| | | | |
|---|---|---|---|
| **492** | A257 5p multicolored | 1.50 | .40 |

American Bicentennial.

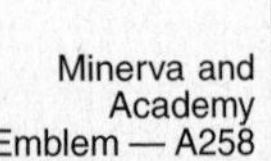

Minerva and Academy Emblem — A258

**1976, July**

| | | | |
|---|---|---|---|
| **493** | A258 2.50p multicolored | 1.75 | .40 |

Polytechnic Military Academy, 50th anniv.

Araucan Indian — A259

Designs: 2p, Condor with broken chain. 3p, Winged woman, symbolizing rebirth.

**1976, Sept. 20** **Litho.** ***Perf. 14½***

| | | | |
|---|---|---|---|
| **494** | A259 1p blue & multi | .40 | .30 |
| **495** | A259 2p blue & multi | 1.75 | .90 |
| **496** | A259 3p yellow & multi | .75 | .40 |
| *a.* | Strip of 3, #494-496 | 3.50 | 3.50 |

3rd anniversary of the Military Junta.

View, Antarctica A260

**1977, Feb. 10** **Litho.** ***Perf. 14½***

| | | | |
|---|---|---|---|
| **497** | A260 2p multicolored | 9.25 | 1.20 |

Visit of President Augusto Pinochet to Antarctica.

School Emblem, Planted Field — A261

**1977, Mar. 10** ***Perf. 14½***

| | | | |
|---|---|---|---|
| **498** | A261 2p multicolored | 1.75 | .40 |

Cent. of advanced agricultural education.

Justice — A262

**1977, Mar. 30** **Litho.** ***Perf. 14½***

| | | | |
|---|---|---|---|
| **499** | A262 2p brown & slate | 1.80 | .40 |

Supreme Court of Justice, sesquicentennial.

Eye with Globe, Caduceus A263

**1977, Mar. 30** **Litho.** ***Perf. 14½***

| | | | |
|---|---|---|---|
| **500** | A263 2p multicolored | 2.25 | .55 |

11th Pan-American Ophthalmological Cong.

Mounted Policeman — A264

Designs: No. 502, Policewoman with children. No. 503, Paine Peaks and Osorno Volcano, crossed rifle emblem. No. 504, Crossed rifle emblem, mounted and motorcycle policemen, helicopter and automobile, horiz.

**1977, Apr. 27**

| | | | |
|---|---|---|---|
| **501** | A264 2p multicolored | .70 | .40 |
| **502** | A264 2p multicolored | .70 | .40 |
| **503** | A264 2p multicolored | .70 | .40 |
| **504** | A264 2p multicolored | .70 | .40 |
| | *Nos. 501-504 (4)* | 2.80 | 1.60 |

Chilean police organization, 50th anniv.

Intelsat Satellite over Globe — A265

**1977, May 17** **Litho.** ***Perf. 14½***

| | | | |
|---|---|---|---|
| **505** | A265 2p multi | 1.75 | .50 |

World Telecommunications Day.

El Mercurio's First Front Page, Press and Ship — A266

**1977, July 5** **Litho.** ***Perf. 14½***

| | | | |
|---|---|---|---|
| **506** | A266 2p multi | .65 | .40 |

El Mercurio de Valparaiso, first Chilean newspaper, 150th anniversary.

St. Francis, Birds and Cross — A267

**1977, July 26** **Litho.** ***Perf. 14½***

| | | | |
|---|---|---|---|
| **507** | A267 5p multi | 2.00 | .40 |

St. Francis of Assisi, 750th death anniv.

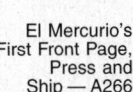

Science and Technology — A268

**1977, Aug. 26** **Litho.** ***Perf. 14½***

| | | | |
|---|---|---|---|
| **508** | A268 4p multi | .80 | .40 |

Young Mother Weaving — A269

No. 510, Handicapped boy in wheelchair & nurse. No. 511, Children dancing in circle. No. 512, Old man & home.

**1977, Sept. 13** **Litho.** ***Perf. 14½***

| | | | |
|---|---|---|---|
| **509** | A269 5p multi | .75 | .40 |
| **510** | A269 5p multi | .75 | .40 |
| **511** | A269 10p multi, horiz. | 1.60 | .40 |
| **512** | A269 10p multi, horiz. | 1.60 | .40 |
| | *Nos. 509-512 (4)* | 4.70 | 1.60 |

4th anniversary of Government Junta and social services of armed forces.

Diego de Almagro — A270

**1977, Oct. 31** **Engr.** ***Perf. 14½***
**513** A270 5p rose & carmine .65 .40

Diego de Almagro (1475-1538), leader of Spanish expedition to Chile.

Bell, Letters, Dove and Child — A271

**1977, Dec. 12** **Litho.** ***Perf. 14½***
**514** A271 2.50p multi .65 .40

Christmas 1977.

Loading Timber — A272

**1978** **Litho.** ***Perf. 15***
**515** A272 10p multi 1.50 .35
**516** A272 20p multi 2.00 .45

No. 516 inscribed "CORREOS," ship is flying Chilean flag.

Papal Arms and Globe — A273

University A274

**1978** **Litho.** ***Perf. 14½***
**521** A273 10p multi 1.50 .30
**522** A274 25p multi 2.50 .75

World Peace Day (10p); Catholic University of Valparaiso, 50th anniversary (25p). Issue dates: 10p, July 28; 25p, July 31.

O'Higgins, by Gil de Castro — A275

**1978, Aug. 20** **Litho.** ***Perf. 15***
**523** A275 10p multi 1.10 .40

Bernardo O'Higgins (1778-1842), soldier and statesman.

Chacabuco Victory Monument — A276

**1978, Sept. 11**
**524** A276 10p multi 1.10 .40

160th anniv. of O'Higgins victory at Chacabuco, and 5th anniv. of military government.

Teacher Writing on Blackboard A277

**1978, Sept. 21**
**525** A277 15p multi 2.25 .50

10th anniversary and 9th Reunion of Inter-american Council for Education, Science and Culture (C.I.E.C.C.), Sept. 21-29.

First National Fleet, by Thomas Somerscales A278

Design: 30p, Last Moments of Rancagua Battle, by Pedro Subercaseaux.

**1978** **Litho.** ***Perf. 15***
**526** A278 20p multi 3.25 .55
**527** A278 30p multi 4.00 .90

Bernardo O'Higgins (1778-1842), soldier and statesman.
Issue dates: 20p, Oct. 9; 30p, Oct. 2.

San Martin-O'Higgins Medal, by Rene Thenot, 1942 — A279

**1978, Oct. 20**
**528** A279 7p multi 1.00 .40

José de San Martin and Bernardo O'Higgins, 200th birth anniversaries.

Council Emblem — A280

**1978, Nov. 27** **Litho.** ***Perf. 14½***
**529** A280 50p multi 5.50 2.00

Intl. Council of Military Sports, 30th anniv.

Three Kings — A281

Virgin and Child — A282

**1978, Dec. 14** **Litho.** ***Perf. 14½***
**530** A281 3p multi 1.00 .35
**531** A282 11p multi 1.60 .45

Christmas 1978.

Philippi Brothers A283

**1978, Dec. 29** **Litho.** ***Perf. 14½x15***
**532** A283 3.50p multi .95 .40

Bernardo E. Philippi (1811-1852) and Rodulfo A. Philippi (1808-1904), scientists and travelers.

No. 477 Surcharged in Bright Green

**1979** **Litho.** ***Perf. 13x14***
**533** A253 3.50p on 10c gray grn .65 .40

Flags of Chile and Salvation Army — A284

**1979, Mar. 17** **Litho.** ***Perf. 14½***
**534** A284 10p multi 1.50 .65

Salvation Army in Chile, 70th anniversary.

Pope Paul VI (1897-1978) A285

**1979, Mar. 30**
**535** A285 11p multi 2.75 .90

Battle of Maipu Monument A286

**1979, Apr. 17** **Litho.** ***Perf. 14½***
**536** A286 8.50p multi 1.75 .50

Bernardo O'Higgins (1778-1842), Liberator of Chile.

Naval Battles — A287

**1979, May 21** **Litho.** ***Perf. 14½***
**537** A287 3.50p Angamos 1.00 .40
**538** A287 3.50p Iquique 1.00 .40
**539** A287 3.50p Punta Gruesa 1.00 .40
*Nos. 537-539 (3)* 3.00 1.20

Centenary of victorious naval battles against Peru.

1903 Ambulance and Red Cross — A288

**1979, June 29** **Litho.** ***Perf. 14½***
**540** A288 25p multi 3.75 1.10

75th anniversary of Chilean Red Cross.

Diego Portales — A289

**1979-86** **Litho.** ***Perf. 13½***
**542** A289 1.50p ocher .50 .40
**543** A289 2p gray ('81) .50 .40
**544** A289 3.50p red .60 .40
**545** A289 4.50p bl grn ('81) .80 .40
**546** A289 5p rose claret 1.00 .40
**547** A289 6p emerald 1.20 .60
**548** A289 7p yellow ('82) 1.10 .60
**549** A289 10p blue ('82) 1.60 .60
**550** A289 12p orange ('86) .70 .40
*Nos. 542-550 (9)* 8.00 4.20

1.50p, 3.50p, 5p and 6p inscribed "D. Portales."

People and Flag — A290

**1979, Aug. 28** **Litho.** ***Perf. 14½***
**551** A290 10p multi 1.25 .60

Yugoslavian immigration, centenary.

Coat of Arms and Mt. Castillo A290a

**1979, Oct. 12** **Litho.** ***Perf. 14½***
**552** A290a 20p multi 2.50 .90

Coyhaique 50th anniv.

IYC Emblem, Playground A291

IYC Emblem, Children's Drawings: 11p, Girl and shadow, vert. 12p, Dancing.

**1979, Oct. 9** ***Perf. 14½***
**553** A291 9.50p multi 1.20 .60
**554** A291 11p multi 1.25 .75
**555** A291 12p multi 1.80 .85
*Nos. 553-555 (3)* 4.25 2.20

International Year of the Child.

Telecom 79 — A292

**1979, Oct. 26** **Litho.** ***Perf. 14½***
**556** A292 15p multi 1.75 .75

3rd World Telecommunications Exhibition, Geneva, Sept. 20-26.

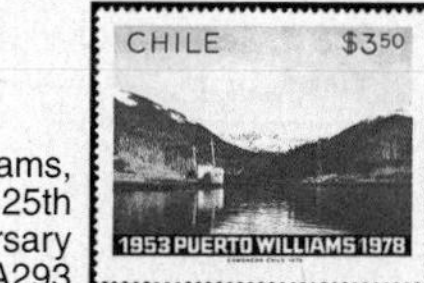

Puerto Williams, 25th Anniversary A293

**1979, Nov. 21**
**557** A293 3.50p multi .85 .40

Adoration of the Kings — A294

**1979, Dec. 4** **Litho.** ***Perf. 15***
**558** A294 3.50p multi .85 .40

Christmas 1979.

Rafael Sotomayor, Minister of War — A295

Military heroes: No. 560, Erasmo Escala. No. 561, Emilio Sotomayor. No. 562, Eleuterio Ramirez.

**1979, Dec. 29** *Perf. 13½*

**559** A295 3.50p ocher & brn .70 .40
**560** A295 3.50p multi .70 .40
**561** A295 3.50p multi .70 .40
**562** A295 3.50p multi .70 .40
*a.* Block of 4, #559-562 3.25 2.50

Bell UH-1 Rescue Helicopter at Tinguiririca Volcano, by S.O. Mococain A296

Air Force, 50th Anniversary: No. 564, Flying boat Catalina Skua over Antarctic, by E.F. Alvarez. No. 565, F5-E Tiger II over Andes, by M.M. Barria.

**1980, Mar. 21** **Litho.** *Perf. 13½*

**563** A296 3.50p shown .80 .40
**564** A296 3.50p Jet .80 .40
**565** A296 3.50p Sea plane .80 .40
*Nos. 563-565 (3)* 2.40 1.20

The Death of Bueras, by Pedro Leon Carmona — A297

**1980, Apr. 14** **Litho.** *Perf. 13½*

**566** A297 12p multi 1.75 .50

Charge of Bueras, Battle of Maipo, 1818.

Rotary International, 75th Anniversary A298

**1980, Apr. 15**

**567** A298 10p multi 1.50 .50

Gen. Manuel Baquedano, by Pedro Subercaseaux A299

Gen. Pedro Lagos, Battle Scene, by Subercaseaux A300

Battle of Morro de Arica Centenary (Subercaseaux Paintings): No. 570, Commander Juan J. San Martin, battle scene.

**1980, June 7** **Litho.** *Perf. 13½*

**568** A299 3.50p multi .80 .40
**569** A300 3.50p multi .80 .40
**570** A300 3.50p multi .80 .40
*Nos. 568-570 (3)* 2.40 1.20

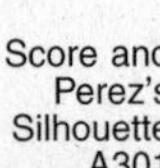

Score and Perez's Silhouette A301

**1980, June 27** **Litho.** *Perf. 13½*

**571** A301 6p multi .85 .40

Osman Perez Freire (1880-1930), composer, and fragment from his song "Ay, Ay, Ay."

Mt. Gasherbrum II, Chilean Flag, Ice Pick — A302

**1980, July 9**

**572** A302 15p multi 1.60 .60

Chilean Himalayan expedition, June 1979.

"Charity," Stained-glass Window — A303

**1980, July 18**

**573** A303 10p multi 1.90 .50

Daughters of Charity, 125th anniv. in Chile.

Condor, Colors of Chile — A304

**1980, Sept. 11** **Litho.** *Perf. 13½*

**574** A304 3.50p multi .90 .40

Plebiscite to vote on new constitution.

Inca Child Mummy — A305

**1980, Sept. 14**

**575** A305 5p shown 1.00 .40
**576** A305 5p Claudio Gay 1.00 .40
*a.* Pair, #575-576 + label 2.25 1.75

Natl. Museum of Natural History (founded by Claudio Gay, 1800-73) sesqui.

Pablo Burchard, by Pedro Lira — A306

**1980, Sept. 27** **Litho.** *Perf. 13½*

**577** A306 3.50p multi .70 .40

Museum of Fine Art centenary (directed by Burchard, 1932).

Santiago International Fair — A307

**1980, Oct. 30**

**578** A307 3.50p multi .75 .40

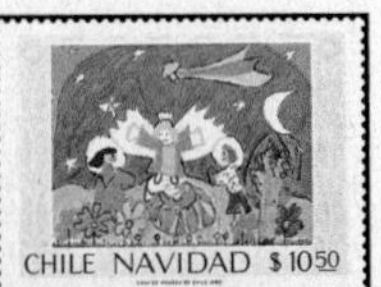

Nativity A308

Christmas 1980: 3.50p, Family, vert.

**1980, Nov. 25** **Litho.** *Perf. 13½*

**579** A308 3.50p multi 1.50 .30
**580** A308 10.50p multi 1.80 .55

Infantryman 1879 — A309

Pacific War period uniforms, 1879.

**1980, Nov. 27**

**581** A309 3.50p shown 1.00 .40
**582** A309 3.50p Cavalry officer 1.00 .40
**583** A309 3.50p Artillery officer 1.00 .40
**584** A309 3.50p Engineer colonel 1.00 .40
*a.* Block of 4, #581-584 7.00 4.00

See Nos. 606-609.

Congress Emblem — A310

**1980, Dec. 1**

**585** A310 11.50p multi 2.25 .60

23rd Intl. Cong. of Military Medicine & Pharmacy.

Eradication of Hoof and Mouth Disease — A311

**1981, Jan. 16** **Litho.** *Perf. 13½*

**586** A311 9.50p multi 1.40 .50

Moai Statues, Easter Island — A312

No. 588, Robinson Crusoe Island. No. 589, Penguins, Antarctic Territory.

**1981, Jan. 28** **Litho.** *Perf. 13½*

**587** A312 3.50p shown 1.60 .40
**588** A312 3.50p multi 2.75 .40
**589** A312 10.50p multi 4.25 1.00
*Nos. 587-589 (3)* 8.60 1.80

National Heroine Javiera Carrera, by O.M. Pizarro, Birth Bicentenary A313

**1981, Mar. 20**

**590** A313 3.50p multi .85 .40

UPU Membership Centenary — A314

**1981, Apr. 1**

**591** A314 3.50p multi .65 .40

C130 Hercules Air Force Transport Plane Unloading Cargo A315

**1981, Apr. 21**

**592** A315 3.50p multi 1.50 .40

Lieutenant Marsh Air Force Base, 1st anniv.

13th World Telecommunications Day — A316

**1981, May 17** **Litho.** *Perf. 13½*

**593** A316 3.50p multi .70 .40

Arturo Prat Naval Base — A317

**1981, June 23** **Litho.** *Perf. 13½*

**594** A317 3.50p multi 1.75 .50

Capt. Jose Luis Araneda — A318

**1981, June 26**

**595** A318 3.50p multi .85 .40

Battle of Sangrar centenary.

Philatelic Society of Chile, 90th Anniv. — A319

**1981, July 29** **Litho.** *Perf. 13½*

**596** A319 4.50p multi 1.50 .50

Minister Recabarren and Chief Conuepan Giving Speeches, by Hector Robles Acuna
A320

**1981, Aug. 7**

| | | |
|---|---|---|
| **597** A320 4.50p multi | 1.50 | .50 |

Temuco city centenary.

Exports — A321

**1981, Aug. 31 Litho. *Perf. 13½***

| | | |
|---|---|---|
| **598** A321 14p multi | 2.00 | .40 |

Presidential Palace — A322

**1981, Sept. 11**

| | | |
|---|---|---|
| **599** A322 4.50p multi | 1.50 | .40 |

Natl. liberation, 8th anniv.

St. Vincent de Paul, 400th Birth Anniv. — A323

**1981, Sept. 27 Litho. *Perf. 13½***

| | | |
|---|---|---|
| **600** A323 4.50p multi | .85 | .40 |

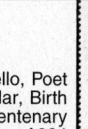

Andres Bello, Poet and Sholar, Birth Bicentenary
A324

**1981, Sept. 29**

| | | |
|---|---|---|
| **601** A324 4.50p Coin | .60 | .35 |
| **602** A324 9.50p Bust, books | 1.00 | .45 |
| **603** A324 11.50p Statue, arms | 1.40 | .60 |
| *Nos. 601-603 (3)* | 3.00 | 1.40 |

2nd Congress of South American Uniformed Police — A325

**1981, Oct. 15**

| | | |
|---|---|---|
| **604** A325 4.50p multi | .85 | .50 |

World Food Day — A326

**1981, Oct. 16**

| | | |
|---|---|---|
| **605** A326 5.50p multi | .80 | .50 |

**Uniform Type of 1980**

1879 Parade Uniforms.

**1981, Nov. 6 *Perf. 13½***

| | | |
|---|---|---|
| **606** A309 5.50p Infantry private | 1.00 | .50 |
| **607** A309 5.50p Cadet | 1.00 | .50 |
| **608** A309 5.50p Cavalryman | 1.00 | .50 |
| **609** A309 5.50p Artilleryman | 1.00 | .50 |
| *a.* Block of 4, #606-609 | 7.00 | 3.00 |

Intl. Year of the Disabled — A327

**1981, Nov. 11**

| | | |
|---|---|---|
| **610** A327 5.50p multi | 1.40 | .50 |

Christmas 1981 — A328

**1981, Nov. 25**

| | | |
|---|---|---|
| **611** A328 5.50p Nativity | .75 | .40 |
| **612** A328 11.50p Three Kings | 1.25 | .60 |

50th Anniv. of Federico Santa Maria Technical University A329

**1981, Dec 1 Litho. *Perf. 13½***

| | | |
|---|---|---|
| **613** A329 5.50p multi | .75 | .50 |

Dario Salas (1881-1941), Educator — A330

**1981, Dec. 4**

| | | |
|---|---|---|
| **614** A330 5.50p multi | .85 | .50 |

FIDA '82, 2nd Natl. Air Force Fair — A331

**1982, Mar. 6 Litho. *Perf. 13½***

| | | |
|---|---|---|
| **615** A331 4.50p multi | .75 | .50 |

1980 Constitution A332

4.50p, Cardinal Caro, family. 11p, Diego Portales. 30p, Bernardo O'Higgins.

**1982, Mar. 11**

| | | |
|---|---|---|
| **616** A332 4.50p multi | .75 | .25 |
| **617** A332 11p multi | 1.75 | .45 |
| **618** A332 30p multi | 3.00 | .90 |
| *Nos. 616-618 (3)* | 5.50 | 1.60 |

Panamerican Institute of Geography and History, 12th General Assembly — A333

**1982, Mar. 22 Litho. *Perf. 13½***

| | | |
|---|---|---|
| **619** A333 4.50p multi | .75 | .50 |

American Air Forces Cooperation System — A334

**1982, Apr. 12**

| | | |
|---|---|---|
| **620** A334 4.50p multi | 1.00 | .50 |

Pedro Montt — A335

**1982, Mar. 27**

| | | |
|---|---|---|
| **621** A335 4.50p light vio | .75 | .50 |

Fish Exports — A336

**1982, May 3 Litho. *Perf. 13½***

| | | |
|---|---|---|
| **622** A336 20p multi | 2.50 | .75 |

Scouting Year — A337

No. 623b, Robert Baden-Powell.

**1982, May 21 Litho. *Perf. 13***

| | | |
|---|---|---|
| **623** A337 Pair | 40.00 | 25.00 |
| *a.-b.* 4.50p, either single | 12.50 | 6.00 |

Battle of Concepcion Centenary — A338

Chacabuco Regiment officers killed in battle.

**1982, June 18 Litho. *Perf. 13½***

| | | |
|---|---|---|
| **624** Block of 4 | 3.50 | 2.50 |
| *a.* A338 4.50p I. Carrera Pinto | .60 | .40 |
| *b.* A338 4.50p A. Perez Canto | .60 | .40 |
| *c.* A338 4.50p J. Montt Salamanca | .60 | .40 |
| *d.* A338 4.50p L. Cruz Martinez | .60 | .40 |

UN World Assembly on Aging, July 26-Aug. 6 A339

**1982, Aug. 5**

| | | |
|---|---|---|
| **625** A339 4.50p multi | 1.25 | .50 |

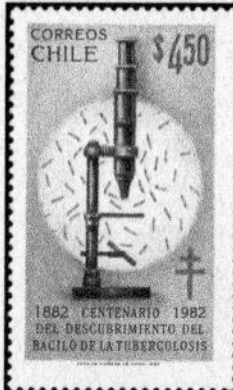

TB Bacillus Centenary — A340

**1982, Aug. 31**

| | | |
|---|---|---|
| **626** A340 4.50p multi | .65 | .40 |

9th Anniv. of National Liberation — A341

**1982, Sept. 11 Litho. *Perf. 13½***

| | | |
|---|---|---|
| **627** A341 4.50p multi | .75 | .50 |

Christmas 1982 — A342

Children's drawings.

**1982, Nov. 2**

| | | |
|---|---|---|
| **628** A342 10p multi | 1.50 | .40 |
| **629** A342 25p multi, vert. | 1.75 | .60 |

**Nos. 416 Surcharged in Green**

Nos. 417 Surcharged in Black

**1982, Nov. *Perf. 14½x15, 14½***

| | | |
|---|---|---|
| **630** A222 1p on 3.50p bl grn & grn (G) | 2.50 | .50 |
| **631** A223 2p on 1.15p blk & car | 3.75 | .50 |

Marist Alumni, 9th World Congress — A342a

Virgin Mary & Marcellus Champagnat (founder of Marist Brotherhood), stained glass window, Church of the Sacred Heart of Jesus, Barcelona.

**1982, Nov. 11 Litho. *Perf. 13½***

| | | |
|---|---|---|
| **631A** A342a 7p multi | 3.75 | 1.00 |

El Sur Newspaper Centenary — A342b

7p, Wooden handpress, masthead.

**1982, Nov. 15**

**631B** A342b 7p multi .75 .50

110th Anniv. of South American Steamship Co. — A342c

**1982, Dec. 20**

**631C** A342c 7p Steamer Copiapo 2.40 .50

60th Anniv. of Radio Club of Chile — A342d

**1982, Dec. 29**

**631D** A342d 7p multi 1.40 1.10

First Anniv. of Postal Agreement with Order of Malta — A343

**1983, Mar. 30 Litho. *Perf. 13½***

**632** 25p Arms of Order of Malta 2.50 .40
**633** 50p Chile 4.00 .80
*a.* Pair, #632-633 8.00 6.50

D.D. No. 20

This and similar inscriptions indicate that the stamps would be sold at a discount if purchased in large quantities.

**D. Portales Type of 1975 Inscribed Diego Portales and**

Ramon Barros Luco A344

Juan Luis Sanfuentes A344a

**1983-88 Litho. *Perf. 13½***

| | | | | | |
|---|---|---|---|---|---|
| **634** | A344 | 1p | grnsh bl | .75 | .40 |
| **635** | A253 | 1p | chalky bl | .75 | .40 |
| **636** | A253 | 1.50p | ocher | .75 | .40 |
| **637** | A344 | 2p | dl vio ('84) | .75 | .40 |
| **638** | A253 | 2p | ol gray | .75 | .40 |
| **639** | A253 | 2.50p | lemon | .75 | .40 |
| **640** | A253 | 5p | red lilac | 1.00 | .40 |
| **641** | A344 | 5p | crim rose | .75 | .40 |
| **642** | A344a | 5p | red ('84) | .75 | .40 |
| **643** | A344 | 7p | ultra | .90 | .40 |
| **644** | A344a | 9p | brn ('84) | .75 | .40 |
| **645** | A344a | 9p | grn ('84) | .75 | .40 |
| **646** | A344 | 10p | black | .75 | .40 |
| **646A** | A344a | 10p | gray ('84) | .75 | .40 |
| **647** | A344a | 15p | ultra ('87) | .75 | .40 |
| *a.* | Booklet pane of 10 | | | 7.50 | |
| **648** | A344a | 20p | yel ('88) | .75 | .40 |
| *b.* | Booklet pane of 10 | | | 7.50 | |

Nos. 644, 647, 648 inscribed "D.S. No. 20."
Issued: No. 640, 8/85.
For surcharge see No. 779.

50th Anniv. of Bureau of Investigation — A345

**1983, June 19 Litho. *Perf. 13½***

**649** A345 20p multi 1.50 .60

Antonio Cardinal Samore (1905-1983) A346

**1983, June 26**

**650** A346 30p multi 2.25 .60

Centenary of Cliff Elevators in Valparaiso — A347

**1983, Aug. 19 Litho. *Perf. 13½***

**651** A347 40p multi 5.25 1.00

Pucara de Quitor Settlement Ruins, San Pedro de Atacama A348

No. 653, Llamas, rock painting, Rio Ibanez, Aisen. No. 654, Duck-shaped jug with human head, Diaguita cultures. No. 655, Puoko Tangata carved stone head, Easter Isld.

**1983, Aug. 26**

**652** A348 7p multi 1.50 .50
**653** A348 7p multi 1.50 .50
**654** A348 7p multi 1.25 .50
**655** A348 7p multi, vert. 1.50 .50
*Nos. 652-655 (4)* 5.75 2.00

10th Anniv. of National Liberation — A349

**1983, Sept. 11 Litho. *Perf. 13½***

**656** A349 7p Angel with broken chains .75 .40
**657** A349 7p Couple, flag .75 .40
**658** A349 10p Family, torch .75 .40
**659** A349 40p Coat of arms, "10" 3.75 .80
*a.* Strip of 4, #656-659 6.00 4.00

For surcharges see Nos. 669-670.

Famous Hondurans — A350

No. 660, Francisco Morazan (1792-1842), Advocate of United Central America. No. 661, Jose Cecilio Del Valle (1777-1834), Scholar and Leader of Pan Americanism.

**1983, Oct. 3 Litho. *Perf. 13½***

**660** A350 7p multi .60 .40
**661** A350 7p multi .60 .40
*a.* Pair, #660-661 1.50 1.00

World Communications Year — A351

**1983, Oct. 13 Litho. *Perf. 13½***

**662** 7p Central P.O. 1.00 .50
**663** 7p Challenger spaceship 1.00 .50
*a.* A351 Pair, #662-663 2.25 2.25

Christmas 1983 — A353

Childrens' Drawings: 10p Chilean Peasant, Hanny Chacon. 30p, Holy Family. Lucrecia Cardenas, vert.

**1983, Nov. 14 Litho. *Perf. 13***

**664** A353 10p multi 1.00 .40
**665** A353 30p multi 1.75 .60

Design descriptions printed on back on top of gum.

State Railways Centenary — A354

Train Cars: a, Presidential coach, 1911. b, Service coach, 1910; tender, 1929. c, Locomotive Type 80, 1929.

**1984, Jan. 4 Litho. *Perf. 13½***

**666** A354 Strip of 3 10.00 8.75
*a.-c.* 9p, any single 2.40 .45

3rd Intl. Air Fair, Santiago, Mar. 3-11 — A355

**1984, Jan. 31 Litho. *Perf. 13½***

**667** A355 9p Flags, plane 1.50 .50

20th Anniv. of Nuclear Energy Commission A356

**1984, Apr. 16 Litho. *Perf. 13***

**668** A356 9p multi .75 .50

**Nos. 656-657 Surcharged in Purple**

**1984, June 11 Litho. *Perf. 13½***

**669** A349 9p on 7p #656 .70 .40
**670** A349 9p on 7p #657 .70 .40
*a.* Pair, #669-670 1.75 1.00

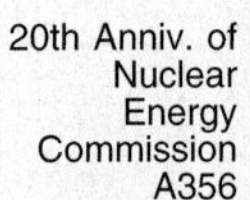

Antarctic Colonization A357

No. 671, Women's expedition. No. 672, Villa las Estrellas Station. No. 673, Scouts, flag, Air Force base.

**1984, June 18**

**671** A357 15p multicolored 1.50 .50
**672** A357 15p multicolored 1.50 .50
**673** A357 15p multicolored 1.50 .50
*a.* Strip of 3, #671-673 7.25 4.50

10th Anniv. of Regionalization — A358

Designs: a, Parinacota Church, Tarapaca. b, El Tatio geyser, Antofagasta. c, Copper mining, Atacama. d, Tololo Observatory, Coquimbo. e, Valparaiso Harbor, Valparaiso. f, Ahu Akivi head sculptures, Easter Isld. g, St. Francis Church, Santiago. h, El Hunique House, O'Higgins. i, Colburn Machicura Dam and Hydroelectric Power Station, Maule. j, Sta. Juana de Guadalcazar Fort, Bio-Bio. k, Indian woman, Araucania. l, Guar Isld. Church, Los Lagos. m, Main road, Gen. del Campo. n, Shepherds' Monument, Magellanes and Antarctic. o, Family, Villa las Estrellas Station, Antarctic.

**1984, July 11**

**674** Sheet of 15 28.00 24.00
*a.-o.* A358 9p multi, any single 1.25 1.25

Capt. Pedro Sarmiento de Gamboa, Map, 1584 — A359

**1984, July 31 Litho. *Perf. 13***

**675** A359 100p multi 5.50 1.10

400th anniv. of Spanish presence in Straits of Magellan.

State Bank of Chile Centenary A360

35p, Founder Antonio Varas de la Barra, coin.

**1984, Sept. 6 Litho. *Perf. 13½***

**676** A360 35p multi 1.50 .55

11th Anniv. of Liberation — A361

20p, Monument to O'Higgins.

**1984, Sept. 11**

**677** A361 20p multi 1.40 .50

Circus Centenary — A362

**1984, Sept. 28 Litho. *Perf. 13½***

**678** A362 45p Clown 2.00 .70

Endangered Species, World Wildlife Emblem A363

**1985, July Litho. *Perf. 13½***

**679** A363 9p Chinchilla *6.50* 2.50
**680** A363 9p Blue whale *6.50* 2.50
**681** A363 9p Sea lions *6.50* 2.50
**682** A363 9p Chilean huemuls *6.50* 2.50
*a.* Block of 4, #679-682 *26.00* *15.00*

Christmas 1984 — A364

Children's drawings.

**1984, Nov. 20 Litho. *Perf. 13½***
**683** A364 9p Shepherds .65 .40
**684** A364 40p Bethlehem 2.40 .60

Santiago University Planetarium Opening — A365

**1984, Dec. 29**
**685** A365 10p multi 3.25 2.00

Flora and Fauna — A366

Wildlife: a, Conepatus chinga. b, Leucocoryne purpurea. c, Himantopus himantopus. d, Lutra felina. e, Balbisia peduncularis. f, Psittacus cyanalysias. g, Pudu pudu. h, Fuschia magellanica. i, Diuca diuca. j, Dusicyon griseus. k, Alstroemeria sierrae. l, Glaucidium nanum.

**1985, Feb.**
**686** Block of 12 24.00 20.00
***a.-l.*** A366 10p, Any single 1.60 .65

American Airforces Cooperation System, 25th Anniv. — A367

**1985, Mar. 26**
**687** A367 45p Emblem, flags 2.25 1.10

Chile-Argentina Peace Treaty — A368

**1985, May 2 Litho. *Perf. 13½***
**688** A368 20p Papal arms, flags 3.25 .60

Fr. Joseph Kentenich (1885-1968), Founder, Intl. Schonstatt Movement of Catholic Laymen — A369

40p, Portrait, La Florida Sanctuary, Santiago.

**1985, May 19 Litho. *Perf. 13½***
**689** A369 40p multi .95 .50

Antarctic Treaty, 25th Anniv. A370

Resources, research: 15p, Krill, pack ice, map. 20p, Seismological Station, O'Higgins' Base. 35p, Georeception Station, dish receiver.

**1985, June 21**
**690** A370 15p multi .90 .35
**691** A370 20p multi 1.20 .50
**692** A370 35p multi 2.10 .75
*Nos. 690-692 (3)* 4.20 1.60

Canis Fulvipes A371

Endangered wildlife: b, Phoenicoparrus jamesi. c, Fulica gigantea. d, Lutra provocax.

**1985, Aug. 9 Litho. *Perf. 13½***
**693** A371 Block of 4 14.00 4.50
***a.-d.*** 20p, any single 1.75 .35

Intl. Youth Year — A372

UN, 40th Anniv. A373

**1985, Aug. 31**
**694** A372 15p multi 1.00 .50
**695** A373 15p multi 1.00 .50
***a.*** Pair, #694-695 2.00 1.00

Gen. Jose Miguel Carrera Verdugo (1785-1821) A374

**1985, Oct. 8 Litho. *Perf. 13½***
**696** A374 40p multi 2.50 .55

Farmer and Ox-drawn Hay Cart — A375

Folklore: b, Street photographer, wet plate camera. c, One-man band. d, Basket maker.

**1985, Oct.**
**697** A375 Block of 4 2.60 1.60
***a.-d.*** 10p, any single .50 .35

For surcharges see Nos. 770-771.

Christmas 1985 — A376

Winning children's drawings, 7th natl. design contest.

**1985, Nov. 4**
**698** A376 15p Nativity .55 .25
**699** A376 100p Father Christmas, vert. 3.75 1.00

Nos. 698-699 inscribed in black on gummed side with child's name, age, school and region.

Holy Family — A376a

**1985 Litho. *Perf. 13½***
**699A** A376a 10p buff & brn .85 .40

For surcharge see No. 768.

16th Armed Forces Conference — A377

20p, Cavalryman, Directorial Escort, 1818. 35p, Officer, Grand Guard, 1813.

**1985, Nov. 15 Litho. *Perf. 13½***
**700** A377 20p multicolored .90 .40
**701** A377 35p multicolored 1.60 .60

Halley's Comet A378

**1985, Nov. 29 Litho. *Perf. 13½***
**702** A378 45p multicolored 1.25 .50
***a.*** Souvenir sheet *42.00* 20.00

No. 702a exists imperf. Value $42.

Natl. Solidarity Campaign A379

**1985**
**703** A379 5p red & blue 2.50 .75

Campaign for Prevention of Forest Fires — A380

**1985, Dec. 27**
**704** 40p Forest .75 .50
**705** 40p Fire destruction .75 .40
***a.*** A380 Pair, #704-705 3.25 2.75

No. 705a has continuous design.

Dungeness Point Lighthouse, Straits of Magellan A381

**1986, Jan. 26**
**706** A381 45p shown 1.50 .60
**707** A381 45p Evangelistas Lighthouse 1.50 .60
***a.*** Pair, #706-707 4.50 2.50

No. 707a continuous design.

View of Santiago, Mackenna A382

**1986, Jan. 28**
**708** A382 30p multi .80 .50

Benjamin Vicuna Mackenna (d. 1886), municipal superintendent of Santiago, 1872-1875.

Diego Portales, Natl. Crest, Text — A382a

**1986, Feb. Litho. *Perf. 13½***
**708A** A382a 12p on 3.50p multi 3.00 1.25

No. 708A not issued without surcharge.

1986 World Cup Soccer Championships, Mexico — A383

Host stadiums: 15p, Natl. Stadium, Chile, 1962. 20p, Aztec Stadium, Mexico, 1970. 35p, Maracana Stadium, Brazil, 1950. 50p, Wembley Stadium, Great Britain, 1966.

**1986, Feb. 18**
**709** A383 15p multi .60 .40
**710** A383 20p multi .80 .40
**711** A383 35p multi 1.20 .50
**712** A383 50p multi 1.90 .75
*Nos. 709-712 (4)* 4.50 2.05

Environmental Conservation A384

**1986, Feb. 28**
**713** A384 20p Water 1.00 .50
**714** A384 20p Air 1.00 .50
**715** A384 20p Soil 1.00 .50
*Nos. 713-715 (3)* 3.00 1.50

Sailing Ship Santiaguillo, Flags — A385

**1986, Mar. 20**
**716** A385 40p multi 1.75 .55

Discovery of Valparaiso Bay, 450th anniv.

A386

**1986, Apr. 9**
**717** A386 45p multi 1.75 .50

Interamerican Development Bank, 25th anniv.

A387

**1986, Apr. 30 Litho. *Perf. 13½***
**718** A387 15p multi .90 .50

St. Rosa de Lima (1586-1617), sanctuary at Pelequen.

Moai Statues, Easter Is. — A388

60p, Raraku Volcano. 100p, Tongariki Ruins.

**1986, May 15**

**719** A388 60p multi 3.75 1.75
*a.* Souvenir sheet *12.50 12.50*
**720** A388 100p multi 6.75 3.25
*a.* Souvenir sheet *20.00 20.00*

AMERIPEX '86 — A389

**1986, May 23**

**721** A389 100p multi 2.75 1.10

Historic Naval Ships — A390

No. 722, Schooner Ancud, 1843. No. 723, Armed merchantman Aguilar, 1830. No. 724, Corvette Esmeralda, 1856. No. 725, Frigate O'Higgins, 1834.

**1986, May 30**

**722** A390 35p multi 1.25 .60
**723** A390 35p multi 1.25 .60
**724** A390 35p multi 1.25 .60
**725** A390 35p multi 1.25 .60
*a.* Block of 4, #722-725 8.00 6.50

See Nos. 752-753.

Paintings by Juan Francisco Gonzalez (1853-1933) A391

No. 726, Rush and Chrysanthemums. No. 727, Gate of La Serena.

**1986, June 24**

**726** A391 30p multi 1.00 .35
**727** A391 30p multi 1.00 .35
*a.* Pair, #726-727 3.00 1.75

Exports A392

Designs: a, Saltpeter. b, Iron. c, Copper. d, Molybdenum.

**1986 Litho. *Perf. 13½***

**728** A392 Block of 4 2.60 1.60
*a.-d.* 12p, any single .50 .35

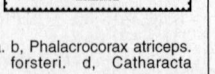

Antarctic Fauna — A393

a, Sterna vittata. b, Phalacrocorax atriceps. c, Aptenodytes forsteri. d, Catharacta lonnberg.

**1986, July 16 Litho. *Perf. 13½***

**729** Block of 4 10.00 5.00
*a.-d.* A393 40p, any single 1.75 .70

Writers A394

No. 730, Pedro de Ona (1570-1643). No. 731, Vicente Huidobro (1893-1948).

**1986, Aug. 19**

**730** A394 20p multi .75 .40
**731** A394 20p multi .75 .40
*a.* Pair, #730-731 2.25 1.00

Has continuous design.

Military Academy, Cent. — A395

No. 732, Major-General, 1878. No. 733, Major, 1950.

**1986, Sept. 8 Litho. *Perf. 13½***

**732** A395 45p multi 1.25 .50
**733** A395 45p multi 1.25 .50
*a.* Pair, #732-733 2.75 2.25

Art — A396

No. 734, Diaguita urn, duck jug. No. 735, Mapuche silver ornament, embroidery.

**1986, Oct. 17 *Perf. 13½***

**734** A396 30p multi .75 .40
**735** A396 30p multi .75 .40
*a.* Pair, #734-735 3.00 1.60

Christmas A397

8th Natl. design contest-winning children's drawings.

**1986, Nov. 19 Litho. *Perf. 13½***

**736** A397 15p multi .70 .50
**737** A397 105p multi 3.00 .70

Nos. 736-737 inscribed in black on gummed side with child's name, age, school and region.

Christmas — A397a

Design: Shepherds see star, Bethlehem.

**1986, Nov. Litho. *Perf. 13½***

**737A** A397a 12p multi *2.50* 2.50

Intl. Peace Year — A398

**1986, Nov. 26**

**738** A398 85p multi 1.75 .60

Natl. Women Volunteers A399

**1986, Dec. 15 Litho. *Perf. 13½***

**739** A399 15p multi 2.50 .50

Crowning of Our Lady of Mt. Carmel, Patron of Chile, by Pius XI, 60th Anniv. — A400

**1986, Dec. 19**

**740** A400 25p multi 1.00 .50

Andean Railways Kitson-Meyer No. 59, 1907, Designed by Robert Sterling A401

**1987, Jan. 27 Litho. *Perf. 13½***

**741** A401 95p multi 3.25 1.25

Arturo Prat Naval Base, Greenwich Island, the Antarctic, 40th Anniv. — A402

No. 742, Storage and power supplies. No. 743, Working and living quarters.

**1987, Feb. 6**

**742** 100p multi 4.50 3.00
**743** 100p multi 4.50 3.00
*a.* A402 Pair, #742-743 13.50 13.00

State Visit of Pope John Paul II, Apr. 1-6, 1987 — A403

Pope John Paul II and: 20p, Christ the Redeemer statue. 25p, Votive Church, Maipu. 90p, Cross of the Seas, Straits of Magellan. 115p, Virgin of the Hill.

**1987 Litho. *Perf. 13½***

**744** A403 20p multi .35 .30
**745** A403 25p multi .50 .30
**746** A403 90p multi 1.60 .60
**747** A403 115p multi 2.25 .95
*a.* Souv. sheet of one 6.75 5.25
**747B** A403 115p multi 2.40 1.00
*Nos. 744-747B (5)* 7.10 3.15

No. 747a sold for 250p.

No. 747B differs from No. 747 in that the Statue of the Virgin has a halo and Pope John Paul II is smiling.

Issue date: Nos. 744-747a, Apr. 6.

World Youth Soccer Championships — A405

b, Concepcion Stadium, kick play. c, Antofagasta Stadium, dribbling the ball. d, Valparaiso Stadium, heading the ball.

**1987, May 28**

**750** A405 Block of 4 5.50 4.00
*a.-d.* 45p any single 1.00 .60

**Souvenir Sheet**

**751** A405 45p Four players 4.00 4.00

No. 751 sold for 150p.

**Naval Ships Type of 1986**

No. 752, Battleship Almirante Latorre, 1913. No. 753, Cruiser O'Higgins, 1936.

**1987, May 29**

**752** A390 60p multi 1.50 .60
**753** A390 60p multi 1.50 .60
*a.* Pair, #752-753 4.25 2.25

Diego Portales (1793-1837), Finance Minister A406

**1987, June 16**

**754** A406 30p multi .75 .50

Public Works Ministry, Cent. — A407

**1987, June 26**

**755** A407 25p multi 1.10 .50

Infantry School, Cent. — A408

**1987, July 9**

**756** A408 50p Entrance 1.00 .35
**757** A408 100p Soldiers, natl. flag 1.40 .65

**Miniature Sheet**

Flora and Fauna — A409

Designs: a, Chiasognathus granti. b, Calidris alba. c, Hippocamelus antisensis. d, Jubaea chilensis. e, Colias vauthieri. f, Pandion haliaetus. g, Cephalorhynchus commersonii. h, Austrocedrus chilensis. i, Jasus frontalis. j, Stephanoides fernandensis. k, Vicugna vicugna. l, Thyrsopteris elegans. m, Lithodes antarctica. n, Pterocnemia pennata. o, Lagidium viscacia. p, Cereus atacamensis.

**1987, July 30**

**758** Sheet of 16 21.00 15.00
*a.-p.* A409 25p any single 1.00 .40

Los Carabineros (Natl. Guard), 60th Anniv. — A404

No. 748, Cavalry showmanship. No. 749, Air-sea rescue.

**1987, Apr. 21**

**748** A404 50p multi 1.25 .50
**749** A404 50p multi 1.25 .50
*a.* Pair, #748-749 3.00 2.00

Intl. Year of Shelter for the Homeless — A410

**1987, Aug. 6**
**759** A410 40p multi 1.10 .50

Legends and Folk Tales — A411

a, The Guitarist of Quinchamali. b, El Caleuche. c, El Pihuychen. d, La Lola.

**1987, July Litho. *Perf. 13½***
**760** A411 Block of 4 4.50 1.60
***a.-d.*** 15p any single .60 .35

Nos. 760a-760d exist ovptd. "D.S. No 20." in golden brown on back. Value $4.50.
For surcharges see Nos. 812, 1104.

FISA '87, Santiago — A412

**1987, Oct. 16 Litho. *Perf. 13½***
**761** A412 20p multi .65 .40

25th Intl. agriculture and exports exhibition.

Rear Admiral Carlos Condell de la Haza (1843-1887), Naval Hero at the Battle of the Pacific
A413

**1987, Nov. 7**
**762** A413 50p multi 1.75 .50

Christmas 1987 — A414

Children's drawings: 30p, Holy Family. 100p, Star Over Bethlehem, horiz.

**1987, Nov. 13**
**763** A414 30p multi .90 .30
**764** A414 100p multi 3.25 .95

COBRE '87, Intl. Conf. on Copper — A415

**1987, Nov. 23**
**765** A415 40p Foundry 2.40 .60
***a.*** Souv. sheet of one 2.75 2.75

No. 765 sold for 150p.

Natl. Antarctic Exploration Commission, 25th Anniv. A415a

**1987, Dec. 11 Litho. *Perf. 13½***
**765B** A415a 45p multi 2.00 .55

Ramon Freire Serrano (1787-1851), Chief of State — A416

**1987, Dec. 29 *Perf. 13x13½***
**766** A416 20p pale lil & rose clar .65 .40

To Smoke Is To Contaminate — A417

**1987, Dec. Litho. *Perf. 13½***
**767** A417 15p blue & ver .65 .40

Natl. Commission for the Control of Smoking.

No. 699A Surcharged in Green

**1987 Litho. *Perf. 13½***
**768** A376a 12p on 10p buff & brn .60 .50

Christmas 1987 — A418

**1987, Dec.**
**769** A418 15p ultra, org yel & blk .65 .40
***a.*** Bklt. pane of 10 7.25

No. 769a exists ovptd. "D.S. No 20." on back.

**No. 697 Surcharged in Black and Rose Red**

**1987, Dec.**
**770** A375 Block of 4 (RR) 3.00 1.50
***a.-d.*** 12p on 10p, #697a-697d .60 .30
**771** A375 Block of 4 (Blk) 3.00 1.50
***a.-d.*** 15p on 10p, #697a-697d .60 .30

St. John Bosco (1815-1888), Educator Canonized in 1934 — A419

**1988, Jan. 29**
**772** A419 40p multi 2.75 .50

20th Music Week, Frutillar A420

**1988, Jan. 27**
**773** A420 30p multi 1.00 .50

FIDA '88, 5th Intl. Aviation Fair — A421

**1988, Mar. 4 Litho. *Perf. 13½***
**774** A421 60p dark blue & blue 1.50 .60

1988 Summer Olympics, Seoul — A422

Flags of Chile and Korea, events: 50p, Shot put, pole vault, javelin. 100p, Swimming, cycling, running.

**1988, Mar. 18 *Perf. 13½***
**775** A422 50p multi 1.50 .60
**776** A422 100p multi 2.75 1.00
***a.*** Souv. sheet of 2, #775-776 4.25 3.75

No. 776a sold for 250p.

Natl. Agricultural Soc., 150th Anniv. A423

**1988, Apr. 8**
**777** A423 45p multi 1.60 .50

Intl. Red Cross and Red Crescent Organizations, 125th Annivs. A424

**1988, May 10**
**778** A424 150p multi 2.25 .65

No. 645 Surcharged

**1988 Litho. *Perf. 13½***
**779** A344a 20p on 9p green .65 .40

Easter Island Folk Art — A425

Designs: Nos. 780, 782, Carved wooden head from Kava Kava. Nos. 781, 783, Bird man stone carving from Tangata Manu.

**1988, Apr. 1 Litho. *Perf. 13½***
**780** A425 20p brick red & blk .50 .40
**781** A425 20p brick red & blk .50 .40
***a.*** Bklt. pane, 6 #780, 4 #781 5.00
***b.*** Pair, #780-781 2.90 2.90
**782** A425 20p yel & blk .50 .40
**783** A425 20p yel & blk .50 .40
***a.*** Bklt. pane, 6 #782, 4 #783 5.00
***b.*** Pair, #782-783 2.90 2.90
*Nos. 780-783 (4)* 2.00 1.60

Nos. 782-783 inscribed "D.S. No 20."
For surcharges see Nos. 813-816, 955-956.

Merino, Biplane, Jet Passenger Plane and Supersonic Fighter Plane — A426

**1988, May 17 Litho. *Perf. 13½***
**784** A426 35p multi 1.40 .50

Commodore Arturo Merino Benitez (b. 1888), aviation pioneer.

Naval Tradition A427

Designs: No. 785, Training ship *Esmeralda*. No. 786, Capt. Arturo Pratt, a stained-glass window in the Naval Museum, Valparaiso.

**1988, May 23**
**785** 50p multi .90 .50
**786** 50p multi .90 .50
***a.*** A427 Pair, #785-786 2.25 1.75

Pontifical Catholic University of Chile, Santiago, Cent. — A429

**1988, June 21**
**787** A429 40p Papal & university arms 1.40 .50

Locomotives — A430

No. 788, Esslingen No. 3331. No. 789, North British No. 45.

**1988, July 22 Litho. *Perf. 13½***
**788** 60p multi 1.00 .70
**789** 60p multi 1.00 .70
***a.*** Souv. sheet, #788-789, imperf 7.50 7.00
***b.*** A430 Pair, #788-789 3.50 2.40

Arica-La Paz Railway, 75th anniv. (No. 788); Antofagasta Bolivia Railway, cent. (No. 789).

Jose Miguel Carrera Natl. Institute, 175th Anniv. A431

**1988, Aug. 10 Litho. *Perf. 13½***
**790** A431 45p multi 1.50 .50

Annexation of Easter Is., Cent. — A432

**1988, Sept. 9**
**791** 50p Ship, officer 2.00 .40
**792** 50p Map, globe 2.00 .40
***a.*** A432 Pair, #791-792 4.50 1.50

**793** 100p Easter Is. folk dancers 3.00 .75
**794** 100p Stone ruins 3.00 .75
*a.* A432 Pair, #793-794 6.50 3.00
*b.* Souv. sheet of 4, #791-794, imperf. 12.50 6.50
*Nos. 791-794 (4)* 10.00 2.30

Miniature Sheet

Flowers — A433

Designs: a, Chloraea chrysantha. b, Lapageria rosea. c, Nolana paradoxa. d, Rhodophiala advena. e, Schizanthus hookeri. f, Acacia caven. g, Cordia decandra. h, Leontochir ovallei. i, Alstroemeria pelegrina. j, Copiapoa cinerea. k, Salpiglossis sinuata. l, Leucocoryne coquimbensis. m, Eucryphia glutinosa. n, Calandrinia longiscapa. o, Desfontainia spinosa. p, Sophora macrocarpa.

**1988, Aug. 23 Litho. *Perf. 13½***
**795** Sheet of 16 24.00 20.00
*a.-p.* A433 30p any single 1.00 .50

First Domestic Airmail Route, 1919 — A434

150p, Clodomiro Figueroa Ponce's aircraft.

**1988, Oct. 11**
**796** A434 150p multi 2.50 1.10

Christmas 1988
A435 A436

Children's drawings: 35p, Nativity, by Paulette Thiers, age 8. 100p, Going to church, by Jose M. Lamas, age 9, horiz.

**1988, Nov. 17**
**797** A435 20p rose lake & org yel .60 .50
*a.* Bklt. pane of 10 8.50
**798** A435 20p rose lake & org yel .60 .50
*a.* Bklt. pane of 10 8.50
**799** A436 35p multi .90 .50
**800** A436 100p multi 1.50 1.10
*Nos. 797-800 (4)* 3.60 2.60

No. 798 inscribed "D.S. No 20."

Artisans — A437

**1988, Oct. 25 Litho. *Perf. 13½***
**801** 25p Potter .75 .40
**802** 25p Weaver .75 .40
*a.* A437 Pair, #801-802 2.10 1.60

No. 802a has continuous design.

Natl. Philatelic Soc., Cent. — A438

**1988, Nov. 24**
**803** A438 40p No. 38, cancellation .85 .60

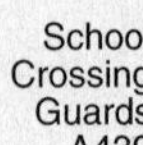

School Crossing Guards A439

**1988, Oct. 26**
**804** A439 45p multi 1.00 .75

A440

Battle scenes and: No. 805, Manuel Bulnes (1799-1866) Commander. No. 806, Cavalryman, Servicemen. No. 807, Roberto Simpson, Commander. No. 808, Seaman, Servicemen.

**1989, Jan. 12 Litho. *Perf. 13½***
**805** 50p multi .85 .40
**806** 50p multi .85 .40
*a.* A440 Pair, #805-806 3.50 1.25
**807** 100p multi 1.60 .85
**808** 100p multi 1.60 .85
*a.* A440 Pair, #807-808 4.00 2.25
*Nos. 805-808 (4)* 4.90 2.50

Battles of 1839: Yungay (50p) and Casma (100p). Nos. 806a, 808a have continuous designs.

Municipal Annivs. — A442

Municipal coats of arms and: 30p, San Ambrosio Church. 35p, Craftsman sculpting marble. 45p, Laja Spring and falls.

**1989, Jan. 20**
**809** A442 30p multi .45 .40
**810** A442 35p multi .70 .40
**811** A442 45p multi .85 .40
*Nos. 809-811 (3)* 2.00 1.20

Founding of Vallenar, 200th anniv. (30p); founding of Combarbala, 200th anniv. (35p); founding of Los Angeles, 250th anniv. (45p).

**Nos. 760a-760d and 780-783 Surcharged**

a

b

**1989, Mar. 20 Litho. *Perf. 13½***
**812** Block of 4 1.75 .75
*a.-d.* A411(a) 25p on 15p #760a-760d, any single .30 .30
**813** A425(b) 25p on 20p #780 .35 .30
**814** A425(b) 25p on 20p #781 .35 .30
*a.* A425(b) Pair, #813-814 1.50 1.25
Complete booklet, 6 #813, 4 #814 5.00
**815** A425(b) 25p on 20p #782 .35 .30
**816** A425(b) 25p on 20p #783 .35 .30
*a.* A425(b) Pair, #815-816 1.50 1.25
Complete booklet, 6 #815, 4 #816 5.00
*Nos. 812-816 (5)* 3.15 1.95

Surcharge differs on Nos. 814, 816.
Issued: Nos. 812-814, 3/20. Nos. 815-816, 11/30.

Women Beatified — A443

No. 818, Sr. Teresa de Los Andes. No. 819, Laura Vicuna.

**1989, Mar. 21 Litho. *Perf. 13½***
**818** A443 40p multicolored 1.00 .50
**819** A443 40p multicolored 1.00 .50
*a.* Pair, #818-819 2.50 2.00

No. 819a has continuous design.

EXFINA '89, Santiago — A444

No. 820, Christopher Columbus. No. 821, Galleons.

**1989, Mar. 31**
**820** 100p multi 1.75 .80
**821** 100p multi 1.75 .80
*a.* A444 Pair, #820-821 4.50 4.00
*b.* Souvenir sheet of 2, #820-821 9.00 5.25
*c.* Souvenir sheet of 2, #820-821 12.00 6.25

No. 821a has continuous design. No. 821b margin pictures Columbus's coat of arms and the Order of the Great Admiralty, No. 821c margin Nos. 55, 69, 18, 76, 37, 1, 20 and 98.

CORFO Development Corp., 50th Anniv. A445

**1989, Apr. 4**
**822** A445 60p Shipping .75 .30
**823** A445 60p Lumber .75 .30
**824** A445 60p Communication .75 .30
**825** A445 60p Coal .75 .30
*a.* Block of 4, #822-825 4.00 3.00

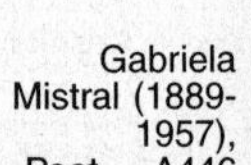

Gabriela Mistral (1889-1957), Poet — A446

**1989, Apr. 7 Litho. *Perf. 13½***
**826** A446 30p Poet, steeple .60 .25
**827** A446 30p Poet, children .60 .25
**828** A446 30p Poet working .60 .25
**829** A446 30p Receiving Nobel Prize, 1945 .60 .25
*a.* Block of 4, #826-829 4.25 3.25

Exports — A447

Nos. 830, 832, Grapes. Nos. 831, 833, Apple.

**1989, Apr. 19**
**830** A447 25p indigo & brt yel grn .45 .30
**831** A447 25p ver & brt yel grn .45 .30
*a.* Bklt. pane, 5 each #830-831 10.00
*b.* Pair, #830-831 2.50 1.00
**832** A447 25p indigo & pale yel org .45 .30
**833** A447 25p ver & pale yel org .45 .30
*a.* Bklt. pane, 5 each #832-833 10.00
*b.* Pair, #832-833 2.50 1.00
*Nos. 830-833 (4)* 1.80 1.20

Nos. 832-833 inscribed "D.S. No 20."
See Nos. 861-864, 943-946. For surcharges see Nos. 956B-956C, 1085-1088.

Military Justice Department, 150th Anniv. — A448

**1989, Apr. 24 Litho. *Perf. 13½***
**834** A448 50p multicolored .85 .80

Monument to the Martyrs of Carabineros de Chile — A449

**1989, Apr. 26**
**835** A449 35p multicolored .95 .70

Surveyor and Penguins A450

**1989, May 29**
**836** A450 150p multicolored 5.00 4.75

Antarctic Research Institute expeditions, 25th anniv.

Naval Engineers, Cent. — A451

No. 837, Naval school. No. 838, Seamen in boiler room. No. 839, Ship, helicopter, submarine. No. 840, *Aquiles* launch, Asmar-Talcahuano.

**1989, May 31**
**837** A451 45p multicolored 1.00 .30
**838** A451 45p multicolored 1.00 .30
**839** A451 45p multicolored 1.00 .30
**840** A451 45p multicolored 1.00 .30
*a.* Block of 4, #837-840 4.50 3.50

Horse-drawn Carriage (Victoria), Vina del Mar — A452

Early transportation: 35p, Launch off Chiloe Is., vert. 40p, Cart, Cautin. 45p, Ferry, Rio Palena. 50p, Car transport, Lake Gral, Carretta. 60p, Incline railroad, Valparaiso. 100p, Cable car (funicular), Santiago.

**1989-92 Litho. *Perf. 13½***
**841** A452 30p black & orange 1.10 .30
**842** A452 60p black & lemon 1.75 .60
**843** A452 60p like No. 842 1.75 .30
**844** A452 100p black & brt yel grn 3.00 1.00

**1989-91**
**845** A452 35p black & brt blue 1.10 .30
**846** A452 40p black & olive 1.25 .30
**847** A452 45p blk & pale blue grn 1.25 .30
*a.* Inscribed "1991" 1.25 .30
**848** A452 45p black & lt ol grn .70 .30
**849** A452 50p black & scarlet .90 .30
*a.* Inscribed "1992" 1.00 .30
*Nos. 841-849 (9)* 12.80 3.70

Nos. 843, 848 inscribed DS No. 20.
Issued: Nos. 841-842, 844, 4/22/89; No. 848, 2/1/91; No. 843, 1992; others, 8/1989.
For surcharge see No. 1002.

**Export Type of 1989**

Nos. 861, 863, Grapes. Nos. 862, 864, Apple.

**1989, May 22**
**861** A447 5p dark blue & gray .50 .40
**862** A447 5p brt red, dark blue & gray .50 .40
*a.* Pair, #861-862 1.40 .90
**863** A447 10p dark blue & gray .50 .40
**864** A447 10p brt red, dark blue & gray .50 .40
*a.* Pair, #863-864 1.40 .90

World Stamp Expo '89 — A453

**1989, Aug. 25 Litho. *Perf. 13½***

**865** A453 250p multicolored 4.75 4.50
*a.* Souvenir sheet of 1 10.00 8.00

A454

UPAE emblem and pre-Columbian peoples: 30p, Atacamena potter. 150p, Selk'nam-onas bow hunter.

**1989, Oct. 12**

**866** A454 30p multicolored 1.25 1.00
**867** A454 150p multicolored 5.00 4.00

Drawing by Christina Lopez A455

**1989, Nov. 20 Litho. *Perf. 13½***

**868** A455 100p multicolored 1.60 .50

Christmas.

Christmas Ornaments — A456

Nos. 869, 871, Balls. Nos. 870, 872, Bells.

**1989**

**869** A456 25p dull green & org .45 .30
**870** A456 25p dull green & org .45 .30
*a.* Bklt. pane, 5 each Nos. 869-870 4.50
*b.* Pair, #869-870 1.50 .80
**871** A456 25p dull green & ver .45 .30
**872** A456 25p dull green & ver .45 .30
*a.* Bklt. pane, 5 each Nos. 871-872 4.50
*b.* Pair, #871-872 1.50 .80
*Nos. 869-872 (4)* 1.80 1.20

Nos. 871-872 inscribed "D.S. No 20."

Miniature Sheet

Wildlife, Natl. Parks A457

Designs: a, Vicuna, Lauca Park. b, Chilean flamingos, Salar de Surire. c, Cactus, La Chimba Reserve. d, Guanaco, Pan de Azucar Park. e, Song bird, Father Jorge Park. f, Terns, Rapa Nui Park. g, Ferret, La Campana Park. h, Duck, Rio Clarillo Park. i, Cypress tree, Rio de Los Cipreses Reserve. j, Black-headed swan, Laguna de Torca Reserve. k, Puma, Laguna del Laja Park. l, Araucaria tree, Villarrica Park. m, Flower, Vicente Perez Rosales Park. n, Lenga tree, Dos Lagunas. o, Sea lion, Laguna San Rafael Park. p, Rhea, Torres del Paine Park.

**1990, Jan. 25**

**873** A457 Sheet of 16 24.00 10.00
*a.-p.* 35p any single .90 .30

1990 World Cup Soccer Championships, Italy — A458

**1990, Feb. 23**

**874** A458 50p Cleated shoe 1.00 .40
**875** A458 50p Hand 1.00 .40
**876** A458 50p Soccer ball 1.00 .40
**877** A458 50p Athlete 1.00 .40
*a.* Block of 4, #874-877 5.50 4.50

Natl. Air Force — A459

Various aircraft: No. 878, Vickers Wibault. No. 879, Curtiss O1E Falcon. No. 880, Pitts S2A. No. 881, Extra 300.

**1990, Mar. 16 Litho. *Perf. 13½***

**878** A459 40p multicolored 1.10 .40
**879** A459 40p multicolored 1.10 .40
**880** A459 40p multicolored 1.10 .40
**881** A459 40p multicolored 1.10 .40
*a.* Souvenir sheet of 4, #878-881 4.50 3.50
*Nos. 878-881 (4)* 4.40 1.60

FIDAE '90.

Discovery of America 500th Anniv. (in 1992) — A460

Maps and 16th cent. men: No. 882, Incan. No. 883, Spanish infantryman.

**1990, Apr. 20 Litho. *Perf. 13½***

**882** 60p multicolored 1.00 .30
**883** 60p multicolored 1.00 .30
*a.* A460 Pair, #882-883 4.00 3.00

Port Cities — A462

**1990, Apr. 27**

**884** A462 40p Valparaiso .85 .40
**885** A462 40p San Vicente .85 .40
*a.* Pair, #884-885 2.10 1.60

Democracy A463

**1990, June 8 Litho. *Perf. 13½***

**886** A463 20p Sunrise .35 .30
**887** A463 30p Peace dove .75 .30
**888** A463 60p Pleasure 1.20 .60
**889** A463 100p Star 2.10 .75
*a.* Souvenir sheet of 4, #886-889 7.50 6.25
*Nos. 886-889 (4)* 4.40 1.95

Equality A464

**1990, June 8**

**890** A464 45p multicolored 1.00 .75
*a.* Souvenir sheet 2.75 2.75

No. 890a margin continues the design.

Naval Tradition A465

No. 891, Transport ship Piloto Pardo. No. 892, Oceanographic research ship Yelcho.

**1990, May 30 Litho. *Perf. 13½***

**891** A465 50p multicolored .95 .40
**892** A465 50p multicolored .95 .40
*a.* Pair, #891-892 2.00 1.50

A466

**1990, June 12**

**893** A466 250p Sir Rowland Hill 3.75 1.25
*a.* Souvenir sheet of 1 6.25 5.00

Penny Black, 150th anniv. No. 893a margin continues the design.

A467

**1990, June 21**

**894** A467 150p multicolored 2.00 1.75

Organization of American States, cent.

Marine Resources — A468

Designs: a, Scallop. b, Clam. c, Swordfish. d, Crab. e, Fish. f, Baiting, processing.

**1990, July 27 Litho. *Perf. 13½***

**895** A468 Block of 6 8.50 4.00
*a.-f.* 40p any single .85 .35

Curimon Convent — A469

**1990, Aug. 1**

**896** A469 50p multicolored .85 .60

250th anniversary of San Felipe.

Environmental Protection — A470

**1990, Sept. 1 Litho. *Perf. 13½***

**897** A470 35p Aerosol propellants .80 .35
**898** A470 35p Deforestation .80 .35
**899** A470 35p Smokestacks .80 .35
**900** A470 35p Oil slick, shore .80 .35
**901** A470 35p Forest fire .80 .35
*a.* Strip of 5, #897-901 9.50 7.50
*b.* Bklt. pane, 2 each #897-901 8.00

**Inscribed "D.S. No 20"**

**902** A470 35p Aerosol propellants .80 .35
**903** A470 35p Deforestation .80 .35
**904** A470 35p Smokestacks .80 .35
**905** A470 35p Oil slick, shore .80 .35
**906** A470 35p Forest fire .80 .35
*a.* Strip of 5, #902-906 9.50 7.50
*b.* Bklt. pane, 2 each #902-906 8.00
*Nos. 897-906 (10)* 8.00 3.50

See Nos. 988-997.

Presidents of Chile — A471

No. 912, Salvador Allende. No. 913, Eduardo Frei. No. 914, Jorge Alessandri. No. 915, Gabriel Gonzalez V. No. 916, Juan Antonio Rios. No. 917, Pedro Aguirre Cerda. No. 918, Juan E. Montero. No. 919, Carlos Ibanez. No. 920, Emiliano Figueroa. No. 921, Arturo Alessandri.

**1990, Sept. 4**

**912** A471 35p multicolored .50 .30
**913** A471 35p multicolored .50 .30
**914** A471 40p multicolored .80 .30
*a.* Inscribed "1992" .80 .30
**915** A471 45p multicolored .80 .30
**916** A471 50p multicolored 1.00 .30
**917** A471 60p multicolored 1.00 .50
**918** A471 70p multicolored 1.25 .50
*a.* Inscribed "1992" 1.25 .50
**919** A471 80p multicolored 1.40 .65
**920** A471 90p multicolored 1.40 .65
*a.* Inscribed "1992" 1.50 .65
**921** A471 100p multicolored 1.50 .75
*a.* Inscribed "1992" 2.00 .90
*Nos. 912-921 (10)* 10.15 4.55

Rodeos A472

Designs: a, Rodeo ring. b, Men on horses. c, Man stopping horse. d, Men, horses, bull.

**1990, Sept. 24**

**926** A472 Block of 4 3.75 2.00
*a.-d.* 45p any single .50 .30

Discovery of America, 500th Anniv. (in 1992) — A473

30p, Phoenicopterus chilensis. 150p, Arctocephalus australis.

**1990, Oct. 12 Litho. *Perf. 13½***

**927** A473 30p multicolored 1.75 1.50
**928** A473 150p multicolored 5.25 5.00

King and Queen of Spain's Visit — A474

No. 930, Arms of King Juan Carlos I, Chilean Arms.

**1990, Oct. 18**

**929** A474 100p shown 1.75 1.50
**930** A474 100p Denomination at LR 1.75 1.50
*a.* Pair, #929-930 3.75 3.25

Malleco Bridge, Cent. — A475

Design: No. 932, Boy waving at train on bridge.

**1990, Oct. 26 Litho. *Perf. 13½***

**931** A475 60p multicolored 1.50 1.00
**932** A475 60p multicolored 1.50 1.00
*a.* Pair, #931-932 3.50 3.00

Chilean Antarctic Territorial Claims, 50th Anniv. — A476

Design: No. 934, Penguins, helicopter, camp.

**1990, Nov. 6** ***Perf. 13½***
**933** 250p multicolored 4.25 2.00
**934** 250p multicolored 4.25 2.00
*a.* A476 Pair, #933-934 12.50 8.50
*b.* Souvenir sheet of 2, #933-934 12.00 12.00

A477 Christmas — A478

150p, Underwater dwelling.

**1990, Nov. 20 Litho.** ***Perf. 13½***
**935** A477 35p lt green & bl grn .55 .45
*a.* Booklet pane of 10 7.50
**936** A477 35p dull org & bl grn .45 .45
*a.* Booklet pane of 10 7.50
**937** A478 35p shown .80 .45
**938** A478 150p multi 3.50 2.75
*Nos. 935-938 (4)* 5.30 4.10

No. 936 inscribed "D.S. No.20."

National Congress A479

No. 939, Congress chamber. No. 940, Early congressional session.

**1990, Dec. 21 Litho.** ***Perf. 13½***
**939** A479 100p multicolored 1.25 1.00
**940** A479 100p multicolored 1.25 1.00
*a.* Pair, #939-940 3.25 2.75

City of Santiago, 450th Anniv. — A480

**1991, Feb. 7**
**941** A480 100p Colorado House 1.50 1.00
**942** A480 100p Skyline 1.50 1.00
*a.* Pair, #941-942 4.50 2.50
*b.* Souvenir sheet of 2, #941-942 5.00 5.00

**Exports Type of 1989**

Nos. 943, 945, Grapes. Nos. 944, 946, Apple.

**1991, Feb. 8** ***Perf. 13½ on 3 Sides***
**943** A447 45p indigo & brt pink .60 .50
**944** A447 45p ver & brt pink .60 .50
*a.* Bklt. pane, 5 each #943-944 10.00
**945** A447 45p indigo & yel .60 .50
**946** A447 45p ver & yel .60 .50
*a.* Bklt. pane, 5 each #945-946 10.00
*Nos. 943-946 (4)* 2.40 2.00

Nos. 945-946 inscribed "D.S. No.20."
For surcharges see Nos. 1085-1088.

Historical Aircraft A481

Designs: a, Voisin. b, S.E. 5a. c, Morane Saulnier MS 35. d, Consolidated PBY-5A/OA-10 Catalina.

**1991, Mar. 21 Litho.** ***Perf. 13½***
**947** A481 150p Block of 4, #a.-d. 8.25 6.00

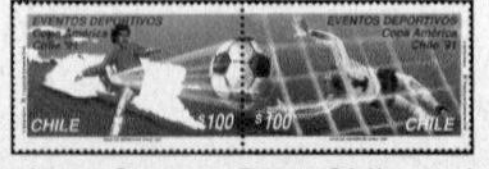


American Soccer Cup, Chile — A482

**1991, Apr. 12 Litho.** ***Perf. 13½***
**948** 100p Player, map 1.25 .75
**949** 100p Ball, goalie 1.25 .75
*a.* A482 Pair, #948-949 2.75 2.25

Coal Mining A483

Design: No. 951, Miners dumping cart of coal.

**1991, Apr. 18**
**950** A483 200p shown 2.25 1.10
**951** A483 200p multicolored 2.25 1.10
*a.* Pair, #950-951 5.00 3.75

Cultural Art — A484

**1991, Apr. 29**
**952** 90p multicolored 1.25 1.00
**953** 90p multicolored 1.25 1.00
*a.* A484 Pair, #952-953 2.75 2.25

Chilean Scientific Society, Cent. — A485

**1991, Apr. 29**
**954** A485 45p blue grn & blk .75 .50

**Nos. 782-783 Surcharged**

a

b

**1991, Apr. 30**
**955** A425(a) 45p on 20p, #782 .75 .40
**956** A425(b) 45p on 20p, #783 .75 .40
*a.* Pair, #955-956 2.00 1.00

Nos. 832-833 Surcharged

**1991, May 6 Litho.** ***Perf. 13½***
**956B** A447 45p on 25p, #832 1.00 .40
**956C** A447 45p on 25p, #833 1.00 .40
*d.* Pair, #956B-956C 2.50 1.25

Santiago Cathedral — A486

**1991, May 9** **Litho & Engr.**
**957** A486 300p red brn, sal & blk 4.00 2.75

World Telecommunications Day — A487

**1991, May 17** **Litho.**
**958** A487 90p multicolored 1.50 1.25

A488

**1991, May 23**
**959** A488 100p Pope Leo XIII 1.25 1.00

Rerum Novarum Encyclical, cent.

A489

Rescue of Shackleton Expedition, 75th anniv.: a, Lt. Luis Pardo, Sir Ernest Shackleton. b, Rescue ship, Yelcho. c, Sailor pointing to survivors. d, Shackleton's ship, Endurance.

**1991, May 28 Litho.** ***Perf. 13½***
**960** A489 50p Block of 4, #a.-d. 5.75 3.50
*e.* Miniature sheet, #960 4.50 3.50

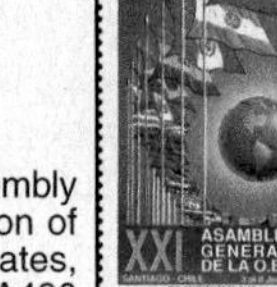


21st General Assembly of Organization of American States, Santiago — A490

**1991, June 5**
**961** A490 70p multicolored 1.25 1.00

New Carabinero School A491

**1991, June 12**
**962** A491 50p multicolored .85 .60

Natl. Merchant Marine Day — A492

**1991, June 26**
**963** A492 45p black & red .85 .60

11th Pan American Games, Havana A493

**1991, July 23**
**964** A493 100p Runners, torch, flags 1.25 1.00
**965** A493 100p Cycling, running, basketball 1.25 1.00
*a.* Pair, #964-965 3.00 2.50

Founding of the City of Los Andes, Bicent. — A494

**1991, July 29**
**966** A494 100p multicolored 1.50 1.25

**Miniature Sheet**

Marine Life — A495

Designs: No. 967a, Octopus vulgaris. b, Durvillaea antarctica. c, Paralichthys adspersus. d, Austromegabalanus psittacus. e, Concholepas concholepas. f, Cancer setosus. g, Lessonia nigrescens. h, Loxechinus albus. i, Homalaspis plana. j, Porphyra columbina. k, Oplegnathus insignis. l, Chorus giganteus. m, Rhynchocinetes typus. n, Engraulis ringens. o, Gracilaria spp. p, Pyura chilensis.

**1991, Aug. 20 Litho.** ***Perf. 13½***
**967** Sheet of 16 24.00 10.00
*a.-p.* A495 50p any single 1.00 .50

1891 Revolution, Cent. — A496

Jose M. Balmaceda (1840-1891) and: No. 968, Machinery. No. 969, Teacher, students at Valentin Letelier School of Medicine.

**1991, Aug. 29**
**968** 100p multicolored 1.40 .60
**969** 100p multicolored 1.40 .60
*a.* A496 Pair, #968-969 2.75 1.50

Chilean Art — A497

Paintings: 50p, Woman in Red, by Pedro Reszka. 70p, The Traveler, by Camilo Mori. 200p, Head of Child, by Benito Rebolledo. 300p, Boy Wearing a Fez, by A. Valenzuela Puelma.

**1991, Sept. 26**
**970** A497 50p multicolored .70 .30
**971** A497 70p multicolored .65 .40
**972** A497 200p multicolored 2.75 1.00
**973** A497 300p multicolored 4.00 1.50
*Nos. 970-973 (4)* 8.10 3.20

Antarctic Treaty, 30th Anniv. — A498

**1991, Oct. 7 Litho. *Perf. 13½***

**974** A498 80p shown 2.25 1.50
**975** A498 80p Birds, sea life 2.25 1.50
*a.* Pair, #974-975 5.00 4.00

Intl. Letter Writing Week — A499

**1991, Oct. 9**

**976** A499 45p shown .60 .45
**977** A499 70p Envelope filled with people 1.00 .65

America Issue — A500

UPAEP emblem, sailing ships and: 150p, Navigator.

**1991, Oct. 14**

**978** A500 50p multicolored 1.75 1.50
**979** A500 150p multicolored 3.50 3.25

A501

**1991, Oct. 21**

**980** 45p blue hat 1.25 1.00
**981** 45p red hat 1.25 1.00
*a.* A501 Pair, #980-981 3.25 2.75
*b.* Souvenir sheet of 2, #980-981 4.50 3.00

Pablo Neruda, (1904-1973), Nobel Prize winner for literature, 1971.

A502

**1991, Nov. 4**

**982** A502 45p Boy with stars .75 .50
**983** A502 100p Girl with stars 1.25 1.00

Christmas.

Christmas
A503 A504

**1991, Nov. 18 Litho. *Perf. 13½***

**984** A503 45p violet & brt pink 1.25 .30
**985** A504 45p violet & brt pink 1.25 .30
*a.* Pair, #984-985 2.75 2.00
*b.* Bklt. pane of 5 #985a 7.50
**986** A503 45p violet & brt pink 1.25 .30
**987** A504 45p violet & brt pink 1.25 .30
*a.* Pair, #986-987 2.75 2.00
*b.* Bklt. pane of 5 #987a 7.50
*Nos. 984-987 (4)* 5.00 1.20

Nos. 986-987 inscribed "D.S. No. 20."
For surcharges see Nos. 1016-1019.

**Environmental Protection Type of 1990**

**1992, Jan. 28 Litho. *Perf. 13½***

**Lemon & Black**

**988** A470 60p like #897 1.00 .40
**989** A470 60p like #898 1.00 .40
**990** A470 60p like #899 1.00 .40
**991** A470 60p like #900 1.00 .40
**992** A470 60p like #901 1.00 .40
*a.* Strip of 5, #988-992 5.25 4.00
*b.* Bklt. pane, 2 each #988-992 10.00

**Inscribed "D.S. No. 20"**

**Orange & Dark Green**

**993** A470 60p like #902 1.00 .40
**994** A470 60p like #903 1.00 .40
**995** A470 60p like #904 1.00 .40
**996** A470 60p like #905 1.00 .40
**997** A470 60p like #906 1.00 .40
*a.* Strip of 5, #993-997 5.25 4.00
*b.* Bklt. pane, 2 each #993-997 10.00
*Nos. 988-997 (10)* 10.00 4.00

Wolfgang Amadeus Mozart, Death Bicent. (in 1991) — A505

**1992, Jan. 31**

**998** A505 60p shown .75 .40
**999** A505 200p Hands at piano 2.25 1.25
*a.* Sheet of 2, #998-999 4.50 4.50

FIDAE '92, Intl. Air and Space Fair — A506

**1992, Mar. 5 Litho. *Perf. 13½***

**1000** A506 60p multicolored .85 .60

16th Population and Housing Census — A507

**1992, Mar.**

**1001** A507 60p multicolored .85 .60

No. 847 Surcharged in Red Brown

**1992, Mar.**

**1002** A452 60p on 45p .85 .60

Chilean Cities A508

Cities' coat of arms and: 80p, Church of San Jose de Maipo. 90p, People making pottery. 100p, Lircunlauta House. 150p, Wine and lumber industries. 250p, Huilquilemu cultural center.

**1992, Apr. 10 Litho. *Perf. 13½***

**1003** A508 80p multicolored .85 .65
**1004** A508 90p multicolored 1.00 .65
**1005** A508 100p multicolored 1.20 .95
**1006** A508 150p multicolored 1.75 1.60
**1007** A508 250p multicolored 2.75 2.10
*Nos. 1003-1007 (5)* 7.55 5.95

80p, San Jose de Maipo, 200th anniv. 90p, Melipilla, 250th anniv. 100p, San Fernando, 250th anniv. 150p, Cauquenes, 250th anniv. 250p, Talca, 250th anniv.

Expo '92, Seville A509

**1992, Apr. 23**

**1008** A509 150p Pavilion 1.40 1.00
**1009** A509 200p Iceberg 2.50 2.00
*a.* Sheet of 2, #1008-1009 *5.00 5.00*

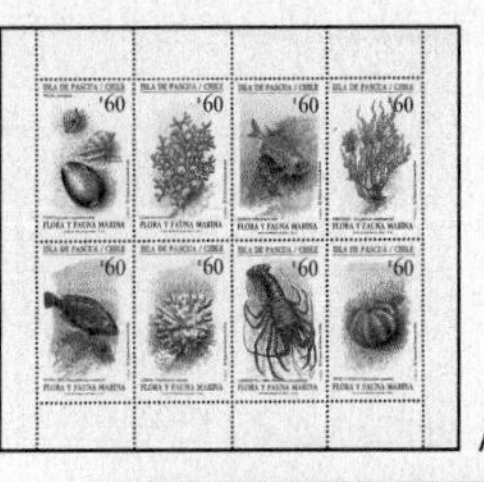

A510

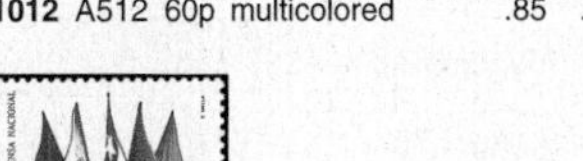

Easter Island — A511

Marine life: No. 1010a, Morula praecipua, Strombus maculatus, Cypraea caputdraconis. b, Codium pocockiae. c, Myripristis tiki. d, Sargassum skottsbergii. e, Pseudolabrus fuentesi. f, Pocillopora danae. g, Panulirus pascuensis. h, Tripneustes gratilla.
No. 1011b, Natives, airplane, petroglyph.

**1992, June 9 Litho. *Perf. 13½***

**1010** A510 60p Sheet of 8, #a.-h. 12.00 10.00
**1011** A511 200p Pair, #a.-b. 5.25 5.00

Natl. Council of the Disabled — A512

**1992, June 23**

**1012** A512 60p multicolored .85 .60

Military Chiefs of Staff, 50th Anniv. — A513

**1992, July 3**

**1013** A513 60p multicolored .85 .60

Submarine Forces, 75th Anniv. A514

Coat of arms and: 250p, Officer using periscope, control room.

**1992, July 4**

**1014** A514 150p multicolored 1.75 1.50
**1015** A514 250p multicolored 2.75 2.50

Nos. 984-987 Surcharged

**1992, Aug. 11 Litho. *Perf. 13½***

**1016** A503 60p on 45p No. 984 1.25 .60
**1017** A504 60p on 45p No. 985 1.25 .60
*a.* Pair, #1016-1017 3.00 1.50
**1018** A503 60p on 45p No. 986 1.25 .60
**1019** A504 60p on 45p No. 987 1.25 .60
*a.* Pair, #1018-1019 3.00 1.50
*Nos. 1016-1019 (4)* 5.00 2.40

Nos. 1018-1019 inscribed "D.S. No. 20."

Emperor Penguins — A515

**1992, Sept. 28 Litho. *Perf. 13½***

**1020** A515 200p shown 1.75 1.75
**1021** A515 250p Adults with young 3.25 2.40
*a.* Souv. sheet of 2, #1020-1021 6.75 6.75

Central Post Office, Santiago, 1772 — A516

**1992, Oct. 9**

**1022** A516 200p multicolored 2.00 1.75

Discovery of America, 500th Anniv. A517

UPAEP emblem and: 200p, Calendar stone, astrolabe, Columbus. 250p, Church, map of Central and South America, sailing ship.

**1992, Oct. 20**

**1023** A517 200p multicolored 3.00 2.75
**1024** A517 250p multicolored 3.50 3.25

Radio Chile, 75th Anniv. — A518

**1992, Oct. 22**

**1025** A518 250p multicolored 2.25 2.00

Bernardo O'Higgins (1778-1842) — A519

**1992, Oct. 23**

**1026** A519 60p multicolored .85 .60

Claudio Arrau, Pianist A520

**1992, Nov. 12 Litho. *Perf. 13½***

**1027** A520 150p As child 1.75 1.10
**1028** A520 200p As adult 2.25 1.50
*a.* Souv. sheet of 2, #1027-1028 4.00 4.00

Natl. Human Rights Day — A521

**1992, Dec. 10**

**1029** A521 100p multicolored 1.00 .60
*a.* Souvenir sheet of 1 1.75 1.75

Christmas — A522

Designs: Nos. 1030, 1032, Denomination at LR. Nos. 1031, 1033, Denomination at LL.

**1992, Dec. 12 Litho. *Perf. 13½***

| No. | Type | Description | Unused | Used |
|---|---|---|---|---|
| 1030 | A522 | 60p buff & brown | 1.25 | .60 |
| 1031 | A522 | 60p buff & brown | 1.25 | .60 |
| a. | | Pair, #1030-1031 | 3.50 | 2.75 |
| b. | | Booklet pane of 5 #1031a | 14.50 | 14.50 |
| 1032 | A522 | 60p buff & red | 1.25 | .60 |
| 1033 | A522 | 60p buff & red | 1.25 | .60 |
| a. | | Pair, #1032-1033 | 3.50 | 2.75 |
| b. | | Booklet pane of 5 #1033a | 14.50 | |
| | | *Nos. 1030-1033 (4)* | 5.00 | 2.40 |

Nos. 1032-1033 inscribed "DS/20."

A523

University of Chile, 150th Anniv.: a, Statue. b, Coat of arms, facade of building.

**1992, Nov. 19 Litho. *Perf. 13½***

| No. | Type | Description | Unused | Used |
|---|---|---|---|---|
| 1034 | A523 | 200p Pair, #a.-b. | 3.50 | 3.00 |
| c. | | Souvenir sheet of 1, #1034 | 6.50 | 6.00 |

Nos. 1034a-1034b have a continuous design.

A524

**1992, Dec. 12**

| No. | Type | Description | Unused | Used |
|---|---|---|---|---|
| 1035 | A524 | 70p black & yellow | 1.25 | 1.00 |

23rd meeting of Latin American Energy Ministers.

Churches of Chiloe — A525

Nos. 1036, 1038, Achao. Nos. 1037, 1039, Castro.

**1993, Mar. 1 Litho. *Perf. 13½***

| No. | Type | Description | Unused | Used |
|---|---|---|---|---|
| 1036 | A525 | 70p black & pink | 1.00 | .75 |
| 1037 | A525 | 70p black & pink | 1.00 | .75 |
| a. | | Pair #1036-1037 | 2.00 | 2.00 |
| b. | | Booklet pane of 5 #1037a | 10.00 | |

**Inscribed "DS/20"**

| No. | Type | Description | Unused | Used |
|---|---|---|---|---|
| 1038 | A525 | 70p black & yellow | 1.00 | .75 |
| 1039 | A525 | 70p black & yellow | 1.00 | .75 |
| a. | | Pair, #1038-1039 | 2.00 | 2.00 |
| b. | | Booklet pane of 5 #1039a | 10.00 | |
| | | *Nos. 1036-1039 (4)* | 4.00 | 3.00 |

See Nos. 1053-1060, 1093-1098.
For surcharges see Nos. 1129-1130.

Arrival of the Jesuits, 400th Anniv.
A526

Canonization of St. Teresa of the Andes, 1993
A527

200p, St. Ignatius of Loyola. 300p, St. Teresa of the Andes.

**1993 Litho. *Perf. 13½***

| No. | Type | Description | Unused | Used |
|---|---|---|---|---|
| 1040 | A526 | 200p multicolored | 2.25 | 2.00 |
| a. | | Souvenir sheet of 1 | 3.25 | 3.25 |
| 1041 | A527 | 300p multicolored | 2.90 | 2.60 |

Issue dates: 200p, Mar. 15; 300p, Mar. 31. No. 1040a sold for 250p.

World Festival of Theatre of the Nations — A528

**1993, Apr. 22**

| No. | Type | Description | Unused | Used |
|---|---|---|---|---|
| 1042 | A528 | 250p multicolored | 2.25 | 2.00 |

Second Space Conference of the Americas
A529

**1993, Apr. 26**

| No. | Type | Description | Unused | Used |
|---|---|---|---|---|
| 1043 | A529 | 150p multicolored | 1.75 | 1.50 |
| a. | | Souvenir sheet of 1 | 3.50 | 3.50 |

No. 1043a sold for 350p.

Clotario Blest (1899-1990), Syndicalist — A530

**1993, Apr. 30**

| No. | Type | Description | Unused | Used |
|---|---|---|---|---|
| 1044 | A530 | 70p multicolored | .85 | .60 |

Intl. Labor Day.

Vicente Huidobro, Poet (1893-1948) — A531

**1993, May 19 Litho. *Perf. 13½***

| No. | Type | Description | Unused | Used |
|---|---|---|---|---|
| 1045 | | 100p shown | 1.00 | .65 |
| 1046 | | 100p Portrait, seated | 1.00 | .65 |
| a. | A531 | Pair, #1045-1046 | 2.50 | 2.00 |

Antique Fire Engines
A532

Nos. 1047, 1902 Watterous Engineering Co. Ltd., Canada. Nos. 1048, 1872 Merryweather, England.

**1993, June 30 Litho. *Perf. 13½***

| No. | Type | Description | Unused | Used |
|---|---|---|---|---|
| 1047 | A532 | 100p multicolored | 2.00 | 1.50 |
| 1048 | A532 | 100p multicolored | 2.00 | 1.50 |
| a. | | Souv. sheet of 2, #1047-1048 | 4.25 | 3.75 |

No. 1048a sold for 400p.

Aircraft
A533

Designs: No. 1049, Douglas B-26 Invader. No. 1050, Mirage M50 Panther. No. 1051, Sanchez Besa. No. 1052, Bell 47D1 helicopter.

**1993, July 13**

| No. | Type | Description | Unused | Used |
|---|---|---|---|---|
| 1049 | A533 | 100p multicolored | 1.00 | .50 |
| 1050 | A533 | 100p multicolored | 1.00 | .50 |
| 1051 | A533 | 100p multicolored | 1.00 | .50 |
| 1052 | A533 | 100p multicolored | 1.00 | .50 |
| a. | | Block of 4, #1049-1052 | 4.50 | 4.00 |

**Church Type of 1993**

Designs: 10p, Chonchi. 20p, Vilupulli. 30p, Llau-llao. 40p, Dalcahue. 50p, Tenaun. 80p, Quinchao. 90p, Quehui. 100p, Nercon.

**1993, July Litho. *Perf. 13½***

| No. | Type | Description | Unused | Used |
|---|---|---|---|---|
| 1053 | A525 | 10p green & black | .30 | .30 |
| 1054 | A525 | 20p black & brown | .30 | .30 |
| 1055 | A525 | 30p black & ver | .30 | .30 |
| 1056 | A525 | 40p black & blue | .40 | .40 |
| 1057 | A525 | 50p blk & grn blue | .50 | .50 |
| 1058 | A525 | 80p black & buff | .85 | .85 |
| a. | | Inscribed "1994" | 1.00 | 1.00 |
| b. | | Booklet pane of 10 #1058a | 8.50 | |
| | | Complete booklet, #1058b | 10.00 | |
| 1059 | A525 | 90p olive & black | .90 | .90 |
| a. | | Booklet pane of 10 | 9.00 | |
| | | Complete booklet, #1059a | 9.50 | |
| 1060 | A525 | 100p gray vio & blk | 1.00 | 1.00 |
| a. | | Booklet pane of 10 | 10.00 | |
| | | Complete booklet, #1060a | 10.50 | |
| | | *Nos. 1053-1060 (8)* | 4.55 | 4.55 |

Issued: No. 1058a, 1/1/94; No. 1059a, 1995; No. 1060a, 2/1/96.
See Nos. 1093-1097.

Natl. Dance, "La Cueca" — A534

**1993, Sept. 15 Litho. *Perf. 13½***

| No. | Type | Description | Unused | Used |
|---|---|---|---|---|
| 1061 | A534 | 70p Cueca chilota | .90 | .40 |
| 1062 | A534 | 70p Cueca central | .90 | .40 |
| 1063 | A534 | 70p Cueca nortina | .90 | .40 |
| | | *Nos. 1061-1063 (3)* | 2.70 | 1.20 |

Paintings — A535

Designs: 80p, Tarde Amanecer, by Mario Carreno, horiz. 90p, Summer, by Gracia Barrios, horiz. 150p, Figura Protegida, by Roser Bru. 200p, Tangueria-Valparaiso, by Nemesio Antunez, horiz.

**1993, Sept. 28**

| No. | Type | Description | Unused | Used |
|---|---|---|---|---|
| 1064 | A535 | 80p multicolored | .80 | .65 |
| 1065 | A535 | 90p multicolored | .95 | .75 |
| 1066 | A535 | 150p multicolored | 1.75 | 1.20 |
| 1067 | A535 | 200p multicolored | 2.25 | 1.60 |
| | | *Nos. 1064-1067 (4)* | 5.75 | 4.20 |

Chilean Mint, 250th Anniv. — A536

**1993, Oct. 7 Litho. & Engr.**

| No. | Type | Description | Unused | Used |
|---|---|---|---|---|
| 1068 | A536 | 250p multicolored | 2.60 | 2.40 |
| a. | | Souvenir sheet of 1 | 3.75 | 3.75 |

A537

**1993, Oct. 19 Litho.**

| No. | Type | Description | Unused | Used |
|---|---|---|---|---|
| 1069 | A537 | 80p multicolored | 1.25 | .60 |

Urban transportation system, 25th anniv.

A538

150p, Cyanoliseus patagonus. 200p, Hippocamelus bisulcus.

**1993, Oct. 12 Litho. *Perf. 13½***

| No. | Type | Description | Unused | Used |
|---|---|---|---|---|
| 1070 | A538 | 150p multicolored | 1.60 | 1.00 |
| 1071 | A538 | 200p multicolored | 2.90 | 1.25 |

America issue.

Chilean Possession of Straits of Magellan, 150th Anniv.
A539

**1993, Oct. 21**

| No. | Type | Description | Unused | Used |
|---|---|---|---|---|
| 1072 | A539 | 100p multicolored | 3.75 | .65 |

Naval Anniversaries
A540

**1993, Oct. 27**

| No. | Type | Description | Unused | Used |
|---|---|---|---|---|
| 1073 | A540 | 80p Sailing ships | 1.00 | .60 |
| 1074 | A540 | 80p Schooner | 1.00 | .60 |
| 1075 | A540 | 80p Assault ship | 1.00 | .60 |
| 1076 | A540 | 80p Patrol boat | 1.00 | .60 |
| | | *Nos. 1073-1076 (4)* | 4.00 | 2.40 |

Sailing of first naval squadron (No. 1073), Arturo Prat Naval Academy (No. 1074), Marine Corps (No. 1075), 175th anniversaries. Alejandro Navarette School for Cadets (No. 1076), 125th anniv.

Intl. Year of Indigenous Peoples
A541

**1993, Nov. 24**

| No. | Type | Description | Unused | Used |
|---|---|---|---|---|
| 1077 | A541 | 100p multicolored | 1.10 | .50 |

Christmas — A542

**1993, Dec. 1 Litho. *Perf. 13½***

| No. | Type | Description | Unused | Used |
|---|---|---|---|---|
| 1078 | A542 | 70p buff & brt lilac | 1.10 | .35 |
| a. | | Booklet pane of 10 | 11.00 | |
| 1079 | A542 | 70p apple grn & brt blue | 2.75 | .35 |
| a. | | Booklet pane of 10 | 17.50 | |

No. 1079 inscribed "DS/20."
For surcharge see No. 1131.

Pygoscelis Adelie — A543

**1993, Dec. 3**

| No. | Type | Description | Unused | Used |
|---|---|---|---|---|
| 1080 | A543 | 200p Nesting | 2.50 | .65 |
| 1081 | A543 | 250p Adult, chicks | 3.25 | 1.00 |
| a. | | Souv. sheet of 2, #1080-1081, imperf. | 7.00 | 7.00 |

Chilean Antarctica.
No. 1081a has simulated perfs.

Chilean Cities — A544

**1993, Dec. 15**

**1082** A544 80p Rancagua .90 .70
**1083** A544 80p Curico .90 .70
**1084** A544 80p Ancud .90 .70
*Nos. 1082-1084 (3)* 2.70 2.10

Rancagua and Curico, 250th anniv. Ancud, 225th anniv.

Nos. 943-946 Surcharged

**1993 Litho. *Perf. 13½on 3 Sides***

**1085** A447 60p on 45p, #943 1.20 .50
**1086** A447 60p on 45p, #944 1.20 .50
*a.* Bklt. pane, 5 each #1085-1086 12.00
**1087** A447 60p on 45p, #945 1.20 .50
**1088** A447 60p on 45p, #946 1.20 .50
*a.* Bklt. pane, 5 each #1087-1088 12.00
*Nos. 1085-1088 (4)* 4.80 2.00

Nos. 1087-1088 inscribed "D.S. No. 20."

Intl. Year of the Family — A545

**1994, Jan. 17 Litho. *Perf. 13½***

**1089** A545 100p multicolored 1.25 1.00

Musical Instruments — A546

Designs: a, Violin. b, Cello.

**1994, Jan. 27 Litho. *Perf. 13½***

**1091** A546 150p Pair, #a.-b. 3.75 3.75

No. 1091 has a continuous design.

### Church Type of 1993

Designs: 80p, Quinchao. 90p, Quehui. Nos. 1097, 1098, Nercon.

**1994-96 Litho. *Perf. 13½***

**1093** A525 80p black & violet .75 .50
*a.* Booklet pane of 10 — —
Complete booklet, #1093a —
**1095** A525 90p red & black .75 .50
*a.* Booklet pane of 10 7.50
Complete booklet, #1095a 7.50
**1097** A525 100p yellow & black .75 .50
*a.* Booklet pane of 10 7.50
Complete booklet, #1097a 7.50
*Nos. 1093-1097 (3)* 2.25 1.50

Issued: 80p, 1/13/94; 90p, 1995; 100p, 2/1/96.

Nos. 1093, 1095, 1097 inscribed "DS/20."

Souvenir Sheet

Natl. Aviation Museum, 50th Anniv. A547

Aircraft: a, Sukhoi SU-30 Flanker. b, Vought-Sikorsky OS-2U3 Kingfisher. c, Lockheed F-117A Nighthawk. d, Northrop F-5E Tiger III.

**1994, Mar. 17 Litho. *Perf. 13***

**1102** A547 300p Sheet of 4, #a.-d. + 2 labels 11.00 10.00

Intl. Air and Space Fair, FIDAE '94. See No. 1159.

College of Agronomy, 50th Anniv. — A548

**1994, Apr. 28 Litho. *Perf. 13***

**1103** A548 220p multicolored 1.75 1.50

No. 760 Surcharged

**1994, May 1 Litho. *Perf. 13½***

**1104** Block of 4 3.75 2.50
*a.-d.* A411 80p on 15p any single .75 .50

Concepcion University, 75th Anniv. A549

Sections of mural, by Jorge Gonzalez Camarena: No. 1105, Cactus plant, skeletons. No. 1106, Flags, pillars, nude woman, faces. No. 1107, Flags, bodies, woman, soldier in armor. No. 1108, Women's faces, pipelines.

**1994, May 14 Litho. *Perf. 13***

**1105** A549 250p multicolored 2.00 1.00
**1106** A549 250p multicolored 2.00 1.00
**1107** A549 250p multicolored 2.00 1.00
**1108** A549 250p multicolored 2.00 1.00
*a.* Strip of 4, #1105-1108 + label 8.50 6.00

No. 1108a is a continuous design.

Chilean Antarctic Institute, 30th Anniv. — A550

Designs: No. 1109, Penguins, buildings. No. 1110, Buildings, coastal waters.

**1994, May 31 *Perf. 13***

**1109** 300p multicolored 2.50 2.00
**1110** 300p multicolored 2.50 2.00
*a.* A550 Pair, #1109-1110 5.00 4.50

No. 1110a is a continuous design.

Antique Fire Engines A551

No. 1111, Merryweather steam pumper, England, 1869. No. 1112, Western lever pumper, US, 1863. No. 1113, Mieusset steam pumper, France, 1905. No. 1114, Merryweather pumper, England, 1903.

**1994, July 19 Litho. *Perf. 13***

**1111** A551 150p multicolored 1.25 1.00
**1112** A551 150p multicolored 1.25 1.00
**1113** A551 150p multicolored 1.25 1.00
**1114** A551 150p multicolored 1.25 1.00
*a.* Block of 4, #1111-1114 5.50 4.50

Javiera Carrera Girls' School, Cent. — A552

**1994, Aug. 10**

**1115** A552 200p multicolored 1.75 1.50

Arms, Sights from Chilean Cities — A553

Designs: 90p, Porvenir, cent. 100p, Villa Alemana, cent. 150p, Constitucion, bicent. 200p, Linares, bicent. 250p, Copiapo, 250th anniv. 300p, La Serena, 450th anniv.

**1994, Aug. 26**

**1116** A553 90p multicolored .75 .30
**1117** A553 100p multicolored .95 .40
**1118** A553 150p multicolored 1.50 .50
**1119** A553 200p multicolored 2.00 .70
**1120** A553 250p multicolored 2.40 1.00
**1121** A553 300p multicolored 2.75 1.00
*Nos. 1116-1121 (6)* 10.35 3.90

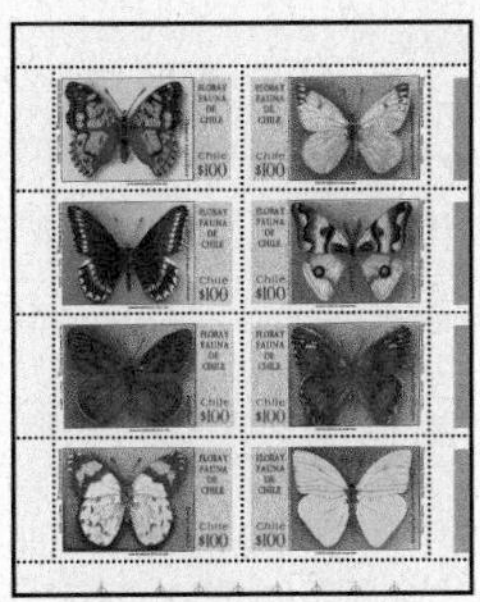

Butterflies — A554

Designs: a, Vanessa terpsichore. b, Hypsochila wagenknechti. c, Battus polydamas. d, Polythysana apollina. e, Satyridae. f, Tetraphloebia stellygera. g, Eroessa chilensis. h, Phoebis sennae.

**1994, June 24 Litho. *Perf. 13***

**1122** A554 100p Sheet of 8, #a.-h. 11.00 11.00

20th Intl. Conference on Data Bases — A555

**1994, Sept. 21 Litho. *Perf. 13½***

**1123** A555 100p multicolored 1.00 .75

America Issue — A556

Early postal transport vehicles: 80p, Van. 220p, DH-60-G, Gypsy Moth.

**1994, Oct. 12**

**1124** A556 80p multicolored 1.25 .50
**1125** A556 220p multicolored 2.25 1.00

A557

**1994, Oct. 31 Litho. & Engr.**

**1126** A557 300p multicolored 2.25 2.00

Beatification of Father Alberto Hurtado.

A558

**1994 Litho. *Perf. 13½***

**1127** A558 80p multicolored 1.25 .75
*a.* Booklet pane of 10 12.50
Complete booklet, #1127a 10.00

**Inscribed "DS/20"**

**1128** A558 80p multicolored 1.25 1.00
*a.* Booklet pane of 10 12.50
Complete booklet, #1128a 13.00

Christmas.

Nos. 1036-1037, 1079 Surcharged

***Perf. 13½ on 3 Sides***

**1994, Nov. 4 Litho.**

**1129** A525 80p on 70p #1036 1.20 .75
**1130** A525 80p on 70p #1037 1.20 .75
*a.* Pair, #1129-1130 2.50 2.00
*b.* Booklet pane, 5 #1130a 6.00
Complete booklet, #1130b 6.00
**1131** A542 80p on 70p #1079 1.20 .75
*a.* Booklet pane, 10 #1131 12.00
Complete booklet, #1131a 12.50

Size and location of surcharge varies.

Miniature Sheet

Intl. Women's Day A559

Designs: a, Star, "Women enriching the future." b, Moon, sun, "Women bringing harmony." c, Bird, "Women bringing peace." d, Earth, "Women changing the world."

**1995, Mar. 8 Litho. *Perf. 13½***

**1132** A559 90p Sheet of 4, #a.-d. 7.00 3.50

Ancud Seminary of Conciliation, 150th Anniv. — A560

**1995, Apr. 27**

**1133** A560 200p multicolored 1.75 1.25

Destroyer Admiral Williams — A561

**1995, Apr. 21**

**1134** A561 100p multicolored 4.75 4.50

World Conference on Social Development — A562

**1995, Apr. 25**

**1135** A562 150p multicolored 1.50 1.25

Order of St. Augustine in Chile, 400th Anniv. A563

Stained glass, Cathedral of Santiago.

**1995, Apr. 28**
**1136** A563 250p multicolored 8.00 3.50

Petroglyphs — A564

Designs: a, Ceremonial mask, Buitre, Limari Province. b, Lamas, Taira Sector, El Loa Province. c, Harpooned whale, El Medano, Taltal Province. d, Two masks, Encanto, Ovalle.

**1995, June 16** **Litho.** ***Perf. 13½***
**1137** A564 150p Block of 4, #a.-d. 10.75 9.75

Miniature Sheet

Motion Pictures, Cent. — A565

Posters: a, Director's chair, camera. b, Charlie Chaplin in "The Kid." c, Lumiere brothers' 1895 Cinematographe. d, "Valparaiso, My Love", with Aldo Francia.

**1995, June 21**
**1138** A565 100p Sheet of 4, #a.-d. 8.00 5.00

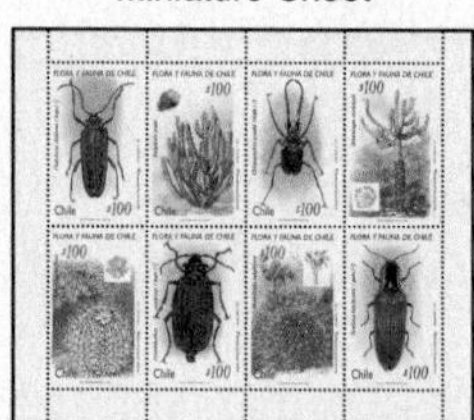

City of Parral, Bicent. A566

**1995, June 30** **Litho.** ***Perf. 13½***
**1139** A566 200p multicolored 1.75 1.00

Miniature Sheet

Insects and Cacti — A567

a, Cheloderus childreni. b, Eulychnia acida. c, Chiasognathus grantii. d, Browningia candelaris. e, Copiapoa dealbata. f, Acanthinodera cummingi. g, Neoporteria subgibbosa. h, Semiotus luteipennis.

**1995, Aug. 10** **Litho.** ***Perf. 13½***
**1140** A567 100p Sheet of 8, #a.-h. 13.50 9.00

2nd World Congress of Police, Santiago A568

**1995, Oct. 2**
**1141** A568 200p multicolored 1.90 1.60

Ministry of Housing and Urban Development, 30th Anniv. A569

Design: Tower of Babel V, by Mario Toral.

**1995, Oct. 5** **Litho.** ***Perf. 13½***
**1142** A569 200p multicolored 1.90 1.60

Andres Bello (1781-1865), Scholar, Author — A570

**1995, Oct. 9** **Litho. & Engr.**
**1143** A570 250p dk brn & blk 2.25 1.75

Andres Bello Covenant, 25th anniv.

UNESCO, UN, FAO, 50th Anniv. — A571

Designs: a, Hands holding book, UNESCO emblem. b, Hands clasped between two globes, UN emblem. c, Hand holding seedling, FAO emblem.

**1995, Oct. 10** **Litho.** ***Perf. 13½***
**1144** A571 100p Strip of 3, #a.-c. 3.50 2.75

America Issue — A572

Children's drawings of environmental protection: 100p, Family in garden, trees, vert. 250p, Three people working with trees.

**1995, Oct. 12** **Litho.** ***Perf. 13½***
**1145** A572 100p multicolored 1.25 .75
**1146** A572 250p multicolored 2.75 2.00

Chilean Soccer, Cent. — A573

Designs: a, Carlos Dittborn. b, Hugo Lepe. c, Eladio Rojas. d, Honorino Landa.

**1995, Nov. 13** **Litho.** ***Perf. 13½***
**1147** A573 100p Sheet of 4, #a.-d. 4.50 2.50

A574

**1995, Oct. 24** **Litho.** ***Perf. 13½***
**1148** A574 250p multicolored 2.50 2.25

51st World Congress of Cape Horn captains.

Gabriela Mistral (1889-1957), 50th Anniv. of Receiving Nobel Prize for Literature — A575

**Litho. & Engr.**

**1995, Nov. 15** ***Perf. 13½***
**1149** A575 300p blue black & blk 2.25 2.00

Eudyptes Chrysolophus A576

**1995, Nov. 22** **Litho.** ***Perf. 13½***
**1150** A576 100p shown 3.00 2.00
**1151** A576 250p Penguins, diff. 4.00 2.50
*a.* Souv. sheet, #1150-1151 11.50 6.50

No. 1151a sold for 600p.

Chilean Export Assoc., 60th Anniv. A577

Cargo ship and: a, Kiwi fruit. b, Grapes. c, Peaches. d, Apples.
Jet plane and: e, Various berries.

**1995, Dec. 1**
**1152** A577 100p Strip of 5, #a.-e. 13.50 8.50

Christmas
A578 A579

**1995, Nov. 13** **Booklet Stamps**
**1153** A578 90p brt blue & blue 1.25 .75
**1154** A579 90p brt blue & blue 1.25 .75
*a.* Bklt. pane, 5 ea #1153-1154 12.50
Complete booklet, #1154a 11.00
**1155** A578 90p brt grn & brown 1.25 .75
**1156** A579 90p brt grn & brown 1.25 .75
*a.* Bklt. pane, 5 ea #1155-1156 10.50
Complete booklet, #1156a 11.00

Nos. 1155-1156 inscribed "DS/20."

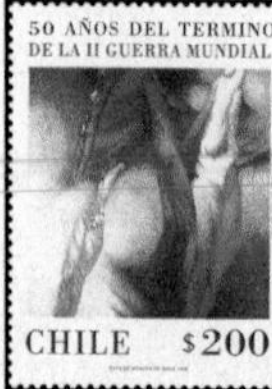

End of World War II, 50th Anniv. — A580

**1995, Dec. 20** **Litho.** ***Perf. 13½***
**1157** A580 200p multicolored 2.75 1.50

Petroleum Production in Chile, 50th Anniv. — A581

Designs: a, Off-shore oil derrick, one main tower. b, Refinery, road trees, building. c, Refinery, up close. d, Off-shore oil derrick, four towers.

**1995, Dec. 29**
**1158** A581 100p Block of 4, #a.-d. 6.00 5.00

**Aviation Type of 1994**

Designs: a, Embraer EMB-145. b, Mirage M5M Elkan. c, DHC-6 Twin Otter Series 300. d, SAAB JAS 39, Gripen.

**1996, Mar. 9** **Litho.** ***Perf. 13½***
**1159** A547 400p Sheet of 4, #a.-d. 14.00 9.00

Intl. Air and Space Fair, FIDAE '96.

Men's High School, La Serena, 175th Anniv. A582

**1996, Apr. 12**
**1160** A582 100p multicolored .95 .70

Espamer '96, World Philatelic Exhibition A583

Designs: No. 1161, Old Train Station, Cordoba. No. 1162, Lope de Vega Theater.

**1996, Apr. 25**
**1161** A583 200p multicolored 3.50 1.50
**1162** A583 200p multicolored 3.50 1.50
*a.* Pair, #1161-1162 6.50 6.00

Accident Prevention — A584

Traffic safety: No. 1163a, Cross street at crosswalk. b, Respect traffic police. c, Obey traffic signals. d, Wait for ride on sidewalk. e, Don't cross street between parked cars. f, Never ride on side of bus. g, Walk beside road facing oncoming traffic. h, Pay attention to where you are walking. i, Don't play on streets. j, Obey traffic rules while riding a bicycle.

Safety in the home: No. 1164a, Extinguish matches after using. b, Be careful with boiling water. c, Curb sharp objects. d, Protect electrical outlets. e, Don't improvise electrical connections. f, Don't play radio or TV too loudly. g, Check all gas connections. h, Don't overload electrical outlets. i, Keep flammable materials away from furnace. j, Keep toys off floor.

Recreational safety: No. 1165a, Swim only in designated areas. b, Keep hands, head inside the car. c, Don't get a sunburn. d, Don't contaminate water with detergents. e, Don't litter. f, Extinguish camp fires. g, Don't bother others when swimming. h, Check car safety features. i, Keep kites away from electrical wires. j, Don't run in swimming pool area.

Safety in the workplace: No. 1166a, Use protective gear. b, Use only safe tools. c, Keep you mind on your work. d, Use proper tools. e, Avoid work accidents. f, Keep stairs free of objects. g, Don't carry objects that obstruct your view. h, Check ladder before using. i, Keep area clean, organized. j, Be aware of protruding nails.

Proper use of drugs and alcohol: No. 1167a, Don't drink and drive. b, Don't drink if you are pregnant. c, Don't encourage friends to drink. d, Alcohol and work don't mix. e, Drinking could destroy your family. f, Drugs can't make you happy. g, Drugs don't make you successful. h, Be happy without drugs. i, For your family say "no" to drugs. j, Drug free, happy and confident.

Safety in schools: No. 1168a, Keep calm in case of fire. b, Don't run along sides of buildings. c, Don't play dangerous jokes. d, Don't sit or stand in high dangerous places. e, Don't run on stairs. f, Don't walk and drink at the same time. g, Don't rock on chairs. h, Don't play with sharp objects. i, Don't open doors abruptly. j, Don't talk to strangers outside the school.

**1996, May 2**

**1163** A584 50p Block of 10, #a.-j. 11.00 8.00
**1164** A584 50p Block of 10, #a.-j. 11.00 8.00
**1165** A584 50p Block of 10, #a.-j. 11.00 8.00
**1166** A584 50p Block of 10, #a.-j. 11.00 8.00
**1167** A584 50p Block of 10, #a.-j. 11.00 8.00
**1168** A584 50p Block of 10, #a.-j. 11.00 8.00

No. 1 Dry Dock, Talcahuano, Cent. — A585

**1996, May 20**

**1169** A585 200p multicolored 1.60 1.40

Sculptures A586

No. 1170, Mariner's Compass, by Ricardo Mesa, vert. No. 1171, Friendship, by Francisca Cerda, vert. No. 1172, Andes Winds, by Benito Rojo. No. 1173, Memory, by Fernando Undurraga.

**1996, June 20 Litho. *Perf. 13½***

**1170** A586 150p multicolored 1.90 1.25
**1171** A586 150p multicolored 1.90 1.25
*a.* Pair, #1170-1171 5.00 5.00
**1172** A586 200p multicolored 2.50 1.25
**1173** A586 200p multicolored 2.50 1.25
*a.* Pair, #1172-1173 6.75 6.75
*Nos. 1170-1173 (4)* 8.80 5.00

Intl. Day Against Use of Illegal Drugs and Drug Trafficking A587

**1996, June 26**

**1174** A587 250p multicolored 3.75 3.50

1996 Summer Olympic Games, Atlanta A588

Designs: a, Boxer's glove. b, Runner's shoe. c, Roller blade. d, Ball.

**1996, July 3**

**1175** A588 450p Block of 4, #a.-d. 14.50 12.50

Order of Mother of God, 50th Anniv. of Presence in Chile — A589

**1996, Aug. Litho. *Perf. 13½***

**1176** A589 200p multicolored 1.75 1.50

Lyceum of San Fernando, 150th Anniv. A590

**1996, Aug. 2**

**1177** A590 200p multicolored 1.75 1.50

4th Intl. Congress of Earth Sciences — A591

Globe showing portions of continents, and: a, Forest fire. b, Smoke stacks creating air pollution. c, Cutting down trees. d, Surveying equipment, desert.

**1996, Aug. 5 Litho. *Perf. 13½***

**1178** A591 200p Block of 4, #a.-d. 7.75 7.75

Minerals — A592

a, Kroehnkita. b, Lapis lazuli. c, Bornite. d, Azurite.

**1996, Aug. 9**

**1179** A592 150p Block of 4, #a.-d. 6.00 5.00

German Immigration, 150th Anniv. — A593

Designs: 250p, House, lake, mountain. 300p, Monument showing arrival on boat.

**1996, Aug. 22**

**1180** A593 250p multicolored 2.00 1.25
**1181** A593 300p multicolored 2.50 1.50

Aptenodytes Patagonica — A594

**1996, Sept. 9 Litho. *Perf. 13½***

**1182** A594 250p shown 3.50 1.75
**1183** A594 300p Molting 4.50 2.25
*a.* Souvenir sheet, #1182-1183 9.50 8.00

Castro Fire Dept., Cent. A595

Designs: a, 1937 Italian pumper. b, 1940 Ford fire truck. c, Gorlitz G.A. Fischer manual 4-speed pumper. d, 1907 pumper.

**1996, Sept. 14**

**1184** A595 200p Block of 4, #a.-d. 8.00 6.50

Ecotourism in National Parks — A596

Designs: a, River rafting. b, Horseback riding. c, Snow skiing. d, Hiking around cacti.

**1996, Sept. 27**

**1185** A596 100p Sheet of 4, #a.-d. 4.25 4.25

Juan José Latorre Benavente (1846-1912), Admiral — A597

**1996, Oct. 8**

**1186** A597 200p multicolored 1.75 1.25

Historical Costumes A598

America issue: No. 1187, Two women, child, dog, vert. No. 1188, Two men with horse, vert. 250p, Two men on horseback.

**1996, Oct. 23**

**1187** A598 100p multicolored 1.20 .75
**1188** A598 100p multicolored 1.20 .75
*a.* Pair, #1187-1188 2.50 2.50
**1189** A598 250p multicolored 2.10 1.40

Church, City of Arica — A599

150p, Fauna, mountains, Parinacota Park.

**1996, Nov. 18 Litho. *Perf. 13½***

**1190** A599 100p multicolored .90 .75
**1191** A599 150p multicolored 1.40 1.00

Christmas — A600

**1996, Nov. 25**

**1192** A600 100p black & multi 1.90 1.40
*a.* Booklet pane of 10 22.50
Complete booklet, #1192a 23.00
**1193** A600 100p orange & multi 1.90 1.40
*a.* Booklet pane of 10 23.50
Complete booklet, #1193a 23.00

No. 1193 is inscribed DS/20.

Mythology A601 A602

**1997, Feb. 12 Litho. *Perf. 13½***

**1194** A601 40p black & blue .35 .30
**1195** A602 110p black & green 1.10 .65
*a* Booklet pane of 10 11.00
Complete booklet, #1195a 11.50
**1196** A602 110p black & orange 1.10 .65
*a.* Booklet pane of 10 11.00
Complete booklet, #1196a 11.50

No. 1195 inscribed DS/20.

Sixth Summit of Spanish-Americana Heads of State and Government — A603

Mural, Visual Memory of the Nation, by Mario Toral: No. 1198, Left half. No. 1199, Right half.

**1996, Nov. 6**

**1198** 110p multicolored 1.00 .60
**1199** 110p multicolored 1.00 .60
*a.* A603 Pair, #1198-1199 2.50 1.50

State Visit of King Carl XVI Gustaf, Queen Silvia of Sweden — A604

Design: Nobel Laureates Pablo Neruda, Gabriela Mistral, Nobel medal.

**1996, Dec. 3**

**1200** A604 300p multicolored 2.50 2.00

UNICEF, 50th Anniv. — A605

**1996, Dec. 11**

**1201** A605 200p multicolored 2.00 1.75

Frontier Region, Cent. — A606

No. 1202, Christian Alliance & Missionary Church, cent. No. 1203, Lonquimay municipality, cent.

**1997**

**1202** A606 110p multicolored 1.00 .75
**1203** A606 110p multicolored 1.25 1.00

Issued: No. 1202, 1/19; No. 1203, 1/25.

Arturo Prat Antarctic Naval Base, 50th Anniv. A607

**1997, Feb. 6** **Litho.** ***Perf. 13½***

**1204** A607 250p Aerial view, vert. 2.25 1.50
**1205** A607 300p shown 2.50 1.75

Controller General of the Republic, 70th Anniv. A608

**1997, Mar. 26**

**1206** A608 110p multicolored 2.25 1.50

Opening of Metro Line 5 — A609

**1997, Apr. 2**

**1207** A609 200p multicolored 2.25 1.50

Interamerican Masonic Confederation, 50th Anniv. — A610

1200p, Emblems, compass, square, book.

**1997, Apr. 8**

**1208** A610 250p shown 2.25 1.50

**Souvenir Sheet**

**1209** A610 1200p multicolored 9.25 9.25

No. 1209 contains one 48x60mm stamp.

Heinrich von Stephan (1831-97) — A611

**1997, Apr. 15**

**1210** A611 250p multicolored 2.50 1.50

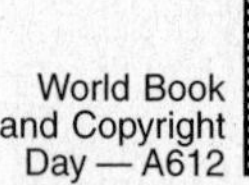

World Book and Copyright Day — A612

**1997, Apr. 23**

**1211** A612 110p multicolored 1.00 .75

Details from "Death to the Invader," by David Alfaro Siqueiros (1896-1974), Muralist A613

**1997, June 26** **Litho.** ***Perf. 13½***

**1212** A613 150p shown 1.75 .75
**1213** A613 200p Detail, diff. 2.00 .60

**Souvenir Sheets**

**1214** A613 1000p like #1212 7.50 6.50
**1215** A613 1000p like #1213 7.50 6.50

Nos. 1214-1215 each contain one 48x36mm stamp.

Providencia, Cent. — A614

**1997, July 17**

**1216** A614 250p multicolored 1.75 1.60

A615

**1997, Sept. 1**

**1217** A615 300p multicolored 2.25 2.00

Diplomatic relations between Chile and Japan, cent. See Japan No. 2578.

A616

**1997, Oct. 1** **Litho.** ***Perf. 13½***

**1218** A616 110p Quality 2.75 .80

1st Radio Broadcast in Chile, 75th Anniv. — A617

**1997** **Litho.** ***Perf. 13½***

**1219** A617 110p multicolored 1.10 .90

Chilean Opera Singers — A618

Singer, opera: 120p, Carlo Morelli, "Rigoletto." 200p, Pedro Navia, "La Bohéme." 250p, Renato Zanelli, "Faust." 300p, Rayèn Quitral, "The Magic Flute." 500p, Ramón Vinay, "Othello."

**1997, Oct. 15**

**1220** A618 120p multicolored 1.10 1.10
**1221** A618 200p multicolored 1.90 1.90
**1222** A618 250p multicolored 2.50 2.50
**1223** A618 300p multicolored 2.75 2.75
**1224** A618 500p multicolored 5.00 5.00
*Nos. 1220-1224 (5)* 13.25 13.25

America Issue — A619

Life of a postman: 110p, Delivering mail on bicycle. 250p, Delivering mail on horseback.

**1997, Oct. 12** **Litho.** ***Perf. 13½***

**1225** A619 110p multicolored 1.25 1.25
**1226** A619 250p multicolored 2.75 2.75

Christmas — A620

**1997** **Litho.** ***Perf. 13½***

**1227** A620 110p multicolored 1.75 .80
*a.* Booklet pane of 10 18.50
Complete booklet, #1227a 19.00
**1228** A620 110p multicolored 1.75 .80
*a.* Booklet pane of 10 18.50
Complete booklet, #1228a 19.00

No. 1228 is inscribed D/S20 and was only issued in booklets.

Chilean Post, 250th Anniv. — A621

Designs: 120p, Postman canceling letters. 300p, Man depositing letter into postbox.

**1997, Dec. 22**

**1229** A621 120p multicolored .90 .90
**1230** A621 300p multicolored 2.25 1.25

Dogs

A622 A623

**1998** **Litho.** ***Perf. 13½***

**1231** A622 120p Great Dane .90 .50
**1232** A623 120p Dalmatian .90 .50
*a.* Pair, #1231-1232 1.75 1.25
*b.* Booklet pane, 5 #1232a 8.75
Complete booklet, #1232b 9.00
**1233** A622 120p Great Dane .90 .50
**1234** A623 120p Dalmatian .90 .50
*a.* Pair, #1233-1234 1.75 1.25
*b.* Booklet pane, 5 #1234a 8.75
Complete booklet, #1234b 9.00

Nos. 1233-1234 are inscribed DS/20.

2nd Summit of the Americas, Santiago — A624

**1998, Apr. 17** **Litho.** ***Perf. 13½***

**1235** A624 150p multicolored 1.40 1.40

**Souvenir Sheet**

**1236** A624 1000p Logo, diff. 10.50 10.50

No. 1236 contains one 26x42mm stamp.

Paintings — A625

350p, "Los Zambos de Calama," by Mauricio Moran. 400p, "Sandia Calada," by Roser Bru.

**1998, May 14** **Litho.** ***Perf. 13½***

**1237** A625 350p multicolored 2.25 2.25
**1238** A625 400p multicolored 2.75 2.75

Capuchin Order in Chile, 150th Anniv. A626

Designs: 150p, Native village, friar writing in book. 250p, Friar aiding injured man.

**1998, May 18**

**1239** A626 150p multicolored 1.10 1.10
**1240** A626 250p multicolored 1.75 1.75

1998 World Cup Soccer Championships, France — A627

Players and: 250p, Crowd. 350p, World Cup Trophy. 500p, Map of France. 700p, Chilean flag.

1500p, Player, vert.

**1998, May 23**

**1241** A627 250p multicolored 1.60 1.50
**1242** A627 350p multicolored 2.75 2.00
**1243** A627 500p multicolored 3.75 3.00
**1244** A627 700p multicolored 4.75 4.25
*Nos. 1241-1244 (4)* 12.85 10.75

**Souvenir Sheet**

**1245** A627 1500p multicolored 10.50 9.00

A628

Antarctic Research: 250p, Logo, penguin. 350p, Penguins, map, logo.

**1998, July 22**

**1246** A628 250p multicolored 1.90 1.50
**1247** A628 350p multicolored 2.75 2.25

No. 1246, Scientific Committee on Antarctic Research, 25th meeting. No. 1247, Natl. Administrators of Antarctic Programs, 10th meeting.

A629

**1998, Apr. 3**

**1248** A629 120p multicolored 1.00 .80

Captain Arturo Prat Chacon, 150th birth anniv.

Army Veterinarian Service, Cent. — A630

350p, Veterinarian listening to horse's heartbeat.

**1998, Apr. 20**

**1249** A630 250p multicolored 1.90 1.50
**1250** A630 350p multicolored 2.75 2.25

A631

**1998, Aug. 31 Litho.** ***Perf. 13½***

**1251** A631 500p multicolored 5.00 3.50

Merchant Marine's Director General of Maritime Territory, 150th Anniv. Intl. Year of the Ocean.

Intl. Year of the Ocean A632

No. 1252, Nautical cartography. No. 1253, Iceberg. 500p, Silhouette of stone head, Easter Island.

**1998, Sept. 10**

**1252** A632 400p multicolored 3.50 2.50
**1253** A632 400p multicolored 3.50 2.50
**1254** A632 500p multicolored 4.50 3.00
*Nos. 1252-1254 (3)* 11.50 8.00

Folk Singers and Composers A633

Designs: 200p, Clara Solovera Cortes (1909-92). 250p, Francisco Flores del Campo (1908-93). 300p, Victor Jara Martinez (1932-73). 350p, Violeta Parra Sandoval (1917-67).

**1998, Sept. 14**

**1255** A633 200p multicolored 1.20 1.00
**1256** A633 250p multicolored 2.10 1.40
**1257** A633 300p multicolored 2.25 1.50
**1258** A633 350p multicolored 2.75 1.90
*Nos. 1255-1258 (4)* 8.30 5.80

World Stamp Day — A634

**1998, Oct. 9 Litho.** ***Perf. 13½***

**1259** A634 250p multicolored 2.10 1.90

Francisco Bilbao (1823-65), Writer — A635

**Litho. & Engr.**

**1998, Oct. 29** ***Perf. 13½***

**1260** A635 250p multicolored 3.25 2.50

Chilean Painters — A636

Designs: 300p, Self-portrait, by Augusto Eguiluz (1894-1969), vert. 450p, Landscape, by Agustin Abarca (1882-1953).

1500p, "Two Nudes," by Henriette Petit (1894-1983).

**1998, Nov. 3 Litho.**

**1261** A636 300p multi 3.00 2.00
**1262** A636 450p multi 3.50 2.75

**Souvenir Sheet**

**1262A** A636 1500p multi 16.50 12.50

No. 1262A contains one 36x47mm stamp.

Catholic University of Valparaiso, 70th Anniv. — A637

**1998, Nov. 18 Litho.** ***Perf. 13½***

**1263** A637 130p multicolored 1.40 1.20

Prominent Women from the University of Chile — A638

America Issue: 120p, Amanda Labarca, edcuator. 250p, Marta Brunet, writer.

**1998, Nov. 19 Litho.** ***Perf. 13½***

**1264** A638 120p multicolored 1.00 .85
**1265** A638 250p multicolored 1.90 1.60

1999 World Scout Jamboree, Chile — A639

Scouting emblems and: 120p, Children of two races, stylized tents. 200p, Robert Baden-Powell. 250p, Stylized doves. 300p, Scout, stylized tents. 1000p, Scouts, leaders seated in semi-circle, vert.

3000p, Jamboree emblem over drawing of Jamboree site at Picarquin, emblems of past jamborees, Intl. Scouting Emblem.

**1998, Dec. 27**

**1266** A639 120p multicolored .85 .75
**1267** A639 200p multicolored 1.20 1.10
**1268** A639 250p multicolored 1.50 1.40
**1269** A639 300p multicolored 1.60 1.50
**1270** A639 1000p multicolored 5.75 5.25
*Nos. 1266-1270 (5)* 10.90 10.00

***Imperf***

**Size: 126x104mm**

**1270A** A639 3000p multi 17.50 17.50

Birds — A640

Designs: 10p, Zonotrichia capensis. 20p, Curaeus curaeus.

**1998, Nov. 29**

**1271** A640 10p multicolored 1.00 .80
*a.* Inscribed "2000" 1.00 .80
**1272** A640 20p multicolored 1.00 .80
*a.* Inscribed "2000" 1.00 .80

See Nos. 1313-1314, 1356, 1385-1386, 1418-1419.

World Equestrian High Jump Record, 50th Anniv. — A641

Captain Alberto Larraguibel and Huaso.

**1999, Feb. 5 Litho.** ***Perf. 13½***

**1273** A641 200p multicolored 1.90 1.60

Temuco Fire Dept., Cent. — A642

Designs: 140p, 1900 pumper. 200p, 1929 Ford. 300p, 1955 Ford K tanker. 350p, 1967 Mercedes Benz hook and ladder truck.

1500p, Firefighter rescuing victim, vert.

**1999, Feb. 18 Litho.** ***Perf. 13½***

**1274** A642 140p multicolored 1.50 .75
**1275** A642 200p multicolored 1.60 1.10
**1276** A642 300p multicolored 2.50 1.75
**1277** A642 350p multicolored 2.75 2.00
*Nos. 1274-1277 (4)* 8.35 5.60

**Souvenir Sheet**

**1278** A642 1500p multicolored 12.50 9.00

Chilean Chamber of Deputies, 1000th Session A643

**1999, Mar. 3** ***Perf. 13½***

**1279** A643 140p multicolored 1.10 .85

Sacred Heart College, 150th Anniv. — A644

**1999, Mar. 15**

**1280** A644 250p multicolored 2.10 1.75

Economic Development Corporation (CORFO), 60th Anniv. — A645

Pedro Aguirre Cerda, former president of Chile.

**1999, Apr. 29** ***Perf. 13½***

**1281** A645 140p multicolored 1.25 1.00

Chilean Insurance Assoc., Cent. — A646

**1999, May 18 Litho.** ***Perf. 13½***

**1282** A646 140p multicolored 2.75 2.25

Chilean Antarctica — A647

Designs: 360p, Leptonychotes weddellii. 450p, Pygoscelis antarctica.

1500p, Arctocephalus gazella, penguins.

**1999, June 15**

**1283** A647 360p multicolored 3.00 1.75
**1284** A647 450p multicolored 5.00 3.25

**Souvenir Sheet**

**1285** A647 1500p multicolored 14.00 9.00

No. 1285 contains one 35x48mm stamp.

Easter Island — A648

**1999, June 25**

**1286** A648 360p multicolored 5.25 2.10

Souvenir Sheet

Barcelona Soccer Club, Cent. — A649

**1999**

**1287** A649 1000p multicolored 10.50 5.00

University of Santiago, 150th Anniv. A650

Designs: 140p, Monument, students in training room, School of Arts and Sciences, 1849. 250p, Technical equipment, building on campus, State Technical University, 1947. 300p, Student looking into microscope, computer, modern building, 1999.

**1999, July 6 Litho.** ***Perf. 13½***

**1288** A650 140p multicolored 1.25 1.00
**1289** A650 250p multicolored 2.10 1.50
**1290** A650 300p multicolored 2.75 2.25
*Nos. 1288-1290 (3)* 6.10 4.75

Alexander von Humboldt (1769-1859), 200th Anniv. of Scientific Research in Latin America A651

Face from monument and: 300p, Bust of Humboldt, wildlife, mountains. 360p, Portrait of Humboldt, penguins, sea.

**1999, July 16**

**1291** A651 300p multicolored 2.50 2.00
**1292** A651 360p multicolored 2.75 2.25

China '99, World Philatelic Exhibition, Beijing A652

Chinese, Chilean flags and: 140p, Pagoda. 450p, Chinese junk.

1500p, Great Wall of China, Gate of Heavenly Peace.

**1999, Aug. 10**

**1293** A652 140p multicolored 1.25 1.00
**1294** A652 450p multicolored 3.50 2.50

**Souvenir Sheet**

**1295** A652 1500p multicolored 11.50 9.00

No. 1295 contains one 60x48mm stamp.

City of Quilpue, Cent. — A653

**1999, Aug. 20**
**1296** A653 250p multicolored 3.25 2.50

Holy Year 2000 — A654

140p, Raúl Cardinal Silva Henriquez (1907-99). 200p, Walking in street clothes, administering sacrament, face of Christ.

**1999, Aug. 9**
**1297** A654 140p shown 1.10 .80
**1298** A654 200p multicolored 1.40 1.20

A655

**1999, Sept. 23** **Litho.** ***Perf. 13½***
**1299** A655 140p multicolored 3.25 2.50

Red Cross blood donation campaign.

2000 World Congress of Authors & Composers, Santiago A656

**1999, Oct. 5**
**1300** A656 170p multicolored 1.60 1.25

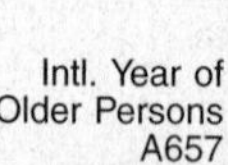
Intl. Year of Older Persons A657

**1999, Oct. 6**
**1301** A657 250p multicolored 1.75 1.50

UPU, 125th Anniv. — A658

**1999, Oct. 9**
**1302** 300p Red mailbox 4.50 4.50
**1303** 360p Gold mailbox 4.50 4.50
*a.* A658 Pair, #1302-1303 + label 10.25 10.25

Nos. 1302-1303 printed in sheets of 16 pairs, with label in central column.

America Issue, A New Millennium Without Arms — A659

**1999, Oct. 12**
**1304** A659 140p shown 2.75 1.75
**1305** A659 320p Broken bomb 3.75 2.00

Labor Management, 75th Anniv. — A660

**1999, Aug. 23**
**1306** A660 320p multicolored 2.40 2.10

Interamerican Development Bank, 40th Anniv. A661

**1999, Oct. 29** **Litho.** ***Perf. 13½***
**1307** A661 360p multicolored 2.50 2.25

Holy Year 2000 — A662

**1999, Dec. 1**
**1308** A662 450p multicolored 2.25 2.25

A663

**1999, Dec. 1**
**1309** A663 170p multicolored 3.00 2.00

**Inscribed "D.S. 20"**

**1310** A663 170p multicolored 2.75 2.00
*a.* Booklet pane of 10 28.50
Complete booklet, #1310a 29.00
*b.* Booklet pane of 5 13.50
Complete booklet, #1310b 14.00

Nos. 1309-1310 each were issued se-tenant with two labels that served as a lottery ticket and stub.

Union Leaders — A664

No. 1311, Luis Emilio Recabarren Serrano (1876-1924), Clotario Leopoldo Blest Riffo (1899-1990). No. 1312, Tucapel Jiménez Alfaro (1921-82), Manuel Bustos Huerta (1943-99).

**1999, Dec. 29** **Litho.** ***Perf. 13½***
**1311** 200p multi 2.00 1.75
**1312** 200p multi 2.00 1.75
*a.* A664 Pair, #1311-1312 + label 4.50 4.50

**Bird Type of 1998**

Designs: 50p, Campephilus magellanicus, vert. 100p, Falco peregrinus cassini, vert.

**2000, Feb.** ***Perf. 13½***
**1313** A640 50p multi .65 .40
**1314** A640 100p multi 1.40 .50

Discovery of Juan Fernández, Archipelago, 425th Anniv. — A665

a, Más Afuera (Alejandro Selkirk) Island, Santa Clara Island, tip of Más a Tierra (Robinson Crusoe) Island. b, Más a Tierra Island. c, Dendroseris litoralis. d, Rhaphythamnus venustus. e, Lobster. f, Lobster's antenna, boat. g, Boat, Gavilea insularis. h, Gavilea insularis.

**2000, Feb. 29** ***Perf. 13¼***
**1315** A665 360p Sheet of 8, #a.-h. 18.00 18.00

Condorito, Cartoon Character by Rene Rios Boettiger Pepo — A666

Condorito: 150p, Celebrating millennium. 260p, As soccer player. 480p, As fire fighter. 980p, On horse.
2000p, With people.

**2000, Mar. 20** ***Perf. 13½***
**1316** A666 150p multi 1.40 1.40
**1317** A666 260p multi 2.25 2.25
**1318** A666 480p multi 5.00 5.00
**1319** A666 980p multi 8.50 8.50
*Nos. 1316-1319 (4)* 17.15 17.15

**Souvenir Sheet**

**1320** A666 2000p multi 15.00 15.00

Easter Island — A667

Designs: 200p, Dancer, stone weapon. 260p, Stone statue and carvings. 340p, Island native, stone statue. 480p, Female dancer, inscribed tablet, map of island.

**2000, Apr. 27** **Litho.** ***Perf. 13¼***
**1321** A667 200p multi 1.90 1.75
**1322** A667 260p multi 2.60 2.40
**1323** A667 340p multi 3.50 3.25
**1324** A667 480p multi 5.00 4.50
*Nos. 1321-1324 (4)* 13.00 11.90

Town of Carahue, Cent. (in 1998) — A668

Bridge and: No. 1325, Locomotive, pottery. No. 1326, Potatoes.

**2000, May 5**
**1325** 220p multi 1.75 1.25
**1326** 220p multi 1.75 1.25
*a.* A668 Pair, #1325-1326 4.25 4.25

El Mercurio Newspaper, Cent. — A669

**2000, June 1**
**1327** A669 370p multi 3.25 3.00

4th Natl. Masonic Convention A670

**2000, June 23**
**1328** A670 460p multi 5.25 4.00

Medicinal Plants — A671

Designs: 200p, Quillaja saponaria. 360p, Fabiana imbricata.

**2000, July 3**
**1329** A671 200p multi 2.50 1.75
**1330** A671 360p multi 4.75 3.50

Discovery of Brazil, 500th Anniv. A672

Designs: 260p, Map of Brazil, butterfly, girl. 1500p, Monkey, parrots, boy.

**2000, July 10**
**1331** A672 260p multi 2.50 2.00

**Souvenir Sheet**

**1332** A672 1500p multi 12.50 12.50

No. 1332 contains one 48x36mm stamp.

Folklore — A673

Religious festivals: 150p, Dancer in devil costume, La Tirana. 200p, Festival of San Pedro de Atacama. 370p, Candlemas Festival, Copiapo. 460p, Chinese dancers, Andacollo.

**2000, July 13**
**1333** A673 150p multi 1.50 1.25
**1334** A673 200p multi 1.75 1.60
**1335** A673 370p multi 3.50 3.25
**1336** A673 460p multi 4.50 3.70
*Nos. 1333-1336 (4)* 11.25 9.80

Prehistoric Animals — A674

No. 1337: a, Milodon. b, Titanosaurus. c, Plesiosaurus. d, Iguanodon.

**2000**
**1337** A674 150p Block of 4, #a-d 5.50 5.00

José de San Martín (1778-1850) A675

**2000, Aug. 25** **Litho.** ***Perf. 13½***
**1338** A675 320p multi 2.60 2.25

World Meteorological Organization, 50th Anniv. — A676

**2000, Aug. 28**
**1339** A676 320p multi 2.40 2.10

Antarctic Fauna — A677

450p, Sphenis magellanicus, vert. 650p, Megaptera novaeangliae. 940p, Orcinus orca. 2000p, Mirounga leonina, vert.

**2000, Sept. 15**

| | | | | |
|---|---|---|---|---|
| 1340-1342 | A677 | Set of 3 | 27.00 | 22.50 |

**Souvenir Sheet**

| | | | | |
|---|---|---|---|---|
| 1343 | A677 | 2000p multi | 25.00 | 15.00 |

No. 1343 contains one 36x48mm stamp.

2000 Summer Olympics, Sydney — A678

Sydney Opera House, Olympic flag and: a, 290p, Chilean flag, tennis player, soccer player, sprinter. b, 290p, Australian flag, archer, high jumper, cyclist.

**2000, Sept. 20**

| | | | | |
|---|---|---|---|---|
| 1344 | A678 | Pair, #a-b | 8.75 | 7.00 |

City of Concepcion, 450th Anniv. A679

Mural by Gregorio De la Fuente: a, Indian holding stick. b, Soldier on white horse. c, Finger pointing upward. d, Seated figure, arms, horse-drawn carriage. e, Horse, statue, train. f, People and rainbow.

**2000, Oct. 2**

| | | | | |
|---|---|---|---|---|
| 1345 | | Horiz. strip of 6 | 21.00 | 21.00 |
| a.-f. | A679 | 250p Any single | 2.00 | 1.25 |

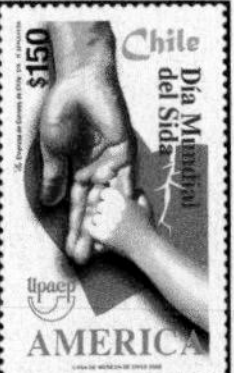

America Issue, World AIDS Day — A680

Designs: 150p, Heart, clasped hands of adult and child. 220p, Clasped hands.

**2000, Oct. 12**

| | | | | |
|---|---|---|---|---|
| 1346-1347 | A680 | Set of 2 | 5.25 | 4.00 |

Penal Reform A681

Designs: 150p, Flag, court proceedings. 2000p, People, doors of Justice Ministry.

**2000, Nov. 16**

| | | | | |
|---|---|---|---|---|
| 1348 | A681 | 150p multi | 1.50 | 1.25 |

**Souvenir Sheet**

| | | | | |
|---|---|---|---|---|
| 1349 | A681 | 2000p multi | 17.50 | 17.50 |

Christmas — A682

Designs: a, Star of Bethlehem. b, Santa Claus flying over town. c, Three Magi on camels. d, Star on top of Christmas tree. e, Boy at mailbox. f, Sleeping child. g, Two Magi, cow. h, Baby Jesus, cow. i, Mary, Joseph. j, Girl putting ornaments on tree.

**2000, Nov. 20** *Perf. 13½*

| | | | | |
|---|---|---|---|---|
| 1350 | A682 | Block of 10 | 22.50 | 22.50 |
| a.-j. | | 150p Any single | 1.50 | 1.25 |

**Inscribed "DS/20"**

***Perf. 13½ on 3 sides***

| | | | | |
|---|---|---|---|---|
| 1351 | A682 | Booklet pane of 10 | 22.50 | |
| a.-j. | | 150p Any single | 1.50 | 1.25 |
| | | Booklet, #1351 | 22.50 | |

National Zoo, 75th Anniv. A683

Various animals and birds, denomination in: a, LL. b, LR. c, UL. d, UR.

**2001, Jan. 13** **Litho.** *Perf. 13½*

| | | | | |
|---|---|---|---|---|
| 1352 | A683 | 160p Block of 4, #a-d | 9.25 | 9.25 |

San Sebastian Festival, Yumbel A684

**2001, Jan. 18**

| | | | | |
|---|---|---|---|---|
| 1353 | A684 | 210p multi | 2.25 | 2.00 |

Father Alberto Hurtado (1901-52) — A685

Hurtado and: 160p, Truck. 340p, Children.

**2001, Jan. 20**

| | | | | |
|---|---|---|---|---|
| 1354-1355 | A685 | Set of 2 | 4.25 | 3.50 |

**Bird Type of 1998**

No. 1356, vert.: a, Sephanoides fernandensis. b, Mimus thenca. c, Pteroptochos megapodius. d, Enicognathus leptorhynchus. Size of Nos. 1356a-1356d: 24x29mm.

**2001, Jan. 29**

| | | | | |
|---|---|---|---|---|
| 1356 | A640 | 160p Block of 4, #a-d | 8.25 | 8.25 |

Assembly of Governors of Inter-American Development Bank and Investment Corporation — A686

**2001, Mar. 16**

| | | | | |
|---|---|---|---|---|
| 1357 | A686 | 230p multi | 1.75 | 1.50 |

Souvenir Sheet

Air Force Anniversaries — A687

No. 1358: a, Lockheed C-130 Hercules, map of Antarctica. b, Flugzeugbau Extra-300, acrobatic squadron. c, North American AT-6 Texan. d, Consolidated PBY-5A/OA-10 Catalina, map of Easter Island.

**2001, Mar. 29**

| | | | | |
|---|---|---|---|---|
| 1358 | A687 | 260p Sheet of 4, #a-d | 9.00 | 9.00 |

Air Force presence in Antarctica, 50th anniv. (No. 1358a); Halcones acrobatic squadron, 20th anniv. (No. 1358b); Aviation Group No. 1, 75th anniv. (No. 1358c); First flight of Easter Island, 50th anniv. (No. 1358d).

Nationalization of Copper Industry, 30th Anniv. — A688

Design: 2000p, Miner and equipment.

**2001, Apr. 26** **Litho.** *Perf. 13¼*

| | | | | |
|---|---|---|---|---|
| 1359 | A688 | 400p multi | 3.50 | 3.00 |

**Souvenir Sheet**

| | | | | |
|---|---|---|---|---|
| 1359A | A688 | 2000p multi | 13.00 | 13.00 |

Organ Donation A689

**2001, May 3**

| | | | | |
|---|---|---|---|---|
| 1360 | A689 | 160p multi | 1.75 | 1.50 |

Easter Island A690

Designs: No. 1361, Stone carvings, map of island and: a, Compass rose. b, Bird and native. No. 1361C, Artifact and map of island.

**2001, June 25**

| | | | | |
|---|---|---|---|---|
| 1361 | A690 | 260p Horiz. pair, #a-b | 7.00 | 6.50 |

**Souvenir Sheet**

| | | | | |
|---|---|---|---|---|
| 1361C | A690 | 2000p multi | 21.00 | 21.00 |

Lynchailurus Colocolo — A691

**2001**

| | | | | |
|---|---|---|---|---|
| 1362 | A691 | 100p multi | 1.25 | .65 |

Endangered species. See Nos. 1394-1395.

Valparaiso Firefighting Corps, 150th Anniv. — A692

Firefighters and: 160p, Manuel Blanco Encalada. 260p, Old pumper, building on fire, modern fire truck. 350p, Flags, building. 490p, Helicopter, rail tank car.
2000p, Helicopter, modern fire truck.

**2001, June 28** **Litho.** *Perf. 13¼*

| | | | | |
|---|---|---|---|---|
| 1363-1366 | A692 | Set of 4 | 11.00 | 9.00 |

**Souvenir Sheet**

| | | | | |
|---|---|---|---|---|
| 1367 | A692 | 2000p multi | 12.00 | 12.00 |

Mushrooms — A693

Designs: 300p, Macrolepiota rhacodes. 400p, Laccata ohiensis.

**2001, July 25** **Litho.** *Perf. 13¼*

| | | | | |
|---|---|---|---|---|
| 1368-1369 | A693 | Set of 2 | 7.75 | 6.50 |

24th Conference of American Armies, Santiago A694

**2001, Aug. 13**

| | | | | |
|---|---|---|---|---|
| 1370 | A694 | 350p multi | 3.00 | 2.75 |

Bernardo O'Higgins (1778-1842), Soldier and Statesman A695

**2001, Aug. 17**

| | | | | |
|---|---|---|---|---|
| 1371 | A695 | 260p multi | 2.10 | 1.90 |

Chilean Antarctic Research A696

Designs: 350p, Researcher, Leptonychotes weddellii. 700p, Researchers, Macronectes giganteus. 2000p, Chionis alba.

**2001, Aug. 29**

| | | | | |
|---|---|---|---|---|
| 1372-1373 | A696 | Set of 2 | 9.25 | 8.50 |

**Souvenir Sheet**

| | | | | |
|---|---|---|---|---|
| 1374 | A696 | 2000p multicolored | 17.50 | 17.50 |

America Issue — UNESCO World Heritage — A697

World Heritage Sites and stamps: 160p, Quinchao Church, #1058. 230p, Tenaun Church, #1057.

**2001, Oct. 9** **Litho.** *Perf. 13¼*

| | | | | |
|---|---|---|---|---|
| 1375-1376 | A697 | Set of 2 | 12.50 | 12.50 |

Cape Horn — A698

**2001, Nov. 22**

| | | | | |
|---|---|---|---|---|
| 1377 | A698 | 220p multi | 2.10 | 1.90 |

El Indice del Indice, by Roberto Matta (1911-2002) A699

**2001, Nov. 5** **Litho.** *Perf. 13¼*

| | | | | |
|---|---|---|---|---|
| 1378 | A699 | 300p multi | 2.90 | 2.50 |

Railroads in Chile, 150th Anniv. — A700

No. 1379 (50x29mm): a, Caldera Station, train cars. b, Locomotive and Copiapó Station.
220p, Train on bridge.

**2001, Nov. 20**

| | | | | |
|---|---|---|---|---|
| 1379 | A700 | 200p Horiz. pair, #a-b | 5.25 | 5.25 |
| 1380 | A700 | 220p multi | 2.75 | 2.75 |

Christmas — A701

Designs: a, Heads of three shepherds. b, Shepherd and cow. c, Joseph and Mary. d, Donkey and Magus. e, Cow and two Magi. f, Head of shepherd. g, Two sheep. h, Infant Jesus. i, Shepherd with staff. j, One sheep.

**2001, Nov.**

**1381** A701 160p Block of 10, #a-j 21.00 21.00

**Inscribed "DS/20"**

**1382** A701 160p Block of 10, #a-j 24.00 24.00
*k.* Booklet pane, #1382 with straight edge at right 21.00 —
Complete booklet, #1382k 21.00

Rotary Intl. Emblem, Map of Chile, Globe, Tropic of Capricorn Monument A702

**2001, Dec. 21**

**1383** A702 240p multi 2.25 2.00

Antofagasta Rotary Club, 75th anniv.

Taxation Department, Cent. — A703

**2002, Jan. 14**

**1384** A703 180p multi 1.40 1.10

**Bird Type of 1998**

Designs: 10p, Turdus falcklandii. 20p, Sturnella loyca.

**2002, Jan. 25**

**1385** A640 10p multi 1.00 .50
**1386** A640 20p multi 1.00 .50

City of Valdivia, 450th Anniv. — A704

**2002, Feb. 9**

**1387** A704 260p multi 2.00 1.75

Carabinero Force, 75th Anniv. — A705

**2002, Apr. 8**

**1388** A705 250p multi 2.25 1.75

Ignacy Domeyko (1802-89), Mineralogist A706

**2002, Apr. 11**

**1389** A706 290p multi *5.25 4.75*

See Poland No. 3645.

City of Villarrica, 450th Anniv. — A707

**2002, Apr. 26**

**1390** A707 290p multi 2.25 2.00

Town of Calbuco, 400th Anniv. — A708

**2002, May 2**

**1391** A708 230p multi 2.10 1.75

Barros Arana Natl. Boarding School — A709

**2002, May 20**

**1392** A709 250p multi 2.00 1.75

Abolition of Death Penalty, 1st Anniv. — A710

**2002, May 29**

**1393** A710 240p multi 2.00 1.75

**Endangered Species Type of 2001**

Designs: 10p, Oreailurus jacobita. 20p, Oncifelis geoffrovi.

**2002, June 5**

**1394** A691 10p multi .80 .40
**1395** A691 20p multi .90 .40

Easter Island — A711

Map of Easter Island and: 250p, Toromiro sophora, moai. 450p, Bird, row of moai statues, native in traditional costume.
2000p, Toromiro sophora and bird.

**2002, July 1**

**1396-1397** A711 Set of 2 7.00 5.75

**Souvenir Sheet**

**1398** A711 2000p multi 17.00 17.00

No. 1398 contains one 47x47mm stamp.

World Heritage Sites — A712

Churches and stamps: 230p, Achao, #1036. 290p, Dalcahue, #1056.

**2002, July 27**

**1399-1400** A712 Set of 2 3.50 3.00

America Issue — Youth, Education, and Literacy A713

Designs: 230p, Adult students. 450p, Woman reading to child, teacher, boy at computer.

**2002, Sept. 9**

**1401-1402** A713 Set of 2 5.25 4.00

Children's Toys — A714

Designs: 290p, Pinwheel. 380p, Kite, vert.

**2002, Sept. 16**

**1403-1404** A714 Set of 2 4.75 3.50

Observatories A715

Designs: 450p, Cerro-Tololo. 550p, Paranal. 2000p, Cerro-Tololo, diff.

**2002, Sept. 27**

**1405-1406** A715 Set of 2 7.00 5.00

**Souvenir Sheet**

**1407** A715 2000p multi 14.00 14.00

No. 1407 contains one 47x47mm stamp.

University of Chile Clinical Hospital, 50th Anniv. — A716

**2002, Oct. 17**

**1408** A716 250p multi 1.75 1.50

Forestry Education, 50th Anniv. — A717

**2002, Oct. 22**

**1409** A717 250p multi 1.75 1.50

12th Convention on International Trade in Endangered Species Conference A718

Designs: 300p, Phoenicoparrus andinus. 450p, Vicugna vicugna.
2000p, Chinchilla lanigera.

**2002, Oct. 29**

**1410-1411** A718 Set of 2 6.25 5.75

**Souvenir Sheet**

**1412** A718 2000p multi 15.00 15.00

No. 1412 contains one 47x47mm stamp.

Protected Whales A719

Designs: 250p, Eubalaena australis. 500p, Balaenoptera acutorostrata.
2000p, Physeter macrocephalus.

**2002, Nov. 2**

**1413-1414** A719 Set of 2 6.25 5.75

**Souvenir Sheet**

**1415** A719 2000p multi 17.00 16.00

Violence Against Women Prevention Day — A720

**2002, Nov. 22**

**1416** A720 230p multi 1.90 1.60

Town of Puerto Varas, 150th Anniv. — A721

**2002, Nov. 29**

**1417** A721 190p multi 1.40 1.10

**Bird Type of 1998**

Designs: 500p, Campephilus magellanicus, vert. 1000p, Falco peregrinus cassini, vert.

**2003, Jan. 15 Litho. *Perf. 13¼***

**1418** A640 500p multi 3.00 2.00
**1419** A640 1000p multi 6.50 4.00

Puerto Montt, 150th Anniv. — A722

**2003, Feb. 13**

**1420** A722 240p multi 1.60 1.40

Claudio Arrau (1903-91), Pianist A723

**2003, June 9 Litho. *Perf. 13¼***

**1421** A723 200p multi 1.60 1.40

First Chilean Postage Stamps, 150th Anniv. A724

No. 1422 — Mailbox, building and: a, #1. b, #2.
2000p, Building, #1 and various other stamps.

**2003, July 1**

**1422** A724 300p Horiz. pair, #a-b 3.00 2.50

**Souvenir Sheet**

**1423** A724 2000p multi 9.00 9.00

America Issue — Flora and Fauna A725

Designs: 240p, Trees, flowers, cactus. 300p, Frog, fox, butterfly, pudu, parrot.

**2003, Oct. 12 Litho. *Perf. 13¼***

**1424-1425** A725 Set of 2 3.75 3.25

Supreme Court, 180th Anniv. A726

**2003, Nov. 5**
**1426** A726 200p multi 1.60 1.40

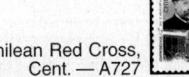

Chilean Red Cross, Cent. — A727

**2003, Nov. 18**
**1427** A727 200p black & red 1.60 1.40

Christmas A728

**2003, Nov. 28**
**1428** A728 190p multi 1.50 1.25

**Inscribed "DS-20"**

**1429** A728 190p multi 1.50 1.25

Powered Flight, Cent. — A729

**2003, Dec. 11**
**1430** A729 200p multi 1.75 1.50

Cristo Redentor Statue, Cent. — A730

**2004, Apr. 22** **Litho.**
**1431** A730 200p multi 1.75 1.50

Seventh World Conference of Grand Masonic Lodges A731

**2004, May 5** ***Perf. 13¼***
**1432** A731 190p multi 1.75 1.50

Pablo Neruda (1904-73), Poet — A732

**2004, June 11**
**1433** A732 300p multi 2.10 1.90

Social Security, 80th Anniv. A733

**2004, Aug. 18**
**1434** A733 190p multi 1.50 1.25

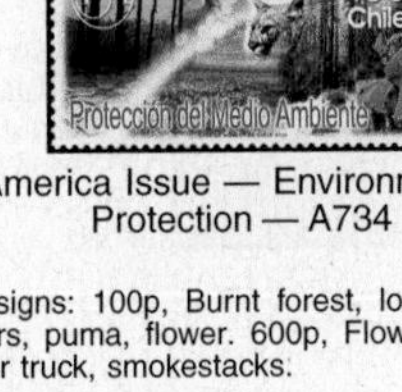

America Issue — Environmental Protection — A734

Designs: 100p, Burnt forest, logs, field of flowers, puma, flower. 600p, Flower, wildlife, tanker truck, smokestacks.

**2004, Sept. 27**
**1435-1436** A734 Set of 2 4.50 4.00

German Institute, Osorno, 150th Anniv. A735

**2004, Oct. 6**
**1437** A735 250p multi *97.50 97.50*

Tematica 2004 National Philatelic Exhibition — A736

**2004, Oct. 19**
**1438** A736 310p multi 2.10 1.90

Naval Telecommunications, Cent. — A737

**2004, Nov. 5**
**1439** A737 400p multi 2.90 2.25

Electricity and Fuel Superintendency, Cent. — A738

**2004, Dec. 7**
**1440** A738 240p multi 2.00 1.60

Chilean Air Force, 75th Anniv. A739

**2005, Mar. 15** **Litho.** ***Perf. 13¼***
**1441** A739 230p multi 2.90 2.60

Law No. 20,000 A740

**2005, May 4**
**1442** A740 220p multi 2.75 2.50

Pope John Paul II (1920-2005) — A741

Pope John Paul II and: a, Child, condor, mountain. b, Crucifix, Chilean flag, mountain. c, Church, Chilean flag.

**2005, May 13**
**1443** A741 Horiz. strip of 3 8.00 8.00
***a.-c.*** 230p Any single 2.00 2.00

Rotary International, Cent. — A742

**2005, June 30** **Litho.** ***Perf. 13¼***
**1444** A742 230p multi 1.60 1.25

Treasury Building, Bicent. A743

**2005, June 30**
**1445** A743 230p multi 1.60 1.25

Publication of Don Quixote, 400th Anniv. — A744

No. 1446: a, Don Quixote on horseback. b, Windmill. c, Windmills. d, Miguel de Cervantes, author.

**2005, July 14**
**1446** Horiz. strip of 4 2.60 2.60
***a.-b.*** A744 10p Either single .60 .60
***c.-d.*** A744 20p Either single .60 .60

See No. 1462.

El Teniente Copper Mine, Cent. — A745

**2005, Aug. 3**
**1447** A745 390p multi 3.50 3.00

Undersecretariat of Aviation, 75th Anniv. — A746

**2005, Aug. 19**
**1448** A746 400p multi 4.50 4.00

Valparaiso Customs House, 150th Anniv. A747

**2005, Sept. 1**
**1449** A747 390p multi 2.50 2.00

Bicentennial Fountain, Santiago A748

**2005, Sept. 5**
**1450** A748 230p multi 1.90 1.50

America Issue — Fight Against Poverty A749

No. 1451: a, Denomination at right. b, Denomination at left.

**2005, Oct. 3** **Litho.** ***Perf. 13¼***
**1451** A749 250p Horiz. pair, #a-b 4.50 4.00

Canonization of Father Alberto Hurtado (1901-52) A750

**2005, Oct. 13** **Litho.** ***Perf. 13¼***
**1452** A750 390p multi 4.50 4.25

Expo Austral 2005 Philatelic Exhibition, Punta Arenas A751

**2005, Oct. 22**
**1453** A751 390p multi 3.50 3.00

New Civil Matrimony Law — A752

**2005, Nov. 18** **Litho.** ***Perf. 13¼***
**1454** A752 260p multi 2.00 1.75

German Clinic, Cent. — A753

**2005, Nov. 23**
**1455** A753 230p multi 2.00 1.75

Restoration of Central Post Office, Santiago — A754

**2005, Nov. 30**
**1456** A754 230p multi 2.00 1.75

Political Constitution A755

**2005, Dec. 1**

**1457** A755 230p multi 2.00 1.75

An unissued version of this stamp, with a different design of a star over a black book, was leaked into the philatelic marketplace. The Chilean government considers these stolen property.

Department of Physical Education, Sports and Recreation, Cent. — A756

**2006, Mar. 6** **Litho.** ***Perf. 13¼***

**1458** A756 230p multi 1.50 1.25

Intl. Women's Day — A757

**2006, Mar. 7**

**1459** A757 390p multi 4.50 3.50

Wulff Castle, Cent. — A758

No. 1460 — Castle, arms of Vina del Mar and: a, Birds. b, Windmill.

**2006, Mar. 21**

**1460** Horiz. pair 3.75 3.25
*a.* A758 230p multi 1.10 1.10
*b.* A758 390p multi 1.90 1.90

Tourism A759

No. 1461: a, Morro de Arica. b, Moais, Easter Island. c, Palafittes, Castro. d, Torres del Paine. e, Penguins, Chilean Antarctic Territory.

**2006, May 19**

**1461** Horiz. strip of 5 7.50 6.50
*a.-e.* A759 230p Any single 1.10 1.10

### Don Quixote Type of 2005

No. 1462: a, Building. b, Windmills. c, Windmill, country name at LR. d, Don Quixote and Sancho Panza.

**2006, May 31**

**1462** Horiz. strip of 4 2.60 2.25
*a.-d.* A744 10p Any single .50 .40

Catholic University of the North, 50th Anniv. A760

No. 1463: a, Students using computers, denomination at UR. b, Students, denomination at LL.

**2006, June 9**

**1463** Horiz. pair 3.00 2.50
*a.-b.* A760 230p Either single 1.10 1.10

Citizenship Plaza, Santiago A761

**2006, July 7**

**1464** A761 390p multi 2.75 2.25

World Quality Forum A762

No. 1465: a, Building. b, Building and flags.

**2006, Aug. 29** **Litho.** ***Perf. 13¼***

**1465** A762 230p Horiz. pair, #a-b 3.00 2.60

America Issue, Energy Conservation A763

No. 1466: a, River and mountains. b, Clouds. c, Oil rigs in water. d, Windmill.

**2006, Sept. 29**

**1466** A763 390p Block of 4, #a-d 15.00 15.00

Adventist University of Chile, Cent. — A764

No. 1467 — University emblem and: a, Building, 1906. b, Family and building, 1922. c, Building, 1960-70. d, Building, 2006.

**2006, Oct. 20**

**1467** Horiz. strip of 4 + central label 7.00 6.00
*a.-d.* A764 250p Any single 1.25 1.25

Antarctic Wildlife A765

No. 1468 — Chilean and Estonian flags and: a, Balaenoptera acutorostrata. b, Aptenodytes forsteri.

**2006, Oct. 25** ***Perf. 13½***

**1468** A765 500p Horiz. pair, #a-b 6.75 5.50

See Estonia No. 555.

Anniversaries — A766

No. 1469: a, Colonization of the Straits of Magellan area, 160th anniv. b, Fort Bulnes, 160th anniv.

**2006, Dec. 7** ***Perf. 13¼***

**1469** A766 250p Horiz. pair, #a-b 3.75 3.25

Gasco, 150th Anniv. A767

No. 1470: a, San Borja facility. b, Gasco headquarters.

**2006, Dec. 14**

**1470** A767 250p Horiz. pair, #a-b 3.75 3.25

Federico Santa Maria Technical University, 75th Anniv. A768

**2006, Dec. 20**

**1471** A768 250p multi 1.75 1.50

Carabineros, 80th Anniv. — A769

No. 1472: a, Carabineros and mountains. b, Carabineros on horseback.

**2007, Apr. 10** **Litho.** ***Perf. 13¼***

**1472** A769 250p Pair, #a-b 3.75 3.00

Tourism A770

No. 1473: a, Valley of the Moon, Antofagasta Region. b, Easter Island, Valparaiso Region. c, Tourism emblem. d, Villarrica-Pucón Volcano, Araucania Region. e, Penguin in Chilean Antarctic.

**2007, May 9**

**1473** Horiz. strip of 5 14.50 14.50
*a.-e.* A770 390p Any single 2.25 2.25

Church Centenaries — A771

No. 1474: a, Parinacota Church. b, San Pedro de Atacama Church.

### Litho. With Foil Application

**2007, June 29**

**1474** A771 250p Pair, #a-b 3.75 3.75

Raul Cardinal Silva Henríquez (1907-99) A772

No. 1475 — Color of portrait and panel: a, Blue violet. b, Red violet. c, Red orange. d, Green.

**2007, Aug. 21** **Litho.**

**1475** Horiz. strip of 4 + central label 9.00 9.00
*a.-d.* A772 250p Any single 1.50 .75

A773

A774

A775

Sculptures by Marta Colvin (1907-95) A776

**2007, Aug. 24** ***Perf. 13¼***

**1476** Horiz. strip of 4 + central label 6.75 6.75
*a.* A773 250p multi 1.25 1.25
*b.* A774 250p multi 1.25 1.25
*c.* A775 250p multi 1.25 1.25
*d.* A776 250p multi 1.25 1.25

Las Condes, 106th Anniv. A777

**2007, Aug. 28**

**1477** A777 330p multi 2.00 1.75

Museums in Santiago — A778

Designs: 10p, Artequin Museum. 20p, National Museum of Fine Arts. 30p, National Museum of Natural History. 50p, Museum of Santiago.

**2007, Aug. 31** **Engr.**

**1478** A778 10p green .65 .40
**1479** A778 20p black .65 .40
**1480** A778 30p purple .65 .40
**1481** A778 50p red .65 .40
*Nos. 1478-1481 (4)* 2.60 1.60

Los Rios Region A779

No. 1482: a, Lake Ranco. b, Huilo Huilo Waterfall. c, Bridge, Valdivia. d, Choshuenco Volcano.

**2007, Oct. 2** **Litho.**

**1482** Horiz strip of 4 + central label 12.00 12.00
*a.-d.* A779 390p Any single 2.50 2.50

Arica and Parinacota Region A780

No. 1483: a, Morro de Arica. b, Parinacota Volcano. c, Anzota Caves. d, Vicunas.

**2007, Oct. 8**

**1483** Horiz strip of 4 + central label 6.00 6.00
*a.-d.* A780 250p Any single 1.25 1.25

Chilean Postal Service, 260th Anniv. A781

No. 1484: a, Half of original General Post Office, Santiago (denomination at UR). b, Half of modern General Post Office, Santiago (denomination at UL). c, Original and modern General Post Offices.

3000p, Statue of postal carrier on bicycle.

### Litho. With Foil Application

**2007, Oct. 9**

**1484** A781 390p Horiz. strip of 3, #a-c 6.50 6.50

### Souvenir Sheet

**1485** A781 3000p multi 17.00 17.00

Comptroller of the Navy, 80th Anniv. — A782

Arms of Chilean Navy and: a, Chilean Navy Building, denomination at UL. b, Naval and Maritime Museum, denomination at UR.

**2007, Oct. 11 Litho. *Perf. 13¼***

**1486** A782 390p Horiz. pair, #a-b 4.50 4.50

America Issue, Education For All — A783

No. 1487: a, Children at computer. b, Boy watching chemistry experiment. c, Children running. d, Children playing musical instruments. e, Boy pointing to globe.

**2007, Nov. 5**

**1487** Horiz. strip of 5 9.75 9.75
***a.-e.*** A783 250p Any single 1.40 1.40

Christmas — A784

No. 1488 — Santa Claus: a, In chimney. b, In automobile. c, Near sleigh. d, In front of fan.

**Litho. With Foil Application**

**2007, Nov. 16**

**1488** A784 250p Block of 4, #a-d 6.50 6.50

Malleco National Reserve, Cent. — A785

No. 1489: a, Tree, flower. b, Tree, puma. c, Waterfall, flowers. d, Forest, fox.

**2007, Nov. 20 Litho.**

**1489** Horiz. strip of 4 + central label 7.75 7.75
***a.-d.*** A785 250p Any single 1.60 1.60

La Nación Newspaper, 90th Anniv. — A786

No. 1490 — Newspaper's office building, Chilean flag and: a, Newspapers at end of production line. b, Newspaper pages.

**2007, Dec. 7**

**1490** A786 250p Horiz. pair, #a-b 2.75 2.75

Santa María de Iquique Massacre, Cent. — A787

No. 1491: a, People, ships. b, Man raising shovel. c, School, dead on ground. d, Wagon, people weeping. e, People hugging, woman weeping.

3000p, Family, vert.

**2007, Dec. 19**

**1491** Horiz. strip of 5 9.75 9.75
***a.-e.*** A787 250p Any single 1.50 1.50

**Souvenir Sheet**

**1492** A787 3000p multi 21.00 21.00

Miniature Sheet

Easter Island A788

No. 1493 — Natives in traditional garb and: a, Ahu Koteriku moais overlooking water. b, Motu Nui, Motu Iti and Motu Kaokao Islets. c, Rock painting. d, Petroglyphs. e, Orongo stone houses. f, Ahu Tahai moai. g, Anakena Beach. h, Rano Kau Volcanic Lake.

No. 1494, vert.: a, Native male. b, Native female.

**2008, Jan. 18**

**1493** A788 390p Sheet of 8, #a-h 18.00 18.00

**Souvenir Sheet**

**1494** A788 1500p Sheet of 2, #a-b 28.50 28.50

Miniature Sheet

Intl. Polar Year A789

No. 1495: a, Antarctic base, penguins. b, Ship and icebergs. c, Helicopter and direction signs. d, Cargo airplane and snow vehicle. e, Man directing small airplane. f, People on snowmobiles.

**2008, Jan. 29 *Perf. 13¼***

**1495** A789 250p Sheet of 6, #a-f 9.25 9.25

Occupations A790

No. 1496, 20p: a, Knife grinder. b, Street sweeper.

No. 1497, 30p: a, Photographer. b, Peanut vendor.

No. 1498, 50p: a, Ice cream vendor. b, Shoeshine man.

No. 1499, 100p: a, Laundry worker. b, Organ grinder.

No. 1500, 500p: a, Street musician. b, Newspaper vendor.

**2008, Feb. 25 Pairs, #a-b Litho.**

**1496-1500** A790 Set of 5 10.00 7.00

Visit to Chile of Italian Pres. Giorgio Napolitano — A791

No. 1501 — Chilean poet Pablo Neruda and: a, His house on Isla Negra, Chile, Chilean flag. b, His house on Isle of Capri, Italy, Italian flag. c, His house on Isla Negra, flags of Chile and Italy. d, Rocks off Capri, flags of Chile and Italy.

**2008, Mar. 17**

**1501** A791 280p Block of 4, #a-d 6.25 6.25

Miniature Sheets

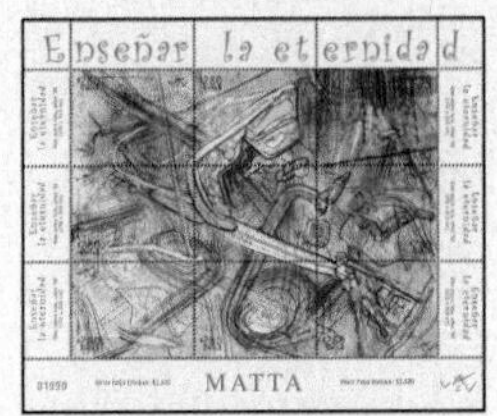

Ensenar la Eternidad, by Roberto Matta — A792

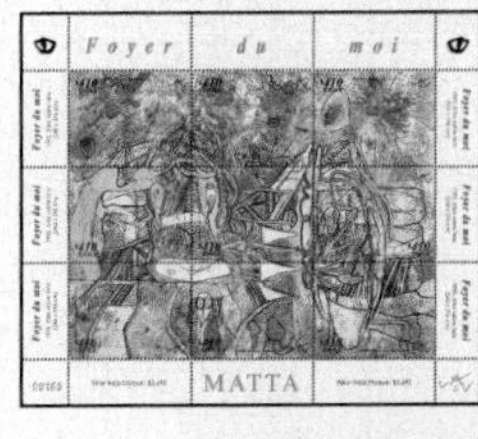

Foyer du Moi, by Matta A793

Espejo de Cronos, by Matta A794

Nos. 1502-1504 — Portion of painting: a, Upper left. b, Top center. c, Upper right. d, Left center. e, Center. f, Right center. g, Lower left. h, Bottom center. i, Lower right.

**2008, Mar. 25 *Perf. 13¼***

**1502** A792 280p Sheet of 9, #a-i 15.00 15.00
**1503** A793 410p Sheet of 9, #a-i 20.00 20.00
**1504** A794 410p Sheet of 9, #a-i 20.00 20.00
*Nos. 1502-1504 (3)* 55.00 55.00

Pres. Salvador Allende (1908-73) A795

**2008, June 26 Litho. *Perf. 13¼***

**1505** A795 410p multi 2.25 2.00

Taltal, 150th Anniv. A796

**2008, July 18**

**1506** A796 280p multi 2.25 1.60

Women's Under-20 Soccer World Championships, Chillán — A797

No. 1507 — Quarter of soccer ball and stadium and: a, Cross. b, Group of people. c, Fruits and vegetables. d, Pottery.

**2008, July 31**

**1507** A797 280p Block of 4, #a-d 6.50 6.50

Chilean Accountancy Association, 50th Anniv. — A798

No. 1508 — Emblem and: a, Accountants, building. b, Map of Western hemisphere.

**2008, Aug. 14**

**1508** A798 280p Horiz. pair, #a-b 3.25 3.25

Bishop Francisco Valdés Subercaseaux (1908-82) — A799

No. 1509 — Bishop Valdés Subercaseaux and: a, Christ of Tromen. b, Osorno Cathedral.

**2008, Sept. 5 Litho. *Perf. 13¼***

**1509** A799 280p Horiz. pair, #a-b 3.00 3.00

Miniature Sheet

La Vida Allende la Muerte, by Roberto Matta A800

No. 1510 — Section of painting: a, Upper left. b, Top center. c, Upper right. d, Left center. e, Center. f, Right center. g, Lower left. h, Bottom center. i, Lower right.

**2008, Sept. 15**

**1510** A800 410p Sheet of 9, #a-i 20.00 20.00

America Issue, National Festivals — A801

Designs; 10p, Cuasimodo. 200p, La Vendimia. 1000p, La Tirana. 2000p, Fiestas Patrias. 5000p, El Rodeo.

**2008, Oct. 30**

**1511** A801 10p multi .25 .25
**1512** A801 200p multi 1.90 1.90
**1513** A801 1000p multi 4.50 4.50
**1514** A801 2000p multi 9.00 9.00
**1515** A801 5000p multi 22.50 22.50
*Nos. 1511-1515 (5)* 38.15 38.15

Miniature Sheet

Torres del Paine National Park, 50th Anniv. A802

No. 1516: a, Fox, Torres del Paine. b, Puma, Grey Glacier. c, Condor (at right), Paine Grande. d, Condor (at left), Cuernos del Paine. e, Guanaco, Cuernos del Paine. f, Guemal, Macizo Paine and Cordillera Paine.

**2008, Nov. 21**

**1516** A802 500p Sheet of 6, #a-f 16.00 16.00

Telethon, 30th Anniv. A803

**2008, Nov. 25**
**1517** A803 280p multi 1.60 1.25

Christmas A804

No. 1518 — Children's art: a, Drawing by Antonia Retamal Figueroa. b, Drawing by Lucas Bastidas Escobar. c, Drawing by Oscar Maya Lazo. d, Drawing of girl, Christmas tree, mountains, Santa Claus. e, Drawing of Christmas tree, cross and handprints.

**2008, Nov. 26**
**1518** Horiz. strip of 5 7.25 7.25
***a.-e.*** A804 280p Any single 1.10 1.10

Osorno, 450th Anniv. A805

**2008, Nov. 28**
**1519** A805 280p multi 2.10 1.50

General Carlos Ibáñez del Campo Carabineros School, Cent. — A806

No. 1520: a, Carabineros, old school building (sepia photograph). b, Carabineros, new school building (color photograph).

**2008, Dec. 10**
**1520** A806 310p Horiz. pair, #a-b 3.25 3.25

Expo Antarctica Chile 2009 Philatelic Exhibition, Pres. Eduardo Frei Montalva Antarctic Base — A807

Designs: 470p, Map of Antarctica, Pres. Eduardo Frei Montalva Antarctic Base. 3000p, Villa Las Estrellas, horiz.

**2009, Mar. 12**
**1521** A807 470p multi 2.90 2.60

**Souvenir Sheet**

**1522** A807 3000p multi 19.00 19.00

Antarctic Treaty, 50th anniv. No. 1522 contains one 48x30mm stamp.

Preservation of Polar Regions and Glaciers A808

Nos. 1523, 1524 — Emblem and map of: a, Arctic area. b, Antarctic area. No. 1524 has vert. stamps.

**Litho. with Foil Application**

**2009, Mar. 18** ***Perf. 13¼***
**1523** A808 470p Vert. pair, #a-b 6.50 6.00

**Souvenir Sheet**

**1524** A808 1500p Sheet of 2, #a-b 19.00 19.00

Miniature Sheets

Independence, Bicent. — A809

No. 1525: a, Chile #92. b, Chile #93. c, Chile #94. d, Chile #95. e, Chile #96. f, Chile #97.
No. 1526, horiz.: a, Chile #83. b, Chile #84. c, Chile #85. d, Chile #86. e, Chile #87. f, Chile #88. g, Chile #89. h, Chile #90. i, Chile #91. j, Bicentennial emblem.

**2009, Apr. 20** **Litho.**
**1525** A809 310p Sheet of 6, #a-f 9.00 9.00
**1526** A809 310p Sheet of 10, #a-j 16.00 16.00

University of Concepción, 90th Anniv. — A810

No. 1527: a, Homage to the Founders, sculpture by Samuel Román. b, Campanile.

**2009, May 14**
**1527** A810 310p Horiz. pair, #a-b 3.75 3.75

Santa María de Los Angeles Diocese, 50th Anniv. A811

No. 1528: a, Virgin Mary, Jesus and angels. b, Los Angeles Cathedral.

**2009, June 10**
**1528** A811 470p Horiz. pair, #a-b 7.25 7.25

Protected Birds — A812

Designs: 10p, Condor. 20p Tricahue parrot. 50p, Chilean flamingo. 100p, Humboldt penguin. 500p, Black-necked swan.

**2009, July 15** **Litho.** ***Perf. 13¼***
**1529** A812 10p black .35 .35
**1530** A812 20p black .35 .35
**1531** A812 50p black .35 .35
**1532** A812 100p black .80 .80
**1533** A812 500p black 3.25 3.25
*Nos. 1529-1533 (5)* 5.10 5.10

21st UPAEP Congress, Santiago A813

**2009, Aug. 17** **Litho.** ***Perf. 13¼***
**1534** A813 500p multi 2.95 2.70

Mutual de Seguros Insurance Company, 90th Anniv. — A814

No. 1535: a, Old building, emblem with black gear. b, Modern building, emblem with blue gray gear.

**Litho. With Foil Application**

**2009, Oct. 14** ***Perf. 13¼***
**1535** A814 310p Horiz. pair, #a-b 4.50 4.50

A815

Winning Art in Bicentennial Stamp Design Contest — A816

No. 1536: a, Flag with mountains and city, by Andrea Barreda, elementary school competition. b, City, by Javiera Monreal Arcil, middle school competition.
No. 1537: a, People in various costumes, by Patricio Díaz Donay, visual arts competition. b, Pepper, by Joshua Arévalo Carreño, university and technical school competition.

**2009, Oct. 15** **Litho.** ***Perf. 13¼***
**1536** A815 310p Pair, #a-b 3.75 3.75
**1537** A816 310p Horiz. pair, #a-b 3.75 3.75

America Issue, Traditional Games — A817

Designs: 310p, Spinning top. 470p, Girl flying kite.

**2009, Oct. 30**
**1538-1539** A817 Set of 2 4.50 4.50

Christmas — A818

No. 1540 — Children: a, Painting nativity scene. b, Drawing pictures of Santa Claus. c, Opening presents under Christmas tree. d, Looking out of window.

**2009, Nov. 26**
**1540** A818 310p Block of 4, #a-d 8.00 8.00

Gabriela Mistral (1889-1957), 1945 Nobel Laureate in Literature — A819

No. 1451: a, Mistral at left, mountain at right. b, Church at left, Mistral at right. c, Mistral at left, church at right. d, Mountain at left, Mistral at right.

**2009, Dec. 18**
**1541** A819 500p Block of 4, #a-d 12.00 12.00

Chile Philatelic Society, 120th Anniv. A820

**2009, Dec. 30**
**1542** A820 500p multi 3.00 2.50

Bicentennial Art by National Art Prize Winners — A821

No. 1543 — Works of art by: a, José Balmes. b, Eugenio Dittborn. c, Guillermo Núñez.

**2010, Mar. 3**
**1543** Horiz. strip of 3 10.00 10.00
***a.-c.*** A821 290p Any single 3.00 3.00

Bicentenary Regatta — A822

No. 1544 — Flags and: a, Ships. b, Map of South America, ship.

**2010, Apr. 15** **Litho.** ***Perf. 13¼***
**1544** A822 430p Horiz. pair, #a-b 5.50 5.50

Miniature Sheet

Pres. Eduardo Frei Montalva Antarctic Air Base, 40th Anniv. A823

No. 1545: a, People near cargo airplane. b, Hangar. c, Airplane over base. d, Helicopter. e, Small airplane. f, Penguin, people, base.

**2010, May 4**
**1545** A823 500p Sheet of 6, #a-f 18.50 18.50

Bauer Tower, Vicuña, 105th Anniv. — A824

Designs: 500p, Tower. 3000p, Tower, diff.

**2010, May 7**
**1546** A824 500p multi 3.00 2.50

**Souvenir Sheet**

**1547** A824 3000p multi 17.00 17.00

2010 World Cup Soccer Championships, South Africa — A825

No. 1548 — Flags of Chile and South Africa, emblem of Chile Soccer Federation and: a, Soccer ball and players. b, Map of Africa, leopard skin.

**2010, June 25**
**1548** A825 500p Vert. pair, #a-b 6.00 5.50

Inauguration of Mini University of Tokyo Atacama Observatory Telescope, Mt. Chajnantor A826

**2010, July 7 Litho. *Perf. 13¼***
**1549** A826 430p multi 2.75 2.50

**Souvenir Sheet**

**1550** A826 3000p multi 17.50 17.50

Valparaiso, UNESCO World Heritage Site — A827

No. 1551: a, British Arch. b, Heroes of Iquique Monument.
No. 1552, horiz.: a, Palacio Polanco. b, Palacio Lyon.
No. 1553: a, Polanco Funicular. b, Artillería Funicular.
No. 1554, horiz.: a, Trolley bus with doors closed. b, Trolley bus with front doors open.

**2010, July 12 Litho. *Perf. 13¼***
**1551** A827 10p Horiz. pair, #a-b .75 .75
**1552** A827 20p Horiz. pair, #a-b .75 .75
**1553** A827 50p Horiz. pair, #a-b 1.25 1.25
**1554** A827 100p Horiz. pair, #a-b 2.25 2.25
*Nos. 1551-1554 (4)* 5.00 5.00

Independence of Latin America, Bicent. — A828

**2010, Sept. 10**
**1555** A828 430p multi 3.00 2.50

La Serena A829

No. 1556: a, Monumental Lighthouse. b, Plaza de Armas Fountain.

**2010, Sept. 15**
**1556** A829 420p Pair, #a-b 5.75 5.75

Bicentennial Naval Review — A830

No. 1557: a, Steamship from 1910 naval review. b, Ships and sailing vessel with flags hoisted from 1910 naval review. c, Ships from 2010, denomination at UR. d, Ships from 2010, denomination at UL.

**2010, Sept. 20**
**1557** A830 430p Block of 4, #a-d 11.50 11.50

**Miniature Sheet**

Antofagasta — A831

No. 1558: a, La Portada. b, Fishing terminal. c, Costanera Avenue. d, Historic District. e, Huanchaca Ruins. f, Antofagasta at night.

**2010, Sept. 24**
**1558** A831 500p Sheet of 6, #a-f 20.00 20.00

Arica A832

No. 1559: a, Fountain, Morro de Arica. b, Fuerza del Sol Carnival.

**2010, Sept. 30 Litho. *Perf. 13¼***
**1559** A832 420p Horiz. pair, #a-b 5.75 5.75

America Issue, National Symbols A833

**2010, Oct. 12 Litho. *Perf. 13¼***
**1560** A833 290p multi 2.75 2.25

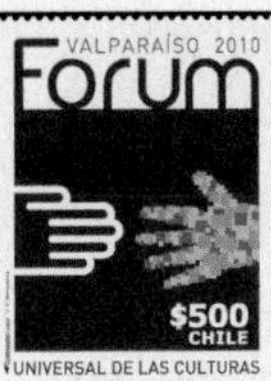

Third International Culture Forum, Valparaíso — A834

**2010, Oct. 19**
**1561** A834 500p multi 3.50 2.75

Irishmen Involved With Chilean Independence — A835

No. 1562: a, Commander General John Mackenna (1771-1814). b, Supreme Director Bernardo O'Higgins (1778-1842).

**2010, Oct. 28**
**1562** A835 500p Horiz. pair, #a-b 6.75 6.75

See Ireland Nos. 1902-1903.

Bicentennial Clock, La Serena University A836

**2010, Oct. 29 Litho. *Perf. 13¼***
**1563** A836 420p multi 3.00 2.50

**Souvenir Sheet**

**1564** A836 3000p Clock, vert. 18.00 18.00

Chile 2010 Bicentennial Philatelic Exhibition A837

**2010, Nov. 12 Litho. *Perf. 13¼***
**1565** A837 290p multi 2.10 1.50

Christmas — A838

**2010, Nov. 26**
**1566** A838 290p multi 2.10 1.50

**Miniature Sheet**

Chilean Army, Bicent. A839

No. 1567: a, Cavalry, back of army vehicle. b, Army vehicle, helicopter, tank, rocket launcher. c, Soldiers, flag, truck. d, Soldiers, people awaiting humanitarian aid. e, Soldiers at fort. f, Bulldozer and road grader. g, Soldiers working on railroad track and building. h, Soldiers on pontoon bridge beside damaged bridge.

**2010, Dec. 2**
**1567** A839 500p Sheet of 8, #a-h 27.00 27.00

Purranque, Cent. — A840

**2011, Apr. 8**
**1568** A840 290p multi 2.10 1.50

Pres. Eduardo Frei Montalva (1911-82) — A841

**2011, May 6**
**1569** A841 290p multi 2.25 1.90

Postal Union of the Americas, Spain and Portugal (UPAEP), Cent. — A842

**2011, May 20**
**1570** A842 290p multi 2.25 1.90

National Congress, Bicent. A843

**2011, July 3**
**1571** A843 290p multi 2.25 1.90

First Competition of Urban Intervention Ideas — A844

**2011, July 29 Litho. *Perf. 13¼***
**1572** A844 500p multi 3.25 3.00

Rapa Nui Face Decorations — A845

Various face decorations.

**2011, Aug. 5**
**1573** A845 10p brown .50 .50
**1574** A845 20p lt brown .50 .50
**1575** A845 50p lt brown .50 .50
**1576** A845 100p brown 1.10 1.10
*Nos. 1573-1576 (4)* 2.60 2.60

FAMAE (Weapons Manufacturer for Chilean Armed Forces), Bicent. A846

**2011, Sept. 30**
**1577** A846 290p multi 2.00 1.50

El Tabo, Cent. A847

No. 1578 — Arms of El Tabo and: a, Nuestra Senora del Rosario Church, El Tabo. b, La Asuncion Church, Las Cruces.

**2011, Oct. 7**
**1578** A847 290p Horiz. pair, #a-b 4.75 4.75

Talca University, 30th Anniv. — A848

No. 1579 — Sculpture and: a, Legal and Social Sciences Building. b, Kinetic Frieze, by Matilde Perez. c, Botanical Garden. d, Curicó Campus Engineering Building.

**2011, Oct. 12**
**1579** A848 290p Block of 4, #a-d 8.25 8.25

Mailbox — A849

**2011, Oct. 21**
**1580** A849 290p multi 2.10 1.90

America issue.

Christmas A850

**2011, Nov. 28**
**1581** A850 310p multi 2.25 1.90

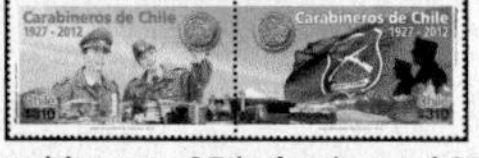

Carabineros, 85th Anniv. — A851

No. 1582 — Anniversary emblem and: a, Male and female carabineros. b, Flag and silhouettes of carabineros.

**2012, Apr. 24**
**1582** A851 310p Horiz. pair, #a-b 4.75 4.75

Diplomatic Relations Between Chile and South Korea, 50th Anniv. A852

**2012, July 23** *Perf. 13¼*
**1583** A852 310p multi 2.40 2.00

University of Chile, 170th Anniv. — A853

No. 1584: a, University building. b, Statue of first University rector, Andrés Bello López (1781-1865). c, Valentín Letelier, (1852-1919) rector. d, Amanda Labarca (1886-1975), educator.

**2012, Sept. 7**
**1584** A853 500p Block of 4, #a-d 15.00 15.00

Trauco (Mythological Forest Dweller) — A854

**2012, Oct. 22**
**1585** A854 310p multi 2.40 1.90

America issue.

Puente Alto, 120th Anniv. A855

**2012, Nov. 12**
**1586** A855 310p multi 2.40 1.90

Christmas — A856

No. 1587: a, Boy and open mail box. b, Children opening Christmas gifts.

**2012, Nov. 30**
**1587** A856 310p Horiz. pair, #a-b 5.25 5.25

Diplomatic Relations Between Thailand and Chile, 50th Anniv. — A857

**2012, Dec. 5**
**1588** A857 500p multi 4.00 3.00

Pontifical Catholic University of Chile, 125th Anniv. — A858

**2013, May 15**
**1589** A858 500p multi 3.75 3.00

Arica-La Paz Railway, Cent. A859

No. 1590: a, Steam locomotive. b, Diesel locomotive.

**2013, May 29**
**1590** A859 310p Horiz. pair, #a-b 4.75 4.75

Salvador Allende School of Public Health at University of Chile, 70th Anniv. — A860

No. 1591: a, Dr. Benjamin Viel (1913-98), Dr. Abraham Horwitz (1910-2000), Dr. Hugo Behm (1913-2011). b, Building.

**2013, June 7**
**1591** A860 500p Pair, #a-b 7.50 7.50

Historic Aricraft A861

No. 1592: a, Voisin biplane, 1910 (airplane used in first flight in Chile). b, Batuco biplane, 1913 (first airplane made in Chile).

No. 1593: a, De Havilland DH-60G "Gipsy Moth," 1929 (airplane used on first airmail route in Chile). b, Junkers R42, 1930 (seaplane flown from Puerto Montt to Straits of Magellan).

No. 1594: a, Blériot XI, 1916 (airplane used in first military flight and first airmail flight in Chile). b, Bristol M1C, 1918 (first airplane to cross the Andes at highest point).

No. 1595: a, Let L-13 "Blanik," 1964 (first glider to cross Andes). b, Bell 47 D-1 "Sioux" helicopter, 1960 (helicopter used in airlift after Valdivia earthquake).

No. 1596: a, PBY-5A Catalina, 1951 (seaplane used in first flight to Easter Island). b, Vought Sikorsky OS2U-3 "Kingfisher," 1947 (seaplane used in first flight from Chile to Antarctica).

**2013, Aug. 9** **Litho.** *Perf. 13¼*

**1592** Horiz. pair .70 .70
*a.-b.* A861 10p Either single .30 .30
**1593** Horiz. pair .70 .70
*a.-b.* A861 20p Either single .30 .30
**1594** Horiz. pair 1.10 1.10
*a.-b.* A861 50p Either single .40 .40
**1595** Horiz. pair 1.60 1.60
*a.-b.* A861 70p Either single .60 .60
**1596** Horiz. pair 2.25 2.25
*a.-b.* A861 100p Either single .85 .85
*Nos. 1592-1596 (5)* 6.35 6.35

Annexation of Easter Island, 125th Anniv. — A862

**2013, Sept. 27** **Litho.** *Perf. 13¼*
**1597** A862 500p multi 3.50 3.00

National Library, 200th Anniv. A863

**2013, Sept. 30** **Litho.** *Perf. 13¼*
**1598** A863 310p multi 2.25 1.90

General José Miguel Carrera National Institute (School for Boys), 200th Anniv. A864

**2013, Sept. 30** **Litho.** *Perf. 13¼*
**1599** A864 430p multi 3.25 2.50

Federation of Catholic University Students, 75th Anniv. — A865

**2013, Oct. 8** **Litho.** *Perf. 13¼*
**1600** A865 310p multi 2.25 1.90

Campaign Against Discrimination A866

**2013, Oct. 25** **Litho.** *Perf. 13¼*
**1601** A866 310p multi 2.25 1.90

America Issue.

Miniature Sheet

San José Mine Rescue, 3rd Anniv. A867

No. 1602: a, Fénix 2 rescue capsule. b, Names of 33 rescued miners. c, Note indicating condition and number of miners sent to surface on probe. d, Monument to the rescue of the miners. e, Drilling equipment at surface. f. 33 Chilean flags.

**2013, Oct. 30** **Litho.** *Perf. 13¼*
**1602** A867 500p Sheet of 6, #a-f 14.50 14.50

Christmas — A868

**2013, Nov. 27** **Litho.** *Perf. 13¼*
**1603** A868 310p multi 1.75 1.40

Public Education in Chile, Cent. — A869

**2013, Dec. 30** **Litho.** *Perf. 13¼*
**1604** A869 310p multi 1.60 1.25

Philatelic Society of Chile, 125th Anniv. A870

**2014, Mar. 18** **Litho.** *Perf. 13¼*
**1605** A870 310p multi 5.50 4.00

Los Angeles, 275th Anniv. — A871

No. 1606: a, Statue of Bernardo O'Higgins. b, Liceo de Hombres. c, Laguna Esmeralda. d, Laja Waterfalls.

**2014, May 26 Litho. *Perf. 13¼***
**1606** A871 310p Block of 4, #a-d 6.50 6.50

Printed in sheets containing four blocks of 4 + 4 labels.

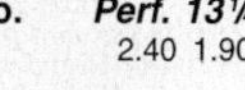

2014 World Cup Soccer Championships, Brazil — A872

**2014, June 16 Litho. *Perf. 13¼***
**1607** A872 500p multi 2.40 1.90

Battle of Rancagua, 200th Anniv. — A873

No. 1608 — Soldiers and: a, Angel holding shield. b, Swordsmen on horseback.

**2014, Sept. 30 Litho. *Perf. 13¼***
**1608** A873 Horiz pair 3.25 3.25
***a.-b.*** 310p Either single 1.40 1.40

Printed in sheets containing 12 pairs and 6 labels.

Exfina 2014 Philatelic Exhibition, Santiago A874

Designs: 470p, Chile #1. 500p, Chile #2. 1500p, Emblem of Philatelic Society of Chile.

**2014, Oct. 14 Litho. *Perf. 13¼***
**1609-1610** A874 Set of 2 4.50 3.50

**Souvenir Sheet**

**1611** A874 1500p multi 6.75 6.75

Philatelic Society of Chile, 125th anniv.

America Issue — A875

No. 1612: a, Lautaro (c. 1534-1557), Mapuche leader of resistance to Spanish rule. b. Caupolicán (d. 1558), Mapuche military leader.

**2014, Oct. 30 Litho. *Perf. 13¼***
**1612** A875 310p Vert. pair, #a-b 3.25 3.25

Christmas — A876

**2014, Nov. 10 Litho. *Perf. 13¼***
**1613** A876 310p multi 1.60 1.25

Chinchorro Mummies — A877

No. 1614: a, Mummy of a child with stake point at top of head. b, Mummy with outer coating missing under eye.

**2014, Nov. 28 Litho. *Perf. 13¼***
**1614** A877 500p Horiz. pair, #a-b 4.75 4.75

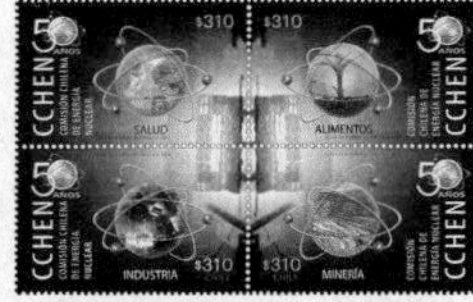

Chilean Nuclear Energy Commission, 50th Anniv. — A878

No. 1615 — Stylized atom with inscription: a, Salud (health). b, Alimentos (food). c, Industria (industry). d, Minería (mining).

**2014, Dec. 10 Litho. *Perf. 13¼***
**1615** A878 310p Block of 4, #a-d 6.25 6.25

**Miniature Sheet**

Talcahuano, 250th Anniv. — A879

No. 1616: a, Cacique Talcahueñu, painting by Héctor Robles Acuña. b, R.H. Huáscar. c, David Fuentes Sosa and his Blériot airplane "Talcahuano." d, Alcalde Luis Macera Dellarossa Coliseum. e, Boats in water near Caleta Tumbes. f, Sailboats off Talcahuano.

**2014, Dec. 12 Litho. *Perf. 13¼***
**1616** A879 500p Sheet of 6, #a-f 14.00 14.00

Hippocamelus Bisulcus — A880

No. 1617 — Huemul: a, Head, with foliage in background. b, Entire animal on hill, head at right. c, Entire animal with head at left. d, Head, Moon in clouds.

**2015, Apr. 7 Litho. *Perf. 13¼***
**1617** A880 600p Block of 4, #a-d 14.00 14.00

Protection of the huemul.

**Miniature Sheet**

Chuquicamata, Cent. — A881

No. 1618: a, Pres. Ramón Barros Luco. b, Steam shovel. c, Chuquicamata Mine. d, Chuquicamata Arch. e, Chile Theater. f, El Salvador Church.

**2015, June 3 Litho. *Perf. 13¼***
**1618** A881 500p Sheet of 6, #a-f 14.50 14.50

2015 Copa América Soccer Championships, Chile — A882

No. 1619 — Map of chile and; a, Soccer ball. b, Mascot and soccer ball.

**2015, June 8 Litho. *Perf. 13¼***
**1619** A882 500p Horiz. pair, #a-b 4.75 4.75

Josefina Martínez Children's Hospital, 75th Anniv. — A883

**2015, July 28 Litho. *Perf. 13¼***
**1620** A883 310p multi 1.50 1.25

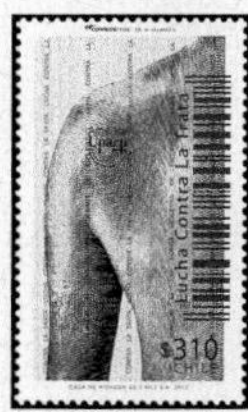

Campaign Against Human Trafficking — A884

Designs: 310p, Man. 500p, Woman.

**2015, Oct. 26 Litho. *Perf. 13¼***
**1621-1622** A884 Set of 2 3.75 3.00

America Issue.

State Defence Council, 120th Anniv. A885

**2015, Oct. 29 Litho. *Perf. 13¼***
**1623** A885 310p multi 1.50 1.25

Maps — A886

Map of: 10p, Santiago, 1541. 50p, Antarctica, 1739. 60p, Antarctica, present day. 80p, Robinson Crusoe Island, 1753. 100p, Robinson Crusoe Island, 1744.

No. 1629 — Map of Easter Island from: a, 1770. b, 1777.

**2015, Nov. 4 Litho. *Perf. 13¼***
**1624** A886 10p multi .35 .35
**1625** A886 50p multi .35 .35
**1626** A886 60p multi .35 .35
**1627** A886 80p multi .35 .35
**1628** A886 100p multi .50 .50
**1629** Horiz. pair 9.00 9.00
***a.-b.*** A886 1000p Either single 4.00 4.00
*Nos. 1624-1629 (6)* 10.90 10.90

Christmas — A887

**2015, Nov. 25 Litho. *Perf. 13¼***
**1630** A887 310p multi 1.50 1.25

Nacimiento A888

No. 1631 — Arms of Nacimiento and: a, Nacimiento Fort. b, Potter and pottery.

**2015, Dec. 21 Litho. *Perf. 13¼***
**1631** Horiz. pair + flanking label 5.25 5.25
***a.-b.*** A888 600p Either single 2.00 2.00

Pelluhue A889

No. 1632 — Arms of Pelluhue and: a, Caleta Curanipe. b, Municipal Stadium. c, Pueño-La Sirena. d, Arcos de Calan, Tregualemu.

**2015, Dec. 28 Litho. *Perf. 13¼***
**1632** A889 310p Block of 4, #a-d 6.00 6.00

**Miniature Sheet**

Symbols of Chilean Justice A890

No. 1633: a, Supreme Court Building. b, Statues at Supreme Court Building. c, Stained-glass window. d, Statue of Blind Justice. e, Court building and eagle sculpture. f, Court building and sculpture of Justice.

**2015, Dec. 29 Litho. *Perf. 13¼***
**1633** A890 500p Sheet of 6, #a-f 13.00 13.00

Naval Aviation A891

No. 1634: a, Dornier Wal No. 16, 1928. b, Fairey III-F Mk 1, 1927.

**2016, Mar. 16 Litho. *Perf. 13¼***
**1634** A891 600p Horiz. pair, #a-b 5.25 5.25

A892

Design: Lieutenant Hernan Merino Correa (1936-65), Soldier Killed in Laguna del Desierto Incident.

**2016, Apr. 25 Litho. *Perf. 13¼***
**1635** A892 500p multi 2.40 1.90

2016 Summer Olympics, Rio de Janeiro — A893

**2016, Oct. 21 Litho. *Perf. 13¼***
**1636** A893 310p multi 1.60 1.25

America issue.

National Monuments — A894

No. 1637: a, San Andrés Church, Pica. b, Matilla Church, Matilla.

**2016, Oct. 27 Litho. *Perf. 13¼***
**1637** A894 310p Horiz. pair, #a-b 3.25 3.25

Christmas — A895

**2016, Nov. 14 Litho. *Perf. 13¼***
**1638** A895 310p multi 1.75 1.25

Radio Bío Bío, 50th Anniv. A896

No. 1639 — Emblem and: a, Concentric circles, map of Chile in blue. b, Speaker holes, map of Chile in red.

**2016, Dec. 7 Litho. *Perf. 13¼***
**1639** A896 500p Horiz. pair, #a-b 4.75 4.75

Costumes of the Selk'nam People — A897

Inscriptions: 10p, Tanu. 20p, Halaháches. 30p, Matan. 50p, Shoort Jóichik. 100p, Kulan. 1000p, Ulen.

**2016, Dec. 29 Litho. *Perf. 13¼***
**1640-1645** A897 Set of 6 6.75 5.00

Pampilla Festival, Coquimbo A898

**2016, Dec. 30 Litho. *Perf. 13¼***
**1646** A898 600p multi 2.90 2.50

Bernardo O'Higgins Military Academy, 200th Anniv. A899

**2017, Mar. 15 Litho. *Perf. 13¼***
**1647** A899 600p multi 2.90 2.50

Independence, 200th Anniv. (in 2018) — A900

No. 1648: a, Fiscal Warehouse Buildings (Edificios Almacenes Fiscales). b, Juan O. Goñi (1854-1919), naval officer, and ship, Esmerelda, in Battle of Iquique. c, José Santiago Campino, first accountant of Chilean Navy. d, Naval Storehouse Building (Edificio de la Dirección de Abastecimiento de la Armada).

**2017, June 15 Litho. *Perf. 13¼***
**1648** Horiz. strip of 4 + label or block of 4 11.50 11.50
*a.-d.* A900 600p Any single 2.50 2.50

Battle of Chacabuco, 200th Anniv. — A901

**2017, Aug. 20 Litho. *Perf. 13¼***
**1649** A901 340p multi 1.75 1.50

Children's Rights A902

No. 1650: a, Sun and heart with faces. b, Faces, crescent Moon and Sun.
1500p, Faces, crescent Moon and Sun, diff.

**2017, Sept. 13 Litho. *Perf. 13¼***
**1650** A902 500p Vert. pair, #a-b 4.75 4.75

**Souvenir Sheet**

**1651** A902 1500p multi 6.75 6.75

Chilean ratification of United Nations Convention on the Rights of the Child, 25th anniv.

Murals by David Alfaro Sisqueiros and Xavier Guerrero at Mexico School, Chillán, 75th Anniv. — A903

**2017, Sept. 14 Litho. *Perf. 13¼***
**1652** A903 360p multi 1.90 1.50

Chilean Postal Service, 270th Anniv. — A904

**2017, Oct. 25 Litho. *Perf. 13¼***
**1653** A904 360p multi 1.90 1.50

Desert Flowers A905

No. 1654: a, Leontochir ovallei. b, Leucocoryne vittata. c, Argylia radiata. d, Rhodophiala phycelloides.

**2017, Oct. 25 Litho. *Perf. 13¼***
**1654** A905 600p Block of 4, #a-d 11.50 11.50

Chilean Postal Service, 270th anniv.

Vicente Pérez Rosales National Park — A906

**2017, Oct. 31 Litho. *Perf. 13¼***
**1655** A906 360p multi 1.90 1.50

America issue.

Christmas — A907

**2017, Dec. 15 Litho. *Perf. 13¼***
**1656** A907 360p multi 1.90 1.50

Violeta Parra (1917-67), Composer and Folklorist — A908

**2017, Dec. 28 Litho. *Perf. 13¼***
**1657** A908 500p multi 2.50 1.90

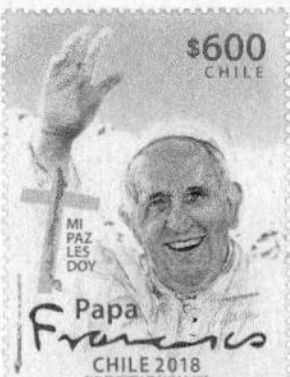
Visit to Chile of Pope Francis — A909

**2018, Jan. 10 Litho. *Perf. 13¼***
**1658** A909 600p multi 2.50 2.00

Battle of Maipú, 200th Anniv. — A910

**2018, Apr. 5 Litho. *Perf. 13¼***
**1659** A910 360p multi 1.75 1.50

Chilean Navy, 200th Anniv. — A911

No. 1660 — Crest of Chilean Navy and: a, Capture of the Esmerelda, 1820. b, First national squadron, 1818. c, Ship and helicopters, 2018. d, Four sailors, 2018.

**2018, Oct. 5 Litho. *Perf. 13¼***
**1660** Horiz. strip of 5 + flanking label 11.00 5.50
*a.-e.* A911 600p Any single 2.50 1.25

Vultur Gryphus A912

**2018, Oct. 13 Litho. *Perf. 13¼***
**1661** A912 360p multi 1.75 1.25

**Souvenir Sheet**

**1662** A912 1500p multi 6.50 6.50

Exfil 2018 Philatelic Exhibition, Santiago. No. 1662 contains one 48x48mm stamp.

Canis Lupus Familiaris A913

**2018, Oct. 31 Litho. *Perf. 13¼***
**1663** A913 360p multi 1.75 1.50

America issue.

Christmas A914

No. 1664 — Winning designs in children's art contest: a, Family and Christmas tree, by Fabián Manquepillán. b, Christmas tree, mailbox and children holding letters, by Emanuel Sepúlveda. c, Santa Claus and reindeer as penguins, by Bárbara Rivera. d, Pyramid of children, by Nicolette Sepúlveda. e, Children and snowman, by Nicolás Sandoval.

**2018, Nov. 20 Litho. *Perf. 13¼***
**1664** Horiz. strip of 5 12.00 6.00
*a.-e.* A914 500p Any single 2.00 1.25

First Flight Over the Andes Mountains by Dagoberto Godoy (1893-1960), Cent. — A915

**2018, Dec. 12** **Litho.** ***Perf. 13¼***
**1665** A915 600p multi 2.75 2.25

July 2, 2019, Total Solar Eclipse A916

**2019, July 2** **Litho.** ***Perf. 13¼***
**1666** A916 830p multi 3.00 2.50

Bass and Jorge Peña Hen (1928-73), Composer and Founder of Children's Symphony Orchestra — A917

**2019, July 12** **Litho.** ***Perf. 13¼***
**1667** A917 370p multi 1.50 1.25

Youth and Children's Orchestras Foundation.

A918

A919

A920

University of Concepción, Cent. — A921

**2019, Aug. 7** **Litho.** ***Perf. 13¼***
**1668** Horiz. strip of 4 + central label 6.00 3.00
*a.* A918 370p multi 1.25 .65
*b.* A919 370p multi 1.25 .65
*c.* A920 370p multi 1.25 .65
*d.* A921 370p multi 1.25 .65

Express Mail Service, 20th Anniv. A922

**2019, Oct. 9** **Litho.** ***Perf. 13¼***
**1669** A922 520p multi 2.10 1.90

Traditional Chilean Foods — A923

Designs: 370p, Marraqueta (bread), cazuela (stew), and vino tinto (red wine). 480p, Mote con huesillo (peach and barley drink), empanadas and paila marina (seafood stew).

**2019, Oct. 25** **Litho.** ***Perf. 13¼***
**1670-1671** A923 Set of 2 3.50 3.00

America issue.

President Frei Antarctic Air Base, 50th Anniv. — A924

No. 1672 — Map and: a, Aerial view of base. b, Heliograph of the Meteorological Center. c, Teniente Marsh Aerodrome. d, Chilean Air Force Bell 412 helicopter and penguins.

**2019, Oct. 29** **Litho.** ***Perf. 13¼***
**1672** A924 1000p Block of 4, #a-d 15.00 7.50

International Year of Indigenous Languages — A925

**2019, Nov. 27** **Litho.** ***Perf. 13¼***
**1673** A925 480p multi 2.00 1.50

Christmas — A926

**2019, Nov. 28** **Litho.** ***Perf. 13¼***
**1674** A926 370p multi 1.50 1.25

Discovery of the Straits of Magellan, 500th Anniv. — A927

No. 1675: a, Yagan woman weaving basket, map of Straits of Magellan. b, Kawesqar people and dog in canoe. c, Ferdinand Magellan (1480-1521), explorer and discoverer of Straits of Magellan, map. d, Map of Straits of Magellan.

**2020, Oct. 21** **Litho.** ***Perf. 13¼***
**1675** A927 1000p Block of 4, #a-d 10.50 5.25

Christmas — A928

**2020, Dec. 12** **Litho.** ***Perf. 13¼***
**1676** A928 370p multi 1.10 .55

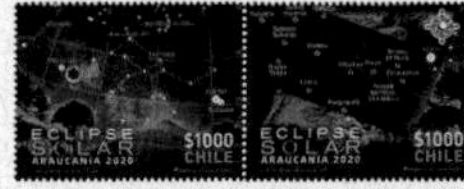
Solar Eclipse of Dec. 14, 2020 A929

No. 1677: a, Astronomical chart and mountain. b, Map of solar eclipse totality.

**2020, Dec. 14** **Litho.** ***Perf. 13¼***
**1677** A929 1000p Horiz. pair, #a-b 5.75 3.00

Diplomatic Relations Between Chile and People's Republic of China, 50th Anniv. — A930

**2020, Dec. 15** **Litho.** ***Perf. 13¼***
**1678** A930 1200p multi 3.50 1.75

America Issue — A931

Architecture: 370p, Parque Bicentenario, Santiago. 500p, Palacio Braun Menéndez, Punta Arenas.

**2020, Dec. 17** **Litho.** ***Perf. 13¼***
**1679-1680** A931 Set of 2 2.50 2.50

Chilean Claims to Antarctic Territory A932

No. 1681 — Map showing Chile and Chilean claim to Antarctic territory and: a, Airplane, ship, snowmobile, researchers, penguin, flora and marine life. b, Sailing ships, seal, whale, penguin, researcher and airplane.

**2021, Mar. 16** **Litho.** ***Perf. 13¼***
**1681** A932 500p Vert. pair, #a-b 3.00 3.00

Gabriela Mistral (1889-1957), 1945 Nobel Laureate in Literature — A933

**2021, Sept. 9** **Litho.** ***Perf. 13¼***
**1682** A933 1500p multi 3.75 3.75

Joint issue between Chile and Spain. See Spain No. 4553.

Independence of Central America, 200th Anniv. — A934

**2021, Sept. 14** **Litho.** ***Perf. 13¼***
**1683** A934 1200p multi 3.00 3.00

Diplomatic Relations Between Chile and Canada, 80th Anniv. A935

**2021, Nov. 18** **Litho.** ***Perf. 13¼***
**1684** A935 500p multi 1.25 1.25

America Issue — A936

Tourist attractions: 500p, Torres del Paine. 1000p, Moais, Easter Island.

**2021, Nov.** **Litho.** ***Perf. 13¼***
**1685-1686** A936 Set of 2 3.75 3.75

Ministry of Foreign Affairs, 150th Anniv. — A937

**2021** **Litho.** ***Perf. 13¼***
**1687** A937 600p multi 1.50 1.50

December 4, 2021 Solar Eclipse Over Antarctica — A938

No. 1688: a, Astronomical chart showing path of eclipse, people in Antarctica viewing eclipse, penguin. b, Map of path of eclipse over Antarctica, compass, penguins, and whale.

**2021, Dec. 4** **Litho.** ***Perf. 13¼***
**1688** A938 1000p Horiz. pair, #a-b 4.75 4.75

Christmas A939

**2021, Dec.** **Litho.** ***Perf. 13¼***
**1689** A939 370p multi .90 .90

## POSTAL FISCAL STAMPS

Revenue stamps and telegraph stamp authorized for postal use until the end of 1914.

Arms — PF1

**1880-91** **Engr.** **Unwmk.** ***Perf. 12***

**AR1** PF1 1c red 2.25 *6.75*
Revenue cancel .40
**AR2** PF1 2c brown 2.25 *5.25*
Revenue cancel .40
**AR3** PF1 5c blue 3.50 *4.50*
Revenue cancel .40
**AR4** PF1 10c green ('91) 13.50 *13.50*
Revenue cancel .40
**AR5** PF1 20c orange ('91) 13.50 *35.00*
Revenue cancel .40

Printed by the American Banknote Co. Issued: 1c, 2c, 11/27/80; 5c, 7/3/80; 10c, 20c, 4/1/91.
Counterfeit postal cancels exist.

Arms — PF2

**1891, Apr. 21**

**AR6** PF2 2c yellow brown 2.00 *12.00*
Telegraph cancel .75
**AR7** PF2 10c olive green 1.00 *12.00*
Telegraph cancel .75
**AR8** PF2 20c blue 8.50 *6.00*
Telegraph cancel .75
**AR9** PF2 1p brown 1.50 *20.00*
Telegraph cancel .75

Printed by Bradbury, Wilkinson & Co. Nos. AR6-AR9 are telegraph stamps, authorized for postal use.
Counterfeit postal cancels exist.
Smaller format stamps of the same design as AR6-AR9 are 1894 telegraph stamps that were not authorized for postal use.

PF3

**1900-13** ***Perf. 14***

**AR10** PF3 1c vermilion 2.25 3.00
Revenue cancel .40
**AR11** PF3 2c brown ('13) 2.25 3.50
Revenue cancel .40
**AR12** PF3 5c blue 3.00 4.50
Revenue cancel .40

Printed by Waterlow & Sons, London. Issued: 1c, 10/25/00; 2c, 1/21/13; 5c, 12/6/00.
Counterfeit postal cancels exist.

## SEMI-POSTAL STAMPS

S. S. Abtao and Captain Policarpo Toro — SP1

S. S. Abtao and Brother Eugenio Eyraud — SP2

***Perf. 14½x15***

**1940, Mar. 1** **Engr.** **Unwmk.**

**B1** SP1 80c + 2.20p dk grn & lake 4.00 2.00
**B2** SP2 3.60p + 6.40p lake & dk grn 4.00 2.00
*a.* Pair, #B1-B2 10.00 8.00
Set, never hinged 10.00

50th anniv. of Chilean ownership of Easter Is. Surtax used for charitable institutions.
Sheets containing 15 of each value, with 9 se-tenant pairs.

**Catalogue values for unused stamps in this section, from this point to the end of the section, are for Never Hinged items.**

Pedro de Valdivia — SP3

Portraits: 10c+10c, Jose Toribio Medina.

**1961, Apr. 29** **Photo.** ***Perf. 13x12½***

**B3** SP3 5c + 5c pale brn & sl grn 1.25 .35
**B4** SP3 10c + 10c buff & vio blk 1.25 .30

Printed without charge by the Spanish Mint as a gift to Chile. The surtax was to aid the 1960 earthquake victims and to increase teachers' salaries. See Nos. CB1-CB2.

### No. 402 Surcharged in Dark Green

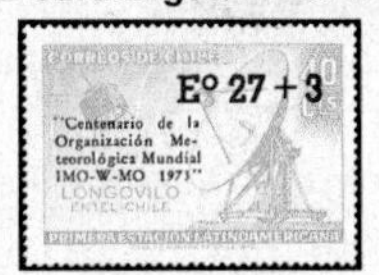

**1974, Mar. 25** **Litho.** ***Perf. 14½***
**B5** A213 27e + 3e on 40c dl grn .85 .40

Cent. of intl. meteorological cooperation.
The 3e surtax of Nos. B5-B10 was for modernization of the postal system.

### No. 412 Surcharged in Dark Blue

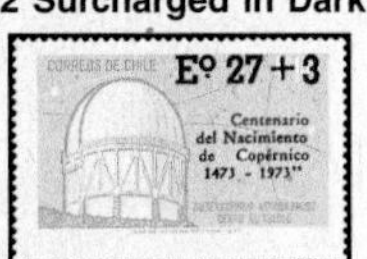

**1974, Apr. 25** **Litho.** ***Perf. 14½***
**B6** A219 27e + 3e on 1.95e 1.00 .40

500th anniversary of the birth of Nicolaus Copernicus (1473-1534), Polish astronomer.

No. 329A Surcharged

**1974, May 2** **Litho.** ***Perf. 14***
**B7** A159 27e + 3e on 1e grnsh bl .65 .40

Centenary of the city of Vina del Mar.

### No. 377 Surcharged in Blk, Nos. 395, 380 in Red

**1974** **Litho.** ***Perf. 14½***

**B8** A193 47e + 3e on 40c grn .40 .40
**B9** A207 67e + 3e on 40c multi .95 .45
**B10** A196 97e + 3e on 40c red brn .65 .40
*Nos. B8-B10 (3)* 2.00 1.25

Issued: No. B8, 6/7; No. B9, 7/9; No. B10, 6/20.

## AIR POST STAMPS

### Surcharged in Black

**Lithographed; Center Engraved**
**1927** **Unwmk.** ***Perf. 13½x14***
**Black Brown & Blue**

**C1** AP1 40c on 10c 350.00 50.00
**C2** AP1 80c on 10c 350.00 65.00
**C3** AP1 1.20p on 10c 350.00 75.00
**C4** AP1 1.60p on 10c 350.00 75.00
**C5** AP1 2p on 10c 350.00 75.00
*Nos. C1-C5 (5)* 1,750. 340.00

Issued for air post service between Santiago and Valparaiso. The stamps picture Bernardo O'Higgins and are not known without surcharge.

Regular Issues of 1915-28 Overprinted or Surcharged in Black, Red or Blue

### Inscribed: "Chile Correos"

**1928-29** ***Perf. 13½x14, 14***

**C6** A39 20c brn org & blk (Bk) .75 .40
**C6A** A55 40c dk vio & blk (R) 1.00 .40
**C6B** A43 1p grn & blk (Bl) 4.25 .80
**C6C** A43 2p red & blk (Bl) 5.00 1.10
*f.* 2p ver & blk (Bl) 120.00 35.00
**C6D** A43 5p ol grn & blk (Bl) 10.00 3.25
**C6E** A50 6p on 10c dp bl & blk (R) 65.00 40.00
**C7** A43 10p org & blk (Bk) ('29) 16.00 6.50
**C8** A43 10p org & blk (Bl) 50.00 35.00
*Nos. C6-C8 (8)* 152.00 87.45

On Nos. C6B to C6D, C7 and C8 the overprint is larger than on the other stamps of the issue.

Nos. 155, 156, 158-161 Ovptd. or Srchd. in Red, Blue or Black

### Inscribed: "Chile Correos"

**1928-32** **Wmk. 215**

**C9** A55 40c vio & blk (R) 1.35 .40
**C10** A43 1p gray grn & blk (Bl) 1.90 .40
**C11** A43 2p red & blk (Bl) 11.00 2.25
**C12** A52 3p on 5c sl bl (R) 65.00 42.50
**C13** A43 5p ol grn & blk (Bl) 8.50 3.00
**C14** A43 10p org & blk (Bk) 45.00 12.00
*Nos. C9-C14 (6)* 132.75 60.55

### Same Overprint on Nos. 166-169, 172 and 158 in Black or Red
### Inscribed: "Correos de Chile"

**1928-30**

**C15** A39 20c (#166) ('29) 1.25 .70
**C16** A39 20c (#172) ('30) .50 .30
**C17** A40 25c bl & blk (R) .60 .30
**C18** A41 30c brn & blk .40 .30
*a.* Double ovpt., one inverted *250.00* *250.00*
**C19** A42 50c dp grn & blk (R) .50 .30
*Nos. C15-C19 (5)* 3.25 1.90

No. 109 Overprinted in Black

### Inscribed: "Chile Correos"

**1932** ***Perf. 13½x14, 14***
**C21** A43 1p yel grn & blk (Bk) 6.00 1.75

Condor on Andes AP1a

Airplane Crossing Andes AP3

Los Cerrillos Airport — AP2

**1931** **Litho.** ***Perf. 13½x14, 14½x14***

**C22** AP1a 5c yellow grn .25 .25
**C23** AP1a 10c yellow brn .25 .25
**C24** AP1a 20c rose .25 .25
**C25** AP2 50c dark blue 3.00 .75
**C26** AP3 50c black brn 1.10 .50
**C27** AP3 1p purple 1.75 .35
**C28** AP3 2p blue blk 2.50 .50
*a.* 2p bluish slate 12.00 3.00
**C29** AP2 5p lt red 4.25 .75
*Nos. C22-C29 (8)* 13.35 3.60

For surcharges see Nos. C51-C53.

Airplane over City — AP4

Two Airplanes over Globe — AP9

Designs: 30c, 40c, 50c, Wings over Chile. 60c, Condor. 70c, Airplane and Star of Chile. 80c, Condor and Statue of Canpolican. 3p, 4p, 5p, Seaplane. 6p, 8p, 10p, Airplane. 20p, 30p, Airplane and Southern Cross. 40p, 50p, Airplane and symbols of space.

***Perf. 13½x14***
**1934-39** **Engr.** **Wmk. 215**

**C30** AP4 10c yel grn ('35) .30 .30
**C31** AP4 15c dk grn ('35) .30 .30
**C32** AP4 20c dp bl ('36) .30 .30
**C33** AP4 30c blk brn ('35) .30 .30
**C34** AP4 40c indigo ('38) .30 .30
**C35** AP4 50c dk brn ('36) .30 .30
**C36** AP4 60c vio blk ('35) .30 .30
**C37** AP4 70c blue ('35) .30 .30
**C38** AP4 80c ol blk ('35) .30 .30

***Perf. 14***

**C39** AP9 1p slate blk .30 .30
**C40** AP9 2p grnsh bl .30 .30
**C41** AP9 3p org brn ('35) .30 .30
**C42** AP9 4p brn ('35) .30 .30
**C43** AP9 5p org red .30 .30
**C44** AP9 6p yel brn ('35) .45 .30
*a.* 6p brown ('39) 2.75 1.90
**C45** AP9 8p grn ('35) .40 .30
**C46** AP9 10p brn lake .45 .30
**C47** AP9 20p olive .45 .30
**C48** AP9 30p gray blk .50 .30
**C49** AP9 40p gray vio 1.00 .70
**C50** AP9 50p brn vio 2.50 .80
*Nos. C30-C50 (21)* 9.95 7.20

Nos. C30-C50 have been re-issued in slightly different colors, with white gum. The first printings are considerably scarcer.
See Nos. C90-C107B, C148-C154.

Types of 1931 Surcharged in Black or Red

*Perf. 13½x14, 14½x14*

**1940 Wmk. 215**

**C51** AP1a 80c on 20c lt rose .40 .25
**C52** AP2 1.60p on 5p lt red 4.25 1.50
**C53** AP3 5.10p on 2p sl bl (R) 7.00 1.75
*Nos. C51-C53 (3)* 11.65 3.50

The surcharge on No. C52 measures 21½mm.

Plane and Weather Vane AP14

Plane and Caravel AP23

Designs (Plane and): 20c, Globe. 30c, Chilean flag. 40c, Star of Chile and Southern Cross. 50c, Mountains. 60c, Tree. 70c, Lakes. 80c, Shore. 90c, Sunrise. 2p, Compass. 3p, Telegraph lines. 4p, Rainbow. 5p, Factory. 10p, Snow-capped mountain.

**1941-42 Wmk. 215 Litho. *Perf. 14***

**C54** AP14 10c ol gray .25 .25
**C55** AP14 20c dp rose .25 .25
**C56** AP14 30c blue vio .25 .25
**C57** AP14 40c dl red brn .25 .25
**C58** AP14 50c red org ('42) .35 .25
**C59** AP14 60c dp green .25 .25
**C60** AP14 70c rose .30 .25
**C61** AP14 80c ultra ('42) 1.50 .45
**C62** AP14 90c dk brown .45 .25
**C63** AP23 1p brt blue .30 .25
**C64** AP23 2p rose lake .80 .30
**C65** AP23 3p dk bl grn & yel grn 1.20 .60
**C66** AP23 4p bl vio & buff 1.75 1.00
**C67** AP23 5p dk org red ('42) 17.00 6.00
**C68** AP23 10p gray grn & bl grn 9.50 6.00
*Nos. C54-C68 (15)* 34.40 16.60

The 1p, dated "1541-1941," commemorates the 400th anniversary of Santiago.

**1942-46 Unwmk.**

**C69** AP14 10c ultra ('43) .25 .25
**C70** AP14 10c rose lil ('45) .25 .25
**C71** AP14 20c dull grn ('43) .25 .25
**C72** AP14 20c cop brn ('45) .25 .25
**C73** AP14 30c dull vio ('44) .25 .25
**C74** AP14 30c ol blk ('45) .25 .25
**C75** AP14 40c red brn ('44) .30 .25
**C76** AP14 40c ultra ('45) .25 .25
**C77** AP14 50c rose ('43) .25 .25
**C78** AP14 50c org red ('45) .25 .25
**C79** AP14 60c orange .25 .25
**C79B** AP14 60c dp grn ('46) .25 .25
**C80** AP14 70c rose ('45) .45 .35
**C81** AP14 80c slate grn .25 .25
**C82** AP14 90c brown ('45) .45 .35
**C83** AP23 1p gray grn & lt bl ('43) .25 .25
**C84** AP23 2p org red ('43) .45 .25
**C85** AP23 3p dk pur & pale org ('43) .45 .25
**C86** AP23 4p bl grn & yel grn .45 .35
**C87** AP23 5p dk rose car ('43) .35 .25
*a.* 5p dk car rose ('44) .40 .40
**C88** AP23 10p sapphire ('43) .45 .35
*Nos. C69-C88 (21)* 6.60 5.65

No. C83 is without dates "1541-1941."
See Nos. C109-C123. For surcharges see Nos. C145-C147.

Coat of Arms and Plane — AP29

**1942, Nov. 5 Engr. *Perf. 14½***

**C89** AP29 100p car lake 40.00 35.00

University of Chile centenary.

**Types of 1934-39**

***Perf. 13½x14***

**1944-55 Unwmk. Engr.**

**C90** AP4 10c yel grn ('55) .25 .25
**C92** AP4 20c deep blue .25 .25
**C93** AP4 30c black brn .25 .25
**C94** AP4 40c indigo .25 .25
**C95** AP4 50c dk brn ('47) .25 .25
**C96** AP4 60c slate vio .25 .25
**C97** AP4 70c blue ('48) .25 .25
**C98** AP4 80c olive blk .25 .25

***Perf. 14***

**C99** AP9 1p slate blk .25 .25
**C100** AP9 2p grnsh bl .25 .25
**C101** AP9 3p org brn ('45) .25 .25
**C102** AP9 4p brown .25 .25
**C103** AP9 5p org red .35 .25
**C104** AP9 6p yel brn ('46) .40 .25
**C105** AP9 8p green .40 .25
**C106** AP9 10p brn lake 1.10 .25
**C107** AP9 20p ol gray ('45) .75 .25
*a.* Imperf., pair 70.00
**C107B** AP9 50p rose vio ('50) 17.50 2.50
*Nos. C90-C107B (18)* 23.50 6.75

Plane and Radio Tower — AP30

**1945 Unwmk. Litho. *Perf. 14***

**C108** AP30 1.60p brt violet .55 .40

See Nos. C118-C119.

**Types of 1941-45**

**1946-48 Wmk. 215**

**C109** AP14 10c rose lil ('47) .25 .25
**C110** AP14 20c dk red brn ('48) .25 .25
**C111** AP14 20c dull grn ('48) 1.50 .30
**C112** AP14 30c black ('48) .25 .25
**C113** AP14 40c ultra ('48) .25 .25
**C114** AP14 60c ol grn ('48) .25 .25
**C115** AP14 80c ol blk ('48) .25 .25
**C116** AP14 90c choc ('48) .25 .25
**C117** AP23 1p gray grn & lt bl ('48) .25 .25
**C118** AP30 1.60p brt violet .25 .25
**C119** AP30 1.80p brt vio ('48) .25 .25
**C119A** AP23 2p org red .40 .25
**C120** AP23 3p dk pur & pale org ('47) 1.50 .30
**C121** AP23 4p bl grn & yel grn ('48) 1.10 .45
**C122** AP23 5p rose car ('47) .80 .25
**C123** AP23 10p sapphire ('47) 1.00 .25
*Nos. C109-C123 (16)* 8.80 4.30

No. C117 is without dates "1541-1941."
For surcharges see Nos. C145, C147.

**Flora and Fauna Type of 1948**

**1948**

**C124** A118 3p Block of 25 60.00 60.00
Never hinged 75.00
*a.-y.* any single 2.00 1.50

**Catalogue values for unused stamps in this section, from this point to the end of the section, are for Never Hinged items.**

Air Line Emblem and Planes — AP32

**1949 Wmk. 215 Litho. *Perf. 14***

**C125** AP32 2p ultra .70 .40

20th anniversary of the establishment of Chile's National Air Line.

Benjamin Vicuna Mackenna — AP33

**1949, Mar. 22 Engr. *Perf. 13½x14***

**C126** AP33 3p dk car rose .40 .30

Factory, Badge and Book — AP34

Design: 10p, Column and cogwheel.

**Unwmk.**

**1949, Nov. 11 Litho. *Perf. 14***

**C127** AP34 5p green 1.00 .45
**C128** AP34 10p red brown 1.50 .55

Centenary of the founding of Chile's School of Arts and Crafts.

Plane and Globe — AP35

**1950, Jan. Engr.**

**C129** AP35 5p green .75 .40
**C130** AP35 10p red brown 1.25 1.00

75th anniv. of the UPU.

Plane over Snow-capped Mountain AP36

Araucarian Pine and Plane AP38

Plane and: 40c, Coast and Sunrise. 60c, Over fishing boat. 2p, Chilean flag. 3p, Dock crane. 4p, Above river. 5p, Blast furnace. 10p, Mountain lake. 20p, Cable cars.

**Imprint: "Especies Valoradas-Chile"**

**1950-54 Wmk. 215 Litho. *Perf. 14***

**C135** AP36 20c yel brn ('54) .50 .30
**C136** AP36 40c purple ('52) .50 .30
**C137** AP36 60c lt bl ('53) 2.40 1.10
**C138** AP38 1p dull green .50 .30
**C139** AP38 2p brown red .50 .30
**C140** AP38 3p violet bl .50 .30
**C141** AP38 4p red org ('54) .50 .30
**C142** AP38 5p violet .50 .30
**C143** AP38 10p yel grn ('53) .50 .30
**C144** AP38 20p red brn ('54) .90 .30
*Nos. C135-C144 (10)* 7.30 3.80

See Nos. C155-C164, C207-C212.

**Nos. C115, C81 and C116 Surcharged with New Value in Carmine or Black**

**1951-52 Wmk. 215**

**C145** AP14 40c on 80c ol blk (C) ('52) .65 .40

**Unwmk.**

**C146** AP14 40c on 80c sl grn (C) ('52) 5.50 3.50

**Wmk. 215**

**C147** AP14 1p on 90c choc .40 .40
*Nos. C145-C147 (3)* 6.55 4.30

**Types of 1934-39**

**1951-53 Unwmk. Engr. *Perf. 14***

**C148** AP9 1p deep blue .30 .25
**C149** AP9 2p blue .40 .25
**C150** AP9 6p bis brn ('52) .50 .25
**C151** AP9 30p dk gray ('53) .65 .90
**C152** AP9 40p dk pur brn 18.00 2.40
**C153** AP9 50p dark purple 25.00 5.00
*Nos. C148-C153 (6)* 44.85 9.05

**Wmk. 215**

**C154** AP9 50p dk pur ('52) .80 .40

**Types of 1950-54**

Designs as Before

Imprint: "Especies Valoradas-Chile"

**1951-55 Unwmk. Litho. *Perf. 14***

**C155** AP36 20c yel brn ('54) .55 .40
**C156** AP36 40c purple .55 .40
**C157** AP36 60c lt blue ('53) .55 .40
**C158** AP38 1p dk bl grn ('55) .55 .40
**C159** AP38 2p brown red .55 .40
**C160** AP38 3p violet bl .55 .40
**C161** AP38 4p red org ('52) .70 .40
**C162** AP38 5p violet .70 .40
**C163** AP38 10p emerald .70 .40
**C164** AP38 20p brown .90 .40
*Nos. C155-C164 (10)* 6.30 4.00

San Martin Crossing Andes — AP40

**Wmk. 215**

**1951, Mar. 16 Engr. *Perf. 14½***

**C165** AP40 5p red violet 1.40 .50

Gen. José de San Martín, death cent.

**Isabella Type of Regular Issue, 1952**

**1952, Mar. 21 *Perf. 14***

**C166** A125 10p carmine 1.00 .40

A souvenir card without franking value was issued for the Hispano-Chilean Philatelic Exhibition at Santiago, Oct. 12, 1969. It contains 2 imperf. stamps similar to Nos. 264 and C166-60c green and 10p rose red. Size: 115x137½mm. Value, $52.

Ancient Fortress — AP42

**1953, Apr. 28**

**C167** AP42 10p brown car 2.75 .80

4th centenary of the founding of Valdivia.

**Stamp Centenary Type of 1953**

**1953, Oct. 15 Engr. *Perf. 14½***

**C168** A131 100p grnsh blue 2.75 1.00

An imperf. souvenir sheet contains one each of Nos. 276 and C168, with inscriptions in black at top and bottom center. Sheet measures 178x229mm, value $850, or 172x226mm, value $130. It is stated that this sheet was not valid for postage.

Early Plane and Stylized Modern Version — AP44

**Unwmk.**

**1954, May 26 Engr. *Perf. 14***

**C170** AP44 3p deep blue .60 .40

25th anniversary of the founding of Chile's National Air Line.

**Domeyko Type of Regular Issue, 1954**

**1954, Aug. 16 *Perf. 13½x14***

**C171** A134 5p reddish brown .40 .30

**Railroad Type of Regular Issue, 1954**

**1954, Sept. 10 Wmk. 215 *Perf. 14½***

**C172** A135 10p dk purple 1.90 .25

An imperforate souvenir sheet contains one each of Nos. 283 and C172. Size: 195x235mm. Value $425.
Size: 174x232mm. Value, $110.

**Presidential Visits Type of 1955**

**1955, May 24**

**C173** A139 100p red 1.90 1.25

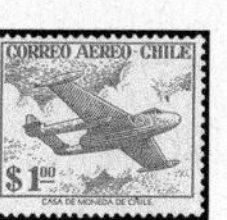


Jet Plane in Clouds AP48

Comet Air Liner AP49

Designs: 2p, Helicopter over bridge. 10p, Oil derricks and plane. 50p, Control tower and plane. 200p, Beechcraft monoplane. 500p, Douglas DC-6.

***Perf. 14½x14, 14x13½ (AP49)***

**1955-56 Engr. Wmk. 215**

**C174** AP48 1p dp red lil ('56) .30 .25
**C175** AP48 2p pale brn ('56) .30 .25
**C176** AP48 10p bluish grn ('56) .30 .25
**C177** AP48 50p rose ('56) .65 .25
**C178** AP49 100p green 1.10 .25
**C179** AP49 200p dp ultra 7.00 .90
**C180** AP49 500p dk carmine 8.25 .90
*Nos. C174-C180 (7)* 17.90 3.05

Stamps similar to type AP49, but inscribed in escudo currency, are listed as type AP58.

**1956-58** **Unwmk.**

Designs: 5p, Train and plane. 20p, Jet plane and Easter Island statue.

**C183** AP48 5p violet .40 .40
**C184** AP48 10p grn ('57) .40 .40
**C185** AP48 20p ultra .40 .40
**C186** AP48 50p rose ('57) .40 .40
**C187** AP49 100p bl grn ('57) .85 .40
*a.* Lithographed ('60) .85 .40
**C188** AP49 200p dp ultra ('57) 1.00 .40
**C189** AP49 500p car ('58) 1.25 .40
*Nos. C183-C189 (7)* 4.70 2.80

Symbols of University Departments AP50

Design: 100p, View of the University.

**1956, Dec. 15** **Unwmk.** ***Perf. 14½***
**C190** AP50 20p green .45 .25
**C191** AP50 100p dk vio bl 1.90 .80

25th anniversary of the Federico Santa Maria Technical University, Valparaiso.

A souvenir sheet contains one each of Nos. 299, C190-C191, imperf. It was not issued for postal use, though some served postally. Size: 185x251mm. Value, $130. Exists on sepia and white papers.

**Mistral Type of Regular Issue, 1958**

**1958, Jan. 10** **Engr.** ***Perf. 14***
**C192** A144 100p green .40 .40

Ambrosio O'Higgins — AP51

**1958, Mar. 23**
**C193** AP51 100p lt blue .80 .40

Founding of the city of Osorno, 500th anniv.

A souvenir sheet contains one each of Nos. 302 and C193, imperf. and printed in red brown. It was not issued for postal use, though some served postally. Size: 155x138mm. Value, $72.50.

**Exhibition Type of Regular Issue**

**1958, Oct. 18** **Unwmk.**
**C194** A146 50p dull green .75 .30

A souvenir sheet contains one each of Nos. 303 and C194, imperforate, printed in deep red or in purple and green. It was not issued for postal use, though some served postally. Size: 188x220mm. Value, $57.

**Bank Type of Regular Issue, 1958**

**1958, Dec. 18** **Engr.** ***Perf. 14***
**C195** A147 50p redsh brown .50 .40

A souvenir sheet contains one each of Nos. 304 and C195, printed in dull violet, imperf. It was not issued for postal use, though some served postally. Size: 128x162mm. Value, $195.

**Antarctic Types of Regular Issue**

**1958** **Litho.** ***Perf. 14***
**C199** A149 20p violet 1.10 .25

**Engr.**

**C200** A150 500p dark blue 5.50 1.75

Symbols of Various Religions — AP52

***Perf. 14½***

**1959, Jan. 23** **Unwmk.** **Engr.**
**C206** AP52 50p dk car rose .65 .40

10th anniversary of the Universal Declaration of Human Rights.

**Types of 1950-54**

Designs: 50p, Plane silhouette over shore. 100p, Plane over map of Antarctica. 200p, Plane over natural arch rock.

**Imprint: "Casa de Moneda de Chile"**

**1959** **Litho.** ***Perf. 14***
**C207** AP38 1p dk blue grn 1.75 .65
*a.* Wmk. 215 30.00
**C208** AP38 10p emerald 1.10 .35
**C209** AP38 20p red brown .70 .35
**C210** AP38 50p yellow grn .70 .35
**C211** AP38 100p car rose .70 .35
**C212** AP38 200p brt blue 1.10 .35
*Nos. C207-C212 (6)* 6.05 2.40

Carlos Anwandter — AP53

**1959, June 18** **Engr.** ***Perf. 14***
**C213** AP53 20p rose carmine .65 .40

Centenary of the German School in Valdivia, founded by Carlos Anwandter.

A souvenir sheet contains one each of Nos. 319 and C213, imperforate. It was not issued for postal use, though some served postally. Size: 144x213mm. Value, $50. Size: 190x273mm. Value, $80.

**IGY Type of Regular Issue, 1958**

**1959, Aug. 28** **Unwmk.** ***Perf. 14***
**C214** A148 50p green 1.00 .25

**Ladrillero Type of Regular Issue**

**1959, Aug. 28** **Litho.**
**C215** A154 50p green .75 .40

**Barros Arana Type of Regular Issue**

**1959, Aug. 28**
**C216** A155 100p purple .85 .40

**Red Cross Type of Regular Issue**

**1959, Oct. 6**
**C217** A156 50p red & blk .95 .40

**WRY Type of Regular Issue, 1960**

**1960, Apr. 7** **Unwmk.** ***Perf. 14½***
**C218** A160 10c violet .70 .40

A souvenir sheet contains two stamps similar to Nos. 330 and C218, the 1c printed in blue, the 10c airmail in maroon. The sheet is imperf., printed on thin cardboard. Size: 160x204mm. Value, $130.

**Type of Regular Issue, 1960-62, and**

José Agustin Eyzaguirre and José Miguel Infante — AP54

Designs: 2c, Palace of Justice. 5c, National memorial. No. C220, Arms of Chile. No. C220A, José Gaspar Marin and J. Gregorio Argomedo. 50c, Archbishop J. I. Cienfuegos and Brother Camilo Henriquez. 1e, Bernardo O'Higgins.

**1960-65** **Unwmk.** **Engr.** ***Perf. 14½***
**C218A** AP54 2c mar & gray vio ('62) .45 .30
**C219** A162 5c vio bl & dl pur ('61) .45 .30

**Wmk. 215**

**C220** A161 10c dk brn & red brn .45 .30

**Unwmk.**

**C220A** AP54 10c vio brn & brn ('64) .70 .30
**C220B** AP54 20c dk bl & dl pur ('64) .45 .30
**C220C** AP54 50c bl grn & ind ('65) 1.75 .30
**C220D** A162 1e dk red & red brn ('63) 1.75 .50
*Nos. C218A-C220D (7)* 6.00 2.30

150th anniv. of the formation of the 1st Natl. Government.

A souvenir sheet contains two airmail stamps: a 5c brown similar to No. C219 (National Memorial) and a 10c green, type A161. The sheet is imperf., printed on heavy paper with papermaker's watermark. Size: 120x168mm. Value, $90.

Map and Rotary Emblem — AP55

**Unwmk.**

**1960, Dec. 1** **Litho.** ***Perf. 14***
**C221** AP55 10c blue .75 .40

South American Rotary Regional Conference, Santiago, 1960.

A souvenir sheet contains one 10c maroon, type AP55, with brown marginal inscription. Size: 118x158mm. Value, $67.50.

The souvenir sheet was overprinted in green "El Mundo Unida Contra la Malaria" and the outline of a mosquito, and released in October, 1962. Value, $115.

Araucan Pine and Plane — AP56

Designs: 2m, Chilean flag and plane. 3m, Plane and dock crane. 4m, Plane above river (vignette like AP39). 5m, Blast furnace. 1c, Plane over mountain lake. 2c, Plane over cable cars. 5c, Plane silhouette over shore. 10c, Plane over map of Antarctica. 20c, Plane over natural arch rock.

**Imprint: "Casa de Moneda de Chile"**

**1960-62** **Litho.** ***Perf. 14***
**C222** AP56 1m orange .50 .40
**C223** AP56 2m yellow grn .50 .40
**C224** AP56 3m violet .50 .40
**C225** AP56 4m gray olive .50 .40
**C226** AP56 5m brt bl grn .50 .40
**C227** AP56 1c ultra .50 .40
**C228** AP56 2c red brn ('61) .60 .40
**C229** AP56 5c yel grn ('61) 3.50 .40
**C230** AP56 10c car rose ('62) .90 .40
**C231** AP56 20c brt bl ('62) 1.00 .40
*Nos. C222-C231 (10)* 9.00 4.00

Oil Derricks and Douglas DC-6 AP57

Beechcraft Monoplane AP58

5m, Train and plane. 2c, Jet plane & Easter Island statue. 5c, Control tower & plane. 10c, Comet airliner. 50c, Douglas DC-6.

***Perf. 14x13½***

**1960-67** **Unwmk.** **Litho.**
**C234** AP57 5m red brown .60 .40
**C235** AP57 1c dull blue .60 .40
**C236** AP57 2c ultra ('62) .60 .40
**C237** AP57 5c rose red ('64) .60 .40
**C238** AP58 10c ultra ('67) .60 .40
**C239** AP58 20c car ('62) .60 .40
**C240** AP58 50c green ('63) .60 .40
*Nos. C234-C240 (7)* 4.20 2.80

Stamps similar to type AP58, but inscribed in peso ($) currency, are listed as type AP49.

**Congress Type of Regular Issue**

**1961, Oct. 5** ***Perf. 14½***
**C245** A164 10c gray green 1.25 .60

**Soccer Type of Regular Issue, 1962**

Designs: 5c, Goalkeeper and stadium, vert. 10c, Soccer players and globe.

**1962, May 30** **Unwmk.** **Engr.**
**C246** A165 5c rose lilac .65 .40
**C247** A165 10c dk carmine .65 .40

A souvenir sheet of four contains one each of Nos. 340-341, C246-C247, imperf., with light brown marginal inscriptions. Size: 123x194mm. Sold for 7.50 escudos (face value, 22 centavos). Value $28.50.

It also exists with a different watermark in a smaller format, size: 122x162mm. Value is the same.

**Hunger Type of Regular Issue**

20c, Mother with empty bowl, horiz.

**1963, Mar. 21** **Litho.** ***Perf. 14***
**C248** A166 20c green .60 .40

**Red Cross Type of Regular Issue**

Design: 20c, Centenary emblem and plane silhouette, horiz.

**1963, Sept. 6** **Unwmk.** ***Perf. 14***
**C249** A167 20c gray & red .60 .40

Fire Engine of 1860's — AP59

**1963, Dec. 20** **Litho.** ***Perf. 14½***
**C250** AP59 30c red .80 .40

Centenary of the Santiago Fire Brigade.

Western Hemisphere — AP60

**1964, Apr. 9** **Unwmk.** ***Perf. 14½***
**C254** AP60 4c ultra .65 .40

Issued in memory of President John F. Kennedy and to honor the Alliance for Progress.

Battle of Rancagua AP61

**1965, May 7** **Engr.** ***Perf. 14½***
**C255** AP61 5c dull grn & sepia .65 .40

Battle of Rancagua, 10/7/14, 150th anniv.

ITU Emblem, Old and New Communication Equipment — AP62

**1965, May 7** **Litho.** ***Perf. 14½x14***
**C256** AP62 40c red & maroon .65 .40

ITU centenary.

**Portrait Type of 1964**

Portraits: No. C257, Enrique Molina. No. C258, Msgr. Carlos Casanueva.

**1965, June** **Litho.** ***Perf. 14***
**C257** A169 60c brt violet .70 .40
**C258** A169 60c green .70 .40

See note after No. 346.

**Skier Type of Regular Issue 1965**

Design: 20c, Skier, horiz.

**1965, Aug. 30** **Unwmk.** ***Perf. 14***
**C259** A172 20c ultra .65 .40

Fishing Boats, Angelmo Harbor AP63

Aviators' Monument AP64

**1965**
**C260** AP63 40c brown .65 .40

***Perf. 14x14½***

**C262** AP64 1e car rose .65 .40

Andrés Bello (1780?-1865), Venezuela-born Writer and Educator — AP65

**1965, Nov. 29 Engr. Unwmk.**

**C263** AP65 10c dk car rose .65 .40

Skiers — AP66

**1966, Apr. 6 Litho. *Perf. 14***

**C264** AP66 4e dk bl & red brn 1.50 .40

World Skiing Championships, Partillo, Aug. 1966.

Basketball — AP67

**1966, Apr. 28**

**C265** AP67 13c rose carmine .65 .40

International Basketball Championships.

Slalom — AP68

***Perf. 14½x15***

**1966, July 20 Litho. Unwmk.**

**C266** AP68 75c rose car & lil .65 .40
**C267** AP68 3e ultra & lt bl .65 .40

Intl. Skiing Championships, Partillo, August 1966. A souvenir sheet of 2 contains imperf. stamps similar to Nos. C266-C267. No gum. Size: 109x140mm. Value, $30.

### Ship Type of Regular Issue

**1966 Litho. *Perf. 14½***

**C268** A175 70c Prus grn & yel grn .65 .40

See note below No. 358.

A souvenir sheet of design A177 was issued imperforate in deep red. Size: 140x119mm. Value $31.

### ICY Type of Regular Issue

**1966, Oct. 28 Unwmk. *Perf. 14½***

**C269** A177 3e blue & carmine .65 .40

A souvenir sheet of 2 contains imperf. stamps similar to Nos. 360 and C269. No gum. Size: 111x140mm. Value $15.

Chilean Flag and Ships — AP69

**1966, Nov. 21 Litho. *Perf. 14***

**C270** AP69 13c dull red brn .65 .40

Centenary of the city of Antofagasta.

### Pardo Type of Regular Issue

40c, Pardo & map of Chile's claim to Antarctica.

**1967, Jan. 6 Unwmk. *Perf. 14½***

**C271** A178 40c ultra .75 .55

See note below No. 361.

### Family Type of Regular Issue

**1967, Apr. 13 Litho. *Perf. 14***

**C272** A179 80c brt bl & blk .65 .40

Ruben Dario and Title Page of "Azul" — AP70

**1967, May 15 Engr. *Perf. 14½***

**C273** AP70 10c dark blue .65 .40

Ruben Dario (pen name of Felix Ruben Garcia Sarmiento, 1867-1916), Nicaraguan poet, newspaper correspondent and diplomat.

### Tree Type of Regular Issue

**1967, June 9 Litho.**

**C274** A180 75c grn & pale rose .50 .40

### Lions Type of Regular Issue

**1967 Litho. *Perf. 14***

**C275** A181 1e purple & yel .55 .40
**C276** A181 5e blue & yel 1.50 .40

A souvenir sheet without franking value contains 3 imperf. stamps, 20c, 1e and 5e, in violet blue and yellow. Size: 110x140mm. Value, $13.50. Also exists with the stamps in violet. Value, $18.

Issue dates: 1e, July 12; 5e, Aug. 11.

### Flag Type of Regular Issue

**1967, Oct. 20 Unwmk. *Perf. 14½***

**C277** A182 50c ultra & crimson .50 .40

ITY Emblem AP71

**1967, Nov. 22 Litho. *Perf. 14½***

**C278** AP71 30c lt vio bl & blk .35 .25

Issued for International Tourist Year, 1967.

### Caro Type of Regular Issue, 1967

**1967, Dec. 4 Engr. *Perf. 14½***

**C279** A183 40c violet .85 .40

### Type of Regular Issue, 1968

**1968, Apr. 23 Litho. *Perf. 14½***

**C280** A184 2e brt violet .85 .40

Sesquicentennial of the Battles of Chacabuco and Maipu. A souvenir sheet of 2 contains imperf. stamps similar to Nos. 367 and C280. Value, $12. A second sheet exists with the 2e in green and the 3e in brown. Size: 139½x100mm. Value, $12.

Another imperforate souvenir sheet was issued in 1971 with Nos. 399, C280 and C303 in original colors. Size: 120x150mm.

### Farm Type of Regular Issue

**1968, June 18 Unwmk.**

**C281** A185 50c blk, org & grn .50 .40

Juan I. Molina, Educator and Scientist AP72

**1968, Aug. 27 Litho. *Perf. 14½***

**C282** AP72 1e bright green .50 .40

Map of Chiloé Province — AP73

***Perf. 14½***

**1968, Oct. 7 Unwmk. Litho.**

**C283** AP73 1e rose claret .60 .40

Anniversaries of the founding of five towns in Chiloé Province.

### Auto Club Type of Regular Issue

**1968, Nov. 10 Engr. *Perf. 14½x14***

**C284** A189 5e ultra .65 .40

British Crown and Map of Chile — AP74

50c, Chilean coat of arms (horiz.; similar to type A161). 3e, British coat of arms, horiz.

**1968, Nov. 12 Litho. *Perf. 14½***

**C285** AP74 50c green & brn .40 .40
**C286** AP74 3e bl & org brn .65 .40

**Engr.**

**C287** AP74 5e purple & mag .95 .40
*Nos. C285-C287 (3)* 2.00 1.20

Visit of Queen Elizabeth II of Great Britain, Nov. 11-18. A souvenir sheet of 3 contains imperf., lithographed stamps similar to Nos. C285-C287. Size: 124½x190mm. The souvenir sheet also publicizes the British-Chilean Philatelic Exhibition. Value, $21.

First Coin Minted in Chile and Coin Press — AP75

Design: 1e, Chile No. 128.

**1968, Dec. 31 Litho. *Perf. 14½***

**C288** AP75 50c ocher & vio brn .55 .40
**C289** AP75 1e lt bl & dp org .55 .40

225th anniversary of the founding of the State Mint (Casa de Moneda de Chile).

A souvenir sheet of 4 contains imperf. stamps similar to Nos. 373-374, C288-C289. Size: 150x119mm. Value, $10.

### Satellite Type of Regular Issue

**1969, May 20 Litho. *Perf. 14½***

**C290** A191 2e rose lilac .65 .40

### Red Cross Type of Regular Issue

**1969, Sept. Litho. *Perf. 14½***

**C291** A192 5e black & red .75 .40

A souvenir card contains 2 imperf. stamps similar to Nos. 376 and C291, with red marginal inscription. Size: 109x140mm. Value $5.

### Dam Type of Regular Issue

**1969, Nov. 18 Litho. *Perf. 14½***

**C292** A193 3e blue .80 .40

### Rodriguez Type of Regular Issue

**1969, Nov. 24**

**C293** A194 30c brown .70 .40

### EXPO '70 Type of Regular Issue

**1969, Dec. 1 Litho. *Perf. 14***

**C294** A195 5e red .65 .40

### Bible Type of 1969

**1969, Dec. 2 *Perf. 14½***

**C295** A196 1e green .60 .40

### ILO Type of Regular Issue

**1969, Dec. 17 *Perf. 14½***

**C296** A197 2e rose lil & blk .45 .40

### Human Rights Year Type of 1969

**1969, Dec. 18**

**C297** A198 4e brown & red .60 .35

A souvenir sheet of 2 contains imperf. stamps similar to Nos. 382 and C297. Size: 110x140mm. Value, $9.

### Easter Island Type of 1970

**1970, Jan. 26**

**C298** A199 50c dull grnsh bl .80 .40

### Ship Type of Regular Issue

**1970, Feb. 4 Litho. *Perf. 14½***

**C299** A200 2e deep ultra .65 .40

### Rotary Type of Regular Issue

**1970, Mar. 18 Litho. *Perf. 14***

**C300** A201 1e rose claret .75 .40

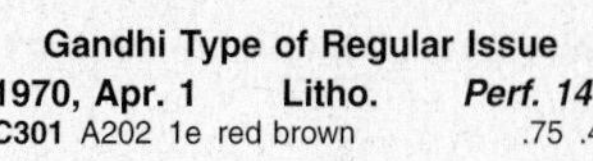

### Gandhi Type of Regular Issue

**1970, Apr. 1 Litho. *Perf. 14½***

**C301** A202 1e red brown .75 .40

### Education Year Type of 1970

**1970, July 17 Litho. *Perf. 14½***

**C302** A204 4e red brown .65 .40

### National Shrine Type of 1970

**1970, July 28 Litho. *Perf. 14½***

**C303** A205 1e ultra .65 .40

An imperforate souvenir sheet containing Nos. 399, C280, and C303 exists. Size: 120x150mm.

### Cancer Type of Regular Issue

**1970, Aug. 11**

**C304** A206 2e brn & lt olive .60 .40

A few stamps are known inscribed "Correos de Chile" instead of "Correos Aereo Chile." Value $350.

### Copper Type of Regular Issue

**1970, Oct. 21 Litho. *Perf. 14½***

**C305** A207 3e grn & lt red brn .80 .40

### United Nations Type of 1970

**1970, Oct. 22**

**C306** A208 5e dk car & grn .75 .40

### Freighter Type of Regular Issue

**1971, Jan. 18 Litho. *Perf. 14***

**C307** A209 5e lt red brown .70 .40

### No. C290 Surcharged in Red

**1971, Jan. 21 Litho. *Perf. 14½***

**C308** A191 52c on 2e rose lil .70 .40

### Liberation Type of Regular Issue

**1971, Feb. 3 *Perf. 14½***

**C309** A210 1e blue gray & vio brn .55 .40

### UNICEF Type of Regular Issue

**1971, Feb. 11 Litho. *Perf. 14½***

**C310** A211 2e blue & grn .60 .40

### Boy Scout Type of Regular Issue

**1971, Feb. 10 *Perf. 14***

**C311** A212 5c dk car & ol .65 .40

### Satellite Type of Regular Issue

**1971, May 25 Litho. *Perf. 14½***

**C312** A213 2e brown .65 .40

### De Ercilla Type of Regular Issue

**1972, Mar. 20 Engr. *Perf. 14***

**C313** A221 2e Prussian blue .45 .40

A souvenir card contains impressions of Nos. 414 and C313 with black marginal inscription commemorating España 75 Philatelic Exhibition. Size: 165x220mm. Value $19.

## AIR POST SEMI-POSTAL STAMPS

**Catalogue values for unused stamps in this section are for Never Hinged items.**

### Type of Semi-Postal Stamps, 1961

Portraits: 10c+10c, Alonso de Ercilla. 20c+20c, Gabriela Mistral.

***Perf. 13x12½***

**1961, Apr. 29 Photo. Unwmk.**

**CB1** SP3 10c + 10c salmon & choc 1.25 .30
**CB2** SP3 20c + 20c gray & dp cl 1.25 .30

Printed without charge by the Spanish Mint as a gift to Chile. The surtax was to aid the 1960 earthquake victims and to increase teachers' salaries.

## ACKNOWLEDGMENT OF RECEIPT STAMPS

AR1

**1894 Unwmk. *Perf. 11½***

| No. | Type | Description | Unused | Used |
|---|---|---|---|---|
| **H1** | AR1 | 5c brown | 5.00 | *5.00* |
| *a.* | | Imperf., pair | 20.00 | |
| *b.* | | Pair, imperf. vert. or horiz. | 20.00 | |

The black stamp of design similar to AR1 inscribed "Avis de Paiement" was prepared for use on notices of payment of funds but was not regularly issued. Value, $30.

A black stamp of design AR1 exists. Value $30.

## POSTAGE DUE STAMPS

Horizontal D1 — Vertical D2

**Horizontal Handstamped**

**1894 Unwmk. *Perf. 13***

| No. | Type | Description | Unused | Used |
|---|---|---|---|---|
| **J1** | D1 | 2c black, *straw* | 19.00 | 19.00 |
| **J2** | D1 | 4c black, *straw* | 19.00 | 19.00 |
| **J3** | D1 | 6c black, *straw* | 19.00 | 19.00 |
| **J4** | D1 | 8c black, *straw* | 19.00 | 19.00 |
| **J5** | D2 | 10c black, *straw* | 19.00 | 19.00 |
| **J6** | D1 | 16c black, *straw* | 19.00 | 19.00 |
| **J7** | D1 | 20c black, *straw* | 19.00 | 19.00 |
| **J8** | D1 | 30c black, *straw* | 19.00 | 19.00 |
| **J9** | D1 | 40c black, *straw* | 19.00 | 19.00 |
| | | *Nos. J1-J9 (9)* | 171.00 | 171.00 |
| *J1a* | D1 | 2c black, *yellow* | 60.00 | 60.00 |
| *J2a* | D1 | 4c black, *yellow* | 40.00 | 40.00 |
| *J3a* | D1 | 6c black, *yellow* | 30.00 | 30.00 |
| *J4a* | D1 | 8c black, *yellow* | 19.00 | 19.00 |
| *J5a* | D2 | 10c black, *yellow* | 19.00 | 19.00 |
| *J6a* | D1 | 16c black, *yellow* | 19.00 | 19.00 |
| *J7a* | D1 | 20c black, *yellow* | 19.00 | 19.00 |
| *J8a* | D1 | 30c black, *yellow* | 19.00 | 19.00 |
| *J9a* | D1 | 40c black, *yellow* | 19.00 | 19.00 |
| | | *Nos. J1a-J9a (9)* | 244.00 | 244.00 |

**Vertical**

| No. | Type | Description | Unused | Used |
|---|---|---|---|---|
| *J1b* | D1 | 2c black, *straw* | 27.50 | 27.50 |
| *J2b* | D1 | 4c black, *straw* | 27.50 | 27.50 |
| *J3b* | D1 | 6c black, *straw* | 27.50 | 27.50 |
| *J4b* | D1 | 8c black, *straw* | 27.50 | 27.50 |
| *J5b* | D2 | 10c black, *straw* | 27.50 | 27.50 |
| *J6b* | D1 | 16c black, *straw* | 27.50 | 27.50 |
| *J7b* | D1 | 20c black, *straw* | 27.50 | 27.50 |
| *J8b* | D1 | 30c black, *straw* | 27.50 | 27.50 |
| *J9b* | D1 | 40c black, *straw* | 27.50 | 27.50 |
| | | *Nos. J1b-J9b (9)* | 247.50 | 247.50 |
| *J1c* | D1 | 2c black, *yellow* | 85.00 | 85.00 |
| *J2c* | D1 | 4c black, *yellow* | 57.50 | 57.50 |
| *J3c* | D1 | 6c black, *yellow* | 42.50 | 42.50 |
| *J4c* | D1 | 8c black, *yellow* | 27.50 | 27.50 |
| *J5c* | D2 | 10c black, *yellow* | 27.50 | 27.50 |
| *J6c* | D1 | 16c black, *yellow* | 27.50 | 27.50 |
| *J7c* | D1 | 20c black, *yellow* | 27.50 | 27.50 |
| *J8c* | D1 | 30c black, *yellow* | 27.50 | 27.50 |
| *J9c* | D1 | 40c black, *yellow* | 27.50 | 27.50 |
| | | *Nos. J1c-J9c (9)* | 350.00 | 350.00 |

Counterfeits exist.

D3

**1895 Litho. *Perf. 11***

| No. | Type | Description | Unused | Used |
|---|---|---|---|---|
| **J19** | D3 | 1c red, *yellow* | 7.50 | 5.50 |
| **J20** | D3 | 2c red, *yellow* | 7.50 | 5.50 |
| **J21** | D3 | 4c red, *yellow* | 7.50 | 5.50 |
| **J22** | D3 | 6c red, *yellow* | 7.50 | 5.50 |
| **J23** | D3 | 8c red, *yellow* | 7.50 | 5.50 |
| **J24** | D3 | 10c red, *yellow* | 7.50 | 5.50 |
| **J25** | D3 | 20c red, *yellow* | 7.50 | 5.50 |
| **J26** | D3 | 40c red, *yellow* | 7.50 | 5.50 |
| **J27** | D3 | 50c red, *yellow* | 7.50 | 5.50 |
| **J28** | D3 | 60c red, *yellow* | 7.50 | 5.50 |
| **J29** | D3 | 80c red, *yellow* | 7.50 | 5.50 |
| **J30** | D3 | 1p red, *yellow* | 13.00 | 13.00 |
| | | *Nos. J19-J30 (12)* | 95.50 | 73.50 |

Nos. J19-J30 were printed in sheets of 100 (10x10) containing all 12 denominations.

Counterfeits of Nos. J19-J42 exist, but usually are perforated 11½ or 14.

No. J19 was surcharge '10c' in a circle. This surcharge was never issued. Value, $13.

**1896 *Perf. 13½***

| No. | Type | Description | Unused | Used |
|---|---|---|---|---|
| **J31** | D3 | 1c red, *straw* | 1.50 | .90 |
| **J32** | D3 | 2c red, *straw* | 1.50 | .90 |
| **J33** | D3 | 4c red, *straw* | 1.50 | .90 |
| **J34** | D3 | 6c red, *straw* | 1.50 | .90 |
| **J35** | D3 | 8c red, *straw* | 1.50 | .90 |
| **J36** | D3 | 10c red, *straw* | 1.50 | .90 |
| **J37** | D3 | 20c red, *straw* | 1.50 | .90 |
| **J38** | D3 | 40c red, *straw* | 13.50 | 7.50 |
| **J39** | D3 | 50c red, *straw* | 13.50 | 7.50 |
| **J40** | D3 | 60c red, *straw* | 13.50 | 7.50 |
| **J41** | D3 | 80c red, *straw* | 20.00 | 12.00 |
| **J42** | D3 | 100c red, *straw* | 20.00 | 12.00 |
| | | *Nos. J31-J42 (12)* | 91.00 | 52.80 |

Counterfeits are perforated 11½ or 14.

D4

**1898 *Perf. 13***

| No. | Type | Description | Unused | Used |
|---|---|---|---|---|
| **J43** | D4 | 1c scarlet | .60 | .50 |
| **J44** | D4 | 2c scarlet | 1.25 | 1.00 |
| **J45** | D4 | 4c scarlet | .60 | .50 |
| **J46** | D4 | 10c scarlet | .60 | .50 |
| **J47** | D4 | 20c scarlet | .60 | .50 |
| | | *Nos. J43-J47 (5)* | 3.65 | 3.00 |

Counterfeits are perforated 11½ or 14.

D5

**1924 *Perf. 12½***

| No. | Type | Description | Unused | Used |
|---|---|---|---|---|
| **J48** | D5 | 2c blue & red | .60 | 1.75 |
| **J49** | D5 | 4c blue & red | .60 | 1.75 |
| **J50** | D5 | 8c blue & red | .60 | 1.75 |
| **J51** | D5 | 10c blue & red | .60 | 1.75 |
| **J52** | D5 | 20c blue & red | .60 | 1.75 |
| **J53** | D5 | 40c blue & red | .60 | 1.75 |
| **J54** | D5 | 60c blue & red | .60 | 1.75 |
| **J55** | D5 | 80c blue & red | .60 | 1.75 |
| **J56** | D5 | 1p blue & red | 1.50 | 5.50 |
| **J57** | D5 | 2p blue & red | 2.75 | 7.50 |
| **J58** | D5 | 5p blue & red | 3.75 | 7.50 |
| | | *Nos. J48-J58 (11)* | 12.80 | 34.50 |
| | | Set, never hinged | 26.00 | |

Nos. J48-J58 were printed in sheets of 150 containing all 11 denominations, and a second printing was printed in sheets of 50 containing the five lower denominations, providing various se-tenants. Stamps from the second printing are of a slightly different shades, with the red appearing pinkish. Second printing stamps are worth 2.5x first printing stamps.

All values of this issue exist imperforate, also with center inverted, but are not believed to have been regularly issued. Those with inverted centers sell for about 10 times normal stamps.

Counterfeits are perforated 11½.

## OFFICIAL STAMPS

Nos. O1A-O16 are departmental Official stamps for use by the Navy department.

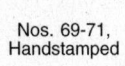

Nos. 69-71, Handstamped

**1906 Unwmk. *Perf. 12***

| No. | Type | Description | Unused | Used |
|---|---|---|---|---|
| **O1A** | A14 | 2c carmine | 175.00 | — |
| **O1B** | A14 | 3c yel brn | 175.00 | — |
| **O1C** | A14 | 5c ultra | 175.00 | — |

Nos. O1A-O1C exist with inverted or vertical overprints, and as pairs, one without overprint.

Counterfeits exist.

O1

**Single-lined frame**
**Control number in violet**

**1907 *Imperf.***

| No. | Type | Description | Unused | Used |
|---|---|---|---|---|
| **O1** | O1 | dl bl, "CARTA" org | *175.00* | *175.00* |
| **O2** | O1 | red, "OFICIO" bl | *350.00* | *250.00* |
| **O3** | O1 | vio, "PAQUETE" red | *250.00* | *250.00* |
| **O4** | O1 | org, *bl*, "EP" vio | *300.00* | *260.00* |
| | | *Nos. O1-O4 (4)* | *1,075.* | *935.00* |

The diagonal inscription in differing color indicates type of usage: CARTA for letters of ordinary weight; OFICIO, heavy letters to 100 grams; PAQUETE, parcels to 100 grams; E P (Encomienda Postal), heavier parcels; C (Certificado), as on No. O8, registration including postage.

Varieties include CARTA, PAQUETE and E P inverted, OFICIO omitted, etc.

Reprints lack control number.

**Double-lined frame**
**Large control number in black**
***Perf. 11***

| No. | Type | Description | Unused | Used |
|---|---|---|---|---|
| **O5** | O1 | bl, "CARTA" yel | 90.00 | 60.00 |
| **O6** | O1 | red, "OFICIO" bl | 160.00 | 80.00 |
| **O7** | O1 | brn, "PAQUETE" grn | 160.00 | 80.00 |
| **O8** | O1 | grn, "C" red | *1,100.* | *600.00* |
| | | *Nos. O5-O8 (4)* | 1,510. | 820.00 |

Nos. O5-O8 exist in tête bêche pairs; with CARTA, OFICIO or PAQUETE double or inverted, and other varieties.

Counterfeits of Nos. O1-O8 exist.

Reprints lack control number.

Regular Issues of 1892-1909 Overprinted in Red — a

**On Stamps of 1904-09**

**1907 *Perf. 12***

| No. | Type | Description | Unused | Used |
|---|---|---|---|---|
| **O9** | A14 | 1c green | 50.00 | *85.00* |
| *a.* | | Inverted overprint | *75.00* | |
| **O10** | A12 | 3c on lp brn | 100.00 | *120.00* |
| *a.* | | Inverted overprint | *150.00* | |
| **O11** | A14 | 5c ultra | 60.00 | *95.00* |
| *a.* | | Inverted overprint | *120.00* | |
| **O12** | A15 | 10c gray & blk | 75.00 | *125.00* |
| **O13** | A15 | 15c vio & blk | 65.00 | *125.00* |
| **O14** | A15 | 20c org brn & blk | 65.00 | *125.00* |
| **O15** | A15 | 50c ultra & blk | 200.00 | *200.00* |

**On Stamp of 1892**
***Rouletted***

| No. | Type | Description | Unused | Used |
|---|---|---|---|---|
| **O16** | A6 | 1p dk brn & blk | 375.00 | *600.00* |
| | | *Nos. O9-O16 (8)* | 990.00 | *1,475.* |

Counterfeits of Nos. O9-O16 exist.

**Regular Issues of 1915-25 Overprinted in Red or Blue**

b

Nos. O21-O22

**1926 *Perf. 13½x14, 14***

| No. | Type | Description | Unused | Used |
|---|---|---|---|---|
| **O17** | A52 | 5c slate bl (R) | 5.00 | 3.25 |
| **O18** | A50 | 10c bl & blk (R) | 8.50 | 4.00 |
| **O19** | A39 | 20c org red & blk (Bl) | 8.50 | 4.00 |
| **O20** | A42 | 50c dp grn & blk (Bl) | 4.25 | 3.00 |
| **O21** | A43 | 1p grn & blk (R) | 8.50 | 4.00 |
| **O22** | A43 | 2p ver & blk (Bl) | 12.50 | 6.00 |
| | | *Nos. O17-O22 (6)* | 47.25 | 24.25 |
| | | Set, never hinged | 80.00 | |

Nos. O21 and O22 are overprinted vertically at each side.

Nos. O17 to O22 were for the use of the Biblioteca Nacional.

**1928 Wmk. 215**

| No. | Type | Description | Unused | Used |
|---|---|---|---|---|
| **O22A** | A42 | 50c dp grn & blk (Bl), #157 | 30.00 | 14.00 |

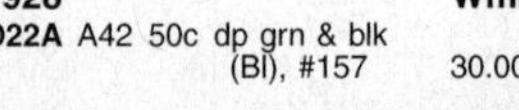

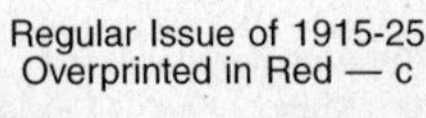

Regular Issue of 1915-25 Overprinted in Red — c

**1928 Unwmk. *Perf. 13½x14, 14***

| No. | Type | Description | Unused | Used |
|---|---|---|---|---|
| **O23** | A50 | 10c bl & blk | 13.00 | 8.00 |
| **O24** | A39 | 20c brn org & blk | 12.50 | 8.00 |
| **O25** | A40 | 25c dl bl & blk | 20.00 | 12.00 |
| **O26** | A42 | 50c dp grn & blk | 20.00 | 12.00 |
| **O27** | A43 | 1p grn & blk | 20.00 | 12.00 |
| | | *Nos. O23-O27 (5)* | 85.50 | 52.00 |
| | | Set, never hinged | 200.00 | |

The overprint on Nos. O23 to O26 is 16½mm high; on No. O27 it is 20mm.

Regular Issues of 1928-30 Overprinted in Red — d

**On Stamp Inscribed: "Correos de Chile"**

**1930-31**

| No. | Type | Description | Unused | Used |
|---|---|---|---|---|
| **O28** | A50 | 10c bl & blk, #173 | 6.00 | 3.00 |

**On Stamp Inscribed: "Chile Correos"**

| No. | Type | Description | Unused | Used |
|---|---|---|---|---|
| **O28A** | A42 | 50c dp grn & blk, #137 | 6.00 | 3.00 |

**Wmk. 215**

**On Stamps Inscribed: "Correos de Chile"**

| No. | Type | Description | Unused | Used |
|---|---|---|---|---|
| **O29** | A50 | 10c bl & blk, #164 | 8.50 | 4.25 |
| **O29A** | A50 | 10c bl & blk, #170 | 8.50 | 4.25 |
| **O30** | A39 | 20c org red & blk, #166 | 4.50 | 2.25 |
| **O31** | A40 | 25c bl & blk, #167 | 4.50 | 2.25 |
| **O32** | A42 | 50c dp grn & blk, #169 | 7.00 | 2.75 |

**On Stamps Inscribed: "Chile Correos"**

| No. | Type | Description | Unused | Used |
|---|---|---|---|---|
| **O33** | A42 | 50c dp grn & blk, #157 | 5.25 | 2.75 |
| **O34** | A43 | 1p grn & blk, #158 | 4.50 | 2.50 |
| | | *Nos. O28-O34 (9)* | 54.75 | 27.00 |
| | | Set, never hinged | 100.00 | |

No. 181 Overprinted in Red

**1933 *Perf. 13½x14***

| No. | Type | Description | Unused | Used |
|---|---|---|---|---|
| **O35** | A61 | 20c brown | 5.00 | 2.50 |

No. 182 Overprinted in Red

**1935 Wmk. 215**

| No. | Type | Description | Unused | Used |
|---|---|---|---|---|
| **O36** | A62 | 10c deep blue | 8.50 | 4.50 |

No. 163 Overprinted in Red

**Inscribed: "Correos de Chile"**

**1934**

| No. | Type | Description | Unused | Used |
|---|---|---|---|---|
| **O37** | A52 | 5c lt grn | 5.00 | 2.00 |

No. 182 Overprinted in Red

**1935**

| No. | Type | Description | Unused | Used |
|---|---|---|---|---|
| **O38** | A62 | 10c dp bl | 3.50 | 1.50 |

**Same Overprint in Black on No. 181**

**1936 *Perf. 13½x14***

| No. | Type | Description | Unused | Used |
|---|---|---|---|---|
| **O39** | A61 | 20c dk brn | 22.00 | 4.00 |

No. 158 Overprinted in Red

**1938** *Perf. 14*
**O40** A43 1p grn & blk 8.50 4.25

**Nos. 204 and 205 Overprinted Type "d" in Black**

**1939** *Perf. 13½x14, 14*
**O41** A78 50c violet 12.50 8.00
**O42** A84 1p org brn 12.50 8.00

Stamps of 1938-40 Overprinted in Black, Red or Blue

**1940-45** *Perf. 13½x14, 14*
**O43** A78 10c sal pink ('45) 5.00 3.00
**O44** A78 15c brn org 6.00 2.00
**O45** A78 20c lt bl (R) ('42) 6.00 2.00
**O46** A78 30c brt mag (Bl) 10.00 5.00
**O47** A78 40c lt grn 5.00 5.00
**O48** A78 50c vio ('45) 12.00 8.00
**O49** A84 1p org brn ('42) 9.00 5.00
**O50** A84 1.80p dp bl (R) ('45) 30.00 15.00
**O51** A84 2p car lake ('42) 8.00 4.00
*Nos. O43-O51 (9)* 91.00 49.00
Set, never hinged 50.00

**Overprint "b" in Black on Nos. 223, 225**

**Unwmk.**

**O58** A84 1p brn org 10.00 4.00
**O59** A84 2p car lake ('46) 10.00 4.00

**Catalogue values for unused stamps in this section, from this point to the end of the section, are for Never Hinged items.**

Regular Issues of 1938-43 Overprinted Diagonally in Carmine, Black or Blue — e

**Wmk. 215, Unwmkd.**

**1948-54** *Perf. 13½x14, 14*
**O60** A78 20c lt bl, #219 (C) 2.50 .80
**O61** A78 30c brt pink, #202 (Bl) ('54) 3.50 2.00
**O62** A78 40c brt grn, #203 ('54) 13.50 5.00
**O63** A78 50c vio #222 ('49) 3.00 .80
**O64** A84 1p org brn, #205 8.50 2.25
**O65** A84 2p car lake, #207 ('54) 10.00 2.25
**O66** A84 5p dk sl grn, #208 (C) ('51) 10.00 2.25
*Nos. O60-O66 (7)* 51.00 15.35

**Overprint "e" Diagonally on Nos. 265 and 275 in Red or Black**

**Wmk. 215, Unwmkd.**

**1953-55** *Perf. 13½x14, 13x14*
**O67** A126 1p dk bl grn, #265 (R) 5.00 1.60
**O68** A126 1p dk bl grn, #265 (Bk) ('55) 4.00 1.60
**O69** A126 1p dk bl grn, #275 (R) ('55) 4.00 1.60
*Nos. O67-O69 (3)* 13.00 4.80

**Overprint "e" Horizontally on Nos. 207, 209 in Black or Blue**

**1955-56** **Wmk. 215** *Perf. 14*
**O70** A84 2p car lake ('56) 10.00 2.50
**O71** A84 10p rose vio (Bl) 21.00 3.50

**Overprint "e" Horizontally on Nos. 293-295 and Types of 1956 Regular Issue in Black or Red**

**1956** **Unwmk.** *Perf. 14x14½*
**O72** A141 2p purple 7.50 1.50
**O73** A142 3p lt vio bl (R) 24.00 5.00
**O74** A141 5p redsh brn 4.50 1.00
**O75** A142 10p vio (19x22¼mm) (R) 9.00 3.50
*a.* Perf. 13½x14 (19½x22½mm) ('58) 24.00 3.50
**O76** A141 50p rose red 15.00 3.50

No. 298 was overprinted, however it was never released.

**No. 310 Overprinted in Red Vertically, Reading Down, Similar to Type "e"**

Size of Overprint: 21x2½mm

**1958** **Litho.** *Perf. 14*
**O77** A149 10p vio blue *125.00 42.50*

**Overprint "e" Horizontally on No. 327 in Red**

**1960** **Unwmk.** *Perf. 13x14*
**O79** A157 5c blue 12.50 2.50

---

## POSTAL TAX STAMPS

**Catalogue values for unused stamps in this section are for Never Hinged items.**

---

Talca Issue.

A 10c blue postal tax stamp, inscribed "Bicentenario de Talca" and picturing a coat of arms, was issued in 1942. It was sold only in Talca and was required for a time on all domestic letters sent from that city. The tax helped pay for Talca's bicentenary celebration. Values: unused, 40c; used, 40c; never hinged, 65c.

---

Nos. 326 and 347 Surcharged

**1970** **Unwmk.** **Litho.** *Perf. 14x13*
**RA1** A159 10c on 2c ultra .65 .40

*Perf. 14x14½*

**RA2** A170 10c on 6c rose lil .65 .40

Chilean Arms — PT1

*Perf. 14½x14*

**1970, Apr. 23** **Litho.** **Unwmk.**
**RA3** PT1 10c blue .65 .40

See No. RA6.

**No. RA3 Surcharged in Red**

a

b

**1971-72**
**RA4** PT1 (a) 15c on 10c bl 2.25 .40
**RA5** PT1 (b) 15c on 10c bl ('72) .65 .40

**Type of 1970**

**1972, July** **Litho.** *Perf. 14½x14*
**RA6** PT1 15c rose red .65 .40

No. RA6 Surcharged in Ultramarine

**1972-73**
**RA7** PT1 20c on 15c rose red .65 .40
**RA8** PT1 50c on 15c rose red ('73) .65 .40

No. RA8 has 9 bars instead of 8.

The surtax on Nos. RA1-RA8 was for modernization of postal system. Compulsory on all inland mail.

---

## PARCEL POST POSTAL TAX STAMP

**Catalogue values for unused stamps in this section are for Never Hinged items.**

Pres. J. J. Prieto V. — PPT1

**Unwmk.**

**1957, Apr. 8** **Litho.** *Perf. 14*
**QRA1** PPT1 15p green 12.50 2.50

The surtax aided the Prieto Foundation. No. QRA1 was required on parcel post entering or leaving Chile.

---

# CHINA

'chī-nə

LOCATION — Eastern Asia
GOVT. — Republic
AREA — 2,903,475 sq. mi.
POP. — 462,798,093 (1948)

10 Candareen = 1 Mace
10 Mace = 1 Tael
100 Cents = 1 Dollar (Yuan) (1897)

### Watermarks

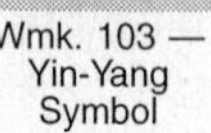

Wmk. 103 — Yin-Yang Symbol

Wmk. 261 — Character Yu (Post) Multiple

### Issues of the Imperial Maritime Customs Post

Imperial Dragon — A1

**1878 Unwmk. Typo. *Perf. 12½***
**Thin Paper**
**Stamps printed 2½-3¼mm apart**

| No. | Type | Description | Unused | Used |
|---|---|---|---|---|
| 1 | A1 | 1c green | 725.00 | 400.00 |
| *b.* | | 1c yellow green | 750.00 | 425.00 |
| 2 | A1 | 3c brown red | 1,100. | 400.00 |
| 3 | A1 | 5c orange | 1,450. | 600.00 |

Imperforate essays of Nos. 1-3 have an extra circle near the dragon's lower left foot. Examples with the circle completely or mostly removed are proofs or unfinished stamps.

**1882**
**Thin Paper**
**Stamps printed 4½mm apart**

| No. | Type | Description | Unused | Used |
|---|---|---|---|---|
| 4 | A1 | 1c green | 600.00 | 400.00 |
| 5 | A1 | 3c brown red | 1,100. | 400.00 |
| 6 | A1 | 5c orange yellow | 20,000. | 1,500. |

Nos. 4-5 exist on both thin paper and medium paper. Both are of equal value.

Nos. 4-5 sometimes show portions of papermaker's watermark "Monckton Kent."

**1883 *Rough to smooth Perf. 12½***
**Medium to Thick Opaque Paper**
**Stamps printed 2½ to 3¼mm apart**

| No. | Type | Description | Unused | Used |
|---|---|---|---|---|
| 7 | A1 | 1c green | 675.00 | 475.00 |
| *c.* | | Vert. pair, imperf. between | *160,000.* | |
| 8 | A1 | 3c brown red | 1,150. | 450.00 |
| *b.* | | Vert. pair, imperf. between | | *230,000.* |
| *d.* | | 3c dark vermilion | 1,600. | 400.00 |
| 9 | A1 | 5c yellow | 1,850. | 650.00 |
| *b.* | | Horiz. pair, imperf. btwn. (rough) | | *60,000.* |
| *c.* | | Vert. pair, imperf. btwn. (smooth) | | *60,000.* |

Nos. 1-9 were printed from plates of 25, 20 or 15 individual copper dies, but only No. 5 exists in the 15-die setting. Many different printings and plate settings exist. All values occur in a wide variety of shades and papers. The effect of climate on certain papers has produced the varieties on so-called toned papers in Nos. 1-15.

Nos. 7-9 were printed with smooth perforations until mid-1885 when the pins became blunt. Stamps with rough perfs are worth approximately 30 percent more than stamps with smooth perfs.

Value for Nos. 8b is for a damaged example.

**Counterfeits, frequently with forged cancellations, occur in all early Chinese issues.**

Imperial Dragon — A2

**1885 Wmk. 103 *Perf. 12½***

| No. | Type | Description | Unused | Used |
|---|---|---|---|---|
| 10 | A2 | 1c green | 175.00 | 110.00 |
| *a.* | | Vert. pair, imperf. btwn. | *20,000.* | *17,500.* |
| *b.* | | Horiz. pair, imperf. btwn. | | — |
| 11 | A2 | 3c lilac | 400.00 | 140.00 |
| *a.* | | Horiz. pair, imperf. btwn. | *22,000.* | *17,500.* |
| *b.* | | Vert. pair, imperf. btwn. | | *24,000.* |
| 12 | A2 | 5c grnsh yellow | 425.00 | 140.00 |
| *a.* | | 5c bister brown | 700.00 | 175.00 |
| *b.* | | Vert. pair, imperf. btwn. | *24,000.* | *24,000.* |
| *c.* | | Horiz. pair, imperf. btwn. | | *52,500.* |
| | | *Nos. 10-12 (3)* | 1,000. | 390.00 |

Nos. 10-12 exist with rough and smooth perforations. Examples with smooth perfs are worth approximately 10 percent more than stamps with rough perfs.

**1888 *Perf. 11½-12***

| No. | Type | Description | Unused | Used |
|---|---|---|---|---|
| 13 | A2 | 1c green | 85.00 | 60.00 |
| 14 | A2 | 3c lilac | 200.00 | 125.00 |
| *b.* | | Double impression | | *1,100.* |
| 15 | A2 | 5c grnsh yellow | 300.00 | 175.00 |
| *b.* | | Horiz. pair, imperf. vert. | | *50,000.* |
| *c.* | | Double impression | 1,100. | 1,100. |
| | | *Nos. 13-15 (3)* | 585.00 | 360.00 |

Nos. 10-15 were printed from plates made of 40 individual copper dies, arranged in two panes of 20 each. Several different settings exist of all values.

Nos. 10d and 13b have a smaller design, measuring 19mmx22mm. The regular design size is 19¼mmx22¼mm.

Imperforates of Nos. 13-15 are considered proofs by most authorities.

Stamps overprinted "Formosa" in English or Chinese are proofs.

For surcharges see Nos. 25-27, 75-77.

"Shou" and "Wu Fu" A3

Dragon and Hydrangea Leaves A4

"Pa Kua" Signs in Corners A5

Dragon and Peony A6

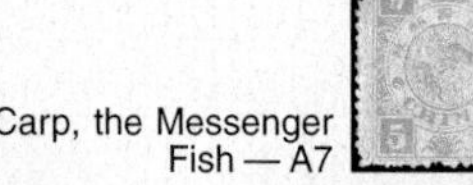

Carp, the Messenger Fish — A7

Dragon, "Pa Kua" and Immortelle A8

Dragons and "Shou" A9

Dragons and Giant Peony — A10

Junk on the Yangtse — A11

**1894 Lithographed in Shanghai**

| No. | Type | Description | Unused | Used |
|---|---|---|---|---|
| 16 | A3 | 1c orange red | 60.00 | *50.00* |
| *a.* | | Vert. pair, imperf. btwn. | *4,500.* | *3,500.* |
| *b.* | | Horiz. pair, imperf. btwn. | *17,500.* | *12,000.* |
| *c.* | | Vert. pair, imperf. horiz. | *3,250.* | *3,250.* |
| 17 | A4 | 2c green | 65.00 | 55.00 |
| *a.* | | Horiz. pair, imperf. btwn. | *3,750.* | *3,500.* |
| 18 | A5 | 3c orange | 57.50 | 30.00 |
| *a.* | | Vert. pair, imperf. btwn. | *3,350.* | *3,500.* |
| *b.* | | Horiz. pair, imperf. btwn. | *5,000.* | *13,340.* |
| 19 | A6 | 4c rose pink | 225.00 | *250.00* |
| *a.* | | Horiz. pair, imperf. btwn. | *14,000.* | |
| 20 | A7 | 5c dull orange | 350.00 | *400.00* |
| *a.* | | Horiz. pair, imperf. btwn. | *18,000.* | *18,000.* |
| 21 | A8 | 6c dark brown | 175.00 | 70.00 |
| *a.* | | Vert. pair, imperf. btwn. | *26,500.* | |
| *b.* | | Horiz. pair, imperf. btwn. | *15,000.* | |
| 22 | A9 | 9c dark green | 200.00 | 135.00 |
| *a.* | | Imperf., pair | *2,250.* | |
| *b.* | | Horiz. pair, imperf. vert. | *4,250.* | *3,750.* |
| *c.* | | Vert. pair, imperf. horiz. | *5,000.* | |
| *d.* | | Vert. pair, imperf. btwn. | *4,750.* | *4,250.* |
| *e.* | | Tete beche pair, vert. | *2,000.* | *1,800.* |
| *f.* | | Tete beche pair, imperf. horiz. | *5,500.* | |
| *g.* | | Tete beche pair, imperf. vert. | *5,500.* | *4,750.* |
| *h.* | | Vert. strip of 3, imperf. btwn. | *5,500.* | |
| *i.* | | Tete beche pair, horiz. | *1,500.* | *1,300.* |
| 23 | A10 | 12c brown orange | 700.00 | 300.00 |
| *b.* | | Vert. pair, imperf. btwn. | — | |
| 24 | A11 | 24c carmine | 900.00 | 400.00 |
| *a.* | | Vert. pair, imperf. btwn. | *37,500.* | — |
| *b.* | | Horiz. pair, imperf. btwn. | | — |
| | | *Nos. 16-24 (9)* | 2,733. | 1,690. |

60th birthday of Tsz'e Hsi, the Empress Dowager. All values exist in several distinct shades.

On Mar. 20, 1896, the Customs Post was changed, by Imperial Edict, effective Jan. 1, 1897, to a National Post and the dollar was adopted as the unit of currency.

Time was required to work out details of the Imperial Post and design new stamps. As a provisional measure, stocks of Nos. 16-24 were ordered surcharged with new values in dollars and cents. It is believed that only the Shanghai office stock of Nos. 16-24 (plus any reserve stock at the printers) was surcharged with small figures of value. Other post offices throughout China were instructed to return all unoverprinted stocks on receipt of the new surcharges.

Early in the year it was apparent that all stamps would be exhausted before the new issues were ready (Nos. 86-97), and since the stones from which Nos. 16-24 had been printed no longer existed, new stones were made from the original transfers. A printing from the new stones was made early in 1897 and surcharged with large figures of value spaced 2½mm below the Chinese characters. During the surcharging, sheets from the 1894 (original) printing were received from outlying post offices and surcharged as they arrived. A small quantity of the 1897 printing reached the public without surcharge (Nos. 16n-24n).

Additional stamps were still required and another printing was made from the new stones and surcharged with large figures, but in a new setting with 1½mm between the Chinese characters and the value. Additional sheets of the 1894 printing were received from the most distant post offices and were also surcharged with the 1½mm setting. Thus there are four different sets of the large-figure surcharges. All these stamps were regularly issued but no attempt was made by the post office to separate printings. Some values are difficult to distinguish as to printing, particularly in used condition.

See No. 73. For surcharges see Nos. 28-72, 74.

**1897 Lithographed in Shanghai**

| No. | Type | Description | Unused | Used |
|---|---|---|---|---|
| *16n* | A3 | 1c pink | *1,300.* | |
| *17n* | A4 | 2c olive green | *1,300.* | |
| *18n* | A5 | 3c chrome yellow | *1,000.* | |
| *p.* | | 3c yellow buff | *1,100.* | |
| *19n* | A6 | 4c pale rose | *1,000.* | |
| *20n* | A7 | 5c yellow | *1,000.* | |
| *21n* | A8 | 6c red brown | *1,100.* | |
| *22n* | A9 | 9c yellowish green | *5,500.* | |
| *p.* | | 9c emerald green | — | |
| *23n* | A10 | 12c yellowish orange | *6,000.* | |
| *24n* | A11 | 24c purplish red | *4,750.* | |

The colors of the 1897 printings are pale or dull; the gum is thin and white. The 1894 printing has a thicker, yellowish gum.

The set of 9 values on thick unwatermarked paper is a special printing of 5,000 sets ordered by P. G. von Mollendorf, a Customs official, for presentation purposes. Value, set $3,100.

For surcharges see Nos. 47-55, 65-72.

### Issues of the Chinese Government Post

Preceding Issues Surcharged in Black

**Small Numerals 2½mm Below Chinese Characters**
**Surcharged on Nos. 13-15**

**1897, Jan. 2 *Perf. 11½-12***

| No. | Type | Description | Unused | Used |
|---|---|---|---|---|
| 25 | A2 | 1c on 1c | 115.00 | *85.00* |
| 26 | A2 | 2c on 3c | 475.00 | 120.00 |
| *a.* | | Double surcharge | — | |
| 27 | A2 | 5c on 5c | 150.00 | 57.50 |
| | | *Nos. 25-27 (3)* | 740.00 | 262.50 |

**Surcharged on Nos. 16-24**

On No. 28 the "½" is 3mm high.

| No. | Type | Description | Unused | Used |
|---|---|---|---|---|
| 28 | A5 | ½c on 3c | 45.00 | 35.00 |
| *a.* | | "1" instead of "½" | 750.00 | 375.00 |
| *b.* | | Horiz. pair, imperf. btwn. | *11,000.* | |
| *c.* | | Vert. pair, imperf. horiz. | *11,000.* | — |
| *d.* | | Double surcharge | *15,000.* | *17,000.* |
| *e.* | | Vert. pair, imperf. btwn. | *11,000.* | |
| 29 | A3 | 1c on 1c | 45.00 | 30.00 |
| *a.* | | Inverted surcharge | *50,000.* | *10,000.* |
| 30 | A4 | 2c on 2c | 40.00 | 22.50 |
| *a.* | | Horiz. pair, imperf. vert. | *8,500.* | |
| *b.* | | Vert. pair, imperf. btwn. | *8,750.* | *8,750.* |
| *c.* | | Double surcharge | *20,000.* | 11,500. |
| *d.* | | Inverted surcharge | — | *15,000.* |
| *e.* | | Horiz. pair, imperf. btwn. | *16,000.* | |
| 31 | A6 | 4c on 4c | 45.00 | 27.50 |
| *a.* | | Double surcharge | *30,000.* | *20,000.* |
| *b.* | | Vert. pair, imperf. btwn. | *27,500.* | — |
| *c.* | | Horiz. pair, imperf. btwn. | *15,000.* | *15,000.* |
| 32 | A7 | 5c on 5c | 50.00 | 22.50 |
| *a.* | | Vert. pair, imperf. btwn. | *20,000.* | *16,750.* |
| 33 | A8 | 8c on 6c | 60.00 | 35.00 |
| *a.* | | Vert. pair, imperf. btwn. | *6,750.* | *6,750.* |
| *b.* | | Vert. strip of 3, imperf. btwn. | *15,000.* | — |
| *c.* | | Horiz. pair, imperf. btwn. | *7,000.* | *5,000.* |
| *e.* | | Horiz. pair, imperf. vert. | *7,000.* | *7,000.* |
| 34 | A8 | 10c on 6c | 140.00 | 90.00 |
| *b.* | | Vert. pair, imperf. btwn. | *11,750.* | *2,500.* |
| *c.* | | Horiz. pair, imperf. vert. | *2,400.* | *2,400.* |
| *d.* | | On #21c | 150.00 | 100.00 |
| 35 | A9 | 10c on 9c | 475.00 | 200.00 |
| *a.* | | Double surcharge | *70,000.* | *40,000.* |
| *b.* | | Inverted surcharge | *950,000.* | — |
| 36 | A10 | 10c on 12c | 500.00 | 225.00 |
| *a.* | | Vert. pair, imperf. horiz. | *4,000.* | |
| *b.* | | Vert. pair, imperf. btwn. | *4,500.* | *4,500.* |
| *c.* | | Horiz. pair, imperf. btwn. | *6,000.* | |
| 37 | A11 | 30c on 24c | 600.00 | 240.00 |
| *a.* | | Vert. pair, imperf. btwn. | *20,000.* | *20,000.* |
| | | *Nos. 28-37 (10)* | 2,000. | 927.50 |

**Small Numerals 4mm Below Chinese Characters**

| No. | Type | Description | Unused | Used |
|---|---|---|---|---|
| *25a* | A2 | 1c on 1c green | 350.00 | *100.00* |
| *28f* | A4 | ½c on 3c orange | 400.00 | 400.00 |
| *i.* | | ½c on 3c olive yellow | 450.00 | 450.00 |
| *29b* | A3 | 1c on 1c vermilion | 500.00 | 400.00 |
| *30f* | A4 | 2c on 2c dark green | 600.00 | 500.00 |
| *31d* | A6 | 4c on 4c dark pink | 700.00 | 500.00 |
| *32b* | A7 | 5c on 5c dull orange | 800.00 | 600.00 |
| *33d* | A8 | 8c on 6c brown | 800.00 | 500.00 |
| *35c* | A9 | 10c on 9c dark green | 1,000. | 700.00 |
| *37b* | A11 | 30c on 24c dark red | 1,200. | 900.00 |

Preceding Issues Surcharged in Black

No. 38 the "½" is 4mm high.

**Large Numerals 2½mm below Chinese characters**
**Surcharged on Nos. 16-24**

**1897, Mar.**

| No. | Type | Description | Unused | Used |
|---|---|---|---|---|
| 38 | A5 | ½c on 3c | 2,500. | 875.00 |
| *b.* | | Inverted surcharge | | *13,500.* |
| 39 | A3 | 1c on 1c | 700.00 | 300.00 |
| 40 | A4 | 2c on 2c | 375.00 | 350.00 |
| 41 | A6 | 4c on 4c | 475.00 | 375.00 |
| *b.* | | Horiz. pair, imperf. btwn. | *15,000.* | |
| 42 | A7 | 5c on 5c | 250.00 | 210.00 |
| 43 | A8 | 8c on 6c | 2,400. | 1,750. |
| 44 | A9 | 10c on 9c | 800.00 | 375.00 |
| 45 | A10 | 10c on 12c | *87,500.* | 3,400. |
| 46 | A11 | 30c on 24c | 1,750. | 1,300. |
| *b.* | | 2mm spacing between "30" and "cents." | *15,000.* | *2,000.* |

**Same Surcharge on Nos. 16n-24n**

| No. | Type | Description | Unused | Used |
|---|---|---|---|---|
| 47 | A5 | ½c on 3c | 37.50 | *40.00* |
| *a.* | | "cen" for "cent" | 850.00 | 700.00 |
| *b.* | | Vert. pair, imperf. btwn. | *6,750.* | *6,000.* |
| *c.* | | Vert. pair, imperf. horiz. | 2,400. | 1,600. |
| *d.* | | As "a" and "c" | *4,500.* | *4,500.* |
| *e.* | | As "a" and "b" | *7,500.* | *7,500.* |
| *f.* | | Horiz. pair, imperf. btwn. | *3,000.* | *3,000.* |
| 48 | A3 | 1c on 1c | 40.00 | 25.00 |
| *a.* | | Horiz. pair, imperf. btwn. | | *4,000.* |
| 49 | A4 | 2c on 2c | 32.50 | 19.00 |
| 50 | A6 | 4c on 4c | 40.00 | 19.00 |
| *a.* | | Horiz. pair, imperf. btwn. | *13,500.* | *13,500.* |
| *b.* | | Vert. pair, imperf. btwn. | | *5,000.* |
| 51 | A7 | 5c on 5c | 50.00 | 30.00 |
| 52 | A8 | 8c on 6c | 600.00 | 300.00 |
| 53 | A9 | 10c on 9c | 300.00 | 125.00 |
| *a.* | | 10c on 9c emerald | 400.00 | 150.00 |
| *b.* | | Pair, one without surcharge | *3,000.* | *2,500.* |
| 54 | A10 | 10c on 12c | 375.00 | 90.00 |
| 55 | A11 | 30c on 24c | 1,200. | 400.00 |
| *a.* | | 2mm spacing btwn "30" and "cents" | *1,700.* | 750.00 |
| *b.* | | Vert. pair, imperf. btwn. | *17,500.* | *17,500.* |

All recorded unused examples of No. 45 are flawed.

**Numerals 1½mm below Chinese characters**

**1897, May**

**Surcharged on Nos. 16-24**

| No. | Type | Description | Unused | Used |
|---|---|---|---|---|
| 56 | A5 | ½c on 3c org yel | 525.00 | 350.00 |
| 57 | A3 | 1c on 1c | 350.00 | 290.00 |
| 58 | A4 | 2c on 2c | 175,000. | *6,000.* |
| 59 | A6 | 4c on 4c | 290.00 | 240.00 |
| 60 | A7 | 5c on 5c | 375.00 | 290.00 |
| 61 | A8 | 8c on 6c | 1,600. | 1,300. |
| 62 | A9 | 10c on 9c | 350.00 | 240.00 |

63 A10 10c on 12c 1,600. 1,000.
64 A11 30c on 24c *80,000.* —

**Same Surcharge on Nos. 16n-24n**

65 A5 ½c on 3c 25.00 *30.00*
a. Inverted surcharge *4,500.* *4,500.*
b. ½mm spacing *8,000.* *8,000.*
c. "t." of "cent." missing — —
d. Horiz. pair, imperf. between *10,000.*
66 A3 1c on 1c 40.00 25.00
67 A4 2c on 2c 35.00 17.50
a. Inverted surcharge *17,500.* *8,750.*
b. Vert. pair, imperf. btwn. *20,000.*
68 A6 4c on 4c 300.00 225.00
a. Inverted surcharge 3,000. 2,000.
69 A7 5c on 5c 300.00 225.00
70 A9 10c on 9c 225.00 110.00
a. Inverted surcharge 3,000. 2,000.
71 A10 10c on 12c 400.00 225.00
72 A11 30c on 24c *13,000.* 2,500.

**Same Surcharge (1½mm Spacing) on Type A12, and**

A12

A12a

**Redrawn Designs Printed from New Stones**

**1897**

73 A12 ½c on 3c yel 250.00 190.00
a. ½mm spacing *6,000.* *4,000.*
74 A12a 2c on 2c yel grn 75.00 35.00
a. Horiz. pair, imperf. btwn. *10,000.* *5,000.*

Nos. 73 and 74 were surcharged on stamps printed from new stones, which differ slightly from the originals. On No. 73 the numeral "3" and symbols in the four corner panels have been enlarged and strengthened. On No. 74, the numeral "2" has a thick, flat base.

**Surcharged on Nos. 13-15**

75 A2 1c on 1c green 500.00 *625.00*
a. On #13b 550.00 575.00
76 A2 2c on 3c lilac 1,100. *1,200.*
77 A2 5c on 5c grnsh yel 375.00 *525.00*

**Revenue Stamps Surcharged in Black**

A13

a

b

c

d

e

f

g

**1897 Unwmk. *Perf. 12 to 15***

78 A13 (a) 1c on 3c red 525.00 350.00
a. No period after "cent" 600.00 400.00
b. Central character with large "box" 625.00 550.00
79 A13 (b) 2c on 3c red 850.00 450.00
a. Inverted surcharge *37,500.* *27,500.*
b. Inverted "S" in "CENTS" *1,000.* *600.00*
c. No period after "CENTS" *950.00* *550.00*
d. Comma after "CENTS" *950.00* *550.00*
e. Double surcharge *140,000.* —
f. Dbl. surch., both inverted *150,000.*
g. Double surch. (blk & grn) *220,000.*
80 A13 (c) 2c on 3c red 500.00 400.00
81 A13 (d) 4c on 3c red *75,000.* *75,000.*
a. Double surcharge (blk & vio) *250,000.* *250,000.*
82 A13 (e) 4c on 3c red 1,650. 800.00
83 A13 (f) $1 on 3c red *900,000.* —
a. No period after "r" —
84 A13 (g) $1 on 3c red 5,000. 3,250.
85 A13 (g) $5 on 3c red 85,000. 55,000.
a. Inverted surcharge *130,000.* *95,000.*

A few examples of the 3c red exist without surcharge; one canceled. Value, unused $85,000. No. 79 with green surcharge is a trial printing. Value, $220,000.

No. 79g is unique. The only canceled example of No. 83 is in a museum.

Normal spacing for No. 78 is 4mm between "one cent" and the Chinese character.

Dragon A14

Carp A15

Wild Goose — A16

**"Imperial Chinese Post" Lithographed in Japan *Perf. 11, 11½, 12***

**1897, Aug. 16 Wmk. 103**

86 A14 ½c purple 7.00 4.50
a. Horiz. pair, imperf. btwn. *800.00*
b. Vert. pair, imperf. btwn. *20,000.*
87 A14 1c yellow 8.00 4.00
88 A14 2c orange 8.00 3.75
a. Vert. pair, imperf. horiz. —
b. Vert. pair, imperf. between 10.00 6.00
c. 2c orange red 10.00 5.00
89 A14 4c brown 11.00 3.75
a. Horiz. pair, imperf. btwn. *3,000.*
b. Horiz. pair, imperf. vert. *3,000.*
90 A14 5c rose red 14.00 5.00
91 A14 10c dk green 40.00 3.75
92 A15 20c maroon 85.00 19.00
93 A15 30c red 140.00 32.50
94 A15 50c yellow grn 100.00 45.00
a. 50c black green 1,750.
b. 50c blue green 5,750.
95 A16 $1 car & rose 325.00 200.00
a. Horiz. pair, imperf. vert. *8,000.*
96 A16 $2 orange & yel 3,000. 1,600.
a. Horiz. pair, imperf. vert. *15,000.*
97 A16 $5 yel grn & pink 1,800. 1,000.

The inner circular frames and outer frames of Nos. 86-91 differ for each denomination.

No. 97 imperforate and unwatermarked was not regularly issued. **Examples have been privately perforated and offered as No. 97.** Shades occur in most values of this issue.

A17

A18

A19

**"Chinese Imperial Post" Engraved in London**

**1898 Wmk. 103 *Perf. 12 to 16***

98 A17 ½c chocolate 6.00 4.00
a. Vert. pair, imperf. btwn. 850.00 475.00
b. Vert. pair, imperf. horiz. 850.00 475.00
99 A17 1c ocher 6.50 4.00
a. Vert. pair, imperf. btwn. 300.00 250.00
b. Horiz. pair, imperf. btwn. 400.00 350.00
100 A17 2c scarlet 8.00 4.00
a. Vert. pair, imperf. btwn. 400.00 200.00
b. Horiz. pair, imperf. vert. 400.00 200.00
101 A17 4c orange brn 7.50 4.00
a. Vert. pair, imperf. btwn. 575.00
b. Horiz. pair, imperf. vert. 500.00 300.00
c. Horiz. pair, imperf. btwn. 700.00 600.00
d. Horiz. strip of 3, imperf. btwn. 2,250. 1,500.
102 A17 5c salmon 11.00 8.00
a. Vert. pair, imperf. btwn. 400.00 300.00
b. Horiz. pair, imperf. btwn. 775.00 500.00
c. Vert. pair, imperf. horiz. 600.00 500.00
d. 5c pale reddish orange 16.00 5.50
e. As "d," vert pair, imperf. btwn. 600.00 500.00
103 A17 10c dk blue grn 17.50 6.00
a. Vert. or horiz. pair, imperf. btwn — —
104 A18 20c claret 70.00 9.00
a. Horiz. pair, imperf. btwn. 850.00 750.00
b. Vert. pair, imperf. horiz. 850.00 750.00
c. Vert. pair, imperf. btwn. 900.00 800.00
105 A18 30c dull rose 60.00 15.00
a. Horiz. pair, imperf. btwn. *2,000.*
b. Vert. pair, imperf. horiz. *1,750.*
c. Vert. pair, imperf. btwn. *1,750.*
106 A18 50c lt green 85.00 20.00
a. Vert. pair, imperf. btwn. *2,250.*
107 A19 $1 red & pale rose 375.00 50.00
108 A19 $2 brn, red & yel 625.00 100.00
109 A19 $5 dp grn & sal 950.00 360.00
a. Horiz. pair, imperf. btwn. *77,500.*
b. Vert. pair, imperf. btwn. *20,000.*
*Nos. 98-109 (12)* 2,222. 584.00

No. 98 surcharged "B. R. A.-5-Five Cents" in three lines in black or green, was surcharged by British military authorities shortly after the Boxer riots for use from military posts in an occupied area along the Peking-Mukden railway. Usually canceled in violet.

See note following No. 122.

**1900(?)-06 Unwmk. *Perf. 12 to 16***

110 A17 ½c brown 7.00 2.75
a. Horiz. pair, imperf. btwn. 400.00 400.00
b. Vert. pair, imperf. btwn. 400.00 400.00
111 A17 1c ocher 8.00 2.75
a. Horiz. pair, imperf. btwn. 350.00 350.00
b. Vert. pair, imperf. btwn. 350.00 350.00
c. Vert. pair, imperf. horiz. 350.00 350.00
112 A17 2c scarlet 10.00 3.00
a. Horiz. pair, imperf. btwn. 350.00 350.00
b. Vert. pair, imperf. btwn. 350.00 350.00
c. Vert. pair, imperf. horiz. 350.00 350.00
d. Horiz. pair, imperf. vert. 350.00 350.00
e. Vert. strip of 3, imperf. btwn. 1,000. 650.00
113 A17 4c orange brn 18.00 3.25
a. Horiz. pair, imperf. btwn. 350.00 350.00
b. Vert. pair, imperf. btwn. 350.00 350.00
114 A17 5c rose red 30.00 5.00
a. Vert. pair, imperf. btwn. 350.00 350.00
b. Vert. pair, imperf. horiz. 350.00 350.00
115 A17 5c orange 37.50 6.00
a. 5c yellow 450.00 100.00
b. Vert. pair, imperf. btwn. 400.00 400.00
c. Horiz. pair, imperf. btwn. 400.00 400.00
116 A17 10c green 40.00 2.75
a. Vert. pair, imperf. btwn. 425.00
b. Horiz. pair, imperf. btwn. 725.00
c. Vert. pair, imperf. horiz. 425.00
d. Vert. strip of 3, imperf. btwn. 700.00
117 A18 20c red brown 50.00 4.00
a. Horiz. pair, imperf. btwn. 600.00
b. Vert. pair, imperf. btwn. 500.00
c. Vert. pair, imperf. horiz. 750.00 375.00
118 A18 30c dull red 50.00 4.00
a. Vert. pair, imperf. btwn. 850.00
119 A18 50c yellow grn 75.00 6.00
a. Horiz. pair, imperf. btwn. 1,000.
b. Vert. pair, imperf. btwn. *2,000.*
120 A19 $1 red & pale rose ('06) 225.00 35.00
121 A19 $2 brn red & yel ('06) 450.00 75.00
122 A19 $5 dp grn & sal 875.00 250.00
*Nos. 110-122 (13)* 1,876. 399.50

See No. 124-130. For surcharges and overprints see Nos. 123, 134-177, J1-J6, Offices in Tibet 1-11.

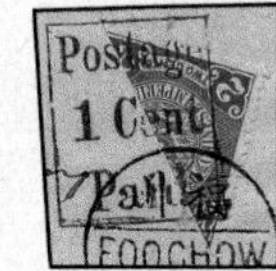
Diagonal Half of No. 112 Surcharged on Stamp and Envelope

**1903**

123 A17 1c on half of 2c scarlet, on cover *1,500.*

Used Oct. 22 to Oct. 24. Value is for cover mailed to post office other than sending office (Foochow) and bearing backstamp showing arrival date. Locally addressed or unaddressed covers without backstamps properly used are worth approximately $900. Others are worth less.

Forgeries are plentiful, particularly on pieces of cover. Certificates of authenticity are mandatory.

**1905-10**

124 A17 2c green ('08) 3.25 3.25
a. Horiz. pair, imperf. btwn. 350.00 350.00
b. Vert. pair, imperf. btwn. 350.00 350.00
c. Horiz. pair, imperf. vert. 350.00 350.00
d. Horiz. strip of 4, imperf. btwn. 800.00 *800.00*
125 A17 3c slate grn ('10) 8.00 2.50
a. Horiz. pair, imperf. btwn. 350.00
b. Vert. pair, imperf. btwn. 350.00
126 A17 4c vermilion ('09) 6.75 2.75
a. Vert. pair, imperf. btwn. 350.00 350.00
127 A17 5c violet 12.00 2.50
a. 5c lilac 10.00 2.75
b. Horiz. pair, imperf. btwn. 550.00
c. Vert. pair, imperf. btwn. 1,000.
d. Vert. pair, imperf. horiz. 600.00
128 A17 7c maroon ('10) 20.00 10.00
129 A17 10c ultra ('08) 25.00 2.75
a. Horiz. pair, imperf. btwn. 400.00 400.00
b. Vert. pair, imperf. btwn. 400.00
c. Vert. pair, imperf. horiz. 400.00 400.00
130 A18 16c olive grn ('07) 60.00 20.00
*Nos. 124-130 (7)* 135.00 43.75

Temple of Heaven, Peking — A20

**1909 *Perf. 14***

131 A20 2c orange & green 8.50 *10.00*
132 A20 3c orange & blue 10.00 *18.00*
133 A20 7c orange & brn vio 11.50 14.00
*Nos. 131-133 (3)* 30.00 *42.00*

1st year of the reign of Hsuan T'ung, who later became Henry Pu-yi and then Emperor Kang Teh of Manchukuo.

**Stamps of 1902-10 Overprinted with Chinese Characters Foochow Issue**

Overprinted in Red or Black

**1912 *Perf. 12 to 16***

134 A17 3c slate grn (R) 300. 175.
135 A19 $1 red & pale rose 3,500. 2,500.
136 A19 $2 brn red & yel 6,000. 3,500.
137 A19 $5 dp grn & sal 7,250. 4,000.

The overprint "Ling Shih Chung Li" or "Provisional Neutrality," signified that the P.O. was

# Easy Online Bidding

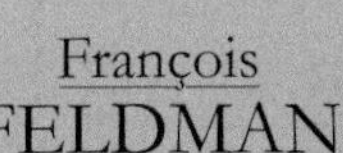

**Philasearch.com**

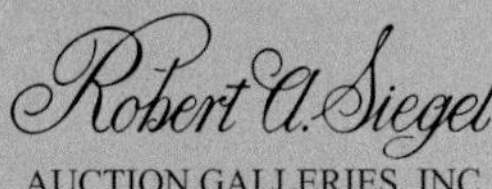

CHERRYSTONE
PHILATELIC AUCTIONEERS

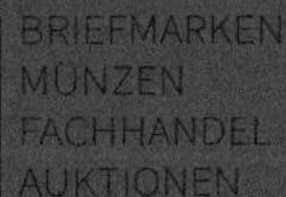

ALEXANDER ODERMATT

Cheshire Stamp Auctions
SANDAFAYRE'S PUBLIC AUCTION

FILATELIA LLACH, S.L.
Fundada en 1915

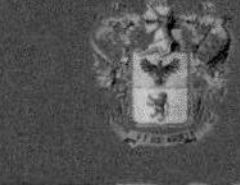

GÖTZ
Internationales Auktionshaus

Postzegelveilingen
VAN LOOY & VAN LOOY

AUCTION GALLERIES Hamburg
vormals SCHWANKE GmbH

**and many more**

conducted neutrally by agreement between the Manchu and opposing forces.

### Nanking Issue

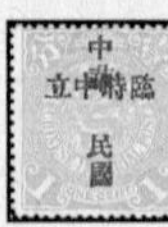

Overprinted in Red or Black

**138** A17 1c ocher (R) 300. 190.
**139** A17 3c slate grn (R) 300. 190.
**140** A17 7c maroon 600. 400.
**141** A18 16c olive grn (R) 3,500. 2,000.
**142** A18 50c yellow grn (R) 3,750. 2,500.
**143** A19 $1 red & pale rose 6,500. 2,250.
**144** A19 $2 brn red & yel 7,500. 4,000.
**145** A19 $5 dp green & sal 11,000. 9,000.

Vertical overprint reads: "Chung Hwa Min Kuo" (Republic of China).

Stamps of this issue were also used in Shanghai and Hankow.

Additional values were overprinted but not issued. Excellent forgeries of the overprints of Nos. 134-145 exist.

### Issues of the Republic

Overprinted in Black or Red

### Overprinted by the Maritime Customs Statistical Department, Shanghai

**146** A17 ½c brown 1.50 1.25
*a.* Inverted overprint 60.00 50.00
*b.* Double overprint 100.00
**147** A17 1c ocher (R) 2.25 1.25
*a.* Vert. pair, imperf. horiz. 200.00 200.00
*b.* Inverted overprint 225.00 150.00
*c.* Double overprint 225.00 200.00
*d.* Horiz. pair, imperf. btwn. 300.00 250.00
*e.* Horiz. pair, imperf. vert. 275.00
*f.* Pair, one without overprint 225.00
**148** A17 2c green (R) 8.00 3.00
*a.* Vert. pair, imperf. btwn. 350.00 300.00
*b.* Horiz. pair, imperf. btwn. 350.00
**149** A17 3c slate grn (R) 3.00 1.50
*a.* Inverted overprint 400.00 100.00
*b.* Horiz. pair, imperf. btwn. 500.00 500.00
*c.* Vert. pair, imperf btwn. 300.00 300.00
*d.* Horiz. pair, imperf. vert. 200.00
*e.* Horiz. strip of 3, imperf btwn. 450.00
*f.* Horiz. strip of 5, imperf btwn. 975.00
**150** A17 4c vermilion 4.75 1.75
*a.* Vert. pair, imperf. btwn. 800.00
**151** A17 5c violet (R) 6.25 1.75
*a.* Horiz. pair, imperf. btwn. —
*b.* Vert. pair, imperf btwn. — 1,000.
**152** A17 7c maroon 8.25 3.50
**153** A17 10c ultra (R) 8.50 1.75
*a.* Double overprint *300.00*
*b.* Pair, one without overprint *900.00*
*c.* Brownish red overprint 22.50 9.00
*d.* Inverted overprint *750.00* *750.00*
**154** A18 16c olive grn (R) 22.50 8.50
**155** A18 20c red brown 21.00 5.00
*a.* Vert. pair, imperf btwn. —
**156** A18 30c rose red 26.00 6.00
**157** A18 50c yel grn (R) 45.00 6.00
**158** A19 $1 red & pale rose 450.00 35.00
*a.* Inverted overprint *27,500.*
**159** A19 $2 brn red & yel 400.00 75.00
*a.* Inverted overprint 725.00 600.00
**160** A19 $5 dp grn & sal 825.00 675.00
*Nos. 146-160 (15)* 1,832. 826.25

Stamps with blue overprint similar to the preceding were not an official issue but were privately made by a printer in Tientsin.

Overprinted in Red

Overprinted by the Commercial Press, Shanghai.

This type differs in that the top character is shifted slightly to right and the bottom character is larger and has small "legs".

**161** A17 1c ocher 10.00 2.00
*a.* Inverted overprint 350.00 350.00
*b.* Vert. pair, imperf. btwn. 425.00
*c.* Double overprint 350.00
*c.* Double overprint 350.00
**162** A17 2c green 37.50 3.50
*a.* Inverted overprint 1,100. 800.00
*b.* Vert. pair, imperf. btwn. 750.00
*c.* Horiz. pair, imperf. btwn. 650.00
*d.* Horiz. strip of 3, imperf. btwn. 850.00

Overprinted in Blue, Carmine or Black

### Overprinted by Waterlow & Sons, London

**163** A17 ½c brown (Bl) 3.00 2.00
*a.* Vert. pair, imperf. btwn. *1,350.* *1,250.*
**164** A17 1c ocher (C) 3.00 2.00
*a.* Horiz. pair, imperf. btwn. *800.00*
**165** A17 2c green (C) 3.75 2.00
**166** A17 3c slate grn (C) 4.50 1.75
*a.* Inverted overprint *1,500.*
*b.* Vert. pair, imperf. btwn. 400.00
*c.* Horiz. pair, imperf. btwn. 400.00
**167** A17 4c vermilion (Bk) 5.75 2.25
**168** A17 5c violet (C) 12.50 2.25
**169** A17 7c maroon (Bk) 40.00 *37.50*
**170** A17 10c ultra (C) 19.50 2.75
*a.* Vert. pair, imperf. btwn. *1,500.* *2,600.*
**171** A18 16c olive grn (R) 57.50 19.00
**172** A18 20c red brn (Bk) 35.00 3.50
**173** A18 30c dull red (Bk) 115.00 6.75
**174** A18 50c yellow grn (R) 170.00 17.50
**175** A19 $1 red & pale rose (Bk) 250.00 27.50
**176** A19 $2 brn red & yel (Bk) 525.00 225.00
**177** A19 $5 dp grn & sal (C) 850.00 525.00
*Nos. 163-177 (15)* 2,095. 876.75

Due to instructions issued to postmasters throughout China at the time of the Revolution, a number of them prepared unauthorized overprints using the same characters as the overprints prepared by the government. While many were made in good faith, some, like the blue overprints from Tientsin, were bogus, and the status of certain others is extremely dubious.

Dr. Sun Yat-sen — A21

**1912, Dec. 14** ***Perf. 14½***

**178** A21 1c orange 6.00 *3.25*
**179** A21 2c yellow grn 6.00 *3.25*
**180** A21 3c slate grn 6.00 *3.25*
**181** A21 5c rose lilac 12.00 3.25
**182** A21 8c dp brown 12.00 5.00
**183** A21 10c dull blue 12.00 5.00
**184** A21 16c olive grn 37.50 20.00
**185** A21 20c maroon 47.50 15.00
**186** A21 50c dk green 130.00 50.00
**187** A21 $1 brown red 340.00 75.00
**188** A21 $2 yellow brn 1,000. 675.00
**189** A21 $5 gray 375.00 *250.00*
*Nos. 178-189 (12)* 1,984. 1,108.

Honoring the leader of the Revolution.

President Yuan Shih-kai — A22

**1912, Dec. 14**

**190** A22 1c orange 4.00 3.00
**191** A22 2c yellow green 4.00 3.00
**192** A22 3c slate green 4.00 3.00
**193** A22 5c rose lilac 4.00 *4.00*
**194** A22 8c deep brown 11.50 4.00
**195** A22 10c dull blue 10.00 2.50
**196** A22 16c olive green 12.00 *12.00*
**197** A22 20c maroon 9.00 *10.00*
**198** A22 50c dark green 55.00 *35.00*
**199** A22 $1 brown red 200.00 60.00
**200** A22 $2 yellow brown 240.00 75.00
**201** A22 $5 gray 725.00 325.00
*Nos. 190-201 (12)* 1,279. 536.50

Honoring the 1st pres. of the Republic.

Junk
A24

Reaping Rice
A25

Gateway, Hall of Classics, Peking — A26

DESIGN A24

London Printing: Vertical shading lines under top panel fine, junk with clear diagonal shading lines on sails, right pennant of junk usually long, lines in water weak except directly under junk.

Peking Printing: Vertical shading lines under top panel and inner vertical frame line much heavier, water and sails of junk more evenly and strongly colored, white wave over "H" of "CHINA" pointed upward, touching the junk.

DESIGN A25

London: Front hat brim thick and nearly straight, left foot touches shadow.

Peking: Front hat brim thin and strongly upturned, left foot and sickle clearly outlined in white, shadow of middle tree lighter than those of the right and left trees.

DESIGN A26

London: Light colored walk clearly defined almost to the doorway, figure in right doorway "T" shaped with strong horizontal cross-bar, white panel in base of central tower rectangular, vertical stroke in top left character uniformly thick at its base, tree to right of doorway ends in minute dots.

Peking: Walk more heavily shaded near doorway, especially at right; figure in right doorway more like a "Y", white panel at base of central tower is a long oval, right vertical stroke in top left character incurved near its base, tree at right has five prominent dots at top.

London Printing: By Waterlow & Sons, London, perf. 14 to 15.

Peking Printing: By the Chinese Bureau of Engraving and Printing, Peking, perf. 14.

### London Printing

**1913, May 5** ***Perf. 14-15***

**202** A24 ½c black brn 1.00 .40
*a.* Horiz. or vert. pair, imperf. btwn. 300.00
**203** A24 1c orange 1.00 .40
*a.* Horiz. pair, imperf. btwn. 300.00 *150.00*
*b.* Vert. pair, imperf. btwn. 300.00
*c.* Horiz. strip of 5, imperf. btwn 850.00
**204** A24 2c yellow grn 3.00 .40
*a.* Horiz. pair, imperf. btwn. 375.00
**205** A24 3c blue grn 7.00 .45
*a.* Horiz. pair, imperf. btwn. 290.00
*b.* Vert. pair, imperf. btwn. *400.00*
**206** A24 4c scarlet 10.00 .70
**207** A24 5c rose lilac 30.00 .60
**208** A24 6c gray 6.00 .90
**209** A24 7c violet 27.50 8.75
**210** A24 8c brown org 50.00 2.50
**211** A24 10c dk blue 40.00 1.10
*a.* Horiz. pair, imperf. btwn. — *2,000.*
*b.* Vert. pair, imperf. btwn. — 2,100.
**212** A25 15c brown 40.00 5.75
**213** A25 16c olive grn 27.50 2.25
**214** A25 20c brown red 50.00 2.75
**215** A25 30c brown vio 50.00 2.00
*a.* Horiz. pair, imperf. btwn. *5,000.* *5,000.*
**216** A25 50c green 80.00 3.50
**217** A26 $1 ocher & blk 260.00 3.00
**218** A26 $2 blue & blk 425.00 25.00
**219** A26 $5 scarlet & blk 825.00 125.00
**220** A26 $10 yel grn & blk 2,350. 950.00
*Nos. 202-220 (19)* 4,283. 1,135.

### First Peking Printing

**1915** ***Perf. 14***

**221** A24 ½c black brn .80 .35
*a.* Vert. pair, imperf. btwn. *600.00*
**222** A24 1c orange .80 .35
**223** A24 2c yellow grn 1.60 .35
**224** A24 3c blue grn 1.75 .35
*a.* Horiz. pair, imperf. btwn. *175.00*
**225** A24 4c scarlet 20.00 .35
**226** A24 5c rose lilac 8.50 .35
*a.* Booklet pane of 4 140.00
**227** A24 6c gray 16.00 .35
**228** A24 7c violet 25.00 4.50
**229** A24 8c brown org 14.00 .40
**230** A24 10c dk blue 15.00 .70
*a.* Booklet pane of 4 140.00
**231** A25 15c brown 42.50 4.50
**232** A25 16c olive grn 22.00 .70
**233** A25 20c brown red 25.00 .70
**234** A25 30c brown vio 17.50 .70
*a.* Hoirz. pair, imperf. btwn. *900.00*
**235** A25 50c green 42.50 .80
*a.* Vert. pair, imperf. btwn. *900.00*
**236** A26 $1 ocher & blk 140.00 .85
**237** A26 $2 blue & blk 350.00 6.00
*a.* Center inverted *175,000.* —
**238** A26 $5 scarlet & blk 800.00 42.50
**239** A26 $10 yel grn & blk 1,100. 300.00
*Nos. 221-239 (19)* 2,643. 364.80

**1919**

**240** A24 1½c violet 3.75 .60
**241** A25 13c brown 9.50 .70
**242** A26 $20 yellow & blk 6,500. 3,900.

Nos. 226 and 230 overprinted in red with five characters in vertical column were for postal savings use.

The higher values of the 1913-19 issues are often overprinted with Chinese characters, which are the names of various postal districts. Stamps were frequently stolen while in transit to post offices. The overprints served to protect them, since the stamps could only be used in the districts for which they were overprinted.

Compare designs A24-A26 with designs A29-A31. For surcharges and overprints see Nos. 247, 288, B1-B3, Sinkiang 1-38.

Yeh Kung-cho, Hsu Shi-chang and Chin Yun-peng — A27

**1921, Oct. 10**

**243** A27 1c orange 6.00 1.75
**244** A27 3c blue green 6.50 1.50
**245** A27 6c gray 7.50 5.00
**246** A27 10c blue 8.50 4.00
*Nos. 243-246 (4)* 28.50 12.25

National Post Office, 25th anniversary.

For overprints see Sinkiang Nos. 39-42.

No. 224 Surcharged in Red

**1922**

**247** A24 2c on 3c blue green 4.50 .70
*a.* Inverted surcharge *175,000.* —

### Second Peking Printing

A29

A30

A31

### Types of 1913-19 Issues Re-engraved

Type A29: Most of the whitecaps in front of the junk have been removed and the water made darker. The shading lines have been removed from the arabesques and pearls above the top inscription. The inner shadings at the top and sides of the picture have been cut away.

Type A30: The heads of rice in the side panels have a background of crossed lines instead of horizontal lines. The Temple of Heaven is strongly shaded and has a door. There are rows of pearls below the Chinese characters in the upper corners. The arabesques above the top inscription have been altered and are without shading lines.

Type A31: The curved line under the inscription at top is single instead of double. There are four vertical lines, instead of eight, at each side of the picture. The trees at the sides of the temple had foliage in the 1913-19 issues, but now the branches are bare. There are numerous other alterations in the design.

**1923** ***Perf. 14***

**248** A29 ½c black brown 1.40 .30
*a.* Horiz. pair, imperf. btwn. 290.00 275.00
*b.* Horiz. pair, imperf. vert. 290.00 275.00
*c.* Vert. pair, imperf. btwn. 250.00
**249** A29 1c orange .80 .30
*a.* Imperf., pair 150.00
*b.* Horiz. pair, imperf. btwn. 150.00
*c.* Booklet pane of 6 90.00
*d.* Booklet pane of 4 45.00
*e.* Vert. pair, imperf. btwn. 150.00
*f.* Vert. pair, imperf. horiz. 150.00
**250** A29 1½c violet 3.00 .90
**251** A29 2c yellow grn 1.60 .30
**252** A29 3c blue green 5.00 .30
*a.* Booklet pane of 6 80.00
**253** A29 4c gray 22.00 .80
*a.* Horiz. pair, imperf. btwn. 300.00

| No. | Type | Description | Unused | Used |
|---|---|---|---|---|
| **254** | A29 | 5c claret | 3.25 | .50 |
| *a.* | | Booklet pane of 4 | 100.00 | |
| **255** | A29 | 6c scarlet | 7.00 | .50 |
| **256** | A29 | 7c violet | 7.00 | .50 |
| **257** | A29 | 8c orange | 14.00 | .50 |
| **258** | A29 | 10c blue | 12.00 | .30 |
| *a.* | | Booklet pane of 6 | 120.00 | |
| *b.* | | Booklet pane of 2 | 150.00 | |
| **259** | A30 | 13c brown | 26.00 | .60 |
| **260** | A30 | 15c dp blue | 8.00 | .60 |
| **261** | A30 | 16c olive grn | 9.00 | .60 |
| **262** | A30 | 20c brown red | 7.00 | .40 |
| **263** | A30 | 30c purple | 26.00 | .40 |
| *a.* | | Horiz. pair, imperf. btwn. | *650.00* | |
| **264** | A30 | 50c dp green | 50.00 | .55 |
| **265** | A31 | $1 org brn & sep | 52.50 | .65 |
| **266** | A31 | $2 blue & red brn | 70.00 | 1.00 |
| **267** | A31 | $5 red & slate | 115.00 | 4.25 |
| **268** | A31 | $10 green & claret | 575.00 | 62.50 |
| **269** | A31 | $20 plum & blue | 1,200. | 175.00 |
| | | *Nos. 248-269 (22)* | 2,216. | 251.75 |

Nos. 249 and 275 exist with webbing watermark from experimental printing. Value, $4,500 each.

To prevent speculation and theft, the dollar denominations were overprinted with single characters in red for use in Kwangsi ($1-$20) and Kweichow ($1-$5).

See Nos. 275, 324. For surcharges and overprints see Nos. 274, 289, 311, 325, 330, 339-340, Szechwan 1-3, Yunnan 1-20, Manchuria 1-20, Sinkiang 47-69, 114, C1-C4.

Temple of Heaven, Peking — A32

**1923, Oct. 17** *Perf. 14*

| No. | Type | Description | Unused | Used |
|---|---|---|---|---|
| **270** | A32 | 1c orange | 5.00 | 1.00 |
| **271** | A32 | 3c blue green | 5.50 | 2.25 |
| **272** | A32 | 4c red | 10.50 | 2.50 |
| **273** | A32 | 10c blue | 16.50 | 5.00 |
| | | *Nos. 270-273 (4)* | 37.50 | 10.75 |

Adoption of Constitution, October, 1923.
For overprints see Sinkiang Nos. 43-46.

No. 253 Surcharged in Red

**1925**

| No. | Type | Description | Unused | Used |
|---|---|---|---|---|
| **274** | A29 | 3c on 4c gray | 3.50 | .35 |
| *a.* | | Inverted surcharge | *300,000.* | *275,000.* |
| *b.* | | Vert. pair, imperf. btwn. | | |

### Junk Type of 1923

**1926**

| No. | Type | Description | Unused | Used |
|---|---|---|---|---|
| **275** | A29 | 4c olive green | 1.60 | .25 |
| *a.* | | Horiz. pair, imperf. vert. | 200.00 | 290.00 |
| *b.* | | Horiz. pair, imperf. btwn. | 200.00 | |
| *c.* | | Horiz. strip of 3, imperf. btwn. | 350.00 | |

Marshal Chang Tso-lin — A34

**1928, Mar. 1** *Perf. 14*

| No. | Type | Description | Unused | Used |
|---|---|---|---|---|
| **276** | A34 | 1c brown orange | 1.50 | 1.50 |
| **277** | A34 | 4c olive green | 3.00 | 3.00 |
| **278** | A34 | 10c dull blue | 9.50 | 5.50 |
| **279** | A34 | $1 red | 72.50 | *80.00* |
| | | *Nos. 276-279 (4)* | 86.50 | 90.00 |

Assumption of office by Marshal Chang Tso-lin. The stamps of this issue were only available for postage in the Provinces of Chihli and Shantung and at the Offices in Manchuria and Sinkiang.

For overprints see Manchuria Nos. 21-24, Sinkiang 70-73.

President Chiang Kai-shek — A35

**1929, May**

| No. | Type | Description | Unused | Used |
|---|---|---|---|---|
| **280** | A35 | 1c brown orange | 3.00 | .40 |
| **281** | A35 | 4c olive green | 5.00 | .75 |
| **282** | A35 | 10c dark blue | 23.00 | 3.50 |
| **283** | A35 | $1 dark red | 90.00 | 70.00 |
| | | *Nos. 280-283 (4)* | 121.00 | 74.65 |

Unification of China.
For overprints see Yunnan Nos. 21-24, Manchuria 25-28, Sinkiang 74-77.

Sun Yat-sen Mausoleum, Nanking — A36

**1929, May 30** *Perf. 14*

| No. | Type | Description | Unused | Used |
|---|---|---|---|---|
| **284** | A36 | 1c brown orange | 2.00 | .75 |
| **285** | A36 | 4c olive green | 2.00 | 1.00 |
| **286** | A36 | 10c dark blue | 9.00 | 2.50 |
| **287** | A36 | $1 dark red | 85.00 | *90.00* |
| | | *Nos. 284-287 (4)* | 98.00 | 94.25 |

The transfer of Dr. Sun Yat-sen's remains from Peiping to the mausoleum at Nanking.
For overprints see Yunnan Nos. 25-28, Manchuria 29-32, Sinkiang 78-81.

Nos. 224 and 252 Surcharged in Red

**1930**

| No. | Type | Description | Unused | Used |
|---|---|---|---|---|
| **288** | A24 | 1c on 3c blue green | 1.60 | *2.75* |
| **289** | A29 | 1c on 3c blue green | 1.20 | .40 |
| *a.* | | No period after "Ct" | 25.00 | 25.00 |

See Nos. 311, 325, 330.

Dr. Sun Yat-sen — A37

Type I Type II

Type I — Double-lined circle in the sun.
Type II — Heavy, single-lined circle in the sun.

### Printed by De la Rue & Co., Ltd., London

***Perf. 11½x12½ (Nos. 304-306), 12½***

**1931, Nov. 12** **Type I** **Engr.**

| No. | Type | Description | Unused | Used |
|---|---|---|---|---|
| **290** | A37 | 1c orange | .55 | .30 |
| **291** | A37 | 2c olive green | .65 | .40 |
| **292** | A37 | 4c green | 1.10 | .30 |
| **293** | A37 | 20c ultra | 1.40 | .30 |
| **294** | A37 | $1 org brn & dk brn | 12.00 | .50 |
| **295** | A37 | $2 blue & org brn | 35.00 | 3.00 |
| **296** | A37 | $5 dull red & blk | 50.00 | 5.00 |
| | | *Nos. 290-296 (7)* | 100.70 | 9.80 |

**1931-37** **Type II**

### Dry Printing

| No. | Type | Description | Unused | Used |
|---|---|---|---|---|
| **297** | A37 | 2c olive grn | .50 | .25 |
| **298** | A37 | 4c green | 7.50 | 1.00 |
| **299** | A37 | 5c green ('33) | .40 | .25 |
| **301** | A37 | 15c scarlet ('34) | .50 | .25 |
| **302** | A37 | 20c ultra ('37) | .90 | .25 |
| **303** | A37 | 25c ultra | 3.00 | 1.00 |
| **304** | A37 | $1 org brn & dk brn | 14.00 | .50 |
| **305** | A37 | $2 blue & org brn | 25.00 | 1.25 |
| **306** | A37 | $5 dull red & blk | 50.00 | 6.00 |
| | | *Nos. 297-306 (9)* | 101.80 | 10.75 |

### Wet Printing

***Perf. 12½x13, 13 (Nos. 304a-306a)***

**1931-32**

| No. | Type | Description | Unused | Used |
|---|---|---|---|---|
| *297a* | A37 | 2c olive grn | 7.50 | 2.00 |
| *298a* | A37 | 4c green | .75 | .25 |
| *299a* | A37 | 5c green | 20.00 | 40.00 |
| **300** | A37 | 15c dk green | 4.25 | 1.25 |
| *303a* | A37 | 25c ultra | .50 | .75 |
| *304a* | A37 | $1 org brn & dk brn | 25.00 | 2.50 |
| *305a* | A37 | $2 blue & org brn | 60.00 | 3.00 |
| *306a* | A37 | $5 dull red & blk | 80.00 | 10.00 |
| | | *Nos. 297a-306a (8)* | 198.00 | 59.75 |

Stamps issued prior to 1933 were printed by a wet paper process (Nos. 297a-306a). Due to shrinkage, they measure 18.5mm-19.5mmx22mm-23mm. No. 298 dry printing occasionally measures only 19.2mm wide; however, this later printing exhibits a tiny vertical line extending from the top of the lower-left tablet between the column and the outer frameline.

See Nos. 631-635 in *Scott Standard Postage Stamp Catalogue*, Vol. 2. For surcharges and overprints see Nos. 341, 343, 678, 682, 684-685, 689-691, 768, 843, 1N1, 2N1-2N5, 2N57-2N59, 2N83-2N84, 2N101-2N106, 2N116, 2N124-2N126, 3N1-3N5, 4N1-4N5, 5N1-5N4, 6N1-6N5, 7N1-7N4, 7N54, 8N2-8N3, 8N43-8N44, 8N54, 8N57, 8N69-8N71, 8N85, 9N1-9N5, Taiwan 19, 21-22, Northeastern Provinces 44, Szechwan 4-11, Yunnan 29-44, Sinkiang 82-97 in this catalogue or Scott Standard catalogue, Vol. 2.

"Nomads in the Desert" — A38

**1932** **Unwmk.** *Perf. 14*

| No. | Type | Description | Unused | Used |
|---|---|---|---|---|
| **307** | A38 | 1c deep orange | 45.00 | 90.00 |
| **308** | A38 | 4c olive green | 45.00 | 90.00 |
| **309** | A38 | 5c claret | 45.00 | 90.00 |
| **310** | A38 | 10c deep blue | 45.00 | 90.00 |
| | | *Nos. 307-310 (4)* | 180.00 | 360.00 |

Northwest Scientific Expedition of Sven Hedin. A small quantity of this issue was sold at face at Peking and several other cities. The bulk of the issue was furnished to Hedin and sold at $5 (Chinese) a set for funds to finance the expedition.

### No. 252 Surcharged in Black Like 288

**1932**

| No. | Type | Description | Unused | Used |
|---|---|---|---|---|
| **311** | A29 | 1c on 3c blue green | 2.75 | 1.60 |

### Martyrs Issue

Teng Keng A39

Ch'en Ying-shih A40

Chu Chih-hsin A45

Sung Chiao-jen A46

Huang Hsing A47

Liao Chung-kai A48

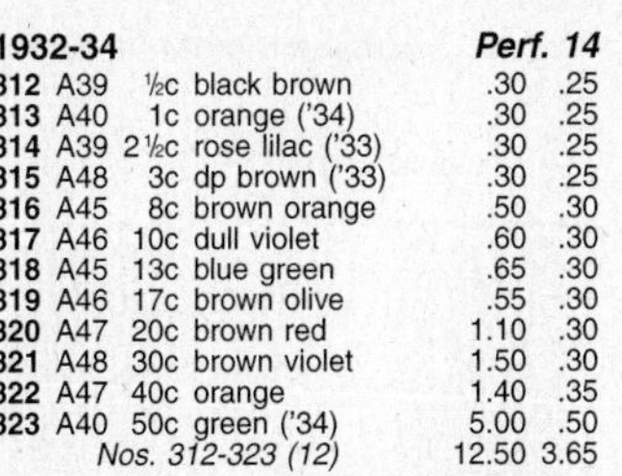

**1932-34** *Perf. 14*

| No. | Type | Description | Unused | Used |
|---|---|---|---|---|
| **312** | A39 | ½c black brown | .30 | .25 |
| **313** | A40 | 1c orange ('34) | .30 | .25 |
| **314** | A39 | 2½c rose lilac ('33) | .30 | .25 |
| **315** | A48 | 3c dp brown ('33) | .30 | .25 |
| **316** | A45 | 8c brown orange | .50 | .30 |
| **317** | A46 | 10c dull violet | .60 | .30 |
| **318** | A45 | 13c blue green | .65 | .30 |
| **319** | A46 | 17c brown olive | .55 | .30 |
| **320** | A47 | 20c brown red | 1.10 | .30 |
| **321** | A48 | 30c brown violet | 1.50 | .30 |
| **322** | A47 | 40c orange | 1.40 | .35 |
| **323** | A40 | 50c green ('34) | 5.00 | .50 |
| | | *Nos. 312-323 (12)* | 12.50 | 3.65 |

Perfs. 12 to 13 and compound and with secret marks are listed as Nos. 402-439. No. 316 re-drawn is No. 485.

For overprints and surcharge see Nos. 342, 472, 474, 478-479, 486-487, 490, 531-536, 539-541, 544-549, 616, 619, 622-624, 647-659, 662-663, 665, 669, 672, 698, 704, 711, 713-715, 720-721, 831, 846-847, 867, 870, 872, 881-882, J120-J121, 1N14-1N15, 1N59, 2N6-2N9, 2N32-2N56, 2N60, 2N76-2N82, 2N85, 2N87-2N90, 2N107-2N115, 2N118, 2N121-2N123, 3N6-3N10, 3N34-3N55, 3N59, 4N6-4N9, 4N39-4N64, 4N69, 5N5-5N8, 5N34-5N60, 5N65, 6N6-6N8, 6N35-6N61, 6N66, 7N5-7N7, 7N30-7N53, 7N55, 7N59, 8N1, 8N4, 8N28-8N42, 8N45, 8N47-8N50, 8N60-8N61, 8N68, 8N73, 8N76-8N79, 8N89, 8N97, 8N99-8N100, 8N103-8N104, 9N72-9N77, Taiwan 14-17, 20, 28A, 74, Northeastern Provinces 6-8, 11, Szechwan 12-23, Yunnan 49-60, Sinkiang 102-113, 140-161, 197.

### Junk Type of 1923

**1933** *Perf. 14*

| No. | Type | Description | Unused | Used |
|---|---|---|---|---|
| **324** | A29 | 6c brown | 25.00 | 3.00 |

### No. 275 Surcharged in Red Like 288

**1933**

| No. | Type | Description | Unused | Used |
|---|---|---|---|---|
| **325** | A29 | 1c on 4c olive green | 3.00 | .35 |
| *a.* | | No period after "Ct" | 30.00 | 25.00 |

Tan Yuan-chang — A49

**1933, Jan. 9**

| No. | Type | Description | Unused | Used |
|---|---|---|---|---|
| **326** | A49 | 2c olive green | 3.00 | 1.50 |
| **327** | A49 | 5c green | 6.50 | .75 |
| **328** | A49 | 25c ultra | 10.00 | 1.75 |
| **329** | A49 | $1 red | 90.00 | 35.00 |
| | | *Nos. 326-329 (4)* | 109.50 | 39.00 |

Tan Yuan-chang, more commonly known as Tan Yen-kai, a prominent statesman in China since the revolution of 1912 and Pres. of the Executive Dept. of the Natl. Government. Placed on sale Jan. 9, 1933, the date of the ceremony in celebration of the completion of the Tan Yuan-chang Memorial Hall and Tomb at Mukden.

For overprints see Yunnan Nos. 45-48, Sinkiang 98-101.

**No. 251 Surcharged in Red Like 288**

**1935** *Perf. 14*

**330** A29 1c on 2c yellow grn 2.50 .25
*a.* No peroid after "Ct" *30.00 25.00*

Emblem of New Life Movement A50

Four Virtues of New Life A51

Lighthouse — A52

**1936, Jan. 1**

**331** A50 2c olive green 1.75 .75
**332** A50 5c green 2.00 .25
**333** A51 20c dark blue 6.00 .70
**334** A52 $1 rose red 40.00 11.00
*Nos. 331-334 (4)* 49.75 12.70

"New Life" movement.

Methods of Mail Transportation A53

Maritime Scene A54

Shanghai General Post Office — A55

Ministry of Communications, Nanking — A56

**1936, Oct. 10**

**335** A53 2c orange 3.00 .70
**336** A54 5c green 1.50 .25
**337** A55 25c blue 5.00 .50
**338** A56 $1 dk carmine 30.00 9.50
*Nos. 335-338 (4)* 39.50 10.95

Founding of the Chinese PO, 40th anniv.

Nos. 260 and 261 Surcharged in Red

**1936, Oct. 11**

**339** A30 5c on 15c dp blue 2.75 .50
**340** A30 5c on 16c olive grn 3.50 1.00

No. 298 Surcharged in Red

**1937**

**341** A37 1c on 4c green (#298a) 1.25 .50
*a.* Upper left character missing
*b.* 1c on 4c green (#298) 750.00 40.00

Nos. 322 and 303 Surcharged in Black or Red

**1938** *Perf. 12½, 14*

**342** A47 8c on 40c orange (Bk) 2.00 .75
**343** A37 10c on 25c ultra (R) 1.75 .30

Dr. Sun Yat-sen — A57

Type I Type II

Type III

Type I — Coat button half circle. Six lines of shading above head. Top frame partially shaded with vertical lines.

Type II — Coat button complete circle. Nine lines of shading above head. Top frame partially shaded with vertical lines.

Type III — Coat button complete circle. Nine lines of shading above head. Top frame line fully shaded with vertical lines.

**Printed by the Chung Hwa Book Co.**
**Type I**

**1938 Unwmk. Engr.** *Perf. 12½*

**344** A57 $1 henna & dk brn 85.00 12.00
**345** A57 $2 dp blue & org brn 17.50 4.25
**346** A57 $5 red & grnsh blk 150.00 19.00
*Nos. 344-346 (3)* 252.50 35.25

**1939** **Type II**

**347** A57 $1 henna & dk brn 20.00 1.00
**348** A57 $2 dp blue & org brn 20.00 4.00

**1939-43** **Type III**

**349** A57 2c olive green .30 .25
**350** A57 3c dull claret .30 .25
**351** A57 5c green .30 .25
**352** A57 5c olive green .30 .25
**353** A57 8c olive green .30 .25
*a.* Vert. pair, imperf. btwn. 250.00
*b.* Horiz. pair, imperf. btwn. 250.00
**354** A57 10c green .30 .25
*a.* Horiz. pair, imperf. btwn. 250.00
**355** A57 15c scarlet 1.25 *2.25*
**356** A57 15c dk vio brn ('43) 17.50 *32.50*
**357** A57 16c olive gray 1.75 .45
*a.* Vert. pair, imperf. btwn. 250.00
**358** A57 25c dk blue .35 *2.00*
**359** A57 $1 henna & dk brn 2.00 2.00
**360** A57 $2 dp blue & org brn 4.50 1.00
*a.* Imperf., pair 300.00
**361** A57 $5 red & grnsh blk 2.75 1.00
*a.* Vert. pair, imperf. btwn. 250.00
*b.* Horiz. pair, imperf. btwn. 250.00
**362** A57 $10 dk green & dull pur 17.50 2.25
**363** A57 $20 rose lake & dk blue 60.00 50.00
*Nos. 349-363 (15)* 109.40 *94.95*

Several values exist imperforate, but these were not regularly issued. No. 361 imperforate is printer's waste.

See Nos. 368-401, 506-524. For surcharges and overprints see Nos. 440-448, 473, 475-477, 480-481, 482-484, 489, 537-538, 615, 618, 620, 660-661, 664, 666-668, 673-676, 680-681, 686, 688, 699-703, 707-709, 717, 719, 830, J67-J68, M2, M11-M12, 1N2-1N13, 1N23-1N42, 1N57-1N58, 2N10-2N31, 2N61-2N75, 2N86, 2N91-2N93, 2N117, 2N119-2N120, 3N11-3N33, 3N56-3N58, 3N60-3N61, 4N10-4N38, 4N65-4N68, 4N70-4N71, 5N9-5N33, 5N61-5N64, 5N66-5N68, 6N9-6N34, 6N62-6N65, 6N67-6N69, 7N8-7N29, 7N56-7N58, 7N60-7N61, 8N5-8N27, 8N46, 8N51-8N53, 8N55-8N56, 8N58-8N59, 8N62-8N67, 8N72, 8N74-8N75, 8N80-8N84, 8N86-8N88, 8N90, 8N95-8N96, 8N98, 8N101-8N102, 8N105-8N106, 9N6-9N71, 9N97, 9N99, Taiwan 78, 84, Northeastern Provinces 9-10, Sinkiang 115-139, 174-188, 196, 198.

Chinese and American Flags and Map of China A58

**Printed by American Bank Note Co.**

**Frame Engr., Center Litho.**

**1939, July 4 Unwmk.** *Perf. 12*

**Flag in Deep Rose and Ultramarine**

**364** A58 5c dark green 2.00 .50
**365** A58 25c deep blue 2.00 .90
**366** A58 50c brown 4.75 1.10
**367** A58 $1 rose carmine 7.50 2.25
*Nos. 364-367 (4)* 16.25 4.75

150th anniv. of the US Constitution.

**Type of 1939-41 Re-engraved**

2c, 1939-41

Re-engraved

8c, 1939-41

Re-engraved

**1940** *Perf. 12½*

**368** A57 2c olive green .30 .25
**369** A57 8c olive green .30 .25

**Type of 1938-41**
**Type III**

**1940 Unwmk.** *Perf. 14*

**370** A57 2c olive green 2.60 1.10
**371** A57 5c green 5.25 2.25
**372** A57 $1 henna & dk brn 115.00 24.00
**373** A57 $2 dp blue & org brn 22.00 5.50
**374** A57 $5 red & grnsh blk 27.00 18.00
*a.* Vert. pair, imperf. btwn. 250.00
*b.* Horiz. pair, imperf. btwn. 250.00
**375** A57 $10 dk grn & dull pur 75.00 13.50
*Nos. 370-375 (6)* 246.85 64.35

See surcharge note following No. 363.

**Type of 1939-41**

**1940 Wmk. 261** *Perf. 12½*

**Type III**

**376** A57 $1 henna & dk brn 7.00 *9.00*
**377** A57 $2 dp blue & org brn 9.00 *9.00*
**378** A57 $5 red & grnsh blk 10.00 *18.00*
**379** A57 $10 dk green & dull pur 15.00 *30.00*
**380** A57 $20 rose lake & dp blue 19.00 *30.00*
*Nos. 376-380 (5)* 60.00 *96.00*

See surcharge note following No. 363.

**Printed by the Dah Tung Book Co.**

Five Cent

Type III - Characters joined

Secret Mark - Characters not joined

Eight Cent

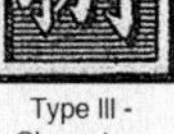
Type III - Characters not joined

Secret Mark - Characters joined

Ten Cent

Type III - Characters sharp and well shaped

Secret Mark - Characters coarse and varying in thickness

Dollar Values

Type III

Secret Mark

**1940 Unwmk.** *Perf. 14*

**Type III with Secret Marks**

**381** A57 5c green .30 .25
**382** A57 5c olive green .30 .25
**383** A57 8c olive green .40 .25
*a.* Without "star" in uniform button 1.50 *2.50*
**384** A57 10c green .30 .25
**385** A57 30c scarlet .35 .25
**386** A57 50c dk blue .45 .25
**387** A57 $1 org brn & sepia 2.50 .25
**388** A57 $2 dp blue & yel brn 1.00 .35
**389** A57 $5 red & slate grn 1.00 .45
**390** A57 $10 dk grn & dull pur 4.00 2.25
**391** A57 $20 rose lake & dk blue 12.00 3.50
*Nos. 381-391 (11)* 22.60 8.30

**Type III with Secret Marks**

**1940 Wmk. 261** *Perf. 14*

**392** A57 5c green .30 .25
**393** A57 5c olive green .30 .25
**394** A57 10c green .35 .25
**395** A57 30c scarlet .25 .25
**396** A57 50c dk blue .55 .25
**397** A57 $1 org brn & sepia 4.50 6.00
**398** A57 $2 dp blue & yel brn 12.50 18.00
**399** A57 $5 red & slate grn 11.50 *18.00*
**400** A57 $10 dk grn & dull pur 16.00 *20.00*
**401** A57 $20 rose lake & dk blue 25.00 37.00
*Nos. 392-401 (10)* 71.25 100.25

Nos. 383, 384, 385, 397, 400 and 401 exist perf. 12½, but were not issued with this perforation.

See surcharge note following No. 363.

**Types of 1932-34 Martyrs Issue with Secret Mark**

1932-34 Issue. In the left Chinese character in bottom row, the two parts are not joined.

Secret Mark, 1940-41 Issue. The two parts are joined

***Perf. 12½, 13 and Compound***

**1940-41 Wmk. 261**

**402** A39 ½c olive blk .30 .25
**403** A40 1c orange .30 .25
**404** A46 2c dp blue ('41) .30 *1.00*
**405** A39 2½c rose lilac .30 *1.00*
**406** A48 3c dp yellow brn .30 *1.00*
**407** A39 4c pale vio ('41) .30 *1.00*
**408** A48 5c dull red org ('41) .30 *1.00*
**409** A45 8c dp orange .30 *1.00*
**410** A46 10c dull violet .30 *1.00*
**411** A45 13c dp yellow grn .35 *1.00*
**412** A48 15c brown car .30 *1.00*
**413** A46 17c brown olive .30 .25
**414** A47 20c lt blue .30 .25
**415** A45 21c olive brn ('41) 1.10 *1.25*
**416** A40 25c red vio ('41) .30 *1.00*
**417** A46 28c olive ('41) .30 *1.00*
**418** A48 30c brown car .45 .25
*a.* Vert. pair, imperf. btwn. 140.00
**419** A47 40c orange .30 .25
**420** A40 50c green .30 .25

**Unwmk.**

**421** A39 ½c olive black .30 .25
**422** A40 1c orange .30 .25
*a.* Without secret mark 2.75 2.75
*b.* Horiz. pair, imperf. vert. 110.00
**423** A46 2c dp blue .30 .25
*a.* Vert. pair, imperf. horiz. 100.00
*b.* Horiz. pair, imperf. between 160.00

**424** A39 2½c rose lilac .30 .25
**425** A48 3c dp yellow brn .30 .25
**426** A39 4c pale violet .30 .25
**427** A48 5c dull red org .30 .25
**428** A45 8c dp orange .30 .25
**429** A46 10c dull violet 3.25 .40
**430** A45 13c dp yel grn .30 .65
**431** A48 15c brown car .35 *1.00*
**432** A46 17c brn olive .40 .25
**433** A47 20c lt blue .30 .25
*a.* Vert. pair, imperf. horiz. 125.00
*b.* Horiz. pair, imperf. vert. 125.00
**434** A45 21c olive brn .50 .35
**435** A40 25c rose vio .35 *.50*
**436** A46 28c olive .70 .50
**437** A48 30c brown car 2.50 2.50
**438** A47 40c orange .35 .35
**439** A40 50c green 3.50 .40
*Nos. 402-439 (38)* 21.60 23.15

Several values exist imperforate, but they were not regularly issued.

Used values are for favor cancels. Postally used examples sell for more.

See surcharge note following No. 323.

Regional Surcharges.

The regional surcharges, Nos. 440-448, 482-484, 486-491, 525-549, have been listed according to the basic stamps, with black or red surcharges. The surcharges of the individual provinces, plus Hong Kong and Shanghai, are noted in small type. The numeral following each letter is the surcharge denomination. These surcharges are identified by the following letters:

| | |
|---|---|
| a — Hong Kong | i — Kwangsi |
| b — Shanghai | j — Kwangtung |
| bx — Anhwei | k — Western Szechwan |
| c — Hunan | l — Yunnan |
| d — Kansu | m — Honan |
| e — Kiangsi | n — Shensi |
| f — Eastern Szechwan | o — Kweichow |
| g — Chekiang | p — Hupeh |
| h — Fukien | |

### Regional Surcharges on Stamps of 1939-40

Hong Kong — a4

Shanghai — b3

Hunan — c3

Kansu — d3

Kiangsi — e3

Eastern Szechwan — f3

Chekiang — g3

**1940-41 Unwmk. *Perf. 12½, 14***

**Carmine Surcharge**

**440** A57 4c on 5c ol grn (#382) (a4) .60 .60
*r.* Lower right character duplicated at left 30.00 32.50

**Black Surcharge**

**441** A57 3c on 5c grn (#351) (b3) 1.25 *1.40*
**442** A57 3c on 5c ol grn (#352) (c3, d3) .65 *2.00*
**443** A57 3c on 5c grn (#381) (b3) .60 *1.25*
**444** A57 3c on 5c ol grn (#382) (e3) .70 *1.00*
*r.* Lower left character duplicated at right (Kiangsi) 42.50 42.50
(b3) Shanghai .65 *1.40*
(f3) Eastern Szechwan .65 *1.60*

The Kansu surcharges of No. 442 are of 6 types. Differences include formation of top part of fen character (at left of "3"), fen with low right hook, height of "3" (5-4mm), space between upper and lower characters (6-9mm), etc.

**1940-41 Wmk. 261 *Perf. 14***

**445** A57 3c on 5c grn (#392) (e3) .60 *1.40*
*r.* Lower left character duplicated at right (Kiangsi) 35.00 35.00
(b3, c3) Shanghai, Hunan .60 *1.60*
**446** A57 3c on 5c ol grn (#393) (f3) .70 *1.75*
(b3) Shanghai .95 *1.75*
*r.* Lower left character duplicated at right (f3) 60.00 65.00

**Red Surcharge**

**447** A57 3c on 5c grn (#392) (g3) 1.25 3.25
**448** A57 3c on 5c ol grn (#393) (g3) 6.00 6.00

Dr. Sun Yat-sen — A59

**Printed by American Bank Note Co.**

**1941 Unwmk. Engr. *Perf. 12***

**449** A59 ½c sepia .30 .30
**450** A59 1c orange .30 .25
**451** A59 2c brt ultra .30 .25
**452** A59 5c green .30 .25
**453** A59 8c red orange .60 .70
**454** A59 8c turq green .30 .25
**455** A59 10c brt green .30 .25
**456** A59 17c olive 4.50 *12.00*
**457** A59 25c rose violet .30 1.00
**458** A59 30c scarlet .35 .25
**459** A59 50c dk blue .50 .25
**460** A59 $1 brown & blk .60 .25
**461** A59 $2 blue & blk .75 .25
*a.* Center inverted *180,000.*
**462** A59 $5 scarlet & blk 1.75 .65
**463** A59 $10 green & blk 5.00 2.75
**464** A59 $20 rose vio & blk 4.00 *6.00*
*Nos. 449-464 (16)* 20.15 25.65

For surcharges see Nos. 488, 491, 542-543, 617, 621, 670, 677, 687, 705-706, 712, 716, 718, M1, M3-M4, 1N16-1N22, 1N43-1N56, 9N78-9N96, 9N98, 9N100.

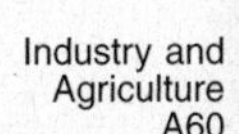

Industry and Agriculture A60

**1941, June 21 *Perf. 12½***

**465** A60 8c green .50 .50
**466** A60 21c red brown .65 .65
**467** A60 28c dk olive grn .85 .85
**468** A60 33c vermilion 1.10 *1.50*
**469** A60 50c dp ultra 1.25 1.25
**470** A60 $1 dk violet 1.75 1.75
*Nos. 465-470 (6)* 6.10 6.50

**Souvenir Sheet**

***Imperf***

**Typo.**

**471** Sheet of 6 100.00 *175.00*
*a.* A60 8c dull green 10.00 *25.00*
*b.* A60 21c dark orange brown 10.00 *25.00*
*c.* A60 28c dull yellow green 10.00 *25.00*
*d.* A60 33c red 10.00 *25.00*
*e.* A60 50c dull blue 10.00 *25.00*
*f.* A60 $1 dark violet 10.00 *25.00*

The Thrift Movement and its aim to "Save for Reconstruction."

Issued in sheets measuring 155x171mm, without gum.

This sheet exists with additional blue marginal overprints in Russian, French and Chinese reading "Souvenir of the Exhibition of the Russian Philatelic Society in China, Shanghai, China, Feb. 28, 1943." Value, $600 unused; $800 used.

The overprinting was applied by the society, and when so overprinted this sheet had no franking power.

Stamps of 1939-41 Overprinted in Carmine or Blue

**1941, Oct. 10 *Perf. 12½, 14, 13***

**472** A40 1c dull orange .30 *20.00*
**473** A57 2c olive grn (C) .30 *20.00*
**474** A39 4c pale violet (C) .30 *20.00*
**475** A57 8c ol grn (#369) (C) .30 *20.00*
**476** A57 10c green (#354) (C) .30 *20.00*
**477** A57 16c ol gray (#357) (C) .30 *20.00*
**478** A45 21c olive brn (C) .30 *20.00*
**479** A46 28c olive (C) .60 *25.00*
**480** A57 30c scarlet 1.00 *25.00*
**481** A57 $1 hn & dk brn (#359) 4.00 *28.00*
*Nos. 472-481 (10)* 7.70 *218.00*

Chinese Republic, 30th anniversary.

Kiangsi — e7

Eastern Szechwan — f7

Chekiang — g7

Fukien — h7

**1941 Unwmk. *Perf. 12½, 14***

**482** A57 7c on 8c (#353) (g7, h7) 1.00 1.10
**483** A57 7c on 8c (#369) (f7) 1.00 .55
**484** A57 7c on 8c (#383) (h7) 1.00 .90
(e7) Kiangsi 1.00 .90
(g7) Chekiang 1.00 1.10
*r.* Without "star" in uniform button 70.00

**Type of 1932-34 Re-engraved**

**1941 Unwmk. *Perf. 14***

**485** A45 8c deep orange 25.00 *60.00*

The original stamps are 19½mm wide, the re-engraved 21mm.

Eleven other values of the Martyrs Issue and types A37 and A57 exist re-engraved, but were not issued.

Hunan — c1

Kiangsi — e1

Fukien — h1

Kwangsi — i1

Kwangtung — j1

**1942 Red Surcharge**

**486** A39 1c on ½c blk brn (#312) (i1) 1.00 *1.75*
(c1) Hunan 2.00 *2.75*
**487** A39 1c on ½c ol blk (#421) (e1) .75 1.60
(c1) Hunan .85 *2.00*
(i1) Kwangsi 1.65 *2.50*
(h1) Fukien 6.00 *9.50*
**488** A59 1c on ½c sepia (#449) (j1) 1.00 *1.60*
(c1) Hunan 1.25 *2.50*

Hunan — c40

Eastern Szechwan — f40

Western Szechwan — k40

Yunnan — l40

**Red Surcharge**

**489** A57 40c on 50c dk bl (#386) (f40) .75 1.25
(k40) Western Szechwan 4.25 *6.00*
(l40) Yunnan 3.75 *5.50*
*r.* Inverted surcharge (Yunnan) 110.00

**Wmk. 261**

**490** A40 40c on 50c grn (#420) (c40) 1.75 *6.50*

**Unwmk.**

**491** A59 40c on 50c dk bl (#459) (c40) 3.25 *8.25*

Dr. Sun Yat-sen — A62

**Central Trust Printing**

***Perf. 10½-11, 11½-12½, 13 and Compounds***

**1942-43 Without Gum Typo.**

**492** A62 10c dp green ('43) .30 *1.50*
**493** A62 16c dull ol brn 13.50 *47.50*
*a.* Perf 10½ 550.00 *550.00*
**494** A62 20c dk ol grn ('43) .30 *1.50*
*a.* Perf. 11 13.50 11.00
**495** A62 25c brown vio .30 *1.00*
**496** A62 30c dull ver .30 *1.00*
*a.* Perf. 11 3.00 5.00
**497** A62 40c dk red brn ('43) .30 *1.00*
*a.* Perf. 11x13 85.00
*b.* Perf. 11 14.00 14.00
**498** A62 50c sage green .30 .25
*a.* Perf. 11 7.00 *13.50*
**499** A62 $1 rose lake .35 .25
*a.* Perf. 11 40.00 40.00
**500** A62 $1 dull grn ('43) .35 .35
**501** A62 $1.50 dp blue ('43) .35 *.45*
*a.* Perf. 11 290.00 290.00
**502** A62 $2 dk blue grn .35 .35
**503** A62 $3 dk yel ('43) .35 .35
**504** A62 $4 red brown .40 .45
**505** A62 $5 cerise ('43) .35 .35
*Nos. 492-505 (14)* 17.80 56.30

Many shades and part-perforate varieties exist.

See Nos. 550 to 563 for other stamps of type A62 with secret mark and new values and colors. For surcharges and overprints see Nos. 525-530, 671, 683, 692-694, 696, 771, 773, 807-809, 811-820, 824-827, 832, 834-834A, 836, 848-850, 852-854, 857, 860-863, 876, 879, M5-M10, Taiwan 55, 86, 99, Kwangsi 6-7, Sinkiang 162-173, 194-195.

**Type of 1938**

**Thin Paper Without Gum**

**1942-44 Unwmk. Engr. *Imperf.***

**506** A57 $10 red brown 1.75 1.25
**507** A57 $20 blue grn 1.75 1.00
**508** A57 $20 rose red ('44) 17.00 11.00
**509** A57 $30 dull vio ('43) 1.25 1.00
**510** A57 $40 rose red ('43) 1.40 1.00
**511** A57 $50 blue 2.00 1.25
**512** A57 $100 org brn ('43) 8.00 5.00

***Rouletted***

**513** A57 $5 lilac gray ('44) 14.00 *14.00*
*a.* Rouletted x perf. 12½ 25.00 30.00
**514** A57 $10 red brown 6.75 5.00
**515** A57 $50 blue 7.25 6.00
*a.* Rouletted x imperf. 6.50 —
*Nos. 506-515 (10)* 61.15 46.50

**1942-45 *Perf. 12½ to 15***

**516** A57 $4 dp blue ('43) .80 1.25
**517** A57 $5 lil gray ('43) 1.75 1.25
**518** A57 $10 red brown 1.75 1.25
**519** A57 $20 blue grn ('43) 1.75 1.00
**520** A57 $20 rose red ('45) 125.00 *175.00*
**521** A57 $30 dull vio ('43) 1.25 1.00
**522** A57 $40 rose ('43) 1.25 1.00
**523** A57 $50 blue 5.50 2.50
**524** A57 $100 org brn ('45) 120.00 *125.00*
*Nos. 516-524 (9)* 259.05 309.25

Beware of Nos. 508 and 512 with faked perforations that are offered as Nos. 520 and 524.

See surcharge note following No. 363.

No. 493 Overprinted in Black or Red

**1942**

**525** A62 (i) 16c (Bk) 85.00 100.00
(c) Hunan 500.00
(k) Western Szechwan 190.00 190.00
(m) Honan 850.00 850.00
(n) Shensi 250.00 260.00
*r.* Perf. 10½ (Kwangsi) 550.00
*s.* Inverted ovpt. (Shensi) 300.00
**526** A62 (d) 16c (R) 60.00 50.00
(bx) Anhwei 550.00 550.00
(e) Kiangsi 77.50 60.00
(f) Eastern Szechwan 120.00 75.00
(h) Fukien 300.00 225.00
(j) Kwangtung 675.00 675.00
(l) Yunnan 60.00 50.00

(o) Kweichow 275.00 200.00
(p) Hupeh, perf. 10½ 925.00 850.00
*r.* Perf. 10½ (E. Szechwan) 500.00
*s.* Horiz. pair, imperf. btwn (Yunnan) 650.00
*t.* Perf. 13 (Hupeh) — —

This overprint means "Domestic Ordinary Letter Surcharge Paid." It was applied in various sizes and types by 14 districts, 9 using red ink, 5 using black. (The Anhwei overprint comes in two types.) These overprinted stamps were briefly sold for $1.16 before the government ordered their sale suspended. The vertical bars and 50c surcharge of Nos. 527-528 were then applied.

### Nos. 525-526 Surcharged "50 cents" and 2 Vertical Bars in Black or Red

Anhwei — bx

Hunan — c

Kansu — d

Kiangsi — e

Eastern Szechwan — f

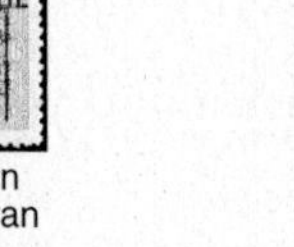

Fukien — h

Kwangsi — i

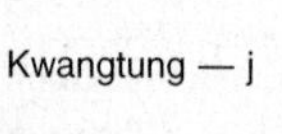

Kwangtung — j

Western Szechwan — k

Yunnan — l

Honan — m

Shensi — n

Kweichow — o

Hupeh — p

**1942** **Unwmk.**

**527** A62 50c on 16c (Bk) (c,f) 3.25 3.00
(i) Kwangsi 6.00 6.00
(k) Western Szechwan 11.00 8.50
(m) Honan 11.50 10.00
(n) Shensi 4.25 *5.00*
*r.* Inverted surch. (W. Szech.) 250.00
*s.* "k" surcharge on #493 350.00
**528** A62 50c on 16c (R) (p) 5.00 5.00
(bx) Anhwei 95.00 *300.00*
(d) Kansu 3.25 *5.00*
(e) Kiangsi 5.50 *10.00*
(h) Fukien 6.50 *8.50*
(j) Kwangtung 6.50 6.00
(l) Yunnan 6.50 8.00
(o) Kweichow 4.00 7.00
*r.* "o" surcharge inverted 300.00
*s.* "p" surch. on #526(f) 100.00 *47.50*

Many varieties of Nos. 527-528 exist, including narrow or wide spacing between the two top characters, or between the vertical bars, or both.

Surcharges on stamps perf. 10½ (basic No. 493a) usually sell at much higher prices.

### No. 493 Surcharged in Black, Red or Carmine

General Issue

Hunan — c50

Eastern Szechwan — f50

Chekiang — g50

Kwangsi — i50

Kwangtung — j50

Western Szechwan — k50

Honan — m50

Shensi — n50

Kweichow — o50

**1943** **Unwmk.**

**529** A62 50c on 16c (Bk) (m50) 11.00 11.00
(n50) Shensi 11.00 11.00
*r.* Perf. 11x13 (Shensi) 95.00
**530** A62 50c on 16c (C) 1.00 *2.00*
(c50) Hunan 3.00 6.00
(f50) Eastern Szechwan 3.75 2.75
(g50) Chekiang 42.50 *50.00*
(i50) Kwangsi 6.50 *7.50*
(j50) Kwangtung 5.00 *7.00*
(k50) Western Szechwan 5.00 *6.50*
(m50) Honan 8.50 *9.50*
(o50) Kweichow 11.00 13.00
*r.* Inverted surch. (Hunan) 65.00
*s.* "05" instead of "50" (Kweichow) 450.00

Many varieties of Nos. 529-530 exist, such as narrow or wide spacing horizontally or vertically between the overprinted Chinese characters.

Surcharges on No. 493a (perf. 10½) usually sell at much higher pricess.

The General Issue type, No. 530, was distributed to all head offices, which in turn supplied the post offices under their direction. It is surcharged in carmine; the other stamps listed under No. 530 are surcharged in red or carmine.

Hunan — c20

Kansu — d20

Kiangsi — e20

Eastern Szechwan — f20

Fukien — h20

Kwangsi — i20

Kwangtung — j20

Western Szechwan — k20

Yunnan — l20

Honan — m20

Shensi — n20

Kweichow — o20

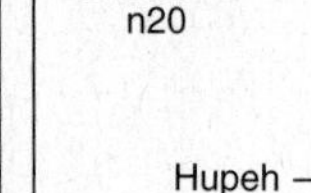

Hupeh — p20

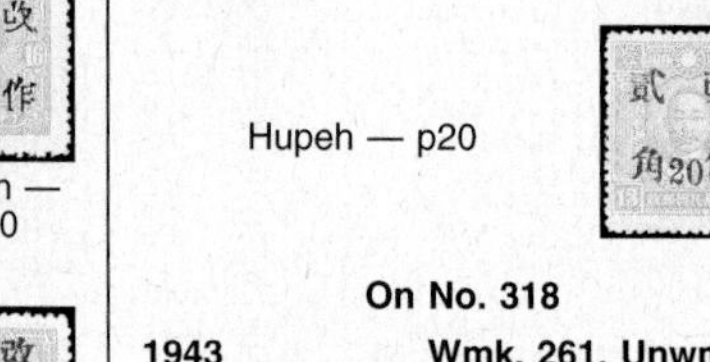

### On No. 318

**1943** **Wmk. 261, Unwmkd.**

**531** A45 20c on 13c (k20) 2.25 *5.00*
(d20) Kansu 2.25 *6.00*
(n20) Shensi 3.50 *5.50*
**532** A45 20c on 13c (i20;R) 1.00 *2.75*
(c20) Hunan 1,100.
(e20) Kiangsi 275.00
(j20) Kwangtung 85.00 95.00
(p20) Hupeh 2.00 *4.00*

### On No. 411

**533** A45 20c on 13c (n20) 2.25 *4.25*
(d20) Kansu 2.75 *7.50*
(k20) Western Szechwan 2.00 *7.50*
(l20) Yunnan 21.00 *35.00*
(m20) Honan 350.00
**534** A45 20c on 13c (p20;R) 1.75 *5.25*
(c20) Hunan 2.50 1.75
(e20) Kiangsi 9.00 2.10
(f20) Eastern Szechwan 2.50 *2.75*
(h20) Fukien 9.50 *11.00*
(i20) Kwangsi 2.00 *2.75*
(j20) Kwangtung 22.00 22.00
(o20) Kweichow 3.75 *3.25*

### On No. 430

**535** A45 20c on 13c (l20) 2.25 *4.75*
(d20) Kansu 2.25 *2.75*
(k20) Western Szechwan 35.00 *42.50*
(m20) Honan 9.50 *9.25*
(n20) Shensi 3.50 *5.50*
**536** A45 20c on 13c (f20;i20;R) 2.25 *3.50*
(c20) Hunan 11.00 *9.75*
(e20) Kiangsi 4.50 *4.00*
(j20) Kwangtung 2.25 *2.75*
(o20) Kweichow 2.25 *10.00*
(p20) Hupeh 2.25 *4.00*

### On No. 357

**537** A57 20c on 16c (k20) 2.25 *2.75*
(c20) Hunan 3.50 *13.50*
(d20) Kansu 3.50 *13.50*
(m20) Honan 11.00 *17.50*
(n20) Shensi 3.50 *13.50*
**538** A57 20c on 16c (e20, o20; R) 2.25 *13.50*
(c20) Hunan 11.00 *17.50*
(i20) Kwangsi 11.00 *13.50*
(j20) Kwangtung 52.50 *55.00*

### On No. 413

**539** A46 20c on 17c (c20;R) 2.75 *4.25*
(i20) Kwangsi 2.25 *2.75*
(j20) Kwangtung 30.00 *42.50*

### On No. 432

**540** A46 20c on 17c (k20) 3.50 *5.50*
(d20) Kansu 3.50 *6.50*
(m20) Honan 40.00 *47.50*
**541** A46 20c on 17c (e20;R) 2.25 *5.50*
(j20) Kwangtung 3.75 *15.00*
(o20) Kweichow 2.50 *6.75*

### On No. 456

**542** A59 20c on 17c (m20) 210.00 *275.00*
**543** A59 20c on 17c (c20;R) 18.00 30.00

### On No. 415

**544** A45 20c on 21c (e20;R) 11.00 *12.00*

### On No. 434

**545** A45 20c on 21c (c20, k20) 2.25 *4.00*
(d20) Kansu 2.50 *6.75*
(l20) Yunnan 2.50 *4.00*
(m20) Honan 2.50 *9.25*

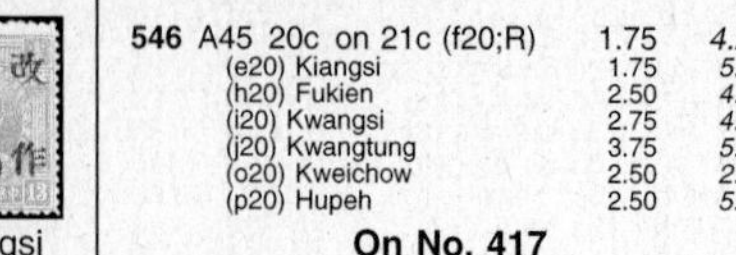

**546** A45 20c on 21c (f20;R) 1.75 *4.25*
(e20) Kiangsi 1.75 *5.50*
(h20) Fukien 2.50 *4.75*
(i20) Kwangsi 2.75 *4.00*
(j20) Kwangtung 3.75 *5.00*
(o20) Kweichow 2.50 *2.75*
(p20) Hupeh 2.50 *5.50*

### On No. 417

**547** A46 20c on 28c (e20;R) 775.00 *725.00*

### On No. 436

**548** A46 20c on 28c (l20) 3.50 *6.25*
(d20) Kansu 17.50 *24.00*
(k20) Western Szechwan 25.00 *65.00*
(m20) Honan 40.00 *47.50*
**549** A46 20c on 28c (e20;R) 1.75 *3.25*
(c20) Hunan 1.90 *4.75*
(h20) Fukien 3.50 *4.75*
(i20) Kwangsi 4.75 *4.75*
(j20) Kwangtung 4.25 *6.25*
(o20) Kweichow 4.75 *4.75*

Many varieties of Nos. 531-549 exist, such as narrow or wide spacing between the overprinted Chinese characters, and "20" higher or lower than illustrated.

### Type of 1942-43 Pacheng Printing

**1944-46** **Unwmk.** ***Perf. 12***

**Without Gum**

**550** A62 30c chocolate .40 *13.00*
**551** A62 $1 green 4.00 *5.00*
**552** A62 $2 dk vio brn .30 .25
*a.* Imperf., pair 30.00 25.00
**553** A62 $2 dk bl grn .30 *2.00*
*a.* Perf. 10½ 47.50 35.00
**554** A62 $2 deep blue 1.75 *6.00*
**555** A62 $3 lt yellow 1.60 *2.00*
**556** A62 $4 violet brn .30 *2.00*
*a.* Imperf., pair 60.00
**557** A62 $5 car ('46) .30 *1.00*
*a.* Perf. 10½ 75.00 75.00
**558** A62 $6 gray vio ('45) .30 *.40*
**559** A62 $10 red brn ('45) .30 .25
*a.* Imperf., pair 60.00
**560** A62 $20 dp ultra ('46) .30 .25
**561** A62 $50 dk green ('46) 4.00 .25
**562** A62 $70 lilac ('46) 5.00 .25
**563** A62 $100 lt brown ('46) .30 .25
*Nos. 550-563 (14)* 19.15 *32.90*

In the Pacheng printing of the Central Trust type stamps, the secret mark "C" has been added below the lower left foliate ornament beneath the sun emblem. On the $3, it is below the right ornament. New values also include a "P" at right of sun emblem on the $6 and $10, and at right of necktie on the $20.

Seven different varieties of paper were used in the printing of Nos. 550-563. Some values exist on laid paper with elephant watermark in sheet.

See surcharge note following No. 505.

Dr. Sun Yat-sen — A63

**1944-46** **Unwmk.** **Typo.** ***Perf. 12½***

**Without Gum**

**565** A63 40c brown red .35 .35
**566** A63 $2 gray brown .35 .35
**567** A63 $3 red .35 .35
*a.* $3 orange red 4.00 4.00
**568** A63 $3 lt red brn ('45) .95 .75
**569** A63 $6 pale lilac gray ('45) .35 .45
**570** A63 $10 dull lake ('45) .35 .35
**571** A63 $20 rose ('45) .35 .35
*a.* Perf. 16 400.00 400.00
**572** A63 $50 lt brown ('46) .45 .55
**573** A63 $70 rose vio ('46) .55 .55
*Nos. 565-573 (9)* 4.05 4.05

For surcharges see Nos. 772, 774, 828, 833, 835, 836A, 839, 842, 851, 864, 868, 873-875, 877, 880. Taiwan 81, 98, Sinkiang 200-201.

Allegory of Savings — A64

**1944-45** **Engr.** ***Perf. 13***

**Without Gum**

**574** A64 $40 indigo ('45) .35 *.90*
**575** A64 $50 yellow grn ('45) .35 .35
**576** A64 $100 yellow brn .35 .35
**577** A64 $200 dk green ('45) .35 .35
*Nos. 574-577 (4)* 1.40 1.95

All four values were printed on thick paper; the first three were also printed on thin paper.

For surcharges see Szechwan Nos. F1, F3.

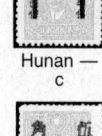

A65

**1944, Dec. 25** **Litho.**

**Without Gum**

**578** A65 $2 deep green .70 *2.00*
**579** A65 $5 fawn .70 *2.00*
**580** A65 $6 dull rose vio 1.40 *3.50*
**581** A65 $10 violet blue 2.75 *7.00*
**582** A65 $20 carmine 5.25 *9.00*
*Nos. 578-582 (5)* 10.80 23.50

50th anniversary of the Kuomintang.

Dr. Sun Yat-sen — A66

**1945, Mar. 12** **Without Gum**

**583** A66 $2 gray green .45 *1.75*
**584** A66 $5 red brown .55 *1.75*
**585** A66 $6 dk vio blue .65 *2.25*
**586** A66 $10 lt blue 1.00 *1.75*
**587** A66 $20 rose 1.25 *4.00*
**588** A66 $30 buff 2.00 *6.00*
*Nos. 583-588 (6)* 5.90 17.50

Death of Dr. Sun Yat-sen, 20th anniv.

Dr. Sun Yat-sen — A67

**1945-46** **Without Gum** ***Perf. 12½***

**589** A67 $2 green .30 .35
**590** A67 $5 dull green .30 .35
**591** A67 $10 dk blue .30 .35
*a.* Imperf., pair 120.00
**592** A67 $20 carmine ('46) .30 .35
*a.* Imperf., pair 120.00
*Nos. 589-592 (4)* 1.20 1.40

For surcharges see Nos. 695, 697, 837, 855, Taiwan 58, 82, 87-88.

Statue of Liberty, Map of China, Flags of Great Britain, China and United States, and Chiang Kai-shek — A68

**Unwmk.**

**1945, July 7** **Engr.** ***Perf. 12***

**Flags in Dark Blue and Red**

**593** A68 $1 deep blue .50 *1.00*
**594** A68 $2 dull green .50 *1.00*
**595** A68 $5 olive gray .50 *1.00*
**596** A68 $6 brown 1.00 *2.00*
**597** A68 $10 rose lilac 5.00 *7.00*
**598** A68 $20 carmine rose 5.00 *9.50*
*Nos. 593-598 (6)* 12.50 *21.50*

Signing of a Treaty in 1943 between Great Britain, the US and China.

Pres. Lin Sen (1864-1943) — A69

**1945, Aug.** **Unwmk.** ***Perf. 12***

**599** A69 $1 dp ultra & blk .65 *4.00*
**600** A69 $2 myrtle grn & blk .65 *4.00*
**601** A69 $5 red & blk .65 *4.00*
**602** A69 $6 purple & blk .90 *4.00*
**603** A69 $10 choc & blk 4.00 *12.00*
**604** A69 $20 olive grn & blk 4.25 *12.00*
*Nos. 599-604 (6)* 11.10 *40.00*

Pres. Chiang Kai-shek — A70

**1945, Oct. 10**

**Flag in Rose Red and Violet Blue**

**605** A70 $2 green .45 *2.00*
**606** A70 $4 dark blue .50 *2.00*
**607** A70 $5 olive gray .50 *3.00*
**608** A70 $6 bister brown 1.50 *4.00*
**609** A70 $10 gray 4.00 *8.00*
**610** A70 $20 red violet 5.00 *8.00*
*Nos. 605-610 (6)* 11.95 27.00

Inauguration of Chiang Kai-shek as president, Oct. 10, 1943.

President Chiang Kai-shek — A71

**1945, Oct. 10** **Typo.** ***Perf. 13***

**Without Gum**

**Flag in Carmine and Blue**

**611** A71 $20 green & blue .30 .25
**612** A71 $50 bister brn & bl .50 .50
**613** A71 $100 blue .50 .40
**614** A71 $300 rose red & blue .50 .40
*Nos. 611-614 (4)* 1.80 1.55

Victory of the Allied Nations over Japan.

**C. N. C. Surcharges**

The green surcharges on Nos. 615 to 621, and the surcharges on Nos. 647 to 721, and 768 to 774 represent Chinese National Currency and were applied at Shanghai.

Stamps of 1938-41 Srchd. in Black with Chinese Characters and New Value in Checkered Rectangle at Bottom, Resrchd. in Green

**1945** ***Perf. 12, 12½***

**615** A57 10c on $20 on 3c (#350) .30 *5.00*
**616** A46 15c on $30 on 2c (#423) .30 *5.00*
*a.* Horiz. pair, imperf. between 90.00
*b.* Vert. pair, imperf. between 85.00
**617** A59 25c on $50 on 1c (#450) .30 *5.00*
**618** A57 50c on $100 on 3c (#350) .30 *5.00*
**619** A40 $1 on $200 on 1c (#422) .30 *5.00*
*a.* Horiz. pair, imperf. between 90.00
**620** A57 $2 on $400 on 3c (#350) .30 *5.00*
**621** A59 $5 on $1000 on 1c (#450) .30 *5.00*
*Nos. 615-621 (7)* 2.10 *35.00*

The black (first) surcharges on Nos. 615 to 621 represent Nanking puppet government currency.

In the green surcharge, the characters at the left express the new value and are either two or four in number.

Types of 1932-34, Re-engraved, and Srchd. in Green with Horiz. Bar and Four or Five Chinese Characters and Ovptd. in Black

***Perf. 14***

**622** A47 $10 on 20c brown red 10.00 *12.00*
**623** A47 $20 on 40c orange 25.00 *29.00*
*a.* Green surcharge inverted 150.00 85.00
**624** A48 $50 on 30c violet brn 18.50 *22.00*
*Nos. 622-624 (3)* 53.50 *63.00*

These provisional surcharges were applied in Honan in National currency to stamps of the Hwa Pei (North China) government. The black overprint reads: "Hwa Pei."

The two-character "Hwa Pei" overprint was applied to various stamps in 1941-43 by the North China puppet government. See Nos. 8N1-8N53, 8N60-8N84.

Dr. Sun Yat-sen — A72

**1945, Dec.** **Typo.** ***Perf. 12***

**Without Gum**

**625** A72 $20 dp carmine .30 .25
**626** A72 $30 dp blue .30 .25
**627** A72 $40 orange .60 1.25
**628** A72 $50 green 1.00 .35
**629** A72 $100 dk brown .30 .25
**630** A72 $200 brown violet .30 .25
*Nos. 625-630 (6)* 2.80 2.60

For surcharges see Nos. 810, 829, 838, 865, J110-J119, Taiwan 75, Kwangsi F2, Szechwan F2, F4, Yunnan 66-67, 71.

**Type of 1931-37**

***Perf. 12½, 13x12½, 13½***

**1946** **Unwmk.**

**631** A37 $1 dk violet .30 *1.50*
**632** A37 $2 olive green .30 *3.00*
**633** A37 $20 brt yellow grn .30 *.55*
**634** A37 $30 chocolate .30 *.50*
**635** A37 $50 red orange .30 *.50*
*Nos. 631-635 (5)* 1.50 6.05

$4 blue and $5 red values were prepared but not issued. Value $400.

For surcharges see Nos. 678, 684, 689-690, 768, 843, Northeastern Provinces No. 44.

Dr. Sun Yat-sen — A73

**1946-47** **Engr.** ***Perf. 14***

**Without Gum**

**636** A73 $20 carmine 6.25 .25
**637** A73 $30 dk blue ('47) .35 .25
**638** A73 $50 purple .25 .25
**639** A73 $70 red org ('47) 18.50 3.00
**640** A73 $100 dk carmine .30 .25
**641** A73 $200 olive grn ('47) .30 .25
**642** A73 $500 brt bl grn ('47) .35 .25
**643** A73 $700 red brown ('47) .30 .25
**644** A73 $1000 rose lake .35 .35
**645** A73 $3000 blue 1.00 .40
**646** A73 $5000 dp green & ver 1.00 .40
*Nos. 636-646 (11)* 28.95 5.90

For surcharges see Nos. 679, 769, 775, 823, 837A, 844-845, 856, 866, 875A, 878, Taiwan 18, 23-28, 54, 76-77, 100, Northeastern Provinces 41-43, Fukien 5-6, Hunan 1, E1, Kwangsi 11, F2, Szechwan F5-F8, Sinkiang 202-204, People's Republic of China 3L53, 3L67-3L68, 6L28.

Stamps of 1932-41 Surcharged in Black

***Perf. 12½, 13, 13x12, 14***

**Wmk. 261**

**647** A45 $20 on 8c (#409) .30 *2.00*
**648** A39 $30 on ½c (#402) 4,000.
**649** A45 $50 on 21c (#415) .30 *.25*
**650** A45 $70 on 13c (#411) .30 .25
**651** A46 $100 on 28c (#417) 1.00 *.65*

**Unwmk.**

**652** A39 $3 on 2½c (#424) 16.00 *8.00*
**653** A48 $10 on 15c (#431) .30 .25
**654** A45 $20 on 8c (#428) .30 .25
**655** A47 $20 on 20c (#433) .35 .35
**656** A39 $30 on ½c (#421) .30 .25
**657** A45 $50 on 21c (#434) .40 *.55*
**657A** A45 $70 on 13c (#318) 210.00 *250.00*
**658** A45 $70 on 13c (#430) .40 *.55*
**659** A46 $100 on 28c (#436) .40 .40

Forgeries of No. 648 exist.

Stamps and Types of 1931-1946 Surcharged in Black or Carmine

***Perf. 12½, 13, 14***

**1946-47** **Wmk. 261**

**660** A57 $50 on 5c green (#392) .35 .85
**661** A57 $50 on 5c ol grn (#393) 25.00 20.00
**662** A48 $50 on 5c dl red org (#408) .30 *1.25*
**663** A40 $100 on 1c org (#403) .30 *1.10*

***Perf. 12, 12½, 12½x13, 13, 14***

**1946-47** **Unwmk.**

**664** A57 $20 on 3c (#350) .30 *.35*
**665** A45 $20 on 8c (#428) .30 .25
**666** A57 $50 on 3c (#350) .30 .25
**667** A57 $50 on 5c (#352) .30 .25
**668** A57 $50 on 5c (#382) .95 *1.75*
**669** A48 $50 on 5c (#427) .30 .25
**670** A59 $50 on 5c (#452) .30 .25
**671** A62 $50 on $1 (#500) .30 .25
**672** A40 $100 on 1c (#422) .30 .25
*a.* Without secret mark (#422a) 67.50 67.50
**673** A57 $100 on 3c (#350) .30 .25
**674** A57 $100 on 8c (#353) 14.00 14.00
**675** A57 $100 on 8c (#369) 2.00 .35
**676** A57 $100 on 8c (#383) .35 .35
*a.* Without "star" in uniform button (No. 383a) 25.00 16.00
**677** A59 $100 on 8c (#454) .30 .25
**678** A37 $100 on $1 (#631) .30 .25
**679** A73 $100 on $20 (#636) .35 .35
**680** A57 $200 on 10c (#354) .75 .25
**681** A57 $200 on 10c (#384) .40 1.10
**682** A37 $200 on $4 dl bl .50 .25
*a.* Double surcharge 16.00
**683** A62 $250 on $1.50 (#501) .30 *2.50*
*a.* Perf. 11 250.00 250.00
**684** A37 $250 on $2 (#632) .50 .25
**685** A37 $250 on $5 car .50 .25
**686** A57 $300 on 10c (#354) .30 .25
**687** A59 $300 on 10c (#455) .30 .25
**688** A57 $500 on 3c (#350) .50 .25
**689** A37 $500 on $20 (#633) .30 .25
**690** A37 $800 on $30 (#634) .30 .25
**691** A37 $1000 on 2c (#297) .65 .35
**692** A62 $1000 on $2 (#552) .30 .25
*a.* Imperf., pair 30.00 20.00
**693** A62 $1000 on $2 (#553) .30 .25
**694** A62 $1000 on $2 (#554) .30 *.55*
**695** A67 $1000 on $2 (#589) .30 .25
**696** A62 $2000 on $5 (#557) .30 .25
**697** A67 $2000 on $5 dl grn (C) (#590) .30 .25
*Nos. 664-697 (34)* 28.05 27.65

Nos. 660-697 have a double row of dots in the surcharge box frame.

Nos. 682 and 685 were not issued without surcharge. No. 682 is perf. 13x13½; No. 685, perf. 12x12½.

The characters at the left express the new value and vary in number.

Stamps of 1938-41 Surcharged in Black

***Perf. 12, 12½, 13, 14***

**1946** **Wmk. 261**

**698** A45 $20 on 8c (#409) 250.00 190.00
**699** A57 $50 on 5c (#392) 3.00 *3.00*
**700** A57 $50 on 5c (#393) 5.00 *8.00*

**1946-48** **Unwmk.**

**700A** A57 $20 on 5c (#381) 900.00
**701** A57 $20 on 8c (#353) .30 .35
**702** A57 $20 on 8c (#369) .35 .35
**703** A57 $20 on 8c (#383) .30 .50
*a.* Without "star" in uniform button (No. 383a) 4.50 4.50
*b.* Inverted surcharge 20.00
*c.* Dbl. surch., one on back 32.50 32.50
*d.* Double surcharge 32.50
**704** A45 $20 on 8c (#428) .30 .25
*a.* Double surcharge 22.50
**705** A59 $20 on 8c (#453) .30 .25
**706** A59 $20 on 8c (#454) .30 .25
*a.* Inverted surcharge 13.00
*b.* Double surcharge 13.00
**707** A57 $50 on 5c (#351) 7.25 6.75
**708** A57 $50 on 5c (#352) .30 .25
*a.* Inverted surcharge 27.50
**709** A57 $50 on 5c (#381) .70 .70
**710** A57 $50 on 5c (#382) .50 .35

711 A48 $50 on 5c (#427) .30 .25
a. Inverted surcharge 27.50
712 A59 $50 on 5c (#452) .50 .25
a. Double surcharge 16.00

Stamps of 1939-41 Surcharged in Blue or Red

**1946 Wmk. 261 *Perf. 12½***
713 A40 $10 on 1c org (#403) .30 .25
a. Inverted surcharge 40.00
714 A48 $20 on 3c dp yel brn (#406) 800.00 800.00

Forgeries of No. 714 exist. Expertizing is recommended.

**1946 Unwmk. *Perf. 12, 12½, 13***
715 A40 $10 on 1c org (#422) .30 .25
a. Without secret mark (#422a) 10.00 12.00
b. Inverted surcharge 8.00 10.00
716 A59 $10 on 1c org (#450) .30 .25
a. Double surcharge 27.50
717 A57 $20 on 2c ol grn (R) (#368) .30 .25
718 A59 $20 on 2c brt ultra (R) (#451) .30 .25
a. Inverted surcharge 20.00
b. Double surcharge 16.00
719 A57 $20 on 3c dl cl (#350) .30 .25
a. Double surcharge 22.50
720 A48 $20 on 3c dp yel brn (#425) .30 .35
721 A39 $30 on 4c pale vio (R) (#426) .30 .25
a. Inverted surcharge 9.00
*Nos. 715-721 (7)* 2.10 1.85

President Chiang Kai-shek — A74

***Perf. 10½-11½***
**1946, Oct. 31 Engr. Unwmk.**
722 A74 $20 carmine 3.00 3.00
723 A74 $30 green 3.00 3.00
724 A74 $50 vermilion 3.00 3.00
725 A74 $100 yellow grn 5.00 5.00
726 A74 $200 yellow org 5.00 5.00
727 A74 $300 magenta 5.00 5.00
*Nos. 722-727 (6)* 24.00 24.00

60th birthday of Chiang Kai-shek.
Printed by Dah Yeh Printing Co.; the earlier ones are gumless, the later ones gummed.
For stamps of Type A74 with additional characters on either side of the portrait see Taiwan Nos. 29-34, Northeastern Provinces 30-35.

**Printed by Dah Tung Book Co.**
**Without Gum**
***Perf. 14***
*722a* A74 $20 carmine 1.10 1.50
*723a* A74 $30 green 1.10 1.50
*724a* A74 $50 vermilion 1.10 1.50
*725a* A74 $100 yellow green 3.00 3.00
*726a* A74 $200 yellow orange 2.00 2.00
*727a* A74 $300 magenta 2.50 2.50
*Nos. 722a-727a (6)* 10.80 12.00

Assembly House, Nanking — A75

**1946, Nov. 15 Litho. *Perf. 14***
**Without Gum**
728 A75 $20 green .75 .40
729 A75 $30 blue .75 .40
730 A75 $50 dk brown .75 .40
a. Horiz. pair, imperf. between 95.00 95.00
731 A75 $100 carmine .75 .40
*Nos. 728-731 (4)* 3.00 1.60

Convening of National Assembly.
For surcharges see Taiwan Nos. 10-13, Northeastern Provinces 26-29.

Entrance to Dr. Sun Yat-sen Mausoleum — A76

**1947, May 5 Engr.**
732 A76 $100 dp green .35 .35
733 A76 $200 deep blue .35 .35
734 A76 $250 carmine .35 .35
735 A76 $350 lt brown .35 .35
736 A76 $400 dp claret .35 .35
*Nos. 732-736 (5)* 1.75 1.75

First anniversary of return of Chinese National Government to Nanking.
See Taiwan Nos. 35-39, Northeastern Provinces 36-40.

Dr. Sun Yat-sen — A77

**1947 *Perf. 12½, 11½x12½***
737 A77 $500 olive green .30 .25
738 A77 $1000 green & car .30 .25
739 A77 $2000 dp blue & red brn .30 .25
740 A77 $5000 org red & blk .30 .25
*Nos. 737-740 (4)* 1.20 1.00

For surcharge see Szechwan No. 50.

Confucius A78

Confucius' Lecturing School A79

Tomb of Confucius A80

Temple of Confucius A81

**1947, Aug. 27 Litho. *Perf. 14***
**Without Gum**
741 A78 $500 carmine rose .60 *.65*
**Engr.**
742 A79 $800 yellow brown .50 *.80*
743 A80 $1250 blue green .50 *1.25*
744 A81 $1800 blue .50 *1.90*
*Nos. 741-744 (4)* 2.10 4.60

Sun Yat-sen and Plum Blossoms — A82

**1947-48 Engr. *Perf. 14***
**Without Gum**
745 A82 $150 dk blue .30 *.25*
746 A82 $250 dp lilac .35 .25
747 A82 $500 blue grn .30 .25
748 A82 $1000 red .30 .25
749 A82 $2000 vermilion .30 .25
750 A82 $3000 blue .30 .25
751 A82 $4000 gray ('48) .30 .25
752 A82 $5000 dk brown .30 .25
753 A82 $6000 rose lil ('48) .30 .25
754 A82 $7000 lt red brn ('48) .30 .25
755 A82 $10,000 dp blue & car 1.10 .25
756 A82 $20,000 car & yel grn .35 .25
757 A82 $50,000 grn & dk bl 1.25 .25
758 A82 $100,000 dl yel & ol grn ('48) 1.80 2.00
759 A82 $200,000 vio brn & dp bl ('48) 2.25 .45
760 A82 $300,000 sep & org brn ('48) 2.25 .55
761 A82 $500,000 dk Prus grn & sep ('48) 3.00 .55
*Nos. 745-761 (17)* 15.05 6.80

See Nos. 788-799. For similar type see Formosa A1. For surcharges see Nos. 770, 804-806, 821-822, 840-841, 858-859, 869, 871, 880A-880B, 885A-885E, 1025-1036, Taiwan 56-57, 59, 89, Fukien 1-4, 7-12, 19-23, Hunan 2-5, C1, F1, Kiangsi 1-3, C1, E1, F1-F2, Kwangsi 8-10, 12-17, Shensi 1-2, C1, E1, Szechwan 24-49, Yunnan 61-62, 69, 205-207, People's Republic of China 3L69-3L70, 3L76, 4L63-4L64, 6L22, 6L27, 6L29, 6L32.

Chinese Flag and Map of Taiwan — A83

**1947, Oct. 25 With Gum**
762 A83 $500 carmine .35 *1.00*
763 A83 $1250 deep green .35 *1.00*

Restoration of Taiwan to China, 2nd anniv.

Mobile Post Office — A84

Street-Corner Branch Post Office — A85

**1947, Nov. 5**
764 A84 $500 carmine .30 *.50*
765 A85 $1000 lilac .30 *1.00*
766 A85 $1250 green .30 *.85*
767 A84 $1800 deep blue .30 *1.10*
*Nos. 764-767 (4)* 1.20 3.45

Stamps and Type of 1943-47 Surcharged in Black or Green

**1947-48 Unwmk. *Perf. 12½, 13, 14***
768 A37 $500 on $20 brt yel grn (#633) .30 .25
769 A73 $1250 on $70 red org (#639) .30 .25
770 A82 $1800 on $350 yel org .30 .25
771 A62 $2000 on $3 dk yel ('48) (#503) .50 .25
772 A63 $2000 on $3 red (#567) .30 .25
a. On #567a 6.50 2.25
773 A62 $3000 on $3 lt yel ('48) (#555) .30 .25
774 A63 $3000 on $3 lt red brn (G) ('48) (#568) .30 .25
*Nos. 768-774 (7)* 2.30 1.75

Nos. 768-774 have a single row of dots in the surcharge box frame.
The characters at the left express the new value and vary in number.

No. 640 Surcharged

**1948, Aug. *Perf. 14***
775 A73 $5000 on $100 dk car 7.00 *80.00*

No. 775 received its surcharge in Kwangsi for use in that province.

Map of China and Mail-carrying Vehicles A86

Rural Mail Delivery A87

Early and Modern Mail Transportation A88

**1947, Dec. 16 Engr. *Perf. 12***
776 A86 $100 violet .30 *1.00*
777 A87 $200 brt green .30 *1.00*
778 A87 $300 red brown .30 *1.00*
779 A88 $400 scarlet .30 *1.00*
780 A88 $500 brt vio blue .30 *1.00*
*Nos. 776-780 (5)* 1.50 5.00

Chinese Postal Administration, 50th anniv.

National Assembly Building and New Constitution — A89

**1947, Dec. 25 *Perf. 14***
**Without Gum**
781 A89 $2000 brt red .50 .60
782 A89 $3000 blue .50 .60
783 A89 $5000 deep green .50 .60
*Nos. 781-783 (3)* 1.50 1.80

1st anniv. of the adoption of China's new constitution, Dec. 25, 1946.

Chinese Stamps of 1947 and 1912 — A90

***Perf. 14, Imperf.***
**1948, Mar. 20 Litho.**
**Without Gum**
784 A90 $5000 dk car rose 1.00 *4.00*
a. Vert. pair, imperf. btwn 40.00
785 A90 $5000 dk green 1.00 *4.00*
a. Vert. pair, imperf. btwn 40.00

Stamp exhibitions at Nanking, Mar. 20 (No. 784), and at Shanghai, May 19 (No. 785).

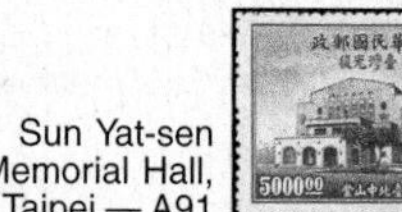

Sun Yat-sen Memorial Hall, Taipei — A91

**1948, Apr. 28 Engr. *Perf. 14***
786 A91 $5000 violet .30 *1.25*
787 A91 $10000 red .30 *2.00*

Restoration of Formosa to China, 3rd anniv.

**Sun Yat-sen Type of 1947-48**
**1948 Without Gum**
788 A82 $20000 rose pink .50 .35
789 A82 $30000 chocolate .30 .25
790 A82 $40000 green .30 .25
791 A82 $50000 dp blue .30 .25
792 A82 $100000 dull grn .30 .25
793 A82 $200000 brn vio .75 .25
794 A82 $300000 yel grn 2.75 1.00
795 A82 $500000 lil rose 1.25 .25
796 A82 $1000000 claret .75 .25
797 A82 $2000000 vermilion 1.50 .25
798 A82 $3000000 ol bis 3.00 .55
799 A82 $5000000 ultra 6.00 .90
*Nos. 788-799 (12)* 17.70 4.80

Zeros for "cents" omitted.
For surcharges see Nos. 841, 871, 880A-880B, 885A-885E, 1025-1028, 1031-1036.

Early Ship and Modern Hai Tien — A92

Passenger Ship Kiang Ya — A93

**1948, Aug. 16 Without Gum**
800 A92 $20000 blue .60 *1.75*
801 A92 $30000 rose lilac .60 *2.00*
802 A93 $40000 yel brown .60 *2.75*
803 A93 $60000 vermilion .60 *2.75*
*Nos. 800-803 (4)* 2.40 9.25

75th anniversary of the China Merchants' Steam Navigation Company.

Type of 1947-48 Surcharged in Black

**1948 Unwmk. *Perf. 14***
804 A82 $4000 on $100 car .30 *25.00*
805 A82 $5000 on $100 car .30 .25
806 A82 $8000 on $700 red brn .35 *.90*
*Nos. 804-806 (3)* .95 26.15

Stamps of 1942-46 Surcharged in Black or Red

**1948** ***Perf. 12½, 13***

**807** A62 $5000 on $1 (#500) .30 .25
**808** A62 $5000 on $1 (#551) 20.00 *20.00*
**809** A62 $5000 on $2 (#502) .30 .25
**810** A72 $10000 on $20 (#625) .30 .25
**811** A62 $20000 on 10c (#492) .30 .25
**812** A62 $20000 on 50c (#498;R) .30 *.50*
**813** A62 $30000 on 30c (#496) .30 *.50*
*a.* Perf. 10½ 22.00 22.00
*Nos. 807-813 (7)* 21.80 22.00

Nos. 492, 556 and 558 Surcharged in Black or Carmine

**1948**

**814** A62 $15,000 on 10c dp grn .30 .25
**815** A62 $15,000 on $4 vio brn .30 .25
**816** A62 $15,000 on $6 gray vio (C) .30 .25
*Nos. 814-816 (3)* .90 .75

No. 498, 494 and 504 Surcharged in Black

**1948** **Unwmk.** ***Perf. 11½, 13***

**817** A62 $15,000 on 50c, perf. 13 .30 *.50*
*a.* Perf. 11½ 10.00 *15.00*
**818** A62 $40,000 on 20c dk ol grn .30 .90
*a.* Perf. 11 10.00 7.50
**819** A62 $60,000 on $4 red brn .45 *.50*
*Nos. 817-819 (3)* 1.05 1.90

**Gold Yuan Surcharges**

(Nos. 820-885E)

Stamps of 1942-47 Surcharged in Black, Carmine or Red

**1948** ***Perf. 14, 13, 11***

**820** A62 ½c on 30c (#496) .30 *5.00*
**821** A82 ½c on $500 (Bk) (#747) .30 .25
**822** A82 ½c on $500 (C) (#747) .30 *.90*
**823** A73 1c on $20 (#636) .30 *2.25*
**824** A62 2c on $1.50 (R) (#501) .30 *3.25*
**825** A62 3c on $5 (#505) .30 *3.25*
**826** A62 4c on $1 (#499) .30 *3.25*
**827** A62 5c on 50c (#498) .30 *1.00*
*a.* Perf. 11 6.50 *8.00*
*Nos. 820-827 (8)* 2.40 *19.15*

On No. 820-827, the position of the surcharged denomination and "Gold Yuan" characters varies, the aim being to obliterate the original denomination.

Stamps of 1940-48 Surcharged in Black, Violet, Carmine, Blue or Green

***Perf. 12, 12½, 13, 14, 12½x13***

**1948-49**

**828** A63 5c on $20 (#571) .30 *1.10*
**829** A72 5c on $30 (C) (#626) .30 *2.00*
*a.* Double surcharge 17.50
**830** A57 10c on 2c (#368) .30 *1.75*
**831** A39 10c on 2½c (#424) .30 *1.10*
**832** A62 10c on 25c (V) (#495) .30 *1.25*
**833** A63 10c on 40c (#565) .30 *1.40*
**834** A62 10c on $1 (#500) .30 *.35*
**834A** A62 10c on $1 (#551) 275.00 *250.00*
**835** A63 10c on $2 (#566) .30 .25
**836** A62 10c on $20 (C) (#560) .30 .25
**836A** A63 10c on $20 (#571) 300.00 *300.00*
**837** A67 10c on $20 (#592) .30 .25
**837A** A73 10c on $20 (#636) 1.00 *3.50*
**838** A72 10c on $30 (C) (#626) .30 *1.50*
**839** A63 10c on $70 (#573) .30 .50
*a.* Double surcharge 15.00
**840** A82 10c on $7000 (#754) 1.00 1.00
**841** A82 10c on $20,000 (#788) .30 *4.75*
**842** A63 20c on $6 (#569) .30 *.35*
**843** A37 20c on $30 (#634) .45 *4.75*
**844** A73 20c on $30 (C) (#637) .65 *3.75*
**845** A73 20c on $100 (#640) .30 *3.00*
*a.* Inverted surcharge 22.00
*b.* Double surcharge 16.00
**846** A39 50c on ½c (#312) 75.00 75.00
**847** A39 50c on ½c (#421) .30 *.65*
*a.* Inverted surcharge 30.00
**848** A62 50c on 20c (#494) .30 *2.00*
**849** A62 50c on 30c (Bl) (#496) .30 *3.00*
**850** A62 50c on 40c (V) (#497) .30 *2.00*
*a.* Perf. 11 9.00 *10.00*
**851** A63 50c on 40c (V) (#565) .30 *1.00*
**852** A62 50c on $4 (#556) 1.00 *3.50*
**853** A62 50c on $4 (Bl) (#556) .30 *2.00*
**854** A62 50c on $20 (C) (#560) .30 *2.00*
**855** A67 50c on $20 (V) (#592) .50 *1.50*
**856** A73 50c on $20 (#636) .30 *1.25*
**857** A62 50c on $70 (C) (#562) .30 .30
**858** A82 50c on $6000 (#753) 2.00 *3.50*
**859** A82 50c on $6000 (Bl) (#753) .30 *1.50*
**860** A62 $1 on 30c (#550) .30 .25
*a.* Perf. 11 22.00 22.00
**861** A62 $1 on 40c (#497) .30 .25
*a.* Perf. 11 4.00 4.00
**862** A63 $1 on $1 (#499) .55 *2.00*
**863** A62 $1 on $5 (#557) .70 .40
**864** A63 $2 on $2 (R) (#566) .30 *1.00*
**865** A72 $2 on $20 (#625) .30 .25
**866** A73 $2 on $100 (#640) .30 .25
**867** A46 $5 on 17c (#432) .90 .90
**868** A63 $5 on $2 (#566) .30 .25
**869** A82 $5 on $3000 (C) (#750) .30 *1.50*
**870** A47 $8 on 20c (#433) .50 .50
**871** A82 $8 on $30,000 (C) (#789) .30 *2.50*
**872** A47 $10 on 40c (#438) 1.25 1.00
**873** A63 $10 on $2 (G) (#566) .30 .35
**874** A63 $10 on $2 (C) (#566) .30 .25
**875** A63 $20 on $2 (C) (#566) .30 .25
**875A** A73 $20 on $20 (#636) 4.75 3.00
**876** A62 $50 on 30c (#496) .30 *.30*
**877** A63 $50 on $2 (Bl) (#566) .30 .25
**878** A73 $80 on $20 (#636) .30 *1.00*
**879** A62 $100 on $1 (#551) .30 *1.00*
*a.* Perf. 11 *100.00* *100.00*
**880** A63 $100 on $2 (C) (#566) .35 .35
**880A** A82 $50,000 on $20,000 (#788) 1.40 .40
**880B** A82 $100,000 on $30,000 (V) (#789) 2.75 .90

**Wmk. 261**

**881** A39 10c on 2½c (#405) .40 *4.00*
**882** A39 50c on ½c (#402) .30 *2.00*
*Nos. 828-882 (61)* 682.45 707.10

Characters at left express the new value. Style of characters and numerals varies.

Nos. Q7 to Q9 Surcharged in Black or Carmine

**1948** **Unwmk.** ***Perf. 12½***

**883** PP2 $200 on $3000 red org .70 .50
**884** PP2 $500 on $5000 dk bl (C) .70 .45
**885** PP2 $1000 on $10,000 vio .70 .50
*Nos. 883-885 (3)* 2.10 1.45

Nos. 788-791 Surcharged in Gold Yuan in Red (Nos. 885A, 885D-885E) or Black (Nos. 885B-885C) at Foochow

**1949, Apr. 30** **Unwmk.** ***Perf. 14***

**885A** $20,000 on $40,000 32.00 *62.00*
**885B** $50,000 on $30,000 32.00 *62.00*
**885C** $100,000 on $20,000 32.00 *62.00*
**885D** $200,000 on $40,000 32.00 *62.00*
**885E** $200,000 on $50,000 32.00 *62.00*
*Nos. 885A-885E (5)* 160.00 *310.00*

Issued in Fukien Postal District.

Dr. Sun Yat-sen — A94

**1949** **Unwmk.** **Engr.** ***Perf. 14***

**Without Gum**

**886** A94 $1 orange .45 *1.00*
**887** A94 $10 green .50 *.65*
**888** A94 $20 vio brown .45 *.65*
**889** A94 $50 dk Prus grn .45 *.65*
**890** A94 $100 org brn .45 *.65*
**891** A94 $200 red org .45 *.65*
**892** A94 $500 rose lilac .45 *.65*
**893** A94 $800 car rose .45 *2.50*
**894** A94 $1000 blue .45 .65

**Redrawn**

**Engr.**

***Perf. 12½***

**895** A94 $10 green .45 *5.00*
*a.* Perf. 14 4.00 *8.00*
*b.* Perf. 13 .45 *5.50*
**896** A94 $20 violet brn .45 *.55*
*a.* Perf. 14 1.10 *4.50*
*b.* Perf. 13 .45 *.90*
*Nos. 886-896 (11)* 5.00 *13.60*

Small "T" at left of necktie on Nos. 895-896a.

**Redrawn**

**1949** **Litho.** ***Perf. 12½***

**Without Gum**

**897** A94 $50 grnsh gray .30 *2.75*
**898** A94 $100 dk org brn .30 *.50*
**899** A94 $200 orange red .60 *3.00*
**900** A94 $500 rose lilac .30 *.50*
**901** A94 $1000 deep blue .30 *.50*
**902** A94 $2000 violet .30 *1.50*
**903** A94 $5000 light blue .30 *.45*
**904** A94 $10,000 sepia .30 *.45*
**905** A94 $20,000 apple grn .30 *1.50*
**906** A94 $50,000 rose pink .30 *1.00*
**907** A94 $80,000 brn red .70 *4.50*
**908** A94 $100,000 bl grn .45 *1.00*
*Nos. 897-908 (12)* 4.45 *17.65*

Diagonal lines have been added to the background of the redrawn design.

Zeros for "cents" omitted on No. 908.

See Nos. 973-981. For surcharges see Nos. 991-1006, 1057-1060, Fukien 13-17, Szechwan 51, Tsingtau 1-4, Yunnan 63-65, 68, 70, People's Republic of China 4L34-4L44, 4L48-4L60, 5L43-5L50, 5L54-5L59, 5L91-5L95, 6L1-6L16, 6L23-6L26, 6L30-6L31, 7L6-7L8, 7L13-7L16, 8L12-8L13, 8L48-8L51.

Plane, Train and Ship — A95

Gold Yuan Surcharge in Black or Other Colors on Revenue Stamps

Two types, 50c on $20:

I — Thick numerals in "20." Vertical stroke in lower right corner of vignette. (Dah Tung Book Co.)

II — Thin "20." No vertical stroke in corner. (Central Trust.)

Two types, $2 on $50, $10 on $30, $100 on $50 and $300 on $50:

III — "Y" in lower right corner of vignette. (Dah Yeh Printing Co.)

IV — No "Y" in corner. (Dah Tung, Central Trust or Chung Ming.)

Two types, $50 on $300 and $1000 on $100:

V — Projection on left frame column below foliate ornament. (Dah Yeh Printing Co.)

VI — No projection. (Dah Tung Book Co.)

**Litho.; Nos. 923, 933, 935-936 Engr.**

**1949** ***Perf. 12½, 13, 14***

**Without Gum**

**913** A95 50c on $20 red brn, I .30 *.50*
*a.* 50c on $20 brown, II .30 *.50*
**914** A95 $1 on $15 red org .30 *9.00*
**915** A95 $2 on $50 dk bl, IV (C) .30 *1.00*
*a.* Type III .40 *1.25*
**916** A95 $3 on $50 dk bl (Bl) .30 *1.00*
**917** A95 $3 on $50 dk bl .30 *1.00*
**918** A95 $5 on $500 brn .30 *.90*
**919** A95 $10 on $30 dk vio, III (Bl) .30 *.45*
*a.* Type IV .70 *1.75*
*b.* Double surcharge, IV
**920** A95 $15 on $20 org brn (Bl) .30 *.45*
**921** A95 $25 on $20 org brn (G) .30 *1.00*
**922** A95 $50 on $50 dk bl (R O) .30 *.45*
**923** A95 $50 on $300 grn, VI (C) .30 *.60*
*a.* $50 on $300 yel grn, V (C) .30 *.50*
**924** A95 $80 on $50 dk bl (Dk Br) .30 *1.25*
**925** A95 $100 on $50 dk bl, IV 1.00 .60
*a.* Type III 8.00 *17.50*
**926** A95 $200 on $50 dk bl .90 .90
**927** A95 $200 on $500 brn (Bl) .60 *1.00*
**928** A95 $300 on $50 dk bl, III (C) 1.25 1.25
*a.* Type IV 1.75 *2.00*
**929** A95 $300 on $50 dk bl (Br) 2.00 2.00
**930** A95 $500 on $15 red org (Bl) 1.50 *4.25*
**931** A95 $500 on $30 dk vio .75 *3.00*
**932** A95 $1000 on $50 dk bl (C) 12.00 9.00
**933** A95 $1000 on $100 ol grn, V 3.00 *4.50*
*a.* Type VI 14.00 *15.00*
**934** A95 $1500 on $50 dk bl (Bl) 2.50 *3.00*
**935** A95 $2000 on $300 grn (Bl) .45 .65
*a.* Horiz. pair, imperf. between
**936** A95 $5000 on $100 ol grn (C) 350.00
*Nos. 913-936 (24)* 379.55
*Nos. 913-935 (23)* 29.55 47.75

No. 936 was officially authorized, but never issued.

**Key pattern of overprinted border inverted and in 2 or 3 detached sections at top and bottom in Blue, Black or Green**

**Without Gum**

**Type A95**

**1949** **Hankow Prints** **Litho.**

**937** A95 $50 on $10 (Bk) 9.50 *11.00*
**938** A95 $100 on $10 11.00 *14.00*
**939** A95 $500 on $10 (Bk) 9.00 *6.50*
**940** A95 $1000 on $10 7.00 *9.00*
**941** A95 $5000 on $20 29.00 25.00
**942** A95 $10,000 on $20 (Bk) 17.50 14.00
**943** A95 $50,000 on $20 20.00 *25.00*
**944** A95 $100,000 on $20 (Bk) 25.00 25.00
**945** A95 $500,000 on $20 350.00 300.00
**946** A95 $2,000,000 on $20 (G) 900.00 375.00
**947** A95 $5,000,000 on $20 1,600. 950.00
*Nos. 937-944 (8)* 128.00 129.50

The $10 stamp is slate green, the $20 red brown.

The basic revenue stamps of Nos. 915-947 were the work of several printers. There are three main types, differing in the bottom label. Nos. 922 and 925 are in a second type: Nos. 923 and 930 in a third. Varieties of paper, color and overprint exist.

Counterfeits exist of Nos. 945-947.

For surcharges and overprints see Nos. 960-970, C63, E13, F3, J122-J126, Hupeh 1-2, People's Republic of China 5L51-5L53, 6L17-6L21.

**Redrawn Coarse Impression**

**1949 Litho. Without Gum**

**Size: 18¼x20¾mm**

**951** A94 $50 green .40 *30.00*
**952** A94 $1000 dp blue .50 *4.00*
**953** A94 $5000 carmine .65 *4.00*
**954** A94 $10,000 brown 4.00 *10.00*
**955** A94 $20,000 orange 1.25 *4.00*
**956** A94 $50,000 blue 3.00 8.00
**957** A94 $200,000 violet 5.00 8.00
**958** A94 $500,000 vio brn 6.00 10.00
*Nos. 951-958 (8)* 20.80 *78.00*

Zeros for "cents" omitted on Nos. 957-958.
See surcharge note following No. 900.

Locomotive and Ship — A96

**1949, May 1 Litho. *Perf. 12½***

**Without Gum**

**959** A96 orange 5.00 2.50
*a.* Rouletted 13.50 10.00

Nos. 959, C62, E12 and F2 were printed without denomination and sold at the daily rate of the yuan. This was necessitated by the gold yuan inflation.

For surcharges and overprints see Nos. 1130, 1213, Taiwan 97, Fukien 18, Kansu 1, People's Republic of China 24-29, 101-104, 4L31-4L33, 4L45-4L47, 4L61-4L62, 7L9-7L12, 8L52-8L54.

Revenue Stamps Overprinted in Black

**1949, May *Perf. 12½, 13, 14***

**Without Gum**

**960** A95 $30 dark violet 125.00 120.00

**Engr.**

**961** A95 $200 violet brown 15.00 12.00
**962** A95 $500 dark green 25.00 20.00
*Nos. 960-962 (3)* 165.00 152.00

A similar overprint appears on Nos. C63, E13, F3, differing in 2nd and 3rd characters of bottom row.

Silver Yuan Surcharge in Black or Other Colors

**1949 Litho.**

**963** A95 1c on $5000 brn (G) 8.50 7.00
**964** A95 4c on $100 ol grn (Bl) 6.00 3.75
**965** A95 4c on $3000 org) 6.00 2.00
**966** A95 10c on $50 dk bl (RV) 8.50 2.75
**967** A95 10c on $1000 car 8.50 8.50
*a.* Inverted surcharge 60.00
**968** A95 20c on $1000 red (V) 8.50 8.50
*b.* Inverted surcharge
**968A** A95 50c on $30 dk vio (C) 47.50 10.00
**969** A95 50c on $50 dk bl (C) 21.00 10.00
**970** A95 $1 on $50 dk bl 25.00 *35.00*
*Nos. 963-970 (9)* 139.50 87.50

Nos. 963-965 and 967 are engraved.

**Sun Type of 1949 Redrawn Coarse Impression**

**1949 *Perf. 12½, 13 or Compound***

**973** A94 1c apple green 29.00 *11.00*
**974** A94 2c orange 9.00 *17.50*
**975** A94 4c blue green .35 *2.00*
**976** A94 10c deep lilac .35 *2.00*
**977** A94 16c orange red .75 *17.50*
**978** A94 20c blue .45 *5.50*
**979** A94 50c dk brown 2.40 *48.00*
**980** A94 100c deep blue 475.00 475.00
**981** A94 500c scarlet 525.00 525.00
*Nos. 973-981 (9)* 1,042. 1,104.

For surcharges see Nos. 1057-1060.

Flying Geese Over Globe — A97

**1949, May Litho. *Perf. 12½***

**Without Gum**

**984** A97 $1 brown org 15.00 *20.00*
**985** A97 $2 blue 75.00 *90.00*
**986** A97 $5 car rose 75.00 *90.00*
**987** A97 $10 blue grn 75.00 *90.00*
*Nos. 984-987 (4)* 240.00 *290.00*

Five other denominations — 10c, 16c, 50c, $20 and $50 — were also printed at Shanghai, but were not issued.

For surcharges see Nos. 1007-1011, 1042-1045, 1061-1063, People's Republic of China 49-56, 5LQ17-5LQ26, 7L17-7L18, 8L14-8L16.

Pigeons, Globe and Wreath — A98

**Engraved and Typographed**

**1949, Aug. 1 Without Gum *Imperf.***

**988** A98 $1 org red & blk 12.00 *17.50*

75th anniv. of the UPU.
Exists with black denomination omitted.

Summer Palace, Peiping A99

Bronze Bull and Kunming Lake A100

**Engraved and Typographed**

**1949, Aug. *Rouletted***

**Without Gum**

**989** A99 15c org brn & grn 8.00 *12.00*
**990** A100 40c dl grn & car 9.25 *12.00*
*a.* 2nd and 3rd characters at top transposed 160.00 200.00

Silver Yuan Surcharge in Black on 1949 Sun Yat-sen Issues

**1949 *Perf. 12½, 14***

**991** A94 1c on $100 org brn (890) 15.00 10.00
**992** A94 1c on $100 dk org brn (898) 15.00 10.00
**993** A94 2½c on $500 rose lil (892) 19.00 11.00
*a.* Inverted surcharge 60.00
**994** A94 2½c on $500 rose lil (900) 21.00 12.00
**995** A94 15c on $10 grn (887) 30.00 40.00
*a.* Inverted surcharge 67.50
**996** A94 15c on $20 vio brn (896) 42.50 *65.00*
*Nos. 991-996 (6)* 142.50 148.00

Silver Yuan Surcharge in Black or Carmine

**997** A94 2½c on $50 grn (951) 2.75 *3.75*
**998** A94 2½c on $50,000 bl (956) 7.50 3.75
**999** A94 5c on $1000 dp bl (952) (C) 6.00 *8.00*
**1000** A94 5c on $20,000 org (955) 4.00 *7.00*
**1001** A94 5c on $200,000 vio (957) (C) 5.50 3.25
**1002** A94 5c on $500,000 vio brn (958) 5.50 3.25
**1003** A94 10c on $5000 car (953) 11.00 *12.00*
**1004** A94 10c on $10,000 brn (954) 11.00 *12.00*
**1005** A94 15c on $200 red org (891) 13.50 *14.00*
**1006** A94 25c on $100 dk org brn (896) 27.50 *40.00*
*Nos. 997-1006 (10)* 94.25 *107.00*

## REPUBLIC OF CHINA

ri-'pə-blik of 'chī-nə

(Taiwan)

LOCATION — Taiwan (since 1949) (Formosa)
GOVT. — Republic
AREA — 13,970 sq. mi.
POP. — 22,113,250 (1999 est.)
CAPITAL — Taipei

Stamps issued and used in Taiwan after Communist forces occupied the Chinese mainland include Taiwan Nos. 91-96, 101-103, J10-J17.

**Catalogue values for unused stamps in this country are for Never Hinged items, beginning with Scott 1124 in the regular postage section, Scott B17 in the semi-postal section, Scott C69 in the airpost section, and Scott J142 in the postage due section.**

**Watermarks**

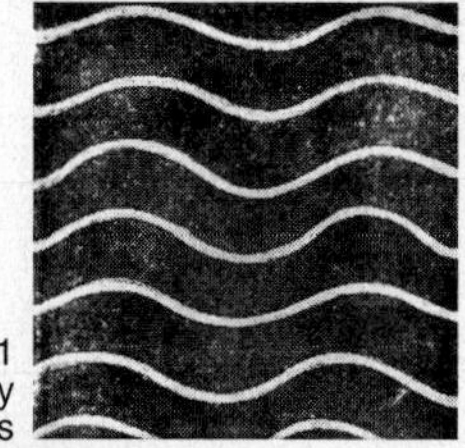

Wmk. 281 — Wavy Lines

Wmk. 323 — Seal Character (found with "Yu" in various arrangements)

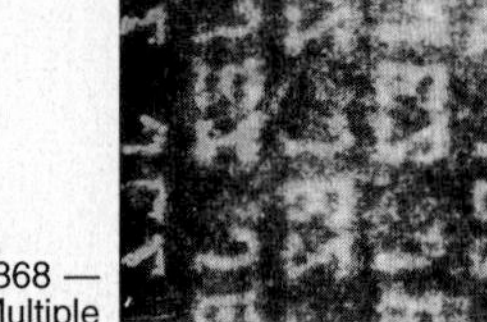

Wmk. 368 — JEZ Multiple

Wmk. 370 — Geometrical Design

Type of 1949 with Value Omitted Surcharged in Various Colors

**1950, Jan. 1 Unwmk. *Perf. 12½***

**Without Gum**

**1007** A97 $1 green (Bk) 150.00 11.00
**1008** A97 $2 green (C) 200.00 20.00
**1009** A97 $5 green (V) 2,000. 110.00
**1010** A97 $10 green (Br) 2,750. 275.00
**1011** A97 $20 green (Dk Bl) 4,500. 900.00
*Nos. 1007-1011 (5)* 9,600. 1,316.

Two printings of the $1 and $2 show minor differences.

Cheng Ch'eng-kung (Koxinga) — A101

**1950, June 26 Typo. *Rouletted***

**Without Gum**

**1012** A101 3c dk gray grn 4.50 15.00
**1013** A101 10c orange brn 3.25 .30
**1014** A101 15c orange yel 14.50 22.00
**1015** A101 20c emerald 4.00 .25
**1016** A101 30c claret 60.00 50.00
**1017** A101 40c red orange 4.50 .30
**1018** A101 50c chocolate 7.25 1.00
**1019** A101 80c carmine 21.50 3.50
**1020** A101 $1 ultra 18.00 1.00
**1021** A101 $1.50 green 67.50 13.00
**1022** A101 $1.60 blue 60.00 1.60
**1023** A101 $2 red violet 24.50 1.25
**1024** A101 $5 aqua 170.00 20.00
*Nos. 1012-1024 (13)* 459.50 129.20

Part perf pairs exist of the 10c, 20c, 80c.

The 10c and 20c were reprinted from new plates. There are slight differences.

For surcharges see Nos. 1070-1072, 1105-1108, 1118-1119. See No. C64.

Nos. 751, 753, 788-791, 793, 795-799 Surcharged in Carmine or Black

**1950 Engr. *Perf. 14***

**Without Gum**

**1025** A82 3c on $30,000 3.75 5.00
**1026** A82 3c on $40,000 (C) 3.25 5.00
**1027** A82 3c on $50,000 (C) 3.25 5.00
**1028** A82 5c on $200,000 3.75 5.00
**1029** A82 10c on $4000 32.00 35.00
**1030** A82 10c on $6000 23.00 26.00
**1031** A82 10c on $20,000 23.00 26.00
**1032** A82 10c on $2,000,000 23.00 15.00
**1033** A82 20c on $500,000 35.00 20.00
**1034** A82 20c on $1,000,000 60.00 20.00
**1035** A82 30c on $3,000,000 90.00 30.00
**1036** A82 50c on $5,000,000 (C) 150.00 45.00
*Nos. 1025-1036 (12)* 450.00 237.00

Issued: Nos. 1025-1027, 3/6; No. 1028, 3/25; No. 1031, 6/10: Nos. 1029-1030, 1032, 1035-1036, 8/1; No. 1033-1034, 8/25.

Forgeries exist.

**Inverted Surcharge**

*1029a* A82 10c on $4000 175.00
*1030a* A82 10c on $6000 375.00
*1031a* A82 10c on $20,000 210.00
*1032a* A82 10c on $2,000,000 225.00
*1033a* A82 20c on $500,000 300.00
*1034a* A82 20c on $1,000,000 300.00

Allegory of Election — A102

***Perf. 12x12½, Imperf.***

**1951, Mar. 20 Engr. Unwmk.**

**Without Gum**

**1037** A102 40c carmine 15.00 2.00
**1038** A102 $1 dp blue 35.00 4.00
**1039** A102 $1.60 purple 62.50 5.00
**1040** A102 $2 brown 85.00 5.00
*Nos. 1037-1040 (4)* 197.50 16.00

Value, imperf. set, $250.

### Souvenir Sheet

*Imperf*

| | | | | |
|---|---|---|---|---|
| **1041** | A102 | $2 dp blue grn | 400.00 | 400.00 |

Adoption of local self-government in Taiwan.

Design A97 Surcharged — A103

**Surcharge in Various Colors**

**1951, July 19** *Perf. 12½*

**Without Gum**

| | | | | |
|---|---|---|---|---|
| **1042** | A103 | $5 grn (R Br) | 75.00 | 15.00 |
| **1043** | A103 | $10 green (Bk) | 150.00 | 16.50 |
| **1044** | A103 | $20 green (R) | 650.00 | 47.50 |
| **1045** | A103 | $50 green (P) | 1,100. | 120.00 |
| | | *Nos. 1042-1045 (4)* | 1,975. | 199.00 |

Farmer and Scroll Announcing Tax Reduction — A104

**1952, Jan. 1 Without Gum** *Perf. 14*

| | | | | |
|---|---|---|---|---|
| **1046** | A104 | 20c red orange | 15.00 | 1.20 |
| **1047** | A104 | 40c dk green | 20.00 | 2.25 |
| **1048** | A104 | $1 brown | 35.00 | 5.25 |
| **1049** | A104 | $1.40 dp blue | 55.00 | 3.75 |
| **1050** | A104 | $2 dk gray | 160.00 | 40.00 |
| **1051** | A104 | $5 brown car | 210.00 | 14.00 |
| | | *Nos. 1046-1051 (6)* | 495.00 | 66.45 |

Land tax reduction of 37.5% in Taiwan. Value, imperf. set, $1,000.

Pres. Chiang Kai-shek, Flag and Followers — A105

**Flag in Violet Blue and Carmine**

**1952, Mar. 1 Unwmk.** *Perf. 14*

**Without Gum**

| | | | | |
|---|---|---|---|---|
| **1052** | A105 | 40c rose car | 16.00 | .50 |
| **1053** | A105 | $1 dp green | 30.00 | 2.25 |
| **1054** | A105 | $1.60 brown org | 62.50 | 1.10 |
| **1055** | A105 | $2 brt blue | 125.00 | 19.00 |
| **1056** | A105 | $5 violet brn | 145.00 | 5.00 |
| | | *Nos. 1052-1056 (5)* | 378.50 | 27.85 |

2nd anniv. of Chiang Kai-shek's return to the presidency.
Value, imperf. set, $550.
See Nos. 1064-1069.

Nos. 975-976, 978-979 Surcharged in Black

**1952, Aug. 1** *Perf. 12½*

**Without Gum**

| | | | | |
|---|---|---|---|---|
| **1057** | A94 | 3c on 4c bl grn | 5.50 | 5.25 |
| **1058** | A94 | 3c on 10c dp lil | 5.50 | 5.25 |
| **1059** | A94 | 3c on 20c blue | 7.75 | 7.50 |
| **1060** | A94 | 3c on 50c dk brn | 8.75 | 8.75 |
| | | *Nos. 1057-1060 (4)* | 27.50 | 26.75 |

Forgeries exist.

Geese Type of 1949 with Value Omitted Surcharged

**1952, Dec. 8**

**Without Gum**

| | | | | |
|---|---|---|---|---|
| **1061** | A97 | $10 green (P) | 87.50 | 16.00 |
| **1062** | A97 | $20 green (R) | 275.00 | 27.50 |
| **1063** | A97 | $50 green (Bk) | 2,150. | 750.00 |
| | | *Nos. 1061-1063 (3)* | 2,513. | 793.50 |

### Chiang Type of 1952 Redrawn

*Perf. 12½*

**1953, Mar. 1 Engr. Unwmk.**

**Without Gum**

**Flag in Dark Blue & Carmine**

| | | | | |
|---|---|---|---|---|
| **1064** | A105 | 10c red orange | 6.00 | 1.60 |
| **1065** | A105 | 20c green | 1.25 | 1.60 |
| **1066** | A105 | 40c rose pink | 17.50 | 2.25 |
| **1067** | A105 | $1.40 blue | 55.00 | 3.50 |
| **1068** | A105 | $2 brown | 135.00 | 7.00 |
| **1069** | A105 | $5 rose violet | 200.00 | 19.00 |
| | | *Nos. 1064-1069 (6)* | 414.75 | 34.95 |

Chiang Kai-shek's return to presidency, 3rd anniv.

Many differences in redrawn design. Value, imperf. set, $650.

Nos. 1020, 1014, 1016 and 1022 Surcharged in Various Colors

**1953** *Rouletted*

**Without Gum**

| | | | | |
|---|---|---|---|---|
| **1070** | A101 | 3c on $1 ultra (C) | 3.25 | 1.00 |
| **1070A** | A101 | 10c on 15c org yel (G) ('54) | 12.00 | 3.00 |
| **1071** | A101 | 10c on 30c cl (Bl) | 12.00 | 6.00 |
| **1072** | A101 | 20c on $1.60 brt bl (Bk) | 7.00 | 3.00 |
| | | *Nos. 1070-1072 (4)* | 34.25 | 13.00 |

Chinese characters and ornamental device at bottom differ on each value.

Issued: No. 1071, 2/1; No. 1070, 5/25; No. 1072, 6/13; No. 1070A, 7/16.

Nurse & Patients — A106

**Cross in Red, Burelage Color in Italics**

**1953, July 1 Litho.** *Perf. 12½*

**Without Gum**

| | | | | |
|---|---|---|---|---|
| **1073** | A106 | 40c brown, *buff* | 15.00 | 2.00 |
| **1074** | A106 | $1.60 blue, *bl* | 35.00 | 2.00 |
| **1075** | A106 | $2 green, *yel* | 55.00 | 2.25 |
| **1076** | A106 | $5 red org, *org* | 95.00 | 10.00 |
| | | *Nos. 1073-1076 (4)* | 200.00 | 16.25 |

Chinese Anti-Tuberculosis Association.

Chiang Kai-shek — A107

**1953, Oct. 31 Engr. Without Gum**

| | | | | |
|---|---|---|---|---|
| **1077** | A107 | 10c dk brown | 4.50 | .25 |
| **1078** | A107 | 20c lilac | 4.50 | .25 |
| **1079** | A107 | 40c dp green | 4.50 | .25 |
| **1080** | A107 | 50c dp pink | 6.75 | .45 |
| **1081** | A107 | 80c brown bis | 20.00 | 2.40 |
| **1082** | A107 | $1 dp olive grn | 9.00 | .25 |
| **1083** | A107 | $1.40 dp blue | 9.00 | .25 |
| **1084** | A107 | $1.60 dp carmine | 9.00 | .25 |
| **1085** | A107 | $1.70 apple grn | 9.50 | 1.35 |
| **1086** | A107 | $2 brown | 9.50 | .25 |
| **1087** | A107 | $3 dark blue | 170.00 | 11.00 |
| **1088** | A107 | $4 aqua | 11.50 | .70 |
| **1089** | A107 | $5 red orange | 14.50 | .70 |
| **1090** | A107 | $10 dk green | 57.50 | 3.50 |
| **1091** | A107 | $20 dk brn lake | 72.50 | 10.00 |
| *a.* | | Souvenir folder | 500.00 | |
| | | *Nos. 1077-1091 (15)* | 412.25 | 31.85 |

67th birthday of Pres. Chiang Kai-shek.

No. 1091a contains Nos. 1077-1091 imperf, arranged in 3 sheets of 5 stamps each.

Silo Highway Bridge — A108

$1.60 and $5, Silo bridge, side view.

**Without Gum**

**Various Frames**

**1954, Jan. 28 Unwmk.** *Perf. 12½*

| | | | | |
|---|---|---|---|---|
| **1092** | A108 | 40c vermilion | 16.00 | 2.00 |
| **1093** | A108 | $1.60 blue violet | 80.00 | 4.00 |
| **1094** | A108 | $3.60 sepia | 60.00 | 11.00 |
| **1095** | A108 | $5 magenta | 140.00 | 19.50 |
| *a.* | | Souvenir folder | *1,500.* | *750.00* |
| | | *Nos. 1092-1095 (4)* | 296.00 | 36.50 |

Opening of Silo bridge, 1st anniversary.

No. 1095a contains one sheet of 4 containing Nos. 1092-1095 imperforate. Beware of stapled folders.

Forest of Evergreens — A109

**1954, Mar. 12** *Perf. 12x12½*

**Without Gum**

| | | | | |
|---|---|---|---|---|
| **1096** | A109 | 40c shown | 22.50 | 1.00 |
| **1097** | A109 | $10 Nursery | 160.00 | 10.00 |

Issued to publicize forest conservation.

Runner — A110

**1954, Mar. 29 Without Gum**

| | | | | |
|---|---|---|---|---|
| **1098** | A110 | 40c dp ultra | 13.50 | .75 |
| **1099** | A110 | $5 carmine | 77.50 | 10.00 |

11th Youth Day, Mar. 29, 1954.

Globe, Bridge and Ship — A111

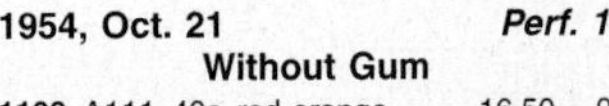

**1954, Oct. 21** *Perf. 12*

**Without Gum**

| | | | | |
|---|---|---|---|---|
| **1100** | A111 | 40c red orange | 16.50 | .90 |
| **1101** | A111 | $5 deep blue | 19.00 | 4.00 |

2nd Overseas Chinese Day, Oct. 21, 1954.

Ex-Prisoner with Broken Chains — A112

Designs: $1, Ex-prisoner with torch and flag, UN emblem. $1.60, Torch and date.

**1955, Jan. 23**

**Without Gum**

| | | | | |
|---|---|---|---|---|
| **1102** | A112 | 40c blue green | 3.50 | .65 |
| **1103** | A112 | $1 sepia | 25.00 | 6.00 |
| **1104** | A112 | $1.60 lake | 25.00 | 4.25 |
| | | *Nos. 1102-1104 (3)* | 53.50 | 10.90 |

Honoring Chinese who fought on the side of the North Korean army, who, when released January 23, 1954, chose to return to the Republic of China.

**Nos. 1019-1021, 1017 Surcharged in Brown, Blue or Green**

a

b

c

**1955** *Rouletted*

**Without Gum**

| | | | | |
|---|---|---|---|---|
| **1105** | A101(a) | 3c on $1 (Br) | 5.50 | .60 |
| **1106** | A101(b) | 10c on 80c (Bl) | 10.75 | 1.00 |
| **1107** | A101(b) | 10c on $1.50 (Bl) | 10.75 | 1.50 |
| **1108** | A101(c) | 20c on 40c (G) | 3.50 | .85 |
| | | *Nos. 1105-1108 (4)* | 30.50 | 3.95 |

Issued: No. 1105, 1108, 2/18; Nos. 1106-1107, 8/1.

Hand Planting Evergreen Tree — A113

Design: $50, Seedling and map of Taiwan.

**1955, Apr. 1** *Perf. 12*

**Without Gum**

| | | | | |
|---|---|---|---|---|
| **1109** | A113 | $20 dp carmine | 35.00 | 1.50 |
| **1110** | A113 | $50 blue | 87.50 | 7.00 |

Issued to publicize forest conservation.

Chiang Kai-shek, Flags, Building — A114

**1955, May 20 Engr. *Perf. 12***
**Without Gum**

| | | | | |
|---|---|---|---|---|
| 1111 | A114 | 20c olive | 6.50 | .40 |
| 1112 | A114 | 40c blue green | 5.50 | .25 |
| 1113 | A114 | $2 car rose | 16.00 | 1.50 |
| 1114 | A114 | $7 dp ultra | 25.00 | 2.50 |
| *a.* | | Souv. sheet of 4, #1111-1114, imperf. | *300.00* | *200.00* |
| | | *Nos. 1111-1114 (4)* | 53.00 | 4.65 |

First anniversary of Pres. Chiang Kai-shek's re-election.

No. 1114a is perf. 12 at right edge of sheet. Value is for sheet with right selvage.

Armed Forces Emblem — A115

**1955, Sept. 3 Without Gum**

| | | | | |
|---|---|---|---|---|
| 1115 | A115 | 40c dk blue | 2.00 | .40 |
| 1116 | A115 | $2 org ver | 20.00 | 1.75 |
| 1117 | A115 | $7 bl grn | 24.00 | 1.75 |
| *a.* | | Sheet of 3, #1115-1117, imperf. | *450.00* | *350.00* |
| | | *Nos. 1115-1117 (3)* | 46.00 | 3.90 |

Armed Forces Day, Sept. 3.

No. 1117a is perf. 12 at right edge of sheet. Value is for sheet with right selvage.

Nos. 1017, 1018 and C64 Surcharged in Magenta

**1955, Sept. 16 Typo. *Rouletted***
**Without Gum**

| | | | | |
|---|---|---|---|---|
| 1118 | A101 | 20c on 40c org | 4.50 | .40 |
| 1119 | A101 | 20c on 50c choc | 5.25 | 1.00 |
| 1120 | AP6 | 20c on 60c dp blue | 22.50 | 3.50 |
| | | *Nos. 1118-1120 (3)* | 32.25 | 4.90 |

Flags of UN and China — A116

**1955, Oct. 24 Engr. *Perf. 11½***
**Without Gum**

| | | | | |
|---|---|---|---|---|
| 1121 | A116 | 40c dk blue | 1.75 | .40 |
| 1122 | A116 | $2 dk car rose | 8.50 | 1.25 |
| 1123 | A116 | $7 slate green | 11.75 | 2.00 |
| | | *Nos. 1121-1123 (3)* | 22.00 | 3.65 |

10th anniv. of the UN, Oct. 24, 1955.

**Catalogue values for unused stamps in this section, from this point to the end of the section, are for Never Hinged items.**

Pres. Chiang Kai-shek — A117

**1955, Oct. 31 Photo. *Perf. 13½***

| | | | | |
|---|---|---|---|---|
| 1124 | A117 | 40c dk bl, rose & brn | 6.50 | .60 |
| 1125 | A117 | $2 grn, red & dk bl | 18.00 | 2.00 |
| 1126 | A117 | $7 brn, red & grn | 23.50 | 3.25 |
| *a.* | | Souv. sheet of 3, #1124-1126, imperf. | *175.00* | *175.00* |
| | | *Nos. 1124-1126 (3)* | 48.00 | 5.85 |

69th birthday of Pres. Chiang Kai-shek.

No. 1126a is perf. 12 at right edge of sheet. Value is for sheet with right selvage. Issued without gum.

Birthplace of Sun Yat-sen — A118

**1955, Nov. 12 Engr. *Perf. 12***
**Without Gum**

| | | | | |
|---|---|---|---|---|
| 1127 | A118 | 40c blue | 3.25 | .40 |
| 1128 | A118 | $2 red brown | 14.50 | 1.25 |
| 1129 | A118 | $7 rose lake | 18.00 | 2.00 |
| | | *Nos. 1127-1129 (3)* | 35.75 | 3.65 |

90th anniversary, birth of Sun Yat-sen.

No. 959a Surcharged in Bright Green

**1956, Feb. 10 Litho. *Rouletted***
**Without Gum**

| | | | | |
|---|---|---|---|---|
| 1130 | A96 | 20c on orange | .75 | .25 |

See No. 1213.

China Map and Transportation Methods — A119

**Wmk. 281**
**1956, Mar. 20 Engr. *Perf. 12***
**Without Gum**

| | | | | |
|---|---|---|---|---|
| 1131 | A119 | 40c dk carmine | 3.00 | .40 |
| 1132 | A119 | $1 intense blk | 9.00 | .80 |
| 1133 | A119 | $1.60 chocolate | 10.00 | .80 |
| 1134 | A119 | $2 dk green | 14.50 | 1.20 |
| | | *Nos. 1131-1134 (4)* | 36.50 | 3.20 |

60th anniv. of the founding of the modern Chinese postal system.

**Souvenir Sheets**
***Imperf***
**Without Gum**

| | | | | |
|---|---|---|---|---|
| 1135 | A119 | $2 magenta | *72.50* | *35.00* |
| 1136 | A119 | $2 red | *72.50* | *35.00* |

Exhib. for the 60th anniv. of the modern Chinese postal system, Mar. 20, 1956.

Children at Play — A120

**1956, Apr. 4 Unwmk. *Perf. 12***
**Without Gum**

| | | | | |
|---|---|---|---|---|
| 1137 | A120 | 40c emerald | 2.10 | .30 |
| 1138 | A120 | $1.60 dk blue | 5.25 | .60 |
| 1139 | A120 | $2 dk carmine | 8.75 | 1.20 |
| | | *Nos. 1137-1139 (3)* | 16.10 | 2.10 |

Children's Day, Apr. 4, 1956.

Early and Modern Locomotives — A121

**1956, June 9 Wmk. 281 Vert.**
**Without Gum**

| | | | | |
|---|---|---|---|---|
| 1140 | A121 | 40c rose car | 5.00 | .30 |
| 1141 | A121 | $2 blue | 7.25 | .75 |
| 1142 | A121 | $8 green | 12.00 | 2.10 |
| | | *Nos. 1140-1142 (3)* | 24.25 | 3.15 |

75th anniversary of Chinese Railroads.

Pres. Chiang Kai-shek
A122 A123

A124

**Various Portraits of Chiang**
***Perf. 14½x13½, 14½ (A123), 13½x14½***
**1956, Oct. 31 Photo. Unwmk.**

| | | | | |
|---|---|---|---|---|
| 1143 | A122 | 20c red orange | 2.50 | .25 |
| 1144 | A122 | 40c carmine rose | 12.00 | .25 |
| 1145 | A123 | $1 brt ultra | 16.00 | .30 |
| 1146 | A123 | $1.60 red lilac | 20.00 | .25 |
| 1147 | A124 | $2 red brown | 28.00 | .60 |
| 1148 | A124 | $8 brt grnsh blue | 62.50 | 1.90 |
| | | *Nos. 1143-1148 (6)* | 141.00 | 3.55 |

70th birthday of Pres. Chiang Kai-shek.

**Types of Special Delivery, Air Post and Registration Stamps of 1949 Surcharged in Black or Maroon**

a

b

c

**1956 Unwmk. Litho. *Rouletted***
**Without Gum**

| | | | | |
|---|---|---|---|---|
| 1150 | SD2(a) | 3c red violet | 6.00 | .60 |
| *a.* | | Perf. 12½ | 2.25 | .30 |
| 1151 | AP5(b) | 3c blue green (M) | 1.50 | .25 |
| 1152 | R2(c) | 10c bright red | 1.75 | .25 |
| | | *Nos. 1150-1152 (3)* | 9.25 | 1.10 |

Issued: No. 1150, 4/25; No. 1151, 11/11; No. 1152, 12/25.

Telecommunications Emblem and Radio Tower — A125

**Wmk. 281**
**1956, Dec. 28 Engr. *Perf. 12***
**Without Gum**

| | | | | |
|---|---|---|---|---|
| 1153 | A125 | 40c deep ultra | 2.75 | .25 |
| 1154 | A125 | $1.40 carmine | 4.75 | .40 |
| 1155 | A125 | $1.60 dark green | 7.25 | .60 |
| 1156 | A125 | $2 chocolate | 9.00 | 1.00 |
| | | *Nos. 1153-1156 (4)* | 23.75 | 2.25 |

Chinese telegraph service, 75th anniv.

Map of China — A126

***Pin Perf., Perf. 12x12½***
**1957 Litho. Wmk. 281**
**Without Gum**

| | | | | |
|---|---|---|---|---|
| 1157 | A126 | 3c brt blue | .40 | .25 |
| 1158 | A126 | 10c violet | 6.25 | .60 |
| 1159 | A126 | 20c red orange | .75 | .25 |
| 1160 | A126 | 40c rose red | 1.00 | .25 |

**Unwmk.**

| | | | | |
|---|---|---|---|---|
| 1161 | A126 | $1 orange brown | 3.75 | .50 |
| 1162 | A126 | $1.60 green | 6.25 | .50 |
| | | *Nos. 1157-1162 (6)* | 18.40 | 2.35 |

Map inscription reads: "Recovery of Mainland."

See Nos. 1177-1182.

Mother Instructing Mencius — A127

Design: $3, Mother tattooing Yueh Fei.

**Without Gum**
**Unwmk.**
**1957, May 12 Engr. *Perf. 12***

| | | | | |
|---|---|---|---|---|
| 1163 | A127 | 40c green | 1.75 | .25 |
| 1164 | A127 | $3 redsh brown | 7.25 | .60 |

Issued to honor Mother's Day, 1957.

Badge of Chinese Boy Scouts — A128

**1957, Aug. 11 Without Gum**

| | | | | |
|---|---|---|---|---|
| 1165 | A128 | 40c lilac | .50 | .25 |
| 1166 | A128 | $1 green | 2.75 | .40 |
| 1167 | A128 | $1.60 dk blue | 3.50 | .50 |
| | | *Nos. 1165-1167 (3)* | 6.75 | 1.15 |

Cent. of the birth of Lord Baden-Powell and to publicize the World Scout Jubilee Jamboree, England, Aug. 1-12.

Globe, Radio Tower and Microphone — A129

**1957, Sept. 16 Without Gum**

| | | | | |
|---|---|---|---|---|
| 1168 | A129 | 40c vermilion | 1.00 | .25 |
| 1169 | A129 | 50c brt rose lilac | 2.00 | .30 |
| 1170 | A129 | $3.50 dark blue | 3.25 | .85 |
| | | *Nos. 1168-1170 (3)* | 6.25 | 1.40 |

30th anniv. of Chinese broadcasting.

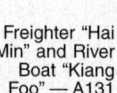

Map of Taiwan — A130

**1957, Oct. 26 Without Gum**

| | | | | |
|---|---|---|---|---|
| 1171 | A130 | 40c blue green | 3.50 | .40 |
| 1172 | A130 | $1.40 lt ultra | 8.75 | 2.25 |
| 1173 | A130 | $2 gray | 12.00 | 2.25 |
| | | *Nos. 1171-1173 (3)* | 24.25 | 4.90 |

Start of construction on the Cross Island Highway, Taiwan.

Freighter "Hai Min" and River Boat "Kiang Foo" — A131

**1957, Dec. 16 Engr. *Perf. 12***
**Without Gum**

| | | | | |
|---|---|---|---|---|
| 1174 | A131 | 40c deep ultra | 1.35 | .25 |
| 1175 | A131 | 80c rose lake | 2.75 | .95 |
| 1176 | A131 | $2.80 vermilion | 4.75 | 1.40 |
| | | *Nos. 1174-1176 (3)* | 8.85 | 2.60 |

85th anniv. of the establishment of the China Merchants Steam Navigation Co.

**Type of 1957**
***Pin Perf., Perf. 12x12½***
**1957, Dec. 25 Typo. Unwmk.**
**Without Gum**
**Dark Blue Frames**

| | | | | |
|---|---|---|---|---|
| 1177 | A126 | 3c brt blue | 1.35 | .25 |
| 1178 | A126 | 10c violet | 2.75 | .50 |
| 1179 | A126 | 20c brick red | .90 | .25 |
| 1180 | A126 | 40c rose red | 1.10 | .25 |
| 1181 | A126 | $1 dp org brn | 6.75 | .70 |
| 1182 | A126 | $1.60 dp green | 7.25 | .80 |
| | | *Nos. 1177-1182 (6)* | 20.10 | 2.75 |

On Feb. 20, 1958, two booklets were issued. One contained 6 #1179 and 22 #1180. The other contained 10 #1179, 30 #1180, and 6 #1181.

Stamps with bars obliterating the face value are specimens.

Butterfly — A132

**Various Insects in Natural Colors**

*Perf. 13½*

**1958, Mar. 20 Unwmk. Photo.**

**1183** A132 10c pale grn, grn & blk 1.50 .40
**1184** A132 40c lem, pink, grn & blk .50 .25
**1185** A132 $1 yel grn & mar 4.00 .60
**1186** A132 $1.40 yel, org & blk 4.75 .75
**1187** A132 $1.60 pale brn & dk pur 5.25 1.00
**1188** A132 $2 brt yel, org & blk 6.00 1.25
*Nos. 1183-1188 (6)* 22.00 4.25

Mme. Chiang Kai-shek Orchid — A133

Orchids: 20c, Formosan Wilson, horiz. $1.40, Klotzsch. $3, Fitzgerald, horiz.

**Orchids in Natural Colors**

**1958, Mar. 20**

**1189** A133 20c chocolate 1.50 .25
**1190** A133 40c purple 1.50 .25
**1191** A133 $1.40 dk vio brn 6.25 .60
**1192** A133 $3 dark blue 7.00 2.00
*Nos. 1189-1192 (4)* 16.25 3.10

World Health Organization Emblem — A134

**1958, May 28 Engr. *Perf. 12***
**Without Gum**

**1193** A134 40c dark blue .60 .25
**1194** A134 $1.60 brick red 1.50 .30
**1195** A134 $2 deep red lilac 1.90 .50
*Nos. 1193-1195 (3)* 4.00 1.05

10th anniv. of the WHO.

President's Mansion, Taipei — A135

**Wmk. 323**

**1958, Sept. 20 Engr. *Perf. 12***
**Without Gum**

**1196** A135 $10 blue green 7.50 .35
*a.* Granite paper 17.00 .50
**1197** A135 $20 car rose 19.00 .60
*a.* Granite paper 42.50 1.50
**1198** A135 $50 red brown 67.50 2.40
**1199** A135 $100 dk blue 170.00 8.00
*Nos. 1196-1199 (4)* 264.00 11.35

Issued: Nos. 1196a, 1197a, 5/24/63.

See Nos. 1349-1351. For surcharge see No. J131.

Taiwan Farm Scene — A136

**1958, Oct. 1 Unwmk.**
**Without Gum**

**1200** A136 20c emerald 1.25 .25
**1201** A136 40c black 1.25 .25
**1202** A136 $1.40 brt magenta 3.00 .30
**1203** A136 $3 ultra 4.50 .75
*Nos. 1200-1203 (4)* 10.00 1.55

10th anniversary of the Joint Commission on Rural Reconstruction.

Pres. Chiang Kai-shek — A137

**1958, Oct. 31 Photo. *Perf. 13½***

**1204** A137 40c multicolored 1.75 .40

Pres. Chiang Kai-shek on his 72nd birthday.

UNESCO Building, Paris — A138

**1958, Nov. 3 Engr. *Perf. 12***
**Without Gum**

**1205** A138 20c dark blue .50 .25
**1206** A138 40c green .50 .25
**1207** A138 $1.40 orange ver 1.25 .40
**1208** A138 $3 red lilac 2.00 .60
*Nos. 1205-1208 (4)* 4.25 1.50

UNESCO Headquarters in Paris opening, Nov. 3.

Flame from Liberty Torch Encircling Globe — A139

**1958, Dec. 10 Unwmk.**
**Without Gum**

**1209** A139 40c green .35 .25
**1210** A139 60c gray brown 1.05 .25
**1211** A139 $1 carmine 1.05 .25
**1212** A139 $3 ultra 1.75 .60
*Nos. 1209-1212 (4)* 4.20 1.35

10th anniversary of the signing of the Universal Declaration of Human Rights.

No. 959a Surcharged in Bright Green

*Rouletted*

**1958, Dec. 11 Litho. Unwmk.**
**Without Gum**

**1213** A96 20c on orange .75 .25

Ballot Box, Scales and Constitution A140

**1958, Dec. 25 Engr. *Perf. 12***
**Without Gum**

**1214** A140 40c green 1.00 .25
**1215** A140 50c dull purple 1.60 .25
**1216** A140 $1.40 car rose 3.75 .40
**1217** A140 $3.50 dk blue 9.50 1.75
*Nos. 1214-1217 (4)* 15.85 2.65

Adoption of the constitution, 10th anniv.

Chu Kwang Tower, Quemoy — A141

**1959-60 Wmk. 323 Litho. *Perf. 12***
**Without Gum**

**1218** A141 3c orange .30 .25
**1218A** A141 5c lt yel grn ('60) 4.75 .30
**1219** A141 10c lilac .45 .25
**1220** A141 20c ultra .55 .25
**1221** A141 40c brown .25 .25
**1222** A141 50c bluish grn 1.60 .25
**1223** A141 $1 rose red 1.10 .25
**1224** A141 $1.40 yel grn 2.10 .25
**1225** A141 $2 gray grn 2.75 .30
**1226** A141 $2.80 rose pink 9.50 .75
**1227** A141 $3 slate blue 8.25 .35
*Nos. 1218-1227 (11)* 31.60 3.45

See Nos. 1270-1283.

ILO Emblem and Headquarters, Geneva — A142

**1959, June 15 Engr. *Perf. 12***
**Without Gum**

**1228** A142 40c blue .40 .25
**1229** A142 $1.60 dk brown 1.00 .25
**1230** A142 $3 brt blue grn 1.40 .30
**1231** A142 $5 orange ver 2.50 .60
*Nos. 1228-1231 (4)* 5.30 1.40

40th anniversary of the ILO.

Bugler and Tents — A143

**1959, July 8 Unwmk.**
**Without Gum**

**1232** A143 40c carmine 1.00 .25
**1233** A143 50c dark blue 1.75 .30
**1234** A143 $5 green 4.50 .70
*Nos. 1232-1234 (3)* 7.25 1.25

10th World Boy Scout Jamboree, Makiling National Park, Philippines, July 17-26.

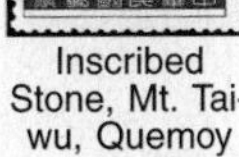

Inscribed Stone, Mt. Taiwu, Quemoy A144

Map of Taiwan Straits A145

**1959, Sept. 3 Engr. *Perf. 12***
**Without Gum**

**1235** A144 40c brown 2.00 .25
**1236** A145 $1.40 ultra 2.10 .25
**1237** A145 $2 green 4.00 .50
**1238** A144 $3 dark blue 4.75 .75
*Nos. 1235-1238 (4)* 12.85 1.75

Defense of Quemoy and Matsu islands. For overprints see Nos. 1258-1259.

Pigeons Circling Globe — A146

**1959, Oct. 4 Without Gum**

**1239** A146 40c blue .70 .25
**1240** A146 $1 rose carmine 1.20 .30
**1241** A146 $2 gray brown 1.60 .25
**1242** A146 $3.50 red orange 2.10 .60
*Nos. 1239-1242 (4)* 5.60 1.40

Intl. Letter Writing Week, Oct. 4-10.

National Taiwan Science Hall, Taipei — A147

**1959, Nov. 12 Photo. *Perf. 13x13½***

**1243** A147 40c shown .35 .25
**1244** A147 $3 Front view 1.25 .90

Emblem — A148

**1959, Dec. 7 Engr. *Perf. 12***
**Without Gum**

**1245** A148 40c blue green .60 .25
**1246** A148 $1.60 red lilac 1.60 .30
**1247** A148 $3 orange 2.40 .75
*Nos. 1245-1247 (3)* 4.60 1.30

Intl. Confederation of Free Trade Unions, 10th anniv.

Sun Yat-sen, Lincoln and Flags — A149

*Perf. 13½, 12*

**1959, Dec. 25 Photo. Unwmk.**

**1248** A149 40c multicolored .65 .30
**1249** A149 $3 multicolored 2.00 .60

Issued to honor Sun Yat-sen and Abraham Lincoln as "Leaders of Democracy."

Mailman on Motorcycle Delivering Night Mail — A150

Postal Launch — A151

**1960, Mar. 20 Engr. *Perf. 11½***
**Without Gum**

**1250** A150 $1.40 dk violet brn 2.40 .40
**1251** A151 $1.60 ultra 2.75 .50

Issued to publicize the Prompt Delivery Service.

WRY Uprooted Oak Emblem — A152

**1960, Apr. 7 Photo. *Perf. 13***

**1252** A152 40c blk, red brn & emer .75 .25
**1253** A152 $3 blk, red org & grn 1.75 .30

World Refugee Year, 7/1/59-6/30/60.

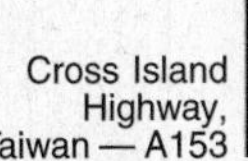

Cross Island Highway, Taiwan — A153

Design: $1, $2, Road through tunnel, vert.

*Perf. 11½*

**1960, May 9 Engr. Unwmk.**
**Without Gum**

**1254** A153 40c green 1.60 .25
**1255** A153 $1 dk blue 3.25 .50
**1256** A153 $2 brown vio 3.00 .40
**1257** A153 $3 brown 5.00 1.00
*a.* Souv. sheet of 2, #1255, 1257, wmk. 323, imperf. *300.00 140.00*
*Nos. 1254-1257 (4)* 12.85 2.15

Opening of the Cross Island Highway, Taiwan.

**Red Overprint on Nos. 1237-1238 Chinese and English: "Welcome U.S. President Dwight D. Eisenhower 1960"**

**1960, June 18 Unwmk. *Perf. 12***

| No. | Type | Denom. | Color | Unused | Used |
|---|---|---|---|---|---|
| **1258** | A145 | $2 | green | 2.25 | .40 |
| **1259** | A144 | $3 | dk blue | 3.00 | .90 |

Eisenhower's visit to China, June 18, 1960.

Phonopost — A154

**1960, June 27 Without Gum**

| No. | Type | Denom. | Color | Unused | Used |
|---|---|---|---|---|---|
| **1260** | A154 | $2 | red orange | 2.50 | .50 |

Phonopost Service of the Chinese armed forces.

Two Horses and Groom, by Han Kan — A155

Paintings from Palace Museum, Taichung: $1, Two Riders, by Wei Yen. $1.60, Flowers and Birds by Hsiao Yung, vert. $2, Pair of Mandarin Ducks by Monk Hui Ch'ung.

**1960, Aug. 4 Photo. *Perf. 13***

| No. | Type | Denom. | Color | Unused | Used |
|---|---|---|---|---|---|
| **1261** | A155 | $1 | ol gray, blk & brn | 6.00 | .70 |
| **1262** | A155 | $1.40 | bis brn, blk & fawn | 8.00 | 1.20 |
| **1263** | A155 | $1.60 | multicolored | 14.00 | 2.10 |
| **1264** | A155 | $2 | beige, blk & gray grn | 20.00 | 4.00 |
| | | | *Nos. 1261-1264 (4)* | 48.00 | 8.00 |

Chinese paintings, 7th-11th centuries.

For other painting types with large straight numerals in the upper corners and large Chinese characters on the side see A186, A241 and A285.

Youth Corps Flag and Summer Activities — A156

Design: $3, similar to 50c, horiz.

**1960, Aug. 20 Engr. *Perf. 12***
**Without Gum**

| No. | Type | Denom. | Color | Unused | Used |
|---|---|---|---|---|---|
| **1265** | A156 | 50c | slate green | .60 | .25 |
| **1266** | A156 | $3 | copper brown | 2.40 | .60 |

Summer activities of China Youth Corps.

Reforestation — A157

$2, Protection of forest. $3, Timber industry.

**1960, Aug. 29 Photo. *Perf. 13½x13***

| No. | Type | Denom. | Color | Unused | Used |
|---|---|---|---|---|---|
| **1267** | A157 | $1 | multicolored | 1.90 | .25 |
| **1268** | A157 | $2 | multicolored | 4.00 | .70 |
| **1269** | A157 | $3 | multicolored | 5.75 | 1.25 |
| *a.* | | | Souvenir sheet of 3 | 30.00 | 22.50 |
| | | | *Nos. 1267-1269 (3)* | 11.65 | 2.20 |

Fifth World Forestry Congress, Seattle, Washington, Aug. 29-Sept. 10.

No. 1269a contains Nos. 1267-1269 assembled as a triptych, 65½x40mm and imperf., but with simulated black perforations.

Chu Kwang Tower, Quemoy — A158

**1960-61 Wmk. 323 Litho. *Perf. 12***
**Without Gum**

| No. | Type | Denom. | Color | Unused | Used |
|---|---|---|---|---|---|
| **1270** | A158 | 3c | lt red brown | .30 | .25 |
| **1271** | A158 | 40c | pale violet | .30 | .25 |
| **1272** | A158 | 50c | orange ('61) | 1.00 | .25 |
| **1273** | A158 | 60c | rose lilac | .75 | .25 |
| **1274** | A158 | 80c | pale green | .30 | .25 |
| **1275** | A158 | $1 | gray grn ('61) | .80 | .25 |
| **1276** | A158 | $1.20 | gray olive | 1.50 | .25 |
| **1277** | A158 | $1.50 | ultra | 1.75 | .25 |
| **1278** | A158 | $2 | car rose ('61) | 1.25 | .25 |
| **1279** | A158 | $2.50 | pale blue | 2.50 | .25 |
| **1280** | A158 | $3 | bluish green | 3.75 | .25 |
| **1281** | A158 | $3.20 | lt red brown | 1.90 | .25 |
| **1282** | A158 | $3.60 | vio blue ('61) | 7.50 | .25 |
| **1283** | A158 | $4.50 | vermilion | 14.00 | .60 |
| | | | *Nos. 1270-1283 (14)* | 37.60 | 3.85 |

Issue dates: Nos. 1272, 1275, 1278 and 1282, Jan. 28, 1961; all others Oct. 5, 1960.

For surcharges see Nos. J132-J134.

**Without Gum**

**1962-64 Granite Paper**

| No. | Type | Denom. | Color | Unused | Used |
|---|---|---|---|---|---|
| *1270a* | A158 | 3c | light red brown | .30 | .25 |
| **1270B** | A158 | 10c | emer ('63) | 1.50 | .25 |
| *1271a* | A158 | 40c | pale violet | .30 | .25 |
| *1274a* | A158 | 80c | pale green | .30 | .25 |
| *1275a* | A158 | $1 | gray grn ('63) | 12.00 | .25 |
| *1278a* | A158 | $2 | carmine rose | 9.00 | .25 |
| *1281a* | A158 | $3.20 | red brn ('64) | 40.00 | .50 |
| **1282A** | A158 | $4 | brt blue grn | 15.00 | .25 |
| *1283a* | A158 | $4.50 | vermilion | 45.00 | 1.00 |
| | | | *Nos. 1270a-1283a (9)* | 123.40 | 3.25 |

Two types of No. 1271a: I. Seven lines in "0" of "40." II. Eight lines in "0."

Issue dates: Nos. 1270a, 1271a, Feb. 20, 1962; No. 1274a, March 20, 1962; No. 1282A, June 30, 1962; Nos. 1278a, 1283a, Dec. 1, 1962; No. 1270B, Dec. 15, 1963; No. 1281a, Jan. 25, 1964.

Sports — A159

***Perf. 12½***

**1960, Oct. 25 Photo. Unwmk.**

| No. | Type | Denom. | Color | Unused | Used |
|---|---|---|---|---|---|
| **1284** | A159 | 50c | Diving | 1.25 | .25 |
| **1285** | A159 | 80c | Discus thrower | 1.00 | .25 |
| **1286** | A159 | $2 | Basketball | 1.75 | .30 |
| **1287** | A159 | $2.50 | Soccer | 3.50 | .55 |
| **1288** | A159 | $3 | Hurdling | 4.00 | .75 |
| **1289** | A159 | $3.20 | Runner | 5.25 | 1.00 |
| | | | *Nos. 1284-1289 (6)* | 16.75 | 3.10 |

Bronze Wine Container, 1751-1111 B.C. — A160

Ancient Chinese Art Treasures: $1, Cauldron, 1111-771 B.C. $1.20, Porcelain vase, 960-1126 A.D. $1.50, Perforated tube, 1111-771 B.C. $2, Jug in shape of monk's cap, 1368-1661 A.D. $2.50, Jade flower vase, 1368-1661, A.D.

**1961 Photo. *Perf. 13***

| No. | Type | Denom. | Color | Unused | Used |
|---|---|---|---|---|---|
| **1290** | A160 | 80c | lt ol, blk & dk vio | 1.20 | .30 |
| **1291** | A160 | $1 | sal, bl & blk | 2.40 | .45 |
| **1292** | A160 | $1.20 | yel, brn & ultra | 4.00 | .60 |
| **1293** | A160 | $1.50 | lil, bl & sep | 6.00 | .80 |
| **1294** | A160 | $2 | pale grn, dk grn & red brn | 10.00 | .85 |
| **1295** | A160 | $2.50 | grnsh bl & dk vio | 16.50 | 1.00 |
| | | | *Nos. 1290-1295 (6)* | 40.10 | 4.00 |

Issue dates: Nos. 1290, 1292, 1295, Feb. 1. Nos. 1291, 1293-1294, May 1.

Flat Bowl, 1111-771 B.C. — A161

80c, Palace perfumer, 1662-1911. $1, Corn vase, 770-221 B.C. $2, Jade tankard, 960-1126 A.D. $4, Glazed washer, 1127-1279 A.D. $4.50, Jade chimera, 8 B.C.-206 A.D.

**1961**

| No. | Type | Denom. | Color | Unused | Used |
|---|---|---|---|---|---|
| **1296** | A160 | 80c | pink, brn, bl & yel | .60 | .30 |
| **1297** | A160 | $1 | cit, blk & brn | 4.00 | 1.00 |
| **1298** | A161 | $1.50 | sal & ind | 4.50 | 1.25 |
| **1299** | A160 | $2 | bl, blk & rose | 23.00 | 2.25 |
| **1300** | A161 | $4 | red, blk & bluish gray | 8.00 | 1.00 |
| **1301** | A161 | $4.50 | grnsh bl, blk & brn | 60.00 | 4.25 |
| | | | *Nos. 1296-1301 (6)* | 100.10 | 10.05 |

Issued: Nos. 1296-1298, 8/15; Nos. 1299-1301, 9/15.

**1962**

Designs: 80c, Topaz twin wine vessels, 1662-1911 A.D. $1, Squat pouring vase, 1751-1111 B.C. $2.40, Vase, 1368-1661 A.D. $3, Wine vase, 1751-1111 B.C. $3.20, Covered porcelain jar, 1662-1911 A.D. $3.60, Perforated disc, 206 B.C.-8 A.D.

| No. | Type | Denom. | Color | Unused | Used |
|---|---|---|---|---|---|
| **1302** | A160 | 80c | crim, blk & ocher | .75 | .30 |
| **1303** | A160 | $1 | blue & vio blk | 3.25 | 1.00 |
| **1304** | A160 | $2.40 | hn brn, blk & bl | 13.50 | 2.00 |
| **1305** | A160 | $3 | blue, blk & pink | 95.00 | 6.00 |
| **1306** | A160 | $3.20 | ultra, lt grn & red | 28.00 | 3.00 |
| **1307** | A160 | $3.60 | yel, blk & brn | 34.00 | 3.25 |
| | | | *Nos. 1302-1307 (6)* | 174.50 | 15.55 |

Issue dates: Nos. 1303-1304, 1307, Jan. 15. Nos. 1302, 1305-1306, Feb. 15.

Farmer with Mechanized Plow — A162

**1961, Feb. 4 Engr. *Perf. 12***
**Without Gum**

| No. | Type | Denom. | Color | Unused | Used |
|---|---|---|---|---|---|
| **1308** | A162 | 80c | rose violet | 1.50 | .25 |
| **1309** | A162 | $2 | green | 3.50 | .50 |
| **1310** | A162 | $3.20 | vermilion | 5.50 | .35 |
| | | | *Nos. 1308-1310 (3)* | 10.50 | 1.10 |

1961 agricultural census.

Madame Chiang Kai-shek and League Emblem — A163

**Unwmk.**

**1961, Mar. 8 Photo. *Perf. 13***
**Portrait in Black**

| No. | Type | Denom. | Color | Unused | Used |
|---|---|---|---|---|---|
| **1311** | A163 | 80c | lt grn & car rose | 3.50 | .25 |
| **1312** | A163 | $1 | yel grn & car rose | 7.25 | .50 |
| **1313** | A163 | $2 | org brn & car rose | 7.25 | .75 |
| **1314** | A163 | $3.20 | lil & car rose | 11.25 | 2.00 |
| | | | *Nos. 1311-1314 (4)* | 29.25 | 3.50 |

10th anniversary of the Chinese Women's Anti-Aggression League.

Spiny Lobster and Mail Order Service Emblem — A164

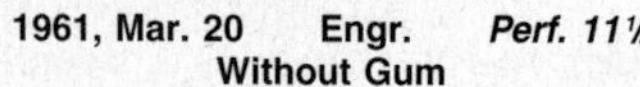

**1961, Mar. 20 Engr. *Perf. 11½***
**Without Gum**

| No. | Type | Denom. | Color | Unused | Used |
|---|---|---|---|---|---|
| **1315** | A164 | $3 | slate green | 6.75 | .75 |

Issued to publicize the mail order service for consumer goods.

Jeme Tien-yow and Pataling Tunnel — A165

$2, Jeme Tien-yow & 1909 locomotive.

**1961, Apr. 26 *Perf. 11½***
**Without Gum**

| No. | Type | Denom. | Color | Unused | Used |
|---|---|---|---|---|---|
| **1316** | A165 | 80c | lilac | 1.75 | .25 |
| **1317** | A165 | $2 | black, horiz. | 5.50 | .75 |

Centenary of the birth of Jeme Tien-yow, builder of the Peking-Kalgan railroad.

Map of China inscribed: "Recovery of the Mainland" A166

Pres. Chiang Kai-shek — A167

**1961, May 20 Photo. *Perf. 13½***

| No. | Type | Denom. | Color | Unused | Used |
|---|---|---|---|---|---|
| **1318** | A166 | 80c | multicolored | 3.00 | .25 |
| **1319** | A167 | $2 | multicolored | 11.00 | 1.50 |
| *a.* | | | Souvenir sheet of 2 | 32.50 | 30.00 |

1st anniversary of Pres. Chiang Kai-shek's 3rd term inauguration.

No. 1319a contains one each of Nos. 1318-1319, imperf. with simulated perforations. Without gum.

Convair 880-M, Biplane of 1921 and Flag — A168

**1961, July 1 *Perf. 13x12½***

| No. | Type | Denom. | Color | Unused | Used |
|---|---|---|---|---|---|
| **1320** | A168 | $10 | multicolored | 7.25 | 1.20 |

40th anniversary of civil air service.

Sun Yat-sen and Chiang Kai-shek A169

Flag and Map of China A170

***Perf. 13½***

**1961, Oct. 10 Unwmk. Photo.**

| No. | Type | Denom. | Color | Unused | Used |
|---|---|---|---|---|---|
| **1321** | A169 | 80c | gray, lt brn & sl | 1.50 | .25 |
| **1322** | A170 | $5 | gray, ultra, red & beige | 9.50 | 1.75 |
| *a.* | | | Souvenir sheet of 2 | 20.00 | 20.00 |

50th anniv. of the Republic of China. No. 1322a contains one each of Nos. 1321-1322, imperf. with simulated perforations. No gum.

Green Lake A171

Lotus Pond A172

Taiwan Scenery: $2, Sun-Moon Lake. $3.20, Wulai waterfalls.

*Perf. 13½x14, 14x13½*

**1961, Oct. 31 Unwmk.**

**1323** A171 80c multicolored 2.50 .25
**1324** A172 $1 multicolored 8.75 1.00
**1325** A172 $2 multicolored 13.50 1.40
**1326** A171 $3.20 multicolored 28.00 2.25
*Nos. 1323-1326 (4)* 52.75 4.90

Oil Refinery — A173

Designs: $1.50, Steel works. $2.50, Aluminum plant. $3.20, Fertilizer plant, horiz.

**1961, Nov. 14** ***Perf. 11½***

**1327** A173 80c multicolored .85 .25
**1328** A173 $1.50 multicolored 5.75 .80
**1329** A173 $2.50 multicolored 8.00 1.00
**1330** A173 $3.20 multicolored 9.25 1.75
*Nos. 1327-1330 (4)* 23.85 3.80

Chinese industrial development and the Golden Jubilee Convention of the Chinese Institute of Engineers, Nov. 13-16.

Atomic Reactor, Tsing-Hwa University A174

Atomic Reactor in Operation A175

Design: $3.20, Atomic symbol and laboratory, Tsing-Hwa, horiz.

**1961-62 Photo.** ***Perf. 12½***

**1331** A174 80c multicolored 3.00 .25
**1332** A175 $2 multicolored 6.75 2.00
**1333** A175 $3.20 multicolored 7.25 1.00
*Nos. 1331-1333 (3)* 17.00 3.25

Inauguration on Apr. 13, 1961, of the 1st Chinese atomic reactor at the National Tsing-Hwa University Institute of Nuclear Science.

Issued: 80c, 12/2; $2, $3.20, 3/20/62.

Microwave Reflector and Telegraph Wires — A176

Design: $3.20, Microwave parabolic antenna and mountains, horiz.

**1961, Dec. 28** ***Perf. 12½***

**1334** A176 80c multicolored 1.75 .25
**1335** A176 $3.20 multicolored 3.75 1.00

80th anniv. of Chinese telecommunications.

Mechanical Postal Equipment and Twine Tying Machine A176a

**Wmk. 323**

**1962, Mar. 20 Engr.** ***Perf. 11½***

**Without Gum**

**1336** A176a 80c chocolate 2.50 .50

Yu Shan Observatory — A177

Map Showing Route of Typhoon Pamela, Sept. 1961 — A177a

Observation Balloon, Earth and Cumulus Clouds — A178

**1962 Without Gum**

**1337** A177 80c brown .75 .25
**1338** A177a $1 bluish black 2.25 .45
**1339** A178 $2 green 4.00 .70
*Nos. 1337-1339 (3)* 7.00 1.40

Issue dates: 80c, $2, Mar. 23; $1, May 7. World Meteorological Day, Mar. 23.

Child Receiving Milk, UN Emblem — A179

**1962, Apr. 4 Without Gum**

**1340** A179 80c rose red .85 .25
**1341** A179 $3.20 green 4.00 .60
*a.* Souvenir sheet of 2 17.50 5.50

15th anniv. of UNICEF. No. 1341a contains one each of Nos. 1340-1341 imperf. with simulated perforations.

Malaria Eradication Emblem — A180

**Unwmk.**

**1962, Apr. 7 Photo.** ***Perf. 13***

**1342** A180 80c dk bl, red & lt grn .65 .25
**1343** A180 $3.60 brn, pink & grn 2.75 .90

WHO drive to eradicate malaria.

Yu Yu-jen — A181

**1962, Apr. 24** ***Perf. 13***

**1344** A181 80c gray, blk & pink 3.00 .40

Issued to honor Yu Yu-jen, newspaper reporter, revolutionary leader and co-worker of Sun Yat-sen, on his 84th birthday.

Cheng Ch'eng-kung (Koxinga) — A182

**1962, Apr. 29**

**1345** A182 80c deep claret 2.40 .25
**1346** A182 $2 dark green 11.00 1.25

300th anniversary (in 1961) of the recovery of Taiwan from the Dutch by Koxinga.

Emblem of Intl. Cooperative Alliance A183

Clasped Hands Across Globe A184

**Wmk. 323**

**1962, July 7 Engr.** ***Perf. 12***

**Without Gum**

**1347** A183 80c brown .50 .25
**1348** A184 $2 violet 3.75 .75

Intl. Cooperative Movement and 40th Intl. Cooperative Day, July 7, 1962.

**Mansion Type of 1958**

**1962, July 20 Without Gum**

**1349** A135 $5 gray green 7.50 .25
**1350** A135 $5.60 violet 10.50 .35
**1351** A135 $6 orange 9.25 .30
*Nos. 1349-1351 (3)* 27.25 .90

**1963 Granite Paper**

*1349a* A135 $5 gray green 6.00 .25
*1350a* A135 $5.60 violet 6.00 .25
*1351a* A135 $6 orange 15.00 .40
*Nos. 1349a-1351a (3)* 27.00 .90

"Art and Science" — A185

$2, "Education," book and UNESCO emblem, horiz. $3.20, "Communications," globes, horiz.

**1962, Aug. 28 Wmk. 323** ***Perf. 12***

**Without Gum**

**1352** A185 80c lilac rose .40 .25
**1353** A185 $2 rose claret 3.00 .50
**1354** A185 $3.20 yellow green 3.00 .40
*Nos. 1352-1354 (3)* 6.40 1.15

UNESCO activities in China.

Emperor T'ai Tsung, T'ang Dynasty, 627-649 — A186

Emperors: $2, T'ai Tsu, Sung dynasty, 960-975. $3.20, T'ai Tsu, Yuan dynasty (Genghis Khan), 1206-27. $4, T'ai Tsu, Ming dynasty, 1368-98.

**1962, Sept. 20 Photo. Unwmk.**

**1355** A186 80c multicolored 20.00 1.25
**1356** A186 $2 multicolored 75.00 9.75
**1357** A186 $3.20 multicolored 125.00 7.25
**1358** A186 $4 multicolored 150.00 17.00
*Nos. 1355-1358 (4)* 370.00 35.25

Lions International Emblem — A187

**1962, Oct. 8** ***Perf. 13½***

**1359** A187 80c multicolored 1.10 .25
**1360** A187 $3.60 multicolored 3.25 1.00
*a.* Souvenir sheet of 2 35.00 17.00

45th anniv. of Lions Intl. No. 1360a contains one each of Nos. 1359-1360, imperf. with simulated perforations.

Pole Vaulting A188

Shooting A189

**1962, Oct. 25 Unwmk.** ***Perf. 13***

**1361** A188 80c multicolored 1.00 .25
**1362** A189 $3.20 multicolored 3.75 .60

Sports meet.

Young Farmers and 4-H Emblem — A190

Design: $3.20, 4-H emblem and rice.

**Wmk. 323**

**1962, Dec. 7 Engr.** ***Perf. 12***

**Without Gum**

**1363** A190 80c carmine .75 .25
**1364** A190 $3.20 green 3.75 .80
*a.* Souvenir sheet of 2 24.00 12.00

10th anniv. of the 4-H Club in China. No. 1364a contains one each of Nos. 1363-1364, imperf. with simulated perforations.

Flag, Liner of China Merchants' Steam Navigation Co. — A191

Design: $3.60, Company's Pacific navigation chart and freighter, horiz.

*Perf. 13½*

**1962, Dec. 16 Unwmk. Photo.**

**1365** A191 80c multicolored 1.25 .25
**1366** A191 $3.60 multicolored 6.50 1.60

90th anniversary of the China Merchants' Steam Navigation Co., Ltd.

Farm Woman, Tractor and Plane Dropping Food over Mainland — A192

*Perf. 12½*

**1963, Mar. 21 Unwmk. Photo.**

**1367** A192 $10 multicolored 7.25 1.20

FAO "Freedom from Hunger" campaign.

Torch, Young Couple and Martyrs' Monument, Canton — A193

**Wmk. 323**

**1963, Mar. 29 Engr.** ***Perf. 11½***

**Without Gum**

**1368** A193 80c purple .60 .25
**1369** A193 $3.20 green 3.50 .60

Issued for the 20th Youth Day.

Swallows, Pagoda and AOPU Emblem — A194

Designs: $2, Northern gannet, horiz. $6, Japanese crane and pine.

**Unwmk.**

**1963, Apr. 1 Photo. *Perf. 13***

| | | | | |
|---|---|---|---|---|
| **1370** A194 | 80c multicolored | 2.40 | .25 |
| **1371** A194 | $2 multicolored | 4.75 | .65 |
| **1372** A194 | $6 multicolored | 20.00 | 3.25 |
| | *Nos. 1370-1372 (3)* | 27.15 | 4.15 |

1st anniversary of the formation of the Asian-Oceanic Postal Union, AOPU.

Refugee Girl (Li Ying) and Map of China A195

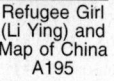

Refugees Fleeing Mainland A196

**Wmk. 323**

**1963, June 27 Engr. *Perf. 11½***

**Without Gum**

| | | | |
|---|---|---|---|
| **1373** A195 | 80c bluish black | 2.40 | .25 |
| **1374** A196 | $3.20 dp claret | 7.25 | .60 |

1st anniv. of the evacuation of Chinese mainland refugees from Hong Kong to Taiwan. Designs from photographs of refugees.

Nurse and Red Cross — A197

Design: $10, Globe and Red Cross.

***Perf. 12½***

**1963, Sept. 1 Unwmk. Photo.**

| | | | |
|---|---|---|---|
| **1375** A197 | 80c black & carmine | 3.00 | .25 |
| **1376** A197 | $10 slate, gray & car | 12.00 | 4.25 |

Centenary of International Red Cross.

Basketball Player, Stadium and Asian Cup — A198

$2, Hands reaching for ball and Asian cup.

**Wmk. 323**

**1963, Nov. 20 Engr. *Perf. 12***

**Without Gum**

| | | | |
|---|---|---|---|
| **1377** A198 | 80c lilac rose | 1.00 | .25 |
| **1378** A198 | $2 violet | 2.75 | .80 |

The 2nd Asian Basketball Championship, Taipei, Nov. 20.

UN Emblem, Torch and Men — A199

Scales and Men of Various Races — A200

**1963, Dec. 10 Wmk. 323 *Perf. 11½***

**Without Gum**

| | | | |
|---|---|---|---|
| **1379** A199 | 80c brt green | .50 | .25 |
| **1380** A200 | $3.20 maroon | 2.25 | .65 |

Universal Declaration of Human Rights, 15th anniversary.

Village and Orchids A201

"Kindle the Fire of Conscience" A202

***Perf. 13½x13***

**1963, Dec. 17 Photo. Unwmk.**

| | | | |
|---|---|---|---|
| **1381** A201 | 40c multicolored | 2.75 | .30 |
| **1382** A202 | $4.50 multicolored | 11.00 | 2.50 |

Contribution of the Good-People-Good-Deeds campaign to improve ethical standards.

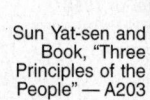

Sun Yat-sen and Book, "Three Principles of the People" — A203

**1963, Dec. 25 *Perf. 13***

| | | | |
|---|---|---|---|
| **1383** A203 | $5 blue & multi | 14.00 | 2.00 |

"Land-to-the-Tillers" program, 10th anniv. An 80c was prepared but not issued.

Torch A204

Hands Unchained A205

**Wmk. 323**

**1964, Jan. 23 Engr. *Perf. 11½***

**Without Gum**

| | | | |
|---|---|---|---|
| **1384** A204 | 80c red orange | .85 | .25 |
| **1385** A205 | $3.20 indigo | 3.75 | .60 |

Liberty Day, 10th anniversary.

Broadleaf Cactus — A206

Designs: $1, Crab cactus. $3.20, Nopalxochia. $5, Grizzly bear cactus.

***Perf. 12½***

**1964, Feb. 27 Unwmk. Photo.**

**Plants in Original Colors**

| | | | |
|---|---|---|---|
| **1386** A206 | 80c dp plum & fawn | 4.50 | .25 |
| **1387** A206 | $1 dk blue & car | 9.50 | 1.20 |
| **1388** A206 | $3.20 green | 9.50 | .60 |
| **1389** A206 | $5 lilac & yellow | 12.50 | 2.40 |
| | *Nos. 1386-1389 (4)* | 36.00 | 4.45 |

Wu Chih-hwei — A207

**Wmk. 323**

**1964, Mar. 25 Engr. *Perf. 11½***

**Without Gum**

| | | | |
|---|---|---|---|
| **1390** A207 | 80c black brown | 2.25 | .40 |

Centenary of the birth of Wu Chih-hwei (1865-1953), politician and leader of the Kuomintang.

Chu Kwang Tower, Quemoy — A208

***Perf. 13x12½***

**1964-66 Wmk. 323 Litho.**

**Granite Paper; Without Gum**

| | | | |
|---|---|---|---|
| **1391** A208 | 3c sepia | .30 | .25 |
| **1392** A208 | 5c brt yel grn ('65) | .30 | .25 |
| **1393** A208 | 10c yellow grn | .30 | .25 |
| **1394** A208 | 20c slate grn ('65) | .30 | .25 |
| **1395** A208 | 40c rose red | .30 | .25 |
| **1396** A208 | 50c brown | .45 | .25 |
| **1397** A208 | 80c orange ('65) | .90 | .25 |
| **1398** A208 | $1 violet ('65) | .45 | .25 |
| **1399** A208 | $1.50 brt lilac ('66) | 9.00 | 1.20 |
| **1400** A208 | $2 lilac rose | 1.15 | .25 |
| **1401** A208 | $2.50 ultra ('65) | 3.50 | .25 |
| **1402** A208 | $3 slate | 5.25 | .40 |
| **1403** A208 | $3.20 brt blue | 5.75 | .30 |
| **1404** A208 | $4 brt green | 4.50 | .25 |
| | *Nos. 1391-1404 (14)* | 32.45 | 4.65 |

Nurses Holding Candles A209

Florence Nightingale and Student Nurse A210

**1964, May 12 Engr. *Perf. 11½***

**Without Gum**

| | | | |
|---|---|---|---|
| **1406** A209 | 80c violet blue | 1.50 | .25 |
| **1407** A210 | $4 red | 6.25 | 1.40 |

Issued for Nurses Day.

Shihmen Reservoir — A211

Designs: $1, Irrigation system. $3.20, Main dam and power plant. $5, Spillway.

***Perf. 12½***

**1964, June 14 Unwmk. Photo.**

| | | | |
|---|---|---|---|
| **1408** A211 | 80c multicolored | 3.00 | .30 |
| **1409** A211 | $1 multicolored | 3.25 | .80 |
| **1410** A211 | $3.20 multicolored | 6.00 | .70 |
| **1411** A211 | $5 multicolored | 19.00 | 3.25 |
| | *Nos. 1408-1411 (4)* | 31.25 | 5.05 |

Completion of Shihmen Reservoir.

15th Century Ship, Modern Liner — A212

**Wmk. 323**

**1964, July 11 Engr. *Perf. 11½***

**Without Gum**

| | | | |
|---|---|---|---|
| **1412** A212 | $2 orange | 1.00 | .25 |
| **1413** A212 | $3.60 brt green | 4.00 | .80 |

China's 10th Navigation Day.

Bananas — A213

**Unwmk.**

**1964, July 25 Photo. *Perf. 14***

| | | | |
|---|---|---|---|
| **1414** A213 | 80c shown | *7.00* | .50 |
| **1415** A213 | $1 Oranges | *20.00* | 2.00 |
| **1416** A213 | $3.20 Pineapple | *23.50* | 2.00 |
| **1417** A213 | $4 Watermelon | *37.50* | 5.00 |
| | *Nos. 1414-1417 (4)* | *88.00* | 9.50 |

Artillery, Warships, Jet Fighters — A214

**Wmk. 323**

**1964, Sept. 3 Engr. *Perf. 11½***

**Without Gum**

| | | | |
|---|---|---|---|
| **1418** A214 | 80c dk blue | 1.60 | .35 |
| **1419** A214 | $6 violet brown | 6.75 | 1.75 |

Issued for the 10th Armed Forces Day.

Unisphere, Flags of China and U.S. A215

Chinese Pavilion, NY World's Fair A216

**1964, Sept. 10 Photo. Unwmk.**

| | | | |
|---|---|---|---|
| **1420** A215 | 80c violet & multi | 1.60 | .25 |
| **1421** A216 | $5 blue & multi | 12.50 | 2.25 |

NY World's Fair, 1964-65. See Nos. 1450-1451.

Cowboy Carrying Calf, and Ranch — A217

**Wmk. 323**

**1964, Sept. 24 Engr. *Perf. 11½***

**Without Gum**

| | | | |
|---|---|---|---|
| **1422** A217 | $2 brown lake | 1.60 | .30 |
| **1423** A217 | $4 dark violet blue | 6.50 | 1.60 |

Animal Protection Week, Sept. 24-30.

Bicycling — A218

Sports: $1, Runner. $3.20, Gymnast on rings. $10, High jump.

**1964, Oct. 10 Without Gum**

| | | | |
|---|---|---|---|
| **1424** A218 | 80c violet blue | .40 | .25 |
| **1425** A218 | $1 rose red | .60 | .40 |
| **1426** A218 | $3.20 dull blue grn | 3.00 | .60 |
| **1427** A218 | $10 lilac | 9.00 | 2.40 |
| | *Nos. 1424-1427 (4)* | 13.00 | 3.65 |

18th Olympic Games, Tokyo, Oct. 10-25.

Xu Guangqi — A219

**1964, Nov. 8 Engr. *Perf. 11½***

**Without Gum**

| | | | |
|---|---|---|---|
| **1428** A219 | 80c indigo | 3.25 | .50 |

Issued to honor Xu Guangqi (1562-1633), scholar and statesman.

Pharmaceutical Industry A220

Textile Industry A221

$2, Chemical industry. $3.60, Cement industry.

**1964, Nov. 11 Photo. Unwmk.**

| | | | | |
|---|---|---|---|---|
| **1429** A220 | 40c multi | | 1.00 | .25 |
| **1430** A221 | $1.50 multi | | 8.00 | 1.75 |
| **1431** A220 | $2 multi | | 4.50 | .75 |
| **1432** A221 | $3.60 multi | | 12.00 | 1.90 |
| | *Nos. 1429-1432 (4)* | | 25.50 | 4.65 |

Dr. Sun Yat-sen — A222

**1964, Nov. 24 Engr. Wmk. 323**
**Without Gum**

| | | | |
|---|---|---|---|
| **1433** A222 | 80c green | 1.95 | .25 |
| **1434** A222 | $3.60 purple | 7.50 | 1.75 |

Founding of the Kuomintang by Sun Yat-sen, 70th anniversary.

Eleanor Roosevelt and Scales of Justice — A223

**Unwmk.**
**1964, Dec. 10 Photo. *Perf. 13***

| | | | |
|---|---|---|---|
| **1435** A223 | $10 violet & brown | 3.25 | .80 |

Issued to honor Eleanor Roosevelt (1884-1962) on the 16th anniversary of the Universal Declaration of Human Rights.

Scales, Code Book and Plum Blossom — A224

**Wmk. 323**
**1965, Jan. 11 Engr. *Perf. 11½***
**Without Gum**

| | | | |
|---|---|---|---|
| **1436** A224 | 80c carmine rose | .60 | .25 |
| **1437** A224 | $3.20 dull slate grn | 4.00 | .80 |

The 20th Judicial Day.

Rotary Emblem and Mainspring — A225

**1965, Feb. 23 Wmk. 323 *Perf. 11½***
**Without Gum**

| | | | |
|---|---|---|---|
| **1438** A225 | $1.50 vermilion | 1.00 | .25 |
| **1439** A225 | $2 emerald | 2.00 | .40 |
| **1440** A225 | $2.50 blue | 2.75 | .60 |
| | *Nos. 1438-1440 (3)* | 5.75 | 1.25 |

Rotary International, 60th anniversary.

Double Carp Design — A226

**Wmk. 323**
**1965, Mar. 29 Engr. *Perf. 11½***
**Granite Paper; Without Gum**

| | | | |
|---|---|---|---|
| **1441** A226 | $5 purple | 12.00 | .40 |
| **1442** A226 | $5.60 dp blue | 10.00 | 5.00 |
| **1443** A226 | $6 brown | 10.50 | .60 |
| **1444** A226 | $10 lilac rose | 12.00 | .40 |
| **1445** A226 | $20 rose car | 23.00 | 1.00 |
| **1446** A226 | $50 green | 40.00 | 4.00 |
| **1447** A226 | $100 crim rose | 160.00 | 12.00 |
| | *Nos. 1441-1447 (7)* | 267.50 | 23.40 |

New dies used to reprint Nos. 1444-1447, 8/20/67. Remainders of Nos. 1441-1447 issued with gum, 11/1/71.

Madame Chiang Kai-shek — A227

**1965, Apr. 17 Photo. Unwmk.**

| | | | |
|---|---|---|---|
| **1448** A227 | $2 multicolored | 10.00 | 1.00 |
| **1449** A227 | $6 salmon & multi | 65.00 | 9.00 |

Chinese Women's Anti-Aggression League, 15th anniversary.

Unisphere and Chinese Pavilion A228

"100 Birds Paying Homage to Queen Phoenix" and Unisphere A229

**1965, May 8**

| | | | |
|---|---|---|---|
| **1450** A228 | $2 blue & multi | 24.00 | .60 |
| **1451** A229 | $10 red, ocher & bis | 36.00 | 4.00 |

New York World's Fair, 1964-65.

ITU Emblem, Old and New Communication Equipment — A230

Design: $5, similar to 80c, vert.

***Perf. 13½x13, 13x13½***
**1965, May 17 Photo. Unwmk.**

| | | | |
|---|---|---|---|
| **1452** A230 | 80c multicolored | 1.25 | .25 |
| **1453** A230 | $5 multicolored | 5.00 | 1.00 |

Centenary of the ITU.

Red Sea Bream — A231

Fish: 80c, White pomfret. $2, Skipjack, vert. $4, Moonfish.

**1965, July 1 *Perf. 13***

| | | | |
|---|---|---|---|
| **1454** A231 | 40c multicolored | 2.25 | .25 |
| **1455** A231 | 80c multicolored | 4.50 | .40 |
| **1456** A231 | $2 multicolored | 10.25 | 1.20 |
| **1457** A231 | $4 multicolored | 22.75 | 2.25 |
| | *Nos. 1454-1457 (4)* | 39.75 | 4.10 |

Issued for Fishermen's Day.

Confucius — A232

Portraits: $2.50, Yueh Fei. $3.50, Wen Tien-hsiang. $3.60, Mencius.

**Wmk. 323**
**1965-66 Engr. *Perf. 11½***
**Without Gum**

| | | | |
|---|---|---|---|
| **1458** A232 | $1 deep carmine | 2.25 | .40 |
| **1459** A232 | $2.50 black brown | 2.00 | .40 |
| **1460** A232 | $3.50 dark red | 10.00 | 2.00 |
| **1461** A232 | $3.60 dark blue | 11.00 | 2.25 |
| | *Nos. 1458-1461 (4)* | 25.25 | 5.05 |

The $2.50 and $3.50 have colored background.

Forgeries of No. 1461 exist.

Issued: Nos. 1458, 1461, 9/28/65; Nos. 1459-1460, 9/3/66.

See Nos. 1507-1508, design A251.

ICY Emblem — A233

Design: $6, ICY emblem, horiz.

**Unwmk.**
**1965, Oct. 24 Photo. *Perf. 13***

| | | | |
|---|---|---|---|
| **1462** A233 | $2 brn, blk & gold | 1.25 | .30 |
| **1463** A233 | $6 brt grn, red & gold | 8.50 | 1.75 |

International Cooperation Year, 1965.

Street Crossing, Traffic Light — A234

**Wmk. 323**
**1965, Nov. 1 Engr. *Perf. 11½***
**Without Gum**

| | | | |
|---|---|---|---|
| **1464** A234 | $1 brown violet | 1.10 | .25 |
| **1465** A234 | $4 crimson rose | 5.50 | 1.00 |

Issued to publicize traffic safety.

Sun Yat-sen — A235

Designs: $4, Dr. Sun Yat-sen, portrait at right. $5, Sun Yat-sen and flags, horiz.

***Perf. 13½***
**1965, Nov. 12 Unwmk. Photo.**

| | | | |
|---|---|---|---|
| **1466** A235 | $1 multicolored | 3.00 | .40 |
| **1467** A235 | $4 multicolored | 6.00 | 1.00 |
| **1468** A235 | $5 multicolored | 17.50 | 4.75 |
| | *Nos. 1466-1468 (3)* | 26.50 | 6.15 |

Children with New Year's Firecrackers A236

Dragon Dance, "Dragon Playing Ball" A237

**1965, Dec. 1 Photo. *Perf. 13***

| | | | |
|---|---|---|---|
| **1469** A236 | $1 multi | 4.00 | .40 |
| **1470** A237 | $4.50 multi | 18.50 | 2.50 |

Lien Po from "Marshal and Prime Minister Reconciled" — A238

Facial Paintings for Chinese Operas: $3, Kuan Yü from "Reunion at Ku City." $4, Gen. Chang Fei from "The Battle of Chang Pan Hill." $6, Buddha from "The Flower-Scattering Angel."

**1966, Feb. 15 Unwmk. *Perf. 11½***

| | | | |
|---|---|---|---|
| **1471** A238 | $1 olive & multi | 8.00 | 1.00 |
| **1472** A238 | $3 multicolored | 17.50 | 2.00 |
| **1473** A238 | $4 multicolored | 38.00 | 4.00 |
| **1474** A238 | $6 ver & multi | 42.50 | 6.00 |
| | *Nos. 1471-1474 (4)* | 106.00 | 13.00 |

Labels with a similar appearance to these stamps exist. These labels have the numbers 1 to 20 in the upper right corner, but lack the "00."

Postal Service Emblem Held by Carrier Pigeon A239

Stone, Mt. Tai-wu, Quemoy, and Mailman A240

postal service emblem and: $3, Postal Museum. $4, Mailman climbing symbolic slope.

**1966, Mar. 20 Photo. *Perf. 12½***

| | | | |
|---|---|---|---|
| **1475** A239 | $1 green & multi | 1.25 | .25 |
| **1476** A240 | $2 multicolored | 4.00 | .60 |
| **1477** A240 | $3 multicolored | 5.50 | .75 |
| **1478** A239 | $4 multicolored | 9.00 | 2.25 |
| | *Nos. 1475-1478 (4)* | 19.75 | 3.85 |

China postal service, 70th anniversary.

Fishing on a Snowy Day, "Five Dynasties" (907-960) — A241

Paintings from Palace Museum: $3.50, Calves on the Plain, Sung artist (960-1126). $4.50, Winter landscape, Sung artist (960-1126). $5, Magpies, by Lin Ch'un, Southern Sung dynasty (1127-1279).

**1966, May 20 Photo. *Perf. 13***

| | | | |
|---|---|---|---|
| **1479** A241 | $2.50 blk, brn & red | 9.00 | .60 |
| **1480** A241 | $3.50 bis brn, blk & gray | 23.75 | .75 |
| **1481** A241 | $4.50 blk, buff & sl | 33.50 | 2.25 |
| **1482** A241 | $5 multicolored | 43.50 | 4.50 |
| | *Nos. 1479-1482 (4)* | 109.75 | 8.10 |

Inauguration of Pres. Chiang Kai-shek for a 4th term.

Dragon Boat Race A242

Lion Dance A243

$4, Lady Chang O flying to the Moon.

**1966 Unwmk.**

| | | | |
|---|---|---|---|
| **1483** A242 | $2.50 multi | 5.50 | .60 |
| **1484** A242 | $4 multi | 10.00 | .80 |
| **1485** A243 | $6 multi | 20.00 | 1.75 |
| | *Nos. 1483-1485 (3)* | 35.50 | 3.15 |

Dragon Boat, Mid-Autumn and Lunar New Year Festivals. Issued: $2.50, 6/23; $4, 9/29; $6, 11/26.

Flags of China and Argentina — A244

**1966, July 9 Photo. *Perf. 13***

| | | | |
|---|---|---|---|
| **1486** A244 | $10 multicolored | 6.00 | .75 |

Argentina's Independence. 150th anniv.

Lin Sen — A245

**Wmk. 323**

**1966, Aug. 1 Engr. *Perf. 11½***
**Without Gum**

| | | | | |
|---|---|---|---|---|
| **1487** | A245 $1 dk brown | | 3.00 | .40 |

Centenary of the birth of Lin Sen (1867-1943), Chairman of the Nationalist Government of China (1931-43).

Flying Geese — A246

**1966-67 *Perf. 11½ Rough***
**Granite Paper; Without Gum**

| | | | | |
|---|---|---|---|---|
| **1496** | A246 | $3.50 brown | 1.50 | .25 |
| **1497** | A246 | $4 vermilion | 1.00 | .25 |
| **1498** | A246 | $4.50 brt green | 1.25 | .25 |
| **1499** | A246 | $5 rose lilac | 1.25 | .25 |
| **1500** | A246 | $5.50 yel grn ('67) | 1.25 | .25 |
| **1501** | A246 | $6 brt blue | 7.50 | .90 |
| **1502** | A246 | $6.50 violet | 1.50 | .50 |
| **1503** | A246 | $7 black | 3.00 | .25 |
| **1504** | A246 | $8 car rose ('67) | 1.50 | .25 |
| | | *Nos. 1496-1504 (9)* | 19.75 | 3.15 |

The $4.50, $5, $6, $7 and $8 were reissued with gum in 1970-71.

For similar design, see Nos. 1566-1567.

Pres. Chiang Kai-shek in Chung San Robe — A247

$5, Chiang Kai-shek in marshal's uniform.

**Unwmk.**

**1966, Oct. 31 Photo. *Perf. 13***

| | | | | |
|---|---|---|---|---|
| **1505** | A247 | $1 multicolored | 2.50 | .25 |
| **1506** | A247 | $5 multicolored | 10.75 | 2.10 |

Chiang Kai-shek's inauguration for a fourth term as president, May 20, 1966.

**Famous Men Type of 1965-66 with Frame Line**

Portraits: No. 1507, Tsai Yuan-pei (1868-1940), educator. No. 1508, Chiu Ching (1875-1907), woman educator and revolutionist.

**1967 Wmk. 323 Engr. *Perf. 11½***
**Without Gum**

| | | | | |
|---|---|---|---|---|
| **1507** | A232 | $1 violet blue | 3.50 | .50 |
| **1508** | A232 | $1 black | 7.25 | .60 |

Issue dates: No. 1507, Jan. 11. No. 1508, July 15.

No. 1507 is on granite paper.

Motorized Mailman and Microwave Station — A248

"Transportation" and Radar Weather Station — A249

**Unwmk.**

**1967, Mar. 15 Photo. *Perf. 13***

| | | | | |
|---|---|---|---|---|
| **1511** | A248 | $1 multicolored | 1.90 | .25 |
| **1512** | A249 | $5 multicolored | 4.25 | .80 |

Issued to publicize the progress in communication and transportation services.

Pres. Chiang Kai-shek and Chinese Flag — A250

Design: $4, Different frame.

**1967, May 20 Litho. *Perf. 13***

| | | | | |
|---|---|---|---|---|
| **1513** | A250 | $1 multicolored | 2.25 | .25 |
| **1514** | A250 | $4 multicolored | 6.50 | 1.25 |

First anniversary of President Chiang Kai-shek's 4th-term inauguration.

Chu Yuan, 332-295 B.C. — A251

Portraits: $2, Li Po (705-760). $2.50, Tu Fu (712-770). $3, Po Chu-i (772-846).

**Granite Paper; Without Gum**
**Wmk. 323**

**1967, June 12 Engr. *Perf. 11½***

| | | | | |
|---|---|---|---|---|
| **1515** | A251 | $1 black | 1.10 | .25 |
| **1516** | A251 | $2 brown | 5.50 | .50 |
| **1517** | A251 | $2.50 brown blk | 7.00 | 1.20 |
| **1518** | A251 | $3 grnsh black | 8.25 | 1.40 |
| | | *Nos. 1515-1518 (4)* | 21.85 | 3.35 |

Issued for Poets' Day.

See design A232.

Hotei, Wood Carving — A252

Handicrafts: $2.50, Vase and plate. $3, Dolls. $5, Palace lanterns.

***Perf. 11½***

**1967, Aug. 12 Unwmk. Photo.**

| | | | | |
|---|---|---|---|---|
| **1519** | A252 | $1 gray & multi | 1.90 | .25 |
| **1520** | A252 | $2.50 multi | 3.75 | .60 |
| **1521** | A252 | $3 multi | 5.75 | 1.00 |
| **1522** | A252 | $5 multi | 11.50 | 3.25 |
| | | *Nos. 1519-1522 (4)* | 22.90 | 5.10 |

Taiwan handicraft industry.

World Map — A253

**Granite Paper; Without Gum**
**Wmk. 323**

**1967, Sept. 25 Engr. *Perf. 11½***

| | | | | |
|---|---|---|---|---|
| **1523** | A253 | $1 vermilion | .35 | .25 |
| **1524** | A253 | $5 blue | 2.75 | .50 |

1st Conference of the World Anti-Communist League, WACL, Taipei, Sept. 25-29.

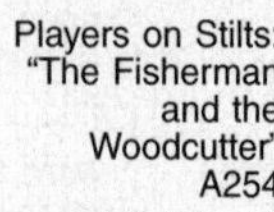

Players on Stilts: "The Fisherman and the Woodcutter" A254

**Unwmk.**

**1967, Oct. 10 Photo. *Perf. 13***

| | | | | |
|---|---|---|---|---|
| **1525** | A254 | $4.50 multi | 2.60 | .60 |

Issued for the 56th National Day.

Maroon Oriole A255

Formosan Birds: $1, Formosan barbet, vert. $2.50, Formosan green pigeon. $3, Formosan blue magpie. $5, Crested serpent eagle, vert. $8, Mikado pheasants.

**1967, Nov. 25 Photo. *Perf. 11***
**Granite Paper**

| | | | | |
|---|---|---|---|---|
| **1526** | A255 | $1 multi | 4.00 | .25 |
| **1527** | A255 | $2 multi | 8.25 | .40 |
| **1528** | A255 | $2.50 multi | 9.25 | .60 |
| **1529** | A255 | $3 multi | 10.00 | .75 |
| **1530** | A255 | $5 multi | 11.00 | 1.25 |
| **1531** | A255 | $8 multi | 12.50 | 2.50 |
| | | *Nos. 1526-1531 (6)* | 55.00 | 5.75 |

Chung Hsing Pagoda A256

Buddha, Changhua A257

Designs: $2.50, Seashore, Yeh Liu Park. $5, National Palace Museum, Taipei.

**Unwmk.**

**1967, Dec. 10 Photo. *Perf. 13***

| | | | | |
|---|---|---|---|---|
| **1532** | A256 | $1 multi | 2.25 | .25 |
| **1533** | A257 | $2.50 multi | 6.00 | .50 |
| **1534** | A257 | $4 multi | 7.50 | 1.00 |
| **1535** | A257 | $5 multi | 8.50 | 2.50 |
| | | *Nos. 1532-1535 (4)* | 24.25 | 4.25 |

Issued for International Tourist Year 1967.

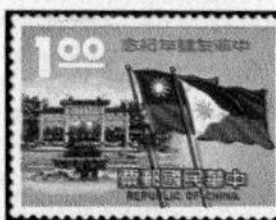
China Park, Manila, and Flags — A258

**1967, Dec. 30 *Perf. 13½***

| | | | | |
|---|---|---|---|---|
| **1536** | A258 | $1 multicolored | .50 | .25 |
| **1537** | A258 | $5 multicolored | 3.50 | .70 |

Sino-Philippine Friendship Year 1966-67.

Sun Yat-sen Building, Yangmingshan
A259 A259a

***Perf. 13x12½***

**1968-75 Litho. Wmk. 323**
**Granite Paper**

| | | | | |
|---|---|---|---|---|
| **1538** | A259 | 5c lt brown | .65 | .25 |
| **1539** | A259 | 10c grnsh black | .65 | .25 |
| **1540** | A259 | 50c brt rose lilac | .30 | .25 |
| **1541** | A259 | $1 vermilion | .40 | .25 |
| **1542** | A259 | $1.50 emerald | 2.25 | .70 |
| **1543** | A259 | $2 plum | 1.90 | .25 |
| **1544** | A259 | $2.50 blue | 1.40 | .25 |
| **1545** | A259 | $3 grnsh blue | 2.25 | .35 |
| | | *Nos. 1538-1545 (8)* | 9.80 | 2.55 |

See Nos. 1702-1709. For overprints see Nos. 1723-1725.

Issued: 50c, $1, $2.50, 1/23/1968; others 7/11/68.

All reprinting of this issue after Sept. 1969 are on a whiter paper with fewer colored fibers.

On Dec. 10, 1969, a booklet containing 12 #1540, 24 #1541, and 8 #1544 was issued.

**Coil Stamps**

***Perf. 13 Horiz.***

**Photo. Unwmk.**

| | | | | |
|---|---|---|---|---|
| **1546** | A259a | $1 carmine rose | 1.20 | .30 |
| **1547** | A259a | $1 vermilion | .55 | .25 |

Issued: No. 1546, 3/20/70; No. 1547, 1/28/75.

Inscription on No. 1546 is in color with white background. On No. 1547 it is white with colored background.

Harvesting Sugar Cane — A260

**Unwmk.**

**1968, Mar. 1 Photo. *Perf. 13***

| | | | | |
|---|---|---|---|---|
| **1548** | A260 | $1 olive & multi | 1.25 | .25 |
| **1549** | A260 | $4 multicolored | 4.00 | .70 |

Jade Cabbage, 1662-1911 — A261

Ancient Art Treasures: $1.50, Jade battle axe. $2, Porcelain flower bowl, 960-1126 A.D., horiz. $2.50, Cloisonné enamel vase, 1723-1736 A.D. $4, Agate flower holder in shape of finger citrus, 1662-1911 A.D., horiz. $5, Sacrificial kettle, 1111-771 B.C.

**1968, Mar. 29 Unwmk. *Perf. 13***

| | | | | |
|---|---|---|---|---|
| **1550** | A261 | $1 rose & multi | 1.90 | .25 |
| **1551** | A261 | $1.50 blue & multi | 6.25 | .50 |
| **1552** | A261 | $2 blue & multi | 6.75 | .70 |
| **1553** | A261 | $2.50 dull rose & multi | 8.25 | 1.00 |
| **1554** | A261 | $4 pink & multi | 11.50 | 1.20 |
| **1555** | A261 | $5 blue & multi | 13.00 | 2.00 |
| | | *Nos. 1550-1555 (6)* | 47.65 | 5.65 |

**For similar artifact designs inscribed "Republic of China," with single-color denominations in slanted numerals and the cents underlined, see types A276, A291, A323, A336, A384, A395, A411.**

**Artifact designs with denominations in outlined numerals begin with type A439.**

View of City in Cathay (1) — A262

Views: No. 1557, City and wall of Forbidden City (2). No. 1558, Wall at right, bridge at left (3). No. 1559, Queen's ship landing at left (4). No. 1560, Palace (5). $5, City wall and gate. $8, Suburb around Great Bridge. Design from scroll "A City in Cathay," painted 1736.

**1968, June 18 Photo. *Perf. 13½***
**Size: 50x29mm**

| | | | | |
|---|---|---|---|---|
| **1556** | A262 | $1 multicolored | 4.00 | .40 |
| **1557** | A262 | $1 multicolored | 4.00 | .40 |
| **1558** | A262 | $1 multicolored | 4.00 | .40 |
| **1559** | A262 | $1 multicolored | 4.00 | .40 |
| **1560** | A262 | $1 multicolored | 4.00 | .40 |
| *a.* | | Strip of 5, #1556-1560 | 20.00 | 20.00 |

**Size: 60x31mm**
***Perf. 13x13½***

| | | | | |
|---|---|---|---|---|
| **1561** | A262 | $5 multicolored | 20.00 | 4.25 |
| **1562** | A262 | $8 multicolored | 35.00 | 6.00 |
| | | *Nos. 1556-1562 (7)* | 75.00 | 12.25 |

See Nos. 1610-1614. For similar designs see types A281, A299, A326, A343.

Entrance Gate, Taroko Gorge — A263

$8, Sun Yat-sen Building, Yangmingshan.

**1968, Feb. 12 Photo. *Perf. 13***

| | | | | |
|---|---|---|---|---|
| **1563** | A263 | $5 multicolored | 4.25 | .60 |
| **1564** | A263 | $8 multicolored | 4.25 | 1.00 |

The 17th Annual Conference of the Pacific Area Travel Association.

Vice President Chen Cheng — A264

**1968, Mar. 5**

| | | | | |
|---|---|---|---|---|
| **1565** | A264 | $1 brown & multi | 2.75 | .25 |

Vice President Chen Cheng (1898-1965).

Flying Geese — A265

**Wmk. 323**

**1968, Mar. 20 Litho. *Perf. 12***

**Granite Paper**

**1566** A265 $1 vermilion 9.00 .25

**Souvenir Sheet**

***Imperf***

**1567** A265 $3 green 21.00 3.50

90th anniv. of Chinese postage stamps. No. 1567 contains one stamp with simulated perforations.

See Nos. 1496-1504.

WHO Emblem and "20" — A266

**1968, Apr. 7 Engr. *Perf. 12***

**Granite Paper**

**1568** A266 $1 green .45 .25
**1569** A266 $5 scarlet 1.60 .50

20th anniv. of WHO.

Symbolic Water Cycle — A267

**Wmk. 323**

**1968, June 6 Litho. *Perf. 11½***

**Granite Paper**

**1570** A267 $1 green & org .60 .25
**1571** A267 $4 brt blue & org 1.40 .30

Hydrological Decade (UNESCO) 1965-74.

Broadcasting to Mainland China A268

Dual Carriers for FM Broadcasting A269

**Wmk. 323**

**1968, Aug. 1 Litho. *Perf. 12***

**Granite Paper**

**1572** A268 $1 bl, vio bl & gray .70 .25
**1573** A269 $4 lt ultra & ver 1.35 .30

40th anniv. of the Broadcasting Corp. of China, and the inauguration of frequency modulation broadcasting.

Human Rights Flame — A270

**1968, Sept. 3 Granite Paper**

**1574** A270 $1 multicolored .60 .25
**1575** A270 $5 multicolored 1.40 .30

International Human Rights Year 1968.

Crop Improvement and Extension Work — A271

**Wmk. 323**

**1968, Sept. 30 Litho. *Perf. 12***

**Granite Paper**

**1576** A271 $1 yel, bister & dk brn .45 .25
**1577** A271 $5 yel, emer & dk grn 1.90 .50

Joint Commission on Rural Reconstruction, 20th anniversary.

Javelin — A272

Designs: $2.50, Weight lifting. $5, Pole vault, horiz. $8, Woman hurdling, horiz.

**Unwmk.**

**1968, Oct. 12 Photo. *Perf. 13***

**1578** A272 $1 multi .60 .25
**1579** A272 $2.50 multi 1.60 .30
**1580** A272 $5 multi 1.60 .60
**1581** A272 $8 pink & multi 1.60 .40
*Nos. 1578-1581 (4)* 5.40 1.55

19th Olympic Games, Mexico City, 10/12-27.

Pres. Chiang Kai-shek and Whampoa Military Academy A273

Designs: $2, Pres. Chiang Kai-shek reviewing forces of the Northern Expedition. $2.50, Suppression of bandits, reconstruction work and New Life Movement emblem. $3.50, Marco Polo Bridge near Peking and victory parade, Nanking. $4, Original copy of Constitution of Republic of China. $5, Nationalist Chinese flag flying over mainland China.

**1968, Oct. 31 *Perf. 11½x12***

**1582** A273 $1 multi .60 .25
**1583** A273 $2 multi 1.75 .30
**1584** A273 $2.50 multi 2.10 .40
**1585** A273 $3.50 multi 3.25 .50
**1586** A273 $4 multi 3.50 .80
**1587** A273 $5 multi 4.00 .90
*Nos. 1582-1587 (6)* 15.20 3.15

Chiang Kai-shek's achievements for China.

Cock — A274

**1968, Nov. 12 Litho. *Perf. 12***

**Granite Paper**

**1588** A274 $1 pink & multi 11.00 .75
**1589** A274 $4.50 lilac & multi 62.50 13.00

Issued for use on New Year's greetings.

Flag — A275

**1968, Dec. 25 Wmk. 323 *Perf. 12½***

**Granite Paper**

**1590** A275 $1 multicolored .50 .25
**1591** A275 $5 lt blue & multi 2.00 .60

Constitution of the Republic of China, 20th anniversary.

Jade Belt Buckle, 1662-1911 — A276

Ancient Art Treasures: $1.50, Yellow jade vase, 960-1126 A.D., vert. $2, Cloisonne enamel square teapot, 1662-1911 A.D. $2.50, Kuei, sacrificial bronze vessel, 722-481 B.C. $4, Heavenly ball vase, 1368-1661 A.D., vert. $5, Gourd-shaped vase, 1662-1911 A.D., vert.

**Unwmk.**

**1969, Jan. 15 Photo. *Perf. 13***

**1592** A276 $1 dl rose & multi .75 .25
**1593** A276 $1.50 rose & multi 2.75 .30
**1594** A276 $2 brt rose & multi 3.50 .40
**1595** A276 $2.50 lt blue & multi 3.75 .60
**1596** A276 $4 tan & multi 4.00 .80
**1597** A276 $5 pale blue & multi 4.25 1.00
*Nos. 1592-1597 (6)* 19.00 3.35

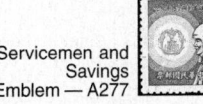

Servicemen and Savings Emblem — A277

**Wmk. 323**

**1969, Feb. 1 Engr. *Perf. 12***

**Granite Paper**

**1598** A277 $1 dull red brown .40 .25
**1599** A277 $4 deep blue 1.75 .55

Military Savings Program, 10th anniv.

Ti (Flute) — A278

Musical Instruments: $2.50, Sheng (13 bamboo pipes connected at the base). $4, P'i p'a (lute). $5, Cheng (zither).

**Unwmk.**

**1969, Mar. 16 Photo. *Perf. 13***

**1600** A278 $1 buff & multi .70 .25
**1601** A278 $2.50 lt ap grn & multi 1.60 .50
**1602** A278 $4 pink & multi 3.50 .75
**1603** A278 $5 lt grnsh bl & multi 2.50 .60
*Nos. 1600-1603 (4)* 8.30 2.10

Sun Yat-sen Building and Kuomintang Emblem — A279

**1969, Mar. 29 Litho. *Perf. 13½***

**1604** A279 $1 multicolored 1.25 .25

10th Natl. Cong. of the Chinese Nationalist Party (Kuomintang), Mar. 29. A $2.50 stamp portraying Sun Yat-sen and Chiang Kai-shek was prepared but not issued.

Double Carp Design — A280

***Perf. 13½x12½***

**1974, Aug. 2 Engr. Wmk. 323**

**Granite Paper**

**1606** A280 $10 dark blue 2.75 .40
**1607** A280 $20 dark brown 6.75 .40
**1608** A280 $50 green 7.25 .75
**1609** A280 $100 bright red 13.00 1.40
*Nos. 1606-1609 (4)* 29.75 2.95

**1969, Apr. 21 *Perf. 11½***

*1606a* A280 $10 4.75 .25
*1607a* A280 $20 7.00 .25
*1608a* A280 $50 8.25 .45
*1609a* A280 $100 15.00 .90
*Nos. 1606a-1609a (4)* 35.00 1.85

**1976, Dec. 15 *Perf. 11½***

**White Paper**

*1606b* A280 $10 3.00 .25
*1607b* A280 $20 5.00 .25
*1608b* A280 $50 7.00 .50
*1609b* A280 $100 10.00 1.00
*Nos. 1606b-1609b (4)* 25.00 2.00

The 1969 issue is 27mm high; 1974 and 1976, 28mm.

See No. 1980.

Bridal Procession A281

Designs: No. 1610, Musicians and standard bearer from bridal procession. $2.50, Emigrant farm family in oxcart. $5, Art gallery. $8, Roadside food stands. Designs from scroll "A City in Cathay," painted in 1736.

***Perf. 13½***

**1969, May 20 Unwmk. Photo.**

**1610** A281 $1 multi 1.75 .25
**1611** A281 $1 multi 1.75 .25
*a.* Pair, #1610-1611 3.75 3.75
**1612** A281 $2.50 multi 5.75 .60
**1613** A281 $5 multi 7.00 1.50
**1614** A281 $8 multi 8.00 2.10
*Nos. 1610-1614 (5)* 24.25 4.70

ILO Emblem — A282

**Wmk. 323**

**1969, June 15 Engr. *Perf. 11½***

**Granite Paper**

**1615** A282 $1 dark blue .55 .25
**1616** A282 $8 dark carmine 1.65 .50

ILO, 50th anniversary.

Family at Dinner Table and Dressing — A283

Designs: $2.50, Housecleaning and obeying traffic rules. $4, Recreation (music, fishing, basketball) and education.

**Wmk. 323**

**1969, July 15 Engr. *Perf. 11½***

**1617** A283 $1 brick red .45 .25
**1618** A283 $2.50 blue 1.40 .35
**1619** A283 $4 green 1.15 .30
*Nos. 1617-1619 (3)* 3.00 .90

Model Citizen's Life Movement.

Pupils in Laboratory and Playing — A284

Design: $1, $5, Pupils with book and various school activities, horiz.

**Granite Paper**

**1969, Sept. 1 Wmk. 323 *Perf. 11½***

**1620** A284 $1 brt red .30 .25
**1621** A284 $2.50 brt green .60 .25
**1622** A284 $4 dk blue 1.50 .30
**1623** A284 $5 brown 1.60 .55
*Nos. 1620-1623 (4)* 4.00 1.35

Free 9-year education system, 1st anniv.

Wild Flowers and Pheasants, by Lu Chih (Ming) — A285

Paintings: $2.50, Bamboo and birds, Sung dynasty. $5, Flowers and Birds, Sung dynasty. $8, Cranes and Flowers, by G. Castiglione, S.J. (1688-1766).

**1969, Oct. 9 Photo. *Perf. 13½***

**1624** A285 $1 multi 1.90 .25
**1625** A285 $2.50 multi 5.75 .80
**1626** A285 $5 multi 11.50 1.75
**1627** A285 $8 multi 16.00 3.00
*Nos. 1624-1627 (4)* 35.15 5.80

Golden Scepter Rose — A286

Roses: $1, "Charles Mollerin," called black rose. $5, Peace. $8, Josephine Bruce.

**1969, Oct. 31 Litho. *Perf. 14***

**1628** A286 $1 lt vio & multi 1.00 .25
**1629** A286 $2.50 lt bl & multi 5.00 .40
**1630** A286 $5 dl org & multi 6.25 .90
**1631** A286 $8 ap grn & multi 5.75 .70
*Nos. 1628-1631 (4)* 18.00 2.25

Rocket and Radar Station — A287

**Wmk. 323**

**1969, Nov. 21 Engr. *Perf. 11½***

**1632** A287 $1 rose claret 1.75 .25

The 30th Air Defense Day.

Symbol of International Cooperation — A288

**1969, Nov. 25**

**1633** A288 $1 rose claret .50 .25
**1634** A288 $5 green 1.40 .40

5th General Assembly of the Asian Parliamentary Union, Taipei, Nov. 24-28.

Pekingese — A289

**1969, Dec. 1 Litho. *Perf. 12***
**Granite Paper**

**1635** A289 50c red & multi 2.40 .50
**1636** A289 $4.50 green & multi 12.00 2.00

Issued for use on New Year's greetings.

Satellite, Earth Station and Map of Taiwan — A290

**Unwmk.**

**1969, Dec. 28 Photo. *Perf. 13***

**1637** A290 $1 brown & multi .45 .25
**1638** A290 $5 vio blue & multi 1.60 .35
**1639** A290 $8 purple & multi 2.25 .65
*Nos. 1637-1639 (3)* 4.30 1.25

Inauguration of the Communication Satellite Earth Station at Chin-Shan-Li, Dec. 28.

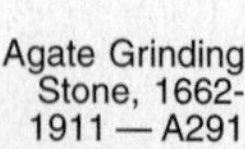

Agate Grinding Stone, 1662-1911 — A291

Ancient Art Treasures: $1, Carved lacquer ware vase, 1662-1911, vert. $2, White jade Chin-li-chih melons, 1662-1911. $2.50, Black jade shepherd and ram, 206 B.C.-220 A.D. $4, Chien-lung twin porcelain vase, 1736-1796, vert. $5, Ju porcelain vase with 3 bulls, 960-1126, vert.

**1970, Jan. 23**

**1640** A291 $1 lt grnsh bl & multi .40 .25
**1641** A291 $1.50 pale bl & multi 1.90 .25
**1642** A291 $2 green & multi 2.50 .30
**1643** A291 $2.50 pink & multi 3.00 .50
**1644** A291 $4 ol bis & multi 5.00 .75
**1645** A291 $5 ultra & multi 6.25 .80
*Nos. 1640-1645 (6)* 19.05 2.85

Hsuan Chuang A292 — Chu Hsi A293

Design: $2.50, Hua To.

**1970 Wmk. 323 Engr. *Perf. 11½***
**Granite Paper**

**1646** A292 $1 car rose .75 .25
**1647** A293 $2.50 blue grn 2.10 .40
**1648** A293 $4 blue 2.50 .50
*Nos. 1646-1648 (3)* 5.35 1.15

Issued in memory of Hsuan Chuang (602-664), who propagated Buddhism in China; Chu Hsi (1130-1200), who developed Neo-Confucianism, and Hua To (3rd century A.D.) physician and surgeon.
Issued: $2.50, 3/17; others, 2/20.

EXPO '70 Pavilion, Emblem and Flags of Participants A294

Design: $5, Chinese pavilion, EXPO '70 emblem, exhibition and Chinese flags.

**Unwmk.**

**1970, Mar. 13 Photo. *Perf. 13***

**1649** A294 $5 org red & multi 1.25 .25
**1650** A294 $8 lt blue & multi 1.75 .60

EXPO '70 International Exhibition, Osaka, Japan, Mar. 15-Sept. 13.

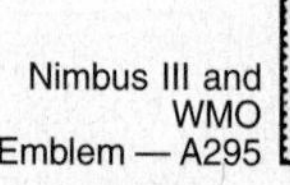

Nimbus III and WMO Emblem — A295

Design: $1, Agricultural meteorological station and tropical landscape, vert.

***Perf. 14x13½, 13½x14***

**1970, Mar. 23 Litho. Wmk. 323**
**Granite Paper**

**1651** A295 $1 green & multi .35 .25
**1652** A295 $8 blue & multi 2.25 .65

10th Annual World Meteorological Day.

Martyrs' Shrine, Taipei — A296 — Shrine's Gate — A297

**Unwmk.**

**1970, Mar. 29 Photo. *Perf. 13***

**1653** A296 $1 multicolored .65 .25
**1654** A297 $8 multicolored 2.40 .65

Completion of the Martyrs' Shrine in Northern Taipei, dedicated to the memory of 72 young revolutionaries who died Mar. 29, 1911.

Yueh Fei Fighting for Lost Territories — A298

Characters from Chinese Operas: $2.50, Emperor Shun and stepmother. $5, The Lady Warrior Chin Liang-yu. $8, Kuan Yu and groom.

**1970, May 4 Unwmk. *Perf. 13½***

**1655** A298 $1 multi .30 .25
**1656** A298 $2.50 multi 1.85 .30
**1657** A298 $5 multi 2.95 .75
**1658** A298 $8 multi 4.00 1.20
*Nos. 1655-1658 (4)* 9.10 2.50

A299

Three Horses Playing A300

Horses: No. 1659, Barren tree at right. No. 1660, Horse standing in river. No. 1661, Tree trunk in lower left corner. No. 1662, Trees in left background. No. 1663, shown. $8, Groom roping horses. Designs from scroll "One Hundred Horses" by Lang Shih-ning (Giuseppe Castiglione, 1688-1766).

***Perf. 13½***

**1970, June 18 Unwmk. Photo.**

**1659** A299 $1 multi 1.40 .25
**1660** A299 $1 multi 1.40 .25
**1661** A299 $1 multi 1.40 .25
**1662** A299 $1 multi 1.40 .25
**1663** A299 $1 multi 1.40 .25
*a.* Strip of 5, #1659-1663 8.00 8.00
**1664** A300 $5 bister & multi 14.00 2.00
**1665** A300 $8 dl yel & multi 16.50 3.00
*Nos. 1659-1665 (7)* 37.50 6.25

Lai-tsu Amusing his Old Parents — A301

Chinese Fairy Tales: No. 1667, Man disguised as deer, and hunters. No. 1668, Boy cooling his father's bed. No. 1669, Boy fishing through ice. No. 1670, Son reunited with old mother. No. 1671, Emperor tasting mother's medicine. No. 1672, Boy saving oranges for mother. No. 1673, Boy saving father from tiger.

**Wmk. 323**

**1970, July 10 Litho. *Perf. 13½***
**Granite Paper**

**1666** A301 10c red & multi .30 .25
**1667** A301 10c car rose & multi .30 .25
**1668** A301 10c lt vio & multi .30 .25
**1669** A301 10c gray & multi .30 .25
**1670** A301 10c emerald & multi .30 .25
**1671** A301 50c bister & multi .50 .25
**1672** A301 $1 sky blue & multi .90 .25
**1673** A301 $1 dp blue & multi .90 .25
*Nos. 1666-1673 (8)* 3.80 2.00

See Nos. 1726-1733.

Man's First Step onto Moon — A302

$1, Pres. Chiang Kai-shek's message brought to the moon. $5, Neil A. Armstrong, Michael Collins, Edwin E. Aldrin, Jr., and moon, horiz.

***Perf. 13½x13, 13x13½***

**1970, July 21 Photo. Unwmk.**

**1674** A302 $1 yellow & multi .50 .25
**1675** A302 $5 lt yel grn & multi 2.75 .40
**1676** A302 $8 blue & multi 3.25 .50
*Nos. 1674-1676 (3)* 6.50 1.15

1st anniv. of man's 1st landing on the moon.

Asian Productivity Year Symbol — A303

**Wmk. 323**

**1970, Aug. 18 Litho. *Perf. 13½***
**Granite Paper**

**1677** A303 $1 emerald & multi .55 .25
**1678** A303 $5 blue & multi 1.25 .40

Issued to publicize Asian Productivity Year.

Flags of China and UN — A304

**1970, Sept. 19 Wmk. 323 *Perf. 12***
**Granite Paper**

**1679** A304 $5 blue, car & blk 2.75 .65

25th anniversary of the United Nations.

Postal Zone Map A305

Postal Code Emblem A306

**1970, Oct. 8 Litho.**

**1680** A305 $1 lt blue & multi .70 .25
**1681** A306 $2.50 green & multi 1.10 .40

Issued to publicize the postal code system.

Eleventh Month Scroll — A307

Designs: A scroll series, "Activities of the 12 Months," painted on silk by a group of painters of the Ch'ien Lung court (1736-1796). Chinese number in parenthesis at right of denomination tells month.

Jan., Feb., Mar.
(一) (二) (三)

***Perf. 13½x13***

**1970-71 Photo. Unwmk.**

**1682** A307 $1 multi 1.60 .40
**1683** A307 $2.50 multi 14.00 3.00
**1684** A307 $5 multi 20.00 4.00

Apr., May, June
(四) (五) (六)

**1685** A307 $1 multi 2.00 .40
**1686** A307 $2.50 multi 6.00 1.00
**1687** A307 $5 multi 9.75 1.40

July, Aug., Sept.
(七) (八) (九)

**1688** A307 $1 multi 1.60 .40
**1689** A307 $2.50 multi 5.00 1.00
**1690** A307 $5 multi 8.00 1.40

Oct., Nov., Dec.

(十) (十一) (十二)

**1691** A307 $1 multi 1.60 .40
**1692** A307 $2.50 multi 5.00 1.00
**1693** A307 $5 multi 8.00 1.40
*Nos. 1682-1693 (12)* 82.55 15.80

Issued: Nos. 1691-1693, 10/21/70; Nos. 1682-1684, 1/14/71; Nos. 1685-1687, 4/26/71; Nos. 1688-1690, 8/27/71.

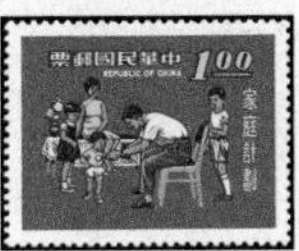

Family at Home — A308

$4, Family of 5 going on an excursion, vert.

***Perf. 13½x14, 14x13½***

**1970, Nov. 11 Litho. Wmk. 323**

**Granite Paper**

**1694** A308 $1 multicolored .50 .25
**1695** A308 $4 yel grn & multi 2.50 .40

Issued to publicize family planning.

Piggy Bank — A309

**1970, Dec. 1** ***Perf. 12½x12***

**Granite Paper**

**1696** A309 50c multi 1.50 .25
**1697** A309 $4.50 blue & multi 9.50 1.50

Issued for use on New Year's greetings.

Tibia Fusus Shells — A310

Rare Taiwan Shells: $2.50, Harpeola kurodai. $5, Conus stupa kuroda. $8, Entemnotrochus rumphii.

**1971, Feb. 25** ***Perf. 13x13½***

**1698** A310 $1 vio & multi .85 .25
**1699** A310 $2.50 multi 2.60 .25
**1700** A310 $5 org & multi 3.50 .40
**1701** A310 $8 grn & multi 4.50 .70
*Nos. 1698-1701 (4)* 11.45 1.60

Sun Yat-sen Building, Yangmingshan — A311

***Perf. 13½x12½***

**1971 Litho. Wmk. 323**

**Granite Paper**

**1702** A311 5c brown .30 .25
**1703** A311 10c dk gray .30 .25
**1704** A311 50c brt rose lilac .30 .25
**1705** A311 $1 vermilion .30 .25
**1706** A311 $1.50 ultra 2.75 .50
**1707** A311 $2 plum 5.75 .50
**1708** A311 $2.50 emerald 1.90 .25
**1709** A311 $3 aqua 6.50 .75
*Nos. 1702-1709 (8)* 18.10 3.00

Passbook and Postal Savings Certificate — A312

$4, People and hand dropping coin into bank.

***Perf. 13½x14***

**1971, Mar. 20 Litho. Wmk. 323**

**1712** A312 $1 yel grn & multi .80 .25
**1713** A312 $4 ver & multi 2.40 .45

Publicizing Chinese Postal Savings Service.

Cooperation Emblem, Farmers — A313

Design: $8, Chinese teaching rice farming to Africans, horiz.

**Unwmk.**

**1971, May 20 Photo.** ***Perf. 13***

**1714** A313 $1 multicolored .75 .25
**1715** A313 $8 multicolored 2.25 .50

Sino-African Technical Cooperation Committee, 10th anniversary.

Rock Monkey — A314

Taiwan Animals: $2, White-face flying squirrel. $3, Chinese pangolin. $5, Formosan sika deer. $2, $3, $5 are horiz.

**1971, June 25** ***Perf. 11½***

**1716** A314 $1 gold & multi .50 .25
**1717** A314 $2 gold & multi 1.60 .25
**1718** A314 $3 gold & multi 2.25 .45
**1719** A314 $5 gold & multi 3.25 .75
*Nos. 1716-1719 (4)* 7.60 1.70

Pitcher — A315

Designs: $2.50, Players at base, horiz. $4, Batter and catcher.

**1971, July 29 Photo.** ***Perf. 13***

**1720** A315 $1 multi .30 .25
**1721** A315 $2.50 multi .70 .25
**1722** A315 $4 multi 1.40 .35
*Nos. 1720-1722 (3)* 2.40 .85

Pacific Regional competition for the 1971 Little League World Series.

Nos. 1541, 1544-1545 Overprinted in Magenta or Red

***Perf. 13x12½***

**1971, Sept. 9 Litho. Wmk. 323**

**Granite Paper**

**1723** A259 $1 vermilion (M) .45 .25
**1724** A259 $2.50 blue (R) .80 .25
**1725** A259 $3 grnsh blue (R) .80 .35
*Nos. 1723-1725 (3)* 2.05 .85

Chinese victory in 1971 Little League World Series, Williamsport, Pa., Aug. 24.

**Fairy Tale Type of 1970**

Chinese Fairy Tales (Filial Piety): No. 1726, Birds and elephant helping in rice field. No. 1727, Son gathering mulberries for mother. No. 1728, Son gathering firewood. No. 1729, Son, mother and bandits. No. 1730, Son carrying heavy burden. 50c, Son digging for bamboo shoots in winter. No. 1732, Man and wife working as slaves. No. 1733, Father, son and carriage.

**1971, Sept. 22** ***Perf. 13½***

**Granite Paper**

**1726** A301 10c dp org & multi .30 .25
**1727** A301 10c lilac & multi .30 .25
**1728** A301 10c ocher & multi .30 .25
**1729** A301 10c dp car & multi .30 .25
**1730** A301 10c lt ultra & multi .30 .25
**1731** A301 50c multicolored .60 .25
**1732** A301 $1 emerald & multi 1.40 .25
**1733** A301 $1 lt red brn & multi 1.40 .25
*Nos. 1726-1733 (8)* 4.90 2.00

Flag of China, "Double Ten" and Anniversary Emblems — A316

Designs (Flag of China and): $2.50, National anthem. $5, Gen. Chiang Kai-shek. $8, Sun Yat-sen.

**1971, Oct. 10 Photo.** ***Perf. 13***

**1734** A316 $1 orange & multi .35 .25
**1735** A316 $2.50 multi .90 .25
**1736** A316 $5 green & multi 2.75 .50
**1737** A316 $8 olive & multi 1.75 .50
*Nos. 1734-1737 (4)* 5.75 1.50

60th National Day.

Bird in Flight (AOPU Emblem) — A317

***Perf. 13½x14***

**1971, Nov. 8 Litho. Wmk. 323**

**1738** A317 $2.50 yellow & multi .85 .25
**1739** A317 $5 orange & multi 1.10 .25

Asian-Oceanic Postal Union Executive Committee Session, Taipei, Nov. 8-15.

"White Frost Hawk," by Lang Shih-ning — A318

**Dog Series I**

Designs: $2, "Star-Glancing Wolf." $2.50, "Golden-Winged Face." $5, "Young Black Dragon." $8, "Young Gray Dragon."

Designs from painting series "Ten Prized Dogs," by Lang Shih-ning (Giuseppe Castiglione, 1688-1766).

***Perf. 13½x13***

**1971, Nov. 16 Litho. Unwmk.**

**1740** A318 $1 Facing left 1.50 .25
**1741** A318 $2 Lying down 3.00 .40
**1742** A318 $2.50 Scratching 4.75 .50
**1743** A318 $5 Facing right 8.00 .75
**1744** A318 $8 Looking back 22.50 2.25
*Nos. 1740-1744 (5)* 39.75 4.15

**Dog Series II**

Designs: $1, "Black with Snow-white Paws." $2, "Yellow Leopard." $2.50, "Flying Magpie." $5, "Heavenly Lion." $8, "Mottled Tiger."

**1972, Jan. 12**

**1745** A318 $1 Facing right 1.10 .25
**1746** A318 $2 Walking 8.50 .80
**1747** A318 $2.50 Sleeping 3.50 .60
**1748** A318 $5 Facing left 12.50 1.40
**1749** A318 $8 Sitting 34.00 7.00
*Nos. 1745-1749 (5)* 59.60 10.05

Squirrels A319

***Perf. 13½x12½***

**1971, Dec. 1 Wmk. 323**

**1750** A319 Block of 4 3.80 2.50
*a.* 50c in UL corner .75 .25
*b.* 50c in UR corner .75 .25
*c.* 50c in LL corner .75 .25
*d.* 50c in LR corner .75 .25

**1751** A319 Block of 4 15.25 7.00
*a.* $4.50 in UL corner 3.25 1.25
*b.* $4.50 in UR corner 3.25 1.25
*c.* $4.50 in LL corner 3.25 1.25
*d.* $4.50 in LR corner 3.25 1.25

New Year 1972.

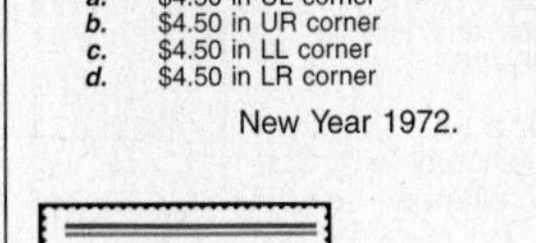

Flags of China and Jordan — A320

**1971, Dec. 16** ***Perf. 13½***

**Granite Paper**

**1752** A320 $5 multicolored 1.90 .25

50th anniversary of the founding of the Hashemite Kingdom of Jordan.

Cargo Ship "Hai King" — A321

$7, Ocean liner & map of Pacific Ocean, vert.

**1971, Dec. 16** ***Perf. 12½***

**1753** A321 $4 grn, dk bl & red 1.45 .25
**1754** A321 $7 ocher & multi 1.45 .30

China Merchants Steam Navigation Co., cent.

Downhill Skiing, Olympic Rings — A322

$5, Cross-country skiing. $8, Giant slalom.

**1972, Feb. 3** ***Perf. 13½***

**1755** A322 $1 org, blk & bl .50 .25
**1756** A322 $5 yel grn, dp org & blk 1.10 .25
**1757** A322 $8 red, gray & blk 1.25 .25
*Nos. 1755-1757 (3)* 2.85 .75

11th Winter Olympic Games, Sapporo, Japan, Feb. 3-13.

Vase, 18th Century — A323

**Porcelain Series I**

Porcelain Masterworks of Ching Dynasty: $2, Covered jar. $2.50, Pitcher. $5, Vase with 5 openings and dragon design. $8, Covered jar with children design.

***Perf. 11½***

**1972, Mar. 20 Photo. Unwmk.**

**1758** A323 $1 violet & multi .50 .25
**1759** A323 $2 plum & blue 2.00 .30
**1760** A323 $2.50 org ver & bl 2.25 .40
**1761** A323 $5 bis brn & bl 3.00 .06
**1762** A323 $8 sl grn & multi 3.50 1.00
*Nos. 1758-1762 (5)* 11.25 2.55

See Nos. 1812-1821, 1864-1868.

Nine Flying Doves — A324

***Perf. 13½x14***

**1972, Apr. 1 Litho. Wmk. 323**

**1763** A324 $1 lt blue & blk .75 .25
**1764** A324 $5 lt violet & blk 2.10 .35

Asian-Oceanic Postal Union, 10th anniv.

"Dignity with Self-reliance" — A325

*Perf. 13½x12½*

**1972-75 Litho. Wmk. 323**

| | | | | |
|---|---|---|---|---|
| **1765** | A325 | 5c brown & yel | .30 | .25 |
| **1766** | A325 | 10c blue & org | .30 | .25 |
| **1767** | A325 | 20c cl & yel grn ('75) | .30 | .25 |
| **1768** | A325 | 50c lil & lil rose | .30 | .25 |
| **1769** | A325 | $1 red & brt bl | .30 | .25 |
| **1770** | A325 | $1.50 yel & dk bl | .60 | .25 |
| **1771** | A325 | $2 maroon & org | .45 | .25 |
| **1772** | A325 | $2.50 emer & ver | .50 | .25 |
| **1773** | A325 | $3 red & lt grn | .90 | .25 |
| | | *Nos. 1765-1773 (9)* | 3.95 | 2.25 |

**Souvenir Sheet**

***Imperf***

| | | | | |
|---|---|---|---|---|
| **1775** | A325 | Sheet of 2 | 6.00 | 3.75 |

No. 1775 commemorates ROCPEX '72 Philatelic Exhibition, Taipei, Oct. 24-Nov. 2. It contains 2 stamps similar to Nos. 1771 and 1773 with simulated perforations.

Issued: $1, $1.50, $2, $3, 5/20/72; 5c, 10c, 50c, $2.50, No. 1775, 10/24/72; 20c, 1975.

For overprints see Nos. 1787-1790.

Emperor Shih-tsung's Procession A326

Messengers on Horseback A327

Designs from scrolls depicting Emperor Shih-tsung's (reigned 1522-1566) journey to and from tombs at Cheng-tien. No. 1776 shows land journey departure and is designed from right to left. No. 1779 shows return trip by boat and is designed from left to right. The 5 stamps of Nos. 1776 and 1780 are numbered 1 to 5 in Chinese (see illustrations with Nos. 1682-1686 for numerals).

**1972 Photo. Unwmk. *Perf. 13½***

| | | | | |
|---|---|---|---|---|
| **1776** | | Strip of 5 | 3.00 | 6.00 |
| *a.* | | A326 $1 shown (1) | .45 | .35 |
| *b.* | | A326 $1 Seven carriages (2) | .45 | .35 |
| *c.* | | A326 $1 Carriage drawn by 23 horses (3) | .45 | .35 |
| *d.* | | A326 $1 Procession (4) | .45 | .35 |
| *e.* | | A326 $1 Emperor under 2 canopies (5) | .45 | .35 |
| **1777** | A327 | $2.50 shown | 1.50 | .50 |
| **1778** | A327 | $5 Guards with flags, fans & spears | 4.50 | 2.00 |
| **1779** | A327 | $8 Sedan chair carried by 28 men | 3.50 | 1.40 |
| **1780** | | Strip of 5 | 3.00 | 6.00 |
| *a.* | | A326 $1 Three barges (1) | .45 | .35 |
| *b.* | | A326 $1 Procession, sedan chairs (2) | .45 | .35 |
| *c.* | | A326 $1 Two barges with trunks (3) | .45 | .35 |
| *d.* | | A326 $1 Procession on land (4) | .45 | .35 |
| *e.* | | A326 $1 Procession, 2 sedan chairs (5) | .45 | .35 |
| **1781** | A326 | $2.50 Courtiers at city welcoming Emperor | 1.50 | .40 |
| **1782** | A327 | $5 Orchestra on horseback | 4.50 | 2.00 |
| **1783** | A326 | $8 Barges | 3.50 | 1.40 |
| | | *Nos. 1776-1783 (8)* | 25.00 | 19.70 |

Issue dates: No. 1776-1779, June 14; Nos. 1780-1783, July 12.

First Day Covers A328

Magnifying Glass, Tongs, Gauge A329

Design: $2.50, Sun Yat-sen stamp of 1971 (type A311) under magnifying glass.

**Wmk. 323**

**1972, Aug. 9 Engr. *Perf. 12***

| | | | | |
|---|---|---|---|---|
| **1784** | A328 | $1 dk vio blue | .30 | .25 |
| **1785** | A328 | $2.50 brt green | .65 | .25 |
| **1786** | A329 | $8 scarlet | .95 | .50 |
| | | *Nos. 1784-1786 (3)* | 1.90 | 1.00 |

Promotion of philately. Printed in sheets of 40. Each sheet contains 4 blocks of 10 stamps surrounded by margins with inscriptions.

Nos. 1768-1770, 1772 Overprinted in Dark Blue or Red

*Perf. 13½x12½*

**1972, Sept. 9 Litho. Wmk. 323**

| | | | | |
|---|---|---|---|---|
| **1787** | A325 | $1 red & brt bl (DB) | .40 | .25 |
| **1788** | A325 | $1.50 yel & dk bl (R) | .65 | .25 |
| **1789** | A325 | $2 mar & org (R) | .75 | .25 |
| **1790** | A325 | $3 red & lt grn (DB) | .80 | .35 |
| | | *Nos. 1787-1790 (4)* | 2.60 | 1.10 |

China's championship victories in the Little League World Series, Gary, Ind., and in the Senior League World Series, Williamsport, Pa., Aug. 1972.

Emperor Yao (2357-2258 B.C.) — A330

Rulers: $4, Emperor Shun (ruled 2255-2208 B.C.). $4.50, Yu, the Great (ruled 2205-2198 B.C.). $5, King T'ang (ruled 1783-1754 B.C.). $5.50, King Wen (ruled 1171-1122 B.C.). $6, King Wu (ruled 1121-1114 B.C.). $7, Chou Kung (died 1105 B.C.). $8, Confucius (551-479 B.C.).

**1972-76 Engr. *Perf. 12***

**Granite Paper**

| | | | | |
|---|---|---|---|---|
| **1791** | A330 | $3.50 dk blue | 1.50 | .25 |
| **1792** | A330 | $4 rose red | .50 | .25 |
| **1793** | A330 | $4.50 bluish lil | 1.60 | .25 |
| **1794** | A330 | $5 brt green | .50 | .25 |
| **1795** | A330 | $5.50 dp claret | 2.00 | .60 |
| **1796** | A330 | $6 dp org | 2.10 | .25 |
| *a.* | | Perf. 13½x12½ ('76) | .80 | .25 |
| **1797** | A330 | $7 sepia | .95 | .25 |
| *a.* | | Perf. 13½x12½ ('76) | .95 | .25 |
| **1798** | A330 | $8 indigo | 1.20 | .25 |
| *a.* | | gray, perf. 13½x12½ ('76) | .60 | .25 |
| | | *Nos. 1791-1798 (8)* | 10.35 | 2.35 |

In the first printing, Nos. 1791-1794, 1796-1798 measure 32mm high. In a 1974 reissue they are 33mm.

**1974, July 25 *Perf. 12***

**Large Wmk. 323**

| | | | | |
|---|---|---|---|---|
| *1791a* | A330 | $3.50 | .90 | .25 |
| *1792a* | A330 | $4 | .60 | .25 |
| *1793a* | A330 | $4.50 | 1.50 | .25 |
| *1794a* | A330 | $5 | .70 | .25 |
| *1796b* | A330 | $6 | 2.10 | .45 |
| *1797b* | A330 | $7 | 1.20 | .25 |
| *1798b* | A330 | $8 | 1.20 | .25 |
| | | *Nos. 1791a-1798b (7)* | 8.20 | 1.95 |

Issued: Nos. 1791-1794, 9/20/1972; Nos. 1795-1798, 4/2/1973; Nos. 1791a-1794a, 1796b-1798b, 7/25/1974; Nos. 1796a-1798a, 1/26/1976.

The 1972 issue was printed using a wet copper plate and the designs are 32mm high. The 1973 printings were done on dry copper plates resulting in a taller design of 33mm. The 1974 printing was printed on a locally made paper with a larger version of the "post" watermark No. 323, using dry copper plates resulting in the design being 33mm high.

Mountain Climbing — A331

Designs (China Youth Corps emblem and): $2.50, Skiing (skiers forming circle). $4, Diving. $8, Parachute jumping.

**Unwmk.**

**1972, Oct. 31 Photo. *Perf. 12***

| | | | | |
|---|---|---|---|---|
| **1800** | A331 | $1 green & multi | .30 | .25 |
| **1801** | A331 | $2.50 blue & multi | .65 | .25 |
| **1802** | A331 | $4 orange & multi | 1.00 | .25 |
| **1803** | A331 | $8 multicolored | 1.30 | .40 |
| | | *Nos. 1800-1803 (4)* | 3.25 | 1.15 |

China Youth Corps, 20th anniversary.

JCI Emblem — A332

**1972, Nov. 12 Litho. Wmk. 323**

| | | | | |
|---|---|---|---|---|
| **1804** | A332 | $1 multicolored | .30 | .25 |
| **1805** | A332 | $5 orange & multi | .60 | .25 |
| **1806** | A332 | $8 multicolored | 1.10 | .40 |
| | | *Nos. 1804-1806 (3)* | 2.00 | .90 |

27th Junior Chamber International (JCI) World Congress, Taipei, Nov. 12-19.

Electronic Mail Sorter A333

Plane, Ship and Pier A334

Progress of Communications System on Taiwan: $5, Highway overpass over railroad.

**Wmk. 323**

**1972, Nov. 12 Engr. *Perf. 11½***

| | | | | |
|---|---|---|---|---|
| **1807** | A333 | $1 red | .35 | .25 |
| **1808** | A334 | $2.50 blue | .80 | .25 |
| **1809** | A334 | $5 dk violet brn | 1.25 | .40 |
| | | *Nos. 1807-1809 (3)* | 2.40 | .90 |

Cow and Calf (Parental Love) — A335

**1972, Dec. 1 Litho. *Perf. 12***

| | | | | |
|---|---|---|---|---|
| **1810** | A335 | 50c red & blk | 2.50 | .25 |
| **1811** | A335 | $4.50 yel, red & brn | 4.50 | .90 |

New Year 1973. Printed in sheets of 80, divided into 4 panes of 20, separated by vertical and horizontal gutters 2 rows wide. 20 red chops meaning "Happy New Year" are printed in the gutters.

**Porcelain Type of 1972 and**

Stem Bowl with Dragons — A336

**Porcelain Series II**

Porcelain Masterworks of Ming Dynasty: $1, Covered vase with fruits and flowers. $2, Vase with ornamental and floral design. $2.50, Vase imitating ancient bronze. $5, Flask with flowers of 4 seasons. $8, Garlic head vase.

**1973 Photo. *Perf. 11½***

| | | | | |
|---|---|---|---|---|
| **1812** | A323 | $1 gray & multi | 2.10 | .25 |
| **1813** | A323 | $2 lt brn & multi | 3.00 | .25 |
| **1814** | A323 | $2.50 brt grn & multi | 4.00 | .25 |
| **1815** | A323 | $5 ultra & multi | 4.50 | .35 |
| **1816** | A323 | $8 olive & multi | 6.50 | .60 |
| | | *Nos. 1812-1816 (5)* | 20.10 | 1.70 |

**Porcelain Series III**

Ming Porcelain: $2, Refuse container with dragons. $2.50, Covered jar with lotus. $5, Covered jar with horses. $8, Bowl with figures of immortals.

| | | | | |
|---|---|---|---|---|
| **1817** | A336 | $1 gray & multi | 1.60 | .25 |
| **1818** | A336 | $2 lt vio & multi | 2.40 | .25 |
| **1819** | A336 | $2.50 dk red & multi | 3.50 | .25 |
| **1820** | A336 | $5 blue & multi | 3.75 | .35 |
| **1821** | A336 | $8 dp org & multi | 5.25 | .60 |
| | | *Nos. 1817-1821 (5)* | 16.50 | 1.70 |

Issued: Nos. 1812-1816, 1/10; Nos. 1817-1821, 3/24.

See Nos. 1864-1868.

Oyster Fairy and Fisherman's Dance A337

$1, Kicking shuttlecock, vert. $5, Rowing boat over land. $8, Old man carrying young lady, vert.

**1973, Feb. 7 Photo. *Perf. 11½***

**Granite Paper**

| | | | | |
|---|---|---|---|---|
| **1822** | A337 | $1 multicolored | .65 | .25 |
| **1823** | A337 | $4 Shown | 1.05 | .25 |
| **1824** | A337 | $5 multicolored | 1.90 | .25 |
| **1825** | A337 | $8 multicolored | 2.10 | .40 |
| | | *Nos. 1822-1825 (4)* | 5.70 | 1.15 |

Chinese folklore popular entertainment.

Bamboo Boat — A338

Taiwanese Handicrafts: $2.50, Painted marble vase, vert. $5, Painted glass plate. $8, Doll, bridegroom carrying bride on back, vert.

*Perf. 13½x14½, 14½x13½*

**1973, Mar. 9 Photo.**

| | | | | |
|---|---|---|---|---|
| **1826** | A338 | $1 multi | .30 | .25 |
| **1827** | A338 | $2.50 multi | 1.10 | .25 |
| **1828** | A338 | $5 multi | 1.75 | .25 |
| **1829** | A338 | $8 multi | 2.40 | .30 |
| | | *Nos. 1826-1829 (4)* | 5.55 | 1.05 |

Federation Emblem, Cargo Hook, Crane A339

Emblem, Tractor, New Buildings A340

**Wmk. 323**

**1973, Apr. 2 Litho. *Perf. 12½***

| | | | | |
|---|---|---|---|---|
| **1830** | A339 | $1 salmon & multi | .45 | .25 |
| **1831** | A340 | $5 blue & blk | 1.45 | .25 |

12th convention of International Federation of Asian and Western Pacific Contractors Association, Taipei, Apr. 2-10.

Pres. Chiang Kai-shek, Flag of China — A341

Design: $4, like $1 with different border.

**Unwmk.**

**1973, May 20 Photo. *Perf. 12***

| | | | | |
|---|---|---|---|---|
| **1832** | A341 | $1 yellow & multi | .65 | .25 |
| **1833** | A341 | $4 dk grn & multi | 2.00 | .50 |

First anniversary of Pres. Chiang Kai-shek's inauguration for a fifth term.

Lin Tse-hsü — A342

**Wmk. 323**

**1973, June 3 Engr. *Perf. 12***

| | | | | |
|---|---|---|---|---|
| **1834** | A342 | $1 sepia | 1.10 | .25 |

Lin Tse-hsü (1785-1850), Governor of Hunan and Kwantung, who destroyed large quantity of opium at Humen, Kwantung, June 3, 1839.

Willows and Palace Gate in the Morning A343

Lady Watering Peonies, Stone Ornament — A344

Design from scroll "Spring Morning in the Han Palace," by Chiu Ying. The five stamps of No. 1835 are numbered 1 to 5 and the five stamps of No. 1838 are numbered 6-10 in Chinese (see illustrations with Nos. 1682-1691 for numerals). The stamps are numbered and listed from right to left.

**1973 Photo. Unwmk. *Perf. 11½***
**Granite Paper**

| | | | | |
|---|---|---|---|---|
| **1835** | | Strip of 5 | 3.50 | 3.50 |
| *a.* | A343 | $1 shown (1) | .45 | .25 |
| *b.* | A343 | $1 Ladies feeding peacocks (2) | .45 | .25 |
| *c.* | A343 | $1 Lady watering peonies (3) | .45 | .25 |
| *d.* | A343 | $1 Pear tree in bloom (4) | .45 | .25 |
| *e.* | A343 | $1 Lady musicians (5) | .45 | .25 |
| **1836** | A344 | $5 shown | 2.75 | .80 |
| **1837** | A344 | $8 Lady musicians | 4.00 | 2.40 |
| **1838** | | Strip of 5 | 3.50 | 3.00 |
| *a.* | A343 | $1 Ladies playing go (6) | .45 | .25 |
| *b.* | A343 | $1 Various games (7) | .45 | .25 |
| *c.* | A343 | $1 Talking and playing music (8) | .45 | .25 |
| *d.* | A343 | $1 Artist painting portrait (9) | .45 | .25 |
| *e.* | A343 | $1 Sentries guarding wall (10) | .45 | .25 |
| **1839** | A344 | $5 Ladies playing go | 2.75 | .80 |
| **1840** | A344 | $8 Girl chasing butterfly | 4.00 | 2.40 |
| | | *Nos. 1835-1840 (6)* | 20.50 | 12.90 |

Issued: Nos. 1835-1837, 6/20; Nos. 1838-1840, 7/18.

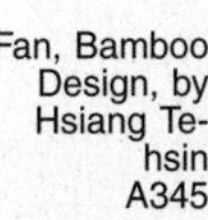

Fan, Bamboo Design, by Hsiang Te-hsin A345

Designs: Painted fans, Ming dynasty.

***Perf. 12½x13***
**1973, Aug. 15 Photo. Wmk. 368**

| | | | | |
|---|---|---|---|---|
| **1841** | A345 | $1 bister & multi | .50 | .25 |
| **1842** | A345 | $2.50 bister & multi | 1.25 | .25 |
| **1843** | A345 | $5 bister & multi | 2.25 | .50 |
| **1844** | A345 | $8 bister & multi | 3.50 | .60 |
| | | *Nos. 1841-1844 (4)* | 7.50 | 1.60 |

See Nos. 1934-1937.

Little League Emblem — A346

**Wmk. 370**
**1973, Sept. 9 Litho. *Perf. 13½***

| | | | | |
|---|---|---|---|---|
| **1845** | A346 | $1 yel, car & dk bl | 1.00 | .25 |
| **1846** | A346 | $4 yel, grn & dk bl | 2.00 | .30 |

Chinese victory in Little League Twin Championships, Gary, Ind., and Williamsport, Pa.

INTERPOL Emblem — A347

**Wmk. 370**
**1973, Sept. 11 Litho. *Perf. 12***

| | | | | |
|---|---|---|---|---|
| **1847** | A347 | $1 blue & org | .70 | .25 |
| **1848** | A347 | $5 green & org | 1.00 | .25 |
| **1849** | A347 | $8 magenta & org | 1.90 | .40 |
| | | *Nos. 1847-1849 (3)* | 3.60 | .90 |

Intl. Criminal Police Organization, 50th anniv.

Ch'iu Feng-chia — A348

**Wmk. 323**
**1973, Oct. 5 Engr. *Perf. 11½***

| | | | | |
|---|---|---|---|---|
| **1850** | A348 | $1 violet black | 1.25 | .25 |

2nd meeting of overseas Hakkas, Taipei, Oct. 5-7, and to honor Ch'iu Feng-chia (1864-1912), Hakka scholar, poet and revolutionist.

Tsengwen Reservoir — A349

Tsengwen Dam — A350

***Perf. 13½***
**1973, Oct. 31 Photo. Unwmk.**

| | | | | |
|---|---|---|---|---|
| **1851** | | Strip of 3 | 1.00 | .70 |
| *a.* | A349 | $1 Upper shore | .30 | .25 |
| *b.* | A349 | $1 shown | .30 | .25 |
| *c.* | A349 | $1 Lower shore | .30 | .25 |

***Perf. 12x11½***

| | | | | |
|---|---|---|---|---|
| **1852** | A350 | $5 shown | 1.40 | .30 |
| **1853** | A350 | $8 Spillway | 2.00 | .60 |
| | | *Nos. 1851-1853 (3)* | 4.40 | 1.60 |

Inauguration of Tsengwen Reservoir. No. 1851 printed in sheets of 15.

Tiger — A351

**Wmk. 370**
**1973, Dec. 1 Litho. *Perf. 12½***

| | | | | |
|---|---|---|---|---|
| **1854** | A351 | 50c multi | 1.40 | .25 |
| **1855** | A351 | $4.50 multi | 2.75 | .40 |

New Year 1974.

"Snow-dotted Eagle," by Lang Shih-ning A352

No. 1857, "Comfortable Ride." No. 1858, "Red Flower Eagle." No. 1859, "Cloud-running Steed." No. 1860, "Sky-running steed." $2.50, "Red Jade Seat." $5, "Thunderclap Steed." $8, "Arabian Champion." Designs from painting series "Ten Prized Horses," by Lang Shih-ning (Giuseppe Castiglione, 1688-1766).

**1973 Litho. Unwmk. *Perf. 13***

| | | | | |
|---|---|---|---|---|
| **1856** | A352 | 50c shown | 1.10 | .25 |
| **1857** | A352 | $1 Pinto, blk tail | 1.25 | .35 |
| **1858** | A352 | $1 Facing left | 1.25 | .35 |
| **1859** | A352 | $1 Facing right | 1.25 | .35 |
| **1860** | A352 | $1 Pinto, white tail | 1.25 | .35 |
| *a.* | | Horiz. or vert. strip of 4, #1857-1860 | 6.00 | 5.00 |
| **1861** | A352 | $2.50 Palomino | 3.25 | .60 |
| **1862** | A352 | $5 Grazing | 5.50 | 2.40 |
| *a.* | | Souvenir sheet of 4 | 60.00 | 35.00 |
| **1863** | A352 | $8 Brown stallion | 8.75 | 1.25 |
| | | *Nos. 1856-1863 (8)* | 23.60 | 5.90 |

No. 1862a contains 4 stamps with simulated perforations similar to Nos. 1856-1857, 1861-1862.

Issued: 50c, $2.50, $5, 11/21; others 12/21.

**Porcelain Types of 1972-73**
**Porcelain Series IV**

Porcelain Masterworks of Sung Dynasty: $1, Vase. $2, Three-tiered vase. $2.50, Lotus-shaped bowl. $5, Incense burner. $8, Incense burner on stand.

**1974, Jan. 16 Photo. *Perf. 11½***

| | | | | |
|---|---|---|---|---|
| **1864** | A323 | $1 ultra & multi | .70 | .25 |
| **1865** | A336 | $2 multicolored | 2.25 | .25 |
| **1866** | A336 | $2.50 red & multi | 2.50 | .30 |
| **1867** | A336 | $5 lilac & multi | 2.75 | .40 |
| **1868** | A336 | $8 green & multi | 2.75 | .50 |
| | | *Nos. 1864-1868 (5)* | 10.95 | 1.70 |

Juggler — A353

Design: $8, Magician producing dishes from his robe, horiz.

**1974, Feb. 6 Photo. *Perf. 11½***

| | | | | |
|---|---|---|---|---|
| **1869** | A353 | $1 yellow & multi | .60 | .25 |
| **1870** | A353 | $8 yellow & multi | 1.80 | .25 |

Taroko Gorge, Hualien — A354

Designs: $2.50, Luce Chapel, Tunghai University. $5, Tzu En Pagoda, Sun Moon Lake. $8, Goddess of Mercy, Keelung.

**1974, Mar. 22 Photo. *Perf. 12***

| | | | | |
|---|---|---|---|---|
| **1871** | A354 | $1 multi | .50 | .25 |
| **1872** | A354 | $2.50 multi | 1.10 | .25 |
| **1873** | A354 | $5 multi | 1.30 | .30 |
| **1874** | A354 | $8 multi | 2.00 | .50 |
| | | *Nos. 1871-1874 (4)* | 4.90 | 1.30 |

Taiwan landmarks.

Fighting Cocks (Brass) — A355

Designs: $2.50, Grapes and bowl with fruit (imitation jade). $5, Fisherman (wood carving), vert. $8, Basket with plastic roses, vert.

***Perf. 13½x14½, 14½x13½***
**1974, Apr. 10**

| | | | | |
|---|---|---|---|---|
| **1875** | A355 | $1 bl grn & multi | .40 | .25 |
| **1876** | A355 | $2.50 brown & multi | .85 | .25 |
| **1877** | A355 | $5 crimson & multi | 1.00 | .30 |
| **1878** | A355 | $8 multicolored | 1.50 | .50 |
| | | *Nos. 1875-1878 (4)* | 3.75 | 1.30 |

Taiwanese handicraft products.

Sun Yat-sen Memorial Hall — A356

Taiwan landmarks: $2.50, Reaching-moon Tower, Cheng Ching Lake. $5, Orchid Island (boats). $8, Penghu Interisland Bridge.

**1974, May 15 Photo. *Perf. 11½***
**Granite Paper**

| | | | | |
|---|---|---|---|---|
| **1879** | A356 | $1 blue & multi | .35 | .25 |
| **1880** | A356 | $2.50 blue & multi | .80 | .25 |
| **1881** | A356 | $5 blue & multi | 1.00 | .25 |
| **1882** | A356 | $8 blue & multi | 1.35 | .30 |
| | | *Nos. 1879-1882 (4)* | 3.50 | 1.05 |

Pres. Chiang and Gate of Whampoa Military Academy A357

Marching Cadets and Entrance Gate A358

**Wmk. 323**
**1974, June 16 Engr. *Perf. 11½***

| | | | | |
|---|---|---|---|---|
| **1883** | A357 | $1 carmine rose | .75 | .25 |
| **1884** | A358 | $14 violet blue | 1.00 | .25 |

50th anniversary of the founding of the Whampoa Military Academy.

Long-distance Runner and Olympic Rings — A359

$8, Women's relay race, Olympic rings.

**1974, June 23 Litho. *Perf. 12½***

| | | | | |
|---|---|---|---|---|
| **1885** | A359 | $1 blue, blk & red | .50 | .25 |
| **1886** | A359 | $8 pink, blk & red | 1.25 | .30 |

80th anniv. of Intl. Olympic Committee.

The Boy Wang Ch'i Fighting Invaders — A360

Folk Tales: No. 1888, T'i Ying pleading for her father before the Emperor. No. 1889, Wen Yen-po flushing out ball caught in tree. No. 1890, Boy Wang Hua returning gold piece he found. No. 1891, Pu Shih, a rich sheep raiser and benefactor. No. 1892, K'ung Yung as a child choosing smallest pear. No. 1893, Tung Yu studying. No. 1894, Szu Ma-kuang saving playmate from drowning in water jar.

**1974, July 15 Wmk. 370 *Perf. 13½***

| | | | | |
|---|---|---|---|---|
| **1887** | A360 | 50c olive & multi | .40 | .25 |
| **1888** | A360 | 50c ultra & multi | .40 | .25 |
| **1889** | A360 | 50c ocher & multi | .40 | .25 |
| **1890** | A360 | 50c red brn & multi | .40 | .25 |
| *a.* | | Block of 4, #1887-1890 | 2.10 | 1.20 |
| **1891** | A360 | $1 green & multi | .70 | .25 |
| **1892** | A360 | $1 lilac & multi | .70 | .25 |
| **1893** | A360 | $1 blue & multi | .70 | .25 |
| **1894** | A360 | $1 car & multi | .70 | .25 |
| *a.* | | Block of 4, #1891-1894 | 3.50 | 2.00 |
| | | *Nos. 1887-1894 (8)* | 4.40 | 2.00 |

For similar designs see A380, A427, A456, A495.

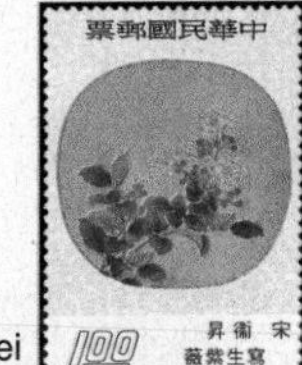

Myrtle, by Wei Sheng — A361

Silk Fan Paintings, Sung Dynasty (960-1279 A.D.): $2.50, Cabbage and Insects, by Hsu Ti. $5, Hibiscus, Cat and Dog, by Li Ti. $8, Pomegranate and Birds, by Wu Ping. Fans from National Palace Museum.

***Perf. 13x12½***
**1974, Aug. 14 Photo. Wmk. 368**

| | | | | |
|---|---|---|---|---|
| **1895** | A361 | $1 multi | .30 | .25 |
| **1896** | A361 | $2.50 multi | 1.00 | .25 |
| **1897** | A361 | $5 multi | 1.75 | .40 |
| **1898** | A361 | $8 multi | 2.50 | .50 |
| | | *Nos. 1895-1898 (4)* | 5.55 | 1.40 |

See Nos. 1950-1953.

Battle at Marco Polo Bridge, July 7, 1937 — A362

**Wmk. 370**
**1974, Sept. 3 Litho. *Perf. 13½***

| | | | | |
|---|---|---|---|---|
| **1899** | A362 | $1 multicolored | 1.25 | .25 |

**Souvenir Sheet**

**Wmk. 323**

**Without Gum; Granite Paper**

**1900** Sheet of 8 8.00 7.00

*a.* A362 $1, single stamp .55 .55

20th Armed Forces Day. No. 1900 commemorates Armed Forces Stamp Exhibition, Sun Yat-sen Memorial Hall, Sept. 3-9.

Chrysanthemum A363

Designs: Various chrysanthemums.

**Unwmk.**

**1974, Sept. 30 Photo. *Perf. 12***

**Granite Paper**

**1901** A363 $1 lilac & multi .30 .25

**1902** A363 $2.50 multi .70 .25

**1903** A363 $5 orange & multi 1.00 .25

**1904** A363 $8 multi 1.60 .35

*Nos. 1901-1904 (4)* 3.60 1.10

Rep. of China Pavilion, EXPO Emblem — A364

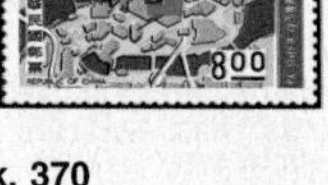

Map of Fair Grounds, Chinese Flag — A364a

**Wmk. 370**

**1974, Oct. 10 Litho. *Perf. 13***

**1905** A364 $1 multi .50 .25

**1906** A364a $8 multi 1.00 .25

EXPO '74, Spokane, Wash., May 4-Nov. 4. Theme, "Preserve the Environment."

Steel Mill, Kaohsiung A365

Taichung Harbor A366

Designs: $1, Taiwan North Link Railroad and map. $2, Oil refinery. $2.50, Electric train. $3.50, Taoyuan International Airport. $4, Taiwan North-South Highway and map. $4.50, Kaohsiung shipyard. $5, Su-ao Port.

***Perf. 13x12½, 12½x13***

**1974, Oct. 31 Wmk. 323**

**1907** A365 50c lilac, yel & brn .30 .25

**1908** A365 $1 green & org .30 .25

**1909** A365 $2 blue & yel .30 .25

**1910** A365 $2.50 emer & org .35 .25

**1911** A366 $3 ocher & ultra .30 .25

**1912** A366 $3.50 sl grn & yel .30 .25

**1913** A366 $4 brown & yel .30 .25

**1914** A366 $4.50 ver & bl .35 .25

**1915** A366 $5 sepia & dk bl .30 .25

*Nos. 1907-1915 (9)* 2.80 2.25

Major construction projects.

See Nos. 2009-2017, 2068-2076. For overprints see Nos. 2064-2065, 2112-2113.

Agaricus Bisporus — A367

Edible Mushrooms: $2.50, Pleurotus ostreatus. $5, Dictyophora indusiata. $8, Flammulina velutipes.

***Perf. 11½***

**1974, Nov. 15 Unwmk. Photo.**

**1916** A367 $1 multi .30 .25

**1917** A367 $2.50 multi .40 .25

**1918** A367 $5 multi .75 .25

**1919** A367 $8 multi .85 .35

*Nos. 1916-1919 (4)* 2.30 1.10

9th Intl. Scientific Congress on the Cultivation of Edible Fungi, Taipei, Nov. 1974.

Batters and World Map — A368

Pitcher and Championship Banners — A369

**Wmk. 323**

**1974, Nov. 24 Litho. *Perf. 13½***

**1920** A368 $1 multicolored .60 .25

**1921** A369 $8 multicolored .90 .25

China's victory in 1974 Little League Baseball World Series Triple Championships.

Rabbit — A370

**Wmk. 323**

**1974, Dec. 10 Photo. *Perf. 12½***

**1922** A370 50c orange & multi .50 .25

**1923** A370 $4.50 brown & multi 2.50 .25

New Year 1975.

Acrobat with Iron Rod — A371

$5, Two acrobats spinning tops, horiz.

**Granite Paper**

**1975, Jan. 15 Unwmk. *Perf. 11½***

**1924** A371 $4 yellow & multi .85 .25

**1925** A371 $5 yellow & multi 1.65 .30

Children Watching Puppet Show A372

Ceremonial New Year Greetings A373

Designs from scroll "Festivals for the New Year," by Ting Kuan-p'eng. Nos. 1926a-1926e are numbered 1-5 in Chinese.

$5, Children buying firecrackers. $8, Children and man with trained monkey.

**1975, Feb. 25 Photo. *Perf. 11½***

**Granite Paper**

**1926** Strip of 5 4.25 3.50

*a.* A372 $1 Ceremonial New Year Greetings (1) .65 .25

*b.* A372 $1 Man with trained monkey (2) .65 .25

*c.* A372 $1 Crowd and musicians (3) .65 .25

*d.* A372 $1 Picnic under a tree (4) .65 .25

*e.* A372 $1 shown (5) .65 .25

**1927** A373 $2.50 shown 3.00 .30

**1928** A373 $5 multi 3.50 .75

**1929** A373 $8 multi 6.00 1.00

*Nos. 1926-1929 (4)* 16.75 5.55

Sun Yat-sen Memorial Hall, Taipei — A374

Sun Yat-sen's Handwriting — A375

Sun Yat-sen, Bronze Statue in Memorial Hall — A376

Sun Yat-sen Memorial Hall, St. John's University, NY — A377

***Perf. 13½x14, 14x13½***

**1975, Mar. 12 Litho.**

**1930** A374 $1 green & multi .40 .25

**1931** A375 $4 yel grn & multi .90 .25

**1932** A376 $5 yellow & multi 1.05 .25

**1933** A377 $8 gray & multi 1.15 .30

*Nos. 1930-1933 (4)* 3.50 1.05

Dr. Sun Yat-sen (1866-1925), statesman and revolutionary leader.

**Fan Type of 1973 Inscribed "Landscape" (1st Character, 2nd Row)**

Painted fans, Ming Dynasty. Second row of inscription gives design description.

***Perf. 12½x13***

**1975, Apr. 16 Photo. Wmk. 368**

**1934** A345 $1 bister & multi .30 .25

**1935** A345 $2.50 bister & multi .95 .25

**1936** A345 $5 bister & multi 2.00 .40

**1937** A345 $8 bister & multi 2.25 1.20

*Nos. 1934-1937 (4)* 5.50 2.10

Yuan-chin coin, 1122-221 B.C. — A378

Ancient Chinese Coins: $4, Pan-liang, 221-207 B.C. $5, Five chu, 206 B.C.-220 A.D. $8, Five chu, 502-557 A.D.

**Wmk. 323**

**1975, May 20 Litho. *Perf. 13***

**1938** A378 $1 salmon & multi .30 .25

**1939** A378 $4 yellow & multi 1.20 .25

**1940** A378 $5 dl yel & multi 1.35 .25

**1941** A378 $8 lt vio & multi 2.00 .25

*Nos. 1938-1941 (4)* 4.85 1.00

The Cloth-bag Monk, by Chang Hung (1577-1668) A379

Chinese Paintings: $4, Lao-tzu Riding Buffalo, by Chao Pu-chih (1053-1110). $5, Portrait of Shih-te, by Wang Wen (1497-1576). $8, Splashed-ink Immortal, by Liang K'ai (early 13th century).

***Perf. 11½***

**1975, June 18 Photo. Unwmk.**

**Granite Paper**

**1942** A379 $2 blk, buff & ver .50 .25

**1943** A379 $4 blk, gray & red 1.90 .25

**1944** A379 $5 blk, yel & ver 2.50 .40

**1945** A379 $8 tan, red & blk 3.75 .60

*Nos. 1942-1945 (4)* 8.65 1.50

Chu Yin Reading by the Light of Fireflies — A380

Folk Tales: No. 1947, Hua Mu-lan going to war for her father. No. 1948, King Kou Chien tasting gall. $5, Chou Ch'u killing tiger.

***Perf. 14x13½***

**1975, July 16 Litho. Wmk. 368**

**1946** A380 $1 olive & multi .30 .25

**1947** A380 $2 bis brn & multi .40 .25

**1948** A380 $2 lt grn & multi .60 .25

**1949** A380 $5 blue & multi 1.20 .25

*Nos. 1946-1949 (4)* 2.50 1.00

See Nos. 2108-2111.

Cherry-Apple Blossoms, by Lin Ch'un — A381

Silk Fan Paintings, Sung Dynasty: $2, Spring Blossoms and Butterfly, by Ma K'uei. $5, Monkeys and Deer, by I Yüan-chih. $8, Tame Sparrow among Bamboo.

***Perf. 13x12½***

**1975, Aug. 15 Litho. Wmk. 323**

**1950** A381 $1 multicolored .30 .25

**1951** A381 $2 multicolored 1.10 .25

**1952** A381 $5 multicolored 1.75 .30

**1953** A381 $8 multicolored 2.75 .50

*Nos. 1950-1953 (4)* 5.90 1.30

See Nos. 2001-2004.

Gen. Chang Tzu-chung (1891-1940) — A382

No. 1955, Maj. Gen. Kao Chih-hong (1908-37). No. 1956, Capt. Sha Shih-chiun (1896-1938). No. 1957, Maj. Gen. Hsieh Chin-yuan (1905-41). No. 1958, Lt. Yen Hai-wen (1916-37). No. 1959, Lt. Gen. Tai An-lan (1905-42).

**Wmk. 323**

**1975, Sept. 3 Engr. *Perf. 12***

**1954** A382 $2 carmine .30 .25

**1955** A382 $2 sepia .30 .25

**1956** A382 $2 dull green .30 .25

**1957** A382 $5 violet black .55 .25

**1958** A382 $5 violet blue .55 .25

**1959** A382 $5 dark blue .55 .25

*Nos. 1954-1959 (6)* 2.55 1.50

Martyrs of the resistance fight against Japan.

Lotus Pond with Willows, by Madame Chiang A383

Paintings by Madame Chiang Kai-shek: $5, Sun Breaks through Mountain Clouds. $8, A Pair of Pine Trees. $10, Fishing and Farming.

*Perf. 13½*

**1975, Oct. 31 Litho. Unwmk.**

| | | | | |
|---|---|---|---|---|
| **1960** | A383 | $2 multicolored | .90 | .25 |
| **1961** | A383 | $5 multicolored | 3.75 | .30 |
| **1962** | A383 | $8 multicolored | 3.75 | .40 |
| **1963** | A383 | $10 multicolored | 4.75 | .75 |
| | | *Nos. 1960-1963 (4)* | 13.15 | 1.70 |

For similar design see type A404.

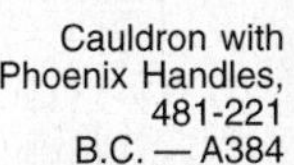

Cauldron with Phoenix Handles, 481-221 B.C. — A384

Ancient Bronzes: $2, Rectangular cauldron, 1122-722 B.C., vert. $8, Flat jar, 481-221 B.C. $10, 3-legged wine vessel, 1766-1122 B.C., vert.

**1975, Nov. 12 Photo. *Perf. 12***

| | | | | |
|---|---|---|---|---|
| **1964** | A384 | $2 pink & multi | .35 | .25 |
| **1965** | A384 | $5 lt blue & multi | 1.05 | .25 |
| **1966** | A384 | $8 yellow & multi | 1.25 | .25 |
| **1967** | A384 | $10 lilac & multi | 1.35 | .25 |
| | | *Nos. 1964-1967 (4)* | 4.00 | 1.00 |

For similar design see type A395. No. 1964 has 7 Chinese characters at left, No. 2005 has 4. No. 1967 has 4 characters at left, No. 2008 has 5.

Dragon, Nine-Dragon Wall, Peihai — A385

**Wmk. 323**

**1975, Dec. 1 Litho. *Perf. 12½***

| | | | | |
|---|---|---|---|---|
| **1968** | A385 | $1 orange & multi | .50 | .25 |
| **1969** | A385 | $5 green & multi | 2.00 | .75 |

New Year 1976.

Techi Dam — A386

Design: $10, Panoramic view of Techi Dam.

**1975, Dec. 17 Unwmk. *Perf. 13½***

| | | | | |
|---|---|---|---|---|
| **1970** | A386 | $2 green & multi | .30 | .25 |
| **1971** | A386 | $10 blue & multi | 1.00 | .35 |

Completion of Techi Dam, Tachia River.

Biathlon and Olympic Rings — A387

Olympic Rings and: $5, Luge. $8, Skiing.

**1976, Jan. 15 Litho. *Perf. 13½***

| | | | | |
|---|---|---|---|---|
| **1972** | A387 | $2 blue & multi | .30 | .25 |
| **1973** | A387 | $5 blue & multi | .50 | .25 |
| **1974** | A387 | $8 blue & multi | .80 | .30 |
| | | *Nos. 1972-1974 (3)* | 1.60 | .80 |

12th Winter Olympic Games, Innsbruck, Austria, Feb. 4-15.

Chin, Oldest Chinese Instrument — A388

Musical Instruments: $5, Se, c. 2900 B.C. $8, Standing kong-ho (harp). $10, Sleeping kong-ho.

**1976, Feb. 11 Unwmk. *Perf. 14***

| | | | | |
|---|---|---|---|---|
| **1975** | A388 | $2 yellow & multi | .60 | .25 |
| **1976** | A388 | $5 orange & multi | .70 | .25 |
| **1977** | A388 | $8 grnsh bl & multi | .90 | .25 |
| **1978** | A388 | $10 multicolored | 1.05 | .30 |
| | | *Nos. 1975-1978 (4)* | 3.25 | 1.05 |

For similar design see Type A407.

**Double Carp Type of 1969**

*Perf. 13½x12½*

**1976, Dec. 15 Engr. Unwmk.**

| | | | | |
|---|---|---|---|---|
| **1980** | A280 | $14 carmine rose | 2.25 | .25 |

Mail Collecting A389

Mail Sorting A390

Postal Service, 80th Anniv.: $8, Mail transport. $10, Mail delivery.

**Wmk. 323**

**1976, Mar. 20 Litho. *Perf. 13½***

| | | | | |
|---|---|---|---|---|
| **1984** | A389 | $2 yellow & multi | .40 | .25 |
| **1985** | A390 | $5 green & multi | .70 | .30 |
| **1986** | A390 | $8 blue & multi | 1.05 | .30 |
| **1987** | A389 | $10 orange & multi | 1.25 | .40 |
| ***a.*** | | Souv. sheet of 4, #1984-1987 | 11.00 | 9.00 |
| | | *Nos. 1984-1987 (4)* | 3.40 | 1.25 |

Pres. Chiang Kai-shek — A391

People Paying Homage A392

No. 1990, Pres. Chiang lying in state. No. 1991, Hearse leaving funeral chapel. $5, People along funeral route. $8, Spirit tablet in Tzuhu Guest House. $10, Tzuhu Guest House, Pres. Chiang's burial place.

**1976, Apr. 4**

| | | | | |
|---|---|---|---|---|
| **1988** | A391 | $2 gray & multi | .40 | .25 |
| **1989** | A392 | $2 gray & multi | .40 | .25 |
| **1990** | A392 | $2 gray & multi | .40 | .25 |
| **1991** | A392 | $2 gray & multi | .40 | .25 |
| **1992** | A392 | $5 gray & multi | .50 | .25 |
| **1993** | A392 | $8 gray & multi | .50 | .25 |
| **1994** | A392 | $10 gray & multi | .60 | .35 |
| | | *Nos. 1988-1994 (7)* | 3.20 | 1.85 |

Pres. Chiang Kai-shek (1887-1975), first death anniversary.

Flags of China and US — A393

**Wmk. 323**

**1976, May 29 Litho. *Perf. 13½***

| | | | | |
|---|---|---|---|---|
| **1995** | A393 | $2 multicolored | .30 | .25 |
| **1996** | A393 | $10 yellow & multi | 1.30 | .40 |

American Bicentennial.

Coin, 12th Century B.C. — A394

Bronze Shovel Coins (pu): $5, Pointed-feet coin, 481-221 B.C. $8, Round-feet coin, 722-481 B.C. $10, Square-feet coin, 3rd-2nd centuries B.C.

**1976, June 16**

| | | | | |
|---|---|---|---|---|
| **1997** | A394 | $2 salmon & multi | .40 | .25 |
| **1998** | A394 | $5 lt blue & multi | 1.05 | .30 |
| **1999** | A394 | $8 gray & multi | 1.30 | .30 |
| **2000** | A394 | $10 multicolored | 1.30 | .30 |
| | | *Nos. 1997-2000 (4)* | 4.05 | 1.15 |

**Fan Painting Type of 1975**

Silk Fan Paintings, Sung Dynasty: $2, Hibiscus, by Li Tung. $5, Lilies, by Lin Ch'un. $8, Deer and Pine, by Mou Chung-fu. $10, Quail and Wild Flowers, by Li An-chung.

*Perf. 13x12½*

**1976, July 14 Litho. Wmk. 323**

| | | | | |
|---|---|---|---|---|
| **2001** | A381 | $2 multicolored | .85 | .25 |
| **2002** | A381 | $5 multicolored | 2.00 | .30 |
| **2003** | A381 | $8 multicolored | 2.10 | .35 |
| **2004** | A381 | $10 multicolored | 2.10 | .30 |
| | | *Nos. 2001-2004 (4)* | 7.05 | 1.20 |

Cauldron, Shang Dynasty — A395

Ancient Bronzes: $5, 3-legged cauldron, Chou Dynasty (1122-722 B.C.). $8, Wine container, Chou Dynasty. $10, Wine vessel with spout, Shang Dynasty (1766-1122 B.C.).

**1976, Aug. 25 Photo. *Perf. 11½***

**Granite Paper**

| | | | | |
|---|---|---|---|---|
| **2005** | A395 | $2 rose & multi | .30 | .25 |
| **2006** | A395 | $5 lt blue & multi | 1.10 | .25 |
| **2007** | A395 | $8 yellow & multi | 1.25 | .25 |
| **2008** | A395 | $10 lilac & multi | 1.35 | .25 |
| | | *Nos. 2005-2008 (4)* | 4.00 | 1.00 |

**Construction Types of 1974**

Designs: $1, Taiwan North Link railroad and map. $2, Railroad electrification. $3, Taichung Harbor. $4, Taiwan North-South Highway and map. $5, Steel Mill, Kaohsiung. $6, Taoyuan International Airport. $7, Kao-hsiung shipyard. $8, Oil refinery. $9, Su-ao Port.

*Perf. 13½x12½, 12½x13½*

**1976 Litho. Wmk. 323**

| | | | | |
|---|---|---|---|---|
| **2009** | A365 | $1 carmine & grn | .30 | .25 |
| **2010** | A365 | $2 orange & multi | .30 | .25 |
| **2011** | A366 | $3 violet & multi | .30 | .25 |
| **2012** | A366 | $4 carmine & multi | .30 | .25 |
| **2013** | A365 | $5 green & brn | .30 | .25 |
| **2014** | A366 | $6 brown & multi | .50 | .25 |
| **2015** | A366 | $7 brown & multi | .40 | .25 |
| **2016** | A365 | $8 carmine & grn | .55 | .25 |
| **2017** | A366 | $9 olive & blue | .75 | .40 |
| | | *Nos. 2009-2017 (9)* | 3.70 | 2.40 |

Chiang Kai-shek and Mother — A396

Sun Yat-sen and Chiang Kai-shek at Canton Station A397

Design: $5, Chiang Kai-shek, portrait.

**1976, Oct. 31 Litho. *Perf. 13½***

| | | | | |
|---|---|---|---|---|
| **2023** | A396 | $2 multicolored | .40 | .25 |
| **2024** | A396 | $5 multicolored | 1.20 | .50 |
| **2025** | A397 | $10 multicolored | 1.20 | .40 |
| | | *Nos. 2023-2025 (3)* | 2.80 | 1.15 |

Pres. Chiang Kai-shek, 90th anniv. of birth.

Flags of Kuomintang and China — A398

Sun Yat-sen and Chiang Kai-shek — A399

**1976, Nov. 12 *Perf. 13½x14***

| | | | | |
|---|---|---|---|---|
| **2026** | A398 | $2 multicolored | .35 | .25 |
| **2027** | A399 | $10 multicolored | 1.10 | .45 |
| ***a.*** | | Souv. sheet of 2, #2026-2027 | 6.00 | 6.00 |

11th National Kuomintang Cong., Taipei.

Brazen Serpent — A400

**1976, Dec. 15 Wmk. 323 *Perf. 12½***

| | | | | |
|---|---|---|---|---|
| **2028** | A400 | $1 red, lilac & gold | .75 | .25 |
| **2029** | A400 | $5 plum, yel & gold | 2.15 | .25 |

New Year 1977.

Bird and Plum Blossoms, by Ch'en Hung-shou — A401

Chinese Paintings: $8, "Wintry Days" (pine), by Yang Wei-chen. $10, Rock and Bamboo, by Hsia Ch'ang.

*Perf. 11½*

**1977, Jan. 12 Photo. Unwmk.**

**Granite Paper**

| | | | | |
|---|---|---|---|---|
| **2030** | A401 | $2 multicolored | .90 | .25 |
| **2031** | A401 | $8 multicolored | 2.75 | .30 |
| **2032** | A401 | $10 multicolored | 3.75 | .75 |
| | | *Nos. 2030-2032 (3)* | 7.40 | 1.30 |

Black-naped Orioles A402

Birds of Taiwan: $8, Common Kingfisher. $10, Chinese pheasant-tailed jacana.

**1977, Feb. 16 Litho.**

| | | | | |
|---|---|---|---|---|
| **2033** | A402 | $2 multicolored | .50 | .25 |
| **2034** | A402 | $8 multicolored | 1.60 | .25 |
| **2035** | A402 | $10 multicolored | 1.75 | .30 |
| | | *Nos. 2033-2035 (3)* | 3.85 | .80 |

See Nos. 2163-2165.

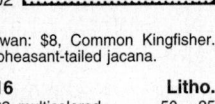

Census Emblem, Industry and Commerce A403

*Perf. 13½*

**1977, Mar. 16 Litho. Unwmk.**

| | | | | |
|---|---|---|---|---|
| **2036** | A403 | $2 red & multi | .30 | .25 |
| **2037** | A403 | $10 purple & multi | .90 | .25 |

Industry and Commerce Census.

Green Mountains Rising into Clouds, by Madame Chiang A404

Landscapes, by Madame Chiang Kai-shek: $5, Boat in the Beauty of Spring. $8, Scholar beside Waterfall. $10, Water Rises to Meet the Bridge.

*Perf. 11½*

**1977, Mar. 31 Unwmk. Photo.**

**Granite Paper**

| | | | | |
|---|---|---|---|---|
| **2038** | A404 | $2 multi | .65 | .25 |
| **2039** | A404 | $5 multi | 2.60 | .40 |
| **2040** | A404 | $8 multi | 3.25 | .50 |
| **2041** | A404 | $10 multi | 3.50 | .60 |
| | | *Nos. 2038-2041 (4)* | 10.00 | 1.75 |

League Emblem — A405

**1977, Apr. 18 Litho. *Perf. 12½***
**2042** A405 $2 carmine & multi .30 .25
**2043** A405 $10 green & multi 1.00 .65

10th World Anti-Communist League Conference.

Blood Donation — A406

Design: $2, Donating blood, horiz.

**1977, May 5 Wmk. 323 *Perf. 13½***
**2044** A406 $2 red & black .30 .25
**2045** A406 $10 red & black .90 .65

Blood donation movement.

San-hsien — A407

Musical Instruments: $5, Tung-hsiao (bamboo flute). $8, Yang-chin (butterfly harpsichord). $10, Pai-hsiao (pipes). Background shows musician playing instrument.

**Unwmk.**
**1977, June 21 Photo. *Perf. 14***
**2046** A407 $2 multicolored .40 .25
**2047** A407 $5 multicolored .65 .25
**2048** A407 $8 multicolored .90 .25
**2049** A407 $10 multicolored 1.10 .30
*Nos. 2046-2049 (4)* 3.05 1.05

Idea Leuconoe — A408

Protected Butterflies: $4, Hebomoia glaucippe formosana. $6, Stichophthalma howqua formosana. $10, Atrophaneura horishana.

**1977, July 20 Litho. *Perf. 13½***
**2050** A408 $2 ver & multi .40 .25
**2051** A408 $4 lt grn & multi 1.15 .25
**2052** A408 $6 lt bl & multi 1.40 .40
**2053** A408 $10 yellow & multi 1.75 .40
*Nos. 2050-2053 (4)* 4.70 1.30

National Palace Museum A409

Temple A410

Children's Drawings: $2, Sea Goddess Festival. $4, Boats on Shore of Lan-yu.

**Wmk. 323**
**1977, Aug. 27 Litho. *Perf. 13½***
**2054** A409 $1 multicolored .30 .25
**2055** A409 $2 multicolored .30 .25
**2056** A409 $4 multicolored .50 .25
**2057** A410 $5 multicolored .60 .25
*Nos. 2054-2057 (4)* 1.70 1.00

8th Exhib. of World School Children's Art.

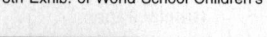

Carved Lacquer Plate, Wan-li Ware — A411

Ancient Carved Lacquer Ware: $5, Bowl, Ching dynasty. $8, Round box, Ming dynasty. $10, Four-tiered box, Ching dynasty.

***Perf. 13x14***
**1977, Sept. 28 Photo. Wmk. 368**
**2058** A411 $2 multicolored .30 .25
**2059** A411 $5 multicolored .90 .30
**2060** A411 $8 multicolored 1.10 .25
**2061** A411 $10 multicolored 1.35 .30
*Nos. 2058-2061 (4)* 3.65 1.10

Lions International, Emblem and Activities — A412

**Unwmk.**
**1977, Oct. 8 Litho. *Perf. 13***
**2062** A412 $2 multicolored .30 .25
**2063** A412 $10 multicolored .85 .25

Intl. Association of Lions Clubs, 60th anniv.

Nos. 2069 and 2075 Overprinted in Claret

***Perf. 13½x12½***
**1977, Sept. 9 Litho. Unwmk.**
**2064** A365 $2 orange & multi .35 .25
**2065** A365 $8 carmine & grn 1.00 .25

Little League baseball championship.

Chinese Quality Mark — A413

***Perf. 13x12½***
**1977, Oct. 14 Litho. Unwmk.**
**2066** A413 $2 red & multi .50 .25
**2067** A413 $10 blue & multi 1.75 .25

International Standardization Day.

**Construction Types of 1974 Redrawn: Numerals Outlined**

Designs as 1976 Issue.

***Perf. 13½x12½, 12½x13½***
**1977 Litho. Unwmk.**
**Granite Paper**
**2068** A365 $1 car & dp grn .30 .25
**2069** A365 $2 ver & multi .30 .25
**2070** A366 $3 violet & multi .65 .25
**2071** A366 $4 carmine & multi .35 .25
**2072** A365 $5 green & multi .30 .25
**2073** A366 $6 sepia & multi .35 .25
**2074** A366 $7 sepia & multi .85 .25
**2075** A365 $8 red lil & multi .80 .25
**2076** A366 $9 olive & multi 1.00 .25
*Nos. 2068-2076 (9)* 4.90 2.25

Numerals are in solid color on Nos. 1907-1915, 2009-2017; in outline on Nos. 2068-2076.

For overprints see Nos. 2064-2065, 2112-2113.

Man and Heart — A414

***Perf. 13½x12½***
**1977, Nov. 12 Litho. Wmk. 323**
**2077** A414 $2 multicolored .35 .25
**2078** A414 $10 multicolored .95 .25

Physical health, cardiac care.

White Stallion — A415

New Year 1978: $5, Two horses, horiz. Designs from painting "100 Horses," by Lang Shih-ning.

***Perf. 12½***
**1977, Dec. 1 Unwmk. Litho.**
**2079** A415 $1 red & multi .50 .25
**2080** A415 $5 emerald & multi 1.60 .30

First Page of Constitution A416

Pres. Chiang Accepting Constitution, 1946 A417

**1977, Dec. 25 Litho. *Perf. 13½***
**2081** A416 $2 multicolored .30 .25
**2082** A417 $10 multicolored 1.10 .30

30th anniversary of the Constitution.

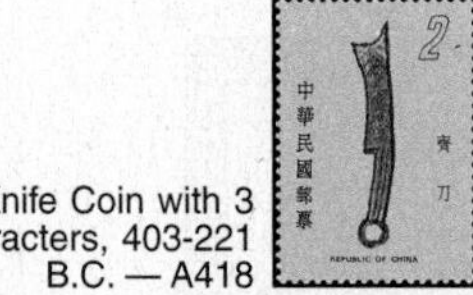
Knife Coin with 3 Characters, 403-221 B.C. — A418

Designs: Ancient knife coins.

**1978, Jan. 18 Wmk. 323 *Perf. 13½***
**2083** A418 $2 salmon & multi .30 .25
**2084** A418 $5 lt blue & blk 1.10 .25
**2085** A418 $8 lt gray & multi 1.20 .25
**2086** A418 $10 tan & multi 1.50 .30
*Nos. 2083-2086 (4)* 4.10 1.05

China No. 1 and Flag of China — A419

Designs: $5, No. 464 (Sun Yat-sen). $10, No. 1204 (Chiang Kai-shek).

**1978, Feb. 21 Litho. *Perf. 13½***
**2087** A419 $2 brown & multi .40 .25
**2088** A419 $5 blue & multi .90 .25
**2089** A419 $10 orange & multi 1.75 .40
*a.* Souv. sheet of 3, #2087-2089 13.50 7.00
*Nos. 2087-2089 (3)* 3.05 .90

Centenary of Chinese postage stamps.

Sun Yat-Sen Memorial Hall — A420

China Nos. 2079 and 2 — A421

***Perf. 14x12½, 12½x14***
**1978, Mar. 20 Wmk. 323**
**2090** A420 $2 multicolored .35 .25
**2091** A421 $10 multicolored 1.00 .25

ROCPEX '78 Phil. Exhib., Taipei, Mar. 20-29.

Chiang Kai-shek with Revolutionary Army — A422

Pres. Chiang Kai-shek (1887-1975); $2, as young man, 1912, vert. $8, Making speech at Mt. Lu, July 17, 1937. $10, Reviewing Armed Forces on National Day, 1956, and Chinese flags, vert.

**1978, Apr. 5 Wmk. 323 *Perf. 13½***
**2092** A422 $2 violet & multi .30 .25
**2093** A422 $5 green & multi .90 .30
**2094** A422 $8 blue & multi 1.15 .30
**2095** A422 $10 vio blue & multi 1.25 .40
*Nos. 2092-2095 (4)* 3.60 1.25

Nuclear Reactor and Plant — A423

***Perf. 13½x12½***
**1978, Apr. 26 Unwmk.**
**2096** A423 $10 multicolored 1.15 .25

First nuclear power plant on Taiwan.

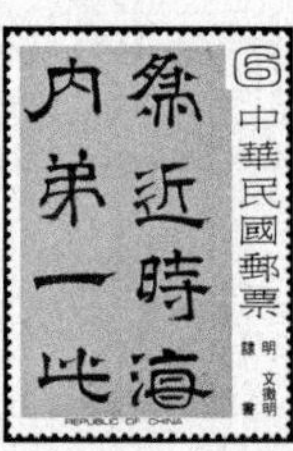

Poem by Wen Cheng-ming (1470-1559) A424

Chinese Calligraphy: $2, Letter by Wang Hsi-chih (307-365). $4, Eulogy by Chu Sui-liang (596-658). $8, From Autobiography of Huai-su, Tang Dynasty. $10, Poem by Ch'ang Piao, Sung Dynasty.

**1978, May 20 Wmk. 323 *Perf. 13½***
**2097** A424 $2 multicolored *.85* .25
**2098** A424 $4 multicolored *3.00* .40
**2099** A424 $6 multicolored *3.00* .60
**2100** A424 $8 multicolored *3.50* .40
**2101** A424 $10 multicolored *4.50* .60
*Nos. 2097-2101 (5)* *14.85* 2.25

Head and Dao Cancer Fund Emblem — A425

**1978, June 15 Litho. *Perf. 13½***
**2102** A425 $2 red, org & ol .35 .25
**2103** A425 $10 dk & lt bl & grn 1.00 .25

Cancer prevention.

Carved Lacquer Vase, Ming Dynasty — A426

Ancient Carved Lacquer Ware: $2, Box with dragon and cloud design, Ch'ing dynasty, horiz. $5, Double box on legs, Ch'ing dynasty, horiz. $8, Round box with peonies, Ming dynasty, horiz.

**1978, July 12**
**2104** A426 $2 gray olive & multi .30 .25
**2105** A426 $5 gray olive & multi .75 .30
**2106** A426 $8 gray olive & multi .90 .25
**2107** A426 $10 gray olive & multi 1.00 .30
*Nos. 2104-2107 (4)* 2.95 1.10

Tsu Ti Practicing with his Sword — A427

Folk Tales: No. 2109, Pan Ch'ao, diplomat and governor. No. 2110, Tien Tan's "Fire Bull Battle." $5, Liang Hung-yu, a general's wife, who served as drummer in battle.

**Wmk. 323**

**1978, Aug. 16 Litho. *Perf. 13½***

**2108** A427 $1 multicolored .30 .25
**2109** A427 $2 bister & multi .95 .25
**2110** A427 $2 gray & multi .95 .25
**2111** A427 $5 multicolored 1.25 .25
*Nos. 2108-2111 (4)* 3.45 1.00

For similar designs see types A456, A495.

Nos. 2071 & 2073 Overprinted in Red

**1978, Sept. 9 *Perf. 12½x13***

**2112** A366 $4 multicolored .30 .25
**2113** A366 $6 multicolored .85 .30

Triple championships won by Chinese teams in Little League World Series. "1978" overprint on $4 at left, on $6 at right.

Ixias Pyrene — A428

Protected Butterflies: $4, Euploea sylvestor swinhoei. $6, Cyrestis thyodamas formosana. $10, Byasa polyeuctes termessus.

**1978, Sept. 20**

**2114** A428 $2 multicolored .50 .25
**2115** A428 $4 multicolored 1.50 .25
**2116** A428 $6 multicolored 1.75 .30
**2117** A428 $10 multicolored 2.40 .30
*Nos. 2114-2117 (4)* 6.15 1.10

Scout Symbols — A429

**1978, Oct. 5 Litho. *Perf. 13½***

**2118** A429 $2 multicolored .65 .25
**2119** A429 $10 multicolored .95 .25

5th Chinese Boy Scout Jamboree, Cheng Ching Lake, Oct. 5-12.

Tropical Tomatoes — A430

Design: $10, Tropical tomatoes, horiz.

**1978, Oct. 23 Wmk. 323**

**2120** A430 $2 multicolored .45 .25
**2121** A430 $10 multicolored 1.50 .30

International Symposium on Tropical Tomatoes, Taiwan, Oct. 23-28.

Sino-Saudi Bridge — A431

Design: $6, Buttresses of bridge, flags of Taiwan and Saudi Arabia, horiz.

**1978, Oct. 31**

**2122** A431 $2 multicolored .50 .25
**2123** A431 $6 multicolored 1.40 .25

Completion of Sino-Saudi Bridge over Cho-Shui River.

National Flag — A432

**1978-80 *Perf. 13½***

**2124** A432 $1 red & dk bl, I .30 .25
*a.* Bklt. pane of 16 ($5, $6, $8, $10, 3 $1, 9 $2) 7.75
*b.* Type II 1.50 .25
**2125** A432 $2 red & dk bl, I .30 .25
*a.* Bklt. pane of 15 + label 11.00
*b.* Type II .30 .25
**2126** A432 $3 yel grn & multi .30 .25
**2127** A432 $4 bis & multi .30 .25
**2128** A432 $5 dk grn & multi, I .30 .25
*a.* Type II .30 .25
**2129** A432 $6 brn org & multi 1.00 .25
**2130** A432 $7 dk brn & multi 1.00 .25
**2131** A432 $8 dk grn & multi, I 1.00 .25
*a.* Type II 1.00 .25
**2132** A432 $10 brt bl & multi .80 .25
**2133** A432 $12 brt rose lil & multi .80 .25
*Nos. 2124-2133 (10)* 6.10 2.50

Two types exist: I. Second line (red) below flag is same width as blue line. II. Second line is a hairline, notably thinner. The $3, $4, $7 and $12 were issued only in type II; $6, $10, No. 2124a, only in type I.

Nos. 2129-2133 have colorless inscriptions and denomination in a panel of solid color. Issued: Nos. 2124, 2125, 2128, 2129, 2121, 11/12/1978; No. 2132, 1/23/1979; No. 2124a, selvage inscription in blue, 10/10/1979, selvage inscription in green or red, 1/23/1980; No. 2125a, selvage inscription in blue, 10/25/1979, selvage inscription in green or red 4/24/1980; Nos. 2125b, 2128a, 2130, 2131a, 2133, 5/31/1980; Nos. 2124b, 2126, 2127, 7/31/1980.

1980 booklets are worth approximately 50 percent more than 1979 booklets.

A432a

**Coil Stamp**

**1980, Jan. 15 *Perf. 12 Horiz.***

**2134** A432a $2 multicolored .90 .25

See Nos. 2288-2300. For overprints see Nos. 2540-2541.

Three Rams, by Emperor Hsuan-tsung — A433

**Wmk. 323**

**1978, Dec. 1 Litho. *Perf. 12½***

**2135** A433 $1 multicolored .40 .25
**2136** A433 $5 multicolored 1.50 .30

New Year 1979.

Taoyuan International Airport — A434

$10, Passenger terminal, control tower.

**1978, Dec. 31 *Perf. 13½***

**2137** A434 $2 multi .40 .25
**2138** A434 $10 multi, horiz. .70 .25

Completion of Taoyuan Intl. Airport.

Oracle Bones and Inscription, 1766-1123 B.C. — A435

Antiquities and Inscriptions: $5, Lehchi cauldron, 722-481 B.C. $8, Small seal (turtle), 206 B.C.-8 A.D. $10, Inscribed stone tablet, 175-183 A.D.

**1979, Jan. 17**

**2139** A435 $2 multicolored .65 .25
**2140** A435 $5 multicolored 1.60 .40
**2141** A435 $8 multicolored 1.90 .30
**2142** A435 $10 multicolored 2.25 .40
*Nos. 2139-2142 (4)* 6.40 1.35

Origin and development of Chinese characters.

Chihkan Tower, 1653 — A436

Taiwan Scenery: $5, Shrine of Confucius, 1665. $8, Shrine of Koxinga, 1661. $10, Eternal Castle and moat.

**1979, Feb. 11 Litho. *Perf. 13½***

**2143** A436 $2 multicolored .45 .25
**2144** A436 $5 multicolored 1.10 .30
**2145** A436 $8 multicolored 1.30 .25
**2146** A436 $10 multicolored 1.60 .30
*Nos. 2143-2146 (4)* 4.45 1.10

Children Playing on Winter Day, Sung Dynasty A437

**1979, Mar. 8**

**2147** A437 Block of 4 15.00 15.00
*a.* $5 in UL corner 3.75 .50
*b.* $5 in UR corner 3.75 .50
*c.* $5 in LL corner 3.75 .50
*d.* $5 in LR corner 3.75 .50
*e.* Souvenir sheet of 4, #2147, imperf. *32.00* 16.00

No. 2147e has simulated perforations.

Lu Hao-tung — A438

***Perf. 13x12½***

**1979, Mar. 29 Engr. Wmk. 323**

**2148** A438 $2 blue 1.00 .25

Lu Hao-tung (1868-1895), revolutionist.

Yellow Jade Brush Holder — A439

Ancient Brush Washers: $5, White jade, Ming Dynasty. $8, Dark green jade, Ch'ing Dynasty. $10, Bluish jade, Ch'ing Dynasty. All horiz.

**Granite Paper**

**Unwmk.**

**1979, Apr. 12 Photo. *Perf. 12***

**2149** A439 $2 multicolored .50 .25
**2150** A439 $5 multicolored 1.25 .30
**2151** A439 $8 multicolored 1.35 .30
**2152** A439 $10 multicolored 1.60 .30
*Nos. 2149-2152 (4)* 4.70 1.15

**For similar artifacts designs with single-color background and denominations in outlined numerals with the cents, see types A453, A469, A489, A523, A547, A582.**

A440

A440a

Designs: National flower plum blossoms.

***Perf. 13½x12½***

**1979-92 Engr. Wmk. 323**

**Granite Paper**

**2153** A440 $10 dk blue 1.50 .25
*a.* Plain paper 1.00 .25
**2154** A440 $20 brown 1.00 .25
*b.* Plain paper 1.10 .25
**2154A** A440 $40 brt car 2.10 .25
*c.* Plain paper 2.00 .25
**2155** A440 $50 dull green 3.50 .75
*a.* Plain paper 2.50 .30
**2156** A440 $100 vermilion 7.00 1.00
*e.* Plain paper 3.50 .60

***Perf. 14x13½***

**2156A** A440a $300 pur & red org 28.00 7.00
*c.* Plain paper 15.00 1.80
**2156B** A440a $500 ver & brn 32.00 6.00
*d.* Plain paper 25.00 3.00
*Nos. 2153-2156B (7)* 75.10 15.50

Issued: Nos. 2153, 2154, 5/20/1979; No. 2155, 6/5/1979; No. 2156, 8/8/1979; No. 2156B, 11/15/1982; No. 2156A, 6/6/1983; No. 2154A, 4/15/1985; Nos. 2154b, 2155a, 1/5/1987; No. 2153a, 5/10/1988; No. 2156e, 3/20/1989; No. 2154Ac, 2/2/1990; Nos. 2156Ac, 2156Bd, 5/1/1991.

City Houses and Garden — A441

Design: $10, Rural landscape, horiz.

***Perf. 13x12½, 12½x13***

**1979, June 5 Litho.**

**2157** A441 $2 multicolored .45 .25
**2158** A441 $10 multicolored .95 .25

Protection of the Environment.

Bankbook and Computer Department A442

Designs: $2, Children at counter, vert. $5, People standing in line, vert. $10, Hand putting coin in savings bank, symbolic tree.

**1979, July 1 Wmk. 323 *Perf. 13½***

**2159** A442 $2 multicolored .30 .25
**2160** A442 $5 multicolored .80 .25
**2161** A442 $8 multicolored 1.10 .25
**2162** A442 $10 multicolored 1.30 .30
*Nos. 2159-2162 (4)* 3.50 1.05

Postal savings, 60th anniversary.

**Bird Type of 1977**

Birds of Taiwan: $2, Swinoe's pheasant. $8, Steere's babbler. $10, Formosan yuhina.

**1979, Aug. 8 *Perf. 11½***

**2163** A402 $2 multicolored .45 .25
**2164** A402 $8 multicolored 1.50 .25
**2165** A402 $10 multicolored 1.75 .40
*Nos. 2163-2165 (3)* 3.70 .90

Rowland Hill, Penny Black — A443

***Perf. 13½x13***

**1979, Aug. 27 Litho. Wmk. 323**

**2166** A443 $10 multicolored 1.25 .30

Sir Rowland Hill (1795-1879), originator of penny postage.

Jar with Rope Design, Shang Dynasty — A444

Ancient Chinese Pottery: $5, Two-handled jar, Shang dynasty. $8, Red jar with "ears," Han dynasty. $10, Green glazed jar, Han dynasty.

**1979, Sept. 12** *Perf. 13½*

**2167** A444 $2 multicolored .45 .25
**2168** A444 $5 multicolored 1.60 .25
**2169** A444 $8 multicolored 1.90 .25
**2170** A444 $10 multicolored 2.25 .35
*Nos. 2167-2170 (4)* 6.20 1.10

Children and IYC Emblem — A445

**1979, Sept. 28 Litho.** *Perf. 13½*

**2171** A445 $2 multicolored .40 .25
**2172** A445 $10 multicolored .80 .30

International Year of the Child.

Trade Symbols, Competition Emblem — A446

**1979, Dec. 9 Litho.** *Perf. 13½*

**2173** A446 $2 blue & multi .40 .25
**2174** A446 $10 green & multi .80 .25

10th National Vocational Training Competition, Taichung, Dec. 9.

Trees on a Winter Plain, by Li Ch'eng — A447

Paintings: $5, Bamboo, Wen T'ung. $8, Old tree, bamboo and rock, by Chao Meng-fu. $10, Twin Pines, by Li K'an.

**1979, Nov. 21**

**2175** A447 $2 multicolored .65 .25
**2176** A447 $5 multicolored 1.90 .40
**2177** A447 $8 multicolored 2.50 .40
**2178** A447 $10 multicolored 3.25 .50
*Nos. 2175-2178 (4)* 8.30 1.55

Monkey — A448

**1979, Dec. 1** *Perf. 12½*

**2179** A448 $1 yellow & multi .85 .25
**2180** A448 $6 tan & multi 2.75 .35

New Year 1980.

Rotary Emblem and "75" — A449

Rotary Intl., 75th Anniv.: $12, Anniv. emblem.

**1980, Feb. 23 Litho.** *Perf. 13½*

**2181** A449 $2 multicolored .40 .25
**2182** A449 $12 multi, vert. .90 .25

Mt. Hohuan — A450

Taiwan Landscapes (East-West Cross-Island Highway): $2, Tunnel of Nine Turns, vert. $12, Bridge, Tien Hsiang, vert.

**1980, Mar. 1 Wmk. 323**

**2183** A450 $2 multicolored .35 .25
**2184** A450 $8 multicolored 1.20 .25
**2185** A450 $12 multicolored 1.90 .45
*Nos. 2183-2185 (3)* 3.45 .95

A451

**1980, Mar. 29 Engr.** *Perf. 13½x12½*
**Granite Paper**

**2186** A451 $2 red brown .80 .25

Shih Chien-Ju (1879-1900), revolutionist.

A452

$2, Chung-cheng Memorial Hall. $8, Quotation. $12, Bronze statue.

**1980, Apr. 4 Litho.** *Perf. 13½*

**2187** A452 $2 multicolored .35 .25
**2188** A452 $8 multicolored .60 .25
**2189** A452 $12 multicolored 1.15 .50
*Nos. 2187-2189 (3)* 2.10 1.00

Chiang Kai-shek (1887-1975).

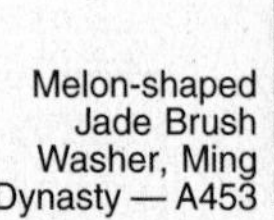

Melon-shaped Jade Brush Washer, Ming Dynasty — A453

Jade Pottery: $2, Jar with dragons, Sung dynasty, vert. $8, Monk's alms bowl, Ch'ing dynasty. $10, Yellow jade brush washer, Ch'ing dynasty.

**1980, May 20 Photo.** *Perf. 12*
**Granite Paper**

**2190** A453 $2 multicolored .50 .25
**2191** A453 $5 multicolored 1.60 .30
**2192** A453 $8 multicolored 1.15 .25
**2193** A453 $10 multicolored 1.75 .40
*Nos. 2190-2193 (4)* 5.00 1.20

Energy Conservation — A454

**1980, July 15 Litho.** *Perf. 13½*

**2194** A454 $2 multicolored .45 .25
**2195** A454 $12 multicolored .90 .30

A455

T'ang Dynasty pottery.

**1980, Aug. 18 Litho.** *Perf. 13½*

**2196** A455 $2 Soldier .50 .25
**2197** A455 $5 Roosters 1.50 .30
**2198** A455 $8 Horse 1.90 .25
**2199** A455 $10 Camel 2.25 .35
*Nos. 2196-2199 (4)* 6.15 1.15

A456

Folk Tales: $1, Grinding mortar into a needle. No. 2201, Confucius Returning Lost Article (shown). No. 2202, Wen Tien-hsiang in jail. $5, Sending coal in snow.

*Perf. 14x13½*

**1980, Sept. 23 Litho. Wmk. 323**

**2200** A456 $1 multicolored .30 .25
**2201** A456 $2 multicolored .80 .25
**2202** A456 $2 multicolored .80 .25
**2203** A456 $5 multicolored 1.40 .25
*Nos. 2200-2203 (4)* 3.30 1.00

Railroad Electrification A457

No. 2205, Taichung Harbor. No. 2206, Chiang Kai-shek Airport. No. 2207, Steel Mill. No. 2208, Sun Yat-sen Freeway. No. 2209, Nuclear power plant. No. 2210, Petrochemical plants. No. 2211, Su-ao Harbor. No. 2212, Kaohsiung shipyard. No. 2213, North link railroad.

**1980, Oct. 10** *Perf. 13½x14*

**2204** A457 $2 shown .35 .25
**2205** A457 $2 multicolored .35 .25
**2206** A457 $2 multicolored .35 .25
**2207** A457 $2 multicolored .35 .25
**2208** A457 $2 multicolored .50 .25
**2209** A457 $2 multicolored .35 .25
**2210** A457 $2 multicolored .35 .25
**2211** A457 $2 multicolored .35 .25
**2212** A457 $2 multicolored .35 .25
**2213** A457 $2 multicolored .50 .25
*a.* Souv. sheet of 10, #2204-2213 14.50 7.50
*b.* Block of 10, #2204-2213 7.50 3.75
*Nos. 2204-2213 (10)* 3.80 2.50

Completion of major construction projects.

10th National Savings Day — A458

$2, Ancient coin and coin banks.

**Wmk. 323**

**1980, Oct. 25 Litho.** *Perf. 13½*

**2214** A458 $2 multicolored .65 .25
**2215** A458 $12 shown 1.00 .30

Landscape, by Ch'iu Ying, Ming Dynasty — A459

**1980, Nov. 12 Litho.** *Perf. 13½*

**2216** A459 Block of 4 12.50 5.00
*a.* $5 in UL corner 2.50 .40
*b.* $5 in UR corner 2.50 .40
*c.* $5 in LL corner 2.50 .40
*d.* $5 in LR corner 2.50 .40
*e.* Souvenir sheet, imperf. 27.50 27.50

No. 2216e has simulated perforations.

Cock — A460

**1980, Dec. 1** *Perf. 12½*

**2217** A460 $1 multicolored .70 .25
**2218** A460 $6 multicolored 3.50 .25
*a.* Souv. sheet, 2 each #2217-2218 12.50 12.50

New Year 1981.

Faces, Flag, Census Form — A461

**1980, Dec. 13** *Perf. 13½*

**2219** A461 $2 shown .30 .25
**2220** A461 $12 Buildings, horiz. 1.20 .30

1980 population and housing census.

TIROS-N Satellite — A462

Design: $10, Central weather bureau, horiz.

**1981, Jan. 28 Litho.** *Perf. 13½*

**2221** A462 $2 multicolored .40 .25
**2222** A462 $10 multicolored 1.00 .25

Completion of meteorological satellite ground station, Taipei.

"Happiness" — A463

New Year 1981 (Calligraphy): No. 2224, Wealth. No. 2225, Longevity. No. 2226, Joy.

**1981, Feb. 3** *Perf. 13½x12½*

**2223** A463 $5 multi, 5 at B 1.00 .25
**2224** A463 $5 multi, 5 at R 1.00 .25
**2225** A463 $5 multi, 5 at L 1.00 .25
**2226** A463 $5 multi, 5 at T 1.00 .25
*a.* Block of 4, #2223-2226 7.50 1.40

International Year of the Disabled — A464

**1981, Feb. 19 Litho.** *Perf. 13½*

**2227** A464 $2 multicolored .35 .25
**2228** A464 $12 multicolored 1.00 .25

Mt. Ali — A465

**1981, Mar. 1**

**2229** A465 $2 shown .35 .25
**2230** A465 $7 Oluanpi Beach 1.00 .25
**2231** A465 $12 Sun Moon Lake 1.40 .40
*Nos. 2229-2231 (3)* 2.75 .90

A $2 multicolored stamp for the 12th National Kuomintang Congress at Taipei was prepared for release Mar. 29, 1981, but not issued. It showed Sun Yat-sen, Chiang Kai-shek, flags of China and the Kuomintang and a map of China.

Children in Forest — A467

Children's Day: Drawings.

**1981, Apr. 4**

**2233** A467 $1 multicolored .30 .25
**2234** A467 $2 multicolored .30 .25
**2235** A467 $5 multicolored .35 .25
**2236** A467 $7 multicolored .40 .25
*Nos. 2233-2236 (4)* 1.35 1.00

Chiang Kai-shek Memorial Hall — A468

**1981, Apr. 5** ***Perf. 12½x13½***

**2237** A468 20c bluish lilac .30 .25
*a.* Photo. ('87) .30 .25
**2238** A468 40c crim rose .30 .25
*a.* Photo. ('87) .30 .25
**2239** A468 50c dull red brn .30 .25
*a.* Photo. ('88) .30 .25
*Nos. 2237-2239 (3)* .90 .75

Chiang Kai-shek (1887-1975).
See Nos. 2601-2603.
Issued: Nos. 2237a-2238a, 1/16/1987; No. 2239, 8/15/1987.

Cloisonne Enamel Brush Washer, 15th Cent. — A469

Cloisonne Enamel: $5, Ritual vessel, 15th cent., vert. $8, Plate, 17th cent. $10, Vase, Ming Dynasty, vert.

**1981, May 20 Photo.** ***Perf. 12***
**Granite Paper**

**2240** A469 $2 multicolored .35 .25
**2241** A469 $5 multicolored 1.15 .30
**2242** A469 $8 multicolored 1.30 .25
**2243** A469 $10 multicolored 1.45 .30
*Nos. 2240-2243 (4)* 4.25 1.10

For similar enamelware stamps see Nos. 2318-2321, 2348-2351, 2410-2413.

Early & Modern Locomotives — A470

**Wmk. 323**

**1981, June 9 Litho.** ***Perf. 12½***

**2244** A470 $2 shown .60 .25
**2245** A470 $14 Trains, horiz. 1.75 .40

Railroad service centenary.

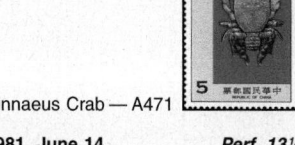

Linnaeus Crab — A471

**1981, June 14** ***Perf. 13½***

**2246** A471 $2 De Haan crab, horiz. .40 .25
**2247** A471 $5 shown .75 .25
**2248** A471 $8 Miers crab, horiz. 1.10 .25
**2249** A471 $14 Rathbun crab 2.00 .40
*Nos. 2246-2249 (4)* 4.25 1.15

Central Weather Bureau, 40th Anniv. — A472

**1981, July 1 Litho.** ***Perf. 13½***

**2250** A472 $2 multicolored .40 .25
**2251** A472 $14 multicolored 1.60 .30

Scene from The Cowherd and the Weaving Maid — A473

Designs: Scenes from the Cowherd and the Weaving Maid.

**1981, Aug. 6 Litho.** ***Perf. 13½x14***

**2252** A473 $2 multicolored .60 .25
**2253** A473 $4 multicolored 1.00 .25
**2254** A473 $8 multicolored 1.75 .25
**2255** A473 $14 multicolored 2.75 .50
*Nos. 2252-2255 (4)* 6.10 1.25

First Lasography Exhibition — A474

Lasography Designs.

**1981, Aug. 15** ***Perf. 13½***

**2256** A474 $2 multicolored .30 .25
**2257** A474 $5 multicolored .35 .25
**2258** A474 $8 multicolored .70 .25
**2259** A474 $14 multicolored 1.20 .50
*Nos. 2256-2259 (4)* 2.55 1.25

Soccer Players A475

**1981, Sept. 9 Litho.** ***Perf. 13½***

**2260** $5 multicolored .60 .25
**2261** $5 multicolored .60 .25
*a.* A475 Pair, #2260-2261 1.40 .65

Sports Day.

A477

70th Anniv. of Republic: No. 2263, Eastward Expedition (soldiers on Hill). No. 2264, Northward Expedition (Chiang on horse). No. 2265, Resistance War with Japan (Chiang, fist raised). No. 2266, Suppression of Communist Rebels (Battle scene). No. 2267, Counter-offensive and unification. $8, Chiang Kai-shek. $14, Sun Yat-sen.

**1981, Oct. 10** ***Perf. 13½***

**2262** A477 $2 multicolored .40 .25
**2263** A477 $2 multicolored .40 .25
**2264** A477 $2 multicolored .40 .25
**2265** A477 $2 multicolored .40 .25
**2266** A477 $3 multicolored .40 .25
**2267** A477 $3 multicolored .40 .25
**2268** A477 $8 multicolored .70 .25
**2269** A477 $14 multicolored 1.60 .45
*a.* Souv. sheet of 8, #2262-2269 11.50 6.50
*Nos. 2262-2269 (8)* 4.70 2.20

No. 2269a issued Oct. 25.

ROCPEX TAIPEI '81 Intl. Philatelic Exhibition, Taipei, Oct. 25-Nov. 2 — A478

**1981, Oct. 25**

**2270** A478 $2 multicolored .30 .25
**2271** A478 $14 multicolored 1.15 .25

Nos. 2269a, 2270-2271 overprinted with four characters meaning "Best of Show" were not valid for postage. They were inserted in a special "ROCPEX" book, edition of 10,000. Value $25.

Boys Playing Games (#2272a) A479

Designs: a.-j. "One Hundred Boys," Sung Dynasty scroll (each stamp is numbered from 1 to 10 in Chinese. See illustrations with Nos. 1682-1691 for numerals.) Two strips of 5 each in continuous design.

**1981, Nov. 12**

**2272** Block of 10 22.50 22.50
*a.-e.* A479 $2 single (top row) 2.00 .25
*f.-j.* A479 $2 single (bottom row) 2.00 .25

New Year 1982 (Year of the Dog) — A480

**Wmk. 323**

**1981, Dec. 1 Litho.** ***Perf. 12½***

**2273** A480 $1 multicolored .70 .25
**2274** A480 $10 multicolored 2.25 .30
*a.* Souv. sheet, 2 ea #2273-2274 12.50 5.00

Information Week, Dec. 6-12 — A481

**1981, Dec. 7** ***Perf. 14x13½***

**2275** A481 $2 multicolored .95 .25

Telecommunications Centenary — A482

**1981, Dec. 28** ***Perf. 14x13½, 13½x14***

**2276** A482 $2 Telephone, vert. .30 .25
**2277** A482 $3 Old, new phones .60 .25
**2278** A482 $8 Submarine cable .85 .25
**2279** A482 $18 Computers, vert. 1.20 .40
*Nos. 2276-2279 (4)* 2.95 1.15

Floral Arrangement — A483

Various floral arrangements in Ming vases.

**Wmk. 323**

**1982, Jan. 23 Litho.** ***Perf. 13½***

**2280** A483 $2 multicolored .40 .25
**2281** A483 $3 multicolored .75 .25
**2282** A483 $8 multicolored 1.10 .25
**2283** A483 $18 multicolored 1.50 .50
*Nos. 2280-2283 (4)* 3.75 1.25

Compare with designs A559, A584.

The Ku Cheng Reunion A484

Designs: Opera scenes.

**Wmk. 323**

**1982, Feb. 15 Litho.** ***Perf. 13½***

**2284** A484 $2 multicolored .70 .25
**2285** A484 $3 multicolored 1.30 .25
**2286** A484 $4 multicolored 1.90 .25
**2287** A484 $18 multicolored 2.50 .50
*Nos. 2284-2287 (4)* 6.40 1.25

**Flag Type of 1978**
**Value Colorless in Colored Panel**

**1981 Litho.** ***Perf. 13½***

**Panel Color**

**2288** A432 $1 dk blue .30 .25
**2289** A432 $1.50 lt olive .30 .25
**2290** A432 $2 dk olive bis .30 .25
**2291** A432 $3 red .30 .25
**2292** A432 $4 blue .50 .25
**2293** A432 $5 sepia .60 .25
**2294** A432 $6 orange .70 .25
**2295** A432 $7 green .85 .25
**2296** A432 $8 magenta .95 .25
**2297** A432 $9 olive grn 1.00 .25
**2298** A432 $10 dk purple 1.20 .25
**2299** A432 $12 lilac 1.40 .25
**2300** A432 $14 dk green 1.75 .40
*Nos. 2288-2300 (13)* 10.15 3.40

Second line (red) below flag is a hairline, notably thinner.
For overprints see Nos. 2540-2541.

Robert Koch — A485

**Wmk. 323**

**1982, Mar. 24 Litho.** ***Perf. 13½***

**2309** A485 $2 multicolored .95 .25

Tubercle Bacillus centenary.

Cheng Shih-liang, Revolutionary — A486

**1982, Mar. 29 Engr.** ***Perf. 13½x12½***
**Granite Paper**

**2310** A486 $2 carmine rose .70 .25

Children's Day — A487

Designs: Various children's drawings.

**1982, Apr. 4** **Litho.**

**2311** A487 $2 multi, vert. .40 .25
**2312** A487 $3 multicolored .40 .25
**2313** A487 $5 multicolored 1.10 .25
**2314** A487 $8 multicolored 1.25 .25
*Nos. 2311-2314 (4)* 3.15 1.00

Dentists' Day — A488

$2, Tooth, boy. $3, Flossing, brushing. $10, Examination.

**1982, May 4 Litho. *Perf. 13½***

| | | | | |
|---|---|---|---|---|
| **2315** | A488 | $2 multicolored | .30 | .25 |
| **2316** | A488 | $3 multicolored | .60 | .25 |
| **2317** | A488 | $10 multicolored | 1.00 | .25 |
| | | *Nos. 2315-2317 (3)* | 1.90 | .75 |

Champleve Enamel Cup and Saucer, 18th Cent. — A489

Painted Enamelware: $5, Cloisonne gold-plated duck Ch'ien-lung period (1736-1795), vert. $8, Incense burner, K'ang-hsi period (1662-1722). $12, Cloisonne pitcher, Ch'ien-lung period, vert.

**1982, May 20 Photo. *Perf. 12***
**Granite Paper**

| | | | | |
|---|---|---|---|---|
| **2318** | A489 | $2 multicolored | .55 | .25 |
| **2319** | A489 | $5 multicolored | 1.35 | .25 |
| **2320** | A489 | $8 multicolored | 1.90 | .25 |
| **2321** | A489 | $12 multicolored | 2.60 | .40 |
| | | *Nos. 2318-2321 (4)* | 6.40 | 1.15 |

See Nos. 2348-2351.

Poets' Day — A490

Tang Dynasty Poetry Illustrations (618-906): $2, Spring Dawn, by Meng Hao-Jan. $3, On Looking for a Hermit and Not Finding Him, by Chia Tao. $5, Summer Dying, by Liu Yu-Hsi. $18, Looking at the Snow Drifts on South Mountain, by Tsu Yung. Chinese characters are to the left of the denominations on Nos. 2322-2325, Nos. 2396-2399 have no characters to the left of the denominations.

**Wmk. 323**

**1982, June 25 Litho. *Perf. 13½***

| | | | | |
|---|---|---|---|---|
| **2322** | A490 | $2 multicolored | *1.15* | .25 |
| **2323** | A490 | $3 multicolored | *3.75* | .25 |
| **2324** | A490 | $5 multicolored | *5.75* | .35 |
| **2325** | A490 | $18 multicolored | *20.00* | 1.90 |
| | | *Nos. 2322-2325 (4)* | *30.65* | 2.75 |

See Nos. 2352-2355.

5th World Women's Softball Championship, Taipei, July 1-12 — A491

**1982, July 2**

| | | | | |
|---|---|---|---|---|
| **2326** | A491 | $2 lt grn & multi | .85 | .25 |
| **2327** | A491 | $18 tan & multi | 1.75 | .40 |

Scouting Year — A492

$2, Crossing bridge, Baden-Powell. $18, Emblem, camp.

**1982, July 18**

| | | | | |
|---|---|---|---|---|
| **2328** | A492 | $2 multicolored | .65 | .25 |
| **2329** | A492 | $18 multicolored | 1.00 | .40 |

Stamp in Tongs — A493

$18, Album stamps magnified.

**1982, Aug. 9**

| | | | | |
|---|---|---|---|---|
| **2330** | A493 | $2 shown | .65 | .25 |
| **2331** | A493 | $18 multicolored | 1.40 | .40 |

Carved Lion, Tsu Shih Temple — A494

Tsu Shih Temple of Sanhsia Architecture: $3, Lion brackets, horiz. $5, Sub-lintels. $18, Tiled roof, horiz.

**1982, Sept. 1 Litho. *Perf. 13½***

| | | | | |
|---|---|---|---|---|
| **2332** | A494 | $2 multicolored | .30 | .25 |
| **2333** | A494 | $3 multicolored | .65 | .25 |
| **2334** | A494 | $5 multicolored | 1.90 | .25 |
| **2335** | A494 | $18 multicolored | 2.60 | .50 |
| | | *Nos. 2332-2335 (4)* | 5.45 | 1.25 |

Hsun Kuan Saving Hsiang-cheng City — A495

Designs: Scenes from The Thirty-Six Examples of Filial Piety, Folk Tale collection by Wu Yen-huan.

**1982, Oct. 15 *Perf. 14x13½***

| | | | | |
|---|---|---|---|---|
| **2336** | A495 | $1 multicolored | .30 | .25 |
| **2337** | A495 | $2 multicolored | .80 | .25 |
| **2338** | A495 | $3 multicolored | 1.00 | .25 |
| **2339** | A495 | $5 multicolored | 1.20 | .25 |
| | | *Nos. 2336-2339 (4)* | 3.30 | 1.00 |

30th Anniv. of China Youth Corps — A496

$2, Riding. $3, Raising flag, vert. $18, Mountain climbing.

**1982, Oct. 31**

| | | | | |
|---|---|---|---|---|
| **2340** | A496 | $2 multicolored | .30 | .25 |
| **2341** | A496 | $3 multicolored | .30 | .25 |
| **2342** | A496 | $18 multicolored | 1.25 | .50 |
| | | *Nos. 2340-2342 (3)* | 1.85 | 1.00 |

Seated Lohan (Buddhist Saint) — A497

Paintings of Lohan, Hanging Scrolls by Liu Sung-nien, 13th cent.

***Perf. 13x12½***

**1982, Nov. 12 Litho. Wmk. 323**

| | | | | |
|---|---|---|---|---|
| **2343** | A497 | $2 multicolored | .75 | .25 |
| **2344** | A497 | $3 multicolored | 2.00 | .25 |
| **2345** | A497 | $18 multicolored | 7.25 | .90 |
| *a.* | | Souv. sheet, #2343-2345 | *37.50* | 13.00 |
| | | *Nos. 2343-2345 (3)* | 10.00 | 1.40 |

No. 2345a comes overprinted in red in the sheet margins. Value, unused $45, Used $20.

New Year 1983 (Year of the Boar) — A498

**1982, Dec. 1 *Perf. 12½***

| | | | | |
|---|---|---|---|---|
| **2346** | A498 | $1 multicolored | 1.40 | .25 |
| **2347** | A498 | $10 multicolored | 3.00 | .25 |
| *a.* | | Souv. sheet, 2 ea #2346-2347 | *17.50* | 5.50 |

**Enamelware Type of 1982**

Designs: $2, Square basin, Ch'ing Dynasty (1644-1911). $3, Vase, Ch'ien-lung period (1736-1795). $4, Tea pot, Ch'ien-lung period. $18, Elephant vase, Ch'ing Dynasty.

**1983, Jan. 5 Photo. *Perf. 12***
**Granite Paper**

| | | | | |
|---|---|---|---|---|
| **2348** | A489 | $2 multi | .65 | .25 |
| **2349** | A489 | $3 multi, vert. | .85 | .25 |
| **2350** | A489 | $4 multi | 1.40 | .25 |
| **2351** | A489 | $18 multi, vert. | 2.25 | .50 |
| | | *Nos. 2348-2351 (4)* | 5.15 | 1.25 |

**Poetry Illustration Type of 1982**

Sung Dynasty Poetry: $2, Seeing the Flowers Fade Away. $3, River. $5, Freckled with Clouds is the Azure Sky. $11, Yielding Fine Fragrance in the Snow. Nos. 2352-2355 vert.

**Wmk. 323**

**1983, Feb. 10 Litho. *Perf. 13½***

| | | | | |
|---|---|---|---|---|
| **2352** | A490 | $2 multicolored | *1.25* | .25 |
| **2353** | A490 | $3 multicolored | *2.50* | .30 |
| **2354** | A490 | $5 multicolored | *8.75* | 1.20 |
| **2355** | A490 | $11 multicolored | *7.50* | .80 |
| | | *Nos. 2352-2355 (4)* | *20.00* | 2.55 |

Mt. Jade, Taiwan A499

$2, Wawa Valley, vert. $3, University Pond, vert.

**1983, Mar. 1**

| | | | | |
|---|---|---|---|---|
| **2356** | A499 | $2 multicolored | .30 | .25 |
| **2357** | A499 | $3 multicolored | .60 | .25 |
| **2358** | A499 | $18 shown | 2.75 | .50 |
| | | *Nos. 2356-2358 (3)* | 3.65 | 1.00 |

400th Anniv. of Arrival of Matteo Ricci (1552-1610), Italian Missionary — A500

***Perf. 14x13½***

**1983, Apr. 3 Litho. Wmk. 323**

| | | | | |
|---|---|---|---|---|
| **2359** | A500 | $2 Astrolabe | .30 | .25 |
| **2360** | A500 | $18 Great Wall | 1.25 | .35 |

Mandarin Phonetic Symbols, 70th Anniv. — A501

$2, Wu Ching-heng, inventor. $18, Children writing.

**Wmk. 323**

**1983, May 22 Litho. *Perf. 13½***

| | | | | |
|---|---|---|---|---|
| **2361** | A501 | $2 multicolored | .35 | .25 |
| **2362** | A501 | $18 multicolored | 1.75 | .35 |

Scenes from Lady White Snake Fairytale — A502

**1983, June 15 *Perf. 14x13½***

| | | | | |
|---|---|---|---|---|
| **2363** | A502 | $2 multicolored | .30 | .25 |
| **2364** | A502 | $3 lt blue & multi | .30 | .25 |
| **2365** | A502 | $3 orange & multi | .30 | .25 |
| **2366** | A502 | $18 multicolored | 4.00 | .60 |
| | | *Nos. 2363-2366 (4)* | 4.90 | 1.35 |

A503

Various bamboo carved objects: $2, Bamboo jug. $3, Tao-t'ieh motif vase. $4, Landscape sculpture. $18, Brush holder, Ming dynasty.

Nos. 2367-2369 Ch'ing dynasty.

**Wmk. 323**

**1983, July 14 Litho. *Perf. 13½***

| | | | | |
|---|---|---|---|---|
| **2367** | A503 | $2 multicolored | .35 | .25 |
| **2368** | A503 | $3 multicolored | .90 | .25 |
| **2369** | A503 | $4 multicolored | 1.10 | .25 |
| **2370** | A503 | $18 multicolored | 2.25 | .50 |
| | | *Nos. 2367-2370 (4)* | 4.60 | 1.25 |

A504

**Wmk. 323**

**1983, Aug. 5 Litho. *Perf. 13½***

| | | | | |
|---|---|---|---|---|
| **2371** | A504 | $2 Globe | .55 | .25 |
| **2372** | A504 | $18 Emblem | .95 | .35 |

World Communications Year.

Fishing Industry (Local Fish) — A505

$2, Epinephelus tauvina. $18, Saurida undosquamis.

**1983, Aug. 20**

| | | | | |
|---|---|---|---|---|
| **2373** | A505 | $2 multicolored | 1.00 | .25 |
| **2374** | A505 | $18 multicolored | 1.75 | .35 |

40th Journalists' Day — A506

**1983, Sept. 1**

| | | | | |
|---|---|---|---|---|
| **2375** | A506 | $2 multicolored | .75 | .25 |

Views of Mongolia and Tibet — A507

**1983, Sept. 15**

| | | | | |
|---|---|---|---|---|
| **2376** | A507 | $2 Village | .45 | .25 |
| **2377** | A507 | $3 Potala Palace | .65 | .25 |
| **2378** | A507 | $5 Sheep grazing | 1.20 | .25 |
| **2379** | A507 | $11 Camel caravan | 2.40 | .30 |
| | | *Nos. 2376-2379 (4)* | 4.70 | 1.05 |

2nd East Asian Bird Protection Conference, Oct. — A508

$2, Lanius cristatus, vert. $18, Butastur indicus.

**1983, Oct. 8 Litho. *Perf. 13½***

| | | | | |
|---|---|---|---|---|
| **2380** | A508 | $2 multicolored | .50 | .25 |
| **2381** | A508 | $18 multicolored | 2.75 | .40 |

A509

Plum Blossoms, photography by Hu Ch'ung-hsien.

**1983, Oct. 31 Litho. *Perf. 14x13½***

| | | | | |
|---|---|---|---|---|
| **2382** | A509 | $2 multicolored | .75 | .25 |
| **2383** | A509 | $3 multi, diff. | .30 | .25 |
| **2384** | A509 | $5 multi, diff. | 1.25 | .30 |
| **2385** | A509 | $11 multi, diff. | .75 | .25 |
| | | *Nos. 2382-2385 (4)* | 3.05 | 1.05 |

A510

$2, JCI and Congress emblems. $18, Globe and emblems, horiz.

**1983, Nov. 6** ***Perf. 13x13½, 13½x13***
**2386** A510 $2 multicolored .30 .25
**2387** A510 $18 multicolored 1.35 .40

Jaycees Intl., 38th World Congress, Taipei.

8th Asian-Pacific Cardiology Congress — A511

$18, Electrocardiogram.

**1983, Nov. 27** **Litho.** ***Perf. 13½***
**2388** A511 $2 shown .30 .25
**2389** A511 $18 multicolored 1.40 .40

New Year 1984 (Year of the Rat) — A512

**1983, Dec. 1** **Litho.** ***Perf. 12½***
**2390** A512 $1 multicolored 1.50 .70
**2391** A512 $10 multicolored 4.75 .30
*a.* Souv. sheet, 2 each #2390-2391 *30.00* 9.00

Literacy Week — A513

$18, Modern family, vert.

**1983, Dec. 17** **Litho.** ***Perf. 13½***
**2392** A513 $2 shown .30 .25
**2393** A513 $18 multicolored 1.50 .40

World Freedom Day — A514

$2, Korean War Patriots. $18, Intl. support.

**1984, Jan. 23** **Litho.** ***Perf. 13½***
**2394** A514 $2 multicolored .35 .25
**2395** A514 $18 multicolored 2.10 .35

Drama Day — A515

Yuan Dynasty Poetry Illustrations by Tien-shih Lin (Poems by): $2, Kuan Yun-shih. $3, Po Pu. $5, Chang Ko-chiu. $18, Shang Cheng-shu. (See note with Nos. 2322-2325.)

**1984, Feb. 15** **Litho.** ***Perf. 13½***
**2396** A515 $2 multicolored *1.05* .25
**2397** A515 $3 multicolored *4.40* .30
**2398** A515 $5 multicolored *5.75* .60
**2399** A515 $18 multicolored *11.50* 2.40
*Nos. 2396-2399 (4)* *22.70* 3.55

A516 A517

A518 Arbor Day — A519

**1984, Mar. 12** **Litho.** ***Perf. 13½x14***
**2400** A516 $2 multicolored 1.00 .25
**2401** A517 $2 multicolored 1.00 .25
**2402** A518 $2 multicolored 1.00 .25
**2403** A519 $2 multicolored 1.00 .25
*a.* Block of 4, #2400-2403 5.75 3.00

Lin Chueh-min — A520

**1984, Mar. 29** **Engr.** ***Perf. 13x12½***
**Granite Paper**
**2404** A520 $2 dark green .75 .25

Central News Agency, 60th Anniv. — A521

$2, Emblem. $10, Emblem, satellite, dish antenna.

***Perf. 14x13½***
**1984, Apr. 1** **Litho.** **Wmk.**
**2405** A521 $2 multicolored .30 .25
**2406** A521 $10 multicolored 1.00 .25

God of Longevity — A522

Paintings by Chang Ta-chien (1899-1983): $2, Five Auspicious Tokens. $18, Lotus Blossoms in Ink Splash.

**Wmk. 323**
**1984, Apr. 20** **Litho.** ***Perf. 11½***
**2407** A522 $2 multicolored 1.25 .25
**2408** A522 $5 multicolored 2.25 .30
**2409** A522 $18 multicolored 6.75 1.25
*Nos. 2407-2409 (3)* 10.25 1.80

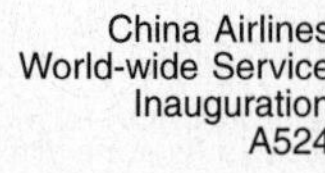
Ch'ing Dynasty Enamelware — A523

$2, Cup, pot, plate, horiz. $3, Wine jug. $4, Teapot. $18, Candle holder.

**1984, May 20** **Photo.** ***Perf. 12***
**Granite Paper**
**2410** A523 $2 multicolored .50 .25
**2411** A523 $3 multicolored .50 .25
**2412** A523 $4 multicolored .75 .25
**2413** A523 $18 multicolored 2.25 .50
*Nos. 2410-2413 (4)* 4.00 1.25

China Airlines World-wide Service Inauguration A524

**1984, May 31** **Litho.** ***Perf. 13½x14***
**2414** A524 $2 Jet circling globe .30 .25
**2415** A524 $7 Globe, jet .75 .25
**2416** A524 $11 New York City .85 .30
**2417** A524 $18 Amsterdam 1.10 .50
*Nos. 2414-2417 (4)* 3.00 1.30

30th Navigation Day — A525

***Perf. 13½x13***
**1984, July 11** **Litho.** **Wmk. 323**
**2418** A525 $2 Container ship .85 .25
**2419** A525 $18 Oil tanker 2.10 .45

1984 Summer Olympics — A526

***Perf. 13½x14, 14x13½***
**1984, June 23**
**2420** A526 $2 Judo, horiz. .30 .25
**2421** A526 $5 Archery .60 .30
**2422** A526 $18 Swimming, horiz. 1.40 .50
*Nos. 2420-2422 (3)* 2.30 1.05

Alpine Plants — A527

$2, Gentiana arisanensis. $3, Epilobium nankotaizanense. $5, Adenophora uehatae. $18, Aconitum fukutomei.

**1984, Aug. 8** ***Perf. 13***
**2423** A527 $2 multi .30 .25
**2424** A527 $3 multi .70 .25
**2425** A527 $5 multi 1.10 .25
**2426** A527 $18 multi 2.00 .50
*Nos. 2423-2426 (4)* 4.10 1.25

The Eighteen Scholars, Sung Dynasty Hanging Scroll — A528

$2, Playing instruments. $3, Playing chess. $5, Practicing calligraphy. $18, Painting.

**Wmk. 323**
**1984, Aug. 20** **Litho.** ***Perf. 13***
**2427** A528 $2 multicolored *1.00* .25
**2428** A528 $3 multicolored *3.00* .25
**2429** A528 $5 multicolored *5.00* .50
**2430** A528 $18 multicolored *15.00* 1.00
*Nos. 2427-2430 (4)* *24.00* 2.00

Athletics Day A529

**1984, Sept. 9**
**2431** $5 Two players 1.10 .25
**2432** $5 One player 1.10 .25
*a.* A529 Pair, #2431-2432 2.25 .75

A531

**1984, Sept. 9**
**2433** A531 $10 "20," map of Asia 1.50 .25

Asian-Pacific Parliamentarians' Union, 20th anniv.

A532

**1984, Oct. 10** **Litho.** ***Perf. 12½***
**2434** A532 $2 No. 1458 .30 .25
**2435** A532 $5 No. 296 .60 .25
**2436** A532 $18 Museum 1.75 .50
*a.* Souv. sheet of 3, #2434-2436 9.50 4.00
*Nos. 2434-2436 (3)* 2.65 1.00

Postal Museum opening.

Flag, Alliance Emblem — A533

**1984, Oct. 16** ***Perf. 13½***
**2437** A533 $2 multicolored 1.00 .25

Grand Alliance for China's Reunification Under the Three Principles of the People Convention, Taipei, Oct. 16-17.

Veteran's Assistance — A534

**1984, Nov. 1** **Litho.** ***Perf. 13½***
**2438** A534 $2 Vignettes .80 .25

Pine Tree A535

Bamboo A535a

Plum Tree — A535b

**1984-88**
**2439** A535 $2 multicolored .30 .25
**2440** A535a $8 multicolored .80 .25
**2441** A535b $10 pale yellow bister background .85 .25
*a.* Grayish tan background .65 .25
*Nos. 2439-2441 (3)* 1.95 .75

Issued: Nos. 2439-2440, 2441a, 11/12; No. 2441,1/12/88.
See Nos. 2495-2503, 3303.

A536

**1984, Dec. 1** *Perf. 12x12½*
**2442** A536 $1 multicolored .90 .25
**2443** A536 $10 multicolored 2.85 .30
*a.* Min. sheet, 2 ea #2442-2443 7.50 2.75

New Year 1985 (Year of the Ox).

Scales, Legal Codes — A537

**1985, Jan. 11** **Litho.** *Perf. 13½*
**2444** A537 $5 multicolored .90 .25

Judicial Day 1985.

Quemoy and Matsu Scenes — A538

$2, Ku-kang Lake, Quemoy. $5, Kuang-hai Stone, Quemoy. $8, Sheng-li Reservoir, Matsu. $10, Tung-chu Lighthouse, Matsu.

**1985, Jan. 23** **Litho.** *Perf. 13½x14*
**2445** A538 $2 multicolored .30 .25
**2446** A538 $5 multicolored .80 .25
**2447** A538 $8 multicolored 1.00 .25
**2448** A538 $10 multicolored 1.25 .25
*Nos. 2445-2448 (4)* 3.35 1.00

Sir Robert Hart (1835-1911) — A539

**1985, Feb. 15** **Litho.** *Perf. 14x13½*
**2449** A539 $2 No. 1 .80 .25

Inspector General of Chinese Customs, 1863-1908, and founder of the Chinese Postal Service.

Lo Fu-hsing (1886-1914) — A540

**1985, Feb. 24** *Perf. 13x13½*
**2450** A540 $2 multicolored .80 .25

Tsou Jung (1882-1905) — A541

**1985, Mar. 29** **Engr.** *Perf. 13½x12½*
**Granite Paper**
**2451** A541 $3 green .80 .25

Chung-cheng Memorial Hall Main Gate — A542

$8, Tzuhu Memorial. $10, Chiang Kai-shek, vert.

**1985, Apr. 5** **Litho.** *Perf. 13*
**2452** A542 $2 shown .40 .25
**2453** A542 $8 multicolored 1.50 .25
**2454** A542 $10 multicolored 1.60 .35
*Nos. 2452-2454 (3)* 3.50 .85

Tenth death anniv. of Chiang Kai-shek.

A543

**1985, May 8** **Litho.** *Perf. 13½*
**2455** A543 $2 Carnation .75 .25
**2456** A543 $2 Day lily .75 .25
*a.* Pair, #2455-2456 2.00 .75

Mother's Day.

Tunnel to Chi-chin Island — A544

**1985, May 18**
**2457** A544 $5 multicolored .90 .25

Kaohsiung Cross-Harbor Tunnel, 1st anniv.

Girl Scouts, 75th Anniv. — A545

**Wmk. 323**
**1985, June 1** **Litho.** *Perf. 13½*
**2458** A545 $2 multicolored .40 .25
**2459** A545 $18 multicolored 2.20 .30

The Book of Odes, Confucius — A545a

**1985, June 22** **Litho.** **Wmk. 323**
**2460** A545a $2 Spring 1.00 .25
**2461** A545a $5 Summer 3.50 .25
**2462** A545a $8 Fall 5.25 .25
**2463** A545a $10 Winter 6.00 .30
*Nos. 2460-2463 (4)* 15.75 1.05

Fruit — A546

*Perf. 13½x14*
**1985, July 5** **Litho.** **Wmk. 323**
**2464** A546 $2 Wax Jambo .55 .25
**2465** A546 $3 Guava 1.25 .25
**2466** A546 $5 Carambola 1.50 .25
**2467** A546 $8 Litchi nut 1.60 .30
*Nos. 2464-2467 (4)* 4.90 1.05

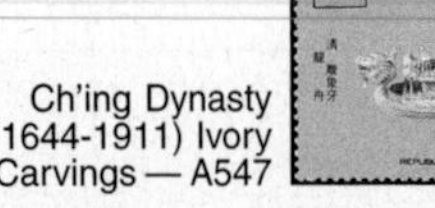

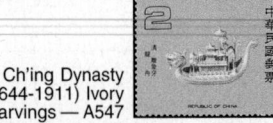

Ch'ing Dynasty (1644-1911) Ivory Carvings — A547

$2, Dragon Boat. $3, Landscape. $5, Melon, water container. $18, Brush holder, vert.

**1985, July 18** **Wmk. 323** *Perf. 13½*
**2468** A547 $2 multicolored .35 .25
**2469** A547 $3 multicolored .30 .25
**2470** A547 $5 multicolored .50 .25
**2471** A547 $18 multicolored 1.90 .50
*Nos. 2468-2471 (4)* 3.05 1.25

T'ang Dynasty (618-907) Aristocrat — A548

Designs: $5, Sung Dynasty (960-1280) palace woman. $8, Yuan Dynasty (1280-1368) aristocrat. $11, Ming Dynasty (1368-1644) aristocrat.

**1985, Aug. 1** **Wmk. 323** *Perf. 13½*
**2472** A548 $2 multicolored .50 .25
**2473** A548 $5 multicolored 2.40 .25
**2474** A548 $8 multicolored 2.75 .30
**2475** A548 $11 multicolored 3.00 .40
*Nos. 2472-2475 (4)* 8.65 1.20

4th Asian Conf. on Costume, Aug. 3.

In the 2 rows of Chinese characters above the denomination, the right row has 3 characters and a dot on Nos. 2472-2475, 4 characters and a dot on Nos. 2549-2552. Nos. 2605-2608, 2660-2663 have solid black numerals.

See Nos. 2549-2552, 2605-2608, 2660-2663, 2721-2724, 2794-2797.

Social Welfare Program — A549

*Perf. 13½x14*
**1985, Aug. 15** **Wmk. 323**
**2476** A549 $2 Heart, bird feeding young .80 .25

Historic Sites — A550

$2, Taipei North Gate. $5, San Domingo Fort, Tamsui. $8, Lung Shun Temple, Lukang. $10, Confucius Temple, Changhua.

**Wmk. 323**
**1985, Sept. 3** **Litho.** *Perf. 13½*
**2477** A550 $2 multicolored .30 .25
**2478** A550 $5 multicolored .90 .25
**2479** A550 $8 multicolored 1.20 .25
**2480** A550 $10 multicolored 1.40 .35
*Nos. 2477-2480 (4)* 3.80 1.10

Bonsai — A551

*Perf. 13½x14*
**1985, Sept. 22** **Wmk. 323**
**2481** A551 $2 Oak .30 .25
**2482** A551 $5 Five-leaf pine .75 .25
**2483** A551 $8 Lohan pine .90 .25
**2484** A551 $18 Banyan 1.80 .50
*Nos. 2481-2484 (4)* 3.75 1.25

Trade Shows — A552

Taipei World Trade Center and show emblems: a, Sporting goods. b, Toys and gifts. c, Electronics. d, Machinery. Se-tenant in continuous design.

**1985, Oct. 5** *Perf. 13½*
**2485** A552 Strip of 4 3.75 1.00
*a.-d.* $2 any single .50 .25

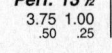

Scenes of Modern Taiwan, Map, Flag — A553

$18, Chiang Kai-shek, Triumphal Arch.

**1985, Oct. 25**
**2486** A553 $2 shown .40 .25
**2487** A553 $18 multicolored 3.15 .50

Defeat of Japanese army, end of World War II, and return of Taiwan to control of the Republic, 40th anniv.

7th Asian Conference on Mental Retardation — A554

**1985, Nov. 8** *Perf. 14x13½*
**2488** A554 $2 multicolored .75 .25
**2489** A554 $11 multicolored 1.75 .25

Sun Yat-sen and Birthplace — A555

**1985, Nov. 12** *Perf. 13½*
**2490** A555 $2 multicolored .50 .25
**2491** A555 $18 multicolored 1.90 .40

Postal Life Insurance, 50th Anniv. — A556

**1985, Dec. 1**
**2492** A556 $2 multicolored .80 .25

New Year 1986 (Year of the Tiger) — A557

**1985, Dec. 1** *Perf. 12½*
**2493** A557 $1 multicolored .60 .25
**2494** A557 $10 multicolored 2.25 .25
*a.* Min. sheet, 2 ea #2493-2494 12.50 3.25

**Flora Types of 1984**

**1986, Jan. 10** **Litho.** *Perf. 13½*
**2495** A535 $1 multicolored .35 .25
**2496** A535a $11 multicolored .75 .25
**2497** A535b $18 multicolored 1.10 .25

**1988, Feb. 12**
**2498** A535 $1.50 multicolored .30 .25
**2499** A535a $7.50 multicolored .70 .25
**2500** A535b $16 multicolored 1.30 .30

No. 2500 has value expressed in dollars and cents. For surcharge, see No. 3303.

**1989, Feb. 24**
**2501** A535 $3 multicolored .30 .25
**2502** A535a $16.50 multicolored 1.25 .30
**2503** A535b $21 multicolored 1.60 .35
*Nos. 2495-2503 (9)* 7.65 2.45

Cultural Renaissance Movement A558

Painting: Hermit Anglers on a Mountain Stream, Ming Dynasty, 1386-1644. Continuous design. (Each stamp is numbered from 1 to 5 in Chinese. See illustrations with Nos. 1682-1691 for numerals.)

**1986, Jan. 28 Litho. *Perf. 13½***

| | | | |
|---|---|---|---|
| **2507** | Strip of 5 | 9.00 | 7.00 |
| ***a.-e.*** | A558 $2 any single | *1.50* | .25 |

See No. 2604.

Floral Arrangements — A559

**Wmk. 323**

**1986, Feb. 20 Litho. *Perf. 13½***

| | | | |
|---|---|---|---|
| **2517** | A559 $2 denom. UL | .35 | .25 |
| **2518** | A559 $5 denom. UR | .75 | .25 |
| **2519** | A559 $8 shown | .85 | .25 |
| **2520** | A559 $10 denom. UL | 1.25 | .30 |
| | *Nos. 2517-2520 (4)* | 3.20 | 1.05 |

Compare with designs A483, A584.

Natl. Postal Service, 90th Anniv. — A560

$2, Unloading express mail at airport. $5, Motorcycle delivery. $8, Technological innovations. $10, Electronic sorting machine.

**1986, Mar. 20**

| | | | |
|---|---|---|---|
| **2521** | A560 $2 multi | .30 | .25 |
| **2522** | A560 $5 multi, vert. | .50 | .25 |
| **2523** | A560 $8 multi, vert. | .75 | .25 |
| **2524** | A560 $10 multi | 1.10 | .30 |
| ***a.*** | Souv. sheet of 4, #2521-2524 | 5.75 | 2.55 |
| | *Nos. 2521-2524 (4)* | 2.65 | 1.05 |

Chen Tien-hua (1875-1905), Revolutionary — A561

**1986, Mar. 29 Engr. *Perf. 13½x12½***
**Granite Paper**

| | | | |
|---|---|---|---|
| **2525** | A561 $2 violet | .80 | .25 |

Yushan Natl. Park — A562

**1986, Apr. 10 Litho. *Perf. 13½***

| | | | |
|---|---|---|---|
| **2526** | A562 $2 multicolored | .40 | .25 |
| **2527** | A562 $5 multi, diff. | 1.00 | .25 |
| **2528** | A562 $8 multi, diff. | 1.30 | .25 |
| **2529** | A562 $10 multi, diff. | 1.60 | .30 |
| | *Nos. 2526-2529 (4)* | 4.30 | 1.05 |

Power Plants — A563

**1986, Apr. 29**

| | | | |
|---|---|---|---|
| **2530** | A563 $2 Hydro-electric | .30 | .25 |
| **2531** | A563 $8 Thermo-electric | .80 | .25 |
| **2532** | A563 $10 Nuclear | 1.15 | .25 |
| | *Nos. 2530-2532 (3)* | 2.25 | .75 |

Economic prosperity through energy development.

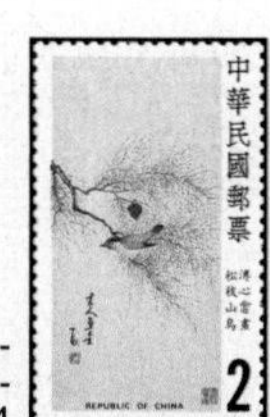

Paintings by P'u Hsin-yu (1896-1963) — A564

**1986, May 22 *Perf. 11½***

| | | | |
|---|---|---|---|
| **2533** | A564 $2 Bird | .90 | .25 |
| **2534** | A564 $8 Landscape | 3.50 | .40 |
| **2535** | A564 $10 Woman in forest | 4.50 | .50 |
| | *Nos. 2533-2535 (3)* | 8.90 | 1.15 |

Asian Productivity Org., 25th Anniv. — A565

**1986, June 3 *Perf. 13x13½***

| | | | |
|---|---|---|---|
| **2536** | A565 $2 multicolored | .30 | .25 |
| **2537** | A565 $11 multicolored | .90 | .25 |

Natl. Productivity Center, 30th anniv.

Coral-reef Fish — A566

Designs: a, Chrysiptera starcki. b, Chelmon rostratus. c, Chaetodon xanthurus. d, Chaetodon quadrimaculatus. e, Chaetodon meyeri. f, Genicanthus semifasciatus. g, Genicanthus semifasciatus. h, Pomacanthus annularis. i, Lienardella fasciata. j, Balistapus undulatus.

**1986, June 27 *Perf. 13½***

| | | | |
|---|---|---|---|
| **2538** | Block of 10 | 5.25 | 4.25 |
| ***a.-j.*** | A566 $2 any single | .50 | .25 |

Protection of Intellectual Property Rights — A567

**1986, June 12**

| | | | |
|---|---|---|---|
| **2539** | A567 $2 Macaw | 1.10 | .25 |

Nos. 2294, 2297 Surcharged

**1986, July 9 Litho. *Perf. 13½***

| | | | |
|---|---|---|---|
| **2540** | A432 $2 on $6 multi | .30 | .25 |
| **2541** | A432 $8 on $9 multi | 1.00 | .25 |

60th Anniv. of northward expedition by the national revolutionary army.

Bridges — A568

$2, Tzu Mu, 1965. $5, Chang Hung, 1968. $8, Kuan Fu, 1977. $10, Kuan Tu, 1983.

**1986, July 30**

| | | | |
|---|---|---|---|
| **2542** | A568 $2 multicolored | .45 | .25 |
| **2543** | A568 $5 multicolored | 1.10 | .25 |
| **2544** | A568 $8 multicolored | 1.60 | .25 |
| **2545** | A568 $10 multicolored | 2.00 | .30 |
| | *Nos. 2542-2545 (4)* | 5.15 | 1.05 |

Love between Liang Shanpo and Chu Yingtai, Folk Tale — A569

Cartoons by Huang Mu-ts'un: a, Yingtai disguised to go to school. b, Yingtai and Shanpo meet in class. c, The friends at pond. d, Yingtai summoned home for arranged marriage. e, Yingtai and Shanpo ascend to heaven as butterflies (each stamp is numbered from 1 to 5 in Chinese. See illustrations with Nos. 1682-1691 for numerals.)

**1986, Aug. 12 *Perf. 12½***

| | | | |
|---|---|---|---|
| **2546** | Strip of 5 | 4.25 | 1.60 |
| ***a.-e.*** | A569 $5 any single | .50 | .25 |

Social Awareness Campaign A570

**1986, Sept. 12 Litho. *Perf. 13½***

| | | | |
|---|---|---|---|
| **2547** | A570 $2 Rainbow, children | .40 | .25 |
| **2548** | A570 $8 Children, adults | .90 | .25 |

Folk Costumes — A571

Designs: $2, Shang Dynasty (1766-1122 B.C.) aristocrat. $5, Warring States (403-221 B.C.) aristocrat. $8, Later Han Dynasty (A.D. 25-221) empress. $10, Flying ribbons gown, Wei and Tsin Dynasties (A.D. 221-420) aristocrat.

**1986, Sept. 23 Litho. *Perf. 13½***

| | | | |
|---|---|---|---|
| **2549** | A571 $2 multicolored | .60 | .25 |
| **2550** | A571 $5 multicolored | 1.40 | .25 |
| **2551** | A571 $8 multicolored | 1.75 | .25 |
| **2552** | A571 $10 multicolored | 2.75 | .35 |
| | *Nos. 2549-2552 (4)* | 6.50 | 1.10 |

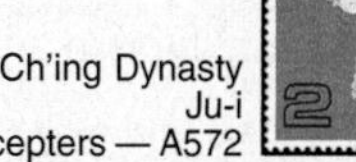

Ch'ing Dynasty Ju-i Scepters — A572

$2, White jade. $3, Red coral. $4, Redwood and gems. $18, Gilded wood.

**1986, Oct. 10 Photo. *Perf. 14x14½***

| | | | |
|---|---|---|---|
| **2553** | A572 $2 multicolored | .30 | .25 |
| **2554** | A572 $3 multicolored | .40 | .25 |
| **2555** | A572 $4 multicolored | .50 | .25 |
| **2556** | A572 $18 multicolored | 2.25 | .40 |
| | *Nos. 2553-2556 (4)* | 3.45 | 1.15 |

See Nos. 2582-2585.

Chiang Kai-shek — A573

Portrait and: $5, Map and flag. $8, Emblem. $10, Flags on globe.

**1986, Oct. 31 Litho. *Perf. 13½***

| | | | |
|---|---|---|---|
| **2557** | A573 $2 multicolored | .30 | .25 |
| **2558** | A573 $5 multicolored | 1.15 | .25 |
| **2559** | A573 $8 multicolored | 1.50 | .25 |
| **2560** | A573 $10 multicolored | 1.90 | .30 |
| ***a.*** | Souv. sheet of 4, #2557-2560 | 12.00 | 6.00 |
| | *Nos. 2557-2560 (4)* | 4.85 | 1.05 |

Cultural Heritage — A574

Architecture: $2, Chin-Kuang Fu land development and defense fund building, 1826. $5, Erh-sha-wan Gun Emplacement, Keelung, 1841, restored 1979. $8, Fort Hsi T'ai, 1886. $10, Matsu Temple, Peng-hu, renovated 1563-1624.

**1986, Nov. 14 Litho. *Perf. 13½***

| | | | |
|---|---|---|---|
| **2561** | A574 $2 multicolored | .30 | .25 |
| **2562** | A574 $5 multicolored | .95 | .25 |
| **2563** | A574 $8 multicolored | 1.15 | .25 |
| **2564** | A574 $10 multicolored | 1.35 | .30 |
| | *Nos. 2561-2564 (4)* | 3.75 | 1.05 |

New Year 1987 (Year of the Hare) — A575

**1986, Dec. 1 *Perf. 12½***

| | | | |
|---|---|---|---|
| **2565** | A575 $1 dl pink & multi | .50 | .25 |
| **2566** | A575 $10 pale grn & multi | 2.50 | .25 |
| ***a.*** | Souv. sheet, 2 each #2565-2566 | *11.50* | 3.50 |

Kenting, 1st Natl. Park — A576

**1987, Jan. 8 Litho. *Perf. 13½***

| | | | |
|---|---|---|---|
| **2567** | A576 $2 Garden | .50 | .25 |
| **2568** | A576 $5 Shore rocks | 1.45 | .25 |
| **2569** | A576 $8 Shore and hill | 1.75 | .25 |
| **2570** | A576 $10 Shore and rocks, diff. | 2.00 | .30 |
| | *Nos. 2567-2570 (4)* | 5.70 | 1.05 |

Folk Art — A577

Puppets: $2, Hand puppet. $5, Marionette. $18, Shadow puppet.

**1987, Feb. 12 Litho. *Perf. 14x13½***

| | | | |
|---|---|---|---|
| **2571** | A577 $2 multicolored | .40 | .25 |
| **2572** | A577 $5 multicolored | 1.00 | .25 |
| **2573** | A577 $18 multicolored | 1.75 | .40 |
| | *Nos. 2571-2573 (3)* | 3.15 | .90 |

Speedpost — A578

**1987, Mar. 20 Litho. *Perf. 14x13½***

| | | | |
|---|---|---|---|
| **2574** | A578 $2 multicolored | .35 | .25 |
| **2575** | A578 $18 multicolored | 1.25 | .30 |

Stamp Day.

Wu Yueh (1878-1905), Revolutionary — A579

**1987, Mar. 29 Engr. *Perf. 13½x12½***

| | | | |
|---|---|---|---|
| **2576** | A579 $2 orange | 1.25 | .25 |

Landscapes Painted by Madame Chiang Kai-shek A580

$2, Singing Creek with Bamboo Orchestra. $5, Mountains Draped in Clouds. $8, Vista of Tranquility. $10, Mountains after a Snowfall.

**1987, Apr. 10 Litho. *Perf. 13½***

| | | | |
|---|---|---|---|
| **2577** | A580 $2 blk, buff & ver | .80 | .25 |
| **2578** | A580 $5 blk, buff & ver | 2.60 | .30 |
| **2579** | A580 $8 blk, buff & ver | 3.50 | .30 |
| **2580** | A580 $10 blk, buff & ver | 4.25 | .50 |
| | *Nos. 2577-2580 (4)* | 11.15 | 1.35 |

Stone Sculptures — A581

Designs: a, Head of a Bodhisattva, sandstone, Northern Wei Dynasty (386-534). b, Standing Buddha, limestone, Northern Ch'i Dynasty (550-577). c, Head of a Bodhisattva, sandstone, T'ang Dynasty (618-907). d, Seated Buddha, alabaster, T'ang Dynasty.

**1987, Apr. 23**

| | | | |
|---|---|---|---|
| **2581** | Strip of 4 | 3.00 | 1.75 |
| *a.-d.* | A581 $5 any single | .60 | .25 |

No. 2581a shows seven Chinese characters at left; No. 2581c shows five.

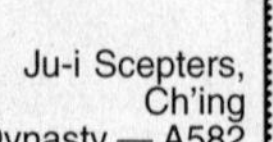

Ju-i Scepters, Ch'ing Dynasty — A582

$2, Silver and gems. $3, Gold and gems. $4, Gilded, jade and inlaid gems. $18, Gilded, inlaid malachite.

**1987, May 7 Photo. *Perf. 14x14½***

| | | | | |
|---|---|---|---|---|
| **2582** | A582 | $2 multicolored | .50 | .25 |
| **2583** | A582 | $3 multicolored | 1.20 | .25 |
| **2584** | A582 | $4 multicolored | 1.90 | .25 |
| **2585** | A582 | $18 multicolored | 2.45 | .45 |
| | | *Nos. 2582-2585 (4)* | 6.05 | 1.20 |

Feitsui Reservoir Inauguration A583

$2, Reservoir. $18, Hsintien Stream, reservoir.

**1987, June 6 Litho. *Perf. 13½x14***

| | | | | |
|---|---|---|---|---|
| **2586** | A583 | $2 multicolored | .50 | .25 |
| **2587** | A583 | $18 multicolored | 2.10 | .30 |

Flower Arrangements by Huang Yung-ch'uan — A584

$8, Flowers in brown vase.

**1987, June 19 *Perf. 13½***

| | | | | |
|---|---|---|---|---|
| **2588** | A584 | $2 denom. LL | .30 | .25 |
| **2589** | A584 | $5 denom. LL | .80 | .25 |
| **2590** | A584 | $8 denom, UR | 1.00 | .25 |
| **2591** | A584 | $10 denom. UR | 1.10 | .25 |
| | | *Nos. 2588-2591 (4)* | 3.20 | 1.00 |

Compare with designs A483, A559.

Lions Club Intl. 70th Annual Convention, Taipei — A585

**1987, July 1**

| | | | | |
|---|---|---|---|---|
| **2592** | A585 | $2 multicolored | .35 | .25 |
| **2593** | A585 | $18 multicolored | 1.75 | .30 |

Sino-Japanese War, 50th Anniv. — A586

$1, Battle front. $2, Chiang Kai-shek giving speech. $5, Public donating funds. $6, Troops marching. $8, Signing of peace treaty. $18, Parade.

**1987, July 7 *Perf. 14x13½***

| | | | | |
|---|---|---|---|---|
| **2594** | A586 | $1 multicolored | .35 | .25 |
| **2595** | A586 | $2 multicolored | .55 | .25 |
| **2596** | A586 | $5 multicolored | .65 | .25 |
| **2597** | A586 | $6 multicolored | .85 | .25 |
| **2598** | A586 | $8 multicolored | 1.20 | .25 |
| **2599** | A586 | $18 multicolored | 1.35 | .45 |
| | | *Nos. 2594-2599 (6)* | 4.95 | 1.70 |

Wang Yun-wu (1888-1979), Lexicographer — A587

**1987, Aug. 14 *Perf. 13½***

| | | | | |
|---|---|---|---|---|
| **2600** | A587 | $2 gray black | .80 | .25 |

**Memorial Hall Type of 1981**

***Perf. 12½x13½***

**1987, Sept. 24 Photo.**

| | | | | |
|---|---|---|---|---|
| **2601** | A468 | 10c lake | .30 | .25 |
| **2602** | A468 | 30c emerald | .30 | .25 |
| **2603** | A468 | 60c brt blue | .30 | .25 |
| | | *Nos. 2601-2603 (3)* | .90 | .75 |

A588

Cultural Renaissance Movement A589

Scroll, 1543, by Weng Chen-ming (1470-1559), a copy of Chao Po-su's *Red Cliff.* Nos. 2604a-2604e and 2604f-2604j are printed in continuous designs. (Each stamp is numbered from 1 to 10 in Chinese. See illustrations with Nos. 1682-1691 for numerals.)

**1987, Sept. 22 Engr. *Perf. 13½***

| | | | |
|---|---|---|---|
| **2604** | Block of 10 | 11.00 | 11.00 |
| *a.-e.* | A588 $3 any single | .80 | .25 |
| *f.-j.* | A589 $3 any single | .80 | .25 |

Folk Costumes — A590

$1.50, Han woman, early Ch'ing Dynasty (1644-1911). $3, Wife of a Ch'ing Dynasty Manchu Bannerman. $7.50, Urban woman wearing Manchu ch'i-p'ao dress, c. 1912. $18, Short jacket over long skirt, c. 1920.

**1987, Oct. 2 Litho.**

| | | | | |
|---|---|---|---|---|
| **2605** | A590 | $1.50 multicolored | *1.00* | .25 |
| **2606** | A590 | $3 multicolored | *1.20* | .25 |
| **2607** | A590 | $7.50 multicolored | *1.40* | .25 |
| **2608** | A590 | $18 multicolored | *1.75* | .60 |
| | | *Nos. 2605-2608 (4)* | *5.35* | 1.35 |

Nos. 2605-2608 have 3 groups of 2 smaller Chinese characters above denomination. Nos. 2660-2663 have 2 groups of 2 and 4 characters.

A591

$3, Ta Chen Tian temple, Taichung. $18, Confucius.

**1987, Nov. 12 *Perf. 13½x14***

| | | | | |
|---|---|---|---|---|
| **2609** | A591 | $3 multicolored | .45 | .25 |
| **2610** | A591 | $18 multicolored | 1.90 | .80 |

Intl. Symposium on Confucianism, Taipei, Nov. 12-17.

A592

**1987, Dec. 1 *Perf. 12½***

| | | | | |
|---|---|---|---|---|
| **2611** | A592 | $1.50 multicolored | .60 | .25 |
| **2612** | A592 | $12 multicolored | 2.40 | .40 |
| *a.* | | Souv. sheet, 2 ea #2611-2612 | 9.75 | 2.50 |

New Year 1988 (Year of the Dragon).

Constitution, 40th Anniv. — A593

**1987, Dec. 25 Litho. *Perf. 13½***

| | | | | |
|---|---|---|---|---|
| **2613** | A593 | $3 multicolored | .45 | .25 |
| **2614** | A593 | $16 multi, diff. | 1.30 | .30 |

Prevent Hypertension Campaign — A594

**1988, Jan. 8 *Perf. 12½x13½***

| | | | | |
|---|---|---|---|---|
| **2615** | A594 | $3 multicolored | .75 | .25 |

Fruit Tree Blossoms — A595

No. 2616, Prunus mume. No. 2617, Prunus armeniaca. No. 2618, Prunus persica.

No. 2619, Paeonia suffruticosa. No. 2620, Punica granatum. No. 2621, Nelumbo nucifera.

No. 2622, Impatiens balsamina. No. 2623, Osmanthus fragrans. No. 2624, Chrysanthemum morifolium.

No. 2625, Hibiscus mutabilis. No. 2626, Camellia japonica. No. 2627, Narcissus tazetta.

**Wmk. 323**

**1988, Feb. 4 Litho. *Perf. 13½***

| | | | | |
|---|---|---|---|---|
| **2616** | A595 | $3 multi | .65 | .25 |
| **2617** | A595 | $7.50 multi | 1.90 | .25 |
| **2618** | A595 | $12 multi | 2.90 | .30 |
| *a.* | | Min. sheet of 3, #2616-2618 | *25.00* | *25.00* |

**Wmk. 323**

**1988, May 5 Litho. *Perf. 13½***

| | | | | |
|---|---|---|---|---|
| **2619** | A595 | $3 multi | .60 | .25 |
| **2620** | A595 | $7.50 multi | 1.75 | .25 |
| **2621** | A595 | $12 multi | 2.60 | .30 |
| *a.* | | Min. sheet of 3, #2619-2621 | *15.00* | *15.00* |

**Wmk. 323**

**1988, Aug. 9 Litho. *Perf. 13½***

| | | | | |
|---|---|---|---|---|
| **2622** | A595 | $3 multi | .60 | .25 |
| **2623** | A595 | $7.50 multi | 1.75 | .25 |
| **2624** | A595 | $12 multi | 2.60 | .30 |
| *a.* | | Min. sheet of 3, #2622-2624 | *12.50* | *12.50* |

**Wmk. 323**

**1988, Nov. 7 Litho. *Perf. 13½***

| | | | | |
|---|---|---|---|---|
| **2625** | A595 | $3 multi | .60 | .25 |
| **2626** | A595 | $7.50 multi | 1.75 | .25 |
| **2627** | A595 | $12 multi | 2.60 | .30 |
| *a.* | | Min. sheet of 3, #2625-2627 | *12.50* | *12.50* |
| | | *Nos. 2616-2627 (12)* | 20.30 | 3.20 |

Tourism Day — A596

Folk art: $3, Modeled dough figurines. $7.50, Blown sweet-malt sugar candy. $16, Sugar paintings.

***Perf. 13½x14***

**1988, Mar. 2 Litho. Wmk. 323**

| | | | | |
|---|---|---|---|---|
| **2628** | A596 | $3 multicolored | .70 | .20 |
| **2629** | A596 | $7.50 multicolored | 1.30 | .30 |
| **2630** | A596 | $16 multicolored | 2.40 | .50 |
| | | *Nos. 2628-2630 (3)* | 4.40 | 1.00 |

A597

***Perf. 13½x12½***

**1988, Mar. 29 Engr. Wmk. 323**

| | | | | |
|---|---|---|---|---|
| **2631** | A597 | $3 brown | .80 | .25 |

Hsu Hsi-lin (1873-1907), hero of the revolution.

A598

$1.50, Biotechnology. $3, Energy resources. $7, Immunization. $7.50, Automation. $10, Telecommunications. $12, Laser technology. $16, Micro-optics. $16.50, Agricultural research.

**1988 Litho. *Perf. 13½***

| | | | | |
|---|---|---|---|---|
| **2632** | A598 | $1.50 multicolored | .30 | .25 |
| **2633** | A598 | $3 multicolored | .30 | .25 |
| **2634** | A598 | $7 multicolored | .35 | .25 |
| **2635** | A598 | $7.50 multicolored | .35 | .25 |
| **2636** | A598 | $10 multicolored | .50 | .30 |
| **2637** | A598 | $12 multicolored | .55 | .30 |
| **2638** | A598 | $16 multicolored | .75 | .60 |
| **2639** | A598 | $16.50 multicolored | 1.00 | .60 |
| | | *Nos. 2632-2639 (8)* | 4.10 | 2.80 |

Industrialization by technological development. Issued: $3, $7.50, $10, $16, Apr. 22; others, May 9.

Police Day — A599

**Wmk. 323**

**1988, June 15 Litho. *Perf. 13½***

| | | | | |
|---|---|---|---|---|
| **2640** | A599 | $3 Traffic control | .35 | .25 |
| **2641** | A599 | $12 Rescue operations | 1.30 | .30 |

Amphibians A600

$1.50, Microhyla butleri. $3, Rana taipehensis. $7.50, Microhyla inornata. $16, Rhacophorus smaragdinus.

**1988, July 8 *Perf. 13½x14***

| | | | | |
|---|---|---|---|---|
| **2642** | A600 | $1.50 multicolored | *1.30* | .25 |
| **2643** | A600 | $3 multicolored | *2.00* | .25 |
| **2644** | A600 | $7.50 multicolored | *2.50* | .30 |
| **2645** | A600 | $16 multicolored | *3.50* | .60 |
| | | *Nos. 2642-2645 (4)* | *9.30* | 1.40 |

China Broadcasting Corp. (BBC), 60th Anniv. — A601

**Wmk. 323**

**1988, Aug. 1 Litho. *Perf. 13½***

| | | | | |
|---|---|---|---|---|
| **2646** | A601 | $3 multicolored | .80 | .25 |

Victory at the Battle of Kinmen, 30th Anniv. — A602

Designs: $1.50, Chiang Kai-shek and artillery commander. $3, With troops. $7.50, Cannon. $12, Tanks.

**1988, Aug. 23**

| | | | | |
|---|---|---|---|---|
| **2647** | A602 | $1.50 multicolored | .40 | .25 |
| **2648** | A602 | $3 multicolored | .60 | .25 |
| **2649** | A602 | $7.50 multicolored | .90 | .25 |
| **2650** | A602 | $12 multicolored | 1.10 | .40 |
| | | *Nos. 2647-2650 (4)* | 3.00 | 1.15 |

Sports Promotion — A603

Nos. 2651-2652, Basketball. Nos. 2653-2654, Baseball.

**1988, Sept. 9**

| | | | | |
|---|---|---|---|---|
| **2651** | | $5 Players | .90 | .25 |
| **2652** | | $5 Players | .90 | .25 |
| *a.* | A603 | Pair, #2651-2652 | 2.25 | 1.10 |
| **2653** | | $5 Batter | .90 | .25 |
| **2654** | | $5 Catcher | .90 | .25 |
| *a.* | A603 | Pair, #2653-2654 | 2.25 | 1.10 |
| | | *Nos. 2651-2654 (4)* | 3.60 | 1.00 |

Nos. 2652a, 2654a have continuous designs.

Yangmingshan Natl. Park — A604

$1.50, Volcanic crater. $3, Lake. $7.50, Tatun Volcanic Range. $16, Dormant volcano.

**1988, Sept. 16**

| | | | | |
|---|---|---|---|---|
| **2655** | A604 | $1.50 multicolored | *.30* | .25 |
| **2656** | A604 | $3 multicolored | *.55* | .25 |
| **2657** | A604 | $7.50 multicolored | *1.00* | .25 |
| **2658** | A604 | $16 multicolored | *2.25* | .50 |
| | | *Nos. 2655-2658 (4)* | *4.10* | 1.25 |

*Lofty Mount Lu,* a Hanging Scroll, 1467, By Shen Chou (1427-1509) — A605

Painting details: a, UL. b, UR. c, LL. d, LR.

**Wmk. 323**

**1988, Oct. 19 Litho. *Perf. 11½***

| | | | | |
|---|---|---|---|---|
| **2659** | A605 | Block of 4 | *7.00* | 5.00 |
| ***a.-d.*** | | $5 any single | *1.50* | .35 |

Folk Costumes — A606

Designs: $2, Shang Dynasty (1766-1122 B.C.) nobleman. $3, Warring States (403-221 B.C.) ruler. $7.50, Wei-Chin Period (221-420) official. $12, Northern Dynasties (502-581) official.

***Perf. 13½x14***

**1988, Nov. 23 Litho. Wmk. 323**

| | | | | |
|---|---|---|---|---|
| **2660** | A606 | $2 multicolored | *.60* | .25 |
| **2661** | A606 | $3 multicolored | *1.00* | .25 |
| **2662** | A606 | $7.50 multicolored | *2.00* | .30 |
| **2663** | A606 | $12 multicolored | *2.75* | .50 |
| | | *Nos. 2660-2663 (4)* | *6.35* | 1.30 |

Nos. 2721-2724 have groups of 2 and 6 Chinese characters above denomination; Nos. 2660-2663 groups of 2 and 4; Nos. 2794-2797 groups of 1 and 5.

A607

**1988, Dec. 1 *Perf. 12½***

| | | | | |
|---|---|---|---|---|
| **2664** | A607 | $2 multicolored | *.65* | .25 |
| **2665** | A607 | $13 multicolored | *5.00* | .50 |
| *a.* | | Souv. sheet, 2 each #2664-2665 | *16.50* | 11.50 |

New Year 1989 (Year of the Snake).

A608

**Wmk. 323**

**1989, Jan. 4 Litho. *Perf. 13½***

| | | | | |
|---|---|---|---|---|
| **2666** | A608 | $3 black | .70 | .25 |

Tai Ch'uan-hsien (1890-1949), party leader.

Pres. Chiang Ching-kuo (1910-88) — A609

**1989, Jan. 13**

| | | | | |
|---|---|---|---|---|
| **2667** | A609 | $3 shown | .30 | .25 |
| **2668** | A609 | $6 Suffrage | .40 | .25 |
| **2669** | A609 | $7.50 Industry | .80 | .30 |
| **2670** | A609 | $16 Children | 1.40 | .50 |
| | | *Nos. 2667-2670 (4)* | 2.90 | 1.30 |

Ni Ying-tien (1884-1910), Revolution Leader — A610

***Perf. 13½x12½***

**1989, Mar. 28 Engr. Wmk. 323**

| | | | | |
|---|---|---|---|---|
| **2671** | A610 | $3 black | .80 | .25 |

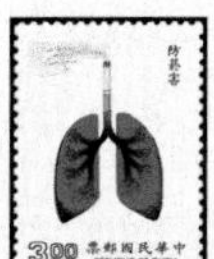

Stop Smoking — A611

***Perf. 13½x12½***

**1989, Apr. 7 Litho. Wmk. 323**

| | | | | |
|---|---|---|---|---|
| **2672** | A611 | $3 multicolored | .80 | .25 |

Lighthouses — A612

75c, Mu Tou Yu. $2, Lu Tao. $2.25, Pen Chia Yu. $3, Pitou Chiao. $4.50, Tungyin Tao. $6, Chilai Pi. $7, Fukwei Chiao. $7.50, Hua Yu. $9, Oluan Pi. $10, Kaohsiung. $10.50, Yuweng Tao. $12, Tungchu Tao. $13, Yeh Liu. $15, Tungchi Yu. $16.50, Chimei Yu.

**1989-91 *Perf. 13½***

| | | | | |
|---|---|---|---|---|
| **2673** | A612 | 75c multi | .30 | .25 |
| **2674** | A612 | $2 multi | .60 | .25 |
| **2675** | A612 | $2.25 multi | .30 | .25 |
| **2676** | A612 | $3 multi | .65 | .25 |
| **2677** | A612 | $4.50 multi | .50 | .25 |
| **2678** | A612 | $6 multi | .65 | .25 |
| **2679** | A612 | $7 multi | .80 | .25 |
| **2680** | A612 | $7.50 multi | 1.60 | .35 |
| **2681** | A612 | $9 multi | 1.00 | .25 |
| **2682** | A612 | $10 multi | 2.10 | .45 |
| **2683** | A612 | $10.50 multi | 1.20 | .25 |
| **2683A** | A612 | $12 multi | 1.35 | .25 |
| **2683B** | A612 | $13 multi | 1.45 | .25 |
| **2683C** | A612 | $15 multi | 1.60 | .25 |
| **2684** | A612 | $16.50 multi | 3.50 | .75 |
| | | *Nos. 2673-2684 (15)* | 17.60 | 4.55 |

Issued: 75c, $2.25, 4/21/1989; $4.50, 8/6/1989; $9, $10.50, $13, 8/16/1989; $7, $15, 5/19/90; $6, $12, 1/9/91; $2, $3, $7.50, $10, $16.50, 5/20/91.

See Nos. 2811-2823.

1st Natl. Wealth Survey — A613

**1989, May 18 Litho. *Perf. 13½***

| | | | | |
|---|---|---|---|---|
| **2685** | A613 | $3 multicolored | .80 | .25 |

*Ch'u Ts'u* Collection of Poems, 722-481 B.C. — A614

Designs: $3, Man overlooking fields. $7.50, Man, woman on path. $12, Man holding staff. $16, Man, stallion, stone gate. Excerpts: $3, "I once tended nine fields of orchids; Also I had planted a hundred rods of melilotus" (Li Sao). $7.50, "No grief is greater than parting of the living; No joy is more than making new friends" (Chiu Ko, shao ssu ming). $12, "Since my heart is straight and good, Why should I be chagrined at living remote and neglected?" (Chiu Chang, she chiang). $16, "The steed will not gallop itself into servitude; The phoenix has no appetite for slave food." (Chiu Pien).

**1989, June 7 Photo. *Perf. 11½x12***

**Granite Paper**

| | | | | |
|---|---|---|---|---|
| **2686** | A614 | $3 multicolored | .35 | .25 |
| **2687** | A614 | $7.50 multicolored | .90 | .35 |
| **2688** | A614 | $12 multicolored | 1.75 | .55 |
| **2689** | A614 | $16 multicolored | 2.00 | .75 |
| | | *Nos. 2686-2689 (4)* | 5.00 | 1.90 |

Compare with types A629, A663. Nos. 2686-2689 have two Chinese characters near denomination. Nos. 2725-2728 have groups of 3 and 4 characters.

Taipei Subway Inauguration A615

$3, Subway tunnel. $16, Entering underground.

**1989, June 27 Litho. *Perf. 13½***

| | | | | |
|---|---|---|---|---|
| **2690** | A615 | $3 multicolored | .45 | .25 |
| **2691** | A615 | $16 multicolored | 1.75 | .60 |

A616

A616a

A616b

Butterflies A616c

$2, Graphium sarpedon connectens. $3, Papilo memnon heronus. $7.50, Princeps demoleus libanius. $9, Pachliopa aristolochiae interpositas.

**Wmk. 323**

**1989, July 14 Litho. *Perf. 13½***

| | | | | |
|---|---|---|---|---|
| **2692** | A616 | $2 multicolored | .75 | .25 |
| **2693** | A616a | $3 multicolored | .75 | .25 |
| **2694** | A616b | $7.50 multicolored | 3.00 | .40 |
| **2695** | A616c | $9 multicolored | 2.40 | .30 |
| | | *Nos. 2692-2695 (4)* | 6.90 | 1.20 |

Compare with design A627.

Ch'ing Dynasty Teapots from I-Hsing of Kiangsu, 1644-1911 — A617

**1989, July 28 *Perf. 13½x14***

| | | | | |
|---|---|---|---|---|
| **2696** | A617 | $2 multicolored | .65 | .25 |
| **2697** | A617 | $3 multi, diff. | .65 | .25 |
| **2698** | A617 | $12 multi, diff. | 2.25 | .45 |
| **2699** | A617 | $16 multi, diff. | 2.40 | .60 |
| | | *Nos. 2696-2699 (4)* | 5.95 | 1.55 |

For stamps with teapot designs and solid black denominations see Nos. 2760-2764.

Intl. Seminar on Fan Chung-yen (989-1052), Military Leader and Civil Service Reformer — A618

***Perf. 14x13½***

**1989, Sept. 1 Litho. Wmk. 323**

| | | | | |
|---|---|---|---|---|
| **2700** | A618 | $12 multicolored | 1.25 | .55 |

*Autumn Colors on the Ch'iao and Hua Mountains,* 14th Cent., by Ch'iao Meng-fu — A619

a, Right side of mountain, trees. b, Trees, left side of mountain. c, House, trees. d, shown.

**Wmk. 323**

**1989, Oct. 5 Litho. *Perf. 13½***

| | | | | |
|---|---|---|---|---|
| **2701** | | Strip of 4 | 10.00 | 4.00 |
| ***a.-d.*** | A619 | $7.50 any single | 2.25 | .50 |

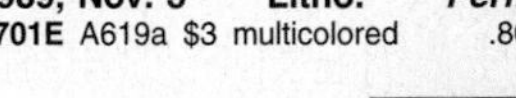

Social Welfare — A619a

**1989, Nov. 3 Litho. *Perf. 13½***

| | | | | |
|---|---|---|---|---|
| **2701E** | A619a | $3 multicolored | .80 | .25 |

Taroko Natl. Park — A620

Designs: $2, Marble gorge, Liwu River. $3, Hohuan Mountain. $12, Waterfall, Cirque of Nanhu. $16, Chingshui Cliff.

**Wmk. 323**

**1989, Nov. 28 Litho. *Perf. 13½***

| | | | | |
|---|---|---|---|---|
| **2702** | A620 | $2 multicolored | .35 | .25 |
| **2703** | A620 | $3 multicolored | .35 | .25 |
| **2704** | A620 | $12 multicolored | 1.00 | .45 |
| **2705** | A620 | $16 multicolored | 1.25 | .50 |
| | | *Nos. 2702-2705 (4)* | 2.95 | 1.45 |

New Year 1990 (Year of the Horse) — A621

**1989, Dec. 1** *Perf. 12½*

**2706** A621 $2 multicolored .40 .25
**2707** A621 $13 multicolored 1.65 .50
*a.* Souv. sheet, 2 ea #2706-2707 8.50 3.00

Yu Lu — A622

Men Shen, "guardian spirits" (likenesses of legendary beings placed on residence doors at the new year): No. 2708, Yu Lu. No. 2709, Shen Shu. No. 2710, Wei-ch'ih Ching-te. No. 2711, Ch'in Shu-pao.

**Wmk. 323**

**1990, Jan. 19 Litho.** *Perf. 13½*

**2708** A622 $3 shown 1.00 .25
**2709** A622 $3 "$3" at LR 1.00 .25
*a.* Pair, #2708-2709 2.00 1.75
**2710** A622 $7.50 "$7.50" at LL 2.40 .40
**2711** A622 $7.50 "$7.50" at LR 2.40 .40
*a.* Pair, #2710-2711 5.00 4.25
*Nos. 2708-2711 (4)* 6.80 1.30

Nos. 2709a, 2711a have continuous designs.

A623

Scenery — A624

Designs: $2, Lishan House, Pear Mountain. $18, Tayu Pass, Tayuling, vert.

**Wmk. 323**

**1990, Feb. 10 Litho.** *Perf. 13½*

**2712** A623 $2 multicolored .55 .25
**2713** A624 $18 multicolored 1.90 .80

Labor Insurance System, 40th Anniv. — A625

**1990, Mar. 1**

**2714** A625 $3 multicolored .80 .25

Liquefied Natural Gas — A626

$3, Terminal, Yung-an Hsiang of Kaohsiung. $16, Container ship, map, refinery.

**1990, Mar. 31 Litho.** *Perf. 13½*

**2715** A626 $3 multi .40 .25
**2716** A626 $16 multi, vert. 1.20 .50

A627

A627a

A627b

Butterflies A627c

$2, Salatura genutia. $3, Hypolimnas misippus. $7.50, Pieris canidia. $9, Precis almana.

**1990, Apr. 20**

**2717** A627 $2 multicolored .35 .25
**2718** A627a $3 multicolored .35 .25
**2719** A627b $7.50 multicolored 1.00 .25
**2720** A627c $9 multicolored 1.40 .35
*Nos. 2717-2720 (4)* 3.10 1.10

Compare with design A616.

Folk Costumes — A628

$2, Official, Sui & T'ang Dynasties (589-907). $3, Official, T'ang & Sung Dynasties (618-1280). $7.50, Royal guardsman, Chin & Yuan Dynasties (1115-1368). $12, Highest ranking civil official, Ming Dynasty (1368-1644).

**1990, May 10 Litho.** *Perf. 13½*

**2721** A628 $2 multicolored .50 .25
**2722** A628 $3 multicolored .60 .25
**2723** A628 $7.50 multicolored 1.35 .25
**2724** A628 $12 multicolored 1.40 .45
*Nos. 2721-2724 (4)* 3.85 1.20

See note after No. 2663.

Yueh Fu Classical Poetry — A629

Lyrics from Tzu-yeh folk songs, Six Dynasties (222-589): $3, Spring Song at Midnight. $7.50, Summer Song at Midnight. $12, Autumn Song at Midnight. $16, Winter Song at Midnight.

**Wmk. 323**

**1990, June 27 Litho.** *Perf. 11½*

**Granite Paper**

**2725** A629 $3 shown .30 .25
**2726** A629 $7.50 Couple, river 1.10 .25
**2727** A629 $12 Washing clothes, river 2.40 .45
**2728** A629 $16 River in winter 3.25 .65
*Nos. 2725-2728 (4)* 7.05 1.60

Compare with designs A614 and A663.

Bonsai — A630

Designs: $3, Pinus thunbergii parl. $6.50, Ehretia microphylla lamk. $12, Buxus harlandii hance. $16, Celtis sinensis pers.

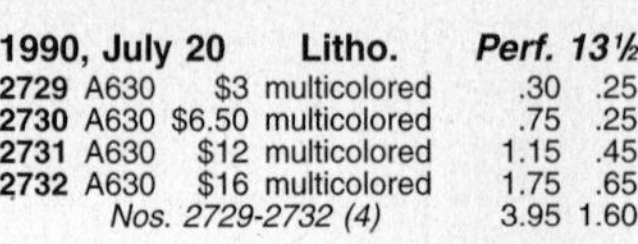

**1990, July 20 Litho.** *Perf. 13½*

**2729** A630 $3 multicolored .30 .25
**2730** A630 $6.50 multicolored .75 .25
**2731** A630 $12 multicolored 1.15 .45
**2732** A630 $16 multicolored 1.75 .65
*Nos. 2729-2732 (4)* 3.95 1.60

Snuff Bottles — A631

$3, Bamboo stem shaped. $6, Peony motif. $9, Amber. $16, White jade.

**1990, Aug. 9**

**2733** A631 $3 multicolored .35 .25
**2734** A631 $6 multicolored .50 .25
**2735** A631 $9 multicolored .95 .35
**2736** A631 $16 multicolored 1.50 .60
*Nos. 2733-2736 (4)* 3.30 1.45

Formosan Firecrest — A632

$3, Laughing thrush. $7.50, White-eared sibia. $16, Yellow tit.

**1990, Aug. 20 Litho.** *Perf. 13½*

**2737** A632 $2 shown .50 .25
**2738** A632 $3 multicolored .50 .25
**2739** A632 $7.50 multicolored 1.15 .25
**2740** A632 $16 multicolored 2.50 .50
*Nos. 2737-2740 (4)* 4.65 1.25

Sports — A633

**1990, Sept. 8 Litho.** *Perf. 13½*

**2741** A633 $2 Sprint .30 .25
**2742** A633 $3 Long jump .30 .25
**2743** A633 $7 Pole vault 1.10 .30
**2744** A633 $16 High hurdle 1.40 .60
*Nos. 2741-2744 (4)* 3.10 1.40

Flying Tigers, 50th Anniv. — A634

**1990, Sept. 26 Litho.** *Perf. 13½*

**2745** A634 $3 multicolored 1.00 .25

Children's Drawings — A635

**1990, Oct. 9**

**2746** A635 $2 Cat .30 .25
**2747** A635 $3 Peacocks .30 .25
**2748** A635 $7.50 Chickens .90 .25
**2749** A635 $12 Cattle 1.30 .40
*Nos. 2746-2749 (4)* 2.80 1.15

National Theater — A636

**Photo. & Engr.**

**1990, Oct. 30** *Perf. 13½*

**2750** A636 $3 shown .45 .25
**2751** A636 $12 Natl. concert hall 1.50 .60

A637

Ancient money.

**1990, Nov. 5 Litho.** *Perf. 13x13½*

**2752** A637 $2 Shell .45 .25
**2753** A637 $3 Oyster .45 .25
**2754** A637 $6.50 Bone .65 .25
**2755** A637 $7.50 Jade .85 .35
**2756** A637 $9 Bronze 1.00 .40
*Nos. 2752-2756 (5)* 3.40 1.50

A638

**1990, Dec. 1** *Perf. 12½*

**2757** A638 $2 multicolored .60 .25
**2758** A638 $13 multicolored 2.50 .60
*a.* Souv. sheet, 2 ea #2757-2758 *10.00* 2.50

New Year 1991 (Year of the Sheep).

Hu Shih (1891-1962), Educator — A639

**Wmk. 323**

**1990, Dec. 17 Engr.** *Perf. 13½*

**2759** A639 $3 purple .80 .25

Teapots, Natl. Palace Museum — A640

Teapots: $2, Blue phoenix, Ming Dynasty. $3, Dragon handle and spout, Ming Dynasty. $9, Blue landscape, flowered top, Ch'ing Dynasty. $12, Rectangular, passion flower motif, Ch'ing Dynasty. $16, Rectangular, flower motif, Ch'ing Dynasty.

**1991, Jan. 18 Photo.** *Perf. 12*

**Granite Paper**

**2760** A640 $2 yel, blk & blue .40 .25
**2761** A640 $3 brt yel grn & blk .55 .25
**2762** A640 $9 pink & multi .85 .30
**2763** A640 $12 violet & multi 1.15 .40
**2764** A640 $16 lt blue & multi 1.30 .60
*Nos. 2760-2764 (5)* 4.25 1.80

God of Happiness A641

God of Joy A642

No. 2766, God of Wealth. No. 2768, God of Longevity.

**1991, Feb. 7 Litho.** *Perf. 13½*

**2765** A641 $3 shown .50 .25
**2766** A641 $3 multi .50 .25
**2767** A642 $7.50 shown 1.10 .25
**2768** A642 $7.50 multi 1.10 .25
*Nos. 2765-2768 (4)* 3.20 1.00

***Perf. 13½ Vert.***

*2765a* A641 $3 *1.20* .25
*2766a* A641 $3 *1.20* .25
*2767a* A642 $7.50 *1.20* .25
*2768a* A642 $7.50 *1.20* .25
*b.* Bklt. pane of 8, 2 each #2765a-2768a + label *14.00*

Native Plants — A643

Designs: $2, Petasites formosanus. $3, Heloniopsis acutifolia. $7.50, Disporum shimadai. $9, Viola nagasawai.

**1991, Mar. 12 Litho. *Perf. 13½***

**2769** A643 $2 multicolored .50 .25
**2770** A643 $3 multicolored .55 .25
**2771** A643 $7.50 multicolored .90 .30
**2772** A643 $9 multicolored 1.10 .35

**1991, June 12**

Designs: $2, Gaultheria itoana. $3, Lysionotus montanus. $7.50, Leontopodium microphyllum. $9, Gentiana flavo-maculata.

**2773** A643 $2 multicolored .30 .25
**2774** A643 $3 multicolored .45 .25
**2775** A643 $7.50 multicolored 1.10 .30
**2776** A643 $9 multicolored 1.30 .35

**1991, Sept. 12**

Designs: $3.50, Rosa transmorrisonensis. $5, Impatiens devolii. $9, Impatiens uniflora. $12, Impatiens tayemonii.

**2777** A643 $3.50 multicolored .40 .25
**2778** A643 $5 multicolored .55 .25
**2779** A643 $9 multicolored 1.00 .30
**2780** A643 $12 multicolored 1.20 .35

**1991, Dec. 12**

Designs: $3.50, Kalanchoe garambiensis. $5, Pieris taiwanensis. $9, Pleione formosana. $12, Elaeagnus oldhamii.

**2781** A643 $3.50 multicolored .40 .25
**2782** A643 $5 multicolored .55 .25
**2783** A643 $9 multicolored .75 .45
**2784** A643 $12 multicolored 1.00 .55
*Nos. 2769-2784 (16)* 12.05 4.95

Hsiung Cheng-Chi (1887-1910), Revolutionary — A644

**1991, Mar. 28 Engr. *Perf. 13½x12½***

**2785** A644 $3 blue .80 .25

Republic of China, 80th Anniv. — A645

$3, Agriculture. $7.50, Science & technology. $12, Cultural activities. $16, Transportation.

**1991, Mar. 28 Litho. *Perf. 13½***

**2786** A645 $3 multicolored .35 .25
**2787** A645 $7.50 multicolored .65 .30
**2788** A645 $12 multicolored 1.10 .50
**2789** A645 $16 multicolored 1.25 .75
*Nos. 2786-2789 (4)* 3.35 1.80

Children's Toys — A646

No. 2790, Bamboo pony. No. 2791, Woven-grass grasshopper. No. 2792, Top. No. 2793, Pinwheels.

**1991, Apr. 20 Litho. *Perf. 13½***

**2790** A646 $3 multicolored .50 .25
**2791** A646 $3 multicolored .50 .25
**2792** A646 $3 multicolored .50 .25
**2793** A646 $3 multicolored .50 .25
*a.* Souv. sheet of 4, #2790-2793 *6.50* 3.50
*Nos. 2790-2793 (4)* 2.00 1.00

See Nos. 2840-2843. Compare with designs A676, A696.

No. 2793a exists with a red overprint in Chinese characters in the selvage. The overprinted sheet was sold at an exhibition in Singapore. Value, $23.

***Perf. 13½ Vert.***

*2790a* A646 $3 *1.00* .25
*2791a* A646 $3 *1.00* .25
*2792a* A646 $3 *1.00* .25
*2793b* A646 $3 *1.00* .25
*c.* Bklt. pane, 2 each #2790a-2793b + label *8.00*
*Nos. 2790a-2793b (4)* 4.00 1.00

Folk Costumes — A647

Ch'ing Dynasty (1644-1911): $2, Winter court hat, Mang robe. $3, Summer court hat, surcoat. $7.50, Winter overcoat. $12, Common hat, traveling robe.

**1991, June 29 Litho. *Perf. 13½***

**2794** A647 $2 multicolored .60 .25
**2795** A647 $3 multicolored .75 .25
**2796** A647 $7.50 multicolored 1.90 .25
**2797** A647 $12 multicolored 2.50 .35
*Nos. 2794-2797 (4)* 5.75 1.10

See note after No. 2663.

Nos. 2794-2797 have groups of one and five Chinese characters.

Traffic Safety Year — A648

$7.50, Don't drink & drive.

**1991, July 17 Litho. *Perf. 13½***

**2798** A648 $3 shown .40 .25
**2799** A648 $7.50 multicolored 1.40 .30

Cloisonne Enamel Lions, Ch'ing Dynasty (1644-1911)
A649 A649a

**1991, July 20 Litho. *Perf. 12½***

**2800** A649 yel grn & multi .55 .25
**2801** A649a violet & multi 2.25 .60
*Nos. 2800-2801 (2)* 2.80 .85

No. 2800 paid basic domestic rate, No. 2801 paid basic express mail rate on date of issue.

Fruits — A650

**1991, Aug. 10 Litho. *Perf. 14x13½***

**2802** A650 $3 Strawberry .40 .25
**2803** A650 $7.50 Grapes .70 .40
**2804** A650 $9 Mango .90 .50
**2805** A650 $16 Sugar apple 1.40 .75
*Nos. 2802-2805 (4)* 3.40 1.90

Birds — A651

Designs: a, Myiophoneus insularis. b, Cinclus pallasii. c, Aix galericulata. d, Nycticorax nycticorax. e, Egretta garzetta. f, Rhyacornis fuliginosus. g, Enicurus scouleri. h, Motacilla cinerea. i, Alcedo atthis. j, Motacilla alba.

**1991, Aug. 24 *Perf. 13½***

**2806** Block of 10 5.75 3.25
*a.-j.* A651 $5 any single .40 .25

Outdoor Activities — A652

**Wmk. 323**

**1991, Sept. 27 Litho. *Perf. 13½***

**2807** A652 $2 Rock climbing .25 .25
**2808** A652 $3 Fishing .35 .25
**2809** A652 $7.50 Bird watching .70 .30
**2810** A652 $10 Playing in water 1.00 .40
*Nos. 2807-2810 (4)* 2.30 1.20

Intl. Federation of Camping and Caravaning, 1991 Rally.

**Lighthouse Type of 1989 Inscription Panel in Blue**

**1991-92 *Perf. 13½***

**2811** A612 50c like #2683C .30 .25
**2812** A612 $1 like #2674 .35 .25
**2813** A612 $3.50 like #2678 .30 .25
**2814** A612 $5 like #2679 .45 .25
*a.* Booklet pane of 10 4.00
**2815** A612 $7 like #2676 .50 .25
**2816** A612 $9 like #2681 .75 .25
**2817** A612 $10 like #2682 .90 .35
**2818** A612 $12 like #2683A 1.00 .40
*a.* $12 Bklt. pane of 5 + label 5.00
**2819** A612 $13 like #2675 1.00 .40
**2820** A612 $19 like #2680 1.50 .65
**2821** A612 $20 like #2683B 1.60 .65
**2822** A612 $26 like #2683 1.75 .90
**2823** A612 $28 like #2684 1.75 .90
*Nos. 2811-2823 (13)* 12.15 5.75

Issued: 50c, $3.50, $5, $12, 10/2; No. 2818a, 9/26/92; $1, $19, $20, 3/2/92; $26, $28, 5/20/92; $7, $9, $10, $13, 8/21/92.

Peacocks by Lan Shih-ning (Giuseppe Castiglione, 1688-1768) — A653

$20, Peacock spreading tail feathers.

***Perf. 12x11½***

**1991, Oct. 30 Photo. Unwmk.**

**Granite Paper**

**2826** A653 $5 multicolored .90 .30
**2827** A653 $20 multicolored 3.25 .80
*a.* Souvenir sheet of 1 5.00 4.25

New Year 1992 (Year of the Monkey) — A654

**Wmk. 323**

**1991, Nov. 30 Litho. *Perf. 12½***

**2828** A654 $3.50 orange & multi .50 .25
**2829** A654 $13 tan & multi 1.75 .50
*a.* Souv. sheet, 2 ea #2828-2829 5.50 2.00

Chinese Books — A655

$3.50, Scroll. $5, Fold bindings. $9, Butterfly bindings. $15, String bindings.

**Wmk. 323**

**1992, Jan. 17 Litho. *Perf. 13½***

**2830** A655 $3.50 multicolored .30 .25
**2831** A655 $5 multicolored .65 .25
**2832** A655 $9 multicolored 1.25 .25
**2833** A655 $15 multicolored 1.90 .50
*Nos. 2830-2833 (4)* 4.10 1.25

Good Fortune and Satisfaction A656

Five Blessings Upon the House A657

Nienhwa paintings: No. 2835, Peace in the Wake of Firecrackers. No. 2837, An Abundance for Every Year.

**1992, Jan. 27 Litho. *Perf. 13½***

**2834** A656 $5 multicolored .55 .25
**2835** A656 $5 multicolored .55 .25
**2836** A657 $12 multicolored 1.45 .50
**2837** A657 $12 multicolored 1.45 .50
*a.* Bklt. pane, 2 each #2834-2837 + label *4.00*
*Nos. 2834-2837 (4)* 4.00 1.50

Lunar New Year.

A658

Lunar New Year: a, like #2664. b, like #2611. c, like #2565. d, like #2493. e, like #2442. f, like #2390. g, like #2346. h, like #2273. i, like #2217. j, like #2828. k, like #2757. l, like #2706.

**Wmk. 323**

**1992, Feb. 18 Litho. *Perf. 12½***

**2838** A658 $5 Block of 12, #a.-l., ver & multi 7.50 2.75
*m.* Sheet of 12, #2838a-2838 l 8.00 3.00

A659

Trees: a, Chamaecyparis formosensis. b, Chamaecyparis taiwanensis. c, Calocedrus formosana. d, Cunninghamia konishii. e. Taiwania crypto- merioides.

**1992, Mar. 12 *Perf. 13½***

**2839** A659 $5 Strip of 5, #a.-e. 3.00 1.50

**Children's Toys Type of 1991**

**1992, Apr. 29 Litho. *Perf. 13½***

**2840** A646 $5 Walking on iron pots .75 .25
*a.* Perf. 13½ vert. .55 .25
**2841** A646 $5 Chopstick gun .75 .25
*a.* Perf. 13½ vert. .55 .25
**2842** A646 $5 Hoop rolling .75 .25
*a.* Perf. 13½ vert. .55 .25
**2843** A646 $5 Grass fighting .75 .25
*a.* Sheet of 4, #2840-2843 *4.75* *4.75*
*b.* As "a," imperf. (simulated perfs), red inscription in sheet margin *13.00* *13.00*
*c.* Perf. 13½ vert. .55 .25
*d.* Bklt. pane, 2 each #2840a-2842a, 2843c + label 4.75
*Nos. 2840-2843 (4)* 3.00 1.00

Issue date: No. 2843b, May 15.

A660

Mother and son in: $3.50, Spring. $5, Summer. $9, Autumn. $10, Winter.

**Wmk. 323**

**1992, May 9 Litho. *Perf. 13½***

**2844** A660 $3.50 multicolored .30 .25
**2845** A660 $5 multicolored .55 .25
**2846** A660 $9 multicolored 1.00 .30
**2847** A660 $10 multicolored 1.10 .35
*Nos. 2844-2847 (4)* 2.95 1.15

Parent-child relationships.

A661

Glassware Decorated with Enamel — Vases: $3.50, Faceted, decorated with bats and longevity characters. $5, Double-lobed, with children at play. $7, Flowered. $17, Tutoring scene.

**Wmk. 323**

**1992, June 25 Litho. *Perf. 13½***

**Background colors**

**2848** A661 $3.50 pink .30 .25
**2849** A661 $5 green .50 .25
**2850** A661 $7 bister .75 .25
**2851** A661 $17 blue 2.25 .55
*Nos. 2848-2851 (4)* 3.80 1.30

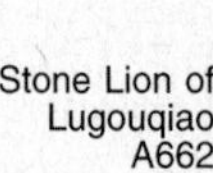

Stone Lion of Lugouqiao A662

Various stone lions.

**Wmk. 323**

**1992, July 7 Engr. *Perf. 13½***

**2852** A662 $5 olive grn & pur .50 .25
**2853** A662 $5 blue & brown .50 .25
**2854** A662 $12 org & olive grn 1.10 .40
**2855** A662 $12 purple & black 1.10 .40
*Nos. 2852-2855 (4)* 3.20 1.30

Compare with designs A614, A629, A663.

Ku Shih Classical Poetry A663

Excerpts: $3.50, "Flesh and body are as closely linked as leaves to a tree." $5, "Once a man and woman get married, conjugal love will last forever without doubt." $9, "Man takes pains to uphold virtue." $15, "Tartar horses lean toward the northern wind."

**1992, Aug. 8 Litho.**

**2856** A663 $3.50 Children playing near tree .30 .25
**2857** A663 $5 Man & woman .65 .25
**2858** A663 $9 Couple near stream 1.15 .30
**2859** A663 $15 Horse, tree 1.60 .50
*Nos. 2856-2859 (4)* 3.70 1.30

Life in the Countryside — A664

Scenes of temple fair: a, Two women, man beating drum, crowd. b, Vendor with basket. c, People playing musical instruments. d, Man with food cart. e, Women with umbrella, basket.

**Wmk. 323**

**1992, Sept. 22 Litho. *Perf. 11½***

**2860** A664 $5 Strip of 5, #a.-e. 4.00 2.75

Silk Tapestries — A665

Ming Dynasty Silk Tapestry Drawing on Life: $5, Two Birds Perched on a Red Camellia Branch. $12, Two Birds Playing on a Peach Branch.

**1992, Oct. 9 Litho. *Perf. 11½***

**Granite Paper**

**2861** A665 $5 multicolored .65 .25
**2862** A665 $12 multicolored 1.75 .50
 *a.* Sheet of 2, #2861-2862 2.75 .75

Chinese Opera — A666

Actors, props: $3.50, Nin Hsiang-ju's carting to a party from "The General and Premier." $5, Hsao En rowing a boat from "The Lucky Pearl." $9, Wang Chao-chun making peace with the frontier from "Chao-chun Serves as an Envoy." $12, Scene with red sedan chair from "Escort to the Wedding."

**Wmk. 323**

**1992, Oct. 21 Litho. *Perf. 13½***

**2863** A666 $3.50 multicolored .30 .25
**2864** A666 $5 multicolored .60 .25
**2865** A666 $9 multicolored 1.05 .30
**2866** A666 $12 multicolored 1.00 .45
*Nos. 2863-2866 (4)* 2.95 1.25

Alishan Forest Railway — A667

**1992, Nov. 5 *Perf. 11½***

**2867** A667 $5 Steam engine .75 .25
**2868** A667 $15 Diesel engine 1.65 .50

Endangered Mammals of Taiwan — A668

Designs: a, Lutra lutra chinensis. b, Pteropus dasymallus formosus. c, Neofelis nebulosa brachyurus. d, Selenarctos thibetanus formosanus.

***Perf. 11½x12***

**1992, Nov. 25 Photo. Unwmk.**

**Granite Paper**

**2869** A668 $5 Block of 4, #a.-d. 3.00 1.25

New Year 1993 (Year of the Rooster) — A669

Design: $13, Rooster facing left.

**Wmk. 323**

**1992, Dec. 1 Litho. *Perf. 12½***

**2870** A669 $3.50 red & multi .55 .25
 *a.* Perf. 13½ vert. .40 .25
**2871** A669 $13 pur & multi 1.35 .35
 *a.* Souv. sheet, 2 ea #2870-2871 4.75 4.75
 *b.* As "a" with added inscription in border 4.75 4.75
 *c.* Bklt. pane, 5 ea #2870-2871 8.00
 *d.* Perf. 13½ vert. 1.00 .40
 *e.* Booklet pane, 6 each #2870a, 2871d + label 8.75

Inscription on No. 2871b reads "Philippine Stamp Exhibition 1992-Taipei" in English and Chinese.

Johann Adam Schall von Bell (1592-1666), Astronomer and Missionary A670

**1992 Dec. 10 *Perf. 11½***

**2872** A670 $5 multicolored .75 .25

Traditional Nienhwas of Window Frames — A671

**Wmk. 323**

**1993, Jan. 7 Litho. *Perf. 11½***

**Background Color**

**2873** A671 $5 brt green .30 .25
**2874** A671 $5 pink .30 .25
**2875** A671 $12 yellow 1.05 .40
**2876** A671 $12 red 1.05 .40
*Nos. 2873-2876 (4)* 2.70 1.30

Lunar New Year.

***Perf. 13½ Vert.***

*2873a* A671 $5 *1.00* .45
*2874a* A671 $5 *1.00* .45
*2875a* A671 $12 *1.00* .45
*2876a* A671 $12 *1.00* .45
 *b.* Booklet pane, 2 each #2873a-2876a + label *9.00*

Nos. 2873a-2876a are 29x43mm.

Traditional Crafts — A672

$3.50, Clip & paste moldings. $5, Lanterns. $9, Pottery jars. $15, Oil paper umbrella.

**1993, Jan. 16**

**2877** A672 $3.50 multi .30 .25
**2878** A672 $5 multi .40 .25
**2879** A672 $9 multi .90 .30
**2880** A672 $15 multi 1.35 .50
*Nos. 2877-2880 (4)* 2.95 1.30

Chinese Creation Story A673

Designs: $3.50, Pan Gu's creation of the universe, vert. $5, Pan Gu transmitted himself into all creatures. $9, Nu Wa created human beings with pestled earth. $19, Nu Wa mended sky with smelted stone, vert.

**1993, Feb. 6 *Perf. 12x11½, 11½x12***

**2881** A673 $3.50 multicolored .30 .25
**2882** A673 $5 multicolored .55 .25
**2883** A673 $9 multicolored 1.05 .50
**2884** A673 $19 multicolored 2.00 1.10
*Nos. 2881-2884 (4)* 3.90 2.10

Lucky Animals — A674

$3.50, Mandarin duck. $5, Chinese unicorn. $10, Deer. $15, Crane.

**Wmk. 323**

**1993, Mar. 2 Litho. *Perf. 13½***

**2885** A674 $3.50 multi .30 .25
**2886** A674 $5 multi .40 .25
**2887** A674 $10 multi .90 .40
**2888** A674 $15 multi 1.35 1.00
*Nos. 2885-2888 (4)* 2.95 1.90

See Nos. 2920-2923.

Water Plants — A675

$5, Nymphaea x hybrida. $9, Nuphar shimadai. $12, Eichhornia crassipes.

**1993, Mar. 12 *Perf. 11½***

**2889** A675 $5 multicolored .60 .25
**2890** A675 $9 multicolored .90 .30
**2891** A675 $12 multicolored 1.15 .40
*Nos. 2889-2891 (3)* 2.65 .95

A676

No. 2892, Sandbag tossing. No. 2893, Bamboo dragonfly twisting. No. 2894, Rubber band skipping. No. 2895, Waist-strength dueling.

**1993 Litho. Wmk. 323 *Perf. 11½***

**2892** A676 $5 multicolored .50 .30
**2893** A676 $5 multicolored .50 .30
**2894** A676 $5 multicolored .50 .30
**2895** A676 $5 multicolored .50 .30
 *a.* Souv. sheet, #2892-2895 3.00 3.00
 *b.* As "a," with green & black inscriptions in border 3.25 3.25
 *c.* As "a," with red inscription in border 3.00 3.00
*Nos. 2892-2895 (4)* 2.00 1.20

Inscriptions on No. 2895b read "AUSTRALIAN STAMP EXHIBITION 1993-TAIPEI" in Chinese and English.

Inscription on No. 2895c reads "Chinese Stamp Exhibition-Thailand" in Chinese.

Nos. 2895b-2895c each have perforations extending into the margin at top (No. 2895c) or bottom (No. 2895b).

Issue dates: Nos. 2892-2895, 2895a, Apr. 20; No. 2895b, Apr. 23; No. 2895c, Apr. 30.

***Perf. 13½ Vert.***

*2892a* A676 $5 *.90* .30
*2893a* A676 $5 *.90* .30
*2894a* A676 $5 *.90* .30
*2895d* A676 $5 *.90* .30
 *e.* Bklt. pane, 2 each #2892a-2894a, 2895d + label *7.50*

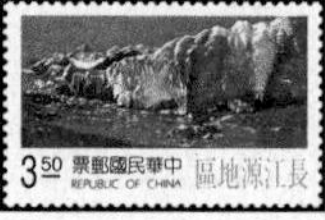

A677

Yangtze River — A678

Designs: No. 2896, Source on Ching-Kang-Chang Plateau. No. 2897, Abrupt bend, Chinsha River. No. 2898, Narrow waterway, Roaring Tiger Gorge, Chinsha River. No. 2899, Sheer cliffs, Chuntang Gorge. $9, Three Small Gorges (Dragon Gate, Pawu, and Titsui).

***Perf. 13x13½***

**1993, May 15 Litho. Wmk. 323**

**2896** A677 $3.50 shown .30 .25
**2897** A677 $3.50 multicolored .30 .25
**2898** A678 $5 shown .60 .25
**2899** A677 $5 multicolored .60 .25
**2900** A677 $9 multicolored 1.10 .30
*Nos. 2896-2900 (5)* 2.90 1.30

Environmental Protection
A679 A680

Children's paintings: $5, No More Noise Pollution, by Yen Chao-min. $17, Clothing My Hometown with Green, by Hu Hui-chun.

*Perf. 12½x13½, 13½x12½*

**1993, June 5**

**2901** A679 $5 multicolored .55 .25
**2902** A680 $17 multicolored 1.60 1.00

Ch'eng-hua Porcelain, Natl. Palace Museum — A681

Cups decorated in tou-ts'ai: $3.50, Human figures. $5, Chickens. $7, Flowers and fruits. $9, Dragon.

**1993, June 30** ***Perf. 12***

**2903** A681 $3.50 multicolored .30 .25
**2904** A681 $5 multicolored .65 .25
**2905** A681 $7 multicolored .90 .40
**2906** A681 $9 multicolored 1.10 .65
*Nos. 2903-2906 (4)* 2.95 1.55

Vocational Training — A682

$3.50, Graphic artist. $5, Computer operator. $9, Carpenter. $12, Welder.

**Wmk. 323**

**1993, July 24 Litho.** ***Perf. 12½***

**2907** A682 $3.50 multicolored .30 .25
**2908** A682 $5 multicolored .45 .25
**2909** A682 $9 multicolored .90 .50
**2910** A682 $12 multicolored 1.25 .75
*Nos. 2907-2910 (4)* 2.90 1.75

Parent-Child Relationship — A683

Silhouettes: $3.50, Adult carrying child on shoulders. $5, Father playing flute for daughter. $9, Father teaching daughter. $10, Father, adult son enjoying wildlife.

**Wmk. 323**

**1993, Aug. 4 Litho.** ***Perf. 11½***

**Background Color**

**2911** A683 $3.50 tan .30 .25
**2912** A683 $5 green .45 .25
**2913** A683 $9 lilac .90 .55
**2914** A683 $10 red brown 1.10 .65
*Nos. 2911-2914 (4)* 2.75 1.70

Souvenir Sheet

Taipei '93, Asian Intl. Philatelic Exhibition — A684

Enjoying Antiques, by Tu Chin, 15th cent: a, Man carrying stick. b, Man selecting antiques from table. c, Man seated in chair. d, Two people at table.

***Perf. 12x11½***

**1993, Aug. 14 Photo. Unwmk.**

**Granite Paper**

**2915** A684 $5 Sheet of 4, #a.-d. 3.25 2.40

Persimmon A685

Loquat A686

**1993, Sept. 10 Litho.** ***Perf. 12½***

**2916** A685 $5 shown .60 .25
**2917** A685 $5 Peach .60 .25
**2918** A686 $12 shown 1.50 .75
**2919** A686 $12 Papaya 1.50 .75
*Nos. 2916-2919 (4)* 4.20 2.00

**Lucky Animals Type of 1993**

**Wmk. 323**

**1993, Sept. 29 Litho.** ***Perf. 13½***

**2920** A674 $1 Blue dragon .30 .25
**2921** A674 $2.50 White tiger .30 .25
**2922** A674 $9 Linnet 1.00 .40
**2923** A674 $19 Black tortoise 1.75 .90
*Nos. 2920-2923 (4)* 3.35 1.80

Taiwan Area Games, Taoyuan A687

Designs: a, Taekwondo. b, Pommel horse.

**Wmk. 323**

**1993, Oct. 20 Litho.** ***Perf. 12½***

**2924** A687 $5 Pair, #a.-b. 1.00 .65

Stone Lions — A688

Stone lions from: $3.50, Taipei New Park. $5, Hsinchu City Council. $9, Hsinchu City God Temple. $12, Fort Providentia, Tainan.

**1993, Oct. 30**

**2925** A688 $3.50 multicolored .30 .25
**2926** A688 $5 multicolored .35 .25
**2927** A688 $9 multicolored .75 .45
**2928** A688 $12 multicolored 1.00 .60
*Nos. 2925-2928 (4)* 2.40 1.55

Syrmaticus Mikado — A689

Designs: a, Hatchling. b, Mother with chicks. c, Immature female, male. d, Adult female, male (profile, showing plumage).

***Perf. 11½***

**1993, Nov. 17 Photo. Unwmk.**

**Granite Paper**

**2929** A689 $5 Strip of 4, #a.-d. 2.25 1.60

New Year 1994 (Year of the Dog) — A690

Design: $13, Dog facing left.

**Wmk. 323**

**1993, Dec. 1 Litho.** ***Perf. 12½***

**2930** A690 $3.50 red & multi .30 .25
*a.* Perf. 13½ vert. .80 .25
*b.* As "a," bklt. pane of 12 + label 3.00
**2931** A690 $13 green & multi 1.10 .55
*a.* Souv. sheet, 2 ea #2930-2931 2.75 1.60
*b.* As "a," overprinted in red 3.00 1.60

No. 2931b is inscribed in Chinese for Kaohsiung Kuo-kuang Stamp Exhibition-1993, and has additional perforations extending into top and bottom margins.

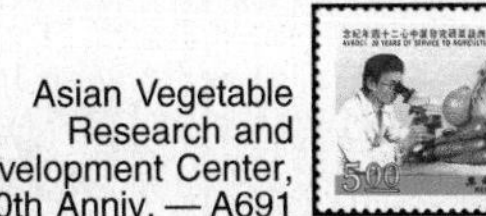

Asian Vegetable Research and Development Center, 20th Anniv. — A691

$13, Researchers in field.

**1993, Dec. 7**

**2932** A691 $5 shown .45 .25
**2933** A691 $13 multicolored 1.50 .75

Formation of Constitutional Court — A692

**Wmk. 323**

**1994, Jan. 11 Litho.** ***Perf. 12½***

**2934** A692 $5 multicolored .75 .30

Paper Making — A693

Designs: No. 2935, Cutting bamboo. No. 2936, Cooking bamboo. No. 2937, Pouring syrup into wooden panel. No. 2938, Stacking panel. No. 2939, Drying paper.

**1994, Jan. 24** ***Perf. 12x12½***

**2935** A693 $3.50 multicolored .30 .25
**2936** A693 $3.50 multicolored .30 .25
**2937** A693 $5 multicolored .50 .25
**2938** A693 $5 multicolored .50 .25
**2939** A693 $12 multicolored 1.00 .65
*Nos. 2935-2939 (5)* 2.60 1.65

See Nos. 2993-2997, 3071-3075, 3098-3102, 3174-3177.

Flowers — A694

$5, Clivia miniata. $12, Cymbidium sinense. $19, Primula malacoides.

**1994, Feb. 17** ***Perf. 12½***

**2940** A694 $5 multicolored .40 .25
**2941** A694 $12 multicolored 1.25 .60
**2942** A694 $19 multicolored 1.85 1.00
*Nos. 2940-2942 (3)* 3.50 1.85

Kinmen Wind Lion Lords — A695

Various Wind Lion Lords.

**1994, Mar. 18 Litho.** ***Perf. 12½***

**2943** A695 $5 green & multi .55 .25
**2944** A695 $9 yellow & multi .80 .40
**2945** A695 $12 org yel & multi 1.30 .50
**2946** A695 $17 blue & multi 1.60 .75
*Nos. 2943-2946 (4)* 4.25 1.90

Children at Play — A696

No. 2947, Playing with paper boat. No. 2948, Fighting with water gun. No. 2949, Throwing paper airplane. No. 2950, Playing "train" with rope.

**Wmk. 323**

**1994, Apr. 2 Litho.** ***Perf. 12½***

**2947** A696 $5 multicolored .50 .25
**2948** A696 $5 multicolored .50 .25
**2949** A696 $5 multicolored .50 .25
**2950** A696 $5 multicolored .50 .25
*a.* Souv. sheet, #2947-2950 2.40 1.25
*Nos. 2947-2950 (4)* 2.00 1.00

***Perf. 13½ Vert.***

*2947a* A696 $5 .45 .25
*2948a* A696 $5 .45 .25
*2949a* A696 $5 .45 .25
*2950b* A696 $5 .45 .25
*c.* Bklt. pane, 2 ea #2947a-2949a, 2950b + label 3.50 1.50
*Nos. 2947a-2950b (4)* 1.80 1.00

A697

Life in the countryside: $5, Playing chess. $10, Playing musical instruments. $12, Telling stories. $19, Drinking tea.

**Wmk. 323**

**1994, Apr. 25 Litho.** ***Perf. 12½***

**2951** A697 $5 multicolored .35 .25
**2952** A697 $10 multicolored .90 .50
**2953** A697 $12 multicolored 1.20 .70
**2954** A697 $19 multicolored 1.75 1.00
*Nos. 2951-2954 (4)* 4.20 2.45

A698

Mother, baby birds: $5, Malay bittern. $7, Little tern, horiz. $10, Common noddy, horiz. $12, Muller's barbet.

**1994, May 7**

**2955** A698 $5 multicolored .35 .30
**2956** A698 $7 multicolored .55 .35
**2957** A698 $10 multicolored .90 .50
**2958** A698 $12 multicolored 1.00 .60
*Nos. 2955-2958 (4)* 2.80 1.75

A699

Protection of Intellectual Property Rights: $5, Palm-shaped book. $15, Human head, computer disk.

**Wmk. 323**

**1994, May 28 Litho.** ***Perf. 12½***

**2959** A699 $5 multicolored .60 .25
**2960** A699 $15 multicolored 1.40 .75

A700

Designs: $5, Care for Lost Children. $17, Care for the aged.

**1994, June 11**

**2961** A700 $5 multicolored .55 .25
**2962** A700 $17 multicolored 1.95 .60

Intl. Olympic Committee, Cent. — A701

**1994, June 23**

**2963** A701 $5 shown .60 .25
**2964** A701 $15 Sporting events 1.90 .75

A702

Shei-pa Natl. Park: $5, Tapachienshan. $7, Shei-san Landslide Scar. $10, Holy Ridge. $17, Shiah-tsuei Lake.

**Wmk. 323**

**1994, July 1 Litho.** ***Perf. 12½***

**2965** A702 $5 multicolored .50 .25
**2966** A702 $7 multicolored .60 .35
**2967** A702 $10 multicolored 1.00 .50
**2968** A702 $17 multicolored 1.50 .90
*Nos. 2965-2968 (4)* 3.60 2.00

A703

$5, Portrait of Chien Mu (b. 1895), educator.

**1994, July 30** ***Perf. 11½x12***
**2969** A703 $5 multicolored .75 .25

Intl. Year of the Family — A704

$5, Rainbow, window. $15, Globe, house.

**1994, Aug. 25** ***Perf. 11½***
**2970** A704 $5 multicolored .50 .25
**2971** A704 $15 yel & multi 1.60 .75

Invention Myths — A705

Designs: $5, Sueirenjy digging wood to obtain fire. $10, Fushijy drawing Pa-Kua. $12, Shennungjy making agricultural tools. $15, Tsang-jier creating written characters.

**1994, Sept. 17 Photo.** ***Perf. 11½***
**Granite Paper**
**2972** A705 $5 multicolored .50 .25
**2973** A705 $10 multicolored 1.05 .50
**2974** A705 $12 multicolored 1.20 .75
**2975** A705 $15 multicolored 1.50 .85
*Nos. 2972-2975 (4)* 4.25 2.35

A706

Design: $5, Dr. Lin Yutang, linguist, writer, 100th birthday.

**Wmk. 323**
**1994, Oct. 8 Litho.** ***Perf. 12½***
**2976** A706 $5 multicolored .80 .30

A707

$5, Cheng Ho's ship. $17, Chart, ship, Cheng Ho.

**1994, Oct. 17**
**2977** A707 $5 multicolored .55 .25
**2978** A707 $17 multicolored 1.65 .75

World Trade Week.

Sun Yat-sen, Founding of Kuomintang, Cent. — A708

Design: $19, Democratic elections, factories, economic development.

**Wmk. 323**
**1994, Nov. 24 Litho.** ***Perf. 12½***
**2979** A708 $5 multicolored .50 .25
**2980** A708 $19 multicolored 1.75 .90

A709

**1994, Nov. 29**
**2981** A709 $3.50 Facing right .50 .25
*a.* Perf. 13½ vert. .80 .25
*b.* As "a," booklet pane of 6 2.00
Complete booklet, 2 #2981b + label 4.00
**2982** A709 $13 Facing left 1.50 .75
*a.* Souv. sheet, 2 ea #2981-2982 3.40 2.00

New Year 1995 (Year of the Boar).

A710

$5, Portrait. $15, Greeting farm family.

**1994, Dec. 24 Litho.** ***Perf. 12½***
**2983** A710 $5 multicolored .50 .25
**2984** A710 $15 multicolored 1.60 .75

Pres. Yen Chia-kan, 1st death anniv.

Horse's Back Roofline — A711

Swallow's Tail Roofline — A711a

Talisman (Stove & Bowl) Roofline — A711b

Cylinder-Shaped Brick Roofline — A711c

Traditional Architecture: Roof lines.

***Perf. 12½x12***
**1995, Jan. 10 Litho. Wmk. 323**
**2985** A711 $5 multicolored .40 .25
**2986** A711a $5 multicolored .40 .25
**2987** A711b $12 multicolored 1.20 .60
**2988** A711c $19 multicolored 1.85 1.00
*Nos. 2985-2988 (4)* 3.85 2.10

See Nos. 3079-3082, 3113-3116, 3187-3190, 3235-3238.

Ancient Chinese Engravings — A712

Various floral designs.

**1995, Jan. 24** ***Perf. 13½***
**Denomination in Black**
**2989** A712 $3.50 multicolored .30 .25
**2990** A712 $5 multicolored .55 .25
**2991** A712 $19 multicolored 1.60 1.00
**2992** A712 $26 multicolored 2.50 1.40
*Nos. 2989-2992 (4)* 4.95 2.90

See Nos. 3018-3021, 3044-3047, 3076-3078, 3178-3181, 3221-3226, 3254-3256, 3299-3300.

**Ancient Skills Type of 1994**

Methods of irrigation: No. 2993, Water wheel. No. 2994, Gear-driven bucket lift. $5, Pedal-powered hoist. $12, Hand-cranked hoist. $13, Using pole with counter-weight to raise bucket.

***Perf. 12x11½***
**1994, Feb. 14 Litho. Wmk. 323**
**2993** A693 $3.50 multicolored .30 .25
**2994** A693 $3.50 multicolored .30 .25
**2995** A693 $5 multicolored 3.25 .25
**2996** A693 $12 multicolored .85 .70
**2997** A693 $13 multicolored .90 .75
*Nos. 2993-2997 (5)* 5.60 2.20

Beauties on an Outing, by Lee Gong-lin — A713

a, Two riders. b, Rider on black horse, woman with child on horse. c, Three riders. d, One rider.

**Unwmk.**
**1995, Mar. 3 Photo.** ***Perf. 12***
**Granite Paper**
**2998** A713 $9 Strip of 4, #a.-d. 3.25 2.00
*e.* Souv. sheet, #2998b-2998c 1.50 1.00

No. 2998 is a continuous design.

Natl. Health Insurance Plan — A714

***Perf. 11½x12½***
**1995, Mar. 1 Litho. Wmk. 323**
**2999** A714 $12 multicolored 1.75 .80

Flowers — A715

$5, Lilium speciosum. $12, Haemanthus multiflorus. $19, Hyacinthus orientalis.

**1995, Mar. 20 Litho.** ***Perf. 12½***
**3000** A715 $5 multicolored .40 .25
**3001** A715 $12 multicolored 1.00 .60
**3002** A715 $19 multicolored 2.00 1.00
*Nos. 3000-3002 (3)* 3.40 1.85

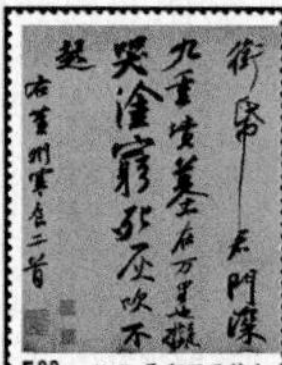
Chinese Calligraphy — A716

Cold Food Observance, poem by Su Shih, red inscriptions at: a, Lower left. b, Middle. c, Upper right. d, Right half of design.

**1995, Apr. 6** ***Perf. 13½***
**3003** Strip of 4 4.00 2.25
*a.-d.* A716 $5 any single .40 .25

Paintings by Tsou I Kuei's — A717

**1995, May 5 Photo.** ***Die Cut***
**Self-Adhesive**
**3004** A717 $5 Red peony .60 .25
**3005** A717 $5 Pink peony .60 .25
*a.* Bklt. pane, 9 ea #3004-3005 12.50

By its nature, No. 3005a is a complete booklet. The peelable backing serves as a booklet cover.

Campaign Against Illegal Drugs — A718

$15, Arm, hypodermic needle.

**Wmk. 323**
**1995, June 1 Litho.** ***Perf. 12½***
**3006** A718 $5 shown .55 .25
**3007** A718 $15 multicolored 1.55 .75

Natl. Taiwan University Hospital, Cent. — A719

Designs: $5, Medical treatment, old hospital. $19, Medical research, new hospital.

**1995, June 20**
**3008** A719 $5 multicolored .65 .25
**3009** A719 $19 multicolored 1.75 1.00

East Coast Scenes — A720

Designs: No. 3010, Green hills above Chichi Bay. No. 3011, Rocky promontory, Shihyuesan. $12, Hsiaoyehlieu. $15, Changhong Bridge.

**Wmk. 323**
**1995, July 1 Litho.** ***Perf. 12½***
**3010** A720 $5 multicolored .40 .25
**3011** A720 $5 multicolored .40 .25
**3012** A720 $12 multicolored 1.00 .65
**3013** A720 $15 multicolored 1.40 .90
*Nos. 3010-3013 (4)* 3.20 2.05

Oncorhynchus Masou Formosanus — A721

Designs: $5, Mating. $7, Female digging a spot to lay eggs. $10, Hatching of fry. $17, Fry swimming in river.

***Perf. 14x14½***
**1995, July 27 Litho. Unwmk.**
**3014** A721 $5 multicolored .40 .25
**3015** A721 $7 multicolored .60 .40
**3016** A721 $10 multicolored .75 .60
**3017** A721 $17 multicolored 1.40 1.00
*Nos. 3014-3017 (4)* 3.15 2.25

**Ancient Chinese Engraving Type**

Various pictures of birds on tree branches.

**Wmk. 323**
**1995, Aug. 18 Litho.** ***Perf. 13½***
**Denomination in Black**
**3018** A712 $2.50 multicolored .30 .25
**3019** A712 $7 multicolored .60 .35
**3020** A712 $13 multicolored 1.10 .80
**3021** A712 $28 multicolored 2.75 1.60
*Nos. 3018-3021 (4)* 4.75 3.00

See Nos. 2989-2992, 3044-3047, 3076-3078, 3178-3181, 3221-3226, 3254-3256, 3299-3300.

Marine Life — A722

No. 3022, Tubastraea aurea. No. 3023, Chromodoris elizabethina. $5, Spirobranchus gigateus. $17, Himerometra magnipinna.

**Wmk. 323**
**1995, Sept. 7 Litho.** ***Perf. 12½***
**3022** A722 $3.50 multicolored .30 .25
**3023** A722 $3.50 multicolored .30 .25
**3024** A722 $5 multicolored .50 .30
**3025** A722 $17 multicolored 1.50 .80
*Nos. 3022-3025 (4)* 2.60 1.60

Louis Pasteur (1822-95) — A723

**1995, Sept. 20**
**3026** A723 $17 multicolored 1.40 .80

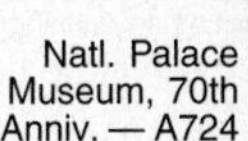

Natl. Palace Museum, 70th Anniv. — A724

Designs: No. 3027, Painting, "Strange Peaks and Myriad Trees." No. 3028, Greenish blue porcelain vase, vert. $5, Bronze X Fu-K'uei Ting vessel, vert. $26, Calligraphy of quatrain in seven-character verse, "The Fragrance of Flowers."

***Perf. 12x11½, 11½x12***

**1995, Oct. 9 Photo. Unwmk.**

| | | | | |
|---|---|---|---|---|
| **3027** | A724 | $3.50 multicolored | .30 | .25 |
| **3028** | A724 | $3.50 multicolored | .30 | .25 |
| **3029** | A724 | $5 multicolored | .50 | .25 |
| **3030** | A724 | $26 multicolored | 2.40 | 1.50 |
| | | *Nos. 3027-3030 (4)* | 3.50 | 2.25 |

A725

End of World War II, 50th Anniv.: $5, Chinese soldiers in battle. $19, Flag, outline map of Taiwan, presidential mansion.

***Perf. 11½x12***

**1995, Oct. 24 Litho. Wmk. 323**

| | | | | |
|---|---|---|---|---|
| **3031** | A725 | $5 multicolored | .60 | .25 |
| **3032** | A725 | $19 multicolored | 2.10 | .65 |
| *a.* | | Souvenir sheet, #3031-3032 | 3.25 | 2.50 |

A726

Sea Turtles: No. 3033, Chelonia mydas. No. 3034, Caretta caretta. No. 3035, Lepidochelys olivacea. No. 3036, Eretmochelys imbricata.

**Wmk. 323**

**1995, Nov. 10 Litho. *Perf. 12½***

| | | | | |
|---|---|---|---|---|
| **3033** | A726 | $5 multicolored | .75 | .25 |
| **3034** | A726 | $5 multicolored | .75 | .25 |
| **3035** | A726 | $5 multicolored | .75 | .25 |
| **3036** | A726 | $5 multicolored | .75 | .25 |
| | | *Nos. 3033-3036 (4)* | 3.00 | 1.00 |

Taiwan Agricultural Research Institute, Cent. — A727

***Perf. 12x11½***

**1995, Nov. 22 Litho. Wmk. 323**

| | | | | |
|---|---|---|---|---|
| **3037** | A727 | $5 In rice field | .70 | .25 |
| **3038** | A727 | $28 In anthurium field | 2.25 | .75 |

New Year 1996 (Year of the Rat) — A728

Designs: $3.50, $13, Different stylized rats.

**Wmk. 323**

**1995, Dec. 1 Litho. *Perf. 12½***

| | | | | |
|---|---|---|---|---|
| **3039** | A728 | $3.50 pink & multi | .45 | .25 |
| *a.* | | Perf. 13½ vert. | .75 | .25 |
| *b.* | | As "a," booklet pane of 6 | 2.10 | |
| | | Complete booklet, 2 #3039b + gutter | 4.25 | |
| **3040** | A728 | $13 olive & multi | 1.25 | .45 |
| *a.* | | Souv. sheet, 2 ea #3039-3040 | 3.00 | 1.50 |

Traditional Wedding Ceremony — A729

Designs: $5, Escorting bride. $12, Kowtowing Heaven, Earth, and ancestors. $19, Seated in bridal chamber.

**1996, Jan. 10**

| | | | | |
|---|---|---|---|---|
| **3041** | A729 | $5 multicolored | .30 | .25 |
| **3042** | A729 | $12 multicolored | 1.00 | .40 |
| **3043** | A729 | $19 multicolored | 1.75 | .60 |
| | | *Nos. 3041-3043 (3)* | 3.05 | 1.25 |

### Ancient Chinese Engraving Type

Various pictures of fruit.

**Wmk. 323**

**1996, Jan. 25 Litho. *Perf. 13½***

**Denomination in Black**

| | | | | |
|---|---|---|---|---|
| **3044** | A712 | $9 multicolored | .75 | .30 |
| **3045** | A712 | $12 multicolored | 1.00 | .50 |
| **3046** | A712 | $15 multicolored | 1.20 | .60 |
| **3047** | A712 | $17 multicolored | 1.40 | .70 |
| | | *Nos. 3044-3047 (4)* | 4.35 | 2.10 |

See Nos. 2989-2992, 3018-3021, 3076-3078, 3178-3181, 3221-3226, 3254-3256, 3299-3300.

Scenic Dwelling at Chü-Ch'ü, by Wang Meng, Yüan Dynasty — A730

Denominations: a, UL. b, UR. c, LL. d, LR.

***Perf. 12½x12***

**1996, Feb. 15 Litho. Unwmk.**

| | | | | |
|---|---|---|---|---|
| **3048** | A730 | Block of 4, #a.-d. | 2.50 | 2.25 |
| *a.-d.* | | $5 any single | .65 | .50 |

A731

Flowers: $5, Bougainvillea spectabilis. $12, Wisteria sinensis. $19, Merremia tuberosa.

**1996, Mar. 8 Unwmk. *Perf. 12½***

| | | | | |
|---|---|---|---|---|
| **3049** | A731 | $5 multicolored | .50 | .25 |
| **3050** | A731 | $12 multicolored | 1.25 | .50 |

**Wmk. 323**

| | | | | |
|---|---|---|---|---|
| **3051** | A731 | $19 multicolored | 1.75 | .75 |
| | | *Nos. 3049-3051 (3)* | 3.50 | 1.50 |

A732

Chinese Postal Service, Cent.: $5, Mailboxes. $9, Instruments of measurement. $12, Methods of mail transport. $13, Computers, plastic card.

**Wmk. 323**

**1996, Mar. 20 Litho. *Perf. 13½***

| | | | | |
|---|---|---|---|---|
| **3052** | A732 | $5 multicolored | .50 | .25 |
| **3053** | A732 | $9 multicolored | .75 | .40 |
| **3054** | A732 | $12 multicolored | .85 | .50 |
| **3055** | A732 | $13 multicolored | 1.00 | .55 |
| *a.* | | Souvenir sheet, #3052-3055 | 3.50 | 1.75 |
| | | *Nos. 3052-3055 (4)* | 3.10 | 1.70 |

Natl. Chiao Tung University, Cent. — A733

**Wmk. 323**

**1996, Apr. 8 Litho. *Perf. 12½***

| | | | | |
|---|---|---|---|---|
| **3056** | A733 | $19 multicolored | 1.90 | .75 |

Penghu Natl. Scenic Areas — A734

No. 3057, Chimei Giant Lion. No. 3058, Chipei Beach. $12, Tungpan Yu. $17, Tingkou Yu.

**1996, May 1**

| | | | | |
|---|---|---|---|---|
| **3057** | A734 | $5 multicolored | .40 | .25 |
| **3058** | A734 | $5 multicolored | .40 | .25 |
| **3059** | A734 | $12 multicolored | 1.10 | .45 |
| **3060** | A734 | $17 multicolored | 1.60 | .65 |
| | | *Nos. 3057-3060 (4)* | 3.50 | 1.60 |

Tzu-Chi Buddhist Compassionate Relief Foundation — A735

$5, Hand holding people. $19, Lotus blossom, sick person.

**Wmk. 323**

**1996, May 11 Litho. *Perf. 13***

| | | | | |
|---|---|---|---|---|
| **3061** | A735 | $5 multicolored | .40 | .25 |
| **3062** | A735 | $19 multicolored | 2.20 | .80 |

First Democratic Presidential Election — A736

New Pres., Vice Pres. and: $3.50, Natl. flag. $5, Presidential office building. $13, Development of Asia-Pacific Operations Hub project. $15, Greeting people at fair.

**1996, May 20 Wmk. 323 *Perf. 12½***

| | | | | |
|---|---|---|---|---|
| **3063** | A736 | $3.50 multicolored | .30 | .25 |
| **3064** | A736 | $5 multicolored | .45 | .25 |
| **3065** | A736 | $13 multicolored | 1.00 | .40 |
| **3066** | A736 | $15 multicolored | 1.10 | .45 |
| *a.* | | Souvenir sheet, #3063-3066 | 3.00 | 1.40 |
| | | *Nos. 3063-3066 (4)* | 2.85 | 1.35 |

South China Sea Archipelago — A737

Outline map of region, Interior Dept. monuments on: $5, Pratas Isl. $17, Itu Aba Isl.

**1996, June 5 Wmk. 323 *Perf. 12½***

| | | | | |
|---|---|---|---|---|
| **3067** | A737 | $5 multicolored | .65 | .25 |
| **3068** | A737 | $17 multicolored | 1.90 | .65 |
| *a.* | | Souvenir sheet, #3067-3068 | 3.00 | 2.00 |

Modern Olympic Games, Cent. — A738

$5, Gymnast, cyclist. $15, Early Greek athletes.

***Perf. 12½x12***

**1996, June 22 Litho. Wmk. 323**

| | | | | |
|---|---|---|---|---|
| **3069** | A738 | $5 multicolored | .50 | .25 |
| **3070** | A738 | $15 multicolored | 1.25 | .45 |

### Ancient Skills Type of 1994

Manufacturing silk: No. 3071, Feeding silkworms. No. 3072, Picking out cocoons. $7, Reeling raw silk. $10, Degumming raw silk. $13, Weaving silk.

**1996, July 5 *Perf. 12***

| | | | | |
|---|---|---|---|---|
| **3071** | A693 | $5 multicolored | .40 | .25 |
| **3072** | A693 | $5 multicolored | .40 | .25 |
| **3073** | A693 | $7 multicolored | .50 | .25 |
| **3074** | A693 | $10 multicolored | .80 | .50 |
| **3075** | A693 | $13 multicolored | 1.10 | .55 |
| | | *Nos. 3071-3075 (5)* | 3.20 | 1.80 |

### Ancient Chinese Engraving Type

**1996, Aug. 5 *Perf. 13½***

**Denomination in Black**

| | | | | |
|---|---|---|---|---|
| **3076** | A712 | $1 Bamboo | .40 | .25 |
| **3077** | A712 | $10 Orchid | .75 | .50 |
| **3078** | A712 | $20 Plum tree branch | 1.60 | .80 |
| | | *Nos. 3076-3078 (3)* | 2.75 | 1.55 |

See Nos. 2989-2992, 3018-3021, 3044-3047, 3178-3181, 3221-3226, 3254-3256, 3299-3300.

A738a A738b

A738c

Column and Beam Construction — A738d

***Perf. 12x11½***

**1996, Aug. 22 Litho. Wmk. 323**

| | | | | |
|---|---|---|---|---|
| **3079** | A738a | $5 Tou-kung (lion) | .50 | .25 |
| **3080** | A738b | $5 Chiue-ti | .50 | .25 |
| **3081** | A738c | $10 Bu-tong | .90 | .40 |
| **3082** | A738d | $19 Dye-tou | 1.60 | .75 |
| | | *Nos. 3079-3082 (4)* | 3.50 | 1.65 |

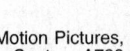

Motion Pictures, Cent. — A739

Chinese movies: No. 3083, Princess Iron Fan, first full-length animated film, 1941. No. 3084, Chin Shan Bi Xie, 1957. $5, Oyster Girl, 1964. $19, City of Sadness, 1989.

**1996, Sept. 17 Litho. *Perf. 12½x12***

| | | | | |
|---|---|---|---|---|
| **3083** | A739 | $3.50 multicolored | .30 | .25 |
| **3084** | A739 | $3.50 multicolored | .30 | .25 |
| **3085** | A739 | $5 multicolored | .50 | .25 |
| **3086** | A739 | $19 multicolored | 1.40 | .55 |
| | | *Nos. 3083-3086 (4)* | 2.50 | 1.30 |

Winning Pictures from Children's Stamp Design Contest — A740

Denomination triangle color, location: a, Red, LR. b, Red, LL. c, Green, LR. d, Green, LL. e, Pink, LL. f, Red, UR. g, Red, UL. h, Green, UR. i, Green, UL. j, Pink, UL. k, Purple, LR. l, Purple, LL. m, Tan, LR. n, Tan, LL. o, Pink, LR. p, Purple, UR. q, Purple, UL. r, Tan, UR. s, Tan, UL. t, Pink, UR.

***Perf. 12½x12***

**1996, Oct. 9 Litho. Unwmk.**

| | | | | |
|---|---|---|---|---|
| **3087** | A740 | $5 Sheet of 20, #a.-t. | 7.50 | 3.75 |

A741

Ancient Chinese paintings: $5, Autumn Scene with Wild Geese. $7, Reeds and Wild Geese. $13, Wild Geese Gathering on a Shore of Reeds. $15, Wild Geese on a Bank in Autumn.

**1996, Oct. 21 Photo. *Perf. 12***

**Granite Paper**

| | | | | |
|---|---|---|---|---|
| **3088** | A741 | $5 multicolored | .45 | .25 |
| **3089** | A741 | $7 multicolored | .55 | .25 |
| **3090** | A741 | $13 multicolored | 1.00 | .40 |

| | | | | |
|---|---|---|---|---|
| **3091** | A741 | $15 multicolored | 1.20 | .45 |
| *a.* | | Souv. sheet, #3088-3091 | 3.60 | 1.60 |
| | | *Nos. 3088-3091 (4)* | 3.20 | 1.35 |

10th Asian Intl. Philatelic Exhib., Taipei '96.

A742

Designs: $5, Computerized letters, numbers, bar coding. $26, Globe, graph line.

***Perf. 12½x12***

**1996, Nov. 1 Litho. Wmk. 323**

| | | | | |
|---|---|---|---|---|
| **3092** | A742 | $5 multicolored | .60 | .25 |
| **3093** | A742 | $26 multicolored | 2.40 | 1.10 |

Merchant's Day, 50th Anniv.

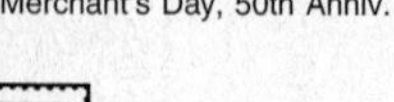

A743

Caring for the Handicapped: $5, Woman in wheelchair working at computer. $19, Handicapped child painting picture.

**Wmk. 323**

**1996, Nov. 15 Litho. *Perf. 12½***

| | | | | |
|---|---|---|---|---|
| **3094** | A743 | $5 multicolored | .65 | .25 |
| **3095** | A743 | $19 multicolored | 1.75 | .75 |

A744

**1996, Dec. 2**

| | | | | |
|---|---|---|---|---|
| **3096** | A744 | $3.50 gray & multi | .30 | .25 |
| *a.* | | Perf. 13½ vert. | .50 | .25 |
| *b.* | | As "a," booklet pane of 6 | 1.90 | |
| | | Complete booklet, 2 #3096b + gutter | 4.80 | |
| **3097** | A744 | $13 blue & multi | 2.00 | .45 |
| *a.* | | Souv. sheet, 2 ea #3096-3097 | 3.50 | 1.25 |
| *b.* | | As "a," overprinted | 3.50 | 1.25 |

New Year 1997 (Year of the Ox).

No. 3097b overprinted in red lilac in sheet margin with Chinese inscription for Kaohsiung Intl. Stamp Exhibition for Chinese Postal Service cent.

**Ancient Skills Type of 1994**

Making porcelain: No. 3098, Pounding stone, looking at bottom of bowl. No. 3099, Painting, shaping. $7, Painting. $10, Glazing. $13, Firing.

***Perf. 11½x12***

**1997, Jan. 15 Litho. Wmk. 323**

| | | | | |
|---|---|---|---|---|
| **3098** | A693 | $5 multicolored | .40 | .25 |
| **3099** | A693 | $5 multicolored | .40 | .25 |
| **3100** | A693 | $7 multicolored | .65 | .25 |
| **3101** | A693 | $10 multicolored | .80 | .30 |
| **3102** | A693 | $13 multicolored | 1.00 | .40 |
| | | *Nos. 3098-3102 (5)* | 3.25 | 1.45 |

Carp Encircled By Dragons — A745

***Perf. 13x12½***

**1997, Feb. 14 Engr. Wmk. 323**

| | | | | |
|---|---|---|---|---|
| **3103** | A745 | $50 carmine | 4.00 | 2.00 |
| **3104** | A745 | $60 dark blue | 4.75 | 2.40 |
| **3105** | A745 | $70 red orange | 5.75 | 2.75 |
| **3106** | A745 | $100 olive green | 8.00 | 4.00 |
| | | *Nos. 3103-3106 (4)* | 22.50 | 11.15 |

See Nos. 3131-3132, 3252-3253, 3369-3370, 3426, 3871, 4312.

Feb. 28, 1947 Rebellion, 50th Anniv. — A746

***Perf. 12x11½***

**1997, Feb. 28 Litho. Wmk. 323**

| | | | | |
|---|---|---|---|---|
| **3107** | A746 | $19 Memorial | 1.75 | .90 |

Woody Plants — A747

$5, Rhododendron x mucronatum. $12, Hibiscus rosa-sinensis. $19, Hydrangea macrophylla.

**Wmk. 323**

**1997, Mar. 12 Litho. *Perf. 12½***

| | | | | |
|---|---|---|---|---|
| **3108** | A747 | $5 multicolored | .50 | .25 |
| **3109** | A747 | $12 multicolored | 1.10 | .50 |
| **3110** | A747 | $19 multicolored | 1.60 | .75 |
| | | *Nos. 3108-3110 (3)* | 3.20 | 1.50 |

Water Resource Protection

A748 A749

**1997, Mar. 22 *Perf. 12½***

| | | | | |
|---|---|---|---|---|
| **3111** | A748 | $5 multicolored | .50 | .25 |
| **3112** | A749 | $19 multicolored | 1.60 | .75 |

A749a

A749b

A749c

Traditional Architecture — A749d

***Perf. 12x12½***

**1997, Apr. 9 Litho. Wmk. 323**

| | | | | |
|---|---|---|---|---|
| **3113** | A749a | $5 Door | .40 | .25 |
| **3114** | A749b | $5 Gable wall | .40 | .25 |
| **3115** | A749c | $10 Carved brick | 1.00 | .50 |
| **3116** | A749d | $19 Column dragon | 1.40 | .65 |
| | | *Nos. 3113-3116 (4)* | 3.20 | 1.65 |

Insects — A750

Designs: $5, Dorcus formosanus. $7, Phyllophorina kotoshoensis. $10, Troides magellanus. $17, Megacrania tsudai.

**1997, Apr. 25 Photo. *Perf. 11½***

**Granite Paper**

| | | | | |
|---|---|---|---|---|
| **3117** | A750 | $5 multicolored | .45 | .25 |
| **3118** | A750 | $7 multicolored | .75 | .35 |
| **3119** | A750 | $10 multicolored | 1.00 | .50 |
| **3120** | A750 | $17 multicolored | 1.55 | .75 |
| | | *Nos. 3117-3120 (4)* | 3.75 | 1.85 |

Minerals — A751

**Wmk. 323**

**1997, May 8 Litho. *Perf. 13***

| | | | | |
|---|---|---|---|---|
| **3121** | A751 | $5 Aragonite | .40 | .25 |
| **3122** | A751 | $5 Alunite | .40 | .25 |
| **3123** | A751 | $12 Enargite | 1.00 | .50 |
| **3124** | A751 | $19 Hokutolite | 1.40 | .65 |
| | | *Nos. 3121-3124 (4)* | 3.20 | 1.65 |

Nanyashan Outlook — A752

No. 3126, Pitou coastline. No. 3127, Stone pillars, Nanya. No. 1328, Tsaoling trail.

**1997, May 31 *Perf. 12½***

| | | | | |
|---|---|---|---|---|
| **3125** | A752 | $5 shown | .50 | .25 |
| **3126** | A752 | $5 multicolored | .50 | .25 |
| **3127** | A752 | $12 multicolored | 1.00 | .50 |
| **3128** | A752 | $19 multicolored | 1.00 | .50 |
| | | *Nos. 3125-3128 (4)* | 3.00 | 1.50 |

A753

Around-The-Island Railway System: $5, Cliffs at Chingshuei, Northern Loop Line. $28, Southbound train passing through tunnel, Central Mountain area.

**Wmk. 323**

**1997, June 12 Litho. *Perf. 13½***

| | | | | |
|---|---|---|---|---|
| **3129** | A753 | $5 multicolored | .55 | .25 |
| **3130** | A753 | $28 multicolored | 1.90 | .75 |

**Carp Type**

**1997, July 3 Engr. *Perf. 13***

| | | | | |
|---|---|---|---|---|
| **3131** | A745 | $300 vio & dark blue | 24.00 | 12.00 |
| **3132** | A745 | $500 dk red & mag | 36.00 | 20.00 |

Electronic Industry's Use of Integrated Circuits — A754

$5, Integrated circuit for computer & telecommunications industry. $26, Wafer linked to portable computer, cellular phone, electronic synthesizer.

**1997, July 16 Litho. *Perf. 12½x12***

| | | | | |
|---|---|---|---|---|
| **3133** | A754 | $5 multicolored | .50 | .25 |
| **3134** | A754 | $26 multicolored | 2.25 | 1.00 |

Chinese Martial Arts — A755

Various stances in martial arts.

**Wmk. 323**

**1997, Aug. 8 Litho. *Perf. 13***

| | | | | |
|---|---|---|---|---|
| **3135** | A755 | $5 shown | .40 | .25 |
| **3136** | A755 | $5 multi, vert. | .40 | .25 |
| **3137** | A755 | $9 multicolored | .65 | .30 |
| **3138** | A755 | $19 multi, vert. | 1.40 | .65 |
| | | *Nos. 3135-3138 (4)* | 2.85 | 1.45 |

Chinese Classical (Yuan) Opera — A756

Designs: No. 3139, Chang Shen playing musical instrument, Tsuei Ying-ying listening outside, from "Hsi Hsiang Chi." No. 3140, Kuan Gung standing on ferry and holding large knife, enemies in distance, from "Dan Daw Huei." $12, Abduction of Wang Chao-juin on horseback, from "Han Guong Chiou." $15, Emperor Tang Ming Huang envisioning concubine, Makueibo, from "Wu Tong Yu."

**1997, Aug. 22**

| | | | | |
|---|---|---|---|---|
| **3139** | A756 | $5 multicolored | .40 | .25 |
| **3140** | A756 | $5 multicolored | .40 | .25 |
| **3141** | A756 | $12 multicolored | .80 | .40 |
| **3142** | A756 | $15 multicolored | 1.20 | .60 |
| | | *Nos. 3139-3142 (4)* | 2.80 | 1.50 |

Sports — A757

**1997, Sept. 9 *Perf. 12½***

| | | | | |
|---|---|---|---|---|
| **3143** | A757 | $5 Badminton | .40 | .25 |
| **3144** | A757 | $12 Bowling | 1.00 | .50 |
| **3145** | A757 | $19 Tennis | 1.25 | .75 |
| | | *Nos. 3143-3145 (3)* | 2.65 | 1.50 |

Ming Dynasty Novel "Journey to the West" — A758

Episodes from novel: No. 3146, "Palm of Buddha," man making inscription while holding pole. No. 3147, "The pilgrimage of T'ang Monk," characters traveling west, one on horse. $5, "The Flaming Mountain," people fighting, fire in background. $20, "The Cobweb Cave," man using pole to fight, spider in cobweb.

**1997, Sept. 24 Photo. *Perf. 11½x12***

**Granite Paper**

| | | | | |
|---|---|---|---|---|
| **3146** | A758 | $3.50 multicolored | .40 | .25 |
| **3147** | A758 | $3.50 multicolored | .40 | .25 |
| **3148** | A758 | $5 multicolored | .50 | .35 |
| **3149** | A758 | $20 multicolored | 1.30 | .65 |
| | | *Nos. 3146-3149 (4)* | 2.60 | 1.50 |

Opening of Second Northern Freeway — A759

Designs: $5, Bitan Bridge crossing, Shindian River. $19, Hsinchu interchange.

**Wmk. 323**

**1997, Aug. 26 Litho. *Perf. 13***

| | | | | |
|---|---|---|---|---|
| **3150** | A759 | $5 multicolored | .50 | .25 |
| **3151** | A759 | $19 multicolored | 1.40 | .65 |

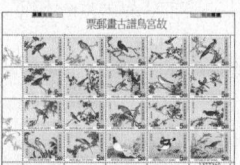

Illustrations from Ching Dynasty Bird Manual — A760

Designs: a, Purple-naped Lory, parrot facing right. b, Common Green Magpie, blue bird, facing left, tail pointed to LR. c, Blue-crowned Hanging Parrot, facing left, looking right. d, Daurian Redstart, two songbirds, facing oposite directions. e, Red-billed Blue Magpie, facing right, looking left. f, Plain Laughing-thrush, facing left, tail pointed to UR. g, Przevalski's Finch, facing left, looking LR. h, Common Rosefinch, viewing belly. I, Mongolian Finch, gray bird, facing left. j, Long-tailed Minivet, two red and black birds. k, Black-naped Oriole, yellow bird, facing left. l, Yellow-throated Bunting, two birds on a thorn bush facing left. m, Bohemian Waxwing, crested bird. n, Mongolian Finch, two brown birds facing left. o, Crested Myna, large brown bird facing left. p, Java Sparrow, bird with white cheek patch. q, Long-tailed Parakeet, facing left. r, Black-winged Starling, black and white bird on ground. s, Cloven-feather Dove, two birds on ground. t, Eurasian Wryneck, brown bird on ground.

**1997, Oct. 9 Photo. *Perf. 11½***
**Granite Paper**

**3152** A760 $5 Sheet of 20, #a.-t. 8.00 5.00

Compare with Nos. 3268-3269.

New Year 1998 (Year of the Tiger) — A761

**Wmk. 323**
**1997, Dec. 1 Litho. *Perf. 12½***

**3153** A761 $3.50 pink & multi .30 .25
*a.* Perf. 14 vert. .30 .25
*b.* As "a," booklet pane of 6 1.90
Complete booklet, 2 #3153b + gutter 3.80
**3154** A761 $13 yellow & multi 1.00 .45
*a.* Souv. sheet, 2 ea #3153-3154 2.60 1.10

Pres. Chiang Ching-kuo (1910-88) — A762

**1998, Jan. 13 Engr. *Perf. 13½***
**3155** A762 $5 Portrait, vert. .75 .30
***Perf. 11½***
**3156** A762 $19 shown 1.60 .90

A763

Common Chinese Expressions of Good Fortune, designs: No. 3157, "Happy Occasion of Abundance," fish, vase with pictures of sun and sea. No. 3158, "Harmonious Union as One," flower with two blooms. No. 3159, "Honor and Wealth," flowers growing in pot, vase of flowers. No. 3160, "All is Lucky," bowl of fruit, vase with branch of fruit blossoms.

***Perf. 11½x12***
**1998, Jan. 23 Litho. Wmk. 323**
**Background Color**

**3157** A763 $5 pink .40 .25
**3158** A763 $5 beige .40 .25
*a.* Pair, 3157-3158 .80 .25
**3159** A763 $12 light yellow .75 .30
**3160** A763 $12 tan .75 .30
*a.* Pair, #3159-3160 1.50 .60
*Nos. 3157-3160 (4)* 2.30 1.10

A764

Herbaceous Flowers: $5, Gaillardia pulchella. $12, Kalanchoe blossfeldiana. $19, Portulaca oleracea.

**Wmk. 323**
**1998, Mar. 1 Litho. *Perf. 12½***

**3161** A764 $5 multicolored .35 .25
**3162** A764 $12 multicolored .80 .40
**3163** A764 $19 multicolored 1.75 .65
*Nos. 3161-3163 (3)* 2.90 1.30

Emperor Shih-tzu, on Hunting Expedition, by Liu Kuan-tao — A765

$5, Horseman drawing bow. $19, Emperor Shih-tzu leading hunting party on horseback.

**1998, Mar. 20 Photo. *Perf. 12***
**Granite Paper**

**3164** A765 $5 multicolored .75 .25

**Size: 64x40mm**

**3165** A765 $19 multicolored 1.50 .50

**Souvenir Sheet**

**3165A** A765 Sheet of 2, b.-c. 2.50 1.00
*b.* A765 $5 multi 1.20 .25
*c.* A765 $19 multi 1.20 .75

No. 3165A is a continuous design.

Children's Folk Rhymes — A766

No. 3166, "A Frog Has One Mouth." No. 3167, "A Little Mouse Climbs an Oil Lamp." $12, "Fireflies." $19, "Egrets."

**Wmk. 323**
**1998, Apr. 4 Litho. *Perf. 11½***

**3166** A766 $5 multicolored .55 .25
**3167** A766 $5 multicolored .55 .25
**3168** A766 $12 multicolored .80 .50
**3169** A766 $19 multicolored 1.85 .65
*Nos. 3166-3169 (4)* 3.75 1.65

Copyright Law in Taiwan, 70th Anniv. — A767

**1998, Apr. 30**
**3170** A767 $19 multicolored 1.40 .65

A768

Portraits of Mythological Character, Chung K'uei: $5, Making ghosts work for him, from Kung Kai's "Chung K'uei Moving," Song Dynasty. $20, Dancing beside small ghost, from "An Auspicious Occasion," Ming Dynasty.

**1998, May 15 Photo. *Perf. 11½***
**Granite Paper**

**3171** A768 $5 multicolored .85 .25
**3172** A768 $20 multicolored 1.50 .75

A769

**Wmk. 323**
**1998, May 25 Litho. *Perf. 11½***
**3173** A769 $15 multicolored 1.25 .60

Intl. Law Assoc., 125th anniv.

**Ancient Skills Type of 1994**

Ships and methods of transport, horiz.: $5, Grain barge. $7, Six-oared boat. $10, One-wheeled carriage. $13, Southern Chinese one-man push cart.

**1998, June 10 *Perf. 12x11½***

**3174** A693 $5 multicolored .45 .25
**3175** A693 $7 multicolored .55 .25
**3176** A693 $10 multicolored .75 .30
**3177** A693 $13 multicolored .90 .40
*Nos. 3174-3177 (4)* 2.65 1.20

**Ancient Chinese Engravings Type of 1995 Redrawn with Chinese Inscription Reading Left to Right**

Various floral designs. Denominations do not include two zeros.

**Wmk. 323**
**1998, July 8 Litho. *Perf. 13½***
**Denomination in Rose**

**3178** A712 $7 like #2989 .45 .25
**3179** A712 $19 like #2990 1.25 .60
**3180** A712 $20 like #2991 1.40 .70
**3181** A712 $26 like #2992 1.75 .85
*Nos. 3178-3181 (4)* 4.85 2.40

See Nos. 2989-2992, 3018-3021, 3044-3047, 3076-3078, 3221-3226, 3254-3256, 3299-3300.

Novel, "Red Chamber Dream," by Tsao Hsueh-chin — A770

Scenes from love story: No. 3182, Chia Pao-yu visits the garden (with group of women). No. 3183, Lin Tai-yu buries flowers (with hoe). $5, Hsueh Pao-chai plays with butterflies. $20, Shih Hsiang-yun in a drunken sleep (on bench).

**1998, July 16 *Perf. 11x11½***

**3182** A770 $3.50 multicolored .30 .25
**3183** A770 $3.50 multicolored .30 .25
**3184** A770 $5 multicolored .40 .25
**3185** A770 $20 multicolored 1.60 1.00
*Nos. 3182-3185 (4)* 2.60 1.75

20th Asia Pacific Jamboree, 8th Taiwan Jamboree — A771

**1998, Aug. 5 Litho. *Perf. 11***

**3186** A771 $5 Emblem .30 .25
**3186A** A771 $5 Tents .30 .25
*b.* Pair, #3186-3186A 1.00 .50

**Traditional Architecture Type of 1995**

Terraces set on raised platforms: No. 3187, Spirit way (carved stone ramp between two staircases). No. 3188, Octagonal base of a column. $10, Carved cornerstone. $19, Carved stone drainage spout.

***Perf. 11½x12***
**1998, Aug. 26 Litho. Wmk. 323**

**3187** A711 $5 multi, vert. .50 .25
**3188** A711 $5 multi, vert. .50 .25
**3189** A711 $10 multi, vert. .75 .30
**3190** A711 $19 multi, vert. 1.25 .55
*Nos. 3187-3190 (4)* 3.00 1.35

Sports Stamps A772

Table tennis: No. 3191, Player awaiting serve. No. 3192, Player serving.
Rugby: No. 3193, Two players. No. 3194, Three players.

**Wmk. 323**
**1998, Sept. 9 Litho. *Perf. 11½***
**Denomination Color**

**3191** $5 green .40 .25
**3192** $5 red .40 .25
*a.* A772 Pair, #3191-3192 .80 .30
**3193** $7 red .50 .25
**3194** $7 blue .50 .25
*a.* A772 Pair, #3193-3194 1.00 .40
*Nos. 3191-3194 (4)* 1.80 1.00

Chinese Fables — A773

Designs: No. 3195, "A Frog in a Well." No. 3196, "The Fox Borrows the Tiger's Ferocity." $12, "Adding Legs to a Drawing of a Snake." $19, "The Snipe and the Clam are at a Deadlock."

**Wmk. 323**
**1998, Sept. 25 Litho. *Perf. 11½***

**3195** A773 $5 multicolored .40 .25
**3196** A773 $5 multicolored .40 .25
**3197** A773 $12 multicolored .80 .40
**3198** A773 $19 multicolored 1.20 .55
*Nos. 3195-3198 (4)* 2.80 1.45

Kinmen National Park — A774

No. 3199, Taiwushan mountain area. No. 3200, Kunningtou Cliff, beach. $12, Teyueh Tower, Huang Hui-huang's house, Shuitou village. $19, Putou Beach, Liehyu Coast.

**1998, Oct. 16**

**3199** A774 $5 multicolored .40 .25
**3200** A774 $5 multicolored .40 .25
**3201** A774 $12 multicolored .90 .40
**3202** A774 $19 multicolored 1.40 .55
*Nos. 3199-3202 (4)* 3.10 1.45

Birds A775

Spizaetus nipalensis: No. 3203, On tree branch. No. 3204, In flight.
Spilornis cheela: No. 3205, On tree branch. No. 3206, In flight.
Ictinaetus malayensis: No. 3207, On tree branch. No. 3208, In flight.
Milvus migrans: No. 3209, Perched on rock. No. 3210, In flight.

**1998, Oct. 30 Litho. *Perf. 11½***

**3203** $5 multicolored .35 .25
**3204** $5 multicolored .35 .25
*a.* A775 Pair, #3203-3204 .70 .25
**3205** $5 multicolored .35 .25
**3206** $5 multicolored .35 .25
*a.* A775 Pair, #3205-3206 .70 .25
**3207** $10 multicolored .65 .25
**3208** $10 multicolored .65 .25
*a.* A775 Pair, #3207-3208 1.30 .50
**3209** $10 multicolored .65 .25
**3210** $10 multicolored .65 .25
*a.* A775 Pair, #3209-3210 1.30 .50
*Nos. 3203-3210 (8)* 4.00 2.00

Ancient Jade Carvings — A776

No. 3211, 2 men mining jade on a mountain. No. 3212, Mountain with 2 pavilions, stream. $7, Figures washing an elephant. $26, Mountain, trees, men.

***Perf. 11½x12, 12x11½***
**1998, Nov. 13 Photo.**
**Granite Paper**

**3211** A776 $5 multi .35 .25
**3212** A776 $5 multi, vert. .35 .25
**3213** A776 $7 multi .50 .25
**3214** A776 $26 multi, vert. 1.60 .80
*a.* Souvenir sheet, #3211-3214 3.50 1.60

New Year 1999 (Year of the Rabbit)
A777 A778

**Wmk. 323**
**1998, Dec. 2 Litho. *Perf. 12½***

**3215** A777 $3.50 multicolored .35 .25
*a.* Perf. 14 vert. .50 .25
*b.* As "a," booklet pane of 6 2.50
Complete bklt., 2 #3215b + gutter 5.00

**3216** A778 $13 multicolored 1.25 .35
*a.* Souv. sheet, 2 ea #3215-3216 3.25 2.00
*b.* As "a," ovptd. in margin, perf. 12½x11¾ 3.25 2.00

No. 3216b was issued 1/30/99 and is inscribed in sheet margin, "ALLIANCE '99 INT'L. FAIR OF PRODUCTS & TRAVEL / Jan. 30-Feb. 1, 1999" and four lines of Chinese text.

Common Expressions of Good Fortune — A779

Expressions, designs: No. 3217, "To have prosperous descendants," gourd on a vine. No. 3218, "A good marriage that soon brings sons," pair of Mandarin ducks, lotus flowers, seeds. No. 3219, "Prosperity from start to finish," egret, flowers. No. 3220, "Reunion and abundance," fish surrounded by flowers.

***Perf. 11½x12***

**1999, Jan. 6 Litho. Wmk. 323**

**3217** A779 $5 multicolored .55 .25
**3218** A779 $5 multicolored .55 .25
**3219** A779 $12 multicolored 1.10 .40
**3220** A779 $12 multicolored 1.10 .40
*Nos. 3217-3220 (4)* 3.30 1.30

### Ancient Chinese Engravings Type of 1995 Redrawn with Chinese Inscription Reading Left to Right; No Zeros

Various pictures of birds on tree branches, bamboo and orchid.

**1999, Jan. 20** ***Perf. 13½***

**Denomination in Red**

**3221** A712 $1 like #3018 .30 .25
**3222** A712 $3.50 like #3019 .30 .25
**3223** A712 $5 like #3020 .35 .25
**3224** A712 $10 like #3021 .60 .30
**3225** A712 $12 like #3076 .80 .35
**3226** A712 $28 like #3077 1.90 .90
*Nos. 3221-3226 (6)* 4.25 2.30

See Nos. 2989-2992, 3018-3021, 3044-3047, 3076-3078, 3178-3181, 3254-3256, 3299-3300.

Indoor Potted Plants — A781

$5, Sinningia speciosa. $12, Saintpaulia x hybrida. $19, Anthurium scherzerianum.

***Perf. 12½***

**1999, Feb. 10 Litho. Unwmk.**

**3228** A781 $5 multicolored .50 .25
**3229** A781 $12 multicolored 1.10 .35
**3230** A781 $19 multicolored 1.90 .65
*Nos. 3228-3230 (3)* 3.50 1.25

Ancient Chinese Painting, "Joy in Peacetime" A782

No. 3231, Woman holding child, boy with small elephant. No. 3232, Boy carrying lantern, crane on leash, people under tree. $7, Family, children playing with toy animals on wheels. $26, Women in front of steps, children playing with toys, boy on edge of balcony.

**1999, Mar. 2 Photo.** ***Perf. 12***

**Granite Paper**

**3231** A782 $5 multicolored .50 .25
**3232** A782 $5 multicolored .50 .25
**3233** A782 $7 multicolored .65 .25
**3234** A782 $26 multicolored 2.00 .65
*a.* Souvenir sheet, #3231-3234 4.50 1.75
*Nos. 3231-3234 (4)* 3.65 1.40

A782a

A782b

A782c

Traditional Architecture — A782d

Decorative features: No. 3235, Hanging cylinder with carving of woman and deer. No. 3236, Taishi screen. $10, Xuanyu (decorative element on gable). $19, Wood carving.

**1999, Mar. 20 Litho. Wmk. 323**

**3235** A782a $5 multicolored .45 .25
**3236** A782b $5 multicolored .45 .25
**3237** A782c $10 multicolored .90 .30
**3238** A782d $19 multicolored 1.75 .50
*Nos. 3235-3238 (4)* 3.55 1.30

Children's Folk Rhymes — A783

Titles: No. 3239, "Baby Sleep." No. 3240, "Be Brave." $12, "Rock, Rock, Rock." $19, "Buggie Flies."

***Perf. 11½x11***

**1999, Apr. 2 Litho. Unwmk.**

**3239** A783 $5 multicolored .55 .25
**3240** A783 $5 multicolored .55 .25
**3241** A783 $12 multicolored 1.00 .30
**3242** A783 $19 multicolored 1.60 .45
*Nos. 3239-3242 (4)* 3.70 1.25

Taiwan's Aboriginal Culture — A784

Celebrations wearing traditional costumes: a, Dancing in row, mountain in background, Atayal Ancestor Festival. b, People wearing hip bells, Saisiat Festival of the Dwarfs. c, Standing arm in arm in circle, Bunun eight-part contrapuntal vocals. d, Row of people standing inside building, Tsou Victory Festival. e, Group outside before large display board, Rukai Harvest Festival. f, Holding bamboo poles in air, Paiwan "Maleveq" Bamboo Festival. g, Men walking while holding millet leaves in air, Puyuma Harvest Ceremony. h, Women dancing in row, tree in background, Ami Harvest Ceremony. i, Holding boat in air, Yami Boat Ceremony.

**Block of 9**

**1999, Apr. 22** ***Perf. 13***

**3243** A784 $5 #a.-i. + label 4.75 4.50

No. 3243 was issued in sheets of 2 blocks + 2 labels. The labels contain the upper and lower halves of Taiwan. The lower block of 9 is in reverse order.

Intl. Council of Nurses, Cent. — A785

**1999, May 12 Litho.** ***Perf. 11½***

**3244** A785 $5 shown .50 .25
**3245** A785 $17 Nurse, world map 1.40 .50

Chinese Classical Opera — A786

Legends of the Ming Dynasty: No. 3246, Fan Li watching Hsi-shih wash yarn, "Wuan Sha Chi.". No. 3247, Tsai Pochieh, Niu looking at moon, Chao Waniang with pipa (stringed instrument) on her back, "The Story of a Pipa." $12, Hung Funu surprising Li Ching, "The Story of Hung Fu." $15, Jueilan setting up incense table, "Paiyueh Pavilion."

**1999, May 27** ***Perf. 13***

**3246** A786 $5 multicolored .40 .25
**3247** A786 $5 multicolored .50 .25
**3248** A786 $12 multicolored 1.10 .30
**3249** A786 $15 multicolored 1.30 .35
*a.* Souvenir sheet, #3246-3249 3.50 1.40
*b.* As "a," imperf., with added inscription 3.50 1.40
*Nos. 3246-3249 (4)* 3.30 1.15

No. 3249b was issued 7/23 and is inscribed in sheet margin with exhibition emblem, two lines of Chinese text and "TAIPEI INTERNATIONAL STAMP EXHIBITION 1999 (INVITATIONAL)."

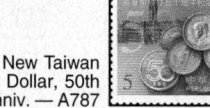

New Taiwan Dollar, 50th Anniv. — A787

**1999, June 15** ***Perf. 11½***

**3250** A787 $5 Coins .40 .25
**3251** A787 $25 Currency 1.60 .60

### Carp Type of 1997 Redrawn With Denominations at Right

**1999, July 1 Engr.** ***Perf. 13½x12½***

**3252** A745 $50 green 3.25 2.40
**3253** A745 $100 brown 7.25 3.25

### Ancient Chinese Engravings Type of 1995 Redrawn with Chinese Inscription Reading Left to Right

***Perf. 13½***

**1999, July 15 Litho. Unwmk.**

**Denomination in Red**

**3254** A712 50c like #3044 .25 .25
**3255** A712 $6 like #3045 .60 .25
**3256** A712 $25 like #3046 2.10 .75
*Nos. 3254-3256 (3)* 2.95 1.25

See Nos. 2989-2992, 3018-3021, 3044-3047, 3076-3078, 3178-3181, 3221-3226, 3299-3300.

Father's Day — A788

Designs: $5, Children with large present, silhouette of their father. $25, Father teaching son how to ride bicycle, girl.

**1999, Aug. 8** ***Perf. 11½***

**3257** A788 $5 multicolored .50 .25
**3258** A788 $25 multicolored 2.00 1.00

Chinese Gourmet Food — A789

Dish, region: a, Peony lobster, Taiwan. b, "Buddha Jumps the Wall" steamed seafood (with blue & white teapot, bowl), Fukien. c, Hors d'oeuvres shaped as star, Canton. d, "Dongpo Pork" (on yellow plate, bowl), Kiangsu and Chekiang. e, "Stewed Fish Jaws" (surrounded by strawberries, pineapple), Shanghai. f, "Beggar's Chicken" (with napkin), Hunan. g, "Carp Jumping over Dragon's Gate," Szechwan. h, "Peking Duck" (in footed dish), Beijing.

***Perf. 11½x11¼***

**1999, Aug 20 Litho. Unwmk.**

**3259** A789 $5 Block of 8, #a.-h. 3.25 1.60

Outdoor Activities — A790

**1999, Sept. 9** ***Perf. 11¼x11½***

**3260** A790 $5 Diving .40 .25
**3261** A790 $6 Rafting .45 .35
**3262** A790 $10 Surfing .90 .40
**3263** A790 $25 Windsurfing 2.25 .40
*Nos. 3260-3263 (4)* 4.00 1.40

Taiwanese Opera — A791

$5, Stage, audience. $6, Dressing room. $10, Actress, tents. $25, Actress as clown.

**1999, Oct. 15 Litho.** ***Perf. 11½x11¼***

**3264** A791 $5 multicolored .35 .25
**3265** A791 $6 multicolored .40 .35
**3266** A791 $10 multicolored .75 .40
**3267** A791 $25 multicolored 1.90 .65
*Nos. 3264-3267 (4)* 3.40 1.65

Illustrations from Ching Dynasty Bird Manual — A792

No. 3268, Yellow-headed parrot. No. 3269, Blue-winged parrotlet (4 characters at LL). $12, African gray parrot (5 characters at UL). $25, King parrot (5 characters at UL).

**1999, Nov. 11 Litho.** ***Perf. 11½***

**3268** A792 $5 multicolored .75 .30
**3269** A792 $5 multicolored .75 .30
**3270** A792 $12 multicolored 1.50 .50
**3271** A792 $25 multicolored 3.25 1.10
*Nos. 3268-3271 (4)* 6.25 2.20

Compare with No. 3152.

See Nos. 3316-3319, 3379-3381, 3509-3512.

New Year 2000 (Year of the Dragon)
A793 A794

**1999, Dec. 1 Litho.** ***Perf. 12½***

**3272** A793 $3.50 multicolored .30 .25
*a.* Perf. 13¼ vert. .30 .25
*b.* As "a," booklet pane of 6 1.60
Complete booklet, 2 #3272b + gutter 3.50
**3273** A794 $13 multicolored 1.00 .40
*a.* Souv. sheet, 2 ea #3272-3273 2.50 1.50

Millennium A795

No. 3274, ROCSAT-1. No. 3275, Deer. $12, Train. $15, Dove, St. Peter's Basilica.

**1999, Dec. 31 Litho.** ***Perf. 11½***

**3274** A795 $5 multicolored .40 .25
**3275** A795 $5 multicolored .40 .25
**3276** A795 $12 multicolored .90 .40
**3277** A795 $15 multicolored 1.10 .55
*a.* Souvenir sheet of 4, #3274-3277, perf. 12 2.75 1.50
*b.* Souvenir sheet of 4, #3274-3277, imperf. 3.00 1.60
*Nos. 3274-3277 (4)* 2.80 1.45

Taipei 2000 Stamp Exhibition (No. 3277b). No. 3277b has simulated perforations.

Calligraphy Tools — A796

Designs: No. 3278, "Colored Cloud Dragon" writing brushes of Ming Emperor Chia-Ching. No. 3279, "Imperial Dragon Fragrance" ink stick of Ming Emperor Lung-Ching, vert. $7, "Clear Heart House" calligraphic work by Tsai Hsiang, Sung Dynasty, vert. $26, Celadon toad inkstone, Sung Dynasty.

**2000, Jan. 12 Photo. *Perf. 11¾***

**Granite Paper**

**3278** A796 $5 multicolored .50 .30
**3279** A796 $5 multicolored .60 .30
**3280** A796 $7 multicolored .70 .40
**3281** A796 $26 multicolored 2.75 1.00
*Nos. 3278-3281 (4)* 4.55 2.00

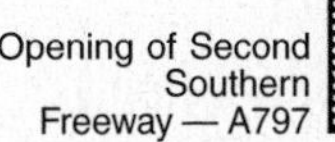

Opening of Second Southern Freeway — A797

Designs: $5, $25, Kaoping River bridge. $12, Interchange.

**2000, Feb. 2 Litho. *Perf. 13x13¼***

**3282** A797 $5 multi .50 .25
**3283** A797 $12 multi .95 .40

**Souvenir Sheet**

***Perf. 12***

**3284** A797 $25 multi 2.00 1.00

No. 3284 contains one 80x30mm stamp.

Seasons — A798

Spring — No. 3285: a, Buds on tree. b, Farmer plowing. c, Cranes. d, Farmers planting. e, Basket of offerings to dead ancestors. f, Farmer's clothing.

Summer — No. 3286: a, Rice seedlings. b, Water wheel. c, Ripened rice. d, Cicada on tree. e, Palm leaf fan. f, Watermelons.

Autumn — No. 3287: a, Farmers in field. b, Granary. c, Dew on grass. d, Reddened maple leaves. e, Leafless tree. f, Hoarfrost on leaves.

Winter — No. 3288: a, Jar on table. b, Snow-covered pine trees. c, Snow-covered mountains. d, Bowl of rice balls. e, Snow-covered plum blossoms. f, House and village.

**2000, Feb. 3 *Perf. 11¾***

**3285** Strip of 6 4.50 3.25
***a.-f.*** A798 $5 multicolored .60 .25
**3286** Strip of 6 4.50 3.25
***a.-f.*** A798 $5 multicolored .60 .25
**3287** Strip of 6 4.50 3.25
***a.-f.*** A798 $5 multicolored .60 .25
**3288** Strip of 6 4.50 3.25
***a.-f.*** A798 $5 multicolored .60 .25
*Nos. 3285-3288 (4)* 18.00 13.00

Issued: No. 3285, 2/3; No. 3286, 5/5; No. 3287, 8/4; No. 3288, 11/3.

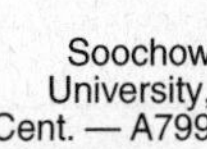

Soochow University, Cent. — A799

Designs: $5 School gate. $25, Justice statue at Law School.

**2000, Mar. 16 *Perf. 13x13¼***

**3289** A799 $5 multi .40 .25
**3290** A799 $25 multi 1.90 1.00

Novel "The Romance of the Three Kingdoms" — A800

No. 3291, Gathering of Liu Bei, Guan Yu and Chang Fei. No. 3292, Guan Yu reading. $5, Three visits to the thatched cottage. $20, Filling boats with straw for making arrows.

**2000, Apr. 12 Litho. *Perf. 11½***

**3291** A800 $3.50 multi .50 .25
**3292** A800 $3.50 multi .50 .25
**3293** A800 $5 multi .65 .35
**3294** A800 $20 multi 1.40 .55
***a.*** Souv. sheet, #3291-3294, perf. 12 3.00 2.60
*Nos. 3291-3294 (4)* 3.05 1.40

Inauguration of New President and Vice-president — A801

a, Pres. Chen Shui-bian, Vice-pres. Lu Hsiu-lien. b, Presidential Office Building.

**2000, May 20 Litho. *Perf. 11¾***

**3295** A801 $5 Pair, #a-b .90 .30
***c.*** Souvenir sheet, 2 #3295 2.25 1.00

Tropic of Cancer Monuments — A802

**2000, June 21 *Perf. 13***

**3296** A802 $5 Hsialiao .40 .25
**3297** A802 $12 Wuho 1.25 .50
**3298** A802 $25 Chingpu 2.25 .90
*Nos. 3296-3298 (3)* 3.90 1.65

**Ancient Chinese Engravings Type of 1995 Redrawn with Chinese Inscription Reading Left to Right**

**2000, July 5 Litho. *Perf. 13½***

**Denomination in Red**

**3299** A712 $32 like #3046 2.25 1.40
**3300** A712 $34 like #3078 2.60 1.40

See Nos. 2989-2992, 3018-3021, 3044-3047, 3076-3078, 3178-3181, 3221-3226, 3254-3256.

Sacred Trees — A803

Designs: $5, Taiwan Giant, Miaoli County. $39, Sleeping Moon, Chiayi County.

**2000, July 20 Litho. *Perf. 11¼x11½***

**3301** A803 $5 multi .30 .25
**3302** A803 $39 multi 2.60 1.25

**No. 2499 Surcharged in Red**

**2000, Aug. 24 Litho. *Perf. 13½***

**3303** A535a $3.50 on $7.50 multi .60 .25

Poisonous Plants — A804

Designs: No. 3304, $5, Lycoris radiata. No. 3305, $5, Cerbera manghas. $12, Abrus precatorius. $20, Nerium indicum.

**2000, Sept. 8 Litho. *Perf. 13***

**3304-3307** A804 Set of 4 3.50 1.60

Sept. 21, 1999 Earthquake, 1st Anniv. — A805

Designs: $5, Map, seismograph reading. $12, Rescue workers. $25, Earthquake preparedness.

**2000, Sept. 21 *Perf. 11¼x11½***

**3308-3310** A805 Set of 3 3.50 1.60

Dragonflies A806

Designs: Nos. 3311, 3315a, $5, Lamelligomphus formosanus. Nos. 3312, 3315b, $5, Anotogaster sieboldii, vert. Nos. 3313, 3315c, $12, Trithemis festiva, vert. Nos. 3314, 3315d, $12, Neurothemis ramburii.

**2000, Oct. 11 *Perf. 13***

**3311-3314** A806 Set of 4 2.75 1.25

**Souvenir Sheet**

**Stamps Without White Margins**

***Perf. 11¾***

**3315** A806 Sheet of 4, #a-d 3.00 1.25

**Bird Manual Type of 1999**

No. 3316, $5, Corn bunting (2 characters at UR). No. 3317, $5, Brambling (3 characters at UL). $12, Bali mynah (3 characters at LR). $25, Indian grackle (2 characters at LR).

**2000, Oct. 26 *Perf. 11½***

**3316-3319** A792 Set of 4 5.50 2.50

Compare No. 3317 with No. 3378.

Tamkang University, 50th Anniv. — A807

$5, Palace Lamp Boulevard, classroom buildings. $25, Maritime Museum, Scroll Plaza.

**2000, Nov. 8 *Perf. 13***

**3320-3321** A807 Set of 2 2.40 1.25

A808

New Year 2001 (Year of the Snake) — A809

**2000, Dec. 1 *Perf. 12½***

**3322** A808 $3.50 multi .80 .25
***a.*** Perf. 13¼ vert. .80 .25
***b.*** As "a," booklet pane of 6 2.40
Booklet, 2 #3322b + gutter 4.80
**3323** A809 $13 multi 1.00 .35
***a.*** Souv. sheet, 2 ea #3322-3323 2.75 1.25
***b.*** As "a," with added marginal inscription in red 2.75 1.25

Added marginal inscription of No. 3323b reads in Chinese "Turn-of-the-Century Intl. Stamp Exhibition, Kaohsiung / Dec. 25, 2000-Jan. 3, 2001" in red

Issued: No. 3323b, 12/25/00.

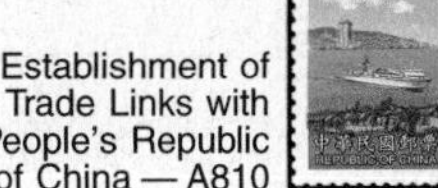

Establishment of Trade Links with People's Republic of China — A810

Ships in Taiwan Strait and: $9, Building. $25, Obelisk.

**2001, Jan. 1 Litho. *Perf. 11½***

**3324-3325** A810 Set of 2 2.50 2.00

A811

Common Chinese expressions of good fortune: No. 3326, $5, "Marital bliss," twin lotus blossoms on one stalk (pink background). No. 3327, $5, "Success in one's career," longan, lichee and walnuts (light green background). No. 3328, $12, "Producing many offspring," split pomegranates (buff background). No. 3329, $12, "Growing old together with wealth and high position," bulbuls flying around peonies (light orange background).

**2001, Jan. 2 *Perf. 11¾x12¼***

**3326-3329** A811 Set of 4 3.75 2.00

See Nos. 3404-3407.

Zodiac Signs — A812

Designs: No. 3330, $5, Aquarius. No. 3331, $12, Gemini. No. 3332, $25, Libra. No. 3333, $5, Capricorn. No. 3334, $12, Taurus. No. 3335, $25, Virgo. No. 3336, $5, Aries. No. 3337, $12, Leo. No. 3338, $25, Sagittarius. No. 3339, $5, Pisces. No. 3340, $12, Cancer. No. 3341, $25, Scorpio.

**2001 *Perf. 12***

**3330-3341** A812 Set of 12 15.00 10.00

Values are for stamps with surrounding selvage.

Issued: Nos. 3330-3332, 2/14. Nos. 3333-3335, 4/20. Nos. 3336-3338, 7/25. Nos. 3339-3341, 11/8.

Fruit — A813

$1, Plums. $3.50, Tangerines. $5, Apples. $7, Pears. $12, Guavas. $20, Longans. $25, Cantaloupes. $40, Grapefruit.

**2001-05 Litho. *Perf. 12½x13¼***

**3342** A813 $1 multi .30 .25
**3343** A813 $3.50 multi .30 .25
***a.*** "Republic of China" 12½mm long ('05) .30 .25
**3344** A813 $5 multi .35 .25
**3345** A813 $7 multi .50 .25
**3346** A813 $12 multi .85 .50
**3347** A813 $20 multi 1.25 .80
***a.*** "Republic of China" 12½mm long ('05) 1.25 .70
**3348** A813 $25 multi 1.60 .85
**3349** A813 $40 multi 3.00 2.60
*Nos. 3342-3349 (8)* 8.15 5.75

Issued: $5, $7, $12, $25, 2/23. $1, $3.50, $20, $40, 8/23. Nos. 3343a, 3347a, 5/16/05.

"Republic of China" on Nos. 3343 and 3347 is 12mm long and is in taller letters.

See Nos. 3408-3411, 3472-3475.

Mount Jade — A814

Designs: No. 3350, $5, Main peak (shown). No. 3351, $5, Western peak, flowers in foreground. $12, Northern peak. $25, Eastern peak.

**2001, Mar. 8 Litho. *Perf. 11½x11¼***

**3350-3353** A814 Set of 4 3.75 3.00

Compare Type A814 with Types A834-A837, A855-A858.

Children's Rhymes — A815

Designs: No. 3354, $5, Little Ball (blue background). No. 3355, $5, Point to the Water Vat (pink background). $12, Pangolin. $25, Shake and Stamp.

**2001, Apr. 4**
**3354-3357** A815 Set of 4 4.50 3.00

Buddhist Statues — A816

Designs: $5, Sakyamuni Buddha, Northern Wei Dynasty. $9, Seated Buddha, Tang Dynasty. $12, Mahavairocana Buddha, Sung Dynasty.

**2001, May 11** ***Perf. 11¼x11½***
**3358-3360** A816 Set of 3 3.00 1.60
*3360a* Souvenir sheet, #3358-3360, perf. 12 3.00 2.00

Agricultural Implements A817

Designs: $5, Rice wind drum. $7, Plow. $10, Bamboo rice baskets. $25, Coir rainwear.

**2001, May 25** ***Perf. 11½x11¼***
**3361-3364** A817 Set of 4 3.75 3.00

Dr. George Leslie Mackay (1844-1901) — A818

**2001, June 1** ***Perf. 11¼x11½***
**3365** A818 $25 multi 1.90 1.60

2001 Kiwanis International Convention — A819

Designs: $5, Girl, Earth. $25, Mother and child, map.

**2001, June 22** ***Perf. 13***
**3366-3367** A819 Set of 2 2.00 1.60

Kites — A820

No. 3368: a, Dragon. b, Phoenix. c, Tiger. d, Fish.

**2001, July 13** ***Perf. 11¼x11½***
**3368** Horiz. strip of 4 1.90 1.50
*a.-d.* A820 $5 Any single .40 .35

**Carp Encircled by Dragons Type of 1997 With Denominations at Right**

**2001, Aug. 3 Engr.** ***Perf. 13***

**Size: 25x33mm**

**3369** A745 $300 red vio & dk bl 16.00 8.00
**3370** A745 $500 red & brown 36.00 16.00

Rapid Transit — A821

Designs: $5, Train, transit system emblem. $12, Passengers in station, fare card. $25, Chientan Station.

**2001, Aug. 14 Litho.** ***Perf. 13***
**3371-3372** A821 Set of 2 1.50 .80

**Souvenir Sheet**

***Perf. 11¾***

**3373** A821 $25 multi 2.25 1.25

No. 3373 contains one 85x42mm stamp.

Fables — A822

Designs: No. 3374, $5, Now Three, Now Four (man and monkeys). No. 3375, $5, Selling the All-Penetrating Sword and Unyielding Shield (men watching man with sword and shield). $12, Waiting by the Tree for the Rabbit. $25, An Old Fool Moves Mountains.

**2001, Sept. 6 Litho.** ***Perf. 11½***
**3374-3377** A822 Set of 4 3.00 2.50

**Bird Manual Type of 1999 and**

Siberian Rubythroat A823

Designs: No. 3379, Waxwing (3 characters at UR). $12, White-rumped munia (2 characters at R). $25, Great barbet (3 characters at LL).

**2001, Sept. 28 Litho.** ***Perf. 11½***
**3378** A823 $5 shown 2.00 1.00
**3379** A792 $5 multi 2.00 1.00
**3380** A792 $12 multi 3.75 1.90
**3381** A792 $25 multi 6.75 3.25
*Nos. 3378-3381 (4)* 14.50 7.15

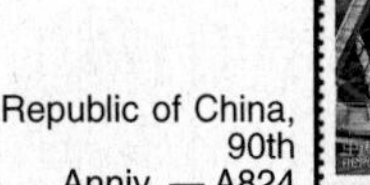

Republic of China, 90th Anniv. — A824

Designs: No. 3382, $5, Terminal, Chiang Kai-shek Intl. Airport. No. 3383, $5, Electronic products made in Republic of China. $12, Dancers at National Theater. $15, Dolphins.

**2001, Oct. 9 Litho.** ***Perf. 11½***
**3382-3385** A824 Set of 4 3.00 2.25

2001 National Games — A825

Athletes and: $5, Torch. $25, Map.

**2001, Oct. 18 Litho.** ***Perf. 12½***
**3386-3387** A825 Set of 2 2.50 2.00

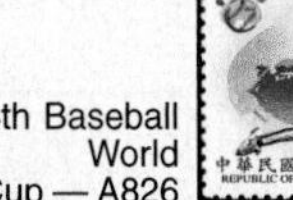

34th Baseball World Cup — A826

Emblem, map and: No. 3388, $5, Pitcher. No. 3389, $5, Batter. $12, Catcher. $20, Runner sliding.

**2001, Oct. 30** ***Perf. 11½***
**3388-3391** A826 Set of 4 3.00 2.40
*3391a* Souvenir sheet, #3388-3391, perf. 12 3.75 3.00

Puppet Theater — A827

Designs: $5, Mozhaonu, from "Thunder Storm." $6, Taiyangnu, from "Rising Winds, Surging Clouds." $10, Kuangdao, from "Thunder Crazy Sword." $25, Chin Chia-chien, from "Thunder Golden Light."

**2001, Nov. 16 Litho.** ***Perf. 11½***
**3392-3395** A827 Set of 4 3.50 2.40

National Defense Medical Center, Cent. — A828

Designs: $5, Medical students, old medical school building. $25, Doctors, new medical school building.

**2001, Nov. 23** ***Perf. 13***
**3396-3397** A828 Set of 2 2.60 2.10

New Year 2002 (Year of the Horse) — A829

Horse and: $3.50, Clouds. $13, Flowers.

**2001, Dec. 3 Litho.** ***Perf. 12½***
**3398** A829 $3.50 multi .40 .25
*a.* Perf. 13¾ vert. .40 .25
*b.* Booklet pane, 12 #3398a 4.50 —
Booklet, #3398b 5.00
**3399** A829 $13 multi 1.20 .80
*a.* Souvenir sheet, 2 each #3398-3399 3.25 2.00

Paul Cardinal Yu Pin (1901-78) — A830

**2001, Dec. 7** ***Perf. 11½***
**3400** A830 $25 multi 2.40 .75
*a.* Souvenir sheet of 1, perf. 12 2.50 1.50

Greetings — A831

No. 3401: a, Pink chrysanthemums, red background. b, White lilies, red background. c, Pink flowers, yellow background. d, Red orange flowers, yellow background. e, Pink flowers, green background. f, Coral roses, blue green background. g, Star and wreath, blue background. h, Poinsettias, blue background. i, Red violet flowers, purple background. j, Yellow flowers, purple background.

**2001, Dec. 12** ***Perf. 12½***
**3401** Sheet of 10 + 10 labels 10.00 4.00
*a.-j.* A831 $5 Any single .60 .40

Labels could be personalized for an additional fee.

Sheets with blank (unprinted) labels were not released.

Fu Hsing Kang College, 50th Anniv. — A832

Designs: $5, Students with flags. $25, Tower, administration building, statue of students.

**2002, Jan. 4** ***Perf. 11½***
**3402-3403** A832 Set of 2 2.75 2.10

**Expressions of Good Fortune Type of 2001**

Designs: No. 3404, $5, "Continuously produce good offspring," lotus and sweet osmanthus flowers in a vase (gradiated pink background). No. 3405, $5, "A high, moral gentleman," orchid and sweet osmanthus in containers (gradiated green background). No. 3406, $12, "A hall full of the rich and famous," flowering crabapple in a vase (gradiated orange background). No. 3407, $12, "Safe and peaceful in all seasons," roses in vase (gradiated purple background).

**2002, Jan. 16** ***Perf. 11¾x12¼***
**3404-3407** A811 Set of 4 2.75 1.60

**Fruit Type of 2001**

**2002-05 Litho.** ***Perf. 12½x13¼***
**3408** A813 $6 Avocados .35 .25
**3409** A813 $10 Lichees .75 .30
*a.* "Republic of China" 12½mm long ('05) .60 .30
**3410** A813 $17 Dates 1.20 .50
*a.* "Republic of China" 12½mm long ('05) 1.00 .55
**3411** A813 $32 Passion fruit 2.20 .85
*a.* "Republic of China" 12½mm long ('05) 2.00 1.00
*Nos. 3408-3411 (4)* 4.50 1.90

Issued: Nos. 3408-3411, 2/8/02; 3409a, 3410a, 3411a, 5/16/05.

"Republic of China" on Nos. 3409-3411 is 12mm long and is in taller letters.

Folk Traditions — A833

Designs: No. 3412, $5, Release of sky lanterns (orange background). No. 3413, $5, Fireworks display (blue background). $10, Matsu procession (lilac background). $20, Dragon boat race (pink background).

**2002, Feb. 26 Litho.** ***Perf. 12½***
**3412-3415** A833 Set of 4 3.25 2.40

See Nos. 3440-3443.

Winter, Mount Hsueh — A834

North Ridge, Mount Hsueh — A835

Autumn, Mount Hsueh — A836

Glacial Cirques, Mount Hsueh — A837

**2002, Mar. 20** ***Perf. 11½***
**3416** A834 $5 multi .35 .35
**3417** A835 $5 multi .35 .35
**3418** A836 $12 multi .80 .70
**3419** A837 $25 multi 1.60 1.40
*Nos. 3416-3419 (4)* 3.10 2.80

Compare with Types A814, A855-A858.

Novel "The Romance of the Three Kingdoms" A838

Designs: No. 3420, $3.50, Three heroes battling Lu Bu (warriors on horseback). No. 3421, $3.50, To the rescue of his master's family (one warrior on horseback). $5, Scraping away the poison from the bone (medicinal bleeding). $20, Playing a lute to make the enemy retreat (horseman and gate).

**2002, Apr. 4**
**3420-3423** A838 Set of 4 4.00 1.75
*a.* Souvenir sheet, #3420-3423, perf. 12 4.00 4.00

Endangered Bird Thalasseus Bernsteini — A839

No. 3424: a, Two birds in flight. b, Bird in flight heading left. c, Bird landing on rock carrying fish. d, Bird on rock with beak open. e, Adult feeding chick. f, Bird diving. g, Bird landing with bill open. h, Bird standing on rock, looking left. i, Adult with chick. j, Adult on nest. $25, Bird in flight.

**2002, May 15 Litho. *Perf. 11½***
**3424** A839 $5 Sheet of 10, #a-j 6.00 3.25

**Souvenir Sheet**
***Perf. 12***
**3425** A839 $25 multi 4.00 1.60

No. 3424 contains ten 40x30mm stamps.

**Dragon & Carp Type of 1997 Redrawn With Denomination at Right**

**2002, June 5 Engr. *Perf. 13¼x12½***
**3426** A745 $80 brown 5.00 3.00

Porcelain Bowls — A840

Ching Dynasty bowls depicting: No. 3427, $5, Peacock (salmon background). No. 3428, $5, Lotus flowers (blue green background). $7, Peonies. $32, Sparrows and bamboo.

**2002, June 21 Litho. *Perf. 11½***
**3427-3430** A840 Set of 4 6.00 4.50

Flowers — A841

Designs: $5, Matthiola incana. $12, Gardenia jasminoides. $25, Michelia figo.

**2002, July 5 *Perf. 13***
**3431-3433** A841 Set of 3 3.50 1.60

Cetaceans A842

Designs: No. 3434, $5, Megaptera novaeangliae, whaling ship. No. 3435, $5, Tursiops truncatus, people on shore attracting cetacean. $10, Orcinus orca, boat following cetaceans. $25, Grampus griseus, people rescuing beached dolphin.

**2002, July 25 Litho. *Perf. 11½x11¼***
**3434-3437** A842 Set of 4 3.50 1.40
*a.* Souvenir sheet, #3434-3437, perf. 12 4.00 2.60

Intl. Paralympic Committee World Table Tennis Championships A843

Player: No. 3438, $5, On crutches. No. 3439, $5, In wheelchair.

**2002, Aug. 13 *Perf. 11½x11¼***
**3438-3439** A843 Set of 2 1.00 .65

**Folk Traditions Type of 2002**

Designs: No. 3440, $5, Launching of water lanterns (green background). No. 3441, $5, Snatching flags for good luck (yellow background). $10, Worship of the just (blue background). $20, Burning the Prince's boat (red orange background).

**2002, Aug. 22 *Perf. 12½***
**3440-3443** A833 Set of 4 3.00 2.25

Republic of China — Vatican City Diplomatic Relations, 60th Anniv. — A844

Designs: $5, Chinese and Vatican flags, Chinese Presidential building, St. Peter's Basilica. $17, Flags, doves, Celso Cardinal Costantini.

**2002, Sept. 20 *Perf. 11½x11¼***
**3444-3445** A844 Set of 2 2.00 1.25

**Bird Manual Type of 1999 and**

White-rumped Munia — A845

Designs: No. 3446, $5, Vernal hanging parrot (3 characters at LL). $12, White-headed greenfinch (4 characters at LL). $25, Yunnan greenfinch (2 characters at UL).

**2002, Oct. 9**

| | | | | |
|---|---|---|---|---|
| **3446** A792 | $5 multi | | .85 | .75 |
| **3447** A845 | $5 multi | | .85 | .75 |
| **3448** A792 | $12 multi | | 1.60 | 1.50 |
| **3449** A792 | $25 multi | | 3.25 | 2.75 |
| | *Nos. 3446-3449 (4)* | | 6.55 | 5.75 |

Taiwanese Opera — A846

Designs: $5, Liang Shan-po and Chu Yingtai. $6, Hsueh Ting-shan and Fan Li-hua. $10, Hsueh Ping-kuei and Wang Pao-chuan. $25, The Living Buddha Chikung.

**2002, Oct. 25**
**3450-3453** A846 Set of 4 3.00 1.50

Koalas — A847

Designs: No. 3454, $5, Adult with cub. No. 3455, $5, Adult on branch. $9, Adult with head on branch. $21, Adult with cub, diff.

**2002, Nov. 15 *Perf. 11¼x11½***
**3454-3457** A847 Set of 4 3.00 1.40
*a.* Souvenir sheet, #3454-3457, perf. 12 3.00 2.25

Knots — A848

Nos. 3458-3459 — Various knots (Denomination location, denomination color and background color): a, UL, orange, light orange. b, UL, purple, yellow. c, UL, green, light green. d, UL, yellow, light blue. e, UL, blue, pink. f, UR, orange, light orange. g, UR, red violet, yellow. h, UR, blue, light green. i, UR, yellow, light blue. j, UR, red violet, pink.

No. 3460 (yellow denominations, olive green background): a, Like #3458a. b, Like #3458b. c, Like #3458c, d, #3458d, e, Like #3458e. f, Like #3458f. g, Like #3458g. h, Like #3458h. i, Like #3458i. j, Like #3458j.

**2002, Nov. 22 Litho. *Perf. 12½***

| | | | |
|---|---|---|---|
| **3458** | Block of 10 | 3.00 | 3.00 |
| *a.-j.* | A848 $3.50 Any single | .30 | .25 |
| *k.* | Sheet of 10 #3458f + 10 attached labels | 15.00 | 15.00 |
| *l.* | Sheet of 10 #3458g + 10 attached labels | 15.00 | 15.00 |
| *m.* | Sheet of 10 #3458h + 10 attached labels | 15.00 | 15.00 |
| *n.* | Sheet of 10 #3458i + 10 attached labels | 15.00 | 15.00 |
| *o.* | Sheet of 10 #3458j + 10 attached labels | 15.00 | 15.00 |
| *p.* | Sheet , #3458a-3458j + 10 attached labels | 15.00 | 15.00 |
| *q.* | Sheet, #3458a, 3458b, 3458d, 3458f, 3458g, 3458i + 6 attached labels ('04) | 10.50 | 10.50 |
| **3459** | Block of 10 | 4.50 | 4.50 |
| *a.-j.* | A848 $5 Any single | .45 | .25 |
| *k.* | Sheet of 10 #3459a + 10 attached labels | 15.50 | 15.50 |
| *l.* | Sheet of 10 #3459b + 10 attached labels | 15.50 | 15.50 |
| *m.* | Sheet of 10 #3459c + 10 attached labels | 15.50 | 15.50 |
| *n.* | Sheet of 10 #3459d + 10 attached labels | 15.50 | 15.50 |
| *o.* | Sheet of 10 #3459e + 10 attached labels | 15.50 | 15.50 |
| *p.* | Sheet of 10 #3459f + 10 attached labels | 15.50 | 15.50 |
| *q.* | Sheet of 10 #3459g + 10 attached labels | 15.50 | 15.50 |
| *r.* | Sheet of 10 #3459h + 10 attached labels | 15.50 | 15.50 |
| *s.* | Sheet of 10 #3459i + 10 attached labels | 15.50 | 15.50 |
| *t.* | Sheet of 10 #3459j + 10 attached labels | 15.50 | 15.50 |
| **3460** | Block of 10 | 22.00 | 22.00 |
| *a.-j.* | A848 $25 Any single | 2.10 | 1.10 |
| *k.* | Sheet of 10 #3460a + 10 attached labels | 30.00 | 30.00 |
| *l.* | Sheet of 10 #3460b + 10 attached labels | 30.00 | 30.00 |
| *m.* | Sheet of 10 #3460c + 10 attached labels | 30.00 | 30.00 |
| *n.* | Sheet of 10 #3460d + 10 attached labels | 30.00 | 30.00 |
| *o.* | Sheet of 10 #3460e + 10 attached labels | 30.00 | 30.00 |
| *p.* | Sheet, #3460a-3460j + 10 attached labels | 30.00 | 30.00 |
| | *Nos. 3458-3460 (3)* | 29.50 | 29.50 |

Nos. 3458k-3458p sold for $185 each; Nos. 3459k-3459u for $200 each; Nos. 3460k-3460p for $400 each. Labels, which were personalized, were separated from stamps on Nos. 3458k-3458p, 3459k-3459u, 3460k-3460p by vertical rows of simulated perforations.

No. 3458q sold for $141 and has labels, which could be personalized, that are separated from the stamps by simulated perforations. Issued 9/30/04.

New Year 2003 (Year of the Ram) — A849

Designs: $3.50, Yellow ram. $13, Red ram.

**2002, Dec. 2 Litho. *Perf. 12¼***

| | | | |
|---|---|---|---|
| **3461** | A849 $3.50 multi | .40 | .25 |
| *a.* | Perf. 12¼ Vert. | .40 | .25 |
| *b.* | As "a," booklet pane of 6 | 2.25 | — |
| | Booklet, 2 #3461b | 5.25 | |
| **3462** | A849 $13 multi | 1.00 | .40 |
| *a.* | Souvenir sheet, 2 each #3461-3462 | 2.75 | 1.50 |
| *b.* | As "a," with Chinese text in red in L & R sheet margins | 2.40 | 1.25 |

Issued: No. 3462b, 1/1/03. Chinese text in left and right sheet margins on No. 3462b commemorates the establishment of Chunghwa Post Co., Ltd.

Street Scene on a Summer Day, by Chen Cheng-po A850

Girl in the White Dress, by Li Mei-shu A851

Courtyard with Banana Trees, by Liao Chi-chun A852

Sunrise, by Kuo Po-chuan A853

***Perf. 11½x11¼, 11¼x11½***
**2002, Dec. 6**

| | | | |
|---|---|---|---|
| **3463** A850 | $5 multi | .40 | .25 |
| **3464** A851 | $5 multi | .40 | .25 |
| **3465** A852 | $10 multi | .70 | .30 |
| **3466** A853 | $20 multi | 1.50 | .50 |
| | *Nos. 3463-3466 (4)* | 3.00 | 1.30 |

Admission to World Trade Organization, 1st Anniv. — A854

**2003, Jan. 1 Litho. *Perf. 11½x11¼***
**3467** A854 $17 multi 2.25 .90

Spring on Wuyen Peak — A855

Glacial Cirques, Mt. Nanhu — A856

Mt. Nanhu — A857

Snow on Mt. Chungyang Chien — A858

**2003, Jan. 23**

| | | | |
|---|---|---|---|
| **3468** A855 | $5 multi | .35 | .25 |
| **3469** A856 | $5 multi | .35 | .25 |
| **3470** A857 | $12 multi | .75 | .30 |
| **3471** A858 | $25 multi | 1.25 | .55 |
| | *Nos. 3468-3471 (4)* | 2.70 | 1.35 |

Compare with Types A814, A834-A837.

**Fruit Type of 2001**

**2003-05 Litho. *Perf. 12½x13¼***

| | | | |
|---|---|---|---|
| **3472** A813 | $9 Rose apples | .60 | .25 |
| *a.* | "Republic of China" 12½mm long ('05) | .60 | .30 |
| **3473** A813 | $13 Kumquats | .90 | .40 |
| **3474** A813 | $15 Lemons | 1.10 | .45 |
| *a.* | "Republic of China" 12½mm long ('05) | .95 | .50 |
| **3475** A813 | $34 Coconuts | 2.00 | 1.00 |
| | *Nos. 3472-3475 (4)* | 4.60 | 2.10 |

Issued: Nos. 3472-3475, 2/14/03; 3472a, 3474a, 5/16/05.

"Republic of China" on Nos. 3472 and 3474 is 12mm long and is in taller letters.

Love — A859

Hearts and: No. 3476, $5, Woman tending to man in wheelchair. No. 3477, $5, Family. $10, Landscape. $25, Girl and dogs.

**2003, Mar. 20 *Perf. 11¼x11½***
**3476-3479** A859 Set of 4 3.00 2.25

Puppet Theater — A860

Designs: No. 3480, $5, *Journey to the West* performed on outdoor stage. No. 3481, $5, Puppets on television. $10, *Mysteries of the Wolf Castle* performed at the National Opera

House. $25, Screening of movie, *Legend of the Sacred Stone.*

**2003, Apr. 3** ***Perf. 11½x11¼***
**3480-3483** A860 Set of 4 3.00 2.25

Merops Philippinus — A861

Designs: Nos. 3484, 3488a, $5, Foraging. Nos. 3485, 3488b, $5, Roosting. Nos. 3486, 3488c, $10, Bathing. Nos. 3487, 3488d, $20, Feeding chick.

**2003, May 8** ***Perf. 12½***

**With White Frame**

**3484-3487** A861 Set of 4 3.00 2.25

**Souvenir Sheet**

**Without White Frame**

**3488** A861 Sheet of 4, #a-d 3.50 3.00

No. 3488 contains four 33x25mm stamps.

Furniture — A862

Designs: No. 3489, $5, Wash basin stand. No. 3490, $5, Canopy bed. $12, Taishi chair. $20, Pahsien table.

**2003, May 22** ***Perf. 11¼x11½***
**3489-3492** A862 Set of 4 3.00 1.50

Folktale "Eight Immortals Cross the Sea" — A863

Immortal: No. 3493, $5, Riding catfish. No. 3494, $5, On donkey. $10, Holding fan. $25, In brown robe.

**2003, June 12**
**3493-3496** A863 Set of 4 6.75 3.50

See Nos. 3535-3538.

Moths — A864

Designs: No. 3497, $5, Antitrygodes divisaria perturbata. No. 3498, $5, Vamuna virilis. $12, Sinna extrema. $20, Thyas juno.

**2003, June 26** ***Perf. 11½x11¼***
**3497-3500** A864 Set of 4 3.00 1.50

Dragonflies — A865

Designs: Nos. 3501, 3505a, $5, Acisoma panorpoides panorpoides. Nos. 3502, 3505b, $5, Sympetrum eroticu ardens, vert. Nos. 3503, 3505c, $10, Anax parthenope julius. Nos. 3504, 3505d, $17, Rhyothemis variegata arria, vert.

**2003, July 25** ***Perf. 12½***

**With White Frames**

**3501-3504** A865 Set of 4 2.60 1.50

**Souvenir Sheet**

**Without White Frames**

***Perf. 11¾***

**3505** A865 Sheet of 4, #a-d 3.00 2.60

Stamp size: Nos. 3505a, 3505c, 33x25mm; Nos. 3505b, 3505d, 25x33mm.

Greetings — A866

No. 3506: a, Cranes. b, Wood carving and red plate. c, Fish and coin. d, Bamboo. e, Wood carving of bird.

No. 3507: a, Vase with tasseled rope. b, Like #3506a. c, Like #3506b. d, Three brown containers. e, Like #3508. f, Dragon. g, Like #3506c. h, Like #3506d. i, Horse and rider. j, Like #3506e.

No. 3508, Vase with flowers.

**2003, Aug. 9** ***Perf. 12½***
**3506** Horiz. strip of 5 1.90 1.90
*a.-e.* A866 $3.50 Any single .35 .25
*f.* Sheet of 10 #3506a+ 10 attached labels 18.00 18.00
*g.* Sheet of 10 #3506b+ 10 attached labels 18.00 18.00
*h.* Sheet of 10 #3506c + 10 attached labels 18.00 18.00
*i.* Sheet of 10 #3506d + 10 attached labels 18.00 18.00
*j.* Sheet of 10 #3506e + 10 attached labels 18.00 18.00
*k.* Sheet , 2 each #3506a-3506e + 10 attached labels 18.00 18.00
**3507** Block of 10 5.00 5.00
*a.-j.* A866 $5 Any single .50 .25
*k.* Sheet of 10 #3507a + 10 attached labels 19.00 19.00
*l.* Sheet of 10 #3507b + 10 attached labels 19.00 19.00
*m.* Sheet of 10 #3507c + 10 attached labels 19.00 19.00
*n.* Sheet of 10 #3507d + 10 attached labels 19.00 19.00
*o* Sheet of 10 #3507e + 10 attached labels 19.00 19.00
*p.* Sheet of 10 #3507f + 10 attached labels 19.00 19.00
*q.* Sheet of 10 #3507g + 10 attached labels 19.00 19.00
*r.* Sheet of 10 #3507h + 10 attached labels 19.00 19.00
*s.* Sheet of 10 #3507i + 10 attached labels 19.00 19.00
*t.* Sheet of 10 #3507j + 10 attached labels 19.00 19.00
*u.* Sheet, #3507a-3507j + 10 attached labels 19.00 19.00
*v.* Sheet, #3507d, 3507e, 3507f, 3507g, 3507h, 3507j + 6 attached labels ('04) 13.50 13.50
**3508** A866 $12 multi 1.25 .65
*a.* Sheet of 10 #3508 + 10 attached labels 25.00 25.00
*Nos. 3506-3508 (3)* 8.15 7.55

Nos. 3506f-3506k sold for $185 each; Nos. 3507k-3507u for $200 each; No. 3508a for $270 each. Labels, which were personalized, were separated from stamps on Nos. 3506f-3506k, 3507k-3507u, 3508a by vertical rows of simulated perforations.

No. 3507v sold for $150 and has labels, which could be personalized, that are separated from the stamps by simulated perforations. Issued 5/30/04.

**Bird Manual Type of 1999 and**

White-throated Laughing Thrush — A867

Designs: No. 3510, Great mynah (2 characters at LR). $12, Yellow-legged buttonquail (3 characters at UL). $25, Crested lark (4 characters at L).

***Perf. 11½x11¼***

**2003, Sept. 10** **Litho.**
**3509** A867 $5 multi .75 .40
**3510** A792 $5 multi .75 .40
**3511** A792 $12 multi 1.60 .85
**3512** A792 $25 multi 3.25 1.60
*Nos. 3509-3512 (4)* 6.35 3.25

Chungshan Park, Taichung — A868

Tourist attractions: No. 3514, $5, Dongshan River Bridge, Ilan. $11, Badlands, Tianliao. $20, Sansiantai, Chenggong.

**2003, Oct. 28** **Litho.** ***Perf. 11½***
**3513-3516** A868 Set of 4 2.75 1.25

Chungshan Park, cent. (No. 3513).

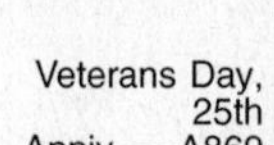

Veterans Day, 25th Anniv. — A869

Veterans Affairs Commission insignia and: $5, Veterans building Central Cross-Island Highway. $25, Veterans, homes and hospital for veterans.

**2003, Oct. 31**
**3517-3518** A869 Set of 2 1.90 .90

The Back Yard, by Lu Tie-jhou A870

A Gold Mine Tower: Jioufen, by Lin Ke-gong A871

Leisurely, by Chen Jin — A872

East Gate, by Li Ze-fan — A873

**2003, Nov. 20**
**3519** A870 $5 multi .40 .25
**3520** A871 $5 multi .40 .25
**3521** A872 $10 multi .70 .30
**3522** A873 $20 multi 1.40 .60
*Nos. 3519-3522 (4)* 2.90 1.40

New Year 2004 (Year of the Monkey) — A874

Monkey holding fruit: $3.50, With tail. $13, In hand.

**2003, Dec. 1** ***Perf. 12¼***
**3523-3524** A874 Set of 2 2.60 1.40
*3523a* Perf. 12¼ vert. .70 .35
*3524a* Sheet, 2 each #3523-3524 4.00 3.50
*3523b* Booklet pane, 12 #3523a 8.50 —
Complete booklet, #3523b 9.00

Springs — A875

Designs: No. 3525, $5, Yangmingshan Hot Springs, fumaroles (light orange background). No. 3526, $5, Suao Cold Springs, Nanfangao Bridge (light blue background). $10, Guanziling Murky Hot Spring, Shuei Huo Tong Yuan. $25, Green Island Seabed Hot Springs, Green Island Lighthouse.

**2003, Dec. 14** ***Perf. 13***
**3525-3528** A875 Set of 4 3.50 1.50
*3528a* Souvenir sheet, #3525-3528 3.50 2.00

Completion of Highway 3 — A876

Designs: $5, Jhonggang Interchange. $25, Cingshuei Service Area.

$20, Cingshuei Service Area, diff.

**2004, Jan. 8** **Litho.** ***Perf. 12½***
**3529-3530** A876 Set of 2 2.00 .90

**Souvenir Sheet**

***Perf. 11½x11¼***

**3531** A876 $20 multi 1.60 1.25

No. 3531 contains one 80x30mm stamp.

Flowers — A877

Designs: No. 3532, $5, Lilium formosanum. No. 3533, $5, Hippeastrum x hybridum. $12, Fressia x hybrida.

**2004, Jan. 17** ***Perf. 12¼***
**3532-3534** A877 Set of 3 1.75 .70
*3534a* Souvenir sheet, of #3532-3534, perf. 13 1.75 1.25
*3534b* As "a," with Taiwan Flower Expo emblem and text added in margin 1.90 1.25

**Eight Immortals Cross the Sea Type of 2003**

Immortal: No. 3535, $5, With crane and flute. No. 3536, $5, With lotus flower. $10, Holding stick, wearing red robe. $25, Carrying flower basket.

**2004, Feb. 25** ***Perf. 11¼x11½***
**3535-3538** A863 Set of 4 3.25 1.50

Red Cross Society, Cent. A878

No. 3539: a, Heart, stylized people with arms raised. b, Heart, stylized people doing Red Cross activities.

**2004, Mar. 9** ***Perf. 11¼x11½***
**3539** A878 $5 Horiz. pair, #a-b 1.10 .55

A Young Girl From Lu Kai, by Yan Shui-long A879

Old Street in Taipei, by Yang San-lang A880

Happy Farmers, by Lee Shih-chiao A881

Fish Shop, by Liu Chi-hsiang A882

***Perf. 11¼x11½, 11½x11¼***

**2004, Mar. 25**
**3540** A879 $5 multi .40 .25
**3541** A880 $5 multi .40 .25
**3542** A881 $10 multi .80 .30
**3543** A882 $20 multi 1.40 .60
*Nos. 3540-3543 (4)* 3.00 1.40

Butterflies A883

Designs: No. 3544, $5, Parantica sita niphonica. No. 3545, $5, Choaspes benjaminii formosanus. $17, Junonia almana. $20, Artipe eryx horiella.

**2004, Apr. 21** ***Perf. 11½x11¼***
**3544-3547** A883 Set of 4 3.00 1.50

Yijhen Folk Art Performers A884

Designs: No. 3548, $5, Eight Generals (buff background). No. 3549, $5, Song Jiang Battle Array (grayish blue background). $11, Drum Dance. $25, Stilt walkers.

**2004, May 11**
**3548-3551** A884 Set of 4 3.00 1.50

Inauguration of Pres. Chen Shui-bian and Vice-President Hsiu-lien Annette Lu — A885

No. 3552 — President, Vice-President and: a, Map of Taiwan, flag, crowd. b, Map of People's Republic of China and Taiwan, handshake, flowers. c, Buildings, crowd. d, Train, highway, buildings.
$12, President, Vice-President, buildings, train, highway.

**2004, May 20** ***Perf. 12½***
**3552** Horiz. strip of 4 1.75 .70
***a.-d.*** A885 $5 Any single .40 .25

**Souvenir Sheet**
***Perf. 12***
**3553** A885 $12 multi 1.50 1.25

No. 3553 contains one 80x30mm stamp.

Opening of Movie, *Harry Potter and the Prisoner of Azkaban* A886

No. 3554: a, $5, Harry, messenger owl, Hedwig, with letter. b, $5, Hedwig, rose background. c, $5, Harry riding Hippogriff. d, $5, Hippogriff, green background. e, $5, Harry, Monster Book of Monsters. f, $25, Crookshanks the Cat.
No. 3555: a, $5, Harry playing quidditch. b, $5, Harry playing quidditch, Dementors. c, $5, Harry and Hermoine riding Hippogriff. d, $5, Harry holding wand, Hogwarts. e, $5, Harry practicing Patronus Charm to repel Dementors. f, $25, Harry thrusting wand.

**2004, June 4** ***Perf. 12***
**Sheets of 6, #a-f**
**3554-3555** A886 Set of 2 10.00 6.00

Postal administrators said that Nos. 3554-3555 would not be not sold directly to customers at foreign addresses. The sheets were made available abroad through Canada Post's philatelic agency, and also were sent to foreign standing order customers.

Old Train Stations — A887

Designs: No. 3556, $5, Keelung Station, rickshaws. No. 3557, $5, Taipei Station, automobile. $15, Hsinchu Station, ox and cart. $25, Taichung Station, wagons.

**2004, June 9** ***Perf. 13½x13¾***
**3556-3559** A887 Set of 4 3.75 1.50

Compare Type A887 with Types A926-A929.

Iron Fort, Nangan Island — A888

Cinbi, Beigan Island — A889

Fujheng, Tungchu Island — A890

Lienyuyikeng, Tungyin Island — A891

**2004, July 1 Litho.** ***Perf. 11½x11¼***

| | | | | | |
|---|---|---|---|---|---|
| **3560** | A888 | $5 | multi | .40 | .25 |
| **3561** | A889 | $5 | multi | .40 | .25 |
| **3562** | A890 | $9 | multi | .60 | .25 |
| **3563** | A891 | $25 | multi | 1.60 | .75 |
| | *Nos. 3560-3563 (4)* | | | 3.00 | 1.50 |

Matsu National Scenic Area.

Crabs — A892

Designs: No. 3564, $3.50, Uca formosensis. No. 3565, $3.50, Uca borealis. $5, Uca arcuata. $25, Uca lactea.

**2004, July 21**
**3564-3567** A892 Set of 4 2.50 1.10

**Souvenir Sheet**

Listening to the Lute, Attributed to Li Sung — A893

No. 3568: a, $5, Lute player. b, $25, Scholar and woman.

**2004, Aug. 6** ***Perf. 12***
**3568** A893 Sheet of 2, #a-b 3.00 3.00

**Souvenir Sheet**

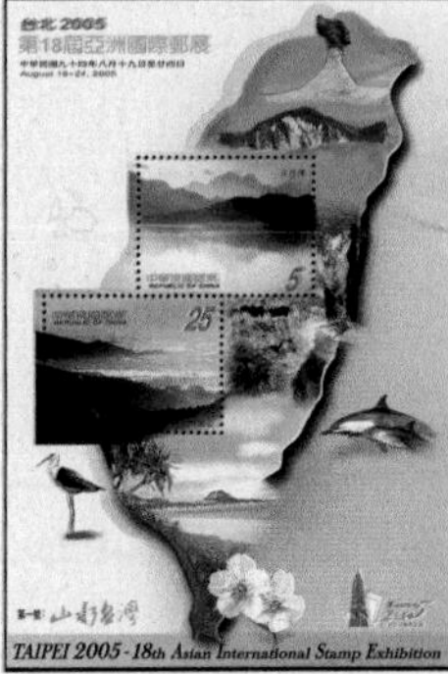


Taipei 2005 Intl. Stamp Exhibition — A894

No. 3569: a, $5, Sun Moon Lake. b, $25, Mt. Ali.

**2004, Aug. 27** ***Perf. 11½x11¼***
**3569** A894 Sheet of 2, #a-b 3.25 3.25

Intl. Day of Peace — A895

**2004, Sept. 21** ***Perf. 12¼x11¾***
**3570** A895 $15 multi 1.10 .55

**Souvenir Sheets**

Hello Kitty A896

No. 3571, oval stamps: a, $5, Dear Daniel, donuts. b, $15, Hello Kitty, Taipei 101 Building.
No. 3572, rectangular stamps: a, $5, Hello Kitty, bird, horiz. b, $15, Dear Daniel, Fisherman's Wharf, Danshuei.

**2004, Sept. 24** ***Perf.***
**3571** A896 Sheet of 2, #a-b 2.00 1.50
***Perf. 12***
**3572** A896 Sheet of 2, #a-b 2.00 1.50

**Sayings With Numbers Greeting Stamps**

One Sea of Smooth Sailing — A897

Two Lions Bring Good Fortune — A898

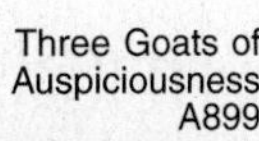

Three Goats of Auspiciousness A899

Safety in All Four Seasons — A900

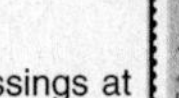

Five Blessings at the Door — A901

Six is Silky Smooth — A902

Married for Seven Lives — A903

Eight Immortals Wish for Your Perfection A904

Nine Means Success — A905

Ten is All Around Perfection A906

**2004, Oct. 10** ***Perf. 12½***

| | | | |
|---|---|---|---|
| **3573** | Block of 10 | 3.25 | 1.10 |
| ***a.*** | A897 $3.50 multi | .30 | .25 |
| ***b.*** | A898 $3.50 multi | .30 | .25 |
| ***c.*** | A899 $3.50 multi | .30 | .25 |
| ***d.*** | A900 $3.50 multi | .30 | .25 |
| ***e.*** | A901 $3.50 multi | .30 | .25 |
| ***f.*** | A902 $3.50 multi | .30 | .25 |
| ***g.*** | A903 $3.50 multi | .30 | .25 |
| ***h.*** | A904 $3.50 multi | .30 | .25 |
| ***i.*** | A905 $3.50 multi | .30 | .25 |
| ***j.*** | A906 $3.50 multi | .30 | .25 |

**Changed Colors**

| | | | |
|---|---|---|---|
| **3574** | Block of 10 | 4.25 | 1.50 |
| ***a.*** | A897 $5 multi | .40 | .25 |
| ***b.*** | A898 $5 multi | .40 | .25 |
| ***c.*** | A899 $5 multi | .40 | .25 |
| ***d.*** | A900 $5 multi | .40 | .25 |
| ***e.*** | A901 $5 multi | .40 | .25 |
| ***f.*** | A902 $5 multi | .40 | .25 |
| ***g.*** | A903 $5 multi | .40 | .25 |
| ***h.*** | A904 $5 multi | .40 | .25 |
| ***i.*** | A905 $5 multi | .40 | .25 |
| ***j.*** | A906 $5 multi | .40 | .25 |
| ***k.*** | Sheet, #3574a-3574j + 10 attached labels ('04) | 11.00 | 11.00 |

No. 3574k sold for $170 and has labels, which could be personalized, that are separated from the stamps by simulated perforations. Issued 10/10/04.

Kaohsiung Medical University. 50th Anniv. — A907

Designs: No. 3575, $5, University gate and buildings. No. 3576, $5, Building, researcher, beaker, mosquito and snake.

**2004, Oct. 16** ***Perf. 12½***
**3575-3576** A907 Set of 2 1.15 .65

Main Peak, Mt. Cilai — A908

North Peak, Mt. Cilai — A909

South Peak, Mt. Cilai — A910

Grasslands, Mt. Cilai — A911

**2004, Oct. 16** ***Perf. 11½x11¼***

| | | | |
|---|---|---|---|
| **3577** A908 $5 multi | .30 | .25 |
| **3578** A909 $5 multi | .30 | .25 |
| **3579** A910 $12 multi | .80 | .40 |
| **3580** A911 $25 multi | 1.60 | .75 |
| *Nos. 3577-3580 (4)* | 3.00 | 1.65 |

Taiwanese Mealist at 2004 Summer Olympics — A912

Designs: No. 3581, $5, Women's Taekwondo. No. 3582, $5, Men's Taekwondo, vert. $9, Archery. $12, Athletes on winner's platform, vert.

***Perf. 11¼x11½, 11½x11¼***

**2004, Oct. 22**

**3581-3584** A912 Set of 4 2.50 1.25

Platalea Minor — A913

Designs: No. 3585, $2.50, Pair in flight. No. 3586, $2.50, Pair standing on one leg. $15, With wings spread. $25, Foraging for food. $20, Birds in water.

**2004, Oct. 30** ***Perf. 13½x13¼***

**3585-3588** A913 Set of 4 3.00 1.65

**Souvenir Sheet**

**3589** A913 $20 multi 2.25 1.75

No. 3589 contains one 80x30mm stamp.

Pres. Yen Chia-kan (1905-93) — A914

**2004, Nov. 5** ***Perf. 13¼x13½***

**3590** A914 $12 multi 1.25 .45

New Year 2005 (Year of the Cock) — A915

Designs: $3.50, Cock on lantern. $13, Lanterns, cock
$5, Cock, hen and chick, horiz.

**2004, Nov. 10** ***Perf. 12¼x11¾***

**3591-3592** A915 Set of 2 2.40 1.25

**Souvenir Sheet**

***Perf. 11¾x11¼***

**3593** A915 $5 multi 1.75 .75

No. 3593 contains one 46x26mm stamp.

Prefectural Hall, Chiayi — A916

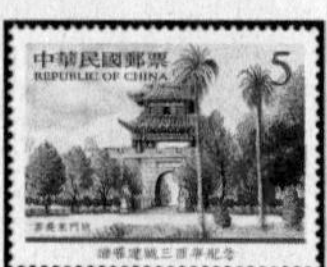

East Gate, Chiayi — A917

**2004, Nov. 20** ***Perf. 13½x13¼***

| | | |
|---|---|---|
| **3594** A916 $5 multi | .80 | .50 |
| **3595** A917 $5 multi | .80 | .50 |

Chiayi, 300th anniv.

Embroidered Squares for Ching Dynasty Civil Official Court Dresses — A918

Designs: No. 3596, $3.50, Manchurian crane (orange background). No. 3597, $3.50, Golden pheasant (green background). $5, Peacock. $25, Goose.

**2005, Jan. 20 Litho.** ***Perf. 11½x11¼***

**3596-3599** A918 Set of 4 2.60 1.40

See Nos. 3727-3730.

Greetings A919

No. 3600 — Cartoon balloon with various keyboard characters creating faces and backgrounds with: a, Hands. b, Envelopes. c, Hearts. d, Flowers.

**2005, Jan. 31** ***Perf. 12½***

| | | |
|---|---|---|
| **3600** Horiz. strip of 4 | 1.60 | .85 |
| *a.-d.* A919 $5 Any single | .40 | .25 |
| *e.* Sheet, #3600a-3600d + 4 attached labels | 11.50 | 11.50 |

No. 3600e sold for $140 and has labels, which could be personalized, that are separated from the stamps by simulated perforations. Sheets exist with various arrangements of stamps and positions of labels respective to the stamps (at left, above or below).

Rotary International, Cent. — A920

Rotary emblem and: $5, Map of Taiwan. $12, Dove.

**2005, Feb. 23** ***Perf. 13½x13¼***

**3601-3602** A920 Set of 2 1.30 1.00

Mangroves A921

Designs: No. 3603, $3.50, Kandelia obovata. No. 3604, $3.50, Rhizophora stylosa. No. 3605, $5, Avicennia marina. No. 3606, $5, Lumnitzera racemosa.

**2005, Mar. 10** ***Perf. 11½x11¼***

**3603-3606** A921 Set of 4 1.25 1.00

Longshan Temple, Mengjia — A922

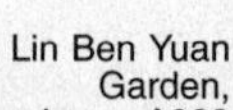

Lin Ben Yuan Garden, Banciao — A923

Designs: $13, Chaotain Temple, Beigang. $15, Fort Anping, Tainan.

**2005, Mar. 18**

| | | |
|---|---|---|
| **3607** A922 $5 multi | .35 | .25 |
| **3608** A923 $5 multi | .35 | .25 |
| **3609** A923 $13 multi | .85 | .40 |
| **3610** A923 $15 multi | .95 | .45 |
| *Nos. 3607-3610 (4)* | 2.50 | 1.35 |

**Souvenir Sheet**

Taipei 2005 Intl. Stamp Exhibition — A924

No. 3611: a, $5, Wood carving, Mandarin Ducks Playing in a Lotus Pond. b, $25, Hand puppets, horiz.

**2005, Apr. 19** ***Perf. 12***

**3611** A924 Sheet of 2, #a-b 2.40 2.40

Coral Reef Fish — A925

Designs: No. 3612, $5, Rhinomuraena quaesita. No. 3613, $5, Pomacanthus semicirculatus. $12, Forcipiger flavissimus. $25, Pterois volitans.

**2005, May 16** ***Perf. 11½x12***

| | | |
|---|---|---|
| **3612-3615** A925 Set of 4 | 3.50 | 1.75 |
| *a.* Sheet, 2 each #3612-3615 | 7.00 | 7.00 |

Changhua Train Station, 1918 — A926

Chiayi Train Station, 1933 — A927

Tainan Train Station, 1936 — A928

Kaohsiung Train Station, 1941 — A929

**2005, June 9** ***Perf. 13½x13¾***

| | | |
|---|---|---|
| **3616** A926 $5 multi | .35 | .25 |
| **3617** A927 $5 multi | .35 | .25 |
| **3618** A928 $15 multi | .90 | .50 |
| **3619** A929 $25 multi | 1.40 | .80 |
| *Nos. 3616-3619 (4)* | 3.00 | 1.80 |

Compare with type A887.

Novel "The Romance of the Three Kingdoms" A930

Designs: No. 3620, $3.50, Mayhem in the Fengyi Pavilion (man and woman near pavilion railing). No. 3621, $3.50, Deterring the Enemy in Changban (horse and rider on bridge). $5, Releasing Tsao Tsao (rider on horse near flag). $20, A Trick in the Bag (man in bed holding bag).

***Perf. 11½x11¼***

**2005, June 23** **Litho.**

| | | |
|---|---|---|
| **3620-3623** A930 Set of 4 | 3.25 | 3.00 |
| *3623a* Souvenir sheet, #3620-3623 | 3.25 | 3.25 |

Lifeline Suicide Prevention Hotline — A931

**2005, July 1** ***Perf. 12x11½***

**3624** A931 $12 multi 1.25 .75

Albert Einstein's Theory of Relativity, Cent. — A932

**2005, July 1**

**3625** A932 $15 multi 1.10 .55

**Souvenir Sheets**

Mickey Mouse A933

No. 3626: a, $5, At ship's wheel, in *Steamboat Willie*. b, $25. As wizard, in *Fantasia*.

No. 3627: a, $5, Holding sword, in *The Prince and the Pauper*. b, $25. With Pluto, in *Mickey's Twice Upon a Christmas*.

**2005, Aug. 3** ***Perf. 12***

**Sheets of 2, #a-b**

**3626-3627** A933 Set of 2 3.50 2.00

Rooster-shaped Wine Vessel — A934

**2005, Aug. 19** ***Perf. 11¼x11½***

| | | |
|---|---|---|
| **3628** A934 $15 multi | .95 | .45 |
| *a.* Sheet of 6, perf. 12 | 5.75 | 3.00 |

Taipei 2005 Intl. Stamp Exhibition.

**Souvenir Sheets**

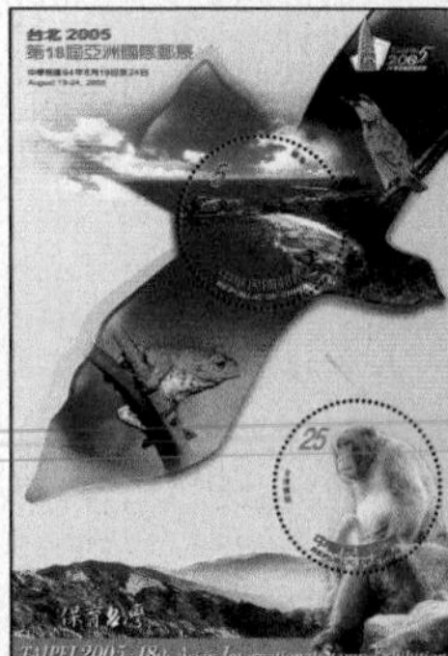

A935

A936

A937

A938

A939

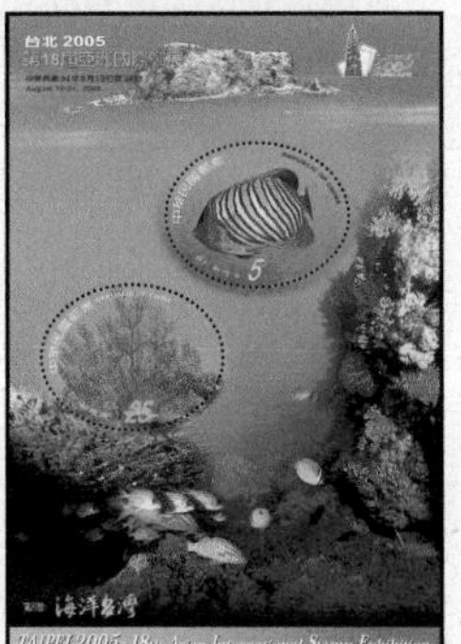
Taipei 2005 Intl. Stamp Exhibition — A940

No. 3629: a, $5, Green Island and shoreline. b, $25, Formosan rock monkey.

No. 3630: a, $5, Microscope. b, $25, DNA double helices, vert.

No. 3631: a, $5, Flowers. $25, Fruit.

No. 3632: a, $5, Ear Shooting Ceremony, vert. b, $25, Dragon boat in race.

No. 3633: a, $5, Bowl of food and ladle. b, $25, Rice cakes.

No. 3634: a, $5, Royal empress angelfish. b, $25, Red horny coral.

**2005** ***Perf.***

**3629** A935 Sheet of 2, #a-b 2.25 .95

***Perf. 13½x13, 13x13½***

**3630** A936 Sheet of 2, #a-b 2.25 .95

***Perf. 13½***

**3631** A937 Sheet of 2, #a-b 2.25 .95

***Perf. 13¼x13½, 13½x13¼***

**3632** A938 Sheet of 2, #a-b 2.25 .95

***Perf. 12***

**3633** A939 Sheet of 2, #a-b 2.25 .95

***Perf.***

**3634** A940 Sheet of 2, #a-b 2.25 .95
*Nos. 3629-3634 (6)* 13.50 5.70

Issued: No. 3629, 8/19; No. 3630, 8/20; No. 3631, 8/21; No. 3632, 8/22; No. 3633, 8/23; No. 3634, 8/24. No. 3629 contains two 38mm diameter stamps. No. 3634 contains two 43x33mm oval stamps.

Novel, "Journey to the West" — A941

Designs: No. 3635, $3.50, Stone Monkey (monkeys at waterfall). No. 3636, $3.50, Buddhist Baby in the River. $5, Making a Pass at Chang E. $20, Taming the Monster of the River of Flowing Sands.

**2005, Sept. 15** ***Perf. 11¼x11½***

**3635-3638** A941 Set of 4 9.00 7.00

**Souvenir Sheet**

Kaohsiung 2005 Intl. Stamp Exhibition — A942

No. 3639: a, $5, Loyalty and Filial Piety, by Cian Syuan, vert. b, Gilt scepter.

***Perf. 13¼x13½, 13½x13¼***

**2005, Oct. 7**

**3639** A942 Sheet of 2, #a-b 2.00 2.00

**Souvenir Sheets**

A943

Opening of Movie, *Harry Potter and the Goblet of Fire* A944

No. 3640: a, $5, Triwizard Cup. b, $5, Harry and Hungarian Horntail. c, $5, Golden Egg. d, $5, Harry swimming. e, $5, Harry summoning Firebolt with wand. f, $25, Harry and Triwizard Cup.

No. 3641: a, $5, Hungarian Horntail. b, $5, Harry on Firebolt. c, $5, Voldemort's snake, Nagini. d, $5, Grindylows. e, $5, Dumbledore's phoenix, Fawkes. f, $25, Merchieftainess.

**2005, Nov. 18** ***Perf. 12***

**3640** A943 Sheet of 6, #a-f 5.00 2.50
**3641** A944 Sheet of 6, #a-f 5.00 2.50

New Year 2006 (Year of the Dog) — A945

Designs: $3.50, Dog at left. $13, Dog at lower right.

$12, Three dogs, horiz.

**2005, Dec. 1** ***Perf. 12¼x11¾***

**3642-3643** A945 Set of 2 2.50 2.00

**Souvenir Sheet**

***Perf. 11¾x11¼***

**3644** A945 $12 multi 1.50 1.00

No. 3644 contains one 46x26mm stamp.

Pets — A946

Designs: $3.50, Siberian husky. $5, Golden retriever. $12, Himalayan cat. $25, Scottish fold cat.

***Perf. 13½x12½***

**2005, Dec. 22** **Litho.**

**Country Name in Green**

**3645** A946 $3.50 multi .30 .25
**3646** A946 $5 multi .35 .25
**3647** A946 $12 multi .75 .35
**3648** A946 $25 multi 1.40 .75
*Nos. 3645-3648 (4)* 2.80 1.60

See Nos. 3652-3655, 3685-3688 3712-3715.

Tea Ceremony — A947

No. 3649: a, Preparation of tea set (dull orange panel). b, Placing of tea leaves in pot (lemon panel). c, Pouring hot water over pots and cups (light green panel). d, Drying of pot and pouring of tea (blue geen panel). e, Smelling and drinking of tea (gray blue panel).

**2006, Jan. 26** ***Perf. 13½***

**3649** A947 Horiz. strip of 5 1.90 1.00
*a.-e.* $5 Any single .35 .25

Taipei 101 Building — A948

Designs: $5, In day. $12, At night.

**2006, Feb. 23** ***Perf. 12***

**3650-3651** A948 Set of 2 3.50 2.25

**Pets Type of 2005**

Designs: $2.50, Labrador retriever. $7, St. Bernard. $10, Siamese cat. $32, Persian cat.

**2006, Mar. 8** ***Perf. 13½x12½***

**Country Name in Blue**

**3652** A946 $2.50 multi .30 .25
**3653** A946 $7 multi .45 .25
**3654** A946 $10 multi .60 .30
**3655** A946 $32 multi 2.00 1.00
*Nos. 3652-3655 (4)* 3.35 1.80

See Nos. 3712-3715.

King Penguins — A949

Aptenodytes patagonicus: No. 3656, $5, Adult and juvenile. No. 3657, $5, Courtship. $9, Swimming and diving, horiz. $12, Gliding and preening, horiz.

$15, Colony, horiz.

***Perf. 11¼x11½, 11½x11¼***

**2006, Mar. 26**

**3656-3659** A949 Set of 4 2.00 1.60

**Souvenir Sheet**

***Perf. 12***

**3660** A949 $15 multi 1.25 1.00

No. 3660 contains one 80x30mm stamp.

**Miniature Sheet**

Children's Art — A950

No. 3661 — Winning drawings in children's stamp design competition: a, Birds with black bills. b, People with red faces. c, Pheasants. d, Chinese celebration. e, Fishing boats and catch. f, People with large flowers and fruit. g, Man painting Chinese lantern. h, Bridge and ducks. i, Train. j, Bees and flowers. k, People with black faces. l, Boy on ladder. m, People and chickens. n, Ring of people around dancers and musicians. o, People and large lions. p, Two cats. q, People and cow. r, Whale and fish. s, People with white faces bending backwards. t, Bus.

**2006, Apr. 4** ***Perf. 11½***

**3661** A950 $5 Sheet of 20, #a-t 6.00 3.50

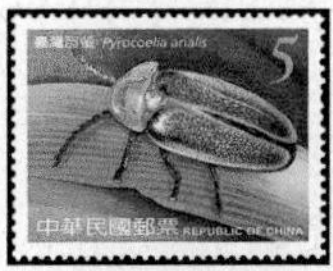
Fireflies — A951

Designs: No. 3662, $5, Pyrocoelia analis. No. 3663, $5, Diaphanes citrinus. No. 3664, $5, Diaphanes niveus. No. 3665, $5, Diaphanes formosus.

**2006, May 25** ***Perf. 13½x13¼***

**3662-3665** A951 Set of 4 1.75 1.00

**Souvenir Sheet**

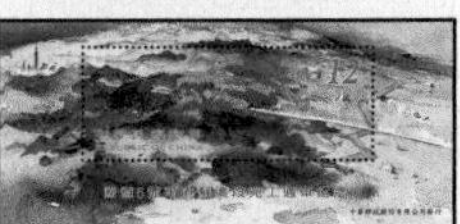
Completion of Nangang to Suao Section of National Expressway 5 — A952

**2006, June 16** **Litho.** ***Perf. 11½***

**3666** A952 $12 multi 1.50 .80

**Souvenir Sheets**

Winnie the Pooh A953

No. 3667: a, $5, Winnie the Pooh pushing Piglet in wheelbarrow. b, $25, Winnie the Pooh, Piglet and Tigger floating in inner tube.

No. 3668: a, $5, Winnie the Pooh and Piglet running in autumn. b, $25, Winnie the Pooh and Tigger ice fishing.

**2006, June 21** ***Perf. 12***

**Sheets of 2, #a-b**

**3667-3668** A953 Set of 2 4.00 2.00

Tourism Greeting Stamps — A954

Designs: Nos. 3669a, 3670a, Satchel and cliff. Nos. 3669b, 3670b, Camera and boat. Nos. 3669c, 3670c, Notebook, pen and bridge. No. 3669d, 3670d, Sailboat and rock. No. 3669e, 3670e, Heart and train.

**2006, June 30** ***Perf. 12½***

**3669** Horiz. strip of 5 1.50 .55
***a.-e.*** A954 $3.50 Any single .30 .25
***f.*** Sheet, 2 each #3669a-3669e, + 5 labels 7.00 —
**3670** Horiz. strip of 5 2.00 .80
***a.-e.*** A954 $5 Any single .40 .25
***f.*** Sheet, 2 each #3670a-3670e, + 5 labels 7.00 —

Nos. 3669f and 3670f each sold for $100. Labels could be personalized.

Fish — A955

Designs: No. 3671, $5, Amphiprion ocellaris. No. 3672, $5, Zanclus cornutus. No. 3673, $12, Coris gaimard. No. 3674, $12, Oxycirrhites typus.

**2006, July 14** ***Perf. 11½***

**3671-3674** A955 Set of 4 2.75 2.25
*3674a* Miniature sheet, 2 each #3671-3674, perf. 11½x12 5.75 5.75

A956

Sung Dynasty Calligraphy and Painting — A957

Designs: $5, Poem by Huang T'ing-chien. $9, Calligraphy on silk, by Mi Fu. Nos. 3677, 3679a, $12, Detail of magpie in flight, from Magpies and Hare, by Ts'ui Po. Nos. 3678, 3679b, $15, Detail of magpie on branch, from Magpies and Hare.

**2006, Aug. 4** ***Perf. 11½***

**Denominations in Black**

**3675-3678** A956 Set of 4 9.00 7.00

**Souvenir Sheet**

**Denominations in Black and Orange**

***Perf. 12½***

**3679** A957 Sheet of 2, #a-b 4.00 3.00

Dragonflies A958

Designs: Nos. 3680, 3684a, $5, Crocothemis servilia servilia. Nos. 3681, 3684b, $5, Orthetrum, pruinosum neglectum, vert. Nos. 3682, 3684c, $12, Diplacodes trivialis, vert. No. 3683, 3684d, $12, Orthetrum sabina sabina.

***Perf. 13x13¼, 13¼x13***

**2006, Aug. 16** **With White Frames**

**3680-3683** A958 Set of 4 2.00 1.75

**Souvenir Sheet**

**Without White Frames**

***Perf. 11¾***

**3684** A958 Sheet of 4, #a-d 2.40 2.00

**Pets Type of 2005**

Designs: $1, Yorkshire terrier. $9, Pomeranian. $15, Abyssinian cat. $20, Norwegian Forest cat.

**2006, Aug. 30** ***Perf. 13½x12½***

**Country Name in Blue**

**3685** A946 $1 multi .30 .25
**3686** A946 $9 multi .55 .25
**3687** A946 $15 multi .90 .45
**3688** A946 $20 multi 1.25 .60
*Nos. 3685-3688 (4)* 3.00 1.55

Aerial Activities — A959

Designs: No. 3689, $3.50, Paragliding. No. 3690, $3.50, Hang gliding, horiz. $12, Ultralight aircraft, horiz. $15, Parasailing.

**2006, Sept. 15** ***Perf. 13½***

**3689-3692** A959 Set of 4 2.50 1.50

Pitta Nympha — A960

Designs: Nos. 3693, 3697a, $5, On branch. Nos. 3694, 3697b, $5, In flight, horiz. Nos. 3695, 3697c, $10, With young at nest, horiz. Nos. 3696, 3697d, $10, With insect in beak.

***Perf. 13¼x13, 13x13¼***

**2006, Sept. 30** **With White Frames**

**3693-3696** A960 Set of 4 2.25 1.10

**Souvenir Sheet**

**Without White Frames**

***Perf. 11¾***

**3697** A960 Sheet of 4, #a-d 2.25 1.10

Cetaceans A961

Designs: No. 3698, $5, Stenella attenuata. No. 3699, $5, Stenella longirostris. $10, Feresa attenuata. $15, Physeter macrocephalus.

***Perf. 13x12 Syncopated***

**2006, Oct. 18** **Litho.**

**3698-3701** A961 Set of 4 2.50 1.50
*3701a* Souvenir sheet, #3698-3701 2.50 1.50

Flowers — A962

Designs: No. 3702, $5, Ludwigia octovalvis. No. 3703, $5, Hygrophila pogonocalyx, vert. $12, Titanotrichum oldhamii, vert.

**2006, Nov. 8** ***Perf. 11½***

**3702-3704** A962 Set of 3 1.75 .90

Scenic Areas — A963

Designs: No. 3705, $5, Jhongshan Building, Yangmingshan National Park. No. 3706, $5, Taroko Gorge, vert. $9, Queen's Head Rock, vert. $12, Sun Moon Lake.

**2006, Nov. 11** ***Perf. 12½***

**3705-3708** A963 Set of 4 2.75 1.50

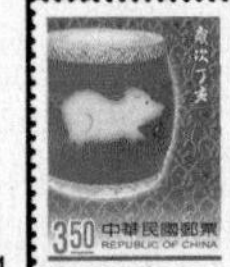

A964

New Year 2007 (Year of the Pig) A965

Designs: $3.50, Pig on drum. $13, Pig and drums.

**2006, Dec. 1** ***Perf. 12¼x11¾***

**3709-3710** A964 Set of 2 1.50 .75

**Souvenir Sheet**

***Perf. 11½x11¼***

**3711** A965 $12 multi 2.40 1.25

**Pets Type of 2005**

Designs: 50c, Border collie. $13, Beagle. $17, American Shorthair cat. $34, Maine Coon cat.

**2006, Dec. 18** ***Perf. 13½x12½***

**Country Name in Green**

**3712** A946 50c multi .30 .25
**3713** A946 $13 multi .75 .40
**3714** A946 $17 multi 1.00 .55
**3715** A946 $34 multi 2.00 1.10
*Nos. 3712-3715 (4)* 4.05 2.30

Inauguration of High Speed Rail Line — A966

No. 3716: a, 700T Series train. b, Hsinchu Station.

**2006, Dec. 25** ***Perf. 11½***

**3716** A966 $12 Horiz. pair, #a-b 1.60 .80

Orchids — A967

Designs: $3.50, Phaius tankervilleae. $5, Spiranthes sinensis. $12, Vanda x hybrida. $25, Cattleya sp.

**2007, Jan. 10** **Litho.** ***Perf. 13½x12½***

**3717** A967 $3.50 multi .30 .25
**3718** A967 $5 multi .35 .25
**3719** A967 $12 multi .80 .40
**3720** A967 $25 multi 1.60 .80
*Nos. 3717-3720 (4)* 3.05 1.70

See Nos. 3751-3754, 3768-3771.

Ching Dynasty Jewelry — A968

Designs: No. 3721, $5, Earrings. No. 3722, $5, Hairpin. $12, Fingernail guard. $25, Ring.

**2007, Jan. 17** ***Perf. 11½***

**3721-3724** A968 Set of 4 2.75 1.50

Valentine's Day — A969

Heart and faces in: $5, White. $20, Red.

**2007, Feb. 6**

**3725-3726** A969 Set of 2 1.50 .75

**Embroidered Squares Type of 2005**

Embroidered squares for Ching Dynasty military officials: No. 3727, $3.50, Cilin (light green background). No. 3728, $3.50, Lion (light orange background). $5, Leopard (bright orange background). $25, Tiger (light blue background).

**2007, Feb. 16** ***Perf. 11½x11¼***

**3727-3730** A918 Set of 4 2.25 1.10

Feb. 28, 1947 Massacre Memorial Museum — A970

**2007, Feb. 28**

**3731** A970 $5 multi 6.00 3.00

Bridges — A971

Designs: No. 3732, $5, Kanjin Bridge, Taoyuan (green panel). No. 3733, $5, Fusing Bridge, Luofu (purple panel). $12, MacArthur Second Bridge, Taipei. $15, Dajhih Bridge, Taipei.

**2007, Apr. 12** **Litho.** ***Perf. 11½x12***

**3732-3735** A971 Set of 4 2.40 1.20

See Nos. 3808-3811.

Lesser Panda — A972

Panda: No. 3736, $5, Eating bamboo. No. 3737, $5, Resting on rock. No. 3738, $10, Walking near tree, vert. No. 3739, $10, Scratching on rock, vert.
$12, Two pandas, vert.

***Perf. 11½x11¼, 11¼x11½***

**2007, Apr. 25**

**3736-3739** A972 Set of 4 2.00 1.00

**Souvenir Sheet**

***Perf. 12***

**3740** A972 $12 multi 1.00 1.00

No. 3740 contains one 40x50mm stamp.

Dharma Drum Mountain Intl. Buddhist Educational Complex A973

Chung Tai Chan Monastery A974

Fo Guang Shan Monastery A975

Tzu Chi Foundation Building A976

**2007, May 24** ***Perf. 13¼x13***

| | | | | |
|---|---|---|---|---|
| 3741 | A973 | $5 multi | .45 | .25 |
| 3742 | A974 | $5 multi | .45 | .25 |
| 3743 | A975 | $5 multi | .45 | .25 |
| 3744 | A976 | $5 multi | .45 | .25 |
| | *Nos. 3741-3744 (4)* | | 1.80 | 1.00 |

Dahlia and Butterflies A977

Iris and Butterfly A978

Clematis and Ladybugs A979

Tung Blossom and Butterflies A980

Rose and Butterfly A981

Sunflower and Insects A982

Bird-of-Paradise Flower and Butterfly A983

Lotus and Butterflies A984

English Daisies and Dragonfly A985

Balloon Flower and Dragonfly A986

**2007, May 28** ***Perf. 12½***

| | | | |
|---|---|---|---|
| 3745 | Block of 10 | 2.10 | 1.10 |
| *a.* | A977 $3.50 multi | .30 | .25 |
| *b.* | A978 $3.50 multi | .30 | .25 |
| *c.* | A979 $3.50 multi | .30 | .25 |
| *d.* | A980 $3.50 multi | .30 | .25 |
| *e.* | A981 $3.50 multi | .30 | .25 |
| *f.* | A982 $3.50 multi | .30 | .25 |
| *g.* | A983 $3.50 multi | .30 | .25 |
| *h.* | A984 $3.50 multi | .30 | .25 |
| *i.* | A985 $3.50 multi | .30 | .25 |
| *j.* | A986 $3.50 multi | .30 | .25 |

**Changed Colors**

| | | | |
|---|---|---|---|
| 3746 | Block of 10 | 3.00 | 1.50 |
| *a.* | A977 $5 multi | .30 | .25 |
| *b.* | A978 $5 multi | .30 | .25 |
| *c.* | A979 $5 multi | .30 | .25 |
| *d.* | A980 $5 multi | .30 | .25 |
| *e.* | A981 $5 multi | .30 | .25 |
| *f.* | A982 $5 multi | .30 | .25 |
| *g.* | A983 $5 multi | .30 | .25 |
| *h.* | A984 $5 multi | .30 | .25 |
| *i.* | A985 $5 multi | .30 | .25 |
| *j.* | A986 $5 multi | .30 | .25 |

Food Preparation Implements A987

Designs: No. 3747, $5, Rice bucket and shelf (light blue background). No. 3748, $5, Steamer (green background). No. 3749, $12, Rice baskets (tan background). No. 3750, $12, Dinnerware (lilac background).

**2007, June 28** ***Perf. 11½x11¼***

| | | | | |
|---|---|---|---|---|
| 3747-3750 | A987 | Set of 4 | 2.25 | 1.10 |

**Orchids Type of 2007 Inscribed "Taiwan" Instead of "Republic of China"**

Designs: $1, Paphiopedilum sp. $2.50, Phalaenopsis aphrodite. $10, Dendrobium sp. $32, Oncidium x hybridum.

**2007, July 12** ***Perf. 13½x12½***

| | | | | |
|---|---|---|---|---|
| 3751 | A967 | $1 multi | .30 | .25 |
| 3752 | A967 | $2.50 multi | .30 | .25 |
| 3753 | A967 | $10 multi | .60 | .30 |
| 3754 | A967 | $32 multi | 2.10 | 1.00 |
| | *Nos. 3751-3754 (4)* | | 3.30 | 1.80 |

End of Martial Law, 20th Anniv. — A988

**2007, July 15** ***Perf. 11¼x11½***

| | | | | |
|---|---|---|---|---|
| 3755 | A988 | $12 multi | .85 | .40 |

Fish — A989

Designs: No. 3756, $5, Nemateleotris magnifica. No. 3757, $5, Balistoides conspicillum. $12, Paracanthurus hepatus. $25, Cetoscarus bicolor.

**2007, July 27** ***Perf. 11½x11¼***

| | | | | |
|---|---|---|---|---|
| 3756-3759 | A989 | Set of 4 | 6.00 | 3.00 |

Chiang Wei-shui (1890-1931), Political and Social Leader — A990

**2007, Aug. 6 Engr.** ***Perf. 11¼x11½***

| | | | | |
|---|---|---|---|---|
| 3760 | A990 | $25 brown | 1.60 | .80 |

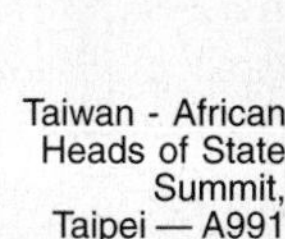
Taiwan - African Heads of State Summit, Taipei — A991

**2007, Sept. 9 Litho.** ***Perf. 11½x11¼***

| | | | | |
|---|---|---|---|---|
| 3761 | A991 | $12 multi | 1.20 | .60 |

Miniature Sheet

Eighteen Scholars of T'ang, by Emperor Hui-tsung. — A992

No. 3762 — Various portions of painting numbered: a, (10-5), 36x30mm. b, (10-4), 51x30mm. c, (10-3), 43x30mm. d, (10-2), 45x30mm. e, (10-1), 43x30mm. f, (10-10), 43x30mm. g, (10-9), 51x30mm. h, (10-8), 43x30mm. i, (10-7), 45x30mm. j, (10-6), 36x30mm.

**2007, Sept. 21** ***Perf. 13¼***

| | | | | |
|---|---|---|---|---|
| 3762 | A992 | Sheet of 10 | 3.00 | 1.50 |
| *a.-j.* | | $5 Any single | .30 | .25 |

Doves — A993

**2007, Sept. 28** ***Perf. 11¼x11½***

| | | | | |
|---|---|---|---|---|
| 3763 | A993 | $5 multi | .80 | .30 |

Portions of the design were applied by a thermographic process producing a shiny, raised effect.

Shells — A994

Designs: No. 3764, $5, Marchia loebbeckei. No. 3765, $5, Harpa major. No. 3766, $12, Epitonium scalare. No. 3767, $12, Cypraea aurantium.

**2007, Oct. 11 Litho.** ***Perf. 11½x11¼***

| | | | | |
|---|---|---|---|---|
| 3764-3767 | A994 | Set of 4 | 2.40 | 1.20 |

**Orchids Type of 2007 Inscribed "Taiwan" Instead of "Republic of China"**

Designs: $7, Ascocentrum sp. $9, Arundina graminifolia. $15, Vanda teres. $20, Epidendrum sp.

**2007, Oct. 24** ***Perf. 13½x12½***

| | | | | |
|---|---|---|---|---|
| 3768 | A967 | $7 multi | .45 | .25 |
| 3769 | A967 | $9 multi | .55 | .30 |
| 3770 | A967 | $15 multi | .95 | .45 |
| 3771 | A967 | $20 multi | 1.25 | .60 |
| | *Nos. 3768-3771 (4)* | | 3.20 | 1.60 |

Birds — A995

Designs: $3.50, Pericrocotus solaris. $5, Parus varius. $12, Luscinia calliope. $25, Phoenicurus auroreus.

**2007, Nov. 3**

| | | | | |
|---|---|---|---|---|
| 3772 | A995 | $3.50 multi | .30 | .25 |
| 3773 | A995 | $5 multi | .30 | .25 |
| 3774 | A995 | $12 multi | .75 | .35 |
| 3775 | A995 | $25 multi | 1.60 | .80 |
| | *Nos. 3772-3775 (4)* | | 2.95 | 1.65 |

See Nos. 3792-3795, 3819-3822, 3845-3848.

Outdoor Activities — A996

Designs: No. 3776, $5, Speed walking. No. 3777, $5, Cycling. $12, Skateboarding. $25, Rollerblading.

**2007, Nov. 9** ***Perf. 11½***

| | | | | |
|---|---|---|---|---|
| 3776-3779 | A996 | Set of 4 | 3.00 | 1.50 |

Scouting, Cent. A997

**2007, Nov. 28** ***Perf. 12½***

| | | | | |
|---|---|---|---|---|
| 3780 | A997 | $12 multi | .80 | .40 |

A998

New Year 2008 (Year of the Rat) A999

**2007, Dec. 3** ***Perf. 12½x11¾***

| | | | | |
|---|---|---|---|---|
| 3781 | A998 | $3.50 Rat at left | .45 | .25 |
| 3782 | A998 | $13 Rat at right | 1.45 | .70 |

**Souvenir Sheet**

***Perf. 12½***

| | | | | |
|---|---|---|---|---|
| 3783 | A999 | $12 multi | 1.75 | .85 |

Democracy Movement Leaders — A1000

Designs: No. 3784, Lei Chen (1897-1979), publisher. No. 3785, Fu Jheng (1927-91), editor. No. 3786, Kuo Yu Shing (1908-85), politician. No. 3787, Huang Hsin Chieh (1928-99), politician.

**2007, Dec. 10 Engr.** ***Perf. 11½***

| | | | | |
|---|---|---|---|---|
| 3784 | A1000 | $5 brown | .35 | .25 |
| 3785 | A1000 | $5 green | .35 | .25 |
| 3786 | A1000 | $5 claret | .35 | .25 |
| 3787 | A1000 | $5 brown black | .35 | .25 |
| | *Nos. 3784-3787 (4)* | | 1.40 | 1.00 |

Liou Family Compound, Shangfangliao — A1001

Lin Family Mansion, Banciao A1002

Li Teng-fang Compound, Dasi A1003

Siao Family Compound, Jiadong A1004

**2008, Jan. 23 Litho. *Perf. 12***

| | | | | |
|---|---|---|---|---|
| **3788** | A1001 | $5 multi | .35 | .25 |
| **3789** | A1002 | $5 multi | .35 | .25 |
| **3790** | A1003 | $5 multi | .35 | .25 |
| **3791** | A1004 | $12 multi | .95 | .45 |
| | | *Nos. 3788-3791 (4)* | 2.00 | 1.20 |

**Birds Type of 2007**

Designs: $1, Dicrurus aeneus. $2.50, Lanius schach. $10, Dendrocitta formosae. $32, Pycnonotus sinensis.

**2008, Jan. 30 *Perf. 13½x12½***

| | | | | |
|---|---|---|---|---|
| **3792** | A995 | $1 multi | .30 | .25 |
| **3793** | A995 | $2.50 multi | .30 | .25 |
| **3794** | A995 | $10 multi | .65 | .30 |
| **3795** | A995 | $32 multi | 2.00 | 1.00 |
| | | *Nos. 3792-3795 (4)* | 3.25 | 1.80 |

A1005

Puppet Theater A1006

No. 3796: a, Mirror Man, denomination at UL. b, Old Oddball, denomination at UR.

No. 3797: a, Shih Yan-wun, denomination at UL. b, Dragon Lady of the Bitter Sea, denomination at UR.

**2008, Feb. 4 *Perf. 11½***

| | | | | |
|---|---|---|---|---|
| **3796** | A1005 | $5 Horiz. pair, #a-b | .80 | .40 |
| **3797** | A1006 | $5 Horiz. pair, #a-b | .80 | .40 |
| *c.* | | Souvenir sheet, #3796-3797, perf. 11½x11 | 1.75 | .80 |

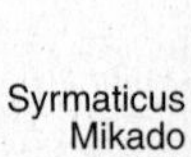

Syrmaticus Mikado A1007

**Litho. & Engr.**

**2008, Mar. 7 *Perf. 12***

| | | | | |
|---|---|---|---|---|
| **3798** | A1007 | $25 multi | 1.75 | .85 |

Taipei 2008 Intl. Stamp Exhibition — A1008

Paintings: $5, Plum Blossoms and Solitary Bird, by Pien Wen-chin. $9, Apricot Blossoms and Peacocks, by Lü Chi. $13, Wild Duck by a Brook, by Ch'en Lin. $15, Bamboo and Shrike, by Li An-chung.

**2008, Mar. 7 Litho. *Perf. 12½***

| | | | | |
|---|---|---|---|---|
| **3799-3802** | A1008 | Set of 4 | 2.75 | 1.40 |
| *3802a* | | Souvenir sheet, #3799-3802, perf. 12½ syncopated | 2.75 | 2.50 |

Miniature Sheets

A1009

Characters From Animated Film, "Finding Nemo" — A1010

No. 3803: a, Turtles (32mm diameter). b, Dory (26x34mm). c, Bubbles (32mm diameter). d, Nemo (34x26mm). e, Pearl (32mm diameter).

No. 3804 (all stamps 32mm diameter): a, Sheldon. b, Squirt. c, Tad. d, Nemo. e, Peach.

***Perf. 13x13½ (#3803b), 13½x13 (#3803d)***

**2008, Apr. 3**

| | | | | |
|---|---|---|---|---|
| **3803** | A1009 | $5 Sheet of 5, #a-e | 1.75 | .85 |
| **3804** | A1010 | $5 Sheet of 5, #a-e | 1.75 | .85 |

Cactus Flowers — A1011

Designs: No. 3805, $5, Hylocerus undatus. No. 3806, $5, Thelocactus bicolor. $12, Rhipsalidopsis gaertneri.

**2008, Apr. 30 Litho. *Perf. 11¼x11½***

| | | | | |
|---|---|---|---|---|
| **3805-3807** | A1011 | Set of 3 | 1.50 | .75 |

**Bridges Type of 2007 Inscribed "Taiwan"**

Designs: No. 3808, $5, Wurih Bridge, Taichung. No. 3809, $5, Jilu Bridge, Nantou, at night. $12, Shueiyun Bridge, Shueili. $15, Sindong Bridge, Miaoli.

**2008, May 12 *Perf. 11½x11¼***

| | | | | |
|---|---|---|---|---|
| **3808-3811** | A971 | Set of 4 | 2.50 | 1.25 |

A1012

A1013

A1014

Inauguration of President Ma Ying-jeou and Vice-president Vincent C. Siew — A1015

**2008, May 20 *Perf. 13½x13¼***

| | | | | |
|---|---|---|---|---|
| **3812** | A1012 | $5 multi | .35 | .25 |
| **3813** | A1013 | $5 multi | .35 | .25 |
| **3814** | A1014 | $13 multi | .85 | .45 |
| **3815** | A1015 | $15 multi | 1.00 | .50 |
| *a.* | | Miniature sheet, #3812-3815, perf. 12 | 2.60 | 1.40 |
| | | *Nos. 3812-3815 (4)* | 2.55 | 1.45 |

Yellow Tiger Flag A1016

Portrait of Jheng Cheng-gong A1017

**2008, May 29 *Perf. 12½***

**Stamps With White Frames**

| | | | | |
|---|---|---|---|---|
| **3816** | A1016 | $5 multi | .35 | .25 |
| **3817** | A1017 | $25 multi | 1.90 | .95 |

**Souvenir Sheet**

***Perf. 13½***

**Stamps Without White Frames**

| | | | | |
|---|---|---|---|---|
| **3818** | | Sheet of 2 | 2.75 | 1.40 |
| *a.* | | A1016 $5 multi | .45 | .25 |
| *b.* | | A1017 $25 multi | 2.25 | 1.10 |

National Taiwan Museum, cent.

**Birds Type of 2007**

Designs: $7, Streptopelia orientalis. $15, Passer montanus. $20, Pica pica. $34, Zosterops japonicus.

**2008, June 5 *Perf. 13½x12½***

| | | | | |
|---|---|---|---|---|
| **3819** | A995 | $7 multi | .50 | .25 |
| **3820** | A995 | $15 multi | 1.00 | .50 |
| **3821** | A995 | $20 multi | 1.40 | .70 |
| **3822** | A995 | $34 multi | 2.25 | 1.10 |
| | | *Nos. 3819-3822 (4)* | 5.15 | 2.55 |

Stag Beetles — A1018

Designs: No. 3823, $5, Neolucanus swinhoei. No. 3824, $5, Dorcus schenklingi. $10, Lucanus datunensis. $12, Cyclommatus asahinai.

**2008, June 5 *Perf. 12¼***

| | | | | |
|---|---|---|---|---|
| **3823-3826** | A1018 | Set of 4 | 2.10 | 1.10 |

Shells — A1019

Designs: No. 3827, $5, Murex troscheli. No. 3828, $5, Lambis chiragra. No. 3829, $12, Spondylus regius. No. 3830, $12, Cymatium pyrum.

**2008, July 9 Litho. *Perf. 13½***

| | | | | |
|---|---|---|---|---|
| **3827-3830** | A1019 | Set of 4 | 2.25 | 1.10 |

Urocissa Caerulea — A1020

Designs: Nos. 3831, 3835a, $5, Adults feeding hatchlings in nest. Nos. 3832, 3835b, $5, Bird holding snake in beak. Nos. 3833, 3835c, $12, Bird in flight. Nos. 3834, 3835d, $12, Bird on branch with spread wings.

**2008, July 9 *Perf. 13x13¼***

**Stamps With White Frames**

| | | | | |
|---|---|---|---|---|
| **3831-3834** | A1020 | Set of 4 | 2.25 | 1.10 |

**Souvenir Sheet**

**Stamps Without White Frames**

***Perf. 11¾***

| | | | | |
|---|---|---|---|---|
| **3835** | A1020 | Sheet of 4, #a-d | 2.25 | 1.10 |

No. 3835 contains four 34x25mm stamps.

Miniature Sheet

A Hundred Deers, by Ignace Sichelbart — A1021

No. 3836 — Parts of painting numbered: a, 8-1 (45x38mm). b, 8-2 (55x38mm). c, 8-3 (45x38mm). d, 8-4 (43x38mm). e, 8-5 (37x38mm). f, 8-6 (43x38mm). g, 8-7 (43x38mm). h, 8-8 (65x38mm).

**2008, July 16 *Perf. 13¼***

| | | | | |
|---|---|---|---|---|
| **3836** | A1021 | Sheet of 8, #a-h | 2.75 | 1.40 |
| *a.-h.* | | $5 Any single | .30 | .25 |

Items From Aboriginal Culture — A1022

Designs: $5, Paiwan earthenware pot. No. 3838, $12, Ami lover's bag (orange background). No. 3839, $12, Rukai men's headdress (lt. green background). $25, Bunun men's neck ornament.

**2008, Aug. 1 *Perf. 11¼x11½***

| | | | | |
|---|---|---|---|---|
| **3837-3840** | A1022 | Set of 4 | 3.50 | 1.75 |

Miniature Sheet

Yimin Festival A1023

No. 3841: a, Erection of lantern poles. b, Bowl of congee, spoon, flowers. c, Sinpu Yimin Temple, horiz. d, Pig competition, horiz.

**2008, Aug. 20 Litho. *Perf. 12½***

| | | | | |
|---|---|---|---|---|
| **3841** | A1023 | $5 Sheet of 4, #a-d | 1.25 | .65 |

New Year 2009 (Year of the Ox) — A1024

Designs: $3.50, Head of ox. $13, Ox. $12, Ox in water, horiz.

**2008, Dec. 1 *Perf. 12¼x11¾***

| | | | | |
|---|---|---|---|---|
| **3842-3843** | A1024 | Set of 2 | 1.75 | .85 |

**Souvenir Sheet**

***Perf. 11¾x11¼***

| | | | | |
|---|---|---|---|---|
| **3844** | A1024 | $12 multi | 1.10 | 1.10 |

No. 3844 contains one 50x30mm stamp.

**Birds Type of 2007 Inscribed "Republic of China (Taiwan)"**

Designs: 50c, Rostratula benghalensis. $9, Turdus poliocephalus. $13, Amaurornis phoenicurus. $17, Cettia acanthizoides.

**2009, Jan. 15 *Perf. 13½x12½***

| | | | | |
|---|---|---|---|---|
| **3845** | A995 | 50c multi | .30 | .25 |
| **3846** | A995 | $9 multi | .55 | .25 |
| **3847** | A995 | $13 multi | .80 | .40 |
| **3848** | A995 | $17 multi | 1.00 | .50 |
| | | *Nos. 3845-3848 (4)* | 2.65 | 1.40 |

Giant Pandas in Taipei Zoo — A1025

Designs: $5, Tuan Tuan on log bridge. $9, Yuan Yuan eating.

$25, Tuan Tuan and Yuan Yuan.

**2009, Jan. 20 *Perf. 11½x11¼***

| | | | | |
|---|---|---|---|---|
| **3849-3850** | A1025 | Set of 2 | 1.25 | .60 |

**Souvenir Sheet**

***Perf. 12***

| | | | | |
|---|---|---|---|---|
| **3851** | A1025 | $25 multi | 1.50 | 1.50 |

No. 3851 contains one 50x40mm stamp.

Ceremonial Objects — A1026

Designs: No. 3852, $5, Gift basket with handle, two women in background. No. 3853, $5, Wooden carrying box, men carrying box in background. No. 3854, $12, Bridal sedan chair, wedding procession in background. No. 3855, $12, Candlesticks, bride and groom holding incense sticks in background.

**2009, Feb. 10** ***Perf. 11½x11¼***

**3852-3855** A1026 Set of 4 2.50 1.25

Shells — A1027

Designs: No. 3856, $5, Strombus sinuatus. No. 3857, $5, Hydatina amplustre. No. 3858, $12, Cymatium hepaticum. No. 3859, $12, Mitra mitra.

**2009, Feb. 26** ***Perf. 13½***

**3856-3859** A1027 Set of 4 2.25 1.10

Flowers — A1028

Designs: $3.50, Lantana camara. $5, Murraya paniculata. $12, Tabebuia chrysantha. $25, Hibiscus sabdariffa.

**2009, Mar. 12** ***Perf. 13½x12½***

**3860** A1028 $3.50 multi .30 .25
**3861** A1028 $5 multi .30 .25
**3862** A1028 $12 multi .75 .35
**3863** A1028 $25 multi 1.50 .75
*Nos. 3860-3863 (4)* 2.85 1.60

See Nos. 3890-3893, 3905-3908, 3934-3937.

Opening of Red and Orange Lines of Kaohsiung Mass Rapid Transit System — A1029

Train and: $5, Central Park Station. $25, World Games Station.

**2009, Apr. 7** ***Perf. 11½x11¼***

**3864-3865** A1029 Set of 2 2.00 1.00

A1030

Pres. Chiang Ching-kuo (1910-88) — A1031

Pres. Chiang: No. 3866, $5, Wearing hat (gray panel). No. 3877, $5, Wearing suit and tie (dull purple panel). $10, Holding cane (blue panel), horiz. $12, Holding baby (brown panel), horiz.

***Perf. 11¼x11½, 11½x11¼***

**2009, Apr. 13**

**3866-3869** A1030 Set of 4 2.25 1.10

**Souvenir Sheet**

**3870** A1031 $25 shown 2.00 1.00

**Dragons Circling Two Carps By Type of 1997 With Denominations at Lower Right and Inscribed "Republic of China (Taiwan)"**

**2009, May 20 Engr.** ***Perf. 13¼x12½***

**3871** A745 $50 cobalt blue 3.25 1.60

Miniature Sheet

Butterflies — A1032

No. 3872: a, $5, Papilio xuthus (butterfly cutout at LL). b, $5, Troides aeacus formosanus (butterfly cutout at LR). c, $12, Graphium agamemnon (butterfly cutout at UL). d, Papilio paris nakaharai (butterfly cutout at UR).

**2009, June 25 Litho.** ***Perf. 11½x12***

**3872** A1032 Sheet of 4, #a-d 2.10 1.10

2009 World Games, Kaohsiung A1033

Designs: $5, Kaohsiung Arena and World Games mascots Kao Mei and Syong Ge. $12, Main Stadium and World Games emblem.

**2009, July 16** ***Perf. 12***

**3873-3874** A1033 Set of 2 1.10 .55
*3874a* Souvenir sheet, #3873-3874 1.10 .55

Ancient Art Treasures — A1034

Designs: No. 3875, $5, Two Qing Dynasty gold gourds. No. 3876, $5, Gold bowl used by Emperor Qianlong. No. 3877, $12, Mughal Empire inlaid round urn. No. 3878, $12, Qing Dynasty gilt ewer.

**2009, July 20** ***Perf. 12¼***

**3875-3878** A1034 Set of 4 2.10 1.10
*3878a* Souvenir sheet, #3875-3878, perf. 12¼x11¾ 2.25 1.10

Sites in Kinmen A1035

Designs: $5, Guningtou. $9, Zhaishan Tunnel. No. 3881, $10, Interior of Qingtian Hall. No. 3882, $10, Lake Taihu.

**2009, July 29** ***Perf. 12½***

**3879-3882** A1035 Set of 4 2.10 1.10

Paintings by Lin Yu-shan (1907-2004) — A1036

No. 3883: a, $5, On the Way Home. b, $25, Two Heads of Cattle.

**2009, Aug. 7 Litho.** ***Perf. 12½x12***

**3883** A1036 Horiz. pair, #a-b, + central label 2.50 1.25

Nursery Rhymes — A1037

Designs: No. 3884, $5, Little Girl and Her Doll (blue denomination). No. 3885, $5, Kingdom of Dolls (king and soldier on horses, yellow denomination). No. 3886, $5, Train, horiz. (red denomination). No. 3887, $5, Thunder Shower, horiz. (fish, fireflies, lotus flower, denomination in orange).

**2009, Aug. 26** ***Perf. 12¼***

**3884-3887** A1037 Set of 4 1.25 .60

21st Summer Deaflympics, Taipei — A1038

Designs: $5, Badminton, running. $25, Taekwondo, tennis.

**2009, Sept. 5** ***Perf. 11½***

**3888-3889** A1038 Set of 2 1.90 .95

**Flowers Type of 2009**

Designs: $1, Calliandra emarginata. $2.50, Bombax ceiba. $10, Delonix regia. $32, Spathodea campanulata.

**2009, Oct. 14 Litho.** ***Perf. 13½x12½***

**3890** A1028 $1 multi .30 .25
**3891** A1028 $2.50 multi .30 .25
**3892** A1028 $10 multi .65 .30
**3893** A1028 $32 multi 2.00 1.00
*Nos. 3890-3893 (4)* 3.25 1.80

Greetings — A1039

No. 3894: a, Necklace (orange background). b, Gift boxes (pink background). c, Bouquet of roses (yellow background). d, Lollipop and candy (light blue background). e, Balloons (orange red background). f, Champagne flutes (blue violet background). g, Hearts (yellow green background). h, Cake and strawberry (rose background). i, Sparklers (red violet background). j, Four-leaf clover (light green background).

No. 3895: a, Necklace (orange red background). b, Gift boxes (yellow green background). c, Bouquet of roses (pink background). d, Lollipop and candy (yellow background). e, Balloons (red background). f, Champagne flutes (red violet background). g, Hearts (orange background). h, Cake and strawberry (green background). i, Sparklers (blue background). j, Four-leaf clover (yellow background).

**2009, Nov. 12** ***Perf. 12½***

**3894** Block of 10 2.50 1.25
*a.-j.* A1039 $3.50 Any single .30 .25
**3895** Block of 10 3.00 1.50
*a.-j.* A1039 $5 Any single .30 .25

Nos. 3894 and 3895 were each printed in sheets containing two blocks + 5 labels.

Ferns — A1040

Designs: $5, Asplenium nidus. $9, Cyathea spinulosa. $12, Cyathea lepifera. $25, Cibotium taiwanense.

**2009, Nov. 26** ***Perf. 11¼x11½***

**3896-3899** A1040 Set of 4 3.25 1.60
*3899a* Souvenir sheet, #3896-3899 3.25 1.60

See Nos. 4060-4063.

A1041

New Year 2010 (Year of the Tiger) A1042

Tiger at: $3.50, Left. $13, Right.

**2009, Dec. 1** ***Perf. 12¼x12½***

**3900-3901** A1041 Set of 2 1.50 .75

**Souvenir Sheet**

***Perf. 12½***

**3902** A1042 $12 multi 1.10 1.10

Anti-Corruption Day — A1043

Background color: $5, Light blue. $25, Mauve.

**2009, Dec. 9 Litho.** ***Perf. 11½***

**3903-3904** A1043 Set of 2 1.90 .95

**Flowers Type of 2009**

Designs: $7, Michelia champaca. $15, Duranta repens. $20, Ixora chinensis. $34, Lagerstroemia speciosa.

**2010, Jan. 20** ***Perf. 13½x12½***

**3905** A1028 $7 multi .45 .25
**3906** A1028 $15 multi .95 .45
**3907** A1028 $20 multi 1.25 .65
**3908** A1028 $34 multi 2.25 1.10
*Nos. 3905-3908 (4)* 4.90 2.45

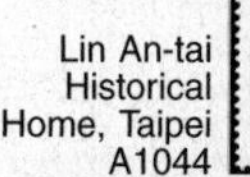

Lin An-tai Historical Home, Taipei A1044

Li Family Compound, Luzhou A1045

Lin Family Compound, Wufeng A1046

Xiaoyun Villa, Shengang A1047

**2010, Feb. 9** ***Perf. 13½x13¼***

**3909** A1044 $5 multi .35 .25
**3910** A1045 $5 multi .35 .25
**3911** A1046 $5 multi .35 .25
**3912** A1047 $12 multi .75 .35
*Nos. 3909-3912 (4)* 1.80 1.10

Little Taiwan, Qimei Islet — A1048

Whale Arch, Xiaomen Islet — A1049

Scenery of Penghu Islands: No. 3914, Basalt rocks, Xiaomen Islet. No. 3916, Twin heart-shaped stone weir, Qimei Islet.

**2010, Feb. 24** ***Perf. 13½***

**3913** A1048 $5 shown .35 .25
**3914** A1048 $5 multi .35 .25
**3915** A1049 $10 shown .65 .30
**3916** A1049 $10 multi .65 .30
*Nos. 3913-3916 (4)* 2.00 1.10

Bridges — A1050

Designs: No. 3917, $5, Jinde Bridge, Donggang (shown). No. 3918, $5, Qigu River Bridge, Tainan. No. 3919, $12, Anyi Bridge, Tainan. No. 3920, $12, Wangyue Bridge, Tainan (blue bridge at night).

**2010, Mar. 10** ***Perf. 11½***

**3917-3920** A1050 Set of 4 2.25 1.10

Mushrooms — A1051

Designs: Nos. 3921, 3925a, $5, Dictyphora multicolor. Nos. 3922, 3925b, $5, Pleurotus salmoneostramineus. Nos. 3923, 3925c, $12, Pseudocolus fusiformis. Nos. 3924, 3925d, $12, Coprinus disseminatus.

**2010, Mar. 25** ***Perf. 13***

**Stamps With White Frames**

**3921-3924** A1051 Set of 4 2.25 1.10

**Miniature Sheet**

**Stamps Without White Frames**

***Perf. 11¾***

**3925** A1051 Sheet of 4, #a-d 2.25 1.10

Crabs — A1052

Designs: No. 3926, $5, Cardisoma carnifex. No. 3927, $5, Scandarma lintou. $10, Sesarmops intermedius. $25, Gecarcoidea lalandii.

**2010, Apr. 15** ***Perf. 11½***

**3926-3929** A1052 Set of 4 3.00 1.50

Scenes From *The Romance of the Three Kingdoms* A1053

Designs: No. 3930, $3.50, Shooting an Arrow at the Halberd Beside the Gate of the Camp (shown). No. 3931, $3.50, Commenting on Heroes Over Wine. $5, Zhou Yu's Anger at Being Tricked by Zhuge Liang Three Times. $20, Holding Meng Huo Captive Seven Times.

**2010, Apr. 29** ***Perf. 11½***

**3930-3933** A1053 Set of 4 2.10 1.10

*3933a* Sheet of 4, #3930-3933, perf. 12 2.10 1.10

**Flowers Type of 2009**

Designs: 50c, Bauhinia variegata. $9, Euphorobia milii. $13, Brunfelsia hopeana. $17, Plumeria rubra.

**2010, May 12 Litho.** ***Perf. 13½x12½***

**3934** A1028 50c multi .30 .25
**3935** A1028 $9 multi .55 .30
**3936** A1028 $13 multi .80 .40
**3937** A1028 $17 multi 1.10 .55
*Nos. 3934-3937 (4)* 2.75 1.50

Long-horned Beetles — A1054

Designs: 75c, Erythrus formosanus. $2.50, Rosalia formosa conviva. $5, Aphrodisium faldermannii yuagii. $25, Anoplophora horsfieldi tonkinensis.

**2010, May 21** ***Perf. 12½x13½***

**3938** A1054 75c multi .30 .25
**3939** A1054 $2.50 multi .30 .25
**3940** A1054 $5 multi .30 .25
**3941** A1054 $25 multi 1.60 .80
*Nos. 3938-3941 (4)* 2.50 1.55

See Nos. 3976-3979, 4027-4030, 4134-4137.

Girl Scouts, Cent. A1055

Emblems and: $5, Two doves, stylized globe. $25, Dove, ribbon hearts.

**2010, June 1** ***Perf. 12½***

**3942-3943** A1055 Set of 2 1.90 .95

**Souvenir Sheet**

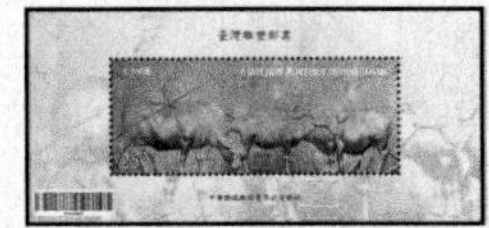

Water Buffaloes, Sculpture by Huang Tu-shui (1895-1930) — A1056

**Litho. & Embossed**

**2010, June 22** ***Perf. 11½x11¼***

**3944** A1056 $25 multi 1.60 .80

A1057

Scenes From Novel "Journey to the West" — A1058

Designs: No. 3945, Complete Enlightenment. No. 3946, Sun Wukong Wreaks Havoc in Heaven. $12, Dreaming of Beheading the Jing River Dragon King. $25, Stealing the Ginseng Fruits.

**2010, July 7 Litho.** ***Perf. 11¼x11½***

**3945** A1057 $5 multi .35 .25
**3946** A1058 $5 multi .35 .25
**3947** A1058 $12 multi .75 .35
**3948** A1058 $25 multi 1.60 .80
*Nos. 3945-3948 (4)* 3.05 1.65

Compare with Nos. 4003-4006.

Lighthouses — A1059

Designs: No. 3949, $5, Chilung Tao Lighthouse (denomination in yellow). No. 3950, $5, Wenkan Tui Lighthouse (denomination in blue). $10, Paisha Chia Lighthouse (denomination in lilac), horiz. $25, Liuchiu Yu Lighthouse (denomination in light green), horiz.

***Perf. 11¼x11½, 11½x11¼***

**2010, July 28**

**3949-3952** A1059 Set of 4 3.00 1.50

See Nos. 4160-4163.

Modern Taiwanese Paintings — A1060

No. 3953: a, $5, Bamboo Grove in Early Summer, by Tsai Yun-yan. b, $25, Pear Espalier, by Lu Yun-sheng.

**2010, Aug. 9** ***Perf. 12x12½***

**3953** A1060 Horiz. pair, #a-b, + central label 1.90 .95

**Souvenir Sheet**

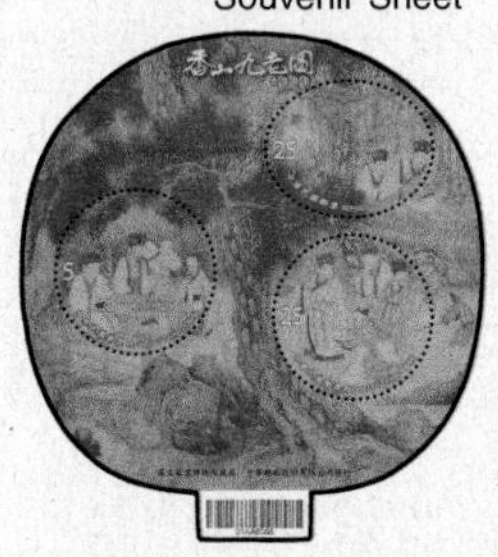

Nine Elders of Mt. Hsiang, by Unknown Painter A1061

No. 3954: a, $5, Servant and elders playing game (35mm diameter). b, $25, Three elders and dancer (35mm diameter). c, $25, Elders in bamboo grove (37x29mm oval stamp).

**2010, Sept. 9** ***Perf.***

**3954** A1061 Sheet of 3, #a-c 3.50 1.75

Stamps Depicting Educators — A1062

Designs: $5, Republic of China No. 1648 (Chu Hsi). $25, Republic of China No. 1798 (Confucius).

***Perf. 11¼x11½***

**2010, Sept. 28** **Litho.**

**3955-3956** A1062 Set of 2 1.90 .95

Shells — A1063

Designs: No. 3957, $5, Thatcheria mirabilis. No. 3958, $5, Tibia martinii. No. 3959, $12, Stellaria solaris. No. 3960, $12, Rapa rapa.

**2010, Oct. 4** ***Perf. 11½x11¼***

**3957-3960** A1063 Set of 4 2.25 1.10

Bridges — A1064

Designs: No. 3961, $5, Lizejian Bridge, Yilan (shown). No. 3962, $5, Taroko Bridge, Hualien. $12, Hongye Bridge, Taitung. $15, Pudu Bridge, Hualien.

**2010, Oct. 20**

**3961-3964** A1064 Set of 4 2.50 1.25

National Taipei University of Technology, Cent. — A1065

No. 3965: a, $5, Building, old gate. b, $25, Sixth Instructional Building, Technology Building, new gate.

**2010, Nov. 1** ***Perf. 12½***

**3965** A1065 Horiz. pair, #a-b 2.00 1.00

A1066 A1067

A1068 A1069

A1070 A1071

A1072 A1073

A1074 A1075

A1076 A1077

A1078 A1079

A1080 A1081

A1082 A1083

A1084

**2010, Nov. 6 Litho.** ***Perf. 13½x13¼***

**3966** Sheet of 9 3.25 1.60
*a.* A1066 $5 multi .35 .25
*b.* A1067 $5 multi .35 .25
*c.* A1068 $5 multi .35 .25
*d.* A1069 $5 multi .35 .25

| | | | |
|---|---|---|---|
| *e.* | A1070 $5 multi | .35 | .25 |
| *f.* | A1071 $5 multi | .35 | .25 |
| *g.* | A1072 $5 multi | .35 | .25 |
| *h.* | A1073 $5 multi | .35 | .25 |
| *i.* | A1074 $5 multi | .35 | .25 |

***Perf. 13¼x13½***

| | | | |
|---|---|---|---|
| **3967** | Sheet of 10 | 3.50 | 1.75 |
| *a.* | A1075 $5 multi | .35 | .25 |
| *b.* | A1076 $5 multi | .35 | .25 |
| *c.* | A1077 $5 multi | .35 | .25 |
| *d.* | A1078 $5 multi | .35 | .25 |
| *e.* | A1079 $5 multi | .35 | .25 |
| *f.* | A1080 $5 multi | .35 | .25 |
| *g.* | A1081 $5 multi | .35 | .25 |
| *h.* | A1082 $5 multi | .35 | .25 |
| *i.* | A1083 $5 multi | .35 | .25 |
| *j.* | A1084 $5 multi | .35 | .25 |

Taipei International Flora Expo.

Qing Dynasty Gilt Copper Censers — A1085

Censer with: No. 3968, $5, Turquoise inlays (shown). No. 3969, $5, Lotus flower designs. $10, Glass and enamel inlays. $25, White jade, turquoise and glass inlays.

**2010, Nov. 18** ***Perf. 11½***

| | | | |
|---|---|---|---|
| **3968-3971** A1085 | Set of 4 | 3.00 | 1.50 |
| *3971a* | Souvenir sheet of 4, #3968-3971, perf. 12 | 3.00 | 1.50 |

New Year 2011 (Year of the Rabbit) — A1086

Designs: $3.50, Two rabbits. $13, One rabbit.
$12, One rabbit, diff.

**2010, Dec. 1** ***Perf. 12¼***

| | | | |
|---|---|---|---|
| **3972-3973** A1086 | Set of 2 | 1.10 | .55 |

**Souvenir Sheet**

***Perf. 12½***

| | | | |
|---|---|---|---|
| **3974** A1086 | $12 multi | .80 | .40 |

No. 3974 contains one 61x37mm stamp.

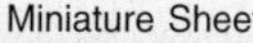

Miniature Sheet

Fireworks Displays — A1087

No. 3975: a, $5, Double Tenth Day display, Taipei (30x30mm). b, $5, New Year's display at Taipei 101 Building (24x48mm). c, $25, Lantern Festival display, Kaohsiung (30x30mm). d, $25, Dragon Boat Festival display, Longtan (24x48mm).

**Litho. With Hologram**

**2011, Jan. 1** ***Perf. 13¼***

| | | | |
|---|---|---|---|
| **3975** A1087 | Sheet of 4, #a-d | 4.25 | 2.10 |

**Long-horned Beetles Type of 2010**

Designs: $1, Aeolesthes oenochrous. $3.50, Doliops similis. $10, Thermistis taiwanensis. $32, Dorysthenes pici.

**2011, Jan. 26 Litho.** ***Perf. 12½x13½***

| | | | |
|---|---|---|---|
| **3976** A1054 | $1 multi | .30 | .25 |
| **3977** A1054 | $3.50 multi | .30 | .25 |
| **3978** A1054 | $10 multi | .70 | .35 |
| **3979** A1054 | $32 multi | 2.25 | 1.10 |
| | *Nos. 3976-3979 (4)* | 3.55 | 1.95 |

Valentine's Day A1088

Quick response code and: $5, Outline of heart. $25, Heart.

**2011, Feb. 14** ***Perf. 12½***

| | | | |
|---|---|---|---|
| **3980-3981** A1088 | Set of 2 | 2.10 | 1.10 |

Values are for stamps with surrounding selvage.

Fish — A1089

Designs: No. 3982, $5, Candidia barbatus. No. 3983, $5, Opsariichthys pachycephalus. $12, Spinibarbus hollandi. $25, Squalidus banarescui.

**2011, Mar. 18** ***Perf. 13½x13¼***

| | | | |
|---|---|---|---|
| **3982-3985** A1089 | Set of 4 | 4.00 | 1.60 |

Miniature Sheet

Butterflies — A1090

No. 3986: a, $5, Euploea eunice hobsoni (butterfly cutout at LL). b, $5, Euploea sylvester swinhoei (butterfly cutout at LR). c, $12, Euploea tulliolus koxinga (denomination at LL). d, $12, Euploea mulciber barsine (denomination at LR).

**2011, Apr. 8** ***Perf. 12½x12***

| | | | |
|---|---|---|---|
| **3986** A1090 | Sheet of 4, #a-d | 2.40 | 1.25 |

National Tsing Hua University, Cent. — A1091

Designs: $5, Second campus gate, old library building. $25, Current campus gate, Humanities and Social Sciences Building.

**2011, Apr. 20** ***Perf. 12½***

| | | | |
|---|---|---|---|
| **3987-3988** A1091 | Set of 2 | 2.10 | 1.10 |

Alpine Flowers — A1092

Designs: No. 3989, $5, Gentiana scabrida var. punctulata. No. 3990, $5, Euphrasia transmorrisonensis. No. 3991, $10, Clematis montana, horiz. No. 3992, $10, Cypripedium formosanum, horiz.

**2011, May 16** ***Perf. 12***

| | | | |
|---|---|---|---|
| **3989-3992** A1092 | Set of 4 | 2.10 | 1.10 |

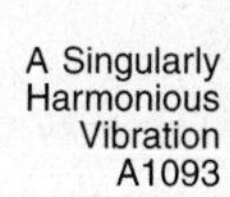

A Singularly Harmonious Vibration A1093

Double Happiness A1094

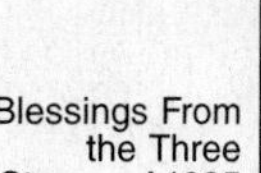

Blessings From the Three Stars — A1095

Four is for Everything Goes as One Wishes — A1096

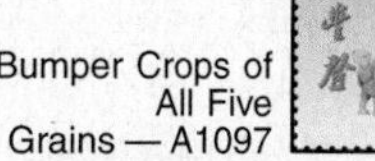

Bumper Crops of All Five Grains — A1097

Spring in All Six Directions A1098

Seven is for a Match Made in Heaven — A1099

The Eight Immortals Wish for Your Longevity A1100

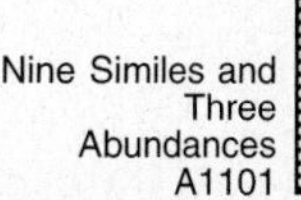

Nine Similes and Three Abundances A1101

Ten Complete A1102

No. 3993 — Color of denomination: a, Blue green. b, Pink. c, Gray. d, Orange red. e, Red violet. f, Red. g, Blue gray. h, Purple. i, Green. j, Olive green.

No. 3994 — Color of denomination: a, Olive green. b, Gray. c, Pink. d, Purple. e, Red. f, Blue gray. g, Orange red. h, Green. i, Red violet. j, Blue green.

**2011, May 27** ***Perf. 12½***

| | | | |
|---|---|---|---|
| **3993** | Block of 10 | 2.50 | 1.25 |
| *a.* | A1093 $3.50 multi | .30 | .25 |
| *b.* | A1094 $3.50 multi | .30 | .25 |
| *c.* | A1095 $3.50 multi | .30 | .25 |
| *d.* | A1096 $3.50 multi | .30 | .25 |
| *e.* | A1097 $3.50 multi | .30 | .25 |
| *f.* | A1098 $3.50 multi | .30 | .25 |
| *g.* | A1099 $3.50 multi | .30 | .25 |
| *h.* | A1100 $3.50 multi | .30 | .25 |
| *i.* | A1101 $3.50 multi | .30 | .25 |
| *j.* | A1102 $3.50 multi | .30 | .25 |
| **3994** | Block of 10 | 3.50 | 1.75 |
| *a.* | A1093 $5 multi | .35 | .25 |
| *b.* | A1094 $5 multi | .35 | .25 |
| *c.* | A1095 $5 multi | .35 | .25 |
| *d.* | A1096 $5 multi | .35 | .25 |
| *e.* | A1097 $5 multi | .35 | .25 |
| *f.* | A1098 $5 multi | .35 | .25 |
| *g.* | A1099 $5 multi | .35 | .25 |
| *h.* | A1100 $5 multi | .35 | .25 |
| *i.* | A1101 $5 multi | .35 | .25 |
| *j.* | A1102 $5 multi | .35 | .25 |

Sea Slugs — A1103

Designs: No. 3995, $5, Mexichromis multituberculata. No. 3996, $5, Chromodoris willani. $12, Gymnodoris ceylonica. $25, Glossodoris averni.

**2011, June 8** ***Perf. 12½***

| | | | |
|---|---|---|---|
| **3995-3998** A1103 | Set of 4 | 3.25 | 1.60 |

Owls — A1104

Designs: No. 3999, $5, Asio otus. No. 4000, $5, Otus sunia. $10, Strix aluco. $25, Glaucidium brodiei.

**2011, July 7 Engr.** ***Perf. 12¾x12½***

| | | | |
|---|---|---|---|
| **3999-4002** A1104 | Set of 4 | 3.25 | 1.60 |

See Nos. 4051-4054, 4122-4125.

Swindling Treasures A1105

Red Boy A1106

Crossing the River on a Turtle's Back A1107

Achieving Nirvana A1108

**2011, July 21** **Litho.**

| | | | |
|---|---|---|---|
| **4003** A1105 | $5 multi | .35 | .25 |
| **4004** A1106 | $5 multi | .35 | .25 |
| **4005** A1107 | $12 multi | .85 | .40 |
| **4006** A1108 | $25 multi | 1.75 | .85 |
| | *Nos. 4003-4006 (4)* | 3.30 | 1.75 |

Scenes from Novel "Journey to the West." Compare with Nos. 3945-3948.

Atayal Facial Tattoos — A1109

**2011, Aug. 1** ***Perf. 12½***

| | | | |
|---|---|---|---|
| **4007** A1109 | $25 multi | 1.75 | .85 |

Souvenir Sheet

Scroll Painting, "Nine Elders of Mt. Hsiang" A1110

No. 4008: a, $5, Three elders and attendant at game table. b, $25, Three elders and three attendants dancing. c, $25, Two elders reading, attendant, tree in foreground.

**2011, Sept. 9** ***Perf. 13½x13¼***

| | | | |
|---|---|---|---|
| **4008** A1110 | Sheet of 3, #a-c | 3.75 | 1.90 |

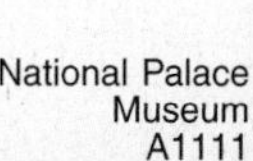

National Palace Museum A1111

Taipei 101 Building — A1112

Sun Moon Lake — A1113

Yushan (Jade Mountain) A1114

Alishan — A1115

Love River, Kaohsiung A1116

Beach, Kenting — A1117

Day Lilies in Liushidan Mountains A1118

Taroko National Park — A1119

Jiufen — A1120

**2011, Sept. 27** *Perf. 12½*

| | | | |
|---|---|---|---|
| 4009 | Block of 10 | 2.50 | 1.25 |
| *a.* | A1111 $3.50 multi | .30 | .25 |
| *b.* | A1112 $3.50 multi | .30 | .25 |
| *c.* | A1113 $3.50 multi | .30 | .25 |
| *d.* | A1114 $3.50 multi | .30 | .25 |
| *e.* | A1115 $3.50 multi | .30 | .25 |
| *f.* | A1116 $3.50 multi | .30 | .25 |
| *g.* | A1117 $3.50 multi | .30 | .25 |
| *h.* | A1118 $3.50 multi | .30 | .25 |
| *i.* | A1119 $3.50 multi | .30 | .25 |
| *j.* | A1120 $3.50 multi | .30 | .25 |
| 4010 | Block of 10 | 3.50 | 1.75 |
| *a.* | A1111 $5 multi | .35 | .25 |
| *b.* | A1112 $5 multi | .35 | .25 |
| *c.* | A1113 $5 multi | .35 | .25 |
| *d.* | A1114 $5 multi | .35 | .25 |
| *e.* | A1115 $5 multi | .35 | .25 |
| *f.* | A1116 $5 multi | .35 | .25 |
| *g.* | A1117 $5 multi | .35 | .25 |
| *h.* | A1118 $5 multi | .35 | .25 |
| *i.* | A1119 $5 multi | .35 | .25 |
| *j.* | A1120 $5 multi | .35 | .25 |

Travel destinations. Nos. 4009 and 4010 were each printed in sheets containing two blocks + 5 labels.

A1121

Republic of China, Cent. A1122

No. 4011: a, Flag of Republic of China, Sun Yat-sen, doves over buildings. b, Presidential Office Building, bananas, pineapple, sugar cane. c, Building, highway bridge, airplane, ship. d, Train, silicon wafers, satellite dish. No. 4012, Flag of Republic of China, Presidential Office Building, Sun Yat-sen.

*Perf. 12½x13¼ Syncopated*

**2011, Oct. 10** **Litho.**

| | | | |
|---|---|---|---|
| 4011 | Horiz. strip of 4 | 3.25 | 1.60 |
| *a.-b.* | A1121 $5 Either single | .35 | .25 |
| *c.* | A1121 $10 multi | .65 | .35 |
| *d.* | A1121 $25 multi | 1.75 | .85 |

**Souvenir Sheet**

**Litho. With Foil Application**

*Perf. 13¼*

4012 A1122 $25 multi 1.75 .85

The syncopation between Nos. 4011a and 4011b is a rectangle, and oval between Nos. 4011b and 4011c and 4011c and 4011d.

Plum Blossoms — A1123

*Perf. 13¼x13½*

**2011, Oct. 10** **Litho. & Engr.**

4013 A1123 $100 multi 6.75 3.25

No. 4013 was printed in sheets of 10 + 8 labels.

Scouting in China, Cent. — A1124

Scout and: $5, City. $12, Mountain, horiz.

*Perf. 12¾x12½, 12½x12¾*

**2011, Nov. 1** **Litho.**

4014-4015 A1124 Set of 2 1.25 .60

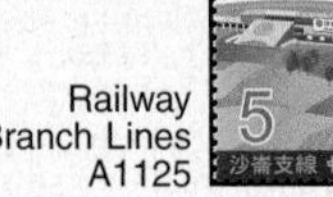
Railway Branch Lines A1125

No. 4016: a, $5, Shalun Branch Line (denomination in pink). b, $5, Jiji Branch Line (denomination in orange). c, $12, Neiwan Branch Line (denomination in blue). d, $12, Liujia Branch Line (denomination in pink). e, $15, Pingxi Branch Line.

**2011, Nov. 12** *Perf. 12½*

| | | | |
|---|---|---|---|
| 4016 | Vert. strip of 5 | 3.50 | 1.75 |
| *a.-b.* | A1125 $5 Either single | .35 | .25 |
| *c.-d.* | A1125 $12 Either single | .80 | .40 |
| *e.* | A1125 $15 multi | 1.00 | .50 |

New Year 2012 (Year of the Dragon) — A1126

Designs: $3.50, Two dragons. $13, Dragon facing left.
$12, Dragon facing right.

**2011, Dec. 1** *Perf. 13*

4017-4018 A1126 Set of 2 1.10 .55

**Souvenir Sheet**

*Perf. 12½*

4019 A1126 $12 multi .80 .40

No. 4019 contains one 64x40mm stamp.

Souvenir Sheet

Alishan Forest Railway, Cent. A1127

No. 4020: a, $5, Diesel engine, tunnel. b, $25, Steam engine.

**2011, Dec. 25** *Perf. 12½x12¾*

4020 A1127 Sheet of 2, #a-b 2.00 1.00

Berries — A1128

Designs: $3.50, Actinidia callosa. $5, Synsepalum dulcificum. $12, Solanum americanum. $25, Solanum verbascifolium.

**2012, Jan. 12** *Perf. 13¼x12½*

| | | | |
|---|---|---|---|
| 4021 | A1128 $3.50 multi | .30 | .25 |
| 4022 | A1128 $5 multi | .35 | .25 |
| 4023 | A1128 $12 multi | .85 | .40 |
| 4024 | A1128 $25 multi | 1.75 | .85 |
| | *Nos. 4021-4024 (4)* | 3.25 | 1.75 |

See Nos. 4084-4087, 4106-4109, 4164-4167..

A1129

Roses A1130

No. 4025: a, Rose. b, Rose, stem and leaves.
$32, Two roses.

**Litho. & Embossed**

**2012, Feb. 10** *Perf. 14½*

| | | | |
|---|---|---|---|
| 4025 | A1129 Horiz. pair + central label | 2.60 | 1.25 |
| *a.* | $12 multi | .85 | .40 |
| *b.* | $25 multi | 1.75 | .85 |

**Souvenir Sheet**

**Litho.**

*Perf.*

4026 A1130 $32 multi 2.25 1.10

No. 4026 is impregnated with a rose scent.

**Long-horned Beetles Type of 2010**

Designs: $7, Leptura formosomontana formosomontana. $12, Pyrestes curticornis. $15, Anaglyptus meridionalis. $20, Anoplophora albopicta.

**2012, Mar. 9** **Litho.** *Perf. 12½x13½*

| | | | |
|---|---|---|---|
| 4027 | A1054 $7 multi | .50 | .25 |
| 4028 | A1054 $12 multi | .85 | .40 |
| 4029 | A1054 $15 multi | 1.00 | .50 |
| 4030 | A1054 $20 multi | 1.40 | .70 |
| | *Nos. 4027-4030 (4)* | 3.75 | 1.85 |

Mushrooms — A1131

Designs: Nos. 4031, 4035a, $5, Amanita rubrovolvata. Nos. 4032, 4035b, $5, Entoloma murraii. Nos. 4033, 4035c, $12, Geastrum sessile. Nos. 4034, 4035d, $12, Clavulinopsis miyabeana.

**2012, Mar. 23** *Perf. 13¼x13*

**Stamps With White Frames**

4031-4034 A1131 Set of 4 2.40 1.25

**Souvenir Sheet**

**Stamps Without White Frames**

*Perf. 12¾x13*

4035 A1131 Sheet of 4, #a-d 2.40 1.25

No. 4035 contains four 26x34mm stamps.

Fish — A1132

Designs: No. 4036, $5, Formosania lacustre. No. 4037, $5, Tanakia himantegus. $12, Channa asiatica. $25, Sinogastromyzon puliensis.

**2012, Apr. 11** *Perf. 12½x13¼*

4036-4039 A1132 Set of 4 3.25 1.60

Scenes From Novel "Outlaws of the Marsh" — A1133

Designs: No. 4040, $5, Demons Released (denomination at LL). No. 4041, $5, Slaying the Tiger on Jingyang Ridge (denomination at LR). $10, Mountain God Temple on a Stormy Night. $25, Knocking the Lord of the West Dead.

**2012, Apr. 25** *Perf. 12½x12¾*

4040-4043 A1133 Set of 4 3.25 1.60

See Nos. 4110-4113.

"A Match Made in Heaven" A1134

"One Child After Another" A1135

Congratulatory greetings: $5, "The Hall is Packed with Wealth and Riches." $12, "A Family Experinces Two Joys."

**2012, May 4** *Perf. 13*

| | | | |
|---|---|---|---|
| 4044 | A1134 $3.50 multi | .30 | .25 |
| 4045 | A1135 $3.50 multi | .30 | .25 |
| 4046 | A1135 $5 multi | .35 | .25 |
| 4047 | A1135 $12 multi | .80 | .40 |
| | *Nos. 4044-4047 (4)* | 1.75 | 1.15 |

**Booklet Stamp**

*Perf. 13½ Vert.*

| | | | |
|---|---|---|---|
| 4048 | A1135 $5 multi | .35 | .25 |
| *a.* | Booklet pane of 12 | 4.25 | — |
| | Complete booklet, #4048a | 4.25 | |

Inauguration of President Ma Ying-jeou and Vice President Wu Den-yih — A1136

No. 4049 — President, Vice president and: a, Flag and Presidential Palace. b, Taipei 101 building, train, ship and airplane. c, Children, dancers, National Theater. d, Map of Taiwan, stylized globe. $32, President, Vice President, flag, Presidential Palace, plum blossoms, horiz.

**2012, May 20** ***Perf. 13¼x13½***

**4049** Horiz. strip of 4 2.40 1.25
*a.-b.* A1136 $5 Either single .35 .25
*c.-d.* A1136 $12 Either single .80 .40

**Souvenir Sheet**

***Perf. 13½x13¼***

**4050** A1136 $32 multi 2.25 1.10

No. 4050 contains one 80x30mm stamp.

### Owls Type of 2011

Designs: No. 4051, $5, Asio flammeus. No. 4052, $5, Otus spilocephalus. $10, Strix leptogrammica. $25, Ninox scutulata.

**2012, June 6 Engr.** ***Perf. 12¾x12½***

**4051-4054** A1104 Set of 4 3.00 1.50

Festivals A1137

Designs: No. 4055, $5, Chinese New Year (fireworks and calligraphic couplets). No. 4056, $5, Lantern Festival (lanterns and sandals). $10, Dragon Boat Festival (herb sachets and covered wine containers). $25, Mid-autumn Festival (Jade Hare, Lady Chang'e, moon cakes).

**2012, June 20 Litho.** ***Perf. 12½***

**4055-4058** A1137 Set of 4 3.00 1.50

Miniature Sheet

Bees and Wasps — A1138

No. 4059: a, $5, Phimenes flavopictus. b, $5, Xanthopimpla pedator. c, $5, Vespa ducalis. d, $10, Apis mellifera. e, $10, Xylocopa tranquebarorum. f, $10, Apis cerana.

**2012, July 12** ***Perf. 13***

**4059** A1138 Sheet of 6, #a-f 3.00 1.50

### Ferns Type of 2009

Designs: No. 4060, $5, Polystichum lepidocaulon. No. 4061, $5, Bolbitis heteroclita. $10, Adiantum malesianum, horiz. $25, Asplenium prolongatum, horiz.

***Perf. 12¾x12½, 12½x12¾***

**2012, July 25**

**4060-4063** A1040 Set of 4 3.00 1.50
*4063a* Sheet of 4, #4060-4063, perf. 12, + label 3.00 1.50

Familial Bonds — A1139

Silhouettes of: $5, Father and daughter. $7, Mother and son. $10, Mother, father and child. $12, Grandparents and child.

**2012, Aug. 24** ***Perf. 12½x13¼***

**4064-4067** A1139 Set of 4 2.40 1.25

Miniature Sheet

Teas and Tourist Attractions — A1140

No. 4068: a, Baozhong tea, Pinglin Tea Museum (bright yellow frame). b, Tieguanyin tea, Maokong Funicular (yellow orange frame). c, Black tea, Sun Moon Lake Wharf (orange frame). d, Oolong tea, Alishan Forest train (bister frame). e, Oriental Beauty tea, Emei Lake Suspension Bridge (red brown frame).

**2012, Sept. 12** ***Perf. 12½***

**4068** A1140 $10 Sheet of 5, #a-e 3.50 1.75

Nos. 4068a-4068e each have a cut-out of a teapot under the denomination.

Cotton Rose A1141

Bird-of-Paradise Flower A1142

Clary Sage A1143

Dancing Lady Orchid A1144

Zinnia A1145

Marigold A1146

Chinese Hibiscus A1147

Fragrant Olive A1148

Flowering Crab Apple A1149

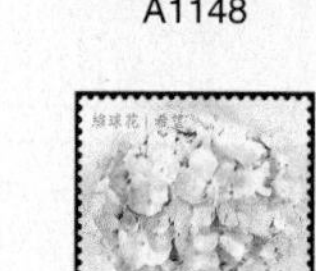

Hydrangea A1150

**2012, Sept. 28** ***Perf. 13¼***

**4069** Block of 10 2.50 1.25
*a.* A1141 $3.50 multi .30 .25
*b.* A1142 $3.50 multi .30 .25
*c.* A1143 $3.50 multi .30 .25
*d.* A1144 $3.50 multi .30 .25
*e.* A1145 $3.50 multi .30 .25
*f.* A1146 $3.50 multi .30 .25
*g.* A1147 $3.50 multi .30 .25
*h.* A1148 $3.50 multi .30 .25
*i.* A1149 $3.50 multi .30 .25
*j.* A1150 $3.50 multi .30 .25

**4070** Block of 10 3.50 1.75
*a.* A1141 $5 multi .35 .25
*b.* A1142 $5 multi .35 .25
*c.* A1143 $5 multi .35 .25
*d.* A1144 $5 multi .35 .25
*e.* A1145 $5 multi .35 .25
*f.* A1146 $5 multi .35 .25
*g.* A1147 $5 multi .35 .25
*h.* A1148 $5 multi .35 .25
*i.* A1149 $5 multi .35 .25
*j.* A1150 $5 multi .35 .25

Miniature Sheets

A1151

Characters From *Toy Story* — A1152

No. 4071: a, $5, Mr. Pricklepants, Peas-in-a-Pod (40x30mm). b, $5, Aliens (35mm diameter). c, $5, Trixie, Buttercup (40x30mm). d, $12, Lotso-Huggin Bear (30x40mm). e, $12, Woody (35mm diameter).

No. 4072: a, $5, Woody on Bullseye (35mm diameter). b, $5, Rex (35mm diameter). c, $5, Hamm (35mm diameter). d, $12, Buzz Lightyear (35mm diameter). e, $12, Jessie (30x40mm).

***Serpentine Die Cut (round stamps), Serpentine Die Cut 14x13½ (horiz. stamps), Serpentine Die Cut 13½x14 (vert. stamps)***

**2012, Oct. 23** **Self-Adhesive**

**4071** A1151 Sheet of 5, #a-e 2.75 1.40
**4072** A1152 Sheet of 5, #a-e 2.75 1.40

Protected Mammals A1153

Designs: No. 4073, $5, Paguma larvata taivana. No. 4074, $5, Mustela nivalis formosana. $10, Martes flavigula chrysopila. $25, Viverricula indica pallida.

**2012, Nov. 7 Litho.** ***Perf. 12½x13¼***

**4073-4076** A1153 Set of 4 3.25 1.60

A1154

Three Friends and a Hundred Birds, by Pien Wen-chin (c. 1356-c. 1428) A1155

No. 4077 — Details from painting of various birds in tree: a, $5. b, $10. c, $12.
$70, Entire painting.

**2012, Nov. 22** ***Perf. 13¼x13***

**4077** A1154 Sheet of 3, #a-c 1.90 .95

**Souvenir Sheet**

**Silk-Faced Paper**

***Perf. 14x14¼***

**4078** A1155 $70 multi 5.00 2.50

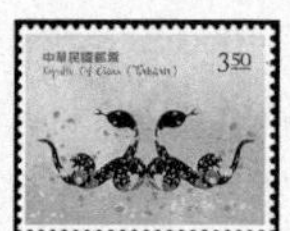

New Year 2013 (Year of the Snake) — A1156

Designs: $3.50, Two snakes. $13, Snake, head at left.
$12, Snake, head at right.

**2012, Dec. 3** ***Perf. 13***

**4079-4080** A1156 Set of 2 1.25 .60

**Souvenir Sheet**

***Perf. 12½***

**4081** A1156 $12 multi .85 .45

No. 4081 contains one 64x40mm stamp.

Marine Life A1157

No. 4082: a, $10, Eurypharynx pelecanoides. b, $10, Bufoceratias shaoi. c, $12, Argyropelecus aculeatus. d, $12, Regalecus glesne.
$25, Histioteuthis celetaria pacifica, vert.

**Litho., Litho. With Foil Application (#4082c)**

**2012, Dec. 12** ***Perf. 14x13¼***

**4082** A1157 Sheet of 4, #a-d 3.00 1.50

**Souvenir Sheet**

***Perf. 13¼x14***

**4083** A1157 $25 multi 1.75 .85

### Berries Type of 2012

Designs: $2.50, Rhodomyrtus tomentosa. $7, Ardisia squamulosa. $10, Hylocereus undatus. $32, Mahonia japonica.

**2013, Jan. 17 Litho.** ***Perf. 13¼x12½***

**4084** A1128 $2.50 multi .30 .25
**4085** A1128 $7 multi .50 .25
**4086** A1128 $10 multi .70 .35
**4087** A1128 $32 multi 2.25 1.10
*Nos. 4084-4087 (4)* 3.75 1.95

Chinese Dishes A1158

No. 4088 — Chopsticks and: a, Kung Pao Chicken, bowl of rice, spoon. b, Mud Crab with Glutinous Rice Cake, cup of green tea, salt shaker. c, Three-cup Chicken, bowl of sauce, salt shaker. d, Hakka Stir-fry, bowl of rice, salt shaker.

**2013, Jan. 31** ***Perf. 13¼x13***

**4088** A1158 $5 Horiz. strip of 4, #a-d 1.40 .70

Compare with Type A1176.

St. Valentine's Day — A1159

Designs: $12, Colored roses. $25, White roses.

**Litho. & Embossed**

**2013, Feb. 4** ***Perf. 13¼x13½***

**4089-4090** A1159 Set of 2 2.50 1.25
*4090a* Souvenir sheet of 2, #4089-4090 2.50 1.25

Grain Farming — A1160

Designs: $5, Oryza sativa. $7, Setaria italica. $10, Zea mays. $25, Triticum aestivum.

**2013, Mar. 5 Litho.** ***Perf. 12½***

**4091-4094** A1160 Set of 4 3.25 1.60

A1161 A1162

A1163

A1164

A1165

Qing Dynasty Embroidery — A1166

**2013, Mar. 20 Litho. *Perf. 14***

| | | | | |
|---|---|---|---|---|
| **4095** | A1161 | $10 multi | .70 | .35 |
| **4096** | A1162 | $10 multi | .70 | .35 |
| **4097** | A1163 | $10 multi | .70 | .35 |
| **4098** | A1164 | $10 multi | .70 | .35 |
| **4099** | A1165 | $10 multi | .70 | .35 |
| | | *Nos. 4095-4099 (5)* | 3.50 | 1.75 |

**Litho. & Embossed With Foil Application**

**Souvenir Sheet**

**Silk-Faced Paper**

***Perf. 13x13¼***

**4100** A1166 $100 multi 6.75 3.50

Children at Play — A1167

Children: No. 4101, $5, Carrying lantern. No. 4102, $5, Flying paper airplanes. No. 4103, $5, With pinwheels. No. 4104, $5, With spinning top. No. 4105, $5, With hand puppets.

**2013, Apr. 2 Litho. *Perf. 12½***

**4101-4105** A1167 Set of 5 1.75 .85

*4105a* Booklet pane of 10, 2 each #4101-4105, perf. 12½ on 3 sides 3.50 —

Complete booklet, #4105a 3.50

See Nos. 4168-4172.

**Berries Type of 2012**

Designs: $1, Ribes formosanum. $15, Garcinia subelliptica. $17, Coffea arabica. $20, Smilax ocreata.

**2013, Apr. 17 *Perf. 13¼x12½***

| | | | | |
|---|---|---|---|---|
| **4106** | A1128 | $1 multi | .30 | .25 |
| **4107** | A1128 | $15 multi | 1.00 | .50 |
| **4108** | A1128 | $17 multi | 1.25 | .60 |
| **4109** | A1128 | $20 multi | 1.40 | .70 |
| | | *Nos. 4106-4109 (4)* | 3.95 | 2.05 |

Capturing Daming Prefecture by Ruse — A1168

Heavenly Inscriptions on Stele — A1169

Lianshan Outlaws Granted Imperial Amnesty A1170

Successful Expedition Against Liao Empire — A1171

**2013, May 10 *Perf. 12½x12¾***

| | | | | |
|---|---|---|---|---|
| **4110** | A1168 | $5 multi | .35 | .25 |
| **4111** | A1169 | $5 multi | .35 | .25 |
| **4112** | A1170 | $10 multi | .70 | .35 |
| **4113** | A1171 | $25 multi | 1.75 | .85 |
| | | *Nos. 4110-4113 (4)* | 3.15 | 1.70 |

Scenes from novel "Outlaws of the Marsh." Compare with Nos. 4040-4043.

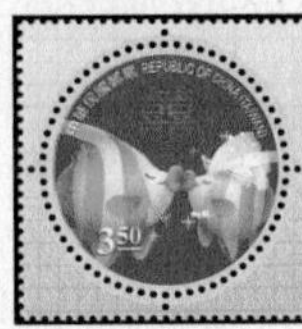
Congratulations A1172

Designs: No. 4114, $3.50, Tropical fish. No. 4115, $3.50, Swans. No. 4116, $5, Penguins. No. 4117, $5, Mandarin ducks.

**2013, May 22 *Perf. 12½***

**4114-4117** A1172 Set of 4 1.25 .60

Values are for stamps with surrounding selvage.

Herbs — A1173

Designs: No. 4118, $5, Mentha x piperita. No. 4119, $5, Rosmarinus officinalis. $12, Salvia elegans. $15, Artemisia indica.

**2013, June 11**

**4118-4121** A1173 Set of 4 2.50 1.25

See Nos. 4179-4182, 4244-4247.

**Owls Type of 2011**

Designs: No. 4122, $5, Otus lettia. No. 4123, $5, Tyto longimembris. $10, Ketupa flavipes. $25, Otus elegans botelensis.

***Perf. 12¾x12½***

**2013, June 26 Engr.**

**4122-4125** A1104 Set of 4 3.00 1.50

Vases — A1174

Designs: $12, Ming Dynasty vase with "One Hundred Deer" design. $25, Qing Dynasty vase with "One Hundred Boys" design.

**2013, July 10 Litho.**

**4126-4127** A1174 Set of 2 2.50 1.25

*4127a* Souvenir sheet of 2, #4126-4127 2.50 1.25

Mushrooms — A1175

Designs: Nos. 4128, 4132a, $5, Ramaria botrytis. Nos. 4129, 4132b, $5, Morchella elata. Nos. 4130, 4132c, $12, Gomphus floccosus. Nos. 4131, 4132d, $12, Aleuria aurantia.

**2013, July 24 *Perf. 12½***

**Stamps With White Frames**

**4128-4131** A1175 Set of 4 2.25 1.10

**Souvenir Sheet**

**Stamps Without White Frames**

***Perf. 12½x13***

**4132** A1175 Sheet of 4, #a-d 2.25 1.10

No. 4132 contains four 26x34mm stamps.

Chinese Dishes A1176

No. 4133 — Chopsticks and: a, Stinky tofu, condiment bowl at UL. b, Taiwanese meatball, two sauce bottles at UL. c, Oyster omelet, teapot and condiment bowl at UL. d, Braised pork rice, salt and pepper shakers at UL.

**2013, Aug. 16 *Perf. 13¼x13***

**4133** A1176 $5 Horiz. strip of 4, #a-d 1.40 .70

Compare with Type A1158.

**Long-horned Beetles Type of 2010**

Designs: No. 4134, Parandra lanyuana. No. 4135, Bunothorax takasagoensis. $10, Oplatocera mandibulata. $25, Cyrtoclytus kusumai.

**2013, Aug. 28 *Perf. 12½x13½***

| | | | | |
|---|---|---|---|---|
| **4134** | A1054 | $5 multi | .35 | .25 |
| **4135** | A1054 | $5 multi | .35 | .25 |
| **4136** | A1054 | $10 multi | .70 | .35 |
| **4137** | A1054 | $25 multi | 1.75 | .85 |
| | | *Nos. 4134-4137 (4)* | 3.15 | 1.70 |

Soong May-ling (Madame Chiang) (1898-2003), First Lady — A1177

**2013, Sept. 12 *Perf. 12¾x12½***

**4138** A1177 $12 multi .80 .40

A1178

Emperor Gaozong Era Artifacts A1179

No. 4139: a, Qing Dynasty gourd-shaped vase. b, Qing Dynasty carved red lacquer bowl, horiz. c, Northern Song Dyanasty plate with celadon glaze, horiz. d, Qing Dynasty jade bear-shaped vessel.

$25, Qing Dynasty New Year's silk tapestry scroll.

**2013, Oct. 8 Litho. *Perf. 12***

**4139** A1178 Sheet of 4 + label 2.50 1.25

| | | | |
|---|---|---|---|
| *a.* | $5 multi | .35 | .25 |
| *b.-c.* | $10 Either single | .65 | .30 |
| *d.* | $12 multi | .85 | .40 |

**Souvenir Sheet**

***Perf. 12¾x12½***

**4140** A1179 $25 multi 1.75 .85

Presidential Office Building, Taipei A1180

Sun Yat-sen Memorial Hall, Taipei A1181

National Palace Museum, Taipei A1182

Taipei 101 Building A1183

Chiang Kai-shek Memorial Hall, Taipei A1184

Jiufen A1185

Alishan A1186

Qingshui Cliff A1187

Queen's Head Rock Formation A1188

Sun Moon Lake A1189

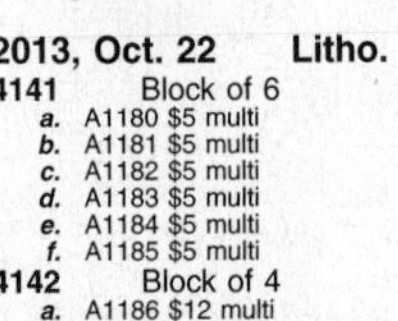

**2013, Oct. 22 Litho. *Perf. 13¼***

**4141** Block of 6 2.10 1.10

| | | | |
|---|---|---|---|
| *a.* | A1180 $5 multi | .35 | .25 |
| *b.* | A1181 $5 multi | .35 | .25 |
| *c.* | A1182 $5 multi | .35 | .25 |
| *d.* | A1183 $5 multi | .35 | .25 |
| *e.* | A1184 $5 multi | .35 | .25 |
| *f.* | A1185 $5 multi | .35 | .25 |

**4142** Block of 4 3.50 1.60

| | | | |
|---|---|---|---|
| *a.* | A1186 $12 multi | .85 | .40 |
| *b.* | A1187 $12 multi | .85 | .40 |
| *c.* | A1188 $12 multi | .85 | .40 |
| *d.* | A1189 $12 multi | .85 | .40 |

Bicycle Paths A1190

Bicyclist on: No. 4143, $5, Yangguang Bridge on Xindian River Bicycle Path, New Taipei City (pale orange panel). No. 4144, $5, Bali Zuoan Bicycle Path, New Taipei City (pink panel). No. 4145, $10, Sankeng Bicycle Path, Taoyuan (green panel). No. 4146, $10, Hsinchu Coast Bicycle Path (yellow panel).

**2013, Nov. 8 Litho. *Perf. 13¼x13***

**Stamp + Label**

**4143-4146** A1190 Set of 4 2.10 1.10

Dragon and Phoenix — A1191

**2013, Nov. 15 Engr. *Perf. 13¼x12½***

**4147** A1191 $50 car & rose 3.50 1.75

Qing Dynasty Bowl, 1723-35 — A1192

Wash Bowl, Southern Song to Yuan Dynasties, 13th-14th Cent. — A1193

Ming Dynasty Jar With Lid, 1465-87 — A1194

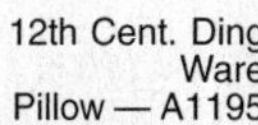

12th Cent. Ding Ware Pillow — A1195

Ming Dynasty Flower Holder — A1196

Qing Dynasty Covered Box, 1874-1908 A1197

Qing Dynasty Jadeite Cabbage and Insects Figurine — A1198

Ru Ware Warming Bowl, 11th-12th Cent. — A1199

Qing Dynasty Stone With Meat Design — A1200

Western Zhoud Dynasty Mao-gong Ding (Ritual Vessel) — A1201

**2013, Nov. 22 Litho. *Perf. 12½***

**4148** Block of 6 2.10 1.10
*a.* A1192 $5 multi .35 .25
*b.* A1193 $5 multi .35 .25
*c.* A1194 $5 multi .35 .25
*d.* A1195 $5 multi .35 .25
*e.* A1196 $5 multi .35 .25
*f.* A1197 $5 multi .35 .25
**4149** Block of 4 3.50 1.60
*a.* A1198 $12 multi .85 .40
*b.* A1199 $12 multi .85 .40
*c.* A1200 $12 multi .85 .40
*d.* A1201 $12 multi .85 .40

Items in National Palace Museum.

New Year 2014 (Year of the Horse) — A1202

Designs: $3.50, Horse with leg lifted. $13, Horse leaping.
$12, Two leaping horses.

**2013, Dec. 2 Litho. *Perf. 13***
**4150-4151** A1202 Set of 2 1.10 .55

**Souvenir Sheet**

***Perf. 12½***

**4152** A1202 $12 multi .85 .40

No. 4152 contains one 64x40mm stamp.

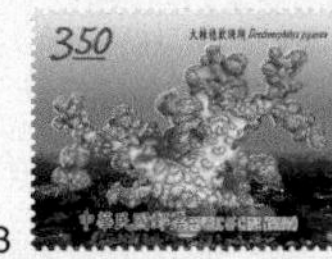

Corals — A1203

Designs: $3.50, Dendronephthya gigantea. $5, Pavona cactus. $10, Acropora granulosa. $15, Melithaea ochracea.

**2014, Jan. 8 Litho. *Perf. 12½x13¼***
**4153-4156** A1203 Set of 4 2.25 1.10

See Nos. 4257-4260, 4308-4311, 4425-4428.

Chinese Desserts A1204

No. 4157: a, Pineapple-filled shortcrust pastries, orange shopping bag and box. b, Mochi, green shopping bag and box. c, Sun cakes, red shopping bag and box. d, Egg yolk pastries, rose lilac shopping bag and box.

**2014, Jan. 22 Litho. *Perf. 13¼x13***
**4157** A1204 $5 Horiz. strip of 4, #a-d 1.40 .70

Lophura Swinhoii A1205

No. 4158: a, Immature male. b, Head of mature male. c, Chicks. d, Hen and chick.
$25, Male and female.

***Perf. 12½x13¼***

**2014, Feb. 20 Litho.**
**4158** A1205 Block of 4 2.25 1.25
*a.-b.* $5 Either single .35 .25
*c.* $10 multi .65 .35
*d.* $12 multi .80 .40

**Souvenir Sheet**

***Perf. 13½***

**4159** A1205 $25 multi 1.75 .85

No. 4159 contains one 80x50mm stamp.

**Lighthouses Type of 2010**

Designs: No. 4160, $5, Fangyuan Lighthouse (denomination in rose), horiz. No. 4161, $5, Chamu Yu Lighthouse (denomination in blue), horiz. $10, Lanyu Lighthouse (denomination in purple), horiz. $25, Sandiaojiao Lighthouse (denomination in yellow), horiz.

**2014, Mar. 6 Litho. *Perf. 12½x12¾***
**4160-4163** A1059 Set of 4 3.00 1.50

**Berries Type of 2012**

Designs: No. 4164, Lycium chinense. No. 4165, Dianella ensifolia. $15, Ampelopsis brevipedunculata var. hancei. $34, Diplocylos palmatus.

***Perf. 13¼x12½***

**2014, Mar. 27 Litho.**
**4164** A1128 $5 multi .35 .25
**4165** A1128 $5 multi .35 .25
**4166** A1128 $15 multi 1.00 .50
**4167** A1128 $34 multi 2.25 1.10
*Nos. 4164-4167 (4)* 3.95 2.10

**Children at Play Type of 2013**

Designs: No. 4168, $5, Boy on hobby horse. No. 4169, $5, Children playing with bamboo helicopters. No. 4170, $5, Child flying kite. No. 4171, $5, Children playing marbles. No. 4172, $5, Children with Lion Dance costumes.

**2014, Apr. 2 Litho. *Perf. 12½***
**4168-4172** A1167 Set of 5 1.75 .85
*4172a* Booklet pane of 10, 2 each #4168-4172, perf. 12½ on 3 sides 3.50 —
Complete booklet, #4172a 3.50

Children at Play Bathing a Buddha, Scroll Painting by Su Hanchen A1206

Children Playing in an Autumn Garden, Scroll Painting by Su Hanchen A1207

Children Playing in Summer, Scroll Painting by Unknown Artist A1208

Children Playing in Autumn, Scroll Painting by Unknown Artist A1209

Children Painting in Winter, Scroll Painting by Unknown Artist — A1210

**2014, Apr. 30 Litho. *Perf. 13¼x12½***
**4173** A1206 $5 multi .35 .25
**4174** A1207 $5 multi .35 .25
**4175** A1208 $10 multi .70 .35
**4176** A1209 $10 multi .70 .35
**4177** A1210 $12 multi .80 .40
*Nos. 4173-4177 (5)* 2.90 1.60

"The Swan Goose Carries a Message" A1211

***Perf. 13½x13¼***

**2014, May 9 Litho. & Engr.**
**4178** A1211 $9 multi .60 .30

See People's Republic of China No. 4189.

**Herbs Type of 2013**

Designs: $3.50, Foeniculum vulgare. $5, Perilla frutescens. $12, Lavandula angustifolia. $25, Ocimum basilicum.

**2014, June 11 Litho. *Perf. 12½***
**4179-4182** A1173 Set of 4 3.00 1.50

**Souvenir Sheet**

Electrification of the Hua-tung Railway — A1212

No. 4183: a, $5, Trains in Hualien Station. b, $12, Train and Kecheng bridge. c, $25, Train exiting Shanli Tunnel.

***Perf. 12½x12¾***

**2014, June 28 Litho.**
**4183** A1212 Sheet of 3, #a-c 3.00 1.50

Cuichi Pond A1213

Tunlu Pond A1214

Designs: $10, Qicai Lake. $12, Jiaming Lake.

**2014, July 17 Litho. *Perf. 13¼***
**4184** A1213 $5 multi .35 .25
**4185** A1214 $5 multi .35 .25
**4186** A1214 $10 multi .70 .35
**4187** A1214 $12 multi .80 .40
*Nos. 4184-4187 (4)* 2.20 1.25

Compare with Nos. 4340-4343.

National Taiwan Library, Cent. A1215

**2014, Aug. 9 Litho. *Perf. 12½***
**4188** A1215 $12 multi .80 .40

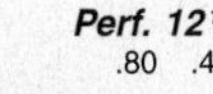

Jugang Tower and Residential Buildings, Kinmen A1216

Wentai Pagoda and Buildings, Kinmen A1217

**2014, Aug. 28 Litho. *Perf. 12½***
**4189** Horiz. pair 1.10 .65
*a.* A1216 $5 multi .35 .25
*b.* A1217 $12 multi .80 .40

Kinmen County, cent.

**Miniature Sheet**

Museums — A1218

No. 4190: a, $5, National Taiwan Museum of Fine Arts (modern building with lawn), Taichung. b, $5, National Taiwan Museum, Taipei (building with 6 pillars). c, $5, National Museum of Taiwan Literature (building with domes at sides). d, $5, National Museum of Taiwan History (building with solar panels). e, $12, National Palace Museum, vert.

**2014, Sept. 10 Litho. *Perf. 12½***
**4190** A1218 Sheet of 5, #a-e, + 4 labels 2.10 1.10

Blue and White Porcelain — A1219

Designs: $5, Qing Dynasty dish with floral design. $10, Ming Dynasty jar with peony design. $12, Ming Dynasty jar with dragon design. $20, Qing Dynasty vase depicting women.
$25, Qing Dynasty plate with bird and flowers design, horiz.

**Litho. & Embossed**

**2014, Sept. 19** *Perf. 13¾x13½*

**4191-4194** A1219 Set of 4 3.25 1.60

**Souvenir Sheet**

*Perf. 13½x13¾*

**4195** A1219 $25 multi 1.75 .85

Miniature Sheet

Taipei 2015 Asian International Stamp Exhibition — A1220

No. 4196: a, $5, Pink azalea blossoms in spring, Mt. Hehuan. b, $5, Tung trees in summer, Pingxi Railway. c, $10, Maple trees in autumn, Wuling Farm. d, $25, Cherry blossoms in winter, Mt. Xue.

**2014, Oct. 3** **Litho.** *Perf. 12½*

**4196** A1220 Sheet of 4, #a-d, + 4 labels 3.00 1.50

Miniature Sheet

Taipei Zoo, Cent. A1221

No. 4197: a, $5, Formosan serow (30x40mm). b, $5, Formosan pangolin (40x30mm). c, $10, Asian elephant (55x38mm). d, $10, Formosan black bear (30x40mm). e, $12, Bengal tiger (55x38mm). f, $12, Giant pandas (38x55mm).

*Perf. 13¼x12½, 12½x13¼*

**2014, Oct. 16** **Litho.**

**4197** A1221 Sheet of 6, #a-f 3.50 1.75

A1222

Scenes From Novel "The Dream of Red Mansions," by Cao Xueqin: No. 4198, $5, Women standing around seated man. No. 4199, $5, Woman and five men looking at garden. $10, Visit of Yuanchun at Lantern Festival. $25, Baochai chasing butterflies.

**2014, Oct. 27** **Litho.** *Perf. 13x13½*

**4198-4201** A1222 Set of 4 3.00 1.50

See Nos. 4228-4231, 4304-4307, 4361-4364.

Flowers in Koji Pottery Vases — A1223

Large vases with: No. 4202, $5, Peonies (yellow green panel). No. 4203, $5, Lotuses (blue panel). $10, Chrysanthemums (orange panel). $25, Camellias (pink lilac panel).

**2014, Nov. 14** **Litho.** *Perf. 13½*

**4202-4205** A1223 Set of 4 3.00 1.50

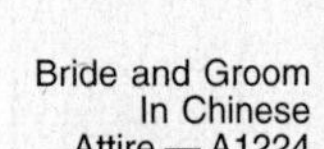

Bride and Groom In Chinese Attire — A1224

Bride and Groom in Western Attire — A1225

Bride and groom with: No. 4206, Red ribbon. No. 4207, Angels and flowers. No. 4208, Red streamer and bow. No. 4209, Hearts and horses.

**2014, Nov. 21** **Litho.** *Perf. 12½*

**4206** A1224 $3.50 multi .25 .25
**4207** A1225 $3.50 multi .25 .25
**4208** A1224 $5 multi .35 .25
**4209** A1225 $5 multi .35 .25
*Nos. 4206-4209 (4)* 1.20 1.00

New Year 2015 (Year of the Ram) — A1226

Designs: $3.50, Bright pink ram. $13, Purple ram.
$12, Two rams.

**2014, Dec. 1** **Litho.** *Perf. 13*

**4210-4211** A1226 Set of 2 1.10 .55

**Souvenir Sheet**

*Perf. 12½*

**4212** A1226 $12 multi .80 .40

No. 4212 contains one 64x40mm stamp.

Archaeological Treasures From Yin Ruins — A1227

No. 4213: a, Marble figurine depicting owl, rose brown background. b, Cauldron with handles, light blue background. c, Oracle bone, rose brown background. d, Mask for horse with turquoise inlays, gray blue background. e, Figurine of human head with crest, light blue background. f, Anthropomorphic figurine with tiger's head, rose brown background. g, Wine container with detachable cap, gray blue background. h, Deer skull with inscriptions, rose brown background.

**2014, Dec. 10** **Litho.** *Perf. 12½*

**4213** A1227 Block of 8 4.25 2.10
*a.-d.* $5 Any single .25 .25
*e.-h.* $12 Any single .80 .40
*i.* Souvenir sheet of 8, #4213a-4213h + 4 labels 4.25 2.10

Jellyfish — A1228

Designs: $5, Pelagia noctiluca. $7, Physophora hydrostatica. $10, Mastigias papua. $12, Cyanea capillata.

**2015, Jan. 8** **Litho.** *Perf. 13¼x13*

**4214-4217** A1228 Set of 4 2.25 1.10

Legumes — A1229

Designs: $5, Arachis hypogaea. $7, Vigna angularis. $10, Glycine max. $25, Vigna radiata.

**2015, Jan. 28** **Litho.** *Perf. 13¼x12½*

**4218-4221** A1229 Set of 4 3.00 1.50

Animals — A1230

Nos. 4222 and 4223: a, Rabbits. b, Squirrels. c, Dogs. d, Bears. e, Elephants. f, Cats. g, Deer. h, Sheep. i, Zebras. j, Giraffes.

**2015, Feb. 12** **Litho.** *Perf. 13¼*

**4222** Block of 10 2.50 1.25
*a.-j.* A1230 $3.50 Any single .25 .25
**4223** Block of 10 3.50 1.75
*a.-j.* A1230 $5 Any single .35 .25

Bo Le Appraises the Horse — A1231

The Ambition of a Swan — A1232

Adept With Both the Pen and the Sword — A1233

Tiny Blade of Grass and Spring Sun — A1234

*Perf. 12½x12¾*

**2015, Mar. 20** **Litho.**

**4224** A1231 $5 multi .35 .25
**4225** A1232 $5 multi .35 .25
**4226** A1233 $5 multi .35 .25
**4227** A1234 $5 multi .35 .25
*Nos. 4224-4227 (4)* 1.40 1.00

Chinese idioms.

Daiyu Burying the Flowers — A1235

Tanchun Starting a Poetry Club — A1236

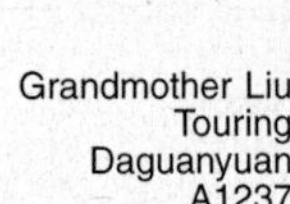

Grandmother Liu Touring Daguanyuan A1237

Miaoyu Tasting Tea — A1238

**2015, Mar. 30** **Litho.** *Perf. 13x13¼*

**4228** A1235 $5 multi .35 .25
**4229** A1236 $5 multi .35 .25
**4230** A1237 $10 multi .65 .30
**4231** A1238 $25 multi 1.60 .80
*Nos. 4228-4231 (4)* 2.95 1.60

Scenes from "The Dream of Red Mansions," by Cao Xueqin. Compare with Nos. 4198-4201, 4304-4307, 4361-4364.

Teresa Teng (1953-95), Singer — A1239

Various photographs of Teng with panel color of: $5, Pink. $9, Orange. $13, Dull rose. $15, Lilac.

**2015, Apr. 15** **Litho.** *Perf. 12½*

**4232-4235** A1239 Set of 4 2.75 1.40

Control Yuan Building, Cent. A1240

**2015, Apr. 24** **Litho.** *Perf. 13¼*

**4236** A1240 $25 multi 1.75 .85

Taipei 2015 Intl. Stamp Exhibition — A1241

No. 4237: a, Dragon. b, Geese.

**2015, Apr. 24** **Litho.** *Perf. 14*

**4237** A1241 Horiz. pair + central label 2.10 1.10
*a.* $5 multi .35 .25
*b.* $25 multi 1.75 .85
*c.* Souvenir sheet of 4, 2 each #4237a-4237b, perf. 13¼x13½ syncopated 4.25 2.25

Black-faced Spoonbills on Zengwen River A1242

Black-winged Stilt, Sicao Wetlands A1243

**2015, Apr. 25** **Litho.** *Perf. 14*

**4238** A1242 $10 multi .65 .30
**4239** A1243 $25 multi 1.75 .85
*a.* Horiz. pair, #4238-4239, + central label 2.40 1.25
*b.* Vert. pair, #4238-4239, no label 2.40 1.25

Taipei 2015 Intl. Stamp Exhibition. Nos 4238-4239 were printed in sheets of 16 (8 of each stamp) + 9 labels.

A1244

Taipei 2015 Intl. Stamp Exhibition — A1245

No. 4240: a, Family, child playing with blocks. b, Family on bicycle.

No. 4241: a, Family, child playing with blocks at left, on bicycle at right. b, Family, child playing with blocks at right, on bicycle at left.

**2015, Apr. 26 Litho. *Perf. 12¾x12½***

| | | | | |
|---|---|---|---|---|
| 4240 | A1244 | Horiz. pair + central label | 2.10 | 1.10 |
| a. | | $5 multi | .35 | .25 |
| b. | | $25 multi | 1.75 | .85 |

**Souvenir Sheet**

| | | | | |
|---|---|---|---|---|
| 4241 | A1245 | Sheet of 2 | 3.50 | 1.75 |
| a.-b. | | $25 Either single | 1.75 | .85 |

Taipei 2015 Intl. Stamp Exhibition — A1246

No. 4242: a, Sky Lantern Festival, Pingxi. b, Xiao Liuqiu coral island.

**2015, Apr. 27 Litho. *Perf. 14***

| | | | | |
|---|---|---|---|---|
| 4242 | A1246 | Horiz. pair + central label | 2.60 | 1.25 |
| a. | | $12 multi | .80 | .40 |
| b. | | $25 multi | 1.75 | .85 |

Taipei 2015 Intl. Stamp Exhibition — A1247

No. 4243 — Scroll paintings: a, Literary Gathering, by Emperor Huizong. b, Elegant Gathering in the Western Garden, by Zhao Mengfu.

**2015, Apr. 28 Litho. *Perf. 13¼x12½***

| | | | | |
|---|---|---|---|---|
| 4243 | A1247 | Horiz. pair + central label | 2.40 | 1.25 |
| a. | | $9 multi | .60 | .30 |
| b. | | $25 multi | 1.75 | .85 |
| c. | | Souvenir sheet of 2, #4243a-4243b, + label | 2.40 | 1.25 |

**Herbs Type of 2013**

Designs: $3.50, Allium schoenoprasum. $5, Borago officinalis. $12, Tropaeolum majus. $25, Chamaemelum nobile.

**2015, June 11 Litho. *Perf. 12½***

| | | | | |
|---|---|---|---|---|
| 4244-4247 | A1173 | Set of 4 | 3.00 | 1.50 |

Liberation of Taiwan in World War II, 70th Anniv. — A1248

Designs: No. 4248, $3.50, Soldiers carrying flags. No. 4249, $3.50, Farm woman holding sheaf of rice, Shimen Reservoir. No. 4250, $5, People cheering Chiang Kai-shek, horiz. No. 4251, $5, Crowd in plaza celebrating Taiwan Retrocession Day, 1963, horiz.

**2015, July 7 Litho. *Perf. 12½***

| | | | | |
|---|---|---|---|---|
| 4248-4251 | A1248 | Set of 4 | 1.10 | .55 |

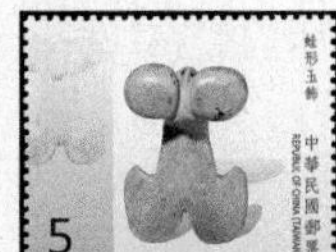

A1249

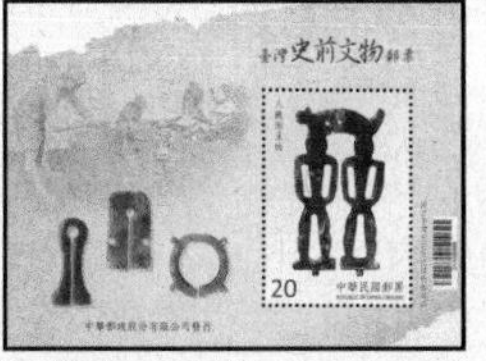

Prehistoric Artifacts — A1250

Designs: $5, Frog-shaped jade ornament. $7, Jade tubes. $9, Circular jade bangle. $12, String of jade beads.
$20, Jade earring.

**2015, Aug. 21 Litho. *Perf. 12½***

| | | | | |
|---|---|---|---|---|
| 4252-4255 | A1249 | Set of 4 | 2.10 | 1.10 |

**Souvenir Sheet**

| | | | | |
|---|---|---|---|---|
| 4256 | A1250 | $20 multi | 1.25 | .60 |

**Corals Type of 2014**

Designs: $3.50, Montipora foliosa. $5, Sarcophyton ehrenbergi. $10, Ellisella robusta. $15, Stylaster gracilis.

**2015, Sept. 10 Litho. *Perf. 12½***

| | | | | |
|---|---|---|---|---|
| 4257-4260 | A1203 | Set of 4 | 2.10 | 1.10 |

A1251

Paintings by Giuseppe Castiglione (Lang Shining) — A1252

Designs: No. 4261, $5, Gathering of Auspicious Signs (flowers in vase). No. 4262, $5, Long-haired Dog Beneath Blossoms. No. 4263, $9, Ayusi Sweeping Bandits with a Lance, horiz. No. 4264, $9, Cochin Lemur, horiz.

No. 4265 — Golden Pheasant in Spring: a, $12. b, $70.

**2015, Oct. 8 Litho. *Perf. 13¼***

| | | | | |
|---|---|---|---|---|
| 4261-4264 | A1251 | Set of 4 | 1.75 | .85 |

**Souvenir Sheet**
**Silk-Faced Paper**

| | | | | |
|---|---|---|---|---|
| 4265 | A1252 | Sheet of 2, #a-b | 5.00 | 2.50 |

Sun Yat-sen (1866-1925), First President of Republic of China — A1253

Various depictions of Sun Yat-sen: $5, $12, horiz.

**2015, Nov. 12 Litho. *Perf. 12½***

| | | | | |
|---|---|---|---|---|
| 4266-4267 | A1253 | Set of 2 | 1.10 | .55 |

Rail Tourism A1254

Designs: $5, Yuli-Taitung Summer Formosa train, railroad bridge. $10, South Link Line train, bridge near coast. $15, Jiji Line Evolution No. 1001 train, bicyclists.

**2015, Nov. 25 Litho. *Perf. 13x13¼***

| | | | | |
|---|---|---|---|---|
| 4268-4270 | A1254 | Set of 3 | 1.90 | .95 |

New Year 2016 (Year of the Monkey) — A1255

Designs: $3.50, Monkey facing right. $13, Monkey facing left.
$12, Two monkeys.

**2015, Dec. 1 Litho. *Perf. 13***

| | | | | |
|---|---|---|---|---|
| 4271-4272 | A1255 | Set of 2 | 1.00 | .50 |

**Souvenir Sheet**
***Perf. 12½***

| | | | | |
|---|---|---|---|---|
| 4273 | A1255 | $12 multi | .75 | .35 |

No. 4273 contains one 64x40mm stamp.

A1256

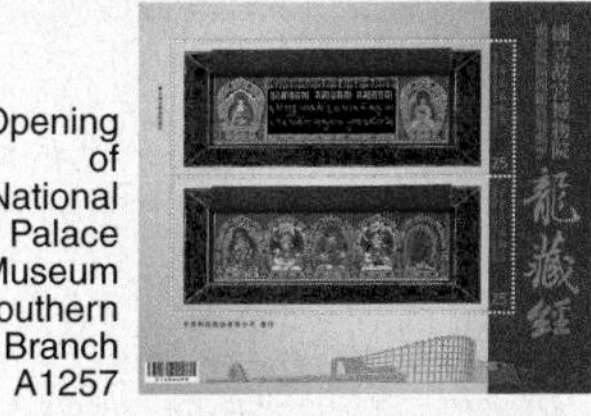

Opening of National Palace Museum Southern Branch A1257

Designs: $5, Right-spiraling conch, Qing dynasty. $10, Jade bowl with handles and lid. $12, Hanging scroll with deities Good Fortune, Wealth and Long Life.

No. 4277: a, Board from Tibetan Kangyar with text and two deities. b, Board from Tibetan Kangyar with five deities.

***Perf. 14¼x14½***
**2015, Dec. 10 Litho.**

| | | | | |
|---|---|---|---|---|
| 4274-4276 | A1256 | Set of 3 | 1.75 | .85 |

**Souvenir Sheet**
***Perf. 14¾***

| | | | | |
|---|---|---|---|---|
| 4277 | A1257 | $25 Sheet of 2, #a-b | 3.00 | 1.50 |

Souvenir Sheets

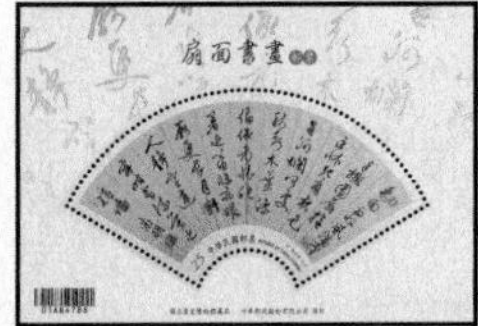

Fan With Verse in Calligraphy by Wen Zhengming (1470-1559) — A1258

**2016, Jan. 13 Litho. *Perf. 13½***

| | | | | |
|---|---|---|---|---|
| 4278 | A1258 | $25 multi | 1.50 | .75 |

**Litho. With Bamboo Veneer Affixed**

| | | | | |
|---|---|---|---|---|
| 4279 | A1258 | $80 multi | 4.75 | 2.40 |

Fruit — A1259

Designs: $1, Atemoyas. $2.50, Papayas. $5, Lychees. $15, Dates.

**2016, Jan. 28 Litho. *Perf. 12½x13½***

| | | | | |
|---|---|---|---|---|
| 4280 | A1259 | $1 multi | .30 | .25 |
| 4281 | A1259 | $2.50 multi | .30 | .25 |
| 4282 | A1259 | $5 multi | .30 | .25 |
| 4283 | A1259 | $15 multi | .90 | .45 |
| | | *Nos. 4280-4283 (4)* | 1.80 | 1.20 |

See Nos. 4365-4368, 4383-4386.

Churches A1260

Designs: No. 4284, $5, Church of St. Joseph, Jinlun (with "Kiokai ni Santo Yosef" sign). No. 4285, $5, Holy Family Church, Taipei. No. 4286, $12, Minor Basilica of the Immaculate Conception, Wanjin. No. 4287, $12, Cathedral of the Holy Rosary, Kaohsiung, vert.

**2016, Feb. 4 Litho. *Perf. 13¼***

| | | | | |
|---|---|---|---|---|
| 4284-4287 | A1260 | Set of 4 | 2.10 | 1.10 |

Souvenir Sheet

Chinese Postal Service, 120th Anniv. A1261

No. 4288 — Mailbox and: a, $5, Bicycle. b, $12, Motorcycle.

**2016, Mar. 18 Litho. *Perf. 13***

| | | | | |
|---|---|---|---|---|
| 4288 | A1261 | Sheet of 2, #a-b | 1.10 | .55 |

Tree Peonies A1262

Peach Blossoms A1263

Herbaceous Peonies A1264

Flowering Crab Apple and Magnolia Blossoms A1265

Corn Poppies and Fringed Iris A1266

Yellow Prickly Roses and Peonies A1267

Carnations A1268

Cherries and Grosbeaks A1269

***Perf. 13¼x12½***
**2016, Mar. 29 Litho.**

| | | | | |
|---|---|---|---|---|
| 4289 | A1262 | $5 multi | .30 | .25 |
| 4290 | A1263 | $5 multi | .30 | .25 |
| 4291 | A1264 | $7 multi | .45 | .25 |
| 4292 | A1265 | $9 multi | .55 | .30 |
| 4293 | A1266 | $10 multi | .65 | .30 |
| 4294 | A1267 | $10 multi | .65 | .30 |
| 4295 | A1268 | $12 multi | .75 | .35 |
| 4296 | A1269 | $12 multi | .75 | .35 |
| | | *Nos. 4289-4296 (8)* | 4.40 | 2.35 |

Paintings by Giuseppe Castiglione (1688-1766).

Miniature Sheet

Taitung County A1270

No. 4297: a, $5, Footbridge, Sanxiantai. b, $5 People watching hot air balloons over Luye Highlands. c, $10, Fishing boat, Lanyu Island. d, $12, National Museum of Prehistory, Taitung.

**2016, Apr. 20 Litho. *Perf. 12½x12¾***
**4297** A1270 Sheet of 4, #a-d 2.00 1.00

Tea Grinding, by Liu Songnian (1174-1224)
A1271

Lu Tong Brewing Tea, by Qian Xuan (1235-1305)
A1272

Tasting Tea, by Wen Zhengming (1470-1559) — A1273

**2016, May 5 Litho. *Perf. 12¾***
**4298** A1271 $5 multi .30 .25
**4299** A1272 $15 multi .95 .45
**4300** A1273 $25 multi 1.60 .80
*Nos. 4298-4300 (3)* 2.85 1.50

South China Sea Peace Initiative — A1274

No. 4301: a, Map of South China Sea, memorial plaque, Taiping Island. b, Taiping Lighthouse. c, Solar panels, Taiping Island National Monument and flags. d, Trail, goat and chickens.

**2016, May 5 Litho. *Perf. 12½x12¾***
**4301** Horiz. strip of 4 2.60 1.40
*a.* A1274 $5 multi .30 .25
*b.* A1274 $9 multi .55 .30
*c.* A1274 $13 multi .80 .40
*d.* A1274 $15 multi .95 .45

Pixelated Faces
A1275

Line-Drawn Faces
A1276

No. 4302 — Images of newly-elected Pres. Tsai Ing-wen and Vice-president Chen Chien-jen with background colors of: a, Light gray brown. b, Orange. c, Brownish gray. d, Turquoise.
$32, 20 pixelated faces.

**2016, May 20 Litho. *Perf. 12½***
**4302** Strip of 4 2.10 1.10
*a.* A1275 $5 multi .30 .25
*b.* A1276 $5 multi .30 .25
*c.* A1275 $12 multi .75 .35
*d.* A1276 $12 multi .75 .35

**Souvenir Sheet**

***Perf. 12½x12¾***
**4303** A1275 $32 multi 2.00 1.00

No. 4303 contains one 80x30mm stamp.

Xiangling Studies Poetry — A1277

White Snow and Pink Plum Blossoms
A1278

Qingwen Repairs a Coat — A1279

Lantern Festival Feast — A1280

**2016, June 29 Litho. *Perf. 14***
**4304** A1277 $5 multi .30 .25
**4305** A1278 $5 multi .30 .25
**4306** A1279 $10 multi .65 .30
**4307** A1280 $25 multi 1.60 .80
*Nos. 4304-4307 (4)* 2.85 1.60

Scenes from "The Dream of Red Mansions," by Cao Xueqin. Compare with Nos. 4198-4201, 4228-4231, 4361-4364.

**Corals Type of 2014**

Designs: $3.50, Euphyllia ancora. $5, Fungia (Pleuractis) taiwanensis. $10, Scleronephthya gracillimum. $15, Anella mollis.

**2016, July 14 Litho. *Perf. 12½x13¼***
**4308-4311** A1203 Set of 4 2.10 1.10

**Carp Encircled by Dragons Type of 1997 With Denomination at Right and Inscribed "Republic of China (Taiwan)"**

**2016, Aug. 3 Engr. *Perf. 13¼x12½***
**4312** A745 $100 dk purple 6.25 3.25

**Fruit Type of 2016**

Designs: $7, Tomatoes. $17, Guavas. $25, Persimmons. $34, Pineapple.

***Perf. 12½x13½***

**2016, Aug. 17 Litho.**
**4313** A1259 $7 multi .45 .25
**4314** A1259 $17 multi 1.10 .55
**4315** A1259 $25 multi 1.60 .80
**4316** A1259 $34 multi 2.25 1.10
*Nos. 4313-4316 (4)* 5.40 2.70

A1281

A1282

A1283

A1284

A1285

A1286

A1287

A1288

A1289

Seals — A1290

***Perf. 13½x12½***

**2016, Sept. 14 Litho.**
**4317** Block of 10 2.50 1.25
*a.* A1281 $3.50 multi .30 .25
*b.* A1282 $3.50 multi .30 .25
*c.* A1283 $3.50 multi .30 .25
*d.* A1284 $3.50 multi .30 .25
*e.* A1285 $3.50 multi .30 .25
*f.* A1286 $3.50 multi .30 .25
*g.* A1287 $3.50 multi .30 .25
*h.* A1288 $3.50 multi .30 .25
*i.* A1289 $3.50 multi .30 .25
*j.* A1290 $3.50 multi .30 .25
**4318** Block of 10 3.00 1.50
*a.* A1281 $5 multi .30 .25
*b.* A1282 $5 multi .30 .25
*c.* A1283 $5 multi .30 .25
*d.* A1284 $5 multi .30 .25
*e.* A1285 $5 multi .30 .25
*f.* A1286 $5 multi .30 .25
*g.* A1287 $5 multi .30 .25
*h.* A1288 $5 multi .30 .25
*i.* A1289 $5 multi .30 .25
*j.* A1290 $5 multi .30 .25

Hu Shih (1891-1962), Writer and Diplomat
A1291

Chien Shih-Liang (1908-83), Chemist
A1292

Wu Ta-You (1907-2000), Physicist — A1293

**2016, Sept. 28 Engr. *Perf. 12½***
**4319** A1291 $5 slate blue .30 .25
**4320** A1292 $5 red violet .30 .25
**4321** A1293 $5 brown .30 .25
*Nos. 4319-4321 (3)* .90 .75

Past presidents of Academia Sinica.

Balloon and Bicyclist
A1294

Bird and Open Box
A1295

**2016, Oct. 21 Litho. *Perf. 14***
**4322** A1294 $5 multi .35 .25
**4323** A1295 $25 multi 1.60 .80

**Souvenir Sheet**

**Litho. & Embossed With Foil Application**

**4324** Sheet of 2 4.00 2.00
*a.* A1294 $32 multi 2.00 1.00
*b.* A1295 $32 multi 2.00 1.00

PhilaTaipei 2016 World Stamp Exhibition, Taipei.

PhilaTaipei 2016 World Stamp Exhibition, Taipei — A1296

No. 4325: a, Yushan, Sun Moon Lake, butterfly, dragon boat. b, Map of Taiwan, birds, Taipei 101 Building, 85 Sky Tower, Kaohsiung.

***Perf. 14 Syncopated***

**2016, Oct. 21 Litho.**
**4325** A1296 Horiz. pair 3.00 1.40
*a.* $13 gold & multi .85 .40
*b.* $32 gold & multi 2.00 1.00
*c.* Souvenir sheet of 4, 2 each #4325a-4325b 6.00 3.00

A1297

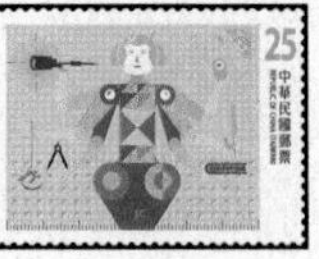

PhilaTaipei 2016 World Stamp Exhibition, Taipei — A1298

**2016, Oct. 22 Litho. *Perf. 13½***
**4326** A1297 $9 multi .60 .30
**4327** A1298 $25 multi 1.60 .80
*a.* Souvenir sheet of 6, 3 each #4326-4327 6.75 3.50

**Souvenir Sheet**

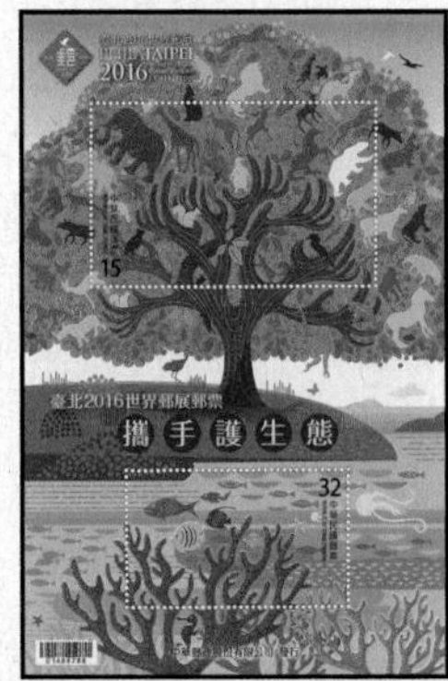

PhilaTaipei 2016 World Stamp Exhibition, Taipei — A1299

No. 4328: a, Animals and birds in tree (64x40mm). b, Fish and marine life in ocean (50x30mm).

**2016, Oct. 22 Litho. *Perf. 14***
**4328** A1299 Sheet of 2 3.00 1.50
*a.* $15 multi .95 .50
*b.* $32 multi 2.00 1.00

PhilaTaipei 2016 World Stamp Exhibition, Taipei — A1300

No. 4329 — Little Yam: a, Mailing letter. b, Holding opened envelope.

**2016, Oct. 22 Litho. *Perf. 13¼x12¾***
**4329** A1300 Horiz. pair + central label 2.00 1.00
*a.* $5 multi .35 .25
*b.* $25 multi 1.60 .80
*c.* Souvenir sheet of 4, 2 each #4329a-4329b, + 2 labels 4.00 2.00

Souvenir Sheet

PhilaTaipei 2016 World Stamp Exhibition, Taipei — A1301

No. 4330: a, Bird carrying flower (39x30mm heart-shaped). b, Person, flowers, hearts (30x40mm).

***Perf. ($17), Perf. 12¾x12½ ($25)***

**2016, Oct. 22 Litho.**

| | | | | |
|---|---|---|---|---|
| **4330** | A1301 | Sheet of 2 | 2.75 | 1.40 |
| *a.* | | $17 multi | 1.10 | .55 |
| *b.* | | $25 multi | 1.60 | .80 |

Souvenir Sheet

Traveler at Shanyin County, Fan Painting by Lan Ying (c. 1585-1664) — A1302

**2016, Oct. 24 Litho. *Perf. 14***

| | | | | |
|---|---|---|---|---|
| **4331** | A1302 | $25 multi | 1.60 | .80 |

New Year 2017 (Year of the Rooster) — A1303

Rooster and: $3.50, Chinese character in black. $13, Fish.
$12, Two roosters, horiz.

**2016, Dec. 1 Litho. *Perf. 13***

| | | | | |
|---|---|---|---|---|
| **4332-4333** | A1303 | Set of 2 | 1.10 | .55 |

**Souvenir Sheet**

***Perf. 12½***

| | | | | |
|---|---|---|---|---|
| **4334** | A1303 | $12 multi | .75 | .40 |

No. 4334 contains one 64x40mm stamp.

Starfish — A1304

Designs: No. 4335, $5, Fromia monilis. No. 4336, $5, Culcita novaeguineae. No. 4337, $5, Acanthaster planci. No. 4338, $5, Linckia laevigata.

**2017, Jan. 5 Litho. *Perf. 12½x12¾***

| | | | | |
|---|---|---|---|---|
| **4335-4338** | A1304 | Set of 4 | 1.40 | 1.40 |

Lions Clubs International, Cent. — A1305

Lions Clubs International emblem, "100," club members and inscription: a, "We Serve." b, "100th Anniversary."

**2017, Jan. 20 Litho. *Perf. 13¼x12½***

| | | | | |
|---|---|---|---|---|
| **4339** | A1305 | Horiz. pair | 1.40 | 1.40 |
| *a.* | | $5 multi | .30 | .30 |
| *b.* | | $15 multi | 1.10 | 1.10 |

Wanli Pond A1306

Baishi Pond A1307

Jialuo Lake A1308

Dagui Lake A1309

**2017, Feb. 23 Litho. *Perf. 14***

| | | | | |
|---|---|---|---|---|
| **4340** | A1306 | $5 multi | .35 | .25 |
| **4341** | A1307 | $5 multi | .35 | .25 |
| **4342** | A1308 | $10 multi | .65 | .30 |
| **4343** | A1309 | $12 multi | .80 | .40 |
| | | *Nos. 4340-4343 (4)* | 2.15 | 1.20 |

Compare with Nos. 4184-4187.

Miniature Sheet

Tainan City A1310

No. 4344: a, $5, Jingzaijiao Tile-paved Salt Fields. b, $9, Tainan Confucian Temple. c, $12, Chikan Lou. d, $12, Anping Sword Lion architectural decoration.

**2017, Mar. 28 Litho. *Perf. 14***

| | | | | |
|---|---|---|---|---|
| **4344** | A1310 | Sheet of 4, #a-d | 2.50 | 1.25 |

Poppies A1311

White and Purple Lilacs A1312

Tiger Lilies and Winding Peonies A1313

Emerald Bamboo and Morning Glories A1314

Lotuses and Arrowhead A1315

Pea Blossoms and Millet Stalks A1316

Cockscomb A1317

Chrysanthemums A1318

**2017, Apr. 26 Litho. *Perf. 13¼x12½***

| | | | | |
|---|---|---|---|---|
| **4345** | A1311 | $5 multi | .35 | .25 |
| **4346** | A1312 | $5 multi | .35 | .25 |
| **4347** | A1313 | $7 multi | .50 | .25 |
| **4348** | A1314 | $9 multi | .60 | .30 |
| **4349** | A1315 | $10 multi | .70 | .35 |
| **4350** | A1316 | $10 multi | .70 | .35 |
| **4351** | A1317 | $12 multi | .80 | .40 |
| **4352** | A1318 | $12 multi | .80 | .40 |
| | | *Nos. 4345-4352 (8)* | 4.80 | 2.55 |

Paintings by Giuseppe Castiglione (1688-1766).

This Infant Can Be Taught — A1319

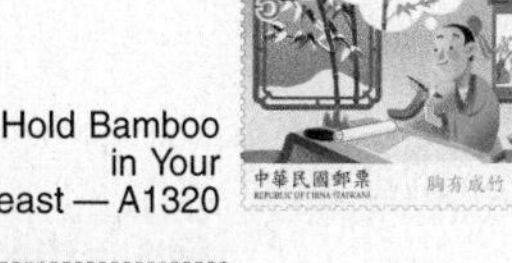

To Hold Bamboo in Your Breast — A1320

To Rub Your Eyes and See Anew — A1321

To Add Eyes to the Dragon — A1322

**2017, May 10 Litho. *Perf. 12½x13¼***

| | | | | |
|---|---|---|---|---|
| **4353** | A1319 | $5 multi | .35 | .25 |
| **4354** | A1320 | $5 multi | .35 | .25 |
| **4355** | A1321 | $5 multi | .35 | .25 |
| **4356** | A1322 | $5 multi | .35 | .25 |
| | | *Nos. 4353-4356 (4)* | 1.40 | 1.00 |

Chinese idioms.

Train and Dongshan River Bridge A1323

Train and Youkeng Bridge A1324

Train and Carp Pond Bridge A1325

Train and Da-an River Bridge A1326

**2017, June 9 Litho. *Perf. 12½x13¼***

| | | | | |
|---|---|---|---|---|
| **4357** | A1323 | $5 multi | .35 | .25 |
| **4358** | A1324 | $5 multi | .35 | .25 |
| **4359** | A1325 | $12 multi | .80 | .40 |
| **4360** | A1326 | $12 multi | .80 | .40 |
| | | *Nos. 4357-4360 (4)* | 2.30 | 1.30 |

Xiangyun Sleeps in Inebriation A1327

Daiyu Burns Manuscripts A1328

Jia Mansion Ransacked A1329

Baoyu Becomes a Monk — A1330

**2017, June 29 Litho. *Perf. 13x13½***

| | | | | |
|---|---|---|---|---|
| **4361** | A1327 | $5 multi | .35 | .25 |
| **4362** | A1328 | $5 multi | .35 | .25 |
| **4363** | A1329 | $10 multi | .65 | .35 |
| **4364** | A1330 | $25 multi | 1.75 | .85 |
| | | *Nos. 4361-4364 (4)* | 3.10 | 1.70 |

Scenes from "The Dream of Red Mansions," by Cao Xueqin. Compare with Nos. 4198-4201, 4228-4231, 4304-4307.

**Fruit Type of 2016**

Designs: $3.50, Mangos. $5, Oranges. $12, Watermelon. $32, Grapes.

**2017, July 20 Litho. *Perf. 12½x13½***

| | | | | |
|---|---|---|---|---|
| **4365** | A1259 | $3.50 multi | .30 | .25 |
| **4366** | A1259 | $5 multi | .35 | .25 |
| **4367** | A1259 | $12 multi | .80 | .40 |
| **4368** | A1259 | $32 multi | 2.10 | 1.10 |
| | | *Nos. 4365-4368 (4)* | 3.55 | 2.00 |

Carrier Dove
A1331 A1332

**2017, Aug. 1 Litho. *Perf. 12½***

| | | | | |
|---|---|---|---|---|
| **4369** | A1331 | ($6) orange & multi | .40 | .25 |
| **4370** | A1332 | ($8) blue & multi | .55 | .25 |

Tungyin Tao Lighthouse A1333

Qinbi Village A1334

Chinese Crested Terns A1335

Dinoflagellates Glowing Blue in Sea Water — A1336

**2017, Aug. 9 Litho. *Perf. 14½x14***

**4371** A1333 $5 multi .35 .25
**4372** A1334 $9 multi .60 .30
**4373** A1335 $10 multi .65 .35
**4374** A1336 $20 multi 1.40 .70
*Nos. 4371-4374 (4)* 3.00 1.60

Matsu Islands tourist attractions.

2017 Summer Universiade, Taipei — A1337

No. 4375 — Universiade mascot Bravo Bear participating in: a, Weight lifting. b, Archery. c, Track. d, Taekwondo. e, Baseball. f, Basketball. g, Volleyball. h, Table tennis.

$25, Stylized figures participating in weight lifting, archery, track, volleyball, taekwondo, table tennis, basketball, and baseball.

***Perf. 13¼x13½ Syncopated***

**2017, Aug. 16 Litho.**

**4375** Block of 8 5.50 3.00
*a.-d.* A1337 $5 Any single .35 .25
*e.-h.* A1337 $15 Any single 1.00 .50

**Souvenir Sheet**

**Litho. & Embossed**

***Perf. 13x12¾ Syncopated***

**4376** A1337 $25 multi 1.75 .85

No. 4376 contains one 100x30mm rectangular stamp.

Magpie, by Xu Beihong A1338

Macaque, by Gao Xifeng A1339

A Secluded Scene of Remote Mountains, by Huang Chun-pi A1340

Pumpkin Vines of Abundant Growth, by Qi Baishi A1341

**2017, Sept. 6 Litho. *Perf. 13¼x12¼***

**4377** A1338 $5 multi .35 .25
**4378** A1339 $12 multi .80 .40
**4379** A1340 $15 multi 1.00 .50
**4380** A1341 $25 multi 1.75 .85
*Nos. 4377-4380 (4)* 3.90 2.00

A1342

Cross-Strait Exchanges, 30th Anniv. A1343

**2017, Sept. 20 Litho. *Perf. 13x12¾***

**4381** A1342 $9 multi .60 .30
**4382** A1343 $28 multi 1.90 .95

**Fruit Type of 2016**

Designs: $3, Asian pears. $6, Rose apples. $8, Bananas. $28, Pomelos.

***Perf. 12¼x13½***

**2017, Sept. 20 Litho.**

**4383** A1259 $3 multi .30 .25
**4384** A1259 $6 multi .40 .25
**4385** A1259 $8 multi .55 .25
**4386** A1259 $28 multi 1.90 .95
*Nos. 4383-4386 (4)* 3.15 1.70

Hydrophasianus Chirurgus — A1344

No. 4387: a, $5, Bird and eggs in nest (denomination in yellow). b, $5, Bird in flight, horiz. (denomination in light blue). c, $10, Juvenile bird walking on water plants, horiz. (denomination in orange). d, $10, Adult and chick walking on water plants (denomination in pink).

$32, Bird grabbing tail feather in beak, horiz.

**2017, Oct. 11 Litho. *Perf. 13***

**4387** A1344 Sheet of 4, #a-d 2.00 1.00

**Souvenir Sheet**

***Perf. 12¾x12½***

**4388** A1344 $32 multi 2.10 1.10

No. 4388 contains one 60x40mm stamp.

National Taipei University of Business, Cent. — A1345

Designs: $8, Japanese era building. $28, Current school building.

***Perf. 12½x13¼***

**2017, Nov. 16 Litho.**

**4389-4390** A1345 Set of 2 2.40 1.25

Cheirostylis Octodactyla — A1346

**2017, Nov. 16 Litho. *Perf. 12½***

**4391** A1346 $35 multi 2.40 1.25

New Year 2018 (Year of the Dog)

A1347 A1348

Design: $15, Dog and fan, horiz.

**2017, Dec. 1 Litho. *Perf. 13***

**4392** A1347 $6 gold & multi .40 .25
**4393** A1348 $13 gold & multi .90 .45

**Souvenir Sheet**

**4394** A1348 $15 gold & multi 1.00 .50

No. 4394 contains one 64x40mm stamp.

Wild Orchids — A1349

Designs: $8, Calanthe puberula. $15, Calanthe sieboldii. $16, Habenaria dentata. $22, Neottia meifongensis. $23, Dendrobium chryseum, horiz. $28, Bulbophyllum pectinatum, horiz. $43, Dendrobium linawianum, horiz.

**2018 Litho. *Perf. 13½x13***

**4395** A1349 $8 multi .55 .25
**4396** A1349 $15 multi 1.00 .50

***Perf. 12½***

**4397** A1349 $16 multi 1.10 .55
**4398** A1349 $22 multi 1.50 .75
**4399** A1349 $23 multi 1.60 .80

***Perf. 13x13½***

**4400** A1349 $28 multi 1.90 .95

***Perf. 12½***

**4401** A1349 $43 multi 3.00 1.50
*Nos. 4395-4401 (7)* 10.65 5.30

**Self-Adhesive**

***Die Cut Perf. 13½x13***

**4402** A1349 $8 multi .55 .25

***Die Cut Perf. 13x13½***

**4403** A1349 $28 multi 1.90 .95

Issued: $8, $15, $28, 1/26; $16, $22, $23, $43, 2/27. See Nos. 4433-4436.

Souvenir Sheet

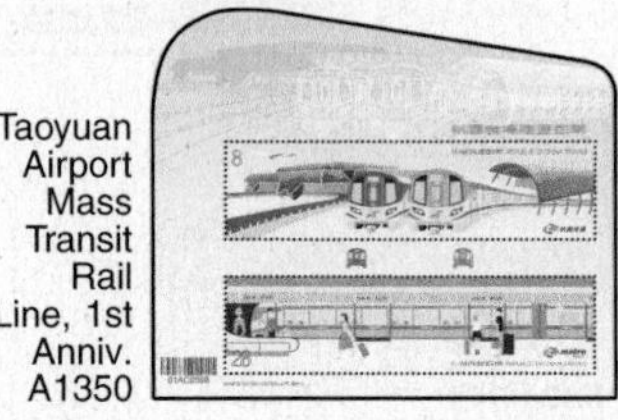

Taoyuan Airport Mass Transit Rail Line, 1st Anniv. A1350

No. 4404: a, $8, Airport, commuter and express trains at station. b, $28, Escalator, passengers on platform, train at station.

**2018, Mar. 2 Litho. *Perf. 13***

**4404** A1350 Sheet of 2, #a-b 2.50 1.25

Jiemei Lakes A1351

Cueifong Lake A1352

Yuanyang Lake A1353

Songluo Lake A1354

***Perf. 13½x13¼***

**2018, Mar. 21 Litho.**

**4405** A1351 $6 multi .40 .25
**4406** A1352 $6 multi .40 .25
**4407** A1353 $8 multi .55 .25
**4408** A1354 $8 multi .55 .25
*Nos. 4405-4408 (4)* 1.90 1.00

A1355

A1356

A1357

A1358

A1359

A1360

A1361

A1362

A1363

Best Wishes — A1364

**2018, Apr. 12 Litho. *Perf. 13¼x12½***

**4409** Block of 10 4.00 2.50
*a.* A1355 $6 multi .40 .25
*b.* A1356 $6 multi .40 .25
*c.* A1357 $6 multi .40 .25
*d.* A1358 $6 multi .40 .25
*e.* A1359 $6 multi .40 .25
*f.* A1360 $6 multi .40 .25
*g.* A1361 $6 multi .40 .25
*h.* A1362 $6 multi .40 .25
*i.* A1363 $6 multi .40 .25
*j.* A1364 $6 multi .40 .25

**4410** Block of 10 5.50 2.50
*a.* A1355 $8 multi .55 .25
*b.* A1356 $8 multi .55 .25
*c.* A1357 $8 multi .55 .25
*d.* A1358 $8 multi .55 .25
*e.* A1359 $8 multi .55 .25
*f.* A1360 $8 multi .55 .25
*g.* A1361 $8 multi .55 .25
*h.* A1362 $8 multi .55 .25
*i.* A1363 $8 multi .55 .25
*j.* A1364 $8 multi .55 .25

Taichung Park A1365

National Taichung Theater A1366

Wuling Farm A1367

Gaomei Wetlands A1368

**2018, May 3 Litho. *Perf. 12¾***

**4411** A1365 $8 multi .55 .25
**4412** A1366 $9 multi .60 .30
**4413** A1367 $12 multi .80 .40
**4414** A1368 $15 multi 1.00 .50
*Nos. 4411-4414 (4)* 2.95 1.45

Taichung City tourist attractions.

Kaomei Lighthouse A1369

Wuchiu Yu Lighthouse A1370

Suao Lighthouse A1371

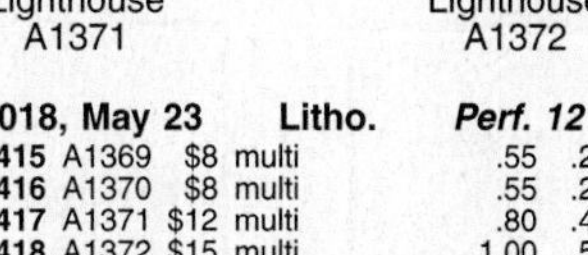

Anping Lighthouse A1372

**2018, May 23 Litho. Perf. 12½**

| | | | | |
|---|---|---|---|---|
| **4415** | A1369 | $8 multi | .55 | .25 |
| **4416** | A1370 | $8 multi | .55 | .25 |
| **4417** | A1371 | $12 multi | .80 | .40 |
| **4418** | A1372 | $15 multi | 1.00 | .50 |
| | | *Nos. 4415-4418 (4)* | 2.90 | 1.40 |

Miniature Sheet

Aerial Views A1373

No. 4419: a, $8, Cattle on Mount Daijan. b, $9, Choir on Mount Jade. c, $13, Sunset over fish farms, Yongan. d, $15, Giant footprints in paddies, Yuli.

**2018, June 8 Litho. Perf. 13¼**

**4419** A1373 Sheet of 4, #a-d 3.00 1.50

Souvenir Sheet

Marine Life A1374

No. 4420: a, $13, Carcharhinus melanopterus. b, $28, Chelonia mydas.

**2018, June 26 Litho. Perf. 12¾**

**4420** A1374 Sheet of 2, #a-b 2.75 1.40

Chinese Poetry — A1375

Scenes depicting poem: $6, Climbing White Stork Tower, by Wang Zhihuan (temple and tree). $8, River Snow, by Liu Zhongyuan (fishing boat in river). $9, Longing, by Wang Wei (woman holding bean and fan). $15, Quiet Night Thoughts, by Li Bai (Moon over shelter with sleeping man).

**2018, July 6 Litho. Perf. 12¾**

**4421-4424** A1375 Set of 4 2.50 1.25

Compare with Nos. 4470-4473, 4556-4559.

**Corals Type of 2014**

Designs: No. 4425, $6, Leptoseris yabei. No. 4426, $6, Clavularia viridis. No. 4427, $15, Lobophytum crassum. No. 4428, $15, Melithaea formosa.

**2018, July 19 Litho. Perf. 12½x13¼**

**4425-4428** A1203 Set of 4 2.75 1.40

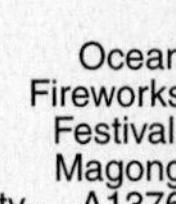

Ocean Fireworks Festival, Magong City — A1376

Erkan Village, Xiyu Island A1377

Low Tide Path, Kueibishan A1378

Daguoye Columnar Basalt A1379

**2018, Aug. 2 Litho. Perf. 12½x13¼**

| | | | | |
|---|---|---|---|---|
| **4429** | A1376 | $6 multi | .40 | .25 |
| **4430** | A1377 | $8 multi | .55 | .25 |
| **4431** | A1378 | $12 multi | .80 | .40 |
| **4432** | A1379 | $15 multi | 1.00 | .50 |
| | | *Nos. 4429-4432 (4)* | 2.75 | 1.40 |

Penghu County tourist attractions.

**Wild Orchids Type of 2018**

Designs: $7, Phalaenopsis equestris. $9, Odontochilus nanlingensis. $10, Bulbophyllum retusiusculum, horiz. $20, Bulbophyllum griffithii, horiz.

***Perf. 13¼x12½***

**2018, Aug. 22 Litho.**

| | | | | |
|---|---|---|---|---|
| **4433** | A1349 | $7 multi | .45 | .25 |
| **4434** | A1349 | $9 multi | .60 | .30 |

***Perf. 12½x13¼***

| | | | | |
|---|---|---|---|---|
| **4435** | A1349 | $10 multi | .65 | .35 |
| **4436** | A1349 | $20 multi | 1.40 | .70 |
| | | *Nos. 4433-4436 (4)* | 3.10 | 1.60 |

Red Sunset, by Lin Chih-chu (1917-2008) A1380

By the Window, by Liao Te-cheng (1920-2015) A1381

Day and Night, by Chen Ting-shih (1916-2002) A1382

Work No. 057, by Lee Chun-shan (1912-84) A1383

***Perf. 12½x12¾, 12¾x12½***

**2018, Sept. 12 Litho.**

| | | | | |
|---|---|---|---|---|
| **4437** | A1380 | $8 multi | .55 | .30 |
| **4438** | A1381 | $8 multi | .55 | .30 |
| **4439** | A1382 | $10 multi | .65 | .35 |
| **4440** | A1383 | $10 multi | .65 | .35 |
| | | *Nos. 4437-4440 (4)* | 2.40 | 1.30 |

Miniature Sheet

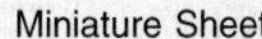

Birds A1384

No. 4441: a, Chlidonias hybrida in flight. b, Chlidonias hybrid on branch, horiz. c, Recurvirostra avosetta. d, Recurvirostra avosetta, horiz.

**2018, Oct. 3 Litho. Perf. 13¼**

| | | | | |
|---|---|---|---|---|
| **4441** | A1384 | Sheet of 4 | 2.00 | 1.00 |
| *a.-b.* | | $7 Either single | .45 | .25 |
| *c.-d.* | | $8 Either single | .55 | .25 |

A1385

Taichung World Flora Exposition — A1386

Designs: $6, Lily. $8, Oncidium orchid. $9, Gladioli. $28, Flamingo flower.

No. 4446: a, $13, Leopard cat mascot holding potted lilies. b, $15. Leopard kitten mascot on pot holding hygrophila. c, $17, Leopard cat mascot holding potted butterfly orchid.

**2018, Oct. 31 Litho. Perf. 14x13¾**

**Stamps + Label**

**4442-4445** A1385 Set of 4 3.50 1.75

**Souvenir Sheet**

***Perf. 13¼ on Top and Bottom***

**4446** A1386 Sheet of 3, #a-c 3.00 1.50

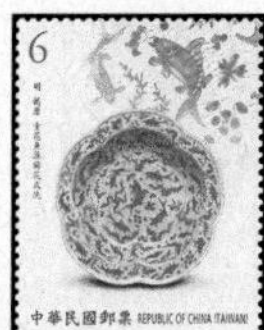

Blue and White Porcelain — A1387

Designs: $6, Ming Dynasty water container with fish design. $9, Ming Dynasty bowl with phoenix and flower design. $15, Qing Dynasty ewer with fruits and flowers design. $16, Qing Dynasty vase with flower design.

$28, Ming Dynasty vase with dragon and lotus blossom designs.

***Perf. 13¾x13½***

**2018, Nov. 15 Litho.**

**4447-4450** A1387 Set of 4 3.00 1.50

**Souvenir Sheet**

**4451** A1387 $28 multi 1.90 .95

Compare with types A1424-A1428.

New Year 2019 (Year of the Pig) — A1388

Designs: $6, Red pig and gold piglet. $13, Pig with plum blossoms and red piglet.

$15, Two pigs with plum blossoms.

**2018, Dec. 3 Litho. Perf. 13**

**4452-4453** A1388 Set of 2 1.25 .60

**Souvenir Sheet**

**4454** A1388 $15 multi 1.00 .50

No. 4454 contains one 64x40mm stamp.

Goldfish — A1389

Goldfish varieties: No. 4455, $6, Red Swallowtail facing right. No. 4456, $6, Ryukin facing left. $12, Dragon Eye. $28, Goose Head Pearl Scale.

**2019, Jan. 24 Litho. Perf. 12½**

**4455-4458** A1389 Set of 4 3.50 1.75

Compare with types A1450-A1453, A1507-A1510.

Dongsha Atoll National Park A1390

Designs: $8, Aerial view of Dongsha Atoll and red-breasted wrasse. $13, Dongsha Coral Reef and yellowhead demoiselle. $15, Dongsha Seagrass Bed and spotted eagle ray. $28, Aerial view of Dongsha Island and white-breasted waterhen.

***Perf. 12½x13½***

**2019, Feb. 21 Litho.**

**4459-4462** A1390 Set of 4 4.25 2.10

Education Benefits Both Students and Teachers A1391

Offering Bricks to Elicit Jade — A1392

Love House and Crow — A1393

True to Life — A1394

***Perf. 12½x12¾***

**2019, Mar. 20 Litho.**

| | | | | |
|---|---|---|---|---|
| **4463** | A1391 | $8 multi | .55 | .25 |
| **4464** | A1392 | $8 multi | .55 | .25 |
| **4465** | A1393 | $8 multi | .55 | .25 |
| **4466** | A1394 | $8 multi | .55 | .25 |
| | | *Nos. 4463-4466 (4)* | 2.20 | 1.00 |

Chinese idioms.

A1395

A1396

A1397

Presidential Office Building, Cent. — A1398

**2019, Apr. 2 Litho. *Perf. 12¾x12½***

| | | | |
|---|---|---|---|
| **4467** | Horiz. strip of 3 | 2.40 | 1.25 |
| *a.* | A1395 $8 multi | .55 | .25 |
| *b.* | A1396 $13 multi | .85 | .40 |
| *c.* | A1397 $15 multi | 1.00 | .50 |

**Souvenir Sheet**

| | | | |
|---|---|---|---|
| **4468** | A1398 $28 multi | 1.90 | .95 |

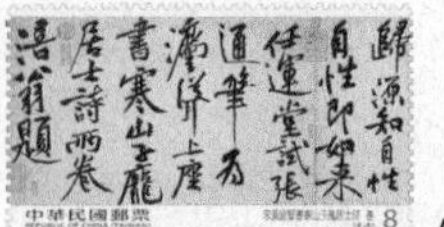
A1399

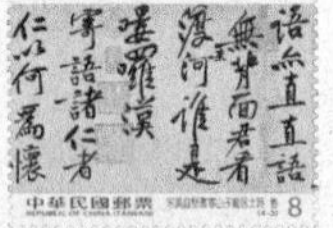
A1400

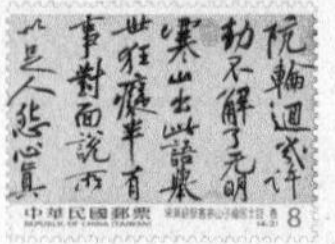
A1401

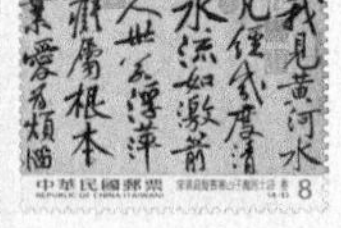
Poetry of Hanshan and Recluse Pang, by Huang Ting-chien (1045-1105) A1402

**2019, May 29 Litho. *Perf. 12½x13¼***

| | | | |
|---|---|---|---|
| **4469** | Horiz. strip of 4 | 2.00 | 1.00 |
| *a.* | A1399 $8 multi | .50 | .25 |
| *b.* | A1400 $8 multi | .50 | .25 |
| *c.* | A1401 $8 multi | .50 | .25 |
| *d.* | A1402 $8 multi | .50 | .25 |

Exists in a sheet containing 4 no. 4469.

"Spring Wind," by Bai Juyi A1403

"Summer Fun on the Farm," by Fan Chengdai A1404

"An Autumn Evening," by Du Mu A1405

"After Snowfall in the Mountains," by Zheng Banqiao A1406

**2019, June 12 Litho. *Perf. 12¾***

| | | | | | |
|---|---|---|---|---|---|
| **4470** | A1403 | $6 multi | | .40 | .25 |
| **4471** | A1404 | $8 multi | | .55 | .25 |
| **4472** | A1405 | $9 multi | | .60 | .30 |
| **4473** | A1406 | $15 multi | | 1.00 | .50 |
| | | *Nos. 4470-4473 (4)* | | 2.55 | 1.30 |

Chinese poetry. Compare with Nos. 4421-4424, 4556-4559.

Festival on South Street, by Kuo Hsueh-hu (1908-2012) A1407

Ferry of the Egret, by Chen Yung-sen (1913-97) A1408

Guitar, by Chang Yi-hsiung (1914-2016) A1409

Studio, by Hsiao Ju-sung (1922-92) A1410

***Perf. 12¾x12½***

**2019, June 21 Litho.**

| | | | | |
|---|---|---|---|---|
| **4474** | A1407 | $8 multi | .55 | .25 |
| **4475** | A1408 | $8 multi | .55 | .25 |
| **4476** | A1409 | $15 multi | 1.00 | .50 |

***Perf. 12½x12¾***

| | | | | |
|---|---|---|---|---|
| **4477** | A1410 | $15 multi | 1.00 | .50 |
| | | *Nos. 4474-4477 (4)* | 3.10 | 1.50 |

Han Dynasty Jade Items From National Palace Museum — A1411

Designs: $6, Jade beast. $8, Jade seal. $13, Jade camel, horiz. $15, Jade bixie beast, horiz.

**2019, July 5 Litho. *Perf. 13¼x13***

| | | | | |
|---|---|---|---|---|
| **4478-4481** | A1411 | Set of 4 | 3.50 | 1.75 |

Compare with Types A1440-A1443.

Lanyang Museum, Toucheng Township, Yilan County A1412

Surfer at Wai'ao, Toucheng Township, Yilan County A1413

Chiang Ku Ceremony, Toucheng Township, Yilan County A1414

Lizejian Bridge Over Dongshan River, Yilan County A1415

**2019, July 16 Litho. *Perf. 13¼***

| | | | | |
|---|---|---|---|---|
| **4482** | A1412 | $6 multi | .40 | .25 |
| **4483** | A1413 | $8 multi | .50 | .25 |
| **4484** | A1414 | $12 multi | .80 | .40 |
| **4485** | A1415 | $13 multi | .85 | .40 |
| | | *Nos. 4482-4485 (4)* | 2.55 | 1.30 |

Yilan County tourist attractions.

Tamsui Church, Tamsui A1416

Thài-Pêng-Kéng Maxwell Memorial Church, Tainan A1417

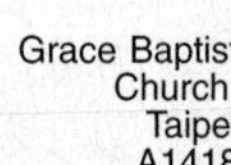
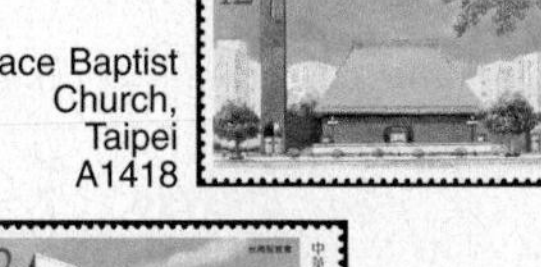
Grace Baptist Church, Taipei A1418

Tainan Holiness Church, Tainan A1419

**2019, Aug. 7 Litho. *Perf. 12¾***

| | | | | |
|---|---|---|---|---|
| **4486** | A1416 | $8 multi | .50 | .25 |
| **4487** | A1417 | $8 multi | .50 | .25 |
| **4488** | A1418 | $12 multi | .80 | .40 |
| **4489** | A1419 | $12 multi | .80 | .40 |
| | | *Nos. 4486-4489 (4)* | 2.60 | 1.30 |

Famous church architecture.

Field of Rapeseed Flowers, East Rift Valley A1420

Qixingtan Bay — A1421

Rafters on Xiuguluan River A1422

Swallow Grotto, Taroko National Park A1423

**2019, Aug. 28 Litho. *Perf. 12¾***

| | | | | |
|---|---|---|---|---|
| **4490** | A1420 | $6 multi | .40 | .25 |
| **4491** | A1421 | $6 multi | .40 | .25 |
| **4492** | A1422 | $12 multi | .80 | .40 |
| **4493** | A1423 | $12 multi | .80 | .40 |
| | | *Nos. 4490-4493 (4)* | 2.40 | 1.30 |

Tourist attractions of Hualien County.

Ming Dynasty Teapot A1424

Qing Dynasty Tea Bowl A1425

Qing Dynasty Teapot A1426

Ming Dynasty Teacup A1427

Ming Dynasty Pilgrim Bottle A1428

**Litho. & Embossed**

**2019, Sept. 9 *Perf. 13¾x13½***

| | | | | |
|---|---|---|---|---|
| **4494** | A1424 | $8 multi | .55 | .25 |
| **4495** | A1425 | $12 multi | .80 | .40 |
| **4496** | A1426 | $13 multi | .85 | .25 |
| **4497** | A1427 | $18 multi | 1.25 | .60 |
| | | *Nos. 4494-4497 (4)* | 3.45 | 1.50 |

**Souvenir Sheet**

| | | | | |
|---|---|---|---|---|
| **4498** | A1428 | $28 multi | 1.90 | .95 |

Blue and white porcelain. Compare with type A1387.

Little Green Man Pedestrian Signal A1429

Electronic Toll Collection A1430

Multipurpose Smartcard for Fare Collection A1431

Transportation Information and Management A1432

**2019, Sept. 25 Litho. *Perf. 13½x13***

| | | | | |
|---|---|---|---|---|
| **4499** | A1429 | $8 multi | .55 | .25 |
| **4500** | A1430 | $8 multi | .55 | .25 |
| **4501** | A1431 | $8 multi | .55 | .25 |
| **4502** | A1432 | $8 multi | .55 | .25 |
| *a.* | | Souvenir sheet of 4, #4499-4502, perf.12¾x12½ | 2.25 | 1.00 |
| | | *Nos. 4499-4502 (4)* | 2.20 | 1.00 |

National Chung Hsing University, Taichung City, Cent. — A1433

Designs: $8, Main entrance. $28, Auditorium.

**2019, Oct. 9 Litho. *Perf. 12½x13¼***

| | | | | |
|---|---|---|---|---|
| **4503-4504** | A1433 | Set of 2 | 2.40 | 1.25 |

Baseball Players A1434

No. 4505: a, Batter. b, Pitcher. c, Catcher. d, Runner.

**2019, Nov. 1 Litho. *Perf. 12½***

| | | | | |
|---|---|---|---|---|
| **4505** | A1434 | Block of 4, #a-d, + 2 central labels | 1.90 | 1.00 |
| *a.-b.* | | $6 Either single | .40 | .25 |
| *c.-d.* | | $8 Either single | .55 | .25 |

Group B Games of World Baseball Softball Confederation Premier 12 Competition, Republic of China.

Keelung Lighthouse A1435

Tungting Tao Lighthouse A1436

Taichung Port Lighthouse A1437

Tamsui Harbor Lighthouse A1438

**2019, Nov. 20 Litho. *Perf. 12½***

| | | | | |
|---|---|---|---|---|
| **4506** | A1435 | $8 multi | .55 | .25 |
| **4507** | A1436 | $8 multi | .55 | .25 |
| **4508** | A1437 | $12 multi | .80 | .40 |
| **4509** | A1438 | $15 multi | 1.00 | .50 |
| | | *Nos. 4506-4509 (4)* | 2.90 | 1.40 |

New Year 2020 (Year of the Rat) — A1439

Designs: $6, Blue green rat. $13, Magenta rat.

$15, Magenta and purple rats, horiz.

**2019, Dec. 3 Litho. *Perf. 13***

| | | | | |
|---|---|---|---|---|
| **4510-4511** | A1439 | Set of 2 | 1.25 | .65 |

**Souvenir Sheet**

***Perf. 12½***

| | | | | |
|---|---|---|---|---|
| **4512** | A1439 | $15 multi | 1.00 | .50 |

No. 4512 contains one 64x40mm stamp.

Jade Hornless Dragons Cup A1440

Jade Bottle With Phoenixes A1441

Jade Goblet A1442

Jade Four-legged Cauldron A1443

***Perf. 13¼x12½***

**2019, Dec. 10 Litho.**

| | | | | |
|---|---|---|---|---|
| **4513** | A1440 | $7 multi | .50 | .25 |
| **4514** | A1441 | $12 multi | .80 | .40 |
| **4515** | A1442 | $15 multi | 1.00 | .50 |
| **4516** | A1443 | $35 multi | 2.40 | 1.25 |
| | | *Nos. 4513-4516 (4)* | 4.70 | 2.40 |

Jade items from National Palace Museum. Compare with Nos. 4478-4481.

Baimi Viaduct A1444

Nan'ao Beixi Bridge A1445

**2020, Jan. 3 Litho. *Perf. 13¼x13***

| | | | | |
|---|---|---|---|---|
| **4517** | A1444 | $28 multi | 1.90 | .95 |
| **4518** | A1445 | $35 multi | 2.40 | 1.25 |

Completion of Suhua Highway Improvement Project.

Dapeng Bay Bridge A1446

Kenting National Park A1447

Little Liuqiu Flower Vase Rock A1448

Hengchun Old Town A1449

**2020, Jan. 10 Litho. *Perf. 12¾***

| | | | | |
|---|---|---|---|---|
| **4519** | A1446 | $6 muti | .40 | .25 |
| **4520** | A1447 | $6 multi | .40 | .25 |
| **4521** | A1448 | $8 multi | .55 | .25 |
| **4522** | A1449 | $15 multi | 1.00 | .50 |
| | | *Nos. 4519-4522 (4)* | 2.35 | 1.25 |

Tourist attractions in Pingtung County.

Red Crane Crest Oranda — A1450

Ranchu — A1451

Broadtail Ryukin — A1452

Pompons A1453

***Perf. 12½x13¼***

**2020, Feb. 26 Litho.**

| | | | | |
|---|---|---|---|---|
| **4523** | A1450 | $6 multi | .40 | .25 |
| **4524** | A1451 | $9 multi | .60 | .30 |
| **4525** | A1452 | $15 multi | 1.00 | .50 |
| **4526** | A1453 | $17 multi | 1.25 | .60 |
| | | *Nos. 4523-4526 (4)* | 3.25 | 1.65 |

Compare with Types A1389, A1450-1453.

Dalongdong Basin Temple, Taipei — A1454

Taiwan Tainan District Court Building, Tainan — A1455

Railway Division of Taiwan Governor General's Bureau of Transportation, Taipei — A1456

Gongziliao Fort, Keelung — A1457

**2020, Mar. 20 Litho. *Perf. 12½***

| | | | | |
|---|---|---|---|---|
| **4527** | A1454 | $8 multi | .55 | .25 |
| **4528** | A1455 | $8 multi | .55 | .25 |
| **4529** | A1456 | $8 multi | .55 | .25 |
| **4530** | A1457 | $8 multi | .55 | .25 |
| | | *Nos. 4527-4530 (4)* | 2.20 | 1.00 |

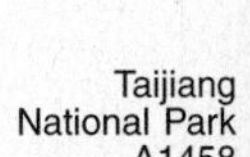

Taijiang National Park A1458

Designs: $6, Oysters and Cigu Lagoon. $8, Black-faced Spoonbill Reserve. $15, Beach morning glories and Wangzailiao Sand Bar. $28, Mangrove blossom and Sicao Mangrove Green Tunnel.

**2020, Apr. 24 Litho. *Perf. 12¾***

| | | | | |
|---|---|---|---|---|
| **4531-4534** | A1458 | Set of 4 | 4.00 | 2.00 |

A1459

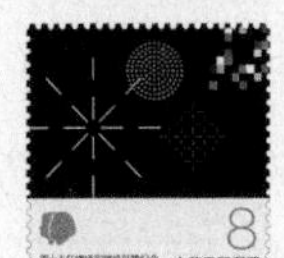

A1460

A1461

A1462

Inauguration of President Tsai Ing-wen and Vice President Lai Ching-te — A1463

**2020, May 20 Litho. *Perf. 12½***

| | | | | |
|---|---|---|---|---|
| **4535** | | Horiz. strip or block of 4 | 3.25 | 1.50 |
| *a.* | A1459 | $8 multi | .55 | .25 |
| *b.* | A1460 | $8 multi | .55 | .25 |
| *c.* | A1461 | $15 multi | 1.00 | .50 |
| *d.* | A1462 | $15 multi | 1.00 | .50 |

**Souvenir Sheet**

| | | | | |
|---|---|---|---|---|
| **4536** | A1463 | $35 multi | 2.40 | 1.25 |

Annular Solar Eclipse A1464

Comet A1465

Total Solar Eclipse A1466

Total Lunar Eclipse A1467

***Perf. 13¼x13½***

**2020, June 20 Litho.**

| | | | | |
|---|---|---|---|---|
| **4537** | A1464 | $6 multi | .40 | .25 |
| **4538** | A1465 | $6 multi | .40 | .25 |

***Perf. 13½x13¼***

| | | | | |
|---|---|---|---|---|
| **4539** | A1466 | $8 multi | .55 | .25 |
| **4540** | A1467 | $8 multi | .55 | .25 |
| *a.* | | Souvenir sheet of 4, #4537-4540, perf. 13¼ | 1.90 | 1.00 |

Sports — A1468

Designs: No. 4541, $6, Badminton. No. 4542, $6, Archery. $8, Weight lifting. $12, Men's pommel horse gymnastics.

**2020, July 10 Litho. *Perf. 12½x12¾***

| | | | | |
|---|---|---|---|---|
| **4541-4544** | A1468 | Set of 4 | 2.25 | 1.10 |

COVID-19 Prevention — A1469

No. 4545: a, Five people wearing masks. b, Manufacturing inspection, bus, train, ambulance, commuter wearing mask, handwashing and medical research.

**2020, July 21 Litho. *Perf. 12¾x12½***

| | | | | |
|---|---|---|---|---|
| **4545** | A1469 | Horiz. pair + central label | 1.90 | .95 |
| *a.* | | $13 multi | .90 | .45 |
| *b.* | | $15 multi | 1.00 | .50 |

Sun Moon Lake A1470

Jiji Green Tunnel A1471

Qingjing Farm A1472

Hehuan Mountain Dark Sky Park A1473

***Perf. 12½x13¼***

| 2020, Aug. 12 | | | Litho. | |
|---|---|---|---|---|
| 4546 | A1470 | $8 multi | .65 | .25 |
| 4547 | A1471 | $8 multi | .65 | .25 |
| 4548 | A1472 | $13 multi | 1.10 | .45 |
| 4549 | A1473 | $15 multi | 1.35 | .55 |
| | *Nos. 4546-4549 (4)* | | 3.75 | 1.50 |

Nantou County tourist attractions.

Hanshan Culture Jade Bird A1474

Liangzhu Culture Jade Ornament A1475

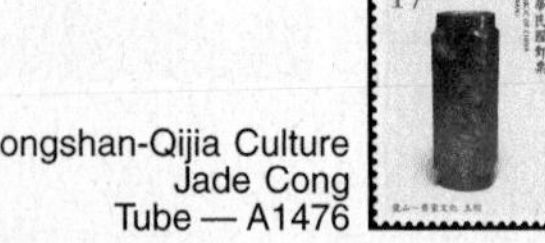
Longshan-Qijia Culture Jade Cong Tube — A1476

Shang Dynasty Jade Disc — A1477

***Perf. 13¼x12½, 12½x13¼***

| 2020, Aug. 26 | | | Litho. | |
|---|---|---|---|---|
| 4550 | A1474 | $8 multi | .55 | .25 |
| 4551 | A1475 | $9 multi | .65 | .30 |
| 4552 | A1476 | $17 multi | 1.25 | .60 |
| 4553 | A1477 | $22 multi | 1.50 | .75 |
| | *Nos. 4550-4553 (4)* | | 3.95 | 1.90 |

Taipei Grand Mosque A1478

Taichung Mosque A1479

***Perf. 12½x13¼***

| 2020, Sept. 29 | | | Litho. | |
|---|---|---|---|---|
| 4554 | A1478 | $15 multi | 1.10 | .55 |
| 4555 | A1479 | $28 multi | 2.00 | 1.00 |

*Plum Blossoms,* Poem by Wang Anshi (1021-86) A1480

*Orchid River,* Poem by Du Mu (803-52) A1481

*New Bamboo,* Poem by Zheng Banqiao (1693-1765) A1482

*Chrysanthemums,* Poem by Yuan Zhen (779-831) A1483

| 2020, Oct. 14 | | Litho. | *Perf. 12¾* | |
|---|---|---|---|---|
| 4556 | A1480 | $8 multi | .55 | .30 |
| 4557 | A1481 | $8 multi | .55 | .30 |
| 4558 | A1482 | $12 multi | .85 | .40 |
| 4559 | A1483 | $15 multi | 1.10 | .55 |
| | *Nos. 4556-4559 (4)* | | 3.05 | 1.55 |

Chinese poetry. Compare with Nos. 4421-4424, 4470-4473.

City Sunsets — A1484

Sunset in: $8, Taichung. $35, Kaohsiung.

| 2020, Oct. 28 | | Litho. | *Perf. 13¼* | |
|---|---|---|---|---|
| 4560-4561 | A1484 | Set of 2 | 3.00 | 1.50 |

A1485

A1486

A1487

A1488

A1489

Details From "Syzygy of the Sun, Moon and the Five Planets," Painting by Xu Yang (1712-c. 1777) A1490

| 2020, Nov. 11 | | Litho. | *Perf. 14* | |
|---|---|---|---|---|
| 4562 | | Block of 6 | 3.30 | 1.80 |
| *a.* | A1485 | $8 multi | .55 | .30 |
| *b.* | A1486 | $8 multi | .55 | .30 |
| *c.* | A1487 | $8 multi | .55 | .30 |
| *d.* | A1488 | $8 multi | .55 | .30 |
| *e.* | A1489 | $8 multi | .55 | .30 |
| *f.* | A1490 | $8 multi | .55 | .30 |

See No. 4592.

Chiutzu Shan Lighthouse A1491

Kuosheng Kan Lighthouse A1492

Peiting Tao Lighthouse A1493

Hualien Kan Lighthouse A1494

Taiping Island Lighthouse — A1495

| 2020, Nov. 23 | | Litho. | *Perf. 12½* | |
|---|---|---|---|---|
| 4563 | A1491 | $8 multi | .55 | .30 |
| 4564 | A1492 | $8 multi | .55 | .30 |
| 4565 | A1493 | $8 multi | .55 | .30 |
| 4566 | A1494 | $12 multi | .85 | .40 |
| 4567 | A1495 | $15 multi | 1.10 | .55 |
| | *Nos. 4563-4567 (5)* | | 3.60 | 1.85 |

New Year 2021 (Year of the Ox) — A1496

Ox facing: $6, Right. $13, Left. $15, Ox facing left, horiz.

| 2020, Dec. 1 | | Litho. | *Perf. 13* | |
|---|---|---|---|---|
| 4568-4569 | A1496 | Set of 2 | 1.40 | .70 |

**Souvenir Sheet**

***Perf. 12½***

| 4570 | A1496 | $15 multi | 1.10 | .55 |
|---|---|---|---|---|

No. 4570 contains one 64x40mm stamp.

Birds A1497

Designs: No. 4571, $8, Elanus caeruleus. No. 4572, $8, Falco peregrinus. $10, Accipiter trivirgatus. $28, Pandion haliaetus.

| 2020, Dec. 8 | | Litho. | *Perf. 13½x13¼* | |
|---|---|---|---|---|
| 4571-4574 | A1497 | Set of 4 | 4.00 | 2.00 |

Blue Cave, Xijiyu, and Green Sea Turtle A1498

Sea Lavender Off Dongjiyu, and Giant Triton A1499

Basalt Stack and Platform, Xiyupingyu, and Greater Crested Tern A1500

Terraced Fields, Dongyupingyu, and Glossogyne Tenuifolia — A1501

| 2021, Jan. 20 | | Litho. | *Perf. 14* | |
|---|---|---|---|---|
| 4575 | A1498 | $6 multi | .45 | .25 |
| 4576 | A1499 | $8 multi | .60 | .30 |
| 4577 | A1500 | $9 multi | .65 | .30 |
| 4578 | A1501 | $15 multi | 1.10 | .55 |
| | *Nos. 4575-4578 (4)* | | 2.80 | 1.40 |

South Penghu Marine National Park.

National Kaohsiung Center for the Arts — A1502

Dome of Light, by Narcissus Quagliata, Formosa Boulevard Metro Station A1503

Lights Along Love River A1504

Port of Kaohsiung A1505

| 2021, Feb. 4 | | Litho. | *Perf. 12½x13¼* | |
|---|---|---|---|---|
| 4579 | A1502 | $6 multi | .45 | .45 |
| 4580 | A1503 | $6 multi | .45 | .45 |
| 4581 | A1504 | $15 multi | 1.10 | 1.10 |
| 4582 | A1505 | $15 multi | 1.10 | 1.10 |
| | *Nos. 4579-4582 (4)* | | 3.10 | 3.10 |

Tourist attractions of Kaohsiung City.

Dr. James L. Maxwell (1836-1921), Medical Missionary — A1506

**Litho. & Engr.**

**2021, Mar. 5** *Perf. 12½*

**4583** A1506 $28 multi 2.00 2.00

Bead Scales — A1507

Upturned Eyes — A1508

Blister Eyes — A1509

Lion's Head — A1510

**2021, Apr. 9** **Litho.** *Perf. 13½x13¼*

| | | | | |
|---|---|---|---|---|
| **4584** | A1507 | $8 multi | .60 | .60 |
| **4585** | A1508 | $8 multi | .60 | .60 |
| **4586** | A1509 | $15 multi | 1.10 | 1.10 |
| **4587** | A1510 | $28 multi | 2.00 | 2.00 |
| | *Nos. 4584-4587 (4)* | | 4.30 | 4.30 |

Compare with types A1389, A1450-A1453.

Mt. Datun, by Ni Chiang-huai (1894-1943) A1511

A Scene from Fengyuan, by Yeh Huo-cheng (1908-93) A1512

Early Summer in South Taiwan, by Huang Shui-wen A1513

Ship of Southern Country, by Huang Ching-shan A1514

**2021, Apr. 21** **Litho.** *Perf. 13½x13¼*

| | | | | |
|---|---|---|---|---|
| **4588** | A1511 | $8 multi | .60 | .60 |
| **4589** | A1512 | $8 multi | .60 | .60 |
| **4590** | A1513 | $12 multi | .85 | .85 |
| **4591** | A1514 | $12 multi | .85 | .85 |
| | *Nos. 4588-4591 (4)* | | 2.90 | 2.90 |

A1515

A1516

A1517

A1518

A1519

Details From "Syzygy of the Sun, Moon and the Five Planets," Painting by Xu Yang (1712-c. 1777) A1520

**2021, May 19** **Litho.** *Perf. 14*

| | | | | |
|---|---|---|---|---|
| **4592** | | Block of 6 | 3.75 | 1.90 |
| *a.* | A1515 $8 multi | | .60 | .30 |
| *b.* | A1516 $8 multi | | .60 | .30 |
| *c.* | A1517 $8 multi | | .60 | .30 |
| *d.* | A1518 $8 multi | | .60 | .30 |
| *e.* | A1519 $8 multi | | .60 | .30 |
| *f.* | A1520 $8 multi | | .60 | .30 |

See No. 4562.

Nankunshen Daitian Temple, Tainan — A1521

Municipal Government Hall, Hsinchu — A1522

Oxford College, Taipei — A1523

Jinguitou Fortress, Magong — A1524

**2021, June 17** **Litho.** *Perf. 13x13¼*

| | | | | |
|---|---|---|---|---|
| **4593** | A1521 | $6 multi | .45 | .25 |
| **4594** | A1522 | $8 multi | .60 | .30 |
| **4595** | A1523 | $10 multi | .70 | .35 |
| **4596** | A1524 | $12 multi | .85 | .45 |
| | *Nos. 4593-4596 (4)* | | 2.60 | 1.35 |

Alpine Flowers — A1525

Designs: No. 4597, $8, Veratrum formosanum. No. 4598, $8, Scabiosa lacerifolia. $15, Geranium hayatanum, horiz. $20, Sedum morrisonense, horiz.

*Perf. 13¼x12½, 12½x13¼*

**2021, June 30** **Litho.**

**4597-4600** A1525 Set of 4 3.75 1.90

A1526

A1527

A1528

Pres. Lee Teng-hui (1923-2020) — A1529

**2021, July 30** **Litho.** *Perf. 12½*

| | | | | |
|---|---|---|---|---|
| **4601** | A1526 | $8 multi | .60 | .30 |
| **4602** | A1527 | $8 multi | .60 | .30 |
| **4603** | A1528 | $15 multi | 1.10 | .55 |
| **4604** | A1529 | $15 multi | 1.10 | .55 |
| | *Nos. 4601-4604 (4)* | | 3.40 | 1.70 |

Miniature Sheet

Rabbit, Children and Flowers A1530

No. 4605: a, Girl with blue dress holding flowers. b, Boy in yellow overalls holding flower. c, Girl in pink dress holding flowers. d, Boy with red pants holding flower. e, Girl with blue and red dress holding flowers. f, Boy with glasses holding flower.

*Perf. 12¼x12½*

**2021, Aug. 11** **Litho.**

| | | | | |
|---|---|---|---|---|
| **4605** | A1530 | Sheet of 6 | 5.50 | 2.60 |
| *a.-b.* | | $8 Either single | .60 | .30 |
| *c.-d.* | | $13 Either single | .95 | .45 |
| *e.-f.* | | $15 Either single | 1.10 | .55 |

Tribute to health care workers of the COVID-19 pandemic.

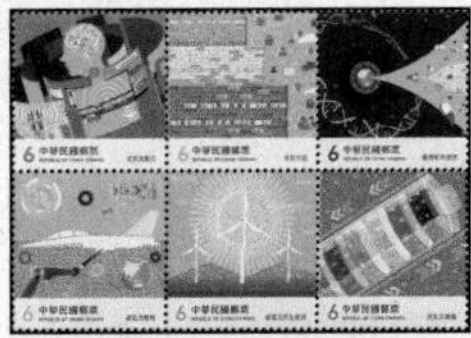

Republic of China's Core Industries — A1531

No. 4606: a, Information and digital technology (head, transmission tower, automobiles). b, Cybersecurity (brick walls and symbols). c, Medical technology and precision health (globe and DNA double helix). d, National defense and strategic industries (jet plane and globe). e, Green and renewable energy (wind generators). f, Strategic stockpile industries (stylized battery).

*Perf. 12¼x12½*

**2021, Aug. 27** **Litho.**

| | | | | |
|---|---|---|---|---|
| **4606** | A1531 | Block of 6 | 2.75 | 1.50 |
| *a.-f.* | | $6 Any single | .45 | .25 |

Longtan Large Tourist Pond, Taoyuan City — A1532

Bade Pond Ecology Park, Taoyuan City A1533

Giant Trees on Lala Mountain, Taoyuan City — A1534

Caota Sand Dunes Geological Park, Taoyuan City — A1535

*Perf. 12¾x12½*

**2021, Sept. 10** **Litho.**

| | | | | |
|---|---|---|---|---|
| **4607** | A1532 | $8 multi | .60 | .30 |
| **4608** | A1533 | $15 multi | 1.10 | .55 |

*Perf. 12½x12¾*

| | | | | |
|---|---|---|---|---|
| **4609** | A1534 | $20 multi | 1.50 | .75 |
| **4610** | A1535 | $28 multi | 2.00 | 1.00 |
| | *Nos. 4607-4610 (4)* | | 5.20 | 2.60 |

Souvenir Sheet

Early Spring, Painting by Guo Xi (c. 1020-c. 1090) A1536

*Perf. 13¼x13½*

**2021, Sept. 29** **Litho.**

**4611** A1536 $35 multi 2.50 1.25

FORMOSAT-7 and Map of Republic of China With Computer Chip Circuit Lines — A1537

Medical Researchers, Pipette, Tube and Symbols of Medical Technology A1538

Airplane, Trains, Ship at Port of Kaohsiung A1539

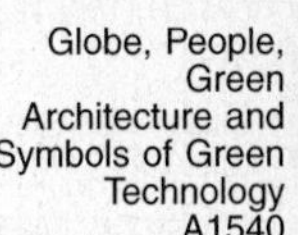

Globe, People, Green Architecture and Symbols of Green Technology A1540

**2021, Oct. 8** **Litho.** *Perf. 12½x12¾*

| | | | | |
|---|---|---|---|---|
| **4612** | A1537 | $6 multi | .45 | .25 |
| **4613** | A1538 | $8 multi | .60 | .30 |
| **4614** | A1539 | $10 multi | .75 | .35 |
| **4615** | A1540 | $28 multi | 2.00 | 1.00 |

Republic of China, 110th anniv.

*The Fisherman on the River,* Poem by Fan Zhongyan (989-1052) A1541

*Singing While Cutting Wood on Mt. Lu,* Poem by Luo Zhongshu (1156-1229) A1542

*Pity the Peasants,* Poem by Li Shen (?-846) A1543

*Exhortation to Learning,* Poem by Yan Zhenqing (709-85) A1544

**2021, Nov. 5 Litho. *Perf. 12¾***

| | | | | |
|---|---|---|---|---|
| **4616** | A1541 $8 multi | | .60 | .30 |
| **4617** | A1542 $8 multi | | .60 | .30 |
| **4618** | A1543 $12 multi | | .90 | .45 |
| **4619** | A1544 $15 multi | | 1.10 | .55 |
| | *Nos. 4616-4619 (4)* | | 3.20 | 1.60 |

Miaoli Dragon Bombing Festival A1545

Liudui Defending the City Walls Festival A1546

Taichung Daoshi Xin Ding Ban Festival A1547

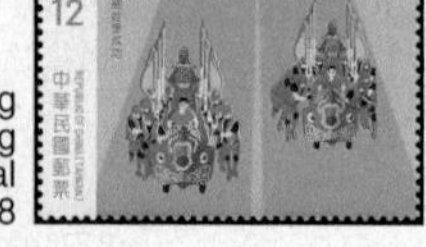

Guoxing Chenggong Festival A1548

**2021, Nov. 24 Litho. *Perf. 12¾***

| | | | | |
|---|---|---|---|---|
| **4620** | A1545 $8 multi | | .60 | .30 |
| **4621** | A1546 $8 multi | | .60 | .30 |
| **4622** | A1547 $12 multi | | .90 | .45 |
| **4623** | A1548 $12 multi | | .90 | .45 |
| | *Nos. 4620-4623 (4)* | | 3.00 | 1.50 |

Hakka festivals.

New Year 2022 (Year of the Tiger) — A1549

Various depictions of a tiger with background color of: $6, Blue green. $13, Bright orange.
$15, Copper, horiz.

**2021, Dec. 1 Litho. *Perf. 13***

**4624-4625** A1549 Set of 2 1.40 .70

**Souvenir Sheet**

***Perf. 12½***

**4626** A1549 $15 multi 1.10 .55

No. 4626 contains one 64x40mm stamp.

Han Dynasty Jade Huan Ring A1550

Warring States Period Jade Dragon Pendant A1551

Warring States Period Jade Beast Pendant A1552

Han Dynasty Jade Disc Depicting Monkeys and Beasts A1553

**2022, Jan. 12 Litho. *Perf. 13¼x12½***

| | | | | |
|---|---|---|---|---|
| **4627** | A1550 $6 multi | | .45 | .25 |
| **4628** | A1551 $15 multi | | 1.10 | .55 |

***Perf. 12½x13¼***

| | | | | |
|---|---|---|---|---|
| **4629** | A1552 $20 multi | | 1.50 | .75 |
| **4630** | A1553 $28 multi | | 2.00 | 1.00 |
| | *Nos. 4627-4630 (4)* | | 5.05 | 2.55 |

Jinlun Bridge, Provincial Highway 9 — A1554

Tongxiao Section, Provincial Highway 61 — A1555

National Freeway 5 Between Toucheng and Su'ao A1556

Provincial Highway 84 Between Toushe and Ershi A1557

**2022, Jan. 26 Litho. *Perf. 12½x13¼***

| | | | | |
|---|---|---|---|---|
| **4631** | A1554 $6 multi | | .45 | .25 |
| **4632** | A1555 $6 multi | | .45 | .25 |
| **4633** | A1556 $8 multi | | .60 | .30 |
| **4634** | A1557 $8 multi | | .60 | .30 |
| | *Nos. 4631-4634 (4)* | | 2.10 | 1.10 |

Endangered Birds A1558

Designs: $8, Butastur indicus. $10, Accipiter soloensis. $12, Pernis ptilorhynchus. $15, Spilornis cheela.

***Perf. 12½x13½***

**2022, Feb. 16 Litho.**

**4635-4638** A1558 Set of 4 3.25 1.60

Souvenir Sheet

George Leslie Mackay (1844-1901), Missionary, Tamsui Church and Hobe Mackay Hospital — A1559

**2022, Mar. 9 Litho. *Perf. 12½x12¾***

**4639** A1559 $28 multi 2.00 1.00

Arrival of Mackay in Taiwan, 150th anniv.

Prionailurus Bengalensis A1560

Designs: $8, Two leopard cats. $28, Three leopard cats.

**2022, Apr. 13 Litho. *Perf. 13x13¼***

**4640-4641** A1560 Set of 2 2.50 1.25

Souvenir Sheet

Inauguration of Taichung Mass Rail Transit System — A1561

No. 4642: a, Train and Taichung Station. b, Train and Taichung City Hall Station.

**2022, Apr. 25 Litho. *Perf. 12½x13½***

| | | | | |
|---|---|---|---|---|
| **4642** | A1561 Sheet of 2 | | 3.50 | 1.75 |
| *a.* | $15 multi | | 1.00 | .50 |
| *b.* | $35 multi | | 2.50 | 1.25 |

Xilou Bridge A1562

Beigang Chaotian Temple A1563

Wannian Canyon, Caoling A1564

Taiping Old Street, Douliu A1565

**2022, May 12 Litho. *Perf. 13¼***

| | | | | |
|---|---|---|---|---|
| **4643** | A1562 $8 multi | | .55 | .25 |
| **4644** | A1563 $8 multi | | .55 | .25 |
| **4645** | A1564 $15 multi | | 1.00 | .50 |
| **4646** | A1565 $15 multi | | 1.00 | .50 |
| | *Nos. 4643-4646 (4)* | | 3.10 | 1.50 |

Yunlin County tourist attractions.

"Two Hearts, One Love" — A1566

"Congratulations on Tying the Knot" — A1567

"Love Is For Life" A1568

"To a Long and Happy Marriage" A1569

**2022, May 20 Litho. *Perf. 13¼x13***

| | | | | |
|---|---|---|---|---|
| **4647** | A1566 $6 multi | | .40 | .25 |
| **4648** | A1567 $6 multi | | .40 | .25 |
| **4649** | A1568 $8 multi | | .55 | .25 |
| **4650** | A1569 $13 multi | | .90 | .45 |
| | *Nos. 4647-4650 (4)* | | 2.25 | 1.20 |

Statue of Confucius, Taihoku High School — A1570

National Taiwan Normal University Library and Administration Building — A1571

**2022, June 1 Litho. *Perf. 12½x12¾***

| | | | | |
|---|---|---|---|---|
| **4651** | A1570 $8 multi | | .55 | .25 |
| **4652** | A1571 $28 multi | | 1.90 | .95 |

National Taiwan Normal University, cent.

Deng Yu-Shian (1906-44), Composer A1572

Hsu Shih (1919-80), Composer A1573

Yang San-Lang (1919-89), Composer A1574

Chou Lan-Ping (1926-71), Composer A1575

**2022, July 6 Litho. *Perf. 13¼x14***

| | | | | |
|---|---|---|---|---|
| **4653** | A1572 $12 multi | | .80 | .40 |
| **4654** | A1573 $12 multi | | .80 | .40 |
| **4655** | A1574 $12 multi | | .80 | .40 |
| **4656** | A1575 $12 multi | | .80 | .40 |
| | *Nos. 4653-4656 (4)* | | 3.20 | 1.60 |

Zither Played in Tune, Poem by Liu Changqing (709-85) A1576

Go, Poem by Wang Anshi (1021-86) A1577

Matched Rhyme to Liu Gongfu's Inscription on Wen Lugong's Calligraphy, Poem by Su Zhe (1039-1112) A1578

Plum Blossoms in Ink, Poem by Wang Mian (1287-1359) A1579

**2022, July 27 Litho. *Perf. 12½x13¼***

| | | | | | |
|---|---|---|---|---|---|
| **4657** | A1576 | $8 | multi | .55 | .25 |
| **4658** | A1577 | $8 | multi | .55 | .25 |
| **4659** | A1578 | $12 | multi | .80 | .40 |
| **4660** | A1579 | $28 | multi | 1.90 | .95 |
| | *Nos. 4657-4660 (4)* | | | 3.80 | 1.85 |

A1580 A1581

A1582 A1583

A1584

24 Solar Terms (Autumn), Paintings by Zhang Ruoai — A1585

***Perf. 13¾x14 Syncopated***

**2022, Aug. 3 Litho.**

| | | | |
|---|---|---|---|
| **4661** | Block of 6 | 3.50 | 1.50 |
| *a.* | A1580 $8 multi | .55 | .25 |
| *b.* | A1581 $8 multi | .55 | .25 |
| *c.* | A1582 $8 multi | .55 | .25 |
| *d.* | A1583 $8 multi | .55 | .25 |
| *e.* | A1584 $8 multi | .55 | .25 |
| *f.* | A1585 $8 multi | .55 | .25 |

Fong Fei-Fei (1953-2012), Singer and Actress — A1586

Fong Fei-Fei wearing hat with panel at left in: $6, Orange. $8, Dark blue. $13, Light red brown. $15, Olive green.

**2022, Aug. 17 Litho. *Perf. 12½***

| | | | | |
|---|---|---|---|---|
| **4662-4665** | A1586 | Set of 4 | 2.75 | 1.40 |

Mazu A1587

Wenchang Dijun A1588

Zhao Gongming (God of Wealth) A1589

Zhusheng Niangniang A1590

**2022, Sept. 21 Litho. *Perf. 13¼x14***

| | | | | | |
|---|---|---|---|---|---|
| **4666** | A1587 | $8 | multi | .50 | .25 |
| **4667** | A1588 | $8 | multi | .50 | .25 |
| **4668** | A1589 | $8 | multi | .50 | .25 |
| **4669** | A1590 | $8 | multi | .50 | .25 |
| | *Nos. 4666-4669 (4)* | | | 2.00 | 1.00 |

Folk deities.

Monopoly Bureau of the Governor-General's Office, Taipei — A1591

Former Tainan Waterworks A1592

Yinshan Temple, New Taipei City — A1593

Ruins of Fengshan City, Kaohsiung A1594

**2022, Oct. 20 Litho. *Perf. 12½x12¾***

| | | | | | |
|---|---|---|---|---|---|
| **4670** | A1591 | $8 | multi | .50 | .25 |
| **4671** | A1592 | $8 | multi | .50 | .25 |
| **4672** | A1593 | $8 | multi | .50 | .25 |
| **4673** | A1594 | $8 | multi | .50 | .25 |
| | *Nos. 4670-4673 (4)* | | | 2.00 | 1.00 |

A1595

A1596

A1597

A1598

A1599

24 Solar Terms (Winter), Paintings by Zhang Ruoai — A1600

***Perf. 13¾x14 Syncopated***

**2022, Nov. 3 Litho.**

| | | | |
|---|---|---|---|
| **4674** | Block of 6 | 4.50 | 2.10 |
| *a.* | A1595 $12 multi | .75 | .35 |
| *b.* | A1596 $12 multi | .75 | .35 |
| *c.* | A1597 $12 multi | .75 | .35 |
| *d.* | A1598 $12 multi | .75 | .35 |
| *e.* | A1599 $12 multi | .75 | .35 |
| *f.* | A1600 $12 multi | .75 | .35 |

Changhua Railway Turntable and Roundhouse A1601

Lukang Tianhou Temple A1602

Wanggong Fishing Port — A1603

Natural Ecological Education Center A1604

**2022, Nov. 11 Litho. *Perf. 12¾***

| | | | | | |
|---|---|---|---|---|---|
| **4675** | A1601 | $8 | multi | .55 | .25 |
| **4676** | A1602 | $8 | multi | .55 | .25 |
| **4677** | A1603 | $12 | multi | .80 | .40 |
| **4678** | A1604 | $28 | multi | 1.90 | .95 |
| | *Nos. 4675-4678 (4)* | | | 3.80 | 1.85 |

Changhua County tourist attractions.

## SEMI-POSTAL STAMPS

China 1913-1919 Issues Surcharge in Red or Blue

**1920, Dec. 1 Unwmk. *Perf. 14, 15***

| | | | | |
|---|---|---|---|---|
| **B1** | A24 | 1c on 2c green | 7.00 | 3.00 |
| **B2** | A24 | 3c on 4c scar (Bl) | 8.00 | 4.00 |
| **B3** | A24 | 5c on 6c gray | 13.00 | 6.00 |
| | | *Nos. B1-B3 (3)* | 28.00 | 13.00 |

The surcharge represents the actual franking value. The extra cent helped victims of the 1919 Yellow River flood.

War Refugees — SP2

**Black Surcharge**

**1944, Oct. 10 Engr. *Perf. 12***

| | | | | |
|---|---|---|---|---|
| **B4** | SP2 | $2 +$2 on 50c + 50c | 3.00 | *4.00* |
| **B5** | SP2 | $4 +$4 on 8c + 8c | 3.00 | *6.00* |
| **B6** | SP2 | $5 +$5 on 21c + 21c | 3.00 | *4.00* |
| **B7** | SP2 | $6 +$6 on 28c + 28c | 5.00 | *5.00* |
| **B8** | SP2 | $10 +$10 on 33c + 33c | 5.50 | *7.00* |
| **B9** | SP2 | $20 +$20 on $1 + $1 | 8.00 | *10.00* |
| *a.* | | Sheet of 6, #B4-B9 | 200.00 | 350.00 |
| | | *Nos. B4-B9 (6)* | 27.50 | *36.00* |

The borders of each stamp differ slightly in design. The surtax was for war refugees.

Nos. B4-B8 exist without surcharge, but were not regularly issued.

Great Wall of China — SP4

**1948, July 5 Litho. *Perf. 14, Imperf.***

**Without Gum**

**Cross in Carmine**

| | | | | |
|---|---|---|---|---|
| **B11** | SP4 | $5000 + $2000 vio | .75 | *3.00* |
| **B12** | SP4 | $10,000 + $2000 brn | .75 | *3.00* |
| **B13** | SP4 | $15,000 + $2000 gray | .75 | *3.00* |
| | | *Nos. B11-B13 (3)* | 2.25 | *9.00* |

The surtax was for anti-tuberculosis work. Value, imperf. set, $3.

**Republic of China (Taiwan)**

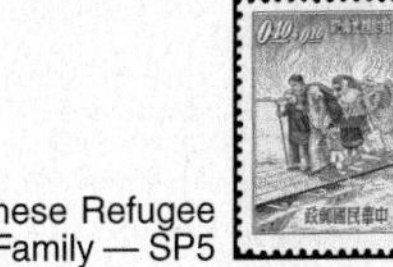
Chinese Refugee Family — SP5

**1954, Oct. 1 Engr. *Perf. 12***

**Without Gum**

| | | | | |
|---|---|---|---|---|
| **B14** | SP5 | 40c + 10c dp bl | 20.00 | 4.00 |
| **B15** | SP5 | $1.60 + 40c lil rose | 55.00 | 21.00 |
| **B16** | SP5 | $5 + $1 red | 100.00 | 87.50 |
| | | *Nos. B14-B16 (3)* | 175.00 | 112.50 |

The surtax was used to aid in the evacuation of Chinese from North Viet Nam.

**Catalogue values for unused stamps in this section, from this point to the end of the section, are for Never Hinged items.**

Sept. 21, 1999 Earthquake Relief — SP6

a, Damaged buildings, map, rescue workers. b, Hands, heart, earthquake fault.

**1999, Nov. 1 Litho. *Imperf.***
**Sheet of 2**

**B17** SP6 $25 +$25, #a.-b. 12.50 7.25

No. B17 has simulated perforations.

Souvenir Sheet

Typhoon Morakot Relief SP7

No. B18: a, Map of Taiwan surrounded by clouds, rescuers and rafts. b, House, construction equipment and workers.

**2009, Oct. 9 Litho. *Imperf.***

**B18** SP7 $25 +$25 Sheet of 2, #a-b 19.50 19.50

No. B18 has simulated perforations.

## AIR POST STAMPS

Curtiss "Jenny" over Great Wall (Bars of Republic flag on tail) — AP1

**Unwmk.**
**1921, July 1 Engr. *Perf. 14***

**C1** AP1 15c bl grn & blk 40.00 *70.00*
**C2** AP1 30c scar & blk 40.00 *70.00*
**C3** AP1 45c dull vio & blk 40.00 *70.00*
**C4** AP1 60c dk blue & blk 52.50 *85.00*
**C5** AP1 90c ol grn & blk 57.50 *90.00*
*Nos. C1-C5 (5)* 230.00 *385.00*

(Nationalist sun emblem on tail) — AP2

**1929, July 5**

**C6** AP2 15c blue grn & blk 10.00 3.00
**C7** AP2 30c dk red & blk 15.00 5.00
**C8** AP2 45c dk vio & blk 24.00 10.00
**C9** AP2 60c dk blue & blk 27.50 12.00
**C10** AP2 90c ol grn & blk 27.50 18.00
*Nos. C6-C10 (5)* 104.00 48.00

Junkers F-13 over Great Wall — AP3

**1932-37**

**C11** AP3 15c gray grn .70 .45
**C12** AP3 25c orange ('33) 5.00 3.00
**C13** AP3 30c red 10.00 2.50
**C14** AP3 45c brown vio 1.00 .45
**C15** AP3 50c dk brown ('33) 1.00 .45
**C16** AP3 60c dk blue 1.00 .45
**C17** AP3 90c olive grn 1.00 1.00
**C18** AP3 $1 yellow grn ('33) 1.50 1.00
**C19** AP3 $2 brown ('37) 1.50 *2.00*
**C20** AP3 $5 brown car ('37) 4.00 *5.00*
*Nos. C11-C20 (10)* 26.70 *16.30*

See Nos. C21-C40. For surcharges and overprints see Nos. C41-C52, C54-C60, 9N111-9N114, 9NC1-9NC7, Szechwan C1, C3-C6, Sinkiang C5-C19.

**Type of 1932-37, with secret mark**

1932-37 Issue, Lower part of left character joined

Secret Mark, 1940-41 Issue, Separated

***Perf. 12, 12½, 12½x13, 13***
**1940-41 Wmk. 261**

**C21** AP3 15c gray green 1.00 1.00
**C22** AP3 25c yellow org 1.25 1.25
**C23** AP3 30c red 1.00 1.00
*a.* Vert. pair, imperf. between *500.00*
**C24** AP3 45c dull rose vio ('41) 1.00 1.00
**C25** AP3 50c brown 1.00 1.00
**C26** AP3 60c dp blue ('41) 1.00 1.00
**C27** AP3 90c olive ('41) 1.00 1.00
**C28** AP3 $1 apple grn ('41) 1.00 1.00
**C29** AP3 $2 lt brown ('41) 1.00 1.00
**C30** AP3 $5 lake 2.50 *3.00*
*Nos. C21-C30 (10)* 11.75 12.25

**Unwmk.**
***Perf. 12½, 13, 13½***

**C31** AP3 15c gray green ('41) .70 *1.00*
**C32** AP3 25c lt orange ('41) .70 *1.00*
**C33** AP3 30c lt red ('41) .70 *1.00*
**C34** AP3 45c dl rose vio ('41) .70 *1.00*
**C35** AP3 50c brown .70 *1.00*
**C36** AP3 60c blue ('41) .70 *1.00*
**C37** AP3 90c lt olive ('41) .70 *1.00*
**C38** AP3 $1 apple grn ('41) .70 *1.00*
*a.* Horiz. pair, imperf. between *500.00*
**C39** AP3 $2 lt brown ('41) 3.00 2.00
**C40** AP3 $5 lake ('41) 2.00 2.00
*Nos. C31-C40 (10)* 10.60 *12.00*

For surcharges see note following No. C20.

**Nos. C11 and C12 Surcharged**

**1946, May 2 Unwmk. *Perf. 14***

**C41** AP3 $53 on 15c 1.50 *1.50*
**C42** AP3 $73 on 25c *2,500.* *1,750.*

Forgeries of No. C42 exist.

**On Nos. C23, C21, C22, C29 and C30**
***Perf. 13, 13x12, 12½***
**Wmk. 261**

**C43** AP3 $23 on 30c red .75 *.75*
**C44** AP3 $53 on 15c gray grn 25.00 *30.00*
**C45** AP3 $73 on 25c yel org 1.00 *1.00*
**C46** AP3 $100 on $2 lt brown 1.50 *2.00*
**C47** AP3 $200 on $5 lake 1.00 *1.00*
*Nos. C43-C47 (5)* 29.25 34.75

**On Nos. C33, C31, C32, C39 and C40**
***Perf. 13, 13x12, 13x12½, 12½***
**Unwmk.**

**C48** AP3 $23 on 30c lt red .75 *1.00*
*a.* Inverted surcharge 400.00
*b.* "2300" omitted 50.00
*c.* Last character (kuo) of surch. omitted 120.00
**C49** AP3 $53 on 15c gray grn .75 *1.00*
*a.* Horiz. pair, imperf. btwn. *1,500.* *675.00*
**C50** AP3 $73 on 25c lt org .75 *1.50*
*a.* Inverted surcharge *1,100.* *350.00*
**C51** AP3 $100 on $2 lt brn .75 *1.00*
**C52** AP3 $200 on $5 lake .75 *1.00*
*a.* Inverted surcharge *400.00*
*Nos. C48-C52 (5)* 3.75 *5.50*

The surcharges on Nos. C41-C52 represent Chinese natl. currency and were applied at Shanghai.

Douglas DC-4 over Sun Yat-sen Mausoleum, Nanking — AP4

**1946, Sept. 10 Litho. *Perf. 14***
**Without Gum**

**C53** AP4 $27 blue .65 *1.00*

For surcharges see Nos. C61, Szechwan C2.

**No. C23 Surcharged in Black**

***Perf. 13x12***
**1948, May 18 Wmk. 261**

**C54** AP3 $10,000 on 30c red .60 *1.25*

**Same, in Black or Carmine, on Nos. C33, C32, C37, C36, C18 and C38**
**Unwmk.**
***Perf. 12½, 13x12½, 14***

**C55** AP3 $10,000 on 30c lt red .60 *1.00*
**C56** AP3 $20,000 on 25c lt org .60 *1.00*
**C57** AP3 $30,000 on 90c lt ol (C) .60 *1.25*
**C58** AP3 $50,000 on 60c blue (C) .60 *1.25*
**C59** AP3 $50,000 on $1 yel grn (C) (#C18) 160.00 150.00
**C60** AP3 $50,000 on $1 ap grn (C) (#C38) .60 *1.10*

No. C53 Surcharged in Black

***Perf. 14***

**C61** AP4 $10,000 on $27 bl .75 *3.00*
*a.* Inverted surcharge *175.00*
*Nos. C54-C61 (8)* 164.35 159.85

Douglas DC-4 and Arrow — AP5

***Perf. 12½***
**1949, May 2 Unwmk. Litho.**
**Without Gum**

**C62** AP5 blue green 7.50 *20.00*
*a.* Rouletted 12.00 *17.50*

See note after No. 959.
For surcharge see No. 1151.
For overprints see Taiwan No. C1, Fukien No. C1, Kansu No. C1, PRC Nos. 26, 102.

Revenue Stamp Overprinted in Blue

**1949, May Engr. *Perf. 14***

**C63** A95 $100 olive green 125.00 125.00

See note after No. 962.

**Republic of China (Taiwan)**

Cheng Ch'eng-kung (Koxinga) — AP6

***Rouletted***
**1950, Sept. 26 Unwmk. Typo.**
**Without Gum**

**C64** AP6 60c deep blue 14.00 30.00

For surcharge see No. 1120.

Plane over City Gate, Taipei — AP7

Jet Planes above Chung Shan Bridge — AP8

Two Doves Near Koxinga Shrine — AP9

**1954 Engr. *Perf. 11½***
**Without Gum**

**C65** AP7 $1 dk brown 18.00 2.40
*a.* Vert. pair, imperf. btwn. 200.00
**C66** AP8 $1.60 olive blk 23.00 1.60
*a.* Vert. pair, imperf. btwn. 140.00
*b.* Horiz. pair, imperf. btwn. 100.00 110.00
**C67** AP9 $5 grnsh blue 33.00 2.00
*Nos. C65-C67 (3)* 74.00 6.00

Issued: No. C66, 8/14; Nos. C65, C67, 9/1.

**No. C67 Surcharged in Red**
**1958, Dec. 11 Without Gum**

**C68** AP9 $3.50 on $5 grnsh bl 11.00 1.25

**Catalogue values for unused stamps in this section, from this point to the end of the section, are for Never Hinged items.**

Sea Gull — AP10

**1959, Mar. 20 Photo. *Perf. 13***

**C69** AP10 $8 blue, gray & blk 8.25 .80

Sabre Jets in Bomb Burst Formation — AP11

Plane Formations: $2, Loop, horiz. $5, Diamond formation passing over grounded plane, horiz.

**1960, Feb. 29 Unwmk. *Perf. 13***

**C70** AP11 $1 multicolored 6.50 .50
**C71** AP11 $2 multicolored 6.00 .50
**C72** AP11 $5 multicolored 10.00 .60
*Nos. C70-C72 (3)* 22.50 1.60

Issued to honor the Chinese Air Force and the "Thunder Tiger" aerobatic team.

Jet Airliner over Pitan Bridge — AP12

Designs: $6, Jet over Tropic of Cancer monument, Kiai, vert. $10, Jet over Lion Head mountain, Sinchu, vert.

**1963, Aug. 14 Photo. *Perf. 13***

**C73** AP12 $2.50 multi 7.25 .25
**C74** AP12 $6 multi 12.50 .40
**C75** AP12 $10 multi 16.00 .65
*Nos. C73-C75 (3)* 35.75 1.30

Boeing 727 over Chilin Pavilion, Grand Hotel — AP13

Design: $8, Boeing 727 over National Palace Museum, Taipei.

**1967, Apr. 1 Unwmk. *Perf. 13***

| | | | | |
|---|---|---|---|---|
| C76 | AP13 $5 multicolored | | 3.75 | .25 |
| C77 | AP13 $8 multicolored | | 5.50 | .50 |

Wild Geese Flying over Mountains — AP14

Wild Geese flying over: $5, The sea. $8, The land, horiz.

**1969, Aug. 14 Photo. *Perf. 13***

| | | | | |
|---|---|---|---|---|
| C78 | AP14 | $2.50 multicolored | 3.00 | .25 |
| C79 | AP14 | $5 multicolored | 4.75 | .45 |
| C80 | AP14 | $8 multicolored | 5.75 | .60 |
| | *Nos. C78-C80 (3)* | | 13.50 | 1.30 |

Presidential Palace and Tzu-Ch'iang Squadron — AP15

$7, China Airlines jet. $12, China flag, jet.

**1980, June 18 Litho. *Perf. 13½***

| | | | | |
|---|---|---|---|---|
| C81 | AP15 | $5 shown | .45 | .30 |
| C82 | AP15 | $7 multicolored | 1.25 | .30 |
| C83 | AP15 | $12 multicolored | 1.75 | .50 |
| | *Nos. C81-C83 (3)* | | 3.45 | 1.10 |

Civil Aeronautics Administration, 37th Anniv. — AP16

Jet Airliners over: $7, Chiang Kai-shek Intl. Airport, vert. $11, Chung Cheng Memorial Hall. $18, Sun Yat-sen Memorial Hall.

***Perf. 14x13½, 13½x14***

**1984, Jan. 20 Litho.**

| | | | | |
|---|---|---|---|---|
| C84 | AP16 | $7 multicolored | .90 | .30 |
| C85 | AP16 | $11 multicolored | .90 | .40 |
| C86 | AP16 | $18 multicolored | 1.00 | .40 |
| | *Nos. C84-C86 (3)* | | 2.80 | 1.10 |

Airplane — AP17

**1987, Aug. 4 Litho. *Perf. 13½***

| | | | | |
|---|---|---|---|---|
| C87 | AP17 | $9 multicolored | .70 | .40 |
| C88 | AP17 | $14 multicolored | .95 | .55 |
| C89 | AP17 | $18 multicolored | 1.25 | .65 |
| | *Nos. C87-C89 (3)* | | 2.90 | 1.60 |

## SPECIAL DELIVERY STAMPS

**Used values of Nos. E1-E8 are for mailer's receipts. Complete unused strips of four are exceptionally scarce because the first section (#1) was to remain in the P.O. booklet.**

**The mailer received the righthand section (#4), usually canceled, as a receipt. The middle two sections were canceled and attached to the letter. Upon arrival at the destination P.O. they were canceled again, usually on the back, with the righthand copy (#3) retained by that P.O. The lefthand copy (#2) was signed by the recipient and returned to the original P.O. as evidence of delivery. Sections 2 and 3 usually are thin or badly damaged.**

**Unused strips of three (#2-4) can be found of Nos. E3-E8.**

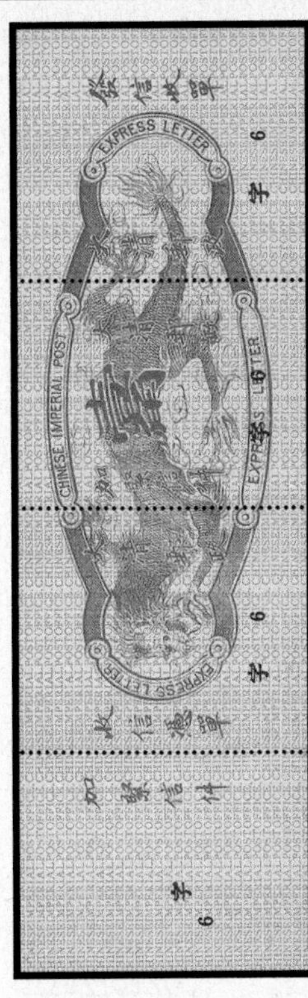

Type E1-E2

Design: Dragon in irregular oval, dragon's head facing downward, with no date, and background with period after "POSTOFFICE."

"Chinese Imperial Post Office" in lines, repeated to form the background which is usually lighter in color than the rest of the design.

Stamp 8x2½ inches, divided into four parts by perforation or serrate rouletting.

**1905 Unwmk. *Perf. 11***

| | | | |
|---|---|---|---|
| E1 | 10c grass green | *12,000.* | *1,700.* |

**Serrate Roulette in Black**

| | | | |
|---|---|---|---|
| E2 | 10c deep green | *15,000.* | 500.00 |

Type, E3-E8

Designs: Dragon's head facing forward. Background with no period after "POSTOFFICE".

**1907-10 No Date**

| | | | |
|---|---|---|---|
| E3 | 10c light bluish green | *4,000.* | 250.00 |

**Background with date at bottom**

**1909-11**

| | | | |
|---|---|---|---|
| E4 | 10c grn (Feb. 1909) | *3,000.* | 400.00 |
| E5 | 10c bl grn (Jan. 1911) | 4,000. | 500.00 |

**"IMPERIAL POST OFFICE" in serifed letters repeated to form the background.**

**No Date, No Border**

**Background of 30 or 28 lines**

**1912**

| | | | |
|---|---|---|---|
| E6 | 10c green (30 lines) | 2,000. | 300.00 |
| *a.* | 28 lines | *2,250.* | *1,500.* |

**Background of 35 lines of sans-serif letters**

**Colored Border**

| | | | |
|---|---|---|---|
| E8 | 10c green | 1,600. | 190.00 |

On No. E8 the medallion in the third section has Chinese characters in the background instead of the usual English inscriptions. E6 and E8 occur with many types of four-character overprints reading "Republic of China," applied locally but unofficially at various post offices.

Type, E9, E10

Design: Wild Goose. Stamp 7½x2¾ inches, divided into five parts.

"CHINESE POST OFFICE" in sans-serif letters, repeated to form the background of 28 lines, with border.

**1913 Serrate Roulette in Black**

| | | | |
|---|---|---|---|
| E9 | 10c green | 900.00 | 110.00 |

Unused values for Nos. E9-E10 are for complete strips of five parts. Used values are for single parts.

**"CHINESE POST OFFICE" in antique letters, forming a background of 29, 30 or 31 lines. No border.**

**1914 Serrate Roulette in Green**

| | | | |
|---|---|---|---|
| E10 | 10c green | 350.00 | 100.00 |

On No. E9 the background is in sans-serif capitals, the Chinese and English inscriptions are on white tablets and the serial numbers are in black.

On No. E10 the background is in antique capitals and extends under the inscriptions. The serial numbers are in green.

**Black overprint on No. E10**

**1916**

| | | |
|---|---|---|
| E10A | 10c green | *550.00* |

Yuan Si-Kai proclaimed himself Emperor of China, Dec. 15, 1915, naming his reign "Hung Hsien." No E10A is overprinted "Hung Hsien" in Chinese characters.

**NOTE:** In February 1916, the Special Delivery Stamps were demonetized and became merely receipts without franking value. To mark this, four of the five sections of the stamp had the letters A, B, C, D either handstamped or printed on them.

SD1

**1941 Unwmk. Typo. *Rouletted***

**Without Gum**

| | | | |
|---|---|---|---|
| E11 | SD1 ($2) car & yel | 40.00 | 32.50 |

Motorcycle Messenger — SD2

**1949, July Litho. *Perf. 12½***

**Without Gum**

| | | | |
|---|---|---|---|
| E12 | SD2 red violet | 9.00 | *32.00* |
| *a.* | Rouletted | 13.00 | *25.00* |

See note after No. 959.

For surcharge and overprints see Nos. 1150, Taiwan E1, Fukien E1.

Revenue Stamp Overprinted in Purple Brown

**1949 Without Gum**

| | | | |
|---|---|---|---|
| E13 | A95 $10 grnsh gray | 55.00 | *90.00* |

See note after No. 962.

## REGISTRATION STAMPS

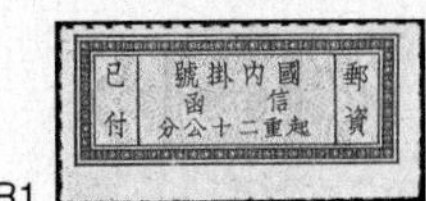

R1

**1941 Unwmk. Typo. *Rouletted***

**Without Gum**

| | | | |
|---|---|---|---|
| F1 | R1 ($1.50) green & buff | 30.00 | 45.00 |

Mountain Scene — R2

**1949, July Litho. *Perf. 12½***

**Without Gum**

| | | | |
|---|---|---|---|
| F2 | R2 carmine | 10.50 | *26.00* |
| *a.* | Rouletted | 14.00 | *24.00* |

See note after No. 959.

For surcharge and overprints see Nos. 1152, Taiwan F1, Fukien F1, PRC 103.

Revenue Stamp Overprinted in Carmine

**1949**
**F3** A95 $50 dark blue 35.00 *45.00*

See note after No. 962.

### POSTAGE DUE STAMPS

Regular Issue of 1902-03 Overprinted in Black

**1904 Unwmk. *Perf. 14 to 15***
**J1** A17 ½c chocolate 16.00 40.00
**J2** A17 1c ocher 16.00 16.00
**J3** A17 2c scarlet 19.50 16.00
*a.* red 20.00 10.00
**J4** A17 4c red brn 20.50 20.00
**J5** A17 5c salmon 23.00 23.00
**J6** A17 10c dk blue grn 40.00 35.00
*a.* Vert. pair, imperf. btwn. 2,000. 2,000.
*Nos. J1-J6 (6)* 135.00 150.00

D1

**1904 Engr.**
**J7** D1 ½c blue 7.00 4.00
*a.* Horiz. pair, imperf. btwn. 3,000. 2,000.
**J8** D1 1c blue 12.00 4.00
**J9** D1 2c blue 12.00 4.00
*a.* Horiz. pair, imperf. btwn. 2,000. 1,800.
**J10** D1 4c blue 15.00 6.00
**J11** D1 5c blue 18.00 7.00
**J12** D1 10c blue 20.00 9.00
**J13** D1 20c blue 50.00 12.00
**J14** D1 30c blue 70.00 40.00
*Nos. J7-J14 (8)* 204.00 86.00

Arabic numeral of value at left on Nos. J12-J14.

**1911**
**J15** D1 1c brown 22.50 *25.00*
**J16** D1 2c brown 37.50 *40.00*

The ½c, 4c, 5c and 20c in brown exist but were not issued as they arrived in China after the downfall of the Ching dynasty.

Issues of 1904 Overprinted in Red

**1912**
**J19** D1 ½c blue 625. *825.*
**J20** D1 4c blue 800. *900.*
**J21** D1 5c blue 900. 900.
**J22** D1 10c blue 1,400. 900.
**J23** D1 20c blue 2,750. 2,600.
**J24** D1 30c blue 2,750. 2,600.

Nos. J15-J16 exist with this overprint, but were not regularly issued. Value, $9,500, each.

Nos. J1-J14 Overprinted in Red

**1912**
**J25** D1 ½c blue 4.00 2.50
**J26** D1 1c brown 5.00 2.50
*a.* Horiz. pair, imperf. btwn. 3,000. 3,000.
*b.* Inverted overprint 550.00 550.00
**J27** D1 2c brown 6.50 3.25
**J28** D1 4c blue 12.00 5.00
**J29** D1 5c blue 220.00 *240.00*
**J30** D1 5c brown 16.00 *8.00*
*a.* Inverted overprint 550.00 340.00
**J31** D1 10c blue 20.00 *10.50*
**J32** D1 20c blue 22.00 14.00
**J33** D1 30c blue 28.00 24.00
*Nos. J25-J33 (9)* 333.50 309.75

Nos. J19-J24 and the two unissued stamps from that set exist additionally overprinted 'Republic of China' in Chinese characters. The same overprint as J25-J33 value for set of 8, $65,000.

Issues of 1904 Overprinted in Black

**1912**
**J34** D1 ½c blue 12.50 9.25
**J35** D1 ½c brown 6.50 2.75
**J36** D1 1c brown 6.50 2.75
*a.* Inverted overprint 350.00 350.00
*b.* Horiz. pair, imperf. btwn. 1,800
**J37** D1 2c brown 8.25 *4.75*
**J38** D1 4c blue 16.50 *8.75*
**J39** D1 5c brown 22.00 *13.00*
*a.* Horiz. pair, imperf. btwn. 3,000. 3,000.
**J40** D1 10c blue 35.00 *25.00*
**J41** D1 20c brown 52.50 *92.50*
**J42** D1 30c blue 90.00 60.00
*Nos. J34-J42 (9)* 249.75 218.75

D4

**Printed by Waterlow & Sons**

**1913, May *Perf. 14, 15***
**J43** D4 ½c blue 3.00 1.50
*a.* Horiz. pair, imperf. btwn. 3,500. 2,600.
**J44** D4 1c blue 3.50 1.50
*a.* Vert. pair, imperf. btwn. 2,500
**J45** D4 2c blue 5.00 3.00
**J46** D4 4c blue 8.00 3.00
**J47** D4 5c blue 12.00 6.00
**J48** D4 10c blue 17.50 8.00
**J49** D4 20c blue 27.50 13.00
**J50** D4 30c blue 35.00 15.00
*Nos. J43-J50 (8)* 111.50 51.00

**Printed by the Chinese Bureau of Engraving & Printing**

**1915 Re-engraved *Perf. 14***
**J51** D4 ½c blue 2.50 *1.00*
**J52** D4 1c blue 3.00 .65
**J53** D4 2c blue 3.25 .65
**J54** D4 4c blue 4.00 .75
**J55** D4 5c blue 5.75 1.50
**J56** D4 10c blue 8.75 2.50
**J57** D4 20c blue 14.00 8.00
**J58** D4 30c blue 40.00 20.00
*Nos. J51-J58 (8)* 81.25 35.05

In the upper part of the stamps of type D4 there is an ornament of five marks like the letter "V". Below this is a curved label with an inscription in Chinese characters. On the 1913 stamps there are two complete background lines between the ornament and the label. The 1915 stamps show only one unbroken line at this place. There are other minute differences in the engraving of the stamps of the two issues.

D5

**1932 *Perf. 14***
**J59** D5 ½c orange .50 *.30*
**J60** D5 1c orange .50 *.30*
**J61** D5 2c orange .50 *.30*
**J62** D5 4c orange .50 *.30*
**J63** D5 5c orange 1.25 *1.50*
**J64** D5 10c orange 1.60 2.00
**J65** D5 20c orange 2.25 3.00
**J66** D5 30c orange 3.25 *4.00*
*Nos. J59-J66 (8)* 10.35 11.70

See Nos. J69-J79. For surcharges see Nos. 1NJ1, 9NJ1-9NJ4.

Nos. 387-388 Overprinted in Black or Red

**1940**
**J67** A57 $1 henna & dk brn (Bk) 10.00 *25.00*
**J68** A57 $2 dl bl & org brn (R) 10.00 *20.00*

**Type of 1932**
**Printed by The Commercial Press, Ltd.**

***Perf. 12½, 12½x13, 13***

**1940-41 Engr.**
**J69** D5 ½c yellow orange .80 *1.25*
**J70** D5 1c yellow orange .80 *1.25*
**J71** D5 2c yel org ('41) .80 *1.25*
**J72** D5 4c yellow orange .80 *1.25*
**J73** D5 5c yel org ('41) 1.20 *1.25*
**J74** D5 10c yel org ('41) .80 *1.25*
**J75** D5 20c yel org ('41) .80 *1.25*
**J76** D5 30c yellow orange .80 *2.00*
**J77** D5 50c yellow orange 1.00 *2.00*
**J78** D5 $1 yellow orange 1.20 *2.00*
**J79** D5 $2 yellow orange 1.50 *3.00*
*Nos. J69-J79 (11)* 10.50 *17.75*

For surcharge see No. 1NJ1.

D6

**Thin Paper Without Gum**

**1944 Typo. *Perf. 13***
**J80** D6 10c bluish green .80 *3.00*
**J81** D6 20c light chalky blue .80 *3.00*
**J82** D6 40c dull rose .80 *3.00*
**J83** D6 50c bluish green .80 *3.00*
**J84** D6 60c dull blue .80 *3.00*
**J85** D6 $1 dull rose .80 *2.00*
**J86** D6 $2 lilac brown .80 *2.00*
*Nos. J80-J86 (7)* 5.60 *19.00*

D7

**1945 Without Gum Unwmk.**
**J87** D7 $2 rose carmine .80 *2.00*
**J88** D7 $6 rose carmine .80 *2.00*
**J89** D7 $8 rose carmine .80 *2.00*
**J90** D7 $10 rose carmine .80 *2.00*
**J91** D7 $20 rose carmine .80 *2.00*
**J92** D7 $30 rose carmine 1.00 *2.00*
*Nos. J87-J92 (6)* 5.00 *12.00*

For surcharges see Nos. J102-J109.

D8

**Thin Paper Without Gum**

**1947 Litho. *Perf. 14***
**J93** D8 $50 plum .80 *2.00*
**J94** D8 $80 plum .80 *2.00*
**J95** D8 $100 plum .80 *2.00*
**J96** D8 $160 plum .80 *2.00*
**J97** D8 $200 plum .80 *2.00*
**J98** D8 $400 violet brown .80 *2.00*
**J99** D8 $500 violet brown .80 *2.00*
*a.* Vert. pair, imperf. between 80.00
**J100** D8 $800 violet brown .80 *2.00*
**J101** D8 $2000 violet brown .80 *2.00*
*Nos. J93-J101 (9)* 7.20 *18.00*

Type of 1945, Redrawn Surcharged in Black

**Without Gum**
**Deep claret**

**1948 Engr. *Perf. 13½x14***
**J102** D7 $1000 on $20 .70 *3.00*
**J103** D7 $2000 on $30 .70 *3.00*
**J104** D7 $3000 on $50 .70 *3.00*
**J105** D7 $4000 on $100 .70 *3.00*
**J106** D7 $5000 on $200 .70 *3.00*
**J107** D7 $10,000 on $300 .70 *3.00*
**J108** D7 $20,000 on $500 .70 *3.00*
**J109** D7 $30,000 on $1000 .70 *3.00*
*Nos. J102-J109 (8)* 5.60 *24.00*

There are many differences in the redrawn design.

No. 627 Surcharged in Black

**1949 *Perf. 12***
**J110** A72 1 (c) on $40 org .70 *10.00*
**J111** A72 2 (c) on $40 org .70 *10.00*
**J112** A72 5 (c) on $40 org .70 *10.00*
**J113** A72 10 (c) on $40 org .70 *10.00*
**J114** A72 20 (c) on $40 org .70 *10.00*
**J115** A72 50 (c) on $40 org .70 *10.00*
**J116** A72 $1 on $40 org .70 *10.00*
**J117** A72 $2 on $40 org .70 *10.00*
**J118** A72 $5 on $40 org 1.00 *10.00*
**J119** A72 $10 on $40 org 1.00 *10.00*
*Nos. J110-J119 (10)* 7.60 *100.00*

## Republic of China (Taiwan)

No. 438 Surcharged in Green or Black

**1951 Unwmk. *Perf. 12½***
**J120** A47 40c on 40c org (G) 47.50 *47.50*
**J121** A47 80c on 40c org (Bk) 47.50 *47.50*

Revenue Stamps Surcharged in Various Colors

**1953 Unwmk. *Perf. 12½, 14***
**Without Gum**
**J122** A95 10c on $50 dk bl (O) 30.00 4.50
**J123** A95 20c on $100 ol grn (Dk Br) 30.00 4.50
**J124** A95 40c on $20 lake 34.00 6.00
**J125** A95 80c on $500 sl grn (Dk Bl) 52.50 9.00
**J126** A95 $1 on $30 dk vio (G) 52.50 15.00
*Nos. J122-J126 (5)* 199.00 39.00

D9

**1956 Unwmk. Litho. *Perf. 12½***
**Without Gum**
**J127** D9 20c rose car, & lt bl 3.25 .40
**J128** D9 40c green & buff 4.50 .60
**J129** D9 80c brown & gray 8.75 1.00
**J130** D9 $1 ultra & pink 10.00 2.00
*Nos. J127-J130 (4)* 26.50 4.00

No. 1197 Surcharged in Dark Violet

**Wmk. 323**
**1961, Dec. 28 Engr. *Perf. 12***
**Without Gum**
**J131** A135 $5 on $20 car rose 12.00 2.40

Nos. 1274, 1282-1283 Surcharged in Black, Carmine Rose or Blue

**1964-65 Litho.**
**J132** A158 10c on 80c pale grn .55 .25
**J133** A158 20c on $3.60 vio bl (CR) ('65) .65 .25
**J134** A158 40c on $4.50 ver (B) ('65) 1.40 .30
*Nos. J132-J134 (3)* 2.60 .80

D10

**1966-76 Wmk. 323 *Perf. 12½***
**Granite Paper; Without Gum**
**J135** D10 10c dk brn & lil .30 .25
**J136** D10 20c blue & yel .40 .25
**J137** D10 50c vio bl & lt bl ('70) .65 .25
**J138** D10 $1 purple & sal .50 .25
**J139** D10 $2 grn & lt bl .65 .25
**J140** D10 $5 red & sal 2.50 .60
*a.* $5 org red & pale yel 2.50 .60

**J141** D10 $10 lil rose & pink ('76) *22.50* 1.00
*Nos. J135-J141 (7)* *27.50* 2.85

The 50c, $10 and No. J140a are gummed. The $1 and $2 were reissued with gum in 1968 and 1973 respectively. No. J140a and the $10 are on ordinary paper.

**Catalogue values for unused stamps in this section, from this point to the end of the section, are for Never Hinged items.**

D11

**1984-88 Litho. *Perf. 12½***

**J142** D11 $1 rose & violet .30 .25
**J143** D11 $2 yellow & blue .30 .25
**J144** D11 $3 pale grn & brt rose lil .30 .25
**J145** D11 $5 blue & yellow .30 .25
**J146** D11 $5.50 rose lil & brt blue .40 .35
**J147** D11 $7.50 bis yel & dp vio .60 .45
**J148** D11 $10 yel & lil rose .50 .30
**J149** D11 $20 sky blue & citron 1.60 1.25
*Nos. J142-J149 (8)* 4.30 3.35

Issued: $3, $5.50, $7.50, $20, Apr. 1, 1988; others, Mar. 15, 1984.

D12

**1998, Sept. 30 Litho. *Perf. 12½***
**Background Color**

**J150** D12 50c orange yellow .30 .25
**J151** D12 $1 pink .30 .25
**J152** D12 $2 deep pink .30 .25
**J153** D12 $5 yellow green .50 .25
**J154** D12 $10 blue .90 .30
**J155** D12 $20 green 1.75 .60
*Nos. J150-J155 (6)* 4.05 1.90

Lotus Flower, Peach, Bats, Coins and Chinese Characters — D13

***Perf. 12½x12¼***
**2008, Nov. 12 Litho.**
**Denomination Color**

**J156** D13 $1 dark red .30 .25
**J157** D13 $3 green .30 .25
**J158** D13 $5 olive green .40 .25
**J159** D13 $10 purple .75 .35
**J160** D13 $20 bister 1.50 .75
*Nos. J156-J160 (5)* 3.25 1.85

**Type of 2008**
***Die Cut Perf. 22***
**2015, Oct. 28 Litho.**
**Self-Adhesive**
**Denomination Color**

**J161** D13 50c red brown .30 .25
**J162** D13 $2 dark blue .30 .25

---

## PARCEL POST STAMPS

PP1

PP2

PP3

**1945-48 Unwmk. Engr. *Perf. 13***
**Without Gum**

**Q1** PP1 $500 green 12.00 1.00
**Q2** PP1 $1000 blue 12.00 1.00
**Q3** PP1 $3000 rose red 22.50 1.60
**Q4** PP1 $5000 brown 140.00 30.00
**Q5** PP1 $10,000 lil gray 250.00 50.00
**Q6** PP1 $20,000 red org *4,500.*
*Nos. Q1-Q5 (5)* 436.50 83.60

No. Q6 was sold through the philatelic counter in Shanghai.

For surcharges see People's Republic of China Nos. 5LQ1-5LQ2, 5LQ27-5LQ28.

***Perf. 12½***

**Q7** PP2 $3000 red org 30.00 2.00
**Q8** PP2 $5000 dk blue 40.00 2.00
**Q9** PP2 $10,000 violet 45.00 5.00
**Q10** PP2 $20,000 dk red 50.00 8.00
*Nos. Q7-Q10 (4)* 165.00 17.00

***Perf. 13½***

**Q11** PP3 $1000 org yel 9.00 1.50
**Q12** PP3 $3000 bl grn 9.00 1.50
**Q13** PP3 $5000 org red 9.00 1.50
**Q14** PP3 $7000 dl blue 9.00 1.50
**Q15** PP3 $10,000 car rose 10.00 2.00
**Q16** PP3 $30,000 olive 10.00 2.00
**Q17** PP3 $50,000 indigo 10.00 2.00
**Q18** PP3 $70,000 org brn 14.00 4.00
**Q19** PP3 $100,000 dp plum 14.00 4.00

**Denomination Tablet Without Inner Frame**

**Q20** PP3 $200,000 dk grn 18.50 6.00
**Q21** PP3 $300,000 pink 18.50 4.00
**Q22** PP3 $500,000 vio brn 18.50 4.00
**Q23** PP3 $3,000,000 sl bl 20.00 10.00
**Q24** PP3 $5,000,000 lilac 20.00 10.00
**Q25** PP3 $6,000,000 ol gray 22.00 10.00
**Q26** PP3 $8,000,000 scar 22.00 11.00
**Q27** PP3 $10,000,000 sage grn 25.00 14.00
*Nos. Q11-Q27 (17)* 258.50 89.00

Zeros for "cents" omitted on Nos. Q23-Q27.

See Taiwan Nos. Q1-Q5. For surcharges see Nos. 883-885, Northeastern Provinces Q1, Szechwan Q1, People's Republic of China 3LQ1-3LQ9, 5LQ3-5LQ16, 5LQ29-5LQ30.

#Q11-Q15, Q23-Q24 Surcharged in Black or Carmine (#Q35)

**1949 Unwmk. *Perf. 13½***

**Q32** PP3 $10 on $3000 5.00 1.00
**Q33** PP3 $20 on $5000 5.00 1.00
**Q34** PP3 $50 on $10,000 5.00 1.00
**Q35** PP3 $100 on $3,000,000 8.00 2.00
**Q36** PP3 $200 on $5,000,000 12.00 2.00
**Q37** PP3 $500 on $1000 22.50 .25
**Q38** PP3 $1000 on $7000 22.50 .30
*Nos. Q32-Q38 (7)* 80.00 7.55

5 characters in each line on Nos. Q33-Q38.

---

## MILITARY STAMPS

No. 454 Overprinted in Dull Red

**1943-44 Unwmk. *Perf. 12***

**M1** A59 8c turquoise green 6.00 *50.00*

Nos. 383, 453-454 Overprinted in Red or Black

**6mm between characters**
***Perf. 14, 12½***

**M2** A57 8c olive green 6.00 *9.00*
*a.* 8mm between characters 6.00 *9.00*
**M3** A59 8c red orange (B) 600.00
**M4** A59 8c turquoise green 12.00 10.00

Forgeries of No. M3 abound.

No. 493 Overprinted in Red

***Perf. 13***

**M5** A62 16c dull olive brn 11.00 *15.00*
*a.* Perf. 10½-11 350.00

No. M5 overprinted in black is a proof.

Stamps of 1942-44 Overprinted in Carmine or Black

**M6** A62 50c sage grn (C) 6.00 *7.00*
**M7** A62 $1 rose lake 8.00 *9.00*
**M8** A62 $1 dull green 8.00 *9.00*
**M9** A62 $2 dk bl grn (C) 10.00 *14.00*
**M10** A62 $2 dk vio brn ('44) 200.00 150.00
*Nos. M6-M10 (5)* 232.00 189.00

Nos. 383 and 357 Overprinted in Red

**1944 *Perf. 12, 14***

**M11** A57 8c olive green 6.00 *10.00*
*a.* Right character inverted 1,000.
**M12** A57 16c olive gray 90.00 *100.00*

Anti-Aircraft Guns — M1

**1945, Jan. 1 Typo. *Perf. 12½***
**Thin Paper Without Gum**

**M13** M1 rose 3.00 *10.00*

For overprints see Northeastern Provinces Nos. M2-M3.

---

## TAIWAN

**(Formosa)**
100 Sen = 1 Yen
100 Cents = 1 Dollar

Stamps and Types of Japan (Taiwan) Overprinted in Black

**Stamps Divided by Lines of Colored Dashes**
Values in Sen and Yen

**1945 Unwmk. Litho. *Imperf.***
**Without Gum**

**1** A1 3s carmine 2.50 10.00
**2** A1 5s blue grn 2.50 2.00
**3** A1 10s pale blue 2.50 .55
*a.* Inverted overprint 375.00
*b.* Double overprint 375.00
**4** A1 30s dk blue 14.00 10.00
**5** A1 40s violet 14.00 7.00
**6** A1 50s gray brn 10.00 5.00
**7** A1 1y olive grn 12.00 10.00

**Same Overprint on Types of Japan**

**8** A99 5y gray grn 40.00 40.00
**9** A100 10y brown vio 60.00 60.00
*a.* Inverted overprint 375.00
*Nos. 1-9 (9)* 157.50 144.55

The basic stamps of this issue were prepared by Japanese authorities for Taiwan use before the end of World War II when the island reverted to Chinese control. They are printed on crude buff or white wove paper. The overprint translates: "For Use in Taiwan, Chinese Republic."

A second overprinting of Nos. 2-3 was made with a different font.

China, Nos. 728-731, Srchd. in Black

**1946 Without Gum *Perf. 14***

**10** A75 70s on $20 green 3.50 *5.50*
*a.* Inverted surcharge *1,200.*
**11** A75 1y on $30 blue 3.50 *5.50*
**12** A75 2y on $50 dk brn 3.50 *5.75*
**13** A75 3y on $100 car 3.75 *5.75*
*Nos. 10-13 (4)* 14.25 *22.50*

Convening of the Chinese Natl. Assembly.

China Issues and Types of 1940-1946 Srchd. in Black — a

***Perf. 12½, 12½x13, 13, 13x12½, 14***
**1946-47**
**Nos. 18, 23-28 Without Gum**

**14** A46 2s on 2c dp bl .80 *1.50*
**15** A48 5s on 5c dl red org .80 *1.00*
**16** A39 10s on 4c pale vio .80 *1.50*
**17** A48 30s on 15c brn car .80 *1.00*
**18** A73 50s on $20 car .80 *1.00*
**19** A37 65s on $20 brt yel grn 1.00 *2.00*
**20** A47 1y on 20c lt bl .80 *2.00*
*a.* Inverted surcharge *950.00*
**21** A37 1y on $30 choc 1.00 *1.75*
**22** A37 2y on $50 red org 1.50 2.00
**23** A73 3y on $100 dk car .80 *2.00*
**24** A73 5y on $200 ol grn .80 *2.00*
**25** A73 10y on $500 brt bl grn .80 *1.50*
**26** A73 20y on $700 red brn 1.00 1.00
**27** A73 50y on $1000 rose lake 2.00 1.50
**28** A73 100y on $3000 blue 2.75 1.60
*Nos. 14-28 (15)* 16.45 *23.35*

The bottom line of the surcharge expresses the new value and consists of 2, 3 or 4 characters.

Nos. 14, 18-19, 21-28 issued in 1947.

**Same Surcharge on China No. 412**

**1947 Wmk. 261 *Perf. 13***

**28A** A48 30s on 15c brn car 135.00 150.00

Type of China, 1946, with additional inscription on both sides of head

**1947 Unwmk. Engr. *Perf. 11, 11½***

**29** A74 70c carmine 3.50 *4.75*
**30** A74 $1 green 3.50 *4.75*
**31** A74 $2 vermilion 3.50 *4.75*
**32** A74 $3 yel grn 3.50 *4.75*
**33** A74 $7 yel org 3.50 *4.75*
**34** A74 $10 magenta 3.50 *4.75*
*Nos. 29-34 (6)* 21.00 *28.50*

60th birthday of Chiang Kai-shek.

Type of China, 1947, with additional inscription above value

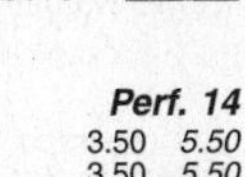

**1947 *Perf. 14***

**35** A76 50c deep green 3.50 *5.50*
**36** A76 $3 deep blue 3.50 *5.50*
**37** A76 $7.50 carmine 3.50 *5.50*
**38** A76 $10 light brown 3.50 *5.50*
**39** A76 $20 deep claret 3.50 *5.50*
*Nos. 35-39 (5)* 17.50 *27.50*

First anniversary of return of Chinese National Government to Nanking.

Dr. Sun Yat-sen — A3

**1947, July 10 Without Gum**

**40** A3 $1 dk brown 1.00 2.50
**41** A3 $2 org brn 1.20 2.00
**42** A3 $3 blue grn 1.20 2.00
**43** A3 $5 vermilion 2.50 *2.75*
**44** A3 $9 deep blue 1.00 1.20
**45** A3 $10 brt rose car 1.00 .80
**46** A3 $20 deep green .85 .70
**47** A3 $50 rose lilac .85 .60
**48** A3 $100 blue .85 .60
**49** A3 $200 dark red .85 .60
*Nos. 40-49 (10)* 11.30 13.75

The 30c gray and $7.50 orange were not regularly issued without surcharge. Value for the two stamps, $450.

See Nos. 63-68. For overprint and surcharges see Nos. 51-53, 69-73, 102, J10-J17.

Type of 1947 Surcharged in Black — b

**1948 Unwmk. *Perf. 14***

51 A3 $25 on $100 blue 2.50 *3.00*
52 A3 $500 on $7.50 org 6.75 3.50
53 A3 $1000 on 30c gray 14.00 9.00
*Nos. 51-53 (3)* 23.25 15.50

**Stamps of China, 1943-48, Surcharged Type "a" in Black or Carmine**

**1948-49 *Perf. 12½, 14***
**Without Gum**

54 A73 $5 on $70 red org (#639) 1.00 *2.50*
55 A62 $10 on $3 dk yel (#555) 4.50 *3.50*
56 A82 $10 on $150 dk bl (C) (#745) 1.20 *1.75*
57 A82 $20 on $250 dp lil (C) (#746) 1.10 *1.20*
58 A67 $100 on $20 car (#592) 1,600. —
59 A82 $1000 on $20,000 rose pink ('49) (#788) 6.50 3.50
*Nos. 54-59 (6)* 1,614. 12.45

The bottom line of the surcharge expresses the new value and consists of 2 or 3 characters.
Forgeries of No. 58 abound.

**Type of 1947**

**1949 Engr. *Perf. 14***

63 A3 $25 olive grn 1.20 1.00
64 A3 $5000 ocher 10.00 2.00
65 A3 $10,000 apple grn 10.00 5.00
66 A3 $20,000 ol bister 10.00 5.00
67 A3 $30,000 indigo 10.00 2.00
68 A3 $40,000 violet brn 9.00 2.00
*Nos. 63-68 (6)* 50.20 17.00

For overprint and surcharges see Nos. 101, 103, J12.

**No. 42 and type of 1947 Surcharged Type "b" in Black, Carmine Violet or Red Violet**

**1949**

69 A3 $300 on $3 bl grn 1.75 1.00
70 A3 $1000 on $3 bl grn (C) 3.00 1.00
71 A3 $2000 on $3 bl grn (V) 2.50 1.00
72 A3 $3000 on $3 bl grn (RV) 12.00 4.25
73 A3 $3000 on $7.50 org 120.00 5.50
*Nos. 69-73 (5)* 139.25 12.75

For overprints see Nos. J10-J11.

**Stamps of China, 1940-47, Surcharged Type "a" in Black or Carmine**

***Perf. 12½, 13x13½, 14***

74 A39 $2 on 2½c rose lil (#424) .80 .80
75 A72 $5 on $40 org (#627) 1.00 *2.00*
76 A73 $5 on $50 pur (C) (#638) 1.00 1.50
77 A73 $5 on $100 dk car (#640) 1.25 .80
78 A57 $20 on 2c ol grn (#368) 1.00 1.75
81 A63 $100 on $20 rose (#571) 1.10 .50
82 A67 $200 on $10 dk bl (C) (#591) 8.00 1.75
84 A57 $500 on $30 dl vio (#521) 18.00 5.00
86 A62 $800 on $4 red brn (#504) 15.00 10.00
87 A67 $5000 on $10 dk bl (#591) 18.00 5.00
88 A67 $10,000 on $20 car (#592) 18.00 4.00
89 A82 $200,000 on $3000 bl (C) (#750) 900.00 50.00
*Nos. 74-89 (12)* 983.15 83.10

Northeastern Provinces No. 47, Surcharged in Green, Red Violet, Black or Blue

**1949-50**

91 A2 2c on $44 (G) 62.50 10.00
92 A2 5c on $44 (RV) ('50) 57.50 20.00
*a.* Violet surcharge 85.00 11.50
93 A2 10c on $44 (RV) ('50) 75.00 6.00
94 A2 20c on $44 (Bk) ('50) 100.00 7.00
*a.* Double surcharge 200.00
95 A2 30c on $44 (Bl) ('50) 110.00 14.00
96 A2 50c on $44 (Bl) ('50) 130.00 17.00
*Nos. 91-96 (6)* 535.00 74.00

There were two printings of Nos. 91-93, with minor differences.

China 959a, Overprinted in Black

**Overprint 15mm Wide**

**1949 Unwmk. *Rouletted 9½***

97 A96 orange 5.50 1.75

**China Nos. 567, 498 and 640 Surcharged Type "a" in Black**

**1948-49 Unwmk. *Perf. 12½, 13, 14***

98 A63 $20 on $3 red 3.50 2.50
99 A62 $50 on 50c sage grn 3.75 5.00
*a.* Perf. 11 50.00 75.00
100 A73 $600 on $100 dk car 6.50 9.00
*Nos. 98-100 (3)* 13.75 16.50

Botton line of surcharge consists of 3 characters.
No. 99 has two settings of surcharge: I. Spacing 10mm between rows of characters. II. Spacing 12mm.

#67, 47 and 68 Surcharged in Violet (#101) or Black

**1949 *Perf. 14***

101 A3 2c on $30,000 ind 52.50 30.00
102 A3 10c on $50 rose lil 52.50 15.00
103 A3 10c on $40,000 vio brn 125.00 45.00
*Nos. 101-103 (3)* 230.00 90.00

Numerals slightly larger on Nos. 101-103.
For similar surcharges on China type A82 see China Nos. 1025-1036.

**AIR POST STAMP**

China No. C62a, Overprinted in Black

**Overprint 15mm Wide**

**1949 Unwmk. *Rouletted 9½***

C1 AP5 blue green 2.50 2.50

**SPECIAL DELIVERY STAMP**

China No. E12a, Overprinted in Black

**Overprint 12½mm Wide**

**1950 Unwmk. *Rouletted 9½***

E1 SD2 red violet 10.00 4.50

**REGISTRATION STAMP**

China No. F2a Overprinted in Black

**Overprint 12mm Wide**

**1950 Unwmk. *Rouletted 9½***

F1 R2 carmine 10.00 4.50

**POSTAGE DUE STAMPS**

D1

**Unwmk.**
**1948, Feb. 10 Litho. *Perf. 14***
**Without Gum**

J1 D1 $1 blue 2.50 *5.00*
J2 D1 $3 blue 2.50 *5.75*
J3 D1 $5 blue 2.50 *5.75*
J4 D1 $10 blue 2.50 *7.75*
J5 D1 $20 blue 2.50 *4.75*
*Nos. J1-J5 (5)* 12.50 *29.00*

Nos. J1-J4 Surcharged in Carmine

**1948, Dec. 4**

J6 D1 $50 on $1 blue 24.00 *13.00*
J7 D1 $100 on $3 blue 24.00 *13.00*
J8 D1 $300 on $5 blue 24.00 *13.00*
J9 D1 $500 on $10 blue 24.00 *13.00*
*Nos. J6-J9 (4)* 96.00 *52.00*

Nos. 70, 72 and 64 Handstamped in Violet

**1949, Aug. 5**

J10 A3 $1000 on $3 bl grn 35.00 22.00
J11 A3 $3000 on $3 bl grn 54.00 29.00
J12 A3 $5000 ocher 120.00 70.00
*Nos. J10-J12 (3)* 209.00 121.00

No. 48 Surcharged in Various Colors

**1950**

J13 A3 4c on $100 bl (Br) 12.00 *20.00*
J14 A3 10c on $100 bl (RV) 22.50 *35.00*
J15 A3 20c on $100 bl (Bk) 10.00 *25.00*
J16 A3 40c on $100 bl (C) 47.50 *90.00*
J17 A3 $1 on $100 bl (Bl) 35.00 *65.00*
*Nos. J13-J17 (5)* 127.00 *235.00*

**PARCEL POST STAMPS**

**Type of China, Parcel Post Stamps of 1945-48 With Added Inscription**

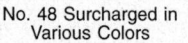

**1949 Unwmk. Engr. *Perf. 14***

Q1 PP3 $100 bluish grn *265.00* 1.00
Q2 PP3 $300 rose car *265.00* 1.00
Q3 PP3 $500 olive green *265.00* 1.00
Q4 PP3 $1000 slate *265.00* 1.00
Q5 PP3 $3000 deep plum *265.00* 1.00
*Nos. Q1-Q5 (5)* *1,325.* 5.00

Chinese characters in lower corners have colorless background; denomination tablet in color.

**OCCUPATION STAMPS**

**Issued Under Japanese Occupation**

Unused values for Japanese occupation issues are for never hinged examples.

Canceled Stamps
Postally used stamps of the Japanese occupation generally have heavy, smudgy cancels.

**Kwangtung**

China No. 297 Overprinted in Black

**1942 Unwmk. *Perf. 12½***

1N1 A37 2c olive green 8.00 8.00
*a.* Inverted overprint 120.00 165.00

**Same Overprint in Red or Black on Stamps of China, 1939-41**

***Perf. 12½, 14***

1N2 A57 3c dl cl (#350) 2.75 2.75
1N3 A57 8c ol grn (#383) 2.75 2.75
1N4 A57 10c grn (#354) (R) 2.50 2.75
1N5 A57 10c grn (#384) (R) 3.50 3.50
1N6 A57 16c ol gray (#357) 7.50 *7.25*
1N7 A57 30c scar (#385) 4.00 3.00
1N8 A57 50c dk bl (#386) (R) 5.00 *9.00*
1N9 A57 $1 org brn & sep (#387) 10.00 *10.00*
1N10 A57 $2 dp bl & yel brn (#388) 12.00 *9.50*
1N11 A57 $5 red & sl grn (#389) 15.00 *10.00*
1N12 A57 $10 dk grn & dl pur (#390) 30.00 *20.00*
1N13 A57 $20 rose lake & dk bl (#391) 13.00 *13.00*

**Same Overprint on China Nos. 422 and 433**

***Perf. 12½***

1N14 A40 1c orange 3.00 *2.40*
*a.* Inverted overprint 87.50 80.00
1N15 A47 20c lt blue 6.00 *5.00*

**Same Overprint on Stamps of China, 1941**

***Perf. 12***

1N16 A59 1c orange 4.50 *4.50*
1N17 A59 5c green 2.50 *4.50*
1N18 A59 8c turq green 2.75 *3.75*
1N19 A59 10c brt green 3.25 *3.75*
1N20 A59 17c olive 4.00 *6.00*
1N21 A59 30c scarlet 6.00 *7.00*
1N22 A59 50c dark blue 4.00 *4.00*
*Nos. 1N1-1N22 (22)* 152.00 *142.40*

Stamps of China, 1939-41 Overprinted in Black

**1942 *Perf. 12½, 14***

1N23 A57 2c olive grn (#368) 1.50 *2.00*
1N24 A57 3c dl claret (#350) 1.50 *2.00*
1N25 A57 5c olive grn (#352) 1.50 *1.25*
1N26 A57 8c olive grn (#353) 300.00 *450.00*
1N27 A57 8c olive grn (#369) 1.00 *1.00*
1N28 A57 10c green (#354) 1.50 *2.00*
1N29 A57 16c ol gray (#357) 1.50 *3.00*
1N30 A57 25c dk bl (#358) 2.00 *4.00*
1N31 A57 30c scarlet (#385) 2.50 *3.00*
1N32 A57 50c dk blue (#386) 2.25 *2.75*
1N33 A57 $1 org brn & sep (#387) 13.00 *17.00*
1N34 A57 $2 dp bl & yel brn (#388) 13.00 *14.00*
1N35 A57 $5 red & sl grn (#389) 14.00 *17.00*
1N36 A57 $10 dk grn & dl pur (#390) 20.00 *20.00*
1N37 A57 $20 rose lake & dk bl (#391) 14.00 *27.50*
*Nos. 1N23-1N25,1N27-1N37 (14)* 89.25 *116.50*

No. 1N26 is valued in fine condition.

**Same Overprint on China Nos. 397-401**

**1942 Wmk. 261 *Perf. 14***

1N38 A57 $1 org brn & sep 10.00 *9.00*
1N39 A57 $2 dp bl & yel brn 9.00 15.00
1N40 A57 $5 red & sl grn 11.00 *14.00*
1N41 A57 $10 dk grn & dl pur 22.50 26.50
1N42 A57 $20 rose lake & dk bl 22.50 24.00
*Nos. 1N38-1N42 (5)* 75.00 88.50

**Same Overprint on Stamps of China, 1941**

**1942 Unwmk. *Perf. 12***

1N43 A59 2c brt ultra 1.00 *2.00*
1N44 A59 5c green 1.00 *2.00*
1N45 A59 8c red org 2.00 *3.00*
1N46 A59 8c turq grn 2.00 *3.00*
1N47 A59 10c brt green 2.00 *5.00*
1N48 A59 17c olive 2.00 *5.00*
1N49 A59 25c rose vio 2.00 *4.00*
1N50 A59 30c scarlet 2.00 *3.00*
1N51 A59 50c dk blue 3.00 *3.00*
1N52 A59 $1 brn & blk 7.00 *8.00*
1N53 A59 $2 bl & blk 7.00 *8.75*

**1N54** A59 $5 scar & blk 13.00 13.00
**1N55** A59 $10 grn & blk 17.00 *17.00*
**1N56** A59 $20 rose vio & blk 11.00 *20.00*
*Nos. 1N43-1N56 (14)* 72.00 *96.75*

China Nos. 354 and 369 Surcharged in Black

**1945 Unwmk. *Perf. 12½***
**1N57** A57 $200 on 10c grn 200.00 110.00
**1N58** A57 $400 on 8c ol grn 200.00 110.00

China No. 422 Surcharged in Black

**1945**
**1N59** A40 $400 on 1c org 750.00 600.00

Forgeries exist.

---

### OCCUPATION POSTAGE DUE STAMPS

China, No. J79 Surcharged Diagonally with New Value Between Parallel Lines in Black

**1945 Unwmk. *Perf. 12½***
**1NJ1** D5 $100 on $2 yel org 825.00 *900.00*
*a.* Inverted surcharge 1,100. 1,100.

---

### MENG CHIANG (Inner Mongolia)

**Nos. 297-298, 301-303 Overprinted**

Characters 4mm High — I

Characters 5mm High — II

**1941 Engr. Unwmk.**
**2N1** A37 2c #297, I 3.00 *2.00*
*a.* Type II 2.00 *2.00*
**2N2** A37 4c #298, II 55.00 —
*a.* Type I 60.00 55.00
**2N3** A37 15c #301, I 6.00 *5.50*
*a.* Type II 45.00 6.00
**2N4** A37 20c #302, II 11.00 8.75
*a.* Type I 12.00 *16.00*
**2N5** A37 25c #303, II 12.00 *14.00*
*a.* Type I 92.50 92.50
*Nos. 2N1-2N5 (5)* 87.00 *30.25*

For surcharge see No. 2N116.

**On Nos. 312, 314, 318, 321**

**1941 *Perf. 14***
**2N6** A39 ½c #312, I 14.00 *17.50*
*a.* Type II 47.50 —
**2N7** A39 2½c #314, II 5.00 *6.00*
*a.* Type I 8.75 *8.75*
**2N8** A45 13c #318, II 7.50 7.50
*a.* Type I 120.00 110.00
**2N9** A48 30c #321, II 87.50 92.50
*Nos. 2N6-2N9 (4)* 114.00 123.50

**On Stamps of 1939-41**

**1941 *Perf. 12½***
**2N10** A57 2c #368, II 2.40 *3.00*
**2N11** A57 3c #350, II 1.00 1.00
*a.* Type I 2.00 2.00
**2N12** A57 5c #352, II 2.10 *2.50*
*a.* Type I 2.75 *6.00*
**2N13** A57 8c #353, I 2.50 2.00
*a.* Type II 2.00 2.00
**2N14** A57 8c #369, II 20.00 11.00
**2N15** A57 10c #354, II 3.00 3.00
**2N16** A57 16c #357, II 6.00 6.00
**2N17** A57 $1 #359, II 30.00 30.00
*a.* Type I 440.00 440.00
*b.* #347, I 87.50 80.00
**2N18** A57 $5 #361, II 100.00 100.00
*Nos. 2N10-2N18 (9)* 167.00 158.50

For surcharges see Nos. 2N117, 2N119.

**On Stamps of 1940 with Secret Marks**

**1941 Unwmk. *Perf. 14***
**2N19** A57 5c #382, II 2.50 *2.00*
**2N20** A57 8c #383, I 4.00 3.25
*a.* Type II 55.00 —
**2N21** A57 10c #384, II 2.25 2.00
*a.* Type I 4.00 4.00
**2N22** A57 30c #385, II 3.00 4.00
*a.* Type I 5.00 5.00
**2N23** A57 50c #386, I 9.00 9.00
*a.* Type II 7.25 7.25
**2N24** A57 $1 #387, I 22.50 *17.50*
*a.* Type II 30.00 29.00
**2N25** A57 $2 #388, I 30.00 22.50
*a.* Type II 35.00 32.50
**2N26** A57 $5 #389, I 42.50 45.00
*a.* Type II 87.50 —
**2N27** A57 $10 #390, II 87.50 87.50
*a.* Type I 87.50 87.50
**2N28** A57 $20 #391, II 120.00 *120.00*
*a.* Type I 120.00 *110.00*
*Nos. 2N19-2N28 (10)* 323.25 *312.75*

For surcharge see No. 2N120.

**On Stamps of 1940 with Secret Marks**

**1941 Wmk. 261 *Perf. 14***
**2N29** A57 10c #394, II 4.50 4.50
**2N30** A57 30c #395, II 6.00 *6.00*
*a.* Type I 120.00 110.00
**2N31** A57 50c #396, II 8.00 *9.00*
*Nos. 2N29-2N31 (3)* 18.50 *19.50*

**On Stamps of 1940-41 (Martyrs) with Secret Marks**

***Perf. 12½, 13 & Compound***

**1941 Wmk. 261**
**2N32** A39 ½c #402, II 12.00 *14.00*
**2N33** A40 1c #403, II 3.00 2.00
*a.* Type I 5.00 3.50
**2N34** A39 2½c #405, I 80.00 72.50
*a.* Type II 80.00 80.00
**2N35** A48 3c #406, II 6.00 4.00
**2N36** A46 10c #410, I 12.50 12.50
*a.* Type II 21.00 —
**2N37** A46 17c #413, II 62.50 —
*a.* Type I 80.00 80.00
**2N38** A40 25c #416, II 8.00 10.00
**2N39** A48 30c #418, II 72.50 77.50
*a.* Type I 77.50 87.50
**2N40** A47 40c #419, II 8.50 7.00
*a.* Type I 14.50 13.00
**2N41** A40 50c #420, I 13.00 14.00
*a.* Type II 60.00 —

**Unwmk.**
**2N42** A39 ½c #421, II 2.00 *3.00*
*a.* Type I 5.00 5.00
**2N43** A40 1c #422, I 2.00 2.00
*a.* Type II 4.25 3.50
**2N44** A46 2c #423, I 8.50 9.00
**2N45** A48 3c #425, II 4.00 3.50
*a.* Type I 5.00 4.00
**2N46** A39 4c #426, II 2.00 2.00
**2N47** A45 8c #428, II 19.00 —
*a.* Type I 100.00 —
**2N48** A46 10c #429, I 24.00 24.00
*a.* Type II 72.50 —
**2N49** A45 13c #430, I 8.00 *7.25*
*a.* Type II 24.00 —
**2N50** A48 15c #431, II 5.00 5.00
**2N51** A46 17c #432, II 5.00 *5.00*
*a.* Type I 7.25 6.00
**2N52** A47 20c #433, II 5.00 *5.00*
*a.* Type I 6.00 *7.00*
**2N53** A45 21c #434, II 5.00 *5.00*
**2N54** A40 25c #435, I 6.00 *8.00*
**2N55** A46 28c #436, II 5.00 *7.00*
**2N56** A40 50c #439, I 21.50 18.00
*a.* Type II 18.00 9.00
*Nos. 2N42-2N56 (15)* 122.00 103.75

For surcharges see Nos. 2N114-2N115, 2N118, 2N121-2N122.

China Nos. 297-298, 302 Surcharged in Black

**1942 Unwmk. *Perf. 12½, 13***
**2N57** A37 1c on 2c ol grn 55.00 55.00
**2N58** A37 2c on 4c grn 14.00 14.00
**2N59** A37 10c on 20c ultra 85.00 42.50
*Nos. 2N57-2N59 (3)* 154.00 111.50

**Same, on China No. 313**

***Perf. 14***
**2N60** A40 ½c on 1c org 62.50 62.50

**Same, on Stamps of China, 1938-41**

***Perf. 12½***
**2N61** A57 1c on 2c (#368) 2.00 1.25
**2N62** A57 4c on 8c (#353) 14.00 *13.00*
*a.* Inverted surcharge 47.50 —
**2N63** A57 4c on 8c (#369) 6.00 7.00
**2N64** A57 5c on 10c (#354) 3.00 3.00
**2N65** A57 8c on 16c (#357) 11.00 7.00
**2N66** A57 50c on $1 (#359) 15.00 *17.50*
*a.* On No. 347 220.00 220.00
*b.* On No. 344 660.00 —
**2N67** A57 $1 on $2 (#360) 87.50 72.50
*Nos. 2N61-2N67 (7)* 138.50 121.25

No. 2N66b was issued without gum.

**Same, on Stamps of China, 1940**

***Perf. 14***
**2N68** A57 4c on 8c (#383) 3.00 *1.50*
**2N69** A57 15c on 30c (#385) 10.00 *10.00*
*a.* Inverted surcharge 55.00 55.00
**2N70** A57 25c on 50c (#386) 10.00 *10.00*
**2N71** A57 50c on $1 (#387) 30.00 *18.00*
**2N72** A57 $1 on $2 (#388) 30.00 *18.00*
**2N73** A57 $5 on $10 (#390) 75.00 *62.50*
**2N74** A57 $10 on $20 (#391) 140.00 *110.00*
*Nos. 2N68-2N74 (7)* 298.00 *230.00*

**Same, on China No. 395**

**1942 Wmk. 261 *Perf. 14***
**2N75** A57 15c on 30c scar 140.00 100.00

**Same, on China Nos. 418 and 419**

***Perf. 12½, 13***
**2N76** A48 15c on 30c brn car 47.50 *47.50*
**2N77** A47 20c on 40c org 20.00 *13.50*
*Nos. 2N75-2N77 (3)* 207.50 *161.00*

**Same, on Stamps of China, 1940-41**

**1942 Unwmk.**
**2N78** A40 ½c on 1c org 3.00 3.00
**2N79** A39 2c on 4c pale vio 6.00 *6.00*
**2N80** A47 10c on 20c lt bl 6.00 *6.00*
**2N81** A47 20c on 40c org 17.50 *14.50*
**2N82** A40 25c on 50c grn 24.00 *24.00*
*Nos. 2N78-2N82 (5)* 56.50 *53.50*

**Same Surcharge on "New Peking" Prints**

***Perf. 14***
**2N83** A37 1c on 2c ol grn 14.50 *25.00*
**2N84** A37 2c on 4c dl grn 1.40 *1.00*
**2N85** A46 5c on 10c dl vio 5.00 *9.00*
**2N86** A57 8c on 16c ol gray 2.00 *2.75*
**2N87** A47 10c on 20c red brn 5.00 7.25
**2N88** A48 15c on 30c brn car 4.00 *4.00*
**2N89** A47 20c on 40c org 9.00 *10.00*
**2N90** A40 25c on 50c grn 6.00 *6.00*
**2N91** A57 50c on $1 org brn & sep 8.50 *14.50*
**2N92** A57 $1 on $2 dp bl & org brn 40.00 *45.00*
**2N93** A57 $5 on $10 dk grn & dl pur 60.00 *80.00*
*Nos. 2N83-2N93 (11)* 155.40 *204.50*

The "New Peking" printings were made by the Chinese Bureau of Engraving and Printing for use in Japanese controlled areas of North China. They are on thin, poor quality paper, with dull gum or without gum and there are slight alterations in the designs.

Dragon-Carved Pillar and Doves — A1

**Wmk. Characters in Circle in Sheet**

**1943 Engr. *Perf. 12xPin-perf. 12***
**2N94** A1 4f deep orange 4.00 *25.00*
**2N95** A1 8f dark blue 5.00 *25.00*

5th anniv. of the Inner Mongolia post and telegraph service.

The watermark, which is 40mm in diameter and covers four stamps, occurs three times in the sheet.

Mining Coal — A2

**1943 Unwmk. Photo. *Perf. 12***
**2N96** A2 4f Prus green 4.00 *10.00*
**2N97** A2 8f brown red 4.00 *10.00*

2nd anniv. of the "Greater East Asia War."

Flying Horse A3

Yun Wang A4

**1944 *Perf. 12½x12, 12x12½***
**2N98** A3 4f rose 3.00 *10.00*
**2N99** A4 8f dull blue 3.00 *10.00*

5th anniv. of the founding of the Federal Autonomous Government of Mongolia, Sept. 1, 1939.

Industrial Plant — A5

**1944, Dec. 8 Photo. *Perf. 12x12½***
**2N100** A5 8f red brown 4.00 *12.00*

3rd anniv. of the "Greater East Asia War" and to encourage production increase.

New Peking Printings of 1942 Overprinted in Black

**1945 Unwmk. Engr. *Perf. 14***
**Without Gum**
**2N101** A37 2c olive grn 12.00 —
**2N102** A37 4c dull grn 20.00 —
**2N103** A37 5c green 21.00 *27.50*
**2N104** A57 $1 org brn & sep 6.00 8.00
**2N105** A57 $2 dp bl & org brn 15.00 19.00
**2N106** A57 $5 red & grnsh blk 50.00 50.00

**Same Overprint on New Peking Printings of Martyrs Issue**
**2N107** A40 1c orange 2.00 *2.50*
**2N108** A45 8c dp orange 3.00 *4.00*
**2N109** A46 10c dl violet 3.00 *4.00*
**2N110** A47 20c red brown 3.00 *4.00*
**2N111** A48 30c brown car 3.00 *4.00*
**2N112** A47 40c orange 2.00 *3.00*
**2N113** A40 50c green 8.00 *10.00*

For surcharges see Nos. 2N123-2N127.

**Stamps of Meng Chiang, 1941, Surcharged in Red or Black**

50c

10c

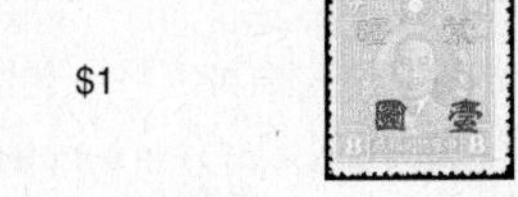

$1

**1945**
**2N114** A39 10c on ½c ol blk (#2N42, II, R) 4.00 *5.00*
*a.* On #2N42a, I 7.25 *8.00*
**2N115** A40 10c on 1c org (#2N43a, II, R) 2.00 *3.00*
*a.* Without secret mark (China #422a) 40.00 *40.00*
*b.* On #2N43, I 3.00 *3.50*
**2N116** A37 50c on 2c ol grn (#2N1a, II, B) 18.00 *35.00*
*b.* On #2N1, I 18.00 *35.00*
**2N117** A57 50c on 2c ol grn (#2N10, II, B)) 1.40 *2.50*
**2N118** A39 50c on 4c pale vio (#2N46, II, R) 2.00 *3.00*
**2N119** A57 50c on 5c ol grn (#2N12, II, R) 1.00 *1.90*
*a.* On #2N12a, I 12.50 *12.50*
**2N120** A57 50c on 5c ol grn (#2N19, II, R) 1.50 *2.75*
*Nos. 2N114-2N120 (7)* 29.90 *53.15*

### Same Surcharge on #2N32, 2N33

**1945** **Wmk. 261**
**2N121** A39 10c on ½c ol blk, II (R) 29.00 *35.00*
**2N122** A40 10c on 1c orange, II (R) 6.00 *7.00*
*a.* On #2N33a, I 35.00 —

### Same Surcharge on Nos. 2N107, 2N101-2N103 and 2N108

**1945** **Unwmk.**
**2N123** A40 10c on 1c org (R) 2.00 *3.00*
**2N124** A37 50c on 2c ol grn (Bk) 5.00 *6.00*
**2N125** A37 50c on 4c dl grn (R) 10.00 *12.00*
**2N126** A37 50c on 5c green 1.00 *3.00*
**2N127** A45 $1 on 8c dp org (R) 4.00 *6.00*
*Nos. 2N123-2N127 (5)* 22.00 *30.00*

## NORTH CHINA

## Honan

### Nos. 297-298, 301-303 Overprinted

I

II

**1941** **Engr.** **Unwmk.**
**3N1** A37 2c #297, II 18.00 18.00
*a.* Type I 30.00 30.00
**3N2** A37 4c #298, I 12.00 7.25
*a.* Type II 32.50 32.50
**3N3** A37 15c #301, I 3.00 *3.00*
*a.* Type II 40.00 3.00
**3N4** A37 20c #302, I 11.00 8.00
**3N5** A37 25c #303, II 24.00 24.00
*Nos. 3N1-3N5 (5)* 68.00 60.25

**1941** ***Perf. 14***
**3N6** A39 ½c #312, I 3.00 *4.00*
*a.* Type II 40.00 —
**3N7** A39 2½c #314, I 4.00 *5.00*
*a.* Type II 4.00 3.00
**3N8** A45 13c #318, II 4.00 *5.00*
*a.* Type I 100.00 100.00
**3N9** A48 30c #321, II 18.00 *22.00*
**3N10** A47 40c #322, II 100.00 *115.00*
*Nos. 3N6-3N10 (5)* 129.00 151.00

### On Stamps of 1939-41

**1941** ***Perf. 12½***
**3N11** A57 2c #368, II 4.00 *2.50*
**3N12** A57 3c #350, I 2.00 *2.50*
*a.* Type II 3.00 2.50
**3N13** A57 5c #352, II 4.00 2.50
*a.* Type I 2.40 2.40
**3N14** A57 8c #353, II 4.00 *2.50*
*a.* Type I 3.00 2.00
**3N15** A57 10c #354, II 8.00 7.00
**3N16** A57 16c #357, II 3.00 *5.00*
**3N17** A57 $1 #359, II 20.00 *25.00*
*a.* Type I 325.00 325.00
*b.* On #347, I 80.00 75.00
**3N18** A57 $5 #361, II 80.00 80.00
*Nos. 3N11-3N18 (8)* 125.00 127.00

For overprints see Nos. 3N56, 3N58, 3N61.

### On Stamps of 1940 with Secret Marks

**1941** **Unwmk.** ***Perf. 14***
**3N20** A57 5c #382, II 5.00 4.00
**3N21** A57 8c #383, II 4.00 *1.00*
**3N22** A57 10c #384, II 6.00 5.00
**3N23** A57 30c #385, I 9.00 *12.00*
*a.* Type II 15.00 11.00
**3N24** A57 50c #386, I 8.00 *8.00*
*a.* Type II 18.00 *17.00*
**3N25** A57 $1 #387, I 12.00 *15.00*
*a.* Type II 80.00 80.00
**3N26** A57 $2 #388, I 18.00 *18.00*
*a.* Type II 24.00 *24.00*
**3N27** A57 $5 #389, I 40.00 35.00
*a.* Type II 62.50 57.50
**3N28** A57 $10 #390, II 65.00 62.50
*a.* Type I 195.00 195.00
**3N29** A57 $20 #391, II 125.00 *140.00*
*a.* Type I 125.00 *140.00*
*Nos. 3N20-3N29 (10)* 292.00 *300.50*

### On Stamps of 1940 with Secret Marks

**1941** **Wmk. 261** ***Perf. 14***
**3N30** A57 5c #392, II 24.00 20.00
**3N31** A57 5c #393, II 15.00 15.00
**3N32** A57 30c #395, I 32.50 31.00
*a.* Type II 40.00 40.00
**3N33** A57 50c #396, II 75.00 *75.00*
*Nos. 3N30-3N33 (4)* 146.50 141.00

### On Stamps of 1940-41 (Martyrs) with Secret Marks

***Perf. 12½, 13 & Compound***

**1941** **Wmk. 261**
**3N34** A39 ½c #402, II 3.00 *3.50*
**3N35** A40 1c #403, II 3.00 2.00
*a.* Type I 20.00 *30.00*
**3N36** A39 2½c #405, II 18.00 *17.00*
**3N37** A46 10c #410, II 20.00 *18.50*
*a.* Type I 35.00 35.00
**3N38** A45 13c #411, II 5.00 5.00
**3N39** A46 17c #413, II 6.00 5.00
*a.* Type I 13.00 9.00
**3N40** A40 25c #416, II 7.50 8.00
**3N41** A47 40c #419, II 9.00 6.00
*a.* Type I 20.00 20.00
*Nos. 3N34-3N41 (8)* 71.50 *65.00*

**Unwmk.**

**3N42** A39 ½c #421, II 4.00 6.00
*a.* Type I 6.00 8.00
**3N43** A40 1c #422, I 3.00 5.00
*a.* Type II 6.00 8.00
**3N44** A46 2c #423, I 15.00 *16.00*
**3N45** A48 3c #425, I 4.00 *6.00*
**3N46** A39 4c #426, II 6.00 *7.00*
**3N47** A46 10c #429, I 50.00 *60.00*
**3N48** A45 13c #430, II 5.50 *7.00*
*a.* Type I 30.00 30.00
**3N49** A48 15c #431, II 6.00 *7.00*
**3N50** A46 17c #432, II 6.00 7.00
*a.* Type I 20.00 20.00
**3N51** A47 20c #433, II 6.00 *8.00*
*a.* Type I 62.50 62.50
**3N52** A45 21c #434, II 7.50 9.00
**3N53** A40 25c #435, I 8.00 10.00
**3N54** A46 28c #436, II 5.00 *8.00*
*Nos. 3N42-3N54 (13)* 126.00 156.00

For overprints see Nos. 3N55, 3N59.

Overprinted in Red

**1942**
**3N55** A39 4c #3N46 6.00 *10.00*
**3N56** A57 8c #3N14 50.00 *60.00*
**3N57** A57 8c #369, II 25.00 *30.00*
*Nos. 3N55-3N57 (3)* 81.00 *100.00*

The fall of Singapore.

Overprinted in Red

**1942**
**3N58** A57 2c #3N11 15.00 *15.00*
**3N59** A39 4c #3N46 20.00 *25.00*
**3N60** A57 8c #369, II 72.50 *72.50*
**3N61** A57 8c #3N14 65.00 *72.50*
*Nos. 3N58-3N61 (4)* 172.50 185.00

Formation of Manchukuo, 10th anniv.

## Hopei

### On Stamps of 1940-41 (Martyrs) with Secret Marks

I

II

***Perf. 11½-13½***

**1941** **Engr.** **Unwmk.**
**4N1** A37 2c #297, II 4.00 *6.00*
*a.* Type I 11.00 *15.00*
**4N2** A37 4c #298, I 4.50 *8.00*
*a.* Type II 85.00 —
**4N3** A37 15c #301, II 5.00 *5.00*
*a.* Type I 4.25 *8.00*
**4N4** A37 20c #302, II 37.50 35.00
**4N5** A37 25c #303, II 35.00 *12.00*
*a.* Type I 95.00 *110.00*
*Nos. 4N1-4N5 (5)* 86.00 *66.00*

### On Nos. 312, 314, 318, 321

**1941** ***Perf. 14***
**4N6** A39 ½c #312, II 3.00 *6.00*
*a.* Type I 10.00 *12.00*
**4N7** A39 2½c #314, II 4.00 *6.00*
*a.* Type I 4.00 *6.00*
**4N8** A45 13c #318, II 5.00 *8.00*
*a.* Type I 5.00 *8.00*
**4N9** A48 30c #321, II 7.00 *10.00*
*Nos. 4N6-4N9 (4)* 19.00 *30.00*

### On Stamps of 1939-41

**1941** ***Perf. 12½***
**4N10** A57 2c #368, II 5.00 3.00
**4N11** A57 2c #349, II 4.00 *2.00*
**4N12** A57 3c #350, II 6.00 2.00
*a.* Type I 3.00 2.00
**4N13** A57 5c #352, II 3.00 2.00
*a.* Type I 4.00 2.00
**4N14** A57 8c #353, II 2.00 1.00
*a.* Type I 2.00 1.60
**4N15** A57 8c #369, II 6.00 6.00
**4N16** A57 10c #354, II 3.00 1.00
**4N17** A57 16c #357, II 4.00 4.00
**4N18** A57 $1 #359, II 175.00 165.00
*a.* On #347, I 250.00 —
**4N19** A57 $2 #360, II 62.50 55.00
*a.* Type I 65.00 65.00
**4N20** A57 $5 #361, I 65.00 65.00
*a.* Type II 65.00 75.00
**4N21** A57 $10 #362, II 200.00 200.00
**4N22** A57 $20 #363, II 450.00 450.00
*Nos. 4N10-4N22 (13)* 985.50 956.00

For overprints see Nos. 4N66-4N68, 4N70.

### On Stamps of 1940 with Secret Marks

**1941** **Unwmk.** ***Perf. 14***

**Type II**

**4N24** A57 5c #382 4.00 1.00
**4N25** A57 8c #383 4.00 1.00
**4N26** A57 10c #384 8.00 3.00
**4N27** A57 30c #385 8.00 3.00
**4N28** A57 50c #386 8.00 3.00
**4N29** A57 $1 #387 12.00 6.00
**4N30** A57 $2 #388 45.00 20.00
**4N31** A57 $5 #389 55.00 50.00
**4N32** A57 $10 #390 65.00 55.00
**4N33** A57 $20 #391 75.00 *72.50*
*Nos. 4N24-4N33 (10)* 284.00 214.50

For overprints see Nos. 4N65, 4N71.

**Type I**

*4N24a* A57 5c 3.00 1.50
*4N25a* A57 8c 80.00 70.00
*4N26a* A57 10c 4.00 2.40
*4N28a* A57 50c 8.00 3.00
*4N29a* A57 $1 11.00 6.00
*4N30a* A57 $2 45.00 32.50
*4N31a* A57 $5 55.00 55.00
*4N32a* A57 $10 45.00 65.00
*4N33a* A57 $20 110.00 110.00
*Nos. 4N24a-4N33a (9)* 361.00 345.40

### On Stamps of 1940 with Secret Marks

**1941** **Wmk. 261** ***Perf. 14***
**4N34** A57 5c #392, II 5.00 3.00
**4N35** A57 5c #393, II 5.00 3.00
**4N36** A57 10c #394, II 4.00 2.00
**4N37** A57 30c #395, II 10.00 10.00
*a.* Type I 15.00 *16.00*
**4N38** A57 50c #396, II 5.00 5.00
*Nos. 4N34-4N38 (5)* 29.00 23.00

### On Stamps of 1940-41 (Martyrs) with Secret Marks

***Perf. 12½, 13 & Compound***

**1941** **Wmk. 261**
**4N39** A39 ½c #402, II 3.00 3.00
**4N40** A40 1c #403, I 2.50 3.00
*a.* Type II 3.00 3.00
**4N41** A46 2c #404, II 4.00 4.00
**4N42** A39 2½c #405, II 5.00 5.00
**4N43** A48 3c #406, II 4.00 4.00
**4N44** A46 10c #410, II 5.00 5.00
*a.* Type I 6.00 6.00
**4N45** A45 13c #411, II 4.00 4.00
**4N46** A46 17c #413, II 5.00 3.50
*a.* Type I 4.25 4.25
**4N47** A40 25c #416, II 7.50 5.00
**4N48** A48 30c #418, II 30.00 30.00
*a.* Type I 50.00 50.00
**4N49** A47 40c #419, II 6.00 6.00
*a.* Type I 6.00 6.00
*Nos. 4N39-4N49 (11)* 76.00 72.50

**Unwmk.**

**4N50** A39 ½c #421, II 3.00 2.00
*a.* Type I 4.00 2.25
**4N51** A40 1c #422, II 4.00 2.00
*a.* Type I 5.00 2.00
**4N52** A46 2c #423 4.00 2.00
**4N53** A48 3c #425, I 4.00 4.00
*a.* Type II 5.50 *4.25*
**4N54** A39 4c #426, II 4.50 2.50
**4N55** A45 8c #428, II 4.00 *2.50*
*a.* Type I 5.00 5.00
**4N56** A46 10c #429, II 5.00 3.00
**4N57** A45 13c #430, I 5.00 *4.00*
*a.* Type II 4.50 4.50
**4N58** A48 15c #431, II 9.00 8.00
**4N59** A46 17c #432, II 8.00 *10.00*
*a.* Type I 8.00 *6.00*
**4N60** A47 20c #433, II 6.00 6.00
*a.* Type I 6.00 6.00
**4N61** A45 21c #434, II 6.00 *8.00*
**4N62** A40 25c #435, I 6.00 *8.00*
*a.* Type II 5.00 *5.00*
**4N63** A46 28c #436, II 5.00 *8.00*
*Nos. 4N50-4N63 (14)* 73.50 70.00

For overprints see Nos. 4N64, 4N69.

### Honan Singapore Overprint in Red

**1942**
**4N64** A39 4c #4N54 5.00 *6.00*
**4N65** A57 8c #4N25 8.00 *10.00*
**4N66** A57 8c #4N14 12.00 *14.00*
**4N67** A57 8c #4N15 12.00 *15.00*
*Nos. 4N64-4N67 (4)* 37.00 *45.00*

### Honan Anniv. of Manchukuo Overprint in Red

**1942**
**4N68** A57 2c #4N10 16.00 *20.00*
**4N69** A39 4c #4N54 7.00 *10.00*
**4N70** A57 8c #4N14 90.00 *105.00*
**4N71** A57 8c #4N25 15.00 *20.00*
*Nos. 4N68-4N71 (4)* 128.00 *155.00*

## Shansi

### Nos. 297-298, 301, 303 Overprinted

I

II

**1941** **Engr.** **Unwmk.** ***Perf. 12½***
**5N1** A37 2c #297, II 65.00 *75.00*
*a.* Type I 87.50 80.00
**5N2** A37 4c #298, I 50.00 62.50
*a.* Type II 125.00 *165.00*
**5N3** A37 15c #301, II 8.00 *10.00*
*a.* Type I 9.00 *11.00*
**5N4** A37 25c #303, II 9.00 *13.50*
*a.* Type I 62.50 *67.50*
*Nos. 5N1-5N4 (4)* 132.00 161.00

### On Nos. 312, 314, 318, 321

**1941** ***Perf. 14***
**5N5** A39 ½c #312, II 55.00 *55.00*
*a.* Type I 4.00 *4.00*
**5N6** A39 2½c #314, II 3.00 *3.00*
*a.* Type I 4.00 4.00
**5N7** A45 13c #318, II 6.00 4.00
*a.* Type I 240.00 240.00
**5N8** A48 30c #321, II 15.00 *12.00*
*Nos. 5N5-5N8 (4)* 79.00 *74.00*

### On Stamps of 1939-41

**1941** ***Perf. 12½***
**5N9** A57 2c #368, II 2.40 2.00
**5N10** A57 3c #350, II 2.00 2.00
*a.* Type I 15.00 15.00
**5N11** A57 5c #352, II 7.00 3.50
*a.* Type I 7.50 5.00
**5N12** A57 8c #353, II 1.50 1.50
*a.* Type I 4.00 3.50
**5N13** A57 8c #369, II 42.50 25.00
**5N14** A57 10c #354, II 17.00 *8.00*
**5N15** A57 16c #357, II 7.50 5.00
**5N16** A57 $1 #359, II 20.00 17.00
**5N17** A57 $2 #360, II 50.00 50.00
**5N18** A57 $5 #361, II 40.00 57.50
*Nos. 5N9-5N18 (10)* 189.90 171.50

For overprints see Nos. 5N62-5N64, 5N66-5N67.

### On Stamps of 1940 with Secret Marks

**1941** **Unwmk.** ***Perf. 14***
**5N19** A57 5c #382, II 3.00 2.00
**5N20** A57 8c #383, II 3.00 2.00
**5N21** A57 10c #384, I 6.00 *2.00*
*a.* Type II 32.50 5.00
**5N22** A57 30c #385, II 9.00 4.00
*a.* Type I 7.50 3.00
**5N23** A57 50c #386, I 7.50 5.00
*a.* Type II 5.75 *5.75*
**5N24** A57 $1 #387, I 18.00 14.00
*a.* Type II 45.00 37.50
**5N25** A57 $2 #388, II 40.00 *25.00*
*a.* Type I 25.00 25.00
**5N26** A57 $5 #389, II 32.50 32.50
*a.* Type I 97.50 97.50
**5N27** A57 $10 #390, II 70.00 70.00
*a.* Type I 75.00 75.00
**5N28** A57 $20 #391, II 70.00 70.00
*a.* Type I 125.00 *135.00*
*Nos. 5N19-5N28 (10)* 259.00 226.50

For overprints see Nos. 5N61, 5N68.

### On Stamps of 1940 with Secret Marks

**1941** **Wmk. 261** ***Perf. 14***
**5N29** A57 5c #392, II 6.00 3.00
**5N30** A57 5c #393, II 3.00 2.00
**5N31** A57 10c #394, II 6.00 3.00
**5N32** A57 30c #395, I 37.50 *80.00*
**5N33** A57 50c #396, I 15.00 11.00
*Nos. 5N29-5N33 (5)* 67.50 99.00

### On Stamps of 1940-41 (Martyrs) with Secret Marks
***Perf. 12½, 13 & Compound***

**1941** **Wmk. 261**
**5N34** A39 ½c #402, II 3.00 3.00
**5N35** A40 1c #403, II 3.00 2.00
*a.* Type I 3.00 2.00
**5N36** A46 2c #404, II 7.50 5.00
**5N37** A39 2½c #405, I 9.00 *10.50*
**5N38** A46 10c #410, I 9.75 9.75
**5N39** A45 13c #411, II 6.00 5.00
**5N40** A46 17c #413, I 47.50 32.50
**5N41** A40 25c #416, II 5.00 5.00
**5N42** A48 30c #418, I 150.00 150.00
*a.* Type II 150.00 150.00
**5N43** A47 40c #419, II 6.00 6.00
*a.* Type I 37.50 37.50
**5N44** A40 50c #420, II 7.50 7.50
*a.* Type I 42.50 42.50
*Nos. 5N34-5N44 (11)* 254.25 236.25

**Unwmk.**
**5N45** A39 ½c #421, II 3.00 *3.75*
*a.* Type I 5.25 *5.75*
**5N46** A40 1c #422, I 4.50 3.00
*a.* Type II 3.00 3.00
**5N47** A46 2c #423, II 4.00 4.00
**5N48** A48 3c #425, I 11.00 9.00
**5N49** A39 4c #426, II 5.00 5.00
**5N50** A45 8c #428, I 17.00 15.00
*a.* Type II 35.00 21.00
**5N51** A46 10c #429, I 50.00 50.00
*a.* Type II 57.50 57.50
**5N52** A45 13c #430, I 30.00 20.00
*a.* Type II 22.50 22.50
**5N53** A48 15c #431, II 6.75 6.75
**5N54** A46 17c #432, II 6.00 6.00
*a.* Type I 6.00 5.50
**5N55** A47 20c #433, II 7.50 6.00
*a.* Type I 7.50 4.00
**5N56** A45 21c #434, II 6.00 6.00
**5N57** A40 25c #435, I 9.00 *5.00*
**5N58** A46 28c #436, II 7.50 6.00
**5N59** A40 50c #439, II 17.00 15.00
*Nos. 5N45-5N59 (15)* 184.25 160.50

For overprints see Nos. 5N60, 5N65.

### Honan Singapore Overprint in Red

**1942**
**5N60** A39 4c #5N49 6.00 *7.00*
**5N61** A57 8c #5N20 18.00 *22.50*
**5N62** A57 8c #5N12 18.00 *18.00*
**5N63** A57 8c #5N13 50.00 *55.00*
*Nos. 5N60-5N63 (4)* 92.00 *102.50*

### Honan Anniv. of Manchukuo Overprint in Red

**1942**
**5N64** A57 2c #5N9 18.00 *17.00*
**5N65** A39 4c #5N49 13.50 *17.00*
**5N66** A57 8c #5N12 50.00 *62.50*
**5N67** A57 8c #5N13 72.50 *85.00*
**5N68** A57 8c #5N20 55.00 55.00
*Nos. 5N64-5N68 (5)* 209.00 *236.50*

## Shantung

### Nos. 297-298, 301-303 Overprinted

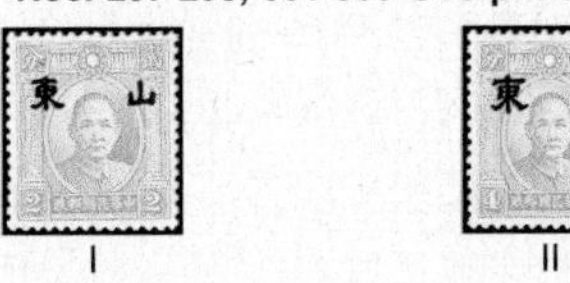

I II

**1941** **Engr.** **Unwmk.** ***Perf. 12½***
**6N1** A37 2c #297, II 2.50 2.00
*a.* Type I 5.00 5.00
**6N2** A37 4c #298, II 8.00 7.25
*a.* Type I 9.25 8.00
**6N3** A37 15c #301, II 3.00 2.50
*a.* Type I 4.00 3.50
**6N4** A37 20c #302, II 6.00 5.00
**6N5** A37 25c #303, II 12.00 7.25
*a.* Type I 265.00 225.00
*Nos. 6N1-6N5 (5)* 31.50 24.00

### On Nos. 312, 314, 318

**1941** ***Perf. 14***
**6N6** A39 ½c #312, II 3.00 2.00
*a.* Type I 3.00 2.00
**6N7** A39 2½c #314, II 3.00 *2.10*
*a.* Type I 4.50 *2.00*
**6N8** A45 13c #318, II 6.00 3.00
*a.* Type I 40.00 25.00
*Nos. 6N6-6N8 (3)* 12.00 7.10

### On Stamps of 1939-41

**1941** ***Perf. 12½***
**6N9** A57 2c #349, II 3.00 *2.00*
**6N10** A57 2c #368, II 2.00 2.00
**6N11** A57 3c #350, II 2.00 2.00
*a.* Type I 3.00 1.50
**6N12** A57 5c #352, II 3.50 2.00
*a.* Type I 3.00 1.50
**6N13** A57 8c #353, II 3.00 2.00
*a.* Type I 2.00 1.00
**6N14** A57 8c #369, II 2.00 2.00
**6N15** A57 10c #354, II 3.50 2.00
**6N16** A57 16c #357, II 5.50 7.50
**6N17** A57 $1 #359, II 27.00 13.00
*a.* Type I 425.00 425.00
*b.* On No. 347, I 62.50 57.50
**6N18** A57 $5 #361, II 60.00 55.00
*Nos. 6N9-6N18 (10)* 111.50 89.50

For overprints see Nos. 6N62, 6N64-6N65, 6N67-6N68.

### On Stamps of 1940 with Secret Marks

**1941** **Unwmk.** ***Perf. 14***
**6N20** A57 5c #382, II 2.00 1.25
**6N21** A57 8c #383, II 3.00 1.00
*a.* Type I 3.00 1.50
**6N22** A57 10c #384, II 3.00 2.00
**6N23** A57 30c #385, II 4.00 2.00
*a.* Type I 7.00 *7.50*
**6N24** A57 50c #386, I 8.00 6.75
*a.* Type II 9.00 8.00
**6N25** A57 $1 #387, II 9.00 5.00
*a.* Type I 24.00 22.50
**6N26** A57 $2 #388, II 18.00 15.00
*a.* Type I 24.50 *27.50*
**6N27** A57 $5 #389, II 30.00 30.00
*a.* Type I 42.50 40.00
**6N28** A57 $10 #390, II 67.50 67.50
*a.* Type I 72.50 72.50
**6N29** A57 $20 #391, II 97.50 97.50
*a.* Type I 100.00 *125.00*
*Nos. 6N20-6N29 (10)* 242.00 228.00

For overprints see Nos. 6N63, 6N69.

### On Stamps of 1940 with Secret Marks

**1941** **Wmk. 261** ***Perf. 14***
**6N30** A57 5c #392, II 3.00 2.00
**6N31** A57 5c #393, II 3.00 2.00
**6N32** A57 10c #394, II 10.00 8.00
**6N33** A57 30c #395, II 7.50 7.00
*a.* Type I 25.00 25.00
**6N34** A57 50c #396, II 10.00 4.25
*a.* Type I 12.00 *11.50*
*Nos. 6N30-6N34 (5)* 33.50 23.25

### On Stamps of 1940-41 (Martyrs) with Secret Marks
***Perf. 12½, 13 & Compound***

**1941** **Wmk. 261**
**6N35** A39 ½c #402, II 4.50 3.00
**6N36** A40 1c #403, II 4.50 2.00
*a.* Type I 3.00 2.00
**6N37** A39 2½c #405, II 25.00 *17.00*
**6N38** A46 10c #410, I 11.00 4.00
**6N39** A45 13c #411, II 10.00 5.00
**6N40** A46 17c #413, II 5.00 5.00
*a.* Type I 11.00 *11.00*
**6N41** A40 25c #416, II 7.50 5.00
**6N42** A48 30c #418, I 60.00 37.50
**6N43** A47 40c #419, II 6.00 6.00
*a.* Type I 37.50 37.50
**6N44** A40 50c #420, II 12.00 9.00
*Nos. 6N35-6N44 (10)* 145.50 93.50

**Unwmk.**
**6N45** A39 ½c #421, II 4.00 2.00
*a.* Type I 7.50 4.25
**6N46** A40 1c #422, II 3.00 2.00
*a.* Type I 3.25 3.25
*b.* On No. 422a, II 97.50 97.50
**6N48** A46 2c #423, II 5.00 2.50
**6N49** A48 3c #425, I 6.00 *5.00*
*a.* Type II 5.00 *6.75*
**6N50** A39 4c #426, II 5.00 3.00
**6N51** A45 8c #428, II 4.00 3.50
*a.* Type I 40.00 40.00
**6N52** A46 10c #429, I 15.00 15.00
**6N53** A45 13c #430, I 6.00 4.50
*a.* Type II 4.50 4.50
**6N54** A48 15c #431, II 5.00 5.00
**6N55** A46 17c #432, II 5.00 4.00
*a.* Type I 5.00 5.00
**6N56** A47 20c #433, II 6.00 4.50
*a.* Type I 6.75 6.75
**6N57** A45 21c #434, II 9.00 5.00
**6N58** A40 25c #435, I 7.00 5.75
**6N59** A46 28c #436, II 5.00 4.00
**6N60** A40 50c #439, II 55.00 55.00
*Nos. 6N45-6N60 (15)* 140.00 120.75

For overprints see Nos. 6N61, 6N66.

### Honan Singapore Overprint in Red

**1942**
**6N61** A39 4c #6N50 5.00 *5.00*
**6N62** A57 8c #6N13 24.50 *30.00*
**6N63** A57 8c #6N21 30.00 24.50
**6N64** A57 8c #6N14 40.00 *40.00*
*Nos. 6N61-6N64 (4)* 99.50 *99.50*

### Honan Anniv. of Manchukuo Overprint in Red

**1942**
**6N65** A57 2c #6N10 9.00 *9.00*
**6N66** A39 4c #6N50 11.00 *11.00*
**6N67** A57 8c #6N13 40.00 *30.00*
**6N68** A57 8c #6N14 65.00 *72.50*
**6N69** A57 8c #6N21 32.50 *37.50*
*Nos. 6N65-6N69 (5)* 157.50 *160.00*

## Supeh

### Nos. 297-298, 301-302 Overprinted

I

II

**1941** **Engr.** **Unwmk.** ***Perf. 12½***
**7N1** A37 2c #297, I 24.00 13.00
*a.* Type II 27.50 15.00
**7N2** A37 4c #298, I 100.00 57.50
*a.* Type II 110.00
**7N3** A37 15c #301, II 8.00 6.00
*a.* Type I 6.00 6.00
**7N4** A37 20c #302, II 15.00 6.00
*Nos. 7N1-7N4 (4)* 147.00 82.50

### On Nos. 312, 314, 318

**1941** ***Perf. 14***
**7N5** A39 ½c #312, I 4.50 4.25
**7N6** A39 2½c #314, II 6.00 4.00
*a.* Type I 5.50 4.00
**7N7** A45 13c #318, II 6.00 5.00
*a.* Type I 160.00 160.00
*Nos. 7N5-7N7 (3)* 16.50 13.25

### On Stamps of 1939-41

**1941** ***Perf. 12½***
**7N8** A57 2c #368, II 5.50 *5.00*
**7N9** A57 3c #350, II 5.50 5.00
*a.* Type I 24.50 24.50
**7N10** A57 5c #352, II 6.00 6.00
*a.* Type I 7.50 8.00
**7N11** A57 8c #353, I 6.00 6.00
*a.* Type II 8.00 5.00
**7N12** A57 8c #369, II 50.00 50.00
**7N13** A57 10c #354, II 9.00 *8.00*
**7N14** A57 16c #357, II 9.00 *9.00*
**7N15** A57 $1 #359, II 18.00 *19.00*
*a.* On No. 347, I 210.00 210.00
*Nos. 7N8-7N15 (8)* 109.00 *108.00*

For overprints see Nos. 7N56-7N58, 7N60-7N61.

### On Stamps of 1940 with Secret Marks

**1941** **Unwmk.** ***Perf. 14***
**7N17** A57 5c #382, II 7.50 4.00
**7N18** A57 8c #383, II 6.00 2.00
**7N19** A57 10c #384, I 7.50 4.25
*a.* Type II 4.25 4.25
**7N20** A57 30c #385, I 8.00 *5.00*
*a.* Type II 12.00 *9.00*
**7N21** A57 50c #386, II 8.00 *5.50*
*a.* Type I 12.00 7.00
**7N22** A57 $1 #387, I 45.00 *30.00*
*a.* Type II 40.00 *50.00*
**7N23** A57 $2 #388, II 29.00 29.00
*a.* Type I 32.50 *40.00*
**7N24** A57 $5 #389, I 50.00 50.00
*a.* Type II 100.00 100.00
**7N25** A57 $10 #390, I 80.00 80.00
*a.* Type II 90.00 90.00
**7N26** A57 $20 #391, II 100.00 *100.00*
*a.* Type I 100.00 *110.00*
*Nos. 7N17-7N26 (10)* 341.00 *309.75*

### On Stamps of 1940 with Secret Marks

**1941** **Wmk. 261** ***Perf. 14***
**7N27** A57 10c #394, II 9.00 8.00
**7N28** A57 30c #395, I 25.00 *25.00*
**7N29** A57 50c #396, I 18.00 *18.50*
*Nos. 7N27-7N29 (3)* 52.00 *51.50*

### On Stamps of 1940-41 (Martyrs) with Secret Marks
***Perf. 12½, 13 & Compound***

**1941** **Wmk. 261**
**7N30** A39 ½c #402, II 5.75 *6.50*
**7N31** A40 1c #403, I 7.00 7.00
*a.* Type II 6.00 6.00
**7N32** A46 2c #404, II 6.00 *6.50*
**7N33** A39 2½c #405, I 40.00 40.00
**7N34** A46 10c #410, I 32.50 32.50
**7N35** A45 13c #411, II 12.00 9.00
**7N36** A46 17c #413, II 9.00 9.00
*a.* Type I 100.00 100.00
**7N37** A40 25c #416, II 10.00 10.00
**7N38** A48 30c #418, I 25.00 15.00
**7N39** A47 40c #419, II 10.00 10.00
*a.* Type I 15.00 15.00
**7N40** A40 50c #420, I 100.00 100.00
*Nos. 7N30-7N40 (11)* 257.25 245.50

**Unwmk.**
**7N41** A39 ½c #421, II 6.00 *7.00*
*a.* Type I 9.00 8.50
**7N42** A40 1c #422, II 4.50 *5.00*
**7N43** A46 2c #423, I 14.50 *15.00*
**7N44** A48 3c #425, I 9.00 *10.00*
**7N45** A39 4c #426, II 11.00 *12.00*
**7N46** A46 10c #429, I 50.00 *55.00*
**7N47** A45 13c #430, I 9.00 *10.00*
**7N48** A48 15c #431, II 7.50 *8.00*
**7N49** A46 17c #432, II 8.00 *9.00*
*a.* Type I 12.00 12.00
**7N50** A47 20c #433, II 12.00 12.00
*a.* Type I 12.00 11.00
**7N51** A45 21c #434, II 12.00 12.00
**7N52** A40 25c #435, I 12.00 12.00
*a.* Type II 18.00 18.00
**7N53** A46 28c #436, II 6.75 *7.50*
*Nos. 7N41-7N53 (13)* 162.25 *174.50*

For overprints see Nos. 7N55, 7N59.

### Honan Singapore Overprint in Red

**1942**
**7N54** A37 4c #298, II 95.00 *110.00*
**7N55** A39 4c #7N45 7.50 *13.00*
**7N56** A57 8c #7N11a 40.00 *40.00*
**7N57** A57 8c #7N12 24.00 *20.00*
*Nos. 7N54-7N57 (4)* 166.50 *183.00*

### Honan Anniv. of Manchukuo Overprint in Red

**1942**
**7N58** A57 2c #7N8 17.00 *24.50*
**7N59** A39 4c #7N45 30.00 *17.00*
**7N60** A57 8c #7N11a 115.00 *130.00*
**7N61** A57 8c #7N12 100.00 *97.50*
*Nos. 7N58-7N61 (4)* 262.00 *269.00*

## North China

### For use in Honan, Hopei, Shansi, Shantung and Supeh (Northern Kiangsu)

Stamps of China, 1931-37 Surcharged North China (Hwa Pei) and Half of Original Value

**1942** **Unwmk.** ***Perf. 14, 12½***
**8N1** A40 ½c on 1c (#313) 2.00 *2.50*
**8N2** A37 1c on 2c (#297) .75 1.10
**8N3** A37 2c on 4c (#298) 1.50 1.25
**8N4** A45 4c on 8c (#316) 150.00 *150.00*

### Same Surcharge on Stamps of 1938-41
***Perf. 12½***

**8N5** A57 1c on 2c (#349) 5.00 *8.50*
**8N6** A57 1c on 2c (#368) .50 .30
**8N7** A57 4c on 8c (#353) 2.10 1.25
**8N8** A57 4c on 8c (#369) .60 .35
**8N9** A57 5c on 10c grn .65 .50
**8N10** A57 8c on 16c ol gray 2.00 .80
**8N11** A57 50c on $1 (#359) 8.00 8.00
**8N12** A57 50c on $1 (#344) 575.00 575.00
**8N13** A57 50c on $1 (#347) 110.00 110.00
**8N14** A57 $1 on $2 (#360) 12.50 12.50
**8N15** A57 $1 on $2 (#345) 40.00 32.50
**8N16** A57 $1 on $2 (#348) 155.00 155.00

No. 8N12 was issued without gum.
For overprint see No. 8N58.

### Same Surcharge on China Nos. 383-388, 390-391
***Perf. 14***

**8N17** A57 4c on 8c ol grn .80 .65
**8N18** A57 5c on 10c grn 1.25 2.00
**8N19** A57 15c on 30c scar 1.50 1.25
*a.* Inverted surcharge 80.00 80.00
**8N20** A57 25c on 50c dk bl 2.00 1.75
**8N21** A57 50c on $1 org brn & sep 4.50 4.50
**8N22** A57 $1 on $2 dp bl & yel brn 5.75 5.75
**8N23** A57 $5 on $10 dk grn & dl pur 50.00 50.00
**8N24** A57 $10 on $20 rose lake & dk bl 50.00 60.00
*Nos. 8N17-8N24 (8)* 115.80 125.90

For overprint see No. 8N55.

### Same Surcharge on China Nos. 394-396
**Wmk. 261**

**8N25** A57 5c on 10c grn 1.00 *1.50*
**8N26** A57 15c on 30c scar 3.50 *5.00*
**8N27** A57 25c on 50c dk bl 1.50 1.50
*Nos. 8N25-8N27 (3)* 6.00 *8.00*

### Same Surcharge on Stamps of 1940-41

**1942** **Wmk. 261** ***Perf. 12½, 13***
**8N28** A40 ½c on 1c org .30 *1.00*
**8N29** A46 1c on 2c dp bl 2.50 2.50
**8N30** A45 4c on 8c dp org 20.00 *24.50*
**8N31** A46 5c on 10c dl vio 3.00 *3.00*
**8N32** A48 15c on 30c brn car 9.75 9.75
**8N33** A47 20c on 40c org 5.75 2.50
**8N34** A40 25c on 50c grn 5.75 5.00
*Nos. 8N28-8N34 (7)* 47.05 48.25

**Unwmk.**
**8N35** A40 ½c on 1c org (#422) .30 .25
*a.* ½c on 1c org (#422a) 37.00 37.00

8N36 A46 1c on 2c dp bl 1.40 1.40
8N37 A39 2c on 4c pale vio 1.00 .85
8N38 A45 4c on 8c dp org 1.25 2.00
8N39 A46 5c on 10c dl vio 3.00 3.00
8N40 A47 10c on 20c lt bl 3.75 .75
8N41 A47 20c on 40c org 4.00 1.00
8N42 A40 25c on 50c grn 32.50 32.50
*Nos. 8N35-8N42 (8)* 47.20 41.75

**Same Surcharge on "New Peking" Prints**

***Perf. 14***

8N43 A37 1c on 2c ol grn .35 .25
8N44 A37 2c on 4c dl grn .90 .25
a. Inverted surcharge 42.50
8N45 A45 4c on 8c dp org .65 .25
8N46 A57 8c on 16c ol gray .35 .25
8N47 A47 10c on 20c red brn 1.75 1.50
8N48 A43 15c on 30c brn car .85 .85
8N49 A47 20c on 40c org 2.10 .50
a. Inverted surcharge 55.00
8N50 A40 25c on 50c grn 1.75 1.50
8N51 A57 50c on $1 org brn & sep 3.50 3.50
8N52 A57 $1 on $2 dp bl & org brn 5.75 3.50
8N53 A57 $5 on $10 dk grn & dl pur 30.00 24.50
*Nos. 8N43-8N53 (11)* 47.95 *36.85*

See note after No. 2N93. For overprints see #8N54, 8N56-8N57, 8N59.

Nos. 8N44, 8N17 and 8N46 with Additional Overprint in Red

**1943 Unwmk. *Perf. 14***

8N54 A37 2c on 4c dl grn .30 *3.00*
8N55 A57 4c on 8c ol grn 1.50 *5.00*
8N56 A57 8c on 16c ol gray 1.50 *8.00*
*Nos. 8N54-8N56 (3)* 3.30 *16.00*

Return of the Foreign Concessions to China.

Nos. 8N44, 8N8 and 8N46 with Additional Overprint in Red

**1943, Aug. 15 *Perf. 14, 12½***

8N57 A37 2c on 4c dl grn .55 *3.00*
8N58 A57 4c on 8c ol grn 1.00 *5.00*
8N59 A57 8c on 16c ol gray 2.00 *3.00*
*Nos. 8N57-8N59 (3)* 3.55 *11.00*

North China Postal Service, 5th anniv.

Stamps of China, 1934-41, Overprinted in Black

**1943, Nov. 1**

8N60 A40 1c org (#313) .85 1.00
8N61 A40 1c org (#422) .85 1.00
8N62 A57 10c grn (#354) .50 1.00
8N63 A57 $2 dp bl & yel brn (#388) 30.00 30.00
8N64 A57 $5 red & grnsh blk (#361) 24.00 24.00
8N65 A57 $5 red & sl grn (#389) 9.75 9.75
8N66 A57 $10 dk grn & dl pur (#390) 14.50 14.50
8N67 A57 $20 rose lake & dk bl (#391) 90.00 *110.00*
*Nos. 8N60-8N67 (8)* 170.45 *191.25*

**Same Overprint on "New Peking" Prints**

8N68 A40 1c orange .30 .25
8N69 A37 2c olive grn .30 *.75*
8N70 A37 4c dull green .30 *1.50*
8N71 A37 5c green .60 *.75*
8N72 A57 9c olive grn .35 *.60*
8N73 A46 10c dl violet .35 *.75*
8N74 A57 16c olive gray .30 *.45*
8N75 A57 18c olive gray .30 *.45*
8N76 A47 20c henna .50 *.60*
8N77 A48 30c brown car .45 .45
8N78 A47 40c brt orange .45 *.75*
a. Inverted overprint 42.50 42.50
8N79 A40 50c green 2.50 2.50
8N80 A57 $1 org brn & sep 4.25 1.25
8N81 A57 $2 bl & org brn 2.50 2.20
8N82 A57 $5 red & sl grn 5.00 *7.50*
8N83 A57 $10 dk grn & dl pur 9.00 9.00
8N84 A57 $20 rose lake & dk bl 10.00 *12.50*
*Nos. 8N68-8N84 (17)* 37.45 *42.25*

See note after No. 2N93. For overprints see Nos. 8N85-8N90, 8N95-8N106.

Nos. 8N70 and 8N62 with Additional Overprint in Red

**1944, Jan. 9**

8N85 A37 4c dull green .35 *2.00*
8N86 A57 10c green .35 *.75*

1st anniv. of the declaration of war against the Allies by North China.

Nos. 8N72, 8N75, 8N79 and 8N80 with Additional Overprint in Red

**1944, Mar. 30**

8N87 A57 9c olive green 1.00 *2.00*
8N88 A57 18c olive gray 6.00 *4.00*
8N89 A40 50c green 9.00 *7.50*
8N90 A57 $1 org brn & sepia 5.50 *3.00*
a. Red overprint inverted 37.00 37.00
*Nos. 8N87-8N90 (4)* 21.50 *16.50*

North China Political Council, 4th anniv.

**Shanghai-Nanking Nos. 9N101-9N104 Surcharged North China (Hwa Pei) and New Value in Red or Black**

a

b

c

d

**1944 *Perf. 12½x12, 12x12½***

8N91 OS1 (a) 9c on 50c org 2.00 8.00
8N92 OS1 (b) 18c on $1 grn (R) 2.00 10.00
a. Double surcharge 37.00 37.00
8N93 OS2 (c) 36c on $2 dp bl (R) 3.00 12.00
8N94 OS2 (d) 90c on $5 car rose 4.00 12.00
*Nos. 8N91-8N94 (4)* 11.00 42.00

Nos. 8N72, 8N75, 8N79 and 8N80 Overprinted in Red or Blue

**1944, Aug. 15**

8N95 A57 9c olive grn 4.00 *4.00*
8N96 A57 18c olive gray 3.00 *4.00*
8N97 A40 50c green 4.00 *5.00*
8N98 A57 $1 org brn & sep (Bl) 5.00 *8.00*
*Nos. 8N95-8N98 (4)* 16.00 *21.00*

6th anniv. of the General P.O. Dept. of North China.

North China Nos. 8N76, 8N79-8N81 Overprinted in Blue or Black

**1944, Dec. 5**

8N99 A47 20c henna (Bl) 3.00 *4.00*
8N100 A40 50c green (Bl) 3.00 *4.00*
8N101 A57 $1 org brn & sep (Bl) 5.75 *8.00*
8N102 A57 $2 bl & org brn 1.75 *3.00*
*Nos. 8N99-8N102 (4)* 13.50 *19.00*

Death of Wang Ching-wei, puppet ruler of China.

North China Nos. 8N76, 8N79-8N81 Overprinted in Red or Black

**1945**

8N103 A47 20c henna 3.00 *5.00*
8N104 A40 50c green (R) 9.00 *10.00*
8N105 A57 $1 org brn & sep 3.25 *4.00*
8N106 A57 $2 bl & org brn 5.75 *6.00*
*Nos. 8N103-8N106 (4)* 21.00 *25.00*

2nd anniv. of the declaration of war.

Shanghai-Nanking Nos. 9N105-9N106 Surcharged in Red

**1945 *Perf. 12x12½***

8N107 OS3 50c on $3 lt org .65 *8.00*
8N108 OS3 $1 on $6 blue .65 *8.00*

Return of the foreign concessions in Shanghai.

Dragon Pillar — OS1

Designs: $2, Long Bridge and White Pagoda. $5, Tower in Imperial City. $10, Marble Boat, Summer Palace.

**1945 Unwmk. Litho. *Perf. 14***

**Various Papers**

8N109 OS1 $1 dull yellow 1.50 *6.00*
8N110 OS1 $2 deep blue .30 *6.00*
8N111 OS1 $5 carmine 3.00 *6.00*
8N112 OS1 $10 dull green .50 *6.00*
*Nos. 8N109-8N112 (4)* 5.30 *24.00*

North China Political Council, 5th anniv.

Dr. Sun Yat-sen — OS2

**Various Papers**

**1945 Without Gum**

8N113 OS2 $1 bister .30 .25
8N114 OS2 $2 dark blue 1.10 .35
8N115 OS2 $5 fawn 2.50 2.50
8N116 OS2 $10 sage green 2.50 *3.00*
8N117 OS2 $20 dull violet 2.50 *3.00*
8N118 OS2 $50 brown 50.00 *60.00*
*Nos. 8N113-8N118 (6)* 58.90 *69.10*

Nos. 8N113-8N118 without "Hwa Pei" overprint are proofs.

Wutai Mountain, Shansi — OS3

Designs: $10, Kaifeng Iron Pagoda. $20, International Bridge, Tientsin. $30, Taishan Mountain, Shantung. $50, General Post Office, Peking.

**Various Papers**

**1945, Aug. 15 Without Gum**

8N119 OS3 $5 gray green .30 *6.00*
8N120 OS3 $10 dull brown .75 *6.00*
8N121 OS3 $20 dull purple .55 *6.00*
8N122 OS3 $30 slate blue 1.10 *6.00*
8N123 OS3 $50 carmine 3.25 10.00
*Nos. 8N119-8N123 (5)* 5.95 *34.00*

North China Postal Directorate, 7th anniv.

---

## SHANGHAI AND NANKING

**China Nos. 299-303 Surcharged**

a

b

**Surcharged Type "b"**

**1942-45 Unwmk. *Perf. 12½, 13½***

9N1 A37 $6 on 5c green .90 *1.25*
9N2 A37 $20 on 15c scar .45 *.90*
9N3 A37 $500 on 15c dk grn .30 *1.25*
9N4 A37 $1000 on 20c ultra 3.50 3.50
9N5 A37 $1000 on 25c ultra 3.50 3.50
*Nos. 9N1-9N5 (5)* 8.65 *10.40*

A $1000 on 20c ultramarine, No. 293, exists.

**Surcharged Type "a" (Nos. 9N6-9N10) or Type "b" (Nos. 9N11-9N40) on Type A57 Stamps of 1939-41**

***Perf. 12½***

9N6 25c on 5c (#352) 2.50 *4.00*
9N7 30c on 2c (#368) .25 *.30*
9N8 50c on 3c (#350) .30 *1.00*
9N9 50c on 5c (#352) .30 .30
9N10 50c on 8c (#353) 2.00 *1.00*
9N11 $1 on 8c (#353) .30 .25
9N12 $1 on 8c (#369) 14.50 14.50
9N13 $1 on 15c (#356) 7.00 .25
9N14 $1.30 on 16c (#357) .30 *1.00*
9N15 $1.50 on 3c (#350) .30 *1.00*
9N16 $2 on 5c (#352) 1.40 1.40
9N17 $2 on 10c (#354) .30 *.35*
9N18 $3 on 15c (#356) 1.00 *.35*
9N19 $4 on 16c (#357) .50 1.00
9N20 $5 on 15c (#356) .30 .30
9N21 $6 on 5c (#351) .75 *1.75*
a. Perf. 14 (#371) 62.50 62.50
9N22 $6 on 5c (#352) .30 *.45*
9N23 $6 on 8c (#353) .50 *1.25*
9N24 $6 on 8c (#369) *990.00 990.00*
9N25 $6 on 10c (#354) .30 .30
9N26 $10 on 10c (#354) .30 .35
9N27 $10 on 16c (#357) .60 .30
9N28 $20 on 3c (#350) .30 *1.00*
9N29 $20 on 15c (#355) 1.40 *3.00*
9N30 $20 on 15c (#356) .50 .50
9N31 $20 on $2 (#360) 3.00 *5.00*
9N32 $100 on 3c (#350) 1.00 .50
9N33 $500 on 8c (#353) 3.00 *5.50*
9N34 $500 on 8c (#369) 42.50 *57.50*
9N35 $500 on 10c (#354) 3.00 *4.25*
9N36 $500 on 15c (#355) 7.00 *3.00*
9N37 $500 on 15c (#356) 1.25 *2.50*
9N38 $500 on 16c (#357) 1.50 *5.00*
9N39 $1000 on 25c (#358) 1.50 *3.00*
9N40 $2000 on $5 (#361) 18.00 *35.00*
*Nos. 9N1-9N23,9N25-9N40 (39)* 126.60 *167.55*

**Nos. 381-391 (Type A57) Surcharged with Type "b"**

***Perf. 14***

9N41 $1 on 8c ol grn .30 *1.00*
9N42 $1.70 on 30c scar .35 *2.00*
a. Perf. 12½ 4.00 6.00
9N43 $2 on 5c ol grn .50 *2.00*
9N44 $2 on $1 org brn & sep 1.25 *3.00*
9N45 $3 on 8c ol grn .75 *.75*
a. $3 on 8c olive green (#383a) 42.50 42.50
b. "3" with flat top .50 .50
9N46 $6 on 5c grn .50 *.60*
9N47 $6 on 5c ol grn 1.00 *2.00*
9N48 $6 on 8c ol grn .45 *1.00*
9N49 $10 on 10c grn .50 *2.50*
a. Perf. 12½ 2.50 *7.50*
9N50 $20 on $2 dp bl & yel brn 2.00 *3.00*
9N51 $50 on 30c scar 2.00 *3.00*
9N52 $50 on 50c dk bl 1.00 *2.00*
9N53 $50 on $5 red & sl grn 2.00 3.00
9N54 $50 on $20 rose lake & dk bl 4.00 *6.00*
9N55 $100 on $10 dk grn & dl pur 4.00 *5.00*
9N56 $200 on $20 rose lake & dk bl 1.00 *2.00*
9N57 $500 on 8c ol grn 13.50 *16.00*
a. $500 on 8c ol grn (#383a) 30.50 30.00
9N58 $500 on 10c grn 3.00 *4.25*
9N59 $1000 on 30c scar 3.00 *4.00*
9N60 $1000 on 50c dk bl 3.00 *4.00*
9N61 $1000 on $2 dp bl & yel brn 5.00 *10.00*
9N62 $2000 on $5 red & sl grn 5.00 *5.00*

**China Nos. 392-395 and 399-401 (Type A57) Surcharged with Type "b"**

**1942-45 Wmk. 261 *Perf. 14***

9N63 $2 on $1 org brn & sep, perf. 12½ 8.00 *1.75*
9N64 $6 on 5c grn .50 *1.05*

**9N65** $6 on 5c ol grn 1.40 *2.00*
**9N66** $50 on $5 red & sl grn .85 *1.25*
*a.* Numeral tablet violet 1.00 *1.25*
**9N67** $100 on $10 dk grn & dl pur .50 *.75*
**9N68** $200 on $20 rose lake & dk bl .60 *.75*
**9N69** $500 on 10c grn 2.50 *3.00*
**9N70** $1000 on 30c scar 3.50 *4.00*
**9N71** $5000 on $10 dk grn & dl pur, perf. 12½ 8.00 *9.75*
*a.* Perf. 14 125.00 125.00
*Nos. 9N41-9N71 (31)* 79.95 *106.40*

Nos. 9N63 and 9N71 were not issued without surcharge. A $50 on 30c scarlet exists.

### Same Surch. on Stamps of 1940-41
***Perf. 12½, 13***
**Wmk. 261**

**9N72** A46 $30 on 2c dp bl 150.00 150.00

A $7.50 on ½c and a $15 on 1c are known.

**Unwmk.**

**9N73** A39 $7.50 on ½c ol blk 2.50 *3.00*
**9N74** A40 $15 on 1c org .35 *1.50*
*a.* Without secret mark 62.50 62.50
**9N75** A46 $30 on 2c dp bl 1.40 *2.00*
**9N76** A40 $200 on 1c org .30 *.35*
**9N77** A45 $200 on 8c dp org .85 *1.25*
*Nos. 9N73-9N77 (5)* 5.40 *8.10*

### Surcharged Type "a" (Nos. 9N78-9N81) or Type "b" (Nos. 9N82-9N96) on Type A59 Stamps of 1941
***Perf. 12***

**9N78** 5c on ½c sepia .30 *.35*
**9N79** 10c on 1c orange .30 *.35*
**9N80** 20c on 1c orange .30 *.50*
**9N81** 40c on 5c green .30 *.50*
**9N82** $5 on 5c grn .30 *.35*
**9N83** $10 on 10c brt grn .30 *.35*
**9N84** $50 on ½c sepia .30 *.35*
**9N85** $50 on 1c orange .45 *.50*
**9N86** $50 on 17c olive .45 *.60*
**9N87** $200 on 5c green .45 *.50*
**9N88** $200 on 8c turq grn .25 *.30*
**9N89** $200 on 8c red org .45 *.75*
**9N90** $500 on $5 scar & blk .50 *.50*
**9N91** $1000 on 1c orange .45 *.65*
**9N92** $1000 on 25c rose vio .50 *.65*
**9N93** $1000 on 30c scarlet 1.25 *.65*
**9N94** $1000 on $2 bl & blk 1.25 *1.25*
**9N95** $1000 on $10 grn & blk .50 *.65*
**9N96** $2000 on $5 scar & blk 1.25 *1.25*
*Nos. 9N78-9N96 (19)* 9.85 *11.00*

Stamps of China 1939-41 Surcharged in Red or Blue

**1943 Unwmk. *Perf. 12, 12½***

**9N97** A57 25c on 5c grn .30 *1.50*
**9N98** A59 50c on 8c red org (Bl) .30 *.90*
**9N99** A57 $1 on 16c ol gray .30 *1.75*
**9N100** A59 $2 on 50c dk bl .30 *.90*
*Nos. 9N97-9N100 (4)* 1.20 *5.05*

Return of the foreign concessions in Shanghai.

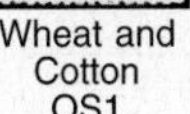

Wheat and Cotton OS1

Purple Mountain, Nanking OS2

***Perf. 12½x12, 12x12½***

**1944 Engr. Unwmk.**

**9N101** OS1 50c orange .90 *6.00*
**9N102** OS1 $1 green .90 *6.00*
**9N103** OS2 $2 deep blue .90 *6.00*
**9N104** OS2 $5 carmine rose .90 *6.00*
*Nos. 9N101-9N104 (4)* 3.60 *24.00*

Puppet government at Nanking, 4th anniv.
For surcharges see Nos. 8N91-8N94, 9N107-9N110.

Map of Foreign Concessions in Shanghai — OS3

**1944 *Perf. 12x12½***

**9N105** OS3 $3 lt orange *15.00 1.10*
**9N106** OS3 $6 blue *15.00 1.10*

1st anniversary of the return of the foreign concessions in Shanghai.
For surcharges see Nos. 8N107-8N108.

### Nos. 9N101-9N104 Surcharged in Black with Type "b"

**1945, Mar. 30**

**9N107** OS1 $15 on 50c orange .90 *1.10*
**9N108** OS1 $30 on $1 green .90 *1.10*
**9N109** OS2 $60 on $2 dp blue .90 *1.10*
**9N110** OS2 $200 on $5 car rose .90 *1.10*
*Nos. 9N107-9N110 (4)* 3.60 *4.40*

### China Nos. C31, C32, C36 and C38 Srchd. in Red, Green, Orange or Carmine

**1945 *Perf. 12½, 13***

**9N111** AP3 $150 on 15c (R) .45 *3.00*
**9N112** AP3 $250 on 25c (G) .45 *3.00*
**9N113** AP3 $600 on 60c (O) .45 *3.00*
**9N114** AP3 $1,000 on $1 (C) .45 *3.00*
*Nos. 9N111-9N114 (4)* 1.80 *12.00*

Issue as air raid precaution propaganda.

## AIR POST STAMPS

### China Nos. C35 and C38 Surcharged in Black

The surcharges on Nos. 9NC1-9NC7 were in Japanese currency because all air mail then was carried by Japanese planes.

The surcharges translate: (10c) "Airmail fee for postcard within the nation has been paid." (20c) "Airmail fee for letter within the nation has been paid."

**1941 Unwmk. *Perf. 12½***

**9NC1** AP3 10(s) on 50c brown .55 *1.00*
**9NC2** AP3 20(s) on $1 apple grn .90 *.90*

Two types of surcharge exist on No. 9NC1.

### Similar Surcharge on No. C28

**1941 Wmk. 261 *Perf. 13***

**9NC3** AP3 20(s) on $1 ap grn 18.00 18.00

### Nos. C37 and C39 Surcharged

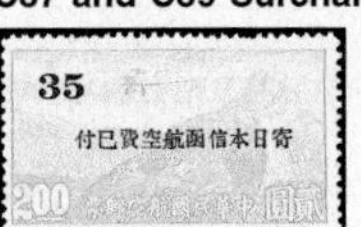

The surcharges translate: (18c and 25c) "Airmail fee for postcard to Japan has been paid." (35c) "Airmail fee for letter to Japan has been paid."

**1941 Unwmk. *Perf. 12½, 13***

**9NC4** AP3 18(s) on 90c lt olive .55 *6.00*
**9NC5** AP3 25(s) on 90c lt olive .45 *6.00*
**9NC6** AP3 35(s) on $2 lt brown .45 *6.00*
*Nos. 9NC4-9NC6 (3)* 1.45 *18.00*

### No. 9NC6 with Additional Surcharge in Red
***Perf. 12½***

**9NC7** AP3 60(s) on 35(s) on $2 .45 *6.00*

## POSTAGE DUE STAMPS

Postage Due Stamps of China 1932 Surcharged in Black

**1945 Unwmk. *Perf. 14***

**9NJ1** D5 $1 on 2c org .90 *10.00*
**9NJ2** D5 $2 on 5c org .90 *10.00*
**9NJ3** D5 $5 on 10c org .90 *10.00*
**9NJ4** D5 $10 on 20c org .90 *15.00*
*Nos. 9NJ1-9NJ4 (4)* 3.60 *45.00*

## Northeastern Provinces

With the end of World War II and the collapse of Manchukuo, the Northeastern Provinces reverted to China. In many Manchurian towns and cities, the Manchukuo stamps were locally handstamped in ideograms: "Republic of China," "China Postal Service" or "Temporary Use for China." A typical example is shown above.

Dr. Sun Yat-sen — A1

### Black Surcharge

**1946, Feb. Unwmk. Typo. *Perf. 14***

**1** A1 50c on $5 red .35 *2.00*
**2** A1 50c on $10 green .90 *3.00*
**3** A1 $1 on $10 green .35 *2.00*
**4** A1 $2 on $20 brown vio .35 *2.00*
**5** A1 $4 on $50 brown .35 *2.00*
*Nos. 1-5 (5)* 2.30 *11.00*

The two characters at left express the new value.

Stamps of China, 1938-41 Overprinted

**1946, Apr. *Perf. 12½, 13, 13½, 14***

**6** A40 1c org (#422) .35 *3.75*
**7** A48 3c dp yel brn (#425) .35 *4.75*
**8** A48 5c dl red org (#427) .35 *4.75*
**9** A57 10c grn (#354) .35 *3.75*
**10** A57 10c grn (#384) .35 *3.75*
**11** A47 20c lt bl (#433) .35 *3.75*
*a.* Horiz. pair, imperf. btwn 100.00
*Nos. 6-11 (6)* 2.10 *24.50*

Dr. Sun Yat-sen — A2

**1946, July Engr. *Perf. 14***
**Without Gum**

**12** A2 5c lake .35 *3.50*
**13** A2 10c orange .35 *3.50*
**14** A2 20c yel grn .35 *4.00*
**15** A2 25c blk brn .35 *3.50*
**16** A2 50c red org .35 *2.75*
**17** A2 $1 blue .35 *2.25*
**18** A2 $2 dk vio .35 *2.75*
**19** A2 $2.50 indigo .35 *3.50*
**20** A2 $3 brown .35 *2.75*
**21** A2 $4 org brn .35 *3.50*
**22** A2 $5 dk grn .35 *2.75*
**23** A2 $10 crimson .35 *1.75*
**24** A2 $20 olive .35 *1.40*
**25** A2 $50 blue vio .40 *1.00*
*Nos. 12-25 (14)* 4.95 *38.90*

Two types of $4, $10, $20 and $50: I- Character *kuo* directly left of sun emblem is open at upper and lower left corners of "box." Diagonal stroke from top center to lower right has no hook at bottom. II- Character is closed at left corners. Diagonal stroke has hook at bottom.

See Nos. 47-52, 61-63. For surcharges see Nos. M1, Taiwan 91-96, People's Republic of China 35-48, 3L37-3L52, 3L55-3L66, 3L71-3L75.

China Nos. 728-731 Surcharged in Black

**1946**

**26** A75 $2 on $20 green .35 *3.25*
**27** A75 $3 on $30 blue .35 *3.25*
**28** A75 $5 on $50 dark brown .35 *3.25*
**29** A75 $10 on $100 carmine .35 *3.25*
*Nos. 26-29 (4)* 1.40 *13.00*

Convening of Chinese National Assembly.

Type of China, 1946, with added inscriptions on both sides of head

**1947 Engr. *Perf. 11, 11½***

**30** A74 $2 carmine .65 *4.00*
**31** A74 $3 green 1.10 *4.00*
**32** A74 $5 vermilion 1.10 *4.00*
**33** A74 $10 yel grn 1.10 *4.00*
**34** A74 $20 yel org 1.40 *4.00*
**35** A74 $30 magenta 1.40 *4.00*
*Nos. 30-35 (6)* 6.75 *24.00*

60th birthday of Chiang Kai-shek.

Type of China, 1947, with additional inscription above value

**1947 Unwmk. Engr. *Perf. 14***

**36** A76 $2 deep green .65 *2.00*
**37** A76 $4 deep blue .65 *2.00*
**38** A76 $6 carmine .65 *2.00*
**39** A76 $10 lt brown .65 *2.00*
**40** A76 $20 deep claret .65 *2.00*
*Nos. 36-40 (5)* 3.25 *10.00*

First anniversary of return of Chinese National Government to Nanking.

China Nos. 644 to 646 and 634 Surcharged in Black

**1947 *Perf. 12½, 14***

**41** A73 $100 on $1000 rose lake 1.10 *4.25*
**42** A73 $300 on $3000 bl 1.10 *4.25*
**43** A73 $500 on $5000 dp grn & ver .55 *5.00*
**44** A37 $500 on $30 choc 1.00 *4.25*
*Nos. 41-44 (4)* 3.75 *17.75*

### Type of 1946

**1947 Engr. *Perf. 14***
**Without Gum**

**47** A2 $44 dk car rose *40.00 85.00*
**48** A2 $100 dp grn .35 *.70*
**49** A2 $200 rose brn .35 *1.40*
**50** A2 $300 bluish grn .35 *2.75*
**51** A2 $500 rose car .35 *.70*
**52** A2 $1000 dp orange .35 *.60*
*Nos. 47-52 (6)* *41.75 91.15*

For surcharges see note following No. 25.

Stamps and Types of 1946-47 Surcharged in Black or Red

**1948 Unwmk. *Perf. 14***

**53** A2 $1500 on 20c yel grn .90 *4.50*
**54** A2 $3000 on $1 blue .45 *5.00*
**55** A2 $4000 on 25c blk brn (R) .45 *4.00*
**56** A2 $8000 on 50c red org .45 *3.25*
**57** A2 $10,000 on 10c org .55 *3.25*
**58** A2 $50,000 on $109 dk grn (R) 1.00 *6.25*
**59** A2 $100,000 on $65 dl grn .90 *6.25*

**60** A2 $500,000 on $22 gray (R) 1.50 *6.25*
*Nos. 53-60 (8)* 6.20 *38.75*

### Type of 1946

**1947, Nov. 5** **Without Gum**

**61** A2 $22 gray 80.00 85.00
**62** A2 $65 dull green 80.00 100.00
**63** A2 $109 dark green 85.00 100.00
*Nos. 61-63 (3)* 245.00 285.00

For surcharges see note following No. 25.

## POSTAGE DUE STAMPS

D1

**1947** **Unwmk.** **Engr.** ***Perf. 14***
**Without Gum**

**J1** D1 10c dark blue .55 *7.75*
**J2** D1 20c dark blue .55 *7.75*
**J3** D1 50c dark blue .55 *5.75*
**J4** D1 $1 dark blue .30 *4.25*
**J5** D1 $2 dark blue .30 *5.50*
**J6** D1 $5 dark blue .30 *5.50*
*Nos. J1-J6 (6)* 2.55 *36.50*

Nos. J4-J6 are known on paper with the papermaker's watermark, "COSMOS BOND."

Nos. J1 to J3 Surcharged in Red

**1948**

**J7** D1 $10 on 10c dark blue .35 *9.00*
**J8** D1 $20 on 20c dark blue .35 *9.00*
**J9** D1 $50 on 50c dark blue .35 *9.00*
*Nos. J7-J9 (3)* 1.05 *27.00*

The surcharge reads "Changed to . . . dollars." Characters at the left express the new value and vary on each denomination.

## MILITARY STAMPS

No. 16 Surcharged in Black

**1947** **Unwmk.** ***Perf. 14***

**M1** A2 $44 on 50c red org 11.00 *40.00*

The surcharge reads: "Army Post. Temporarily for 44 dollars."

China No. M13 Overprinted in Black

**Thin Paper Without Gum**
***Perf. 12½***

**M2** M1 rose 2.75 *18.00*

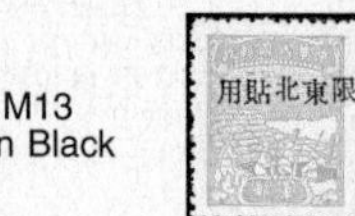

China No. M13 Overprinted in Black

**M3** M1 rose 62.50 *80.00*

## PARCEL POST STAMP

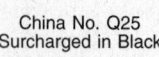

China No. Q25 Surcharged in Black

**1948** **Unwmk.** **Engr.** ***Perf. 13½***
**Without Gum**

**Q1** PP3 $500,000 on $5,000,000 lil 180.00

Used value is for CTO.

The use of this handstamp from Anhwei has not been verified.

## FUKIEN PROVINCE

Stamps of China, 1945-49, Surcharged

**1949** **Engr.** ***Perf. 14***
**Without Gum**

**1** A82 1c on $500 bl grn 10.00 *6.25*
**2** A82 1c on $7000 lt red brn 15.00 *22.50*
**3** A82 2c on $2,000,000 ver 5.00 *6.75*
**4** A82 2½c on $50,000 dp bl 35.00 35.00
**5** A73 4c on $100 dk car 4.50 4.50
**6** A73 10c on $200 ol grn 7.25 9.00
**7** A82 10c on $3000 bl 5.50 *4.50*
**8** A82 10c on $4000 gray 7.25 *10.75*
**9** A82 10c on $6000 rose lil 4.50 *6.25*
**10** A82 10c on $100,000 dl grn 5.75 *6.75*
**11** A82 10c on $1,000,000 cl 5.75 *6.25*
**12** A82 40c on $200,000 brn vio 9.00 *10.00*
*Nos. 1-12 (12)* 114.50 128.50

The surcharge on No. 2 is handstamped and in slightly larger characters.
Issue dates: No. 2, May 10; others, June.

China Nos. 973, 975-978 Overprinted

**1949, June** **Litho.** ***Perf. 12½, 13***

**13** A94 1c apple grn 18.00 5.50
**14** A94 4c blue green 5.50 2.00
**15** A94 10c deep lilac 55.00 27.50
**16** A94 16c orange red 11.00 *27.50*
**17** A94 20c blue 55.00 27.50
*Nos. 13-17 (5)* 144.50 90.00

### Same Overprint on China No. 959

**1949, July** **Litho.** ***Perf. 12½***

**18** A96 orange 72.50 72.50

### Same Overprint on Fukien Nos. 1, 3-4, 8, 11 in Black or Red

**1949, June** **Engr.** ***Perf. 14***

**19** A82 1c on $500 bl grn 150.00 150.00
**20** A82 2c on $2,000,000 ver 55.00 55.00
**21** A82 2½c on $50,000 dp bl 90.00 90.00
**22** A82 10c on $4000 gray 37.50 37.50
**23** A82 10c on $1,000,000 cl 145.00 145.00
*Nos. 19-23 (5)* 477.50 477.50

## AIR POST STAMP

### China #C62 Overprinted as #13-17

**1949, July** **Litho.** ***Perf. 12½***

**C1** AP5 blue green 72.50 37.50

## SPECIAL DELIVERY STAMP

### China #E12 Overprinted as #13-17

**1949, July** **Litho.** ***Perf. 12½***

**E1** SD2 red violet 50.00 35.00

## REGISTRATION STAMP

### China #F2 Overprinted as #13-17

**1949, July** **Litho.** ***Perf. 12½***

**F1** R2 carmine 50.00 35.00

## HUNAN PROVINCE

China No. 640 Surcharged

**1949, May** **Engr.** ***Perf. 14***

**1** A73 on $100 dk car 14.50 8.50

The first printing of surcharge on No. 1 is in smaller characters.

China Nos. 797, 788, 750, 747 Surcharged

**1949, May** **Engr.** ***Perf. 14***

**2** A82 1c on $2,000,000 ver 27.50 27.50
**3** A82 2c on $20,000 rose pink 27.50 27.50
**4** A82 5c on $3000 blue 35.00 *40.00*
**5** A82 10c on $500 blue grn 30.00 27.50
*Nos. 2-5 (4)* 120.00 122.50

## AIR POST STAMP

China No. 790 Surcharged

**1949, May** **Engr.** ***Perf. 14***

**C1** A82 On $40,000 green 22.50 *24.00*

## SPECIAL DELIVERY STAMP

### China No. 637 Surcharged as No. F1 in Red

**1949, May** **Engr.** ***Perf. 14***

**E1** A73 On $30 dark blue 27.50 27.50

## REGISTRATION STAMP

China No. 754 Surcharged

**1949, May** **Engr.** ***Perf. 14***

**F1** A82 On $7000 lt red brn 27.50 27.50

## HUPEH PROVINCE

China Type A95 Surcharged

**1949, May** **Litho.**

**1** A95 1c on $20 red brn 67.50 67.50
**2** A95 10c on $20 red brn 67.50 67.50

## KANSU PROVINCE

China No. 959 Handstamped in Purple

**1949, Aug.** **Litho.** ***Perf. 12½***

**1** A96 orange *1,100.*

## AIR POST STAMP

### Same Handstamp Overprinted on China No. C62 in Red

**1949, Aug.** **Litho.** ***Perf. 12½***

**C1** AP5 blue green *1,100.*

Counterfeits exist.

## KIANGSI PROVINCE

China Nos. 789-791 Surcharged

**1949** **Engr.** ***Perf. 14***

**1** A82 On $30,000 choc 57.50 55.00
**2** A82 On $40,000 green 57.50 55.00
**3** A82 On $50,000 dp bl 57.50 55.00
*Nos. 1-3 (3)* 172.50 165.00

## AIR POST STAMP

### Similar Surcharge on China No. 754

**1949** **Engr.** ***Perf. 14***

**C1** A82 On $7000 lt red brn 62.50 62.50

Third and fourth characters in right column of surcharge read "Air Mail" in Chinese on No. C1, "Registered" on Nos. F1-F2.

## SPECIAL DELIVERY STAMP

### Similar Surcharge on China No. 750

**1949** **Engr.** ***Perf. 14***

**E1** A82 On $3000 blue 67.50 45.00

See note below No. C1.

## REGISTRATION STAMPS

### Similar Surcharge on China Nos. 747 and 754

**1949** **Engr.** ***Perf. 14***

**F1** A82 On $500 bl grn 67.50 45.00
**F2** A82 On $7000 lt red brn 67.50 55.00

## KWANGSI PROVINCE

China Nos. 811 and 818 Also Surcharged in Red

**1949, May 21** **Typo.**

6 A62 5c on $20,000 on 10c dp grn 30.00 30.00
7 A62 5c on $40,000 on 20c dk ol grn 67.50 67.50

**China Stamps of 1946-48 Surcharged in Black or Red**

a

b

**1949** **Engr.** ***Perf. 14***

**Type "a" Surcharge**

8 A82 ½c on $500,000 lil rose 40.00 27.50
9 A82 1c on $200,000 brn vio 35.00 12.00
10 A82 2c on $300,000 yel grn 120.00 72.50
11 A73 5c on $3000 blue 35.00 20.00
12 A82 5c on $3000 blue 18.00 11.00
13 A82 5c on $40,000 grn 35.00 20.00

**Type "b" Surcharge**

14 A82 13c on $50,000 dp bl (R) 25.00 16.00
15 A82 13c on $50,000 dp bl 100.00 25.00
16 A82 17c on $7000 lt red brn 27.50 27.50
17 A82 21c on $100,000 dl grn 32.50 29.00
*Nos. 8-17 (10)* 468.00 260.50

**SHENSI PROVINCE**

China Nos. 747, 750 Surcharged

**1949, May** **Engr.** ***Perf. 14***

1 A82 On $500 bl grn 45.00 45.00
2 A82 On $3000 blue 45.00 45.00

**AIR POST STAMP**

**Similar Surcharge on China No. 754**

**1949, May** **Engr.** ***Perf. 14***

C1 A82 On $7000 lt red brn 55.00 55.00

**SPECIAL DELIVERY STAMP**

**Similar Surcharge on China No. 746 in Red**

**1949, May** **Engr.** ***Perf. 14***

E1 A82 On $250 dp lil 62.50 62.50

**REGISTRATION STAMPS**

**Similar Surcharge on China Nos. 626, 637 in Red**

**1949, May** **Typo.** ***Perf. 12***

F1 A72 on $30 dp bl 62.50 62.50
F2 A73 on $30 dk bl 55.00 55.00

**SZECHWAN PROVINCE**

Re-engraved Issue of China, 1923, Overprinted

**1933** **Unwmk.** ***Perf. 14***

1 A29 1c orange 11.00 1.00
2 A29 5c claret 11.00 1.40
3 A30 50c deep green 32.50 6.75
*Nos. 1-3 (3)* 54.50 9.15

The overprint reads "For use in Szechwan Province exclusively."

**Same on Sun Yat-sen Issue of 1931-37**
**Type II**

**1933-34** ***Perf. 12½***

4 A37 2c olive grn 2.00 1.00
5 A37 5c green 22.50 2.40
6 A37 15c dk green 7.75 3.50
7 A37 15c scar ('34) 9.00 12.00
8 A37 25c ultra 7.50 1.75
9 A37 $1 org brn & dk brn 22.50 4.00
10 A37 $2 bl & org brn 55.00 6.75
11 A37 $5 dl red & blk 125.00 37.50
*Nos. 4-11 (8)* 251.25 68.90

**Same on Martyrs Issue of 1932-34**

**1933** ***Perf. 14***

12 A39 ½c black brn .80 .80
13 A40 1c orange 1.25 .55
14 A39 2½c rose lilac 3.50 3.75
15 A48 3c deep brown 3.00 3.00
16 A45 8c brown org 1.75 1.50
17 A46 10c dull violet 4.50 .55
18 A45 13c blue green 5.00 1.00
19 A46 17c brown olive 5.50 1.40
20 A47 20c brown red 8.50 1.00
21 A48 30c brown violet 6.75 1.00
22 A47 40c orange 18.00 1.40
23 A40 50c green 37.50 2.10
*Nos. 12-23 (12)* 96.05 18.05

Stamps of China, 1947-48, Surcharged

**1949** **Engr.** ***Perf. 14***

24 A82 on $150 dk bl 72.50 55.00
25 A82 on $250 dp lil 72.50 55.00
26 A82 on $500 bl grn 21.00 12.50
27 A82 on $1000 red 55.00 42.50
28 A82 on $2000 ver 21.00 9.50
29 A82 on $3000 blue 21.00 9.50
30 A82 on $4000 gray 21.00 9.50
31 A82 on $5000 dk brn 62.50 *62.50*
32 A82 on $6000 rose lil 21.00 21.00
33 A82 on $7000 lt red brn 55.00 45.00
34 A82 on $10,000 dk bl & car 30.50 16.00
35 A82 on $20,000 rose pink 22.50 16.00
36 A82 on $30,000 choc 29.00 22.50
37 A82 on $50,000 grn & dk bl 29.00 25.00
38 A82 on $50,000 dp bl 29.00 22.50
39 A82 on $100,000 dl yel & ol 29.00 22.50
40 A82 on $100,000 dl grn 29.00 25.00
41 A82 on $200,000 vio brn & dp bl 29.00 22.50
42 A82 on $200,000 brn vio 29.00 22.50
43 A82 on $300,000 sep & org brn 40.00 27.50
44 A82 on $300,000 yel grn 55.00 40.00
45 A82 on $500,000 dk Prus grn & sep 29.00 22.50
46 A82 on $1,000,000 claret 55.00 40.00
47 A82 on $2,000,000 ver 29.00 27.50
48 A82 on $3,000,000 ol bis 29.00 27.50
49 A82 on $5,000,000 ultra 110.00 67.50
*Nos. 24-49 (26)* 1,026. 769.00

Several of Nos. 24-49 exist with inverted surcharge and a few with bottom character of left row repeated in right row, same position.

Counterfeits exist.

China No. 737 Surcharged in Black

**1949** ***Perf. 12½***

50 A77 2c on $500 ol grn 40.00 *55.00*

China No. 975 Handstamp Surcharged in Purple

**1949** **Litho.**

51 A94 2½c on 4c bl grn 55.00 *40.00*

**AIR POST STAMPS**

**China Nos. C55-C58, C60-C61 Surcharged**

***Perf. 12½, 13x12½, 14***

**1949, July** **Unwmk.**

C1 AP3 On $10,000 on 30c 9.00 15.00
*a.* On #C54 500.00
C2 AP4 On $10,000 on $27 14.50 *20.00*
*a.* Second surcharge inverted 250.00
*b.* On #C53 125.00
C3 AP3 On $20,000 on 25c 14.50 *20.00*
C4 AP3 On $30,000 on 90c 16.00 *27.50*
C5 AP3 On $50,000 on 60c 125.00 *155.00*
C6 AP3 On $50,000 on $1 17.00 *30.00*
*Nos. C1-C6 (6)* 196.00 *267.50*

**REGISTRATION STAMPS**

Stamps of China, 1944-47, Surcharged

**Engraved; Typographed (A72)**

**1949** ***Perf. 12, 13, 14***

F1 A64 On $100 yel brn 77.50
F2 A72 On $100 dk brn 77.50
F3 A64 On $200 dk grn 155.00
F4 A72 On $200 brn vio 72.50
F5 A73 On $200 ol grn 77.50
F6 A73 On $500 brt bl grn 155.00
F7 A73 On $700 red brn 275.00
F8 A73 On $5000 dp grn & ver 120.00
*Nos. F1-F8 (8)* 1,010.

**PARCEL POST STAMP**

China No. Q10 Surcharged

**1949** **Engr.** ***Perf. 12½***

Q1 PP2 1c on $20,000 dk red — —

**TSINGTAU PROVINCE**

China Nos. 890, 903, 900, 894 Handstamp Surcharged in Purple (#1-2), Blue (#3) or Red (#4)

**Engraved; Lithographed**

**1949, May** ***Perf. 14, 12½***

1 A94 1c on $100 org brn 100.00 90.00
2 A94 4c on $5000 lt bl 100.00 90.00
3 A94 6c on $500 rose lil 100.00 90.00
4 A94 10c on $1000 bl 100.00 90.00
*Nos. 1-4 (4)* 400.00 360.00

**YUNNAN PROVINCE**

Stamps of China, 1923-26, Overprinted

The overprint reads "For exclusive use in the Province of Yunnan." It was applied to prevent stamps being purchased in the depreciated currency of Yunnan and used elsewhere.

**1926** **Unwmk.** ***Perf. 14***

1 A29 ½c blk brn 1.10 .35
2 A29 1c orange 1.75 .35
3 A29 1½c violet 3.75 4.25
4 A29 2c yellow grn 2.75 .50
5 A29 3c blue green 2.75 .35
6 A29 4c olive grn 3.50 .50
7 A29 5c claret 3.50 .50
8 A29 6c red 5.25 1.25
9 A29 7c violet 5.50 1.90
10 A29 8c brown org 4.75 1.40
11 A29 10c dark blue 3.00 .30
12 A30 13c brown 3.00 1.90
13 A30 15c dark blue 3.00 1.90
14 A30 16c olive grn 3.50 1.90
15 A30 20c brown red 8.50 3.25
16 A30 30c brown vio 8.00 5.75
17 A30 50c deep green 8.00 5.75
18 A31 $1 org brn & sep 20.50 14.00
19 A31 $2 blue & red brn 35.00 14.00
20 A31 $5 red & slate 240.00 260.00
*Nos. 1-20 (20)* 367.10 320.10

Unification Issue of China, 1929, Overprinted in Red

**1929** ***Perf. 14***

21 A35 1c brown org 2.25 2.25
22 A35 4c olive grn 3.75 *5.75*
23 A35 10c dark blue 12.00 15.00
24 A35 $1 dark red 120.00 130.00
*Nos. 21-24 (4)* 138.00 153.00

**Similar Overprint in Black on Sun Yat-sen Mausoleum Issue**
**Characters 15½-16mm apart**

25 A36 1c brown orange 2.25 2.00
26 A36 4c olive green 2.25 *3.75*
27 A36 10c dark blue 9.00 *20.00*
28 A36 $1 dark red 77.50 *95.00*
*Nos. 25-28 (4)* 91.00 *120.75*

London Print Issue of China, 1931-37, Overprinted

**1932-34** **Unwmk.** ***Perf. 12½***

**Type I (double circle)**

29 A37 1c orange 4.00 2.75
30 A37 2c olive grn 5.00 *5.50*
31 A37 4c green 3.25 *5.50*
32 A37 20c ultra 3.25 *3.00*
33 A37 $1 org brn & dk brn 50.00 *55.00*
34 A37 $2 bl & org brn 82.50 *85.00*
35 A37 $5 dl red & blk 250.00 *295.00*
*Nos. 29-35 (7)* 398.00 *451.75*

**Type II (single circle)**

36 A37 2c olive grn 26.00 26.00
37 A37 4c green 17.00 10.75
38 A37 5c green 15.00 10.00
39 A37 15c dk green 8.00 *8.75*
40 A37 15c scar ('34) 8.00 *10.00*
41 A37 25c ultra 11.00 *11.50*
42 A37 $1 org brn & dk brn 67.50 67.50
43 A37 $2 bl & org brn 125.00 125.00
44 A37 $5 dl red & blk 260.00 260.00
*Nos. 36-44 (9)* 537.50 529.50

Nos. 36-39, 41-44 were overprinted in London as well as in Peking. The London overprints are 11mm in length; the Peking overprints are 12mm in length. There are other minor differences. Value of London overprints is significantly more than the Peking overprints, which are valued above.

Tan Yuan-chang Issue of China, 1933, Overprinted

**1933** *Perf. 14*

| No. | Type | Value | Color | Unused | Used |
|---|---|---|---|---|---|
| 45 | A49 | 2c | olive green | 1.75 | 1.75 |
| 46 | A49 | 5c | green | 3.00 | 2.40 |
| 47 | A49 | 25c | ultra | 5.25 | *7.00* |
| 48 | A49 | $1 | red | 80.00 | *105.00* |
| | | | *Nos. 45-48 (4)* | 90.00 | *116.15* |

Martyrs Issue of China, 1932-34, Overprinted

**1933**

| No. | Type | Value | Color | Unused | Used |
|---|---|---|---|---|---|
| 49 | A39 | ½c | blk brown | 1.75 | 1.60 |
| 50 | A40 | 1c | orange | 3.50 | 2.75 |
| 51 | A39 | 2½c | rose lilac | 4.00 | 4.50 |
| 52 | A48 | 3c | deep brown | 6.25 | 2.25 |
| 53 | A45 | 8c | brown org | 2.75 | 2.75 |
| 54 | A46 | 10c | dull vio | 4.00 | 4.50 |
| 55 | A45 | 13c | blue grn | 2.50 | 1.10 |
| 56 | A46 | 17c | brn olive | 12.50 | 12.50 |
| 57 | A47 | 20c | brown red | 3.25 | 3.25 |
| 58 | A48 | 30c | brown vio | 10.00 | 10.00 |
| 59 | A47 | 40c | orange | 55.00 | 70.00 |
| 60 | A40 | 50c | green | 55.00 | 70.00 |
| | | | *Nos. 49-60 (12)* | 160.50 | 185.20 |

China No. 324 was overprinted with characters arranged vertically, like Sinkiang No. 114, but was not issued.

China Stamps of 1945-49 Surcharged in Black or Blue

### Engraved; Lithographed; Typographed

**1949** *Perf. 12, 12½, 14*

| No. | Type | Value | Color | Unused | Used |
|---|---|---|---|---|---|
| 61 | A82 | 1c | on $200,000 brn vio | *25.00* | *35.00* |
| 62 | A82 | 1.2c | on $40,000 grn | *25.00* | *35.00* |
| 63 | A94 | 6c | on $200 red org | *25.00* | *35.00* |
| 64 | A94 | 10c | on $20,000 org | *25.00* | *35.00* |
| 65 | A94 | 12c | on $50 dk Prus grn (Bl) | *25.00* | *35.00* |
| 66 | A72 | 12c | on $50 grnsh gray (Bl) | *25.00* | *35.00* |
| 67 | A72 | 12c | on $200 brn vio (Bl) | *25.00* | *35.00* |
| 68 | A94 | 30c | on $20 vio brn | *25.00* | *35.00* |
| 69 | A82 | $1.20 | on $100,000 dl grn | *40.00* | *50.00* |
| | | | *Nos. 61-69 (9)* | *240.00* | *330.00* |

China No. 888 and 630 Surcharged

**1949** **Engr.** *Perf. 14*

| No. | Type | Value | Color | Unused | Used |
|---|---|---|---|---|---|
| 70 | A94 | 4c | on $20 vio brn | 360.00 | 225.00 |

**Typo.** *Perf. 12*

| No. | Type | Value | Color | Unused | Used |
|---|---|---|---|---|---|
| 71 | A72 | 12c | on $200 brn vio | 310.00 | 200.00 |

## MANCHURIA

### Kirin and Heilungkiang Issue

Stamps of China, 1923-26, Overprinted

The overprint reads: "For use in Ki-Hei District" the two names being abbreviated.

The intention of the overprint was to prevent the purchase of stamps in Manchuria, where the currency was depreciated, and their resale elsewhere.

**1927** **Unwmk.** *Perf. 14*

| No. | Type | Value | Color | Unused | Used |
|---|---|---|---|---|---|
| 1 | A29 | ½c | black brn | 1.90 | .35 |
| 2 | A29 | 1c | orange | 1.90 | .35 |
| 3 | A29 | 1½c | violet | 2.50 | 1.90 |
| 4 | A29 | 2c | yellow grn | 2.50 | 1.90 |
| 5 | A29 | 3c | blue grn | 1.75 | .75 |
| 6 | A29 | 4c | olive grn | .85 | .35 |
| 7 | A29 | 5c | claret | 1.75 | .35 |
| 8 | A29 | 6c | red | 2.50 | 1.90 |
| 9 | A29 | 7c | violet | 5.25 | 1.90 |
| 10 | A29 | 8c | brown org | 3.50 | 1.90 |
| 11 | A29 | 10c | dk blue | 1.90 | .50 |
| 12 | A30 | 13c | brown | 4.00 | 3.00 |
| 13 | A30 | 15c | dk blue | 4.00 | 3.00 |
| 14 | A30 | 16c | olive grn | 4.00 | 2.75 |
| 15 | A30 | 20c | brown red | 6.00 | 3.50 |
| 16 | A30 | 30c | brown vio | 8.75 | 3.50 |
| 17 | A30 | 50c | dp green | 12.00 | 4.25 |
| 18 | A31 | $1 | org brn & sep | 26.00 | 8.75 |
| 19 | A31 | $2 | bl & red brn | 70.00 | 19.00 |
| 20 | A31 | $5 | red & slate | 325.00 | 325.00 |
| | | | *Nos. 1-20 (20)* | 486.05 | 384.90 |

Several values of this issue exist with inverted overprint, double overprint and in pairs with one overprint omitted. These "errors" were not regularly issued. Forgeries also exist.

Chang Tso-lin Stamps of 1928 Overprinted in Red or Blue

**1928** *Perf. 14*

| No. | Type | Value | Color | Unused | Used |
|---|---|---|---|---|---|
| 21 | A34 | 1c | brown org (R) | 2.75 | 1.75 |
| 22 | A34 | 4c | olive grn (R) | 1.75 | 1.75 |
| 23 | A34 | 10c | dull blue (R) | 5.00 | 3.75 |
| 24 | A34 | $1 | red (Bl) | 50.00 | 45.00 |
| | | | *Nos. 21-24 (4)* | 59.50 | 52.25 |

### Unification Issue of China, 1929, Overprinted in Red as in 1928

**1929**

| No. | Type | Value | Color | Unused | Used |
|---|---|---|---|---|---|
| 25 | A35 | 1c | brown orange | 2.00 | 2.00 |
| 26 | A35 | 4c | olive green | 3.75 | 3.25 |
| 27 | A35 | 10c | dark blue | 13.00 | 12.50 |
| 28 | A35 | $1 | dark red | 110.00 | *100.00* |
| | | | *Nos. 25-28 (4)* | 128.75 | *117.75* |

### Similar Overprint in Black on Sun Yat-sen Mausoleum Issue of China Characters 15-16mm apart

**1929** *Perf. 14*

| No. | Type | Value | Color | Unused | Used |
|---|---|---|---|---|---|
| 29 | A36 | 1c | brown orange | 2.25 | *2.50* |
| 30 | A36 | 4c | olive green | 2.75 | *3.00* |
| 31 | A36 | 10c | dark blue | 8.50 | 10.00 |
| 32 | A36 | $1 | dark red | 85.00 | 85.00 |
| | | | *Nos. 29-32 (4)* | 98.50 | 100.50 |

## SINKIANG

Stamps of China, 1913-19, Overprinted in Black or Red

The first character of overprint is ½mm out of alignment, to the left, and the overprint measures 16mm.

**1915** **Unwmk.** *Perf. 14*

| No. | Type | Value | Color | Unused | Used |
|---|---|---|---|---|---|
| 1 | A24 | ½c | black brn | 1.75 | .95 |
| 2 | A24 | 1c | orange | 1.75 | .70 |
| 3 | A24 | 2c | yellow grn | 2.40 | 1.25 |
| 4 | A24 | 3c | slate grn | 2.40 | .65 |
| 5 | A24 | 4c | scarlet | 4.75 | 1.10 |
| 6 | A24 | 5c | rose lilac | 3.50 | .95 |
| 7 | A24 | 6c | gray | 6.50 | 2.75 |
| 8 | A24 | 7c | violet | 12.00 | *8.50* |
| 9 | A24 | 8c | brown orange | 8.00 | 5.50 |
| 10 | A24 | 10c | dark blue | 5.50 | 2.75 |
| 11 | A25 | 15c | brown | 6.50 | 3.50 |
| 12 | A25 | 16c | olive grn | 13.00 | 9.25 |
| 13 | A25 | 20c | brown red | 13.00 | 7.25 |
| 14 | A25 | 30c | brown violet | 14.50 | 11.00 |
| 15 | A25 | 50c | deep green | 40.00 | 18.50 |
| 16 | A26 | $1 | ocher & blk (R) | 145.00 | 62.50 |
| *a.* | | | Second & third characters of overprint transposed | *70,000.* | |
| | | | *Nos. 1-16 (16)* | 280.55 | 137.10 |

Stamps of China, 1913-19, Overprinted in Black or Red

The five characters of overprint are correctly aligned and measure 15½mm.

**1916-19**

| No. | Type | Value | Color | Unused | Used |
|---|---|---|---|---|---|
| 17 | A24 | ½c | black brn | 2.00 | 2.40 |
| 18 | A24 | 1c | orange | 3.25 | 1.75 |
| 19 | A24 | 1½c | violet | 4.50 | 4.00 |
| 20 | A24 | 2c | yellow grn | 3.25 | 1.75 |
| 21 | A24 | 3c | slate grn | 5.50 | .70 |
| 22 | A24 | 4c | scarlet | 5.50 | 1.25 |
| 23 | A24 | 5c | rose lilac | 5.50 | .90 |
| 24 | A24 | 6c | gray | 8.00 | 1.25 |
| 25 | A24 | 7c | violet | 8.00 | *11.00* |
| 26 | A24 | 8c | brown org | 8.75 | 8.50 |
| 27 | A24 | 10c | dark blue | 8.75 | 1.25 |
| 28 | A25 | 13c | brown | 4.75 | *8.00* |
| 29 | A25 | 15c | brown | 6.00 | *8.50* |
| 30 | A25 | 16c | olive grn | 5.50 | 4.00 |
| 31 | A25 | 20c | brown red | 4.50 | 3.00 |
| 32 | A25 | 30c | brown vio | 6.75 | 6.00 |
| 33 | A25 | 50c | deep green | 9.25 | 5.50 |
| 34 | A26 | $1 | ocher & blk (R) | 29.00 | 11.00 |
| 35 | A26 | $2 | dk bl & blk (R) | 27.50 | 12.00 |
| 36 | A26 | $5 | scar & blk (R) | 110.00 | 37.50 |
| 37 | A26 | $10 | yel grn & blk (R) | 275.00 | 175.00 |
| 38 | A26 | $20 | yel & blk (R) | 1,435. | 875.00 |
| | | | *Nos. 17-38 (22)* | 1,976. | 1,180. |

For overprint see No. C4.

China Nos. 243-246 Overprinted

**1921** *Perf. 14*

| No. | Type | Value | Color | Unused | Used |
|---|---|---|---|---|---|
| 39 | A27 | 1c | orange | 1.75 | 1.75 |
| 40 | A27 | 3c | blue green | 3.50 | 3.50 |
| 41 | A27 | 6c | gray | 13.50 | 13.50 |
| 42 | A27 | 10c | blue | 80.00 | 80.00 |
| | | | *Nos. 39-42 (4)* | 98.75 | 98.75 |

Constitution Issue of China, 1923, Overprinted

**1923**

| No. | Type | Value | Color | Unused | Used |
|---|---|---|---|---|---|
| 43 | A32 | 1c | orange | 1.55 | 1.55 |
| 44 | A32 | 3c | blue green | 6.50 | 6.50 |
| 45 | A32 | 4c | red | 9.75 | 9.75 |
| 46 | A32 | 10c | blue | 27.50 | 27.50 |
| | | | *Nos. 43-46 (4)* | 45.30 | 45.30 |

### Stamps of China, 1923-26, Overprinted as in 1916-19, in Black or Red

**1924**

### Re-engraved

| No. | Type | Value | Color | Unused | Used |
|---|---|---|---|---|---|
| 47 | A29 | ½c | black brn | 1.50 | *3.00* |
| 48 | A29 | 1c | orange | 1.50 | 1.25 |
| 49 | A29 | 1½c | violet | 2.75 | *5.00* |
| 50 | A29 | 2c | yellow grn | 4.25 | 1.40 |
| 51 | A29 | 3c | blue grn | 4.25 | 1.25 |
| 52 | A29 | 4c | gray | 4.25 | *6.75* |
| 53 | A29 | 5c | claret | 1.40 | 3.00 |
| 54 | A29 | 6c | red | 7.50 | 10.00 |
| 55 | A29 | 7c | violet | 8.50 | 7.50 |
| 56 | A29 | 8c | org brn | 17.00 | *15.00* |
| 57 | A29 | 10c | dark blue | 6.75 | 1.90 |
| 58 | A30 | 13c | red brown | 6.00 | *8.50* |
| 59 | A30 | 15c | deep blue | 8.75 | 6.75 |
| 60 | A30 | 16c | olive grn | 10.00 | 9.75 |
| 61 | A30 | 20c | brown red | 8.50 | 6.25 |
| 62 | A30 | 30c | brown vio | 9.75 | 6.75 |
| 63 | A30 | 50c | deep green | 10.00 | 6.75 |
| 64 | A31 | $1 | org brn & sep (R) | 18.00 | 8.50 |
| 65 | A31 | $2 | bl & red brn (R) | 40.00 | 12.00 |
| 66 | A31 | $5 | red & slate (R) | 95.00 | 19.00 |
| 67 | A31 | $10 | grn & claret (R) | 350.00 | 170.00 |
| 68 | A31 | $20 | plum & bl (R) | 425.00 | 325.00 |
| | | | *Nos. 47-68 (22)* | 1,041. | 635.30 |

See #69, 114. For overprints see #C1-C3.

### Same Overprint on China No. 275

**1926**

| No. | Type | Value | Color | Unused | Used |
|---|---|---|---|---|---|
| 69 | A29 | 4c | olive green | 8.00 | 5.50 |

Chang Tso-lin Stamps of China, 1928, Overprinted in Red or Blue

**1928** *Perf. 14*

| No. | Type | Value | Color | Unused | Used |
|---|---|---|---|---|---|
| 70 | A34 | 1c | brn org (R) | 1.75 | 1.75 |
| 71 | A34 | 4c | ol grn (R) | 2.75 | 2.75 |
| 72 | A34 | 10c | dull bl (R) | 6.50 | 6.50 |
| 73 | A34 | $1 | red (Bl) | 55.00 | 55.00 |
| | | | *Nos. 70-73 (4)* | 66.00 | 66.00 |

### Unification Issue of China, 1929, Overprinted in Red as in 1928

**1929**

| No. | Type | Value | Color | Unused | Used |
|---|---|---|---|---|---|
| 74 | A35 | 1c | brown org | 2.75 | 2.75 |
| 75 | A35 | 4c | olive grn | 4.75 | 4.75 |
| 76 | A35 | 10c | dk blue | 11.50 | 11.50 |
| 77 | A35 | $1 | dk red | 90.00 | 90.00 |
| | | | *Nos. 74-77 (4)* | 109.00 | 109.00 |

### Similar Overprint in Black on Sun Yat-sen Mausoleum Issue of China Characters 15mm apart

**1929** *Perf. 14*

| No. | Type | Value | Color | Unused | Used |
|---|---|---|---|---|---|
| 78 | A36 | 1c | brown org | 2.25 | 2.25 |
| 79 | A36 | 4c | olive grn | 3.50 | *3.50* |
| 80 | A36 | 10c | dark blue | 8.00 | *8.00* |
| 81 | A36 | $1 | dark red | 95.00 | 95.00 |
| | | | *Nos. 78-81 (4)* | 108.75 | 108.75 |

Stamps of Sun Yat-sen Issue of 1931-37 Overprinted

**1932** **Type I** *Perf. 12½*

| No. | Type | Value | Color | Unused | Used |
|---|---|---|---|---|---|
| 82 | A37 | 1c | orange | 1.75 | *4.00* |
| 83 | A37 | 2c | olive grn | 4.25 | *5.75* |
| 84 | A37 | 4c | green | 2.50 | *6.50* |
| 85 | A37 | 20c | ultra | 4.00 | *8.25* |
| 86 | A37 | $1 | org brn & dk brn | 12.00 | *20.00* |
| 87 | A37 | $2 | bl & org brn | 35.00 | *42.50* |
| 88 | A37 | $5 | dl red & blk | 40.00 | *60.00* |
| | | | *Nos. 82-88 (7)* | 99.50 | *147.00* |

No. 83 was overprinted in Shanghai in 1938. The overprint differs in minor details.

**1932-38** **Type II**

| No. | Type | Value | Color | Unused | Used |
|---|---|---|---|---|---|
| 89 | A37 | 2c | olive grn | .45 | *2.00* |
| 90 | A37 | 4c | green | 1.25 | *4.00* |
| 91 | A37 | 5c | green | .80 | *4.00* |
| 92 | A37 | 15c | dk green | 1.10 | *4.00* |
| 93 | A37 | 15c | scar ('34) | 1.10 | *4.00* |
| 93A | A37 | 20c | ultra ('38) | .80 | *2.75* |
| 94 | A37 | 25c | ultra | 1.25 | *4.00* |
| 95 | A37 | $1 | org brn & dk brn | 9.50 | *11.00* |
| 96 | A37 | $2 | bl & org brn | 20.00 | *32.50* |
| 97 | A37 | $5 | dl red & blk | 40.00 | *65.00* |
| | | | *Nos. 89-97 (10)* | 76.25 | *133.25* |

Nos. 89, 90 and 94 were overprinted in London, Peking and Shanghai. Nos. 92, 95-97 exist with London and Peking overprints. Nos. 91 and 93 exist with Peking and Shanghai overprints. No. 93A is a Shanghai overprint. The overprints differ in minor details.

### Tan Yuan-chang Issue of China, 1933, Overprinted as in 1928

**1933** *Perf. 14*

| No. | Type | Value | Color | Unused | Used |
|---|---|---|---|---|---|
| 98 | A49 | 2c | olive grn | 3.75 | 3.75 |
| 99 | A49 | 5c | green | 4.75 | 4.75 |
| 100 | A49 | 25c | ultra | 15.00 | 15.00 |
| 101 | A49 | $1 | red | 75.00 | 95.00 |
| | | | *Nos. 98-101 (4)* | 98.50 | 118.50 |

Stamps of China Martyrs Issue of 1932-34 Overprinted

**1933-34**

| No. | Type | Value | Color | Unused | Used |
|---|---|---|---|---|---|
| 102 | A39 | ½c | black brown | .30 | *3.50* |
| 103 | A40 | 1c | orange | 1.10 | *4.25* |
| 104 | A39 | 2½c | rose lilac | .30 | *3.25* |
| 105 | A48 | 3c | deep brown | .30 | *3.25* |
| 106 | A45 | 8c | brown orange | .75 | *3.50* |
| 107 | A46 | 10c | dull violet | .30 | *3.25* |
| 108 | A45 | 13c | blue green | .30 | *4.50* |
| 109 | A46 | 17c | brown olive | .30 | *2.50* |
| 110 | A47 | 20c | brown red | 1.10 | *6.50* |
| 111 | A48 | 30c | brown violet | .40 | *4.50* |
| 112 | A47 | 40c | orange | .60 | *3.25* |
| 113 | A40 | 50c | green | .70 | *2.50* |
| | | | *Nos. 102-113 (12)* | 6.45 | *44.75* |

Nos. 102-113 were originally overprinted in Peking. In 1938, Nos. 103-105, 108-112 were overprinted in Shanghai. The two overprints differ in minor details. No. 105, Shanghai overprint, is scarce. Value $35.

### China No. 324 Overprinted as in 1916-19

**1936** *Perf. 14*

| | | | | |
|---|---|---|---|---|
| **114** | A29 | 6c brown | 20.00 | *25.00* |

### Stamps of China, 1939-40 Overprinted in Black

### Type III

**1940-45** **Unwmk.** *Perf. 12½*

| | | | | |
|---|---|---|---|---|
| **115** | A57 | 2c olive green | .85 | *3.00* |
| **116** | A57 | 3c dull claret ('41) | .30 | *3.00* |
| **117** | A57 | 5c green | .30 | *3.00* |
| **118** | A57 | 5c olive green | .30 | *3.00* |
| **119** | A57 | 8c olive green ('41) | .30 | *3.00* |
| **120** | A57 | 10c green ('41) | .30 | *3.00* |
| **121** | A57 | 15c scarlet | .55 | *4.00* |
| **122** | A57 | 16c olive gray ('41) | .40 | *3.00* |
| **123** | A57 | 25c dark blue | .55 | *5.00* |
| **124** | A57 | $1 hn & dk brn (type II) | 6.25 | *11.00* |
| **125** | A57 | $2 dp bl & org brn (type I) | 4.50 | *11.00* |
| **126** | A57 | $5 red & grnsh blk | 26.00 | *32.50* |
| | | *Nos. 115-126 (12)* | 40.60 | *84.50* |

*Perf. 14*

**With Secret Marks**

| | | | | |
|---|---|---|---|---|
| **127** | A57 | 8c ol grn (#383a) | 1.10 | *3.00* |
| *a.* | | On #383 | 19.00 | *22.50* |
| **128** | A57 | 10c green ('41) | 10.00 | *15.00* |
| **129** | A57 | 30c scarlet ('45) | .30 | *3.00* |
| **130** | A57 | 50c dk blue ('45) | .55 | *3.50* |
| **131** | A57 | $1 org brn & sep | .55 | *4.00* |
| **132** | A57 | $2 dp bl & org brn | .55 | *4.00* |
| **133** | A57 | $5 red & sl grn | .65 | *6.00* |
| **134** | A57 | $10 dk grn & dl pur | 1.90 | *5.00* |
| **135** | A57 | $20 rose lake & dk bl | 3.50 | *8.00* |
| | | *Nos. 127-135 (9)* | 19.10 | *51.50* |

### Wmk. Character Yu (Post) (261)

*Perf. 14*

| | | | | |
|---|---|---|---|---|
| **136** | A57 | 5c olive green | .30 | *2.50* |
| **137** | A57 | 10c green | .35 | *3.75* |
| **138** | A57 | 30c scarlet | .35 | *5.00* |
| **139** | A57 | 50c dark blue | .45 | *2.50* |
| | | *Nos. 136-139 (4)* | 1.45 | *13.75* |

Martyrs Issue, 1940-41, Overprinted in Black

***Perf. 12, 12½, 13, 13x12, 13½x13***

**1941-45** **Wmk. 261**

| | | | | |
|---|---|---|---|---|
| **140** | A40 | 1c orange | .35 | *2.40* |
| **141** | A39 | 2½c rose lilac | .35 | *4.50* |
| **142** | A45 | 8c dp org ('45) | 5.75 | 12.00 |
| **143** | A46 | 10c dull vio | .45 | *3.00* |
| **144** | A45 | 13c dp yel grn | 1.00 | *5.50* |
| **145** | A46 | 17c brown olive | 1.00 | *5.25* |
| **146** | A40 | 25c red vio ('45) | 2.00 | *7.25* |
| **147** | A47 | 40c orange ('45) | 3.50 | *9.25* |
| | | *Nos. 140-147 (8)* | 14.40 | *49.15* |

**Unwmk.**

| | | | | |
|---|---|---|---|---|
| **148** | A39 | ½c olive blk | .35 | *3.25* |
| **149** | A40 | 1c orange ('45) | .35 | *2.40* |
| **150** | A46 | 2c dp blue ('45) | 3.25 | *3.75* |
| **151** | A48 | 3c dp yel brn | .35 | *4.50* |
| **152** | A39 | 4c pale vio ('45) | .35 | *4.50* |
| **153** | A45 | 8c dp orange | .35 | *5.50* |
| **154** | A45 | 13c dp yel grn ('45) | .65 | *4.00* |
| **155** | A48 | 15c brn car ('45) | .35 | *4.00* |
| **156** | A46 | 17c brn ol ('45) | 1.00 | *4.50* |
| **157** | A47 | 20c lt blue ('45) | .35 | *3.25* |
| **158** | A45 | 21c ol brn ('45) | 1.25 | *4.50* |
| **159** | A46 | 28c olive ('45) | 1.45 | *5.50* |
| **160** | A47 | 40c orange ('45) | 3.00 | *14.00* |
| **161** | A40 | 50c green ('45) | 2.00 | *7.00* |
| | | *Nos. 148-161 (14)* | 15.05 | *70.65* |

Stamps of China, 1942-43 Overprinted in Carmine, Black or Red

**1944** **Without Gum** *Perf. 12½, 13*

| | | | | |
|---|---|---|---|---|
| **162** | A62 | 10c dp grn (C) | 1.75 | *7.75* |
| **163** | A62 | 20c dk ol grn (C) | 2.00 | *7.75* |
| **164** | A62 | 25c violet brn | .30 | *8.50* |
| **165** | A62 | 30c dk orange | .95 | *9.00* |
| **166** | A62 | 40c red brown | .30 | *8.50* |
| **167** | A62 | 50c sage green | .30 | *5.00* |
| *a.* | | Perf. 11 | 16.00 | 24.00 |
| **168** | A62 | $1 rose lake | 3.75 | 5.00 |
| **169** | A62 | $1 dull green | .30 | *8.50* |
| **170** | A62 | $1.50 dp bl (C) | .30 | *9.50* |
| **171** | A62 | $2 dk bl grn (R) | 2.40 | *7.00* |
| **172** | A62 | $3 yellow | .30 | *12.00* |
| **173** | A62 | $5 cerise | 2.40 | *11.00* |
| | | *Nos. 162-173 (12)* | 15.05 | *99.50* |

For surcharges see Nos. 194-195.

### Same Overprint on Stamps of China, 1942-43, in Black

**1944-46** ***Imperf.***

| | | | | |
|---|---|---|---|---|
| **174** | A57 | $10 red brown | 140.00 | 125.00 |
| **175** | A57 | $20 rose red | 6.75 | *17.00* |
| **176** | A57 | $30 dull vio | 5.00 | *17.00* |
| **177** | A57 | $40 rose red | 5.00 | *17.00* |
| **178** | A57 | $50 blue ('46) | 1,080. | *1,170.* |
| **179** | A57 | $100 orange brn | 14.50 | *22.50* |

*Perf. 13½*

| | | | | |
|---|---|---|---|---|
| **180** | A57 | $4 dp blue | 2.00 | *13.50* |
| **181** | A57 | $5 lilac gray | 3.50 | *13.50* |
| **182** | A57 | $10 red brn | 3.50 | *13.50* |
| **183** | A57 | $20 blue grn | 2.00 | *15.00* |
| **184** | A57 | $20 rose red | 140.00 | 140.00 |
| **185** | A57 | $30 dull vio | 4.00 | *17.00* |
| **186** | A57 | $40 rose | 4.00 | *16.00* |
| **187** | A57 | $50 blue | 4.50 | *17.00* |
| **188** | A57 | $100 orange brn | 160.00 | 140.00 |
| | | *Nos. 174-177,179-188 (14)* | 494.75 | *584.00* |

Beware of trimmed examples of Nos. 182 and 187 offered as Nos. 174 and 178.

Nos. 162 and 164 Surcharged in Black

**1944, Aug. 1**

| | | | | |
|---|---|---|---|---|
| **194** | A62 | 12c on 10c dp grn | 9.00 | *27.50* |
| **195** | A62 | 24c on 25c brn vio | 9.00 | *27.50* |

Stamps of China, 1940-41, Overprinted in Black at Chengtu, Szechwan

**1943**

| | | | | |
|---|---|---|---|---|
| **196** | A57 | 10c green (#354) | 25.00 | *45.00* |
| **197** | A47 | 20c lt blue (#433) | 25.00 | *45.00* |

**Wmk. 261** ***Perf. 14***

| | | | | |
|---|---|---|---|---|
| **198** | A57 | 50c dk blue (#396) | 25.00 | *30.00* |

China Nos. 565 and 567 Overprinted in Black

**1945** **Unwmk.** ***Perf. 12½***

| | | | | |
|---|---|---|---|---|
| **200** | A63 | 40c brown red | .45 | 20.00 |
| **201** | A63 | $3 red | .45 | 18.00 |

China Nos. 640-642, 788, 751, 753 Surcharged in Black or Red

**1949** **Engr.** ***Perf. 14***

| | | | | |
|---|---|---|---|---|
| **202** | A73 | 1c on $100 dk car | 29.00 | *60.00* |
| **203** | A73 | 3c on $200 ol grn (R) | 29.00 | *60.00* |
| **204** | A73 | 5c on $500 brt bl grn (R) | 29.00 | *60.00* |
| **205** | A82 | 10c on $20,000 rose pink | 25.00 | *50.00* |
| **206** | A82 | 50c on $4000 gray (R) | 100.00 | *175.00* |
| **207** | A82 | $1 on $6000 rose lil | 110.00 | *175.00* |
| | | *Nos. 202-207 (6)* | 322.00 | *580.00* |

### AIR POST STAMPS

Sinkiang Nos. 53, 57, 59, 32 Overprinted in Red

**1932-33** **Unwmk.** ***Perf. 14***

| | | | | |
|---|---|---|---|---|
| **C1** | A29 | 5c claret ('33) | 400.00 | 290.00 |
| **C2** | A29 | 10c dark blue ('33) | 400.00 | 225.00 |
| **C3** | A30 | 15c deep blue | 2,700. | 775.00 |
| **C4** | A25 | 30c brown violet | 1,170. | 990.00 |

**Counterfeits exist of Nos. C1-C4.**

### Air Post Stamps of China, 1932-37 Handstamped in Dull Red

**1942**

| | | | | |
|---|---|---|---|---|
| **C5** | AP3 | 15c gray green | 7.25 | *9.00* |
| **C6** | AP3 | 25c orange | 425.00 | 375.00 |
| **C7** | AP3 | 30c red | 15.50 | *27.50* |
| **C8** | AP3 | 45c brown vio | 11.00 | *18.00* |
| **C9** | AP3 | 50c dk brown | 45.00 | *50.00* |
| **C10** | AP3 | 60c dk blue | 11.00 | *21.00* |
| **C11** | AP3 | 90c olive grn | 57.50 | *80.00* |
| **C12** | AP3 | $1 yellow grn | 12.00 | *20.00* |
| | | *Nos. C5-C12 (8)* | 584.25 | *600.50* |

### Same Handstamped Overprint on Air Post Stamps of China, 1940-41 in Dull Red

**1942** **Wmk. 261** ***Perf. 12½, 13, 13½***

| | | | | |
|---|---|---|---|---|
| **C13** | AP3 | 15c gray green | 6.75 | *15.00* |
| **C14** | AP3 | 25c yellow orange | 6.75 | *17.00* |

**1942** **Unwmk.**

| | | | | |
|---|---|---|---|---|
| **C15** | AP3 | 25c light orange | 6.75 | 13.50 |
| **C16** | AP3 | 30c light red | 6.75 | 13.50 |
| **C17** | AP3 | 50c brown | 9.00 | 15.00 |
| **C18** | AP3 | $2 light brown | 42.50 | 42.50 |
| **C19** | AP3 | $5 lake | 42.50 | 42.50 |
| | | *Nos. C15-C19 (5)* | 107.50 | 127.00 |

Twelve values exist with this overprint in black. Their status has not been determined. Inverted overprints exist in both red and black.

Official Perforated Characters

For use on official mail, various Sinkiang stamps were perforated with an arrangement of four Chinese characters ("For Official Business Only"). These include Nos. 1-38, 47-69, 114.

### OFFICES IN TIBET

12 Pies = 1 Anna
16 Annas = 1 Rupee

Stamps of China, Issues of 1902-10, Surcharged

**1911** **Unwmk.** ***Perf. 12 to 16***

| | | | | |
|---|---|---|---|---|
| **1** | A17 | 3p on 1c ocher | 27.50 | *45.00* |
| *a.* | | Inverted surcharge | *3,500.* | |
| **2** | A17 | ½a on 2c grn | 27.50 | *45.00* |
| **3** | A17 | 1a on 4c ver | 27.50 | *45.00* |
| **4** | A17 | 2a on 7c mar | 27.50 | *45.00* |
| **5** | A17 | 2½a on 10c ultra | 35.00 | *55.00* |
| **6** | A18 | 3a on 16c ol grn | 70.00 | *80.00* |
| *a.* | | Large "S" in "Annas" | *1,250.* | |
| **7** | A18 | 4a on 20c red brn | 70.00 | *80.00* |
| **8** | A18 | 6a on 30c rose red | 125.00 | *140.00* |
| **9** | A18 | 12a on 50c yel grn | 325.00 | *400.00* |
| **10** | A19 | 1r on $1 red & pale rose | 900.00 | *900.00* |
| **11** | A19 | 2r on $2 red & yel | 1,620. | *1,800.* |
| | | *Nos. 1-11 (11)* | 3,255. | 3,635. |

Beware of fake overprints.

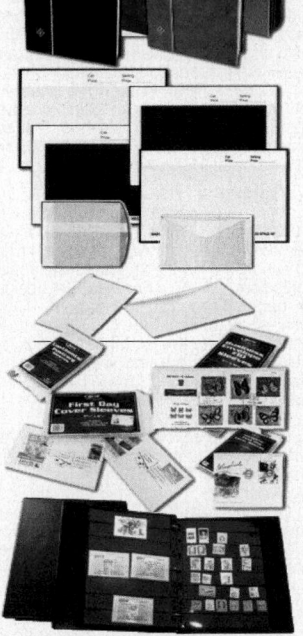

# PEOPLE'S REPUBLIC OF CHINA

'pē-pəls ri-'pə-blik of 'chī-nə

LOCATION — Eastern Asia
GOVT. — Communist Republic
POP. — 1,339,724,852 (2010 est.)
CAPITAL — Beijing (Peking)

The communists completed their conquest of all mainland China in 1949. They established the Central Government and General Postal Administration in Peking. They ordered all but two regions to stop selling regional issues by June 30, 1950, extending validity one year from that date. The Northeast and Port Arthur-Dairen regions were exempted because their currency had a different value. These two regions stopped using separate issues at the end of 1950. Thereafter unified issues were used throughout mainland China.

On July 1, 1997 Hong Kong returned to Chinese control as an administrative district. Hong Kong stamps issued under Chinese rule will continue to be listed under "Hong Kong."

**Reprints**

After currency revaluation Mar. 1, 1955, reprints were prepared and put on sale by the Philatelic Agency in order to supply stocks of exhausted issues for collectors. Minor differences in design or paper distinguish the reprints. They are of commemorative and special issues up to the gymnastics set of 1952. Reprints are less expensive. Values are for original issues. Reprint distinctions are footnoted.

**Used Stamps**

Most used stamps before 1970 exist primarily canceled to order. Postally used stamps generally sell for ½ the unused value.

Beginning in 1987 the PRC stopped furnishing quantities of used stamps to the philatelic market. When available, used stamps of these issues sell for the same or more than unused stamps.

**China Post Issue Numbers**

Commemorative issues, beginning in 1949, and special issues, beginning in 1951, bear 4 numbers in lower margin: 1. Issue number. 2. Total of stamps in set. 3. Position of stamp in set. 4. Cumulative number of stamp (usually in parenthesis). A fifth number, the year of issue, was added in 1952.

The numbering system varies at times, and changed in 1992 to listing the year of issue followed by the set number on the right hand lower margin. Stamps with the "R" prefix do not have serial numbers on them.

We have listed the China Post issue number on all sets to 1992. In certain sets listings include parenthetically the position-in-set number. During some periods these parentheses in listings hold the stamp's cumulative number.

**Gum**

All stamps to the beginning of 1960 were issued without gum, except as noted. After that date, most stamps have gum, which is translucent and almost invisible. Catalogue values are for stamps with fresh, untoned paper and gum. Stamps with toned paper or gum sell for approximately 20% to 50% less. All issues are unwatermarked, unless otherwise noted.

100 fen = 1 yuan ($)

**Catalogue values for unused stamps in this country are for Never Hinged items, beginning with Scott 487 in the regular postage section, Scott B1 in the semi-postal section.**

Lantern and Gate of Heavenly Peace — A1

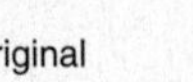

Original

Reprint

*Reprints have altered ornament on lantern base. On originals, it is a full oval; on reprints, only a partial circle. Value, set: unused $11; used $3.*

**China Post No. C1**

**1949, Oct. 8 Litho. *Perf. 12½***

| | | | | | |
|---|---|---|---|---|---|
| 1 | A1 | $30 | blue | 7.25 | 5.50 |
| 2 | A1 | $50 | rose red | 8.25 | 5.50 |
| 3 | A1 | $100 | green | 12.00 | 6.00 |
| 4 | A1 | $200 | maroon | 12.00 | 6.00 |
| | | | *Nos. 1-4 (4)* | 39.50 | 23.00 |

1st session of Chinese People's Consultative Political Conference. See Nos. 1L121-1L124.

Globe and Hand Holding Hammer — A2

Original

Reprint

*Reprints show heavier shading on index finger and thumb. Value, set $6.50 unused or $3.50 used.*

**China Post No. C3**

**1949, Nov. 16**

| | | | | | |
|---|---|---|---|---|---|
| 5 | A2 | $100 | carmine | 14.50 | 10.00 |
| 6 | A2 | $300 | slate green | 14.50 | 10.00 |
| 7 | A2 | $500 | dark blue | 42.50 | 10.00 |
| | | | *Nos. 5-7 (3)* | 71.50 | 30.00 |

Asiatic and Australasian Congress of the World Federation of Trade Unions, Peking.

The $100, imperf., is of dubious status.

See Nos. 1L133-1L135.

Conference Hall, Peking — A3

Mao Tse-tung on Rostrum — A4

Original

Reprint

*Nos. 8-9: First character in top inscription shows a square, reprints an oblong.*

*Nos. 10-11: Originals have heavy cross-hatching and lines which touch back of head and top of rostrum. Reprints have lighter lines which do not touch head or top of rostrum. Reprints, value set $19 unused, $8 used.*

**China Post No. C2**

**1950, Feb. 1 Engr. *Perf. 14***

| | | | | | |
|---|---|---|---|---|---|
| 8 | A3 | $50 | red | 12.50 | 8.00 |
| 9 | A3 | $100 | blue | 12.50 | 8.00 |
| 10 | A4 | $300 | red brown | 13.50 | 9.50 |
| 11 | A4 | $500 | green | 21.00 | 16.00 |
| | | | *Nos. 8-11 (4)* | 59.50 | 41.50 |

Chinese People's Consultative Political Conference. See Nos. 1L136-1L139.

Gate of Heavenly Peace (actual size) — A5

**China Post No. R1**

First Issue: Top line of shading broken at right.

**1950, Feb. 10 Litho. *Perf. 12½***

| | | | | | |
|---|---|---|---|---|---|
| 12 | A5 | $200 | green | 13.00 | 6.50 |
| 13 | A5 | $300 | brown red | 1.00 | *1.00* |
| 14 | A5 | $500 | red | 1.00 | 1.00 |
| 15 | A5 | $800 | orange | 12.00 | 1.00 |
| 16 | A5 | $1000 | dull violet | 5.00 | 1.00 |
| 17 | A5 | $2000 | olive | 18.00 | 3.00 |
| 18 | A5 | $5000 | brt pink | 2.00 | *2.75* |
| 19 | A5 | $8000 | blue | 1.00 | *9.00* |
| 20 | A5 | $10,000 | brown | 1.25 | *9.00* |
| | | | *Nos. 12-20 (9)* | 54.25 | *34.25* |

**China Post No. R2**

**1950, June 9 Typo.**

Second Issue: Top line of shading extends to frame line at right.

| | | | | | |
|---|---|---|---|---|---|
| 21 | A5 | $1000 | dull violet | 2.25 | 2.10 |
| 22 | A5 | $3000 | red brown | 1.75 | 1.75 |
| 23 | A5 | $10,000 | brown | 1.00 | *2.50* |
| | | | *Nos. 21-23 (3)* | 5.00 | *6.35* |

Other Gate of Heavenly Peace issues are illustrated where they are listed. See A10, A13, A14 and A42 for similar designs.

For similar types with Chinese characters in upper right corner see Northeast China A28, A29, Port Arthur & Darien A11, North China A8.

As part of the second issue, a $4,000 value in deep blue was prepared by not issued. Value, $7,500.

China Nos. 959, C62, E12, F2 Surcharged in Blue, Black, Green or Red

**China Post Nos. SC1 and SC4**

***Rouletted, Perf. 12½ (#27, 29)***

**1950, Mar. Litho.**

| | | | | | |
|---|---|---|---|---|---|
| 24 | SD2 | $100 | on red vio (Bl) | 1.50 | *8.50* |
| a. | | | Perf. 12½ | 12.50 | 6.50 |
| 25 | R2 | $200 | on red (Bk) | 7.50 | 8.00 |
| a. | | | Perf. 12½ | 60.00 | 3.25 |
| 26 | AP5 | $300 | on bl grn (Bk) | 1.40 | *3.25* |
| a. | | | Perf. 12½ | 1.60 | 1.10 |
| 27 | A96 | $500 | on org (Gr) | 1.00 | .60 |
| a. | | | Perf. 14 | 80.00 | 67.50 |
| 28 | A96 | $800 | on org (R) | 8.50 | 1.00 |
| a. | | | Perf. 12½ | 30.00 | 5.50 |
| b. | | | Perf. 14 | *850.00* | 90.00 |
| 29 | A96 | $1000 | on org (Bk) | 1.00 | .70 |
| a. | | | Perf. 14 | 27.50 | 3.00 |
| | | | *Nos. 24-29 (6)* | 20.90 | 22.05 |

In Nos. 24-29 the rouletted stamps are China Post No. SC4, the perforated stamps are China Post No. SC1.

Harvesters with Ox — A6

**China Post No. SC2**

**1950, May**

| | | | | | |
|---|---|---|---|---|---|
| 30 | A6 | $20,000 | on $10,000 red | *725.00* | 130.00 |

No. 30 is surcharged on an unissued stamp of East China. Value, without surcharge (unissued) *$1,500*.

Flag, Mao Tse-tung, Gate of Heavenly Peace — A7

Original

Reprint

*Originals have a single curved line in jacket button, reprints have an extra dot in button. Value, set unused $32.50 used $11.50.*

**China Post No. C4**

**1950, July 1 *Perf. 14***

**Yellow Stars**

| | | | | | |
|---|---|---|---|---|---|
| 31 | A7 | $800 | green & red | 60.00 | 17.50 |
| 32 | A7 | $1000 | brn & red | 85.00 | 22.50 |
| 33 | A7 | $2000 | dk brn & red | 100.00 | 24.00 |
| 34 | A7 | $3000 | dk blue & red | 150.00 | 35.00 |
| | | | *Nos. 31-34 (4)* | 395.00 | 99.00 |

Inauguration of the People's Republic, Oct. 1, 1949. See Nos. 1L150-1L153.

Sun Yat-sen Stamps of Northeastern Provinces Surcharged in Red, Black or Blue

**China Post No. SC3**

**1950, July 1 Engr.**

| | | | | | |
|---|---|---|---|---|---|
| 35 | A2 | $50 | on 20c yel grn | 8.00 | *8.00* |
| 36 | A2 | $50 | on 25c blk brn | 5.00 | 5.50 |
| 37 | A2 | $50 | on 50c red org (Bk) | 1.75 | *2.25* |
| 38 | A2 | $100 | on $2.50 ind | 1.40 | *2.00* |
| 39 | A2 | $100 | on $3 brn (Bk) | 2.25 | *4.25* |
| 40 | A2 | $100 | on $4 org brn, Type II (Bl) | 4.75 | *7.00* |
| a. | | | Type I | *450.00* | *225.00* |
| 41 | A2 | $100 | on $5 dk grn (Bk) | 7.00 | 6.00 |
| 42 | A2 | $100 | on $10 crim, Type II (Bl) | 23.00 | 12.00 |
| a. | | | Type I | *2,250.* | — |
| 43 | A2 | $400 | on $20 ol, Type II (Bl) | 87.50 | 87.50 |
| a. | | | Type I | *800.00* | *275.00* |
| 44 | A2 | $400 | on $44 dk car rose (Bl) | 2.75 | *5.50* |
| 45 | A2 | $400 | on $65 dl grn | 140.00 | 100.00 |
| 46 | A2 | $400 | on $100 dp grn | 22.00 | 15.00 |
| 47 | A2 | $400 | on $200 rose brn (Bk) | 47.50 | 22.00 |
| 48 | A2 | $400 | on $300 bluish grn | 60.00 | 26.00 |
| | | | *Nos. 35-48 (14)* | 412.90 | 303.00 |

Flying Geese Type of China Surcharged in Red, Blue, Green, Brown or Black

**China Post No. SC5**

**1950, Aug. 1 *Perf. 12½, Imperf.***

| | | | | | |
|---|---|---|---|---|---|
| 49 | A97 | $50 | on 10c dk bl (R) | .40 | 1.00 |
| 50 | A97 | $100 | on 16c ol, imperf. (Bl) | .45 | 1.00 |
| 51 | A97 | $100 | on 50c dl grn, imperf. (Bl) | .45 | 1.00 |
| 52 | A97 | $200 | on $1 org (G) | .60 | 1.00 |
| 53 | A97 | $200 | on $2 bl (Br) | 5.00 | 4.00 |
| 54 | A97 | $400 | on $5 car rose (Bk) | 1.00 | 2.00 |
| 55 | A97 | $400 | on $10 bl grn (Bk) | 2.50 | *5.00* |
| 56 | A97 | $400 | on $20 pur (Bk) | 3.00 | *6.50* |
| | | | *Nos. 49-56 (8)* | 13.40 | 21.50 |

Dove of Peace, by Picasso — A8

**China Post No. C5**

**1950, Aug. 1 Engr. *Perf. 14***

| | | | | | |
|---|---|---|---|---|---|
| 57 | A8 | $400 | brown | 30.00 | 8.50 |
| 58 | A8 | $800 | green | 32.50 | 10.00 |
| 59 | A8 | $2000 | blue | 50.00 | 15.00 |
| | | | *Nos. 57-59 (3)* | 112.50 | 33.50 |

World Peace Campaign. See Nos. 1L154-1L156.

*Paper of originals appears bright under ultraviolet lamp. That of reprints looks dull. Value, set unused $7.50 used $3.25.*

Chinese Flag and "1" — A9

$800

Original

Reprint

*Reprints are a brighter red, leaves beside "1" are gray brown instead of reddish brown. On the large format stamp, the arrangement of dots in background differs in relationship to large star: in the originals the dots run about parellel to the bottom edge of the upper right point of the large star, in the reprints the dots run in lines almost parellel to the left edge of the top point of the large star. Value, set unused $20 used $9.*

### China Post No. C6

**1950** **Engr. & Litho.**

**Flag in Red & Yellow**

**60** A9 $100 purple 50.00 18.00
**61** A9 $400 red brown 55.00 20.00
**62** A9 $800 green 80.00 17.50
**63** A9 $1000 lt olive 115.00 30.00
**64** A9 $2000 blue 175.00 45.00
*Nos. 60-64 (5)* 475.00 130.50

1st anniv. of the Chinese People's Republic. Size of $800: 38x46mm; others 26x32mm.

Issue dates: No. 62, Oct. 1; others Oct. 31. See Nos. 1L157-1L161.

Gate of Heavenly Peace (actual size) — A10

### China Post No. R3

Third Issue: Cloud almost touches character at upper left. Cloud breaks inner frame line at top.

**1950** **Litho.**

**65** A10 $100 lt grnsh bl 45.00 22.00
**66** A10 $200 green 325.00 16.00
**67** A10 $300 dk carmine 2.25 *4.25*
**68** A10 $400 grnsh gray 8.25 *4.50*
**69** A10 $500 carmine 2.00 *2.75*
**70** A10 $800 orange 8.25 1.90
**71** A10 $2000 gray olive 3.25 3.25
*Nos. 65-71 (7)* 394.00 *54.65*

Issued: $800, 10/8; $500, $2000, 12/1; others, 10/6.

"Communication" and Map of China — A11

Original

Reprint

*Originals have 3 lines below horizontal bar (2nd character); reprints have four. Value, set unused $3.50, used $1.50.*

### China Post No. C7

**1950, Nov. 1** **Litho.**

**72** A11 $400 green & brn 37.50 15.00
**73** A11 $800 carmine & grn 40.00 13.00

First All-China Postal Conference, Peking. See Nos. 1L162-1L163.

Stalin and Mao Tse-tung A12

### China Post No. C8

**1950, Dec. 1** **Engr.** ***Perf. 14***

**74** A12 $400 red 22.50 15.00
**75** A12 $800 dp green 22.50 16.00
**76** A12 $2000 dk blue 37.50 22.50
*Nos. 74-76 (3)* 82.50 53.50

Signing of Sino-Soviet Treaty of Friendship, Alliance and Mutual Assistance. See Nos. 1L176-1L178.

*Paper of originals appears bright under ultraviolet lamp. That of reprints looks dull. Value, set unused $18.50, used $7.*

### East China Issue of 1949 Surcharged in Red, Black, Brown or Blue

Train and Postal Runner — A12a

### China Post No. SC7

**1950, Dec.** **Litho.** ***Perf. 12½***

**77** A12a $50 on $10 dp ultra (R) .65 1.10
**78** A12a $100 on $15 org ver (Bk) .65 1.10
*a.* $100 on $15 red (Bk), perf. 14 3.00 3.00
**79** A12a $300 on $50 car (Bk) .70 3.00
**80** A12a $400 on $1600 vio bl (Br) 2.00 2.25
**81** A12a $400 on $2000 brn vio (Bl) 1.00 1.25
*Nos. 77-81 (5)* 5.00 8.70

### East China Issue of 1949 Surcharged in Red or Black

Chairman Mao — A12b

### China Post No. SC6

**1950, Dec.**

**82** A12b $50 on $10 ultra (R) .90 .70
**83** A12b $400 on $15 ver (Bk) 1.00 .90
**84** A12b $400 on $2000 grn (Bk) 3.00 3.00
*Nos. 82-84 (3)* 4.90 4.60

(actual size) — A13

### China Post No. R4

Fourth Issue: Similar to 3rd issue, but large cloud does not break inner frame line at top.

**1950-51** **Litho.**

**85** A13 $100 lt blue 1.00 *2.00*
**86** A13 $200 dull green 14.00 4.50
**87** A13 $300 dull lilac .75 *5.00*
**88** A13 $400 gray grn 8.50 1.75
**89** A13 $500 carmine .85 1.75
**90** A13 $800 orange 80.00 3.00
*a.* Imperf., pair *725.00*
**91** A13 $1000 violet 1.50 *2.75*
**92** A13 $2000 olive 300.00 7.50
**93** A13 $3000 brown 1.00 *3.50*
**94** A13 $5000 pink 1.00 *5.50*
*Nos. 85-94 (10)* 408.60 *37.25*

Issued: $200, $300, $500, $800, $2000, $5000, 12/22/50; others 6/8/51.

(actual size) — A14

### China Post No. R5

Fifth Issue: Colored network on surface in salmon.

**1951, Jan. 18** **Engr.** ***Perf. 14***

**95** A14 $10,000 brown 2.50 *35.00*
**96** A14 $20,000 olive 4.00 *15.00*
**97** A14 $30,000 green 175.00 *110.00*
**98** A14 $50,000 violet 275.00 80.00
**99** A14 $100,000 scar 3,000. 425.00
**100** A14 $200,000 blue 3,500. 800.00
*Nos. 95-100 (6)* 6,957. 1,465.

Unit Issue of China Surcharged

### China Post No. SC8

**1951, May 2** **Litho.** ***Perf. 12½***

**101** SD2 $5 on rose lilac 3.00 *3.25*
**102** AP5 $10 on brt grn 2.00 *2.25*
**103** R2 $15 on red 1.00 *1.00*
**104** A96 $25 on orange 1.00 *1.00*
*Nos. 101-104 (4)* 7.00 7.50

Issued for use in Northeast China, but available for use throughout China. Nos. 101-104 rouletted (China Post No. SC9) were sold for philatelic purposes only. Value, set unused $8, used $7.

Chairman Mao Tse-tung — A15

### China Post No. C9

**1951, July 1** **Engr.** ***Perf. 14***

**105** A15 $400 chestnut 11.00 7.50
**106** A15 $500 deep green 14.00 7.00
**107** A15 $800 crimson 16.00 6.00
*Nos. 105-107 (3)* 41.00 20.50

Chinese Communist Party, 30th anniv.

*Reprints are on whiter, thinner and harder paper. Value, set unused $20, used $8.*

Picasso Dove A16

### China Post No. C10

**1951, Aug. 15** ***Perf. 12½***

**108** A16 $400 orange brn 24.00 19.00
**109** A16 $800 blue grn 22.50 12.00
**110** A16 $1000 dull vio 31.00 19.00
*Nos. 108-110 (3)* 77.50 50.00

*Reprints are perf 14. Value, set unused $32.50, used $11.*

### Remittance Stamp of China Surcharged in Carmine or Black

(same size) — A17

### China Post No. SC10

**Engraved, Commercial Press**

**1951, Sept.** ***Perf. 12, 12½, 13***

**111** A17 $50 on $2 bl grn (C) 1.00 *2.00*

***Rouletted 9½***

**Typo., Kang Hwa Printing Co.**

**112** A17 $50 on $2 gray bl (C) 3.75 *4.50*
**113** A17 $50 on $5 red org (Bk) 1.00 *2.50*
**114** A17 $50 on $50 gray (C) 6.00 *7.50*

***Perf. 13***

**Lithographed, Central Trust Co.**

**115** A17 $50 on $50 gray blk (C) .75 *1.00*

***Perf. 10x11½, 11½x9½, 11½x10***

**Lithographed, Chung Hwa Book Co.**

**116** A17 $50 on $50 gray (C) 3.50 6.00
*a.* Perf. 11½ 2.50 2.50
*Nos. 111-116 (6)* 16.00 *23.50*

National Emblem — A18

### China Post No. S1

**Engraved; Background Network Lithographed in Yellow**

**1951, Oct. 1** ***Perf. 14***

**117** A18 $100 Prus blue 19.00 6.50
**118** A18 $200 brown 13.00 6.00
**119** A18 $400 orange 12.00 6.00
**120** A18 $500 green 14.00 8.00
**121** A18 $800 carmine 16.00 6.50
*Nos. 117-121 (5)* 74.00 33.00

*Reprints exist but are difficult to distinguish; paper whiter, and colors slightly brighter. Value, set unused $18 or used $5.*

Rough Perfs

Rough perforations are normal on many early issues. These include Nos. 122-123, 136-140, 155-176, 239-240, 299-300, 453-456, 467-482, 629-634, 684-707, 737-745 and probably others.

Lu Hsun and Quotation — A19

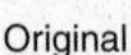

Original

Reprint

*Reprints have dot in triangle at lower right; no dot in original. Value, set unused $5, used $2.25.*

**China Post No. C11**

**1951, Oct. 19 Litho. *Perf. 12½***

| | | | | |
|---|---|---|---|---|
| **122** | A19 | $400 lilac | 11.00 | 6.50 |
| **123** | A19 | $800 green | 20.00 | 10.00 |

15th anniversary of the death of Lu Hsun (1881-1936), writer.

Peasant Uprising, Chintien A20

Design: Nos. 126-127, Coin of Taiping Regime and decrees of peasant government.

Original

Reprint

*Reprints of Nos. 124-125 have additional short stroke at upper left.*

Original

Reprint

*Reprints of Nos. 126-127 have two short strokes on scale near tail of right dragon on coin. Value, Nos. 124-127 unused $8.50, used $3.75.*

**China Post No. C12**

**1951, Dec. 15 Engr. *Perf. 14***

| | | | | |
|---|---|---|---|---|
| **124** | A20 | $400 green | 19.00 | 12.00 |
| **125** | A20 | $800 scarlet | 13.00 | 10.00 |
| **126** | A20 | $800 orange | 13.00 | 10.00 |
| **127** | A20 | $1000 deep blue | 22.00 | 10.50 |
| | | *Nos. 124-127 (4)* | 67.00 | 42.50 |

Centenary of Taiping Peasant Rebellion.

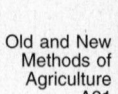

Old and New Methods of Agriculture A21

Original

Reprint

*One short horizontal line between legs of plower; 2 lines in reprints. Value, set unused $8.50, used $3.50.*

**China Post No. S2**

**1952, Jan. 1**

| | | | | |
|---|---|---|---|---|
| **128** | A21 | $100 scarlet | 11.00 | 7.00 |
| **129** | A21 | $200 bright blue | 11.00 | 7.00 |
| **130** | A21 | $400 deep brown | 12.00 | 8.00 |
| **131** | A21 | $800 green | 14.00 | 8.00 |
| | | *Nos. 128-131 (4)* | 48.00 | 30.00 |

Agrarian reform.

Potala Monastery, Lhasa — A22

**China Post No. C13**

Nos. 134-135, Farmer plowing with yaks.

**1952, Mar. 15 *Perf. 12½***

| | | | | |
|---|---|---|---|---|
| **132** | A22 | $400 vermilion | 17.50 | 10.00 |
| **133** | A22 | $800 claret | 15.00 | 7.50 |
| **134** | A22 | $800 blue grn | 15.00 | 7.50 |
| **135** | A22 | $1000 dull vio | 17.50 | 10.00 |
| | | *Nos. 132-135 (4)* | 65.00 | 35.00 |

Liberation of Tibet.

*Reprints, perf 14, have a small Chinese character at lower left of the vignette which is missing in the original. Value, set unused $16, used $7.*

Some reprints of No. 132 are perf 14x14½. Value, $200.

Children of Four Races — A23

**China Post No. C14**

**1952, Apr. 12 Litho.**

| | | | | |
|---|---|---|---|---|
| **136** | A23 | $400 dull grn | 1.50 | .40 |
| **137** | A23 | $800 vio blue | 1.75 | .55 |

Intl. Child Protection Conf., Vienna.

Hammer and Sickle on Numeral 1 — A24

**China Post No. C15**

Labor Day: No. 139, Dove rising from worker's hand. No. 140, Dove, hammer, wheat & chimneys.

**1952, May 1**

| | | | | |
|---|---|---|---|---|
| **138** | A24 | $800 scarlet | 2.00 | .45 |
| **139** | A24 | $800 blue grn | 2.00 | .45 |
| **140** | A24 | $800 orange brn | 2.00 | .45 |
| | | *Nos. 138-140 (3)* | 6.00 | 1.35 |

Physical Exercises — A25

**China Post No. S4**

Stamps printed in blocks of four for each color, each block representing a specific setting-up exercise; exercises coincided with a national radio program. Where exercise positions are identical within the block, the serial number in the LL margin of each stamp (and in parenthesis in the listings below) is the only means of differentiation.

**1952, June 20**

| | | | | |
|---|---|---|---|---|
| **141** | A25 | Block of 4 | 140.00 | 100.00 |
| *a.* | | $400 vermilion (1) | 8.50 | 6.00 |
| *b.* | | $400 vermilion (2) | 8.50 | 6.00 |
| *c.* | | $400 vermilion (3) | 8.50 | 6.00 |
| *d.* | | $400 vermilion (4) | 8.50 | 6.00 |
| **142** | A25 | Block of 4 | 140.00 | 100.00 |
| *a.* | | $400 blue (5) | 8.50 | 6.00 |
| *b.* | | $400 blue (6) | 8.50 | 6.00 |
| *c.* | | $400 blue (7) | 8.50 | 6.00 |
| *d.* | | $400 blue (8) | 8.50 | 6.00 |
| **143** | A25 | Block of 4 | 140.00 | 100.00 |
| *a.* | | $400 brown red (9) | 8.50 | 6.00 |
| *b.* | | $400 brown red (10) | 8.50 | 6.00 |
| *c.* | | $400 brown red (11) | 8.50 | 6.00 |
| *d.* | | $400 brown red (12) | 8.50 | 6.00 |
| **144** | A25 | Block of 4 | 140.00 | 100.00 |
| *a.* | | $400 yellow green (13) | 8.50 | 6.00 |
| *b.* | | $400 yellow green (14) | 8.50 | 6.00 |
| *c.* | | $400 yellow green (15) | 8.50 | 6.00 |
| *d.* | | $400 yellow green (16) | 8.50 | 6.00 |
| **145** | A25 | Block of 4 | 140.00 | 100.00 |
| *a.* | | $400 red orange (17) | 8.50 | 6.00 |
| *b.* | | $400 red orange (18) | 8.50 | 6.00 |
| *c.* | | $400 red orange (19) | 8.50 | 6.00 |
| *d.* | | $400 red orange (20) | 8.50 | 6.00 |
| **146** | A25 | Block of 4 | 140.00 | 100.00 |
| *a.* | | $400 dull blue (21) | 8.50 | 6.00 |
| *b.* | | $400 dull blue (22) | 8.50 | 6.00 |
| *c.* | | $400 dull blue (23) | 8.50 | 6.00 |
| *d.* | | $400 dull blue (24) | 8.50 | 6.00 |
| **147** | A25 | Block of 4 | 140.00 | 100.00 |
| *a.* | | $400 orange (25) | 8.50 | 6.00 |
| *b.* | | $400 orange (26) | 8.50 | 6.00 |
| *c.* | | $400 orange (27) | 8.50 | 6.00 |
| *d.* | | $400 orange (28) | 8.50 | 6.00 |
| **148** | A25 | Block of 4 | 140.00 | 100.00 |
| *a.* | | $400 dull purple (29) | 8.50 | 6.00 |
| *b.* | | $400 dull purple (30) | 8.50 | 6.00 |
| *c.* | | $400 dull purple (31) | 8.50 | 6.00 |
| *d.* | | $400 dull purple (32) | 8.50 | 6.00 |
| **149** | A25 | Block of 4 | 140.00 | 100.00 |
| *a.* | | $400 yellow bister (33) | 8.50 | 6.00 |
| *b.* | | $400 yellow bister (34) | 8.50 | 6.00 |
| *c.* | | $400 yellow bister (35) | 8.50 | 6.00 |
| *d.* | | $400 yellow bister (36) | 8.50 | 6.00 |
| **150** | A25 | Block of 4 | 140.00 | 100.00 |
| *a.* | | $400 sky blue (37) | 8.50 | 6.00 |
| *b.* | | $400 sky blue (38) | 8.50 | 6.00 |
| *c.* | | $400 sky blue (39) | 8.50 | 6.00 |
| *d.* | | $400 sky blue (40) | 8.50 | 6.00 |
| | | *Nos. 141-150 (10)* | 1,400. | 1,000. |

*Originals are on thin gray paper, colors darker. Reprints on thicker white paper, colors brighter. Value, set of blocks unused $55, used $37.50.*

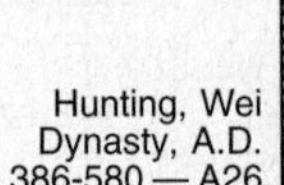

Hunting, Wei Dynasty, A.D. 386-580 — A26

**China Post No. S3**

Designs from Murals in Cave Temples at Tunhuang, Kansu Province: No. 152, Lady attendants, Sui Dynasty, 581-617 A.D. No. 153, Gandharvas (mythology), Tang Dynasty, 618-906. No. 154, Dragon, Tang Dynasty.

**1952, July 1 Engr.**

| | | | | |
|---|---|---|---|---|
| **151** | A26 | $800 slate green (1) | 2.00 | .65 |
| **152** | A26 | $800 chocolate (2) | 2.00 | .65 |
| *a.* | | Vert. pair, imperf. between | 500.00 | |
| **153** | A26 | $800 indigo (3) | 2.00 | .65 |
| **154** | A26 | $800 dk vio (4) | 2.00 | .65 |
| | | *Nos. 151-154 (4)* | 8.00 | 2.60 |

"Glorious Mother Country," 1st series.

Marco Polo Bridge, near Peking — A27

**China Post No. C16**

Designs: No. 156, Cavalry passing through Great Wall. No. 157, Departure of New Fourth Army. No. 158, Mao Tse-tung and Gen. Chu Teh planning counter-attack.

**1952, July 7 Litho. *Perf. 14***

| | | | | |
|---|---|---|---|---|
| **155** | A27 | $800 brt blue | 2.50 | .75 |
| **156** | A27 | $800 blue grn | 2.50 | .75 |
| **157** | A27 | $800 plum | 2.50 | .75 |
| **158** | A27 | $800 scarlet | 2.50 | .75 |
| | | *Nos. 155-158 (4)* | 10.00 | 3.00 |

15th anniversary of war against Japan.

Soldier, Sailor & Airman — A28

Soldier & Tanks — A28a

**China Post No. C17**

No. 161, Sailor & warships, horiz. No. 162, Airman & planes, horiz.

**1952, Aug. 1 Engr. *Perf. 12½***

| | | | | |
|---|---|---|---|---|
| **159** | A28 | $800 carmine | 2.50 | .65 |
| **160** | A28a | $800 deep green | 2.50 | .65 |
| **161** | A28a | $800 purple | 2.50 | .65 |
| **162** | A28a | $800 orange brown | 2.50 | .65 |
| | | *Nos. 159-162 (4)* | 10.00 | 2.60 |

25th anniv. of People's Liberation Army.

Huai River Sluice Dam — A29

**China Post No. S5**

No. 164, Train on the Chengtu-Chungking Railway. No. 165, Oil refinery and derricks in the Northwest. No. 166, Mechanized state farm.

**1952, Oct. 1 *Perf. 14***

| | | | | |
|---|---|---|---|---|
| **163** | A29 | $800 dk violet | 2.50 | .75 |
| **164** | A29 | $800 red | 2.50 | .75 |
| **165** | A29 | $800 dk vio brn | 2.50 | .75 |
| **166** | A29 | $800 dp green | 2.50 | .75 |
| | | *Nos. 163-166 (4)* | 10.00 | 3.00 |

"Glorious Mother Country," 2nd series.

Doves and Globe — A30

**China Post No. C18**

Designs: Nos. 167-168, Picasso dove over Pacific, vert. $2500, as No. 169.

**1952, Oct. 2 *Perf. 14***

| | | | | |
|---|---|---|---|---|
| **167** | A30 | $400 maroon | 1.75 | .50 |
| **168** | A30 | $800 red | 1.00 | .40 |
| **169** | A30 | $800 brown orange | 1.00 | .40 |
| **170** | A30 | $2500 deep green | 3.00 | .70 |
| | | *Nos. 167-170 (4)* | 6.75 | 2.00 |

Peace Conf. of the Asian and Pacific Regions.

Volunteers on the March — A31

**China Post No. C19**

No. 172, Chinese peasants loading supplies. No. 173, Volunteers attacking across river. No. 174, Meeting of Chinese & Korean troops.

**1952, Oct. 25**

| | | | | |
|---|---|---|---|---|
| **171** | A31 | $800 blue green (1) | 2.25 | .50 |
| **172** | A31 | $800 vermilion (2) | 2.75 | .60 |
| **173** | A31 | $800 violet (3) | 2.75 | .60 |
| **174** | A31 | $800 lake brown (4) | 2.75 | .60 |
| | | *Nos. 171-174 (4)* | 10.50 | 2.30 |

2nd anniv. of Chinese Volunteers in Korea.

Woman Textile Worker — A32

**China Post No. C21**

Design: No. 176, Farm woman with sickle.

**1953, Mar. 10**

| | | | | |
|---|---|---|---|---|
| **175** | A32 | $800 carmine | 1.75 | .50 |
| **176** | A32 | $800 emerald | 1.75 | .50 |

International Women's Day.

Textile Worker — A33

**China Post No. R6**

$200, Shepherdess. $250, Stone lion. $800, Lathe operator. $1600, Coal miners. $2000, Corner tower of Forbidden City, Peking.

**1953 Litho. *Perf. 14, 12½ ($250)***

| | | | | |
|---|---|---|---|---|
| **177** | A33 | $50 magenta | .75 | .30 |
| **178** | A33 | $200 emerald | 1.50 | .50 |
| **179** | A33 | $250 ultra | 4.50 | 2.00 |

**180** A33 $800 blue grn .85 .35
**181** A33 $1600 gray 1.25 1.00
**182** A33 $2000 red org 2.25 .45
*Nos. 177-182 (6)* 11.10 4.60

Issued: Nos. 177-181, Mar. 25; No. 182, May 23.

Karl Marx — A34

**China Post No. C22**

**1953, May 20 Engr. *Perf. 14***

**183** A34 $400 dk brown 2.50 .75
**184** A34 $800 slate grn 2.25 .75

135th anniv. of the birth of Karl Marx.

Workers and Banners — A35

**China Post No. C23**

**1953, June 25**

**185** A35 $400 Prus blue 2.25 .65
**186** A35 $800 carmine 2.25 .65

7th All-China Trade Union Congress.

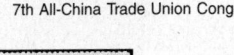

Picasso Dove — A36

**China Post No. C24**

**1953, July 25**

**187** A36 $250 blue grn 3.00 .90
**188** A36 $400 orange brn 2.00 .70
**189** A36 $800 purple 2.00 .60
*Nos. 187-189 (3)* 7.00 2.20

World Peace.

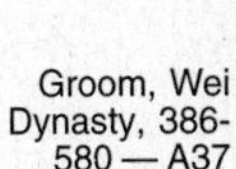

Groom, Wei Dynasty, 386-580 — A37

**China Post No. S6**

Scenes from Tunhuang Murals: No. 191, Court Players, Wei Dynasty. No. 192, Battle Scene, Sui Dynasty, 581-617. No. 193, Ox-drawn palanquin, Tang Dynasty, 618-906.

**1953, Sept. 1**

**190** A37 $800 dp green (1) 2.00 .75
**191** A37 $800 red org (2) 2.00 .75
**192** A37 $800 Prus blue (3) 2.00 .75
**193** A37 $800 carmine (4) 2.00 .75
*Nos. 190-193 (4)* 8.00 3.00

"Glorious Mother Country," 3rd series.

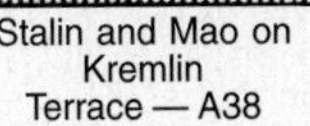

Stalin and Mao on Kremlin Terrace — A38

Statue of Stalin at Volga-Don Canal — A39

**China Post No. C20**

Designs: No. 195, Lenin proclaiming Soviet power. No. 197, Stalin as orator.

**1953, Oct. 5**

**194** A38 $800 green (1) 2.75 1.25
**195** A38 $800 carmine (2) 2.75 1.25
**196** A39 $800 brt blue (3) 3.75 2.00
**197** A39 $800 org brn (4) 4.00 1.50
*Nos. 194-197 (4)* 13.25 6.00

Russian October Revolution, 35th anniv.

Stamps in same designs with two additional characters meaning "Soviet" in the single-line Chinese inscription, and in different colors, were unofficially released at several small post offices in Hunan, Fukien and Canton areas in February, 1953, but were withdrawn after only a small number had been sold. Value, set $30,000. unused, $12,000 canceled.

Compass, 3rd Century B.C. — A40

**China Post No. S7**

No. 199, Seismoscope, later Han Dynasty. No. 200, Drum cart to measure distance, Chin Dynasty. No. 201, Armillary sphere, Ming Dynasty.

**1953, Dec. 1**

**198** A40 $800 indigo (1) 2.00 .90
**199** A40 $800 dk green (2) 2.00 .90
**200** A40 $800 dk blue (3) 2.00 .90
**201** A40 $800 choc (4) 2.00 .90
*Nos. 198-201 (4)* 8.00 3.60

Major inventions by ancient and medieval Chinese scientists.

"Glorious Mother Country," 4th series.

Francois Rabelais — A41

**China Post No. C25**

Designs: $400, Jose Marti, Cuban revolutionary. $800, Chu Yuan (350-275 B.C.), philosopher. $2200, Nicolaus Copernicus, astronomer.

**1953, Dec. 30**

**202** A41 $250 slate grn (3) 1.50 .50
**203** A41 $400 brown blk (4) 1.50 .50
**204** A41 $800 indigo (1) 1.50 .50
**205** A41 $2200 choc (2) 2.50 .85
*Nos. 202-205 (4)* 7.00 2.35

(same size) Gate of Heavenly Peace — A42

**China Post No. R7**

Sixth Issue: Inscription at upper right.

**1954, Apr. 16 Litho.**

**206** A42 $50 carmine .55 .35
**207** A42 $100 lt blue .55 .35
**208** A42 $200 green .55 .35
**209** A42 $250 ultra 3.75 .95
**210** A42 $400 gray grn 1.10 .25
**211** A42 $800 orange .65 .25
**212** A42 $1600 gray .90 *.75*
**213** A42 $2000 olive 1.40 .60
*Nos. 206-213 (8)* 9.45 3.85

Textile Plant, Harbin — A43

**China Post No. S8**

Designs: $200, Tangku Harbor. $250, Tienshui-Lanchow railroad bridge, Kansu Province. $400, Heavy machine-building plant, Taiyuan, Shansi. No. 218, Automatic blast, furnace, Anshan, Manchuria. No. 219, Fushun open-cut coal mine. $2000, Automatic power plant, Northeast. $3200, Prospecting in Tayeh district, Hupeh.

**1954, May 1 Engr.**

**214** A43 $100 brown olive 1.60 1.00
**215** A43 $200 blue green 2.10 1.00
**216** A43 $250 violet 1.90 .75
**217** A43 $400 black 1.90 1.00
**218** A43 $800 claret 1.90 .75
**219** A43 $800 indigo 1.90 .75
**220** A43 $2000 red 2.10 1.00
**221** A43 $3200 dark brown 2.10 1.00
*Nos. 214-221 (8)* 15.50 7.25

Economic progress.

Lenin — A44

**China Post No. C26**

$400, Lenin and Stalin Monument, Gorki, horiz. $2000, Lenin proclaiming Soviet power.

**1954, June 30 Engr.**

**222** A44 $400 deep green 2.50 1.25
**223** A44 $800 dark brown 3.50 1.50
**224** A44 $2000 deep carmine 4.00 2.00
*Nos. 222-224 (3)* 10.00 4.75

30th anniversary of the death of Lenin.

Pottery Vessels, Neolithic Period, 2000 B.C. — A45

**China Post No. S9**

Archeological Treasures: No. 226, Stone clime, Shang Dynasty, c. 1200 B.C. No. 227, Kuo Chi Tsu-pai bronze basin, Middle Chou Dynasty, 816 B.C. No. 228, Lacquered box and wine cup, Warring States Period, 403-221 B.C.

**1954, Aug. 25**

**225** A45 $800 brown 2.00 .60
**226** A45 $800 indigo 2.00 .60
**227** A45 $800 Prus bl 2.00 .60
**228** A45 $800 dk car 2.00 .60
*Nos. 225-228 (4)* 8.00 2.40

"Glorious Mother Country," 5th series.

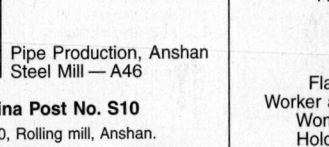

Pipe Production, Anshan Steel Mill — A46

**China Post No. S10**

Design: $800, Rolling mill, Anshan.

**1954, Oct. 1**

**229** A46 $400 Prus green 3.25 .75
**230** A46 $800 vio brown 3.25 .75

Stalin Statue, by Tomsky — A47

**China Post No. C27**

Designs: $800, Stalin portrait. $2000, Stalin viewing hydroelectric plant.

**1954, Oct. 15 Size: 21x45mm**

**231** A47 $400 black 5.00 .90

**Size: 26x37mm**

**232** A47 $800 black brown 2.25 .80

**Size: 42x26mm**

**233** A47 $2000 deep red 3.00 .80
*Nos. 231-233 (3)* 10.25 2.50

First anniversary of the death of Stalin.

Exhibition Building, Peking A48

**China Post No. C28**

**1954, Nov. 7**

**234** A48 $800 brown, *cream* 57.50 12.00
*a.* Size: 53½x24mm 72.50 20.00

Russian Economic and Cultural Exhibition, Peking. No. 234 measures 52½x24½mm.

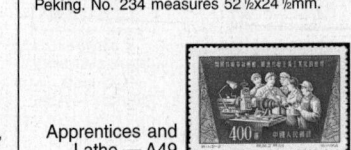

Apprentices and Lathe — A49

**China Post No. S11**

Progress in Technology: $800, Heavy machinery and workers.

**1954, Dec. 15**

**235** A49 $400 dk olive grn 2.40 .70
**236** A49 $800 bright red 3.60 .80

Woman Worker Voting — A50

People Celebrating Opening of Congress — A51

**China Post No. C29**

**1954, Dec. 30**

**237** A50 $400 deep claret 3.50 2.00
**238** A51 $800 bright red 4.25 2.25

First National Congress.

Flags, Worker and Woman Holding Constitution A52

**China Post No. C30**

**1954, Dec. 30**

**239** A52 $400 brown, *buff* 3.50 .75
**240** A52 $800 brt red, *yel* 4.25 1.50

Adoption of Constitution.

High-tension Pylon — A53

**China Post No. S12**

**1955, Feb. 25**

**241** A53 $800 dk Prus bl 6.75 1.50

Development of electric power.

Factory Health Workers and Red Cross — A54

### China Post No. C31

**1955, June 25 Engr.; Cross Typo.**

| | | | | |
|---|---|---|---|---|
| **242** | A54 | 8f dp grn & red | 20.00 | 3.00 |

50th anniversary of Chinese Red Cross.

Stalin and Mao in Kremlin — A55

Soviet Specialist and Chinese Worker — A56

### China Post No. C32

**1955, July 25 Engr.**

| | | | | |
|---|---|---|---|---|
| **243** | A55 | 8f brown red | 20.00 | 1.50 |
| **244** | A56 | 20f olive blk | 27.50 | 3.25 |

5th anniv. of Sino-Soviet Friendship Treaty.

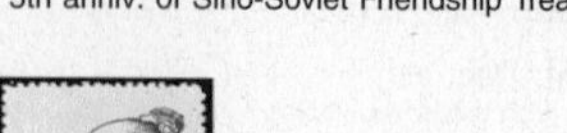

Chang Heng (78-139), Astronomer — A57

### China Post No. C33

Portraits of Scientists: No. 246, Tsu Chung-chih (429-500), mathematician. No. 247, Chang Sui (683-727), astronomer. No. 248, Li Shih-chen (1518-1593), physician and pharmacologist.

**1955, Aug. 25** ***Perf. 14***

| | | | | |
|---|---|---|---|---|
| **245** | A57 | 8f sepia, *buff* | 6.00 | 1.25 |
| *a.* | | Min. sheet, sepia, *white* | 90.00 | 20.00 |
| **246** | A57 | 8f dp grn, *buff* | 6.00 | 1.25 |
| *a.* | | Min. sheet, deep green, *white* | 90.00 | 20.00 |
| **247** | A57 | 8f black, *buff* | 6.00 | 1.25 |
| *a.* | | Min. sheet, blk, *white* | 90.00 | 20.00 |
| **248** | A57 | 8f claret, *buff* | 6.00 | 1.25 |
| *a.* | | Min. sheet, claret, *white* | 90.00 | 20.00 |
| | | *Nos. 245-248 (4)* | 24.00 | 5.00 |

Miniature sheets contain one imperf. stamp.

Steel Pouring Ladle — A58

### China Post No. S13

No. 250, High tension line (2). No. 251, Mechanized coal mining (3). No. 252, Tank cars and derricks (4). No. 253, Heavy machine shop (5). No. 254, Soldier on guard (6). No. 255, Spinning machine (7). No. 256, Workers discussing 5-year plan (8). No. 257, Combine harvester (9). No. 258, Milk production (10). No. 259, Dam (11). No. 260, Pottery industry (12). No. 261, Truck (13). No. 262, Ship at dock (14). No. 263, Geological survey (15). No. 264, Higher education (16). No. 265, Family (17). No. 266, Workers' rest home (18).

**1955-56 Litho.**

| | | | | |
|---|---|---|---|---|
| **249** | A58 | 8f shown (1) | 4.25 | .90 |
| **250** | A58 | 8f multicolored | 4.25 | .90 |
| **251** | A58 | 8f multicolored | 4.25 | .90 |
| **252** | A58 | 8f multicolored | 4.25 | .90 |
| **253** | A58 | 8f multicolored | 4.25 | .90 |
| **254** | A58 | 8f multicolored | 4.25 | .90 |
| **255** | A58 | 8f multicolored | 4.25 | .90 |
| **256** | A58 | 8f multicolored | 4.25 | .90 |
| **257** | A58 | 8f multicolored | 4.25 | .90 |
| **258** | A58 | 8f multicolored | 4.25 | .90 |
| **259** | A58 | 8f multicolored | 4.25 | .90 |
| **260** | A58 | 8f multi ('56) | 4.25 | .90 |
| **261** | A58 | 8f multicolored | 4.25 | .90 |
| **262** | A58 | 8f multicolored | 4.25 | .90 |
| **263** | A58 | 8f multicolored | 4.25 | .90 |
| **264** | A58 | 8f multicolored | 4.25 | .90 |
| **265** | A58 | 8f multicolored | 4.25 | .90 |
| **266** | A58 | 8f multi ('56) | 4.25 | .90 |
| | | *Nos. 249-266 (18)* | 76.50 | 16.20 |

1st 5 Year Plan. Issued: Nos. 249-257, 10/1; Nos. 258-259, 261-265, 12/15; Nos. 260, 266, 2/24/56.

Lenin — A59

### China Post No. C34

**1955, Dec. 15 Engr.** ***Perf. 14***

| | | | | |
|---|---|---|---|---|
| **267** | A59 | 8f dk blue grn | 22.50 | 1.75 |
| **268** | A59 | 20f dk rose car | 27.50 | 2.75 |

85th anniversary of the birth of Lenin.

Engels — A60

### China Post No. C35

**1955, Dec. 15**

| | | | | |
|---|---|---|---|---|
| **269** | A60 | 8f deep orange | 20.00 | 1.75 |
| **270** | A60 | 20f brown | 30.00 | 2.75 |

135th anniversary of the birth of Friedrich Engels (1820-1895), German socialist.

Storming Lu Ting Bridge A61

Crossing Great Snow Mountains A62

### China Post No. C36

**1955, Dec. 30**

| | | | | |
|---|---|---|---|---|
| **271** | A61 | 8f dark red | 20.00 | 1.25 |
| **272** | A62 | 8f dark blue | 28.00 | 3.50 |

Long March of Chinese Communist army, 20th anniversary.

Miner A63

Gate of Heavenly Peace A64

### China Post No. R8

Designs: 1f, Machinist. 2f, Airman. 2½f, Nurse. 4f, Soldier. 8f, Steel worker. 10f, Scientist. 20f, Farm woman. 50f, Sailor.

**1955-56 Litho.** ***Perf. 14***

| | | | | |
|---|---|---|---|---|
| **273** | A63 | ½f orange brn | 1.75 | .70 |
| **274** | A63 | 1f purple | 1.75 | .35 |
| **275** | A63 | 2f green | 3.50 | .80 |
| **276** | A63 | 2½f blue ('56) | 3.00 | .40 |
| **277** | A63 | 4f gray olive | 2.25 | .50 |
| **278** | A63 | 8f red org (Peking printing) | 15.00 | .75 |
| *a.* | | Perf. 12½ (Shanghai printing) | 400.00 | 40.00 |
| **279** | A63 | 10f claret ('56) | 7.00 | .70 |
| **280** | A63 | 20f dp blue | 12.00 | .80 |
| **281** | A63 | 50f gray | 3.75 | .95 |
| | | *Nos. 273-281 (9)* | 50.00 | 5.95 |

### China Post No. R9

**Engr.**

| | | | | |
|---|---|---|---|---|
| **282** | A64 | $1 claret ('56) | 5.00 | .60 |
| **283** | A64 | $2 sepia ('55) | 4.00 | .60 |
| **284** | A64 | $5 indigo ('56) | 8.50 | 1.00 |
| **285** | A64 | $10 dp org ('56) | 15.00 | 8.00 |
| **286** | A64 | $20 gray vio ('56) | 23.50 | *17.50* |
| | | *Nos. 282-286 (5)* | 56.00 | 27.70 |

Nos. 282-286 are the 7th Gate Issue. Used values for Nos. 282-286 are for postally used examples.

Trucks, Mountains, Highway Map — A65

Suspension Bridge over Tatu River — A66

### China Post No. S14

No. 289, 1st truck arriving in Lhasa, & the Potala.

**1956, Mar. 10 Engr.**

| | | | | |
|---|---|---|---|---|
| **287** | A65 | 4f dp blue | 4.25 | .95 |
| **288** | A66 | 8f dk brown | 2.40 | .65 |
| **289** | A65 | 8f carmine | 2.40 | .65 |
| | | *Nos. 287-289 (3)* | 9.05 | 2.25 |

Completion of Sikang-Tibet and Chinghai-Tibet Highways.

Summer Palace and Marble Boat — A67

### China Post No. S15

Famous Views of Imperial Peking: No. 291, Peihai Park with Jade Belt Marble Bridge. No. 292, Gate of Heavenly Peace. No. 293, Temple of Heaven. No. 294, Great Throne Hall, Forbidden City.

**1956-57**

| | | | | |
|---|---|---|---|---|
| **290** | A67 | 4f car rose (1) | 6.00 | 1.00 |
| **291** | A67 | 4f blue grn (2) | 6.00 | 1.00 |
| **292** | A67 | 8f red org (3) ('57) | 9.00 | 1.00 |
| **293** | A67 | 8f Prus blue (4) | 9.00 | 1.00 |
| **294** | A67 | 8f yellow brn (5) | 9.00 | 1.00 |
| | | *Nos. 290-294 (5)* | 39.00 | 5.00 |

Issued: No. 292, 2/20/57; others, 6/15/56.

No. 292 exists with sun rays in background. Values: unused, $250,000; used, $80,000.

Salt Making — A68

### China Post No. S16

Designs: No. 296, Dwelling of the Eastern Han period. No. 297, Duck hunting and harvesting. No. 298, Carriage crossing bridge.

**1956, Oct. 1**

| | | | | |
|---|---|---|---|---|
| **295** | A68 | 4f gray olive | 2.00 | .40 |
| **296** | A68 | 4f slate blue | 2.00 | .40 |
| **297** | A68 | 8f gray brown | 2.00 | .40 |
| **298** | A68 | 8f sepia | 2.00 | .40 |
| | | *Nos. 295-298 (4)* | 8.00 | 1.60 |

Murals, Tung Han Dynasty, 250 B.C.-220 A.D., found near Chengtu.

Ancient Coins and "Save" — A69

### China Post No. S17

**1956, Oct. 1**

| | | | | |
|---|---|---|---|---|
| **299** | A69 | 4f yellow brown | 10.00 | 1.25 |
| **300** | A69 | 8f rose red | 14.00 | 2.00 |

Promotion of saving.

Gate of Heavenly Peace — A70

### China Post No. C37

**1956, Nov. 10**

| | | | | |
|---|---|---|---|---|
| **301** | A70 | 4f dk green | 14.00 | .90 |
| **302** | A70 | 8f brt red | 17.50 | .90 |
| **303** | A70 | 16f dk carmine | 27.50 | 1.50 |
| | | *Nos. 301-303 (3)* | 59.00 | 3.30 |

8th National Congress of the Communist Party of China.

Sun Yat-sen — A71

### China Post No. C38

**1956, Nov. 12**

| | | | | |
|---|---|---|---|---|
| **304** | A71 | 4f brown, *cream* | 22.50 | 2.00 |
| **305** | A71 | 8f dp blue, *cream* | 32.50 | 3.25 |

90th anniversary of birth of Sun Yat-sen.

Weight Lifting — A72

### China Post No. C39

**1957, Mar. 20 Litho.** ***Perf. 12½***

**Hibiscus red and green; inscription brown**

| | | | | |
|---|---|---|---|---|
| **306** | A72 | 4f Shot put (2) | 3.00 | .50 |
| **307** | A72 | 4f shown (5) | 3.00 | .50 |
| **308** | A72 | 8f Track (1) | 3.00 | .50 |
| **309** | A72 | 8f Soccer (3) | 3.00 | .50 |
| **310** | A72 | 8f Bicycling (4) | 3.00 | .50 |
| | | *Nos. 306-310 (5)* | 15.00 | 2.50 |

First National Workers' Sports Meeting.

Truck Factory No. 1, Changchun A73

### China Post No. C40

China's truck industry: 8f, Trucks rolling off assembly line.

**1957, May 1 Engr.** ***Perf. 14***

| | | | | |
|---|---|---|---|---|
| **311** | A73 | 4f light brown | 3.00 | .75 |
| **312** | A73 | 8f slate green | 4.00 | .75 |

Nanchang Uprising A74

### China Post No. C41

No. 314, Mao and Chu Teh at Chingkanshan. No. 315, Crossing Yellow River. No. 316, Liberation of Nanking, 4/23/49.

**1957**

| | | | | |
|---|---|---|---|---|
| **313** | A74 | 4f blk vio (1) | 31.00 | 3.25 |
| **314** | A74 | 4f slate grn (2) | 31.00 | 2.75 |
| **315** | A74 | 8f red brn (3) | 31.00 | 2.75 |
| **316** | A74 | 8f dp blue (4) | 31.00 | 2.75 |
| | | *Nos. 313-316 (4)* | 124.00 | 11.50 |

People's Liberation Army, 30th anniv. Issued: Nos. 313, 315, 8/10; No. 314, 8/30; No. 316, 12/30.

Congress Emblem — A75

### China Post No. C42

**1957, Sept. 30**

| | | | | |
|---|---|---|---|---|
| **317** | A75 | 8f chocolate | 9.00 | 1.50 |
| **318** | A75 | 22f indigo | 12.00 | 1.10 |

4th Intl. Trade Union Cong., Leipzig, 10/4-15.

Yangtze River Bridge — A76

**China Post No. C43**

20f, Road leading to and over bridge.

**1957, Oct. 1**

**319** A76 8f scarlet 3.00 .60
**320** A76 20f slate blue 5.25 1.20

Completion of Yangtze River Bridge at Wuhan.

Fireworks over Kremlin — A77

**China Post No. C44**

Designs: 8f, Hammer and sickle over globe and broken chain. 20f, Stylized dove and olive branch. 22f, Hands of three races holding book with Marx and Lenin. 32f, Star and pylon.

**1957, Nov. 7**

**321** A77 4f brt red 5.00 .95
**322** A77 8f chocolate 6.00 .95
**323** A77 20f dp green 11.00 .95
**324** A77 22f red brown 13.50 2.50
**325** A77 32f dp blue 27.50 3.00
*Nos. 321-325 (5)* 63.00 8.35

40th anniv. of Russian October Revolution.

Map of Yellow River Basin — A78

**China Post No. S19**

No. 327, Sanmen Gorge dam & powerhouse. No. 328, Ocean liner on Yellow River. No. 329, Dam, irrigation canals & tree-bordered fields.

**1957, Dec. 30**

**326** A78 4f deep orange (1) 19.00 2.25
**327** A78 4f deep blue (2) 19.00 2.25
**328** A78 8f deep lake (3) 31.00 2.00
**329** A78 8f blue green (4) 31.00 2.00
*Nos. 326-329 (4)* 100.00 8.50

Yellow River control plan.

Old Man and Young Drummer — A79

**China Post No. S20**

**1957, Dec. 30** **Litho.**

**330** A79 8f shown (1) 2.60 .70
**331** A79 8f Plowman (2) 2.60 .70
**332** A79 8f Woman planting tree (3) 2.60 .70
**333** A79 8f Harvest (4) 2.60 .70
*Nos. 330-333 (4)* 10.40 2.80

Agricultural cooperation.

Train on Bridge, Ship and Train — A80

**China Post No. C45**

Designs (Congratulatory Banner and): 4f, Crane, dove and flowers. 8f, Crane with hot ingots, cotton bolls and wheat.

**1958, Jan. 30** **Engr.**

**334** A80 4f emer, *cream* 2.50 1.50
**335** A80 8f red, *cream* 2.50 1.50
**336** A80 16f ultra, *cream* 2.50 1.50
*Nos. 334-336 (3)* 7.50 4.50

Fulfillment of First Five-Year Plan.

Sungyu Pagoda, Honan — A81

**China Post No. S21**

Ancient Pagodas: No. 338, Chienhsun Pagoda, Yunnan. No. 339, Sakyamuni Pagoda, Shansi. No. 340, Flying Rainbow Pagoda, Shansi.

**1958, Mar. 15** **Engr.**

**337** A81 8f sepia (1) 4.75 1.10
**338** A81 8f Prus blue (2) 4.75 1.10
**339** A81 8f maroon (3) 4.75 1.10
**340** A81 8f dp green (4) 4.75 1.10
*Nos. 337-340 (4)* 19.00 4.40

Trilobite, Kaoli — A82

**China Post No. S22**

Designs: 8f, Lufeng dinosaur. 16f, Choukoutien sino-megaceros.

**1958, Apr. 15**

**341** A82 4f blue 2.50 .80
**342** A82 8f sepia 3.50 .50
**343** A82 16f slate green 3.75 .50
*Nos. 341-343 (3)* 9.75 1.80

Prehistoric animals of China.

Heroes Monument — A83

**China Post No. C47**

**1958, May 1**

**344** A83 8f scarlet 42.50 4.25
*a.* Souvenir sheet, imperf. *275.00* 110.00

Unveiling of People's Heroes Monument, Peking. No. 344a issued May 30.

Karl Marx — A84

**China Post No. C46**

Design: 22f, Marx Speaking to German Workers' Educational Association, London, painting by Zhukow.

**1958, May 5**

**345** A84 8f chocolate 22.00 1.75
**346** A84 22f dk green 28.00 4.00

Karl Marx (1818-83), 140th birth anniv.

Cogwheels and Factories — A85

**China Post No. C48**

**1958, May 25**

**347** A85 4f brt grnsh bl 22.50 2.25
**348** A85 8f red lilac 35.00 3.50

8th All-China Trade Union Cong., Peking.

Dove over Globe — A86

**China Post No. C49**

**1958, June 1**

**349** A86 8f violet blue 10.00 1.75
**350** A86 20f blue green 17.50 3.25

4th Congress of the Intl. Democratic Women's Federation, Vienna, June 1958.

Mother and Child — A87

**China Post No. S18**

Children's Day: No. 352, Watering sunflowers. No. 353, Playing hide-and-seek. No. 354, Sailing toy boat.

**1958, June 1** **Litho.**

**351** A87 8f green & multi (1) 25.00 2.40
**352** A87 8f green & multi (2) 25.00 2.40
**353** A87 8f green & multi (3) 25.00 2.40
**354** A87 8f green & multi (4) 25.00 2.40
*Nos. 351-354 (4)* 100.00 9.60

Kuan Han-ching — A88

**China Post No. C50**

Designs (Operas): 4f, "Dream of Butterflies." 20f, "The Riverside Pavilion."

**1958, June 20** **Engr.**

**355** A88 4f indigo, *cr* 32.50 3.00
**356** A88 8f brown, *cr* 35.00 2.50
**357** A88 20f black, *cr* 50.00 4.50
*a.* Souvenir sheet of 3, *ivory* 475.00 100.00
*Nos. 355-357 (3)* 117.50 10.00

700th anniversary of publication of works of Kuan Han-ching (1210-1280), dramatist. No. 357a contains 3 imperf. stamps similar to Nos. 355-357. Size: 130x100mm. Issued June 28.

Planetarium — A89

**China Post No. S23**

20f, Telescope and stars over Peking.

**1958, June 25**

**358** A89 8f dk green 9.00 2.00
**359** A89 20fr indigo 13.50 2.50

First Chinese planetarium, Peking.

Marx and Engels — A90

**China Post No. C51**

8f, Cover of 1st edition of the Communist Manifesto.

**1958, July 1**

**360** A90 4f dk red vio 29.00 3.50
**361** A90 8f Prus blue 34.00 2.00

110th anniversary of publication of the Communist Manifesto.

Wild Goose and Broadcasting Tower — A91

**China Post No. C52**

**1958, July 10**

**362** A91 4f ultra 20.00 3.75
**363** A91 8f deep green 25.00 2.00

1st Conference of the Ministers of Posts and Telecommunications of Socialist Countries, Moscow, Dec. 3-17, 1957.

Peony and Doves — A92

**China Post No. C53**

8f, Olive branch with ribbon & clouds. 22f, Atomic energy symbol over factories.

**1958, July 20**

**364** A92 4f red 20.00 3.25
**365** A92 8f green 16.00 2.75
**366** A92 22f red brown 27.50 5.00
*Nos. 364-366 (3)* 63.50 11.00

Congress for Disarmament and International Cooperation, Stockholm, July 17-22.

Bronze Weather Vane — A93

**China Post No. S24**

Designs: No. 368, Weather balloon. No. 369, Typhoon tower and weather map of Asia.

**1958, Aug. 25**

**367** A93 8f yel bis & blk (1) 2.25 .65
**368** A93 8f blue & blk (2) 2.25 .65
**369** A93 8f brt grn & blk (3) 2.25 .65
*Nos. 367-369 (3)* 6.75 1.95

Meteorological services in ancient and modern China.

"5" Encircling IUS Emblem — A94

**China Post No. C54**

**1958, Sept. 4**

**370** A94 8f rose lilac 25.00 2.25
**371** A94 22f dp blue grn 42.50 3.75

Intl. Union of Students, 5th Cong., Peking, 9/4-13.

Nos. 370-371 exist with incorrect inscription. Values: No. 370, unused $15,000; used $6,000; No. 371, unused $160,000; used $120,000.

Telegraph Building, Peking — A95

**China Post No. C56**

**1958, Sept. 29**

**372** A95 4f greenish black 6.00 1.00
**373** A95 8f rose red 6.00 1.00

Opening of Telegraph Building, Peking.

Exhibition Emblem and Exhortation — A96

**China Post No. C55**

Designs: No. 375, Dragon over clouds signifying "aiming high." No. 376, Flying horses, signifying "great leap forward" in production.

**1958, Oct. 1**

| | | | | |
|---|---|---|---|---|
| **374** | A96 | 8f slate grn (1) | 20.00 | 1.50 |
| **375** | A96 | 8f rose car (2) | 20.00 | 1.50 |
| **376** | A96 | 8f red brown (3) | 20.00 | 1.75 |
| | | *Nos. 374-376 (3)* | 60.00 | 4.75 |

National Exhibition of Industry and Communications, Peking.

Worker and Excavator — A97

**China Post No. S26**

Design: 8f, Completed dam and pylon.

**1958, Oct. 25**

| | | | | |
|---|---|---|---|---|
| **377** | A97 | 4f dark brown | 3.50 | .75 |
| **378** | A97 | 8f deep Prussian blue | 5.50 | .60 |

13 Ming Tombs Reservoir completion.

Sputnik 3 in Orbit — A98

**China Post No. S25**

Designs: 4f, Sputnik over armillary sphere. 10f, Trajectories of 3 Sputniks over earth.

**1958, Oct. 30**

| | | | | |
|---|---|---|---|---|
| **379** | A98 | 4f scarlet | 8.00 | 1.25 |
| **380** | A98 | 8f dp violet bl | 6.00 | 1.10 |
| **381** | A98 | 10f dp green | 9.00 | 1.90 |
| | | *Nos. 379-381 (3)* | 23.00 | 4.25 |

Anniversary of first earth satellite launched by the USSR.

Chinese and North Korean Soldiers — A99

**China Post No. C57**

Designs: No. 383, Chinese soldier embracing Korean woman. No. 384, Chinese girl presenting flowers to returning soldier.

**1958, Nov. 20**

| | | | | |
|---|---|---|---|---|
| **382** | A99 | 8f brt purple (1) | 7.50 | .90 |
| **383** | A99 | 8f chestnut (2) | 7.50 | 1.25 |
| **384** | A99 | 8f rose car (3) | 7.50 | 1.25 |
| | | *Nos. 382-384 (3)* | 22.50 | 3.40 |

Return of the Chinese Volunteers from Korea.

Forest and Mountains — A100

**China Post No. S27**

Afforestation: No. 386, Mounted forest patrol. No. 387, Mechanized lumbering, horiz. No. 388, Tree-planting: "Turning the Country Green," horiz.

**1958, Dec. 15**

| | | | | |
|---|---|---|---|---|
| **385** | A100 | 8f dp blue grn (1) | 5.50 | 1.00 |
| **386** | A100 | 8f slate grn (2) | 5.50 | 1.00 |
| **387** | A100 | 8f dk purple (3) | 5.50 | 1.00 |
| **388** | A100 | 8f indigo (4) | 5.50 | 1.00 |
| | | *Nos. 385-388 (4)* | 22.00 | 4.00 |

Peony — A101

**China Post No. R10**

Designs: 3f, Lotus. 5f, Chrysanthemums.

**1958, Sept. 25** **Litho.**

| | | | | |
|---|---|---|---|---|
| **389** | A101 | 1½f lilac rose | 3.75 | 1.00 |
| **390** | A101 | 3f blue grn | 15.00 | 2.40 |
| **391** | A101 | 5f dp orange | 2.00 | .55 |
| | | *Nos. 389-391 (3)* | 20.75 | 3.95 |

Atomic Reactor — A102

**China Post No. S28**

**1958, Dec. 30** **Engr.**

| | | | | |
|---|---|---|---|---|
| **392** | A102 | 8f shown | 18.00 | 2.50 |
| **393** | A102 | 20f Cyclotron | 25.00 | 3.00 |

Inauguration of China's first atomic reactor and cyclotron, Peking.

Children Launching Model Planes — A103

**China Post No. S29**

8f, Gliders over trees. 10f, Parachutists descending. 20f, Small monoplanes in mid-air.

**1958, Dec. 30**

| | | | | |
|---|---|---|---|---|
| **394** | A103 | 4f carmine | 2.25 | .50 |
| **395** | A103 | 8f dp slate grn | 2.25 | .50 |
| **396** | A103 | 10f dk brown | 3.00 | .65 |
| **397** | A103 | 20f Prus blue | 4.00 | .85 |
| | | *Nos. 394-397 (4)* | 11.50 | 2.50 |

Sports-aviation publicity.

Camel Carrying Load — A104

**China Post No. S30**

Designs: No. 399, Pomegranates. No. 400, Rooster. No. 401, Theatrical figure.

**1959, Jan. 1**

| | | | | |
|---|---|---|---|---|
| **398** | A104 | 8f vio & blk (1) | 17.50 | 1.10 |
| **399** | A104 | 8f dp bl grn & blk (2) | 17.50 | 1.10 |
| **400** | A104 | 8f red & blk (3) | 17.50 | 1.10 |
| **401** | A104 | 8f dp bl & blk (4) | 17.50 | 1.10 |
| | | *Nos. 398-401 (4)* | 70.00 | 4.40 |

Paper cut-outs (folk art).

Red Flag, Mao and Workers — A105

**China Post No. C58**

Designs: 8f, Traditional and modern blast furnaces. 10f, Steel works and workers.

**1959**

| | | | | |
|---|---|---|---|---|
| **402** | A105 | 4f brt red | 30.00 | 1.75 |
| **403** | A105 | 8f lake | 30.00 | 1.75 |
| **404** | A105 | 10f deep red | 35.00 | 2.25 |
| | | *Nos. 402-404 (3)* | 95.00 | 5.75 |

"Great Leap Forward" in steel production.
Issue dates: 4f, 8f, Feb. 19; 10f, May 25.

Women Workers and Atomic Model — A106

**China Post No. C59**

Design: 22f, Chinese and Soviet women holding banners dated "3.8."

**1959, Mar. 8**

| | | | | |
|---|---|---|---|---|
| **405** | A106 | 8f emerald, *cr* | 3.00 | .60 |
| **406** | A106 | 22f magenta, *cr* | 4.50 | 1.25 |

International Women's Day.

Natural History Museum — A107

**China Post No. S31**

**1959, Apr. 1**

| | | | | |
|---|---|---|---|---|
| **407** | A107 | 4f greenish blue | 3.25 | 1.00 |
| **408** | A107 | 8f olive brown | 3.25 | .75 |

Opening of Museum of Natural History, Peking.

Wheat — A108

**China Post No. C60**

Designs on Chinese Flag: No. 410, Rice. No. 411, Cotton bolls. No. 412, Soybeans, rapeseed and peanuts.

**1959, Apr. 25**

| | | | | |
|---|---|---|---|---|
| **409** | A108 | 8f red (1) | 5.00 | .70 |
| **410** | A108 | 8f red (2) | 5.00 | .70 |
| **411** | A108 | 8f red (3) | 5.00 | .70 |
| **412** | A108 | 8f red (4) | 5.00 | .70 |
| *a.* | | Block of 4, #409-412 | 47.50 | 12.00 |

Successful harvest, 1958.

A109

**China Post No. C61**

Designs: 4f, Marx, Lenin and workers. 8f, Black, yellow and white fists holding banner. 22f, Steel workers parading with banners dated "5.1."

**1959, May 1**

| | | | | |
|---|---|---|---|---|
| **413** | A109 | 4f ultra | 7.50 | 1.60 |
| **414** | A109 | 8f red | 10.00 | 1.25 |
| **415** | A109 | 22f emerald | 20.00 | 2.25 |
| | | *Nos. 413-415 (3)* | 37.50 | 5.10 |

International Labor Day.

A110

**China Post No. S34**

8f, Peking airport. 10f, Plane loading on runway.

**1959, June 20**

| | | | | |
|---|---|---|---|---|
| **416** | A110 | 8f lilac & blk | 24.00 | 2.00 |
| **417** | A110 | 10f ol gray & blk | 32.50 | 2.50 |

Opening of new Peking Airport.

Students with Marx-Lenin Banners — A111

**China Post No. C62**

Design: 8f, Workers with banners of Mao.

**1959, July 1** **Photo.** ***Perf. 11x11½***

| | | | | |
|---|---|---|---|---|
| **418** | A111 | 4f gray, red & dk brn | 32.50 | 12.00 |
| **419** | A111 | 8f bis, red & dk brn | 60.00 | 8.00 |

40th anniv. of the May 4th students' uprising.

Frederick Joliot-Curie — A112

**China Post No. C63**

22f, Three races, dove and olive branch.

**1959, July 25** **Engr.** ***Perf. 11½***

| | | | | |
|---|---|---|---|---|
| **420** | A112 | 8f violet brn | 10.00 | 2.75 |
| **421** | A112 | 22f dk violet | 20.00 | 3.25 |

10th anniv. of the World Peace Movement.

Stamp Printing Plant, Peking — A113

**China Post No. C65**

**1959, Aug. 15** ***Perf. 11x11½***

| | | | | |
|---|---|---|---|---|
| **422** | A113 | 8f dp blue grn | 15.00 | 2.00 |

Sino-Czechoslovak cooperation in stamp production.

Table Tennis — A114

**China Post No. C66**

**1959, Aug. 30** **Litho.** ***Perf. 14***

| | | | | |
|---|---|---|---|---|
| **423** | A114 | 4f black & blue | 8.50 | 1.25 |
| **424** | A114 | 8f black & red | 7.50 | .90 |

25th World Table Tennis Championships, Dortmund, German Democratic Republic.

Soviet Space Rocket — A115

**China Post No. S33**

**1959, Sept. 10** **Photo.** ***Perf. 11½***

| | | | | |
|---|---|---|---|---|
| **425** | A115 | 8f Prus bl, red & blk | 25.00 | 3.25 |

Launching of first Russian space rocket, Jan. 2, 1959.

Backyard Steel Production — A116

**China Post No. S35**

Designs: No. 426, Sun rising over "industry and agriculture." No. 428, Farming. No. 429, Trade. No. 430, Education. No. 431, Militia. No. 432, Communal dining. No. 433, Nursery. No. 434, Care for the aged. No. 435, Health services. No. 436, Flutist; culture and sports. No. 437, Flower symbolizing unity of industry, agriculture, trade, education and armed forces.

Position-in-set number in ( ).

**1959, Sept. 25** **Engr.**

| | | | | |
|---|---|---|---|---|
| **426** | A116 | 8f rose (1) | 5.00 | .80 |
| **427** | A116 | 8f violet brn (2) | 5.00 | .80 |
| **428** | A116 | 8f dp orange (3) | 5.00 | .80 |
| **429** | A116 | 8f slate grn (4) | 5.00 | .80 |
| **430** | A116 | 8f dp blue (5) | 5.00 | .80 |
| **431** | A116 | 8f olive (6) | 5.00 | .80 |
| **432** | A116 | 8f indigo (7) | 5.00 | .80 |
| **433** | A116 | 8f lilac rose (8) | 5.00 | .80 |
| **434** | A116 | 8f gray blk (9) | 5.00 | .80 |
| **435** | A116 | 8f emerald (10) | 5.00 | .80 |
| **436** | A116 | 8f dk violet (11) | 5.00 | .80 |
| **437** | A116 | 8f red (12) | 5.00 | .80 |
| | | *Nos. 426-437 (12)* | 60.00 | 9.60 |

First anniversary of Peoples' Communes.

Mao and Gate of Heavenly Peace — A117

**China Post No. C67**

Designs: No. 439, Marx, Lenin and Kremlin. 22f, Dove over globe.

*Perf. 11½ x 11*

**1959, Sept. 28** **Photo.**

**With Gum**

**438** A117 8f lt brown & red 55.00 3.75
**439** A117 8f dull blue & red 25.00 2.25
**440** A117 22f blue grn & red 27.50 8.50
*Nos. 438-440 (3)* 107.50 14.50
Set, never hinged 170.00

National Emblem — A118

**China Post No. C68**

**1959, Oct. 1** **Litho.** ***Perf. 14***

**441** A118 4f pale grn, red & gold 12.00 2.10
**442** A118 8f gray, red & gold 14.00 2.10
**443** A118 10f lt blue, red & gold 22.50 3.75
**444** A118 20f pale brn, red & gold 32.50 4.75
*Nos. 441-444 (4)* 81.00 12.70

Blast Furnaces — A119

**China Post No. C69**

No. 446, Large coal mine. No. 447, Planer, Wuhan heavy machinery plant. No. 448, Wuhan Yangtze River Bridge. No. 449, Combine harvester. No. 450, Hsinankiang hydroelectric station. No. 451, Spinning machine. No. 452, Kirin chemical fertilizer plant.

**Engraved and Photogravure**

**1959, Oct. 1** ***Perf. 11½ x 11***

**With Gum**

**445** A119 8f brown & rose red (1) 4.50 1.50
**446** A119 8f brown & gray (2) 4.50 1.50
**447** A119 8f brown & yel brn (3) 4.50 1.50
**448** A119 8f brown & stl bl (4) 4.50 1.50
**449** A119 8f brown & org (5) 4.50 1.50
**450** A119 8f brown & ol (6) 4.50 1.50
**451** A119 8f brown & bl grn (7) 4.50 1.50
**452** A119 8f brown & vio (8) 4.50 1.50
*Nos. 445-452 (8)* 36.00 12.00
Set, never hinged 62.50

Celebration at Gate of Heavenly Peace — A120

**China Post No. C70**

Designs: 10f, Workers and factory, vert. 20f, People rejoicing, vert.

**1959, Oct. 1** **Litho.** ***Perf. 14***

**453** A120 8f cream & multi 9.50 3.25
**454** A120 10f cream & multi 17.50 3.75
**455** A120 20f cream & multi 22.50 5.50
*Nos. 453-455 (3)* 49.50 12.50

Mao Proclaiming Republic — A121

**China Post No. C71**

**1959, Oct. 1** **Engr.**

**456** A121 20f deep carmine 450.00 75.00

Nos. 438-456 commemorate 10th anniversary of the Proclamation of the People's Republic of China.

A122

**China Post No. C64**

Designs: No. 457, Pioneers' emblem. No. 458, Pioneer Bugler. No. 459, Schoolgirl. No. 460, Girl using rain gauge. No. 461, Boy planting tree. No. 462, Girl figure skater.

**1959, Nov. 10** **Photo.** ***Perf. 11½***

**457** A122 4f red yel & blk (1) 13.00 1.00
**458** A122 4f Prus bl & red (2) 13.00 1.00
**459** A122 8f brn & red (3) 12.00 1.00
**460** A122 8f dk bl & red (4) 12.00 1.00
**461** A122 8f red & grn (5) 12.00 1.00
**462** A122 8f mag & red (6) 12.00 1.00
*Nos. 457-462 (6)* 74.00 6.00

10th anniversary of the Young Pioneers. Black inscription on No. 457 engraved.

A123

**China Post No. C73**

4f, Exhibition emblem, communications symbols. 8f, Exhibition emblem & chimneys.

**1959, Dec. 1** **Engr.**

**463** A123 4f dark blue 2.75 .80
**464** A123 8f red 3.25 .80

Exhibition of Industry and Communications, Peking.

Palace of Nationalities A124

**China Post No. S36**

**Engraved, Frame Lithographed**

**1959, Dec. 10** ***Perf. 14***

**465** A124 4f red & blk 13.00 1.75
**466** A124 8f brt grn & blk 14.00 1.50

Inauguration of the Cultural Palace of Nationalities, Peking.

Athletes' Monument and Track — A125

**China Post No. C72**

Sports: No. 468, Parachuting. No. 469, Marksmanship. No. 470, Diving. No. 471, Table tennis. No. 472, Weight lifting. No. 473, High jump. No. 474, Rowing. No. 475, Track. No. 476, Basketball. No. 477, Traditional Chinese fencing. No. 478, Motorcycling. No. 479, Gymnastics. No. 480, Bicycling. No. 481, Horsemanship. No. 482, Soccer.

**1959, Dec. 28** **Litho.**

**467** A125 8f bis, blk & gray (1) 7.50 1.00
**468** A125 8f dl bl, blk & gray (2) 7.50 1.00
**469** A125 8f red brn & blk (3) 7.50 1.00
**470** A125 8f grn, blk & brn (4) 7.50 1.00
**471** A125 8f brt grn, blk, brn & gray (5) 7.50 1.00
**472** A125 8f gray, blk & brn (6) 7.50 1.00
**473** A125 8f dl bl, blk & brn (7) 7.50 1.00
**474** A125 8f Prus grn, blk & brn (8) 7.50 1.00
**475** A125 8f org, blk & brn (9) 7.50 1.00
**476** A125 8f dl vio, blk & brn (10) 7.50 1.00
**477** A125 8f lt ol, blk & brn (11) 7.50 1.00
**478** A125 8f bl, blk & gray (12) 7.50 1.00
**479** A125 8f gray bl, blk, grn, & bl (13) 7.50 1.00
**480** A125 8f gray, blk, brn, & vio (14) 7.50 1.00
**481** A125 8f red org, blk, brn, & gray (15) 7.50 1.00
**482** A125 8f lt gray, blk, brn, & red (16) 7.50 1.00
*Nos. 467-482 (16)* 120.00 16.00

First National Sports Meeting, Peking.

Wheat and Main Pavilion — A126

**China Post No. S37**

Designs (Pavilion and): 8f, Meteorological symbols. 10f, Domestic animals. 20f, Fish.

**1960, Jan. 20** **Engr. & Litho.**

**Cream Background**

**483** A126 4f black & org 2.00 .85
**484** A126 8f black & dull bl 2.00 .85
**485** A126 10f black & org brn 2.00 .85
**486** A126 20f black & grnsh bl 2.25 1.00
*Nos. 483-486 (4)* 8.25 3.55

Opening of the National Agricultural Exhibition Halls, Peking.

With Gum

From No. 487 onward all stamps were issued with gum except as noted.

**Catalogue values for unused stamps in this section, from this point to the end of the section, are for Never Hinged items without gum toning.**

Conference Hall, Tsunyi — A127

**China Post No. C74**

Designs: 8f, Mao addressing conference. 10f, Crossing Chinsha River.

**Engraved (4f, 10f); Photogravure (8f)**

**1960, Jan. 25** ***Perf. 11x11½***

**487** A127 4f violet & blue 60.00 9.50
**488** A127 8f red & multi 77.50 7.75
**489** A127 10f slate green 140.00 11.00
*Nos. 487-489 (3)* 277.50 28.25

25th anniversary of the Communist Party Conference at Tsunyi.

Clara Zetkin (1857-1933) — A128

**China Post No. C76**

8f, Mother, child and dove. 10f, Woman tractor driver. 22f, Women of three races.

**1960, Mar. 8** **Photo.** ***Perf. 11½x11***

**490** A128 4f black & multi 6.50 1.00
**491** A128 8f black & multi 11.00 1.00
**492** A128 10f black & multi 15.00 1.50
**493** A128 22f black & multi 17.50 2.25
*Nos. 490-493 (4)* 50.00 5.75

50th anniv. of International Women's Day.

Chinese and Russian Workers — A129

**China Post No. C75**

Designs: 8f, Chinese and Russian flags. 10f, Chinese and Russian soldiers.

**1960, Mar. 10**

**494** A129 4f dk brown 26.00 5.00
**495** A129 8f red, yel & blk 34.00 3.00
**496** A129 10f dp blue 47.50 9.00
*Nos. 494-496 (3)* 107.50 17.00

10th anniv. of Sino-Soviet Treaty of Friendship. Black inscription engraved on No. 495.

Flags of Hungary and China — A130

**China Post No. C78**

Design: 8f, Parliament Building, Budapest.

**1960, Apr. 4** ***Perf. 11 x 11½***

**497** A130 8f yel, blk, red & grn 52.50 7.25
**498** A130 8f blue, red & blk 52.50 7.25

15th anniv. of the liberation of Hungary.

Lenin Speaking — A131

**China Post No. C77**

Designs: 8f, Portrait of Lenin. 20f, Lenin talking with Smolny Palace guard.

**Engraved (4f, 20f); Engraved and Photogravure (8f)**

**1960, Apr. 22** ***Perf. 11½ x 11***

**499** A131 4f violet brn 27.50 1.90
**500** A131 8f org red & blk 30.00 2.75
**501** A131 20f dk brown 50.00 4.50
*Nos. 499-501 (3)* 107.50 9.15

90th anniversary of the birth of Lenin.

Lunik 2, Moon and Russian Arms — A132

**China Post No. S39**

Design: 10f, Lunik 3 over moon.

**1960, Apr. 30** **Engr.** ***Perf. 11½***

**502** A132 8f red 11.00 1.90
**503** A132 10f green 17.50 2.50

Russian space flights.

Pioneers and Flags of Czechoslovakia and China — A133

View of Prague with Charles Bridge — A134

**China Post No. C79**

***Perf. 11½x11; 11x11½***

**1960, May 9** **Photo.**

| No. | Type | Description | Unused | Used |
|---|---|---|---|---|
| **504** | A133 | 8f yellow & multi | 50.00 | 6.50 |
| **505** | A134 | 8f deep green | 50.00 | 6.50 |

Liberation of Czechoslovakia, 15th anniv.

Nostril Bouquet — A135

**China Post No. S38**

Various goldfish: No. 507, Black-back dragon eye (2). No. 508, Bubble eye (3). No. 509, Red tiger head (4). No. 510, Pearl scale (5). No. 511, Blue dragon eye (6). No. 512, Skyward eye (7). No. 513, Red cap (8). No. 514, Purple cap (9). No. 515, Red head (10). No. 516, Red and white dragon eye (11). No. 517, Red dragon eye (12).

**1960, June 1** ***Perf. 11x11½***

| No. | Type | Description | Unused | Used |
|---|---|---|---|---|
| **506** | A135 | 4f shown (1) | *110.00* | *7.00* |
| **507** | A135 | 4f multi | *110.00* | *7.00* |
| **508** | A135 | 4f multi | *130.00* | *7.00* |
| **509** | A135 | 4f multi | *110.00* | *7.00* |
| **510** | A135 | 8f multi | *300.00* | *7.00* |
| **511** | A135 | 8f multi | *130.00* | *7.00* |
| **512** | A135 | 8f multi | *240.00* | *7.00* |
| **513** | A135 | 8f multi | *75.00* | *10.50* |
| **514** | A135 | 8f multi | *75.00* | *10.50* |
| **515** | A135 | 8f multi | *75.00* | *10.50* |
| **516** | A135 | 8f multi | *350.00* | *10.50* |
| **517** | A135 | 8f multi | *90.00* | *20.00* |
| | | *Nos. 506-517 (12)* | *1,795.* | *111.00* |

Unused values for Nos. 506-517 are for examples with untoned gum.

Sow with Litter — A136

**China Post No. S40**

No. 519, Pig being inoculated. No. 520, Pigs. No. 521, Pig and mechanized feeding. No. 522, Pig and bales.

**1960, June 15**

| No. | Type | Description | Unused | Used |
|---|---|---|---|---|
| **518** | A136 | 8f red & blk (1) | *120.00* | *9.25* |
| **519** | A136 | 8f dp grn & blk (2) | *120.00* | *9.25* |
| **520** | A136 | 8f lil rose & blk (3) | *120.00* | *9.25* |
| **521** | A136 | 8f lt yel grn & blk (4) | *120.00* | *9.25* |
| **522** | A136 | 8f org & blk (5) | *120.00* | *9.25* |
| | | *Nos. 518-522 (5)* | *600.00* | *46.25* |

Flag Inscribed "Serving the Workers" — A137

**China Post No. C81**

Design: 8f, Inscribed stone seal.

**1960, July 30** **Photo.** ***Perf. 11½x11***

| No. | Type | Description | Unused | Used |
|---|---|---|---|---|
| **523** | A137 | 4f lt grn, red, pink & brn | *47.50* | *7.00* |

**Photogravure & Engraved**

| No. | Type | Description | Unused | Used |
|---|---|---|---|---|
| **524** | A137 | 8f pale bl, red & bis | *60.00* | *5.50* |

3rd Natl. Cong. for Literature and Arts, Peking.

Flowers, Flags of North Korea and China — A138

**China Post No. C82**

Design: 8f, Flying horse of Korea.

**1960, Aug. 15** **Photo.**

| No. | Type | Description | Unused | Used |
|---|---|---|---|---|
| **525** | A138 | 8f red & multi | *85.00* | *10.00* |
| **526** | A138 | 8f ultra, red & indigo | *110.00* | *10.00* |

15th anniversary of the liberation of Korea.

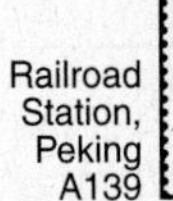

Railroad Station, Peking A139

**China Post No. S42**

Design: 10f, Train arriving at station.

**1960, Aug. 30** ***Perf. 11½***

| No. | Type | Description | Unused | Used |
|---|---|---|---|---|
| **527** | A139 | 8f blue, cream & brn | *47.50* | *15.00* |
| **528** | A139 | 10f bluish grn, cr & ind | *67.50* | *16.00* |

Opening of new Peking Railroad Station.

Girls and Flags of North Viet Nam and China — A140

Lake of the Returning Sword, Hanoi — A141

**China Post No. C83**

**1960, Sept. 2** ***Perf. 11x11½, 11½x11***

| No. | Type | Description | Unused | Used |
|---|---|---|---|---|
| **529** | A140 | 8f red & multi | *20.00* | *5.50* |
| **530** | A141 | 8f red, gray grn & gray | *27.50* | *3.50* |

15th anniversary of the Democratic Republic of North Viet Nam.

Worker and Fresh-air Installation — A142

**China Post No. S43**

Designs: No. 532, Exterminator. No. 533, Window cleaning. No. 534, Medical examination of child. No. 535, Physical exercise.

**1960, Sept. 10** ***Perf. 11½***

| No. | Type | Description | Unused | Used |
|---|---|---|---|---|
| **531** | A142 | 8f black & orange (1) | *13.50* | *1.25* |
| **532** | A142 | 8f indigo & slate (2) | *13.50* | *1.25* |
| **533** | A142 | 8f brown & blue (3) | *13.50* | *1.25* |
| **534** | A142 | 8f maroon & ocher (4) | *13.50* | *1.25* |
| **535** | A142 | 8f indigo & brt grn (5) | *13.50* | *1.25* |
| | | *Nos. 531-535 (5)* | *67.50* | *6.25* |

National health campaign.

Great Hall of the People A143

**China Post No. S41**

Design: 10f, Inside view.

**1960, Oct. 1**

| No. | Type | Description | Unused | Used |
|---|---|---|---|---|
| **536** | A143 | 8f yellow & multi | *47.50* | *15.00* |
| **537** | A143 | 10f brown & multi | *67.50* | *17.00* |

Completion of the Great Hall of the People, Peking.

Dr. Norman Bethune — A144

**China Post No. C84**

No. 539, Dr. Bethune operating on a soldier.

**Photo. (No. 538); Engr. (No. 539)**

**1960, Nov. 20** ***Perf. 11½x11***

| No. | Type | Description | Unused | Used |
|---|---|---|---|---|
| **538** | A144 | 8f red & multi | *24.00* | *3.00* |
| **539** | A144 | 8f sepia | *24.00* | *3.00* |

Dr. Norman Bethune (1890-1939), Canadian surgeon with 8th Route Army.

Engels Addressing Congress at The Hague — A145

**China Post No. C80**

**1960, Nov. 28** **Engr.**

| No. | Type | Description | Unused | Used |
|---|---|---|---|---|
| **540** | A145 | 8f shown | *50.00* | *3.25* |

**Photo.**

| No. | Type | Description | Unused | Used |
|---|---|---|---|---|
| **541** | A145 | 10f Portrait of Engels | *55.00* | *8.00* |

140th anniversary of the birth of Friedrich Engels (1820-1895), German Socialist.

"Hwang Shi Ba" — A146

**China Post No. S44**

**1960-61** **Photo.**

**Various Chrysanthemums in Natural Colors**

| No. | Type | Description | Unused | Used |
|---|---|---|---|---|
| **542** | A146 | 4f bl gray (1) | *22.50* | *3.25* |
| **543** | A146 | 4f pink (2) | *22.50* | *3.25* |
| **544** | A146 | 8f dk gray (3) | *25.00* | *3.25* |
| **545** | A146 | 8f dp blue (4) | *25.00* | *3.25* |
| **546** | A146 | 8f green (5) | *25.00* | *3.25* |
| **547** | A146 | 8f magenta (6) | *25.00* | *3.25* |
| **548** | A146 | 8f olive (7) | *24.00* | *3.25* |
| **549** | A146 | 8f grnsh bl (8) | *25.00* | *3.25* |
| **550** | A146 | 10f gray (9) | *30.00* | *4.75* |
| **551** | A146 | 10f choc (10) | *32.00* | *4.75* |
| **552** | A146 | 20f dp blue (11) | *57.50* | *5.50* |
| **553** | A146 | 20f brt red (12) | *57.50* | *6.50* |
| **554** | A146 | 22f olive bis (13) | *135.00* | *9.25* |
| **555** | A146 | 22f carmine (14) | *215.00* | *12.00* |
| **556** | A146 | 30f grnsh gray (15) | *300.00* | *13.00* |
| **557** | A146 | 30f brt pink (16) | *200.00* | *8.25* |
| **558** | A146 | 35f dp green (17) | *135.00* | *10.00* |
| **559** | A146 | 52f brt lilac rose (18) | *135.00* | *20.50* |
| | | *Nos. 542-559 (18)* | *1,491.* | *120.50* |

Issued: Nos. 548-550, 557-559, 12/10/60; Nos. 545-547, 554-556, 1/18/61; Nos. 542-544, 2/24/61.

Freighter — A147

**China Post No. S32**

**1960, Dec. 15** ***Perf. 11½***

**Without Gum**

| No. | Type | Description | Unused | Used |
|---|---|---|---|---|
| **560** | A147 | 8f deep blue | *14.00* | *2.25* |

1st 10,000-ton Chinese-built freighter, launching.

Pantheon, Paris — A148

**China Post No. C85**

Design: 8f, Proclamation of the Commune.

**Engraved and Photogravure**

**1961, Mar. 18** ***Perf. 11½x11***

| No. | Type | Description | Unused | Used |
|---|---|---|---|---|
| **561** | A148 | 8f gray blk & red | *37.50* | 5.75 |
| **562** | A148 | 8f brown & red | *37.50* | 6.75 |

90th anniversary of the Paris Commune.

Championship Symbol and Jasmine — A149

**China Post No. C86**

Designs: 10f, Table tennis racket and ball; Temple of Heaven. 20f, Table tennis match. 22f, Peking workers' gymnasium.

**1961, Apr. 5** **Photo.** ***Perf. 11***

| No. | Type | Description | Unused | Used |
|---|---|---|---|---|
| **563** | A149 | 8f multicolored | *7.50* | *.75* |
| **564** | A149 | 10f multicolored | *8.50* | *1.00* |
| **565** | A149 | 20f multicolored | *9.50* | *1.50* |
| **566** | A149 | 22f multicolored | *11.00* | *2.00* |
| *a.* | | Souv. sheet, #563-566 | *1,000.* | *700.00* |
| | | *Nos. 563-566 (4)* | *36.50* | *5.25* |

26th World Table Tennis Championships, Peking.

Jeme Tien-yow — A150

**China Post No. C87**

Design: 10f, Train and tunnel, Peking-Changchow Railroad.

**1961, June 20** ***Perf. 11½x11***

| No. | Type | Description | Unused | Used |
|---|---|---|---|---|
| **567** | A150 | 8f ol grn & blk | *11.00* | *1.25* |
| **568** | A150 | 10f org brn & brn | *26.50* | *3.75* |

Centenary of the birth of Jeme Tien-yow, railroad construction engineer.

Congress Building, Shanghai A151

**China Post No. C88**

Designs: 8f, August 1st Building, Nanchang. 10f, Provisional Central Government Office, Juikin. 20f, Pagoda Hill, Yenan. 30f, Gate of Heavenly Peace, Peking.

**1961, July 1** ***Perf. 11½***

| No. | Type | Description | Unused | Used |
|---|---|---|---|---|
| **569** | A151 | 4f gold, red & cl | *105.00* | *11.50* |
| **570** | A151 | 8f gold, red & bl grn | *105.00* | *11.50* |
| **571** | A151 | 10f gold, red & yel brn | *92.50* | *7.00* |
| **572** | A151 | 20f gold, red & ultra | *180.00* | *14.00* |
| **573** | A151 | 30f gold, red & org red | *210.00* | *26.00* |
| | | *Nos. 569-573 (5)* | *692.50* | *70.00* |

40th anniv. of the Chinese Communist Party.

August 1 Building, Nanchang — A152

**China Post No. R11**

3f, 4f, 5f, Trees & Sha Cho Pa Building, Juikin. 8f, 10f, 20f, Pagoda Hill, Yenan. 22f, 30f, 50f, Gate of Heavenly Peace, Peking.

**1961-62** **Engr.** ***Perf. 11***

**Without Gum**

**Size: 24x16mm**

| No. | Type | Description | Unused | Used |
|---|---|---|---|---|
| **574** | A152 | 1f vio blue | *15.00* | *.70* |
| **575** | A152 | 1½f maroon | *45.00* | *2.50* |
| **576** | A152 | 2f indigo | *18.00* | *1.10* |
| **577** | A152 | 3f dull vio | *67.50* | *3.25* |
| **578** | A152 | 4f green | *4.00* | *.75* |
| **579** | A152 | 5f gray | *4.00* | *.60* |
| **580** | A152 | 8f dark olive | *4.00* | *.50* |
| **581** | A152 | 10f brt lil rose | *10.00* | *.50* |
| **582** | A152 | 20f grnsh bl | *3.00* | *.50* |
| **583** | A152 | 22f brown | *1.75* | *.50* |
| **584** | A152 | 30f blue | *3.00* | *.50* |
| **585** | A152 | 50f vermilion | *3.00* | *.50* |
| | | *Nos. 574-585 (12)* | *178.25* | *11.90* |

Issued: 1f, 1½f, 5f, 7/20/62; others 7/20/61.

See Nos. 647-654, 1059-1064.

Flowers, Flags of Mongolia and China — A153

**China Post No. C89**

Design: 10f, Parliament, Ulan Bator, and statue of Sukhe Bator.

**1961, July 11 Photo. *Perf. 11x11½***

| | | | | |
|---|---|---|---|---|
| **586** | A153 | 8f crim, ultra & yel | *120.00* | *20.00* |
| **587** | A153 | 10f orange, blk & yel | *175.00* | *27.50* |

40th anniv. of the Mongolian People's Republic.

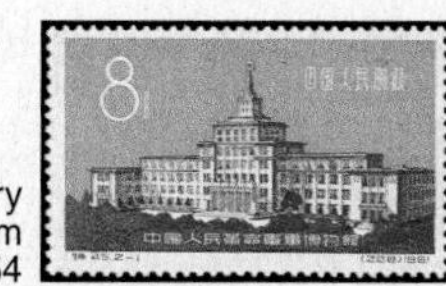

Military Museum A154

**China Post No. S45**

**Photo. & Engr.**

**1961, Aug. 1 *Perf. 11½***

| | | | | |
|---|---|---|---|---|
| **588** | A154 | 8f gray bl, brn & grn | *120.00* | *3.25* |
| *a.* | | Inscribed series "(229)" (error) | *200.00* | *17.50* |
| **589** | A154 | 10f gray, blk & grn | *130.00* | *3.75* |

Opening of the People's Revolutionary Military Museum.

Uprising at Wuchang A155

Sun Yat-sen A156

**China Post No. C90**

***Perf. 11x11½, 11½x11***

**1961, Oct. 10 Photo.**

| | | | | |
|---|---|---|---|---|
| **590** | A155 | 8f gray & blk | *62.50* | *5.00* |
| **591** | A156 | 10f tan & black | *77.50* | *5.50* |

50th anniversary of the 1911 Revolution.

Donkey — A157

**China Post No. S46**

Designs: 8f, 10f, 20f, 22f, Horses; 30f, 50f, Camels. Ceramic statuettes from Tang Dynasty (618-906) graves.

**1961, Nov. 10 *Perf. 11½x11***

**Statuettes in Original Colors**

| | | | | |
|---|---|---|---|---|
| **592** | A157 | 4f dull blue | *25.00* | *2.10* |
| **593** | A157 | 8f gray green | *25.00* | *2.10* |
| **594** | A157 | 8f dp purple | *25.00* | *2.10* |
| **595** | A157 | 10f dp blue | *25.00* | *2.10* |
| **596** | A157 | 20f olive | *28.00* | *2.60* |
| **597** | A157 | 22f blue grn | *52.00* | *3.75* |
| **598** | A157 | 30f red brown | *105.00* | *9.50* |
| **599** | A157 | 50f slate | *65.00* | *5.75* |
| | | *Nos. 592-599 (8)* | *350.00* | *30.00* |

Rejoicing Tibetans — A158

**China Post No. S47**

Designs: 8f, Woman sower. 10f, Celebration of bumper crop. 20f, People's representatives. 30f, Tibetan children.

**1961, Nov. 25**

| | | | | |
|---|---|---|---|---|
| **600** | A158 | 4f brn & ocher | *85.00* | *4.00* |
| **601** | A158 | 8f brn & lt bl grn | *75.00* | *3.50* |
| **602** | A158 | 10f brn & yel | *105.00* | *4.00* |
| **603** | A158 | 20f brn & rose | *185.00* | *9.00* |
| **604** | A158 | 30f brn & bluish gray | *250.00* | *10.00* |
| | | *Nos. 600-604 (5)* | *700.00* | *30.50* |

Rebirth of the Tibetan people.

Lu Hsun — A159

**China Post No. C91**

**1962, Feb. 26**

| | | | | |
|---|---|---|---|---|
| **605** | A159 | 8f red brown & blk | *7.25* | *1.75* |

80th anniv. of the birth of Lu Hsun, writer.

An Chi Bridge, Chao Hsien A160

**China Post No. S50**

Bridges of Ancient China: 8f, Pao Tai, Soochow. 10f, Chu Pu, Kwan Hsien. 20f, Chen Yang, San Kiang.

**1962, May 15 *Perf. 11***

| | | | | |
|---|---|---|---|---|
| **606** | A160 | 4f dk gray blue | *5.75* | *1.00* |
| **607** | A160 | 8f dp green | *5.75* | *1.00* |
| **608** | A160 | 10f brown | *33.00* | *3.75* |
| **609** | A160 | 20f grnsh blue | *24.00* | *2.50* |
| | | *Nos. 606-609 (4)* | *68.50* | *8.25* |

Tu Fu — A161

**China Post No. C93**

4f, Tu Fu memorial pavilion, Chengtu.

**1962, May 25 *Perf. 11½x11***

| | | | | |
|---|---|---|---|---|
| **610** | A161 | 4f ol bis & blk | *65.00* | *3.00* |
| **611** | A161 | 8f grnsh bl & blk | *75.00* | *4.00* |

Poet Tu Fu, 1,250th anniversary of birth.

Cranes and Bamboo — A162

**China Post No. S48**

10f, Two cranes in flight. 20f, Crane on rock.

**1962, June 10**

| | | | | |
|---|---|---|---|---|
| **612** | A162 | 8f tan & multi | *25.00* | *2.50* |
| **613** | A162 | 10f blue & multi | *50.00* | *4.75* |
| **614** | A162 | 20f bister & multi | *67.50* | *8.00* |
| | | *Nos. 612-614 (3)* | *142.50* | *15.25* |

"The Sacred Crane," from paintings by Chen Chi-fo.

Cuban Soldier and Flag — A163

**China Post No. S51**

Designs: 10f, Sugar cane worker. 22f, Militiaman and woman.

**1962, July 10 *Perf. 11x11½***

| | | | | |
|---|---|---|---|---|
| **615** | A163 | 8f car, rose & blk | *50.00* | *6.50* |
| **616** | A163 | 10f green & blk | *100.00* | *11.00* |
| **617** | A163 | 22f ultra & blk | *225.00* | *47.50* |
| | | *Nos. 615-617 (3)* | *375.00* | *65.00* |

Support of Cuba.

Torch and Map of Algeria — A164

**China Post No. S52**

Design: 22f, Algerian soldiers and flag.

**1962, July 10 *Perf. 11½x11***

| | | | | |
|---|---|---|---|---|
| **618** | A164 | 8f dp brown & red org | *2.75* | *1.20* |
| **619** | A164 | 22f ocher & dp brn | *8.25* | *1.90* |

Support of Algeria.

Mei Lan-fang — A165

**China Post No. C94**

Designs (Mei Lan-fang in Women's Roles): No. 621, Beating drum. No. 622, With fan. 10f, Lady Yu with swords. 20f, With bag. 22f, Heavenly Maiden, horiz. 30f, With spinning wheel, horiz. 50f, Kneeling, horiz. $3, Scene from opera "Drunken Beauty."

**1962 *Perf. 11½x11, 11x11½***

| | | | | |
|---|---|---|---|---|
| **620** | A165 | 4f tan & multi | *220.00* | *35.00* |
| **621** | A165 | 8f tan & multi | *120.00* | *15.00* |
| **622** | A165 | 8f gray & multi | *120.00* | *15.00* |
| **623** | A165 | 10f gray & multi | *220.00* | *20.00* |
| **624** | A165 | 20f lt grn & multi | *220.00* | *30.00* |
| **625** | A165 | 22f cream & multi | *375.00* | *65.00* |
| **626** | A165 | 30f lt blue & multi | *475.00* | *80.00* |
| **627** | A165 | 50f buff & multi | *475.00* | *80.00* |
| | | *Nos. 620-627 (8)* | *2,225.* | *340.00* |

**Souvenir Sheet**

***Perf. 11***

| | | | | |
|---|---|---|---|---|
| **628** | A165 | $3 brown & multi | *18,500.* | *6,250.* |

Stage art of Mei Lan-fang, actor.

Issued: 4f, 8f, 10f, 8/8; $3, 9/15; others 9/1.

Nos. 620-627 exist imperf. Value, set unused $6,750, used $2,350.

No. 628 contains one 48x58mm stamp and almost always has some faults. Values above are for fault-free examples. Value for No. 628 with small faults, unused $11,000. Excellent forgeries exist.

Flower Drum Dance, Han — A166

**China Post No. S49**

Folk Dances: 8f, Ordos, Mongolia. 10f, Catching shrimp, Chuang. 20f, Friend, Yi. 30f, Fiddle dance, Tibet. 50f, Tambourine dance, Uighur.

Cumulative numbers 246-251 at lower right.

**1962, Oct. 15 Litho. *Perf. 12½***

**Without Gum**

| | | | | |
|---|---|---|---|---|
| **629** | A166 | 4f cream & multi | *3.00* | *.80* |
| **630** | A166 | 8f cream & multi | *3.00* | *.80* |
| **631** | A166 | 10f cream & multi | *3.75* | *1.00* |
| **632** | A166 | 20f cream & multi | *5.00* | *1.50* |
| **633** | A166 | 30f cream & multi | *6.00* | *1.75* |
| **634** | A166 | 50f cream & multi | *7.00* | *2.25* |
| | | *Nos. 629-634 (6)* | *27.75* | *8.10* |

See Nos. 696-707.

Lenin Leading Soldiers — A167

Soldiers Storming Winter Palace — A167a

**China Post No. C95**

**1962, Nov. 7 Photo. *Perf. 11½***

| | | | | |
|---|---|---|---|---|
| **635** | A167 | 8f black & red | *90.00* | *6.00* |
| **636** | A167a | 20f slate grn & red | *175.00* | *13.00* |

45th anniversary of the Russian Revolution.

Monument and Map of Albania — A168

**China Post No. C96**

Design: 10f, Albanian flag and Girl Pioneer.

**1962, Nov. 28 *Perf. 11½x11***

| | | | | |
|---|---|---|---|---|
| **637** | A168 | 8f Prus blue & sepia | *4.50* | *1.50* |
| **638** | A168 | 10f red, yel, & blk | *6.75* | *1.75* |

50th anniversary of Albanian independence.

Tsai Lun, Inventor of Papermaking — A169

**China Post No. C92**

Designs: No. 640, Paper making. No. 641, Sun Szu-miao, physician. No. 642, Writing medical treatise. No. 643, Shen Ko, geologist. No. 644, Making field notes. No. 645, Kuo Shou-chin, astronomer. No. 646, Astronomical instrument.

Cumulative numbers 297-304 at lower right.

**1962, Dec. 1 *Perf. 11½x11***

| | | | | |
|---|---|---|---|---|
| **639** | A169 | 4f multicolored | *10.50* | *1.20* |
| **640** | A169 | 4f multicolored | *13.50* | *1.20* |
| **641** | A169 | 8f multicolored | *15.00* | *1.60* |
| **642** | A169 | 8f multicolored | *15.00* | *3.00* |
| **643** | A169 | 10f multicolored | *15.00* | *4.75* |
| **644** | A169 | 10f multicolored | *15.00* | *4.75* |
| **645** | A169 | 20f multicolored | *24.00* | *8.00* |
| **646** | A169 | 20f multicolored | *29.00* | *8.00* |
| | | *Nos. 639-646 (8)* | *137.00* | *32.50* |

Scientists of ancient China.

No. 639 exists with an extra character in the inscription. Value, unused *$12,500*, used *$2,500*.

**Building Type of 1961**

**China Post No. R12**

Designs: 1f, 2f, Building, Nanchang. 3f, 4f, Trees and Sha Cho Pa Building. 8f, 10f, 20f, Pagoda Hill, Yenan. 30f, Gate of Heavenly Peace, Peking.

**1962, Jan. Litho. *Rough Perf. 12½***

**Size: 21x16mm**

**Without Gum**

| | | | | |
|---|---|---|---|---|
| **647** | A152 | 1f ultra | *1.50* | *.50* |
| **648** | A152 | 2f greenish gray | *2.60* | *.50* |
| **649** | A152 | 3f violet gray | *1.50* | *.50* |
| **650** | A152 | 4f green | *1.50* | *.50* |
| **651** | A152 | 8f dk olive, perf. 14 | *10.00* | *.50* |
| *b.* | | Perf. 11x11½ | *20.00* | |
| **652** | A152 | 10f brt rose lilac | *6.75* | *.50* |
| **653** | A152 | 20f slate blue | *11.00* | *1.00* |
| **654** | A152 | 30f dull blue | *8.00* | *1.00* |
| | | *Nos. 647-654 (8)* | *42.85* | *5.00* |

Tank Monument, Havana — A170

Crowd in Peking A171

**China Post No. C97**

Designs: No. 656, Cuban revolutionaries. No. 658, Crowd in Havana. No. 659, Cuban soldier. No. 660, Castro and Cuban flag.

***Perf. 11½, 11x11½***

**1963, Jan. 1** **Photo.**

**655** A170 4f red & blk brn 75.00 5.00
**656** A170 4f green & blk 75.00 5.00
**657** A171 8f dull red & brn 110.00 12.50
**658** A171 8f dull red & brn 110.00 20.00
**659** A170 10f ocher & blk 160.00 22.50
**660** A170 10f red, blue & blk 190.00 50.00
*Nos. 655-660 (6)* 720.00 115.00

4th anniversary of the Cuban revolution.

Green Dragontail — A172

**China Post No. S56**

No. 661, Tibetan clouded yellow (1). No. 662, Tritailed glory (2). No. 663, Neumogeni jungle queen (3). No. 664, Washan swordtail (4). No. 665, Striped ringlet (5). No. 667, Dilunulated peacock (7). No. 668, Yamfly (8). No. 669, Golden kaiser-i-hind (9). No. 670, Mushaell hairstreak (10). No. 671, Yellow orange-tip (11). No. 672, Great jay (12). No. 673, Striped punch (13). No. 674, Hainan violet-beak (14). No. 675, Omeiskipper (15). No. 676, Philippines birdwing (16). No. 677, Richtofenis red apollo (17). No. 678, Blue-banded king crow (18). No. 679, Solskyi copper (19). No. 680, Yunnan clipper (20).

**1963** **Without Gum** ***Perf. 11***

**661** A172 4f multi 21.00 2.00
**662** A172 4f multi 21.00 2.00
**663** A172 4f multi 21.00 2.00
**664** A172 4f multi 21.00 2.00
**665** A172 4f multi 21.00 2.00
**666** A172 8f shown (6) 28.00 2.50
**667** A172 8f multi 28.00 2.50
**668** A172 8f multi 28.00 2.50
**669** A172 8f multi 28.00 2.50
**670** A172 8f multi 28.00 2.50
**671** A172 10f multi 36.00 3.00
**672** A172 10f multi 36.00 3.00
**673** A172 10f multi 36.00 3.00
**674** A172 10f multi 36.00 3.00
**675** A172 10f multi 36.00 3.00
**676** A172 20f multi 55.00 8.00
**677** A172 20f multi 55.00 8.00
**678** A172 22f multi 67.50 12.50
**679** A172 30f multi 90.00 20.00
**680** A172 50f multi 105.00 22.50
*Nos. 661-680 (20)* 797.50 108.50

Issued: Nos. 666-675, July 15; others Apr. 5.

Karl Marx — A173

**China Post No. C98**

Designs: No. 682, "Workers of the World, Unite" on cover of first edition of Communist Manifesto. No. 683, Marx and Engels.

**1963, May 5** ***Perf. 11½***

**Without Gum**

**681** A173 8f black, gold & sal (1) 30.00 3.50
**682** A173 8f gold & red (2) 30.00 4.00
**683** A173 8f gold & choc (3) 25.00 4.00
*Nos. 681-683 (3)* 85.00 11.50

145th anniversary of birth of Karl Marx (1818-1883), German political philosopher.

Child with Top — A174

**China Post No. S54**

Child: No. 685, eating berries. No. 686, as traffic policeman. No. 687, with windmill. No. 688, listening to caged cricket. No. 689, with sword. No. 690, embroidering. No. 691, with umbrella. No. 692, playing with sand. No. 693, playing table tennis. No. 694, learning to add. No. 695, with kite.

**1963, June 1** **Litho.** ***Perf. 12½***

**Without Gum**

**Multicolored Designs**

**684** A174 4f grnsh gray (1) 5.25 .80
**685** A174 4f tan (2) 5.25 .80
**686** A174 8f gray (3) 5.25 .60
**687** A174 8f blue (4) 5.25 .80
**688** A174 8f tan (5) 5.25 .80
**689** A174 8f dp gray (6) 5.25 .80
**690** A174 8f citron (7) 5.25 1.20
**691** A174 8f gray (8) 5.25 1.20
**692** A174 10f green (9) 7.75 1.90
**693** A174 10f violet (10) 7.75 1.90
**694** A174 20f bister (11) 17.00 4.75
**695** A174 20f green (12) 17.00 4.75
*Nos. 684-695 (12)* 91.50 20.30

Children's Day. Value, imperf set unused $600, used $200.

**Dance Type of 1962**
**China Post No. S53**

Folk Dances: 4f, Weavers' dance, Puyi. 8f, Kazakh. 10f, Olunchun. 20f, Labor dance, Kaochan. 30f, Reed pipe dance, Miao. 50f, Fan dance, Korea.

Cumulative numbers 261-266 at lower right.

**1963, June 15** ***Perf. 12½***

**Without Gum**

**696** A166 4f cream & multi 3.00 .40
**697** A166 8f cream & multi 3.00 .50
**698** A166 10f cream & multi 4.00 .60
**699** A166 20f cream & multi 5.00 1.75
**700** A166 30f cream & multi 5.00 1.75
**701** A166 50f cream & multi 8.00 3.25
*Nos. 696-701 (6)* 28.00 8.25

**China Post No. S55**

**1963, June 30** **Without Gum**

Folk Dances: 4f, "Wedding Ceremony," Yu. 8f, "Encircling Mountain Forest," Pai. 10f, Long drum dance, Yao. 20f, Third day of the third month dance, Li. 30f, Knife dance, Kawa. 50f, Peacock dance, Thai.

Cumulative numbers 279-284 at lower right.

**702** A166 4f cream & multi 3.00 .40
**703** A166 8f cream & multi 3.00 .50
**704** A166 10f cream & multi 3.00 .60
**705** A166 20f cream & multi 6.00 1.25
**706** A166 30f cream & multi 6.00 1.25
**707** A166 50f cream & multi 6.00 1.25
*Nos. 702-707 (6)* 27.00 5.25

Giant Panda Eating Apples — A175

**China Post No. S59**

Designs: No. 709, Giant panda eating bamboo shoots. 10f, Two pandas, horiz.

**1963, Aug. 5** **Photo.** ***Perf. 11½x11***

**Size: 28x38mm**

**708** A175 8f pale blue & blk 45.00 3.50
**709** A175 8f pale blue & blk 45.00 6.00

**Size: 50x29mm**

***Perf. 11½***

**710** A175 10f olive & blk 60.00 4.00
*Nos. 708-710 (3)* 150.00 13.50

Value, imperf set unused $400, used $150.

Table Tennis Player — A176

**China Post No. C99**

No. 712, Trophies won by Chinese team.

**1963, Sept. 10** **Engr.** ***Perf. 11½***

**711** A176 8f dk olive grn 28.00 2.75
**712** A176 8f brown 28.00 2.75

27th World Table Tennis Championships.

Snub-nosed Langur — A177

**China Post No. S60**

Designs: 10f, Two monkeys playing. 22f, Two monkeys grooming.

**1963, Sept. 23** **Photo.** ***Perf. 11½x11***

**713** A177 8f gray & multi 20.00 2.25
**714** A177 10f gray & multi 20.00 2.25
**715** A177 22f gray & multi 35.00 7.75
*Nos. 713-715 (3)* 75.00 12.25

Value, imperf set unused $300, used $130.

Jade-green Screen Mountain — A178

**China Post No. S57**

Hwang Shan Landscapes (Yellow Mountains), Anhwei Province: No. 717, "Guests Welcoming Pines" (2). No. 718, Pines and Rock Behind the Sea (3). No. 719, Terrace of Keeping Cool (4). No. 720, Mount of Heavenly Capital (5). No. 721, Mount of Scissors (6). No. 722, Forest of Ten Thousand Pines (7). No. 723, "Brush Blooming in Dream" (8). No. 724, Mount of Lotus Flower (9). No. 725, Cumulus Cloud over West Sea (10). No. 726, Old Pines of Hwang Shan (11). No. 727, "Watching the Clouds over West Sea" (12). No. 728, Mount of Stalagmites (13). No. 729, "Stone Monkey Watching the Sea" (14). No. 730, Forest of Lions (15). No. 731, Three Fairy Tales of Pen Lai (16).

Nos. 724-731 horiz.

**Engraved and Photogravure**

**1963, Oct. 15** ***Perf. 11½***

**716** A178 4f shown (1) 67.50 5.50
**717** A178 4f multi 67.50 5.50
**718** A178 4f multi 67.50 5.50
**719** A178 4f multi 67.50 5.50
**720** A178 8f multi 50.00 5.00
**721** A178 8f multi 50.00 5.00
**722** A178 8f multi 50.00 6.00
**723** A178 8f multi 50.00 5.00
**724** A178 10f multi 105.00 9.00
**725** A178 10f multi 105.00 9.00
**726** A178 10f multi 105.00 9.00
**727** A178 10f multi 105.00 9.00
**728** A178 20f multi 135.00 14.00
**729** A178 22f multi 135.00 13.00
**730** A178 30f multi 295.00 40.00
**731** A178 50f multi 295.00 60.00
*Nos. 716-731 (16)* 1,750. 206.00

Soccer Player — A179

Athletes and Banners A180

**China Post No. C100**

No. 733, Discus, women's. No. 734, Diving, men's. No. 735, Gymnastics, women's.

**Engraved and Photogravure**

**1963, Nov. 17** ***Perf. 11***

**732** A179 8f gray, red & blk (1) 19.00 2.00
**733** A179 8f gray, ultra & blk (2) 19.00 2.00
**734** A179 8f lt grn, brn & blk (4) 19.00 2.00
**735** A179 8f gray, lil rose & blk (5) 19.00 2.00

**Photo.**

***Perf. 11½***

**736** A180 10f red & multi (3) 65.00 6.00
*Nos. 732-736 (5)* 141.00 14.00

Games of the Newly Emerging Forces, Djakarta.

Clay Rooster and Goat — A181

**China Post No. S58**

Chinese Folk Toys: No. 738, Cloth camel. No. 739, Cloth tigers. No. 740, Clay ox and rider. No. 741, Cloth rabbit, wooden doll, clay roosters. No. 742, Straw rooster. No. 743, Cloth donkey and bird. No. 744, Clay lion. No. 745, Cloth tiger and tumbler doll.

**1963, Dec. 10** **Litho.** ***Perf. 11½***

**Toys Multicolored; Without Gum**

**737** A181 4f bister (1) 2.25 1.00
**738** A181 4f gray (4) 2.25 1.00
**739** A181 4f lt blue (7) 2.25 1.00
**740** A181 8f bister (2) 2.25 1.00
**741** A181 8f gray (5) 2.25 1.00
**742** A181 8f lt blue (8) 2.25 1.00
**743** A181 10f bister (3) 4.50 1.00
**744** A181 10f gray (6) 4.50 1.00
**745** A181 10f lt blue (9) 4.50 1.00
*Nos. 737-745 (9)* 27.00 9.00

Armed Vietnamese Family — A182

**China Post No. C101**

Liberation of South Viet Nam: No. 747, Militia with Vietnamese flag.

**1963, Dec. 20** **Photo.** ***Perf. 11½x11***

**746** A182 8f tan, blk & red 11.00 2.00
**747** A182 8f red & multi 11.00 2.00

Flags of Cuba and China — A183

**China Post No. C102**

Design: No. 749, Boy waving Cuban flag.

**1964, Jan. 1**

**748** A183 8f red, yel, bl & ind 65.00 7.00
**749** A183 8f multicolored 65.00 7.00

5th anniversary of the liberation of Cuba.

Woman Driving Tractor — A184

**China Post No. S64**

Woman of the People's Commune: No. 751, harvesting. No. 752, picking cotton. No. 753, picking fruit. No. 754, reading book. No. 755, on guard duty.

**1964, Mar. 8**

**750** A184 8f ol, pink & brn (1) 5.50 1.00
**751** A184 8f brn yel & org (2) 5.50 1.00
**752** A184 8f gray & multi (3) 5.50 1.00
**753** A184 8f black, org & bl (4) 5.50 1.00
**754** A184 8f green & multi (5) 5.50 2.00
**755** A184 8f lilac & multi (6) 5.50 2.00
*Nos. 750-755 (6)* 33.00 8.00

Chinese and African Men — A185

**China Post No. C103**

Design: No. 757, African drummer.

**1964, Apr. 12 Photo. *Perf. 11***

| | | | |
|---|---|---|---|
| **756** A185 8f red & multi | *5.00* | *.95* |
| **757** A185 8f black & dk brn | *5.00* | *.95* |

African Freedom Day.

Marx, Engels, Lenin and Stalin A186

**China Post No. C104**

Design: No. 759, Banners and workers.

**1964, May 1 *Perf. 11½***

| | | |
|---|---|---|
| **758** A186 8f gold, red & blk | *55.00* | *7.50* |
| **759** A186 8f gold, red & blk | *55.00* | *7.50* |

Labor Day.

Orchard, Yenan — A187

**China Post No. S65**

Yenan, Shrine of the Chinese Revolution: No. 761, Central Auditorium, Yang Chia Ling. No. 762, Mao's office and residence. No. 763, Auditorium, Wang Chia Ping. No. 764, Border Region Assembly Hall. No. 765, Pagoda Hill and Bridge.

**1964, July 1 Photo. *Perf. 11x11½***

| | | |
|---|---|---|
| **760** A187 8f multicolored (1) | *24.00* | *3.00* |
| **761** A187 8f multicolored (2) | *24.00* | *3.00* |
| **762** A187 8f multicolored (3) | *24.00* | *3.00* |
| **763** A187 8f multicolored (4) | *24.00* | *3.00* |
| **764** A187 8f multicolored (5) | *24.00* | *3.00* |
| **765** A187 52f multicolored (6) | *155.00* | *19.50* |
| *Nos. 760-765 (6)* | *275.00* | *34.50* |

Map and Flag of Viet Nam — A188

**China Post No. C105**

**1964, July 20 *Perf. 11½***

| | | |
|---|---|---|
| **766** A188 8f multicolored | *60.00* | *6.00* |

Victory in South Viet Nam.

Alchemist's Glowing Crucible — A189

**China Post No. S61**

No. 768, Night-shining jade (2). No. 769, Purple Kuo's cap (3). No. 770, Chao pink (4). No. 771, Yao yellow (5). No. 772, Twin beauty (6). No. 773, Ice-veiled ruby (7). No. 774, Gold-sprinkled Chinese ink (8). No. 775, Cinnabar jar (9). No. 776, Lan Tien jade (10). No. 777, Imperial robe yellow (11). No. 778, Hu red (12). No. 779, Pea green (13). No. 780, Wei purple (14). No. 781, Intoxicated celestial peach (15).

No. 782, Glorious crimson & great gold pink.

**1964, Aug. 5 *Perf. 11½x11***

| | | |
|---|---|---|
| **767** A189 4f shown (1) | *24.00* | *2.10* |
| **768** A189 4f multi | *24.00* | *2.10* |
| **769** A189 8f multi | *15.00* | *2.10* |
| **770** A189 8f multi | *15.00* | *2.10* |
| **771** A189 8f multi | *15.00* | *2.10* |
| **772** A189 8f multi | *15.00* | *2.10* |
| **773** A189 8f multi | *15.00* | *2.10* |
| **774** A189 10f multi | *26.00* | *2.10* |
| **775** A189 10f multi | *26.00* | *2.10* |
| **776** A189 10f multi | *26.00* | *2.10* |
| **777** A189 10f multi | *26.00* | *2.10* |
| **778** A189 10f multi | *26.00* | *2.10* |
| **779** A189 20f multi | *95.00* | *18.50* |
| **780** A189 43f multi | *155.00* | *23.00* |
| **781** A189 52f multi | *240.00* | *34.00* |
| *Nos. 767-781 (15)* | *743.00* | *100.70* |

**Souvenir Sheet**

***Perf. 11½***

**Without Gum**

| | | |
|---|---|---|
| **782** A189 $2 multi | *2,500.* | *925.00* |

No. 782 contains one 48x59mm stamp.

Eight values depicting theatrical masks of the Peking Opera were prepared in 1964 but not issued. The designs are as design type A398: 4f, Meng Lang. 4f, Li Kui. 8f, Huang Gai. 8f, Monkey King. 10f, Lu Zhishen. 10f, Lian Po. 20f, Zhang Fei. 20f, Dou Erdun. The unissued stamps are numbered 352-359 and dated "1964." Sound examples are rare and sell for between $125,000 and $275,000. See Nos. 1574-1581.

Wine Cup — A190

**China Post No. S63**

Sacrificial bronze vessels of Yin dynasty, prior to 1050 B.C.: No. 784, Ku beaker (2). No. 785, Kuang wine urn (3). No. 786, Chia wine cup (4). No. 787, Tsun wine vessel (5). No. 788, Yu wine urn (6). No. 789, Tsun wine vessel (7). No. 790, Ceremonial cauldron (8).

**Engraved and Photogravure**

**1964, Aug. 25 *Perf. 11½x11***

| | | |
|---|---|---|
| **783** A190 4f shown (1) | *15.50* | *1.75* |
| **784** A190 4f multi | *15.50* | *1.75* |
| **785** A190 8f multi | *14.00* | *1.75* |
| **786** A190 8f multi | *14.00* | *1.75* |
| **787** A190 10f multi | *32.50* | *2.00* |
| **788** A190 10f multi | *32.50* | *2.00* |
| **789** A190 20f multi | *57.50* | *4.75* |
| **790** A190 20f multi | *57.50* | *4.75* |
| *Nos. 783-790 (8)* | *239.00* | *20.50* |

Grain Harvest — A191

**China Post No. S66**

Designs: No. 792, Students planting trees. No. 793, Study period. No. 794, Scientific experimentation.

**1964, Sept. 26 Photo.**

| | | |
|---|---|---|
| **791** A191 8f multicolored (1) | *7.25* | *1.25* |
| **792** A191 8f multicolored (2) | *7.25* | *1.25* |
| **793** A191 8f multicolored (3) | *7.25* | *1.25* |
| **794** A191 8f multicolored (4) | *7.25* | *1.25* |
| *Nos. 791-794 (4)* | *29.00* | *5.00* |

Youth helping in agriculture.

Marx, Engels, Trafalgar Square, London — A192

**China Post No. C107**

**1964, Sept. 28 *Perf. 11½***

| | | |
|---|---|---|
| **795** A192 8f red, gold & red brn | *130.00* | *25.00* |

Centenary of the First International.

**Gold Ink**

Stamps with gold ink often show some tarnishing. Values are for untarnished gold color. Tarnished stamps will sell for less.

People with Banners — A193

**China Post No. C106**

No. 797, Gate of Heavenly Peace and Chinese flag. No. 798, People with banners, facing left.

**1964, Oct. 1**

| | | |
|---|---|---|
| **796** A193 8f cream & multi (1) | *50.00* | *7.50* |
| **797** A193 8f cream & multi (2) | *50.00* | *7.50* |
| **798** A193 8f cream & multi (3) | *50.00* | *7.50* |
| ***a.*** Souvenir sheet of 3 | *4,250.* | *1,350.* |
| ***b.*** Strip of 3, #796-798 | *450.00* | *80.00* |
| *Nos. 796-798 (3)* | *150.00* | *22.50* |

15th anniv. of the People's Republic.

No. 798a contains No. 798b in continuous design without separating perfs. No. 798a almost always has disturbed gum, with interleaving paper sticking to it, or tarnished gilt. Such examples sell for considerably less than the very fine example valued above.

Values for No. 798b are for an unfolded strip.

Oil Derricks — A194

**China Post No. S67**

Oil industry: 4f, Geological surveyors and truck, horiz. 8f, "Christmas tree" and extraction accessories. 10f, Oil refinery. 20f, Tank cars, horiz.

**1964, Oct. 1**

| | | |
|---|---|---|
| **799** A194 4f lt blue & multi | *85.00* | *11.00* |
| **800** A194 8f shown | *140.00* | *15.00* |
| **801** A194 8f lilac & multi | *80.00* | *8.00* |
| **802** A194 10f slate & multi | *80.00* | *8.00* |
| **803** A194 20f brown & multi | *270.00* | *30.00* |
| *Nos. 799-803 (5)* | *655.00* | *72.00* |

Albanian and Chinese Flags — A195

**China Post No. C108**

10f, Enver Hoxha and Albanian coat of arms.

**1964, Nov. 29 *Perf. 11x11½***

| | | |
|---|---|---|
| **804** A195 8f red & multi | *40.00* | *13.50* |
| **805** A195 10f red, yel & blk | *62.50* | *22.00* |

20th anniv. of the liberation of Albania.

Power Dam Construction — A196

**China Post No. S68**

No. 807, Installation of turbogenerator rotor. No. 808, Main dam. 20f, Pylon.

**1964, Dec. 15 *Perf. 11½***

| | | |
|---|---|---|
| **806** A196 4f multicolored | *92.50* | *10.00* |
| **807** A196 8f multicolored | *87.50* | *5.00* |
| **808** A196 8f multicolored | *115.00* | *5.00* |
| **809** A196 20f multicolored | *280.00* | *27.50* |
| *Nos. 806-809 (4)* | *575.00* | *47.50* |

Hsin An Kiang Dam and hydroelectric power station.

Fertilizer Industry A197

**China Post No. S69**

Chemical Industry: No. 811, Plastics. No. 812, Medicines. No. 813, Rubber. No. 814, Insecticides. No. 815, Industrial acids. No. 816, Industrial alkaloids. No. 817, Synthetic fibers.

**1964, Dec. 30 Photo. & Engr.**

| | | |
|---|---|---|
| **810** A197 8f red & blk (1) | *10.00* | *1.50* |
| **811** A197 8f yel grn & blk (2) | *10.00* | *1.50* |
| **812** A197 8f brown & blk (3) | *10.00* | *1.50* |
| **813** A197 8f lilac rose & blk (4) | *10.00* | *1.50* |
| **814** A197 8f blue & blk (5) | *10.00* | *1.50* |
| **815** A197 8f orange & blk (6) | *10.00* | *1.50* |
| **816** A197 8f violet & blk (7) | *10.00* | *1.50* |
| **817** A197 8f brt green & blk (8) | *10.00* | *1.50* |
| *Nos. 810-817 (8)* | *80.00* | *12.00* |

Mao Studying Map A198

Mao Tse-tung — A199

**China Post No. C109**

Design: No. 819, Victory at Lushan Pass.

**1965, Jan. 31 Photo. *Perf. 11***

| | | |
|---|---|---|
| **818** A198 8f red & multi | *75.00* | *22.50* |
| **819** A198 8f red & multi | *75.00* | *22.50* |

***Perf. 11½x11***

| | | |
|---|---|---|
| **820** A199 8f gold & multi | *125.00* | *30.00* |
| *Nos. 818-820 (3)* | *275.00* | *75.00* |

Tsunyi Conference, 30th anniversary.

Conference Hall, Bandung — A200

**China Post No. C110**

No. 822, Asians and Africans applauding.

**1965, Apr. 18** ***Perf. 11½x11***

| | | | | |
|---|---|---|---|---|
| **821** | A200 | 8f cream & multi | *4.00* | *.90* |
| **822** | A200 | 8f cream & multi | *4.00* | *.90* |

10th anniversary of the Bandung, Indonesia, Conference, Apr. 1955.

Lenin — A201

### China Post No. C111

**1965, Apr. 25** ***Perf. 11½***

| | | | | |
|---|---|---|---|---|
| **823** | A201 | 8f red, choc & salmon | *30.00* | *5.00* |

95th anniversary of the birth of Lenin.

Chinese Player — A202

### China Post No. C112

No. 825, European woman (2). No. 826, Chinese woman (3). No. 827, European man (4).

**1965, Apr. 25** ***Perf. 11½***

| | | | | |
|---|---|---|---|---|
| **824** | A202 | 8f shown (1) | *.90* | *.45* |
| **825** | A202 | 8f multi | *.90* | *.45* |
| **826** | A202 | 8f multi | *.90* | *.45* |
| **827** | A202 | 8f multi | *.90* | *.45* |
| ***a.*** | | Block of 4, #824-827 | *10.00* | *5.00* |

28th World Table Tennis Championships, Ljubljana, Yugoslavia, Apr. 15-25.

Climbers on Mt. Minya Konka — A203

### China Post No. S70

Mountain Climbers: No. 829, on Muztagh Ata. No. 830, on Mt. Jolmo Lungma (Mt. Everest). No. 831, Women camping on Kongur Tiubie Tagh. No. 832, on Shisha Pangma.

**1965, May 25** **Photo. & Engr.**

| | | | | |
|---|---|---|---|---|
| **828** | A203 | 8f blue, blk & ol (1) | *17.00* | *2.10* |
| **829** | A203 | 8f blue, blk & ol (2) | *17.00* | *2.10* |
| **830** | A203 | 8f ultra, blk & gray (3) | *17.00* | *2.10* |
| **831** | A203 | 8f lt bl, blk & yel gray (4) | *17.00* | *2.10* |
| **832** | A203 | 8f ultra, blk & gray (5) | *17.00* | *2.10* |
| | | *Nos. 828-832 (5)* | *85.00* | *10.50* |

Chinese mountaineering achievements, 1957-64.

Marx and Lenin — A204

### China Post No. C113

**1965, June 21** **Photo.** ***Perf. 11½x11***

| | | | | |
|---|---|---|---|---|
| **833** | A204 | 8f red, yel & blk | *27.50* | *4.50* |

Postal Ministers' Congress, Peking.

Tseping Valley — A205

### China Post No. S73

Chingkang Mountains, Cradle of the Chinese Revolution: No. 835, San Wan Tsun (2). No. 836, Octagon Bldg., Mao Ping (3). No. 837, River and Bridge at Lung Shih (4). No. 838, Ta Ching Tsun (5). No. 839, Bridge across the Lung Yuan (6). No. 840, Hwang Yang Mountain (7). No. 841, Chingkang peaks (8).

**1965, July 1** ***Perf. 11x11½***

| | | | | |
|---|---|---|---|---|
| **834** | A205 | 4f shown (1) | *42.50* | *8.50* |
| **835** | A205 | 8f multi | *42.50* | *3.00* |
| **836** | A205 | 8f multi | *42.50* | *3.00* |
| **837** | A205 | 8f multi | *45.00* | *3.00* |
| **838** | A205 | 8f multi | *45.00* | *3.00* |
| **839** | A205 | 10f multi | *72.50* | *3.00* |
| **840** | A205 | 10f multi | *72.50* | *10.00* |
| **841** | A205 | 52f multi | *45.00* | *19.00* |
| | | *Nos. 834-841 (8)* | *407.50* | *52.50* |

Soldiers with Books A206

### China Post No. S74

No. 843, Soldiers reading Little Red Books (2). No. 844, With shell and artillery (3). No. 845, Rifle instruction (4). No. 846, Sewing jacket (5). No. 847, Bayonet charge (6). No. 848, With Banner (7). No. 849, Military band (8).

**1965, Aug. 1** ***Perf. 11½***

**Without Gum**

| | | | | |
|---|---|---|---|---|
| **842** | A206 | 8f shown (1) | *50.00* | *6.50* |
| **843** | A206 | 8f multi | *50.00* | *6.50* |
| **844** | A206 | 8f multi | *50.00* | *6.50* |
| **845** | A206 | 8f multi | *50.00* | *6.50* |
| **846** | A206 | 8f multi | *50.00* | *6.50* |
| **847** | A206 | 8f multi | *50.00* | *11.00* |
| **848** | A206 | 8f multi | *50.00* | *11.00* |
| **849** | A206 | 8f multi | *50.00* | *11.00* |
| | | *Nos. 842-849 (8)* | *400.00* | *65.50* |

People's Liberation Army. Nos. 846-849 vertical.

"Welcome to Peking" — A207

### China Post No. C114

No. 851, Chinese and Japanese young men. No. 852, Chinese and Japanese girls. No. 853, Musical entertainment. No. 854, Emblem of meeting.

**1965, Aug. 25** ***Perf. 11½x11***

| | | | | |
|---|---|---|---|---|
| **850** | A207 | 4f yellow & multi | *2.00* | *1.00* |
| **851** | A207 | 8f pink & multi | *2.00* | *1.00* |
| **852** | A207 | 8f multicolored | *3.75* | *1.00* |
| **853** | A207 | 10f multicolored | *4.50* | *2.00* |
| **854** | A207 | 22f lt blue & multi | *9.25* | *3.00* |
| | | *Nos. 850-854 (5)* | *21.50* | *8.00* |

Chinese-Japanese Youth Meeting, Peking.

North Vietnamese Soldier — A208

Peoples of the World A209

### China Post No. C117

Designs: No. 856, Soldier with guns. No. 857, Soldier giving victory salute.

**1965, Sept. 2** ***Perf. 11½x11***

| | | | | |
|---|---|---|---|---|
| **855** | A208 | 8f red & red brn (1) | *4.50* | *1.25* |
| **856** | A208 | 8f red & blk (2) | *4.50* | *1.25* |
| **857** | A208 | 8f red & vio brn (3) | *4.50* | *1.25* |

***Perf. 11½***

| | | | | |
|---|---|---|---|---|
| **858** | A209 | 8f black & red (4) | *7.00* | *1.75* |
| | | *Nos. 855-858 (4)* | *20.50* | *5.50* |

Struggle of the people of Viet Nam.

Mao Tse-tung at His Desk A210

Crossing Yellow River A211

Victory Monument A212

### China Post No. C115

Design: No. 862, Recruits in cart.

**1965, Sept. 3** ***Perf. 11***

| | | | | |
|---|---|---|---|---|
| **859** | A210 | 8f red & multi (1) | *65.00* | *15.00* |

***Perf. 11x11½, 11½x11***

| | | | | |
|---|---|---|---|---|
| **860** | A211 | 8f red & dk grn (2) | *45.00* | *3.75* |
| **861** | A212 | 8f red & dk brn (3) | *45.00* | *3.75* |
| **862** | A211 | 8f red & dk grn (4) | *45.00* | *3.75* |
| | | *Nos. 859-862 (4)* | *200.00* | *26.25* |

20th anniversary of victory over Japan.

2nd National Games — A213

National Games Opening Ceremonies — A214

### China Post No. C116

***Perf. 11½x11, 11 (A214)***

**1965, Sept. 28**

| | | | | |
|---|---|---|---|---|
| **863** | A213 | 4f Soccer (1) | *21.50* | *1.75* |
| **864** | A213 | 4f Archery (2) | *21.50* | *1.75* |
| **865** | A213 | 8f Javelin (3) | *21.50* | *1.75* |
| **866** | A213 | 8f Gymnastics (4) | *21.50* | *1.75* |
| **867** | A213 | 8f Volleyball (5) | *21.50* | *1.75* |
| **868** | A214 | 10f shown (6) | *57.50* | *4.00* |
| **869** | A213 | 10f Bicyling (7) | *63.00* | *4.00* |
| **870** | A213 | 20f Diving (8) | *69.00* | *7.50* |
| **871** | A213 | 22f Hurdles (9) | *69.00* | *7.50* |
| **872** | A213 | 30f Weight lifting (10) | *80.00* | *20.00* |
| **873** | A213 | 43f Basketball (11) | *80.00* | *25.00* |
| | | *Nos. 863-873 (11)* | *526.00* | *76.75* |

Government Building — A215

### China Post No. R13

1½f, 5f, 22f, Gate of Heavenly Peace. 2f, 8f, 30f, People's Hall. 3f, 10f, 50f, Military Museum.

**1964-66** ***Perf. 11½x11***

**Without Gum**

| | | | | |
|---|---|---|---|---|
| **874** | A215 | 1f brown | *.60* | *.35* |
| **875** | A215 | 1½f red lilac | *.60* | *.35* |
| **876** | A215 | 2f green | *.60* | *.35* |
| **877** | A215 | 3f blue grn | *.60* | *.35* |
| **878** | A215 | 4f brt blue | *.70* | *.35* |
| **879** | A215 | 5f vio brn ('66) | *2.25* | *.35* |
| **880** | A215 | 8f rose red | *.80* | *.35* |
| **881** | A215 | 10f gray olive | *2.25* | *.35* |
| **882** | A215 | 20f violet | *2.25* | *.35* |
| **883** | A215 | 22f orange | *2.25* | *.35* |
| **884** | A215 | 30f yellow grn | *3.50* | *.50* |
| **885** | A215 | 50f dp blue ('66) | *16.00* | *4.00* |
| | | *Nos. 874-885 (12)* | *32.40* | *8.00* |

No. 878 exists as perf. 12. No 880 exists with other perforation varieties. Nos. 879 and 885 were issued March 10, 1966; all others issued June 17, 1964.

Textile Workers — A216

### China Post No. S71

No. 887, Machine shop (2). No. 888, Welder (3). No. 889, Students (4). No. 890, Militia (5).

**1965, Nov. 30**

| | | | | |
|---|---|---|---|---|
| **886** | A216 | 8f shown (1) | *55.00* | *3.25* |
| **887** | A216 | 8f multicolored | *55.00* | *3.25* |
| **888** | A216 | 8f multicolored | *55.00* | *3.25* |
| **889** | A216 | 8f multicolored | *55.00* | *3.25* |
| **890** | A216 | 8f multicolored | *55.00* | *3.25* |
| | | *Nos. 886-890 (5)* | *275.00* | *16.25* |

Women workers.

Soccer A217

### China Post No. S72

Children's Sports: No. 892, Racing. No. 893, Tobogganing and skating. No. 894, Gymnastics. No. 895, Swimming. No. 896, Rifle practice. No. 897, Jumping rope. No. 898, Table tennis.

**1966, Feb. 25** ***Perf. 11***

| | | | | |
|---|---|---|---|---|
| **891** | A217 | 4f emer & multi (1) | *1.60* | *.55* |
| **892** | A217 | 4f yel brn & multi (2) | *1.60* | *.55* |
| **893** | A217 | 8f blue & multi (3) | *1.60* | *.55* |
| **894** | A217 | 8f yellow & multi (4) | *1.60* | *.70* |
| **895** | A217 | 8f grnsh bl & multi (5) | *1.60* | *.70* |
| **896** | A217 | 8f green & multi (6) | *1.60* | *.70* |
| **897** | A217 | 10f org & multi (7) | *5.00* | *1.50* |
| **898** | A217 | 52f grnsh gray & multi (8) | *15.00* | *7.00* |
| | | *Nos. 891-898 (8)* | *29.60* | *12.25* |

Mobile Transformer A218

### China Post No. S62

New Industrial Machinery: No. 900, Electron microscope, vert. No. 901, Lathe. No. 902, Vertical boring and turning machine, vert. No. 903, Gear-grinding machine. No. 904, Hydraulic press. No. 905, Milling machine. No. 906, Electron accelerator, vert.

***Perf. 11x11½, 11½x11***

**1966, Mar. 30** **Photo. & Engr.**

| | | | | |
|---|---|---|---|---|
| **899** | A218 | 4f yellow & blk (1) | *55.00* | *3.00* |
| **900** | A218 | 8f blk & lt ultra (2) | *55.00* | *2.00* |
| **901** | A218 | 8f sal pink & blk (3) | *55.00* | *2.00* |
| **902** | A218 | 8f olive & blk (4) | *55.00* | *2.00* |
| **903** | A218 | 8f rose lil & blk (5) | *55.00* | *2.00* |
| **904** | A218 | 10f gray & blk (6) | *70.00* | *8.50* |
| **905** | A218 | 10f bl grn & blk (7) | *70.00* | *11.00* |
| **906** | A218 | 22f lilac & blk (8) | *80.00* | *9.00* |
| | | *Nos. 899-906 (8)* | *495.00* | *39.50* |

Military and Civilian Workers — A219

### China Post No. S75

Women in Various Occupations: No. 908, Train conductor. No. 909, Red Cross worker. No. 910, Kindergarten teacher. No. 911, Road sweeper. No. 912, Hairdresser. No. 913, Bus conductor. No. 914, Traveling saleswoman. No. 915, Canteen worker. No. 916, Rural mail carrier.

**1966, May 10** ***Perf. 11x11½***

**907** A219 8f red & multi (1) *2.75 1.10*
**908** A219 8f pale grn & multi (2) *2.75 1.10*
**909** A219 8f yellow & multi (3) *2.75 1.10*
**910** A219 8f green & multi (4) *2.75 1.10*
**911** A219 8f salmon & multi (5) *2.75 1.10*
**912** A219 8f pale bl & bl (6) *2.75 1.10*
**913** A219 8f yellow & multi (7) *2.75 1.10*
**914** A219 8f tan & multi (8) *2.75 1.10*
**915** A219 8f yel grn & multi (9) *2.75 1.10*
**916** A219 8f green & multi (10) *2.75 1.10*
*Nos. 907-916 (10) 27.50 11.00*

Statue "Thunderstorm" A220

**China Post No. C119**

22f, Open book and association emblem.

**1966, June 27** ***Perf. 11***

**917** A220 8f red & black *12.50 3.00*
**918** A220 22f red, gold & yel *24.00 4.50*

Afro-Asian Writers' Assoc. Conf., Peking.

Sun Yat-sen — A221

**China Post No. C120**

**1966, Nov. 12** ***Perf. 11½x11***

**919** A221 8f sepia & lt buff *105.00 27.50*

Birth centenary of Sun Yat-sen.

Athletes Holding Portrait of Mao A222

Two Women Athletes with Little Red Book — A223

**China Post No. C121**

No. 921, Athletes holding Little Red Books. No. 923, Athletes reading Mao texts.

**1966, Dec. 31** ***Perf. 11***

**920** A222 8f red & multi (1) *90.00 16.50*
**921** A222 8f red & multi (2) *90.00 16.50*

***Perf. 11x11½***

**922** A223 8f blue & multi (3) *70.00 17.00*
**923** A223 8f blue & multi (4) *70.00 17.00*
*Nos. 920-923 (4) 320.00 67.00*

1st Athletic Games of the New Emerging Nations.

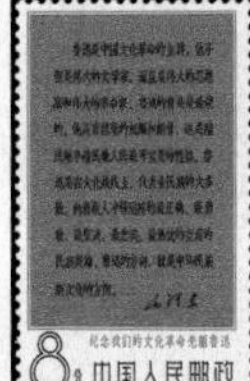

Appreciation of Lu Hsun by Mao — A224

**China Post No. C122**

Designs: No. 925, Portrait of Lu Hsun. No. 926, Lu Hsun's handwriting (3 vert. rows).

**Engr. & Photo.; Photo. (#925)**

**1966, Dec. 31** ***Perf. 11½***

**924** A224 8f red & black (1) *100.00 25.00*
**925** A224 8f red & multi (2) *200.00 25.00*
**926** A224 8f red & black (3) *100.00 25.00*
*Nos. 924-926 (3) 400.00 75.00*

Lu Hsun, Revolutionary writer (1881-1936).

"Be Resolute ...," by Mao Tse-tung — A225

**China Post No. C124**

Designs: No. 928, Drilling crew fighting natural gas fire, horiz. No. 929, Attempt to close fire-engulfed valve.

**Sizes: Nos. 927, 929, 26x38mm; No. 928, 49x29mm**

***Perf. 11½x11, 11½ (No. 928)***

**1967, Mar. 10** **Photo.**

**927** A225 8f red, gold & blk *75.00 17.50*
**928** A225 8f brick red & blk *75.00 17.50*
**929** A225 8f brick red & blk *75.00 17.50*
*Nos. 927-929 (3) 225.00 52.50*

Heroic oil well firefighters.

Liu Ying-chun — A226

**China Post No. C123**

No. 931, With book by Mao (2). No. 932, Holding bridle of horse (3). No. 933, With film slide (4). No. 934, Lecturing (5). No. 935, Fatal attempt to stop runaway horse (6).

**1967, Mar. 25** ***Perf. 11½x11***

**930** A226 8f shown (1) *95.00 17.50*
**931** A226 8f multi *95.00 17.50*
**932** A226 8f multi *95.00 17.50*
**933** A226 8f multi *95.00 17.50*
**934** A226 8f multi *95.00 17.50*
**935** A226 8f multi *95.00 17.50*
*Nos. 930-935 (6) 570.00 105.00*

In memory of soldier Liu Ying-chun, hero.

Third 5-Year Plan A227

**China Post No. C118**

Design: No. 936, Banners, 3 workers and male soldier facing right (industrial growth). No. 937, Banners, 3 workers and female militia member facing left (agricultural growth).

**1967, Apr. 15** ***Perf. 11***

**936** A227 8f red & multi *112.50 19.00*
**937** A227 8f red & multi *112.50 19.00*

Third Five-Year Plan.

Mao Tse-tung A228

Thoughts of Mao A229

**China Post No. W1**

**1967, Apr. 20** ***Perf. 11½***

**938** A228 8f red & multi *110.00 45.00*

**Red & Gold**

**939** A229 8f 39 characters *110.00 55.00*
**940** A229 8f 50 characters *110.00 55.00*
**941** A229 8f 39 characters in 6 lines *110.00 55.00*
**942** A229 8f 53 characters *110.00 55.00*
**943** A229 8f 46 characters *110.00 55.00*
*a.* Strip of 5, #939-943 *2,000. 525.00*

**Gold & Red**

**944** A229 8f 41 characters *160.00 90.00*
**945** A229 8f 49 characters *160.00 90.00*
**946** A229 8f 35 characters *160.00 90.00*
**947** A229 8f 22 characters *160.00 90.00*
**948** A229 8f 29 characters *160.00 90.00*
*a.* Strip of 5, #944-948 *2,600. 725.00*
*Nos. 938-948 (11) 1,460. 770.00*

Thoughts of Mao Tse-tung.

Values for Nos. 943a and 948a are for unfolded strips without tarnishing. Strips with folds and/or tarnishing sell for much less.

For Nos. 938-1046, beware of forgeries, removed cancels and repairs. No numbers appear below design on Nos. 938-1046.

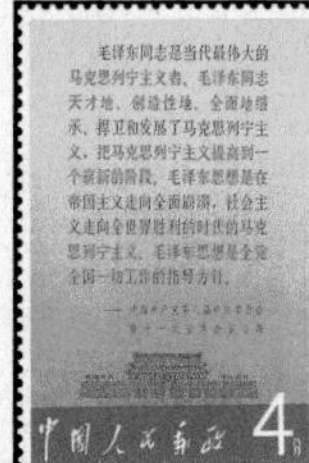

Gate of Heavenly Peace and Text from C. C. P. Communique Praising Mao — A230

Mao and Lin Piao — A231

**China Post No. W2**

No. 950, Mao and poem. No. 951, Mao among people of various races. No. 952, Mao facing left and Red Guards with books. No. 953, Mao with upraised right hand. No. 954, Mao leaning on rail, horiz. 10f, Mao and Lin Piao in discussion, horiz.

**Engraved and Photogravure**

**1967** ***Perf. 11x11½***

**Size: 36x56mm**

**949** A230 4f yel, red & mar *140.00 47.50*

**Photo.**

**950** A230 8f yel, brn, & red *140.00 47.50*
**951** A230 8f yel, red & multi *140.00 47.50*
**952** A230 8f yel, red & multi *140.00 47.50*

**Size: 36x50mm, 50x36mm**

***Perf. 11***

**953** A231 8f black & multi *175.00 42.50*
**954** A231 8f lt blue & multi *400.00 160.00*
**955** A231 8f black & multi *135.00 42.50*
**956** A231 10f black & multi *400.00 160.00*
*Nos. 949-956 (8) 1,670. 595.00*

"Mao Tse-tung Our Great Teacher."

Issued: Nos. 949-953, 5/1; Nos. 954-956, 9/20.

Mao Text (4 lines) A232

Parade of Supporters A233

**China Post No. W3**

Design: No. 958, Mao text (5 lines).

**Engraved and Photogravure**

**1967, May 23** ***Perf. 11½***

**957** A232 8f black, red & yel *325.00 135.00*
**958** A232 8f black, red & yel *325.00 160.00*

**Photo.**

***Perf. 11***

**959** A233 8f multicolored *325.00 160.00*
*Nos. 957-959 (3) 975.00 455.00*

25th anniversary of Mao Tse-tung's "Talks on Literature and Art" in Yenan.

A stamp was prepared in August 1967 for the 40th anniversary of the Autumn Harvest March. It was not issued, but a few examples have entered the marketplace. It depicts Mao Tse-tung on the left and Lin Piao on the right at podium, against a blue sky. A cut example comprising the right half of the stamp was sold in a Jan. 2010 Hong Kong auction for the equivalent of U.S. $285,000. Presumably, an intact example would sell for far more.

Mao Tse-tung — A234

**China Post No. W4**

**1967** **Engr.** ***Perf. 11***

**960** A234 4f brown *137.50 30.00*
**961** A234 8f carmine *275.00 50.00*
**962** A234 35f dk brown *55.00 12.50*
**963** A234 43f vermilion *60.00 12.50*
**964** A234 52f carmine *70.00 17.50*
*Nos. 960-964 (5) 597.50 122.50*

46th anniv. of Chinese Communist Party. Issue dates: 8f, July 1; others Sept. 18.

Mao, "Sun of the Revolution" — A235

**China Post No. W6**

No. 966, Mao and people of various races.

**1967, Oct. 1** ***Perf. 11½x11***

**965** A235 8f multicolored *100.00 40.00*
**966** A235 8f multicolored *225.00 47.50*

People's Republic of China, 18th anniv.

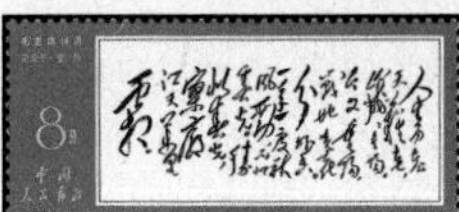

"September 9" — A236

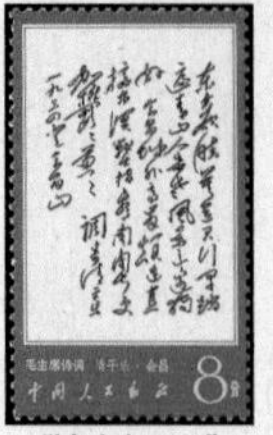

"Huichang"
A237

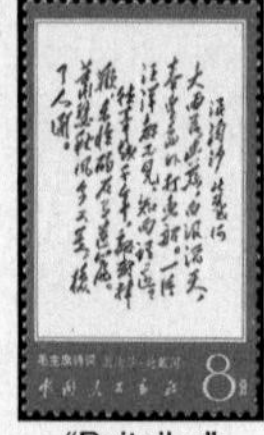

"Peitaiho"
A238

Reply to Comrade Kuo Mo-jo
A239

Mao Tse-tung Writing Poems
A240

**China Post No. W7**

Poems by Mao: No. 967, "The Long March." No. 968, "Liupanshan." No. 969, shown. No. 970, "The Cave of the Fairies." No. 971, "Snow." No. 972, "Lushan Pass." No. 975, "Conquest of Nanking." No. 976, "The Yellow Crane Pavilion." No. 977, "Swimming." No. 979, "Changsha."

**1967-68 Photo. *Perf. 11***

**Size: 79x18½mm**

**967** A236 4f 9 charac-ters, UL panel *140.00 100.00*
**968** A236 4f 11 charac-ters, UL panel *140.00 33.00*

**Size: 60x24mm**

***Perf. 11½***

**969** A236 8f shown, 10 characters in UL panel *100.00 50.00*
**970** A236 8f 21 charac-ters in UL panel *130.00 50.00*
**971** A236 8f 11 charac-ters in UL panel *115.00 67.50*
**972** A236 8f 9 characters in UL panel *115.00 67.50*

**Size: 29x50mm**

**973** A237 8f shown *675.00 155.00*
**974** A238 8f shown *875.00 250.00*
**975** A238 8f 3 rows in bottom panel *600.00 160.00*
**976** A238 8f 2 rows in bottom panel *310.00 155.00*

**Size: 52x38mm**

***Perf. 11***

**977** A239 8f 3 short vert. rows, at left of poem *450.00 160.00*
**978** A239 10f shown *67.50 33.00*
**979** A239 10f undivided text *145.00 33.00*
**980** A240 10f red, yel & multi *145.00 50.00*
*Nos. 967-980 (14)* *4,008. 1,364.*

Issued: Nos. 969-970, 980, 10/1; Nos. 973-974, 977, 5/20/68; others 7/20/68.

Lin Piao's Epigram on Mao Tse-tung — A241

**China Post No. W8**

**1967, Dec. 26 Photo. *Perf. 11x11½***

**981** A241 8f red & gold *42.50 15.00*

Mao and Parade of Artists
A242

"Raid on White Tiger Regiment"
A243

"Red Detachment of Women"
A244

**China Post No. W5**

No. 983, "The Red Lantern," vert. No. 985, "Shachiapang" (women & soldier). No. 986, "On the Dock". No. 987, "Taking Bandits' Fort". No. 989, "The White-haired Girl". No. 990, Mao with Orchestra & Chorus (50x36mm).

**1968 *Perf. 11½x11; 11 (983, 990)***

**982** A242 8f shown (56x36mm) *160.00 40.00*
**983** A242 8f multi *160.00 40.00*
**984** A243 8f shown *160.00 40.00*
**985** A243 8f multi *160.00 40.00*
**986** A243 8f multi *160.00 40.00*
**987** A243 8f multi *160.00 40.00*
**988** A244 8f shown *160.00 40.00*
**989** A244 8f multi *160.00 40.00*
**990** A242 8f multi *160.00 40.00*
*Nos. 982-990 (9)* *1,440. 360.00*

Mao's direction for revolutionary literature and art. Issued: Nos. 982-987, Jan. 30; Nos. 988-990, May 1.

"Unite still more closely . . ." — A245

**China Post No. W9**

**1968, May 31 Photo. *Perf. 11***

**991** A245 8f red, gold & red brn *400.00 100.00*

Mao Tse-tung's statement of support of Afro-Americans.

Statement about Cultural Revolution — A246

**China Post No. W10**

Directives of Chairman Mao: No. 993, Experiences of Revolutionary Committee. No. 994, Leadership role of Revolutionary Committee. No. 995, Basic principle of reform. No. 996, Purpose of Cultural Revolution.

**1968, July 20 Photo. *Perf. 11½***

**No. of Lines Over Signature**

**992** A246 8f 6 *475.00 250.00*
**993** A246 8f 5 *475.00 250.00*
**994** A246 8f 4½ *475.00 250.00*
**995** A246 8f 4 *475.00 250.00*
**996** A246 8f 8 *475.00 250.00*
*a.* Strip of 5, #992-996 *7,000. 2,350.*
*Nos. 992-996 (5)* *2,375. 1,250.*

Value for No. 996a is for an unfolded strip.

Lin Piao's Statement, July 26, 1965
A247

**China Post No. W11**

**1968, Aug. 1 Engr. & Photo.**

**997** A247 8f red, gold & blk *37.50 11.00*

Chinese People's Liberation Army, 41st anniv.

Mao Tse-tung Going to An Yuan, 1921 — A248

**China Post No. W12**

**1968, Aug. 1 *Perf. 11x11½***

**998** A248 8f multicolored *225.00 50.00*

Shade varieties include varying amount of red in clouds.

An 8f stamp was prepared in Sept. 1968, showing black writing on a red background, regarding Chairman Mao's inscriptions to Japanese Labor Friends. It was not issued, but a few examples have reached the marketplace. Value, *$175,000.*

Directive of Chairman Mao — A249

**China Post No. W13**

**1968, Nov. 30 *Perf. 11½***

**999** A249 8f red & blk brn *240.00 50.00*

China Map, Worker, Farmer and Soldier — A249a

**China Post No. W14**

**1968, Nov. 25 Photo. *Perf. 11½x11***

**999A** A249a 8f red, bl & bis *135,000. 80,000.*

Map inscribed: "The entire nation is red." Although officially issued in Canton Nov. 25, some post offices began selling the stamp Nov. 24. Because of inaccuracies in the map (the archipelagos of Xisha and Nanshi were omitted), the stamp was withdrawn from sale Nov. 26.

No. 999A most often is found repaired. Values are for sound, unrepaired examples.

Counterfeits exist.

Two values were prepared to celebrate the Great Victory of the Cultural Revolution but were not issued, although a few examples were sold through the post office at Hebei prior to the recall and issue date. Values for sound stamps: 8f, Mao Tse-tung and Lin Piao, $300,000; 8f, map and workers, $1,150,000.

Woman, Miner and Soldier Holding Little Red Book — A250

**China Post No. W16**

**1968, Dec. 26 *Perf. 11x11½***

**1000** A250 8f multicolored *65.00 15.00*

Canceled-to-order

From about this point on stamps are valued postally used.

Yangtze Bridge, Nanking — A251

Road across Bridge
A252

**China Post No. W15**

No. 1003, Side view. 10f, Aerial view.

**Lithographed, *Perf. 11½x11 (A251);* Photogravure, *Perf. 11½ (A252)***

**1969, May 1 Without Gum**

**1001** A251 4f multicolored *8.75 3.00*
**1002** A252 8f multicolored *72.50 11.00*
**1003** A252 8f multicolored *22.50 6.00*
**1004** A251 10f multicolored *6.75 3.00*
*Nos. 1001-1004 (4)* *110.50 23.00*

Inauguration of Yangtze Bridge at Nanking on Dec. 29, 1968.

Singer and Pianist — A253

**China Post No. W17**

(Piano Music from the Opera, "The Red Lantern"): No. 1006, Woman singer and pianist.

**1969, Aug. 1 Photo. *Perf. 11x11½***

**Without Gum**

**1005** A253 8f multicolored *40.00 12.50*
**1006** A253 8f multicolored *110.00 18.50*

Harvest — A254

**China Post No. W18**

No. 1008, Two harvesters. No. 1009, Harvesters with Little Red Books. No. 1010, Red Cross Worker examining baby.

**1969, Oct. 1** **Without Gum**

| No. | Type | Description | Unused | Used |
|---|---|---|---|---|
| **1007** | A254 | 4f shown | *13.50* | *3.50* |
| **1008** | A254 | 8f multi | *62.50* | *8.50* |
| **1009** | A254 | 8f multi | *82.50* | *19.00* |
| **1010** | A254 | 10f multi | *9.00* | *3.75* |
| | | *Nos. 1007-1010 (4)* | *167.50* | *34.75* |

Agriculture students.

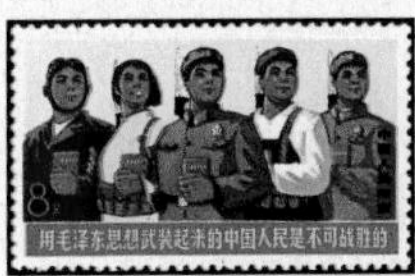

Armed Forces and Slogan A255

Guarding the Coast A256

**China Post No. W19**

Designs: No. 1013, 43f, Snow patrol, vert.

**1969, Oct. 1** ***Perf. 11½***

**Without Gum**

| No. | Type | Description | Unused | Used |
|---|---|---|---|---|
| **1011** | A255 | 8f red & multi | *72.50* | *15.00* |
| **1012** | A256 | 8f blue & multi | *15.50* | *4.50* |
| **1013** | A256 | 8f blue & multi | *15.50* | *4.50* |
| **1014** | A256 | 35f black & multi | *12.00* | *6.00* |
| **1015** | A256 | 43f black & multi | *15.50* | *8.00* |
| | | *Nos. 1011-1015 (5)* | *131.00* | *38.00* |

Defense of Chen Pao-tao (Damansky Islands) in Ussuri River.

Farm Woman — A257

**China Post No. RW2**

Designs: 8f, Foundry worker. 10f, Soldier.

**1969, Oct. 1** ***Perf. 10; 11½***

**Without Gum**

| No. | Type | Description | Unused | Used |
|---|---|---|---|---|
| **1016** | A257 | 4f ver & dk pur | *2.75* | *.80* |
| *a.* | | Perf 11½ | *8.25* | *1.60* |
| **1017** | A257 | 8f ver & dk brn | *3.25* | *.80* |
| *a.* | | Perf 11½ | *5.00* | *1.60* |
| **1018** | A257 | 10f ver & blk | *5.50* | *1.75* |
| *a.* | | Perf 11½ | — | *900.00* |
| | | *Nos. 1016-1018 (3)* | *11.50* | *3.35* |

Perforation

Nos. 1016-1018 and some succeeding issues bear two kinds of perforation: clean (Peking) and rough (Shanghai).

Building A258

Communist Party Building, Shanghai A259

Agriculture Building, Canton A260

Foundry Worker A261

Type I

**China Post Nos. RW1 and R14**

Two types of 8f Gate of Heavenly Peace:
I — Strong, definite halo around sun.
II — Halo missing, white shades gradually into red.

No. 1022, 1929 Party Day House, Pu Tien. No. 1023, Mao's Home and Office, Yunnan. No. 1024, Woman Tractor Driver. No. 1025, Gate of Heavenly Peace. No. 1026, Heroes Monument. No. 1027, Pagoda Hill, Yenan. No. 1028, Gate of Heavenly Peace (no sun). No. 1029, Monument, Tsu Ping. No. 1030, Conference Hall, Tsunyi. No. 1031, Highway ('72). No. 1032, Shao Shan Village, Birthplace of Mao. No. 1033, Conference Hall. No. 1034, Chingkang Peaks. No. 1035, as 4f, different view. No. 1036, People's Hall, Peking.

**1969-72** **Photo.** ***Perf. 10***

**Without Gum**

| No. | Type | Description | Unused | Used |
|---|---|---|---|---|
| **1019** | A258 | 1f shown | *.50* | *.50* |
| **1020** | A259 | 1½f shown | *1.30* | *.95* |
| *a.* | | Perf. 11½ | *8.75* | *4.50* |
| **1021** | A260 | 2f shown | *.50* | *.40* |
| **1022** | A260 | 3f multi | *.75* | *.40* |
| **1023** | A260 | 4f multi | *.95* | *.30* |
| **1024** | A261 | 5f multi | *1.90* | *.75* |
| **1025** | A260 | 8f multi, type II | *4.25* | *1.30* |
| *a.* | | Type I | *8.50* | *1.60* |
| **1026** | A259 | 8f multi | *2.40* | *2.10* |
| *a.* | | Perf. 11½ | *8.50* | *4.00* |
| **1027** | A260 | 8f multi | *20.00* | *3.25* |
| **1028** | A260 | 8f multi | *1.00* | *.40* |
| **1029** | A260 | 10f multi | *1.00* | *.40* |
| **1030** | A259 | 20f multi | *3.50* | *1.90* |
| *a.* | | Perf. 11½ | *25.00* | *6.00* |
| **1031** | A260 | 20f multi | *3.00* | *.50* |
| **1032** | A260 | 22f multi | *1.60* | *.75* |
| **1033** | A260 | 35f multi | *1.25* | *.65* |
| **1034** | A260 | 43f multi | *3.00* | *.65* |
| **1035** | A259 | 50f multi | *2.50* | *.75* |
| **1036** | A260 | 52f multi | *5.25* | *.85* |
| **1037** | A261 | $1 shown | *6.00* | *2.25* |
| | | *Nos. 1019-1037 (19)* | *60.65* | *19.05* |

China Post No. RW1 includes Nos. 1019, 1024-1027, 1030, 1035, and 1037. The rest are China Post No. R14.

Issue dates: Nos. 1025 and 1027, Oct. 1, 1969; Nos. 1030 and 1035, Jan. 1, 1970; Nos. 1020, 1024 and 1026, April 1, 1970; No. 1037, April 20, 1970; Nos. 1019 and 1031, Dec. 20, 1971; Nos. 1023 and 1028, March 25, 1972; others, Sept. 25, 1971.

Kin Hsün-hua — A262

**China Post No. W21**

**1970, Jan.** **Without Gum** ***Perf. 11½***

| No. | Type | Description | Unused | Used |
|---|---|---|---|---|
| **1045** | A262 | 8f red & black | *45.00* | *17.50* |
| *a.* | | 8f red & gray brown | *55.00* | *15.00* |

Death of Kin Hsün-hua in Kirin border flood.

Mounted Patrol — A263

**China Post No. 1046**

**1970, Aug. 1** **Without Gum**

| No. | Type | Description | Unused | Used |
|---|---|---|---|---|
| **1046** | A263 | 8f yel grn & multi | *25.00* | *9.25* |

People's Liberation Army, 43rd anniv.

Commemorative stamps from Nos. 1047 to 1142 and 1211-1214, carry a cumulative number in parentheses at lower left and the year at lower right. Where such numbers help to identify, they are quoted in parentheses.

Cpl. Yang Tse-jung A264

Ensemble A265

**China Post No. N1**

No. 1048, Armed guards (2) horiz. No. 1049, Yang leaping through forest (3). No. 1051, Yang in folk costume (5). No. 1052, Four actors (6) horiz.

***Perf. 11½x11 (1047, 1049), 11x11½ (1048,1052), 11½ (1050-1051)***

**1970-1971**

**Without Gum**

| No. | Type | Description | Unused | Used |
|---|---|---|---|---|
| **1047** | A264 | 8f shown (1) | *65.00* | *14.00* |
| **1048** | A264 | 8f multi | *22.00* | *2.75* |
| **1049** | A264 | 8f multi | *27.50* | *4.75* |
| **1050** | A265 | 8f shown (4) | *105.00* | *14.00* |
| **1051** | A265 | 8f multi | *16.75* | *3.75* |
| **1052** | A264 | 8f multi | *38.00* | *8.25* |
| | | *Nos. 1047-1052 (6)* | *274.25* | *47.50* |

Scenes from opera "Taking Tiger Mountain by Strategy."

Frontier Guard — A266

**China Post No. N2**

**1971, Jan.** **Litho.** ***Perf. 10***

**Without Gum**

| No. | Type | Description | Unused | Used |
|---|---|---|---|---|
| **1053** | A266 | 4f multicolored | *6.50* | *1.90* |
| *a.* | | Perf. 11½ | *7.00* | *1.90* |
| *b.* | | Perf. 11½x10 | *8.00* | *3.00* |
| *c.* | | Perf. 10x11½ | *8.00* | *3.50* |

Banner of the Commune A267

Street Battle, Paris, 1871 A268

**China Post No. N3**

10f, Proclamation of the Commune. 22f, Rally.

***Perf. 11½x11, 11x11½***

**1971, Mar. 18** **Litho. & Engr.**

**Without Gum**

| No. | Type | Description | Unused | Used |
|---|---|---|---|---|
| **1054** | A267 | 4f sal & multi | *49.00* | *18.00* |
| **1055** | A268 | 8f ver, pink & brn | *315.00* | *50.00* |
| **1056** | A267 | 10f ver, pink & dk brn | *20.00* | *11.00* |
| **1057** | A268 | 22f ver, pink & dk brn | *15.00* | *10.00* |
| | | *Nos. 1054-1057 (4)* | *399.00* | *89.00* |

Centenary of the Paris Commune.

**Redrawn Building Type of 1961**

**China Post No. R12**

Designs: 2f, 3f, August 1 building, Nanchang. 4f, 52f, Gate of Heavenly Peace, Peking. 10f, 20f, Pagoda Hill, Yenan.

**1971, July 1** **Litho.** ***Perf. 11x11½***

**Size: 21x16mm**

**Without Gum**

| No. | Type | Description | Unused | Used |
|---|---|---|---|---|
| **1059** | A152 | 2f slate green | *2.00* | *.75* |
| **1060** | A152 | 3f sepia | *3.00* | *1.25* |
| **1061** | A152 | 4f brt pink | *5.00* | *2.00* |
| **1062** | A152 | 10f brt rose lil | *1.50* | *1.25* |
| **1063** | A152 | 20f dk blue grn | *3.75* | *1.25* |
| **1064** | A152 | 52f orange | *2.50* | *3.00* |
| | | *Nos. 1059-1064 (6)* | *17.75* | *9.50* |

Paper of Nos. 1059-1064 is white. That of Nos. 647-654 is toned.

Communist Party Building, Shanghai A269

People and Factories — A270

**China Post No. N4**

Designs: No. 1068, Peasant Movement Training Institute. No. 1069, Ching Kang Peaks. No. 1070, Conference Building, Tsunyi. No. 1071, Pagoda Hill, Yenan. No. 1073, People and People's Hall, Peking. No. 1074, People and Pagoda Hill, Yenan. 22f, Gate of Heavenly Peace, Peking.

**1971, July 1** **Photo.** ***Perf. 11½***

**Red and Gold Frame**

**Without Gum**

| No. | Type | Description | Unused | Used |
|---|---|---|---|---|
| **1067** | A269 | 4f vermilion (12) | *47.50* | *4.00* |
| **1068** | A269 | 4f brt grn (13) | *47.50* | *4.00* |
| **1069** | A269 | 8f grnsh bl & red (14) | *60.00* | *4.00* |
| **1070** | A269 | 8f ol blk (15) | *70.00* | *4.00* |
| **1071** | A269 | 8f bis, grn & red (16) | *70.00* | *4.00* |
| **1072** | A270 | 8f yel, red & multi (18) | *70.00* | *6.50* |
| **1073** | A270 | 8f yel, red & multi (19) | *70.00* | *6.50* |
| **1074** | A270 | 8f yel, red & multi (20) | *70.00* | *6.50* |
| *a.* | | Strip of 3, #1072-1074 | *375.00* | *60.00* |
| **1075** | A269 | 22f red, gold & brn (17) | *35.00* | *7.25* |
| | | *Nos. 1067-1075 (9)* | *540.00* | *46.75* |

50th anniv. of the Chinese Communist Party. No. 1073 has date of 1921-1971 at top. No. 1074a has a continuous design and is valued as an unfolded strip.

Chinese Welcome — A271

**China Post No. N5**

No. 1077, Chinese & African players. No. 1078, Chinese & African girl players. 43f, Games' emblem.

**1971, Nov. 3** **Litho.** ***Perf. 11½***

**Without Gum**

| No. | Type | Description | Unused | Used |
|---|---|---|---|---|
| **1076** | A271 | 8f lil rose & multi | *27.50* | *5.75* |
| **1077** | A271 | 8f lt yellow & multi | *27.50* | *5.75* |
| **1078** | A271 | 8f dk grn & multi | *27.50* | *5.75* |
| **1079** | A271 | 43f grn, gold & org | *115.00* | *16.00* |
| | | *Nos. 1076-1079 (4)* | *197.50* | *33.25* |

Afro-Asian Table Tennis Games, Peking.

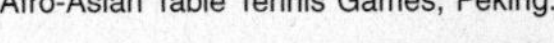

Enver Hoxha — A272

**China Post No. N6**

No. 1081, Party's birthplace. No. 1082, Albanian flag. 52f, Albanian partisans, horiz.

**1971, Nov. 3** **Photo.** ***Perf. 11***

**Without Gum**

| No. | Type | Description | Unused | Used |
|---|---|---|---|---|
| **1080** | A272 | 8f Prus blue & multi | *32.50* | *8.00* |
| **1081** | A272 | 8f buff & multi | *20.00* | *7.00* |
| **1082** | A272 | 8f red, yel & multi | *20.00* | *7.00* |
| **1083** | A272 | 52f lt blue & multi | *35.00* | *10.00* |
| | | *Nos. 1080-1083 (4)* | *107.50* | *32.00* |

30th anniversary of the founding of Albanian Communist Party.

Yenan Pagoda and 1942 Meeting House — A273

**China Post No. N8**

No. 1085, Uniformed choir (34). No. 1086, "Brother & Sister" (35). No. 1087, Outdoor performance (36). No. 1088, "The Red Signal Lantern" (37). No. 1089, Dancer from "The Red Company of Women" (38).

**1972, May 23 Photo. *Perf. 11***
**Without Gum**

**1084** A273 8f shown (33) *25.00* *7.50*
**1085** A273 8f multi *25.00* *7.50*
**1086** A273 8f multi *25.00* *7.50*
**1087** A273 8f multi *25.00* *7.50*
**1088** A273 8f multi *25.00* *7.50*
**1089** A273 8f multi *25.00* *7.50*
*Nos. 1084-1089 (6)* *150.00* *45.00*

30th anniversary of the publication of the Discussions on Literature and Art at the Yenan Forum.

Various Ball Games A274

Workers' Gymnastics — A275

**China Post No. N9**

No. 1092, Tug of war (41). No. 1093, Mountain climbers and tents (42). No. 1094, Children diving & swimming (43).

**1972, June 10**

**1090** A274 8f shown (39) *47.50* *5.00*
**1091** A275 8f shown (40) *24.00* *5.00*
**1092** A275 8f multi *24.00* *5.00*
**1093** A275 8f multi *21.50* *5.00*
**1094** A275 8f multi *24.00* *5.00*
*Nos. 1090-1094 (5)* *141.00* *25.00*

10th anniversary of Mao Tse-tung's edict on physical culture.

Ocean Freighter Fenglei A276

**China Post No. N7**

No. 1096, Tanker Taching No. 30 (30). No. 1097, Cargo-passenger ship Changzeng (31). No. 1098, Dredger Xienfeng (32).

**1972, July 10 Photo. *Perf. 11½***
**Without Gum**

**1095** A276 8f shown (29) *77.50* *12.50*
**1096** A276 8f multi *40.00* *11.00*
**1097** A276 8f multi *40.00* *11.00*
**1098** A276 8f multi *62.50* *12.50*
*Nos. 1095-1098 (4)* *220.00* *47.00*

Table Tennis Players' Welcome — A277

**China Post No. N11**

No. 1099, Championship emblem, vert. (45). No. 1101, Table tennis (47). No. 1102, Women from different countries, vert. (48).

**1972, Sept. 2 *Perf. 11½x11, 11x11½***
**Without Gum**

**1099** A277 8f multi *13.50* *5.00*
**1100** A277 8f shown (46) *37.50* *5.00*
**1101** A277 8f multi *25.00* *5.00*
**1102** A277 22f multi *22.00* *6.00*
*Nos. 1099-1102 (4)* *98.00* *21.00*

First Asian table tennis championships.

Wang Chin-hsi — A278

**China Post No. N10**
**Engraved and Photogravure**

**1972, Dec. 25 *Perf. 11½x11***
**1103** A278 8f multicolored (44) *65.00* *20.00*

Wang Chin-hsi, the Iron Man, fighter for the working class.

Workers on Cliffs along Canal — A279

**China Post No. N12**

No. 1105, Canal flowing through tunnel (50). No. 1106, Bridge (51). No. 1107, Canal along cliffs (52).

**1972, Dec. 30**

**1104** A279 8f multi (49) *30.00* *7.00*
**1105** A279 8f multicolored *30.00* *7.00*
**1106** A279 8f multicolored *40.00* *10.00*
**1107** A279 8f multicolored *40.00* *10.00*
*Nos. 1104-1107 (4)* *140.00* *34.00*

Construction of Red Flag Canal, Linhsien county, Honan.

Giant Panda — A280

**China Post No. N14**

Designs: Pandas in various positions. The 8f stamps are horizontal.

***Perf. 11½x11, 11x11½***
**1973, Jan. 15 Photo.**
**Designs in Black and Red**

**1108** A280 4f lt yel grn (61) *10.00* *8.00*
**1109** A280 8f buff (59) *10.00* *6.00*
**1110** A280 8f lt tan (60) *10.00* *6.00*
**1111** A280 10f pale grn (58) *115.00* *18.00*
**1112** A280 20f pale bl gray (57) *57.50* *10.00*
**1113** A280 43f pale lil (62) *17.00* *14.00*
*Nos. 1108-1113 (6)* *219.50* *62.00*

Woman Coal Miner — A281

**China Post No. N15**

No. 1115, Committee member (64). No. 1116, Telephone line worker (65).

**1973, Mar. 8 Photo. *Perf. 11½x11***

**1114** A281 8f shown (63) *24.00* *5.00*
**1115** A281 8f multi *17.50* *6.00*
**1116** A281 8f multi *17.50* *5.00*
*Nos. 1114-1116 (3)* *59.00* *16.00*

Intl. Working Women's Day. Designs are after paintings from an exhib. for 30th anniv. of the Yenan Forum on Literature and Art.

Dancing Girl — A282

**China Post No. N19**

No. 1118, Musician, boy (87). No. 1119, Girl with scarf (88). No. 1120, Boy with tambourine (89). No. 1121, Girl with drum (90).

**1973, June 1 Photo. *Perf. 11***

**1117** A282 8f shown (86) *3.00* *1.75*
**1118** A282 8f multi *3.00* *1.75*
**1119** A282 8f multi *3.00* *1.75*
**1120** A282 8f multi *3.00* *1.75*
**1121** A282 8f multi *3.00* *1.75*
*a.* Strip of 5, #1117-1121 *65.00* *20.00*
*Nos. 1117-1121 (5)* *15.00* *8.75*

Values for No. 1121a are for an unfolded strip.

Tournament Emblem — A283

**China Post No. N20**

No. 1123, Visitors from Asia, Africa and Latin America arriving by plane (92). No. 1124, Woman player (93). No. 1125, African, Asian & Latin American women (94).

**1973, Aug. 25 Photo. *Perf. 11½***

**1122** A283 8f multi (91) *16.00* *2.75*
**1123** A283 8f multicolored *13.00* *2.75*
**1124** A283 8f multicolored *13.00* *2.75*
**1125** A283 22f multicolored *13.00* *2.75*
*Nos. 1122-1125 (4)* *55.00* *11.00*

Asian, African and Latin American Table Tennis Friendship Invitational Tournament.

The White-haired Girl — A284

**China Post No. N13**

Designs: Scenes from the ballet "The White-haired Girl." Nos. 1126, 1129 vert.

**1973, Sept. 25 Photo. *Perf. 11½***

**1126** A284 8f multi (53) *40.00* *11.00*
**1127** A284 8f multi (54) *50.00* *11.00*
**1128** A284 8f multi (55) *40.00* *11.00*
**1129** A284 8f multi (56) *45.00* *11.00*
*Nos. 1126-1129 (4)* *175.00* *44.00*

Fair Building, Canton A285

**China Post No. N21**

**1973, Oct. 15 Photo. *Perf. 11***
**1130** A285 8f multicolored (95) *30.00* *3.00*

Export Commodities Fall Fair, Canton.

Teapot with Blue Phoenix Design — A286

**China Post No. N16**

Excavated Works of Art: No. 1132, Silver pot with horse design. No. 1133, Black pottery horse. No. 1134, Woman, clay figurine. No. 1135, Carved stone pillar base. No. 1136, Galloping bronze horse. No. 1137, Bronze inkwell (toad). No. 1138, Bronze lamp, Chang Hsin Palace. No. 1139, Bronze tripod. No. 1140, Square bronze pot. 20f, Bronze wine vessel. 52f, Painted red clay tripod.

**1973, Nov. 20 *Perf. 11½***

**1131** A286 4f ol bis & multi (66) *5.50* *.75*
**1132** A286 4f ver & multi (67) 5.50 *.75*
**1133** A286 8f yel grn & multi (68) *4.50* *.75*
**1134** A286 8f brt rose & multi (69) *4.50* *.75*
**1135** A286 8f lt vio & multi (70) *4.50* *.75*
**1136** A286 8f yel bis & multi (71) *4.50* *.75*
**1137** A286 8f lt bl & multi (72) *4.50* *.75*
**1138** A286 8f gray & multi (73) *4.50* *.75*
**1139** A286 10f yel bis & multi (74) *4.50* *.75*
**1140** A286 10f dp org & multi (75) *4.50* *.75*
**1141** A286 20f lil & multi (76) *9.00* *2.00*
**1142** A286 52f grn & multi (77) *14.50* *4.00*
*Nos. 1131-1142 (12)* *70.50* *13.50*

Marginal Markings

Marginal inscriptions on stamps of 1974-91 start at lower left with "J" for commemoratives and "T" for "special issues," followed by three numbers indicating (a) set sequence for the year, (b) total of stamps in set, and (c) number of stamp within set. At right appears the year date. Listings include the "c" number parenthetically. The "a" number is included only when it will help identify stamps not illustrated.

Example: T26 (6-3), the 3rd stamp of 6 from the 26th special set. Set numbers and or positions will be shown only when they help identify a stamp. An illustrated single stamp set will not have these numbers in the listings.

Woman Gymnast — A287

**China Post No. T.1.**

Designs: No. 1144, Gymnast on rings. No. 1145, Aerial split over balance beam, woman. No. 1146, Gymnast on parallel bars. No. 1147, Uneven bars, woman. No. 1148, Gymnast on horse.

**1974, Jan. 1 Photo. *Perf. 11½x11***

**1143** A287 8f lt grn & multi (1) *10.00* *3.50*
**1144** A287 8f lt vio & multi (2) *10.00* *3.50*
**1145** A287 8f lt blue & multi (3) *10.00* *3.50*
**1146** A287 8f sal & multi (4) *12.50* *4.50*
**1147** A287 8f yel & multi (5) *10.00* *4.50*
**1148** A287 8f lil rose & multi (6) *12.50* *4.50*
*Nos. 1143-1148 (6)* *65.00* *24.00*

Girls Twirling Bamboo Diabolos A288

**China Post No. T.2.**

Designs: No. 1149, Lion Dance, vert. No. 1150, Handstand on chairs, vert. No. 1152, Men balancing jar. No. 1153, Plate spinning, vert. No. 1154, Twirling umbrella, vert.

**1974, Jan. 21 *Perf. 11***

**1149** A288 8f brn & multi (1) *7.00* *2.75*
**1150** A288 8f Prus bl & multi (2) *7.00* *2.75*
**1151** A288 8f lilac & multi (3) *10.00* *2.75*
**1152** A288 8f dull bl & multi (4) *7.00* *2.75*
**1153** A288 8f ol grn & multi (5) *7.00* *2.75*
**1154** A288 8f gray & multi (6) *10.00* *2.75*
*Nos. 1149-1154 (6)* *48.00* *16.50*

Traditional acrobatics.

Shao Shan — A289

Site of 1st National Communist Party Congress — A289a

Peasant Movement Institute, Kwangchow — A289b

Headquarters of Nanchang Uprising — A289c

Great Hall of the People, Beijing — A289d

View of Wen Chia Shih — A289e

Tien An Men, Beijing — A289f

Tzeping in Chingkang Mountains — A289g

Site of Kutien Meeting — A289h

Tsunyi Conference Site — A289i

Yenan (bridge) — A289j

Hsi Pai Ho, Communist Party Meeting Site — A289k

Fairy Cave, Lushan — A289l

Monument to People's Heroes — A289m

Transportation by Railroad — A289n

Trucks on Mountain Road — A289o

**China Post No. R15**

**1973-74 Litho. *Perf. 11***

**Without Gum**

| | | | | |
|---|---|---|---|---|
| **1163** | A289 | 1f sl grn & pale grn | .65 | .35 |
| **1164** | A289a | 1½f car & buff | .65 | .35 |
| **1165** | A289b | 2f dk blue & pale grn | .70 | .35 |
| **1166** | A289c | 3f dk ol & yel | .70 | .35 |
| **1167** | A289d | 4f red & yel | 1.50 | .35 |
| **1168** | A289e | 5f brn & lt yel | .80 | .35 |
| **1169** | A289f | 8f dull mag & buff | 1.00 | .35 |
| *a.* | | Perf. 11½x12 | 17.50 | 9.75 |
| **1170** | A289g | 10f blue & buff | .80 | .40 |
| **1171** | A289h | 20f dk red & buff | 2.40 | .40 |
| **1172** | A289i | 22f vio & lt yel | 5.00 | 1.60 |
| **1173** | A289j | 35f mar & lt yel | 4.25 | 1.75 |
| **1174** | A289k | 43f red brn & buff | 5.00 | 2.00 |
| **1175** | A289l | 50f dk blue & pink | 4.00 | .50 |
| **1176** | A289m | 52f sepia & buff | 3.00 | .50 |

**China Post No. R16**

**Photogravure & Engraved**

| | | | | |
|---|---|---|---|---|
| **1177** | A289n | $1 multicolored | 5.00 | 1.00 |
| **1178** | A289o | $2 multicolored | 6.50 | 1.10 |
| | | *Nos. 1163-1178 (16)* | *41.95* | *11.70* |

Issue dates: No. 1177, Oct. 20, 1973; No. 1178, Feb. 20, 1974; all others April 1, 1974.

Capital Stadium — A290

**China Post No. R17**

Design: 8f, Hotel Peking.

**1974, Dec. 1 Photo. *Perf. 11***

**Without Gum**

**1179** A290 4f black & yel grn .85 .25

Nos 1179 and 1180 also exist with gum.

**1180** A290 8f black & ultra .50 .25

"Veteran Secretary" A291

Well Diggers A292

**China Post No. T.3.**

Designs: Nos. 1183-1186 horizontal.

**1974, Apr. 20 Photo. *Perf. 11***

| | | | | |
|---|---|---|---|---|
| **1181** | A291 | 8f shown (1) | 4.50 | 2.25 |
| **1182** | A292 | 8f shown (2) | 4.50 | 2.25 |
| **1183** | A291 | 8f Spring hoeing (3) | 5.50 | 2.25 |
| **1184** | A291 | 8f Farmers (4) | 5.50 | 2.25 |
| **1185** | A292 | 8f Farm (5) | 5.50 | 2.25 |
| **1186** | A291 | 8f Bumper crops (6) | 5.50 | 2.50 |
| | | *Nos. 1181-1186 (6)* | *31.00* | *13.75* |

Paintings by farmers of Huhsien County, shown at exhibition in Peking.

Mailman on Motorcycle — A293

**China Post No. J.1.**

**1974, May 15 Photo. *Perf. 11***

| | | | | |
|---|---|---|---|---|
| **1187** | A293 | 8f shown (1) | 10.00 | 4.50 |
| **1188** | A293 | 8f People of the world (2) | 10.00 | 3.50 |
| **1189** | A293 | 8f Great Wall (3) | 15.00 | 3.50 |
| | | *Nos. 1187-1189 (3)* | *35.00* | *11.50* |

Centenary of the UPU.

Barefoot Doctor Inoculating Children — A294

**China Post No. N18**

Designs (Barefoot Doctors): No. 1191, Crossing stream at night to reach patient, vert. No. 1192, Gathering herbs, vert. No. 1193, Acupuncture treatment for farmer in the field.

***Perf. 11x11½, 11½x11***

**1974, June 26 Photo.**

| | | | | |
|---|---|---|---|---|
| **1190** | A294 | 8f multicolored (82) | 16.50 | 2.00 |
| **1191** | A294 | 8f multicolored (83) | 22.50 | 3.00 |
| **1192** | A294 | 8f multicolored (84) | 19.50 | 2.00 |
| **1193** | A294 | 8f multicolored (85) | 16.50 | 2.00 |
| | | *Nos. 1190-1193 (4)* | *75.00* | *9.00* |

Steel Worker Wang Chin-hsi A295

**China Post No. T.4.**

No. 1195, Workers studying Mao's writings around campfire. No. 1196, Drilling for oil in winter. No. 1197, Scientific industrial management. No. 1198, Oil derricks and farms.

**1974, Sept. 30 Photo. *Perf. 11***

| | | | | |
|---|---|---|---|---|
| **1194** | A295 | 8f multi (5-1) | 9.25 | 3.00 |
| **1195** | A295 | 8f multi (5-2) | 8.75 | 2.75 |
| **1196** | A295 | 8f multi (5-3) | 8.75 | 2.75 |
| **1197** | A295 | 8f multi (5-4) | 8.75 | 2.75 |
| **1198** | A295 | 8f multi (5-5) | 9.25 | 3.00 |
| | | *Nos. 1194-1198 (5)* | *44.75* | *14.25* |

Workers of Taching as examples of achievement.

Members of Tachai Commune — A296

**China Post No. T.5.**

No. 1200, Farmers leveling mountains and fields in winter. No. 1201, Scientific farming. No. 1202, Trucks carrying surplus harvest. No. 1203, Young workers with banner.

**1974, Sept. 30**

| | | | | |
|---|---|---|---|---|
| **1199** | A296 | 8f multi (5-1) | 5.50 | 1.50 |
| **1200** | A296 | 8f multi (5-2) | 5.50 | 1.50 |
| **1201** | A296 | 8f multi (5-3) | 5.50 | 1.50 |
| **1202** | A296 | 8f multi (5-4) | 6.50 | 1.50 |
| **1203** | A296 | 8f multi (5-5) | 6.50 | 1.50 |
| | | *Nos. 1199-1203 (5)* | *29.50* | *7.50* |

Farmers of Tachai as examples of achievement.

Arms of Republic and Members of Ethnic Groups A297

**China Post No. J.2.**

**1974, Oct. 1**

**1204** A297 8f multi (1-1) 40.00 8.50

Taching Steel Worker — A298

**China Post No. J.3.**

Designs: No. 1206, Tachai farm woman. No. 1207, Soldier, planes and ships.

**1974, Oct. 1**

| | | | | |
|---|---|---|---|---|
| **1205** | A298 | 8f multi (3-1) | 4.50 | 2.00 |
| **1206** | A298 | 8f multi (3-2) | 4.50 | 2.00 |
| **1207** | A298 | 8f multi (3-3) | 4.50 | 2.00 |
| *a.* | | Strip of 3, #1205-1207 | 25.00 | 12.00 |

People's Republic of China, 25th anniv.

Values for No. 1207a are for an unfolded strip.

Export Commodities Fair Building, Canton — A299

**China Post No. T.6.**

**1974, Oct. 15**

**1208** A299 8f multicolored 12.50 2.00

Chinese Export Commodities Fair, Canton.

Guerrillas' Monument, Permet, Albania A300

Albanian Patriots and Coat of Arms A301

**China Post No. J.4.**

**1974, Nov. 29 Photo. *Perf. 11½x11***

| | | | | |
|---|---|---|---|---|
| **1209** | A300 | 8f multicolored | 8.50 | 2.75 |
| **1210** | A301 | 8f multicolored | 8.50 | 2.75 |

Albania's liberation, 30th anniversary.

Water-cooled Generator — A302

**China Post No. N17**

Industrial Products: No. 1212, Motorized rice sprouts transplanter. No. 1213, Universal cylindrical grinding machine. No. 1214, Open-air rock drill, vert. All dated 1973.

**Photogravure and Engraved**

**1974, Dec. 23 *Perf. 11***

| | | | | |
|---|---|---|---|---|
| **1211** | A302 | 8f vio & multi (78) | 67.50 | 10.50 |
| **1212** | A302 | 8f yel grn & multi (79) | 90.00 | 22.50 |
| **1213** | A302 | 8f ver & multi (80) | 67.50 | 10.50 |
| **1214** | A302 | 8f blue & multi (81) | 135.00 | 22.50 |
| | | *Nos. 1211-1214 (4)* | *360.00* | *66.00* |

Congress Delegates A303

**China Post No. J.5.**

Designs: No. 1216, Red flags, constitution and flowers. No. 1217, Worker, farmer and soldier, agriculture and industry.

**1975, Jan. 25 Photo. *Perf. 11½***

| | | | | |
|---|---|---|---|---|
| **1215** | A303 | 8f gold & multi (3-1) | 16.00 | 4.00 |
| **1216** | A303 | 8f gold & multi (3-2) | 20.00 | 4.00 |
| **1217** | A303 | 8f gold & multi (3-3) | 25.00 | 10.00 |
| | | *Nos. 1215-1217 (3)* | *61.00* | *18.00* |

Fourth National People's Congress, Peking.

Teacher Studying Revolutionary Works — A304

**China Post No. T.9.**

No. 1219, Teacher, children and horse. No. 1220, Outdoors class. No. 1221, Class held in boat.

**1975, Mar. 8 Photo. *Perf. 11***

| | | | | |
|---|---|---|---|---|
| **1218** | A304 | 8f multi (4-1) | 18.00 | 5.25 |
| **1219** | A304 | 8f multi (4-2) | 29.00 | 6.25 |
| **1220** | A304 | 8f multi (4-3) | 21.00 | 5.25 |
| **1221** | A304 | 8f multi (4-4) | 18.00 | 4.25 |
| | | *Nos. 1218-1221 (4)* | *86.00* | *21.00* |

Rural women teachers and for International Working Women's Day.

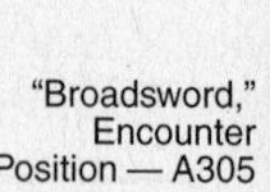

"Broadsword," Encounter Position — A305

### China Post No. T.7.

No. 1223, Exercise with 2 swords (woman). No. 1224, Graceful boxing (woman). No. 1225, Man leaping with spear. No. 1226, Woman holding fighting staff. 43f, 2 women with spears against man with 3-section staff.

**1975, June 10 Photo.** ***Perf. 11x11½***

**Size: 39x29mm**

| No. | Type | Description | Unused | Used |
|---|---|---|---|---|
| **1222** | A305 | 8f (6-1) | *6.00* | *2.10* |
| **1223** | A305 | 8f (6-2) | *7.00* | *2.10* |
| **1224** | A305 | 8f (6-3) | *5.00* | *2.10* |
| **1225** | A305 | 8f (6-4) | *5.00* | *2.10* |
| **1226** | A305 | 8f (6-5) | *6.00* | *2.10* |

**Size: 59x29mm**

| No. | Type | Description | Unused | Used |
|---|---|---|---|---|
| **1227** | A305 | 43f red & multi (6-6) | *12.00* | *7.75* |
| | | *Nos. 1222-1227 (6)* | *41.00* | *18.25* |

Wushu ("Kung Fu"), self-defense exercises. Tête bêche in sheets of 50 (5x10). Value, set of pairs $120.

Mass Judgment and Criticisms — A306

### China Post No. T.8.

No. 1229, Brigade leader writing wall newspaper. No. 1230, Study and criticism on battlefield, horiz. No. 1231, Former "slave" led into battle by criticism of Lin Piao and Confucius, horiz.

***Perf. 11½x11, 11x11½***

**1975, Aug. 20 Photo.**

| No. | Type | Description | Unused | Used |
|---|---|---|---|---|
| **1228** | A306 | 8f red & multi (4-1) | *20.00* | *4.25* |
| **1229** | A306 | 8f red & multi (4-2) | *20.00* | *4.25* |
| **1230** | A306 | 8f red & multi (4-3) | *18.50* | *4.25* |
| **1231** | A306 | 8f red & multi (4-4) | *20.00* | *4.25* |
| | | *Nos. 1228-1231 (4)* | *78.50* | *17.00* |

Campaign to encourage criticism of Lin Piao and Confucius.

Athletes Studying Theory of Dictatorship of Proletariat A307

### China Post No. J.6.

3rd National Sports Meet: No. 1232, Women athletes leading parade, vert. No. 1234, Women volleyball players. No. 1235, Runner, soldier, farmer and worker, vert. No. 1236, Young athlete and various sports. No. 1237, Athletes of various races and horse race. 35f, Children and diving tower, vert.

**1975, Sept. 12 Photo.** ***Perf. 11½***

| No. | Type | Description | Unused | Used |
|---|---|---|---|---|
| **1232** | A307 | 8f multi (7-1) | *4.00* | *1.00* |
| **1233** | A307 | 8f multi (7-2) | *8.50* | *1.00* |
| **1234** | A307 | 8f multi (7-3) | *14.00* | *1.50* |
| **1235** | A307 | 8f multi (7-4) | *4.00* | *1.00* |
| **1236** | A307 | 8f multi (7-5) | *4.00* | *1.00* |
| **1237** | A307 | 8f multi (7-6) | *4.00* | *1.00* |
| **1238** | A307 | 35f multi (7-7) | *4.00* | *2.00* |
| | | *Nos. 1232-1238 (7)* | *42.50* | *8.50* |

Mountaineers A308

Mt. Everest A309

### China Post No. T.15.

Design: No. 1240, Mountaineers raising Chinese flag on summit, horiz.

**1975 Photo.** ***Perf. 11½x11, 11x11½***

| No. | Type | Description | Unused | Used |
|---|---|---|---|---|
| **1239** | A308 | 8f multi (3-2) | *2.75* | *1.00* |
| **1240** | A308 | 8f multi (3-3) | *2.75* | *1.00* |
| **1241** | A309 | 43f multi (3-1) | *4.00* | *1.25* |
| | | *Nos. 1239-1241 (3)* | *9.50* | *3.25* |

Chinese Mt. Everest expedition.

Agricultural Workers with Book A310

### China Post No. J.7.

No. 1243, Workers carrying load. No. 1244, Woman driving harvester combine.

**1975, Oct. 1** ***Perf. 11½***

| No. | Type | Description | Unused | Used |
|---|---|---|---|---|
| **1242** | A310 | 8f multi (3-1) | *9.00* | *1.90* |
| **1243** | A310 | 8f multi (3-2) | *9.00* | *1.90* |
| **1244** | A310 | 8f multi (3-3) | *13.00* | *1.90* |
| | | *Nos. 1242-1244 (3)* | *31.00* | *5.70* |

National Conference to promote learning from Tachai's achievements in agriculture.

Girl Giving Boy Red Scarf — A311

### China Post No. T.14.

Designs (Children): No. 1246, Putting up wall posters criticizing Lin Piao and Confucius. No. 1247, Studying. No. 1248, Harvesting. 52f, Physical training.

**1975, Dec. 1 Photo.** ***Perf. 11½***

| No. | Type | Description | Unused | Used |
|---|---|---|---|---|
| **1245** | A311 | 8f multi (5-1) | *4.50* | *1.25* |
| **1246** | A311 | 8f multi (5-2) | *4.50* | *1.25* |
| **1247** | A311 | 8f multi (5-3) | *4.50* | *1.25* |
| **1248** | A311 | 8f multi (5-4) | *4.50* | *1.25* |
| **1249** | A311 | 52f multi (5-5) | *9.00* | *2.50* |
| | | *Nos. 1245-1249 (5)* | *27.00* | *7.50* |

Moral, intellectual and physical progress of Chinese children.

Woman Plowing Rice Field — A312

### China Post No. T.13.

No. 1251, Mechanized rice planting. No. 1252, Drainage and irrigation. No. 1253, Woman spraying insecticide over cotton field. No. 1254, Combine.

**1975, Dec. 15** ***Perf. 11***

| No. | Type | Description | Unused | Used |
|---|---|---|---|---|
| **1250** | A312 | 8f multi (5-1) | *7.50* | *1.75* |
| **1251** | A312 | 8f multi (5-2) | *7.50* | *1.75* |
| **1252** | A312 | 8f multi (5-3) | *5.25* | *1.75* |
| **1253** | A312 | 8f multi (5-4) | *5.25* | *1.75* |
| **1254** | A312 | 8f multi (5-5) | *5.25* | 1.75 |
| | | *Nos. 1250-1254 (5)* | *30.75* | *8.75* |

Priority program of farm mechanization.

Farmland and Irrigation Canal A313

### China Post No. J.8.

Designs: No. 1256, Irrigation canal (16-2). No. 1257, Fertilizer plant (16-3). No. 1258, Textile plant (16-4). No. 1259, Anshan Iron and Steel Co. (16-5). No. 1260, Coal freight trains (16-6). No. 1261, Hydroelectric station (16-7). No. 1262, Ship building (16-8). No. 1263, Oil industry (16-9). No. 1264, Pipe line and port (16-10). No. 1265, Train on viaduct (16-11). No. 1266, Scientific research (16-12). No. 1267, Classroom (16-13). No. 1268, Health Center (16-14). No. 1269, Apartment houses (16-15). No. 1270, Department store (16-16).

**1976 Photo.** ***Perf. 11½***

| No. | Type | Description | Unused | Used |
|---|---|---|---|---|
| **1255** | A313 | 8f shown (16-1) | *10.00* | *2.25* |
| **1256** | A313 | 8f multi | *9.00* | *2.25* |
| **1257** | A313 | 8f multi | *20.00* | *2.25* |
| **1258** | A313 | 8f multi | *9.50* | *2.25* |
| **1259** | A313 | 8f multi | *9.50* | *2.25* |
| **1260** | A313 | 8f multi | *11.50* | *2.25* |
| **1261** | A313 | 8f multi | *11.50* | *2.25* |
| **1262** | A313 | 8f multi | *11.50* | *2.25* |
| **1263** | A313 | 8f multi | *11.50* | *2.25* |
| **1264** | A313 | 8f multi | *11.50* | *2.25* |
| **1265** | A313 | 8f multi | *11.50* | *2.25* |
| **1266** | A313 | 8f multi | *8.00* | *2.25* |
| **1267** | A313 | 8f multi | *30.00* | *5.50* |
| **1268** | A313 | 8f multi | *8.00* | 2.25 |
| **1269** | A313 | 8f multi | *15.00* | *2.25* |
| **1270** | A313 | 8f multi | *37.50* | *5.50* |
| | | *Nos. 1255-1270 (16)* | *225.50* | *42.50* |

Nos. 1255-1270 commemorate fulfillment of 4th Five-year Plan.

Issued: Nos. 1255-1259, 2/20; Nos. 1260-1264, 4/9; Nos. 1265-1270, 6/12.

Heart Surgery with Acupuncture Anesthesia — A314

### China Post No. T.12.

Operating Room and: No. 1272, Man driving tractor with severed arm restored. No. 1273, Man exercising broken arm in cast. No. 1274, Patient threading needle after cataract operation.

**1976, Apr. 9 Photo.** ***Perf. 11½***

| No. | Type | Description | Unused | Used |
|---|---|---|---|---|
| **1271** | A314 | 8f brn & multi (4-1) | *9.00* | *2.00* |
| **1272** | A314 | 8f yel grn & multi (4-2) | *23.50* | *3.00* |
| **1273** | A314 | 8f bl grn & multi (4-3) | *8.75* | *1.75* |
| **1274** | A314 | 8f vio bl & multi (4-4) | *8.75* | *1.75* |
| | | *Nos. 1271-1274 (4)* | *50.00* | *8.50* |

Achievements in medical and health services.

Students in May 7 School A315

### China Post No. J.9.

Designs: No. 1276, Students as farm workers. No. 1277, Production brigade.

**1976, May 7 Photo.** ***Perf. 11½***

| No. | Type | Description | Unused | Used |
|---|---|---|---|---|
| **1275** | A315 | 8f multi (3-1) | *11.00* | *2.00* |
| **1276** | A315 | 8f multi (3-2) | *4.50* | *2.00* |
| **1277** | A315 | 8f multi (3-3) | *11.00* | *2.00* |
| | | *Nos. 1275-1277 (3)* | *26.50* | *6.00* |

Chairman Mao's May 7 Directive, 10th anniv.

Mass Training in Swimming A316

### China Post No. J.10.

No. 1279, Swimmers crossing Yangtze River. No. 1280, Swimmers walking into the surf.

**1976, July 16 Photo.** ***Perf. 11½***

**Size: 47x27mm**

| No. | Type | Description | Unused | Used |
|---|---|---|---|---|
| **1278** | A316 | 8f multi (3-1) | *8.50* | *2.00* |

**Size: 35x27mm**

| No. | Type | Description | Unused | Used |
|---|---|---|---|---|
| **1279** | A316 | 8f multi (3-2) | *8.50* | *2.00* |
| **1280** | A316 | 8f multi (3-3) | *8.50* | *2.00* |
| | | *Nos. 1278-1280 (3)* | *25.50* | *6.00* |

Chairman Mao's swim in Yangtze River, 10th anniversary.

Workers, Peasants and Soldiers Going to College A317

### China Post No. T.18.

No. 1282, Classroom. No. 1283, Instruction on construction site. No. 1284, Computer room. No. 1285, Graduates returning home.

**1976, Sept. 6 Photo.** ***Perf. 11½***

| No. | Type | Description | Unused | Used |
|---|---|---|---|---|
| **1281** | A317 | 8f multi (5-1) | *11.00* | *2.75* |
| **1282** | A317 | 8f multi (5-2) | *11.00* | *2.75* |
| **1283** | A317 | 8f multi (5-3) | *13.00* | *3.50* |
| **1284** | A317 | 8f multi (5-4) | *17.00* | *3.50* |
| **1285** | A317 | 8f multi (5-5) | *11.00* | *3.25* |
| | | *Nos. 1281-1285 (5)* | *63.00* | *15.75* |

Success of proletarian education system.

Power Line Repair by Woman — A318

### China Post No. T.16.

No. 1287, Insulator repair. No. 1288, Cherry picker. No. 1289, Transformer repair.

**1976, Sept. 15**

| No. | Type | Description | Unused | Used |
|---|---|---|---|---|
| **1286** | A318 | 8f multi (4-1) | *9.00* | *1.75* |
| **1287** | A318 | 8f multi (4-2) | *9.00* | *1.75* |
| **1288** | A318 | 8f multi (4-3) | *6.00* | *1.75* |
| **1289** | A318 | 8f multi (4-4) | *6.00* | *1.75* |
| | | *Nos. 1286-1289 (4)* | *30.00* | *7.00* |

Maintenance of high power lines.

Lu Hsun — A319

### China Post No. J.11.

No. 1291, Lu Hsun sick, writing in bed. No. 1292, Lu Hsun with worker, soldier and peasant.

**Photo. & Engr.**

**1976, Oct. 19** ***Perf. 11x11½***

| No. | Type | Description | Unused | Used |
|---|---|---|---|---|
| **1290** | A319 | 8f multi (3-1) | *6.50* | *2.00* |

**Photo.**

| No. | Type | Description | Unused | Used |
|---|---|---|---|---|
| **1291** | A319 | 8f multi (3-2) | *16.50* | *4.00* |
| **1292** | A319 | 8f multi (3-3) | *10.00* | *2.00* |
| | | *Nos. 1290-1292 (3)* | *33.00* | *8.00* |

Lu Hsun (1881-1936), writer and revolutionary leader.

Old Farmer Tying Towel on Student's Head — A320

### China Post No. T.17.

Designs: No. 1294, Student teaching farm woman, horiz. No. 1295, Students climbing mountain for new water resources. No. 1296, Student testing wheat, horiz. 10f, Student feeding lamb. 20f, Frontier guards, horiz.

**1976, Dec. 22 Photo.** ***Perf. 11½***

| No. | Type | Description | Unused | Used |
|---|---|---|---|---|
| **1293** | A320 | 4f multi (6-1) | *4.50* | *.85* |
| **1294** | A320 | 8f multi (6-2) | *4.50* | *.90* |
| **1295** | A320 | 8f multi (6-3) | *4.50* | *.90* |
| **1296** | A320 | 8f multi (6-4) | *10.00* | *3.25* |
| **1297** | A320 | 10f multi (6-5) | *7.00* | *.90* |
| **1298** | A320 | 20f multi (6-6) | *8.00* | 2.60 |
| | | *Nos. 1293-1298 (6)* | *38.50* | *9.40* |

Students' efforts to help poor country people.

Mao's Home, Shaoshan — A321

### China Post No. T.11.

Shaoshan, Mao's birthplace: No. 1300, School building. No. 1301, Farmers' Association building. 10f, Railroad station.

**1976, Dec. 26** ***Perf. 11***

| No. | Type | Description | Unused | Used |
|---|---|---|---|---|
| **1299** | A321 | 4f multi (4-1) | *6.00* | *1.50* |
| **1300** | A321 | 8f multi (4-2) | *6.00* | *1.50* |
| **1301** | A321 | 8f multi (4-3) | *11.50* | *1.50* |
| **1302** | A321 | 10f multi (4-4) | *6.00* | *1.50* |
| | | *Nos. 1299-1302 (4)* | 29.50 | *6.00* |

Chou En-lai — A322

**China Post No. J.13.**

No. 1304, Chou giving report at 10th Party Congress. No. 1305, Chou with Wang Chin-hsi, famous oil worker, horiz. No. 1306, Chou with people of Tachai, 1973, horiz.

**1977, Jan. 8 Photo. *Perf. 11½***

| | | | | |
|---|---|---|---|---|
| **1303** | A322 8f multi (4-1) | | *3.75* | *1.60* |
| **1304** | A322 8f multi (4-2) | | *7.50* | *1.60* |
| **1305** | A322 8f multi (4-3) | | *3.75* | *1.60* |
| **1306** | A322 8f multi (4-4) | | *12.50* | *1.60* |
| | *Nos. 1303-1306 (4)* | | *27.50* | *6.40* |

Premier Chou En-lai (1898-1976), a founder of Chinese Communist Party, 1st death anniversary.

Liu Hu-lan, an Inspiration — A323

**China Post No. J.12.**

Liu Hu-lan, Chinese heroine: No. 1307, Liu Hu-lan monument. No. 1308, Mao Tse-tung quotation: "A great life-a glorious death."

**1977, Jan. 31**

| | | | |
|---|---|---|---|
| **1307** | A323 8f multi (3-1) | *24.00* | *4.00* |
| **1308** | A323 8f multi (3-2) | *6.50* | *2.00* |
| **1309** | A323 8f multi (3-3) | *6.50* | *2.00* |
| | *Nos. 1307-1309 (3)* | *37.00* | *8.00* |

Uprising in Taiwan — A324

**China Post No. J.14.**

Design: 10f, Gate of Heavenly Peace, Peking; Sun Moon Lake, Taiwan, Taiwanese people holding PRC flag.

**1977, Feb. 28 Photo. *Perf. 11***

| | | | |
|---|---|---|---|
| **1310** | A324 8f multi (2-1) | *9.00* | *1.25* |
| **1311** | A324 10f multi (2-2) | *11.00* | *1.75* |

Uprising of the people of Taiwan, 2/28/47.

Sharpshooters — A325

**China Post No. T.10.**

Militia Women: No. 1313, Women horse-back riders. No. 1314, Underground defense tunnel.

**1977, Mar. 8 *Perf. 11½***

| | | | |
|---|---|---|---|
| **1312** | A325 8f multi (3-1) | *7.50* | *3.00* |
| **1313** | A325 8f multi (3-2) | *7.50* | *3.00* |
| **1314** | A325 8f multi (3-3) | *11.00* | *3.00* |
| | *Nos. 1312-1314 (3)* | *26.00* | *9.00* |

Coal Mining — A326

Sheepherding — A326a

Export (Loading Railroad Car onto Ship) — A326b

Forestry — A326c

Hydroelectric Station — A326d

Fishery — A326e

Combine in Field — A326f

Radio Tower, Mail Truck — A326g

Steel Production — A326h

Trucks on Mountain Road — A326i

Textiles — A326j

Tractor Assembly Line — A326k

Offshore Oil Rigs, Birds, Setting Sun — A326l

Railroad Bridge, Yangtze Gorge — A326m

**China Post No. R18**

**1977 Photo. *Perf. 11½***

| | | | | |
|---|---|---|---|---|
| **1315** | A326 | 1f yel grn, red & blk | *.45* | *.30* |
| **1316** | A326a | 1½f bl grn, yel grn & brn | *.50* | *.30* |
| **1317** | A326b | 2f org, bl & blk | *.50* | *.30* |
| **1318** | A326c | 3f ol & dk grn | *.60* | *.30* |
| **1319** | A326d | 4f lil, org & blk | *.85* | *.30* |
| **1320** | A326e | 5f lt ol & ultra | *.85* | *.30* |
| **1321** | A326f | 8f red & yel | *.85* | *.30* |
| **1322** | A326g | 10f lt grn, org & bl | *.85* | *.30* |
| **1323** | A326h | 20f org, yel & brn | *.95* | *.30* |
| **1324** | A326i | 30f bl, gray grn & blk | *1.25* | *.35* |
| **1325** | A326j | 40f multicolored | *1.40* | *.35* |
| **1326** | A326k | 50f cit, red & blk | *1.25* | *.35* |
| **1327** | A326l | 60f pur, lt & dk org | *1.25* | *.50* |
| **1328** | A326m | 70f blue & multi | *2.00* | *.75* |
| | | *Nos. 1315-1328 (14)* | *13.55* | *5.00* |

Nos. 1316, 1317 and 1325 exist imperf. Value, pair each $1,000.

Issue dates: Nos. 1318, 1322-1323, 1325-1328, March 18; all others Aug. 11.

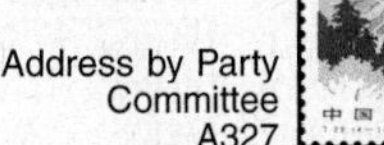

Address by Party Committee A327

**China Post No. T.22.**

Designs: No. 1330, Planting new rice fields. No. 1331, Farmers reading wall newspaper. No. 1332, Land reclamation.

**1977, Apr. 9 *Perf. 11x11½***

| | | | |
|---|---|---|---|
| **1329** | A327 8f multi (4-1) | *7.50* | *1.00* |
| **1330** | A327 8f multi (4-2) | *7.50* | *1.00* |
| **1331** | A327 8f multi (4-3) | *7.50* | *1.00* |
| **1332** | A327 8f multi (4-4) | *7.50* | *1.00* |
| | *Nos. 1329-1332 (4)* | *30.00* | *4.00* |

Building Tachai-type communities throughout China.

Worker at Microphone — A328

**China Post No. J.15.**

Designs: No. 1334, Drilling for oil during snowstorm. No. 1335, Crowd advancing under Red banner. No. 1336, Workers, industrial complex, rocket blast-off.

**1977, Apr. 25 *Perf. 11***

| | | | |
|---|---|---|---|
| **1333** | A328 8f multi (4-1) | *7.00* | *1.25* |
| **1334** | A328 8f multi (4-2) | *7.00* | *1.25* |
| **1335** | A328 8f multi (4-3) | *7.00* | *1.25* |
| **1336** | A328 8f multi (4-4) | *7.00* | *1.25* |
| | *Nos. 1333-1336 (4)* | *28.00* | *5.00* |

Conference on learning from Taching workers in industry.

Mongolians Hailing Anniversary A329

**China Post No. J.16.**

10f, Iron and steel complex, iron ore train. 20f, Cattle grazing in improved pasture.

**1977, May 1 *Perf. 11x11½***

| | | | |
|---|---|---|---|
| **1337** | A329 8f multi (3-1) | *5.00* | *.85* |
| **1338** | A329 10f multi (3-2) | *1.50* | *.75* |
| **1339** | A329 20f multi (3-3) | *3.00* | *1.10* |
| | *Nos. 1337-1339 (3)* | *9.50* | *2.70* |

30th anniversary of Inner Mongolian Autonomous Region.

1877 Flag of Romania and Oak Leaves A330

Mihai Viteazu Memorial (16th Century Hero) A331

**China Post No. J.17.**

10f, Battle of Smirdan, by N. Grigorescu.

**1977, May 9 Photo. *Perf. 11***

| | | | |
|---|---|---|---|
| **1340** | A330 8f multi (3-1) | *5.25* | *1.25* |
| **1341** | A331 10f multi (3-2) | *1.10* | *1.00* |
| **1342** | A331 20f multi (3-3) | *1.10* | *1.00* |
| | *Nos. 1340-1342 (3)* | *7.45* | *3.25* |

Centenary of Romanian independence.

Yenan "Let 100 Flowers Bloom" — A332

**China Post No. J.18.**

No. 1344, Hammer, sickle, gun & flowers; "Proletarian revolutionary literature will prosper."

**1977, May, 23**

| | | | |
|---|---|---|---|
| **1343** | A332 8f grn, red & gold | *1.90* | *.75* |
| **1344** | A332 8f lt brn, red & gold | *1.90* | *.75* |

Yenan Forum on Literature & Art, 35th anniv.

Zhu De — A333

**China Post No. J.19.**

Designs: No. 1346, Zhu De, last address to Congress. No. 1347, Zhu De at his desk, horiz. No. 1348, Zhu De on horseback as commander of Red Army.

**1977, July 6 Photo. *Perf. 11½***

| | | | |
|---|---|---|---|
| **1345** | A333 8f multi (4-1) | *3.50* | *.70* |
| **1346** | A333 8f multi (4-2) | *3.50* | *.70* |
| **1347** | A333 8f multi (4-3) | *4.25* | *.80* |
| **1348** | A333 8f multi (4-4) | *4.25* | *.80* |
| | *Nos. 1345-1348 (4)* | *15.50* | *3.00* |

Zhu De (1886-1976), Commander of Red Army, Chairman of National People's Congress.

Military under Mao's Banner — A334

**China Post No. J.20.**

No. 1350, Red Flag, Soldiers, Chingkang Mountains. No. 1351, Guerrilla fighters returning to base. No. 1352, Guerrillas crossing Yangtze. No. 1353, National defense.

**1977, Aug. 1**

| | | | |
|---|---|---|---|
| **1349** | A334 8f multi (5-1) | *9.50* | *1.50* |
| **1350** | A334 8f multi (5-2) | *5.50* | *1.50* |
| **1351** | A334 8f multi (5-3) | *8.00* | *1.50* |
| **1352** | A334 8f multi (5-4) | *8.00* | *1.50* |
| **1353** | A334 8f multi (5-5) | *6.50* | *1.50* |
| | *Nos. 1349-1353 (5)* | *37.50* | *7.50* |

Liberation Army Day, 50th anniversary of People's Army.

Gate of Heavenly Peace, People and Red Flags A335

**China Post No. J.23.**

Designs: No. 1355, People marching under Red Flag with Mao's portrait. No. 1356, People marching under Red Flag with hammer and sickle.

**1977, Aug. 22 Photo. *Perf. 11½x11***

| | | | |
|---|---|---|---|
| **1354** | A335 8f multi (3-1) | *16.00* | *3.75* |
| **1355** | A335 8f multi (3-2) | *16.00* | *3.75* |
| **1356** | A335 8f multi (3-3) | *16.00* | *3.75* |
| | *Nos. 1354-1356 (3)* | *48.00* | *11.25* |

11th National Congress of the Communist Party of China.

Chairman Mao — A336

**China Post No. J.21.**

Designs (Mao Portraits): No. 1358, as young man in Shansi. No. 1359, addressing Communist Party in Plenary Session. No. 1360, Proclaiming People's Republic at Gate of Heavenly Peace. No. 1361, at airport with Chou En-lai and Zhu De, horiz. No. 1362, Reviewing Army as old man.

**1977, Sept. 9 Photo. *Perf. 11½***

| No. | Type | Description | Unused | Used |
|---|---|---|---|---|
| **1357** | A336 | 8f multi (6-1) | 7.00 | 1.10 |
| **1358** | A336 | 8f multi (6-2) | 7.00 | 1.10 |
| **1359** | A336 | 8f multi (6-3) | 7.00 | 1.10 |
| **1360** | A336 | 8f multi (6-4) | 7.00 | 1.10 |
| **1361** | A336 | 8f multi (6-5) | 10.00 | 1.10 |
| **1362** | A336 | 8f multi (6-6) | 7.00 | 1.10 |
| | | *Nos. 1357-1362 (6)* | 45.00 | 6.60 |

Mao-Tse-tung (1893-1976), first death anniversary.

Mao Memorial Hall A337

**China Post No. J.22.**

Completion of Mao Memorial Hall: No. 1364, Chairman Hua's inscription.

**1977, Sept. 9**

| No. | Type | Description | Unused | Used |
|---|---|---|---|---|
| **1363** | A337 | 8f lt ultra & multi | 6.00 | 1.50 |
| **1364** | A337 | 8f lt grn, tan & gold | 8.50 | 2.25 |

Tractors Moving Drilling Tower A338

**China Post No. T.19.**

No. 1366, Shui Pow Tsi oil well and women workers. No. 1367, Construction of oil pipe line, Taching, and silos. No. 1368, Tung Fang Hung oil refinery, Peking. No. 1369, Taching oil loaded into tanker in harbor. 20f, Off-shore drilling platform "Pohai No. 1."

**1978, Jan. 31 Photo. *Perf. 11***

| No. | Type | Description | Unused | Used |
|---|---|---|---|---|
| **1365** | A338 | 8f multi (6-1) | 2.00 | 1.00 |
| **1366** | A338 | 8f multi (6-2) | 2.00 | 1.00 |
| **1367** | A338 | 8f multi (6-3) | 2.00 | 1.00 |
| **1368** | A338 | 8f multi (6-4) | 5.00 | 1.00 |
| **1369** | A338 | 8f multi (6-5) | 5.00 | 1.00 |
| **1370** | A338 | 20f multi (6-6) | 4.00 | 2.00 |
| | | *Nos. 1365-1370 (6)* | 20.00 | 7.00 |

Development of Chinese oil industry.

"Army Teaching Militia" A339

**China Post No. T.23.**

No. 1372, "Army helping with rice planting."

**1978, Feb. 5 Photo. *Perf. 11***

| No. | Type | Description | Unused | Used |
|---|---|---|---|---|
| **1371** | A339 | 8f multi (2-1) | 7.00 | 1.25 |
| **1372** | A339 | 8f multi (2-2) | 7.00 | 1.25 |

Army and people working as a family.

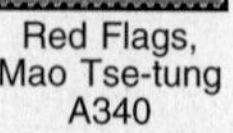

Red Flags, Mao Tse-tung A340

Constitution and Red Flags A341

**China Post No. J.24.**

No. 1375, Atom symbol over symbols of agriculture & industry. All designs include Great Hall of the People, Peking, & flowers.

**1978, Feb. 26**

| No. | Type | Description | Unused | Used |
|---|---|---|---|---|
| **1373** | A340 | 8f multi (3-1) | 6.00 | .85 |
| **1374** | A341 | 8f multi (3-2) | 6.00 | .85 |
| **1375** | A340 | 8f multi (3-3) | 6.00 | .85 |
| | | *Nos. 1373-1375 (3)* | 18.00 | 2.55 |

5th National People's Congress.

Mao's Eulogy for Lei Feng A342

Lei Feng, Studying Mao's Works A343

**China Post No. J.26.**

No. 1377, Chairman Hua's thoughts (5 lines).

**1978, Mar. 5**

| No. | Type | Description | Unused | Used |
|---|---|---|---|---|
| **1376** | A342 | 8f gold & red (3-1) | 9.00 | 2.00 |
| **1377** | A342 | 8f gold & red (3-2) | 9.00 | 2.00 |
| **1378** | A343 | 8f multicolored (3-3) | 9.00 | 2.00 |
| | | *Nos. 1376-1378 (3)* | 27.00 | 6.00 |

Lei Feng (1940-1962), communist fighter; 15th anniversary of Chairman Mao's eulogy "Learn from Comrade Lei Feng."

Hsiang Ching-yu A344

Yang Kai-hui A345

**China Post No. J.27.**

**1978, Mar. 8**

| No. | Type | Description | Unused | Used |
|---|---|---|---|---|
| **1379** | A344 | 8f multi (2-1) | 4.00 | 1.00 |
| **1380** | A345 | 8f multi (2-2) | 4.00 | 1.00 |

Hsiang Ching-yu, pioneer of Women's Movement, executed 1928; Yang Kai-hui, communist fighter, executed 1930.

A346

A346a

A346b

**China Post No. J.25.**

No. 1381, Conference emblem. No. 1382, Banners symbolizing industry, agriculture, defense & science. No. 1383, Red flag, atom symbol & globe.

**1978, Mar. 18 Litho. *Perf. 11½x11***

| No. | Type | Description | Unused | Used |
|---|---|---|---|---|
| **1381** | A346 | 8f gold & red (3-1) | 4.00 | .90 |
| **1382** | A346a | 8f multi (3-2) | 4.00 | .90 |
| **1383** | A346b | 8f multi (3-3) | 4.00 | .90 |
| *a.* | | Souvenir sheet of 3 | 500.00 | 250.00 |
| | | *Nos. 1381-1383 (3)* | 12.00 | 2.70 |

Natl. Science Conf. No. 1383a contains Nos. 1381-1383 with simulated perforations. Sold for 50f.

Release of Weather Balloon — A347

**China Post No. T.24.**

Weather Observations: No. 1385, Radar station, typhoon watch. No. 1386, Computer, weather maps. No. 1387, Local weather observers. No. 1388, Rockets intercepting hail clouds.

**1978, Apr. 25 Photo. *Perf. 11x11½***

| No. | Type | Description | Unused | Used |
|---|---|---|---|---|
| **1384** | A347 | 8f multi (5-1) | 1.50 | .70 |
| **1385** | A347 | 8f multi (5-2) | 1.50 | .70 |
| **1386** | A347 | 8f multi (5-3) | 1.50 | .70 |
| **1387** | A347 | 8f multi (5-4) | 1.50 | .70 |
| **1388** | A347 | 8f multi (5-5) | 1.50 | .70 |
| | | *Nos. 1384-1388 (5)* | 7.50 | 3.50 |

Galloping Horse — A348

**China Post No. T.28.**

Designs: Galloping Horses, by Hsu Peihung (1895-1953). 40f, 50f, 60f, 70f, $5, horiz.

**1978, May 5 *Perf. 11½x11, 11x11½***

| No. | Type | Description | Unused | Used |
|---|---|---|---|---|
| **1389** | A348 | 4f multi (10-1) | 3.00 | 1.00 |
| **1390** | A348 | 6f multi (10-2) | 3.00 | 1.00 |
| **1391** | A348 | 8f multi (10-3) | 3.00 | 1.00 |
| **1392** | A348 | 10f multi (10-4) | 4.00 | 1.00 |
| **1393** | A348 | 20f multi (10-5) | 4.00 | 1.00 |
| **1394** | A348 | 30f multi (10-6) | 8.50 | 2.00 |
| **1395** | A348 | 40f multi (10-7) | 6.50 | 1.75 |
| **1396** | A348 | 50f multi (10-8) | 25.00 | 3.00 |
| **1397** | A348 | 60f multi (10-9) | 8.00 | 2.00 |
| **1398** | A348 | 70f multi (10-10) | 7.00 | 2.00 |
| | | *Nos. 1389-1398 (10)* | 72.00 | 15.75 |

**Souvenir Sheet**

| No. | Type | Description | Unused | Used |
|---|---|---|---|---|
| **1399** | A348 | $5 multicolored | 550.00 | 250.00 |

No. 1399 contains one stamp showing 4 horses, size: 89x39mm.

Children Playing Soccer — A349

**China Post No. T.21.**

Designs: No. 1401, Children on the beach. No. 1402, Little girls dancing. No. 1403, Children taking long walks. 20f, Children exercising for good health.

**Size: 22x27mm**

**1978, June 1 *Perf. 11½***

| No. | Type | Description | Unused | Used |
|---|---|---|---|---|
| **1400** | A349 | 8f multi (5-2) | 1.00 | .60 |
| **1401** | A349 | 8f multi (5-3) | 1.00 | .60 |
| **1402** | A349 | 8f multi (5-4) | 1.00 | .60 |
| **1403** | A349 | 8f multi (5-5) | 1.00 | .60 |

**Size: 48x28mm**

| No. | Type | Description | Unused | Used |
|---|---|---|---|---|
| **1404** | A349 | 20f multi (5-1) | 1.25 | .95 |
| | | *Nos. 1400-1404 (5)* | 5.25 | 3.35 |

Build up your health while young.

Synthetic Fiber Feeder — A350

**China Post No. T.25.**

Designs: No. 1406, Drawing out threads. No. 1407, Weaving. No. 1408, Dyeing and printing. No. 1409, Finished products.

**1978, June 15 Photo. *Perf. 11½***

| No. | Type | Description | Unused | Used |
|---|---|---|---|---|
| **1405** | A350 | 8f multi (5-1) | 1.00 | .60 |
| **1406** | A350 | 8f multi (5-2) | 1.00 | .60 |
| **1407** | A350 | 8f multi (5-3) | 1.00 | .60 |
| **1408** | A350 | 8f multi (5-4) | 1.00 | .60 |
| **1409** | A350 | 8f multi (5-5) | 1.00 | .60 |
| *a.* | | Strip of 5, #1405-1409 | 12.00 | 11.00 |
| | | *Nos. 1405-1409 (5)* | 5.00 | 3.00 |

Chemical fiber industry. No. 1409a has continuous design. No. 1409a is valued as an unfolded strip. Folded strips sell for less.

Conference Emblem A351

"Develop Economy and Ensure Supplies" A352

**China Post No. J.28.**

**1978, June 20 *Perf. 13***

| No. | Type | Description | Unused | Used |
|---|---|---|---|---|
| **1410** | A351 | 8f multi (2-1) | 2.25 | .75 |
| **1411** | A352 | 8f multi (2-2) | 2.25 | .75 |

Natl. Conf. on Learning from Taching and Tachai in Finance and Trade.

New Pastures, Mongolia — A353

**China Post No. T.27.**

Designs: No. 1413, Kazakh shepherds selecting sheep for breeding. No. 1414, Mechanized shearing of sheep, Tibet.

**1978, June 30 Photo. *Perf. 11½***

| No. | Type | Description | Unused | Used |
|---|---|---|---|---|
| **1412** | A353 | 8f multi (3-1) | 4.00 | .80 |
| **1413** | A353 | 8f multi (3-2) | 4.00 | .80 |
| **1414** | A353 | 8f multi (3-3) | 4.00 | .80 |
| | | *Nos. 1412-1414 (3)* | 12.00 | 2.40 |

Learning from Tachai in developing animal husbandry and new pastoral areas.

Coke Oven A354

**China Post No. T.26.**

Iron and Steel Industry: No. 1416, Iron furnace. No. 1417, Pouring steel. No. 1418, Steel rolling. No. 1419, Finished iron and steel products.

**1978, July 22**

| No. | Type | Description | Unused | Used |
|---|---|---|---|---|
| **1415** | A354 | 8f multi (5-1) | 2.25 | .50 |
| **1416** | A354 | 8f multi (5-2) | 2.25 | .50 |
| **1417** | A354 | 8f multi (5-3) | 2.25 | .50 |
| **1418** | A354 | 8f multi (5-4) | 2.25 | .50 |
| **1419** | A354 | 8f multi (5-5) | 2.25 | .50 |
| | | *Nos. 1415-1419 (5)* | 11.25 | 2.50 |

Iron Fist to Prevent Revisionism — A355

**China Post No. T.32.**

No. 1421, "Carrying forward revolutionary tradition." No. 1422, "Strenuous training in military skills to wipe out enemy."

**1978, Aug. 1 Photo. *Perf. 11½***

| No. | Type | Description | Unused | Used |
|---|---|---|---|---|
| **1420** | A355 | 8f multi (3-1) | 3.50 | .70 |
| **1421** | A355 | 8f multi (3-2) | 3.50 | .70 |
| **1422** | A355 | 8f multi (3-3) | 3.50 | .70 |
| | | *Nos. 1420-1422 (3)* | 10.50 | 2.10 |

"Learn from Hard-boned 6th Company." (A military unit since 1939).

Jug in Shape of Sheep — A356

### China Post No. T.29.

Arts and Crafts: 4f, Giant lion (toy; horiz.). No. 1425, Rhinoceros (lacquer ware; horiz). 10f, Cat (embroidery). 20f, Bag (weaving; horiz.). 30f, Teapot in shape of peacock (cloisonné). 40f, Plate with lotus, and swan-shaped box (lacquer ware; horiz.). 50f, Dragon flying in sky (ivory). 60f, Sun rising (jade; horiz.). 70f, Flight to human world (ivory). $3, Flying fairies (arts and crafts; horiz.).

**1978, Aug. 26**

| | | | | |
|---|---|---|---|---|
| **1423** | A356 | 4f multi (10-1) | .95 | .45 |
| **1424** | A356 | 8f multi (10-2) | .95 | .45 |
| **1425** | A356 | 8f multi (10-3) | .95 | .45 |
| **1426** | A356 | 10f multi (10-4) | .95 | .55 |
| **1427** | A356 | 20f multi (10-5) | .95 | .55 |
| **1428** | A356 | 30f multi (10-6) | 2.00 | .80 |
| **1429** | A356 | 40f multi (10-7) | 2.50 | 1.10 |
| **1430** | A356 | 50f multi (10-8) | 6.00 | 2.75 |
| **1431** | A356 | 60f multi (10-9) | 3.50 | 2.75 |
| **1432** | A356 | 70f multi (10-10) | 3.50 | 1.60 |
| | | *Nos. 1423-1432 (10)* | *22.25* | *11.45* |

**Souvenir Sheet**

| | | | | |
|---|---|---|---|---|
| **1433** | A356 | $3 multi | 300.00 | 190.00 |

No. 1433 contains one 85x36mm stamp.

Women, Atom Symbol, Rocket and Wheat — A357

### China Post No. J.30.

**1978, Sept. 8 Photo. *Perf. 11***

| | | | | |
|---|---|---|---|---|
| **1434** | A357 | 8f multicolored | 3.00 | 1.00 |

4th National Women's Congress.

Ginseng — A358

### China Post No. T.30.

Medicinal Plants: No. 1436, Horn of plenty. No. 1437, Blackberry lily. No. 1438, Balloon-flower. 55f, Rhododendron dauricum.

**1978, Sept. 15**

| | | | | |
|---|---|---|---|---|
| **1435** | A358 | 8f multi (5-1) | 1.50 | .35 |
| **1436** | A358 | 8f multi (5-2) | 1.50 | .35 |
| **1437** | A358 | 8f multi (5-3) | 1.50 | .35 |
| **1438** | A358 | 8f multi (5-4) | 1.50 | .35 |
| **1439** | A358 | 55f multi (5-5) | 6.00 | 1.25 |
| | | *Nos. 1435-1439 (5)* | *12.00* | *2.65* |

Flag, Wheat, Cogwheel, Plane, Atom Symbols — A359

### China Post No. J.31.

**1978, Oct. 11 Photo. *Perf. 11***

| | | | | |
|---|---|---|---|---|
| **1440** | A359 | 8f multicolored | 4.00 | 1.00 |

9th National Trade Union Congress.

Youth League Emblem — A360

### China Post No. J.32.

**1978, Oct. 16**

| | | | | |
|---|---|---|---|---|
| **1441** | A360 | 8f multicolored | 4.25 | 1.00 |

10th Natl. Communist Youth League Cong.

Chinese and Japanese Girls Exchanging Gifts — A361

Great Wall and Mt. Fuji — A362

### China Post No. J.34.

**1978, Oct. 22**

| | | | | |
|---|---|---|---|---|
| **1442** | A361 | 8f multicolored | 2.75 | .75 |
| **1443** | A362 | 55f multicolored | 4.50 | 1.50 |

Signing of Sino-Japanese Peace and Friendship Treaty.

Moslem, Chinese and Mongolian People — A363

### China Post No. J.29.

No. 1445, Loading coal at Holan Mountain. 10f, Irrigated rice fields & boxthorn.

**1978, Oct. 25**

| | | | | |
|---|---|---|---|---|
| **1444** | A363 | 8f multi (3-1) | 4.00 | 1.00 |
| **1445** | A363 | 8f multi (3-2) | 4.00 | 1.00 |
| **1446** | A363 | 10f multi (3-3) | 4.75 | 1.00 |
| | | *Nos. 1444-1446 (3)* | *12.75* | 3.00 |

20th anniversary of founding of Ningsia Moslem Autonomous Region.

Chinsha River Bridge, West Szechuan — A364

### China Post No. T.31.

Highway Bridges: No. 1448, Hsinhong bridge, Wuhsi. No. 1449, Chiuhsikou bridge, Fengdu. No. 1450, Chinsha River bridge, West Szechuan. 60f, Shangyeh bridge, Sanmen. $2, Hsiang-kiang River bridge.

**1978, Nov. 1 Photo. *Perf. 11½x11***

| | | | | |
|---|---|---|---|---|
| **1447** | A364 | 8f multi (5-1) | 2.00 | .40 |
| **1448** | A364 | 8f multi (5-2) | 1.60 | .40 |
| **1449** | A364 | 8f multi (5-3) | 1.60 | .40 |
| **1450** | A364 | 8f multi (5-4) | 1.60 | .40 |
| **1451** | A364 | 60f multi (5-5) | 3.50 | 1.25 |
| | | *Nos. 1447-1451 (5)* | *10.30* | *2.85* |

**Souvenir Sheet**

| | | | | |
|---|---|---|---|---|
| **1452** | A364 | $2 multi | 300.00 | 180.00 |

No. 1452 contains one 86x37mm stamp.

Mechanical Transplanting of Rice Seedlings — A365

### China Post No. T.34.

Paintings: No. 1454, Spraying fields. No. 1455, Seed selection. No. 1456, Trade. No. 1457, Delivery of public grain in city.

**1978, Nov. 30 *Perf. 11½***

| | | | | |
|---|---|---|---|---|
| **1453** | A365 | 8f multi (5-1) | 3.25 | 1.50 |
| **1454** | A365 | 8f multi (5-2) | 3.25 | 1.50 |
| **1455** | A365 | 8f multi (5-3) | 3.25 | 1.50 |
| **1456** | A365 | 8f multi (5-4) | 3.25 | 1.50 |
| **1457** | A365 | 8f multi (5-5) | 3.25 | 1.50 |
| *a.* | | Strip of 5, #1453-1457 | *25.00* | *16.50* |

Agricultural progress. No. 1457a has a continuous design. Value is for unfolded strip. Folded strips are worth less.

Dancers and Fireworks — A366

### China Post No. J.33.

Designs: No. 1459, Industry, vert. 10f, Agriculture, vert.

**1978, Dec. 11 Photo. *Perf. 11***

| | | | | |
|---|---|---|---|---|
| **1458** | A366 | 8f multi (3-1) | 4.50 | 1.00 |
| **1459** | A366 | 8f multi (3-2) | 3.00 | 1.00 |
| **1460** | A366 | 10f multi (3-3) | 1.50 | 1.00 |
| | | *Nos. 1458-1460 (3)* | *9.00* | *3.00* |

20th anniversary of Kwangsi Chuang Autonomous Region.

Miners with Pneumatic Drill — A367

### China Post No. T.20.

Mine Development: 4f, Old Tibetan peasant reporting to surveyor. 10f, Open-cut mining with power shovel. 20f, Loaded electric train in pit.

**1978, Dec. 29 Photo. & Engr.**

| | | | | |
|---|---|---|---|---|
| **1461** | A367 | 4f multi (4-1) | 2.50 | 1.00 |
| **1462** | A367 | 8f multi (4-2) | 3.50 | 1.75 |
| **1463** | A367 | 10f multi (4-3) | 2.50 | 1.00 |
| **1464** | A367 | 20f multi (4-4) | 2.50 | 1.00 |
| | | *Nos. 1461-1464 (4)* | *11.00* | *4.75* |

A368

### China Post No. T.35.

Golden Pheasants: 4f, Roosting on rock. 8f, In flight. 45f, Seeking food.

**1979, Jan. 25 Photo. *Perf. 11½***

| | | | | |
|---|---|---|---|---|
| **1465** | A368 | 4f multi (3-1) | 2.00 | 1.00 |
| **1466** | A368 | 8f multi (3-2) | 2.50 | 2.00 |
| **1467** | A368 | 45f multi (3-3) | 4.00 | 3.00 |
| | | *Nos. 1465-1467 (3)* | *8.50* | *6.00* |

Albert Einstein, Equation — A369

### China Post No. J.36.

**1979, Mar. 14 Photo. *Perf. 11½x11***

| | | | | |
|---|---|---|---|---|
| **1468** | A369 | 8f multi | 2.50 | 1.25 |

Phoenix Battling Monster, Praying Woman — A370

### China Post No. T.33.

60f, Man riding dragon to heaven. Designs from silk paintings found in Changsha tomb, Warring States Period (475-221 B.C.).

**1979, Mar. 29 *Perf. 11***

| | | | | |
|---|---|---|---|---|
| **1469** | A370 | 8f multi (2-1) | 2.50 | 1.50 |
| **1470** | A370 | 60f multi (2-2) | 3.50 | 1.50 |

Summer Palace — A371

### China Post No. R20

**Photo., Photo. & Engr. ($5)**

**1979-80 *Perf. 13***

| | | | | |
|---|---|---|---|---|
| **1471** | A371 | $1 Pagoda ('80) | 2.00 | .70 |
| **1472** | A371 | $2 Shown | 1.75 | .80 |
| **1473** | A371 | $5 Temple, Beihai Park | 5.75 | 1.50 |
| | | *Nos. 1471-1473 (3)* | *9.50* | *3.00* |

Issued: $1, Nov. 24, 1980; $2, June 16, 1979; $5, June 20, 1980.

Hammer and Sickle "51" and Bars from "International" A372

### China Post No. J.35.

**1979, May 1 Photo. *Perf. 11***

| | | | | |
|---|---|---|---|---|
| **1474** | A372 | 8f multicolored | 2.50 | 1.00 |

International Labor Day, 90th anniv.

"Tradition of May 4th Movement" A373

Young Woman, Rocket, Antenna, Nuclear Reactor — A374

### China Post No. J.37.

**1979, May 4**

| | | | | |
|---|---|---|---|---|
| **1475** | A373 | 8f multicolored | 1.25 | .65 |
| **1476** | A374 | 8f multicolored | 1.25 | .65 |

60th anniversary of May 4th Movement.

IYC Emblem, Children Holding Balloons A375

Children of Three Races, IYC Emblem A376

### China Post No. J.38.

**1979, May 25 *Perf. 11½***

| | | | | |
|---|---|---|---|---|
| **1477** | A375 | 8f multicolored | 2.00 | 1.00 |
| **1478** | A376 | 60f multicolored | 12.00 | 4.50 |

International Year of the Child.

Great Wall in Spring — A377

### China Post No. T.38.

Designs (The Great Wall): No. 1480, in summer. No. 1481, in autumn. 60f, in winter. $2, Guard tower.

**1979, June 25 Photo. *Perf. 11***

| | | | | |
|---|---|---|---|---|
| **1479** | A377 | 8f multi (4-1) | 2.00 | .95 |
| **1480** | A377 | 8f multi (4-2) | 2.00 | .95 |
| **1481** | A377 | 8f multi (4-3) | 2.00 | 1.00 |
| **1482** | A377 | 60f multi (4-4) | 10.00 | 4.50 |
| | | *Nos. 1479-1482 (4)* | *16.00* | *7.40* |

**Souvenir Sheet**

| | | | | |
|---|---|---|---|---|
| **1483** | A377 | $2 multi | 175.00 | 60.00 |

For overprint see No. 1492.

Roaring Tiger — A379

**China Post No. T.40.**

Manchurian Tiger: 8f, Two young tigers. 60f, Tiger at rest.

**1979, July 20** ***Perf. 11½x11***

**1484** A379 4f multi (3-1) *4.25 1.00*
**1485** A379 8f multi (3-2) *2.50 1.00*
**1486** A379 60f multi (3-3) *3.00 1.75*
*Nos. 1484-1486 (3) 9.75 3.75*

Mechanical Harvesting — A380

**China Post No. T.39.**

Work of the Communes: No. 1488, Forestry. No. 1489, Raising ducks. No. 1490, Women weaving baskets. 10f, Fishing.

**1979, Aug. 10** ***Perf. 11½***

**1487** A380 4f multi (5-1) *6.00 2.00*
**1488** A380 8f multi (5-2) *3.25 1.00*
**1489** A380 8f multi (5-3) *3.25 1.00*
**1490** A380 8f multi (5-4) *3.25 1.00*
**1491** A380 10f multi (5-5) *4.00 1.75*
*Nos. 1487-1491 (5) 19.75 6.75*

**No. 1483 Overprinted with Gold Inscription and "1979"**

**China Post No. J.41.**

Souvenir Sheet

**1979, Aug. 25** **Photo.** ***Perf. 11***

**1492** A377 $2 multi (1-1) *575.00 200.00*

31st International Stamp Exhibition, Riccione, Italy.
Forged overprints exist.

Games Emblem, Sports A381

**China Post No. J.43.**

No. 1494, Soccer, badminton, high jump, speed skating. No. 1495, Fencing, skiing, gymnastics, diving. No. 1496, Motorcycling, table tennis, basketball, archery. No. 1497, Emblem only.

**1979, Sept. 15** ***Perf. 11½x11***

**1493** A381 8f multi (4-1) *1.25 .80*
**1494** A381 8f multi (4-2) *1.25 .80*
**1495** A381 8f multi (4-3) *1.25 .80*
**1496** A381 8f multi (4-4) *1.25 .80*
*a.* Block of 4, #1493-1496 *7.50 5.00*

**Souvenir Sheet**

***Perf. 11½***

**1497** A381 $2 multi, vert. *90.00 45.00*

4th National Games. Size of stamp in No. 1497: 22x26mm.

Flag and Rainbow A382

**China Post No. J.44.**

Design: No. 1499, Flag and mountains.

**1979, Oct. 1** **Photo.** ***Perf. 11½***

**1498** A382 8f multicolored *2.40 1.00*
**1499** A382 8f multicolored *5.25 1.50*

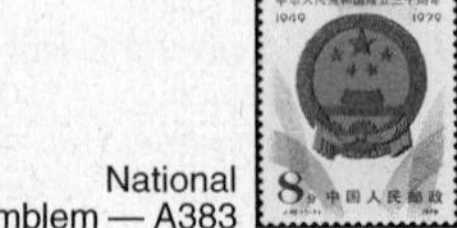

National Emblem — A383

**China Post No. J.45.**

**1979, Oct. 1** **Photo.** ***Perf. 11½***

**1500** A383 8f multicolored *5.75 1.50*

**Souvenir Sheet**

**1501** A383 $1 multicolored *110.00 35.00*

Dancers — A384

**China Post No. J.47.**

Designs: Nos. 1503-1505, various dances.

**1979, Oct. 1** **Photo.** ***Perf. 11½***

**1502** A384 8f multi (4-1) *.85 .40*
**1503** A384 8f multi (4-2) *.85 .40*
**1504** A384 8f multi (4-3) *.85 .40*
**1505** A384 8f multi (4-4) *.85 .40*
*a.* Block of 4, #1502-1505 *12.00 5.00*

Tractor, Aerial Crop Spraying, Irrigation — A385

**China Post No. J.48.**

No. 1507, Gear, computers. No. 1508, Rocket, submarine, jets. No. 1509, Atom symbol.

**1979, Oct. 1** **Photo.** ***Perf. 11½***

**1506** A385 8f multi (4-1) *2.75 1.00*
**1507** A385 8f multi (4-2) *2.75 1.00*
**1508** A385 8f multi (4-3) *1.60 .90*
**1509** A385 8f multi (4-4) *2.25 .90*
*Nos. 1506-1509 (4) 9.35 3.80*

National Anthem — A386

**China Post No. J.46.**

**1979, Oct. 1** **Engr.** ***Perf. 11***

**1510** A386 8f multicolored *12.50 2.00*

Exhibition Emblem — A387

**China Post No. J.40.**

**1979, Oct. 3**

**1511** A387 8f multicolored *1.25 1.00*

Junior National Scientific and Technological Exhibition.

Children Flying Model Planes — A388

**China Post No. T.41.**

No. 1513, Girls and microscope. No. 1514, Children and telescope. No. 1515, Boy catching butterflies. No. 1516, Girl taking meteorological readings. No. 1517, Boys sailing model boat. No. 1518, Girl with book.

**1979, Oct. 3**

**1512** A388 8f multi (6-1) *1.50 .70*
**1513** A388 8f multi (6-2) *1.50 .70*
**1514** A388 8f multi (6-3) *1.50 .70*
**1515** A388 8f multi (6-4) *1.50 .70*
**1516** A388 8f multi (6-5) *1.50 .70*
**1517** A388 60f multi (6-6) *7.00 3.00*
*Nos. 1512-1517 (6) 14.50 6.50*

**Souvenir Sheet**

***Perf. 11***

**1518** A388 $2 multi *1,500. 850.00*

Study Science from Childhood. No. 1518 contains one stamp, size: 90x40mm.

Yu Shan Mountain — A389

**China Post No. T.42.**

Taiwan Landscapes: No. 1520, Sun and Moon Lake. No. 1521, Chihkan Tower. No. 1522, Suao-Hualien Highway. 55f, Tian Xiang Falls. 60f, Banping Mountain.

**1979, Oct. 20** **Photo.** ***Perf. 11x11½***

**1519** A389 8f multi (6-1) *1.50 .85*
**1520** A389 8f multi (6-2) *1.50 .85*
**1521** A389 8f multi (6-3) *1.50 .85*
**1522** A389 8f multi (6-4) *1.50 .85*
**1523** A389 55f multi (6-5) *4.00 1.50*
**1524** A389 60f multi (6-6) *11.00 3.00*
*Nos. 1519-1524 (6) 21.00 7.90*

Arts Symbols — A390

**China Post No. J.39.**

8f, Seals and modernization symbols.

**1979, Oct. 30**

**1525** A390 4f multicolored *1.25 .65*
**1526** A390 8f multicolored *2.00 .85*

4th Natl. Cong. of Literary and Art Workers.

Train in Tunnel — A391

**China Post No. T.36.**

Railroads: No. 1528, Mountain bridge. No. 1529, Freight train.

**1979, Oct. 30** **Photo. & Engr.**

**1527** A391 8f multi (3-1) *3.00 1.00*
**1528** A391 8f multi (3-2) *3.00 1.25*
**1529** A391 8f multi (3-3) *3.00 1.50*
*Nos. 1527-1529 (3) 9.00 3.75*

Chrysanthemum Petal — A392

**China Post No. T.37.**

Camellias: No. 1531, Lion head. No. 1532, Camellia chryantha. 10f, Small osmanthus leaf. 20f, Baby face. 30f, Cornelian. 40f, Peony camellia. 50f, Purple gown. 60f, Dwarf rose. 70f, Willow leaf spinel pink. $2, Red jewelry.

**1979, Nov. 10** **Photo.** ***Perf. 11x11½***

**1530** A392 4f multi (10-1) *5.25 1.00*
**1531** A392 8f multi (10-2) *1.75 .65*
**1532** A392 8f multi (10-3) *1.75 .65*
**1533** A392 10f multi (10-4) *1.75 .65*
**1534** A392 20f multi (10-5) *1.75 1.00*
**1535** A392 30f multi (10-6) *14.00 3.00*
**1536** A392 40f multi (10-7) *2.75 1.25*
**1537** A392 50f multi (10-8) *1.50 1.00*
**1538** A392 60f multi (10-9) *3.25 1.00*
**1539** A392 70f multi (10-10) *3.50 1.00*
*Nos. 1530-1539 (10) 37.25 11.20*

**Souvenir Sheet**

***Perf. 11½x11***

**1540** A392 $2 multi *225.00 130.00*

No. 1540 contains one 86x36mm stamp.

**No. 1540 Overprinted and Numbered in Gold in Margin**

**China Post No. J.42.**

**Souvenir Sheet**

Souvenir Sheet

**1979, Nov. 10**

**1541** A392 $2 multi (1-1) *400.00 150.00*

People's Republic of China Phil. Exhib., Hong Kong, 1979.
Forged overprints exist.

Norman Bethune Treating Soldier — A393

**China Post No. J.50.**

Design: 70f, Bethune statue.

**1979, Nov. 12**

**1542** A393 8f multi (2-2) *1.50 .45*
**1543** A393 70f multi (2-1) *4.50 2.00*

Dr. Norman Bethune, 40th death anniv.

Central Archives Hall — A394

**China Post No. J.51.**

Intl. Archives Weeks: No. 1545, Gold archive cabinet, vert. 60f, Pavilion.

***Perf. 11x11½, 11½x11***

**1979, Nov. 26** **Photo.**

**1544** A394 8f multi (3-1) *2.00 1.00*
**1545** A394 8f multi (3-2) *2.00 1.00*
**1546** A394 60f multi (3-3) *11.00 2.25*
*Nos. 1544-1546 (3) 15.00 4.25*

Monkey King in Waterfall Cave — A395

**China Post No. T.43.**

Monkey King, Scenes from Pilgrimage to the West (Novel): No. 1548, Fighting Necha, son of Prince Li. No. 1549, In Mother Queen's peach orchard. No. 1550, In the alchemy furnace. 10f, Subduing the white bone demon. 20f, With palm leaf fan. 60f, In cobweb cave. 70f, Walking on scripture-seeking route.

**1979, Dec. 1** ***Perf. 11½x11***

**1547** A395 8f multi (8-1) *5.25 1.75*
**1548** A395 8f multi (8-2) *5.25 1.75*
**1549** A395 8f multi (8-3) *5.25 1.75*
**1550** A395 8f multi (8-4) *5.25 1.75*
**1551** A395 10f multi (8-5) *7.25 1.75*
**1552** A395 20f multi (8-6) *7.25 1.75*
**1553** A395 60f multi (8-7) *32.50 10.00*
**1554** A395 70f multi (8-8) *19.50 6.00*
*Nos. 1547-1554 (8) 87.50 26.50*

Stalin Delivering Speech — A396

**China Post No. J.49.**

Joseph Stalin (1879-1953): No. 1555, Portrait of Stalin, vert.

***Perf. 11x11½, 11½x11***

**1979, Dec. 21** **Engr.**

**1555** A396 8f brown (2-1) *1.50 1.00*
**1556** A396 8f black (2-2) *2.00 1.60*

A397

### China Post No. T.44.

No. 1557, Peony (16-1). No. 1558, Squirrels and grapes (16-2). No. 1559, Crabs candle and wine (16-3). No. 1560, Tadpoles in mountain spring (16-4). No. 1561, Chicks (16-5). No. 1562, Lotus (16-6). No. 1563, Red plum (16-7). No. 1564, Kingfisher (16-8). No. 1565, Bottle gourd (16-9). No. 1566, Voice of autumn (16-10). No. 1567, Wisteria (16-11). No. 1568, Chrysanthemums (16-12). No. 1569, Shrimp (16-13). No. 1570, Litchi (16-14). No. 1571, Cabbages, mushrooms (16-15). No. 1572, Peaches (16-16).

No. 1573, Hyacynth.

**1980 Photo.** ***Perf. 11½***

| No. | Type | Description | Unused | Used |
|---|---|---|---|---|
| **1557** | A397 | 4f multi | *2.50* | *1.00* |
| **1558** | A397 | 4f multi | *2.50* | *1.00* |
| **1559** | A397 | 8f multi | *2.00* | *.75* |
| **1560** | A397 | 8f multi | *2.00* | *.75* |
| **1561** | A397 | 8f multi | *2.00* | *.75* |
| **1562** | A397 | 8f multi | *2.00* | *.75* |
| **1563** | A397 | 8f multi | *2.00* | *.75* |
| **1564** | A397 | 8f multi | *2.00* | *.75* |
| **1565** | A397 | 10f multi | *5.00* | *1.75* |
| **1566** | A397 | 20f multi | *5.00* | *1.75* |
| **1567** | A397 | 30f multi | *6.00* | *2.00* |
| **1568** | A397 | 40f multi | *30.00* | *8.00* |
| **1569** | A397 | 50f multi | *7.50* | *2.00* |
| **1570** | A397 | 55f multi | *7.50* | *3.00* |
| **1571** | A397 | 60f multi | *37.50* | *8.00* |
| **1572** | A397 | 70f multi | *15.00* | *5.00* |
| | | *Nos. 1557-1572 (16)* | *130.50* | *38.00* |

**Souvenir Sheet**

| No. | Type | Description | Unused | Used |
|---|---|---|---|---|
| **1573** | A397 | $2 multi | *240.00* | *125.00* |

Qi Baishi paintings. Issued: Nos. 1557-1560, 1569-1572, 1/15; others, 5/20. No. 1573 contains one 37½x61mm stamp.

A398

### China Post No. T.45.

Opera Masks: No. 1574, Meng Liang Mask from Hongyang Cave Opera. No. 1575, Li Kui, from Black Whirlwind. No. 1576, Huang Gai, from Meeting of Heroes. No. 1577, Monkey King. 10f, Lu Zhishen, from Wild Boar Forest. 20f, Lian Po, from Reconciliation between the General and Minister. 60f, Zhang Fei, from Reed Marsh. 70f, Dou Erdun, from Stealing the Emperor's Horse.

**1980, Jan. 25** ***Perf. 11½x11***

| No. | Type | Description | Unused | Used |
|---|---|---|---|---|
| **1574** | A398 | 4f multi (8-1) | *4.25* | *1.25* |
| **1575** | A398 | 4f multi (8-2) | *28.00* | *5.50* |
| **1576** | A398 | 8f multi (8-3) | *4.00* | *1.25* |
| **1577** | A398 | 8f multi (8-4) | *3.50* | *1.75* |
| **1578** | A398 | 10f multi (8-5) | *4.00* | *1.75* |
| **1579** | A398 | 20f multi (8-6) | *4.00* | *1.75* |
| **1580** | A398 | 60f multi (8-7) | *7.00* | *3.00* |
| **1581** | A398 | 70f multi (8-8) | *8.00* | *4.00* |
| | | *Nos. 1574-1581 (8)* | *62.75* | *20.25* |

A set of eight similar to Nos. 1574-1581 was prepared but not issued in 1964. See note below No. 782.

Speed Skating, Olympic Rings — A399

### China Post No. J.54.

Olympic Rings and: No. 1582, Chinese flag. No. 1584, Figure skating. 60f, Downhill skiing.

**1980, Feb. 13**

| No. | Type | Description | Unused | Used |
|---|---|---|---|---|
| **1582** | A399 | 8f multi (4-1) | *2.50* | *.75* |
| **1583** | A399 | 8f multi (4-2) | *2.50* | *.75* |
| **1584** | A399 | 8f multi (4-3) | *2.50* | *.75* |
| **1585** | A399 | 60f multi (4-4) | *9.00* | *3.00* |
| | | *Nos. 1582-1585 (4)* | *16.50* | *5.25* |

13th Winter Olympic Games, Lake Placid, NY, Feb. 12-24.

Monkey, New Year — A400

### China Post No. T.46.
### Engraved and Photogravure

**1980, Feb. 15** ***Perf. 11½***

| No. | Type | Description | Unused | Used |
|---|---|---|---|---|
| **1586** | A400 | 8f multicolored | *1,900.* | *675.00* |

Excellent forgeries of No. 1586 exist.

Clara Zetkin — A401

### China Post No. J.53.
### Photogravure & Engraved

**1980, Mar. 8** ***Perf. 11½x11***

| No. | Type | Description | Unused | Used |
|---|---|---|---|---|
| **1587** | A401 | 8f black & yellow | *2.50* | *1.10* |

International Working Women's Day, 70th anniv., founded by Clara Zetkin (1857-1933).

Orchard — A402

### China Post No. T.48.

Afforestation: 8f, Trees lining highway. 10f, Aerial seeding. 20f, Trees surrounding factory.

**1980, Mar. 12** ***Perf. 11x11½***

| No. | Type | Description | Unused | Used |
|---|---|---|---|---|
| **1588** | A402 | 4f multi (4-1) | *3.25* | *.95* |
| **1589** | A402 | 8f multi (4-2) | *3.25* | *.95* |
| **1590** | A402 | 10f multi (4-3) | *1.50* | *.75* |
| **1591** | A402 | 20f multi (4-4) | *1.50* | *.75* |
| | | *Nos. 1588-1591 (4)* | *9.50* | *3.40* |

Apsaras, Symbols of Modernization — A403

### China Post No. J.52.

**1980, Mar. 15 Photo.** ***Perf. 11½***

| No. | Type | Description | Unused | Used |
|---|---|---|---|---|
| **1592** | A403 | 8f multicolored | *3.50* | *1.40* |

2nd National Conference of the Scientific and Technical Association of China.

Mail Transport A404

### China Post No. T.49.

**1980, Mar. 20** ***Perf. 11x11½***

| No. | Type | Description | Unused | Used |
|---|---|---|---|---|
| **1593** | A404 | 2f Ship (4-1) | *1.75* | *1.50* |
| **1594** | A404 | 4f Bus (4-2) | *5.50* | *2.00* |
| **1595** | A404 | 8f Train (4-3) | *4.75* | *2.00* |
| **1596** | A404 | 10f Jet (4-4) | *3.75* | *2.25* |
| | | *Nos. 1593-1596 (4)* | *15.75* | *7.75* |

Forgeries exist.

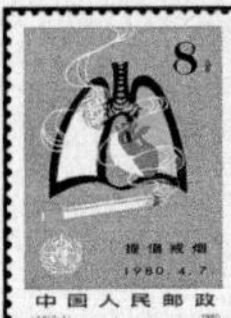

Lungs, Heart, Cigarette, WHO Emblem — A405

### China Post No. J.56.

**1980, Apr. 7** ***Perf. 11½x11***

| No. | Type | Description | Unused | Used |
|---|---|---|---|---|
| **1597** | A405 | 8f shown (2-1) | *2.00* | *.60* |
| **1598** | A405 | 60f Faces (2-2) | *14.00* | *3.50* |

Fight against cigarette smoking.

Statue of Chien Chen (688-763) — A406

### China Post No. J.55.

Loan to China by Japan of statue of Chien Chen (Jian Zhen), Buddhist missionary to Japan (754-763): No. 1600, Chien Chen Memorial Hall, Yangchou, horiz. 60f, Chien Chen's ship, horiz. His name in Japan is Ganjin.

**1980, Apr. 13** ***Perf. 11x11½, 11½x11***

| No. | Type | Description | Unused | Used |
|---|---|---|---|---|
| **1599** | A406 | 8f multi (3-1) | *4.00* | *1.10* |
| **1600** | A406 | 8f multi (3-2) | *4.00* | *1.10* |
| **1601** | A406 | 60f multi (3-3) | *35.00* | *7.75* |
| | | *Nos. 1599-1601 (3)* | *43.00* | *9.95* |

Lenin's 110th Birthday — A407

### China Post No. J.57.
### Photogravure and Engraved

**1980, Apr. 22** ***Perf. 11½x11***

| No. | Type | Description | Unused | Used |
|---|---|---|---|---|
| **1602** | A407 | 8f multicolored | *4.75* | *1.10* |

Swallow Chick Kite — A408

### China Post No. T.50.

Kites: No. 1604, Slender-swallow (4-2). No. 1605, Semi-slender swallow (4-3). No. 1606, Dual swallows (4-4).

**1980, May 10 Photo.** ***Perf. 11½***

| No. | Type | Description | Unused | Used |
|---|---|---|---|---|
| **1603** | A408 | 8f shown (4-1) | *5.50* | *1.75* |
| **1604** | A408 | 8f multi | *5.50* | *1.75* |
| **1605** | A408 | 8f multi | *5.50* | *1.75* |
| **1606** | A408 | 70f multi | *30.00* | *6.25* |
| | | *Nos. 1603-1606 (4)* | *46.50* | *11.50* |

Hare Running from Fallen Papaya — A409

### China Post No. T.51.

**1980, June 1 Photo.** ***Perf. 11x11½***

| No. | Type | Description | Unused | Used |
|---|---|---|---|---|
| **1607** | | Strip of 4 + label | *20.00* | *20.00* |
| *a.* | | A409 8f shown (4-1) | *2.00* | *1.60* |
| *b.* | | A409 8f Hare fox, monkey running away (4-2) | *2.00* | *1.60* |
| *c.* | | A409 8f Lion instructing animals (4-3) | *2.00* | *1.60* |
| *d.* | | A409 8f Discovery of fallen papaya (4-4) | *2.00* | *1.60* |
| *e.* | | Bklt. pane, 2 #1607 | *500.00* | |
| | | Complete booklet | *750.00* | |

Gu Dong fairy tale.

Beware of complete booklets of No. 1607e with forged booklet covers.

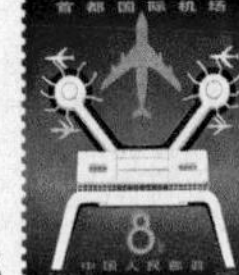

Terminal Building, Jets — A410

### China Post No. T.47.

**1980, June 20** ***Perf. 11½***

| No. | Type | Description | Unused | Used |
|---|---|---|---|---|
| **1608** | A410 | 8f Shown (2-1) | *4.00* | *1.40* |
| **1609** | A410 | 10f Runways, jets (2-2) | *4.00* | *1.40* |

Peking Intl. Airport opening.

Sika Stag — A411

### China Post No. T.52.

8f, Doe and fawn (3-2). 60f, Herd (3-3).

**1980, July 18 Photo.** ***Perf. 11½***

| No. | Type | Description | Unused | Used |
|---|---|---|---|---|
| **1610** | A411 | 4f Shown (3-1) | *2.60* | *1.40* |
| **1611** | A411 | 8f multi | *2.60* | *1.40* |
| **1612** | A411 | 60f multi | *12.75* | *5.25* |
| | | *Nos. 1610-1612 (3)* | *17.95* | *8.05* |

White Lotus — A412

### China Post No. T.54.

No. 1614, Rose-tipped snow (4-2). No. 1615, Buddha's seat (4-3). No. 1616, Variable charming face (4-4).

No. 1617, Fresh lotus on rippling water.

**1980, Aug. 4**

| No. | Type | Description | Unused | Used |
|---|---|---|---|---|
| **1613** | A412 | 8f Shown (4-1) | *6.00* | *2.00* |
| **1614** | A412 | 8f multi | *6.00* | *2.00* |
| **1615** | A412 | 8f multi | *6.00* | *2.00* |
| **1616** | A412 | 70f multi | *60.00* | *8.00* |
| | | *Nos. 1613-1616 (4)* | *78.00* | *14.00* |

**Souvenir Sheet**

| No. | Type | Description | Unused | Used |
|---|---|---|---|---|
| **1617** | A412 | $1 multi | *300.00* | *120.00* |

No. 1617 contains one 48x88mm stamp.

Pearl Cave, Sword-cut Stone Sculptures — A413

### China Post No. T.53.

Guilin Landscapes: No. 1619, Three mountains, distant views. No. 1620, Nine-horse fresco hill. No. 1621, Egrets around aged banyan. No. 1622, Western hills at sunset, vert. No. 1623, Moonlight on Lijiang River, vert. 60f, Springhead, ancient ferry, vert. 70f, Scenic path, Yangshue, vert.

**1980, Aug. 30 Photo.** ***Perf. 11½***

| No. | Type | Description | Unused | Used |
|---|---|---|---|---|
| **1618** | A413 | 8f multi (8-1) | *2.00* | *1.00* |
| **1619** | A413 | 8f multi (8-2) | *2.00* | *1.00* |
| **1620** | A413 | 8f multi (8-3) | *2.00* | *1.00* |
| **1621** | A413 | 8f multi (8-4) | *2.00* | *1.00* |
| **1622** | A413 | 8f multi (8-5) | *2.00* | *1.00* |
| **1623** | A413 | 8f multi (8-6) | *2.00* | *1.00* |
| **1624** | A413 | 60f multi (8-7) | *20.00* | *4.00* |
| **1625** | A413 | 70f multi (8-8) | *25.00* | *5.00* |
| | | *Nos. 1618-1625 (8)* | *57.00* | *15.00* |

Entrance Gate and Good Fairies — A414

Great Wall, Symbols of Chicago, San Francisco and New York — A415

**China Post No. J.59.**

**1980, Sept. 13 Photo.** ***Perf. 11x11½***
**1626** A414 8f multicolored *2.00 .90*
**1627** A415 70f multicolored *14.00 3.75*

Exhibitions of the People's Republic of China in San Francisco, Chicago and New York, Sept.-Dec. Sheets of 12 were sold only at the US exhibitions at increasing prices. Value, set of two sheets of 12, $1,500.

Romanian Flag, Warrior and Scroll — A416

**China Post No. J.61.**

**1980, Sept. 20 Photo.** ***Perf. 11½x11***
**1628** A416 8f multicolored *2.50 1.40*

2050th anniv. of Dacia, 1st independent Romanian state.

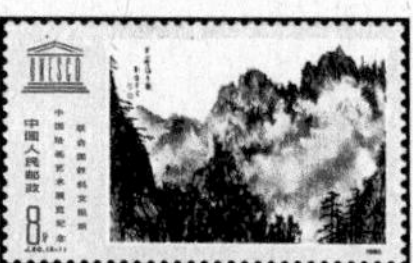

UNESCO Exhibition of Drawings and Paintings A417

**China Post No. J.60.**

No. 1629, Sea of Clouds, by Liu Haisu (3-1). No. 1630, Oriole and Magnolia, by Yu Feian, vert., (3-2). No. 1631, Camels, by Wu Zuoren (3-3).

**1980, Oct. 8** ***Perf. 11½***
**1629** A417 8f multi *2.00 .85*
**1630** A417 8f multi *2.00 .85*
**1631** A417 8f multi *2.00 .85*
*Nos. 1629-1631 (3) 6.00 2.55*

Scenes from Tarrying Garden A418

**China Post No. T.56.**

No. 1632, Quxi Tower (4-1). No. 1633, Yuancui Pavilion (4-2). No. 1634, Hanbi Shanfang (4-3). No. 1635, Guanyun Peak (4-4).

**1980, Oct. 25 Photo.** ***Perf. 11½***
**1632** A418 8f multi *7.25 4.00*
**1633** A418 8f multi *7.25 4.00*
**1634** A418 10f multi *12.00 4.00*
**1635** A418 60f multi *62.50 22.50*
*Nos. 1632-1635 (4) 89.00 34.50*

Xu Guangqi (1562-1633), Agronomist — A419

**China Post No. J.58.**

Scientists of Ancient China: No. 1637, Li Bing, hydraulic engineer, 3rd century B.C. No. 1638, Jia Sixie, agronomist, 5th century. 60f, Huang Daopo, textile expert, 13th century.

**Photogravure and Engraved**

**1980, Nov. 20** ***Perf. 11½x11***
**1636** A419 8f multi (4-1) *8.00 2.00*
**1637** A419 8f multi (4-2) *8.00 2.00*
**1638** A419 8f multi (4-3) *8.00 2.00*
**1639** A419 60f multi (4-4) *50.00 11.00*
*Nos. 1636-1639 (4) 74.00 17.00*

Shooting, Olympic Rings — A420

**China Post No. J.62.**

**1980, Nov. 26** **Photo.**
**1640** A420 4f shown (5-1) *2.25 .45*
**1641** A420 8f Gymnastics (5-2) *2.25 .45*
**1642** A420 8f Diving (5-3) *2.25 .45*
**1643** A420 10f Volleyball (5-4) *2.25 .75*
**1644** A420 60f Archery (5-5) *14.00 2.75*
*Nos. 1640-1644 (5) 23.00 4.85*

Return to International Olympic Committee, 1st anniversary.

Chinese River Dolphin — A421

**China Post No. T.57.**

**Photogravure & Engraved**

**1980, Dec. 25** ***Perf. 11x11½***
**1645** A421 8f shown (2-1) *4.25 .75*
*a.* Booklet pane of 6 *50.00*
**1646** A421 60f Dolphins (2-2) *9.75 1.90*
*a.* Booklet pane of 1 *50.00*

Stamps from No. 1645a have straight edges on top or bottom.

Cock — A422

**China Post No. T.58.**

**Photogravure & Engraved**

**1981, Jan. 5** ***Perf. 11½***
**1647** A422 8f multicolored 35.00 6.00
*a.* Booklet pane of 12 275.00
Complete booklet 225.00

New Year 1981.
Stamps from booklet pane have straight edges on top or bottom.

Early Morning in Xishuang Bana — A423

**China Post No. T.55.**

No. 1649, Dai mountain village (6-2). No. 1650, Rainbow over Lanchang River (6-3). No. 1651, Ancient temple vert. (6-4). No. 1652, Moonlit night, vert. (6-5). No. 1653, Phoenix tree, vert. (6-6).

***Perf. 11x11½, 11½x11***

**1981, Jan. 20** **Photo.**
**1648** A423 4f shown (6-1) 7.00 1.50
**1649** A423 4f multi 2.60 .75
**1650** A423 8f multi 2.60 .75
**1651** A423 8f multi 2.60 .75
**1652** A423 8f multi 2.60 .75
**1653** A423 60f multi 13.00 3.50
*Nos. 1648-1653 (6)* 30.40 8.00

Flower Basket Palace Lantern — A424

**China Post No. T.60.**

Designs: Palace lanterns.

**1981, Feb. 19 Photo.** ***Perf. 11½***
**1654** A424 4f multi (6-1) 2.00 1.00
**1655** A424 8f multi (6-2) 2.00 1.00
**1656** A424 8f multi (6-3) 2.00 1.00
**1657** A424 8f multi (6-4) 2.00 1.00
**1658** A424 20f multi (6-5) 4.50 3.50
**1659** A424 60f multi (6-6) 25.00 7.50
*Nos. 1654-1659 (6)* 37.50 15.00

Crossing River, Scene from Marking the Gunwale — A425

**China Post No. T.59.**

Scenes from Marking the Gunwale fable: No. 1660, Text (5-1). No. 1662, Dropping sword in water (5-3). No. 1663, Marking gunwale (5-4). No. 1664, Searching for sword (5-5).

**1981, Mar. 10 Photo.** ***Perf. 11x11½***
**1660** A425 8f multi 2.00 1.25
**1661** A425 8f shown (5-2) 2.00 1.25
**1662** A425 8f multi 2.00 1.25
**1663** A425 8f multi 2.00 1.25
**1664** A425 8f multi 2.00 1.25
*a.* Bklt. pane, 2 each #1660-1664 50.00
Complete booklet, #1664a 55.00
*b.* Strip of 5, #1660-1664 16.00 10.00

Chinese Juniper — A426

**China Post No. T.61.**

Designs: Miniature landscapes: No. 1665, Chinese elm, vert. (6-1). No. 1666, Juniper, vert. (6-2). No. 1667, Maidenhair tree, vert. (6-3). No. 1669, Persimmon (6-5). No. 1670, Juniper (6-6).

**1981, Mar. 31** ***Perf. 11½***
**1665** A426 4f multi 3.00 1.40
**1666** A426 8f multi 2.00 1.10
**1667** A426 8f multi 2.00 1.10
**1668** A426 10f shown (6-4) 2.00 1.10
**1669** A426 20f multi 2.00 1.25
**1670** A426 60f multi 12.50 4.25
*Nos. 1665-1670 (6)* 23.50 10.20

Vase with Tiger-shaped Handles — A427

**China Post No. T.62.**

Cizhou Kiln Ceramic Pottery: 4f, Vase with 2 tigers, Song Dynasty. No. 1672, Black glazed jar, Jin Dynasty. No. 1673, Amphora. No. 1674, Jar with 2 phoenixes (Yuan Dynasty). 10f, Flat flask, Yuan Dynasty.

**1981, Apr. 15 Photo.** ***Perf. 11½x11***
**1671** A427 4f multi, vert. (6-1) 1.50 .90
**1672** A427 8f multi (6-2) 1.50 .90
**1673** A427 8f multi, vert. (6-3) 1.50 .90
**1674** A427 8f multi (6-4) 1.50 .90
**1675** A427 10f multi (6-5) 1.50 .90
**1676** A427 60f multi (6-6) 7.50 3.75
*Nos. 1671-1676 (6)* 15.00 8.25

Panda and Colored Stamps — A428

**China Post No. J.63.**

**1981, Apr. 29 Photo.** ***Perf. 11½x11***
**1677** A428 8f shown (2-1) 1.25 .50
**1678** A428 60f Boat, bird (2-2) 4.75 1.60
*a.* Booklet pane (8 #1677, souv. sheet with 1677-1678) 20.00
Complete booklet, #1678a 23.00

Qinchuan Steer — A429

**China Post No. T.63.**

Cattle Breeds: No. 1680, Binhu buffalo. No. 1681, Yak. No. 1682, Black and white dairy cows. 10f, Pasture red cow. 55f, Simmental cross-breed.

**1981, May 5** ***Perf. 11x11½***
**1679** A429 4f multi (6-1) 2.65 1.00
**1680** A429 8f multi (6-2) 4.00 1.25
**1681** A429 8f multi (6-3) 3.65 1.25
**1682** A429 8f multi (6-4) 3.00 1.00
**1683** A429 10f multi (6-5) 3.00 1.00
**1684** A429 55f multi (6-6) 4.75 1.00
*Nos. 1679-1684 (6)* 21.05 6.50

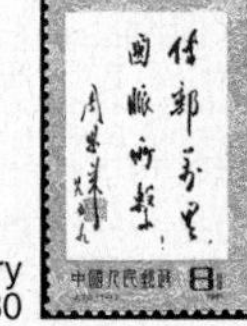

Mail Delivery Slogan — A430

**China Post No. J.70.**

**1981, May 9** ***Perf. 11***
**1685** A430 8f multicolored 1.25 .35

13th World Telecommunications Day — A431

**China Post No. J.69.**

**1981, May 17** ***Perf. 11½x11***
**1686** A431 8f multicolored 1.50 .35

Construction Worker — A432

**China Post No. J.65.**

No. 1688, Miner (4-2). No. 1689, Children crossing street (4-3). No. 1690, Farm worker (4-4).

**1981, May 20** ***Perf. 11½***
**1687** A432 8f shown (4-1) 1.75 .60
**1688** A432 8f multi 1.75 .60
**1689** A432 8f multi 1.75 .60
**1690** A432 8f multi 1.75 .60
*Nos. 1687-1690 (4)* 7.00 2.40

National Safety Month.

Telephone Building, Peking — A433

**China Post No. R19**

**1981, June 5 Engr.** ***Perf. 11½x11***
**1691** A433 8f violet brown 1.40 .65

Swaythling Cup, Men's Team Table Tennis — A434

**China Post No. J.71.**

36th World Table Tennis Championships Victory — No. 1692: a, St. Bride Vase, men's singles (7-3). b, Iran Cup, men's doubles (7-4). c, G. Geist Prize, women's singles (7-5). d, W.J. Pope Trophy, women's doubles (7-6). e, Heydusek Prize, mixed doubles (7-7). No.

1694, Marcel Corbillon Cup, women's team. Nos. 1693-1694 printed in sheets of 16 (8 each) + 2 labels.

**1981, June 30 Photo. *Perf. 11½x11***

| | | | | |
|---|---|---|---|---|
| **1692** | | Strip of 5 | 6.50 | 3.75 |
| ***a.-e.*** | A434 | 8f multi | .45 | .25 |
| **1693** | A434 | 20f multi (7-1) | 1.75 | .85 |
| **1694** | A434 | 20f multi (7-2) | 1.75 | .85 |

Chinese Communist Party, 60th Anniv. — A435

**China Post No. J.64.**

**1981, July 1 Photo. *Perf. 11x11½***

| | | | | |
|---|---|---|---|---|
| **1695** | A435 | 8f multicolored | 1.50 | .60 |

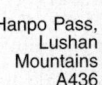

Hanpo Pass, Lushan Mountains A436

**China Post No. T.67.**

No. 1696, Five-veteran Peak, vert. (7-1). No. 1698, Yellow Dragon Pool, vert. (7-3). No. 1699, Sunlit Peak (7-4). No. 1700, Three-layer Spring, vert. (7-5). No. 1701, Stone and pines (7-6). No. 1702, Dragon-head Cliff, vert. (7-7).

**Photogravure & Engraved**

**1981, July 20 *Perf. 12½x12***

| | | | |
|---|---|---|---|
| **1696** | 8f multi | 2.40 | .70 |
| **1697** | 8f shown (7-2) | 2.40 | .70 |
| **1698** | 8f multi | 2.40 | .70 |
| **1699** | 8f multi | 2.40 | .70 |
| **1700** | 8f multi | 2.40 | .70 |
| **1701** | 8f multi | 2.40 | .70 |
| **1702** | 60f multi | 23.00 | 4.75 |
| | *Nos. 1696-1702 (7)* | 37.40 | 8.95 |

Tremella Fuciformis — A437

**China Post No. T.66.**

Edible mushrooms: No. 1704, Dictyophora indusiata (6-2). No. 1705, Hericium erinaceus (6-3). No. 1706, Russula rubra (6-4). No. 1707, Lentinus edodes (6-5). No. 1708, Agaricus bisporus (6-6).

**1981, Aug. 6 Photo. *Perf. 11½***

| | | | | |
|---|---|---|---|---|
| **1703** | A437 | 4f shown (6-1) | 1.30 | .55 |
| **1704** | A437 | 8f multi | 1.30 | .55 |
| **1705** | A437 | 8f multi | 1.30 | .55 |
| **1706** | A437 | 8f multi | 1.30 | .55 |
| **1707** | A437 | 10f multi | 1.30 | .55 |
| **1708** | A437 | 70f multi | 11.00 | 2.50 |
| | | *Nos. 1703-1708 (6)* | 17.50 | 5.25 |

Quality Month — A438

**China Post No. J.66.**

**1981, Sept. 1 Photo. *Perf. 11½x11***

| | | | | |
|---|---|---|---|---|
| **1709** | A438 | 8f Silver medal (2-1) | 2.75 | .75 |
| **1710** | A438 | 8f Gold medal (2-2) | 2.75 | .75 |

Lunan Stone Forest, Yunn — A439

**China Post No. T.64.**

Designs: Views of limestone formations, Lunan Stone Forest. Nos. 1711-1713 horiz.

**1981, Sept. 18 *Perf. 11½***

| | | | | |
|---|---|---|---|---|
| **1711** | A439 | 8f multi (5-1) | 1.40 | .60 |
| **1712** | A439 | 8f multi (5-2) | 1.40 | .60 |
| **1713** | A439 | 8f multi (5-3) | 1.40 | .60 |
| **1714** | A439 | 10f multi (5-4) | 1.40 | .60 |
| **1715** | A439 | 70f multi (5-5) | 13.00 | 4.75 |
| | | *Nos. 1711-1715 (5)* | 18.60 | 7.15 |

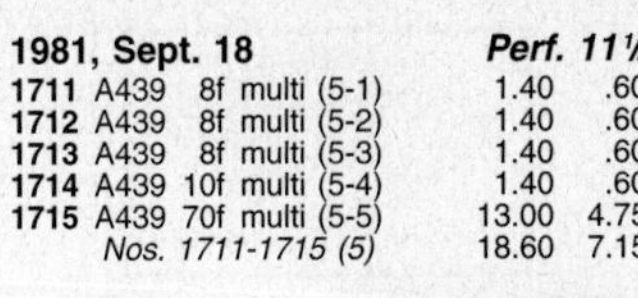

Lu Xun, Writer, Birth Centenary — A440

**China Post No. J.67.**

**1981, Sept. 25**

| | | | | |
|---|---|---|---|---|
| **1716** | A440 | 8f shown (2-1) | 2.25 | .50 |
| **1717** | A440 | 20f Portrait (diff.) (2-2) | 3.50 | 1.50 |

Sun Yat-sen and Text — A441

**China Post No. J.68.**

70th Anniv. of 1911 Revolution: No. 1719, 72 Martyrs Grave, Huang Hua Gang. No. 1720, Hubei Provincial Government Headquarters, 1911.

**1981, Oct. 10 Photo. *Perf. 11x11½***

| | | | | |
|---|---|---|---|---|
| **1718** | A441 | 8f multi (3-1) | 1.90 | .60 |
| **1719** | A441 | 8f multi (3-2) | 1.90 | .60 |
| **1720** | A441 | 8f multi (3-3) | 1.90 | .60 |
| | | *Nos. 1718-1720 (3)* | 5.70 | 1.80 |

Asian Conference of Parliamentarians on Population and Development, Peking, Oct. 27 — A442

**China Post No. J.73.**

**1981, Oct. 27 *Perf. 11½x11, 11x11½***

| | | | | |
|---|---|---|---|---|
| **1721** | A442 | 8f Tree, vert. (2-1) | .90 | .40 |
| **1722** | A442 | 70f shown (2-2) | 1.80 | 1.10 |

Xishuang Banna — A443

Mt. Hua — A443a

Mt. Tai — A443b

Huang Guo Shu Falls — A443c

Hainan Island — A443d

Tiger Hill, Suzhou — A443e

Great Wall — A443f

Immense Forest — A443g

Mt. Tian — A443h

Grassland, Inner Mongolia — A443i

Stone Forest — A443j

Banping Mountain — A443k

Mt. Qomolangma — A443l

Seven-Star Crag — A443m

Three Gorges, Changjiang River — A443n

Guilin landscape — A443o

Mt. Huangshan — A443p

**China Post No. R21**

Nos. 1731-1739 are horizontal.

***Perf. 11¼, 13x13¼ (#1726, 1729), 13¼x13 (#1731)***

**1981-83 Engr.**

| | | | | | |
|---|---|---|---|---|---|
| **1723** | A443 | 1f | blue green | .35 | .25 |
| **1724** | A443a | 1½f | red orange | .35 | .25 |
| **1725** | A443b | 2f | gray green | .35 | .25 |
| **1726** | A443c | 3f | red brown | .40 | .25 |
| **1727** | A443d | 4f | purple | .50 | .25 |
| **1728** | A443e | 5f | brown | .45 | .25 |
| **1729** | A443f | 8f | blue | .45 | .25 |
| **1730** | A443g | 10f | purplish brn | .50 | .25 |
| **1731** | A443h | 20f | blue green | .50 | .25 |
| **1732** | A443i | 30f | light brown | .50 | .25 |
| **1733** | A443j | 40f | blue black | .60 | .25 |
| **1734** | A443k | 50f | violet | .80 | .25 |
| **1735** | A443l | 70f | greenish blk | 1.00 | .50 |
| **1736** | A443m | 80f | rose lake | 1.15 | .70 |
| **1737** | A443n | $1 | violet black | 1.25 | .75 |
| **1738** | A443o | $2 | green | 2.00 | 1.40 |
| **1739** | A443p | $5 | Prussian blue | 5.00 | 2.75 |
| | | | *Nos. 1723-1739 (17)* | 16.15 | 9.10 |

Issued: Nos. 1737-1739, 10/9/82; Nos. 1732, 1734-1736 4/1/83.

**China Post No. R22**

**Photo.**

***Perf. 11½***

| | | | | | |
|---|---|---|---|---|---|
| *1726a* | A443 | 3f | tan & brown | .30 | .25 |
| *1727a* | A443 | 4f | pink & purple | .30 | .25 |
| *1727b* | | | Perf. 11½x11 | 7.50 | 7.50 |
| *1729a* | A443 | 8f | blue | .35 | .25 |
| *1730a* | A443 | 10f | dark brown | .60 | .50 |
| *1731a* | A443 | 20f | blue green | 1.40 | .80 |
| | | | *Nos. 1726a-1731a (5)* | 2.95 | 2.05 |

Nos. 1727a, 1729a, 1730a exist tagged. Values 10-15% higher.

Cowrie Shell and Shell-shaped Coin — A444

**China Post No. T.65.**

Ancient Coins. T.65.

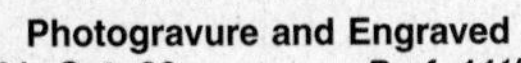

**Photogravure and Engraved**

**1981, Oct. 29 *Perf. 11½x11***

| | | | | |
|---|---|---|---|---|
| **1740** | A444 | 4f shown (8-1) | 1.35 | .50 |
| **1741** | A444 | 4f Shovel (8-2) | 1.35 | .50 |
| **1742** | A444 | 8f Shovel, diff. (8-3) | 1.35 | .50 |
| **1743** | A444 | 8f Shovel, diff. (8-4) | 1.75 | .50 |
| **1744** | A444 | 8f Knife (8-5) | 1.75 | .50 |
| **1745** | A444 | 8f Knife (8-6) | 1.75 | .50 |
| **1746** | A444 | 60f Knife, diff. (8-7) | 8.00 | 2.50 |
| **1747** | A444 | 70f Gong (8-8) | 10.50 | 3.00 |
| | | *Nos. 1740-1747 (8)* | 27.80 | 8.50 |

See Nos. 1765-1772.

A445

**China Post No. J.72.**

**1981, Nov. 10 Photo. *Perf. 11½x11***

| | | | | |
|---|---|---|---|---|
| **1748** | A445 | 8f multicolored | 1.40 | .40 |

Intl. Year of the Disabled.

A446

**China Post No. T.69.**

Twelve Beauties, from The Dream of Red Mansions, by Cao Xueqin: No. 1749, Daiyu (12-1). No. 1750, Baochai (12-2). No. 1751, Yuanchun (12-3). No. 1752, Yingchun (12-4). No. 1753, Tanchun (12-5). No. 1754, Xichun (12-6). No. 1755, Xiangyuh (12-7). No. 1756, Liwan (12-8). No. 1757, Xifeng (12-9). No. 1758, Sister Qiao (12-10). No. 1759, Keqing (12-11). No. 1760, Miaoyu (12-12).

No. 1761, Baoyu, Daiyu.

**1981-82 Photo. *Perf. 11***

| | | | | |
|---|---|---|---|---|
| **1749** | A446 | 4f multi | 5.00 | .95 |
| **1750** | A446 | 4f multi | 3.00 | .95 |
| **1751** | A446 | 8f multi | 4.00 | 1.50 |
| **1752** | A446 | 8f multi | 3.00 | 1.00 |
| **1753** | A446 | 8f multi | 3.00 | 1.00 |
| **1754** | A446 | 8f multi | 3.00 | 1.00 |
| **1755** | A446 | 8f multi | 3.00 | 1.25 |
| **1756** | A446 | 10f multi | 3.00 | 1.25 |
| **1757** | A446 | 20f multi | 3.00 | 1.25 |
| **1758** | A446 | 30f multi | 5.00 | 1.75 |
| **1759** | A446 | 40f multi | 22.50 | 6.00 |
| **1760** | A446 | 80f multi | 8.00 | 2.75 |
| | | *Nos. 1749-1760 (12)* | 65.50 | 20.65 |

**Souvenir Sheet**

| | | | | |
|---|---|---|---|---|
| **1761** | A446 | $2 multi | *210.00* | *95.00* |

No. 1761 contains one 59x39mm stamp.

Issued: Nos. 1749, 1751, 1753, 1755, 1757, 1759, 1761, 11/20/81; others, 4/24/82.

A447

**China Post No. J.76.**

8f, Girl playing (2-1). 20f, Girl holding trophy (2-2).

**1981, Dec. 21 Photo.**

| | | | | |
|---|---|---|---|---|
| **1762** | A447 | 8f multi | 1.40 | .30 |
| **1763** | A447 | 20f multi | 2.75 | .60 |

Women's team victory in 3rd World Cup Volleyball Championship.

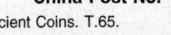

A448

**China Post No. T.70.**

**Photogravure & Engraved**

| **1982, Jan. 5** | | *Perf. 11½* | |
|---|---|---|---|
| **1764** A448 8f multicolored | | 7.75 | 3.00 |
| *a.* Booklet pane of 10 + label | | 77.50 | |
| Complete booklet, #1764a | | 85.00 | *85.00* |

New Year 1982 (Year of the Dog).

Stamps from No. 1764a have straight edges at top or bottom.

**Coin Type of 1981**

**China Post No. T.71.**

No. 1765, Guilian mask (8-1). No. 1766, Shu shovel (8-2). No. 1767, Xia zhuan shovel (8-3). No. 1768, Han Dan shovel (8-4). No. 1769, Knife (8-5). No. 1770, Ming knife (8-6). No. 1771, Jin hua knife (8-7). No. 1772, Yi Liu Hua coin (8-8).

| **1982, Feb. 12** | | |
|---|---|---|
| **1765** A444 4f multi | 1.20 | .65 |
| **1766** A444 4f multi | 1.20 | .65 |
| **1767** A444 8f multi | 1.20 | .65 |
| **1768** A444 8f multi | 1.20 | .65 |
| **1769** A444 8f multi | 1.20 | .65 |
| **1770** A444 8f multi | 1.20 | .80 |
| **1771** A444 70f multi | 4.25 | 2.25 |
| **1772** A444 80f multi | 5.50 | 3.00 |
| *Nos. 1765-1772 (8)* | 16.95 | 9.30 |

Nie Er (1912-1935), Natl. Anthem Composer A449

**China Post No. J.75.**

| **1982, Feb. 15** | *Perf. 11x11½* | |
|---|---|---|
| **1773** A449 8f multicolored | 2.25 | .55 |

Intl. Drinking Water and Sanitation Decade, 1981-1990 — A450

**China Post No. J.77.**

| **1982, Mar. 1** | *Perf. 11½x11* | |
|---|---|---|
| **1774** A450 8f multicolored | 1.75 | .50 |

TB Bacillus Centenary A451

**China Post No. J.74.**

| **1982, Mar. 24** | *Perf. 11x11½* | |
|---|---|---|
| **1775** A451 8f multicolored | 1.50 | .50 |

Fire Control — A452

**China Post No. T.76.**

No. 1776, Water hoses (2-1). No. 1777, Chemical extinguisher (2-2).

| **1982, May 8 Photo.** | *Perf. 11½x11* | |
|---|---|---|
| **1776** A452 8f multicolored | 1.50 | .50 |
| **1777** A452 8f multicolored | 1.50 | .50 |

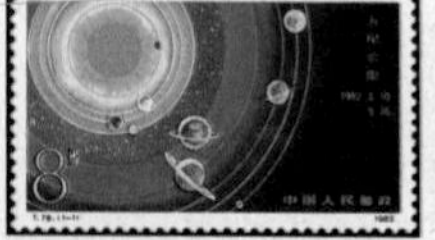

Syzygy of the Nine Planets, Mar. 10 and May 16 — A453

**China Post No. T.78.**

| **1982, May 16** | *Perf. 11½* | |
|---|---|---|
| **1778** A453 8f multicolored | 2.25 | .60 |

Medicinal Herbs — A454

**China Post No. T.72.**

No. 1779, Hemerocallis flava (6-1). No. 1780, Fritillaria unibracteata (6-2). No. 1781, Aconitum carmichaeli (6-3). No. 1782, Lilium brownii (6-4). No. 1783, Arisaema (6-5). No. 1784, Paeonia lactiflora (6-6).

No. 1785, Iris tectorum maxim.

| **1982, May 20** | *Perf. 11½x11* | |
|---|---|---|
| **1779** A454 4f multi | .65 | .45 |
| **1780** A454 8f multi | .65 | .45 |
| **1781** A454 8f multi | .65 | .45 |
| **1782** A454 10f multi | 1.40 | .65 |
| **1783** A454 20f multi | 1.75 | .75 |
| **1784** A454 70f multi | 5.25 | 1.50 |
| *Nos. 1779-1784 (6)* | 10.35 | 4.25 |

**Souvenir Sheet**

| **1785** A454 $2 multi | 30.00 | 19.50 |
|---|---|---|

No. 1785 contains one 89x39mm stamp.

Soong Ching Ling (1893-1981), Sun Yat-sen's Widow — A455

**China Post No. J.82.**

8f, Addressing Consultative Conf. (2-1). 20f, Portrait (2-2).

| **1982, May 29** | *Perf. 11½* | |
|---|---|---|
| **1786** A455 8f multi | 1.00 | .45 |
| **1787** A455 20f multi | 4.00 | 1.40 |

Sable — A456

**China Post No. T.68.**

| **1982, June 20 Photo.** | *Perf. 11½* | |
|---|---|---|
| **1788** A456 8f shown (2-1) | 1.50 | .60 |
| **1789** A456 80f Sable, diff. (2-2) | 5.00 | 3.75 |
| *a.* Bklt. pane of 8, 6 8f plus sheetlet of 2 (8f, 80f) | 30.00 | |
| Complete booklet, #1789a | 35.00 | |

A457

**China Post No. J.78.**

| **1982, June 30** | *Perf. 11½x11* | |
|---|---|---|
| **1790** A457 8f multicolored | 1.75 | .40 |

Natl. census, July 1.

A458

**China Post No. J.81.**

| **1982, July 25 Photo.** | *Perf. 11½x11* | |
|---|---|---|
| **1791** A458 8f multicolored | 1.40 | .40 |

2nd UN Conference on Peaceful Uses of Outer Space, Vienna, Aug. 9-21.

Strolling in Autumn Woods, by Shen Zhou, Ming Dynasty A459

**China Post No. T.77.**

Fan Paintings (Ming or Qing Dynasty): No. 1793, Jackdaw on Withered Tree, by Tang Yin. No. 1794 Bamboo and Sparrows, by Zhou Zhimian. 10f, Writing Poem under Pine, by Chen Hongshou and Bai Han. 20f, Chrysanthemums, by Yun Shouping, Qing. 70f, Birds, Crape Myrtle and Chinese Parasol, by Wang Wu, Qing.

| **1982, July 31** | *Perf. 11½* | |
|---|---|---|
| **1792** A459 4f multi (6-1) | 3.00 | .80 |
| **1793** A459 8f multi (6-2) | 1.30 | .70 |
| **1794** A459 8f multi (6-3) | 1.30 | .70 |
| **1795** A459 10f multi (6-4) | 2.10 | .75 |
| **1796** A459 20f multi (6-5) | 2.10 | .80 |
| **1797** A459 70f multi (6-6) | 6.00 | 2.25 |
| *Nos. 1792-1797 (6)* | 15.80 | 6.00 |

A460

**China Post No. J.79.**

| **1982, Aug. 25** | *Perf. 11½x11* | |
|---|---|---|
| **1798** A460 8f multicolored | 1.00 | .35 |

60th anniv. of Chinese Geological Society.

A461

**China Post No. T.73.**

| **1982, Aug. 25 Photo.** | *Perf. 11½x11* | |
|---|---|---|
| **1799** A461 4f Orpiment (4-1) | .75 | .30 |
| **1800** A461 8f Stibnite (4-2) | .75 | .30 |
| **1801** A461 10f Cinnabar (4-3) | 1.50 | .30 |
| **1802** A461 20f Wolframite (4-4) | 1.50 | .55 |
| *Nos. 1799-1802 (4)* | 4.50 | 1.45 |

Souvenir Sheet

Messenger, Tomb Mural, Jiayu Pass, Wei-Jin Period — A462

**China Post No. J.85.**

| **1982, Aug. 25** | | |
|---|---|---|
| **1803** A462 $1 multicolored | 29.00 | 12.50 |

All-China Philatelic Federation, 1st Cong.

12th Natl. Communist Party Congress — A463

**China Post No. J.86.**

| **1982, Sept. 1** | *Perf. 11½* | |
|---|---|---|
| **1804** A463 8f multicolored | 2.75 | .45 |

Hoopoe — A464

**China Post No. T.79.**

No. 1806, Swallows (5-2). No. 1807, Oriole (5-3). No. 1808, Chickadees (5-4). No. 1809, Woodpecker (5-5).

No. 1810, Cuckoos.

| **1982, Sept. 10** | *Perf. 11½x11* | |
|---|---|---|
| **1805** A464 8f shown (5-1) | 1.00 | .40 |
| **1806** A464 8f multi | 1.00 | .40 |
| **1807** A464 8f multi | 1.00 | .40 |
| **1808** A464 20f multi | 2.50 | .80 |
| **1809** A464 70f multi | 7.25 | 3.25 |
| *Nos. 1805-1809 (5)* | 12.75 | 5.25 |

**Souvenir Sheet**

| **1810** A464 $2 multi | 55.00 | 20.00 |
|---|---|---|

No. 1810 contains one 56x36mm stamp.

Japan-China Relations Normalization, 10th Anniv. — A465

**China Post No. J.84.**

Flower Paintings: 8f, Plum blossoms, by Guan Shanyue. 70f, Hibiscus, by Xiao Shufang.

| **1982, Sept. 29** | *Perf. 11* | |
|---|---|---|
| **1811** A465 8f multi (2-1) | 1.40 | .40 |
| **1812** A465 70f multi (2-2) | 2.50 | 1.00 |

World Food Day — A466

**China Post No. J.80.**

| **1982, Oct. 16** | *Perf. 11½* | |
|---|---|---|
| **1813** A466 8f multicolored | 1.75 | .40 |

Guo Morou (1892-1978), Acad. of Sciences Pres. — A467

**China Post No. J.87.**

Designs: Portraits.

| **1982, Nov. 16 Photo.** | *Perf. 11½x11* | |
|---|---|---|
| **1814** A467 8f multi (2-1) | .75 | .50 |
| **1815** A467 20f multi (2-2) | 1.75 | .60 |

Bodhisattva, 11th Cent. Sculpture — A468

**China Post No. T.74.**

Liao Dynasty Buddha Sculptures, Lower Huayan Monastery.

**1982, Nov. 19** ***Perf. 11***

**1816** A468 8f multi (4-1) 1.70 .40
**1817** A468 8f multi (4-2) 1.70 .40
**1818** A468 8f multi (4-3) 2.50 .40
**1819** A468 70f multi (4-4) 6.75 3.00
*Nos. 1816-1819 (4)* 12.65 4.20

**Souvenir Sheet**

***Perf. 11x11½***

**1820** A468 $2 multicolored 50.00 22.00

No. 1820 contains one 36x55mm stamp.

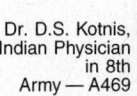

Dr. D.S. Kotnis, Indian Physician in 8th Army — A469

**China Post No. J.83.**

***Perf. 11½x11, 11x11½***

**1982, Dec. 9** **Photo.**

**1821** A469 8f Portrait, vert. (2-1) .40 .30
**1822** A469 70f Riding horse (2-2) 1.60 1.60

11th Communist Youth League Natl. Congress — A470

**China Post No. J.88.**

**1982, Dec. 20** ***Perf. 11x11½***

**1823** A470 8f multicolored 1.50 .50

Bronze Wine Container — A471

**China Post No. T.75.**

Western Zhou Dynasty Bronze (1200-771 B.C.): No. 1825, Three-legged cooking pot. No. 1826, Food bowl. No. 1827, Three-legged cooking pot (diff.). No. 1828, Animal-shaped wine container. 10f, Wine container with lid. 20f, Round food bowl. 70f, Square wine container.

**Photogravure & Engraved**

**1982, Dec. 25** ***Perf. 11***

**1824** A471 4f multi (8-1) 1.75 .90
**1825** A471 4f multi (8-2) 1.75 .90
**1826** A471 8f multi (8-3) 1.75 .90
**1827** A471 8f multi (8-4) 3.00 1.40
**1828** A471 8f multi (8-5) 1.75 .90
**1829** A471 10f multi (8-6) 2.75 .90
**1830** A471 20f multi (8-7) 3.50 1.60
**1831** A471 70f multi (8-8) 17.50 5.00
*Nos. 1824-1831 (8)* 33.75 12.50

A472

**China Post No. T.80.**

**1983, Jan. 5** ***Perf. 11½***

**1832** A472 8f multicolored 14.00 3.75
*a.* Booklet pane of 12 150.00 *77.50*
Complete booklet, #1832a 100.00

New Year 1983 (Year of the Pig).

Stamps from No. 1832a have straight edges at top or bottom and sell for less as singles than No. 1832.

A473

**China Post No. T.81.**

Stringed Instruments.

**1983, Jan. 20** ***Perf. 11½x11, 11x11½***

**1833** A473 4f Konghou (5-1) 3.75 .80
**1834** A473 8f Ruan (5-2) 3.75 .80
**1835** A473 8f Qin, horiz. (5-3) 3.75 .80
**1836** A473 10f Piba (5-4) 3.75 .80
**1837** A473 70f Sanxian (5-5) 29.00 5.25
*Nos. 1833-1837 (5)* 44.00 8.45

A474

**China Post No. J.89.**

No. 1838, Monument, Jiangan (2-1). No. 1839, Erqi Memorial Tower, Zhengzhou (2-2).

**1983, Feb. 7** **Photo.** ***Perf. 11½x11***

**1838** A474 8f multi 1.35 .50
**1839** A474 8f multi 1.65 .50

60th Anniv. of Peking-Hankow Railroad Workers' Strike.

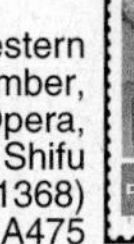

The Western Chamber, Traditional Opera, by Wang Shifu (1271-1368) A475

**China Post No. T.82.**

Scenes from the opera.

**1983, Feb. 21** **Photo.** ***Perf. 11x11½***

**1840** A475 8f multi (4-1) 3.50 1.30
**1841** A475 8f multi (4-2) 3.50 1.30
**1842** A475 10f multi (4-3) 6.00 1.60
**1843** A475 80f multi (4-4) 27.50 5.00
*Nos. 1840-1843 (4)* 40.50 9.20

**Souvenir Sheet**

**Photogravure and Engraved**

***Perf. 12***

**1844** A475 $2 multicolored 155.00 50.00

No. 1844 contains one 27x48mm stamp.

Karl Marx (1818-1883) — A476

**China Post No. J.90.**

8f, Portrait (2-1). 20f, Making speech (2-2).

**Photogravure & Engraved**

**1983, Mar. 14** ***Perf. 11½x11***

**1845** A476 8f multicolored .90 .50
**1846** A476 20f multicolored 1.40 .60

Tomb of the Yellow Emperor — A477

**China Post No. T.84.**

8f, Tomb, vert. (3-1). 10f, Hall of Founder of Chinese Culture (3-2). 20f, Cypress tree, vert. (3-3).

**Photogravure & Engraved**

**1983, Apr. 5** ***Perf. 11½***

**1847** A477 8f multi 1.50 .60
**1848** A477 10f multi 2.00 .60
**1849** A477 20f multi 3.25 .90
*Nos. 1847-1849 (3)* 6.75 2.10

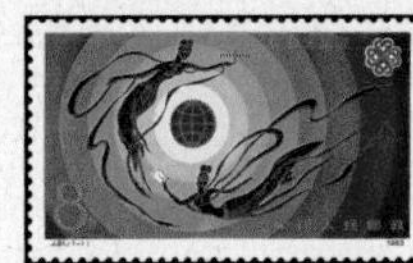

World Communications Year — A478

**China Post No. J.91.**

**1983, Apr. 28** **Photo.** ***Perf. 11½***

**1850** A478 8f multicolored 1.75 .50

Male Chinese Alligator A479

**China Post No. T.85.**

20f, Female, hatching eggs (2-2).

**Photogravure & Engraved**

**1983, May 24** ***Perf. 11***

**1851** A479 8f shown (2-1) 1.10 .50
**1852** A479 20f multicolored 1.90 .75

Kitten, by Tan Arxi — A480

**China Post No. T.86.**

Various children's drawings.

**1983, June 1** ***Perf. 11½x11***

**1853** A480 8f multi (4-1) .45 .30
**1854** A480 8f multi (4-2) .45 .30
**1855** A480 8f multi (4-3) .45 .30
**1856** A480 8f multi (4-4) .45 .30
*Nos. 1853-1856 (4)* 1.80 1.20

6th Natl. People's Congress — A481

**China Post No. J.94.**

8f, Hall (2-1). 20f, Natl. anthem score (2-2).

**1983, June 6** ***Perf. 11x11½***

**1857** A481 8f multicolored 1.50 .50
**1858** A481 20f multicolored 3.75 .90

Terra Cotta Figures, Qin Dynasty (221-207 BC) — A482

**China Post No. T.88.**

No. 1859, Soldiers (4-1). No. 1860, Heads (4-2). No. 1861, Soldiers, horses (4-3). No. 1862, Excavation site (4-4).

No. 1863, Soldier leading horse.

**1983, June 30**

**1859** A482 8f multi 1.25 .55
**1860** A482 8f multi 1.25 .55
**1861** A482 10f multi 2.00 .65
**1862** A482 70f multi 5.75 2.40
*a.* Bklt. pane of 8 (#1859, 3 #1860, 3 #1861, #1862) *97.50 75.00*
*Nos. 1859-1862 (4)* 10.25 4.15

**Souvenir Sheet**

**1863** A482 $2 multi *70.00 25.00*
*a.* Booklet pane of 1 *70.00*
Complete booklet, #1862a, #1863a 100.00 *65.00*

No. 1863 contains one 59x39mm stamp.

A483

**China Post No. T.87.**

Female roles in Peking opera: 4f, Sun Yujiao (8-1). No. 1865, 8f, Chen Miaochang (8-2). No. 1866, 8f, Bai Suzhen (8-3). No. 1867, 8f, Sister Thirteen (8-4). 10f, Qin Xianglian (8-5). 20f, Yang Yuhuan (8-6). 50f, Cui Yingying (8-7). 80f, Mu Guiying (8-8).

**1983, July 20** **Photo.** ***Perf. 11***

**1864** A483 4f multi 2.40 .65
**1865** A483 8f multi 2.40 .65
**1866** A483 8f multi 2.40 .65
**1867** A483 8f multi 2.40 .65
**1868** A483 10f multi 2.40 .65
**1869** A483 20f multi 2.40 .65
**1870** A483 50f multi 13.50 3.00
**1871** A483 80f multi 17.50 4.25
*Nos. 1864-1871 (8)* 45.40 11.15

A484

**China Post No. J.92.**

Paintings by Liu Lingcang: No. 1872, Li Bai (4-1). No. 1873, Du Fu (4-2). No. 1874, Han Yu (4-3). No. 1875, Liu Zongyuan (4-4).

**1983, Aug. 10** **Photo.** ***Perf. 11½***

**1872** A484 8f multi 2.25 .40
**1873** A484 8f multi 2.25 .40
**1874** A484 8f multi 2.25 .40
**1875** A484 70f multi 13.00 3.25
*Nos. 1872-1875 (4)* 19.75 4.45

Poets and philosophers of ancient China.

5th Natl. Women's Congress A485

**China Post No. J.95.**

**1983, Sept. 1** **Photo.** ***Perf. 11½***

**1876** A485 8f multicolored 1.00 .40

5th National Games — A486

**China Post No. J.93.**

No. 1877, Emblem (6-1). No. 1878, Gymnast (6-2). No. 1879, Badminton (6-3). No. 1880, Diving (6-4). No. 1881, High jump (6-5). No. 1882, Wind surfing (6-6).

**1983, Sept. 16** **Photo.** ***Perf. 11½***

**1877** A486 4f multi .70 .35
**1878** A486 8f multi .70 .35
**1879** A486 8f multi .70 .35
**1880** A486 8f multi .70 .35
**1881** A486 20f multi 1.25 .40
**1882** A486 70f multi 4.50 2.25
*Nos. 1877-1882 (6)* 8.55 4.05

Family Planning — A487

**China Post No. T.91.**

No. 1883, One child (2-1). No. 1884, Cultivated land (2-2).

**1983, Sept. 19** **Perf. *11x11½***

| No. | Type | Description | Unused | Used |
|---|---|---|---|---|
| **1883** | A487 | 8f multicolored | .50 | .30 |
| **1884** | A487 | 8f multicolored | .50 | .30 |

10th Intl. Trade Union Congress A488

**China Post No. J.98.**

**1983, Oct. 18** **Litho.** **Perf. *11½***

| No. | Type | Description | Unused | Used |
|---|---|---|---|---|
| **1885** | A488 | 8f multicolored | 1.00 | .40 |

Mute Swans — A489

**China Post No. T.83.**

Cygnus Olor: No. 1886, One swan (4-1). No. 1887, Two swans (4-2). No. 1888, Four swans (4-3). No. 1889, Six swans (4-4).

***Perf. 11x11½ on 3 sides***

**1983, Nov. 18** **Photo.**

| No. | Type | Description | Unused | Used |
|---|---|---|---|---|
| **1886** | A489 | 8f multi | .65 | .30 |
| **1887** | A489 | 8f multi | 2.30 | .50 |
| **1888** | A489 | 10f multi | 2.30 | .50 |
| **1889** | A489 | 80f multi | 5.25 | 1.75 |
| *a.* | | Booklet pane, 7 #1886, 1 each #1887-1889 | 32.50 | *20.00* |
| | | Complete booklet, #1889a | 50.00 | *27.50* |
| | | *Nos. 1886-1889 (4)* | 10.50 | 3.05 |

A490

**China Post No. J.96.**

Various photos.

**1983, Nov. 24** **Photo.** **Perf. *11½***

| No. | Type | Description | Unused | Used |
|---|---|---|---|---|
| **1890** | A490 | 8f multi (4-1) | 1.40 | .50 |
| **1891** | A490 | 8f multi (4-2) | 1.40 | .50 |
| **1892** | A490 | 8f multi (4-3) | 1.40 | .50 |
| **1893** | A490 | 8f multi (4-4) | 1.40 | .50 |
| | | *Nos. 1890-1893 (4)* | 5.60 | 2.00 |

85th birth anniv. of Liu Shaoqi, political leader.

A491

**China Post No. J.99.**

**1983, Nov. 29** **Photo.** **Perf. *11½***

| No. | Type | Description | Unused | Used |
|---|---|---|---|---|
| **1894** | A491 | 8f No. 117 (2-1) | .80 | .35 |
| **1895** | A491 | 20f No. 4L1 (2-2) | 1.20 | .45 |

CHINAPEX '83 Natl. Philatelic Exhibition.

A492

**China Post No. J.97.**

Various portraits.

**1983, Dec. 26** **Photo.** **Perf. *11½***

| No. | Type | Description | Unused | Used |
|---|---|---|---|---|
| **1896** | A492 | 8f 1925 (4-1) | 1.25 | .35 |
| **1897** | A492 | 8f 1945 (4-2) | 1.25 | .35 |
| **1898** | A492 | 10f 1952 (4-3) | 6.00 | 1.00 |
| **1899** | A492 | 20f 1961 (4-4) | 3.50 | .60 |
| | | *Nos. 1896-1899 (4)* | 12.00 | 2.30 |

90th birth anniv. of Mao Tse-tung.

A493

**China Post No. T.90.**

**Photogravure and Engraved**

**1984, Jan. 5** **Perf. *11½***

| No. | Type | Description | Unused | Used |
|---|---|---|---|---|
| **1900** | A493 | 8f multicolored | 7.00 | 2.50 |
| *a.* | | Booklet pane of 12 | *65.00* | *30.00* |
| | | Complete booklet, #1900a | *75.00* | *60.00* |

New Year 1984 (Year of the Rat).

Stamps from No. 1900a have straight edge at top or bottom.

Beauties Wearing Flowers A494

**China Post No. T.89.**

Portions of painting by Zhou Fang (Tang Dynasty).

**1984, Mar. 24** **Photo.** **Perf. *11***

| No. | Type | Description | Unused | Used |
|---|---|---|---|---|
| **1901** | A494 | 8f multi (3-1) | 2.50 | .40 |
| **1902** | A494 | 10f multi (3-2) | 4.00 | .60 |
| **1903** | A494 | 70f multi (3-3) | 12.50 | 3.00 |
| | | *Nos. 1901-1903 (3)* | 19.00 | 4.00 |

**Souvenir Sheet**

| No. | Type | Description | Unused | Used |
|---|---|---|---|---|
| **1904** | A494 | $2 Entire painting | *210.00* | 55.00 |

No. 1904 contains one 162x40mm stamp.

Chinese Roses — A495

**China Post No. T.93.**

No. 1905, Spring of Shanghai (6-1). No. 1906, Rosy Dawn of Pujiang River (6-2). No. 1907, Pearl (6-3). No. 1908, Black whirlwind (6-4). No. 1909, Yellow flower in battlefield (6-5). No. 1910, Blue Phoenix (6-6).

**1984, Apr. 20** **Photo.** **Perf. *11½***

| No. | Type | Description | Unused | Used |
|---|---|---|---|---|
| **1905** | A495 | 4f multi | .80 | .30 |
| **1906** | A495 | 8f multi | .80 | .30 |
| **1907** | A495 | 8f multi | .80 | .30 |
| **1908** | A495 | 10f multi | .80 | .35 |
| **1909** | A495 | 20f multi | 1.75 | .45 |
| **1910** | A495 | 70f multi | 4.00 | 1.40 |
| | | *Nos. 1905-1910 (6)* | 8.95 | 3.10 |

Ren Bishi (1904-50), Statesman — A496

**China Post No. J.100.**

**1984, Apr. 30** **Perf. *11½x11***

| No. | Type | Description | Unused | Used |
|---|---|---|---|---|
| **1911** | A496 | 8f multicolored | 1.75 | .50 |

Crested Ibis — A497

**China Post No. T.94.**

**1984, May 15** **Photo.** **Perf. *11x11½***

| No. | Type | Description | Unused | Used |
|---|---|---|---|---|
| **1912** | A497 | 8f Flying (3-1) | 1.00 | .25 |
| **1913** | A497 | 8f Wading (3-2) | 1.00 | .25 |
| **1914** | A497 | 80f Perching (3-3) | 3.00 | 1.40 |
| | | *Nos. 1912-1914 (3)* | 5.00 | 1.90 |

Chinese Red Cross Society, 80th Anniv. A498

**China Post No. J.102.**

**1984, May 29** **Perf. *11½***

| No. | Type | Description | Unused | Used |
|---|---|---|---|---|
| **1915** | A498 | 8f multicolored | 1.75 | .40 |

Gezhou Dam, Yangtze River A499

**China Post No. T.95.**

8f, Dam (3-1). 10f, Bridge, vert. (3-2). 20f, Lock Gate #2 (3-3).

**1984, June 15** **Photo.**

| No. | Type | Description | Unused | Used |
|---|---|---|---|---|
| **1916** | A499 | 8f multi | .50 | .35 |
| **1917** | A499 | 10f multi | .75 | .40 |
| **1918** | A499 | 20f multi | 1.60 | .75 |
| | | *Nos. 1916-1918 (3)* | 2.85 | 1.50 |

Zhuo Zheng Garden, Suzhou — A500

**China Post No. T.96.**

No. 1919, Inverted Image Tower (4-1). No. 1920, Loquat Garden (4-2). No. 1921, Water Court, Xiao Cang Lang (4-3). No. 1922, Yuanxiang Hall, Yiyu Study (4-4).

**Photogravure & Engraved**

**1984, June 30** **Perf. *11½x11***

| No. | Type | Description | Unused | Used |
|---|---|---|---|---|
| **1919** | A500 | 8f multi | .75 | .45 |
| **1920** | A500 | 8f multi | .75 | .45 |
| **1921** | A500 | 10f multi | .85 | .45 |
| **1922** | A500 | 70f multi | 2.25 | 1.50 |
| | | *Nos. 1919-1922 (4)* | 4.60 | 2.85 |

1984 Summer Olympics — A501

**China Post No. J.103.**

No. 1923, Shooting (6-1). No. 1924, High jump (6-2). No. 1925, Weight lifting (6-3). No. 1926, Gymnastics (6-4). No. 1927, Volleyball (6-5). No. 1928, Diving (6-6).

No. 1929, Athletes, rings.

**1984, July 28** **Photo.** **Perf. *11½***

| No. | Type | Description | Unused | Used |
|---|---|---|---|---|
| **1923** | A501 | 4f multi | .35 | .35 |
| **1924** | A501 | 8f multi | .40 | .40 |
| **1925** | A501 | 8f multi | .40 | .40 |
| **1926** | A501 | 10f multi | .45 | .45 |
| **1927** | A501 | 20f multi | .50 | .50 |
| **1928** | A501 | 80f multi | 1.25 | 1.25 |
| | | *Nos. 1923-1928 (6)* | 3.35 | 3.35 |

**Souvenir Sheet**

| No. | Type | Description | Unused | Used |
|---|---|---|---|---|
| **1929** | A501 | $2 multi | 12.50 | 6.00 |

No. 1929 contains one 61x38mm stamp.

Calligraphy — A502

**China Post No. T.98.**

Artworks by Wu Changshuo: No. 1931, A Pair of Peaches (8-2). No. 1932, Lotus (8-3). No. 1933, Wisteria (8-4). No. 1934, Peony (8-5). No. 1935, Chrysanthemum (8-6). No. 1936, Plum Blossom (8-7). No. 1937, Seal Cutting (8-8).

**1984, Aug. 27** **Photo.** **Perf. *11½***

| No. | Type | Description | Unused | Used |
|---|---|---|---|---|
| **1930** | A502 | 4f shown (8-1) | .65 | .30 |
| **1931** | A502 | 4f multi | .65 | .30 |
| **1932** | A502 | 8f multi | 1.35 | .30 |
| **1933** | A502 | 8f multi | .60 | .30 |
| **1934** | A502 | 8f multi | 5.50 | 1.60 |
| **1935** | A502 | 10f multi | 1.25 | .50 |
| **1936** | A502 | 20f multi | 1.35 | .50 |
| **1937** | A502 | 70f multi | 3.50 | 1.60 |
| | | *Nos. 1930-1937 (8)* | 14.85 | 5.40 |

Luanhe River Water Diversion Project — A503

**China Post No. T.97.**

***Perf. 11½x11, 11 (#1939)***

**1984, Sept. 11** **Photo.**

| No. | Type | Description | Unused | Used |
|---|---|---|---|---|
| **1938** | A503 | 8f multi (3-1) | .45 | .40 |
| **1939** | A503 | 10f multi, horiz. (3-2) | .45 | .40 |
| **1940** | A503 | 20f multi (3-3) | .65 | .50 |
| | | *Nos. 1938-1940 (3)* | 1.55 | 1.30 |

Chinese-Japanese Youth — A504

**China Post No. J.104.**

**1984, Sept. 24** **Photo.** **Perf. *11½***

| No. | Type | Description | Unused | Used |
|---|---|---|---|---|
| **1941** | A504 | 8f Neighbors (3-1) | .50 | .30 |
| **1942** | A504 | 20f Planting tree (3-2) | .75 | .40 |
| **1943** | A504 | 80f Dancing (3-3) | 1.50 | .90 |
| | | *Nos. 1941-1943 (3)* | 2.75 | 1.60 |

People's Republic, 35th Anniv. — A505

**China Post No. J.105.**

No. 1944, Engineer (5-1). No. 1945, Farm woman (5-2). No. 1946, Scientist (5-4). No. 1947, Soldier (5-5). No. 1948, Cranes (5-3).

**1984, Oct. 1** **Photo.** **Perf. *11½x11***

**Size: 26x35mm**

| No. | Type | Description | Unused | Used |
|---|---|---|---|---|
| **1944** | A505 | 8f multi | .40 | .30 |
| **1945** | A505 | 8f multi | .40 | .30 |
| **1946** | A505 | 8f multi | .40 | .30 |
| **1947** | A505 | 8f multi | .40 | .30 |

**Size: 36x48mm**

***Perf. 11***

| No. | Type | Description | Unused | Used |
|---|---|---|---|---|
| **1948** | A505 | 20f multi | 1.50 | 1.00 |
| | | *Nos. 1944-1948 (5)* | 3.10 | 2.20 |

110th Birth Anniv. of Chen Jiageng — A506

**China Post No. J.106.**

8f, Chen Jiageng (2-1). 80f, Jimei School (2-2).

**1984, Oct. 21** **Photo.** **Perf. *12½x12***

| No. | Type | Description | Unused | Used |
|---|---|---|---|---|
| **1949** | A506 | 8f multi | .65 | .25 |
| **1950** | A506 | 80f multi | 2.10 | .75 |

The Maiden's Study — A507

**China Post No. T.99.**

Scenes from The Peony Pavilion, by Tang Xianzu: No. 1952, In the dreamland (4-2). No. 1953, Du Liniang drawing self-portrait (4-3). No. 1954, Married to Liu Mengmai (4-4).
No. 1955, Playing in the garden.

**Photogravure & Engraved**

| **1984, Oct. 30** | | *Perf. 11* | |
|---|---|---|---|
| **1951** A507 8f shown (4-1) | | .75 | .40 |
| **1952** A507 8f multi | | .75 | .40 |
| **1953** A507 20f multi | | 1.60 | .80 |
| **1954** A507 70f multi | | 3.25 | 1.75 |
| | *Nos. 1951-1954 (4)* | 6.35 | 3.35 |

**Souvenir Sheet**

***Perf. 11½***

| | | |
|---|---|---|
| **1955** A507 $2 multi | *40.00* | *20.00* |

No. 1955 contains one 90x60mm stamp.

Emei Shan Mountain Scenery A508

**China Post No. T.100.**

No. 1956, Baoguo Temple (6-1). No. 1957, Leiyin Temple (6-2). No. 1958, Hongchun Lawn (6-3). No. 1959, Elephant bath (6-4). No. 1960, Woyun Temple (6-5). No. 1961, Shining Cloud Sea at Jinding (6-6).

| **1984, Nov. 16** | | *Perf. 11* | |
|---|---|---|---|
| **1956** A508 4f multi | | 1.00 | .50 |
| **1957** A508 8f multi | | .70 | .35 |
| **1958** A508 8f multi | | .40 | .40 |
| **1959** A508 10f multi | | .90 | .45 |
| **1960** A508 20f multi | | 1.75 | .90 |
| **1961** A508 80f multi | | 5.50 | 2.25 |
| | *Nos. 1956-1961 (6)* | 10.25 | 4.85 |

A509

**China Post No. J.101.**

Portraits: 8f, During the Long March (3-1). 10f, At 7th Natl. Party Congress (3-2). 20f, In motorcade (3-3).

| **1984, Dec. 15** **Photo.** | | *Perf. 11½x11* | |
|---|---|---|---|
| **1962** A509 8f multi | | .45 | .45 |
| **1963** A509 10f multi | | .55 | .50 |
| **1964** A509 20f multi | | .80 | .50 |
| | *Nos. 1962-1964 (3)* | 1.80 | 1.45 |

Former party secretary Ren Bishi (1904-50).

Flower Arrangement — A510

**China Post No. T.101.**

| **1984, Dec. 25** | *Perf. 11* | |
|---|---|---|
| **1965** A510 8f multi | 1.50 | .40 |

Chinese insurance industry.

New Year 1985 (Year of the Ox) — A511

**China Post No. T.102.**

**Photogravure & Engraved**

| **1985, Jan. 5** | *Perf. 11½* | |
|---|---|---|
| **1966** A511 8f multi | 1.50 | .50 |
| *a.* Bklt. pane of 4 + 8 plus label | 20.00 | 10.00 |
| Complete booklet, #1966a | 30.00 | |

Stamps from No. 1966a have straight edge at top or bottom.

Zunyi Meeting, 50th Anniv. A512

**China Post No. J.107.**

Paintings: 8f, The Zunyi Meeting, by Liu Xiangping. 20f, The Red Army Successfully Arrived in Northern Shaanxi, by Zhao Yu.

| **1985, Jan. 15** **Photo.** | *Perf. 11x11½* | |
|---|---|---|
| **1967** A512 8f multi (2-1) | 1.10 | .30 |
| **1968** A512 20f multi (2-2) | 1.90 | .70 |

A513

**China Post No. T.104.**

Lantern Folk Festival: No. 1969, Lotus of Good Luck. No. 1970, Auspicious dragon and phoenix. No. 1971, A hundred flowers blossoming. 70f, Prosperity and affluence.

| **1985, Feb. 28** | | *Perf. 11½* | |
|---|---|---|---|
| **1969** A513 8f multi (4-1) | | 1.05 | .40 |
| **1970** A513 8f multi (4-2) | | 1.05 | .40 |
| **1971** A513 8f multi (4-3) | | 1.05 | .40 |
| **1972** A513 70f multi (4-4) | | 3.25 | 1.05 |
| | *Nos. 1969-1972 (4)* | 6.40 | 2.25 |

A514

**China Post No. J.108.**

| **1985, Mar. 8** | | |
|---|---|---|
| **1973** A514 20f multicolored | 1.20 | .35 |

UN Decade for Women (1976-85).

Mei (Prunus mume) — A515

**China Post No. T.103.**

No. 1974, Green calyx (6-1). No. 1975, Pendant mei (6-2). No. 1976, Contorted dragon (6-3). No. 1977, Cinnabar (6-4). No. 1978, Versicolor mei (6-5). No. 1979, Apricot mei (6-6).

No. 1980, Duplicate and condensed fragrance mei.

| **1985, Apr. 5** | | *Perf. 11* | |
|---|---|---|---|
| **1974** A515 8f multi | | .90 | .35 |
| **1975** A515 8f multi | | .90 | .35 |
| **1976** A515 8f multi | | .90 | .35 |
| **1977** A515 10f multi | | 1.60 | .35 |
| **1978** A515 20f multi | | 2.50 | .75 |
| **1979** A515 80f multi | | 6.50 | 2.25 |
| | *Nos. 1974-1979 (6)* | 13.30 | 4.40 |

**Souvenir Sheet**

***Perf. 11½***

| | | |
|---|---|---|
| **1980** A515 $2 multi | *47.50* | *20.00* |

No. 1980 contains one 93x52mm stamp.

Huizo Guild Hall, Guangzhou — A516

**China Post No. J.109.**

| **1985, May 1** **Photo.** | *Perf. 11* | |
|---|---|---|
| **1981** A516 8f multi | 1.10 | .30 |

All-China Fed. of Trade Unions.

Intl. Youth Year — A517

**China Post No. J.110.**

| **1985, May 4** | **Photo.** | |
|---|---|---|
| **1982** A517 20f multicolored | 1.00 | .30 |

A518

**China Post No. T.106.**

Paintings of giant pandas: 8f, 20f, 50f, 80f, by Han Meilin; $3, by Wu Zuoren. T.106.

| **1985, May 24** | | *Perf. 11½* | |
|---|---|---|---|
| **1983** A518 8f multi (4-1), vert. | | 1.15 | .35 |
| **1984** A518 20f multi (4-2) | | 1.40 | .40 |
| **1985** A518 50f multi (4-3), vert. | | 1.40 | .50 |
| **1986** A518 80f multi (4-4) | | 3.75 | .70 |
| | *Nos. 1983-1986 (4)* | 7.70 | 1.95 |

**Souvenir Sheet**

***Perf. 11x11½***

| | | |
|---|---|---|
| **1987** A518 $3 multi, vert. | 7.50 | 3.00 |
| *a.* Ovptd. in sheet margin | 6.25 | |

No. 1987 contains one 39x59mm stamp.
No. 1987a ovptd. in sheet margin with panda hologram, PJZ-4 and horizontal Chinese inscription in gold. Issued 10/9/96.
No. 1987a was sold in a mount affixed to a small card.

Xian Xinghai (1905-1945), Composer — A519

**China Post No. J.111.**

Design: Bust, by Cao Chongen and music from The Yellow River Cantata.

| **1985, June 13** **Photo.** | *Perf. 11½x11* | |
|---|---|---|
| **1988** A519 8f multicolored | 1.00 | .35 |

Agnes Smedley, 1892-1950 (3-1) — A520

**China Post No. J.112.**

American journalists: 20f, Anna Louise Strong, 1885-1970 (3-2). 80f, Edgar Snow, 1905-1972 (3-3).

| **1985, June 25** | | | |
|---|---|---|---|
| **1989** A520 8f multicolored | | .40 | .30 |
| **1990** A520 20f multicolored | | .50 | .30 |
| **1991** A520 80f multicolored | | 1.05 | .60 |
| | *Nos. 1989-1991 (3)* | 1.95 | 1.20 |

Zheng He's West Seas Expedition, 580th Anniv. — A521

**China Post No. J.113.**

No. 1992, Portrait of the navigator. No. 1993, Peace envoy. 20f, Trade, cultural exchange. 80f, Honored for navigational feats.

| **1985, July 11** | | *Perf. 11½* | |
|---|---|---|---|
| **1992** A521 8f multi (4-1) | | .40 | .30 |
| **1993** A521 8f multi (4-2) | | .40 | .30 |
| **1994** A521 20f multi (4-3) | | .75 | .45 |
| **1995** A521 80f multi (4-4) | | 1.75 | .90 |
| | *Nos. 1992-1995 (4)* | 3.30 | 1.95 |

Self-portrait — A522

Xu Beihong, 1895-1953, Painter — A522a

**China Post No. J.114.**

| **1985, July 19** *Perf. 11½x11, 11x11½* | | |
|---|---|---|
| **1996** A522 8f multi (2-1) | .40 | .25 |
| **1997** A522a 20f multi (2-2) | .90 | .40 |

A523

**China Post No. J.115.**

Designs: 8f, Lin Zexu, 1785-1850, statesman, patriot. 80f, Burning opium at Humen, bas-relief.

| **1985, Aug. 30** | *Perf. 11* | |
|---|---|---|
| **1998** A523 8f multi (2-1) | .40 | .35 |

**Size: 51x22mm**

| | | |
|---|---|---|
| **1999** A523 80f multi (2-2) | 1.15 | .50 |

Lin Zexu's ban of the opium trade catalyzed the Anglo-Chinese Opium Wars.

A524

**China Post No. J.116.**

8f, Prosperity (3-1). 10f, Celebration (3-2). 20f, Abundant Harvest (3-3).

| **1985, Sept. 1** | | *Perf. 11½x11* | |
|---|---|---|---|
| **2000** A524 8f multi | | .55 | .30 |
| **2001** A524 10f multi | | .75 | .35 |
| **2002** A524 20f multi | | 1.40 | .40 |
| | *Nos. 2000-2002 (3)* | 2.70 | 1.05 |

Tibet Autonomous Region, 20th anniv.

End of World War II, 40th Anniv. — A525

**China Post No. J.117.**

Woodcuts by Wu Biduan: 8f, The Chinese Army Rose Against the Japanese Agressors at Logouqiao (2-1). 80f, The Eighth Route Army and Militia Fought Around the Great Wall (2-2).

**1985, Sept. 3** *Perf. 11*
**2003** A525 8f multi .50 .30
**2004** A525 80f multi .95 .55

2nd Natl. Worker's Games, Sept. 8-15, Beijing — A526

**China Post No. J.118.**

Competitors from various events and: 8f, Men's bicycling (2-1). 20f, Women hurdlers (2-2).

**1985, Sept. 8** *Perf. 11x11½*
**2005** A526 8f multi .50 .45
**2006** A526 20f multi .75 .60

Xinjiang Uygur Autonomous Region, 30th Anniv. — A527

**China Post No. J.119.**

8f, Oasis in the Gobi, woman (3-1). 10f, Oil field, Lake Tianchi (3-2). 20f, Tianshan pasture, woman (3-3).

**1985, Oct. 1** **Photo.** *Perf. 11½*
**2007** A527 8f multi .55 .30
**2008** A527 10f multi .65 .30
**2009** A527 20f multi .95 .35
*Nos. 2007-2009 (3)* 2.15 .95

Size of No. 2008, 60x30mm.

1st Natl. Youth Games, Oct. 6-15, Zhengzhou — A528

**China Post No. J.121.**

8f, Girls' track & field (2-1). 20f, Boys' basketball (2-2).

**1985, Oct. 6** *Perf. 11½x11*
**2010** A528 8f multi .50 .30
**2011** A528 20f multi .80 .40

Forbidden City Main Buildings — A529

**China Post No. J.120.**

**1985, Oct. 10** *Perf. 11½*
**2012** A529 8f multi (4-1) .35 .30
**2013** A529 8f multi (4-2) .35 .30
**2014** A529 20f multi (4-3) .35 .30
**2015** A529 80f multi (4-4) .70 .70
*a.* Vert. strip of 4, #2012-2015 2.75 2.75

Palace Museum, 60th anniv.

Zou Taofen (1895-1935), Journalist — A530

**China Post No. J.122.**

**1985, Nov. 5** *Perf. 11½x11*
**2016** A530 8f Portrait (2-1) .35 .35
**2017** A530 20f Epitaph by Zhou Enlai (2-2) .35 .35
*a.* Pair, #2016-2017 1.70 .90

December 9th Revolution, 50th Anniv. — A531

**China Post No. J.125.**

**1985, Dec. 9** *Perf. 11½*
**2018** A531 8f Memorial Pavilion 1.10 .30

New Year 1986 — A532

**China Post No. T.107.**

**Photogravure & Engraved**

**1986, Jan. 5** *Perf. 11½*
**2019** A532 8f multicolored 1.50 .50
*a.* Bklt. pane of 4 + 8 with label btwn 8.00
Complete booklet, #2019a 20.00

Natl. Space Industry — A533

**China Post No. T.108.**

4f, 1st experimental satellite. No. 2021, Recoverable satellite. No. 2022, Underwater rocket launch. 10f, Rocket launch. 20f, Earth satellite receiver. 70f, Satellite trajectory diagram.

**1986, Feb. 1** **Photo.**
**2020** A533 4f multi (6-1) .45 .35
**2021** A533 8f multi (6-2) .45 .35
**2022** A533 8f multi (6-3) .45 .35
**2023** A533 10f multi (6-4) .45 .40
**2024** A533 20f multi (6-5) 1.00 .40
**2025** A533 70f multi (6-6) 2.25 .80
*Nos. 2020-2025 (6)* 5.05 2.65

Dong Biwu (1886-1975), Party Founder — A534

**China Post No. J.123.**

**Photogravure and Engraved**

**1986, Mar. 5** *Perf. 11½x11*
**2026** A534 8f 1975 (2-1) .90 .30
**2027** A534 20f 1945 (2-2) 1.10 .65

Lin Boqu (1886-1960), Party Leader — A535

**China Post No. J.124.**

**1986, Mar. 20**
**2028** A535 8f shown (2-1) .75 .30
**2029** A535 20f Lin standing (2-2) 1.00 .50

Marshal He Long (1896-1969), Revolution Leader — A536

**China Post No. J.126.**

20f, On horseback (2-2).

**1986, Mar. 22** *Perf. 11x11½*
**2030** A536 8f shown (2-1) 1.10 .30
**2031** A536 20f multicolored 1.25 .45

Halley's Comet — A537

**China Post No. T.109.**

**1986, Apr. 11** **Photo.** *Perf. 11½*
**2032** A537 20f dk bl & gray 1.00 .30

White Crane — A538

**China Post No. T.110.**

8f, Two cranes (3-1). 10f, One flying (3-2), vert. 70f, Four cranes (3-3), vert.
$2, Flock.

**1986, May 22** *Perf. 11x11½, 11½x11*
**2033** A538 8f multi .60 .30
**2034** A538 10f multi .60 .30
**2035** A538 70f multi 1.60 .75
*Nos. 2033-2035 (3)* 2.80 1.35

**Souvenir Sheet**

**2036** A538 $2 multi *12.50 4.50*

No. 2036 contains one 116x25mm stamp.

Li Weihan (1896-1984), Party Leader — A539

**China Post No. J.127.**

**1986, June 2** *Perf. 11x11½*
**2037** A539 8f Portrait (2-1) .50 .30
**2038** A539 20f Writing (2-2) .65 .50

Intl. Peace Year — A540

**China Post No. J.128.**

**1986, June 16** *Perf. 11*
**2039** A540 8f multi 1.00 .30

Mao Dun (1896-1981), Writer — A541

**China Post No. J.129.**

**1986, July 4** *Perf. 11x11½*
**2040** A541 8f Portrait (2-1) .70 .30
**2041** A541 20f Portrait, diff. (2-2) .95 .50

Wang Jiaxiang (1906-1974), Party Leader — A542

**China Post No. J.130.**

**1986, Aug. 15**
**2042** A542 8f Portrait (2-1) .50 .30
**2043** A542 20f Portrait, diff. (2-2) .65 .50

Teacher's Day — A543

**China Post No. J.131.**

**1986, Sept. 10** *Perf. 11*
**2044** A543 8f multi 1.00 .30

Magnolia Liliflora — A544

**China Post No. T.111.**

No. 2045, Blossom (3-1). No. 2046, Two blossoms (3-2). No. 2047, Blossom, diff. (3-3). No. 2048, Three blossoms.

**1986, Sept. 23** *Perf. 11x11½*
**2045** A544 8f multi .45 .30
**2046** A544 8f multi .45 .30
**2047** A544 70f multi 2.60 1.60
*Nos. 2045-2047 (3)* 3.50 2.20

**Souvenir Sheet**

**2048** A544 $2 multi *13.50 8.00*

No. 2048 contains one 132x70mm stamp.

Inner Mongolia — A545

Tibet — A545a

Northeastern China — A545b

Hunan — A545c

So. Yangtze River — A545d

Beijing — A545e

Yunnan — A545f

Shanghai — A545g

Anhui — A545h

No. Shaanxi — A545i

Sichuan — A545j

Taiwan — A545k

Fujian — A545l

Zhejiang — A545m

**China Post No. R23**

Folk Houses.

***Perf. 13x13½, 11x11½, (1½f, 3f, #2057-2062)***

**1986, Apr. 1** **Photo.**

| | | | | |
|---|---|---|---|---|
| **2049** | A545 | 1f multi | .30 | .25 |
| **2050** | A545a | 1½f multi | .30 | .25 |
| **2051** | A545b | 2f multi | .30 | .25 |
| **2052** | A545c | 3f multi | .30 | .25 |
| **2053** | A545d | 4f multi | .30 | .25 |
| **2054** | A545e | 8f multi | .30 | .25 |
| **2055** | A545f | 10f multi | .30 | .25 |
| **2056** | A545g | 20f multi | .30 | .25 |
| **2057** | A545h | 30f multi | .30 | .25 |
| **2058** | A545i | 40f multi | .40 | .30 |
| **2059** | A545j | 50f multi | .60 | .40 |
| **2060** | A545k | 90f multi | .80 | .55 |
| **2061** | A545l | $1 multi | .85 | .65 |
| **2062** | A545m | $1.10 multi | .90 | .75 |
| | | *Nos. 2049-2062 (14)* | 6.25 | 4.90 |

Issue dates: 3f, Dec. 25; 4f, $1, Oct. 15; 20f, 50f, Sept. 10; 40f, Nov. 15; others, Apr. 1.

Postal forgeries of No. 2056 exist.

See Nos. 2198-2204.

**1989-90** **Photo.**

| | | | |
|---|---|---|---|
| *2055a* | Perf. 11x11½ ('89) | 1.00 | .65 |
| *2056a* | Perf. 11x11½ ('89) | 1.00 | .65 |
| *2057a* | Perf. 13x13½ ('90) | .50 | .35 |
| *2058a* | Perf. 13x13½ | 6.00 | *3.00* |
| *2059a* | Perf. 13x13½ ('89) | 1.00 | .60 |
| *2061a* | Perf. 13x13½ ('90) | 1.90 | 1.00 |
| | *Nos. 2055a-2061a (6)* | 11.40 | 6.25 |

Souvenir Sheet

All-China Philatelic Federation, 2nd Congress — A546

**China Post No. J.135.**

**1986, Oct. 17** **Litho.** ***Perf. 11½***

**2063** A546 $2 Jade lion *6.50 3.50*

Leaders of the 1911 Revolution A547

**China Post No. J.132.**

**1986, Oct. 10** **Photo.** ***Perf. 11x11½***

| | | | | |
|---|---|---|---|---|
| **2064** | A547 | 8f Sun Yat-sen (3-1) | 1.00 | .40 |
| **2065** | A547 | 10f Huang Xing (3-2) | 1.40 | .70 |
| **2066** | A547 | 40f Zhang Taiyan (3-3) | 3.00 | 1.50 |
| | | *Nos. 2064-2066 (3)* | 5.40 | 2.60 |

Souvenir Sheet

Sun Yat-sen (1866-1925) — A548

**China Post No. J.133.**

**1986, Nov. 12** ***Perf. 11½***

**2067** A548 $2 multicolored *12.50 6.00*

Marshal Zhu De (1886-1976) — A549

**China Post No. J.134.**

Designs: 20f, Orating.

**1986, Dec. 1** **Engr.** ***Perf. 11½x11***

| | | | | |
|---|---|---|---|---|
| **2068** | A549 | 8f sepia (2-1) | 1.75 | .35 |
| **2069** | A549 | 20f myrtle grn (2-2) | 3.25 | .50 |

Sports of Ancient China — A550

**China Post No. T.113.**

Stone carvings: No. 2070, Archery (4-1), vert. No. 2071, Weiqi (4-2). No. 2072, Golf (4-3). No. 2073, Soccer (4-4), vert.

***Perf. 11½x11, 11x11½***

**1986, Dec. 20** **Photo.**

| | | | | |
|---|---|---|---|---|
| **2070** | A550 | 8f multi | .50 | .30 |
| **2071** | A550 | 8f multicolored | .50 | .30 |
| **2072** | A550 | 10f multicolored | .75 | .40 |
| **2073** | A550 | 50f multicolored | 3.00 | 1.75 |
| | | *Nos. 2070-2073 (4)* | 4.75 | 2.75 |

A551

**China Post No. T.112.**

**Photogravure & Engraved**

**1987, Jan. 5** ***Perf. 11½***

| | | | | |
|---|---|---|---|---|
| **2074** | A551 | 8f blk, dk pink & yel grn | 1.20 | .40 |
| *a.* | | Bklt. pane of 4 + 8 + label | *10.50* | — |
| | | Complete booklet, #2074a | 19.50 | |

New Year 1987 (Year of the Hare).

A552

**China Post No. J.136.**

8f, Traveling (3-1). 20f, Cave writing (3-2). 40f, Mountain climbing (3-3).

**1987, Feb. 20** **Photo.** ***Perf. 11½***

| | | | | |
|---|---|---|---|---|
| **2075** | A552 | 8f multi | .65 | .30 |
| **2076** | A552 | 20f multi | 2.10 | 1.25 |
| **2077** | A552 | 40f multi | 3.75 | 2.25 |
| | | *Nos. 2075-2077 (3)* | 6.50 | 3.80 |

Xu Xiake (1587-1621), Ming Dynasty geographer.

Birds of Prey A553

**China Post No. T.114.**

No. 2078, Kite (4-1). No. 2079, Sea eagle (4-2), vert. No. 2080, Vulture (4-3), vert. No. 2081, Buzzard (4-4).

**1987, Mar. 20**

| | | | | |
|---|---|---|---|---|
| **2078** | A553 | 8f multi | .60 | .30 |
| **2079** | A553 | 8f multi | .60 | .30 |
| **2080** | A553 | 10f multi | .95 | .30 |
| **2081** | A553 | 90f multi | 5.75 | 1.25 |
| | | *Nos. 2078-2081 (4)* | 7.90 | 2.15 |

Liao Zhongkai (1877-1925), National Party Leader — A554

**China Post No. J.137.**

20f, Liao, He Xiangning (2-2).

**1987, Apr. 23** ***Perf. 11½x11***

| | | | | |
|---|---|---|---|---|
| **2082** | A554 | 8f shown (2-1) | .75 | .30 |
| **2083** | A554 | 20f multi | 1.30 | .35 |

Kites — A555

**China Post No. T.115.**

No. 2084, Hawk (4-1). No. 2085, Dragon (4-2). No. 2086, Symbolic octagon (4-3). No. 2087, Phoenix (4-4).

**1987, Apr. 1**

| | | | | |
|---|---|---|---|---|
| **2084** | A555 | 8f multi | .75 | .35 |
| **2085** | A555 | 8f multi | .75 | .35 |
| *a.* | | Pair, #2084-2085 | 2.75 | 2.25 |
| **2086** | A555 | 30f multi | 2.00 | .95 |
| **2087** | A555 | 30f multi | 2.00 | .95 |
| *a.* | | Pair, #2086-2087 | 5.25 | 4.00 |
| | | *Nos. 2084-2087 (4)* | 5.50 | 2.60 |

Nos. 2085a, 2087a have continuous designs.

A556

**China Post No. J.138.**

Portraits of Ye Jianying (1897-1986), central committee vice chairman.

**1987, Apr. 28**

| | | | | |
|---|---|---|---|---|
| **2088** | A556 | 8f multi (3-3) | .85 | .30 |
| **2089** | A556 | 10f multi (3-2) | 1.25 | .40 |
| **2090** | A556 | 30f multi (3-1) | 4.50 | 1.50 |
| | | *Nos. 2088-2090 (3)* | 6.60 | 2.20 |

Caves of the Thousand Buddhas, Dunhuang, Gansu Province A557

**China Post No. T.116.**

Wall Paintings: 8f, Worshipping Bodhisattvas, Northern Liang Dynasty. 10f, Deer King Jatka, Northern Wei Dynasty. 20f, Heavenly Musicians, Northern Wei Dynasty. 40f, Flying Devata, Northern Wei Dynasty. $2, Mahasattva Jataka.

**1987, May 20** ***Perf. 11½***

| | | | | |
|---|---|---|---|---|
| **2091** | A557 | 8f multi (4-1) | .60 | .30 |
| **2092** | A557 | 10f multi (4-2) | .75 | .30 |
| **2093** | A557 | 20f multi (4-3) | 1.90 | .75 |
| **2094** | A557 | 40f multi (4-4) | 3.25 | 1.25 |
| | | *Nos. 2091-2094 (4)* | 6.50 | 2.60 |

**Souvenir Sheet**

**2095** A557 $2 multi *25.00 15.00*

No. 2095 contains one 92x73mm stamp.

See Nos. 2149-2152, 2283-2286, 2407-2411, 2505-2508, 2704-2707.

Children's Day Festival — A558

**China Post No. T.117.**

Children's drawings: No. 2096, Happy Holiday, by Yan Qinghui, age 7. No. 2097, Peace and Happiness, by Liu Yuan, age 7.

**1987, June 1** ***Perf. 12½x12***

| | | | | |
|---|---|---|---|---|
| **2096** | A558 | 8f shown (2-1) | .65 | .25 |
| **2097** | A558 | 8f multi, vert. (2-2) | .85 | .45 |

Rural Development — A559

**China Post No. T.118.**

No. 2098, Village, southeast China (4-1). No. 2099, Market, horiz. (4-2). No. 2100, Dairy industry, horiz. (4-3). No. 2101, Theater, horiz. (4-4).

**1987, June 25** ***Perf. 11½***

| | | | | |
|---|---|---|---|---|
| **2098** | A559 | 8f multi | .55 | .45 |
| **2099** | A559 | 8f multi | .55 | .45 |
| **2100** | A559 | 10f multi | .75 | .60 |
| **2101** | A559 | 20f multi | 1.50 | 1.25 |
| | | *Nos. 2098-2101 (4)* | 3.35 | 2.75 |

Postal Savings Bank Inauguration — A560

**China Post No. T.119.**

**1987, July 1**

**2102** A560 8f multicolored 1.30 .30

Esperanto Language Movement, Cent. — A561

**China Post No. J.139.**

**1987, July 26**

**2103** A561 8f lt olive grn, blk & brt blue 1.15 .30

People's Liberation Army, 60th Anniv. — A562

**China Post No. J.140.**

No. 2104, Flag, Great Wall (4-1). No. 2105, Rocket launch, soldier, village (4-2). No. 2106, Submarine, sailor (4-3). No. 2107, Aircraft, pilot (4-4).

**1987, Aug. 1** ***Perf. 11***

| | | | | |
|---|---|---|---|---|
| **2104** | A562 | 8f multi | .55 | .30 |
| **2105** | A562 | 8f multi | .55 | .30 |
| **2106** | A562 | 10f multi | 1.30 | .35 |
| **2107** | A562 | 30f multi | 1.80 | .60 |
| | | *Nos. 2104-2107 (4)* | 4.20 | 1.55 |

Intl. Year of Shelter for the Homeless A563

**China Post No. J.141.**

**1987, Aug. 20** ***Perf. 11***

**2108** A563 8f gray, dk car rose & blk 1.00 .30

Chinese Art Festival, Sept. 5-25, Beijing — A564

**China Post No. J.142.**

**1987, Sept. 5** ***Perf. 11***

**2109** A564 8f brt red, gold & blk 1.90 .40

Fairy Tales — A565

**China Post No. T.120.**

4f, Pan Gu inventing the universe. No. 2111, Nu Wa creating man. No. 2112, Yi shooting nine suns. 10f, Chang'e flying to the moon. 20f, Kua Fu pursuing the sun. 90f, Jing Wei filling the sea.

**1987, Sept. 25** ***Perf. 11½***

**2110** A565 4f multi (6-1) .55 .30
**2111** A565 8f multi (6-2) .65 .30
**2112** A565 8f multi (6-3) .65 .30
**2113** A565 10f multi (6-4) .80 .30
**2114** A565 20f multi (6-5) 1.10 .50
**2115** A565 90f multi (6-6) 2.50 1.50
*Nos. 2110-2115 (6)* 6.25 3.20

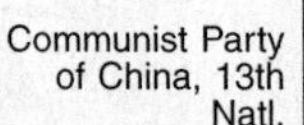

Communist Party of China, 13th Natl. Congress — A566

**China Post No. J.143.**

**1987, Oct. 25** ***Perf. 11***

**2116** A566 8f multicolored 1.60 .40

Yellow Crane Tower — A567

**China Post No. T.121.**

No. 2118, Yue Yang Tower (4-2). No. 2119, Teng Wang Pavilion (4-3). No. 2120, Peng Lai Pavilion (4-4).

**1987, Oct. 30**

**2117** A567 8f shown (4-1) .45 .25
**2118** A567 8f multi .45 .25
**2119** A567 10f multi .60 .35
**2120** A567 90f multi 3.50 2.40
*a.* Min. sheet of 4, #2117-2120 *17.50 9.00*
*Nos. 2117-2120 (4)* 5.00 3.25

No. 2120a sold for $1.50.

6th Natl. Games — A568

**China Post No. J.144.**

No. 2121, Pole vault (4-1). No. 2122, Softball (4-2). No. 2123, Weight lifting (4-3). No. 2124, Diving (4-4).

**1987, Nov. 20** ***Perf. 11½x11***

**2121** A568 8f multi .35 .25
**2122** A568 8f multi .35 .25
**2123** A568 30f multi .60 .35
**2124** A568 50f multi 1.00 .55
*Nos. 2121-2124 (4)* 2.30 1.40

Souvenir Sheet

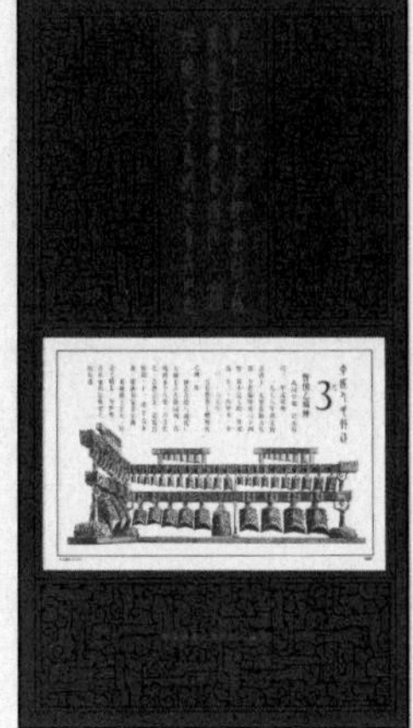

Bronze Bells from the Tomb of Marquis Yi of the Zeng State (c. 433 B.C.), Hubei Province A569

**China Post No. T.122.**

**1987, Dec. 10** **Litho.** ***Imperf.***

**2125** A569 $3 multicolored *9.50 4.50*

Classic Literature A570

**China Post No. T.123.**

Outlaws of the Marsh: 8f, Shi Jin practicing martial arts. 10f, Sagacious Lu, the "Tattooed Monk," uprooting a willow tree. 30f, Lin Chong seeking shelter from snow storm at the Mountain Spirit Temple. 50f, Song Jiang helps Ward Chief Chao Gai flee. $2, Outlaws of the Marsh capture treasures.

**1987, Dec. 20** **Photo.** ***Perf. 11***

**2126** A570 8f multi (4-1) .40 .25
**2127** A570 10f multi (4-2) .50 .25
**2128** A570 30f multi (4-3) 1.60 .60
**2129** A570 50f multi (4-4) 2.50 1.25
*Nos. 2126-2129 (4)* 5.00 2.35

**Souvenir Sheet**

***Perf. 11½x11***

**2130** A570 $2 multi *32.00 16.00*

No. 2130 contains one 90x60mm stamp.
See Nos. 2216-2219, 2373-2377, 2449-2452, 2822-2826, 2889-2893.

New Year 1988 (Year of the Dragon) — A571

**China Post No. T.124.**

**Photo. & Engr.**

**1988, Jan. 5** ***Perf. 11½***

**2131** A571 8f multicolored *3.00* .45
*a.* Bklt. pane of 4 + 8 with label between *20.00* —
Complete booklet, #2131a *32.50*

Cai Yuanpei (1868-1940), Education Reformer — A572

**China Post No. J.145.**

**1988, Jan. 11** **Photo.** ***Perf. 11½x11***

**2132** A572 8f shown (2-1) .60 .25
**2133** A572 20f Seated (2-2) .90 .50

Tao Zhu (1908-1969), Party Leader — A573

**China Post No. J.146.**

**1988, Jan. 16** ***Perf. 11x11½***

**2134** A573 8f shown (2-1) .80 .30
**2135** A573 20f Tao, diff. (2-2) 1.05 .50

Folklore — A574

**China Post No. T.125.**

**1988, Feb. 10**

**2136** A574 8f shown (4-1) .45 .25
**2137** A574 10f multi, diff. (4-2) .60 .25
**2138** A574 20f multi, diff. (4-3) .75 .40
**2139** A574 30f multi, diff. (4-4) 1.50 .70
*Nos. 2136-2139 (4)* 3.30 1.60

A575

**China Post No. J.147.**

**1988, Mar. 25** **Photo.** ***Perf. 11½***

**2140** A575 8f multicolored 1.00 .30

7th Natl. People's Congress.

A576

**China Post No. J.148.**

8f, Wuzhi Mountain (4-1). 10f, Wanquan River (4-2). 30f, "End of the Earth" (4-3). $1.10, "Deer Turning Its Head" (4-4).

**1988, Apr. 20** **Photo.** ***Perf. 11½***

**2141** A576 8f multi .35 .25
**2142** A576 10f multi .45 .25
**2143** A576 30f multi .65 .30
**2144** A576 $1.10 multi .85 .50
*Nos. 2141-2144 (4)* 2.30 1.30

Establishment of Hainan Province.

Modern Scientists — A577

**China Post No. J.149.**

Designs: 8f, Li Siguang, geologist. 10f, Zhu Kezhen, meteorologist and geographer. 20f, Wu Youxun, physicist. 30f, Hua Luogeng, mathematician.

**1988, Apr. 28** ***Perf. 11x11½***

**2145** A577 8f multi (4-1) .45 .25
**2146** A577 10f multi (4-2) .55 .25
**2147** A577 20f multi (4-3) .70 .30
**2148** A577 30f multi (4-4) 1.20 .60
*Nos. 2145-2148 (4)* 2.90 1.40

**Wall Paintings Type of 1987**

**China Post No. T.126.**

Caves of the Thousand Buddhas, Dunhuang, Gansu Province: No. 2149, Hunting, Western Wei Dynasty. No. 2150, Fishing, Western Wei Dynasty. 10f, Farming, Northern Zhou Dynasty. 90f, Building a Pagoda, Northern Zhou Dynasty.

**1988, May 25** ***Perf. 11½x11***

**2149** A557 8f multi (4-1) .50 .25
**2150** A557 8f multi (4-2) .50 .25
**2151** A557 10f multi (4-3) .65 .30
**2152** A557 90f multi (4-4) 2.10 .75
*Nos. 2149-2152 (4)* 3.75 1.55

Environmental Protection — A578

**China Post No. T.127.**

No. 2153, Soil (4-1). No. 2154, Air (4-2). No. 2155, Water (4-3). No. 2156, Prevent noise pollution (4-4).

**1988, June 5** **Photo.** ***Perf. 11***

**2153** 8f multi .40 .30
**2154** 8f multi .40 .30
**2155** 8f multi .40 .30
**2156** 8f multi .40 .30
*a.* A578 Block of 4, #2153-2156 2.50 1.75

Souvenir Sheet

China Nos. 1-3 A579

**China Post No. J.150.**

**Photo. & Engr.**

**1988, July 2** ***Perf. 13***

**2157** A579 $3 multicolored *9.00 6.00*

Postage stamps of China, 110th anniv.

11th Asian Games (in 1990), Beijing — A580

**China Post No. J.151.**

8f, Emblem (2-1). 30f, Character trademark (2-2).

**1988, July 20** **Photo.** ***Perf. 11x11½***

**2158** A580 8f multi .30 .25
**2159** A580 30f multi .70 .45

See No. 2300a.

Signing of the Sino-Japanese Peace Treaty, 10th Anniv. — A581

**China Post No. J.152.**

**1988, Aug. 12** **Photo.** ***Perf. 11***

**2160** A581 8f Peony (2-1) .30 .25
**2161** A581 $1.60 Sakura (2-2) .85 .50
*a.* Pair, #2160-2161 2.00 1.50

Achievements in Construction A582

**China Post No. T.128.**

Designs: 8f, Coal-loading wharf, Ch'in-huang-tao Port. 10f, Ethylene refinery, Qilu. 20f, Pao-shan steel plant, Shanghai. 30f, Central Television Broadcasting Station.

**1988, Sept. 2 Photo. *Perf. 11***

**2162** A582 8f multi (4-1) .50 .25
**2163** A582 10f multi (4-2) .70 .30
**2164** A582 20f multi (4-3) .85 .30
**2165** A582 30f multi (4-4) .95 .40
*Nos. 2162-2165 (4)* 3.00 1.25

See Nos. 2221-2224, 2279-2282, 2354-2357.

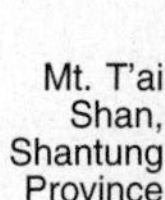

Mt. T'ai Shan, Shantung Province A583

**China Post No. T.130.**

8f, T'ai Shan Temple (4-1). 10f, Ladder to Heaven (4-2). 20f, Daguang peak (4-3). 90f, Sun-watching peak (4-4).

**1988, Sept. 14 Photo. & Engr.**

**2166** A583 8f multi .35 .25
**2167** A583 10f multi .40 .35
**2168** A583 20f multi .75 .40
**2169** A583 90f multi 3.00 1.25
*Nos. 2166-2169 (4)* 4.50 2.25

Liao Chengzhi (1908-1983), Party Leader — A584

**China Post No. J.153.**

**1988, Sept. 25 Photo. *Perf. 11½x11***

**2170** A584 8f shown (2-1) .40 .25
**2171** A584 20f Writing (2-2) .75 .45

Marshal Peng Dehuai (1898-1974), Party Leader — A585

**China Post No. J.155.**

20f, Peng in uniform (2-2).

**1988, Oct. 24 Photo. *Perf. 11x11½***

**2172** A585 8f shown (2-1) .50 .25
**2173** A585 20f multi 1.35 .60

1st Natl. Farmers' Games — A586

**China Post No. J.154.**

**1988, Oct. 9 Photo. *Perf. 11½***

**2174** A586 8f Cycling (2-1) .35 .25
**2175** A586 20f Javelin (2-2) .65 .40

Literary Masterpieces — A587

**China Post No. T.131.**

*The Romance of the Three Kingdoms,* by Luo Guanzhong, 14th cent.: No. 2176, Three heroes' sworn brotherhood (4-1). No. 2177, Battle between Lu Bu and the heroes, vert. (4-2). No. 2178, Struggle between man and woman at Fengyi Pavilion (4-3). No. 2179, Two noblemen, vert. (4-4). No. 2180, Guan Yu's battle through five passes.

***Perf. 11½x11, 11x11½***

**1988, Nov. 25 Photo.**

**2176** A587 8f multicolored .55 .25
**2177** A587 8f multicolored .55 .35
**2178** A587 30f multicolored 1.40 .70
**2179** A587 50f multicolored 1.80 1.20
*Nos. 2176-2179 (4)* 4.30 2.50

**Souvenir Sheet**

***Perf. 11***

**2180** A587 $3 multicolored *27.50 16.00*

See Nos. 2310-2313, 2403-2406, 2539-2543.

Intl Volunteers' Day — A588

**China Post No. J.156.**

**1988, Dec. 5 Photo. *Perf. 11***

**2181** A588 20f multicolored 1.00 .30

A589

**China Post No. T.132.**

Milu, *Elaphurus davidianus*

**1988, Dec. 20 Photo. *Perf. 11½x11***

**2182** A589 8f Buck (2-1) .70 .25
**2183** A589 40f Herd (2-2) 1.80 3.00

Exist imperf. Value, pairs each $7.50.

Orchids A590

**China Post No. T.129.**

8f, Da yi pin (4-1). 10f, Dragon (4-2). 20f, Large phoenix tail (4-3). 50f, Silver-edged black (4-4).
Red lotus petal.

**1988, Dec. 25 *Perf. 12***

**2184** A590 8f multi .70 .30
**2185** A590 10f multi .85 .35
**2186** A590 20f multi 1.10 .45
**2187** A590 50f multi 1.40 .75
*a.* Strip of 4, #2184-2187 6.25 3.75
*Nos. 2184-2187 (4)* 4.05 1.85

**Souvenir Sheet**

***Perf. 11½x11***

**2188** A590 $2 multi *16.00 8.00*

No. 2188 contains one 55x37mm stamp.

A591

**China Post No. R24**

Grotto Statuary: $2, Buddha. $5, Warrior, Longmen Grotto, Henan. $10, Goddess. $20, Woman and birds.

**Photo & Engr.**

**1988-89 *Perf. 11½x11***

**2189** A591 $2 buff & reddish blk 2.25 .30
**2190** A591 $5 buff & grnh blk 3.00 .65
**2191** A591 $10 buff & brn blk 6.95 1.25
*a.* Souv. sheet of 1, buff & sep *25.00* 20.00
**2192** A591 $20 buff & indigo 16.50 2.50
*Nos. 2189-2192 (4)* 28.70 4.70

Issued: $2, 11/30; $5, 8/10; $10, 10/15; $20, 10/20.

No. 2191a released on Oct. 12, 1989, for the China Natl. Philatelic Exhibition and the 40th anniv. of the People's Republic.

Nos. 2189-2192, 2191a are almost always found with small ink spots on the stamps. Values are for stamps in this condition.

A592

**China Post No. T.133.**

**Photo. & Engr.**

**1989, Jan. 5 *Perf. 11½***

**2193** A592 8f multicolored 1.25 .30
*a.* Bklt. pane of 4+8 with label between *10.00* —
Complete booklet, #2193a *15.00*

New Year 1989 (Year of the Snake).

Stamps from No. 2193a have one or two straight edges and sell for less as singles than No. 2193.

Qu Qiubai (1899-1935), Party Leader (J.157) — A593

**China Post No. J.157.**

**1989, Jan. 29 Photo. *Perf. 11x11½***

**2194** A593 8f multi (2-1) .55 .30
**2195** A593 20f multi, diff. (2-2) .90 .45

Brown-eared Pheasant, *Crossoptilon mantchuricum* (T.134) — A594

**China Post No. T.134.**

**1989, Feb. 21 *Perf. 11½***

**2196** A594 8f multi (2-1) .80 .25
**2197** A594 50f multi, diff. (2-2) 1.40 .40

Shandong — A594a

Guangxi — A594b

Ningxia — A594c

Shanxi — A594d

Qinghai — A594e

Guizhou — A594f

Jiangxi — A594g

**China Post Nos. R25-R27**

**1989-91 Photo. *Perf. 13x13½***

**2198** A594a 5f multicolored .30 .25
**2199** A594b 15f blk, gray & brt grn .30 .25
**2200** A594c 25f blk, gray & rose .30 .25
**2201** A594d 80f blk, gray & pale bl .60 .25
**2202** A594e $1.30 blk, gray & brn red .60 .35
**2203** A594f $1.60 blk, gray & pale ultra .75 .35
**2204** A594g $2 multicolored 1.00 .35
*Nos. 2198-2204 (7)* 3.85 2.05

Issued: 5f, 6/10/91; 15f, 11/25/90; 25f, 11/10/90; 80f, 9/20/90; $1.30, $1.60, 3/10/89; $2, 4/25/91.

China Post Nos.: R25, $1.30, and $1.60; R26, 15f, 25f, and 80f; R27, 5f, and $2.00.

Silk Painting Excavated from Han Tomb No. 1 at Mawangdui, Changsha A595

**China Post No. T.135.**

8f, In the Heavens (3-1). 20f, On the Earth, vert. (3-2). 30f, In the Netherworld, vert. (3-3). $5, Entire painting.

**1989, Mar. 25 Photo. *Perf. 11x11½***

**2208** A595 8f multi .50 .25
*a.* Perf. 11½ 5.50 5.50

***Perf. 11½x11***

**2209** A595 20f multi .50 .25
*a.* Perf. 11½ 5.50 5.50
**2210** A595 30f multi .50 .25
*a.* Perf. 11½ 5.50 5.50
*Nos. 2208-2210 (3)* 1.50 .75

**Textured Paper, Without Gum**

**Size: 90x165mm**

***Imperf***

**2211** A595 $5 multi *4.50 4.00*

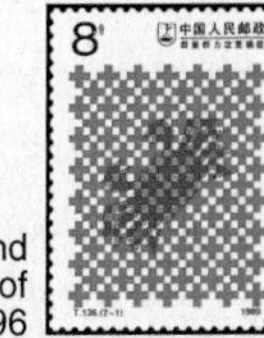

Prevention and Resistance of Cancer — A596

**China Post No. T.136.**

20f, Woman's thermogram (2-2).

**1989, Apr. 7 Litho. *Perf. 12***

**2212** A596 8f shown (2-1) .35 .25
**2213** A596 20f multicolored .65 .30

May Fourth Movement, 70th Anniv. — A597

**China Post No. J.158.**

**1989, May 4 Photo. *Perf. 11***

**2214** A597 8f Bas-relief .90 .30

Interparliamentary Union, Cent. — A598

**China Post No. J.159.**

**1989, June 29 Photo. *Perf. 11x11½***

**2215** A598 20f multi .90 .30

**Literature Type of 1987**

**China Post No. T.138.**

Outlaws of the Marsh: 8f, Wu Song slaying a tiger on Jingyang Ridge. 10f, Qin Ming dodging arrows. 20f, Hua Rong shooting a wild goose on Mt. Liangshan. $1.30, Li Kui fighting Zhang Shun from a junk.

**1989, July 25 Photo. *Perf. 11***

**2216** A570 8f multi (4-1) .35 .25
**2217** A570 10f multi (4-2) .35 .25
**2218** A570 20f multi (4-3) .50 .35
**2219** A570 $1.30 multi (4-4) .95 .50
*Nos. 2216-2219 (4)* 2.15 1.35

Asia-Pacific Telecommunity, 10th Anniv. — A599

**China Post No. J.160.**

**1989, Aug. 4 Litho. *Perf. 12***

**2220** A599 8f multi .80 .25

**Type of 1988**

**China Post No. T.139.**

Achievements in Engineering and Construction: 8f, Beijing Intl. Telecommunications Building, vert. 10f, Xi Qu Coal Mine, Gu Jiao,

Shanxi Province. 20f, Long Yang Gorge Hydroelectric Power Station, Qinghai Province. 30f, Da Yao Shan Tunnel of the Guangzhou-Heng Yang Railway.

**1989, Aug. 10 Photo. *Perf. 11***

| | | | | |
|---|---|---|---|---|
| **2221** | A582 | 8f multi (4-1) | .35 | .25 |
| **2222** | A582 | 10f multi (4-2) | .35 | .25 |
| **2223** | A582 | 20f multi (4-3) | .35 | .30 |
| **2224** | A582 | 30f multi (4-4) | .40 | .30 |
| | | *Nos. 2221-2224 (4)* | 1.45 | 1.10 |

Mt. Huashan A601

**China Post No. T.140.**

Designs: 8f, Five prominent peaks. 10f, View from atop Huashan. 20f, 1000-foot precipice. 90f, Blue Dragon Ridge.

**1989, Aug. 25 Photo. & Engr.**

| | | | | |
|---|---|---|---|---|
| **2225** | A601 | 8f multi (4-1) | .35 | .25 |
| **2226** | A601 | 10f multi (4-2) | .45 | .25 |
| **2227** | A601 | 20f multi (4-3) | .50 | .35 |
| **2228** | A601 | 90f multi (4-4) | 1.10 | .55 |
| | | *Nos. 2225-2228 (4)* | 2.40 | 1.40 |

Modern Art — A602

**China Post No. T.141.**

Paintings: 8f, *The Fable of the White Snake,* by Ye Qianyu. 20f, *Li River in Fine Rain,* by Li Keran. 50f, *Marching Together,* by Wu Zuoren.

**1989, Sept. 1 Photo.**

| | | | | |
|---|---|---|---|---|
| **2229** | A602 | 8f multi (3-1) | .50 | .25 |
| **2230** | A602 | 20f multi (3-2) | .60 | .25 |
| **2231** | A602 | 50f multi (3-3) | 1.10 | .40 |
| | | *Nos. 2229-2231 (3)* | 2.20 | .90 |

People's Political Conference — A603

**China Post No. J.161.**

**1989, Sept. 21 *Perf. 12***

| | | | | |
|---|---|---|---|---|
| **2232** | A603 | 8f No. 2 | 1.25 | .30 |

A604

Confucius (551-479 B.C.) — A605

**China Post No. J.162.**

Designs: 8f, The lecture in the Apricot Temple, Qufu. $1.60, Confucius riding in an ox cart.

**1989, Sept. 28 Photo. *Perf. 11***

| | | | | |
|---|---|---|---|---|
| **2233** | A604 | 8f shown (2-1) | .50 | .30 |
| **2234** | A604 | $1.60 multi (2-2) | 1.50 | .90 |

**Souvenir Sheet Without Gum**

**Litho. *Imperf.***

| | | | | |
|---|---|---|---|---|
| **2235** | A605 | $3 multicolored | *5.75* | *3.25* |

A606

Gate of Heavenly Peace A607

**China Post No. J.163.**

**1989, Oct. 1 Photo. *Perf. 11x11½***

| | | | | |
|---|---|---|---|---|
| **2236** | A606 | 8f shown (4-1) | .30 | .25 |
| **2237** | A606 | 10f Flowers (4-2) | .30 | .25 |
| **2238** | A606 | 20f Five stars (4-3) | .35 | .25 |
| **2239** | A606 | 40f Construction (4-4) | .55 | .25 |
| | | *Nos. 2236-2239 (4)* | 1.50 | 1.00 |

**Souvenir Sheet Without Gum**

**Litho. *Imperf.***

| | | | | |
|---|---|---|---|---|
| **2240** | A607 | $3 shown | 4.50 | 3.00 |

PRC, 40th anniv.

Photography, Sesquicentennial A608

**China Post No. T.142.**

**1989, Oct. 15 Photo. *Perf. 11***

| | | | | |
|---|---|---|---|---|
| **2241** | A608 | 8f multicolored | .75 | .30 |

Li Dazhao (1889-1927), Party Leader — A609

**China Post No. J.164.**

**1989, Oct. 29 Photo. *Perf. 11x11¼***

| | | | | |
|---|---|---|---|---|
| **2242** | A609 | 8f Li, soldiers (2-1) | .75 | .30 |
| *a.* | | Perf. 11½x11¼ | 6.00 | 6.00 |
| **2243** | A609 | 20f Li, text (2-2) | 1.25 | .30 |
| *a.* | | Perf. 11½x11¼ | 6.00 | 6.00 |

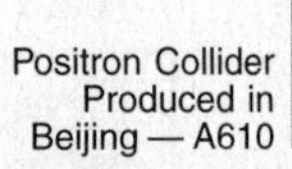

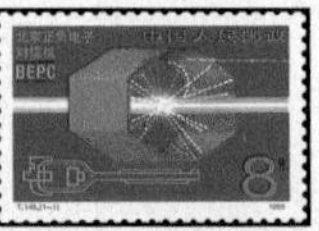

Positron Collider Produced in Beijing — A610

**China Post No. T.145.**

**1989, Nov. 1 *Perf. 11***

| | | | | |
|---|---|---|---|---|
| **2244** | A610 | 8f multicolored | .90 | .60 |

Rocket Defense — A611

**China Post No. T.143.**

Designs: 4f, Transporting 3 rockets. 8f, Disassembled rocket on transport. 10f, Launch, vert. 20f, Stage separation in space.

**1989, Nov. 15 Litho. *Perf. 12***

| | | | | |
|---|---|---|---|---|
| **2245** | A611 | 4f multicolored (4-1) | .35 | .25 |
| **2246** | A611 | 8f multicolored (4-2) | .50 | .25 |
| **2247** | A611 | 10f multicolored (4-3) | .60 | .30 |
| **2248** | A611 | 20f multicolored (4-4) | .80 | .40 |
| | | *Nos. 2245-2248 (4)* | 2.25 | 1.20 |

A612

Views of West Lake A613

**China Post No. T.144.**

**1989, Nov. 25 Photo. *Perf. 11x11½***

| | | | | |
|---|---|---|---|---|
| **2249** | A612 | 8f multi (4-1) | .45 | .25 |
| **2250** | A612 | 10f multi, diff. (4-2) | .60 | .30 |
| **2251** | A612 | 30f multi, diff. (4-3) | .75 | .35 |
| **2252** | A612 | 40f multi, diff. (4-4) | .95 | .40 |
| | | *Nos. 2249-2252 (4)* | 2.75 | 1.30 |

**Souvenir Sheet**

***Perf. 11½x11***

| | | | | |
|---|---|---|---|---|
| **2253** | A613 | $5 multicolored | 7.50 | 3.50 |

11th Asian Games — A614

**China Post No. J.165.**

Various stadiums.

**1989, Dec. 15 *Perf. 11x11½***

| | | | | |
|---|---|---|---|---|
| **2254** | A614 | 8f multi (4-1) | .30 | .25 |
| **2255** | A614 | 10f multi (4-2) | .30 | .25 |
| **2256** | A614 | 30f multi (4-3) | .30 | .25 |
| **2257** | A614 | $1.60 multi (4-4) | .55 | .40 |
| | | *Nos. 2254-2257 (4)* | 1.45 | 1.15 |

See Nos. 2295-2300.

A615

**China Post No. T.146.**

**Photo & Engr.**

**1990, Jan. 5 *Perf. 11½***

| | | | | |
|---|---|---|---|---|
| **2258** | A615 | 8f multicolored | 1.75 | .30 |
| *a.* | | Bklt. pane of 12 + 4 labels | *18.00* | *21.00* |
| | | Complete booklet, #2258a | 25.00 | |
| *b.* | | As. No. 2258, perf. 11½x11 | 16.00 | 16.00 |

New Year 1990 (Year of the Horse).

Stamps from No. 2258a have straight edges at top or bottom and sell for less as singles than No. 2258.

Narcissus — A616

**China Post No. T.147.**

**1990, Feb. 10 Photo. *Perf. 11x11½***

| | | | | |
|---|---|---|---|---|
| **2259** | A616 | 8f multi (4-1) | .35 | .25 |
| **2260** | A616 | 20f multi, diff. (4-2) | .45 | .30 |
| **2261** | A616 | 30f multi, diff. (4-3) | .65 | .30 |
| **2262** | A616 | $1.60 multi, diff. (4-4) | .80 | .40 |
| | | *Nos. 2259-2262 (4)* | 2.25 | 1.25 |

Norman Bethune (1890-1939), Surgeon — A617

**China Post No. J.166.**

**Litho. & Engr.**

**1990, Mar. 3 *Perf. 11x11½***

| | | | | |
|---|---|---|---|---|
| **2263** | A617 | 8f In Canada (2-2) | .30 | .25 |
| **2264** | A617 | $1.60 In China (2-1) | .60 | .50 |
| *a.* | | Pair, #2263-2264 | 1.60 | 1.25 |

See Canada Nos. 1264-1265.

Intl. Women's Day — A618

**China Post No. J.167.**

**1990, Mar. 8 Photo. *Perf. 11½x11***

| | | | | |
|---|---|---|---|---|
| **2265** | A618 | 20f multicolored | 1.10 | .30 |

Afforestation A619

**China Post No. T.148.**

8f, Bird, flora (4-1). 10f, Buildings (4-2). 20f, Great Wall, forest, (4-3). 30f, Bushes, evergreens (4-4).

**1990, Mar. 12 *Perf. 11***

| | | | | |
|---|---|---|---|---|
| **2266** | A619 | 8f multi | .30 | .25 |
| **2267** | A619 | 10f multi | .30 | .25 |
| **2268** | A619 | 20f multi | .40 | .25 |
| **2269** | A619 | 30f multi | .50 | .25 |
| | | *Nos. 2266-2269 (4)* | 1.50 | 1.00 |

Pottery — A620

**China Post No. T.149.**

**1990, Apr. 10 Litho. *Perf. 12***

| | | | | |
|---|---|---|---|---|
| **2270** | A620 | 8f multi (4-1) | .30 | .25 |
| **2271** | A620 | 20f multi (4-2) | .30 | .25 |
| **2272** | A620 | 30f multi (4-3) | .50 | .30 |
| **2273** | A620 | 50f multi (4-4) | .65 | .30 |
| | | *Nos. 2270-2273 (4)* | 1.75 | 1.10 |

Li Fuchun (1900-1975), Party Leader — A621

**China Post No. J.168.**

**1990, May 22 Photo. *Perf. 11x11½***

| | | | | |
|---|---|---|---|---|
| **2274** | A621 | 8f shown | .60 | .30 |
| **2275** | A621 | 20f In uniform (2-2) | .90 | .35 |

Bronze Head — A622

**China Post No. T.151.**

Bronze treasures from Emperor Qin Shi Huang Mausoleum: 50f, Horse head. $5, Chariots.

**1990, June 20 Photo. *Perf. 11½x11***

| | | | | |
|---|---|---|---|---|
| **2276** | A622 | 8f shown (2-1) | .65 | .25 |
| **2277** | A622 | 50f multicolored (2-2) | 1.10 | .35 |

**Miniature Sheet**

**Size: 141x79mm**

| | | | | |
|---|---|---|---|---|
| **2278** | A622 | $5 multicolored | *7.50* | *4.25* |

**Achievements Type of 1988**

**China Post No. T.152.**

Designs: 8f, 2nd automobile factory. 10f, Yizheng Joint Corporation of Chemical Fiber Industry. 20f, Shengli Oil Field. 30f, Qinshan Nuclear Power Station.

**1990, June 30 Litho. *Perf. 12***

| | | | | |
|---|---|---|---|---|
| **2279** | A582 | 8f shown (4-1) | .40 | .25 |
| **2280** | A582 | 10f multicolored (4-2) | .40 | .25 |
| **2281** | A582 | 20f multicolored (4-3) | .50 | .25 |
| **2282** | A582 | 30f multicolored (4-4) | .70 | .30 |
| | | *Nos. 2279-2282 (4)* | 2.00 | 1.05 |

**Wall Paintings Type of 1987**

**China Post No. T.150.**

8f, Flying Devatas. 10f, Worshipping Bodhisatva. 30f, Savior Avolokitesvara. 50f, Indra.

**1990, July 10 *Perf. 11½x11***

| | | | | |
|---|---|---|---|---|
| **2283** | A557 | 8f multi (4-1) | .45 | .25 |
| **2284** | A557 | 10f multi, vert. (4-2) | .45 | .25 |
| **2285** | A557 | 30f multi, vert. (4-3) | .60 | .30 |
| **2286** | A557 | 50f multi (4-4) | 1.15 | .40 |
| | | *Nos. 2283-2286 (4)* | 2.65 | 1.20 |

Snow Leopard (Uncia Uncia) — A624

**China Post No. T.153.**

**1990, July 20 Photo. *Perf. 11½***

**2287** A624 8f multicolored (2-1) .40 .25
**2288** A624 50f multicolored (2-2) .75 .30

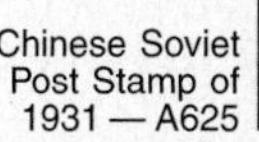

Chinese Soviet Post Stamp of 1931 — A625

**China Post No. J.169.**

Design: 20f, Chinese Red Post issue of West Fukien, 1929.

**1990, Aug. 1 Litho. *Perf. 12***

**2289** A625 8f multi (2-1) .60 .25
**2290** A625 20f multi, diff. (2-2) 1.10 .25

Zhang Wentian (1900-1990) A626

**China Post No. J.170.**

**1990, Aug. 30 *Perf. 11x11½***

**2291** A626 8f shown (2-1) .55 .25
**2292** A626 20f multi, diff. (2-2) 1.10 .25

Intl. Literacy Year — A627

**China Post No. J.171.**

**1990, Sept. 8 *Perf. 11½x11***

**2293** A627 20f multicolored .75 .30

Chinese Films — A628

**China Post No. T.154.**

**1990, Sept. 21 Litho. *Perf. 11***

**2294** A628 20f multicolored 1.25 .25

11th Asian Games, Beijing — A629

**China Post No. J.172.**

4f, Running (6-1). 8f, Gymnastics (6-2). 10f, Karate (6-3). 20f, Volleyball (6-4). 30f, Swimming (6-5). $1.60, Shooting (6-6).

**1990, Sept. 22 *Perf. 11x11½***

**2295** A629 4f multi .30 .25
**2296** A629 8f multi .30 .25
**2297** A629 10f multi .30 .25
**2298** A629 20f multi .30 .25
**2299** A629 30f multi .40 .30
**2300** A629 $1.60 multi .90 .65
*a.* Souv. sheet of 12, #2158-2159, 2254-2257, 2295-2300 *11.00 6.00*
*Nos. 2295-2300 (6)* 2.50 1.95

Souvenir Sheet

Sportphilex '90, Beijing — A629a

**1990, Sept. 21 Litho. *Perf. 11½***

**2300B** A629a $10 multi *20.00 15.00*

No. 2300B exists imperf. Value, *$700.*

Modern Scientists — A630

**China Post No. J.173.**

Designs: 8f, Lin Qiaozhi, obstetrician. 10f, Zhang Yuzhe, astronomer. 20f, Hou Debang, chemist. 30f, Ding Ying, agronomist.

**1990, Oct. 10 Litho. *Perf. 12***

**2301** A630 8f multicolored (4-1) .45 .25
**2302** A630 10f multicolored (4-2) .45 .25
**2303** A630 20f multicolored (4-3) .75 .25
**2304** A630 30f multicolored (4-4) .80 .25
*Nos. 2301-2304 (4)* 2.45 1.00

Mt. Hengshan A631

**China Post No. T.155.**

Designs: 8f, Towering Temple. 10f, South Sacred Mountain. 20f, Forested mountainside. 50f, Imposing Zhurong Peak.

**Photo. & Engr.**

**1990, Nov. 5 *Perf. 11***

**2305** A631 8f multicolored (4-1) .35 .30
**2306** A631 10f multicolored (4-2) .50 .30
**2307** A631 20f multicolored (4-3) .65 .35
**2308** A631 50f multicolored (4-4) 1.05 .45
*Nos. 2305-2308 (4)* 2.55 1.40

See Nos. 2342-2345. 2628-2631.

Souvenir Sheet

China Philatelic Federation, 3rd Congress — A632

**China Post No. J.174.**

**1990, Nov. 28 *Perf. 11½x11***

**2309** A632 $2 multicolored 4.50 4.00

Two types of No. 2309 exist. Either two or three of the horizontal bars in seventh character from top right are connected at left side. Value for No. 2309 is for the first type. Examples with three bars connected, value $7.50.

**Literature Type of 1988**
**China Post No. T.157.**

Romance of the Three Kingdoms by Luo Guanzhong: No. 2310, Night Attack on Wuchao. No. 2311, Making Three Calls at the Thatched Cottage. 30f, Rescuing the Master Single-handedly. 50f, Turning the Changban Bridge Upside Down.

**1990, Dec. 10 Photo. *Perf. 11½x11***

**2310** A587 20f multicolored (4-1) .50 .25
**2311** A587 20f multi, vert. (4-2) .50 .25
**2312** A587 30f multicolored (4-3) .60 .30
**2313** A587 50f multi, vert. (4-4) .90 .35
*Nos. 2310-2313 (4)* 2.50 1.15

Han Xizai's Night Revels by Gu Hongzhong — A633

**China Post No. T.158.**

Designs: a, Guests enjoying food, music (5-1). b, Music and dance (5-2). c, Hand washing (5-3). d, Musicians (5-4). e, Guests departing (5-5).

**1990, Dec. 20 Litho. *Perf. 12***

**2314** Strip of 5 5.00 3.25
*a.-e.* A633 50f any single .70 .40

New Year 1991 (Year of the Sheep) — A634

**China Post No. T.159.**
**Photo. & Engr.**

**1991, Jan. 5 *Perf. 11½***

**2315** A634 20f multicolored 1.75 .40
*a.* Bklt. pane of 12 + label 17.50 —
Complete booklet, #2315a 22.50

Stamps from No. 2315a have straight edges at top or bottom and sell for less as singles than No. 2315.

Dujiangyan Irrigation Project A635

**China Post No. T.156.**

Designs: 20f, Yuzui, flood control. 50f, Feishayan, drainage. 80f, Baopingkou, water volume control.

**1991, Feb. 20 Photo. *Perf. 11½x11***

**2316** A635 20f multicolored .40 .25
**2317** A635 50f multicolored .80 .45
**2318** A635 80f multicolored 1.40 .80
*Nos. 2316-2318 (3)* 2.60 1.50

A636

**China Post No. J.175.**

**1991, Mar. 18**

**2319** A636 20f multicolored 1.30 .40

Paris Commune, 120th anniv.

A637

**China Post No. T.160.**

**1991, Apr. 20 Photo. *Perf. 10***

**2320** A637 20f multi (2-1) .85 .30
*a.* Perf. 11½x11 1.50 .90

***Perf. 11½x11***

**2321** A637 50f Child & adult hands (2-2) 1.05 .30

Family planning.

Horned Animals — A638

**China Post No. T.161.**

No. 2322, Saiga tatarica (4-1). No. 2323, Budorcas taxicolor (4-2). No. 2324, Ovis ammon (4-3). No. 2325, Capra ibex (4-4).

**1991, May 10 *Perf. 11x11½***

**2322** A638 20f multi .30 .25
**2323** A638 20f multi .30 .25
*a.* Perf. 11 *7.00 7.00*
**2324** A638 50f multi .50 .30
*a.* Perf. 11 *17.50 17.50*
**2325** A638 $2 multi .75 .35
*Nos. 2322-2325 (4)* 1.85 1.15

No. 2322 exists imperf. Value, pair *$140.*

A639

**China Post No. J.176.**

25f, Song and dance (2-1). 50f, Golden bridge (2-2).
$2, PRC No. 132, cranes.

**1991, May 23 Photo. *Perf. 11***

**2326** A639 25f multi .45 .30
**2327** A639 50f multi .75 .40

**Souvenir Sheet**

**2328** A639 $2 multi *10.00 4.50*

Occupation of Tibet, 40th anniv.

A640

**China Post No. J.177.**

**1991, June 22 *Perf. 11½x11***

**2329** A640 20f multicolored 1.00 .35

Antarctic Treaty, 30th anniv.

Rhododendrons A641

**China Post No. T.162.**

Varieties of rhododendrons: No. 2330, Delavayi (8-1). No. 2331, Molle (8-2). No. 2332, Simsii (8-3). No. 2333, Fictolacteum (8-4). No. 2334, Agglutinatum, vert. (8-5). No. 2335, Fortunei, vert. (8-6). No. 2336, Giganteum, vert. (8-7). No. 2337, Rex, vert. (8-8).
$5, Wardii.

**1991, June 25 Litho. *Perf. 12***

**2330** A641 10f multi .30 .25
**2331** A641 15f multi .30 .25
**2332** A641 20f multi .30 .25
**2333** A641 20f multi .30 .25
**2334** A641 50f multi .55 .25
**2335** A641 80f multi .80 .35
**2336** A641 90f multi .95 .50
**2337** A641 $1.60 multi 1.60 .75
*Nos. 2330-2337 (8)* 5.10 2.85

**Souvenir Sheet**
***Perf. 11½***

**2338** A641 $5 multi *11.50 8.50*

No. 2338 contains one 80x40mm stamp.

Chinese Communist Party, 70th Anniv. — A642

**China Post No. J.178.**

50f, Hammer and sickle (2-2).

**1991, July 1 Photo. *Perf. 11x11½***

**2339** A642 20f shown (2-1) .80 .30
**2340** A642 50f multicolored 1.20 .50

Peasant Uprising, 209B.C. — A643

**China Post No. J.179.**

**1991, July 7**

**2341** A643 20f brown 1.15 .25

**Mt. Hengshan Type of 1990**
**China Post No. T.163.**

Designs: No. 2342, Monastery on mountainside. No. 2343, Snow-covered mountain top. 55f, Inscription carved into mountainside. 80f, Hidden monastery.

**Photo. & Engr.**

**1991, July 20 *Perf. 11***

**2342** A631 20f multi (4-1) .45 .25
**2343** A631 20f multi (4-2) .45 .25
**2344** A631 55f multi (4-3) .95 .30
**2345** A631 80f multi (4-4) 1.35 .45
*Nos. 2342-2345 (4)* 3.20 1.25

Intl. Union for Quaternary Research, 13th Conf. — A644

**China Post No. J.180.**

**1991, Aug. 2 Photo. *Perf. 11x11½***

**2346** A644 20f multicolored 1.10 .30
*a.* Perf. 11½ *13.00 13.00*

Chengde Mountain Resort A645

**China Post No. T.164.**

Ch'ing Dynasty Royal Gardens: 15f, Pine valleys. 20f, Mid-lake pavilion. 90f, Islet, maple trees. $2, Chengde Royal Summer Resort.

**1991 *Perf. 11½x11***

**2347** A645 15f multi (3-1) .30 .25
**2348** A645 20f multi (3-2) .40 .30
**2349** A645 90f multi (3-3) .90 .60
*Nos. 2347-2349 (3)* 1.60 1.15

**Souvenir Sheet**

**2350** A645 $2 multicolored *8.00 3.75*

No. 2350 contains one 90x40mm stamp. Issue dates: $2, Aug. 19; others, Aug. 10.

A646

**China Post No. J.181.**

Chen Yi, (b. 1901), party leader.

**1991, Aug. 26 Photo. *Perf. 11½x11***

**2351** A646 20f shown (2-1) .95 .25
**2352** A646 50f Verse (2-2) 1.70 .40

A647

**China Post No. T.168.**

**1991, Sept. 14**

**2353** A647 80f Disaster relief 1.65 .40

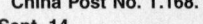

**Achievements Type of 1988**
**China Post No. T.165.**

20f, Luoyang glassworks. 25f, Urumchi chemical fertilizer project. 55f, Dalian expressway, Shenyang. 80f, Xichang satellite launching center.

**1991, Sept. 20 Litho. *Perf. 12***

**2354** A582 20f multi (4-1) .35 .25
**2355** A582 25f multi (4-2) .35 .30
**2356** A582 55f multi (4-3) .65 .35
**2357** A582 80f multi (4-4) .80 .45
*Nos. 2354-2357 (4)* 2.15 1.35

Revolutionary Heroes — A648

**China Post No. J.182.**

Designs: No. 2358, Xu Xilin (1873-1907). No. 2359, Qiu Jin (1879-1907). No. 2360, Song Jiaoren (1882-1913).

***Perf. 10 (#2358), 11x11½***

**1991, Oct. 10 Photo.**

**2358** A648 20f multi (3-1) .85 .35
*a.* Perf. 11x11½ 6.00 1.60
**2359** A648 20f multi (3-2) .60 .30
**2360** A648 20f multi (3-3) .60 .30
*Nos. 2358-2360 (3)* 2.05 .95

Jingdezhen Chinaware A649

**China Post No. T.166.**

Designs: 15f, Glazed wine pot and warming bowl, Song Dynasty, vert. No. 2362, Porcelain vase, Yuan Dynasty, vert. No. 2363, Jar, Ming Dynasty. 25f, Porcelain vase, Ch'ing Dynasty, vert. 50f, Modern underglazed plate, vert. $2, Modern octagonal eggshell bowl.

***Perf. 11¼x11½, 11½x11¼ (#2363, 2366)***

**1991, Oct. 11 Photo.**

**2361** A649 15f multi (6-1) .45 .25
**2362** A649 20f multi (6-2) .45 .25
**2363** A649 20f multi (6-3) .45 .25
**2364** A649 25f multi (6-4) .45 .25
**2365** A649 50f multi (6-5) .45 .30
**2366** A649 $2 multi (6-6) 1.10 .50
*Nos. 2361-2366 (6)* 3.35 1.80

***Perf. 11¼x11, 11x11¼ (#2363a, 2366a)***

**1991**

*2361a* A649 15f multi .55 .25
*2362a* A649 20f multi .55 .25
*2363a* A649 20f multi .55 .25
*2364a* A649 25f multi .55 .30
*2365a* A649 50f multi .55 .30
*2366a* A649 $2 multi 1.00 .55
*Nos. 2361a-2366a (6)* 3.75 1.90

Tao Xingzhi, Educator, Birth Cent. — A650

**China Post No. J.183.**

50f, Wearing robe (2-2).

**1991, Oct. 18 Litho. *Perf. 12***

**2367** A650 20f shown (2-1) .65 .25
**2368** A650 50f multicolored 1.00 .35

Xu Xiangqian, Revolutionary Leader, 90th Birth Anniv. — A651

**China Post No. J.184.**

**1991, Nov. 8 *Perf. 11x11½***

**2369** A651 20f shown (2-1) .70 .30
**2370** A651 50f In uniform (2-2) 1.05 .40

1st Women's Soccer World Championships, Guangdong Province — A652

**China Post No. J.185.**

Designs: 50f, Woman kicking soccer ball.

**1991, Nov. 16 *Perf. 11½x11***

**2371** A652 20f red & multi (2-1) .40 .30
**2372** A652 50f grn & multi (2-2) .50 .35

**Literature Type of 1987**
**China Post No. T.167.**

Outlaws of the Marsh: 20f, Dai Zong sends a false letter from Liangshan Marsh. No. 2374, Ten feet of steel alone captures Stumpy Tiger Wang. No. 2375, Mistress Gu breaks open the jail in Dengzhou to rescue the Xie Brothers. 90f, Sun Li offers a plan to attack Zhu Family manor. $3, Mount Liangshan gallants raid the execution grounds.

**1991, Nov. 19 *Perf. 11***

**2373** A570 20f multi (4-1) .30 .25
**2374** A570 25f multi (4-2) .30 .30
**2375** A570 25f multi (4-3) .35 .35
**2376** A570 90f multi (4-4) 1.20 .55
*Nos. 2373-2376 (4)* 2.15 1.45

**Souvenir Sheet**
***Perf. 11x11½***

**2377** A570 $3 multicolored *9.00 5.00*

No. 2377 contains one 60x90mm stamp.

---

Beginning with No. 2378 stamps are inscribed "CHINA" and are numbered chronologically with the year followed by the number of the set. Additional numbers in parentheses indicate the number and position of each stamp in a set. A typical inscription looks like this: 1992-2 (2-2)T. We will note these only when helpful in identifying stamps.

---

New Year 1992, Year of the Monkey
A653 A654

20f, Monkey, peach. 50f, Magpies, plum branches.

**Photo. & Engr.**

**1992, Jan. 25 *Perf. 11½***

**2378** A653 20f multicolored .60 .30
**2379** A654 50f multicolored 1.00 .35

Storks — A655

**1992, Feb. 20 Photo. *Perf. 11x11½***

**2380** A655 20f Ciconia nigra .45 .25
**2381** A655 $1.60 Ciconia ciconia 1.15 .45

Conifers — A656

Designs: 20f, Metasequoia glyptostroboides. 30f, Cathaya argyrophylla. 50f, Taiwania flousiana. 80f, Abies beshanzuensis.

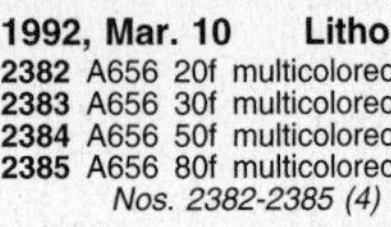

**1992, Mar. 10 Litho. *Perf. 12½***

**2382** A656 20f multicolored .40 .25
**2383** A656 30f multicolored .40 .25
**2384** A656 50f multicolored .50 .30
**2385** A656 80f multicolored .80 .35
*Nos. 2382-2385 (4)* 2.10 1.15

Marine Life — A660

20f, Pagrosomus major. 25f, Penaeus chinesis. 50f, Chlamys farreri. 80f, Laminaria japonica.

**1992, Apr. 15 Photo. *Perf. 11***

**2386** A660 20f multi .40 .25
**2387** A660 25f multi .40 .25
**2388** A660 50f multi .45 .25
**2389** A660 80f multi .55 .30
*Nos. 2386-2389 (4)* 1.80 1.05

Publication of "Discussions on Literature and Art at the Yenan Forum," 50th Anniv. — A661

**1992, May 23 Photo. *Perf. 11½x11***

**2390** A661 20f org, blk & red 1.10 .30

A662

**1992, June 5 Litho. *Perf. 12***

**2392** A662 20f multicolored 1.30 .30

UN Conf. on Human Development, 20th anniv.

A663

Insects: 20f, Coccinella septempunctata. 30f, Sympetrum croceolum. 50f, Chrysopa septempunctata. $2, Tenodera aridifolia sinensis.

**1992, June 28**

**2393** A663 20f multicolored .30 .25
**2394** A663 30f multicolored .30 .25
**2395** A663 50f multicolored .35 .30
**2396** A663 $2 multicolored .95 .45
*Nos. 2393-2396 (4)* 1.90 1.25

1992 Summer Olympics, Barcelona A664

20f, Basketball, vert. 25f, Women's gymnastics. 50f, Women's diving. 80f, Weight lifting, vert.
$5, Runners.

**1992, July 25 Photo. *Perf. 11***

**2397** A664 20f multi .40 .25
**2398** A664 25f multi .45 .25
**2399** A664 50f multi .45 .30
**2400** A664 80f multi .60 .35
*Nos. 2397-2400 (4)* 1.90 1.15

**Souvenir Sheet**

**2401** A664 $5 multi 3.75 1.75

No. 2401 contains one 54x40mm stamp.

Intl. Space Year — A665

**1992, Aug. 18 Litho. *Perf. 12***
**2402** A665 20f multicolored 1.30 .30

**Literature Type of 1988**

Romance of the Three Kingdoms by Luo Guanzhong: 20f, Verbal battle with scholars. 30f, Goading Sun Quan with sarcasm, vert. 50f, Jiang Gan stealing the letter. $1.60, Gathering arrows with straw-covered boats, vert.

***Perf. 11½x11, 11x11½***
**1992, Aug. 25 Photo.**
**2403** A587 20f multi .40 .25
**2404** A587 30f multi .45 .30
**2405** A587 50f multi .45 .30
**2406** A587 $1.60 multi .95 .45
*Nos. 2403-2406 (4)* 2.25 1.30

**Wall Paintings Type of 1987**

20f, Bodhisattva, vert. 25f, Musical performance, vert. 55f, Flight of a dragon. 80f, Envoy to the western regions. $5, Avalokitesvara-Bodhisattva, vert.

**1992, Sept. 15 *Perf. 11***
**2407** A557 20f multicolored .40 .25
**2408** A557 25f multicolored .45 .30
**2409** A557 55f multicolored .45 .30
**2410** A557 80f multicolored .80 .40
*Nos. 2407-2410 (4)* 2.10 1.25

**Souvenir Sheet**
***Perf. 11½***
**2411** A557 $5 multicolored *4.25 2.00*

No. 2411 contains one 52x70mm stamp.

Normalization of Diplomatic Relations Between China and Japan, 20th Anniv. — A666

20f, Cranes, Great Wall of China, Mt. Fuji. $2, Japanese, Chinese children, dove.

**1992, Sept. 29 Photo. *Perf. 11x11½***
**2412** A666 20f multicolored .45 .25
**2413** A666 $2 multicolored 1.70 .55

A667

Statue of Mazu, Chinese Goddess of the Sea.

**1992, Oct. 4 Litho. *Perf. 12***
**2414** A667 20f multicolored 1.10 .30

A667a

**1992, Oct. 12 Photo. *Perf. 11½x11***
**2414A** A667a 20f multicolored 1.60 .30

14th Chinese Communist Party Congress.

Jiao Yulu (1922-1964), Communist Party Leader — A668

**1992, Oct. 28 Litho. *Perf. 12***
**2415** A668 20f multicolored 1.30 .30

Famous Men — A669

Designs: 20f, Xiong Qinglai, mathematician. 30f, Tang Feifan, microbiologist. 50f, Zhang Xiaoqian, physician. $1, Liang Sicheng, architect.

**1992, Nov. 20**
**2416** A669 20f multicolored .35 .25
**2417** A669 30f multicolored .40 .25
**2418** A669 50f multicolored .55 .25
**2419** A669 $1 multicolored .85 .30
*Nos. 2416-2419 (4)* 2.15 1.05

Luo Ronghuan, Leader of People's Army, 90th Anniv. of Birth — A670

**1992, Nov. 26 Photo. *Perf. 11x11½***
**2420** A670 20f In dress uniform .75 .25
**2421** A670 50f In field uniform 1.20 .35

Constitution of the People's Republic of China, 10th Anniv. — A671

**1992, Dec. 4 *Perf. 11½x11***
**2422** A671 20f multicolored 1.60 .40

Liu Bocheng, Leader of People's Army, Birth Cent. — A672

Designs: 20f, In dress uniform. 50f, During period of Long March, vert.

**1992, Dec. 4 *Perf. 11x11½, 11½x11***
**2423** A672 20f multicolored .75 .25
**2424** A672 50f multicolored 1.20 .30

Quingtian Stone Carvings — A673

10f, Spring. 20f, Chinese sorghum. 40f, Harvest. $2, Blooming flowers, full moon.

**1992, Dec. 15 Litho. *Perf. 12***
**2425** A673 10f multicolored .30 .25
**2426** A673 20f multicolored .30 .25
**2427** A673 40f multicolored .40 .25
**2428** A673 $2 multicolored .65 .30
*Nos. 2425-2428 (4)* 1.65 1.05

New Year 1993 (Year of the Rooster)
A674 A675

**Photo. & Engr.**
**1993, Jan. 5 *Perf. 11½***
**2429** A674 20f red & black .70 .25
**2430** A675 50f red, white & blk .95 .30

Madam Song Quingling, Chinese Communist Leader, Birth Cent. — A676

**1993, Jan. 20 Photo. *Perf. 11x11½***
**2431** A676 20f Portrait .90 .30
*a.* Perf. 11 5.00 5.00
**2432** A676 $1 With children 1.70 .45
*a.* Perf. 11 5.00 5.00

No. 2431 exists imperf. Value, pair $140.

Camelus Bactrianus Ferus — A677

**1993, Feb. 20 Litho. *Perf. 12***
**2433** A677 20f shown .40 .25
**2434** A677 $1.60 Adult, young .90 .35

8th Natl. People's Congress — A678

**1993, Mar. 15 Litho. *Perf. 12***
**2435** A678 20f multicolored 1.25 .25

A679

Game of Weiqi (Go): 20f, Painting of players of ancient times. $1.60, Game board showing Chinese-style position.

**1993, Apr. 30 Litho. *Perf. 12***
**2436** A679 20f multi .65 .25
**2437** A679 $1.60 multi 1.30 .40

A680

20th Cent. Revolutionaries: 20f, Li Jishen (1885-1959), horiz. 30f, Zhang Lan (1872-1955). 50f, Shen Junru (1875-1963). $1, Huang Yanpei (1878-1965), horiz.

**1993, May 15 Litho. *Perf. 12***
**2438** A680 20f multi .45 .25
**2439** A680 30f multi .45 .25
**2440** A680 50f multi .50 .30
**2441** A680 $1 multi .70 .35
*Nos. 2438-2441 (4)* 2.10 1.15

See Nos. 2483-2486.

A681

**1993, May 9 Photo. *Perf. 12***
**2442** A681 50f Runner (2-1) .35 .25
**2443** A681 50f Mascot (2-2) .35 .25
*a.* Pair, #2442-2443 .85 .75

First East Asian Games. No. 2443a printed in continuous design.

A682

Bamboo: 20f, Phyllostachys nigra. 30f, Phyllostachys aureosulcata spectabilis. 40f, Bambusa ventricosa. $1, Pseudosasa amabilis. $5, Phyllostachys heterocycla pubescens, horiz.

**1993, June 15 Litho. *Perf. 12½***
**2444** A682 20f multi .35 .25
**2445** A682 30f multi .45 .25
**2446** A682 40f multi .60 .30
**2447** A682 $1 multi .75 .35
*Nos. 2444-2447 (4)* 2.15 1.15

**Souvenir Sheet**
**Photo.**
***Perf. 11***
**2448** A682 $5 multicolored 3.25 2.25
*a.* As #2448, added inscription 7.50 7.50

No. 2448 contains one 54x40mm stamp.

No. 2448a is inscribed in sheet margin with hologram of panda at left, Chinese inscription for CHINA '96 and PJZ-3 at bottom, and flag and tagged security emblem at right. Soaking in water may affect the hologram. Issued: May 10, 1996.

**Literature Type of 1987**

Outlaws of the Marsh: 20f, Chai Jin is trapped in Gaotang. 30f, Shi Qian steals armor. 50f, Xu Ning teaches how to use barbed lance. $2, Shi Xiu leaps from building to rescue condemned man from execution.

**1993, Aug. 20 Photo. *Perf. 11***
**2449** A570 20f multi .45 .25
**2450** A570 30f multi .50 .25
**2451** A570 50f multi .60 .30
**2452** A570 $2 multi 1.10 .40
*Nos. 2449-2452 (4)* 2.65 1.20

Changbai Mountains A683

**1993, Sept. 3 *Perf. 11½x11***
**2453** A683 20f Tianchi .45 .25
**2454** A683 30f Alpine tundra .55 .25
**2455** A683 50f Waterfall .65 .30
**2456** A683 $1 Mixed forest .85 .35
*Nos. 2453-2456 (4)* 2.50 1.15

Seventh Natl. Games — A684

**1993, Sept. 4**
**2457** A684 20f multicolored .75 .30

Longmen Grottoes — A685

Designs: 20f, Rocana, Ancestor Worshipping Temple. 30f, Sakyamuni, Middle Binyang Cave, Northern Wei. 50f, Maharaja, devas treading on Yaksha. $1, Bodhisattva at the left side of Rocana, Guyang Cave, Northern Wei. $5, Ancestor Worshipping Temple.

**1993, Sept. 5 Litho. *Perf. 12***
**2458** A685 20f multi .30 .25
**2459** A685 30f multi .45 .25
**2460** A685 50f multi .65 .30
**2461** A685 $1 multi 1.20 .45
*Nos. 2458-2461 (4)* 2.60 1.25

**Souvenir Sheets**
**2462** A685 $5 multicolored *3.00 2.25*
*a.* Overprinted in gold *7.50 4.50*
*b.* Overprinted in silver *5.00 3.50*

No. 2462 contains one 120x40mm stamp.

Overprint in margin of No. 2462a includes Chinese characters and "PJZ-1." Bangkok '95 (No. 2462a). No. 2462a sold for $6.

No. 2462a exists with serial number inscribed in sheet margin. The same number is inscribed on Thailand No. 1615b. These were sold as a set. Value for the two sheets with matching numbers, $26.50.

Sheet margin of No. 2462b contains silver lettering in Chinese for Thailand stamp exhibition and "PJZ-7." No. 2462b exists with serial

number inscribed in sheet margin. Value: *$11.50.*
Issued: No. 2462a, 8/95; No. 2462b, 12/5/97.

Honey Bees — A686

10f, Queen and two bees. 15f, Extracting nectar. 20f, Two Zhonghua bees. $2, Two bees in flight.

**1993, Sept. 21 Photo. *Perf. 11½***

| | | | | |
|---|---|---|---|---|
| **2463** | A686 10f multi | .35 | .25 |
| *a.* | Perf. 11x11½ | 5.00 | 5.00 |
| **2464** | A686 15f multi | .35 | .25 |
| *a.* | Perf. 11x11½ | 5.00 | 5.00 |
| **2465** | A686 20f multi | .35 | .25 |
| **2466** | A686 $2 multi | .85 | .50 |
| | *Nos. 2463-2466 (4)* | 1.90 | 1.25 |

Lacquerware A687

**1993, Oct. 20 Photo. *Perf. 12***

| | | | |
|---|---|---|---|
| **2467** | A687 20f Bowl | .40 | .25 |
| **2468** | A687 30f Duck | .45 | .25 |
| **2469** | A687 50f Round tray | .55 | .25 |
| **2470** | A687 $1 Lidded box | .60 | .30 |
| | *Nos. 2467-2470 (4)* | 2.00 | 1.05 |

Paintings, by Zheng Banqiao A688

Designs: 10f, Bamboo, rock on fan. No. 2472, Orchard. No. 2473, Orchard, bamboo, rock on scroll, vert. 30f, Bamboo, rock on scroll, vert. 50f, Vase and chrysanthemums. $1.60, Chinese calligraphy on fan.

**1993, Nov. 22 Litho. *Perf. 12½***

| | | | |
|---|---|---|---|
| **2471** | A688 10f multi (6-1) | .35 | .25 |
| **2472** | A688 20f multi (6-2) | .35 | .25 |
| **2473** | A688 20f multi (6-3) | .35 | .25 |
| **2474** | A688 30f multi (6-4) | .70 | .30 |
| **2475** | A688 50f multi (6-5) | .70 | .30 |
| **2476** | A688 $1.60 multi (6-6) | 1.25 | .35 |
| | *Nos. 2471-2476 (6)* | 3.70 | 1.70 |

No. 2476 exists imperf. Value, pair *$240.*

A689

**1993, Nov. 26 *Perf. 12***

| | | | |
|---|---|---|---|
| **2477** | A689 20f multicolored | .90 | .30 |

Yang Hucheng, birth cent.

Mao Tse-tung (1893-1976) — A690

$1, Portrait, seated.
$5, Standing by Great Wall.

**1993 Photo. *Perf. 11½***

| | | | |
|---|---|---|---|
| **2478** | A690 20f shown | *1.15* | .35 |
| **2479** | A690 $1 multicolored | *3.25* | .55 |

**Souvenir Sheet**

| | | | |
|---|---|---|---|
| **2480** | A690 $5 multicolored | *4.75* | *3.00* |
| *a.* | Overprinted in gold in margin | *4.00* | *5.50* |

No. 2480 contains one 48x58mm stamp. No. 2480a sold for $8.
No. 2478 exists imperf. Value, pair *$350.*
Issued: $5, 11/16; 20f, $1, 12/26; No. 2480a, 4/9/99.

New Year 1994 (Year of the Dog)
A691 A692

**1994, Jan. 5 Photo. *Perf. 11½***

| | | | |
|---|---|---|---|
| **2481** | A691 20f multi | .65 | .25 |
| **2482** | A692 50f yel, red & blk | .95 | .30 |

**20th Cent. Revolutionaries Type**

Designs: No. 2483, Chen Qiyou, horiz. No. 2484, Chen Shutong. No. 2485, Ma Xulun. No. 2486, Xu Deheng, horiz.

**1994, Feb. 25 Litho. *Perf. 12***

| | | | |
|---|---|---|---|
| **2483** | A680 20f blk & brn (4-1) | .50 | .30 |
| **2484** | A680 20f blk & brn (4-2) | .50 | .30 |
| **2485** | A680 50f blk & brn (4-3) | .55 | .30 |
| **2486** | A680 50f blk & brn (4-4) | .55 | .30 |
| | *Nos. 2483-2486 (4)* | 2.10 | 1.20 |

Sturgeon A693

20f, Huso dauricus. 40f, Acipenser sinensis. 50f, Psephurus gladius. $1, Acipenser dabryanus.

**1994, Mar. 18 Litho. *Perf. 12½***

| | | | |
|---|---|---|---|
| **2487** | A693 20f multi | .30 | .25 |
| **2488** | A693 40f multi | .35 | .25 |
| **2489** | A693 50f multi | .40 | .30 |
| **2490** | A693 $1 multi | .50 | .40 |
| | *Nos. 2487-2490 (4)* | 1.55 | 1.20 |

Afforestation Campaign A694

Designs: 15f, Sand dunes. 20f, Flowers on sand dune. 40f, Forest of poplars. 50f, Oasis.

**1994, Apr. 21 Litho. *Perf. 12***

| | | | |
|---|---|---|---|
| **2491** | A694 15f multi | .35 | .25 |
| **2492** | A694 20f multi | .45 | .25 |
| **2493** | A694 40f multi | .50 | .25 |
| **2494** | A694 50f multi | .60 | .30 |
| | *Nos. 2491-2494 (4)* | 1.90 | 1.05 |

Teapots — A695

Style of teapot: 20f, Round, three-legged. 30f, Square, four-legged. 50f, Eight diagrams. $1, Round-eared.

**1994, May 5 Litho. *Perf. 12***

| | | | |
|---|---|---|---|
| **2495** | A695 20f multi | .30 | .25 |
| **2496** | A695 30f multi | .35 | .25 |
| **2497** | A695 50f multi | .40 | .30 |
| **2498** | A695 $1 multi | .75 | .35 |
| | *Nos. 2495-2498 (4)* | 1.80 | 1.15 |

Huangpu Military School, 70th Anniv. — A696

**1994, June 16 Litho. *Perf. 12***

| | | | |
|---|---|---|---|
| **2499** | A696 20f multicolored | 1.25 | .25 |

Intl. Olympic Committee, Cent. — A697

**1994, June 23**

| | | | |
|---|---|---|---|
| **2500** | A697 20f multicolored | .80 | .25 |

Ancient Chinese Writers — A698

Designs: 20f, Tao Yuanming holding basket of flowers. 30f, Cao Zhi holding sword at side. 50f, Si Maqian writing on scroll. $1, Qu Yuan walking away with sword under arm.

**1994, June 25**

| | | | |
|---|---|---|---|
| **2501** | A698 20f multi | .30 | .25 |
| **2502** | A698 30f multi | .55 | .25 |
| **2503** | A698 50f multi | .60 | .30 |
| **2504** | A698 $1 multi | .90 | .35 |
| | *Nos. 2501-2504 (4)* | 2.35 | 1.15 |

**Wall paintings Type of 1987**

10f, Flying Devata. 20f, Vimalakirti. 50f, Z. Yichao on the march. $1.60, Sorceresses.

**1994, July 16 Photo. *Perf. 11***

| | | | |
|---|---|---|---|
| **2505** | A557 10f multi | .35 | .25 |
| **2506** | A557 20f multi | .60 | .25 |
| **2507** | A557 50f multi | .65 | .30 |
| **2508** | A557 $1.60 multi | 1.00 | .35 |
| | *Nos. 2505-2508 (4)* | 2.60 | 1.15 |

Zhaojun's Marriage to Xiongnu A699

**1994, Aug. 25 Photo. *Perf. 11½x11***

| | | | |
|---|---|---|---|
| **2509** | A699 20f Zhaojun | .50 | .25 |
| **2510** | A699 50f Leaving home | 1.05 | .30 |

**Souvenir Sheet**

***Perf. 11½***

| | | | |
|---|---|---|---|
| **2511** | A699 $3 Wedding | 4.25 | 2.10 |

No. 2511 contains one 85x46mm stamp.

Sixth Far East and South Pacific Games for the Disabled, Beijing — A700

**1994, Sept. 4 Litho. *Perf. 12***

| | | | |
|---|---|---|---|
| **2512** | A700 20f multicolored | 1.25 | .25 |

Wulingyuan State Forest Park A701

20f, South Gate to Heaven. 30f, Shentangwan. 50f, No. One Bridge. $1, Writing-brush Peak. $3, Picturesque corridor.

**1994, Sept. 25 Litho. *Perf. 12***

| | | | |
|---|---|---|---|
| **2513** | A701 20f multi, vert. | .35 | .25 |
| **2514** | A701 30f multi, vert. | .45 | .25 |
| **2515** | A701 50f multi | .55 | .35 |
| **2516** | A701 $1 multi | .80 | .40 |
| | *Nos. 2513-2516 (4)* | 2.15 | 1.25 |

**Souvenir Sheet**

***Perf. 11½x12***

| | | | |
|---|---|---|---|
| **2517** | A701 $3 multicolored | *3.25* | *1.75* |

No. 2517 contains one 50x36mm stamp.

Wuyi Mountains A702

Designs: a, Jade-girl Peak (4-1). b, Nine-bend Brook (4-2). c, Guadun Village (4-3). d, Alpine Grassland (4-4).

**1994, Sept. 30 *Perf. 12***

| | | | |
|---|---|---|---|
| **2518** | Strip of 4 | 2.40 | 1.50 |
| *a.-d.* | A702 50f any single | .35 | .25 |

No. 2518 exists imperf. Value, *$225.*

Listening to the Rapids, by Fu Baoshi (1904-65) — A703

Paintings: No. 2520, Appreciating a Painting. No. 2521, Dadi's Thatched Hut. 40f, Playing the Ruan. 50f, At Hupao. $1, The Road to Shanyin.

**1994, Oct. 5**

| | | | |
|---|---|---|---|
| **2519** | A703 10f multi (6-1) | .35 | .25 |
| **2520** | A703 20f multi (6-2) | .35 | .25 |
| **2521** | A703 20f multi (6-3) | .35 | .25 |
| **2522** | A703 40f multi (6-4) | .50 | .30 |
| **2523** | A703 50f multi (6-5) | .60 | .35 |
| **2524** | A703 $1 multi (6-6) | 1.10 | .40 |
| | *Nos. 2519-2524 (6)* | 3.25 | 1.80 |

Cranes — A704

20f, Whooping crane. $2, Black-necked crane.

**Photo. & Engr.**

**1994, Oct. 9 *Perf. 11x11½***

| | | | |
|---|---|---|---|
| **2528** | A704 20f multi | .65 | .25 |
| **2529** | A704 $2 multi | 1.05 | .55 |

See US Nos. 2867-2868.

Souvenir Sheet

UPU, 120th Anniv. — A705

**1994, Oct. 9 Litho. *Perf. 12***

| | | | |
|---|---|---|---|
| **2530** | A705 $3 multicolored | 2.50 | 1.30 |
| *a.* | Ovptd. in sheet margin | 3.50 | 2.00 |

No. 2530a ovptd. in sheet margin with UPU hologram, vertical Chinese inscription in gold. Issued: July 18, 1996.

Gorges of Yangtze River — A706

Designs: 10f, Baidicheng. No. 2532, Qutang Gorge. No. 2533, Wuxia Gorge. 30f, Goddess Peak. 50f, Xiling Gorge. $1, Qu Yuan Memorial Temple.
$5, The Three Gorges.

**1994, Nov. 4 Photo. *Perf. 12***

| | | | |
|---|---|---|---|
| **2531** | A706 10f multi (6-1) | .40 | .25 |
| **2532** | A706 20f multi (6-2) | .40 | .25 |
| **2533** | A706 20f multi (6-3) | .40 | .25 |
| **2534** | A706 30f multi (6-4) | .40 | .25 |
| **2535** | A706 50f multi (6-5) | .50 | .30 |
| **2536** | A706 $1 multi (6-6) | .55 | .35 |
| | *Nos. 2531-2536 (6)* | 2.65 | 1.65 |

**Souvenir Sheet**

***Perf. 11½x11***

| | | | |
|---|---|---|---|
| **2537** | A706 $5 multicolored | 4.25 | 2.00 |

No. 2537 contains one 116x35mm stamp.

### Souvenir Sheet

All-China Philatelic Federation, 4th Congress — A707

**1994, Nov. 17 Litho. *Perf. 11***
**2538** A707 $3 multicolored 4.25 1.30

### Literature Type of 1988

Romance of the Three Kingdoms by Luo Guanzhong: 20f, Composing a poem with a lance in hands. 30f, Liu Bei's marriage, vert. 50f, Overwhelming Xiaoyaojin with prowess. $1, Campsites burned, vert.
$5, Fierce battle at Chibi.

***Perf. 11½x11, 11x11½***
**1994, Nov. 24 Photo.**
**2539** A587 20f multicolored .35 .25
**2540** A587 30f multicolored .45 .25
**2541** A587 50f multicolored .50 .30
**2542** A587 $1 multicolored .60 .35
*Nos. 2539-2542 (4)* 1.90 1.15

### Souvenir Sheet
***Perf. 11***
**2543** A587 $5 multicolored 6.50 2.60

No. 2543 contains one 158x36mm stamp.

Special Economic Zones — A708

Designs: a, Shenzhen (5-1). b, Zhuhai (5-2). c, Shantou (5-3). d, Xiamen (5-4). e, Hainan (5-4).

**1994, Dec. 10 Litho. *Perf. 12***
**2544** A708 50f Strip of 5, #a.-e. 2.40 *1.90*

Pagodas of Ancient China — A709

Designs: No. 2545, Dayan Pagoda, Cien Temple. No. 2546, Zhenguo Pagoda, Kaiyuan Temple. 50f, Liuhe Pagoda, Kaihua Temple. $2, Youguo Temple.

### Photo. & Engr.
**1994, Dec. 15 *Perf. 11½x11***
**2545** 20f tan, brn & blk (4-1) .30 .25
**2546** 20f tan, brn & blk (4-2) .35 .25
**2547** 50f tan, brn & blk (4-3) .40 .25
**2548** $2 tan, brn & blk (4-4) .75 .30
*a.* Souvenir sheet of 4, #2545-2548 *5.75 3.00*
*Nos. 2545-2548 (4)* 1.80 1.05

No. 2548a sold for $5.

New Year 1995 (Year of the Boar)
A711 A712

### Photo. & Engr.
**1995, Jan. 5 *Perf. 11½***
**2550** A711 20f multicolored 1.25 .25
**2551** A712 50f multicolored 1.35 .30

Winter Scenes — A713

Designs: 20f, Snow willows, Cold River. 50f, Ice & snow on jade trees, vert.

**1995, Jan. 12 Litho. *Perf. 12***
**2552** A713 20f multicolored .65 .25
**2553** A713 50f multicolored 1.25 .30

Mt. Dinghushan A714

Designs: 15f, Topographical map. No. 2555, Stream flowing down from mountain. No. 2556, Buildings on mountain side. $2.30, Silver pheasants.

**1995, Feb. 15 Litho. *Perf. 12½***
**2554** A714 15f multi (4-1) .30 .25
**2555** A714 20f multi (4-2) .35 .30
**2556** A714 20f multi (4-3) .35 .30
**2557** A714 $2.30 multi (4-4) 1.00 .35
*Nos. 2554-2557 (4)* 2.00 1.20

World Summit for Social Development, Copenhagen A715

**1995, Mar. 6 Photo. *Perf. 11x11½***
**2558** A715 20f multicolored 3.25 .40

Owls — A716

**1995, Mar. 22 Photo. *Perf. 11½***
**2559** A716 10f Eagle owl .35 .25
**2560** A716 20f Long-eared owl .40 .25
**2561** A716 50f Snowy owl .55 .35
**2562** A716 $1 Grass owl 1.05 .40
*Nos. 2559-2562 (4)* 2.35 1.25

Sweet Osmanthus A717

No. 2563, Thunbergii (4-1). No. 2564, Latifolius (4-2). No. 2565, Aurantiacus (4-3). No. 2566, Semperflorens (4-4).

**1995, Apr. 14 Litho. *Perf. 12***
**2563** A717 20f multicolored .30 .25
**2564** A717 20f multicolored .30 .25
**2565** A717 50f multicolored .35 .30
**2566** A717 $1 multicolored .60 .40
*Nos. 2563-2566 (4)* 1.55 1.20

A souvenir sheet of 4, Nos. 2563-2566, exists, both perf and imperf. Value, perf $4.25, imperf $100.

43rd World Table Tennis Championships, Tianjin — A718

**1995, May 1 Litho. *Perf. 12***
**2567** A718 20f Athlete .90 .25
**2568** A718 50f Arena 1.25 .30
*a.* Souv. sheet of 2, #2567-2568 *19.00 9.25*

No. 2568a sold for $7. Issued 8/14/95.

Spring Outing A719

Designs: No. 2569, Group riding horses. No. 2570, Three riding horses.

**1995, May 23 Litho. *Perf. 12***
**2569** A719 50f multi (2-1) .30 .30
**2570** A719 50f multi (2-2) .70 .30
*a.* Pair, #2569-2570 3.25 1.00

No. 2570a is a continuous design.

Shadow Play — A720

Various costumed characters.

**1995, June 8 Photo. *Perf. 12x12½***
**2571** A720 20f multi (4-1) .45 .25
**2572** A720 40f multi (4-2) .45 .25
**2573** A720 50f multi (4-3) .65 .30
**2574** A720 50f multi (4-4) .65 .30
*Nos. 2571-2574 (4)* 2.20 1.10

Highway Interchanges, Beijing — A721

**1995, June 20 Photo. *Perf. 11½x11***
**2575** A721 20f Siyuan .40 .25
**2576** A721 30f Tianningsi .45 .25
**2577** A721 50f Yuting .55 .25
**2578** A721 $1 Anhui .75 .30
*Nos. 2575-2578 (4)* 2.15 1.05

Diplomatic Relations Between China & Thailand, 20th Anniv. — A722

No. 2579, Elephants walking right into water. No. 2580, Elephants walking left into water.

**1995, July 1**
**2579** $1 multi (2-1) .45 .30
**2580** $1 multi (2-2) .45 .30
*a.* A722 Pair, #2579-2580 1.25 .85

Taihu Lake — A723

Lake scenes: No. 2581, Yellow trees. No. 2582, Structures on bank, boats, hills. No. 2583, Structures across inlet. No. 2584, Red trees, home. 230f, Winter scene. 500f, Houses on cliff, lighthouse.

**1995, July 20 Photo. *Perf. 11½***
**2581** A723 20f multi (5-1) .30 .25
**2582** A723 20f multi (5-2) .30 .25
**2583** A723 50f multi (5-3) .35 .30
**2584** A723 50f multi (5-4) .35 .30
**2585** A723 230f multi (5-5) .85 .70
*Nos. 2581-2585 (5)* 2.15 1.80

### Souvenir Sheet
***Perf. 11***
**2586** A723 500f multicolored 3.00 1.90
*a.* Ovptd. in sheet margin 7.00 4.75

No. 2586 contains one 90x60mm stamp with continuing design.

No. 2586a issued 3/24/97. Gold overprint in sheet margin contains an emblem, Chinese inscription saying "Hong Kong Returns to China" and "PJZ-5."

Posts of Ancient China — A724

**1995, Aug. 17 Photo. *Perf. 12***
**2587** A724 20f Yucheng .75 .25
**2588** A724 50f Jimingshan 1.15 .30

Shaolin Temple, 1500th Anniv. — A725

No. 2589, Entrance (4-1). No. 2590, Pagoda Forest (4-2). No. 2591, Martial arts (4-3). No. 2592, Historical rescue (4-4).

**1995, Aug. 30**
**2589** A725 20f multicolored .55 .25
**2590** A725 20f multicolored .55 .25
**2591** A725 50f multicolored .70 .25
**2592** A725 100f multicolored 1.35 .45
*Nos. 2589-2592 (4)* 3.15 1.20

Cultural Relics of Tibet — A726

20f, Jar. 30f, Casque. 50f, Celestial motion chart. 100f, Pearl mandala.

**1995, Sept. 1**
**2593** A726 20f multicolored .30 .25
**2594** A726 30f multicolored .35 .25
**2595** A726 50f multicolored .45 .25
**2596** A726 100f multicolored .50 .30
*Nos. 2593-2596 (4)* 1.60 1.05

Wildlife — A727

**1995, Sept. 1 *Perf. 11x11½***
**2597** A727 20f Koalas .40 .25
**2598** A727 $2.90 Pandas 1.55 .75

See Australia No. 1459.

End of World War II, 50th Anniv. — A728

10f, July 7th event. No. 2600, Victory at Taier village. No. 2601, Soldier, hundred-regiment battle. No. 2602, Guerrilla war. No. 2603, Troops on parade, joining forces at Mangyo. 60f, Aircraft donated by Chinese living abroad. No. 2605, Taiwan recovered. No. 2606, Japanese surrender aboard USS Missouri.

**1995, Sept. 3**
**2599** A728 10f multi (8-1) .40 .25
**2600** A728 20f multi (8-2) .40 .25
**2601** A728 20f multi (8-3) .40 .25
**2602** A728 50f multi (8-4) .45 .25
**2603** A728 50f multi (8-5) .45 .25
**2604** A728 60f multi (8-6) .55 .30
**2605** A728 100f multi (8-7) .80 .40
**2606** A728 100f multi (8-8) .80 .40
*Nos. 2599-2606 (8)* 4.25 2.35

4th World Conference on Women, Beijing — A729

Symbols of: 15f, Equality. 20f, Development. 50f, Peace. 60f, Friendship.

**1995, Sept. 4 *Perf. 12***
**2607** A729 15f multi .30 .25
**2608** A729 20f multi .30 .25
**2609** A729 50f multi .35 .25
**2610** A729 60f multi .40 .30
*Nos. 2607-2610 (4)* 1.35 1.05

The Great Wall — A730

### China Post No. R28

230f, Shanhaiguan Pass. 290f, Jinshanling.

**1995, Oct. 5 Photo. *Perf. 12½***

**2611** A730 60f shown .30 .25
**2612** A730 230f multicolored .85 .30
**2613** A730 290f multicolored 1.05 .35
*Nos. 2611-2613 (3)* 2.20 .90

See Nos. 2755, 2792-2795, 2907-2910, 2934-2941, 2952-2955.

Jiuhua Mountains — A731

10f, Sunrise at Peak Terrace, horiz. No. 2615, Hall of Meditation. No. 2616, Temple of Bodhisattva, horiz. No. 2617, Sunset at Zhiyuan, horiz. No. 2618, Great Rock. No. 2619, Phoenix Pine, horiz.

**1995, Oct. 9 *Perf. 12***

**2614** A731 10f multi (6-1) .35 .25
**2615** A731 20f multi (6-2) .35 .25
**2616** A731 20f multi (6-3) .35 .25
**2617** A731 50f multi (6-4) .45 .30
**2618** A731 50f multi (6-5) .45 .30
**2619** A731 290f multi (6-6) 1.35 .45
*Nos. 2614-2619 (6)* 3.30 1.80

Motion Pictures, Cent. — A732

Projector and: 20f, Black and white film. 50f, Color film.

**1995, Oct. 13**

**2620** A732 20f blue & black .45 .25
**2621** A732 50f multicolored .80 .30

A733

UN, 50th Anniv. — A733a

Designs: 20f, UN flag, Headquarters. 50f, Stylized flags, UN emblem, "50."

**1995, Oct. 24 Litho.**

**2622** A733 20f multi .45 .25
**2623** A733a 50f multi 1.15 .30

Sanqing Mountains A734

No. 2624, Good Fortune Land. No. 2625, Sichun Goddess. 50f, Bodhisattva Enjoys Music. 100f, Huge Boa out of Mountain.

**1995, Nov. 1 Photo. *Perf. 12***

**2624** A734 20f multi (4-1) .35 .25
**2625** A734 20f multi (4-2) .35 .25
**2626** A734 50f multi, vert. (4-3) .40 .25
**2627** A734 100f multi, vert. (4-4) .60 .40
*Nos. 2624-2627 (4)* 1.70 1.15

### Mt. Hengshan Type of 1990

Songshan Mountains: 20f, Ancient Temple of Mount Song. 50f, Moon waiting at Songmen Gate. 60f, Shaolin Temple. $1, Panorama view of Mt. Song.

**Photo. & Engr.**

**1995, Nov. 10 *Perf. 11***

**2628** A631 20f multi .30 .25
**2629** A631 50f multi .30 .25
**2630** A631 60f multi .30 .30
**2631** A631 $1 multi .70 .40
*Nos. 2628-2631 (4)* 1.60 1.20

Scenic Views of Hong Kong — A735

Designs: 20f, Victoria Harbor. 50f, Central Plaza at night. 60f, Hong Kong Cultural Center. 290f, Repulse Bay.

**1995, Nov. 28 Photo. *Perf. 12***

**2632** A735 20f multi .30 .25
**2633** A735 50f multi .30 .25
**2634** A735 60f multi .35 .30
**2635** A735 290f multi 1.15 .40
*Nos. 2632-2635 (4)* 2.10 1.20

No. 2635 exists imperf. Value, pair *$140.*

Sun Zi's Art of War — A736

Drawings depicting: No. 2637, Discussing strategy. 30f, Capturing Ying. 50f, Battle at Ailing. 100f, Meeting of sovereigns, Huangchi.

**1995, Dec. 4 *Perf. 11x11½***

**2636** A736 20f multi (5-1) .35 .25
**2637** A736 20f multi (5-2) .35 .25
**2638** A736 30f multi (5-3) .45 .25
**2639** A736 50f multi (5-4) .50 .30
**2640** A736 100f multi (5-5) 1.00 .45
*Nos. 2636-2640 (5)* 2.65 1.50

New Year 1996 (Year of the Rat)
A737 A738

**Photo. & Engr.**

**1996, Jan. 5 *Perf. 11½***

**2641** A737 20f multi .80 .25
**2642** A738 50f multi 1.90 .35

3rd Asian Winter Games — A739

No. 2643, Speed skating. No. 2644, Ice hockey. No. 2645, Figure skating. No. 2646, Skiing.

**1996, Feb. 4 Litho. *Perf. 12***

**2643** A739 50f multi (4-1) .30 .25
**2644** A739 50f multi (4-2) .30 .25
**2645** A739 50f multi (4-3) .30 .25
**2646** A739 50f multi (4-4) .30 .25
*a.* Block of 4, #2643-2646 1.40 1.00

China/Korea Submarine Fiber Optic Cable System — A740

**1996, Feb. 8 Litho. *Perf. 12***

**2647** A740 20f multicolored 1.10 .25

First day covers are dated 12/15/95.
See Korea No. 1863.

Shenyang Imperial Palace A741

Designs: No. 2648, Buildings, denomination UL. No. 2649, Buildings, denomination LR.

**1996, Mar. 18 Photo. *Perf. 12***

**2648** A741 50f multi (2-1) .35 .25
**2649** A741 50f multi (2-2) .35 .25
*a.* Pair, Nos. 2648-2649 1.25 .75

China Post, Cent. — A742

Post Office buildings: 10f, Tianjin Posts Bureau. 20f, Beijing Postal Administration. 50f, Directorate of Posts of China. 100f, Beijing postal hub.
500f, China #78-85.

**1996, Mar. 20 *Perf. 11½***

**2650** A742 10f multi .35 .25
**2651** A742 20f multi .45 .25
**2652** A742 50f multi .45 .30
**2653** A742 100f multi .60 .40
*Nos. 2650-2653 (4)* 1.85 1.20

### Souvenir Sheet

***Perf. 11***

**2654** A742 500f multicolored *6.75* 3.25

No. 2654 contains one 89x59mm stamp.
No. 2654 exists with a red overprint in the bottom margin. Value, $15.

Huang Binhong, Artist — A743

No. 2655, Calligraphy. No. 2656, Landscape. 40f, Qingcheng Mts. No. 2658, View from Xiing. No. 2659, Colored landscape. 230f, Flowers.

**1996, Apr. 5 *Perf. 11½***

**2655** A743 20f multi (6-1) .35 .25
**2656** A743 20f multi (6-2) .35 .25
**2657** A743 40f multi (6-3) .55 .30
**2658** A743 50f multi (6-4) .60 .30
**2659** A743 50f multi (6-5) .60 .35
**2660** A743 230f multi (6-6) 2.35 .50
*Nos. 2655-2660 (6)* 4.80 1.95

Aircraft A744

**1996, Apr. 17 *Perf. 12***

**2661** A744 20f F-8 (4-1) .45 .25
**2662** A744 50f A-5 (4-2) .75 .30
**2663** A744 50f Yun-7 (4-3) .75 .30
**2664** A744 100f Yun-12 (4-4) 1.20 .40
*Nos. 2661-2664 (4)* 3.15 1.25

Potted Landscapes A745

Nos. 2665-2666, Lijing & Divine Peak. Nos. 2667-2668, Melting Snow & Eagle Rock. Nos. 2668-2669, Manch & Rosy Clouds.

**1996, Apr. 18**

**2665** A745 20f multi (6-1) .30 .25
**2666** A745 20f multi (6-2) .30 .25
*a.* Pair, #2665-2666 .75 .50
**2667** A745 50f multi (6-3) .30 .25
**2668** A745 50f multi (6-4) .30 .25
*a.* Pair, #2667-2668 1.00 .60
**2669** A745 100f multi (6-5) .35 .30
**2670** A745 100f multi (6-6) .35 .30
*a.* Pair, #2669-2670 1.50 1.00
*Nos. 2665-2670 (6)* 1.90 1.60

Iron Trees — A746

No. 2671, Cycas revoluta. No. 2672, Cycas panzhihuaensis. 50f, Cycas pectinata. 230f, Cycas multipinnata.

**1996, May 2 Litho. *Perf. 12***

**2671** A746 20f multi (4-1) .30 .25
**2672** A746 20f multi (4-2) .30 .25
**2673** A746 50f multi (4-3) .30 .25
**2674** A746 230f multi (4-4) .70 .30
*Nos. 2671-2674 (4)* 1.60 1.05

Nos. 2671-2674 exist imperf. Value, set of pairs *$325.*

China-San Marino Relations, 25th Anniv. — A747

No. 2675, Great Wall of China (2-1). No. 2676, Mt. Titano (2-2).

**1996, May 6 Photo. *Perf. 12***

**2675** A747 100f multi .40 .30
**2676** A747 100f multi .40 .30
*a.* Pair, #2675-2676 1.20 .80

See San Marino Nos. 1356-1357.

Artifacts from Hemudu Ruins A748

Designs: 20f, Agricultural tool. 50f, Pile to support building. 100f, Paddles for boats. 230f, Bird and sun carved in wood.

**1996, May 12 Litho. *Perf. 12***

**2677** A748 20f multi .30 .25
**2678** A748 50f multi .30 .25
**2679** A748 100f multi .35 .30
**2680** A748 230f multi .70 .40
*Nos. 2677-2680 (4)* 1.65 1.20

### Souvenir Sheet

CHINA '96, 9th Asian Intl. Philatelic Exhibition — A749

**1996, May 18 *Perf. 11½x12***

**2681** A749 500f multicolored *8.00* 3.00
*a.* Overprinted in gold *7.00* 5.00

No. 2681 exists imperf. Value, $25.
Overprint in margin of No. 2681a includes Chinese characters, Shanghai '97 exhibition emblem, and "PJZ-6." Issued in 1998.

Children's Activities — A750

Designs: 20f, Singing, playing musical instruments. 30f, Pushing child in wheelchair, holding umbrella. 50f, Placing flag on South Pole, penguins. 100f, Planting tree.

**1996, June 1 *Perf. 12***

**2682** A750 20f multi .30 .25
**2683** A750 30f multi .35 .25
**2684** A750 50f multi .40 .25
**2685** A750 100f multi .55 .30
*Nos. 2682-2685 (4)* 1.60 1.05

Modern Olympic Games, Cent. — A751

**1996, June 23 Photo. *Perf. 12***
**2686** A751 20f multicolored 1.25 .25

Protection of Land — A752

Stylized designs representing: 20f, Making use of land. 50f, Protection of farmland.

**1996, June 25 *Perf. 11x11½***
**2687** A752 20f multi .50 .25
**2688** A752 50f multi .80 .30

A753

Military Terraces — A754

**1996, July 9 Litho. *Perf. 12***
**2689** A753 20f multi .65 .25
**2690** A754 50f multi .95 .30

Vehicles A755

No. 2691, Red Flag, 4-door limousine. No. 2692, Dongfeng, stake truck. 50f, Jiefang, 4-door truck. 100f, Beijing, canvas-topped jeep.

**1996, July 15 Photo. *Perf. 12***
**2691** A755 20f multi (4-1) .35 .25
**2692** A755 20f multi (4-2) .35 .25
**2693** A755 50f multi (4-3) .50 .25
**2694** A755 100f multi (4-4) .70 .35
*Nos. 2691-2694 (4)* 1.90 1.10

New Tangshan Built Following 1976 Earthquake A756

No. 2695, Farm cottages (4-1). No. 2696, Factory (4-2). No. 2697, Street (4-3). No. 2698, Port (4-4).

**1996, July 28 *Perf. 11½***
**2695** A756 20f multi .30 .25
**2696** A756 50f multi .30 .25
**2697** A756 50f multi .30 .25
**2698** A756 100f multi .40 .30
*Nos. 2695-2698 (4)* 1.30 1.05

30th Intl. Geological Conference A757

**1996, Aug. 4 Litho. *Perf. 12***
**2699** A757 20f multicolored 1.00 .30

Tianchi Lake, Tianshan Mountains A758

20f, High mountain lake. No. 2701, Splendid Waterfalls. No. 2702, Snow-capped peaks. 100f, Lakeside scenery.

**1996, Aug. 8**
**2700** A758 20f multi (4-1) .40 .25
**2701** A758 50f multi, vert. (4-2) .55 .25
**2702** A758 50f multi, vert. (4-3) .55 .25
**2703** A758 100f multi (4-4) .70 .30
*Nos. 2700-2703 (4)* 2.20 1.05

**Wall Paintings Type of 1987**

10f, Illustration of Mount Wutai. 20f, King of Khotan, vert. 50f, Savior Avalokitesvara. 100f, Worshipping Bodhisattvas.
$5, Thousand Arm Avalokitesvara.

**1996, Aug. 15 Photo. *Perf. 11***
**2704** A557 10f multi, vert. .35 .25
**2705** A557 20f multi .35 .25
**2706** A557 50f multi .45 .30
**2707** A557 100f multi .70 .40
*Nos. 2704-2707 (4)* 1.85 1.20

**Souvenir Sheet**
**2708** A557 500f multicolored 8.00 2.60

No. 2708 contains one 46x102mm stamp.

Mausoleums of Western Xia — A759

Designs: No. 2709: Mausoleum terrace. No. 2710, Ornament on Divine Gate. 50f, Stele. 100f, Stele remnant, Shouling.

**1996, Aug. 22 Photo. *Perf. 11½***
**2709** A759 20f multi (4-1) .40 .25
**2710** A759 20f multi (4-2) .40 .25
**2711** A759 50f multi (4-3) .45 .25
**2712** A759 100f multi (4-4) .70 .30
*Nos. 2709-2712 (4)* 1.95 1.05

Railways in China A760

Designs: 15f, Datong-Quinhuangdao Railway. 20f, Lanzhou-Xinjiang Two-Track Railway. 50f, Beijing-Kowloon Railway. 100f, Beijing Western Railway Station

**1996, Sept. 1**
**2713** A760 15f multi .35 .25
**2714** A760 20f multi .50 .25
**2715** A760 50f multi .50 .30
**2716** A760 100f multi 1.05 .55
*Nos. 2713-2716 (4)* 2.40 1.35

A761

Chinese Archives: No. 2717, Archives on tortoise shells, Shang Dynasty. No. 2718, Archives on wood slips, Han Dynasty. 50f, Iron scrolls, Ming Dynasty. 100f, Books of Ch'ing Dynasty.

**1996, Sept. 2 Litho. *Perf. 12***
**2717** A761 20f multi (4-1) .60 .25
**2718** A761 20f multi (4-2) .60 .25
**2719** A761 50f multi (4-3) .85 .30
**2720** A761 100f multi (4-4) 1.75 .45
*Nos. 2717-2720 (4)* 3.80 1.25

A762

**1996, Sept. 10 *Perf. 12***
**2721** A762 20f Portrait .45 .25
**2722** A762 50f In uniform .75 .35

Ye Ting (1896-1946), co-founder of Chinese People's Liberation Army.

96th Conference of Inter-Parliamentary Union — A763

**1996, Sept. 16 *Perf. 11½***
**2723** A763 20f multi .75 .25

Shanghai A764

No. 2724, Communication (6-1). No. 2725, Lujiazui (6-2). No. 2726, Jinqiao (6-3). No. 2727, Zhanghiang (6-4). No. 2728, Waigaoqiao (6-5). No. 2729, Residential (6-6).
No. 2730, Panoramic view.

**Photo. & Engr.**

**1996, Sept. 21 *Perf. 11½***
**2724** A764 10f multicolored .30 .25
**2725** A764 20f multicolored .35 .25
**2726** A764 20f multicolored .40 .25
**2727** A764 50f multicolored .45 .30
**2728** A764 60f multicolored .50 .30
**2729** A764 100f multicolored .90 .35
*Nos. 2724-2729 (6)* 2.90 1.70

**Souvenir Sheet**

***Perf. 11***
**2730** A764 500f multicolored 7.50 4.25
*a.* Margin ovptd. 6.75 6.50

No. 2730 contains one 90x45mm stamp.
No. 2730a issued 10/20/01. It is inscribed in margin with multicolored emblems and gold "PJZ-14," "APEC CHINA 2001," and Chinese characters.

Space Navigation A765

**1996, Oct. 7 Litho. *Perf. 12***
**2731** A765 20f Rocket lift-off .45 .25
**2732** A765 100f Satellite in orbit .65 .35

Singapore Waterfront A766

Design: 290f, Panmen, Suzhou, China.

**1996, Oct. 9 Photo. *Perf. 11½***
**2733** A766 20f multi .30 .25
**2734** A766 290f multi 1.00 .40

See Singapore Nos. 768-769.

Victory of Long March, 60th Anniv. A767

Designs: 20f, Red Army through Marshland. 50f, Reunion of Three Armies.

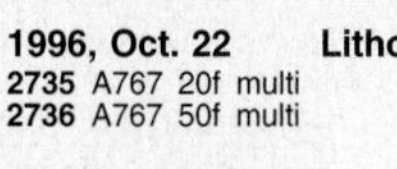

**1996, Oct. 22 Litho. *Perf. 12***
**2735** A767 20f multi 1.10 .30
**2736** A767 50f multi 2.15 .50

Colored Sculpture of Tianjin — A768

Designs: 20f, The Two Immortals. No. 2738, Making Candy. No. 2739, Returning from Fishing. 100f, Xi Chun in Painting.

**1996, Nov. 5 Photo. *Perf. 11½***
**2737** A768 20f multi (4-1) .45 .25
**2738** A768 50f multi (4-2) .55 .25
**2739** A768 50f multi (4-3) .55 .25
**2740** A768 100f multi (4-4) .65 .30
*Nos. 2737-2740 (4)* 2.20 1.05

Hong Kong — A769

20f, Bank of China. 40f, Container Terminal. 60f, Kai Tak Airport. 290f, Stock Exchange.

**1996, Dec. 19 Litho. *Perf. 12***
**2741** A769 20f multi (4-1) .45 .25
**2742** A769 40f multi (4-2) .45 .25
**2743** A769 60f multi (4-3) .60 .25
**2744** A769 290f multi (4-4) 1.75 .35
*Nos. 2741-2744 (4)* 3.25 1.10

Nos. 2741-2744 exist imperf. Value, set of pairs *$700.*

Visit China — A770

**1997, Jan. 1**
**2745** A770 50f multi 1.00 .25

A771

**1997, Jan. 1**
**2746** A771 50f multicolored .90 .25

First natl. agricultural census.

New Year 1997 (Year of the Ox)
A772 A773

**Photo. & Engr.**

**1997, Jan. 5 *Perf. 11½***
**2747** A772 50f multi (2-2) 1.00 .25
**2748** A773 150f multi (2-1) 2.30 .50

Paintings by Pan Tianshou (1897-1971) A774

No. 2749, Pines on the Yellow Mountain. No. 2750, Rosy Clouds of Dawn. No. 2751, Clearing Up after Mould Rains. No. 2752, Chrysanthemum and Bamboo. No. 2753,

Sleeping Cat. No. 2754, A Corner of Lingyan Brook.

**1997, Mar. 14 Photo. *Perf. 11½***

**2749** A774 50f multi (6-1) .35 .25

**2750** A774 50f multi (6-2) .35 .25

**2751** A774 100f multi (6-3) .75 .35

**2752** A774 100f multi (6-4) .75 .35

**2753** A774 150f multi (6-5) 1.40 .40

**2754** A774 150f multi (6-6) 1.40 .40

*Nos. 2749-2754 (6)* 5.00 2.00

**Great Wall Type of 1995**
**China Post No. R29**

**1997, Apr. 1 Photo. *Perf. 13x12***

**2755** A730 50f multicolored .30 .25

A776

Tea: No. 2756, People forming circle beside tea tree. No. 2757, Statue of tea sage. No. 2758, Tea utensils, horiz. No. 2759, Painting of tea party, horiz.

**1997, Apr. 8 Litho. *Perf. 12***

**2756** A776 50f multi (4-1) .60 .25

**2757** A776 50f multi (4-2) .60 .25

**2758** A776 150f multi (4-3) 1.05 .40

**2759** A776 150f multi (4-4) 1.05 .40

*Nos. 2756-2759 (4)* 3.30 1.30

A777

Stylized designs depicting: No. 2760, Celebration. No. 2761, Unity (group of people), horiz. 200f, Advance (horses running), horiz.

**1997, May 1 Photo. *Perf. 11½***

**2760** A777 50f multi (3-1) .40 .25

**2761** A777 50f multi (3-2) .40 .25

**2762** A777 200f multi (3-3) 1.15 .35

*Nos. 2760-2762 (3)* 1.95 .85

Inner Mongolia Autonomous Region, 50th anniv.

Pheasants A778

Designs: 50f, Chinese copper pheasant. 540f, Common pheasant.

**Litho. & Engr.**

**1997, May 9 *Perf. 11½x11***

**2763** A778 50f multi (2-1) .30 .25

**2764** A778 540f multi (2-2) 1.40 1.00

See Sweden Nos. 2225-2226.

Dong Architecture — A779

No. 2765, Zengchong Drum Tower. No. 2766, Bai'er Drum Tower. No. 2767, Wind and Rain Bridge over the River, horiz. No. 2768, Wind and Rain Bridge in the Field, horiz.

**1997, June 2 Litho. *Perf. 12***

**2765** A779 50f multi (4-1) .30 .25

**2766** A779 50f multi (4-2) .30 .25

*a.* Pair, #2765-2766 1.05 .60

**2767** A779 150f multi (4-3) .40 .25

**2768** A779 150f multi (4-4) .40 .25

*a.* Pair, #2767-2768 1.75 1.10

*Nos. 2765-2768 (4)* 1.40 1.00

Maiji Grottoes — A780

Statues: No. 2769, Buddha and Xieshi Bodhisattva. No. 2770, Xieshi Bodhisattva and his disciple. 100f, Maid. No. 2772, Buddha. No. 2773, Xieshi Bodhisattva. 200f, Provider.

**1997, June 13**

**2769** A780 50f multi (6-1) .35 .25

**2770** A780 50f multi (6-2) .35 .25

**2771** A780 100f multi (6-3) .50 .25

**2772** A780 150f multi (6-4) .60 .30

**2773** A780 150f multi (6-5) .60 .30

**2774** A780 200f multi (6-6) .85 .35

*Nos. 2769-2774 (6)* 3.25 1.70

A780a

A781

Texts surrounded by flowers: 50f, Sino-British Joint Declaration. 150f, Basic Law of the Hong Kong Special Adminstrative Region. 800f, Deng Xiaoping.

**1997, July 1 Litho. *Perf. 12***

**2774A** A780a 50f multi (2-1) .30 .25

**2774B** A780a 150f multi (2-2) .80 .50

**Souvenir Sheets**

**2774C** A781 800f multi 3.50 2.40

*d.* Overprinted in sheet margin 5.00 3.25

**Litho. (stamp) & Embossed (margin)**

***Perf. 13½***

**2775** A781 $50 gold & multi *30.00 30.00*

*a.* Overprinted in margin *37.50 37.50*

Deng Xiaoping (1904-97), return of Hong Kong to China.

No. 2775 was released in special souvenir folder.

No. 2744C exists imperf. Value, *$500.*

No. 2774Cd contains gold Chinese inscription for Hong Kong's Return Exhibition Tour, emblem, and "PJZ-8" in sheet margin. Issued: 6/19/98.

Overprint in margin on No. 2775a is Chinese inscription, "2000-1" and "(2-1)J." Issued: 1/1/00.

Ancient Temples of Wutai Mountain A782

Designs: 40f, Taihuai Township. No. 2777, Nanchan Temple. No. 2778, Foguang Temple. No. 2779, Xiantong Temple. No. 2780, Bodhisattva Summit. 200f, Zhenhai Temple.

**1997, July 26 Litho. *Perf. 12***

**2776** A782 40f multi (6-1) .35 .25

**2777** A782 50f multi (6-2) .40 .25

**2778** A782 50f multi (6-3) .40 .25

**2779** A782 150f multi (6-4) .65 .30

**2780** A782 150f multi (6-5) .65 .30

**2781** A782 200f multi (6-6) .80 .35

*Nos. 2776-2781 (6)* 3.25 1.70

Chinese People's Liberation Army, 70th Anniv. A783

No. 2782, Land Force. No. 2783, Naval Force. No. 2784, Air Force. No. 2785, Strategic Missile Troops. 200f, Joint military maneuvers.

**1997, Aug. 1**

**2782** A783 50f multi (5-1) .45 .25

**2783** A783 50f multi (5-2) .45 .25

**2784** A783 50f multi (5-3) .45 .25

**2785** A783 50f multi (5-4) .45 .25

**2786** A783 200f multi (5-5) 1.90 .75

*Nos. 2782-2786 (5)* 3.70 1.75

Shoushan Stone Carvings — A784

Designs: No. 2787, "Rhythm of Autumn," vert. No. 2788, "Rhinoceros under Sunshine,", vert. No. 2789, "Jade's Fragrance," (basket of fruit). No. 2790, "Drunken Joy."

800f, Qianlong's Chain Seals.

**1997, Aug. 17 Litho. *Perf. 12***

**2787** A784 50f multi (4-1) .50 .25

**2788** A784 50f multi (4-2) .50 .25

**2789** A784 150f multi (4-3) .90 .30

**2790** A784 150f multi (4-4) .90 .30

*Nos. 2787-2790 (4)* 2.80 1.10

**Souvenir Sheet**

**2791** A784 800f multi 4.00 3.00

No. 2791 contains one 60x60mm stamp.

**Great Wall Type of 1995**
**China Post No. R29**

Gates: 30f, Huangyaguan. 100f, Badaling. 150f, Joyongguan. 200f, Zijingguan.

**1997, Sept. 1 Photo. *Perf. 13x12***

**2792** A730 30f yellow & black .30 .45

**2793** A730 100f vermilion & black .50 .45

**2794** A730 150f green & black .70 .45

**2795** A730 200f red & black .85 .50

*Nos. 2792-2795 (4)* 2.35 1.85

Communist Party of China, 15th Natl. Congress — A785

**1997, Sept. 12 Litho. *Perf. 12***

**2796** A785 50f multicolored 1.00 .30

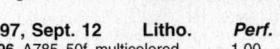

A786

No. 2797, China Rose. No. 2798, New Zealand Monthly Rose.

**1997, Oct. 9 Photo. *Perf. 11½***

**2797** 150f multi (2-1) .50 .30

**2798** 150f multi (2-2) .50 .30

*a.* A786 Pair, #2797-2798 1.50 1.40

See New Zealand Nos. 1469-1470.

Eighth Natl. Games — A788

**1997, Oct. 12 Litho. *Perf. 12***

**2799** A788 50f Athletes (2-1) .30 .25

**2800** A788 150f Stadium )2-2) .60 .30

*a.* Souv. sheet, #2799-2800 4.00 2.60

No. 2800a sold for 300f.

Temple of Heaven, Beijing A789

No. 2801, Hall of Prayers for Bumper Harvests. No. 2802, Imperial Vault of Heaven. No. 2803, Circular Mound Altar. No. 2804, Fasting Palace.

**1997, Oct. 16 Litho. *Perf. 12***

**2801** A789 50f multi (4-1) .30 .25

**2802** A789 50f multi (4-2) .30 .25

*a.* Pair, #2801-2802 1.25 .70

**2803** A789 150f multi (4-3) .45 .25

**2804** A789 150f multi (4-4) .45 .25

*a.* Pair, #2803-2804 2.15 1.10

*Nos. 2801-2804 (4)* 1.50 1.00

Mt. Huangshan — A790

a, Mt. Huangshan at sunrise (8-1). b, Xihai Peaks (8-2). c, Flying Rock in surging clouds (8-3). d, Beihai in drifting clouds (8-4). e, Yuping Peak (8-5). f, Mystical stone (8-6). g, Tiandu Peak over clouds (8-7). h, Fabled Abode of Immortals (8-8).

**1997, Oct. 20 Photo. *Perf. 11½***

**Sheet of 8 + Label**

**2805** A790 200f #a.-h. 9.00 6.50

Nos. 2805d, 2805e are each 36x46mm.

22nd UPU Congress, Beijing, 1999.

City Wall of Xi'an — A791

Designs: No. 2806, Surrounding tower. No. 2807, Arrow Tower. No. 2808, Watch Tower. No. 2809, Corner Tower.

**1997, Oct. 24 Litho. *Perf. 12***

**2806** A791 50f multi (4-1) .30 .25

**2807** A791 50f multi (4-2) .30 .25

**2808** A791 150f multi (4-3) .50 .25

**2809** A791 150f multi (4-4) .50 .25

*Nos. 2806-2809 (4)* 1.60 1.00

Three Gorges Dam Project on Yangtze River — A792

No. 2810, New channel being opened to navigation. No. 2811, Damming Yangtze River.

**1997, Nov. 8 Photo. *Perf. 11½***

**2810** A792 50f multi (2-1) .35 .25

**2811** A792 50f multi (2-2) .35 .25

*a.* Pair, #2810-2811 1.25 .75

Macao Landmarks A793

50f, Ma Kok Temple. 100f, Lin Fong Temple. 150f, St. Paul's Ruins. 200f, Guia Lighthouse.

**1997, Nov. 11 Litho. *Perf. 12***

**2812** A793 50f multi (4-1) .30 .25

**2813** A793 100f multi (4-2) .40 .25

**2814** A793 150f multi (4-3) .45 .35

**2815** A793 200f multi (4-4) .60 .40

*Nos. 2812-2815 (4)* 1.75 1.25

Steel Production Exceeds 100 Million Tons in 1996 — A794

50f, Ancient method of producing steel. 150f, Modern mill, pouring steel from smelter.

**1997, Nov. 25**

**2816** A794 50f multi (2-1) .40 .25
**2817** A794 150f multi (2-2) .95 .40

Telecommunications A795

Stylized designs: No. 2818, Digital transmissions. No. 2819, Computer, "X-changing" data. No. 2820, Computer receiving signals, Chinese landmarks. No. 2821, Cellular phone transmission, man's head.

**1997, Dec. 10**

**2818** A795 50f multi (4-1) .30 .25
**2819** A795 50f multi (4-2) .30 .25
**2820** A795 150f multi (4-3) .50 .25
**2821** A795 150f multi (4-4) .50 .25
*Nos. 2818-2821 (4)* 1.60 1.00

**Literature Type of 1987**

Outlaws of the Marsh: 40f, Huyan Zhuo coaxes Guan Sheng in a moonlit night. No. 2823, Lu Junyi captures Shi Wengong. No. 2824, Yan Qing defeats sky supporting pillar. 150f, Thunderbolt defeats Imperial Army.

800f, Heroes of Mount Liangshan take seats in order of rank.

**1997, Dec. 22 Photo. *Perf. 11***

**2822** A570 40f multi (4-1) .35 .25
**2823** A570 50f multi (4-2) .50 .25
**2824** A570 50f multi (4-3) .50 .25
**2825** A570 150f multi (4-4) .95 .40
*Nos. 2822-2825 (4)* 2.30 1.15

**Souvenir Sheet**

**2826** A570 800f multicolored 4.00 2.75

No. 2826 contains one 60x90mm stamp.

New Year 1998 (Year of the Tiger)
A796 A797

**Photo. & Engr.**

**1998, Jan. 5 *Perf. 11½***

**2827** A796 50f multi (2-1) .85 .25
**2828** A797 150f multi (2-2) 1.90 .40

Gardens of Lingnan A798

**1998, Jan. 18 Litho. *Perf. 12***

**2829** A798 50f Keyaun (4-1) .50 .25
**2830** A798 50f Liangyuan (4-2) .50 .25
**2831** A798 100f Qinghui (4-3) .65 .30
**2832** A798 200f Yuyin Villa (4-4) 1.15 .35
*Nos. 2829-2832 (4)* 2.80 1.15

Deng Xiaoping (1904-97) — A799

No. 2833, At middle age. No. 2834, During Liberation War. No. 2835, With Mao Tse-tung. 100f, As Chairman of Central Military Commission. 150f, Making speech on 35th anniversary of People's Republic. 200f, Making speech, hand raised, 1992.

**1998, Feb. 19 Photo. *Perf. 11½***

**2833** A799 50f multi (6-1) .55 .25
**2834** A799 50f multi (6-2) .55 .25
**2835** A799 50f multi (6-3) .55 .25
**2836** A799 100f multi (6-4) .80 .30
**2837** A799 150f multi (6-5) 1.15 .40
**2838** A799 200f multi (6-6) 1.40 .55
*Nos. 2833-2838 (6)* 5.00 2.00

Chinese People's Police A800

Designs: 40f, Golden shield. No. 2840, Blitz operation. No. 2841, Cooperation between police and people. 100f, Traffic control. 150f, Fire police. 200f, Border guards.

**1998, Feb. 28 Litho. *Perf. 12***

**2839** A800 40f multi (6-1) .45 .25
**2840** A800 50f multi (6-2) .55 .25
**2841** A800 50f multi (6-3) .55 .25
**2842** A800 100f multi (6-4) .70 .30
**2843** A800 150f multi (6-5) .95 .30
**2844** A800 200f multi (6-6) 1.25 .35
*Nos. 2839-2844 (6)* 4.45 1.70

A801

**1998, Mar. 5**

**2845** A801 50f multi (1-1) 1.00 .25

Ninth Natl. People's Congress, Beijing.

A802

Chou En-lai (1898-1976), Communist Party leader: No. 2846, In military uniform on horse. No. 2847, As First Premier, walking. No. 2848, As diplomat wearing lei. No. 2849, Standing and applauding.

**1998, Mar. 5 Photo. *Perf. 11½***

**2846** A802 50f multi (4-1) 1.05 .25
**2847** A802 50f multi (4-2) 1.05 .25
**2848** A802 150f multi (4-3) 1.45 .50
**2849** A802 150f multi (4-4) 1.45 .50
*Nos. 2846-2849 (4)* 5.00 1.50

Nine-Village Valley A803

Designs: No. 2850, Fangcao Lake. No. 2851, Wuhua Lake. No. 2852, Shuzheng Waterfalls. No. 2853, Nuorilang Waterfalls.

No. 2854, Long Lake.

**1998, Mar. 26 Litho. *Perf. 12***

**2850** A803 50f multi (4-1) .40 .25
**2851** A803 50f multi (4-2) .40 .25
**2852** A803 150f multi (4-3) .70 .35
**2853** A803 150f multi (4-4) .70 .35
*Nos. 2850-2853 (4)* 2.20 1.20

**Souvenir Sheet**

**2854** A803 800f multicolored 3.50 2.75

No. 2854 contains one 93x52mm stamp.

Dai Architecture A804

No. 2855, Building on stilts. No. 2856, Well. No. 2857, Pavilion. No. 2858, Pagoda.

**1998, Apr. 12 Photo. *Perf. 11½***

**2855** A804 50f multi (4-1) .40 .25
**2856** A804 50f multi (4-2) .40 .25
**2857** A804 150f multi (4-3) .70 .35
**2858** A804 150f multi (4-4) .70 .35
*Nos. 2855-2858 (4)* 2.20 1.20

Construction, Hainan Special Economic Zone — A805

No. 2859, Urban construction, Haikou. No. 2860, Economic development zone, Yangpu. No. 2861, Phoenix Intl. Airport, Sanya. No. 2862, Natl. tourism and resort zone, Yalongwan.

**1998, Apr. 13 Litho. *Perf. 12***

**2859** A805 50f multi (4-1) .30 .25
**2860** A805 50f multi (4-2) .30 .25
*a.* Pair, #2859-2860 1.20 .65
**2861** A805 150f multi (4-3) .55 .30
**2862** A805 150f multi (4-4) .55 .30
*a.* Pair, #2861-2862 2.00 1.00
*Nos. 2859-2862 (4)* 1.70 1.10

Ancient Academies A806

Designs: No. 2863, Yingtian. No. 2864, Songyang. No. 2865, Yuelu. No. 2866, Bailu.

**1998, Apr. 29**

**2863** A806 50f multi (4-1) .35 .25
**2864** A806 50f multi (4-2) .35 .25
**2865** A806 150f multi (4-3) .65 .35
**2866** A806 150f multi (4-4) .65 .35
*Nos. 2863-2866 (4)* 2.00 1.20

Beijing University, Cent. — A807

**1998, May 4 Litho. *Perf. 12***

**2867** A807 50f multicolored 1.00 .25

22nd UPU Congress, Beijing — A808

50f, Emblem (2-1). 540f, Emblem, vert. (2-2).

**1998, May 15 Litho. *Perf. 12***

**2868** A808 50f multicolored .30 .25
**2869** A808 540f multicolored 1.75 .85

Shennongjia Nature Reserve A809

No. 2870, Mountain peaks. No. 2871, River, gorge. No. 2872, Primitive forest. No. 2873, Grasslands.

**1998, June 6**

**2870** A809 50f multi (4-1) .30 .25
**2871** A809 50f multi (4-2) .30 .25
**2872** A809 150f multi (4-3) .55 .35
**2873** A809 150f multi (4-4) .55 .35
*Nos. 2870-2873 (4)* 1.70 1.20

Chongqing A810

**1998, June 18 Litho. *Perf. 12***

**2874** A810 50f Great Hall (2-1) .60 .25
**2875** A810 150f Port (2-2) 1.00 .45

Xilinguole Grassland A811

Designs: No. 2876, Sheep grazing, sheep herders. No. 2877, Cattle grazing, flowers. 150f, Poplar and birch forest, deer.

800f, Horses at Xilinguole River Bend.

**1998, June 24**

**2876** A811 50f multi (3-1) .40 .25
**2877** A811 50f multi (3-2) .40 .25
**2878** A811 150f multi (3-3) .85 .40
*Nos. 2876-2878 (3)* 1.65 .90

**Souvenir Sheet**

**2879** A811 800f multicolored 4.25 2.75

No. 2879 contains one 56x36mm stamp.

Paintings, by He Xiangning (1878-1972) A812

50f, Tiger (3-1). 100f, Lion, vert. (3-2). 150f, Plum blossom, vert. (3-3).

***Perf. 12½ Syncopated***

**1998, June 27 Photo.**

**2880** A812 50f multi .50 .25
**2881** A812 100f multi .75 .35
**2882** A812 150f multi .95 .50
*Nos. 2880-2882 (3)* 2.20 1.10

Jingpo Lake — A813

Views of lake: No. 2883, Bridge, houses on cliff, boat. No. 2884, Islands, boats at shore. No. 2885, Boat, island. No. 2886, Waterfalls.

**1998, Aug. 15 Litho. *Perf. 12***

**2883** A813 50f multi (4-1) .30 .25
**2884** A813 50f multi (4-2) .30 .25
**2885** A813 50f multi (4-3) .30 .25
**2886** A813 50f multi (4-4) .30 .25
*a.* Strip of 4, #2883-2886 2.75 1.25

Würzburg Palace A814

Puning Temple, Chengde A815

**1998, Aug. 20 Litho. *Perf. 12***

**2887** A814 50f multi (2-1) .35 .25
**2888** A815 540f multi (2-2) 1.90 1.40

See Germany Nos. 2012-2013.

**Literature Type of 1987**

Romance of the Three Kingdoms: No. 2889, Liu Bei finds a guardian for his heir at Baidi City. No. 2890, Zhuge Liang leads his army home, vert. 100f, Death of Zhuge Liang. 150f, Three Kingdoms united under the reign of Jin, vert.

800f, The Stratagem of Empty City.

**1998, Aug. 26 Photo. *Perf. 11½***

| | | | | |
|---|---|---|---|---|
| **2889** | A570 | 50f multi (4-1) | .30 | .25 |
| **2890** | A570 | 50f multi (4-2) | .30 | .25 |
| **2891** | A570 | 100f multi (4-3) | .50 | .35 |
| **2892** | A570 | 150f multi (4-4) | .75 | .55 |
| | | *Nos. 2889-2892 (4)* | 1.85 | 1.40 |

**Souvenir Sheet**

| | | | | |
|---|---|---|---|---|
| **2893** | A570 | 800f multicolored | 5.00 | 3.00 |

No. 2893 contains one 158x37mm stamp.

The Louvre, France — A817

Design: 200f, Hall of Heavenly Peace, Imperial Palace, China.

**1998, Sept. 12 Photo. *Perf. 13x13½***

| | | | | |
|---|---|---|---|---|
| **2895** | A817 | 50f multi (2-1) | .75 | .25 |
| **2896** | A817 | 200f multi (2-2) | .85 | .55 |

See France Nos. 2669-2670.

Cliff Paintings of Helan Mountains A818

50f, Human face (3-1). 100f, Hunting (3-2). 150f, Ox (3-3).

**1998, Sept. 23 Litho. *Perf. 12***

| | | | | |
|---|---|---|---|---|
| **2897** | A818 | 50f multi | .30 | .25 |
| **2898** | A818 | 100f multi | .40 | .35 |
| **2899** | A818 | 150f multi | .55 | .45 |
| | | *Nos. 2897-2899 (3)* | 1.25 | 1.05 |

Longquan Pottery and Porcelain — A819

Designs: No. 2900, Vase with five spouts. No. 2901, Vase with phoenix ears. No. 2902, Double gourd vase. 150f, Ewer.

**1998, Oct. 13**

| | | | | |
|---|---|---|---|---|
| **2900** | A819 | 50f multi (4-1) | .30 | .25 |
| **2901** | A819 | 50f multi (4-2) | .30 | .25 |
| **2902** | A819 | 50f multi (4-3) | .30 | .25 |
| **2903** | A819 | 150f multi (4-4) | .65 | .50 |
| | | *Nos. 2900-2903 (4)* | 1.55 | 1.25 |

Mausoleum of Yandi — A820

Designs: 50f, Meridian Gate. 100f, Saluting Pavilion. 150f, Tomb.

**1998, Oct. 28 Litho. *Perf. 12***

| | | | | |
|---|---|---|---|---|
| **2904** | A820 | 50f multi (3-1) | .35 | .25 |
| **2905** | A820 | 100f multi (3-2) | .55 | .30 |
| **2906** | A820 | 150f multi (3-3) | .80 | .45 |
| *a.* | | Souvenir sheet, #2904-2906 | 3.25 | 1.75 |
| | | *Nos. 2904-2906 (3)* | 1.70 | 1.00 |

**Great Wall Type of 1995**
**China Post No. R29**

10f, Jiumenko Pass. 300f, Niagziguan Pass. 420f, Pianguan Pass. 500f, Bianjing Tower.

**1998, Nov. 1 Photo. *Perf. 13x12***

| | | | | |
|---|---|---|---|---|
| **2907** | A730 | 10f apple grn & blk | .30 | .25 |
| **2908** | A730 | 300f olive & black | 1.30 | 1.25 |
| **2909** | A730 | 420f brn org & blk | 1.70 | 1.60 |
| **2910** | A730 | 500f blue, blk & brn | 2.00 | 1.75 |
| | | *Nos. 2907-2910 (4)* | 5.30 | 4.85 |

Major Campaigns in Liberation War — A821

No. 2911, Making plans. No. 2912, Conquering Jinzhou. No. 2913, Battle in Huaihai. No. 2914, Liberating Beijing. 150f, People moving supplies.

**1998, Nov. 14 Litho. *Perf. 12***

| | | | | |
|---|---|---|---|---|
| **2911** | A821 | 50f red & multi (5-1) | .50 | .25 |
| **2912** | A821 | 50f gray & multi (5-2) | .50 | .25 |
| **2913** | A821 | 50f org yel & multi (5-3) | .50 | .25 |
| **2914** | A821 | 50f org & multi (5-4) | .50 | .25 |
| **2915** | A821 | 150f brn org & multi (5-5) | 1.20 | .75 |
| | | *Nos. 2911-2915 (5)* | 3.20 | 1.75 |

Liu Shaoqi (1898-1969), Communist Party Leader — A822

Various portraits.

**1998, Nov. 24 Photo. *Perf. 11½***

| | | | | |
|---|---|---|---|---|
| **2916** | A822 | 50f multi (4-1), vert. | .45 | .25 |
| **2917** | A822 | 50f multi (4-2), vert. | .45 | .25 |
| **2918** | A822 | 50f shown (4-3) | .45 | .25 |
| **2919** | A822 | 150f multi (4-4) | 1.25 | .50 |
| | | *Nos. 2916-2919 (4)* | 2.60 | 1.25 |

Chillon Castle, Lake Geneva — A823

Bridge 24, Slender West Lake, Yangzhou — A824

**1998, Nov. 25 *Perf. 11x11½***

| | | | | |
|---|---|---|---|---|
| **2920** | A823 | 50f multi (2-1) | .35 | .25 |
| **2921** | A824 | 540f multi (2-2) | 1.75 | 1.00 |

See Switzerland Nos. 1037-1039.

Lingqu Canal A825

No. 2922, Dam. No. 2923, Bridge over canal, vert. 150f, Boat approaching lock, vert.

**1998, Dec. 1 Litho. *Perf. 12***

| | | | | |
|---|---|---|---|---|
| **2922** | A825 | 50f multi (3-1) | .40 | .25 |
| **2923** | A825 | 50f multi (3-2) | .40 | .25 |
| **2924** | A825 | 150f multi (3-3) | .85 | .45 |
| | | *Nos. 2922-2924 (3)* | 1.65 | .95 |

Buildings in Macao A826

Designs: 50f, Building complex, Nanwan. 100f, Friendship Bridge. 150f, Macao Stadium. 200f, Macao Intl. Airport.

**1998, Dec. 12 Litho. *Perf. 12***

| | | | | |
|---|---|---|---|---|
| **2925** | A826 | 50f multi (4-1) | .35 | .25 |
| **2926** | A826 | 100f multi (4-2) | .60 | .30 |
| **2927** | A826 | 150f multi (4-3) | .80 | .40 |
| **2928** | A826 | 200f multi (4-4) | 1.00 | .60 |
| | | *Nos. 2925-2928 (4)* | 2.75 | 1.55 |

11th Communist Party Congress, 20th Anniv. — A827

50f, Deng Xiaoping (2-1). 150f, Handbill, buildings (2-2).

**1998, Dec. 18**

| | | | | |
|---|---|---|---|---|
| **2929** | A827 | 50f multicolored | .90 | .25 |
| **2930** | A827 | 150f multicolored | 1.60 | .45 |

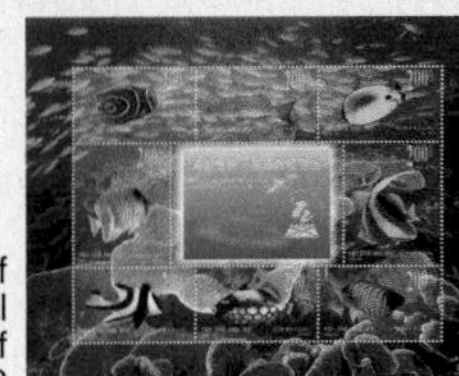

Fish of the Coral Reef A828

a, Pomacanthus imperator (8-1). b, Plectropomus maculatus (8-2). c, Chaetodon plebeius (8-3). d, Chaetodon chrysurus (8-4), vert. e, Heniochus acuminatus (8-5), vert. f, Lutjanus sebae (8-6). g, Balistoides conspicillum (8-7). h, Pygoplites diancanthus (8-8).

**1998, Dec. 22 Photo. *Perf. 11½***

**Sheet of 8**

| | | | | |
|---|---|---|---|---|
| **2931** | A828 | 200f #a.-h. + label | 8.75 | 6.00 |
| *i.* | | As No. 2931, with margin ovptd. in gold | *8.00* | *8.00* |

UPU, 22nd Congress, Beijing '99 World Philatelic Exhibition.

Nos. 2931d-2931e are each 40x49mm.

No. 2931i issued 7/15/00. No. 2931i inscribed in margin in gold "PJZ-12," "1997-1999" and Chinese characters. Inscription for best philatelic item from 1997-99.

New Year 1999 (Year of the Rabbit)
A829 A830

50f, Stylized rabbit (2-1). 150f, Symbol for rabbit (2-2).

**Photo. & Engr.**

**1999, Jan. 5 *Perf. 11½***

| | | | | |
|---|---|---|---|---|
| **2932** | A829 | 50f multicolored | 1.50 | .25 |
| **2933** | A830 | 150f multi | 2.20 | .50 |

**Great Wall Type of 1995**
**China Post No. R29**

5f, Hushan Section. 20f, Shanhaiguan Pass. 40f, Jinshanling Section. 80f, Mutianyu Section. 270f, Pingxingguan Pass. 320f, Desheng Pass. 440f, Yanmen Pass. 540f, Zhenbei Tower.

**1999, Mar. 1 Photo. *Perf. 13x12***

| | | | | |
|---|---|---|---|---|
| **2934** | A730 | 5f bl, blk & bl grn | .30 | .25 |
| **2935** | A730 | 20f vio & blk | .35 | .25 |
| **2936** | A730 | 40f pink & blk | .40 | .30 |
| **2937** | A730 | 80f grn, blk & ol | .50 | .40 |
| **2938** | A730 | 270f grn, blk & brn | 1.30 | .65 |
| **2939** | A730 | 320f vio, blk & bwn | 1.75 | 1.10 |
| **2940** | A730 | 440f red brn, blk & bwn | 3.25 | 2.00 |
| **2941** | A730 | 540f blue & black | 3.00 | 1.50 |
| | | *Nos. 2934-2941 (8)* | 10.85 | 6.45 |

Stone Carvings of the Han Dynasty — A831

No. 2942, Plowing fields with oxen. No. 2943, Group weaving. No. 2944, Three figures dancing in front of fire. No. 2945, Horses, carriage. No. 2946, Group in assassination attempt. No. 2947, Goddess Chang'e.

**1999, Mar. 16 *Perf. 12***

| | | | | |
|---|---|---|---|---|
| **2942** | A831 | 50f dark green & blk | .30 | .25 |
| **2943** | A831 | 50f brown & blk | .30 | .25 |
| **2944** | A831 | 50f dark blue & blk | .30 | .25 |
| **2945** | A831 | 150f dark brown & blk | .55 | .45 |
| **2946** | A831 | 150f brown olive & blk | .55 | .45 |
| **2947** | A831 | 150f dark purple & blk | .55 | .45 |
| | | *Nos. 2942-2947 (6)* | 2.55 | 2.10 |

A832

Chinese Ceramics (Porcelain from the Jun Kiln): 80f, Halberd-shaped cup. 100f, Cup. 150f, Dual-handled stove. 200f, Dual-handled vase with base.

**1999, Apr. 8 Photo. *Perf. 11½***

| | | | | |
|---|---|---|---|---|
| **2948** | A832 | 80f multi (4-1) | .35 | .25 |
| **2949** | A832 | 100f multi (4-2) | .45 | .30 |
| **2950** | A832 | 150f multi (4-3) | .65 | .45 |
| **2951** | A832 | 200f multi (4-4) | .90 | .60 |
| | | *Nos. 2948-2951 (4)* | 2.35 | 1.60 |

**Great Wall Type of 1995**
**China Post No. R29**

Designs: 60f, Huanghua Tower. $10, Huama section. $20, Sanguankou Pass. $50 Jiayuguan Pass.

**1999, May 1 Photo. *Perf. 13x12***

| | | | | |
|---|---|---|---|---|
| **2952** | A730 | 60f multicolored | .30 | .30 |

**Size: 28x22mm**

***Perf. 11½***

**Photo. & Engr.**

| | | | | |
|---|---|---|---|---|
| **2953** | A730 | $10 multicolored | 4.00 | 3.00 |
| **2954** | A730 | $20 multicolored | 8.00 | 5.75 |
| **2955** | A730 | $50 multicolored | 20.00 | 14.50 |
| | | *Nos. 2952-2955 (4)* | 32.30 | 23.55 |

A833

**1999, May 1 Litho. *Perf. 12***

| | | | | |
|---|---|---|---|---|
| **2956** | A833 | 80f shown (2-1) | .55 | .25 |
| **2957** | A833 | 200f Tree (2-2) | 1.10 | .55 |

Kunming World Horticultural Fair.

Red Deer — A834

**1999, May 18 Litho. *Perf. 11x11½***

| | | | | |
|---|---|---|---|---|
| **2958** | A834 | 80f Bucks | .35 | .25 |
| **2959** | A834 | 80f Does | .35 | .25 |
| *a.* | | Pair, #2958-2959 | 1.60 | .70 |

See Russia No. 6514.

Beauty of Putuo Mountain A835

No. 2960, Puji Temple (6-1). No. 2961, Nantian Gate, vert. (6-2). No. 2962, 100-step Sand (6-3). No. 2963, Pantuo Rock (6-4). No. 2964, Fanyin Cave, vert. (6-5). No. 2965, Fayu Temple (6-6).

**1999, June 3 Litho. *Perf. 12***

| | | | | |
|---|---|---|---|---|
| **2960** | A835 | 30f multicolored | .35 | .25 |
| **2961** | A835 | 60f multicolored | .40 | .25 |
| **2962** | A835 | 60f multicolored | .40 | .25 |
| **2963** | A835 | 80f multicolored | .45 | .30 |
| **2964** | A835 | 80f multicolored | .45 | .30 |
| **2965** | A835 | 280f multicolored | 1.15 | .75 |
| | | *Nos. 2960-2965 (6)* | 3.20 | 2.10 |

Fang Zhimin (1899-1935), Revolutionary — A836

**1999, Aug. 21 Photo. *Perf. 11¼***

| | | | | |
|---|---|---|---|---|
| **2966** | A836 | 80f Close-up (2-1) | .65 | .35 |
| **2967** | A836 | 80f Standing (2-2) | .65 | .35 |

Souvenir Sheet

China 1999 World Philatelic Exhibition — A837

**1999, Aug. 21** ***Perf. 11½x11¼***
**2968** A837 800f multicolored 5.00 3.75

Exists overprinted in upper corners in gold. Value, $7.50.

A838

22nd UPU Congress — A839

Congress sites: 80f, 1st, Bern. 540f, 22nd, Beijing.
800f, Inscription by Pres. Jiang Zemin.

**1999, Aug. 23** **Litho.** ***Perf. 12***
**2969** A838 80f multi (2-1) .35 .25
**2970** A838 540f multi (2-2) 1.90 1.25

**Souvenir Sheet**
***Perf. 12¼***
**2971** A839 800f multicolored 5.00 3.25

UPU, 125th Anniv. — A840

**1999, Sept. 7** **Litho.** ***Perf. 12***
**2972** A840 80f multicolored 1.10 .35

Intl. Year of the Elderly — A841

**1999, Sept. 9**
**2973** A841 80f multicolored 1.10 .25

Chinese People's Political Consultative Conference, 50th Anniv. — A842

60f, Building (2-1). 80f, Mao Zedong, vert. (2-2).

**1999, Sept. 21**
**2974** A842 60f multi .40 .25
**2975** A842 80f multi 1.20 .35

Ethnic Groups in China — A843

Designs (stamp number following "56-" at LR): a, Han (1). b, Mongols (2). c, Hui (3). d, Tibetans (4). e, Uygurs (5) f, Miao (6). g, Yi (7). h, Zhuang (8). i, Bouyei (9). j, Koreans (10). k, Manchu (11). l, Dongs (12). m, Yao (13). n, Bai (14). o, Tujia (15). p, Hani (16). q, Kazak (17). r, Dai (18). s, Li (19). t, Lisu (20). u, Va (21). v, She (22). w, Gaoshan (23). x, Lahu (24). y, Shui (25). z, Dongxiang (26). aa, Naxi (27). ab, Jingpo (28). ac, Kirgiz (29). ad, Tu (30). ae, Daur (31). af, Mulam (32). ag, Qiang (33). ah, Blang (34). ai, Salas (35). aj, Maonan (36). ak, Gelao (37). al, Xibe (38). am, Achang (39). an, Pumi (40). ao, Tajiks (41). ap, Nu (42). aq, Uzbeks (43). ar, Russians (44). as, Ewenki (45). at, De'ang (46). au, Bonan (47). av, Yugur (48). aw, Jing (49). ax, Tartars (50). ay, Drung (51). az, Oroqen (52). ba, Hezhe (53). bb, Moiba (54). bc, Lhoba (55). bd, Jino (56).

**1999, Oct. 7** **Photo.** ***Perf. 13¼***
**2976** A843 80f Sheet of 56, #a.-bd. 26.00 17.00
*be.* As #2976, overprinted in margin *45.00 45.00*

No. 2976be includes the inscription "PJZ-17," in the selvage at the bottom right of the sheet.

Mountains A844

**1999, Oct. 5** ***Perf. 11½x11¼***
**2977** A844 80f Lushan (2-1) .50 .30
**2978** A844 80f Kuryongyon (2-2) .50 .30

Project Hope, 10th Anniv. — A845

**1999, Oct. 30** **Photo.** ***Perf. 11½***
**2979** A845 80f multi 1.10 .30

Scientific and Technological Achievements — A846

Designs: No. 2980, Cambrian era fossil. No. 2981, Underwater robot. No. 2982, Best result of Goldbach conjecture, vert. No. 2983, 2.16m telescope, vert.

**1999, Nov. 1** **Litho.** ***Perf. 12***
**2980** A846 80f multi (4-1) .50 .25
**2981** A846 80f multi (4-2) .50 .25
*a.* Pair, #2980-2981 2.00 1.75
**2982** A846 80f multi (4-3) .50 .25
**2983** A846 80f multi (4-4) .50 .25
*a.* Pair, #2982-2983 2.00 1.75
*Nos. 2980-2983 (4)* 2.00 1.00

Li Lisan (1899-1967), Minister of Labor — A847

No. 2984, As young man (2-1). No. 2985, Wearing glasses (2-2).

**1999, Nov. 19** **Photo.** ***Perf. 11½***
**2984** A847 80f multi .80 .30
**2985** A847 80f multi .80 .30

Return of Macao to China A848

Designs: 80f, Sino-Portuguese declaration, flower. 150f, Basic Law of Macao Special Administrative Region, Great Wall.
800f, $50, Deng Xiaoping.

**1999-2000** **Photo.** ***Perf. 11¾x11½***
**2986** A848 80f multi (2-1) .70 .25
**2987** A848 150f multi (2-2) .90 .50

**Souvenir Sheets**
***Perf. 13***
**2988** A848 800f multi 4.00 2.40

**Litho. (stamp) & Embossed (margin)**
***Perf. 12***
**2989** A848 $50 multi *20.00 15.00*
*a.* Overprinted in margin *40.00 40.00*

No. 2988 contains one 60x50mm stamp with star-shaped perforations in the corners.
Overprint in margin on No. 2989a is Chinese inscription, "2000-1" and "(2-2)J."
Issued: No. 2989a, 1/1/00; others, 12/20/99.

Nie Rongzhen (1899-1992), Military Leader — A849

**1999, Dec. 29** **Litho.** ***Perf. 12***
**2990** A849 80f In uniform (2-1) 1.00 .30
**2991** A849 80f Seated (2-2) 1.00 .30

Millennium — A850

No. 2992, Sun Yat-sen, #590. No. 2993, #2214. No. 2994, #2339. No. 2995, #2601. No. 2996, Mao Zedong, #456. 200f, #2248. 260f, #2730. 280f, Deng Xiaoping, #2774C.

**1999, Dec. 31** **Litho.** ***Perf. 12***
**2992** A850 60f multi (8-1) .40 .25
**2993** A850 60f multi (8-2) .40 .25
**2994** A850 80f multi (8-3) .55 .30
**2995** A850 80f multi (8-4) .55 .30
**2996** A850 80f multi (8-5) .55 .30
**2997** A850 200f multi (8-6) 1.15 .65
**2998** A850 260f multi (8-7) 1.30 .75
**2999** A850 280f multi (8-8) 1.50 .85
*Nos. 2992-2999 (8)* 6.40 3.65

New Year 2000 (Year of the Dragon) — A851

80f, Dragon (2-1). $2.80, Rising sun (2-2).

**Photo. & Engr.**
**2000, Jan. 5** ***Perf. 11½x11¾***
**3000** A851 80f copper & multi *8.75 .85*
**3001** A851 $2.80 copper & multi *13.25 1.25*

A852

Spring Festival: No. 3002, Welcoming the Spring Festival. No. 3003, Bidding farewell to outgoing year. $2.80, Offering sacrifices to god of land.
$8, Family reunion, horiz.

**2000, Jan. 29** **Photo.** ***Perf. 11¼***
**3002** A852 80f multi (3-1) .50 .25
**3003** A852 80f multi (3-2) .50 .25
**3004** A852 $2.80 multi (3-3) 1.60 .80
*Nos. 3002-3004 (3)* 2.60 1.30

**Souvenir Sheet**
***Perf. 11¼x11***
**3005** A852 $8 multi *4.50 3.50*
*a.* Ovptd. in sheet margin *9.00 5.75*

Nos. 3002-3004 were issued in miniature sheets of 9. Value, $8, each.
No. 3005 contains one 90x60mm stamp.
No. 3005a contains gold Chinese inscription for New Century Philatelic Exhibition, "2000," and "PJZ-11" in sheet margin. Issued: 4/28.

A853

Wildlife.

**2000, Feb. 25** **Photo.** ***Perf. 13¼x13***
**3006** A853 Sheet of 10 + 2 labels 7.50 7.50
*a.* 30f Nipponia nippon .30 .25
*b.* 60f Teinopalpus aureus .30 .25
*c.* 80f Ailuropoda melanoleuca .30 .25
*d.* $1 Crossoptilon manichuricum .35 .25
*e.* $1.50 Acipenser sinensis .50 .25
*f.* $2 Rhinopithecus roxellanae .65 .35
*g.* $2.60 Lipotes vexillifer .80 .40
*h.* $2.80 Grus japonensis .85 .45
*i.* $3.70 Panthera tigris 1.20 .60
*j.* $5.40 Alligator sinensis 1.75 .95

Cultural Relics — A854

Designs; 60f, Neolithic Age jade dragon. No. 3008, Dragon-shaped ornament. No. 3009, Carved tile with dragon. No. 3010, Copper mirror with dragon. No. 3011, Bronze dragon. $2.80, Dragon on sandalwood throne.

**2000, Mar. 7** **Litho.** ***Perf. 12***
**3007** A854 60f multi (6-1) .85 .25
**3008** A854 80f multi (6-2) 1.25 .30
**3009** A854 80f multi (6-3) 1.25 .30
**3010** A854 80f multi (6-4) 1.25 .30
**3011** A854 80f multi (6-5) 1.25 .30
**3012** A854 $2.80 multi (6-6) 4.25 1.75
*Nos. 3007-3012 (6)* 10.10 3.20

Yangtze River Highway Bridges A855

**2000, Mar. 26** **Litho.** ***Perf. 12***
**3013** A855 80f Wanxian (4-1) .50 .30
**3014** A855 80f Huangshi (4-2) .50 .30
**3015** A855 80f Tongling (4-3) .50 .30
**3016** A855 $2.80 Jiangyin (4-4) 1.80 .75
*Nos. 3013-3016 (4)* 3.30 1.65

Landscapes in Dali — A856

Designs: No. 3017, Cangshan Mountain and Erhai Lake. No. 3018, Pagodas at Chongsheng Temple. No. 3019, Jizu Mountain. $2.80, Shibao Mountain.

*Perf. 11¾x11½*

**2000, Apr. 19** **Photo.**

**3017** A856 80f multi (4-1) .40 .25
**3018** A856 80f multi (4-2) .40 .25
**3019** A856 80f multi (4-3) .40 .25
**3020** A856 $2.80 multi (4-4) 1.40 .70
*Nos. 3017-3020 (4)* 2.60 1.45

Legend of Mulan A857

Mulan: No. 3021, Weaving cloth. No. 3022, Joining army. No. 3023, On expedition. No. 3024, Returning home.

**2000, Apr. 30** **Litho.** ***Perf. 12***

**3021** A857 80f multi (4-1) .30 .30
**3022** A857 80f multi (4-2) .30 .30
**3023** A857 80f multi (4-3) .30 .30
**3024** A857 80f multi (4-4) .30 .30
***a.*** Strip, #3021-3024 *2.00 1.60*

Taer Lamasery A858

No. 3025, Good Luck Treasure Pagoda. No. 3026, Big Golden Tile Palace. No. 3027, Big Scripture Hall. $2.80, Banqen residence.

**2000, May 5**

**3025** A858 80f multi (4-1) .35 .30
**3026** A858 80f multi (4-2) .35 .30
**3027** A858 80f multi (4-3) .35 .30
**3028** A858 $2.80 multi (4-4) 1.00 .75
*Nos. 3025-3028 (4)* 2.05 1.65

Cai Chang and Li Fuchun — A859

**2000, May 22**

**3029** A859 80f multi 1.00 .30

Stampin' the Future Children's Stamp Design Contest Winners A860

Various children's drawings: No. 3030, 30f, (8-1). No. 3031, 60f, (8-2). No. 3032, 60f, (8-3). No. 3033, 80f, (8-4). No. 3034, 80f, (8-5). No. 3035, 80f, (8-6). $2.60, (8-7). $2.80, (8-8).

*Perf. 11½x11¼*

**2000, June 1** **Photo.**

**3030-3037** A860 Set of 8 4.95 2.50

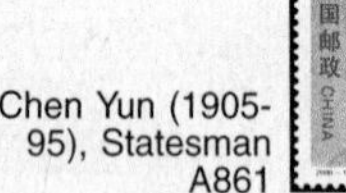

Chen Yun (1905-95), Statesman A861

No. 3038, 80f, As a young man (4-1). No. 3039, 80f, In uniform, vert. (4-2). No. 3040, 80f, In black jacket, vert. (4-3). $2.80, As old man (4-4).

*Perf. 13x13¼, 13¼x13*

**2000, June 13**

**3038-3041** A861 Set of 4 3.75 1.50

Pots — A862

Designs: No. 3042, 80f, Wine vessel (2-1). No. 3043, 80f, Horse milk pot (2-2).

**2000, June 28** **Litho.** ***Perf. 12***

**3042-3043** A862 Set of 2 1.60 .50

See Kazakhstan No. 305.

Laoshan Mountain A863

No. 3044, 80f, Huge Peak (4-1). No. 3045, 80f, Yangkou Bay (4-2). No. 3046, 80f, Beijiu Lake (4-3). $2.80, Taiqing Palace (4-4).

*Perf. 11½x11¼*

**2000, July 15** **Photo.**

**3044-3047** A863 Set of 4 3.25 1.75
*3047a* Souvenir sheet, #3044-3047 *5.00 4.00*

Souvenir Sheet

All-China Philatelic Federation, Fifth Congress — A864

**2000, July 18** **Litho.** ***Perf. 12***

**3048** A864 $8 multi 4.75 3.75
***a.*** Margin ovptd. in gold 5.75 5.00

No. 3048a issued 9/21/01. It is inscribed in margin in gold "PJZ-13," "2001," with Chinese characters and Nanjing 2001 Philatelic Exhibition mascot.

Small Carp Leap Through Dragon Gate Legend — A865

No. 3049: a, Grandma Carp tells a story (5-1). b, Small Carp look for Dragon Gate (5-2). c, Help from Uncle Crab (5-3). d, Small Carp leap through Dragon Gate (5-4). e, Aunt Swallow passes on a letter (5-5).

**2000, Aug. 8** **Photo.** ***Perf. 11½***

**3049** A865 80f Horiz. strip of 5, #a-e 3.25 2.00
***f.*** Booklet pane, #3049 + 2 labels, perf. 12 9.00
Booklet, #3049f 10.00

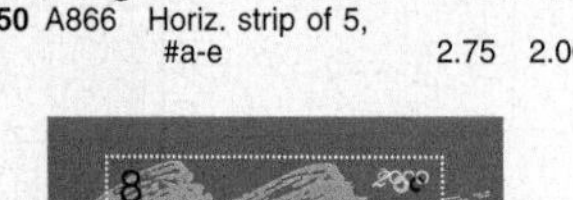

Shenzhen Special Economic Zone — A866

No. 3050: a, 80f, Financial Center district (5-1). b, 80f, China Intl. Exhibition Center (5-2). c, 80f, Yantian Harbor area (5-3). d, 80f, Shenzhen Bay tourist area (5-4). e, $2.80, Shekou industrial district (5-5).

**2000, Aug. 26** **Litho.** ***Perf. 12***

**3050** A866 Horiz. strip of 5, #a-e 2.75 2.00

2000 Summer Olympics, Sydney — A867

**2000, Sept. 15** **Photo.** ***Perf. 13¼x13***

**3051** A867 $8 multi *4.00 3.00*
***a.*** Sheet of 2 *32.00 32.00*

No. 3051a issued 10/31/00.

Beaches A868

a, Coconuts Bay, PRC (2-1). b, Varadero Beach, Cuba (2-2).

**2000, Sept. 26** **Litho.** ***Perf. 12***

**3052** A868 Pair 1.60 .75
***a.-b.*** 80f Any single .85 .25

See Cuba Nos. 4108-4109.

Masks and Puppets — A869

No. 3053, Tan background (2-1). No. 3054, Violet blue background (2-2).

**2000, Oct. 9** **Photo.** ***Perf. 13x13½***

**3053-3054** A869 80f Set of 2 1.95 .60

See Brazil Nos. 2767-2768.

Relics from the Tomb of Prince Jing of Zhongshan — A870

No. 3055, 80f, Eternal Fidelity palace lamp (4-1). No. 3056, 80f, Bronze pot (4-2). No. 3057, 80f, Boshan incense burner (4-3). $2.80, Cup (4-4).

**2000, Oct. 20** ***Perf. 13½x13¼***

**3055-3058** A870 Set of 4 2.25 1.75

Ancient Thinkers — A871

No. 3059, 60f, Confucius (6-1). No. 3060, 80f, Mencius (6-2). No. 3061, 80f, Lao Zi (6-3). No. 3062, 80f, Zhuang Zi (6-4). No. 3063, 80f, Mo Zi (6-5). $2.80, Xun Zi (6-6).

**Photo. & Engr.**

**2000, Nov. 11** ***Perf. 11¼x11***

**3059-3064** A871 Set of 6 8.75 2.50

Test of Shenzhou Spacecraft, 1st Anniv. — A872

No. 3065: a, Launch (2-1). b, In orbit (2-2).

**2000, Nov. 20** **Photo.** ***Perf. 11½***

**3065** A872 Pair *4.50 3.00*
***a.-b.*** 80f Any single .80 .35
***c.*** Sheet, 6 #3065 *40.00 40.00*

World Meteorological Organization, 50th Anniv. — A873

Designs: No. 3066, 80f, Weather satellite (4-1). No. 3067, 80f, Weather measuring equipment on Qinghai-Tibetan Plateau (4-2). No. 3068, 80f, Weather-predicting computer (4-3). $2.80, Airplane for cloud seeding (4-4).

**2000, Nov. 22** **Litho.** ***Perf. 12***

**3066-3069** A873 Set of 4 3.75 1.50

Flowers — A874

No. 3070, 80f, Scarlet kaffir lily (4-1). No. 3071, 80f, Noble clivia (4-2). No. 3072, 80f, Golden striated lily (4-3). $2.80, White kaffir lily (4-4).

*Perf. 11¼x11½*

**2000, Dec. 12** **Photo.**

**3070-3073** A874 Set of 4 3.00 1.75
*3073a* Souv. sheet, #3070-3073 5.00 4.00

Ancient Bells — A875

No. 3074, 80f, Jingshu bell (4-1). No. 3075, 80f, Su chime bell (4-2). No. 3076, 80f, Jingyun bell (4-3). $2.80, Qianlong bell (4-4).

**2000, Dec. 31** ***Perf. 11¼x11½***

**3074-3077** A875 Set of 4 2.90 1.60

Advent of New Millennium — A876

Designs: 60f, Sun, moon, date, time, building (5-1). No. 3079, 80f, Dove, Earth (5-2). No. 3080, 80f, Map, leaf, infant's hands (5-3). No. 3081, 80f, Circuitboard, head, Earth, horiz. (5-4). $2.80, Moon, stars, sundial (5-5).

**2001, Jan. 1** **Litho.** ***Perf. 12***

**3078-3082** A876 Set of 5 7.00 2.00

New Year 2001 (Year of the Snake) — A877

Snake and: 80f, Flower (2-1). $2.80, Chinese character for snake (2-2).

**Photo. & Engr.**

**2001, Jan. 5** ***Perf. 11½x11¾***

**3083** A877 80f multi 4.50 .75
***a.*** Sheet of 6 *17.00 17.00*
**3084** A877 $2.80 multi 5.25 1.25
***a.*** Sheet of 6 *23.00 23.00*

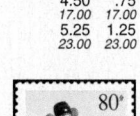

Clown Roles in Peking Opera — A878

Designs: No. 3085, 80f, Tang Qin (6-1). No. 3086, 80f, Lin Lihua (6-2). No. 3087, 80f, Gao Lishi (6-3). No. 3088, 80f, Jiang Gan (6-4). No. 3089, 80f, Yang Xiangwu (6-5). $2.80, Shi Qian (6-6).

**2001, Feb. 15** **Photo.** ***Perf. 11½x11***

**3085-3090** A878 Set of 6 5.50 2.25

Wildlife — A879

**2001, Mar. 16** ***Perf. 13¼x13***

**3091** Sheet of 10 + 2 labels *6.50 6.50*
***a.*** A879 30f Budorcas taxicolor .30 .25
***b.*** A879 60f Psephurus gladius .30 .30
***c.*** A879 60f Elaphurus davidianus .30 .30
***d.*** A879 80f Acipenser dabryanus .35 .35
***e.*** A879 80f Capra ibex .35 .35
***f.*** A879 80f Haliaeetus pelagicus .35 .35
***g.*** A879 80f Camelus bactrianus .35 .35
***h.*** A879 $1 Uncia uncia .45 .45
***i.*** A879 $2.60 Martes zibellina 1.15 1.15
***j.*** A879 $5.40 Saiga tatarica 2.40 2.40

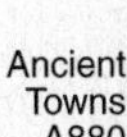

Ancient Towns A880

Designs: No. 3092, 80f, Zhouzhuang, Kunshan (6-1). No. 3093, 80f, Tongli, Wujiang (6-2). No. 3094, 80f, Wuzhen, Tongxiang (6-3). No. 3095, 80f, Nanxun, Huzhou (6-4). No. 3096, 80f, Luzhi, Wuxian (6-5). $2.80, Xitang, Jiashan (6-6).

**2001, Apr. 7 Photo. *Perf. 11½x11¼***
**3092-3097** A880 Set of 6 4.25 2.10
*3097a* Booklet pane, #3092-3097 + 6 labels *9.00*
Booklet, #3097a *11.50*

Strange Stories From a Chinese Studio, by Pu Songling — A881

Designs: 60f, Ying Ning (4-1). No. 3099, 80f, A Bao (4-2). No. 3100, 80f, Mask of Evildoer (4-3). $2.80, Stealing Peach (4-4).
$8, Taoist Priest from Laoshan.

**2001, Apr. 21 *Perf. 11½***
**3098-3101** A881 Set of 4 3.25 2.00

**Souvenir Sheet**
***Perf. 13½x13***

**3102** A881 $8 multi *6.50 6.50*

No. 3102 contains one 90x60mm stamp.

Yongle Temple Murals — A882

No. 3103: a, Lady Queen Mother (4-1). b, Jade Lady Presenting Treasure (4-2). c, Celestial Worthy of the East (4-3). d, Venus and Mercury (4-4).

**2001, May 5 Litho. *Perf. 12***
**3103** Horiz. strip of 4 3.00 2.50
*a.* A882 60f multi .30 .25
*b.-c.* A882 80f Any single .40 .35
*d.* A882 $2.80 multi 1.10 .95

Mount Wudang — A883

Designs: 60f, Nanyan Hall (3-1). No. 3105, 80f, Zixiao Temple (3-2). No. 3106, 80f, Taizi Slope (3-3).
$8, Golden Crown in spring.

***Perf. 11¼x11½***
**2001, May 26 Photo.**
**3104-3106** A883 Set of 3 2.60 1.00

**Souvenir Sheet**
***Perf. 12¼x12½***

**3107** A883 $8 multi + label *6.00 4.75*

No. 3107 contains one 47x71mm stamp.

Ancient Chinese Receptacles — A884

Designs: No. 3108, 80f, Earthenware vase. No. 3109, 80f, Porcelain coffee pot.

**2001, June 12 *Perf. 11¼x11½***
**3108-3109** A884 Set of 2 1.25 .60

See Belgium Nos. 1858-1859.

Dragon Boat Festival — A885

Designs: No. 3110, Dragon boat race (3-1). No. 3111, Making Zongzi (3-2). $2.80, Expelling five poisons (3-3).

**2001, June 25 Photo. *Perf. 13x13½***
**3110** A885 80f multi .60 .25
*a.* Sheet of 9 *3.00* —
**3111** A885 80f multi .60 .25
*a.* Sheet of 9 *3.00* —
**3112** A885 $2.80 multi 1.45 .90
*a.* Sheet of 9 *10.00* —
*Nos. 3110-3112 (3)* 2.65 1.40

Nos. 3110-3112 each issued in sheets of 40.

Early Leaders of the Communist Party — A886

Designs: No. 3113, 80f, Wang Jinmei (5-1). No. 3114, 80f, Zhao Shiyan (5-2). No. 3115, 80f, Deng Enming (5-3). No. 3116, 80f, Cai Hesen (5-4). No. 3117, 80f, He Shuheng (5-5).

**2001, June 28 *Perf. 11¼x11***
**3113-3117** A886 Set of 5 4.25 2.00

Communist Party, 80th Anniv. — A887

**2001, July 1 Photo. *Perf. 13x13¼***
**3118** A887 80f multi 1.75 .40
*a.* Sheet of 8 *12.50* —

No. 3118 issued in sheets of 40.

Emblem of 2008 Summer Olympics, Beijing — A888

**2001, July 14 *Perf. 13x13¼***
**3119** A888 80f multi + label 1.30 .75
*a.* Sheet of 36 + 39 labels *35.00* —

No. 3119 printed in sheets of 12 stamp + label pairs with one large central label. See Hong Kong No. 940, Macao No. 1067.
No. 3119a contains 12 each of No. 3119, Hong Kong No. 940 (with different adjacent label), and Macao No. 1067 (with different adjacent label).

Waterfalls — A889

Designs: No. 3120, 80f, Yinlianzhuitan (3-1). No. 3121, 80f, Doupotang, horiz. (3-2). No. 3122, 80f, Dishuitan (3-3).
$8, Huangguoshu.

***Perf. 12¼x12, 12x12¼***
**2001, July 22 Litho.**
**3120-3122** A889 Set of 3 2.40 .95

**Souvenir Sheet**
***Perf. 12***

**3123** A889 $8 multi *4.75 4.75*

No. 3123 contains one 40x60mm stamp.

Beidaihe Beach A890

Designs: 60f, Pigeon Nest (4-1). No. 3125, 80f, Zhonghai Beach (4-2). No. 3126, 80f, Lianfeng Hill (4-3). $2.80, Tiger Stone (4-4).

**2001, Aug. 5 Litho. *Perf. 12***
**3124-3127** A890 Set of 4 2.15 1.75

21st Universiade A891

Emblem, "2001" and: 60f, Concentric circles (3-1). 80f, Runners (3-2). $2.80, Hemispheres of globe (3-3).

**2001, Aug. 22 Litho.**
**3128-3130** A891 Set of 3 1.75 1.40
*3129a* Sheet of 20 +20 labels *18.00*

No. 3129a exists with different margin designs.
Sheets of four No. 3129 plus four labels were not placed on sale but were included with 2001 year sets. Uncut sheets containing two of these sheets also exist.

Datong River Diversion Project A892

Designs: No. 3131, 80f, Sluice gates (4-1). No. 3132, 80f, Xianming Gorge water pipeline (4-2). No. 3133, 80f, Tunnel (4-3). $2.80, Zhuanglang River Aqueduct (4-4).

**2001, Aug. 26**
**3131-3134** A892 Set of 4 3.25 1.75

Wuhu Bridge A893

View from: 80f, Shore (2-1). $2.80, Roadway (2-2).

**Photo. & Engr.**
**2001, Sept. 20 *Perf. 11½x11¼***
**3135-3136** A893 Set of 2 2.40 1.20

Orchids — A894

Designs: No. 3137, 80f, Paphiopedilum malipoense (4-1). No. 3138, 80f, Paphiopedilum dianthum (4-2). No. 3139, 80f, Paphiopedilum markianum (4-3). $2.80, Paphiopedilum appletonianum (4-4).

**2001, Sept. 28 Photo. *Perf. 12½***
**3137-3140** A894 Set of 4 3.25 2.00
*3140a* Souvenir sheet, #3137-3140 *6.50* 3.00

Ancient Gold Masks A895

Designs: No. 3141, 80f, Mask of San Xing Dui (2-1). No. 3142, 80f, Funerary mask of King Tutankhamun, Egypt (2-2).

**2001, Oct. 12 *Perf. 11¾x11½***
**3141-3142** A895 Set of 2 3.75 .80

See Egypt Nos. 1807-1808.

People's Republic of China as 2001 Asia-Pacific Economic Cooperation Head — A896

**2001, Oct. 20 Litho. *Perf. 12***
**3143** A896 80f multi .90 .35

**Souvenir Sheet**

Ertan Hydroelectric Plant — A897

**2001, Oct. 20 Litho. *Perf. 12¼***
**3144** A897 $8 multi *6.50 3.00*

Horses, Zhaoling Mausoleum A898

Horse: a, Facing right, galloping (6-1). b, Facing right, galloping, diff. (6-2). c, Facing right, walking (6-3). d, With attendant (6-4). e, Facing left, walking (6-5). f, Facing left, galloping (6-6).

**2001, Oct. 28 Photo. *Perf. 12***
**Fawn Background**
**3145** Horiz. strip of 6 3.50 2.40
*a.* A898 60f multi .30 .25
*b.-e.* A898 80f multi .40 .30
*f.* A898 $2.80 multi 1.00 .90
*g.* Sheet, 2 each #3145a-3145c, white background, photo. & embossed *16.00* —
*h.* Sheet, 2 each #3145d-3145f, white background, photo. & embossed *16.00* —

Sailing Ships A899

No. 3146: a, Chinese junk, 13th cent. (2-1). b, Portuguese caravel, 15th cent. (2-2).

**2001, Nov. 8 *Perf. 13x13¼***
**3146** A899 80f Horiz. pair, #a-b 2.40 1.00

See Portugal No. 2454.

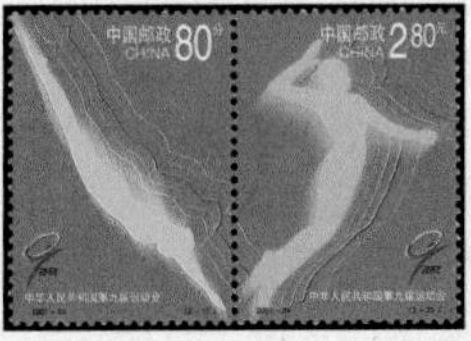

9th Natl. Games A900

No. 3147: a, 80f, Diving (2-1). b, $2.80, Volleyball (2-2).

**2001, Nov. 11 Litho. *Perf. 12***
**3147** A900 Horiz. pair, #a-b 2.25 1.50
*c.* Souvenir sheet, #3147 *3.25 2.40*

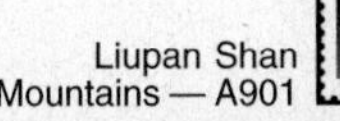

Liupan Shan Mountains — A901

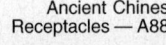

Various landscapes: No. 3148, 80f (4-1). No. 3149, 80f (4-2). No. 3150, 80f (4-3). $2.80, (4-4).

**Photo. & Engr.**

**2001, Nov. 24** ***Perf. 11¼x11½***

**3148-3151** A901 Set of 4 3.25 2.00

Xiu Xian and the White Snake — A902

Designs: No. 3152, Women, umbrella (4-1). No. 3153, Three men (4-2). No. 3154, Man with sword, man with bowl (4-3). $2.80, Women on bridge (4-4).

***Perf. 11½, 11½x11 (#3153-3154)***

**2001, Dec. 5** **Photo.**

| | | | | |
|---|---|---|---|---|
| **3152** | A902 | 80f multi | .50 | .30 |
| *a.* | | Booklet pane of 1 | *1.10* | — |
| **3153** | A902 | 80f multi | .50 | .30 |
| *a.* | | Booklet pane of 1 | *1.10* | — |
| **3154** | A902 | 80f multi | .50 | .30 |
| *a.* | | Booklet pane of 1 | *1.10* | — |
| **3155** | A902 | $2.80 multi | 1.65 | .90 |
| *a.* | | Booklet pane of 1 | *4.00* | — |
| | | Booklet, #3152a-3155a | *8.00* | |
| | | *Nos. 3152-3155 (4)* | 3.15 | 1.80 |

Admission to World Trade Organization — A903

**2001, Dec. 11** **Photo.** ***Perf. 13¼x13***

**3156** A903 80f multi 1.60 .80

Koxinga's Recovery of Taiwan from the Dutch, 340th Anniv. A904

Koxinga and: No. 3157, 80f, Warriors, ships (3-1). No. 3158, 80f, Warriors, horse (3-2). $2.80, People, trees (3-3).

***Perf. 11½x11¼***

**2001, Dec. 13** **Photo.**

**3157-3159** A904 Set of 3 3.25 1.50

**Souvenir Sheet**

Qinhai - Tibet Railway A905

**2001, Dec. 29** ***Perf. 13¼***

**3160** A905 $8 multi 6.50 3.25

New Year 2002 (Year of the Horse) — A906

Designs: 80f, Ceramic horse (2-1). $2.80, Flowers, Chinese symbol for horse (2-2).

**Photo. & Engr.**

**2002, Jan. 5** ***Perf. 11½***

**3161-3162** A906 Set of 2 5.25 2.00

Nos. 3161-3162 each exist in a miniature sheet of six. Value, each $18.50.

Art of Badashanren (1626-1705) — A907

Designs: 60f, Two Eagles (6-1). No. 3164, 80f, Pine Tree (6-2). No. 3165, 80f, Lotus Flowers (6-3). No. 3166, 80f, Chysanthemum in Vase (6-4). $2.60, Two Magpies on a Rock (6-5). $2.80, Landscape After Dong Yuan (6-6).

***Perf. 11¼x11½***

**2002, Jan. 20** **Photo.**

**3163-3168** A907 Set of 6 4.75 3.00

Environmental Protection — A908

**China Post No. R30**

Designs: 5f, Keeping birth rate low. 10f, Forest conservation. 30f, Conservation of mineral resources. 60f, Preventing air pollution. 80f, Conservation of water. $1.50, Conservation of ocean resources.

***Perf. 12¾x13¼ Syncopated***

**2002** **Photo.**

| | | | | |
|---|---|---|---|---|
| **3169** | A908 | 5f multi | .30 | .25 |
| **3170** | A908 | 10f multi | .30 | .25 |
| **3171** | A908 | 30f multi | .30 | .25 |
| **3172** | A908 | 60f multi | .35 | .25 |
| **3173** | A908 | 80f multi | .40 | .25 |
| **3174** | A908 | $1.50 multi | .75 | .40 |
| | | *Nos. 3169-3174 (6)* | 2.40 | 1.65 |

Issued: 10f, 60f, 2/1; others, 4/1. See Nos. 3334-3335.

Birds — A909

**China Post No. R31**

Designs: 80f, Yellow-bellied tragopan. $1, Biddulph's ground jay. $2, Taiwan blue magpies. $4.20, Alashan redstart. $5.40, Kozlov's bunting.

**2002** ***Perf. 13¼***

| | | | | |
|---|---|---|---|---|
| **3175** | A909 | 80f multi | .40 | .30 |
| *a.* | | Booklet pane of 10 +2 labels | 5.00 | |
| | | Booklet, #3175a | 5.00 | |
| **3176** | A909 | $1 multi | .50 | .35 |
| **3177** | A909 | $2 multi | .90 | .65 |
| **3178** | A909 | $4.20 multi | 1.60 | 1.25 |
| **3179** | A909 | $5.40 multi | 2.00 | 1.50 |
| | | *Nos. 3175-3179 (5)* | 5.40 | 4.05 |

Issued: 80f, $1, $2, 2/1; Nos. 3178, 3179, 4/1. No. 3175a, 12/7.

See Nos. 3336-3337, 3547-3548.

Flowers A910

No. 3180: a, Camellia nitidissima (2-1). b, Couroupita guianensis (2-2).

**2002, Feb. 5** ***Perf. 13¼x13***

**3180** A910 80f Horiz. pair, #a-b 1.50 .80

See Malaysia Nos. 861-864.

Musical Instruments — A911

Designs: 60f, Yaqin (5-1). No. 3182, 80f, Erhu (5-2). No. 3183, 80f, Banhu (5-3). No. 3184, 80f, Satar (5-4). $2.80, Matouqin (5-5).

**2002, Feb. 23** **Litho.** ***Perf. 12***

**3181-3185** A911 Set of 5 3.25 2.00

**Souvenir Sheet**

The Royal Carriage, by Yan Liben A912

**2002, Mar. 16** **Photo.**

**3186** A912 $8 multi 13.00 6.00

Song Dynasty Pottery and Porcelain from Ruyao Kilns — A913

Designs: 60f, Wine vessel (4-1). No. 3188, 80f, Three-legged basin (4-2). No. 3189, 80f, Bowl (4-3). $2.80, Dish (4-4).

**2002, Mar. 30** **Litho.**

**3187-3190** A913 Set of 4 2.50 2.00

Strange Stories from a Chinese Studio, by Pu Songling — A914

No. 3191: a, 60f, Xi Fangping (4-1). b, 80f, Pianpian (4-2).

No. 3192: a, 80f, Tian Qilang (4-3). b, $2.80, Bai Qiulian (4-4).

**2002, Apr. 21** **Photo.** ***Perf. 11½***

| | | | | |
|---|---|---|---|---|
| **3191** | A914 | Vert. pair, #a-b | 1.50 | .75 |
| **3192** | A914 | Horiz. pair, #a-b | 2.25 | 1.00 |

Qianshan Mountain — A915

No. 3193: a, Wuliang Taoist Temple (4-1). b, Maitreya Peak (4-2). c, Longquan Temple (4-3). d, Terrace of Immortals (4-4).

**2002, Apr. 26** ***Perf. 12***

| | | | | |
|---|---|---|---|---|
| **3193** | A915 | Horiz. strip of 4 | 3.25 | 1.90 |
| *a.-c.* | | 80f Any single | .30 | .25 |
| *d.* | | $2.80 multi | .90 | .70 |

Ancient City of Lijiang A916

Designs: No. 3194, 80f, Sifang Street (3-1). No. 3195, 80f, Stream, vert. (3-2). $2.80, House of Naxi people (3-3).

**2002, May 1** ***Perf. 11½***

| | | | | |
|---|---|---|---|---|
| **3194-3196** | A916 | Set of 3 | 2.50 | 1.50 |
| *a.* | | Souvenir sheet, #3194-3196 | 4.75 | 3.25 |

No. 3196a sold for $6.60.

Ruyi (Good Luck Symbol) A917

**2002, May 10** **Litho.** ***Perf. 12***

**3197** A917 80f multi + label 1.10 .50

Exists in miniature sheet of 4 + 4 vert. labels (value $6) and in sheet of 16 + 16 horiz. labels (value $20).

**Stamps with Attached Labels**

Starting with No. 3197, stamps listed as having attached labels are known to have been issued in dozens of different sheets having various margin and label designs, various numbers of stamps and labels in the sheets, and different stamp and label combinations. Little information has been made available about these sheets, and all seem to have been sold for prices significantly above face value. Labels on these sheets do not seem to have been personalizable with personal photos but have illustrations with approved designs.

2002 World Cup Soccer Championships, Japan and Korea — A918

No. 3198: a, 80f, Player (2-1). b, $2.80, Players (2-2).

**2002, May 16** **Photo.** ***Perf. 12¼***

**3198** A918 Horiz. pair, #a-b 1.90 1.25

A souvenir sheet containing People's Republic of China No. 3198, Hong Kong Nos. 978a-978b and Macao 1091a-1091b exists, and sold for premium over face value. Value $45.

Lighthouses — A919

Nautical charts and: No. 3199, 80f, Maota Pagoda Lighthouse (5-1). No. 3200, 80f, Jiangxin Pagoda Lighthouses (5-2). No. 3201, 80f, Huaniaoshan Lighthouse (5-3). No. 3202, 80f, Laotieshan Lighthouse (5-4). No. 3203, 80f, Lin'gao Lighthouse (5-5).

**Photo. & Engr.**

**2002, May 18** ***Perf. 11½x11***

**3199-3203** A919 Set of 5 3.25 1.50

Yellow River Dams A920

Designs: No. 3204, 80f, Lijia Gorge (4-1). No. 3205, 80f, Liujia Gorge (4-2). No. 3206, 80f, Qingtong Gorge (4-3). No. 3207, 80f, Sanmen Gorge (4-4).

$8, Xiaolangdi, vert.

**2002, June 8** **Photo.** ***Perf. 12***

**3204-3207** A920 Set of 4 1.60 1.25

**Souvenir Sheet**

***Perf. 13x13¼***

**3208** A920 $8 multi 4.25 3.00

No. 3208 contains one 40x60mm stamp.

Dazu Stone Carvings — A921

Designs: No. 3209, 80f, Avalokitesvara of the Sun and Moon, North Mountain (4-1). No. 3210, 80f, Samantabhadra, North Mountain (4-2). No. 3211, 80f, Three Avatamasaka Sages, Holy Summit Mountain (4-3). No. 3212, 80f, Statue in Cave of the Three Emperors, Stone Gate Mountain (4-4).

$8, Avalokitesvara of a Thousand Hands, Holy Summit Mountain.

**2002, June 18 Litho. *Perf. 12***

**3209-3212** A921 Set of 4 2.40 1.00

**Souvenir Sheet**

**Photo.**

***Perf. 13x13¼***

**3213** A921 $8 multi 4.75 2.75

No. 3213 contains one 40x60mm stamp.

Desert Flowers — A922

No. 3214: a, Ammopiptanthus mongolicus (4-1). b, Calligonum rubicandum (4-2). c, Hedysarum scoparium (4-3). d, Tamarix leptostachys (4-4).

**2002, June 29 Photo. *Perf. 13x13¼***

**3214** Vert. strip of 4 2.65 1.50
***a.-c.*** A922 80f Any single .35 .25
***d.*** A922 $2 multi .70 .60

Antarctic Scenes — A923

Designs: No. 3215, 80f, Penguins (3-1). No. 3216, 80f, Aurora Australis (3-2). $2, Bird, Grove Mountains (3-3).

**2002, July 15 Litho. *Perf. 12***

**3215-3217** A923 Set of 3 2.25 1.25

Qinghai Lake — A924

Designs: No. 3218, 80f, Lake shore (3-1). No. 3219, 80f, Birds on rock (3-2). $2.80, View of lake and birds (3-3).

**2002, July 20**

**3218-3220** A924 Set of 3 2.75 1.40

Early Communist Party Leaders — A925

Designs: No. 3221, 80f, Huang Gonglue (1898-1931) (5-1). No. 3222, 80f, Xu Jishen (1901-31) (5-2). No. 3223, 80f, Cai Shengxi (1906-32) (5-3). No. 3224, 80f, Wei Baqun (1894-1932) (5-4). No. 3225, 80f, Liu Zhidan (1903-36) (5-5).

**2002, Aug. 1 Photo.**

**3221-3225** A925 Set of 5 2.75 1.50

Scientists of Ancient China — A926

Designs: No. 3226, 80f, Bian Que (4-1). No. 3227, 80f, Liu Hui (4-2). No. 3228, 80f, Su Song (4-3). No. 3229, 80f, Song Yingxing (4-4).

**Photo. & Engr.**

**2002, Aug. 20 *Perf. 11¼x11***

**3226-3229** A926 Set of 4 2.70 1.25

Yandangshan Mountain — A927

Designs: No. 3230, 80f, Xianshengmen Gate (4-1). No. 3231, 80f, Dalongqui Pond (4-2). No. 3232, 80f, Beidou Cave, horiz. (4-3). No. 3233, 80f, Guanyin Peak, horiz. (4-4).

**2002, Sept. 7 Litho. *Perf. 12¾***

**3230-3233** A927 Set of 4 1.50 1.25

Mid-Autumn Festival — A928

Designs: No. 3234, 80f, Family reunion (3-1). No. 3235, 80f, People looking at Moon (3-2). $2, The Moon as a matchmaker (3-3).

**2002, Sept. 21 *Perf. 12***

**3234-3236** A928 Set of 3 2.70 1.40

Each printed in sheets of 20. Sheets of nine containing three of each stamp exist with a decorative border (value $25) and a border with Chinese text for the Beijing 2002 Stamp Exhibition (value $55).

Peng Zhen (1902-97) — A929

Designs: No. 3237, 80f, Head of Peng Zhen (2-1). No. 3238, 80f, Peng Zhen standing (2-2).

**2002, Oct. 12 *Perf. 11¾x12***

**3237-3238** A929 Set of 2 1.60 .60

Architecture in Slovakia and China — A930

No. 3239: a, Bojnice Castle, Slovakia (2-1). b, Handan Congtai Pavilion, China (2-2).

**Photo. & Engr.**

**2002, Oct. 12 *Perf. 11¼x11***

**3239** A930 80f Horiz. pair, #a-b 1.25 .60

See Slovakia No. 410.

Dong Yong and Lady — A931

No. 3240: a, Dong Yong's filial love moves immortals (5-1). b, Dong Yong marries seventh immortal maiden (5-2). c, Immortal maiden weaving brocade (5-3). d, Dong Yong returns home (5-4). e, Everlasting love (5-5).

**2002, Oct. 26 Litho. *Perf. 13¼x13***

**3240** Horiz. strip of 5 2.25 2.00
***a.-d.*** A931 80f Any single .35 .25
***e.*** A931 $2 multi .70 .50

Nos. 3240a-3240e exist in booklet panes of one that made up a booklet that had limited distribution to people with standing order accounts. Value, $8, for complete booklet.

Flower A932

**2002, Nov. 8 Litho. *Perf. 12***

**3241** A932 80f multi + label .75 .50

Exists in a miniature sheet of 4 + 4 labels. Value, $4. See Stamps With Attached Labels note after No. 3197.

Souvenir Sheet

Hukou Waterfall A933

**Photo. (Margin Photo. & Embossed)**

**2002, Nov. 8 *Perf. 13¼x13***

**3242** A933 $8 multi *17.50 6.50*

Museums A934

Designs: No. 3243, 80f, Shanxi History Museum (5-1). No. 3244, 80f, Shanghai Museum (5-2). No. 3245, 80f, Henan Museum (5-3). No. 3246, 80f, Tibet Museum (5-4). No. 3247, 80f, Tianjin Natural Museum.

**2002, Nov. 9 Photo. *Perf. 12¾***

**3243-3247** A934 Set of 5 3.25 1.50

Martial Arts — A935

No. 3248: a, Kung Fu (2-1). b, Taekwondo (2-2)

**2002, Nov. 20 Photo. *Perf. 12***

**3248** A935 80f Vert. pair, #a-b 1.10 .80

No. 3248 is a joint issue with South Korea No. 2109.

Gibbons — A936

Designs: No. 3249, 80f, Hylobates lar (4-1). No. 3250, 80f, Hylobates leucogenys (4-2). No. 3251, 80f, Hylobates concolor (4-3). $2, Hylobates hoolock (4-4).

**Photo. & Engr.**

**2002, Dec. 7 *Perf. 11¼x11***

**3249-3252** A936 Set of 4 2.10 1.40

New Year 2003 (Year of the Ram) — A937

Designs: 80f, Ram (2-1). $2, Chinese symbol (2-2).

**Photo. & Engr.**

**2003, Jan. 5 *Perf. 11½***

**3253-3254** A937 Set of 2 6.50 3.50

Sheets of 8 + central label of Nos. 3253-3254 exist. Value, each $37.50. Sheets of 6 of Nos. 3253-3254 also exist. Value, each $30.

Yangliuqing New Year Woodprints A938

Designs: No. 3255, 80f, Five boys wrestling for a lotus (4-1). No. 3256, 80f, Zhong Kui, vert. (4-2). No. 3257, 80f, Steaing the herb of immortality (4-3). $2, Wealth in a jade hall (4-4).

**2003, Jan. 25 Photo. *Perf. 12***

**3255-3258** A938 Set of 4 4.25 1.90

A sheet containing two each Nos. 3255-3258 exists. Value $22.50.

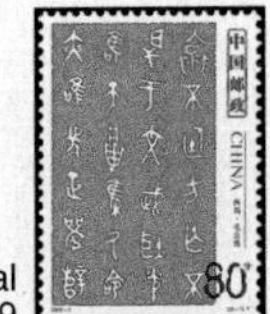

Seal Characters — A939

Designs: No. 3259, 80f, 24 characters (2-1). No. 3260, 80f, 12 characters (2-2).

**2003, Feb. 22 Litho.**

**3259-3260** A939 Set of 2 4.50 1.25

A sheet exists containg four each Nos. 3259-3260. Value $55.

Knot — A940

**2003, Feb. 3**

**3261** A940 80f multi + label 1.00 .60

See Stamps With Attached Labels note after No. 3197. Exists in sheets of 4 stamps + 4 labels. Value $13.

Perf 12¾ examples come from a sheetlet containing four examples with labels below the stamps that also contain four No. 3375. The sheetlet sold for $15.

Lilies — A941

Designs: 60f, Lilium taliense (4-1). No. 3263, 80f, Lilium lankongense (4-2). No. 3264, 80f, Lilium distichum (4-3). $2, Lilium lophophorum (4-4).

$8, Lilium leucanthum.

**2003, Mar. 5 Photo. *Perf. 13x13¼***

**3262-3265** A941 Set of 4 4.25 2.25

**Souvenir Sheet**

***Perf. 13¼***

**3266** A941 $8 multi 5.00 2.50

Nos. 3262-3265 each exist in sheets of 10. Value, set of 4, $35.

No. 3266 contains one 75x53mm stamp.

Arch Bridges A942

Designs: No. 3267, 80f, Maple Bridge (4-1). No. 3268, 80f, Xiaoshang Bridge (4-2). No. 3269, 80f, Lugouqiao Bridge (4-3). No. 3270, 80f, Double Dragon Bridge (4-4).

**Photo. & Engr.**

**2003, Mar. 29** ***Perf. 11½***
**3267-3270** A942 Set of 4 2.00 1.25

A sheet of 8 exists for each of Nos. 3267-3270. Value, set of 2, $72.50.

Chinese and Iranian Buildings — A943

Designs: No. 3271, 80f, Bell Tower, Xian, China (2-1). No. 3272, 80f, Mosque, Isfahan, Iran (2-2).

**2003, Apr. 15** **Photo.** ***Perf. 13x13¼***
**3271-3272** A943 Set of 2 3.25 1.50

Joint issue between China, People's Republic and Iran. See Iran No. 2856.
A sheet exists containing 4 each Nos. 3271-3272. Value $25.

Souvenir Sheet

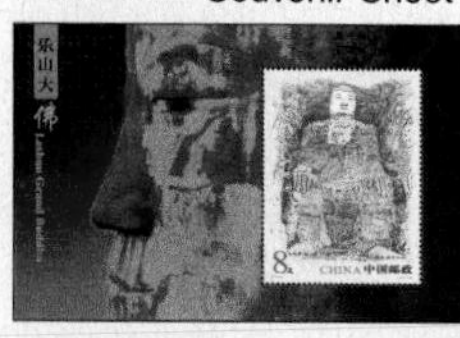

Leshan Giant Buddha A944

**Photo. & Engr.**

**2003, Apr. 28** ***Perf. 12***
**3273** A944 $8 multi 8.50 3.50

Gulangyu Island A945

No. 3274: a, Eight Diagram Building (3-1). b, Sunlight Rock (3-2). c, Shuzhuang Park (3-3)

**2003, May 2** **Photo.** ***Perf. 12***
**3274** Horiz. strip of 3 3.25 1.50
*a.-b.* A945 80f Either single .35 .25
*c.* A945 $2 multi .75 .60
*d.* Souvenir sheet, #3274 5.25 3.00

A souvenir sheet exists containing 3 No. 3274. Value $50.

Campaign to Combat Epidemic of Severe Acute Respiratory Syndrome — A946

**2003, May 19** ***Perf. 13¼x13***
**3275** A946 80f multi *35.00 11.00*

Beware of counterfeits of No. 3275.

Strange Stories from a Chinese Studio, by Pu Songling — A947

Designs: 10f, Xiang Yu (6-1). 30f, Tiger of Zhaocheng (6-2). 60f, Huanniang (6-3). 80f, Ah Xiu (6-4). $1.50, Wang Gui'an (6-5). $2, Goddess (6-6).
$8, Princess of Dongting Lake, horiz.

**2003, May 16** ***Perf. 12***
**3276-3281** A947 Set of 6 2.50 2.50

**Souvenir Sheet**

***Perf. 13¼x13***

**3282** A947 $8 multi 7.25 3.75

No. 3282 contains one 90x60mm stamp.
Sheets exist containing 4 each of Nos. 3276-3277, 3278-3279 and 3280-3281. Value, set $42.50

1976 Meteorite Shower Over Jilin — A948

Designs: No. 3283, 80f, Meteorites falling (3-1). No. 3284, 80f, Dispersal of meteorites (3-2). $2, Meteorite (3-3).

**2003, June 21** **Litho.**
**3283-3285** A948 Set of 3 2.25 1.75

A sheet exists containing 3 each of Nos. 3283-3285. Value $45.

Master-of-Nets Garden, Suzhou — A949

No. 3286: a, 80f, Late Spring Cottage (4-1). b, 80f, Pavilion Greeting the Moon and Breeze (4-2). c, 80f, Veranda of Bamboo (4-3). d, $2, Hall of Ten Thousand Volumes (4-4).

**2003, June 29** **Photo.** ***Perf. 12¾***
**3286** A949 Horiz. strip of 4, #a-d 2.60 2.00

A sheet exists containing 2 No. 3286. Value $17.50.

Tibetan Antelopes — A950

Designs: 80f, Antelopes and mountain (2-1). $2, Antelope's head, adult with young (2-2).

**Photo. & Engr.**

**2003, July 20** ***Perf. 11x11¼***
**3287-3288** A950 Set of 2 1.95 1.50

Sheets exist containing 3 each of Nos. 3287-3288. Value, set $25.

Kongtong Mountain — A951

No. 3289: a, 80f, Town of Huangcheng (4-1). b, 80f, Gorge of Playing the Zither (4-2). c, 80f, Pagoda Courtyard (4-3). d, $2, Peak of Thunder (4-4).

**2003, July 26** **Litho.** ***Perf. 12***
**3289** A951 Block of 4, #a-d 2.25 2.00

A sheet exists containing 2 No. 3289. Value, $65.

Sailing Ship — A952

**2003, Aug. 5**
**3290** A952 80f multi + label 1.00 1.00

See Stamps With Attached Labels note after No. 3197. No. 3290 exists in sheets of 4 stamps + 4 labels. Value $5.

Powered Flight, Cent. — A953

Designs: 80f, Foreign airplanes (2-1). $2, Chinese airplanes (2-2).

**2003, Aug. 9** **Photo.** ***Perf. 12¾***
**3291-3292** A953 Set of 2 2.40 1.25

A sheet exists containing 6 each of Nos. 3291-3292. Value, $22.

Jinci Temple Painted Statues — A954

Designs: No. 3293, 80f, Ruyi maid (4-1). No. 3294, 80f, Maid holding a towel (4-2). No. 3295, 80f, Maid carrying a royal seal (4-3). $2, Maid singing and dancing (4-4).

**2003, Aug. 16** ***Perf. 11¾x12***
**3293-3296** A954 Set of 4 3.00 1.50

Sheets exist containing four each of Nos. 3293-3294 and 3295-3296. Value, set of 2 sheets $40. Value, set of 2 sheets with gold overprint $45.

Three Gorges Project A955

Designs: No. 3297, 80f, Dam and reservoir (3-1). No. 3298, 80f, Ship locks (3-2). $2, Power plant and high tension wire towers (3-3).

**2003, Aug. 20** **Litho.** ***Perf. 12***
**3297-3299** A955 Set of 3 3.25 1.40

A sheet exists containing 3 each of Nos. 3297-3299. Value, $22.

Traditional Sports of Ethnic Minorities — A956

Designs: No. 3300, 80f, Wrestling (4-1). b, No. 3301, 80f, Archery (4-2). No. 3302, 80f, Horse racing (4-3). No. 3303, 80f, Swinging (4-4).

**2003, Sept. 5** **Photo.** ***Perf. 13x13½***
**3300-3303** A956 Set of 4 2.65 1.10
*3303a* Souvenir sheet, #3300-3303 4.25 2.00

No. 3303a sold for $5. Sheets exist containing four each of No. 3300-3301 and 3302-3303. Value, set $19.
The sheets exist with overprint in selvage. Value, set $30.

Tiananmen Gate, Beijing A957

**2003, Sept. 10** **Litho.** ***Perf. 12***
**3304** A957 80f multi + label 1.00 .50

See Stamps With Attached Labels note after No. 3197. Two different sheets each containing four examples of No. 3304 were included in a souvenir folder sold only at the International Stamp and Coin Expo in Beijing in 2004. Value, set of 2 $8. Two additional sheets of four stamps + four labels, perf. 12½, exist. Value, set of 2 $30.

General Yue Fei (1103-42) — A958

Designs: No. 3305, 80f, Mother tattooing "Loyalty to the Country" on Yue Fei's back (3-1). No. 3306, 80f, Yue Fei standing with sword (3-2). $2, Yue Fei seated (3-3).

**2003, Sept. 25**
**3305-3307** A958 Set of 3 3.25 1.25

A sheet exists containing 3 each of Nos. 3305-3307. Value, $30.

Souvenir Sheet

Water Diversion Projects A959

**2003, Sept. 26** **Photo.** ***Perf. 12¾***
**3308** A959 $8 multi 3.75 2.50

Book Printing A960

Designs: No. 3309, 80f, Ritual of Zhou, China (2-1). No. 3310, 80f, Hungarian Illuminated Chronicle, 1473 (2-2).

**2003, Sept. 30** **Litho.** ***Perf. 12***
**3309-3310** A960 Set of 2 1.95 .80

Nos. 3309-3310 have large perforation holes at the stamp corners. A sheet exists containing 4 each of Nos. 3309-3310 in se-tenant pairs. Value, $27.50.
See Hungary Nos. 3863-3864.

Double Ninth Festival — A961

Designs: No. 3311, 80f, Climbing mountain (3-1). No. 3312, 80f, Enjoying the beauty of chrysanthemums (3-2). $2, Playing chess and drinking wine (3-3).

**2003, Oct. 4** **Photo.** ***Perf. 11½***
**3311-3313** A961 Set of 3 2.60 1.25

A sheet exists containing 3 each of Nos. 3311-3313 in strips of 3. Value, $15.

Launch of First Manned Chinese Spacecraft A962

No. 3314: a, 80f, Astronaut, Shenzhou spacecraft (2-1). b, $2, Yang Liwei, flag (2-2).

**2003, Oct. 16** ***Perf. 13x13¼***
**3314** A962 Pair, #a-b 10.00 6.00

A booklet containing No. 3314, Hong Kong No. 1062 and Macao No. 1128 exists. The booklet sold for a premium over face value. Value, $20.

Folktale of Liang Shanbo and Zhu Yingtai — A963

Designs: No. 3315, 80f, Zhu Yingtai, disguised as a man, and Liang Shanbo become sworn brothers at Caoqiao (5-1). No. 3316, 80f, Classmates for three years (5-2). No. 3317, 80f, Bidding farewell (5-3). No. 3318, 80f, Sad parting on the terrace (5-4). $2, Turning into butterflies (5-5).

**2003, Oct. 18** ***Perf. 12***
**3315-3319** A963 Set of 5 4.25 1.75

A booklet containing booklet panes of 1 of each of Nos. 3315-3319 exists. Value, $7.50. A sheet exists containing 2 each of Nos. 3315-3319. Value, $18. The sheet exists overprinted in the selvage. Value, $30.

China 2003 Intl. Stamp Exhibition, Mianyang — A964

**2003, Nov. 20** **Photo.** ***Perf. 13¼***
**3320** A964 80f multi 1.00 .60

No. 3320 exists as a minature sheet of 8. Value, $10. The sheet exists overprinted in the selvage. Value, $13.

World AIDS Day — A965

**2003, Dec. 1** ***Perf. 11¼x11***
**3321** A965 80f multi 2.00 1.00

No. 3321 exists as a miniature sheet of 8. Value, $27.50.

Mao Zedong (1893-1976) A966

Mao: No. 3322, 80f, Seated in folding chair (4-1). No. 3323, 80f, Standing (4-2). No. 3324, 80f, Seated on bench (4-3). No. 3325, 80f, Seated at desk (4-4).

**Litho. & Engr.**

**2003, Dec. 6** ***Perf. 12***
**3322-3325** A966 Set of 4 15.00 6.75

A sheet exists containing 2 each of Nos. 3322-3325 in se-tenant strips of 4. Value, $40.

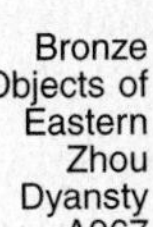

Bronze Objects of Eastern Zhou Dyansty A967

Designs: No. 3326, 60f, Square plate with turtle and fish patterns (8-1). No. 3327, 60f, Gui of the Duke of Qin (handled bowl with lid) (8-2). No. 3328, 80f, Iron-footed tripod of the King of Zhongshan (8-3). No. 3329, 80f, Gourd-shaped ladle of Yi, the Marquis of Zeng (8-4). No. 3330, 80f, Divine animal wine vessel, vert. (8-5). No. 3331, 80f, Wine vessel with phoenix pattern, vert. (8-6). $1, Square pot with lotus and cranes design, vert. (8-7). $2, Tripod with a dragon-shaped handle, vert. (8-8).

***Perf. 11½x11¼, 11¼x11½***

**2003, Dec. 13** **Photo. & Engr.**
**3326-3333** A967 Set of 8 6.50 2.75

A sheet of 8 No. 3328 exists. Value, $40.

**Environmental Protection Type of 2002**
**China Post No. R30**

Designs: 50f, Prevention and control of desertification. $4.50, Protection of biodiversity.

***Perf. 12¾x13¼ Syncopated***

**2004, Jan. 1** **Photo.**
**3334** A908 50f multi .35 .35
**3335** A908 $4.50 multi 1.75 .90

**Bird Type of 2002**
**China Post No. R31**

Designs: $5, Yellow-bellied tit. $6, Yunnan nuthatch.

**2004, Jan. 1** ***Perf. 13¼***
**3336** A909 $5 multi 1.75 1.60
**3337** A909 $6 multi 2.00 1.90

New Year 2004 (Year of the Monkey) — A968

**2004, Jan. 5** ***Perf. 13 Syncopated***
**3338** A968 80f multi 2.10 1.25
*a.* Booklet pane of 10 25.00 —
Complete booklet, #3338a 27.00

Sheets of 4 and sheets of 6 exist. Value, set $65.

Taohuawu New Year Pictures — A969

Designs: No. 3339, 80f, Feelings of Pipa (4-1). No. 3340, 80f, Kylin Bringing a Son (4-2). No. 3341, 80f, Liu Hai Playing with the Golden Toad (4-3). $2, Ten Beauties Playing Football (4-4).

**2004, Jan. 14** **Litho.** ***Perf. 12***
**3339-3342** A969 Set of 4 3.25 1.25
*3342a* Souvenir sheet, #3339-3342 5.50 3.75

A sheet of 2 each of Nos. 3339-3342 in se-tenant blocks of 4 exists. Value, $7. Sheet exists with overprint in selvage. Value, $21.

Deng Yingchao (1904-92), Communist Party Leader — A970

No. 3343: a, Holding book. b, Portrait.

**2004, Feb. 4** **Litho. & Engr.**
**3343** A970 80f Vert. pair, #a-b 1.10 1.00

No. 3343 exists in miniature sheets of 10. Value, $11.

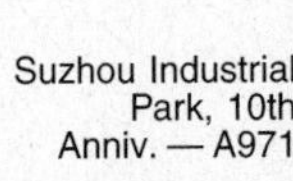

Suzhou Industrial Park, 10th Anniv. — A971

**2004, Mar. 1** **Photo.** ***Perf. 13x13¼***
**3344** A971 80f multi 1.00 .50

No. 3344 exists in miniature sheets of 12. Value, $27.50.
See Singapore No. 1084.

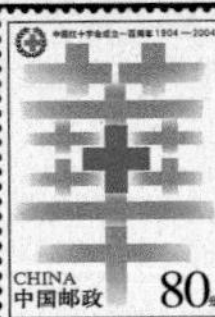

Red Cross Society, Cent. — A972

**2004, Mar. 10** ***Perf. 11¼x11***
**3345** A972 80f multi 1.10 .35

Stories Explaining Chinese Idioms — A973

Idioms: No. 3346, 80f, Trying to learn the Handan walk (4-1). No. 3347, 80f, Lord Ye's love for dragon (4-2). No. 3348, 80f, Filling a position in a Yu band (4-3). No. 3349, 80f, When the snipe and the clam grapple (4-4).

***Perf. 12½x13¼ Syncopated***

**2004, Apr. 2**
**3346-3349** A973 Set of 4 1.60 1.25

A sheet of 2 each of Nos. 3346-3349 in se-tenant strips of 4 exists. Value, $12.

Peacocks A974

Designs: No. 3350, 80f, Blue peacock (2-1). No. 3351, 80f, Albino peacock, vert. (2-2). $6, Green peacocks.

**2004, Apr. 13** ***Perf. 12¾***
**3350-3351** A974 Set of 2 1.00 .60

**Souvenir Sheet**

***Perf. 13¼x13***

**3352** A974 $6 multi 4.50 3.25

No. 3352 contains one 60x40mm stamp

Nanxi River A975

No. 3353: a, River and mountain (4-1). b, Tree and boat in foreground, mountains in background (4-2). c, Rocks, boat in river (4-3). d, Boat, spit of land with trees (4-4).

**2004, Apr. 24** **Photo.** ***Perf. 12¾***
**3353** Horiz. strip of 4 2.00 1.60
*a.* A975 60f multi .30 .25
*b.-c.* A975 80f Either single .40 .30
*d.* A975 $2 multi .75 .55

Danxia Mountain A976

Designs: 60f, Sengmao Peak (4-1). No. 3355, 80f, Xianlong Lake (4-2). No. 3356, 80f, Chahu Peak (4-3). $2, Jinjiang River (4-4).

**2004, May 1** **Litho. & Engr.** ***Perf. 12***
**3354-3357** A976 Set of 4 1.75 1.40

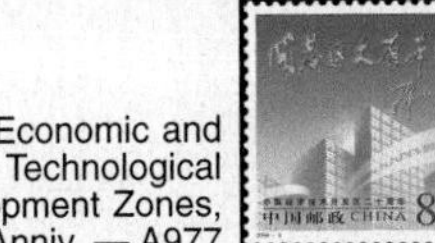

Economic and Technological Development Zones, 20th Anniv. — A977

**2004, May 4** **Litho.**
**3358** A977 80f multi 1.00 .40

Exists in a sheet of 8 stamps + 8 labels. Value, $7.50.

Hometowns of Returned Chinese — A978

Designs: No. 3359, 80f, Xinglong Overseas Chinese Farm (4-1). No. 3360, 80f, Jinan University (4-2). No. 3361, 80f, Fuqing Rongqiao Development Zone (4-3). No. 3362, 80f, Kaiping (4-4).

**2004, May 15** **Photo.** ***Perf. 11x11¼***
**3359-3362** A978 Set of 4 2.75 1.10

Sima Guang Breaking the Vat — A979

Designs: No. 3363, 80f, Sima Guang falling into water (3-1). No. 3362, 80f, Breaking vat (3-2). No. 3363, $2, Rescued (3-3).

**2004, June 1** ***Perf. 12***
**3363-3365** A979 Set of 3 2.40 1.25

A sheet of 2 each of Nos. 3363-3365 exists. Value, $19.50.

Scenes of Villages of Southern Anhui Province — A980

Designs: No. 3366, 80f, Archway (4-1). No. 3367, 80f, Old buildings (4-2). No. 3368, 80f, Buildings on South Lake (4-3). No. 3369, 80f, Moon Pond (4-4).

**Photo. & Engr.**

**2004, June 25** ***Perf. 11x11¼***
**3366-3369** A980 Set of 4 2.70 1.25

Liu Yi Delivering a Letter — A981

Designs: No. 3370, 80f, Dragon Princess asking Liu Yi to deliver a letter (4-1). No. 3371, 80f, Delivering letter to Dongting Lake (4-2). No. 3372, 80f, Family reunion (4-3). $2, Couple embracing (4-4).

**2004, July 17** **Photo.** ***Perf. 13¼x13***
**3370** A981 80f multi .35 .30
*a.* Booklet pane of 1 .90 —
**3371** A981 80f multi .35 .30
*a.* Booklet pane of 1 .90 —
**3372** A981 80f multi .35 .30
*a.* Booklet pane of 1 .90 —
**3373** A981 $2 multi .75 .30
*a.* Booklet pane of 1 2.50 —
Complete booklet, #3370a-3373a 6.75
*Nos. 3370-3373 (4)* 1.80 1.20

Complete booklet sold for $6.

Nos. 3370a-3373a exist with additional overprint in the margin. Value for complete booklet, $9.

**Souvenir Sheet**

Eight Immortals Crossing the Sea — A982

**2004, July 30** ***Perf. 12 Syncopated***
**3374** A982 $6 multi 5.00 5.00

Peony
A983

**2004, July 31** **Litho.** ***Perf. 12¾***
**3375** A983 80f multi + label .85 .50

See Stamps With Attached Labels note after No. 3197. Perf 12¾ examples come from a sheet containing four examples with labels below the stamps that also contain four No. 3261. The sheetlet sold for $15. Value, $14.

2004 Summer Olympics, Athens — A984

Olympic rings and: No. 3376, 80f, Parthenon, Athens (2-1). No. 3377, 80f, Hall of Good Harvest, Temple of Heaven, Beijing.

**2004, Aug. 13** **Photo.** ***Perf. 12¾***
**3376-3377** A984 Set of 2 1.00 1.00

Perf. 12¾ examples come from a sheet containing four examples with labels below the stamps that also contain four No. 3261. The sheetlet sold for $15. Value, $14.
See Greece Nos. 2124-2125.

A985

Deng Xiaoping (1904-97), Chinese Leader

Designs: No. 3378, 80f, Walking (2-1). No. 3379, 80f, Saluting, horiz. (2-2).
$6, Seated.

**2004, Aug. 22** ***Perf. 12 Syncopated***
**3378-3379** A985 Set of 2 1.90 1.00

**Souvenir Sheet**

***Perf. 13 Syncopated***

**3380** A985a $6 brnz & multi 5.00 2.25

No. 3380 contains one 47x57mm stamp.

South China Tiger — A986

Designs: 80f, Head (2-1). $2, Adult and young (2-2).

**2004, Aug. 23** **Litho.** ***Perf. 12***
**3381-3382** A986 Set of 2 1.25 .90

A sheet of 4 each of Nos. 3381-3382 in se-tenant pairs exists. Value, $17.50.

People's Congress, 50th Anniv. — A987

Designs: No. 3383, 80f, Congress members arriving at Huairentang Hall of Zhongnanhai (2-1). No. 3384, 80f, Interior of Great Hall of the People (2-2).

**2004, Sept. 15** ***Perf. 13¼***
**3383-3384** A987 Set of 2 2.20 .80

A sheet containing 3 pairs of Nos. 3383-3384 exists. Value, $13.

Bloodstone Seals — A988

No. 3385: a, 80f, Seal of Emperor Qianlong (2-1). b, $2, Seal of Emperor Jiaqing (2-2).

**Litho. & Embossed**

**2004, Sept. 17** ***Perf. 13x13¼***
**3385** A988 Pair, #a-b 2.75 1.10

A sheet cointaining four pairs of No. 3385 exists. Value, $10.

Celery Wormwood — A989

Designs: No. 3386, 80f, Purple flowers (4-1). No. 3387, 80f, Blue flowers (4-2). No. 3388, 80f, Red flowers (4-3). $2, Yellow flowers (4-4).

**2004, Sept. 19** **Photo.** ***Perf. 13¼x13***
**3386-3389** A989 Set of 4 1.75 1.50

A sheet containing 2 strips of 3386-3389 exists. Value, $11.

Chinese and Romanian Handicrafts — A990

Designs: No. 3390, 80f, Drum with tigers and birds, China (2-1). No. 3391, 80f, Cucuteni pottery jar, Romania (2-2).

**2004, Sept. 22** ***Perf. 13 Syncopated***
**3390-3391** A990 Set of 2 1.10 1.00

A sheet containing 4 pairs of Nos. 3390-3391 exists. Value, $13.
See Romania No. 4668.
Sheet exists with additional overprint in selvage. Value, $16.

National Symbols — A991

Designs: No. 3392, 80f, Flag (2-1). No. 3393, 80f, Arms, vert. (2-2).

***Perf. 13¼x13 Syncopated, 13x13¼ Syncopated***

**2004, Sept. 30**
**3392-3393** A991 Set of 2 2.50 2.50

A sheet of 4 self-adhesive examples of both Nos. 3392 and 3393 was included in a souvenir folder sold only at the International Stamp and Coin Expo in Beijing in 2004. Value, $25.

Landscapes of Chinese Borderlands A992

Designs: No. 3394, 80f, Forest, Xing'an Mountains (12-1). No. 3395, 80f, Lake in Yalu River Basin (12-2). No. 3396, 80f, Reefs in Yellow Sea (12-3). No. 3397, 80f, Zhoushan Archipelago (12-4). No. 3398, 80f, Coast of Taiwan (12-5). No. 3399, 80f, Xisha Islands (12-6). No. 3400, 80f, Karst landscape, Southern Guangxi (12-7). No. 3401, 80f, Rain forest, Southern Yunnan (12-8). No. 3402, 80f, Mt. Qomolangma (12-9). No. 3403, 80f, Pamirs (12-10). No. 3404, 80f, Badain Jaran Desert (12-11). No. 3405, 80f, Hulun Buir Steppe (12-12).

**2004, Oct. 1** ***Perf. 12¾***
**3394-3405** A992 Set of 12 3.75 3.50
*3405a* Sheet of 12, #3394-3405 + central label 8.00 7.50

Buildings in China and Spain — A993

Designs: No. 3406, 80f, Jinmao Tower, China (2-1). No. 3407, 80f, Park Guell, Spain.

**2004, Oct. 8** ***Perf. 13¼x13***
**3406-3407** A993 Set of 2 1.40 .90

See Spain Nos. 3319-3320.

Miniature Sheet

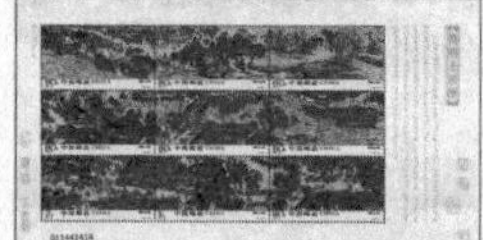

The Festival of Pure Brightness on the River, by Zhang Zeduan — A994

No. 3408 — Various details from painting: a, 60f, Trees (9-1). b, 80f, Trees, people on horseback (9-2). c, 80f, Buildings, boats on river (9-3). d, 80f, Buildings, boats on river, diff. (9-4). e, 80f, Bridge (9-5). f, 80f, Buildings, boats on river (9-6). g, 80f, Buildings (9-7). h, $1, Tower (9-8). i, $2, Intersection (9-9).

**Litho. & Engr.**

**2004, Oct. 18** ***Perf. 12***
**3408** A994 Sheet of 9, #a-i 15.00 9.75

Phoenix A995

**2004, Nov. 1** **Litho.** ***Perf. 12¾***
**3409** A995 80f multi + label .80 .30

A sheet of 4 No. 3409 + label exists. Value, $6.
A sheet of 10 serpentine die cut 12¼ self-adhesive stamps like No. 3409 + 10 labels depicting Snoopy for 25 yuan. Value, $15.

Pavilions — A996

Designs: No. 3410, 80f, Aiwan (4-1). No. 3411, 80f, Pipa (4-2). No. 3412, 80f, Lan (4-3). No. 3413, 80f, Zuiweng (4-4).

**2004, Nov. 6** **Photo.** ***Perf. 13¼x13***
**3410-3413** A996 Set of 4 1.60 1.00

A sheet of 2 each of Nos. 3410-3413 exists. Value, $14.

Ancient Calligraphy — A997

Designs: No. 3414, 80f, Yiying stele (4-1). No. 3415, 80f, Zhangqian stele (4-2). No. 3416, 80f, Caoquan stele (4-3). No. 3417, 80f, Shimen song (4-4).

**Photo. & Engr.**

**2004, Dec. 5** ***Perf. 11¼x11***
**3414-3417** A997 Set of 4 3.25 .90

A sheet of 2 each of Nos. 3414-3417 exists. Value, $16.

New Year 2005 (Year of the Rooster) — A998

***Perf. 13 Syncopated***

**2005, Jan. 5** **Photo.**
**3418** A998 80f multi 1.75 .40
*a.* Booklet pane of 10 16.00 —
Complete booklet, #3418a 17.00

No. 3418 exists in sheets of 4 and 6. Value, $20 and $24, respectively.
The sheet of 6 exists with an additional overprint "PJZ-18." Value, $60. Some also exist overprinted "PJZ-17." Value, $200.

Tarim-Baihe Gas Pipeline — A999

No. 3419: a, 80f, Derrick (2-1). b, $3, Pipes (2-2).

**2005, Jan. 8** **Litho.** ***Perf. 12***
**3419** A999 Horiz. pair, #a-b 2.25 1.25

Historic Structures in Taiwan — A1000

No. 3420: a, North Gate, Taipei City Wall (5-1). b, Confucian Temple (5-2). c, Longshan Temple, Lugang (5-3). d, Erkunshen Cannon Fort, Tainan (5-4). e, Matsu Temple, Penghu (5-5).

***Perf. 13 Syncopated***

**2005, Jan. 30** **Litho. & Engr.**
**3420** Vert. strip of 5 3.25 1.75
*a.-d.* A1000 80f Any single .30 .25
*e.* A1000 $1.50 multi .60 .45

Exists in a sheet with 2 No. 3420. Value, $6.

Yangjiabu New Year Woodprints — A1001

Designs: No. 3421, 80f, Door God (4-1). No. 3422, 80f, Abundance for year (4-2). No. 3423, 80f, Good news on New Year's Day (4-3). No. 3424, 80f, Goddess strewing flowers from heaven (4-4).

**2005, Feb. 1 Litho. *Perf. 13¼x13***
**3421-3424** A1001 Set of 4 1.75 1.10
*3424a* Souvenir sheet, #3421-3424 7.50 2.50

No. 3424a sold for $4.80. A miniature sheet containing 2 of each stamp exists. Value, $8.

Magnolias A1002

Designs: No. 3425, 80f, Magnolia denudata (4-1). No. 3426, 80f, Magnolia delavayi (4-2). No. 3427, 80f, Magnolia grandiflora (4-3). No. 3428, 80f, Magnolia liliflora (4-4).

**2005, Mar. 5 Photo. *Perf. 13x13¼***
**3425-3428** A1002 Set of 4 2.50 1.10

Great Wall of China A1003

**2005, Apr. 1 Litho. *Perf. 12¾***
**3429** A1003 80f multi + label .60 .30

See Stamps With Attached Labels note after No. 3197. See note following No. 3462. See No. 3846A.

Earth Day — A1004

**2005, Apr. 22 Photo. *Perf. 13¼***
**3430** A1004 80f multi 1.00 .30

A ring of syncopated perforations surrounds the vignette.

Jigong Mountains A1005

No. 3431: a, Mountain at daybreak (4-1). b, Garden in clouds (4-2). c, Moon Pond (4-3). d, Black Dragon Waterfall (4-4).

***Perf. 12½ Syncopated***

**2005, Apr. 28 Litho.**
**3431** Horiz. strip of 4 2.70 1.25
*a.-d.* A1005 80f Any single .35 .25

No. 3431 exists in a sheet comprised of two strips of 4. Value, $6.

All-China Federation of Trade Unions, 80th Anniv. — A1006

**2005, May 1 *Perf. 12***
**3432** A1006 80f multi .80 .40

Paintings of Flower Arrangements A1007

Designs: No. 3433, 80f, Magnolia Flowers, by Chen Hongshou (2-1). No. 3434, 80f, Flower Vase in a Window Niche, by Ambrosius Bosschaert the Elder (2-2).

***Perf. 12½ Syncopated***

**2005, May 18 Photo.**
**3433-3434** A1007 Set of 2 2.40 .50

See Liechtenstein Nos. 1315-1316.

Dalian Bay Area Views A1008

No. 3435: a, Tiger Beach (4-1). b, Bangchui Island (4-2). c, Golden Pebble Beach (4-3). d, Lushunkou (4-4).

**2005, May 21 *Perf. 12¾ Syncopated***
**3435** Horiz. strip of 4 3.75 1.25
*a.-d.* A1008 80f Any single .40 .25

Exists in a sheet with 2 No. 3435. Value, $7.

Fudan University, Cent. — A1009

**Litho., Engr. & Embossed**

**2005, May 27 *Perf. 12***
**3436** A1009 80f multi 1.60 .25

Hans Christian Andersen (1805-75), Author — A1010

No. 3437 — Fairy tales by Andersen: a, The Emperor's New Clothes (5-1). b, The Little Mermaid (5-2). c, Thumbelina (5-3). d, The Little Match Girl (5-4). e, The Ugly Duckling (5-5).

***Perf. 13¼ Syncopated***

**2005, June 1 Photo.**
**3437** Horiz. strip of 5 3.00 1.40
*a.-e.* A1010 60f Any single .30 .25
*f.* Booklet pane of 1, #3437a .50 —
*g.* Booklet pane of 1, #3437b .50 —
*h.* Booklet pane of 1, #3437c .50 —
*i.* Booklet pane of 1, #3437d .50 —
*j.* Booklet pane of 1, #3437e .50 —
Complete booklet, #3437f-3437j 6.00

The complete booklet sold for $6.

A sheet of ten serpentine die cut 10 self-adhesive stamps containing two of each of the designs of Nos. 3437a-3437e and ten labels exists. Value, $10.

Voyages of Admiral Zheng He, 600th Anniv. — A1011

No. 3438: a, Admiral Zheng He (3-1). b, Building, map of voyages (3-2). c, Compass, drawing of ship (3-3)

$6, Ship, horiz.

**2005, June 28 Litho.**
**3438** Horiz. strip of 3 3.00 1.00
*a.-c.* A1011 80f Any single .30 .25

**Souvenir Sheet**

**3439** A1011 $6 multi 4.00 2.50

No. 3439 contains one 70x50mm stamp.

Nantong Museum A1012

No. 3440: a, Southern Hall (2-1). b, Central Hall (2-2).

**Photo. & Engr.**

**2005, July 16 *Perf. 12½x12¾***
**3440** A1012 80f Horiz. pair, #a-b 1.90 .75

Xianghai National Nature Reserve A1013

Designs: No. 3441, 80f, Red-crowned cranes in nest (4-1). No. 3442, 80f, Three birds in flight, trees (4-2). No. 3443, 80f, Birds at lake (4-3). No. 3444, 80f, Eagles flying above steppe (4-4).

**2005, July 30 Photo. *Perf. 12¾***
**3441-3444** A1013 Set of 4 2.50 1.00

**Miniature Sheet**

People's Army Generals A1014

No. 3445: a, Yang Jingyu (5-1). b, Zuo Quan (5-2). c, Peng Xuefeng (5-3). d, Luo Binghui (5-4). e, Guan Xiangying (5-5).

**2005, Aug. 1 *Perf. 12***
**3445** A1014 80f Sheet of 10, 2 each #a-e 7.00 4.00

End of World War II, 60th Anniv. A1015

No. 3446: a, Soldiers with machine guns (4-1). b, Bugler (4-2). c, Soldier holding gun, troops landing in Normandy (4-3). d, Conquering Berlin (4-4).

$6, Dove, vert.

***Perf. 12¾ Syncopated***

**2005, Aug. 15 Litho.**
**3446** A1015 80f Block of 4, #a-d 3.00 1.25

**Souvenir Sheet**

**Photo.**

***Perf. 12¾***

**3447** A1015 $6 multi 4.50 2.00

Tibet Autonomous Region, 40th Anniv. A1016

**2005, Aug. 26 Photo. *Perf. 13¼***
**3448** A1016 80f multi 2.10 .30

Chinese Motion Pictures, Cent. — A1017

**2005, Aug. 28 Litho. *Perf. 12¾x13***
**3449** A1017 80f multi 1.30 .25

Exists in a sheet of 8 stamps + 8 labels.

"Five Happinesses Arrive" — A1018

**2005, Sept. 16 *Perf. 12¾***
**3450** A1018 80f multi + label 1.00 .35

See Stamps With Attached Labels note after No. 3197. See note following No. 3462.

Fanjing Mountain Nature Reserve A1019

No. 3451: a, Golden Summit (4-1). b, Mushroom Rock (4-2). c, Forest (4-3). d, Heiwan River (4-4).

**2005, Sept. 18 Photo. *Perf. 13x13¼***
**3451** Horiz. strip of 4 1.60 1.25
*a.-d.* A1019 80f Any single .30 .25

Exists in a sheet with 2 No. 3451. Value, $7.50.

Farm Technology A1020

Sheep and: No. 3452, 80f, Chinese water wheel (2-1). No. 3453, 80f, Dutch windmill (2-2).

**2005, Sept. 22 *Perf. 12***
**3452-3453** A1020 Set of 2 2.00 .50

See Netherlands Nos. 1203-1204.

Exists in a sheet with 4 No. 3453 and 8 No. 3452. Value, $27.50.

**Miniature Sheet**

People's Liberation Army Generals — A1021

No. 1021: a, Su Yu (10-1). b, Xu Haidong (10-2). c, Huang Kecheng (10-3). d, Chen Geng (10-4). e, Tan Zheng (10-5). f, Xiao Jinguang (10-6). g, Zhang Yunyi (10-7). h, Luo Ruiqing (10-8). i, Wang Shusheng (10-9). j, Xu Guangda (10-10).

**Litho. & Engr.**

**2005, Sept. 27 *Perf. 13¼x13***
**3454** A1021 80f Sheet of 10, #a-j 8.00 3.25

**Miniature Sheet**

Goddess of the River Luo, by Gu Kaizhi A1022

Various painting details with width of: a, 50mm (10-1). b, 50mm (10-2). c, 60mm (10-3). d, 40mm (10-4). e, 60mm (10-5). f, 60mm (10-6). g, 60mm (10-7). h, 50mm (10-8). i, 40mm (10-9). j, 50mm (10-10).

**2005, Sept. 28 *Perf. 12***
**3455** A1022 80f Sheet of 10, #a-j 15.00 7.50

Xinjiang Uygur Autonomous Region, 50th Anniv. — A1023

No. 3456: a, Male dancers and musicians (3-1). b, Male and female dancers (3-2). c, Women carrying plates of food (3-3).

***Perf. 12x12½ Syncopated***

**2005, Oct. 1** **Litho.**

**3456** A1023 Horiz. strip of 3 2.15 1.00
*a.-c.* 80f Any single .30 .25

Souvenir Sheet

10th National Games, Jiangsu Province A1024

**2005, Oct. 12** **Photo.** ***Perf. 12¾***

**3457** A1024 $6 multi 4.25 2.00

Wild Cats — A1025

Designs: No. 3458, 80f, Panthera pardus orientalis (2-1). No. 3459, 80f, Puma concolor (2-2).

**2005, Oct. 13** **Photo.** ***Perf. 13x13¼***

**3458-3459** A1025 Set of 2 1.75 .50

See Canada Nos. 2122-2123.

"Be Safe Every Year" A1026

**2005, Nov. 6** **Litho.** ***Perf. 13¼***

**3460** A1026 80f red & blk + label 3.50 1.00

See Stamps With Attached Labels note after No. 3197. A serpentine die cut 10 self-adhesive stamp of type A1026 exists. Value, $22.50.

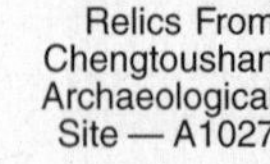

Relics From Chengtoushan Archaeological Site — A1027

**2005, Nov. 6** **Photo.** ***Perf. 12½***

**3461** A1027 80f multi 1.60 .25

"Beam With Delight" A1028

**2005, Nov. 11** **Litho.** ***Perf. 12¾***

**3462** A1028 80f multi + label 1.10 .25

See Stamps With Attached Labels note after No. 3197. A sheet of 2 each of Nos. 3429, 3450 and 3462 exists. Value, $6.

2008 Summer Olympics, Beijing — A1029

Designs: No. 3463, Beijing Olympics emblem, Olympic rings (6-1).

No. 3464 — Beijing Olympic mascots with emblem on chest: a, Beibei (6-2). b, Jingjing (6-3). c, Huanhuan (6-4). d, Yingying (6-5). e, Nini (6-6).

No. 3465: a, Like #3463. b, Like #3464a. c, Like #3464b. d, Like #3464c. e, Like #3464d. f, Like #3464e.

**2005, Nov. 12** **Photo.** ***Perf. 13¼x13***

**3463** A1029 80f multi .65 .25

**3464** A1029 80f Horiz. strip of 5, #a-e 10.00 7.50

**Self-Adhesive**

***Serpentine Die Cut 11¾***

**3465** A1029 80f Sheet, 2 each #a-f *26.00 26.00*

A sheet of 5 30x30mm stamps with the Beijing Olympics emblem and Olympic rings was issued in 2008. Value, $15.

New Year 2006 (Year of the Dog) — A1030

***Perf. 13 Syncopated***

**2006, Jan. 5** **Photo.**

**3466** A1030 80f multi 1.60 .25
*a.* Sheet of 6 *9.00 7.25*
*b.* Booklet pane of 10 10.00 —
Complete booklet, #3466b 12.50

A sheet of 4 exists that was a giveaway for standing-order customers. Value, $15.

Wuqiang New Year Woodprints — A1031

Designs: No. 3467, 80f, Being Safe All Year Round (4-1). No. 3468, 80f, Five Blessings Approach Your Door (4-2). No. 3469, 80f, Flower of Prosperity Blossoms (4-3). No. 3470, 80f, Lion Rolling the Embroidered Ball (4-4).

**Litho. & Engr.**

**2006, Jan. 22** ***Perf. 12***

**3467-3470** A1031 Set of 4 2.75 1.25
*3470a* Souvenir sheet, #3467-3470 *8.00 2.50*
*3470b* Souvenir sheet, 2 each #3467-3470 *9.00 6.00*

Lanterns — A1032

Designs: No. 3471, 80f, Fish lantern (5-1). No. 3472, 80f, Chinese white cabbage lantern (5-2). No. 3473, 80f, Lotus lantern (5-3). No. 3474, 80f, Dragon and phoenix lantern (5-4). $1.50, Butterfly lantern (5-5).

**2006, Feb. 12** **Photo.** ***Perf. 13¼x13***

**3471-3475** A1032 Set of 5 5.00 2.00
*3475a* Sheet, 2 each #3471-3475 *14.00 8.00*

Abolition of Agricultural Tax — A1033

***Perf. 13½ Syncopated***

**2006, Feb. 22**

**3476** A1033 80f multi 7.00 2.00

Lijiang River — A1034

No. 3477: a, Yangdi (4-1). b, Langshi (4-2). c, Huangbu (4-3). d, Xingping (4-4).

**2006, Feb. 25** ***Perf. 12¾***

**3477** A1034 Horiz. strip of 4 4.00 2.00
*a.-d.* 80f Any single .60 .25

Relic Plants — A1035

Designs: No. 3478, 80f, Ginkgo biloba (4-1). No. 3479, 80f, Glyptostrobus pensilis (4-2). No. 3480, 80f, Davidia involucrata (4-3). No. 3481, 80f, Liriodendron chinense (4-4).

***Perf. 12x12¼ Syncopated***

**2006, Mar. 12** **Litho.**

**3478-3481** A1035 Set of 4 4.75 1.50

Dogs — A1036

Designs: Nos. 3482, 3486a, 80f, Pekingese (4-1). Nos. 3483, 3486b, 80f, Pug, vert. (4-2). Nos. 3484, 3486c, 80f, Chow chow (4-3). Nos. 3485, 3486d, 80f, Tibetan mastiff, vert. (4-4).

***Perf. 13¼ Syncopated***

**2006, Mar. 19** **Litho. & Engr.**

**3482-3485** A1036 Set of 4 2.70 1.40

**Self-Adhesive**

***Serpentine Die Cut 11¾ on 2 Sides***

**3486** A1036 80f Sheet, 2 each #3486a-3486d 10.00 *7.00*

Qingcheng Mountain — A1037

Designs: 60f, Remote mountain gate (4-1). No. 3488, 80f, Winding path (4-2). No. 3489, 80f, Ancient temple (4-3). No. 3490, 80f, Spring (4-4).

**2006, Apr. 12** ***Perf. 13¼ Syncopated***

**3487-3490** A1037 Set of 4 5.25 1.50

Statues in Yungang Grottoes — A1038

Designs: No. 3491, 80f, Sakyamuni (4-1). No. 3492, 80f, Bodhisattva (4-2). No. 3493, 80f, Head of Bodhisattva (4-3). No. 3494, 80f, Xieshi Bodhisattva (4-4).
$6, Sakyamuni, diff.

***Perf. 13¼x13½ Syncopated***

**2006, Apr. 13** **Photo.**

**3491-3494** A1038 Set of 4 6.25 1.00

**Souvenir Sheet**

***Perf. 13 Syncopated***

**3495** A1038 $6 multi 6.50 3.00

No. 3495 contains one 40x60mm stamp.

Tianzhu Mountain A1039

Designs: 60f, Green Dragon Mountain Stream (4-1). No. 3497, 80f, Taoist Practice Terrace (4-2). No. 3498, 80f, Sanzu Temple (4-3). No. 3499, 80f, Qingtian Peak (4-4).

**2006, Apr. 22** ***Perf. 11½x11¼***

**3496-3499** A1039 Set of 4 2.40 1.00

Scientists A1040

Designs: No. 3500, 80f, Liang Xi (1883-1958), forester (4-1). No. 3501, 80f, Mao Yisheng (1896-1989), civil engineer (4-2). No. 3502, 80f, Yan Jici (1900-96), physicist (4-3). No. 3503, 80f, Zhou Peiyuan (1902-93), physicist (4-4).

**Litho. & Engr.**

**2006, May 13** ***Perf. 12***

**3500-3503** A1040 Set of 4 8.50 2.00

Lighthouses — A1041

No. 3504: a, Dagu Lighthouse (4-1). b, Guishan Island Lighthouse (4-2). c, Wusongkou Lighthouse (4-3). d, Mulantou Lighthouse (4-4).

**2006, May 22** **Photo.** ***Perf. 12¾***

**3504** A1041 Horiz. strip of 4 4.00 1.50
*a.-d.* 80f Any single .40 .25

Chinese Space Program, 50th Anniv. A1042

No. 3505: a, Geospace Double Star Exploration (2-1). b, Shenzhou 6 (2-2).

***Perf. 12x11¼ Syncopated***

**2006, June 8** **Litho.**

**3505** A1042 80f Horiz. pair, #a-b 2.25 1.00

Silver and Gold Objects — A1043

Designs: No. 3506, 80f, Jeeweled Qing Dynasty cup, China (2-1). No. 3507, 80f, Tankard with Biblical designs, by Peter Rohde, Poland.

**2006, June 20** **Photo.** ***Perf. 13¼x13***

**3506-3507** A1043 Set of 2 2.40 .65

See Poland No. 3829.

Olympic Rings and Emblem of 2008 Summer Olympics, Beijing — A1043a

**2006, June 23** **Litho.** ***Perf. 12***

**3507A** A1043a 80f multi + label 1.25 .45

See Stamps With Attached Labels note after No. 3197. Printed in sheets of 15 stamps + 15 labels, sheets of 5 stamps + 5 labels, sheets of 4 stamps + 4 labels to right of stamps, sheets of 4 stamps + 4 labels below stamps, and sheets of 8 stamps + 8 labels. Value, set of 5 sheets $50.

Early Communist Leaders — A1044

Designs: No. 3508, 80f, Gao Junyu (1896-1925) (5-1). No. 3509, 80f, Wang Hebo (1882-1927) (5-2). No. 3510, 80f, Su Zhaozheng (1885-1929) (5-3). No. 3511, 80f, Peng Pai (1896-1929) (5-4). No. 3512, 80f, Deng Xhongxia (1894-1933) (5-5).

**2006, June 30 — Litho. & Engr.**

**3508-3512** A1044 Set of 5 *35.00 12.50*

Opening of Qinghai-Tibet Railway — A1045

Designs: No. 3513, 80f, Bridge across Kekexili, antelopes (3-1). No. 3514, 80f, Train crossing Danggula Mountains, cattle (3-2). No. 3515, 80f, Lhasa Railway Station, birds (3-3).

***Perf. 12½x12 Syncopated***

**2006, July 1 — Litho.**

**3513-3515** A1045 Set of 3 6.75 2.00

Kanasi Nature Reserve A1046

Designs: No. 3516, 80f, Kanasi Lake (4-1). No. 3517, 80f, Crouching Dragon Bend (4-2). No. 3518, 80f, Celestial Bend (4-3). No. 3519, 80f, Moon Bend (4-4).

**2006, July 8 — Photo. — *Perf. 12¾***

**3516-3519** A1046 Set of 4 6.00 1.75

Earthquake Protection and Damage Mitigation — A1047

**2006, July 26 — *Perf. 13½x13***

**3520** A1047 80f multi 4.00 .65

2008 Summer Olympics, Beijing — A1048

Designs: Nos. 3521, 3525a, 60f, Basketball (4-1). Nos. 3522, 3525b, 80f, Fencing (4-2). Nos. 3523, 3525c, Sailing (4-3). Nos. 3524, 3525d, $3, Gymnastics (4-4).

**2006, Aug. 8 — Photo. — *Perf. 13¼x13***

**3521-3524** A1048 Set of 4 4.25 2.00

**Self-Adhesive**

***Serpentine Die Cut 11¾***

**3525** A1048 Sheet of 8, 2 each #a-d 20.00 *10.00*

Portions of the designs of Nos. 3525a-3525d were applied by a thermographic process, producing a shiny, raised effect.

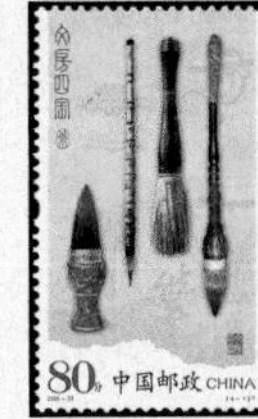

Treasures of the Study — A1049

Designs: No. 3526, 80f, Brushes (4-1). No. 3527, 80f, Ink (4-2). No. 3528, 80f, Paper (4-3). No. 3529, 80f, Ink stone (4-4).

***Perf. 12x12½ Syncopated***

**2006, Sept. 10 — Litho.**

**3526-3529** A1049 Set of 4 8.50 1.90

A sheet of 2 each of Nos. 3526-3529 exists. Value, $60.

All-China Federation of Returned Overseas Chinese, 50th Anniv. — A1050

***Perf. 12½x12 Syncopated***

**2006, Sept. 25**

**3530** A1050 80f multi 1.00 .30

Musical Instruments A1051

Designs: No. 3531, 80f, Seven-stringed qin, China (2-1). No. 3532, 80f, Bösendorfer piano, Austria (2-2).

***Perf. 13x12½ Syncopated***

**2006, Sept. 26 — Litho.**

**3531-3532** A1051 Set of 2 2.60 .60

See Austria Nos. 2066-2067.

Chinese Export Commodities Fair — A1052

***Perf. 13½x13¼ Syncopated***

**2006, Oct. 15 — Photo.**

**3533** A1052 80f multi 1.60 .25

Long March, 70th Anniv. A1053

Designs: No. 3534, 80f, Setting Out (4-1). No. 3535, 80f, Zunyi Conference (4-2). No. 3536, 80f, Speedily Occupy the Luding Bridge (4-3). No. 3537, 80f, The Red Army Through the Marshland (4-4).

$6, Reunion.

**2006, Oct. 22 — *Perf. 13x13¼***

**3534-3537** A1053 Set of 4 4.75 1.60

**Souvenir Sheet**

**3538** A1053 $6 multi 6.50 2.50

No. 3538 contains one 80x50mm stamp. A souvenir sheet of one of No. 3535 exists.

No. 3538 exists imperf.

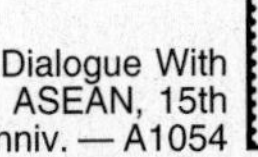

Dialogue With ASEAN, 15th Anniv. — A1054

***Perf. 12½x12 Syncopated***

**2006, Oct. 30 — Litho.**

**3539** A1054 80f multi 1.50 .30

"Enjoying Prosperity Year After Year" — A1055

"Happy New Year" — A1055a

***Perf. 12¾ Syncopated***

**2006, Nov. 1 — Photo.**

**3540** A1055 80f multi .35 .25

**3541** A1055a $3 multi 1.35 .85

A souvenir sheet containing Nos. 3540-3541 exists. Value, $19.

See note following No. 3628. See Nos. 3708a, 3869b, 3978a, 4048a, 4158a, 4238a, 4326a, 4409a, 4488a, 4582a, 4683a.

Beijing Summit of Forum on China-Africa Cooperation A1056

**2006, Nov. 3 — Litho. — *Perf. 13¼***

**3542** A1056 80f multi 1.25 .25

Buildings Associated With Dr. Sun Yat-sen (1826-1925) — A1057

Designs: No. 3543, 80f, Sun Yat-sen Villa (4-1). No. 3544, 80f, Mausoleum (4-2). No. 3545, 80f, Sun Yat-sen Memorial Hall (4-3). No. 3546, 80f, Sun Yat-sen University (4-4).

***Perf. 13¼ Syncopated***

**2006, Nov. 12 — Litho. & Engr.**

**3543-3546** A1057 Set of 4 4.00 1.75

**Birds Type of 2002**

**China Post No. R31**

Designs: 40f, Chinese monal pheasant. $1.20, Taiwan yuhinas.

***Perf. 13½ Syncopated***

**2006, Nov. 15 — Photo.**

**3547** A909 40f multi .30 .25

**3548** A909 $1.20 multi .45 .35

Heavenly Steed, Silk Roll Painting A1058

No. 3549: a, Horse and rider. b, People looking at horse.

**2006, Dec. 3 — Photo. — *Perf. 12¾***

**3549** A1058 $1.20 Horiz. pair, #a-b 1.50 1.00

Wu Lanfu (1906-88), Politician — A1059

**2006, Dec. 23 — *Perf. 13¼x13***

**3550** A1059 $1.20 multi *11.00 4.00*

Trains A1060

Designs: No. 3551, $1.20, Locomotive, blue background (4-1). No. 3552, $1.20, Locomotive, red brown background (4-2). No. 3553, $1.20, Box car (4-3). No. 3554, $1.20, Log cars and gateway (4-4).

$6, Locomotive and city skyline.

**2006, Dec. 28 — *Perf. 13x13¼***

**3551-3554** A1060 Set of 4 *32.50 10.00*

**Souvenir Sheet**

***Perf. 13¼x13***

**3555** A1060 $6 multi *12.50 8.00*

No. 3555 contains one 90x40mm stamp.

China Post, 110th Anniv. A1061

***Perf. 12x11½ Syncopated***

**2006, Dec. 30 — Litho.**

**3556** A1061 $1.20 multi 1.50 .60

A sheet containing 6 No. 3556 exists. Value, $8.50.

New Year 2007 (Year of the Pig) — A1062

***Perf. 13 Syncopated***

**2007, Jan. 5 — Photo.**

**3557** A1062 $1.20 multi 1.25 .35

*a.* Souvenir sheet of 6 11.00 *6.00*

*b.* Booklet pane of 10 10.00 —

Complete booklet, #3557b 12.50

A sheet containing 4 No. 3557 exists. Value, $12.50.

6th Asian Winter Games — A1063

***Perf. 12x12½ Syncopated***

**2007, Jan. 28 — Litho.**

**3558** A1063 $1.20 multi 1.30 .35

Shiwan Pottery Figurines — A1064

Designs: No. 3559, $1.20, Ta Xue Xun Mei (2-1). No. 3560, $1.20, Wang Zhaojun Chu Sai (2-2).

**2007, Feb. 3 — Photo. — *Perf. 13¼x13***

**3559-3560** A1064 Set of 2 1.25 .65

*3560a* Miniature sheet, 4 each #3559-3560 7.00 3.50

"Divine Birds of the Sun" A1065

**2007, Feb. 9 — Litho. — *Perf. 12***

**3561** A1065 $1.20 multi + label .65 .35

See Stamps With Attached Labels note after No. 3197. Printed in sheets of 6 + 6 labels (value, $11), 8 + 8 labels and 15 + 15 labels (value, $20).

Mianzhu New Year Woodcuts — A1066

Designs: No. 3562, $1.20, Zuo Zuo Ti Dao (4-1). No. 3563, $1.20, Mu Guiying (4-2). No. 3564, $1.20, Shuang Xi Tong Zi (4-3). No. 3565, $1.20, Zhang Xian She Gou (4-4).

***Perf. 12x11½ Syncopated***

**2007, Feb. 10** **Litho. & Engr.**

**3562-3565** A1066 Set of 4 3.00 1.50
*3565a* Souvenir sheet of 4, #3562-3565 6.50 2.50
*3565b* Miniature sheet of 8, 2 each #3562-3565 19.00 5.25

A lithographed sheet similar to No. 3565b on a textured silk-faced paper exists. Value, $16.

Beijing Opera — A1067

Designs: 80f, Lin Xiangru (6-1). No. 3567, $1.20, Song Shijie (6-2). No. 3568, $1.20, Zhou Yu (6-3). No. 3569, $1.20, Xu Xian (6-4). No. 3570, $1.20, Gao Chong (6-5). No. 3571, $1.20, Ren Tanghui (6-6).

**2007, Mar. 10** **Photo.** ***Perf. 13¼x13***

**3566-3571** A1067 Set of 6 3.75 1.90

Postal Savings Bank A1068

**2007, Mar. 20** ***Perf. 12¾***

**3572** A1068 $1.20 multi 1.00 .35
*a.* Miniature sheet of 8 *9.00 4.50*

Writings of Li Keran — A1069

Designs: No. 3573, $1.20, Man viewing waterfall (6-1). No. 3574, $1.20, Mountains with red-leaved trees (6-2). No. 3575, $1.20, People looking at scroll (6-3). No. 3576, $1.20, Crane flying above man under tent (6-4). No. 3577, $1.20, Cattle and driver in pond (6-5). No. 3578, $1.20, Raining in Jiangnan (6-6).

***Perf. 13x13¼ Syncopated***

**2007, Mar. 26**

**3573-3578** A1069 Set of 6 6.50 2.25

Modern Chinese Drama, Cent. — A1070

***Perf. 13 Syncopated***

**2007, Apr. 6** **Litho.**

**3579** A1070 $1.20 multi .80 .35

Yangzhou Garden — A1071

No. 3580: a, He Garden (3-1). b, Ge Garden (3-2). c, Xu Garden (3-3).

***Perf. 12x11½ Syncopated***

**2007, Apr. 8**

**3580** A1071 Horiz. strip of 3 1.75 1.40
*a.-c.* $1.20 Any single .50 .35

Dances — A1072

Designs: No. 3581, $1.20, Dragon dance (2-1). No. 3582, $1.20, Lion dance (2-2).

**2007, Apr. 13** **Litho.** ***Perf. 12¾x13***

**3581-3582** A1072 Set of 2 2.25 .75

See Indonesia No. 2100.

Torch Relay for 2008 Summer Olympics, Beijing — A1073

**2007, Apr. 27** ***Perf. 12***

**3583** A1073 $1.20 multi + label 1.75 .60
*a.* Sheet of 4 + 4 labels 3.00 2.50

See Stamps With Attached Labels note after No. 3197.

Inner Mongolia Autonomous Region, 60th Anniv. — A1074

Designs: No. 3584, $1.20, Horsemen, wrestlers, archer (2-1). No. 3585, $1.20, Seven women (2-2).

***Perf. 12½x12 Syncopated***

**2007, May 1**

**3584-3585** A1074 Set of 2 1.25 .70
*3585a* Souvenir sheet, #3584-3585 2.90 1.50

Mausoleums of Qing Emperors — A1075

Designs: No. 3586, $1.20, Zhaoling Mausoleum (3-1). No. 3587, $1.20, Xiaoling Mausoleum (3-2). No. 3588, Tailing Mausoleum (3-3).

**2007, May 12** **Photo.** ***Perf. 12¾***

**3586-3588** A1075 Set of 3 2.40 1.00

Tongji University, Cent. — A1076

**2007, May 20** ***Perf. 12½ Syncopated***

**3589** A1076 $1.20 multi 1.25 .50

Kong Rong and Pears A1077

Nos. 3590 and 3591: a, Denomination at LL (2-1). b, Denomination at LR (2-2).

**2007, June 1** ***Perf. 13¼x13***

**3590** A1077 $1.20 Horiz. pair, #a-b 1.45 .85

**Self-Adhesive**

**Booklet Stamps**

***Serpentine Die Cut 11¾***

**3591** A1077 $1.20 Horiz. pair, #a-b .85 .85
*c.* Booklet pane, 4 #3591 5.00

Chongqing — A1078

No. 3592: a, City skyline (2-1). b, City and highway interchange (2-2).

***Perf. 12x11½ Syncopated***

**2007, June 8** **Litho.**

**3592** A1078 $1.20 Horiz. pair, #a-b 1.60 .90

Wudalianchi Natl. Park — A1079

No. 3593: a, Heilong Mountain (3-1). b, Sanchi Pool (3-2). c, Sea of Rock (3-3).

**2007, June 19** **Photo.** ***Perf. 12¾***

**3593** A1079 Horiz. strip of 3 2.40 1.25
*a.-c.* $1.20 Any single .45 .35

Return of Hong Kong, 10th Anniv. — A1080

Designs: No. 3594, $1.20, Flags of People's Republic of China and Hong Kong, doves, monument (3-1). No. 3595, $1.20, "CEPA" and stylized buildings (3-2). No. 3596, $1.20, Hong Kong buildings, bridge (3-3).

***Perf. 13¼x12¾ Syncopated***

**2007, July 1**

**3594-3596** A1080 Set of 3 2.40 1.50

A souvenir sheet containing Nos. 3594-3596 and Hong Kong No. 1275 sold for $12.95 in Hong Kong currency. Value, $27.50.

Pres. Yang Shangkun (1907-98) — A1081

Designs: No. 3597, $1.20, Standing in uniform (2-1). No. 3598, $1.20, Seated at desk, horiz. (2-2).

***Perf. 11½x11, 11x11½***

**2007, July 5** **Photo. & Engr.**

**3597-3598** A1081 Set of 2 1.70 .85

Nanji Islands Marine Reserve A1082

Shells and: No. 3599, $1.20, Sanpanwei (3-1). No. 3600, $1.20, Longchuanjiao (3-2). No. 3601, $1.20, Dashaao (3-3).

***Perf. 12¾x12½ Syncopated***

**2007, July 10** **Photo.**

**3599-3601** A1082 Set of 3 1.95 1.00

Emblem of People's Liberation Army — A1083

**2007, July 15** **Litho.** ***Perf. 12***

**3602** A1083 $1.20 multi + label 1.25 .45

See Stamps With Attached Labels note after No. 3197.

Souvenir Sheet

All-China Philatelic Federation, 6th Congress — A1084

***Perf. 12½ Syncopated***

**2007, July 28** **Litho. & Engr.**

**3603** A1084 $6 multi 3.75 2.25

A sheet of 2 No. 3603 exists. Value, $9.

People's Liberation Army, 80th Anniv. — A1085

Designs: No. 3604, $1.20, Soldiers saluting (4-1). No. 3605, $1.20, Soldier carrying sack (4-2). No. 3606, $1.20, Soldier with rifle (4-3). No. 3607, $1.20, Soldiers wearing UN Peacekeeper berets (4-4).

***Perf. 13¼x12½ Syncopated***

**2007, Aug. 1** **Photo.**

**3604-3607** A1085 Set of 4 3.50 2.00

A sheet of eight (two each Nos. 3604-3607) exists. Value, $10.

Olympic Sports — A1086

Designs: Nos. 3608, 3614a, $1.20, Diving (6-1). Nos. 3609, 3614b, $1.20, Shooting (6-2). Nos. 3610, 3614c, $1.20, Athletics (6-3). Nos. 3611, 3614d, $1.20, Volleyball (6-4). Nos. 3612, 3614e, $1.20, BMX bicycling (6-5). Nos. 3613, 3614f, $1.20, Weight lifting (6-6).

**2007, Aug. 8** **Photo.** ***Perf. 13¼x13***

**3608-3613** A1086 Set of 6 4.00 2.25
*3613a* Sheet of 10, #3521-3524, 3608-3613, + label 21.00 18.00

**Self-Adhesive**

***Serpentine Die Cut 11¾***

**3614** Miniature sheet of 12, 2 each #a-f *23.00*
*a.-f.* A1086 $1.20 Any single .40 .30

No. 3613a sold for $18.60.

Tengchong Volcano Area A1087

Designs: No. 3615, $1.20, Rehai (3-1). No. 3616, $1.20, Volcanoes, vert. (3-2). No. 3617, $1.20, Shenzhu Valley, vert. (3-3).

***Perf. 12x12½ Syncopated, 12½x12 Syncopated***

**2007, Aug. 18**

**3615-3617** A1087 Set of 3 1.50 1.00

Nos. 3615-3617 were printed together in a sheet of 15 stamps + a horizontal label. The first row consists of the label and 2 No. 3615; the second row, 3 No. 3615; the third row, 5 No. 3616; and the fourth row, 5 No. 3617.

Jin Hu A1088

No. 3618: a, Da Chibi (2-1). b, Maoer Mountain (2-2).

***Perf. 12¾ Syncopated***

**2007, Sept. 2** **Litho.**

**3618** A1088 $1.20 Horiz. pair, #a-b 1.45 .95

2007 Women's Soccer World Cup, People's Republic of China — A1089

**2007, Sept. 10** **Photo.** ***Perf. 13¼***

**3619** A1089 $1.20 multi 1.75 .75

Values are for stamps with surrounding selvage.

2007 World Summer Special Olympics, Shanghai A1090

**2007, Oct. 2** ***Perf. 13¼***

**3620** A1090 $1.20 multi 1.00 .40

Historic Sites in Three Gorges Reservoir Area A1091

Designs: No. 3621, $1.20, Zhang Fei Temple (4-1). No. 3622, $1.20, Shibaozhai Village, vert. (4-2). No. 3623, $1.20, Ancient Dachang, vert. (4-3). No. 3624, $1.20, Quyuan's Grave (4-4).

***Perf. 13¼ Syncopated***

**2007, Oct. 13** **Litho. & Engr.**

**3621-3624** A1091 Set of 4 2.00 1.50

17th Natl. Communist Party Congress A1092

Designs: No. 3625, $1.20, Memorial for First Natl. Communist Party Congress (2-1). No. 3626, $1.20, Site of Second Plenary Session of the Seventh Central Committee.

$6, Dove and monument.

***Perf. 13¼x13 Syncopated***

**2007, Oct. 15** **Photo.**

**3625-3626** A1092 Set of 2 2.75 1.00

**Souvenir Sheet**

***Perf. 13¼x13***

**3627** A1092 $6 multi 5.25 2.75

No. 3627 contains one 60x40mm stamp.

A souvenir sheet of 2 of Nos. 3625-3626 exists. Value, $65.

"Happiness" A1093

***Perf. 12¾ Syncopated***

**2007, Nov. 1** **Photo.**

**3628** A1093 $1.20 multi .45 .40

A sheet containing Nos. 3628, 3541 and four labels exists. Value, $10.

Ancient Calligraphy — A1094

Designs: No. 3629, $1.20, Proclamation (6-1). No. 3630, $1.20, Zhang Menglong Stele (6-2). No. 3631, $1.20, Inscription for Sweet Spring at Jiucheng Palace (6-3). No. 3632, $1.20, Preface for Sacred Religion at Wild Goose Pagoda (6-4). No. 3633, $1.20, Yan Qinli Stele (6-5). No. 3634, $1.20, Mysterious Pagoda Stele (6-6).

***Perf. 12x11½ Syncopated***

**2007, Nov. 5** **Litho.**

**3629-3634** A1094 Set of 6 4.25 2.25

A sheet containing 2 each of lithographed and embossed examples of Nos. 3629-3634 exists. Value, $10.

Mountains A1095

Designs: No. 3635, $1.20, Mount Gongga, People's Republic of China (2-1). No. 3636, $1.20, Popocatepetl, Mexico (2-2).

***Perf. 12¾ Syncopated***

**2007, Nov. 22**

**3635-3636** A1095 Set of 2 2.00 .75

See Mexico Nos. 2561-2562.

Launch of China's First Lunar Probe — A1096

**2007, Nov. 26** **Litho. & Embossed**

**3637** A1096 $1.20 multi 4.00 1.75

Emblem of Expo 2010, Shanghai A1097

Mascot of Expo 2010 A1098

***Perf. 11½ Syncopated***

**2007, Dec. 19** **Litho.**

**3638** A1097 $1.20 multi .60 .45
*a.* Booklet pane of 1 .70 —

**3639** A1098 $1.20 multi .60 .45
*a.* Booklet pane of 1 .70 —
*b.* Booklet pane of 10, 5 each #3638-3639 7.00 —
Complete booklet, #3638a, 3639a, 3639b 7.00

Compare with Type A1131.

Venues at 2008 Summer Olympics, Beijing — A1099

Designs: 80f, China Agricultural University Gymnasium (6-1). No. 3641, $1.20, Laoshan Mountain Bike Course (6-2). No. 3642, $1.20, National Indoor Stadium (6-3). No. 3643, $1.20, Beijing University Gymnasium (6-4). No. 3644, $1.20, National Aquatics Center (6-5). No. 3645, $3, Qingdao Olympic Sailing Center (6-6).

$6, National Stadium.

**2007, Dec. 20** **Photo.** ***Perf. 13x13¼***

**3640-3645** A1099 Set of 6 3.75 2.75

**Souvenir Sheet**

***Perf. 13***

**3646** A1099 $6 multi 4.00 2.75

No. 3646 contains one pentagonal 65x62mm stamp.

A self-adhesive sheet of 2 each of Nos. 3640-3645 exists. Value, $22.50.

New Year 2008 (Year of the Rat) — A1100

***Perf. 12¾ Syncopated***

**2008, Jan. 5** **Photo.**

**3647** A1100 $1.20 multi 1.25 .40
*a.* Booklet pane of 10 8.00 —
Complete booklet, #3647a 19.00

Miniature sheets containing 4 and 6 stamps exist. Value, $11 and $12, respectively.

Zhuxian New Year Woodprints — A1101

Designs: No. 3648, $1.20, Gate guardian (4-1). No. 3649, $1.20, Woman lecturing son (4-2). No. 3650, $1.20, Come back with fruitful result (4-3). No. 3651, $1.20, Chivalrous women (4-4).

**2008, Jan. 15** **Photo.** ***Perf. 13¼x13***

**3648-3651** A1101 Set of 4 3.25 1.75
*3651a* Souvenir sheet of 4, #3648-3651 4.00 2.25

No. 3651a sold for $7.20. A miniature sheet containing two each of Nos. 3648-3651 exists. Value, $12.50.

Beijing Opera Characters — A1102

Designs: 80f, Zhang Fei (6-1). No. 3653, $1.20, Cao Cao (6-2). No. 3654, $1.20, Bao Zheng (6-3). No. 3655, $1.20, Lian Po (6-4). No. 3656, $1.20, Xu Yanzhao (6-5). No. 3657, $1.20, Yang Yansi (6-6).

***Perf. 12x11½ Syncopated***

**2008, Feb. 23** **Litho.**

**3652-3657** A1102 Set of 6 4.75 2.25

Miniature Sheet

Birds A1103

No. 3658: a, Urocissa caerulea (6-1). b, Emberiza koslowi (6-2). c, Tragopan caboti (6-3). d, Garrulax sukatschewi (6-4). e, Chrysolophus pictus (6-5). f, Podoces biddulphi (6-6).

**2008, Feb. 28** **Photo.** ***Perf. 13¼x13***

**3658** A1103 $1.20 Sheet of 6, #a-f 6.50 2.50

11th National People's Congress A1104

**2008, Mar. 5**

**3659** A1104 $1.20 multi 1.40 .40

Olympic Torch Relay A1105

Designs: $1.20, Lighting of torch in Greece, mascot holding torch (2-1). $3, Torch, torch bearer, vert. (2-2).

**2008, Mar. 5** **Photo.** ***Perf. 13¼***

**3660-3661** A1105 Set of 2 2.40 1.25
*3661a* Souvenir sheet, #3660-3661 6.00 3.00

No. 3661a sold for $6.30. A sheet containing 4 self-adhesive examples each of Nos. 3660-3661 exists. Value, $15.

Suzhou-Nantong Yangtze River Bridge — A1106

No. 3662 — Denomination at: a, Left (2-1). b, Right (2-2).

**2008, Apr. 12** ***Perf. 13¼***

**3662** A1106 $1.20 Horiz. pair, #a-b 2.15 .90

Boao Forum For Asia A1107

No. 3663: a, Dongyu Island (2-1). b, Forum venue (2-2).

***Perf. 12x11½ Syncopated***

**2008, Apr. 13** **Litho.**

**3663** A1107 $1.20 Horiz. pair, #a-b 1.95 .90

Qiandao Lake A1108

No. 3664 — Islands with denomination at: a, Left (2-1). b, Right (2-2).

**2008, Apr. 16** ***Perf. 12¾ Syncopated***

**3664** A1108 $1.20 Horiz. pair, #a-b 1.75 .90
*c.* Souvenir sheet, #3664 4.25 2.00

No. 3664c sold for $3.60.

A1109

Olympic Expo, Beijing — A1110

**2008, Apr. 30 Photo. *Perf. 11¼x11***
**3665** A1109 $1.20 multi 1.10 .40

**Litho.**
***Perf. 12½***
**3666** A1110 $1.20 multi 1.10 .40

A circle of perforations surrounds the circular design on No. 3665.

Summer Palace A1111

Designs: No. 3667, $1.20, Shiqikong Bridge (6-1). No. 3668, $1.20, Corridor (6-2). No. 3669, $1.20, Boat (6-3). No. 3670, $1.20, Garden of Harmonious Pleasures (6-4). No. 3671, $1.20, Yudai Bridge (6-5). No. 3672, $1.20, Houhu Lake (6-6).

$6, Tower of the Fragrance of Buddha, vert.

**Litho. & Engr.**
**2008, May 10 *Perf. 12***
**3667-3672** A1111 Set of 6 3.00 2.00

**Souvenir Sheet**
***Perf. 12x11¾***
**3673** A1111 $6 multi 6.50 2.00

No. 3673 contains one 50x62mm stamp.

Cao Chong Weighs the Elephant A1112

Cao Chong: Nos. 3674, 3676, $1.20, Marking water level on boat carrying elephant (2-1). Nos. 3675, 3677, $1.20, Replacing elephant with weighable objects (2-2).

**2008, June 1 Photo. *Perf. 13x13¼***
**3674-3675** A1112 Set of 2 1.60 1.00

**Booklet Stamps**
**Self-Adhesive**
***Serpentine Die Cut 11¾***
**3676-3677** A1112 Set of 2 .85 —
*3677a* Booklet pane of 8, 4 each #3676-3677 3.50 —
Complete booklet, #3677a 4.00

Temples — A1113

Designs: No. 3678, $1.20, White Horse Temple, China (2-1). No. 3679, $1.20, Mahabodhi Temple, India (2-2).

**2008, June 6 *Perf. 13¼x13***
**3678-3679** A1113 Set of 2 2.15 .75

See India No. 2246.

Development on the Taiwan Strait A1114

Designs: No. 3680, $1.20, Minjiang River development (4-1). No. 3681, $1.20, Port of Xiamen (4-2). No. 3682, $1.20, Exhibition Hall (4-3). No. 3683, $1.20, Fujian-Taiwan Kinship Museum (4-4).

**2008, June 18 *Perf. 12¾***
**3680-3683** A1114 Set of 4 3.25 1.50

A sheet containing 2 each of Nos. 3680-3683 + 1 label exists. Value, $7.

Second Land Survey — A1115

Designs: No. 3684, $1.20, Satellite, rural land survey (2-1). No. 3685, $1.20, Theodolite, urban land survey (2-2).

***Perf. 12¾x12½***
**2008, June 25 Litho.**
**3684-3685** A1115 Set of 2 1.60 .75

Qiuci Grotto Murals — A1116

Designs: No. 3686, $1.20 Heavenly Kings (4-1). No. 3687, $1.20, Bodhisattva (4-2). No. 3688, $1.20, Flying Apsaras, horiz. (4-3). No. 3689, $1.20, Maitreya Preaching, horiz. (4-4).

**2008, July 6 Photo. *Perf. 13¼***
**3686-3689** A1116 Set of 4 4.25 1.50

General Qi Jiguang (1528-88) — A1117

Qi Jiguang: No. 3690, $1.20, Standing (2-1). No. 3691, $1.20, On horse (2-2).

***Perf. 12x12½ Syncopated***
**2008, July 19 Litho.**
**3690-3691** A1117 Set of 2 1.90 .90

Opening of 2008 Summer Olympics, Beijing A1118

**2008, Aug. 8 Photo. *Perf. 13¼***
**3692** A1118 $1.20 multi 2.25 .50

A sheet of 8 self-adhesive stamps similar to No. 3692 exists. Value, $11. A sheet of 8 stamps with a holographic background exists. Value, $35.

Olympex 2008 Philatelic Exhibition, Beijing — A1119

Designs: No. 3693, $1.20, Greece #127 (2-1). No. 3694, $1.20, Portugal #RA14 (2-2). $6, Greece #127, gold medal and mascots of 2004 Summer Olympics.

**2008, Aug. 8 Photo. *Perf. 13¼x13***
**3693-3694** A1119 Set of 2 1.60 .85

**Souvenir Sheet**
**Litho.**
***Perf.***
**3695** A1119 $6 multi 4.50 3.50

No. 3695 contains one 56mm diameter stamp. No. 3695 exists on silk paper. Value, $20.

2008 Summer Olympics Gold Medal A1119a

**2008, Aug. 9 Litho. *Perf. 12***
**3695A** A1119a $1.20 multi + label *4.00 4.00*

See Stamps With Attached Labels note after No. 3197. No. 3695A was printed in sheets of various sizes, with many sheets having pre-printed labels depicting Olympic athletes.

Closing of 2008 Summer Olympics — A1120

Designs: No. 3696, $1.20, National Stadium, Beijing (4-1). No. 3697, $1.20, Tower, Forbidden City, Beijing (4-2). No. 3698, $1.20, Millennium Wheel, London (4-3). No. 3699, $1.20, Tower of London (4-4).

**2008, Aug. 24 Photo. *Perf. 13¼***
**3696-3699** A1120 Set of 4 3.00 2.25

A sheet containing 3 self-adhesive examples each of Nos. 3696-3699 exists. Value, $11.

China Central Television, 50th Anniv. — A1121

***Perf. 13½x13 Syncopated***
**2008, Sept. 2**
**3700** A1121 $1.20 multi .85 .40

Emblem of 2008 Paralympic Games, Beijing A1122

Paralympic Games Mascot A1123

**2008, Sept. 6 *Perf. 13¼x13***
**3701** A1122 $1.20 multi .65 .40
**3702** A1123 $1.20 multi .65 .40

University of Science and Technology, 50th Anniv. — A1124

***Perf. 12x11¼ Syncopated***
**2008, Sept. 20 Litho.**
**3703** A1124 $1.20 multi 1.25 .40

Ningxia Hui Autonomous Region, 50th Anniv. — A1125

No. 3704: a, Windmills (3-1). b, Trees and wildlife in desert (3-2). c, People holding flower bouquets (3-3).

***Perf. 13¼x12¾ Syncopated***
**2008, Sept. 23 Photo.**
**3704** A1125 Horiz. strip of 3 1.40 1.25
*a.* 80f multi .25 .25
*b.-c.* $1.20 Either single .45 .35

Airports A1126

No. 3705: a, Beijing Capital International Airport (3-1). b, Shanghai Pudong International Airport (3-2). c, Guangzhou Baiyun International Airport (3-3).

**2008, Sept. 28 *Perf. 12¾***
**3705** Vert. strip of 3 3.25 1.50
*a.-c.* A1126 $1.20 Any single .45 .35

Guangxi Zhuang Autonomous Region, 50th Anniv. — A1127

No. 3706: a, Dancers (3-1). b, Building (3-2). c, Port (3-3).

***Perf. 12¾ Syncopated***
**2008, Oct. 18 Litho.**
**3706** A1127 Horiz. strip of 3 1.25 1.25
*a.* 80f multi .25 .25
*b.-c.* $1.20 Either single .45 .35

**Happy New Year Type of 2006 and**

"Blossom of Fortune" — A1128

***Perf. 11¾ Syncopated***
**2008, Oct. 9 Litho.**
**3707** A1128 $1.20 multi .50 .35

**Souvenir Sheet**
**3708** Sheet of 2, #3707, 3708a *12.00 8.00*
*a.* A1055a $3 gold & multi *6.25 6.25*

Seventh Asia-Europe Meeting, Beijing — A1129

***Perf. 12x11¼ Syncopated***
**2008, Oct. 24**
**3709** A1129 $1.20 multi 1.60 .40
*a.* Miniature sheet of 12 8.50 8.50

"Harmony" — A1130

**2008, Dec. 3 *Perf. 12***
**3710** A1130 $1.20 multi + label .50 .40

See Stamps With Attached Labels note after No. 3197.

Expo 2010, Shanghai — A1131

**2008, Dec. 13** ***Perf. 12***

**3711** A1131 $1.20 multi + label 1.10 .45

See Stamps With Attached Labels note after No. 3197. Compare with Type A1097.

A1132

Reform in China, 30th Anniv. A1133

***Perf. 12x11¼ Syncopated***

**2008, Dec. 18** **Litho.**

**3712** A1132 $1.20 multi 1.25 .60
*a.* Miniature sheet of 8 12.50 6.50

**Souvenir Sheet**

**Photo.**

***Perf.***

**3713** A1133 $6 multi + label 4.25 3.00

A sheet containing 2 examples of No. 3713 exists. Value, $12.

New Year 2009 (Year of the Ox) — A1134

***Perf. 13 Syncopated***

**2009, Jan. 5** **Photo.**

**3714** A1134 $1.20 multi 1.60 .45
*a.* Miniature sheet of 6 17.00 5.00
*b.* Booklet pane of 10 8.50 —
Complete booklet, #3714b 11.00

A sheet of 4 No. 3714 exists. Value, $7.

Bo Yibo (1908-2007), Politician — A1135

Bo Yibo: No. 3715, $1.20, Standing (2-1). No. 3716, $1.20, Seated, horiz. (2-2).

**2009, Jan. 15** ***Perf. 13¼x13, 13x13¼***

**3715-3716** A1135 Set of 2 2.75 .90

Zhangzhou New Year Woodprints A1136

Designs: No. 3717, $1.20, Lion holding a sword in mouth (4-1). No. 3718, $1.20, The coming flood of wealth, vert. (4-2). No. 3719, $1.20, Goddess sending children, vert. (4-3). No. 3720, $1.20, Rat marrying off its daughter (4-4).

**2009, Jan. 18** ***Perf. 12***

**3717-3720** A1136 Set of 4 2.00 1.50
*3720a* Souvenir sheet, #3717-3720 + label 2.50 2.50
*3720b* Miniature sheet of 8, 2 each #3717-3720 4.50 4.50

No. 3720b exists on silk paper. Value, $5.50.

A1137

24th Winter Universiade, Harbin A1138

**2009, Feb. 18** **Litho.** ***Perf. 12¾***

**3721** A1137 $1.20 multi .80 .40
**3722** A1138 $1.20 multi .80 .40

Electric Power Grid Construction — A1139

No. 3723: a, Power station (3-1). b, Transmission towers and power lines (3-2). c, Light bulb, city skyline (3-3).

***Perf. 12x12½ Syncopated***

**2009, Feb. 24**

**3723** A1139 $1.20 Horiz. strip of 3, #a-c 2.00 1.50

Paintings by Shi Tao (1642-1707) — A1140

No. 3724: a, Chaohu Lake (30x55mm) (6-1). b, Enjoying Fountain Sound (25x55mm) (6-2). c, Double Chrysanthemums (30x55mm) (6-3). d, Plum Blossoms and Bamboo (25x55mm) (6-4). e, Horse and its Owner (30x55mm) (6-5). f, Lotus (25x55mm) (6-6).

**2009, Mar. 22** **Litho.** ***Perf. 12½x13***

**3724** Horiz. strip of 6 8.50 3.00
*a.* A1140 80f multi .35 .25
*b.-f.* A1140 $1.20 Any single .65 .45

A1141

China 2009 World Stamp Exhibition, Luoyang — A1142

Designs: No. 3725, $1.20, Vase (2-1). No. 3726, $1.20, Jar with stopper (2-2).
$6, National Beauty and Heavenly Fragrance.

***Perf. 12¾ Syncopated***

**2009, Apr. 10** **Litho. & Embossed**

**3725-3726** A1141 Set of 2 1.10 .85

**Souvenir Sheet**

**Litho.**

***Perf. 13 Syncopated***

**3727** A1142 $6 multi 3.50 3.00

Nos. 3725 and 3726 both exist in sheets of 4. Value, set $7.50.
No. 3727 exists in a sheet of 2. Value, $10. No. 3727 exists in a sheet of 2 on silk paper. Value, $19.

China at World Expos — A1143

Scenes from Expos from: No. 3728, $1.20, 1904, 1915, 1926, 1933 (red panel) (4-1). No. 3729, $1.20, 1982, 1982 (brown panel) (4-2). No. 3730, $1.20, 1999 (green panel) (4-3). No. 3731, $1.20, 2010 (blue panel) (4-4).

***Perf. 13¼x12¾ Syncopated***

**2009, May 1** **Photo.**

**3728-3731** A1143 Set of 4 3.00 2.00
*3731a* Miniature sheet of 8, 2 each #3728-3731 7.00 7.00

Fenghuang — A1144

No. 3732: a, North Gate (3-1). b, Rainbow Bridge (3-2). c, Street (3-3).

***Perf. 12¾ Syncopated***

**2009, May 23** **Litho.**

**3732** A1144 Horiz. strip of 3 1.25 1.25
*a.-c.* $1.20 Any single .40 .35

Children's Art — A1145

Designs: Nos. 3733, 3737, 80f, Love for the Motherland (yellow orange panel) (4-1). Nos. 3734, 3738, $1.20, Happy Life, horiz. (red panel) (4-2). Nos. 3735, 3739, $1.20, Peace Lovers (blue panel) (4-3). Nos. 3736, 3740, $1.20, Enthusiasm for Science, horiz. (green panel) (4-4).

***Perf. 13¼x13, 13x13¼***

**2009, June 1** **Photo.**

**3733-3736** A1145 Set of 4 2.00 1.40

**Booklet Stamps**

**Self-Adhesive**

***Serpentine Die Cut 12***

**3737-3740** A1145 Set of 4 1.40 1.40
*3740a* Booklet pane of 8, 2 each #3737-3740 3.00

Hangzhou Bay Bridge — A1146

No. 3741: a, Bridge. b, Marine platform.

**2009, June 18** **Litho.** ***Perf. 12***

**3741** A1146 $1.20 Horiz. pair, #a-b 1.95 .80

Li Xiannian (1909-92), People's Republic of China President — A1147

Designs: No. 3742, $1.20, Wearing army uniform and cap (3-1). No. 3743, $1.20, Wearing gray suit with collar buttoned (3-2). No. 3744, $1.20, Wearing gray suit and eyeglasses (3-3).

**2009, June 23** **Photo.** ***Perf. 13¼x13***

**3742-3744** A1147 Set of 3 1.95 1.25

A1148

16th Asian Games, Guangzhou A1149

**2009, June 30** **Photo.** ***Perf. 13¼***

**3745** A1148 $1.20 multi .95 .50
**3746** A1149 $1.20 multi .95 .50

A sheet containing four each of Nos. 3745-3746 exists. Value, $8.

Great Hall of the People A1150

Designs: No. 3747, East Gate (2-1). No. 3748, Great Auditorium (2-2).

**2009, July 18** **Litho.** ***Perf. 13¼x12½***

**3747** A1150 $1.20 multi .55 .45
**3748** A1150 $1.20 multi .55 .45
*a.* Booklet pane of 2, #3747-3748 1.10 —
*b.* Booklet pane of 8, 4 each #3747-3748 4.50 —
Complete booklet, #3748a, 3748b 7.50

Sanjiangyuan Nature Reserve — A1151

No. 3749: a, Geladandong (3-1). b, Eling Lake (3-2). c, Dza Chu (3-3).

***Perf. 13¼x12½ Syncopated***

**2009, July 25** **Photo.**

**3749** A1151 Horiz. strip of 3 2.65 1.25
*a.-c.* $1.20 Any single .40 .35

Flag, 60th Anniv. A1152

**2009, Aug. 2** **Litho.** ***Perf. 13¼***

**3750** A1152 $1.20 multi + label .80 .60

A souvenir sheet of 4 No. 3750 + one label exists.

Labrang Lamasery A1153

No. 3751: a, Grand Sutra Hall (2-1). b, Gongtang Pagoda (2-2).

*Perf. 13x12¾ Syncopated*

**2009, Aug. 2**

**3751** A1153 $1.20 Vert. pair, #a-b .90 .80

Stork Tower — A1154

Golden Gate — A1155

**2009, Aug. 14** **Photo.**

**3752** A1154 $1.20 multi .55 .40
**3753** A1155 $1.20 multi .55 .40

A1156

Huang Long Scenic Area A1157

Designs: No. 3754, $1.20, Guest Welcome Ponds (3-1). No. 3755, $1.20, Waterfall (3-2). No. 3756, $1.20, Erdao Lake (3-3).
$6, Five-color Ponds.

**2009, Aug. 27** ***Perf. 12¾***

**3754-3756** A1156 Set of 3 1.25 1.10

**Souvenir Sheet**

***Perf. 13¼x12¾ Syncopated***

**3757** A1157 $6 multi 2.50 2.50

A miniature sheet containing 2 each of Nos. 3754-3756 exists. Value, $6.

National Library of China — A1158

Books and: No. 3758, $1.20, Old building (2-1). No. 3759, $1.20, Modern building (2-2).

**2009, Sept. 9** ***Perf. 13¼ Syncopated***

**3758-3759** A1158 Set of 2 1.10 1.10

Miniature Sheet

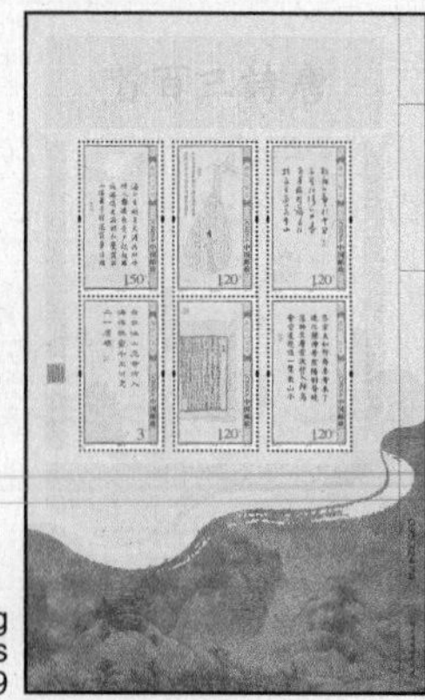

Tang Poems A1159

No. 3760: a, $1.20, Downstream to Jiangling, by Il Bai (boat near rocks) (6-1). b, $1.20, A View of Taishan Mountain, by Du Fu (mountains) (6-2). c, $1.20, The Song of Pipa, by Bai Juyi (musician) (6-3). d, $1.20, To One Unnamed, by Li Shangyin (book) (6-4). e, $1.50, Looking at the Moon and Thinking of One Far Away, by Zhang Jiulin (Moon) (6-5). f, $3, On the Stork Tower, by Wang Zhihuan (Stork Tower) (6-6).

**Litho., Engr. & Silk-screened**

***Perf. 12¾x13¼ Syncopated***

**2009, Sept. 13**

**3760** A1159 Sheet of 6, #a-f 16.00 6.50

Lanzhoui University, Cent. — A1160

***Perf. 13x12½ Syncopated***

**2009, Sept. 17** **Litho.**

**3761** A1160 $1.20 multi 1.10 .50

Chinese People's Political Consultative Conference, 60th Anniv. — A1161

Flowers and: No. 3762, $1.20, Conference emblem (2-1). No. 3763, $1.20, Conference venue, horiz. (2-2).

***Perf. 13¼ Syncopated***

**2009, Sept. 17**

**3762-3763** A1161 Set of 2 1.50 1.10

A1162

Beijing-Hangzhou Grand Canal — A1163

Designs: No. 3764, $1.20, Lantern Lighting Pagoda (6-1). No. 3765, $1.20, Boats and Tianhou Temple (6-2). No. 3766, $1.20, Shanshan Guild Hall (6-3). No. 3767, $1.20, Qingjiang Water Gate (6-4). No. 3768, $1.20, Boats and Wenfeng Pagoda (6-5). No. 3769, $1.20, Gongchen Bridge (6-6).
$6, Canal.

***Perf. 13x13¼ Syncopated***

**2009, Sept. 26** **Photo.**

**3764-3769** A1162 Set of 6 3.25 2.10

**Souvenir Sheet**

***Perf. 13¼ Syncopated***

**3770** A1163 $6 multi 3.00 3.00

A1164

People's Republic of China, 60th Anniv. A1165

Designs: No. 3771, $1.20, Marchers (4-1). No. 3772, $1.20, Tractors pulling floats bearing Chinese symbols (4-2). No. 3773, $1.20, Flag, emblems of Macao and Hong Kong (4-3). No. 3774, $1.20, Olympic rings and torch (4-4).
$6, Flag.

***Perf. 13x12½ Syncopated***

**2009, Oct. 1**

**3771-3774** A1164 Set of 4 1.80 1.50

**Souvenir Sheet**

***Perf. 13¼x13½ Syncopated***

**3775** A1165 $6 multi 3.00 3.00

A miniature sheet containing two each of Nos. 3771-3774 exists. Value, $6.

National Day Parade A1166

Designs: No. 3776, $1.20, Infantry Group (red background) (4-1). No. 3777, $1.20, Army and 2nd Artillery Group (green background) (4-2). No. 3778, $1.20, Navy Equipment Group (blue background) (4-3). No. 3779, $1.20, Air Group (orange background) (4-4).

***Perf. 13¼x12½ Syncopated***

**2009, Oct. 1**

**3776-3779** A1166 Set of 4 2.25 2.00

A miniature sheet containing two each of Nos. 3776-3779 exists. Value, $9.

"Music" A1167

**2009, Sept. 29** **Litho.** ***Perf. 12***

**3780** A1167 $1.20 multi + label .75 .35

See Stamps With Attached Labels note after No. 3197.

"Happiness With the Spring" A1168

**2009, Oct. 9** ***Perf. 13 Syncopated***

**3781** A1168 $1.20 multi .75 .35

A souvenir sheet containing Nos. 3781 and 3708a exists. Value, $13.

A1169

11th National Games, Shandong — A1170

***Perf. 13¼x13 Syncopated***

**2009, Oct. 16**

**3782** A1169 $1.20 multi .50 .45
**3783** A1170 $1.20 multi .50 .45
*a.* Souvenir sheet, #3782-3783 3.25 1.75

No. 3783a sold for $3.60.

Ancient Academies — A1171

Designs: No. 3784, $1.20, Stone Drum Academy (4-1). No. 3785, $1.20, Anding Academy (4-2). No. 3786, $1.20, Ehu Academy (4-3). No. 3787, $1.20, Dongpo Academy (4-4).

***Perf. 13¼ Syncopated***

**2009, Nov. 15** **Photo.**

**3784-3787** A1171 Set of 4 3.25 1.50

A souvenir sheet containing two each of Nos. 3784-3787 exists. Value, $6.

Guangji Bridge — A1172

No. 3788: a, Building at left on shore, bridge, ships (3-1). b, Ships, central part of bridge (3-2). c, Bridge, building at right on shore (3-3).

***Perf. 12¾ Syncopated***

**2009, Nov. 16** **Litho.**

**3788** A1172 Horiz. strip of 3 1.10 1.10
*a.-c.* $1.20 Any single .35 .35

Ma Lianliang (1901-66), Opera Performer, in Kong Ming Borrows the East Wing A1173

Ma Lianliang in Zhao the Orphan A1174

***Perf. 13¼x13½ Syncopated***

**2009, Nov. 28** **Photo.**

**3789** A1173 $1.20 multi .60 .35
**3790** A1174 $1.20 multi .60 .35

Return of Macao to China, 10th Anniv. — A1175

Doves and: No. 3791, $1.20, Golden Lotus sculpture, flags of People's Republic of China and Macao (3-1). No. 3792, $1.20, "CEPA," buildings (3-2). $1.50, Bridge, buildings (3-3).

***Perf. 13¼x13 Syncopated***

**2009, Dec. 20**

**3791-3793** A1175 Set of 3 1.25 1.25
*3793a* Souvenir sheet, #3791-3793, Macao #1302a-1302c 2.40 2.40

See Macao Nos. 1302-1303. No. 3793a was not offered for sale in Macao.

16th Asian Games, Guangzhou — A1176

**2009, Dec. 25** **Litho.** ***Perf. 12***

**3794** A1176 $1.20 multi + label 1.00 .40

Compare with Type A1148. See Stamps With Attached Labels note after No. 3197.

Gutian Conference, 80th Anniv. A1177

***Perf. 13¼x13 Syncopated***

**2009, Dec. 28**

**3795** A1177 $1.20 multi .80 .35

Ballet Dancers in Red Detachment of Women — A1178

Designs: No. 3796, $1.20, Dancer in red (2-1). No. 3797, $1.20, Dancers in blue (2-2).

**2010, Jan. 1 Photo. *Perf. 13¼***

**3796-3797** A1178 Set of 2 2.00 1.00

New Year 2010 (Year of the Tiger) — A1179

**2010, Jan. 5 *Perf. 12¾ Syncopated***

**3798** A1179 $1.20 multi 1.60 .40
*a.* Booklet pane of 10 4.00 —
Complete booklet, #3798a 7.50

No. 3798 exists in sheets of 4 and 6. Value, $10 each.

Gen. Song Renqiong (1909-2005) A1180

Designs: No. 3799, $1.20, Wearing cap (2-1). No. 3800, $1.20, Reading book (2-2).

***Perf. 13 Syncopated***

**2010, Jan. 8 Litho.**

**3799-3800** A1180 Set of 2 2.15 .70

Expo 2010, Shanghai A1181

Designs: 80f, Expo Center (4-1). No. 3802, $1.20, China Pavilion (4-2). No. 3803, $1.20, Expo Performance Center (4-3). $3, Theme Pavilion (4-4).
$6, Shanghai Expo Park, vert.

***Perf. 13¼x13 Syncopated***

**2010, Jan. 21 Photo.**

**3801-3804** A1181 Set of 4 2.00 2.00

**Souvenir Sheet**

***Perf. 13x12¾ Syncopated***

**3805** A1181 $6 multi 6.00 4.50

No. 3805 contains one 30x75mm stamp. A sheet containing two each of Nos. 3801-3804 exists. A sheet containing two examples of No. 3805 exists.

Liangping New Year Woodprints — A1182

Designs: No. 3806, $1.20, Gate god (4-1). No. 3807, $1.20, Stealing the immortal grass (4-2). No. 3808, $1.20, Peace leads to happiness (4-3). No. 3809, $1.20, Exiting the pass with a stolen token (4-4).

**2010, Feb. 6 *Perf. 13¼x13***

**3806-3809** A1182 Set of 4 1.40 1.40
*3809a* Souvenir sheet, #3806-3809 + label 2.50 2.50
*3809b* Souvenir sheet of 8, 2 each #3806-3809 on fabric-faced paper *10.00 8.00*
*3809c* As "b," plain paper *6.25 6.25*

No. 3809a sold for $7.20.

Intl. Women's Day, Cent. — A1183

***Perf. 13¼x13 Syncopated***

**2010, Mar. 8**

**3810** A1183 $1.20 multi 1.10 .40

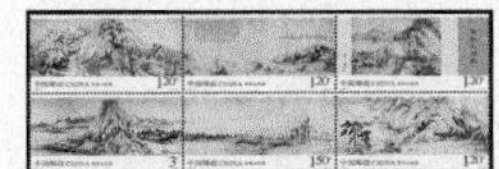

Dwelling in Fuchun Mountains, Painting by Huang Gongwang — A1184

No. 3811 — Various parts of painting with inscription: a, (6-1). b, (6-2). c, (6-3). d, (6-4). e, (6-5). f, (6-6).

**2010, Mar. 20 *Perf. 13¼***

**3811** A1184 Block of 6 16.00 10.00
*a.-d.* $1.20 Any single .60 .35
*e.* $1.50 multi .75 .50
*f.* $3 multi 1.25 .95

Tomb Sweeping Festival — A1185

Designs: No. 3812, $1.20, Ancestor worship (3-1). No. 3813, $1.20, Spring outing (3-2). No. 3814, $1.20, Planting willows (3-3).

***Perf. 13¼x13½ Syncopated***

**2010, Apr. 5 Litho.**

**3812-3814** A1185 Set of 3 2.15 1.10

A sheet containing three each of Nos. 3812-3814 exists.

Idioms — A1186

Designs: No. 3815, $1.20, The foolish old man removes the mountains (4-1). No. 3816, $1.20, Sleeping on brushwood and tasting gall (4-2). No. 3817, $1.20, Mao Sui recommending himself (4-3). No. 3818, $1.20, Rising to practice swordplay upon hearing the rooster crow (4-4).

***Perf. 13¼x13½ Syncopated***

**2010, Apr. 18 Photo.**

**3815-3818** A1186 Set of 4 1.40 1.40

Opening of Expo 2010, Shanghai — A1187

**2010, May 1 *Perf. 13¼ Syncopated***

**3819** A1187 $1.20 multi 1.00 .40

A sheet of six exists.

A1188

A1189

Ancient Calligraphy — A1190

No. 3820 — Preface to the Orchid Pavilion: a, Denomination at right (6-1). b, Denomination at left (6-2).

No. 3821 — Poems Composed During the Cold Food Festival in Huangzhou: a, Denomination at right (6-3). b, Denomination at left (6-4).

No. 3822 — Elegiac Lament for My Nephew: a, Denomination at right (6-5). b, Denomination at left (6-6).

**2010, May 15 *Perf. 13x13¼***

**3820** A1188 $1.20 Horiz. pair, #a-b .70 .70
**3821** A1189 $1.20 Horiz. pair, #a-b .70 .70
**3822** A1190 $1.20 Horiz. pair, #a-b .70 .70
*Nos. 3820-3822 (3)* 2.10 2.10

A sheet containing two each Nos. 3820-3822 exists.

Tenth Global Travel and Tourism Summit, Beijing A1191

**2010, May 25 *Perf. 13¼ Syncopated***

**3823** A1191 $1.20 multi 3.50 .50

Wen Yanbo's Ball Goes Into Hole in Tree — A1192

Wen Yanbo Retrieves Ball With Water — A1193

**2010, June 1 *Perf. 13 Syncopated***

**3824** A1192 $1.20 multi .35 .35
**3825** A1193 $1.20 multi .35 .35
*a.* Booklet pane of 2, #3824-3825 .70 —
*b.* Booklet pane of 8, 4 each #3824-3825 3.00 —
Complete booklet, #3825a, 3825b 4.00

A1194

Environmental Protection — A1195

***Perf. 13¼x13½ Syncopated***

**2010, June 5**

**3826** A1194 $1.20 multi 1.25 .40
**3827** A1195 $1.20 multi 1.25 .40

Kunqu Opera — A1196

Designs: No. 3828, $1.20, Washing the Silken Gauze (3-1). No. 3829, $1.20, The Peony Pavilion (3-2). No. 3830, $1.20, The Palace of Long Life (3-3).

***Perf. 13¼ Syncopated***

**2010, June 12 Photo.**

**3828-3830** A1196 Set of 3 1.10 1.10

A miniature sheet containing 3 each of Nos. 3828-3830 exists.

Pearl River Scenes A1197

Designs: No. 3831, $1.20, Five Goats Statue, Guangzhou (4-1). No. 3832, $1.20, Guangzhou Center for the Performing Arts (4-2). No. 3833, $1.20, Guangzhou skyline (4-3). No. 3834, $1.20, Guangzhou Intl. Convention and Exhibition Center (4-4).

***Perf. 13¼x13 Syncopated***

**2010, June 28**

**3831-3834** A1197 Set of 4 1.40 1.40
*3834a* Souvenir sheet of 8, 2 each #3831-3834 *9.50 4.75*

Loulan A1198

Designs: No. 3835, $1.20, Ruins of Buddhist stupa (2-1). No. 3836, $1.20, Ruins of building (2-2).

**2010, July 3 Litho.**

**3835-3836** A1198 Set of 2 .70 .70

Maritime Day — A1199

***Perf. 13½x13 Syncopated***

**2010, July 11 Photo.**

**3837** A1199 $1.20 multi .80 .35

Composers A1200

Designs: No. 3838, $1.20, Johann Sebastian Bach (1685-1750) (4-1). No. 3839, $1.20, Joseph Haydn (1732-1809) (4-2). No. 3840, $1.20, Wolfgang Amadeus Mozart (1756-91) (4-3). $4.50, Ludwig van Beethoven (1770-1827) (4-4).

***Perf. 13¼x12¾ Syncopated***

**2010, July 25 Litho. & Engr.**

**3838-3841** A1200 Set of 4 2.40 2.40

Legend of the Cowherd and the Weaving Maid — A1201

Designs: No. 3842, Dress-linked affection (4-1). No. 3843, Happy lovers (4-2). No. 3844, Carrying children to chase wife (4-3). No. 3845, Heavenly reunion (4-4).

***Perf. 13¼x13¾ Syncopated***

**2010, Aug. 16** **Photo.**

**3842** A1201 $1.20 multi .40 .35
*a.* Booklet pane of 1 + 5 labels .60 —
**3843** A1201 $1.20 multi .40 .35
*a.* Booklet pane of 1 + 5 labels .60 —
**3844** A1201 $1.20 multi .40 .35
*a.* Booklet pane of 1 + 5 labels .60 —
**3845** A1201 $1.20 multi .40 .35
*a.* Booklet pane of 1 + 5 labels .60 —
Complete booklet, #3842a-3845a 5.25
*Nos. 3842-3845 (4)* 1.60 1.40

Complete booklet sold for $8.

2010 Asian Para Games, Guangzhou A1202

**2010, Sept. 3** ***Perf. 13***

**3846** A1202 $1.20 multi 1.10 .35

Values are for stamp with adjacent selvage.

**Great Wall Type of 2005**

**2010, Sept. 3** **Litho.** ***Perf. 12***

**3846A** A1003 $1.20 multi + label *5.00 5.00*

See note following No. 3462.

A1203

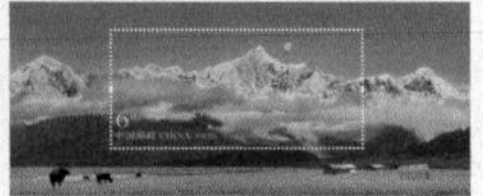

Shangri-La (Zhongdian) — A1204

Designs: No. 3847, $1.20, Songzanlin Lamasery (4-1). No. 3848, $1.20, Napa Lake and grassland (4-2). No. 3849, $1.20, Pudacuo National Park (4-3). No. 3850, $1.20, Dukezong (4-4).
$6, Meili Snow Mountain.

***Perf. 13¼x13 Syncopated***

**2010, Sept. 13**

**3847-3850** A1203 Set of 4 1.50 1.50

**Souvenir Sheet**

***Perf. 13¼x13¾ Syncopated***

**3851** A1204 $6 multi 2.50 1.90

Confucius and Buildings — A1205

No. 3852: a, $1.20, Confucius and temple (3-1). b, $1.20, Family home of Confucius (3-2). c, $3, Cemetery of Confucius (3-3).

***Perf. 13¼ Syncopated***

**2010, Sept. 28** **Litho.**

**3852** A1205 Horiz. strip of 3, #a-c 2.00 1.60
*d.* Souvenir sheet, #3852a-3852c 5.25 3.00

Huai River Water Control Project A1206

Designs: No. 3853, $1.20, Nanwan Reservoir (4-1). No. 3854, $1.20, Linhuaigang Water Control Project (4-2). No. 3855, $1.20, Huai River Outflow Project (4-3). No. 3856, $1.20, Nansi Lake Water Control Project (4-4).

***Perf. 12¾x13 Syncopated***

**2010, Oct. 14**

**3853-3856** A1206 Set of 4 1.50 1.50

Flora — A1207

Drawings of: No. 3857, $1.20, Plum blossom (4-1). No. 3858, $1.20, Orchid (4-2). No. 3859, $1.20, Bamboo (4-3). No. 3860, $1.20, Chrysanthemums (4-4).

**2010, Oct. 18** ***Perf. 13¼ Syncopated***

**3857-3860** A1207 Set of 4 2.50 1.50
*3860a* Souvenir sheet of 8, 2 each #3857-3860 *20.00 15.00*

No. 3860a exists imperf.

Zhu Xi (Chu Hsi) (1130-1200), Philosopher — A1208

Designs: No. 3861, $1.20, Portrait of Zhu Xi (2-1). No. 3862, $1.20, Zhu Xi, student and horse (2-2).

***Perf. 13¼x13½ Syncopated***

**2010, Oct. 22** **Litho. & Engr.**

**3861-3862** A1208 Set of 2 1.00 .75

A souvenir sheet of two exists.

2010 Asian Games, Guangzhou — A1209

Designs: 80f, Badminton (6-1). No. 3864, $1.20, Wushu (6-2). No. 3865, $1.20, Hurdles (6-3). No. 3866, $1.20, Equestrian (6-4). No. 3867, $1.20, Dragon boat racing (6-5). $3, Weiqi (6-6).

***Perf. 13¼ Syncopated***

**2010, Nov. 12** **Photo.**

**3863-3868** A1209 Set of 6 4.25 2.60
*3868a* Sheet of 12, 2 each #3863-3868 *8.00 8.00*

**Souvenir Sheet**

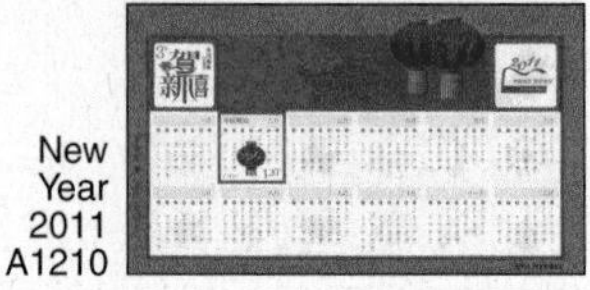

New Year 2011 A1210

No. 3869: a, $1.20, Chinese lantern, calendar for February 2011. b, $3, Like #3541, with copper frame.

***Serpentine Die Cut 12¼***

**2010, Oct. 9** **Self-Adhesive** **Litho.**

**3869** A1210 Sheet of 2, #a-b, + 13 labels *4.75 4.75*

Traditional Chinese Medicine Stores — A1211

Designs: No. 3870, $1.20, Tongren Tang (4-1). No. 3871, $1.20, Huqing Yu Tang (4-2). No. 3872, $1.20, Lei Yongshang (4-3). No. 3873, $1.20, Chen Liji (4-4).

***Perf. 13¼ Syncopated***

**2010, Nov. 20** **Photo.**

**3870-3873** A1211 Set of 4 1.50 1.50

High-speed Train A1212

***Perf. 13¼x12¾ Syncopated***

**2010, Dec. 7** **Photo.**

**3874** A1212 $1.20 multi 2.15 .80

Chinese Capital Markets A1213

Bar graph and: No. 3875, $1.20, Bull, computers at capital market (2-1). No. 3876, $1.20, City, satellite dish, train (2-2).

***Perf. 13¼ Syncopated***

**2010, Dec. 12** **Litho.**

**3875-3876** A1213 Set of 2 2.15 1.25
*3876a* Souvenir sheet of 8, 4 each #3875-3876 *30.00 20.00*

New Year 2011 (Year of the Rabbit) — A1214

***Perf. 13 Syncopated***

**2011, Jan. 5** **Photo.**

**3877** A1214 $1.20 multi .80 .60
*a.* Booklet pane of 10 8.00 —
Complete booklet, #3877a 8.00
*b.* Souvenir sheet of 6 *12.50 10.00*

A souvenir sheet containing 4 No. 3877 exists. Value, $12.50.

Fengxiang New Year Woodprints — A1215

Designs: No. 3878, $1.20, General Yuchi Jingde (4-1). No. 3879, $1.20, Fortune boy (4-2). No. 3880, $1.20, Beauties (4-3). No. 3881, $1.20, Fortune flower vase (4-4).

***Perf. 13¼x13¾ Syncopated***

**2011, Jan. 10** **Litho.**

**3878-3881** A1215 Set of 4 2.00 1.50

Sheet of eight containing two each Nos. 3878-3881 on plain and fabric-faced paper exist.

Early Leaders of the Communist Party of China — A1216

Designs: No. 3882, $1.20, Chen Yannian (1898-1927) (5-1). No. 3883, $1.20, Zhang Tailei (1898-1927) (5-2). No. 3884, $1.20, Luo Yinong (1902-28) (5-3). No. 3885, $1.20, Yun Daiying (1895-1931) (5-4). No. 3886, $1.20, Xiang Ying (1898-1941) (5-5).

**2011, Feb. 21**

**3882-3886** A1216 Set of 5 3.00 1.90

Liangzhu Jade — A1217

Designs: No. 3887, $1.20, Cong (carved block of jade) (2-1). No. 3888, $1.20, Bi (ring of jade) (2-2).

**2011, Mar. 8** **Photo.**

**3887-3888** A1217 Set of 2 2.10 .75

Scenes From "The Scholars," Novel by Wu Jingzi — A1218

Designs: 80f, Lotus painter Wang Mian (6-1). No. 3890, $1.20, Fanjin passing the Imperial exam (6-2). No. 3891, $1.20, Two lamp wicks (6-3). No. 3892, $1.20, Ma Er tours West Lake (6-4). No. 3893, $1.20, Mr. and Mrs. Du Shaoqing (6-5). No. 3894, $1.20, Shen Qunzhi selling writings by Sheli Bridge (6-6).

**2011, Mar. 21**

**3889-3894** A1218 Set of 6 2.10 2.10

A sheet of 12 containing two each of Nos. 3889-3894 exists.

Chinese Calligraphy A1219

Designs: No. 3895, $1.20, Pingfu Tie, by Lu Ji (4-1). No. 3896, $1.20, Chuyue Tie, by Wang Xizhi (4-2). No. 3897, $1.20, Gushi Si Tie, by Zhangxu (4-3). No. 3898, $1.20, Zixu Tie, by Huaisu (4-4).

**2011, Apr. 15** ***Perf. 13¼ Syncopated***

**3895-3898** A1219 Set of 4 2.65 1.50

A sheet of eight containing two each Nos. 3895-3896, printed on rice paper exists.

Military Aircraft A1220

Designs: No. 3899, $1.20, J-10 fighter (3-1). No. 3900, $1.20, JH-7 fighter (3-2). No. 3901, $1.20, AC313 helicopter (3-3).

***Perf. 13¼x12¾ Syncopated***

**2011, Apr. 17** **Litho.**

**3899-3901** A1220 Set of 3 1.50 1.25

World Reading Day — A1221

**2011, Apr. 23** ***Perf. 13 Syncopated***

**3902** A1221 $1.20 multi .60 .50

Tsinghua University, Cent. — A1222

**2011, Apr. 24** **Litho. & Embossed**

**3903** A1222 $1.20 multi .80 .50

Expo 2011, Xi'an — A1223

Designs: $1.20, Emblem (2-1). $3, Mascot (2-2).

***Perf. 13¼x13¾ Syncopated***

**2011, Apr. 28** **Photo.**

**3904-3905** A1223 Set of 2 2.00 1.40

26th Summer Universiade, Shenzhen — A1224

No. 3906: a, $1.20, Emblem (50x30mm, 4-1). b, $1.20, Mascot (30x30mm, 4-2).

No. 3907: a, $1.20, Shenzhen Universiade Sports Center (50x30mm, 4-3). b, $3, Torch, Chinese and English text (30x30mm, 4-4).

**2011, May 4** **Litho.** ***Perf. 13¼***

**Horiz. Pairs, #a-b**

**3906-3907** A1224 Set of 2 2.10 2.10

*3907a* Sheet of 8 2 each #3906a-3906b, 3907a-3907b *6.50 5.50*

Cloud Brocade — A1225

Designs: No. 3908, $1.20, Dragon (3-1). No. 3909, $1.20, Crane insignia of first-rank civil official (3-2). No. 3910, $1.20, Fish (Double happiness, 3-3).

***Perf. 13¼x12¾***

**2011, May 10** **Photo.**

**3908-3910** A1225 Set of 3 1.50 1.25

*3910a* Souvenir sheet of 3, #3908-3910, + 3 labels *5.50 3.50*

Emblem of Communist Party of China — A1226

**2011, May 21** **Litho.** ***Perf. 13¼***

**3911** A1226 $1.20 multi + label 1.00 .75

See Stamps With Attached Labels note after No. 3187.

Liberation of Tibet, 60th Anniv. — A1227

Designs: No. 3912, $1.20, Potala Palace, Chinese soldiers, Tibetans and livestock (3-1). No. 3913, $1.20, Airplane over building, dancers (3-2). No. 3914, $1.20, Building, dancers (3-3).

***Perf. 13¼x13¾ Syncopated***

**2011, May 23** **Photo.**

**3912-3914** A1227 Set of 3 1.50 1.25

Scientists A1228

Designs: No. 3915, $1.20, Bei Shizhang (1903-2009), biologist (4-1). No. 3916, $1.20, Qian Xuesen (1911-2009), rocket scientist (4-2). No. 3917, $1.20, Hou Xianglin (1912-2008), chemical engineer (4-3). No. 3918, $1.20, Qian Sanqiang (1913-92), nuclear physicist (4-4).

***Perf. 13x12¾ Syncopated***

**2011, May 25**

**3915-3918** A1228 Set of 4 2.25 1.50

Ming and Qing Dynasty Furniture A1230

No. 3919: a, 80f, Qing Dynasty rosewood-embedded copper dragon throne (6-1). b, $1.20, Ming Dynasy pearwood folding chair (6-2).

No. 3920: a, $1.20, Ming Dynasty pearwood official's armchair with carved Chinese characters (6-3). b, $1.20, Ming Dynasty pearwood armchair with carved dragons (6-4).

No. 3921: a, $1.20, Qing Dynasty rosewood-embedded marble armchair (6-5). b, $1.20, Ming Dynasty marble-embedded rosewood drum stool (6-6).

***Perf. 13¼x13¾ Syncopated***

**2011, June 20** **Litho.**

**3919** A1230 Horiz. pair, #a-b .65 .65

*c.* Booklet pane, #3919a-3919b + 2 labels *.90* —

**3920** A1230 $1.20 Horiz. pair, #a-b .75 .75

*c.* Booklet pane, #3920a-3920b + 2 labels *1.10* —

**3921** A1230 $1.20 Horiz. pair, #a-b .75 .75

*c.* Booklet pane, #3921a-3921b + 2 labels *1.10* —

*d.* Booklet pane, #3919a-3919b, 3920a-3920b, 3921a-3921b *3.25* —

Complete booklet, #3919c, 3920c, 3921c, 3921d *6.50*

*Nos. 3919-3921 (3)* 2.15 2.15

A1231

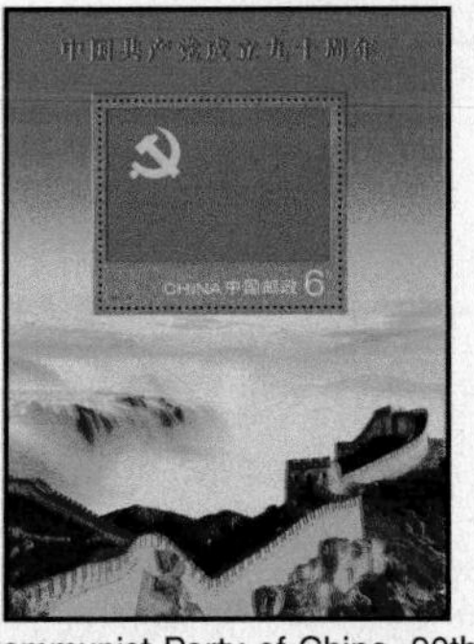

Communist Party of China, 90th Anniv. — A1232

Flag of the Communist Party of China and: No. 3922, $1.20, People and building (6-1). No. 3923, $1.20, Soldiers and monument (6-2). No. 3924, $1.20, Sculpture and building (6-3). No. 3925, $1.20, City skyline, sculpture of bull (6-4). No. 3926, $1.20, City skyline and modern building (6-5). No. 3927, $1.20, Beijing National Stdium, Chinese Pavilion, Shanghai (6-6).

$6, Flag of the Communist Party of China.

**2011, June 22** **Photo.** ***Perf. 13¼***

**3922-3927** A1231 Set of 6 3.25 2.50

*3924a* Sheet of 6, 2 each #3922-3924 *8.75 8.75*

*3927a* Sheet of 6, 2 each #3925-3927 *8.75 8.75*

**Souvenir Sheet**

***Perf. 13¼x13***

**3928** A1232 $6 multi 3.50 2.75

Opening of Beijing-Shanghai High Speed Railway — A1233

***Perf. 13¼x12¾ Syncopated***

**2011, June 30**

**3929** A1233 $1.20 multi 1.75 .90

Cycling A1234

Designs: No. 3930, $1.20, Cyclists on bike path (2-1). No. 3931, $1.20, Cyclists racing (2-2).

**2011, July 2** **Litho.**

**3930-3931** A1234 Set of 2 1.00 .80

Folk Vocal Arts — A1235

Designs: No. 3932, $1.20, Xiangsheng (4-1). No. 3933, $1.20, Singer with drum (4-2). No. 3934, $1.20, Pingtan (4-3). No. 3935, $1.20, Performer in black robe (4-4).

**2011, July 8** ***Perf. 13¼ Syncopated***

**3932-3935** A1235 Set of 4 1.50 1.50

*3935a* Sheet of 8, 4 each #3932-3935 *9.50 9.50*

Chinese Culture Abroad — A1236

No. 3936: a, Chinese Festival, London Eye (4-1). b, Chinese Benevolent Association sculpture and building, Buddhist temple, modern building (4-2). c, Chinatown, Transamerica Pyramid, San Francisco (4-3). d, Chinese school building, mountain (4-4).

***Perf. 13¼x13¾ Syncopated***

**2011, July 10**

**3936** Horiz. strip of 4 3.00 2.60

*a.-c.* A1236 $1.20 Any single .40 .40

*d.* A1236 $4.50 multi 1.40 1.40

Cargo Ships A1237

No. 3937: a, Cosco Asia container ship (4-1). b, Xinsheng Hai bulk transport ship (4-2).

***Perf. 13¼x12¾ Syncopated***

**2011, Aug. 8** **Photo.**

**3937** A1237 $1.20 Horiz. pair, #a-b 1.00 .85

Peonies A1238

Lilies A1239

Sunflowers — A1240

Chinese Rose A1241

Carnations — A1242

Camellias — A1243

Azalea Flowers A1244

Lotus Flowers A1245

Plum Blossoms — A1246

Magnolia Blossoms — A1247

**2011, Sept. 1** **Litho.** ***Perf. 12***

**3938** A1238 $1.20 multi + label .65 .50

**3939** A1239 $1.20 multi + label .65 .50

**3940** A1240 $1.20 multi + label .65 .50

**3941** A1241 $1.20 multi + label .65 .50

**3942** A1242 $1.20 multi + label .65 .50

**3943** A1243 $1.20 multi + label .65 .50

**3944** A1244 $1.20 multi + label .65 .50

**3945** A1245 $1.20 multi + label .65 .50

**3946** A1246 $1.20 multi + label .65 .50

**3947** A1247 $1.20 multi + label .65 .50

*Nos. 3938-3947 (10)* 6.50 5.00

See Stamps With Attached Labels note after No. 3197.

Traditional Games of Ethnic Minorities A1248

No. 3948, $1.20: a, Men in board shoe race (4-1). b, Women with bamboo poles (4-2).

No. 3949, $1.20: a, Top spinning (4-3). b, Stilt racing (4-4).

***Perf. 13x12¾ Syncopated***

**2011, Sept. 10** **Photo.**

**Vert. Pairs, #a-b**

| | | | |
|---|---|---|---|
| **3948-3949** | A1248 | Set of 2 | 1.50 1.50 |

A1249

Lord Guan Yu (?-219) A1250

Lord Guan Yu: No. 3950, $1.20, On horse (2-1). No. 3951, $1.20, Seated, reading annals (2-2).

***Perf. 13x13¼ Syncopated***

**2011, Sept. 12**

| | | | |
|---|---|---|---|
| **3950-3951** | A1249 | Set of 2 | 2.75 1.00 |

**Souvenir Sheet**

***Perf. 13¼x13 Syncopated***

| | | | |
|---|---|---|---|
| **3952** | A1250 | $6 multi | 6.50 6.00 |

A limited edition souvenir sheet of 6 containing three each Nos. 3950-3951 exists.

Details From the Scroll of the 87 Immortals — A1251

Various details with stamps numbered: No. 3953, $1.20, (6-1). No. 3954, $1.20, (6-2). No. 3955, $1.20, (6-3). No. 3956, $1.20, (6-4). $1.50, (6-5). $3, (6-6).

***Perf. 13¼ Syncopated***

**2011, Sept. 26** **Litho.**

| | | | |
|---|---|---|---|
| **3953-3958** | A1251 | Set of 6 | 3.00 3.00 |
| *3958a* | Booklet pane of 6, #3953-3958 | | *4.00 —* |
| | Complete booklet, #3958a | | *12.50* |

A1252

Chinese Revolution, Cent. — A1253

Designs: No. 3959, $1.20, Wuchang Uprising (2-1). No. 3960, $1.20, Revolution leaders (2-2).

$6, Dr. Sun Yat-sen (1866-1925), leader of revolution.

***Perf. 13¼x13 Syncopated***

**2011, Oct. 10** **Photo.**

| | | | |
|---|---|---|---|
| **3959-3960** | A1252 | Set of 2 | 1.00 .85 |
| *3960a* | Sheet of 8, 4 each #3959-3960 | | *8.00 7.00* |

**Souvenir Sheet**

***Perf. 13¼x12¾ Syncopated***

| | | | |
|---|---|---|---|
| **3961** | A1253 | $6 multi | 2.00 2.00 |

A1254

Rebuilding Efforts After May 12, 2008 Sichuan Earthquake — A1255

Designs: No. 3962, $1.20, Clock, rebuilt town (4-1). No. 3963, $1.20, Sculpture, rebuilt sections of ancient town (4-2). No. 3964, $1.20, Sculpture, buildings (4-3). No. 3965, $1.20, Flag, sculpture, rebuilt village (4-4).

$6, Rebuilt town, sculpture, wind generators.

***Perf. 13¼ Syncopated***

**2011, Oct. 13** **Litho.**

| | | | |
|---|---|---|---|
| **3962-3965** | A1254 | Set of 4 | 2.25 1.50 |

**Souvenir Sheet**

***Perf. 13 Syncopated***

| | | | |
|---|---|---|---|
| **3966** | A1255 | $6 multi | 2.00 2.00 |

A1256

Tianjin Binhai New Area A1257

Building and: No. 3967, $1.20, New downtown (3-1). No. 3968, $1.20, Yujiabao Financial District (3-2). No. 3969, $1.20, Map of National Animation Industry Park (3-3).

$6, Port, crane, container ship.

***Perf. 13¼x12¾ Syncopated***

**2011, Oct. 21** **Photo.**

| | | | |
|---|---|---|---|
| **3967-3969** | A1256 | Set of 3 | 1.25 1.25 |

**Souvenir Sheet**

***Perf. 13x13¾ Syncopated***

| | | | |
|---|---|---|---|
| **3970** | A1257 | $6 multi | 1.90 1.90 |

A1258

China 2011 Intl. Philatelic Exhibition, Wuxi — A1259

Designs: No. 3971, $1.20, Flat-sided container with spout and handle (2-1). No. 3972, $1.20, A-fu (2-2).

$6, Yu Zhuang Qiu, by Ni Zan.

***Perf. 13¼x13¾ Syncopated***

**2011, Oct. 10**

| | | | |
|---|---|---|---|
| **3971-3972** | A1258 | Set of 2 | .75 .75 |
| *3972a* | Sheet of 8, 4 each #3971-3972 + label | | *6.50 6.50* |

**Souvenir Sheet**

***Perf. 13¼x13 Syncopated***

| | | | |
|---|---|---|---|
| **3973** | A1259 | $6 multi | 1.90 1.90 |

No. 3973 exists imperf. Value, $42.50.

Xinhua News Agency, 80th Anniv. — A1260

Various buildings: No. 3974, $1.20, Red electric wave (4-1). No. 3975, $1.20, Anti-Japanese War (4-2). No. 3976, $1.20, War of Liberation (4-3). No. 3977, $1.20, Going global (4-4).

***Perf. 13¼ Syncopated***

**2011, Nov. 7** **Litho.**

| | | | |
|---|---|---|---|
| **3974-3977** | A1260 | Set of 4 | 1.50 1.50 |

Bird on Branch — A1261

**2011, Oct. 9** ***Perf. 11¾ Syncopated***

| | | | |
|---|---|---|---|
| **3978** | A1261 | $1.20 multi | .40 .40 |
| *a.* | Souvenir sheet of 2, #3708a, 3978 | | *3.75 3.75* |

Armillary Spheres — A1262

Designs: No. 3980, $1.20, Simplified armillary sphere built by Guo Shoujing, 1276 (2-1). No. 3981, $1.20, Equatorial armillary sphere built by Tycho Brahe, 1595 (2-2).

***Perf. 13¼x12¾ Syncopated***

**2011, Dec. 10** **Litho. & Engr.**

| | | | |
|---|---|---|---|
| **3980-3981** | A1262 | Set of 2 | 1.00 .90 |

See Denmark Nos. 1576-1577.

New Year 2012 (Year of the Dragon) — A1263

***Perf. 12¾ Syncopated***

**2012, Jan. 5** **Photo.**

| | | | |
|---|---|---|---|
| **3982** | A1263 | $1.20 multi | 1.50 1.00 |
| *a.* | Booklet pane of 10 | | 15.00 — |
| | Complete booklet, #3982a | | 16.00 |

Limited edition sheets of 4 and 6 stamps exist.

Bank of China, Cent. A1264

Designs: $1.20, Old bank building (2-1). $1.50, Modern bank building (2-2).

**2012, Feb. 5** ***Perf. 13 Syncopated***

| | | | |
|---|---|---|---|
| **3983-3984** | A1264 | Set of 2 | 3.50 2.00 |

Emblem and Building of Zhonghua Book Company — A1265

***Perf. 13¼x13¾ Syncopated***

**2012, Feb. 23** **Litho.**

| | | | |
|---|---|---|---|
| **3985** | A1265 | $1.20 multi | 1.30 .50 |

Diplomatic Relations Between People's Republic of China and Israel, 20th Anniv. — A1266

Designs: No. 3986, $1.20, Waxwing, five-pointed star (2-1). No. 3987, $1.20, White dove, Star of David (2-2).

**2012, Mar. 20** **Litho. & Embossed**

| | | | |
|---|---|---|---|
| **3986-3987** | A1266 | Set of 2 | 1.50 1.50 |

See Israel Nos. 1923-1924.

Asian-Pacific Postal Union, 50th Anniv. — A1267

**2012, Apr. 1** **Photo.** ***Perf. 13x13¼***

| | | | |
|---|---|---|---|
| **3988** | A1267 | $1.20 multi | .80 .80 |

Musicians A1268

Designs: No. 3989, $1.20, Xiao Youmei (1884-1940) (4-1). No. 3990, $1.20, Liu Tianhua (1895-1932) (4-2). No. 3991, $1.20, He Lvting (1903-99) (4-3). No. 3992, $1.20, Ma Sicong (1912-87) (4-4).

**2012, Apr. 15** ***Perf. 13 Syncopated***

| | | | |
|---|---|---|---|
| **3989-3992** | A1268 | Set of 4 | 2.15 1.60 |

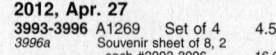

Chinese Characters — A1269

Embellished character for: No. 3993, $1.20, Good luck (fu) (4-1). No. 3994, $1.20, Richness (lu) (4-2). No. 3995, $1.20, Longevity (shou) (4-3). No. 3996, $1.20, Happiness (xi) (4-4).

**Litho With Foil Application**

**2012, Apr. 27**

| | | | |
|---|---|---|---|
| **3993-3996** | A1269 | Set of 4 | 4.50 2.50 |
| *3996a* | Souvenir sheet of 8, 2 each #3993-3996 | | *16.00 13.00* |

Communist Youth League, 90th Anniv. — A1270

Designs: 80f, Building, flag of Youth League (2-1). $1.20, Emblem, Great Wall of China, boy and girl (2-2).

***Perf. 13x12¾ Syncopated***

**2012, May 4** **Photo.**
**3997-3998** A1270 Set of 2 1.30 .65
*3998a* Souvenir sheet of 8, 4 each #3997-3998 *6.00 4.50*

International Nurses Day — A1271

**2012, May 12**
**3999** A1271 $1.20 multi .40 .40

Nanjing University, 110th Anniv. — A1272

***Perf. 13¼x13¾ Syncopated***

**2012, May 20** **Litho.**
**4000** A1272 $1.20 multi .40 .40

Publication of *Talks at Yan'an Forum on Literature and Art*, 70th Anniv. — A1273

Flowers and: No. 4001, $1.20, Former building of Chinese Communist Party Central Committee (2-1). No. 4002, $1.20, National Performing Arts Center, Beijing (2-2).

**2012, May 23** **Photo.**
**4001-4002** A1273 Set of 2 1.25 .80

Tables A1274

No. 4003: a, Ming Dynasty pear wood drawing table (50x30mm) (4-1). b, Qing Dynasty square pear wood table (40x30mm) (4-2).

No. 4004: a, Ming Dynasty pear wood incense stand with base (40x30mm) (4-3). b, Ming Dynasty rock wood table (50x30mm) (4-4).

***Perf. 13¼x13 Syncopated***

**2012, June 9** **Litho. & Embossed**
**4003** A1274 $1.20 Horiz. pair, #a-b 1.00 .75
*c.* Booklet pane of 1 #4003a + 2 labels .40 —
*d.* Booklet pane of 1 #4003b + 2 labels .40 —
**4004** A1274 $1.20 Horiz. pair, #a-b 1.00 .75
*c.* Booklet pane of 1 #4004a + 2 labels .40 —
*d.* Booklet pane of 1 #4004b + 2 labels .40 —
*e.* Booklet pane of 4, #4003a-4003b, 4004a-4004b 1.50 —
Complete booklet, #4003c, 4003d, 4004c, 4004d, 4004e 5.25

Third Asian Beach Games, Haiyang — A1275

Designs: No. 4005, $1.20, Beach volleyball (3-1). No. 4006, $1.20, Inline skating (3-2). No. 4007, $1.20, Waterskiing (3-3).

***Perf. 13¼ Syncopated***

**2012, June 16** **Photo.**
**4005-4007** A1275 Set of 3 1.25 1.25

Rocket Launch and Spacecraft — A1276

**2012, June 25** **Litho.** ***Perf. 12***
**4008** A1276 $1.20 multi + label .40 .40

See Stamps With Attached Labels note after No. 3197.

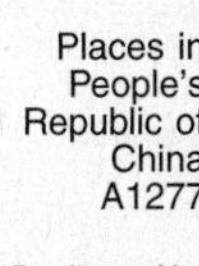

Places in People's Republic of China A1277

Designs: No. 4009, $1.20, Jingangshan Mountain (6-1). No. 4010, $1.20, Ruijin (6-2). No. 4011, $1.20, Zunyi (6-3). No. 4012, $1.20, Huining (6-4). No. 4013, $1.20, Yan An (6-5). No. 4014, $1.20, Xibaipo (6-6).

***Perf. 13¼x12¾ Syncopated***

**2012, June 30** **Litho. & Engr.**
**4009-4014** A1277 Set of 6 2.25 2.25
*4014a* Sheet of 12, 2 each #4009-4014 5.75 5.75

Full Coverage in Insurance Systems — A1278

***Perf. 13¼x13¾ Syncopated***

**2012, July 1** **Photo.**
**4015** A1278 $1.20 gold & red 1.50 .75

Emblem of Chinese Olympic Committee — A1279

**2012, July 17** **Litho.** ***Perf. 12***
**4016** A1279 $1.20 multi + label 1.00 .70

See Stamps With Attached Labels note after No. 3197.

National Museum and Stamps — A1280

No. 4017 — Museum and: a, $1.20, People's Republic of China #787. b, $3, People's Republic of China #790.

***Perf. 13¼ Syncopated***

**2012, July 8** **Litho. & Engr.**
**4017** A1280 Horiz. pair, #a-b 1.40 1.40

2012 Summer Olympics, London — A1281

Designs: No. 4018, $1.20, Soccer (4-1). No. 4019, $1.20, Tennis (4-2). No. 4020, $1.20, Equestrian (4-3). No. 4021, $1.20, Hurdles (4-4).

***Perf. 13¼x13 Syncopated***

**2012, July 27** **Photo.**
**4018-4021** A1281 Set of 4 1.50 1.50
*4021a* Sheet of 8, 2 each #4018-4021 *6.25 6.25*

Generals — A1282

Designs: No. 4022, $1.20, Zhao Bosheng (1897-1933) (5-1). No. 4023, $1.20, Duan Dechang (1904-33) (5-2). No. 4024, $1.20, Xie Zichang (1897-1935) (5-3). No. 4025, $1.20, Zeng Zhongsheng (1900-35) (5-4). No. 4026, $1.20, Dong Zhentang (1895-1937) (5-5).

***Perf. 13¼x13¾ Syncopated***

**2012, Aug. 1**
**4022-4026** A1282 Set of 5 2.00 1.90

A1283

Silk Road — A1284

Designs: No. 4027, $1.20, Buildings, figurines of camel and man (4-1). No. 4028, $1.20, Building, horse figurine (4-2). No. 4029, $1.20, Mountains, pitcher (4-3). No. 4030, $1.20, Cliff buildings, horse and rider figurine (4-4).

***Perf. 13¼x12¾ Syncopated***

**2012, Aug. 1**
**4027-4030** A1283 Set of 4 1.50 1.50
*4030a* Sheet of 8, 2 each #4027-4030 *7.25 7.25*

**Souvenir Sheet**

***Perf. 13¼ Syncopated***

**4031** A1284 $6 shown 1.90 1.90

Liu Sanjie — A1285

Designs: No. 4032, $1.20, Song fairy (4-1). No. 4033, $1.20, Singing, horiz. (4-2). No. 4034, $1.20, Couple with embroidered ball, horiz. (4-3). No. 4035, $1.20, Riding a carp to heaven (4-4).

***Perf. 13¼x13½ Syncopated, 13 Syncopated***

**2012, Aug. 23**
**4032-4035** A1285 Set of 4 2.20 1.50
*4032a* Booklet pane of 1 .65 —
*4033a* Booklet pane of 1 .65 —
*4034a* Booklet pane of 1 .65 —
*4035a* Booklet pane of 1 .65 —
Complete booklet, #4032-4035a 3.95

Complete booklet sold for $8.

Hetian Jade — A1286

Designs: No. 4036, $1.20, Figurine of dragon (4-1). No. 4037, $1.20, Bi with grain design, vert. (4-2). No. 4038, $1.20, Cup on plate (4-3). No. 4039, $1.20, Figurine of children washing elephant, vert. (4-4).

**Litho. & Embossed**

**2012, Aug. 28** ***Perf. 12***
**4036-4039** A1286 Set of 4 1.50 1.50
*4039a* Souvenir sheet of 4, #4036-4039 + label 2.40 2.40

A1287

Sanxingdui Bronze Relics — A1288

Designs: No. 4040, $1.20, Mask (2-1). No. 4041, $1.20, Statue of person kneeling (2-2). $6, Statue of person standing.

***Perf. 13¼x13½ Syncopated***

**2012, Sept. 26** **Litho.**
**4040-4041** A1287 Set of 2 .80 .80

**Souvenir Sheet**

***Perf. 13x13¼***

**4042** A1288 $6 multi 1.90 1.90

**Miniature Sheet**

Song Poetry — A1289

No. 4043: a, 80f, Sand of Silk Washing, by Yan Shu (6-1). b, $1.20, Meditating on the Past at Chibi, by Su Shi (6-2). c, $1.20, Fairy of the Magpie Bridge, by Qin Guan (6-3). d, $1.20, A Twig of Plum Blossoms (6-4). e, $1.20, Ode to the Plum Blossom, by Lu You (6-5). f, $3, This Unconstrained Poem to Chen Tongfu, by Xin Qiji (6-6).

***Perf. 13x13¼ Syncopated***

**2012, Aug. 31**
**4043** A1289 Sheet of 6, #a-f 3.75 3.75

Yanbian Culture A1290

Designs: No. 4044, $1.20, Harvest Dance (3-1). No. 4045, $1.20, Dancers (3-2). No. 4046, $1.20, Hymn for harmony (3-3).

***Perf. 13¼x13 Syncopated***

**2012, Sept. 3** **Photo.**

**4044-4046** A1290 Set of 3 2.00 1.25
*4046a* Sheet of 9, 3 each #4044-4046 27.50 3.75

Qin Dynasty Liye Bamboo Slips A1291

No. 4047: a, Multiplication table, denomination at UL (2-1). b, Calendar, denomination at UR (2-2).

***Perf. 13¼ Syncopated***

**2012, Sept. 13**

**4047** A1291 $1.20 Horiz. pair, #a-b .80 .80

"Good Fortune" — A1292

***Perf. 11¾ Syncopated***

**2012, Oct. 9** **Litho.**

**4048** A1292 $1.20 multi .40 .40
*a.* Souvenir sheet of 2, #3708a, 4048 *1.90 1.90*

Porcelain Objects From Dehua Kiln A1293

No. 4049, $1.20: a, Three-legged pot with dragon decoration (4-1). b, Vase with handles (4-2).
No. 4050, $1.20: a, Seated Guanyin figurine (4-3). b, Bodhidharma figurine (4-4).

***Perf. 13¼ Syncopated***

**2012, Oct. 20** **Photo.**

**Horiz. Pairs, #a-b**

**4049-4050** A1293 Set of 2 2.00 1.60

History of Merchants A1294

Designs: No. 4051, $1.20, Steamship, 1872 (3-1). No. 4052, $1.20, Shekou skyline (3-2). $1.50, Hong Kong skyline (3-3)

***Perf. 13¼x13 Syncopated***

**2012, Oct. 26** **Litho.**

**4051-4053** A1294 Set of 3 1.75 1.25
*4053a* Souvenir sheet of 6, 2 each #4051-4053 *4.75 4.75*

A1295

18th National Congress of Chinese Communist Party — A1296

No. 4054: a, Rocket launch (2-1). b, Great Wall of China (2-2).

***Perf. 13¼ Syncopated***

**2012, Nov. 8** **Photo.**

**4054** A1295 $1.20 Horiz. pair, #a-b .80 .80

**Souvenir Sheet**

***Perf. 13 Syncopated***

**4055** A1296 $6 multi 2.00 2.00

A sheet containing four No. 4054 exists.

Bridges A1297

Designs: No. 4056, $1.20, Taizhou Yangtze River Bridge (2-1). No. 4057, $1.20, Bosporus Bridge, Istanbul, Turkey (2-2).

***Perf. 13¼x13 Syncopated***

**2012, Nov. 26** **Litho.**

**4056-4057** A1297 Set of 2 .80 .80

See Turkey No. 3319.

Auditing — A1298

No. 4058: a, Three-legged pot, bas-relief (4-1). b, Imperial Chinese chop (4-2). c, Auditing document of Communist era with red circular seal, building, star, hammer and sickle (4-3). d, Modern auditing documents, building (4-4).

***Perf. 13 Syncopated***

**2012, Nov. 30** **Photo.**

**4058** A1298 Horiz. strip of 4 1.60 1.60
*a.-d.* $1.20 Any single .40 .40

Confucius Institute — A1299

No. 4059: a, $1.20, Stylized dove and globe (2-1). b, $3, Panda (2-2).

**2012, Dec. 1**

**4059** A1299 Horiz. pair, #a-b 1.40 1.40

Constitution of People's Republic of China, 30th Anniv. — A1300

***Perf. 13½x13¼ Syncopated***

**2012, Dec. 4** **Litho.**

**4060** A1300 $1.20 multi 1.00 .40

New Year 2013 (Year of the Snake) — A1301

***Perf. 12¾ Syncopated***

**2013, Jan. 5** **Photo.**

**4061** A1301 $1.20 multi *.95 .40*
*a.* Booklet pane of 10 *8.75* —
Complete booklet, #4061a 8.75

A limited edition sheet of 6 stamps exists.

Offshore Oil Exploration A1302

Designs: No. 4062, $1.20, Exploration ship (3-1). No. 4063, $1.20, Offshore drilling rig (3-2). $3, Production ship (3-3).

***Perf. 13¼x13 Syncopated***

**2013, Jan. 18**

**4062-4064** A1302 Set of 3 1.75 1.75

Heart and Flowers A1303

**2013, Feb. 28** **Litho.** ***Perf. 12***

**4065** A1303 $1.20 multi + label .40 .40

See Stamps With Attached Labels note after No. 3197.

Lanterns A1304

**2013, Mar. 3**

**4066** A1304 $1.20 multi + label .40 .40

See Stamps With Attached Labels note after No. 3197.

12th National People's Congress — A1305

***Perf. 13¼x13½ Syncopated***

**2013, Mar. 5** **Photo.**

**4067** A1305 $1.20 multi .40 .40
*a.* Souvenir sheet of 6 9.50 4.50

Mao Zedong's Instruction to Follow Examples of Comrade Lei Feng, 50th Anniv. — A1306

Lei Feng (1940-62), model soldier: 80f, Holding gun (4-1). No. 4069, $1.20, Studying book (4-2). No. 4070, $1.20, Polishing object (4-3). No. 4071, $1.20, Holding baby (4-4).

***Perf. 13¼ Syncopated***

**2013, Mar. 5** **Litho. & Engr.**

**4068-4071** A1306 Set of 4 1.40 1.40
*4071a* Sheet of 8, 2 each #4068-4071 *12.50 5.50*

Party School of the Central Committee, 80th Anniv. — A1307

***Perf. 13 Syncopated***

**2013, Mar. 13** **Litho.**

**4072** A1307 $1.20 multi .40 .40

Peach Blossoms — A1308

Various peach blossoms in decorative frames: No. 4073, 80f, (12-1). No. 4074, 80f, (12-2). No. 4075, $1.20. (12-3). No. 4076, $1.20, (12-4). No. 4077, $1.20, (12-5). No. 4078, $1.20 (12-6). No. 4079, $1.20, (12-7). No. 4080, $1.20, (12-8). No. 4081, $1.20, (12-9). No. 4082, $1.20 (12-10). No. 4083, $1.20, (12-11). $1.50, (12-12).

***Perf. 13¼x13 Syncopated***

**2013, Mar. 16** **Photo.**

**4073-4084** A1308 Set of 12 6.50 4.50
*4078a* Sheet of 12, 2 each #4073-4078 *5.50 5.50*
*4084a* Sheet of 12, 2 each #4079-4084 *6.50 6.50*

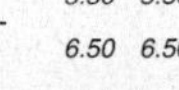

World Water Day — A1309

**2013, Mar. 22**

**4085** A1309 $1.20 multi .40 .40

Painting of Women Producing Silk — A1310

Details from painting: No. 4086, $1.20, Women beating silk in basin (3-1). No. 4087, $1.20, Women working silk thread (3-2). No. 4088, $1.20, Women pulling silk cloth (3-3).
$6, Entire painting.

***Perf. 13 Syncopated***

**2013, Apr. 13** **Litho.**

**4086-4088** A1310 Set of 3 1.25 1.25

**Souvenir Sheet**

***Perf. 13½ Syncopated***

**4089** A1310 $6 multi 2.00 2.00

No. 4089 contains one 59x37mm stamp.

Cloisonné Ware — A1311

Designs: 80f, Yuan Dynasty three-legged pot (6-1). No. 4091, $1.20, Ming Dynasty container (6-2). No. 4092, $1.20, Qing Dynasty Zun vessel (6-3). No. 4093, $1.20, Qing Dynasty pot with spout and handle (6-4). No. 4094, $1.20, Hanging vase with handle (6-5). $3, Ming Dynasty bottle vase (6-6).

***Perf. 13¼x13½ Syncopated***

**2013, Apr. 21**

**4090-4095** A1311 Set of 6 3.00 3.00
*4095a* Sheet of 12, 2 each #4090-4095 *7.75 7.75*

Souvenir Sheet

7th Congress of All-China Philatelic Federation — A1312

**2013, Apr. 25** **Litho. & Embossed**
**4096** A1312 $6 multi 2.00 2.00

Earthquake Relief — A1313

***Perf. 13x12½ Syncopated***
**2013, May 3** **Photo.**
**4097** A1313 $1.20 multi *7.50 7.50*

Mother's Day — A1314

**Litho. With Foil Application**
***Perf. 13x12¾ Syncopated***
**2013, May 11**
**4098** A1314 $1.20 multi .95 .40

Exists in a sheet of 8. Value, $42.50.

Galloping Horse — A1315

**2013, May 19** **Litho.** ***Perf. 12***
**4099** A1315 $1.20 multi + label .40 .40

See Stamps With Attached Labels note after No. 3197.

Town Scenes A1316

Designs: No. 4100, $1.20, Qiantong (8-1). No. 4101, $1.20, Laitan (8-2). No. 4102, $1.20, Heping (8-3). No. 4103, $1.20, Jingziuan (8-4). No. 4104, $1.20, Heshun (8-5). No. 4105, $1.20, Tangjiawan (8-6). No. 4106, $1.20, Lizhuang (8-7). No. 4107, $1.20, Jingsheng (8-8).

***Perf. 13¼x12¾ Syncopated***
**2013, May 19** **Litho. & Engr.**
**4100-4107** A1316 Set of 8 3.25 3.25

Zhangjiajie Tianzi Mountain A1317

Xiapu Beaches — A1318

Qilian Yu Island Group, Paracel Islands — A1319

Panjin Red Beach — A1320

Longsheng Terraced Fields — A1321

Fields and Irrigation Canals, Xinghua — A1322

***Perf. 13x12¾ Syncopated***
**2013, May 19** **Photo.**

| | | | | |
|---|---|---|---|---|
| **4108** | A1317 | 80f multi | .25 | .25 |
| **4109** | A1318 | 80f multi | .25 | .25 |
| **4110** | A1319 | $1.20 multi | .40 | .40 |
| **4111** | A1320 | $1.20 multi | .40 | .40 |
| **4112** | A1321 | $1.50 multi | .50 | .50 |
| **4113** | A1322 | $3 multi | 1.00 | 1.00 |
| | | *Nos. 4108-4113 (6)* | 2.80 | 2.80 |

Tadpoles and Pond Life — A1323

No. 4114 — Tadpoles and: a, Shrimp. b, Goldfish. c, Crab. d, Turtles. e, Frog.

***Perf. 13x12½ Syncopated***
**2013, June 1** **Photo.**

| | | | |
|---|---|---|---|
| **4114** | Horiz. strip of 5 | 1.90 | 1.90 |
| *a.* | A1323 80f multi | .25 | .25 |
| *b.-e.* | A1323 $1.20 Any single | .40 | .40 |
| *f.* | Booklet pane of 5, #4114a-4114e | 1.90 | — |
| | Complete booklet, #4114f | 3.75 | |

Gold and Bronze Statues of Buddha — A1324

Buddha statue from: 80f, Five Dynasties period (6-1). No. 4116, $1.20, Song Dynasty (6-2). No. 4117, $1.20, Ming Dynasty (6-3). No. 4118, $1.20, Ming Dynasty, diff. (6-4). No. 4119, $1.20, Ming Dynasty, diff. (6-5). No. 4120, $1.20, Ming Dynasty, diff. (6-6).
$6, Five Buddha statues.

***Perf. 13¼ Syncopated***
**2013, June 16** **Litho.**
**4115-4120** A1324 Set of 6 2.25 2.25

**Souvenir Sheet**
***Perf. 13 Syncopated***
**4121** A1324 $6 multi 2.00 2.00

No. 4121 contains one 74x83mm stamp.
No. 4115-4120 exist in a sheet of 12 (2 of each value).

Four Arts of Chinese Scholars — A1325

Designs: No. 4122, $1.20, Scholar playing a qin (4-1). No. 4123, $1.20, Scholars playing game of Go (4-2). No. 4124, $1.20, Scholars learning calligraphy (4-3). No. 4125, $1.20, Scholar and wall painting (4-4).

***Perf. 13¼ Syncopated***
**2013, July 13** **Litho.**
**4122-4125** A1325 Set of 4 1.60 1.60

A sheet containing two No. 4122-4125 exists. The stamps exist printed on silk paper.

Longhu Mountain A1326

No. 4126: a, Elephant Trunk Hill (3-1). b, Rocks of Immortals (3-2). c, Zhengyi Taoist Abbey (3-3).
$6, Longhu Mountain and lake, horiz.

***Perf. 13¼ Syncopated***
**2013, July 27** **Photo.**
**4126** A1326 $1.20 Horiz. strip of 3, #a-c 1.25 1.25

**Souvenir Sheet**
***Perf. 13x13½ Syncopated***
**4127** A1326 $6 multi 2.00 2.00

Ship A1327

Stars A1328

Knot A1329

Painting of Bamboo A1330

***Die Cut Perf. 12¾ Syncopated***
**2013, Aug. 8** **Photo.**
**Self-Adhesive**
**4128** A1327 80f multi .25 .25

***Die Cut Perf. 13¼x13 Syncopated***

| | | | | |
|---|---|---|---|---|
| **4129** | A1328 | $1.20 multi | .40 | .40 |
| **4130** | A1329 | $2.40 multi | .80 | .80 |
| **4131** | A1330 | $3 multi | 1.00 | 1.00 |
| | | *Nos. 4128-4131 (4)* | 2.45 | 2.45 |

Mascot of 2014 Youth Olympic Games, Nanjing A1331

**2013, Aug. 15** **Litho.** ***Perf. 12***
**4132** A1331 $1.20 multi + label .40 .40

See Stamps With Attached Labels note after No. 3197.

China-ASEAN Expo, 10th Anniv. — A1332

***Perf. 13¼x12¾ Syncopated***
**2013, Aug. 15** **Photo.**
**4133** A1332 $1.20 multi .40 .40

Cats — A1333

Cat breed: No. 4134, $1.20, Chinese Li Hua (4-1). No. 4135, $1.20, Maine Coon (4-2). No. 4136, $1.20, Abyssinian, vert. (4-3). No. 4137, $1.20, Exotic shorthair, vert. (4-4).

***Perf. 13 Syncopated, 13¼x13¾ Syncopated (#4136-4137)***
**2013, Aug. 18** **Litho. & Engr.**
**4134-4137** A1333 Set of 4 1.60 1.60

Sun and Peonies A1334

**2013, Aug. 26** **Litho.** ***Perf. 12***
**4138** A1334 $1.20 multi + label .40 .40

See Stamps with Attached Labels note after No. 3197.

12th National Games, Liaoning A1335

Designs: No. 4139, $1.20, Rhythmic gymnastics (2-1). No. 4140, $1.20, Fencing (2-2).

***Perf. 13¼x13 Syncopated***
**2013, Aug. 31** **Litho.**
**4139-4140** A1335 Set of 2 .80 .80
*4140a* Souvenir sheet of 2, #4139-4140 *1.40 1.40*

Wei Guoqing (1913-89), Political and Military Leader — A1336

Wei Guoqing: No. 4141, $1.20, Wearing army cap (2-1). No. 4142, $1.20, Without cap (2-2).

***Perf. 13¼x13¾ Syncopated***
**2013, Sept. 2** **Litho.**
**4141-4142** A1336 Set of 2 .80 .80

Yu Yuan Garden, Shanghai A1337

Designs: 80f, Zigzag Bridge and Mid-lake Pavilion (4-1). No. 4144, $1.20, Grand Rockery (4-2). No. 4145, $1.20, Yuan-yu Building (4-3). No. 4146, $1.20, Exquisite Jade Rock (4-4).

***Perf. 13¼x12¾ Syncopated***
**2013, Sept. 7** **Litho. & Engr.**
**4143-4146** A1337 Set of 4 1.50 1.50

Nanhua Temple A1338

No. 4147: a, Cao Xi Gate (4-1). b, Mahavira Hall (4-2). c, Ling Zhao Pagoda (4-3). d, Liu Zu Hall (4-4).

***Perf. 13¼x13 Syncopated***
**2013, Sept. 7** **Photo.**
**4147** Horiz. strip of 4 1.60 1.60
*a.-d.* A1338 $1.20 Any single .40 .40

Poets — A1339

Designs: No. 4148, $1.20, Jia Yi (200 B.C.-168 B.C.) (4-1). No. 4149, $1.20, Sima Xiangru (179 B.C.-118 B.C.) (4-2). No. 4150, $1.20, Yang Xiong (53 B.C.-18 A.D.) (4-3). No. 4151, $1.20, Ban Gu (32-92) (4-4).

***Perf. 13¼ Syncopated***
**2013, Sept. 15** **Photo.**
**4148-4151** A1339 Set of 4 1.60 1.60

Table Tennis — A1340

Players: No. 4152, $1.20, Woman (2-1). No. 4153, $1.20, Man (2-2).

***Perf. 13½x13 Syncopated***

**2013, Sept. 27** **Photo.**
**4152-4153** A1340 Set of 2 1.95 .80

See Sweden No. 2715.

Chinese Technical Achievements A1341

Designs: 80f, Rendezvous of Shenzhou and Tiangong spacecraft (4-1). No. 4155, $1.20, Beidou Navigation Satellite System (4-2). No. 4156, $1.20, Liaoning Aircraft Carrier (4-3). No. 4157, $1.20, Jiaolong Manned Submersible (4-4).

***Perf. 13x12¾ Syncopated***

**2013, Sept. 29** **Photo.**
**4154-4157** A1341 Set of 4 2.75 1.50
*4157a* Souvenir sheet of 4, #4154-4157 1.50 1.50

Fish and Flowers — A1342

***Perf. 12¾x12 Syncopated***

**2013, Oct. 9** **Litho.**
**4158** A1342 $1.20 multi .40 .40
*a.* Souvenir sheet of 2, #3708a, 4158, perf. 11¾ syncopated 2.50 2.50

Tenth China Art Festival — A1343

***Perf. 13¼x13 Syncopated***

**2013, Oct. 11** **Litho.**
**4159** A1343 $1.20 multi .40 .40

Xi Zhongxun (1913-2002), Communist Party Official — A1344

Xi Zhnongxun: No. 4160, $1.20, As young man in military uniform (2-1). No. 4161, $1.20, As older man (2-2).

***Perf. 13¼x13½ Syncopated***

**2013, Oct. 15** **Litho. & Engr.**
**4160-4161** A1344 Set of 2 .80 .80

21st Intl. Congress of Supreme Audit Institutions, Beijing A1345

No. 4162: a, Congress emblem, Gate of Heavenly Peace (2-1). b, Emblem of Intl. Organization of Supreme Audit Institutions, Great Wall of China (2-2)

***Perf. 13¼ Syncopated***

**2013, Oct. 22** **Litho.**
**4162** A1345 $1.20 Horiz. pair, #a-b 1.95 .80

Hybrid Rice A1346

No. 4163: a, Seed production (2-1). b, Stalk of rice, rice bowl (2-2).

**2013, Oct. 25 Litho.** ***Perf. 13¼x13¾***
**4163** A1346 $1.20 Horiz. pair, #a-b .80 .80

Mao Zedong (1893-1976), Chairman of People's Republic of China — A1347

Various paintings of Mao Zedong: No. 4164, $1.20, With boats in background (4-1). No. 4165, $1.20, With opened overcoat (4-2). No. 4166, $1.20, With arm extended, vert. (4-3). No. 4167, $1.20, Watching waves come ashore (4-4).

***Perf. 13¼ Syncopated***

**2013, Nov. 16** **Litho.**
**4164-4167** A1347 Set of 4 1.60 1.60

Wuhan University, 120th Anniv. — A1348

***Perf. 13 Syncopated***

**2013, Nov. 29** **Litho.**
**4168** A1348 $1.20 multi .40 .40

Chinese Junk A1349

**2013, Nov. 22 Litho.** ***Perf. 12***
**4169** A1349 $1.20 multi + label .40 .40

See Stamps With Attached Labels note under No. 3197.

First Moon Landing by Chinese Space Vehicles A1350

No. 4170: a, $1.20, Chang'e 3 Lander (2-1). b, $1.50, Yutu Moon Rover (2-2).

***Perf. 13¼x13 Syncopated***

**2014, Jan. 1** **Photo.**
**4170** A1350 Horiz. pair, #a-b .90 .90

New Year 2014 (Year of the Horse) — A1351

***Perf. 12¾ Syncopated***

**2014, Jan. 5** **Photo.**
**4171** A1351 $1.20 multi .85 .40
*a.* Booklet pane of 10 4.00 —
Complete booklet, #4171a 6.50

Diplomatic Relations Between France and People's Republic of China, 50th Anniv. A1352

Desings: No. 4172, $1.20, Qinhuai River, Nanjing (2-1). No. 4173, $1.20, Seine River, Paris (2-2).

***Perf. 13x12½ Syncopated***

**2014, Jan. 27** **Litho. & Engr.**
**4172-4173** A1352 Set of 2 .80 .80

See France Nos. 4587-4588.

Birds of Prey — A1353

Designs: No. 4174, $1.20, Aquila heliaca (4-1). No. 4175, $1.20, Circus cyaneus, horiz. (4-2). No. 4176, $1.50, Accipiter gentilis, horiz. (4-3). No. 4177, $1.50, Falco tinnunculus (4-4).

***Perf. 12¾ Syncopated (vert. stamps), 13x12½ Syncopated***

**2014, Feb. 23** **Litho. & Engr.**
**4174-4177** A1353 Set of 4 1.75 1.75

Bathing Horses, by Zhao Mengfu (1254-1322) A1354

No. 4179: a, 7 horses and rider. (50x38mm) (3-1). b, 5 horses, 3 riders, 3 grooms, Chinese text (57x38mm) (3-2). c, 2 horses, 2 men (50x38mm) (3-3).
$6, Entire painting.

***Perf. 13¼ Syncopated***

**2014, Mar. 1** **Litho.**
**4178** Horiz. strip of 3 1.40 1.40
*a.-b.* A1354 $1.20 Either single .40 .40
*c.* A1354 $1.50 multi .50 .50

**Souvenir Sheet**

***Perf. 13½x14 Syncopated***

**4179** A1354 $6 multi 2.00 2.00

No. 4179 contains one 153x31mm stamp.

Strengthening of Consumer Rights in China — A1355

Designs: No. 4180, $1.20, Scales, book and Consumer Rights Day emblem (2-1). No. 4181, $1.20, Hands, bowl, shirt, house, steering wheel. (2-2).

***Perf. 13¼x13¾ Syncopated***

**2014, Mar. 15** **Litho.**
**4180-4181** A1355 Set of 2 .80 .80

Internet Life — A1356

Designs: No. 4182, $1.20, Internet icons, man and woman touching hands (4-1). No. 4183, $1.20, Computer screen, mouse, man pushing shopping cart with Internet icons (4-2). No. 4184, $1.20, Hand holding smart phone showing picture of man on laptop computer (4-3). $1.50, Clouds with Internet icons, people on hills (4-4).

***Perf. 13¼x13½ Syncopated***

**2014, Apr. 20** **Photo.**
**4182-4185** A1356 Set of 4 1.75 1.75

Exists in a sheet of 2 each, No. 4182-4185.

Theme Pavilion and Emblem — A1357

Botanical Pavilion and Mascot — A1358

***Perf. 13 Syncopated***

**2014, Apr. 25** **Photo.**
**4186** A1357 $1.20 multi (2-1) .65 .40
**4187** A1358 $1.20 multi (2-2) .65 .40

Intl. Horticultural Exposition, Qingdao.

Chinese People's Association for Friendship With Foreign Countries, 60th Anniv. A1359

***Perf. 13¼ Syncopated***

**2014, May 3** **Litho.**
**4188** A1359 $1.20 multi .40 .40

Wild Goose Delivering Letters A1360

***Perf. 13¼x13 Syncopated***

**2014, May 10** **Litho. & Engr.**
**4189** A1360 $1.20 multi .40 .40

See Republic of China No. 4178.

Buddhist Art — A1361

Designs: No. 4190, $1.20, Sakyamuni Buddha (4-1). No. 4191, $1.20, Amitayus Buddha (4-2). No. 4192, $1.20, Green Tara (4-3). No. 4193, $1.20, White Tara (4-4).
$6, Sahasra-bhuja Sahasra-netra Avalokitesvara.

***Perf. 13¼x13 Syncopated***

**2014, May 18** **Litho.**
**4190-4193** A1361 Set of 4 1.60 1.60

**Souvenir Sheet**

***Perf. 13x13¼ Syncopated***

**4194** A1361 $6 multi 1.90 1.90

No. 4194 contains one 66x108mm stamp.
A sheet containing 2 each No. 4190-4193 exists. Value, $12.50.

Birds in Bamboo Forest A1362

**2014, May 28 Litho. *Perf. 12***
**4195** A1362 $1.20 multi + label .40 .40

See Stamps With Attached Labels note after No. 3197.

Premiere of Animated Movie *The Monkey King* A1363

Designs: No. 4196, 80f, Monkey King seeking weapon in Dragon King's palace (6-1). No. 4197, 80f, Horses in water and in flight (6-2). No. 4198, $1.20, Monkey King, other monkeys, banner (6-3). No. 4199, $1.20, Monkey King in peach tree (6-4). No. 4200, $1.20, Monkey King in battle (6-5). No. 4201, $1.20, Monkey King breaking picture frame (6-6).

***Perf. 13¼x12¾ Syncopated***

**2014, June 1 Photo.**
**4196-4201** A1363 Set of 6 2.10 2.10
*4201a* Booklet pane of 6, #4196-4201 2.10 —
Complete booklet, #4201a 2.10

Huangpu Military Academy, 90th Anniv. A1364

***Perf. 13¼x12¾ Syncopated***

**2014, June 16 Litho. & Engr.**
**4202** A1364 $1.20 multi .40 .40

*The Dream of Red Mansions,* Novel by Cao Xueqin — A1365

Scenes from novel: No. 4203, $1.20, Lady Dowager sends for her motherless granddaughter (4-1). No. 4204 $1.20, Confounded monk ends a confounding case (4-2). No. 4205, $1.20, Grandmother Liu saw Madam Phoenix first (4-3). $1.50, Baoyu recognizes the gold locket (4-4).

$6, Spirit of Baoyu.

***Perf. 13 Syncopated***

**2014, June 21 Photo.**
**4203-4206** A1365 Set of 4 1.75 1.75

**Souvenir Sheet**

**4207** A1365 $6 multi 2.00 2.00

No. 4207 contains one 45x70mm stamp. Compare with Nos. 4375-4379.

Huangmei Opera — A1366

Designs: 80f, A Happy Marriage with a Fairy (3-1). No. 4209, $1.20, Royal Son-in-law (3-2). No. 4210, $1.20, Collecting Grass for Pig (3-3).

***Perf. 13¼ Syncopated***

**2014, July 6 Litho.**
**4208-4210** A1366 Set of 3 1.10 1.10

Fruit — A1367

Designs: No. 4211, $1.20, Apples (4-1). No. 4212, $1.20, Peaches (4-2). No. 4213, $1.50, Pomegranates (4-3). No. 4214, $1.50, Kumquats (4-4).

***Perf. 13¼x13 Syncopated***

**2014, July 15 Litho.**
**4211-4214** A1367 Set of 4 1.75 .75

Exists in a sheet of 2 each, No. 4211-4214.

2014 Youth Olympic Games, Nanjing — A1368

***Perf. 13¼x13½ Syncopated***

**2014, Aug. 16 Litho.**
**4215** A1368 $1.20 multi .40 .40

Basin A1369

**2014, Aug. 20 Litho. *Perf. 12***
**4216** A1369 $1.20 multi + label .40 .40

See Stamps With Attached Labels note after No. 3197.

Deng Xiaoping (1904-97), Leader of People's Republic of China — A1370

Deng Xiaoping: No. 4217, $1.20, In military uniform, Red Army flag (4-1). No. 4218, $1.20, At lectern, United Nations Building and flag (4-2). No. 4219, $1.50, Reading speech, microphones, teapot, flag of Chinese Communist Party (4-3). No. 4220, $1.50, With extended arm, flag of People's Republic of China (4-4)

***Perf. 13 Syncopated***

**2014, Aug. 22 Litho.**
**4217-4220** A1370 Set of 4 1.75 1.75

Exists in a sheet of 2 each, No. 4217-4220.

Zhuge Liang (181-234), Chancellor of Shu Han — A1371

Designs: No. 4221, $1.20, Zhuge Liang standing (2-1). No. 4222, $1.20, Zhuge Liang writing (2-2).

$6, Zhuge Liang standing, diff.

***Perf. 13¼ Syncopated***

**2014, Aug. 28 Litho.**
**4221-4222** A1371 Set of 2 .80 .80

**Souvenir Sheet**

**4223** A1371 $6 multi 2.00 2.00

No. 4223 contains one 38x62mm stamp.
A sheet containing 4 each No. 4221-4222 exists.

Teacher's Day — A1372

Designs: $1.20, Candles in hot-air balloon basket, eyeglasses and book on desk (2-1). $1.50, Tree with symbols of education, stylized faces (2-2).

***Perf. 13¼x13¾ Syncopated***

**2014, Sept. 10 Photo.**
**4224-4225** A1372 Set of 2 .90 .90

Exists in a sheet of 4 each, No. 4224-4225.

**Miniature Sheet**

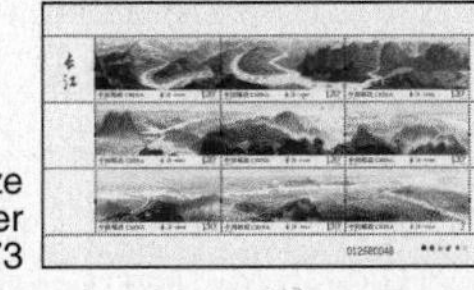

Yangtze River A1373

No. 4226: a, $1.20, River running through mountains (9-1). b, $1.20, River passing Chongqing (9-2). c, $1.20, Three Gorges (9-3). d, $1.20, Hubei and Hunan (9-4). e, $1.20, Mount Lu and Jiujang River (9-5). f, $1.20, Yellow Mountain (9-6). g, $1.50, Bridges over river (9-7). h, $1.50, River passing towns (9-8). i, $3, River running into sea (9-9).

***Perf. 13¼x12¾ Syncopated***

**2014, Sept. 13 Photo.**
**4226** A1373 Sheet of 9, #a-i 4.50 4.50

People's Congress, 60th Anniv. — A1374

60th anniv. emblem and: No. 4227, $1.20, Building and people (2-1). No. 4228, $1.20, Great Hall of the People and flags (2-2).

***Perf. 12¾x12½ Syncopated***

**2014, Sept. 15 Litho.**
**4227-4228** A1374 Set of 2 1.65 .80

National Rejuvenation A1375

Ribbons and: 80f, Buildings, flags and ship (4-1). No. 4230, $1.20, Buildings, construction cranes, harvesters (4-2). No. 4231, $1.20, China Central Television Building, Ferris wheel, buildings, dancers (4-3). No. 4232, $1.20, Ethnic dancers and musicians, buildings (4-4).

***Perf. 13 Syncopated***

**2014, Sept. 20 Photo.**
**4229-4232** A1375 Set of 4 1.50 1.50
*4232a* Souvenir sheet of 4, #4229-4232 1.50 1.50

Filial Piety — A1376

Designs: No. 4233, $1.20, Yu Shun, elephants and birds (4-1). No. 4234, $1.20, Wife of Jiang Shi holding tray with bowl and plate, carp jumping from spring (4-2). No. 4235, $1.50, Hua Mulan with spear on horseback (4-3). No. 4236, $1.50, Sun Simao studying medicine (4-4).

***Perf. 13¼ Syncopated***

**2014, Sept. 30 Litho. & Engr.**
**4233-4236** A1376 Set of 4 1.75 1.75

Exists in a sheet of 2 each, No. 4233-4236.

A1377

A1378

Xinjiang Production and Construction Corps, 60th Anniv. — A1379

***Perf. 13 Syncopated***

**2014, Oct. 7 Litho.**
**4237** Horiz. strip of 3 1.25 1.25
*a.* A1377 $1.20 multi .40 .40
*b.* A1378 $1.20 multi .40 .40
*c.* A1379 $1.20 multi .40 .40

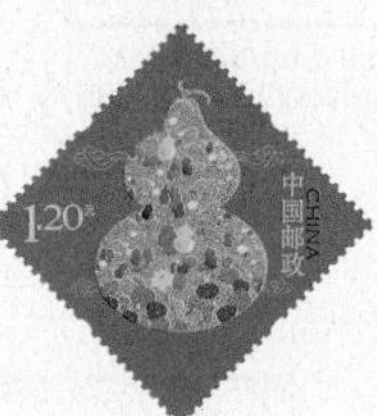

Calabash A1380

***Perf. 12¾ Syncopated***

**2014, Oct. 9 Litho.**
**4238** A1380 $1.20 multi .40 .40
*a.* Souvenr sheet of 2, #3708a (perf. 12 syncopated), #4238 1.40 1.40

Scientists — A1381

Designs: No. 4239, $1.20, Wang Ganchang (1907-98), nuclear physicist (6-1). No. 4240, $1.20, Zhou Jiuzhang (1907-68), spacecraft engineer (6-2). No. 4241, $1.20, Guo Yonghuai (1909-68), physicist (6-3). No. 4242, $1.20, Deng Jiaxian (1924-86), nuclear physicist (6-4). No. 4243, $1.20, Zhu Guangya (1924-2011), nuclear physicist (6-5). No. 4244, $1.20, Wang Xuan (1937-2006), computer scientist (6-6).

***Perf. 13¼ Syncopated***

**2014, Oct. 16 Photo.**
**4239-4244** A1381 Set of 6 2.40 2.40

Sail Your Dreams A1382

**2014, Oct. 31 Litho. *Perf. 13¼***
**4245** A1382 $1.20 multi + label .40 .40

See Stamps With Attached Labels note after No. 3197.

Meeting of Leaders of Asia-Pacific Economic Cooperation, Beijing — A1383

**2014, Nov. 10 Litho. *Perf. 13¼x13***

**4246** A1383 $1.20 multi .40 .40

10th China Intl. Aviation and Aerospace Exhibition — A1384

No. 4247: a, Helicopter, airplanes, city skyline (2-1). b, Space Station, rockets, astronaut (2-2).

**2014, Nov. 11 Litho. *Perf. 13¼x13***

**4247** A1384 $1.20 Horiz. pair, #a-b .80 .80

Chinese Character for "Congratulations" — A1385

**2014, Nov. 12 Litho. *Perf. 12***

**4248** A1385 $1.20 multi + label .40 .40

See Stamps With Attached Labels note after No. 3197.

Chinese Arctic and Antarctic Research Expeditions, 30th Anniv. — A1386

No. 4249: a, $1.20, Map of Antarctica, research expedition station, buildings, penguins (2-1). b, $1.50, Map of Arctic region, ship, buildings and polar bears (2-2).

***Perf. 13x12¾ Syncopated***

**2014, Nov. 20 Litho.**

**4249** A1386 Vert. pair, #a-b .90 .90

Double Happiness — A1387

**2014, Dec. 1 Litho. *Perf. 13¼x13***

**4250** A1387 $3 multi 1.00 1.00

Values are for stamp with surrounding selvage.

Miniature Sheet

Yuan Dramatic Works A1388

No. 4251: a, 80f, Sand and Sky — Autumn Thoughts, by Ma Zhiyuan (6-1). b, $1.20, Sheep on the Slope — Meditation on the Past at Tong Pass, by Zhang Yanghao (6-2). c, $1.20, Dou E Yuan, by Guan Hanqing (6-3). d, $1.20, Over the Wall, by Bai Pu (6-4). e, $1.50, The Orphan of Zhao, by Ji Junxiang (6-5). f, $3, Premature Death of a Beautiful Young Girl, by Zheng Guangzu (6-6).

**Litho. & Engr.**

**2014, Dec. 1 *Perf. 13¼***

**4251** A1388 Sheet of 6, #a-f 3.00 3.00

New Year 2015 (Year of the Ram) — A1389

***Perf. 13 Syncopated***

**2015, Jan. 5 Photo.**

**4252** A1389 $1.20 multi .75 .40

*a.* Booklet pane of 10 4.00 —

Complete booklet, #4252a 6.75

Exists in a sheet of 4. Value, $17.50.

Greeting Chinese New Year — A1390

***Perf. 13 Syncopated***

**2015, Jan. 10 Litho.**

**4253** A1390 $1.20 multi .40 .40

Exists in a sheet of 8.

Zunyi Conference, 80th Anniv. — A1391

Designs: No. 4254. $1.20, Conference site (2-1). No. 4255, $1.20, Conference participants (2-2).

***Perf. 13¼x13 Syncopated***

**2015, Jan. 15 Litho.**

**4254-4255** A1391 Set of 2 .80 .80

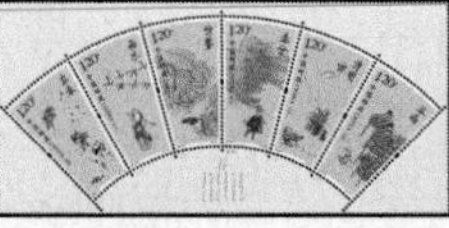

24 Solar Terms A1392

No. 4256: a, Beginning of Spring (children and flowers) (6-1). b, Rain water (fisherman and birds). (6-2). c, Waking of insects (cowherd and bulls) (6-3). d, Spring equinox (boy on bull) (6-4). e, Pure brightness (kite flying) (6-5). f, Grain rain (women tending to vegetables on racks, rabbits) (6-6).

***Perf. 13 Syncopated***

**2015, Feb. 4 Photo.**

**4256** A1392 $1.20 Block of 6, #a-f 2.40 2.40

Values are for stamps with surrounding selvage.

Court Ladies Swinging Fans, by Zhou Fang A1393

No. 4257 — Painting details numbered: a, (3-1). b, (3-2). c, (3-3).

$6, Entire painting.

***Perf. 13¼x13 Syncopated***

**2015, Mar. 22 Litho.**

**4257** Horiz. strip of 3 1.40 1.40

*a.-b.* A1393 $1.20 Either single .40 .40

*c.* A1393 $1.50 multi .50 .50

**Souvenir Sheet**

***Perf. 12¾x12½ Syncopated***

**4258** A1393 $6 multi 2.00 2.00

No. 4258 contains one 157x28mm stamp.

Writers A1394

Designs: No. 4259, $1.20, Tang Xianzu (1550-1616) (6-1). No. 4260, $1.20, Feng Menglong (1574-1645) (6-2). No. 4261, $1.20, Pu Songling (1640-1715) (6-3). No. 4262, $1.20, Hong Sheng (1645-1704) (6-4). No. 4263, $1.20, Kong Shangren (1648-1718) (6-5). No. 4264, $1.20, Cao Xueqin (c.1715-c.1763) (6-6).

***Perf. 13 Syncopated***

**2015, Apr. 4 Litho. & Engr.**

**4259-4264** A1394 Set of 6 2.40 2.40

Slender West Lake A1395

Designs: No. 4265, $1.20, Lotus Bridge (3-1). No. 4266, $1.20, Twenty-four Bridge (3-2). $1.50, White Pagoda (3-3).

***Perf. 13¼x13 Syncopated***

**2015, Apr. 18 Litho. & Engr.**

**4265-4267** A1395 Set of 3 1.25 1.25

Exists in a sheet containing 3, No. 4265-4267. Value, $12.50.

Scenes from *Journey to the West*, by Wu Cheng'en — A1396

Designs: No. 4268, $1.20, Great sage equalling heaven (4-1). No. 4269, $1.20, Sun Wukong surrendered to Buddha (4-2). No. 4270, $1.50, Tang monk makes vows to go to the West (4-3). No. 4271, $1.50, Tang monk disciples Monkey King (4-4).

$6, Making havoc in heaven.

***Perf. 13¼ Syncopated***

**2015, May 3 Litho.**

**4268-4271** A1396 Set of 4 1.75 1.75

**Souvenir Sheet**

**Photo.**

***Perf. 13¼x13 Syncopated***

**4272** A1396 $6 multi 2.00 2.00

Vacation Activities A1397

Designs: 80f, Man taking photograph. $1.20, Family in automobile on bridge. $3, Backpacking.

***Die Cut Perf. 12½ Syncopated***

**2015, May 19 Photo.**

**Self-Adhesive**

**4273** A1397 80f multi .25 .25

**4274** A1397 $1.20 multi .40 .40

**4275** A1397 $3 multi 1.00 1.00

*Nos. 4273-4275 (3)* 1.65 1.65

World Metrology Day — A1398

***Perf. 13¼x12¾ Syncopated***

**2015, May 20 Litho.**

**4276** A1398 $1.20 multi .40 .40

Ships A1399

Designs: No. 4277, $1.20, Space tracking ship (4-1). No. 4278, $1.20, Liquified natural gas tanker (4-2). No. 4279, $1.20, Floating Production Storage and Offloading ship (4-3). $1.50, Guided missile destroyer (4-4).

***Perf. 13¼x12¾ Syncopated***

**2015, June 3 Litho.**

**4277-4280** A1399 Set of 4 1.75 1.75

World Environment Day — A1400

***Perf. 13¼x12¾ Syncopated***

**2015, June 5 Photo.**

**4281** A1400 $1.20 multi .40 .40

Exists in a sheet of 6.

Father's Day — A1401

**Litho. With Foil Application**

***Perf. 13¼x13 Syncopated***

**2015, June 13**

**4282** A1401 $1.20 multi .95 .40

Exists in a sheet of 8. Value, $12.50.

Rainbows, Hearts and Gift Box — A1402

**2015, June 18 Litho. *Perf. 13¼***

**4283** A1402 $1.20 multi + label .40 .40

See Stamps With Attached Labels note after No. 3197.

Mickey Mouse A1403

**2015, June 20 Litho. *Perf. 12***

**4284** A1403 $1.20 multi .40 .40

See Stamps With Attached Labels note after No. 3197.

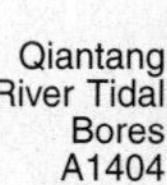

Qiantang River Tidal Bores A1404

No. 4285: a, Crossing bores (3-1). b, Spectators watching wave (3-2). c, Spectators watching reverse bore (3-3).

***Perf. 13¼x12¾ Syncopated***

**2015, July 1 Litho. & Engr.**

**4285** Horiz. strip of 3 1.40 1.40
*a.-b.* A1404 $1.20 Either single .40 .40
*c.* A1404 $1.50 multi .50 .50

Peace Dove A1405

**2015, July 3 Litho. *Perf. 13¼***

**4286** A1405 $1.20 multi + label .40 .40

See Stamps With Attached Labels note after No. 3197.

Qingyuan Mountain A1406

Designs: 80f, Sky Lake (3-1). No. 4288, $1.20, Rock carvings (3-2). No. 4289, $1.20, Statue of Lao Zi (3-3).

***Perf. 13¼x12¾ Syncopated***

**2015, July 18 Litho. & Engr.**

**4287-4289** A1406 Set of 3 1.10 1.10

Stylized Athletes A1407

**2015, July 20 Litho. *Perf. 13¼***

**4290** A1407 $1.20 multi + label .40 .40

See Stamps With Attached Labels note after No. 3197.

Happiness of the People — A1408

Buildings and: 80f, Fruit sellers, machine (4-1). No. 4292, $1.20, Bus, medical care (4-2). No. 4293, $1.20, Automobile, person in wheelchair, voters (4-3). No. 4294, $1.20, Ferris wheel, tai chi, woman pushing baby carriage (4-4).

***Perf. 13x12¾ Syncopated***

**2015, July 25 Photo.**

**4291-4294** A1408 Set of 4 1.40 1.40
*4294a* Souvenir sheet of 4, #4291-4294 1.40 1.40

Awarding of 2022 Winter Olympics to Beijing — A1409

***Perf. 13¼x13½ Syncopated***

**2015, July 31 Photo.**

**4295** A1409 $1.20 multi .40 .40

Lord Bao (999-1062), Government Official — A1410

Designs: No. 4296, $1.20, Lord Bao throwing inkstone into water (2-1). No. 4297, $1.20, Case of Chen Shimei (2-2).
$6, Lord Bao seated.

***Perf. 13¼ Syncopated***

**2015, Aug. 8 Photo.**

**4296-4297** A1410 Set of 2 .75 .75

**Souvenir Sheet**

***Perf. 13¼x13½ Syncopated***

**4298** A1410 $6 multi 1.90 1.90

No. 4298 contains one 60x67mm stamp.
A sheet of 6 exists comprised of 3 each, No. 4296-4297.

Mandarin Ducks — A1411

***Perf. 13x12¾ Syncopated***

**2015, Aug. 20 Litho. & Engr.**

**4299** A1411 $1.20 multi .40 .40

Exists in a sheet of 8.

Lunar Exploration by China — A1412

**2015, Aug. 20 Litho. *Perf. 13¼***

**4300** A1412 $1.20 multi + label .40 .40

See Stamps With Attached Labels note after No. 3197.

Miniature Sheet

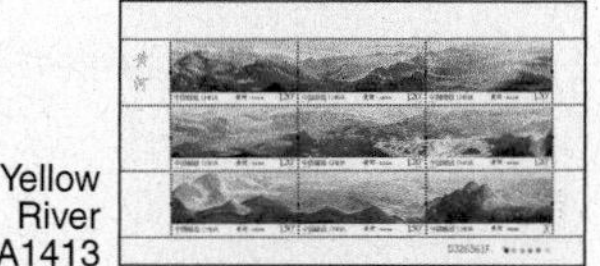

Yellow River A1413

No. 4301: a, $1.20, Beginning of river (9-1). b, $1.20, Nine Bays (9-2). c, $1.20, River bend in Hinterland (9-3). d, $1.20, Great bend (9-4). e, $1.20, River approaching Hukou Waterfalls (9-5). f, $1.20, Hukou Waterfalls and Sanjing (9-6). g, $1.50, Helou area (9-7). h, $1.50, Zhongshou Plain (9-8). i, $3, Mountains and buildings in foreground (9-9).

***Perf. 13¼x12¾ Syncopated***

**2015, Aug. 23 Photo.**

**4301** A1413 Sheet of 9, #a-i 4.25 4.25

Tibet Autonomous Region, 50th Anniv. A1414

No. 4302: a, Tibetans, symbols of Tibet, cranes and mountains (3-1). b, Tibetans, doves, buildings (3-2). c, Tibetan family, house, symbols of Tibet (3-3).

***Perf. 13¼x12¾ Syncopated***

**2015, Sept. 1 Photo.**

**4302** Horiz. strip of 3 1.25 1.25
*a.-c.* A1414 $1.20 Any single .40 .40

Victory in World War II, 70th Anniv. A1415

Soldiers and: No. 4303, 80f, September 18 Memorial Museum (13-1). No. 4304, 80f, Northeast China Revolutionary Martyrs Memorial Hall (13-2). No. 4305, $1.20, Museum of the War of Chinese People's Resistance Against Japanese Aggression (13-3). No. 4306, $1.20, Shanghai Songhu Anti-Japanese War Memorial Hall (13-4). No. 4307, $1.20, Museum of Victims in the Nanjing Massacre by Japanese Invaders (13-5). No. 4308, $1.20, Taierzhuang Campaign Memorial Hall (13-6). No. 4309, $1.20, Yan'an Revolutionary Memorial Hall (13-7). No. 4310, $1.20, Memorial Hall of Former Site of the Eighth Route Army Headquarters (13-8). No. 4311, $1.20, Hundred Regiments Offensive Memorial Hall (13-9). No. 4312, $1.20, Pingxingguan Victory Memorial Hall (13-10). No. 4313, $1.20, Museum of Tunnel Warfare at Ranzhuang (13-11). No. 4314, $1.20, New Fourth Army Memorial Hall (13-12). No. 4315, $1.20, Memorial Hall of Anti-Japanese War in Western Yunnan (13-13).
$6, Statue of soldier with sword, vert.

***Perf. 13¼x13 Syncopated***

**2015, Sept. 3 Photo.**

**4303-4315** A1415 Set of 13 4.75 4.75

**Souvenir Sheet**

**4316** A1415 $6 multi 1.90 1.90

No. 4316 contains one 50x60mm stamp.

Flying Fairies A1416

**2015, Sept. 9 Litho. *Perf. 13¼***

**4317** A1416 $1.20 multi .40 .40

See Stamps With Attached Labels note after No. 3197.

Birthday Cake A1417

**2015, Sept. 10 Litho. *Perf. 12***

**4318** A1417 $1.20 multi .40 .40

See Stamps With Attached Labels note after No. 3197.

Synthetic Crystalline Bovine Insulin, 50th Anniv. — A1418

***Perf. 13x12¾ Syncopated***

**2015, Sept. 17 Photo.**

**4319** A1418 $1.20 multi .40 .40

10th International Garden Expo, Wuhan — A1419

Designs: $1.20, Buildings (2-1). $1.50, Buildings, diff. (2-2).

***Perf. 13x12¾ Syncopated***

**2015, Sept. 25 Photo.**

**4320-4321** A1419 Set of 2 .85 .85

United Nations, 70th Anniv. — A1420

Designs: $1.20, United Nations emblem, stylized dove (2-1). $1.50, United Nations Headquarters, arrows (2-2).

***Perf. 13¼x13 Syncopated***

**2015, Sept. 26 Litho.**

**4322-4323** A1420 Set of 2 .85 .85

Xianjiang Production and Construction Corps, 60th Anniv. A1421

No. 4324: a, Building, wind generators, airplane, train, bridge (3-1). b, Agricultural products, city skyline, airplane, bridge over river, doves, farm community (3-2). c, Dancers (3-3).

***Perf. 13¼x13 Syncopated***

**2015, Oct. 1 Photo.**

**4324** Horiz. strip of 3 1.25 1.25
*a.-c.* A1421 $1.20 Any single .40 .40

Tianjin University, 120th Anniv. — A1422

***Perf. 13x12¾ Syncopated***

**2015, Oct. 2 Photo.**

**4325** A1422 $1.20 multi .40 .40

Good Fortune and Longevity — A1423

***Perf. 12¾ Syncopated***

**2015, Oct. 9 Litho.**

**4326** A1423 $1.20 multi .40 .40
*a.* Souvenir sheet of 2, #3708a (perf. 12¾), 4326 1.40 1.40

Palace Museum A1424

Designs: No. 4327, $1.20, Meridian Gate (4-1). No. 4328, $1.20, Hall of Supreme Harmony (4-2). No. 4329, $1.50, Corner Tower (4-3). No. 4330, $1.50, Gate of Heavenly Purity (4-4).

***Perf. 13¼x12 Syncopated***

**2015, Oct. 10 Litho.**

**Stamp + Label**

**4327-4330** A1424 Set of 4 1.75 1.75

Poets — A1425

Designs: No. 4331, $1.20, Du Fu (712-70) (4-1). No. 4332, $1.20, Su Dongpo (1037-1101) (4-2). No. 4333, $1.20, Bai Juyi (772-846) (4-3). No. 4334, $1.20, Cao Zhi (192-232) (4-4).

***Perf. 13¼ Syncopated***

**2015, Nov. 12 Litho. & Engr.**

**4331-4334** A1425 Set of 4 1.50 1.50

Delivery of First ARJ21 Airplane to Chengdu Airlines A1426

***Perf. 13¼x13 Syncopated***

**2015, Nov. 28** **Photo.**

**4335** A1426 $1.20 multi .40 .40

Chinese Values — A1427

Designs: No. 4336, $1.20, Bird's nest (importance of family) (3-1). No. 4337, $1.20, Ox (dreams and spirit, 47x28mm) (3-2). $1.50, Child daydreaming (unity of personal and national dreams) (3-3).

***Perf. 13 Syncopated, 13¼x13 Syncopated (#4337)***

**2015, Nov. 29** **Photo.**

**4336-4338** A1427 Set of 3 1.25 1.25

Exists in a sheet containing 3, No. 4336-4338. Value, $10.

New Year 2016 (Year of the Monkey) — A1428

Designs: No. 4339, $1.20, Monkey with peach (2-1). No. 4340, $1.20, Three monkeys (2-2).

***Perf. 13 Syncopated***

**2016, Jan. 5** **Litho. & Engr.**

**4339-4340** A1428 Set of 2 .75 .75
*4340a* Booklet pane of 10, 5 each #4339-4340 7.50 —
Complete booklet, #4340a 7.50
*4340b* Souvenir sheet of 4, 2 each #4339-4340 4.50 4.50

Children Celebrating Chinese New Year — A1429

***Perf. 13 Syncopated***

**2016, Jan. 10** **Litho.**

**4341** A1429 $1.20 multi .40 .40

Paintings by Liu Haisu (1896-1994) A1430

Designs: No. 4342, $1.20, Land So Rich in Beauty (3-1). No. 4343, $1.20, Ink Lotus (3-2). $1.50, Yellow Mountain Renzi Waterfall (3-3).

**Litho. (#4342), Photo. (#4343), Litho. & Engr. (#4344)**

**2016, Mar. 16** ***Perf. 13 Syncopated***

**4342-4344** A1430 Set of 3 1.25 1.25

China Post, 120th Anniv. A1431

Designs: No. 4345, $1.20, Mailbox, post office, statue of postman on horse, bicycle (4-1). No. 4346, $1.20, All-day automated kiosk, modern post office interior (4-2). No. 4347, $1.20, Airplane, parcel sorting conveyors, mail van (4-3). No. 4348, $1.20, Automated savings bank kiosks, credit cards (4-4).

***Perf. 13¼x13 Syncopated***

**2016, Mar. 20** **Litho.**

**4345-4348** A1431 Set of 4 1.50 1.50

Painting of Gaoyi Tu, by Sun Wei — A1432

No. 4349: a, Right side of painting (47x35mm) (3-1). b, Center of painting (62x35mm) (3-2). c, Left side of painting (47x35mm) (3-3).
$6, Entire painting.

***Perf. 13¼ Syncopated***

**2016, Apr. 2** **Photo.**

**4349** Horiz. strip of 3 1.25 1.25
*a.-b.* A1432 $1.20 Either single .40 .40
*c.* A1432 $1.50 multi .45 .45

**Souvenir Sheet**

***Perf. 13½x13¾ Syncopated***

**4350** A1432 $6 multi 1.90 1.90

No. 4350 contains one 134x35mm stamp.

Jiaotong University, 120th Anniv. — A1433

***Perf. 13½ Syncopated***

**2016, Apr. 8** **Photo.**

**4351** A1433 $1.20 multi .40 .40

Song Ci (1186-1249), Forensic Medicine Expert A1434

Song Ci, Scribe and Child A1435

***Perf. 13½ Syncopated***

**2016, Apr. 13** **Litho. & Engr.**

**4352** A1434 $1.20 multi .40 .40
**4353** A1435 $1.50 multi .45 .45

Nationwide Reading — A1436

***Perf. 13¼x13½ Syncopated***

**2016, Apr. 23** **Litho.**

**4354** A1436 $1.20 multi .40 .40

A1437

Tangshan International Horticulture Exposition A1438

***Perf. 13 Syncopated***

**2016, Apr. 29** **Litho.**

**4355** A1437 $1.20 multi .40 .40
**4356** A1438 $1.50 multi .45 .45

24 Solar Terms A1439

No. 4357: a, Beginning of summer (woman, butterflies and flowers) (6-1). b, Lesser fullness of grain (woman at loom) (6-2). c, Grain in beard (man in rice paddy) (6-3). d, Summer solstice (crouching children and flowers) (6-4). e, Lesser heat (man and goat near water wheel) (6-5). f, Greater heat (children looking at scroll under vines) (6-6).

***Perf. 13 Syncopated***

**2016, May 5** **Photo.**

**4357** A1439 $1.20 Block of 6, #a-f 2.25 2.25

Values are for stamps with surrounding selvage.

Scientists — A1440

Designs: No. 4358, $1.20, Ding Wenjiang (1887-1936), geologist (4-1). No. 4359, $1.20, Jin Shanbao (1895-1997), agronomist (4-2). No. 4360, $1.20, Ye Qisun (1898-1977), physicist (4-3). No. 4361, $1.20, Ye Duzheng (1916-2013), meteorologist (4-4).

***Perf. 13¼ Syncopated***

**2016, May 8** **Litho. & Engr.**

**4358-4361** A1440 Set of 4 1.50 1.50

Snow-covered Landscape A1441

Wanfeng Peaks Forest — A1442

Sand Lake — A1443

Xixi National Wetland Park — A1444

***Perf. 13x12¾ Syncopated***

**2016, May 12** **Photo.**

**4362** A1441 40f multi .25 .25
**4363** A1442 $1 multi .30 .30
**4364** A1443 $2 multi .60 .60
**4365** A1444 $4.20 multi 1.25 1.25
*Nos. 4362-4365 (4)* 2.40 2.40

Ancient Chinese Towns A1445

Designs: No. 4366, $1.20, Zhentong (6-1). No. 4367, $1.20, Qiliping (6-2). No. 4368, $1.20, Qingyan (6-3). No. 4369, $1.20, Zhujiajiao (6-4). No. 4370, $1.20, Sanhe (6-5). No. 4371, $1.20, Huangyao (6-6).

***Perf. 13¼x12¾ Syncopated***

**2016, May 19** **Litho. & Engr.**

**4366-4371** A1445 Set of 6 2.25 2.25

Cultural Heritage Day A1446

No. 4372 — Inscription on emblem: a, $1.20, China Intangible Cultural Heritage (2-1). b, $1.50, China Cultural Heritage (2-2).

***Perf. 13¼x13½ Syncopated***

**2016, June 11** **Litho.**

**4372** A1446 Horiz. pair, #a-b .85 .85

Opening of Shanghai Disney Resort A1447

Designs: $1.20, Mickey and Minnie Mouse (2-1). $1.50, Tinker Bell, Enchanted Storybook Castle (2-2).

***Perf. 13¼x13 Syncopated***

**2016, June 16** **Photo.**

**4373-4374** A1447 Set of 2 .85 .85
*4374a* Souvenir sheet of 2, #4373-4374 1.25 1.25

No. 4374a sold for $4.

A1448

*The Dream of Red Mansions,* Novel by Cao Xueqin — A1449

Scenes from novel: No. 4375, $1.20, Xifeng abuses her power (4-1). No. 4376, $1.20, Lingguan writes on the ground (4-2). No. 4377, $1.20, Qingwen, the maid, tearing the fan (4-3). $1.50, Baoyu receives a flogging (4-4).
$6, Rong-guo House makes itself ready for an important visitor.

***Perf. 13 Syncopated***

**2016, June 18** **Photo.**

**4375-4378** A1448 Set of 4 1.60 1.60

**Souvenir Sheet**

**4379** A1449 $6 multi 1.90 1.90

Compare with Nos. 4203-4207.

Longxing Temple, Zhengding A1450

Designs: $1.20, Moni Hall (2-1). $1.50, Dabei Pavilion (2-2).

***Perf. 13¼x13 Syncopated***

**2016, June 26** **Litho.**

**4380-4381** A1450 Set of 2 .85 .85

Pass the Flame
A1451

**2016, July 8 Litho. *Perf. 13¼***
**4382** A1451 $1.20 multi + label .40 .40

See Stamps With Attached Labels note after No. 3197.

Artifacts From Ruins of Yin
A1452

No. 4383: a, 80f, Oracle bone with inscription (3-1). b, $1.20, Bronze ware (3-2). c, $1.50, Jadeware (3-3)

***Perf. 11¾ Syncopated***
**2016, July 13 Litho. & Engr.**
**4383** A1452 Horiz. strip of 3, #a-c 1.10 1.10

Fruit — A1453

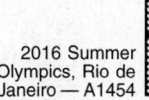

Designs: No. 4384, $1.20, Apricots (4-1). No. 4385, $1.20, Grapes (4-2). No. 4386, $1.50, Watermelons (4-3). No. 4387, $1.50, Litchis (4-4).

***Perf. 13¼x13 Syncopated***
**2016, July 23 Litho. & Embossed**
**4384-4387** A1453 Set of 4 1.75 1.75

Exists in a sheet containing 2 each of Nos. 4384-4387.

2016 Summer Olympics, Rio de Janeiro — A1454

Designs: $1.20, Women's volleyball (2-1). $1.50, Men's relay race (2-2).

***Perf. 13 Syncopated***
**2016, Aug. 5 Photo.**
**4388-4389** A1454 Set of 2 .80 .80

Red-billed Leiothrix — A1455

***Perf. 13x12¾ Syncopated***
**2016, Aug. 9 Litho. & Engr.**
**4390** A1455 $1.20 multi .40 .40

Miniature Sheet

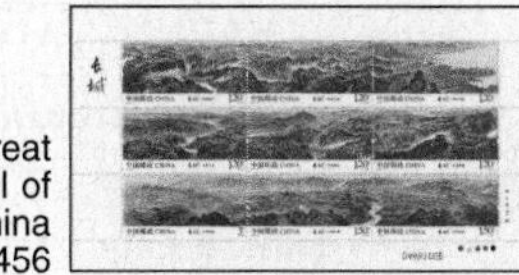

Great Wall of China
A1456

No. 4391: a, $1.20, Shanhai Pass and Old Dragon Head (9-1). b, $1.20, Hushan Great Wall (9-2). c, $1.20, Jinshanling, Jiumenkou and Huangyaguan (9-3). d, $1.20, Gubeikou, Huanghuacheng, Mutianyu, Badaling and Juyongguan (9-4). e, $1.20, Zijingguan, Pingxingguan, Niangziguan, Yanmenguan, Deshengkou and Bianjinlou (9-5). f, $1.20, Pianguan (9-6). g, $1.50, Zhenbeitai and Huamachi (9-7). h, $1.50, Sanguankou (9-8). i, $3, Yumenguan and Jiayuguan (9-9).

***Perf. 13¼x12¾ Syncopated***
**2016, Aug. 20 Litho. & Engr.**
**4391** A1456 Sheet of 9, #a-i 4.00 4.00

G20 Summit, Hangzhou
A1457

***Perf. 13¼x13 Syncopated***
**2016, Aug. 27 Photo.**
**4392** A1457 $1.20 multi .40 .40

**Silk-Faced Paper**
**4392A** A1457 $1.20 multi .40 .40

No. 4392 exists in a sheet of 8 on regular and silk papers.

Full Moon on Mid-Autumn Night — A1458

***Perf. 13¼ Syncopated***
**2016, Aug. 28 Litho.**
**4393** A1458 $1.20 multi .40 .40

Microperforations surround the Moon in the vignette.
Exists in a sheet of 6.

A1459

Xuan Zang, Character From *Journey to the West* — A1460

Xuan Zang: No. 4394, $1.20, Walking with items on back (2-1). No. 4395, $1.20, Translating Buddhist scriptures (2-2).

***Perf. 13¼ Syncopated***
**2016, Sept. 4 Photo.**
**4394-4395** A1459 Set of 2 .75 .75

**Souvenir Sheet**
***Perf. 13¼x13 Syncopated***
**4396** A1460 $6 multi 1.90 1.90

Foreign Trade — A1461

Buildings, ships and: No. 4397, $1.20, Doves, lectern and microphones (6-1). No. 4398, $1.20, Train, offshore platform (6-2). No. 4399, $1.20, Truck at airport (6-3). No. 4400, $1.20, Arrow charts, stacks of coins (6-4). No. 4401, $1.50, Sculpture, dancers and fireworks (6-5). No. 4402, $1.50, Crane and shipping containers (6-6).

***Perf. 13¼x13½ Syncopated***
**2016, Sept. 10 Photo.**
**4397-4402** A1461 Set of 6 2.40 2.40
*4402a* Souvenir sheet of 6, #4397-4402 3.50 3.50

No. 4402a sold for $11.

39th International Organization for Standardization General Assembly, Beijing — A1462

***Perf. 13¼x13½ Syncopated***
**2016, Sept. 11 Litho.**
**4403** A1462 $1.20 multi .75 .35

Sichuan University, 120th Anniv. — A1463

***Perf. 13 Syncopated***
**2016, Sept. 28 Litho.**
**4404** A1463 $1.20 multi .35 .35

Filial Piety — A1464

Designs: No. 4405, $1.20, Carrying rice for more than 1,000 li (4-1). No. 4406, $1.20, Personally checking his mother's prescriptions (4-2). No. 4407, $1.50, Wenji returning to Han (4-3). No. 4408, $1.50, Gu Kaizhi painting his mother (4-4).

***Perf. 13¼ Syncopated***
**2016, Oct. 7 Litho. & Engr.**
**4405-4408** A1464 Set of 4 1.60 1.60

New Year 2017 (Year of the Rooster) — A1465

***Perf. 12¾ Syncopated***
**2016, Oct. 9 Litho.**
**4409** A1465 $1.20 multi .35 .35
*a.* Souvenir sheet of 2, #3708a (perf. 12¾ syncopated), 4409 1.25 1.25

Poverty Alleviation Day — A1466

***Perf. 13¼ Syncopated***
**2016, Oct. 14 Litho.**
**4410** A1466 $1.20 multi .35 .35

Red Army
A1467

Designs: No. 4411, $1.20, Start of the Long March (6-1). No. 4412, $1.20, Zunyi Conference (6-2). No. 4413, $1.20, Army crossing the Chishui River four times (6-3). No. 4414, $1.20, Army crossing the Snow Mountain and grasslands (6-4). No. 4415, $1.50, Union of the three Red Armies (6-5). No. 4416, $1.50, Soldiers and flags (6-6).

***Perf. 13¼x13 Syncopated***
**2016, Oct. 22 Litho.**
**4411-4416** A1467 Set of 6 2.40 2.40

End of Long March, 80th anniv.

Lighthouses — A1468

No. 4417: a, Huayang Lighthouse (5-1). b, Chigua Lighthouse (5-2). c, Zhubi Lighthouse (5-3). d, Yongshu Lighthouse (5-4). e, Meiji Lighthouse (5-5).

***Perf. 13¼ Syncopated***
**2016, Oct. 28 Photo.**
**4417** Horiz. strip of 5 2.00 2.00
*a.-c.* A1468 $1.20 Any single .35 .35
*d.-e.* A1468 $1.50 Either single .45 .45

Sun Yat-sen (1866-1925), First President of Republic of China — A1469

Designs: No. 4418, $1.20, Museum of Dr. Sun Yat-sen (4-1). No. 4419, $1.20, Statue of Sun Yat-sen, vert. (4-2). No. 4420, $1.50, Sun Yat-sen Memorial Hall (4-3). No. 4421, $1.50, Sun Yat-sen Memorial Secondary School, vert. (4-4).

***Perf. 13 Syncopated, 13¼ Syncopated (vert. stamps)***
**2016, Nov. 12 Photo.**
**4418-4421** A1469 Set of 4 1.60 1.60

A1470

China 2016 International Stamp Exhibition, Nanning — A1471

Designs: No. 4422, $1.20, Zhuang brocade (2-1). No. 4423, $1.20, Silk ball and tassels (2-2).

***Perf. 13¼ Syncopated***
**2016, Dec. 2 Litho.**
**4422-4423** A1470 Set of 2 .70 .70

**Souvenir Sheet**
***Perf. 13¼x13½ Syncopated***
**4424** A1471 $6 multi 1.75 1.75

New Year 2017 (Year of the Rooster) — A1472

Designs: No. 4425, $1.20, Rooster running (2-1). No. 4426, $1.20, Rooster and chicks (2-2).

*Perf. 13 Syncopated*

**2017, Jan. 5 Litho. & Engr.**

**4425-4426** A1472 Set of 2 .70 .70
*4426a* Booklet pane of 10, 5 each #4425-4426 3.50 —
Complete booklet, #4426a 3.50
*4426b* Souvenir sheet of 4, 2 each #4425-4426 1.40 1.40

New Year's Greetings A1473

*Perf. 13 Syncopated*

**2017, Jan. 10 Litho.**

**4427** A1473 $1.20 multi .35 .35

Miniature Sheet

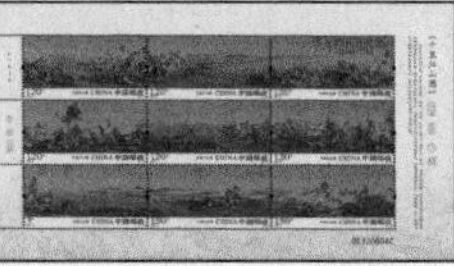

One Thousand Li of Rivers and Mountains, Painting by Wang Ximeng (1096-1119) — A1474

No. 4428 — Various parts of painting numbered: a, $1.20, (9-1). b, $1.20, (9-2). c, $1.20, (9-3). d, $1.20, (9-4). e, $1.20, (9-5). f, $1.20, (9-6). g, $1.50, (9-7). h, $1.50, (9-8). i, $3 (9-9).

*Perf. 13¼x13 Syncopated*

**2017, Feb. 25 Photo.**

**4428** A1474 Sheet of 9, #a-i 4.00 4.00

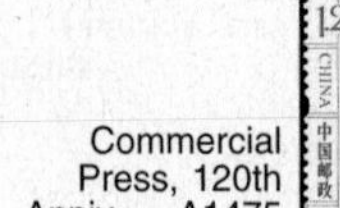

Commercial Press, 120th Anniv. — A1475

*Perf. 13 Syncopated*

**2017, Feb. 27 Litho.**

**4429** A1475 $1.20 multi .35 .35

Development of Beijing, Tianjin and Hebei Province — A1476

Designs: No. 4430, $1.20, City, train, airplane, ship, highways. (3-1). No. 4431, $1.20, Buildings, wind generators, cars at charging stations, cyclists on road (3-2). No. 4432, $1.50, Manufacturing, agriculture, trucks at warehouse, airplane (3-3).

*Perf. 13 Syncopated*

**2017, Mar. 9 Litho.**

**4430-4432** A1476 Set of 3 1.25 1.25
*4432a* Souvenir sheet of 3, #4430-4432 1.75 1.75

No. 4432a sold for $5.80.

Four Seasons — A1477

Designs: No. 4433, $1.20, Spring Swallows Flying Through Willows (4-1). No. 4434, $1.20, Paddling in a Summer Lotus Pond (4-2). No. 4435, $1.50, Rooster Crowing at Autumn Harvest (4-3). No. 4436, $1.50, Plum Blossoms in Winter (4-4).

*Perf. 13¼ Syncopated*

**2017, Mar. 20 Photo.**

**4433-4436** A1477 Set of 4 1.60 1.60

Scenes From *Journey to the West,* by Wu Cheng'en — A1478

Designs: No. 4437, $1.20, White dragon horse is reined in (4-1). No. 4438, $1.20, Zhu Bajie recruited by Sanzang (4-2). No. 4439, $1.50, Friar Sand joins the pilgrims (4-3). No. 4440, $1.50, Wuzhuang Temple Monkey (4-4).

*Perf. 13x13¼ Syncopated*

**2017, Mar. 30 Photo.**

**4437-4440** A1478 Set of 4 1.60 1.60

Jade Figurines of Hongshan Culture — A1479

No. 4441: a, Dragon (3-1). b, Phoenix (3-2). c, Man (3-3).

*Perf. 13¼ Syncopated*

**2017, Apr. 9 Litho. & Embossed**

**4441** A1479 $1.20 Horiz. strip of 3, #a-c 1.10 1.10

A1480

A1481

Inner Mongolian Autonomous Region, 70th Anniv. A1482

*Perf. 13 Syncopated*

**2017, May 1 Photo.**

**4442** Horiz. strip of 3 1.10 1.10
*a.* A1480 $1.20 multi .35 .35
*b.* A1481 $1.20 multi .35 .35
*c.* A1482 $1.20 multi .35 .35

Belt and Road Forum for International Cooperarion, Beijing A1483

*Perf. 13 Syncopated*

**2017, May 14 Photo.**

**4443** A1483 $1.20 multi .35 .35

No. 4443 exists in sheets of 8 on silk paper.

Dinosaurs — A1484

No. 4444: a, $1.20, Tsintaosaurus (6-1). b, $1.20, Yangchuanosaurus (6-2). c, $1.20, Huayangosaurus (6-3). d, $1.20, Sinosauropteryx (6-4). e, $1.50, Gigantoraptor (6-5). f, $3, Microraptor (6-6).
$6, Mamenchisaurus.

*Perf. 13 Syncopated*

**2017, May 19 Litho. & Engr.**

**4444** A1484 Sheet of 6, #a-f 2.75 .75

**Souvenir Sheet**

*Perf. 12½x12¾ Syncopated*

**4445** A1484 $6 multi 1.75 1.75

No. 4445 contains one 49x68mm stamp.

Zhejiang University, 120th Anniv. A1485

*Perf. 13 Syncopated*

**2017, May 21 Litho. & Embossed**

**4446** A1485 $1.20 multi .35 .35

Children at Play — A1486

Children: No. 4447, 80f, Rolling iron rings (6-1). No. 4448, 80f, Playing leapfrog (6-2). No. 4449, $1.20, Tossing beanbag (6-3). No. 4450, $1.20, On swings (6-4). No. 4451, $1.20, Kicking shuttlecock (6-5). No. 4452, $1.20, Playing hopscotch (6-6).

*Perf. 13¼x13½ Syncopated*

**2017, May 31 Litho. & Engr.**

**4447-4452** A1486 Set of 6 1.90 1.90

One Belt and One Road A1487

**2017, June 11 Litho. *Perf. 13¼***

**4453** A1487 $1.20 multi + label .35 .35

See Stamps With Attached Labels note after No. 3197.

International Day Against Drug Abuse and Illicit Trafficking A1488

*Perf. 13 Syncopated*

**2017, June 26 Photo.**

**4454** A1488 $1.20 multi .35 .35

Return of Hong Kong, 20th Anniv. — A1489

Buildings and: No. 4455, $1.10, Flags of Hong Kong and People's Republic of China, people waving flags, people in dragon and lion costumes (3-1). No. 4456, $1.20, Doves (3-2). No. 4457, $1.50, Airplane, train, bridge (3-3).

*Perf. 13¼x13 Syncopated*

**2017, July 1 Photo.**

**4455-4457** A1489 Set of 3 1.25 1.25

See Hong Kong No. 1855.

Emblem of Chinese Soccer Super League A1490

**2017, July 24 Litho. *Perf. 13¼***

**4458** A1490 $1.20 multi + label .35 .35

See Stamps With Attached Labels note after No. 3197.

Neolithic Age Jade Phoenix A1491

Western Zhou Dynasty Phoenix Wine Container A1492

Tang Dynasty Celadon Pot With Phoenix-head Cover A1493

Tang Dynasty Golden Phoenix A1494

Ming Dynasty Phoenix and Peonies Silk Tapestry A1495

Qing Dynasty Phoenix and Peonies Porcelain Jar A1496

*Perf. 13¼x13½ Syncopated*

**2017, July 29 Litho. & Embossed**

**4459** A1491 $1.20 multi .35 .35

**Litho. & Engr.**

**4460** A1492 $1.20 multi .35 .35

**Litho. & Embossed**

**4461** A1493 $1.20 multi .35 .35

**Litho. & Embossed With Foil Application**

**4462** A1494 $1.20 multi .35 .35

**Litho.**

**4463** A1495 $1.50 multi .45 .45
**4464** A1496 $1.50 multi .45 .45
*Nos. 4459-4464 (6)* 2.30 2.30

A1497

Chinese People's Liberation Army, 90th Anniv. — A1498

Designs: No. 4465, $1.20, Soldier, tanks and helicopters (6-1). No. 4466, $1.20, Sailor, ship and airplane (6-2). No. 4467, $1.20, Air Force pilot and airplane (6-3). No. 4468, $1.20, Rocket Force member, trucks and rocket launch (6-4). No. 4469, $1.20, Strategic Support Force member at computer, digital code (6-5). No. 4470, $1.20, Armed Police Force member, ship and helicopter (6-6).

$6, Soldiers, sailor and flag.

***Perf. 13¼x13½ Syncopated***

**2017, Aug. 1 Photo.**

**4465-4470** A1497 Set of 6 2.25 2.25

**Souvenir Sheet**

**4471** A1498 $6 multi 1.90 1.90

2017 BRICS (Brazil, Russia, India, China and South Africa) Summit, Xiamen — A1499

***Perf. 13¼x13½ Syncopated***

**2017, Aug. 19 Photo.**

**4472** A1499 $1.20 multi .40 .40

**Litho.**

***Perf. 13¼x13½ Syncopated***

**On Silk-Faced Paper**

**4472A** A1499 $1.20 multi .40 .40

No. 4472A exists in sheets of 8.

13th National Games, Tianjin and Luoyang — A1500

Mascots playing: No. 4473, $1.20, Volleyball and tennis (2-1). No. 4474, $1.20, Table tennis and gymnastics (2-2)

***Perf. 13¼ Syncopated***

**2017, Aug. 27 Litho.**

**4473-4474** A1500 Set of 2 .75 .75

*4474a* Souvenir sheet of 2, #4473-4474 .75 .75

Magpies — A1501

***Perf. 13x13¼ Syncopated***

**2017, Aug. 28 Litho. & Engr.**

**4475** A1501 $1.20 multi .40 .40

No. 4475 comes printed in sheets of 8.

Composers A1502

Designs: No. 4476, $1.20, Franz Schubert (1797-1828) (4-1). No. 4477, $1.20, Frédéric Chopin (1810-49) (4-2). No. 4478, $1.50, Franz Liszt (1811-86) (4-3). No. 4479, $1.50, Gustav Mahler (1860-1911) (4-4).

***Perf. 13 Syncopated***

**2017, Sept. 9 Litho. & Engr.**

**4476-4479** A1502 Set of 4 1.75 1.75

Scientific and Technological Innovations A1503

Designs: No. 4480, $1.20, Radio telescope (5-1). No. 4481, $1.20, Mozi Quantum Science Experiment Satellite (5-2). No. 4482, $1.20, Discovery 1 research ship (5-3). No. 4483, $1.50, Bohai Rim agricultural project (5-4). No. 4484, $1.50, Sunway TaihuLight supercomputer (5-5).

***Perf. 13x12¾ Syncopated***

**2017, Sept. 17 Litho.**

**4480-4484** A1503 Set of 5 2.00 2.00

Zhang Qian (d. 113 B.C.), Diplomat and Developer of Silk Road Trade Routes — A1504

Designs: No. 4485, $1.20, Zhang Qian facing left (2-1). No. 4486, $1.20, Zhang Qian giving rolled-up scroll to another man (2-2).

$6, Zhang Qian holding open scroll.

***Perf. 13x13¼ Syncopated***

**2017, Sept. 20 Photo.**

**4485-4486** A1504 Set of 2 .75 .75

**Souvenir Sheet**

***Perf. 13x12¾ Syncopated***

**4487** A1504 $6 silver & multi 1.90 1.90

No. 4487 contains one 60x90mm stamp.

New Year 2018 (Year of the Dog) — A1505

***Perf. 12½ Syncopated***

**2017, Oct. 9 Litho.**

**4488** A1505 $1.20 gold & multi .40 .40

*a.* Souvenir sheet of 2, #3708a, perf. 12½ syncopated, 4488 1.40 1.40

Cantonese Opera — A1506

Designs: No. 4489, $1.20, Fragrant Mountain Birthday Celebration (3-1). No. 4490, $1.20, Six States Installation of Minister (3-2). $1.50, The Imperial Emperor of Heaven Holds Court (3-3).

***Perf. 13¼x13½ Syncopated***

**2017, Oct. 15 Photo.**

**4489-4491** A1506 Set of 3 1.25 1.25

A1507

Designs: No. 4492, $1.20, Monument, building, boat and bridge (2-1). No. 4493, $1.20, Wind turbines, solar panels, airplane, road, rocket, ship and high-speed train (2-2).

$6, Hammer and sickle, Gate of Heavenly Peace.

***Perf. 13x12¾ Syncopated***

**2017, Oct. 18 Photo.**

**4492-4493** A1507 Set of 2 .75 .75

**Souvenir Sheet**

***Perf.***

**4494** A1507 $6 gold & multi 1.90 1.90

19th National Congress of the Communist Party of People's Republic of China.

No. 4494 contains one 56mm diameter stamp.

Journalist's Day — A1508

***Perf. 13¼x13½ Syncopated***

**2017, Nov. 8 Photo.**

**4495** A1508 $1.20 sil & multi .40 .40

Statues Depicting Lions — A1509

Designs: No. 4496, $1.20, Iron Lion of Cangzhou (2-1). No. 4497, $1.20, Stone Lion, Temple Phnom Bakheng, vert. (2-2).

***Perf. 13x13¼ Syncopated, 13¼x13½ Syncopated***

**2017, Nov. 16 Litho. & Engr.**

**4496-4497** A1509 Set of 2 .75 .75

See Cambodia Nos. 2458-2459.

Development of High-Speed Rail Transportation — A1510

Designs: No. 4498, $1.20, Construction of elevated high-speed rail line, high-speed train and tunnels (4-1). No. 4499, $1.20, High-speed trains at servicing depot (4-2). No. 4500, $1.20, Completed high-speed rail bridges (4-3). No. 4501, $1.20, High-speed railway stations (4-4).

$6, High-speed trains and city skylines.

***Perf. 13¼x13 Syncopated***

**2017, Nov. 25 Photo.**

**4498-4501** A1510 Set of 4 1.50 1.50

**Souvenir Sheet**

***Perf. 12¾ Syncopated***

**4502** A1510 $6 gold & multi 1.90 1.90

No. 4502 contains one 78x46mm stamp.

Disney Princesses and Castle — A1511

**2017, Dec. 2 Litho. *Perf. 13¼***

**4503** A1511 $1.20 multi + label .40 .40

See Stamps with Attached Labels note after No. 3197.

Xiongan New Area A1512

No. 4504: a, Sculpture, gate, front page of *Renmin Ribao* newspaper (2-1). b, Gate of Heavenly Peace, buildings, lion statue (2-2).

***Perf. 13x12¾ Syncopated***

**2017, Dec. 22 Litho.**

**4504** A1512 $1.20 Horiz. pair, #a-b .75 .75

Emblem of 2022 Winter Olympics, Beijing A1513

Emblem of 2022 Winter Paralympics, Beijing A1514

***Perf. 13¼x13½ Syncopated***

**2017, Dec. 31 Photo.**

**4505** A1513 $1.20 multi .40 .40

**4506** A1514 $1.20 multi .40 .40

New Year 2018 (Year of the Dog) — A1515

Designs: No. 4507, $1.20, Dog facing right (2-1). No. 4508, $1.20, Dog and puppy (2-2).

***Perf. 13 Syncopated***

**2018, Jan. 5 Litho. & Engr.**

**4507-4508** A1515 Set of 2 .80 .80

*a.* Booklet pane of 10, 5 each #4507-4508 4.00 —

Complete booklet, #4508a 4.00

*b.* Souvenir sheet of 4, 2 each #4507-4508 1.60 1.60

New Year's Greetings A1516

***Perf. 13x12¾ Syncopated***

**2018, Jan. 10 Photo.**

**4509** A1516 $1.20 multi .40 .40

Paper Cuttings — A1517

Designs: No. 4510, $1.20, Luhua Dang, character from Beijing Opera (4-1). No. 4511, $1.20, Shepherd and sheep (4-2). No. 4512, $1.20, Jiangwa leading Meixiang on horse (4-3). No. 4513, $1.20, The son's farewell to his mother (4-4).

***Perf. 13¼ Syncopated***

**2018, Jan. 24 Litho.**

**4510-4513** A1517 Set of 4 1.60 1.60

Lantern Festival — A1518

Designs: No. 4514, $1.20, Family eating rice dumpling balls (3-1). No. 4515, $1.20, People looking at large lanterns (3-2). $1.50, Dragon and lion dance (3-3).

***Perf. 13¼x13½ Syncopated***

**2018, Mar. 2 Photo.**

**4514-4516** A1518 Set of 3 1.25 1.25

Exists in a sheet containing 3 sets, No. 4514-4516.

13th National People's Congress A1519

***Perf. 13x12¾ Syncopated***

**2018, Mar. 5 Litho.**

**4517** A1519 $1.20 multi .40 .40

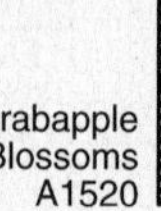

Crabapple Blossoms A1520

Designs: No. 4518, $1.20, Malus prunifolia (4-1). No. 4519, $1.20, Malus micromalus (4-2). No. 4520, $1.20, Malus honanensis (4-3). No. 4521, $1.20, Malus sieboldii (4-4).

***Perf. 13x12¾ Syncopated***

**2018, Mar. 25 Litho. & Engr.**

**4518-4521** A1520 Set of 4 1.60 1.60

Central Academy of Fine Arts, Cent. A1521

***Perf. 13x12¾ Syncopated***

**2018, Apr. 1 Litho. & Engr.**

**4522** A1521 $1.20 gold & multi .40 .40

A1522

*The Dream of Red Mansions,* Novel by Cao Xueqin — A1523

Designs: No. 4523, $1.20, Miao Yu makes tea (4-1). No. 4524, $1.20, Xi Chun painting (4-2). No. 4525, $1.20, Pinger and her attendants at dressing table (4-3). $1.50, Baoyu visits Bamboo Lodge at night (4-4).

$6, Tanchun and the Crab Flower Club.

***Perf. 13 Syncopated***

**2018, Apr. 22 Litho.**

**4523-4526** A1522 Set of 4 1.60 1.60

**Souvenir Sheet**

***Perf. 12¾ Syncopated***

**4527** A1523 $6 multi 1.90 1.90

Karl Marx (1818-83), Political Theorist — A1524

Designs: No. 4528, $1.20, Statue of Marx (2-1). No. 4529, $1.20, Statues of Marx and Friedrich Engels, book covers (2-2).

***Perf. 13¼ Syncopated***

**2018, May 5 Photo.**

**4528-4529** A1524 Set of 2 .75 .75

I Looked Up to Them and They Seemed to Become More High, by Feng Zikai (1898-1975) A1525

Autumn Mountain Stream, by Guan Shanyue (1912-2000) A1526

Two Eagles, by Li Kuchan (1898-1983) — A1527

***Perf. 13¼ Syncopated***

**2018, May 11 Litho. & Engr.**

**4530** A1525 $1.20 multi .40 .40

**Litho.**

**4531** A1526 $1.20 multi .40 .40

**Photo.**

**4532** A1527 $1.50 multi .45 .45

*Nos. 4530-4532 (3)* 1.25 1.25

Buffalo A1528

**2018, May 19 Litho. *Perf. 13¼***

**4533** A1528 $1.20 multi + label .40 .40

See Stamps With Attached Labels note after No. 3197.

Relics of the Silk Road — A1529

Designs: No. 4534, $1.20, Gilt bronze figurine of silkworm (4-1). No. 4535, $1.20, Gold horse figurine (4-2). No. 4536, $1.20, Agate wine cup with head of animal (4-3). No. 4537, $1.20, Gold-painted blue glass plate (4-4).

***Perf. 13 Syncopated***

**2018, May 19 Litho. & Embossed**

**4534-4537** A1529 Set of 4 1.50 1.50

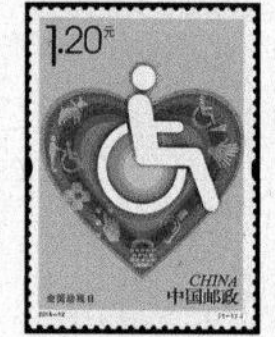

National Day of the Disabled — A1530

***Perf. 13¼x13½ Syncopated***

**2018, May 20 Litho.**

**4538** A1530 $1.20 multi .40 .40

Scientists and Scientific Works — A1531

Designs: No. 4539, $1.20, Li Shizhen (1518-93), compiler of medical knowledge (4-1). No. 4540, $1.20, *Compendium of Materia Medica,* by Li Shizhen (4-2). No. 4541, $1.20, Song Yingxing (1587-1666), scientist and encyclopedia writer (4-3). No. 4542, $1.20, *Exploitation of the Works of Nature,* by Song Yingxing (4-4).

***Perf. 13¼x13½ Syncopated***

**2018, May 26 Litho.**

**4539-4542** A1531 Set of 4 1.50 1.50

Sites in Kashgar Prefecture A1532

Designs: 80f, Ancient town of Kashgar (4-1). No. 4544, $1.20, Ruins of Stone City, Tashkurgan (4-2). No. 4545, $1.20, Zepu Jinhu Yang National Forest Park (4-3). No. 4546, $1.20, Khunjerab Pass border gate (4-4).

***Perf. 13 Syncopated***

**2018, June 9 Photo.**

**4543-4546** A1532 Set of 4 1.40 1.40

Shanghai Cooperation Organization Summit, Qingdao A1533

***Perf. 13 Syncopated***

**2018, June 9 Litho.**

**4547** A1533 $1.20 multi .40 .40

**On Silk-Faced Paper**

***Perf. 13¼x13 Syncopated***

**4547A** A1533 $1.20 multi .40 .40

A1534

Qu Yuan (c. 340-278 B.C.), Poet A1535

Qu Yuan: No. 4548, $1.20, Seated behind table (The Lament) (2-1). No. 4549, $1.20, Pointing to sky (Asking the Heaven) (2-2).

$6, Qu Yuan holding scroll.

***Perf. 13x13¼ Syncopated***

**2018, June 18 Photo.**

**4548-4549** A1534 Set of 2 .75 .75

**Souvenir Sheet**

***Perf. 13 Syncopated***

**4550** A1535 $6 multi 1.90 1.90

Uprightness and Incorruptibility A1536

Designs: No. 4551, $1.20, Han treasuring incorruptibility (4-1). No. 4552, $1.20, Yang Xu hung fish to refuse gifts (4-2). No. 4553, $1.20, Yu Qian's sleeves swaying in the breeze (4-3). No. 4554, $1.20, Yu Chenglong making public declaration to refuse gifts (4-4).

***Perf. 13¼ Syncopated***

**2018, June 24 Litho.**

**4551-4554** A1536 Set of 4 1.50 1.50

Buildings and Doves A1537

**2018, July 1 Litho. *Perf. 13¼***

**4555** A1537 $1.20 multi + label .35 .35

See Stamps With Attached Labels note after No. 3197.

Fruits — A1538

Designs: No. 4556, $1.20, Pineapples (4-1). No. 4557, $1.20, Cherries (4-2). No. 4558, $1.20, Mangos (4-3). $1.50, Oranges (4-4).

***Perf. 13¼x13 Syncopated***

**2018, July 14 Litho.**

**4556-4559** A1538 Set of 4 1.60 1.60

National Heroes — A1539

Designs: No. 4560, $1.20, Guan Tianpei (1781-1841), admiral (5-1). No. 4561, $1.20, Lin Zexu (1785-1850), viceroy (5-2). No. 4562, $1.20, Feng Zicai (1818-1903), general (5-3). No. 4563, $1.20, Liu Yongfu (1837-1917), President of Republic of Formosa (5-4). No. 4564, $1.20, Deng Shichang (1849-94), naval officer (5-5).

***Perf. 13¼x13½ Syncopated***

**2018, July 29 Photo.**

**4560-4564** A1539 Set of 5 1.75 1.75

Landscapes of the Four Seasons, by Liu Songnian (c. 1155-1224) A1540

Various sections of the painting numbered: No. 4565, 80f, (4-1). No. 4566, 80f, (4-2). No. 4567, $1.20, (4-3). No. 4568, $1.20, (4-4).

***Perf. 13¼x13 Syncopated***

**2018, Aug. 4 Litho. & Engr.**

**4565-4568** A1540 Set of 4 1.25 1.25

*4568a* Souvenir sheet of 4, #4565-4568 1.25 1.25

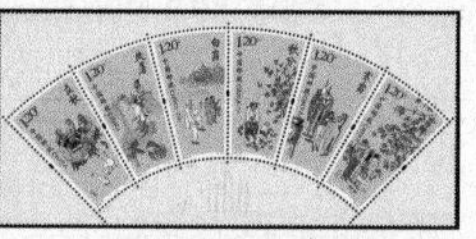

24 Solar Terms A1541

No. 4569: a, Autumn begins (family at table) (6-1). b, Stopping the heat (people winnowing rice) (6-2). c, White dews (people in tai chi poses) (6-3). d, Autumn equinox (man and boy picking fruit) (6-4). e, Cold dews (woman and tailor) (6-5). f, Hoarfrost falls (man with camera, two women in coats near tree with changing leaves) (6-6).

***Perf. 13 Syncopated***

**2018, Aug. 7 Photo.**

**4569** A1541 $1.20 Block of 6, #a-f 2.10 2.10

Values are for stamps with surrounding selvage.

Geese in Flight — A1542

*Perf. 13 Syncopated*

**2018, Aug. 17** **Litho. & Engr.**

**4570** A1542 $1.20 multi .35 .35

Yangtze River Economic Belt — A1543

Designs: No. 4571, $1.20, Ecology protection plan (6-1). No. 4572, $1.20, Multimoda transport corridor (6-2). No. 4573, $1.20, Transformation and upgrading of industry (6-3). No. 4574, $1.20, New urbanization (6-4). No. 4575, $1.50, Airplane, train and ships at port (6-5). No. 4576, $1.50, Regional coordinated development (6-6).

*Perf. 13¼x13 Syncopated*

**2018, Aug. 26** **Litho.**

**4571-4576** A1543 Set of 6 2.25 2.25

*4576a* Souvenir sheet of 6, #4571-4576 2.25 2.25

Miniature Sheet

Book of Songs A1544

No. 4577: a, 80f, The Songs of Zhou and the South (woman, birds and flowers) (6-1). b, $1.20, The Songs of Qin (man in robe) (6-2). c, $1.20, The Songs of Qin (two men and wheel) (6-3). d, $1.20, Minor Songs of the Kingdom (four men) (6-4). e, $1.50, Minor Songs of the Kingdom (three cranes and six fish) (6-5). f, $3, Songs of Lu (horses) (6-6).

*Perf. 13 Syncopated*

**2018, Sept. 8** **Litho. & Engr.**

**4577** A1544 Sheet of 6, #a-f 2.60 2.60

Round Moon Over Mid-Autumn Festival — A1545

*Perf. 13¼x13 Syncopated*

**2018, Sept. 15** **Litho.**

**4578** A1545 $1.20 multi .35 .35

Perforations encircle most of the moon.

Windmills, Solar Panels, Factory, Airships, Computer and Head A1546

Houses and People of Ningxia Hui Autonomous Region A1547

City — A1548

Designs: a, Innovation driven. b, Poverty alleviation. c, Establishing autonomous region by ecological way.

*Perf. 13 Syncopated*

**2018, Sept. 19** **Litho.**

| | | | |
|---|---|---|---|
| **4579** | Horiz. strip of 3 | 1.10 | 1.10 |
| ***a.*** | A1546 $1.20 multi | .35 | .35 |
| ***b.*** | A1547 $1.20 multi | .35 | .35 |
| ***c.*** | A1548 $1.20 multi | .35 | .35 |

Ningxia Hui Autonomous Region, 60th anniv.

Farmers' Harvest Festival A1549

*Perf. 13 Syncopated*

**2018, Sept. 23** **Photo.**

**4580** A1549 $1.20 multi .35 .35

International Day of Older Persons — A1550

*Perf. 13¼ Syncopated*

**2018, Oct. 1** **Litho.**

**4581** A1550 $1.20 gold & multi .35 .35

Happiness and Longevity — A1551

*Perf. 12½ Syncopated*

**2018, Oct. 9** **Litho.**

**4582** A1551 $1.20 gold & multi .35 .35

***a.*** Souvenir sheet of 2, #3708a (perf. 12½ syncopated), 4582 1.25 1.25

Dancers and Buildings A1552

Ships, Trains and City Skyline A1553

Waterfront Houses Near Mountains A1554

Designs: a, Harmonious homeland. b, Openning-up door. c, Eco-friendly land.

*Perf. 13 Syncopated*

**2018, Oct. 18** **Photo.**

| | | | |
|---|---|---|---|
| **4583** | Horiz. strip of 3 | 1.10 | 1.10 |
| ***a.*** | A1552 $1.20 multi | .35 | .35 |
| ***b.*** | A1553 $1.20 multi | .35 | .35 |
| ***c.*** | A1554 $1.20 multi | .35 | .35 |

Guangxi Zhuang Autonomous Region, 60th anniv.

Qingzhou Navigational Channel Bridge A1555

East Artificial Island A1556

Tunnel — A1557

*Perf. 13¼ Syncopated*

**2018, Oct. 30** **Photo.**

| | | | |
|---|---|---|---|
| **4584** | A1555 $1.20 multi | .35 | .35 |
| **4585** | A1556 $1.20 multi | .35 | .35 |
| **4586** | A1557 $1.20 multi | .35 | .35 |
| | *Nos. 4584-4586 (3)* | 1.05 | 1.05 |

Opening of Hong Kong-Zhuhai-Macao Bridge. See Hong Kong No. 1970.

China International Import Expo Emblem A1558

China International Import Expo Mascot A1559

*Perf. 13¼ Syncopated*

**2018, Nov. 5** **Photo.**

| | | | |
|---|---|---|---|
| **4587** | A1558 $1.20 multi | .35 | .35 |
| **4588** | A1559 $1.20 multi | .35 | .35 |

2022 Winter Olympics, Beijing — A1560

Designs: No. 4589, $1.20, Cross-country skiing (4-1). No. 4590, $1.20, Alpine skiing (4-2). No. 4591, $1.20, Biathlon (4-3). No. 4592, $1.20, Freestyle skiing (4-4).

*Perf. 13 Syncopated*

**2018, Nov. 16** **Photo.**

**4589-4592** A1560 Set of 4 1.40 1.40

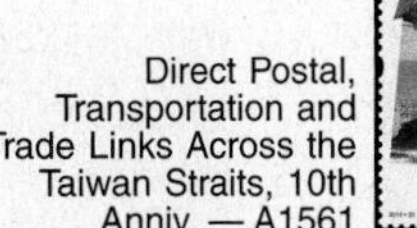
Direct Postal, Transportation and Trade Links Across the Taiwan Straits, 10th Anniv. — A1561

*Perf. 13¼ Syncopated*

**2018, Dec. 15** **Photo.**

**4593** A1561 $1.20 multi .35 .35

A1562

Governmental Reform, 40th Anniv. — A1563

Designs: No. 4594, $1.20, Leaders at table, statue of bull, tractor in field (2-1). No. 4595, $1.20, Dancers, buildings, airplane and train (2-2).

$6, People raising hands in Tiananmen Square.

*Perf. 13x12¾ Syncopated*

**2018, Dec. 18** **Photo.**

**4594-4595** A1562 Set of 2 .70 .70

**Souvenir Sheet**

*Perf. 13¼ Syncopated*

**4596** A1563 $6 multi 1.75 1.75

New Year 2019 (Year of the Pig) — A1564

Designs: No. 4597, $1.20, Pig (2-1). No. 4598, $1.20, Two pigs and three piglets (2-2).

*Perf. 13 Syncopated*

**2019, Jan. 5** **Litho. & Engr.**

| | | | |
|---|---|---|---|
| **4597-4598** | A1564 Set of 2 | .70 | .70 |
| *4597a* | Souvenir sheet of 6 | 3.25 | 3.25 |
| *4598a* | Booklet pane of 10, 5 each #4597-4598 | 3.50 | — |
| | Complete booklet, #4598a | 3.50 | |
| *4598b* | Souvenir sheet of 4, 2 each #4597-4598 | 1.40 | 1.40 |
| *4598c* | Souvenir sheet of 6 #4598 | 3.25 | 3.25 |

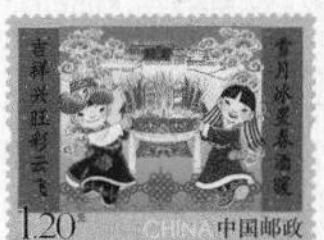
New Year Greetings A1565

*Perf. 13 Syncopated*

**2019, Jan. 10** **Litho.**

**4599** A1565 $1.20 multi .35 .35

***a.*** Souvenir sheet of 8 3.00 3.00

Knot A1566

**2019, Jan. 26** **Litho.** ***Perf. 13¼***

**4600** A1566 $1.20 multi + label .35 .35

See Stamps With Attached Labels note after No. 3197.

A1567

Designs: No. 4601, $1.20, Purple Sand tea pot and cup (2-1). No. 4602, $1.20, Silver tea pot (2-2).

*Perf. 13 Syncopated*

**2019, Feb. 8** **Photo.**

**4601-4602** A1567 Set of 2 .75 .75

Diplomatic relations between People's Republic of China and Portugal, 40th anniv. See Portugal Nos. 4091-4092.

Arbor Day — A1568

***Perf. 13¼ Syncopated***

**2019, Mar. 12 Photo.**

**4603** A1568 $1.20 multi .35 .35

Marathon Runners — A1569

Various marathon runners with denomination at: No. 4604, $1.20, UL (2-1). No. 4605, $1.20, UR (2-2).

***Perf. 13¼ Syncopated***

**2019, Mar. 31 Photo.**

**4604-4605** A1569 Set of 2 .70 .70

A1570

*Journey to the West,* Novel by Wu Cheng'en (c. 1500-c.1580) — A1571

Designs: No. 4606, $1.20, Monkey subdues the white-boned demon (4-1). No. 4607, $1.20, Battles with the Red Boy (4-2). No. 4608, $1.50, In the Kingdom of Chechi, the Monkey King shows his powers (4-3). No. 4609, $1.50, Escape from the Kingdom of Women (4-4).

$6, Immortals subdue the water buffalo.

***Perf. 13¼x13 Syncopated***

**2019, Apr. 20 Photo.**

**4606-4609** A1570 Set of 4 1.60 1.60

**Souvenir Sheet**

***Perf. 13x13¼ Syncopated***

**4610** A1571 $6 multi 1.90 1.90

No. 4606-4609 exists in a sheet of 8 with 2 sets of each.

2019 International Horiticultural Exhibition, Beijing A1572

Designs: 80f, Emblem, roses, Great Wall of China (2-1). $1.20, Mascots and exhibition buildings (2-2).

***Perf. 13¼x13 Syncopated***

**2019, Apr. 29 Photo.**

**4611-4612** A1572 Set of 2 .60 .60

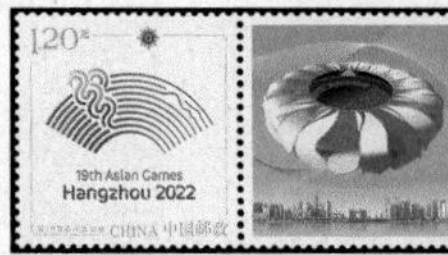

May Fourth Movement, Cent. — A1573

"100" and: No. 4613, $1.20, Sculptures, May 4th movement spirit (2-1). No. 4614, $1.20, Doves and people with raised hands, new era of endeavor (2-2).

***Perf. 11¾x12¼ Syncopated***

**2019, May 4 Litho.**

**4613-4614** A1573 Set of 2 .70 .70

2022 Asian Games, Hangzhou — A1574

**2019, May 11 Litho. *Perf. 13¼***

**4615** A1574 $1.20 multi + label .35 .35

See Stamps With Attached Labels note after No. 3197.

Peonies — A1575

Designs: No. 4616, $1.20, Paeonia lactiflora (4-1). No. 4617, $1.20, Paeonia veitchii (4-2). No. 4618, $1.20, Paeonia obovata (4-3). No. 4619, $1.20, Paeonia mairei (4-4).

***Perf. 13 Syncopated***

**2019, May 11 Litho. & Engr.**

**4616-4619** A1575 Set of 4 1.40 1.40

Exists in sheet of 8 with 2 sets, No. 4616-4619.

Ancient Cities A1576

Designs: No. 4620, 80f, Yangliuqing (4-1). No. 4621, 80f, Guangfu (4-2). No. 4622, $1.20, Nianbadu (4-3). No. 4623, $1.20, Furong (4-4).

***Perf. 13¼x13 Syncopated***

**2019, May 19 Litho. & Engr.**

**4620-4623** A1576 Set of 4 1.25 1.25

Exists in sheet of 8 with 2 sets, No. 4620-4623.

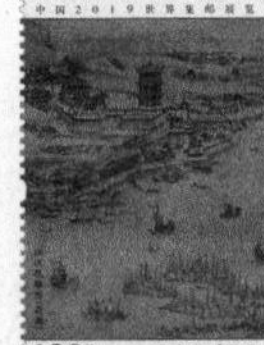

Children at Play — A1577

Children: No. 4624, 80f, Completing jigsaw puzzle (4-1). No. 4625, 80f, Building sand castle (4-2). No. 4626, $1.20, Roller skating (4-3). No. 4627, $1.20, Playing with building blocks (4-4).

***Perf. 13¼ Syncopated***

**2019, June 1 Photo.**

**4624-4627** A1577 Set of 4 1.25 1.25

*4627a* Souvenir sheet of 8, 2 each #4624-4627 3.00 3.00

A1578

China 2019 World Stamp Exhibition, Wuhan — A1579

Various details of *The Three Towns of Wuhan*: No. 4628, $1.20, (2-1). No. 4629, $1.20 (2-2).

$6, Bronze Zun-pan from tomb of Zenghouyi.

***Perf. 13¼ Syncopated***

**2019, June 11 Litho.**

**4628-4629** A1578 Set of 2 .70 .70

*4629a* Souvenir sheet of 8, 4 each #4628-4629 3.75 3.75

**Souvenir Sheet**

**Litho. & Engr.**

***Perf.***

**4630** A1579 $6 multi 1.75 1.75

Yiwu Train A1580

Madrid Train A1581

***Perf. 13½ Syncopated***

**2019, June 15 Litho. & Engr.**

**4631** Horiz. pair .70 .70

*a.* A1580 $1.20 multi .35 .35

*b.* A1581 $1.20 multi .35 .35

Chine-Europe Railway Express. See Spain No. 4364.

Seventh World Military Games, Wuhan A1582

Designs: No. 4632, 80f, Javelin (4-1). No. 4633, 80f, Obstacle course (4-2). No. 4634, $1.20, Naval pentathlon (4-3). No. 4625, $1.20, Four-person formation skydiving (4-4).

***Perf. 13¼x13 Syncopated***

**2019, July 10 Photo.**

**4632-4635** A1582 Set of 4 1.25 1.25

*4635a* Souvenir sheet of 8, 2 each #4632-4635 3.00 3.00

Poyang Lake A1583

Designs: 80f, Stone Bell Mountain (3-1). No. 4637, $1.20, Shoe-shape Island (3-2). No. 4638, $1.20, Birds over Poyang Lake National Wetland Park (3-3).

***Perf. 13½x13 Syncopated***

**2019, July 20 Photo.**

**4636-4638** A1583 Set of 3 .95 .95

Five Sacred Mountains — A1584

Designs: No. 4639, $1.20, Sunrise on Mount Tai (5-1). No. 4640, $1.20, Mount Hua in Late Autumn (5-2). No. 4641, $1.20, Mount Zhurong in Rain (5-3). No. 4642, $1.20, Mount Heng in Snow (5-4). No. 4643, $1.20, Mounts Taishi and Shaoshi (5-5).

***Perf. 13 Syncopated***

**2019, Aug. 3 Litho. & Engr.**

**4639-4643** A1584 Set of 5 1.75 1.75

*4643a* Souvenir sheet of 5, #4639-4643 1.75 1.75

Ancient Mythology — A1585

Designs: No. 4644, 80f, Suiren producing fire by drilling in wood (6-1). No. 4645, 80f, Fuxi drawing trigrams (6-2). No. 4646, $1.20, Shennong tasting herbs (6-3). No. 4647, $1.20, Leizu and the origins of Chinese silk (6-4). No. 4648, $1.20, Cangjie creating Chinese characters (6-5). No. 4649, $1.20, Yu the Great taming waters (6-6).

**2019, Aug. 6 Photo. *Perf. 13¼***

**4644-4649** A1585 Set of 6 1.90 1.90

Highways to Tibet A1586

Designs: 80f, Sichuan-Tibet Highway (2-1). $1.20, Qinghai-Tibet Highway (2-2).

***Perf. 13¼x13 Syncopated***

**2019, Aug. 10 Litho. & Embossed**

**4650-4651** A1586 Set of 2 .55 .55

A1587

Lu Ban (c. 507-444 B.C.), God of Carpenters and Masons — A1588

Lu Ban holding: No. 4652, $1.20, Model of building (2-1). No. 4653, $1.20, Hammer and chisel (2-2).

$6, Lu Ban holding invention.

***Perf. 13x13¼ Syncopated***

**2019, Aug. 24 Photo.**

**4652-4653** A1587 Set of 2 .70 .70

*4653a* Souvenir sheet of 6, 3 each #4652-4653 2.75 2.75

**Souvenir Sheet**

***Perf. 13 Syncopated***

**4654** A1588 $6 multi 1.75 1.75

Chinese People's Political Consultative Conference, 70th Anniv. A1589

National Political Consultative Conference Auditorium, Beijing A1590

***Perf. 13¼x13½ Syncopated***

**2019, Sept. 21 Photo.**

**4655** A1589 $1.20 gold & multi .35 .35

***Perf. 13 Syncopated***

**4656** A1590 $1.20 gold & multi .35 .35

Guangdong-Hong Kong-Macao Greater Bay Area — A1591

Designs: No. 4657, $1.20, Drone, Pearl River and buildings (3-1). No. 4658, $1.20, Bridge, airplane over runway, ship near port (3-2). No. 4659, $1.20, Dragon boats, buildings, bicyclist, woman in traditional costume, runners, Tsai chi practitioner (3-3).

***Perf. 13¼x13 Syncopated***

**2019, Sept. 26** **Photo.**

**4657-4659** A1591 Set of 3 1.00 1.00
*4659a* Souvenir sheet of 3, #4657-4659 1.00 1.00

Opening of Beijing Daxing International Airport — A1592

***Perf. 13¼x13 Syncopated***

**2019, Sept. 26** **Photo.**

**4660** A1592 $1.20 multi + label .35 .35

A1593

People's Republic of China, 70th Anniv. A1594

Designs: No. 4661, $1.20, Drone, airplane, satellite, robotic arm, woman and man with computer, buildings and train (5-1). No. 4662, $1.20, People at governmental meeting (5-2). No. 4663, $1.20, Athletes and entertainers, China Central Television Building (5-3). No. 4664, $1.20, Buildings, school children, farmer, doctor, nurse and patient (5-4). No. 4665, $1.20, Wind generators, solar panels, woman and chld watering tree (5-5).

$6, Ship, doves, 70th anniv. emblem.

***Perf. 13 Syncopated***

**2019, Oct. 1** **Photo.**

**4661-4665** A1593 Set of 5 1.75 1.75
*4665a* Souvenir sheet of 10, 2 each #4661-4665 4.50 4.50

**Souvenir Sheet**

**4666** A1594 $6 multi 1.75 1.75

Chaotianmen Bridge, Chongqing A1595

Saratov Bridge, Saratov, Russia — A1596

***Perf. 12x12¼ Syncopated***

**2019, Oct. 2** **Litho.**

**4667** A1595 $1.20 multi .35 .35
**4668** A1596 $1.20 multi .35 .35

Diplomatic relations between People's Republic of China and Russia, 70th anniv.

Chinese Incense Burner on Hook, c. 880 — A1597

Slovakian Bronze Horse Harness Fitting, c. 795 — A1598

***Perf. 13¼x13 Syncopated***

**2019, Oct. 6** **Litho. & Embossed**

**4669** A1597 $1.20 multi .35 .35
**4670** A1598 $1.20 multi .35 .35

Diplomatic relations between People's Republic of China and Slovakia, 70th anniv. See Slovakia No. 828.

Famous Men — A1599

Designs: No. 4671, 80f, Wang Shouren (1472-1529), philosopher (6-1). No. 4672, 80f, Huang Zongxi (1610-95), philosopher (6-2). No. 4673, 80f, Gu Yanwu (1613-82), philologist (6-3). No. 4674, $1.20, Wang Fuzhi (1619-92), historian (6-4). No. 4675, $1.20, Dai Zhen (1724-77), philosopher (6-5). No. 4676, $1.20, Zhang Xuecheng (1738-1801), historian (6-6).

***Perf. 13¼ Syncopated***

**2019, Oct. 7** **Litho. & Engr.**

**4671-4676** A1599 Set of 6 1.75 1.75

Nankai University, Tianjin, Cent. A1600

***Perf. 13x13¼ Syncopated***

**2019, Oct. 17** **Litho.**

**4677** A1600 $1.20 multi .35 .35

Chang'e 4 Probe — A1601

Cloned Monkeys A1602

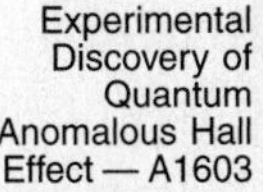

Experimental Discovery of Quantum Anomalous Hall Effect — A1603

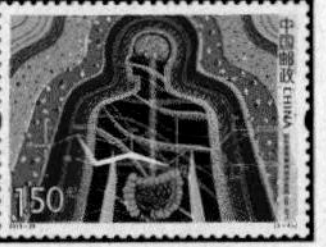

Human Body and Chemical Diagram for New Drug to Treat Alzheimer's Disease — A1604

China Spallation Neutron Source — A1605

**Litho. With Foil Application**

**2019, Nov. 1** ***Perf. 13 Syncopated***

**4678** A1601 $1.20 gold & multi .35 .35
**4679** A1602 $1.20 gold & multi .35 .35
**4680** A1603 $1.20 gold & multi .35 .35
**4681** A1604 $1.50 gold & multi .45 .45
**4682** A1605 $1.50 gold & multi .45 .45
*Nos. 4678-4682 (5)* 1.95 1.95

Golden Rat — A1606

***Perf. 12¾ Syncopated***

**2019, Nov. 1** **Photo.**

**4683** A1606 $1.20 gold & multi .35 .35
*a.* Souvenir sheet of 2, #3708a (perf. 12¾ syncopated), 4683 1.25 1.25

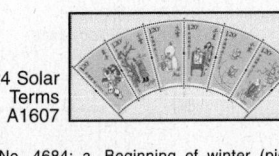

24 Solar Terms A1607

No. 4684: a, Beginning of winter (pigs, woman and bok choy) (6-1). b, Slight snow (man pruning tree) (6-2). c, Great snow (children making snowman) (6-3). d, The winter solstice (woman knitting and child painting) (6-4). e, Slight cold (children on chairs with ice skate blades) (6-5). f, Great cold (man and child looking at tree in snow) (6-6).

***Perf. 13 Syncopated***

**2019, Nov. 8** **Photo.**

**4684** A1607 $1.20 Block of 6, #a-f 2.10 2.10

Values are for stamps with surrounding selvage.

Poverty Alleviation A1608

Designs: No. 4685, $1.20, Flag of People's Republic of China, family, medical clinic, school (6-1). No. 4686, $1.20, Boat on river, Chixi Village (6-2). No. 4687, $1.20, Tree, buildings in Shibadong Village (6-3). No. 4688, $1.20, Raspberries, women, motorized cart, Minning Village (6-4). No. 4689, $1.20, Statue of man, buildings in Lankao County (6-5). No. 4690, $1.20, Peaches, sculpture, truck, buildings in Jinggangshan City (6-6).

***Perf. 13 Syncopated***

**2019, Nov. 29** **Photo.**

**4685-4690** A1608 Set of 6 2.10 2.10

Emblems of 2022 Winter Olympics and Paralympics, Beijing — A1609

No. 4691 — Emblem of: a, Winter Olympics. b, Winter Paralympics.

**2019, Dec. 7** **Litho.** ***Perf. 12***

**4691** A1609 $1.20 Vert. pair, #a-b, + 2 labels .70 .70

Return of Macao to People's Republic of China, 20th Anniv. — A1610

Designs: No. 4692, $1.20, Flags of People's Republic of China and Macao, people, Lotus Flower sculpture (3-1). No. 4693, $1.20, Dragon, dancers, buildings of Macao (3-2). $1.50, Buildings and bridges of Macao (3-3).

***Perf. 13¼x13 Syncopated***

**2019, Dec.20** **Photo.**

**4692-4694** A1610 Set of 3 1.10 1.10

New Year 2020 (Year of the Rat) — A1611

Designs: No. 4695, $1.20, Rat (2-1). No. 4696, $1.20, Three rats (2-2).

***Perf. 13 Syncopated***

**2020, Jan. 5** **Litho. & Engr.**

**4695-4696** A1611 Set of 2 .70 .70
*4696a* Booklet pane of 10, 5 each #4695-4696 3.50 —
Complete booklet, #4696a 3.50

Mascot of 2022 Winter Olympics, Beijing A1612

Mascot of 2022 Winter Paralympics, Beijing A1613

***Perf. 13x13¼ Syncopated***

**2020, Jan. 16** **Photo.**

**4697** A1612 $1.20 multi .35 .35
**4698** A1613 $1.20 multi .35 .35

Paper Cutting Art — A1614

Designs: No. 4699, $1.20, Sanniang Teaches Her Son (4-1). No. 4700, $1.20, Celebrating Spring Festival With Waist Drums (4-2). No. 4701, $1.20, Wang Xiao Serves With a Donkey (4-3). No. 4702, $1.20, Auspicious Road for Ginseng Digging (4-4).

***Perf. 13¼x12¾ Syncopated***

**2020, Feb. 8** **Litho.**

**4699-4702** A1614 Set of 4 1.40 1.40

Paintings by Wu Guanzhong (1919-2010) A1615

Designs: No. 4703, $1.20, Sorghum and Cotton (6-1). No. 4704, $1.20, Melon Vines (6-2). No. 4705, $1.20, Water Lane (6-3). No. 4706, $1.50, Spring Snow in Daba Mountains (50x30mm) (6-4). No. 4707, $1.50, Double Swallows (50x30mm) (6-5). $3, Dancing Cranes (50x30mm) (6-6).

***Perf. 13¼ Syncopated (vert. stamps), 13¼x13 Syncopated (horiz. stamps)***

**2020, Mar. 20** **Litho.**

**4703-4708** A1615 Set of 6 2.75 2.75

Launch of First Chinese Satellite, Dong Fang Hong I, 50th Anniv. — A1616

***Perf. 13 Syncopated***

**2020, Apr. 24** **Litho.**

**4709** A1616 $1.20 multi .35 .35

Campaign Against COVID-19 — A1617

No. 4710: a, Military and medical staffers wearing mask, city and airplane (2-1). b, Medical worker wearing protective gear, ambulance, patient on ventilator (2-2).

***Perf. 13¼ Syncopated***

**2020, May 11** **Photo.**

**4710** A1617 $1.20 Horiz. pair, #a-b 12.75 12.75

Ancient Asian Civilizations A1618

Designs: No. 4711, $1.20, Ziggurat of Ur (6-1). No. 4712, $1.20, Akkadian-language tablet with Gilgamesh Flood Myth, vert. (6-2). No. 4713, $1.20, Harappan seal, vert. (6-3). No. 4714, $1.20, Mohenjo-daro ruins (6-4). No. 4715, $1.20, Liangzhu jade cong, vert. (6-5). No. 4716, $1.20, Ruins at Shimao archaeological site (6-6).

***Perf. 13¼x13 Syncopated (horiz. stamps), 13¼ Syncopated (vert. stamps)***

**2020, May 15** **Litho. & Engr.**

**4711-4716** A1618 Set of 6 2.10 2.10

A1619

*The Dream of Red Mansions,* Novel by Cao Xueqin — A1620

Designs: No. 4717, $1.20, Yuanyang vows never to marry (4-1). No. 4718, $1.20, Baoqin stands in snow (4-2). No. 4719, $1.20, You Sanjie returns the love token sword (4-3). $1.50, Malicious talk makes Lady Wang have a search made of the garden (4-4).

$6, Xiangyun sleeps among the peonies.

***Perf. 13 Syncopated***

**2020, May 17** **Photo.**

**4717-4720** A1619 Set of 4 1.50 1.50

**Souvenir Sheet**

***Perf. 13¼x13***

**4721** A1620 $6 multi 1.75 1.75

Roses — A1621

Designs: No. 4722, $1.20, Red rose and swallows in flight (4-1). No. 4723, $1.20, Pink roses and ducks (4-2). No. 4724, $1.50, White roses and birds in flight (4-3). No. 4725, $1.50, Purple roses and swans (4-4).

**Litho. & Embossed With Holographic Foil Affixed**

**2020, May 20** ***Perf. 13¼ Syncopated***

**4722-4725** A1621 Set of 4 1.50 1.50

Ascent of Mount Everest by Chinese Mountaineering Team, 60th Anniv. — A1622

***Perf. 13 Syncopated***

**2020, May 25** **Photo.**

**4726** A1622 $1.20 multi .35 .35

Scenes From *Calabash Brothers* Animated Series A1623

Various characters: No. 4727, 80f (6-1). No. 4728, 80f (6-2). No. 4729, $1.20, (6-3). No. 4730, $1.20, (6-4). No. 4731, $1.20 (6-5). No. 4732, $1.20, (6-6).

***Perf. 13¼x13 Syncopated***

**2020, June 1** **Photo.**

**4727-4732** A1623 Set of 6 1.90 1.90

Harbin Institute of Technology, Cent. — A1624

***Perf. 13¼x13½ Syncopated***

**2020, June 6** **Litho. & Engr.**

**4733** A1624 $1.20 multi .35 .35

Souvenir Sheet

Eighth Congress of All-China Philatelic Federation — A1625

***Perf. 13¼ Syncopated***

**2020, June 18** **Photo. & Litho.**

**4734** A1625 $6 multi 1.75 1.75

Astronomical Phenomena — A1626

Designs: No. 4735, $1.20, Annular eclipse (5-1). No. 4736, $1.20, Total lunar eclipse (5-2). No. 4737, $1.20, Meteor shower (5-3). No. 4738, $1.50, Comet (5-4). No. 4739, $1.50, Transit of Mercury (5-5).

***Perf. 13¼x13 Syncopated***

**2020, June 21** **Litho.**

**4735-4739** A1626 Set of 5 1.90 1.90

A1627

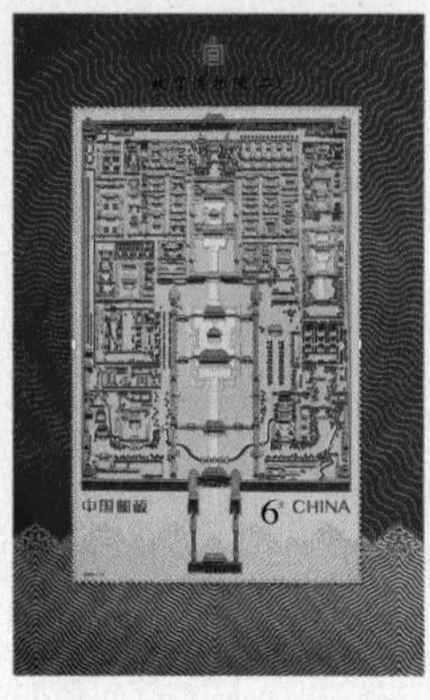

Palace Museum A1628

Designs: No. 4740, $1.20, Golden Water Bridge (4-1). No. 4741, $1.20, Hall of Complete Harmony (4-2). No. 4742, $1.50, Palace of Heavenly Purity (4-3). No. 4743, $1.50, Pavilion of One Thousand Autumns (4-4).

$6, Map of Palace Museum.

***Perf. 13x12¾ Syncopated***

**2020, July 11** **Litho. & Engr.**

**4740-4743** A1627 Set of 4 1.60 1.60

**Souvenir Sheet**

**Photo.**

***Perf. 13¼x13½ Syncopated***

**4744** A1628 $6 gold & multi 1.75 1.75

Pudong New Area — A1629

No. 4745: a, Buildings and roadway, Shanghai Pilot Free Trade Zone (33x44mm, 5-1). b, Airplane and robot, Zhangjiang Science City (33x44mm, 5-2). c, Graphs and Lujiazui Financial City (50x44mm, 5-3). d, Fireworks, wind generators, cyclists and buildings of East Bund (33x44mm, 5-4). e, Cyclist, bridges, ships at Yangshan Port (33x44mm, 5-5).

***Perf. 13¼ Syncopated***

**2020, July 20** **Litho.**

**4745** Horiz. strip of 5 1.75 1.75

***a.-e.*** A1629 $1.20 Any single .35 .35

A1630

Hua Tuo (c. 140-208), Physician — A1631

Hua Tuo: No. 4746, $1.20, Wearing brown robe, holding bowl of cannabis boil powder (2-1). No. 4747, $1.20, Wearing blue robe, developing wuqinxi (2-2).

***Perf. 13x13¼ Syncopated***

**2020, Aug. 19** **Litho.**

**4746-4747** A1630 Set of 2 .70 .70

**Souvenir Sheet**

***Perf. 13x13½ Syncopated***

**4748** A1631 $6 multi 1.75 1.75

Publication of Chinese Edition of *The Communist Manifesto*, Cent. A1632

***Perf. 13¼x12¾ Syncopated***

**2020, Aug. 22** **Litho.**

**4749** A1632 $1.20 multi .35 .35

Scientists A1633

Designs: No. 4750, $1.20, Wang Daheng (1915-2011), optical engineer (4-1). No. 4751, $1.20, Huang Kun (1919-2005), physicist (4-2). No. 4752, $1.20, Yu Min (1926-2019), nuclear physicist (4-3). No. 4753, $1.20, Chen Jingrun (1933-96), mathematician (4-4).

***Perf. 13¼x12¾ Syncopated***

**2020, Sept. 19** **Litho. & Engr.**

**4750-4753** A1633 Set of 4 1.40 1.40

A1634

Mogao Caves A1635

Designs: No. 4754, $1.20, Shakyamuni Buddha (4-1). No. 4755, $1.20, Flying Apsaras, horiz. (4-2). No. 4756, $1.20, Statues of Buddha and Bodhisattvas, horiz. (4-3). No. 4757, $1.20, Seated Bodhisattva (4-4).

$6, Statues of Buddha and disciples, Bodhisattvas and Heavenly Kings.

***Perf. 13 Syncopated (vert. stamps), 13¼ Syncopated (horiz. stamps)***

**2020, Sept. 26** **Photo. & Litho.**

**4754-4757** A1634 Set of 4 1.40 1.40

**Souvenir Sheet**

***Perf. 13¼x13½ Syncopated***

**4758** A1635 $6 gold & multi 1.75 1.75

Launch of Tianwen-1 Mars Probe — A1636

***Perf. 13¼ Syncopated***

**2020, Sept. 26** **Photo.**

**4759** A1636 $1.20 sil & multi .35 .35

Chagan Lake A1637

Designs: No. 4760, $1.20, Birds at Chagan Lake (3-1). No. 4761, $1.20, Fishing village in winter (3-2). No. 4762, $1.50, Fish jumping out of nets of fishermen (3-3).

***Perf. 13¼x13 Syncopated***

**2020, Oct. 18** **Photo.**

**4760-4762** A1637 Set of 3 1.25 1.25

Participation of Chinese Troops in Korean War, 70th Anniv. A1638

***Perf. 13¼x13 Syncopated***

**2020, Oct. 25** **Photo.**

**4763** A1638 $1.20 gold & multi .35 .35

Seventh National Census — A1639

***Perf. 13¼x13 Syncopated***

**2020, Nov. 1** **Litho. & Embossed**

**4764** A1639 $1.20 multi .35 .35

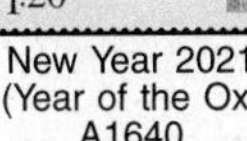

New Year 2021 (Year of the Ox) A1640

New Year's Blessing A1641

***Perf. 13 Syncopated***

**2020, Nov. 5** **Photo.**

**4765** A1640 $1.20 multi .40 .40

**4766** A1641 $3 gold & multi .95 .95

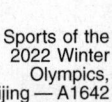

Sports of the 2022 Winter Olympics, Beijing — A1642

Designs: No. 4767, $1.20, Short track speed skating (5-1). No. 4768, $1.20, Figure skating (5-2). No. 4769, $1.20, Speed skating (5-3). No. 4770, $1.20, Curling (5-4). No. 4771, $1.20, Ice hockey (5-5).

***Perf. 13 Syncopated***

**2020, Nov. 7** **Photo.**

**4767-4771** A1642 Set of 5 1.90 1.90

Assistance for Chinese Citizens Abroad A1643

Designs: No. 4772, $1.20, Chinese woman with microphone, smartphone connecting with 24-hour consular services number (3-1). No. 4773, $1.20, Stylized globe and various consular services (3-2). No. 4774, $1.20, Great Wall of China, children with passport and flag of People's Republic of China, and adults (3-3).

***Perf. 13¼x13 Syncopated***

**2020, Nov. 12** **Photo.**

**4772-4774** A1643 Set of 3 1.10 1.10

Diplomatic Relations Between People's Republic of China and Ethiopia, 50th Anniv. A1644

Designs: No. 4775, $1.20, Olympic Forest Park, Beijing (2-1). No. 4776, $1.20, Sheger Park, Addis Ababa (2-2).

***Perf. 13¼x12¾ Syncopated***

**2020, Nov. 24** **Photo.**

**4775-4776** A1644 Set of 2 .75 .75

Friedrich Engels (1820-95), Co-author of *The Communist Manifesto* — A1645

Engels: No. 4777, $1.20, As young man (2-1). No. 4778, $1.20, As older man, writing (2-2).

***Perf. 13¼ Syncopated***

**2020, Nov. 28** **Litho.**

**4777-4778** A1645 Set of 2 .75 .75

Implementation of the Civil Code — A1648

***Perf. 13¼ Syncopated***

**2021, Jan. 1** **Litho.**

**4781** A1648 $1.20 multi .40 .40

A1649

New Year 2021 (Year of the Ox) — A1650

***Perf. 13 Syncopated***

**2021, Jan. 5** **Litho. & Engr.**

**4782** A1649 $1.20 multi .40 .40

**4783** A1650 $1.20 multi .40 .40

*a.* Souvenir sheet of 4, 2 each #4782-4783 1.60 1.60

*b.* Booklet pane of 10, 5 each #4782-4783 4.00 —

Complete booklet, #4783b 4.00

Male and Female Police Officers and Police Flag — A1651

Police Emblem and Police in Action — A1652

***Perf. 13 Syncopated***

**2021, Jan. 10** **Photo.**

**4784** A1651 $1.20 multi .40 .40

**4785** A1652 $1.20 gold & multi .40 .40

Police Day.

A1653

A1654

A1655

A1656

Five Oxen, Painting by Han Huang (723-87) A1657

Design: $6, Entire painting.

***Serpentine Die Cut 12***

**2021, Mar. 20** **Litho. & Engr.**

**4786** Horiz. strip of 5 1.75 1.75

*a.* A1653 80f multi .25 .25

*b.* A1654 $1.20 multi .35 .35

*c.* A1655 $1.20 multi .35 .35

*d.* A1656 $1.20 multi .35 .35

*e.* A1657 $1.50 multi .45 .45

**Souvenir Sheet**

***Imperf***

**4787** A1657 $6 multi 1.90 1.90

No. 4787 contains one 205x35mm stamp.

Xiamen University, Cent. A1658

***Perf. 12½ Syncopated***

**2021, Apr. 6** **Litho. & Engr.**

**4788** A1658 $1.20 multi .40 .40

Chinese Aircraft A1659

Designs: No. 4789, $1.20, Stealth fighter (4-1). No. 4790, $1.20, Military transport airplanes (4-2). No. 4791, $1.20, Tactical utility helicopter (4-3). No. 4792, $1.20, Amphibious airplane (4-4).

***Perf. 13¼x13 Syncopated***

**2021, Apr. 17** **Litho.**

**4789-4792** A1659 Set of 4 1.50 1.50

*Journey to the West,* Novel by Wu Cheng'en (c. 1500-c. 1580) — A1660

Designs: No. 4793, $1.20, The Monkey King and his double (4-1). No. 4794, $1.20, Baited for the palm-leaf fan throne (4-2). No. 4795, $1.20, Trapped in the Lesser Leiyin Temple (4-3). No. 4796, $1.20, Falling in trouble in the Spider Cave (4-4).

**Photo., Litho. (#4796)**

**2021, Apr. 23** ***Perf. 13 Syncopated***

**4793-4796** A1660 Set of 4 1.50 1.50

Tsinghua University, 110th Anniv. — A1661

**Litho., Label Litho. & Engr.**

**2021, Apr. 24** ***Perf. 13¼***

**4797** A1661 $1.20 multi + label .40 .40

Mountains Near Linyi — A1662

Sayram Lake — A1663

Bamboo Sea Near Yibin — A1664

Badain Jaran Desert — A1665

Saihanba National Forest Park — A1666

Fragrant Hills, Beijing — A1667

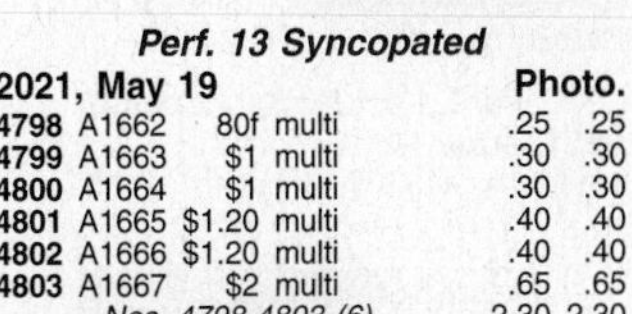

***Perf. 13 Syncopated***

**2021, May 19** **Photo.**

**4798** A1662 80f multi .25 .25

**4799** A1663 $1 multi .30 .30

**4800** A1664 $1 multi .30 .30

**4801** A1665 $1.20 multi .40 .40

**4802** A1666 $1.20 multi .40 .40

**4803** A1667 $2 multi .65 .65

*Nos. 4798-4803 (6)* 2.30 2.30

Fujian Tulous A1668

Designs: No. 4804, $1.20, Zhengcheng Building (4-1). No. 4805, $1.20, Eryi Building (4-2). No. 4806, $1.20, Tianluoken Tulou Cluster (4-3). No. 4807, $1.20, Chengqi Building (4-4).

***Perf. 13 Syncopated***

**2021, May 19** **Litho. & Engr.**

**4804-4807** A1668 Set of 4 1.50 1.50

Diplomatic Relations Between People's Republic of China and Pakistan, 70th Anniv. A1669

Ports of: No. 4808, $1.20, Zhuhai, People's Republic of China (2-1). No. 4809, $1.20, Gwadar, Pakistan (2-2).

***Perf. 13 Syncopated***

**2021, May 21** **Litho.**

**4808-4809** A1669 Set of 2 .75 .75

Values are for stamps with selvage at top and bottom.

Children's Art — A1670

No. 4810: a, 80f, My Chinese Dream (3-1). b, $1.20, Charm of Chinese Culture (3-2). c, $1.20, Hopes and Dreams (3-3).

***Perf. 13¼x13½ Syncopated***

**2021, June 1** **Photo.**

**4810** A1670 Vert. strip of 3, #a-c 1.00 1.00

Cultural Relics of the Silk Road — A1671

Designs: No. 4811, $1.20, Han Dynasty silver box (4-1). No. 4812, $1.20, Tang Dynasty glazed jug (4-2). No. 4813, $1.20, Five Dynasties and Ten Kingdoms Period blue glazed pottery from Persia (4-3). No. 4814, $1.20, Song Dynasty blue-glazed plate (4-4).

***Perf. 13x13½ Syncopated***

**2021, June 12** **Litho.**

**4811-4814** A1671 Set of 4 1.50 1.50

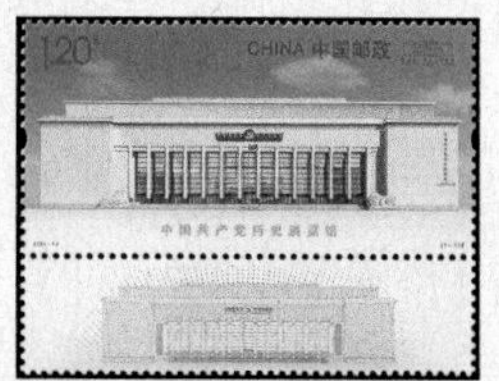

Opening of Museum of the Communist Party of China, Beijing — A1672

***Perf. 13¼x13 Syncopated***

**2021, June 20** **Litho.**

**4815** A1672 $1.20 multi + label .40 .40

Competition Venues for the 2022 Winter Olympics, Beijing A1673

Designs: No. 4816, $1.20, Shougang Big Air Stadium (4-1). No. 4817, $1.20, National Aquatics Center (4-2). No. 4818, $1.20, National Ski Jumping Center (4-3). No. 4819, $1.20, Yanqing National Sliding Center (4-4). $6, National Speed Skating Oval.

***Perf. 13¼x13 Syncopated***

**2021, June 23** **Litho. & Engr.**

**4816-4819** A1673 Set of 4 1.50 1.50

**Souvenir Sheet**

**Litho. & Engr. With Foil Application**

***Perf. Syncopated***

**4820** A1673 $6 multi 1.90 1.90

No. 4820 contains one 111x62mm oval stamp.

Communist Party of China, Cent. — A1674

**2021, July 1** **Litho.** ***Perf. 13¼***

**4821** A1674 $1.20 multi + label .40 .40

See Stamps With Attached Labels note after No. 3197.

A1675

A1676

A1677

A1678

A1679

A1680

A1681

A1682

A1683

A1684

A1685

A1686

A1687

A1688

A1689

A1690

A1691

A1692

A1693

Communist Party of China, Cent. A1694

***Perf. 13¼x13 Syncopated***

**2021, July 1** **Photo.**

| | | | |
|---|---|---|---|
| **4822** | Sheet of 20 | 8.00 | 8.00 |
| *a.* | A1675 $1.20 multi (20-1) | .40 | .40 |
| *b.* | A1676 $1.20 multi (20-2) | .40 | .40 |
| *c.* | A1677 $1.20 multi (20-3) | .40 | .40 |
| *d.* | A1678 $1.20 multi (20-4) | .40 | .40 |
| *e.* | A1679 $1.20 multi (20-5) | .40 | .40 |
| *f.* | A1680 $1.20 multi (20-6) | .40 | .40 |
| *g.* | A1681 $1.20 multi (20-7) | .40 | .40 |
| *h.* | A1682 $1.20 multi (20-8) | .40 | .40 |
| *i.* | A1683 $1.20 multi (20-9) | .40 | .40 |
| *j.* | A1684 $1.20 multi (20-10) | .40 | .40 |
| *k.* | A1685 $1.20 multi (20-11) | .40 | .40 |
| *l.* | A1686 $1.20 multi (20-12) | .40 | .40 |
| *m.* | A1687 $1.20 multi (20-13) | .40 | .40 |
| *n.* | A1688 $1.20 multi (20-14) | .40 | .40 |
| *o.* | A1689 $1.20 multi (20-15) | .40 | .40 |
| *p.* | A1690 $1.20 multi (20-16) | .40 | .40 |
| *q.* | A1691 $1.20 multi (20-17) | .40 | .40 |
| *r.* | A1692 $1.20 multi (20-18) | .40 | .40 |
| *s.* | A1693 $1.20 multi (20-19) | .40 | .40 |
| *t.* | A1694 $1.20 multi (20-20) | .40 | .40 |

2020 Summer Olympics, Tokyo — A1695

Designs: No. 4823, $1.20, Table tennis (2-1). No. 4824, $1.20, Weight lifting (2-2).

***Perf. 13 Syncopated***

**2021, July 23** **Litho.**

**4823-4824** A1695 Set of 2 .75 .75

The 2020 Summer Olympics were postponed untile 2021 because of the COVID-19 pandemic.

Liberation of Tibet, 70th Anniv. — A1696

***Perf. 13 Syncopated***

**2021, Aug. 19** **Photo.**

**4825** A1696 $1.20 gold & multi .40 .40

A1697

Animated Cartoon, *Prince Nezha's Triumph Against the Dragon King*: No. 4826, 80f, Birth of Nezha (6-1). No. 4827, 80f, Nezha playing as child (6-2). No. 4828, $1.20, Killing Ao Bin (6-3). No. 4829, $1.20, Fighting the Dragon King (6-4). No. 4830, $1.20, Rebirth of Nezha (6-5). No. 4831, $1.20, Conquering the sea and protecting the people (6-6).

***Perf. 13¼x13 Syncopated***

**2021, Aug. 28** **Photo.**

**4826-4831** A1697 Set of 6 2.00 2.00

Cotton Roses — A1698

Designs: No. 4832, $1.20, Hibiscus mutabilis (4-1). No. 4833, $1.20, Hibiscus mutabilis Jinqiuhong (4-2). No. 4834, $1.20, Hibiscus mutabilis Chongbanbai (4-3). No. 4835, $1.20, Hibiscus mutabilis Zuifurong (4-4).

***Perf. 13 Syncopated***

**2021, Sept. 7** **Litho. & Engr.**

**4832-4835** A1698 Set of 4 1.50 1.50

Peking Union Medical College Hospital, Cent. A1699

**2021, Sept. 15 Litho. *Perf. 13¼***

**4836** A1699 $1.20 multi + label .40 .40

See Stamps With Attached Labels note after No. 3197.

Shooter A1700

Rowers and Mascots A1701

***Perf. 13¼x13 Syncopated***

**2021, Sept. 15 Litho.**

| | | | |
|---|---|---|---|
| **4837** | Horiz. pair | .80 | .80 |
| *a.* | A1700 $1.20 multi | .40 | .40 |
| *b.* | A1701 $1.20 multi | .40 | .40 |
| *c.* | Souvenir sheet of 2, #4837a-4837b | .80 | .80 |

14th Games of the People's Republic of China.

Souvenir Sheet

A Land So Rich in Beauty, Painting by Fu Baoshi (1904-65) and Guan Shanyue (1912-2000) — A1702

***Perf. 13x13¼ Syncopated***

**2021, Sept. 25 Litho. & Engr.**

**4838** A1702 $6 multi 1.90 1.90

1911 Revolution, 110th Anniv. A1703

***Perf. 13 Syncopated***

**2021, Oct. 10 Photo.**

**4839** A1703 $1.20 gold & multi .40 .40

2020 United Nations Biodiversity Conference, Kunming — A1704

***Perf. 13¼x13 Syncopated***

**2021, Oct. 11 Litho. & Engr.**

**4840** A1704 $1.20 multi .40 .40

The Biodiversity Conference, scheduled for 2020 was postponed because of the COVID-19 pandemic. The first session was held virtually in 2021, with the second session to be held in 2022 in Kunming. Values are for stamps with surrounding selvage.

Shandong University, 120th Anniv. — A1705

***Perf. 13 Syncopated***

**2021, Oct. 15 Litho. & Engr.**

**4841** A1705 $1.20 multi + label .40 .40

See Stamps With Attached Labels note after No. 3197.

Sustainable Development of Transportation — A1706

Designs: No. 4842, $1.20, High-speed train, cruise liner, truck, bus, automobile, airplanes and airport (4-1). No. 4843, $1.20, Trucks and tunnel (4-2). No. 4844, $1.20, Bus, bridge and cyclists (4-3). No. 4845, $1.20, Freight train and ship at cargo terminal (4-4).

***Perf. 13¼x13 Syncopated***

**2021, Oct. 15 Photo.**

**4842-4845** A1706 Set of 4 1.50 1.50

Henan Opera — A1707

Designs: No. 4846, $1.20, Hua Mulan (3-1). No. 4847, $1.20, Sesame Official (3-2). No. 4848, $1.20, Chaoyanggou Village (3-3).

***Perf. 13¼x13½ Syncopated***

**2021, Oct. 18 Litho.**

**4846-4848** A1707 Set of 3 1.10 1.10

People's Republic of China's Seating at the United Nations, 50th Anniv. A1708

***Perf. 13¼x13 Syncopated***

**2021, Oct. 25 Photo.**

**4849** A1708 $1.20 multi .40 .40

## SEMI-POSTAL STAMPS

**Catalogue values for unused stamps in this section are for Never Hinged items.**

Girl Holding Ball — SP1

### China Post No. T.92

**1984, Feb. 16 Photo. *Perf. 11½***

| | | | |
|---|---|---|---|
| **B1** | SP1 8f + 2f shown (2-1) | 1.25 | .30 |
| **B2** | SP1 8f + 2f Boy, panda (2-2) | 1.25 | .30 |

Surtax for China Children's Fund.

Hands Reading Braille — SP2

### China Post No. T.105

No. B4, Sign language, lip reading. No. B5, Artificial limb. No. B6, Handicapped person in wheelchair.

**1985, Mar. 15 Photo. *Perf. 11½***

| | | | |
|---|---|---|---|
| **B3** | SP2 8f + 2f shown (4-1) | .60 | .35 |
| **B4** | SP2 8f + 2f multi (4-2) | .60 | .35 |
| **B5** | SP2 8f + 2f multi (4-3) | .60 | .35 |
| **B6** | SP2 8f + 2f multi (4-4) | .60 | .35 |
| | *Nos. B3-B6 (4)* | 2.40 | 1.40 |

Surtax for China Welfare Fund.

Children — SP3

### China Post No. T.137

No. B7, Friends. No. B8, Penguins. No. B9, Bird, Moon, Sun. No. B10, Girl, boy playing ball.

**1989, June 1 Litho. *Perf. 12***

| | | | |
|---|---|---|---|
| **B7** | SP3 8f +4f multi (4-1) | .30 | .25 |
| **B8** | SP3 8f +4f multi (4-2) | .30 | .25 |
| **B9** | SP3 8f +4f multi (4-3) | .30 | .25 |
| **B10** | SP3 8f +4f multi (4-4) | .30 | .25 |
| *a.* | Strip of 4, #B7-B10 | 1.50 | 1.50 |

Intl Children's Day, 40th anniv., and 10th Intl. Year of the Child. Surtax for China Children's Fund.

Flood Victims Relief SP4

**1998, Sept. 10 Photo. *Perf. 13x13½***

**B10B** SP4 50f + 50f label 1.20 .40

Sichuan Earthquake Relief — SP5

**2008, May 20 Photo. *Perf. 13x13¼***

**B11** SP5 $1.20 + $1 multi + label *6.50 3.75*

## AIR POST STAMPS

Mail Plane and Temple of Heaven AP1

### China Post No. A1

**1951, May 1 Engr. *Perf. 12½***

**Without Gum**

| | | | |
|---|---|---|---|
| **C1** | AP1 $1000 carmine | 1.00 | .40 |
| **C2** | AP1 $3000 green | 1.00 | .40 |
| **C3** | AP1 $5000 orange | 1.00 | .40 |
| *a.* | Pair, imperf. between | 600.00 | — |
| **C4** | AP1 $10,000 vio brn & grn | 3.00 | 1.00 |
| **C5** | AP1 $30,000 dk bl & brn | 24.00 | 4.25 |
| | *Nos. C1-C5 (5)* | 30.00 | 6.45 |

Planes at Airport — AP2

### China Post No. A2

Designs: 28f, Plane over winding mountain highway. 35f, Plane over railroad yard. 52f, Plane over ship.

**1957-58 Without Gum *Perf. 14***

| | | | |
|---|---|---|---|
| **C6** | AP2 16f indigo | 16.00 | 1.00 |
| **C7** | AP2 28f olive black | 16.00 | 1.00 |
| **C8** | AP2 35f slate | 16.00 | 5.00 |
| **C9** | AP2 52f Prus blue ('58) | 16.00 | 2.00 |
| | *Nos. C6-C9 (4)* | 64.00 | 9.00 |

## POSTAGE DUE STAMPS

Grain and Cogwheel — D1

### China Post No. D1

**1950, Sept. 1 Typo. *Perf. 12½***

**Without Gum**

| | | | |
|---|---|---|---|
| **J1** | D1 $100 steel blue | .30 | 5.00 |
| **J2** | D1 $200 steel blue | .30 | 5.00 |
| **J3** | D1 $500 steel blue | .30 | 5.00 |
| **J4** | D1 $800 steel blue | 30.00 | 10.00 |
| **J5** | D1 $1000 steel blue | .45 | 5.00 |
| **J6** | D1 $2000 steel blue | .70 | 5.00 |
| **J7** | D1 $5000 steel blue | .70 | 5.00 |
| **J8** | D1 $8000 steel blue | .70 | 15.00 |
| **J9** | D1 $10,000 steel blue | 2.00 | 25.00 |
| | *Nos. J1-J9 (9)* | 35.45 | 80.00 |

D2

### China Post No. D2

**1954, Aug. 18 Litho. *Perf. 14***

**Without Gum**

| | | | |
|---|---|---|---|
| **J10** | D2 $100 red | 1.50 | 1.25 |
| **J11** | D2 $200 red | 1.00 | 1.25 |
| **J12** | D2 $500 red | 1.50 | 1.25 |
| **J13** | D2 $800 red | 1.00 | 1.25 |
| **J14** | D2 $1600 red | 1.00 | 1.25 |
| | *Nos. J10-J14 (5)* | 6.00 | 6.25 |

## MILITARY STAMP

Red Star, 8-1 in Center — M1

### China Post No. M1

**1953, Aug. Litho. *Perf. 14***

**Without Gum**

**M1** M1 $800 yel, org & red *300.00 125.00*

This stamp also was printed in deep purple, orange & red (value, *$3,500.*), and blue, orange & red (value, *$315,000*). These were not issued.

While it has been assumed for many years that each color was for a separate branch of the armed forces (army, air force and navy), there is no documentation to support that theory. Quantities printed also do not correspond to the number of servicemen in each branch.

M2

### China Post No. M2

**1995 Litho. *Perf. 12***

**M4** M2 20f multicolored 13.00 *4.00*

## NORTHEAST CHINA

The Northeast Liberation Area included the provinces of Liaoning, Kirin, Jehol and Heilungkiang, the area generally known as Manchuria under the Japanese. The first post war issues were local overprints on stamps of Manchukuo. In early 1946, a Ministry of Posts and Telegraphs served the areas already liberated, and in August, 1946, a Communications Committee of the Political Council was established. In June, 1947, these postal services were subordinated to the Harbin General Post Office, and this was extended to Changchun on Oct. 22, 1948, and to Mukden on Nov. 4, 1948. It was rapidly extended to cover all Manchuria.

Rough Perfs

Rough perforations are normal on most regional issues.

**All Stamps Issued without Gum**

Mao Tse-tung
A1 A2

**1946, Feb. Unwmk. Litho.**

**1L1** A1 $1 violet 22.50 25.00
**1L2** A2 $2 vermilion 2.50 5.00
**1L3** A2 $5 orange 2.75 5.00
*a.* Booklet pane of 6 250.00
**1L4** A2 $10 blue 3.00 4.00
*a.* Booklet pane of 6 250.00
*Nos. 1L1-1L4 (4)* 30.75 39.00

Value, imperf set $125.

For surcharges see Nos. 1L20-1L23, 1L49-1L50, 1L89, 1L91, 1L93.

Map of China, Lion, Hyena and Chiang Kai-shek — A3

**1946, Dec. 12 *Perf. 10½***

**1L5** A3 $1 violet 2.25 4.00
**1L6** A3 $2 orange 2.25 4.00
**1L7** A3 $5 org brn 7.50 *12.00*
**1L8** A3 $10 lt grn 12.00 20.00
*a.* Imperf., pair 60.00
*Nos. 1L5-1L8 (4)* 24.00 40.00

10th anniversary of the capture of Chiang Kai-shek at Sian.

Railroad Workers, Chengchow — A4

**1947, Feb. 7 *Perf. 10½***

**1L9** A4 $1 pink 3.00 *4.00*
**1L10** A4 $2 dull grn 3.00 *4.00*
**1L11** A4 $5 pink 4.00 *5.00*
**1L12** A4 $10 dull grn 8.00 *9.00*
*Nos. 1L9-1L12 (4)* 18.00 *22.00*

24th anniversary of the Chengchow railroad workers' strike and massacre.

Women (Worker, Soldier and Farmer) — A5

**Wmk. Chinese Characters in Sheet**

**1947, Mar. 8 *Perf. 10½x11***

**1L13** A5 $5 brick red 5.00 8.00
**1L14** A5 $10 brown 5.00 8.00

International Women's Day, March 8. Exists imperf.

Same Overprinted in Green ("Northeast Postal Service")

**1947, Mar. 18**

**1L15** A5 $5 brick red 9.50 12.00
**1L16** A5 $10 brown 9.50 12.00

Exists imperf.

Children Carrying Banner — A6

**1947, Apr. 4 *Perf. 11x10½***

**Granite Paper**

**1L17** A6 $5 rose red 7.00 10.00
**1L18** A6 $10 lt green 12.00 15.00
**1L19** A6 $30 orange 17.50 20.00
*Nos. 1L17-1L19 (3)* 36.50 45.00

Children's Day.

Nos. 1L1-1L2 Surcharged in Red, Brown, Black, Blue or Green

**1947, Apr. Unwmk. *Perf. 11***

**1L20** A1 $50 on $1 vio (R) 30.00 *32.50*
*a.* Brown surcharge 30.00 *32.50*
**1L21** A2 $50 on $2 ver 30.00 *32.50*
*a.* Brown surcharge 30.00 *32.50*
**1L22** A1 $100 on $1 vio 30.00 *32.50*
*a.* Green surcharge 30.00 *32.50*
**1L23** A2 $100 on $2 ver (Bl) 30.00 *32.50*
*a.* Green surcharge 30.00 *32.50*
*Nos. 1L20-1L23 (4)* 120.00 *130.00*

Farmer and Worker — A7

**Wmk. Chinese Characters in Sheet**

**1947, May 1 *Perf. 10½x11***

**Granite Paper**

**1L24** A7 $10 orange red 6.00 *8.00*
**1L25** A7 $30 ultra 10.00 *15.00*
**1L26** A7 $50 gray green 6.50 *8.00*
*Nos. 1L24-1L26 (3)* 22.50 *31.00*

Labor Day. Value, imperf. pairs, set $425.

Ax Severing Chain — A8

**1947, May 4 *Perf. 11***

**1L27** A8 $10 brt green 8.00 *10.00*
**1L28** A8 $30 brown 8.00 *10.00*
**1L29** A8 $50 violet 10.00 *15.00*
*Nos. 1L27-1L29 (3)* 26.00 *35.00*

28th anniversary of the students' revolt at Peking University against the 1918 peace treaty. Value, imperf. pairs, set $525.

Workers with Banner: "Oppose Imperialist Aggression" A9

**1947, May 30 *Perf. 10½x11***

**Banner in Red**

**1L30** A9 $2 brt lilac 7.50 *10.00*
**1L31** A9 $5 brt green 7.50 *10.00*
**1L32** A9 $10 yellow 9.50 *10.00*
**1L33** A9 $20 violet 9.00 *10.00*
**1L34** A9 $30 red brown 9.00 *12.00*
**1L35** A9 $50 dk blue 12.00 *15.00*
**1L36** A9 $100 brown 15.00 *20.00*
*a.* Souvenir sheet of 7 375.00 *475.00*
*Nos. 1L30-1L36 (7)* 69.50 *87.00*

22nd anniversary of the Shanghai-Nanking Road incident. No. 1L36a is on granite paper and contains 7 imperf. stamps similar to Nos. 1L30-1L36. Size: 215x158mm. Value, imperf. pairs, ordinary paper, set $1,300.

Mao and Communist Flag — A10

**1947, July 1 *Perf. 10½x11***

**1L37** A10 $10 red 20.00 *24.00*
**1L38** A10 $30 brt lilac 20.00 *24.00*
**1L39** A10 $50 rose brn 60.00 *65.00*
**1L40** A10 $100 vermilion 70.00 *80.00*
*Nos. 1L37-1L40 (4)* 170.00 *193.00*

26th anniversary of the founding of the Chinese Communist Party.

Hand Holding Rifle — A11

**1947, July 7 *Perf. 10½***

**1L41** A11 $10 orange 10.00 *12.00*
**1L42** A11 $30 green 10.00 *12.00*
**1L43** A11 $50 dull blue 15.00 14.00
**1L44** A11 $100 brown 20.00 18.00
*a.* Souvenir sheet of 4 475.00 *600.00*
*Nos. 1L41-1L44 (4)* 55.00 56.00

10th anniversary of the start of Sino-Japanese War. No. 1L44a contains 4 imperf. stamps similar to Nos. 1L41-1L44. Size: 149x107mm.

Exist imperf. Value, set of pairs $1,100.

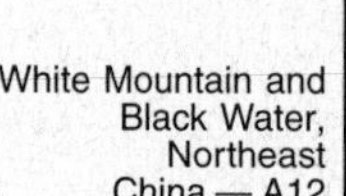

White Mountain and Black Water, Northeast China — A12

**Wmk. Zigzag Lines (141)**

**1947, Aug. 15 *Perf. 10½***

**1L45** A12 $10 brown org 10.00 *20.00*
**1L46** A12 $30 lt ol grn 10.00 *20.00*
**1L47** A12 $50 blue grn 30.00 *32.00*
**1L48** A12 $100 sepia 45.00 *52.00*
*Nos. 1L45-1L48 (4)* 95.00 *124.00*

2nd anniversary of the reoccupation of Northeast China and the surrender of Japan.

Exist imperf. Value, set of pairs $700.

Nos. 1L1-1L2 Surcharged in Black, Red, Green or Blue

**1947, Aug. 29 Unwmk. *Perf. 11***

**1L49** A1 $5 on $1 vio 40.00 40.00
*a.* Red surcharge 40.00 40.00
*b.* Green surcharge 40.00 40.00
**1L50** A2 $10 on $2 ver 40.00 40.00
*a.* Blue surcharge 40.00 40.00
*b.* Green surcharge 40.00 40.00

Map of Manchuria — A13

**1947, Sept. 18 Unwmk.**

**White Paper**

**1L51** A13 $10 gray green 7.00 10.00
**1L52** A13 $20 rose lilac 7.00 10.00
**1L53** A13 $30 black brown 13.00 10.00
**1L54** A13 $50 carmine 13.00 10.00
*Nos. 1L51-1L54 (4)* 40.00 40.00

16th anniversary of Japanese attack on Mukden, Sept. 18, 1931.

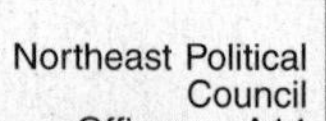

Northeast Political Council Offices — A14

**1947, Oct. 10 *Perf. 10½***

**1L55** A14 $10 yel orange 50.00 *75.00*
**1L56** A14 $20 rose red 50.00 *75.00*
**1L57** A14 $100 brown 110.00 *120.00*
*Nos. 1L55-1L57 (3)* 210.00 *270.00*

35th anniversary of the founding of the Chinese Republic.

Mao Tse-tung (Value figures repeated) — A15

**1947, Oct. 10 White Paper *Perf. 11***

**1L58** A15 $1 brown 3.50 *6.00*
**1L59** A15 $5 gray green 2.50 *6.00*
**1L60** A15 $10 brt green 18.00 *25.00*
**1L61** A15 $15 bluish lilac 18.00 *25.00*
**1L62** A15 $20 brt rose 1.00 *6.00*
**1L63** A15 $30 green 1.00 *8.00*
**1L64** A15 $50 black brown 25.00 *30.00*
**1L65** A15 $90 blue 6.50 *10.00*
*Nos. 1L58-1L65 (8)* 75.50 *116.00*

**Newsprint**

**1L66** A15 $100 red .80
*a.* White paper 8.00 5.00
**1L67** A15 $500 red orange 40.00 40.00
*a.* White paper 32.50 30.00

Type A22 resembles A15, but has "YUAN" at upper right.

The $1, $90 were also printed on newsprint. See footnote following No. 1L72.

See Nos. 1L68-1L72. For surcharges see Nos. 1L84-1L88, 1L90, 1L92, 1L94.

**White Paper**

**1947, Nov. Redrawn**

**1L68** A15 $50 lt grn 1.00 *3.00*
**1L69** A15 $150 red org, wmkd. Chinese characters 2.25 4.00
*a.* Unwatermarked 2.75
**1L70** A15 $250 bluish lil .90 *1.50*
*a.* Wmkd. Chinese characters 1.25 *1.50*

Nos. 1L69 and 1L69a exist in same sheet.

**1947, Dec. Unwmk. Newsprint**

**1L71** A15 $300 green 55.00 30.00
**1L72** A15 $1000 yellow 1.50 *2.00*
*a.* White paper 1.50 *2.00*
*Nos. 1L68-1L72 (5)* 60.65 40.50

Panel below portrait 8½x3mm on Nos. 1L68-1L70; 7x3mm on No. 1L58-1L67. Nos. 1L68-1L70 have different ornamental border. Nos. 1L71-1L72 without zeros for cents.

For surcharges see Nos. 1L90, 1L92, 1L94.

Hand Holding Torch — A16

**1947, Dec. 12 Unwmk. *Perf. 11***

**White Paper**

**1L73** A16 $30 rose red 17.50 *22.50*
**1L74** A16 $90 dk bl 19.00 *22.50*
**1L75** A16 $150 green 21.00 *27.50*
*Nos. 1L73-1L75 (3)* 57.50 *72.50*

11th anniversary of the capture of Chiang Kai-shek at Sian.

Tomb of Gen. Li Chao-lin — A17

**1948, Mar. 9 Unwmk. *Perf. 10½x11***

**1L76** A17 $30 green 24.00 *26.00*
*a.* Granite paper, wmkd. 24.00 *26.00*
**1L77** A17 $150 vio gray 24.00 *26.00*
*a.* Granite paper, wmkd. 24.00 *26.00*

2nd anniversary of the assassination of Gen. Li Chao-lin, Commander of 3rd Army.

Globe and Banner — A18

**Wmk. Chinese Characters in Sheet**

**1948, May 1** *Perf. 11x10½*

1L78 A18 $50 red 17.00 *20.00*
1L79 A18 $150 green 9.50 *20.00*
1L80 A18 $250 lilac 9.50 *40.00*
*Nos. 1L78-1L80 (3)* 36.00 *80.00*

Labor Day.

Student, Torch and Banner — A19

**1948, May 4 Unwmk.** *Perf. 10½x11*

**Granite paper**

1L81 A19 $50 green 21.00 *25.00*
1L82 A19 $150 brown 21.00 *25.00*
1L83 A19 $250 red 25.00 *30.00*
*Nos. 1L81-1L83 (3)* 67.00 80.00

Youth Day, May 4.

Nos. 1L58, 1L61, 1L59, 1L63, 1L65, 1L2-1L4, 1L68-1L69, 1L71 Srchd. in Black, Blue, Red or Green

**1948-49** *Perf. 11*

1L84 A15 $100 on $1 75.00 90.00
a. Blue surcharge 50.00 50.00
1L85 A15 $100 on $15 28.00 28.00
a. Blue surcharge 50.00 50.00
1L86 A15 $300 on $5 (R) 55.00 42.50
1L87 A15 $300 on $30 (R) 20.00 20.00
1L88 A15 $300 on $90 (R) 15.00 15.00
1L89 A2 $500 on $2 12.00 12.00
1L90 A15 $500 on $50 (R, '49) 30.00 25.00
1L91 A2 $1500 on $5 (Bl) 12.00 10.00
1L92 A15 $1500 on $150 (G; '49) 25.00 25.00
a. Blue surcharge 50.00 50.00
1L93 A2 $2500 on $10 (R) 15.00 15.00
1L94 A15 $2500 on $300 ('49) 20.00 20.00
*Nos. 1L84-1L94 (11)* 307.00 302.50

Crane Operator — A20

**Wmk. Chinese Characters in Sheet**

**1948, May** *Perf. 11*

1L95 A20 $100 red & pink 4.50 6.00
1L96 A20 $300 vio brn & yel 7.50 10.00
1L97 A20 $500 bl & grn 11.00 15.00
*Nos. 1L95-1L97 (3)* 23.00 31.00

6th All-China Labor Conference, Harbin.

Farmer, Worker and Soldier Saluting — A21

**1948, Dec. 3 Unwmk.** *Perf. 11x10½*

**White paper**

1L98 A21 $500 vermilion 17.50 *26.00*
1L99 A21 $1500 brt grn 20.00 *32.00*
1L100 A21 $2500 brown 32.50 *45.00*
*Nos. 1L98-1L100 (3)* 70.00 *103.00*

Liberation of Northeast China.

Values for Nos. 1L98-1L100 are for fine stamps.

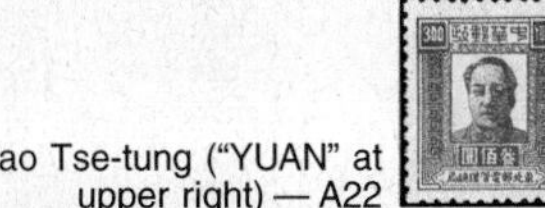

Mao Tse-tung ("YUAN" at upper right) — A22

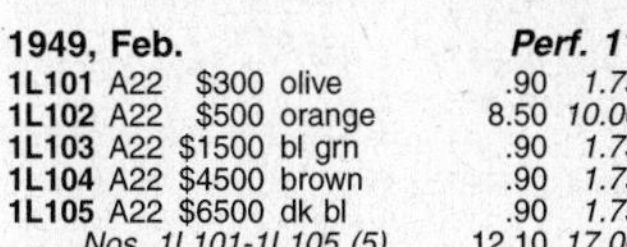

**1949, Feb.** *Perf. 11*

1L101 A22 $300 olive .90 *1.75*
1L102 A22 $500 orange 8.50 *10.00*
1L103 A22 $1500 bl grn .90 *1.75*
1L104 A22 $4500 brown .90 *1.75*
1L105 A22 $6500 dk bl .90 *1.75*
*Nos. 1L101-1L105 (5)* 12.10 *17.00*

See type A15. For surcharges see Nos. 1L126-1L129, 1L131-1L132.

Workers, Globe and Flag — A23

**1949, May 1** *Perf. 11½*

1L106 A23 $1000 red & dl bl .65 *1.75*
1L107 A23 $1500 red & pale bl .65 *1.75*
1L108 A23 $4500 rose & ol brn .85 *1.75*
1L109 A23 $6500 dl org & grn .85 *1.75*
1L110 A23 $10,000 mar & ultra 4.00 *5.00*
*Nos. 1L106-1L110 (5)* 7.00 *12.00*

Labor Day.

Fields and Factories — A24

**1949** *Perf. 10, 11*

1L111 A24 $5000 Prus bl 7.75 *7.75*
1L112 A24 $10,000 org brn .60 *2.00*
1L113 A24 $50,000 green .90 *3.25*
1L114 A24 $100,000 violet 1.25 *13.00*
*Nos. 1L111-1L114 (4)* 10.50 *26.00*

Production in agriculture and industry.

Workers with Flags — A25

**1949, July 1** *Perf. 11*

1L115 A25 $1500 vio, lt bl & red 1.50 *2.00*
1L116 A25 $4500 dk brn, lt bl & ver 1.50 *2.25*
1L117 A25 $6500 gray, lt bl & rose red 3.25 *5.50*
*Nos. 1L115-1L117 (3)* 6.25 *9.75*

28th anniversary of the founding of the Chinese Communist Party.

Heroes' Monument, Harbin — A26

**1949, Aug. 15** *Perf. 11½x11*

1L118 A26 $1500 brick red 1.50 *4.00*
1L119 A26 $4500 yel grn 2.00 *4.00*
1L120 A26 $6500 lt blue 4.00 *6.00*
*Nos. 1L118-1L120 (3)* 7.50 *14.00*

4th anniversary of the Reoccupation, and the surrender of Japan.

---

東北貼用

**"Northeast Postal Service"**

The following commemorative issues are similar to those of the People's Republic of China, 1949-1950, with the 4 characters shown added in different sizes and various arrangements.

**Reprints** were also issued similar to those of the PRC.

---

**Chinese Lantern Type of PRC, 1949**
**China Post No. C1NE**

**1949, Sept. 12 Litho.** *Perf. 12½*

1L121 A1 $1000 dp blue 35.00 11.00
1L122 A1 $1500 scarlet 35.00 13.00
1L123 A1 $3000 green 65.00 *17.50*
1L124 A1 $4500 maroon 65.00 *17.50*
*Nos. 1L121-1L124 (4)* 200.00 *59.00*

*Reprints exist. Value, set $14.*

Factory — A27

**1949, Oct.** *Perf. 11x10½*

1L125 A27 $1500 orange 1.50 *3.00*

For surcharge see No. 1L130.

Nos. 1L101, 1L103-1L105, 1L125 Surcharged in Black or Green

**1949, Nov. 20**

1L126 A22 $2000 on $300 37.50 *40.00*
1L127 A22 $2000 on $4500 (G) 50.00 *50.00*
1L128 A22 $2500 on $1500 .70 *25.00*
1L129 A22 $2500 on $6500 37.50 *40.00*
1L130 A27 $5000 on $1500 .60 *2.00*
1L131 A22 $20,000 on $4500 .40 *7.00*
1L132 A22 $35,000 on $300 .50 *11.00*
*Nos. 1L126-1L132 (7)* 127.20 *175.00*

**Globe and Hammer Type of PRC**
**China Post No. C3NE**

**1949, Nov. 15** *Perf. 12½*

1L133 A2 $5000 crimson 650.00 250.00
1L134 A2 $20,000 dp green 950.00 275.00
1L135 A2 $35,000 vio blue 1,250. 325.00
*Nos. 1L133-1L135 (3)* 2,850. 850.00

*Reprints, value; Nos. 1L133-1L134, each $2; No. 1L135, $575.*

**Mao and Conference Hall Types of PRC**
**China Post No. C2NE**

**1950, Feb. 1** *Perf. 14*

1L136 A3 $1000 vermilion 35.00 29.00
1L137 A3 $1500 dp blue 35.00 29.00
1L138 A4 $5000 dk vio brn 60.00 45.00
1L139 A4 $20,000 green 60.00 *55.00*
*Nos. 1L136-1L139 (4)* 190.00 158.00

*Reprints exist. Value, set $13.*

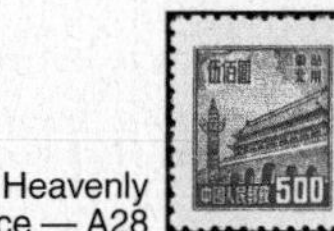

Gate of Heavenly Peace — A28

**1950** *Perf. 10, 10½, 11*

**Narrow horizontal shading**

1L140 A28 $500 olive 2.00 2.00
1L141 A28 $1000 orange 2.25 4.00
1L142 A28 $1000 lil rose 4.00 4.00
1L143 A28 $2000 gray grn 1.75 *2.50*
1L144 A28 $2500 yellow 4.50 4.50
1L145 A28 $5000 dp org 35.00 2.00
1L146 A28 $10,000 brn org 2.50 2.50
1L147 A28 $20,000 vio brn 1.50 *3.00*
1L148 A28 $35,000 dp blue 1.50 *4.00*
1L149 A28 $50,000 brt grn 22.50 20.00
*Nos. 1L140-1L149 (10)* 77.50 48.50

See A29.

**Flag and Mao Type of PRC**
**China Post No. C4NE**

**1950, July 1** *Perf. 14*

**Yellow Stars**

1L150 A7 $5000 grn & red 200.00 115.00
1L151 A7 $10,000 brn & red 225.00 115.00
1L152 A7 $20,000 dk brn & red 225.00 115.00
1L153 A7 $30,000 dk vio bl & red 375.00 150.00
*Nos. 1L150-1L153 (4)* 1,025. 495.00

*Reprints exist. Value, set $55.*

**Picasso Dove Type of PRC**
**China Post No. C5NE**

**1950, Aug. 1 Engr.** *Perf. 14*

1L154 A8 $2500 brown 16.00 *20.00*
1L155 A8 $5000 green 21.00 20.00
1L156 A8 $20,000 blue 28.00 20.00
*Nos. 1L154-1L156 (3)* 65.00 60.00

*Reprints exist. Value, set $6.*

**Flag Type of PRC**
**China Post No. C6NE**

**1950, Oct. 1 Engr. & Litho.**

**Flag in Red & Yellow**

1L157 A9 $1000 purple 160.00 32.50
1L158 A9 $2500 org brn 175.00 32.50
1L159 A9 $5000 dp grn 190.00 40.00
1L160 A9 $10,000 olive 200.00 45.00
1L161 A9 $20,000 blue 225.00 100.00
*Nos. 1L157-1L161 (5)* 950.00 250.00

Size of No. 1L159: 38x47mm, others 26x33mm.

*Reprints exist. Value, set $30.*

**Postal Conference Type of PRC**
**China Post No. C7NE**

**1950, Nov. 1 Litho.**

1L162 A11 $2500 grn & dp org 45.00 20.00
1L163 A11 $5000 car & grn 45.00 20.00

*Reprints exist. Value, set, $5.*

Gate of Heavenly Peace — A29

**China Post No. RN1-RN2**

**1950-51** *Perf. 10½*

**Wide horizontal shading**

1L164 A29 $5000 orange 15.00 *15.00*
1L165 A29 $30,000 scarlet 9.00 *20.00*
1L166 A29 $100,000 violet 16.00 *24.00*

**Wmk. Zigzag Lines (141)**

1L167 A29 $250 brown 1.75 *2.50*
1L168 A29 $500 olive 1.75 *2.50*
1L169 A29 $1000 lil rose 2.00 *4.00*
1L170 A29 $2000 dl grn ('51) 3.00 *4.00*
1L171 A29 $2500 yellow 1.75 *4.00*
1L172 A29 $5000 orange 3.75 *4.00*
1L173 A29 $10,000 brn org ('51) 2.50 *4.00*
1L174 A29 $12,500 maroon 1.75 *4.00*
1L175 A29 $20,000 dp brn ('51) 2.75 *7.50*
*Nos. 1L164-1L175 (12)* 61.00 *95.50*

A $50,000 green was prepared, but not issued. Value $200.

Nos. 1L167, 1L168, 1L172 and 1L174 exist on grayish paper.

**Stalin and Mao Tse-tung Type of PRC**

**Unwmk.**

**1950, Dec. 1 Engr.** *Perf. 14*

1L176 A12 $2500 red 24.00 17.50
1L177 A12 $5000 dp green 29.00 17.50
1L178 A12 $20,000 dk blue 29.00 17.50
*Nos. 1L176-1L178 (3)* 82.00 52.50

*Reprints exist. Value, set $16.*

---

## NORTHEAST CHINA PARCEL POST STAMPS

Locomotive — PP1

**1951 Litho.** *Perf. 10½*

1LQ1 $100,000 purple *500.00*

***Imperf***

1LQ2 $300,000 brown *1,600.*
1LQ3 $500,000 grnsh bl *2,400.*
1LQ4 $1,000,000 ver *4,750.*

Value, Nos. 1LQ2-1LQ4 perf. 10½, $2,650.
For similar type see North China PP1.

---

## PORT ARTHUR AND DAIREN

The Liaoning Postal Administration was established on April 1, 1946, in accordance with the Sino-Soviet Treaty, but was renamed one week later the Port Arthur and Dairen Postal Administration. On Apr. 3, 1947, it was combined with telecommunications and renamed the Kwantung Post and Telegraph General Administration.

On May 1, 1949, the name was again changed to Port Arthur and Dairen Post and Telegraph Administration. Postal tariffs were based on local currency and both Manchukuo and Japanese stamps were overprinted for use.

**Gum**

Nos. 2L1-2L35, 2L37-2L55 and 2L62-2L66 were issued with gum.

Manchukuo Nos. 162 and 94 Handstamp Surcharged in Violet ("Liaoning Post")

**1946, Mar. 15**

**2L1** A19 20f on 30f buff 72.50 72.50
**2L2** A18 1y on 12f org 37.50 37.50

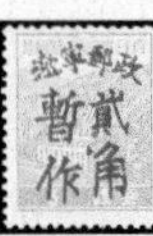

Same Surcharge on Japan Nos. 260, 337, 195, 244, 263, 342 in Violet, Red or Black

**1946, Apr. 1**

**2L3** A85 20f on 3s grn (V) 19.50 *21.00*
**2L4** A151 1y on 17s gray vio (R) 16.00 *18.00*
**2L5** A57 5y on 6s car 30.00 30.00
**2L6** A57 5y on 6s crim 30.00 20.00
**2L7** A88 5y on 6s org 22.00 22.00
**2L8** A154 15y on 40s dk vio 110.00 *125.00*
*Nos. 2L1-2L8 (8)* 337.50 346.00

Surcharge sideways on Nos. 2L5-2L6.

Japan Nos. 260 and 263 Surcharged

**1946, Apr.**

**2L9** A85 1y on 3s grn —
**2L10** A88 5y on 6s org —

Sha Ho Kow (suburb of Dairen) issue. The status of this issue is in question.

Manchukuo Nos. 84, 88 and 98 Handstamp Surcharged in Green, Red or Black

**1946, May 1**

**2L11** A16 1y on 1f red brn (G) 18.00 *24.00*
**2L12** A18 5y on 4f lt ol grn (R) 24.00 *32.50*
**2L13** A19 15y on 30f chnt brn 52.50 *62.50*
*Nos. 2L11-2L13 (3)* 94.50 *119.00*

Transfer of postal administration and Labor Day.

Manchukuo Nos. 159, 86 and 94 Surcharged in Green, Red or Black

**1946, July 7**

**2L14** A17 1y on 6f crim rose (G) 11.50 *20.00*
**2L15** A17 5y on 2f lt grn (R) 52.50 *85.00*
**2L16** A18 15y on 12f dp org 110.00 110.00
*Nos. 2L14-2L16 (3)* 174.00 215.00

Outbreak of war with Japan, 9th anniv.

Manchukuo Nos. 94, 84 and 158 Surcharged in Black, Green or Red

**1946, Aug. 15**

**2L17** A18 1y on 12f dp org 22.50 *27.50*
**2L18** A16 5y on 1f red brn (G) 52.50 50.00
**2L19** A10 15y on 5f gray blk (R) 110.00 100.00
*Nos. 2L17-2L19 (3)* 185.00 177.50

Surrender of Japan, first anniversary.

Manchukuo Nos. 159, 94 and 86 Surcharged in Green, Black or Red

**1946, Oct. 10**

**2L20** A17 1y on 6f crim rose (G) 32.50 30.00
**2L21** A18 5y on 12f dp org 57.50 55.00
**2L22** A17 15y on 2f lt grn (R) 110.00 100.00
*Nos. 2L20-2L22 (3)* 200.00 185.00

35th anniversary of Chinese revolution.

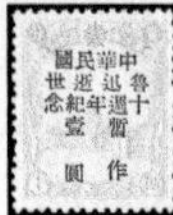

Manchukuo Nos. 84, 159 and 94 Surcharged in Black, Green or Blue

**1946, Oct. 19**

**2L23** A16 1y on 1f red brn 50.00 50.00
**2L24** A17 5y on 6f crim rose (G) 100.00 100.00
**2L25** A18 15y on 12f dp org (Bl) 135.00 135.00
*Nos. 2L23-2L25 (3)* 285.00 285.00

10th anniversary of the death of Lu Hsun (1881-1936), writer.

Manchukuo Nos. 86, 159 and 95 Surcharged in Red, Green or Black

**1947, Feb. 20**

**2L26** A17 1y on 2f lt grn (R) 85.00 85.00
**2L27** A17 5y on 6f crim rose (G) 175.00 175.00
**2L28** A18 15y on 13f dk red brn 325.00 325.00
*Nos. 2L26-2L28 (3)* 585.00 585.00

29th anniversary of the Red (USSR) Army.

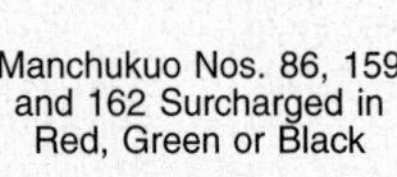

Manchukuo Nos. 86, 159 and 162 Surcharged in Red, Green or Black

**1947, May 1**

**2L29** A17 1y on 2f lt grn (R) 24.00 24.00
**2L30** A17 5y on 6f crim rose (G) 67.50 65.00
**2L31** A19 15y on 30f buff 110.00 100.00
*Nos. 2L29-2L31 (3)* 201.50 189.00

Labor Day.

Manchukuo Nos. 86, 88, 98 and 162 Surcharged ("Kwantung Postal Service, China")

**1947, Sept. 15**

**2L32** A17 5y on 2f lt grn 40.00 40.00
**2L33** A18 15y on 4f lt ol grn 65.00 62.50
**2L34** A19 20y on 30f red brn 100.00 95.00
**2L35** A19 20y on 30f buff 110.00 100.00
*Nos. 2L32-2L35 (4)* 315.00 297.50

Manchukuo Nos. 86 and 159 Surcharged in Red and Green

Sacred Golden Kite (same size) — A1

**1948, Feb. 20**

**2L36** A17 10y on 2f lt grn (R) 150.00 150.00
**2L37** A17 20y on 6f crim rose (G) 190.00 190.00
**2L38** A1 100y on bl & red brn 800.00 800.00

30th anniversary of the Red (USSR) Army. No. 2L38 is on an ungummed label for the 2600th anniv. of the Japanese Empire.

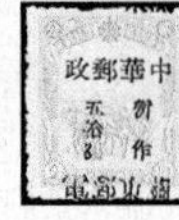

Japan No. 260 and Manchukuo Nos. 84, 86 and 88 Surcharged in Red, Blue or Black

**1948, July**

**2L39** A85 5y on 3s grn (R) 125.00 125.00
**2L40** A16 10y on 1f red brn (Bl) 250.00 250.00
**2L41** A17 50y on 2f lt grn 500.00 500.00
**2L42** A18 100y on 4f lt ol grn (R) 900.00 900.00

**Smaller Characters on Bottom Line**

**2L43** A17 10y on 2f lt grn (R) 300.00 250.00
**2L44** A16 50y on 1f red brn 350.00 300.00

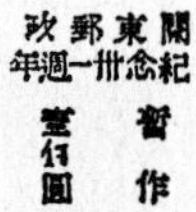

Stamps of Manchukuo Nos. 84, 86 and 88 Surcharged in Blue, Red or Black

**1948, Nov. 1**

**2L45** A16 10y on 1f red brn (Bl) 275.00 600.00
**2L46** A17 50y on 2f lt grn (R) 450.00 600.00
**2L47** A18 100y on 4f lt ol grn 1,100. 600.00

31st anniversary of the Russian Revolution.

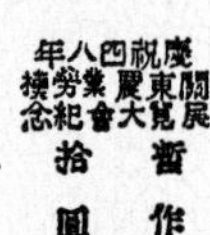

Manchukuo Nos. 86 and 161 Surcharged in Red or Green

**1948, Nov. 15**

**2L48** A17 10y on 2f lt grn 1,050. 1,050.
**2L49** A17 50y on 20f brn (G) 1,200. 1,200.

Kwantung Agricultural and Industrial Exhibition.

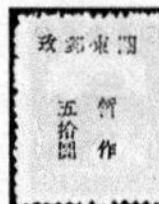

Manchukuo Nos. 86, 88 and 161 Surcharged in Red, Black or Green

**1949, Jan.**

**2L50** A17 20y on 2f lt grn (R) 500.00
**2L51** A18 50y on 4f lt ol grn 700.00
**2L52** A17 100y on 20f brn (G) 700.00

**Without Gum**

From No. 2L56 onward all stamps were issued without gum except as noted.

Farmer and Worker A2

Train and Ship A3

Ship at Dock (No. 2L55) — A4

(No. 2L56)

**1949 Litho. *Perf. 11, 11½***

**2L53** A2 5y pale grn 10.00 *12.00*
**2L54** A3 10y orange 20.00 25.00
**2L55** A4 50y vermilion 22.50 30.00
**2L56** A4 50y red (redrawn) 24.00 30.00
*Nos. 2L53-2L56 (4)* 76.50 97.00

Issue dates: No. 2L56, July 7; others Apr. 1.
For surcharges see Nos. 2L62-2L66.

Worker, Flag and Means of Transport — A5

**1949, May 1 *Perf. 11***

**2L57** A5 10y rose pink 55.00 *55.00*
*a.* 10y vermilion 75.00 75.00

Labor Day. No. 2L57a is from a worn plate.

Mao Tse-tung and Red Flag — A6

**1949, July 1**

**2L59** A6 50y red 45.00 45.00

28th anniversary of the founding of the Chinese Communist Party.

Heroes Monument, Dairen — A7

**1949, Sept.**

**2L60** A7 10y red, bl & olive 45.00 45.00
*a.* 10y red, blue & pale blue 100.00 85.00

4th anniversary of victory over Japan and opening of the Dairen Industrial Fair.

**Nos. 2L53-2L54 Surcharged in Red or Black**

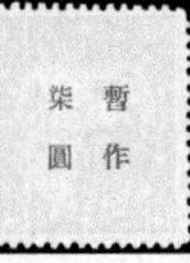

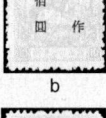

a

b

c

**1949, Sept. With Gum**

**2L62** A2(a) 7y on 5y (R) 40.00 40.00
**2L63** A2(a) 7y on 5y 40.00 40.00
**2L64** A2(b) 50y on 5y (R) 95.00 95.00
**2L65** A3(b) 100y on 10y 500.00 400.00
**2L66** A3(c) 500y on 10y (R) 650.00 475.00
*Nos. 2L62-2L66 (5)* 1,325. 1,050.

Size of surcharge on No. 2L63: 16x19mm.
A 500y on 5y, red surcharge "c," and a 500y on 10y orange, surcharge "b" were prepared but not issued.

Stalin and Lenin — A8

**1949, Nov. 7 *Perf. 11x11½***

**2L68** A8 10y dl bl grn (shades) 125.00 *150.00*

32nd anniversary of the Russian Revolution.

Workers Saluting Mao, Star and Flag — A9

**1949, Nov. 16** *Perf. 11*
**2L69** A9 35y dk bl, red, & yel 175.00 *110.00*

Founding of the People's Republic of China.

Stalin — A10

**1949, Dec. 20** *Perf. 11½*
**2L70** A10 20y dull magenta *90.00 110.00*
**2L71** A10 35y rose red *90.00 110.00*

70th birthday of Stalin.

Gate of Heavenly Peace — A11

**China Post No. RL1**

**1950, Mar. 10 Typo.** *Perf. 10½*
**2L72** A11 10y Prus blue *425.00 400.00*
**2L73** A11 20y dull grn *225.00 150.00*
**2L74** A11 35y red *15.00 20.00*
**2L75** A11 50y deep pur *15.00 25.00*
**2L76** A11 100y lilac rose *55.00 55.00*
*Nos. 2L72-2L76 (5) 735.00 650.00*

## NORTH CHINA

The North China Liberation Area included the provinces of Hopeh, Chahar, Shansi and Suiyuan. The original postal service, begun in the Shansi-Hopeh-Chahar Border Area in December, 1937, became the North China Postal and Telegraph Administration in May, 1949.

**All Stamps Issued without Gum Except as Noted**

**Large Victory Issue**

A1

**Wmk. Wavy Lines**

**1946, Mar.** *Perf. 10½*

**Granite Paper**

**Size: 34½x42mm**

**3L1** A1 $1 red brown 4.50 4.50
*a.* Newsprint 10.00 12.00
**3L2** A1 $2 gray grn 4.50 4.50
**3L3** A1 $4 vermilion 5.00 5.00
**3L4** A1 $5 vio brn 16.00 16.00
**3L5** A1 $8 vio bl 16.00 16.00
**3L6** A1 $10 dp car 5.00 5.00
**3L7** A1 $12 yellow 15.00 15.00
**3L8** A1 $20 lt green 34.00 34.00
*Nos. 3L1-3L8 (8)* 100.00 100.00

Defeat of Japan.

**Small Victory Issue**

***Perf. 10½x10, 9½ rough***

**1946, May Unwmk.**

**Granite paper**

**Size: 20x21mm**

**3L9** A1 $1 red org 1.60 *2.25*
**3L10** A1 $2 green 2.50 2.25
**3L11** A1 $3 lt lilac 4.75 *8.50*
**3L12** A1 $5 dull pur 6.25 .40
**3L13** A1 $8 dk blue 13.50 *17.50*
**3L14** A1 $10 rose red 2.50 *4.50*
**3L15** A1 $15 purple *77.50 67.50*
**3L16** A1 $20 green 4.75 *6.25*
**3L17** A1 $30 brt grnsh bl 4.00 *7.25*
**3L18** A1 $40 brt rose lilac 4.75 3.25
**3L19** A1 $50 brown *36.00* .75
**3L20** A1 $60 myrtle green *67.50* 1.60

**Wmk. Wavy Lines**

**3L21** A1 $100 orange 9.00 *4.50*
**3L22** A1 $200 dull blue 12.00 *4.50*
**3L23** A1 $500 rose 57.50 *70.00*
*Nos. 3L9-3L23 (15) 304.10 201.00*

**North China Postal and Telegraph Administration**

Charging Infantrymen A2

Agriculture and Industry A3

**1949, Jan. Unwmk.** *Imperf.*

**White Paper**

**3L24** A2 50c brown lake 3.50 *4.00*
**3L25** A2 $1 Prussian blue 3.50 *4.00*

**Newsprint**

**3L26** A2 $2 apple green 3.50 *4.00*
**3L27** A2 $3 dull violet 3.50 *4.00*
**3L28** A2 $5 brown 3.50 *4.00*
**3L29** A3 $6 deep rose 3.50 3.00
*a.* White paper 3.50 3.50
**3L30** A2 $10 blue grn 1.25 *3.00*
**3L31** A2 $12 dp car 3.75 *5.00*
*Nos. 3L24-3L31 (8)* 26.00 *31.00*

No. 3L29 issued in Peking, others in Tientsin.

**Remittance Stamps of China Surcharged**

A4

壹
$1

叁
$3

**1949, Jan. Engr.** *Perf. 13*

**Small Central Characters**

**3L32** A4 50c on $50 brn blk 3.25 *3.50*
**3L33** A4 $1 on $50 gray blk 5.50 *2.75*
**3L34** A4 $3 on $50 gray 5.50 2.50

**Large Central Characters**

**3L35** A4 50c on $50 blk 2.50 1.60
**3L36** A4 $6 on $20 dk vio brn 7.50 1.60
*Nos. 3L32-3L36 (5)* 24.25 11.95

Issued in Tientsin.
For surcharges see Nos. 3LQ10-3LQ21.

**Sun Yat-sen Type A2 of Northeastern Provinces and China No. 640 Srchd. in Black, Red, Green or Blue**

#3L37-3L45, 3L47-3L50, 3L52

#3L46, 3L51, 3L53

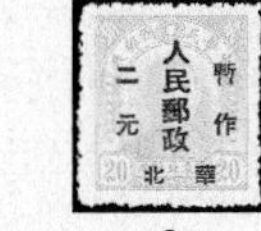
c

Type "b," bottom character of left vertical row (yuan) differs. Type "c," top character of right vertical row differs.

**1949, Mar. 7** *Perf. 14*
**3L37** A2 50c on 5c lake .85 *2.75*
**3L38** A2 $1 on 10c org .85 *2.25*
**3L39** A2 $2 on 20c yel grn 80.00 25.00
**3L40** A2 $3 on 50c red org .85 *1.75*
**3L41** A2 $4 on $5 dk grn 9.50 2.25
**3L42** A2 $6 on $10 crim 2.75 *2.25*
**3L43** A2 $10 on $300 bluish grn 6.00 *3.25*
**3L44** A2 $12 on $1 bl 4.00 *3.25*
**3L45** A2 $18 on $3 brn 7.00 *1.75*
**3L46** A2 $20 on 50c red org (Bl) 2.75 1.50
**3L47** A2 $20 on $20 ol, II 5.50 *4.50*
*a.* Type I 20.00 *13.50*
**3L48** A2 $30 on $2.50 ind (R) 7.00 *4.00*
**3L49** A2 $40 on 25c blk brn (R) 9.00 *6.25*
**3L50** A2 $50 on $109 dk grn (R) 17.50 9.00
**3L51** A2 $80 on $1 bl (R) 22.50 4.50
**3L52** A2 $100 on $65 dl grn (R) 30.00 9.00
**3L53** A73 $100 on $100 dk car, surch. 16mm wide (Bl) 30.00 3.25
*a.* Surcharge 14mm wide 30.00 10.00

**1949, Apr.**
**3L55** A2 (c) $2 on 20c yel grn 1.75 *3.25*
**3L56** A2 (c) $3 on 50c red org .85 *2.25*
**3L57** A2 (c) $4 on $5 dk grn 7.00 4.25
**3L58** A2 (c) $6 on $10 crim, I 4.50 9.50
*a.* Type II 15.00 10.00
**3L59** A2 (c) $12 on $1 blue 1.75 *1.75*

d

e

**1949, Apr.** **Type "d"**
**3L60** A2 $1 on 25c blk grn (G) .50 *1.25*
**3L61** A2 $10 on $300 bluish grn (R) 13.00 5.75
**3L62** A2 $20 on 50c red org (G) 26.00 *55.00*
**3L63** A2 $20 on $20 ol (R) 11.00 4.25
**3L64** A2 $40 on 25c blk brn (R) 11.00 5.00
**3L65** A2 $50 on $109 dk grn, surch. 15mm wide (R) 13.00 *13.00*
*a.* Surcharge 13mm wide 30.00 *30.00*
**3L66** A2 $80 on $1 bl (R) 8.00 6.50

**Type "d" On Stamps on China**

**3L67** A73 $100 on $100 dk car (G) 65.00 35.00
**3L68** A73 $300 on $700 red brn (Bl) 20.00 12.50
**3L69** A82 $500 on $500 bl grn (R) 20.00 4.50
**3L70** A82 $3000 on $3000 bl (R) 20.00 8.25

**Type "e" On Stamps of Northeastern Provinces**

**1949, Aug.**
**3L71** A2 $10 on $10 crim, II (Bl) 8.00 3.50
*a.* Type I 12.50 12.00
**3L72** A2 $30 on 20c yel grn (R) 8.00 2.25
**3L73** A2 $50 on $44 dk car rose (Bl) 8.00 1.25
**3L74** A2 $100 on $3 brn (Bl) 14.00 6.50
**3L75** A2 $200 on $4 org brn, II (Bl) 40.00 24.00
*a.* Type I 1,100. 450.00

**On China No. 754 in Blue**

**3L76** A82 $10 on $7000 lt red brn 12.50 8.50
*Nos. 3L37-3L76 (39)* 549.90 *304.50*

Overprints on Nos. 3L71 and 3L76 have 2 characters in center row.

Farmer and Worker on Globe — A5

**1949, May 1 Engr.** *Perf. 14*
**3L77** A5 $20 crimson 9.50 9.50
**3L78** A5 $40 dark blue 9.50 9.50
**3L79** A5 $60 brown org 9.50 9.50
**3L80** A5 $80 dk green 9.50 9.50
**3L81** A5 $100 purple 9.50 9.50
*Nos. 3L77-3L81 (5)* 47.50 47.50

Labor day. Exists imperf. Value, set $50. Also issued in blocks of 4, imperf between. Value, unused or used, $17.50.

Mao Tse-tung (Chinese Numeral) — A6

Mao Tse-tung (Arabic Numeral) — A7

**1949, July 1** *Perf. 14*
**3L82** A6 $10 red 8.00 *8.00*
**3L83** A7 $20 dk blue 2.00 *7.00*
**3L84** A6 $50 orange 13.00 8.00
**3L85** A7 $80 dk green 5.50 *8.00*
**3L86** A6 $100 purple 10.00 10.00
**3L87** A7 $120 olive 2.00 *7.00*
**3L88** A6 $140 vio brn 10.00 *12.00*
*Nos. 3L82-3L88 (7)* 50.50 *60.00*

28th anniv. of the founding of the Chinese Communist Party. Value, imperf, set $150.

Gate of Heavenly Peace — A8

**1949, Nov. 26 Litho.** *Perf. 12½*
**3L89** A8 $50 orange *1.00 7.00*
**3L90** A8 $100 crimson .50 *2.00*
**3L91** A8 $200 green 2.00 *2.00*
**3L92** A8 $300 rose brn 15.00 4.50
**3L93** A8 $400 blue 15.00 4.50
**3L94** A8 $500 brown 15.00 2.50
**3L95** A8 $700 violet 8.00 7.00
*Nos. 3L89-3L95 (7)* 56.50 29.50

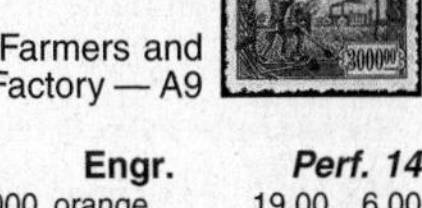
Farmers and Factory — A9

**1949, Dec. Engr.** *Perf. 14*
**3L96** A9 $1000 orange 19.00 6.00
**3L97** A9 $3000 dark blue 1.00 *1.50*
**3L98** A9 $5000 crimson 1.00 *2.75*
**3L99** A9 $10,000 red brown 1.00 *5.75*
*Nos. 3L96-3L99 (4)* 22.00 *16.00*

## NORTH CHINA PARCEL POST STAMPS

**Parcel Post Stamps of China Nos. Q23-Q27 (Type PP3) Srchd. in Red, Black (#3LQ6-3LQ9) or Blue (#3LQ2)**

政郵民人
元百捌
北 華
a

b

c

**1949, June**

**Surcharged Type "a"**

**3LQ1** $300 on $6,000,000 55.00
**3LQ2** $400 on $8,000,000 55.00
**3LQ3** $500 on $10,000,000 55.00
**3LQ4** $800 on $5,000,000 55.00
**3LQ5** $1000 on $3,000,000 75.00

**Surcharged Type "b"**

**3LQ6** $500 on $3,000,000 75.00
**3LQ7** $1000 on $5,000,000 90.00

**Surcharged Type "c"**

**3LQ8** $3000 on $8,000,000 225.00
**3LQ9** $5000 on $10,000,000 300.00
*Nos. 3LQ1-3LQ9 (9)* 985.00

Nos. 3LQ8-3LQ9 have large numerals unboxed.

### Remittance Stamps of China (like North China Type A4) Surcharged in Black or Red

政郵民人
紙印裹包
元　六
北　華

a

b

**Peking Surcharge "a"**

**1949, June Litho. *Perf. 13***

| | | | |
|---|---|---|---|
| **3LQ10** | $6 on $5 ver | 11.00 | 3.50 |
| **3LQ11** | $20 on $50 gray | 11.00 | 3.50 |
| **3LQ12** | $50 on $20 dk vio brn | 11.00 | 3.50 |
| **3LQ13** | $100 on $10 ol grn | 11.00 | 7.00 |

**Tientsin Surcharge "b"**

**Engr. *Perf. 14***

| | | | |
|---|---|---|---|
| **3LQ14** | $20 on $1 brn org | 14.00 | 15.00 |
| *a.* | Perf. 12½ | 22.50 | 7.50 |
| **3LQ15** | $30 on $2 dk grn | 14.00 | 20.00 |
| *a.* | Red surcharge | 22.50 | 11.00 |
| **3LQ16** | $30 on $10 ol grn | 125.00 | 15.00 |
| **3LQ17** | $100 on $10 gray grn (R) | 14.50 | 25.00 |

**Litho.**

***Perf. 13***

| | | | |
|---|---|---|---|
| **3LQ18** | $50 on $5 red | 14.00 | 125.00 |

**Engr.**

***Perf. 14***

| | | | |
|---|---|---|---|
| **3LQ19** | $20 on $1 org brn | 40.00 | 17.00 |

***Perf. 12½***

| | | | |
|---|---|---|---|
| **3LQ20** | $100 on $10 yel grn (R) | 65.00 | 30.00 |

**Typo.**

***Roulette 9½***

| | | | |
|---|---|---|---|
| **3LQ21** | $30 on $2 bl grn (R) | 50.00 | 20.00 |

The surcharge on No. 3LQ19 is without first and last lines.

Nos. 3LQ14, 3LQ14a, 3LQ15, 3LQ15a, 3LQ16-3LQ17, 3LQ19-3LQ20 issued with gum.

Locomotive — PP1

**1949, Nov. Engr. *Perf. 14***

| | | | | |
|---|---|---|---|---|
| **3LQ22** | PP1 | $500 crim | 17.50 | *17.50* |
| **3LQ23** | PP1 | $1000 dp bl | *175.00* | 50.00 |
| **3LQ24** | PP1 | $2000 green | *250.00* | 75.00 |
| **3LQ25** | PP1 | $5000 dp ol | *350.00* | 125.00 |
| **3LQ26** | PP1 | $10,000 org | *650.00* | 250.00 |
| **3LQ27** | PP1 | $20,000 red brn | *1,400.* | 750.00 |
| **3LQ28** | PP1 | $50,000 brn pur | *3,000.* | 1,200. |
| | | *Nos. 3LQ22-3LQ28 (7)* | 5,843. | 2,468. |

## NORTHWEST CHINA

The Northwest China Liberation Area consisted of the provinces of Sinkiang, Tsinghai, Ningsia and the western part of Shensi. The area was first established as the Shensi-Kansu-Ningsia Border Area in October, 1936, after the Long March to Yenan. Remote Sinkiang was not included until late 1949.

**All Stamps Issued without Gum**

Pagoda on Yenan Hill — A1

**1945, Mar. Litho. *Imperf.***

| | | | |
|---|---|---|---|
| **4L1** | A1 | $1 green | 26.00 |
| **4L2** | A1 | $5 dk blue | 150.00 |
| **4L3** | A1 | $10 rose red | 25.00 |
| **4L4** | A1 | $50 dull pur | 30.00 |
| **4L5** | A1 | $100 yel org | 55.00 |
| | | *Nos. 4L1-4L5 (5)* | 286.00 |

**Rouletted 9**

| | | | |
|---|---|---|---|
| *4L1a* | A1 | $1 | 95.00 |
| *4L2a* | A1 | $5 | 160.00 |
| *4L3a* | A1 | $10 | 100.00 |

First issue; denomination in Chinese and Arabic. Heavy shading at top of vignette. Columns at sides.

See types A2, A3 and A4. For surcharges see Nos. 4L6-4L10, 4L23.

**Nos. 4L1-4L2 Surcharged in Red**

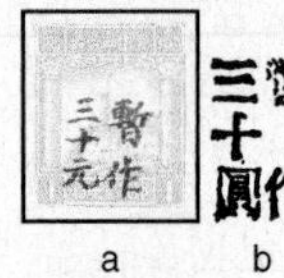

a b

c d

**1946, Nov.**

| | | | |
|---|---|---|---|
| **4L6** | A1 (a) | $30 on $1 grn | 35.00 |
| **4L7** | A1 (b) | $30 on $1 grn | *160.00* |
| *a.* | | Rectangular lower left character | *1,000.* |
| **4L8** | A1 (c) | $30 on $1 grn | 20.00 |
| **4L9** | A1 (b) | $60 on $1 grn | 2,500. |
| **4L10** | A1 (d) | $90 on $5 dk bl | 37.50 |

Surcharge on Nos. 4L7a is type "b" as illustrated. Surcharge on No. 4L7 differs from "b," having lower left character as in type "a."

Surcharge on No. 4L9 the upper left surcharge character differs from that shown in "b."

Pagoda on Yenan Hill — A2

**1948, June**

| | | | |
|---|---|---|---|
| **4L11** | A2 | $100 buff | 175.00 |
| **4L12** | A2 | $300 rose pink | 8.00 |
| **4L13** | A2 | $500 red | 8.50 |
| **4L14** | A2 | $1000 blue | 8.00 |
| **4L15** | A2 | $2000 yel grn | 24.00 |
| **4L16** | A2 | $5000 dull pur | 22.50 |
| | | *Nos. 4L11-4L16 (6)* | 246.00 |

Second issue; denominations in Chinese only. Many shades and proofs exist.

For surcharge see No. 4L24.

Pagoda on Yenan Hill (same size) — A3

**1948, Dec.**

| | | | |
|---|---|---|---|
| **4L17** | A3 | 10c yel org | 10.00 |
| **4L18** | A3 | 20c lemon | 10.00 |
| **4L19** | A3 | $1 dk blue | 10.00 |
| **4L20** | A3 | $2 vermilion | 10.00 |
| **4L21** | A3 | $5 pale bl grn | 25.00 |
| **4L22** | A3 | $10 violet | 35.00 |
| | | *Nos. 4L17-4L22 (6)* | 100.00 |

Third issue; ornamental border at sides. Many shades exist.

Nos. 4L2 and 4L13 Surcharged in Red or Black

**1949, Jan.**

| | | | | |
|---|---|---|---|---|
| **4L23** | A1 | $1 on $5 dk bl | 80.00 | 80.00 |
| **4L24** | A2 | $2 on $500 red | 40.00 | 40.00 |

Pagoda on Yenan Hill — A4

**1949, May 1**

| | | | | |
|---|---|---|---|---|
| **4L25** | A4 | 50c yel to olive | .85 | *2.00* |
| **4L26** | A4 | $1 dl bl to indigo | .85 | *2.00* |
| **4L27** | A4 | $3 ol yel to org yel | .85 | *2.00* |
| **4L28** | A4 | $5 blue green | 2.25 | *3.00* |
| *a.* | | Upper left character as on #4L25 | | |
| **4L29** | A4 | $10 vio to dp vio | 7.50 | *9.00* |
| **4L30** | A4 | $20 pink to rose red | 13.50 | *20.00* |
| | | *Nos. 4L25-4L30 (6)* | 25.80 | *38.00* |

Fourth issue; light shading at top of vignette, columns without ornaments at sides. Many shades exist.

China Nos. 959, F2 and E12 Overprinted ("People's Post, Shensi")

**1949, June 13 Engr. *Perf. 12½***

| | | | | |
|---|---|---|---|---|
| **4L31** | A96 | orange | 25.00 | 16.00 |
| **4L32** | R2 | carmine | 35.00 | 35.00 |
| **4L33** | SD2 | red vio | 35.00 | 35.00 |
| | | *Nos. 4L31-4L33 (3)* | 95.00 | 86.00 |

Stamps of China, Sun Yat-sen Type A94 of 1949, Overprinted in Black or Red ("People's Post, Shensi")

**Lithographed; Engraved**

**1949, July 1 *Perf. 14, 12½***

| | | | |
|---|---|---|---|
| **4L34** | $10 green (887) | 1.25 | 3.00 |
| **4L35** | $20 vio brn (888) | 1.25 | *3.00* |
| **4L36** | $20 vio brn (896) | 1.25 | 4.00 |
| **4L37** | $50 dk Prus grn (889; R) | 6.00 | 8.00 |
| **4L38** | $50 grn (951) | 6.00 | 8.00 |
| **4L39** | $100 org brn (890) | 14.50 | 15.00 |
| **4L40** | $500 ros lil (892) | 20.00 | 25.00 |
| **4L41** | $1000 dp bl (952; R) | 27.50 | 30.00 |
| **4L42** | $2000 vio (902;R) | 30.00 | 35.00 |
| **4L43** | $5000 car (953) | 45.00 | 30.00 |
| **4L44** | $10,000 brn (954) | 80.00 | 90.00 |
| | *Nos. 4L34-4L44 (11)* | 232.75 | 251.00 |

**Kansu-Ningsia-Tsinghai Area, Lanchow Overprints**

China Nos. 959a, F2 and E12 Overprinted ("People's Post, Kansu")

**1949, Oct. Engr. *Rouletted***

| | | | | |
|---|---|---|---|---|
| **4L45** | A96 | orange | 22.50 | 22.50 |

***Perf. 12½***

| | | | | |
|---|---|---|---|---|
| **4L46** | R2 | carmine | 32.50 | 32.50 |
| **4L47** | SD2 | red vio | 32.50 | 32.50 |
| | | *Nos. 4L45-4L47 (3)* | 87.50 | 87.50 |

Stamps of China, Sun Yat-sen Type A94 of 1949, Overprinted ("People's Post, Kansu")

**Engraved; Lithographed**

**1949, Oct. *Perf. 14, 12½***

| | | | |
|---|---|---|---|
| **4L48** | $10 grn (887) | 2.25 | 2.25 |
| **4L49** | $20 vio brn (888) | 2.25 | 3.25 |
| **4L50** | $50 dk Prus grn (889) | 5.25 | *8.25* |
| **4L51** | $100 org brn (890) | 3.50 | 3.25 |
| **4L52** | $100 dk org brn (898) | 5.25 | *6.00* |
| **4L53** | $200 red org (891) | 6.50 | 5.25 |
| **4L54** | $500 rose lil (892) | 6.50 | 5.25 |
| **4L55** | $1000 blue (894) | 3.50 | 3.25 |
| **4L56** | $1000 dp bl (901) | 6.50 | *7.50* |
| **4L57** | $2000 vio (902) | 11.00 | *15.00* |
| **4L58** | $5000 lt bl (903) | 22.00 | *27.50* |
| **4L59** | $10,000 sepia (904) | 30.00 | *37.50* |
| **4L60** | $20,000 ap grn (905) | 60.00 | *72.50* |
| | *Nos. 4L48-4L60 (13)* | 164.50 | 196.75 |

No. 4L54-4L60 exist with wider spaced overprints.

China Nos. 959, F2 and 791-792 Surcharged in Black or Red ("People's Post, Sinkiang")

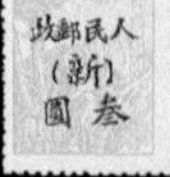

**1949, Oct.**

| | | | | |
|---|---|---|---|---|
| **4L61** | A96 | $1 on org | 12.00 | *13.50* |
| **4L62** | R2 | $3 on car | 18.00 | *20.00* |
| **4L63** | A82 | 10c on $50,000 dp bl (R) | 40.00 | 40.00 |
| **4L64** | A82 | $1.50 on $100,000 dl grn (R) | 80.00 | 80.00 |
| | | *Nos. 4L61-4L64 (4)* | 150.00 | 153.50 |

**Northwest People's Post**

Mao Tse-tung A5

Great Wall A6

**1949, Oct. 15 Litho. *Imperf.***

| | | | | |
|---|---|---|---|---|
| **4L65** | A5 | $50 rose | 7.00 | *3.75* |
| *a.* | | $200 cliche in $50 plate | *225.00* | |
| **4L66** | A6 | $100 dark blue | 1.75 | *2.00* |
| **4L67** | A5 | $200 orange | 6.50 | *6.00* |
| **4L68** | A6 | $400 sepia | 12.00 | *7.50* |
| | | *Nos. 4L65-4L68 (4)* | 27.25 | *19.25* |

## EAST CHINA

The East China Liberation Area included the provinces of Shantung, Kiangsu, Chekiang, Anhwei and Fukien. The original postal service established in Shantung in 1941, became the East China Posts and Telegraph General Office in July, 1948.

**All Stamps Issued without Gum**

Mao Tse-tung — A1

**1948, Mar. Litho. *Perf. 10½***

| | | | | |
|---|---|---|---|---|
| **5L1** | A1 | $50 yel org | 2.00 | *3.00* |
| **5L2** | A1 | $100 dp rose | 6.00 | *8.00* |
| **5L3** | A1 | $200 dk vio bl | 6.00 | *8.00* |
| **5L4** | A1 | $300 brt grn | 7.50 | *8.00* |
| **5L5** | A1 | $500 dp blue | 2.50 | *8.00* |
| **5L6** | A1 | $800 vermilion | 7.50 | *8.00* |
| **5L7** | A1 | $1000 dk blue | 12.00 | *15.00* |
| **5L8** | A1 | $5000 rose | 30.00 | 30.00 |
| **5L9** | A1 | $10,000 dp car | 75.00 | 75.00 |
| | | *Nos. 5L1-5L9 (9)* | 148.50 | *163.00* |

Many varieties, including unissued imperforates exist.

Transportation and Tower — A2

***Perf. 9 to 11 and compound***

**1949, Apr. Litho.**

| | | | | |
|---|---|---|---|---|
| **5L10** | A2 | $1 yel grn | .95 | *1.00* |
| **5L11** | A2 | $2 blue grn | .60 | *1.00* |
| **5L12** | A2 | $3 dull red | .60 | *1.00* |
| **5L13** | A2 | $5 pale brn (ovpt. 4x4mm) | .60 | *1.00* |
| *a.* | | Without overprint | 65.00 | 65.00 |
| *b.* | | Overprint 3x3mm | 1.25 | *3.00* |
| *c.* | | As "b," purple overprint | 65.00 | |
| **5L14** | A2 | $10 ultra | .90 | *1.00* |
| **5L15** | A2 | $13 brt vio | .60 | *1.00* |
| **5L16** | A2 | $18 brt blue | .60 | *1.00* |
| **5L17** | A2 | $21 vermilion | .90 | *1.00* |
| **5L18** | A2 | $30 gray | .60 | *3.00* |
| **5L19** | A2 | $50 crimson | 2.25 | *4.00* |
| **5L20** | A2 | $100 olive | 27.50 | 27.50 |
| | | *Nos. 5L10-5L20 (11)* | 36.10 | *42.50* |

Seventh anniv. of Shantung Communist Postal Administration. The overprint on the $5, character "yu" meaning "Posts," obliterates Japanese flag on tower, erroneously included in design. Value, imperfs. of Nos. 5L10-5L12, 5L13c, 5L14-5L20 on different paper, set $150.

Train and Postal Runner (1949.2.7) — A3

**1949, Apr. Litho. *Perf. 8 to 11***

**5L21** A3 $1 brt emer .30 *1.50*
**5L22** A3 $2 blue grn .30 *1.50*
**5L23** A3 $3 dk red .30 *1.50*
**5L24** A3 $5 brown .35 *2.00*
**5L25** A3 $10 ultra .60 *2.25*
**5L26** A3 $13 brt vio .35 *1.75*
**5L27** A3 $18 brt blue .35 *1.75*
**5L28** A3 $21 vermilion 3.50 *4.00*
**5L29** A3 $30 slate .35 *2.25*
**5L30** A3 $50 crimson .45 *2.25*
**5L31** A3 $100 olive 2.00 *3.50*
*Nos. 5L21-5L31 (11)* 8.85 24.25

7th anniv. of Shantung P. O., Feb. 7. Imperf. sets were sold by the Philatelic Dept., Tientsin P.O. Value $40. See Nos. 5L69-5L76. For surcharges see People's Republic of China Nos. 77-81.

Mao, Soldiers, Map — A4

***Perf. 9½ to 11 and comp.***

**1949, Apr.**

**5L32** A4 $1 brt emer .40 *1.00*
**5L33** A4 $2 blue grn .40 *1.00*
**5L34** A4 $3 dull red .40 *1.00*
**5L35** A4 $5 brown .40 *1.00*
**5L36** A4 $10 ultra .60 *1.00*
**5L37** A4 $13 brt vio .60 *1.50*
**5L38** A4 $18 brt blue .60 *1.50*
**5L39** A4 $21 vermilion .60 *1.50*
**5L40** A4 $30 gray .60 *1.50*
**5L41** A4 $50 crimson .60 *1.50*
**5L42** A4 $100 olive 6.75 *8.00*
*Nos. 5L32-5L42 (11)* 11.95 *20.50*

Victory of Hwai-Hai (Hwaiying and Haichow). Imperf. sets were sold by the Philatelic Dept., Tientsin P.O. Value, set $100.

### Stamps of China, Sun Yat-sen Type of 1949, Surcharged in Red or Black

(Nanking) — a

(Wuhu) — b

**1949, May 4 Engr. *Perf. 12½***

**5L43** A94 (a) $1 on $10 grn (895, R) 1.00 2.00
*a.* Perf. 13 3.25 3.00
**5L44** A94 (a) $3 on $20 vio brn (896) 3.00 4.00
*a.* Perf. 13 3.00 4.50
*b.* Perf. 14 5.75 5.50
*c.* Surcharge inverted 200.00

### Sun Yat-sen Type A94 Surcharged Type "b"

**Lithographed, Engraved**

**1949, May *Perf. 12½, 14***

**5L45** $30 on $1000 dp bl (901 10.00 7.50
**5L46** $30 on $1000 bl (894) 10.00 7.50
**5L47** $50 on $200 org red (899) 10.00 7.50
**5L48** $100 on $5000 lt bl (903, R) 22.50 20.00
**5L49** $300 on $10,000 sep (904, R) 67.50 60.00
**5L50** $500 on $200 org red (899) 100.00 85.00
*Nos. 5L45-5L50 (6)* 220.00 187.50

Many varieties exist.

China Nos. 913a and 913 Srchd. in Blue, Green, Black or Red, (East China)

**1949, May Litho. *Perf. 12½***

**5L51** A95 $5 on 50c on $20 brn, II (B) 17.50 16.00
*a.* Green surcharge 100.00 *100.00*
**5L52** A95 $10 on 50c on $20 brn, II 17.50 16.00
**5L53** A95 $20 on 50c on $20 red brn, II (R) 17.50 16.00
*a.* Type I (R) 21.00 21.00
*Nos. 5L51-5L53 (3)* 52.50 48.00

Stamps of China, Sun Yat-sen Type of 1949, Srchd. in Black or Red, (Hangchow)

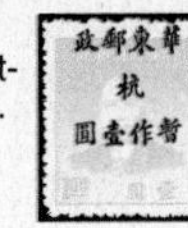

**Engr., Litho. (No. 5L57)**

**1949, June 25 *Perf. 14, 12½***

**5L54** A94 $1 on $1 org (886) 4.00 4.00
**5L55** A94 $3 on $20 vio brn (896, R) 2.00 2.00
**5L56** A94 $5 on $100 org brn (890) 7.50 7.50
**5L57** A94 $5 on $100 dk org brn (898) 5.00 5.00
**5L58** A94 $10 on $50 dk Prus grn (889, R) 24.00 24.00
**5L59** A94 $13 on $10 grn (895) 2.75 *2.75*
*Nos. 5L54-5L59 (6)* 45.25 45.25

### East China Liberation Area

Maps of Shanghai and Nanking — A5

**1949, May 30 Litho. *Perf. 8½ to 11***

**5L60** A5 $1 orange ver .30 *3.50*
**5L61** A5 $2 blue green .30 *3.50*
**5L62** A5 $3 brt violet .40 *3.50*
**5L63** A5 $5 violet brn .40 *.50*
**5L64** A5 $10 ultra .40 *1.00*
**5L65** A5 $30 slate .40 *3.00*
**5L66** A5 $50 carmine .40 *3.00*
**5L67** A5 $100 olive .40 *1.00*
**5L68** A5 $500 orange 15.00 8.00
*Nos. 5L60-5L68 (9)* 18.00 *27.00*

Liberation of Shanghai and Nanking. Many shades, paper and perforation varieties and imperfs. exist.

### Train and Postal Runner Type Dated "1949"

**1949, July-1950, Feb. *Perf. 12½, 14***

**5L69** A3 $10 dp ultra .30 *.25*
**5L70** A3 $15 orange ver .30 *.45*
*a.* $15 red, perf. 14 .50 .30
**5L71** A3 $30 slate green .30 .25
*a.* Perf. 12½ .50 .30
**5L72** A3 $50 carmine .30 *.50*
**5L73** A3 $60 bl grn, perf. 14 .30 *1.50*
**5L74** A3 $100 ol, perf. 14 8.00 2.00
**5L75** A3 $1600 vio bl ('50) .90 *4.00*
**5L76** A3 $2000 brn vio ('50) 1.00 *4.00*
*Nos. 5L69-5L76 (8)* 11.40 *12.95*

Chu Teh, Mao, Troops with Flags — A7

**1949, Aug. 17 *Perf. 12½***

**5L77** A7 $70 orange .40 *.35*
**5L78** A7 $270 crimson .50 *.35*
**5L79** A7 $370 emerald .60 .50
**5L80** A7 $470 vio brn 1.00 .60
**5L81** A7 $570 blue .50 *.50*
*Nos. 5L77-5L81 (5)* 3.00 2.30

22nd anniv. of the People's Liberation Army. For similar type see Southwest China A1.

Mao Tse-tung — A8

**1949, Oct.**

**5L82** A8 $10 dk blue 8.00 *15.00*
**5L83** A8 $15 vermilion 10.00 *15.00*
**5L84** A8 $70 brown .50 .50
**5L85** A8 $100 vio brn .50 .50
**5L86** A8 $150 orange .50 .50
**5L87** A8 $200 grnsh gray .50 .50
**5L88** A8 $500 gray bl .50 .50
**5L89** A8 $1000 rose .50 .50
**5L90** A8 $2000 emerald .50 .50
*Nos. 5L82-5L90 (9)* 21.50 *33.50*

For surcharges see People's Republic of China Nos. 82-84.

Stamps of China, Sun Yat-sen Type of 1949 Surcharged in Black or Red

**1949, Nov. Litho. *Perf. 12½***

**5L91** A94 $400 on $200 org red (899) 22.50 1.50
**5L92** A94 $1000 on $50 grnsh gray (897, R) 2.25 .70
**5L93** A94 $1200 on $100 dk org brn (898) .30 *1.50*
**5L94** A94 $1600 on $20,000 ap grn (905) .30 *3.00*
**5L95** A94 $2000 on $1000 dp bl (952,R) .30 *.75*
*a.* Perf. 14 45.00 25.00
*Nos. 5L91-5L95 (5)* 25.65 *7.45*

---

## EAST CHINA PARCEL POST STAMPS

Parcel Post Stamps of China 1945-48 Surcharged, (Shantung)

**1949, Aug. 1 Engr. *Perf. 13***

**5LQ1** PP1 $200 on $500 grn *10.00* 8.00
**5LQ2** PP1 $500 on $1000 bl 30.00 18.00

**Type PP3 *Perf. 13½***

**5LQ3** $200 on $200,000 dk grn 32.50 32.00
**5LQ4** $200 on $10,000,000 sage grn 32.50 32.00
**5LQ5** $500 on $7000 dl bl 65.00 65.00
**5LQ6** $500 on $50,000 indigo 12.00 12.00
**5LQ7** $1000 on $10,000 car rose 12.00 12.00
**5LQ8** $1000 on $100,000 dk rose brn 37.50 12.00
**5LQ9** $1000 on $300,000 pink 12.00 37.00
**5LQ10** $1000 on $500,000 vio brn 90.00 12.00
**5LQ11** $1000 on $8,000,000 org ver 15.00 90.00
**5LQ12** $2000 on $5,000,000 dl vio 30.00 30.00
**5LQ13** $2000 on $6,000,000 brn blk 55.00 55.00
**5LQ14** $3000 on $30,000 ol 60.00 60.00
**5LQ15** $3000 on $70,000 org brn 30.00 30.00
**5LQ16** $5000 on $3,000,000 dl bl 90.00 90.00
*Nos. 5LQ1-5LQ16 (16)* 613.50 595.00

### China Type A97, No. 987 Surcharged

華東郵政
$200 $500
$1000 $2000
$5000 $10,000

**1949, Sept. 7 Litho. *Perf. 12½***

**5LQ17** $200 on $10 35.00 15.00
**5LQ18** $500 on $10 35.00 15.00
**5LQ19** $1000 on $10 35.00 15.00
**5LQ20** $2000 on $10 50.00 32.50
**5LQ21** $5000 on $10 75.00 50.00
**5LQ22** $10,000 on $10 150.00 75.00
*Nos. 5LQ17-5LQ22 (6)* 380.00 202.50

Flying Geese Type of China, 1949, and China Nos. 984-986 Surcharged in Red or Black

**1950, Jan. 28**

**5LQ23** A97 $5000 on 10c bl vio (R) 30.00 25.00
**5LQ24** A97 $10,000 on $1 brn org 45.00 40.00
**5LQ25** A97 $20,000 on $2 bl 75.00 70.00
**5LQ26** A97 $50,000 on $5 car rose 130.00 130.00
*Nos. 5LQ23-5LQ26 (4)* 280.00 265.00

Parcel Post Stamps of China Type PP3, Nos. Q1-Q2, Q12-Q13 Surcharged in Red or Black

**1950, Jan. 28 Engr. *Perf. 13, 13½***

**5LQ27** $5000 on $500 grn (R) .75 *15.00*
**5LQ28** $10,000 on $1000 bl (R) 80.00 65.00
**5LQ29** $20,000 on $3000 bl grn 140.00 110.00
**5LQ30** $50,000 on $5000 org red 7.50 *75.00*
*Nos. 5LQ27-5LQ30 (4)* 228.25 265.00

---

## CENTRAL CHINA

The Central Chinese Liberation Area included the provinces of Honan, Hupeh, Hunan and Kiangsi. The area was established between August and September, 1949, following the occupation of Hankow by Red Army forces.

### All Stamps Issued without Gum

### Hupeh Postal and Telegraph Administration

Stamps of China, Sun Yat-sen Type A94 of 1949, Surcharged ("Chinese P.O., Temporary Use")

**Engraved; Lithographed**

**1949, June 4 *Perf. 14, 12½***

**Thin parallel lines**

**6L1** $1 on $200 red org (891) 4.00 *4.50*
**6L2** $6 on $10,000 sep (904) 4.00 *4.50*
**6L3** $15 on $1 org (886) 4.00 *4.50*
**6L4** $30 on $100 org brn (890) 7.50 6.00
**6L5** $30 on $100 dk org brn (898) 4.00 *4.50*
**6L6** $50 on $20 vio brn (896) 25.00 14.00
**6L7** $80 on $1000 dp bl (901) 5.50 5.00

**Thick parallel lines**

**6L8** $1 on $200 red org (891) 7.00 7.00
**6L9** $3 on $5000 lt bl (903) 3.50 *4.00*
**6L10** $10 on $500 rose lil (892) 3.50 *4.00*
**6L11** $10 on $500 rose lil (900) 5.25 *5.75*
**6L12** $50 on $20 vio brn (888) 7.00 *7.50*
**6L13** $50 on $20 vio brn (896) 4.00 *5.00*
**6L14** $80 on $1000 bl (894) 6.50 5.00
**6L15** $80 on $1000 dp bl (901) 27.00 16.00
**6L16** $100 on $50 dk Prus grn (903) 5.00 *6.00*
*Nos. 6L1-6L16 (16)* 122.75 103.25

### Kiangsi Postal and Telegraph Administration.

Central Trust Revenue Stamps of China Surcharged ("People's Post, Kiangsi")

(same size) — A1

$30

$60

**1949, June 20 Engr. *Perf. 12½***

**6L17** A1 $3 on $30 pur 2.50 3.00
**6L18** A1 $15 on $15 red org 7.00 3.00
**6L19** A1 $30 on $50 dk bl 7.00 3.00
**6L20** A1 $60 on $50 dk bl 7.00 3.00
**6L21** A1 $130 on $15 red org 4.00 3.00

The $15 surcharge has 3 characters in left vertical row, the $130 surcharge has 5.

### Same Surcharge on Sun Yat-sen Issues of China, 1945-49

**Engraved, Lithographed**

*Perf. 14, 12½*

**6L22** A82 $1 on $250 dp lil (746) 6.50 16.00
**6L23** A94 $5 on $1000 dp bl (901) 6.50 16.00
**6L24** A94 $5 on $2000 vio (902) 6.50 16.00
**6L25** A94 $5 on $5000 lt bl (903) 3.50 12.00
**6L26** A94 $10 on $1000 bl (894) 6.50 16.00
**6L27** A82 $20 on $4000 gray 4.50 10.00
**6L28** A73 $30 on $100 dk car 6.50 16.00
**6L29** A82 $30 on $20,000 rose pink 4.50 10.00
**6L30** A94 $80 on $500 rose lil (900) 4.00 12.00
**6L31** A94 $100 on $1000 dp bl (901) 3.50 12.00
**6L32** A82 $200 on $250 dp lil 4.50 12.00
*Nos. 6L17-6L32 (16)* 84.50 163.00

### Central China Posts and Telegraph Administration

Farmer, Soldier and Worker
A2 A3

I — Top white line of square character (yuan) at upper left does not touch left vertical stroke. No gap in shading between soldier's feet.

II — Top line connects with left vertical stroke. Gap in shading between feet.

***Perf. 10 to 11½ & Comp.***

**1949** **Litho.**

**6L33** A2 $1 orange 10.00 12.00
**6L34** A2 $3 brn org 6.00 8.00
**6L35** A2 $6 emerald 7.50 10.00
**6L36** A3 $7 yel brn 1.00 *4.00*
**6L37** A2 $10 bl grn .30 *3.00*
**6L38** A3 $14 org brn 35.00 35.00
**6L39** A2 $15 ultra 2.00 *5.00*
**6L40** A2 $30 grn, type I .30 *3.00*
*a.* Type II .80 .70
**6L41** A3 $35 gray bl 25.00 *30.00*
**6L42** A2 $50 rose vio 12.00 14.00
**6L43** A3 $70 dp grn .70 3.00
**6L44** A2 $80 pink .90 *10.00*
**6L45** A3 $100 bl grn .80 *8.00*
**6L46** A3 $220 rose red 4.00 *6.00*
*Nos. 6L33-6L46 (14)* 105.50 151.00

Nos. 6L33 and 6L34 exist imperf. Value, each $13.50.

For surcharges & overprints see Nos. 6L63-6L65, 6L66-6L73, 6L75, 6L90-6L98, 6L100-6L108.

Star Enclosing Map of Hankow Area — A4

Two types of $500:
I — Thick numerals of "500." No period after "500."
II — Thin numerals and period.

Two types of $1000:
I — No period after "1000."
II — Period after "1000."

**1949, July**

**6L48** A4 $110 org brn 1.00 *1.25*
**6L49** A4 $130 violet 5.00 3.00
**6L50** A4 $200 dp org .50 *.50*
**6L51** A4 $290 brown 1.75 1.25
**6L52** A4 $370 dk bl 1.75 1.25
**6L53** A4 $500 lt bl, I 7.50 1.50
*a.* $500 blue, II 20.00 7.00
**6L54** A4 $1000 dull red, II 20.00 2.00
*a.* $1000 dark red, I 27.50 14.00
**6L55** A4 $5000 brown 5.00 5.00
**6L56** A4 $10,000 brt pink 6.00 6.00
*Nos. 6L48-6L56 (9)* 48.50 21.75

For surcharges and overprints see Nos. 6L74, 6L76-6L81, 6L99, 6L109.

Hankow River Customs Building — A5

River Wall, Wuchang — A6

Design: $290, $370, River scene, Hanyang.

**1949, Aug. 16** ***Perf. 11***

**6L57** A5 $70 green 3.00 3.00
**6L58** A5 $220 crimson 3.00 3.00
**6L59** A5 $290 brown 3.00 3.00
**6L60** A5 $370 brt blue 3.00 3.00
**6L61** A6 $500 purple 7.00 7.00
**6L62** A6 $1000 vermilion 7.00 7.00
*Nos. 6L57-6L62 (6)* 26.00 26.00

Liberation of Hankow, Wuchang and Hanyang.
Exist imperf. Twice the value of used.
For overprints see Nos. 6L82-6L87.

Nos. 6L35, 6L39 and 6L40 Surcharged in Red ("Honan Renminbi Currency")

**1949, July**

**6L63** A2 $7 on $6 emer 7.00 7.00
**6L64** A2 $14 on $15 ultra 7.50 *7.50*
**6L65** A2 $70 on $30 grn 9.00 *10.00*
*Nos. 6L63-6L65 (3)* 23.50 24.50

Surcharge shown is for $70. The $7 has 5 characters in left column and no bottom line.

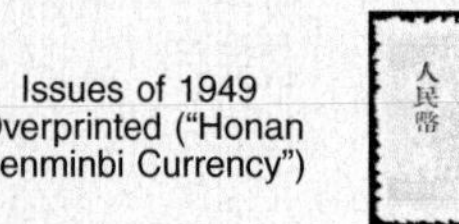

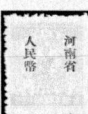

Issues of 1949 Overprinted ("Honan Renminbi Currency")

**1949, Aug.**

**6L66** A2 $3 brn org .95 *2.00*
**6L67** A3 $7 yel brn .95 *2.00*
**6L68** A2 $10 bl grn 1.90 *4.00*
**6L69** A3 $14 org brn 1.90 *5.00*
**6L70** A2 $30 yel grn (6L40a) 2.00 *5.00*
**6L71** A3 $35 gray bl .95 *5.00*
**6L72** A2 $50 rose vio 7.00 *8.00*
**6L73** A3 $70 dp grn 2.00 *5.00*
**6L74** A4 $110 org brn 7.00 *8.00*
**6L75** A3 $220 rose red 6.00 6.00
**6L76** A4 $290 brown 6.00 *8.00*
**6L77** A4 $370 blue 10.00 *12.00*
**6L78** A4 $500 bl, II 12.00 *15.00*
**6L79** A4 $1000 dk red, I 25.00 *30.00*
**6L80** A4 $5000 brown 100.00 *125.00*
**6L81** A4 $10,000 brt pink 200.00 *225.00*
*Nos. 6L66-6L81 (16)* 383.65 *465.00*

Width of the overprint varies slightly.

Nos. 6L57-6L62 Overprinted ("Honan Renminbi Currency")

**1949, Aug.** ***Perf. 11***

**6L82** A5 $70 green 2.50 *10.00*
**6L83** A5 $220 crimson 4.00 *15.00*
**6L84** A5 $290 brown 4.00 *18.00*
**6L85** A5 $370 brt bl 6.00 *18.00*
**6L86** A6 $500 purple 6.00 *22.00*
**6L87** A6 $1000 vermilion 8.00 *30.00*
*Nos. 6L82-6L87 (6)* 30.50 *113.00*

Width of overprint on Nos. 6L82-6L85, 7mm; on Nos. 6L86-6L87, 12mm.
Exist imperf. About the same value.

### Changchow Issue Surcharged in Red ("Honan Renminbi Currency")

(same size) Mao Tse-tung — A7

**1949, Sept.** ***Perf. 10***

**6L88** A7 $290 on $30 yel grn 30.00 *32.50*
**6L89** A7 $370 on $30 yel grn 37.50 *50.00*

Issues of 1949 Surcharged

**1950, Jan.**

**6L90** A2 $200 on $1 .55 *1.75*
**6L91** A2 $200 on $3 3.00 1.60
**6L92** A2 $200 on $6 .55 *1.75*
**6L93** A3 $200 on $7 3.00 1.60
**6L94** A3 $200 on $14 3.00 1.60
**6L95** A3 $200 on $35 3.25 2.40
**6L96** A3 $200 on $70 3.00 1.60
**6L97** A2 $200 on $80 3.00 1.60
**6L98** A3 $200 on $220 3.00 1.60
**6L99** A4 $200 on $370 .50 *1.75*
**6L100** A3 $300 on $70 .50 *2.50*
**6L101** A2 $300 on $80 .50 *1.75*
**6L102** A3 $300 on $220 .30 *1.75*
**6L103** A2 $1200 on $3 27.50 27.50
**6L104** A3 $1200 on $7 5.25 5.00
**6L105** A3 $1500 on $14 7.00 6.75
**6L106** A2 $2100 on $1 35.00 35.00
**6L107** A2 $2100 on $6 35.00 35.00
**6L108** A3 $2100 on $35 10.00 9.00
**6L109** A4 $5000 on $370 4.50 4.50
*Nos. 6L90-6L109 (20)* 148.40 146.00

Two types of surcharge exist, differing in spacing of characters in top row.

### CENTRAL CHINA PARCEL POST STAMPS

Star and Map of Hankow — PP1

**1949, Nov.** **Litho.** ***Perf. 11, 11½***

**6LQ1** PP1 $5000 brown 4.50 *5.75*
**6LQ2** PP1 $10,000 scarlet 19.00 17.00
**6LQ3** PP1 $20,000 dk sl grn 9.50 *18.00*
**6LQ4** PP1 $50,000 vermilion 5.00 *35.00*
*Nos. 6LQ1-6LQ4 (4)* 38.00 *75.75*

### SOUTH CHINA

The South China Liberation Area included the provinces of Kwangtung and Kwangsi and Hainan Island. The South China Postal and Telegraph Administration was organized on or about Nov. 4, 1949.

**All Stamps Issued without Gum**

Pearl River Bridge, Canton — A1

**1949, Nov. 4** **Litho.** ***Imperf.***

**7L1** A1 $10 green .85 *4.00*
**7L2** A1 $20 sepia .85 *4.00*
**7L3** A1 $30 violet .85 *4.00*
**7L4** A1 $50 carmine .85 *4.00*
**7L5** A1 $100 ultramarine 1.50 *4.00*
*Nos. 7L1-7L5 (5)* 4.90 *20.00*

For surcharges see Nos. 7L19-7L23.

China Nos. 993-995 With Additional Overprint in Red ("Liberation of Swatow")

**1949, Nov. 9**

**7L6** A94 2½c on $500 rose lil (993) 35.00 35.00
*a.* Handstamped 80.00 80.00
**7L7** A94 2½c on $500 rose lil (994) 40.00 40.00
*a.* Handstamped 95.00 95.00
**7L8** A94 15c on $10 grn (995) 50.00 50.00
*a.* Handstamped 175.00 175.00

**On Unit Issues of China, 1949**

**7L9** A96 org (959) 19.00 12.50
**7L10** AP5 bl grn (C62) 24.00 *27.50*
**7L11** SD2 red vio (E12) 24.00 *27.50*
**7L12** R2 car (F2) 20.00 *27.50*

**On Sun Yat-sen and Flying Geese Issues of China**

**7L13** A94 2c org (974) 150.00 *200.00*
**7L14** A94 4c bl grn (975) 300.00 *400.00*
**7L15** A94 10c dp lil (976) 20.00 *20.00*
**7L16** A94 20c bl (978) 40.00 *32.50*
**7L17** A97 $1 brn org (984) 45.00 30.00
**7L18** A97 $10 bl grn (987) 450.00 400.00
*Nos. 7L6-7L18 (13)* 1,217. 1,303.

Forgeries exist of Nos. 7L13-7L14, 7L18.

Nos. 7L1-7L3 Surcharged in Red or Green

**1950, Jan.**

**7L19** A1 $300 on $30 vio (R) 4.00 6.00
**7L20** A1 $500 on $20 brn (R) 4.00 6.00
**7L21** A1 $800 on $30 vio (G) 5.00 8.00
**7L22** A1 $1000 on $10 gray grn (R) 5.00 8.00
**7L23** A1 $1000 on $20 brn (R) 5.00 8.00
*Nos. 7L19-7L23 (5)* 23.00 36.00

### SOUTHWEST CHINA

The Southwest China Liberation Area included the provinces of Kweichow, Szechwan, Yunnan, Sikang and Tibet. The Southwest Postal and Telegraph Administration was organized on or about Nov. 15, 1949 after the liberation of Kweiyang, capital of Kweichow Province.

**All Stamps Issued without Gum**

Chu Teh, Mao and Troops — A1

**1949, Dec.** **Litho.** ***Perf. 12½***

**8L1** A1 $10 deep blue 4.00 *4.25*
**8L2** A1 $20 rose claret .45 *2.00*
**8L3** A1 $30 dp org .60 *2.00*
**8L4** A1 $50 gray grn 1.00 *2.00*
**8L5** A1 $100 carmine .90 *1.50*
**8L6** A1 $200 blue 1.25 *1.50*
**8L7** A1 $300 bl vio 1.50 *2.00*
**8L8** A1 $500 dk gray 3.00 *4.00*
**8L9** A1 $1000 pale pur 11.00 *12.00*
**8L10** A1 $2000 green 20.00 *20.00*
**8L11** A1 $5000 orange 57.50 *60.00*
*Nos. 8L1-8L11 (11)* 101.20 *111.25*

For surcharges and overprints see Nos. 8L21-8L29, 8L40-8L47, 8L55.

China Nos. 974-975, 984, 986-987 Surcharged ("Kweichow People's Post")

**1949, Dec. 1** ***Perf. 12½***

**8L12** A94 $20 on 2c org 12.00 *15.00*
**8L13** A94 $50 on 4c bl grn 18.00 18.00
**8L14** A97 $100 on $1 brn org 30.00 21.00
**8L15** A97 $400 on $5 car rose 60.00 *65.00*
**8L16** A97 $2000 on $10 bl grn 210.00 130.00
*Nos. 8L12-8L16 (5)* 330.00 249.00

Map of China, Flag Planted in Southwest — A2

**1950, Jan.** **Litho.** ***Perf. 9 to 11½***

**8L17** A2 $20 dark blue 1.25 *2.50*
**8L18** A2 $30 green 2.75 *3.00*
**8L19** A2 $50 red 1.75 *3.50*
**8L20** A2 $100 brown 2.75 *3.50*
*Nos. 8L17-8L20 (4)* 8.50 *12.50*

Liberation of the Southwest.
For surcharges see Nos. 8L30-8L39, 8L56-8L59.

**Nos. 8L5-8L6 Surcharged**

No. 8L22

$300

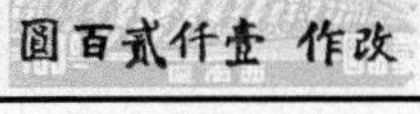

$1200

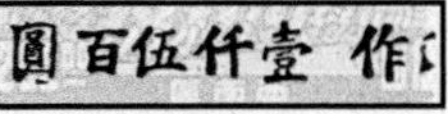

$1500

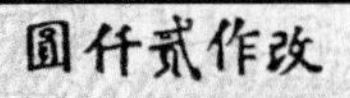

$2000

*Perf. 12½*

| | | | | |
|---|---|---|---|---|
| **8L21** | A1 | $300 on $100 car | 3.50 | 12.00 |
| **8L22** | A1 | $500 on $100 car | 3.50 | 12.00 |
| **8L23** | A1 | $1200 on $100 car | 7.00 | 20.00 |
| **8L24** | A1 | $1500 on $200 bl | 7.00 | 20.00 |
| **8L25** | A1 | $2000 on $200 bl | 11.00 | 26.00 |
| | | *Nos. 8L21-8L25 (5)* | 32.00 | 90.00 |

Nos. 8L5-8L6 Overprinted ("East Szechwan")

**1950, Jan.**

| | | | | |
|---|---|---|---|---|
| **8L26** | A1 | $100 carmine | 9.00 | 18.00 |
| **8L27** | A1 | $200 blue | 9.00 | 22.00 |

Nos. 8L5-8L6 Handstamp Surcharged

**1950, Jan.**

| | | | | |
|---|---|---|---|---|
| **8L28** | A1 | $1200 on $100 car | 15.00 | *27.50* |
| **8L29** | A1 | $1500 on $200 bl | 40.00 | *27.50* |

Many varieties, including wide and narrow settings, exist.

**Nos. 8L17-8L20 Surcharged in Black or Red**

$60

$150

$300

$1500

$3000

$5000

$10,000

$20,000

$50,000

**1950** *Perf. 9 to 11½*

| | | | | |
|---|---|---|---|---|
| **8L30** | A2 | $60 on $30 | 12.00 | 9.00 |
| **8L31** | A2 | $150 on $30 | 12.00 | 9.00 |
| **8L32** | A2 | $300 on $20 (R) | 2.00 | *4.00* |
| **8L33** | A2 | $300 on $100 | 12.00 | 9.00 |
| **8L34** | A2 | $1500 on $100 | 72.50 | 22.50 |
| **8L35** | A2 | $3000 on $50 | 7.75 | *22.50* |
| **8L36** | A2 | $5000 on $50 | 3.50 | *22.50* |
| **8L37** | A2 | $10,000 on $50 | 120.00 | 42.50 |
| **8L38** | A2 | $20,000 on $50 | 4.00 | *42.50* |
| **8L39** | A2 | $50,000 on $50 | 5.75 | *60.00* |
| | | *Nos. 8L30-8L39 (10)* | 251.50 | 243.50 |

Nos. 8L5-8L7 Overprinted ("West Szechwan")

**1950, Jan.** *Perf. 12½*

| | | | | |
|---|---|---|---|---|
| **8L40** | A1 | $100 carmine | 22.50 | *24.00* |
| **8L41** | A1 | $200 pale blue | 30.00 | *32.50* |
| **8L42** | A1 | $300 blue violet | 40.00 | *42.50* |
| | | *Nos. 8L40-8L42 (3)* | 92.50 | 99.00 |

**Nos. 8L4-8L7 Surcharged**

No. 8L43

No. 8L44

No. 8L45

No. 8L46

No. 8L47

**1950, Jan.**

| | | | | |
|---|---|---|---|---|
| **8L43** | A1 | $500 on $100 | 8.75 | 8.75 |
| *a.* | | Narrow spacing | 70.00 | 60.00 |
| **8L44** | A1 | $800 on $100 | 8.75 | 8.75 |
| **8L45** | A1 | $1000 on $50 | 11.00 | 11.00 |
| **8L46** | A1 | $2000 on $200 | 22.50 | 27.50 |
| **8L47** | A1 | $3000 on $300 | 35.00 | 45.00 |
| | | *Nos. 8L43-8L47 (5)* | 86.00 | 101.00 |

Two lines of surcharge 7mm apart on No. 8L43, 4mm on No. 8L43a.

**China Nos. 975 and 977 Surcharged**

No. 8L48

No. 8L50

*Perf. 12½, 13 or Compound*

**1950, Jan.**

| | | | | |
|---|---|---|---|---|
| **8L48** | A94 | $100 on 4c | 7.50 | *13.50* |
| **8L49** | A94 | $200 on 4c | 12.00 | *22.50* |
| **8L50** | A94 | $800 on 16c | 67.50 | 67.50 |
| **8L51** | A94 | $1000 on 16c | 300.00 | *375.00* |
| | | *Nos. 8L48-8L51 (4)* | 387.00 | 478.50 |

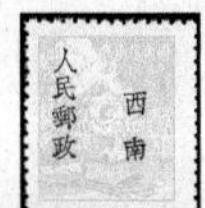

Unit Issue of China Overprinted ("Southwest People's Post")

**1950, Jan.** **Engr.** *Rouletted*

| | | | | |
|---|---|---|---|---|
| **8L52** | A96 | orange | 150.00 | 175.00 |
| *a.* | | Perf. 12½ | 225.00 | 250.00 |

*Perf. 12½*

| | | | | |
|---|---|---|---|---|
| **8L53** | SD2 | red violet | 225.00 | 250.00 |
| **8L54** | R2 | carmine | 225.00 | 250.00 |
| | | *Nos. 8L52-8L54 (3)* | 600.00 | 675.00 |

On No. 8L54, space between overprint columns is 3mm and right column is raised to height of left.

Nos. 8L3, 8L17-8L20 Surcharged in Black or Red

**1950, Mar.** *Perf. 12½, 9 to 11½*

| | | | | |
|---|---|---|---|---|
| **8L55** | A1 | $800 on $30 | 45.00 | 45.00 |
| **8L56** | A2 | $1000 on $50 | 9.00 | *12.00* |
| **8L57** | A2 | $2000 on $100 | 13.50 | *18.00* |
| **8L58** | A2 | $4000 on $20 (R) | 35.00 | *40.00* |
| **8L59** | A2 | $5000 on $30 | 55.00 | 55.00 |
| | | *Nos. 8L55-8L59 (5)* | 157.50 | *170.00* |

## CHRISTMAS ISLAND

'kris-məs 'ī-lənd

LOCATION — In the Indian Ocean, 230 miles south of Java
GOVT. — A territory of Australia
AREA — 52 sq. mi.
POP. — 2,373 (1999 est.)

Australia took over Christmas Island from Singapore in 1958.

**Catalogue values for all unused stamps in this country are for Never Hinged items.**

Queen Elizabeth II — A1

**Engr.; Name and Value Typo. in Black**

**1958, Oct. 15** **Unwmk.** *Perf. 14½*

| | | | | |
|---|---|---|---|---|
| **1** | A1 | 2c yellow orange | .45 | .80 |
| **2** | A1 | 4c brown | .55 | .35 |
| **3** | A1 | 5c lilac | .55 | .50 |
| **4** | A1 | 6c dull blue | 1.60 | .35 |
| **5** | A1 | 8c gray brown | 3.00 | .50 |
| **6** | A1 | 10c violet | 2.25 | .35 |
| **7** | A1 | 12c carmine rose | 3.25 | 2.00 |
| **8** | A1 | 20c ultramarine | 2.25 | 2.00 |
| **9** | A1 | 50c yellow green | 3.25 | 2.00 |
| **10** | A1 | $1 greenish blue | 3.50 | 2.00 |
| | | *Nos. 1-10 (10)* | 20.65 | 10.85 |
| | | Set, hinged | 11.00 | |

Map of Island A2

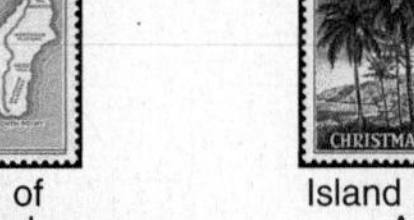

Island Scene A3

4c, Moonflower. 5c, Robber crab. 8c, Phosphate train. 10c, Crane loading phosphate. 12c, Flying fish cove. 20c, Loading ship. 50c, Frigate bird. $1, Yellow-billed tropic bird.

*Perf. 14x14½, 14½x14*

**1963, Aug. 28** **Engr.**

| | | | | |
|---|---|---|---|---|
| **11** | A2 | 2c orange | 1.00 | .55 |
| **12** | A2 | 4c red brown | .40 | .25 |
| **13** | A2 | 5c rose lilac | .40 | .35 |
| **14** | A3 | 6c slate | .35 | *.45* |
| **15** | A2 | 8c black | 2.00 | .45 |
| **16** | A2 | 10c violet | .35 | .25 |
| **17** | A3 | 12c dull red | .30 | .40 |
| **18** | A3 | 20c dark blue | 1.00 | .35 |
| **19** | A3 | 50c green | 1.25 | .35 |

**Size: 35x21mm**

| | | | | |
|---|---|---|---|---|
| **20** | A3 | $1 orange yellow | 1.75 | .45 |
| | | *Nos. 11-20 (10)* | 8.80 | 3.85 |
| | | Set, hinged | 6.50 | |

"Simpson and His Donkey" by Wallace Anderson — A3a

**1965, Apr. 14** **Photo.** *Perf. 13½x13*

| | | | | |
|---|---|---|---|---|
| **21** | A3a | 10c brt grn, sepia & blk | .55 | *1.25* |

ANZAC issue. See note after Australia No. 387.

Moorish Goddess — A4

Fish: 1c, Golden striped grouper. 3c, Forceps fish. 4c, Queen triggerfish. 5c, Regal angelfish. 9c, Surgeonfish. 10c, Turkeyfish. 15c, Saddleback butterflyfish. 20c, Clown butterflyfish. 30c, Ghost pipefish. 50c, Lined surgeonfish. $1, Meyer's butterflyfish.

**1968-70** **Photo.** *Perf. 13½*

| | | | | |
|---|---|---|---|---|
| **22** | A4 | 1c multicolored | .55 | .55 |
| **23** | A4 | 2c multicolored | .75 | .25 |
| **24** | A4 | 3c multicolored | .75 | .35 |
| **25** | A4 | 4c multicolored | .75 | .25 |
| *a.* | | Dark blue ("4c") omitted | 3,000. | |
| **26** | A4 | 5c multicolored | .75 | .30 |
| **27** | A4 | 9c multicolored | .75 | .60 |
| **28** | A4 | 10c multicolored | .75 | .30 |
| **29** | A4 | 15c multicolored | 6.00 | 3.00 |
| **30** | A4 | 20c multicolored | 1.75 | .90 |
| **31** | A4 | 30c multicolored | 6.00 | 3.00 |
| **32** | A4 | 50c multicolored | 2.25 | *2.50* |
| **33** | A4 | $1 multicolored | 2.25 | *2.50* |
| | | *Nos. 22-33 (12)* | 23.30 | 14.50 |
| | | Set, hinged | 15.00 | |

Issued: 15c, 30c, 12/14/70; others, 5/6/68.

**Christmas Issues**

"Hark the Herald Angels Sing" — A5

**1969, Nov. 10** **Photo.** *Perf. 13½*

| | | | | |
|---|---|---|---|---|
| **34** | A5 | 5c dk blue, gold, buff & red | .35 | .35 |

A6

3c, The Ansidei Madonna, by Raphael. 5c, Virgin and Child, by Morando.

**1970, Oct. 26** **Photo.** *Perf. 14x14½*

| | | | | |
|---|---|---|---|---|
| **35** | A6 | 3c gold & multi | .25 | .25 |
| **36** | A6 | 5c silver & multi | .25 | .25 |

A7

5c, Adoration of the Shepherds, Seville School. 20c, Adoration of the Shepherds, by Guido Reni.

**1971, Oct. 4**

| | | | | |
|---|---|---|---|---|
| **37** | A7 | 6c black & multi | .50 | .50 |
| **38** | A7 | 20c dark blue & multi | 1.15 | 1.15 |

"Flying Fish," 1887 — A8

Ships and Map of Christmas Island: 1c, "Eagle," 1714. 2c, "Redpole," 1890. 3c, "Hoi Houw," 1959. 4c, "Pigot," 1771. 5c, "Valetta," 1968. 7c, "Asia," 1805. 8c, "Islander," 1929-60. 9c, "Imperieuse," 1888 (incorrectly inscribed "Imperious"). 10c, "Egeria," 1887. 20c, "Thomas," 1615. 25c, "Gordon," 1864. 30c, "Cygnet," 1688. 35c, "Triadic," 1958. 50c, "Amethyst," 1857. $1, "Royal Mary," 1643.

**1972-73 Photo. *Perf. 14½x13½***

**39** A8 1c yel green & multi .30 *.55*
**40** A8 2c lt red brn & multi .35 *.65*
**41** A8 3c dp rose & multi .35 *.70*
**42** A8 4c multicolored .45 *.70*
**43** A8 5c multicolored .45 *.70*
**44** A8 6c lilac & multi .45 *.70*
**45** A8 7c lt green & multi .45 *.70*
**46** A8 8c blue & multi .50 *.70*
**47** A8 9c org & multi .75 *.65*
**48** A8 10c lem & multi .45 *.50*
**49** A8 20c tan & multi .50 *.80*
**50** A8 25c multicolored .60 *1.60*
**51** A8 30c multicolored .75 *1.00*
**52** A8 35c tan & multi .80 *1.00*
**53** A8 50c ultra & multi .90 *1.60*
**54** A8 $1 yellow & multi 1.25 *1.90*
*Nos. 39-54 (16)* 9.30 *14.45*

Issued: 6c, 7c, 8c, 20c, 2/5/72; 1c, 2c, 3c, $1, 6/5/72; 4c, 5c, 9c, 50c, 2/6/73; 10c, 25c, 30c, 35c, 6/4/73.

A9 56
"Peace" "Joy" — A9a

**1972, Oct. 2 Litho. *Perf. 14½***

**55** A9 3c black & multi .50 .50
**56** A9a 3c black & multi .50 .50
*a.* Pair, #55-56 1.25 1.25
**57** A9 7c black & multi .65 .65
**58** A9a 7c black & multi .65 .65
*a.* Pair, #57-58 1.50 1.50
*Nos. 55-58 (4)* 2.30 2.30

Mother and Child, Christmas Island Map — A10

**1973, Oct. 2 Photo. *Perf. 14½x13½***

**59** A10 7c blue & multi .60 .60
**60** A10 25c brt green & multi 1.75 1.75

Christmas.

Mother and Child with Star and Cross — A11

**1974, Oct. 2 Photo. *Perf. 13½x14½***

**61** A11 7c black & lilac rose .55 .55
**62** A11 30c black & yellow 1.60 *2.00*

Christmas.

Flight into Egypt — A12

**1975, Oct. 2 Photo. *Perf. 14½x13½***

**63** A12 10c gold, black & yel .40 .40
**64** A12 35c gold, vio blk & rose .90 *1.25*

Christmas.

Star of Bethlehem and Dove
A13 A14

**1976, Oct. 2 Photo. *Perf. 13½***

**65** A13 10c red & multi .25 .35
**66** A14 10c red & multi .25 .35
*a.* Pair, #65-66 .90 *1.50*
**67** A13 35c blue & multi .40 .55
**68** A14 35c blue & multi .40 .55
*a.* Pair, #67-68 1.10 *1.75*
*Nos. 65-68 (4)* 1.30 1.80

Christmas.

Andrew Clunies-Ross (first settler) — A15

Famous Visitors: 1c, William Dampier, explorer, buccaneer. 2c, Capt. Willem de Vlamingh, Dutch explorer. 3c, Vice Adm. John F. L. P. Maclear, Royal Navy. 4c, John Murray, oceanographer, scientist. 5c, Adm. Pelham Aldrich and crew collecting specimen. 7c, Joseph Jackson Lister, naturalist, and arenga listeri plant. 8c, Adm. William Henry May. 9c, Henry Nicholas Ridley, botanist. 10c, George Clunies-Ross, pioneer phosphate miner. 20c, Capt. Joshua Slocum. 45c, Charles William Andrews, zoologist, and frigate birds. 50c, Karl Richard Hanitsch, zoologist, and fruit pigeon. 75c, Victor W. W. Saunders Purcell, Sinologist. $1, Fam Choo Beng, educator. $2, Harold Spencer-Jones, astronomer.

**1977-78 Photo. *Perf. 14x13½***

**69** A15 1c multicolored .25 *.80*
**70** A15 2c multicolored .25 *.90*
**71** A15 3c multicolored .25 *.90*
**72** A15 4c multicolored .25 *.90*
**73** A15 5c multicolored .30 *.40*
**74** A15 6c multicolored .30 *.70*
**75** A15 7c multicolored .30 *.45*
**76** A15 8c multicolored .30 *.75*
**77** A15 9c multicolored .35 *1.75*
**78** A15 10c multicolored .30 *.55*
**79** A15 20c multicolored .35 *.70*
**80** A15 45c multicolored .65 .45
**81** A15 50c multicolored .90 *2.00*
**82** A15 75c multicolored .70 *1.25*
**83** A15 $1 multicolored .80 *1.25*
**84** A15 $2 multicolored 1.30 *2.00*
*Nos. 69-84 (16)* 7.55 *15.75*

Issued: 1c, 6c, 9c, $1, 4/30/77; 2c, 3c, 4c, $2, 2/22/78; 5c, 7c, 45c, 50c, 5/31/78; 8c, 10c, 20c, 75c, 9/1/78.

Australian Arms, Map of Christmas Island — A16

**1977, June 2 Litho. *Perf. 14½x13½***

**85** A16 45c multicolored .50 .50

25th anniv. of reign of Elizabeth II.

Souvenir Sheet

The Twelve Days of Christmas — A17

Twelve Days of Christmas: a, Partridge in a pear tree. b, 2 turtle doves. c, 3 French hens. d, 4 calling birds. e, 5 gold rings. f, 6 geese. g, 7 swans. h, 8 maids a-milking. i, 9 ladies dancing. j, 10 lords a-leaping. k, 11 pipers piping. l, 12 drummers drumming.

**Unwmk.**

**1977, Oct. 20 Litho. *Perf. 14***

**86** A17 Sheet of 12 1.50 *2.00*
*a.-l.* 10c, any single .25 .25
*m.* Wmk. 373 ('78) 2.75 *3.75*

Christmas.

Common Design Types pictured following the introduction.

**Elizabeth II Coronation Anniversary**
Common Design Types
Souvenir Sheet

**1978, Apr. 21 Litho. *Perf. 15***

**87** Sheet of 6 3.50 *4.00*
*a.* CD326 45c White swan of Bohun .55 *.60*
*b.* CD327 45c Elizabeth II .55 *.60*
*c.* CD328 45c Abbott's booby .55 *.60*

No. 87 contains 2 se-tenant strips of Nos. 87a-87c, separated by horizontal gutter with commemorative and descriptive inscriptions.

Souvenir Sheet

The Song of Christmas — A18

Song of Christmas: a, Christ Child. b, Herald angels. c, Redeemer. d, Israel. e, Star. f, Three Wise Men. g, Manger. h. "All He stands for." i, "Shepherds came."

**1978, Oct. 2 Litho. *Perf. 14***

**88** A18 Sheet of 9 1.50 *1.75*
*a.-i.* 10c single stamp .25 .25

Christmas. Each stamp design incorporates one letter of "Christmas."

IYC Emblem and Children — A19

No. 89 — Children holding hands or playing with country name in: a, Yellow green. b, Blue green. c, Lilac. d, Red, e, Bister.

**1979, Apr. 20 Litho. *Perf. 14***

**89** Strip of 5 1.50 2.25
*a.-e.* A19 20c single stamp .25 .45

International Year of the Child.

Rowland Hill and No. 25 — A20

Sir Rowland Hill (1795-1879), originator of penny postage, and Christmas Island stamps: a, #1. b, #11. c, #21. d, #25. e, #34.

**1979, Aug. 27 Litho. *Perf. 13x13½***

**90** Strip of 5 1.10 1.75
*a.-e.* A20 20c any single .25 .40

Three Kings Bearing Gifts — A21

Christmas: 55c, Virgin and Child, globe.

**1979, Oct. 22 Litho. *Perf. 14x14½***

**91** A21 20c multicolored .25 *.30*
**92** A21 55c multicolored .45 *.70*

25 Years of Golf — A22

**1980, Feb. 12 Litho. *Perf. 14½x14***

**93** A22 20c shown .35 .55
**94** A22 55c Clubhouse .95 1.40

Surveyor, Phosphate Industry — A23

No. 96, Drilling for samples. No. 97, Sample analysis. No. 98, Mine planning. No. 99, Jungle clearing. No. 100, Overburden removal. No. 101, Open cut mining. No. 102, Restoration. No. 103, Screening and stockpiling. No. 104, Loading train. No. 105, Rail transport. No. 106, Drying. No. 107, Crushing. No. 108, Pipeline. No. 109, Bulk storage. No. 110, Loading ship.

**1980-81 Litho. *Perf. 14x14½***

**95** A23 15c shown .25 .25
**96** A23 22c multicolored .25 .25
**97** A23 40c multicolored .30 .30
**98** A23 55c multicolored .45 .45
**99** A23 15c multicolored .25 .25
**100** A23 22c multicolored .25 .25
**101** A23 40c multicolored .30 .30
**102** A23 55c multicolored .45 .45
**103** A23 22c multicolored .30 .30
**104** A23 28c multicolored .35 .35
**105** A23 40c multicolored .45 .45
**106** A23 60c multicolored .55 .55
**107** A23 22c multicolored .30 .30
**108** A23 28c multicolored .35 .35
**109** A23 40c multicolored .45 .45
**110** A23 60c multicolored .55 .55
*Nos. 95-110 (16)* 5.80 5.80

Issued: Nos. 96-98, 5/5/80; Nos. 99-102, 7/14/80; Nos. 103-106, 2/9/81; NOs. 107-110, 5/4/81.

Souvenir Sheet

Christmas — A24

**1980, Oct. 6 Litho. *Perf. 13½x13***

**111** A24 Sheet of 6 1.60 *2.25*
*a.* 15c Angel .25 .25
*b.* 22c Virgin and child .25 .35
*c.* 60c Angel .30 .35
*d.* 15c Angel holding soldier .25 .35
*e.* 22c Kneeling woman and man .25 .35
*f.* 60c Chinese, Indian, European children .30 .35

Christmas. No. 111 contains 2 strips of 3 (Nos. 111a-111c and 111d-111f) with gutter between.

Cryptoblepharus Egeriae — A25

Reptiles: 30c, Emoia nativitata. 40c, Lepidodactylus listeri. 60c, Cyrtodactylus nov.

**1981, Aug. 10 Litho. *Perf. 13x13½***

**112** A25 24c shown .25 .25
**113** A25 30c multicolored .30 .30
**114** A25 40c multicolored .45 .45
**115** A25 60c multicolored .55 .55
*Nos. 112-115 (4)* 1.55 1.55

Souvenir Sheet

Christmas — A26

**1981, Oct. 19 Litho. *Perf. 14½x14***

| | | | | |
|---|---|---|---|---|
| **116** | A26 | Sheet of 4 | 1.60 | *2.00* |
| *a.* | | 18c Angels, star | .25 | *.30* |
| *b.* | | 24c Nativity | .25 | *.35* |
| *c.* | | 40c Children praying to Jesus | .50 | *.60* |
| *d.* | | 60c Children praying | .55 | *.75* |

Reef Heron — A27

2c, Noddies. 3c, Glossy swiftlet. 4c, Imperial pigeon. 5c, Christmas Isld. silvereyes. 10c, Thrush. 25c, Silver bosunbird. 30c, Christmas Isld. emerald doves. 40c, Brown boobies. 50c, Red-footed boobies. 65c, Christmas Isld. frigatebird. 75c, Golden bosunbirds. 80c, Nankeen kestrel, vert. $1, Christmas Isld. hawk owl, vert. $2, Goshawk, vert. $4, Abbott's boobies, vert.

**1982-83 Litho. *Perf. 14***

| | | | | |
|---|---|---|---|---|
| **117** | A27 | 1c shown | .65 | .25 |
| **118** | A27 | 2c multicolored | .65 | .25 |
| **119** | A27 | 3c multicolored | .65 | .75 |
| **120** | A27 | 4c multicolored | .65 | .75 |
| **121** | A27 | 5c multicolored | .80 | .95 |
| **122** | A27 | 10c multicolored | .65 | .75 |
| **123** | A27 | 25c multicolored | 1.00 | .75 |
| **124** | A27 | 30c multicolored | .70 | .75 |
| **125** | A27 | 40c multicolored | .70 | .60 |
| **126** | A27 | 50c multicolored | .70 | .60 |
| **127** | A27 | 65c multicolored | .70 | .60 |
| **128** | A27 | 75c multicolored | .85 | .75 |
| **129** | A27 | 80c multicolored | 1.00 | *2.00* |
| **130** | A27 | $1 multicolored | 2.00 | 2.25 |
| **131** | A27 | $2 multicolored | 1.75 | *4.00* |
| **132** | A27 | $4 multicolored | 2.75 | 3.00 |
| | | *Nos. 117-132 (16)* | 16.20 | 19.00 |

Issued: 1c, 2c, 25c $4, 3/8; 3c, 4c, 10c, $2, 6/14; 40c, 50c, 65c, 75c, 8/23; 5c, 30c, 80c, $1, 2/21/83.

Christmas — A28

Paper sculptures.

**1982, Oct. 18 Litho. & Embossed**

| | | | | |
|---|---|---|---|---|
| **135** | A28 | 27c Joseph | .30 | .30 |
| **136** | A28 | 50c Angel | .40 | .40 |
| **137** | A28 | 75c Mary, Baby Jesus | .50 | .65 |
| *a.* | | Strip of 3, #135-137 | 1.30 | 1.60 |

25th Anniv. of Boat Club — A29

Designs: Various boating activities.

***Perf. 14x14½, 14½x14***

**1983, May 2 Litho.**

| | | | | |
|---|---|---|---|---|
| **138** | A29 | 27c multicolored | .30 | .30 |
| **139** | A29 | 35c multicolored | .30 | .30 |
| **140** | A29 | 50c multi, horiz. | .45 | .45 |
| **141** | A29 | 75c multi, horiz. | .45 | .45 |
| | | *Nos. 138-141 (4)* | 1.50 | 1.50 |

25th Anniv. of Australian Territory — A30

24c, Maps. golden bosun bird, kangaroo. 30c, Map, flag. 85c, Boeing 727, maps.

**1983, Oct. 1 Litho. *Perf. 14***

| | | | | |
|---|---|---|---|---|
| **142** | A30 | 24c multicolored | .70 | .45 |
| **143** | A30 | 30c multicolored | .80 | .80 |
| **144** | A30 | 85c multicolored | 1.60 | 2.00 |
| | | *Nos. 142-144 (3)* | 3.10 | 3.25 |

Christmas — A31

Designs: Christmas candles.

**1983, Oct. 31 Litho. *Perf. 13½x13***

| | | | | |
|---|---|---|---|---|
| **145** | A31 | 24c multicolored | .25 | .30 |
| **146** | A31 | 30c multicolored | .35 | .50 |
| **147** | A31 | 85c multicolored | .75 | 1.50 |
| | | *Nos. 145-147 (3)* | 1.35 | 2.30 |

Red Land Crab — A32

30c, Feeding. 40c, Migration. 55c, Developmental stages. 85c, Adult female, young.

**1984, Feb. 20 Litho. *Perf. 14x14½***

| | | | | |
|---|---|---|---|---|
| **148** | A32 | 30c multicolored | .30 | .30 |
| **149** | A32 | 40c multicolored | .40 | .40 |
| **150** | A32 | 55c multicolored | .40 | .40 |
| **151** | A32 | 85c multicolored | .80 | .80 |
| | | *Nos. 148-151 (4)* | 1.90 | 1.90 |

Local Fungi — A33

30c, Leucocoprinus fragilissimus. 40c, Microporus xanthopus. 45c, Trogia anthidepas. 55c, Haddowia longipes. 85c, Phillipsia domingensis.

**1984, Apr. 30 *Perf. 13½x14½***

| | | | | |
|---|---|---|---|---|
| **152** | A33 | 30c multicolored | .45 | .45 |
| **153** | A33 | 40c multicolored | .50 | .50 |
| **154** | A33 | 45c multicolored | .65 | .65 |
| **155** | A33 | 55c multicolored | .75 | .75 |
| **156** | A33 | 85c multicolored | .95 | .95 |
| | | *Nos. 152-156 (5)* | 3.30 | 3.30 |

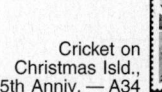

Cricket on Christmas Isld., 25th Anniv. — A34

**1984, July 23 Litho. *Perf. 14***

| | | | | |
|---|---|---|---|---|
| **157** | A34 | 30c Runout | .50 | *.75* |
| **158** | A34 | 40c Catch at point | .55 | *1.00* |
| **159** | A34 | 55c Batsman | .65 | *1.25* |
| **160** | A34 | 85c Batsman hitting | .75 | *1.50* |
| | | *Nos. 157-160 (4)* | 2.45 | *4.50* |

Souvenir Sheet

Christmas; Ausipex '84 — A35

**1984, Sept. 21 Litho. *Perf. 13½***

| | | | | |
|---|---|---|---|---|
| **161** | A35 | Sheet of 3 + 3 labels | 2.60 | 2.60 |
| *a.* | | 30c Father Christmas arriving | .45 | .45 |
| *b.* | | 55c Distributing gifts | .75 | .75 |
| *c.* | | 85c Waving good-bye | 1.25 | 1.25 |

Crabs — A36

No. 162, Birgus latro. No. 163, Cardiosoma hirtipes. No. 164, Gecarcoidea natalis. No. 165, Ocypode ceratophthalma. No. 166, Ceonobita rugosa. No. 167, Metasesarma rousseauxi. No. 168, Coenobita brevimana. No. 169, Geograpsus stormi. No. 170, Grapsus tenuicrustatus. No. 171, Geograpsus grayi. No. 172, Ocypode cordimana. No. 173, Geograpsus crinipes.

**1985 Litho. *Perf. 13x13½***

| | | | | |
|---|---|---|---|---|
| **162** | A36 | 30c multicolored | 1.00 | .90 |
| **163** | A36 | 33c multicolored | 1.00 | .90 |
| **164** | A36 | 33c multicolored | 1.10 | 1.00 |
| **165** | A36 | 40c multicolored | 1.10 | 1.00 |
| **166** | A36 | 45c multicolored | 1.10 | 1.25 |
| **167** | A36 | 45c multicolored | 1.25 | 1.50 |
| **168** | A36 | 55c multicolored | 1.25 | 1.50 |
| **169** | A36 | 60c multicolored | 1.75 | 1.75 |
| **170** | A36 | 60c multicolored | 2.25 | 2.50 |
| **171** | A36 | 85c multicolored | 2.50 | 2.50 |
| **172** | A36 | 90c multicolored | 2.50 | *3.25* |
| **173** | A36 | 90c multicolored | 3.00 | *4.00* |
| | | *Nos. 162-173 (12)* | 19.80 | 22.05 |

Issued: 30c, 40c, 55c, 85c, 1/30; Nos. 163, 166, 169, 172, 4/29; Nos. 164, 167, 170, 173, 7/22.

Once in Royal David's City — A37

Songs: 33c, While Shepherds Watched Their Flocks by Night. 45c, Away in a Manger. 60c, We Three Kings of Orient Are. 90c, Hark! The Herald Angels Sing.

**1985, Oct. 28 Litho. *Perf. 14x14½***

| | | | | |
|---|---|---|---|---|
| **174** | A37 | 27c multicolored | .80 | *1.25* |
| **175** | A37 | 33c multicolored | .90 | *1.40* |
| **176** | A37 | 45c multicolored | 1.10 | *1.50* |
| **177** | A37 | 60c multicolored | 1.20 | *1.60* |
| **178** | A37 | 90c multicolored | 1.30 | *1.75* |
| *a.* | | Strip of 5, #174-178 | 6.75 | *9.00* |
| | | *Nos. 174-178 (5)* | 5.30 | *7.50* |

Christmas.

Halley's Comet — A38

33c, Over island. 45c, Edmond Halley. 60c, Over phosphate shipping. 90c, Over Flying Fish Cove.

**1986, Apr. 30 Litho. *Perf. 14***

| | | | | |
|---|---|---|---|---|
| **179** | A38 | 33c multicolored | .40 | *.70* |
| **180** | A38 | 45c multicolored | .50 | *1.10* |
| **181** | A38 | 60c multicolored | .75 | *2.10* |
| **182** | A38 | 90c multicolored | 1.10 | *2.50* |
| | | *Nos. 179-182 (4)* | 2.75 | *6.40* |

Indigenous Flowers — A39

**1986, June 30 Litho. *Perf. 14***

| | | | | |
|---|---|---|---|---|
| **183** | A39 | 33c Ridley's orchid | .85 | .55 |
| **184** | A39 | 45c Hanging flower | .60 | *.85* |
| **185** | A39 | 60c Hoya | .60 | *1.50* |
| **186** | A39 | 90c Sea hibiscus | .70 | *2.00* |
| | | *Nos. 183-186 (4)* | 2.75 | *4.90* |

**Royal Wedding Issue, 1986**

Common Design Type

Designs: 33c, Couple in Buckingham Palace garden. 90c, Andrew operating helicopter.

**1986, July 23 Litho. *Perf. 14½x14***

| | | | | |
|---|---|---|---|---|
| **187** | CD338 | 33c multicolored | .45 | *.45* |
| **188** | CD338 | 90c multicolored | 1.00 | *1.75* |

Christmas — A40

Santa Claus at Christmas Island: 30c, Speedboating. 36c, At the beach. 55c, Fishing. 70c, Golfing. $1, Sleeping in hammock.

**1986, Sept. 30 Litho. *Perf. 13x13½***

| | | | | |
|---|---|---|---|---|
| **189** | A40 | 30c multicolored | .80 | .60 |
| **190** | A40 | 36c multicolored | .95 | .60 |
| **191** | A40 | 55c multicolored | 1.40 | 1.50 |
| **192** | A40 | 70c multicolored | 2.50 | *3.50* |
| **193** | A40 | $1 multicolored | 2.50 | *4.00* |
| | | *Nos. 189-193 (5)* | 8.15 | 10.20 |

Visiting Ships, Cent. — A41

**1987, Jan. 21 *Perf. 14½***

| | | | | |
|---|---|---|---|---|
| **194** | A41 | 36c Flying Fish | 1.00 | .80 |
| **195** | A41 | 90c Egeria | 1.90 | 2.50 |

Wildlife — A42

1c, Blind snake. 2c, Blue-tailed skink. 3c, Insectivorous bat. 5c, Green cricket. 10c, Christmas Is. fruit bat. 25c, Gecko. 30c, Praying mantis. 36c, Hawk owl. 40c, Bull-mouth helmet shell. 41c, Nudibranch. 50c, Textile cone shell. 65c, Brittle-stars. 75c, Royal angelfish. 90c, Christmas Is. white butterfly. $1, Mimic butterfly. $2, Shrew. $5, Green turtle.

**1987-89 Litho. *Perf. 14***

| | | | | |
|---|---|---|---|---|
| **196** | A42 | 1c multicolored | .40 | .90 |
| **197** | A42 | 2c multicolored | .40 | .90 |
| **198** | A42 | 3c multicolored | .75 | .90 |
| **199** | A42 | 5c multicolored | 1.10 | .90 |
| **200** | A42 | 10c multicolored | .90 | .90 |
| **201** | A42 | 25c multicolored | .90 | 1.00 |
| **202** | A42 | 30c multicolored | 1.00 | 1.25 |
| **203** | A42 | 36c multicolored | 2.25 | 1.75 |
| **204** | A42 | 40c multicolored | 1.50 | 2.75 |
| **204A** | A42 | 41c multi ('89) | 3.25 | 1.00 |
| **205** | A42 | 50c multicolored | 1.60 | 2.75 |
| **206** | A42 | 65c multicolored | 1.00 | *1.25* |
| **207** | A42 | 75c multicolored | 1.00 | *1.75* |
| **208** | A42 | 90c multicolored | 3.25 | 3.00 |
| **209** | A42 | $1 multicolored | 3.25 | 3.00 |
| **210** | A42 | $2 multicolored | 3.25 | *6.50* |
| **211** | A42 | $5 multicolored | 4.00 | *6.50* |
| *a.* | | Sheet of 16, #196-204, 205-211 | *47.50* | *47.50* |
| | | *Nos. 196-211 (17)* | 29.80 | 37.00 |

Issued: 1c, 2c, 25c, $5, 3/25; 3c, 10c, 36c, $2, 6/24; 40c, 50c, 65c, 75c, 8/26; 5c, 30c, 90c, $1, 3/1/88; 41c, 9/1/89.

Stamps contained in No. 211a inscribed "1988" at bottom.

For overprint see Nos. 246-247.

Souvenir Sheet

Santa Claus Delivering Presents — A43

**1987, Oct. 7 Litho. *Perf. 13½***

| | | | | |
|---|---|---|---|---|
| **212** | A43 | Sheet of 4 | 5.50 | 5.50 |
| *a.* | | 30c multicolored | .60 | .60 |
| *b.* | | 37c multicolored | .65 | .65 |
| *c.* | | 90c multicolored | 1.75 | 1.75 |
| *d.* | | $1 multicolored | 1.90 | 1.90 |

Christmas. Nos. 212a-212d printed in a continuous design.

Australia Bicentennial — A44

Designs: a, First Fleet sighted by 5 Aborginals on land. b, Four Aboriginals on land, one in canoe. c, Ships entering bay, kangaroos. d, Europeans land. e, Flag raising.

**1988, Jan. 26 Litho. *Perf. 13***
**213** Strip of 5 10.00 10.00
*a.-e.* A44 37c any single 1.75 1.75

Nos. 213a-213e printed in a continuous design. See Cocos Islands No. 172.

Annexation of the Island, Cent. — A45

37c, Capt William Henry May. 53c, Annexation ceremony. 95c, HMS Imperieuse. $1.50, Building cairn of stones.

**1988, June 8 Litho. *Perf. 14½***
**214** A45 37c multicolored .65 .65
**215** A45 53c multicolored .90 .90
**216** A45 95c multicolored 1.50 1.50
**217** A45 $1.50 multicolored 2.00 2.00
*Nos. 214-217 (4)* 5.05 5.05

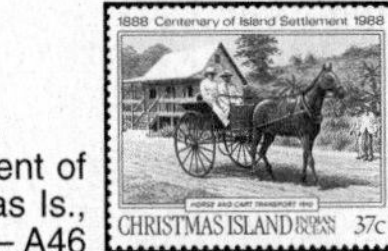

Settlement of Christmas Is., Cent. — A46

Transportation: 37c, Horse and cart, 1910. 55c, Phosphate mining, 1910. 70c, Steam locomotive, 1914. $1, Arrival of first aircraft, 1957.

**1988, Aug. 24 Litho. *Perf. 14½***
**218** A46 37c multicolored .95 .55
**219** A46 55c multicolored 1.40 .75
**220** A46 70c multicolored 1.40 1.00
**221** A46 $1 multicolored 2.25 1.60
*Nos. 218-221 (4)* 6.00 3.90

Christmas Presents — A47

32c, Bucket, shovel, boat. 39c, Snorkeling equipment. 90c, Toy soldier, doll, stuffed animals. $1, Race car, truck, plane.

**1988, Nov. 15 *Perf. 14x14½***
**222** A47 32c multicolored .50 .50
**223** A47 39c multicolored .60 .60
**224** A47 90c multicolored 1.25 1.25
**225** A47 $1 multicolored 1.50 1.00
*Nos. 222-225 (4)* 3.85 3.35

Chinese New Year — A48

**1989, Jan. 31 *Perf. 14½***
**226** A48 39c Good harvest .70 .70
**227** A48 70c Prosperity 1.00 1.00
**228** A48 90c Good fortune 1.25 1.25
**229** A48 $1 Progress 1.50 1.50
*Nos. 226-229 (4)* 4.45 4.45

Sir John Murray (1841-1914), Oceanographer A49

39c, Portrait. 80c, Murray Hill (map). $1, Murray's equipment. $1.10, HMS Challenger.

**1989, Mar. 16 *Perf. 14½x14***
**230** A49 39c multicolored .70 .70
**231** A49 80c multicolored 1.25 1.25
**232** A49 $1 multicolored 1.60 1.60
**233** A49 $1.10 multicolored 1.90 1.90
*Nos. 230-233 (4)* 5.45 5.45

Malay-Hari Raya Folk Celebration — A50

39c, Children. 55c, Tambourine player. 80c, Girl. $1.10, Minaret.

**1989, May 31 *Perf. 14***
**234** A50 39c multicolored .50 .50
**235** A50 55c multicolored .85 .85
**236** A50 80c multicolored 1.10 1.10
**237** A50 $1.10 multicolored 1.75 1.75
*Nos. 234-237 (4)* 4.20 4.20

Ferns — A51

41c, Huperzia phlegmaria. 65c, Asplenium polydon. 80c, Davallia denticulata. $1.10, Asplenium nidus.

**1989, Aug. 16**
**238** A51 41c multicolored .90 .90
**239** A51 65c multicolored 1.25 1.25
**240** A51 80c multicolored 1.40 1.25
**241** A51 $1.10 multicolored 2.10 2.10
*Nos. 238-241 (4)* 5.65 5.50

Christmas — A52

Biblical scenes: 36c, Joseph. 41c, Manger. 80c, Shepherds see star. $1.10, Magi riding camels.

**1989, Oct. 4 Litho. *Perf. 14½x15***
**242** A52 36c multicolored .65 .55
**243** A52 41c multicolored .70 .60
**244** A52 80c multicolored 1.75 .90
**245** A52 $1.10 multicolored 1.90 1.25
*Nos. 242-245 (4)* 5.00 3.30

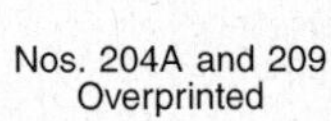

Nos. 204A and 209 Overprinted

**1989, Oct. 18 Litho. *Perf. 14***
**246** A42 41c multicolored *1.40* .60
**247** A42 $1 multicolored *4.75* 1.40

STAMPSHOW '89, Melbourne.
No. 247 is dated "1989."

1st Sighting of Christmas Is., 375th Anniv. — A53

Sightings of the island: 41c, John Milward, master of the British East India ship *Thomas,* 1615. $1.10, William Mynors, captain of *Royal Mary,* 1643.

**1990, Jan. 31 Litho. *Perf. 14x15***
**248** A53 41c multicolored 2.00 .50
**249** A53 $1.10 multicolored 2.40 1.50

Transport Through the Ages — A55

1c, Phosphate transport. 2c, Phosphate train. 3c, Rail car, vert. 5c, Road train. 10c, Trishaw, vert. 15c, Terex. 25c, Long bus. 30c, Passenger rake, vert. 40c, Passenger barge, vert. 50c, Kolek canoe. 65c, Flying doctor, ambulance. 75c, Tradestore van. 90c, Vintage truck. $1, Water tanker. $2, Traction engine. $5, Steam locomotive, flat car.

***Perf. 14x13½, 13½x14***
**1990 Litho. Unwmk.**
**254** A55 1c multicolored .25 .25
**255** A55 2c multicolored .45 .45
**256** A55 3c multicolored .30 .30
**257** A55 5c multicolored .50 .50
**258** A55 10c multicolored .45 .45
**259** A55 15c multicolored .75 .75
**260** A55 25c multicolored .40 .40
**261** A55 30c multicolored .40 .40
**262** A55 40c multicolored .45 .45
**263** A55 50c multicolored .65 .65
**264** A55 65c multicolored 3.75 1.75
**265** A55 75c multicolored 1.75 1.75
**266** A55 90c multicolored 1.75 1.75
**267** A55 $1 multicolored 1.90 1.90
**268** A55 $2 multicolored 2.50 2.50
**269** A55 $5 multicolored 3.50 *3.75*
*Nos. 254-269 (16)* 19.75 18.00

Issued: 1c, 3c, 10c, 25c, 30c, 40c, 50c, $5, Apr. 18; others, Aug. 22.

World Wildlife Fund — A56

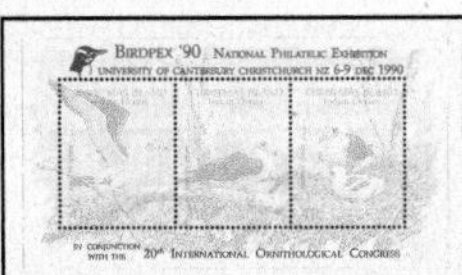
No. 274e

Abbott's boobies *(Sula abbotti):* 20c, Adult (facing left). 29c, Adult (facing right). No. 273, Adults, nest, hatchling. No. 274a, Adult landing on tree branch. No. 274b, Adult resting on branch. No. 274c, Adult, young in nest.

***Perf. 14x14½***
**1990, June 6 Litho. Unwmk.**
**270** A56 10c shown 1.25 1.25
**271** A56 20c multicolored 1.75 1.75
**272** A56 29c multicolored 2.00 2.00
**273** A56 41c multicolored 3.25 3.25
*Nos. 270-273 (4)* 8.25 8.25

**Souvenir Sheet**
***Perf. 14½***
**274** Sheet of 3 8.25 8.25
*a.-c.* A56 41c any single 2.50 2.50
*d.* Overprinted in purple *13.50* *13.50*
*e.* Overprinted in green *17.50* *17.50*

No. 274d overprint reads "WORLD STAMP EXHIBITION / AUCKLAND, NEW ZEALAND, 24 AUGUST-2 SEPTEMBER 1990."

Issued: No. 274d, Aug. 24; No. 274e, Dec. 6.

Centenary of Visit by Botanist Henry Ridley — A57

**1990, July 11 Litho. *Perf. 14½***
**275** A57 41c No. 77 .85 *.90*
**276** A57 75c Ridley, vert. 1.30 *2.00*

Christmas — A58

Flowers: 38c, Corymborkus veratrifolia. 43c, Hoya aldrichii. 80c, Quisqualis indica. $1.20, Barringtonia racemosa.

**1990, Oct. 3 Litho. *Perf. 14½***
**294** A58 38c multicolored 1.00 1.00
**295** A58 43c multicolored 1.30 1.10
**296** A58 80c multicolored 2.10 2.25
**297** A58 $1.20 multicolored 3.00 *3.75*
*Nos. 294-297 (4)* 7.40 8.10

1st Phosphate Mining Lease, Cent. — A59

**1991, Feb. 13 Litho. *Perf. 14½***
**298** A59 43c Freighter 1.15 1.15
**299** A59 43c Loading rail cars 1.15 1.15
**300** A59 85c Shay locomotive 1.30 1.30
**301** A59 $1.20 Bucket shovel 1.90 1.90
**302** A59 $1.70 Reforestation 2.25 2.25
*a.* Strip of 5, #298-302 8.00 8.00
*Nos. 298-302 (5)* 7.75 7.75

Island Police Force — A60

No. 303, Community relations. No. 304, Traffic control. 90c, Customs and quarantine. $1.20, Search and rescue.

**1991, Apr. 17 Litho. *Perf. 14½***
**303** A60 43c multicolored 1.75 1.75
**304** A60 43c multicolored 1.75 1.75
**305** A60 90c multicolored 2.50 2.50
**306** A60 $1.20 multicolored 3.25 3.25
*a.* Souvenir sheet of 4, #303-306 9.25 9.25
*Nos. 303-306 (4)* 9.25 9.25

Maps — A61

75c, Goos Atlas, 1666. $1.10, Apres De Manevillette, 1745. $1.20, Comberford, 1667.

**1991, June 19 Litho. *Perf. 14***
**307** A61 43c shown, 1991 1.10 1.10
**308** A61 75c multicolored 2.10 2.10
**309** A61 $1.10 multicolored 2.75 2.75
**310** A61 $1.20 multicolored 3.00 3.00
*Nos. 307-310 (4)* 8.95 8.95

Trees — A62

43c, Bruguiera gymnorrhiza. 70c, Syzygium operculatum. 85c, Ficus microcarpa. $1.20, Arenga listeri.

**1991, Aug. 21 Litho. *Perf. 14***
**311** A62 43c multicolored 1.25 1.25
**312** A62 70c multicolored 1.75 1.75
**313** A62 85c multicolored 2.00 2.00
**314** A62 $1.20 multicolored 2.25 2.25
*Nos. 311-314 (4)* 7.25 7.25

Christmas — A63

Drawings of "What Christmas Means to Me" by: No. 315a, S'ng Yen Luiw. b, Liew Ann Nee. c, Foo Pang Chuan. d, Too Lai Peng. e, Jesamine Wheeler. 43c, Ho Puay Ha. $1, Ng Hooi Hua. $1.20, Yani Kawi.

**1991, Oct. 2 Litho. *Perf. 14½***
**315** Strip of 5 4.25 4.25
*a.-e.* A63 38c any single .75 .75
**316** A63 43c multicolored .85 .70
**317** A63 $1 multicolored 1.90 1.90
**318** A63 $1.20 multicolored 2.10 2.10
*Nos. 315-318 (4)* 9.10 8.95

A64

War Time Evacuation, 50th Anniv.: No. 319, Conference to decide upon evacuation. No. 320, Europeans awaiting barge. $1.05, Barge approaching waiting ship. $1.20, Remaining population waving to TSS Islander.

**1992, Feb. 19 Litho. *Perf. 14½***

| | | | | |
|---|---|---|---|---|
| **319** | A64 | 45c multicolored | 1.25 | 1.25 |
| **320** | A64 | 45c multicolored | 1.25 | 1.25 |
| **321** | A64 | $1.05 multicolored | 2.60 | 2.60 |
| **322** | A64 | $1.20 multicolored | 2.75 | 2.75 |
| | | *Nos. 319-322 (4)* | 7.85 | 7.85 |

Shells — A65

5c, Cypraea tigris. 10c, Cypraea caput-serpentis. 15c, Lambis scorpius. 20c, Chlamys pallium. 25c, Engina mendicaria. 30c, Drupa ricinus. 40c, Distorsio reticulata. 45c, Turbo petholatus. 50c, Cantharus pulcher. 60c, Conus capitaneus. 70c, Turbo lajonkairii. 80c, Lambis chiragra. 90c, Angaria delphinus. $1, Vasum ceramicum. $2, Tonna perdix. $5, Drupa rubusidaea.

**1992 Litho. *Perf. 15x14½***

| | | | | |
|---|---|---|---|---|
| **326** | A65 | 5c multicolored | .60 | *.90* |
| **327** | A65 | 10c multicolored | .90 | .80 |
| **328** | A65 | 15c multicolored | 1.40 | .80 |
| **329** | A65 | 20c multicolored | 1.40 | .80 |
| **330** | A65 | 25c multicolored | 1.40 | .80 |
| **331** | A65 | 30c multicolored | 1.40 | .80 |
| **332** | A65 | 40c multicolored | 1.40 | .80 |
| **333** | A65 | 45c multicolored | 1.75 | .90 |
| **334** | A65 | 50c multicolored | 1.75 | .90 |
| **335** | A65 | 60c multicolored | 2.25 | 1.00 |
| **336** | A65 | 70c multicolored | 2.75 | 1.25 |
| **337** | A65 | 80c multicolored | 2.75 | 1.75 |
| **338** | A65 | 90c multicolored | 2.75 | 2.00 |
| **339** | A65 | $1 multicolored | 2.75 | 2.10 |
| **340** | A65 | $2 multicolored | 2.00 | *3.50* |
| **341** | A65 | $5 multicolored | 5.00 | *5.50* |
| | | *Nos. 326-341 (16)* | 32.25 | 24.60 |

Issued: 10c, 20c, 30c, 45c, 60c, 80c, $1, $2, 4/15; 5c, 15c, 25c, 40c, 50c, 70c, 90c, $5, 8/19.

For overprint see No. 348.

Sinking of Eidsvold and Nissa Maru, 50th Anniv. — A66

Designs: 45c, Eidsvold hit by torpedo. 80c, Eidsvold sinking. $1.05, Nissa Maru hit by torpedo. $1.20, Nissa Maru sinking.

**1992, June 17 Litho. *Perf. 14x13½***

| | | | | |
|---|---|---|---|---|
| **343** | A66 | 45c multicolored | 2.25 | 2.25 |
| **344** | A66 | 80c multicolored | 3.00 | 3.00 |
| **345** | A66 | $1.05 multicolored | 3.50 | 3.50 |
| **346** | A66 | $1.20 multicolored | 3.75 | 3.75 |
| | | *Nos. 343-346 (4)* | 12.50 | 12.50 |

Christmas — A67

Coastline, booby birds: a, 40c, Plants on shore, birds. b, 40c, Birds, rocks offshore. c, 45c, Birds on shore. d, $1.05, Birds in flight, coastline. e, $1.20, Forest, rocky coastline.

**1992, Oct. 7 Litho. *Perf. 14½***

| | | | | |
|---|---|---|---|---|
| **347** | A67 | Strip of 5, #a.-e. | 7.00 | *9.00* |

No. 341 Ovptd. in Red Violet

**1992, Sept. 1 Litho. *Perf. 15x14½***

| | | | | |
|---|---|---|---|---|
| **348** | A65 | $5 on #342 | 11.00 | 8.75 |

Kuala Lumpur Philatelic Exhibition.

Starting with No. 349, Christmas Island stamps are valid for postage on items mailed in Australia and Australian stamps are valid on items posted on Christmas Island.

Seabirds — A68

Designs: a, Abbott's booby. b, Christmas Island frigatebird. c, Common noddy. d, Golden bosunbird. e, Brown booby.

**1993, Mar. 4 Litho. *Perf. 14½x14***

| | | | | |
|---|---|---|---|---|
| **349** | A68 | 45c Strip of 5, #a.-e. | 3.75 | *4.25* |
| *f.* | | Souvenir sheet of 5, #a.-e. | 4.00 | *4.50* |
| *g.* | | As "f," overprinted | *9.00* | *9.00* |
| *h.* | | As "f," overprinted | *7.00* | *7.00* |

No. 349g Ovptd. in Gold in sheet margin with Taipei '93 emblem and: "ASIAN INTERNATIONAL INVITATION STAMP EXHIBITION / TAIPEI '93" in Chinese and English.

No. 349h Ovptd. in Gold in Sheet Margin with "INDOPEX '93 / 6TH ASIAN INTERNATIONAL PHILATELIC EXHIBITION 1993 / PAMERAN INTERNASIONAL PENGUMPULAN / KEENAM DI ASIA TAHUN 1993" and show emblem.

Issued: No. 349g, 4/93; No. 349h, 5/29/93.

Scenic Views — A69

**1993, June 1 *Perf. 14x14½***

| | | | | |
|---|---|---|---|---|
| **350** | A69 | 85c Dolly Beach | 1.75 | 1.75 |
| **351** | A69 | 95c Blow holes | 2.10 | 2.10 |
| **352** | A69 | $1.05 Merrial Beach | 2.25 | 2.25 |
| **353** | A69 | $1.20 Rain forest | 2.50 | 2.50 |
| | | *Nos. 350-353 (4)* | 8.60 | 8.60 |

Christmas — A70

40c, Turtle on beach. 45c, Crabs, wave. $1, Frigatebird, rainforest.

**1993, Sept. 2 Litho. *Perf. 14½x14***

| | | | | |
|---|---|---|---|---|
| **354** | A70 | 40c multicolored | 1.25 | 1.25 |
| **355** | A70 | 45c multicolored | 1.25 | 1.25 |
| **356** | A70 | $1 multicolored | 2.50 | 2.50 |
| | | *Nos. 354-356 (3)* | 5.00 | 5.00 |

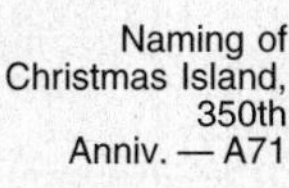

Naming of Christmas Island, 350th Anniv. — A71

**1993, Dec. 1 Litho. *Perf. 14x14½***

| | | | | |
|---|---|---|---|---|
| **357** | A71 | $2 multicolored | 3.75 | 3.75 |

New Year 1994 (Year of the Dog) — A72

**1994, Jan. 20 Litho. *Perf. 14x14½***

| | | | | |
|---|---|---|---|---|
| **358** | A72 | 45c shown | 1.25 | *1.50* |
| **359** | A72 | 45c Pekingese | 1.25 | *1.50* |
| *a.* | | Pair, #358-359 | 3.00 | *4.00* |
| *b.* | | Souvenir sheet of 1, #359a | 4.00 | *4.00* |
| *c.* | | As "b," overprinted | *4.75* | *4.75* |
| *d.* | | As "b," overprinted | *7.75* | *7.75* |
| *e.* | | As "b," overprinted | *8.00* | *8.00* |
| *f.* | | As "b," overprinted | *15.50* | *15.50* |

No. 359c Ovptd. in gold in sheet margin with dog and "Melbourne / STAMP & COIN SHOW / 11-13 February 1994;" No. 359d with "HONG KONG '94 STAMP EXHIBITION" and show emblem; No. 359e with "Canberra /Stamp Show '94 / 19-21 March / 1994" and show emblem; No. 359f with "QUEENSLAND STAMP & COIN SHOW 1994 / JUNE 11, 12, 13."

Issued: No. 359c, 2/11/94; No. 359d, 2/18/94; No. 359e, 3/19/94; No. 359f, 1995.

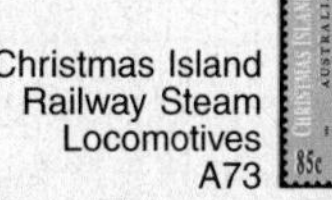

Christmas Island Railway Steam Locomotives A73

85c, Locomotive No. 4. 95c, Locomotive No. 9. $1.20, Locomotive No. 1.

**1994, May 19 Litho. *Perf. 14x14½***

| | | | | |
|---|---|---|---|---|
| **360** | A73 | 85c multicolored | 2.00 | 2.00 |
| **361** | A73 | 95c multicolored | 2.25 | 2.25 |
| **362** | A73 | $1.20 multicolored | 2.60 | 2.60 |
| | | *Nos. 360-362 (3)* | 6.85 | 6.85 |

Orchids — A74

a, Brachypeza archytas. b, Thelasis capitata. c, Corymborkis veratrifolia. d, Flickingeria nativitatis. e, Dendrobium crumenatum.

**1994, Aug. 16 Litho. *Perf. 14½x14***

| | | | | |
|---|---|---|---|---|
| **363** | A74 | 45c Strip of 5, #a.-e. | 7.00 | 7.00 |

Christmas — A75

**1994, Sept. 8 Litho. *Perf. 14x14½***

| | | | | |
|---|---|---|---|---|
| **364** | A75 | 40c Angel | .70 | .60 |
| **365** | A75 | 45c Wise man | .90 | .60 |
| **366** | A75 | 80c Bethlehem | 1.50 | 1.50 |
| | | *Nos. 364-366 (3)* | 3.10 | 2.70 |

New Year 1995 (Year of the Boar) — A76

Design: 85c, Stylized boar, diff.

**1995, Jan. 12 Litho. *Perf. 14x14½***

| | | | | |
|---|---|---|---|---|
| **367** | A76 | 45c shown | .80 | .80 |
| **368** | A76 | 85c multicolored | 1.40 | 1.40 |
| *a.* | | Souvenir sheet, #367-368 | 3.00 | 3.00 |
| *b.* | | As "a," overprinted | *7.00* | *7.00* |
| *c.* | | As "a," overprinted | *15.00* | *15.00* |

No. 368b ovptd. in gold in sheet margin with outline of boar and: "STAMP & COIN FAIR / ROYAL EXHIBITION BUILDING / MELBOURNE VIC. 3000 . 10-12 FEB 1995."

No. 368c ovptd. in sheet margin with Taiwan flag and map of Australia with flag, and also Chinese characters, dates and "STAMP TAIWAN, SYDNEY, / AUSTRALIA MAY 20-28 1995."

Christmas Island Golf Course, 40th Anniv. — A77

**1995, May 11 Litho. *Perf. 14***

| | | | | |
|---|---|---|---|---|
| **369** | A77 | $2.50 multicolored | 6.00 | 6.00 |

Christmas — A78

Santa Claus riding great frigatebird: 40c, Reading map. 45c, Dropping presents. 80c, Waving.

**1995, Sept. 14 Litho. *Perf. 14x14½***

| | | | | |
|---|---|---|---|---|
| **370** | A78 | 40c multicolored | .90 | .75 |
| **371** | A78 | 45c multicolored | 1.00 | .75 |
| **372** | A78 | 80c multicolored | 1.50 | 1.50 |
| | | *Nos. 370-372 (3)* | 3.40 | 3.00 |

End of World War II, 50th Anniv. — A79

No. 373a, RAAF reconnaissance flight, 1945. No. 373b, Arrival of HMS Rother, 1945.

**Litho. & Engr.**

**1995, Oct. 12 *Perf. 14x14½***

| | | | | |
|---|---|---|---|---|
| **373** | | Pair | 2.75 | 2.75 |
| *a.-b.* | A79 | 45c any single | 1.00 | 1.00 |

Angelfish — A80

**1995, Oct. 12 Litho.**

| | | | | |
|---|---|---|---|---|
| **374** | A80 | 75c Lemonpeel | 1.25 | *1.75* |
| **375** | A80 | $1 Emperor | 1.90 | *2.50* |

See also Nos. 381-387.

New Year 1996 (Year of the Rat) — A81

**Litho. with Foil Application**

**1996, Jan. 9 *Perf. 14x14½***

| | | | | |
|---|---|---|---|---|
| **376** | A81 | 45c Facing right | 1.25 | 1.25 |
| **377** | A81 | 45c Facing left | 1.25 | 1.25 |
| *a.* | | Pair, #376-377 | 3.00 | 3.00 |
| *b.* | | Souvenir sheet, #377a | 3.75 | 3.75 |
| *c.* | | As "b," overprinted | *10.00* | *10.00* |

No. 377c overprinted in gold in sheet margin "STAMP AND COIN FAIR / MELBOURNE / 23-25 February 1996."

Fish — A82

20c, Pinktail triggerfish. 30c, Longnose filefish. 45c, Princess anthias. 85c, Green moon wrasse. 90c, Spotted boxfish. 95c, Moorish idol. $1.20, Glass bigeye.

**1996-97 Litho. *Perf. 14x14½***

| | | | | |
|---|---|---|---|---|
| **381** | A82 | 20c multicolored | .40 | .40 |
| **382** | A82 | 30c multicolored | .60 | .50 |
| **383** | A82 | 45c multicolored | .90 | .50 |
| **384** | A82 | 85c multicolored | 1.75 | *2.00* |
| **385** | A82 | 90c multicolored | 1.00 | 1.00 |
| **386** | A82 | 95c multicolored | 1.75 | 1.75 |
| **387** | A82 | $1.20 multicolored | 2.25 | *3.25* |
| | | *Nos. 381-387 (7)* | 8.65 | 9.40 |

Issued: 20c, 30c, 45c, 90c, 4/18/96; 85c, 95c, $1.20, 7/17/97.

Birds — A83

**1996, July 11 Litho. *Perf. 14½x14***

| | | | | |
|---|---|---|---|---|
| **399** | A83 | 45c White-eye | 1.25 | 1.25 |
| **400** | A83 | 85c Hawk-owl | 2.00 | 2.00 |

Christmas — A84

Sailing ships, words from Christmas carol: 40c, "I Saw Three Ships." 45c, "Come sailing in." 80c, "On Christmas day in the morning."

**1996, Sept. 12 Litho. *Perf. 14***
**401** A84 40c multicolored 1.00 .75
**402** A84 45c multicolored 1.10 .90
**403** A84 80c multicolored 1.60 1.60
*Nos. 401-403 (3)* 3.70 3.25

Exploration of Australian Coast & Christmas Island by Willem de Vlamingh, 300th Anniv. — A85

"Portrait of a Dutch Navigator," by Jan Verkolje.

**1996, Oct. 27 Litho. *Perf. 14***
**404** A85 45c multicolored 1.25 1.25

No. 404 was issued se-tenant with Australia No. 1571 (No. 1571a). Value, pair $4.

New Year 1997 (Year of the Ox) — A86

Constellation and: No. 405, Ox facing right. No. 406, Ox facing left.

**Litho. with Foil Application**

**1997, Jan. 6 *Perf. 14x14½***
**405** A86 45c multicolored 1.00 1.00
**406** A86 45c multicolored 1.00 1.00
*a.* Pair, #405-406 2.75 2.75
*b.* Souvenir sheet, #405-406 3.00 3.00

Christmas — A87

Santa on Christmas Island: 40c, Reading letters. 45c, Making toys. 80c, In sleigh.

**1997, Sept. 11 Litho. *Perf. 14x14½***
**407** A87 40c multicolored .65 .65
**408** A87 45c multicolored .75 .75
**409** A87 80c multicolored 1.75 1.75
*Nos. 407-409 (3)* 3.15 3.15

New Year 1998 (Year of the Tiger) — A88

**Litho. with Foil Application**

**1998, Jan. 5 *Perf. 14x14½***
**410** A88 45c shown 1.25 1.25
**411** A88 45c Looking backward 1.25 1.25
*a.* Pair, #410-411 3.00 3.00
*b.* Souvenir sheet of 2, #410-411 3.50 3.50

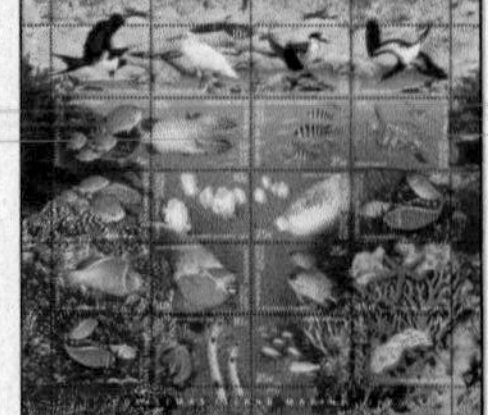
Marine Life — A89

Designs: a, 5c, Frigatebird. b, 5c, Ambon chromis, denomination LR. c, 5c, Ambon chromis, denomination LL. d, 5c, Pink anemonefish, denomination, UR. e, 5c, Pink anemonefish, denomination LL. f, 10c, Eastern reef egret. g, 10c, Whitelined cod. h, 10c, Pyramid butterfly fish. i, 10c, Dusky parrotfish. j, 10c, Spotted garden eel. k, 25c, Sooty tern. l, 25c, Scissortail sergeant. m, 25c, Thicklip wrasse. n, 25c, Blackaxil chromis. o, 25c, Orange anthias. p, 45c, Brown booby. q, 45c, Green turtle. r, 45c, Pink anemonefish. s, 45c, Blue sea star. t, 45c, Kunie's chromodoris.

**1998, Mar. 12 Litho. *Perf. 14***
**412** A89 Sheet of 20, #a.-t. 10.00 10.00

Tree Flowers of Christmas — A90

**1998, Sept. 3 Litho. *Perf. 14½x14***
**413** A90 40c Orchid tree .80 .80
**414** A90 80c Flame tree 1.60 1.60
**415** A90 95c Sea hibiscus 1.60 1.60
*Nos. 413-415 (3)* 4.00 4.00

New Year 1999 (Year of the Rabbit) — A91

**Litho. with Foil Application**

**1999, Jan. 14 *Perf. 14x14½***
**416** A91 45c shown 1.00 1.00
**417** A91 45c Rabbit looking left 1.00 1.00
*a.* Pair, #416-417 2.75 2.75
*b.* Souvenir sheet, #417a 3.25 3.25

Festivals on Christmas Island — A92

Children's drawings: No. 418, Carrying balloons in parade, by Fong Jason. No. 419, Giant crab, by Siti Zanariah Zainal. 85c, Children at night, by Tan Diana, vert. $1.20, Green mosque, tree, by Anwar Ramian, vert.

**1999, July 15 Litho. *Perf. 14x14½***
**418** A92 45c multicolored .75 .75
**419** A92 45c multicolored .75 .75
*a.* Pair, #418-419 1.75 1.75

***Perf. 14½x14***
**420** A92 85c multicolored 1.00 1.00
**421** A92 $1.20 multicolored 1.75 1.75
*Nos. 418-421 (4)* 4.25 4.25

Christmas — A93

Designs: 40c, Santa Claus in hammock. 45c, Santa, birds, crab, lizard, cake. 95c, Santa, booby-drawn sleigh.

**1999, Sept. 9 Litho. *Perf. 14x14½***
**422** A93 40c multicolored .95 .80
**423** A93 45c multicolored 1.10 .95
**424** A93 95c multicolored 1.75 1.75
*Nos. 422-424 (3)* 3.80 3.50

New Year 2000 (Year of the Dragon) — A94

**Litho. with Foil Application**

**2000, Jan. 13 *Perf. 14x14½***
**425** A94 45c shown 1.10 1.10
**426** A94 45c Dragon facing left 1.10 1.10
*a.* Pair, #425-426 3.00 3.00
*b.* Souvenir sheet, #426a 3.50 3.50

Faces of Christmas Island — A95

Ordinary people: a, Yeow Jian Min, without shirt. b, Ida Chin, with blue shirt. c, Ho Tak Wah, old man. d, Thomas Faul and James Neill. e, Siti Sanniah Kawi, with striped blouse.

**2000, Apr. 13 Litho. *Perf. 14½x14***
**427** A95 45c Strip of 5, #a.-e. 4.75 4.75

Christmas — A96

No. 428: a, We three kings of Orient are. b, Bearing gifts we traverse afar. 45c, Star of wonder, star of night.

**2000, Sept. 5 Litho. *Perf. 14½x14***
**428** Pair 1.90 1.90
*a.-b.* A96 40c Any single .60 .60
**429** A96 45c multi .60 .60

New Year 2001 (Year of the Snake) — A97

Snake color: 45c, Green. $1.35, Silver.

**Litho. with Foil Application**

**2001, Jan. 8 *Perf. 14x14½***
**430-431** A97 Set of 2 3.00 3.00
*a.* Souvenir sheet, #430-431 4.00 *4.00*

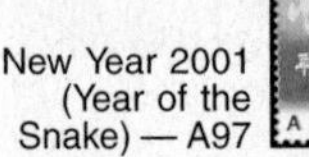

Fungi — A98

Designs: $1, Chaetocalathus semisupinus. $1.50, Pycnoporus sanguineus.

**2001, Oct. 25 Litho. *Perf. 14x14½***
**432-433** A98 Set of 2 4.00 *4.00*

New Year 2002 (Year of the Horse) A99

Zodiac Animals and Their Chinese Characters A100

Designs: 45c, Purple horse. $1.35, Gold horse.

No. 436: a, Rat. b, Ox. c, Tiger. d, Rabbit. e, Dragon. f, Snake. g, Horse. h, Sheep. i, Monkey. j, Cock. k, Dog. l, Boar.

**Litho. With Gold Foil Application**

**2002, Jan. 8 *Perf. 14x14½***
**434-435** A99 Set of 2 3.00 3.00
*a.* Souvenir sheet, #434-435 4.00 4.00
**436** Sheet of 14, #a-l, #435a 12.00 12.00
*a.-d.* A100 5c Any single .55 .55
*e.-h.* A100 15c Any single, orange background .60 .60
*i.-l.* A100 25c Any single, orange background .65 .65

See Nos. 442, 447, 451, 456, 462-463.

Worldwide Fund for Nature (WWF) — A101

Christmas Island birds — No. 437: a, Imperial pigeon. b, Hawk owl.
$1, Goshawk. $1.50, Thrush.

**2002, May 1 Litho. *Perf. 14½x14***
**437** A101 45c Horiz. pair, #a-b 1.60 1.60
**438** A101 $1 multi 1.60 1.60
**439** A101 $1.50 multi 2.75 2.75
*Nos. 437-439 (3)* 5.95 5.95

**Zodiac Animals Type of 2002 and**

New Year 2003 (Year of the Ram) — A102

Designs: 50c, Yellow and orange ram. $1.50, Blue ram.

No. 442: a, Rat. b, Ox. c, Tiger. d, Rabbit. e, Dragon. f, Snake. g, Horse. h, Sheep. i, Monkey. j, Cock. k, Dog. l, Boar.

**Litho. With Gold Foil Application**

**2003, Jan. 7 *Perf. 14x14½***
**440-441** A102 Set of 2 3.50 3.50
*a.* Souvenir sheet, #440-441 4.00 4.00
**442** Sheet of 14, #a-l, #441a 12.00 12.00
*a.-d.* A100 10c Any single, red violet background .50 .50
*e.-h.* A100 15c Any single, red violet background .60 .60
*i.-l.* A100 25c Any single, red violet background .70 .70

See No. 463.

Christmas — A103

Designs: 45c, Arrival of Santa Claus on whale shark. 50c, Santa giving gifts to red crabs.

**2003, Oct. 31 Litho. *Perf. 14½x14***
**443-444** A103 Set of 2 3.00 3.00

**Zodiac Animals Type of 2002 and**

New Year 2004 (Year of the Monkey) — A104

Designs: 50c, Yellow and orange monkey. $1.45, Red orange monkey, lotus flower.

No. 447: a, Rat. b, Ox. c, Tiger. d, Rabbit. e, Dragon. f, Snake. g, Horse. h, Sheep. i, Monkey. j, Cock. k, Dog. l, Boar.

**Litho. With Gold Foil Application**

**2004, Jan. 6 *Perf. 14x14½***
**445-446** A104 Set of 2 4.50 4.50
*446a* Souvenir sheet, #445-446 5.50 5.50
**447** Sheet of 14, #a-l, #446a 12.00 12.00
*a.-d.* A100 10c Any single, light and dark blue background .50 .50
*e.-h.* A100 15c Any single, light and dark blue background .60 .60
*i.-l.* A100 25c Any single, light and dark blue background .70 .70

No. 446a exists with a 2004 Hong Kong Stamp Expo overprint in sheet margin in red. This sheet was sold at the show and was sold at some post offices in Australia, but not on Christmas Island. Value: *$15.*

See No. 463.

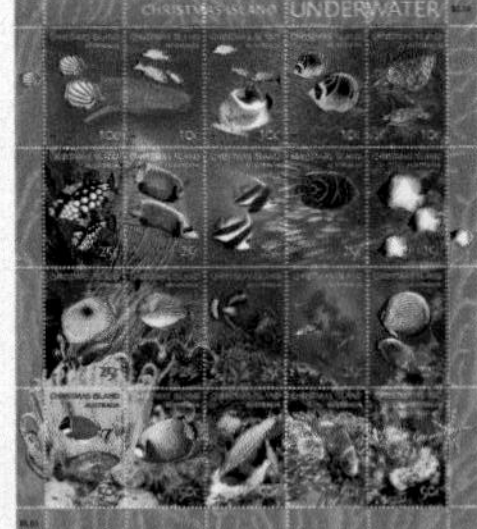

Marine Life A105

No. 448: a, Two butterflyfish, rear of whale shark. b, Three striped fish, front of whale shark. c, Four fish. d, Two fish. e, Two green turtles. f, Two triggerfish (polka dots), red coral at LL. g, Two fish with thin horizontal stripes with yellow tails. h, Two fish with thick vertical stripes. i, Black and white fish. j, Three fish. k, Yellow fish with black spot, blue fish, red coral, yellow coral. l, Striped fish, clam. m, Black fish, small red fish. n Red fish, divers. o, Two striped fish, red coral under denomination. p, Blue and yellow fish, red and white spotted fish, yellow coral. q, Blue and yellow fish, yellow coral, sea anemones. r, Three blue fish with orange spots. s, Sea anemone and two anemonefish. t, Nudibranch, red coral and starfish.

**2004, July 13 Litho. *Perf. 14½x14***

**448** A105 Sheet of 20 11.00 11.00
*a.-e.* 10c Any single .25 .25
*f.-o.* 25c Any single .45 .45
*p.-t.* 50c Any single .95 .95

### Zodiac Animals Type of 2002 and

New Year 2005 (Year of the Cock) — A106

Designs: 50c, Cock, spirals at right. $1.45, Cock, spirals at right.

No. 451: a, Rat. b, Ox. c, Tiger. d, Rabbit. e, Dragon. f, Snake. g, Horse. h, Sheep. i, Monkey. j, Cock. k, Dog. l, Boar.

### Litho. With Gold Foil Application

**2005, Jan. 4 *Perf. 14x14½***

**449-450** A106 Set of 2 4.50 4.50
*450a* Souvenir sheet, #449-450 4.50 4.50
*450b* As "a," with Taipei 2005 emblem overprinted in margin 5.00 5.00
**451** Sheet of 14, #a-l, #450a 14.00 14.00
*a.-d.* A100 10c Any single, red and yellow background .45 .45
*e.-h.* A100 15c Any single, red and yellow background .45 .45
*i.-l.* A100 25c Any single, red and yellow background .65 .65

See No. 463.

Christmas — A107

Santa Claus, birds and: 45c, Palm tree, presents. 90c, Sleigh, crabs.

**2005, Nov. 1 Litho. *Perf. 14¼x14***

**452** A107 45c multi 1.25 1.25
*a.* Booklet pane of 4 5.00 —
**453** A107 90c multi 2.25 2.25

No. 452a exists with two different margins. These two panes were issued in a booklet that also contained three examples of Australia No. 2423a. The entire booklet sold for $9.95.

### Zodiac Animals Type of 2002 and

New Year 2006 (Year of the Dog) — A108

Designs: 50c, Purple dog. $1.45, Copper dog.

No. 456: a, Rat. b, Ox. c, Tiger. d, Rabbit. e, Dragon. f, Snake. g, Horse. h, Sheep. i, Monkey. j, Cock. k, Dog. l, Boar.

### Litho. With Copper Foil Application

**2006, Jan. 5 *Perf. 14x14½***

**454-455** A108 Set of 2 3.25 3.25
*455a* Souvenir sheet, #454-455 3.25 3.25
**456** Sheet of 14, #a-l, #455a 9.00 9.00
*a.-d.* A100 10c Any single, brown and yellow background .30 .30
*e.-h.* A100 15c Any single, brown and yellow background .35 .35
*i.-l.* A100 25c Any single, brown and yellow background .50 .50

See No. 463.

Buildings — A109

Designs: 50c, Mosque. $1.45, Tai Jin House.

No. 458: a, Tai Pak Kong Temple. b, Soon Tian Temple.

**2006, June 13 Litho. *Perf. 14½x14***

**457** A109 50c multi 1.25 1.25
**458** A109 $1 Horiz. pair, #a-b 4.50 4.50
**459** A109 $1.45 multi 3.25 3.25
*Nos. 457-459 (3)* 9.00 9.00

### Zodiac Animals Types of 1996-2006 and

New Year 2007 (Year of the Boar) — A110

Zodiac Animals — A111

Designs: Nos. 460, 463l, 50c, Boar facing right. $1.45, Boar facing left.

No. 462: a, Rat. b, Ox. c, Tiger. d, Rabbit. e, Dragon. f, Snake. g, Horse. h, Sheep. i, Monkey. j, Cock. k, Dog. l, Boar.

### Litho. With Copper Foil Application

**2007, Jan. 9 *Perf. 14x14½***

**460-461** A110 Set of 2 4.25 4.25
*461a* Souvenir sheet, #460-461 4.25 4.25
**462** Sheet of 14, #a-l, #461a 10.00 10.00
*a.-d.* A100 10c Any single, multicolored background .25 .25
*e.-h.* A100 15c Any single, multicolored background .30 .25
*i.-l.* A100 25c Any single, multicolored background .50 .50

### Self-Adhesive

***Serpentine Die Cut 12¼ Syncopated (#463a-463l), Serpentine Die Cut (#463m)***

**463** Sheet of 13 19.00
*a.* A81 50c Like #376 1.10 1.10
*b.* A86 50c Like #405 1.10 1.10
*c.* A88 50c Like #410 1.10 1.10
*d.* A91 50c Like #416 1.10 1.10
*e.* A94 50c Like #425 1.10 1.10
*f.* A97 50c Like #430 1.10 1.10
*g.* A99 50c Like #434 1.10 1.10
*h.* A102 50c Like #440 1.10 1.10
*i.* A104 50c Like #445 1.10 1.10
*j.* A106 50c Like #449 1.10 1.10
*k.* A108 50c Like #454 1.10 1.10
*l.* A110 50c Like #460 1.10 1.10
*m.* A111 $1 multi 3.00 3.00
*n.* Booklet pane, 2 each #463a-463b 4.00
*o.* Booklet pane, 2 each #463c-463d 4.00
*p.* Booklet pane, 2 each #463e-463f 4.00
*q.* Booklet pane, 2 each #463g-463h 4.00
*r.* Booklet pane, 2 each #463i-463j 4.00
*s.* Booklet pane, 2 each #463k-463l 4.00
Complete booklet, #463n-463s 25.00

Complete booklet sold for $12.95.

Christmas — A112

Santa Claus: 45c, In boat. 50c, Hoisted by crane. $1.10, On beach.

**2007, Nov. 1 Litho. *Perf. 14x14½***

**464-466** A112 Set of 3 4.00 4.00

New Year 2008 (Year of the Rat) — A113

Designs: 50c, Rat. $1.45, Chinese character for "rat."

No. 469: a, Rat, diff. b, Ox. c, Dragon. d, Snake. e, Tiger. f, Rabbit. g, Horse. h, Pig. i, Goat. j, Monkey. k, Rooster. l, Dog.

### Litho. With Foil Application

**2008, Jan. 8 *Perf. 14***

**467** A113 50c multi 1.00 1.00
*a.* Perf. 14¾x14 *7.00 7.00*

***Perf. 14¾x14***

**468** A113 $1.45 multi 2.75 2.75
*a.* Souvenir sheet, #467a, 468 3.75 3.75
*b.* As "a," with Olympex emblem in margin 3.75 3.75
**469** Sheet of 14, #467a, 468, 469a-469l 11.00 11.00
*a.-d.* A113 10c Any single .25 .25
*e.-h.* A113 15c Any single .35 .35
*i.-l.* A113 25c Any single .50 .50
*m.* Booklet pane of 4, #469a, 469b, 2 #468 6.75 —
*n.* Booklet pane of 4, #469e, 469f, 2 #467a 2.75 —
*o.* Booklet pane of 4, #469c, 469d, 2 #467a 2.75 —
*p.* Booklet pane of 4, #469g, 469i, 2 #467a 3.00 —
*q.* Booklet pane of 4, #469j, 469k, 2 #467a 3.25 —
*r.* Booklet pane of 4, #469h, 469l, 2 #467a 3.00 —
Complete booklet, #469m-469r 22.00

Complete booklet sold for $10.95. Issued: No. 468b, 8/8. See Nos. 512g, 546d.

Territorial Status of Christmas Island, 50th Anniv. — A114

No. 470: a, Gecarcoidea natalis. b, Papasula abbotti. c, Asplenium listeri.

$1.45, Seal of Union of Christmas Island Workers. $2.45, Christmas Island flag.

**2008, June 10 Litho. *Perf. 14¼***

**470** Horiz. strip of 3 3.75 3.75
*a.-c.* A114 50c Any single 1.00 1.00
**471** A114 $1.45 multi 3.50 3.50
**472** A114 $2.45 multi 5.50 5.50
*Nos. 470-472 (3)* 12.75 12.75

Christmas — A115

Designs: Nos. 473, 475, 50c, Christmas tree, bird, crabs and shells. Nos. 474, 476, $1.20, Crabs with gifts and Christmas lights.

**2008, Oct. 31 Litho. *Perf. 14½x14***

**473-474** A115 Set of 2 3.00 3.00

***Serpentine Die Cut 11¼ Syncopated***

### Self-Adhesive

**475** A115 50c multi 1.00 1.00
*a.* Booklet pane of 10 10.00

### Booklet Stamp

**476** A115 $1.20 multi 2.00 2.00
*a.* Booklet pane of 5 10.00

No. 475 was also printed in sheets of 10.

Christmas With Personalized Picture — A116

Designs as before.

***Serpentine Die Cut 11½x11¼ Syncopated***

**2008, Oct. 31 Litho.**

### Self-Adhesive

**477** A116 50c multi *4.00 4.00*
**478** A116 $1.20 multi *7.00 7.00*

Nos. 477-478 each were sold in sheets of 20 and have personalized pictures and a straight edge at right, and lack separations between the stamp and the personalized photo. Sheets of 20 of No. 477 sold for $23, and No. 478 sold for $37.

New Year 2009 (Year of the Ox) — A117

Designs: 55c, Rat. $1.65, Chinese character for "ox."

No. 481: a, Rat. b, Ox, diff. c, Dragon. d, Snake. e, Tiger. f, Rabbit. g, Horse. h, Pig. i, Goat. j, Monkey. k, Rooster. l, Dog.

### Litho. With Foil Application

**2009, Jan. 8 *Perf. 14¾x14***

**479** A117 55c multi .90 .90
**480** A117 $1.65 multi 2.75 2.75
*a.* Souvenir sheet, #479-480 4.00 4.00
**481** Sheet of 14, #479-480, 481a-481l 13.00 13.00
*a.-d.* A117 10c Any single .30 .30
*e.-h.* A117 20c Any single .35 .35
*i.-l.* A117 25c Any single .50 .50
*m.* Booklet pane of 4, #481b, 481e, 2 #480 6.50 —
*n.* Booklet pane of 4, #481c, 481f, 2 #479 2.75 —
*o.* Booklet pane of 4, #481d, 481g, 2 #479 2.75 —
*p.* Booklet pane of 4, #481i, 481j, 2 #479 3.00 —
*q.* Booklet pane of 4, #481k, 481l, 2 #479 3.00 —
*r.* Booklet pane of 4, #481a, 481h, 2 #479 2.75 —
Complete booklet, #481m-481r 21.00

No. 479 was issued in a sheet of 9 + 9 labels that could be personalized and removed. The sheet sold for $15.95. Gutter strips of 10 of No. 484 exist with five labels forming a picture featuring the 12 Zodiac animals.

Complete booklet sold for $12.95. See Nos. 512h, 546e.

Christmas — A118

**2009, Nov. 2 Litho. *Perf. 14¾x14***

**482** A118 $1.25 multi 3.25 3.25

### Booklet Stamp
### Self-Adhesive

***Serpentine Die Cut 11¼ Syncopated***

**483** A118 $1.25 multi 3.25 3.25
*a.* Booklet pane of 5 16.50

New Year 2010 (Year of the Tiger) — A119

Designs: 55c, Tiger. $1.65, Chinese character for "tiger."

No. 486: a, Rat. b, Ox. c, Dragon. d, Snake. e, Tiger, diff. f, Rabbit. g, Horse. h, Pigs. i, Goat. j, Monkey. k, Rooster. l, Dog.

### Litho. With Foil Application

**2010, Jan. 12 *Perf. 14¾x14***

**484** A119 55c multi 1.25 1.25
**485** A119 $1.65 multi 3.25 3.25
*a.* Souvenir sheet, #484-485 5.50 5.50
**486** Sheet of 14, #484-485, 486a-486l 14.50 14.50
*a.-d.* A119 10c Any single .30 .30
*e.-h.* A119 20c Any single .40 .40
*i.-l.* A119 25c Any single .55 .55
*m.* Booklet pane of 4, #486e, 486f, 2 #485 8.00 —
*n.* Booklet pane of 4, #486c, 486d, 2 #484 3.25 —
*o.* Booklet pane of 4, #486g, 486i, 2 #484 4.00 —
*p.* Booklet pane of 4, #486j, 486k, 2 #484 4.00 —
*q.* Booklet pane of 4, #486h, 486l, 2 #484 4.00 —
*r.* Booklet pane of 4, #486a, 486b, 2 #484 3.25 —
Complete booklet, #486m-486r 23.00

Complete booklet sold for $12.95. A sheet of 13 self-adhesive stamps containing a round $1 stamp depicting a flower and stamps similar to Nos. 467, 479, 484, 486c, 486d, 486f, 486g, 486h, 486i, 486j, 486k, 486l, sold for $9.95.

No. 484 was issued in a sheet of 9 + 9 labels that could be personalized and removed. The sheet sold for $15.95. Gutter strips of 10 of No. 484 exist with five labels forming a picture featuring the 12 Zodiac animals.

A sheet containing lithographed versions of Nos. 486a-486l and 12 labels that could not be personalized sold for $10.

See Nos. 512i, 546f.

Worldwide Fund for Nature (WWF) — A120

No. 487 — Christmas Island frigatebird: a, Adult on nest. b, Adults and chick at nest.
No. 488 — Christmas Island frigatebird: a, Chick and adult at nest. b, Adult in flight.

**2010, Aug. 17 Litho. *Perf. 14¼***

**487** Horiz. pair 4.25 4.25
*a.-b.* A120 60c Either single 1.60 1.25
**488** Horiz. pair 9.75 9.75
*a.-b.* A120 $1.80 Either single 4.25 2.75
*c.* Souvenir sheet, #487a-487b, 488a-488b 14.00 14.00

Christmas — A121

Golden bosunbird: 60c, Carrying gift. $1.30, Flying away from gift on beach.

**2010, Nov. 1 Litho. *Perf. 14¾x14***

**489** A121 60c multi 2.25 2.25
**490** A121 $1.30 multi 4.50 4.50

**Booklet Stamp**
**Self-Adhesive**

***Serpentine Die Cut 11¼ Syncopated***

**491** A121 60c multi 2.25 2.25
*a.* Booklet pane of 10 22.50
**491B** A121 $1.30 multi 4.50 4.25
*c.* Booklet pane of 5 22.50

New Year 2011 (Year of the Rabbit) — A122

Designs: 60c, Rabbit. $1.80, Chinese character for "rabbit."
No. 494: a, Rat. b, Ox. c, Dragon. d, Snake. e, Tiger. f, Rabbit, diff. g, Horse. h, Pig. i, Goat. j, Monkey. k, Rooster. l, Dog.

**Litho. With Foil Application**

**2011, Jan. 11 *Perf. 14¾x14***

**492** A122 60c multi 1.25 1.25
**493** A122 $1.80 multi 3.75 3.75
*a.* Souvenir sheetof 2, #492-493 5.50 5.50
**494** Sheet of 14, #492-493, 494a-494l 13.00 13.00
*a.-d.* A122 15c Any single .30 .30
*e.-h.* A122 20c Any single .40 .40
*i.-l.* A122 25c Any single .50 .50
*m.* Booklet pane of 4, #494a, 494b, 2 #492 3.75 —
*n.* Booklet pane of 4, #494e, 494f, 2 #492 4.00 —
*o.* Booklet pane of 4, #494g, 494i, 2 #492 4.25 —
*p.* Booklet pane of 4, #494h, 494l, 2 #492 4.25 —
*q.* Booklet pane of 4, #494j, 494k, 2 #492 4.25 —
*r.* Booklet pane of 4, #494c, 494d, 2 #493 9.75 —
Complete booklet, #494m-494r 31.00

Complete booklet sold for $14.95. A sheet of 12 containing Nos. 494a-494l + 12 labels that could not be personalized sold for $15.95.
See Nos. 512j, 546g.

Crabs A123

No. 495: a, Red crab. b, Robber crab.
No. 496: a, Jackson's crab. b, Blue crab.

**2011, June 7 Litho. *Perf. 14¾x14***

**495** A123 60c Horiz. pair, #a-b 4.00 4.00
**496** A123 $1.20 Horiz. pair, #a-b 7.50 7.50

Christmas — A124

Santa Claus: 55c, Giving cracker to crab. $1.50, In water holding flippers.

**2011, Oct. 31 *Perf. 14x14¾***

**497** A124 55c multi 1.75 1.75
**498** A124 $1.50 multi 4.00 4.00

**Booklet Stamps**
**Self-Adhesive**

***Serpentine Die Cut 11¼ Syncopated***

**499** A124 55c multi 1.75 1.75
*a.* Booklet pane of 10 17.50
**500** A124 $1.50 multi 4.00 4.00
*a.* Booklet pane of 5 20.00

New Year 2012 (Year of the Dragon) — A125

Designs: 60c, Dragon. $1.80, Chinese character for "dragon."
No. 503: a, Rat. b, Ox. c, "Dragon" in circle. d, Snake. e, Tiger. f, Rabbit. g, Horse. h, Pig. i, Goat. j, Monkey. k, Rooster. l, Dog.

**Litho. with Foil Application**

**2012, Jan. 10 *Perf. 14¾x14***

**501** A125 60c multi 1.40 1.40
**502** A125 $1.80 multi 4.00 4.00
*a.* Souvenir sheet of 2, #501-502 5.50 5.50
*b.* As "a," with 2012 Beijing Intl. Stamp & Coin Expo overprint in sheet margin in gold 5.00 5.00
**503** Sheet of 14, #501-502, 503a-503l 11.00 11.00
*a.-d.* A125 15c Any single .35 .35
*e.-h.* A125 20c Any single .45 .45
*i.-l.* A125 25c Any single .55 .55
*m.* Booklet pane of 4, #503c, 503d, 2 #502 8.75 —
*n.* Booklet pane of 4, #503g, 503i, 2 #501 4.00 —
*o.* Booklet pane of 4, #503j, 503k, 2 #501 4.00 —
*p.* Booklet pane of 4, #503h, 503l, 2 #501 4.00 —
*q.* Booklet pane of 4, #503a, 503b, 2 #501 3.50 —
*r.* Booklet pane of 4, #503e, 503f, 2 #501 3.75 —
Complete booklet, #503m-503r 28.00

Complete booklet sold for $12.95.
Issued: No. 502b, 11/2.
See Nos. 512k, 546h.

Ferns — A126

No. 504: a, Tectaria devexa. b, Asplenium listeri.
No. 505: a, Bolbitis heteroclita. b, Pteris tripartita.

**2012, May 1 Litho. *Perf. 14x14¾***

**504** Horiz. pair 3.00 3.00
*a.-b.* A126 60c Either single 1.25 1.25
**505** Horiz. pair 6.00 6.00
*a.-b.* A126 $1.20 Either single 2.50 2.50

Christmas — A127

Designs: 55c, Sand sculpture of Santa Claus, frigatebirds, turtle and crabs. $1.60, Santa Claus decorating sand sculpture of Christmas tree, starfish, crabs, bird.

**2012, Nov. 1 *Perf. 14¾x14***

**506** A127 55c multi 1.50 1.50
**507** A127 $1.60 multi 3.75 3.75
*a.* Souvenir sheet of 2, #506-507 5.25 5.25

**Booklet Stamp**
**Self-Adhesive**

***Serpentine Die Cut 11¼ Syncopated***

**508** A127 $1.60 multi 3.75 3.75
*a.* Booklet pane of 5 19.00

**New Year Types of 2008-12 and**

New Year 2013 (Year of the Snake) A128

Rat and Apples A129

Flower — A130

Designs: No. 509, 60c, Snake. $1.80, Chinese character for "snake."
No. 511: a, Rat and apples. b, Ox and cherries. c, Dragon and tomatoes. d, Snake amd eggs. e, Tiger and fish. f, Rabbit and oranges. g, Horse and bananas. h, Boar and spinach. i, Goat and onions. j, Monkey and grapes. k, Rooster and pumpkins. l, Dog and milk bottles.
No. 512: a, Like No 511g. b, Like No. 511h. c, Like No. 511i. d, Like No. 511j. e, Like No. 511k. f, Like No. 511l. g, Rat with purple foil. h, Ox with purple foil. i, Tiger with purple foil. j, Rabbit with purple foil. k, Dragon with purple foil. l, Like No. 509.

**Litho. With Foil Application**

**2013, Jan. 13 *Perf. 14¾x14***

**509** A128 60c multi 1.25 1.25
**510** A128 $1.80 multi 3.75 3.75
*a.* Souvenir sheet of 2, #509-510 5.25 5.25
*b.* As "a," with emblem overprinted in gold in sheet margin 4.75 4.75
**511** Sheet of 14, #509-510, 511a-511l 10.00 10.00
*a.-d.* A129 15c Any single .30 .30
*e.-h.* A129 20c Any single .40 .40
*i.-l.* A129 25c multi .55 .55
*m.* Booklet pane of 4, #511d, 511g, 2 #510 9.00 —
*n.* Booklet pane of 4, #511i, 511j, 2 #509 4.00 —
*o.* Booklet pane of 4, #511k, 511l, 2 #509 4.00 —
*p.* Booklet pane of 4, #511a, 511h, 2 #509 3.50 —
*q.* Booklet pane of 4, #511b, 511e, 2 #509 3.50 —
*r.* Booklet pane of 4, #511c, 511f, 2 #509 3.50 —
Complete booklet, #511m-511r 27.50

Issued: No. 510b, 9/26. China International Collection Expo (No. 510b).

**Self-Adhesive**

***Serpentine Die Cut 12¼, Serpentine Die Cut (#512m)***

**512** Sheet of 13 25.00
*a.-b.* A129 20c Either single .70 .70
*c.-f.* A129 25c Any single .90 .90
*g.* A113 50c pur & multi 1.75 1.75
*h.* A117 55c pur & multi 2.00 2.00
*i.* A119 55c pur & multi 2.00 2.00
*j.* A122 60c pur & multi 2.10 2.10
*k.* A125 60c pur & multi 2.10 2.10
*l.* A128 60c pur & multi 2.10 2.10
*m.* A130 $1 pur & multi 3.75 3.75

Complete booklet sold for $12.95. No. 512 sold for $9.95.
See Nos. 546i.

Fish — A131

No. 513: a, Cocos angelfish. b, Ladder wrasse.
$1.20, Redtooth triggerfish. $1.80, Red-striped pigfish.

**2013, May 21 Litho. *Perf. 14x14¾***

**513** Horiz. pair 2.50 2.50
*a.-b.* A131 60c Either single 1.25 1.25
**514** A131 $1.20 multi 2.50 2.50
**515** A131 $1.80 multi 3.50 3.50
*Nos. 513-515 (3)* 8.50 8.50

Flowering Shrubs A132

No. 516: a, Colubrina pedunculata. b, Abutilon listeri.
No. 517: a, Urena lobata var. sinuata. b, Indigofera hirsuta.
No. 518, Like No. 516a. No. 519, Like No. 516b.

**2013, June 18 *Perf. 14¾x14***

**516** A132 60c Horiz. pair, #a-b 2.40 2.40
**517** A132 $1.20 Horiz. pair, #a-b 4.50 4.50

**Booklet Stamps**
**Self-Adhesive**

***Serpentine Die Cut 11¼ Syncopated***

**518** A132 60c multi 1.25 1.25
**519** A132 60c multi 1.25 1.25
*a.* Booklet pane of 10, 5 each #518-519 16.00

Christmas — A133

Designs: 55c, Santa Claus riding on frigatebird. $1.80, Frigatebird and crab in balloon gondola.

**2013, Nov. 1 Litho. *Perf. 14x14¾***

**520** A133 55c multi 1.10 1.10
**521** A133 $1.80 multi 3.50 3.50
*a.* Souvenir sheet of 2, #520-521 5.00 5.00

**Booklet Stamps**
**Self-Adhesive**

***Serpentine Die Cut 11¼ Syncopated***

**522** A133 $1.80 multi 3.50 3.50
*a.* Booklet pane of 5 20.00

**Litho. With Foil Application**

**523** A133 $1.80 multi 3.50 3.50
*a.* Booklet pane of 10 40.00

New Year 2014 (Year of the Horse) — A134

Designs: 60c, Horse. $1.80, Chinese character for "horse."
No. 526: a, Rat. b, Ox. c, Dragon. d, Snake. e, Tiger. f, Rabbit. g, Horse, diff. h, Pig. i, Goat. j, Monkey. k, Rooster. l, Dog.

**Litho. With Foil Application**

**2014, Jan. 7 *Perf. 14¾x14***

**524** A134 60c multi 1.10 1.10
**525** A134 $1.80 multi 3.25 3.25
*a.* Souvenir sheet of 2, #524-525 4.50 4.50
**526** Sheet of 14, #524-525, 526a-526l 8.75 8.75
*a.-d.* A134 15c Any single .25 .25
*e.-h.* A134 20c Any single .35 .35
*i.-l.* A134 25c Any single .45 .45
*m.* Booklet pane of 4, #526g, 526i, 2 #525 7.75 —
*n.* Booklet pane of 4, #526j, 526k, 2 #524 3.25 —
*o.* Booklet pane of 4, #526h, 526l, 2 #524 3.25 —
*p.* Booklet pane of 4, #526a, 526b, 2 #524 3.00 —
*q.* Booklet pane of 4, #526e, 526f, 2 #524 3.25
*r.* Booklet pane of 4, #526c, 526d, 2 #524 3.00 —
Complete booklet, #526m-526r 23.50

Complete booklet sold for $12.95. See No. 546j.

Christmas Island National Park — A135

Designs: No. 527a, Forest. No. 527b, Beach. $1.40, Sea cliffs. $2.10, Wetlands.

**2014, June 17 Litho. *Perf. 14x14¾***

**527** Horiz. pair 3.00 3.00
*a.-b.* A135 70c Either single 1.40 1.40

**528** A135 $1.40 multi 2.75 2.75
**529** A135 $2.10 multi 4.00 4.00
*Nos. 527-529 (3)* 9.75 9.75

Red Crab Migration — A136

Designs: 70c, Red crab. $2.10, Red crabs migrating.

**2014, Aug. 12 Litho.** ***Perf. 14x14¾***
**530-531** A136 Set of 2 5.25 5.25

Christmas — A137

Designs: 65c, Crab offering gift to Santa Claus. $1.80, Crab holding gift-wrapped coconut.

**2014, Oct. 31 Litho.** ***Perf. 14¾x14***
**532** A137 65c multi 1.25 1.25
**533** A137 $1.80 multi 3.25 3.25
*a.* Souvenir sheet of 2, #532-533 4.50 4.50

**Booklet Stamps Self-Adhesive**

***Serpentine Die Cut 11¼ Syncopated***

**534** A137 65c multi 1.25 1.25
*a.* Booklet pane of 10 + 10 etiquettes 12.50
**535** A137 $1.80 multi 3.25 3.25
*a.* Booklet pane of 5 16.50

New Year 2015 (Year of the Goat) — A138

Designs: 70c, Goat. $2.10, Chinese character for "goat."

No. 538: a, Rat. b, Ox. c, Dragon. d, Snake. e, Goat, diff. f, Monkey. g, Rooster. h, Dog. i, Tiger. j, Rabbit. k, Horse. l, Pig.

**Litho. With Foil Application**

**2015, Jan. 8** ***Perf. 14¾x14***
**536** A138 70c multi 1.10 1.10
**537** A138 $2.10 multi 3.25 3.25
*a.* Souvenir sheet of 2, #536-537 4.50 4.50
**538** Sheet of 14, #536-537, 538a-538l 9.00 9.00
*a.-d.* A138 15c Any single .25 .25
*e.-h.* A138 25c Any single .40 .40
*i.-l.* A138 30c Any single .50 .50
*m.* Booklet pane of 4, #538e, 538f, 2 #537 8.00 —
*n.* Booklet pane of 4, #538g, 538h, 2 #536 3.25 —
*o.* Booklet pane of 4, #538a, 538l, 2 #536 3.25 —
*p.* Booklet pane of 4, #538b, 538i, 2 #536 3.25 —
*q.* Booklet pane of 4, #538c, 538j, 2 #536 3.25
*r.* Booklet pane of 4, #538d, 538k, 2 #536 3.25 —
Complete booklet, #538m-538r 24.50

Complete booklet sold for $14.95. See No. 546k.

Christmas — A139

Designs: 65c, Waterfall, Christmas tree made of red crabs. $1.80, Red crabs, snowman made of turtle and coconut.

**2015, Oct. 30 Litho.** ***Perf. 14¾x14***
**539** A139 65c multi .95 .95
**540** A139 $1.80 multi 2.60 2.60
*a.* Souvenir sheet of 2, #539-540 3.75 3.75

**Booklet Stamps Self-Adhesive**

***Serpentine Die Cut 11¼ Syncopated***

**541** A139 $1.80 multi 2.60 2.60
*a.* Booklet pane of 5 13.00

**Litho. With Foil Application**

**542** A139 65c multi .95 .95
*a.* Booklet pane of 10 9.50

**New Year Types of 2008-15 and**

New Year 2016 (Year of the Monkey) A140

Peach A141

Designs: $1, Monkey. $3, Chinese character for "monkey."

No. 545: a, Rat. b, Rabbit. c, Goat. d, Dog. e, Ox. f, Dragon. g, Monkey, diff. h, Pig. i, Tiger. j, Snake. k, Horse. l, Rooster.

**Litho. With Foil Application**

**2016, Feb. 3** ***Perf. 14¾x14***
**543** A140 $1 multi 1.50 1.50
**544** A140 $3 multi 4.50 4.50
*a.* Souvenir sheet of 2, #543-544 6.00 6.00
**545** Sheet of 14, #543-544, 545a-545l 12.00 12.00
*a.-d.* A140 20c Any single .30 .30
*e.-h.* A140 30c Any single .45 .45
*i.-l.* A140 50c Any single .75 .75
*m.* Booklet pane of 4, #543, 544, 545a, 545e 6.75 —
*n.* Booklet pane of 4, #545b, 545i, 2 #543 4.25 —
*o.* Booklet pane of 4, #545f, 545j, 2 #543 4.25 —
*p.* Booklet pane of 4, #543, 544, 545c, 545k 7.25 —
*q.* Booklet pane of 4, #545g, 545l, 2 543 4.25 —
*r.* Booklet pane of 4, #545d, 545h, 2 #543 3.75 —
Complete booklet, #545m-545r 30.50

**Self-Adhesive**

***Serpentine Die Cut 12¼ Syncopated, Serpentine Die Cut (#546m)***

**546** Sheet of 13 14.50
*a.* A140 20c Like #545d .35 .35
*b.* A140 30c Like #545h .50 .50
*c.* A140 50c Like #545l .85 .85
*d.* A113 50c Rat .85 .85
*e.* A117 55c Ox .90 .90
*f.* A119 55c Tiger .90 .90
*g.* A122 60c Rabbit 1.00 1.00
*h.* A125 60c Dragon 1.00 1.00
*i.* A128 60c Snake 1.00 1.00
*j.* A134 60c Horse 1.00 1.00
*k.* A136 70c Goat 1.10 1.10
*l.* A140 $1 Like #543 1.60 1.60
*m.* A141 $2 multi 3.25 3.25

Complete booklet sold for $20.95. No. 546 sold for $9.95.

**With Personalized Photo at Right Like Type A116 Litho.**

***Serpentine Die Cut 11½x11¼ Syncopated***

**Self-Adhesive**

**547** A140 $1 gold & multi 2.40 2.40

No. 547 was printed in a sheet of 20 and has personalized pictures and a straight edge at right and lack separations between the stamp and the personalized photo. Sheets of 20 sold for $33 each.

Robber Crab — A142

Various depictions of crab with denomination in: No. 548a, Greenish yellow. No. 548b, Turquoise green. $2, Red.

**2016, Apr. 26 Litho.** ***Perf. 14x14¾***
**548** Horiz. pair 3.00 3.00
*a.-b.* A142 $1 Either single 1.50 1.50
**549** A142 $2 multi 3.00 3.00

Shells — A143

No. 550: a, Lambis scorpius. b, Tectus niloticus.

No. 551: a, Conus canonicus. b, Tridacna squamosa.

**2016, Aug. 23 Litho.** ***Perf. 14x14¾***
**550** Horiz. pair 3.00 3.00
*a.-b.* A143 $1 Either single 1.50 1.50
**551** Horiz. pair 6.00 6.00
*a.-b.* A143 $2 Either single 3.00 3.00

Christmas — A144

Birds and: 65c, Santa Claus in sleigh. $1.80, Rudolph, the red-nosed reindeer.

**2016, Oct. 31 Litho.** ***Perf. 14¾x14***
**552** A144 65c multi 1.00 1.00
**553** A144 $1.80 multi 2.75 2.75
*a.* Souvenir sheet of 2, #552-553 3.75 3.75

**Booklet Stamps Self-Adhesive**

***Serpentine Die Cut 11¼ Syncopated***

**554** A144 $1.80 multi 2.75 2.75
*a.* Booklet pane of 5 14.00

**Litho. With Foil Application**

**555** A144 65c multi 1.00 1.00
*a.* Booklet pane of 10 + 10 etiquettes 10.00

New Year 2017 (Year of the Rooster) — A145

Designs: $1, Rooster. $3, Chinese character for "rooster."

No. 558: a, Rat. b, Rabbit. c, Goat. d, Dog. e, Ox. f, Dragon. g, Monkey. h, Pig. i, Tiger. j, Snake. k, Horse. l, Chicks.

**Litho. With Foil Application**

**2017, Jan. 10** ***Perf. 14¾x14***
**556** A145 $1 multi 1.50 1.50
**557** A145 $3 multi 4.50 4.50
*a.* Souvenir sheet of 2, #556-557 6.00 6.00
**558** Sheet of 14, #556-557, 558a-558l 12.00 12.00
*a.-d.* A145 20c Any single .30 .30
*e.-h.* A145 30c Any single .45 .45
*i.-l.* A145 50c Any single .75 .75
*m.* Booklet pane of 4, #556, 557, 558d, 558l 7.50 —
*n.* Booklet pane of 4, #558a, 558h, 2 #556 4.00 —
*o.* Booklet pane of 4, #558e, 558i, 2 #556 4.50 —
*p.* Booklet pane of 4, #558b, 558f, 2 #556 4.00 —
*q.* Booklet pane of 4, #558j, 558k, 2 #556 4.75 —
*r.* Booklet pane of 4, #556, 557, 558c, 558g 7.25 —
Complete booklet, #558m, 558n, 558o, 558p, 558q, 558r 32.00

**With Personalized Photo at Right Like Type A116 Self-Adhesive Litho.**

***Serpentine Die Cut 11½x11¼ Syncopated***

**559** A145 $1 multi 2.50 2.50

Complete booklet sold for $20.95.

No. 559 was printed in a sheet of 20 and has personalized pictures and a straight edge at right and lack separations between the stamp and the personalized photo. Sheets of 20 sold for $33 each.

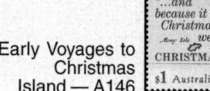

Early Voyages to Christmas Island — A146

Quotation, map of Christmas Island and: $1, Mary, ship of island's discoverer William Mynors. $2, William Dampier and crab.

**2017, Aug. 15 Litho.** ***Perf. 14x14¾***
**560** A146 $1 multi 1.60 1.60
**561** A146 $2 multi 3.25 3.25
*a.* Souvenir sheet of 2, #560-561 5.00 5.00

Christmas — A147

Designs: 65c, Reindeer and elf on golf course. $2, Santa Claus swinging golf club.

**2017, Nov. 1 Litho.** ***Perf. 14¾x14***
**562** A147 65c multi 1.00 1.00
**563** A147 $2 multi 3.25 3.25
*a.* Souvenir sheet of 2, #562-563 4.25 4.25

**Booklet Stamps Self-Adhesive**

***Serpentine Die Cut 11¼ Syncopated***

**564** A147 $2 multi 3.25 3.25
*a.* Booklet pane of 5 16.50

**Litho. & Silk-Screened**

**565** A147 65c multi 1.00 1.00
*a.* Booklet pane of 10 + 10 etiquettes 10.00

New Year 2018 (Year of the Dog) — A148

Designs: $1, Dog. $3, Chinese character for "dog."

No. 568: a, Rat and Narcissus. b, Rabbit and Jonquil. c, Goat and Larkspur. d, Dog and Marigold. e, Ox and Carnation. f, Dragon and Sweet pea. g, Monkey and Gladiolus. h, Pig and Chrysanthemum. i, Tiger and Violet. j, Snake and Passion flower. k, Horse and Rose. l, Rooster and Aster.

**Litho. With Foil Application**

**2018, Jan. 8** ***Perf. 14¾x14***
**566** A148 $1 gold & multi 1.60 1.60
**567** A148 $3 gold & multi 5.00 5.00
*a.* Souvenir sheet of 2, #566-567 6.75 6.75
**568** Sheet of 14, #566-567, 568a-568l 13.50 13.50
*a.-d.* A148 20c Any single .35 .35
*e.-h.* A148 30c Any single .50 .50
*i.-l.* A148 50c Any single .80 .80
*m.* Booklet pane of 4, #566-567, 568d, 568h 7.50 —
*n.* Booklet pane of 4, #568a, 568e, 2 #566 4.25 —
*o.* Booklet pane of 4, #568b, 568i, 2 #566 4.50 —
*p.* Booklet pane of 4, #568f, 568j, 2 #566 4.75 —
*q.* Booklet pane of 4, #568c, 568k, 2 #566 4.50 —
*r.* Booklet pane of 4, #566-567, 568g, 568l 9.00 —
Complete booklet, #568m, 568n, 568o, 568p, 568q, 568r 35.00

**With Personalized Photo at Right Like Type A116 Self-Adhesive Litho.**

***Serpentine Die Cut 11½x11¼ Syncopated***

**569** A148 $1 multi 2.75 2.75

Complete booklet sold for $20.95.

No. 569 was printed in a sheet of 20 and has personalized pictures and a straight edge at right and lack separations between the stamp and the personalized photo. Sheets of 20 sold for $33 each.

Illustrations of Birds by John Gerrard Keulemans (1842-1912) — A149

Designs: No. 570, Christmas boobook. No. 571, White-tailed tropicbird. No. 572, Brown goshawk. No. 573, Christmas white-eye.

**2018, Aug. 28 Litho.** ***Perf. 14¾x14***
**570** A149 $1 multi 1.50 1.50
**571** A149 $1 multi 1.50 1.50
**572** A149 $2 multi 3.00 3.00
**573** A149 $2 multi 3.00 3.00
*a.* Souvenir sheet of 4, #570-573 9.00 9.00
*Nos. 570-573 (4)* 9.00 9.00

Christmas — A150

Designs: 65c, Santa Claus and Golden bosunbird on surfboard. $2, Red-footed booby with Christmas tree on surfboard.

**2018, Nov. 1 Litho. *Perf. 14¾x14***

574 A150 65c multi .95 .95
575 A150 $2 multi 3.00 3.00
a. Souvenir sheet of 2, #574-575 4.00 4.00

### Booklet Stamps
### Self-Adhesive
***Serpentine Die Cut 11¼ Syncopated***

576 A150 $2 multi 3.00 3.00
a. Booklet pane of 5 15.00

### Litho. & Silk-Screened

577 A150 65c multi .95 .95
a. Booklet pane of 10 + 10 etiquettes 9.50

New Year 2019 (Year of the Pig) — A151

Designs: $1, Pig. $3, Chinese character for "pig."

No. 568: a, Rat and kangaroo. b, Rabbit and platypus. c, Goat and echidna. d, Dog and dingo. e, Ox and wombat. f, Dragon and frilled lizard. g, Monkey and ringtail possum. h, Pig and koala. i, Tiger and Tasmanian Tiger. j, Snake and goanna. k, Horse and kookaburra. l, Rooster and emu.

### Litho. With Foil Application

**2019, Jan. 8 *Perf. 14¾x14***

578 A151 $1 multi 1.50 1.60
579 A151 $3 multi 4.50 4.50
a. Souvenir sheet of 2, #578-579 6.00 6.00
580 Sheet of 14, #578-579, 580a-580l 12.00 12.00
a.-d. A151 20c Any single .30 .30
e.-h. A151 30c Any single .45 .45
i.-l. A151 50c Any single .75 .75
m. Booklet pane of 4, #578, 579, 580a, 580h 7.00 —
n. Booklet pane of 4, #580e, 580i, 2 #578 4.25 —
o. Booklet pane of 4, #580b, 580f, 2 #578 3.75 —
p. Booklet pane of 4, #580j, 580k, 2 #578 4.75 —
q. Booklet pane of 4, #578, 579, 580c, 580g 7.00 —
r. Booklet pane of 4, #580d, 580l, 2 #578 4.25 —
Complete booklet, #580m, 580n, 580o, 580p, 580q, 580r 31.00

### With Personalized Photo at Right Like Type A116
### Litho.
***Serpentine Die Cut 11½x11¼ Syncopated***
### Self-Adhesive

581 A151 $1 multi — —

No. 581 was printed in a sheet of 20 and has personalized pictures, a straight edge at right and lacks separation between the stamp and the personalized photo. Sheets of 20 sold for $33 each.

Complete booklet sold for $20.95.

Explorers — A152

Designs: $1, Captain John Fiot Lee Pearse Maclear (1838-1907), discoverer of Flying Fish Cove. $2, Captain Pelham Aldrich (1844-1930), explorer of Christmas Island jungle and discoverer of phosphates.

**2019, Aug. 27 Litho. *Perf. 14x14¾***

582-583 A152 Set of 2 4.00 4.00
583a Souvenir sheet of 2, #582-583 4.00 4.00

Christmas — A153

Designs: 65c, Santa Claus, crab and bird at dinner table. $2.20, Reindeer, crab and bird at dinner table.

**2019, Nov. 1 Litho. *Perf. 14¾x14***

584 A153 65c multi .90 .90
585 A153 $2.20 multi 3.00 3.00
a. Souvenir sheet of 2, #584-585 4.00 4.00

### Booklet Stamps
### Self-Adhesive
***Serpentine Die Cut 11¼ Syncopated***

586 A153 $2.20 multi 3.00 3.00
a. Booklet pane of 5 15.00

### Litho. & Silk-Screened

587 A153 65c multi .90 .90
a. Booklet pane of 20 + 20 etiquettes 18.00
Complete booklet, #587a 18.00

New Year 2020 (Year of the Rat) — A154

Designs: Nos. 588, 591a, Rat with fan. Nos. 589, 591b, Rat with red robe. Nos. 590, 591c, Rat with bowl.

No. 592: a, Ox. b, Goat. c, Dog. d, Rabbit. e, Horse. f, Monkey. g, Tiger. h, Dragon. i, Rooster. j, Rat. k, Snake. l, Pig.

### Litho. & Embossed

**2020, Jan. 8 *Perf. 14¼***

588 A154 $1.10 multi 1.50 1.50
a. Booklet pane of 4 6.00 —
589 A154 $2.50 multi 3.50 3.50
a. Booklet pane of 4, 2 each #588, 589 10.00 —
590 A154 $3.30 multi 4.50 4.50
a. Booklet pane of 4, 2 each #588, 590 12.00 —
Complete booklet, #589a, 590a, 3 #588a 40.00
*Nos. 588-590 (3)* 9.50 9.50

### Souvenir Sheet

591 Sheet of 3 9.50 9.50
a. A154 $1.10 multi (50x50mm diamond-shaped) 1.50 1.50
b. A154 $2.50 multi (50x50mm diamond-shaped) 3.50 3.50
c. A154 $3.30 multi (50x50mm diamond-shaped) 4.50 4.50

### Miniature Sheet

592 Sheet of 15, #591a-591c, 592a-592l 19.00 19.00
a.-c. A154 10c Any single (30x30mm) .25 .25
d.-f. A154 50c Any single (30x30mm) .70 .70
g.-i. A154 70c Any single (30x30mm) .95 .95
j.-l. A154 $1 Any single (30x30mm) 1.25 1.25

### Booklet Stamp
### Self-Adhesive
### Litho.
***Serpentine Die Cut 11½ Syncopated***

593 A154 $2.50 multi 3.50 3.50
a. Booklet pane of 5 17.50

Complete booklet sold for $29.95. The three examples of No. 588a in the complete booklet have different pane margins. A sheet containing self-adhesive stamps like Nos. 592a-592l sold for $15.50.

Crabs — A155

Designs: No. 594, $1.10, Bright-eyed crab. No. 595, $1.10, Kuhl's ghost crab. No. 596, $2.20, Red nipper. No. 597, $2.20, White-stripe crab.

**2020, Aug. 17 Litho. *Perf. 14x14¾***

594-597 A155 Set of 4 9.75 9.75
597a Souvenir sheet of 4, #594-597 9.75 9.75

Christmas — A156

Designs: 65c, Santa Claus conducting choir of birds. $2.20, Reindeer, red crabs and giant geckos playing percussion instruments.

**2020, Oct. 30 Litho. *Perf. 14x14¾***

598 A156 65c multi .95 .95
599 A156 $2.20 multi 3.25 3.25
a. Souvenir sheet of 2, #598-599 4.25 4.25

### Booklet Stamps
### Self-Adhesive
***Serpentine Die Cut 11¼ Syncopated***

600 A156 $2.20 multi 3.25 3.25
a. Booklet pane of 5 16.50

### Litho. With Foil Application

601 A156 65c multi .95 .95
a. Booklet pane of 10 + 10 etiquettes 9.50

A157

New Year 2021 (Year of the Ox) — A157a

Ox with: $1.10, Flowers. $2.20, Chinese knot. $3.30, Ring of gold coins.

No. 606: a, Rabbit. b, Horse. c, Pig. d, Tiger. e, Ram. f, Monkey. g, Rat. h, Snake. i, Dog. j, Ox. k, Dragon. l, Rooster.

No. 610: a, Rabbit. b, Horse. c, Pig. d, Tiger. e, Goat. f, Monkey. g, Rat. h, Snake. i, Dog. j, Ox. k, Dragon. l, Rooster. m, Chinese characters for "Happy New Year."

### Litho. & Embossed

**2021, Jan. 8 *Perf. 14¼***

602 A157 $1.10 multi 1.75 1.75
603 A157 $2.20 multi 3.50 3.50
604 A157 $3.30 multi 5.00 5.00
*Nos. 602-604 (3)* 10.25 10.25

### Souvenir Sheet
### Litho. & Embossed With Foil Application

605 Sheet of 3 10.50 10.50
a. A157 $1.10 multi (50x50mm diamond-shaped) 1.75 1.75
b. A157 $2.20 multi (50x50mm diamond-shaped) 3.50 3.50
c. A157 $3.30 multi (50x50mm diamond-shaped) 5.00 5.00

### Miniature Sheet

606 Sheet of 15, #605a-605c, 606a-606l 21.00 21.00
a.-c. A157 10c Any single (30x30mm, perf. 14¼x14) .25 .25
d.-f. A157 40c Any single (30x30mm, perf. 14¼x14) .60 .60
g.-i. A157 70c Any single (30x30mm, perf. 14¼x14) 1.10 1.10
j.-l. A157 $1 Any single (30x30mm, perf. 14¼x14) 1.50 1.50

### Booklet Stamps
### Litho.
***Perf. 14¼***

607 A157 $1.10 multi 1.75 1.75
a. Booklet pane of 4 7.75 —
608 A157 $2.20 multi 3.50 3.50
a. Booklet pane of 4, #608 at LR, 3 #607 8.75 —
b. Booklet pane of 4, #608 at UL, 3 #607 8.75 —
609 A157 $3.30 multi 5.25 5.25
a. Booklet pane of 4, #609 at UL, 3 #607 10.50 —
b. Booklet pane of 4, #609 at LR, 3 #607 10.50 —
Complete booklet, #607a, 608a, 608b, 609a, 609b 46.50
*Nos. 607-609 (3)* 10.50 10.50

### Litho. (#610a-610l), Litho. With Foil Application (#610m)
***Serpentine Die Cut 13½ Syncopated (#610a-610l), Serpentine Die Cut (#610m)***
### Self-Adhesive

610 Sheet of 13 24.00
a.-c. A157 10c Any single .30 .30
d.-f. A157 40c Any single .65 .65
g.-i. A157 70c Any single 1.10 1.10
j.-l. A157 $1 Any single 1.60 1.60
m. A157a $8 gold & red 13.00 13.00

Complete booklet sold for $29.95. No. 610 sold for $15.50 and contains twelve 26x26mm stamps and one 34mm diameter stamp.

Turtles — A158

Designs: No. 611, $1.10, Eretmochelys imbricata, head at right. No. 612, $1.10, Eretmochelys imbricata, head at left. No. 613, $2.20, Chelonia mydas, head at left. No. 614, $2.20, Chelonia mydas facing forward.

**2021, Aug. 10 Litho. *Perf. 14x14¾***

611-614 A158 Set of 4 9.75 9.75
614a Souvenir sheet of 4, #611-614 9.75 9.75

Christmas — A159

Designs: 65c, Santa Claus snorkeling with crab and turtle. $2.40, Crabs, turtle and Christmas gifts.

**2021, Nov. 1 Litho. *Perf. 14¾x14***

615 A159 65c multi 1.00 1.00
616 A159 $2.40 multi 3.75 3.75
a. Souvenir sheet of 2, #615-616 4.75 4.75

### Booklet Stamps
### Self-Adhesive
***Serpentine Die Cut 11¼ Syncopated***

617 A159 $2.40 multi 3.75 3.75
a. Booklet pane of 5 19.00

### Litho. With Foil Application

618 A159 65c multi 1.00 1.00
a. Booklet pane of 10 + 10 etiquettes 10.00

A160

New Year 2022 (Year of the Tiger) — A161

Tiger with: $1.10, Flowers. $2.20, Small tiger and firecrackers. $3.30, Small tiger, Chinese knot and peaches.

No. 622: a, Rabbit. b, Horse. c, Pig. d, Tiger. e, Goat. f, Rooster. g, Rat. h, Snake. i, Dog. j, Ox. k, Dragon. l. Monkey.

No. 623: a, Rabbit. b, Horse. c, Pig. d, Tiger. e, Goat. f, Rooster. g, Rat. h, Snake. i, Dog. j, Ox. k, Dragon. l. Monkey. m, Chinese characters.

### Litho. With Foil Application

**2022, Jan. 6 *Perf. 14¾x14***

619 A160 $1.10 gold & multi 1.60 1.60
a. Booklet pane of 4 6.50 —
620 A160 $2.20 gold & multi 3.25 3.25
a. Booklet pane of 4, 2 each #619, 620 10.00 —
621 A160 $3.30 gold & multi 4.75 4.75
a. Booklet pane of 4, 2 each #619, 621 13.00 —
b. Souvenir sheet of 3, #619-621 9.75 9.75
Complete booklet, #620a, 621a, 3 #619a 42.50
*Nos. 619-621 (3)* 9.60 9.60

### Miniature Sheet

622 A160 Sheet of 15, #619-621, 622a-622l 19.50 19.50
a.-c. 10c Any single .30 .30
d.-f. 40c Any single .55 .55
g.-i. 70c Any single 1.00 1.00
j.-l. $1 Any single 1.40 1.40

### Litho. With Foil Application
***Serpentine Die Cut 13x12½ Syncopated (#623a-623l), Serpentine Die Cut (#623m)***
### Self-Adhesive

623 Sheet of 13 21.50
a.-c. A160 10c Any single .30 .30
d.-f. A160 40c Any single .55 .55
g.-i. 70c Any single 1.00 1.00
j.-l. $1 Any single 1.40 1.40
m. A161 $8 red & gold 11.50 11.50

Complete booklet sold for $29.95 and contains 3 examples of No. 619a, each with different pane margins. No. 623 sold for $15.50 and contains twelve 24x34mm stamps and one 38mm diameter stamp.

Christmas — A162

Designs: 65c, Santa Claus leaving airplane to greet butterflies, bird and crabs. $2.60, Reindeer as airplane pilot, crabs, butterflies and building.

**2022, Nov. 1 Litho.** ***Perf. 14¾x14***

624 A162 65c multi .85 .85
625 A162 $2.60 multi 3.50 3.50
a. Souvenir sheet of 2, #624-625 4.50 4.50

**Booklet Stamps**
**Self-Adhesive**

***Serpentine Die Cut 11¼ Syncopated***

626 A162 $2.60 multi 3.50 3.50
a. Booklet pane of 5 17.50

**Litho. With Foil Application**

627 A162 65c multi .85 .85
a. Booklet pane of 10 + 10 etiquettes 8.50
a. Booklet pane of 20 + 20 etiquettes 19.50
Complete booklet, #627b 19.50

Complete booklet sold for $14.95.

## CILICIA

sə-ˈli-sh͟ē-͵ə

LOCATION — A territory of Turkey, in Southeastern Asia Minor
GOVT. — Former French occupation
AREA — 6,238 sq. mi.
POP. — 383,645
CAPITAL — Adana

British and French forces occupied Cilicia in 1918 and in 1919 its control was transferred to the French. Eventually part of Cilicia was assigned to the French Mandated Territory of Syria but by the Lausanne Treaty of 1923 which fixed the boundary between Syria and Turkey, Cilicia reverted to Turkey.

40 Paras = 1 Piaster

**Issued under French Occupation**

Numbers in parentheses are those of basic Turkish or French stamps.

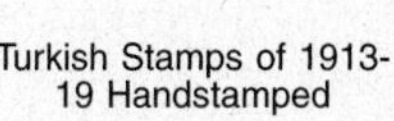

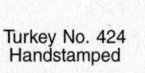

Turkish Stamps of 1913-19 Handstamped

***Perf. 11½, 12, 12½, 13½***

**1919 Unwmk.**

**On Pictorial Issue of 1913**

2 A24 2pa red lilac (254) 9.00 9.00
a. Inverted overprint 20.00 20.00
b. Double overprint 30.00 30.00
3 A25 4pa dk brn (255) 7.25 7.25
a. Inverted overprint 20.00 20.00
b. Double overprint 22.50 22.50
4 A27 6pa dk blue (257) 27.50 20.00
a. Inverted overprint 32.50 32.50
b. Double overprint 50.00 50.00
5 A32 1¾pi slate & red brn (262) 8.75 8.75
a. Inverted overprint 20.00 20.00
b. Double overprint 22.50 22.50

**On Issue of 1915**

6 A17 1pi blue (300) 4.00 4.00
a. Inverted overprint 10.00 10.00
b. Double overprint 10.00 10.00
c. In pair with unovptd. stamp 20.00 20.00
7 A21 20pa car rose (318) 13.50 12.00
a. Inverted overprint 20.00 20.00
b. Double overprint 35.00 35.00
9 A22 20pa car rose (330) 35.00 32.50
a. Inverted overprint 45.00 45.00
b. Double overprint 45.00 45.00

**On Commemorative Issue of 1916**

9A A41 5pa grn (345) 130.00 92.50
10 A41 20pa ultra (347) 7.25 7.25
a. Double overprint 15.00 15.00
11 A41 1pi vio & blk (348) 9.50 9.50
a. Double overprint 27.50 27.50
b. Perf 12½ 9.50 9.50
c. In pair with unovptd. stamp 19.00 19.00
12 A41 5pi yel brn & blk (349) 4.00 4.00
a. Double overprint 7.50 7.50

**On Issue of 1916-18**

13 A44 10pa grn (424) 8.75 8.75
a. Perf 11½ (424a) 8.75 8.75
b. Double overprint 24.00 24.00
14 A47 50pa ultra (428) 45.00 35.00
a. Perf 11½ (428a) 45.00 35.00
b. Double overprint 90.00 90.00
15 A51 25pi car, *straw* (434) 8.75 8.75
16 A52 50pi car (437) 8.75 8.75
17 A52 50pi ind (438) 32.50 32.50

**On Issue of 1917**

18 A53 5pi on 2pa Prus blue (547) 15.00 15.00
a. Perf 11½ (547c) 15.00 15.00

**On Issue of 1919**

19 A47 50pa ultra (555) 40.00 32.50
a. Perf 11½ (555a) 40.00 32.50
b. Double overprint 80.00 80.00
20 A48 2pi org brn & indigo (556) 40.00 32.50
21 A49 5pi pale bl & blk (557a) 40.00 32.50
a. Perf 11½ (557) 40.00 32.50
b. Perf 11½x12½ (557b) 40.00 32.50
c. Double overprint 95.00 95.00

**On Newspaper Stamp of 1916**

22 A10 5pa on 10pa gray grn (P137) 4.75 4.75
d. Inverted overprint 11.00 11.00
e. Double overprint 14.00 14.00

**On Semi-Postal Stamps of 1915**

22A A21 20pa car rose (B8) 92.50 80.00
22B A21 1pi ultra (B9) 2,250. 1,700.
22C A21 1pi ultra (B13) 1,900. 1,200.

**On Semi-Postal Stamps of 1916**

23 A17 1pi bl (B19) 10.50 10.50
a. Inverted overprint 16.00 16.00
b. Double overprint 16.00 16.00
c. Perf 13¼ 25.00 25.00
24 A21 20pa car rose (B28) 4.00 4.00
a. Inverted overprint 7.50 7.50
b. Double overprint 10.00 10.00
25 A21 1pi ultra (B29) 8.75 8.75
a. Inverted overprint 15.00 15.00
b. Double overprint 25.00 25.00

Turkish Stamps of 1913-18 Handstamped

**1919 On Pictorial Issue of 1913**

31 A24 2pa red lil (254) 5.00 5.00
a. Inverted overprint 8.00 8.00
b. Double overprint 12.00 12.00
c. In pair with unovptd. stamp 16.00 16.00
32 A25 4pa dk brn (255) 15.00 15.00
a. Inverted overprint 25.00 25.00
b. Double overprint 45.00 45.00

**On Issue of 1915**

33 A17 1pi blue (300) 13.50 13.50
a. Inverted overprint 22.50 22.50
b. Double overprint 40.00 40.00
34 A22 20pa car rose (330) 5.00 5.00
a. Inverted overprint 11.00 11.00
b. Double overprint 17.50 17.50
c. In pair with unovptd. stamp 22.50 22.50

**On Commemorative Issue of 1916**

35 A41 20pa ultra (347) 15.00 15.00
a. Inverted overprint 32.50 32.50
b. Perf 12½ (347a) 17.50 17.50
36 A41 1pi vio & blk (348) 3.60 3.60
a. Inverted overprint 7.50 7.50
b. Perf 12½ (348a) 3.75 3.75

**On Issue of 1917**

40 A53 5pi on 2pa Prus bl (547) 13.50 13.50
a. Perf 11½ (547c) 13.50 13.50

**On Newspaper Stamp of 1916**

41 A10 5pa on 10pa gray grn (P137) 27.50 27.50
a. Inverted overprint 50.00 50.00
b. In pair with unovptd. stamp 60.00 60.00

**On Semi-Postal Stamp of 1915**

41A A21 20pa car rose (B8) 225.00 150.00

**On Semi-Postal Stamps of 1916**

42 A17 1pi blue (B19) 6.50 6.50
a. Inverted overprint 14.00 14.00
b. Double overprint 15.00 15.00
c. Perf 12 (B19a) 8.00 8.00
d. Perf 12x13¼ (B19b) 8.00 8.00
43 A21 20pa car rose (B28) 4.25 4.25
a. Inverted overprint 10.00 *10.00*
b. Double overprint 11.00 *11.00*
*Nos. 31-43 (11)* 333.85 258.85

Turkish Stamps of 1913-19 Handstamped

**1919 On Pictorial Issue of 1913**

51 A24 2pa red lil (254) 11.00 11.00
a. Inverted overprint 18.00 18.00
b. Double overprint 27.50 27.50
c. In pair with unovptd. stamp 45.00 45.00
52 A25 4pa dk brn (255) 4.50 4.50
a. Inverted overprint 9.00 9.00
b. Double overprint 12.00 12.00

**On Issue of 1915**

53 A17 1pi blue (300) 5.50 5.50
a. Inverted overprint 13.00 13.00
b. Double overprint 17.00 17.00
55 A22 5pa ocher (328) 40.00 35.00
a. Double overprint 80.00 80.00
56 A22 20pa car rose (330) 4.00 4.00
a. Inverted overprint 10.00 10.00
b. Double overprint 14.00 14.00
c. In pair with unovptd. stamp 25.00 25.00

**On Commemorative Issue of 1916**

57 A41 20pa ultra (347) 4.00 4.00
a. Inverted overprint 8.00 8.00
b. Double overprint 12.00 12.00
c. Double overprint, one inverted 9.50 9.50
d. In pair with unovptd. stamp 17.50 17.50
58 A41 1pi vio & blk (348) 4.50 4.50
a. Inverted overprint 7.50 7.50
b. Double overprint 10.00 10.00
59 A41 5pi yel brn & blk (349) 12.00 12.00
a. Inverted overprint 18.00 18.00
b. Double overprint 24.00 24.00

**On Issue of 1916**

59A A17 1pi blue (372) — —

**On Issue of 1916-18**

60 A43 5pa org (421) 45.00 40.00
a. Inverted overprint 70.00 70.00
b. Perf 11½ (421a) 45.00 40.00
61 A46 1pi dl vio (426) 13.50 13.50
a. Inverted overprint 21.00 21.00
b. Double overprint 35.00 35.00
63 A52 50pi green, *straw* (439) 35.00 27.50

**On Issue of 1917**

64 A53 5pi on 2pa Prus bl (547) 32.50 27.50
a. Double overprint 75.00 75.00
b. Perf 11½ (421a) 32.50 27.50

**On Newspaper Stamp of 1916**

65 A10 5pa on 10pa gray grn (P137) 8.75 8.75
a. Inverted overprint 13.50 13.50
b. Double overprint 24.00 24.00

**On Semi-Postal Stamp of 1915**

65A A21 20pa car rose (B8) 1,200. 850.00

**On Semi-Postal Stamps of 1916**

66 A17 1pi blue (B19) 30.00 30.00
a. Inverted overprint 55.00 55.00
67 A19 20pa car (B26) 13.50 13.50
a. Inverted overprint 17.50 17.50
b. Double overprint 17.50 17.50
68 A21 20pa car rose (B28) 180.00 92.50
69 A21 20pa car rose (B31) 8.00 8.00
a. Inverted overprint 15.00 15.00
b. Double overprint 22.50 22.50
69C A21 1pi ultra (401) 110.00 80.00
*Nos. 51-69C (20)* 1,762. 1,272.

Turkey No. 424 Handstamped

**1919**

71 A44 10pa green (420) 9.50 9.50
a. Inverted overprint 17.50 17.50
b. Double overprint 25.00 25.00
c. Perf 11½ (420a) 11.00 11.00

"T.E.O." stands for "Territoires Ennemis Occupés."

Turkish Stamps of 1913-19 Overprinted in Black, Red or Blue

In this setting there are various broken and wrong font letters and the letter "i" is sometimes replaced by a "t."

**1919 On Pictorial Issue of 1913**

75 A30 1pi blue (R) (260) 4.75 4.75
a. Inverted overprint 11.00 11.00
b. Double overprint 11.00 11.00
c. Double overprint, one inverted 20.00 20.00

**On Issue of 1915**

76 A21 20pa car rose (318) 8.75 8.75

**On Commemorative Issue of 1916**

76A A41 5pa grn (345) 200.00 110.00
77 A41 20pa ultra (347) 13.50 13.50
a. Inverted overprint 20.00 20.00
b. Double overprint 30.00 30.00
c. Perf 12½ (347a) 13.50 13.50
78 A41 1pi vio & blk (348) 24.00 24.00
a. Inverted overprint 35.00 35.00
b. Double overprint 60.00 60.00
c. Double overprint, one inverted 65.00 65.00

**On Issue of 1916-18**

79 A43 5pa org (Bl) (421) 4.75 4.75
a. Inverted overprint 10.00 10.00
b. Double overprint 13.00 13.00
c. Double overprint, one inverted 11.00 11.00
d. Perf 11½ (421a) 5.00 5.00
80 A44 10pa grn (424) 8.75 8.75
a. Inverted overprint 16.00 16.00
b. Double overprint 22.50 22.50
c. Double overprint, one inverted 20.00 20.00
d. Perf 11½ (424a) 9.00 9.00
81 A45 20pa dp rose (Bk) (425) 27.50 27.50
a. Double overprint 60.00 60.00
82 A45 20pa dp rose (Bl) (425) 2.00 2.00
a. Inverted overprint 6.00 6.00
b. Double overprint 8.00 8.00
c. Double overprint, one inverted 10.00 10.00
83 A48 2pi org brn & indigo (429) 1.60 1.60
a. Double overprint 6.00 6.00
b. Perf 11½ (429a) 1.75 1.75
83C A49 5pi pale blue & black (R) (430) 1.75 1.75
a. Inverted overprint 10.00 10.00
b. Double overprint 10.00 10.00
c. Double overprint, one inverted 13.00 13.00
d. Perf 11½ (430a) 1.75 1.75
84 A51 25pi car, *straw* (434) 6.50 6.50
a. Inverted overprint 15.00 15.00
b. Double overprint 20.00 20.00
c. Double overprint, one inverted 13.50 13.50
85 A52 50pi grn, *straw* (439) 92.50 87.50
a. Inverted overprint 150.00 150.00
b. Double overprint 150.00 150.00
c. Double overprint, one inverted 160.00 160.00

**On Issue of 1917**

85A A53 5pi on 2pa Prus bl (547) —
86 A53 5pi on 2pa Prus bl (548) 13.50 13.50
a. Perf 11½ (548c) 13.50 13.50

**On Newspaper Stamps of 1916-19**

87 A10 5pa on 10p gray grn (P137) 3.00 3.00
a. Inverted overprint 5.50 5.50
b. Double overprint 7.00 7.00
c. Double overprint, one inverted 13.50 13.50
88 A21 5pa on 2pa ol grn (P173) 1.50 1.50
a. Inverted overprint 5.50 5.50
b. Double overprint 7.00 7.00
c. Double overprint, one inverted 6.50 6.50

**On Semi-Postal Stamps of 1915-17**

90 A21 20pa car rose (B28) 8.75 8.75
a. Double overprint 16.00 16.00
91 A41 10pa car (B42) 4.50 4.50
a. Inverted overprint 7.75 7.75
b. Double overprint 9.50 9.50
c. Double overprint, one inverted 12.50 12.50
d. Perf 12½ (B42b) 3.25 3.25
92 A11 10pa on 20pa vio brn (B38) 3.25 3.25
a. Inverted overprint 10.00 10.00
b. Double overprint 12.50 12.50
c. Double overprint, one inverted 14.50 14.50
93 SP1 10pa red vio (B46) 3.25 3.25
a. Overprint sideways 8.50 8.50

It is understood that the newspaper and semi-postal stamps overprinted "Cilicie" were used as ordinary postage stamps.

A1

**1920 Blue Surcharge** *Perf. 11½*

98 A1 70pa on 5pa red 2.40 2.40
a. Double surcharge 40.00 40.00
b. Triple surcharge 250.00
c. Inverted surcharge 35.00 35.00
d. Double overprint, one inverted 47.50 47.50
e. In pair with unovptd. stamp 120.00
99 A1 3½pi on 5pa red 3.00 2.75
a. Se-tenant with No. 98, horiz. pair 120.00 120.00
b. As "a," inverted surcharge 240.00 240.00
c. Double surcharge 40.00 40.00
d. Inverted surcharge 35.00 35.00
e. Double surcharge, one inverted 47.50 47.50

Nos. 98-99 exist with a variety of surcharge misspellings. For detailed listings, see the *Scott Classic Specialized Catalogue.*

French Offices in Turkey No. 26 Surcharged

**1920** *Perf. 14x13½*

100 A3 20pa on 10c rose red (I) 2.25 2.25
a. "PARAS" omitted 72.50 72.50

Three types of "20" exist on No. 100: I, "2" bold; II "2" faint; III, "0" distinctly taller than "2." See the *Scott Classic Specialized Catalogue of Stamps and Covers* for detailed listings.

Stamps of France, 1900-17, Surcharged

**1920**

101 A16 5pa on 2c vio brn 1.75 1.75
102 A22 10pa on 5c green 2.25 2.25
103 A22 20pa on 10c red 4.50 4.50
104 A22 1pi on 25c blue 3.00 2.50
105 A20 2pi on 15c gray green 12.00 12.00
106 A18 5pi on 40c red & gray bl 26.00 26.00
107 A18 10pi on 50c bis brn & lav 32.50 32.50
108 A18 50pi on 1fr claret & ol grn 180.00 180.00
109 A18 100pi on 5fr dk bl & buff 900.00 900.00
*Nos. 101-109 (9)* 1,162. 1,162.

Nos. 106 to 109 surcharged in four lines.
"O.M.F." stands for "Occupation Militaire Francaise."

**1917 Stamps of France Surcharged**

No. 110

No. 115

**1920**

110 A16 5pa on 2c vio brn (109b) 13.00
111 A22 10pa on 5c grn (110b) 13.00
b. Double surcharge 75.00
c. On ordinary paper (110) 19.00
112 A22 20pa on 10c red (162) 9.75
a. Inverted surcharge 75.00
b. Double surcharge 67.50
113 A22 1pi on 25c bl (168d) 6.00
114 A20 2pi on 15c gray grn (139c) 27.00
115 A18 5pi on 40c red & gray bl (121) 50.00
116 A18 20pi on 1fr claret & ol grn (125) 190.00
a. "O.M.F. Cilicie" omitted 625.00
b. Double surcharge 625.00
*Nos. 110-116 (7)* 308.75

On Nos. 115 and 116 "SAND. EST" is placed vertically. "Sand. Est" is an abbreviation of Sandjak de l'Est (Eastern County).
Nos. 110-116 were prepared for use, but never issued.

Stamps of France, 1900-17, Surcharged

**First Setting: 1.75-2mm spacing between "Cilicie" and figures of value**

**1920**

117 A16 5pa on 2c vio brn 1.50 1.50
a. Inverted surcharge 32.50 27.50
b. "Cililie" 35.00 35.00
c. Surcharge 5pi (error) 60.00 60.00
h. Double surcharge 35.00 35.00
119 A22 10pa on 5c grn 1.50 1.50
a. Inverted surcharge 30.00 26.00
b. Surch. 5pa (error), upright 55.00 55.00
c. Surch. 5pa (error), invtd. 75.00 67.50
121 A22 20pa on 10c red 1.75 1.75
a. Inverted surcharge 32.50 27.50
b. Surch. 10pa (error), upright 60.00 60.00
c. Surch. 10pa (error), invtd. 80.00 72.50
f. Double surcharge 35.00 35.00
g. Double surcharge, one inverted 47.50 47.50
122 A22 1pi on 25c blue 2.00 2.00
a. Double surcharge 72.50 72.50
b. Inverted surcharge 55.00 52.50
123 A20 2pi on 15c gray green 2.25 2.25
a. Double surcharge 45.00 45.00
b. Inverted surcharge 35.00 32.50
c. Double surcharge, one inverted 55.00 55.00
124 A18 5pi on 40c red & gray blue 4.00 4.00
a. Double surcharge 65.00 65.00
b. Inverted surcharge 40.00 40.00
e. "PIASRTES" 72.50 72.50
125 A18 10pi on 50c bis brn & lav 12.50 12.50
a. Double surcharge 60.00 60.00
b. Inverted surcharge 55.00 47.50
c. First "S" in "PIASTRES" inverted 110.00 110.00
e. "PIASRTES" 72.50 72.50
126 A18 50pi on 1fr clar & ol grn 17.50 17.50
a. Inverted surcharge 130.00
b. Double surcharge 180.00
e. "PIASRTES" 87.50
127 A18 100pi on 5fr dk bl & buff 45.00 45.00
a. Inverted surcharge 180.00
d. "PIASRTES" *925.00*
*Nos. 117-127 (9)* 88.00 88.00

This surcharge has "O.M.F." in thicker letters than the preceding issues.
There were two printings of this surcharge, which may be distinguished by the spacing between "Cilicie" and figures of value. See the *Scott Classic Specialized Catalogue of Stamps and Covers* for detailed listings.
For overprints see Nos. C1-C2.

## AIR POST STAMPS

**Nos. 123 and 124 Handstamped**

*Perf. 14x13½*

**1920, July 15 Unwmk.**

C1 A20 2pi on 15c gray grn *9,250.* 9,250.
C2 A18 5pi on 40c red & gray blue 9,500. 9,500.
a. "PIASRTES"

A very limited number of Nos. C1 and C2 were used on two air mail flights between Adana and Aleppo. At a later date impressions from a new handstamp were struck "to oblige" on stamps of the regular issue of 1920 (Nos. 123, 124, 125 and 126) that were in stock at the Adana Post Office.
Counterfeits exist.

## POSTAGE DUE STAMPS

**Turkish Postage Due Stamps of 1914 Handstamped**

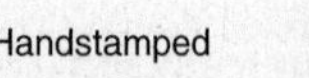

Handstamped

**1919 Unwmk.** *Perf. 12*

J1 D1 5pa claret 22.00 22.00
a. Inverted overprint 35.00 35.00
b. Double overprint 50.00 50.00
J2 D2 20pa red 22.50 22.50
a. Inverted overprint 35.00 35.00
b. Double overprint 50.00 50.00
J3 D3 1pi dark blue 35.00 35.00
a. Inverted overprint 50.00 50.00
J4 D4 2pi slate 45.00 45.00
a. Inverted overprint 65.00 65.00
*Nos. J1-J4 (4)* 124.50 124.50

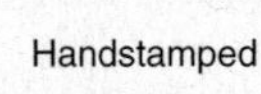

Handstamped

J5 D1 5pa claret 26.00 26.00
a. Inverted overprint 40.00 40.00
b. Double overprint 55.00 55.00
J6 D2 20pa red 30.00 30.00
a. Inverted overprint 45.00 45.00
b. Double overprint 60.00 60.00
J7 D3 1pi dark blue 35.00 35.00
a. Inverted overprint 47.50 47.50
J8 D4 2pi slate 35.00 35.00
a. Inverted overprint 47.50 47.50
*Nos. J5-J8 (4)* 126.00 126.00

Handstamped

J9 D1 5pa claret 22.00 22.00
a. Inverted overprint 32.50 32.50
b. Double overprint 32.50 32.50
J10 D2 20pa red 22.50 22.50
a. Inverted overprint 32.50 32.50
b. Double overprint 35.00 35.00
J11 D3 1pi dark blue 35.00 35.00
a. Inverted overprint 47.50 47.50
J12 D4 2pi slate 22.00 22.00
a. Inverted overprint 32.50 32.50
*Nos. J9-J12 (4)* 101.50 101.50

Postage Due Stamps of France Surcharged

**1921**

J13 D2 1pi on 10c choc 15.00 15.00
a. Inverted overprint 130.00
J14 D2 2pi on 20c olive grn 15.00 15.00
a. Inverted overprint 130.00
J15 D2 3pi on 30c red 15.00 15.00
a. Inverted overprint 92.50
J16 D2 4pi on 50c vio brn 14.00 14.00
a. Inverted overprint 92.50
*Nos. J13-J16 (4)* 59.00 59.00

# COCHIN CHINA

'kō-chən 'chī-nə

LOCATION — The southernmost state of French Indo-China in the Cambodian Peninsula.
GOVT. — French Colony
AREA — 26,476 sq. mi.
POP. — 4,615,968
CAPITAL — Saigon

100 Centimes = 1 Franc

**Surcharged in Black on Stamps of French Colonies**

a

b

c

**1886-87 Unwmk.** *Perf. 14x13½*

1 A9(a) 5c on 25c yel, *straw* 225.00 120.00
2 A9(b) 5c on 2c brn, *buff* 40.00 *32.50*
3 A9(b) 5c on 25c yel, *straw* 32.50 27.50
a. Inverted surcharge *275.00* *275.00*
4 A9(c) 5c on 25c blk, *rose* ('87) 60.00 47.50
a. Double surch., one of type b *3,750.* *2,750.*
b. Triple surch., two of type b — —
c. Inverted surcharge 375.00 375.00
d. Double surch., both type "c" *2,750.* *3,250.*
e. Triple surch., types "a," "b" and "c" *8,750.*
*Nos. 1-4 (4)* 357.50 227.50

**1888**

5 A9 15c on half of 30c brn, *bis* 125.00

No. 5 was prepared but not issued.
The so-called Postage Due stamps were never issued.
Stamps of Cochin China were superseded by those of Indo-China in 1892.

## COCOS ISLANDS

ˈkō-kəs ˈī-ləndz

### (Keeling Islands)

LOCATION — Indian Ocean, 1,330 miles northwest of Australia, 580 miles southwest of Java
GOVT. — A territory of Australia
AREA — 6 sq. mi.
POP. — 670 (1994)

Of 27 small coral islands making up two atolls, two islands are inhabited. Cocos Islands stamps are also valid within Australia.

12 Pence = 1 Shilling
100 Cents = 1 Dollar (1969)

**Catalogue values for all unused stamps in this country are for Never Hinged items.**

Copra Industry A1

Super Constellation A2

Map of Islands — A3

Designs: 1sh, Coco palms. 2sh, Sailboat (dukong). 2sh3p, Fairy tern.

***Perf. 14½***

**1963, June 11 Unwmk. Engr.**

| No. | Type | Description | Unused | Used |
|---|---|---|---|---|
| 1 | A1 | 3p dk red brown | 1.25 | 1.25 |
| 2 | A2 | 5p vio blue | 1.50 | .85 |
| 3 | A3 | 8p red | 1.75 | 1.25 |
| 4 | A1 | 1sh green | 1.75 | .85 |
| 5 | A3 | 2sh dull purple | 7.00 | 2.50 |
| 6 | A2 | 2sh3p green | 13.00 | 4.00 |
| | | *Nos. 1-6 (6)* | 26.25 | 10.70 |
| | | Set, hinged | 13.00 | |

"Simpson and His Donkey" by Wallace Anderson — A3a

**1965, Apr. 14 Photo. *Perf. 13½x13***

| No. | Type | Description | Unused | Used |
|---|---|---|---|---|
| 7 | A3a | 5p brt grn, sepia & blk | .85 | .85 |

ANZAC issue. See note after Australia No. 387.

Nos. 8-31 are valid for postage in Australia.

Turbo Lajonkairii A4

Blenny A5

Designs: 2c, Tridacna crocea (shell). 3c, Tridacna derasa (shell). 5c, Porites cocosensis (coral). 6c, Flyingfish. 10c, Banded rail (bird). 15c, Java sparrow. 20c, Red-tailed tropic bird. 30c, Sooty tern. 50c, Eastern reef heron. $1, Great frigate bird.

***Perf. 13½***

**1969, July 9 Unwmk. Photo.**

**Size: 21½x27mm, 26½x22mm**

| No. | Type | Description | Unused | Used |
|---|---|---|---|---|
| 8 | A4 | 1c multicolored | .30 | *.55* |
| 9 | A4 | 2c multicolored | 1.00 | .70 |
| 10 | A5 | 3c multicolored | .40 | .25 |
| 11 | A5 | 4c multicolored | .30 | *.45* |
| *a.* | | Salmon omitted | 2,000. | |
| 12 | A5 | 5c multicolored | .35 | .30 |
| 13 | A5 | 6c multicolored | .60 | .65 |
| 14 | A5 | 10c multicolored | .75 | .75 |
| 15 | A5 | 15c multicolored | .90 | .30 |
| 16 | A5 | 20c multicolored | .75 | .30 |
| 17 | A5 | 30c multicolored | .75 | .30 |
| 18 | A4 | 50c multicolored | .90 | .50 |

**Size: 21½x34mm**

| No. | Type | Description | Unused | Used |
|---|---|---|---|---|
| 19 | A4 | $1 multicolored | 2.00 | 1.25 |
| | | *Nos. 8-19 (12)* | 9.00 | 6.30 |

"Dragon" A6

"Juno" A7

***Perf. 13½x13, 13x13½***

**1976, Mar. 29 Photo.**

| No. | Type | Description | Unused | Used |
|---|---|---|---|---|
| 20 | A6 | 1c shown | .30 | .30 |
| 21 | A7 | 2c shown | .30 | .30 |
| 22 | A7 | 5c "Beagle" | .30 | .30 |
| 23 | A7 | 10c "Sydney" | .35 | .35 |
| 24 | A7 | 15c "Emden" | .55 | .55 |
| 25 | A7 | 20c "Ayesha" | .55 | .55 |
| 26 | A6 | 25c "Islander" | .55 | .55 |
| 27 | A6 | 30c "Cheshire" | .55 | .55 |
| 28 | A7 | 35c "Jukung" | .55 | .55 |
| 29 | A7 | 40c "Scotia" | .55 | .55 |
| 30 | A6 | 50c "Orontes" | .70 | .70 |
| 31 | A6 | $1 Royal Yacht "Gothic" | .90 | .90 |
| | | *Nos. 20-31 (12)* | 6.15 | 6.15 |

Historic ships.

Flag, Southern Cross, Islands' Map — A8

Council Emblem, Sailboat — A9

**1979, Sept. 3 Litho. *Perf. 15½***

| No. | Type | Description | Unused | Used |
|---|---|---|---|---|
| 32 | A8 | 20c multicolored | .35 | *.35* |
| 33 | A9 | 50c multicolored | .55 | *.75* |

Inauguration of Cocos Islands' postal service (20c), and establishment of Cocos Islands Council (50c).

Forcipiger Flavissimus — A10

Fish: 2c, Chaetodon ornatissimus. 5c, Anthias. 10c, Chaetodon meyeri. 15c, Halichoeres. 20c, Amphiprion clarkii. 22c, Balistapus undulatus. 25c, Cheilinus fasciatus. 28c, Macropharyngodon meleagris. 30c, Chaetodon madagascariensis. 35c, Centropyge colini. 40c, Bodianus axillaris. 50c, Corisgaimardi. 55c, Anampses meleagrides. 60c, Epinepnelus tauvina. $1, Paracanthurus hepatus. $2, Chaetodon trifasciatus.

**1979-80 Litho. *Perf. 15½***

| No. | Type | Description | Unused | Used |
|---|---|---|---|---|
| 34 | A10 | 1c multicolored | .25 | *1.00* |
| 35 | A10 | 2c multicolored | .25 | *.35* |
| 36 | A10 | 5c multicolored | .35 | *1.10* |
| 37 | A10 | 10c multi ('80) | .25 | *1.00* |
| 38 | A10 | 15c multicolored | .30 | .35 |
| 39 | A10 | 20c multicolored | .40 | .35 |
| 40 | A10 | 22c multi ('80) | .35 | .35 |
| 41 | A10 | 25c multi ('80) | .40 | *1.00* |
| 42 | A10 | 28c multi ('80) | .35 | .35 |
| 43 | A10 | 30c multicolored | .50 | .45 |
| 44 | A10 | 35c multicolored | .55 | *1.25* |
| 45 | A10 | 40c multicolored | .65 | .55 |
| 46 | A10 | 50c multicolored | .85 | .75 |
| 47 | A10 | 55c multi ('80) | .60 | *1.10* |
| 48 | A10 | 60c multi ('80) | .70 | .75 |
| 49 | A10 | $1 multicolored | 1.15 | *2.25* |
| 50 | A10 | $2 multi ('80) | 2.25 | *2.75* |
| | | *Nos. 34-50 (17)* | 10.15 | *15.70* |

Sailboats in Lagoon — A11

Christmas: 25c, Yachts and seagulls, vert.

**1979, Oct. 22 Litho. *Perf. 15½***

| No. | Type | Description | Unused | Used |
|---|---|---|---|---|
| 51 | A11 | 25c multicolored | .40 | .30 |
| 52 | A11 | 55c multicolored | .60 | *.70* |

Star of Bethlehem, Map of Cocos Islands — A12

Christmas (Map of Cocos Islands and): 28c, Three kings. 60c, Nativity.

**1980, Oct. 22 Litho. *Perf. 13½x13***

| No. | Type | Description | Unused | Used |
|---|---|---|---|---|
| 53 | A12 | 15c multicolored | .25 | .25 |
| 54 | A12 | 28c multicolored | .30 | .30 |
| 55 | A12 | 60c multicolored | .70 | .70 |
| | | *Nos. 53-55 (3)* | 1.25 | 1.25 |

Flag and Arms of Great Britain — A13

Australian Territory Status, 25th Anniv. (British Flag and Arms of Past Administrators): No. 57, Ceylon, 1878, 1942-1946. No. 58, Straits Settlements, 1886. No. 59, Singapore, 1946. No. 60, Australia (flag), 1955.

**1980, Nov. 24 Litho. *Perf. 13½x13***

| No. | Type | Description | Unused | Used |
|---|---|---|---|---|
| 56 | A13 | 22c multicolored | .25 | .25 |
| 57 | A13 | 22c multicolored | .25 | .25 |
| 58 | A13 | 22c multicolored | .25 | .25 |
| 59 | A13 | 22c multicolored | .25 | .25 |
| 60 | A13 | 22c multicolored | .25 | .25 |
| *a.* | | Strip of 5, Nos. 56-60 | 1.75 | 1.75 |

Eye of the Wind, Map of Cocos Islands — A14

28c, Expedition routes, horiz. 35c, Francis Drake, Golden Hinde. 60c, Prince Charles, Eye of the Wind.

**1980, Dec. 18 *Perf. 13x13½, 13½x13***

| No. | Type | Description | Unused | Used |
|---|---|---|---|---|
| 61 | A14 | 22c shown | .35 | .35 |
| 62 | A14 | 28c multicolored | .35 | .35 |
| 63 | A14 | 35c multicolored | .35 | .35 |
| 64 | A14 | 60c multicolored | .60 | .60 |
| | | *Nos. 61-64 (4)* | 1.65 | 1.65 |

Operation Drake circumnavigation.

Livestock in Quarantine — A15

22c, Aerial view of station. 60c, Livestock, diff.

**1981, May 12 Litho. *Perf. 13½x13***

| No. | Type | Description | Unused | Used |
|---|---|---|---|---|
| 65 | A15 | 22c multicolored | .30 | .30 |
| 66 | A15 | 45c shown | .40 | .40 |
| 67 | A15 | 60c multicolored | .70 | .70 |
| | | *Nos. 65-67 (3)* | 1.40 | 1.40 |

West Island Quarantine Station opening.

Catalina Guba II — A16

Inauguration of Air Service to Indian Ocean: No. 69, Avro Lancastrian. No. 70, Douglas DC4 Skymaster, Lockheed Constellation. No. 71, Lockheed Electra. No. 72, Boeing 727.

**1981, June 23 Litho. *Perf. 13½x13***

| No. | Type | Description | Unused | Used |
|---|---|---|---|---|
| 68 | A16 | 22c multicolored | .30 | .30 |
| 69 | A16 | 22c multicolored | .30 | .30 |
| 70 | A16 | 22c multicolored | .30 | .30 |
| 71 | A16 | 22c multicolored | .30 | .30 |
| 72 | A16 | 22c multicolored | .30 | .30 |
| *a.* | | Strip of 5, #68-72 | 1.75 | 1.75 |

Prince Charles and Lady Diana — A17

**1981, July 29 Litho. *Perf. 13½x13***

| No. | Type | Description | Unused | Used |
|---|---|---|---|---|
| 73 | A17 | 24c multicolored | .25 | .25 |
| 74 | A17 | 60c multicolored | .70 | .70 |

Royal Wedding.

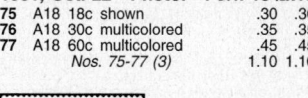

Angels We Have Heard on High — A18

Christmas: Carols: 30c, Shepherds Why this Jubilee. 60c,

**1981, Oct. 22 Photo. *Perf. 13½x13***

| No. | Type | Description | Unused | Used |
|---|---|---|---|---|
| 75 | A18 | 18c shown | .30 | .30 |
| 76 | A18 | 30c multicolored | .35 | .35 |
| 77 | A18 | 60c multicolored | .45 | .45 |
| | | *Nos. 75-77 (3)* | 1.10 | 1.10 |

Sesquicentennial of Charles Darwin's Visit — A19

**1981, Dec. 28 Litho. *Perf. 13½x13***

| No. | Type | Description | Unused | Used |
|---|---|---|---|---|
| 78 | A19 | 24c Coral | .30 | .30 |
| 79 | A19 | 45c Darwin, coral | .40 | .40 |
| 80 | A19 | 60c Beagle, coral | .55 | .55 |
| | | *Nos. 78-80 (3)* | 1.25 | 1.25 |

**Souvenir Sheet**

| No. | Type | Description | Unused | Used |
|---|---|---|---|---|
| 81 | | Sheet of 2 | 1.00 | 1.00 |
| *a.* | | A19 24c Atoll | .45 | .45 |
| *b.* | | A19 24c Atoll, diff. | .45 | .45 |

125th Anniv. of Annexation to the British Dominions — A20

**1982, Mar. 31 Litho. *Perf. 13½x14***

| No. | Type | Description | Unused | Used |
|---|---|---|---|---|
| 82 | A20 | 24c Queen Victoria | .30 | .30 |
| 83 | A20 | 45c British flag | .50 | .50 |
| 84 | A20 | 60c Capt. Fremantle | .60 | .60 |
| | | *Nos. 82-84 (3)* | 1.40 | 1.40 |

Scouting Year — A21

***Perf. 13½x14, 14x13½***

**1982, July 21 Litho.**

| No. | Type | Description | Unused | Used |
|---|---|---|---|---|
| 85 | A21 | 27c Baden-Powell | .40 | .40 |
| 86 | A21 | 75c Emblem, map, vert. | .90 | .90 |

Macroglossum Corythus — A22

1c, Presic villida, vert. 2c, Cephonodes picus. 10c, Chasmina candida, vert. 20c, Nagia linteola. 25c, Eublemma rivula, vert. 30c, Eurrhyparodes tricoloralis, vert. 35c, Hippotion boerhaviae. 40c, Euploea core corinna, vert. 45c, Psara hipponalis. 50c, Danaus chrysippus. 55c, Hypolimas misippus, vert. 60c, Spodoptera litura, vert. $1, Achaea janata, vert. $2, Hippotion velox. $3, Utetheisa pulchelloides.

**1982, Sept. 6**

| No. | Type | Description | Unused | Used |
|---|---|---|---|---|
| 87 | A22 | 1c multicolored | 1.00 | .65 |
| 88 | A22 | 2c multicolored | .40 | *.50* |
| 89 | A22 | 5c shown | 1.50 | .80 |
| 90 | A22 | 10c multicolored | .40 | *.50* |
| 91 | A22 | 20c multicolored | .40 | *.60* |
| 92 | A22 | 25c multicolored | .40 | *.70* |
| 93 | A22 | 30c multicolored | .40 | *.60* |
| 94 | A22 | 35c multicolored | 1.75 | .80 |
| 95 | A22 | 40c multicolored | .40 | *.75* |
| 96 | A22 | 45c multicolored | .50 | *.75* |
| 97 | A22 | 50c multicolored | .60 | *1.40* |
| 98 | A22 | 55c multicolored | .55 | *.90* |
| 99 | A22 | 60c multicolored | .60 | *1.75* |
| 100 | A22 | $1 multicolored | 2.25 | 2.75 |
| 101 | A22 | $2 multicolored | 1.50 | *2.75* |
| 102 | A22 | $3 multicolored | 2.00 | *2.50* |
| | | *Nos. 87-102 (16)* | 14.65 | *18.70* |

Christmas — A23

**1982, Oct. 25** *Perf. 13x13½*

**104** A23 21c Holy Family .25 .25
**105** A23 35c Angel .30 .30
**106** A23 75c Flight into Egypt .90 .90
*Nos. 104-106 (3)* 1.45 1.45

Christmas — A24

The Birth of Christ: a, God Will Look After Us; b, Our Baby King Jesus; c, Your Saviour is Born; d, Wise Men Followed the Star; e, And Worship the Lord.

**1983, Oct. 31 Litho.** *Perf. 14x13½*

**107** A24 Strip of 5 1.50 1.50
*a.-e.* 24c any single .25 .25

Cocos-Malay Culture — A25

Festive Occasions: 45c, Hari Raya. 75c, Melenggok dance. 85c, Wedding.

**1984, Jan. 27 Litho.** *Perf. 14x13½*

**108** A25 45c multicolored .50 .40
**109** A25 75c multicolored .75 .65
**110** A25 85c multicolored .90 .75
*Nos. 108-110 (3)* 2.15 1.80

75th Anniv. of Barrel Mail (1909-1955) — A26

Designs: 35c, Mail distribution, Direction Isld. 55c, Jukongs retrieving barrels from ocean liner. 70c, Morea receiving outgoing barrel mail, 1909. $1, Barrel mail recovery.

**1984, Apr. 20 Litho.** *Perf. 13½x14*

**111** A26 35c multicolored .55 .55
**112** A26 55c multicolored .95 .95
**113** A26 70c multicolored 1.10 1.10
*Nos. 111-113 (3)* 2.60 2.60

**Souvenir Sheet**

**114** A26 $1 multicolored 2.25 *2.25*

375th Anniv. of Islands' Discovery — A27

30c, Capt. William Keeling. 65c, The Hector. 95c, Astrolabe. $1.10, Map, 1666.

**1984, July 10 Litho.** *Perf. 14x13½*

**115** A27 30c multicolored .60 .50
**116** A27 65c multicolored 1.20 1.15
**117** A27 95c multicolored 1.50 1.40
**118** A27 $1.10 multicolored 1.75 1.75
*Nos. 115-118 (4)* 5.05 4.80

AUSIPEX '84 — A28

45c, Malay Settlement, Home Island. 55c, West Island Air Strip, settlement. $2, Jukong ships racing, Melbourne Exhibition Center.

**1984, Sept. 21 Litho.** *Perf. 13½*

**119** A28 45c multicolored .65 .55
**120** A28 55c multicolored .70 .70

**Souvenir Sheet**

**121** A28 $2 multicolored 2.75 2.75

Christmas — A29

**1984, Oct. 31 Litho.** *Perf. 13½*

**122** A29 24c Fish .40 .40
**123** A29 35c Butterfly .60 *1.10*
**124** A29 55c Bird 1.00 *1.50*
*Nos. 122-124 (3)* 2.00 *3.00*

**Souvenir Sheet**

Act of Self-Determination — A30

Integration with Australia: a, Australians welcoming Cocos islanders. b, Australian flag over the islands.

**1984, Nov. 30 Litho.** *Perf. 13½x14*

**125** A30 Sheet of 2 2.50 2.50
*a.-b.* 30c any single 1.10 1.10

Crafts — A31

**1985, Jan. 30** *Perf. 14x13½*

**126** A31 30c Boat building .55 .35
**127** A31 45c Blacksmith .80 .50
**128** A31 55c Woodcarving 1.15 .80
*Nos. 126-128 (3)* 2.50 1.65

Cable-laying Ships — A32

**1985, Apr. 24** *Perf. 13½x14*

**129** A32 33c Scotia 1.45 1.00
**130** A32 65c Anglia 2.10 1.60
**131** A32 80c Patrol 2.10 *2.10*
*Nos. 129-131 (3)* 5.65 4.70

Birds — A33

33c, Redfooted booby, vert. 60c, Nankeen night heron. $1, Buff-banded rail.

**1985, July 17** *Perf. 13½*

**132** A33 33c multicolored 2.50 2.50
**133** A33 60c multicolored 2.75 2.75
**134** A33 $1 multicolored 3.00 3.00
*a.* "Block" of 3, #132-134 9.00 9.00

Nos. 132-134 printed in a continuous design.

Seashells — A34

1c, Trochus maculatus. 2c, Smaragdia rangiana. 3c, Chama. 4c, Cypraea moneta. 5c, Drupa morum. 10c, Conus miles. 15c, Terebra maculata. 20c, Fragum fragum. 30c, Turbo lajonkairii. 33c, Mitra fissurata. 40c, Lambis lambis. 50c, Tridacna squamosa. 60c, Cypraea histrio. $1, Phillidia varicosa. $2, Halgerda tessellata. $3, Harminoea cymbalum.

**1985-86 Litho.** *Perf. 13½x14*

**135** A34 1c multicolored .65 *1.25*
**136** A34 2c multicolored .65 *1.25*
**137** A34 3c multicolored .65 *1.25*
**138** A34 4c multicolored 1.10 *1.25*
**139** A34 5c multicolored .65 *1.25*
**140** A34 10c multicolored .75 *1.75*
**141** A34 15c multicolored 2.25 1.50
**142** A34 20c multicolored 2.25 1.75
**143** A34 30c multicolored 2.25 1.75
**144** A34 33c multicolored 2.25 1.75
**145** A34 40c multicolored 2.25 1.75
**146** A34 50c multicolored 2.25 *2.25*
**147** A34 60c multicolored 2.25 *2.75*
**148** A34 $1 multicolored 3.25 *3.25*
**149** A34 $2 multicolored 3.25 *4.00*
**150** A34 $3 multicolored 3.75 *4.50*
*Nos. 135-150 (16)* 30.45 33.25

Issue dates: 1c, 5c, 33c, $1, Sept. 18. 2c, 3c, 10c, $3, Jan. 29, 1986. 15c-30c, 40c, Apr. 30, 1986. 4c, 50c, 60c, $2, July 30, 1986.

For surcharges see Nos. 225, 228-229, 231-233.

**Souvenir Sheet**

Christmas — A35

a, Star LR. b, Star LL. c, Star UR. d, Star UL.

**1985, Oct. 30** *Perf. 13½x14*

**151** A35 Sheet of 4 2.50 2.50
*a.-d.* 27c any single .60 .60

Darwin's Visit to the Islands — A36

33c, Charles Darwin. 60c, Map of voyage. $1, HMS Beagle.

**1986, Apr. 1 Litho.** *Perf. 14x13½*

**152** A36 33c multicolored .75 .75
**153** A36 60c multicolored 1.50 *2.25*
**154** A36 $1 multicolored 2.25 *2.75*
*Nos. 152-154 (3)* 4.50 *5.75*

Christmas — A37

30c, Coconut palm, holly. 90c, Shell, ornament. $1, Tropical fish, bell.

**1986, Oct. 20 Litho.** *Perf. 13½x14*

**155** A37 30c multicolored .70 .70
**156** A37 90c multicolored 2.50 *3.00*
**157** A37 $1 multicolored 2.50 *3.00*
*Nos. 155-157 (3)* 5.70 *6.70*

Sailboats — A38

a, Jukong. b, Ocean racers. c, Sarimanok. d, Ayesha. No. 158 has a continuous design.

**1987, Jan. 28**

**158** Strip of 4 5.00 *6.00*
*a.-d.* A38 36c any single .95 *1.25*

Island Views — A39

70c, Direction Island. 90c, West Island. $1, Golf course, Cocos.

**1987, Apr. 8**

**159** A39 70c multicolored 1.60 1.60
**160** A39 90c multicolored 2.25 *2.50*
**161** A39 $1 multicolored 2.60 *3.25*
*Nos. 159-161 (3)* 6.45 *7.35*

Communications A40

**1987, July 29 Litho.** *Perf. 13½x14*

**162** A40 70c Radio 1.25 *1.50*
**163** A40 75c Air service 1.25 *1.75*
**164** A40 90c Satellite 1.50 *2.25*
**165** A40 $1 Airmail 1.75 *2.25*
*Nos. 162-165 (4)* 5.75 *7.75*

Industries — A41

**1987, Sept. 16**

**166** A41 45c Batik printing 1.10 *1.50*
**167** A41 65c Boat building 1.50 *2.00*
**168** A41 75c Copra production 1.75 *2.25*
*Nos. 166-168 (3)* 4.35 *5.75*

Industrial activities of the Cocos Malay people.

Christmas — A42

30c, Peace on Earth. 90c, Unity. $1, Goodwill Towards All.

**1987, Oct. 28** *Perf. 14x13½*

**169** A42 30c multicolored .45 .45
**170** A42 90c multicolored 1.25 *1.90*
**171** A42 $1 multicolored 1.60 *1.90*
*Nos. 169-171 (3)* 3.30 *4.25*

Australia Bicentennial — A43

Arrival of the First Fleet, Sydney Cove, Jan. 1788: a, Five aboriginals on shore. b, Four aboriginals on shore, one in canoe. c, Ships entering bay, kangaroos. d, Europeans land, white cranes. e, Flag raising.

**1988, Jan. 26 Litho.** *Perf. 13*

**172** Strip of 5 8.50 8.50
*a.-e.* A43 37c any single 1.05 1.05

No. 172 has a continuous design. See Christmas Is. No. 213.


Life Cycle of the Coconut — A44

**1988, Apr. 13 Litho.** *Perf. 14x13½*

**173** A44 37c Flower .60 .60
**174** A44 65c Small nut stage 1.10 1.10
**175** A44 90c Mature nuts 1.30 1.30
**176** A44 $1 Seedlings 1.75 1.75
*a.* Souvenir sheet of 4, #173-176 6.75 6.75
*Nos. 173-176 (4)* 4.75 4.75

For surcharge see No. O1.

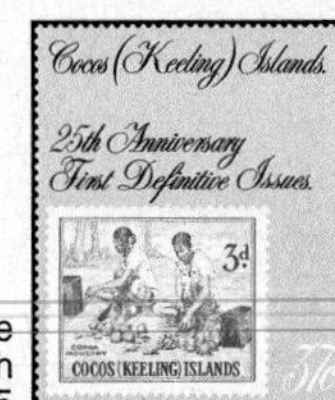

Cocos Postage Stamps, 25th Anniv. — A45

**Litho. & Engr.**

**1988, June 15** *Perf. 15x14*

**177** A45 37c No. 1 1.00 1.00
**178** A45 55c No. 4 1.35 *1.50*
**179** A45 65c No. 2 1.50 *2.25*
**180** A45 70c No. 3 1.75 *2.25*
**181** A45 90c No. 5 2.00 *2.50*
**182** A45 $1 No. 6 2.25 *2.50*
*Nos. 177-182 (6)* 9.85 *12.00*

For overprint and surcharge see Nos. 216, 236.

Flowering Plants — A46

1c, Pisonia grandis. 2c, Cocos nucifera. 5c, Morinda citrifolia. 10c, Cordia subcordata. 30c, Argusia argentea. 37c, Calophyllum inophyllum. 40c, Barringtonia asiatica. 50c, Caesalpinia bonduc. 90c, Terminalia catappa. $1, Pemphis acidula. $2, Scaevola sericea. $3, Hibiscus tiliaceus.

**1988-89 Litho. *Perf. 14x13½***

| No. | Type | Description | Unused | Used |
|---|---|---|---|---|
| **183** | A46 | 1c multicolored | .55 | *.90* |
| **184** | A46 | 2c multicolored | .55 | *.90* |
| **185** | A46 | 5c multicolored | 1.10 | 1.00 |
| **186** | A46 | 10c multicolored | .75 | *1.00* |
| **189** | A46 | 30c multicolored | 1.10 | *1.40* |
| **190** | A46 | 37c multicolored | 1.60 | 1.25 |
| **191** | A46 | 40c multicolored | 1.10 | *1.40* |
| **192** | A46 | 50c multicolored | 1.40 | *3.00* |
| **194** | A46 | 90c multicolored | 2.00 | *4.25* |
| **195** | A46 | $1 multicolored | 2.00 | *2.50* |
| **197** | A46 | $2 multicolored | 2.50 | *2.75* |
| **198** | A46 | $3 multicolored | 3.75 | *4.00* |
| | | *Nos. 183-198 (12)* | 18.40 | *24.35* |

Issued: 1c, 5c, 37c, $3, 7/29; 2c, 10c, 30c, $2, 1/18/89; 40c, 50c, 90c, $1, 4/19/89.

For self-adhesive sheet of 3 see No. 217.

### Souvenir Sheet

**1988, July 30**

| No. | Type | Description | Unused | Used |
|---|---|---|---|---|
| **199** | A46 | $3 like No. 198 | *7.50* | *7.50* |

SYDPEX '88.

Christmas — A47

**1988, Oct. 12 Litho. *Perf. 13½x14***

| No. | Type | Description | Unused | Used |
|---|---|---|---|---|
| **200** | A47 | 32c multicolored | .85 | .85 |
| **201** | A47 | 90c multicolored | 1.90 | 1.90 |
| **202** | A47 | $1 multicolored | 2.25 | 2.25 |
| | | *Nos. 200-202 (3)* | 5.00 | 5.00 |

1st Aerial Survey of the Indian Ocean Air Route, 50th Anniv. — A48

40c, P.G. Taylor, pilot. 70c, *Guba II* seaplane and crew. $1, *Guba II* landing off Direction Island. $1.10, Unissued 5sh stamp of Australia, 1939.

**1989, July 19 Litho. *Perf. 14x13½***

| No. | Type | Description | Unused | Used |
|---|---|---|---|---|
| **203** | A48 | 40c multicolored | .90 | .90 |
| **204** | A48 | 70c multicolored | 1.40 | 1.40 |
| **205** | A48 | $1 multicolored | 2.00 | 2.00 |
| **206** | A48 | $1.10 multicolored | 2.25 | 2.25 |
| | | *Nos. 203-206 (4)* | 6.55 | 6.55 |

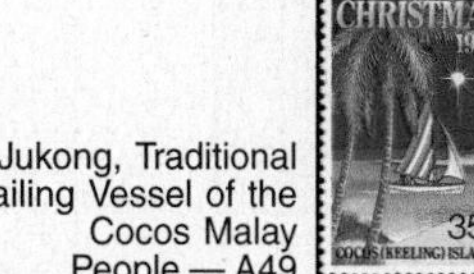

Jukong, Traditional Sailing Vessel of the Cocos Malay People — A49

**1989, Oct. 18 Litho. *Perf. 14x13½***

| No. | Type | Description | Unused | Used |
|---|---|---|---|---|
| **207** | A49 | 35c multicolored | .85 | .85 |
| **208** | A49 | 80c multicolored | 1.90 | 1.90 |
| **209** | A49 | $1.10 multicolored | 2.75 | 2.75 |
| | | *Nos. 207-209 (3)* | 5.50 | 5.50 |

Christmas.

A50

Designs: 40c, HMAS *Sydney*. 70c, SMS *Emden*. $1, Steam launch belonging to the *Emden*. $1.10, HMAS *Sydney* and naval crest.

**1989, Nov. 9 Litho. *Perf. 13½x14***

| No. | Type | Description | Unused | Used |
|---|---|---|---|---|
| **210** | | Strip of 4 + label | 6.75 | 6.75 |
| *a.* | | A50 40c multicolored | .60 | .60 |
| *b.* | | A50 70c multicolored | 1.15 | 1.15 |
| *c.* | | A50 $1 multicolored | 1.60 | 1.60 |
| *d.* | | A50 $1.10 multicolored | 1.75 | 1.75 |
| *e.* | | Souvenir sheet of 4, #210a-210d | 8.25 | 8.25 |

Naval Engagement of the HMAS *Sydney* and the German Raider SMS *Emden*, 75th Anniv.

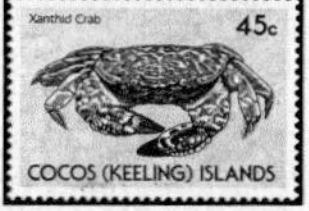

Crabs — A52

45c, Xanthid. 75c, Ghost. $1, Red-backed mud crab. $1.30, Coconut, vert.

**1990, May 31 Litho. *Perf. 14½***

| No. | Type | Description | Unused | Used |
|---|---|---|---|---|
| **212** | A52 | 45c multicolored | 1.20 | 1.20 |
| **213** | A52 | 75c multicolored | 2.10 | 2.10 |
| **214** | A52 | $1 multicolored | 2.40 | 2.40 |
| **215** | A52 | $1.30 multicolored | 3.00 | 3.00 |
| | | *Nos. 212-215 (4)* | 8.70 | 8.70 |

No. 180 Ovptd. in Red

### Litho. & Engr.

**1990, Aug. 24 *Perf. 15x14***

| No. | Type | Description | Unused | Used |
|---|---|---|---|---|
| **216** | A45 | 70c gray, black & red | *9.50* | *9.50* |

### Flowering Plants Type of 1988

**1990, Aug. 24 Photo. *Rouletted 9½***

**Self-Adhesive**

| No. | Type | Description | Unused | Used |
|---|---|---|---|---|
| **217** | | Sheet of 3 | 8.75 | 8.75 |
| *a.* | | A46 10c like No. 186 | .30 | .30 |
| *b.* | | A46 90c like No. 194 | 2.00 | 2.00 |
| *c.* | | A46 $2 like No. 197 | 4.50 | 4.50 |

World Stamp Exhibition, New Zealand 1990. Nos. 217a-217c inscribed 1990.

Explorers and Their Ships — A54

45c, Capt. Keeling, Hector, 1609. 75c, Capt. Fitzroy, Beagle, 1836. $1, Capt. Belcher, Samarang, 1846. $1.30, Capt. Fremantle, Juno, 1857.

**1990, Aug. 24 Litho. *Perf. 14½***

| No. | Type | Description | Unused | Used |
|---|---|---|---|---|
| **218** | A54 | 45c violet brown | 1.60 | 1.50 |
| **219** | A54 | 75c pale bl & vio brn | 2.75 | *3.50* |
| **220** | A54 | $1 pale yel & vio brn | 3.25 | *4.25* |
| **221** | A54 | $1.30 buff & vio brn | 5.25 | *6.50* |
| *a.* | | Souv. sheet of 4, #218-221, imperf. | 11.00 | 11.00 |
| | | *Nos. 218-221 (4)* | 12.85 | 15.75 |

Christmas — A55

**1990, Dec. 12 Litho. *Rouletted 5***

| No. | Type | Description | Unused | Used |
|---|---|---|---|---|
| **222** | A55 | 40c Star at left | 1.00 | 1.00 |
| *a.* | | Bklt. pane of 10 + 2 labels | 20.00 | |
| **223** | A55 | 70c Star in center | 1.75 | 1.75 |
| *a.* | | Bklt. pane, 4 #222, 2 #223 + 6 labels | 25.00 | |
| **224** | A55 | $1.30 Star at right | 3.50 | 3.50 |
| | | *Nos. 222-224 (3)* | 6.25 | 6.25 |

### Nos. 140, 141, 143, 146-147, 179 Surcharged in Blue or Black

No. 225

No. 228

No. 229

No. 231

No. 232

No. 233

No. 236

### Litho., Litho. & Engr.

**1990-91 *Perf. 13½x14, 15x14***

| No. | Type | Description | Unused | Used |
|---|---|---|---|---|
| **225** | A34 | (1c) on 30c #143 | *6.50* | *6.50* |
| **228** | A34 | (43c) on 10c #140 | *47.50* | *47.50* |
| **229** | A34 | (43c) on 10c #140 | *19.00* | *19.00* |
| **231** | A34 | 70c on 60c #147 (bk) | *10.00* | *10.00* |
| **232** | A34 | 80c on 50c #146 (bk) | *10.00* | *10.00* |
| **233** | A34 | $1.20 on 15c #141 (bk) | *10.00* | *10.00* |
| **236** | A45 | $5 on 65c #179 | *45.00* | *45.00* |
| | | *Nos. 225-236 (7)* | *148.00* | *148.00* |

Issued: No. 236, 11/11; No. 228, 12/18; Nos. 225, 229, 231-233, 1/1991.

Beaded Sea Star — A56

75c, Feather star. $1, Slate pencil urchin. $1.30, Globose sea urchin.

**1991, Feb. 28 Litho. *Perf. 14½***

| No. | Type | Description | Unused | Used |
|---|---|---|---|---|
| **237** | A56 | 45c shown | 1.05 | 1.05 |
| **238** | A56 | 75c multicolored | 1.50 | 1.50 |
| **239** | A56 | $1 multicolored | 2.10 | 2.10 |
| **240** | A56 | $1.30 multicolored | 2.50 | 2.50 |
| | | *Nos. 237-240 (4)* | 7.15 | 7.15 |

Hari Raya — A57

**1991, Mar. Litho. *Perf. 14½***

| No. | Type | Description | Unused | Used |
|---|---|---|---|---|
| **241** | A57 | 45c multicolored | 1.10 | 1.10 |
| **242** | A57 | 75c multi, diff. | 1.60 | 1.60 |
| **243** | A57 | $1.30 multi, diff. | 3.00 | 3.00 |
| | | *Nos. 241-243 (3)* | 5.70 | 5.70 |

Christmas — A58

**1991, Nov. 6 Litho. *Perf. 15½***

| No. | Type | Description | Unused | Used |
|---|---|---|---|---|
| **244** | A58 | 38c Child praying | .85 | .85 |
| **245** | A58 | 43c Child sleeping | 1.05 | 1.05 |
| **246** | A58 | $1 Child singing | 2.10 | 2.10 |
| **247** | A58 | $1.20 Child in wonder | 2.75 | 2.75 |
| | | *Nos. 244-247 (4)* | 6.75 | 6.75 |

### Souvenir Sheet

| No. | Type | Description | Unused | Used |
|---|---|---|---|---|
| **248** | | Sheet of 4 | 7.00 | 7.00 |
| *a.* | | A58 38c Two children | .75 | .75 |
| *b.* | | A58 43c Three girls | .85 | .85 |
| *c.* | | A58 $1 Boy, two girls | 2.00 | 2.00 |
| *d.* | | A58 $1.20 Boy, girl | 2.25 | 2.25 |

Nos. 248a-248d are in a continuous design depicting a children's choir.

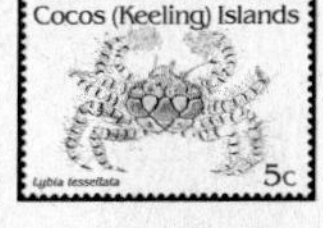

Crustaceans A59

Designs: 5c, Lybia tessellata. 10c, Pilodius areolatus. 20c, Trizopagurus strigatus. 30c, Lophozozymus pulchellus. 40c, Thalamitoides quadridens. 45c, Calcinus elegans, vert. 50c, Clibarius humilis. 60c, Trapezia rufopunctata, vert. 80c, Pylopaguropsis magnimanus, vert. $1, Trapezia ferruginea, vert. $2, Trapezia guttata, vert. $3, Trapezia cymodoce, vert.

**1992 Litho. *Perf. 14½***

| No. | Type | Description | Unused | Used |
|---|---|---|---|---|
| **249** | A59 | 5c multicolored | 1.20 | *1.60* |
| **250** | A59 | 10c multicolored | 1.20 | *1.75* |
| **251** | A59 | 20c multicolored | 1.20 | *1.75* |
| **252** | A59 | 30c multicolored | 1.25 | *2.50* |
| **253** | A59 | 40c multicolored | 1.40 | *2.50* |
| **254** | A59 | 45c multicolored | 1.50 | *2.50* |
| **255** | A59 | 50c multicolored | 1.50 | *4.00* |
| **256** | A59 | 60c multicolored | 1.75 | *4.00* |
| **257** | A59 | 80c multicolored | 2.10 | *4.00* |
| **258** | A59 | $1 multicolored | 2.75 | *4.00* |
| **259** | A59 | $2 multicolored | 5.50 | 5.50 |
| **260** | A59 | $3 multicolored | 8.50 | 7.00 |
| | | *Nos. 249-260 (12)* | 29.85 | *41.10* |

Issued: 10c, 30c, 50c, 80c, $1, $2, 8/11; others, 2/28.

Discovery of America, 500th Anniv. — A60

**1992, May 22 Litho. *Perf. 14½***

| No. | Type | Description | Unused | Used |
|---|---|---|---|---|
| **261** | A60 | $1.05 multicolored | 3.75 | *4.25* |

Buff-banded Rail — A61

No. 262: a, 10c, Bird looking for food. b, 15c, Adult with chick. c, 30c, Two adults eating. d, 45c, Adult with eggs, hatchling.

No. 263: a, 45c, Two birds, one in water. b, 85c, Chick in nest. c, $1.20, Bird's head.

**1992, June 18 Litho. *Perf. 14***

| No. | Type | Description | Unused | Used |
|---|---|---|---|---|
| **262** | A61 | Strip of 4, #a.-d. | 5.25 | 5.25 |

### Souvenir Sheet

| No. | Type | Description | Unused | Used |
|---|---|---|---|---|
| **263** | A61 | Sheet of 3, #a.-c. | 8.00 | 8.00 |

World Wildlife Fund (No. 262).

World War II, 50th Anniv. — A62

45c, Royal Air Force Spitfire fighters. 85c, Japanese bombing of Kampong. $1.20, Sunderland reconnaissance flying boat.

**1992, Oct. 13 Litho. *Perf. 14½***

| No. | Type | Description | Unused | Used |
|---|---|---|---|---|
| **264** | A62 | 45c multicolored | 1.75 | 1.75 |
| **265** | A62 | 85c multicolored | 3.00 | 3.00 |
| **266** | A62 | $1.20 multicolored | 4.25 | 4.25 |
| | | *Nos. 264-266 (3)* | 9.00 | 9.00 |

Festive Season — A63

40c, Storm waves on reef edge. 80c, Direction Island. $1, Moorish idols among coral.

**1992, Nov. 10 Litho. *Perf. 15x14½***

**267** A63 40c multicolored 1.40 1.40
**268** A63 80c multicolored 2.50 2.50
**269** A63 $1 multicolored 3.25 3.25
*Nos. 267-269 (3)* 7.15 7.15

Corals — A64

45c, Lobophyllia hemprichii. 85c, Pocillopora eydouxi. $1.05, Fungia scutaria. $1.20, Sarcophyton sp.

**1993, Jan. 28 Litho. *Perf. 14½***

**270** A64 45c multicolored .80 .80
**271** A64 85c multicolored 1.45 1.45
**272** A64 $1.05 multicolored 2.00 2.00
**273** A64 $1.20 multicolored 2.50 2.50
*Nos. 270-273 (4)* 6.75 6.75

A65

Island Currency Tokens: 45c, 5r token, 1968. 85c, Island scene token, 1968. $1.05, 150r token, 1977. $1.20, Token, 1910.

**1993, Mar. 30 Litho. *Perf. 15x14½***

**274** A65 45c multicolored 1.20 1.20
**275** A65 85c multicolored 2.00 2.00
**276** A65 $1.05 multicolored 2.60 2.60
**277** A65 $1.20 multicolored 3.25 3.25
*Nos. 274-277 (4)* 9.05 9.05

A66

Education: 5c, Primary classroom activities. 45c, Secondary studies. 85c, Crafts, traditional basket weaving. $1.05, Office staff, higher education. $1.20, Marine officers, coxswain's training.

**1993, June 1 Litho. *Perf. 14½***

**278** A66 5c multicolored .80 .80
**279** A66 45c multicolored 1.25 1.25
**280** A66 85c multicolored 2.10 2.10
**281** A66 $1.05 multicolored 2.40 2.40
**282** A66 $1.20 multicolored 2.75 2.75
*Nos. 278-282 (5)* 9.30 9.30

Air-Sea Rescue Service — A67

45c, Men in lifeboat. 85c, Westwind Seascan. $1.05, R.J. Hawke inter-island ferry.

**1993, Aug. 17 Litho. *Perf. 14½***

**283** A67 45c multicolored 2.00 2.00
**284** A67 85c multicolored 3.00 3.00
**285** A67 $1.05 multicolored 4.00 4.00
*a.* Souvenir sheet of 3, #283-285 11.00 11.00
*Nos. 283-285 (3)* 9.00 9.00

A limited printing exists of No. 285a overprinted *Taipei '95* for the 1995 show. Value, $110.

Festive Season — A68

**1993, Oct. 24 Litho. *Perf. 14½***

**286** A68 40c pink & multi 1.25 1.25
**287** A68 80c blue & multi 2.50 2.50
**288** A68 $1 yellow & multi 3.50 3.50
*Nos. 286-288 (3)* 7.25 7.25

From No. 289 on, Cocos Island stamps are valid for postage in Australia.

Map and Reef Life — A69

Reef triggerfish — No. 289: a, Two fish, purple coral (b). b, Three fish. c, Two fish. d, Two fish, red coral (e). e, One fish.

Green turtles — No. 290: a, Eggs, turtles. b, Two turtles (c). c, Group of baby turtles. d, Baby turtle. e, Fish, large turtle.

Pyramid butterflyfish — No. 291: a, Three fish. b, Two small, one large fish, coral (c). c, One small, one large fish, coral (d). d, Three fish, coral (e). e, Coral, one fish.

Junkongs sailing craft — No. 292: a, One boat, red sail. b, Two boats, one blue & white sail, one red sail. c, One boat, yellow sail. d, Two boats sailing away. e, Two boats, one red sail, one white & blue sail.

**1994, Feb. 17 Litho. *Perf. 14½x14***

**289** A69 5c Strip of 5, #a.-e. 1.25 *1.60*
**290** A69 10c Strip of 5, #a.-e. 1.60 *2.00*
**291** A69 20c Strip of 5, #a.-e. 2.00 *2.75*
**292** A69 45c Strip of 5, #a.-e. 4.75 *5.25*
*f.* Sheet of 20, #289-292 10.00 *13.00*
*Nos. 289-292 (4)* 9.60 11.60

No. 292 also produced in sheets of 20.

Puppets — A70

**1994, June 16 Litho. *Perf. 14½x14***

**293** A70 45c Prabu Abjasa .80 .80
**294** A70 90c Prabu Pandu 1.50 1.50
**295** A70 $1 Judistra 1.60 1.60
**296** A70 $1.35 Abimanju 2.10 2.10
*Nos. 293-296 (4)* 6.00 6.00

Christmas — A71

**1994, Oct. 31 Litho. *Perf. 14x14½***

**297** A71 40c Angel .70 .70
**298** A71 45c Wise man .90 .90
**299** A71 80c Bethlehem 1.40 1.40
*Nos. 297-299 (3)* 3.00 3.00

Seabirds — A72

45c, White-tailed tropicbird, masked booby. 85c, Great frigatebird, white tern.

**1995, Mar. 16 Litho. *Perf. 14x14½***

**300** A72 45c multicolored .80 .80
**301** A72 85c multicolored 1.60 1.60
*a.* Souvenir sheet of 2, #300-301 3.00 3.00
*b.* As "a," overprinted *15.00* *15.00*

No. 301b ovptd. in gold in sheet margin with Jakarta '95 exhibition emblem and: "8th Asian International Philatelic Exhibition / PAMERAN FILATELI INTERNASIONAL ASIA VIII."

No. 301b issued 8/19/95.

Insects — A73

No. 302: a, Yellow crazy ant. b, Aedes mosquito. c, Hawk moth. d, Scarab beetle. e, Lauxaniid fly.

$1.20, Common eggfly butterfly.

**1995, July 13 Litho. *Perf. 14½x14***

**302** A73 45c Strip of 5, #a.-e. 5.25 5.25
**303** A73 $1.20 multicolored 2.50 2.50

Fish — A74

Designs: 5c, Redspot wrasse. 30c, Gilded triggerfish. 40c, Saddled butterflyfish. 45c, Ringeyed hawkfish. 75c, Orangespine unicornfish. 80c, Blue tang. 85c, Humpback wrasse. 90c, Threadfin butterflyfish. $1, Bluestripe snapper. $1.05, Longnosed butterflyfish. $1.20, Freckled hawkfish. $2, Powder blue surgeonfish.

**1995-97 Litho. *Perf. 14x14½***

**304** A74 5c multicolored .40 .40
**305** A74 30c multicolored .60 .60
**306** A74 40c multicolored .95 .95
**307** A74 45c multicolored 1.10 1.10
**308** A74 75c multicolored 1.60 1.60
**309** A74 80c multicolored 1.75 1.75
**310** A74 85c multicolored 1.75 1.75
**311** A74 90c multicolored 2.00 2.00
**312** A74 $1 multicolored 2.25 2.25
**313** A74 $1.05 multicolored 2.25 2.25
**314** A74 $1.20 multicolored 3.00 3.00
**315** A74 $2 multicolored 5.25 5.25
*Nos. 304-315 (12)* 22.90 22.90

Issued: 40c, 80c, $1.05, 11/1/95; 30c, 45c, 85c, $2, 8/8/96; 5c, 75c, 90c, $1, $1.20, 8/14/97.

See Nos. 327-329, 335.

Festive Season — A75

Designs: 45c, Greeting others, asking forgiveness. 75c, Drum beaters celebrate Hari Raya Puasa. 85c, Sharing food with friends.

**1996, Feb. 19 Litho. *Perf. 14***

**316** A75 45c multicolored .65 .65
**317** A75 75c multicolored 1.60 1.60
**318** A75 85c multicolored 1.75 1.75
*Nos. 316-318 (3)* 4.00 4.00

Animals Imported Into Australia Through Cocos Islands Quarantine Station — A76

45c, Black rhinoceros. 50c, Alpacas. $1.05, Boran cattle. $1.20, Ostrich.

**1996, June 13 Litho. *Perf. 14½x14***

**319** A76 45c multicolored 1.20 1.20
**320** A76 50c multicolored 1.35 1.35
**321** A76 $1.05 multicolored 2.40 2.40
**322** A76 $1.20 multicolored 3.25 3.25
*Nos. 319-322 (4)* 8.20 8.20

A77

Festive Season: 45c, Tambourine, dancing on shore, bird. 75c, Woman clapping, sailboats racing. 85c, Fish, night scene on beach.

**1997, Jan. 6 Litho. *Perf. 14x14½***

**323** A77 45c multicolored .95 .95
**324** A77 75c multicolored 1.50 1.50
**325** A77 85c multicolored 1.90 1.90
*Nos. 323-325 (3)* 4.35 4.35

A78

Children's drawings: a, Gift package. b, Mosque. c, Cocos Malay woman. d, Island scene. e, Two dancers.

**1998, Jan. 22 Litho. *Perf. 14***

**326** A78 45c Strip of 5, #a.-e. 4.00 4.00

Festive Season.

### Fish Type of 1995

Designs: 70c, Crowned squirrelfish. 95c, Sixstripe wrasse. $5, Goldback anthias.

**1998, Aug. 13 Litho. *Perf. 14x14½***

**327** A74 70c multicolored 1.15 1.15
**328** A74 95c multicolored 1.35 1.35
**329** A74 $5 multicolored 7.50 7.50
*Nos. 327-329 (3)* 10.00 10.00

Jukong Boats, Hari Raya Festival — A79

a, Women placing items in leaves, people along beach. b, Two women, boats along beach. c, Flowers, man in boat. d, Palm trees, two men, man in boat. e, Two people in boat.

**1999, Feb. 11 Litho. *Perf. 14½x14***

**330** A79 45c Strip of 5, #a.-e. 4.25 4.25

Flora and Fauna — A80

a, 45c, Two birds on tree branch. b, 25c, Bird in flight. c, 10c, Sailboat with sail down. d, 5c, Sailboat with red sails. e, 45c, Two birds in flight. f, 25c, Butterflies. g, 10c, School of fish. h, 5c, School of fish swimming left, coral. i, 45c, Red hibiscus flower. j, 25c, Three birds in flight. k, 10c, Two moorish idols. l, 5c, Turtles. m, 45c, Butterfly, flowers. n, 25c, Moth with wings folded, flowers. o, 10c, Two gold fish. p, 5c, Various fish swimming right. q, 45c, Yellow hibiscus. r, 25c, Butterfly on flowers. s, 10c, Two birds in flight. t, 5c, Large fish, coral.

**1999, June 17 Litho. *Perf. 14x14½***

**331** A80 Sheet of 20, #a.-t. 16.00 16.00

Faces of Cocos Islands — A81

Ordinary people: a, Ratma Anthoney, with white shirt. b, Nakia Haji Dolman, with multicolored head covering. c, Muller Eymin, with white head covering. d, Courtney Press, with flowered outfit. e, Mhd Abu-Yazid, with blue shirt with stripes.

**2000, Apr. 13 Litho. *Perf. 14x14½***

**332** A81 45c Strip of 5, #a.-e. 4.50 4.50

Worldwide Fund for Nature — A82

No. 333: a, Purple crab. b, Little nipper crab.

No. 334: a, Horn-eyed ghost crab. b, Smooth-banded ghost crab.

**2000, June 20 Litho. *Perf. 14x14¾***

| | | | | |
|---|---|---|---|---|
| 333 | A82 | 5c Pair, #a-b | 1.00 | 1.00 |
| 334 | A82 | 45c Pair, #a-b | 2.00 | 2.00 |

### Fish Type of 1995

No. 335: a, Wideband fusilier. b, Striped surgeonfish. c, Orangeband surgeonfish. d, Indo-Pacific sergeant.

**2001, Feb. 8 Litho. *Perf. 14x14½***

| | | | | |
|---|---|---|---|---|
| 335 | | Block of 4 | 5.00 | 5.00 |
| *a.-d.* | | A74 45c Any single | .90 | .90 |

Turtles A83

No. 336: a, Loggerhead. b, Hawksbill. c, Leatherback. d, Green.

**2002, Oct. 1 Litho. *Perf. 14x14½***

| | | | | |
|---|---|---|---|---|
| 336 | A83 | Block of 4 | 6.00 | 6.00 |
| *a.-d.* | | 45c Any single | 1.10 | 1.10 |

Shore Birds — A84

No. 337: a, Eastern reef egret. b, Sooty tern. c, Ruddy turnstone. d, Whimbrel.

**2003, June 17**

| | | | | |
|---|---|---|---|---|
| 337 | | Horiz. strip of 4 | 7.50 | 7.50 |
| *a.-d.* | | A84 50c Any single | 1.45 | 1.45 |

Royal Visit, 50th Anniv. — A85

Queen Elizabeth II and: No. 338a, Cocos Malay musicians. No. 338b, Royal Yacht Gothic. $1, Clunies Ross (Oceania) House. $1.45, Dignitary presenting model of Malay jukong.

**2004, Mar. 16**

| | | | | |
|---|---|---|---|---|
| 338 | A85 | 50c Horiz. pair, #a-b | 2.75 | 2.75 |
| 339 | A85 | $1 multi | 2.75 | 2.75 |
| 340 | A85 | $1.45 multi | 3.50 | 3.50 |
| *a.* | | Souvenir sheet, #338a, 338b, 339, 340 | 10.00 | 10.00 |
| *b.* | | As "a," with 2004 World Stamp Championship emblem ovptd. in gold in margin | *15.00* | *15.00* |
| | | *Nos. 338-340 (3)* | 9.00 | 9.00 |

No. 340b issued 8/28.

Worldwide Fund for Nature (WWF) — A86

Designs: No. 341a, Blacktip reef shark. No. 341b, Gray reef sharks. $1, Blacktip reef sharks. $1.45, Gray reef shark.

**2005, Jun 21 *Perf. 14½x14***

| | | | | |
|---|---|---|---|---|
| 341 | A86 | 50c Horiz. pair, #a-b | 3.50 | 3.50 |
| 342 | A86 | $1 multi | 3.50 | 3.50 |
| 343 | A86 | $1.45 multi | 5.00 | 5.00 |
| | | *Nos. 341-343 (3)* | 12.00 | 12.00 |

Wildlife A87

No. 344: a-e, Various birds. f-t, Various fish and marine life.

**2006, June 13 *Perf. 14¾x14***

| | | | | |
|---|---|---|---|---|
| 344 | A87 | Sheet of 20 | 21.00 | 21.00 |
| *a.-e.* | | 10c Any single | .50 | .50 |
| *f.-o.* | | 25c Any single | .80 | .80 |
| *p.-t.* | | 50c Any single | 1.75 | 1.75 |

Mollusks — A88

Designs: No. 345a, Oriental moonsnail. No. 345b, Perly nautilus. $1, Partridge tun. $1.45, Giant clam.

**2007, Mar. 20 *Perf. 14x14½***

| | | | | |
|---|---|---|---|---|
| 345 | A88 | 50c Horiz. pair, #a-b | 4.50 | 4.50 |
| 346 | A88 | $1 multi | 4.50 | 4.50 |
| 347 | A88 | $1.45 multi | 4.50 | 4.50 |
| | | *Nos. 345-347 (3)* | 13.50 | 13.50 |

Birds — A89

No. 345, a, Black-winged stilt. b, Chinese pond heron.

$1, White-breasted waterhen, horiz. $1.45, Saunders' tern, horiz.

**2008, Feb. 26 *Perf. 14***

| | | | | |
|---|---|---|---|---|
| 348 | A89 | 50c Horiz. pair, #a-b | 4.50 | 4.50 |
| 349 | A89 | $1 multi | 4.50 | 4.50 |
| 350 | A89 | $1.45 multi | 7.00 | 7.00 |
| | | *Nos. 348-350 (3)* | 16.00 | 16.00 |

History of Cocos Islands A90

No. 351: a, Sighting of islands by Captain William Keeling, 1609. b, Visit of Charles Darwin, 1836.

$1.10, Control of islands by Clunies Ross family, 1827-1978. $1.65, Australian territory, 1955.

**2009, Apr. 21 *Perf. 14¼***

| | | | | |
|---|---|---|---|---|
| 351 | A90 | 55c Horiz. pair, #a-b | 4.50 | 4.50 |
| 352 | A90 | $1.10 multi | 4.50 | 4.50 |
| 353 | A90 | $1.65 multi | 7.00 | 7.00 |
| | | *Nos. 351-353 (3)* | 16.00 | 16.00 |

Flowers A91

No. 354: a, Ipomoea pes-caprae. b, Hibiscus tiliaceus.

No. 355: a, Suriana maritima. b, Morinda citrifolia.

**2010, Sept. 15 Litho. *Perf. 14¾x14***

| | | | | |
|---|---|---|---|---|
| 354 | A91 | 60c Horiz. pair, #a-b | 4.75 | 4.75 |
| 355 | A91 | $1.20 Horiz. pair, #a-b | 9.50 | 9.50 |

Boats — A92

Designs: 60c, Jukongs. $1.20, Small boat. $1.80, Glass-bottom boat, horiz. $3, Yacht, horiz.

***Perf. 14¾x14, 14x14¾***

**2011, Jan. 18 Litho.**

| | | | | |
|---|---|---|---|---|
| 356 | A92 | 60c multi | 1.25 | 1.25 |
| 357 | A92 | $1.20 multi | 2.40 | 2.40 |
| 358 | A92 | $1.80 multi | 3.75 | 3.75 |
| 359 | A92 | $3 multi | 6.00 | 6.00 |
| | | *Nos. 356-359 (4)* | 13.40 | 13.40 |

### Miniature Sheet

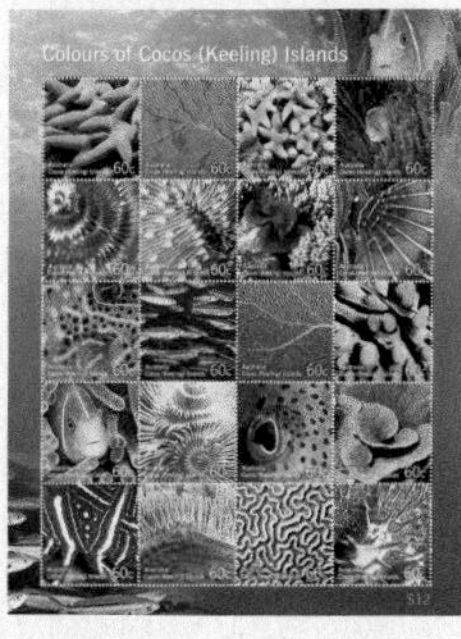

Marine Life A93

No. 360: a, Sea cucumbers with red coloring. b, Fan coral with breaks at right. c, Sea cucumbers with purple coloring. d, Pink anemonefish in sea anemone. e, Christmas tree worm, tip at upper left. f, Mushroom coral. g, Giant clam. h, Fin of Spotted lionfish. i, Eye of Scribbled filefish (brown and blue fish). j, School of Neon fusiliers. k, Fan coral (intact). l, Nudibranch. m, Pink anemonefish in sea anemone, close-up. n, Christmas tree worms. o, Eye of Foster's hawkfish (pink and red fish). p, Foliaceous coral. q, Durban dancing shrimp. r, Magnificent sea anemone. s, Brain coral. t, Crown of thorns sea star.

**2011, Sept. 6 *Perf. 14¼***

| | | | | |
|---|---|---|---|---|
| 360 | A93 | Sheet of 20 | 25.00 | 25.00 |
| *a.-t.* | | 60c Any single | 1.25 | 1.25 |

A sheet of 9 stamps containing stamps similar to Nos. 360a, 360b, 360d, 360e, 360j, 360l, 360m, 360n, and 360t but with glossy varnish was sold only with a set of nine gift cards for $9.99.

Colorful Skies Over Cocos Islands — A94

Skies over: 60c, Pier. $1.20, Rocks in water. $1.80, Beach. $3, Palm trees.

**2012, May 22 *Perf. 14x14¾***

| | | | | |
|---|---|---|---|---|
| 361-364 | A94 | Set of 4 | 13.00 | 13.00 |

Butterflies — A95

No. 365: a, Meadow argus. b, Common crow.

No. 366: a, Australian painted lady. b, Varied eggfly.

**2012, Aug. 2**

| | | | | |
|---|---|---|---|---|
| 365 | A95 | Horiz. pair | 3.00 | 3.00 |
| *a.-b.* | | 60c Either single | 1.50 | 1.50 |
| 366 | A95 | Horiz. pair | 6.00 | 6.00 |
| *a.-b.* | | $1.20 Either single | 3.00 | 3.00 |

Cocos Islands Postage Stamps, 50th Anniv. — A96

Designs: 5c, Sea turtle and underwater photographer. 60c, Man in outrigger canoe. $1, Sailboarder. $1.20, Coconut. $2, Egret.

**2013, June 4 *Perf. 14¾x14***

| | | | | |
|---|---|---|---|---|
| 367-371 | A96 | Set of 5 | 11.00 | 11.00 |
| *371a* | | Souvenir sheet of 5, #367-371 | 11.00 | 11.00 |

A booklet containing five of No. 368 was produced locally and in very limited quantities. Value $110.

Barrel Mail — A97

Designs: 60c, Men and barrels in ocean, cover franked with Australia #213. $3, Men on shore signaling ship, cover franked with Australia #166 and 236.

**2013, Aug. 6 Litho. *Perf. 14¼***

| | | | | |
|---|---|---|---|---|
| 372-373 | A97 | Set of 2 | 7.75 | 7.75 |

Historical Cocos Islands Maps — A98

Designs: No. 374a, 17th cent. map with natives at right. No. 374b, Map from 18th cent. with French inscriptions. $1.40, Map from 19th cent. $2.10, Map from 20th cent.

**2014, June 24 Litho. *Perf. 14¼***

| | | | | |
|---|---|---|---|---|
| 374 | | Horiz. pair | 2.80 | 2.80 |
| *a.-b.* | | A98 70c Either single | 1.40 | 1.40 |
| 375 | A98 | $1.40 multi | 2.75 | 2.75 |
| 376 | A98 | $2.10 multi | 4.00 | 4.00 |
| | | *Nos. 374-376 (3)* | 9.55 | 9.55 |

Battle of the Cocos Islands, Cent. — A99

Warships: 70c, HMAS Sydney. $3.50, SMS Emden.

**2014, Oct. 14 Litho. *Perf. 14¼***

| | | | | |
|---|---|---|---|---|
| 377-378 | A99 | Set of 2 | 7.25 | 7.25 |

Worldwide Fund for Nature (WWF) — A100

Birds: No. 379, 70c, Herald petrels. No. 380, 70c, Oriental pratincoles. No. 381, 70c, Little curlews. No. 382, 70c, Indian yellow-nosed albatrosses.

**2015, Apr. 22 Litho. *Perf. 14¼***

| | | | | |
|---|---|---|---|---|
| 379-382 | A100 | Set of 4 | 4.50 | 4.50 |

A101

Uninhabited Islands A102

No. 383: a, Pulu Klapa Satu (green water in foreground). b, Pulu Maraya (white beach in foreground).

No. 384: a, Pulu Blan Madar (at twilight). b, Pulu Beras (at midday).

**2015, Aug. 25 Litho. *Perf. 14¾x14***

| | | | | |
|---|---|---|---|---|
| 383 | A101 | Horiz. pair | 2.00 | 2.00 |
| *a.-b.* | | 70c Either single | 1.00 | 1.00 |
| 384 | A102 | Horiz. pair | 4.00 | 4.00 |
| *a.-b.* | | $1.40 Either single | 2.00 | 2.00 |

Dolphins — A103

Designs: No. 385, $1, Common dolphin. No. 386, $1, Indo-Pacific bottlenose dolphin. No. 387, $1, Spinner dolphin.

**2016, May 17 Litho. *Perf. 14x14¾***
**385-387** A103 Set of 3 4.50 4.50

A104

Art A105

Nos. 388 and 389 — Various works with denomination at: a, UL. b, UR.

**2016, Oct. 18 Litho. *Perf. 14x14¾***
**388** A104 Horiz. pair 3.25 3.25
*a.-b.* $1 Either single 1.60 1.60
**389** A105 Horiz. pair 6.50 6.50
*a.-b.* $2 Either single 3.25 3.25
*c.* Souvenir sheet of 4, #388a, 388b, 389a, 389b 9.75 9.75

Fruit A106

No. 390: a, West Indian limes. b, Rose apples.
No. 391: a, Sapodillas. b, Breadfruit.

**2017, May 30 Litho. *Perf. 14x14¾***
**390** A106 Horiz. pair 3.00 3.00
*a.-b.* $1 Either single 1.50 1.50
**391** A106 Horiz. pair 6.00 6.00
*a.-b.* $2 Either single 3.00 3.00
*c.* Souvenir sheet of 4, #390a, 390b, 391a, 391b 9.00 9.00

Airplanes — A107

Designs: No. 392, $1, Consolidated Model 28-3. No. 393, $1, Avro Lancastrian. No. 394, $1, Lockheed Electra. No. 395, $1, Boeing 727.

**2017, Oct. 31 Litho. *Perf. 14x14¾***
**392-395** A107 Set of 4 6.25 6.25
*395a* Souvenir sheet of 4, #392-395 6.25 6.25

Basket Weaving — A108

Hands of weaver making: No. 396, $1, Rice parcels. No. 397, $1, Basket with handle. $2, Round basket.

**2018, June 26 Litho. *Perf. 14x14¾***
**396-398** A108 Set of 3 6.00 6.00
*398a* Souvenir sheet of 3, #396-398 6.00 6.00

Shadow Puppets — A109

Puppet facing: No. 399, $1, Right. No. 400, $1, Left, diff. No. 401, $2, Right, diff. No. 402, $2, Left, diff.

**2018, Oct. 16 Litho. *Perf. 14¾x14***
**399-402** A109 Set of 4 8.75 8.75
*402a* Souvenir sheet of 4, #399-402 8.75 8.75

Water Sports — A110

Designs: No. 403, $1, Windsurfing. No. 404. $1, Surfing. No. 405, $2, Snorkeling. No. 406, $2, Kitesurfing.

**2019, May 28 Litho. *Perf. 14x14¾***
**403-406** A110 Set of 4 8.50 8.50
*406a* Souvenir sheet of 4, #403-406 8.50 8.50

Boobies — A111

Designs: No. 407, $1.10, Brown boobies. No. 408, $1.10, Red-footed booby. $2.20, Masked boobies.

**2020, May 12 Litho. *Perf. 14¾x14***
**407-409** A111 Set of 3 6.00 6.00
*409a* Souvenir sheet of 3, #407-409 6.00 6.00

1902 Scrip — A112

1910 Ivorine Tokens — A113

1968 Plastic Tokens — A114

1977 Metal Coins — A115

**2020, Oct. 20 Litho. *Perf. 14x14¾***
**410** A112 $1.10 multi 1.60 1.60
**411** A113 $1.10 multi 1.60 1.60
**412** A114 $2.20 multi 3.25 3.25
**413** A115 $2.20 multi 3.25 3.25
*a.* Souvenir sheet of 4, #410-413 9.75 9.75
*Nos. 410-413 (4)* 9.70 9.70

Currencies used in Cocos Islands under rule by Clunies-Ross family.

Manta Rays — A116

Various photographs of manta rays with denomination at: No. 414, $1.10, UL. No. 415, $1.10, UR. No. 416, $2.20, UL. No. 417, $2.20, UR.

**2021, May 18 Litho. *Perf. 14x14¾***
**414-417** A116 Set of 4 10.50 10.50
*417a* Souvenir sheet of 4, #414-417 10.50 10.50

Jukongs — A117

Various jukongs with panel color of: $1.10, Orange. $2.20, Light blue.

**2022, May 17 Litho. *Perf. 14x14¾***
**418-419** A117 Set of 2 4.75 4.75
*419a* Souvenir sheet of 2, #418-419 4.75 4.75

Pandanus — A118

Designs: No. 420, $1.10, Pandanus leaves. No. 421, $1.10, Pandanus flowers. No. 422, $1.10, Whole pandanus fruit. No. 423, $1.10, Sectioned pandanus fruit.

**2022, Oct. 4 Litho. *Perf. 14¾x14***
**420-423** A118 Set of 4 5.75 5.75
*423a* Souvenir sheet of 4, #420-423 5.75 5.75

### OFFICIAL STAMP

No. 175 Ovptd. and Srchd. in Dark Blue

**1991, Jan. 25 Litho. *Perf. 14x13½***
**O1** A44 (43c) on 90c multi *115.00*

No. O1 was not sold to the public unused. Used value is for a canceled-to-order example. Mint examples exist in the marketplace. Value, $250.

## COLOMBIA

kə-'ləm-bē-ə

LOCATION — On the northwest coast of South America, bordering on the Caribbean Sea and the Pacific Ocean
GOVT. — Republic
AREA — 456,535 sq. mi.
POP. — 39,309,422 (1999 est.)
CAPITAL — Bogota

In 1810 the Spanish Viceroyalty of New Granada gained its independence and with Venezuela and Ecuador formed the State of Greater Colombia. In 1832 this state split into three independent units as Venezuela, Ecuador and the Republic of New Granada. The name of the country has been, successively, Granadine Confederation (1858-61), United States of New Granada (1861), United States of Colombia (1861-65), and the Republic of Colombia (1885 to date).

100 Centavos = 1 Peso

**Catalogue values for unused stamps in this country are for Never Hinged items, beginning with Scott 594 in the regular postage section, Scott B1 in the semi-postal section, Scott C200 in the airpost section, Scott CE1 in the airpost special delivery section, Scott E2 in the special delivery section, and Scott RA33 in the postal tax section.**

In the earlier days many towns did not have handstamps for canceling and stamps were canceled with pen and ink. Pen cancellations, therefore, do not indicate fiscal use. (Postage stamps were not used for revenue purposes.) Used values for Nos. 1-128 are for stamps with illegible manuscript cancels or handstamp cancels of Bogota or Medellin. Stamps with legible manuscript or other handstamped town-name cancels sell for more.

Fractions of many Colombian stamps of both early and late issues are found canceled, their use to pay postage having been tolerated even though forbidden by the postal laws and regulations. Many are known to have been made for philatelic purposes.

### Watermarks

Wmk. 116 — Crosses and Circles

Wmk. 127 — Quatrefoils

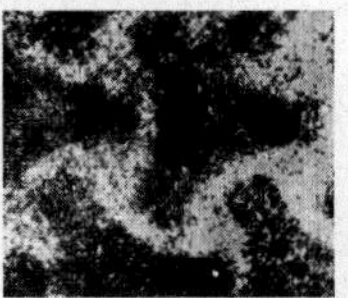
Wmk. 194 — Multiple Curvilinear Triangles

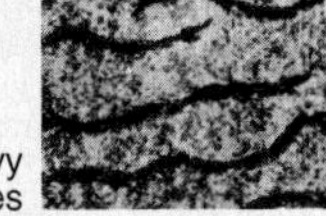
Wmk. 229 — Wavy Lines

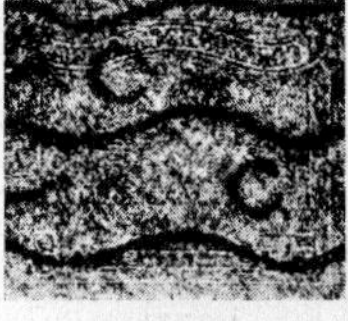
Wmk. 255 — Wavy Lines and C Multiple

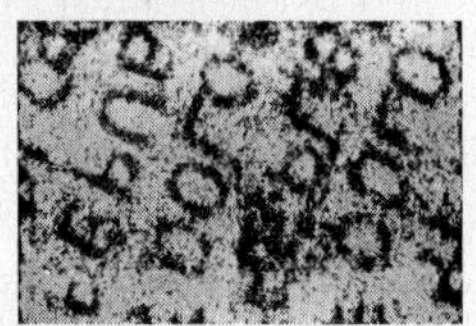
Wmk. 331 — REPUBLICA DE COLOMBIA

Wmk. 334 — Rectangles

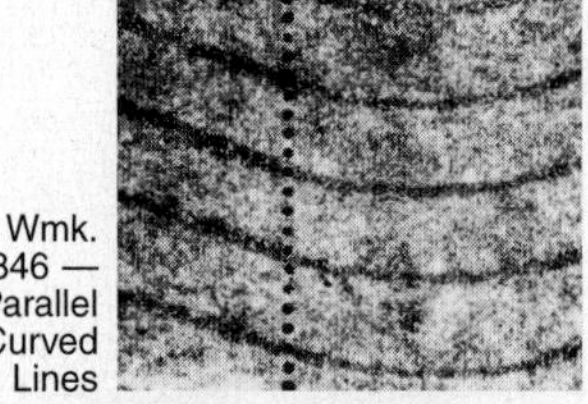
Wmk. 346 — Parallel Curved Lines

Stamps inscribed "Colombia" that show the Panama Canal area were used in Panama and can be found in Vol. 5.

### Granadine Confederation

Coat of Arms — A1

Type A1 — Asterisks in frame. Wavy lines in background.
Type A2 — Diamond-shaped ornaments in frame. Straight lines in background. Numerals larger.

**1859 Unwmk. Litho. *Imperf.***
**Wove Paper**

| | | | |
|---|---|---|---|
| **1** | A1 2½c green | 120.00 | 120.00 |
| *a.* | 2½c yellow green | 120.00 | 120.00 |
| **2** | A1 5c blue | 140.00 | 87.50 |
| *a.* | Tête bêche pair | *4,500.* | *10,000.* |
| *b.* | "50" instead of "5" | | *7,500.* |
| **3** | A1 5c violet | 375.00 | 120.00 |
| *a.* | Tête bêche pair | *6,250.* | *6,000.* |
| *b.* | "50" instead of "5" | | *15,000.* |
| **4** | A1 10c red brown | 140.00 | 80.00 |
| *a.* | 10c buff | 140.00 | 80.00 |

**6** A1 20c blue 120.00 90.00
*a.* 20c gray blue 120.00 90.00
*b.* Se-tenant with 5c —
*c.* Tête bêche pair *40,000. 32,500.*
**7** A1 1p carmine 72.50 *120.00*
*a.* 1p rose 110.00 150.00
**8** A1 1p rose, *bluish* 225.00

The 10c green is an essay.

*Reprints of No. 7 are in brown rose or brown red. Wavy lines of background are much broken; no dividing lines between stamps.*

Coat of Arms — A2

**1860** **Laid Paper**
**9** A2 5c lilac 325.00 200.00

**Wove Paper**

**10** A2 5c gray lilac 90.00 90.00
*a.* 5c lilac 90.00 90.00
**11** A2 10c yellow buff 90.00 90.00
*a.* Tête bêche pair *5,000. 5,000.*
**12** A2 20c blue 260.00 175.00

### United States of New Granada

Arms of New Granada — A3

**1861**
**13** A3 2½c black 1,050. 400.00
**14** A3 5c yellow 375.00 150.00
*a.* 5c buff 375.00 150.00
**16** A3 10c blue 1,250. 175.00
**17** A3 20c red 400.00 400.00
**18** A3 1p pink 1,000. 400.00

There are 54 varieties of the 5c, 20c, and 1 peso.

Forgeries exist of Nos. 13-18.

### United States of Colombia

Coat of Arms — A4

**1862**
**19** A4 10c blue 250.00 125.00
**20** A4 20c red *11,000.* 725.00
**21** A4 50c green 250.00 160.00
**22** A4 1p red lilac 550.00 160.00
**23** A4 1p red lil, *bluish* *4,500. 1,000.*

No. 23 is on a thinner, coarser wove paper than Nos. 19-22.

Coat of Arms — A5

**1863**
**24** A5 5c yellow 100.00 65.00
*a.* Star after "Cent" 110.00 72.50
**25** A5 10c blue 175.00 50.00
*a.* Period after "10" 200.00 50.00
**26** A5 20c red 225.00 75.00
*a.* Star after "Cent" 250.00 82.50
*b.* Transfer of 50c in stone of 20c *10,000. 2,500.*

**Bluish Paper**

**28** A5 10c blue 175.00 32.50
*a.* Period after "10" 190.00 35.00
**29** A5 50c green 210.00 75.00
*a.* Star after "Cent" 210.00 77.50

Ten varieties of each.

Coat of Arms — A6

**1864** **Wove Paper**
**30** A6 5c orange 60.00 37.50
*a.* Tête bêche pair 475.00 400.00
**31** A6 10c blue 55.00 15.00
*a.* Period after 10 55.00 15.00
**32** A6 20c scarlet 100.00 55.00
**33** A6 50c green 85.00 65.00
**34** A6 1p red violet 400.00 150.00

Two varieties of each.

Arms of Colombia
A7 A9

A8

**1865**
**35** A7 1c rose 12.00 12.00
*a.* bluish pelure paper 30.00 21.00
**36** A8 2½c black, *lilac* 21.00 14.00
**37** A9 5c yellow 47.50 20.00
*a.* 5c orange 47.50 20.00
**38** A9 10c violet 67.50 4.50
**39** A9 20c blue 67.50 20.00
**40** A9 50c green 120.00 52.50
**41** A9 50c grn (small figures) 120.00 52.50
**42** A9 1p vermilion 125.00 18.00
*a.* 1p rose red 125.00 18.00
*b.* Period after "PESO" 150.00 20.00

Ten varieties of each of the 5c, 10c, 20c, and 50c, and six varieties of the 1 peso. No. 36 was used as a carrier stamp.

A10 A11 A12

A13

A14

A15

A16

**1866** **White Wove Paper**
**45** A10 5c yellow 72.50 27.50
**46** A11 10c lilac 17.00 5.25
*a.* Pelure paper 21.00 11.50
**47** A12 20c light blue 42.50 21.00
*a.* Pelure paper 67.50 52.50
**48** A13 50c green 17.00 13.00
**49** A14 1p rose red, *bluish* 92.50 32.50
*a.* 1p vermilion 92.50 32.50
**51** A15 5p blk, *green* 500.00 190.00
**52** A16 10p blk, *vermilion* 350.00 190.00

There are several varieties of the 1 peso having the letters "U," "N," "S" and "O" smaller.

A17

A18

A19

A20

A21

TEN CENTAVOS:

Type I — "B" of "COLOMBIA" over "V" of "CENTAVOS".

Type II — "B" of "COLOMBIA" over "VO" of "CENTAVOS."

ONE PESO:

Type I — Long thin spear heads. Diagonal lines in lower part of shield.

Type II — Short thick spear heads. Horizontal and a few diagonal lines in lower part of shield.

Type III — Short thick spear heads. Crossed lines in lower part of shield. Ornaments at each side of circle are broken. (See No. 97.)

**1868**
**53** A17 5c orange 67.50 52.50
**54** A18 10c lilac (I) 4.25 1.10
*a.* 10c red violet (I) 4.25 1.10
*b.* 10c lilac (II) 4.25 1.10
*c.* 10c red violet (II) 4.25 1.10
*d.* Printed on both sides 7.50 2.50
**55** A19 20c blue 3.00 1.25
**56** A20 50c yellow green 3.50 2.40
**57** A21 1p ver (II) 4.25 2.10
*a.* Tête bêche pair 140.00 100.00
*b.* 1p rose red (I) 60.00 27.50
*c.* 1p rose red (II) 4.00 2.10
*Nos. 53-57 (5)* 82.50 59.35

See Nos. 83-84, 96-97.

*Counterfeits or reprints.*

*10c — There is a large white dot at the upper left between the circle enclosing the "X" and the ornament below.*

*50c — There is a shading of dots instead of dashes below the ribbon with motto. There are crossed lines in the lowest section of the shield instead of diagonal or horizontal ones.*

*1p — The ornaments in the lettered circle are broken. There are crossed lines in the lowest section of the shield. These counterfeits, or reprints, are on white paper, wove and laid, on colored wove paper and in fancy colors.*

A22

Two varieties

**1869-70** **Wove Paper**
**59** A22 2½c black, *lilac* 4.75 2.50
*a.* Laid paper ('70) 325.00 250.00
*b.* Laid batonné paper ('70) 30.00 24.00

Nos. 59, 59a, 59b were used as carrier stamps.

*Counterfeits, or reprints, are on magenta paper wove or ribbed.*

A23

A24

**1870** **Wove Paper**
**62** A23 5c orange 2.00 1.25
*a.* 5c yellow 2.00 1.25
**63** A24 25c black, *blue* 16.00 13.00

See No. 89.

*In the counterfeits, or reprints, of No. 63, the top of the "2" of "25" does not touch the down stroke. The counterfeits are on paper of various colors.*

A25

A26

5 pesos — The ornament at the left of the "C" of "Cinco" cuts into the "C," and the shading of the flag is formed of diagonal lines.

10 pesos — The stars have extra rays between the points, and the central part of the shield has some horizontal lines of shading at each end.

**Surface Colored, Chalky Paper**

**1870**
**64** A25 5p blk, *green* 100.00 67.50
**65** A26 10p blk, *vermilion* 120.00 67.50

See Nos. 77-79, 125-126.

A27

A28

A29

TEN CENTAVOS:

Type I — "S" of "CORREOS" 2½mm high. First "N" of "NACIONALES" small.

Type II — "S" of "CORREOS" 2mm high. First "N" of "NACIONALES" wide.

**1871-74** **Thin Porous Paper**
**66** A27 1c green ('72) 3.50 3.50
**67** A27 1c rose ('73) 3.50 3.50
*a.* 1c carmine ('73) 3.50 3.50
**68** A28 2c brown 1.60 1.60
*a.* 2c red brown 1.60 1.60
**69** A29 10c vio (I) ('74) 2.50 2.50
*a.* 10c lilac (I) ('74) 2.50 2.50
*b.* 10c violet (II) ('74) 2.50 2.50
*c.* 10c lilac (II) ('74) 2.50 2.50
*d.* As #69, laid paper ('72) 140.00 140.00
*e.* As "b," laid paper ('72) 140.00 140.00
*Nos. 66-69 (4)* 11.10 11.10

*Counterfeits or reprints.*

*1c — The outer frame of the shield is broken near the upper left corner and the "A" of "Colombia" has no cross-bar.*

*2c — There are scratches across "DOS" and many white marks around the letters on the large "2." The counterfeits, or reprints, are on white wove and bluish white laid paper.*

Condor — A30

Liberty Head
A31 A32

5 pesos, redrawn — The ornament at the left of the "C" only touches the "C," and the shading of the flag is formed of vertical and diagonal lines.

10 pesos, redrawn — The stars are distinctly five pointed, and there is no shading in the central part of the shield.

**1877** **Wove Paper**
**73** A30 5c purple 7.25 2.10
*a.* 5c lilac 7.25 2.10
**74** A31 10c bister brown 3.50 .90
*a.* 10c red brown 3.50 .90
*b.* 10c violet brown 3.50 .90
**75** A32 20c blue 4.25 1.40
*a.* 20c violet blue 25.00 3.50
**77** A26 10p blk, *rose* 120.00 67.50
**78** A25 5p blk, *lt grn,* redrawn 42.50 32.50
**79** A26 10p blk, *rose,* redrawn 17.00 2.75
*a.* 10p blk, *dark rose,* redrawn 17.00 2.75
*Nos. 73-79 (6)* 194.50 107.15

Stamps of the issues of 1871-77 are known with private perforations of various gauges, also with sewing machine perforation.

*In the counterfeits, or reprints, of the 5 pesos the ornament at the left of the "C" of "Cinco" is separated from the "C" by a black line.*

*In the counterfeits, or reprints, of the 10 pesos the outer line of the double circle containing "10" is broken at the top, below "OS" of "Unidos," and the vertical lines of shading contained in the double circle are very indistinct. There is a colorless dash below the loop of the "P" of "Pesos."*

**1876-79** **Laid Paper**
**80** A30 5c lilac 85.00 65.00
**81** A31 10c brown 47.50 2.75
**82** A32 20c blue 100.00 67.50
**83** A20 50c green ('79) 97.50 65.00
**84** A21 1p pale red (II) ('79) 62.50 15.00
*Nos. 80-84 (5)* 392.50 215.25

**1879** **Wove Paper**
**89** A24 25c green 32.50 32.50

**1881** **Blue Wove Paper**
**93** A30 5c violet 20.00 13.00
*a.* 5c lilac 20.00 13.00
**94** A31 10c brown 12.00 2.50
**95** A32 20c blue 12.00 3.75
**96** A20 50c yellow green 12.50 7.50
**97** A21 1p ver (III) 17.00 7.50
*Nos. 93-97 (5)* 73.50 34.25

For types of 1p, see note over No. 53.

*Reprints of the 10c and 20c are much worn. On the 10c the letters "TAVOS" of "CENTAVOS" often touch. On the 20c the letters "NT" of "VEINTE" touch and the left arm of the "T" is too long. Reprints of the 25c, 50c and 1p have the characteristics previously described. The reprints are on white wove or laid paper, on colored papers, and in fancy colors. Stamps on green paper exist only as reprints.*

A34

A35

A36

1 centavo — The period before "UNION" is round and there are rays between the stars and the condors.
2 centavos — The "2's" and "C's" in the corners are placed upright.
5 centavos — The last star at the right almost touches the frame.
10 centavos — The letters of the inscription are thin; there are rays between the stars and the condor.

**1881 White Wove Paper *Imperf.***

**103** A34 1c green 5.00 4.00
**104** A35 2c vermilion 2.10 1.60
*a.* 2c rose 2.50 1.60
**106** A34 5c blue 5.00 1.60
*a.* Printed on both sides
**107** A36 10c violet 4.25 1.25
**108** A34 20c black 4.75 2.00
*Nos. 103-108 (5)* 21.10 10.45

The stamps of this issue are found with perforations of various gauges, also sewing machine perforation, all of which are unofficial.
See Nos. 112, 114-115.

Liberty Head — A37

**1881 *Imperf.***

**109** A37 1c blk, *green* 3.50 *5.00*
**110** A37 2c blk, *lilac rose* 3.50 *5.00*
**111** A37 5c blk, *lilac* 8.50 1.75
*Nos. 109-111 (3)* 15.50 *11.75*

Nos. 109 to 111 are found with regular or sewing machine perforation, unofficial.
*Reprints:*
*1c — The top line of the stamp and the top frame extend to the left. 2c — There is a curved line over the scroll below the "AV" of "CENTAVOS."*
*5c — There are scratches across the "5" in the upper left corner. All three values were reprinted on the three colors of paper of the originals.*

A37a

**Redrawn**

1 centavo — The period before "UNION" is square and the rays between the stars and the condor have been wholly or partly erased.
2 centavos — The "2's" and "C's" in the corners are placed diagonally.
5 centavos — The last star at the right touches the wing of the condor.
10 centavos — The letters of the inscription are thick; there are no rays under the stars; the last star at the right touches the wing of the condor and this wing touches the frame.

**1883 *Imperf.***

**112** A34 1c green 4.75 4.25
**113** A37a 2c rose 2.10 1.75
**114** A34 5c blue 4.00 1.00
*a.* 5c ultramarine 4.00 1.00
*b.* Printed on both sides, reverse ultra 25.00 20.00
**115** A36 10c violet 5.00 1.40
*Nos. 112-115 (4)* 15.85 8.40

The stamps of this issue are found with regular or sewing machine perforation, privately applied.

A38

A39

**1883 *Perf. 10½, 12, 13½***

**116** A38 1c gray grn, *grn* 1.00 1.00
*a.* Imperf., pair 5.00 5.00
**117** A39 2c red, *rose* 1.00 *1.25*
*a.* 2c org red, *rose* 1.00 *1.25*
*b.* 2c red, *buff* 12.00 12.00
*c.* Imperf., pair (#117 or 117a) 7.75 7.75
*d.* "DE LOS" in very small caps 15.00 15.00
**118** A38 5c blue, *blue* 2.50 1.50
*a.* 5c dk bl, *blue* 2.50 1.00
*b.* 5c blue 3.25 2.50
*c.* Imperf., pair (#118 or 118a) 7.75 7.75
*d.* As "b," imperf., pair 12.00 12.00
**119** A39 10c org, *yel* 1.25 *1.40*
*a.* "DE LOS" in large caps 60.00 26.00
*b.* Imperf., pair 16.00 16.00
**120** A39 20c vio, *lilac* 1.40 1.40
*a.* Imperf., pair 16.00 16.00
**122** A38 50c brn, *buff* 3.00 3.25
*a.* Perf. 12 3.00 3.25
**123** A38 1p claret, *bluish* 5.50 1.90
*a.* Imperf., pair 16.00 16.00
*Nos. 116-123 (7)* 15.65 11.70

**Redrawn Types of 1877**

**1883 (?) *Perf. 10½, 12***

**125** A25 5p orange brown 10.00 6.00
**126** A26 10p black, *gray* 10.00 7.25

**1886 *Perf. 10½, 11½, 12***

**127** A25 5p brown, *straw* 10.00 5.50
*a.* Imperf., pair 32.50 32.50
**128** A26 10p black, *rose* 10.00 5.50
*a.* Imperf., pair 32.50 32.50

**Republic of Colombia**

A40

Simón Bolívar A41

Pres. Rafael Núñez A42

**1886 *Perf. 10½ and 13½***

**129** A40 1c grn, *grn* 1.75 .70
*a.* Imperf., pair 6.75 6.75
**130** A41 5c blue, *bl* 1.75 .40
*a.* 5c ultra, *blue* 1.75 .40
*b.* Imperf., pair (#130) 6.75 6.75
**131** A42 10c orange 3.50 .70
*a.* Imperf., pair 9.25 9.25
*b.* Pelure paper 4.50 1.00
*Nos. 129-131 (3)* 7.00 1.80

Gen. Antonio Jose de Sucre y Alcala A43

Gen. Antonio Nariño A44

**1887**

**133** A43 2c org red, *rose* 2.25 1.00
*a.* 2c orange red, *yellowish* 6.00 6.00
*b.* 2c orange red 7.25 7.25
*c.* Imperf., pair (#133) 10.00 10.00
**134** A44 20c pur, *grysh* 3.00 1.10
*a.* Imperf., pair 8.50 8.50
*b.* Pelure paper 3.50 2.25

*Impressions of No. 134 on white, blue or greenish blue paper were not regularly issued.*

Arms — A45

**1888**

**135** A45 50c brn, *buff* 1.75 *1.90*
*a.* Imperf., pair 6.00 6.00
**136** A45 1p claret, *bluish* 8.00 2.10
**137** A45 1p claret 3.50 1.60
**138** A45 5p org brn 8.50 6.50
**139** A45 5p black 14.50 9.50
**140** A45 10p black, *rose* 21.00 6.75
*Nos. 135-140 (6)* 57.25 28.35

See Nos. 155, 158-159.

Nariño — A46

**1889**

**141** A46 20c pur, *grayish* 1.90 1.25
*a.* Imperf., pair 9.25 9.25

*Impressions on white, blue or greenish blue paper were not regularly issued.*

A47

A48

A49

A50

A51

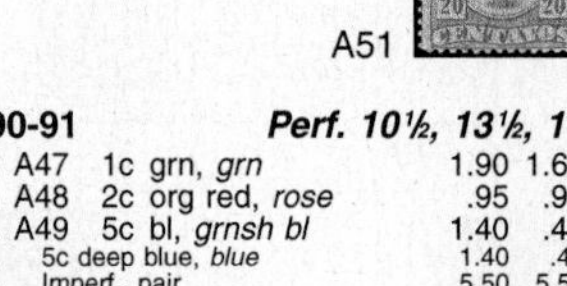

**1890-91 *Perf. 10½, 13½, 11***

**142** A47 1c grn, *grn* 1.90 1.60
**143** A48 2c org red, *rose* .95 .95
**144** A49 5c bl, *grnsh bl* 1.40 .40
*a.* 5c deep blue, *blue* 1.40 .40
*b.* Imperf., pair 5.50 5.50
**146** A50 10c brn, *yel* 1.00 .40
*a.* 10c brown, *buff* 1.00 .40
**147** A51 20c vio, pelure paper 3.50 *3.50*
*Nos. 142-147 (5)* 8.75 *6.85*

A52

A52a

A53

A53a

A54

***Perf. 10½, 12, 13½, 14 to 15½***

**1892-99 Ordinary Paper**

**148** A47 1c red, *yel* .85 .40
**149** A52 2c red, *rose* 42.50 42.50
**150** A52 2c green .50 .30
*a.* 2c yellow green .50 .30
**151** A49 5c blk, *buff* 13.00 .35
**152** A52a 5c org brn, *pale buff* 1.00 .30
*a.* 5c red brown, *salmon* ('97) 1.00 .30
**153** A50 10c bis brn, *rose* .75 .40
*a.* 10c brown, *brownish* 2.00 1.60
**154** A53 20c brn, *bl* .75 .40
*a.* 20c red brown, *blue* .75 .40
*b.* 20c yel brn, *grnsh bl* ('97) 5.50 *13.00*
*c.* 20c brown, *buff* ('97) 19.00 13.00
**155** A45 50c vio, *vio* 1.25 .75
**156** A53a 50c red vio, *vio* ('99) 1.75
**157** A54 1p bl, *grnsh* 2.10 .90
*a.* 1p blue, *buff* 2.10 .90
**158** A45 5p red, *pale rose* 8.50 3.25
**159** A45 10p blue 16.00 3.25
*a.* Thin, pale rose paper 27.50 7.25
*Nos. 148-159 (12)* 88.95
*Nos. 148-155,157-159 (11)* 52.80

Type A53a is a redrawing of type A45. The letters of the inscriptions are slightly larger and the numerals "50" slightly smaller than in type A45.
The 20c brown on white paper is believed to be a chemical changeling.
Nos. 148, 150-152a, 153-155, 157, 159 exist imperf. Value per pair, $6-9.

A56

**1899**

**162** A56 1c red, *yellow* .70 .35
**163** A56 5c red brn, *sal* .70 .35
**164** A56 10c brn, *lil rose* 2.00 .95
**165** A56 50c blue, *lilac* 1.40 1.25
*Nos. 162-165 (4)* 4.80 2.90

**Cartagena Issues**

A57

**1899 Blue Overprint *Imperf.***

**167** A57 5c red, *buff* 30.00 30.00
*a.* Sewing machine perf. 30.00 30.00
**168** A57 10c ultra, *buff* 30.00 30.00
*a.* Sewing machine perf. 30.00 30.00

Nos. 167 and 167a differ slightly from the illustration.

**Bolivar No. 55 Overprinted with 7 Parallel Wavy Lines and**

A58

A59

A60

A61

***Perf. 14 (#169), Sewing Machine Perf.***

**1899 Purple Overprint**

**169** A18 1c black 60.00 60.00
**170** A58 1c brn, *buff* 20.00 20.00
*a.* Altered from 10c 30.00 30.00
**171** A59 2c blk, *buff* 20.00 20.00
*a.* Altered from 10c 30.00 30.00
**172** A60 5c mar, *grnsh bl* 18.00 18.00
*a.* Perf. 12 18.00 18.00
*b.* Without overprint 10.50 10.50
**173** A61 10c red, *sal* 18.00 18.00
*a.* Perf. 12 18.00 18.00
*Nos. 169-173 (5)* 136.00 136.00

No. 169 is Bolivar type A18.
Types A58 and A59 illustrate Nos. 170a and 171a, which were made from altered plates of the 10c (No. 168). Nos. 170 and 171 were made from altered plate of the 5c denomination (No. 167), show part of the top flag of the "5" and differ slightly from the illustrations.
Nos. 170-173 exist imperf. Values about same as perf.

A62

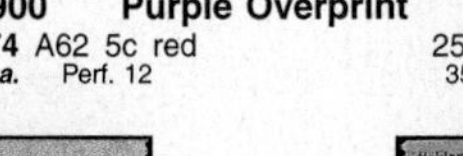

**1900 Purple Overprint *Imperf.***

**174** A62 5c red 25.00 25.00
*a.* Perf. 12 35.00 35.00

A63

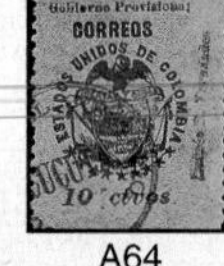
A64

**"Gobierno Provisorio" at Top**

**1900 Litho. *Perf. 12 Vertically***

**175** A63 1c (ctvo) blk, *bl grn* 47.50 8.00
*a.* "cvo." 120.00 14.50
*b.* "cvos." 47.50 8.00
*c.* "centavo" 55.00 47.50

**176** A63 2c black 26.00 6.00
**177** A63 5c blk, *pink* 26.00 6.00
*a.* Name at side (V) 62.50 9.00
**178** A63 10c blk, *pink* 26.00 6.00
*a.* Name at side (V) 62.50 9.00
**179** A63 20c blk, *yellow* 47.50 8.00
*a.* Name at side (G) 92.50 12.00
*Nos. 175-179 (5)* 173.00 34.00

### "Gobierno Provisional" at Top Name at Side in Black or Green

**180** A64 1c (ctvo.) blk, *bl grn* 47.50 8.00
*a.* "centavo" 125.00 47.50
**181** A64 2c blk, *bl grn* 30.00 5.00
**182** A64 5c blk (G) 30.00 5.00
*a.* "ctvos." smaller 47.50 9.00
**183** A64 10c blk, *pink* 30.00 5.00
**184** A64 20c blk, *yel* (G) 47.50 8.00
*Nos. 180-184 (5)* 185.00 31.00

Issues of the rebel provisional government in Cucuta.

A65

A66

### Purple Overprint

**1901** *Sewing Machine Perf.*

**185** A65 1c black 1.00 1.00
*a.* Without overprint 2.25 2.25
*b.* Double overprint 2.50 2.50
*c.* Imperf., pair 2.50 2.50
*d.* Inverted overprint 1.25 1.25
**186** A66 2c blk, *rose* 1.00 1.00
*a.* Imperf., pair 2.50 2.50
*b.* Without overprint 2.25 2.25
*c.* Double overprint 2.50 2.50

A67

A68

**1901** **Rose Overprint**

**187** A67 1c blue 1.00 1.00
*a.* Imperf., pair 4.00 4.00
**188** A68 2c brown 1.00 1.00
*a.* Imperf., pair 4.00 4.00
*b.* Without overprint 1.00 1.00

A69

A70

### *Sewing Machine or Regular Perf. 12, 12½*

**1902** **Magenta Overprint**

**189** A69 5c violet 2.25 2.25
*a.* Without overprint 2.25 2.25
*b.* Double overprint 2.25 2.25
*c.* Imperf., pair 4.75 4.75
**190** A70 10c yel brn 2.25 2.25
*a.* Double overprint 2.25 2.25
*b.* Imperf., pair 4.75 4.75
*c.* Without overprint 2.25 2.25
*d.* Printed on both sides 3.25 3.25

A71

A72

**1902** **Magenta Overprint**

**191** A71 5c yel brn 2.25 2.25
*a.* Without overprint 2.10 2.10
*b.* Imperf., pair 6.00 6.00
**192** A71 10c black 1.75 1.75
*a.* Without overprint 1.50 1.50
*b.* Imperf., pair 9.00 9.00
**193** A72 20c maroon 5.50 4.50
*b.* Imperf., pair 15.00 15.00
*Nos. 191-193 (3)* 9.50 8.50

Nos. 191-193 exist tête bêche. Value of 10c and 20c, each $15.

Washed examples of Nos. 167-174, 185-193 are offered as "without overprint."

### Barranquilla Issues

Magdalena River A75

Iron Quay at Sabanilla A76

La Popa Hill — A77

**1902-03** *Imperf.*

**194** A75 2c green 1.60 1.60
**195** A75 2c dk bl 1.60 1.60
**196** A75 2c rose 22.50 22.50
**197** A76 10c scarlet 1.10 1.10
**198** A76 10c orange 13.00 13.00
**199** A76 10c rose 1.75 1.75
**200** A76 10c maroon 1.90 1.90
**201** A76 10c claret 1.90 1.90
**202** A77 20c violet 3.50 3.50
*a.* Laid paper 9.50
**203** A77 20c dl bl 9.50 9.50
**204** A77 20c dl bl, *pink* *125.00 125.00*
**205** A77 20c car rose 20.00 20.00
*Nos. 194-205 (12)* *203.35 203.35*

### *Sewing Machine Perf. and Perf. 12*

*194a* A75 2c green 9.50 9.50
*195a* A75 2c dark blue 9.50 9.50
*196a* A75 2c carmine *47.50 47.50*
*197a* A76 10c scarlet 4.75 4.75
*198a* A76 10c orange *35.00 35.00*
*199a* A76 10c rose 6.50 6.50
*200a* A76 10c maroon 6.50 6.50
*201a* A76 10c claret 6.00 6.00
*202b* A77 20c purple .70 .70
*c.* 20c lilac .70 .70
*203a* A77 20c dull blue 9.50 9.50
*204a* A77 20c dull blue, *rose* *150.00 150.00*
*205b* A77 20c carmine rose *72.50 72.50*
*Nos. 194a-205b (12)* *357.95 357.95*

See Nos. 240-245.

Cruiser "Cartagena" A78

Bolívar A79

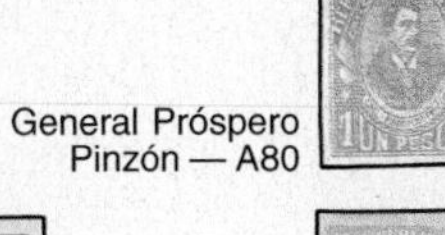
General Próspero Pinzón — A80

A81

A82

**1903-04** *Imperf.*

**209** A78 5c blue 2.75 2.75
**210** A78 5c bister 4.50 4.50
**211** A79 50c yellow 3.75 3.75
**212** A79 50c green 4.50 4.50
**213** A79 50c scarlet 4.50 4.50
**214** A79 50c carmine 4.50 4.50
*a.* 50c rose 4.50 4.50
**215** A79 50c pale brown 4.50 4.50
**216** A80 1p yellow brn 1.60 1.60
**217** A80 1p magenta 2.50 2.50
**218** A80 1p blue 2.50 2.50
**219** A80 1p violet 25.00 25.00
**220** A81 5p claret 5.50 5.50
**221** A81 5p pale brown 8.00 8.00
**222** A81 5p blue green 7.50 7.50
**223** A82 10p pale green 7.75 7.75
**224** A82 10p claret 25.00 25.00
*Nos. 209-224 (16)* 114.35 114.35

Nos. 216 and 217 measure 20½x26½mm and No. 218, 18x24mm. Stamps of this issue exist with forged perforations.

### *Perf. 12*

*209a* A78 5c blue 9.50 9.50
*210a* A78 5c bister 9.50 9.50
*211a* A79 50c yellow 9.50 9.50
*b.* 50c orange 25.00 25.00
*212a* A79 50c green 25.00 25.00
*213a* A79 50c scarlet 11.50 11.50
*214b* A79 50c rose 11.50 11.50
*215a* A79 50c pale brown 11.50 11.50
*216a* A80 1p yellow brown 5.25 5.25
*217a* A80 1p rose 7.50 7.50
*218a* A80 1p blue 9.50 7.50
*219a* A80 1p violet 62.50 62.50
*220a* A81 5p claret 20.00 20.00
*221a* A81 5p pale brown 22.50 22.50
*222a* A81 5p blue green 22.50 22.50
*223a* A82 10p pale green 30.00 30.00
*224a* A82 10p claret 77.50 77.50
*Nos. 209a-224a (16)* 345.25 343.25

**Laid Paper** *Imperf.*

**240** A76 10c dk bl, *lil* 6.25 6.25
**241** A76 10c dk bl, *bluish* 3.75 3.75
**242** A76 10c dk bl, *brn* 3.75 3.75
**243** A76 10c dk bl, *sal* 9.25 9.25
**244** A76 10c dk bl, *grnsh bl* 5.00 5.00
**245** A76 10c dk bl, *dp rose* 3.75 3.75
*Nos. 240-245 (6)* 31.75 31.75

### *Perf. 12*

*240a* A76 10c dk bl, *lilac* 13.50 13.50
*241a* A76 10c dk bl, *bluish* 9.25 9.25
*242a* A76 10c dk bl, *brn* 9.25 9.25
*243a* A76 10c dk bl, *salmon* 72.50 72.50
*244a* A76 10c dk bl, *grnsh bl* 20.00 20.00
*245a* A76 10c dk bl, *deep rose* 9.25 9.25
*Nos. 240a-245a (6)* 133.75 133.75

A82a

### *Imperf., Sewing Machine Perf.*

**1902** **Typeset**

**255** A82a 10c black, *rose* 3.50 3.50
**256** A82a 20c blk, *orange* 2.50 2.50

This issue was printed in either Cali or Popayan.

### Medellin Issue

A83

**1902**

**257** A83 1c grn, *straw* .35 *.50*
**258** A83 2c salmon, *rose* .35 *.50*
**259** A83 5c dp bl, *grnsh* .35 *.50*
**260** A83 10c pale brn, *straw* .35 *.50*
**261** A83 20c pur, *rose* .45 *.50*
**262** A83 50c dl rose, *grnsh* 2.25 *3.00*
**263** A83 1p blk, *yellow* 4.50 *6.75*
**264** A83 5p slate, *blue* 35.00 35.00
**265** A83 10p dk brn, *rose* 22.50 22.50
*Nos. 257-265 (9)* 66.10 69.75

For overprint see No. L8.

### Imperf., Pairs

*257a* A83 1c 11.00 11.00
*258a* A83 2c 11.00 11.00
*259a* A83 5c 11.00 11.00
*260a* A83 10c 11.00 11.00
*261a* A83 20c 11.00 11.00
*262a* A83 50c 11.00 11.00
*263a* A83 1p 27.50 27.50
*264a* A83 5p 80.00 80.00
*265a* A83 10p 50.00 50.00

### Regular Issue

A84

A85

A86

A87

A88

A89

A90

A91

A92

**1902** *Imperf.*

**266** A84 2c blk, *rose* .25 .25
**267** A85 4c red, *grn* .25 .25
**268** A86 5c grn, *grn* .25 .25
**269** A87 10c blk, *pink* .25 .25
*c.* 10c blk, *rose* 1.10 1.10
**270** A88 20c brn, *buff* .25 .25
**271** A89 50c dk grn, *rose* 1.40 1.40
**272** A90 1p pur, *buff* .60 .60
**273** A91 5p grn, *bl* 4.25 4.25
**274** A92 10p grn, *pale grn* 13.00 6.50
*Nos. 266-274 (9)* 20.50 14.00

For overprint see No. H4.

### *Sewing Machine Perf.*

*266a* A84 2c blk, *rose* 1.90 1.90
*267a* A85 4c red, *grn* 1.60 1.60
*268a* A86 5c grn, *blue* 1.90 1.90
*269a* A87 10c blk, *pink* 1.90 1.90
*270a* A88 20c brn, *buff* 3.25 2.50
*271a* A89 50c dk grn, *rose* 6.50 5.25
*272a* A90 1p pur, *buff* 7.75 6.50
*273a* A91 5p grn, *blue* 35.00 35.00
*274a* A92 10p grn, *pale grn* 65.00 65.00
*Nos. 266a-274a (9)* 124.80 121.55

**1903** *Perf. 12*

*266b* A84 2c blk, *rose* 1.40 1.40
*269b* A87 10c blk, *pink* 1.60 1.60
*270b* A88 20c brn, *buff* 1.60 1.60
*272b* A90 1p pur, *buff* 3.25 3.25
*273b* A91 5p grn, *blue* 27.50 27.50
*274b* A92 10p grn, *pale grn* 52.50 45.00
*Nos. 266b-274b (6)* 87.85 80.35

**1903** *Imperf.*

**284** A85 4c blue, *grn* .35 .35
**285** A86 5c blue, *blue* .35 .35
**286** A88 20c blue,*buff* .35 .35
**288** A89 50c blue, *rose* 1.75 1.75
*Nos. 284-288 (4)* 2.80 2.80

### *Sewing Machine Perf.*

*284a* A85 4c blue, *grn* 2.25 1.75
*285a* A86 5c blue, *blue* 2.25 1.75
*286a* A88 20c blue, *buff* 3.25 2.50
*288a* A89 50c blue, *rose* 6.50 5.75
*Nos. 284a-288a (4)* 14.25 11.75

### *Perf. 12*

*284b* A85 4c blue, *grn* 2.50 2.50
*285b* A86 5c blue, *blue* 2.50 2.50
*286b* A88 20c blue, *buff* 3.50 3.50
*288b* A89 50c blue, *rose* 9.75 9.75
*Nos. 284b-288b (4)* 18.25 18.25

A93

**1904** **Pelure Paper** *Imperf.*

**303** A93 ½c yellow brn 1.10 1.10
**304** A90 1c blue green 1.10 1.10
*a.* 1c yellow green 1.10 1.10
**306** A84 2c blue .90 .65
**307** A86 5c carmine 1.00 1.00
**308** A87 10c violet 1.10 .90
*Nos. 303-308 (5)* 5.20 4.75

For overprint see No. H13.

**1904** *Perf. 13*

*303a* A93 ½c yellow brown 4.25 4.25
*304b* A90 1c blue green 5.50 5.00
*c.* 1c yellow green 7.50 7.00
*306a* A84 2c blue 2.50 2.50

### *Perf. 12*

*307a* A86 5c carmine 2.25 2.25
*308a* A87 10c violet 2.25 2.25
*Nos. 303a-308a (5)* 16.75 16.25

A94

A95

Pres. José Manuel Marroquín — A96

**Imprint: "Lit. J.L.Arango Medellin. Col."**

**1904 Wove Paper *Perf. 12***

| | | | | |
|---|---|---|---|---|
| **314** | A94 | ½c yellow | .85 | .25 |
| **315** | A94 | 1c green | .85 | .25 |
| **316** | A94 | 2c rose | .85 | .25 |
| **317** | A94 | 5c blue | 1.40 | .25 |
| **318** | A94 | 10c violet | 1.75 | .25 |
| **319** | A94 | 20c black | 1.75 | .25 |
| **320** | A95 | 1p brown | 19.00 | 3.00 |
| **321** | A96 | 5p red & blk, *yel* | 60.00 | 60.00 |
| **322** | A96 | 10p bl & blk, *grnsh* | 60.00 | 60.00 |
| | | *Nos. 314-322 (9)* | 146.45 | 124.50 |

**Redrawn**

| | | | | |
|---|---|---|---|---|
| *314a* | A94 | ½c | .85 | .25 |
| *315a* | A94 | 1c | .85 | .25 |
| *316a* | A94 | 2c | .85 | .25 |
| *317a* | A94 | 5c | 1.40 | .25 |
| *319a* | A94 | 20c | 1.75 | .25 |
| | | *Nos. 314a-319a (5)* | 5.70 | 1.25 |

**Imperf., Pairs**

| | | | | |
|---|---|---|---|---|
| *314b* | A94 | ½c | 3.25 | 3.25 |
| *315b* | A94 | 1c | 2.50 | 2.50 |
| *316b* | A94 | 2c | 3.25 | 3.25 |
| *317b* | A94 | 5c | 3.25 | 3.25 |
| *318a* | A94 | 10c | 4.25 | 4.25 |
| *319b* | A94 | 20c | 7.75 | 7.75 |
| *320a* | A95 | 1p | 65.00 | 65.00 |
| | | *Nos. 314b-320a (7)* | 89.25 | 89.25 |

On the redrawn types, the imprint is close to the base of the design instead of being spaced from it. On the redrawn 2c and 5c, the lower end of the vertical white line below "OR" of "CORREOS" forms a hook which turns to the right instead of to the left as in the originals.

See Nos. 325-330. For surcharges see Nos. 351-354, L1-L7, L9-L13, L15-L25.

A97

100p has different frame.

**1903 *Imperf.***

| | | | | |
|---|---|---|---|---|
| **323** | A97 | 50p org yel, *pale pink* | 92.50 | 92.50 |
| **324** | A97 | 100p dk bl, *dk rose* | 77.50 | 77.50 |

**Imprint: "Lit. Nacional"**

***Perf. 10, 13, 13½ and Compound***

**1908**

| | | | | |
|---|---|---|---|---|
| **325** | A94 | ½c orange | .85 | .25 |
| *a.* | | ½c yellow | .85 | .25 |
| *b.* | | Imperf., pair | 2.50 | 1.90 |
| *c.* | | Without imprint | 5.25 | 5.25 |
| **326** | A94 | 1c yel grn | .75 | .25 |
| *a.* | | Without imprint | .75 | .25 |
| *d.* | | Imperf., pair | 4.00 | 3.25 |
| **327** | A94 | 2c red | .75 | .25 |
| *a.* | | 2c carmine | .75 | .25 |
| *b.* | | Imperf., pair | 4.00 | 3.25 |
| **328** | A94 | 5c blue | .60 | .25 |
| *a.* | | Imperf., pair | 4.25 | 5.25 |
| **329** | A94 | 10c violet | *50.00* | 1.00 |
| **330** | A94 | 20c gray blk | *50.00* | 1.00 |
| | | *Nos. 325-330 (6)* | *102.95* | 3.00 |

The above stamps may be easily distinguished from those of 1904 by the perforation, by the height of the design, 24mm instead of 23mm, and by the "Lit. Nacional" imprint.

Camilo Torres A99

Policarpa Salavarrieta A100

Bolívar Demanding Liberation of Slaves — A105

Designs: 2c, Nariño. 5c, Bolívar. 10c, Francisco José de Caldas. 20c, Francisco de Paula Santander. 10p, Bolívar Resigning.

**1910, Aug. Engr. *Perf. 12***

| | | | | |
|---|---|---|---|---|
| **331** | A99 | ½c violet & blk | .50 | .30 |
| *a.* | | Center inverted | 390.00 | 390.00 |
| **332** | A100 | 1c deep green | .40 | .25 |
| **333** | A100 | 2c scarlet | .40 | .25 |
| **334** | A100 | 5c deep blue | 1.25 | .45 |
| **335** | A100 | 10c plum | 10.00 | 5.00 |
| **336** | A100 | 20c black brn | 15.00 | 5.50 |
| **337** | A105 | 1p dk violet | 85.00 | 25.00 |
| **338** | A105 | 10p claret | 325.00 | 250.00 |
| | | *Nos. 331-338 (8)* | 437.55 | 286.75 |

Colombian independence centenary.

Caldas A107

Monument to Battle of Boyacá A113

View of Cartagena A114

Coat of Arms A118

Designs: 1c, Torres. 2c, Narino. 4c, Santander. 5c, Bolivar. 10c, Jose Maria Cordoba. 1p, Sucre. 2p, Rufino Cuervo. 5p, Antonio Ricaurte y Lozano.

**1917 Engr. *Perf. 14***

| | | | | |
|---|---|---|---|---|
| **339** | A107 | ½c bister | .35 | .25 |
| **340** | A107 | 1c green | .30 | .25 |
| **341** | A107 | 2c car rose | .30 | .25 |
| **342** | A107 | 4c violet | .90 | .30 |
| **343** | A107 | 5c dull blue | 3.00 | .25 |
| **344** | A107 | 10c gray | 3.00 | .25 |
| **345** | A113 | 20c red | 1.50 | .25 |
| **346** | A114 | 50c carmine | 1.75 | .25 |
| **347** | A107 | 1p brt blue | 12.00 | .40 |
| **348** | A107 | 2p orange | 13.50 | .45 |
| **349** | A107 | 5p gray | 40.00 | 11.00 |
| **350** | A118 | 10p dk brown | 47.50 | 11.50 |
| | | *Nos. 339-350 (12)* | 124.10 | 25.40 |

The 1c, 5c, 10c, 50c, 2p, 5p and 10p also exist perf. 11½ and 11½ compounded with 14.

Litho. varieties of Nos. 343, 345 and 346 are counterfeits made to defraud the government.

Imperforate examples of Nos. 339-350 are not known to have been regularly issued.

See Nos. 373-374, 400-405. For overprints and surcharges see Nos. 369-370, 377, 409-410, 440, C1, O3, O5-O9.

Nos. 318-319, 329-330 Surcharged in Red

**1918 On Issue of 1904**

| | | | | |
|---|---|---|---|---|
| **351** | A94 | ½c on 20c black | 1.25 | .35 |
| **352** | A94 | 3c on 10c violet | 3.00 | .60 |

**On Issue of 1908**

| | | | | |
|---|---|---|---|---|
| **353** | A94 | ½c on 20c gray blk | 10.00 | 6.25 |
| **354** | A94 | 3c on 10c violet | 15.00 | 5.00 |
| | | *Nos. 351-354 (4)* | 29.25 | 12.20 |

Nos. 351-354 inclusive exist with surcharge reading up or down. On one stamp in each sheet the letter "S" in "Especie" is omitted. All denominations exist with a small zero before the decimal in the surcharge.

A119

**1918 Litho. *Perf. 13½***

| | | | | |
|---|---|---|---|---|
| **358** | A119 | 3c red | .95 | .25 |
| *a.* | | Imperf., pair | 5.00 | 5.00 |

A120

**1920 Engr. *Perf. 14***

| | | | | |
|---|---|---|---|---|
| **359** | A120 | 3c red, *org* | .40 | .25 |
| *a.* | | Imperf., pair | 3.75 | 3.75 |

See No. 371-372. For surcharge see No. 453.

A121

A122

A123

***Perf. 10, 13½ and Compound***

**1920-21 Litho.**

| | | | | |
|---|---|---|---|---|
| **360** | A121 | ½c yellow | 1.40 | .50 |
| **361** | A121 | 1c green | .85 | .25 |
| **362** | A121 | 2c red | .65 | .25 |
| **363** | A122 | 3c green | .65 | .25 |
| *a.* | | 3c yellow green | .65 | .25 |
| **364** | A121 | 5c blue | 1.25 | .25 |
| **365** | A121 | 10c violet | 6.00 | 1.50 |
| **366** | A121 | 20c deep green | 6.75 | 4.00 |
| **367** | A123 | 50c dark red | 8.50 | 4.00 |
| | | *Nos. 360-367 (8)* | 26.05 | 11.00 |

The tablet with "PROVISIONAL" was added separately to each design on the various lithographic stones and its position varies slightly on different stamps in the sheet. For some values there were two or more stones, on which the tablet was placed at various angles.

Nos. 360-366 exist imperf.

See No. 375.

**No. 342 Surcharged in Red**

a

(15mm wide) — b

**1921**

| | | | | |
|---|---|---|---|---|
| **369** | A107 (a) | 3c on 4c violet | .95 | .25 |
| *a.* | | Double surcharge | 22.50 | |
| **370** | A107 (b) | 3c on 4c violet | 3.75 | 2.00 |

See No. 377.

**Types of 1917-21**

**1923-24 Engr. *Perf. 13½***

| | | | | |
|---|---|---|---|---|
| **371** | A120 | 1½c chocolate | 1.25 | .60 |
| **372** | A120 | 3c blue | .50 | .25 |
| **373** | A107 | 5c claret ('24) | 3.00 | .25 |
| **374** | A107 | 10c blue | 9.25 | .50 |

**Litho.**

| | | | | |
|---|---|---|---|---|
| **375** | A121 | 10c dark blue | 12.50 | 7.25 |
| | | *Nos. 371-375 (5)* | 26.50 | 8.85 |

**No. 342 Surcharged in Red**

(18mm wide)

**1924**

| | | | | |
|---|---|---|---|---|
| **377** | A107 | 3c on 4c vio | 3.75 | 1.50 |
| *a.* | | Double surcharge | 22.50 | |
| *b.* | | Double surch., one invtd. | 22.50 | |
| *c.* | | With added surch. "3cs." in red | | |

A124

**1924-25 Litho. *Perf. 10, 10x13½***

| | | | | |
|---|---|---|---|---|
| **379** | A124 | 1c red | .85 | .25 |
| **380** | A124 | 3c dp blue ('25) | .85 | .25 |

Exist imperf. Value, each pair $6.25.

A125 A126

**Black, Red or Green Srch. & Ovpt.**

**Imprint of Waterlow & Sons**

**1925 *Perf. 14, 14½***

| | | | | |
|---|---|---|---|---|
| **382** | A125 | 1c on 3c bis brn | .70 | .25 |
| **383** | A126 | 4c violet (R) | .50 | .25 |
| *a.* | | Inverted surcharge | 12.50 | 8.75 |

**Imprint of American Bank Note Co.**

***Perf. 12***

| | | | | |
|---|---|---|---|---|
| **384** | A125 | 1c on 3c bis brn | 7.50 | 6.25 |
| *a.* | | Inverted surcharge | 19.00 | 19.00 |
| **385** | A126 | 4c violet (G) | .50 | .30 |
| *a.* | | Inverted overprint | 12.50 | 9.50 |
| | | *Nos. 382-385 (4)* | 9.20 | 7.05 |

Correos
Provisional

Revenue stamps of basic types A125 and A126 were handstamped as above in violet or blue by the Cali post office in 1925, but were not authorized by the government. Denominations so overprinted are 1c, 2c, 3c, 4c and 5c.

A127 A128

***Perf. 10, 13½x10***

**1926 Litho. Wmk. 194**

| | | | | |
|---|---|---|---|---|
| **395** | A127 | 1c yellow green | .50 | .25 |
| **396** | A128 | 4c blue | .55 | .25 |

Exist imperf. Value, each pair $5.

**Types of 1917 and**

Sabana Station — A129

**1926-29 Unwmk. Engr. *Perf. 14***

| | | | | |
|---|---|---|---|---|
| **400** | A107 | 4c deep blue | .50 | .25 |
| **401** | A118 | 8c dark blue | .60 | .25 |
| **402** | A107 | 30c olive bister | 6.00 | .70 |
| **403** | A129 | 40c brn & yel brn | 9.25 | 1.25 |
| **404** | A107 | 5p violet | 9.25 | .90 |
| *a.* | | Perf. 11 ('29) | 12.00 | 1.00 |
| **405** | A118 | 10p green | 15.00 | 2.50 |
| *a.* | | Perf. 11 ('29) | 30.00 | 4.75 |
| | | *Nos. 400-405 (6)* | 40.60 | 5.85 |

For surcharges & overprint see Nos. 409-410, 453, O4.

Death of Bolívar — A130

**1930, Dec. 17 *Perf. 12½***

| | | | | |
|---|---|---|---|---|
| **408** | A130 | 4c dk blue & blk | .80 | .35 |

Cent. of the death of Simón Bolívar. See Nos. C80-C82.

Nos. 400 and 402 Surcharged in Red or Dark Blue

**1932, Jan. 20 *Perf. 14***

| | | | | |
|---|---|---|---|---|
| **409** | A107 | 1c on 4c dp bl (R) | .30 | .25 |
| *a.* | | Inverted surcharge | 5.25 | 5.25 |

| | | | | |
|---|---|---|---|---|
| **410** | A107 | 20c on 30c ol bis | 10.00 | .70 |
| *a.* | | Inverted surcharge | 21.00 | |
| *b.* | | Double surcharge | 21.00 | |

Emerald Mine A131

Oil Wells A132

Coffee Cultivation A133

Platinum Mine A134

Gold Mining A135

Christopher Columbus A136

**Imprint: "Waterlow & Sons Ltd. Londres"**

**1932 Wmk. 229 *Perf. 12½***

| | | | | |
|---|---|---|---|---|
| **411** | A131 | 1c green | .60 | .25 |
| **412** | A132 | 2c red | .60 | .25 |
| **413** | A133 | 5c brown | .70 | .25 |
| **414** | A134 | 8c blue blk | 4.75 | .60 |
| **415** | A135 | 10c yellow | 3.50 | .25 |
| **416** | A136 | 20c dk blue | 10.00 | .40 |
| | | *Nos. 411-416 (6)* | 20.15 | 2.00 |

See Nos. 441-442, 464-466a, 517. For surcharges see Nos. 455, 527, O1, O10-O11, O13, RA30.

Pedro de Heredia — A137

***Perf. 11½***

**1934, Jan. 10 Unwmk. Litho.**

| | | | | |
|---|---|---|---|---|
| **417** | A137 | 1c dark green | 3.00 | .80 |
| **418** | A137 | 5c chocolate | 3.75 | .65 |
| **419** | A137 | 8c dark blue | 3.00 | .80 |
| | | *Nos. 417-419 (3)* | 9.75 | 2.25 |

Cartagena, 400th anniv. See Nos. C111-C114.

Coffee Picking — A138

**1934, Dec. Engr. *Perf. 12***

| | | | | |
|---|---|---|---|---|
| **420** | A138 | 5c brown | 3.00 | .25 |

Soccer A139

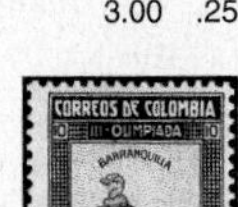

Condor A145

Allegory of Olympic Games at Barranquilla A140

Foot Race — A141

Tennis — A142

Pier at Puerto Colombia — A143

View of the Bay — A144

Designs: 4c, Discus Thrower. 10c, Hurdling. 15c, Athlete in stadium. 18c, Baseball. 24c, Swimming. 50c, View of Barranquilla. 1p, Post and Telegraph Building. 2p, Monument to Flag. 5p, Coat of Arms.

**1935, Jan. 26 Litho. *Perf. 11½***

| | | | | |
|---|---|---|---|---|
| **421** | A139 | 2c bluish grn & buff | 1.60 | .50 |
| **422** | A139 | 4c deep green | 1.60 | .50 |
| **423** | A140 | 5c dk brn & yel | 1.60 | .50 |
| *a.* | | Horiz. pair, imperf. btwn. | 240.00 | |
| **424** | A141 | 7c dk carmine | 3.00 | 1.75 |
| **425** | A142 | 8c blk & pink | 2.50 | 2.50 |
| **426** | A141 | 10c brown & bl | 3.50 | 1.75 |
| **427** | A143 | 12c indigo | 4.25 | 3.00 |
| **428** | A141 | 15c bl & red brn | 7.25 | 5.50 |
| **429** | A141 | 18c dk vio & buff | 10.00 | 8.25 |
| **430** | A144 | 20c purple & grn | 8.50 | 7.00 |
| **431** | A144 | 24c bluish grn & ultra | 8.50 | 6.75 |
| **432** | A144 | 50c ultra & buff | 13.00 | 10.00 |
| **433** | A145 | 1p drab & blue | 110.00 | 60.00 |
| **434** | A145 | 2p dull grn & gray | 125.00 | 100.00 |
| **435** | A145 | 5p pur blk & bl | 425.00 | 450.00 |
| **436** | A145 | 10p black & gray | 500.00 | 525.00 |
| | | *Nos. 421-436 (16)* | 1,225. | 1,183. |

3rd Natl. Olympic Games, Barranquilla. Counterfeits of 10p exist.

Oil Wells A155

Gold Mining A157

**Imprint: "American Bank Note Co."**

**1935, Mar. Unwmk. Engr. *Perf. 12***

| | | | | |
|---|---|---|---|---|
| **437** | A155 | 2c carmine rose | .45 | .25 |
| **439** | A157 | 10c deep orange | 25.00 | .25 |

See Nos. 468, 470, 498, 516. For surcharge and overprints see Nos. 496, 596, O2.

No. 347 Surcharged in Black

**1935, Aug. *Perf. 14***

| | | | | |
|---|---|---|---|---|
| **440** | A107 | 12c on 1p brt bl | 4.75 | 1.50 |

**Types of 1932**

**Imprint: "Lit. Nacional Bogotá"**

**1935-36 Litho. *Perf. 11, 11½, 12½***

| | | | | |
|---|---|---|---|---|
| **441** | A131 | 1c lt green | .25 | .25 |
| *a.* | | Imperf., pair | 6.00 | |
| **442** | A133 | 5c brown ('36) | .70 | .25 |
| *a.* | | Imperf., pair | 6.00 | 4.00 |

For overprints and surcharges, see Nos. 527, O1.

Bolívar A159

Tequendama Falls A160

**Wmk. Wavy Lines. (229)**

**1937 Engr. *Perf. 12½***

| | | | | |
|---|---|---|---|---|
| **443** | A159 | 1c deep green | .25 | .25 |
| *a.* | | Perf. 14 | .25 | .25 |
| **444** | A160 | 12c deep blue | 5.00 | 1.50 |

See No. 570. For surcharges and overprints see Nos. 454, 456, C231, C326, O12.

Soccer Player A161

Discus Thrower A162

Runner — A163

**1937, Jan. 4 Photo. Unwmk.**

| | | | | |
|---|---|---|---|---|
| **445** | A161 | 3c lt green | 1.40 | .85 |
| **446** | A162 | 10c carmine rose | 3.75 | 1.75 |
| **447** | A163 | 1p black | 32.50 | 26.00 |
| | | *Nos. 445-447 (3)* | 37.65 | 28.60 |

National Olympic Games, Manizales. For surcharge see No. 452.

Exposition Palace A164

Stadium at Barranquilla A165

Monument to the Colors — A166

**1937, Jan. 4**

| | | | | |
|---|---|---|---|---|
| **448** | A164 | 5c violet brown | 2.50 | .40 |
| **449** | A165 | 15c blue | 7.00 | 5.00 |
| **450** | A166 | 50c orange brn | 20.00 | 9.00 |
| | | *Nos. 448-450 (3)* | 29.50 | 14.40 |

Barranquilla National Exposition.

Stamps of 1926-37 Surcharged in Black

***Perf. 12½, 14 (#453)***

**1937-38 Unwmk.**

| | | | | |
|---|---|---|---|---|
| **452** | A161 | 1c on 3c lt grn | 1.00 | 1.00 |
| *a.* | | Inverted surcharge | 5.00 | 2.25 |
| **453** | A118 | 5c on 8c dk bl | .55 | .45 |
| *a.* | | Inverted surcharge | 5.00 | 2.25 |

**Wmk. 229**

| | | | | |
|---|---|---|---|---|
| **454** | A160 | 2c on 12c dp bl | .55 | .45 |
| **455** | A134 | 5c on 8c bl blk | .65 | .65 |
| *a.* | | Invtd. surcharge | 5.00 | 2.00 |
| **456** | A160 | 10c on 12c dp bl ('38) | 5.50 | 1.00 |
| *a.* | | Dbl. surcharge | 11.00 | 11.00 |
| | | *Nos. 452-456 (5)* | 8.25 | 3.55 |

Calle del Arco A168

Entrance to Church of the Rosary A169

Arms of Bogotá A170

Gonzálo Jiménez de Quesada A171

Bochica A172

Santo Domingo Convent A173

Mass of the Conquistadors A174

**1938, July 27 Unwmk. *Perf. 12½***

| | | | | |
|---|---|---|---|---|
| **457** | A168 | 1c yellow green | .25 | .25 |
| **458** | A169 | 2c scarlet | .25 | .25 |
| **459** | A170 | 5c brown blk | .40 | .25 |
| **460** | A171 | 10c brown | .75 | .50 |
| **461** | A172 | 15c brt blue | 3.75 | 1.60 |
| **462** | A173 | 20c brt red vio | 3.75 | 1.75 |
| **463** | A174 | 1p red brown | 50.00 | 29.00 |
| | | *Nos. 457-463 (7)* | 59.15 | 33.60 |

Bogotá, 400th anniversary.

**Types of 1932**

**Imprint: "Litografia Nacional Bogotá"**

**1938, Dec. 5 Litho. *Perf. 10½, 11***

| | | | | |
|---|---|---|---|---|
| **464** | A132 | 2c rose | 1.00 | .35 |
| **465** | A135 | 10c yellow | 2.50 | .35 |
| **466** | A136 | 20c dull blue | 10.00 | 1.25 |
| *a.* | | 20c dark blue, perf. 12½ ('44) | 62.50 | 6.25 |
| | | *Nos. 464-466 (3)* | 13.50 | 1.95 |

**Types of 1935 and**

Bolívar A175

Coffee Picking A176

Arms of Colombia A177

Christopher Columbus A178

Caldas A179

Sabana Station A180

**Imprint: "American Bank Note Co."**

**Wmk. 255**

**1939, Mar. 3 Engr. *Perf. 12***

| | | | | |
|---|---|---|---|---|
| **467** | A175 | 1c green | .25 | .25 |
| **468** | A155 | 2c car rose | .25 | .25 |
| **469** | A176 | 5c dull brown | .25 | .25 |
| **470** | A157 | 10c deep orange | .50 | .25 |
| **471** | A177 | 15c dull blue | 1.75 | .25 |
| **472** | A178 | 20c violet blk | 19.00 | .25 |
| **473** | A179 | 30c olive bister | 5.50 | .35 |
| **474** | A180 | 40c bister brn | 17.00 | 3.75 |
| | | *Nos. 467-474 (8)* | 44.50 | 5.60 |

See Nos. 497-499, 515, 518, 574. For surcharges and overprints see Nos. 506-507, 520-522, 596, RA26, RA47.

Gen. Santander
A181

Allegory
A182

Gen. Santander
A183

Statue at Cúcuta
A184

Birthplace of Santander
A185

Church at Rosario
A186

Paya
A187

Bridge at Boyacá
A188

Death of General Santander
A189

Invasion of the Liberators
A190

***Perf. 13x13½, 13½x13***

**1940, May 6 Engr. Wmk. 229**

**475** A181 1c olive green .25 .25
**476** A182 2c dk carmine .50 .35
**477** A183 5c sepia .25 .25
**478** A184 8c carmine 1.75 1.50
**479** A185 10c orange yel .80 .60
**480** A186 15c dark blue 2.00 1.40
**481** A187 20c green 2.75 2.00
**482** A188 50c violet 6.00 5.00
**483** A189 1p deep rose 20.00 17.50
**484** A190 2p orange 62.50 60.00
*Nos. 475-484 (10)* 96.80 88.85

Death of General Francisco Santander, cent.

Tobacco Plant
A194

Gen. Santander
A195

Garcia Rovira
A196

R. Galan
A197

Antonio Sucre — A198

**1940-43 Engr. Wmk. 255 *Perf. 12***

**488** A194 8c rose car & grn 1.25 .65
**489** A195 15c dp blue ('43) 1.25 .25
**490** A196 20c slate ('41) 4.75 .50
**491** A197 40c brown bis ('41) 2.75 .50
**492** A198 1p black 5.00 1.25
*Nos. 488-492 (5)* 15.00 3.15

See Nos. 500, 554. For overprint see No. RA28.

Arms of Palmira — A199

**Unwmk.**

**1942, July 4 Litho. *Perf. 11***

**493** A199 30c claret 5.50 .75

8th Natl. Agricultural Exposition, held at Palmira.

Paradise of Isaacs, Palmira — A200

**1942, July 4**

**494** A200 50c lt blue grn 5.50 .85

Issued in honor of the writer, Jorge Isaacs.

Signing Treaty of the Wisconsin — A201

**1942, Nov. 21 *Perf. 10½***

**495** A201 10c dull orange 3.75 .50
*a.* "2. XI.1902" instead of "21. XI. 1902" 22.50 22.50
*b.* Perf. 12 6.00 6.00

40th anniv. of the signing of the Treaty of the Wisconsin, Nov. 21, 1902.

No. 470 Surcharged in Black

**1944 Wmk. 255 *Perf. 12***

**496** A157 5c on 10c dp org .25 .25

Counterfeits exist of No. 496 with inverted or double surcharge.

**Types of 1935-41 and**

National Shrine
A202

San Pedro Alejandrino
A203

**Imprint: "Columbian Bank Note Co."**

**1944-45 Unwmk. Engr. *Perf. 11***

**497** A175 1c green .25 .25
**498** A155 2c rose .25 .25
**499** A176 5c dull brown .25 .25
**500** A196 20c gray black 3.75 .75
**501** A202 30c dl ol grn ('45) 2.25 1.25
**502** A203 50c rose 2.25 1.25
*Nos. 497-502 (6)* 9.00 4.00

No. 499 Surcharged in Black

**1944, Oct.**

**506** A176 1c on 5c dull brn .25 .25
**507** A176 2c on 5c dull brn .25 .25

Nos. 506 and 507 exist with inverted or double surcharge, created by favor.

Flag
A204

Arms
A205

Murillo Toro
A206

Hospital of St. John of God
A207

Virrey Solis — A208

**1944, Oct. 10 Litho.**

**508** A204 2c ultra & bis .30 .25
*a.* Sheet of 18 15.00
*b.* Imperf., pair 15.00
**509** A205 5c ultra & bis .30 .25
*a.* Sheet of 22 18.00
*b.* Imperf., pair 15.00
**510** A206 20c blk & bluish grn 1.00 .80
*a.* Sheet of 8 16.00
*b.* Imperf., pair 22.50
**511** A207 40c blk & red 4.00 3.50
*a.* Sheet of 4 27.50
**512** A208 1p blk & red 11.00 10.00
*a.* Sheet of 2 32.50
*Nos. 508-512 (5)* 16.60 14.80

**Souvenir Sheet**

***Perf. 11x11½ All Around, Stamps Imperf.***

**513** Sheet of 5, #508-512 25.00 *40.00*
Never hinged 40.00

75th anniv. of Gen. Benevolent Assoc. of Cundinamarca.

Nos. 508-513 were printed in composite sheets containing one each of Nos. 508a, 509a, 510a, 511a and 512a, and two of 513. Fifty of these were presented to government officials.

Murillo Toro — A210

**1944, Nov. 10 *Perf. 11***

**514** A210 5c lt brown .40 .25

**Types of 1932-39 and**

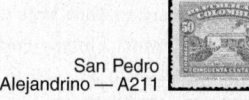

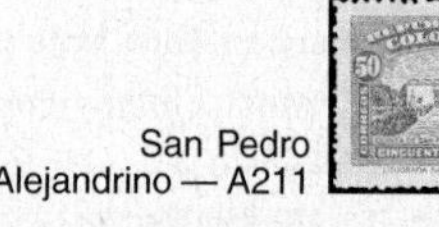
San Pedro Alejandrino — A211

**Imprint: "Litografia Nacional Bogota"**

**1944 Litho. *Perf. 12½***

**515** A175 1c dp green .25 .25
*a.* 1c olive green .35 .25
*b.* Imperf., pair 1.75 1.75
**516** A155 2c dk carmine .25 .25
*a.* Imperf., pair 1.75 1.75
**517** A135 10c yellow org 3.50 .45
**518** A179 30c gray olive 12.00 1.75
*a.* Imperf., pair 35.00
**519** A211 50c rose 12.00 5.25
*Nos. 515-519 (5)* 28.00 7.95

No. 469 Overprinted in Green, Blue or Red

**Wmk. 255**

**1945, July 19 Engr. *Perf. 12***

**520** A176 5c dull brn (G) .40 .25
**521** A176 5c dull brn (R) .40 .25
**522** A176 5c dull brn (Bl) .40 .25
*Nos. 520-522 (3)* 1.20 .75

Portraits are Joseph Stalin, Franklin D. Roosevelt and Winston Churchill.

Nos. 520-522 exist with overprint inverted. Value, $20 each.

Clock Tower, Cartagena — A212

**1945, Nov. 15**

**523** A212 50c olive black 4.25 1.60

For overprints see Nos. 543-544.

Sierra Nevada of Santa Marta — A213

Designs: 30c, Seaplane Tolima. 50c, San Sebastian Fort, Cartagena.

**Unwmk.**

**1945, Dec. 14 Litho. *Perf. 11***

**524** A213 20c light green 2.50 1.40
**525** A213 30c pale blue 2.50 1.40
**526** A213 50c salmon pink 2.50 1.40
*Nos. 524-526 (3)* 7.50 4.20

25th anniv. of the 1st airmail service in America, according to the inscription, but earlier services are known to have existed.

No. 442 Surcharged in Black

**1946, Mar. 8 *Perf. 12½***

**527** A133 1c on 5c brown .25 .25
*a.* Inverted surcharge 5.00
*b.* Perf. 11x11½ 6.00 6.00

Gen. Antonio Jose de Sucre — A216

**Wmk. 255**

**1946, Apr. 16 Engr. *Perf. 12***

**Size: 19x26½mm**

**528** A216 1c brn & turq grn .25 .25
**529** A216 2c vio & rose car .25 .25

**Size: 23x31mm**

**530** A216 5c sepia & blue .25 .25
**531** A216 9c dk grn & red .80 *1.25*
**532** A216 10c ultra & org .65 .50
**533** A216 20c blk & dp org .65 .50
**534** A216 30c brn red & grn .90 .40
**535** A216 40c ol blk & red vio .90 .40
**536** A216 50c dp brn & vio .90 .40
*Nos. 528-536 (9)* 5.55 4.20

Map of South America — A217

**Unwmk.**

**1946, June 7 Litho. *Perf. 11***

**537** A217 15c ultra .65 .50
*a.* Imperf., pair 5.00

National Observatory — A218

**1946, Aug.**

**538** A218 5c fawn .30 .25
*a.* Imperf., pair 6.00

See No. 565.

Andrés Bello — A219

**Wmk. 255**

**1946, Sept. 3 Engr. *Perf. 12***

| | | |
|---|---|---|
| **539** A219 3c sepia | .25 | .25 |
| **540** A219 10c orange | .60 | .35 |
| **541** A219 15c slate black | .70 | .35 |
| *Nos. 539-541,C145 (4)* | 1.80 | 1.20 |

Bello (1781-1865), poet and educator.

Joaquín de Cayzedo y Cuero — A220

**1946, Sept. 20 Wmk. 229 *Perf. 12½***

| | | |
|---|---|---|
| **542** A220 2p bluish green | 4.50 | 1.25 |

See No. 568. For surcharge see No. 613.

Type of 1945, Overprinted in Black or Green

**1946, Dec. 6 Wmk. 255 *Perf. 12***

| | | |
|---|---|---|
| **543** A212 50c red (Bk) | 4.00 | 2.75 |
| *a.* Double overprint | 25.00 | |
| **544** A212 50c red (G) | 4.00 | 2.75 |
| *a.* Double overprint | 25.00 | |

5th Central American and Caribbean Championship Games.

Coffee — A221

**Engraved and Lithographed**

**1947, Jan. 10 Wmk. 229 *Perf. 12½***

| | | |
|---|---|---|
| **545** A221 5c multicolored | .40 | .25 |

Colombian Orchid: Masdevallia Nycterina — A222

Designs (Orchids): 2c, Miltonia vexillaria. No. 548, Cattleya chocoensis. No. 549, Odontoglossum crispum. No. 550, Cattleya dowiana aurea. 10c, Cattleya labiata trianae.

**1947, Feb. 7 Wmk. 255 *Perf. 12***

| | | |
|---|---|---|
| **546** A222 1c multicolored | 1.25 | .25 |
| **547** A222 2c multicolored | 1.25 | .25 |
| **548** A222 5c multicolored | 1.25 | .25 |
| **549** A222 5c multicolored | 1.25 | .25 |
| **550** A222 5c multicolored | 1.25 | .25 |
| **551** A222 10c multicolored | 2.25 | .35 |
| *Nos. 546-551 (6)* | 8.50 | 1.60 |

Antonio Nariño A228

Alberto Urdaneta y Urdaneta A229

***Perf. 12½***

**1947, May 9 Litho. Unwmk.**

| | | |
|---|---|---|
| **552** A228 5c blue, *grnsh* | .40 | .25 |
| **553** A229 10c red brn, *grnsh* | .40 | .25 |
| *Nos. 552-553,C146-C147 (4)* | 2.10 | 1.30 |

4th Pan-American Press Congress, 1946.

**Sucre Type of 1940**

**1947 Wmk. 255 Engr. *Perf. 12***

| | | |
|---|---|---|
| **554** A198 1p violet | 2.75 | 1.25 |

José Celestino Mutis and José Jerónimo Triana — A230

Miguel A. Caro and Rufino J. Cuervo — A231

**1947 Wmk. 229 *Perf. 12½***

| | | |
|---|---|---|
| **555** A230 25c olive green | .50 | .40 |
| **556** A231 3p dark purple | 4.00 | 3.75 |

See Nos. 567, 569. For surcharge see No. 610.

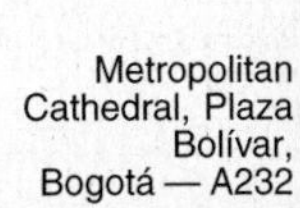

Metropolitan Cathedral, Plaza Bolívar, Bogotá — A232

National Capitol — A233

Ministry of Foreign Affairs — A234

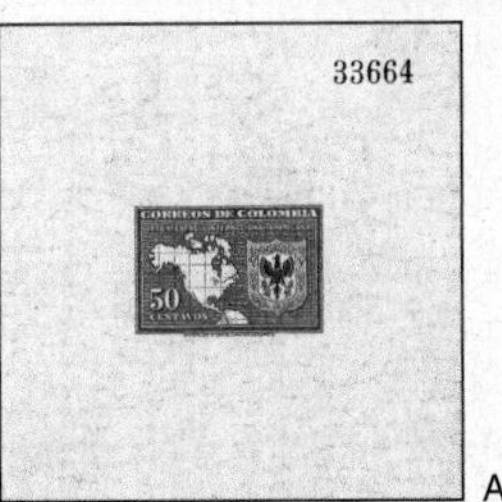

A235

**1948, Apr. 2**

| | | |
|---|---|---|
| **557** A232 5c black brown | .25 | .25 |
| **558** A233 10c orange | .60 | .55 |
| **559** A234 15c dark blue | .60 | .55 |
| *Nos. 557-559,C148-C149 (5)* | 2.70 | 2.60 |

**Miniature Sheet**

***Imperf***

| | | |
|---|---|---|
| **560** A235 50c slate | 2.00 | 1.60 |

9th Pan-American Conf., Bogotá.

No. RA5A Overprinted in Black

**1948 Unwmk. *Perf. 12½***

**Without Gum**

| | | |
|---|---|---|
| **561** PT3 1c yellow orange | .25 | .25 |

The letter "C" is the initial of "CORREOS." Exists with inverted overprint. Value $5.

Nos. RA33, RA24 and RA25 Overprinted in Black

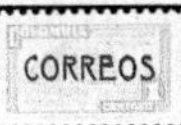


**1948 Wmk. 255 *Perf. 12.***

| | | |
|---|---|---|
| **562** PT6 1c olive | .25 | .25 |
| **563** PT6 2c green | .25 | .25 |
| **564** PT6 20c brown | .25 | .25 |
| *Nos. 562-564 (3)* | .75 | .75 |

Nos. 561-564 exist with inverted and double overprints.

**Observatory Type of 1946**

**Unwmk.**

**1948, June 30 Litho. *Perf. 11***

| | | |
|---|---|---|
| **565** A218 5c blue | .25 | .25 |

Simón Bolívar — A236

**Wmk. 255**

**1948, May 29 Engr. *Perf. 12***

| | | |
|---|---|---|
| **566** A236 15c green | .40 | .25 |

**Types of 1946-47**

**1948 Unwmk. *Perf. 12½***

| | | |
|---|---|---|
| **567** A230 25c green | .25 | .25 |
| **568** A220 2p dp green | .55 | .25 |
| **569** A231 3p dp red violet | .55 | .35 |
| *Nos. 567-569 (3)* | 1.35 | .85 |

**Falls Type of 1937**

**1948 Wmk. 229**

| | | |
|---|---|---|
| **570** A160 10c red | .25 | .25 |

For overprints see Nos. C231, C326.

Carlos Martinez Silva — A237

***Perf. 13½***

**1948, Dec. 21 Unwmk. Litho.**

| | | |
|---|---|---|
| **571** A237 40c carmine | .40 | .25 |

Juan de Dios Carrasquilla — A238

**1949, May 20 Wmk. 229 *Perf. 12½***

| | | |
|---|---|---|
| **572** A238 5c bister | .35 | .25 |

75th anniv. of the foundation of the Colombian Soc. of Agriculture.

Julio Garavito Armero — A239

**Wmk. 229**

**1949, Apr. 24 Engr. *Perf. 12***

| | | |
|---|---|---|
| **573** A239 4c green | .35 | .25 |

Issued to honor Julio Garavito Armero (1865-1920), mathematician.

**Coffee Type of 1939**

Imprint: "American Bank Note Co."

**1949, Aug. 4 Wmk. 255**

| | | |
|---|---|---|
| **574** A176 5c blue | .25 | .25 |

Arms of Colombia — A240

**1949, Oct. 7 Unwmk. *Perf. 13***

| | | |
|---|---|---|
| **575** A240 15c blue | .25 | .25 |

Issued to honor the new Constitution. See Nos. C164-C165.

Shield and Tree — A241

**1949, Oct. 13 Wmk. 229 *Perf. 12½***

| | | |
|---|---|---|
| **576** A241 5c olive | .25 | .25 |

4th anniv. of Colombia's 1st Forestry Cong. and propaganda for the government's reforestation program.

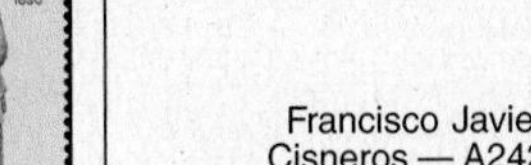

Francisco Javier Cisneros — A242

**1949, Dec. 15 Photo. Unwmk.**

| | | |
|---|---|---|
| **577** A242 50c red vio & yel | 1.10 | .60 |
| **578** A242 50c green & vio | 1.10 | .60 |
| **579** A242 50c brown & lt bl | 1.10 | .60 |
| *Nos. 577-579 (3)* | 3.30 | 1.80 |

50th anniv. (in 1948) of the death of Francisco Javier Cisneros.

Masdevallia Chimaera A243

Odontoglossum Crispum A244

Eastern Hemisphere — A245

Designs: 3c, Cattleya labiata trianae. 4c, Masdevallia nycterina. 5c, Cattleya dowiana aurea. 11c, Miltonia vexillaria. 18c, Santo Domingo post office.

**1950, Aug. 22 Photo. *Perf. 13***

| | | |
|---|---|---|
| **580** A243 1c brown | .25 | .25 |
| **581** A244 2c violet | .25 | .25 |
| **582** A243 3c rose lilac | .30 | .25 |
| **583** A243 4c emerald | .40 | .25 |
| **584** A243 5c red orange | .60 | .25 |
| **585** A244 11c red | 1.75 | 1.25 |
| **586** A244 18c ultra | 2.75 | .50 |
| *Nos. 580-586 (7)* | 6.30 | 3.00 |

**Miniature Sheet**

***Imperf***

| | | |
|---|---|---|
| **587** A245 50c orange yel | 2.00 | 2.00 |

75th anniv. (in 1949) of the UPU. See No. C199. For surcharge see No. C232.

Antonio Baraya — A246

***Perf. 12½***

**1950, Nov. 27 Unwmk. Engr.**

| | | |
|---|---|---|
| **588** A246 2c red | .25 | .25 |

Colombian Farm — A247

**1950, Dec. 28 Photo. *Perf. 11½***

| | | |
|---|---|---|
| **589** A247 5c dp car & buff | .25 | .25 |
| **590** A247 5c bl grn & gray | .25 | .25 |
| **591** A247 5c vio bl & gray | .25 | .25 |
| *Nos. 589-591 (3)* | .75 | .75 |

Issued to publicize rural life.

Arms of Bogotá A248

Arms of Colombia A249

*Perf. 12x12½*

**1950, Dec. 28 Engr. Wmk. 255**

**592** A248 5p deep green 2.75 1.50
**593** A249 10p red orange 6.75 2.00

**Catalogue values for unused stamps in this section, from this point to the end of the section, are for Never Hinged items.**

Map and Badge — A250

*Perf. 12½x13*

**1951, Jan. 30 Photo. Unwmk.**

**594** A250 20c red, yel & bl .55 .25

60th anniversary (in 1947) of the formation of the Colombian Society of Engineers.

Guillermo Valencia — A251

**1951, Oct. 20 Engr. *Perf. 13x13½***

**595** A251 25c black 1.10 .25

Issued to honor Guillermo Valencia (1873-1943), newspaper founder, governor of Cauca, presidential candidate, author.

No. 468 Overprinted in Black

**1951, Dec. 11 Wmk. 255 *Perf. 12***

**596** A155 2c carmine rose .30 .25

Issued to publicize the reversion of the Mares oil concession to Colombia.

Nicolas Osorio — A252

No. 598, Pompilio Martinez. No. 599, Ezequiel Uricoechea. No. 600, Jose M. Lombana.

*Perf. 11½*

**1952, Aug. 6 Unwmk. Engr.**

**Various Frames**

**597** A252 1c deep blue .25 .25
**598** A252 1c deep blue .25 .25
**599** A252 1c deep blue .25 .25
**600** A252 1c deep blue .25 .25
*Nos. 597-600 (4)* 1.00 1.00

Nos. 597-600 were printed in a single sheet containing four panes of twenty-five each, separated by double rows of ornamental tabs. Although inscribed "sobretasa," the stamps were for ordinary postage.

**Types of Postal Tax Stamps of 1945-50 and**

Communications Building
A253 A253a

**1952 *Perf. 12***

**601** A253 5c ultra .35 .25

**Wmk. 255**

**602** PT10 20c brown 10.00 4.50
**603** PT6 25c dk gray *42.50 42.50*
**604** PT10 25c blue green 1.00 .25
**605** A253a 50c orange yel 25.00 13.00
**606** A253a 1p rose carmine 2.25 .30
**607** A253a 2p lilac rose 25.00 9.75
**608** A253a 2p violet 3.00 .65
*Nos. 601-608 (8)* 109.10 71.20

Although inscribed "sobretasa," Nos. 601-608 were issued for ordinary postage.
For surcharges see Nos. 612, RA48.

Cathedral of Manizales — A254

*Perf. 11½*

**1952, Oct. 10 Photo. Unwmk.**

**609** A254 23c blue & gray blk .50 .25

Centenary of city of Manizales.
For surcharge see No. 619.

No. 555 Surcharged in Blue

**1952, Oct. 30 Wmk. 229 *Perf. 12½***

**610** A230 15c on 25c olive green .45 .25

Latin American Siderurgical Conf., 1952. See No. C226.

Queen Isabella I and Monument — A255

*Perf. 12½*

**1953, Mar. 10 Unwmk. Engr.**

**611** A255 23c blue & black .95 .70

5th cent. of the birth of Queen Isabella I of Spain.
For surcharge see No. 693.

**Nos. 606 and 568 Surcharged with New Values in Dark Blue**

**1953, Oct. 19 Wmk. 255**

**612** A253a 40c on 1p rose car 1.50 .25
**613** A220 50c on 2p dp green 1.50 .25

Manuel Ancizar — A256

Portraits: 23c, José Jeronimo Triana. 30c, Manuel Ponce de Leon. 1p, Agustin Codazzi.

*Perf. 12½x13*

**1953, Nov. Engr. Unwmk.**

**Frames in Black**

**614** A256 14c rose red .65 .65
**615** A256 23c ultra .55 .25
**616** A256 30c chocolate .45 .25
**617** A256 1p emerald .45 .25
*Nos. 614-617 (4)* 2.10 1.40

Cent. (in 1950) of the establishment of the Chorographic Commission. For surcharges and overprint see Nos. 620, 687, 690, 692, C284.

Murillo Toro and Map — A257

**Black Surcharge**

**Engraved and Lithographed**

**1953, Dec. 12 Wmk. 255 *Perf. 12***

**618** A257 5c on 5p multi .40 .25

2nd Natl. Phil. Exhib., Bogotá, Dec. 1953. See No. C237.

**Nos. 609 and 614 Surcharged with New Value or New Value and Ornaments**

**1953 Unwmk. *Perf. 11½, 12½x13***

**619** A254 5c on 23c (C) .45 .25
**620** A256 5c on 14c (Bk) .45 .25

No. 614 surcharged "CINCO" in blue is listed as No. 687.

Symbolical of St. Francis Receiving Christ's Wounds — A258

**1954, Apr. 23 Photo. *Perf. 11½***

**621** A258 5c sepia & green .40 .25

400th anniversary of the establishment of Colombia's first Franciscan community.

Soldier, Map and Arms — A259

**1954, June 13 Engr. *Perf. 13***

**622** A259 5c dull blue .25 .25

1st anniv. of the assumption of the presidency by Gen. Gustavo Rojas Pinilla. See Nos. C255, 637a.

Sports Emblem — A260

Design: 10c, Stadium and athlete holding arms of Colombia.

**1954, July 18 Unwmk.**

**623** A260 5c deep blue .60 .25
**624** A260 10c red .90 .25
*Nos. 623-624,C256-C257 (4)* 3.60 1.10

7th Natl. Athletic Games, Cali, July 1954.

History Academy Seal — A261

**1954, July 24**

**625** A261 5c ultra & green .30 .25

50th anniversary (in 1952) of the Colombian Academy of History.

Convent and Cell of St. Peter Claver — A262

**1954, Sept. 9**

**627** A262 5c dark green .25 .25
*a.* Souvenir sheet 8.00 *12.00*

300th anniv. of the death of St. Peter Claver.
No. 627a contains one stamp similar to No. 627, but printed in greenish black. Sheet size: 121x129½mm. See Nos. C258-C258a.

Mercury — A263

**1954, Oct. 29**

**628** A263 5c orange .55 .25
*Nos. 628,C259-C260 (3)* 1.65 .75

1st Intl. Fair and Exhibition, Bogota, 1954.

Tapestry Madonna — A264

College Cloister A265

Designs: 10c, Brother Cristobal de Torres. 20c, College chapel and arms.

***Perf. 12½x11½, 11½x12½***

**1954, Dec. 6**

**629** A264 5c orange & blk .40 .25
**630** A264 10c blue .40 .25
**631** A265 15c violet brn .40 .25
**632** A265 20c black & brn 1.00 .35
*a.* Souvenir sheet 6.50 *10.50*
*Nos. 629-632,C263-C266 (8)* 6.65 2.55

Founding of the Senior College of Our Lady of the Rosary, Bogota, 300th anniv. (in 1953).
No. 632a contains four stamps similar to Nos. 629-632, but printed in different colors: 5c yellow and black, 10c green, 15c dull violet, 20c black and light-blue.

Steel Mill — A266

**1954, Dec. 12 *Perf. 12½x13***

**633** A266 5c ultra & blk .50 .25

Issued to mark the opening of the Paz del Rio steel mill, October 1954. See No. C267.

José Marti — A267

**1955, Jan. 28 *Perf. 13½x13***

**634** A267 5c deep carmine .25 .25

Centenary of the birth of José Marti (1853-1895), Cuban patriot. See No. C268.

Arms, Flags and Soldiers Building Bridge — A268

**1955, Mar. 23 *Perf. 12½***

**635** A268 10c claret .30 .25

Issued to honor Colombian soldiers who served in Korea, 1951-53. See Nos. 637a, C269.

Fleet Emblem
A269

M. S. City of Manizales and New York Skyline
A270

**1955, Apr. 12** **Unwmk.**

| | | | | |
|---|---|---|---|---|
| **636** | A269 15c deep green | | .25 | .25 |
| **637** | A270 20c violet | | .45 | .25 |
| *a.* | Souvenir sheet | | 7.50 | *10.00* |
| | *Nos. 636-637,C270-C271 (4)* | | 1.95 | 1.15 |

Grand-Colombian Merchant Fleet.

No. 637a contains four stamps similar to Nos. 622, 635-637, but printed in different colors: 5c blue, 10c dark carmine, 15c green, 20c purple.

Hotel Tequendama and Church of San Diego — A271

**1955, May 16** **Photo.** ***Perf. 11½x12***

| | | | |
|---|---|---|---|
| **638** | A271 5c blue | .25 | .25 |

See No. C273.

Bolivar's Country Estate, Bogotá — A272

**1955, Sept. 28** **Engr.** ***Perf. 12½***

| | | | |
|---|---|---|---|
| **639** | A272 5c deep ultra | .25 | .25 |

50th anniv. of Rotary Intl. See No. C274.

Belalcazar, Jiménez de Quesada and Balboa — A273

Caravels and Columbus
A274

5c, San Martin, Bolivar and Washington.

**Engraved and Photogravure**

**1955, Oct. 29** ***Perf. 13x12½***

| | | | | |
|---|---|---|---|---|
| **640** | A273 | 2c yel grn & brn | .50 | .25 |
| **641** | A273 | 5c brt bl & brn | .50 | .25 |
| **642** | A274 | 23c lt ultra & blk | .55 | .25 |
| *a.* | | Souvenir sheet | 24.00 | 24.00 |
| | | *Nos. 640-642,C275-C280 (9)* | 29.85 | 15.00 |

7th Cong. of the Postal Union of the Americas and Spain, Bogota, Oct. 12-Nov. 9, 1955.

No. 642a contains one each of Nos. 640-642, printed in slightly different shades.

José Eusebio Caro — A275

**1955, Nov. 29** **Engr.** ***Perf. 13½x13***

| | | | |
|---|---|---|---|
| **643** | A275 5c brown | .35 | .25 |

José Eusebio Caro (1817-53), poet. See No. C281.

**Departmental Issue**

Map — A276

View of San Andres Harbor — A277

Cattle at Waterhole
A278

Designs: 2c, Docks, Atlantico. 3c, "Industry," Antioquia. 4c, Cartagena Harbor, Bolivar. No. 647, Steel Mill, Boyaca. No. 648, Cattle, Cordoba. No. 649, Map. No. 650, San Andres Harbor. No. 651, Cacao picker, Cauca. 10c, Coffee picker, Caldas. 15c, Salt Mine Chapel, Zipaquira, Cundinamarca. 20c, Tropical plants and map, Choco. 23c, Harvester, Huila. 25c, Banana plantation, Magdalena. 30c, Gold mining, Nariño. 40c, Tobacco plantation, Santander. 50c, Oil wells, North Santander. 60c, Cotton plantation, Tolima. 1p, Sugar industry, Cauca. 3p, Amazon river at Leticia, Amazonas. 5p, Windmills and panoramic view, La Guajira. 10p, Rubber plantation, Vaupes.

***Perf. 13½x13, 13x13½, 13***

**Engr.; Engr. & Litho.**

**1956** **Unwmk.**

**Various Frames**

| | | | | |
|---|---|---|---|---|
| **644** | A277 | 2c car & grn | .25 | .25 |
| **645** | A276 | 3c brn vio & blk | .25 | .25 |
| **646** | A277 | 4c grn & blk | .25 | .25 |
| **647** | A276 | 5c dk brn & bl | .25 | .25 |
| **648** | A277 | 5c ol & dk vio brn | .30 | .25 |
| **649** | A276 | 5c bl & blk | .25 | .25 |
| **650** | A277 | 5c car & grnsh bl | .25 | .25 |
| **651** | A277 | 5c ol grn & red brn | .25 | .25 |
| **652** | A276 | 10c org & blk | .40 | .25 |
| **653** | A276 | 15c ultra & blk | .25 | .25 |
| **654** | A276 | 20c dk brn & bl | .25 | .25 |
| **655** | A277 | 23c ultra & ver | .30 | .25 |
| **656** | A277 | 25c ol grn & blk | .30 | .25 |
| **657** | A277 | 30c ultra & brn | .25 | .25 |
| **658** | A277 | 40c dl pur & red brn | .25 | .25 |
| **659** | A277 | 50c dk grn & blk | .25 | .25 |
| **660** | A277 | 60c pale brn & grn | .25 | .25 |
| **661** | A278 | 1p mag & grnsh bl | 1.90 | .25 |
| **662** | A278 | 2p grn & red brn | 2.75 | .25 |
| **663** | A278 | 3p car & blk | 4.25 | .50 |
| **664** | A278 | 5p brn & lt ultra | 7.50 | 1.00 |
| **665** | A276 | 10p red brn & grn | 20.00 | 6.00 |
| | | *Nos. 644-665 (22)* | 40.95 | 12.25 |

Nos. 645, 647, 649, 652-654 measure 27x32mm, No. 665 27x37mm. See Nos. 681-684, 685, 688-689. For surcharges and overprints see Nos. 685, 688-689, C289, C312.

Columbus and Proposed Lighthouse
A279

**1956, Oct. 12** **Photo.** ***Perf. 12***

| | | | |
|---|---|---|---|
| **666** | A279 3c gray black | .50 | .25 |

Issued in honor of Christopher Columbus. See Nos. C285, C306.

Altar of St. Elizabeth and Tomb of Jimenez de Quesada — A280

**1956, Nov. 19** **Unwmk.**

| | | | |
|---|---|---|---|
| **667** | A280 5c red lilac | .25 | .25 |

7th cent. of St. Elizabeth of Hungary, patron saint of Sante Fé de Bogotá. See No. C286.

St. Ignatius of Loyola — A281

**1956, Nov. 26** **Engr.** ***Perf. 12½x13***

| | | | |
|---|---|---|---|
| **668** | A281 5c blue | .25 | .25 |

400th anniv. of the death of St. Ignatius of Loyola. See No. C287. For overprint see No. C324.

Javier Pereira — A282

**1956, Dec. 28** **Unwmk.** ***Perf. 12***

| | | | |
|---|---|---|---|
| **669** | A282 5c blue | .25 | .25 |

Issued to honor 167-year-old Javier Pereira. See No. C288.

Emblem and Dairy Farm — A283

Designs: 2c, Emblem and tractor. 5c, Emblem, coffee and corn.

**1957, Mar. 5** **Photo.** ***Perf. 14x13½***

| | | | |
|---|---|---|---|
| **670** | A283 1c lt ol grn | .25 | .25 |
| **671** | A283 2c lt brn | .25 | .25 |
| **672** | A283 5c lt bl | .25 | .25 |
| | *Nos. 670-672,C292-C296 (8)* | 3.00 | 2.05 |

Agrarian Savings Bank of Colombia, 25th anniv.

For overprint see No. C322.

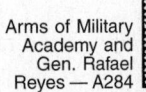

Arms of Military Academy and Gen. Rafael Reyes — A284

Design: 10c, Arms and Academy.

**1957, July 20** **Engr.** ***Perf. 12½***

| | | | | |
|---|---|---|---|---|
| **673** | A284 | 5c blue | .25 | .25 |
| **674** | A284 | 10c orange | .40 | .25 |
| *a.* | | Souv. sheet of 2 | 20.00 | 20.00 |
| | | *Nos. 673-674,C299-C300 (4)* | 1.40 | 1.00 |

50th anniv. of the Colombian Military Academy.

No. 674a contains one each of Nos. 673-674 in slightly different shades.

For overprints see Nos. C328, C312.

Statue of José Matias Delgado — A285

**1957, Sept. 16** **Photo.** ***Perf. 12***

| | | | |
|---|---|---|---|
| **675** | A285 2c rose brn | .25 | .25 |

Issued in honor of Jose Matias Delgado, liberator of El Salvador. See No. C301.

Santo Michelena, Marcos y Crespo, P. Alcantara Herran and UPU Monument
A286

**1957, Oct. 10** **Unwmk.**

| | | | |
|---|---|---|---|
| **676** | A286 5c green | .30 | .25 |
| **677** | A286 10c gray | .30 | .25 |
| | *Nos. 676-677,C302-C303 (4)* | 1.30 | 1.00 |

Intl. Letter Writing Week and 14th UPU Cong.

St. Vincent de Paul and Children — A287

**1957, Oct. 18**

| | | | |
|---|---|---|---|
| **678** | A287 1c dark olive green | .25 | .25 |

Colombian Society of St. Vincent de Paul, cent. See No. C304. For overprint see No. C323.

Fencer — A288

**1957, Nov. 22** **Photo.** ***Perf. 12***

| | | | |
|---|---|---|---|
| **679** | A288 4c lilac | .25 | .25 |

3rd South American Fencing Championship. See No. C305. For overprint see No. C332.

Francisco José de Caldas and Hypsometer
A289

**1958, May 12** **Unwmk.** ***Perf. 12***

| | | | |
|---|---|---|---|
| **680** | A289 10c black | .50 | .25 |
| | *Nos. 680,C309-C310 (3)* | 1.65 | .75 |

International Geophysical Year, 1957-58.

**Departmental Issue**
**Type of 1956**

Designs as before.

**1958** **Engr.** ***Perf. 13***

| | | | | |
|---|---|---|---|---|
| **681** | A276 | 3c ultra & brn | .25 | .25 |
| **682** | A276 | 3c ol grn & pur | .25 | .25 |
| **683** | A276 | 10c grn & brn | .25 | .25 |
| **684** | A276 | 10c dk bl & brn | .25 | .25 |
| | | *Nos. 681-684 (4)* | 1.00 | 1.00 |

Nos. 646, C291, 614, 653, 655, 616, C308, 615 and 611 Surcharged or Overprinted in Dark Blue or Green

***Perf. 12½, 12½x13, 13***

**1958-59** **Unwmk.**

| | | | | |
|---|---|---|---|---|
| **685** | A277 | 2c on 4c grn & blk | .25 | .25 |
| **686** | AP48 | 5c dp plum & multi ('59) | .25 | .25 |
| **687** | A256 | 5c on 14c blk & rose red ("CINCO") ('59) | .30 | .30 |
| **688** | A276 | 5c on 15c ultra & blk | .25 | .25 |
| **689** | A277 | 5c on 23c ultra & ver (G) | .25 | .25 |
| **690** | A256 | 5c on 30c blk & choc ("CINCO") | .25 | .25 |
| **691** | AP40 | 10c on 25c rose vio | .25 | .25 |
| **692** | A256 | 20c on 23c blk & ultra (G) ("VEINTE") ('59) | .30 | .25 |
| **693** | A255 | 20c on 23c lt bl & blk ('59) | .30 | .25 |
| | | *Nos. 685-693 (9)* | 2.40 | 2.30 |

On No. 686 the words "Correo Extra Rapido" are obliterated in dark blue.

Father Rafael Almanza and Church of San Diego, Bogota — A290

**1958, Oct. 23** **Photo.** ***Perf. 14x13***

| | | | |
|---|---|---|---|
| **695** | A290 10c purple | .30 | .25 |
| | *Nos. 695,C313-C314 (3)* | 1.00 | .75 |

For overprint see No. C336.

Msgr. R. M. Carrasquilla and Church — A291

**1959, Jan. 22** *Perf. 14x13*

**696** A291 10c dk red brn .25 .25
*Nos. 696,C315-C316 (3)* 1.30 .75

Cent. of the birth of Msgr. R. M. Carrasquilla (1857-1930), rector of Our Lady of the Rosary Seminary, Bogotá. For overprints see Nos. C335, C341.

Miss Universe 1959 — A292

**1959, June 26** **Photo.** *Perf. 11½*

**697** A292 10c multi .80 .25
*Nos. 697,C317-C318 (3)* 47.55 46.65

Luz Marina Zuluaga, Miss Universe, 1959.
For overprint see No. C342.

Jorge Eliecer Gaitan — A293

**1959, July 28** **Engr.** *Perf. 12x13½*

**698** A293 10c on 3c gray bl (Bl) .25 .25
**699** A293 30c rose vio .45 .25
*Nos. 698-699,C319-C320 (4)* 4.70 3.30

Issued in honor of Jorge Eliecer Gaitan (1898-1948), lawyer and politician.
No. 698 exists without blue surcharge.

Gen. Francisco de Paula Santander — A294

Designs: Nos. 701, 703, Simon Bolivar.

**1959** **Litho.** **Wmk. 331** *Perf. 12½*

**700** A294 5c brown & yel .25 .25
**701** A294 5c ultra & bl .25 .25
**702** A294 10c gray & grn .30 .25
**703** A294 10c gray & red .30 .25
*Nos. 700-703,C389 (5)* 4.60 1.45

Capitol, Bogota — A295

**1959**

**704** A295 2c dk bl & red brn .25 .25
**705** A295 3c blk brn & lilac .25 .25

Stamp of 1859 and Mail Transport by Mule — A296

Designs (various stamps of 1859 and): 10c, Mail boat on the Magdalena river. 15c, as 5c. 25c, Train.

**Unwmk.**

**1959, Dec. 1** **Photo.** *Perf. 12*

**709** A296 5c org & grn .25 .25
**710** A296 10c rose cl & bl .25 .25
**711** A296 15c car rose & grn .40 .40
**712** A296 25c bl & red brn .50 .50
*Nos. 709-712,C351-C354 (8)* 6.00 4.25

Centenary of Colombian postage stamps.

Two-Toed Sloth — A297

Designs: 10c, Alexander von Humboldt. 20c, Spider monkey.

**1960, Feb. 12** *Perf. 12*

**713** A297 5c grnsh bl & brn .25 .25
**714** A297 10c blk & dp car .25 .25
**715** A297 20c cit & gray brn .45 .25
*Nos. 713-715,C357-C359 (6)* 8.30 5.40

Cent. of the death of Alexander von Humboldt (1769-1859), German naturalist and geographer.
For overprint and surcharge see Nos. C411, C413.

Anthurium Andreanum — A298

Flower: 20c, Espeletia grandiflora.

**1960, May 10**

**716** A298 5c multi .85 .25
**717** A298 20c brn, yel & gray ol .85 .25
*Nos. 716-717,C360-C370 (13)* 17.85 18.30

See Nos. C420-C425. For overprint see No. C412.

Lincoln Statue, Washington — A299

**Wmk. 331**

**1960, June 10** **Litho.** *Perf. 10½*

**718** A299 20c rose lil & blk .35 .25
*Nos. 718,C375-C376 (3)* 2.25 1.50

Florero House, Cradle of the Republic A300

Arms of Santa Cruz de Mompox A301

Design: 5c, First coins of Republic.

**Unwmk.**

**1960, July 19** **Photo.** *Perf. 12*

**719** A301 5c grn & ocher .25 .25
**720** A300 20c ol bis & mar .25 .25
**721** A301 20c multi .25 .25
*Nos. 719-721,C377-C385 (12)* 7.90 6.05

Colombia's independence, 150th anniv.

St. Isidore and Farm Animals — A302

Design: 20c, Nativity by Gregorio de Arce Vasquez y Ceballos.

**1960, Sept. 26** *Perf. 12*

**722** A302 10c multi .25 .25
**723** A302 20c multi .25 .25
*Nos. 722-723,C387 (3)* .75 .75

St. Isidore the Farmer, patron saint of the rural people.

See Nos. 747, C388, C439-C440.

UN Headquarters and Emblem — A303

**Wmk. 331**

**1960, Oct. 24** **Litho.** *Perf. 11*

**724** A303 20c blk & pink .25 .25

**Souvenir Sheet**

***Imperf***

**725** A303 50c dk brn, brt grn & blk 3.75 3.75

15th anniversary of the United Nations.

Pan-American Highway through Colombia — A304

**1961, Mar. 7** **Unwmk.** *Perf. 10½x11*

**726** A304 20c brn & grnsh bl 1.00 .70
*Nos. 726,C390-C393 (5)* 3.40 2.90

8th Pan-American Highway Congress, Bogota, May 20-29, 1960.

Alfonso Lopez — A305

**1961, Mar. 22** **Photo.** *Perf. 12½*

**727** A305 10c brt rose & brn .25 .25
**728** A305 20c vio & brn .25 .25
*Nos. 727-728,C394-C395 (4)* 1.25 1.00

Alfonso Lopez (1886-1959), President of Colombia. See No. C396.

Cauca River Bridge, Cali A306

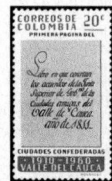

Page from Resolutions of Confederated Cities A307

**1961-62** *Perf. 12½x13, 13½x13*

**729** A306 10c red brn, bl, grn & red ('62) .50 .25
**730** A307 20c pale brn & blk .50 .25
*Nos. 729-730,C397-C401 (7)* 4.05 2.45

50th anniversary (in 1960) of the Department of Valle del Cauca.

View of Cucuta and Arms — A308

No. 732, Arms of Ocana and Pamplona.

**1961, Aug. 29** *Perf. 13x13½*

**731** A308 20c bl, blk, yel & red .30 .25
**732** A308 20c ocher, ultra & red .30 .25
*Nos. 731-732,C402-C403 (4)* 1.50 1.00

50th anniv. (in 1960) of the Department of North Santander.

Arms of Popayan — A309

Designs: No. 734, Arms of Barranquilla. No. 735, Arms of Bucaramanga.

***Perf. 12½x13***

**1961, Oct. 10** **Unwmk.**

**Arms in Multicolor**

**733** A309 10c blue & silver .25 .25
**734** A309 20c blue & yellow .25 .25
**735** A309 20c blue & gold .25 .25
*Nos. 733-735,C404-C408 (8)* 2.80 2.00

Issued to honor Atlantico Department.

Basketball — A310

**1961, Dec. 16** **Litho.** *Perf. 13½x14*

**736** A310 20c shown .30 .25
**737** A310 20c Runners .30 .25
**738** A310 20c Boxers .50 .25
**739** A310 25c Soccer .30 .25
*Nos. 736-739,C414-C418 (9)* 4.50 2.65

4th Bolivarian Games, Barranquilla, 1961.

Colombian Anti-Malaria Emblem — A311

Design: 50c, Malaria eradication emblem and mosquito in swamp.

**1962, Apr. 12** **Unwmk.** *Perf. 12*

**740** A311 20c lt bis & red .25 .25
**741** A311 50c bis & ultra .30 .25
*Nos. 740-741,C426-C428 (5)* 5.45 5.15

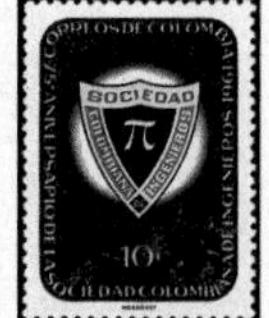

Engineers Society Emblem — A312

**1962, June 12** **Photo.** *Perf. 11½x12*

**742** A312 10c multi .25 .25
*Nos. 742,C429-C432 (5)* 3.40 3.30

Colombian Society of Engineers, 75th anniv.

Flags of American Nations — A313

**1962, June 28** *Perf. 13*

**Flags in National Colors**

**743** A313 25c blk & org ver .25 .25

**Souvenir Sheet**

**744** A313 2.50p blk & yel 5.50 5.50

70th anniv. of the founding of the Organization of American States.
See No. C433.

Woman Casting Ballot and Statue of Policarpa Salavarrieta — A314

*Perf. 12x12½*

**1962, July 20 Litho. Wmk. 229**

**745** A314 10c lt bl, gray & blk .25 .25

Issued to publicize women's political rights. See Nos. 752, C434, C448-C450.

Scouts at Campfire and Tents — A315

*Perf. 11½x12*

**1962, July 28 Photo. Unwmk.**

**746** A315 10c brt grnsh bl & brn .35 .30
*Nos. 746,C435-C438 (5)* 6.75 5.40

Colombian Boy Scouts, 30th anniv.

**St. Isidore Type of 1960 Redrawn**

**1962, Aug. 28** ***Perf. 12***

**747** A302 10c pink & multi .50 .25
*Nos. 747,C439-C440 (3)* 5.25 5.00

The frame on No. 747 is solid color with white inscription similar to type AP82.

Railroad Map of Colombia — A316

**1962, Sept. 28** ***Perf. 12½***

**748** A316 10c blk, gray, grn & red .25 .25
*Nos. 748,C441-C444 (5)* 7.75 5.50

Progress of Colombian railroads and the completion of the Atlantic Line from Santa Marta to Bogota.

Post Horn — A317

*Perf. 13½x14*

**1962, Oct. 18 Litho. Wmk. 346**

**749** A317 20c gold, dl gray vio & blk .25 .25
*Nos. 749,C445-C446 (3)* .90 .75

50th anniv. of the founding of the Postal Union of the Americas and Spain, UPAE.

"Virgin of the Rock" — A318

**1963, Mar. 11 Wmk. 346**

**750** A318 60c multi .25 .25

Vatican II, the 21st Ecumenical Council of the Roman Catholic Church. See No. C447.

Red Cross Centenary Emblem — A319

**1963, May 1** ***Perf. 12x12½***

**751** A319 5c olive bister & red .30 .25

Centenary of International Red Cross.

**Women's Rights Type of 1962**

**1963, July 11 Wmk. 346**

**752** A314 5c org, gray & blk .25 .25
*Nos. 752,C448-C450 (4)* 1.30 1.00

Manuel Mejia J. and Flag of National Coffee Growers Assn. — A320

*Perf. 12½x13*

**1965, Feb. 10 Engr. Unwmk.**

**753** A320 25c rose & blk .25 .25
*Nos. 753,C464-C466 (4)* 6.50 1.15

Manuel Mejia J. (1887-1958), banker and manager of the National Coffee Growers Association.

Julio Arboleda (1817-62), Writer, Soldier and Statesman A321

**1966, Mar. 9 Litho.** ***Perf. 14x13½***

**754** A321 5c lt brn, lt yel grn & blk .30 .25

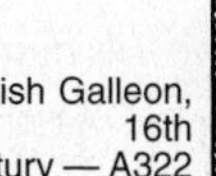

Spanish Galleon, 16th Century — A322

History of Maritime Mail: 15c, Rio Hacha brigantine, 1850. 20c, Uraba canoe. 40c, Magdalena River steamship and barge, 1900. 50c, Modern motor ship and sea gull.

**1966, June 16 Photo. Unwmk.**

**755** A322 5c org & multi .40 .25
**756** A322 15c car rose, blk & brn .40 .25
**757** A322 20c brt grn, org & blk .40 .25
**758** A322 40c dp bl & multi .50 .25
**759** A322 50c pale bl & multi 1.25 .60
*Nos. 755-759 (5)* 2.95 1.60

Plumed Hogfish — A323

Design: 10p, Bat ray and brittle starfish.

**1966, Aug. 25 Photo.** ***Perf. 12½x13***

**760** A323 80c multi .25 .25
**761** A323 10p multi 8.50 5.50
*Nos. 760-761,C481-C483 (5)* 27.25 19.90

Arms of Venezuela, Colombia and Chile — A324

**1966, Oct. 11 Litho.** ***Perf. 14x13½***

**762** A324 40c yel & multi .25 .25
*Nos. 762,C484-C485 (3)* .95 .75

Visits of Eduardo Frei and Raul Leoni, presidents of Chile and Venezuela.

Camilo Torres, 1766-1816, Lawyer — A325

Portraits: 60c, Jorge Tadeo Lozano (1771-1816), naturalist. 1p, Francisco Antonio Zea (1776-1822), naturalist and politician.

*Perf. 13½x14*

**1967, Jan. 18 Litho. Unwmk.**

**763** A325 25c vio & bis .25 .25
**764** A325 60c dk red brn & bis .25 .25
**765** A325 1p grn & bis .40 .25
*Nos. 763-765,C486-C487 (5)* 1.70 1.25

Issued to honor famous men of Colombia.

Map of South America and Arms — A326

**1967, Feb. 2 Litho.** ***Perf. 14x13½***

**766** A326 40c multi .30 .25
**767** A326 60c multi .30 .25
*Nos. 766-767,C488 (3)* 1.10 .75

Declaration of Bogota for cooperation and world peace, signed by Colombia, Chile, Ecuador, Peru and Venezuela.

Monochaetum Orchid and Bee — A327

Orchid: 2p, Passiflora vitifolia and butterfly.

**1967, May 23 Litho.** ***Perf. 14***

**768** A327 25c multi .35 .25
**769** A327 2p multi 2.50 1.50
*Nos. 768-769,C489-C491 (5)* 8.70 3.15

1st Natl. Orchid Exhib. and the Topical Phil. Flora and Fauna Exhib., Medellin, Apr. 1967.

Lions Emblem — A328

**1967, July 12 Litho.** ***Perf. 13½x14***

**770** A328 10p multi 3.50 2.00

50th anniv. of Lions Intl. See No. C492.

SENA Emblem — A329

**Lithographed and Embossed**

**1967, Sept. 20 Unwmk.**

**771** A329 5p gold, brt grn & blk 1.50 .25

10th anniv. of Natl. Apprenticeship Service, SENA. See No. C494.

Gold Diadem in Calima Style — A330

Pre-Columbian Art: 3p, Gold statuette, ornamental globe and bird, horiz.

*Perf. 13½x14, 14x13½*

**1967, Oct. 13 Photo.**

**772** A330 1.60p brt rose lil, gold & brn .95 .25
**773** A330 3p dk bl, gold & brn 1.25 .40
*Nos. 772-773,C495-C497 (5)* 20.85 11.40

Meeting of the UPU Committee of Postal Studies, Bogota, Oct., 1967.

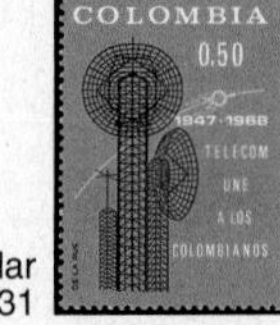

Radar Installation — A331

1p, Map of communications network.

**1968, May 14 Litho.** ***Perf. 13½x14***

**774** A331 50c brt yel grn, blk & org brn .25 .25
**775** A331 1p multi .35 .25
*Nos. 774-775,C498-C499 (4)* 1.15 1.00

20th anniv. of the National Telecommunications Service (TELECOM).

The Eucharist — A332

**1968, June 6 Litho.** ***Perf. 13½x14***

**776** A332 60c multi .25 .25
*Nos. 776,C500-C501 (3)* .80 .75

39th Eucharistic Cong., Bogotá, 8/18-25.

St. Augustin, by Gregorio Vasquez — A333

Designs: 60c, The Gathering of Manna, by Gregorio Vasquez. 1p, The Marriage of the Virgin, by Baltazar de Figueroa. 5p, Jeweled monstrance, c. 1700. 10p, Pope Paul VI, painting by Roman Franciscan nuns.

**1968, Aug. 13 Photo.** ***Perf. 13***

**777** A333 25c multicolored .25 .25
**778** A333 60c multicolored .25 .25
**779** A333 1p multicolored .25 .25
**780** A333 5p multicolored .65 .25
**781** A333 10p multicolored 1.25 .45
***a.*** Souvenir sheet of 2 3.75 3.75
*Nos. 777-781,C502-C506 (10)* 9.55 4.95

39th Eucharistic Congress. Bogotá, Aug. 18-25. No. 781a contains two imperf. stamps similar to Nos. 780-781.

Pope Paul VI — A334

**1968, Aug. 22 Litho.** ***Perf. 13½x14***

**782** A334 25c multi .30 .25
*Nos. 782,C507-C509 (4)* 1.30 1.00

Visit of Pope Paul VI to Colombia, 8/22-24.

Arms of National University — A335

**1968, Oct. 29 Litho.** ***Perf. 13½x14***
**783** A335 80c multi .35 .25

Centenary of the founding of the National University. See No. C510.

Stamp of Antioquia, 1868 — A336

**1968, Nov. 20 Litho.** ***Perf. 12x12½***
**784** A336 30c emer & bl .30 .25

**Souvenir Sheet**

**785** A336 5p lt olive & blue 5.00 5.00

Cent. of the 1st postage stamps of Antioquia and the 7th Natl. Phil. Exhib., Medellin, Nov. 20-29.

Institute Emblem — A337

**1969, Mar. 5 Litho.** ***Perf. 13½x14***
**786** A337 20c multi .35 .25

25th anniv. (in 1967) of the Inter-American Agricultural Sciences Institute. See No. C511.

Battle of Boyaca (Detail), by José Maria Espinosa A338

Design: 30c, Army of liberation crossing Pisba Pass, by Francisco Antonio Caro.

**1969, July 24 Litho.** ***Perf. 13½x14***
**787** A338 20c gold & multi .35 .25
**788** A338 30c gold & multi .35 .25
*Nos. 787-788,C517 (3)* 1.70 .85

Fight for independence, sesquicentennial.

"Poverty" — A339

**1970, Mar. 1 Litho.** ***Perf. 14***
**789** A339 30c bl & multi .75 .25

Colombian Institute for Family Welfare and 10th anniv. of the Children's Rights Law.

Greek Mask and Pre-Columbian Symbol of Literary Contest — A340

**1970, Sept. 12 Litho.** ***Perf. 14x13½***
**790** A340 30c dk brn, red org & ocher 1.00 .25

3rd Latin American Theatrical Festival of the Universities, Manizales, Sept. 12-20.

Colombian Stamps, Envelope and Emblem — A341

**1970, Sept. 24 Litho.** ***Perf. 14x13½***
**791** A341 2p brt bl & multi .75 .25

Issued to publicize Philatelic Week.

Arms of Ibague and Discobolus A342

**1970, Oct. 13**
**792** A342 80c buff, emer & sepia .40 .25

9th National Games in Ibague.

St. Theresa, by Baltazar de Figueroa — A343

**1970, Oct. 28 Litho.** ***Perf. 13½x14***
**793** A343 2p multi .75 .25

Elevation of St. Theresa (1515-1582), to Doctor of the Church. See No. C568. For overprint see No. C568.

Casa Cural — A344

**1971, May 20 Litho.** ***Perf. 14x13½***
**794** A344 1.10p multi .80 .25

Fourth centenary (in 1970) of the founding of Guacari, Valle. See No. 809.

Dancers and Music, Currulao — A345

1p, Chicha Maya dancers and music.

**1971 Litho.** ***Perf. 13½x14***
**795** A345 1p pink & multi 1.00 .25
**796** A345 1.10p lt bl & multi 1.00 .25

**Souvenir Sheets**

***Imperf***

| | | | |
|---|---|---|---|
| **797** | Sheet of 3 | 8.00 | 6.00 |
| *a.* | A345 2.50p Napanga | 1.50 | .65 |
| *b.* | A345 2.50p Joropo | 1.50 | .65 |
| *c.* | A345 5p Guabina | 3.35 | 1.25 |
| **798** | Sheet of 3 | 8.00 | 6.00 |
| *a.* | A345 4p Bambuco | 1.50 | 1.00 |
| *b.* | A345 4p Cumbia | 1.50 | 1.00 |
| *c.* | A345 4p Currulao | 3.35 | 1.00 |

Issued: No. 795, 12/20; No. 796, 8/5; Nos. 797-798, 8/10.

Constitutional Assembly, by Delgado — A346

**1971, Oct. 2** ***Perf. 14***
**801** A346 80c multi 1.00 .25

Sesquicentennial of Gran Colombian Constitutional Assembly in Rosario del Cucuta. See No. C589. For overprint see No. C589.

Arrows Emblem — A347

**1972, Feb. 24** ***Perf. 13½x14***
**802** A347 60c blk & gray .30 .25

Inter-Governmental Committee on European Migration, 20th anniversary.

Student and World Map — A348

**1972, Mar. 15** ***Perf. 14x13½***
**803** A348 1.10p lt grn & brn 1.00 .25

20th anniv. of ICETEX, an organization which furnishes financial help for educational purposes and for technical studies abroad.

UN Emblem, Soldier and Frigate — A349

**1972, Apr. 7**
**804** A349 1.20p lt bl & multi 1.00 .25

Colombian Battalion in Korea, 20th anniv.

Mother Francisca Josefa del Castillo — A350

**1972, Apr. 6** ***Perf. 13½x14***
**805** A350 1.20p brn & multi 1.00 .25

Tercentenary (in 1971) of the birth of Mother Francisca Josefa del Castillo, Poor Clare abbess and writer.

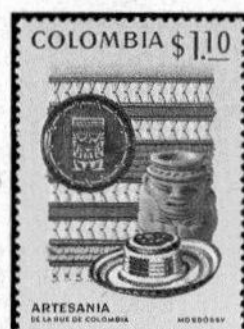

Handicraft — A351

**1972, Apr. 11**
**806** A351 1.10p multi .60 .25
*Nos. 806,C569-C571 (4)* 1.80 1.00

Colombian artisans.

Maxillaria Triloris — A352

**1972, Apr. 20**
**807** A352 20p green & multi 9.75 .75

10th Natl. Phil. Exhib., Medellin.

Emeralds — A353

**1972, June 16 Litho.** ***Perf. 13½x14***
**808** A353 1.10p multi 2.00 .25

**Type of 1971**

Design: Antonio Nariño House.

**1972, June 17** ***Perf. 14x13½***
**809** A344 1.10p multi 1.00 .25

4th centenary, town of Leyva.

San Andres and Providencia Islands — A354

**1972, June 24** ***Perf. 13½x14***
**810** A354 60c bl & multi 1.00 .25

Sesquicentennial of annexation by Colombia of San Andres and Providencia Islands.

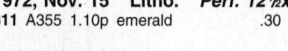

Postal Service Emblem — A355

**1972, Nov. 15 Litho.** ***Perf. 12½x12***
**811** A355 1.10p emerald .30 .25

Family — A356

**1972, Nov. 23**
**812** A356 60c orange .30 .25

Social progress.

Radio League Emblem — A357

**1973, Apr. 6 Litho.** ***Perf. 12x12½***
**813** A357 60c lt bl, ultra & red .30 .25

40th anniversary of the Colombian Radio Amateurs' League.

Human Figure, Tamalameque — A358

Excavated Ceramic Artifacts: 1p, Winged urn, Tairona. 1.10p, Jug, Muisca.

**1973, June 15 Litho.** ***Perf. 13½x14***
**814** A358 60c lt bl & multi .40 .25
**815** A358 1p org & multi .80 .25
**816** A358 1.10p vio bl & multi .80 .25
*Nos. 814-816,C583-C586 (7)* 8.00 2.75

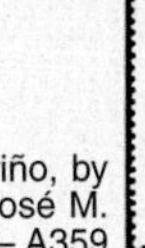

Antonio Nariño, by José M. Espinosa — A359

**1973, Dec. 13 Litho.** ***Perf. 13½x14***

**817** A359 60c multi .25 .25

Sesquicentennial of the death of General Antonio Nariño (1765-1823).

Child — A360

**1973, Dec. 17**

**818** A360 1.10p multi .25 .25

National Campaign for Children's Welfare.

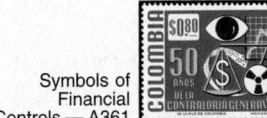

Symbols of Financial Controls — A361

**1973, Dec. 20 Litho.** ***Perf. 14x13½***

**819** A361 80c ultra, ocher & blk .25 .25

50th anniv. of Comptroller-general's Office.

Mother Laura Montoya — A362

**1974, June 18 Litho.** ***Perf. 13½x14***

**820** A362 1p multi .25 .25

Mother Laura Montoya (1874-1949), founder and Mother Superior of the Missionaries of Mary Immaculata and St. Catherine of Siena.

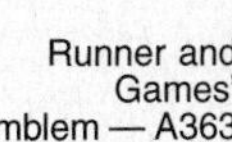

Runner and Games' Emblem — A363

**1974, July 18 Litho.** ***Perf. 14x13½***

**821** A363 2p ver, yel & brn .35 .25

10th National Games, Pereira.

José Rivera — A364

**1974, Aug. 3 Litho.** ***Perf. 14x13½***

**822** A364 10p grn & multi 1.30 .25

50th anniv. of the publication of "La Voragine" (The Whirlpool) by José Eustasio Rivera.

Abstract Pattern — A365

**1974, Oct. 24 Litho.** ***Perf. 13½x14***

**823** A365 1.10p multi .90 .25

Cent. of Natl. Insurance Co. See No. C610.

Train Emerging from Tunnel — A366

**1974, Nov. 27 Litho.** ***Perf. 13½x14***

**824** A366 1.10p multi .90 .25

Centenary of the Antioquia railroad.

Boy, Puppy and Soccer Ball — A367

Christmas: 1p, Girl with racket and kitten.

**1974, Dec. 9**

**825** A367 80c multi .50 .25
**826** A367 1p multi .50 .25

A368

**1975, Apr. 11 Litho.** ***Perf. 14x13½***

**827** A368 80c Gold Animal .45 .25
**828** A368 1.10p Gold necklace .45 .25
*Nos. 827-828,C621-C622 (4)* 6.65 1.35

Pre-Columbian Sinu culture artifacts.
For surcharge see No. 840.

Guglielmo Marconi — A369

**1975, June 2 Litho.** ***Perf. 13½x14***

**829** A369 3p multi .75 .25

Birth centenary of Guglielmo Marconi (1874-1937), Italian electrical engineer and inventor.

Santa Marta Cathedral — A370

**1975, July 26**

**830** A370 80c multi .30 .25

400th anniv. of Santa Marta City. See No. C623.

Rafael Nuñez — A371

**1975, Sept. 28 Litho.** ***Perf. 13½x14***

**831** A371 1.10p multi .30 .25

Rafael Nunez (1825-1894), philosopher, poet, political leader, birth sesquicentenary.
For surcharge see No. 848.

A372

A372a

Arms of Medellin — A372b

**1975-79** ***Perf. 13½x14, 12 (1.20p)***

| | | | | | |
|---|---|---|---|---|---|
| **832** | A372 | 1p | shown | .40 | .25 |
| **833** | A372b | 1.20p | Ibagué | .35 | .25 |
| **834** | A372b | 1.20p | Tunja | .25 | .25 |
| **835** | A372a | 1.50p | Cucuta | .55 | .25 |
| **836** | A372b | 1.50p | Cartagena | .25 | .25 |
| **836A** | A372b | 4p | Sogamoso | 1.00 | .25 |
| **837** | A372 | 5p | Popayan | .50 | .25 |
| **838** | A372b | 5p | Barranquilla | .55 | .25 |
| **839** | A372a | 10p | San Gil | 1.00 | .25 |
| **839A** | A372a | 10p | Socorro | 1.00 | .25 |
| | | | *Nos. 832-839A (10)* | 5.85 | 2.50 |

1p for the tercentenary of Medellin; No. 835, the cent. of Cucuta's reconstruction.

Issued: 1p, 11/4; No. 835, 11/29; No. 836, 2/10/76; No. 833, 7/30/76; No. 834, 12/20/76; No. 837, 8/30/77; No. 838, 9/20/77; 10p, 8/9/79; 4p, 9/14/79.

See Nos. 905-913, C818. For surcharge see No. 849.

No. 827 Surcharged

**1975** ***Perf. 14x13½***

**840** A368 1.20p on 80c multi .35 .25

Purace Indians, Cauca — A373

**1976, Nov. 10 Litho.** ***Perf. 13½x14***

**841** A373 1.50p multi .25 .25

Callicore — A374

5p, Morpho (butterfly). 20p, Anthurium.

**1976, Nov. 17** ***Perf. 12***

**842** A374 3p multicolored .90 .25
**843** A374 5p multicolored 1.50 .25
**844** A374 20p multicolored 4.25 1.00
*Nos. 842-844 (3)* 6.65 1.50

Rotary Emblem — A375

**1976, Dec. 3 Litho.** ***Perf. 12***

**845** A375 1p multicolored .25 .25

Rotary Club of Colombia, 50th anniversary.

Declaration of Independence, by John Trumbull — A376

**1976, Dec. 21 Litho.** ***Perf. 12***

**846** A376 Strip of 3 10.00 *11.50*
***a.-c.*** 30p any single 2.75 2.00

American Bicentennial. No. 846 printed in sheets of 4 triptychs.

Policeman with Dog — A377

**1976, Dec. 29** ***Perf. 13½x14***

**847** A377 1.50p multicolored .25 .25

Honoring the National Police.
For surcharge see No. 850.

Nos. 831, 834, 847 Surcharged in Light Brown

**1977, June Litho.** ***Perf. 13½x14, 12***

**848** A371 2p on 1.10p multi .65 .25
**849** A372b 2p on 1.20p multi .50 .25
**850** A377 2p on 1.50p multi .50 .25
*Nos. 848-850 (3)* 1.65 .75

Souvenir Sheet

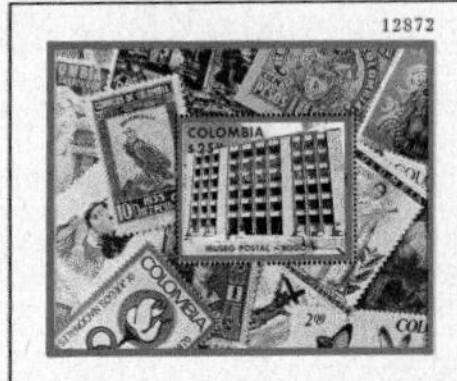

Postal Museum, Bogota A378

**1977, July 27 Litho.** ***Perf. 14***

**855** A378 25p multi 3.50 3.50

Postal Museum, Bogota.

Mother and Child — A379

**1977-78 Litho.** ***Perf. 12***

**856** A379 2p multi .50 .25
**857** A379 2.50p multi ('78) 2.25 .25

National good nutrition plan.
Issue dates: 2p, Aug. 30; 2.50p, Jan. 26.

Jacana and Eichhornia — A380

20p, Mayan cotinga and pyrostegia venusta.

**1977, Sept. 6 Litho. *Perf. 14***

**858** A380 10p multicolored 2.50 .25
**859** A380 20p multicolored 4.00 .50
*Nos. 858-859,C644-C647 (6)* 10.20 1.75

Fidel Cano, by Francisco Cano — A381

**1977, Sept. 16 *Perf. 14***

**860** A381 4p multicolored .25 .25

90th anniversary of El Espectador, newspaper founded by Fidel Cano.

Abacus and Alphabet — A382

**1977, Sept. 16 *Perf. 13½x14***

**861** A382 3p multicolored .25 .25

Popular education.

Cattleya Triannae — A383

**1978-79 Litho. *Perf. 12***

**862** A383 2.50p multi .75 .25
**863** A383 3p multi ('79) .75 .25

Issue dates: 2.50p, Apr. 18. 3p, May 10.

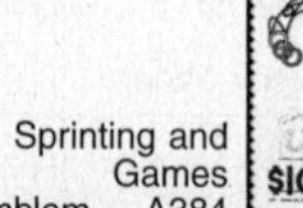

Sprinting and Games Emblem — A384

Sports: a, sprinting. b, basketball. c, baseball. d, boxing. e. bicycling. f, fencing. g, soccer. h, gymnastics. i, judo. j, weight lifting. k, wrestling. l, swimming. m, tennis. n, target shooting. o, volleyball. p, water polo.

**1978, June 27 Litho. *Perf. 14***

**868** Sheet of 16 29.00 29.00
*a.-p.* A384 10p, any single 1.25 .25

13th Central American and Caribbean Games, Medellin.

"Sigma 2" by Alvaro Herrán — A385

**1978, June 30**

**869** A385 8p multicolored .55 .25

Chamber of Commerce, Bogota, centenary.

Gen. Tomás Cipriano de Mosquera (1778-1878), Statesman — A386

**1978, Oct. 6 Litho. *Perf. 12***

**870** A386 6p multicolored .45 .25

Anthurium Narinenses — A387

**1979, July 23 *Perf. 12***

**871** A387 3p red & multi .30 .25
**872** A387 3p purple & multi .30 .25
**873** A387 3p rose & purple .30 .25
**874** A387 3p white & multi .30 .25
*a.* Block of 4, #871-874 2.50 2.50

Gen. Rafael Uribe, by Acevedo Bernal — A388

**1979, Oct. 31 Litho. *Perf. 12***

**875** A388 8p multicolored .50 .25

Gen. Uribe, statesman, 60th death anniv.

Village, by Leonor Alarcon A389

**1979, Nov. 22 *Perf. 14***

**876** A389 15p multicolored 1.50 .60

Community Work Boards, 20th anniversary.

Introduction of Color Television — A390

**1980, Mar. 4 Litho. *Perf. 14***

**877** A390 5p multicolored .60 .25

Bullfight, Arms of Cali — A391

**1980, Mar. 25**

**878** A391 5p multicolored .70 .25

Cali Tourist Festival, 12/25/79-1/2/80.

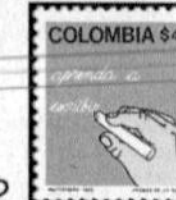


"Learn to Write" — A392

a, shown. b, "a." c, "b." d, "c." e, "ch." f, "d." g, "e." h, "f." i, "g." j, "h." k, "i." l, "j." m, "k." n, "l." o, "ll." p, "m." q, "n." r, "ñ." s, "o." t, "p." u, "q." v, "r." w, "s." x, "t." y, "u." z, "v." aa, "w." ab, "x." ac, "y." ad, "z."

**1980, Apr. 25 Litho. *Perf. 12½***

**879** Block of 30 27.50 27.50
*a.-ad.* A392 4p any single .75 .25

Each stamp shows letter of alphabet and corresponding animal or subject. Issued in sheets of 90 (10x9).

Villavicencio Festival A393

Design: 9p, Vallenato festival.

**1980 Litho. *Perf. 14***

**880** A393 5p multicolored .55 .25
**881** A393 9p multicolored .55 .25

Issue dates: 5p, July 15; 9p, June 17.

Gustavo Uribe Ramirez and Tree — A394

**1980, Aug. 5 Litho. *Perf. 12***

**882** A394 10p multicolored 1.20 .25

Gustavo Uribe Ramirez (1893-1968), ecologist.

Narino Palace (Former Presidential Residence) A395

**1980, Sept. 19 Litho. *Perf. 14***

**883** A395 5p multicolored .70 .25

Monument to First Pioneers of 1819, Armenia — A396

**1980, Oct. 14**

**884** A396 5p multicolored .60 .25

11th National Games, Neiva — A397

**1980, Nov. 28 *Perf. 13½x14***

**885** A397 5p multicolored .60 .25

Fight against Cancer — A398

**1980, Dec. 9**

**886** A398 10p multicolored .50 .25

Xavier University Law Faculty, 50th Anniversary — A399

**1980, Dec. 16 Litho. *Perf. 14½***

**887** A399 20p multicolored .85 .30

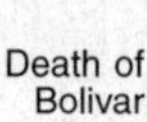

Death of Bolivar A400

**1980, Dec. 17 *Perf. 12***

**888** A400 25p multicolored 1.25 .60

Simon Bolivar, death sesquicentennial. See No. C696.

José Maria Obando, President of Colombia — A401

115th Anniv. of Constitution (Former Presidents): b, Jose Hilario Lopez. c, Manuel Murillo Toro. d, Santiago Perez. e, Rafael Reyes. f, Carlos E. Restrepo. g, Jose Vicente Concha. h, Miguel Abadia Mendez. i, Eduardo Santos. j, Mariano Ospina Perez.

**1981, June 9 Litho. *Perf. 12***

**889** Strip of 10 *9.00*
*a.-j.* A401 5p multicolored .90 .25

**1981, Sept. 23 Litho. *Perf. 12***

Designs: a, Rafael Nunez (1825-94). b, Marco Fidel Suarez (1855-1927). c, Pedro Nel Ospina (1858-1927). d, Enrique Olaya Herrera (1880-1937). e, Alfonso Lopez Pumarejo (1886-1959). f, Aquileo Parra (1825-1900). g, Santos Gutierrez (1820-72). h, Tomas Cipriano de Mosquera (1789-1878). i, Mariano Ospina Rodriguez. j, Pedro Alcantara Herran (1800-72).

**890** Strip of 10 *65.00*
*a.-j.* A401 7p multicolored 6.50 .50

**1981, Aug. 11 Litho. *Perf. 12***

Designs like No. 889.

**891** Strip of 10 *75.00*
*a.-j.* A401 7p multicolored 7.50 1.00

**1981, Nov. 11 Litho. *Perf. 12***

Designs: a, Manuel Maria Mallarino. b, Santos Acosta. c, Eustorgio Salgar. d, Julian Trujillo. e, Francisco Javier Zaldua. f, Guillermo Leon Valencia. g, Laureano Gomez. h, Manuel A. Sanclemente. i, Miguel Antonio Caro. j, Jose Eusebio Otalora.

**892** Strip of 10 *45.00*
*a.-j.* A401 7p multicolored 4.50 .40

**1981, Dec. 15 Litho. *Perf. 12***

Designs: a, Ruben Piedrahita Arango. b, Jorge Holguin. c, Ramon Gonzalez Valencia. d, Jose Manuel Marroquin. e, Carlos Holguin. f, Bartolome Calvo. g, Sergio Camargo. h, Jose Maria Rojas Garrido. i, J.M. Campo Serrano. j, Eliseo Payan.

**893** Strip of 10 *30.00*
*a.-j.* A401 7p multicolored 3.00 .30

**1982, May 3 *Perf. 12***

Designs: a, Simon Bolivar. b, Francisco de Paula Santander. c, Joaquin Mosquera. d, Domingo Caicedo. e, Jose Ignacio de Marquez. f, Roberto Urdaneta Arbelaez. g, Carlos Lozano y Lozano. h, Guillermo Quintero Calderon. i, Jose de Obaldia. j, Juan de Dios Aranzazu.

**894** Strip of 10 12.50
*a.-j.* A401 7p multicolored 1.20 .25

See No. 1110, 1329.

Jose Maria Villa and West Bridge over Cauca River — A404

**1981, Nov. 25 Litho. *Perf. 14x13½***

**895** A404 60p multicolored 1.50 .30

Agrarian, Mineral and Industrial Credit Bank, 50th Anniv. — A405

**1981, Dec. 9 Litho. *Perf. 14***

| | | | |
|---|---|---|---|
| **896** | A405 15p multicolored | 1.00 | .25 |

Los Nevados Park — A406

**1981, Dec. 10 Litho. *Perf. 13½x14***

| | | | |
|---|---|---|---|
| **897** | A406 20p multicolored | 1.00 | .25 |

Girl Sitting on Fence — A407

**1982, Feb. 22 Litho. *Perf. 12½x12***

| | | | |
|---|---|---|---|
| **898** | Strip of 3 | 5.00 | 5.00 |
| *a.* | A407 30p shown | 1.10 | .40 |
| *b.* | A407 30p Girl, basket | 1.10 | .40 |
| *c.* | A407 30p Boy, wheelbarrow | 1.10 | .40 |

Floral Bouquet — A408

Various floral arrangements (background): a, Flowers in vase (gray). b, Roses (red). c, Daisies (green). d, Roses (blue). e, Assorted (red). f, Yellow & orange flowers (green). g, Assorted (lilac). h, Roses (gray). i, Pink flowers (green). j, Flowers in basket (gray).

**1982, July 28**

| | | | |
|---|---|---|---|
| **900** | Strip or block of 10 | 16.00 | 16.00 |
| *a.-j.* | A408 7p, any single | 1.50 | .30 |

Hipotecario Bank, 50th Anniv. — A409

**1982, July 29 *Perf. 14***

| | | | |
|---|---|---|---|
| **901** | A409 9p black & green | .50 | .25 |

St. Thomas Aquinas (1225-1274) — A410

Paintings by Zurbaran.

**1982 Litho. *Perf. 12***

| | | | |
|---|---|---|---|
| **902** | A410 5p multicolored | .60 | .25 |
| **903** | A410 5p St. Teresa of Avila | .60 | .25 |
| **904** | A410 5p St. Francis of Assisi | .60 | .25 |
| | *Nos. 902-904 (3)* | 1.80 | .75 |

Issued: No. 902, 8/6; No. 903, 9/28; No. 904, 10/4.

### Arms Type of 1975

No. 905, Buga. No. 906, San Juan de Pasto. No. 907, Rionegro. No. 908, Santa Fe de Bogota. No. 909, Santiago de Cali. No. 910, Honda. No. 911, Cartago. No. 912, Antioquia ('86).

**1982-90 Litho. *Perf. 14, 12 (50p)***

| | | | |
|---|---|---|---|
| **905** | A372 10p | .40 | .25 |
| **906** | A372 10p multicolored | 1.25 | .25 |
| **907** | A372 16p multicolored | .70 | .25 |
| **908** | A372 20p multicolored | 1.00 | .25 |
| **909** | A372 20p multicolored | .30 | .25 |
| **910** | A372 23p multicolored | .75 | .25 |
| **911** | A372 50p multicolored | .70 | .25 |
| **912** | A372 55p multicolored | 1.00 | .25 |
| | *Nos. 905-912 (8)* | 6.10 | 2.00 |

Issued: 16p, 23p, No. 905, 12/7; No. 908, 3/1/83; No. 906, 4/12/83; No. 909, 7/25/86; 55p, 8/5/86; 50p, 5/30/90.
See No. C818.

Gabriel Marquez, 1982 Nobel Prize, Literature — A412

**1982, Dec. 10 *Perf. 13½x14***

| | | | |
|---|---|---|---|
| **917** | A412 7p gray & green | .25 | .25 |

See Nos. C731-C732.

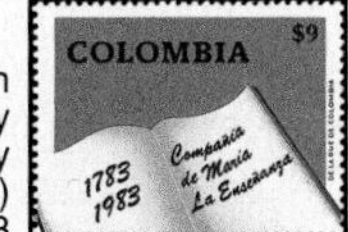

Public Education Bicentenary (Society of Mary for Education) A413

**1983, May 6**

| | | | |
|---|---|---|---|
| **918** | A413 9p gold & blk | .35 | .25 |

José Maria Espinosa Prieto, Painter — A414

**1983, June 3 *Perf. 12***

| | | | |
|---|---|---|---|
| **919** | A414 9p Self-portrait, 1860 | .40 | .25 |

250th Anniv. of City of Cucuta — A415

**1983, June 23 Litho. *Perf. 12***

| | | | |
|---|---|---|---|
| **920** | A415 9p multicolored | .35 | .25 |

Porfirio Barba-Jacob (1883-1942), Poet — A416

**1983, July 29 Litho. *Perf. 13½x14***

| | | | |
|---|---|---|---|
| **921** | A416 9p Portrait | .35 | .25 |

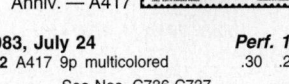

Simon Bolivar, 200th Birth Anniv. — A417

**1983, July 24 *Perf. 12***

| | | | |
|---|---|---|---|
| **922** | A417 9p multicolored | .30 | .25 |

See Nos. C736-C737.

Royal Spanish Botanical Expedition, 200th Anniv. — A418

No. 923, Cinchona lancefolia. No. 924, Passiflora laurifolia. No. 925, Cinchona cordiflora.

**1983, Aug. 18 *Perf. 14***

| | | | |
|---|---|---|---|
| **923** | A418 9p multicolored | .25 | .25 |
| **924** | A418 9p multicolored | .25 | .25 |
| **925** | A418 60p multicolored | 1.75 | .40 |
| | *Nos. 923-925,C738-C740 (6)* | 5.05 | 2.80 |

Dawn in the Andes, by Alejandro Obregon — A420

**1983, Oct. 5 Litho. *Perf. 12***

| | | | |
|---|---|---|---|
| **928** | A420 20p multicolored | .40 | .25 |

See No. C741.

Francisco de Paula Santander (1792-1840), General — A421

**1984, Mar. 6 Litho. *Perf. 14½x14***

| | | | |
|---|---|---|---|
| **929** | A421 12p light olive green | .30 | .25 |
| **930** | A421 12p pale carmine | .30 | .25 |
| **931** | A421 12p light ultra | .30 | .25 |
| | *Nos. 929-931 (3)* | .90 | .75 |

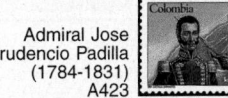

Admiral Jose Prudencio Padilla (1784-1831) A423

**1984, May 17 Litho. *Perf. 12***

| | | | |
|---|---|---|---|
| **933** | A423 10p multicolored | .40 | .25 |

Luis Antonio Calvo (1882-1945) Composer A424

**1984, July 26**

| | | | |
|---|---|---|---|
| **934** | A424 18p multicolored | .40 | .25 |

Diego Fallon (1834-1905), Educator, Musician, Poet — A425

**1984, Aug. 31 *Perf. 12***

| | | | |
|---|---|---|---|
| **935** | A425 20p multicolored | .45 | .25 |

Candelario Obeso (1849-1884), Writer — A426

**1984, Sept. 4 *Perf. 14x13½***

| | | | |
|---|---|---|---|
| **936** | A426 20p multicolored | .45 | .25 |

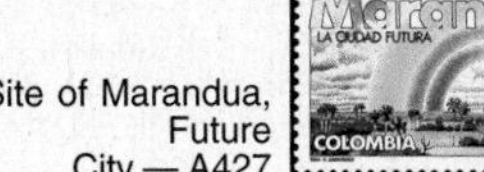

Site of Marandua, Future City — A427

**1984, Sept. 28 *Perf. 12***

| | | | |
|---|---|---|---|
| **937** | A427 15p multicolored | .35 | .25 |

See No. C744.

Christmas 1984 — A428

Nativity and Children Playing, by Jose Uriel Sierra, Age 7.

**1984, Dec. 14**

| | | | |
|---|---|---|---|
| **938** | A428 12p multicolored | .35 | .25 |

See No. C746.

Dr. Luis Eduardo Lopez, Education Minister — A429

**1984, Dec. 21**

| | | | |
|---|---|---|---|
| **939** | A429 22p multicolored | .45 | .25 |

Maria Concepcion Loperena de Fernandez de Castro, Independence War Heroine — A430

**1985, Jan. 6**

| | | | |
|---|---|---|---|
| **940** | A430 12p multicolored | .35 | .25 |

Gonzalo Mejia (1885-1956) A431

12p, Portrait, biplane, camera.

**1985, Feb. 25**

| | | | |
|---|---|---|---|
| **941** | A431 12p multicolored | .45 | .25 |

Aviation, motion picture and meat exporting industrialist.

Self-portrait with Wife — A432

**1985, Feb. 25**

| | | | |
|---|---|---|---|
| **942** | A432 37p multicolored | .80 | .30 |

Pedro Nel Gomez (1899-1984), painter. See No. C748.

Fauna — A433

No. 943, Hydrochaeris hydrochaeris. No. 944, Felis pardalis. No. 945, Tremarctos ornatus, vert. No. 946, Tapirus pinchaque.

**1985 *Perf. 14***

| | | | |
|---|---|---|---|
| **943** | A433 12p multicolored | .50 | .30 |
| | ***Perf. 13*** | | |
| **944** | A433 15p multicolored | .50 | .25 |
| **945** | A433 15p multicolored | .50 | .25 |
| **946** | A433 20p multicolored | .85 | .30 |
| | *Nos. 943-946,C758 (5)* | 3.85 | 1.35 |

Carlos Gardel (1890-1935), Entertainer — A434

15p, Portrait, Fokker F-31 Trimotor.

**1985, June 23** ***Perf. 14***
**947** A434 15p multicolored .30 .25

Camina Literacy Program — A435

**1985, Nov. 25** ***Perf. 13½x14***
**948** A435 15p Tree, alphabet .30 .25

Christmas 1985 — A436

**1985, Dec. 4** **Litho.** ***Perf. 13***
**949** A436 15p multicolored .40 .25

Rafael Pombo Children's Foundation. See No. C755.

Eduardo Carranza (b. 1913), Poet — A437

**1986, Feb. 13**
**950** A437 18p multicolored .30 .25

Colombian Free University, Cent. — A438

**1986, Feb. 14**
**951** A438 18p multicolored .30 .25

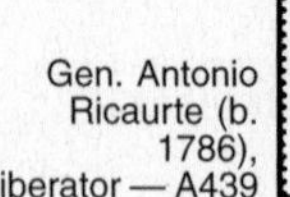

Gen. Antonio Ricaurte (b. 1786), Liberator — A439

**1986, May 7** **Litho.** ***Perf. 13***
**952** A439 18p Leiva birthplace .30 .25

Jose Asuncion Silva (1865-1896), Poet, and Scene from Nocturno — A440

**1986, May 30** **Litho.** ***Perf. 12***
**953** A440 18p multicolored .30 .25

Fernando Gomez Martinez (1897-1985), Journalist — A441

**1986, June 19**
**954** A441 24p multicolored .30 .25

Santiago de Cali, 450th Anniv. — A442

**1986, July 25** **Litho.** ***Perf. 13***
**955** A442 25p La Merced .30 .25

A443

Monsignor Jose Vicente Castro Silva (1885-1968), rector of the Mayor del Rosario School: portrait by Ricardo Gomez.

**1986, Aug. 4** **Litho.** ***Perf. 12***
**956** A443 20p multicolored .35 .25

Natl. University — A444

**1986, Oct. 14** **Litho.** ***Perf. 12***
**957** A444 40p multicolored .60 .40

Faculties: Fine Arts, cent., and Architecture, 50th anniv.

Rafael Maya (1897-1980), Poet, and Salamanca University Entrance — A445

**1986, Oct. 15**
**958** A445 25p multicolored .35 .25

See No. C772.

Condor in Flight — A446

Inia goefrenis A446a

No. 962, Inia goeffrensis. No. 963, Procyon cancrivorus. No. 964, Monachus tropicalis. No. 965, Pteronura brasiliensis. No. 966, Trichechus manatus. No. 967, Odocoileus virginianus. No. 968, Trogon personatus personatus. Nos. 962-968 horiz.

**1986-89** **Litho.** ***Perf. 12***
**959** A446 20p ultra .35 .25
**960** A446 25p ultra ('87) .50 .25

***Perf. 14½x14, 14x14½***
**961** A446a 30p grn ('87) .50 .25
**962** A446a 30p dull vio ('87) .50 .25

**Engr.**
**Wmk. 334**
**963** A446a 35p chest brn ('88) .75 .25
**964** A446a 35p dark grn ('88) .75 .25
**965** A446a 40p deep org ('88) .75 .25
**966** A446a 40p gray ('88) .85 .25
**967** A446a 40p tan ('89) .85 .25
**968** A446a 45p dark vio ('88) .85 .25
*Nos. 959-968 (10)* 6.65 2.50

Issued: 20p, 11/6; 25p, 5/25; No. 961, 6/8; No. 962, 12/24; No. 963, 8/6; No. 964, 9/20; No. 965, 9/20; No. 966, 11/29; No. 967, 4/29; No. 968, 12/16.
See Nos. 996-1001, C778-C781.

A447

**1987, Jan. 29** **Unwmk.** ***Perf. 12***
**969** A447 25p multicolored .50 .25

Pedro Uribe Mejia (1886-1972), pioneer of Colombian coffee industry.

Santa Barbara Church — A448

**1987, May 3** ***Perf. 13½x13***
**970** A448 500p multicolored 5.00 1.75

Mompox, 450th anniv.

Writers — A449

Portraits and scenes from works: 70p, Jorge Isaacs (1837-1895), novelist, and scene from *Maria*. 90p, Aurelio Martinez Mutis (1884-1954), poet, and scene from *La Epopeya del Condor.*

**1987** ***Perf. 12***
**971** A449 70p multicolored .90 .25
**972** A449 90p multicolored 1.25 .40

Issue dates: 70p, July 28. 90p, Sept. 2.

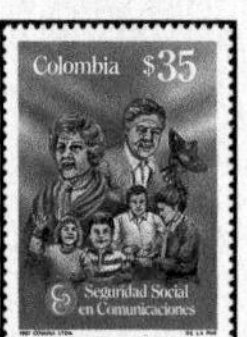

A450

Social Security & Communications.

**1987** **Litho.** ***Perf. 13½x13***
**973** A450 35p multicolored .40 .25

A451

Natl. Anthem, Cent.: Score, lyricist Rafael Nunez and composer Oreste Sindici. Dated 1987.

**1988, May 25** **Litho.** ***Perf. 12***
**974** A451 70p multicolored .90 .25

Human Rights — A452

***Perf. 14½x14, 14x14½***
**1988-89** **Engr.**
**975** A452 30p Life .35 .25
**976** A452 35p Suffrage .35 .25
**977** A452 40p Association, horiz. .45 .25
**978** A452 45p Culture, horiz. .35 .25
*Nos. 975-978 (4)* 1.50 1.00

Issued: 30p, 35p, 5/12; 40p, 7/1; 45p, 10/27/89.
See Nos. C797, C807.

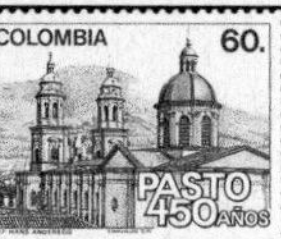

Pasto, 450th Anniv. — A453

**1988, May 20** **Litho.** ***Perf. 12***
**979** A453 60p Cathedral, Pasto .70 .35

Dated 1987.

Bogota Aqueduct and Sewage System, Cent. — A454

**1988, May 20**
**980** A454 100p Waterfall 1.25 .35

Maria Currea de Aya (1888-1985), Women's Rights Activist — A455

**1988, May 27**
**981** A455 80p multicolored .95 .25

A456

Sailfish, Istiaophorus Americanus.

***Perf. 14x13½***
**1988, July 19** **Engr.** **Wmk. 334**
**982** A456 (A) dark blue 4.00 2.25
**983** A456 (B) Prus blue 1.00 .40

At the time of issue, No. 982 was sold for 400p and No. 983 for 100p. See type A486.

A457

**Unwmk.**
**1988, Aug. 10** **Litho.** ***Perf. 12***
**984** A457 120p multicolored 1.25 .35

San Bartolome College, founded in 1604.

Jorge Alvarez Lleras (1885-1952), Engineer and Director of the Natl. Astronomical Observatory A458

**1988, Aug. 17**
**985** A458 90p multicolored 1.00 .45

Pres. Eduardo Santos (1888-1974) — A459

**1988, Aug. 30**
**986** A459 80p multicolored .85 .25

Andres Bello Seminary — A460

**Unwmk.**

**1988, Dec. 27 Litho. *Perf. 12***
**987** A460 115p multicolored 1.25 .25

Adpostal, 25th Anniv. — A461

**1989, May 3**
**988** A461 45p multicolored .40 .25

Military Leaders — A462

*Bolivar and Santander at the Los Llanos Campaign* A463

**1989 Litho. *Perf. 12***
**989** A462 40p Santander .60 .25
**990** A462 40p Bolivar .60 .25
**991** A463 45p multicolored .60 .25
*Nos. 989-991 (3)* 1.80 .75

Liberation campaign, 170th anniv.
Issued: No. 989, 8/25; No. 990, 7/25; 45p, 8/7.

From Boyaca to Santa Fe A464

**1989, Aug. 7 Litho. *Perf. 12***
**992** 45p multicolored 1.50 .45
**993** 45p multicolored 1.50 .45
*a.* A464 Pair, #992-993 4.00 2.00

Liberation campaign, 170th anniv.

Liberation Campaign Triptych — A466

Designs: a, Gen. Santander, liberation force. b, Simon Bolivar riding mount. c, Insurgent cavalry.

**Unwmk.**

**1989, Aug. 7 Litho. *Perf. 13***
**994** A466 Strip of 3 4.50 1.75
*a.-c.* 45p any single 1.25 .55

Liberation Campaign, 170th anniv.

Tunja, 450th Anniv. — A467

**1989, Aug. 8 *Perf. 12***
**995** A467 45p multicolored .40 .25

**Fauna Type of 1988**

Designs: No. 996, Harpia harpyja, horiz. No. 997, Urocyon cinereoargenteus. No. 998, Dendrobates histrionicus. No. 999, Phenacosaurus indenenae. No. 1000, Cebuella pygmaea. No. 1001, Eurypyga helias, horiz.

***Perf. 14½x14, 14x14½***
**1989-90 Engr. Wmk. 334**
**996** A446a 45p black 1.00 .25
**997** A446a 50p blue gray .60 .25
**998** A446a 50p deep claret .40 .25
**999** A446a 55p red brown .85 .25
**1000** A446a 60p brown .60 .25
**1001** A446a 60p org brown .60 .25
*Nos. 996-1001 (6)* 4.05 1.50

Issued: 45p, 9/7; Nos. 997, 1000, 3/1/90; No. 998, 4/25; 55p, 8/18; No. 1001, 8/6.

City of Armenia, Cent. — A468

**1989, Aug. 30 Unwmk. *Perf. 12***
**1011** A468 135p multicolored 1.25 .80

Espeletia Hartwegiana — A469

**1990, Mar. 28 Litho. *Perf. 12***
**1012** A469 60p multicolored .35 .25

Gen. Francisco De Paula Santander (1792-1840) A470

**1990, May 6 *Perf. 14x13½***
**1013** A470 50p multicolored .35 .25
*Nos. 1013,C823-C827 (6)* 3.30 2.75

See Nos. 1046-1047.

General Santander Police Academy, 50th Anniv. — A471

**1990, May 16 *Perf. 12***
**1014** A471 60p multicolored .40 .25

Department of La Guajira — A473

**1990, July 1 *Perf. 12***
**1016** A473 60p multicolored .60 .25

Ceiba Pentandra A474

**1990, July 15 Litho. *Perf. 12***
**1017** A474 60p multicolored .50 .25

Tibouchina lepidota — A475

**1990, Aug. 8 Litho. *Perf. 12***
**1018** A475 70p multicolored .90 .25

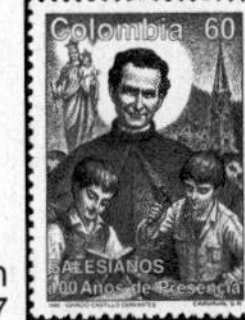


Ceroxylon quindiuense — A476

**Unwmk.**

**1990, Aug. 28 Litho. *Perf. 14***
**1019** A476 70p multicolored .50 .25

St. John Bosco — A477

**1990, Sept. 28 *Perf. 12***
**1020** A477 60p multicolored .60 .25

Salesian Order in Colombia, cent.

A478

**1991, Mar. 28 Litho. *Perf. 12***
**1021** A478 70p multicolored .40 .25

Miraculous Christ, Pilgrimage Church of Buga.

Moths and Butterflies A479

No. 1022, Callithea philotima. No. 1023, Anaea syene, vert. No. 1024, Thecla coronata, vert. No. 1025, Agrias amydon. No. 1026, Morpho rhetenor. No. 1027, Heliconius longarenus.

**1991, Apr. 18 Litho. *Perf. 14***
**1022** A479 70p multicolored .90 .25
**1023** A479 70p multicolored .90 .25
**1024** A479 80p multicolored 1.10 .25
**1025** A479 80p multicolored 1.20 .25
**1026** A479 170p multicolored 2.50 .35
**1027** A479 190p multicolored 2.50 .35
*Nos. 1022-1027 (6)* 9.10 1.70

Nos. 1025-1027 are airmail.

New Constitution A480

**1991, July 4 Litho. *Perf. 14***
**1028** A480 70p multicolored .40 .25

A481

**1991, July 19 *Perf. 12***
**1029** A481 80p multicolored .40 .30

Pres. Dario Echandia Olaya (1897-1989). See No. 1042.

A482

**1991, Aug. 7**
**1030** A482 70p multicolored .35 .25

Col. Antanasio Girardot (1791-1813).

A483

**1991, Aug. 15 Litho. *Perf. 14***
**1031** A483 80p multicolored .50 .25

Luis Carlos Galan Sarmiento (1943-1989), political reformer.

A484

Pre-Columbian Artifacts: 80p, Statue of cat god. No. 1033, Pitcher from tomb of high official. No. 1034, Statue with two heads. 210p, Flying fish, horiz.

**1991, Aug. 24 *Perf. 12***
**1032** A484 80p multicolored .75 .25
**1033** A484 90p multicolored .90 .25
**1034** A484 90p multicolored .90 .25
**1035** A484 210p multicolored 2.00 .30
*Nos. 1032-1035 (4)* 4.55 1.05

Nos. 1034-1035 are airmail.

Colonial Architecture A485

80p, Cloister of St. Augustine, Tunja. No. 1037, Community Bridge, Chia. No. 1038, Roadside Chapel, Pamplona. 190p, Church of Immaculate Conception, Bogota.

**1991 Litho. *Perf. 12***
**1036** A485 80p multi .75 .25
**1037** A485 90p multi 1.25 .25
**1038** A485 90p multi, vert. 1.00 .30
**1039** A485 190p multi, vert. 2.00 .35
*Nos. 1036-1039 (4)* 5.00 1.15

Issue dates: No. 1037, Sept. 9; others, Sept. 27. Nos. 1038-1039 are airmail.

Istiaphorus Americanus A486

**1991, Sept. 3 *Perf. 14***
**1040** A486 830p multicolored 5.75 1.50

Colombian Police Force, Cent. — A487

**1991, Oct. 12** *Perf. 12*
**1041** A487 80p multicolored .60 .25

**President Type of 1991**

Pres. Alberto Lleras Camargo (1906-1990)

**1991, Nov. 5**
**1042** A481 80p multicolored .45 .25

Sogamoso City Hall — A489

**1991, Dec. 17** **Litho.** *Perf. 12*
**1043** A489 80p multicolored .50 .25

A490

Designs: No. 1044, Diana Turbay Quintero (1950-91), journalist. No. 1045, Indalecio Lievano Aguirre (1917-82), diplomat.

**1992** **Litho.** *Perf. 14*
**1044** A490 80p multicolored .45 .25
**1045** A490 80p multicolored .45 .25

Issued: No. 1044, Jan. 24; No. 1045, Apr. 21.

**Santander Type of 1990 and**

Battle of Boyaca A491a

**1992, Apr. 2** *Perf. 14*
**Size: 26x37mm**
**1046** A470 80p Monument .50 .30
**1047** A470 190p Portrait 1.20 .70

**Souvenir Sheet**
*Perf. 13½x14*
**1047A** A491a 950p multicolored 5.25 5.25

Nos. 1047-1047A are airmail. Gen. Francisco de Paula Santander, bicent. of birth.

A492

Ministers of Justice: 100p, Enrique Low Murtra (1939-91). 110p, Rodrigo Lara Bonilla (1946-84).

**1992, Apr. 30** **Litho.** *Perf. 12*
**1048** A492 100p multicolored .60 .30
**1049** A492 110p multicolored .70 .30

A493

**1992, May 18** *Perf. 14*
**1050** A493 110p multicolored .50 .40

15th natl. games, Barranquilla.

Wildlife — A494

No. 1051, Oroaetus icidori. No. 1052, Tremarctos ornatus.

**1992, Apr. 14** **Litho.** *Perf. 12*
**1051** A494 (B) multicolored 1.60 .80
**1052** A494 (A) multicolored 8.50 3.50

Nos. 1051-1052 had face values of 200p and 950p respectively on date of issue.

Endangered Species — A495

No. 1053, Crocodylus acutus. No. 1054, Vultur gryphus, vert.

**1992, Aug. 4**
**1053** A495 100p multicolored 1.25 .40
**1054** A495 100p multicolored 1.25 .40

On No. 1053 acutus is misspelled.

A496

**1992, Aug. 24** **Litho.** *Perf. 14*
**1055** A496 100p multicolored .60 .30
**1056** A496 110p multicolored .60 .30

Maria Lopez de Escobar, founder of the House of the Mother and Child. No. 1056 is airmail.

A497

**1992, Sept. 23** **Litho.** *Perf. 12*
**1057** A497 100p multicolored .50 .30

Conference of First Ladies of the Americas and Caribbean, Cartagena.

Recycling — A498

**1992, Oct. 9** **Litho.** *Perf. 12*
**1058** A498 100p multicolored .50 .30

Discovery of America, 500th Anniv. — A499

Paintings: 100p, Zenaida, by Ana Mercedes Hoyos. No. 1060, Estudio Para 1/500, by Beatriz Gonzalez. No. 1061, Blue Eagle, by Alejandro Obregon. 230p, Cantileo, by Luis Luna. 260p, Corn, by Antonio Caro. 400p, Grand Curtain, by Luis Caballero. 440p, Homage to Guatavita, by Alejandro Obregon.

**1992, Oct. 5** **Litho.** *Perf. 13½x14*
**1059** A499 100p multicolored .50 .30
**1060** A499 110p multicolored .50 .30
**1061** A499 110p multicolored .50 .30
**1062** A499 230p multicolored 1.25 .70
**1063** A499 260p multicolored 1.50 .80
*Nos. 1059-1063 (5)* 4.25 2.40

**Souvenir Sheets**
*Perf. 12*
**1064** A499 400p multicolored 3.50 3.50
**1065** A499 440p multicolored 3.50 3.50

Nos. 1061-1063 are airmail.

World Post Day — A500

**1992, Oct. 19** **Litho.** *Perf. 12*
**1066** A500 (B) multicolored 1.20 .65

No. 1066 had face value of 200p on day of issue.

Christmas A501

Children's paintings of: 100p, Nativity scene. 110p, Adoration of the Magi.

**1992, Nov. 20** **Litho.** *Perf. 12*
**1067** A501 100p multicolored .60 .30
**1068** A501 110p multicolored .60 .30

No. 1068 is airmail.

Three Musicians, by Fernando Botero — A502

**1993, Feb. 5** **Litho.** *Perf. 12*
**1069** A502 (B) multicolored 1.25 .80

No. 1069 had a face value of 250p on day of issue.

Lions Intl. Campaign Against Amblyopia A503

**1993, Mar. 26** *Perf. 14*
**1070** A503 100p multicolored .40 .30

Holy Week in Popayan — A504

**1993, Apr. 5** *Perf. 14x13½*
**1071** A504 (B) multicolored 1.25 .80

No. 1071 had a face value of 250p on day of issue.

A505

**1993, Apr. 7** *Perf. 12*
**1072** A505 (B) multicolored 1.25 .80

Pan American Health Org., 90th anniv.
No. 1072 had a face value of 250p on day of issue.

A506

**1993, Apr. 14**
**1073** A506 (B) multicolored 1.25 .80

Franciscans of Mary Immaculate, cent. No. 1073 had a face value of 250p on day of issue.

A507

**1993, Apr. 22** **Litho.** *Perf. 14*
**1074** A507 (B) multicolored .90 .80

EXFILBO '93, 18th Natl. Philatelic Exhibition. No. 1074 had a face value of 250p on day of issue.

Guillermo Cano, writer — A508

**1993, July 2** **Litho.** *Perf. 12*
**1075** A508 250p multicolored 1.25 .75

Human Rights — A509

Rights: a, 150p, Of prisoners. b, 150p, Of the elderly. c, 200p, Of the infirm. d, 200p, Of children. e, 220p, Of women. f, 220p, Of the poor. g, 460p, To clean environment. h, 520p, Of indigenous people.
Painting: 800p, Peace, Rights, and Freedom, by Alfredo Vivero, vert.

**1993, June 10** *Perf. 14*
**1076** A509 Block of 8, #a.-h. 12.00 7.50

**Souvenir Sheet**
**1077** A509 800p multicolored 5.50 5.50

Nos. 1076e-1076h are airmail.

Amazon Region of Colombia — A510

No. 1078a, Parrot. No. 1078b, Anaconda. No. 1079a, Victoria regia. No. 1079b, Flor ipecacuana. 880p, Map, native, horiz.

**1993 Litho. *Perf. 12***
**1078** A510 150p Pair, #a.-b. 1.50 1.25
**1079** A510 220p Pair, #a.-b. 2.00 1.50

**Souvenir Sheet**

**1080** A510 880p multicolored 5.00 5.00

Nos. 1079-1080 are airmail.

Famous People A511

Designs: a, 150p, Alberto Pumarejo (1893-1970). b, 150p, Lorencita Villegas de Santos (1892-1960). c, 200p, Meliton Rodriguez (1875-1942). d, 200p, Tomas Carrasquilla (1858-1940).

**1993 Litho. *Perf. 14x13½***
**1081** A511 Block of 4, #a.-d. 4.00 2.75

Christmas — A512

**1993, Nov. 30 *Perf. 12***
**1082** A512 200p Holy Family .95 .60
**1083** A512 220p Shepherd 1.60 1.10

No. 1083 is airmail.

Tourism — A513

Designs: No. 1084a, San Andres Providence. b, Cocuy Natl. Park. c, Lake Cocha. d, Waterfalls, Serrania de la Macarena. 250p, Lake Otun. No. 1086a, Chicamocha River. b, Sierra Nevada de Santa Marta mountains. 520p, Penol Reservoir.

**1993, Dec. 1 Litho. *Perf. 12***
**1084** A513 220p Block of 4, #a.-d. 4.50 3.00
**1085** A513 250p multicolored 1.25 .75
**1086** A513 460p Pair, #a.-b. 4.75 3.00
**1087** A513 520p multicolored 2.75 1.50
*Nos. 1084-1087 (4)* 13.25 8.25

Nos. 1084, 1086-87 are airmail.

A514

**1993, Dec. 21 Litho. *Perf. 14***
**1088** A514 150p multicolored .75 .40

Natl. Museum, 170th anniv.

Marie Poussepin — A515

**1994, Jan. 25 Litho. *Perf. 14***
**1089** A515 300p multicolored 1.40 .80

A516

Birds: 180p, Ognorhynchus icterotis. 240p, Rallus semiplumbeus. 270p, Semnornis ramphastinus. 560p, Anas cyanoptera.

**1994, Mar. 4**
**1090** A516 180p multi 1.40 .40
**1091** A516 240p multi 1.60 .55
**1092** A516 270p multi, horiz. 2.00 .70
**1093** A516 560p multi, horiz. 4.00 1.40
*Nos. 1090-1093 (4)* 9.00 3.05

Nos. 1092-1093 are airmail.

A517

**1994, Apr. 11 Litho. *Perf. 14***
**1094** A517 300p multicolored 1.40 .80

Air Force, 75th anniv.

Latin American Presidential Summit, Cartagena — A518

**1994, June 14 Litho. *Perf. 14***
**1095** A518 300p shown 1.00 .65
**1096** A518 630p Flags 2.10 1.60

No. 1096 is airmail.

1994 World Cup Soccer Championships, US — A519

World Cup Trophy and: 180p, Soccer player, Colombian flag. 270p, Two players with ball. 560p, Soccer ball, Colombian flag, vert.

1110p, Soccer player offering hand to another.

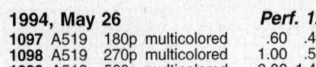

**1994, May 26 *Perf. 12***
**1097** A519 180p multicolored .60 .40
**1098** A519 270p multicolored 1.00 .55
**1099** A519 560p multicolored 2.00 1.40
*Nos. 1097-1099 (3)* 3.60 2.35

**Souvenir Sheet**

**1100** A519 1110p multicolored 5.50 5.50

Nos. 1098-1099 are airmail.

Ricardo Rendon (1894-1931), Artist — A520

**1994, June 30 Litho. *Perf. 12***
**1101** A520 240p black 1.25 .65

1993 Census — A521

**1994, Aug. 12 *Perf. 14***
**1102** A521 240p multicolored 1.00 .40

Ministry of Communications Inravision, 30th Anniv. — A522

**1994, Aug. 3**
**1103** A522 180p multicolored .80 .40

Intl. Year of the Family — A523

**1994, Sept. 1 Litho. *Perf. 14***
**1104** A523 300p multicolored 1.25 .65

America Issue — A524

Methods of mail delivery: 270p, Horse, bicycle. 300p, Men holding stamps showing truck, ship, plane.

**1994, Oct. 18 Litho. *Perf. 13***
**1105** A524 270p multicolored 1.60 .65
**1106** A524 300p multicolored 2.40 .70

No. 1105 is airmail.

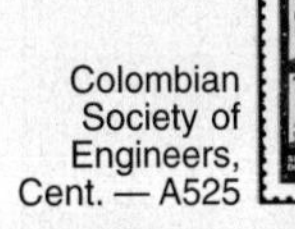


Colombian Society of Engineers, Cent. — A525

**1994, Oct. 20 Litho. *Perf. 12***
**1107** A525 180p multicolored .75 .40

Christmas — A526

**1994, Nov. 22 Litho. *Perf. 13½x13***
**1108** A526 270p Magi .95 .65
**1109** A526 300p Holy family 1.10 .70

No. 1108 is airmail.

**Former President Type of 1981**

Miniature Sheet of 20

Designs: a, Jose Miguel Pey. b, Jorge Tadeo Lozano. c, Antonio Narino. d, Camilo Torres. e, Jose Fernandez Madrid. f, Jose Maria del Castillo y Rada. g, Custodio Garcia Rovira. h, Antonio Villavicencio. i, Liborio Mejia. j, Rafael Urdaneta. k, Juan Garcia del Rio. l, Jose Maria Melo. m, Tomas Herrera. n, Froilan Largacha. o, Salvador Camacho Roldan. p, Ezequiel Hurtado. q, Dario Echandia Olaya. r, Alberto Lleras Camargo. s, Gustavo Rojas Pinilla. t, Carlos Lleras Restrepo.

**1995, Apr. 4 Litho. *Perf. 12***
**1110** A401 270p #a.-t. 35.00 35.00

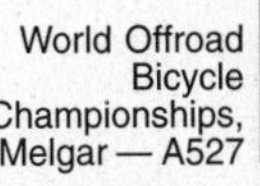

World Offroad Bicycle Championships, Melgar — A527

**1995, Mar. 30 *Perf. 14***
**1111** A527 400p multicolored 1.50 .90

A528

**1995, Oct. 12 Litho. *Perf. 12***
**1112** A528 220p multicolored 1.00 .45

Gen. Jose Maria Obando (1795-1861), President.

A529

**1995, Nov. 28 *Perf. 14***
**1113** A529 400p Clean air 1.50 .75
**1114** A529 400p Clean water 1.50 .75

Preserve the environment. America issue.

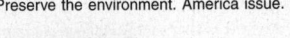

Christmas A530

Stained glass windows: 220p, Flight into Egypt. 330p, Nativity.

**1995, Dec. 18 *Perf. 12***
**1115** A530 220p multicolored .75 .40
**1116** A530 330p multicolored 1.10 .65

No. 1116 is airmail.

Bogotá to Boyacá World Cycling Championship A531

**1995, Oct. 4 Litho. *Perf. 12***
**1117** A531 400p multicolored 1.75 .75

León De Greiff (1895-1976), Poet — A532

**1996, May 2** **Litho.** ***Perf. 12***
**1118** A532 400p black 1.40 .60

Mosquera Courtyard, Natl. Capitol — A533

**1996, July 18** **Litho.** ***Perf. 14***
**1119** A533 400p multicolored 1.25 .60

Medellin Rapid Transit System — A534

**1996, July 2** ***Perf. 12***
**1120** A534 500p multicolored 2.00 .90

A535

**1996, June 20**
**1121** A535 500p multicolored 1.50 .75

Community of St. John of God in Colombia, 400th anniv.

A536

Arms: a, Santa Maria la Antigua del Darien. b, San Sebastian de Mariquita. c, Villa de la Marinilla. d, Villa of Santa Cruz of Mompox.

**1996, June 25**
**1122** A536 400p Block of 4, #a.-d. 4.75 4.75
*e.* As "d," inscribed AEREO 15.00 15.00
*f.* Block of 4, #1122a-1122c, 1122e 20.00 20.00

Issued in sheets of 16 stamps.

1996 Summer Olympic Games, Atlanta A537

**1996, July 16**
**1123** A537 500p multicolored 1.60 .75

SAYCO (Colombian Authors and Composers Society), 50th Anniv. — A538

**1996, Aug. 17** **Litho.** ***Perf. 12***
**1124** A538 400p multicolored 1.40 .60

Exfilbo '96, 20th Natl. Philatelic Exhibition — A539

Jewelry from Gold Museum, Bogotá.

**1996, Oct. 19** **Litho.** ***Perf. 12***
**1125** A539 400p multicolored 1.40 .60

Souvenir Sheet

Founders Theater, Manizales, 30th Anniv. — A540

Drop curtain: a, Eagle, people watching man drawing on ground, vert. b, People, animals on hillside.

**1996, Oct. 28** ***Perf. 14***
**1126** A540 4000p #a.-b. 25.00 25.00

Christmas A541

No. 1127, Mailman handing woman letter. No. 1128, Woman reading letter, mailman holding bundle of mail.

**1996, Nov. 22**
**1127** A541 400p multicolored 1.75 .40
**1128** A541 400p multicolored 1.75 .40

No. 1128 is airmail.

America Issue — A542

No. 1129, Men's costume. No. 1130, Women's costume.

**1996, Nov. 29** ***Perf. 12***
**1129** A542 500p multicolored 1.50 .60
**1130** A542 500p multicolored 1.50 .60

Historical Landmarks — A543

a, Cemetery, Santa Cruz of Mompox. b, Carved face, San Agustin Archaelogical Park. c, Entrance, Palace of the Inquisition, Cartagena de Indias. d, Inside ruins, Tierradentro Archaelogical Park.

**1996, Dec. 6** ***Perf. 14***
**1131** A543 400p Block of 4, #a.-d. 10.00 10.00

Alvaro Gomez Hurtado (1919-95), Politician, Writer — A544

**1997, Mar. 18** **Litho.** ***Perf. 12***
**1132** A544 400p multicolored 1.50 .75

Bogotá Journalists Assoc., 50th Anniv. — A545

**1997, July 10** **Litho.** ***Perf. 12***
**1133** A545 400p multicolored 1.00 .40

Natl. Festival of Porro A546

**1997, June 26** ***Perf. 13½x14***
**1134** A546 400p multicolored 1.00 .40

Pres. Virgilio Barco (1921-97) — A547

**1997, Nov. 27** **Litho.** ***Perf. 14***
**1135** A547 500p multicolored 1.15 .40

Colombia in Peace — A548

500p, Children playing. 1100p, Children dancing.

**1997, Dec. 30** **Litho.** ***Perf. 12***
**1136** A548 500p multicolored 1.25 .40
**1137** A548 1100p multicolored 2.50 .90

No. 1137 is airmail.

America Issue — A549

500p, Postman by day. 1100p, Postman by night.

**1997, Dec. 30**
**1138** A549 500p multicolored 1.75 .50
**1139** A549 1100p multicolored 3.75 1.25

No. 1139 is airmail.

Jorge Eliecer Gaitan (1903-48), Politician — A550

**1998, Apr. 24** **Litho.** ***Perf. 14***
**1140** A550 500p multicolored 1.75 .80

Free University, 75th Anniv. — A551

**1998, July 1** **Litho.** ***Perf. 14***
**1141** A551 500p black & red 2.50 .75

Santander Industrial University, 50th Anniv. — A552

**1998, May 14** ***Perf. 12***
**1142** A552 500p multicolored 1.75 .80

City of Manizales, 150th Anniv. A553

**1998, July 24** **Litho.** ***Perf. 12***
**1143** A553 500p multicolored 2.50 .75

A554

Pre-Columbian art, agency: a, Tairona, Bank of the Republic. b, Malagana, Controller General. c, Quimbaya, Bank Superintendent.

**1998, July 24**
**1144** A554 500p Strip of 3, #a.-c. 7.25 7.25

Natl. financial agencies, 70th anniv.

A555

**1998, Aug. 21** ***Perf. 14***
**1145** A555 500p multicolored 2.50 .80

Pres. Misael Pastrana Borrero (1923-97).

University of the Andes, 50th Anniv. — A556

**1998, Sept. 28**
**1146** A556 500p multicolored 2.10 .80

Christmas — A557

Designs: 500p, Woman kneeling down to get water with bowl, cherubs in sky. No. 1148a, Magi. No. 1148b, Nativity scene.

**1998, Nov. 19 Litho. *Perf. 14***
**1147** A557 500p multicolored 1.25 .75
**1148** A557 1000p Pair, #a.-b. 4.75 3.25

No. 1148 is airmail.

A558

Emblems of Colombian Academies: a, Language. b, Medicine. c, Law. d, History. e, Science. f, Ecomonics. g, Religion.

**1998, Dec. 15 *Perf. 12***
**Sheet of 7 + Label**
**1149** A558 500p #a.-g. 15.00 13.50

A559

**1999, Apr. 16 *Perf. 14***
**1150** A559 1000p multicolored 2.10 1.00

Gen. José Hilario López.

Famous Women — A559a

America Issue: 600p, Soledad Román de Nuñez. 1200p, Bertha Herández de Ospina.

**1999, Mar. 25 Litho. *Perf. 12***
**1151** A559a 600p multicolored 1.50 1.50
**1152** A559a 1200p multicolored 2.75 2.75

No. 1152 is airmail.

Turtles — A560

a, Chelonia mydas. b, Dermochelys coriacea. c, Eretmochelys imbricata.

**1999, Apr. 16 *Perf. 14***
**1153** A560 1300p Strip of 3, #a.-c. 12.50 12.50

Dr. Eduardo Zuleta Angel, Diplomat (b. 1899) — A561

**1999, Sept. 9 Litho. *Perf. 12***
**1154** A561 600p multicolored 1.35 1.35

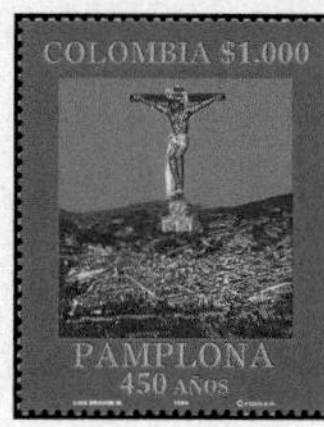
Pamplona, 450th Anniv. — A562

**1999 Litho. *Perf. 12***
**1155** A562 1000p multicolored 2.50 2.50

Sovereign Military Order of Malta, 900th Anniv. — A563

**1999, June 24 *Perf. 14***
**1156** A563 1200p multicolored 4.75 4.00

Japanese Immigration to Colombia A564

Designs: a, Red at right. b, Red at left.

**1999, May 12 *Perf. 13½x14***
**1157** A564 1300p Pair, #a.-b. 5.50 5.50

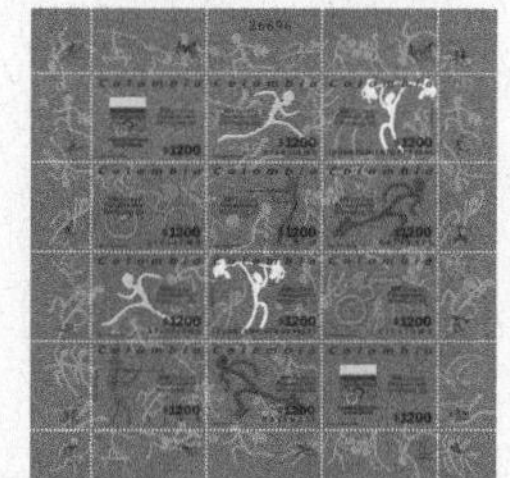
Pan American Games, Winnipeg, Manitoba — A565

Designs: a, Flag, Olympic rings. b, Runner facing right. c, Weight lifter facing left. d, Cyclist facing right. e, Shooter facing left. f, Roller skater facing right. g, Runner facing left. h, Weight lifter facing right. i, Cyclist facing left. j, Shooter facing right. k, Roller skater facing left. l, Like "a," with lilac vertical line under "12."

**1999, July 23 Litho. *Perf. 14***
**1158** A565 1200p Sheet of 12, #a.-l. 30.00 30.00

Luis A. Robles (b. 1849) — A566

**1999, Oct. 27**
**1159** A566 600p multi 1.10 1.10

Manufacture of Aspirin, Cent. — A567

**1999, Dec. 1 *Perf. 12¾***
**1160** A567 600p multi 1.10 1.10

Value is for stamp with surrounding selvage.

UPU, 125th Anniv. — A568

**1999, Oct. 29 *Perf. 14¼***
**1161** A568 1000p "125" 1.75 1.75
**1162** A568 1300p "1874-1999" 2.75 2.75

Inter-American Development Bank, 40th Anniv. — A569

Abstract art: a, "Colombia" in yellow. b, "Colombia" in red.

**1999, Nov. 19 *Perf. 14x14¼***
**1163** A569 1000p Pair, #a.-b. 3.50 3.50

America Issue, A New Millennium Without Arms — A570

a, Stylized hands. b, Large flower at LR.

**1999, Nov. 9 *Perf. 14***
**1164** A570 1200p Pair, #a.-b. 4.50 4.50

Christmas — A571

a, Holy Family, animals. b, Angel, Magi.

**1999, Nov. 29 *Perf. 13½x14***
**1165** A571 600p Pair, #a.-b. 2.40 2.40

Millennium — A572

Designs: a, Nude man, flag, dove. b, Globe, rainbow, "2000."

**2000, Jan. 3 *Perf. 14***
**1166** A572 1000p Pair, #a.-b. 4.00 4.00

University of Medellin, 50th Anniv. — A573

**2000, Feb. 1 Litho. *Perf. 14***
**1167** A573 1000p multi 2.00 2.00

Father José Rafael Faría Bermúdez (1896-1979) — A574

**2000, Mar. 6 Litho. *Perf. 14***
**1168** A574 1300p multi 2.60 2.60

2000 Summer Olympics, Sydney — A575

**2000, Apr. 21**
**1169** A575 1000p multi 2.00 2.00

Popayán Religious Music Festival — A576

**2000, July 7**
**1170** A576 1000p multi 2.25 2.25

America Issue, Campaign Against AIDS — A577

**2000, Sept. 19 Litho. *Perf. 14x13½***
**1171** A577 1000p multi 4.00 4.00

Radio Station HJCK, 50th Anniv. — A578

**2000, Sept. 28 Litho. *Perf. 14***
**1172** A578 1000p multi 2.00 2.00

Birth Registration — A579

**2000, Nov. 14 Litho. *Perf. 14¼***
**1173** A579 1000p multi 2.00 2.00

Paintings — A580

No. 1174: a, Archangel, by Fernando Botero. b, Gypsy Woman With Tamourine, by Jean-Baptiste-Camille Corot. c, Vera Sergine Renoir, by Renoir. d, Man on Horse, by Botero. e, Mother Superior, by Botero. f, A Town, by Botero. g, Flowers, by Botero. h, Cézanne, by Botero. i, Patio, by Botero. j, Absinthe Drinker in Grenelle, by Toulouse-Lautrec. k, A Little Valley, by Corot. l, The Studio, by Botero.

**2001, Jan. 31 *Perf. 12***
**1174** Sheet of 12 32.50 32.50
*a.-l.* A580 650p Any single 2.00 2.00

Children's Day — A581

**2001, Mar. 15 Litho. *Perf. 14***
**1175** A581 1100p multi 3.75 3.50

Abolition of Slavery, 150th Anniv. — A582

**2001, May 21 Litho. *Perf. 14¼x14***
**1176** A582 1100p multi 4.00 3.50

Discovery of Magdalena River, 500th Anniv. — A583

**2001, June 13 Litho. *Perf. 14***
**1177** A583 1100p multi 4.00 3.50

Copa America Soccer Tournament A584

**2001, July 18 Litho. *Perf. 12¾***
**1178** A584 1900p multi 5.25 5.00

Values are for examples with surrounding selvage.

America Issue — Los Katios Natl. Park, UNESCO World Heritage Site — A585

**2001, Aug. 17 *Perf. 13¾x14***
**1179** A585 2100p multi 8.00 7.00

Year of Dialogue Among Civilizations — A586

**2001, Oct. 9 *Perf. 14***
**1180** A586 650p multi 2.75 2.25

Reclining Woman, by Fernando Botero — A587

**2001, Oct. 23 *Perf. 14¼***
**1181** A587 1100p multi 4.50 4.00

Christmas — A588

**2001, Nov. 19 *Perf. 14***
**1182** A588 1100p multi 4.50 4.00

National Beauty Pageant A589

Flag, Miss Colombia Vanesa A. Mendoza Bustos and: a, Cartagena de Indias. b, St. Francis of Assisi Cathedral, Quibdo.

**2002, Jan. 22 *Perf. 14x14¼***
**1183** A589 800p Horiz. pair, #a-b 3.75 2.75

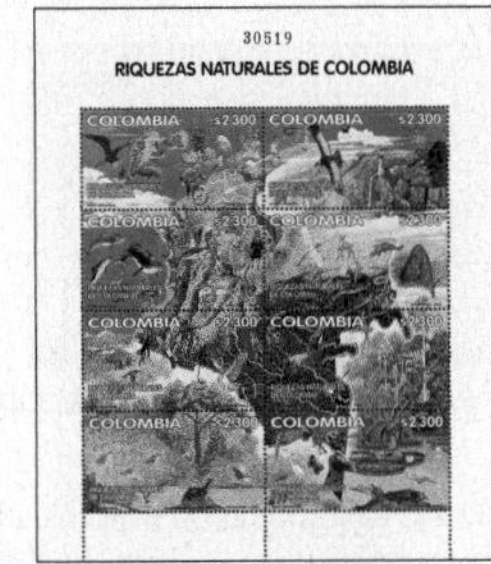

Natural Riches of Colombia — A590

Parts of map of Colombia, various wildlife and/or natives and: a, Bird and clouds at left. b, Turtle at upper left. c, Fish and whales at left. d, Man on horse at center. e, Volcano at upper left. f, Red and blue parrots at right. g, Flamingos at left. h, Snake at upper left.

**2002, Feb. 1 *Perf. 14¼x14***
**1184** A590 2300p Sheet of 8, #a-h 50.00 45.00

Children's Day — A591

**2002, Feb. 18 *Perf. 12***
**1185** A591 1400p multi 2.75 2.75

New Emblem of Adpostal — A592

**2002, Mar. 7 *Perf. 14***
**1186** A592 800p multi 1.75 1.75

7th South American Games — A593

**2002, Jan. 7**
**1187** A593 2100p multi 4.00 4.00

Oxyura Jamaicensis A594

**2002, Apr. 30 Litho. *Perf. 12***
**1188** A594 3900p multi 7.25 7.25

Souvenir Sheet

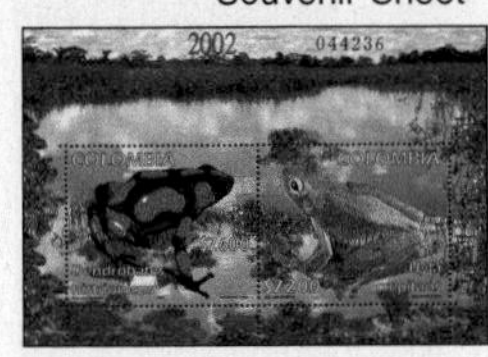

Frogs A595

No. 1189: a, 7200p, Hyla crepitans. b, 7600p, Dendrobates histrionicus.

**2002, Apr. 30 *Perf. 13¾x14***
**1189** A595 Sheet of 2, #a-b 27.50 27.50

Souvenir Sheet

Butterflies — A596

No. 1190: a, Dryas iulia. b, Dryadula phaetusa, vert.

**2002, Apr. 30 *Perf. 12***
**1190** A596 13,700p Sheet of 2, #a-b *50.00 50.00*

Foundation for Reconstructive Surgery, 25th Anniv. — A597

**2002, May 24 *Perf. 14***
**1191** A597 1000p multi 2.00 2.00

Pre-Columbian Art — A598

No. 1192, 800p: a, Nariño pectoral. b, Nariño disc.
No. 1193, 1400p: a, Calima diadem. b, Calima pectoral.
No. 1194, 2100p: a, Anthropomorphic Tairona pectoral. b, Round Tairona pectoral.

**2002, June 7 *Perf. 13½x14***
**Horiz. Pairs, #a-b**
**1192-1194** A598 Set of 3 *40.00 40.00*

Surgical Society of Bogota San José Hospital, Cent. A599

No. 1195: a, Early doctors and nurse. b, Hospital.

**2002, July 22 *Perf. 14***
**1195** A599 800p Horiz. pair, #a-b 3.00 3.00

Consuelo Araújo Noguera (1940-2001), Assassinated Former Minister of Culture — A600

**2002, Aug. 1**
**1196** A600 1400p multi 2.75 2.75

Union Network International — A601

**2002, Aug. 12**
**1197** A601 1000p multi 1.90 1.90

America Issue — Youth, Education and Literacy — A602

No. 1198: a, Person reading book. b, Letters amd words.

**2002, Oct. 9**
**1198** A602 2500p Horiz. pair, #a-b 7.25 7.25

Christmas A603

**2002, Nov. 6 Litho. *Perf. 14x13¾***
**1199** A603 800p multi 2.75 2.00

Colombian History Academy, Cent. — A604

No. 1200: a, Mural scene with Simon Bolivar at UR. b, Mural scene with horsemen at top. c, Mural scene with man with outstretched arms at UL. d, Cafetal, 1956. e, Batalla de Palonegro, 1905. f, Tigre Cazando Sabanera, 1963. g, El Barqueo, 1936. h, Colombia Asesinada, 1902. i, Dos Mujeres, 1951. j, Bearded man at left, Plaza de Santander. k, Carriage, Plaza de Santander. l, Horse, man and woman, Plaza de Santander.

**2002, Nov. 19 *Perf. 13¾x14***
**1200** A604 800p Sheet of 12, #a-l *45.00 45.00*

Peace Treaty Ending War of 1,000 Days, Cent. — A605

**2002, Nov. 21 *Perf. 14x13¾***
**1201** A605 1600p multi 4.50 4.50

Carnival — A606

No. 1202: a, shown. b, Participants holding masks on sticks. c, Participants on float.

**2003, Jan. 4** *Perf. 14*

| | | | |
|---|---|---|---|
| **1202** | Horiz. strip of 3 | 6.50 | 6.50 |
| *a.-b.* | A606 1000p Either single | 1.25 | 1.25 |
| *c.* | A606 1200p multi | 1.60 | 1.60 |

Printed in sheets of 3 horizontal strips and 2 horiz. strips of 3 labels.

Articulated Bus, Bogota — A607

**2003, Mar. 13** *Perf. 12*

**1203** A607 1000p multi 2.00 2.00

Departments — A608

No. 1204 — Caldas Department: a, 1200p, Arms. b, 1200p, Government office building, Manizales, horiz. c, 1200p, Campesinos, 1957. d, 2400p, Church, Salamina. e, 2400p, Neira, 1997, horiz. f, 2400p, Enea Chapel, Manizales. g, 2800p, Laguna Verde, Villamaria. h, 2800p, Aguadas, horiz. i, 2800p, Devil's carnival, Riosucio. j, 4100p, Miner, Marmato. k, 4100p, Mariposas del Eje Cafetero, 2001, horiz. l, 4100p, Pacora.

No. 1205, 1000p — Huila Department: a, Arms. b, Government office building, Neiva, horiz. c, La Gaitana. d, Bordones Waterfall, Isnos. e, San Agustín World Heritage Archaeological Park, horiz. f, Lavapatas Spring, San Agustín. g, La Tatacoa Desert, Villavieja. h, Liberty tree, Gigante, horiz. i, Sombrero maker, Suaza. j, Nuestra Señora de los Dolores Church, Aipe. k, Paisaje, horiz. l, Dancers.

No. 1206 — 2400p: a, Historic center of Barichara. b, Ophthalmologic Foundation of Santander, Bucaramanga, horiz. c, Girón. d, Santander Industrial University Intl. Piano Festival, 20th anniv. emblem. e, Petroleum Christ Statue, refinery, Barrancabermeja, horiz. f, Church, San Andrés. g, Gustavo Cote Uribe (1918-94), writer. h, Chamber of Commerce, Bucaramanga, horiz. i, Carnival of Eastern Colombia, Bucaramanga. j, Historic center of Albania. k, Chicamocha River Canyon, Cepitá, horiz. l, Entreguerras.

**Sheets of 12, #a-l, + 8 labels**

**2003** *Perf. 12*

| | | | | |
|---|---|---|---|---|
| **1204** | A608 | Caldas | *45.00* | *45.00* |
| **1205** | A608 | Huila | *19.00* | *19.00* |
| **1206** | A608 | Santander | *40.00* | *40.00* |

Issued: No. 1204, Apr. 11. No. 1205, June 29. No. 1206, July 22. Size of horiz. stamps: 46x37mm.

See Nos. 1224-1226, 1246, 1265-1267, 1273, 1288-1289, 1316, 1335-1336, 1359, 1377, 1393, 1430, 1454, 1476, 1532-1533. 1552, 1607.

Fish and Coral of the Rosario Islands — A609

**2003, Jan. 16** **Litho.** *Perf. 12*

**1207** A609 1000p multi 3.50 3.00

Hapalopsittaca Fuertesi — A610

**2003, June 13**

**1208** A610 1000p multi 3.50 3.00

Souvenir Sheets

Orchids A611

No. 1209 — 2400p: a, Masdevallia ignea. b, Miltoniopsis vexillaria.

No. 1210 — 2800p: a, Odontoglossum crispum, horiz. b, Masdevallia macrura.

No. 1211, vert. — 5000p: a, Cimbidium. b, Oncidium obryzatum.

No. 1212 — 7000p: a, Cattleya dowiana. b, Cattleya trianaei (49x49mm).

**Sheets of 2, #a-b**

***Perf. 14¼, 13¾x14 (#1212b)***

**2003, June 13**

**1209-1212** A611 Set of 4 57.50 57.50

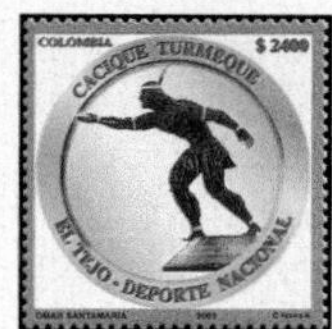

Tejo, National Sport — A612

No. 1213: a, Players, tree in foreground (49x39mm). b, Players, light poles (49x39mm). c, Cacique Turmeque.

**2003, July 25** *Perf. 12*

| | | | |
|---|---|---|---|
| **1213** | Horiz. strip of 3 | 11.00 | 11.00 |
| *a.-c.* | A612 2400p Any single | 2.25 | 2.25 |

America Issue A613

Flora and fauna: a, Denomination at UR. b, Denomination at LR.

**2003, Oct. 9** **Litho.** *Perf. 12*

**1214** A613 1600p Vert. pair, #a-b 6.25 6.25

Printed in sheets of four pairs and four labels.

Souvenir Sheet

Colombia Libraries National Reading Plan — A614

No. 1215: a, 1200p, Building. b, 4100p, Building, diff.

**2003, Oct. 30** **Litho.** *Perf. 12*

**1215** A614 Sheet of 2, #a-b 9.00 9.00

General Ramón Arturo Rincón Quiñones (1922-75) — A615

**2003, Oct. 31**

**1216** A615 1000p multi 1.90 1.90

Souvenir Sheet

Administrative Security Deparment, 50th Anniv. — A616

**2003, Oct. 31**

**1217** A616 4100p multi 6.50 6.50

Armed Forces — A617

No. 1218 — Arms and mottos: a, General Command of Military Forces. b, National Army. c, National Navy. d, Air Force. e, Colombian Forces in Korea, 50th anniv.

**2003, Nov. 7**

| | | | |
|---|---|---|---|
| **1218** | Vert. strip of 5 | 8.50 | 8.50 |
| *a.-e.* | A617 1200p Any single | 1.10 | .60 |

Christmas A618

No. 1219: a, Good Shepherd, sheep. b, Tree, comet, airplane, rabbit. c, Rabbits, dog. d, Automobile, angel, reindeer, horse. e, Sheep, woman with basket, swan, house. f, Branch with leaves, horse and rider, duck, Indian with bow and arrow.

**2003, Dec. 2** **Litho.** *Perf. 12*

| | | | |
|---|---|---|---|
| **1219** | Block of 6 | 12.00 | 12.00 |
| *a.-f.* | A618 1000p Any single | 1.40 | 1.40 |

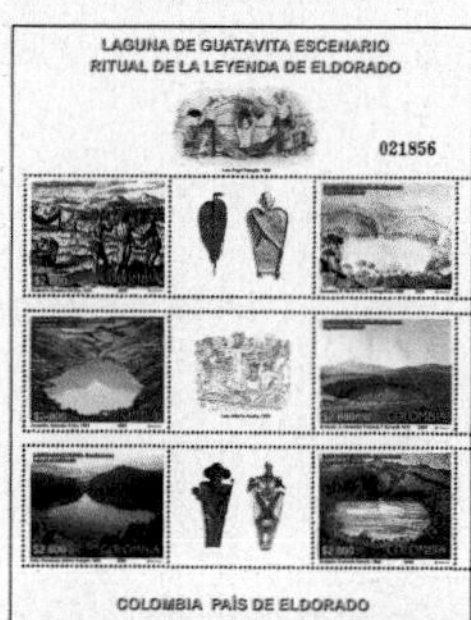

Colombia and the Eldorado Legend — A619

No. 1220: a, Print of Eldorado ceremony, by Teodoro De Bry, 1595. b, Watercolor painting of Lake Guatavita, by M. María Paz, 1855. c, Watercolor painting of Lake Guatavita, by Gonzalo Ariza, 1984. d, Print of Lake Guatavita, by A. Humboldt Thibault and F. Schoell, 1813. e, Photo of Lake Guatavita, by Fernando Urbina Rangel, 1983. f, Print of Lake Guatavita, by Eustacio Barreto, 1883.

No. 1221 — Muisca raft: a, 1700p, Front. b, 2000p, Back, vert.

**2004, Mar. 10**

**1220** A619 2800p Sheet of 6, #a-f, + 3 labels 32.00 32.00

**Souvenir Sheet**

**1221** A619 Sheet of 2, #a-b 7.00 7.00

Locomotives — A620

No. 1222, 1100p: a, 2-8-2. b, 4-8-0.
No. 1223, 1300p: a, 2-6-2. b, 4-6-2.

**2004, Mar. 19** **Horiz. Pairs, #a-b**

**1222-1223** A620 Set of 2 8.00 8.00

Nos. 1222-1223 each printed in sheets of four pairs and two pairs of labels.

**Departments Type of 2003**

No. 1224, 1100p — Nariño Department: a, Galeras Volcano, San Juan de Pasto, horiz. b, Statue of Gen. Antonio Nariño. c, Nariño Government Building, San Juan de Pasto, horiz. d, Farm, Catambuco, horiz. e, Nuestra Señora de las Lajas Sanctuary, Ipiales. f, Sandoná city center, horiz. g, Gallery of Mirrors, horiz. h, Barnizadores de Pasto Chorography Commission. i, Golden palms, horiz. j, El Morro, Tumaco, horiz. k, Virgen de la Playa Sanctuary, San Pablo. l, Festival of Whites and Blacks, horiz.

No. 1225, 2000p — Tolima Department: a, Nevado del Tolima, horiz. b, Tolima arms. c, Ambalema, horiz. d, Bowls, La Chamba, horiz. e, Natural Bridge, Icononzo. f, Hermitage, Mariquita, horiz. g, Matachos, horiz. h, Prison, Ibagué. i, Alberto Castilla Conservatory Room, horiz. j, Fishermen, Magdalena River, horiz. k, Cacique Calarcá. l, Tolima Art Museum, Ibagué.

No. 1226, 3000p — Chocó Department: a, Coat of Arms. b, Quibdó skyline, horiz. c, Indian girls. d, San Pacho Fiesta. e, Carrasquilla College, Quibdó, horiz. f, Houses, Nóvita. g, Canoe on San Juan River. h, Women grinding corn meal, horiz. i, Nuestra Senora del Rosario Church, Condoto. j, Utría Bay. k, Bellavista Church, Bojayá, horiz. l, Goldsmith, Acandi.

Horiz. stamps are 46x37mm.

**Sheets of 12, #a-l, +8 labels**

**2004** **Litho.** *Perf. 13¾x14*

| | | | | |
|---|---|---|---|---|
| **1224** | A608 | Nariño | 20.00 | 20.00 |
| **1225** | A608 | Tolima | 35.00 | 35.00 |
| **1226** | A608 | Chocó | 50.00 | 50.00 |
| | *Nos. 1224-1226 (3)* | | 105.00 | 105.00 |

Issued: No. 1224, 8/5; No. 1225, 4/16. No. 1226, 11/17

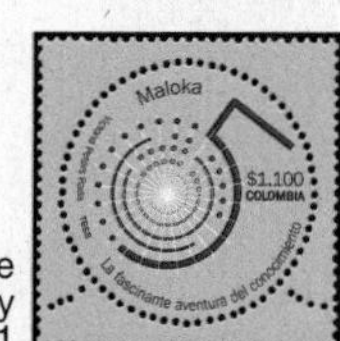

Maloka Science and Technology Center — A621

**2004, July 6** **Litho.** *Perf. 12¾*

**1227** A621 1100p multi 1.75 1.75

Values are for stamps with surrounding selvage.

2004 Summer Olympics, Athens A622

**2004, Aug. 5** *Perf. 13¾x14*

**1228** A622 4400p multi 9.00 9.00

Natl. Association of Contractors, 60th Anniv. — A623

No. 1229: a, Denomination in white. b, Denomination in black.

**2004, Aug. 5** *Perf. 14x13¾*
**1229** Pair 5.00 5.00
*a.-b.* A623 2800p Either single 2.25 2.25

Printed in sheets containing 6 pairs and one large central label.

FIFA (Fédération Internationale de Football Association), Cent. — A624

**2004, Aug. 25** *Perf. 13¼x14*
**1230** A624 3500p multi 4.75 4.75

Women's Citizenship, 50th Anniv. — A625

**2004, Sept. 24** *Perf. 14*
**1231** A625 15,000p multi 12.50 12.50

Fair and Expositions Corporation, 50th Anniv. — A626

**2004, Oct. 14** *Perf. 13½x13*
**1232** A626 1300p multi 1.60 1.60

Colombian Radio Announcers Association, 50th Anniv. — A627

**2004, Oct. 21** *Perf. 14*
**1233** A627 1700p multi 3.25 3.25

17th National Games A628

**2004, Dec. 10** **Litho.** *Perf. 12¾*
**1234** A628 7000p multi + label 12.50 12.50

Printed in sheets of 4 + 5 labels.

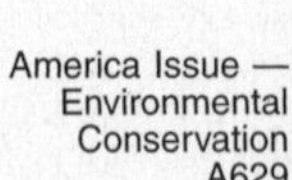

America Issue — Environmental Conservation A629

Designs: No. 1235, 5000p, Whale, Gorgona National Nature Park. No. 1236, 5000p, Hammerhead sharks, Malpelo Flora and Fauna Sanctuary.

**2004, Dec. 14** *Perf. 14*
**1235-1236** A629 Set of 2 9.00 9.00

Miniature Sheet

Christmas — A630

No. 1237 — Inscriptions: a, Jesús en la mansion de su padre. b, Eterna sumision a Dios. c, Jesús desciende al seno de su madre. d, Aceptacion de milagro divino. e, La ilusion de Maria. f, Voluntad divina en manos del emperador. g, Paciencia, expectativa y anhelo. h, Belén: Humilde hospedaje. i, Nacimiento, la faz de Dios encarnado.

**2004, Dec. 15**
**1237** A630 2800p Sheet of 9, #a-i 28.50 28.50

Pre-Columbian Gold Artifacts From Gold Museum — A631

No. 1238, 1200p: a, Tumaco ear covering. b, Zenú nose ring.
No. 1239, 1800p: a, Cauma nose ring. b, Tierradentro bracelet.

**Pairs, #a-b**

**2005, Jan. 21** *Perf. 12x12½*
**1238-1239** A631 Set of 2 6.50 6.50

Issued: No. 1238, 1/21; No. 1239, 3/28.

Rotary International, Cent. A632

**2005, Feb. 23** *Perf. 13½x14*
**1240** A632 3100p multi 3.00 3.00

Souvenir Sheet

Butterflies — A633

No. 1241: a, Protographium tyastes panamensis. b, Dismorphia zaela laura. c, Actinote ozomene.

**2005, June 7** **Litho.** *Perf. 14¼*
**1241** A633 4600p Sheet of 3, #a-c 20.00 20.00

FENALCO (Natl. Federation of Retailers), 60th Anniv. — A634

**2005, June 10** *Perf. 14*
**1242** A634 1200p multi 1.75 1.75

Souvenir Sheets

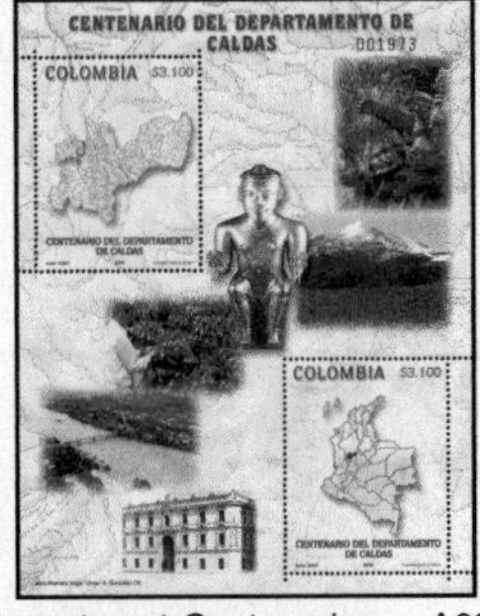

Department Centenaries — A635

No. 1243, 3100p: a, Map of Caldas Department. b, Map of Colombia highlighting Caldas.
No. 1244, 3700p: a, Map of Huila Department. b, Map of Colombia highlighting Huila.
No. 1245, 4200p: a, Map of Atlantico Department. b, Map of Colombia highlighting Atlantico.

**Sheets of 2, #a-b**

**2005, June** *Perf. 14x13½*
**1243-1245** A635 Set of 3 35.00 35.00

**Departments Type of 2003**

No. 1246 — San Andrés y Providencia Department: a, Aerial view of San Andrés, horiz. b, Arms. c, Aerial view of Johnny Cay, horiz. d, Cayo Cangrejo, horiz. e, Artisan. f, Culture House, San Andrés, horiz. g, Morgan Head, Santa Catalina Island, horiz. h, Island view. i, Ensenada, San Andrés, horiz. j, Island architecture, horiz. k, Baptist Church, San Andrés. l, Aerial view of Providencia and Santa Catalina Islands.
Horiz. stamps are 46x37mm.

**2005, July 20** *Perf. 13¾x14*
**1246** A608 1200p Sheet of 12, #a-l 30.00 30.00

Bogota Botanical Gardens — A636

**2005, Aug. 5** *Perf. 14*
**1247** A636 1400p multi 1.75 1.75

15th Bolivarian Games A637

**2005, Aug. 11** *Perf. 13¾x14*
**1248** A637 3500p multi 3.75 3.75

Association of Graduates of the University of the Andes, 50th Anniv. — A638

**2005, Sept. 14** *Perf. 14*
**1249** A638 2000p multi 3.00 3.00

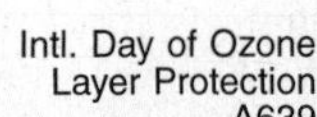

Intl. Day of Ozone Layer Protection A639

**2005, Sept. 16**
**1250** A639 2000p multi 3.00 3.00

Souvenir Sheet

Publication of Don Quixote, 400th Anniv. — A640

No. 1251 — Paintings of Miguel de Cervantes by: a, Ricardo Rendón Bravo. b, Eduardo Ramírez Villamizar, vert. c, Santiago Martínez Delgado, vert.

*Perf. 13½x14 (#1251a), 14x13½*

**2005, Oct. 25**
**1251** A640 1300p Sheet of 3, #a-c 6.50 6.50

Colpatria Bank, 50th Anniv. — A641

**2005, Nov. 2** *Perf. 14x13½*
**1252** A641 1200p multi 1.40 1.40

Arms of City of Facatativá — A642

**2005, Oct. 30** **Litho.** *Perf. 14*
**1253** A642 1800p multi 1.75 1.75

Latin Union, 50th Anniv. A643

**2005, Dec. 1** *Perf. 13½x14*
**1254** A643 5000p multi 6.00 6.00

Printed in sheets of 4.

Souvenir Sheet

America Issue, Fight Against Poverty A644

**2005, Nov. 30** *Perf. 14x13½*
**1255** A644 Sheet of 2 #1255a 13.00 13.00
*a.* 5000p Single stamp 6.25 6.25

Souvenir Sheet

Escuela de Lanceros (Military School), 50th Anniv. A645

**2005, Nov. 30** ***Perf. 14***

**1256** A645 Sheet of 2 #1256a 31.00 31.00
*a.* 10,000p Single stamp 9.50 9.50

Christmas A646

**2005, Dec. 9** ***Perf. 14***

**1257** A646 3100p multi 5.75 5.75

Printed in sheets of 7.

Colombian Journalism A647

**2006, Feb. 9** **Litho.**

**1258** A647 2000p multi 3.00 3.00

St. Francis Xavier (1506-52) — A648

**2006, Apr. 7**

**1259** A648 4500p multi 4.25 4.25

Pope John Paul II (1920-2005) — A649

**2006, Apr. 4**

**1260** A649 4800p multi 4.25 4.25

Frederic Chopin (1810-49), Composer — A650

**2006, May 25** ***Perf. 13½x13***

**1261** A650 5300p multi 5.00 5.00

Printed in sheets of 4.

### Gold Artifacts Type of 2005

No. 1262: a, Quimbaya striated lime receptacle with handles. b, Quimbaya thin lime receptacle.

**2006, Jan. 26** ***Perf. 12x12½***

**1262** A631 1500p Pair, #a-b 3.75 3.75

Italian Cultural Institute of Bogota, 50th Anniv. A651

No. 1263: a, Lute at lower left. b, Violin at lower right.

**2006, Feb. 23** ***Perf. 14***

**1263** A651 1300p Horiz. pair, #a-b 3.50 3.50

Souvenir Sheet

Rayo Museum, 25th Anniv. A652

No. 1264: a, Artwork in blue, white, red, yellow and black. b, Artwork in white, blue, tan and black.

**2006, Jan. 21** ***Perf. 13½x13***

**1264** A652 Sheet, 2 each #a-b 7.00 7.00
*a.-b.* 1300p Either single 1.50 1.50

### Departments Type of 2003

No. 1265 — Valle del Cauca Department: a, Mapping Commission drawing of Cali, horiz. b, Arms of Valle del Cauca. c, Arms and panoramic view of Sevilla, horiz. d, Calima Lake, El Darién, horiz. e, La Ermita, Santiago de Cali. f, Port of Buenaventura, horiz. g, Railroad station, Palmira, horiz. h, Sugar cane. i, Salsa dancers, Cali, horiz. j, El Paraiso Museum, El Cerrito, horiz. k, Basilica, Buga. l, Aerial view of Valle del Cauca, horiz.

No. 1266 — Boyacá Department: a, Plaza de Bolivar, Tunja, horiz. b, Arms of Boyacá. c, Mapping Commission drawing of Campo de Boyacá, horiz. d, Bolivar Monument, Campo de Boyacá, horiz. e, Altar of the Virgin of Chiquinquirá. f, Panoramic view of Garagoa, horiz. g, Plaza de los Libertadores, Duitama, horiz. h, Emeralds. i, Plaza Mayor, Villa de Leyva, horiz. j, Sierra Nevada del Cocuy, horiz. k, Temple of the Sun, Sogamoso. l, El Salitre Farm, Paipa, horiz.

No. 1267 — Quindío Department: a, Quindío Pass, 1836, horiz. b, Quimbaya culture sculpture. c, Coffee plantation house, Quimbaya, horiz. d, Coffee bean picker, Pijao, horiz. e, Valle de Cocora, Salento. f, Botanical Gardens, Calarca, horiz. g, La Estación Metropolitan Cultural Center, Armenia, horiz. h, Monument and government building, Armenia. i, Free Cemetery, Circasia, horiz. j, Aerial view of Buenavista, horiz. k, San José Temple, Génova. l, Founding of Armenia, horiz.

Horizontal stamps are 46x37mm.

### Sheets of 12, #a-l, + 8 labels

**2006** ***Perf. 13½x14***

**1265** A608 1300p Valle del Cauca 20.00 20.00
**1266** A608 2000p Boyacá 30.00 30.00
**1267** A608 3300p Quindío 45.00 45.00
*Nos. 1265-1267 (3)* 95.00 95.00

20th Central American and Caribbean Games — A653

**2006, July 15** **Litho.** ***Perf. 14***

**1268** A653 2000p multi 2.50 2.50

Pres. Alberto Lleras Camargo (1906-90) — A654

Denominations: a, 1300p. b, 3300p.

**2006, Dec. 6** **Litho.** ***Perf. 14x13¾***

**1269** A654 Horiz. pair, #a-b + alternating labels 7.00 7.00

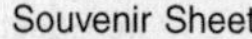

Souvenir Sheet

America Issue, Energy Conservation — A655

No. 1270: a, Left hand. b, Right hand.

**2006, Dec. 28** ***Perf. 12***

**1270** A655 5000p Sheet of 2, #a-b 12.00 12.00

Christmas A656

Denominations: a, 1300p. b, 3300p.

**2006, Dec. 13** ***Perf. 13¾x14***

**1271** A656 Vert. pair, #a-b 5.75 5.75

General José Maria Cordova Military School, Cent. — A657

**2007, May 30** ***Perf. 14***

**1272** A657 10,000p multi 11.00 11.00

### Departments Type of 2003

No. 1273 — Sucre Department: a, Coat of arms. b, St. Francis of Assisi Cathedral, Sincelejo, horiz. c, Palm trees, Tolú. d, Cattle, Sucre. e, Bull ring, Sincelejo, horiz. f, Church, Corozal. g, Musical score of "Fiesta en Corraleja." h, Painting of fandango dancers, horiz. i, Fisherman, Caimito. j, Palm trees, Sincelejo. k, Cane weaver, Sampués, horiz. l, Hammocks, Morroa.

Horizontal stamps are 46x37mm.

### Sheet of 12, #a-l, + 8 Labels

**2007, May 30** ***Perf. 12***

**1273** A608 3300p Sucre 50.00 50.00

Miniature Sheet

Scouting, Cent. A658

No. 1274: a, International and Colombian Scouting emblems, Scouts with Lord Robert Baden-Powell. b, Emblem of 21st World Scout Jamboree, Colombian Scouting emblem, children's drawing of Colombian scout. c, Scouting emblem, Lord Robert Baden-Powell. d, International and Colombian Scouting emblems, animal track.

**2007, June 26** ***Perf. 14***

**1274** A658 1500p Sheet of 8, 2 each #a-d, + central label 13.00 13.00

Souvenir Sheet

El Espectador Newspaper, 120th Anniv. — A659

No. 1275: a, Newspaper from 1887. b, Paperboy, horiz.

**2007, June 28** ***Perf. 12***

**1275** A659 4500p Sheet of 2, #a-b 17.50 17.50

Pan American Games, Rio de Janeiro — A660

**2007, July 9** ***Perf. 14***

**1276** A660 3700p multi 3.75 3.75

Fourth Spanish Language Intl. Congress A661

**2007, June 25**

**1277** A661 5300p multi + label 7.25 7.25

Caja de Compensación Familiar, 50th Anniv. — A662

**2007, Oct. 10** **Litho.** ***Perf. 14***

**1278** A662 3500p multi 4.75 4.75

Colombian Association of Engineers, 50th Anniv. — A663

**2007, Oct. 17**

**1279** A663 1400p multi 1.50 1.50

Bogota Honors and Awards A664

No. 1280: a, 2007 UNESCO World Book Capital. b, Venice Biennale Golden Lion Award for Architecture. c, 2007 Latin American Cultural Capital.

**2007, Oct. 23**

**1280** A664 3700p Horiz. strip of 3, #a-c 20.00 20.00

Minuto de Dios, 50th Anniv. — A665

**2007, Nov. 22**

**1281** A665 1600p multi 2.00 2.00

Christmas A666

**2007, Nov. 27**
**1282** A666 3300p multi 3.75 3.75

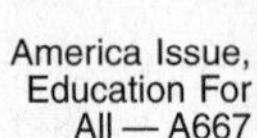
America Issue, Education For All — A667

**2007, Dec. 13**
**1283** A667 3500p multi 4.25 4.25

Pres. Carlos Lleras Restrepo (1908-94) — A668

**2008, Apr. 8** **Litho.** ***Perf. 12***
**1284** A668 1400p multi 1.75 1.75

Colombian Friendship With Japan, Cent. — A669

**2008, May 22** ***Perf. 14***
**1285** A669 5200p multi 6.25 6.25

New Emblem of Postal Network of Colombia — A670

**2008, May 28**
**1286** A670 2100p multi 2.50 2.50

Compare with Type A685.

National Institute for the Blind, 50th Anniv. — A671

**Litho. & Embossed**

**2008, June 10**
**1287** A671 1400p multi 1.75 1.75

**Departments Type of 2003**

No. 1288 — Antioquia Department: a, Medellín skyline, horiz. b, Arms of Antioquia. c, Necoclí, horiz. d, Silleteros Parade, horiz. e, Purse. f, Rafael Uribe Uribe Palace of Culture, horiz. g, Molas, horiz. h, Lipaugus weberi. i, Waterfall, Támesis, horiz. j, Coffee cups, horiz. k, Santa Fé de Antioquia Church. l, Orquideorama, Medellín Botanical Gardens, horiz.

No. 1289 — Amazonas Department: a, Departmental emblem. b, Monkey, Isla de los Micos, horiz. c, Victoria Regia water lily. d, Butterfly, Puerto Nariño. e, Indigenous child, horiz. f, Caiman. g, Beaded mask. h, Dolphin, horiz. i, Amazonas landscape. j, Flower. k, Fisherman casting net, horiz. l, Fruits at Plaza de Mercado, Puerto Leticia.

Horizontal stamps are 50x40mm.

**Sheets of 12, #a-l, + 8 labels**

**2008** **Litho.** ***Perf. 13¾x14***
**1288** A608 1500p Antioquia 17.50 17.50

***Perf. 12***
**1289** A608 1600p Amazonas 24.00 24.00

Issued: No. 1288, 10/22; No. 1289, 7/18.

Battle of Maracaibo Lake, 185th Anniv. A672

**2008, July 30** ***Perf. 12***
**1290** A672 3900p multi 5.00 5.00

Treaty of Amity and Commerce Between Colombia and Switzerland, Cent. — A673

**2008, July 31** ***Perf. 14***
**1291** A673 5200p multi 6.00 6.00

2008 Summer Olympics, Beijing — A674

**2008, Aug. 1**
**1292** A674 5000p multi 5.75 5.75

**Souvenir Sheet**

**1293** A674 10,000p multi 11.50 11.50

Aguadas, Bicent. — A675

**2008, Aug. 15**
**1294** A675 3500p multi 4.00 4.00

Accordion Festival, Villanueva — A676

**2008, Sept. 25**
**1295** A676 5600p multi 6.00 6.00

Pres. Alfonso López Michelsen (1913-2007) — A677

**2008, Oct. 8**
**1296** A677 5100p multi 4.50 4.50

**Miniature Sheet**

Ministry of Communications, 85th Anniv. — A678

No. 1297 — Arms of Colombia and: a, Stylized person, emblem for Government Online program. b, Children, emblem for Computers for Education progam, vert. c, Girl with "@" balloon, campaign for clean Internet. d, Emblem for Compartel, vert.

**2008, Oct. 29**
**1297** A678 1500p Sheet of 4, #a-d 5.50 5.50

Episcopal Conference of Colombia, Cent. — A679

**2008, Nov. 6**
**1298** A679 1500p multi 1.40 1.40

18th Carlos Lleras Restrepo National Games — A680

**2008, Nov. 21**
**1299** A680 1500p multi 1.40 1.40

Natl. Department of Planning, 50th Anniv. — A681

**2008, Dec. 9**
**1300** A681 1500p multi 1.40 1.40

Christmas — A682

Adoration of the Shepherds, by Gregorio Vásquez de Arce y Ceballos: a, 1400p. b, 3500p.

**2008, Dec. 12**
**1301** A682 Vert. pair, #a-b 6.00 6.00

**Miniature Sheet**

Luis Angel Arango Library, 50th Anniv. A683

No. 1302 — Open book with: a, Ship page and "B." b, Sun page and "L." c, Dove page and "a." d, Face page and "A."

**2008, Dec. 16** ***Perf. 13¾x14***
**1302** A683 1300p Sheet of 4, #a-d 5.75 5.75

America Issue, National Festivals A684

Paintings: No. 1303, 1400p, November 11, 1811, Absolute Independence of Cartagena, by Cecilia Porras. No. 1304, 1400p, Liberty Indian, by unknown artist, vert.

**2008, Dec. 29** ***Perf. 13¾x14, 14x13¾***
**1303-1304** A684 Set of 2 3.25 3.25

4-72 Colombia Postal Network Emblem — A685

Designs: 200p, Emblem on blue background with red frame. 400p, Emblem against blue background, and three arrows against red, blue and yellow backgrounds. 500p, Emblem against white background with blue frame. 600p, Emblem and map of Colombia.

**2009, Mar. 1** **Litho.** ***Perf. 14***
**1305-1308** A685 Set of 4 1.40 1.40

**Souvenir Sheet**

Cali Philatelic Club, 70th Anniv. A686

No. 1309: a, Necklace with flower-shaped pendant. b, Miltoniopsis roezlii, vert.

**2009, Mar. 12** ***Perf. 12***
**1309** A686 2000p Sheet of 2, #a-b 7.25 7.25

Inter-America Development Bank, 50th Anniv. — A687

**2009, Mar. 27**
**1310** A687 3700p multi 3.25 3.25

President Julio César Turbay (1916-2005) A688

**2009, Apr. 1** ***Perf. 14x13½***
**1311** A688 1700p multi 1.60 1.60

Printed in sheets of 9 + 6 labels.

Naval School for Non-Commissioned Officers, Barranquilla, 75th Anniv. — A689

**2009, Apr. 17** ***Perf. 14***
**1312** A689 4000p multi 4.25 4.25

Colombian War School, Cent. — A690

**2009, May 8** ***Perf. 12***
**1313** A690 5500p multi 5.50 5.50

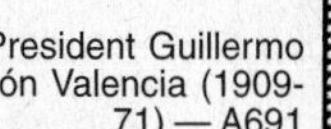

President Guillermo León Valencia (1909-71) — A691

**2009, May 27**

**1314** A691 4200p multi 5.00 5.00

Fight of July 20, 1810, by Julián Rubiano Chávez — A692

**2009, June 25** ***Perf. 12***

**1315** A692 1700p multi 1.75 1.75

### Departments Type of 2003
Miniature Sheet

No. 1316 — La Guajira Department: a, Arms of La Guajira. b, Francisco el Hombre, mural in La Guajira Cultural Center, horiz. c, Waterfall, Montes de Oca. d, Phoenicopterus ruber. e, Domingueka, Kogui village, horiz. f, Cape of La Vela. g, Majayuts (Wayuu women). h, Riohacha Cathedral, horiz. i, Cardinalis phoeniceus. j, Aloe vulgaris. k, Caesalpinia coriaria, horiz. l, Wayuu mochilas (bags).

Horizontal stamps are 50x40mm.

**Sheet of 12, #a-l, + 8 Labels**

**2009, July 24 Litho.** ***Perf. 12***

**1316** A608 1700p La Guajira 24.00 24.00

Miniature Sheet

Heliconia Varieties A693

No. 1317: a, Heliconia stricta. b, Heliconia rostrata. c, Heliconia wagneriana. d, Heliconia orthotricha. e, Heliconia psittacorum.

**2009, Aug. 14 Litho.** ***Perf. 12***

**1317** A693 2000p Sheet of 5, #a-e, + 5 labels 11.00 11.00

Miniature Sheet

First Colombian Postage Stamps, 150th Anniv. — A694

No. 1318: a, Colombia #1. b, Colombia #6. c, Colombia #4. d, Colombia #3. e, Colombia #7. f, Map of Colombia and text on gray background.

10,000p, Like No. 1318f with blue background.

**2009, Aug. 25** ***Perf. 12***

**1318** A694 4000p Sheet of 6, #a-f 28.00 28.00

**Souvenir Sheet**

**1319** A694 10,000p multi 11.50 11.50

America Issue, Traditional Games — A695

No. 1320 — Chaza player: a, Bare-handed. b, Holding racquet.

**2009, Oct. 13 Litho.** ***Perf. 14***

**1320** A695 5000p Horiz. pair, #a-b 12.00 12.00

Rafael Uribe Uribe (1859-1914), General — A696

**2009, Oct. 20**

**1321** A696 1500p multi 1.75 1.75

Madrid Town Hall — A697

**2009, Nov. 13**

**1322** A697 10,000p multi 12.00 12.00

Madrid, Cundinamarca Department, 450th anniv.

Miniature Sheet

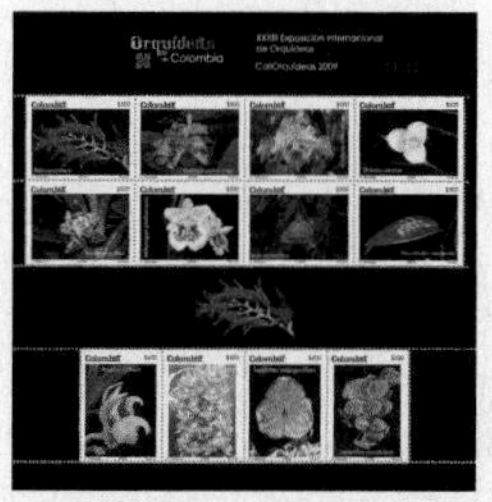

Orchids A698

No. 1323: a, 500p, Ada aurantiaca (many flowers). b, 500p, Cattleya patinii cogn. c, 500p, Cattleya schroderae. d, 500p, Dracula amaliae. e, 500p, Huntleya gustavi. f, 500p, Miltoniopsis phalaenopsis. g, 500p, Ada aurantiaca (one flower). h, 500p, Pleurothallis casapensis. i, 600p, Anguloa cliftonii, vert. j, 600p, Cycnoche barthriorum, vert. k, 600p, Lepanthes telipogoniflora, vert. l, 600p, Lepanthes calodictyon, vert.

**2009, Nov. 20**

**1323** A698 Sheet of 12, #a-l 11.00 11.00

33rd Intl. Orchid Exposition, Cali.

Miniature Sheet

Independence, Bicent. — A699

No. 1324: a, Bishop Andrés Rosillo y Meruelo (1758-1835). b, Josè Félix de Restrepo (1760-1832), statesman. c, Camilo Torres Tenorio (1766-1816), President of the Congress. d, Bishop Juan Fernández de Sotomayor (1777-1849). e, Antonio Villavicencio y Berástegui (1775-1816), President of the United Provinces of New Granada. f, Juan de Dios Morales (1767-1810), governmental minister and revolutionary. g, José María Carbonel (1778-1816), revolutionary agitator. h, Antonio Morales Galavís (1784-1852), military commander. i, José Ramón de Leyva (1747-1816), military commander. j, Nicolás Mauricio de Omaña, priest, lawyer.

**2009, Nov. 24**

**1324** A699 6000p Sheet of 10, #a-j 70.00 70.00

Christmas — A700

**2009, Nov. 27** ***Perf. 12***

**1325** A700 5000p multi 7.75 7.75

Souvenir Sheet

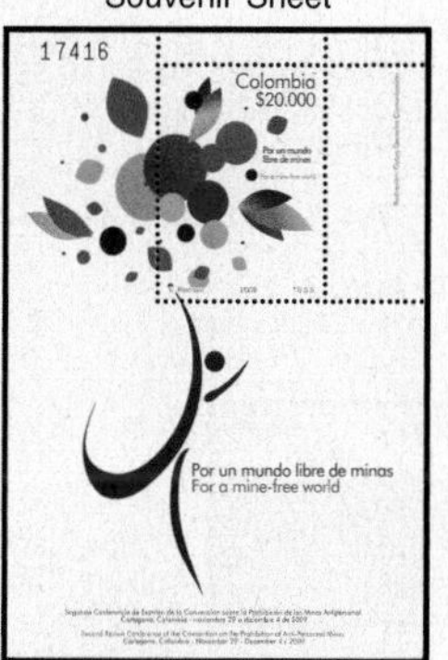

Campaign for a Mine-free World — A701

**2009, Dec. 3** ***Perf. 14***

**1326** A701 20,000p multi 25.00 20.00

Winning Designs in Stamp Design Contest A702

No. 1327: a, Abstract face, by Vito. b, Collage, by Caracha. c, People holding hands, by D. Bueno.

**2009, Dec. 15**

**1327** A702 1800p Horiz. strip of 3, #a-c 7.50 7.50

Miniature Sheet

Famous People A703

No. 1328: a, Mercedes Abrego (1770-1813), spy. b, Gerardo Molina R. (1906-91), politician. c, Virginia Gutiérrez (1922-99), social anthropologist. d, María Mercedes Carranza (1945-2003), poet. e, Gonzalo Arango (1931-76), poet. f, Adolfo Mejía (1905-76), composer. g, General Benjamin Herrera (1853-1924). h, César Uribe Piedrahita (1896-1951), medical writer. i, Emilio Robledo (1875-1962), medical educator. j, Luis Duque Gómez (1916-2000), archaeologist. k, Enrique A. Becerra (1883-1954), jurist. l, Hugo Escobar Sierra (1927-2003), politician.

**2010, Jan. 28** ***Perf. 13½x14***

**1328** A703 4000p Sheet of 12, #a-l 60.00 60.00

### Presidents Type of 1981
Miniature Sheet

No. 1329 — Presidents, coup leaders and other leaders of Colombia: a, Virgilio Barco Vargas. b, Julio César Turbay Ayala. c, Alfonso López Michelsen. d, Misael Pastrana Borrero. e, Carlos Lemos Simmonds. f, Victor Mosquera Chaux. g, Indalecio Liévano Aguirre. h, Rafael Azuero Manchola. i, Gabriel París Gordillo. j, Deogracias Fonseca. k, Rafael Navas Pardo. l, Luis Ernesto Ordóñez. m, Diego Euclides de Angulo. n, Clímaco Calderón Reyes. o, Andrés Cerón Serrano. p, Ignacio Gutiérrez Vergara. q, Juan José Nieto Gil. r, Rufino Cuervo. s, Manuel Rodríguez Torices. t, José Joaquín Camacho.

**2010, Jan. 28** ***Perf. 14***

**1329** Sheet of 20 47.50 47.50

*a.-t.* A401 1900p Any single 2.00 2.00

Ninth South American Games, Medellin A704

**2010, Feb. 18**

**1330** A704 5800p multi 8.00 8.00

Pope John Paul II (1920-2005) — A705

**2010, Feb. 19** ***Perf. 13x13¼***

**1331** A705 4400p multi 5.50 5.50

Miniature Sheet

Endangered Birds — A706

No. 1332: a, Crax alberti. b, Ognorhynchus icterotis. c, Hapalopsittaca fuertesi. d, Amazilia castaneiventris. e, Rallus semiplumbeus. f, Coeligena prunellei. g, Grallaria gigantea. h, Bangsia aureocincta. i, Hypopyrrhus pyrohypogaster.

**2010, Apr. 6** ***Perf. 13¼x13***

**1332** A706 1900p Sheet of 9, #a-i 22.50 22.50

Souvenir Sheet

Expo 2010, Shanghai — A707

**2010, May 7** ***Perf. 13¾x14***

**1333** A707 5000p multi 6.00 6.00

Miniature Sheet

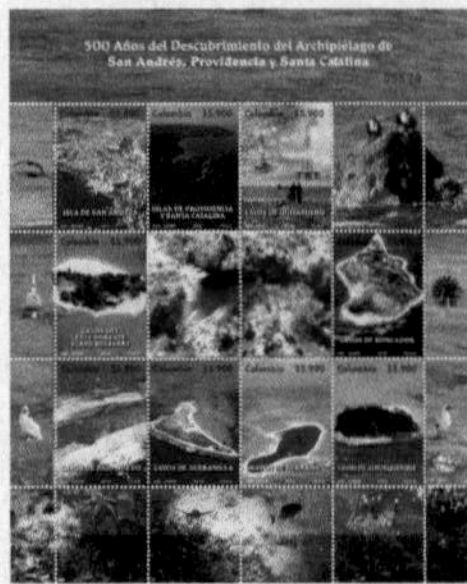

Discovery of San Andrés, Providencia and Santa Catalina Archipelago, 500th Anniv. — A708

No. 1334: a, San Andrés Island. b, Providencia and Santa Catalina Islands. c, Quitasueño Keys. d, Bolivar Key. e, Roncador Keys. f, Bajo Nuevo Keys. g, Serranilla Keys. h, Serrana Keys. i, Alburquerque Keys.

**2010, June 12 Litho. *Perf. 14***
**1334** A708 5900p Sheet of 9, #a-i, + 3 labels 85.00 85.00

**Departments Type of 2003**

No. 1335 — Guainía Department: a, Arms of Guainía. b, Princess Inírida Monument, horiz. c, Egretta alba. d, Cerro Mavicure. e, Canoe on Inírida River, horiz. f, Curripaco baskets. g, Guacamaya superba. h, Confluence of the Guaviare and Inírida Rivers, horiz. i, Remanso. j, Cualé Rapids. k, Children from Paujil, horiz. l, Coco Petroglyphs.

No. 1336 — Atlántico Department: a, Arms of Atlántico. b, Palacio de la Cultura, Barranquilla, horiz. c, Tubará rock paintings. d, Fluvicola pica. e, Julio Flórez Museum, Usiacurí, horiz. f, Tocagua Marsh, Luruaco. g, Bull's head carnival mask. h, San Antonio de Padua Church, Soledad, horiz. i, Tabebuya rosea. j, Iraca Palm handicrafts. k, Pier at Puerto Colombia, horiz. l, Customs House, Barranquilla.

Horiz. stamps are 50x40mm.

**Sheets of 12, #a-l, + 8 labels**

**2010 *Perf. 12x12½***
**1335** A608 600p Guainía 15.00 15.00
**1336** A608 2000p Atlántico 35.00 35.00

Issued: No. 1335, 7/24; No. 1336, 6/15.

Gonzalo Jiménez de Quesada Police Academy — A709

**2010, June 24 *Perf. 14***
**1337** A709 2000p multi 2.50 2.50

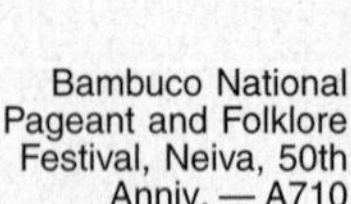

Bambuco National Pageant and Folklore Festival, Neiva, 50th Anniv. — A710

**2010, June 22 *Perf. 13¼x13***
**1338** A710 4200p multi 5.50 5.50

Admiral Padilla Naval Academy — A711

**2010, July 3 *Perf. 14***
**1339** A711 500p multi 4.00 4.00

Miniature Sheet

Norte de Santander Department, Cent. — A712

No. 1340: a, Map of Norte de Santander Department. b, Government building. c, Estoraques Nature Area. d, Catatumbo River. e, Santa Ana de Ocaña Cathedral. f, Santa Clara de Pamplona Cathedral.

**2010, July 14 Litho.**
**1340** A712 6000p Sheet of 6, #a-f 47.50 47.50

Teresa Pizarro de Angulo (c. 1930-2000), National Beauty Pageant Director — A713

**2010, Aug. 3**
**1341** A713 5900p multi 8.00 8.00

Pinillos National College, Bicent. (in 2009) — A714

**2010, Aug. 27 Litho. *Perf. 14***
**1342** A714 4000p multi 5.25 5.25

America Issue, National Symbols A715

No. 1343: a, Colombian flag. b, Colombian coat of arms.

**2010, Oct. 12 *Perf. 13½x14***
**1343** A715 2100p Horiz. pair, #a-b 6.50 6.50

Medellin Institute of Fine Arts, Cent. — A716

**2010, Oct. 19 *Perf. 14x13¾***
**1344** A716 4400p multi 5.50 5.50

Miniature Sheet

Valle del Cauca Department, Cent. — A717

No. 1345: a, Map of Valle del Cauca Department. b, Sula granti. c, Overo Chapel. d, Pance River, Farallones Park. e, llama Culture vessel. f, Sonso Lake, Buga.

**2010, Nov. 18 *Perf. 14***
**1345** A717 4000p Sheet of 6, #a-f 32.50 32.50

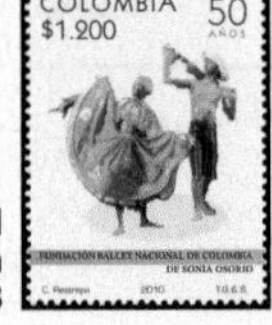

Colombia National Ballet, 50th Anniv. — A718

**2010, Nov. 22**
**1346** A718 1200p multi 6.00 6.00

Christmas A719

**2010, Nov. 23 *Perf. 13x13¼***
**1347** A719 5000p multi 6.50 6.50

Eduardo Caballero Calderón (1910-93), Writer — A720

**2010, Dec. 1 *Perf. 14***
**1348** A720 3000p multi 4.00 4.00

Miniature Sheet

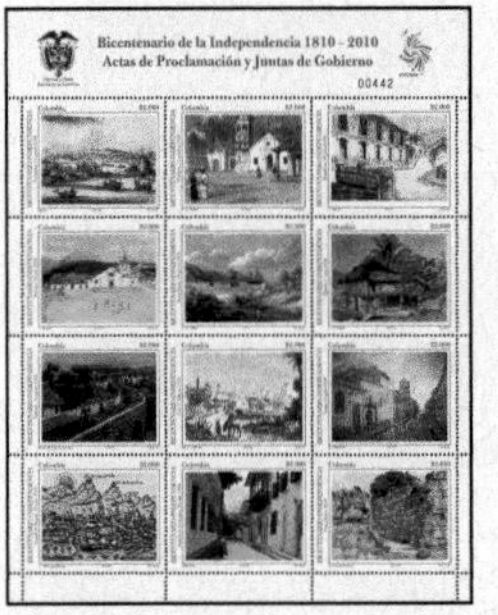

Independence, Bicent. — A721

No. 1349 — Various paintings depicting scenes from towns declaring independence in 1810: a, Caratgena. b, Mompox. c, Pamplona. d, Socorro. e, Santa Marta. f, Chocó. g, Popayán. h, Cali. i, Tunja. j, Santa Fé de Bogotá. k, Santa Fé de Antioquia. l, Pore.

**2010, Oct. 22 *Perf. 13½x14***
**1349** A721 2000p Sheet of 12. #a-l 32.50 32.50

Radio Station HJCK, Bogota — A722

**2011, Feb. 10 *Perf. 14***
**1350** A722 600p multi 1.50 1.50

4-72 Colombia Postal Network Emblem and "Es Tu Correo!" — A723

**Frame Color**
***Serpentine Die Cut 12½***

**2011, Mar. 22 Self-Adhesive**
**1351** A723 10,000p blue 13.50 13.50
**1352** A723 20,000p red 27.50 27.50

El Catolicismo Newspaper, 162nd Anniv. — A724

**2011, Mar. 30 *Perf. 13x13¼***
**1353** A724 1700p multi 2.75 2.75

Souvenir Sheet

Biological Diversity — A725

**2011, Apr. 11 *Perf. 13***
**1354** A725 6100p multi 10.00 10.00

Office of the Attorney General — A726

**2011, May 10 *Perf. 14***
**1355** A726 1600p multi 3.00 3.00

Under-20 World Cup Soccer Championships, Colombia — A727

**2011, July 21 Litho. *Perf. 13¼x13***
**1356** A727 2000p multi 3.25 3.25

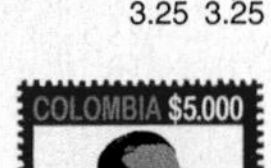

Rufino José Cuervo (1844-1911), Writer — A728

**2011, July 27 *Perf. 14***
**1357** A728 5000p multi 8.00 8.00

Alfonso López Pumarejo National Carabiniers School, 50th Anniv. — A729

**2011, Aug. 9 *Perf. 14***
**1358** A729 2100p multi 3.25 3.25

**Departments Type of 2003**
Miniature Sheet

No. 1359 — Norte de Santander Department: a, Arms of Norte de Santander. b, Virgin of Torcoroma and church, horiz. c, Locomotive. d, Sculpture of Barí Indian. e, Laguna Brava and Sisavita Complex, horiz. f, Southern tamandua, El Bojoso Reserve. g, Clock Tower, Cucuta. h, Street in La Play de Belén, horiz. i, Historic church, Rosario. j, Piedras Negras National Park. k, Pamplona University, horiz. l, Páramo de Guerrero.

Horiz. stamps are 46x37mm.

**Sheet of 12, #a-l, + 8 labels**

**2011, Aug. 25 *Perf. 13¼x13***
**1359** A608 3000p Norte de Santander *55.00 55.00*

Souvenir Sheet

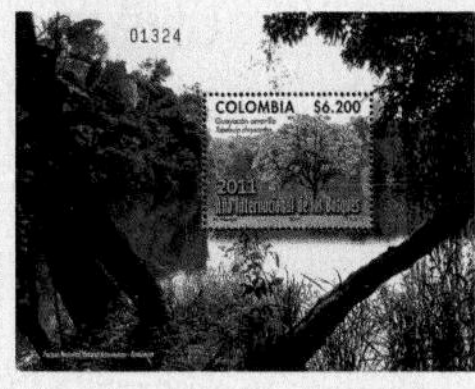

Intl. Year of Forests A730

**2011, Aug. 30** ***Perf. 14***
**1360** A730 6200p multi 10.00 10.00

Miniature Sheet

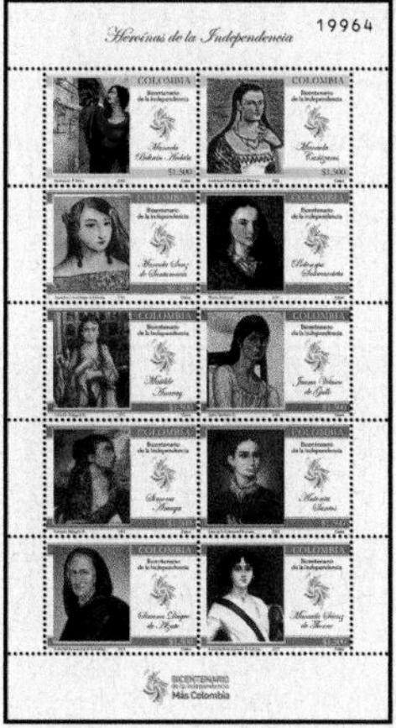

Heroines of Independence — A731

No. 1361: a, Manuela Beltrán Archila. b, Manuela Cañizares. c, Manuela Sanz de Santamaría. d, Policarpa Salvarrieta. e, Matilde Anaray. f, Juana Velasco de Gallo. g, Simona Amaya. h, Antonia Santos. i, Simona Duque de Alzate. j, Manuela Sáenz de Thorne.

**2011, Sept. 12** ***Perf. 13x13¼***
**1361** A731 1500p Sheet of 10, #a-j 24.00 24.00

Intl. Year of People of African Descent — A732

**2011, Oct. 12** ***Perf. 13¼x13***
**1362** A732 5000p multi 8.00 8.00

2011 Pan American Games, Guadalajara, Mexico — A733

**2011, Oct. 19** ***Perf. 14***
**1363** A733 600p multi 1.00 1.00

Souvenir Sheet

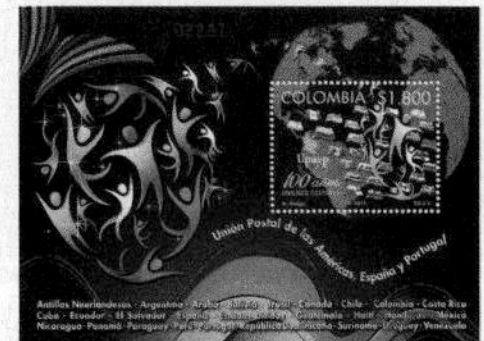

Postal Union of the Americas, Spain and Portugal (UPAEP), Cent. — A734

**2011, Nov. 11**
**1364** A734 1800p multi 3.00 3.00

Bolívar House, Bucaramanga A735

**2011, Nov. 15** ***Perf. 13x13¼***
**1365** A735 1200p multi 2.00 2.00

Declaration of Independence of Cartagena, 200th Anniv. — A736

**2011, Nov. 26** ***Perf. 14***
**1366** A736 6000p multi 9.00 9.00

Emblem of United Nations AIDS Program — A737

**2011, Dec. 1**
**1367** A737 1900p multi 3.25 3.25

Mailbox — A738

**2011, Dec. 2** **Litho.**
**1368** A738 500p multi 1.25 1.25

America issue.

Christmas A739

**2011, Dec. 2**
**1369** A739 1600p multi 2.75 2.75

Souvenir Sheet

El Tiempo Newspaper, Cent. — A740

**2011, Dec. 13** ***Perf. 13x13¼***
**1370** A740 4000p multi 6.50 6.50

2012 Summer Olympics, London — A741

No. 1371: a, Swimming, fencing, wrestling. b, Equestrian, running, cycling. c, Judo, boxing, weight lifting. d, Shot put, soccer, tennis.

**2012, Mar. 6** ***Perf. 14x14¼***
**1371** Horiz. strip of 4 20.00 20.00
*a.-d.* A741 3000p Any single 4.00 4.00

Nos. 1371a-1371d were printed in sheets of 8 containing two of each stamp.

National Police Magazine, Cent. — A742

**2012, Mar. 23** ***Perf. 14***
**1372** A742 2000p multi 3.50 3.50

National Police Symphony, Cent. — A743

**2012, Mar. 23**
**1373** A743 6400p multi 11.00 11.00

Diplomatic Relations Between Colombia and South Korea, 50th Anniv. — A744

No. 1374: a, Ginseng flowers and root. b, Coffee bush and beans.

**2012, May 1** ***Perf. 13x13¼***
**1374** A744 600p Horiz. pair, #a-b 2.50 2.50

See South Korea No. 2379.

Souvenir Sheet

Neiva, 400th Anniv. A745

**2012, May 4** ***Perf. 14***
**1375** A745 4000p multi 6.50 6.50

Souvenir Sheet

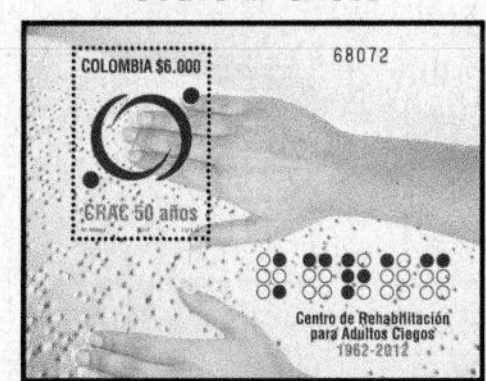

Rehabilitation Center for Blind Adults, 50th Anniv. — A746

**2012, June 3** **Litho. & Embossed**
**1376** A746 6000p multi 10.00 10.00

**Departments Type of 2003**

Miniature Sheet

No. 1377 — Cauca Department: a, Arms of Cauca. b, Puracé National Park, horiz. c, Gorgona National Park. d, Samanea saman. e, Laguna Grande de la Magdalena, horiz. f, Niña Maria de Caloto icon. g, Street in San Sebastian. h, Nuestra Senñora de la Asuncion Cathedral, Popayán, horiz. i, Battle of Bajo Palacé. j, Tierradentro National Archaeological Park. k, San Andrés Church, Pisimbalá, horiz. l, Megaptera novaeangliae.

Horiz. stamps are 46x37mm.

**Sheet of 12, #a-l, + 8 labels**

**2012, July 24** **Litho.** ***Perf. 12x12½***
**1377** A608 1200p Cauca 24.00 24.00

Miniature Sheet

Famous Men A747

No. 1378: a, Diego de Torres y Moyachoque (1549-90), Turmequé cacique. b, Pantaléon Germán Ribón (1774-1816), military leader. c, Cayetano Betancur (1910-82), philosopher. d, Luis Bermúdez (1912-94), composer.

**2012, Aug. 16** ***Perf. 13¼***
**1378** A747 4600p Sheet of 4, #a-d 30.00 30.00

Rafael Pombo (1833-1912), Writer of Children's Literature — A748

**2012, Aug. 23** ***Perf. 13x13¼***
**1379** A748 2100p multi + label 3.50 3.50

Voceadores de Prensa, Painting by Débora Arango Pérez (1907-2005) — A749

**2012, Aug. 28** ***Perf. 14***
**1380** A749 2400p multi 4.00 4.00

19th National Games and 3rd Paranational Games — A750

**2012, Sept. 5**
**1381** A750 1500p multi 2.75 2.75

Art by Omar Rayo — A751

No. 1382 — Art with stripes of: a, White, black and red. b, White, black and yellow. c, White, green, yellow, red and blue.

**2012, Sept. 20** ***Perf. 13x13¼***
**1382** Horiz. strip of 3 5.00 5.00
*a.-c.* A751 1000p Any single 1.50 1.50

Jorge Palacios Preciado (1940-2003), Historian — A752

**2012, Sept. 29**
**1383** A752 500p multi .85 .85

Plaza Mayor, Leyva — A753

**2012, Oct. 4**
**1384** A753 4500p multi 8.50 8.50

First Congress of the United Provinces of New Granada, Bicent.

Souvenir Sheet

America Issue, Myths and Legends A754

No. 1385: a, El Hojarasquin. b, El Ribiel and El Tesoro de Morgan.

**2012, Oct. 9**
**1385** A754 4000p Sheet of 2, #a-b 13.00 13.00

Fedepalma (National Federation of Oil Palm Growers), 50th Anniv. — A755

**2012, Oct. 24** ***Perf. 14***
**1386** A755 6000p multi 9.50 9.50

Gen. Francisco de Paula Santander (1792-1840) — A756

**2012, Nov. 16** ***Perf. 13¼***
**1387** A756 1000p multi 1.75 1.75

Christmas — A757

**2012, Dec. 14** ***Perf. 14***
**1388** A757 2500p multi 4.25 4.25

Medals Won at 2012 Summer Olympics, London — A758

**2012, Dec. 18** ***Perf. 13***
**1389** A758 1800p multi 4.00 4.00

A souvenir sheet containing one 30,000p stamp depicting medals won at the 2012 Summer Olympics was produced in limited quantities.

Miniature Sheet

Proclamation of State Constitutions, 200th Anniv. — A759

No. 1391 — Seals of state of: a, Socorro. b, Cundinamarca. c, Tunja. d, Antioquia. e, Cartagena de Indias. f, Neiva.

**Litho. & Embossed**

**2012, Dec. 19** ***Perf. 13¼x13***
**1391** A759 500p Sheet of 6, #a-f 5.00 5.00

Renaming of Las Hermosas National Natural Park After Gloria Valencia de Castaño (1927-2011), Television Personality A760

**2013, Apr. 29** **Litho.**
**1392** A760 1800p multi + label 2.00 2.00

**Departments Type of 2003**

Miniature Sheet

No. 1393 — Cundinamarca Department: a, Arms of Cundinamarca. b, Tequendama Falls, Soacha, horiz. c, Poster commemorating bicentennial of Cundinamarca's independence. d, Basilica del Santo Cristo, Ubaté. e, Salt Cathedral, Zipaquirá, horiz. f, Ironworks, Pacho. g, Lagunas del Cerro, Machetá. h, Cliffs, Suesca, horiz. i, St. John the Baptist Parish Church, San Juan de Rioseco. j, Chapel, Siecha. k, Bridge of the Commoners, Chía, horiz. l, Versalles Falls, Guaduas.
Horiz. stamps are 46x37mm.

**2013, July 16** ***Perf. 13¼x13***
**Sheet of 12, #a-l, + 8 labels**
**1393** A608 2100p Cundinamarca 27.00 27.00

2013 World Games, Cali A761

**2013, July 26** **Litho.** ***Perf. 14***
**1394** A761 2200p multi + label 2.40 2.40

Deportivo Independiente Medellín Soccer Team, Cent. — A762

**2013, July 28** ***Perf. 14x13½***
**1395** A762 4500p multi 4.75 4.75

Town of Río de Oro, 355th Anniv. — A763

**2013, Aug. 1** ***Perf. 13½x14***
**1396** A763 800p multi .85 .85

Alfonso Palacio Rudas (1912-96), Politician — A764

**2013, Aug. 9** **Litho.**
**1397** A764 7000p multi 7.50 7.50

Soledad Acosta de Samper (1833-1913), Writer — A765

**2013, Sept. 3** ***Perf. 13¼x13***
**1398** A765 2500p multi 2.60 2.60

Campaign Against Crime — A766

**2013, July 19** **Litho.** ***Perf. 14x13½***
**1399** A766 2000p multi 2.25 2.25

Aspects of Life of Coffee Pickers A767

**2013, July 30** **Litho.** ***Perf. 14½x14¼***
**1400** A767 2000p multi 2.25 2.25

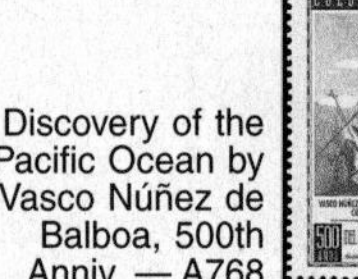


Discovery of the Pacific Ocean by Vasco Núñez de Balboa, 500th Anniv. — A768

**2013, Sept. 9** **Litho.** ***Perf. 13½x14***
**1401** A768 1400p multi 1.50 1.50

Pres. Alfonso López Michelsen (1913-2007) — A769

**2013, Sept. 9** **Litho.** ***Perf. 13½x14***
**1402** A769 2500p multi 2.60 2.60

Christmas — A770

**2013, Nov. 26** **Litho.** ***Perf. 14x13½***
**1403** A770 3500p multi 3.75 3.75

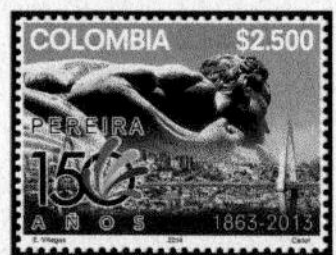


Pereira, 150th Anniv. (in 2013) — A771

**2014, Mar. 13** **Litho.** ***Perf. 13x13¼***
**1404** A771 2500p multi 2.60 2.60

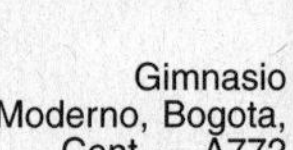

Gimnasio Moderno, Bogota, Cent. — A772

**2014, Mar. 18** **Litho.** ***Perf. 13x13¼***
**1405** A772 800p multi .85 .85

Jaguar Mask A773

**2014, May 13** **Litho.** ***Perf. 13½***
**1406** A773 7200p multi + label 7.75 7.75

Artisans of Colombia, 50th anniv. No. 1406 was printed in sheets of 4 + 4 labels.

Souvenir Sheet

2014 World Cup Soccer Championships, Brazil — A774

No. 1407: a, Soccer ball. b, Emblem of the Colombian Soccer Federation, vert.

**2014, May 23** **Litho.** ***Perf. 13¾***
**1407** A774 2600p Sheet of 2, #a-b 5.50 5.50
*c.* Booklet pane of 2, #1407a-1407b *10.00* —
Complete booklet, 5 #1407c *50.00*

Issued: No. 1407c, 7/8. Each example of No. 1407c in the complete booklet has a different pane margin. These pane margins differ from the sheet margin on No. 1407.

Official Journal, 150th Anniv. — A775

**2014, Oct. 9 Litho. *Perf. 13x13¼***
1408 A775 1300p multi 1.25 1.25

4-72 Colombia Postal Network Emblem and Text — A776

***Serpentine Die Cut 12¼x12¾***
**2014, Aug. 25 Litho.**
**Self-Adhesive**
**Frame Color**
1409 A776 10,000p blue 10.50 10.50
1410 A776 20,000p red 21.00 21.00

Scouting in Colombia, Cent. (in 2013) — A777

**2014, Nov. 22 Litho. *Perf. 13¼x13***
1411 A777 3000p multi 2.60 2.60

Fanny Mikey (c. 1930-2008), Founder of Bogota Ibero-American Theater Festival — A778

**2014, Dec. 2 Litho. *Perf. 13¼x13***
1412 A778 500p multi .45 .45

Christmas — A779

***Perf. 13½x13¼***
**2014, Dec. 10 Litho.**
1413 A779 100p multi .25 .25

Augusto Ramirez Ocampo (c. 1934-2011), Politician — A780

**2014, Dec. 23 Litho. *Perf. 13¼x13***
1414 A780 1000p multi .85 .85

Gabriel García Márquez (1927-2014), 1982 Nobel Literature Laureate — A781

**2015, July 14 Litho. *Perf. 13¼x13***
1415 A781 200p multi .25 .25

**Souvenir Sheet**
***Imperf***
1416 A781 10,000p multi 7.00 7.00

No. 1416 contains one 45x56mm stamp.

Fauna — A782

Designs: 200p, Allobates juanii. 500p, Eriocnemis mirabilis. 1000p, Diglossa gloriosissima. 2000p, Crocodylus intermedius. 5000p, Ateles hybridus. 10,000p, Phyllobates terribilis. 20,000p, Batrachemys dahli.

***Serpentine Die Cut 12¾***
**2015, July 14 Litho.**
**Self-Adhesive**
1417 A782 200p multi .25 .25
1418 A782 500p multi .35 .35
1419 A782 1000p multi .70 .70
1420 A782 2000p multi 1.40 1.40
1421 A782 5000p multi 3.50 3.50
1422 A782 10,000p multi 7.00 7.00
1423 A782 20,000p multi 14.00 14.00
*Nos. 1417-1423 (7)* 27.20 27.20

20th National and 4th Paranational Games, Chocó and Tolima — A783

**2015, Nov. 7 Litho. *Perf. 13¼x13***
1424 A783 5000p multi + label 3.25 3.25

**Souvenir Sheet**
**Litho. & Embossed With Foil Application**
***Perf. 13***
1425 A783 12,000p gold & multi 7.75 7.75

No. 1425 contains one 40x52mm stamp.

Manuel Mejía Vallejo (1923-89), Writer — A784

***Serpentine Die Cut 12¾***
**2015, Nov. 12 Litho.**
**Self-Adhesive**
1426 A784 20,000p multi 13.00 13.00

Paulina Vega Dieppa, 2014 Miss Universe — A785

**2015, Nov. 14 Litho. *Perf. 13¼x13***
1427 A785 20,000p multi 13.00 13.00

National Police School of Criminal Investigation, Cent. (in 2014) — A786

**2015, Dec. 10 Litho. *Perf. 13¼x13***
1428 A786 1000p multi .65 .65

Christmas — A787

**2015, Dec. 11 Litho. *Perf. 13¼x13***
1429 A787 10,000p multi 6.25 6.25

**Departments Type of 2003**
Miniature Sheet

No. 1430 — Risaralda Department: a, Arms of Risaralda. b, Cathedral of Our Lady of Poverty, Pereira, horiz. c, Pseudoscada lavinia. d, Santa Rosa de Cabal Thermal Springs. e, House of Culture, Marsella, horiz. f, Immaculate Mary Church, Marsella. g, Magnolia wolfi. h, Emberá-Chamí women, horiz. i, Dosquebradas Viaduct. j, Alouatta seniculus. k, Oxypogon stubelii, horiz. l, Old Railway Station, Pereira.

Horiz. stamps are 46x37mm.

**2015, Dec. 14 Litho. *Perf. 13¼x13***
**Sheet of 12, #a-l, + 8 labels**
1430 A608 100p Risaralda .75 .75

Aerial Mapping — A788

**2016, Apr. 19 Litho. *Perf. 13¼x13***
1431 A788 5000p multi 3.50 3.50

Agustín Codazzi Geographical Institute.

José Francisco Socarrás Colina (1906-95), Physician and Educator A789

**2016, May 18 Litho. *Perf. 13½***
1432 A789 10,000p multi 6.50 6.50

Values are for stamps with surrounding selvage.

Rafael Escalona (1926-2009), Composer — A790

**2016, May 26 Litho. *Perf. 13¼x13***
1433 A790 5000p multi 3.25 3.25

ARC Gloria and Humpback Whales — A791

**2016, June 8 Litho. *Perf. 13x13¼***
1434 A791 2000p multi 1.40 1.40

Colombian Ocean Commission.

2016 Summer Olympics, Rio de Janeiro — A792

Designs: 500p, Dove and olive branch. 25,000p, Dove and olive branch, diff.

**2016, July 7 Litho. *Perf. 13¼x13***
1435 A792 500p multi + label .35 .35

**Souvenir Sheet**
**Silk-Faced Paper**
***Perf. 13¼***
1436 A792 25,000p multi 16.50 16.50

No. 1436 contains one 30x60mm stamp.

A793

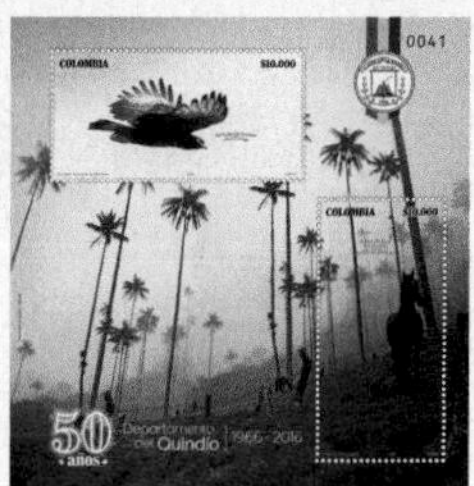

Quindío Department, 50th Anniv. — A794

No. 1437 — Arms of Quindío Department and: a, Spizaetus isidori. b, Horse and Ceroxylon quindiuense spp.

No. 1438: a, Spizaetus isidori. b, Horse and Ceroxylon quindiuense spp., vert.

**2016, July 29 Litho. *Perf. 13x13¼***
1437 A793 200p Pair, #a-b .30 .30

***Perf. 13¼***
1438 A794 10,000p Sheet of 2, #a-b 13.00 13.00

No. 1437 was printed in sheets of 16, containing 8 each Nos. 1437a-1437b + 4 labels.

Malpelo Fauna and Flora Sanctuary UNESCO World Heritage Site — A795

**2016, Aug. 11 Litho. *Perf. 13x13¼***
1439 A795 2000p multi + label 1.40 1.40

Souvenir Sheet

Peace Dove Watering Plant A796

***Perf. 13¼x13½***
**2016, Sept. 13 Litho.**
**Flocked Paper**
1440 A796 10,000p multi 7.00 7.00

No. 1440 is impregnated with a floral scent.

Ismael Enrique Arciniegas (1865-1938), Poet — A797

**2016, Nov. 4 Litho. *Perf. 13½***
1441 A797 20,000p multi 13.00 13.00

Values are for stamps with surrounding selvage.

Colombian Geological Service, Cent. — A798

**2016, Nov. 10 Litho. *Perf. 13½***
1442 A798 20,000p multi 13.00 13.00

Miniature Sheet

Tourist Network of Heritage Towns A799

No. 1443: a, Monument, Ciénaga, Magdalena Department. b, Santa Barbara Church, Santa Cruz de Mompox, Bolívar Department. c, Public Market, Santa Cruz de Lorica, Córdoba Department. d, Church, Aguadas, Caldas Department. e, Fountain and staute, Salamina, Caldas Department. f, Basilica of Our Lady of Monguí, Monguí, Boyacá Department. g, Central plaza and fountain, Villa de Leyva, Boyacá Department, h, Santa Barbara Church, Santa Fe de Antioquia, Antioquia Department. i, Church and building, Jericó, Antioquia Department. j, Building, Jardín, Antioquia Department. k, Lord of the Miracles Basilica, Guadelajara de Buga, Valle del Cauca Department. l, Navarro Bridge, Honda, Tolima Department. m. St. Michael Archangel Cathedral, Villa de Guaduas, Cundinamarca Department. n, Cathedral, Barichara, Santander Department. o, Building, San Juan Girón, Santander Department. p, St. Joseph's Church, La Playa de Belén, Norte de Santander Department. q, Cathedral, El Soccoro, Santander Department.

**2016, Nov. 15 Litho. *Perf. 13½***
**1443** A799 100p Sheet of 17, #a-q, + 3 labels *34.00 34.00*

Hands and Relay Network — A800

**2016, Dec. 3 Litho. *Perf. 13x13¼***
**1444** A800 5000p multi 3.50 3.50

**Souvenir Sheet**
**Self-Adhesive**
***Serpentine Die Cut***

**1445** A800 20,000p multi 13.50 13.50

No. 1445 contains one 28x36mm oval stamp on a 150mm diameter backing paper that is covered by a spinnable paper wheel that is attached by a metal grommet at the center.

Miniature Sheets

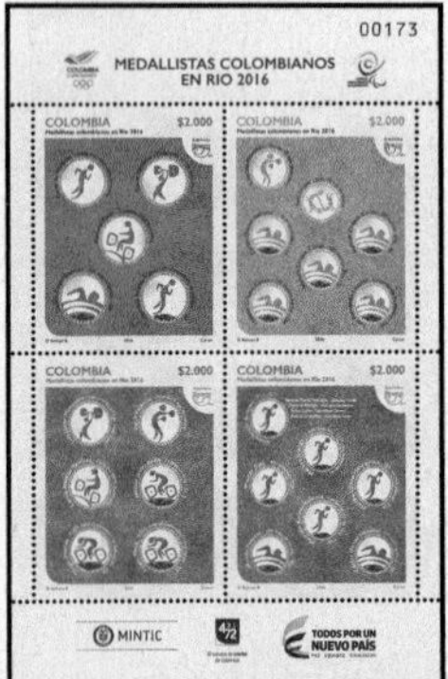

Medalists at 2016 Summer Olympics — A801

Nos. 1446 and 1447 — Emblem of sporting event and names of: a, Five gold medalists. b, Seven silver medalists. c, Six bronze medalists. d, Seven bronze medalists.

**2016, Dec. 12 Litho. *Perf. 14***
**1446** A801 2000p Sheet of 4, #a-d 5.50 5.50
**1447** A801 10,000p Sheet of 4, #a-d 27.00 27.00

America Issue.

Colombian Antarctic Program — A802

**2016, Dec. 13 Litho. *Perf. 13¼x13***
**1448** A802 10,000p multi 6.75 6.75

Christmas A803

**2016, Dec. 14 Litho. *Perf. 14***
**1449** A803 500p multi .35 .35

Sucre Department, 50th Anniv. — A804

No. 1450 — Arms of Sucre Department and: a, Dancers. b, Church.

**2017, Mar. 1 Litho. *Perf. 13x13¼***
**1450** A804 2000p Pair, #a-b 2.75 2.75

Printed in sheets of 16, containing 8 each Nos. 1450a-1450b + 4 labels.

Souvenir Sheet

Telegraph Key and Map of Colombia — A805

**2017, Mar. 24 Litho. *Perf. 13¼x13***
**1451** A805 2000p multi 1.40 1.40

Pres. Manuel Murillo Toro (1816-80).

Risaralda Department, 50th Anniv. — A806

No. 1452 — Arms of Risaralda Department and: a, Clouds covering Tatamá and Los Nevados National Parks. b, Bangsia aureocincta.

**2017, Apr. 7 Litho. *Perf. 13x13¼***
**1452** A806 500p Pair, #a-b .70 .70

Printed in sheets of 16, containing 8 each Nos. 1452a-1452b + 4 labels.

Enrique Santos Castillo (1917-2001), Lawyer and Journalist — A807

**2017, Apr. 17 Litho. *Perf. 13¼x13***
**1453** A807 5000p multi 3.50 3.50

**Departments Type of 2003**
Miniature Sheet

No. 1454 — Cesar Department: a, Arms of Cesar. b, 50th anniversary emblem of Cesar Department, horiz. c, 50th anniversary emblem of Vallenato Legend Festival. d, Ardea alba. e, Fisherman fishing Zapatosa Marsh, horiz. f, Vallenato musician playing accordion. g, Train hauling coal. h, Río Guatapurí, horiz. i, Cañaguate tree in bloom, Valledupar. j, Almojábana Monument, La Paz. k, Tamalameque folk dancers, horiz. l, Kankuama bags.

Horiz. stamps are 46x37mm.

**2017, Apr. 27 Litho. *Perf. 13¼x13***
**Sheet of 12, #a-l, + 8 labels**
**1454** A608 100p Cesar .85 .85

Julio Flórez (1867-1923), Poet — A808

**2017, May 26 Litho. *Perf. 13¼***
**1455** A808 1000p multi .70 .70

First Grand Masonic Lodge, 300th Anniv. — A809

**2017, July 6 Litho. *Perf. 13¼x13***
**1456** A809 500p multi .35 .35

**Souvenir Sheet**
***Perf. 13½x13***

**1457** A809 10,000p multi 6.75 6.75

National Federation of Coffee Growers, 90th Anniv. — A810

**2017, July 10 Litho. *Perf. 13¼***
**1458** A810 50p multi .25 .25

Matamoros Corporation, 30th Anniv. (in 2016) — A811

**2017, Aug. 14 Litho. *Perf. 13½***
**1459** A811 20,000p multi 13.50 13.50

No. 1459 was printed in sheets of 2.

A812

No. 1460: a, Neon pink "I." b, Neon orange "C." c, Neon green "C."

**2017, Aug. 24 Litho. *Perf. 13¼***
**1460** A812 500p Horiz. strip of 3, #a-c 1.00 1.00

Caro y Cuervo Institute, 75th anniv.

Visit of Pope Francis to Colombia — A813

Design: 10,000p, Pope Francis, vert.

**2017, Aug. 30 Litho. *Perf. 13x13¼***
**1461** A813 5000p gold & sil 3.50 3.50

**Souvenir Sheet**
***Perf. 13¼x13***

**1462** A813 10,000p gold & sil 6.75 6.75

Miniature Sheet

National University of Colombia, 150th Anniv. — A814

No. 1463: a, Balance (symbol of social sciences and humanities. b, Sesquicentenario symbols in deep turquoise-blue circle. c, Sesquicentenario symbols surrounding University crest, white background. d, Wheat (symbol of agriculture). e, Harp (symbol of arts). f, 19th century University monogram. g, University crest. h, Greek letter "pi" (symbol of science). i, Bowl of Hygieia (symbol of health sciences). j, Sesquicentenario symbols surrounding University crest, blue violet bacground. k, Sesquicentenario symbols in white circle. l, Greek letter "phi" (symbol of engineering).

**2017, Aug. 31 Litho. *Perf. 13¼***
**1463** A814 2000p Sheet of 12, #a-l, + 8 labels 16.50 16.50

A815

Design: Policarpa Salvarrieta (1795-1817), executed spy for revolutionary forces.

**2017, Sept. 14 Litho. *Perf. 13½***
**1464** A815 100p multi .25 .25

Ara Ararauna — A816

**2017, Sept. 22 Litho. *Perf. 13¼***
**1465** A816 1000p multi .70 .70

Bio Program.

America Issue — A817

No. 1466 — Tourist attractions: a, Caño Cristales River. b, Serranía de la Lindosa.

**2017, Oct. 9 Litho. *Perf. 13x13¼***
**1466** A817 1000p Pair, #a-b 1.40 1.40

New Future of Colombia Association, 25th Anniv. (in 1998) — A818

**2017, Oct. 18 Litho. *Perf. 13¼x13***
**1467** A818 2000p multi 1.40 1.40

Lions Clubs International, Cent. — A819

**2017, Oct. 30 Litho. *Perf. 13¼x13***
**1468** A819 5000p blue & yel 3.25 3.25

18th Bolivarian Games, Santa Marta — A820

No. 1469: a, Emblem. b, Mascot Ajaytuké.

**2017, Nov. 10 Litho. *Perf. 13¼***
**1469** A820 3000p Pair, #a-b 4.00 4.00

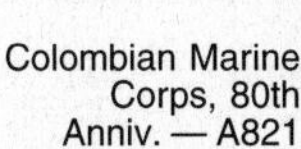

Colombian Marine Corps, 80th Anniv. — A821

**2017, Nov. 30 Litho. *Perf. 13x13¼***
**1470** A821 10,000p multi 6.75 6.75

Christmas — A822

***Serpentine Die Cut 12¾x12½***
**2017, Dec. 1 Litho.**
**Self-Adhesive**
**1471** A822 4000p gold & multi 2.75 2.75

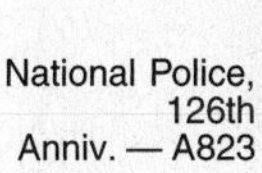

National Police, 126th Anniv. — A823

**2017, Dec. 7 Litho. *Perf. 13x13¼***
**1472** A823 1000p multi .70 .70

Publication of *María,* Novel by Jorge Isaacs (1837-95), 150th Anniv. — A824

***Perf. 13½x13¼***
**2017, Dec. 15 Litho.**
**1473** A824 4000p multi 2.75 2.75

Improvement and Decoration Society of Bogota, Cent. — A825

**2017, Dec. 20 Litho. *Perf. 13***
**1474** A825 200p multi .25 .25

Miniature Sheet

Endemic Birds — A826

No. 1475: a, Capito hypoleucus. b, Pyrrhura calliptera. c, Vireo caribaeus. d, Pyrrhura viridicata. e, Anisognathus melanogenys. f, Bangsia melanochlamys. g, Metallura iracunda. h, Cercomacra parkeri. i, Ramphomicron dorsale. j, Bucco noanamae. k, Atlapetes flaviceps. l, Coeligena orina. m, Hummingbird and "CO Colombia."

**2018, Jan. 23 Litho. *Perf. 14¼***
**1475** A826 1000p Sheet of 13, #a-m 9.25 9.25

**Departments Type of 2003**
Miniature Sheet

No. 1476 — Meta Department: a, Arms of Meta. b, Aerial view of Villavicencio, horiz. c, Joropo Music International Tournament, 50th anniv. d, Laguna de Lomalinda Natural Regional Park. e, Cuadrillas de San Martín Festival, horiz. f, Maloca Museum of Pope Francis, Villavicencio. g, Llano cowboys moving herd of cattle. h, Laguna del Amor, Puerto Rico, horiz. i, Dancers at Joropódromo. j, Monument at geographical center of Colombia, Puerto López. k, Sikuani canoe, horiz. l, Hato Santa Helena.

Horiz. stamps are 46x37mm.

**2018, Jan. 26 Litho. *Perf. 13¼x13***
**Sheet of 12, #a-l, + 8 labels**
**1476** A608 500p Meta 4.25 4.25

Miniature Sheet

Barranquilla Carnival, Cent. — A827

No. 1477: a, Carnival emblem. b, Alicia Lafaurie Roncallo, first Carnival Queen. c, Carnival reveler wearing tiger head covering and makeup. d, Torito Ribeño dancers. e, Cumbia singer. f, Fire-breathing clown.

**2018, Feb. 9 Litho. *Perf. 13x13¼***
**1477** A827 3000p Sheet of 6, #a-f 12.50 12.50

Corn Dishes — A828

No. 1478 — Ear of corn and: a, Mazamorra and arepas. b, Empanadas and tamales. c, Envueltos. d, Tortas, chicha and buñuelas.

**2018, Mar. 15 Litho. *Perf. 13x13¼***
**1478** Block or horiz. strip of 4 15.00 15.00
*a.-d.* A828 5000p Any single 3.75 3.75

National Institute of Health, Cent. — A829

**2018, Mar. 20 Litho. *Perf. 13½***
**1479** A829 2000p multi 1.50 1.50

General Rafael Reyes Prieto Military School, 109th Anniv. — A830

**2018, May 5 Litho. *Perf. 13x13¼***
**1480** A830 20,000p multi 14.00 14.00

Butterflies — A831

No. 1481 — Flowers and: a, Danaus plexippus. b, Morpho peleides.

**2018, May 9 Litho. *Perf. 13x13¼***
**1481** A831 10,000p Pair, #a-b 14.00 14.00

See Mexico Nos. 3104-3105.

Miniature Sheet

Barranquilla Attractions — A832

No. 1482: a, Plaza de Intendencia Fluvial. b, Gran Malecón del Río. c, Yellow Butterflies Monument. d, Port of Barranquilla. e, Metropolitan Cathedral. f, Barranquilla sign.

**2018, May 18 Litho. *Perf. 13¼***
**1482** A832 5000p Sheet of 6, #a-f 21.00 21.00

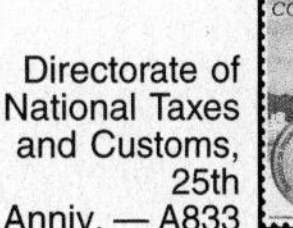

Directorate of National Taxes and Customs, 25th Anniv. — A833

**2018, June 1 Litho. *Perf. 13x13¼***
**1483** A833 10,000p multi 7.00 7.00

International History Festival, Villa de Leyva — A834

**2018, June 15 Litho. *Perf. 13¼***
**1484** A834 1000p multi .70 .70

Miniature Sheet

Ceramic Art of Cecilia Vargas Muñoz A835

No. 1485: a, Chiva Expreso del Café . b, Sculpture of mammal without tail. c, Sculpture of mammal with tail. d, Chiva Expreso Macondo.

**2018, July 13 Litho. *Perf. 13x13¼***
**1485** A835 5000p Sheet of 4, #a-d 14.00 14.00

Awarding of 2016 Nobel Peace Prize to Pres. Juan Manuel Santos Calderón — A836

**2018, July 18 Litho. *Perf. 13¼x13***
**1486** A836 2000p multi 1.40 1.40

23rd Central American and Caribbean Sports Games, Barranquilla — A837

No. 1487: a, Mascot. b, Emblem.

**2018, July 19 Litho. *Perf. 13½***
**1487** A837 2000p Pair, #a-b 2.75 2.75

Miniature Sheet

Commissioning of ARC Gloria as Training Ship, 50th Anniv. — A838

No. 1482: a, Ship with flag at right, builidngs at LR. b, Ship and bridge. c, Stylized ship with flag at right. d, Aerial view of ship. e, View of ship's stern, large flag. f, 50th anniversary emblem.

**2018, July 24 Litho. *Perf. 13¼x13***
**1488** A838 5000p Sheet of 6, #a-f 21.00 21.00

Miniature Sheet

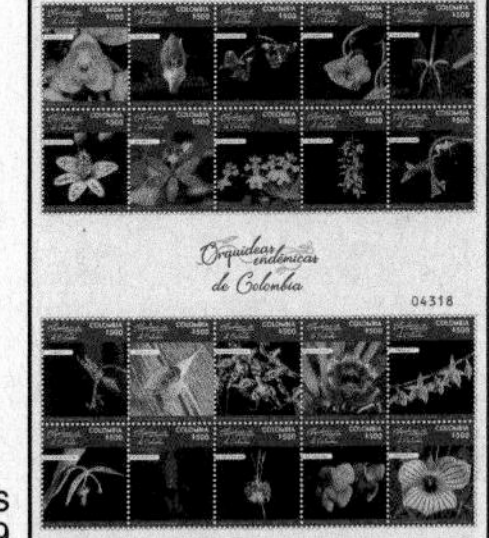

Orchids A839

No. 1489: a, Acineta antioquiae. b, Anguloa uniflora. c, Coryanthes mastersiana. d, Coryanthes misasii. e, Epidendrum ciliare. f, Epidendrum fimbriatum. g, Epidendrum sp. h, Erycina glossomystax. i, Gongora gratulabunda (multiple orchids). j, Gongora gratulabunda (single orchid). k, Gongora sp. l, Lepanthes sp. m, Odontoglossum gloriosum. n, Pescatorea pulvinaris. o, Platistele sp. p, Pleurothallis gracilicolumna. q, Pleurothallis jaramilloi. r, Psychopsis krameriana. s, Stelis nanegalensis. t, Telipogon pulcher.

**2018, Aug. 9 Litho. *Perf. 13½***
**1489** A839 500p Sheet of 20, #a-t 6.50 6.50

Presidential Guard Batallion, 90th Anniv. — A840

**2018, Aug. 13 Litho. *Perf. 13½x13***

**1490** A840 200p multi .25 .25

Miniature Sheet

Catatumbo Region and Ocaña Province of Norte de Santander Department — A841

No. 1491: a, Catatumbo River, El Tarra. b, Pineapple cultivation, Teorama. c, Pink bean cultivation, Abrego. d, Páramo de Guerrero, Cáchira and Villa Caro. e, Site of the Convention of Ocaña, Ocaña. f, Cliffs, La Playa de Belén.

**2018, Aug. 17 Litho. *Perf. 13x13½***

**1491** A841 1000p Sheet of 6, #a-f 4.00 4.00

Miniature Sheet

Risaralda Bird Festival A842

No. 1492 — Birds and butterflies: a, Dacnis hartlaubi. b, Penelope perspicax. c, Pipreola jucunda. d, Boissonneaua jardini. e, Myiarchus apicalis. f, Eueides isabella arquata. g, Eueides procula edias. h, Heliconius cydno cydnides. i, Heliconius erato chestertoni. j, Heliconius doris obscurus. k, Calliphlox mitchelli. l, Picumnus granadensis. m, Tangara ruficervix. n, Bangsia melanochlamys. o, Chlorochrysa nitidissima.

**2018, Aug. 24 Litho. *Perf. 13***

**1492** A842 1000p Sheet of 15, #a-o 9.75 9.75

Military Communications, 74th Anniv. — A843

**2018, Aug. 31 Litho. *Perf. 13½x13***

**1493** A843 20,000p multi 13.00 13.00

Souvenir Sheet

Domesticated Animals — A844

No. 1494: a, Horses, rabbit, cow, cat. dog, geese. b, Cow, donkey, sheep, dogs, goats, chickens, pigs.

**2018, Oct. 9 Litho. *Perf. 13x13½***

**1494** A844 4000p Sheet of 2, #a-b 5.00 5.00

America issue.

University of Caldas, 75th Anniv. — A845

**2018, Oct. 23 Litho. *Perf. 13***

**1495** A845 10,000p multi 6.25 6.25

Restoration of Polish Independence, Cent. — A846

**2018, Nov. 9 Litho. *Perf. 13x13½***

**1496** A846 5000p multi 3.25 3.25

National Civil Registry, 70th Anniv. — A847

**2018, Dec. 5 Litho. *Perf. 13***

**1497** A847 2000p multi 1.25 1.25

Christmas — A848

***Serpentine Die Cut***

**2018, Dec. 11 Litho.**

**On Plastic Film**

**Self-Adhesive**

**1498** A848 10,000p multi 6.25 6.25

Details of Mural, "History of the Lord of the Miracles of Buga," by Gustavo Rojas — A856

A849

A850

A851

A852

A853

A854

A855

**2018, Dec. 13 Litho. *Perf. 13x13½***

| | | | |
|---|---|---|---|
| **1499** | Sheet of 8 | 20.00 | 20.00 |
| *a.* | A849 4000p multi | 2.50 | 2.50 |
| *b.* | A850 4000p multi | 2.50 | 2.50 |
| *c.* | A851 4000p multi | 2.50 | 2.50 |
| *d.* | A852 4000p multi | 2.50 | 2.50 |
| *e.* | A853 4000p multi | 2.50 | 2.50 |
| *f.* | A854 4000p multi | 2.50 | 2.50 |
| *g.* | A855 4000p multi | 2.50 | 2.50 |
| *h.* | A856 4000p multi | 2.50 | 2.50 |

Carlos Gaviria Díaz (1937-2015), Politician — A857

No. 1500: a, Gaviria Díaz facing right. b, Gaviria Díaz seated with legs crossed. c, Gaviria Díaz facing forward. d, Books authored by Gaviria Díaz.

**2018, Dec. 17 Litho. *Perf. 13¼***

**1500** A857 500p Block of 4, #a-d 1.25 1.25

Diplomatic Relations Between Colombia and India, 60th Anniv. — A858

**2019, Jan. 28 Litho. *Perf. 13¼***

**1501** A858 4000p multi 2.60 2.60

No. 1501 was printed in sheets of 8 + 4 flanking labels.

Miniature Sheet

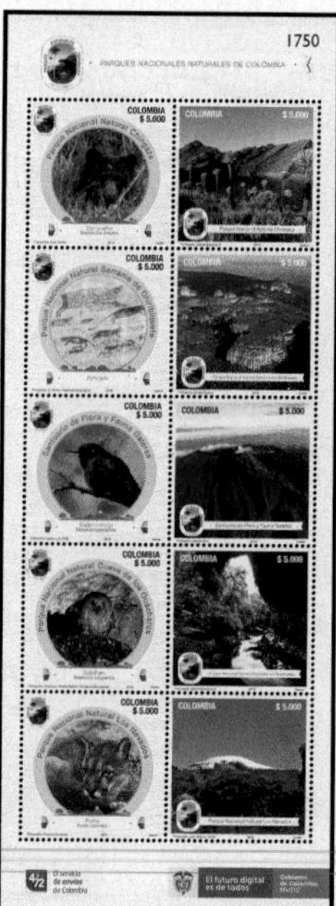

Colombian Parks — A859

No. 1502: a, Tremarctos ornatus, Chingaza National Natural Park. b, Lake and hills, Chingaza National Natural Park. c, Rock painting, Serranía de Chiribiquete National Natural Park. d, Aerial view of Chiribiquete National Natural Park. e, Metallura tyrianthina, Galeras Flora and Fauna Sanctuary. f, Volcano, Galeras Flora and Fauna Sanctuary. g, Steatornis caripensis, Cueva de los Guácharos National Natural Park. h, Cave, Cueva de los Guácharos National Natural Park. i, Puma concolor, Los Nevados National Natural Park. j, Mountain, Los Nevados National Natural Park.

**2019, Apr. 5 Litho. *Perf. 14¼***

**1502** A859 5000p Sheet of 10, #a-j 31.00 31.00

Latin American Integration Association A860

**2019, Apr. 12 Litho. *Perf. 13½***

**1503** A860 20,000p multi 12.50 12.50

Values are for stamps with surrounding selvage.

Gilberto Alejandro Durán Díaz (1919-89), Composer and Accordion Player — A861

**2019, Apr. 21 Litho. *Perf. 13***

**1504** A861 500p multi .30 .30

Mohandas K. Gandhi (1869-1948), Indian Nationalist Leader — A862

**2019, May 5 Litho. *Perf. 13¼x13***

**1505** A862 10,000p multi 6.00 6.00

Miniature Sheet

19th Century Colombian Watercolor Landscapes — A863

No. 1506: a, Market of Plaza Mayor, Santa Fé de Bogotá, by José Santiago del Castillo, 1837 (80x30mm). b, Los Llanos, Casanare Province, by Manuel María Paz, 1856 (40x30mm). c, Main House, Cachirí, Soto Province, by Carmelo Fernández, 1850 (40x30mm). d, Scene of the Battle of Boyaca, Tunja Province, by Fernández, 1850 (40x30mm). e, Bridge over Funza River, Bogotá, Cundinamarca Province, by María Paz, 1858 (40x30mm). f, Ambalema, Magdalena River, Tolima, by Edward Mark, 1846 (40x30mm). g, San Felipe Castle and La Popa Hill, Cartagena de Indias, by Mark, 1845 (40x30mm). h, Santa Marta, by Mark, 1844 (40x30mm). i, View of the Farallones de Cali from a Street in Cali, Buenaventura Province, by María Paz, 1853 (40x30mm). j, View of Village of Puracé from Alto de los Pesares, Popayán Province, by María Paz, 1855 (40x30mm). k, View of Cumbal and Chiles Volcanos, Túquerres Province, by María Paz, 1853 (40x30mm). l, Cabin, Chocó Province, by Mark, 1843 (40x30mm). m, City of Antioquia, by Henry Price, 1852 (80x30mm).

**2019, May 13 Litho. *Perf. 13x13¼***

**1506** A863 2000p Sheet of 13, #a-m 15.50 15.50

Colombian independence, 200th anniv.

Diplomatic Relations Between Colombia and Russia, 160th Anniv. — A864

No. 1507: a, Russian Tsar Alexnder II (1818-81) and balalaika. b, Colombian President Mariano Ospina Rodríguez (1805-85) and tiple.

**2019, May 24 Litho.** ***Perf. 13x13¼***
**1507** A864 20,000p Horiz. pair, #a-b 24.00 24.00

Riosucio Carnival — A865

**2019, May 28 Litho.** ***Perf. 13x13¼***
**1508** A865 10,000p multi 6.00 6.00

Colombian Air Force, Cent. — A866

**2019, June 13 Litho.** ***Perf. 13x13¼***
**1509** A866 10,000p multi 6.25 6.25

Diplomatic Relations Between Colombia and Morocco, 40th Anniv. — A867

No. 1510: a, Hassan tower, Rabat, Morocco. b, Monserrate Monastery, Bogota, Colombia.

**2019, June 19 Litho.** ***Perf. 13x13¼***
**1510** A867 10,000p Pair, #a-b 12.50 12.50

51st International Joropo Tournament, Villavicencio — A868

**2019, June 28 Litho.** ***Perf. 13¼x13***
**1511** A868 2000p multi 1.25 1.25

Colombian National Army, 200th Anniv. — A869

**2019, July 29 Litho.** ***Perf. 13¼x13***
**1512** A869 5000p multi 3.00 3.00

Miniature Sheet

19th Century Watercolors of Colombians — A870

No. 1513: a, A Llapanga and Mestizo of Cauca, by Manuel María Paz, 1855. b, Customs, Plaza Mayor, Bogota, by François Désiré Roulin, 1824. c, Exterior of Houses of Nóvita, Chocó Province, by Marí Paz, 1853. d, Habitants of the Shores of the Magdalena, by Ramón Torres Méndez, c. 1850. e, Beggar of Sogamoso, by Edward Mark, 1845. f, Peasant of Ibagué, by Mark, 1847. g, Dinner at Santa Marta, by Roulin, 1823. h, Prortait of Three Young Boys of Túquerres, by María Paz, 1853. i, Notables of the Capital, by Carmelo Fernández, 1851. j, Family of Churruyes Indians on a Trip, by José María Gutiérrez de Alba, 1871. k, Peasant of Guaduas, by Mark, 1846. l, Antioquia, by Henry Price, 1852.

**2019, Aug. 15 Litho.** ***Perf. 14***
**1513** A870 5000p Sheet of 12, #a-l 35.00 35.00

Colombian independence, 200th anniv.

Solidarity Foundation for Colombia, 44th Anniv. — A871

**2019, Aug. 25 Litho.** ***Perf. 13¼x13***
**1514** A871 500p multi .30 .30

Souvenir Sheet

Marly Clinic, Bogota, 115th Anniv. A872

**2019, Aug. 28 Litho.** ***Perf. 13x13¼***
**1515** A872 20,000p multi 12.00 12.00

Miniature Sheet

Traditional Dishes — A873

No. 1516: a, Sugar cane and panela (unrefined sugar). b, Panela. c, Plantain chips and dip. d, Green plantains, caramelized plantains.

**2019, Oct. 9 Litho.** ***Perf. 13x13¼***
**1516** A873 2000p Sheet of 4, #a-d 4.75 4.75

America issue.

Jorge Barón Television Production Company, 50th Anniv. — A874

**2019, Oct. 15 Litho.** ***Perf. 13¼x13***
**1517** A874 5000p multi 3.00 3.00

Radio Broadcasting in Colombia, 90th Anniv. — A875

**2019, Oct. 30 Litho.** ***Perf. 13x13¼***
**1518** A875 500p multi .30 .30

Miniature Sheet

Art Depicting Colombian Women of the 19th Century — A876

No. 1519 — Inscriptions: a, Frutera de la Mesa (Fruit Seller), attributed to Ramón Torres Méndez, 19th cent. b, Mujeres Blancas (White Women), Ocaña Province, by Carmelo Fernández, 1851. c, Sombrerera de Guaduas (Sombrero Maker of Guaduas), by Edward Mark, 1846. d, Plaza de Quibdó, Chocó Province, by Manuel María Paz, 1853. e, Campesinas Conduciendo Naranjas al Mercado de Bogotá (Peasants Bringing Oranges to Market in Bogotá), by Torres Méndez, 19th cent. f, Hilanderas de Lana (Wool Spinners), Pasto Province, by María Paz, 1853. g, Lavadoras de Oro Río Guadalupe (Gold Washers), Río Guadalupe, Medellin Province, by Henry Price, 1852. h, Bogotá, Mujeres del Pueblo (Bogotá, Village Women), attributed to Torres Méndez, 1872. i, Mujer de Vélez (Vélez Woman), attributed to Torres Méndez, 19th cent. j, Beata Carmelita (Blessed Carmelite), attributed to Torres Méndez, 19th cent. k, Llapangas de Popayán (Llapangas of Popayán), Popayán Province, by María Paz, 1855. l, India de Funza (Indian of Funza), attributed to Torres Méndez, 19th cent.

**2019, Nov. 14 Litho.** ***Perf. 13½***
**1519** A876 2000p Sheet of 12, #a-l 14.00 14.00

Colombian Independence, 200th anniv.

Lawyers' Club, Cent. — A877

**2019, Nov. 14 Litho.** ***Perf. 13¼x13***
**1520** A877 5000p multi 3.00 3.00

Andean Community, 50th Anniv. — A878

**2019, Nov. 21 Litho.** ***Perf. 13¼x13***
**1521** A878 2000p multi 1.25 1.25

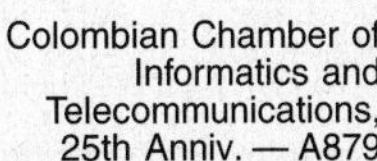
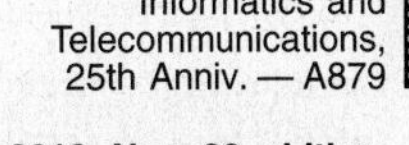

Colombian Chamber of Informatics and Telecommunications, 25th Anniv. — A879

**2019, Nov. 28 Litho.** ***Perf. 13¼x13***
**1522** A879 5000p multi 3.00 3.00

21st National Games and 5th Paranational Games, Bolívar Deparatment A880

**2019, Nov. 29 Litho.** ***Perf. 13½***
**1523** A880 5000p multi 3.00 3.00

Values are for stamps with surrounding selvage.

Bogota District Printing Office, Cent. — A881

**2019, Dec. 2 Litho.** ***Perf. 13¼x13***
**1524** A881 5000p multi 3.00 3.00

Avianca Airlines, Cent. — A882

No. 1525: a, SCADTA emblem, map of Colombia, crowd of people near seaplane. b, Seaplane with pilot and ground crew.

**2019, Dec. 2 Litho.** ***Perf. 13¼x13***
**1525** A882 2000p Pair, #a-b 2.25 2.25

Superintendent of Public Home Services, 25th Anniv. — A883

**2019, Dec. 3 Litho.** ***Perf. 13¼x13***
**1526** A883 5000p multi 3.25 3.25

Souvenir Sheet

Athletes A884

No. 1527: a, Weight lifter Leidy Y. Solís Arboleta, BMX bicyclist Mariana Pajón Londoño, boxer Ingrit L. Valencia Victoria, Triple jumper Caterine Ibargüen Mena. b, Bowler María José Rodríguez, archer Valentina Acosta Giraldo, tennis players Robert C. Farah Maksoud and Juan Sebastián Cabal Valdés. c, Runner Anthony José Zambrano, weight lifter Francisco Mosquera Valencia, diver Daniel Restrepo García, cyclist Egan Arley Bernal Gómez.

**2019, Dec. 3 Litho.** ***Perf. 13¼x13***
**1527** A884 5000p Sheet of 3, #a-c 9.25 9.25

Pereira Campus of Free University of Colombia, 50th Anniv. — A885

**2019, Dec. 9 Litho.** ***Perf. 13x13¼***
**1528** A885 2000p multi 1.25 1.25

Rotary International Projects in Colombia — A886

**2019, Dec. 10 Litho. *Perf. 13***
**1529** A886 500p multi .30 .30

Promotion of Tourism in Santander Department — A887

**2019, Dec. 12 Litho. *Perf. 13¼x13***
**1530** A887 5000p multi 3.25 3.25

Christmas — A888

**2019, Dec. 12 Litho. *Perf. 13¼x13***
**1531** A888 5000p multi 3.25 3.25

**Departments Type of 2003**
Miniature Sheets

No. 1532 — Caquetá Department: a, Arms of Caquetá. b, Thraupis episcopus, horiz. c, El Paujil. d, Araracuara Canyon and Caquetá River. e, Sanjuanero dancers, horiz. f, Maloca of an indigenous community. g, Las Dalias Nature Reserve, La Montañita. h, Our Lady of Lourdes Cathedral, Florencia, horiz. i, St. John the Baptist Parish Church, El Doncello. j, Milán. k, Prafa Museum, Belén de los Andaquíes, horiz. l, Chairá Lake.

No. 1533 — Putumayo Department: a, Arms of Putumayo. b, Sunset on Putumayo River, Puerto Asís, horiz. c, Woman weaving. d, Betsknaté y Kalusturinda Carnival of Forgiveness, Sibundoy Valley. e, Ara ararauna, horiz. f, Putumayo Governmental Building, Mocoa. g, End of the World Waterfall, Mocoa. h, Indigenous mask makers, horiz. i, Pirarucu ceviche. j, Plukenetia volubilis fruits. k, St. Michael Archangel Cathedral, Mocoa, horiz. l, Piedra del Pijili, Orito.

Horiz. stamps are 46x37mm.

**2019 Litho. *Perf. 13¼x13***
**Sheets of 12, #a-l, + 8 labels**
**1532** A608 2000p Caquetá 15.00 15.00
**1533** A608 2000p Putumayo 15.00 15.00

Issued: No. 1532, 12/20; No. 1533, 12/27.

A889

A890

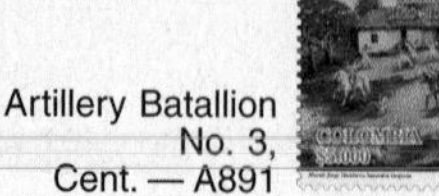

Artillery Batallion No. 3, Cent. — A891

**2020, Jan. 17 Litho. *Perf. 13x13¼***
**1534** Horiz. strip of 3 9.00 9.00
*a.* A889 5000p multi 3.00 3.00
*b.* A890 5000p multi 3.00 3.00
*c.* A891 5000p multi 3.00 3.00

Miniature Sheet

Diplomatic Relations Between Colombia and People's Republic of China, 40th Anniv. — A892

No. 1535 — UNESCO World Heritage Sites: a, Terracotta Army of Emperor Qin Shi Huang, People's Republic of China. b, Walls of Cartagena, Colombia. c, Great Wall of China. d, Stone sculptures, San Agustín Archaeological Park, Colombia.

**2020, Feb. 7 Litho. *Perf. 13***
**1535** A892 5000p Sheet of 4, #a-d 11.50 11.50

Miniature Sheet

Guadalajara de Buga, 450th Anniv. — A893

No. 1536: a, 1844 map of Guadalajara de Buga, Puente de la Libertad over Río Guadalajara. b, Sculpture of Rodrigo Díez de Fuenmayor, old train station. c, Bowls of Manjar blanco and Guiso Bugueño. d, Chloroceryle amazona, fishermen in Laguna de Sonso Nature Reserve.

**2020, Mar. 4 Litho. *Perf. 13x13¼***
**1536** A893 2000p Sheet of 4, #a-d 4.00 4.00

Miniature Sheet

2020 Risaralda Bird Festival A894

No. 1537: a, Spizaetus isidori. b, Pseudocolopteryx acutipennis. c, Rupicola peruvianus. d, Machaeropterus striolatus. e, Ceratopipra erythrocephala. f, Atlapetes flaviceps. g, Penelope perspicax. h, Bangsia melanochlamys. i, Hapalopsittaca fuertesi. j, Megoleria susiana susanna.

**2020, Mar. 20 Litho. *Perf. 13***
**1537** A894 5000p Sheet of 10, #a-j 25.00 25.00

A895

Design: Leonardo da Vinci (1452-1519), sculptor and painter.

**2020, May 29 Litho. *Perf. 13¼***
**On Paper Faced With Synthetic Fabric**
**1538** A895 5000p multi 2.75 2.75

Miniature Sheet

Colombian Parks — A896

No. 1539: a, Podocnemis expansa, El Tuparro National Natural Park (35x35mm). b, Maipures Rapids, El Tuparro National Natural Park (35x35mm). c, Coeligena helianthea, Sumapaz National Natural Park (35x35mm). d, Laguna Larga, Sumapaz National Natural Park (35x35mm). e, Cardinalis phoeniceus, Macuira National Natural Park (35x35mm). f, Aleewolu Dunes, Macuira National Natural Park (35x35mm). g, Sphyrna lewini, Malpelo Flora and Fauna Sanctuary (35x35mm). h, Malpelo Island, Malpelo Flora and Fauna Sanctuary (35x35mm). i, "60 años" and National Natural Parks of Colombia emblem (70x35mm).

**2020, June 6 Litho. *Perf. 14¼x14½***
**1539** A896 500p Sheet of 9, #a-i 2.40 2.40

Mono Núñez Andean Music Festival — A897

**2020, June 28 Litho. *Perf. 13¼***
**1540** A897 200p multi .25 .25

National Grand Masonic Lodge, Cent. — A898

**2020, July 10 Litho. *Perf. 13½x13***
**1541** A898 2000p multi 1.10 1.10

RegioTram de Occidente Tramway Project — A899

**2020, July 16 Litho. *Perf. 13x13¼***
**1542** A899 5000p multi 2.75 2.75

No. 1542 was printed in sheets of 9 + 6 labels.

Miniature Sheet

Colombian Parks — A900

No. 1543: a, Anas georgica, Isla de la Corota Flora and Fauna Sanctuary. b, Aerial view of Isla de la Corota Flora and Fauna Sanctuary. c, Leptosciurus pucheranil, Las Hermosas Gloria Valencia de Castaño National Natural Park. d, Flora near Laguna las Mellizas, Las Hermosas Gloria Valencia de Castaño National Natural Park. e, Merganetta armetta, Nevado del Huila National Natural Park. f, Mountain, Nevado del Huila National Natural Park. g, Eriocnemis vestita, Doña Juana Cascabel Volcanic Complex National Natural Park. h, Laguna del Silencio, Doña Juana Cascabel Volcanic Complex National Natural Park. i, Lepanthes sp., Puracé National Natural Park. j, San Juan Hot Springs, Puracé National Natural Park.

**2020, Aug. 14 Litho. *Perf. 14½***
**1543** A900 2000p Sheet of 10, #a-j 11.00 11.00

Julio Garavito Armero (1865-1920), Astronomer A901

**2020, Aug. 14 Litho. *Perf. 13x13¼***
**1544** A901 5000p multi 2.75 2.75

Campaign Against COVID-19 in Colombia — A902

**2020, Aug. 26 Litho. *Perf. 13¼x13***
**1545** A902 10,000p multi 5.50 5.50

Miniature Sheet

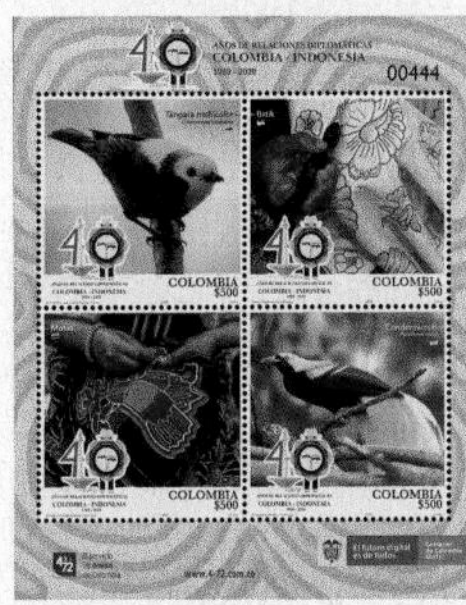

Diplomatic Relations Between Colombia and Indonesia, 40th Anniv. — A903

No. 1546 — 40th anniv. emblem and: a, Chlorochrysa nitidissima, flag of Colombia. b, Artisan making batik, flag of Indonesia. c, Artisan making mola, flag of Colombia. d, Paradisaea minor, flag of Indonesia.

**2020, Sept. 16 Litho. *Perf. 13½***
**1546** A903 500p Sheet of 4, #a-d 1.10 1.10

Reactivation of Aviation in Colombian Army, 25th Anniv. — A904

**2020, Sept. 25 Litho. *Perf. 13¼x13***
**1547** A904 100p multi .25 .25

Miniature Sheet

Colombian Parks — A905

No. 1548: a, Bangsia aureocincta, Tatamá National Natural Park. b, Valle de las Lagunas, Tatamá National Natural Park. c, Otoglossum scansor, Las Orquidéas National Natural Park. d, Páramo Morro Pelao, Las Orquidéas National Natural Park. e, Alouatta seniculus, Otún Quimbaya Flora and Fauna Sanctuary. f, Hills, Otún Quimbaya Flora and Fauna Sanctuary. g, Andinobates opisthomelas, Selva de Florencia National Natural Park. h, El Escondido Volcano, Selva de Florencia National Natural Park.

**2020, Sept. 29 Litho. *Perf. 14½***
**1548** A905 2000p Sheet of 8, #a-h 8.50 8.50

National Association of Public Services and Communications Companies, 25th Anniv. — A906

**2020, Oct. 6 Litho. *Perf. 13½x13***
**1549** A906 2000p multi 1.10 1.10

Miniature Sheet

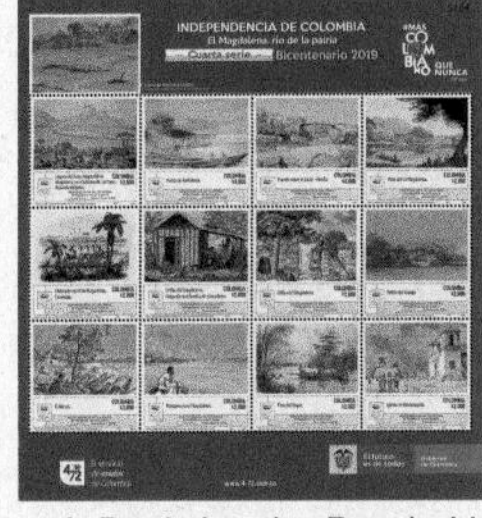

Artwork Depicting the People Living Near the Magdalena River — A907

No. 1550 — Inscriptions: a, Laguna del Buey, origen del río Magdalena, en el páramo de Las Papas - Provincia de Neiva (Laguna del Buey, origin of the Magdalena River, in the moors of Las Papas, Province of Neiva), by Manuel María Paz. b, Puerto de Ambalema (Port of Ambalema), by Edward Walhouse Mark. c, Puente sobre el Gualì - Honda (Bridge over the Gualí, Honda), by Mark. d, Vista del río Magdalena (View of the Magdalena River), by Mark. e, Champán en el río Magdalena, Colombia (Champagne on the Magdalena River, Colombia), by Ramón Torres Méndez. f, Orillas del Magdalena, Hogar de una familia de pescadores (Home of a family of fishermen on the banks of the Magdalena), by François Désiré Roulin. g, Orillas del Magdalena (Banks of the Magdalena), by Roulin. h, Peñón del Conejo (Rabbit Rock), by Mark. i, El Banco (The bank), by Mark. j, Mompox en el Magdalena (Mompon on the Magdalena), by Mark. k, Paso del Dique, by A. De Neuville. l, Iglesia en Barranquilla (Church in Barranquilla), by Mark.

**2020, Oct. 15 Litho. *Perf. 13½***
**1550** A907 2000p Sheet of 12, #a-l 12.50 12.50

Colombian independence, 200th anniv.

Diplomatic Relations Between Colombia and Austria, Cent. — A908

No. 1551: a, Nikolaus Joseph von Jacquin (1727-1817), botanist, Cordia sebestena, Psiguria pedata. b, José Celeestino Mutis (1732-1808), priest and botanist, Bomarea multiflora.

**2020, Oct. 26 Litho. *Perf. 13x13½***
**1551** A908 5000p Horiz. pair, #a-b 5.25 5.25

No. 1551 was printed in sheets containing two pairs.

**Departments Type of 2003**
Miniature Sheet

No. 1552 — Bolívar Department: a, Arms of Bolívar. b, Santa Cruz de Mompox, horiz. c, Pink Sea of Galerazamba (salt mine). d, Saguinus oedipus. e, Fishermen off Santa Catalina de Alejandría, horiz. f, Fabric art of Mampuján. g, Items made by San Jacinto artisans. h, Walls of Cartagena de Indias, horiz. i, Son de Negros dancer, Gamero. j, Crax alberti. k, El Guamo, Montes de María, horiz. l, Guillermo Piñeres Botanical Garden, Turbaco. Horiz. stamps are 46x37mm.

**2020, Oct. 29 Litho. *Perf. 13¼x13***
**Sheet of 12, #a-l, + 8 labels**
**1552** A608 1000p Bolívar 6.25 6.25

Organization of the Andrés Bello Agreement for Educational, Scientific, Technological and Cultural Integration, 50th Anniv. — A909

**2020, Oct. 29 Litho. *Perf. 13x13½***
**1553** A909 2000p multi 1.10 1.10

Miniature Sheet

Colombian Parks — A910

No. 1554: a, Lagothrix lagotricha, Amacayacu National Natural Park. b, Lago Tigre, Amacayacu National Natural Park. c, Tapirus terrestris, Cahuinarí National Natural Park. d, Maloka Bora-Miraña, Cahuinarí National Natural Park. e, Dendropsophus triangulum, Serranía de los Churumbelos National Natural Park. f, Caquetá River, Serra ía de los Churumbelos National Natural Park. g, Panthera onca, Alto Fragua Indi Wasi National Natural Park. h, Fragua Grande River Basin, Alto Fragua Indi Wasi National Natural Park. i, Harpia harpyja, Nukak National Reserve. j, Tepuis, Nukak National Reserve.

**2020, Oct. 30 Litho. *Perf. 14¼***
**1554** A910 5000p Sheet of 10, #a-j 26.00 26.00

Miniature Sheet

America Issue A911

No. 1555 — Buildings in: a, Magdalena. b, La Guajira. c, San Andrés y Providencia. d, Antioquia. e, Boyaca. f, Tolima.

**2020, Nov. 25 Litho. *Perf. 13x13¼***
**1555** A911 2000p Sheet of 6, #a-f 6.75 6.75

Miniature Sheet

Colombian Parks — A912

No. 1556: a, Pipile cumanensis, Orito Ingi-Ande Medicinal Plants Flora Sanctuary. b, Passiflora sp., Orito Ingi-Ande Medicinal Plants Flora Sancturary. c, Caiman crocodilus, Río Puré Natural National Park. d, Boats on Río Puré, Río Puré Natural National Park. e, Indigenous people in ceremony, Yaigojé Apaporis Natural National Park. f, La Playa Rapids on Río Apaporis, Yaigojé Apaporis Natural National Park. g, Saguinus nigricollis, Puinawai Natural National Reserve. h, Guacamaya Rapids, Puinawai Natural National Reserve. i, Inia geoffrensis, La Paya Natural National Park. j, Río Putumayo, La Paya Natural National Park.

**2020, Nov. 27 Litho. *Perf. 14¼***
**1556** A912 2000p Sheet of 10, #a-j 11.50 11.50

Souvenir Sheet

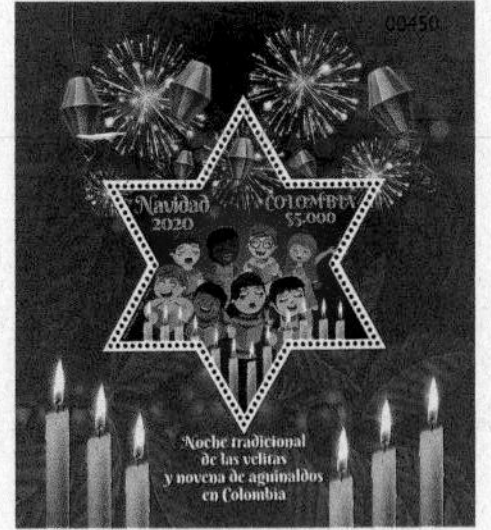

Christmas — A913

**2020, Dec. 7 Litho. *Perf. 14***
**1557** A913 5000p multi 3.00 3.00

Ocaña, 450th Anniv. A914

No. 1558: a, Temple of San Francisco. b, 1888 drawing of people of the San Agustí neighborhood.

**2020, Dec. 14 Litho. *Perf. 13x13¼***
**1558** A914 2000p Pair, #a-b 2.40 2.40

Colombian National Radio, 80th Anniv. — A915

**2020, Dec. 21 Litho. *Perf. 13¼x13***
**1559** A915 500p multi .30 .30

### Miniature Sheet

Colombian Parks — A916

No. 1560: a, Ocypode gaudichaudii, Cabo Manglares, Bajo Mira y Frontera National Integrated Management District. b, Arco del Morro, Cabo Manglares, Bajo Mira y Frontera National Integrated Management District. c, Sphyraena idiastes, Yuruparí-Malpelo National Integrated Management District. d, Diver and marine life, Yuruparí-Malpelo National Integrated Management District. e, Oophaga lehmanni, Farallones de Cali National Natural Park. f, Peaks of the Farallones, Farallones de Cali National Natural Park. g, Anolis gorgonae, Gorgona National Natural Park. h, Cerro Trinidad, Gorgona National Natural Park. i, Chauna chavaria, Los Katíos National Natural Park. j, Atrato River, Los Katíos National Natural Park.

**2020, Dec. 29 Litho.** ***Perf. 14½***

**1560** A916 2000p Sheet of 10, #a-j 12.00 12.00

### Miniature Sheet

Colombian Parks — A917

No. 1561: a, Begonia killipiana, Munchique National Natural Park. b, Pico de Piedra, Munchique National Natural Park. c, Anadara tuberculosa, Sanquianga National Natural Park. d, Mangrove trees, Hondo Estuary, Sanquianga National Natural Park. e, Megaptera novaeangliae, Uramba Bahía Málaga National Natural Park. f, Juanchaco Beach, Uramba Bahía Málaga National Natural Park. g, Atelopus spurelli, Utría National Natural Park. h, Blanca Beach, Utría National Natural Park.

**2021, Jan. 20 Litho.** ***Perf. 14½***

**1561** A917 200p Sheet of 8, #a-h .90 .90

### Miniature Sheet

Famous People A918

No. 1562: a, Rodrigo Arenas Betancourt (1919-95), sculptor. b, Enrique Grau (1920-2004), painter and sculptor. c, Fernando González Ochoa (1895-1964), writer. d, Manuel Zapata Olivella (1920-2004), writer. e, Cecilia Porras (1920-71), painter. f, Alejandro Obregón (1920-92), painter.

**2021, Feb. 24 Litho.** ***Perf. 13x13¼***

**1562** A918 500p Sheet of 6, #a-f 1.75 1.75

### Miniature Sheets

Liberation Campaign of 1819 — A919

Travel and Transportation in the 19th Century — A920

No. 1563 — Inscription under picture: a, El paso del Ejército Libertador por los Llanos en 1819 (The passage of the Liberation Army through the Llanos in 1819) (40x30mm). b, Avance de los lanceros llaneros hacia Santafé (Advance of the Llaneros lancers toward Santafé) (40x30mm). c, Cruce de la cordillera orinetal por el Ejército Libertador (Liberation Army crossing the eastern mountains) (40x30mm). d, Combate de Paya. Trincherón y poblado de Paya (Combat of Paya. Fort and town of Paya) (40x30mm). e, Combate de Gámeza (Combat of Gámeza (40x30mm). f, Batalla del Pantano de Vargas (Battle of Vargas Swamp) (40x30mm). g, Alegoría honores al coronel de la Légion Brítanica James Rooke. Batalla del Pantano de Vargas (Allegory honoring British Legion Colonel James Rooke. Battle of Vargas Swamp) (80x30mm). h, Carga de lancerso Batalla del Pantano de Vargas (Charge of the lancers. Battle of Vargas Swamp) (40x30mm). i, Casa de postas o de teja, sitio primer encuentro de tropas. Batalla de Boyacá (Casa de Teja, site of first troop encounter. Battle of Boyacá) (40x30mm). j, Caballería, infantería, y artillería del ejército español. Campo de la batalla de Boyacá (Cavalry, infantry and artillery of Spanish army on Boyacá battleground) (40x30mm). k, Carga de la vanguardia del Ejército Libertador al mando de general de brigada F. P. Santander. Batalla de Boyacá (Charge of the vanguard of the Liberation Army under the command of Brigadier General Francisco Santander. Battle of Boyacá) (40x30mm).

No. 1564 — Inscription: a, Actividad portuaria en Santa Marta (Santa Marta port activity). b, Champán de Magdalena (Magdalena sampan). c, Vapor en el río Catatumbo (Río Catatumbo steamboat). d, La Ceja, camino de Guanacas (La Caya, on the way to Guanacas). e, Camino para Novitá en la montaña de Tamaná. Provincia del Chocó (Road to Novitáon Mount Tamaná, Chocó Province). f, Puente del río Ingará. Provincia del Chocó (Río Ingará Bridge, Chocó Province). g, Puente de cuerdas de la Plata (Tarabita) (Cord bridge (Tarabita) over Río la Plata). h, Mujer campesina de Gachetá en viaje (Peasant woman from Gachetá on journey). i, Indios cargueros conduciendo un piano de Honda a Bogotá (Indians carrying piano crate from Honda to Bogotá). j, India carguera (indian carrying crate). k, Tren de viaje de un cura de las tierras altas (Travel convoy of priest). l, Conducción de muebles (Furniture transport).

**2021, Apr. 20 Litho.** ***Perf. 13x13¼***

**1563** A919 2000p Sheet of 11, #a-k 11.50 11.50

***Perf. 13¼***

**1564** A920 5000p Sheet of 12, #a-l 31.50 31.50

Colombian independence, 200th anniv.

Ministry of Foreign Affairs, 200th Anniv. — A921

**Litho. & Embossed**

**2021, Apr. 29** ***Perf. 13x13¼***

**1565** A921 5000p gold & multi 2.60 2.60

### Miniature Sheet

People and Governmental Items of Colombia of the Early 19th Century — A922

No. 1566: a, Preamble of the 1821 Constitution of the Republic of Colombia. b, Drawing of original church, Villa del Rosario. c, Historic church of Cucutá, Villa del Rosario (site of writing and signing of first constitution). d, Birthplace of Francisco de Paula Santander, Villa del Rosario. e, 1821 map of the Republic of Colombia. f, 1821 coat of arms of the Republic of Colombia. g, 1821 coin of the Republic of Colombia. h, Public education. i, People of the Llanos, 1821. j, People on Paseo del Agua Nueva, Bogotá, 1848. k, People drinking chicha. l, Signatures on 1821 Constitution of the Republic of Colombia.

**2021, May 6 Litho.** ***Perf. 13¼***

**1566** A922 2000p Sheet of 12, #a-l 13.00 13.00

Colombian independence, 200th anniv.

### Souvenir Sheet

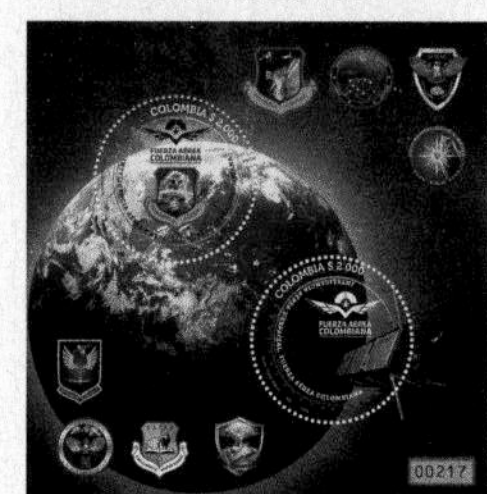

Colombian Air Force — A923

No. 1567: a, Emblem of Air and Space Intelligence branch of Colombian Air Force. b, FACSAT-1 Satellite in space.

**2021, May 27 Litho.** ***Perf.***

**1567** A923 2000p Sheet of 2, #a-b 2.25 2.25

San Juan and San Pedro Folk Festivals, 60th Anniv. A924

No. 1568: a, Dancers, musical notes on staff. b, Festival attendees.

**2021, July 4 Litho.** ***Perf. 14***

**1568** A924 5000p Pair, #a-b 5.25 5.25

### Miniature Sheet

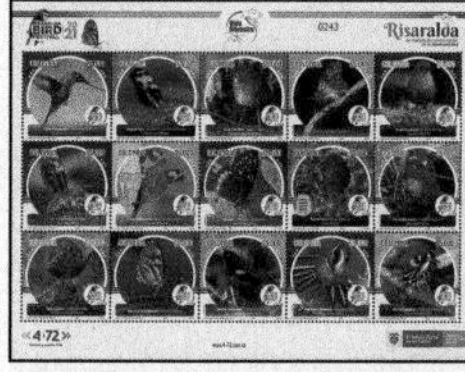

Birds and Butterflies — A925

No. 1569: a, Sword-billed hummingbird. b, Orange-spotted tiger butterfly. c, Brown-banded antpitta. d, Catasticta prioneris albescens. e, Equatorial antpitta. f, Tiger mimic-white butterfly. g, Yellow-eared parrots. h, Tarricina longwing butterfly. i, Chami antpitta. j, Bicolored antpitta. k, Slate-crowned antpitta. l, Ithomia alienassa. m, Chestnut-bellied flowerpiercer. n, Buffy helmetcrest. o, Crescent-faced antpitta.

**2021, July 12 Litho.** ***Perf. 13***

**1569** A925 5000p Sheet of 15, #a-o 39.00 39.00

Risaralda Bird Festival.

Association of Footwear and Similar Industries, 20th Anniv. — A926

**2021, July 13 Litho.** ***Perf. 13¼x13***

**1570** A926 1000p multi .55 .55

Jorge Oñate (1949-2021), Singer and Composer — A927

**2021, July 15 Litho.** ***Perf. 13¼x13***

**1571** A927 5000p multi 2.60 2.60

National Council for Economic and Social Policy, 54th Anniv. — A928

**2021, July 21 Litho.** ***Perf. 13¼x13***

**1572** A928 2000p multi 1.10 2.60

### Souvenir Sheet

La Gran Colombia University, Bogota, 70th Anniv. — A929

No. 1573: a, University building, small crest and 70th anniv. emblem. b, Windows, door and sidewalk of university building, large crest and 70th anniv. emblem.

**2021, July 22 Litho.** ***Perf. 13x13¼***

**1573** A929 1000p Sheet of 2, #a-b 1.10 1.10

Flags, Coats of Arms and Seals A930

No. 1574 — Inscriptions: a, Escudo de armas del Estado Libre e Independiente de Cundinamarca (coat of arms of the Free and Independent State of Cundinamarca), 1813-15. b, Bandfera del Estado Libre e Indpendiente de Cundinamarca (flag of the Free and Independent State of Cundinamarca), 1813-14. c, Primera bandera de las Provincias Unidas de Nueva Granada (first flag of the United Provinces of New Granada), 1814-15. d, Escudo provisional de las Provincias Unidas de Nueva Granada (provisional coat of arms of the United Provinces of New Granada), 1814. e, Bandera de la República de Colombia (flag of the Republic of Colombia), 1819-30. f, Primer escudo de la República de Colombia (first coat of arms of the Republic of Colombia), 1819-20. g, Sello provisional de la República de Nueva Granada (Provisional seal of the Republic of New Granada), 1820. h, Escudo de la República de Colombia (coat of arms of the Republic of Colombia), 1821-30. i, Escudo propuesto para la República de Nueva Granada (proposed coat of arms of the Republic of New Granada), 1833. j, Escudo de la República de Nueva Granada (coat of arms of the Republic of New Granada), 1834. k, Bandera de la República de Nueva Granada y la Confederación Granadina (flag of the Republic of New Granada and the Granadine Confederation), 1834-58, 1858-61. l, Escudo provisional de la República de Nueva Granada (provisional coat of arms of the Republic of New Granada), 1854.

**2021, Aug. 5 Litho.** ***Perf. 13½***
**1574** A930 2000p Sheet of 12, #a-l 13.00 13.00

Colombian independece, 200th anniv.

Miniature Sheet

Redoubt of Paya A931

No. 1575 — Inscriptions: a, Delineado del Reducto del Paya, ca. 1817-18 (Drawing of the outline of the Redoubt. c. 1817-19). b, Lugar donde se dio el primer triunfo de la Campaña Libertadora, 1819 (Aerial view of Redoubt). c, Ubicación sobre el poblado de Paya (Aerial view of Redoubt and town of Paya). d, Vista estratégica, localizado en la vereda El Morro en la cordillera Oriental (View of Redoubt and nearby hills and valley). e, Panorámica del foso ylos muros de defensa (View of Redoubt's defensive walls and surrounding pit). f, Detalle, al fondo las veredas de Soapaga, Abejón, y Boca de Monte (Walkways of the Redoubt.).

**2021, Aug. 5 Litho.** ***Perf. 13¼***
**1575** A931 2000p Sheet of 6, #a-f 6.50 6.50

Miniature Sheet

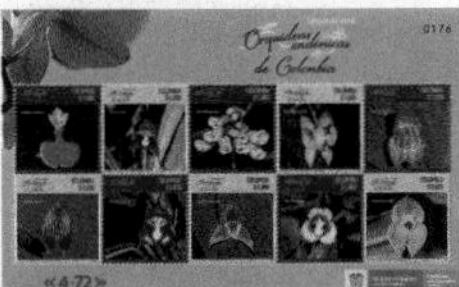

Orchids A932

No. 1576; a, Comparettia ignea. b, Dracula minax. c, Elleanthus escobarii. d, Lepanthes nicolasii. e, Lepanthes yubarta. f, Lepanthes discolor. g, Dracula nosferatu. h, Lepanthes niesseniae. i, Dracula tsubotae. j, Lepanthes ophelma.

**2021, Aug. 12 Litho.** ***Perf. 13¼***
**1576** A932 5000p Sheet of 10, #a-j 26.50 26.50

Regional Autonomous Corporation of Guavio — A933

No. 1577: a, Dendropsophus molitor. b, Lake near Ubalá. c, Guavio Reservoir. d, Spizaetus isidori. e, Coeligena helianthea. f, Siecha Lake, Guasca. g, Geranoaetus melanoleucus. h, Anolis heterodermus.

**2021, Aug. 20 Litho.** ***Perf. 13x13¼***
**1577** A933 2000p Sheet of 8, #a-h 8.50 8.50

Miniature Sheet

Socorro Tourist Attractions — A934

No. 1578: a, Basilica of Our Lady of Socorro. b, Statue of Manuela Beltrán, leader of 1780 peasant revolt. c, Capuchin Monastery. d, Statue of José Antonio Galán (c. 1749-82), leader of 1781 insurrection. e, Medal depicting José A. Morales (1913-78), composer. f, Walls of the Capitol. g, Houses along cobblestoned street. h, Horacio Rodríguez Plata Cultural Center. i, Sculptures on José A. Morales Square.

**2021, Aug. 17 Litho.** ***Perf. 13x13¼***
**1578** A934 2000p Sheet of 9, #a-i 9.50 9.50

Miniature Sheet

Coffee Cultural Landscape UNESCO World Heritage Site — A935

No. 1579: a, Woman carrying shopping bags in Salamina. b, Man raking coffee beans. c, Man drinking cup of coffee near Willys jeep. d, Building in Mirador National Park. e, Trees and mountains at dawn. f, Momotus momota. g, Belén de Umbría. h, Buildings in El Cairo. i, Aerial view of valley. j, Quimbaya culture statues. k, House on coffee-producing farm, Risaralda. l, House's windows, lamp and hanging plant, Valle del Cauca.

**2021, Sept. 23 Litho.** ***Perf. 13***
**1579** A935 2000p Sheet of 12, #a-l 14.00 14.00

Miniature Sheet

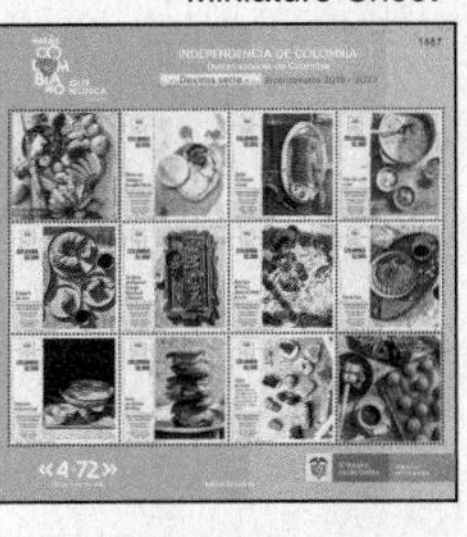

Desserts A936

No. 1580: a, Obleas con arequipe y bocadillo veleño (wafers with caramel and guava jelly). b, Liberal de arequipe y moras (roll cake with caramel and blackberries). c, Arroz con leche y coco (rice pudding with coconut). d, Enyucado con anís (cassava cake with anise). e, Tartaleta de chocolate amargo, tamarindo y marañón (dark chocolate tartlet with tamarind and cashews). f, Merengón de fresa y crema de diente de leon (meringue with strawberry cream and dandelions). g, Flan de coco (coconut flan). h, Esponjado de limón y sal (lemon and salt sponge cake). i, Cucas con helado de malta (malt ice cream cookie sandwiches). j, Dulces del portal (assorted desserts).

**2021, Sept. 24 Litho.** ***Perf. 13½***
**1580** A936 2000p Sheet of 10, #a-j, + 2 labels 10.50 10.50

Colombian independence, 200th anniv.

Miniature Sheet

Colombian Foods — A937

No. 1581: a, Caldo de costilla y papa de Paloquemao (Paloquemao rib and potato broth). b, Posta negra Catagenera (Cartagena marinated beef). c, Arepas made with various ingredients. d, Empanaditas fritas (fried empanadas). e, Ajiaco Bogotano (Bogota potato and chicken soup). f, Frijolada Antioqueña (Antioquia beans). g, Encocado de Almejas (clam and coconut milk stew). h, Cayeye (mashed plantain). i, Pan de Bono, Lulada con Aguardiente y Empanaditas de Pipián (cheese bread, lemon juice cocktail, and pumpkin seed empanadas). j, Envolturas con Hojas (wrapped foods).

**2021, Sept. 24 Litho.** ***Perf. 13½***
**1581** A937 2000p Sheet of 10, #a-j, + 2 labels 10.50 10.50

Miniature Sheet

Tourism A938

No. 1582: a, Sculpture of musicians, San Jacinto. b, Woman holding plate of food. c, Woven artisanal fiber goods, Usiacurí. d, Yagua man at tree.

**2021, Oct. 8 Litho.** ***Perf. 13x13¼***
**1582** A938 5000p Sheet of 4, #a-d 11.00 11.00

America issue.

Miniature Sheet

Colombian Association of Micro, Small and Medium Industries — A939

No. 1583: a, Statue of a hat maker. b, Finished and unfinished hats. c, Jewelry. d, Gold miner. e, Worker holding bleached cane syrup. f, Pans containing unrefined cane sugar.

**2021, Nov. 5 Litho.** ***Perf. 13x13¼***
**1583** A939 2000p Sheet of 6, #a-f 6.25 6.25

Miniature Sheet

Scenes of Everyday Life in 19th Century Colombia — A940

No. 1584: a, Market in Mompox. b, Trapiche (sugar cane juice extractor). c, Procession in Bogota. d, Angelito dancers on shore of Río Magdalena. e, Woman preparing chocolate. f, Harvesters preparing tobacco leaves for drying. g, People roasting food on shores of Río Meta. h, People at store's counter. i, Women playing cards. j, Musician and dancers. k, Musicians, dancers and dog. l, Harpist.

**2021, Nov. 6 Litho.** ***Perf. 13½***
**1584** A940 2000p Sheet of 12, #a-l 12.50 12.50

Miniature Sheet

Tenth Festival of Flowers, Madrid, Cundinamarca Department — A941

No. 1585 — Floral display: a, Commemorating Madrid's 461st anniversary. b, Of pink, red, orange and purple flowers. c, Between brick pathways. d, Near church.

**2021, Nov. 13 Litho.** ***Perf. 13¼x13***
**1585** A941 2000p Sheet of 4, #a-d 4.25 4.25

Miniature Sheet

Arcabuco Tourist Attractions — A942

No. 1586: a, Church and park with statues in fountain. b, Statue depicting guardian angel. c, Las Chorreras Waterfall. d, View of Arcabuco from hilltop at sunset.

**2021, Nov. 19 Litho. *Perf. 13x13¼***
**1586** A942 5000p Sheet of 4, #a-d 10.50 10.50

Miniature Sheet

Gulf of Morrosquillo Regional Tourist Attractions — A943

No. 1587: a, Dama de Blanco and tourist transportation, Tolú. b, Gyr cattle. c, Seagull Monument, Tolú. d, Playa Caimán, Coveñas. e, Fregata magnificens. f, Virgin of the Seas statue, Tolú. g, Sailboats on shore. h, Ciénaga de la Caimanera, Coveñas. i, Alouatta seniculus.

**2021, Nov. 22 Litho. *Perf. 13x13¼***
**1587** A943 2000p Sheet of 9, #a-i 9.25 9.25

Miniature Sheet

Artisans and Tradesmen — A944

No. 1588: a, Weaver. b, Water haulers with donkey, Bogota. c, Carrier of sticks. d, Pig herders. e, Mail carriers and horse. f, Women making corn bread. g, Donkey drover. h, Indigenous woman carrying sacks. i, Potters transporting pots. j, Indigenous people transporting corpse to cemetery. k, Cook using bellows. l, Musicians.

**2021, Nov. 26 Litho. *Perf. 13½***
**1588** A944 5000p Sheet of 12, #a-l 30.50 30.50

Miniature Sheet

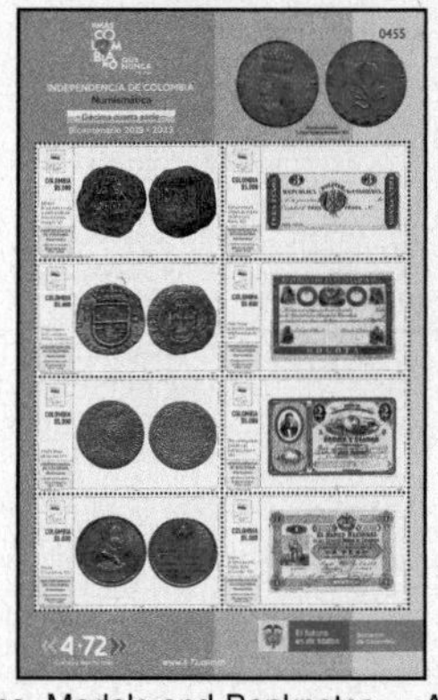

Coins, Medals and Banknotes — A945

No. 1589: a, Obverse and reverse of first coin of New Kingdom of Granada minted in 1621 in Cartagena. b, 1822 3-peso banknote printed after Cucúta Congress. c, Obverse and reverse of first gold coin minted in the Americas, 1622. d, 1843 banknote of Republic of New Granada. e, Obverse and reverse of 1819 medal depicting Simón Bolívar. f, 1861 2-peso private banknote of Granadine Confederation. g, Obverse and reverse of medal depicting Bolívar minted in September 1828. h, 1881 1-peso United States of Colombia banknote.

**Litho. & Embossed (coins and medals), Litho. (banknotes)**

**2021, Dec. 1 *Perf. 13¾***
**1589** A945 5000p Sheet of 8, #a-h 20.50 20.50

Miniature Sheet

City of Armenia Tourist Attractions — A946

No. 1590: a, St. Francis of Assisi Parish Church. b, Locomotive 70. c, Parade of cargo-laden Willys Jeeps. d, Dialogues of Thought, sculpture by Efrén Fernández Varón (1938-2019).

**2021, Dec. 15 Litho. *Perf. 13x13¼***
**1590** A946 5000p Sheet of 4, #a-d 10.00 10.00

Miniature Sheet

Colombian Medalists at 2020 Summer Olympics, Tokyo — A947

No. 1591 — Emblems depicting sports of medalists: a, José Gregorio Lemos Rivas, Carlos Daniel Serraano Zarate, and Nelson Crispin Corzo. b, Mauricio Valencia, Darian Faisury Jiménez Sánchez, and Mayerli Buitrago Ariza. c, Anthony José Zambrano de la Cruz, Luis Javier Mosquera Lozano, Sandra Lorena Arenas Campuzano, Mariana Pajón Londoño, and Carlos Alberto Ramírez Yepes. d, Moisés Fuentes Garcísa, Corzo, and Serrano Zarate. e, Serrano Zarate, Corzo, and Laura C. González Rodríguez. f, Jean Carlos Mina Aponzá, Lemos Rivas, Diego F. Meneses M., Angie Lizeth Pabón Mamiam, and Luis F. Lucimí V. g, Jiménez Sánchez, Juan José Betancourt Q., Yesenia M. Restrepo Muñoz, Diego Dueñas G., and Fabio Torres Silva.

**Litho. & Embossed With Foil Application**

**2021, Dec. 16 *Perf. 14***
**1591** A947 20,000p Sheet of 7, #a-g, + 2 labels 69.00 69.00

The 2020 Summer Olympics was postponed until 2021 because of the COVID-19 pandemic.

Christmas — A948

**Litho. & Embossed With Foil Application**

**2021, Dec. 16 *Perf. 13½x13***
**1592** A948 2000p sil & multi 1.00 1.00

Diplomatic Relations Between Colombia and Mexico, 200th Anniv. — A949

No. 1593 — Stylized butterfly at: a, Left. b, Right.

**2021, Dec. 20 Litho. *Perf. 14x13½***
**1593** A949 5000p Horiz. pair, #a-b 5.00 5.00

See Mexico Nos. 3227-3228.

Miniature Sheet

Cali Festivals A950

No. 1594: a, Two dancers on record. b, Three performers. c, Two performers. d, Male dancers lifting female dancer.

**2021, Dec. 27 Litho. *Perf. 13x13¼***
**1594** A950 5000p Sheet of 4, #a-d 10.00 10.00

15th World Salsa Festival (Nos. 1594a, 1594d), 25th Petronio Alvarez Festival of Pacific Music (Nos. 1594b, 1594c).

Miniature Sheet

Blacks and Whites' Carnival, Pasto A951

No. 1595: a, Dragon's head from parade float (bright yellow green panel). b, Caricatures of people from side of small float (purple black panel). c, Masked carnival participant (cerise panel). d, Parade participant with frog on top of mask (orange panel). e, Musicians wearing costumes (dark violet panel). f, Dance troupe (rose red panel). g, Child with painted face wearing costume and hat (bright purple panel). h, Costumed dancers (ocher panel). i, Artisan cutting decorated Pasto-lacquered wooden object (scarlet panel). j, Decorated container commemorating 500th anniversary of the discovery of the Americas, 1992 (blue green panel).

**2021, Dec. 28 Litho. *Perf. 14x13½***
**1595** A951 2000p Sheet of 10, #a-j 10.00 10.00

Miniature Sheet

Grand Masonic Lodge of Colombia, Cent. — A952

No. 1596 — Emblem of: a, Grand Lodge (rose background). b, Lodge No. 1 (rose lilac background). c, Lodge No. 2 (yellow background). d, Lodge No. 3 (dull gray blue background). e, Lodge No. 4 (pale emerald background). f, Lodge No. 5 (pale yellow green background).

**2022, Feb. 17 Litho. *Perf. 13¼x13***
**1596** A952 2000p Sheet of 6, #a-f 6.25 6.25

Miniature Sheet

Diplomatic Relations Between Colombia and Egypt, 65th Anniv. — A953

No. 1597: a, Bust of Queen Nefertiti. b, Simón Bolívar (1783-1830), liberator of South American countries. c, Parrot. d, Falcon.

**2022, Feb. 23 Litho. *Perf. 13¼***
**1597** A953 2000p Sheet of 4, #a-d 4.25 4.25

See Egypt No.

Miniature Sheet

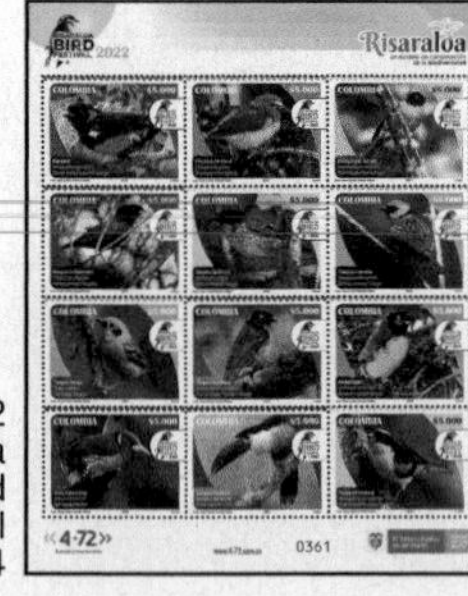

2022 Risaralda Bird Festival A954

No. 1598: a, Scarlet-bellied mountain tanager. b, Blue-naped chlorophonia. c, Black-headed hemispingus. d, Golden-crowned tanager. e, Rufous-throated tanager. f, Saffron-crowned tanager. g, Golden tanager. h, Lacrimose mountain tanager. i, Hooded mountain tanager. j, Red-headed barbet. k, Black-billed mountain toucan. l, Blue-winged mountain tanager.

**2022, Mar. 17 Litho.** ***Perf. 13x13¼***
**1598** A954 5000p Sheet of 12, #a-l 32.00 32.00

Medellin Coin Club, 31st Anniv. (in 2021) — A955

**2022, Mar. 25 Litho.** ***Perf. 13¼x13***
**1599** A955 20,000p multi 10.50 10.50

Miniature Sheet

Restoration of Stained Glass Windows of Cathedral Basilica of Our Lady of the Rosary, Manizales — A956

No. 1600 — Window depicting: a, St. Matthew, 1846. b, Tobias and St. Raphael the Archangel, 1851. c, Christ's Descent from the Cross, 1878. d, Christ the King, 1952. e, Saints John Chrysostom and Gregory of Nazianzus, 1956. f, Crucified Lord, 1956. g, 27 Figures, 1957. h, Melchizedek and Abraham, 1958. i, Young Jesus Preaching to the Doctors in the Temple, 1963. j, North Rosette, 1971. k, Tares Among the Wheat, 1971. l, The Wise and Foolish Virgins, 1972.

**2022, Mar. 30 Litho.** ***Perf. 13½***
**1600** A956 1000p Sheet of 12, #a-l 6.50 6.50

Miniature Sheet

Settlement of La Dorada, 135th Anniv. — A957

No. 1601: a, Cerro Golilludo, Nevado del Ruiz volcano. b, Fisheman casting net. c, Sculpture of fish, Santander Park, La Dorada. d, Mexico railroad Station, La Dorada.

**2022, Apr. 1 Litho.** ***Perf. 13x13¼***
**1601** A957 20,000p Sheet of 4, #a-d 42.50 42.50

Miniature Sheet

Diplomatic Relations Between Colombia and the United States, 200th Anniv. — A958

No. 1602: a, Vultur gryphus. b, Glen Canyon National Recreation Area, Utah and Arizona. c, Serranía de Chiribiquete National Natural Park, Colombia. d, Haliaeetus leucocephalus.

**2022, May 2 Litho.** ***Perf. 13x13¼***
**1602** A958 5000p Sheet of 4, #a-d 10.00 10.00

Miniature Sheet

New Granada Military University, 40th Anniv. — A959

No. 1603: a, University crest. b, Students on Cajicá campus. c, Buildings of Bogota campus. d, Bearers of the Torch, sculpture by Gilbert Senchi, and flagpoles.

**2022, May 6 Litho.** ***Perf. 13¼***
**1603** A959 2000p Sheet of 4, #a-d 4.25 4.25

Miniature Sheet

Diplomatic Relations Between Colombia and South Korea, 60th Anniv. — A960

No. 1604: a, Jaguar. b, Mt. Halla, Jeju Island, South Korea. c, Malpelo Island, Colombia. d, Panthera tigris altaica.

**2022, May 6 Litho.** ***Perf. 13x13¼***
**1604** A960 5000p Sheet of 4, #a-d 10.50 10.50

Miniature Sheet

Diplomatic Relations Between Colombia and Peru, 200th Anniv. — A962

No. 1606: a, Moray Archaeological Center, Cusco, Peru. b, Caño Cristales, Sierra de la Macarena, Colombia. c, Vicugna vicugna mensalis. d, Bradypus variegatus.

**2022, May 27 Litho.** ***Perf. 13x13¼***
**1606** A962 2000p Sheet of 4, #a-d 4.25 4.25

**Departments Type of 2003**

Miniature Sheet

No. 1607 — Córdoba Department: a, Arms of Córdoba. b, Montería, horiz. c, Zenú hatmaker making hat. d, Urrá Hydroelectric Dam, Tierralta. e, Agamia agami, horiz. f, Bullerengue musicians. g, Porro Festival, San Pelayo. h, Men driving cattle, horiz. i, Completed sombrero. j, Sombrero, maracas, and flute. k, Buildings on Río Sinú, Lorica, horiz. l, Sinuano cheese.

Horiz. stamps are 49x37mm.

**2022, June 21 Litho.** ***Perf. 13¼x13***
**Sheet of 12, #a-l, + 8 labels**
**1607** A608 1000p Córdoba 6.00 6.00

Miniature Sheets

A963

A964

Colombian Parks — A965

No. 1608: a, Verongula sp., Corales de Profundidad National Natural Park. b, Kallymenia, Corales de Profundidad National Natural Park. c, Bradypus variegatus, Tayrona National Natural Park. d, Siete Olas Beach, Tayrona National Natural Park. e, Phoenicopterus ruber, Los Flamencos Flora and Fauna Sancturary. f, Navío Quebrado Lake, Los Flamencos Flora and Fauna Sanctuary. g, Egretta thula, Ciénaga Grande de Santa Marta Flora and Fauna Sanctuary. h, Trees near water, Ciénaga Grande de Santa Marta Flora and Fauna Sanctuary.

No. 1609: a, Eusmilia fastigiana, Corales de Rosario y de San Bernardo National Natural Park. b, Underwater scene, Rosario Archipelago, Corales de Rosario y de San Bernardo National Natural Park. c, Boa constrictor, Salamanca Island Road Park. d, Caño Loro, Salamanca Island Road Park. e, Cnemidophorus lemnistcatus lemnistcatus, Old Providence McBean Lagoon National Natural Park. f, Three Brothers Cays, Old Providence McBean Lagoon National Natural Park. g, Dermochelys coriacea, Playona Acandí Flora and Fauna Sanctuary. h, Shoreline, Playona Acandí Flora ana Fauna Sanctuary.

No. 1610: a, Phalacrocorax brasilianus, Bahía Portete-Kaurrele National Natural Park. b, Mangroves, Bahía Portete-Kaurrele National Natural Park. c, Corytophanes cristatus, Paramillo National Natural Park. d, Cerro Murrucucú, Paramillo National Natural Park. e, Libanothamnus sp., Sierra Nevada de Santa Marta National Natural Park. f, Vista from Valledupar, Sierra Nevada de Santa Marta National Natural Park. g, Ara macao, Los Colorados Flora and Fauna Sanctuary. h, Handroanthus serratifolius, Los Colorados Flora and Fauna Sanctuary. i, Procyon lotor, El Corchal "El Mono Hernández" Flora and Fauna Sanctuary. j, Pterocarpus officinalis, El Corchal "El Mono Hernández" Flora and Fauna Sancturay.

**2022 Litho.** ***Perf. 14½***
**1608** A963 2000p Sheet of 8, #a-h 7.75 7.75
**1609** A964 2000p Sheet of 8, #a-h 7.50 7.50
**1610** A965 2000p Sheet of 10, #a-j 9.50 9.50
*Nos. 1608-1610 (3)* 24.75 24.75

Issued: No. 1608, 6/24; Nos. 1609-1610, 7/19.

National Goal to Plant 180,000,000 Trees — A966

**2022, June 27 Litho.** ***Perf. 13x13¼***
**1611** A966 5000p multi 2.50 2.50

## SEMI-POSTAL STAMP

**Catalogue values for unused stamps in this section are for Never Hinged items.**

Girl Giving First Aid — SP1

*Perf. 13½x14*

**1966, Apr. 26 Litho. Unwmk.**

| | | | | |
|---|---|---|---|---|
| **B1** | SP1 | 5c + 5c multicolored | .25 | .25 |

Issued for the Red Cross.

## AIR POST STAMPS

No. 341 Overprinted

**1919 Unwmk.** ***Perf. 14***

| | | | | |
|---|---|---|---|---|
| **C1** | A107 | 2c car rose | 3,500. | 1,200. |
| *a.* | | Numerals "1" with serifs | *6,000.* | *2,000.* |

Used for the first experimental flight from Barranquilla to Puerto Colombia, 6/18/19.

### Issued by Compania Colombiana de Navegacion Aerea

From 1920 to 1932 the internal airmail service of Colombia was handled by the Compania Colombiana de Navegacion Aerea (1920) and the Sociedad Colombo-Alemana de Transportes Aéreos, known familiarly as "SCADTA" (1920-1932).

These organizations, under government contracts, operated and maintained their own post offices and issued stamps which were the only legal franking for airmail service during this period, both in the internal and international mails. All letters had to bear government stamps as well.

Woman and Boy Watching Plane — AP1

Designs: No. C3, Clouds and small biplane at top. No. C4, Tilted plane viewed close-up from above. No. C5, Flier in plane watching biplane. No. C6, Lighthouse. No. C7, Fuselage and tail of biplane. No. C8, Condor on cliff. No. C9, Plane at rest; pilot foreground. No. C10, Ocean liner.

**1920, Feb. Unwmk. Litho.** ***Imperf.***
**Without Gum**

| | | | | |
|---|---|---|---|---|
| **C2** | AP1 | 10c multi | 4,500. | 1,750. |
| **C3** | AP1 | 10c multi | 4,500. | 1,750. |
| **C4** | AP1 | 10c multi | 4,500. | 1,750. |
| **C5** | AP1 | 10c multi | 4,500. | 1,750. |
| **C6** | AP1 | 10c multi | 4,500. | 1,750. |
| **C7** | AP1 | 10c multi | 12,500. | 2,500. |
| **C8** | AP1 | 10c multi | 8,000. | 3,000. |
| **C9** | AP1 | 10c multi | 4,500. | 1,750. |
| **C10** | AP1 | 10c multi | 6,000. | 1,500. |

Nos. C2-C10 were overprinted on the nine lighter-colored varieties of a set of 18 publicity labels produced by the Curtiss Co. for inclusion with packs of cigarettes. These labels were printed se-tenant, in panes of 18 (3x6). Value for the set of 18 values without overprint: $4,750.

No. C8 exists uniquely on cover with the overprint omitted.

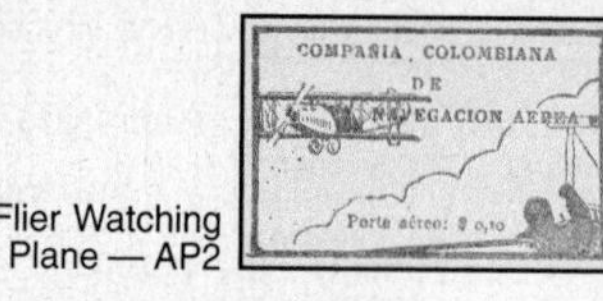

Flier Watching Plane — AP2

AP2a

AP2b

**1920, Mar.**

| | | | | |
|---|---|---|---|---|
| **C11** | AP2 | 10c green | 60.00 | *92.50* |
| **C11A** | AP2a | 10c green | 65.00 | *750.00* |
| **C11B** | AP2b | 10c green | 65.00 | *750.00* |
| **C11C** | AP2a | 10c red brown | 65.00 | — |
| **C11D** | AP2b | 10c red brown | 65.00 | — |

### No. C11 Handstamp Surcharged

**1920, Mar.**

| | | | | |
|---|---|---|---|---|
| **C11E** | AP2 | 30c on 10c | 250.00 | — |

### Nos. C11C-C11D Handstamp Surcharged

**1920, Dec.**

| | | | | |
|---|---|---|---|---|
| **C11F** | AP2a | 20c on 10c | 250.00 | — |
| **C11G** | AP2b | 20c on 10c | 250.00 | — |
| **C11H** | AP2b | 30c on 10c | 250.00 | — |
| *i.* | | "0.30." | | |

No. C11C exists with "0-30." surcharge, however there is no evidence of postal usage.

### Issued by Sociedad Colombo-Alemana de Transportes Aereos (SCADTA)

Seaplane over Magdalena River — AP3

**1920-21 Litho.** ***Perf. 12***

| | | | | |
|---|---|---|---|---|
| **C12** | AP3 | 10c yellow ('21) | 60.00 | 47.50 |
| **C13** | AP3 | 15c blue ('21) | 65.00 | 52.50 |
| **C14** | AP3 | 30c blk, *rose* | 30.00 | 16.00 |
| *a.* | | Horiz. pair, imperf. btwn. | 600.00 | |
| **C15** | AP3 | 30c rose ('21) | 60.00 | 45.00 |
| **C16** | AP3 | 50c pale green | 60.00 | *125.00* |
| *a.* | | Horiz. pair, imperf. btwn. | 600.00 | |
| | | *Nos. C12-C16 (5)* | 275.00 | 286.00 |

For surcharges see Nos. C17-C24, C36-C37.

### No. C16 Handstamp Surcharged in Violet, Black, Gray, or Blue Green

a

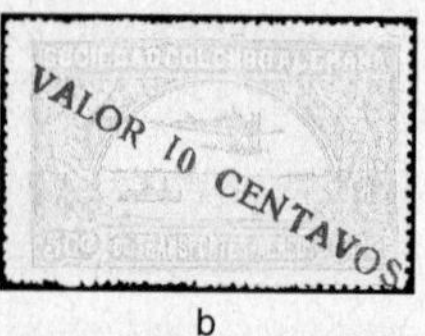

b

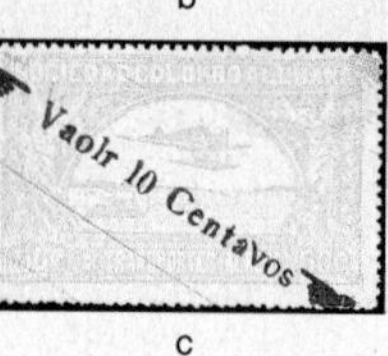

c

d

e

f

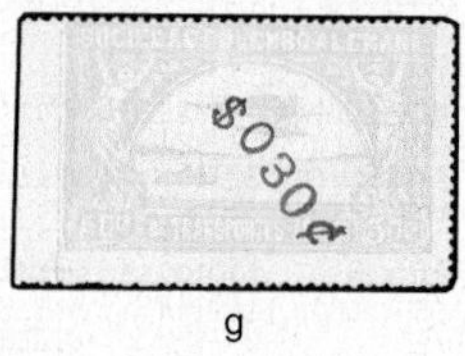

g

**1921-23**

| | | | | |
|---|---|---|---|---|
| **C17** | AP3 (a) | 10c on 50c (V or B) ('23) | 1,500. | 825. |
| **C18** | AP3 (b) | 10c on 50c (G or bl grn) | 1,900. | 825. |
| **C19** | AP3 (c) | 10c on 50c (B) | 1,500. | 825. |
| *a.* | | Imperf. | | — |
| **C20** | AP3 (b) | 30c on 50c (V or B) | 925. | 575. |
| **C21** | AP3 (d) | 30c on 50c (V or B) | 925. | 575. |
| **C22** | AP3 (e) | 30c on 50c (V) | 4,500. | 950. |
| **C23** | AP3 (f) | 30c on 50c (V or G) | 3,250. | 950. |
| **C24** | AP3 (g) | 30c on 50c (V) | 3,250. | 950. |
| **C24A** | AP3 (g) | 20c on 50c (V) | | — |
| **C24B** | AP3 | 30c on 50c "c 30" (V), on cover | | — |

### No. C16 with Typwritten Surcharge in Red or Violet

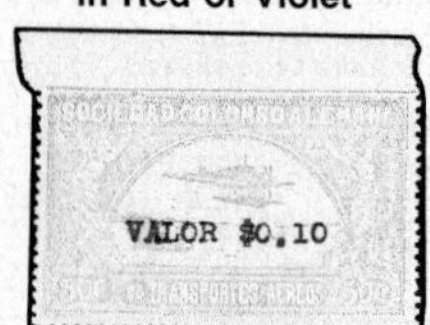


**1921**

| | | | | |
|---|---|---|---|---|
| **C24C** | AP3 | 10c on 50c (R or V) | — | 600. |
| **C24D** | AP3 | 30c on 50c (V) | | *3,000.* |

Plane over Magdalena River AP4

Plane over Bogota Cathedral AP5

**1921** ***Perf. 11½***

| | | | | |
|---|---|---|---|---|
| **C25** | AP4 | 5c orange yellow | 4.50 | 4.00 |
| **C26** | AP4 | 10c slate green | 2.10 | 1.50 |
| **C27** | AP4 | 15c orange brown | 2.10 | 1.60 |
| **C28** | AP4 | 20c red brown | 4.50 | 2.10 |
| *a.* | | Horiz. pair, imperf. vert. | *225.00* | |
| **C29** | AP4 | 30c green | 2.10 | 1.10 |
| **C30** | AP4 | 50c blue | 3.25 | 1.25 |
| **C31** | AP4 | 60c vermilion | 85.00 | 32.50 |
| **C32** | AP5 | 1p gray black | 22.50 | 5.00 |
| **C33** | AP5 | 2p rose | 40.00 | 20.00 |
| **C34** | AP5 | 3p violet | 110.00 | 72.50 |
| **C35** | AP5 | 5p olive green | 325.00 | 300.00 |
| | | *Nos. C25-C35 (11)* | 601.05 | 441.55 |

Exist imperf.
For surcharge see No. C52.

### Nos. C16 and C12 Handstamp Surcharged in Black or Violet

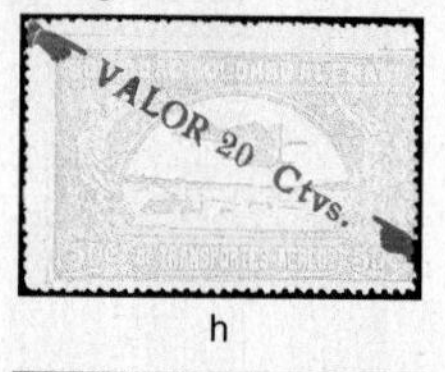

h

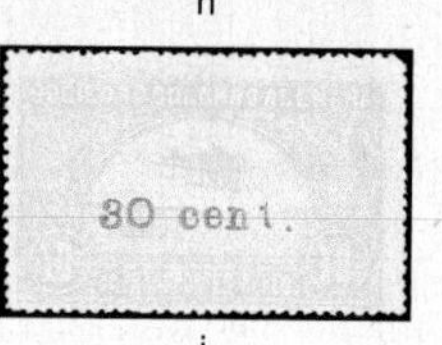

i

**1921-22** ***Perf. 12***

| | | | | |
|---|---|---|---|---|
| **C36** | AP3 (h) | 20c on 50c (B or V) | 3,500. | 1,500. |
| **C37** | AP3 (i) | 30c on 10c (V) | 1,500. | 575. |

Seaplane over Magdalena River AP6

Plane over Bogota Cathedral AP7

**1923-28 Wmk. 116** ***Perf. 14x14½***

| | | | | |
|---|---|---|---|---|
| **C38** | AP6 | 5c orange yellow | 1.75 | .25 |
| **C39** | AP6 | 10c green | 1.75 | .25 |
| **C40** | AP6 | 15c carmine | 1.75 | .25 |
| **C41** | AP6 | 20c gray | 1.75 | .25 |
| **C42** | AP6 | 30c blue | 1.75 | .25 |
| **C43** | AP6 | 40c purple ('28) | 12.50 | 8.00 |
| **C44** | AP6 | 50c green | 2.10 | .25 |
| **C45** | AP6 | 60c brown | 3.25 | .25 |
| **C46** | AP6 | 80c olive grn ('28) | 32.50 | 30.00 |
| **C47** | AP7 | 1p gray | 14.50 | 3.25 |
| **C48** | AP7 | 2p orange brown | 21.00 | 6.00 |
| **C49** | AP7 | 3p claret | 37.50 | 25.00 |
| **C50** | AP7 | 5p olive brown | 67.50 | 32.50 |
| | | *Nos. C38-C50 (13)* | 199.60 | 106.50 |

For surcharges and overprints see Nos. C51, C53-C54, CF1.

### Nos. C41 and C31 Surcharged in Carmine and Dark Blue

No. C51

No. C52

**1923**

| | | | | |
|---|---|---|---|---|
| **C51** | AP6 | 30c on 20c gray (C) | 92.50 | 57.50 |
| **C52** | AP4 | 30c on 60c ver | 85.00 | 37.50 |

Nos. C41-C42 Overprinted in Black

**1928 Wmk. 116 *Perf. 14x14½***

| | | | | | |
|---|---|---|---|---|---|
| **C53** | AP6 | 20c | gray | 80.00 | 62.50 |
| **C54** | AP6 | 30c | blue | 80.00 | 62.50 |

Goodwill flight of Lt. Benjamin Mendez from New York to Bogota.

Magdalena River and Tolíma Volcano AP8

Columbus' Ship and Plane AP9

**1929, June 1 Wmk. 127 *Perf. 14***

| | | | | | |
|---|---|---|---|---|---|
| **C55** | AP8 | 5c | yellow org | 1.25 | .25 |
| **C56** | AP8 | 10c | red brown | 1.25 | .25 |
| **C57** | AP8 | 15c | deep green | 1.25 | .25 |
| **C58** | AP8 | 20c | carmine | 1.25 | .25 |
| **C59** | AP8 | 30c | gray blue | 1.25 | .25 |
| **C60** | AP8 | 40c | dull violet | 1.25 | .25 |
| **C61** | AP8 | 50c | dk olive grn | 2.50 | .25 |
| **C62** | AP8 | 60c | orange brown | 3.75 | .25 |
| **C63** | AP8 | 80c | green | 11.00 | 3.25 |
| **C64** | AP9 | 1p | ultra | 12.00 | 2.50 |
| **C65** | AP9 | 2p | brown orange | 18.00 | 5.75 |
| **C66** | AP9 | 3p | redsh pur | 42.50 | 18.00 |
| **C67** | AP9 | 5p | olive green | 100.00 | 37.50 |
| | | | *Nos. C55-C67 (13)* | 197.25 | 69.00 |

For surcharges and overprints see Nos. C80-C95, CF2, CF4.

**For International Airmail**

AP10

AP11

**1929, June 1 Wmk. 127 *Perf. 14***

| | | | | | |
|---|---|---|---|---|---|
| **C68** | AP10 | 5c | yellow org | 6.25 | *7.25* |
| **C69** | AP10 | 10c | red brown | 1.25 | *3.00* |
| **C70** | AP10 | 15c | deep green | 1.25 | *3.00* |
| **C71** | AP10 | 20c | carmine | 1.25 | *3.75* |
| **C72** | AP10 | 25c | violet blue | 1.25 | .85 |
| **C73** | AP10 | 30c | gray blue | 1.25 | .95 |
| **C74** | AP10 | 50c | dk olive grn | 1.25 | *1.90* |
| **C75** | AP10 | 60c | brown | 2.50 | *3.00* |
| **C76** | AP11 | 1p | blue | 5.50 | *7.25* |
| **C77** | AP11 | 2p | red orange | 8.50 | *10.00* |
| **C78** | AP11 | 3p | violet | 100.00 | 100.00 |
| **C79** | AP11 | 5p | olive green | 125.00 | *140.00* |
| | | | *Nos. C68-C79 (12)* | 255.25 | *280.95* |

This issue was sold abroad for use on correspondence to be flown from coastal to interior points of Colombia. Cancellations are those of the country of origin rather than Colombia.

For overprint see No. CF3.

**Nos. C63, C66 and C64 Surcharged in Black**

m

n

**1930, Dec. 15**

| | | | | | |
|---|---|---|---|---|---|
| **C80** | AP8(m) | 10c | on 80c | 7.00 | 7.00 |
| **C81** | AP9(n) | 20c | on 3p | 12.50 | 12.50 |
| **C82** | AP9(n) | 30c | on 1p | 15.00 | 12.50 |
| | | | *Nos. C80-C82 (3)* | 34.50 | 32.00 |

Simon Bolivar (1783-1830).

**Colombian Government Issues**

Nos. C55-C67 Overprinted in Black

o

p

**Wmk. 127**

**1932, Jan. 1 Typo. *Perf. 14***

| | | | | | |
|---|---|---|---|---|---|
| **C83** | AP8(o) | 5c | yellow org | 10.00 | 10.00 |
| **C84** | AP8(o) | 10c | red brown | 2.25 | .60 |
| **C85** | AP8(o) | 15c | deep green | 3.75 | 3.75 |
| **C86** | AP8(o) | 20c | carmine | 1.90 | .35 |
| *a.* | | | Double overprint | — | |
| **C87** | AP8(o) | 30c | gray blue | 1.90 | .60 |
| **C88** | AP8(o) | 40c | dull violet | 2.50 | 1.25 |
| **C89** | AP8(o) | 50c | dk ol grn | 5.00 | 3.75 |
| **C90** | AP8(o) | 60c | orange brn | 4.25 | 3.75 |
| **C91** | AP8(o) | 80c | green | 17.00 | 17.00 |
| **C92** | AP9(p) | 1p | blue | 14.50 | 12.00 |
| **C93** | AP9(p) | 2p | brown org | 37.50 | 35.00 |
| **C94** | AP9(p) | 3p | pale rose vio | 77.50 | 65.00 |
| **C95** | AP9(p) | 5p | olive green | 125.00 | *140.00* |
| | | | *Nos. C83-C95 (13)* | 303.05 | 293.05 |

Coffee AP12

Gold AP16

Designs: 10c, 50c, Cattle. 15c, 60c, Petroleum. 20c, 40c, Bananas. 3p, 5p, Emerald.

**1932-39 Wmk. 127 Photo. *Perf. 14***

| | | | | | |
|---|---|---|---|---|---|
| **C96** | AP12 | 5c | org & blk brn | .90 | .25 |
| **C97** | AP12 | 10c | lake & blk | 1.00 | .25 |
| **C98** | AP12 | 15c | bl grn & vio blk | .50 | .25 |
| **C99** | AP12 | 15c | ver & vio blk ('39) | 4.00 | .25 |
| **C100** | AP12 | 20c | car & ol blk | .85 | .25 |
| **C101** | AP12 | 20c | bl grn & ol brn ('39) | 4.25 | .35 |
| **C102** | AP12 | 30c | dk bl & blk brn | 2.40 | .25 |
| **C103** | AP12 | 40c | dk vio & ol bis | 1.10 | .25 |
| **C104** | AP12 | 50c | dk grn & brnsh blk | 6.75 | 1.50 |
| **C105** | AP12 | 60c | dk brn & blk vio | 1.40 | .25 |
| **C106** | AP12 | 80c | grn & blk brn | 9.50 | 2.00 |
| **C107** | AP16 | 1p | dk bl & ol bis | 10.00 | 1.25 |
| **C108** | AP16 | 2p | org brn & ol bis | 16.00 | 2.75 |
| **C109** | AP16 | 3p | vio & blue grn | 26.00 | 7.25 |
| **C110** | AP16 | 5p | gray grn & turq bl | 57.50 | 21.00 |
| | | | *Nos. C96-C110 (15)* | 142.15 | 38.10 |

For overprint see No. CF5.

**Nos. C104, C106-C108 Surcharged**

a

b

**1934, Jan. 5**

| | | | | | |
|---|---|---|---|---|---|
| **C111** | AP12(a) | 10c | on 50c | 4.50 | 4.50 |
| **C112** | AP12(a) | 15c | on 80c | 6.25 | 6.25 |
| **C113** | AP16(b) | 20c | on 1p | 6.50 | 6.50 |
| **C114** | AP16(b) | 30c | on 2p | 7.25 | 7.25 |
| | | | *Nos. C111-C114 (4)* | 24.50 | 24.50 |

400th anniversary of Cartagena.

**Nos. C100 and C103 Surcharged in Black or Carmine**

**1939, Jan. 15**

| | | | | | |
|---|---|---|---|---|---|
| **C115** | AP12 | 5c | on 20c (Bk) | .35 | .35 |
| **C116** | AP12 | 5c | on 40c (C) | .40 | .25 |
| **C117** | AP12 | 15c | on 20c (Bk) | 1.50 | .50 |
| *a.* | | | Double surcharge | 50.00 | |
| *b.* | | | Pair, one with dbl. surch. | 60.00 | |
| *c.* | | | Inverted surcharge | 50.00 | 50.00 |

**No. CF5 Surcharged in Black**

| | | | | | |
|---|---|---|---|---|---|
| **C118** | AP12 | 5c | on 20c | .70 | .70 |
| | | | *Nos. C115-C118 (4)* | 2.95 | 1.80 |

Nos. C102-C103 Surcharged in Black or Red

**1940, Oct. 20**

| | | | | | |
|---|---|---|---|---|---|
| **C119** | AP12 | 15c | on 30c | 1.75 | .55 |
| *a.* | | | Inverted surcharge | 50.00 | |
| **C120** | AP12 | 15c | on 40c (R) | 2.75 | .80 |
| *a.* | | | Double surcharge | 50.00 | |

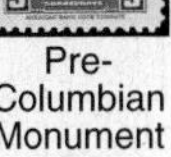

Pre-Columbian Monument AP18

Proclamation of Independence AP22

Designs: 10c, 40c, Symbol of Legend of El Dorado. 15c, 50c, Spanish Fortifications, Cartagena. 20c, 60c, Colonial Bogotá. 2p, 5p, National Library, Bogota.

**Unwmk.**

**1941, Jan. 28 Engr. *Perf. 12***

| | | | | | |
|---|---|---|---|---|---|
| **C121** | AP18 | 5c | gray black | .25 | .25 |
| **C122** | AP18 | 10c | yellow org | .25 | .25 |
| **C123** | AP18 | 15c | carmine rose | .25 | .25 |
| **C124** | AP18 | 20c | yellow grn | .35 | .25 |
| *a.* | | | Horiz. pair, imperf. vert. | 87.50 | |
| **C125** | AP18 | 30c | deep blue | .35 | .25 |
| **C126** | AP18 | 40c | rose lake | 1.40 | .25 |
| **C127** | AP18 | 50c | turq green | 1.40 | .25 |
| **C128** | AP18 | 60c | sepia | 1.40 | .25 |
| **C129** | AP18 | 80c | olive blk | 3.25 | .40 |
| **C130** | AP22 | 1p | blue & blk | 4.00 | .50 |
| **C131** | AP22 | 2p | red org & blk | 8.00 | 2.00 |
| **C132** | AP22 | 3p | violet & blk | 16.00 | 6.50 |
| **C133** | AP22 | 5p | lt green & blk | 40.00 | 20.00 |
| | | | *Nos. C121-C133 (13)* | 76.90 | 31.40 |

See Nos. C151-C163, C217-C225. For overprints see Nos. C175-C198, C200-C216, C226, C290.

San Sebastian Fort, Cartagena AP24

National Capitol, Bogotá AP27

Designs: 5c, 20c, 50c, San Sebastian Fort, Cartagena. 10c, 30c, 60c, Tequendama Waterfall. 15c, 40c, 80c, Bay of Santa Maria.

**Unwmk.**

**1945, Nov. 3 Litho. *Perf. 11***

| | | | | | |
|---|---|---|---|---|---|
| **C134** | AP24 | 5c | blue gray | .25 | .25 |
| **C135** | AP24 | 10c | yellow org | .25 | .25 |
| **C136** | AP24 | 15c | rose | .25 | .25 |
| **C137** | AP24 | 20c | lt yel grn | .30 | .25 |
| **C138** | AP24 | 30c | ultra | .30 | .25 |
| **C139** | AP24 | 40c | claret | .50 | .25 |
| **C140** | AP24 | 50c | bluish grn | .55 | .25 |
| **C141** | AP24 | 60c | lt vio brn | 2.25 | .80 |
| **C142** | AP24 | 80c | dk slate grn | 3.50 | .80 |
| **C143** | AP27 | 1p | dk blue | 5.00 | .75 |
| **C144** | AP27 | 2p | red orange | 7.00 | 2.50 |
| | | | *Nos. C134-C144 (11)* | 20.15 | 6.60 |

Part-perforate varieties exist for all denominations except 80c.

**Imperf., Pairs**

| | | | |
|---|---|---|---|
| *C134a* | AP24 | 5c | 8.50 |
| *C135a* | AP24 | 10c | 8.50 |
| *C136a* | AP24 | 15c | 8.50 |
| *C137a* | AP24 | 20c | 8.50 |
| *C138a* | AP24 | 30c | 8.50 |
| *C139a* | AP24 | 40c | 8.50 |
| *C140a* | AP24 | 50c | 8.50 |
| *C141a* | AP24 | 60c | 8.50 |
| *C142a* | AP24 | 80c | 10.50 |
| *C143a* | AP27 | 1p | 17.50 |
| *C144a* | AP27 | 2p | 60.00 |
| | | *Nos. C134a-C144a (11)* | 156.00 |

**Bello Type of Regular Issue, 1946**

**Wmk. 255**

**1946, Sept. 3 Engr. *Perf. 12***

| | | | | | |
|---|---|---|---|---|---|
| **C145** | A219 | 5c | deep blue | .25 | .25 |

Francisco José de Caldas AP29

Manuel del Socorro Rodriguez AP30

***Perf. 12½***

**1947, May 9 Litho. Unwmk.**

| | | | | | |
|---|---|---|---|---|---|
| **C146** | AP29 | 5c | dp bl, *grnsh* | .50 | .35 |
| **C147** | AP30 | 10c | red org, *grnsh* | .80 | .45 |

4th Pan-American Press Congress (1946).

Chancellery Patio — AP31

Capitol, Patio Rafael Nunez — AP32

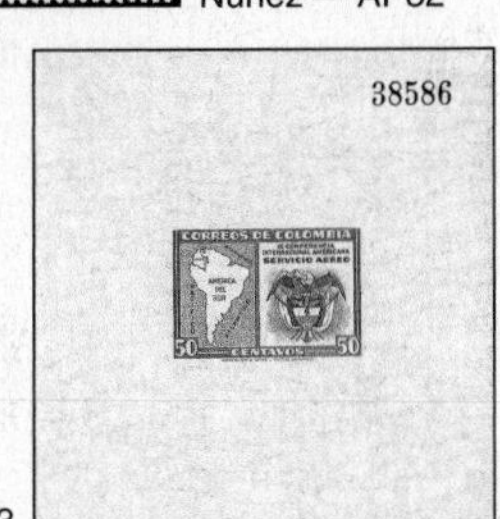

AP33

**1948, Apr. 2 Engr. Wmk. 229**

| | | | | | |
|---|---|---|---|---|---|
| **C148** | AP31 | 5c | dark brown | .25 | .25 |
| **C149** | AP32 | 15c | deep blue | 1.00 | 1.00 |

**Miniature Sheet**

***Imperf***

| | | | | | |
|---|---|---|---|---|---|
| **C150** | AP33 | 50c | brown | 1.90 | 1.90 |

9th Pan-American Conference, Bogotá.

**Types of 1941**

**1948, July 21 Unwmk. *Perf. 12***

| | | | | | |
|---|---|---|---|---|---|
| **C151** | AP18 | 5c | orange yel | .25 | .25 |
| **C152** | AP18 | 10c | scarlet | .25 | .25 |
| **C153** | AP18 | 15c | deep blue | .25 | .25 |
| **C154** | AP18 | 20c | violet | .25 | .25 |
| **C155** | AP18 | 30c | yellow grn | .35 | .25 |
| **C156** | AP18 | 40c | gray | .40 | .25 |
| **C157** | AP18 | 50c | rose lake | .40 | .25 |
| **C158** | AP18 | 60c | olive gray | .70 | .25 |
| **C159** | AP18 | 80c | red brn | .85 | .25 |
| **C160** | AP22 | 1p | ol grn & vio brn | 1.50 | .30 |
| **C161** | AP22 | 2p | dp grn & brt bl | 2.50 | .65 |
| **C162** | AP22 | 3p | rose car & blk | 5.50 | 3.75 |
| **C163** | AP22 | 5p | lt brn & turq grn | 14.00 | 7.00 |
| | | | *Nos. C151-C163 (13)* | 27.20 | 13.95 |

**"Air Week" 5c Blue**

The War and Air Department issued a 5c blue stamp in May, 1949, to publicize Air Week (Semana de Aviacion). This stamp had no franking value and its use was optional during May 16-23.

Justice and Liberty — AP34

Design: 10c, Liberty holding tablet of laws.

**1949, Oct. 7 Unwmk. *Perf. 13***

**C164** AP34 5c blue green .25 .25
**C165** AP34 10c orange .25 .25

Issued to honor the new Constitution.

Wing — AP35

**For Domestic Postage**

**1950, June 22 Litho. *Perf. 12***

**C166** AP35 5c org yel .25 .30
**C167** AP35 10c brown red .35 .30
**C168** AP35 15c lt blue .40 .40
**C169** AP35 20c lt green .60 *.95*
**C170** AP35 30c lilac gray 1.50 *2.40*
**C171** AP35 60c chocolate 1.90 *3.50*

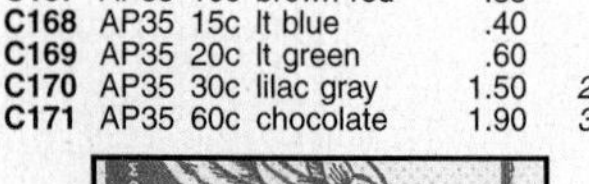

With Network

**With Network as in Parenthesis**

**C172** AP35 1p dk gray (yel) 14.00 *16.00*
**C173** AP35 2p bl (pale grn) 14.00 *20.00*
**C174** AP35 5p claret (claret) 40.00 *60.00*
*Nos. C166-C174 (9)* 73.00 *103.85*

No. C172 was issued both with and without network.

Nos. C151-C157 and C160-C163 Overprinted in Black

**1950, July 18**

**C175** AP18 5c orange yel .25 .25
**C176** AP18 10c scarlet .25 .25
**C177** AP18 15c deep blue .25 .25
**C178** AP18 20c violet .25 .25
**C179** AP18 30c yellow green .30 .25
**C180** AP18 40c gray 2.50 .80
**C181** AP18 50c rose lake .75 .40
**C182** AP22 1p ol grn & vio brn 4.00 4.50
**C183** AP22 2p dp grn & brt bl 7.50 6.00
**C184** AP22 3p rose car & blk 10.00 16.00
**C185** AP22 5p lt brn & turq grn 35.00 52.50
*Nos. C175-C185 (11)* 61.05 81.45

Nos. C151-C163 Overprinted in Black

**1950, July 12**

**C186** AP18 5c orange yel .25 .25
**C187** AP18 10c scarlet .25 .25
**C188** AP18 15c deep blue .25 .25
**C189** AP18 20c violet .25 .25
**C190** AP18 30c yellow green .25 .25
**C191** AP18 40c gray .55 .25
**C192** AP18 50c rose lake .55 .25
**C193** AP18 60c olive gray .85 .25
**C194** AP18 80c red brown 1.25 .50
**C195** AP22 1p ol grn & vio brn 1.50 .70
**C196** AP22 2p dp grn & brt bl 4.50 2.40
**C197** AP22 3p rose car & blk 10.00 12.00
**C198** AP22 5p lt brn & turq grn 30.00 35.00
*Nos. C186-C198 (13)* 50.45 52.60

On Nos. C175-C198, "L" stands for LANSA, "A" for AVIANCA.

**UPU Type**
Miniature Sheet

**Unwmk.**

**1950, Aug. 22 Photo. *Imperf.***

**C199** A245 50c gray 2.25 2.25

75th anniv. (in 1949) of the UPU.

**Catalogue values for unused stamps in this section, from this point to the end of the section, are for Never Hinged items.**

Types of 1941 Overprinted at Lower Right in Black

**Unwmk.**

**1951, Sept. 15 Engr. *Perf. 12***

**C200** AP18 40c orange yel 1.60 1.00
**C201** AP18 50c ultra 2.10 1.40
**C202** AP18 60c gray 1.60 1.00
**C203** AP18 80c car rose 1.50 1.00
**C204** AP22 1p red org & red brn 6.00 6.00
**C205** AP22 2p rose car & bl 7.25 7.25
**C206** AP22 3p choc & emer 18.00 20.00
**C207** AP22 5p org & gray 47.50 52.50
*Nos. C200-C207 (8)* 85.55 90.15

Types of 1941 Overprinted at Lower Right in Black

**1951-54**

**C208** AP18 40c orange yel 5.50 .55
**C209** AP18 50c ultra 16.00 .65
**C210** AP18 60c gray 4.50 .55
*a.* Overprint centered 5.00 .55
**C211** AP18 80c car rose 1.00 .35
**C212** AP22 1p red org & red brn 4.75 .50
**C213** AP22 1p ol grn & vio brn ('54) 7.00 .95
**C214** AP22 2p rose car & bl 4.75 .70
**C215** AP22 3p choc & emer 8.75 2.10
**C216** AP22 5p org & gray 16.00 2.25
*Nos. C208-C216 (9)* 68.25 8.60

All values except the 2p and 3p exist without overprint.

**Types of 1941**

**1952, May 10 Engr.**

**C217** AP18 5c ultra .50 .25
**C218** AP18 10c ultra .50 .25
**C219** AP18 15c ultra .50 .25
**C220** AP18 20c ultra .90 .40
**C221** AP18 30c ultra 2.50 .95

**Color Change**

**C222** AP18 5c car rose .50 .25
**C223** AP18 10c car rose .50 .25
**C224** AP18 20c car rose .95 .25
**C225** AP18 30c car rose 2.00 .55
*Nos. C217-C225 (9)* 8.85 3.40

Type of 1941 Surcharged in Blue

**1952, Oct. 30**

**C226** AP18 70c on 80c car rose 2.00 .80

Latin American Siderurgical Conf., 1952.

Type of Postal Tax Stamps, 1948-50, Nos. 602 and 604 Surcharged or Overprinted in Black

**1953 Wmk. 255 *Perf. 12***

**C227** PT10 5c on 8c blue .25 .25
**C228** PT10 15c on 20c brown .30 .25
**C229** PT10 15c on 25c bl grn 1.50 .25
**C230** PT10 25c blue green .80 .25
*Nos. C227-C230 (4)* 2.85 1.00

Many varieties of overprint or surcharge exist on Nos. C227-C231.

No. 570 Overprinted in Blue

**1953, Aug. Wmk. 229 *Perf. 12½***

**C231** A160 10c red .25 .25

**"Extra Rapido"**

Stamps inscribed "Extra Rapido" are for use on domestic airmail carried by airlines other than AVIANCA.

No. 585 Surcharged and Overprinted in Dark Blue

**1953 Unwmk. *Perf. 13***

**C232** A244 5c on 11c red .50 .35

Capitol and Arms — AP37

**Revenue Stamps Overprinted "Correo Extra-Rapido"**
Gray Security Paper

**1953 Wmk. 255 Engr. *Perf. 12***

**C233** AP37 1c on 2c green .25 .25
**C234** AP37 50c red orange .25 .25

AP38

**Real Estate Tax Stamps Ovptd. "Correo Extra-Rapido" in Black or Carmine**

**1953**

**C235** AP38 5c red orange .25 .25
**C236** AP38 20c brown (C) .30 .25

On 20c, overprint is at bottom of stamp and two lines of ornaments cover real estate tax inscription at top.

Castillo y Rada and Map — AP39

**Real Estate Tax Stamp Surcharged "Correo Aereo, II Exposicion Filatelica Nacional, Bogota Dicbre 1953, 15 Centavos"**

**1953, Dec. 12 Engr. & Litho.**

**C237** AP39 15c on 10p multi .50 .35

2nd Natl. Philatelic Exhib., Bogota, Dec. 1953.

No. RA45 Overprinted in Black

**1953**

**C238** PT10 10c purple .25 .25

Galeras Volcano AP40

Retreat of San Diego AP41

Designs: No. C241, Las Lajas Shrine, Narino. No. C242, 50c, Bolivar monument. 20c, 80c, Ruiz mountain, Manizales. 40c, George Isaacs monument, Cali. 60c, Mono Fountain, Tunja. 1p, Stadium, Medellin. 2p, Pastelillo Fort, Cartagena. 3p, Santo Domingo University gate. 5p, Las Lajas Shrine. 10p, Map of Colombia.

***Perf. 13½x13, 13***

**1954, Jan. 15 Engr. Unwmk.**

**C239** AP40 5c dp red vio .25 .25
**C240** AP41 10c black .25 .25
**C241** AP40 15c red orange .25 .25
**C242** AP40 15c car rose .25 .25
**C243** AP40 20c brown .25 .25
**C244** AP40 30c brown org .25 .25
**C245** AP40 40c blue .35 .25
**C246** AP40 50c dk violet brn .40 .25
**C247** AP40 60c dk brown .50 .25
**C248** AP40 80c red brown .75 .25

**Size: 37x27mm**
**Center in Black**

**C249** AP41 1p deep blue 3.75 .25
**C250** AP41 2p dark green 5.00 .40
**C251** AP41 3p carmine rose 12.00 1.40

**Size: 38x32mm, 32x38mm**

**C252** AP41 5p dk grn & red brn 15.00 3.50
**C253** AP40 10p gray grn & red org 22.00 7.50
*Nos. C239-C253 (15)* 61.25 15.55

See Nos. C307-C308. For surcharges and overprints see Nos. 691, C321, C325, C330, C333-C334, C343-C346.

Condor Carrying Shield — AP42

**Inscribed: "Correo Extra-Rapido"**

**1954, Apr. 23 Litho. *Perf. 12½***

**C254** AP42 5c reddish lilac .95 .30

For overprint see No. RA53.

**Soldier-Map-Arms Type**

**1954, June 13 Engr. *Perf. 13***

**C255** A259 15c carmine .40 .25

See No. C271a.

**Games Type**

Design: 20c, Stadium and Athlete holding arms of Colombia.

**1954, July 18**

**C256** A260 15c chocolate .70 .25
**C257** A260 20c deep blue green 1.40 .35

Church of St. Peter Claver, Cartagena — AP45

**1954, Sept. 9**

**C258** AP45 15c brown 1.25 .35
*a.* Souvenir sheet 8.00 *12.00*

St. Peter Claver, 300th death anniv.

No. C258a contains one stamp similar to No. C258, but printed in red brown.

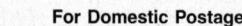

### Mercury Type

**1954, Oct. 29**
**C259** A263 15c deep blue .55 .25

**Inscribed "Extra Rapido"**
**C260** A263 50c scarlet .55 .25

Archbishop Manuel José Mosquera, Death Cent. — AP47

**Inscribed: "Correo Extra Rapido"**

**1954, Nov. 17**
**C261** AP47 2c yellow green .25 .25

Virgin of Chiquinquira AP48

**Inscribed: "Correo Extra Rapido"**

**1954, Dec. 4** **Engr. & Litho.**
**C262** AP48 5c org brn & multi .25 .25

See No. C291. For overprint see No. 686.

### College Types

Designs: 20c, Brother Cristobal de Torres. 50c, College chapel and arms.

***Perf. 12½x11½, 11½x12½***
**1954, Dec. 6** **Engr.** **Unwmk.**
**C263** A264 15c orange & blk .50 .25
**C264** A264 20c ultra .85 .25
**C265** A265 25c dark brown .85 .25
**C266** A265 50c black & car 2.25 .70
*a.* Souvenir sheet 12.00 *16.00*
*Nos. C263-C266 (4)* 4.45 1.45

No. C266a contains four stamps similar to Nos. C263-C266, but printed in different colors: 15c red and black, 20c pale purple, 25c brown, 50c black and olive green.

### Steel Mill Type

**1954, Dec. 12** ***Perf. 12½x13***
**C267** A266 20c green & blk 1.75 .60

### Marti Type

**1955, Jan. 28** ***Perf. 13½x13***
**C268** A267 15c deep green .30 .25

### Korean Veterans Type

**1955, Mar. 23** ***Perf. 12½***
**C269** A268 20c dark green .55 .25

### Merchant Fleet Types

**1955, Apr. 12** ***Perf. 12½***
**C270** A269 25c black .40 .25
**C271** A270 50c dark green .85 .40
*a.* Souvenir sheet 9.50 *12.00*

No. C271a contains 4 stamps similar to Nos. C255, C269-C271, but printed in different colors; 15c lilac red, 20c olive, 25c bluish black, 50c bluish green.

Marco Fidel Suarez (1855-1927), Pres. 1918-21 — AP56

**Inscribed: "Correo Extra Rapido"**

**1955, April 23** ***Perf. 13***
**C272** AP56 10c deep blue .25 .25

### Hotel-Church Type

**1955, May 16** **Photo.** ***Perf. 11½x12***
**C273** A271 15c rose brown .40 .25

### Rotary Type

**Unwmk.**
**1955, Oct. 17** **Engr.** ***Perf. 13***
**C274** A272 15c dk carmine rose .40 .25

Atahualpa, Tisquesuza and Montezuma AP59

Ferdinand the Catholic and Queen Isabella I — AP60

Designs: 15c, O'Higgins, Santander and Sucre. 20c, Marti, Hidalgo and Petion. 1p, Artigas, Solano Lopez and Murillo. 2p, Abdon Calderon, Baron de Rio Branco and José de La Mar.

**1955, Oct. 12** **Engr. & Photo.**

**Inscribed: "Extra Rapido"**
**C275** AP59 2c dull brn & blk .45 .25
**C276** AP60 5c dk brn & yel .45 .25

**Regular Air Post**
**C277** AP59 15c rose car & blk .55 .25
**C278** AP59 20c pale brn & blk .85 .25
*a.* Souvenir sheet of 2 30.00 30.00

**Inscribed: "Extra Rapido"**
**C279** AP60 1p ol gray & brn 15.00 7.50
**C280** AP60 2p lilac & blk 11.00 5.75
*Nos. C275-C280 (6)* 28.30 14.25

7th Cong. of the Postal Union of the Americas and Spain, Bogota, Oct. 12-Nov. 9, 1955.

No. C278a contains one each of Nos. C277-C278 printed in different shades.

### Caro Type

**1955, Nov. 29** **Engr.** ***Perf. 13½x13***
**C281** A275 15c gray green .40 .25

University of Salamanca — AP62

**Inscribed: "Extra Rapido"**

**1955, Nov. 29** **Unwmk.** ***Perf. 13***
**C282** AP62 20c dark brown .25 .25

University of Salamanca, 7th centenary.

Type of Postal Tax Stamp of 1948-50 Surcharged

**1956** **Wmk. 255** **Engr.** ***Perf. 12***
**C283** PT10 2c on 8c blue .25 .25

No. 617 Overprinted in Black

**1956** **Unwmk.** ***Perf. 12½x13***
**C284** A256 1p black & emerald .40 .25

### Columbus Type

**1956, Oct. 11** **Photo.** ***Perf. 12***
**C285** A279 15c intense blue .65 .25

See No. C306.

### St. Elizabeth Type

**1956, Nov. 19**
**C286** A280 15c red brown .50 .25

### St. Ignatius Type

**1956, Nov. 26** **Engr.** ***Perf. 12½x13***
**C287** A281 5c brown .25 .25

Javier Pereira — AP63

**1956, Dec. 28** **Unwmk.** ***Perf. 12***
**C288** AP63 20c rose carmine .25 .25

Issued to honor 167-year-old Javier Pereira.

No. 649 and Type of 1941 Overprinted in Red

**1957** ***Perf. 13½x13***
**C289** A276 5c blue & black 7.50 3.25

***Perf. 12***
**C290** AP22 5p orange & gray 11.00 7.50

The overprint measures 14mm.

### Virgin Type of 1954

**Engraved and Lithographed**

**1957, May 23** **Unwmk.** ***Perf. 13***
**C291** AP48 5c dp plum & multi .25 .25

### Bank Type

No. C292, 20c, Emblem, cow, horse & herd. 10c, Emblem & tractor. 15c, Emblem, coffee & corn. No. C293, Emblem & dairy farm.

**1957** **Photo.** ***Perf. 14x13½***
**C292** A283 5c chocolate .25 .25
**C293** A283 5c orange .25 .25
**C294** A283 10c green .55 .25
**C295** A283 15c black .35 .25
**C296** A283 20c dull red .85 .30
*Nos. C292-C296 (5)* 2.25 1.30

No. C292 is inscribed "Extra Rapido."
Issued: No. C292, 3/5; others 5/23.

Cyclist — AP64

**1957, July 6** **Unwmk.** ***Perf. 12***
**C297** AP64 2c brown .25 .25
**C298** AP64 5c ultra .25 .25

Seventh Bicycle Tour of Colombia.

### Academy Type

Designs: 15c, Coat of arms and Gen. Rafael Reyes. 20c, Coat of arms and Academy.

**1957, July 20** **Engr.** ***Perf. 12½***
**C299** A284 15c rose carmine .30 .25
**C300** A284 20c brown .45 .25

### Delgado Type

**1957, Sept. 15** **Photo.** ***Perf. 12***
**C301** A285 10c slate blue .25 .25

### UPU Type

**1957, Oct. 10**
**C302** A286 15c dark red brown .30 .25
**C303** A286 25c dark blue .40 .25

### St. Vincent de Paul Type

**1957, Oct. 18**
**C304** A287 5c rose brown .25 .25

### Fencing Type

**1957, Nov. 23** ***Perf. 12***
**C305** A288 20c dark red brown .50 .30

### Columbus Type Inscribed "Extra Rapido"

**1958, Jan. 8** **Unwmk.** ***Perf. 12***
**C306** A279 3c dark green .25 .25

### Scenic Type

Design: 25c, Las Lajas Shrine.

**1958, June 20** **Engr.** ***Perf. 13***
**C307** AP40 25c dark blue .30 .25
**C308** AP40 25c rose violet .30 .25

### IGY Type

**1958, May 12** **Photo.** ***Perf. 12***
**C309** A289 25c green .50 .25

**Inscribed "Extra Rapido"**
**C310** A289 1p purple .65 .25

No. 659 Ovptd. in Carmine

**1958, Oct. 16** **Engr.** ***Perf. 13***
**C312** A277 50c dk green & blk .50 .25

### Almanza Type

**1958, Oct. 23** **Photo.** ***Perf. 14x13***
**C313** A290 25c dark gray .40 .25

**Inscribed "Extra Rapido"**
**C314** A290 10c olive green .30 .25

### Carrasquilla Type

**1959, Jan. 22** **Photo.** ***Perf. 14x13***
**C315** A291 25c carmine rose .25 .25
**C316** A291 1p dark blue .80 .25

### Miss Universe Type

**1959, June 26** **Unwmk.** ***Perf. 11½***
**C317** A292 1.20p multicolored 1.75 1.40
**C318** A292 5p multicolored 45.00 45.00

Gaitan Type Inscribed and Surcharged in Black or Blue

**1959, July 28** **Engr.** ***Perf. 12x13½***
**C319** A293 2p on 1p black 2.00 1.40
**C320** A293 2p on 1p black (Bl) 2.00 1.40

The 1p black, type A293, exists without surcharge. Value $10.

No. C247 Surcharged in Dark Blue

**1959, Aug. 24** **Unwmk.** ***Perf. 13***
**C321** AP40 50c on 60c dk brown 2.25 .40

Regular and Air Post Issues of 1948-59 Ovptd. in Black or Red

**1959-60**
**C322** A283 5c orange .50 .50
**C323** A287 5c rose brn ('60) .50 .35
**C324** A281 5c brown (R) .45 .40
**C325** AP41 10c black .35 .25
*a.* Double overprint 2.50 2.50
**C326** A160 10c red, #C231 .35 .25
*a.* Double overprint 1.40 1.40
**C328** A284 15c rose car .35 .25
*a.* Inverted overprint 3.00 3.00
**C330** AP40 20c brown .35 .25
*a.* Double overprint 1.40 1.40
**C331** A284 20c brown .35 .25
**C332** A288 20c dk red brn ('60) .40 .25
**C333** AP40 25c rose vio ('60) .35 .25
**C334** AP40 25c dark blue .35 .25
**C335** A291 25c car rose .35 .25
**C336** A290 25c dark gray .35 .25
**C338** AP40 30c brown org .35 .25
**C340** AP40 50c on 60c dk brn .50 .25
**C341** A291 1p dark blue 1.15 .25
*a.* Double overprint 2.50 2.50
**C342** A292 1.20p brn, ultra, car & ol 1.40 1.15
**C343** AP41 2p dk grn & blk 2.75 .25
**C344** AP41 3p car rose & blk 6.75 .85
*a.* Double overprint 10.00 10.00

**C345** AP41 5p dk grn & red brn 9.00 1.15
- *a.* Double overprint 10.00 10.00
- *b.* Inverted overprint 10.00 10.00

**C346** AP40 10p gray grn & red org 12.00 3.25
*Nos. C322-C346 (21)* 38.90 11.15

Issued following agreement between the Colombian government and AVIANCA to unify the air postage used on all mail carried by AVIANCA.

Vertical overprint on Nos. C342 and C346.

Airmail Stamp of 1919 and Planes — AP66

60c, Nos. C349a, C350a, Planes of 1919 and 1959. Nos. C349b, C350b, Stamp of 1919 and Planes.

**Unwmk.**

**1959, Dec. 5 Photo. *Perf. 12***

**C347** AP66 35c lt bl, blk & red .65 .25
**C348** AP66 60c yel grn & gray 1.10 .75

**Souvenir Sheets**

**C349** Sheet of 2 11.50 11.50
- *a.* AP66 1p orange & gray 2.00 1.50
- *b.* AP66 1p lilac, gray & red 2.00 1.50

**Inscribed "Extra Rapido"**

**1960, May 17**

**C350** Sheet of 2 11.00 11.00
- *a.* AP66 1.50p red orange & gray 2.00 1.50
- *b.* AP66 1.50p olive, gray & rose 2.00 1.50

Nos. C347-C350 for the 40th anniv. of air post service and of the AVIANCA company.

**Type of Regular Issue and**

1859 Stamp and Seaplane — AP67

Designs (various stamps of 1859 and): 10c, Map of Colombia. 25c, Pres. Mariano Ospina. 1.20p, Plane over mountains.

**1959, Dec. 1 Photo. *Perf. 12***

**C351** A296 25c choc & red .50 .35
**C352** AP67 50c ver & ultra 1.25 .65
**C353** AP67 1.20p yel grn & car 2.60 1.60

**Inscribed "Extra Rapido"**

**C354** A296 10c lemon & vio .25 .25
*Nos. C351-C354 (4)* 4.60 2.85

Souvenir Sheet

Tête Bêche 5c Stamps of 1859 AP68

**Wmk. 331**

**1959, Dec. 23 Litho. *Imperf.***

**C355** AP68 5p blue, *pink* 19.00 19.00

Cent. of Colombian postage stamps.

No. C355 exists with inscription "VALOR $5.10" instead of "VALOR $5."

Eldorado Airport, Bogota — AP69

**1960, Jan. 5 Wmk. 331 *Perf. 12½***

**C356** AP69 35c black & ocher .65 .25
**C356A** AP69 60c ver & gray .75 .45

**Inscribed "Extra Rapido"**

**C356B** AP69 1p Prus bl & gray 1.25 .70
*Nos. C356-C356B (3)* 2.65 1.40

Ant Bear — AP70

1.30p, Armadillo. 1.45p, Parrot fish.

**Unwmk.**

**1960, Feb. 12 Photo. *Perf. 12***

**C357** AP70 35c sepia 1.60 .25
**C358** AP70 1.30p rose car & dk brn 3.00 2.40
**C359** AP70 1.45p lt bl, bl & yel 2.75 2.00
*Nos. C357-C359 (3)* 7.35 4.65

Alexander von Humboldt, German naturalist and geographer (1769-1859).

**Flower Type**

Nos. C360, C362, C366, Passiflora mollissima. Nos. C361, C364, C367, Odontoglossum luteo purpureum. Nos. C363, C369, Anthurium andreanum. Nos. C365, C370, Stanhopea tigrina. No. C368, Espeletia grandiflora.

**1960, May 10 Photo. *Perf. 12***

**Flowers in Natural Colors**

**C360** A298 5c dark blue .25 .25
**C361** A298 35c maroon .55 .25
**C362** A298 60c dark blue 1.10 .70
**C363** A298 1.45p dark brown 1.25 1.10

**Inscribed "Extra Rapido"**

**C364** A298 5c maroon .25 .25
**C365** A298 10c brown .25 .25
**C366** A298 1p dark blue 2.50 *3.00*
**C367** A298 1p maroon 2.50 *3.00*
**C368** A298 1p brown 2.50 *3.00*
**C369** A298 1p brown 2.50 *3.00*
**C370** A298 1p brown 2.50 *3.00*
*Nos. C360-C370 (11)* 16.15 *17.80*

See Nos. C420-C425.

Fleeing Family and Uprooted Oak Emblem — AP71

***Perf. 10, 11***

**1960, May 24 Litho. Wmk. 331**

**C371** AP71 60c bl grn & gray .40 .25

World Refugee Year, 7/1/59-6/30/60.

Souvenir Sheet

Pan-American Highway Through Colombia AP72

**1960, May 28 Litho. *Imperf.***

**C372** AP72 2.50p brn & aqua 7.50 7.25

8th Pan-American Highway Congress, Bogota, May 20-29.

**Lincoln Type**

**1960, June 6 *Perf. 10½***

**C375** A299 40c dl red brn & blk 1.50 1.00
**C376** A299 60c rose red & blk .40 .25

No. C376 exists imperforate. Value $25.

**Type of Regular Issue and**

Joaquin Camacho, Jorge Tadeo Lozano and Jose Miguel Pey — AP73

Flag, Coins and Arms of Mompox and Cartagena — AP74

No. C378, Arms of Cartagena. 35c, 1.45p, Colombian flag. 60c, Andres Rosillo, Antonio Villavicencio and Joaquin Caicedo. 1p, Manuel de Bernardo Alvarez and Joaquin Gutierrez. 1.20p, Jose Antonio Galan statue. 1.30p, Front page of newspaper La Bagatela, 1811. 1.65p, Antonia Santos, Jose Acevedo y Gomez and Liborio Mejia.

**Unwmk.**

**1960, July 20 Photo. *Perf. 12***

**C377** AP73 5c lilac & brn .25 .25
**C378** A301 5c dp bl grn & multi .25 .25
**C379** AP73 35c multicolored .25 .25
**C380** AP73 60c red brn & grn .45 .25
**C381** AP73 1p ver & sl grn 1.10 .70
**C382** A301 1.20p ultra & ind 1.10 .70
**C383** AP73 1.30p orange & blk 1.10 .70
**C384** AP73 1.45p multicolored 1.40 1.10
**C385** AP73 1.65p green & brn 1.25 1.10
*Nos. C377-C385 (9)* 7.15 5.30

**Souvenir Sheet**

**Stamps Inscribed "Extra Rapido"**

**C386** AP74 Sheet of 4 7.25 7.25
- *a.* 50c deep claret & multi 1.00 1.00
- *b.* 50c green & multi 1.00 1.00
- *c.* 1p brown olive, yel, blue & car 1.00 1.00
- *d.* 1p lilac & gray 1.00 1.00

150th anniv. of Colombia's independence.

**St. Isidore Type**

Designs: 35c, No. C388a, St. Isidore and farm animals. No. C388b, Nativity.

**Unwmk.**

**1960, Sept. 26 Photo. *Perf. 12***

**C387** A302 35c multicolored .25 .25

**Souvenir Sheet**

**Stamps Inscribed "Extra Rapido"**

**C388** A302 Sheet of 2 9.75 9.75
- *a.* 1.50p multicolored 3.00 3.00
- *b.* 1.50p multicolored 3.00 3.00

See Nos. C439-C440.

**Type of Regular Issue, 1959**

**Wmk. 331**

**1960, Nov. 23 Litho. *Perf. 12½***

**C389** A294 35c Bolivar 3.50 .45

**Pan-American Highway Type**

**1961, Mar. 7 Unwmk. *Perf. 10½x11***

**C390** A304 10c rose lil & emer .60 .55
**C391** A304 20c ver & lt bl .60 .55
**C392** A304 30c black & emer .60 .55

**Inscribed "Extra Rapido"**

**C393** A304 10c dk blue & emer .60 .55
*Nos. C390-C393 (4)* 2.40 2.20

8th Pan-American Highway Congress, Bogota, May 20-29, 1960.

**Lopez Type**

**1961, Mar. 22 Photo. *Perf. 12½***

**C394** A305 35c blue & brown .50 .25

**Inscribed "Extra Rapido"**

**C395** A305 10c emerald & brn .25 .25

**Souvenir Sheet**

**C396** A305 1p lilac & brn 5.75 5.75

Brother Damian and San Francisco Church, Cali — AP75

Designs: 10c, View of Cali, vert. No. 398, Emblem of University del Valle, vert. 1.30p, Fine Arts School, Cali. 1.45p, Agricultural College, Palmira.

***Perf. 13x13½, 13½x13***

**1961, Aug. 17 Photo. Unwmk.**

**C397** AP75 35c vio brn & ol .40 .25
**C398** AP75 35c olive & grn .40 .25
**C399** AP75 1.30p sepia & pink 1.00 .50
**C400** AP75 1.45p multicolored 1.00 .70

**Inscribed: "Extra Rapido"**

**C401** AP75 10c brn & yel grn .25 .25
*Nos. C397-C401 (5)* 3.05 1.95

50th anniv. (in 1960) of the department of Valle del Cauca.

View of Cucuta — AP76

10c, Church of the Rosary, Cucuta, vert.

**1961, Aug. 29**

**C402** AP76 35c brn ol & grn .65 .25

**Inscribed: "Extra Rapido"**

**C403** AP76 10c dk brn & gray grn .25 .25

50th anniv. (in 1960) of the department of North Santander.

Old and New Ships of Barranquilla AP77

Arms and View of San Gil AP78

Hotel, Popayan AP79

Statue of Christ in Procession AP80

Design: 1.45p, View of Velez.

***Perf. 12½x13, 13x12½***

**1961, Oct. 10 Photo. Unwmk.**

**C404** AP77 35c gold & bl .45 .25
**C405** AP78 35c bl grn, yel & red .45 .25
**C406** AP79 35c car & brn .45 .25
**C407** AP78 1.45p brown & grn .45 .25

**Inscribed: "Extra Rapido"**

**C408** AP80 10c brown & yel .25 .25
*Nos. C404-C408 (5)* 2.05 1.25

**Types of Regular and Air Post**

Souvenir Sheets

Designs, No. C409: 35c, Barranquilla arms. 40c, Popayan arms. c, Arms and view of San Gil. d, Holy Week in Popayan.

No. C410: a, Old and new ships at Barranquilla. b, Hotel, Popayan. c, Bucaramanga arms. d, Holy Week in Popayan.

**C409** Sheet of 4 11.50 11.50
- *a.* A309 35c gold & multi 1.00 1.00
- *b.* A309 40c gold & multi 1.00 1.00
- *c.* AP78 1p blue, yellow & red 2.00 2.00
- *d.* AP80 1p car rose & yellow 2.00 2.00

**Stamps Inscribed: "Extra Rapido"**

**C410** Sheet of 4 11.50 11.50
- *a.* AP77 50c gold & car rose 1.50 1.50
- *b.* AP79 50c gold & blue 1.50 1.50
- *c.* A309 50c pink & multi 1.50 1.50
- *d.* AP80 50c blue & yellow 1.50 1.50

Nos. C404-C408 are in honor of the Atlantico Department. Nos. C409-C410 are in honor of the Departments of Atlantico, Cauca and Santander.

Nos. 713, 716 and 715 Overprinted and Surcharged

**1961, Sept. *Perf. 12***

**C411** A297 5c grnsh bl & brn .35 .25
**C412** A298 5c multicolored .35 .25
**C413** A297 10c on 20c cit & gray brn .35 .25
*Nos. C411-C413 (3)* 1.05 .75

"Aereo" in script on No. C412.

See Nos. C420-C425.

### Sports Type

Designs: No. C414, Women divers. No. C415, Tennis, mixed doubles. 1.45p, No. C419b, Baseball. No. C417, Torch bearer. Nos. C418, C419a, Bolivar statue and flags of six participating nations. No. C419c, Soccer. No. C419d, Basketball.

**1961, Dec. 16 Litho. *Perf. 13½x14***

**C414** A310 35c ultra, yel & brn .75 .25
**C415** A310 35c car, yel & brn .75 .25
**C416** A310 1.45p Prus grn, yel & brn 1.10 .65

**Inscribed: "Extra Rapido"**

**C417** A310 10c car lake, yel & brn .25 .25
**C418** A310 10c ol, yel, bl & red .25 .25
*Nos. C414-C418 (5)* 3.10 1.65

**Souvenir Sheet**

**Stamps Inscribed: "Extra Rapido"**

***Imperf***

**C419** Sheet of 4 7.25 7.25
*a.* A310 50c multi .60 .60
*b.* A310 50c multi .60 .60
*c.* A310 1p multi 1.25 1.25
*d.* A310 1p multi 1.25 1.25

### Flower Type of 1960

5c, Passiflora mollissima. 10c, Espeletia grandiflora. 20c, 2p, Odontoglossum luteo purpureum. 25c, Stanhopea tigrina. 60c, Anthurium Andreanum.

**Unwmk.**

**1962, Jan. 30 Photo. *Perf. 12***

**Flowers in Natural Colors**

**C420** A298 5c gray .25 .25
**C421** A298 10c gray blue .25 .25
**C422** A298 20c rose lilac .25 .25
**C423** A298 25c citron .40 .25
**C424** A298 60c light brown .40 .25

**Inscribed "Extra Rapido"**

**C425** A298 2p salmon pink 3.75 1.25
*Nos. C420-C425 (6)* 5.30 2.50

### Anti-Malaria Type

Designs: 40c, Colombian anti-malaria emblem. 1p, 1.45p, Malaria eradication emblem and mosquito in swamp.

**1962, Apr. 12 Litho. *Perf. 12***

**C426** A311 40c yellow & red .25 .25
**C427** A311 1.45p gray & ultra .65 .40

**Inscribed "Extra Rapido"**

**C428** A311 1p yel grn & ultra 4.00 4.00
*Nos. C426-C428 (3)* 4.90 4.65

WHO drive to eradicate malaria.

### Type of Regular Issue, 1962 and

Abelardo Ramos and Engineering School, Cauca — AP81

Designs: 10c, Miguel Triana, Andres A. Arroyo and Monserrate shrine with cable cars. 15c, Diodoro Sanchez and first meeting place of Engineers Society. 2p, Engineers Society emblem.

**1962, June 12 Photo. *Perf. 11½x12***

**C429** AP81 5c blue & dp rose .25 .25
**C430** AP81 10c green & sepia .25 .25
**C431** AP81 15c lilac & sepia .40 .30

**Inscribed: "Extra Rapido"**

**C432** A312 2p blk, yel, red & bl 2.25 2.25
*Nos. C429-C432 (4)* 3.15 3.05

75th anniv. of the founding of the Colombian Soc. of Engineers and 6th Natl. Cong. of Engineers.

### American States Type

**1962, June 28 Photo. *Perf. 13***

**Flags in National Colors**

**C433** A313 35c black & blue .35 .25

### Women's Rights Type

***Perf. 12x12½***

**1962, July 20 Litho. Wmk. 229**

**C434** A314 35c buff, gray & blk .25 .25

See Nos. C448-C450.

### Scout Type

Designs: 15c, No. C438, Scouts at campfire and tents. 40c and No. C437, Girl Scouts.

***Perf. 11½x12***

**1962, July 26 Photo. Unwmk.**

**C435** A315 15c brown & rose .30 .25
**C436** A315 40c dp cl & pink .40 .30
**C437** A315 1p blue & buff .70 .55

**Inscribed "Extra Rapido"**

**C438** A315 1p purple & yel 5.00 4.00
*Nos. C435-C438 (4)* 6.40 5.10

Nos. C435 and C438 for 30th anniv. of the Colombian Boy Scouts. Nos. C436 and C437 for the 25th anniv. of the Girl Scouts.

Nativity by Gregorio Vasquez — AP82

Design: 2p, St. Isidore, similar to type A302.

**Inscribed "Extra Rapido"**

**Unwmk.**

**1962, Aug. 28 Photo. *Perf. 12***

**C439** AP82 10c gray & multi .25 .25
**C440** AP82 2p gray & multi 4.50 4.50

See Nos. C387-C388.

### Type of Regular Issue, 1962 and

Locomotives of 1854 and 1961 — AP82a

Pres. Aquileo Parra and Magdalena River Bridge — AP83

Design: 10c, Railroad map of Colombia.

**1962, Sept. 28 Photo. *Perf. 12½***

**C441** AP82a 5c sep & slate grn .25 .25
**C442** A316 10c multicolored .25 .25

**Engr.**

**C443** AP83 1p dull pur & brn 2.00 .25

**Inscribed: "Extra Rapido."**

**C444** AP83 5p bl, brn & dl grn 5.00 4.50
*Nos. C441-C444 (4)* 7.50 5.25

Progress of Colombian railroads and completion of the Atlantic Line from Santa Maria to Bogota.
No. C444 inscribed "EXTRA RAPIDO."

### UPAE Type

Designs: 50c, Map of Americas and carrier pigeon. 60c, Post horn.

***Perf. 13½x14***

**1962, Oct. 18 Litho. Wmk. 346**

**C445** A317 50c slate grn & gold .40 .25
**C446** A317 60c gold & plum .25 .25

Pope John XXIII — AP84

**1963, Mar. 11**

**C447** AP84 60c gold, red brn, buff & red .40 .25

Vatican II, the 21st Ecumenical Council of the Roman Catholic Church.

### Women's Rights Type of 1962

**1963-64 *Perf. 12x12½***

**C448** A314 5c sal, gray & blk ('64) .25 .25
**C449** A314 45c pale grn, gray & blk .40 .25
**C450** A314 45c brt pink, gray & blk .40 .25
*Nos. C448-C450 (3)* 1.05 .75

Games Emblem AP85

**1963, Aug. 12 *Perf. 13x14***

**C451** AP85 20c gray & multi .35 .25
**C452** AP85 80c buff & multi .35 .25

South American Athletic Championships (22nd for men, 12th for women), Cali, June 30-July 7.

Bolivar Statue by Arenas-Betancourt — AP86

***Perf. 14x13½***

**1963, Aug. 30 Unwmk.**

**C453** AP86 1.90p olive bis & blue .25 .25

Centenary of the city of Pereira.
For surcharge see No. C574.

Tennis Player — AP87

**1963, Oct. 11 *Perf. 13½x14***

**C454** AP87 55c multicolored .25 .25

30th South American Tennis Championships, Medellin, Oct. 3-13.

Pres. John F. Kennedy and Alliance for Progress Emblem — AP88

**1963, Dec. 17 Litho. *Perf. 14x13½***

**C455** AP88 10c multicolored .25 .25

President John F. Kennedy (1917-1963).

Church of the True Cross, National Pantheon, Bogota — AP89

2p, Christ of the Martyrs, bell and tomb.

***Perf. 13½x14***

**1964, Mar. 10 Photo. Unwmk.**

**C459** AP89 1p multicolored .25 .25
**C460** AP89 2p multicolored .35 .25

View of Cartagena AP90

**1964, Mar. 18 Litho. *Perf. 14x13½***

**C461** AP90 3p vio, bl, ocher & brn 1.50 .60

Cartagena's independence in 1811, Simon Bolivar's visit in 1812 and the siege of 1815.

Eleanor Roosevelt — AP91

**1964, Nov. 10 Photo. *Perf. 12***

**C462** AP91 20c ol & dl red brn .25 .25

Eleanor Roosevelt (1884-1962).

Alberto Castilla and Score of "El Bunde" — AP92

**1964, Nov. 10 Unwmk.**

**C463** AP92 30c ol bis & Prus grn .25 .25

Department of Tolima and Maestro Alberto Castilla (1878-1937) who in 1906 founded the Tolima Conservatory of Music in Ibague.

### Mejia Type

Mejia portrait and: 45c, Women picking coffee. 5p, Mules carrying coffee bags. 10p, Loading coffee on freighter "Manuel Mejia."

**1965, Feb. 10 Engr. *Perf. 12½x13***

**C464** A320 45c brown & blk .25 .25
**C465** A320 5p gray grn & blk 2.50 .25
**C466** A320 10p ultra & blk 3.50 .40
*Nos. C464-C466 (3)* 6.25 .90

ITU Emblem — AP93

**1965, Oct. 25 Photo. *Perf. 12***

**C467** AP93 80c Prus bl, lt bl & red .25 .25

Cent. of the ITU.

Cattleya Truanae — AP94

**1965, Oct. 3 Litho. *Perf. 13½x14***

**C468** AP94 20c yellow & multi 1.00 .40

Fifth Philatelic Exhibition.

Cent. of the Telegraph in Colombia — AP95

No. C469, Pres. Manuel Murillo Toro statue, telegraph and orbits. No. C470, Telegraph and satellites over South America, horiz.

**1965, Nov. 1 *Perf. 13½x14, 14x13½***

**C469** AP95 60c multicolored .25 .25
**C470** AP95 60c multicolored .25 .25

Junkers F-13 Seaplane, 1920 — AP96

History of Colombian Aviation: 10c, Dornier Wal, 1924. 20c, Dornier Mercur, 1926. 50c, Trimotor Ford, 1932. 60c, De Havilland biplane, 1930. 1p, Douglas DC-4, 1947. 1.40p, Douglas DC-3, 1944. 2.80p, Superconstellation 1049, 1951. 3p, Boeing 720B jet, 1961.

***Perf. 14x13½***

**1965-66 Photo. Unwmk.**

**C471** AP96 5c multicolored .25 .25
**C472** AP96 10c multicolored .25 .25
**C473** AP96 20c multicolored .25 .25
**C474** AP96 50c multicolored .25 .25

C475 AP96 60c multicolored .40 .25
C476 AP96 1p multicolored .75 .25
C477 AP96 1.40p multicolored 1.00 .25
C478 AP96 2.80p multicolored 2.60 .60
C479 AP96 3p multicolored 3.40 .85
*Nos. C471-C479 (9)* 9.15 3.20
*Nos. C471-C479,CE4 (10)* 9.70 3.45

Issued: 5c, 60c, 3p, 12/13/65; 10c, 1p, 1.40p, 7/15/66; 20c, 50c, 2.80p, 12/14/66.

Automobile Club Emblem and Car on Road — AP97

**1966, Feb. 16 Litho. *Perf. 14x13½***
C480 AP97 20c multicolored .60 .25

25th anniv. (in 1965) of the Automobile Club of Colombia.

### Fish Type

Fish: 2p, Flying fish. 2.80p, Queen angelfish. 20p, King mackerel.

**1966, Aug. 25 Photo. *Perf. 12½x13***
C481 A323 2p multicolored .50 .25
C482 A323 2.80p multicolored 1.00 .90
C483 A323 20p multicolored 17.00 13.00
*Nos. C481-C483 (3)* 18.50 14.15

### Coat of Arms Type

**1966, Oct. 11 Litho. *Perf. 14x13½***
C484 A324 1p ultra & multi .40 .25
C485 A324 1.40p red & multi .30 .25

### Portrait Type

80c, Father Felix Restrepo Mejia, S.J. (1887-1965), theologian, scholar. 1.70p, José Joaquin Casas (1866-1951), educator, diplomat.

***Perf. 13½x14***
**1967, Jan. 18 Litho. Unwmk.**
C486 A325 80c dk bl & bis .30 .25
C487 A325 1.70p blk & bis .50 .25

### Declaration of Bogota Type

**1967, Feb. 2 Litho. *Perf. 14x13½***
C488 A326 3p multicolored .50 .25

See note after No. 767.

### Orchid Type

Orchids: 1p, Cattleya dowiana aurea, vert. 1.20p, Masdevallia coccinea, vert. 5p, Catasetum macrocarpum and bee.

**1967, May 23 Litho. *Perf. 14***
C489 A327 1p multicolored .90 .25
C490 A327 1.20p multicolored .70 .25
C491 A327 5p multicolored 4.25 .90
*a.* Souv. sheet of 3, #C489-C491 26.00 25.00
*Nos. C489-C491 (3)* 5.85 1.40

### Lions Type

**1967, July 12 Litho. *Perf. 13½x14***
C492 A328 25c multicolored .25 .25

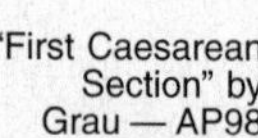

"First Caesarean Section" by Grau — AP98

***Perf. 14x13½***
**1967, Sept. 7 Litho. Unwmk.**
C493 AP98 80c multicolored .25 .25

Issued to publicize the 6th Congress of Colombian Surgeons, Bogota, Sept. 25.

### SENA Type
### Lithographed and Embossed

**1967, Sept. 20 *Perf. 13½x14***
C494 A329 2p gold, ver & blk .50 .25

### Pre-Columbian Art Type

Designs: 30c, Bird pectoral. 5p Ornamental pectoral. 20p, Pitcher.

**1967, Oct. 13 Photo. *Perf. 13½x14***
C495 A330 30c ver, gold & brn .40 .25
C496 A330 5p red, gold & brn 3.25 .50
*a.* Souvenir sheet of 2 12.00 12.00
C497 A330 20p vio, gold & brn 15.00 10.00
*Nos. C495-C497 (3)* 18.65 10.75

No. C496a also commemorates the 6th Natl. Phil. Exhib. No. C496a contains 2 imperf. stamps in changed colors similar to Nos. C495-C496 (30c has green background and 5p maroon background).

### Telecommunications Type

Designs: 50c, Signal lights. 1p, Early Bird satellite, Southern Cross and radar.

***Perf. 13½x14***
**1968, May 14 Litho. Unwmk.**
C498 A331 50c blk, ver & emer .25 .25
C499 A331 1p ultra, yel & gray .30 .25

### Eucharist Type

**1968, June 6 Litho. *Perf. 13½x14***
C500 A332 80c rose lil, red, yel & blk .25 .25
C501 A332 3p bl, red, yel & blk .30 .25

### Eucharistic Congress Type

Designs: 80c, The Last Supper, by Gregorio Vasquez, horiz. 1p, St. Francis Xavier Preaching, by Gregorio Vasquez. 2p, The Dream of the Prophet Elias, by Gregorio Vasquez. 3p, Monstrance, c. 1700. 20p, Pope Paul VI, painting by Roman Franciscan nuns.

**1968, Aug. 13 Photo. *Perf. 13***
C502 A333 80c multicolored .25 .25
C503 A333 1p multicolored .40 .25
C504 A333 2p multicolored .45 .25
C505 A333 3p lil & multi .80 .25
C506 A333 20p gold & multi 5.00 2.50
*Nos. C502-C506 (5)* 6.90 3.50

Shrine of the Eucharist, Bogotá — AP99

1.20p, Pope Paul VI giving blessing and Papal arms. 1.80p, Cathedral of Bogotá.

***Perf. 14x13½, 13½x14***
**1968, Aug. 22 Litho.**
C507 AP99 80c multi .30 .25
C508 AP99 1.20p multi, vert. .30 .25
C509 AP99 1.80p multi, vert. .40 .25
*Nos. C507-C509 (3)* 1.00 .75

Visit of Pope Paul VI to Colombia.

Computer Symbols — AP100

**1968, Oct. 29 Litho. *Perf. 13½x14***
C510 AP100 20c buff, car & grn .25 .25

Cent. of the Natl. University and the 1st Data Processing Cong. in 1967 at the University.

### Agriculture Institute Type

**1968, Mar. 5 Litho. *Perf. 13½x14***
C511 A337 1p gray & multi .25 .25

Microscope and Pen — AP101

**1969, Mar. 24 Litho. *Perf. 14***
C512 AP101 5p blk, yel, ver & pur 2.00 .35

20th anniv. (in 1968) of the University of the Andes.

Alexander von Humboldt and Andes — AP102

**1969, May 3 Litho. *Perf. 14x13½***
C513 AP102 1p grn & brn .65 .35

Alexander von Humboldt (1769-1859), German naturalist and traveler.

Map of Colombia, Amphibian Plane and Letter — AP103

Design: 1.50p, No. C516b, Globe, letter, and jet of Avianca airlines.

**1969, June 18 Litho. *Perf. 14x13½***
C514 AP103 1p multi .45 .25
C515 AP103 1.50p multi .65 .25

### Souvenir Sheet
### *Imperf*

C516 Sheet of 2 7.25 7.25
*a.* AP103 5p green & multi 1.00 1.00
*b.* AP103 5p violet & multi 1.00 1.00

50th anniv. of the 1st air post flight in Colombia. No. C516 also for 8th Natl. Philatelic Exhibition, EXFILBA 69, Barranquilla, June 18-22. No. C516 contains 2 stamps in the designs of the 1p and 1.50p.

### Independence Type

2.30p, Simon Bolivar, José Antonio Anzoategui, Francisco de Paula Santander and victorious army entering Bogotá, 9/18/1819; painting by Ignacio Castillo Cervantes.

**1969, July 24 Litho. *Perf. 13½x14***
C517 A338 2.30p gold & multi 1.00 .35

Social Security Emblem — AP104

**1969, Oct. 29 Litho. *Perf. 13½x14***
C518 AP104 20c emer & blk .25 .25

20th anniv. of the Colombian Institute of Social Security.

Neurosurgeons' Congress Emblem — AP105

**1969, Oct. 29**
C519 AP105 70c vio, red & yel .50 .30

Issued to publicize the 13th Congress of Latin-American Neurosurgeons, Bogotá.

Junkers F-13 — AP106

Nos. C521, C522b, Globe with airlines from Bogota & Boeing jet. No. C522a, like No. C520.

**1969, Nov. 28 Litho. *Perf. 14x13½***
C520 AP106 2p grn & multi .60 .25
C521 AP106 3.50p ultra & multi 1.00 .50

### Souvenir Sheet
### *Imperf*

C522 Sheet of 2 6.50 6.50
*a.* AP106 3.50p lt grn & multi .75 .75
*b.* AP106 5p ultra & multi 1.00 1.00

50th anniv. of AVIANCA; No. C522 also publicizes the 1st Interamerican Phil. Exhib., Bogota, Nov. 28-Dec. 7.

No. C522 contains 2 imperf. stamps.

Child Mailing Letter — AP107

Christmas: 1.50p, Praying child and gifts.

**1969, Dec. 16 Litho. *Perf. 13½x14***
C523 AP107 60c ocher & multi .60 .25
C524 AP107 1p multicolored .65 .25
C525 AP107 1.50p multicolored .75 .25
*Nos. C523-C525 (3)* 2.00 .75

Radar Station and Pre-Columbian Head — AP108

**1970, Mar. 25 Litho. *Perf. 14x13½***
C526 AP108 1p dl grn, blk & brick red .95 .25

Issued to publicize the opening of the communications satellite earth station at Chocontá in Cundinamarca Province.

Emblem of Colombian Youth Sports Institute — AP109

2.30p, Games' emblem (dove and 3 rings).

**1970, Apr. 6 Litho. *Perf. 13½x14***
C527 AP109 1.50p dk ol grn, yel & blk .30 .25
C528 AP109 2.30p red & multi .40 .25

9th Natl. Youth Games, Ibague, July 10-20.

Art Exhibition Emblem — AP110

**1970, Apr. 30 Litho. *Perf. 13½x14***
C529 AP110 30c multicolored .25 .25

2nd Biennial Art Exhib., Medellin, 6/1-7/14.

Eduardo Santos, Rural and Urban Buildings AP111

**1970, June 18 Litho. *Perf. 14x13½***
C530 AP111 1p grn, yel & blk .25 .25

Issued to commemorate the founding (in 1939) of the Territorial Credit Institute.

UN Emblem, Scales and Dove — AP112

**1970, June 26 *Perf. 13½x14***
C531 AP112 1.50p dk bl, lt bl & yel .25 .25

25th anniversary of United Nations.

EXFILCA Emblem — AP113

**1970, Nov. Litho. *Perf. 13½x14***

**C532** AP113 10p bl, gold & blk 4.50 .25

EXFILCA 70, 2nd Interamerican Philatelic Exhib., Caracas, Venezuela, Nov. 27-Dec. 6.

Mother Juana Ruperta in Napanga Costume and Music by Efrain Orozco — AP114

Designs: 1p, Dancers from Eastern Plains and music by Alejandro Wills. No. C535, Guabina man, woman and folk song. No. C536, Bambuco man and woman, and music. No. C537, Man and woman dancing the Cumbia, and music.

**1970-71 Litho. *Perf. 13½x14***

| | | | | |
|---|---|---|---|---|
| **C533** | AP114 | 60c dp lil rose & multi | .80 | .25 |
| **C534** | AP114 | 1p ultra & multi | .75 | .25 |
| **C535** | AP114 | 1.30p bl & multi | .85 | .25 |
| **C536** | AP114 | 1.30p emer & multi ('71) | 1.00 | .25 |
| **C537** | AP114 | 1.30p lil & multi ('71) | .70 | .25 |
| | | *Nos. C533-C537 (5)* | 4.10 | 1.25 |

Athlete and Games Emblem — AP115

Design: 2p, Games emblem.

**1971, Mar. 11**

| | | | | |
|---|---|---|---|---|
| **C542** | AP115 | 1.50p multicolored | 1.10 | 1.00 |
| **C543** | AP115 | 2p blk, org & grn | 1.00 | .75 |

6th Pan-American Games, Cali, 7/30-8/13.

Gilberto Alzate Avendano AP116

**1971, Apr. 29 Litho. *Perf. 14x13½***

**C544** AP116 1p bl & multi .85 .25

Avendano (1910-60), journalist, popular leader.

Commemorative Medal — AP117

**Lithographed and Embossed**

**1971, June 21 *Perf. 14x13½***

**C545** AP117 1p slate grn & gold .60 .30

Centenary (in 1970) of the Bank of Bogota.

Olympic Center AP118

Soccer AP119

Designs (Games Emblem and): Nos. C546-C546C, Olympic Center. No. 547, Soccer. No. C548, Wrestling. No. C549, Bicycling. No. C550, Volleyball. No. C551, Diving (women). No. C552, Fencing. No. C553, Sailing. No. C554, Equestrian. No. C555, Jumping. No. C556, Rowing. No. C557, Cali emblem. No. C558, Basketball (women). No. C559, Stadium. No. C560, Baseball. No. C561, Hockey. No. C562, Weight lifting. No. C563, Medals. No. C564, Boxing. No. C565, Gymnastics (women). No. C566, Sharpshooting.

**1971, July 16 Litho. *Perf. 13½x14***

**Multicolored and Emblem Color:**

| | | | | |
|---|---|---|---|---|
| **C546** | AP118 | 1.30p yellow | 2.60 | .30 |
| **C546A** | AP118 | 1.30p green | 2.60 | .30 |
| **C546B** | AP118 | 1.30p blue | 2.60 | .30 |
| **C546C** | AP118 | 1.30p carmine | 2.60 | .30 |
| **C547** | AP119 | 1.30p emerald | 2.60 | .30 |
| **C548** | AP119 | 1.30p lilac | 2.60 | .30 |
| **C549** | AP119 | 1.30p blue | 2.60 | .30 |
| **C550** | AP119 | 1.30p carmine | 2.60 | .30 |
| **C551** | AP119 | 1.30p blue | 2.60 | .30 |
| **C552** | AP119 | 1.30p carmine | 2.60 | .30 |
| **C553** | AP119 | 1.30p blue | 2.60 | .30 |
| **C554** | AP119 | 1.30p gray | 2.60 | .30 |
| **C555** | AP119 | 1.30p green | 2.60 | .30 |
| **C556** | AP119 | 1.30p blue | 2.60 | .30 |
| **C557** | AP118 | 1.30p orange | 2.60 | .30 |
| **C558** | AP119 | 1.30p carmine | 2.60 | .30 |
| **C559** | AP118 | 1.30p light blue | 2.60 | .30 |
| **C560** | AP119 | 1.30p plum | 2.60 | .30 |
| **C561** | AP119 | 1.30p yel grn | 2.60 | .30 |
| **C562** | AP119 | 1.30p pink | 2.60 | .30 |
| **C563** | AP118 | 1.30p deep org | 2.60 | .30 |
| **C564** | AP119 | 1.30p plum | 2.60 | .30 |
| **C565** | AP119 | 1.30p lilac rose | 2.60 | .30 |
| **C566** | AP119 | 1.30p green | 2.60 | .30 |
| *a.* | | Sheet of 25, #C546-C566 | 65.00 | 60.00 |

6th Pan American Athletic Games, Cali. No. C546B appears twice in sheet.

Battle of Carabobo, by Martin Tovar y Tovar AP120

**1971, Nov. 25 Litho. *Perf. 13½x14***

**C567** AP120 1.50p multicolored 1.20 .25

Sesquicentennial of the Battle of Carabobo.

St. Theresa Type Overprinted

**1972 Litho. *Perf. 13½x14***

**C568** A343 2p multicolored .60 .25

See note after No. 793.

Vendor — AP121

Designs: 50c, Woman wearing shawl, and woven shawl. 3p, Fruit vendor (puppet).

**1972, Apr. 11 Litho. *Perf. 13½x14***

| | | | | |
|---|---|---|---|---|
| **C569** | AP121 | 50c multicolored | .35 | .25 |
| **C570** | AP121 | 1p multicolored | .35 | .25 |
| **C571** | AP121 | 3p multicolored | .50 | .25 |
| | | *Nos. C569-C571 (3)* | 1.20 | .75 |

Colombian artisans.

Mormodes Rolfeanum AP122

**1972, Apr. 20 *Perf. 14x13½***

**C572** AP122 1.30p multicolored 1.15 .25

7th World Orchidology Congress, Medellin.

Congo Grande Dancer — AP123

**1972, June 21 Litho. *Perf. 13½x14***

**C573** AP123 1.30p multicolored .60 .25

International Carnival of Barranquilla.

No. C453 Surcharged in Brown

**1972, Oct. 5 Litho. *Perf. 14x13½***

**C574** AP86 1.30p on 1.90p .85 .25

Laureano Gomez, by Ridriguez Cubillos — AP124

No. C576, Guillermo Leòn Valencia Muñoz.

**1972 *Perf. 13½x14***

| | | | | |
|---|---|---|---|---|
| **C575** | AP124 | 1.30p multicolored | .25 | .25 |
| **C576** | AP124 | 1.30p multicolored | .25 | .25 |

Laureano Gomez (1898-1966), Guillermo Leon Valencia Munoz (1909-71), Presidents of Colombia.

Issued: No. C575, 10/17; No. C576, 11/28.

Benito Juarez — AP125

**1972, Dec. 12 *Perf. 13½x14***

**C577** AP125 1.50p multicolored .25 .25

Benito Juarez (1806-1872), revolutionary leader and president of Mexico.

Rebecca Fountain — AP126

**1972, Dec. 19 Litho.**

| | | | | |
|---|---|---|---|---|
| **C578** | AP126 | 80c multicolored | .70 | .45 |
| **C579** | AP126 | 1p multicolored | .65 | .25 |

"Bucaramanga" AP127

**1972, Dec. 22 *Perf. 14x13½***

**C580** AP127 5p multicolored 1.00 .25

Founding of Bucaramanga, 350th anniv.

Xavier University AP128

**1973, May 8 Litho. *Perf. 14x13½***

| | | | | |
|---|---|---|---|---|
| **C581** | AP128 | 1.30p lt grn & sep | .30 | .25 |
| **C582** | AP128 | 1.50p lt bl & sep | .30 | .25 |

350th anniversary of the founding of Xavier University in Bogotá.

**Ceramic Type**

Excavated Ceramic Artifacts: 1p, Winged urn, Tairona. 1.30p, Woman and child, Sinu. 1.70p, Two-headed figure, Quimbaya. 3.50p, Man, Tumaco.

**1973 Litho. *Perf. 13½x14***

| | | | | |
|---|---|---|---|---|
| **C583** | A358 | 1p multicolored | 1.75 | 1.20 |
| **C584** | A358 | 1.30p multicolored | 1.00 | .25 |
| **C585** | A358 | 1.70p multicolored | 1.25 | .25 |
| **C586** | A358 | 3.50p multicolored | 2.00 | .30 |
| | | *Nos. C583-C586 (4)* | 6.00 | 2.00 |

Issue dates: 1p, Oct. 11; others, June 15.

Battle of Maracaibo, by Manuel F. Rincon — AP129

**1973, July 24 Litho. *Perf. 14x13½***

**C587** AP129 10p bl & multi 2.50 .25

Battle of Maracaibo, sesquicentennial.

Bank Emblem — AP130

**1973, Oct. 1 Litho. *Perf. 14x13½***

**C588** AP130 2p multicolored .30 .25

50th anniv. of the Bank of the Republic.

**No. 801 Overprinted "AEREO"**

**1973, Oct. 11 *Perf. 14***

**C589** A346 80c multicolored .30 .25

Pres. Pedro Nel Ospina, by Coroleano Leudo — AP131

**1973, Nov. 9 *Perf. 13½x14***

**C590** AP131 1.50p multicolored .25 .25

50th anniversary of the Ministry of Communications founded under Pres. Ospina.

Arms of Toro — AP132

**1973, Dec. 1**

**C591** AP132 1p multicolored .25 .25

Founding of Toro, Valle del Cauca, 4th cent.

Bolivar, Battle of Bombona AP133

**1973, Dec. 7 Litho. *Perf. 14x13½***

**C592** AP133 1.30p multicolored .25 .25

Sesquicentennial (in 1972) of the Battle of Bombona.

Nicolaus Copernicus — AP134

**1974, Feb. 19 Litho. *Perf. 13½x14***

**C593** AP134 2.50p multicolored .70 .25

500th anniversary of the birth of Nicolaus Copernicus (1473-1543), Polish astronomer.

Andes, Map of South America — AP135

**1974, May 11 Litho. *Perf. 14***

**C594** AP135 2p multicolored .50 .25

Meeting of Communications Ministers of Members of the Andean Group, Cali, May 7-11, 1974.

Television Set — AP136

**1974, July 16 Litho. *Perf. 14x13½***

**C595** AP136 1.30p org, blk & brn .40 .25

20th anniversary of Colombian television and 10th anniversary of INRAVISION, the National Institute of Radio and Television.

Championship Emblem — AP137

**1974, Aug. 5 Litho. *Perf. 14x13½***

**C596** AP137 4.50p multicolored .40 .25

2nd World Swimming Championships, Cali.

Condor AP138

**1974, Aug. 28 *Perf. 14***

**C597** AP138 1.50p multicolored .65 .25

Bank of Colombia centenary.

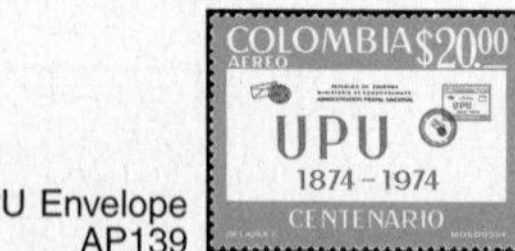
UPU Envelope AP139

**1974, Sept. 9 Litho. *Perf. 14***

**C598** AP139 20p multicolored 2.75 2.60

Centenary of Universal Postal Union.

Symbol of Flight — AP140

**1974, Sept. *Perf. 12x12½***

**C599** AP140 20c olive .60 .25

Gen. José Maria Cordoba — AP141

**1974, Oct. 14 Litho. *Perf. 13½x14***

**C609** AP141 1.30p multicolored .25 .25

Sesquicentennial of the Battles of Junin and Ayacucho.

**Insurance Type**

Design: 3p, Abstract pattern.

**1974, Oct. 24 Litho. *Perf. 13½x14***

**C610** A365 3p multicolored .30 .25

White-tailed Trogon, Letter — AP142

Designs (UPU Letter and): 1.30p, Keelbilled Toucan, horiz. 2p, Peruvian cock-of-the-rock, horiz. 2.50p, Scarlet macaw.

***Perf. 13½x14, 14x13½***

**1974, Nov. 14**

| | | | | |
|---|---|---|---|---|
| **C611** | AP142 | 1p multicolored | 1.25 | .25 |
| **C612** | AP142 | 1.30p multicolored | 1.25 | .25 |
| **C613** | AP142 | 2p multicolored | 1.90 | .25 |
| **C614** | AP142 | 2.50p multicolored | 1.90 | .25 |
| | | *Nos. C611-C614 (4)* | 6.30 | 1.00 |

Centenary of Universal Postal Union.
For surcharge see No. C656.

Forest No. 1, by Roman Roncancio AP143

Boy with Thorn in Finger, by Gregorio Vazquez AP144

Paintings: 3p, Women Fruit Vendors, by Miguel Diaz Vargas (1886-1956). 5p, Annunciation, Santafereña School, 17th-18th cent.

***Perf. 13½x14, 14x13½***

**1975, Mar. 12 Litho.**

| | | | | |
|---|---|---|---|---|
| **C615** | AP143 | 2p multicolored | .75 | .25 |
| **C616** | AP144 | 3p multicolored | .50 | .25 |
| **C617** | AP144 | 4p multicolored | .65 | .25 |
| **C618** | AP144 | 5p multicolored | 1.10 | .25 |
| | | *Nos. C615-C618 (4)* | 3.00 | 1.00 |

Modern and Colonial Colombian paintings.

Trees and Lake — AP145

Design: 6p, Victoria regia, Amazon River.

**1975, Mar. 12 *Perf. 14x13½***

| | | | | |
|---|---|---|---|---|
| **C619** | AP145 | 1p yellow & multi | .25 | .25 |
| **C620** | AP145 | 6p yellow & multi | .75 | .25 |

Nature conservation of trees and Amazon Region.

**Gold Treasure Type**

Designs: 2p, Nose pendant. 10p, Alligator-shaped staff ornament.

**1975, Apr. 11 Litho. *Perf. 14x13½***

| | | | | |
|---|---|---|---|---|
| **C621** | A368 | 2p grn, gold & brn | 1.00 | .25 |
| **C622** | A368 | 10p multicolored | 4.75 | .60 |

El Rodadero, Santa Maria — AP146

**1975, July 26 Litho. *Perf. 14x13½***

**C623** AP146 2p multicolored .25 .25

400th anniversary of Santa Marta City.

AP147

**1975, Aug. 31 Litho. *Perf. 13½x14***

**C624** AP147 4p multicolored .25 .25

Intl. Women's Year 1975. Maria de Jesus Paramo de Collazos founded 1st normal school for women in Bucaramanga in 1875.

"Sugar Cane" — AP148

**1976, Mar. 12 Litho. *Perf. 13½x14***

**C625** AP148 5p blk & grn 1.25 .25

4th Congress of Latin-American and Caribbean sugar-exporting countries, Cali, 3/8-12.

View of Bogota AP149

**1976, July 2 Litho. *Perf. 12***

| | | | | |
|---|---|---|---|---|
| **C626** | AP149 | 10p shown | 1.40 | .90 |
| **C627** | AP149 | 10p Barranquilla | 1.40 | .90 |
| **C628** | AP149 | 10p Cali | 1.40 | .90 |
| **C629** | AP149 | 10p Medellin | 1.40 | .90 |
| *a.* | | Block of 4, #C626-C629 | 6.25 | 6.25 |

Habitat, UN Conf. on Human Settlements, Vancouver, Canada, May 31-June 11.

University Emblem and "90" — AP150

**1976, Aug. 6 Litho. *Perf. 13½x14***

**C630** AP150 5p lt blue & multi .50 .25

Univ. of Colombia day school, 90th anniv.

Miguel Samper — AP151

**1976, Oct. 29 Litho. *Perf. 13½x14***

**C631** AP151 2p multicolored .25 .25

Samper (1825-99), economist and writer.

Telephone, 1895 — AP152

**1976, Nov. 2**

**C632** AP152 3p multicolored .25 .25

Centenary of first telephone call by Alexander Graham Bell, Mar. 10, 1876.

747 Jumbo Jet — AP153

**1976, Dec. 3 Litho. *Perf. 12***

**C633** AP153 2p multicolored .25 .25

Inauguration of 747 jumbo jet service by Avianca.
For surcharge see No. C636.

Convent, Church and Plaza de San Francisco AP154

**1976, Dec. 29 Litho. *Perf. 14***

**C634** AP154 6p multicolored .50 .25

150th anniv. of the Congress of Panama.

Souvenir Sheet

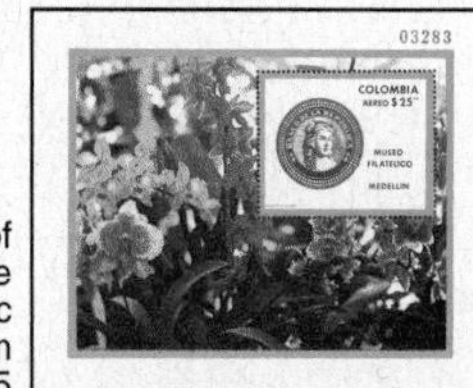
Bank of the Republic Emblem AP155

**1977, June 6 Litho. *Perf. 14***

**C635** AP155 25p multicolored 12.00 12.00

Opening of Philatelic Museum of Medellin under auspices of Banco de la Republica.

**No. C633 Surcharged in Light Brown**

**1977, June Litho. *Perf. 12***

**C636** AP153 3p on 2p multi .25 .25

Coffee — AP156

**1977-78 Litho. *Perf. 12½***

| | | | | |
|---|---|---|---|---|
| **C640** | AP156 | 3p multi | .50 | .25 |
| **C641** | AP156 | 3.50p multi ('78) | .50 | .25 |

Colombian coffee.

Coffee Grower, Pack Mule — AP157

**1977, Aug. 9 Litho. *Perf. 13½x14***

**C642** AP157 10p multicolored .50 .25

National Federation of Coffee Growers, 50th anniversary.

Beethoven and 9th Symphony — AP158

**1977, Aug. 17**

**C643** AP158 8p multicolored 1.25 .25

Sesquicentennial of the death of Ludwig van Beethoven (1770-1827).

### Bird Type

Tropical Birds and Plants: No. C644, Woodpecker and Meriania. C645, Purple gallinule and water lilies. No. C646, Xipholaena punicea and Cochlospermum orinocense. No. C647, Crowned flycatcher and Jacaranda copaia.

**1977, Sept. 6 Litho. *Perf. 14***

| | | | | | |
|---|---|---|---|---|---|
| **C644** | A380 | 5p | multicolored | .75 | .25 |
| **C645** | A380 | 5p | multicolored | .75 | .25 |
| **C646** | A380 | 10p | multicolored | 1.10 | .25 |
| **C647** | A380 | 10p | multicolored | 1.10 | .25 |
| | *Nos. C644-C647 (4)* | | | 3.70 | 1.00 |

Games' Emblem — AP159

**1977, Sept. 9 *Perf. 12x12½***

**C648** AP159 6p multicolored .25 .25

13th Central American and Caribbean Games, Medellin, 1978.

La Cayetana, by Enrique Grau — AP160

No. C650, Water Nymphs, by Beatriz Gonzalez.

**1977, Sept. 13 *Perf. 14x13½***

| | | | | | |
|---|---|---|---|---|---|
| **C649** | AP160 | 8p | multicolored | 1.25 | .25 |
| **C650** | AP160 | 8p | multicolored | 1.25 | .25 |

Women's suffrage, 20th anniversary.

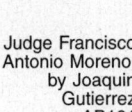

Judge Francisco Antonio Moreno, by Joaquin Gutierrez AP161

Design: 25p, Viceroy Manuel de Guirior.

**1977, Sept. 13 *Perf. 12***

| | | | | | |
|---|---|---|---|---|---|
| **C651** | AP161 | 20p | multicolored | 1.60 | .75 |
| **C652** | AP161 | 25p | multicolored | 2.40 | 1.10 |

Bicentenary of National Library.

Federico Lleras Acosta — AP162

**1977, Sept. 27 Litho. *Perf. 14***

**C653** AP162 5p multicolored .30 .25

Dr. Federico Lleras Acosta, veterinarian and bacteriologist; birth centenary.

Cauca University Arms — AP163

**1977, Oct. 14**

**C654** AP163 5p multicolored .30 .25

Sesquicentennial of the University of Cauca.

CUDECOM Building, Bogota — AP164

**1977, Oct. 14**

**C655** AP164 1.50p multicolored .25 .25

Colombian Society of Engineers, 90th anniv.

### No. C612 Surcharged with New Value and Bars in Brown

**1977, Dec. 3 Litho. *Perf. 14x13½***

**C656** AP142 2p on 1.30p multi .30 .25

Lost City, Tayrona Culture — AP165

**1978, Apr. 18 Litho. *Perf. 12½***

**C657** AP165 3.50p multicolored .25 .25

Creator of Energy, by Arenas Betancourt — AP166

**1978, Apr. 25 *Perf. 12***

**C658** AP166 4p blue & multi .35 .25

Sesquicentennial of Antioquia University Law School.

Column of the Slaves — AP167

**1978, May 9**

**C659** AP167 2.50p multicolored .25 .25

Sesquicentennial of Ocana Convention (meeting of various political groups).

Statue of Catalina, Cartagena — AP168

**1978, May 30 Litho. *Perf. 12***

**C660** AP168 4p blk & lt bl .25 .25

Sesquicentennial of University of Cartagena.

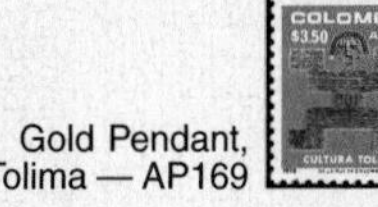

Gold Pendant, Tolima — AP169

**1978, July 11 Litho. *Perf. 12x12½***

**C661** AP169 3.50p multicolored .25 .25

Apotheosis of Spanish Language, by Luis Alberto Acuña — AP170

**1978, Aug. 9 *Perf. 14***

| | | | | |
|---|---|---|---|---|
| **C662** | AP170 | Strip of 3 | 5.75 | 5.00 |
| *a.-c.* | | 11p, any single | 1.40 | 1.25 |

Millennium of Spanish language.

Presidential Guard — AP171

**1978, Aug. 16 *Perf. 13½x14***

**C663** AP171 9p multicolored .45 .45

Presidential Guard Battalion, 50th anniv.

Figure, Muisca Culture — AP172

**1978, Sept. 12 Litho. *Perf. 12½***

**C664** AP172 3.50p multicolored .30 .25

Apse of Carmelite Church — AP173

**1978, Oct. 12 *Perf. 13***

**C665** AP173 30p multicolored 2.60 .40

### Souvenir Sheet

***Perf. 13½x14***

**C666** AP173 50p multicolored 4.50 3.75

ESPAMER '78 Philatelic Exhibition, Bogota, Oct. 12-21.

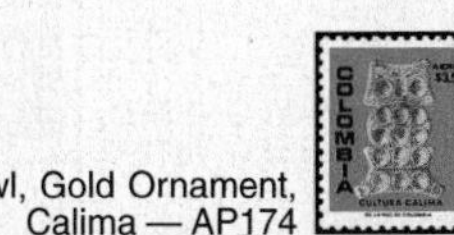

Owl, Gold Ornament, Calima — AP174

No. C669, Gold frog, Quimbaya culture. No. C670, Gold nose pendant, Tairona, horiz.

**1978-80 Litho. *Perf. 12½***

| | | | | | |
|---|---|---|---|---|---|
| **C667** | AP174 | 3.50p | multi | .50 | .25 |
| **C668** | AP174 | 4p | multi ('79) | .30 | .25 |
| **C669** | AP174 | 4p | multi ('79) | .50 | .25 |
| **C670** | AP174 | 5p | multi ('80) | .80 | .25 |
| | *Nos. C667-C670 (4)* | | | 2.10 | 1.00 |

Virgin and Child, by Gregorio Vasquez — AP175

**1978, Nov. 28 *Perf. 13½x14***

**C671** AP175 2.50p multicolored .25 .25

Christmas 1978.

Bull Ring, Cathedral, Manizales AP176

**1979, Jan. 6 Litho. *Perf. 14***

**C672** AP176 7p multicolored .80 .25

Manizales Fair.

Children Playing Hopscotch, and IYC Emblem — AP177

No. C674, Child at blackboard and UNESCO emblem. No. C675, The Paper Collector, by Omar Gordillo, and UN emblem.

**1979, July 19 *Perf. 13½x14, 14x13½***

| | | | | | |
|---|---|---|---|---|---|
| **C673** | AP177 | 8p | multi | .40 | .30 |
| **C674** | AP177 | 12p | multi, horiz. | .55 | .45 |
| **C675** | AP177 | 12p | multi | .55 | .45 |
| | *Nos. C673-C675 (3)* | | | 1.50 | 1.20 |

International Year of the Child.

Rio Prado Hydroelectric Station AP178

**1979, Aug. 24 *Perf. 13½x14***

**C676** AP178 5p multicolored .80 .25

Tomb, 6th Century AP179

**1979, Sept. 25 Litho. *Perf. 14***

**C677** AP179 8p multicolored .80 .35

San Augustin Archaeological Park.

Gonzalo Jimenez de Quesada, by C. Leudo — AP180

**1979, Oct. 11 *Perf. 12***

**C678** AP180 20p multicolored 3.25 1.00

Gonzalo Jimenez de Quesada (1500-1579), Spanish conquistador.

Hill, Penny Black, Colombia No. 1 AP181

**1979, Oct. 23 *Perf. 13½x14***

**C679** AP181 15p multicolored .90 .25

Sir Rowland Hill (1795-1879), originator of penny postage.

Amazon Region AP182

Tourism: 14p, San Fernando Fortress.

**1979 Litho. *Perf. 13½x14***

| | | | | | |
|---|---|---|---|---|---|
| **C680** | AP182 | 7p | multicolored | .60 | .25 |
| **C681** | AP182 | 14p | multicolored | 1.60 | .75 |

Issue dates: 7p, Nov. 16; 14p, Nov. 9.
See Nos. C717-C719.

AP183

Creche Sculptures: No. C682, Three Kings and soldiers. No. C683, Nativity. No. C684, Shepherds.

**1979, Nov. 30 *Perf. 12***

| | | | | | |
|---|---|---|---|---|---|
| **C682** | AP183 | 3p | multicolored | 1.25 | 1.10 |
| **C683** | AP183 | 3p | multicolored | 1.25 | 1.10 |
| **C684** | AP183 | 3p | multicolored | 1.25 | 1.10 |
| *a.* | Strip of 3, #C682-C684 | | | 4.50 | 3.50 |

Christmas 1979.

AP184

Magdalena Bridge, Avianca emblem.

**1979, Dec. 5 *Perf. 14***

| | | | | | |
|---|---|---|---|---|---|
| **C685** | AP184 | 15p | multicolored | .70 | .25 |

Barranquilla, 350th anniversary; Avianca National Airline, 60th anniversary.

AP185

Boy Playing Flute, by Judith Leyster.

**1980, Feb. 15 *Perf. 13½x14***

| | | | | | |
|---|---|---|---|---|---|
| **C686** | AP185 | 6p | multicolored | .60 | .25 |

2nd Intl. Music Competition, Ibague, Dec. 1979.

Gen. Antonio José de Sucre, 150th Death Anniversary AP186

**1980, Feb. 15 Litho. *Perf. 12½x12***

| | | | | | |
|---|---|---|---|---|---|
| **C687** | AP186 | 12p | multicolored | .60 | .25 |

The Watchman, by Edgar Negret — AP187

**1980, Feb. 26 *Perf. 12x12½***

| | | | | | |
|---|---|---|---|---|---|
| **C688** | AP187 | 25p | multicolored | 2.50 | 1.40 |

Virgin Mary, by Real del Sarte, 1929 — AP188

**1980, May 23 Litho. *Perf. 14x13½***

| | | | | | |
|---|---|---|---|---|---|
| **C689** | AP188 | 12p | multicolored | .60 | .25 |

Apparition of the Virgin Mary to Sister Catalina Labouri Gontard, 150th anniv.

San Gil Produce Market, by Luis Roncancio AP189

**1980, May 27 *Perf. 13½x14***

| | | | | | |
|---|---|---|---|---|---|
| **C690** | AP189 | 12p | multicolored | .70 | .25 |

Pres. Enrique Olaya Herrera, by Miguel Diaz Vargas — AP190

**1980, Oct. 28 Litho. *Perf. 12***

| | | | | | |
|---|---|---|---|---|---|
| **C691** | AP190 | 20p | multicolored | 1.40 | .40 |

Enrique Olaya Herrera (1880-1936), president, 1930-1934.

The Boy Fishing in a Bucket AP191

Christmas (Christmas Stories by Rafael Pombo): No. C693, The Frog and the Mouse. No. C694, The Seven Lives of the Cat.

**1980, Nov. 21 Litho. *Perf. 14½***

| | | | | | |
|---|---|---|---|---|---|
| **C692** | AP191 | 4p | multicolored | .60 | .25 |
| **C693** | AP191 | 4p | multicolored | .60 | .25 |
| **C694** | AP191 | 4p | multicolored | .60 | .25 |
| | *Nos. C692-C694 (3)* | | | 1.80 | .75 |

28th World Golf Cup, Cajica — AP192

**1980, Dec. 9 Litho. *Perf. 13½x14***

| | | | | | |
|---|---|---|---|---|---|
| **C695** | AP192 | 30p | multicolored | 5.50 | 3.00 |

**Bolivar Type**

Simon Bolivar Death Sesquicentennial: 6p, Portrait, last words to Colombia, vert.

**1980, Dec. 17 *Perf. 12***

| | | | | | |
|---|---|---|---|---|---|
| **C696** | A400 | 6p | multicolored | .80 | .45 |

St. Peter Claver Holding Cross — AP193

**1981, Jan. 13 *Perf. 14½***

| | | | | | |
|---|---|---|---|---|---|
| **C697** | AP193 | 15p | multicolored | .80 | .30 |

St. Peter Claver (1580-1654), helped American Indians.

Sculptured Bird, San Augustin — AP194

Archaeological Finds: No. C699, Funeral chamber, Tierradentro. No. C700, Chamber hallway, Tierradentro. No. C701, Statue of man, San Augustin.

**1981, May 12 Litho. *Perf. 14***

| | | | | | |
|---|---|---|---|---|---|
| **C698** | AP194 | 7p | multicolored | 1.25 | .25 |
| **C699** | AP194 | 7p | multicolored | 1.25 | .25 |
| **C700** | AP194 | 7p | multicolored | 1.25 | .25 |
| **C701** | AP194 | 7p | multicolored | 1.25 | .25 |
| *a.* | Block of 4, #C698-C701 | | | 6.00 | 5.00 |

See Nos. C707-C710D.

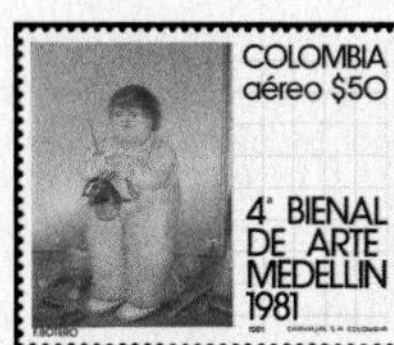


Child with Hobby Horse, by Fernando Botero AP195

4th Biennial Arts show, Medellin: 20p, Square Abstract, by Omar Rayo. 25p, Flowers, by Alejandro Obregon.

**1981, May 15 *Perf. 12***

| | | | | | |
|---|---|---|---|---|---|
| **C702** | AP195 | 20p | multicolored | 1.35 | .25 |
| **C703** | AP195 | 25p | multicolored | 1.50 | .40 |
| **C704** | AP195 | 50p | multicolored | 2.75 | .75 |
| | *Nos. C702-C704 (3)* | | | 5.60 | 1.40 |

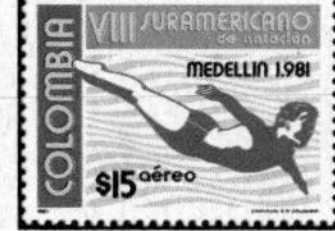


8th South American Swimming Championships, Medellin AP196

**1981, June 5**

| | | | | | |
|---|---|---|---|---|---|
| **C705** | AP196 | 15p | multicolored | .60 | .25 |

Santamaria Bull Ring, 50th Anniv. AP197

**1981, June 9 Litho. *Perf. 12***

| | | | | | |
|---|---|---|---|---|---|
| **C706** | AP197 | 30p | multicolored | 3.25 | 1.75 |

Quimbaya Culture — AP197a

**1981, Sept. 23 Litho. *Perf. 14***

**Yellow Background**

| | | | | |
|---|---|---|---|---|
| **C707** | 9p | Man | 1.25 | .25 |
| **C708** | 9p | Seated man | 1.25 | .25 |
| **C709** | 9p | Seal, print | 1.25 | .25 |
| **C710** | 9p | Jug | 1.25 | .25 |
| *e.* | AP197a Block of 4, #C707-C710 | | 6.00 | 3.50 |

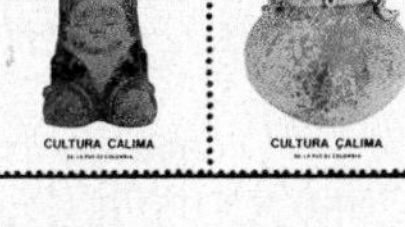

Calima Culture AP197b

No. C710A, Anthropomorphic container. No. C710B, Jar. No. C710C, Anthropomorphic jar. No. C710D, Urn.

**1981, Dec. 17 White Background**

| | | | | |
|---|---|---|---|---|
| **C710A** | 9p | multicolored | 1.75 | .25 |
| **C710B** | 9p | multicolored | 1.75 | .25 |
| **C710C** | 9p | multicolored | 1.75 | .25 |
| **C710D** | 9p | multicolored | 1.75 | .25 |
| *f.* | AP197b Block of 4, #C710A-C710D | | 9.00 | 9.00 |

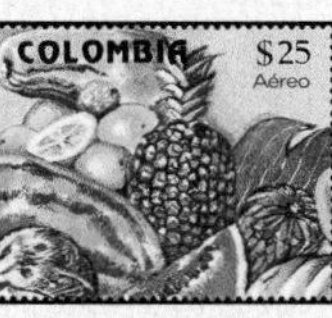


Fruit — AP198

**1981, Nov. 3 Litho. *Perf. 14***

| | | | |
|---|---|---|---|
| **C711** | Block of 6 | 25.00 | 20.00 |
| *a.-f.* | AP198 25p, any single | 4.00 | 1.50 |

Revolt of the Comuneros, 200th Anniv. AP199

**1981, Nov. 21 Litho. *Perf. 12***

| | | | | | |
|---|---|---|---|---|---|
| **C712** | AP199 | 20p | multicolored | .90 | .40 |

Jose Manuel Restrepo, Historian, 1775?-1860? — AP200

**1981, Dec. 1 Litho. *Perf. 12***

| | | | | | |
|---|---|---|---|---|---|
| **C713** | AP200 | 35p | multicolored | 1.25 | .75 |

Andres Bello, 1780?-1865 — AP201

**1981, Dec. 11 Litho. *Perf. 12***

| | | | | | |
|---|---|---|---|---|---|
| **C714** | AP201 | 18p | multicolored | .70 | .25 |

Colombia's Admission to UPU, 100th Anniv. — AP202

30p, No. 103. 50p, Hemispheres, Nos. 104-108.

**1981 Litho. *Perf. 12***

| | | | | | |
|---|---|---|---|---|---|
| **C715** | AP202 | 30p | multicolored | 1.25 | .35 |

**Size: 100x70mm**

***Imperf***

| | | | | | |
|---|---|---|---|---|---|
| **C716** | AP202 | 50p | multicolored | 4.50 | 4.50 |

Issued: No. C715, Dec. 18. No. C716, Dec. 28.

### Tourism Type of 1979

No. C717, Solano Bay. No. C718, Tota Lake, Boyaca. No. C719, Corrales, Boyaca.

**1982 Litho. *Perf. 12***

| | | | | |
|---|---|---|---|---|
| **C717** | AP182 20p multicolored | .60 | .25 |
| **C718** | AP182 20p multicolored | .60 | .25 |
| **C719** | AP182 20p multicolored | .60 | .25 |
| | *Nos. C717-C719 (3)* | 1.80 | .75 |

Issued: No. C717, 6/2; others, 6/16.

1982 World Cup — AP202a

Players and team emblems: a, "America." b, "A. B." c, "Cali." d, "C." e, "C/D." f, "Junior F.B.C." g, "D/M." h, Stadium. i, "M." j, "Club Atletico Nacional." k, "D/P." l, "Quindio." m, "Santa Fe." n, "T." o, "Santa Marta."

**1982, June 21 *Perf. 14***

| | | | |
|---|---|---|---|
| **C720** | Sheet of 15 | 10.00 | 6.75 |
| ***a.-o.*** | AP202a 9p, any single | .80 | .30 |

Bogota Gun Club Centenary AP202b

**1982, July 16 *Perf. 12***

**C721** AP202b 20p multicolored .70 .25

Gold Crocodile Figure, Tairona Culture AP202c

Tairona Culture Exhibit, Gold Museum: Various figures. Nos. C723-C727 vert.

**1982, July 28**

**Gold, Black and**

| | | | |
|---|---|---|---|
| **C722** | AP202c 25p light brown | 2.50 | .95 |
| **C723** | AP202c 25p bright pink | 2.50 | .95 |
| **C724** | AP202c 25p green | 2.50 | .95 |
| **C725** | AP202c 25p dark blue | 2.50 | .95 |
| **C726** | AP202c 25p violet | 2.50 | .95 |
| **C727** | AP202c 25p red | 2.50 | .95 |
| | *Nos. C722-C727 (6)* | 15.00 | 5.70 |

Government Buildings, Pereira AP203

**1982, Aug. 4 Litho. *Perf. 12***

**C728** AP203 35p multicolored 1.25 .40

Biplane in Flight, by Edgar Antonio Bustos — AP204

**1982, Aug. 5 *Perf. 14***

**C729** AP204 18p multicolored 1.20 .25

American Air Forces Cooperation System.

Magdalena River — AP205

**1982, Oct. 21 Litho. *Perf. 12***

**C730** AP205 30p multicolored 1.40 .35

### Marquez Type

**1982, Dec. 10 *Perf. 13½x14***

| | | | |
|---|---|---|---|
| **C731** | A412 25p gray & blue | .70 | .25 |
| **C732** | A412 30p gray & brown | 1.00 | .25 |

San Andres Archipelago AP206

**1983, Apr. 9 Litho. *Perf. 12***

**C733** AP206 25p Liberty Fort .60 .25

Opening of Las Gaviotas (The Seagulls) Ecological Center, Bogota AP207

**1983, June 1 Litho.**

**C734** AP207 12p multicolored .40 .25

50th Anniv. of Radio Amateurs League — AP208

**1983, June 11 *Perf. 14x13½***

**C735** AP208 12p multicolored .30 .25

### Bolivar Type

**1983, July 24 *Perf. 12***

| | | | |
|---|---|---|---|
| **C736** | A417 30p multicolored | .80 | .25 |
| **C737** | A417 100p multicolored | 2.50 | 1.75 |

### Botanical Exhibition Type

No. C738, Begonia guaduensis. No. C739, Chinchona ovaliflora. No. C740, Begonia urticae.

**1983, Aug. 18 *Perf. 14***

| | | | |
|---|---|---|---|
| **C738** | A418 12p multicolored | .40 | .25 |
| **C739** | A418 12p multicolored | .40 | .25 |
| **C740** | A418 40p multicolored | 2.00 | 1.40 |
| | *Nos. C738-C740 (3)* | 2.80 | 1.90 |

Cartagena, 450th Anniv. AP208a

12p, Customs Square. 35p, Historic sites, Cartagena.

**1983, Sept. 9 Litho. *Perf. 12***

| | | | |
|---|---|---|---|
| **C740A** | AP208a 12p multi | .50 | .25 |
| **C740B** | AP208a 35p multi | 1.25 | .30 |

### Painting Type

**1983, Oct. 5 Litho. *Perf. 12***

**C741** A420 30p multicolored 1.50 .50

Scouting Year — AP209

**1983, Oct. 24**

**C742** AP209 12p multicolored .25 .25

Coffee Beans — AP210

**1984, Mar. 28 Litho. *Perf. 14½x14***

**C743** AP210 14p multicolored .25 .25

### Marandua City Type

**1984, Sept. 28 *Perf. 12***

**C744** A427 30p multicolored .75 .25

AP211

**1984, Nov. 2**

**C745** AP211 45p multicolored 1.50 .80

45th Cong. of Americanists, Bogota, 1985.

### Christmas Type

**1984, Dec. 14**

**C746** A428 14p multicolored .35 .25

AP212

Design: Dove, map and flags of Colombia, Mexico, Costa Rica and Venezuela.

**1985, Feb. 15**

**C747** AP212 40p multicolored 1.50 .30

Contadora Group of Latin American countries.

### Gomez Type

**1985, Feb. 25**

**C748** A432 40p multicolored 1.00 .30

Birds — AP213

14p, Dryocopus lineatus nuperus. 20p, Xiphorhynchus picus. 50p, Eriocnemis cupreoventris. 55p, Momotus momota.

**1985**

| | | | |
|---|---|---|---|
| **C749** | AP213 14p multicolored | .80 | .30 |
| **C750** | AP213 20p multicolored | 1.50 | .30 |
| **C751** | AP213 50p multicolored | 3.50 | 1.00 |
| **C752** | AP213 55p multicolored | 4.50 | 1.25 |
| | *Nos. C749-C752 (4)* | 10.30 | 2.85 |

Issued: 14p, 4/12; 20p, 50p, 8/6; 55p, 8/29.

AP214

**1985, July 15**

**C753** AP214 20p multicolored .30 .25

Admiral Padilla Naval School, 50th anniv.

1985 Census — AP215

**1985, Oct. 15 *Perf. 12***

**C754** AP215 20p multicolored .45 .25

### Christmas Type

**1985, Dec. 4 Litho. *Perf. 13***

**C755** A436 20p Girl, Christmas tree .40 .25

Alfonso Lopez Pumarejo (1886-1959), President, 1934-38, 1942-45 — AP216

**1986, Jan. 31**

**C756** AP216 24p multicolored .35 .25

Coffee Berries, Natl. Cycling Team — AP217

**1986, Feb. 4**

**C757** AP217 60p multicolored 1.25 .75

Natl. Coffee Producers Assoc. sponsorship of natl. cycling team, 25th anniv.

### Fauna Type of 1985

**1986, Feb. 18**

**C758** A433 50p Pudu mephistophiles 1.50 .25

World Communications Day — AP218

**1986, May 17 Litho. *Perf. 13***

**C759** AP218 50p multicolored .65 .25

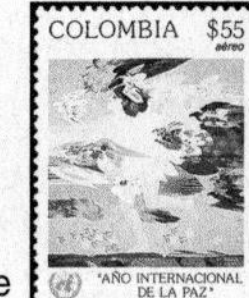

Intl. Peace Year — AP219

**1986, June 13 Litho. *Perf. 13***

**C760** AP219 55p multicolored 1.00 .45

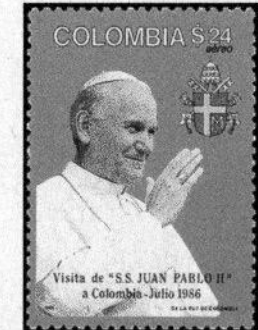

AP220

24p, Portrait, papal arms. 55p, Portrait, Medellin cathedral, horiz. 60p, Blessing crowd, horiz.
200p, Praying, Madonna of Bogota.

**1986, July 1 Litho. *Perf. 13***

| | | | | |
|---|---|---|---|---|
| **C761** | AP220 | 24p multicolored | 1.50 | .25 |
| **C762** | AP220 | 55p multicolored | 1.50 | .25 |
| **C763** | AP220 | 60p multicolored | 1.50 | .25 |
| | | *Nos. C761-C763 (3)* | 4.50 | .75 |

**Souvenir Sheet**

| | | | | |
|---|---|---|---|---|
| **C764** | AP220 | 200p multicolored | 4.50 | 3.50 |

Visit of Pope John Paul II.
Nos. C762-C763 each printed in sheets of 20 with se-tenant labels picturing religious symbols.

AP221

**1986, July 15 *Perf. 12***

| | | | | |
|---|---|---|---|---|
| **C765** | AP221 | 25p multicolored | .30 | .25 |

Enrique Santos Montejo (1886-1971), journalist.

Bach, Handel and Schutz, Composers AP222

**1986, July 17 *Perf. 13***

| | | | | |
|---|---|---|---|---|
| **C766** | AP222 | 70p Bach | 1.60 | .40 |
| **C767** | AP222 | 100p Text, music | 2.10 | .55 |

Salesian Order Education in Colombia, Cent. — AP223

**1986, July 23 *Perf. 12***

| | | | | |
|---|---|---|---|---|
| **C768** | AP223 | 25p De La Salle, founder | .35 | .25 |

Completion of Coal Mining Complex, El Cerrejon AP224

**1986, July 29 Litho. *Perf. 12***

| | | | | |
|---|---|---|---|---|
| **C769** | AP224 | 55p multi | 1.25 | .75 |

AP225

Natl. Constitution, Cent. — AP226

25p, The Five Signators, by R. Vasquez, detail, & Bogota Cathedral. 200p, Pres. Nunez & Miguel Antonio Caro, Natl. Council of Delegates chairman, & Presidential Palace, constitution.

**1986, Aug. 5 Litho. *Perf. 14***

| | | | | |
|---|---|---|---|---|
| **C770** | AP225 | 25p multi | .35 | .25 |

**Souvenir Sheet**

***Perf. 12***

| | | | | |
|---|---|---|---|---|
| **C771** | AP226 | 200p multi | 3.00 | 3.00 |

**Poet Type**

Federico Garcia Lorca (1898-1936), poet, and birthplace, Fuentevaqueros, Granada, Spain.

**1986, Sept. 26 Litho. *Perf. 12***

| | | | | |
|---|---|---|---|---|
| **C772** | A445 | 60p multi | 1.00 | .50 |

Gratitude for Intl. Aid after the Armero Mudslide Disaster — AP227

**1986, Nov. 13**

| | | | | |
|---|---|---|---|---|
| **C773** | AP227 | 50p multi | 1.00 | .75 |

Christmas — AP228

Wood sculpture: Virgin Mestiza, Nerina.

**1986, Dec. 19 Litho. *Perf. 12***

| | | | | |
|---|---|---|---|---|
| **C774** | AP228 | 25p multi | .35 | .25 |

The Apotheosis of Popayan, by Ephrain Martinez Zambrano (1898-1956) — AP229

**1987, Jan. 13**

| | | | | |
|---|---|---|---|---|
| **C775** | | 100p Popayan riding horse | 2.50 | 1.25 |
| **C776** | | 100p Onlookers | 2.50 | 1.25 |
| *a.* | | AP229 Pair, #C775-C776 | 5.00 | 3.50 |

AP230

**1987, Mar. 16 Litho. *Perf. 12***

| | | | | |
|---|---|---|---|---|
| **C777** | AP230 | 30p multi | .50 | .25 |

The Conversion of St. Augustine of Hippo, 1600th anniv.

**Type of 1987**

30p, Phoenicopterus ruber. 35p, Pseudemys scripta, horiz. No. C780, Crax alberti. No. C781, Symphysodon aequifasciatum, horiz.

***Perf. 14½x14, 14x14½***

**1987-89 Wmk. 334**

| | | | | |
|---|---|---|---|---|
| **C778** | A446a | 30p lake | .35 | .25 |
| **C779** | A446a | 35p dark red brn | .40 | .25 |
| **C780** | A446a | 45p dark blue gray | .30 | .25 |
| **C781** | A446a | 45p blue | .30 | .25 |
| | | *Nos. C778-C781 (4)* | 1.35 | 1.00 |

Issue dates: 30p, June 8. 35p, Dec. 24. No. C780, Dec. 6, 1988. No. C781, June 23, 1989.

AP231

***Perf. 13½x13***

**1987, Apr. 10 Unwmk.**

| | | | | |
|---|---|---|---|---|
| **C783** | AP231 | 25p multi | .30 | .25 |

Natl. University School of Mining, Medellin, cent.

Purebred Horses — AP232

**1987, June 17 *Perf. 12***

| | | | | |
|---|---|---|---|---|
| **C784** | AP232 | 60p White horse | 1.25 | .30 |
| **C785** | AP232 | 70p Black horse | 1.25 | .30 |

El Espectador Newspaper, Cent. — AP233

Design: Frontispieces from 1887, 1915, 1948, 1974 and portraits of founder Don Fidel Cano, editors Don Luis Cano, Luis Gabriel Cano Isaza and Alfonso Cano Isaza.

**1987, July 24 *Perf. 12½x12***

| | | | | |
|---|---|---|---|---|
| **C786** | AP233 | 60p multi | .85 | .25 |

Intl. Year of Shelter for the Homeless — AP234

**1987, Sept. 21 *Perf. 14***

| | | | | |
|---|---|---|---|---|
| **C787** | AP234 | 60p multi | 1.00 | .25 |

Flags — AP235

**1987, Nov. 27 Litho. *Perf. 13x13½***

| | | | | |
|---|---|---|---|---|
| **C788** | AP235 | 80p multi | 1.00 | .30 |

Ist Meeting of the eight Latin-American Presidents, Acapulco, Nov.

Christmas — AP236

**1987, Dec. 8 Litho. *Perf. 14***

| | | | | |
|---|---|---|---|---|
| **C789** | AP236 | 30p multi | .45 | .25 |

Rural Telephone System — AP237

**1988, Feb. 4 Litho. *Perf. 14***

| | | | | |
|---|---|---|---|---|
| **C790** | AP237 | 70p multi | .80 | .30 |

Founding of Bogota, 450th Anniv. — AP238

**1988, Apr. 11 Litho. *Perf. 12***

| | | | | |
|---|---|---|---|---|
| **C791** | AP238 | 70p multi | .80 | .25 |

Bogota, 450th Anniv. — AP238a

80p, Modern district, vert. 90p, Colonial district.

**Unwmk.**

**1988, July 1 Litho. *Perf. 12***

| | | | | |
|---|---|---|---|---|
| **C792** | AP238a | 80p multi | .75 | .25 |
| **C793** | AP238a | 90p multi | .85 | .30 |

Gold Artifacts — AP239

Artifacts in the Gold Museum: 70p, Mask. 80p, Two-headed human figure inside a circle, Muisca tribe. 90p, Ritual figure of the Quimbaya.

**1988 *Perf. 12***

| | | | | |
|---|---|---|---|---|
| **C794** | AP239 | 70p multi | 1.10 | .50 |
| **C795** | AP239 | 80p multi | 1.50 | .60 |
| **C796** | AP239 | 90p multi | 2.00 | .75 |
| | | *Nos. C794-C796 (3)* | 4.60 | 1.85 |

Issue dates: 70p, May 13; 80p, 90p, Oct. 7.

**Human Rights Type**

***Perf. 14x14½***

**1988, July 1 Engr. Wmk. 334**

| | | | | |
|---|---|---|---|---|
| **C797** | A452 | 40p Communication, horiz. | .40 | .25 |

AP240

**1988, Sept. 28 Litho. *Perf. 12***

| | | | | |
|---|---|---|---|---|
| **C798** | AP240 | 80p multi | .90 | .25 |

Zipa Tisquesusa (d. 1538), Chibcha Indian leader during revolt against Spanish Conquistadors.

Christmas — AP241

**1988, Nov. 23 Litho. *Perf. 12***

| | | | | |
|---|---|---|---|---|
| **C799** | AP241 | 40p multi | .60 | .25 |

Agustin Nieto Caballero (1889-1975), Educator AP242

**Unwmk.**

**1989, Mar. 18 Litho. *Perf. 12***

| | | | | |
|---|---|---|---|---|
| **C800** | AP242 | 100p multi | 1.00 | .50 |

Pres. Laureano Gomez (1889-1965) — AP243

**1989, Mar. 29**
**C801** AP243 45p multi .45 .25

Intl. Coffee Organization AP244

**1989, Apr. 3**
**C802** AP244 110p multi 1.00 .50

12th Session of the UN Commission on Human Rights — AP245

**1989, Apr. 28**
**C803** AP245 100p multi 1.00 .40

French Revolution, Bicent. — AP246

**1989, June 29 Litho. *Perf. 12***
**C804** AP246 100p multi .90 .40

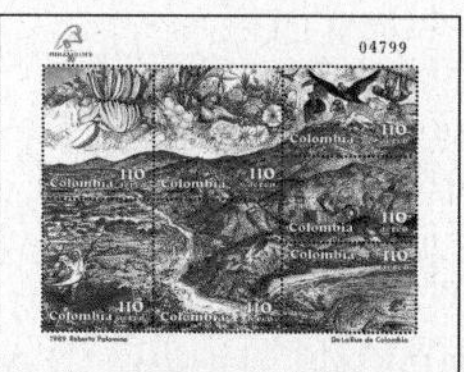

PHILEXFRANCE '89 — AP247

a, Bananas, tropical fruits. b, Fruits, flowers. c, Birds, animals. d, Precious gems, metals and mineral resources. e, View of fields, Colombian carrying produce basket. f, Waterfall. g, Fish, coast.

**1989 Litho. *Perf. 14***
**C805** AP247 Pane of 7 17.50 17.50
***a.-g.*** 110p any single 1.75 .40

No. C805 printed in sheets containing panes of 7, rouletted between.

Souvenir Sheet

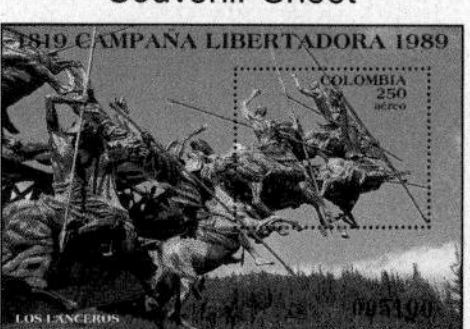

*Los Lanceros,* by R. Arenas Betancur — AP248

**1989 Litho. *Perf. 12***
**C806** AP248 250p multicolored 2.25 1.25

**Human Rights Type**

***Perf. 14½x14***

**1989, Aug. 18 Engr. Wmk. 334**
**C807** A452 55p Family .40 .25

Natl. Anti-Drugs Campaign — AP249

**Unwmk.**

**1989, Aug. 23 Litho. *Perf. 12***
**C808** AP249 115p multicolored 1.00 .25

America Issue — AP250

UPAE emblem and artifacts or customs of pre-Columbian peoples: 115p, Quimbaya, Calima or Tolima gold smiths. 130p, Potter and Sinu ceramic figurine.

**1989 *Perf. 12***
**C809** AP250 115p multicolored 1.25 .40
**C810** AP250 130p multicolored 1.25 .60

Issue dates: 115p, Oct. 12; 130p, Aug. 23.

Joaquin Quijano Mantilla (1878-1944), Journalist AP251

**1989, Sept. 29 *Perf. 12***
**C811** AP251 170p multicolored 1.50 .50

Arts and Crafts in Barro-Raquira AP252

**1989 Litho. *Perf. 12***
**C812** AP252 55p multicolored .40 .25

Christmas.

Boeing 767 — AP253

**1989, Dec. 5 Litho. *Perf. 12***
**C813** AP253 130p multicolored 1.25 .30

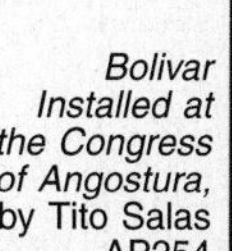

*Bolivar Installed at the Congress of Angostura,* by Tito Salas AP254

**1989, Dec. 12**
**C814** AP254 130p multicolored 1.10 .50

Creation of the Republic, 1819.

Fathers of the Nation Leaving the Constitutional Convention — AP255

**1989, Dec. 12**
**C815** AP255 130p shown 1.00 .50
**C816** AP255 130p Arms 1.00 .50
**C817** AP255 130p Temple of the Rosary 1.00 .50
*Nos. C815-C817 (3)* 3.00 1.50

Constitution of the Republic, 1821.

**Arms Type of Regular Issue, 1982**

**1990, Mar. 1 Litho. *Perf. 12***
**C818** A372 60p Velez .30 .25

Presidential Summit, Cartagena AP256

130p, Plaza de la Aduana.

**1990, Feb. 15 Litho. *Perf. 12***
**C819** AP256 130p multi .55 .25

Colombian National Radio, 50th Anniv. — AP257

**1990, Feb. 16 Litho. *Perf. 12***
**C820** AP257 150p multicolored 1.00 .25

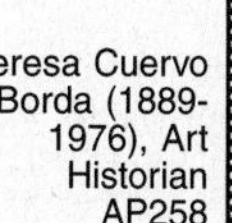

Teresa Cuervo Borda (1889-1976), Art Historian AP258

**1990, Mar. 28 Litho. *Perf. 12***
**C821** AP258 60p multicolored .35 .25

Second Latin American Theater Festival, Bogota — AP259

**1990, Apr. 10**
**C822** AP259 150p buff, tan & gold 1.00 .25

**Santander Type**

No. C823, Santander holding the Constitution. No. C824, Central Cemetery, Bogota and National Pantheon. No. C825, Santander, as organizer of public education. No. C826, "Postman of New Granada" (Man and burro) by Joseph Brown and Jose Maria del Castillo, horiz. 500p, Santander on death bed.

**1990, May 6 *Perf. 14x13½***
**C823** A470 60p multicolored .25 .25
**C824** A470 60p multicolored .25 .25
**C825** A470 70p multicolored .35 .25
**C826** A470 70p multicolored .35 .25
*Nos. C823-C826 (4)* 1.20 1.00

**Souvenir Sheet**

***Perf. 12***

**C827** A470 500p multi 1.75 1.50

No. C827 contains one 54x40mm stamp.

First Postage Stamp, 150th Anniv. — AP260

**1990, May 6 *Perf. 14***
**C828** AP260 150p multicolored .80 .40

Trans-Caribbean Fiber Optic Cable — AP261

**1990, May 19 *Perf. 12***
**C829** AP261 150p multicolored 1.00 .40

Institute of Industrial Development, 25th Anniv. — AP262

**1990, May 22**
**C830** AP262 60p multicolored .40 .25

Souvenir Sheet

World Cup Soccer Championships, Italy — AP263

**1990, June 8**
**C831** AP263 500p multicolored 4.50 3.50

AP264

**1990, June 27**
**C832** AP264 130p multicolored .80 .25

Organization of American States, cent.

AP265

**1990, July 26**
**C833** AP265 170p multicolored 1.25 .50

Museum of Gold, 50th Anniv.

Dolphins, Marine Birds — AP266

170p, Jungle fauna, vert.

**1990, Oct. 12 Litho. *Perf. 12***
**C834** AP266 150p shown 2.50 .25
**C835** AP266 170p multi 2.50 .25

AP267

**1990, Nov. 16 Litho. *Perf. 12***
**C836** AP267 70p multicolored .50 .25

Monastery of Our Lady of Las Lajas.

AP268

**1991, Feb. 8 Litho. *Perf. 12***
**C837** AP268 170p multicolored 1.25 .50

Newspaper Publishing, 200th Anniv.

Christmas — AP269

**1990, Nov. 1 Litho. *Perf. 12***
**C838** AP269 70p multicolored .60 .25

AP270

Whales and Dolphins: 80p, Megaptera novaeangliae, breaching. 170p, Megaptera novaeangliae, diving. 190p, Inia geoffrensis, Sotalia fluviatilis, horiz.

**1991, May 31 Litho. *Perf. 14***
**C839** AP270 80p multicolored 1.25 .25
**C840** AP270 170p multicolored 2.50 .30
**C841** AP270 190p multicoloed 3.25 .30
*Nos. C839-C841 (3)* 7.00 .85

America Issue — AP271

190p, Ship arriving in New World.

**1991, Oct. 11 Litho. *Perf. 14***
**C842** AP271 90p shown .60 .30
**C843** AP271 190p multi 1.25 .50

Adoration of the Magi — AP272

**1991, Dec. 20 Litho. *Perf. 14***
**C844** AP272 90p multicolored .60 .30

Christmas.

Country Flags — AP273

**1991, Dec. 2**
**C845** AP273 190p multi 1.00 .50

Fifth summit of Latin American presidents.

AP274

**1992, Feb. 8 Litho. *Perf. 12***
**C846** AP274 210p multicolored 1.25 .60

8th UNCTAD Conference, Cartagena.

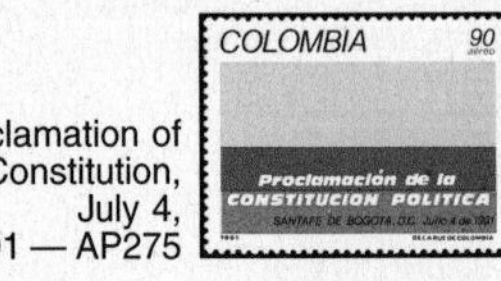

Proclamation of New Constitution, July 4, 1991 — AP275

**1991, Nov. 27 Litho. *Perf. 14***
**C847** AP275 90p multicolored .40 .25

Export Products — AP276

90p, Flowers. 210p, Fruits, vegetables, horiz.

**1992, Mar. 11 *Perf. 12***
**C848** AP276 90p multi .60 .30
**C849** AP276 210p multi 1.40 .65

Copyright Protection — AP277

**1992, Apr. 13 Litho. *Perf. 12***
**C850** AP277 190p multicolored 1.40 .60

1992 Summer Olympics — AP278

**1992, June 4 Litho. *Perf. 14***
**C851** AP278 110p multicolored 1.25 .30

Earth Summit '92 — AP279

a, Tree, mountain landscape. b, Birds in tree.

**1992, June 2 Litho. *Perf. 14***
**C852** A279 230p Pair, #a.-b. 2.50 2.00

America Issue — AP280

Paintings: 230p, Discovery of America by Christopher Columbus, by Salvador Dali. 260p, Magical America, Myth and Legend, by Alfredo Vivero.

**1992, July 22 *Perf. 14x13½***
**C853** AP280 230p multicolored 1.75 .70
**C854** AP280 260p multicolored 2.00 .75

McDonnell Douglas MD83 — AP281

**1992, Sept. 22 Litho. *Perf. 12***
**C855** AP281 110p multicolored .75 .30

Curtain of Colon Theatre — AP282

**1992, Oct. 12 Litho. *Perf. 12***
**C856** AP282 230p multicolored 1.25 .65

Gloria Lara, 1938-82 — AP283

**1992, Nov. 27 Litho. *Perf. 12***
**C857** AP283 230p multicolored 2.00 .65

AP284

**1993, June 7 Litho. *Perf. 12***
**C858** AP284 220p multicolored 1.25 .60

1993 American Soccer Cup, Ecuador.

Intl. Year of Indigenous People — AP285

**1993, July 1 *Perf. 14***
**C859** AP285 460p multicolored 2.50 1.25

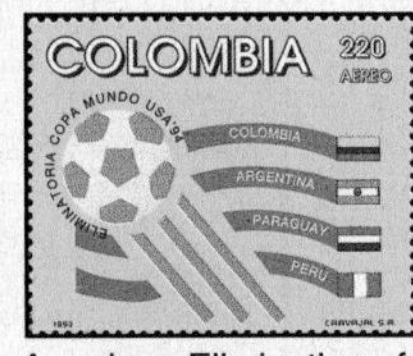

South American Eliminations for 1994 World Cup Soccer Championships, US — AP286

**1993, July 31 Litho. *Perf. 12***
**C860** AP286 220p multicolored 1.60 .60

AP287

America Issue (Endangered species): a, 220p, Saguinus oedipus. b, 220p, Porphyrula martinica. c, 460p, Rupicola peruviana. d, 520p, Trichecus manatus.

**1993, Oct. 19 Litho. *Perf. 12***
**C861** AP287 Block of 4, #a.-d. 7.50 7.50

AP288

**1994, Mar. 21 Litho. *Perf. 12***
**C862** AP288 630p multicolored 3.00 1.50

Intl. Decade for Natural Disaster Reduction.

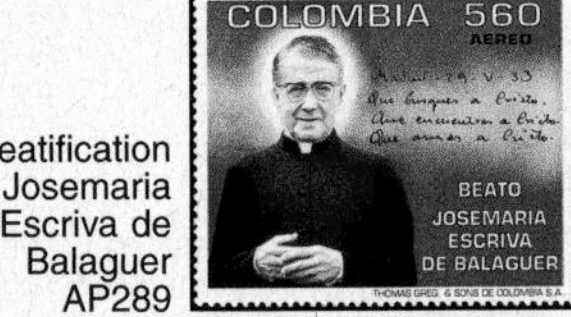

Beatification of Josemaria Escriva de Balaguer AP289

**1994, May 17 Litho. *Perf. 13½x14***
**C863** AP289 560p multicolored 2.25 1.40

First Airmail Delivery, 75th Anniv. — AP290

Design: 270p, William Knox Martin, airplane over Port Colombia, 1919.

**1994, July 29 Litho. *Perf. 14***
**C864** AP290 270p multicolored 1.25 .55

Natl. Institute of Medical Law & Forensic Sciences, 80th Anniv. — AP291

**1994, Oct. 27 Litho. *Perf. 12***
**C865** AP291 560p multicolored 2.25 1.25

Sociedad Colombo-Alemana de Transportes Aereos (SCADTA), 75th Anniv. — AP292

**1995, Jan. 2 Litho. *Perf. 12***
**C866** AP292 330p No. C15 1.10 .50

Flora and Fauna AP293

Iguana iguana: No. C867a, Facing right. b, Facing left.

Rain forest: No. C868a, Nuts on branch, flowers. b, Waterfall, hanging red flower.

**1995, Jan. 17**
**C867** AP293 650p Pair, #a.-b. 5.00 5.00
**C868** AP293 750p Pair, #a.-b. 5.00 5.00

Nos. C867-C868 are continuous designs.

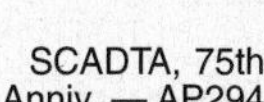
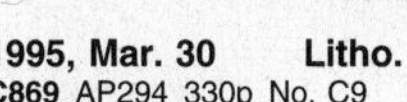

SCADTA, 75th Anniv. — AP294

**1995, Mar. 30** **Litho.** ***Perf. 14***
**C869** AP294 330p No. C9 1.50 .75

FAO, 50th Anniv. — AP295

**1995, Apr. 25** **Litho.** ***Perf. 13x13½***
**C870** AP295 750p multicolored 2.50 1.50

Andres Bello Organization, 25th Anniv. — AP296

**1995, Apr. 27** ***Perf. 13½x13***
**C871** AP296 650p multicolored 2.50 1.25

Colombian Firefighters, Cent. — AP297

**1995, May 5** ***Perf. 12***
**C872** AP297 330p multicolored 1.50 .75

Fenalco, 50th Anniv. — AP298

**1995, May 25** ***Perf. 13½***
**C873** AP298 330p multicolored 1.25 .65

UN, 50th Anniv. — AP299

**1995, June 21** ***Perf. 12***
**C874** AP299 750p multicolored 2.75 1.50

First Pacific Ocean Games — AP300

**1995, June 23**
**C875** AP300 750p multicolored 2.75 1.50

11th Summit of Non-Aligned Countries, Cartagena AP302

**1995, Oct. 13** **Litho.** ***Perf. 12***
**C877** AP302 650p multicolored 2.75 1.25

Motion Pictures, Cent. — AP303

Design: 330p, Charlie Chaplin and Jackie Coogan in "The Kid," Estela López Pomareda in "Maria," first Colombian feature length film.

**1995, Oct. 19** ***Perf. 14***
**C878** AP303 330p black & sepia 1.50 .75

AP304

**1995, Nov. 23** ***Perf. 12***
**C879** AP304 650p multicolored 2.10 1.00

Andes Development Corporation (CAF), 25th Anniv.

AP305

Fight against illegal drug trafficking: No. C880, Locating illegally grown plants. No. C881, Hands in handcuffs, horiz.

**1995, Nov. 21** ***Perf. 14***
**C880** AP305 330p multicolored .70 .45
**C881** AP305 330p multicolored .70 .45

Miniature Sheet of 16

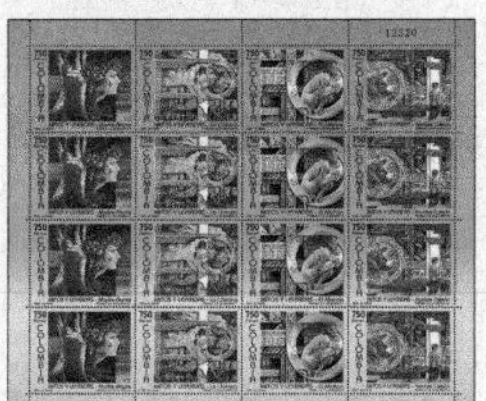

Myths and Legends — AP306

Madre-Monte: a.-d.
La Llorona: e.-h.
El Mohán: i.-l.
Hombre Caimán: m.-p.
Background color changes from top to bottom rows. Top row is blue. Row 2 is blue green. Row 3 is green. Row 4 is lilac. Each design comes in all four colors.

**1995, Dec. 6**
**C882** AP306 750p #a.-p. 40.00 40.00

See No. C886.

José Asunción Silva (1865-96), Poet — AP307

**1996, Apr. 23** **Litho.** ***Perf. 12***
**C883** AP307 400p multicolored 1.25 .75

Isla de Providencia — AP308

**1996, Apr. 25** ***Perf. 14***
**C884** AP308 800p multicolored 2.75 1.40

Policarpa Salavarrieta (1796-1817), Patriot — AP309

**1996, Apr. 26**
**C885** AP309 900p multicolored 3.00 1.50

### Myths and Legends Type

Designs: a, Kogui Creation. b, Yonna Wayu. c, Jaguar Man. d, Master of the Animals.

**1996, Aug. 12** **Litho.** ***Perf. 13½x14***
**C886** AP306 900p Block of 4, #a.-d. 13.00 13.00

Metropolitan Basilica, Medellin — AP310

**1996, July 12**
**C887** AP310 400p multicolored 1.05 .55

National Archives Building — AP311

**1996, July 30** **Litho.** ***Perf. 14***
**C888** AP311 400p multicolored 1.05 .55

CERLALC, 25th Anniv. — AP312

**1996, Aug. 16** **Litho.** ***Perf. 12***
**C889** AP312 800p multicolored 2.75 1.25

UNESCO.

Pioneers in Petroleum Industry — AP313

a, Jorge Isaacs, pumping oil. b, Francisco Burgos Rubio, refinery at night. c, Diego Martínez Camargo, derrick. d, Prisciliano Cabrales Lora, off-shore drilling. e, Manuel María Palacio, oil tanker loading offshore. f, Roberto De Mares, refinery, lake. g, General Virgilio Barco Maldonado, men positioning equipment. h, Roustabout, "ECOPETROL" emblem.

**1996, Sept. 5** **Litho.** ***Perf. 13½x14***
**C890** AP313 800p Block of 8, #a.-h. 20.00 20.00

Colombian Golf Federation, 50th Anniv. — AP314

**1996, Sept. 19** **Litho.** ***Perf. 12***
**C891** AP314 400p multicolored 2.25 .60

Covenant for the Children — AP315

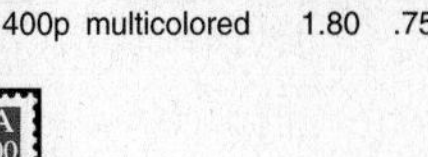

**1997, Feb. 28** **Litho.** ***Perf. 14***
**C892** AP315 400p multicolored 1.80 .75

AP316

**1997, Apr. 25** ***Perf. 12***
**C893** AP316 800p multicolored 3.75 1.75

Motion pictures in Colombia, cent.

AP317

**1997, May 13** **Litho.** ***Perf. 12***
**C894** AP317 400p multicolored 1.90 .75

Social Security Institute, 50th anniv.

Ericsson in Colombia, Cent. AP318

**1997, May 22** ***Perf. 13½x14***
**C895** AP318 900p multicolored 4.50 2.00

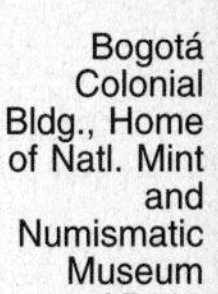

Bogotá Colonial Bldg., Home of Natl. Mint and Numismatic Museum AP319

**1997, July 10** ***Perf. 12***
**C896** AP319 800p multicolored 3.00 1.40

Phytelephas Seemannii AP320

**1997, July 23** ***Perf. 13½x14***
**C897** AP320 900p multicolored 3.00 .90

Cordoba Cattle Fair — AP321

**1997, June 21** *Perf. 14*
**C898** AP321 400p multicolored 1.50 .45

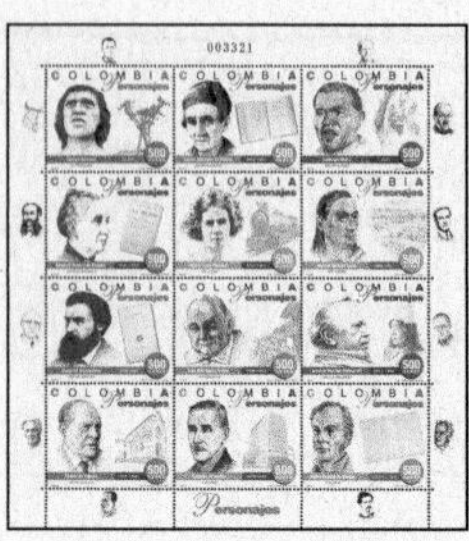

Personalities — AP322

No. C899: a, Cacique Gaitana, 16th cent., Indian resistance leader. b, Josefa Acevedo de Gómez (1803-61), writer. c, Domingo Bioho (d. 1621), black leader. d, Soledad Acosta de Samper (1831-1913), historian. e, Maria Cano Márquez (1897-1967), popular leader. f, Manuel Quintín Lame (1880-1967), native leader. g, Ezequiel Uricoechea (1834-80), linguist, naturalist. h, Juan Rodríguez Freyle (1566-1642), colonial reporter. i, Gerardo Reichel-Dolmatoff (1912-94), archaeologist. j, Ramón de Zubiría (1922-95), writer, educator. k, Esteban Jaramillo (1874-1947), economist. l, Pedro Fermín de Vargas (1762-c. 1810), economist.

No. C900: a, Luis Carlos "el tuerto" López (1879-1950), poet. b, Aurelio Arturo (1906-74), poet. c, Enrique Pérez Arbeláez (1896-1972), botanist. d, José Maria González Benito (1843-1903), mathematician, astronomer. e, José Manuel Rivas Sacconi (1917-91), diplomat. f, Eduardo Lemaitre Román (1914-94), historian. g, Diójenes Arrieta (1848-93), politician. h, Gabriel Turbay Abunader (1901-47), politician, diplomat. i, Guillermo Echavarría Misas (1888-1985), aviation pioneer. j, Juan Friede Alter (1901-90), historian. k, Fabio Lozano Torrijos (1865-1947), diplomat. l, Lino de Pombo (1797-1862), engineer, diplomat.

**Sheets of 12**

**1997, Dec. 19 Litho.** *Perf. 13½x14*
**C899** AP322 500p #a.-l. 25.00 25.00
**C900** AP322 500p #a.-l. 25.00 25.00

Colombian Society of Orthopedic Surgery and Traumatology, 50th Anniv. — AP323

**1997** *Perf. 12*
**C901** AP323 1000p multicolored 3.00 1.00

AP324

**1998, Apr. 30 Litho.** *Perf. 14*
**C902** AP324 1000p multicolored 3.00 .80

Organization of American States, 50th anniv.

AP325

**1998, May 22**
**C903** AP325 1000p bl & org 3.00 .80

4th Bolivar Philatelic Exhibition, Santa Fe de Bogota.

World Health Organization, 50th Anniv. — AP326

**1998, Apr. 7** *Perf. 12*
**C904** AP326 1100p multicolored 3.00 1.00

1998 World Cup Soccer Championships, France — AP327

Stylized designs: a, Foot. b. Soccer ball. c, Hand.

**1998, June 9 Litho.** *Perf. 14*
**C905** AP327 1100p Strip of 3, #a.-c. 12.00 12.00

Intl. Year of the Ocean AP328

**1998, May 22** *Perf. 12*
**C906** AP328 1100p ARC Gloria 3.75 .95

Myths and Legends — AP329

Designs: a, Bochica. b, Chimingagua. c, Bachue and Huitica.

*Perf. 13¼x12¾*

**1998, Nov. 27 Litho.**
**C907** AP329 1000p Strip of 3, #a.-c. 17.00 15.00

## AIR POST SPECIAL DELIVERY STAMPS

**Catalogue values for unused stamps in this section are for Never Hinged items.**

Post Horn and Wings — APSD1

**Unwmk.**

**1958, May 19 Litho.** *Perf. 12*
**CE1** APSD1 25c dk bl & red .55 .25

No. CE1 Ovptd. in Red

**1959**
**CE2** APSD1 25c dk bl & red .50 .25

Jet Plane and Envelope APSD2

**1963, Oct. 4** *Perf. 14*
**CE3** APSD2 50c red & blk .25 .25

**Aviation Type**

80c, Boeing 727 jet, 1966.

*Perf. 14x13½*

**1966, Dec. 14 Photo. Unwmk.**
**CE4** AP96 80c crim & multi .55 .25

## AIR POST REGISTRATION STAMPS

**Issued by Sociedad Colombo-Alemana de Transportes Aereos (SCADTA)**

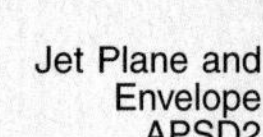

No. C41 Overprinted in Red

**1923 Wmk. 116** *Perf. 14x14½*
**CF1** AP6 20c gray 4.75 1.10

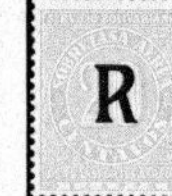

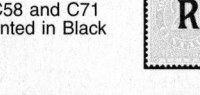

Nos. C58 and C71 Overprinted in Black

**1929 Wmk. 127** *Perf. 14*
**CF2** AP8 20c carmine 8.00 7.00
**CF3** AP10 20c carmine 6.50 6.00

**Colombian Government Issues**

No. C86 Overprinted in Black

**1932**
**CF4** AP8 20c carmine 6.50 6.00

No. C100 Overprinted

**CF5** AP12 20c car & ol blk 6.00 1.25

For surcharge see No. C118.

## SPECIAL DELIVERY STAMPS

Special Delivery Messenger — SD1

**1917 Unwmk. Engr.** *Perf. 14*
**E1** SD1 5c dark green *60.00 150.00*

**Catalogue values for unused stamps in this section, from this point to the end of the section, are for Never Hinged items.**

SD2

**1987, July 31 Litho.** *Perf. 14*
**E2** SD2 25p emerald & ver .30 .30
**E3** SD2 30p emerald & ver .35 .35

## REGISTRATION STAMPS

R1

R2

**1865 Unwmk. Litho.** *Imperf.*
**F1** R1 5c black 87.50 47.50
**F2** R2 5c black 110.00 50.00

R3 R4

**Vertical Lines in Background**

**1870** **White Paper**
**F3** R3 5c black 3.00 2.50
**F4** R4 5c black 3.00 2.50

**Horizontal Lines in Background**

**F5** R3 5c black 10.00 8.50
**F6** R4 5c black 3.00 2.50
*Nos. F3-F6 (4)* 19.00 16.00

*Reprints of Nos. F3 to F6 show either crossed lines or traces of lines in background.*

R5

**1881** *Imperf.*
**F7** R5 10c violet 60.00 52.50
*a.* Sewing machine perf. 67.50 60.00
*b.* Perf. 11 75.00 62.50

R6

**1883** *Perf. 12, 13½*
**F8** R6 10c red, *yellow* 2.00 *2.50*

R7

**1889-95** *Perf. 12, 13½*
**F9** R7 10c org, *grysh* 9.50 4.50
**F10** R7 10c red, *yelsh* 9.50 4.50
**F11** R7 10c dp brn, *rose buff* ('95) 2.00 1.60
**F12** R7 10c yel brn, *lt buff* ('92) 2.00 1.60
*Nos. F9-F12 (4)* 23.00 12.20

Nos. F9-F12 exist imperf.

R9

**1902** *Imperf.*
**F13** R9 20c red brown, *blue* 1.60 1.60
*a.* Sewing machine perf. 4.75 4.75
*b.* Perf. 12 4.75 4.75

**Medellin Issue**

R10

**1902 Laid Paper *Perf. 12***
F16 R10 10c blk vio 15.00 15.00
*a.* Wove paper 21.00 21.00

**Regular Issue**
***Imperf***

**1903**
F17 R9 20c blue, *blue* 1.60 1.60
*a.* Sewing machine perf. 4.75 4.75
*b.* Perf. 12 4.75 4.75

R11

**1904 Pelure Paper *Imperf.***
F19 R11 10c purple 3.75 3.75
*a.* Sewing machine perf. 5.00 3.75
*b.* Perf. 12 6.25 5.00

R12

**Imprint: "J. L. Arango"**

**1904 Wove Paper *Perf. 12***
F20 R12 10c purple 2.50 .60
*a.* Imperf., pair 7.75 7.75

**Imprint: "Lit. Nacional"**

**1909 *Perf. 10, 14, 10x14, 14x10***
F21 R12 10c purple 2.75 .85
*a.* Imperf., pair 6.25 6.25

For overprints see Nos. LF1-LF4.

Execution at Cartagena in 1816 — R13

**1910, July 20 Engr. *Perf. 12***
F22 R13 10c red & black 21.00 *90.00*

Centenary of National Independence.

Pier at Puerto Colombia R14

Tequendama Falls — R15

***Perf. 11, 11½, 14, 11½x14***
**1917, Aug. 25**
F23 R14 4c green & ultra .55 *3.50*
*a.* Center inverted 575.00 575.00
F24 R15 10c deep blue 8.00 .60

R16

**1925 Litho. *Perf. 10x13½***
F25 R16 (10c) blue 4.25 1.90
*a.* Imperf., pair 15.00 12.50
*b.* Perf. 13½x10 7.50 5.00

## ACKNOWLEDGMENT OF RECEIPT STAMPS

AR1

**1893 Unwmk. Litho. *Perf. 13½***
H1 AR1 5c ver, *blue* 4.75 4.75

**1894 *Perf. 12***
H2 AR1 5c vermilion 4.50 *5.00*

AR2

**1902-03 *Imperf.***
H3 AR2 10c blue, *blue* 3.50 5.00
*a.* 10c, blue, *greenish blue* 3.50 5.00
*b.* Sewing machine perf. 3.50 5.00
*c.* Perf. 12 3.50 5.00

The handstamp "AR" in circle is believed to be a postmark.

AR2a

**Purple Handstamp**

**1903 *Imperf.***
H4 AR2a 10c black, *pink* 25.00 25.00

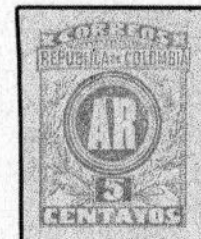
AR3

**1904 Pelure Paper *Imperf.***
H12 AR3 5c pale blue 10.50 10.50
*a.* Perf. 12 10.50 10.50

No. 307 Overprinted in Black, Green or Violet

H13 A86 5c carmine 17.50 17.50

AR4

**1904 *Perf. 12***
H16 AR4 5c blue 3.25 2.75
*a.* Imperf., pair 8.75 8.75

For overprints see Nos. LH1-LH2.

General José Acevedo y Gómez — AR5

**1910, July 20 Engr.**
H17 AR5 5c orange & green 7.00 *17.50*

Centenary of National Independence.

Sabana Station AR6

Map of Colombia AR7

**1917 *Perf. 14***
H18 AR6 4c bister brown 5.50 *6.00*
H19 AR7 5c orange brown 5.50 *4.50*
*a.* Imperf., pair 14.00

## LATE FEE STAMPS

LF1

**1886 Unwmk. Litho. *Perf. 10½***
I1 LF1 2½c blk, *lilac* 4.00 3.25
*a.* Imperf., pair 15.00 15.00

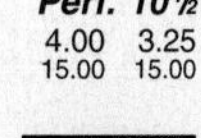

LF2

**1892 *Perf. 12, 13½***
I2 LF2 2½c dk bl, *rose* 3.50 2.50
*a.* Imperf., pair 15.00
I3 LF2 2½c ultra, *pink* 3.50 2.50

LF3

**1902 *Imperf.***
I4 LF3 5c vio, *brn rose* 1.00 1.00
*a.* Perf. 12 2.10 2.10

LF4

**1914 *Perf. 10, 13½***
I6 LF4 2c vio brown 5.00 5.00
I7 LF4 5c blue green 5.00 4.25

Overprints illustrated above are unauthorized and of private origin.

## POSTAGE DUE STAMPS

These are not, strictly speaking, postage due stamps but were issued to cover an additional fee, "Sobreporte," charged on mail to foreign countries with which Colombia had no postal conventions.

D1

D2

D3

**1866 Unwmk. Litho. *Imperf.***
J1 D1 25c black, *blue* 80.00 55.00
J2 D2 50c black, *yellow* 55.00 *80.00*
J3 D3 1p black, *rose* 160.00 *125.00*
*Nos. J1-J3 (3)* 295.00 260.00

## DEPARTMENT STAMPS

These stamps are said to be for interior postage, to supersede the separate issues for the various departments.

Regular Issues Handstamped in Black, Violet, Blue or Green — a

**On Stamps of 1904**

**1909 Unwmk. *Perf. 12***
L1 A94 ½c yellow 2.50 2.50
*a.* Imperf., pair 7.50 7.50
L2 A94 1c yel grn 3.75 2.50
L3 A94 2c red 5.50 3.75
*a.* Imperf., pair 15.00 15.00
L4 A94 5c blue 6.25 4.00
L5 A94 10c violet 8.75 8.75
L6 A94 20c black 14.00 14.00
L7 A95 1p brown 22.50 21.00

**On Stamp of 1902**
L8 A83 10p dk brn, *rose* 25.00 25.00
*Nos. L1-L8 (8)* 88.25 81.50

**On Stamps of 1908**
***Perf. 10, 13, 13½ and Compound***
L9 A94 ½c orange 2.90 2.90
*a.* Imperf., pair 7.50 7.50
L10 A94 1c green 5.00 5.00
*a.* Without imprint 6.25 6.25
L11 A94 2c red 5.50 5.50
*a.* Imperf., pair
L12 A94 5c blue 5.50 5.50
*a.* Imperf., pair 15.00 15.00
L13 A94 10c violet 8.75 8.75

**On Tolima Stamp of 1888**
***Perf. 10½***
L14 A23 1p red brn 27.50 27.50
*Nos. L9-L14 (6)* 55.15 55.15

Regular Issues Handstamped — b

**On Stamps of 1904**
***Perf. 12***
L15 A94 ½c yellow 2.50 2.50
L16 A94 1c yellow grn 4.25 4.25
L17 A94 2c red 7.50 7.50
L18 A94 5c blue 7.50 7.50
L19 A94 10c violet 10.00 10.00
L20 A94 20c black 14.00 14.00
L21 A94 1p brown 25.00 25.00
*Nos. L15-L21 (7)* 70.75 70.75

**On Stamps of 1908**
***Perf. 10, 13, 13½***
L22 A94 ½c orange 2.75 2.75
L23 A94 1c yellow grn 7.75 7.75
L24 A94 2c red 6.25 6.25
*a.* Imperf., pair 15.00 15.00
L25 A94 5c light blue 7.50 7.50
*Nos. L22-L25 (4)* 24.25 24.25

The handstamps on Nos. L1-L25 are, as usual, found inverted and double.

## DEPARTMENT REGISTRATION STAMPS

**Registration Stamps of 1904 Handstamped like Nos. L1-L25**

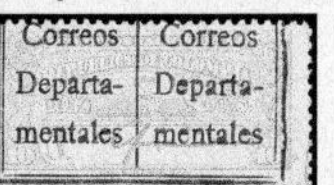


**1909 Unwmk. *Perf. 12***
LF1 R12 (a) 10c purple 30.00 30.00
LF2 R12 (b) 10c purple 30.00 30.00

**On Registration Stamp of 1909**
***Perf. 10, 13***
LF3 R12 (a) 10c purple 30.00 30.00
LF4 R12 (b) 10c purple 30.00 30.00
*Nos. LF1-LF4 (4)* 120.00 120.00

Nos. LF1-LF4 exist with overprints in black, and with overprints inverted and double.

Nos. LF1-LF4 exist imperf. Value per pair, $125.

## DEPARTMENT ACKNOWLEDGMENT OF RECEIPT STAMPS

Acknowledgment of Receipt Stamp of 1904 Hstmpd.

**1909 Unwmk. *Perf. 12***
**LH1** AR4 (a) 5c blue 30.00 30.00
*a.* Imperf., pair 125.00
**LH2** AR4 (b) 5c blue 30.00 30.00
*a.* Imperf., pair 125.00

## LOCAL STAMPS FOR THE CITY OF BOGOTA

A1

**Pelure Paper**

**1889 Unwmk. Litho. *Perf. 12***
**LX1** A1 ½c black 1.10 1.10
*a.* Imperf., pair 7.25 7.25

*Impressions on bright blue and blue-gray paper were not regularly issued.*

A2

**White Wove Paper**

**1896 *Perf. 12, 13½***
**LX2** A2 ½c black 1.10 1.10

A3

**1903 *Imperf.***
**LX3** A3 10c black, *pink* 7.25 1.40
*a.* Perf. 12 7.25 1.40

## OFFICIAL STAMPS

### Stamps of 1917-1937 Overprinted in Black or Red

a

b

**1937 Unwmk. *Perf. 11, 12, 13½***
**O1** A131 (a) 1c green .25 .25
**O2** A157 (a) 10c dp org .25 .25
**O3** A107 (b) 30c olive bis 2.10 1.00
**O4** A129 (b) 40c brn & yel brn 1.60 .80
**O5** A114 (b) 50c car 1.60 .80
**O6** A107 (b) 1p lt bl 13.00 5.50
**O7** A107 (b) 2p org 15.00 6.50
**O8** A107 (b) 5p gray 47.50 *52.50*
**O9** A118 (b) 10p dk brn 110.00 *125.00*

**Wmk. 229**
***Perf. 12½***
**O10** A132 (a) 2c red .25 .25
**O11** A133 (a) 5c brn .25 .25
**O12** A160 (a) 12c dp bl (R) 1.00 .50
**O13** A136 (b) 20c dk bl (R) 1.60 .80
*Nos. O1-O13 (13)* 194.40 194.40

Tall, wrong font "I's" in OFICIAL exist on all stamps with "a" overprint.

## POSTAL TAX STAMPS

"Greatest Mother" — PT1

***Perf. 11½***
**1935, May 27 Unwmk. Litho.**
**RA1** PT1 5c olive blk & scar 4.00 1.25

Required on all mail during Red Cross Week in 1935 (May 27-June 3) and in 1936.

Mother and Child — PT2

***Perf. 10½, 10½x11***
**1937, May 24 Unwmk.**
**RA2** PT2 5c red 2.75 .90

Required on all mail during Red Cross Week. The tax was for the Red Cross.

Ministry of Posts and Telegraphs Building — PT3

**1939-45 Litho. *Perf. 10½, 12½***
**RA3** PT3 ¼c dp bl .25 .25
**RA3A** PT3 ¼c dk vio brn ('45) .25 .25
**RA4** PT3 ½c pink .25 .25
**RA5** PT3 1c violet .30 .25
**RA5A** PT3 1c yel org ('45) 1.75 .70
**RA6** PT3 2c pck grn .55 .25
**RA7** PT3 20c lt brn 4.50 1.50
*Nos. RA3-RA7 (7)* 7.85 3.45

Obligatory on all mail. The tax was for the construction of the new Communications Building.

The 25c of type PT3 and PT4 were not usable on postal matter.

For overprint see No. 561.

Ministry of Posts and Telegraphs Building — PT4

***Perf. 12½x13***
**1940, Jan. 20 Engr. Wmk. 229**
**RA8** PT4 ¼c ultra .25 .25
**RA9** PT4 ½c carmine .25 .25
**RA10** PT4 1c violet .25 .25
**RA11** PT4 2c bl grn .30 .25
**RA12** PT4 20c brown 1.25 .25
*Nos. RA8-RA12 (5)* 2.30 1.25

See note after No. RA7. See No. RA18.

"Protection" — PT5

**1940, Apr. 25 Wmk. 255 *Perf. 12***
**RA13** PT5 5c rose carmine .30 .25

See No. RA17.

Postal Tax Stamps of 1939 Surcharged in Black

**1943 Unwmk. *Perf. 10½***
**RA14** PT3 ½c on 1c violet .25 .25
*a.* Inverted surcharge 2.00
**RA15** PT3 ½c on 2c pck grn .25 .25
**RA16** PT3 ½c on 20c lt brn .25 .25
*Nos. RA14-RA16 (3)* .75 .75

**Types of 1940**
**Imprint: "Litografia Colombia Bogota S.A."**

**1944 Litho. *Perf. 11***
**RA17** PT5 5c dark rose .40 .25

**Imprint: "Lito-Colombia Bogota-Colombia"**

**RA18** PT4 ¼c ultra .25 .25

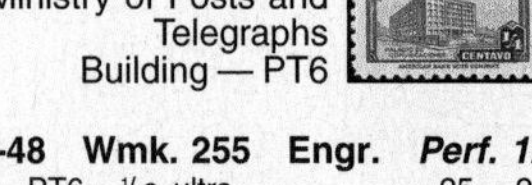
Ministry of Posts and Telegraphs Building — PT6

**1945-48 Wmk. 255 Engr. *Perf. 12***
**RA19** PT6 ¼c ultra .25 .25
**RA20** PT6 ¼c sepia ('46) .25 .25
**RA21** PT6 ½c car rose .25 .25
**RA22** PT6 ½c dp mag ('46) .25 .25
**RA23** PT6 1c vio ('46) .25 .25
**RA23A** PT6 1c red org ('46) .25 .25
**RA24** PT6 2c grn ('46) .25 .25
**RA25** PT6 20c brn ('47) 7.50 .30
*a.* 20c red brown ('48) .70 .25
*Nos. RA19-RA25 (8)* 9.25 2.05

These stamps were obligatory on all mail. The surtax was for the construction of the new Communications Building. See Nos. 603, RA33. For overprints see Nos. 562-564.

No. 469 Overprinted in Carmine

**1946, May 25**
**RA26** A176 5c dull brown .40 .25

The surtax was for the Red Cross.

Ministry of Posts and Telegraphs Building — PT7

**1946 Unwmk. Litho. *Perf. 11***
**RA27** PT7 3c blue .25 .25

No. 490 Overprinted in Carmine

**1947 Wmk. 255 *Perf. 12***
**RA28** A196 20c gray black 5.25 2.90

Arms of Colombia and Red Cross — PT8

***Perf. 12½***
**1947, Sept. Unwmk. Engr.**
**RA29** PT8 5c car lake .25 .25

The surtax of Nos. RA29 and RA40 was for the Red Cross. See No. RA40.

No. 466 Overprinted in Carmine

**RA30** A136 20c dark blue 32.50 20.00

**Catalogue values for unused stamps in this section, from this point to the end of the section, are for Never Hinged items.**

**Type of 1945**

**1947 Wmk. 255 Engr. *Perf. 12***
**RA33** PT6 1c olive bister .30 .25

Black Surcharge — PT9

**1948 Unwmk. Litho. *Perf. 11***
**RA36** PT9 1c on 5c lt brn .30 .25
**RA37** PT9 1c on 10c lt vio .30 .25
**RA38** PT9 1c on 25c red .30 .25
**RA39** PT9 1c on 50c ultra .30 .25
*Nos. RA36-RA39 (4)* 1.20 1.00

**Type of 1947**

**1948 *Perf. 10½***
**RA40** PT8 5c vermilion .25 .25

Ministry of Posts and Telegraphs Building — PT10

**1948-50 Wmk. 255 Engr. *Perf. 12***
**RA41** PT10 1c rose car ('49) .30 .25
**RA42** PT10 2c green ('50) .30 .25
**RA43** PT10 3c blue .30 .25
**RA44** PT10 5c gray .30 .25
**RA45** PT10 10c purple .30 .25
*Nos. RA41-RA45 (5)* 1.50 1.25

A 25c stamp of type PT10 was for use on telegrams, later for regular postage. See Nos. 602, 604. For overprints and surcharge see Nos. C227-C230, C238, C283, RA51.

Mother and Child — PT11

**Dark Blue Surcharge**

**Unwmk.**
**1950, May 25 Litho. *Perf. 11***
**RA46** PT11 5c on 2c gray, red, blk & yel 1.25 .90
*a.* "195" instead of "1950" 2.50 2.50
*b.* Top bar and "19" of "1950" omitted 2.50 2.50

Marginal perforations omitted, creating 26 straight-edged stamps in each sheet of 44. Surtax for Red Cross.

No. 574 Overprinted in Black

**1950, May 26 Wmk. 255 *Perf. 12***
**RA47** A176 5c blue .25 .25
*a.* Inverted overprint 8.00

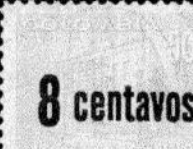

Telegraph Stamp Surcharged in Black

**RA48** A253a 8c on 50c org yel .25 .25

Fiscal stamps of type A253a were available for postal use after May 9, 1952. See Nos. 605-608.

Arms and Cross PT12

Bartolome de Las Casas Aiding Youth PT13

***Perf. 12½***
**1951, May Unwmk. Engr.**
**RA49** PT12 5c red .25 .25
**RA50** PT13 5c carmine .25 .25

The surtax was for the Red Cross.

No. RA43 Surcharged in Black

**1951 Wmk. 255 *Perf. 12***
**RA51** PT10 1c on 3c blue .25 .25

**Type of 1951**
**Engraved; Cross Lithographed**
**1953 Unwmk. *Perf. 12½***
**RA52** PT13 5c grn & car .35 .25

Surtax of Nos. RA52-RA60 for the Red Cross.

No. C254 Overprinted in Carmine

**1954**
**RA53** AP42 5c lilac rose 2.00 .90

St. Peter Claver Offering Gifts to Slaves — PT14

**Engraved; Cross Typographed**
**1955, May 2 Unwmk. *Perf. 13***
**RA54** PT14 5c dp plum & red .30 .25

Death of St. Peter Claver, 300th anniv.

Jean Henri Dunant and Santiago Samper Brush — PT15

**Photo.; Red Cross & "Cruz Roja" Engr.**
**1956, June 1 Unwmk. *Perf. 13***
**RA55** PT15 5c brown & red .45 .25

Nurses and Ambulances — PT16

**1958, June 2 Photo. *Perf. 12***
**RA56** PT16 5c gray & red .25 .25

St. Louisa de Marillac and Church — PT17

No. RA58, Henri Dunant and battle scene.

**1960, Sept. 1 Litho. *Perf. 11***
**RA57** PT17 5c brown & rose .30 .25
**RA58** PT17 5c vio blue & rose .30 .25

No. RA57 for 3rd cent. of the Sisters of Charity. No. RA58 for cent. (in 1959) of the Red Cross idea.

Manuelita de la Cruz — PT18

**1961, Nov. 2 Engr. *Perf. 13***
**RA59** PT18 5c dull pur & red .25 .25
**RA60** PT18 5c brown & red .25 .25

Issued in memory of Red Cross Nurse Manuelita de la Cruz, who died in the line of duty during the floods of 1955. Obligatory on domestic mail for a month.

Red Cross Worker, Patient — PT19

**1965, Apr. 30 Photo. *Perf. 12***
**RA61** PT19 5c blue gray & red .25 .25

Obligatory on domestic mail during May.

Nurse's Cap — PT20

**1967, June 1 Litho. *Perf. 12***
**RA62** PT20 5c brt bl & red .25 .25

Red Cross — PT21

**1969, July 1 Litho. *Perf. 12x12½***
**RA63** PT21 5c vio bl & red .25 .25

Child Care — PT22

**1970, July 1 Litho. *Perf. 12½x12***
**RA64** PT22 5c light bl & red .25 .25

## ANTIOQUIA

ant-ē-'ō-kē-ə

Originally a State, now a Department of the Republic of Colombia. Until the revolution of 1885, the separate states making up the United States of Colombia were sovereign governments in their own right. On August 4, 1886, the National Council of Bogotá, composed of two delegates from each state, adopted a new constitution which abolished the sovereign rights of states, which then became departments with governors appointed by the President of the Republic. The nine original states represented at the Bogotá Convention retained some of their previous rights, as management of their own finances, and all issued postage stamps until as late as 1904. For Panama's issues, see Panama Nos. 1-30.

Coat of Arms
A1 A2

A3

A4

**Wove Paper**

**1868 Unwmk. Litho. *Imperf.***
1 A1 2½c blue *1,000. 750.*
2 A2 5c green *750. 575.*
3 A3 10c lilac *3,000. 1,000.*
4 A4 1p red *675. 750.*

*Reprints of Nos. 1, 3 and 4 are on a bluish white paper and all but No. 3 have scratches across the design.*

A5

A6

A7

A8

A9

A10

**1869**
5 A5 2½c blue 7.50 6.50
6 A6 5c green 11.00 10.00
7 A7 5c green 11.00 10.00
8 A8 10c lilac 14.50 7.00
9 A9 20c brown 14.50 7.00
10 A10 1p rose red 29.00 26.00
*a.* 1p vermilion 55.00 50.00
*Nos. 5-10 (6)* 87.50 66.50

*Reprints of Nos. 7, 8 and 10 are on a bluish white paper; reprints of Nos. 5 and 10a on white paper. The 10c blue is believed to be a reprint.*

A11

A12

A13

A14

A15

A16

A17

A18

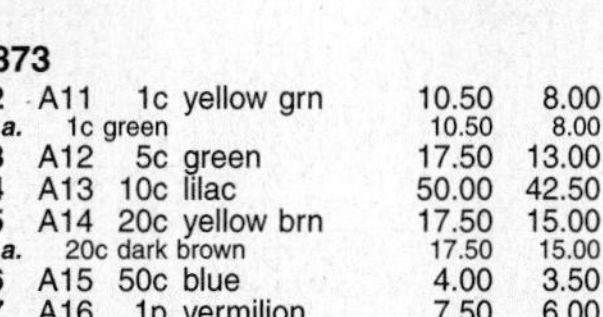

**1873**
12 A11 1c yellow grn 10.50 8.00
*a.* 1c green 10.50 8.00
13 A12 5c green 17.50 13.00
14 A13 10c lilac 50.00 42.50
15 A14 20c yellow brn 17.50 15.00
*a.* 20c dark brown 17.50 15.00
16 A15 50c blue 4.00 3.50
17 A16 1p vermilion 7.50 6.00
18 A17 2p black, *yellow* 17.50 16.00
19 A18 5p black, *rose* 130.00 110.00

A19

A20

Liberty Head
A21 A22

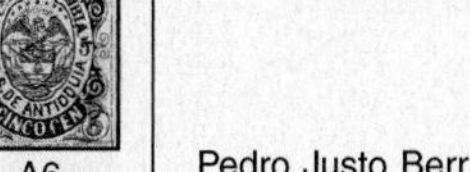

Pedro Justo Berrio — A23

**1875-85**
20 A19 1c blk, *grn*, unglazed ('76) 3.20 4.75
*a.* Glazed paper 5.25 6.50
*b.* 1c blk, *lt grn*, laid paper ('85) 7.50 7.00
21 A19 1c black ('76) 2.25 2.00
*a.* Laid paper 325.00 225.00
22 A19 1c bl grn ('85) 5.00 8.00
23 A19 1c red lil, laid paper ('85) 5.00 8.00
24 A20 2½c blue 5.00 3.75
*a.* Pelure paper ('78) *1,500. 1,100.*
25 A21 5c green 32.50 29.00
*a.* Laid paper 325.00 175.00
26 A22 5c green 32.50 29.00
*a.* Laid paper 325.00 175.00
27 A23 10c lilac 50.00 42.50
*a.* Laid paper 325.00 250.00
28 A20 10c vio, pelure paper ('78) *900.00 675.00*

Arms
A24

Liberty
A25

A26

A27

**1878-85**
29 A24 2½c blue, pelure paper 5.50 5.00
30 A24 2½c green ('83) 5.00 4.25
*a.* Laid paper ('83) 160.00 110.00
31 A24 2½c blk, *buff* ('85) 14.50 13.00
32 A25 5c green ('83) 9.00 8.00
*a.* Pelure paper 65.00 55.00
*b.* Laid paper ('82) 80.00 *26.00*
33 A25 5c violet ('83) 19.00 15.00
*a.* 5c blue violet ('83) 19.00 15.00
34 A26 10c vio, laid paper ('82) 375.00 125.00
35 A26 10c scar ('83) 5.00 4.25
*a.* Tete beche pair 225.00 225.00
36 A27 20c brown ('83) 9.00 8.00
*a.* Laid paper ('82) 12.00 11.00

A28

A29

Liberty — A30

**1883-85**
37 A28 5c brown 10.50 7.00
*a.* Laid paper 450.00 175.00
38 A28 5c green ('85) 275.00 90.00
*a.* Laid paper ('85) 325.00 150.00
39 A28 5c yel, laid paper ('85) 11.00 9.00
40 A29 10c bl grn, laid paper 11.00 9.50
41 A29 10c bl, *bl* ('85) 11.00 9.00
42 A29 10c lil, laid paper ('85) 24.00 15.00
*a.* Wove paper ('85) 3,360. 1,680.
43 A30 20c bl, laid paper ('85) 9.00 8.00

Coat of Arms — A31

**1886 Wove Paper**
55 A31 1c grn, *pink* 1.25 1.10
56 A31 2½c blk, *orange* 1.25 1.10
57 A31 5c ultra, *buff* 5.00 4.00
*a.* 5c blue, *buff* 7.50 6.50
58 A31 10c rose, *buff* 3.50 3.25
*a.* Transfer of 50c in stone of 10c 275.00 275.00

**59** A31 20c dk vio, *buff* 3.50 3.25
**61** A31 50c yel brn, *buff* 6.50 5.50
**62** A31 1p yel, *grn* 10.50 9.00
**63** A31 2p green, *pink* 10.50 9.00
*Nos. 55-63 (8)* 42.00 36.20

**1887-88**

**64** A31 1c red, *vio* 1.00 .90
**65** A31 2½c lil, *pale lil* 1.00 1.00
**66** A31 5c car, *buff* 1.25 1.25
**67** A31 5c red, *grn* 7.50 3.50
**68** A31 10c brn, *grn* 1.50 *2.00*
*Nos. 64-68 (5)* 12.25 8.65

### Medellin Issue

A32

A33

A34

**1888** **Typeset**

**69** A32 2½c blk, *yellow* 32.50 29.00
**70** A33 5c blk, *yellow* 17.50 15.00
**71** A34 5c red, *yellow* 10.50 9.00
*Nos. 69-71 (3)* 60.50 53.00

Two varieties of No. 69, six of No. 70 and ten of No. 71.

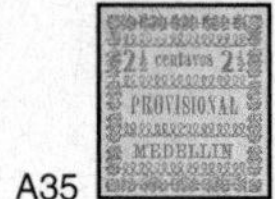
A35

**1889**

**72** A35 2½c red 16.00 13.00

Ten varieties including "eentavos."

### Regular Issue

Coat of Arms — A36

**1889** **Litho.** ***Perf. 13½***

**73** A36 1c blk, *rose* .50 .50
**74** A36 2½c blk, *blue* .50 .50
**75** A36 5c blk, *yellow* .60 .60
**76** A36 10c blk, *green* .60 .60
*Nos. 73-76 (4)* 2.20 2.20

A37

A38

A39

A40

Coat of Arms — A41

**1890**

**78** A37 20c blue 2.75 2.75
**79** A38 50c vio brn 5.00 5.00
*a.* Transfer of 20c in stone of 50c 200.00 200.00
**80** A38 50c green 4.50 4.50
**81** A39 1p red 4.00 4.00
**82** A40 2p blk, *mag* 29.00 29.00
**83** A41 5p blk, *org red* 45.00 45.00
*Nos. 78-83 (6)* 90.25 90.25

Nos. 73-76, 82-83 exist imperf.

The so-called "errors" of Nos. 73 to 76, printed on paper of wrong colors, are essays or, possibly, reprints. They exist perforated and imperforate.

See No. 96.

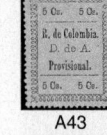

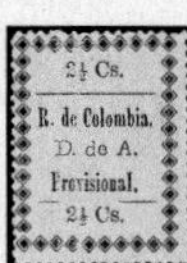
A42

A43

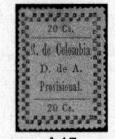

A44

A45

**1890** **Typeset** ***Perf. 14***

**84** A42 2½c blk, *buff* 4.50 4.50
**85** A43 5c blk, *orange* 4.50 4.50
**86** A44 10c blk, *buff* 14.00 14.00
**87** A44 10c blk, *rose* 18.00 18.00
**88** A45 20c blk, *orange* 18.00 18.00
*Nos. 84-88 (5)* 59.00 59.00

20 varieties of the 5c, 10 each of the other values.

A46

**1892** **Litho.** ***Perf. 13½***

**89** A46 1c brn, *brnsh* .80 .80
**90** A46 2½c pur, *lil* .80 .80
**92** A46 5c blk, *gray* 4.50 2.25
*a.* Transfer of 2½c in stone of 5c 400.00
*Nos. 89-92 (3)* 6.10 3.85

**1893**

**93** A46 1c blue .50 .50
**94** A46 2½c green .80 .80
**95** A46 5c vermilion .50 .50
**96** A36 10c pale brown .50 .50
*Nos. 93-96 (4)* 2.30 2.30

A47

**1896** ***Perf. 14***

**97** A47 2c gray .50 .50
**98** A47 2c lilac rose .50 .50
**99** A47 2½c brown .50 .50
**100** A47 2½c steel blue .50 .50
**101** A47 3c orange .50 .50
**102** A47 3c olive grn .50 .50
**103** A47 5c green .50 .50
**104** A47 5c yellow buff .60 .60
**105** A47 10c brown vio 1.10 1.10
**106** A47 10c violet 1.10 1.10
**107** A47 20c brown org 2.75 2.75
**108** A47 20c blue 2.75 2.75
**109** A47 50c gray brn 2.75 2.75
**110** A47 50c rose 2.75 2.75
**111** A47 1p blue & blk 35.00 35.00
**112** A47 1p rose red & blk 35.00 35.00
**113** A47 2p orange & blk 110.00 110.00
**114** A47 2p dk grn & blk 110.00 110.00
**115** A47 5p red vio & blk 200.00 200.00
**116** A47 5p purple & blk 200.00 200.00
*Nos. 97-116 (20)* 707.30 707.30

#115-116 with centers omitted are proofs.

General José María Córdoba — A48

**1899** ***Perf. 11***

**117** A48 ½c grnsh bl .50 .50
**118** A48 1c slate blue .50 .50
**119** A48 2c slate brown .50 .50
**120** A48 3c red .50 .50
**121** A48 4c bister brown .50 .50
**122** A48 5c green .50 .50
**123** A48 10c scarlet .50 .50
**124** A48 20c gray violet .50 .50
**125** A48 50c olive bister .50 .50
**126** A48 1p greenish blk .50 .50
**127** A48 2p olive gray .50 .50
*Nos. 117-127 (11)* 5.50 5.50

Numerous part-perf. and imperf. varieties of Nos. 117-127 exist.

Used values for Nos. 117-127 are for favor-canceled stamps with oval cancels in violet. Postally used examples are valued at $3.50 each.

A49

A50

A50a

**1901** **Typeset** ***Perf. 12***

**128** A49 1c red .50 .50
**129** A50 1c ultra 1.25 1.25
**130** A50 1c bister 1.25 1.25
**130A** A50a 1c dull red 1.25 1.25
**130B** A50a 1c ultra 9.00 9.00
*Nos. 128-130B (5)* 13.25 13.25

Eight varieties of No. 128, four varieties of Nos. 129-130B.

A51

A52

Atanasio Girardot
A53

Dr. José Félix Restrepo
A54

**1902** **Litho.** **Wove Paper**

**131** A51 1c brt rose .50 .50
*a.* Laid paper 1.25 1.25
*b.* Imperf., pair 5.50
**132** A51 2c blue .50 .50
*a.* Transfer of 3c in stone of 2c 12.00 12.00
**133** A51 3c green .50 .50
*a.* Imperf., pair 10.00
**134** A51 4c dull violet .50 .50
**135** A52 5c rose red .50 .50
**136** A53 10c rose lilac .50 .50
*a.* Small head 11.50 11.50
*b.* 10c rose 2.00 2.00
**137** A53 20c gray green .50 .50
**138** A53 30c brt rose .50 .50
**139** A53 40c blue .50 .50
**140** A53 50c brn, *yel* .50 .50

**Laid Paper**

**141** A54 1p purple & blk 1.60 1.60
**142** A54 2p rose & blk 1.60 1.60
**143** A54 5p sl bl & blk 3.00 3.00
*Nos. 131-143 (13)* 11.20 11.20

**1903** **Wove Paper**

**143A** A51 1c blue .50 .50
**144** A51 2c violet .50 .50
*a.* Imperf. 6.00

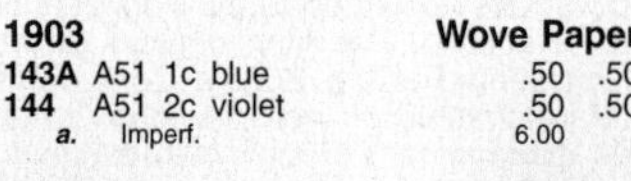
A55

A56

A57

Designs: 1p, Francisco Antonio Zea. 2p, Custodio Garcia Rovira. 3p, La Pola (Policarpa Salavarrieta). 4p, J. M. Restrepo. 5p, José Fernández Madrid. 10p, Juan del Corral.

**1903-04**

**145** A55 4c yellow brn .70 .60
**146** A55 5c blue .70 .60
**147** A56 10c yellow .70 .60
**148** A56 20c purple .70 .60
**149** A56 30c brown 1.75 1.75
**150** A56 40c green 1.75 1.75
**151** A56 50c rose .70 .60
**152** A57 1p olive gray 1.75 1.75
**153** A57 2p purple 1.75 1.75
**154** A57 3p dark blue 1.75 1.75
**155** A57 4p dull red 3.00 3.00
**156** A57 5p red brown 9.00 4.25
**157** A57 10p scarlet 19.00 11.00
*Nos. 145-157 (13)* 43.25 30.00

Nos. 145-146, 151, 153-157 exist imperf. Value of pairs, $8 to $10.

### Manizales Issue

Stamps of these designs are local private post issues.

OFFICIAL STAMPS Stamps of 1903-04 with overprint "OFICIAL" were never issued.

## REGISTRATION STAMPS

R1

**1896** **Unwmk.** **Litho.** ***Perf. 14***

**F1** R1 2½c rose 2.50 2.50
**F2** R1 2½c dull blue 2.50 2.50

Córdoba — R2

R3

**1899** ***Perf. 11***

**F3** R2 2½c dull blue .50 .50
**F4** R3 10c red lilac .50 .50

R4

**1902** ***Perf. 12***

**F5** R4 10c purple, *blue* .60 .60
*a.* Imperf. —

## ACKNOWLEDGMENT OF RECEIPT STAMPS

AR1

**1902-03** **Unwmk.** **Litho.** ***Perf. 12***

**H1** AR1 5c black, *rose* 2.25 2.25
**H2** AR1 5c slate ('03) .75 .75

## LATE FEE STAMPS

Córdoba — LF1

**1899** **Unwmk.** **Litho.** ***Perf. 11***

**I1** LF1 2½c dark green .70 .70
*a.* Imperf., pair 10.00

LF2

**1901 Typeset *Perf. 12***
**I2** LF2 2½c red violet 2.00 2.00
*a.* 2½c purple 2.00 2.00

LF3

**1902 Litho.**
**I3** LF3 2½c violet .50 .50

City of Medellin

Stamps of the designs shown were not issued by any governmental agency but by the Sociedad de Mejoras Publicas.

## BOLIVAR

bə-ˈlē-ˌvär

Originally a State, now a Department of the Republic of Colombia. (See Antioquia.)

A1

**1863-66 Unwmk. Litho. *Imperf.***
**1** A1 10c green *1,200.* *600.00*
*a.* Five stars below shield *2,500.* *2,400.*
**2** A1 10c red ('66) 55.00 *60.00*
*a.* Diagonal half used as 5c on cover 240.00
*b.* Five stars below shield 175.00 145.00
**3** A1 1p red 13.50 *15.50*

Fourteen varieties of each. Counterfeits of Nos. 1 and 1a exist.

Coat of Arms
A2 A3

A4

A5

**1873**
**4** A2 5c blue 14.50 14.50
**5** A3 10c violet 14.50 14.50
**6** A4 20c yellow green 65.00 65.00
**7** A5 80c vermilion 130.00 130.00
*Nos. 4-7 (4)* 224.00 224.00

A6

A7

A8

**1874-78**
**8** A6 5c blue 55.00 28.00
**9** A7 5c blue ('78) 16.00 14.50
**10** A8 10c violet ('77) 8.00 7.50
*Nos. 8-10 (3)* 79.00 50.00

Bolívar — A9

**Dated "1879"**

**1879 White Wove Paper *Perf. 12½***
**11** A9 5c blue .60 .60
*a.* Imperf., pair 4.00
**12** A9 10c violet .50 .50
**13** A9 20c red .60 .60
*a.* 20c green (error) 22.50 22.50

**Bluish Laid Paper**
**15** A9 5c blue .60 .60
*a.* Imperf., pair 10.00
**16** A9 10c violet 3.25 3.25
*a.* Imperf., pair 17.50
**17** A9 20c red .80 .80
*a.* Imperf., pair 8.00
*Nos. 11-17 (6)* 6.35 6.35

Stamps of 80c and 1p on white wove paper and 1p on bluish laid paper were prepared but not placed in use.

**Dated "1880"**

**1880 White Wove Paper *Perf. 12½***
**19** A9 5c blue .60 .60
*a.* Imperf., pair 4.00
**20** A9 10c violet .80 .80
*a.* Imperf., pair 4.00
**21** A9 20c red .80 .80
*a.* 20c green (error) 28.00 28.00
**23** A9 80c green 5.00 5.00
**24** A9 1p orange 5.50 5.50
*a.* Imperf., pair 22.00
*Nos. 19-24 (5)* 12.70 12.70

**Bluish Laid Paper**
**25** A9 5c blue .60 .60
*a.* Imperf., pair 4.00
**26** A9 10c violet 5.00 5.00
**27** A9 20c red .80 .80
*a.* Imperf., pair 12.00
**28** A9 1p orange 900.00
*a.* Imperf. *1,000.*

A11

A12

A13

A15

A16

**Dated "1882"**
**White Wove Paper**

**1882 *Perf. 12, 16x12***
**29** A11 5c blue .70 .70
**30** A12 10c lilac .70 .70
**31** A13 20c red .70 .70
**33** A15 80c green 1.25 1.25
**34** A16 1p orange 1.25 1.25
*Nos. 29-34 (5)* 4.60 4.60

Nos. 29, 30 and 34 are known imperforate. They are printer's waste and were not issued through post offices.

A17

**1882 Engr. *Perf. 12***
**35** A17 5p blue & rose red 1.25 1.25
*a.* Imperf., pair 11.00
*b.* Perf. 16 16.00 13.50
*c.* Perf. 14 13.50 13.50
**36** A17 10p brown & blue 3.50 3.50
*a.* Imperf., pair 18.00
*b.* Perf. 16 14.50 12.00
*c.* Rouletted 17.00 17.00

**Dated "1883"**

**1883 Litho. *Perf. 12, 16x12***
**37** A11 5c blue .50 .50
*a.* Imperf., pair 2.00
*b.* Perf. 12 25.00 5.00
**38** A12 10c lilac .60 .60
**39** A13 20c red .60 .60
**41** A15 80c green .60 .60
**42** A16 1p orange 3.25 3.25
*a.* Perf. 16x12 5.00 5.00
*Nos. 37-42 (5)* 5.55 5.55

**1884 Dated "1884"**
**43** A11 5c blue 1.40 1.40
*a.* Perf. 12 32.50 32.50
**44** A12 10c lilac 1.00 1.00
**45** A13 20c red 1.00 1.00
*a.* Perf. 12 16.00 16.00
**47** A15 80c green 1.40 1.40
*a.* Perf. 12 8.00 8.00
**48** A16 1p orange 1.25 1.25
*Nos. 43-48 (5)* 6.05 6.05

**1885 Dated "1885"**
**49** A11 5c blue .50 .50
**50** A12 10c lilac .50 .50
**51** A13 20c red .50 .50
**53** A15 80c green .50 .50
**54** A16 1p orange .60 .60
*Nos. 49-54 (5)* 2.60 2.60

The note after No. 34 will also apply to imperforate stamps of the 1884-85 issues.

A18

**1891 *Perf. 14***
**55** A18 1c black .60 .60
**56** A18 5c orange .60 .60
*a.* Imperf., pair 1.75
**57** A18 10c carmine .60 .60
**58** A18 20c blue 1.25 1.25
**59** A18 50c green 2.00 2.00
**60** A18 1p purple 2.00 2.00
*Nos. 55-60 (6)* 7.05 7.05

For overprint see Colombia No. 169.

Bolívar
A19

José Fernández Madrid
A20

Manuel Rodriguez Torices
A21

José María García de Toledo
A22

**1903 Laid Paper *Imperf.***
**62** A19 50c dk bl, *pink* 1.25 1.25
*a.* Bluish paper 1.25 1.25
**63** A19 50c sl grn, *pink* 1.25 1.25
*a.* Rose paper 4.50 4.50
*b.* Greenish blue paper 6.50 6.50
*c.* Yellow paper 9.00 9.00
*d.* Brown paper 9.00 9.00
*e.* Salmon paper 16.00 16.00
**64** A19 50c pur, *pink* 4.50 4.50
*a.* White paper 9.00 9.00
*b.* Brown paper 9.00 9.00
*c.* Greenish blue paper 9.00 9.00
*d.* Lilac paper 9.00 9.00

*e.* Rose paper 8.00 8.00
*f.* Yellow paper 9.00 9.00
*g.* Salmon paper 13.00 13.00
*h.* As "a," wove paper 20.00 20.00
**65** A20 1p org, *sal* 1.25 1.25
*a.* Yellow paper 10.00 10.00
*b.* Greenish blue paper 32.50 32.50
**66** A20 1p gray grn, *lil* 3.25 3.25
*a.* Yellow paper 14.00 14.00
*b.* Salmon paper 16.00 16.00
*c.* Green paper 16.00 16.00
*d.* White wove paper 24.00
**67** A21 5p car rose, *lil* 1.25 1.25
*a.* Brown paper 2.50 2.50
*b.* Yellow paper 2.50 2.50
*c.* Greenish blue paper 10.00 10.00
*d.* Bluish paper 13.00 13.00
*e.* Salmon paper 16.00 16.00
*f.* Rose paper 20.00 20.00
**68** A22 10p dk bl, *bluish* 2.75 2.75
*a.* Greenish blue paper 2.75 2.75
*b.* Rose paper 16.00 16.00
*c.* Salmon paper 16.00 16.00
*d.* Yellow paper 16.00 16.00
*e.* Brown paper 16.00 16.00
*f.* Lilac paper 24.00 24.00
*g.* White paper 20.00 20.00
**69** A22 10p pur, *grnsh bl* 7.50 7.50
*a.* Bluish paper 16.00 16.00
*b.* Rose paper 15.00 15.00
*c.* Yellow paper 16.00 16.00
*d.* Brown paper 16.00 16.00
*Nos. 62-69 (8)* 23.00 23.00

***Sewing Machine Perf.***
**Laid Paper**
**70** A19 50c dk bl, *pink* 2.25 2.25
*a.* Bluish paper 2.25 2.25
**71** A19 50c sl grn, *pink* 4.50 4.50
**72** A19 50c pur, *grnsh bl* 9.00 9.00
*a.* White paper 9.00 9.00
*b.* White wove paper 16.00
**73** A20 1p org, *sal* 4.50 4.50
**74** A20 1p gray grn, *lil* 20.00 20.00
*a.* Yellow paper 20.00 20.00
**75** A21 5p car rose, *yel* 3.50 3.50
*a.* Lilac paper 9.00 9.00
*b.* Brown paper 9.00 9.00
*c.* Bluish paper 12.00 12.00
*d.* White wove paper 20.00
**76** A22 10p dk bl, *grnsh bl* 10.00 10.00
*a.* Bluish paper 14.00 14.00
*b.* Yellow paper 20.00 20.00
*c.* As "b," wove paper 24.00
**77** A22 10p pur, *grnsh bl* 15.00 15.00
*a.* Bluish paper 26.00 26.00
*b.* Rose paper 17.00 17.00
*c.* Yellow paper 26.00 26.00
*Nos. 70-77 (8)* 68.75 68.75

José María del Castillo y Rada
A23

Manuel Anguiano
A24

Pantaleón C. Ribón — A25

**1904 *Sewing Machine Perf.***
**89** A23 5c black .50 .50
**90** A24 10c brown .50 .50
**91** A25 20c red .60 .60
**92** A25 20c red brown 1.25 1.25
*Nos. 89-92 (4)* 2.85 2.85

**Imperf., pairs**
*89a* A23 5c black 8.00 8.00
*90a* A24 10c brown 6.00 6.00
*91a* A25 20c red 15.00 15.00
*92a* A25 20c red brown 15.00 15.00

A26

A27

A28

**1904 *Imperf.***
**93** A26 ½c black 1.25 1.25
*a.* Tête bêche pair 7.50 7.50
**94** A27 1c blue 2.50 2.50
**95** A28 2c purple 2.75 2.75
*Nos. 93-95 (3)* 6.50 6.50

### REGISTRATION STAMPS

Simón Bolívar — R1

**White Wove Paper**

***Perf. 12½, 16x12***

**1879 Unwmk. Litho.**

| No. | Design | Description | Unused | Used |
|---|---|---|---|---|
| F1 | R1 | 40c brown | 1.50 | 1.50 |

**Bluish Laid Paper**

| No. | Design | Description | Unused | Used |
|---|---|---|---|---|
| F2 | R1 | 40c brown | 1.50 | 1.50 |
| a. | | Imperf., pair | 8.00 | |

**Dated "1880"**

**1880 White Wove Paper**

| No. | Design | Description | Unused | Used |
|---|---|---|---|---|
| F3 | R1 | 40c brown | 1.50 | 1.50 |

**Bluish Laid Paper**

| No. | Design | Description | Unused | Used |
|---|---|---|---|---|
| F4 | R1 | 40c brown | 1.50 | 1.50 |
| a. | | Imperf., pair | 8.00 | |

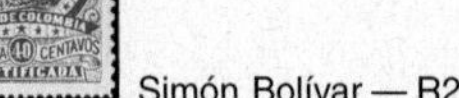

Simón Bolívar — R2

**Dated "1882" to "1885"**
**White Wove Paper**

**1882-85** ***Perf. 16x12***

| No. | Design | Description | Unused | Used |
|---|---|---|---|---|
| F5 | R2 | 40c brown (1882) | .70 | .70 |
| F6 | R2 | 40c brown (1883) | .60 | .60 |
| F7 | R2 | 40c brown (1884) | .60 | .60 |
| F8 | R2 | 40c brown (1885) | .60 | .60 |
| | | *Nos. F5-F8 (4)* | 2.50 | 2.50 |

***Perf. 12***

| No. | Design | Description | Unused | Used |
|---|---|---|---|---|
| *F5a* | R2 | 40c | 40.00 | |
| *F6a* | R2 | 40c | 32.50 | |
| *F7a* | R2 | 40c | 32.50 | |
| *F8a* | R2 | 40c | 32.50 | |
| | | *Nos. F5a-F8a (4)* | 137.50 | |

R3

**1903 Laid Paper** ***Imperf.***

| No. | Design | Description | Unused | Used |
|---|---|---|---|---|
| F9 | R3 | 20c orange, *rose* | 1.25 | 1.25 |
| a. | | Salmon paper | 2.50 | 2.50 |
| b. | | Greenish blue paper | 13.00 | 13.00 |

***Sewing Machine Perf.***

| No. | Design | Description | Unused | Used |
|---|---|---|---|---|
| F10 | R3 | 20c orange, *rose* | 5.50 | 5.50 |
| a. | | Salmon paper | 5.50 | 5.50 |
| b. | | Greenish blue paper | 13.00 | 13.00 |

R4

**1904 Wove Paper**

| No. | Design | Description | Unused | Used |
|---|---|---|---|---|
| F11 | R4 | 5c black | 6.50 | 6.50 |

### ACKNOWLEDGMENT OF RECEIPT STAMPS

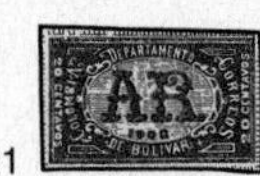

AR1

**1903 Unwmk. Litho.** ***Imperf.***

**Laid Paper**

| No. | Design | Description | Unused | Used |
|---|---|---|---|---|
| H1 | AR1 | 20c org, *rose* | 5.50 | 5.50 |
| a. | | Yellow paper | 2.75 | 2.75 |
| b. | | Greenish blue paper | 11.00 | 11.00 |
| H2 | AR1 | 20c dk bl, *yel* | 4.50 | 4.50 |
| a. | | Brown paper | 7.50 | 7.50 |
| b. | | Rose paper | 5.50 | 5.50 |
| c. | | Salmon paper | 15.00 | 15.00 |
| d. | | Greenish blue paper | 15.00 | 15.00 |

***Sewing Machine Perf.***

| No. | Design | Description | Unused | Used |
|---|---|---|---|---|
| H3 | AR1 | 20c org, *grnsh bl* | 13.50 | 13.50 |
| a. | | Yellow paper | 15.00 | 15.00 |
| H4 | AR1 | 20c dk bl, *yel* | 15.00 | 15.00 |
| a. | | Lilac paper | 15.00 | 15.00 |
| | | *Nos. H1-H4 (4)* | 38.50 | 38.50 |

AR2

**1904 Wove Paper**

| No. | Design | Description | Unused | Used |
|---|---|---|---|---|
| H5 | AR2 | 2c red | 2.50 | 2.50 |

### LATE FEE STAMPS

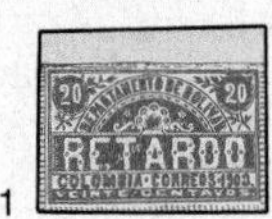

LF1

**1903 Unwmk. Litho.** ***Imperf.***

**Laid Paper**

| No. | Design | Description | Unused | Used |
|---|---|---|---|---|
| I1 | LF1 | 20c car rose, *bluish* | 1.25 | 1.25 |
| I2 | LF1 | 20c pur, *bluish* | 1.25 | 1.25 |
| a. | | Rose paper | 4.50 | 4.50 |
| b. | | Brown paper | 4.50 | 4.50 |
| c. | | Lilac paper | 4.50 | 4.50 |
| d. | | Yellow paper | 14.00 | 14.00 |

***Sewing Machine Perf.***

| No. | Design | Description | Unused | Used |
|---|---|---|---|---|
| I3 | LF1 | 20c car rose, *bluish* | 7.50 | 7.50 |
| I4 | LF1 | 20c pur, *bluish* | 7.50 | 7.50 |
| a. | | Rose paper | 13.00 | 13.00 |
| b. | | Lilac paper | 13.00 | 13.00 |
| c. | | Yellow paper | 24.00 | 24.00 |
| | | *Nos. I1-I4 (4)* | 17.50 | 17.50 |

## BOYACA

bō-yä-cä

Originally a State, now a Department of the Republic of Colombia. (See Antioquia.)

Diego Mendoza Pérez — A1

**1902 Unwmk. Litho.** ***Perf. 13½***

**Wove Paper**

| No. | Design | Description | Unused | Used |
|---|---|---|---|---|
| 1 | A1 | 5c blue green | 1.60 | 1.60 |
| a. | | Bluish paper | 190.00 | 190.00 |
| b. | | Imperf., pair | 32.50 | 32.50 |

**Laid Paper**

***Perf. 12***

| No. | Design | Description | Unused | Used |
|---|---|---|---|---|
| 2 | A1 | 5c green | 225.00 | 225.00 |

Coat of Arms
A2 A3

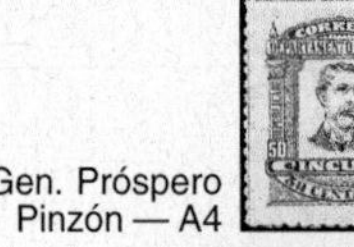

Gen. Próspero Pinzón — A4

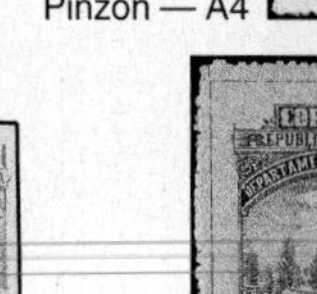

A5

Monument of Battle of Boyacá — A6

President José Manuel Marroquin — A7

**1903 Litho.** ***Imperf.***

| No. | Design | Description | Unused | Used |
|---|---|---|---|---|
| 4 | A2 | 10c dark gray | .60 | .60 |
| 5 | A3 | 20c red brown | .70 | .70 |
| 6 | A5 | 1p red | 6.50 | 6.50 |
| a. | | 1p claret | 7.50 | 7.50 |
| 8 | A6 | 5p black, *rose* | 2.50 | 2.50 |
| a. | | 5p black, *buff* | 24.00 | 24.00 |
| 9 | A7 | 10p black, *buff* | 2.50 | 2.50 |
| a. | | 10p black, *rose* | 24.00 | 24.00 |
| b. | | As "a," tête bêche pair | 50.00 | |
| | | *Nos. 4-9 (5)* | 12.80 | 12.80 |

***Perf. 12***

| No. | Design | Description | Unused | Used |
|---|---|---|---|---|
| 10 | A2 | 10c dark gray | .70 | .70 |
| 11 | A3 | 20c red brown | .80 | .80 |
| 12 | A4 | 50c green | .70 | .70 |
| 13 | A4 | 50c dull blue | 5.00 | 5.00 |
| 14 | A5 | 1p red | .70 | .70 |
| a. | | 1p claret | 6.00 | 6.00 |
| 16 | A6 | 5p black, *rose* | 22.00 | 22.00 |
| a. | | 5p black, *buff* | 19.00 | 19.00 |
| 17 | A7 | 10p black, *buff* | 2.25 | 2.25 |
| a. | | 10p black, *rose* | 22.00 | 22.00 |
| b. | | Tête bêche pair | 24.00 | 24.00 |
| | | *Nos. 10-17 (7)* | 32.15 | 32.15 |

Statue of Bolívar — A8

**1904**

| No. | Design | Description | Unused | Used |
|---|---|---|---|---|
| 18 | A8 | 10c orange | .50 | .50 |
| a. | | Imperf., pair | 7.50 | 7.50 |

### CAUCA

Stamps of these designs were issued by a provincial post between 1879(?) and 1890.

Stamps of this design are believed to be of private origin and without official sanction.

Items inscribed "No hay estampillas" (No stamps available) and others inscribed "Manuel E. Jiménez" are considered by specialists to be receipt labels, not postage stamps.

## CUNDINAMARCA

kün-di-nə-'mär-kə

Originally a State, now a Department of the Republic of Colombia. (See Antioquia.)

Coat of Arms
A1 A2

**1870 Unwmk. Litho.** ***Imperf.***

| No. | Design | Description | Unused | Used |
|---|---|---|---|---|
| 1 | A1 | 5c blue | 10.50 | 10.50 |
| 2 | A2 | 10c red | 32.50 | 32.50 |

*The counterfeits, or reprints, show traces of the cuts made to deface the dies.*

A3

A4

A5

A6

**1877-82**

| No. | Design | Description | Unused | Used |
|---|---|---|---|---|
| 3 | A3 | 10c red ('82) | 7.00 | 7.00 |
| a. | | Laid paper ('77) | 9.00 | 9.00 |
| 4 | A4 | 20c green ('82) | 15.00 | 15.00 |
| a. | | Laid paper ('77) | 24.00 | 24.00 |
| 7 | A5 | 50c purple ('82) | 16.00 | 16.00 |
| 8 | A6 | 1p brown ('82) | 24.00 | 24.00 |
| | | *Nos. 3-8 (4)* | 62.00 | 62.00 |

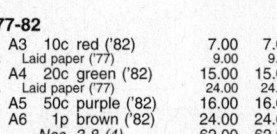

A7

Redrawn

**1884**

| No. | Design | Description | Unused | Used |
|---|---|---|---|---|
| 10 | A7 | 5c blue | 1.60 | 1.60 |
| 11 | A7 | 5c blue (redrawn) | 1.60 | 1.60 |
| a. | | Tête bêche pair | 160.00 | 160.00 |

The redrawn stamp has no period after "COLOMBIA."

A8

A9

A10

A11

**1883 Typeset**

| No. | Design | Description | Unused | Used |
|---|---|---|---|---|
| 13 | A8 | 10c black, *yellow* | 30.00 | 30.00 |
| 14 | A9 | 50c black, *rose* | 30.00 | 30.00 |
| a. | | 50c black, *mag* | 30.00 | 30.00 |
| 15 | A10 | 1p black, *brown* | 75.00 | 75.00 |
| 16 | A11 | 2r black, *green* | *2,200.* | |

Typeset varieties exist: 4 of the 10c, 2 each of 50c and 1p.

Some experts doubt that No. 16 was issued. The variety without signature and watermarked "flowers" is believed to be a proof. Forgeries exist.

A12

**1886 Litho.**

| No. | Design | Description | Unused | Used |
|---|---|---|---|---|
| 17 | A12 | 5c blue | 1.60 | 1.60 |
| 18 | A12 | 10c red | 10.00 | 10.00 |
| 19 | A12 | 10c red, *lilac* | 5.50 | 5.50 |
| 20 | A12 | 20c green | 8.50 | 8.50 |
| a. | | 20c yellow green | 10.00 | 10.00 |

| | | | | |
|---|---|---|---|---|
| 21 | A12 | 50c purple | 11.00 | 11.00 |
| 22 | A12 | 1p orange brown | 11.50 | 11.50 |
| | | *Nos. 17-22 (6)* | 48.10 | 48.10 |

*Nos. 17 to 22 have been reprinted. The colors are aniline and differ from those of the original stamps. The impression is coarse and blurred.*

A13

A14

A15

A16

A17

A18

A19

A20

A21

**1904** ***Perf. 10½, 12***

| | | | | |
|---|---|---|---|---|
| 23 | A13 | 1c orange | .50 | .50 |
| 24 | A14 | 2c gray blue | .50 | .50 |
| 25 | A15 | 3c rose | .70 | .70 |
| 26 | A15 | 5c olive grn | .70 | .70 |
| 27 | A16 | 10c pale brn | .70 | .70 |
| 28 | A17 | 15c pink | .70 | .70 |
| 29 | A18 | 20c blue, *grn* | .70 | .70 |
| 30 | A18 | 20c blue | 1.25 | 1.25 |
| 31 | A19 | 40c blue | 1.25 | 1.25 |
| 32 | A19 | 40c blue, *buff* | 42.50 | 42.50 |
| 33 | A20 | 50c red vio | 1.25 | 1.25 |
| 34 | A21 | 1p gray grn | 1.25 | 1.25 |
| | | *Nos. 23-34 (12)* | 52.00 | 52.00 |

***Imperf***

| | | | | |
|---|---|---|---|---|
| 23a | A13 | 1c orange | 1.50 | 1.50 |
| 24a | A14 | 2c blue | 1.50 | 1.50 |
| *b.* | | 2c slate | 13.00 | 13.00 |
| 25a | A15 | 3c rose | 1.75 | 1.75 |
| 26a | A15 | 5c olive green | 3.25 | 3.25 |
| 27a | A16 | 10c pale brown | 4.00 | 4.00 |
| 28a | A17 | 15c pink | 1.00 | 1.00 |
| 29a | A18 | 20c blue, *green* | 4.00 | 4.00 |
| 30a | A18 | 20c blue | 4.00 | 4.00 |
| 31a | A19 | 40c blue | 1.40 | 1.40 |
| 32a | A19 | 40c blue, *buff* | 42.50 | 42.50 |
| 33a | A20 | 50c red violet | 1.40 | 1.40 |
| 34a | A21 | 1p gray green | 1.40 | 1.40 |
| | | *Nos. 23a-34a (12)* | 67.70 | 67.70 |

## REGISTRATION STAMPS

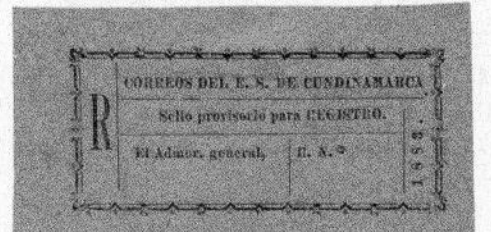
R1

**1883** **Unwmk.** ***Imperf.***

| | | | | |
|---|---|---|---|---|
| F1 | R1 | black, *orange* | 35.00 | 35.00 |

R2

**1904** ***Perf. 12***

| | | | | |
|---|---|---|---|---|
| F2 | R2 | 10c bister | 1.75 | 1.75 |
| *a.* | | Imperf. | 7.50 | 7.50 |

## INSURED LETTER STAMP

IL1

**1883** ***Imperf.***

**Thin Paper with Vertical Mesh**

| | | | | |
|---|---|---|---|---|
| G1 | IL1 | 20c blk, *emerald grn* | 160.00 | 240.00 |

Magdalena

Items inscribed "No hay estampillas" (No stamps available) are considered by specialists to be not postage stamps but receipt labels.

Panama

Issues of Panama as a state and later Department of Colombia are listed with the Republic of Panama issues (Nos. 1-30).

# SANTANDER

sän-ˌtän-ˈdeˌəˌr

Originally a State, now a Department of the Republic of Colombia.
(See Antioquia.)

Coat of Arms
A1 A2

**1884** **Unwmk.** **Litho.** ***Imperf.***

| | | | | |
|---|---|---|---|---|
| 1 | A1 | 1c blue | .60 | .60 |
| *a.* | | 1c gray blue | 1.00 | 1.00 |
| 2 | A2 | 5c red | 1.00 | 1.00 |
| 3 | A2 | 10c bluish purple | 3.75 | 3.75 |
| *a.* | | Tête bêche pair | — | |
| | | *Nos. 1-3 (3)* | 5.35 | 5.35 |

No. 2 exists unofficially perforated 14.

A3

**1886** ***Imperf.***

| | | | | |
|---|---|---|---|---|
| 4 | A3 | 1c blue | 1.75 | 1.75 |
| 5 | A3 | 5c red | .60 | .60 |
| 6 | A3 | 10c red violet | 1.00 | 1.00 |
| *a.* | | 10c deep violet | 1.00 | 1.00 |
| *b.* | | Inscribed "CINCO CENTAVOS" | 52.50 | 52.50 |
| | | *Nos. 4-6 (3)* | 3.35 | 3.35 |

The numerals in the upper corners are omitted on No. 5, while on No. 6 there are no numerals in the side panels. No. 6 exists unofficially perforated 12.

A4

**1887**

| | | | | |
|---|---|---|---|---|
| 7 | A4 | 1c blue | .50 | .50 |
| *a.* | | 1c ultramarine | 3.50 | 3.50 |
| 8 | A4 | 5c red | 3.50 | 3.50 |
| 9 | A4 | 10c violet | 11.00 | 11.00 |
| | | *Nos. 7-9 (3)* | 15.00 | 15.00 |

A5

A6

A7

**1889** ***Perf. 11½ and 13½***

| | | | | |
|---|---|---|---|---|
| 10 | A5 | 1c blue | .70 | .70 |
| 11 | A6 | 5c red | 2.50 | 2.50 |
| 12 | A7 | 10c purple | .90 | .90 |
| *a.* | | Imperf., pair | 40.00 | *40.00* |
| | | *Nos. 10-12 (3)* | 4.10 | 4.10 |

A8

**1892** ***Perf. 13½***

| | | | | |
|---|---|---|---|---|
| 13 | A8 | 5c red, *rose buff* | 2.00 | 2.00 |

A9

**1895-96**

| | | | | |
|---|---|---|---|---|
| 14 | A9 | 5c brown | 1.40 | 1.40 |
| 15 | A9 | 5c yel grn ('96) | 1.40 | 1.40 |

A10

A11

A12

**1899** ***Perf. 10***

| | | | | |
|---|---|---|---|---|
| 16 | A10 | 1c black, *green* | .70 | .70 |
| 17 | A11 | 5c black, *pink* | .75 | .75 |

***Perf. 13½***

| | | | | |
|---|---|---|---|---|
| 18 | A12 | 10c blue | 1.50 | 1.50 |
| *a.* | | Perf. 12 | 2.00 | 2.00 |
| | | *Nos. 16-18 (3)* | 2.95 | 2.95 |

A13

**1903** ***Imperf.***

| | | | | |
|---|---|---|---|---|
| 19 | A13 | 50c red | 1.20 | 1.20 |
| *a.* | | 50c rose | 1.20 | 1.20 |
| *b.* | | "SANTENDER" | 5.00 | 5.00 |
| *c.* | | "Corrcos" | 5.00 | 5.00 |
| *d.* | | "Corceos" | 5.00 | 5.00 |
| *e.* | | Tête bêche pair | 10.00 | 10.00 |
| *f.* | | Pair, one without overprint | 5.50 | 5.50 |

The overprint "Correos de Departmento Bucaramanga" on the 50c red revenue stamp has been proved to be a cancellation.

A14

A15

Arms
A16

Locomotive
A17

A18

A19

A20

**1904** ***Imperf.***

| | | | | |
|---|---|---|---|---|
| 22 | A14 | 5c dark green | .50 | .50 |
| *a.* | | 5c yellow green | .80 | .80 |
| 24 | A15 | 10c rose | .25 | .25 |
| 25 | A16 | 20c brown violet | .50 | .50 |
| 26 | A17 | 50c yellow | .70 | .70 |
| 27 | A18 | 1p black | .50 | .50 |
| 28 | A19 | 5p dark blue | .70 | .70 |
| 29 | A20 | 10p carmine | .80 | .80 |
| | | *Nos. 22-29 (7)* | 3.95 | 3.95 |

**1905**

| | | | | |
|---|---|---|---|---|
| 30 | A14 | 5c pale blue | 1.20 | 1.20 |
| 31 | A15 | 10c red brown | 1.20 | 1.20 |
| 32 | A16 | 20c yellow green | 1.20 | 1.20 |
| 33 | A17 | 50c red violet | 1.20 | 1.20 |
| 34 | A18 | 1p dark blue | 2.25 | 2.25 |
| 35 | A19 | 5p pink | 1.20 | 1.20 |
| 36 | A20 | 10p red | 3.25 | 3.25 |
| | | *Nos. 30-36 (7)* | 11.50 | 11.50 |

A21

**1907** ***Imperf.***

| | | | | |
|---|---|---|---|---|
| 37 | A21 | ½c on 50c rose | 1.60 | *3.25* |

City of Cucuta

Stamps of these and similar designs on white and yellow paper, with and without surcharges of ½c, 1c or 2c, are believed to have been produced without government authorization.

# TOLIMA

tə-lē-mə

Originally a State, now a Department of the Republic of Colombia.
(See Antioquia.)

A1

**1870** **Unwmk.** **Typeset** ***Imperf.***

**White Wove Paper**

| | | | | |
|---|---|---|---|---|
| 1 | A1 | 5c black | 125.00 | 125.00 |
| 2 | A1 | 10c black | 150.00 | 150.00 |
| *a.* | | Vert. se-tenant pair | *1,500.* | *1,500.* |

Printed from two settings. Setting I, ten types of 5c. Setting II, six types of 5c and four types of 10c. No. 2a is contained in a unique strip of 3.

**Blue Laid Batonné Paper**

| | | | | |
|---|---|---|---|---|
| 3 | A1 | 5c black | *950.00* | |

**Buff Laid Batonné Paper**

| | | | | |
|---|---|---|---|---|
| 4 | A1 | 5c black | 300.00 | 200.00 |

**Blue Wove Paper**

| | | | | |
|---|---|---|---|---|
| 5 | A1 | 5c black | 140.00 | 90.00 |

**Blue Vertically Laid Paper**

| | | | | |
|---|---|---|---|---|
| 6 | A1 | 5c black | 225.00 | 140.00 |
| *a.* | | Paper with ruled blue vertical lines | | |

**Blue Horizontally Laid Paper**

| | | | | |
|---|---|---|---|---|
| 7 | A1 | 5c black | 200.00 | 150.00 |

**Blue Quadrille Paper**

| | | | | |
|---|---|---|---|---|
| 8 | A1 | 5c black | 300.00 | 160.00 |

Ten varieties each of Nos. 3-5 and 7; 20 varieties each of Nos. 6 and 8.

*Official imitations were made in 1886 from new settings of the type. There are only 2 varieties of each value. They are printed on blue and white paper, wove, batonné, laid, etc.*

A2

A3

A4

A5

**Yellowish White Wove Paper**

**1871 Litho. *Imperf.***

| No. | Type | Description | Unused | Used |
|---|---|---|---|---|
| 9 | A2 | 5c deep brown | 4.50 | 4.50 |
| *a.* | | 5c red brown | 4.50 | 4.50 |
| *b.* | | Value reads "CINGO" | 80.00 | 80.00 |
| 10 | A3 | 10c blue | 12.50 | 12.50 |
| 11 | A4 | 50c green | 16.00 | 16.00 |
| 12 | A5 | 1p carmine | 26.00 | 26.00 |
| | | *Nos. 9-12 (4)* | 59.00 | 59.00 |

The 5p stamps, type A2, are bogus varieties made from an altered die of the 5c.

*The 10c, 50c and 1 peso stamps have been reprinted on bluish white wove paper. They are from new plates and most copies show traces of fine lines with which the dies had been defaced. Reprints of the 5c have a large cross at the top. The 10c on laid batonné paper is known only as a reprint.*

A6

A7

A8

A9

**1879**

**Grayish or White Wove Paper**

| No. | Type | Description | Unused | Used |
|---|---|---|---|---|
| 14 | A6 | 5c yellow brown | .90 | .90 |
| *a.* | | 5c purple brown | .90 | .90 |
| 15 | A7 | 10c blue | 1.00 | 1.00 |
| 16 | A8 | 50c green, *bluish* | 1.00 | 1.00 |
| *a.* | | White paper | 3.25 | 3.25 |
| 17 | A9 | 1p vermilion | 4.50 | 4.50 |
| *a.* | | 1p carmine rose | 18.00 | 18.00 |
| | | *Nos. 14-17 (4)* | 7.40 | 7.40 |

A10

**1883 *Imperf.***

| No. | Type | Description | Unused | Used |
|---|---|---|---|---|
| 18 | A6 | 5c orange | .90 | .90 |
| 19 | A7 | 10c vermilion | 1.90 | 1.90 |
| 20 | A10 | 20c violet | 3.00 | 3.00 |
| | | *Nos. 18-20 (3)* | 5.80 | 5.80 |

Coat of Arms — A12

**1884 *Imperf.***

| No. | Type | Description | Unused | Used |
|---|---|---|---|---|
| 23 | A12 | 1c gray | .50 | .50 |
| 24 | A12 | 2c rose lilac | .50 | .50 |
| *a.* | | 2c slate | .50 | .50 |
| 25 | A12 | 2½c dull orange | .50 | .50 |
| 26 | A12 | 5c brown | .50 | .50 |
| 27 | A12 | 10c blue | .70 | .70 |
| *a.* | | 10c slate | .50 | .50 |
| 28 | A12 | 20c lemon | .70 | .70 |
| *a.* | | Laid paper | 10.00 | 10.00 |
| 29 | A12 | 25c black | .60 | .60 |
| 30 | A12 | 50c green | .60 | .60 |
| 31 | A12 | 1p vermilion | .80 | .80 |
| 32 | A12 | 2p violet | 1.20 | 1.20 |
| *a.* | | Value omitted | 60.00 | 60.00 |
| 33 | A12 | 5p yellow | .80 | .80 |
| 34 | A12 | 10p lilac rose | 2.25 | 2.25 |
| *a.* | | Laid paper | 60.00 | 60.00 |
| *b.* | | 10p gray | *350.00* | |
| | | *Nos. 23-34 (12)* | 9.65 | 9.65 |

A13

A14

Condor with Long Wings Touching Flagstaffs
A15 A16

**1886 Litho. *Perf. 10½, 11***

**White Paper**

| No. | Type | Description | Unused | Used |
|---|---|---|---|---|
| 36 | A13 | 5c brown | 2.75 | 2.75 |
| *a.* | | 5c yellow brown | 2.75 | 2.75 |
| *b.* | | Imperf., pair | 35.00 | |
| 37 | A14 | 10c blue | 7.50 | 7.50 |
| *a.* | | Imperf., pair | 35.00 | |
| 38 | A15 | 50c green | 6.50 | 6.50 |
| *a.* | | Imperf., pair | 35.00 | |
| 39 | A16 | 1p vermilion | 5.50 | 5.50 |
| *a.* | | Imperf., pair | 52.50 | |
| | | *Nos. 36-39 (4)* | 22.25 | 22.25 |

*No. 38 has been reprinted in pale gray green, perforated 10½, and No. 39 in bright vermilion, perforated 11½. The impressions show many signs of wear.*

**Lilac Tinted Paper**

| No. | Type | Description | Unused | Used |
|---|---|---|---|---|
| *36c* | A13 | 5c orange brown | 25.00 | 25.00 |
| *37b* | A14 | 10c blue | 25.00 | 25.00 |
| *38b* | A15 | 50c green | 19.00 | 19.00 |
| *39b* | A16 | 1p vermilion | 17.00 | 17.00 |
| | | *Nos. 36c-39b (4)* | 86.00 | 86.00 |

Items similar to A15 and A16 but with condor with long wings and upper flag-staffs omitted are forgeries.

A17

A18

Condor with Short Wings
A19 A20

**1886 White Paper *Perf. 12***

| No. | Type | Description | Unused | Used |
|---|---|---|---|---|
| 44 | A19 | 1c gray | 12.50 | 12.50 |
| 45 | A17 | 2c rose lilac | 13.00 | 13.00 |
| 46 | A18 | 2½c dull org | 37.50 | 37.50 |
| 47 | A19 | 5c brown | 17.00 | 16.00 |
| 48 | A20 | 10c blue | 16.00 | 16.00 |
| 49 | A20 | 20c lemon | 13.00 | 13.00 |
| *a.* | | Tête bêche pair | 550.00 | 550.00 |
| 50 | A20 | 25c black | 12.50 | 12.50 |
| 51 | A20 | 50c green | 7.50 | 7.50 |
| 52 | A20 | 1p vermilion | 10.00 | 8.50 |
| 53 | A20 | 2p violet | 14.50 | 14.50 |
| *b.* | | Tête bêche pair | 375.00 | 375.00 |
| 54 | A20 | 5p orange | 26.00 | 26.00 |
| 55 | A20 | 10p lilac rose | 15.00 | 15.00 |
| | | *Nos. 44-55 (12)* | 194.50 | 192.00 |

**Imperf., Pairs**

| No. | Type | Description | Unused | Used |
|---|---|---|---|---|
| *44a* | A19 | 1c | 35.00 | |
| *47a* | A19 | 5c | 57.50 | |
| *48a* | A20 | 10c | 57.50 | |
| *52a* | A20 | 1p | 42.50 | |
| *53a* | A20 | 2p | 52.50 | |
| *54a* | A20 | 5p | 80.00 | |
| *55a* | A20 | 10p | 35.00 | |

A23

**1888 *Perf. 10½***

| No. | Type | Description | Unused | Used |
|---|---|---|---|---|
| 62 | A23 | 5c red | .50 | .50 |
| 63 | A23 | 10c green | .60 | .60 |
| 64 | A23 | 50c blue | 1.50 | 1.50 |
| 65 | A23 | 1p red brown | 4.00 | 4.00 |
| | | *Nos. 62-65 (4)* | 6.60 | 6.60 |

For overprint see Colombia No. L14.

**1895 *Perf. 12, 13½***

| No. | Type | Description | Unused | Used |
|---|---|---|---|---|
| 66 | A23 | 1c blue, *rose* | .50 | .50 |
| 67 | A23 | 2c grn, *lt grn* | .50 | .50 |
| 68 | A23 | 5c red | .50 | .50 |
| *a.* | | Vert. pair, imperf. btwn. | 25.00 | |
| 69 | A23 | 10c green | 1.00 | 1.00 |
| 70 | A23 | 20c blue, *yellow* | .60 | .60 |
| 71 | A23 | 1p brown | 4.50 | 4.50 |
| | | *Nos. 66-71 (6)* | 7.60 | 7.60 |

**Imperf., Pairs**

| No. | Type | Description | Unused | Used |
|---|---|---|---|---|
| *62a* | A23 | 5c | 17.00 | |
| *63a* | A23 | 10c | 24.00 | |
| *64a* | A23 | 50c | 29.00 | 29.00 |
| *65a* | A23 | 1p | 42.50 | |
| *66a* | A23 | 1c | 42.50 | |
| *67a* | A23 | 2c | 42.50 | |
| *70a* | A23 | 20c | 47.50 | |

"No Hay Estampillas"

Items inscribed "No hay estampillas" (No stamps available) are considered by specialists to be not postage stamps but receipt labels.

"Honda Issue"

This item seems to be of private origin.

A24

A25

A26

A27

A28

A29

A30

A31

***Sewing Machine or Regular Perf. 12***

**1903-04 Litho.**

| No. | Type | Description | Unused | Used |
|---|---|---|---|---|
| 79 | A24 | 4c black, *green* | .50 | .50 |
| 80 | A25 | 10c dull blue | .50 | .50 |
| 81 | A26 | 20c orange | 1.00 | 1.00 |
| 82 | A27 | 50c black, *rose* | 1.00 | 1.00 |
| *a.* | | 50c black, *buff* | 1.00 | 1.00 |
| 84 | A28 | 1p brown | 1.00 | 1.00 |
| 85 | A29 | 2p gray | .50 | .50 |
| 86 | A30 | 5p red | .50 | .50 |
| *a.* | | Tête bêche pair | 16.00 | *24.00* |
| 87 | A31 | 10p black, *blue* | .50 | .50 |
| *a.* | | 10p black, *light green* | .50 | .50 |
| *b.* | | 10p black, *grn,* glazed | 7.50 | 7.50 |
| | | *Nos. 79-87 (8)* | 5.50 | 5.50 |

***Imperf***

| No. | Type | Description | Unused | Used |
|---|---|---|---|---|
| *79a* | A24 | 4c black, *green* | .50 | .50 |
| *80a* | A25 | 10c dull blue | .50 | .50 |
| *81a* | A26 | 20c orange | 2.50 | 2.50 |
| *82b* | A27 | 50c black, *rose* | 3.50 | 3.50 |
| *c.* | | 50c black, *buff* | 3.50 | 3.50 |
| *84a* | A28 | 1p brown | .50 | .50 |
| *85a* | A29 | 2p gray | .50 | .50 |
| *86b* | A30 | 5p red | .50 | .50 |
| *c.* | | Tête bêche pair | 24.00 | *32.50* |
| *87c* | A31 | 10p black, *blue* | 5.00 | 5.00 |
| *d.* | | Tête bêche pair | | |
| *e.* | | 10p black, *light green* | 7.50 | 7.50 |
| *f.* | | 10p black, *green,* glazed | 37.50 | 37.50 |
| | | *Nos. 79a-87c (8)* | 13.50 | 13.50 |

## COMORO ISLANDS

'kä-mə-,rō 'ī-ləndz

LOCATION — In Mozambique Channel between Madagascar and Mozambique
GOVT. — Republic
AREA — 838 sq. mi.
POP. — 562,723 (1999 est.)
CAPITAL — Moroni

The Comoro Archipelago consists of the islands of Mayotte, Anjouan, Grand Comoro (Grande Comore) and Moheli, which issued their own stamps as French protectorates or colonies from 1887-1914. The archipelago was attached to Madagascar from 1914 to 1946, when it became a separate French territory. In July 1975, Anjouan, Grand Comoro and Moheli united to declare independence as the State of Comoro. Mayotte remained French.

100 Centimes = 1 Franc

**Catalogue values for all unused stamps in this country are for Never Hinged items.**

Anjouan Bay — A2

Comoro Woman Grinding Grain — A3

Moroni Mosque on Grand Comoro — A4

**1950 Unwmk. Engr. *Perf. 13***

**30** A2 10c blue .30 .50
**31** A2 50c green .30 .50
**32** A2 1fr dk ol brn .40 .50
**33** A3 2fr brt grn .75 .50
**34** A3 5fr purple 1.10 .75
**35** A3 6fr vio brn 1.25 1.10
**36** A4 7fr red 1.10 .75
**37** A4 10fr dk grn 1.25 1.00
**38** A4 11fr dp ultra 1.50 1.25
*Nos. 30-38 (9)* 7.95 6.85

Imperforates

Most Comoro Islands stamps exist imperforate in issued and trial colors, and also in small presentation sheets in issued colors.

Common Design Types pictured following the introduction.

**Military Medal Issue**
Common Design Type

**1952 Engraved and Typographed**

**39** CD101 15fr multi 45.00 37.50

Mosque of Ouani, Anjouan A5

Coelacanth A6

**1952-54 Engr.**

**40** A5 15fr dark brown 1.75 1.50
**41** A5 20fr red brown 3.75 3.25
**42** A6 40fr aqua & indigo ('54) 23.50 17.00
*Nos. 40-42 (3)* 29.00 21.75

**FIDES Issue**
Common Design Type

Design: 9fr, Women at water pump.

**1956 Unwmk. *Perf. 13x12½***

**43** CD103 9fr dp vio 2.25 1.60

**Human Rights Issue**
Common Design Type

**1958 Engr. *Perf. 13***

**44** CD105 20fr ol grn & dk bl 9.00 9.00

**Flower Issue**
Common Design Type

**1959 Photo. *Perf. 12½x12***

**45** CD104 10fr Colvillea 5.25 4.25

View of Dzaoudzi and Radio Symbol — A8

Comoro radio station: 25fr, Radio tower and radio waves over Islands.

**1960, Dec. 23 Engr. *Perf. 13***

**46** A8 20fr maroon, vio bl & grn 1.50 1.10
**47** A8 25fr ultra, brn & grn 1.75 .90

Harpa Conoidalis — A9

Sea Shells: 50c, Cypraecassis rufa. 2fr, Murex ramosus. 5fr, Turbo marmoratus. 20fr, Pterocera scorpio. 25fr, Charonia tritonis.

**1962, Jan. 13 Photo.**
**Shells in Natural Colors**

**48** A9 50c lilac & brn 1.00 1.00
**49** A9 1fr yel & red 1.00 1.00
**50** A9 2fr pale grn & pink 2.40 2.40
**51** A9 5fr yel & grn 2.75 2.75
**52** A9 20fr salmon & brn 10.00 10.00
**53** A9 25fr bister & pink 14.00 14.00
*Nos. 48-53,C5-C6 (8)* 69.65 62.65

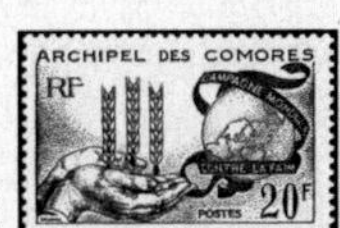


Wheat Emblem and Globe — A10

**1963, Mar. 21 Engr. *Perf. 13***

**54** A10 20fr choc & dk grn 4.75 4.00

FAO "Freedom from Hunger" campaign.

**Red Cross Centenary Issue**
Common Design Type

**1963, Sept. 2 Unwmk. *Perf. 13***

**55** CD113 50fr emer, gray & car 7.50 6.00

**Human Rights Issue**
Common Design Type

**1963, Dec. 10 Engr.**

**56** CD117 15fr dk red & yel grn 7.50 6.00

Tobacco Pouch — A13

Designs: 4fr, Censer. 10fr, Carved lamp.

**1963, Dec. 27 *Perf. 13***
**Size: 22x36mm**

**57** A13 3fr multi .75 .75
**58** A13 4fr org, dp cl & sl grn 1.00 1.00
**59** A13 10fr org brn, dk red brn & grn 2.00 2.00
*Nos. 57-59,C8-C9 (5)* 16.25 11.25

**Philatec Issue**
Common Design Type

**1964, Mar. 31**

**60** CD118 50fr dk bl, red & grn 4.00 3.50

Grand Comoro Canoe — A14

Design: 30fr, Boutre felucca.

**Size: 22x37mm**

**1964, Aug. 7 Photo. *Perf. 13x12½***

**61** A14 15fr multi 2.75 2.25
**62** A14 30fr lt grn & multi 5.00 4.00
*Nos. 61-62,C10-C11 (4)* 18.00 10.10

Spiny Lobster — A15

Designs: 12fr, Hammerhead shark, horiz. 20fr, Turtle, horiz. 25fr, Merou fish.

**1965, Dec. 20 Engr. *Perf. 13***

**63** A15 1fr grn, lil & ocher 1.25 .75
**64** A15 12fr org red, slate & gray 2.75 1.60
**65** A15 20fr org, red & bl grn 4.00 1.75
**66** A15 25fr bl grn, dk brn & red 7.00 3.25
*Nos. 63-66 (4)* 15.00 7.35

Hotel Itsandra, Moroni — A16

Design: 15fr, Lake Salé, Grand Comoro.

**1966, Dec. 19 Photo. *Perf. 12½x13***

**67** A16 15fr multi 1.10 .70
**68** A16 25fr multi 1.25 .70
*Nos. 67-68,C18-C19 (4)* 14.35 8.50

Comoro Sunbird — A17

Birds: 10fr, Malachite kingfisher. 15fr, Rothschild's fody. 30fr, Cuckoo-roller.

**1967, June 20 Photo. *Perf. 12½x13***
**Size: 36x23mm**

**69** A17 2fr ocher & multi 2.50 1.50
**70** A17 10fr lil & multi 4.25 2.00
**71** A17 15fr yel grn & multi 6.25 3.00
**72** A17 30fr pink & multi 13.00 6.50
*Nos. 69-72,C20-C21 (6)* 48.50 27.50

For surcharge see No. 133.

**WHO Anniversary Issue**
Common Design Type

**1968, May 4 Engr. *Perf. 13***

**73** CD126 40fr grn, vio & dp car 2.40 1.75

Surgeonfish A19

Design: 25fr, Imperial angelfish.

**1968, Aug. 1 Engr. *Perf. 13***
**Size: 36x22mm**

**74** A19 20fr vio bl, yel & red brn 3.25 3.25
**75** A19 25fr Prus bl, dk bl & org 4.00 4.00
*Nos. 74-75,C23-C24 (4)* 24.00 15.75

For surcharge & overprint see Nos. C52, C74.

**Human Rights Year Issue**
Common Design Type

**1968, Aug. 10 Engr. *Perf. 13***

**76** CD127 60fr brn, grn & org 3.25 3.25

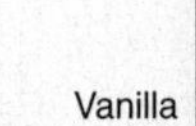

Msoila Prayer Rug and Praying Man — A20

Each stamp shows a different prayer position.

**1969, Feb. 27 Engr. *Perf. 13***

**77** A20 20fr bl grn, rose red & pur 1.10 .75
**78** A20 30fr pur, rose red & bl grn 1.25 1.10
**79** A20 45fr rose red, pur & bl grn 2.25 1.40
*Nos. 77-79 (3)* 4.60 3.25

Vanilla Flower — A21

Design: 15fr, Flower of ylang-ylang tree. 25fr, Poinsettia (country name at upper left).

**1969-70 Photo. *Perf. 12½x13***
**Size: 36x23mm**

**80** A21 10fr multi 1.00 .50
**81** A21 15fr multi 1.40 .70
**82** A21 25fr multi ('70) 3.25 1.50
*Nos. 80-82,C26-C28 (6)* 21.65 13.45

Issued: Nos. 80-81, 3/20. No. 82, 3/5.

**ILO Issue**
Common Design Type

**1969, Nov. 24 Engr. *Perf. 13***

**83** CD131 5fr org, emerald & gray 1.25 .75

**UPU Headquarters Issue**
Common Design Type

**1970, May 20 Engr. *Perf. 13***

**84** CD133 65fr pur, bl grn & red brn 5.50 2.00

Chiromani Costume, Anjouan — A22

25fr, Bouiboui costume, Grand Comoro.

**1970, Oct. 30 Photo. *Perf. 12½x13***

**85** A22 20fr grn, yel & red 1.60 .80
**86** A22 25fr brn, yel & dk bl 1.90 1.10

Friday Mosque — A23

**1970, Dec. 18 Engr. *Perf. 13***

**87** A23 5fr rose car, grn & grnsh bl .75 .75
**88** A23 10fr dp lil, grn & vio 1.00 .75
**89** A23 40fr cop red, grn & dp brn 1.75 1.40
*Nos. 87-89 (3)* 3.50 2.90

Great White Egret — A24

Birds: 10fr, Comoro pigeon. 15fr, Green-backed heron. 25fr, Comoro blue pigeon. 35fr, Humbolt's flycatcher. 40fr, Allen's gallinule.

**1971, Mar. 12 Photo. *Perf. 12½x13***

**90** A24 5fr multi 1.50 .80
**91** A24 10fr yel & multi 2.00 .80
**92** A24 15fr bl & multi 3.25 1.75
**93** A24 25fr org & multi 4.75 2.00
**94** A24 35fr yel grn & multi 6.50 2.50
**95** A24 40fr gray & multi 8.00 3.25
*Nos. 90-95 (6)* 26.00 11.10

For overprint see No. 145.

Pyrostegia Venusta — A25

Flowers: 3fr, Dogbane, horiz. 20fr, Frangipani.

**Size: 22x36mm, 36x22mm**

**1971, July 19 Photo. *Perf. 13***

**96** A25 1fr ver & grn .95 .85
**97** A25 3fr yel, grn & red 1.40 1.00
**98** A25 20fr ver & grn 3.50 2.50
*Nos. 96-98,C37-C38 (5)* 17.35 11.50

For surcharges see Nos. 131-132, C75, C83.

Lithograph Cone — A26

Sea Shells: 10fr, Pacific lettered cone. 20fr, Aulicus cone. 35fr, Polita nerita. 60fr, Snake-head cowrie.

**1971, Oct. 4**

**99** A26 5fr lt ultra & multi 1.25 1.00
**100** A26 10fr multi 1.75 1.40
**101** A26 20fr vio & multi 3.75 2.25
**102** A26 35fr lt bl & multi 7.25 2.75
**103** A26 60fr lt vio & multi 9.50 3.50
*Nos. 99-103 (5)* 23.50 10.90

For surcharge see No. 150.

**De Gaulle Issue**

Common Design Type

Designs: 20fr, Gen. de Gaulle, 1940. 35fr, Pres. de Gaulle, 1970.

**1971, Nov. 9 Engr. *Perf. 13***

**104** CD134 20fr dk car & blk 4.00 2.50
**105** CD134 35fr dk car & blk 5.00 3.25

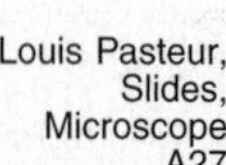

Louis Pasteur, Slides, Microscope A27

**1972, Aug. 2**

**106** A27 65fr indigo, org, & ol brn 5.50 4.75

Sesquicentennial of the birth of Louis Pasteur (1822-1895), chemist.

**Type of Air Post Issue 1971**

Designs: 10fr, View of Goulaivoini. 20fr, Bay, Mitsamiouli. 35fr, Gate and fountain, Foumbouni. 50fr, View of Moroni.

**1973, June 28 Photo. *Perf. 13***

**107** AP10 10fr bl & multi 1.00 .30
**108** AP10 20fr grn & multi 1.50 .75
**109** AP10 35fr bl & multi 2.50 1.25
**110** AP10 50fr bl & multi 2.75 1.75
*Nos. 107-110,C53 (5)* 17.25 10.55

For overprint see No. 143.

Bank of Madagascar and Comoros — A28

Buildings in Moroni: 15fr, Post and Telecommunications Administration. 20fr, Prefecture.

**1973, July 10 Photo. *Perf. 13x12½***

**111** A28 5fr multi .65 .55
**112** A28 15fr multi .90 .80
**113** A28 20fr multi 1.25 1.00
*Nos. 111-113 (3)* 2.80 2.35

For surcharge see No. 134.

Salimata Hamissi Mosque — A29

20fr, Zaouiyat Chaduli Mosque, vert.

***Perf. 12½x13, 13x12½***

**1973, Oct. 20 Photo.**

**114** A29 20fr multi 1.25 .95
**115** A29 35fr multi 2.10 1.25

For surcharges see Nos. 135, 138.

Cheikh Mausoleum A30

Design: 50fr, Mausoleum of President Said Mohamed Cheikh (different view).

**1974, Mar. 16 Engr. *Perf. 13***

**116** A30 35fr grn, ol brn & blk 1.60 1.10
**117** A30 50fr grn, ol brn & blk 2.50 1.25

For surcharge see No. 140.

Koran Stand, Anjouan — A31

Designs: 15fr, Carved combs, vert. 20fr, 3-legged table, vert. 75fr, Sugar press.

**1974, May 10 Photo. *Perf. 12½x13***

**118** A31 15fr emer & multi 1.25 .60
**119** A31 20fr grn & multi 1.40 .65
**120** A31 35fr multi 2.25 1.10
**121** A31 75fr multi 4.50 2.00
*Nos. 118-121 (4)* 9.40 4.35

For overprints and surcharge see Nos. 137, 141, 149.

UPU Emblem, Symbolic Postmark — A32

**1974, Oct. 9 Engr. *Perf. 13x12½***

**122** A32 30fr multi 2.00 1.75

Centenary of Universal Postal Union.
For surcharge see No. 155.

Bracelet — A33

**1975, Feb. 28 Engr. *Perf. 13***

**123** A33 20fr shown 1.10 .95
**124** A33 35fr Diadem 1.90 1.25
**125** A33 120fr Saber 5.00 3.25
**126** A33 135fr Dagger 7.00 4.00
*Nos. 123-126 (4)* 15.00 9.45

For surcharges see Nos. 136, 142, 151, 154.

Mohani Village, Moheli A34

50fr, Djoezi Village, Moheli. 55fr, Chirazi tombs.

**1975, May 26 Photo. *Perf. 13***

**127** A34 30fr vio bl & multi 2.00 1.00
**128** A34 50fr Prus bl & multi 3.25 1.50
**129** A34 55fr grn & multi 3.50 2.50
*Nos. 127-129 (3)* 8.75 5.00

For overprints and surcharge see Nos. 139, 146, 148.

Scuba Diver Photographing Coelacanth — A35

**1975, June 27 Engr. *Perf. 13***

**130** A35 50fr multi 8.25 5.75

1975 coelacanth expedition.
For overprint see No. 147.

**STATE OF COMORO**

In 1978 the islands' name became the Federal and Islamic Republic of the Comoros.

Issues of 1971-75 Srchd. and Ovptd. with Bars and: "ETAT COMORIEN" in Black, Silver or Red

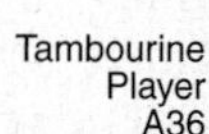

Tambourine Player A36

No. 153, Women dancers & tambourine players.

**Printing & Perforations as Before, Photogravure (A36)**

**1975 *Perf. 13 (A36)***

**131** A25 5fr on 1fr *.40 .25*
**132** A25 5fr on 3fr *.40 .25*
**133** A17 10fr on 2fr *1.25 .50*
**134** A28 15fr on 20fr (R) *.80 .25*
**135** A29 15fr on 20fr (S) *.80 .25*
**136** A33 15fr on 20fr *.80 .25*
**137** A31 20fr *1.00 .25*
**138** A29 25fr on 35fr *1.00 .25*
**139** A34 30fr *1.00 .60*
**140** A30 30fr on 35fr *1.00 .30*
**141** A31 30fr on 35fr *1.00 .30*
**142** A33 30fr on 35fr *1.00 .60*
**143** AP10 35fr *1.25 .75*
**144** SP2 35fr on 35fr + 10fr *1.25 .75*
**145** A24 40fr *2.75 1.50*
**146** A34 50fr *1.90 1.90*
**147** A35 50fr *2.50 1.25*
**148** A34 50fr on 55fr (S) *1.90 .95*
**149** A31 75fr *2.00 .55*
**150** A26 75fr on 60fr (S) *4.00 2.00*
**151** A33 100fr on 120fr *2.50 .90*
**152** A36 100fr bl & multi *3.25 1.75*
**153** A36 100fr on 150fr (S) *2.50 .90*
**154** A33 200fr on 135fr *6.00 2.40*
**155** A32 500fr on 30fr *12.00 6.75*
*Nos. 131-155 (25) 54.25 26.40*

Nos. 152-153 exist without overprint or surcharge. Value, each $90.

No. 155 exists with red surcharge. Value $12.

Litho. & Embossed "Gold Foil" Stamps

These stamps generally are of a different design format than the rest of the issue. Since there is a commemorative inscription tieing them to the issue a separate illustration is not being shown.

Apollo-Soyuz — A37

Spacecraft and astronauts: 10fr, Soyuz lift-off, Alexei A. Leonov and Valeri N. Kubasov, vert. 30fr, Apollo lift-off, Thomas P. Stafford, Vance D. Brand, Donald K. Slayton, vert. 50fr, Meeting in space. 100fr, Chairman Brezhnev, President Ford talking with astronauts and cosmonauts. 200fr, Spacecraft preparing to dock. 400f, Return to Earth. 500fr, Spacecraft, mission emblems. 1500fr, Apollo-Soyuz crew. No. 164, Preparing to dock, diff.

**1975, Dec. 15 Litho. *Perf. 13½***

**156** A37 10fr multicolored .40 .25
**157** A37 30fr multicolored .50 .25
**158** A37 50fr multicolored .70 .55
**159** A37 100fr multicolored 1.00 .60
**160** A37 200fr multicolored 2.00 1.25
**161** A37 400fr multicolored 4.00 2.50
*Nos. 156-161 (6)* 8.60 5.40

**Litho. & Embossed**

**Size: 45x45mm**

**162** A37 1500fr gold & multi 17.50 —

**Souvenir Sheets**

**Litho.**

**163** A37 500fr multicolored 4.50 1.75

**Litho. & Embossed**

**164** A37 1500fr gold & multi 17.50 —

Nos. 159-164 are airmail. No. 163 contains one 64x44mm stamp. No. 164 contains one 45x45mm stamp.

No. 162 exists in a souvenir sheet of 1. Value $50.

For overprints see Nos. 477-478.

A38

American Revolution, Bicent. — A39

Designs: 15fr, Lewis and Clark, Blackfoot Indian. 25fr, John C. Fremont, Kit Carson, Indian dancer. 35fr, Daniel Boone, Buffalo Bill Cody, wagon train. 40fr, Richard E. Egan, Johnny Frey, Pony Express. 75fr, Henry Wells, William G. Fargo, stagecoach. 400fr, Frontiersman, Indian. 500fr, Leland Stanford, Thomas C. Dunant, transcontinental railroad. 1000fr, George Washington, winter at Valley Forge. 1500fr, John Paul Jones, ship.

**1976, Jan. 15 Litho.**

**165** A38 15fr multicolored .25 .25
**166** A38 25fr multicolored .45 .25
**167** A38 35fr multicolored .75 .35
**168** A38 40fr multicolored .85 .45
**169** A38 75fr multicolored 1.50 .60
**170** A38 500fr multicolored 6.25 2.50
*Nos. 165-170 (6)* 10.05 4.40

**Litho. & Embossed**

**171** A39 1000fr gold & multi 13.50 —

**Souvenir Sheets**

**Litho.**

**172** A38 400fr multicolored 5.50 1.75

**Litho. & Embossed**

**173** A39 1500fr gold & multi 16.50 —

Nos. 170-173 are airmail. See Nos. 230, 232 and note after No. 479.

No. 171 exists in a souvenir sheet of 1. Value $55.

1976 Winter Olympics, Innsbruck — A40

5fr, Women's figure skating. 30fr, Slalom skiing. 35fr, Speed skating. 50fr, Downhill skiing. 200fr, Ski jumping. 400fr, Cross country skiing. No. 180, 1000fr, Downhill skier, hockey. 500fr, Hockey. No. 182, 1000fr, Olympic Rings.

**1976, Mar. 30 Litho.**

**174** A40 5fr multicolored .25 .25
**175** A40 30fr multicolored .25 .25
**176** A40 35fr multicolored .50 .25

**177** A40 50fr multicolored .65 .50
**178** A40 200fr multicolored 2.10 1.00
**179** A40 400fr multicolored 4.50 1.25
*Nos. 174-179 (6)* 8.25 3.50

**Litho. & Embossed**

**Size: 56x35mm**

**180** A40 1000fr multicolored *13.00* —

**Souvenir Sheets**

**Litho.**

**181** A40 500fr multicolored 7.00 1.75

**Litho. & Embossed**

**182** A40 1000fr multicolored *11.00* —

Nos. 178-182 are airmail. Nos. 181-182 contain one 58x35mm stamp. For overprint see No. 471.

No. 162 exists in a souvenir sheet of 1. Value $45.

1976 Summer Olympics, Montreal — A41

20fr, Runner, Athens, 1896. 25fr, Sprints. 40fr, High jump, Paris, 1900. 75fr, High jump. 100fr, Women stretching, St. Louis, 1904. 500fr, Uneven parallel bars.

400fr, Olympic Stadium, Montreal.

**1976, Mar. 30** **Litho.**

**183** A41 20fr multicolored .25 .25
**184** A41 25fr multicolored .35 .25
**185** A41 40fr multicolored .50 .25
**186** A41 75fr multicolored 1.00 .45
**187** A41 100fr multicolored 1.10 .50
**188** A41 500fr multicolored 6.00 1.75
*Nos. 183-188 (6)* 9.20 3.45

**Souvenir Sheet**

**189** A41 400fr multicolored 5.00 1.25

Nos. 187-189 are airmail.

For overprint see No. 476.

Fairy Tales A42

15fr, Hansel & Gretel. 30fr, Alice in Wonderland. 35fr, Pinocchio. 40fr, Good Little Henry. 50fr, Peter and the Wolf. 400fr, Thousand and One Nights.

**1976, June 28**

**190** A42 15fr multicolored .25 .25
**191** A42 30fr multicolored .50 .25
**192** A42 35fr multicolored .65 .25
**193** A42 40fr multicolored .65 .25
**194** A42 50fr multicolored 1.00 .25
**195** A42 400fr multicolored 6.50 2.00
*Nos. 190-195 (6)* 9.55 3.25

No. 195 is airmail. Nos. 190-191, 193, 195 are vert.

Invention of Telephone, Cent. — A43

Designs: 10fr, A. G. Bell, 1st telephone. 25fr, Charles Bourseul, Paris-London phone service, 1891. 75fr, Philipp Reis, telephone operators. 100fr, Earth to Moon to Earth communications. 200fr, Satellite. 400fr, Ship-to-Satellite communications. No. 201, Satellite in orbit, antenna. No. 203, Global communications.

**1976, July 1**

**196** A43 10fr multicolored .25 .25
**197** A43 25fr multicolored .35 .25
**198** A43 75fr multicolored 1.00 .30
**199** A43 100fr multicolored 1.40 .50
**200** A43 200fr multicolored 2.25 .90
**201** A43 500fr multicolored 5.50 1.75
*Nos. 196-201 (6)* 10.75 3.95

**Souvenir Sheets**

**202** A43 400fr multicolored 7.00 1.75
**203** A43 500fr multicolored 7.00 1.75

Nos. 199-203 are airmail. Nos. 202-203 contain a 73x44mm stamp. For overprint see No. 472.

Comoro Flag, Map and Government Buildings — A44

**1976, Nov. 18** **Litho.** ***Perf. 13½***

**204** A44 30fr multi .75 .30
**205** A44 50fr multi 1.50 .30

1st anniversary of independence.

For overprints and surcharges see Nos. 353-372.

Viking Probe to Mars — A45

Designs: 5fr, Nicolaus Copernicus, rocket launch. 10fr, Albert Einstein, Carl Sagan, Thomas Young, horiz. 25fr, Viking probe orbiting Mars. 35fr, Discovery of America by Vikings, horiz. 100fr, Flag, Viking landing on Mars. 500fr, Viking emblem, surface of Mars, horiz. 400fr, Viking probe. No. 212, Wagon train, frontiersman, rocket launch. No. 214, Viking on Martian surface, robotic shovel.

**1976, Nov. 23**

**206** A45 5fr multicolored .30 .25
**207** A45 10fr multicolored .30 .25
**208** A45 25fr multicolored .40 .25
**209** A45 35fr multicolored .40 .25
**210** A45 100fr multicolored 1.40 .40
**211** A45 500fr multicolored 8.00 1.50
*Nos. 206-211 (6)* 10.80 2.90

**Litho. & Embossed**

**Size: 57x39mm**

**212** A45 1500fr gold & multi *14.00* —

**Souvenir Sheets**

**Litho.**

**213** A45 400fr multicolored *5.00* 1.50

**Litho. & Embossed**

**214** A45 1500fr gold & multi *15.00* —

American Revolution, bicentennial. Nos. 211-214 are airmail. No. 213 contains one 60x42mm stamp.

No. 212 exists in a souvenir sheet of 1. Value $50.

UN Postal Administration, 25th Anniv. — A46

Designs: 15fr, UN #24, irrigating field. 30fr, UN #43, doctor, nurse. 50fr, UN #162, mother holding child. 75fr, UN #42, communications satellite in orbit. 200fr, UN #32, Concorde, Zeppelin. 400fr, UN #18, cargo plane. 500fr, People passing letters around globe.

**1976, Nov. 25** **Litho.**

**215** A46 15fr multicolored .25 .25
**216** A46 30fr multicolored .30 .25
**217** A46 50fr multicolored .60 .30
**218** A46 75fr multicolored .80 .30
**219** A46 200fr multicolored 2.50 1.00
**220** A46 400fr multicolored 5.00 2.00
*Nos. 215-220 (6)* 9.45 4.10

**Souvenir Sheet**

**221** A46 500fr multicolored *5.00* 2.00

Nos. 219-221 are airmail. No. 221 contains one 57x40mm stamp. For overprints see Nos. 282-284, 473.

Nos. 215-220 exist as souvenir sheets of one. Value, set, $45.

Comoro Flag, UN Headquarters and Emblem — A47

**1976, Nov. 25**

**222** A47 40fr multicolored 1.40 .30
**223** A47 50fr multicolored 1.90 .40

1st anniv. of UN membership.

**Type of 1976 and**

US Bicentennial — A48

Civil War Battles: 10fr, Fort Sumter, Lincoln. 30fr, Bull Run, Gen. P.G.T. Beauregard, vert. 50fr, Antietam, Gen. Joseph E. Johnston. 100fr, Gettysburg, Gen. Meade. 200fr, Chattanooga, Gen. Sherman, vert. 400fr, Appomattox, Gen. Pickett. 500fr, Surrender at Appomattox, Generals Lee and Grant. 1000fr, Lincoln, battlefield. No. 230, Pres. Kennedy, lunar lander.

**1976, Dec. 30** **Litho.**

**224** A48 10fr multicolored .25 .25
**225** A48 30fr multicolored .30 .25
**226** A48 50fr multicolored .65 .25
**227** A48 100fr multicolored 1.10 .45
**228** A48 200fr multicolored 2.50 .80
**229** A48 400fr multicolored 5.00 1.50
*Nos. 224-229 (6)* 9.80 3.50

**Litho. & Embossed**

**Size: 61x51mm**

**230** A39 1500fr gold & multi *17.00* —

**Souvenir Sheets**

**Litho.**

**231** A48 500fr multicolored *6.50* 1.75

**Litho. & Embossed**

**232** A39 1000fr gold & multi *9.50* —

American Revolution bicentennial. Nos. 227-232 are airmail. No. 231 contains one 60x42mm stamp.

No. 224-229 exist as souvenir sheets of one. Value, set, $32.50.

No. 230 exists in a souvenir sheet of one. Value $50.

Endangered Species — A49

15fr, Andean condor, vert. 20fr, Australian tiger cat. 35fr, Leopard, vert. 40fr, White rhinoceros. 75fr, Nyala, vert. 400fr, Orangutan.

500fr, Lemur, vert.

**1976, Dec. 30** **Litho.**

**233** A49 15fr multicolored .30 .25
**234** A49 20fr multicolored .65 .25
**235** A49 35fr multicolored 1.00 .25
**236** A49 40fr multicolored 1.25 .45
**237** A49 75fr multicolored 3.00 .55
**238** A49 400fr multicolored 8.00 1.50
*Nos. 233-238 (6)* 14.20 3.25

**Souvenir Sheet**

**239** A49 500fr multicolored 7.00 1.75

Nos. 238-239 airmail. No. 239 contains one 40x58mm stamp.

See note after No. 479.

Endangered Species — A50

10fr, Wolf. 30fr, Aye-aye. 40fr, Cephalopus zebra. 50fr, Giant tortoise. 200fr, Ocelot. 400fr, Penguin.

500fr, Sumatran tiger.

**1977, Apr. 14**

**240** A50 10fr multicolored .25 .25
**241** A50 30fr multicolored .45 .25
**242** A50 40fr multicolored .90 .30
**243** A50 50fr multicolored 1.00 .30
**244** A50 200fr multicolored 3.00 .75
**245** A50 400fr multicolored 6.50 1.50
*Nos. 240-245 (6)* 12.10 3.35

**Souvenir Sheet**

**246** A50 500fr multicolored 8.00 1.50

Nos. 244-246 airmail. No. 246 contains one 58x40mm stamp.

Giffard Airship, 1851 and Paris-St. Germain Train, 1837, France — A51

Airships & Locomotives: 25fr, Santos-Dumont's airship, 1906, Brazilian Tander 120FIN, Brazil. 50fr, Astra, 1914, Trans-Siberian Express, 1905, Russia. 75fr, R.34, 1919, Southern Belle, 1910, Great Britain. 200fr, Navy airship, Pacific Class locomotive, 1930, US. No. 252, Hindenburg, Rheingold Express, 1933, Germany. No. 253, Graf-Zeppelin, 1928, Nord-Express Type 231, 1925, Germany.

**1977, Apr. 14**

**247** A51 20fr multicolored .30 .25
**248** A51 25fr multicolored .30 .25
**249** A51 50fr multicolored .75 .25
**250** A51 75fr multicolored 1.10 .25
**251** A51 200fr multicolored 2.75 .60
**252** A51 500fr multicolored 6.25 1.60
*Nos. 247-252 (6)* 11.45 3.20

**Souvenir Sheet**

**253** A51 500fr multi, horiz. 6.00 2.00

Nos. 251-253 are airmail. No. 253 contains one 58x39mm stamp.

Nobel Prize, 75th Anniv. A52

Nobel Prize winners: 30fr, Medicine. 40fr, Physics. 50fr, Literature. 100fr, Physics. 200fr, Chemistry. 400fr, Peace.

500fr, Nobel medal.

**1977, July 7**

**254** A52 30fr multicolored .75 .25
**255** A52 40fr multicolored .75 .25
**256** A52 50fr multicolored 1.25 .25
**257** A52 100fr multicolored 3.25 .25
**258** A52 200fr multicolored 5.50 .75
**259** A52 400fr multicolored 12.50 1.25
*Nos. 254-259 (6)* 24.00 3.00

**Souvenir Sheet**

**260** A52 500fr multicolored 5.50 1.75

Nos. 258-260 are airmail.

See note after No. 479.

Peter Paul Rubens, 400th Birth Anniv. — A53

Portraits: 20fr, Portrait of the Artist's Daughter, Clara. 25fr, Suzanne Fourment. 50fr, Toilet of Venus, (detail). 75fr, Ceres (detail). 200fr, Young Woman with Blonde Braided Hair. No. 266, Helene Fourment in her Wedding Dress. No. 267, Self-portrait.

**1977, July 7**

**261** A53 20fr multicolored .25 .25
**262** A53 25fr multicolored .30 .25
**263** A53 50fr multicolored .65 .25
**264** A53 75fr multicolored 1.10 .30

| | | | | |
|---|---|---|---|---|
| **265** | A53 | 200fr multicolored | 2.50 | .60 |
| **266** | A53 | 500fr multicolored | 6.25 | 1.50 |
| | | *Nos. 261-266 (6)* | 11.05 | 3.15 |

**Souvenir Sheet**

**267** A53 500fr multicolored 5.50 1.75

Nos. 265-267 are airmail.
See note after No. 479.

Fish — A54

30fr, Swordfish. 40fr, Gaterin. 50fr, Sea scorpion. 100fr, Chaetodon lunula. 200fr, Amphiprion. 400fr, Tetrodon.
500fr, Coelacanth.

**1977, Nov. 21**

| | | | | |
|---|---|---|---|---|
| **268** | A54 | 30fr multicolored | .50 | .25 |
| **269** | A54 | 40fr multicolored | 1.00 | .25 |
| **270** | A54 | 50fr multicolored | 1.75 | .25 |
| **271** | A54 | 100fr multicolored | 3.25 | .45 |
| **272** | A54 | 200fr multicolored | 4.00 | .75 |
| **273** | A54 | 400fr multicolored | 7.50 | 1.50 |
| | | *Nos. 268-273 (6)* | 18.00 | 3.45 |

**Souvenir Sheet**

**274** A54 500fr multicolored 8.00 2.00

Nos. 272-274 airmail. No. 274 contains one 52x47mm stamp.

Space Exploration A55

30fr, Jupiter lander. 50fr, Voyager probe, Uranus, vert. 75fr, Pioneer probe, Venus. 100fr, Space shuttle, vert. 200fr, Viking III, Mars. 400fr, Apollo-Soyuz, vert.
500fr, Allegory of the Sun.

**1977, Nov. 21**

| | | | | |
|---|---|---|---|---|
| **275** | A55 | 30fr multicolored | .30 | .25 |
| **276** | A55 | 50fr multicolored | .60 | .25 |
| **277** | A55 | 75fr multicolored | 1.00 | .25 |
| **278** | A55 | 100fr multicolored | 1.10 | .40 |
| **279** | A55 | 200fr multicolored | 2.50 | .60 |
| **280** | A55 | 400fr multicolored | 5.00 | 1.25 |
| | | *Nos. 275-280 (6)* | 10.50 | 3.00 |

**Souvenir Sheet**

**281** A55 500fr multicolored 5.00 1.75

Nos. 279-281 airmail. No. 281 contains one 52x42mm stamp.

**No. 219 Overprinted in One Line in Gold, Silver or Red "Paris-New-York - 22 Nov. 1977"**

**1977, Nov. 22**

| | | | | |
|---|---|---|---|---|
| **282** | A46 | 200fr multicolored | 6.00 | 2.75 |
| **283** | A46 | 200fr multicolored (S) | 30.00 | — |
| **284** | A46 | 200fr multicolored (R) | 10.00 | — |
| | | *Nos. 282-284 (3)* | 46.00 | 2.75 |

Birds — A56

15fr, Porphyrula alleni. 20fr, M. superciliosus. 35fr, Alcedo vintsioides johannae. 40fr, Terpsiphone. 75fr, Nectarinia comorensis. 400fr, Egretta alba.
500fr, Foudia eminentissima, horiz.

**1978, Feb. 6**

| | | | | |
|---|---|---|---|---|
| **285** | A56 | 15fr multicolored | .35 | .25 |
| **286** | A56 | 20fr multicolored | .50 | .25 |
| **287** | A56 | 35fr multicolored | .70 | .30 |
| **288** | A56 | 40fr multicolored | 1.00 | .40 |
| **289** | A56 | 75fr multicolored | 2.00 | .50 |
| **290** | A56 | 400fr multicolored | 8.00 | 2.25 |
| | | *Nos. 285-290 (6)* | 12.55 | 3.95 |

**Souvenir Sheet**

**291** A56 500fr multicolored 6.00 1.75

Nos. 290-291 are airmail. For overprint and surcharges see Nos. 444-448.

World Cup Soccer Championships, Argentina — A57

Designs: 30fr, Greece, 5th. cent. B.C. 50fr, Brittany, 19th cent. 75fr, London, 14th cent. 100fr, Italy, 18th cent. 200fr, England, 19th cent. 400fr, English Cup match, 1891. 500fr, English Cup final, 1962. No. 298, Player, satellite. No. 300, Players.

**1978, Feb. 6**

| | | | | |
|---|---|---|---|---|
| **292** | A57 | 30fr multicolored | .30 | .25 |
| **293** | A57 | 50fr multicolored | .60 | .25 |
| **294** | A57 | 75fr multicolored | .75 | .30 |
| **295** | A57 | 100fr multicolored | 1.10 | .40 |
| **296** | A57 | 200fr multicolored | 2.50 | .60 |
| **297** | A57 | 400fr multicolored | 5.00 | 1.25 |
| | | *Nos. 292-297 (6)* | 10.25 | 3.05 |

**Litho. & Embossed**

**Size: 60x42mm**

**298** A57 1000fr gold & multi 11.00 —

**Souvenir Sheets**

**Litho.**

**299** A57 500fr multicolored 6.00 1.75

**Litho. & Embossed**

**300** A57 1000fr gold & multi 9.00 4.00

Nos. 296-300 are airmail. No. 300 contains one 60x42mm stamp.

No. 298 exists in a souvenir sheet of 1. Value $50.

For overprints and surcharges see Nos. 402-408, 449-453.

Composers A58

30fr, J.S. Bach. 40fr, W.A. Mozart. 50fr, Berlioz. 100fr, Verdi. 200fr, Tchaikovsky. 400fr, George Gershwin.
500fr, Beethoven.

**1978, Apr. 5** **Litho.**

| | | | | |
|---|---|---|---|---|
| **301** | A58 | 30fr multicolored | .90 | .25 |
| **302** | A58 | 40fr multicolored | 1.10 | .25 |
| **303** | A58 | 50fr multicolored | 1.50 | .30 |
| **304** | A58 | 100fr multicolored | 3.00 | .30 |
| **305** | A58 | 200fr multicolored | 4.50 | .60 |
| **306** | A58 | 400fr multicolored | 9.00 | 1.25 |
| | | *Nos. 301-306 (6)* | 20.00 | 2.95 |

**Souvenir Sheet**

**307** A58 500fr multicolored 9.00 1.75

Nos. 305-307 are airmail. For overprints and surcharges see Nos. 454-458.

Albrecht Durer, 450th Death Anniv. — A59

Portraits: 20fr, Oswolt Krel. 25fr, Elspeth Tucher. 50fr, Hieronymus Holzschuher. 75fr, Young Woman. 200fr, Emperor Maximilian I. No. 313, Young Woman, (detail). No. 314, Self-portrait.

**1978, Apr. 5**

| | | | | |
|---|---|---|---|---|
| **308** | A59 | 20fr multicolored | .25 | .25 |
| **309** | A59 | 25fr multicolored | .30 | .25 |
| **310** | A59 | 50fr multicolored | .65 | .30 |
| **311** | A59 | 75fr multicolored | 1.00 | .30 |
| **312** | A59 | 200fr multicolored | 2.50 | .60 |
| **313** | A59 | 500fr multicolored | 6.00 | 1.60 |
| | | *Nos. 308-313 (6)* | 10.70 | 3.30 |

**Souvenir Sheet**

**314** A59 500fr multicolored 5.50 1.75

Nos. 312-314 airmail. No. 314 contains one 42x52mm stamp. See note after No. 479.

Issues Not Valid for Postage

The government changed in May 1978. A number of sets that had not been issued seem to have been invalid for postage until they were overprinted with the new country name. These are a set of 9 for the 25th anniv. of Elizabeth's coronation, a set of 7 for butterflies, a set of 6 for the 10th Intl. Communications Year, a set of 7 for the history of aviation, a set of 9 for Rubens, and a set of 9 for Durer.

These sets, unoverprinted, exist both mint and cancelled to order. They are no scarcer than the previous listed issues.

See note after No. 479.

**Islamic Republic**

Nos. 204-205 Surcharged and Overprinted with 3 Lines and: "République / Fédérale / et Islamique / des Comores"

**1978, July 24** **Litho.** ***Perf. 13½***

| | | | | |
|---|---|---|---|---|
| **353** | A44 | 30fr multi | 1.75 | — |
| **354** | A44 | 40fr on 30fr multi | 1.75 | — |
| **355** | A44 | 50fr multi | 1.75 | — |
| **356** | A44 | 100fr on 50fr multi | 1.75 | — |
| | | *Nos. 353-356 (3)* | 1.50 | |

Nos. 353 and 355 were also overprinted to commemorate World Cup Soccer winner; Albrecht Dürer; Railroad anniversary; Voyager I and II; 1980 Olympic Games; World Cup Soccer, Espana '82.

Nos. 353, 355 Overprinted

**1978, July 25** **Litho.** ***Perf. 13½***

| | | | | |
|---|---|---|---|---|
| **357** | A44 | 30fr multi | *8.50* | — |
| **358** | A44 | 50fr multi | *12.50* | — |

Coronation of Queen Elizabeth II, 25th anniv.

Nos. 353, 355 Overprinted

**1978, July 26** **Litho.** ***Perf. 13½***

| | | | | |
|---|---|---|---|---|
| **359** | A44 | 30fr multi | *6.00* | — |
| **360** | A44 | 50fr multi | *9.00* | — |

Birth of Capt. James Cook, 250th anniv.

Nos. 353, 355 Overprinted

**1978, July 31** **Litho.** ***Perf. 13½***

| | | | | |
|---|---|---|---|---|
| **365** | A44 | 30fr multi | *6.00* | — |
| **366** | A44 | 50fr multi | *10.00* | — |

Intl. Civil Aviation Organization.

Nos. 353, 355 Overprinted

**1978, Aug. 3** **Litho.** ***Perf. 13½***

| | | | | |
|---|---|---|---|---|
| **371** | A44 | 30fr multi | *7.00* | — |
| **372** | A44 | 50fr multi | *8.00* | — |

Intl. Year of the Child (in 1979).

Europe-Africa A66

Various satellites or spacecraft.

**1978, Dec. 16**

| | | | | |
|---|---|---|---|---|
| **386** | A66 | 10fr multicolored | .25 | .25 |
| **387** | A66 | 25fr multicolored | .25 | .25 |
| **388** | A66 | 35fr multicolored | .30 | .25 |
| **389** | A66 | 50fr multicolored | .55 | .25 |
| **390** | A66 | 100fr multicolored | 1.00 | .60 |
| **391** | A66 | 500fr multicolored | 5.00 | 1.25 |
| | | *Nos. 386-391 (6)* | 7.35 | 2.85 |

**Souvenir Sheet**

**392** A66 500fr multicolored 5.50 1.75

Nos. 390-392 airmail. No. 392 contains one 61x40mm stamp.

Sir Rowland Hill — A67

20fr, Saxony #1. 30fr, Netherlands #1. 40fr, Great Britain #2. 75fr, US #2. 200fr, France #33. 400fr, Basel #3L1. 1500fr, British Guiana #13.

500fr, Moheli, Mayotte, Anjouan, Grand Comoro #1. No. 401, 1500fr, Hill, Mauritius #3.

**1978, Dec. 16**

| | | | | |
|---|---|---|---|---|
| **393** | A67 | 20fr multi | .25 | .25 |
| **394** | A67 | 30fr multi | .30 | .25 |
| **395** | A67 | 40fr multi | .60 | .25 |
| **396** | A67 | 75fr multi | .75 | .30 |
| **397** | A67 | 200fr multi | 2.10 | .60 |
| **398** | A67 | 400fr multi | 4.50 | 1.25 |
| | | *Nos. 393-398 (6)* | 8.50 | 2.90 |

**Litho. & Embossed**

**Size: 39x58mm**

**399** A67 1500fr multi 13.00 —

**Souvenir Sheets**

**Litho.**

**400** A67 500fr multi 5.50 1.75

**Litho. & Embossed**

**401** A67 1500fr multi 13.00 —

Nos. 397-401 are airmail. No. 400 contains one 57x49mm stamp. No. 401 contains one 58x39mm stamp.

No. 399 exists in a souvenir sheet of 1. Value $35.

**Nos. 292-297, 299 Ovptd. in Black & Silver**

**1978, Dec. 16**

| | | | | |
|---|---|---|---|---|
| **402** | A57 | 30fr multicolored | .30 | .25 |
| **403** | A57 | 50fr multicolored | .60 | .25 |
| **404** | A57 | 75fr multicolored | .90 | .25 |
| **405** | A57 | 100fr multicolored | 1.10 | .45 |
| **406** | A57 | 200fr multicolored | 2.25 | .60 |
| **407** | A57 | 400fr multicolored | 4.75 | 1.25 |
| | | *Nos. 402-407 (6)* | 9.90 | 3.05 |

**Souvenir Sheet**

**408** A57 500fr multicolored 5.50 1.25

Nos. 406-407 are airmail.

Exists with Country name in red on silver. Value approx. triple those of overprints in black.

Galileo and Voyager I — A68

Exploration of Solar System: 30fr, Kepler and Voyager II. 40fr, Copernicus and Voyager I, 100fr, Huygens and Voyager II. 200fr, William Herschel and Voyager II. 400fr, Urbain Leverrier and Voyager II. 500fr, Voyagers I and II, symbolic solar system.

**1979, Feb. 19 Litho. *Perf. 13***

| | | | | |
|---|---|---|---|---|
| **409** | A68 | 20fr multi | .25 | .25 |
| **410** | A68 | 30fr multi | .30 | .25 |
| **411** | A68 | 40fr multi | .50 | .25 |
| **412** | A68 | 100fr multi | 1.10 | .25 |
| **413** | A68 | 200fr multi | 1.90 | .50 |
| **414** | A68 | 400fr multi | 4.00 | 1.00 |
| | | *Nos. 409-414 (6)* | 8.05 | 2.50 |

**Souvenir Sheet**

| | | | | |
|---|---|---|---|---|
| **415** | A68 | 500fr multi | 5.00 | 1.50 |

Nos. 413-415 airmail.

Philidor, Anderssen, Steinitz and King — A69

100fr, Chess pieces and board, Venetian chess player. 500fr, Chess Grand Masters Alekhine, Spassky, Fischer, and bishop.

**1979, Feb. 19**

| | | | | |
|---|---|---|---|---|
| **416** | A69 | 40fr multi | .50 | .25 |
| **417** | A69 | 100fr multi | 1.00 | .25 |
| **418** | A69 | 500fr multi | 5.00 | 1.50 |
| | | *Nos. 416-418 (3)* | 6.50 | 2.00 |

Chess Grand Masters. No. 418 airmail.
Nos. 416-418 exist as souvenir sheets of one. Value, set, $30.

Nos. 419-425 are reserved for Summer Olympics set of 6 with one souvenir sheet, released Mar. 28, 1979. Values: set, unused $7; set, used $3; souvenir sheet, unused $6; souvenir sheet, used $3.

Charaxes Defulvata — A71

Fauna: 50fr, Leptosomus discolor. 75fr, Bee eater.

**1979, Apr. 10 Litho. *Perf. 12½***

| | | | | |
|---|---|---|---|---|
| **426** | A71 | 30fr multi | 2.00 | .30 |
| **427** | A71 | 50fr multi | 5.00 | 1.00 |
| **428** | A71 | 75fr multi | 7.00 | 2.00 |
| | | *Nos. 426-428 (3)* | 14.00 | 3.30 |

Otto Lilienthal and Glider A72

History of Aviation: No. 430, Wright brothers and Flyer A. No. 431, Louis Bleriot and Bleriot XI. 100fr, Claude Dornier and Dornier-Wal hydrofoil. 200fr, Charles Lindbergh and Spirit of St. Louis.

**1979, May 2 *Perf. 13***
**Black Overprint and Surcharge**

| | | | | |
|---|---|---|---|---|
| **429** | A72 | 30fr multi | .50 | .50 |
| **430** | A72 | 50fr multi | .80 | .80 |
| **431** | A72 | 50fr on 75fr multi | .80 | .80 |
| **432** | A72 | 100fr multi | 1.60 | 1.60 |
| **433** | A72 | 200fr multi | 2.50 | 2.50 |
| | | *Nos. 429-433 (5)* | 6.20 | 6.20 |

No. 433 airmail.
For unoverprinted stamps see note after No. 314.

Papilio Dardanus Cenea — A73

Butterflies: 15fr, Papilio dardanus. 30fr, Chrysiridia croesus. 50fr, Precis octavia. 75fr, Bunaea alcinoe.

**1979, May 2**
**Black Overprint and Surcharge**

| | | | | |
|---|---|---|---|---|
| **434** | A73 | 5fr on 20fr multi | .25 | .25 |
| **435** | A73 | 15fr multi | .35 | .25 |
| **436** | A73 | 30fr multi | .70 | .45 |
| **437** | A73 | 50fr multi | 1.40 | .95 |
| **438** | A73 | 75fr multi | 2.25 | 1.50 |
| | | *Nos. 434-438 (5)* | 4.95 | 3.40 |

For unoverprinted stamps see note after No. 314.

Man Reading Proclamation A74

No. 439, Coronation coach. No. 440, Drummer. No. 441, With crown, orb, scepter. No. 443, St. Edward's Crown.

**1979, May 2 Litho. *Perf. 13½***
**Black Surcharge and Overprint**

| | | | | |
|---|---|---|---|---|
| **439** | A74 | 5fr on 25fr multi | .25 | .25 |
| **440** | A74 | 10fr multi | .30 | .30 |
| **441** | A74 | 50fr on 40fr multi | .70 | .70 |
| **442** | A74 | 50fr on 200fr shown | 1.10 | 1.10 |
| **443** | A74 | 100fr multi | 1.40 | 1.40 |
| | | *Nos. 439-443 (5)* | 3.75 | 3.75 |

No. 442 is airmail.
For unoverprinted stamps see note after No. 314.

**Nos. 285-289 (Birds) Overprinted or Surcharged like A72-A74**

**1979, May 2 Litho. *Perf. 13***

| | | | | |
|---|---|---|---|---|
| **444** | A56 | 15fr multi | .25 | .30 |
| **445** | A56 | 30fr on 35fr multi | .60 | .70 |
| **446** | A56 | 50fr on 20fr multi | 1.10 | 1.25 |
| **447** | A56 | 50fr on 40fr multi | 1.10 | 1.25 |
| **448** | A56 | 200fr on 75fr multi | 3.50 | 4.00 |
| | | *Nos. 444-448 (5)* | 6.55 | 7.50 |

**Nos. 292-296 (Soccer) Overprinted or Surcharged like A72-A74**

**1979, May 2 Litho. *Perf. 13***

| | | | | |
|---|---|---|---|---|
| **449** | A57 | 1fr on 100fr multi | .25 | .25 |
| **450** | A57 | 2fr on 75fr multi | .25 | .25 |
| **451** | A57 | 3fr on 30fr multi | .25 | .25 |
| **452** | A57 | 50fr multi | .90 | .55 |
| **453** | A57 | 200fr multi | 2.25 | 2.25 |
| | | *Nos. 449-453 (5)* | 3.90 | 3.55 |

No. 453 airmail.

**Nos. 301-305 (Composers) Overprinted or Surcharged like A72-A74**

**1979, May 2 *Perf. 13½***

| | | | | |
|---|---|---|---|---|
| **454** | A58 | 5fr on 100fr multi | .25 | .25 |
| **455** | A58 | 30fr multi | 1.25 | 1.25 |
| **456** | A58 | 40fr multi | 1.75 | 1.75 |
| **457** | A58 | 50fr multi | 2.25 | 2.25 |
| **458** | A58 | 50fr on 200fr multi | 3.50 | 3.50 |
| | | *Nos. 454-458 (5)* | 9.00 | 9.00 |

No. 458 airmail.

Intl. Year of the Child — A75

Intl. Year of the Child emblem and: 20fr, Astronaut on moon, child in astronaut costume. 30fr, Luger, child with snowboard. 40fr, Woman from Dürer painting, child practicing Chinese calligraphy. 100fr, Steam locomotive, child with toy train. 200fr, Adults and children playing soccer. 400fr, Olympic rower, child in rowboat.
500fr, Karl Benz, boy in toy car, horiz.
No. 465A, Louis Blériot, child with remote-control airplane, horiz.
No. 465B, Capt. James Cook, child with teddy bear and toy gun, horiz.

**1979, May 30 Litho. *Perf. 13½***

| | | | | |
|---|---|---|---|---|
| **459** | A75 | 20fr multi | .25 | .25 |
| **460** | A75 | 30fr multi | .30 | .25 |
| **461** | A75 | 40fr multi | .40 | .25 |
| **462** | A75 | 100fr multi | 1.00 | .35 |
| **463** | A75 | 200fr multi | 2.00 | .50 |
| **464** | A75 | 400fr multi | 4.00 | 1.10 |
| | | *Nos. 459-464 (6)* | 7.95 | 2.70 |

**Souvenir Sheet**

| | | | | |
|---|---|---|---|---|
| **465** | A75 | 500fr multi | 5.75 | 2.75 |

**Litho. & Embossed**
**Size: 51x42mm**

| | | | | |
|---|---|---|---|---|
| **465A** | A75 | 1500fr gold & multi | 13.50 | — |

**Souvenir Sheet**
***Perf. 13¼***

| | | | | |
|---|---|---|---|---|
| **465B** | A75 | 1500fr gold & multi | 13.50 | — |

Nos. 463-465A are airmail. Nos. 465 and 465B each contain one 51x42mm stamp.

Litchi Nuts — A76

**1979, June 15 Litho. *Perf. 12½***

| | | | | |
|---|---|---|---|---|
| **466** | A76 | 60fr shown | 1.00 | .30 |
| **467** | A76 | 70fr Papayas | 1.25 | .45 |
| **468** | A76 | 100fr Avocados | 1.40 | .55 |
| **469** | A76 | 125fr Bananas | 1.90 | .90 |
| | | *Nos. 466-469 (4)* | 5.55 | 2.20 |

For surcharges see Nos. 515, 533.

Basketball Players — A77

**1979, Aug. 28 Litho. *Perf. 13***

| | | | | |
|---|---|---|---|---|
| **470** | A77 | 200fr multi | 2.50 | 1.40 |

Indian Ocean Olympics.

**Nos. 176, 198, 218, 187, 159-160 and Type A78 Overprinted in Black**

Nimbus Weather Satellite A78

No. 475, Apollo-Soyuz. No. 479, Molniya.

**Printing & Perfs. as Before, Litho. (A78)**

**1979, Sept. 15 *Perf. 13 (A78)***

| | | | | |
|---|---|---|---|---|
| **471** | A40 | 35fr multi | .70 | .70 |
| **472** | A43 | 75fr multi | 1.50 | 1.50 |
| **473** | A46 | 75fr multi | 1.50 | 1.50 |
| **474** | A78 | 75fr multi | 1.50 | 1.50 |
| **475** | A78 | 100fr multi | 2.10 | 2.10 |
| **476** | A41 | 100fr multi | 2.10 | 2.10 |
| **477** | A37 | 100fr multi | 2.10 | 2.10 |
| **478** | A37 | 200fr multi | 4.25 | 4.25 |
| **479** | A78 | 200fr multi | 4.25 | 4.25 |
| | | *Nos. 471-479 (9)* | 20.00 | 20.00 |

Nos. 476-479 airmail.
For type A78 see note after No. 314.

Nos. 166-167, 169, 235-236, 257, 262, 309, 311, the unissued Rubens set (4 values) and Durer set (5 values) exist with this overprint, supposedly also issued Sept. 15. Value, set of 18 $12.

Dugout on Beach A80

Anjouan Puppet A81

**1980, Jan. 4 Litho. *Perf. 13***

| | | | | |
|---|---|---|---|---|
| **498** | A80 | 60fr multi | 1.00 | .25 |
| **499** | A81 | 100fr multi | 1.50 | .45 |

For surcharge see No. 534.

Sultan Said Ali — A82

**1980, Feb. 20 *Perf. 12½x13***

| | | | | |
|---|---|---|---|---|
| **500** | A82 | 40fr shown | .75 | .25 |
| **501** | A82 | 60fr Sultan Ahmed | 1.00 | .25 |

Sherlock Holmes, Doyle — A83

**1980, Feb. 25 *Perf. 12½***

| | | | | |
|---|---|---|---|---|
| **502** | A83 | 200fr multi | 4.75 | 1.75 |

Sir Arthur Conan Doyle (1859-1930), writer.
For surcharge see No. 513.

Grand Mosque, Holy Ka'aba, Mecca A84

**1980, Mar. 12 *Perf. 13x12½***

| | | | | |
|---|---|---|---|---|
| **503** | A84 | 75fr multi | 1.00 | .40 |

Hegira, 1350th anniv.
For surcharge see No. 514.

Year of the Holy City of Jerusalem — A85

**1980, Mar. 12 *Perf. 13x13½***

| | | | | |
|---|---|---|---|---|
| **504** | A85 | 60fr multi | 1.00 | .40 |

Kepler, Copernicus and Pluto — A86

**1980, Apr. 30 Litho. *Perf. 12½***

| | | | | |
|---|---|---|---|---|
| **505** | A86 | 400fr multi | 4.50 | 2.25 |

Discovery of Pluto, 50th anniversary.
For surcharge see No. 531.

Muscle System, Avicenna — A87

**1980, Apr. 30** **Engr.** ***Perf. 13***
**506** A87 60fr multi 1.00 .40

Avicenna, Arab physician, birth millennium.

Soccer Players A88

World Cup Soccer 1982; Various soccer scenes. 60fr, 150fr, 500fr, vert.

**1981, Feb. 20** **Litho.** ***Perf. 12½***
**507** A88 60fr multi .65 .25
**508** A88 75fr multi .75 .25
**509** A88 90fr multi 1.25 .25
**510** A88 100fr multi 1.10 .45
**511** A88 150fr multi 1.90 .60
*Nos. 507-511 (5)* 5.65 1.80

**Souvenir Sheet**

**512** A88 500fr multi 5.00 1.50

For overprints & surcharge see Nos. 532, 555-560.

Nos. 502-503, 469 Surcharged

and

Merops Superciliosus — A89

**Red, Black or Blue Surcharge**

***Perf. 12½, 13x12½ (No. 514)***

**1981, Feb.** **Litho.**
**513** A83 15fr on 200fr multi .50 .50
**514** A84 20fr on 75fr multi .50 .50
**515** A76 40fr on 125fr multi (Bk) 1.50 1.50
**516** A89 60fr on 75fr multi (Bl) 3.00 3.00
*Nos. 513-516 (4)* 5.50 5.50

A90

Space Exploration: 50fr, Apollo program, vert. 75fr, 100fr, 500fr, Columbia space shuttle.

**1981, July 13** **Litho.** ***Perf. 14***
**517** A90 50fr multi .60 .25
**518** A90 75fr multi .75 .25
**519** A90 100fr multi 1.25 .30
**520** A90 450fr multi 6.00 1.50
*Nos. 517-520 (4)* 8.60 2.30

**Souvenir Sheet**

**521** A90 500fr multi 4.00 1.50

For overprints and surcharges see Nos. 599, 804F.

Prince Charles and Lady Diana, Buckingham Palace — A91

200fr, Highwood House. 450fr, Carnarvon Castle.

**1981, Sept. 1** **Litho.** ***Perf. 14½***
**522** A91 125fr shown .90 .30
**523** A91 200fr multicolored 1.35 .60
**524** A91 450fr multicolored 3.00 1.25
*a.* Souvenir sheet of 3 6.50 2.00
*Nos. 522-524 (3)* 5.25 2.15

Royal wedding. No. 524a contains Nos. 522-524 in changed colors.
For overprints see Nos. 551-553.

**Official Stamp Flag Type**

**1981, Oct.** **Litho.** ***Perf. 13***
**526** O1 5fr multi .25 .25
**527** O1 15fr multi .25 .25
**528** O1 25fr multi .30 .25
**529** O1 35fr multi .40 .25
**530** O1 75fr multi .75 .35
*Nos. 526-530 (5)* 1.95 1.35

**Nos. 505, 509, 468, 499 Surcharged**

No. 531

No. 532

No. 533

No. 534

**1981, Nov.** **Litho.** ***Perf. 12½***
**531** A86 5fr on 400fr multi .40 .40
**532** A88 20fr on 90fr multi .80 .80
**533** A76 45fr on 100fr multi 2.00 .25
**534** A81 45fr on 100fr multi 2.00 .25
*Nos. 531-534 (4)* 5.20 1.70

75th Anniv. of Grand Prix — A92

Winners and their Cars: 20fr, Mercedes, 1914. 50fr, Delage, 1925. 75fr, Rudi Caracciola, 1926. 90fr, Stirling Moss, 1955. 150fr, Maserati, 1957.
500fr, Changing wheels, vert.

**1981, Dec. 28** **Litho.** ***Perf. 12½***
**535** A92 20fr multicolored .25 .25
**536** A92 50fr multicolored .50 .25
**537** A92 75fr multicolored .70 .25
**538** A92 90fr multicolored .90 .35
**539** A92 150fr multicolored 1.30 .45
*Nos. 535-539 (5)* 3.65 1.55

**Souvenir Sheet**

***Perf. 13***

**540** A92 500fr multicolored 6.00 1.75

For overprint see No. 600.

Scouting Year — A93

**1982, Jan. 5** ***Perf. 12½***
**541** A93 50fr Climbing rocks .60 .25
**542** A93 75fr Boating .85 .25
**543** A93 250fr Sailing 3.00 .90
**544** A93 350fr Sailing, diff. 3.75 1.10
*Nos. 541-544 (4)* 8.20 2.50

**Souvenir Sheet**

***Perf. 13***

**545** A93 500fr Baden-Powell 6.50 1.75

For overprint see No. 601.

21st Birthday of Princess of Wales — A94

Various portraits of Princess Diana.

**1982, July 1** **Litho.** ***Perf. 14***
**546** A94 200fr multi 2.00 .60
**547** A94 300fr multi 3.25 .90

**Souvenir Sheet**

**548** A94 500fr multi 5.00 1.50

Johannes von Goethe (1749-1832) — A95

**1982, July**
**549** A95 75fr multi .75 .25
**550** A95 350fr multi 3.75 .90

**Nos. 522-524a Overprinted in Blue**

**1982, July 31** ***Perf. 14½***
**551** A91 125fr multi 1.25 .60
**552** A91 200fr multi 2.00 .90
**553** A91 450fr multi 3.75 2.00
*a.* Souvenir sheet of 3 7.50 7.50
*Nos. 551-553 (3)* 7.00 3.50

Birth of Prince William of Wales, June 21.

**Nos. 507-512 Overprinted with Finalists and Score in Red**

**1982, Sept. 20** **Litho.** ***Perf. 12½***
**555** A88 60fr multi .65 .25
**556** A88 75fr multi .75 .35
**557** A88 90fr multi 1.00 .45
**558** A88 100fr multi 1.10 .45
**559** A88 150fr multi 1.40 .60
*Nos. 555-559 (5)* 4.90 2.10

**Souvenir Sheet**

**560** A88 500fr multi 5.00 1.50

Italy's victory in 1982 World Cup.

Paintings by Norman Rockwell — A96

**1982, Oct. 11** **Litho.** ***Perf. 14***
**561** A96 60fr 1931 .65 .25
**562** A96 75fr 1925 .70 .25
**563** A96 100fr 1922 1.25 .25
**564** A96 150fr 1919 1.40 .55
**565** A96 200fr 1924 2.00 .60
**566** A96 300fr 1918 3.50 1.00
*Nos. 561-566 (6)* 9.50 2.90

Sultans of Anjouan A97

30fr, Said Mohamed Sidi, vert. 60fr, Ahmed Abdallah, vert. 75fr, Salim. 300fr, Sidi, Abdallah.

**1982, Dec.** ***Perf. 12½x13, 13x12½***
**567** A97 30fr multicolored .40 .25
**568** A97 60fr multicolored .75 .25
**569** A97 75fr multicolored 1.00 .25
**570** A97 300fr multicolored 3.50 1.40
*Nos. 567-570 (4)* 5.65 2.15

Landscapes A98

**1983, Sept. 30** **Litho.** ***Perf. 13***
**571** A98 60fr D'Ziani Lake .75 .30
**572** A98 100fr Sunset 1.25 .45
**573** A98 175fr Anjouan, vert. 2.00 .75
**574** A98 360fr Itsandra 4.00 1.25
**575** A98 400fr Anjouan, diff. 5.00 1.60
*Nos. 571-575 (5)* 13.00 4.35

For surcharge see No. 815S.

Woman from Moheli — A99

**1983, Oct. 17** **Litho.** ***Perf. 12½x13***
**576** A99 30fr shown .45 .25
**577** A99 45fr Woman, diff. .65 .25
**578** A99 50fr Man from Mayotte .70 .25
*Nos. 576-578 (3)* 1.80 .75

Horses A100

**1983, Nov. 30** **Litho.** ***Perf. 13***
**579** A100 75fr Arabian .60 .25
**580** A100 100fr Anglo-Arabian .90 .30
**581** A100 125fr Lippizaner 1.10 .40
**582** A100 150fr Tennessee 1.35 .50
**583** A100 200fr Appaloosa 1.75 .70
**584** A100 300fr Pure English 2.75 1.00
**585** A100 400fr Clydesdale 3.50 1.25
**586** A100 500fr Andalusian 4.50 1.50
*Nos. 579-586 (8)* 16.45 5.90

Double Portrait, by Raphael — A101

200fr, Girl, fresco detail. 300fr, St. George Killing Dragon. 400fr, Balthazar Castiglione.

**1983, Dec. 30 Litho. *Perf. 13***

| | | | | |
|---|---|---|---|---|
| **587** | A101 | 100fr shown | 1.10 | .45 |
| **588** | A101 | 200fr multicolored | 2.25 | .80 |
| **589** | A101 | 300fr multicolored | 2.75 | .90 |
| **590** | A101 | 400fr multicolored | 5.00 | 1.25 |
| | | *Nos. 587-590 (4)* | 11.10 | 3.40 |

For surcharges see Nos. 703, 800E, 815M.

Ships and Automobiles A102

No. 591, William Fawcett. No. 592, De Dion, 1885. No. 593, Lightning. No. 594, Benz Victoria, 1893. No. 595, Rapido. No. 596, Columbia Electric, 1901. No. 597, Sindia. No. 598, Fiat, 1902.

**1984, Oct. 9 Litho. *Perf. 12½***

| | | | | |
|---|---|---|---|---|
| **591** | A102 | 100fr multi | 1.10 | .30 |
| **592** | A102 | 100fr multi | 1.35 | .30 |
| **593** | A102 | 150fr multi | 1.70 | .45 |
| **594** | A102 | 150fr multi | 2.00 | .60 |
| **595** | A102 | 200fr multi | 2.25 | .75 |
| **596** | A102 | 200fr multi | 2.75 | .75 |
| **597** | A102 | 350fr multi | 4.00 | 1.00 |
| **598** | A102 | 350fr multi | 4.50 | 1.10 |
| | | *Nos. 591-598 (8)* | 19.65 | 5.25 |

For surcharge see No. 812Q.

**Nos. 521, 540, 545, C126, C131 Ovptd. in Black, Blue, Red or Gold**

No. 599

No. 600

No. 601

No. 603

No. 599, '85 / HAMBOURG (Bk). No. 600, TSUKUBA EXPO '85 (Bl). No. 601, ARGENTINA '85/BUENOS AIRES (R). No. 602, Rome, ITALIA '85 emblem (R). No. 603, OLYM - PHILEX/ '85 / LAUSANNE (G).

**1985, Mar. 11 *Perf. 14, 13***

**Souvenir Sheets**

| | | | | |
|---|---|---|---|---|
| **599** | A90 | 500fr multi | 5.00 | 5.00 |
| **600** | A92 | 500fr multi | 5.00 | 5.00 |
| **601** | A93 | 500fr multi | 5.00 | 5.00 |
| **602** | AP31 | 500fr multi | 5.00 | 5.00 |
| **603** | AP32 | 500fr multi | 5.00 | 5.00 |
| | | *Nos. 599-603 (5)* | 25.00 | 25.00 |

Nos. 602-603 airmail.

Victor Hugo (1802-1885), Author, Pantheon, Paris A103

Anniversaries and events: 200fr, IYY, Jules Verne (1828-1905), author. 300fr, IYY, Mark Twain (1835-1910), author. 450fr, Queen Mother, 85th birthday, vert. 500fr, Statue of Liberty, cent., vert.

**1985, May 27 Litho. *Perf. 13***

| | | | | |
|---|---|---|---|---|
| **604** | A103 | 100fr multi | 1.10 | .30 |
| **605** | A103 | 200fr multi | 2.00 | .60 |
| **606** | A103 | 300fr multi | 3.00 | .90 |
| **607** | A103 | 450fr multi | 4.50 | 1.25 |
| **608** | A103 | 500fr multi | 5.50 | 1.50 |
| | | *Nos. 604-608 (5)* | 16.10 | 4.55 |

For surcharges see Nos. 704, 800A.

Sea Shells A104

75fr, Lambis chiragra. 125fr, Strombe lentifinosum. 200fr, Tonna gala. 300fr, Cymbium glans. 450fr, Lambis crocata.

**1985, Oct. 23 *Perf. 14***

| | | | | |
|---|---|---|---|---|
| **609** | A104 | 75fr multicolored | 1.10 | .25 |
| **610** | A104 | 125fr multicolored | 1.50 | .35 |
| **611** | A104 | 200fr multicolored | 2.40 | .60 |
| **612** | A104 | 300fr multicolored | 3.75 | .90 |
| **613** | A104 | 450fr multicolored | 5.75 | 1.40 |
| | | *Nos. 609-613 (5)* | 14.50 | 3.50 |

Comoros Admission to UN, 10th Anniv. A105

**1985, Nov. 12 Litho. *Perf. 13x12½***

| | | | | |
|---|---|---|---|---|
| **614** | A105 | 5fr multi | .25 | .25 |
| **615** | A105 | 30fr multi | .25 | .25 |
| **616** | A105 | 75fr multi | .80 | .25 |
| **617** | A105 | 125fr multi | 1.25 | .50 |
| **618** | A105 | 400fr multi | 4.25 | 1.50 |
| | | *Nos. 614-618 (5)* | 6.80 | 2.75 |

For surcharge see No. 800F.

Moroni Rotary Club, 20th Anniv. A106

**1985, Nov. 30 *Perf. 13***

| | | | | |
|---|---|---|---|---|
| **619** | A106 | 25fr multi | .40 | .25 |
| **620** | A106 | 75fr multi | .90 | .40 |
| **621** | A106 | 125fr multi | 1.10 | .45 |
| **622** | A106 | 500fr multi | 4.00 | 2.00 |
| | | *Nos. 619-622 (4)* | 6.40 | 3.10 |

Mushrooms A107

75fr, Boletus edulis. 125fr, Sarcoscypha coccinea. 200fr, Hypholoma fasciculare. 350fr, Astraeus hygrometricus. 500fr, Armillariella mellea.

**1985, Dec. 24 *Perf. 13½***

| | | | | |
|---|---|---|---|---|
| **623** | A107 | 75fr multicolored | 1.00 | .30 |
| **624** | A107 | 125fr multicolored | 1.20 | .45 |
| **625** | A107 | 200fr multicolored | 2.25 | .60 |
| **626** | A107 | 350fr multicolored | 4.00 | .90 |
| **627** | A107 | 500fr multicolored | 5.50 | 1.50 |
| | | *Nos. 623-627 (5)* | 13.95 | 3.75 |

For surcharge see No. 815R.

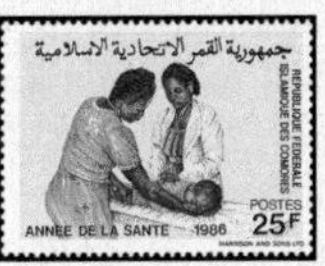

Health Year — A108

25fr, Pediatric examination. 100fr, Weighing child. 200fr, Immunization.

**1986, Oct. 2 Litho. *Perf. 15x14½***

| | | | | |
|---|---|---|---|---|
| **628** | A108 | 25fr multicolored | .25 | .25 |
| **629** | A108 | 100fr multicolored | 1.20 | .60 |
| **630** | A108 | 200fr multicolored | 2.25 | 1.25 |
| | | *Nos. 628-630 (3)* | 3.70 | 2.10 |

For surcharge see No. 705.

Musical Instruments A109

**1986, Dec. 24 Litho. *Perf. 13***

| | | | | |
|---|---|---|---|---|
| **631** | A109 | 75fr Ndzoumara | .80 | .40 |
| **632** | A109 | 125fr Ndzedze | 1.10 | .60 |
| **633** | A109 | 210fr Gaboussi | 1.90 | .90 |
| **634** | A109 | 500fr Ngoma | 5.50 | 1.75 |
| | | *Nos. 631-634 (4)* | 9.30 | 3.65 |

For surcharges see Nos. 796P, 796T, 800L, 815A.

Role of Women in National Development — A110

75fr, Working fields. 125fr, Harvesting crops, vert. 1000fr, Basketweaving.

**1987, Mar. 7 Litho. *Perf. 13***

| | | | | |
|---|---|---|---|---|
| **635** | A110 | 75fr multi | .50 | .30 |
| **636** | A110 | 125fr multi | 1.00 | .50 |
| **637** | A110 | 1000fr multi | 9.50 | 3.50 |
| | | *Nos. 635-637 (3)* | 11.00 | 4.30 |

Service Organizations A111

Emblems and activities: 75fr, Nos. 642, Kiwanis or 643c, Rotary Intl. for child survival. 125fr, Nos. 641, Kiwanis or 643b, Lions Intl. for aid to the handicapped. 210fr, No. 643a, Kiwanis helping poor and homeless children.

**1988 Litho. *Perf. 13½***

| | | | | |
|---|---|---|---|---|
| **638** | A111 | 75fr dk bl, lt bl & multi | .65 | .30 |
| **639** | A111 | 125fr dk brn, lt brn & multi | 1.25 | .45 |
| **640** | A111 | 210fr org, yel & multi | 1.90 | .75 |
| **641** | A111 | 425fr red, pink & multi | 4.00 | 1.75 |
| **642** | A111 | 500fr bl, yel & multi | 5.50 | 2.00 |
| **643** | | Strip of 3 | 11.50 | 6.00 |
| *a.* | A111 | 210fr grn, lt grn & multi | 2.10 | .75 |
| *b.* | A111 | 425fr pur, pink & multi | 4.50 | 1.75 |
| *c.* | A111 | 500fr red, orange & multi | 6.00 | 2.00 |
| | | *Nos. 638-643 (6)* | 24.80 | 11.25 |

For surcharges see Nos. 654-656, 815B, 815W.

A112

1988 Olympics, Calgary and Seoul — A113

75fr, Women's figure skating. 100fr, Running. 125fr, Women's speed skating. 150fr, Equestrian. 350fr, Two-man luge. 400fr, Biathlon. 500fr, Pole vault. 600fr, Soccer.

No. 652, Women's downhill skiing, satellite. No. 653, Track, satellite.

**1988 Litho. *Perf. 13½***

| | | | | |
|---|---|---|---|---|
| **644** | A112 | 75fr multicolored | .65 | .25 |
| **645** | A112 | 100fr multicolored | 1.00 | .30 |
| **646** | A112 | 125fr multicolored | 1.00 | .40 |
| **647** | A112 | 150fr multicolored | 1.50 | .50 |
| **648** | A112 | 350fr multicolored | 3.25 | .90 |
| **649** | A112 | 400fr multicolored | 4.00 | 1.40 |
| **650** | A112 | 500fr multicolored | 4.00 | 1.25 |
| **651** | A112 | 600fr multicolored | 6.00 | 1.50 |
| | | *Nos. 644-651 (8)* | 21.40 | 6.50 |

**Souvenir Sheets**

| | | | | |
|---|---|---|---|---|
| **652** | A113 | 750fr multicolored | 7.75 | 1.50 |
| **653** | A113 | 750fr multicolored | 7.75 | 1.50 |

Nos. 649 and 651-653 are airmail.

For surcharges see Nos. 800C, 800M, 815V.

**No. 643 and Service Organization Types Surcharged**

No. 655, like #643b. No. 656, like #643c.

**1988, July 18 Litho. *Perf. 13½***

| | | | | |
|---|---|---|---|---|
| **654** | | Strip of 3 | 4.75 | 5.00 |
| *a.* | | A111 75fr on 210fr #643a | .65 | .45 |
| *b.* | | A111 200fr on 425fr #643b | 1.75 | .90 |
| *c.* | | A111 300fr on 500fr #643c | 2.75 | 1.25 |
| **655** | A111 | 125fr on 425fr pur, lt pur & multi, blk letters | .90 | .60 |
| **656** | A111 | 400fr on 500fr car, pink & multi | 3.25 | 2.00 |
| | | *Nos. 654-656 (3)* | 8.90 | 7.60 |

Nos. 655-656 not issued without surcharge.

Discovery of America, 500th Anniv. (in 1992) — A114

Designs: 75fr, Christopher Columbus, *Santa Maria*. 125fr, Martin Alonzo Pinzon (c. 1441-1493), *Pinta*. 150fr, Vicente Yanez Pinzon (c. 1460-1523), *Nina*. 250fr, Search for Cipango, legendary rich islands off the coast of Asia. 375fr, *Santa Maria* shipwrecked. 450fr, Preparing for 4th voyage. 750fr, Samana Cay landing.

**1988, Apr. 18 Litho. *Perf. 13½***

| | | | | |
|---|---|---|---|---|
| **657** | A114 | 75fr multi | .65 | .25 |
| **658** | A114 | 125fr multi | 1.10 | .30 |
| **659** | A114 | 150fr multi | 1.50 | .45 |
| **660** | A114 | 250fr multi | 2.10 | .75 |
| **661** | A114 | 375fr multi | 3.75 | 1.00 |
| **662** | A114 | 450fr multi | 4.50 | 1.25 |
| | | *Nos. 657-662 (6)* | 13.60 | 4.00 |

**Souvenir Sheet**

| | | | | |
|---|---|---|---|---|
| **663** | A114 | 750fr multi, horiz. | 7.75 | 1.50 |

Nos. 661-663 airmail. No. 663 contains one 42x30mm stamp.

For surcharges see Nos. 702, 815D.

1992 Summer Olympics, Barcelona A115

**1988, Apr. 18**

| | | | | |
|---|---|---|---|---|
| **664** | A115 | 75fr Discus, vert. | .60 | .25 |
| **665** | A115 | 100fr shown | .90 | .30 |
| **666** | A115 | 125fr Cycling | 1.25 | .35 |
| **667** | A115 | 150fr Wrestling | 1.50 | .50 |
| **668** | A115 | 375fr Basketball, vert. | 3.75 | 1.00 |
| **669** | A115 | 600fr Tennis, vert. | 6.00 | 1.25 |
| | | *Nos. 664-669 (6)* | 14.00 | 3.65 |

**Souvenir Sheet**

| | | | | |
|---|---|---|---|---|
| **670** | A115 | 750fr Marathon, vert. | 7.75 | 1.50 |

Nos. 668-670 are airmail.

Famous Men — A116

Rotary Intl. A117

150fr, Yuri Gagarin (1934-68), USSR, cosmonaut. 300fr, Jean-Henri Dunant, Red Cross founder. 400fr, Roger Clemens, baseball player. 500fr, Garry Kasparov, USSR, 1985 world chess champion. 600fr, Paul Harris, US, Rotary founder. 750fr, Neil Armstrong walking on the Moon, John F. Kennedy. No. 678, The Thinker by Rodin, Rotary Intl. emblem.

**1988, Dec. 6 Litho. *Perf. 13½***

| | | | | |
|---|---|---|---|---|
| **671** | A116 | 150fr multi | 1.75 | .50 |
| **672** | A116 | 300fr multi | 1.75 | .50 |
| **673** | A116 | 400fr multi | 1.75 | .50 |
| **674** | A116 | 500fr multi | 1.75 | .50 |
| **675** | A116 | 600fr multi | 1.75 | .50 |
| *a.* | | Souv. sheet of 5, #671-675 + label | 10.00 | — |
| | | *Nos. 665-669 (5)* | 18.40 | 3.50 |

**Litho. & Embossed**

| | | | | |
|---|---|---|---|---|
| **676** | A117 | 1500fr gold & multi | 15.00 | — |

**Souvenir Sheets**

**Litho.**

| | | | | |
|---|---|---|---|---|
| **677** | A116 | 750fr multi | 7.75 | 1.50 |

**Litho. & Embossed**

| | | | | |
|---|---|---|---|---|
| **678** | A117 | 1500fr gold & multi | 15.00 | — |

Intl. Red Cross, 125th anniv. (300fr), Rotary Intl. (600fr, Nos. 676, 678). Nos. 674-678 are airmail.

Nos. 672-673 exist in souv. sheets of 1.

No. 676 exists in a souvenir sheet of 1. Value $42.50.

Inventors and Sportsmen — A118

Portraits and modes of transportation: Designs: 75fr, Alain Prost, F-1 MacLaren-Honda. 125fr, George Stephenson and locomotive *Borsig of 1935.* 500fr, Ettore Bugatti (1881-1947), 1939 Bugatti Aravis Type 57. 600fr, Rudolf Diesel (1858-1913) and V200 BB diesel-electric locomotive. 750fr, Dennis Conner, captain of the *Stars and Stripes,* winner of the 1987 America's Cup. No. 684, Michael Fay, patron of the *New Zealand,* an entry in the America's Cup. No. 685, Enzo Ferrari and 1989 Ferrari Formula 1, horiz.

**1988, Dec. 27 Litho. *Perf. 13½***

| | | | | |
|---|---|---|---|---|
| **679** | A118 | 75fr multi | .75 | .45 |
| **680** | A118 | 125fr multi | 1.25 | .25 |
| **681** | A118 | 500fr multi | 5.00 | 1.25 |
| **682** | A118 | 600fr multi | 6.00 | 1.25 |
| **683** | A118 | 750fr multi | 7.00 | 1.25 |
| **684** | A118 | 1000fr multi | 10.00 | 1.25 |
| | | *Nos. 679-684 (6)* | 30.00 | 5.70 |

**Souvenir Sheet**

| | | | | |
|---|---|---|---|---|
| **685** | A118 | 1000fr multi | 10.00 | 1.50 |

Nos. 683-685 are airmail.

Nos. 679-684 exist in souv. sheets of 1.

Scouts, Butterflies and Birds — A119

Scouts involved in various activities and species: 50fr, Gathering specimens, *Papilio nireus aristophontes oberthur* female. 75fr, Studying specimen and male. 150fr, Cooking out, *Charaxes fulvescens separanus poulton.* 375fr, Picking mushrooms, *Lonchura cucullatus.* 450fr, Examining specimen, *Charaxes castor comoranus rothschild.* 500fr, Identifying specimen, *Zosterops maderaspatana.* 750fr, Studying specimens, *Foudia omissa* and *Charaxes paradoxa lathy* female. No. 692, Photographing specimen, *Junonia rhadama.* No. 694, Examining specimen, *Agapornis cana cana.*

**1989 Litho.**

| | | | | |
|---|---|---|---|---|
| **686** | A119 | 50fr multi | .50 | .25 |
| **687** | A119 | 75fr multi | .60 | .25 |
| **688** | A119 | 150fr multi | 1.40 | .30 |
| **689** | A119 | 375fr multi | 4.00 | .75 |
| **690** | A119 | 450fr multi | 4.75 | 1.00 |
| **691** | A119 | 500fr multi | 5.75 | 1.25 |
| | | *Nos. 686-691 (6)* | 17.00 | 3.80 |

**Litho. & Embossed**

| | | | | |
|---|---|---|---|---|
| **692** | A119 | 1500fr gold & multi | 16.00 | — |

**Souvenir Sheets**

**Litho.**

| | | | | |
|---|---|---|---|---|
| **693** | A119 | 750fr multi | 10.00 | 1.50 |

**Litho. & Embossed**

| | | | | |
|---|---|---|---|---|
| **694** | A119 | 1500fr gold & multi | 13.00 | — |

Nos. 690-694 are airmail. Issue dates: Nos. 692, 694, May 15; others, Mar. 15.

No. 692 exists in a souvenir sheet of 1. Value $42.50.

For surcharges see Nos. 800D, 815T.

Gold Medalists of the 1988 Summer Olympics A120

Communication satellites, various equestrians and their mounts: 75fr, Nicole Uphoff, West Germany, individual dressage, and Aussat K3. 150fr, Pierre Durand, France, individual jumping, and Brazilsat. 375fr, Janos Martinek, Hungary, individual modern pentathlon, and ECS 4. 600fr, Mark Todd, New Zealand, individual three-day event, and Olympus. 750fr, Team jumping, West Germany, and satellite. No. 699, Pierre Durand, France, individual show jumping. No. 701, Nicole Uphoff, West Germany, individual dressage.

**1989, Apr. 10 Litho. *Perf. 13½***

| | | | | |
|---|---|---|---|---|
| **695** | A120 | 75fr multi | .65 | .25 |
| **696** | A120 | 150fr multi | 1.25 | .35 |
| **697** | A120 | 375fr multi | 3.00 | .75 |
| **698** | A120 | 600fr multi | 5.00 | 1.25 |
| | | *Nos. 695-698 (4)* | 9.90 | 2.60 |

**Litho. & Embossed**

| | | | | |
|---|---|---|---|---|
| **699** | A120 | 1500fr gold & multi | 16.00 | — |

**Souvenir Sheets**

**Litho.**

| | | | | |
|---|---|---|---|---|
| **700** | A120 | 750fr multi | 6.75 | 1.50 |

**Litho. & Embossed**

| | | | | |
|---|---|---|---|---|
| **701** | A120 | 1500fr gold & multi | 13.00 | — |

No. 701 contains one 39x38mm stamp. Nos. 698-701 are airmail.

No. 699 exists in a souvenir sheet of 1. Value $45.

For surcharges see Nos. 796Q, 804I.

**Nos. 660, 588, 605 and 630 Surcharged**

**1989 Litho. *Perfs. as Before***

| | | | | |
|---|---|---|---|---|
| **702** | A114 | 25fr on 250fr #660 | .40 | .25 |
| **703** | A101 | 150fr on 200fr #588 | 1.50 | .50 |
| **704** | A103 | 150fr on 200fr #605 | 1.50 | .50 |
| **705** | A108 | 150fr on 200fr #630 | 1.50 | .50 |
| | | *Nos. 702-705 (4)* | 4.90 | 1.75 |

1992 Summer Olympics, Barcelona — A121

**1989, Apr. 26 Litho. *Perf. 13½***

| | | | | |
|---|---|---|---|---|
| **706** | A121 | 75fr Running | .65 | .25 |
| **707** | A121 | 150fr Soccer | 1.25 | .40 |
| **708** | A121 | 300fr Tennis | 2.50 | .60 |
| **709** | A121 | 375fr Baseball | 3.25 | .80 |
| **710** | A121 | 500fr Pommel horse | 4.00 | 1.00 |
| **711** | A121 | 600fr Table tennis | 5.00 | 1.25 |
| | | *Nos. 706-711 (6)* | 16.65 | 4.30 |

**Souvenir Sheet**

| | | | | |
|---|---|---|---|---|
| **712** | A121 | 750fr Equestrian | 6.75 | 1.50 |

Nos. 710-712 are airmail.

For surcharges see Nos. 796J, 796K, 800J, 812R.

Dr. Joseph-Ignace Guillotin (1738-1814) — A122

French Revolution, Bicent.: 150fr, French artillery, Gen. Francois-Christophe Kellermann (1735-1820). 375fr, Royalist insurgents & leader, Jean Cottereau (1757-94). 600fr, King Louis XVI (1774-92), troops. 1000fr, Storming of the Bastille & Jacques Necker, statesman (1732-1804). No. 717, Lafayette, Mounier, Sieyes & Declaration of the Rights of Man and Citizen. No. 719, Robespierre & St. Just before the Convention on 9 Thermidor.

**1989, Oct. 25 Litho. *Perf. 13½***

| | | | | |
|---|---|---|---|---|
| **713** | A122 | 75fr multicolored | .70 | .25 |
| **714** | A122 | 150fr multicolored | 1.25 | .35 |
| **715** | A122 | 375fr multicolored | 3.00 | .60 |
| **716** | A122 | 600fr multicolored | 5.00 | 1.25 |
| | | *Nos. 713-716 (4)* | 9.95 | 2.45 |

**Litho. & Embossed**

| | | | | |
|---|---|---|---|---|
| **717** | A122 | 1500fr gold & multi | 13.00 | — |

**Souvenir Sheets**

**Litho.**

| | | | | |
|---|---|---|---|---|
| **718** | A122 | 1000fr multicolored | 8.50 | 1.75 |

**Litho. & Embossed**

| | | | | |
|---|---|---|---|---|
| **719** | A122 | 1500fr gold & multi | 13.00 | |

Philexfrance 1989. No. 716-719 are airmail.

No. 714 incorrectly inscribed "Francois-Etienne."

Nos. 713-716 exist in souvenir sheets of 1.

No. 717 exists in a souvenir sheet of 1. Value $22.

For surcharges see Nos. 796B, 800W, 804J.

Airport Pavilion — A124

Designs: 10fr, 25fr, Airport pavilion. 50fr, 75fr, 150fr, Federal Assembly.

**1990, Apr. 1 Litho. *Perf. 13***

| | | | | |
|---|---|---|---|---|
| **722** | A124 | 5fr brn, org & brt red | .25 | .25 |
| **723** | A124 | 10fr brn, org & brt bl | .25 | .25 |
| **724** | A124 | 25fr brn, org & brt grn | .25 | .25 |
| **725** | A124 | 50fr blk & brt red | .45 | .25 |
| **726** | A124 | 75fr blk & brt bl | .75 | .30 |
| **727** | A124 | 150fr blk & grn | 1.40 | .60 |
| | | *Nos. 722-727 (6)* | 3.35 | 1.90 |

World Cup Soccer Championships, Italy — A125

Players from: 50fr, Brazil. 75fr, England. 100fr, Federal Republic of Germany. 150fr, Belgium. 375fr, Italy. 600fr, Argentina. 750fr, Argentina and Italy.

**1990 Litho. *Perf. 13½***

| | | | | |
|---|---|---|---|---|
| **728** | A125 | 50fr multicolored | .45 | .25 |
| **729** | A125 | 75fr multicolored | .65 | .30 |
| **730** | A125 | 100fr multicolored | .80 | .35 |
| **731** | A125 | 150fr multicolored | 1.10 | .45 |
| **732** | A125 | 375fr multicolored | 3.00 | 1.00 |
| **733** | A125 | 600fr multicolored | 5.00 | 1.25 |
| | | *Nos. 728-733 (6)* | 11.00 | 3.60 |

**Litho. & Embossed**

| | | | | |
|---|---|---|---|---|
| **734** | A125 | 1500fr gold & multi | 13.00 | 5.00 |

**Souvenir Sheets**

**Litho.**

| | | | | |
|---|---|---|---|---|
| **735** | A125 | 750fr multicolored | 6.75 | 1.50 |

**Litho. & Embossed**

| | | | | |
|---|---|---|---|---|
| **736** | A125 | 1500fr gold & multi | 13.00 | — |

Nos. 732-736 are airmail.

Nos. 728-733 exist in a souvenir sheet of 6. Value, $12.50.

No. 734 exists in a souvenir sheet of 1. Value $22.50.

For surcharges see Nos. 796L, 796O, 804K.

Telecom '91 — A125a

75fr, Emblem, vert.

**1990, Oct. 29 Litho. *Perf. 13½***

| | | | | |
|---|---|---|---|---|
| **736A** | A125a | 75fr multi | 1.00 | .60 |
| **736B** | A125a | 150fr shown | 2.00 | 1.25 |

Nos. 736A-736B exist imperf.

A126

Designs: 75fr, Hubble Space Telescope placed in orbit. 150fr, Pope John Paul II, Pres. Gorbachev meet Dec. 3, 1989. 200fr, Kevin Mitchell, San Francisco Giants, Natl. League Most Valuable Player, 1989. 250fr, De Gaulle, France, and Adenauer, West Germany, meet in Sept. 1962. 300fr, Cassini probe to Titan, 2002. 375fr, Bullet train and Concorde, France. 450fr, Garry Kasparov, World Chess Champion. 500fr, Paul Harris (1868-1947), founder of Rotary Intl.

**1990, Nov. 26 Litho. *Perf. 13½***

| | | | | |
|---|---|---|---|---|
| **737** | A126 | 75fr sil & multi | .75 | .25 |
| **738** | A126 | 150fr sil & multi | 1.50 | .40 |
| **739** | A126 | 200fr sil & multi | 2.00 | .40 |
| **740** | A126 | 250fr sil & multi | 2.50 | .40 |
| **741** | A126 | 300fr sil & multi | 3.00 | .50 |
| **742** | A126 | 375fr sil & multi | 3.75 | .65 |
| **743** | A126 | 450fr sil & multi | 4.50 | 1.00 |
| **744** | A126 | 500fr sil & multi | 5.25 | .75 |
| | | *Nos. 737-744 (8)* | 23.25 | 4.35 |

Nos. 743-744 are airmail.

No. 737-744 exist in souv. sheets of 1. Value, set of 8 $50.

For surcharges see Nos. 796A, 796R, 800I, 804A, 804L, 815E, 815U.

A127

Winter Olympics participants: 75fr, Edi Reinalter, Switzerland, slalom, 1948. 100fr, Canadian hockey team, 1924. 375fr, Gratia Van der Oye, women's slalom, Holland, 1936. 600fr, Heikki Hasu, Finland, combined cross country and ski jumping, 1948. 750fr, Helene Engelman & Alfred Berger, Austria, pairs figure skating, 1924. No. 751, Speed skater, horiz. No. 751A, Luge, horiz.

**1990, Dec. 10**

| | | | | |
|---|---|---|---|---|
| **746** | A127 | 75fr multicolored | .60 | .25 |
| **747** | A127 | 100fr multicolored | .75 | .30 |
| **748** | A127 | 375fr multicolored | 3.50 | 1.00 |
| **749** | A127 | 600fr multicolored | 6.00 | 1.25 |
| | | *Nos. 746-749 (4)* | 10.85 | 2.80 |

**Souvenir Sheet**

| | | | | |
|---|---|---|---|---|
| **750** | A127 | 750fr multicolored | 7.00 | 1.50 |

**Litho. & Embossed**

| | | | | |
|---|---|---|---|---|
| **751** | A127 | 1500fr gold & multi | 16.00 | — |

**Souvenir Sheet**

| | | | | |
|---|---|---|---|---|
| **751A** | A127 | 1500fr gold & multi | 15.00 | — |

1992 Winter Olympics, Albertville. Nos. 748-751A are airmail. No. 750 contains one 36x41mm stamp.

No. 751 exists in a souvenir sheet of 1. Value $22.

For surcharges see Nos. 796M, 800K, 804M, 812S.

A128

Ground station, Moroni Volo-Volo.

**1991, May 17 Litho. *Perf. 13½***

| | | | | |
|---|---|---|---|---|
| **752** | A128 | 75fr multicolored | 1.00 | .25 |
| **753** | A128 | 150fr multicolored | 1.60 | .45 |
| **754** | A128 | 225fr multicolored | 2.40 | .75 |
| **755** | A128 | 300fr multicolored | 3.50 | 1.00 |
| **756** | A128 | 500fr multicolored | 5.50 | 1.25 |
| | | *Nos. 752-756 (5)* | 14.00 | 3.70 |

For surcharge see 815N.

Indian Ocean Conference A129

**1991, June 17**

| | | | | |
|---|---|---|---|---|
| **757** | A129 | 75fr multicolored | .50 | .25 |
| **758** | A129 | 150fr multicolored | 1.40 | .75 |
| **759** | A129 | 225fr multicolored | 2.00 | 1.00 |
| | | *Nos. 757-759 (3)* | 3.90 | 2.00 |

World War II, 50th Anniv. — A130

Actors, Films: 150fr, Errol Flynn, Objective Burma. 300fr, Henry Fonda, The Longest Day. 450fr, Humphrey Bogart, Sahara.

**1991, Aug. 5**

| | | | | |
|---|---|---|---|---|
| **760** | A130 | 150fr sil & multi | 1.75 | .45 |
| **761** | A130 | 300fr sil & multi | 3.25 | .75 |
| **762** | A130 | 450fr sil & multi | 5.00 | .90 |
| | | *Nos. 760-762 (3)* | 10.00 | 2.10 |

No. 762 is airmail. Nos. 760-762 exist in souvenir sheets of 1. Value, set of 3 $15.

For surcharges see Nos. 796D, 800H, 804B, 804G.

A131

Charles de Gaulle — A132

De Gaulle and: 125fr, Battle of Koufra. 375fr, Battle of Britain. 500fr, Battle of Monte Cassino. 1000fr, Airplanes. 1500fr, De Gaulle at podium.

**1991, Aug. 5 Litho. *Perf. 13½***

| | | | | |
|---|---|---|---|---|
| **763** | A131 | 125fr multi | 1.50 | .30 |
| **764** | A131 | 375fr multi | 3.00 | .75 |
| **765** | A131 | 500fr multi | 5.00 | .90 |
| | | *Nos. 763-765 (3)* | 9.50 | 1.95 |

**Souvenir Sheet**

| | | | | |
|---|---|---|---|---|
| **766** | A131 | 1000fr multi | 12.00 | 2.00 |

**Litho. & Embossed**

| | | | | |
|---|---|---|---|---|
| **767** | A132 | 1500fr gold & multi | 16.00 | — |

Nos. 765-767 are airmail. No. 767 exists in souvenir sheet of 1. Value $20.

For surcharges see Nos. 796G, 804N, 816I.

Anniversaries and Events — A133

Designs: 100fr, Satellite Columbus in polar orbit. 150fr, Gandhi. 250fr, Jean-Henri Dunant. 300fr, Wolfgang Amadeus Mozart. 375fr, Brandenburg Gate. 400fr, Konrad Adenauer. 450fr, Elvis Presley. 500fr, Ferdinand von Zeppelin.

**1991, Nov. 18 Litho. *Perf. 13½***

| | | | | |
|---|---|---|---|---|
| **768** | A133 | 100fr multicolored | 1.25 | .30 |
| **769** | A133 | 150fr multicolored | 1.60 | .35 |
| **770** | A133 | 250fr multicolored | 2.50 | .60 |
| **771** | A133 | 300fr multicolored | 3.00 | .60 |
| **772** | A133 | 375fr multicolored | 4.25 | .90 |
| **773** | A133 | 400fr multicolored | 5.00 | .90 |
| **774** | A133 | 450fr multicolored | 5.50 | 1.00 |
| *a.* | | Souv. sheet, #771, 774 | — | — |
| **775** | A133 | 500fr multicolored | 5.50 | 1.00 |
| *a.* | | Souv. sheet, #772-773, 775 | — | — |
| | | *Nos. 768-775 (8)* | 28.60 | 5.65 |

Nobel Peace Prize, 90th anniv. (No. 770). Mozart, bicent. of death (No. 771). Brandenburg Gate, bicent. (No. 772). Konrad Adenauer, 25th anniv. of death (No. 773). Elvis Presley, 15th anniv. of death (in 1992) (No. 774). Count Zeppelin, 75th anniv. of death (in 1992) (No. 775).

Nos. 774-775 are airmail. Nos. 768-775 exist in souvenir sheets of 1. Value, set $50.

For surcharges see Nos. 796F, 796H, 800G, 804C, 804O, 815F, 815O, 816J.

Mushrooms A134

75fr, Cepe comestible. 150fr, Geastre en etoile. 600fr, Pezize ecarlate.

**1992, Mar. 23 Litho. *Perf. 13½***

| | | | | |
|---|---|---|---|---|
| **776** | A134 | 75fr multicolored | .80 | .40 |
| **777** | A134 | 150fr multicolored | 1.50 | .60 |
| **778** | A134 | 600fr multicolored | 6.00 | 1.50 |
| | | *Nos. 776-778 (3)* | 8.30 | 2.50 |

No. 778 is airmail. Nos. 776-778 exist imperf. and in souvenir sheets of one. Values, imperf set $12; set of souvenir sheets $10.

Shells — A135

125fr, Conus textile. 150fr, Cypraecassis rufa. 500fr, Leporicypraea mappa. 750fr, Nautilus pompilius.

**1992, Mar. 23**

| | | | | |
|---|---|---|---|---|
| **779** | A135 | 125fr multicolored | 1.60 | .50 |
| **780** | A135 | 150fr multicolored | 1.75 | .65 |
| **781** | A135 | 500fr multicolored | 6.00 | 1.90 |
| | | *Nos. 779-781 (3)* | 9.35 | 3.05 |

**Souvenir Sheet**

| | | | | |
|---|---|---|---|---|
| **782** | A135 | 750fr multicolored | 10.50 | 2.00 |

Nos. 781-782 are airmail. Nos. 779-781 exist imperf. and in souvenir sheets of one. Values, imperf set $15; set of souvenir sheets $12. No. 782 exists imperf. Value, $12.

For surcharges see Nos. 800N, 816K.

Space Programs A136

Designs: 75fr, Mercury rocket, chimpanzee Ham, US. 125fr, Mars Observer, US. No. 785, Veronica rocket, cat Felix, France. No. 786, Mars rover, US, Mars car, USSR. 500fr, Phobos project, USSR. 600fr, Sputnik II, dog Laika, USSR. 1000fr, Viking, US, vert.

**1992, Mar. 30 Litho. *Perf. 13½***

| | | | | |
|---|---|---|---|---|
| **783** | A136 | 75fr multicolored | 1.25 | .25 |
| **784** | A136 | 125fr multicolored | 1.75 | .30 |
| **785** | A136 | 150fr multicolored | 2.25 | .70 |
| **786** | A136 | 150fr multicolored | 2.10 | .70 |
| **787** | A136 | 500fr multicolored | 6.50 | 1.25 |
| *a.* | | Souv. sheet, #784, 786-787 | 20.00 | — |
| **788** | A136 | 600fr multicolored | 7.75 | 1.40 |
| *a.* | | Souv. sheet, #783, 785, 788 | 20.00 | — |
| | | *Nos. 783-788 (6)* | 21.60 | 4.60 |

**Souvenir Sheet**

| | | | | |
|---|---|---|---|---|
| **789** | A136 | 1000fr multicolored | 13.00 | 2.25 |

Nos. 787-789 are airmail. Nos. 783-788 exist imperf. and in souvenir sheets of one. Values: imperf set, $32.50; set of souvenir sheets, $25. No. 789 contains one 30x42mm stamp.

For surcharges see Nos. 800O, 804Q.

Voyages of Discovery A137

Designs: 75fr, Space shuttle Endeavour, sailing ship Endeavour, Capt. Cook. 100fr, Satellite, sailing ship Golden Hinde, Sir Francis Drake. 150fr, ISO observation satellite, sailing ship Susan Constant, John Smith. 225fr, Probe B, sailing ship Discovery, Robert F. Scott. 375fr, Magellan probe over Venus, sailing ship, Ferdinand Magellan. 500fr, Newton probe, sailing ship Sao Gabriel, Vasco da Gama.

1000fr, Hermes-Columbus space shuttle, Columbus and his fleet.

**1992, May 28 Litho. *Perf. 13½***

| | | | | |
|---|---|---|---|---|
| **790** | A137 | 75fr multicolored | 1.25 | .25 |
| **791** | A137 | 100fr multicolored | 1.40 | .30 |
| **792** | A137 | 150fr multicolored | 2.25 | .45 |
| **793** | A137 | 225fr multicolored | 2.75 | .75 |
| **794** | A137 | 375fr multicolored | 5.25 | 1.00 |
| **795** | A137 | 500fr multicolored | 6.00 | 1.25 |
| *a.* | | Souvenir sheet of 6, #790-795 | 15.00 | 7.00 |
| | | *Nos. 790-795 (6)* | 18.90 | 4.00 |

**Souvenir Sheet**

| | | | | |
|---|---|---|---|---|
| **796** | A137 | 1000fr multicolored | 13.00 | 2.25 |

Nos. 794-796 are airmail. Nos. 790-795 exist imperf. in souvenir sheets of one. Values: imperf sets $35; set of souvenir sheets $45.

For surcharges see Nos. 796E, 800P, 804P.

**Various Stamps Surcharged**

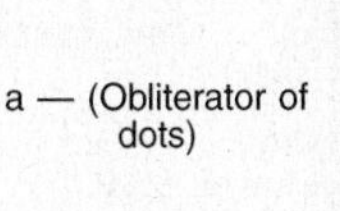

a — (Obliterator of dots)

**Methods and Perfs as Before**

**1992-95**

| | | | | |
|---|---|---|---|---|
| **796A** | A126 | 10fr on 300fr #741 | — | |
| **796B** | A122 | 15fr on 375fr #715 | — | |
| **796C** | AP41 | 25fr on 210fr #C164 | — | |
| **796D** | A130 | 25fr on 300fr #761 | — | |
| **796E** | A137 | 25fr on 375fr #794 | — | |
| **796F** | A133 | 35fr on 400fr #773 | — | |
| **796G** | A131 | 50fr on 375fr #764 | — | |
| **796H** | A133 | 50fr on 375fr #772 | — | |
| **796I** | AP34 | 50fr on 475fr #C138 | — | |
| **796J** | A121 | 75fr on 300fr #708 | — | — |
| **796K** | A121 | 75fr on 375fr #709 | — | |
| **796L** | A125 | 75fr on 375fr #732 | — | |
| **796M** | A127 | 75fr on 375fr #748 | — | |
| **796N** | AP42 | 75fr on 600fr #C170 | — | |
| **796O** | A125 | 100fr on 375fr #732 | — | |
| **796P** | A109 | 150fr on 210fr #633 | — | |
| **796Q** | A120 | 150fr on 375fr #697 | — | — |
| **796R** | A126 | 150fr on 375fr #742 | — | |
| **796S** | AP40 | 150fr on 450fr #C162 | — | |
| **796T** | A109 | 150fr on 500fr #634 | — | |
| **796U** | AP42 | 150fr on 500fr #C169 | — | |

No. 796J exists with quadruple surcharge.

No. 796Q exists with inverted surcharge and with double surcharge, one inverted.

Organization of African Unity, 30th Anniv. — A138

**1993, Feb. 15 Litho. *Perf. 13½x13***

| | | | | |
|---|---|---|---|---|
| **797** | A138 | 25fr blue & multi | .25 | .25 |
| **798** | A138 | 50fr pink & multi | .50 | .25 |

***Perf. 12***

| | | | | |
|---|---|---|---|---|
| **799** | A138 | 75fr green & multi | 1.40 | .45 |
| **800** | A138 | 150fr vermilion & multi | 2.25 | 1.00 |
| | | *Nos. 797-800 (4)* | 4.40 | 1.95 |

**Various Stamps Surcharged**

b — (Bar obliterator)

**Methods and Perfs as Before**

**1992-95**

| | | | | |
|---|---|---|---|---|
| **800A** | A103 | 50fr on 450fr #607 | — | |
| *x.* | | Zero in surcharge thin at top and bottom | — | |
| **800B** | AP47 | 75fr on 800fr #C192 | — | |
| **800C** | A112 | 100fr on 350fr #648 | — | — |
| **800D** | A119 | 100fr on 375fr #689 | — | |
| *g.* | | Zero in surcharge thin at top and bottom | — | |
| *y.* | | 150fr on 375fr #689 (error) | — | |
| **800E** | A101 | 100fr on 400fr #590 | — | — |
| **800F** | A105 | 100fr on 400fr #618 | — | |
| *h.* | | Zero in surcharge thin at top and bottom | — | |
| **800G** | A133 | 100fr on 400fr #773 | — | |
| *i.* | | Zero in surcharge thin at top and bottom | — | |
| **800H** | A130 | 125fr on 450fr #762 | — | |
| **800I** | A126 | 150fr on 250fr #740 | — | — |
| **800J** | A121 | 150fr on 375fr #709 | — | |
| *z.* | | Zero in surcharge thin at top and bottom | — | |
| **800K** | A127 | 150fr on 375fr #748 | — | |
| *a.* | | Zero in surcharge thin at top and bottom | — | |
| **800L** | A109 | 150fr on 500fr #634 | — | — |
| *k.* | | Zero in surcharge thin at top and bottom | — | |
| **800M** | A112 | 150fr on 500fr #650 | — | |
| *b.* | | Zero in surcharge thin at top and bottom | — | |
| **800N** | A135 | 150fr on 500fr #781 | — | — |
| **800O** | A136 | 150fr on 500fr #787 | — | |
| **800P** | A137 | 150fr on 500fr #795 | — | |
| *c.* | | Zero in surcharge thin at top and bottom | — | |
| **800Q** | AP41 | 150fr on 500fr #C165 | — | |
| *d.* | | Zero in surcharge thin at top and bottom | — | |
| **800R** | AP44 | 150fr on 500fr #C177 | — | |
| *l.* | | Zero in surcharge thin at top and bottom | — | |
| *m.* | | Denomination above obliterator | — | |
| *n.* | | As "l," denomination above obliterator | — | |
| **800S** | AP45 | 150fr on 500fr #C181 | — | |
| *e.* | | Zero in surcharge thin at top and bottom | — | |
| **800T** | AP42 | 150fr on 500fr #C185 | — | |
| *o.* | | Zero in surcharge thin at top and bottom | — | |
| **800U** | AP47 | 150fr on 500fr #C191 | — | |
| **800V** | AP50 | 150fr on 500fr #C212 | — | |
| *p.* | | Zero in surcharge thin at top and bottom | — | |
| **800W** | A122 | 150fr on 600fr #716 | — | |

Surcharge on No. 800W is sideways reading top to bottom. Nos. 800B and 800F exist with inverted surcharge, Nos. 800F, 800R, 800W, and perhaps other values exist with misplaced surcharge.

No. 800F exists with zeros in surcharge in different sizes.

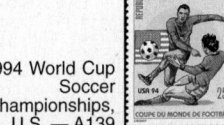

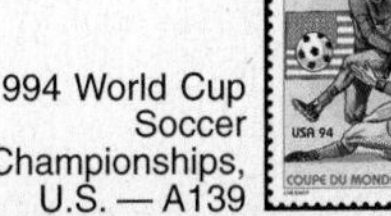
1994 World Cup Soccer Championships, U.S. — A139

**1993, May 12 Litho. *Perf. 13x12½***

**801** A139 25fr red & multi .25 .25
**802** A139 75fr brown & multi .65 .30
**803** A139 100fr blue & multi 1.40 .40
**804** A139 150fr green & multi 1.60 .60
*Nos. 801-804 (4)* 3.90 1.55

### Various Stamps Surcharged Type "b" in Black or Red

### Methods and Perfs as Before

**1992-95**

**804A** A126 200fr on 300fr #741 —
*s.* Zero in surcharge thin at top and bottom —
**804B** A130 200fr on 300fr #761 —
**804C** A133 200fr on 300fr #771 —
*w.* Zero in surcharge thin at top and bottom — —
**804D** AP45 200fr on 300fr #C180 —
*x.* Zero in surcharge thin at top and bottom —
**804E** AP47 200fr on 300fr #C190 —
*t.* Zero in surcharge thin at top and bottom —
**804F** A90 200fr on 450fr #520 —
*u.* Overprint right side up —
*y.* Overprint right side up, zero in surcharge thin at top and bottom —
**804G** A130 200fr on 450fr #762 —
*a.* Zero in surcharge thin at top and bottom —
*b.* As "a," two obliterators —
**804H** AP40 200fr on 450fr #C162 —
*c.* Zero in surcharge thin at top and bottom —
**804I** A120 225fr on 375fr #697 —
**804J** A122 225fr on 375fr #715 —
**804K** A125 225fr on 375fr #732 —
**804L** A126 225fr on 375fr #742 —
**804M** A127 225fr on 375fr #748 —
*v.* "f" in surcharge omitted —
**804N** A127 225fr on 375fr #764 —
**804O** A133 225fr on 375fr #772 —
**804P** A137 225fr on 375fr #794 —
**804Q** A136 225fr on 500fr #787 —

### Red Surcharge

**804R** AP40 200fr on 300fr #C161 —

Surcharge on No. 804F is inverted.
No. 804D exists with "020fr" surcharge. Nos. 804D and 804F exist with zeroes in surcharge in different sizes.

Intl. Telecommunications Day — A140

**1993, May 17**

**805** A140 50fr red & multi .30 .25
**806** A140 75fr blue & multi .50 .30
**807** A140 100fr green & multi .90 .40
**808** A140 150fr black & multi 1.25 .60
*Nos. 805-808 (4)* 2.95 1.55

### Miniature Sheet

Prehistoric Animals — A141

Designs: a, 75fr, Edaphosaurus. b, 75fr, Moschops. c, 75fr, Sauroctonus. d, 75fr, Ornitholestes. e, 75fr, Kentrosaurus. f, 75fr, Compsognathus. g, 75fr, Styracosaurus. h, 75fr, Acanthopholis. i, 150fr, Edmontonia. j, 150fr, Struthiomimus. k, 450fr, Dromiceiomimus. l, 450fr, Iguanodon. m, 150fr, Diatryma. n, 150fr, Uintatherium. o, 525fr, Synthetoceras. p, 525fr, Euryapteryx.
1200fr, Tyrannosaurus rex.

**1994, Apr. 5 Litho. *Perf. 13½***

**809** A141 Sheet of 16, #a.-p. 17.50 9.00

### Souvenir Sheet

**810** A141 1200fr multicolored 11.50 3.00

No. 810 is airmail and contains one 42x60mm stamp.

### Miniature Sheets

Flora A142

No. 811a: 75fr, Hibiscus syriacus. b, 75fr, Anacardier. c, 75fr, Suillus lutens. d, 150fr, Pyrostegia venusta. e, 150fr, Manioc. f, 150fr, Lycogala epidendron. g, 525fr, Allamanda cathartica. h, 525fr, Cacao. i, 525fr, Clathrus ruber.
Butterflies, insects: No. 812a, 75fr, Colotis zoe. b, 150fr, Acherontia atropos. c, 450fr, Danaus chrysippus. d, 75fr, Charaxes comoranus. e, 150fr, Euchloron megaera. f, 450fr, Papilio phorbanta. g, 75fr, Hypurgus ova. h, 150fr, Onthophagus catta. i, 450fr, Echinosoma bolivari.

**1994, May 24 Litho. *Perf. 13½***

**811** A142 Sheet of 9 16.00 5.50
*j.* Souvenir sheet of 3, #811a, 811d, 811g *16.00 5.00*
*k.* Souvenir sheet of 3, #811b, 811e, 811h *16.00 5.00*
*l.* Souvenir sheet of 3, #811c, 811f, 811i *16.00 5.00*
**812** A142 Sheet of 9, #a.-i. 15.00 5.00
*j.* Souv. sheet of 3, #812a-812c *16.00 5.00*
*k.* Souv. sheet of 3, #812d-812f *16.00 5.00*
*l.* Souv. sheet of 3, #812g-812i *16.00 5.00*

For surcharges see No. 826F.

Independence, 20th Anniv. — A142a

Designs: 100fr, 200fr, 300fr, Maps of Grand Comoro, Moheli, Mayotte and Anjouan.

**1995 (?) Litho. *Perf. 13x12¾***

**812M** A142a 100fr multi
**812N** A142a 200fr multi — —
**812O** A142a 300fr multi

For surcharge see No. 826M.

### Various Stamps Surcharged in Gold

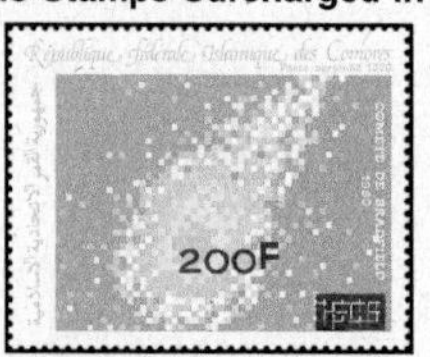
c — (Wide numerals, obliterator of small sqares in grid)

### Methods and Perfs as Before

**1996, Dec.**

**812P** AP40 200fr on 300fr #C161 —
**812Q** A102 200fr on 350fr #598 —
**812R** A121 200fr on 375fr #709 —
*v.* "2" same size as "0" —
**812S** A127 200fr on 375fr #748 —
**812T** AP31 200fr on 400fr #C125 — —
**812U** AP44 200fr on 500fr #C177 —

Size of numerals and obliteration grids varies.

A143

Diana, Princess of Wales (1961-97): Various portraits.

**1997, Dec. 15 Litho. *Perf. 14***

**813** A143 150fr Sheet of 12, #a.-l. 10.00 4.00
**814** A143 375fr Sheet of 6, #a.-f. 12.00 5.00

### Souvenir Sheet

**815** A143 1000fr multicolored 5.50 2.25

### Various Stamps Surcharged Type "c" in Black

### Methods and Perfs as Before

**1996, Dec.**

**815A** A109 200fr on 210fr #633 —
**815B** A111 200fr on 210fr #640 —
**815C** AP41 200fr on 210fr #C164 — —
**815D** A114 200fr on 250fr #660 —
**815E** A126 200fr on 250fr #740 —
**815F** A133 200fr on 250fr #770 —
**815G** AP30 200fr on 250fr #C116 — —
**815H** AP38 200fr on 250fr #C151 —
**815I** AP38 200fr on 250fr #C152 —
*x.* Pair, #815H-815I + label —
**815J** AP42 200fr on 250fr #C168 —
**815K** AP42 200fr on 250fr #C184 —
**815L** AP28 200fr on 260fr #C110 — —
**815M** A101 200fr on 300fr #589 —
*y.* With gold obliterator over old value — —
**815N** A128 200fr on 300fr #755 —
**815O** A133 200fr on 300fr #771 —
**815P** AP31 200fr on 300fr #C124 —
**815Q** AP37 200fr on 300fr #C150 —
**815R** A107 200fr on 350fr #626 —
**815S** A98 200fr on 360fr #574 —
**815T** A119 200fr on 375fr #689 —
**815U** A126 200fr on 375fr #742 —
**815V** A112 200fr on 400fr #649 —
**815W** A111 200fr on 425fr #641 —

Size of surcharge numerals and obliteration grid varies. Black surcharge on No. 815My is misplaced. No. 815Q exists with misplaced surcharge that is faintly tripled, a surcharge with thinner zeroes, and a pair containing No. C150 next to No. 815Q with misplaced surcharge that is faintly tripled and has thinner zeroes. No. 815W exists with an inverted surcharge and with a double surcharge, one inverted.

Mother Teresa (1910-97) — A144

**1997, Dec. 15 Litho. *Perf. 14***

**816** A144 200fr multicolored 1.50 1.00

No. 816 was issued in sheets of 9.

Aromatic Plants — A144a

Designs: 25fr, 50fr, 1000fr, Piper nigrum. 100fr, 125fr, 200fr, Cinnamomum ceylanicum. 300fr, Syzigium aromaticum. 500fr, Myristica fragrans.

**1997, Dec. 15 Litho. *Perf. 14***

**816A** A144a 25fr multi —
**816B** A144a 50fr multi —
**816C** A144a 100fr multi —
**816D** A144a 125fr multi —
**816E** A144a 200fr multi —
**816F** A144a 300fr multi —
**816G** A144a 500fr multi —
**816H** A144a 1000fr multi —

### Various Stamps Surcharged Type "c" in Black

### Methods and Perfs as Before

**1996, Dec.**

**816I** A131 200fr on 500fr #765 — —
**816J** A133 200fr on 500fr #775 — —
**816K** A135 200fr on 500fr #781 — —
**816L** AP42 200fr on 500fr #C169 — —
**816M** AP42 200fr on 500fr #C185 — —
**816N** AP42 200fr on 600fr #C170 — —
**816O** AP42 200fr on 600fr #C186 — —

Size of surcharge and obliteration grid varies.

### Vertical Pairs from No. B4 Surcharged with Silver Bar to Obliterate Surtax

### Methods and Perfs as before.

**1996, Dec.**

**816P** Surcharged pair of #B4a, B4e —
*t.* SP3 200fr on 200fr+10fr Galileo —
*u.* SP3 200fr on 200fr+10fr Planet A & 3 stars —
**816Q** Surcharged pair of #B4b, B4f —
*v.* SP3 200fr on 200fr+10fr Copernicus —
*w.* SP3 200fr on 200fr+10fr ICE —
**816R** Surcharged pair of #B4c, B4g —
*x.* SP3 200fr on 200fr+10fr Kepler —
*y.* SP3 200fr on 200fr+10fr Planet A & 5 stars —
**816S** Surcharged pair of #B4d, B4h —
*z.* SP3 200fr on 200fr+10fr Halley —
*aa.* SP3 200fr on 200fr+10fr Vega —

A full sheet of Nos. 816P-816S is not known to exist.

Cats — A145

Designs, vert: 75fr, Silver banded. 150fr, Lac de Van. No. 819, 200fr, European short hair. No. 820, 200fr, Somali. No. 821, 375fr, Japanese bobtail. No. 822, 375fr, Egyptian mau.
No. 823, each 375fr: a, Poupée de chiffon. b, Maine coon. c, Norwegian forest cat. d, Persian. e, Droop-eared. f, Marbled American short hair.
No. 824, each 375fr: a, Manx. b, Cashmere. c, British shorthair. d, Cornish rex. e, American curl. f, Ocicat.
No. 825, 1500fr, Silver-chocolate Somali. No. 826, 1500fr, Chocolate Persian, vert.

**1998, June 3 Litho. *Perf. 14***

**817-822** A145 Set of 6 7.50 7.50

### Sheets of 6

**823-824** A145 Set of 2 24.00 24.00

### Souvenir Sheets

**825-826** A145 Set of 2 15.00 6.00

### No. C215D Surcharged Type "c" in Red or Black

### Methods and Perfs as Before

**1997 (?)**

**826A** AP52a 100fr on 225fr — —
**826B** AP52a 200fr on 225fr — —
**826C** AP52a 200fr on 225fr (Bk) —
**826D** AP52a 500fr on 225fr —
**826E** AP52a 600fr on 225fr —

Size of surcharge numerals varies. No. 826B exists with inverted surcharge, No. 826C exists with double surcharge.

### No. 811 Surcharged on Six Stamps

d — (Obliterator of Triangles and Wavy Lines)

### Methods and Perfs as Before

**1998 (?)**

**826F** Sheet of 9 —
*g.* A142 200fr on 150fr Pyrostegia venusta —
*h.* A142 200fr on 150fr Manioc —
*i.* A142 200fr on 150fr Lycogala epidendron —
*j.* A142 200fr on 525fr Allamanda cathartica —
*k.* A142 200fr on 525fr Cacao —
*l.* A142 200fr on 525fr Clathrus ruber —

The three 75fr stamps on the sheet received no surcharge.

### No. 812O Surcharged

e — (Obliterator of Bars, Dots, and Semicircles)

### Methods and Perfs as Before

**1998 (?)**

**826M** A142a 100fr on 300fr —

Size of surcharge numerals varies.

Marine Life — A146

No. 827, each 150fr: a, Pomacanthus imperator. b, Cephalopholis miniata. c, Diver. d, Nautilus pompilius. e, Sphyraena barracuda. f, Manta birostris. g, Lutjanus sebae. h, Chaetodonplus duboulayi. i, Amphiprion bicinctus.

No. 828, vert , each 150fr: a, Istiophorus platypterus. b, Sterna fuscata. c, Larus pipixcan. d, Hippocampus kuda. e, Amphiprion ocellaris (2 fish). f, Octopus vulgaris. g, Chaetodon striatus. h, Actini aquina. i, Acanthurus leucosternon.

No. 829: a, Diomedea exulans. b, Delphinus delphis. c, Sailboat. d, Sphyrna zygaena. e, Loligo forbesi. f, Galeocerdo cuvieri. g, Pomacanthus imperator, diff. h, Amphiprion ocellaris (1 fish). i, Forcipiger flavissimus. j, Electrophorus electricus. k, Dermochelys coriaoea. l, Asterias rubens.

No. 830, 1500fr, Mastigias papua, vert. No. 831, 1500fr, Sepia officinalis. No. 832, 1500fr, Zancius canescens.

**1998, Aug. 10 Litho. *Perf. 14***

**Sheets of 9 or 12**

**827-828** A146 Set of 2 13.00 13.00
**829** A146 200fr #a.-l. 12.00 12.00

**Souvenir Sheets**

**830-832** A146 Set of 3 22.50 22.50

Nos. 830-832 each contain one 51x38mm or 38x51mm stamp.

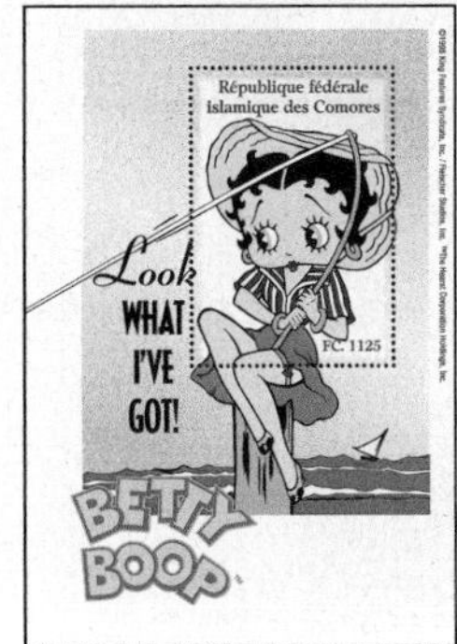


Betty Boop — A146a

No. 832A: b, Wearing hula skirt, dancing. c, With dog, wearing blue dress, in pink heart. d, Wearing polka dot dress. e, In bathtub. f, Face in red heart. g, Holding top hat. h, With flamingos. i, With dog, Wearing red dress, blue ribbon. j, Wearing hula skirt, on surf board.

1125fr, With fishing pole.

**1998 Litho. *Perf. 13¼***

**832A** A146a 300fr Sheet of 9, #b-j 14.00 14.00

**Souvenir Sheet**

**832K** A146a 1125fr multi 6.00 6.00

No. 832A contains nine 35x41mm stamps.

Popeye — A146b

No. 832L: m, Wimpy. n, Popeye, Olive Oyl, ship's wheel. o, Swee'Pea. p, Head of Popeye. q, Popeye. r, Head of Olive Oyl. s, Jeep. t, Olive Oyl. u, Brutus.

No. 832V, 1125fr, Popeye with spinach can. No. 832W, 1125fr, Like #832Ln, horiz.

**1998**

**832L** A146b 450fr Sheet of 9, #m-u 20.00 20.00

**Souvenir Sheets**

**832V-832W** A146b Set of 2 11.50 11.50

No. 832L contains nine 35x51mm stamps, No. 832W contains one 60x50mm stamp.

Coelacanth A147

World Wildlife Fund: a, Swimming right, colored background. b, Swimming right, white background. c, In net. d, Swimming left.

No. 833E: f, Like #833a. g, Like #833d. h, Like #833c. i, Like #833b.

**1998**

**833** A147 200fr Strip of 4, #a-d 11.50 11.50
**833E** A147 375fr Sheet of 4, #f-i 5.00 5.00

No. 833 was issued in sheets of 3 vertical strips.

No. 833E exists imperf. Value $45.

I Love Lucy — A147a

No. 833F, vert. — Lucy: g, With black ribbon in hair. h, Wearing burlap sack. i, With trapeze in mouth. j, With one arm raised. k, On telephone. l, Wearing red and white apron. m, Wearing bright green dress. n, Wearing blue dress. o, With fishing gear.

1125fr, With Ricky, with fishing gear.

**1998 Litho. *Perf. 13¼***

**833F** A147a 250fr Sheet of 9, #g-o 13.00 13.00

**Souvenir Sheet**

**833P** A147a 1125fr multi 7.00 7.00

No. 833F contains nine 35x51mm stamps.

Diana, Princess of Wales (1961-97) — A148

Nos. 834-835, 835J, Various portraits.

No. 836, 1125fr, Wearing scarf, green dress. No. 837, 1125fr, Wearing black and white hat and outfit.

**1998 Litho. *Perf. 13½***

**Sheets of 9**

**834** A148 250fr #a.-i. 11.50 11.50
**835** A148 350fr #a.-i. 14.50 14.50
**835J** A148 450fr #k.-s. 18.00 18.00

**Souvenir Sheets**

**836-837** A148 Set of 2 10.00 10.00

Nos. 835, 835J contain 42x51mm stamps. Nos. 836-837 each contain one 42x60mm stamp.

Entertainers A149

No. 838: Various portraits of Grace Kelly (Princess Grace of Monaco) (1929-92).

No. 839: Various portraits of Frank Sinatra (1915-98).

**1998 Sheets of 9**

**838** A149 300fr #a.-i. 13.00 13.00
**839** A149 500fr #a.-i. 21.00 21.00

Classic Automobiles A150

No. 840, each 150fr: a, 1936 Jaguar SS. b, 1939 Lincoln Continental. c, 1903 Mercedes. d, 1936 MG-TA. e, 1946 Oldsmobile Custom Cruiser 98. f, 1933 Pontiac. g, 1940 Rolls-Royce Silver Ghost 40/50. h, 1950 Studebaker Starlight Coupe. i, 1932 Ford V8.

No. 841, each 150fr: a, 1927 Alfa Romeo RLSS. b, 1933 DuPont Model G. c, Bentley Speed Six. d, 1932 Cadillac 355. e, 1955 Corvette. f, 1934 Chrysler Airflow. g, Buick Coupe deVille. h, Model T Ford. i, 1920 Duesenberg Model A.

No. 842, 1500fr, Rolls-Royce Phantom II Continental. No. 843, 1500fr, 1927 Daimler Double Six.

**1998, Oct. 29 Litho. *Perf. 14***

**Sheets of 9**

**840-841** A150 Set of 2 13.00 13.00

**Souvenir Sheets**

**842-843** A150 Set of 2 17.00 17.00

Birds — A151

No. 844, 75fr, Macareux moine. No. 845, 75fr, Calliste à tête verte. No. 846, 150fr, Soutmanga de la reine Christine. No. 847, 150fr, Rale d'eau. No. 848, 200fr, Lophophore replendissant. No. 849, 200fr, Francolin noir. No. 850, 375fr, Mesia â oreillonis argentes. No. 851, 375fr, Mérion splendide.

No. 852: a, Canard plongeur austral. b, Garrot a ceil d'or. c, Harle huppé. d, Canard colvert. e, Canard branchu. f, Sarcelle elegante.

No. 853: a, Emérillon. b, Nyctale de tengmalm. c, Aigle royal d, Kétoupa malais. e, Caracara. f, Chouette à lunettes

No. 854, Jacana du mexique. No. 855, Toucan de cuvier.

**1999, Jan. 23 Litho. *Perf. 14***

**844-851** A151 Set of 8 8.50 8.50

**Sheets of 6, #a-f**

**852-853** A151 375fr Set of 2 22.50 22.50

**Souvenir Sheets**

**854-855** A151 1500fr Set of 2 16.00 16.00

Fauna — A152

No. 856, vert, each 150fr: a, Giraffa camaloprdalis. b, Macaca fusata. c, Loxodonta africana. d, Ovis dalli. e, Phoenicopterus ruber. f, Orcinus orca. g, Ursus horribilis. h, Lemur catta.

No. 857, vert, each 150fr: a, Pongo pygmaeus. b, Ceratotherium simum. c, Ailuropoda melanoleuca. d, Tursiops truncartus. e, Felis caracel. f, Eudyptes chrysocome. g, Bison bison. h, Panthera uncia.

No. 858, vert, each 150fr: a, Phascolarctos cinereus. b, Ammotragus levia. c, Hippopatamus amphibius. d, Saimiri boliviensis. e, Acinonyx jubatus. f, Gorilla gorilla. g, Branta sandvicensis. h, Thalarctos maritimus.

No. 859, each 150fr: a, Panthera tigris. b, Phoca groenlandica. c, Acipenser sturio. d, Lepidochelys kempii. e, Ailuropoda melanoleuca. f, Isurus oxyrinchus. g, Chelydra serpentina. h, Eretmochelys imbricata.

Each 1500fr: No. 860: Pan troglodytes, vert. No. 861, Panthera tigris altaica, vert. No. 862, Oryx gazella, vert. No. 863, Hippotigris zebra. No. 864, Diceros bicornis. No. 865, Panthera leo. No. 866, Amazona viridgenalis. No. 867, Pygoscelis papua, vert.

**1999, Jan. 25 Sheets of 8**

**856-859** A152 Set of 4 25.00 25.00

**Souvenir Sheets**

**860-867** A152 Set of 8 65.00 65.00

Fish — A153

No. 868, 75fr, Pomacantus imperator. No. 869, 75fr, Heniochus intermedium. No. 870, 150fr, Mirolaprichthys. No. 871, 150fr, Pomacanthus paru. No. 872, 375fr, Ostzacion tuberculatus. No. 873, 375fr, Colisa calia.

No. 874, each 150fr: a, Coris aygula. b, Chromis caeruleys. c, Euxiphipops navarchus. d, Pseudobalistes fuscus. e, Zebrasoma flavescens. f, Mycteroperca urba. g, Epinephelus flavocaeruleus. h, Equetus lanceolatus. i, Acanthurus leucostemon.

No. 875, each 150fr: a, Chaetodon tinkeri. b, Ostzaciidae. c, Seatophagus argus. d, Adioryx coruscus. e, Pygoplites diacanthus. f, Paracanthurus hepatus. g, Chaetodon plebius. h, Lythrypnus dalli. i, Myrichthys oculatus.

Each 1500fr: No. 876, Amphipzion percula. No. 877, Cymnothorne undulatus.

**1998, Oct.-Nov. Litho. *Perf. 14***

**868-873** A153 Set of 6 7.00 7.00

**Sheets of 9**

**874-875** A153 Set of 2 14.00 14.00

**Souvenir Sheets**

**876-877** A153 Set of 2 16.00 16.00

Marine Life — A154

No. 878, 75fr, Tubastrea aurea. No. 879, 75fr, Condylachtis gigantea. No. 880, 150fr, Paracanthurus hepatus. No. 881, 150fr, Balistoides conspicillum. No. 882, 200fr, Diodon holocanthus. No. 883, 200fr, Sebastes rubrivintus. No. 884, 375fr, Trygonorhina fasciata. No. 885, 375fr, Phocoenoides dalli.

No. 886, each 150fr: a, Epinephelus guttatus. b, Diademichthys lineatus. c, Plotosus lineatus. d, Rhinomuraena quaesita. e, Zanclus cornutus. f, Persephona punctata. g, Murex pecten. h, Tetrosomus gibbosus.

No. 887, each 150fr: a, Lythrypnus dalli. b, Premnas biaculeatus. c, Pseudanthias tuka. d, Capros aper. e, Balistoides conspicillum. f,

Oreaster reticulatus. g, Octopus joubini. h, Fasciolaris tulipa.

Each 1500fr: No. 888, S. picturatus. No. 889, Megaptera novaeangliae.

**1999**

| | | | | |
|---|---|---|---|---|
| **878-885** | A154 | Set of 8 | 8.50 | 8.50 |

**Sheets of 8**

| | | | | |
|---|---|---|---|---|
| **886-887** | A154 | Set of 2 | 15.00 | 15.00 |

**Souvenir Sheets**

| | | | | |
|---|---|---|---|---|
| **888-889** | A154 | Set of 2 | 19.00 | 19.00 |

Prehistoric Animals — A155

No. 890, each 150fr: a, Meganeura. b, Archaeopteryx. c, Peteinosaurus. d, Eudimorphodon. e, Brachiosaurus. f, Gallimimus. g, Tarbosaurus. h, Parasaurolophus. i, Sauropelta. j, Herrarasaurus. k, Stegosaurus. l, Lambeosaurus.

No. 891, each 150fr: a, Ramphorhinchus. b, Quetzalcoatlus. c, Pterodactylus. d, Pteranodon. e, Dimorphodon. f, Camarasaurus. g, Tenontosaurus. h, Protoceratops. i, Coelurosaurus. j, Mixosaurus. k, Ceresiosaurus. l, Sharovipteryx.

Each 1500fr: No. 892, Ceratosaurus. No. 893, Mesosaurus. No. 894, Megazostrodon. No. 895, Diatryma.

**1999** **Sheets of 12**

| | | | | |
|---|---|---|---|---|
| **890-891** | A155 | Set of 2 | 19.00 | 19.00 |

**Souvenir Sheets**

| | | | | |
|---|---|---|---|---|
| **892-895** | A155 | Set of 4 | 32.50 | 32.50 |

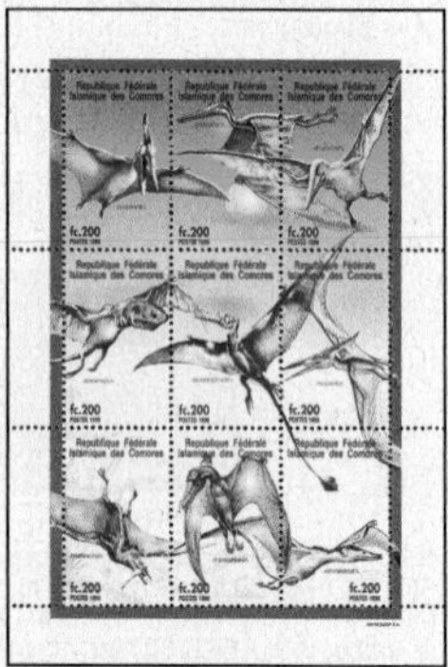

Prehistoric Animals, Lemurs and Butterflies — A156

Prehistoric animals — No. 895A — Prehistoric sea creatures: b, Eurhinodelphis. c, Stenopterygius. d, Ichthyosaurus. e, Pakicetus. f, Xenacanthus. g, Zygorhiza. h, Basilosaurus. i, Mesosaurus. j, Cetotherium. No. 896: a, Elasmosaurus (b). b, Quetzalcoatl (c). c, Mesadactylus (b). d, Dimorphodon (e). e, Rhamphorhynchus (c, d, f, i). f, Pteranodon (c, i). g, Pterodactylus (h). h, Eudimorphodon (i). i, Ornithodesmus (g, h).

Lemurs — No. 897: a, Haplorhinien primitif. b, Aye aye (c, e, f). c, Lemur vari. d, Indri. e, Makis varis (f, i). f, Potto. g, Lemur catta. h, Lemur macaos. i, Microcebe souris.

Butterflies — No. 898: a, Charaxes nobilis. b, Charaxes eupale. c, Charaxes brutus. d, Lobobunea turlini. e, Papilio nobilis. f, Athletes gigas. g, Papilio antimachus. h, Epiphora albida. i, Papilio zalmoxis.

**1998** **Sheets of 9** ***Perf. 13¼x13½***

| | | | | |
|---|---|---|---|---|
| **895A** | A156 150fr #b-j | | 6.50 | 6.50 |
| **896** | A156 200fr #a.-i. | | 9.75 | 9.75 |
| **897** | A156 250fr #a.-i. | | 12.00 | 12.00 |
| **898** | A156 300fr #a.-i. | | 14.50 | 14.50 |

See Nos. 928-933.

A157

Endangered Species — A157a

Designs: 75fr, Galago crassicaudatus. 150fr, Vulpes vulpes. 200fr, Anomalurus pusillus. 375fr, Loxodonta africana, vert.

Primates, vert: Nos. 903a-903c, Various views of Pan troglodytes. Nos. 903d-903f, Various views of gorilla gorilla. Nos. 903g-903i, Various views of pongo pygmaeus.

No. 904, each 375fr: a, Tragelaphus strepsiceros. b, Capra hircus. c, Egretta alba. d, Tockus flavirostris.

No. 905, each 375fr: a, Ursus maritimus. b, Megaptera novaeangliae. c, Phoca vitulina. d, Aptenodytes forsteri.

No. 906, each 375fr: a, Pelecanus occidentalis. b, Orcinus orca. c, Delphinus delphis. d, Iguana iguana.

No. 907: a, Panthera tigris altaica. b, Camelus bactrianus. c, Canus lupus. d, Cuon alpinus. e, Rangifer tarandus dawsoni. f, Gulo gulo.

Each 1500fr: No. 908, Loxodonta africana, vert. No. 909, Ursus thibetanus.

***Perf. 14, 14½x14 (#904-906)***

**1999, Jan. 25** **Litho.**

| | | | | |
|---|---|---|---|---|
| **899-902** | A157 | Set of 4 | 4.50 | 4.50 |
| **903** | A157 | 150fr Sheet of 9, #a.-i. | 8.00 | 8.00 |

**Sheets of 4**

| | | | | |
|---|---|---|---|---|
| **904-906** | A157a | Set of 3 | 24.00 | 24.00 |

**Sheet of 6**

| | | | | |
|---|---|---|---|---|
| **907** | A157 | 375fr #a.-f. | 12.00 | 12.00 |

**Souvenir Sheets**

| | | | | |
|---|---|---|---|---|
| **908-909** | A157 | Set of 2 | 16.00 | 16.00 |

Mushrooms

A158 A159

No. 910, 75fr, Russula xerampelina. No. 911, 75fr, Catathelasma imperiale. No. 912, 150fr, Cortinarius violaceus. No. 913, 150fr, Cortinarius camphoratus. No. 914, 200fr, Rozites caperata. No. 915, 200fr, Coprinus picaceus. No. 916, 375fr, Coprinus cromatus. No. 917, 375fr, Russula cavipes.

No. 918, each 150fr: a, Boletus edulis. b, Suillus grevillei. c, Boletinus cavipes. d, Morchella esculenta. e, Morchella conica. f, Clitocybe dealbata. g, Hygrocybe nigrescens. h, Clitocybe geotropa. i, Lepiota cristata.

No. 919, each 150fr: a, Amanita citrina. b, Amanita phalloides. c, Cortinarius praestans. d, Phallus impudicus. e, Cortinarius bicolor. f, Cortinarius renidens. g, Lactarius torminosus. h, Boletus satanas. i, Cystolepiota bucknalii.

No. 920, each 375fr: a, Amanita muscaria. b, Coprinus comatus. c, Clitocybe odora. d, Cantharellus cibarius. e, Mycena epipterygia. f, Marasmius oreades.

No. 921, each 375fr: a, Boletus edulis. b, Laccaria laccata. c, Agaricus campestris. d, Hypholoma fasciculare. e, Lepiota procera. f, Russula aurata.

Each 1500fr: No. 922, Ramaria aurea, horiz. No. 923, Panellus serotinus. No. 924, Macrolepiota procera. No. 925, Amanita muscaria. No. 926, Hebeloma crustuliniforme. No. 927, Lepiota molybdites.

**1999** **Litho.** ***Perf. 14***

| | | | | |
|---|---|---|---|---|
| **910-917** | A158 | Set of 8 | 8.50 | 8.50 |

**Sheets of 9**

| | | | | |
|---|---|---|---|---|
| **918-919** | A158 | Set of 2 | 14.00 | 14.00 |

**Sheets of 6**

| | | | | |
|---|---|---|---|---|
| **920-921** | A159 | Set of 2 | 24.00 | 24.00 |

**Souvenir Sheets**

| | | | | |
|---|---|---|---|---|
| **922-925** | A158 | Set of 4 | 32.50 | 32.50 |
| **926-927** | A159 | Set of 2 | 16.00 | 16.00 |

Raptors — A160

No. 927A — Birds: b, Souimanga royal. c, Martin-pecheur huppe. d, Pie-grieche. e, Barbican a tete roughe. f, Beau-marquet. g, Rollier a poitrine lilas. h, Pintade vulturine. i, Grenadier. j, Outarde korhaon.

No. 928: a, Sparrow hawk. b, Red-tailed buzzard. c, Dark kite. d, African fish eagle. e, Bald eagle. f, Fawn-colored vulture. g, Peregrine falcon. h, Osprey. i, Harpie eagle.

Dinosaurs — No. 929: a, Dilophosaurus. b, Megalosaurus. c, Ceratosaurus. d, Coelophysis. e, Tyrannosaurus. f, Deinonychus. g, Allosaurus. h, Stegosaurus. i, Albertosaurus.

Gems — No. 930: a, Ruby. b, Liroconite. c, Emerald. d, Euclase. e, Diamond. f, Chrysoberyl. g, Plancheite. h, Kasolite. i, Indigolite.

Meteorites — No. 931: a, Martian. b, Antarctic. c, C2 Chondrite. d, Archondrite. e, Octaedrite moyenne. f, Iron. g, Tektite. h, Chondrite olivine. i, Iron, diff.

Mushrooms — No. 932: a, Paxillus atrotomentosus. b, Craterellus cornucopioides. c, Boletus satanas. d, Clavaria truncata. e, Phallus impudicus. f, Scleroderma aurantiacum. g, Amanita citrina. h, Catathe lasma. i, Inocybe fastigiata.

1125fr, Wulfenite.

**1998** **Sheets of 9** ***Perf. 13¼x13½***

| | | | | |
|---|---|---|---|---|
| **927A** | A160 | 175fr #b-j | 10.00 | 10.00 |
| **928** | A160 | 200fr #a.-i. | 11.00 | 11.00 |
| **929** | A160 | 250fr #a.-i. | 11.50 | 11.50 |
| **930** | A160 | 375fr #a.-i. | 15.00 | 15.00 |
| **931** | A160 | 400fr #a.-i. | 16.00 | 16.00 |
| **932** | A160 | 400fr #a.-i. | 16.00 | 16.00 |

**Souvenir Sheet**

| | | | | |
|---|---|---|---|---|
| **933** | A160 | 1125fr multicolored | 4.50 | 4.50 |

No. 933 contains one 36x51mm stamp.

Captions on Nos. 928e and 928h are transposed.

See Nos. 896-898.

### "Illegal" Stamps

Comoro Islands postal officials have declared as "illegal" the following items:

Muhammad Ali, sheet of nine 300fr stamps (previously No. 934);

Muhammad Ali, 1125fr souvenir sheet (previously No. 935);

Babe Ruth, sheet of nine 375fr stamps;

Babe Ruth, two 1125fr souvenir sheets;

Ocean Life, sheet of nine stamps with values of 100, 150, 250, 300, 350, 400, 450, and 500fr;

Horses, sheet of nine stamps with values of 100, 150, 250, 300, 350, 400, 450, and 500fr;

Pandas, sheet of nine stamps with values of 100, 150, 250, 300, 350, 400, 450, and 500fr;

Flora and Fauna: 25fr Harpe costata, 25fr Hibiscus, 50fr Volute lapponica, 50fr Tournesol de Comoros, 100fr Ghetonia mydas, 125fr Octopus vulgaris, 150fr Ylang ylang, 300fr Coelacanth, 300fr Tellina variegata.

Famous People: 250fr, Willy Messerschmitt, Messerschmitt BF-109G-6/R6. 300fr, Louis Pasteur, rabies vaccine administered to Joseph Meister. 350fr, Dr. Albert Schweitzer. 400fr, Ferdinand von Zeppelin, flying Zeppelin. 475fr, Henri Dunant, Nobel Prize. 500fr, Albert Einstein, Gravity Probe B. 550fr, Ayrton Senna, race car. 600fr, Pope John Paul II. 750fr, Iranian Pres. Mohammad Khatami, Pope John Paul II. 800fr, Crew of Apollo 11. 1125fr souvenir sheet, Lindbergh, Spirit of St. Louis.

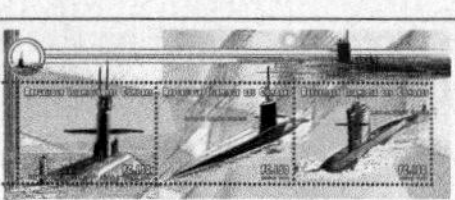

Submarines — A161

No. 934: a, USS Salt Lake City, US. b, Le Terrible, France. c, Amethyste, France.

**1999** **Litho.** ***Perf. 13¼***

| | | | | |
|---|---|---|---|---|
| **934** | A161 | 150fr Sheet of 3, #a-c | 3.00 | 3.00 |

Automobiles — A161a

No. 935: a, Cadillac Eldorado, Cadillac Series 62, US. b, Aston Martin DB2 IV Mark III, Austin Healey. c, Alfa Romeo Superlegera, Alfa Romeo Giuletta.

1125fr, Aston Martin DB5.

**1999**

| | | | | |
|---|---|---|---|---|
| **935** | A161a | 200fr Sheet of 3, #a-c | 3.00 | 3.00 |

**Souvenir Sheet**

| | | | | |
|---|---|---|---|---|
| **935D** | A161a | 1125fr multi | 5.50 | 5.50 |

No. 935D contains one 51x30mm stamp.

Motorcycles — A162

No. 935E: f, Honda NR. g, Christian Leliard and motorcycle. h, Joe S. Wright and motorcycle.

**1999**

| | | | | |
|---|---|---|---|---|
| **935E** | A162 | 250fr Sheet of 3, #f-h | 4.00 | 4.00 |

Helicopters — A162a

No. 936: a, Westland Wessex. b, MIL MI-8. c, Sikorsky 5-76 Spirit.

**1999**

| | | | | |
|---|---|---|---|---|
| **936** | A162a | 300fr Sheet of 3, #a-c | 4.50 | 4.50 |

Dogs and Sleds — A163

No. 937: a, Alaskan malamute, US. b, Greenlandic. c, Siberian husky.

**1999**

| | | | | |
|---|---|---|---|---|
| **937** | A163 | 400fr Sheet of 3, #a-c | 6.00 | 6.00 |

Airplanes A164

No. 938: a, Tupolev Tu-160. b, Lockheed F-117A. c, Rafale C.01.

No. 939: a, Ilyshin Il-76. b, Boeing E-3. c, Concorde.

1125fr, Concorde, diff.

**1999** **Litho.** ***Perf. 13¼***

**Sheets of 3**

| | | | | |
|---|---|---|---|---|
| **938** | A164 | 375fr #a.-c. | 5.00 | 5.00 |
| **939** | A164 | 450fr #a.-c. | 6.50 | 6.50 |

**Souvenir Sheet**

| | | | | |
|---|---|---|---|---|
| **940** | A164 | 1125fr mulicolored | 6.75 | 6.75 |

No. 940 contains one 50x30mm stamp.

Trains — A165

No. 941: a, Series E. b, Series 9100. c, Kitson-Still I-C-I.

No. 942: a, HST 125. b, TGV. c, RTG.

1125fr, Sereis DD40AX.

**1999 Litho. *Perf. 13¼***

**Sheets of 3**

**941** A165 400fr #a.-c. 6.50 6.50
**942** A165 500fr #a.-c. 8.00 8.00

**Souvenir Sheet**

**943** A165 1125fr mulicolored 6.00 6.00

No. 943 contains one 50x30mm stamp.

Space Achievements A166

No. 944: a, Shuttles Discovery, Buran. b, Ariane V. c, John Glenn, Saturn V.

No. 945: a, Valentina Tereshkova, Soyuz 4. b, Dogs Laika, Bielka. c, Yuri Gagarin, Vostok 1.

1125fr, Space Shuttle Discovery, John Glenn.

**1999 Litho. *Perf. 13¼***

**Sheets of 3**

**944** A166 500fr #a.-c. 7.00 7.00
**945** A166 600fr #a.-c. 9.00 9.00

Souvenir Sheet

**946** A166 1125fr multi 6.00 6.00

No. 946 contains one 51x30mm stamp.

Teams in 1998 World Cup Soccer Tournament — A167

Players in 1998 World Cup Soccer Tournament — A168

No. 947, 150fr: a, Italy. b, Chile, c, Cameroun. d, Austria. e, Netherlands. f, Belgium. g, South Korea. h, Mexico.

No. 948, 250fr: a, France. b, Brazil. b, Scotland. c, Morocco. d, Norway. e, Spain. f, Nigeria. g, Paraguay. h, Bulgaria.

No. 949, 300fr: a, France. b, South Africa. c, Saudi Arabia. d, Denmark. e, Germany. f, United States. g, Yugoslavia. h, Iran.

No. 950, 500fr: a, England. b, Colombia. c, Romania. d, Tunisia. e, Argentina. f, Croatia. g, Jamaica. h, Japan.

No. 951, 350fr: a, Desailly, French flag. b, Ronaldo, Brazilian flag. c, Suker, Croatian flag. d, Kluivert, Netherlands flag. e, French players, World Cup trophy. f, Brazilian player (yellow and green shirt). g, Croatian player (checked shirt). h, Netherlands player (orange shirt).

**1998 Litho. *Perf. 13x13½***

**Sheets of 8, #a-h**

**947-950** A167 Set of 4 40.00 40.00
**951** A168 multi 12.00 12.00

Trucks A169

No. 952: a, Truck with ornamentation over cab. b, Blue truck. c, Green truck. d, Yellow truck.

**1999 Litho. *Perf. 13¼***

**952** A169 350fr Sheet of 4, #a-d *10.00 10.00*

Automobile Racing, Chess, Tennis and Table Tennis, Fishing and Diving — A170

No. 953, 250fr — Automobile racing: a, Giuseppe Farina and Alfa 1500. b, Juan Fangio and Mercedes 2.5L. c, Jack Brabham and Cooper Climax 2.5L. d, Jim Clark and Lotus Climax 1.5L.

No. 954, 300fr — Chess players: a, Garry Kasparov. b, Akiba Rubinstein. c, Max Euwe. d, Mikhail Botvinnik.

No. 955, 375fr — Fishing and diving: a, Shark fishing. b, Sport fishing. c, Diver, back half of shark. d, Diver, front half of shark.

No. 956, 500fr — Chess players: a, Bent Larsen. b, José Raúl Capablanca. c, Boris Spassky. d, Bobby Fischer.

No. 957, 600fr — Tennis and table tennis: a, Female tennis player. b, Male table tennis player. c, Female table tennis player. d, Male tennis player.

No. 958, 1125fr — Chess players: a, Samuel Reshevsky. b, Vassili Smyslov.

No. 959, 1125fr — Fishing and diving: a, Sport fishing, diff. b, Divers and marine life.

No. 960, 1125fr — Tennis and table tennis: a, Male table tennis player, diff. b, Women tennis players.

**1999 *Perf. 13¼***

**Sheets of 4, #a-d**

**953-957** A170 Set of 5 47.50 47.50

**Souvenir Sheets of 2, #a-b**

**958-960** A170 Set of 3 16.00 16.00

Nos. 816E, 816G Surcharged

**Methods and Perfs. As Before**

**2001, June 16**

**963** A144a 100fr on 500fr multi — —
**964** A144a 125fr on 200fr multi — —

Traditional Costumes — A171

Designs: 125fr, Woman. No. 966, 150fr, No. 969, 300fr, Woman, diff. No. 967, 150fr, No. 968, 300fr, Man.

**2002, Apr. 8 Litho. *Perf. 13¼x13***

**965-969** A171 Set of 5 *8.50 8.50*

Flowers — A172

Designs: 50fr, Cananga odorata. 600fr, Vanilla planifolia.

**2003, Oct. 9**

**970-971** A172 Set of 2 *5.25 5.25*

Marine Mammals A173

Designs: 75fr, Peponocephala electra. 1000fr, Megaptera novaeangliae.

**2003, Oct. 9 *Perf. 13x13¼***

**972-973** A173 Set of 2 *9.00 9.00*

Wood Handicrafts — A174

Designs: 100fr, Carved door. 300fr, Candleholder.

**2003, Oct. 9 *Perf. 13¼x13***

**974-975** A174 Set of 2 *3.25 3.25*

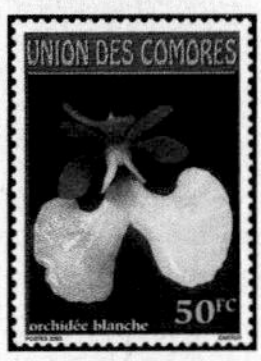

Orchids — A175

Orchid color: 50fr, White. 75fr, Yellow. 100fr, Mauve. 600fr, Red.

**2003, Oct. 9**

**976-979** A175 Set of 4 *6.50 6.50*

Diplomatic Relations Between Comoro Islands and People's Republic of China, 30th Anniv. — A176

No. 980: a, 125fr, Chinese President Hu Jintao and Comoro Islands President Azali Assoumani, country flags. b, 125fr, Coelacanth, Worldwide Fund for Nature emblem, country arms. c, 300fr, Comoros Islands Broadcasting Center, country arms. d, 600fr, Comoros Islands People's Palace, country flags.

**2006, Jan. 1 Litho. *Perf. 12***

**980** A176 Block of 4, #a-d 5.75 5.75

Comoro Islands postal officials have declared as "illegal" the following items:

Impressionist Paintings, sheet of five 500fr stamps.

Paintings in the Louvre, six different sheets of two 500fr stamps.

American Actors and Actresses, four different sheets of four 350fr stamps.

European Astronauts, three souvenir sheets of one 500fr stamp.

Disneyland, 50th anniv., souvenir sheet of one 500fr stamp.

Léopold Sédar Senghor (1906-2001), First President of Senegal — A177

***Perf. 13x13¼, 13¼x13***

**2007, June 1 Litho.**

**980E** A177 125fr pur & blk —
**981** A177 125fr grn & multi .70 .70
**982** A177 125fr yel & multi, vert. .70 .70
**983** A177 300fr grn & blk 1.75 1.75
**983A** A177 300fr blue & multi —
**984** A177 300fr red vio & blk, vert. 1.75 1.75
**985** A177 350fr pur & multi, vert. 2.00 2.00
**986** A177 500fr brn & blk, vert. 2.75 2.75
*Nos. 981-983, 984-986 (6)* 9.65 9.65

Dated 2006.

Medicinal Plants — A178

Designs: 75fr, Cymbopogon citratus. 125fr, Ocimum suave. 150fr, Aloe molucaca. 250fr, Like 75fr. 300fr, Like 150fr. 500fr, Like 125fr.

**2007, June 1 *Perf. 13¼x13***

**987-992** A178 Set of 6 7.75 7.75

A179

Transportation and Space — A180

No. 993 — Military aircraft and flags: a, 125fr, B-24 Liberator, U.S. flag. b, 150fr, Mitsubishi G4-M3, Japanese flag. c, 225fr, Petlyakov Pe-2, Russian flag. d, 300fr, Savoia-Marchetti SM-79, Italian flag. e, 400fr, Nakajima Ki84, Japanese flag. f, 1000fr, Dornier DO-335, German flag.

3000fr, Mitsubishi A6M5, Japanese flag.

**2008, Oct. 1 *Perf. 13x13¼***

**993** A179 Sheet of 6, #a-f 12.50 12.50

**Souvenir Sheet**

***Perf. 13¼ Syncopated***

**994** A180 3000fr multi 17.00 17.00

**Medical Vehicles**

No. 995 — Red Cross flag and: a, 125fr, English ambulance. b, 150fr, ASLAV-A, Australia. c, 225fr, Red Cross vehicle, U.S. d, 300fr, Devon Air Ambulance helicopter, United Kingdom. e, 400fr, USNS Mercy. f, 1000fr, Medical worker on motorcycle, Hong Kong.

3000fr, M1133 Medical evacuation vehicle, U.S.

**2008, Oct. 1 *Perf. 13x13¼***

**995** A179 Sheet of 6, #a-f 12.50 12.50

**Souvenir Sheet**

***Perf. 13¼ Syncopated***

**996** A180 3000fr multi 17.00 17.00

**Submarines**

No. 997: a, 125fr, Nautilus, 1800. b, 150fr, Brandtaucher, 1850. c, 225fr, Pioneer, 1861. d, 300fr, Flach, 1866. e, 400fr, Ictineo I 1858. f, 1000fr, Resurgam, 1878.

3000fr, Turtle, 1776.

**2008, Oct. 1 *Perf. 13x13¼***

**997** A179 Sheet of 6, #a-f 12.50 12.50

**Souvenir Sheet**

***Perf. 13¼ Syncopated***

**998** A180 3000fr multi 17.00 17.00

**U.S. High Speed Trains**

No. 999 — Acela Express and U.S. landmarks: a, 125fr, Hollywood sign. b, 150fr, Golden Gate Bridge. c, 225fr, World Trade Center. d, 300fr, Statue of Liberty. e, 400fr, San Francisco skyline. f, 1000fr, White House.

3000fr, U.S. Capitol.

**2008, Oct. 1 *Perf. 13x13¼***

**999** A179 Sheet of 6, #a-f 12.50 12.50

**Souvenir Sheet**

***Perf. 13¼ Syncopated***

**1000** A180 3000fr multi 17.00 17.00

### Chinese High Speed Trains

No. 1001 — Maglev, flag of People's Republic of China, and Chinese landmarks: a, 200fr, Xian. b, 250fr, Tea house. c, 350fr, Pudong. d, 450fr, Great Wall of China. e, 500fr, Potala Palace. f, 1000fr, Gate of Heavenly Peace.
3000fr, Great Wall of China, diff.

**2008, Oct. 1** *Perf. 13x13¼*
**1001** A179 Sheet of 6, #a-f 15.50 15.50

**Souvenir Sheet**

*Perf. 13¼ Syncopated*

**1002** A180 3000fr multi 17.00 17.00

### Japanese High Speed Trains

No. 1003 — Shinkansen, Japanese flag, and Japanese landmarks: a, 200fr, Amanohashidate. b, 250fr, Itsukushima Shrine. c, 350fr, Umeda Sky Building, Osaka. d, 450fr, Buildings in Shiodome. e, 500fr, Temple in Kyoto. f, 1000fr, Himeji Castle.
3000fr, Minato Mirai 21.

**2008, Oct. 1** *Perf. 13x13¼*
**1003** A179 Sheet of 6, #a-f 15.50 15.50

**Souvenir Sheet**

*Perf. 13¼ Syncopated*

**1004** A180 3000fr multi 17.00 17.00

### Automobiles

No. 1005: a, 200fr, 1886 Daimler. b, 250fr,1906 Renault GP. c, 350fr, 1923 Ford Model T. d, 450fr, 1954 Mercedes Benz 300 SL. e, 500fr, 1988 Ferrari Testarossa. f, 1000fr, 2007 Bugatti Veyron.
3000fr, 2007 Lamborghini Murcielago LP640 Versace.

**2008, Oct. 1** *Perf. 13x13¼*
**1005** A179 Sheet of 6, #a-f 15.50 15.50

**Souvenir Sheet**

*Perf. 13¼ Syncopated*

**1006** A180 3000fr multi 17.00 17.00

### Airplanes and Airports

No. 1007 — Airplane at airport and flag: a, 200fr, Changri Airport, Singapore flag. b, 250fr, John F. Kennedy Airport, New York, and U.S. flag. c, 350fr, Frankfort Airport, German flag. d, 450fr, Narita Airport, Tokyo, Japanese flag. e, 500fr, Beijing Airport, flag of People's Republic of China. f, 1000fr, Schiphol Airport, Amsterdam, Netherlands flag.
3000fr, 2007 Heathrow Airport, London, British flag.

**2008, Oct. 1** *Perf. 13x13¼*
**1007** A179 Sheet of 6, #a-f 15.50 15.50

**Souvenir Sheet**

*Perf. 13¼ Syncopated*

**1008** A180 3000fr multi 17.00 17.00

### Mars Probes

No. 1009 — Mars and: a, 200fr, Spirit. b, 250fr, Mars Polar. c, 350fr, Viking. d, 450fr, Mars Climate. e, 500fr, Phoenix. f, 1000fr, Sojourner.
3000fr, Mariner 3.

**2008, Oct. 1** *Perf. 13x13¼*
**1009** A179 Sheet of 6, #a-f 15.50 15.50

**Souvenir Sheet**

*Perf. 13¼ Syncopated*

**1010** A180 3000fr multi 17.00 17.00

### Ocean Liners

No. 1011: a, 200fr, Titanic. b, 250fr, Golden Princess. c, 350fr, Mauretania. d, 450fr, MS Queen Victoria. e, 500fr, Queen Elizabeth 2. f, 1000fr, Queen Mary 2.
3000fr, Pacific Princess.

**2008, Oct. 1** *Perf. 13x13¼*
**1011** A179 Sheet of 6, #a-f 15.50 15.50

**Souvenir Sheet**

*Perf. 13¼ Syncopated*

**1012** A180 3000fr multi 17.00 17.00

### Postal Vehicles

No. 1013: a, 125fr, English postal van, carrier pigeon with letter, British flag. b, 150fr, Swiss postal bus, Horn, Swiss flag. c, 225fr, Spanish postal truck, posthorn, Spanish flag. d, 300fr, Swedish postal truck, carrier pigeon with letter, Swedish flag. e, 400fr, Israeli postal van, carrier pigeon with letter, Israeli flag. f, 1000fr, German postal buses, post horn, German flag.
3000fr, Hungarian postal van, posthorn, Hungarian flag.

**2009, Jan. 5** *Perf. 13x13¼*
**1013** A179 Sheet of 6, #a-f 12.50 12.50

**Souvenir Sheet**

*Perf. 13¼ Syncopated*

**1014** A180 3000fr multi 16.50 16.50

Dated 2008.

### Subway Trains

No. 1015: a, 125fr, Beijing train and system map, Forbidden City, flag of People's Republic of China. b, 150fr, London train and system map, Big Ben, British flag. c, 225fr, Paris train and system map, Eiffel Tower, French flag. d, 300fr, Tokyo train and system map, Tokyo Tower, Japanese flag. e, 400fr, New York train and system map, Statue of Liberty, U.S. flag. f, 1000fr, Moscow train and system map, Red Square, Russian flag.
3000fr, Madrid train and system map, Statue of Bear and Tree, Spanish flag.

**2009, Jan. 5** *Perf. 13x13¼*
**1015** A179 Sheet of 6, #a-f 12.50 12.50

**Souvenir Sheet**

*Perf. 13¼ Syncopated*

**1016** A180 3000fr multi 16.50 16.50

Dated 2008.

### German High Speed Trains

No. 1017 — ICE, flag of Germany and: a, 125fr, Cologne Cathedral. b, 150fr, Neuschwanstein Castle. c, 225fr, Göltsch Viaduct. d, 300fr, Kaiser Wilhelm Memorial Church, Berlin. e, 400fr, Brandenburg Gate. f, 1000fr, Eltz Castle.
3000fr, Brandenburg Gate, diff.

**2009, Jan. 5** *Perf. 13x13¼*
**1017** A179 Sheet of 6, #a-f 12.50 12.50

**Souvenir Sheet**

*Perf. 13¼ Syncopated*

**1018** A180 3000fr multi 16.50 16.50

Dated 2008.

### French High Speed Trains

No. 1019 — TGV, flag of France and: a, 125fr, Notre Dame Cathedral, Paris. b, 150fr, Louvre Museum. c, 225fr, Hôtel de Ville, Paris. d, 300fr, Eiffel Tower. e, 400fr, Moulin Rouge. f, 1000fr, Arc de Triomphe.
3000fr, Eiffel Tower, diff.

**2009, Jan. 5** *Perf. 13x13¼*
**1019** A179 Sheet of 6, #a-f 12.50 12.50

**Souvenir Sheet**

*Perf. 13¼ Syncopated*

**1020** A180 3000fr multi 16.50 16.50

Dated 2008.

### Fire Trucks

No. 1021: a, 125fr, Zuk, Poland. b, 150fr, Isuzu Forward, Japan. c, 225fr, Pegaso 7217, Spain. d, 300fr, A LF 16/12, Germany. e, 400fr, WPFD Engine 3, U.S. f, 1000fr, Scientific Support Truck, United Kingdom.
3000fr, Palm Beach fire truck, U.S.

**2009, Jan. 5** *Perf. 13x13¼*
**1021** A179 Sheet of 6, #a-f 12.50 12.50

**Souvenir Sheet**

*Perf. 13¼ Syncopated*

**1022** A180 3000fr multi 16.50 16.50

Dated 2008.

### Sailing Ships and Lighthouses

No. 1023 — Various lighthouses and: a, 125fr, Lettie G, 1893. b, 150fr, Maple Leaf, 1904. c, 225fr, Etoile, 1930. d, 300fr, Brigantine St. Lawrence, 1952. e, 400fr, Cuauhtemoc, 1982. f, 1000fr, Royal clipper, 2001.
3000fr, Belle Poule, 1834.

**2009, Jan. 5** *Perf. 13x13¼*
**1023** A179 Sheet of 6, #a-f 12.50 12.50

**Souvenir Sheet**

*Perf. 13¼ Syncopated*

**1024** A180 3000fr multi 16.50 16.50

Dated 2008.

### Airplanes

No. 1025: a, 125fr, Airbus A380. b, 150fr, Concorde F-BTSD. c, 225fr, Concorde G-BOAC. d, 300fr, Airbus A380, diff. e, 400fr, Airbus A380, diff. f, 1000fr, Concorde F-BVFC.
3000fr, Concorde F-BTSD, diff.

**2009, Jan. 5** *Perf. 13x13¼*
**1025** A179 Sheet of 6, #a-f 12.50 12.50

**Souvenir Sheet**

*Perf. 13¼ Syncopated*

**1026** A180 3000fr multi 16.50 16.50

Dated 2008.

### Antique Automobiles

No. 1027: a, 200fr, 1893 Duryea. b, 250fr, 1897 Oldsmobile. c, 350fr, 1896 Ford. d, 450fr, 1903 Vauxhall. e, 500fr, 1886 Daimler Maybach. f, 1000fr, 1906 Haynes.
3000fr, 1904 Mercedes Simplex.

**2009, Jan. 5** *Perf. 13x13¼*
**1027** A179 Sheet of 6, #a-f 15.00 15.00

**Souvenir Sheet**

*Perf. 13¼ Syncopated*

**1028** A180 3000fr multi 16.50 16.50

Dated 2008.

### Combat Vehicles

No. 1029: a, 200fr, Jino Motors truck, South Korea. b, 250fr, PTU, Singapore. c, 350fr, BRDM, Russia. d, 450fr, KRAZ AVC-30, Ukraine. e, 500fr, Avalanche truck, Russia. f, 1000fr, Fahd 240/30, Egypt.
3000fr, 1904 Humber Flying Pig MK2, FV1611, Great Britain.

**2009, Jan. 5** *Perf. 13x13¼*
**1029** A179 Sheet of 6, #a-f 15.00 15.00

**Souvenir Sheet**

*Perf. 13¼ Syncopated*

**1030** A180 3000fr multi 16.50 16.50

Dated 2008.

### Motorcycles and Their Inventors

No. 1031: a, 200fr, 1885 Daimler, Karl Benz. b, 250fr, 1901 NSU, Christian Schmidt. c, 350fr, 1920 Excelsior 20R, William G. Henderson. d, 450fr, 1914 Indian V-Twin, Oscar Hedstrom. e, 500fr, 1927 Böhmerland, Albin Hugo Liebisch. f, 1000fr, 1923 BMW R32, Max Friz.
3000fr, 1905 Scott, Alfred Angus Scott.

**2009, Jan. 5** *Perf. 13x13¼*
**1031** A179 Sheet of 6, #a-f 15.00 15.00

**Souvenir Sheet**

*Perf. 13¼ Syncopated*

**1032** A180 3000fr multi 16.50 16.50

Dated 2008.

A181

Birds and Lighthouses, Famous People — A182

No. 1033: a, 125fr, Alopochen aegyptiacus, El Montaza Lighthouse, Egypt. b, 150fr, Larus dominicanus, Agulhas Lighthouse, South Africa. c, 225fr, Gavia stellata, Europa Point Lighthouse, Gibraltar. d, 300fr, Oceanites oceanicus, Ilha do Goa Lighthouse, Mozambique. e, 400fr, Thalassarche cauta, Walvis Bay Lighthouse, Namibia. f, 1000fr, Pelecanus rufescens, Bwene Lighhouse, Tanzania.
3000fr, Phaethon aethereus, Lagos Lighthouse, Nigeria.

**2009, Jan. 7** *Perf. 13x13¼*
**1033** A181 Sheet of 6, #a-f 12.50 12.50

**Souvenir Sheet**

*Perf. 13¼ Syncopated*

**1034** A182 3000fr multi 16.50 16.50

Dated 2008.

### Scouting Centenary (in 2007)

No. 1035 — Robert Baden-Powell, Scouting emblem and: a, 125fr, Two Scouts saluting. b, 150fr, Two Scouts reading map. c, 225fr, Two Scouts standing with book. d, 300fr, Three Scouts looking at plant. e, 400fr, Two Scouts standing. f, 1000fr, Scouts and tent.
3000fr, Scouts practicing first aid.

**2009, Jan. 7** *Perf. 13x13¼*
**1035** A181 Sheet of 6, #a-f 12.50 12.50

**Souvenir Sheet**

*Perf. 13¼ Syncopated*

**1036** A182 3000fr multi 16.50 16.50

Dated 2008.

### Medical Pioneers

No. 1037: a, 125fr, Sir Humphry Davy. b, 150fr, Robert Koch. c, 225fr, Emil Adolf von Behring. d, 300fr, Louis Pasteur. e, 400fr, Sir Frederick Banting. f, 1000fr, Sir Alexander Fleming.
3000fr, Jean Henri Dunant.

**2009, Jan. 7** *Perf. 13x13¼*
**1037** A181 Sheet of 6, #a-f 12.50 12.50

**Souvenir Sheet**

*Perf. 13¼ Syncopated*

**1038** A182 3000fr multi 16.50 16.50

Dated 2008.

### Classical Composers

No. 1039: a, 125fr, Joseph Haydn. b, 150fr, Louis Hector Berlioz. c, 225fr, Franz Schubert. d, 300fr, Ludwig van Beethoven. e, 400fr, Franz Liszt. f, 1000fr, Johannes Brahms.
3000fr, Wolfgang Amadeus Mozart.

**2009, Jan. 7** *Perf. 13x13¼*
**1039** A181 Sheet of 6, #a-f 12.50 12.50

**Souvenir Sheet**

*Perf. 13¼ Syncopated*

**1040** A182 3000fr multi 16.50 16.50

Dated 2008.

### Ornithologists

No. 1041: a, 125fr, John James Audubon and Corvus cristatus. b, 150fr, John Gould and Trogon ambiguus. c, 225fr, Audubon and Columba migratoria. d, 300fr, Gould and Tanager darwinii. e, 400fr, Audubon and Corvus corax. f, 1000fr, Gould and Astrapia nigra.
3000fr, Gould, Audubon, two birds.

**2009, Jan. 7** *Perf. 13x13¼*
**1041** A181 Sheet of 6, #a-f 12.50 12.50

**Souvenir Sheet**

*Perf. 13¼ Syncopated*

**1042** A182 3000fr multi 16.50 16.50

Dated 2008.

### Paleontologists

No. 1043: a, 125fr, Barnum Brown and Archaeopteryx. b, 150fr, Thomas Condon and Gallimimus. c, 225fr, Robert Broom and Irritator. d, 300fr, William Buckland and Dimorphodon. e, 400fr, Edward Drinker Cope and Parasaurolophus. f, 1000fr, Edwin H. Colbert and Allosaurus.
3000fr, Roy Chapman Andrews and fossil dinosaur egg.

**2009, Jan. 7** *Perf. 13x13¼*
**1043** A181 Sheet of 6, #a-f 12.50 12.50

**Souvenir Sheet**

*Perf. 13¼ Syncopated*

**1044** A182 3000fr multi 16.50 16.50

Dated 2008.

### Humanists

No. 1045: a, 125fr, Miriam Makeba and Nelson Mandela. b, 150fr, Mahatma Gandhi. c, 225fr, Mother Teresa. d, 300fr, Yassir Arafat. e, 400fr, Shirin Ebadi. f, 1000fr, Mohammed El-Baradei.
3000fr, Dr. Martin Luther King, Jr.

**2009, Jan. 7** *Perf. 13x13¼*
**1045** A181 Sheet of 6, #a-f 12.50 12.50

**Souvenir Sheet**

*Perf. 13¼ Syncopated*

**1046** A182 3000fr multi 16.50 16.50

Dated 2008.

### Aviators

No. 1047: a, 125fr, Edward Rickenbacker. b, 150fr, Jimmy Doolittle. c, 225fr, Beryl Markham. d, 300fr, Elinor Smith. e, 400fr, Antoine de Saint-Exupéry. f, 1000fr, Charles Lindbergh.

3000fr, Wiley Post.

**2009, Jan. 7** ***Perf. 13x13¼***

**1047** A181 Sheet of 6, #a-f 12.50 12.50

**Souvenir Sheet**

***Perf. 13¼ Syncopated***

**1048** A182 3000fr multi 16.50 16.50

Dated 2008.

### Astronauts and Cosmonauts

No. 1049: a, 125fr, Yuri Gagarin and Vostok 1. b, 150fr, Neil Armstrong and Apollo 11. c, 225fr, Alan Shepard, Jr. and Apollo 14. d, 300fr, Valentina Tereshkova and Vostok 6. e, 400fr, Pavel Popovich and Soyuz 14. f, 1000fr, John Glenn and Mercury 6.

3000fr, Yang Liwei and Shenzhou 5.

**2009, Jan. 7** ***Perf. 13x13¼***

**1049** A181 Sheet of 6, #a-f 12.50 12.50

**Souvenir Sheet**

***Perf. 13¼ Syncopated***

**1050** A182 3000fr multi 16.50 16.50

Dated 2008.

### Mineralogists

No. 1051: a, 200fr, Ignacy Domeyko and sulfur. b, 250fr, James Dwight Dana and barite. c, 350fr, William Niven and rhodochrosite. d, 450fr, George Kunz and legrandite. e, 500fr, Waldemar Brogger and pyrite. f, 1000fr, Otto von Abich and rutile.

3000fr, Max von Laue and calcite.

**2009, Jan. 7** ***Perf. 13x13¼***

**1051** A181 Sheet of 6, #a-f 15.00 15.00

**Souvenir Sheet**

***Perf. 13¼ Syncopated***

**1052** A182 3000fr multi 16.50 16.50

Dated 2008.

### Entomologists

No. 1053: a, 200fr, Nathan Banks and Nymphalis antiopa. b, 250fr, Louis Agassiz and Apatura ilia. c, 350fr, Henry Walter Bates and Gonepterix rhamni. d, 450fr, Per Olof Christopher Aurivillus and Biston betularius. e, 500fr, John Henry Comstock and Parnassius apollo. f, 1000fr, Jean Henri Fabre and Acronicta aceris.

3000fr, William Kirby and Acherontia atropos.

**2009, Jan. 7** ***Perf. 13x13¼***

**1053** A181 Sheet of 6, #a-f 15.00 15.00

**Souvenir Sheet**

***Perf. 13¼ Syncopated***

**1054** A182 3000fr multi 16.50 16.50

Dated 2008.

### Mycologists

No. 1055: a, 200fr, Charles Horton Peck and Chroogomphus vinicolor. b, 250fr, Michel Adanson and Macrolepiota procera. c, 350fr, Miles Joseph Berkeley and Paxillus involutus. d, 450fr, Andrea Cesalpino and Tricholoma flavovirens. e, 500fr, Eduard Fischer and Phallus impudicus. f, 1000fr, Charles Edwin Bessey and Armillariella mellea.

3000fr, Peter Adolph Karsten and Marasmius oreades.

**2009, Jan. 7** ***Perf. 13x13¼***

**1055** A181 Sheet of 6, #a-f 15.00 15.00

**Souvenir Sheet**

***Perf. 13¼ Syncopated***

**1056** A182 3000fr multi 16.50 16.50

Dated 2008.

### Explorers

No. 1057: a, 200fr, Ferdinand Magellan. b, 250fr, Vasco da Gama. c, 350fr, Christopher Columbus. d, 450fr, James Cook. e, 500fr, Marco Polo. f, 1000fr, Amerigo Vespucci.

3000fr, Columbus, diff.

**2009, Jan. 7** ***Perf. 13x13¼***

**1057** A181 Sheet of 6, #a-f 15.00 15.00

**Souvenir Sheet**

***Perf. 13¼ Syncopated***

**1058** A182 3000fr multi 16.50 16.50

Dated 2008.

### David Livingstone

No. 1059 — Livingstone, map of Africa, and: a, 200fr, Livingstone with compass. b, 250fr, Lion attacking man. c, 350fr, Livingstone with rifle. d, 450fr, Men reading newspapers, African man and boy. e, 500fr, Livingstone with daughter. f, 1000fr, Livingstone reading book to Africans.

3000fr, Meeting Henry M. Stanley.

**2009, Jan. 7** ***Perf. 13x13¼***

**1059** A181 Sheet of 6, #a-f 15.00 15.00

**Souvenir Sheet**

***Perf. 13¼ Syncopated***

**1060** A182 3000fr multi 16.50 16.50

Dated 2008.

### Nobel Peace Prize Recipients

No. 1061: a, 200fr, Jane Addams, 1931, and peace marchers. b, 250fr, Nelson Mandela, 1993, and globe. c, 350fr, Kofi Annan, 2001, United Nations emblem and dove. d, 450fr, Mother Teresa, 1979, and children. e, 500fr, Aung San Suu Kyi, 1991, Burmese children. f, 1000fr, Wangari Muta Maathai, 2004, globe and dove.

3000fr, Dr. Albert Schweitzer, 1952, map of Africa, Red Cross, hands.

**2009, Jan. 7** ***Perf. 13x13¼***

**1061** A181 Sheet of 6, #a-f 15.00 15.00

**Souvenir Sheet**

***Perf. 13¼ Syncopated***

**1062** A182 3000fr multi 16.50 16.50

Dated 2008.

### World Chess Champions

No. 1063: a, 200fr, Boris Spassky. b, 250fr, Bobby Fischer. c, 350fr, Anatoly Karpov. d, 450fr, Garry Kasparaov. e, 500fr, Vladimir Kramnik. f, 1000fr, Viswanathan Anand.

3000fr, Tigran Petrosian.

**2009, Jan. 7** ***Perf. 13x13¼***

**1063** A181 Sheet of 6, #a-f 15.00 15.00

**Souvenir Sheet**

***Perf. 13¼ Syncopated***

**1064** A182 3000fr multi 16.50 16.50

Dated 2008.

### Vincent Van Gogh

No. 1065 — Self-portraits and: a, 200fr, Vincent's Bedroom in Arles. b, 250fr, Olive Trees and the Alpilles in the Background. c, 350fr, Wheat Field with Cypresses. d, 450fr, The Night Café in the Place Lamartine in Arles. e, 500fr, The Red Vineyard. f, 1000fr, Starry Night.

3000fr, Starry Night over the Rhone.

**2009, Jan. 7** ***Perf. 13x13¼***

**1065** A181 Sheet of 6, #a-f 15.00 15.00

**Souvenir Sheet**

***Perf. 13¼ Syncopated***

**1066** A182 3000fr multi 16.50 16.50

Dated 2008.

### 70th Birthday of Romy Schneider

No. 1067 — Schneider and scenes from her films: a, 200fr, Le Trio Infernal, 1974. b, 250fr, Adorable Sinner, 1959. c, 350fr, Ludwig, 1972. d, 450fr, Sissi: The Young Empress, 1956. e, 500fr, César and Rosalie, 1972. f, 1000fr, Max and the Junkmen, 1971.

3000fr, Christine, 1958.

**2009, Jan. 7** ***Perf. 13x13¼***

**1067** A181 Sheet of 6, #a-f 15.00 15.00

**Souvenir Sheet**

***Perf. 13¼ Syncopated***

**1068** A182 3000fr multi 16.50 16.50

Dated 2008.

A183

Mushrooms and Fauna — A184

No. 1069 — Mushrooms: a, 125fr, Amanita caesarea. b, 150fr, Amanita pantherina. c, 225fr, Pleurotus eryngii. d, 300fr, Amanita rubescens. e, 400fr, Boletus edulis. f, 1000fr, Pluteus leoninus.

3000fr, Amanita phalloides.

**2009, Mar. 2** ***Perf. 13x13¼***

**1069** A183 Sheet of 6, #a-f 11.50 11.50

**Souvenir Sheet**

***Perf. 13¼ Syncopated***

**1070** A184 3000fr multi 15.50 15.50

### Camels

No. 1071: a, 125fr, Camelus dromedarius. b, 150fr, Camelus bactrianus. c, 225fr, Camelus bactrianus, diff. d, 300fr, Camelus dromedarius, diff. e, 400fr, Camelus dromedarius, diff. f, 1000fr, Camelus bactrianus, diff.

3000fr, Two Camelus bactrianus.

**2009, Mar. 2** ***Perf. 13x13¼***

**1071** A183 Sheet of 6, #a-f 11.50 11.50

**Souvenir Sheet**

***Perf. 13¼ Syncopated***

**1072** A184 3000fr multi 15.50 15.50

### Gorillas

No. 1073: a, 125fr, Gorilla gorilla gorilla. b, 150fr, Gorilla gorilla. c, 225fr, Gorilla beringei graueri. d, 300fr, Gorilla beringei beringei. e, 400fr, Gorilla beringei. f, 1000fr, Gorilla gorilla diehli.

3000fr, Gorilla gorilla, diff.

**2009, Mar. 2** ***Perf. 13x13¼***

**1073** A183 Sheet of 6, #a-f 11.50 11.50

**Souvenir Sheet**

***Perf. 13¼ Syncopated***

**1074** A184 3000fr multi 15.50 15.50

### Dogs

No. 1075: a, 125fr, Aidi. b, 150fr, Africanis. c, 225fr, Sloughi. d, 300fr, Basenji. e, 400fr, Boerboel. f, 1000fr, Azawakh.

3000fr, Rhodesian ridgeback.

**2009, Mar. 2** ***Perf. 13x13¼***

**1075** A183 Sheet of 6, #a-f 11.50 11.50

**Souvenir Sheet**

***Perf. 13¼ Syncopated***

**1076** A184 3000fr multi 15.50 15.50

### Beetles

No. 1077: a, 125fr, Trachelophorus giraffa. b, 150fr, Cicindela campestris. c, 225fr, Leptinotarsa decemlineata (light blue frame). d, 300fr, Gelastorcoris oculatus (light blue frame). e, 400fr, Scarites guineensis. f, 1000fr, Goliathus albosignatus.

3000fr, Staphylinus olens.

**2009, Mar. 2** ***Perf. 13x13¼***

**1077** A183 Sheet of 6, #a-f 11.50 11.50

**Souvenir Sheet**

***Perf. 13¼ Syncopated***

**1078** A184 3000fr multi 15.50 15.50

### Bees and Wasps

No. 1079: a, 125fr, Chrysis ignita. b, 150fr, Megarhyssa macrurus. c, 225fr, Leptinotarsa decemlineata (yellowish green frame). d, 300fr, Gelastorcoris oculatus (yellowish green frame). e, 400fr, Parazumia symmorpha. f, 1000fr, Pteromalus puparum.

3000fr, Sphex ichneumoneus.

**2009, Mar. 2** ***Perf. 13x13¼***

**1079** A183 Sheet of 6, #a-f 11.50 11.50

**Souvenir Sheet**

***Perf. 13¼ Syncopated***

**1080** A184 3000fr multi 15.50 15.50

### Fish

No. 1081: a, 125fr, Latimeria chalumnae. b, 150fr, Synanceia verrucosa. c, 225fr, Scorpaena scrofa. d, 300fr, Periophthalmus argentilineatus. e, 400fr, Lophius americanus. f, 1000fr, Pristis microdon.

3000fr, Narcine brasiliensis.

**2009, Mar. 2** ***Perf. 13x13¼***

**1081** A183 Sheet of 6, #a-f 11.50 11.50

**Souvenir Sheet**

***Perf. 13¼ Syncopated***

**1082** A184 3000fr multi 15.50 15.50

### Shells and Lighthouses

No. 1083: a, 125fr, Pleurotomaria fricana and Hood Point Lighthouse. b, 150fr, Patella ferruginea and Swakopmund Lighthouse. c, 225fr, Tectus pyramis and Cape Columbine Lighthouse. d, 300fr, Monodonta turbinata and Seal Point Lighthouse. e, 400fr, Mesalia opalina and Moroni Lighthouse. f, 1000fr, Cypraea diliculum and Cape Agulhas Lighthouse.

3000fr, Ranella olearia and Umhlanga Rocks Lighthouse.

**2009, Mar. 2** ***Perf. 13x13¼***

**1083** A183 Sheet of 6, #a-f 11.50 11.50

**Souvenir Sheet**

***Perf. 13¼ Syncopated***

**1084** A184 3000fr multi 15.50 15.50

### Cats

No. 1085: a, 200fr, Sokoke. b, 250fr, Abyssinian. c, 350fr, Egyptian Mau. d, 450fr, Sokoke, diff. e, 500fr, Abyssinian, diff. f, 1000fr, Egyptian Mau, diff.

3000fr, Felis nigripes.

**2009, Mar. 2** ***Perf. 13x13¼***

**1085** A183 Sheet of 6, #a-f 14.50 14.50

**Souvenir Sheet**

***Perf. 13¼ Syncopated***

**1086** A184 3000fr multi 15.50 15.50

### Owls

No. 1087: a, 200fr, Otus pembaensis. b, 250fr, Ptilopsis granti. c, 350fr, Tyto alba. d, 450fr, Asio otus. e, 500fr, Strix woodfordii. f, 1000fr, Tyto soumagnei.

3000fr, Bubo africanus.

**2009, Mar. 2** ***Perf. 13x13¼***

**1087** A183 Sheet of 6, #a-f 14.50 14.50

**Souvenir Sheet**

***Perf. 13¼ Syncopated***

**1088** A184 3000fr multi 15.50 15.50

### Kingfishers

No. 1089: a, 200fr, Megaceryle maxima. b, 250fr, Alcedo atthis. c, 350fr, Halcyon senegalensis. d, 450fr, Ipsidina picta. e, 500fr, Todiramphus chloris. f, 1000fr, Alcedo cristata.

3000fr, Halcyon malimbica.

**2009, Mar. 2** ***Perf. 13x13¼***

**1089** A183 Sheet of 6, #a-f 14.50 14.50

**Souvenir Sheet**

***Perf. 13¼ Syncopated***

**1090** A184 3000fr multi 15.50 15.50

### Butterflies

No. 1091: a, 200fr, Crenis pechuelli. b, 250fr, Charaxes zingha. c, 350fr, Taenaris catops turdula. d, 450fr, Danaus chrysippus alcippus. e, 500fr, Anaea cyanae. f, 1000fr, Epiphile orea negrina.

3000fr, Cithaeria aurora.

**2009, Mar. 2** ***Perf. 13x13¼***

**1091** A183 Sheet of 6, #a-f 14.50 14.50

**Souvenir Sheet**

***Perf. 13¼ Syncopated***

**1092** A184 3000fr multi 15.50 15.50

### Dolphins

No. 1093: a, 200fr, Stenella coeruleoalba. b, 250fr, Stenella attenuata. c, 350fr, Sousa plumbea. d, 450fr, Stenella longirostris. e, 500fr, Tursiops truncatus. f, 1000fr, Lissodelphis peronii.

3000fr, Lagenorhynchus cruciger.

**2009, Mar. 2** ***Perf. 13x13¼***

**1093** A183 Sheet of 6, #a-f 14.50 14.50

**Souvenir Sheet**

***Perf. 13¼ Syncopated***

**1094** A184 3000fr multi 15.50 15.50

### Frogs

No. 1095: a, 200fr, Xenopos laevis. b, 250fr, Astyloternus robustus. c, 350fr, Mantella aurantiaca. d, 450fr, Rana goliath. e, 500fr, Pyxicephalus adspersus. f, 1000fr, Breviceps mossambicus.

3000fr, Phrynomantis bifasciatus.

**2009, Mar. 2** ***Perf. 13x13¼***

**1095** A183 Sheet of 6, #a-f 14.50 14.50

**Souvenir Sheet**

***Perf. 13¼ Syncopated***

**1096** A184 3000fr multi 15.50 15.50

### Prehistoric Animals

No. 1097: a, 200fr, Heterodontosaurus. b, 250fr, Malawisaurus. c, 350fr, Carnotaurus. d, 450fr, Rhamphorhynchus. e, 500fr, Ouranosaurus. f, 1000fr, Herrerasaurus.

3000fr, Abrictosaurus.

**2009, Mar. 2** ***Perf. 13x13¼***
**1097** A183 Sheet of 6, #a-f 14.50 14.50

**Souvenir Sheet**

***Perf. 13¼ Syncopated***

**1098** A184 3000fr multi 15.50 15.50

## SEMI-POSTAL STAMPS

**Anti-Malaria Issue**

Common Design Type

***Perf. 12½x12***

**1962, Apr. 7** **Engr.** **Unwmk.**
**B1** CD108 25fr + 5fr brt pink 3.50 3.50

WHO drive to eradicate malaria.

Nurse Feeding Infant — SP1

**1967, July 3** **Engr.** ***Perf. 13***
**B2** SP1 25fr + 5fr multi 3.25 3.25

For the Red Cross.

Mother and Child — SP2

**1974, Aug. 10** **Engr.** ***Perf. 13***
**B3** SP2 35fr + 10fr red & dk brn 2.75 2.75

For the Red Cross.
For surcharge see No. 144.

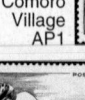

Space Achievements — SP3

World Philatelic Programs emblems (stamp collecting or Halley's Comet) and astronomer or satellite: a, Galileo. b, Copernicus. c, Kepler. d, Halley. e, *Planet A,* Japan, and 3 stars. f, *ICE,* US. g, *Planet A,* 5 stars. h, *Vega,* USSR.

**Miniature Sheet**

**1988** **Litho.** ***Perf. 13½***
**B4** Sheet of 8 15.00 15.00
***a.-h.*** SP3 200fr +10fr multi 1.50 1.50

See No. C193.
For surcharges see Nos. 816P-816S.

## AIR POST STAMPS

Comoro Village AP1

Comoro Men and Moroni Mosque AP2

Design: 200fr, Mosque of Ouani, Anjouan.

**1950-54** **Unwmk.** **Engr.** ***Perf. 13***
**C1** AP1 50fr grn & red brn 3.75 1.20
**C2** AP2 100fr dk brn & red 5.75 1.50
**C3** AP1 200fr dk grn, rose brn & pur ('54) 22.00 8.00
*Nos. C1-C3 (3)* 31.50 10.70

**Liberation Issue**

Common Design Type

**1954, June 6**
**C4** CD102 15fr sepia & red 32.50 19.00

Madrepora Fructicosa — AP3

100fr, Coral, shells and sea anemones.

**1962, Jan. 13** **Photo.** ***Perf. 12½x13***
**C5** AP3 100fr multi 13.50 13.50
**C6** AP3 500fr multi 25.00 18.00

**Telstar Issue**

Common Design Type

**1962, Dec. 5** **Engr.** ***Perf. 13***
**C7** CD111 25fr dp vio, dl pur & red lil 4.50 2.75

**Type of Regular Issue**

**Unwmk.**

**1963, Dec. 27** **Engr.** ***Perf. 13***

**Size: 26½x48mm**

**C8** A13 65fr Baskets 4.25 3.00
**C9** A13 200fr Pendant 8.25 4.50

**Boat Type of Regular Issue**

**1964, Aug. 7** **Photo.** ***Perf. 13***

**Size: 27x48mm**

**C10** A14 50fr Mayotte pirogue 4.00 1.60
**C11** A14 85fr Schooner 6.25 2.25

Olympic Torch and Boxers — AP4

**1964, Oct. 10** **Engr.** ***Perf. 13***
**C12** AP4 100fr red brn, dk brn & gray grn 6.50 6.50

18th Olympic Games, Tokyo, Oct. 10-25.

Order of Star of Grand Comoro — AP5

**1964, Dec. 10** **Photo.** ***Perf. 13***
**C13** AP5 500fr multi 17.50 15.00

**ITU Issue**

Common Design Type

**1965, May 17** **Engr.** ***Perf. 13***
**C14** CD120 50fr gray, grnsh bl & ol 18.00 9.00

**French Satellite A-1 Issue**

Common Design Type

Designs: 25fr, Diamant rocket and launching installations. 30fr, A-1 satellite.

**1966, Jan. 17** **Engr.** ***Perf. 13***
**C15** CD121 25fr dk pur & ultra 3.75 3.75
**C16** CD121 30fr dk pur & ultra 5.00 5.00
***a.*** Strip of 2, #C15-C16 + label 9.00 9.00

**French Satellite D-1 Issue**

Common Design Type

**1966, May 16** **Engr.** ***Perf. 13***
**C17** CD122 30fr dk grn, org & brn 4.00 4.00

Old Gun Battery, Dzaoudzi AP6

200fr, Ksar Castle, Mutsamudu, vert.

**1966, Dec. 19** **Photo.** ***Perf. 13***
**C18** AP6 50fr multi 4.25 2.10
**C19** AP6 200fr multi 7.75 5.00

**Bird Type of Regular Issue**

Birds: 75fr, Madagascar paradise flycatchers. 100fr, Blue-cheeked bee eaters.

**1967, June 20** **Photo.** ***Perf. 13***

**Size: 27x48mm**

**C20** A17 75fr yel grn & multi 10.00 6.50
**C21** A17 100fr lt bl & multi 12.50 8.00

Woman Skier — AP7

**1968, Apr. 29** **Engr.** ***Perf. 13***
**C22** AP7 70fr brt grn, lt bl & choc 4.75 3.75

10th Winter Olympic Games, Grenoble, France, Feb. 6-18, 1968.

**Fish Type of Regular Issue**

50fr, Moorish idol. 90fr, Diagramma lineatus.

**1968, Aug. 1** **Engr.** ***Perf. 13***

**Size: 47½x27mm**

**C23** A19 50fr plum blk & yel 7.50 3.75
**C24** A19 90fr brt grn, yel & gray grn 9.25 4.75

For surcharge & overprint see Nos. C52, C74.

Swimmer, Butterfly Stroke AP8

**1969, Jan. 27** **Photo.** ***Perf. 12½***
**C25** AP8 65fr ver, grnsh bl & blk 5.25 3.50

19th Olympic Games, Mexico City, 10/12-27.

**Flower Type of Regular Issue**

50fr, Heliconia sp. 85fr, Tuberose. 200fr, Orchid (angraecum eburneum).

**1969, Mar. 20** **Photo.** ***Perf. 13***

**Size: 27x48mm**

**C26** A21 50fr multi, vert. 3.50 2.75
**C27** A21 85fr multi, vert. 4.25 3.50
**C28** A21 200fr multi, vert. 8.25 4.50
*Nos. C26-C28 (3)* 16.00 10.75

**Concorde Issue**

Common Design Type

**1969, Apr. 17** **Engr.**
**C29** CD129 100fr pur & brn org 18.00 12.00

View of EXPO, Globe and Moon — AP9

90fr, Geisha, map of Japan & EXPO emblem.

**1970, Sept. 13** **Photo.** ***Perf. 13***
**C30** AP9 60fr slate & multi 4.50 2.40
**C31** AP9 90fr multi 5.50 3.25

EXPO '70 International Exposition, Osaka, Japan, Mar. 15-Sept. 13.

Sunset over Mutsamudu AP10

Map of Archipelago AP11

Designs: 20fr, Sada Village, Mayotte. 65fr, Old Iconi Palace, Grand Comoro. 85fr, Nioumatchoua Island, Moheli.

**1971, May 3** **Photo.** ***Perf. 13***
**C32** AP10 15fr dk bl & multi 1.20 .65
**C33** AP10 20fr multi 1.75 .80
**C34** AP10 65fr grn & multi 3.75 1.60
**C35** AP10 85fr bl & multi 5.50 2.50

**Engr.**

**C36** AP11 100fr brn red, grn & vio bl 7.50 5.50
*Nos. C32-C36 (5)* 19.70 11.05

See Nos. 107-110, C45-C49, C53, C62-C64. For overprints & surcharges see Nos. 143, C69, C71, C73, C76-C77, C79-C80, C82, C84.

**Flower Type of Regular Issue**

Flowers: 60fr, Hibiscus schizopetalus. 85fr, Acalypha sanderii.

**1971, July 19** **Photo.** ***Perf. 13***

**Size: 27x48mm**

**C37** A25 60fr grn, ver & yel 5.00 2.40
**C38** A25 85fr grn, red & yel 6.50 4.75

For surcharge see No. C75.

Mural, Moroni Airport AP12

Designs: 85fr, Mural in Arrival Hall, Moroni Airport. 100fr, View of Moroni Airport.

**1972, Mar. 30** **Photo.** ***Perf. 13***
**C39** AP12 65fr gray & multi 2.00 .85
**C40** AP12 85fr gray & multi 2.25 1.20

**Engr.**

**C41** AP12 100fr brn, bl & slate grn 4.00 2.10
*Nos. C39-C41 (3)* 8.25 4.15

New airport in Moroni.

Eiffel Tower and Moroni Telephone Exchange AP13

75fr, Frenchman and Comoro Islander talking on telephone, radio tower and beacons.

**1972, Apr. 24**
**C42** AP13 35fr dl red & gray 1.25 .85
**C43** AP13 75fr dk car, vio & bl 2.25 .95

First radio-telephone connection between France and Comoro Islands.

Underwater Spear-fishing — AP14

**1972, July 5 Engr. *Perf. 13***
**C44** AP14 70fr vio bl, brt grn & mar 8.75 5.50

For surcharge see No. C78.

### Types of 1971

Designs: 20fr, Cape Sima. 35fr, Bambao Palace. 40fr, Domoni Palace. 60fr, Gomajou Peninsula. 100fr, Map of Anjouan Island.

**1972, Nov. 15 Photo.**
**C45** AP10 20fr brn & multi .90 .65
**C46** AP10 35fr dk grn & multi 1.20 .80
**C47** AP10 40fr bl & multi 1.75 .95
**C48** AP10 60fr grnsh blk & multi 2.50 1.60

**Engr.**

**C49** AP11 100fr mar, bl & sl grn 13.50 7.25
*Nos. C45-C49 (5)* 19.85 11.25

Pres. Said Mohamed Cheikh (1904-70) — AP15

**1973, Mar. 16 Photo. *Perf. 13***
**C50** AP15 20fr multi 1.25 .80
**C51** AP15 35fr multi 1.60 1.00

For overprints see Nos. C70, C72.

### No. C24 Surcharged

**1973, Apr. 30 Engr. *Perf. 13***
**C52** A19 120fr on 90fr multi 13.00 7.25

Intl. Commission for Coelacanth Studies.

Map of Grand Comoro — AP16

**1973, June 28 Engr. *Perf. 13***
**C53** AP16 135fr vio, bl & dk brn 9.50 6.50

See Nos. C65, C68. For surcharges see Nos. C90-C92.

Karthala Volcano — AP17

**1973, July 16 Photo. *Perf. 13x12½***
**C54** AP17 120fr multi 7.50 5.50

Eruption of Karthala, Sept. 1972.
For surcharge see No. C89.

Armauer G. Hansen — AP18

Design: 150fr, Nicolaus Copernicus (1473-1543), Polish astronomer.

**1973, Sept. 5 Engr. *Perf. 13***
**C55** AP18 100fr brn, dk bl & sl grn 7.00 3.50
**C56** AP18 150fr grnsh bl, vio bl & choc 8.00 5.25

Cent. of the discovery of the Hansen bacillus, the cause of leprosy.
For overprint & surcharge see Nos. C81, C93.

Pablo Picasso (1881-1973) AP19

**1973, Sept. 30 Photo.**
**C57** AP19 200fr blk & multi 12.00 9.75

**Souvenir Sheet**

**C58** AP19 100fr blk & multi 16.00 14.50

For overprint see No. C87.

Order of the Star of Anjouan — AP20

**1974, Jan. 7 Photo. *Perf. 13***
**C59** AP20 500fr brn, bl & gold 13.00 9.50

For overprint see No. C95.

Said Omar ben Soumeth — AP21

135fr, Grand Mufti Said Omar, horiz.

**1974, Jan. 31 *Perf. 13x13½, 13½x13***
**C60** AP21 135fr blk & multi 4.50 2.75
**C61** AP21 200fr blk & multi 5.50 3.50

For overprint & surcharge see Nos. C85, C88.

### Types of 1971-73

Designs (Views on Mayotte): 20fr, Moya Beach. 35fr, Chiconi. 90fr, Port Mamutzu. 120fr, Map of Mayotte.

**1974, Aug. 31 Photo. *Perf. 13***
**C62** AP10 20fr bl & multi 1.20 .95
**C63** AP10 35fr grn & multi 2.50 2.00
**C64** AP10 90fr multi 6.25 3.50

**Engr.**

**C65** AP16 120fr ultra & grn 9.00 5.50
*Nos. C62-C65 (4)* 18.95 11.95

Jet Take-off AP22

**1975, Jan. 10 Engr. *Perf. 13***
**C66** AP22 135fr multi 7.25 4.75

First direct route Moroni-Hahaya-Paris.
For surcharge see No. C86.

Rotary Emblem, Meeting House, Map — AP23

**1975, Feb. 23 Photo. *Perf. 13***
**C67** AP23 250fr multi 10.50 7.25

Rotary Intl., 70th anniv., Moroni Rotary Club, 10th anniv.
For surcharge see No. C94.

### Map Type of 1973

Design: 230fr, Map of Moheli, horiz.

**1975, May 26 Engr. *Perf. 13***
**C68** AP16 230fr ocher, ol grn & bl 11.00 8.00

### STATE OF COMORO

Issues of 1968-75 Surcharged and Overprinted in Black, Silver, Red or Orange

**1975 Printing & Perfs. as Before**
**C69** AP10 10fr on 20fr #C62 *.60* .25
**C70** AP15 20fr (S) *1.00* .25
**C71** AP10 30fr on 35fr (R) #C63 *1.00* .25
**C72** AP15 35fr (S) *1.25* .75
**C73** AP10 40fr (O) *1.50* .75
**C74** A19 50fr *2.50* 1.25
**C75** A25 75fr on 60fr *2.00* 1.10
**C76** AP10 75fr on 60fr *2.00* 1.10
**C77** AP10 75fr on 65fr (O) *2.00* 1.10
**C78** AP14 75fr on 70fr *2.50* 1.25
**C79** AP11 100fr #C36 *4.00* 2.00
**C80** AP11 100fr #C49 *4.00* 2.00
**C81** AP18 100fr *4.00* 2.00
**C82** AP10 100fr on 85fr (O) *2.50* 1.50
**C83** A25 100fr on 85fr *2.50* 1.50
**C84** AP10 100fr on 90fr *2.50* 1.50
**C85** AP21 100fr on 135fr (S) *2.50* 1.50
**C86** AP22 100fr on 135fr *3.00* 2.00
**C87** AP19 200fr (S) *8.00* 4.00
**C88** AP21 200fr (S) *6.00* 3.50
**C89** AP17 200fr on 120fr *8.00* 4.00
**C90** AP16 200fr on 120fr *6.00* 3.50
**C91** AP16 200fr on 135fr *6.00* 3.50
**C92** AP16 200fr on 230fr *6.00* 3.50
**C93** AP18 400fr on 150fr *10.00* 5.25
**C94** AP23 400fr on 250fr *10.00* 5.25
**C95** AP20 500fr *12.00* 7.25
*Nos. C69-C95 (27)* 113.35 61.80

See postage section for airmail stamps that are part of joint postage/airmail sets.

Rotary Emblem, Landscape AP26

**1979, July 31 Litho. *Perf. 13x12½***
**C107** AP26 400fr multi 7.00 3.00

Rotary International.

IYC Emblem, Mother and Child — AP27

**1979, July 31 *Perf. 13x13½***
**C108** AP27 250fr multi 3.50 3.50

Intl. Year of the Child. See No. CB1. For surcharges see Nos. C121, C202.

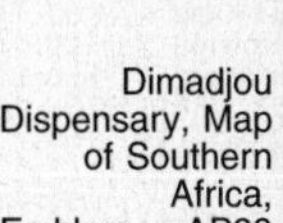

Dimadjou Dispensary, Map of Southern Africa, Emblem — AP28

260fr, Globe, Concorde, emblem.

**1980, Feb. 23 Litho. *Perf. 12½***
**C109** AP28 100fr shown 1.25 .40
**C110** AP28 260fr multicolored 3.00 1.00

Rotary International, 75th anniv. and Moroni Rotary Club, 15th anniv. (100fr).
For surcharges see Nos. 815L, C119-C120.

First Transatlantic Flight, 50th Anniversary AP29

**1980, May 30 Litho. *Perf. 13***
**C111** AP29 200fr multi 3.50 1.75

### No. C111 Surcharged in Blue

**1981, Feb. Litho. *Perf. 13***
**C112** AP29 30fr on 200fr multi 1.00 .35

The Dove and the Rainbow, by Picasso AP30

Picasso Birth Centenary: 70fr, Still Life on a Sideboard. 150fr, Studio with Plaster Head. 250fr, Bowl and Pot, vert. 500fr, The Red Tablecloth.

**1981, June 30 Litho. *Perf. 12½***
**C113** AP30 40fr multi .55 .25
**C114** AP30 70fr multi .95 .25
**C115** AP30 150fr multi 1.90 .50
**C116** AP30 250fr multi 3.25 .70
**C117** AP30 500fr multi 6.25 1.50
*Nos. C113-C117 (5)* 12.90 3.20

For surcharges see Nos. 815G, C118.

### Nos. C114, C109-C110, CB1 Srchd.

**1981, Nov. Litho. *Perf. 12½, 13***
**C118** AP30 10fr on 70fr multi .40 .40
**C119** AP28 10fr on 100fr multi .80 .80
**C120** AP28 50fr on 260fr multi 2.00 .25
**C121** AP27 50fr on 200fr+30fr multi 2.00 .25
*Nos. C118-C121 (4)* 5.20 1.70

Manned Flight Bicentenary AP31

Balloons: 100fr, Montgolfiere, 1783. 200fr, Lunardi, 1784. 300fr, Blanchard and Jeffries, 1785. 400fr, Giffard, 1852, horiz.
500fr, Paris Siege. 1870.

**1983, Apr. 20 Litho. *Perf. 13***

| | | | | |
|---|---|---|---|---|
| **C122** | AP31 | 100fr multicolored | 1.00 | .30 |
| **C123** | AP31 | 200fr multicolored | 1.90 | .50 |
| **C124** | AP31 | 300fr multicolored | 3.25 | .90 |
| **C125** | AP31 | 400fr multicolored | 4.50 | 1.25 |
| | | *Nos. C122-C125 (4)* | 10.65 | 2.95 |

**Souvenir Sheet**

| | | | | |
|---|---|---|---|---|
| **C126** | AP31 | 500fr multicolored | 5.50 | 1.50 |

For overprints and surcharges see Nos. 602, 812T, 815P.

Pre-Olympic Year Sailing AP32

150fr, Type 470, pink and yellow sail. 200fr, Flying Dutchman. 300fr, Type 470, white sails. 400fr, Finn.
500fr, Soling.

**1983, June 30 Litho. *Perf. 13***

| | | | | |
|---|---|---|---|---|
| **C127** | AP32 | 150fr multi | 1.50 | .40 |
| **C128** | AP32 | 200fr multi | 2.25 | .50 |
| **C129** | AP32 | 300fr multi | 3.25 | .90 |
| **C130** | AP32 | 400fr multi | 4.75 | 1.00 |
| | | *Nos. C127-C130 (4)* | 11.75 | 2.80 |

**Souvenir Sheet**

| | | | | |
|---|---|---|---|---|
| **C131** | AP32 | 500fr multi | 5.50 | 1.50 |

For overprint and surcharge see Nos. 603, C206.

1984 Summer Olympics AP33

60fr, Basketball, 2 players. 100fr, Basketball, 6 players. 165fr, Basketball, 4 players. 175fr, Baseball catcher, horiz. 200fr, Baseball, horiz.
500fr, Basketball, diff.

**1984, July 10 Litho. *Perf. 13***

| | | | | |
|---|---|---|---|---|
| **C132** | AP33 | 60fr multicolored | .50 | .25 |
| **C133** | AP33 | 100fr multicolored | .90 | .40 |
| **C134** | AP33 | 165fr multicolored | 1.50 | .65 |
| **C135** | AP33 | 175fr multicolored | 1.60 | .65 |
| **C136** | AP33 | 200fr shown | 1.90 | .80 |
| | | *Nos. C132-C136 (5)* | 6.40 | 2.75 |

**Souvenir Sheet**

| | | | | |
|---|---|---|---|---|
| **C137** | AP33 | 500fr multicolored | 8.00 | 1.50 |

Nos. C132-C134 vert.

Development Conference — AP34

475fr, Tools for development.

**1984, July 2 Litho. *Perf. 13***

| | | | | |
|---|---|---|---|---|
| **C138** | AP34 | 475fr multi | 5.50 | 2.00 |

For surcharge see No. 796I.

Audubon Bicentenary AP35

100fr, Hirundo rustica, vert. 125fr, Icterus galbula, vert. 150fr, Buteo lineatus. 500fr, Sphyropieus varius.

**1985, Jan. 15 Litho. *Perf. 13***

| | | | | |
|---|---|---|---|---|
| **C139** | AP35 | 100fr multicolored | 1.25 | .40 |
| **C140** | AP35 | 125fr multicolored | 1.50 | .50 |
| **C141** | AP35 | 150fr multicolored | 2.00 | .60 |
| **C142** | AP35 | 500fr multicolored | 5.25 | 2.00 |
| | | *Nos. C139-C142 (4)* | 10.00 | 3.50 |

Moroni Port Missile Defense — AP36

No. C146, Ngome Ntsoudjini Scout troop.

**1985, May 20 Litho. *Perf. 13x12½***

| | | | | |
|---|---|---|---|---|
| **C145** | AP36 | 200fr multi | 3.00 | 1.25 |
| **C146** | AP36 | 200fr multi | 3.00 | 1.25 |
| *a.* | | Pair, #C145-C146 + label | 6.00 | 6.00 |

PHILEXAFRICA '85, Lome.
For surcharges see Nos. C207-C208.

Natl. Flag, Sun, Outline Map of Islands — AP37

**1985, July 6**

| | | | | |
|---|---|---|---|---|
| **C147** | AP37 | 10fr multi | .30 | .25 |
| **C148** | AP37 | 15fr multi | .30 | .25 |
| **C149** | AP37 | 125fr multi | 2.25 | .60 |
| **C150** | AP37 | 300fr multi | 5.50 | 1.50 |
| | | *Nos. C147-C150 (4)* | 8.35 | 2.60 |

Natl. independence, 10th anniv.
For surcharge see No. 815Q.

Runners AP38

**1985, Nov. 12**

| | | | | |
|---|---|---|---|---|
| **C151** | AP38 | 250fr shown | 2.75 | 1.75 |
| **C152** | AP38 | 250fr Mining | 2.75 | 1.75 |
| *a.* | | Pair, #C151-C152 + label | 6.00 | 6.00 |

PHILEXAFRICA '85, Lome, Togo, 11/16-24.
For surcharges see Nos. 815H-815I, C204-C205.

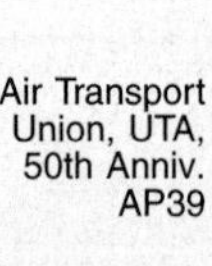

Air Transport Union, UTA, 50th Anniv. AP39

25fr, F-AOUL seaplane. 75fr, Camel driver, DC-8. 100fr, Noratlas and Heron DC-4s. 125fr, UTA cargo plane. 1000fr, Aircraft, 1935-1985.

**1985, Dec. 30 Litho. *Perf. 13***

| | | | | |
|---|---|---|---|---|
| **C153** | AP39 | 25fr multi | .25 | .25 |
| **C154** | AP39 | 75fr multi | .75 | .30 |
| **C155** | AP39 | 100fr multi | 1.10 | .40 |
| *a.* | | Souv. sheet of 3, #C153-C155, perf. 12½ | 3.50 | 2.25 |
| **C156** | AP39 | 125fr multi | 1.40 | .60 |

**Size: 40x52mm**

***Perf. 12½x13***

| | | | | |
|---|---|---|---|---|
| **C157** | AP39 | 1000fr multi | 12.00 | 6.00 |
| *a.* | | Souv. sheet of 2, #C156-C157, perf. 12½ | 13.00 | 8.00 |
| | | *Nos. C153-C157 (5)* | 15.50 | 7.55 |

Halley's Comet AP40

Comets, astronomers and probes: 125fr, Edmond Halley, Giotto probe. 150fr, Giacobini-Zinner, 1959. 225fr, Encke, 1961. 300fr, Bradfield, 1980. 450fr, Planet A probe.

**1986, Mar. 7 *Perf. 13***

| | | | | |
|---|---|---|---|---|
| **C158** | AP40 | 125fr multi | 1.25 | .45 |
| **C159** | AP40 | 150fr multi | 1.50 | .50 |
| **C160** | AP40 | 225fr multi | 2.50 | .90 |
| **C161** | AP40 | 300fr multi | 3.00 | 1.25 |
| **C162** | AP40 | 450fr multi | 5.00 | 1.75 |
| | | *Nos. C158-C162 (5)* | 13.25 | 4.85 |

For surcharges see Nos. 796S, 804H, 804R, 812P.

1986 World Cup Soccer Championships, Mexico — AP41

Various soccer plays.

**1986, June 11 Litho. *Perf. 13***

| | | | | |
|---|---|---|---|---|
| **C163** | AP41 | 125fr multi | 1.25 | .45 |
| **C164** | AP41 | 210fr multi | 2.25 | .80 |
| **C165** | AP41 | 500fr multi | 5.50 | 2.00 |
| **C166** | AP41 | 600fr multi | 6.00 | 2.25 |
| | | *Nos. C163-C166 (4)* | 15.00 | 5.50 |

For surcharges see Nos. 796C, 800Q, 815C.

Tennis at the 1988 Summer Olympics — AP42

Various players.

**1987, Jan. 28 Litho. *Perf. 13½***

| | | | | |
|---|---|---|---|---|
| **C167** | AP42 | 150fr multi | 1.75 | .45 |
| **C168** | AP42 | 250fr multi | 3.00 | .75 |
| **C169** | AP42 | 500fr multi | 5.50 | 1.50 |
| **C170** | AP42 | 600fr multi | 6.75 | 1.75 |
| | | *Nos. C167-C170 (4)* | 17.00 | 4.45 |

For overprints and surcharges see Nos. 796N, 796U, 815J, 816L, 816N, C183-C186, C203.

World Wildlife Fund AP43

Various pictures of the mongoose lemur.

**1987, Feb. 18 *Perf. 13***

| | | | | |
|---|---|---|---|---|
| **C171** | AP43 | 75fr multi, vert. | 2.00 | .50 |
| **C172** | AP43 | 100fr multi | 3.00 | .75 |
| **C173** | AP43 | 125fr multi | 5.00 | 1.00 |
| **C174** | AP43 | 150fr multi | 6.00 | 1.25 |
| | | *Nos. C171-C174 (4)* | 16.00 | 3.50 |

1988 Winter Olympics, Calgary — AP44

150fr, Slalom. 225fr, Ski jumping. 500fr, Women's giant slalom. 600fr, Luge.

**1987, Apr. 10 Litho. *Perf. 13½***

| | | | | |
|---|---|---|---|---|
| **C175** | AP44 | 150fr multi | 1.25 | .45 |
| **C176** | AP44 | 225fr multi | 2.25 | .75 |
| **C177** | AP44 | 500fr multi | 5.50 | 1.60 |
| **C178** | AP44 | 600fr multi | 6.00 | 2.25 |
| | | *Nos. C175-C178 (4)* | 15.00 | 5.05 |

For surcharges see Nos. 800R, 812U.

AP45

Aviation History — AP46

Designs: 200fr, Inventors Didier Daurat and Raymond Vanier with 1935 Air Blue F-ANR1. 300fr, Farman biplane, 1st scheduled airmail delivery, Paris-LeMans-St. Nazaire, Aug. 17, 1918. 500fr, Bleriot aircraft, 1st scheduled airmail delivery, Villacoublay-Vendome-Poitiers-Pauillac, Oct. 15, 1913. 1000fr, Henri Pequet and his aircraft, Feb. 18, 1911.

**1987, Dec. 29 Litho. *Perf. 13***

| | | | | |
|---|---|---|---|---|
| **C179** | AP45 | 200fr multi | 2.00 | .65 |
| **C180** | AP45 | 300fr multi | 3.00 | 1.00 |
| **C181** | AP45 | 500fr multi | 5.00 | 1.60 |

***Perf. 12½x13***

| | | | | |
|---|---|---|---|---|
| **C182** | AP46 | 1000fr multi | 10.00 | 2.25 |
| | | *Nos. C179-C182 (4)* | 20.00 | 5.50 |

Airmail history exposition, Allahabad.
For surcharges see Nos. 800S, 804D.

**Nos. C167-C170 Ovptd. in Red for 1988 Olympic Tennis Champions**

Overprint includes name of athlete and "Medaille d'or / Seoul" or "Medaille / d'argent / Seoul."

**1988, Nov. Litho. *Perf. 13½***

| | | | | |
|---|---|---|---|---|
| **C183** | AP42 | 150fr "Miloslav Mecir / (Tchec.)" | 1.25 | .75 |
| **C184** | AP42 | 250fr "Tim Mayotte / (U.S.A.)" | 1.90 | 1.40 |
| **C185** | AP42 | 500fr "Steffi Graf / (R.F.A.)" | 5.00 | 2.75 |
| **C186** | AP42 | 600fr "Gabriela Sabatini / (Argentine)" | 6.00 | 3.75 |
| | | *Nos. C183-C186 (4)* | 14.15 | 8.65 |

For surcharges see Nos. 800T, 815K, 816M, 816O.

Early Aviators and Aircraft AP47

100fr, Alberto Santos-Dumont (1873-1932), & *Bagatelle,* 1st documented power flight in Europe, Oct. 23, 1906. 150fr, Wright Brothers & *Flyer A.* 200fr, Louis Bleriot (1872-1936) & *Bleriot XI,* 1st crossing of the English Channel in a heavier-than-air craft, July 25, 1909. 300fr, Henri Farman (1874-1958) & Voisin biplane, 1st fixed-route 1-kilometer circular flight, Jan. 13, 1908. 500fr, Gabriel (1880-1973) & Charles (1882-1912) Voisin, established 1st biplane factory (1908), & Voisin biplane. 800fr, Roland Garros (1888-1918), 1st trans-Mediterranean flight, Sept. 23, 1913.

**1988, Dec. 7 Litho. *Perf. 13***

| | | | | |
|---|---|---|---|---|
| **C187** | AP47 | 100fr pur | .90 | .45 |
| **C188** | AP47 | 150fr brt lil rose | 1.60 | .60 |
| **C189** | AP47 | 200fr blk | 2.00 | .90 |
| **C190** | AP47 | 300fr dark yel org | 3.00 | .90 |
| **C191** | AP47 | 500fr dark blue | 5.00 | 1.50 |
| **C192** | AP47 | 800fr lt olive grn | 7.50 | 3.00 |
| | | *Nos. C187-C192 (6)* | 20.00 | 7.35 |

For surcharges see Nos. 800B, 800U, 804E, C209.

Souvenir Sheet

Space Achievements — AP48

Design: World Philatelic Programs stamp collecting emblem, Soviet satellite and Edmond Halley.

**1988 Litho. *Perf. 13½***

| | | | | |
|---|---|---|---|---|
| **C193** | AP48 | 750fr multi | 8.00 | 1.50 |

Nos. C108, C168, C151-C152, C128, C145-C146 and C189 Surcharged

**1989 Litho. *Perfs. as Before***

| | | | | |
|---|---|---|---|---|
| **C202** | AP27 | 5fr on 250fr #C108 | .25 | .25 |
| **C203** | AP42 | 25fr on 250fr #C168 | .25 | .25 |
| **C204** | AP38 | 50fr on 250fr #C151 | .50 | .25 |
| **C205** | AP38 | 50fr on 250fr #C152 | .50 | .25 |
| *a.* | | Pair, #C204-C205 + label | 1.25 | 1.25 |
| **C206** | AP32 | 150fr on 200fr #C128 | 1.40 | .60 |
| **C207** | AP36 | 150fr on 200fr #C145 | 1.40 | .60 |
| **C208** | AP36 | 150fr on 200fr #C146 | 1.40 | .60 |
| *a.* | | Pair, #C207-C208 + label | 6.00 | 6.00 |
| **C209** | AP47 | 150fr on 200fr #C189 | 1.40 | .60 |
| | | *Nos. C202-C209 (8)* | 7.10 | 3.40 |

World Cup Soccer, Championships, Italy — AP50

Various soccer plays and map of Italy.

**1990, June Litho. *Perf. 13***

| | | | | |
|---|---|---|---|---|
| **C210** | AP50 | 75fr multicolored | .60 | .30 |
| **C211** | AP50 | 150fr multicolored | 1.40 | .60 |
| **C212** | AP50 | 500fr multicolored | 4.25 | 1.90 |
| **C213** | AP50 | 1000fr multicolored | 8.75 | 4.00 |
| | | *Nos. C210-C213 (4)* | 15.00 | 6.80 |

For surcharge see No. 800V.

Souvenir Sheet

Garry Kasparov, Anatoly Karpov, Russian Chess Champions — AP51

**Litho. & Embossed**

**1991, Aug. 5 *Perf. 13½***

| | | | | |
|---|---|---|---|---|
| **C214** | AP51 | 1500fr gold & multi | 12.00 | — |

World Chess Championships.

1992 Summer Olympics, Barcelona AP52

**Litho. & Embossed**

**1992, July 28 *Perf. 13½***

| | | | | |
|---|---|---|---|---|
| **C215** | AP52 | 1500fr gold & multi | 26.50 | 12.00 |

Sculpted Table — AP52a

**1994 (?) Litho. *Perf. 13¼x13½***

**Background Color**

| | | | | |
|---|---|---|---|---|
| **C215A** | AP52a | 15fr blue | — | 5.00 |
| **C215B** | AP52a | 75fr green | — | — |
| **C215C** | AP52a | 100fr pink | — | — |
| **C215D** | AP52a | 225fr orange | — | — |

For surcharges see Nos. 826A-826E.

Sea Turtles — AP53

**1995 Litho. *Perf. 13½x13¼***

**Frame Color**

| | | | | |
|---|---|---|---|---|
| **C216** | AP53 | 10fr blue | 15.00 | 15.00 |
| **C217** | AP53 | 25fr pink | — | — |
| **C218** | AP53 | 30fr green | 25.00 | 25.00 |
| **C219** | AP53 | 50fr lilac | 50.00 | 50.00 |

No. C215A Surcharged in Blue Violet

***Perf. 13¼x13½***

**2001, June 16 Litho.**

| | | | | |
|---|---|---|---|---|
| **C220** | AP52a | 300fr on 15fr | — | — |

## AIR POST SEMI-POSTAL STAMP

**Type of Air Post 1979**

Design: IYC emblem, mother and son.

**1979, July 31 Photo. *Perf. 13½x13***

| | | | | |
|---|---|---|---|---|
| **CB1** | AP27 | 200fr + 30fr multi | 3.50 | 3.50 |

International Year of the Child.
For surcharge see No. C121.

## POSTAGE DUE STAMPS

Anjouan Mosque — D1

**1950 Unwmk. Engr. *Perf. 14x13***

| | | | | |
|---|---|---|---|---|
| **J1** | D1 | 50c deep green | 1.20 | .95 |
| **J2** | D1 | 1fr black brown | 1.20 | 1.00 |

Coelacanth — D2

**1954**

| | | | | |
|---|---|---|---|---|
| **J3** | D2 | 5fr dk brown & green | 1.10 | 1.00 |
| **J4** | D2 | 10fr gray & red brown | 1.50 | 1.50 |
| **J5** | D2 | 20fr indigo & blue | 2.75 | 2.50 |
| | | *Nos. J3-J5 (3)* | 5.35 | 5.00 |

Hibiscus — D3

2fr, Pineapple, vert. 5fr, White butterfly. 10fr, Chameleon. 15fr, Blooming banana, vert. 20fr, Orchids. 30fr, Allamanda cathartica. 40fr, Cashews, vert. 50fr, Custard apple, vert. 100fr, Breadfruit. 200fr, Vanilla. 500fr, Ylang ylang.

**1977, Nov. 19 Litho. *Perf. 13½***

| | | | | |
|---|---|---|---|---|
| **J6** | D3 | 1fr shown | .35 | .25 |
| **J7** | D3 | 2fr multicolored | .35 | .25 |
| **J8** | D3 | 5fr multicolored | .35 | .25 |
| **J9** | D3 | 10fr multicolored | .35 | .25 |
| **J10** | D3 | 15fr multicolored | .35 | .25 |
| **J11** | D3 | 20fr multicolored | .35 | .25 |
| **J12** | D3 | 30fr multicolored | .50 | .25 |
| **J13** | D3 | 40fr multicolored | .95 | .25 |
| **J14** | D3 | 50fr multicolored | 1.10 | .25 |
| **J15** | D3 | 100fr multicolored | 2.10 | .75 |
| **J16** | D3 | 200fr multicolored | 4.50 | .95 |
| **J17** | D3 | 500fr multicolored | 10.75 | 1.50 |
| | | *Nos. J6-J17 (12)* | 22.00 | 5.45 |

## OFFICIAL STAMPS

Comoro Flag — O1

***Perf. 13x12½***

**1979-85 Litho. Unwmk.**

| | | | | |
|---|---|---|---|---|
| **O1** | O1 | 5fr multi | .25 | .25 |
| **O2** | O1 | 10fr multi | .25 | .25 |
| **O3** | O1 | 20fr multi | .25 | .25 |
| **O4** | O1 | 30fr multi | .50 | .25 |
| **O5** | O1 | 40fr multi | .65 | .25 |
| **O6** | O1 | 60fr multi ('80) | .60 | .25 |
| **O7** | O1 | 75fr multi ('85) | .40 | .25 |
| **O8** | O1 | 100fr multi | 1.25 | .60 |
| | | *Nos. O1-O8 (8)* | 4.15 | 2.35 |

See Nos. 526-530.

Pres. Said Mohamed Cheikh (1904-1970) — O2

**1980-85**

| | | | | |
|---|---|---|---|---|
| **O9** | O2 | 100fr multi | 1.00 | .40 |
| **O10** | O2 | 125fr multi ('85) | 2.00 | 1.50 |
| **O11** | O2 | 400fr multi | 3.00 | 1.25 |
| | | *Nos. O9-O11 (3)* | 6.00 | 3.15 |

# CONGO, DEMOCRATIC REPUBLIC

ˌde-mə-ˈkra-tik ri-ˈpə-blik of ˈkäŋ-ˌgō

LOCATION — Central Africa
GOVT. — Republic
AREA — 895,348 sq. mi. (estimated)
POP. — 22,480,000 (est. 1971)
CAPITAL — Kinshasa (Leopoldville)

Congo was an independent state, founded by Leopold II of Belgium, until 1908 when it was annexed to Belgium as a colony. Congo became an independent republic in 1960. The name was changed to Republic of Zaire, Oct. 28, 1971. In 1998 some issues again used the name Congo Democratic Republic. See Zaire in Vol. 6 for later issues.

100 Centimes = 1 Franc
100 Sengi = 1 Li-Kuta,
100 Ma-Kuta = 1 Zaire (1967)

**Catalogue values for all unused stamps in this country are for Never Hinged items.**

Belgian Congo Flower Issue of 1952-53 Overprinted or Surcharged

***Perf. 11½***

**1960, June 30 Photo. Unwmk.**

**Flowers in Natural Colors**

**Size: 21x25½mm**

**Granite Paper**

| | | | | |
|---|---|---|---|---|
| **323** | A86 | 10c dp plum & ocher | .25 | .25 |
| **324** | A86 | 10c on 15c red & yel grn | .25 | .25 |
| **325** | A86 | 20c grn & gray | .25 | .25 |
| **326** | A86 | 40c grn & sal | .25 | .25 |
| **327** | A86 | 50c on 60c bl grn & pink | .25 | .25 |
| **328** | A86 | 50c on 75c dp plum & gray | .25 | .25 |
| **329** | A86 | 1fr car & yel | .30 | .25 |
| **330** | A86 | 1.50fr vio & ap grn | .30 | .25 |
| **331** | A86 | 2fr ol grn & buff | .30 | .25 |
| **332** | A86 | 3fr ol grn & pink | .45 | .25 |
| **333** | A86 | 4fr choc & lil | 1.50 | 1.00 |
| **334** | A86 | 5fr dp plum & lt bl grn | .55 | .25 |
| **335** | A86 | 6.50fr dk car & lil | .70 | .25 |
| **336** | A86 | 8fr grn & lt yel | .80 | .30 |
| **337** | A86 | 10fr dp plum & pale ol | 1.50 | .30 |
| **338** | A86 | 20fr vio bl & dl sal | 3.50 | .80 |

Nos. 324, 327-328 exist without "CONGO" overprint but with surcharge, also without surcharge but with "CONGO." Inverted and double overprints exist. Values from $10 to $50 each.

Belgian Congo Flower Issue of 1952-53 Overprinted or Surcharged

**Size: 22x32mm**

| | | | | |
|---|---|---|---|---|
| **339** | A86 | 50fr dp plum & gray bl | 19.00 | 6.00 |
| **340** | A86 | 100fr grn & buff | 45.00 | 10.00 |
| | | *Nos. 323-340 (18)* | 75.40 | 21.40 |

Belgian Congo Nos. 306-317, Ovptd. or Srchd. in Red, Blue, Black or Brown

| | | | | |
|---|---|---|---|---|
| **341** | A92 | 10c bl & brn (R) | .25 | .25 |
| **342** | A93 | 20c red org & sl (Bl) | .25 | .25 |
| **343** | A92 | 40c brn & bl (Bk) | .25 | .25 |
| **344** | A93 | 50c brt ultra, red & sep (R) | .25 | .25 |
| **345** | A92 | 1fr brn, grn & blk (Br) | .25 | .25 |
| **346** | A93 | 1.50fr blk & org yel (R) | .25 | .25 |
| **347** | A92 | 2fr crim, blk & brn (Bl) | .45 | .25 |
| **348** | A93 | 3.50fr on 3fr blk, gray & lil rose (Bk) | .65 | .25 |
| **349** | A92 | 5fr brn, dk brn & brt grn (Br) | .85 | .25 |
| **350** | A93 | 6.50fr bl, brn & org yel (R) | 1.00 | .25 |
| *a.* | | Black overprint | 1.10 | .60 |
| **351** | A92 | 8fr org brn, ol bis & lil (Br) | 1.25 | .30 |
| **352** | A93 | 10fr multi (R) | 1.50 | .40 |
| | | *Nos. 341-352 (12)* | 7.20 | 3.20 |

Inverted and double overprints exist. Values from $15 to $20 each.

Belgian Congo No. 318 Overprinted

**1960**

| | | | | |
|---|---|---|---|---|
| **353** | A94 | 50c gldn brn, ocher & red brn | 1.00 | .90 |

**Belgian Congo Nos. 321-322 Overprinted and Surcharged**

**Inscription in French**

| | | | | |
|---|---|---|---|---|
| **354** | A95 | 3.50fr on 3fr gray & org red | .85 | .50 |

**Inscription in Flemish**

| | | | | |
|---|---|---|---|---|
| **355** | A95 | 3.50fr on 3fr gray & org red | .85 | .50 |
| | | *Nos. 353-355 (3)* | 2.70 | 1.90 |

Nos. 353-355 are known with inverted double and triple overprints. Value, each $11. Overprints in other colors are proofs.

Nos. 354-355 exist with surcharge omitted. Value, set $165.

Map of Congo — A93a

**1960 Photo. *Perf. 11½***

| No. | Type | Description | Unused | Used |
|---|---|---|---|---|
| **356** | A93a | 20c brown | .25 | .25 |
| **357** | A93a | 50c rose red | .25 | .25 |
| **358** | A93a | 1fr green | .25 | .25 |
| **359** | A93a | 1.50fr red brn | .25 | .25 |
| **360** | A93a | 2fr rose car | .25 | .25 |
| **361** | A93a | 3.50fr lilac | .25 | .25 |
| **362** | A93a | 5fr brt bl | .25 | .25 |
| **363** | A93a | 6.50fr gray | .25 | .25 |
| **364** | A93a | 10fr orange | .30 | .25 |
| **365** | A93a | 20fr ultra | .70 | .25 |
| | | *Nos. 356-365 (10)* | 3.00 | 2.50 |

Congo's Independence.

Nos. 356-365 exist imperf. Value, set unused $25.

For overprints see Nos. 371-380.

Flag, People and Broken Chain — A94

**1961, Jan. 4 Unwmk. *Perf. 11½***

**Flag in Blue and Yellow**

| No. | Type | Description | Unused | Used |
|---|---|---|---|---|
| **366** | A94 | 2fr rose vio | .25 | .25 |
| **367** | A94 | 3.50fr vermilion | .25 | .25 |
| **368** | A94 | 6.50fr yel brn | .25 | .25 |
| **369** | A94 | 10fr brt grn | .35 | .25 |
| **370** | A94 | 20fr car rose | .50 | .30 |
| | | *Nos. 366-370 (5)* | 1.60 | 1.30 |

Signing of the Independence Agreement by Belgium, Jan. 4, 1959.

**Nos. 356-365 Overprinted in Blue, Black or Red**

**1961**

| No. | Type | Description | Unused | Used |
|---|---|---|---|---|
| **371** | A93a | 20c brn (Bl) | 1.60 | 1.60 |
| **372** | A93a | 50c rose red (Bk) | 1.60 | 1.60 |
| **373** | A93a | 1fr grn (R) | 1.60 | 1.60 |
| **374** | A93a | 1.50fr red brn (Bl) | 1.60 | 1.60 |
| **375** | A93a | 2fr rose car (Bk) | 1.60 | 1.60 |
| **376** | A93a | 3.50fr lil (Bl) | 1.60 | 1.60 |
| **377** | A93a | 5fr brt bl (R) | 1.60 | 1.60 |
| **378** | A93a | 6.50fr gray (R) | 1.60 | 1.60 |
| **379** | A93a | 10fr org (Bk) | 1.60 | 1.60 |
| **380** | A93a | 20fr ultra (R) | 1.60 | 1.60 |
| | | *Nos. 371-380 (10)* | 16.00 | 16.00 |

Coquilhatville Conf., Apr.-May, 1961.

Nos. 371-380 exist with inverted overprints. Value $15 each.

Pres. Joseph Kasavubu A95

Kasavubu and Map of Congo A96

10fr-100fr, Kasavubu in uniform and map.

***Perf. 11½***

**1961, June 30 Unwmk. Photo.**

**Portrait and Inscription in Dark Brown**

| No. | Type | Description | Unused | Used |
|---|---|---|---|---|
| **381** | A95 | 10c yellow | .25 | .25 |
| **382** | A95 | 20c dp rose | .25 | .25 |
| **383** | A95 | 40c bl grn | .25 | .25 |
| **384** | A95 | 50c salmon | .25 | .25 |
| **385** | A95 | 1fr lilac | .25 | .25 |
| **386** | A95 | 1.50fr lt brn | .25 | .25 |
| **387** | A95 | 2fr brt grn | .25 | .25 |
| **388** | A96 | 3.50fr rose pink | .25 | .25 |
| **389** | A96 | 5fr gray | *6.50* | .25 |
| **390** | A96 | 6.50fr ultra | 1.00 | .25 |
| **391** | A96 | 8fr olive | 1.00 | .25 |
| **392** | A95 | 10fr lt vio | 2.25 | .80 |
| **393** | A95 | 20fr orange | 2.25 | .25 |
| **394** | A95 | 50fr lt bl | 3.75 | .35 |
| **395** | A95 | 100fr apple green | 6.25 | .55 |
| | | *Nos. 381-395 (15)* | 25.00 | 4.70 |

First anniversary of independence.

Exists imperf. Value, set $70.

**Nos. 381-387, 389 and 392 Overprinted**

No. 396

No. 403

**1961**

**Portrait and Inscription in Dark Brown**

| No. | Type | Description | Unused | Used |
|---|---|---|---|---|
| **396** | A95 | 10c yellow | .25 | .25 |
| **397** | A95 | 20c dp rose | .25 | .25 |
| **398** | A95 | 40c bl grn | .25 | .25 |
| **399** | A95 | 50c salmon | .55 | .35 |
| **400** | A95 | 1fr lilac | .55 | .35 |
| **401** | A95 | 1.50fr lt brn | 1.50 | 1.00 |
| **402** | A95 | 2fr brt grn | 1.50 | 1.00 |
| **403** | A96 | 5fr gray | 1.50 | 1.00 |
| **404** | A95 | 10fr lt vio | 1.50 | 1.00 |
| | | *Nos. 396-404 (9)* | 7.85 | 5.45 |

Congolese parliament re-opening, 7/1961.

Nos. 396-404 exist with inverted overprints. Value $9 each.

Dag Hammarskjold and Map of Africa with Congo — A97

**1962, Jan. 20 Photo. *Perf. 11½***

**Gray Background**

| No. | Type | Description | Unused | Used |
|---|---|---|---|---|
| **405** | A97 | 10c dk brn | .25 | .25 |
| **406** | A97 | 20c Prus bl | .25 | .25 |
| **407** | A97 | 30c brown | .25 | .25 |
| **408** | A97 | 40c dk bl | .25 | .25 |
| **409** | A97 | 50c brn red | .25 | .25 |
| **410** | A97 | 3fr ol grn | *4.50* | *1.25* |
| **411** | A97 | 6.50fr dk vio | 1.25 | .30 |
| **412** | A97 | 8fr red brn | 1.50 | .45 |
| | | *Nos. 405-412 (8)* | 8.50 | 3.25 |

**Souvenir Sheets**

***Imperf***

| No. | Type | Description | Unused | Used |
|---|---|---|---|---|
| **413** | A97 | 25fr blk brn | 8.00 | 8.00 |
| *a.* | | Overprint in green | 4.00 | 4.00 |
| *b.* | | Overprint in blue | 50.00 | |

Dag Hammarskjold, Sec. Gen. of the UN, 1953-61.

Nos. 405-412 exist imperf. Value, set unused $12.

No 413a is overprinted "30 Juin 1962" on stamp and "2eme Anniversaire de l'Independance" on sheet margin. Issued June 30, 1962.

For overprints see Nos. 417-424.

Malaria Eradication Emblem and Mosquito — A98

**1962, June 15 Granite Paper**

| No. | Type | Description | Unused | Used |
|---|---|---|---|---|
| **414** | A98 | 1.50fr yel, blk & dk red | .25 | .25 |
| **415** | A98 | 2fr yel grn, brn & bl grn | .25 | .25 |
| **416** | A98 | 6.50fr ultra, blk & mar | .25 | .25 |
| | | *Nos. 414-416 (3)* | .75 | .75 |

WHO drive to eradicate malaria.

Nos. 414-416 exist imperf. Value, set unused $2.

Nos. 405-412 Overprinted in Blue, Purple, Black or Carmine

**1962, Oct. 15 Gray Background**

| No. | Type | Description | Unused | Used |
|---|---|---|---|---|
| **417** | A97 | 10c dk brn (Bl) | .25 | .25 |
| **418** | A97 | 20c Prus bl (P) | .25 | .25 |
| **419** | A97 | 30c brn (Bk) | .25 | .25 |
| **420** | A97 | 40c dk bl (C) | .25 | .25 |
| **421** | A97 | 50c brn red (Bl) | *2.50* | *1.00* |
| **422** | A97 | 3fr ol grn (P) | .25 | .25 |
| **423** | A97 | 6.50fr dk vio (Bk) | .25 | .25 |
| **424** | A97 | 8fr red brn (C) | .40 | .25 |
| | | *Nos. 417-424 (8)* | 4.40 | 2.75 |

Reorganization of Adoula administration.

Inverted overprints exist. Value, $10 each.

Canceled to Order

Starting in 1963, values in the used column are for "canceled to order" stamps. Postally used examples sell for much more.

A99

**1963, Jan. 28 Engr. *Perf. 10½x13***

| No. | Type | Description | Unused | Used |
|---|---|---|---|---|
| **425** | A99 | 2fr dull purple | *1.25* | .75 |
| **426** | A99 | 4fr red | .25 | .25 |
| **427** | A99 | 7fr dark blue | .25 | .25 |
| **428** | A99 | 20fr slate green | .40 | .25 |
| | | *Nos. 425-428 (4)* | 2.15 | *1.50* |

Congo's 1st participation at the UPU Cong., New Delhi, Mar. 1963.

Nos. 425-428 exist imperf. Value, set unused $30.

An imperf sheet containing No. 428 in brown exists. Value $35.

For overprints see Nos. 468-471.

Shoebill — A100

Birds: 10c, Pelicans. 20c, Crested guinea fowl, horiz. 30c, Openbill. 40c, White-bellied storks, horiz. 2fr, Marabou. 3fr, Greater flamingos, horiz. 4fr, Congolese peacock. 5fr, Hartlaub ducks, horiz. 6fr, Secretary bird. 7fr, Black-casqued hornbill, horiz. 8fr, Sacred ibis and nest. 10fr, Crowned crane, horiz. 20fr, Saddle-bill stork, horiz.

**1963 Unwmk. Photo. *Perf. 11½***

| No. | Type | Description | Unused | Used |
|---|---|---|---|---|
| **429** | A100 | 10c pink, ultra & ocher | .25 | .25 |
| **430** | A100 | 20c rose red, bl & blk | .25 | .25 |
| **431** | A100 | 30c grn, ocher & blk | .25 | .25 |
| **432** | A100 | 40c gray, org & blk | .25 | .25 |
| **433** | A100 | 1fr brn, emer & gray | .25 | .25 |
| **434** | A100 | 2fr gray, red & ind | *3.25* | .60 |
| **435** | A100 | 3fr ol grn, blk & rose | .25 | .25 |
| **436** | A100 | 4fr car rose, vio bl & grn | .25 | .25 |
| **437** | A100 | 5fr lake, lt bl & blk | .45 | .25 |
| **438** | A100 | 6fr pur, yel & blk | *3.50* | .60 |
| **439** | A100 | 7fr bl grn, blk & ind | .55 | .25 |
| **440** | A100 | 8fr yel, org & blk | .65 | .25 |
| **441** | A100 | 10fr bl, blk & rose | .65 | .25 |
| **442** | A100 | 20fr cit, red & blk | 1.20 | .25 |
| | | *Nos. 429-442 (14)* | 12.00 | 4.20 |

Nos. 429-442 exist imperf. Value, set unused $60.

Nos. 436 and 438 exist in imperf sheets of one. Value, each $45.

Cinchona Ledgeriana A101

Red Cross Nurse A102

10c, 30c, 5fr, Strophanthus sarmentosus.

***Perf. 12½x13½, 13½x12½***

**1963, May 25 Engr. Unwmk.**

**Cross in Red**

| No. | Type | Description | Unused | Used |
|---|---|---|---|---|
| **443** | A101 | 10c vio & dl grn | .25 | .25 |
| **444** | A101 | 20c magenta & bl | .25 | .25 |
| **445** | A101 | 30c grn & org | .25 | .25 |
| **446** | A101 | 40c bl & vio | .25 | .25 |
| **447** | A101 | 5fr ol & rose claret | .25 | .25 |
| **448** | A101 | 7fr org & blk | .25 | .25 |
| **449** | A102 | 9fr gray olive & red | .25 | .25 |
| **450** | A102 | 20fr purple & red | *2.50* | .75 |
| | | *Nos. 443-450 (8)* | 4.25 | 2.50 |

International Red Cross centenary.

Nos. 443-450 exist imperf. Value, set unused $35.

A souvenir sheet of three contains imperf. 5fr, 7fr, and 20fr stamps similar to Nos. 447, 448 and 450, but in changed colors. Size: 109x75mm. Value $55.

Men Joining Hands and Map of Congo — A103

**1963, June 29 Photo. *Perf. 11½***

| No. | Type | Description | Unused | Used |
|---|---|---|---|---|
| **451** | A103 | 4fr multi | 1.00 | .25 |
| **452** | A103 | 5fr multi | .25 | .25 |
| **453** | A103 | 9fr multi | .25 | .25 |
| **454** | A103 | 12fr multi | .25 | .25 |
| | | *Nos. 451-454 (4)* | 1.75 | 1.00 |

Issued to celebrate national reconciliation.

Nos. 451-454 exist imperf. Value, set unused $12.50.

Bulldozer and Kabambare Sewer, Leopoldville A104

Designs: 30c, 5fr, 12fr, Excavator and blueprint. 50c, 9fr, Building Ituri road.

**1963, July 1 Engr. Unwmk.**

| No. | Type | Description | Unused | Used |
|---|---|---|---|---|
| **455** | A104 | 20c multi | .25 | .25 |
| **456** | A104 | 30c multi | .25 | .25 |
| **457** | A104 | 50c multi | .25 | .25 |
| **458** | A104 | 3fr multi | 1.10 | .25 |
| **459** | A104 | 5fr multi | .25 | .25 |
| **460** | A104 | 9fr multi | .25 | .25 |
| **461** | A104 | 12fr multi | .25 | .25 |
| | | *Nos. 455-461 (7)* | 2.60 | 1.75 |

Issued to publicize aid to Congo by the European Economic Community.

Nos. 455-461 exist imperf. Value, set unused $40.

Leopoldville Airport N'Djili — A105

5fr, 7fr, 50fr, Tail assembly and airport.

**1963, Nov. 30 Photo. *Perf. 11½***

| No. | Type | Description | Unused | Used |
|---|---|---|---|---|
| **462** | A105 | 2fr gray, yel & red brn | .25 | .25 |
| **463** | A105 | 5fr mag, vio & yel | .25 | .25 |
| **464** | A105 | 6fr bl, yel & dk brn | 1.75 | .25 |
| **465** | A105 | 7fr multi | .25 | .25 |
| **466** | A105 | 30fr lil, yel & ol | .40 | .25 |
| **467** | A105 | 50fr multi | .60 | .25 |
| | | *Nos. 462-467 (6)* | 3.50 | 1.50 |

Issued to publicize Air Congo.

Nos. 462-467 exist imperf. Value, set unused $30.

For surcharge see No. 606.

**Nos. 425-428 Overprinted with Silver Frame on Three Sides and Black Inscription**

**Engraved and Typographed**

**1963, Dec. 10 *Perf. 10½x13***

| No. | Type | Description | Unused | Used |
|---|---|---|---|---|
| **468** | A99 | 2fr dull purple | .25 | .25 |
| **469** | A99 | 4fr red | .25 | .25 |
| **470** | A99 | 7fr dark blue | .25 | .25 |
| **471** | A99 | 20fr slate green | .35 | .25 |
| | | *Nos. 468-471 (4)* | 1.10 | 1.00 |

Universal Declaration of Human Rights, 15th anniv.

Nos. 468-471 exist with side date panels transposed ("1963" at left, "1948" at right). Value, each $55. Nos. 468-471 exist imperf. Value, set $30.

Laboratory Technician and Atomic Emblem — A106

1.50fr, 60fr, University. 8fr, 75fr, First African nuclear reactor. 25fr, 100fr, University and crest.

**1964, Feb. 1 Photo. Perf. 14x12½**

**472** A106 50c multi .25 .25
**473** A106 1.50fr multi .25 .25
**474** A106 8fr multi *2.75 2.50*
**475** A106 25fr multi .25 .25
**476** A106 30fr multi .30 .25
**477** A106 60fr multi .50 .30
**478** A106 75fr multi .60 .50
**479** A106 100fr multi 1.00 .80
*a.* Souv. sheet of 3 6.50 6.50
*Nos. 472-479 (8)* 5.90 5.10

Lovanium University, Leopoldville, 10th anniv.

No. 479a contains 3 imperf. multicolored stamps: 20fr, design as 50c; 30fr, as 8fr; 100fr.

Nos. 472-479 exist imperf. Value, set unused $30.

### Belgian Congo Issues of 1952-59 Overprinted and Surcharged in Black on Metallic Panels

Nos. 480 and 482

Nos. 481 and 483

**1964 Perf. 11½**

**480** A93 1fr on 20c red org & sl (#307) .25 .25
**481** A86 2fr on 1.50fr (#273) *11.00 3.75*
**482** A93 5fr on 6.50fr (#315) .25 .25
**483** A86 8fr on 6.50fr (#278) 1.10 .35

### Republic Issues of 1960-61 Surcharged in Black on Overprinted Metallic Rectangles or Ovals

Nos. 487-488

Nos. 489-489a

Nos. 490-491

**484** A86 1fr on 6.50fr (#335) .25 .25
**485** A93 1fr on 20c (#342) .25 .25
**486** A86 2fr on 1.50fr (#330) .25 .25
**487** A95 3fr on 20c (#382) .45 .25
**488** A95 4fr on 40c (#383) .55 .25
**489** A93 5fr on 6.50fr ("Congo" red) (#350) .90 .25
*a.* "Congo" black .90 .25
**490** A93a 6fr on 6.50fr (#363) .90 .30
**491** A93a 7fr on 20c (#356) .90 .35
*Nos. 480-491 (12)* 17.05 6.75

Pole Vault — A107

7fr, 20fr, Javelin, vert. 8fr, 100fr, Hurdling.

***Perf. 11½***

**1964, July 13 Unwmk. Photo.**

**Granite Paper**

**492** A107 5fr gray, dk brn & car .25 .25
**493** A107 7fr rose, vio & emer .95 .35
**494** A107 8fr org, yel, red brn & vio bl .25 .25
**495** A107 10fr bl, vio brn & mag .25 .25
**496** A107 20fr gray grn, red brn & ver .25 .25
**497** A107 100fr lil, dk brn & grn .95 .25
*a.* Souv. sheet of 3 10.00 10.00
*Nos. 492-497 (6)* 2.90 1.60

18th Olympic Games, Tokyo, Oct. 10-25. No. 497a contains 3 imperf. stamps (20fr orange & dark brown, pole vault; 30fr citron and dark brown, hurdling; 100fr dull green and dark brown, javelin). Sheet issued Sept. 10.

Nos. 492-497 exist imperf. Value, set unused $75.

National Palace, Leopoldville A108

**1964, Sept. 15 Granite Paper**

**498** A108 50c lil rose & bl .25 .25
**499** A108 1fr bl & lil rose .25 .25
**500** A108 2fr brn red & vio .25 .25
**501** A108 3fr emer & red .25 .25
**502** A108 4fr org & vio bl .25 .25
**503** A108 5fr gray vio & emer .25 .25
**504** A108 6fr sep & org .25 .25
**505** A108 7fr gray ol & red brn .25 .25
**506** A108 8fr rose red & vio bl *1.50* .30
**507** A108 9fr vio bl & rose red .25 .25
**508** A108 10fr brn ol & grn .25 .25
**509** A108 20fr bl & brn org .25 .25
**510** A108 30fr dk car rose & grn .25 .25
**511** A108 40fr ultra & dk car rose .35 .25
**512** A108 50fr brn org & grn .40 .25
**513** A108 100fr slate & ver .75 .25
*Nos. 498-513 (16)* 6.00 4.05

Nos. 498-513 exist imperf. Value, set unused $25.

For overprints and surcharges see Nos. 574-577, 593-598, 609-615, 670-671, 673-674, 676-677, 680, 684-687.

Pres. John F. Kennedy (1917-63) — A109

**1964, Dec. 8 Photo. Perf. 13½**

**514** A109 5fr dk bl & blk .25 .25
**515** A109 6fr rose claret & blk .25 .25
**516** A109 9fr brn & blk .25 .25
**517** A109 30fr pur & blk .50 .25
**518** A109 40fr dl grn & blk *2.75* .80
**519** A109 60fr red brn & blk 1.00 .30
*Nos. 514-519 (6)* 5.00 2.10

**Souvenir Sheet**

**520** A109 150fr blk & mar 6.50 6.50

Nos. 514-519 exist imperf. Value, set unused $90. No. 520 exists imperf. Value, unused $90.

Rocket and Unisphere — A110

**Engraved and Typographed**

**1965, Mar. 1 Unwmk. Perf. 12**

**521** A110 50c lil & blk .25 .25
**522** A110 1.50fr bl & lil .25 .25
**523** A110 2fr red brn & brt grn .25 .25
**524** A110 10fr brt grn & dk red .70 .50
**525** A110 18fr vio bl & brn .25 .25
**526** A110 27fr rose red & grn .30 .25
**527** A110 40fr gray & org .35 .25
*Nos. 521-527 (7)* 2.35 2.00

New York World's Fair, 1964-65.

Nos. 521-527 exist imperf. Value, set unused $20.

Basketball — A111

6fr, 40fr, Soccer, horiz. 15fr, 60fr, Volleyball.

**1965, Apr. Photo. Perf. 13½**

**528** A111 5fr blk, grnsh bl & ocher .25 .25
**529** A111 6fr blk, bl gray & crim .25 .25
**530** A111 15fr blk, org & yel grn .25 .25
**531** A111 24fr blk, rose lil & brt grn .40 .25
**532** A111 40fr blk, brt grn & ultra *1.60* .40
**533** A111 60fr blk, bl & red lil .50 .25
*Nos. 528-533 (6)* 3.25 1.65

First African Games, Leopoldville, Mar. 31-Apr. 7, 1965.

Nos. 528-533 exist imperf. Value, set unused $17.50.

For surcharges see Nos. 604-605.

Earth and Satellites — A112

Designs: 9fr, 15fr, 20fr, 40fr, Satellites at left, globe at right.

***Perf. 14x14½***

**1965, June 28 Photo. Unwmk.**

**534** A112 6fr blk, sal & vio .25 .25
**535** A112 9fr blk, lt grn & gray .25 .25
**536** A112 12fr org, gray & blk .25 .25
**537** A112 15fr grn, ultra & blk .25 .25
**538** A112 18fr blk, lt grn & gray 1.20 .25
**539** A112 20fr blk, sal & vio .25 .25
**540** A112 30fr grn, ultra & blk .25 .25
**541** A112 40fr org, gray & blk .35 .25
*Nos. 534-541 (8)* 3.05 2.00

Cent. of the ITU.

Nos. 534-541 exist imperf. Value, set unused $47.50.

Congolese Paratrooper and Parachutes A113

**1965, July 5 Perf. 13x14**

**542** A113 5fr brt bl & brn .25 .25
**543** A113 6fr org & brn .25 .25
**544** A113 7fr br grn & brn .30 .25
**545** A113 9fr brt pink & brn .25 .25
**546** A113 18fr lem & brn .25 .25
*Nos. 542-546 (5)* 1.30 1.25

Fifth anniversary of independence.

Nos. 542-546 exist imperf. Value, set unused $17.50.

Matadi Harbor and ICY Emblem A114

ICY Emblem and: 8fr, 25fr, Katanga mines. 9fr, 60fr, Tshopo Dam, Stanleyville.

**1965, Oct. 25 Photo. Perf. 13x14**

**547** A114 6fr ultra, blk & yel .25 .25
**548** A114 8fr org red, blk & bl .25 .25
**549** A114 9fr bl grn, blk & brn org .25 .25
**550** A114 12fr car rose, blk & gray .75 .30
**551** A114 25fr ol, blk & rose red .25 .25
**552** A114 60fr gray, blk & org .50 .25
*Nos. 547-552 (6)* 2.25 1.55

International Cooperation Year, 1965.

Nos. 547-552 exist imperf. Value, set unused $20.

For overprints and surcharges see Nos. 559-560, 607-608.

Soldiers Giving First Aid — A115

The Army Serving the Country: 7fr, Bridge building. 9fr, Feeding child. 19fr, Maintenance of telegraph lines. 20fr, House building. 30fr, Soldier and flag. (19fr, 20fr, 30fr, vert.)

***Perf. 12½x13, 13x12½***

**1965, Nov. 17**

**553** A115 5fr sal, brn & red .25 .25
**554** A115 7fr yel & grn .25 .25
**555** A115 9fr ol & brn .25 .25
**556** A115 19fr brt grn & brn .80 .45
**557** A115 20fr lt bl & brn .25 .25
**558** A115 30fr multi .40 .25
*Nos. 553-558 (6)* 2.20 1.70

See Nos. 582-586.

Nos. 553-558 exist imperf. Value, set unused $17.50.

For surcharges see Nos. 602, 678-679, 683.

### Nos. 551-552 Overprinted on Metallic Strip

**1966, Mar. 23 Photo. Perf. 13x14**

**559** A114 25fr ol & blk 1.40 .55
**560** A114 60fr gray & blk 1.40 .65

6th World Meteorological Day.

Nos. 559-560 exist with inverted overprint and black missing. Value, each $15.

Woman's Head and Goat — A116

10fr, Sculptured heads. 12fr, Sitting figure and two heads, vert. 53fr, Figure with earrings and kneeling woman with bowl, vert.

***Perf. 11½x13, 13x11½***

**1966, Apr. 23 Litho. Unwmk.**

**561** A116 10fr red, blk & gray .25 .25
**562** A116 12fr grn, blk & bl .25 .25
**563** A116 15fr dp bl, blk & lil .30 .25
**564** A116 53fr dp rose, blk & vio bl 1.30 1.00
*Nos. 561-564 (4)* 2.10 1.75

Intl. Negro Arts Festival, Dakar, Senegal, Apr. 1-24.

Nos. 561-564 exist imperf. Value, set unused $15.

Pres. Joseph Desiré Mobutu and Fishing Industry — A117

Pres. Mobutu and: 4fr, Pyrethrum harvest. 6fr, Building industry. 8fr, Winnowing rice. 10fr, Cotton harvest. 12fr, Banana harvest. 15fr, Coffee harvest. 24fr, Pineapple harvest. No. 573a, Pres. Mobutu without cap, and men rolling up sleeves.

**1966, May 1 Photo. Perf. 11½**

**565** A117 2fr dk brn & dk bl .25 .25
**566** A117 4fr dk brn & org .25 .25
**567** A117 6fr dk brn & ol .50 .25
**568** A117 8fr dk brn & brt grnsh bl .25 .25
**569** A117 10fr dk brn & brn red .25 .25
**570** A117 12fr dk brn & vio .25 .25
**571** A117 15fr dk brn & lt ol grn .25 .25
**572** A117 24fr dk brn & lil rose .25 .25
*Nos. 565-572 (8)* 2.25 2.00

**Souvenir Sheet**

***Perf. 11x11½***

**573** Sheet of 4 2.00 1.50
*a.* A117 15fr red, black & ultra .50 .35

Lt. Gen. Joseph Desiré Mobutu, Pres. of Congo, and publicizing the "Back to Work" campaign.

Nos. 565-572 exist imperf. Value, set unused $15. No. 573 exists imperf. Value, unused $15.

For surcharges see Nos. 601, 603, 616, 619-624, 672, 675, 681-682.

Nos. 510-513 Overprinted

**1966, June 13 Perf. 11½**

**574** A108 30fr dk car rose & grn 1.10 1.10
**575** A108 40fr ultra & dk car rose 1.20 1.20
**576** A108 50fr brn org & grn 1.40 1.40
**577** A108 100fr slate & ver 1.40 1.40
*Nos. 574-577 (4)* 5.10 5.10

Inauguration of WHO Headquarters, Geneva.

Nos. 574-577 exist with inverted overprint. Value, set $25.

Soccer Player
A118

30fr, 2 soccer players. 50fr, 3 soccer players. 60fr, Jules Rimet Cup, soccer ball & globe.

**1966, July 25 Photo. *Perf. 14***

**578** A118 10fr ocher, vio & grn .25 .25
**579** A118 30fr brt rose lil, vio & ap grn .45 .25
**580** A118 50fr ap grn, Prus bl & tan 1.50 1.00
**581** A118 60fr brt grn, dk brn & gold 1.50 .50
*Nos. 578-581 (4)* 3.70 2.00

World Cup Soccer Championship, Wembley, England, July 11-30.

Nos. 578-581 exist imperf. Value, set unused $20.

For overprints see Nos. 587-590.

### Army Type of 1965

The Army Serving the Country: 2fr, Soldiers giving first aid. 6fr, Feeding child. 10fr, House building, vert. 18fr, Bridge building. 24fr, Soldier and flag, vert.

**1966, Aug. 8 *Perf. 12½x13, 13x12½***

**582** A115 2fr sal pink, grn blue & red .25 .25
**583** A115 6fr ultra red brn .25 .25
**584** A115 10fr yel grn & red brn .50 .30
**585** A115 18fr car rose & vio .25 .25
**586** A115 24fr multi .25 .25
*Nos. 582-586 (5)* 1.50 1.30

Nos. 582-586 exist imperf. Value, set unused $10.

### Nos. 578-581 Overprinted in Black, Carmine or Green

**1966, Nov. 14 Photo. *Perf. 14***

**587** A118 10fr pair, B and C .75 .75
**588** A118 30fr pair, B and G 2.25 2.00
**589** A118 50fr pair, B and C 3.50 3.00
**590** A118 60fr pair, B and C 4.50 4.00
*Nos. 587-590 (4)* 11.00 9.75

England's victory in the World Soccer Cup Championship.

The two colors of the overprint alternate in the sheets.

Nos. 587-590 exist with inverted overprint. Value, set $75.

Souvenir Sheets

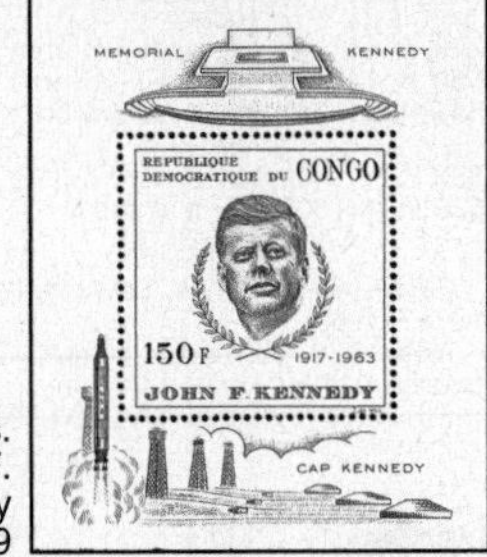


Pres. John F. Kennedy
A119

**1966, Dec. 28 Engr. *Perf. 13***

**591** A119 150fr brown 22.50 17.50
**592** A119 150fr slate 22.50 17.50

Issued in memory of Pres. John F. Kennedy.

No. 591 has slate green, No. 592 deep orange marginal design.

Two imperf. sheets exist: 150fr brown with violet blue margin and 150fr slate with lilac margin. Size: 65x76mm. Values, $20 each.

Perforated sheets exist in imperf. colors. Value, set $200.

Nos. 498-503 Surcharged in Black, Red or Maroon and

Map of Africa, Torch
A120

**1967, Sept. 11 Photo. *Perf. 11½***

**593** A108 1k on 2fr .25 .25
*a.* Inverted overprint 5.00
**594** A108 3k on 5fr .25 .25
**595** A108 5k on 4fr .35 .25
**596** A108 6.60k on 1fr (R) .50 .25
*a.* Inverted overprint 5.00
**597** A108 9.60k on 50c .70 .30
*a.* Inverted overprint 5.00
**598** A108 9.80k on 3fr (M) .75 .50
*Nos. 593-598 (6)* 2.80 1.80

### Souvenir Sheet

**599** A120 50k grnsh bl, blk & red 2.75 2.75

Fourth meeting of the Org. for African Unity, Kinshasa (Leopoldville), Sept. 9-11.

No. 599 exists imperf. Value, unused $17.50.

No. 599 in other colors was not a postal issue.

Souvenir Sheet

Horn Blower and EXPO Emblem
A121

**1967, Sept. 28 Engr. *Perf. 11½***

**600** A121 50k dk brn 3.50 3.50

EXPO '67, International Exhibition, Montreal, Apr. 28-Oct. 27, 1967.

No. 600 exists imperf. Value, unused $20.

### Nos. 565-566 and 582 Overprinted and Surcharged on Metallic Panel in Magenta or Brown

No. 601

No. 602

***Perf. 11½, 12½x13***

**1967, Oct. 9 Photo.**

**601** A117 4k on 2fr (M) .25 .25
**602** A115 5k on 2fr (B) .45 .25
**603** A117 21k on 4fr (M) 1.40 .75
*Nos. 601-603 (3)* 2.10 1.25

Promulgation of the Constitution, June 4, 1967.

Nos. 528 and 530 Surcharged and Overprinted

**1967, Oct. 16 Photo. *Perf. 13½***

**604** A111 1k on 5fr multi .35 .25
**605** A111 9.60k on 15fr multi .75 .65

First Congolese Games, Kinshasa, June 25-July 2, 1967.

Nos. 604-605 exist with red overprint. Value, set $25.

### No. 465 Surcharged and Overprinted

**1967, Oct. 16 *Perf. 11½***

**606** A105 9.60k on 7fr multi 1.10 .25

1st flight of the BAC 111 in the service of Air Congo, May 14, 1967.

### Nos. 547 and 549 Surcharged in Red or Black

**1968, Feb. 10 Photo. *Perf. 13x14***

**607** A114 1k on 6fr (R) .35 .25
**608** A114 9k on 9fr (B) .90 .65

Intl. Children's Day. The surcharge is on a rectangle printed in metallic ink.

### Nos. 498, 504 and 501 Surcharged in Blue or Red

**1968, Feb. 10 *Perf. 11½***

**609** A108 5k on 50c lil rose & bl (Bl) .45 .25
**610** A108 10k on 6fr sepia & org (R) .60 .50
**611** A108 15k on 3fr emer & red (R) .80 .80
*Nos. 609-611 (3)* 1.85 1.55

International Tourist Year. The surcharge is on a rectangle printed in metallic ink.

### Nos. 500, 498 and 502 Surcharged in Black, Violet Blue or Gold

No. 612

No. 613

No. 614

No. 615

**1968, July Photo. *Perf. 11½***

**612** A108 1k on 2fr .30 .25
**613** A108 2k on 50c (VBl) .45 .25
**614** A108 2k on 50c (G) .45 .25
**615** A108 9.60k on 4fr 2.00 1.10
*Nos. 612-615 (4)* 3.20 1.85

The surcharge on No. 612 consists of a black rectangle and new denomination in upper right corner; the surcharge on No. 613 has a violet blue rectangle with denomination printed in white on it; on No. 614 the rectangle is gold and the denomination black; on No. 615 the rectangle is black and the denomination white.

Nos. 612-615 exist with inverted surcharge. Value, set $7.50.

### No. 565 Surcharged in White on Black Rectangle

**1968, Oct. Photo. *Perf. 11½***

**616** A117 10k on 2fr dk brn & dk bl .70 .25

Leopard — A122

**1968, Nov. 5 Litho. *Perf. 10½***

**617** A122 2k brt grnsh bl & blk .30 .25
**618** A122 9.60k red & blk 1.50 .25

Nos. 617-618 exist imperf. Value, set unused $20.

Nos. 617-618 exist with inverted surcharge. Values: No. 617, $300; No. 618, $140.

Mobutu Type of 1966 Surcharged

**1968, Dec. 20 Photo. *Perf. 11½***

**619** A117 15s on 2fr sep & brt bl .25 .25
**620** A117 1k on 6fr sep & brn .25 .25
**621** A117 3k on 10fr sep & emer .25 .25
**622** A117 5k on 12fr sep & org .30 .25
**623** A117 20k on 15fr sep & brt grn 1.00 .50
**624** A117 50k on 24fr sep & brt lil 2.75 1.25
*Nos. 619-624 (6)* 4.80 2.75

Nos. 619-624 exist imperf. Value, set $15.

Human Rights Flame — A123

**1968, Dec. 30** *Perf. 12½x13*

**625** A123 2k lt ultra & brt grn .25 .25
**626** A123 9.60k grn & dp car .75 .30
**627** A123 10k brt lil & brn .75 .35
**628** A123 40k org brn & pur 2.50 1.25
*Nos. 625-628 (4)* 4.25 2.15

International Human Rights Year.
Nos. 625-628 exist imperf. Value, set unused $15.

Type of 1968 Overprinted in Gold

**1969, Jan. 27** Photo. *Perf. 12½x13*

**629** A123 2k ap grn & red brn .25 .25
**630** A123 9.60k rose & emer .75 .30
**631** A123 10k gray & ultra .75 .35
**632** A123 40k grnsh bl & pur 2.50 1.25
*Nos. 629-632 (4)* 4.25 2.15

4th summit meeting of OCAM (Organisation Communitee Afrique et Malgache), Kinshasa, Jan. 27.
Nos. 629-632 exist imperf. Value, set unused $15.

Kinshasa Fair Emblem and Cotton Boll — A124

Fair Emblem and: 6k, Copper. 9.60k, Coffee. 9.80k, Diamond. 11.60k, Oil palm fruits.

**1969, May 2** Photo. *Perf. 12½x13*

**633** A124 2k brt pur, gold & red lil .25 .25
**634** A124 6k grn, gold & bl grn .95 .40
**635** A124 9.60k brn, gold & lt brn 1.25 .40
**636** A124 9.80k ultra & gold 1.40 .60
**637** A124 11.60k hn brn, gold & brn 1.60 .80
*Nos. 633-637 (5)* 5.45 2.45

Kinshasa Fair, Limete, June 30-July 21.
Nos. 633-637 exist imperf. Value, set unused $25.

Fair Entrance, Emblem A125

Fair Emblem and: 3k, Gecomin Mining Co. Pavilion. 10k, Administration Building. 25k, Pavilion of the Organization for African Unity.

**1969, June 30** Photo. *Perf. 11½*
**Granite Paper**

**638** A125 2k brt rose lil & gold .25 .25
**639** A125 3k blue & gold .25 .25
**640** A125 10k lt ol grn & gold .75 .40
**641** A125 25k copper red & gold 1.75 1.00
*Nos. 638-641 (4)* 3.00 1.90

Kinshasa Fair, Limete, June 30-July 21.
Nos. 638-641 exist imperf. Value, set unused $15.

Congo Arms A126

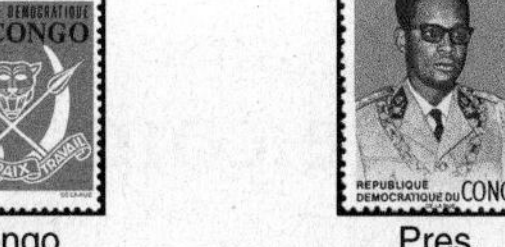


Pres. Mobutu A127

**1969, July-Sept.** Litho. *Perf. 14*

**642** A126 10s org & blk .25 .25
**643** A126 15s ultra & blk .25 .25
**644** A126 30s brt grn & blk .25 .25
**645** A126 60s brt rose lil & blk .25 .25
**646** A126 90s dp bister & blk .25 .25

*Perf. 13*

**647** A127 1k sky bl & multi .25 .25
**648** A127 2k org & multi .25 .25
**649** A127 3k multi .30 .25
**650** A127 5k brt rose & multi .40 .25
**651** A127 6k ultra & multi .40 .25
**652** A127 9.60k multi .75 .40
**653** A127 10k lt lil & multi 1.00 .50
**654** A127 20k yel & multi 1.75 1.00
**655** A127 50k multi 5.00 2.50
**656** A127 100k fawn & multi 10.00 6.00
*Nos. 642-656 (15)* 21.35 12.90

Nos. 642-656 exist imperf. Value, set unused $25.

Well Driller, by Oscar Bonnevalle A128

Paintings: 4k, Preparation of cocoa, by Jean Van Noten. 8k, Dock workers, by Constantin Meunier. 10k, Poultry shop, by Henri Evenepoel. 15k, Steel industry, by Constantin Meunier.

*Perf. 13x14, 14x13 (8k)*

**1969, Dec. 15** Litho.

**Size: 41x41mm**

**657** A128 3k multi .25 .25
**658** A128 4k multi .25 .25

**Size: 28x41mm**

**659** A128 8k multi .45 .30

**Size: 41x41mm**

**660** A128 10k multi .65 .40
**661** A128 15k multi 1.40 .50
*Nos. 657-661 (5)* 3.00 1.70

50th anniv. of the ILO.
Nos. 657-661 exist imperf. Value, set unused $15.

Souvenir Sheet

Adoration of the Kings, by Rubens — A129

**1969, Dec.** Engr. *Perf. 13*

**662** A129 50k red lilac 5.50 5.50

Issued for Christmas 1969.
No. 662 exists imperf. Value, unused $15.

Pres. Mobutu, Map and Flag of Congo — A130

**1970, June 30** Litho. *Perf. 13½x13*

**663** A130 10s multi .25 .25
**664** A130 90s pur & multi .25 .25
**665** A130 1k brn & multi .25 .25
**666** A130 2k multi .25 .25
**667** A130 7k multi .35 .25
**668** A130 10k multi .55 .25
**669** A130 20k multi 1.10 .50
*Nos. 663-669 (7)* 3.00 2.00

10th anniversary of independence.
Nos. 663-669 exist imperf. Value, set unused $12.

Issues of 1964-1966 Surcharged

*Perf. 11½, 12½x13, 13x12½*

**1970, Sept. 24** Photo.

**670** A108 10s on 1fr (#499) .25 .25
**671** A108 20s on 2fr (#500) .25 .25
**672** A117 20s on 2fr (#565) .80 .45
**673** A108 30s on 3fr (#501) .25 .25
**674** A108 40s on 4fr (#502) .25 .25
**675** A117 40s on 4fr (#566) .80 .45
**676** A108 60s on 7fr (#505) 2.60 1.60
**677** A108 90s on 9fr (#507) 2.60 1.60
**678** A115 90s on 9fr (#555) .55 .40
**679** A115 1k on 7fr (#554) .55 .40
**680** A108 1k on 6fr (#504) .45 .25
**681** A117 1k on 12fr (#570) 2.50 1.60
**682** A117 2k on 24fr (#572) 1.10 .50
**683** A115 2k on 24fr (#586) 1.10 .50
**684** A108 3k on 30fr (#510) 2.00 1.10
**685** A108 4k on 40fr (#511) .45 .25
**686** A108 5k on 50fr (#512) 7.50 4.25
**687** A108 10k on 100fr (#513) 2.00 1.10
*Nos. 670-687 (18)* 26.00 15.45

Telecommunications Building, Geneva — A131

Designs: 2k, 6.60k, UPU Headquarters, Bern. 9.80k, 10k, 11k, UN Headquarters, NY.

**1970, Oct. 24** Photo. *Perf. 11½*

**688** A131 1k pink & grn .25 .25
**689** A131 2k org & grn .25 .25
**690** A131 6.60k grnsh bl & rose car .40 .25
**691** A131 9.60k yel & vio bl .50 .35
**692** A131 9.80k lt ultra & brn .50 .35
**693** A131 10k lt pur & brn .50 .35
**694** A131 11k rose & brn .70 .45
*Nos. 688-694 (7)* 3.10 2.25

ITU; new UPU Headquarters, Bern; 25th anniv. of the UN.
Nos. 688-694 exist imperf. Value, set unused $35.

Pres. Mobutu, Congolese Flag and Arch — A132

**1970, Nov. 24** Litho. *Perf. 13*

**695** A132 2k yel & multi .25 .25
**696** A132 10k bl & multi 1.00 .50
**697** A132 20k red & multi 2.75 1.75
*Nos. 695-697 (3)* 4.00 2.50

Fifth anniversary of new government.
Nos. 695-697 exist imperf. Value, set unused $6.
Stamps of design A132 denominated 1k, 6k, and 11k were printed but not issued. Value, set $125.

Apollo 11 in Flight — A133

Designs: 2k, Astronaut and spacecraft on moon. 7k, Pres. Mobutu decorating astronauts' wives. 10k, Pres. Mobutu with Neil A. Armstrong, Col. Edwin E. Aldrin, Jr. and Lt. Col. Michael Collins. 30k, Armstrong, Aldrin and Collins in space suits.

**1970, Dec. 24** *Perf. 13x13½*

**698** A133 1k bl & blk .30 .25
**699** A133 2k brt pur & blk .50 .25
**700** A133 7k dl org & blk 1.50 .85
**701** A133 10k rose red & blk 2.00 1.25
**702** A133 30k grn & blk 5.50 3.50
*Nos. 698-702 (5)* 9.80 6.10

Visit of US Apollo 11 astronauts and their wives to Kinshasa.
Nos. 698-702 exist imperf. Value, set unused $30.

Metopodontus Savagei A134

Designs: Various insects of Congo.

**1971, Jan. 25** Photo. *Perf. 11½*

**703** A134 10s dl rose & multi .75 .30
**704** A134 50s gray & multi .75 .30
**705** A134 90s multi .75 .30
**706** A134 1k citron & multi .75 .30
**707** A134 2k gray grn & multi .75 .30
**708** A134 3k lt vio & multi 1.75 .60
**709** A134 5k bl & multi 5.00 2.00
**710** A134 10k multi 7.00 2.50
**711** A134 30k grn & multi 16.00 6.75
**712** A134 40k ocher & multi 25.00 10.00
*Nos. 703-712 (10)* 58.50 23.35

Nos. 703-712 exist imperf. Value, set unused $65.

Colotis Protomedia A135

Various butterflies and moths of Congo.

**1971, Feb. 24**

**713** A135 10s lt ultra & multi .75 .35
**714** A135 20s choc & multi .75 .35
**715** A135 70s dp org & multi .75 .35
**716** A135 1k vio bl & multi .75 .35
**717** A135 3k multi 1.75 .60
**718** A135 5k dk grn & multi 4.75 1.50
**719** A135 10k multi 6.25 2.00
**720** A135 15k emer & multi 11.00 3.50
**721** A135 25k yel & multi 17.50 4.50
**722** A135 40k multi 24.00 11.00
*Nos. 713-722 (10)* 68.25 24.50

Nos. 713-722 exist imperf. Value, set unused $75.

UN Emblem, Racial Unity — A136

**1971, Mar. 21** Photo. *Perf. 11½*

**723** A136 1k lt grn & multi .25 .25
**724** A136 4k gray & multi .25 .25
**725** A136 5k lt lil & multi .40 .25
**726** A136 10k lt bl & multi .75 .35
*Nos. 723-726 (4)* 1.65 1.10

Intl. year against racial discrimination.
Nos. 723-726 exist imperf. Value, set unused $10.

Hypericum Bequaertii — A137

Flowers: 4k, Dissotis brazzae. 20k, Begonia wollastonii. 25k, Cassia alata.

**1971, May 24** Litho. *Perf. 14*

**727** A137 1k multi 1.00 .25
**728** A137 4k multi 1.75 .45
**729** A137 20k multi 9.25 2.50
**730** A137 25k multi 12.00 3.25
*Nos. 727-730 (4)* 24.00 6.45

Nos. 727-730 exist imperf. Value, set unused $30.

Obelisk at N'sele, Pres. Mobutu — A138

**1971, May 20** Photo. *Perf. 11½*

**731** A138 4k gold & multi .60 .25

Fourth anniversary of the People's Revolutionary Movement.
No. 731 exists imperf. Value, unused $10.

Radar Station — A139

Designs: 1k, Waves. 6k, Map of Africa with telecommunications network.

**1971, June 25 Photo. *Perf. 11½***

| | | | | |
|---|---|---|---|---|
| **732** | A139 | 1k rose & multi | .25 | .25 |
| **733** | A139 | 3k yel & multi | .55 | .35 |
| **734** | A139 | 6k lt bl & multi | 1.40 | 1.00 |
| | | *Nos. 732-734 (3)* | 2.20 | 1.60 |

3rd World Telecommunications Day, May 17 (1k); opening of satellite telecommunications ground station, Kinshasa, June 30 (3k); Pan-African telecommunication system (6k).

Nos. 732-734 exist imperf. Value, set unused $15.

Grass Monkeys — A140

Designs: 20s, Moustached monkeys, vert. 70s, De Brazza's monkeys. 1k, Yellow baboons. 3k, Pygmy chimpanzee, vert. 5k, Mangabeys, vert. 10k, Owlfaced monkeys. 15k, Diana monkeys. 25k, Black-and-white colobus, vert. 40k, L'Hoest's monkeys, vert.

**1971, Aug.**

| | | | | |
|---|---|---|---|---|
| **735** | A140 | 10s vio & multi | .75 | .35 |
| **736** | A140 | 20s lt bl & multi | .75 | .35 |
| **737** | A140 | 70s ocher & multi | 1.25 | .45 |
| **738** | A140 | 1k gray & multi | 1.25 | .45 |
| **739** | A140 | 3k rose & multi | 2.00 | 1.00 |
| **740** | A140 | 5k brn & multi | 4.50 | 2.50 |
| **741** | A140 | 10k multi | 8.75 | 4.75 |
| **742** | A140 | 15k multi | 14.00 | 6.50 |
| **743** | A140 | 25k brt bl & multi | 23.50 | 11.00 |
| **744** | A140 | 40k red & multi | 32.50 | 16.00 |
| | | *Nos. 735-744 (10)* | 89.25 | 43.35 |

Nos. 735-744 exist imperf. Value, set unused $120.

Hotel Inter-Continental, Kinshasa A141

**1971, Oct. 2 Photo. *Perf. 13***

| | | | | |
|---|---|---|---|---|
| **745** | A141 | 2k silver & multi | .25 | .25 |
| **746** | A141 | 12k gold & multi | .55 | .25 |

Nos. 745-746 exist imperf. Value, set unused $6.

Man Reading — A142

Designs: 2.50k, Open book and abacus. 7k, Five letters surrounding symbolic head.

**1971, Oct. 24**

| | | | | |
|---|---|---|---|---|
| **747** | A142 | 50s multi | .25 | .25 |
| **748** | A142 | 2.50k multi | .25 | .25 |
| **749** | A142 | 7k multi | 1.25 | .75 |
| | | *Nos. 747-749 (3)* | 1.75 | 1.25 |

Fight against illiteracy.

Nos. 747-749 exist imperf. Value, set unused $10.

Succeeding issues are listed in Vol. 6 under Zaire. Beginning in 1998, Zaire reverted to using the Congo name, at least temporarily. Until the situation is resolved, the current stamps inscribed "Congo" will be listed under Zaire.

## SEMI-POSTAL STAMPS

Women Carrying Food, Wheat Emblem, and Tractor — SP22

**1963, Mar. 21 Photo. *Perf. 14x13***

| | | | | |
|---|---|---|---|---|
| **B48** | SP22 | 5fr + 2fr multi | .25 | .25 |
| **B49** | SP22 | 9fr + 4fr multi | .45 | .25 |
| **B50** | SP22 | 12fr+ 6fr multi | .50 | .25 |
| **B51** | SP22 | 20fr+ 10fr multi | 2.25 | 1.75 |
| | | *Nos. B48-B51 (4)* | 3.45 | 2.50 |

FAO "Freedom from Hunger" campaign.

Nos. B48-B51 exist imperf. Value, set unused $30.

No. B51 exists in an imperf sheet of one, in light and dark violet. Value $30.

# CONGO, PEOPLE'S REPUBLIC

'pē-pəls ri-'pə-blik of 'käŋ-gō

(ex-French)

LOCATION — West Africa at equator
GOVT. — Republic
AREA — 132,046 sq. mi.
POP. — 2,716,814 (1999 est.)
CAPITAL — Brazzaville

The former French colony of Middle Congo became a member state of the French Community on November 28, 1958, and achieved independence on August 15, 1960. For some years before 1958, the colony was joined with three other French territories to form French Equatorial Africa. Issues of Middle Congo (1907-1933) are listed under that heading.

100 Centimes = 1 Franc

**Catalogue values for all unused stamps in this country are for Never Hinged items.**

Allegory of New Republic — A7

**1959 Unwmk. Engr. *Perf. 13***
**89** A7 25fr brn, dp clar, org & ol .75 .25

1st anniv. of the proclamation of the Republic.

Imperforates

Most stamps of the Republic of the Congo exist imperforate in issued and trial colors, and also in small presentation sheets in issued colors.

Common Design Types pictured following the introduction.

**C.C.T.A. Issue**
Common Design Type

**1960 Unwmk. *Perf. 13***
**90** CD106 50fr dl grn & plum 1.00 1.00

President Fulbert Youlou — A8

**1960**
**91** A8 15fr grn, blk & car .35 .35
**92** A8 85fr indigo & car 2.00 .45

Flag, Map and UN Emblem — A9

**1961, Mar. 11 *Perf. 13***
**Flag in Green, Yellow & Red**
**93** A9 5fr vio brn & dk bl .25 .25
**94** A9 20fr org & dk bl .45 .25
**95** A9 100fr grn & dk bl 2.00 .80
*Nos. 93-95 (3)* 2.70 1.30

Congo's admission to United Nations.

Rainbow Runner — A10

Fish: 50c, 3fr, Rainbow runner. 1fr, 2fr, Sloan's viperfish. 5fr, Hatchet fish. 10fr, A deep-sea fish.

**1961, Nov. 28 Engr.**
**96** A10 50c brn, ol grn & sal .30 .25
**97** A10 1fr bl grn & sepia .30 .25
**98** A10 2fr ultra, sep & dk grn .30 .25
**99** A10 3fr dk bl, grn & salmon .45 .30
**100** A10 5fr red brn, grn & blk .70 .30
**101** A10 10fr blue & red brn 1.40 .45
*Nos. 96-101 (6)* 3.45 1.80

Brazzaville Market — A11

**1962, Mar. 23 Unwmk. *Perf. 13***
**102** A11 20fr blk, red & grn .90 .25

**Abidjan Games Issue**
Common Design Type

20fr, Boxing. 50fr, Running, finish line.

**1962, July 21 Photo. *Perf. 12½x12***
**103** CD109 20fr car, brt pink, brn & blk .45 .25
**104** CD109 50fr car, brt pink, brn & blk .90 .30
*Nos. 103-104,C7 (3)* 3.85 1.80

**African-Malgache Union Issue**
Common Design Type

**1962, Sept. 8**
**105** CD110 30fr multicolored 1.50 .50

Waves Around Globe — A11a

Design: 100fr, Orbit patterns around globe.

**1963, Sept. 19 *Perf. 12½***
**106** A11a 25fr org, grn & ultra .75 .30
**107** A11a 100fr lt red brn, bl & plum 1.75 .90

Issued to publicize space communications.

King Makoko's Collar — A12

**Unwmk.**
**1963, Oct. 21 Engr. *Perf. 13***
**108** A12 10fr showm .45 .25
**109** A12 15fr Kebekebe mask .60 .25

UNESCO Emblem, Scales and Tree — A12a

**1963, Dec. 10 Unwmk. *Perf. 13***
**110** A12a 25fr grn, dk bl & brn .90 .30

15th anniv. of the Universal Declaration of Human Rights.

Barograph and WMO Emblem — A12b

**1964, Mar. 23 Engr.**
**111** A12b 50fr grn, red brn & ultra 1.50 .60

Fourth World Meteorological Day.

Mechanic with Machine — A13

**1964, Apr. 8**
**112** A13 20fr grnsh bl, mag & dk brn .90 .30

Training of technicians.

Corn and Tools — A14

**1964, Apr. 24 Unwmk. *Perf. 13***
**113** A14 80fr brn, grn & brn car 1.60 .60

Importance of manual labor.

Diaboua Ballet A15

Kébékébé Dance A16

**1964, May 8 Engr.**
**114** A15 30fr multicolored 1.25 .30
**115** A16 60fr multicolored 2.25 .65

Carved Figure — A17

**1964, May 22**
**116** A17 50fr brn red & sepia 1.50 .55

Classroom — A18

**1964, May 26**
**117** A18 25fr dk brn, red & blue .90 .30

Issued to publicize education.

**Type of Air Post Issue, 1963, Inscribed**

Fire Squid — A19

**1964, Aug. 15 Photo. *Perf. 13x12***
**118** AP5 20fr lt bl, red, ocher, dk brn & grn .80 .25

1st anniv. of the revolution and Natl. Feast Day, Aug. 15.

15fr, Johnson's deep-sea angler (fish).

**1964, Oct. 20 Engr. *Perf. 13***
**119** A19 2fr ver, lt grn & brn .80 .50
**120** A19 15fr vio, lt ol grn & dp cl 2.75 1.50

**Cooperation Issue**
Common Design Type

**1964, Nov. 7 Unwmk. *Perf. 13***
**121** CD119 25fr car, brt grn & dk brn .90 .35

Communications Emblems — A20

**1965, Jan. 1 Litho. *Perf. 12½x13***
**122** A20 25fr ol, red brn & blk .90 .25

Issued to commemorate the establishment of the national postal administration.

Sitatunga A21

Dancer on Stilts A22

Design: 20fr, Elephant, horiz.

**1965, Mar. 15 Engr. *Perf. 13***
**123** A21 15fr redsh brn, dl grn & bl 1.00 .40
**124** A21 20fr blk, dp bl & sl grn 1.00 .40
**125** A22 85fr lil & multi 3.50 1.50
*Nos. 123-125 (3)* 5.50 2.30

Pres. Alphonse Massamba-Debat — A23

**1965-66 Photo. *Perf. 12x12½***
**126** A23 20fr dk brn, grn & yel .40 .25
**127** A23 25fr brn, bl grn, emer & blk ('66) .40 .25
**128** A23 30fr brn, bl grn, org & blk ('66) .70 .25
*Nos. 126-128 (3)* 1.50 .75

Soccer Player — A24

Designs: 25fr, Games' emblem (map of Africa and runners). 50fr, Field ball player. 85fr, Runner. 100fr, Bicyclist.

**1965, July 17 Photo. *Perf. 12½***
**Size: 28x28mm**
**129** A24 25fr blk, red, yel & grn .50 .30
**Size: 34x34mm**
**130** A24 40fr yel grn & multi .70 .45
**131** A24 50fr red & multi .70 .45
**132** A24 85fr blk & multi 1.25 .65
**133** A24 100fr yel & multi 1.75 .65
*a.* Min. sheet of 5, #129-133 7.50 7.50
*Nos. 129-133 (5)* 4.90 2.60

1st African Games, Brazzaville, July 18-25.

Arms of Congo — A25

**1965, Nov. 15 Litho. *Perf. 12½x13***
**134** A25 20fr multicolored .90 .25

Cooperative Village — A26

30fr, Gymnastic drill team with streamers.

**1966, Feb. 18 *Perf. 12½x13***
**135** A26 25fr multicolored .90 .25
**136** A26 30fr multicolored .90 .30

Sculptured Mask — A27

Designs: 30fr, Weaver, painting. 85fr, String instrument, painting, horiz.

***Perf. 13x12½, 12½x13***
**1966, Apr. 9 Photo.**
**137** A27 30fr multicolored .70 .30
**138** A27 85fr multicolored 1.90 .70
**139** A27 90fr multicolored 2.25 1.00
*Nos. 137-139 (3)* 4.85 2.00

Intl. Negro Arts Festival, Dakar, Senegal, 4/1-24.

Men and Clocks — A28

**1966, Apr. 15 *Perf. 12½x12***
**140** A28 70fr pale brn, ocher & dk brn 1.60 .50

Introduction of the shorter work day (less lunch time, earlier quitting time).

WHO Headquarters, Geneva — A29

**1966, May 3 Photo. *Perf. 12½x13***
**141** A29 50fr org yel, vio & bl 1.50 .50

Inauguration of the WHO Headquarters, Geneva.

Church of St. Peter Claver — A30

**1966, June 15 Photo. *Perf. 13x12½***
**142** A30 70fr multicolored 1.50 .40

Women's Basketball — A31

Sport: 1fr, Women's volleyball, horiz. 3fr, Women's field ball, horiz. 5fr, Athletes of various races. 10fr, Torch bearer. 15fr, Soccer and gold medal of First African Games.

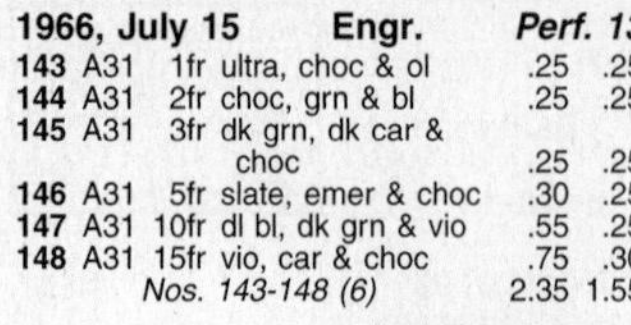
**1966, July 15 Engr. *Perf. 13***
**143** A31 1fr ultra, choc & ol .25 .25
**144** A31 2fr choc, grn & bl .25 .25
**145** A31 3fr dk grn, dk car & choc .25 .25
**146** A31 5fr slate, emer & choc .30 .25
**147** A31 10fr dl bl, dk grn & vio .55 .25
**148** A31 15fr vio, car & choc .75 .30
*Nos. 143-148 (6)* 2.35 1.55

Jules Rimet Cup and Globe — A32

**1966, July 15 Photo. *Perf. 12½x12***
**149** A32 30fr brt red, gold, blk & bl 1.25 .45

8th World Soccer Cup Championship, Wembley, England, July 11-30.

Savorgnan de Brazza School — A33

**1966, Sept. 15 Photo. *Perf. 12½x12***
**150** A33 30fr dk pur, grn, yel & blk 1.00 .25

Pointe-Noire Railroad Station — A34

**1966, Oct. 15 Engr. *Perf. 13***
**151** A34 60fr grn, red & brn 1.50 .60

Student with Microscope — A35

**1966, Nov. 28 Engr. *Perf. 13***
**152** A35 90fr brn, grn & ind 1.50 .70

20th anniv. of UNESCO.

Balumbu Mask — A36

Masks: 10fr, Kuyu. 15fr, Bakwélé. 20fr, Batéké.

**1966, Dec. 12 Engr. *Perf. 13***
**153** A36 5fr car rose & dk brn .45 .25
**154** A36 10fr Prus bl & brn .50 .25
**155** A36 15fr sep, dl org & dk bl .60 .25
**156** A36 20fr dp bl & multi .80 .25
*Nos. 153-156 (4)* 2.35 1.00

Order of the Revolution and Map — A37

Learning the Alphabet — A38

Design: 45fr, Harvesting and loading sugar cane, and sugar mill.

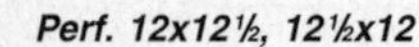
***Perf. 12x12½, 12½x12***
**1967, Mar. 15 Photo.**
**157** A37 20fr org & multi .80 .30
**158** A38 25fr blk, ocher & dk car .80 .35
**159** A38 45fr blk, yel grn & lt bl 1.50 .30
*Nos. 157-159 (3)* 3.10 .95

Issued to honor the members of the Order of the Revolution (20fr); to publicize the literacy campaign (25fr); to publicize sugar production (45fr).

Mahatma Gandhi — A39

**1967, Apr. 21 Engr. *Perf. 13***
**160** A39 90fr blue & black 2.25 .75

Issued in memory of Mohandas K. Gandhi (1869-1948), Hindu nationalist leader.

"Elegant Lady" — A40

Dolls: 10fr, Fruit vendor 25fr, Woman pounding saka-saka. 30fr, Mother and child.

**1967, June Photo. *Perf. 13x12½***
**161** A40 5fr gold & multi .25 .25
**162** A40 10fr yel grn & multi .45 .25
**163** A40 25fr lt ultra & multi .50 .25
**164** A40 30fr multicolored .60 .25
*Nos. 161-164 (4)* 1.80 1.00

ITY Emblem, Village and Waterfall — A41

**1967, July 5 Engr. *Perf. 13***
**165** A41 60fr rose cl, org & ol grn 1.10 .40

Issued for International Tourist Year, 1967.

### Europafrica Issue

Symbols of Cooperation — A42

**1967, July 20 Photo. *Perf. 12x12½***
**166** A42 50fr multicolored 1.00 .30

Arms of Brazzaville — A43

**1967, Aug. 15 Litho. *Perf. 12½x13***
**167** A43 30fr yel & multi .90 .35

Fourth anniversary of the revolution.

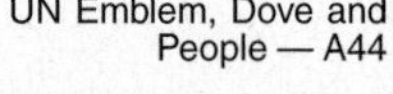
UN Emblem, Dove and People — A44

**1967, Oct. 24 Photo. *Perf. 13x12½***
**168** A44 90fr bl, dk brn, red brn & yel 1.75 .60

Issued for United Nations Day, Oct. 24.

Boy and UNICEF Emblem — A45

**1967, Dec. 11 Engr. *Perf. 13***
**169** A45 90fr mar, blk & ultra 1.75 .60

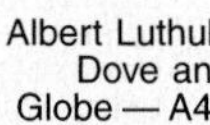
21st anniv. of UNICEF.

Albert Luthuli, Dove and Globe — A46

**1968, Jan. 29 Engr. *Perf. 13***
**170** A46 30fr brt grn & ol bis 1.00 .35

Albert Luthuli (1899-1967) of South Africa, winner of 1960 Nobel Peace Prize.

Arms of Pointe Noire — A47

**1968, Feb. 20 Litho. *Perf. 12½x13***
**171** A47 10fr brt pink & multi .90 .30

Motherhood — A48

**1968, May 25 Engr. *Perf. 13***
**172** A48 15fr dk car rose, sky bl & blk .90 .30

Issued for Mother's Day.

Mayombe Viaduct — A49

**1968, June 24**
**173** A49 45fr mar, slate grn & bl 2.00 .45

A50

5fr, Daimler, 1889. 20fr, Berliet, 1897. 60fr, Peugeot, 1898. 80fr, Renault, 1900. 85fr, Fiat, 1902.

**1968, July 29 Photo. *Perf. 13x12½***
**174** A50 5fr multi .45 .25
**175** A50 20fr multi .90 .30
**176** A50 60fr multi 1.75 .40
**177** A50 80fr multi 2.75 .70
**178** A50 85fr multi 3.25 .90
*Nos. 174-178,C67-C68 (7)* 17.85 6.05

Tanker, Refinery and Map of Area Served A50a

**1968, July 30** ***Perf. 12½***
**179** A50a 30fr multicolored .90 .30

Issued to commemorate the opening of the Port Gentil (Gabon) Refinery, June 12, 1968.

WHO Emblem and Tree of Life — A51

**1968, Nov. 28** **Engr.** ***Perf. 13***
**180** A51 25fr dk grn, red & dp lil .90 .30

20th anniv. of WHO.

**Development Bank Issue**
Common Design Type

**1969, Sept. 10** **Engr.** ***Perf. 13***
**181** CD130 25fr car rose, grn & ocher .50 .25
**182** CD130 30fr bl, grn & ocher .50 .25

Bicycle — A52

Bicycles & Motorcycles: 75fr, Hirondelle. 80fr, Folding bicycle. 85fr, Peugeot. 100fr, Excelsior Manxman. 150fr, Norton. 200fr, Brough Superior "Old Bill." 300fr, Matchless and N.L.G.-J.A.P.S.

**1969, Oct. 6** **Engr.** ***Perf. 13***
**183** A52 50fr multicolored 1.25 .30
**184** A52 75fr multicolored 1.50 .30
**185** A52 80fr multicolored 1.75 .40
**186** A52 85fr multicolored 2.00 .50
**187** A52 100fr multicolored 3.00 .85
**188** A52 150fr multicolored 4.00 1.00
**189** A52 200fr multicolored 5.25 1.75
**190** A52 300fr multicolored 9.50 2.75
*Nos. 183-190 (8)* 28.25 7.85

Mayombe Train and Tourist Year Emblem — A53

40fr, Train and Mbamba Tunnel, vert.

***Perf. 13x12½, 12½x13***
**1969, Oct. 20** **Photo.**
**191** A53 40fr multicolored 2.40 .40
**192** A53 60fr multicolored 4.00 .65

Issued for African Tourist Year.

Loutete Cement Works — A54

Loutete Cement Works: 15fr, Mixing tower, vert. 25fr, Cable transport, vert. 30fr, General view of plant.

**1969, Dec. 10** **Engr.** ***Perf. 13***
**193** A54 10fr dk gray, rose cl & dk ol .25 .25
**194** A54 15fr Prus bl, red brn & pur .50 .25
**195** A54 25fr mar, brn & Prus bl .60 .25
**196** A54 30fr vio brn, ultra & blk .70 .25
*a.* Min. sheet of 4, #193-196 2.75 2.75
*Nos. 193-196 (4)* 2.05 1.00

**ASECNA Issue**
Common Design Type

**1969, Dec. 12**
**197** CD132 100fr dull brown 2.00 .40

Pineapple Harvest and ILO Emblem — A55

30fr, Worker at lathe and ILO emblem.

**1969, Dec. 20** **Engr.** ***Perf. 13***
**198** A55 25fr bl, olive & brn .60 .25
**199** A55 30fr rose red, choc & slate .85 .35

50th anniv. of the ILO.

SOTEXCO Textile Plant, Kinsoundi — A56

20fr, Women in spinnery. 25fr, Hand-printing textiles. 30fr, Checking woven cloth.

**1970, Jan. 20**
**200** A56 15fr grn, blk & lil .45 .25
**201** A56 20fr plum, car & sl grn .45 .25
**202** A56 25fr bl, slate & brn .60 .25
**203** A56 30fr gray, car rose & brn .60 .25
*Nos. 200-203 (4)* 2.10 1.00

Hotel Cosmos, Brazzaville — A57

**1970, Jan. 30**
**204** A57 90fr slate grn, bl & red brn 1.40 .50

**The status of the three sets for Kennedy, etc., Summer Olympics, and Baroque paintings is not certain.**

Linzolo Church A58

Diosso Gorge A59

Design: 90fr, Foulakari waterfall.

**1970** **Engr.** ***Perf. 13***
**205** A58 25fr multicolored .80 .25
**206** A59 70fr multicolored 1.50 .30
**207** A59 90fr multicolored 2.25 .40
*Nos. 205-207 (3)* 4.55 .95

Issue dates: 25fr, Feb. 10; others, Feb. 25.

Volvaria Esculenta — A60

Mushrooms: 10fr, Termitomyces entolomoides. 15fr, Termitomyces microcarpus. 25fr, Termitomyces aurantiacus. 30fr, Termitomyces mammiformis. 50fr, Tremella fuciformis.

**1970, Mar. 31** **Photo.** ***Perf. 13***
**208** A60 5fr multicolored 3.00 .50
**209** A60 10fr multicolored 4.50 .75
**210** A60 15fr multicolored 6.50 1.00
**211** A60 25fr multicolored 12.50 2.00
**212** A60 30fr multicolored 17.50 3.00
**213** A60 50fr multicolored 35.00 5.00
*Nos. 208-213 (6)* 79.00 12.25

Laying Coaxial Cable — A61

Design: 30fr, Full view of rail car; 3 cable layers on railway roadbed.

**1970, Apr. 30** **Engr.** ***Perf. 13***
**214** A61 25fr dk brn & multi 1.00 .30
**215** A61 30fr brn & multi 1.25 .60

Issued to publicize the laying of the coaxial cable linking Brazzaville and Pointe Noire.
For surcharges see Nos. 263-264.

**UPU Headquarters Issue**
Common Design Type

**1970, May 20**
**216** CD133 30fr dk pur, gray & mag 1.00 .25

Mother Feeding Child — A62

Design: 90fr, Mother nursing infant.

**1970, May 30** **Photo.**
**217** A62 85fr vio bl & multi 1.00 .30
**218** A62 90fr lil & multi 1.10 .40

Issued for Mother's Day.

Dag Hammarskjold, UN Emblem — A63

UN Emblem and: No. 220, Trygve Lie, horiz. No. 221, U Thant, horiz.

**1970, June 20** **Engr.** ***Perf. 13***
**219** A63 100fr scar, dk red & dk pur 1.40 .80
**220** A63 100fr dk red, ultra & ind 1.40 .80
**221** A63 100fr grn, emer & dk red 1.40 .80
*a.* Souv. sheet of 3, #219-221 5.50 5.50
*Nos. 219-221 (3)* 4.20 2.40

25th anniv. of the UN and to honor its Secretaries General.

Brillantaisia Vogeliana A64

Sternotomis Variabilis A65

Plants and Beetles: 2fr, Plectranthus decurrens. 3fr, Myrianthemum mirabile. 5fr, Connarus griffonianus. 15fr, Chelorrhina polyphemus. 20fr, Metopodontus savagei.

***Perf. 12½x12, 12x12½***
**1970, June 30** **Photo.**
**222** A64 1fr dk grn & multi .70 .25
**223** A64 2fr multicolored .70 .25
**224** A64 3fr indigo & multi .70 .25
**225** A64 5fr lemon & multi 1.40 .25
**226** A65 10fr lilac & multi 2.25 .40
**227** A65 15fr orange & multi 3.25 .40
**228** A65 20fr multicolored 3.25 .60
*Nos. 222-228 (7)* 12.25 2.40

For surcharge see No. 288.

Stegosaurus A66

Prehistoric Fauna: 20fr, Dinotherium, vert. 60fr, Brachiosaurus, vert. 80fr, Arsinoitherium.

**1970, July 20**
**229** A66 15fr dl grn, ocher & red brn 1.75 .30
**230** A66 20fr lt bl & multi 3.50 .65
**231** A66 60fr lt bl & multi 6.25 .95
**232** A66 80fr lt bl & multi 8.00 1.75
*Nos. 229-232 (4)* 19.50 3.65

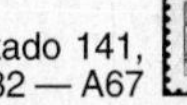
Mikado 141, 1932 — A67

Locomotives: 60fr, Steam locomotive 130+032, 1947. 75fr, Alsthom BB 1100, 1962. 85fr, Diesel BB BB 302, 1969.

**1970, Aug. 20** **Engr.** ***Perf. 13***
**233** A67 40fr mag, bl grn & blk 2.75 .80
**234** A67 60fr blk, bl & grn 3.25 .90
**235** A67 75fr red, bl & blk 4.50 1.25
**236** A67 85fr car, sl grn & ocher 7.50 1.75
*Nos. 233-236 (4)* 18.00 4.70

Cogniauxia Padolaena — A68

Tropical Flowers: 2fr, Celosia cristata. 5fr, Plumeria acutifolia. 10fr, Bauhinia variegata. 15fr, Poinsettia. 20fr, Thunbergia grandiflora.

**1971, Feb. 10** **Photo.** ***Perf. 12x12½***
**237** A68 1fr lil & multi .25 .25
**238** A68 2fr yel & multi .25 .25
**239** A68 5fr ultra & multi .25 .25
**240** A68 10fr yel & multi 1.10 .25
**241** A68 15fr multicolored 1.60 .30
**242** A68 20fr dk red & multi 2.75 .40
*Nos. 237-242 (6)* 6.20 1.70

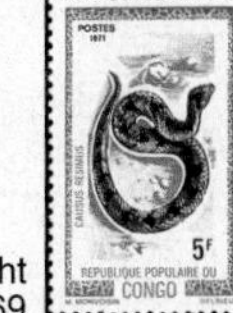
Green Night Adder — A69

Reptiles: 10fr, African Egg-eating snake, horiz. 15fr, Flap-necked chameleon. 20fr, Nile crocodile, horiz. 25fr, Rock python, horiz. 30fr, Gaboon viper. 40fr, Brown house snake, horiz. 45fr, Jameson's mamba.

***Perf. 12x12½, 12½x12***
**1971, June 26** **Photo.**
**243** A69 5fr multicolored .40 .25
**244** A69 10fr multicolored .40 .25
**245** A69 15fr multicolored 1.40 .25
**246** A69 20fr red & multi 2.25 .25
**247** A69 25fr grn & multi 3.00 .35
**248** A69 30fr multicolored 3.75 .75
**249** A69 40fr bis & multi 4.25 .95
**250** A69 45fr multicolored 5.75 1.00
*Nos. 243-250 (8)* 21.20 4.05

Pseudimbrasia Deyrollei — A70

Caterpillars: 15fr, Bunaea alcinoe, vert. 20fr, Epiphora vacuna ploetzi. 25fr, Imbrasia eblis. 30fr, Imbrasia dione, vert. 40fr, Holocera angulata.

**1971, July 3** ***Perf. 13***
**251** A70 10fr ver, blk & grn 1.00 .25
**252** A70 15fr multicolored 1.50 .30
**253** A70 20fr yel grn, blk & ocher 2.25 .40
**254** A70 25fr multicolored 3.50 .60
**255** A70 30fr red, blk & yel 5.00 .90
**256** A70 40fr bl, blk & org 6.75 1.25
*Nos. 251-256 (6)* 20.00 3.70

Boy Scout — A70a

Scouts, Lord Baden-Powell — A70b

Designs: c, Scout facing left. d, Scout facing forward. e, Lord Baden-Powell.

**Embossed on Metallic Foil**

**1971, July 14** ***Die Cut Perf. 10½***

**256A** A70a 90fr Block of 4, #b.-e, silver 12.00 12.00
**256F** A70b 1000fr gold *30.00 30.00*

No. 256F is airmail.

Cymothoe Sangaris — A71

Butterflies and Moths: 40fr, Papilio dardanus, vert. 75fr, Iolaus timon. 90fr, Papilio phorcas, vert. 100fr, Euchloron megaera.

**1971, Oct. 15** ***Perf. 12½x12, 12x12½***

| | | | | |
|---|---|---|---|---|
| **257** | A71 | 30fr yel & multi | 1.75 | .40 |
| **258** | A71 | 40fr grn & multi | 3.25 | .65 |
| **259** | A71 | 75fr multicolored | 5.25 | 1.25 |
| **260** | A71 | 90fr multicolored | 7.00 | 1.90 |
| **261** | A71 | 100fr ultra & multi | 9.50 | 2.50 |
| | | *Nos. 257-261 (5)* | 26.75 | 6.70 |

Black and White Men Working Together — A72

**1971, Oct. 30** ***Perf. 13x12½***

**262** A72 50fr org & multi 1.75 .50

Intl. Year Against Racial Discrimination.

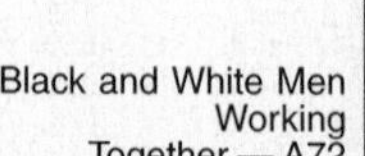
Nos. 214-215 Surcharged

**1971, Nov. 18** **Engr.** ***Perf. 13***

| | | | | |
|---|---|---|---|---|
| **263** | A61 | 30fr on 25fr multicolored | .65 | .30 |
| **264** | A61 | 40fr on 30fr multicolored | .95 | .35 |

Inauguration of cable service between Brazzaville and Pointe Noire. Words of surcharge arranged differently on No. 264.

Map of Congo — A73

**1971, Dec. 31** **Photo.** ***Perf. 12½x13***

| | | | | |
|---|---|---|---|---|
| **265** | A73 | 30fr bl & multi | .35 | .25 |
| **266** | A73 | 40fr yel grn & multi | .45 | .25 |
| **267** | A73 | 100fr gray & multi | 1.10 | .40 |
| | | *Nos. 265-267 (3)* | 1.90 | .90 |

"Labor, Democracy, Peace."

Lion — A74

2fr, African elephants. 3fr, Leopard. 4fr, Hippopotamus. 5fr, Gorilla, vert. 20fr, Potto. 30fr, De Brazza's monkey. 40fr, Pygmy chimpanzee, vert.

**1972, Jan. 31** **Engr.** ***Perf. 13***

| | | | | |
|---|---|---|---|---|
| **268** | A74 | 1fr grn & multi | .35 | .25 |
| **269** | A74 | 2fr dk red & multi | .50 | .25 |
| **270** | A74 | 3fr red brn & multi | .80 | .25 |
| **271** | A74 | 4fr vio & multi | 1.00 | .25 |
| **272** | A74 | 5fr brn & multi | 1.10 | .25 |
| **273** | A74 | 20fr org & multi | 2.75 | .35 |
| **274** | A74 | 30fr ocher & multi | 3.50 | .45 |
| **275** | A74 | 40fr Prus bl & multi | 5.25 | .75 |
| | | *Nos. 268-275 (8)* | 15.25 | 2.80 |

WHO, 25th Anniv. — A75

***Perf. 12½x13, 13x12½***

**1973, June 30** **Typo.**

| | | | | |
|---|---|---|---|---|
| **276** | A75 | 40fr WHO Emblem | .65 | .25 |
| **277** | A75 | 50fr WHO emblem, horiz. | .95 | .25 |

Kronenbourg Brewery — A76

Brewery Trademark and: 40fr, Laboratory. 75fr, Vats and controls. 85fr, Automatic control room. 100fr, Pressure room. 250fr, Bottling plant.

**1973, July 15** **Engr.** ***Perf. 13***

| | | | | |
|---|---|---|---|---|
| **278** | A76 | 30fr red & multi | .50 | .25 |
| **279** | A76 | 40fr red & multi | .60 | .25 |
| **280** | A76 | 75fr red & multi | 1.20 | .30 |
| **281** | A76 | 85fr red & multi | 1.75 | .40 |
| **282** | A76 | 100fr red & multi | 1.90 | .55 |
| **283** | A76 | 250fr red & multi | 3.75 | 1.00 |
| | | *Nos. 278-283 (6)* | 9.70 | 2.75 |

Kronenbourg Brewery, Brazzaville.

Golwe Locomotive, 1935 — A77

Locomotives: 40fr, Diesel, 1935. 75fr, Diesel Whithcomb, 1946. 85fr, Diesel CC200.

**1973, Aug. 1** **Engr.** ***Perf. 13***

| | | | | |
|---|---|---|---|---|
| **284** | A77 | 30fr indigo & multi | 2.00 | .50 |
| **285** | A77 | 40fr vio bl & multi | 3.00 | .85 |
| **286** | A77 | 75fr multicolored | 4.25 | 1.50 |
| **287** | A77 | 85fr multicolored | 5.50 | 2.75 |
| | | *Nos. 284-287 (4)* | 14.75 | 5.60 |

No. 225 Srchd. and Ovptd. in Ultramarine

**1973, Aug. 16** **Photo.** ***Perf. 12½x12***

**288** A64 100fr on 5fr multicolored 1.75 .60

African solidarity in drought emergency.

**African Postal Union Issue**

Common Design Type

**1973, Sept. 12** **Engr.** ***Perf. 13***

**289** CD137 100fr bl grn, vio & brn 1.60 .50

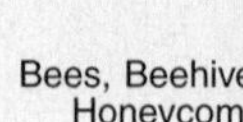

Bees, Beehive, Honeycomb A78

**1973, Dec. 10** **Engr.** ***Perf. 13***

| | | | | |
|---|---|---|---|---|
| **290** | A78 | 30fr sl grn, dk red & bl | 1.10 | .25 |
| **291** | A78 | 40fr sl bl, sl grn & lt grn | 1.50 | .25 |

"Work and economy."

Family, UN and FAO Emblems — A79

40fr, Grain, emblems. 100fr, Grain, emblems, vert.

**1973, Dec. 10**

| | | | | |
|---|---|---|---|---|
| **292** | A79 | 30fr dk car & dk brn | .50 | .25 |
| **293** | A79 | 40fr dk grn, yel & ind | .60 | .25 |
| **294** | A79 | 100fr grn, brn & org | 1.40 | .40 |
| | | *Nos. 292-294 (3)* | 2.50 | .90 |

World Food Program, 10th anniversary.

Amilcar Cabral, Cattle and Child — A80

**1974, July 15** **Engr.** ***Perf. 13***

**295** A80 100fr multicolored 1.60 .60

First death anniversary of Amilcar Cabral (1924-1973), leader of anti-Portuguese guerrilla activity in Portuguese Guinea.

Félix Eboué, Cross of Lorraine — A81

**1974, Aug. 31** **Litho.** ***Perf. 13***

| | | | | |
|---|---|---|---|---|
| **296** | A81 | 30fr bl & multi | .80 | .30 |
| **297** | A81 | 40fr brt pink & multi | 1.60 | .60 |

Félix A. Eboué (1884-1944), Governor of Chad, first colonial governor to join Free French in WWII, 30th death anniversary.

Pineapples — A82

**1974, Nov. 12**

| | | | | |
|---|---|---|---|---|
| **298** | A82 | 30fr shown | .60 | .30 |
| **299** | A82 | 30fr Bananas | .70 | .30 |
| **300** | A82 | 30fr Safous | .70 | .30 |
| **301** | A82 | 40fr Avocados | 1.25 | .30 |
| **302** | A82 | 40fr Mangos | 1.25 | .30 |
| **303** | A82 | 40fr Papaya | 1.25 | .30 |
| **304** | A82 | 40fr Orange | 1.25 | .30 |
| | | *Nos. 298-304 (7)* | 7.00 | 2.10 |

Charles de Gaulle and Conference Building A83

**1974, Nov. 25** **Engr.** ***Perf. 13***

**305** A83 100fr multicolored 5.00 1.90

Brazzaville Conference, 25th anniversary.

George Stephenson and Various Locomotives — A84

**1974, Dec. 15**

**306** A84 75fr slate grn & ol 4.00 1.00

George Stephenson (1781-1848), English inventor and railroad founder.

**UDEAC Issue**

Presidents and Flags of Cameroun, CAR, Congo, Gabon and Meeting Center A84a

**1974, Dec. 8** **Photo.** ***Perf. 13***

**307** A84a 40fr gold & multi .65 .25

See note after Cameroun No. 595.
See No. C195.

Irish Setter — A85

**1974, Dec. 15** **Photo.** ***Perf. 13x13½***

| | | | | |
|---|---|---|---|---|
| **308** | A85 | 30fr shown | 1.25 | .30 |
| **309** | A85 | 40fr Borzoi | 1.50 | .30 |
| **310** | A85 | 75fr Pointer | 3.25 | .75 |
| **311** | A85 | 100fr Great Dane | 4.50 | .80 |
| | | *Nos. 308-311 (4)* | 10.50 | 2.15 |

**1974, Dec. 15**

Designs: Cats.

| | | | | |
|---|---|---|---|---|
| **312** | A85 | 30fr Havana chestnut | 1.25 | .30 |
| **313** | A85 | 40fr Red Persian | 1.50 | .30 |
| **314** | A85 | 75fr Blue British | 3.50 | .75 |
| **315** | A85 | 100fr African serval | 5.00 | .80 |
| | | *Nos. 312-315 (4)* | 11.25 | 2.15 |

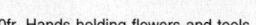

Labor Party Flags and People — A86

40fr, Hands holding flowers and tools.

**1974, Dec. 31** **Engr.** ***Perf. 13x12½***

| | | | | |
|---|---|---|---|---|
| **316** | A86 | 30fr red & multi | .65 | .25 |
| **317** | A86 | 40fr red & multi | .95 | .25 |

5th anniversary of Congolese Labor Party and of introduction of red flag.

Symbols of Development — A87

U Thant and UN Headquarters — A88

Paul G. Hoffman and UN Emblem — A89

***Perf. 13x12½, 12½x13***

**1975, Feb. 28** **Litho.**

**318** A87 40fr multicolored .90 .35
**319** A88 50fr light blue & multi .90 .35
**320** A89 50fr yellow & multi .90 .35
*Nos. 318-320 (3)* 2.70 1.05

National economic development.

Map of China and Mao Tse-tung A90

**1975, Mar. 9** **Engr.** ***Perf. 13***

**321** A90 75fr multicolored 5.50 1.50

25th anniv. of the PRC.

Woman Breaking Bonds, Women's Activities, Map of Congo — A91

**1975, June 20** **Litho.** ***Perf. 12½***

**322** A91 40fr gold & multi .80 .35

Revolutionary Union of Congolese Women, URFC, 10th anniversary.

CARA Soccer Team A92

Design: 40fr, Team captain and manager receiving trophy, vert.

**1975, July 15** **Litho.** ***Perf. 12½***

**323** A92 30fr multicolored .65 .25
**324** A92 40fr multicolored .95 .25

CARA team, winners of African Soccer Cup 1974.

Citroen, 1935 — A93

Designs: Early autombiles.

**1975, July 17** ***Perf. 12***

**325** A93 30fr shown 1.10 .40
**326** A93 40fr Alfa Romeo, 1911 1.35 .40
**327** A93 50fr Rolls Royce, 1926 1.75 .55
**328** A93 75fr Duryea, 1893 3.50 .70
*Nos. 325-328 (4)* 7.70 2.05

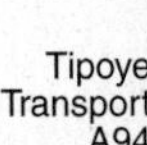

Tipoye Transport A94

**1975, Aug. 5**

**329** A94 30fr shown .90 .40
**330** A94 40fr Dugout canoe 1.00 .65

Traditional means of transportation.

Raising Red Flag — A95

**1975, Aug. 15**

**331** A95 30fr shown .80 .25
**332** A95 40fr National Conference .80 .25

2nd anniv. of installation of popular power (30fr) and 3rd anniv. of Natl. Conf. (40fr).

Line Fishing — A96

Traditional Fishing: 30fr, Trap fishing, horiz. 60fr, Spear fishing. 90fr, Net fishing, horiz.

**1975, Aug. 31** **Litho.** ***Perf. 12***

**333** A96 30fr multicolored .80 .25
**334** A96 40fr multicolored .80 .30
**335** A96 60fr multicolored 1.25 .50
**336** A96 90fr multicolored 2.50 1.00
*Nos. 333-336 (4)* 5.35 2.05

Woman Pounding "Foufou" — A97

Household Tasks: No. 338, Woman chopping wood. 40fr, Woman preparing manioc, horiz.

**1975, Sept. 5**

**337** A97 30fr multicolored .60 .25
**338** A97 30fr multicolored .60 .25
**339** A97 40fr multicolored .90 .25
*Nos. 337-339 (3)* 2.10 .75

Musical Instruments — A98

**1975, Sept. 20** ***Perf. 12½***

**340** A98 30fr Esanga .75 .25
**341** A98 40fr Kalakwa 1.25 .25
**342** A98 60fr Likembe 1.50 .30
**343** A98 75fr Ngongui 2.00 .40
*Nos. 340-343 (4)* 5.50 1.20

Dzeke (Congolese) Shell Money — A99

Ancient Money: No. 346, like No. 344. Nos. 345, 347, Okengo, Congolese, iron bar. 40fr, Gallic coin, c. 60 B.C. 50fr, Roman denarius, 37 B.C. 60fr, Danubian coin, 2nd cent. B.C. 85fr, Greek stater, 4th cent. B.C.

**1975-76** **Engr.** ***Perf. 13***

**344** A99 30fr red & multi .60 .25
**345** A99 30fr vio & multi .60 .25
**346** A99 35fr ol & multi .90 .25
**347** A99 35fr dk car rose & multi .90 .25
**348** A99 40fr Prus bl & brn .90 .25
**349** A99 50fr Prus bl & ol 1.00 .30
**350** A99 60fr dk grn & brn 1.25 .35
**351** A99 85fr mag & sl grn 2.10 .45
*Nos. 344-351 (8)* 8.25 2.35

Nos. 346-347 inscribed "1976" and issued Mar. 1976; others issued Oct. 5, 1975.

Moschops A100

Pre-historic Animals: 70fr, Tyrannosaurus. 95fr, Cryptocleidus. 100fr, Stegosaurus.

**1975, Oct. 15** **Litho.** ***Perf. 13***

**352** A100 55fr multicolored 2.25 .30
**353** A100 75fr multicolored 3.25 .35
**354** A100 95fr multicolored 5.75 .75
**355** A100 100fr multicolored 8.00 1.25
*Nos. 352-355 (4)* 19.25 2.65

Albert Schweitzer (1875-1965), Medical Missionary — A101

**1975, Oct. 15** **Engr.**

**356** A101 75fr ol, brn & red 1.50 .40

Alexander Fleming — A102

Designs: No. 358, André Marie Ampère. No. 359, Clement Ader.

**1975, Nov. 15** **Engr.** ***Perf. 13***

**357** A102 60fr brn, grn & blk 1.60 .45
**358** A102 95fr blk, red & grn 2.50 .65
**359** A102 95fr red, blue & indigo 2.50 .65
*Nos. 357-359 (3)* 6.60 1.75

Fleming (1881-1955), developer of penicillin; Ampère (1775-1836), physicist; Ader (1841-1925), aviation pioneer.

UN Emblem "ONU" and "30" — A103

**1975, Dec. 20** **Engr.** ***Perf. 13***

**360** A103 95fr car, ultra & grn 1.60 .50

United Nations, 30th anniversary.

Women's Broken Chain A104

Design: 60fr, Equality between man and woman, globe, IWY emblem.

**1975, Dec. 20** **Litho.** ***Perf. 12½***

**361** A104 35fr mag, ocher & gray .90 .25
**362** A104 60fr ultra, brn & blk 1.75 .50

International Women's Year, 1975.

Pres. Marien Ngouabi, Flag and Workers A105

Echo of the P.C.T. — A106

**1975, Dec. 31** ***Perf. 12½x12, 13x12½***

**363** A105 30fr multicolored .55 .25
**364** A106 35fr multicolored .65 .25

6th anniversary of the Congolese Labor Party (P.C.T.). See No. C215.

A.G. Bell and 1876 Telephone A107

**1976, Apr. 25** **Litho.** ***Perf. 12½x13***

**365** A107 35fr yel, brn & org brn .65 .25

Cent. of 1st telephone call by Alexander Graham Bell, Mar. 10, 1876. See No. C229.

Women Selling Fruit and Vegetables A108

**1976, Sept. 19** **Litho.** ***Perf. 12½x13***

**366** A108 35fr shown .50 .25
**367** A108 60fr Market scene 1.20 .30

Congolese Coiffure — A109

Designs: Various women's hair styles.

**1976, Oct. 10** **Litho.** ***Perf. 13***

**368** A109 35fr multicolored .55 .25
**369** A109 60fr multicolored .90 .25
**370** A109 95fr multicolored 1.40 .35
**371** A109 100fr multicolored 1.60 .40
*Nos. 368-371 (4)* 4.45 1.25

Pole Vault, Map of Central Africa — A110

95fr, Long jump and map of Central Africa.

**1976, Oct. 25** ***Perf. 12½***

**372** A110 60fr yel & multi .70 .25
**373** A110 95fr yel & multi 1.25 .40
*Nos. 372-373,C230-C231 (4)* 6.45 2.50

Gold medalists, 1st Central African Games, Yaoundé, July 27-30, 1975.

Antelope — A111

**1976, Oct. 27** **Litho.** ***Perf. 12½***

**Size: 36x36mm**

**374** A111 5fr shown .55 .25
**375** A111 10fr Buffalos .65 .25
**376** A111 15fr Hippopotamus 1.00 .30
**377** A111 20fr Wart hog 2.00 .35
**378** A111 25fr Elephants 2.25 .40
*Nos. 374-378 (5)* 6.45 1.55

**1976, Dec. 8 Size: 26x36mm**

Birds — 5fr, Saddle-bill storks. 10fr, Malachite kingfisher. 20fr, Crowned cranes.

**379** A111 5fr multicolored 1.25 .25

**Size: 36x36mm**

**380** A111 10fr multicolored 1.50 .25
**381** A111 20fr multicolored 2.40 .60
*Nos. 379-381 (3)* 5.15 1.10

Bicycling, Map of Participants — A112

**1976, Dec. 21 Photo. *Perf. 12½x13***

**382** A112 35fr shown .35 .25
**383** A112 60fr Fieldball .60 .25
**384** A112 80fr Running 1.00 .35
**385** A112 95fr Soccer 1.25 .40
*Nos. 382-385 (4)* 3.20 1.25

First Central African Games, Libreville, Gabon, June-July 1976.

Heliotrope — A113

Flowers: 5fr, Water lilies. 15fr, Bird-of-paradise flower.

**1976, Dec. 23 Photo. *Perf. 12½x13***

**386** A113 5fr multicolored .30 .25
**387** A113 10fr multicolored .40 .25
**388** A113 15fr multicolored .70 .25
*Nos. 386-388 (3)* 1.40 .75

Torch and Olive Branches — A114

**1976, Dec. 25 Litho. *Perf. 12½x13***

**389** A114 35fr multicolored .90 .25

National Pioneer Movement.

The Spirit of '76 — A115

125fr, Pulling down George III statue. 150fr, Battle of Princeton. 175fr, Generals of Revolutionary War. 200fr, Burgoyne's surrender at Saratoga. 500fr, Battle of Lexington.

**1976, Dec. 29 Litho. *Perf. 14***

**390** A115 100fr multicolored 1.00 .25
**391** A115 125fr multicolored 1.10 .35
**392** A115 150fr multicolored 1.60 .40
**393** A115 175fr multicolored 2.00 .50
**394** A115 200fr multicolored 2.25 .60
*Nos. 390-394 (5)* 7.95 2.10

**Souvenir Sheet**

**395** A115 500fr multicolored 5.75 1.50

American Bicentennial.

Dugout Canoe Race — A116

Design: 60fr, 2-man dugout canoes.

**1977, Mar. 27 Litho. *Perf. 13x13½***

**396** A116 35fr multicolored .60 .25
**397** A116 60fr multicolored 1.00 .35

Dugout canoe races on Congo River.

Lilan Goua — A117

Fresh-water Fish: 15fr, Liko ko. 25fr, Liyanga. 35fr, Mbessi. 60fr, Mongandza.

**1977, June 15 Litho. *Perf. 12½***

**398** A117 10fr multicolored .75 .25
**399** A117 15fr multicolored .90 .25
**400** A117 25fr multicolored 1.25 .25
**401** A117 35fr multicolored 2.00 .30
**402** A117 60fr multicolored 3.50 .45
*Nos. 398-402 (5)* 8.40 1.50

Traditional Headdress A118

**1977, June 30 Litho. *Perf. 12½***

**403** A118 35fr shown .45 .30
**404** A118 60fr Leopard cap .90 .35

See Nos. C234-C235.

Bondjo Wrestling — A119

40fr, 50fr, Bondjo wrestling, diff. 40fr, horiz.

**1977, July 15**

**405** A119 25fr multicolored .50 .25
**406** A119 40fr multicolored .60 .25
**407** A119 50fr multicolored .70 .30
*Nos. 405-407 (3)* 1.80 .80

"Schwaben" LZ 10, 1911 — A120

Zeppelins: 60fr, "Viktoria Luise." LZ 11, 1913. 100fr, LZ 120. 200fr, LZ 127. 300fr, "Graf Zeppelin II" LZ 130.

**1977, Aug. 5 Litho. *Perf. 11***

**408** A120 40fr multicolored .50 .25
**409** A120 60fr multicolored .75 .25
**410** A120 100fr multicolored 1.25 .30
**411** A120 200fr multicolored 2.50 .60
**412** A120 300fr multicolored 4.00 .95
*Nos. 408-412 (5)* 9.00 2.35

History of the Zeppelin. Exist imperf. See No. C236.

Coat of Arms and Rising Sun — A121

**1977, Aug. 15**

**413** A121 40fr multicolored .90 .25

14th anniversary of the revolution.

Victor Hugo and The Hunchback of Notre Dame A122

Designs (Hugo and): 60fr, Les Miserables. 100fr, Les Travailleurs de la Mer (octopus).

**1977, Aug. 20 Engr. *Perf. 13***

**414** A122 35fr multicolored .75 .30
**415** A122 60fr multicolored 1.00 .30
**416** A122 100fr multicolored 1.90 .45
*Nos. 414-416 (3)* 3.65 1.05

Victor Hugo (1802-1885), French novelist.

Mao Tse-tung — A123

**Lithographed; Gold Embossed**

**1977, Sept. 9 *Perf. 12x12½***

**417** A123 400fr red & gold 16.00 8.00

Chairman Mao Tse-tung (1893-1976), Chinese Communist leader, 1st death anniv.

Peter Paul Rubens — A124

**1977, Sept. 20 Gold Embossed**

**418** A124 600fr gold & lt bl 10.00 6.00

Peter Paul Rubens (1577-1640), painter.

Child Leading Blind Woman Across Street — A125

**1977, Oct. 22 Litho. *Perf. 12½x13***

**419** A125 35fr multicolored 1.00 .25

World Health Day: To see is life.

Paul Kamba and Records — A126

**1977, Oct. 29**

**420** A126 100fr multicolored 1.60 .50

Paul Kamba (1912-1950), musician.

Trajan Vuia and Flying Machine A127

Designs: 75fr, Louis Bleriot and plane. 100fr, Roland Garros and plane. 200fr, Charles Lindbergh and Spirit of St. Louis. 300fr, Tupolev Tu-144. 500fr, Lindbergh and Spirit of St. Louis over ship in Atlantic.

**1977, Nov. 18 Litho. *Perf. 14***

**421** A127 60fr multicolored .60 .25
**422** A127 75fr multicolored .90 .25
**423** A127 100fr multicolored 1.10 .30
**424** A127 200fr multicolored 2.25 .50
**425** A127 300fr multicolored 3.25 .70
*Nos. 421-425 (5)* 8.10 2.00

**Souvenir Sheet**

**426** A127 500fr multicolored 5.75 1.25

History of aviation.

Elizabeth II and Prince Philip — A128

Design: 300fr, Elizabeth II wearing Crown.

**1977, Dec. 21**

**427** A128 250fr multicolored 2.25 .65
**428** A128 300fr multicolored 2.75 .70

Reign of Queen Elizabeth II, 25th anniv. See No. C239. For overprints see Nos. 468-469, C244.

King Baudouin — A129

Design: No. 430, Charles de Gaulle.

**1977, Dec. 21**

**429** A129 200fr multicolored 2.25 .65
**430** A129 200fr multicolored 2.25 .65

King Baudouin of Belgium and Charles de Gaulle, president of France.

Ambete Sculpture — A130

Congolese art: 85fr, Babembe sculpture.

**1978, Feb. 18 Engr. *Perf. 13***

**431** A130 35fr lt brn & multi .65 .25
**432** A130 85fr lt grn & multi 1.50 .45

St. Simon, by Rubens — A131

Rubens Paintings: 140fr, Duke of Lerma. 200fr, Madonna and Saints. 300fr, Rubens and his Wife Helena Fourment. 500fr, Farm at Laeken.

**1978, Mar. 7 Litho. *Perf. 13½x14***

**433** A131 60fr gold & multi .60 .25
**434** A131 140fr gold & multi 1.50 .30
**435** A131 200fr gold & multi 2.25 .45
**436** A131 300fr gold & multi 3.50 .65
*Nos. 433-436 (4)* 7.85 1.65

**Souvenir Sheet**

**437** A131 500fr gold & multi 6.00 1.40

Peter Paul Rubens, 400th birth anniv.

Pres. Ngouabi and Microphones A132

60fr, Ngouabi at his desk, horiz. 100fr, Portrait.

*Perf. 12½x13, 13x12½*

**1978, Mar. 18** **Litho.**

**438** A132 35fr multicolored .45 .25
**439** A132 60fr multicolored .50 .25
**440** A132 100fr multicolored .90 .40
*Nos. 438-440 (3)* 1.85 .90

Pres. Marien Ngouabi, 1st death anniv.

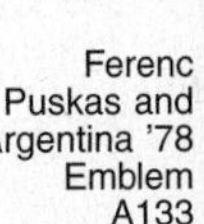

Ferenc Puskas and Argentina '78 Emblem A133

Players and Emblem: 75fr, Giacinto Facchetti. 100fr, Bobby Moore. 200fr, Raymond Kopa. 300fr, Pele. 500fr, Franz Beckenbauer.

**1978, Apr. 4** ***Perf. 14x13½***

**441** A133 60fr multicolored .60 .25
**442** A133 75fr multicolored .70 .25
**443** A133 100fr multicolored 1.10 .25
**444** A133 200fr multicolored 2.25 .55
**445** A133 300fr multicolored 3.25 .75
*Nos. 441-445 (5)* 7.90 2.05

**Souvenir Sheet**

**446** A133 500fr multicolored 6.25 1.25

11th World Cup Soccer Championship, Argentina, June 1-25.
For overprints see Nos. 481-486.

Pearl S. Buck and Chinese Women A134

Nobel Prize winners: 75fr, Fridtjof Nansen, refugees and Nansen passport. 100fr, Henri Bergson, book and flame. 200fr, Alexander Fleming and Petri dish. 300fr, Gerhart Hauptmann and book. 500fr, Henri Dunant and Red Cross Station.

**1978, Apr. 29**

**447** A134 60fr multicolored .60 .25
**448** A134 75fr multicolored .70 .25
**449** A134 100fr multicolored 1.10 .30
**450** A134 200fr multicolored 2.00 .50
**451** A134 300fr multicolored 2.75 .60
*Nos. 447-451 (5)* 7.15 1.90

**Souvenir Sheet**

**452** A134 500fr multicolored 6.00 1.40

African Buffalos — A135

Endangered animals and Wildlife Fund Emblem: 35fr, Okapi, vert. 85fr, Rhinoceros. 150fr, Chimpanzee, vert. 200fr, Hippopotamus. 300fr, Buffon's kob, vert.

**1978** ***Perf. 14½***

**453** A135 35fr multicolored 1.25 .45
**454** A135 60fr multicolored 1.75 .55
**455** A135 85fr multicolored 4.25 .85
**456** A135 150fr multicolored 6.00 1.25
**457** A135 200fr multicolored 8.00 1.75
**458** A135 300fr multicolored 15.00 2.50
*Nos. 453-458 (6)* 36.25 7.35

Issue dates: 35fr, Aug. 11; others, July 11.

Emblem, Young People, Gun and Fist — A136

**1978, July 28** ***Perf. 12½***

**459** A136 35fr multicolored .80 .30

11th World Youth Festival, Havana, 7/28-8/5.

Pyramids and Camels A137

Seven Wonders of the Ancient World: 50fr, Hanging Gardens of Babylon. 60fr, Statue of Zeus, Olympia. 95fr, Colossus of Rhodes. 125fr, Mausoleum of Halicarnassus. 150fr, Temple of Artemis, Ephesus. 200fr, Lighthouse, Alexandria. 300fr, Map of Eastern Mediterranean showing locations. 50fr, 60fr, 95fr, 125fr, 200fr, vertical.

**1978, Aug. 12** **Litho.** ***Perf. 14***

**460** A137 35fr multicolored .50 .25
**461** A137 50fr multicolored .60 .25
**462** A137 60fr multicolored .75 .25
**463** A137 95fr multicolored 1.00 .30
**464** A137 125fr multicolored 1.25 .45
**465** A137 150fr multicolored 1.75 .55
**466** A137 200fr multicolored 2.25 .75
**467** A137 300fr multicolored 3.25 1.00
*Nos. 460-467 (8)* 11.35 3.80

**Nos. 427-428 Overprinted in Silver**

No. 468

No. 469

**1978, Sept.** **Litho.** ***Perf. 14***

**468** A128 250fr multicolored 2.25 .90
**469** A128 300fr multicolored 2.75 1.25

25th anniversary of coronation of Queen Elizabeth II. See No. C244.

Kwame Nkrumah and Map of Africa A138

**1978, Sept. 23** **Litho.** ***Perf. 13x12½***

**470** A138 60fr multicolored .80 .40

Nkrumah (1909-72), Pres. of Ghana.

Wild Boar Hunt A139

Local hunting and fishing: 50fr, Fish smoking. 60fr, Hunter with spears and dog, vert.

**1978** **Litho.** ***Perf. 12***

**471** A139 35fr multicolored 2.00 .25
**472** A139 50fr multicolored .80 .25
**473** A139 60fr multicolored 2.75 .25
*Nos. 471-473 (3)* 5.55 .75

Issue dates: 35fr, 60fr, Oct. 5; 50fr, Oct. 10.

View of Kalchreut, by Dürer A140

Paintings by Dürer: 150fr, Elspeth Tucher, vert. 250fr, "The Great Piece of Turf," vert. 350fr, Self-portrait, vert.

**1978, Nov. 23** **Litho.** ***Perf. 14***

**474** A140 65fr multicolored .60 .25
**475** A140 150fr multicolored 1.40 .35
**476** A140 250fr multicolored 2.25 .65
**477** A140 350fr multicolored 3.50 .90
*Nos. 474-477 (4)* 7.75 2.15

Albrecht Dürer (1471-1528), German painter.

Basketmaker — A141

Productive Labor: 90fr, Woodcarver. 140fr, Women hoeing field.

**1978, Nov. 18** **Litho.** ***Perf. 12½***

**Size: 25x36mm**

**478** A141 85fr multicolored .90 .40
**479** A141 90fr multicolored 1.00 .40

**Size: 27x48mm**

***Perf. 12***

**480** A141 140fr multicolored 1.50 .65
*Nos. 478-480 (3)* 3.40 1.45

**Nos. 441-446 Overprinted in Silver**

a

b

c

d

e

f

**1978, Nov.** ***Perf. 14x13½***

**481** A133 (a) 60fr multicolored .65 .25
**482** A133 (b) 75fr multicolored .75 .35
**483** A133 (c) 100fr multicolored 1.05 .45
**484** A133 (d) 200fr multicolored 2.10 .65
**485** A133 (e) 300fr multicolored 3.00 1.00
*Nos. 481-485 (5)* 7.55 2.70

**Souvenir Sheet**

**486** A133 (f) 500fr multicolored 6.00 2.40

Winners, World Soccer Cup Championships 1962-1978.

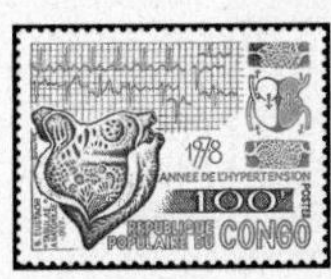


Heart and Charts — A142

**1978, Dec. 16** **Engr.** ***Perf. 13***

**487** A142 100fr multicolored 1.60 .50

Fight against hypertension.

Party Emblem and Road A143

**1978, Dec. 31** **Litho.** ***Perf. 12½x12***

**488** A143 60fr multicolored .75 .25

Congolese Labor Party, 9th anniversary.

Capt. Cook, Polynesians and House — A144

Capt. James Cook (1728-1779): 150fr, Island scene. 250fr, Polynesian longboats. 350fr, Capt. Cook's ships off Hawaii.

**1979, Jan. 16** ***Perf. 14½***

**489** A144 65fr multicolored .70 .25
**490** A144 150fr multicolored 1.75 .35
**491** A144 250fr multicolored 2.75 .60
**492** A144 350fr multicolored 3.50 1.00
*Nos. 489-492 (4)* 8.70 2.20

Pres. Marien Ngouabi — A145

**1979, Mar. 18** **Litho.** ***Perf. 12***

**493** A145 35fr multicolored .35 .25
**494** A145 60fr multicolored .50 .25

Assassination of President Ngouabi, 2nd anniv.

"1979," IYC Emblem, Child — A146

A146a

**1979, Apr. 30 Litho. *Perf. 12½x13***

**495** A146 45fr multicolored .45 .25
**496** A146 75fr multicolored .90 .35

**Souvenir Sheet**

***Perf. 14½***

**496A** A146a 250fr multicolored 2.75 1.00

International Year of the Child.
Issued: 45fr, 75fr, Apr. 30; 250fr, Sept. 5.

Pottery Vases and Solanum A147

Design: 150fr, Mail runner, Concorde, train, UPU emblem, envelope.

**1979, June 8 Litho. *Perf. 13***

**497** A147 60fr multicolored 1.75 .60

**Engr.**

**498** A147 150fr multicolored 3.50 1.25

Philexafrique II, Libreville, Gabon, June 8-17. Nos. 497, 498 each printed in sheets of 10 with 5 labels showing exhibition emblem.

Rowland Hill, Diesel Locomotive, Germany No. 78 — A148

Designs (Rowland Hill and): 100fr, Old steam locomotive and France No. B10. 200fr, Diesel locomotive and US No. 245. 300fr, Steam locomotive and England-Australia First Aerialpost vignette, 1919. 500fr, Electric train, Concorde and Middle Congo No. 75.

**1979, June 30 *Perf. 14***

**499** A148 65fr multicolored .60 .25
**500** A148 100fr multicolored 1.00 .25
**501** A148 200fr multicolored 2.25 .50
**502** A148 300fr multicolored 3.00 .75
*Nos. 499-502 (4)* 6.85 1.75

**Souvenir Sheet**

**503** A148 500fr multicolored 5.75 1.25

Sir Rowland Hill (1795-1879), originator of penny postage.

Salvador Allende, Flags, Demonstrators — A149

**1979, July 21 Litho. *Perf. 12½***

**504** A149 100fr multicolored 1.60 .50

Salvador Allende, president of Chile.

Old Man Telling Stories A150

**1979, July 28**

**505** A150 45fr multicolored .80 .25

Story telling as education.

Handball Players — A151

75fr, Players and ball. 250fr, Pres. Ngouabi, cup on map of Africa, player.

**1979, July 31 Litho. *Perf. 12½***

**Size: 40x30mm, 30x40mm**

**506** A151 45fr multi .60 .25
**507** A151 75fr multi, vert. 1.00 .25

**Size: 22x40mm**

***Perf. 12x12½***

**508** A151 250fr multicolored 2.75 1.00

Marien Ngouabi Handball Cup.

Map and Flag of Congo — A152

**1979, Aug. 15**

**509** A152 50fr multicolored .80 .25

16th anniversary of revolution.

Souvenir Sheet

Virgin and Child, by Dürer A153

**1979, Aug. 13 *Perf. 13½***

**510** A153 500fr red brn & lt grn 6.50 2.50

Albrecht Dürer (1471-1528), German engraver and painter.

Bach and Contemporary Instruments — A155

No. 512, Albert Einstein, astronauts on moon.

**1979, Sept. 10 *Perf. 13½***

**511** A155 200fr multicolored 2.25 .75
**512** A155 200fr multicolored 2.25 .75

Yoro Fishing Port — A156

**1979, Sept. 26 Litho. *Perf. 12½***

**513** A156 45fr shown .65 .25
**514** A156 75fr Port at night .95 .35

Mukukulu Dam A157

**1979, Oct. 5 *Perf. 12½x12***

**515** A157 20fr multicolored .60 .25
**516** A157 45fr multicolored 1.10 .30

Emblem, Control Tower, Jets — A158

**1979, Dec. 12 Litho. *Perf. 12½***

**517** A158 100fr multicolored 1.60 .50

ASECNA (Air Safety Board), 20th anniv.

Congolese Labor Party, 10th Anniversary A159

**1979, Dec. 31**

**518** A159 45fr multicolored .80 .25

Post Office, 15th Anniv. — A160

**1980, Mar. 30 Litho. *Perf. 12½***

**519** A160 45fr multicolored .60 .25
**520** A160 95fr multicolored 1.10 .30

Visit of Pope John Paul II — A161

**1980, May 5**

**521** A161 100fr multicolored 3.50 1.00

Rotary International, 75th Anniversary — A162

**1980, May 10 Litho. *Perf. 12½***

**522** A162 150fr multicolored 1.50 .50

Pointe Noire Foundry — A163

**1980, June 18 Litho. *Perf. 12½***

**523** A163 30fr shown .30 .25
**524** A163 35fr Different view .50 .25

Claude Chappe, Tower A164

**1980, June 21 Litho. *Perf. 12½***

**525** A164 200fr multicolored 2.50 1.00

Claude Chappe (1763-1805), French engineer.

Mossaka Harbor A165

**1980, June 23**

**532** A165 45fr shown .60 .25
**533** A165 90fr Different view 1.10 .25

Papilio Dardanus (Front and Back) — A167

15fr, Kalima aethiops. 20fr, Papilio demodocus. 60fr, Euphaedra. 90fr, Hypolimnas misippus.
300fr, Charaxes smaragdalis.

**1980, July 12 Litho. *Perf. 12½***

**534** A167 5fr shown .60 .30
*a.* Perf. 12½x13 1.60 1.60
**535** A167 15fr multicolored 1.40 .30
*a.* Perf. 12½x13 2.00 2.00
**536** A167 20fr multicolored 1.40 .40
*a.* Perf. 12½x13 2.40 2.40
**537** A167 60fr multicolored 3.25 .75
**538** A167 90fr multicolored 6.50 1.00
*Nos. 534-538 (5)* 13.15 2.75

**Souvenir Sheet**

**539** A167 300fr multicolored 12.00 17.00

July 31st Hospital A168

**1980, July 31**

**540** A168 45fr multicolored .80 .25

Human Rights Emblem, People — A169

500fr, Man breaking chain.

**1980, Aug. 2**

**541** A169 350fr shown 2.75 1.00
**542** A169 500fr multicolored 4.50 1.50

Human Rights Convention, 32nd anniv.

Citizens and Congolese Arms — A170

95fr, Dove on flag, fists, vert. 150fr, Dove holding Congolese arms.

**1980, Aug. 15 *Perf. 12½***

**543** A170 75fr shown .70 .30
**544** A170 95fr multicolored .90 .30
**545** A170 150fr multicolored 1.50 .60
*Nos. 543-545 (3)* 3.10 1.20

August 13-15th Revolution, 17th anniv.

Coffee and Cocoa Trees on Map of Congo — A171

Coffee and Cocoa Day: 95fr, Branches, map of Congo.

**1980, Aug. 18 *Perf. 13½x13***

**546** A171 45fr multicolored .60 .25
**547** A171 95fr multicolored 1.10 .40

Logging — A172

**1980, Aug. 28**

**548** A172 70fr shown .80 .30
**549** A172 75fr Wood transport .80 .30

Pres. Neto of Angola, 1st Death Anniv. — A173

**1980, Sept. 11**

**550** A173 100fr multicolored .90 .30

Lark — A174

Designs: Birds.

**1980, Sept. 17**

**551** A174 45fr multi, horiz. .90 .30
**552** A174 75fr multi, horiz. 1.10 .30
**553** A174 90fr multi, horiz. 1.40 .35
**554** A174 150fr multicolored 2.25 .50
**555** A174 200fr multicolored 3.00 1.00
**556** A174 250fr multicolored 3.50 1.25
*a* Souv. sheet of 6, #551-556 22.50 17.50
*Nos. 551-556 (6)* 12.15 3.70

World Tourism Conference, Manila, Sept. 27 — A175

**1980, Sept. 27 Litho. *Perf. 13½x13***

**557** A175 100fr multicolored 1.00 .35

First Day of School Term A176

**1980, Oct. 2 Photo. *Perf. 13***

**558** A176 50fr multicolored .70 .25

First House in Brazzaville A177

Brazzaville Centenary: 65fr, First native village. 75fr, Old Town Hall, 1912. 150fr, View from bank of Bacongo, 1912. 200fr, Meeting of explorer Savorgnan de Brazza and chief Makoko, 1880.

**1980, Oct. 3 Litho. *Perf. 12½***

**559** A177 45fr multicolored .50 .25
**560** A177 65fr multicolored .70 .30
**561** A177 75fr multicolored 1.00 .40
**562** A177 150fr multicolored 1.75 .65
**563** A177 200fr multicolored 2.25 1.00
*Nos. 559-563 (5)* 6.20 2.60

Boys on Bank of Congo River A178

**1980, Oct. 30**

**564** A178 80fr shown .85 .25
**565** A178 150fr Djoue Bridge 1.90 .40

Revolutionary Stadium and Athletes — A179

**1980, Nov. 20 *Perf. 13x12½***

**566** A179 60fr multicolored .80 .25

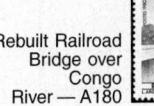

Rebuilt Railroad Bridge over Congo River — A180

**1980, Nov. 29 *Perf. 13x13½***

**567** A180 75fr multicolored .90 .30

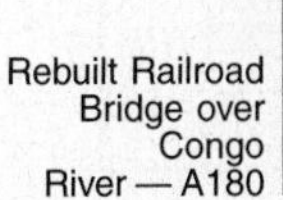

Mangoes, Loudima Fruit Packing Station — A181

**1980, Dec. 2 *Perf. 13***

**568** A181 10fr shown .25 .25
**569** A181 25fr Oranges .50 .25
**570** A181 40fr Citrons .60 .25
**571** A181 85fr Mandarins 1.10 .30
*Nos. 568-571 (4)* 2.45 1.05

African Postal Union, 5th Anniversary — A182

**1980, Dec. 24 *Perf. 13½***

**572** A182 100fr multicolored .90 .30

Moungouni Earth Satellite Station — A183

**1980, Dec. 30 *Perf. 12½***

**573** A183 75fr multicolored .80 .25

Hertzian Wave Communication, Brazzaville A184

**1980, Dec. 30 *Perf. 12½x12***

**574** A184 150fr multicolored 1.60 .40

1980 African Handball Champion Team A185

100fr, Receiving cup, vert.

***Perf. 12½x13, 13x12½***

**1981, Jan. 26 Litho.**

**575** A185 100fr multicolored 1.25 .35
**576** A185 150fr shown 1.50 .60

Pres. Denis Sassou-Nguesso A186

**1981, Feb. 5 Litho. *Perf. 12½***

**577** A186 45fr multicolored .45 .25
**578** A186 75fr multicolored .60 .25
**579** A186 100fr multicolored .90 .25
*Nos. 577-579 (3)* 1.95 .75

Luna 17, 1970. A187

Space Conquest: 150fr, Space shuttle in orbit. 200fr, Shuttle, space station. 300fr, Shuttle, landing field. 500fr, Shuttle lift-off.

**1981, May 4 Litho. *Perf. 14x13½***

**580** A187 100fr multicolored 1.00 .25
**581** A187 150fr multicolored 1.40 .40
**582** A187 200fr multicolored 2.00 .55
**583** A187 300fr multicolored 2.75 .80
*Nos. 580-583 (4)* 7.15 2.00

**Souvenir Sheet**

**584** A187 500fr multicolored 5.00 1.40

For overprint see No. 725.

Fight Against Apartheid — A188

**1981, May 5 Litho. *Perf. 12½***

**585** A188 100fr deep blue .90 .25

Twin Palm Tree of Louingui — A189

**1981, May 22 *Perf. 12x12½***

**586** A189 75fr multicolored 1.00 .25

13th World Telecommunications Day — A190

**1981, June 6 *Perf. 12½***

**587** A190 120fr multicolored 1.50 .50

Rubber Extraction — A191

**1981, June 27 *Perf. 13***

**588** A191 50fr shown .60 .25
**589** A191 70fr Sap draining .90 .30

Intl. Year of the Disabled — A192

**1981, June 29 Engr.**

**590** A192 45fr multicolored .60 .25

See No. B7.

Bird Trap A194

Designs: Animal traps. 10fr vert.

**1981, July**

**596** A194 5fr multicolored .90 .25
**597** A194 10fr multicolored .90 .25
**598** A194 15fr multicolored 1.40 .25
**599** A194 20fr multicolored 1.40 .25
**600** A194 30fr multicolored 2.00 .25
**601** A194 35fr multicolored 2.00 .30
*Nos. 596-601 (6)* 8.60 1.55

Mausoleum of King Maloango A195

150fr, Mausoleum, portrait.

**1981, July 4 Litho. *Perf. 12½***

**602** A195 75fr shown .70 .25
**603** A195 150fr multicolored 1.25 .40

Prince Charles and Lady Diana, Coach — A196

Royal wedding: Couple and coaches.

**1981, Sept. 1 Litho. *Perf. 14½***

**604** A196 100fr multicolored 1.00 .25
**605** A196 200fr multicolored 2.00 .55
**606** A196 300fr multicolored 3.25 .80
*Nos. 604-606 (3)* 6.25 1.60

**Souvenir Sheet**

**607** A196 400fr multicolored 4.00 1.10

World Food Day — A197

**1981, Oct. 16 Litho. *Perf. 13½x13***

**608** A197 150fr multicolored 1.75 .55

12th World UPU Day — A198

**1981, Oct. 24 Engr. *Perf. 13x12½***

**609** A198 90fr multicolored 1.00 .25

Royal Guard — A199

**1981, Oct. 31 Litho. *Perf. 12½x13***

**610** A199 45fr multicolored .90 .25

Eradication of Manioc Beetle — A200

**1981, Nov. 18 Litho. *Perf. 12½***

**611** A200 75fr multicolored 1.20 .25

Natl. Red Cross — A201

10fr, Bandaging patient. 35fr, Treating child. 60fr, Drawing well water.

**1981, Nov. 18 *Perf. 13***

**612** A201 10fr multicolored .30 .25
**613** A201 35fr multicolored .50 .25
**614** A201 60fr multicolored .80 .25
*Nos. 612-614 (3)* 1.60 .75

Giant Baobab ("Tree of Savorgnan de Brazza") — A202

**1981, Dec. 19 Litho. *Perf. 13***

**615** A202 45fr multicolored 1.00 .25
**616** A202 75fr multicolored 1.40 .30

Fetish Figure — A203

Designs: Various carved figures.

**1981, Dec. 19 *Perf. 12½***

**617** A203 15fr multicolored .30 .25
*a.* Perf. 12½x13 .30 .25
**618** A203 25fr multicolored .40 .25
*a.* Perf. 12½x13 .40 .25
**619** A203 45fr multicolored .50 .25
**620** A203 50fr multicolored .60 .25
*a.* Perf. 12½x13 .60 .35
**621** A203 60fr multicolored .70 .25
*Nos. 617-621 (5)* 2.50 1.25

Caves of Bangou — A204

**1981, Dec. 29 *Perf. 13x13½***

**622** A204 20fr multicolored .45 .25
**623** A204 25fr multicolored .45 .25

King Makoko and His Queen, Ivory Sculptures by R. Engongodzo A205

25fr, Woman, facing right, vert. 35fr, Woman, facing left, vert.

***Perf. 13½x13, 13x13½***

**1982, Feb. 27 Litho.**

**624** A205 25fr multicolored .35 .25
**625** A205 35fr multicolored .45 .25
**626** A205 100fr shown 1.00 .30
*Nos. 624-626 (3)* 1.80 .80

George Stephenson (1781-1848) and Inter City 125, Gt. Britain A206

Locomotives: 150fr, Sinkansen Bullet Train, Japan. 200fr, Advanced Passenger Train, Gt. Britain. 300fr, TGV-001, France.

**1982, Mar. 2 Litho. *Perf. 12½***

**627** A206 100fr multicolored 1.00 .25
**628** A206 150fr multicolored 1.60 .40
**629** A206 200fr multicolored 2.25 .55
**630** A206 300fr multicolored 3.25 .80
*Nos. 627-630 (4)* 8.10 2.00

Scouting Year — A207

100fr, Looking through binoculars. 150fr, Reading map. 200fr, Helping woman. 300fr, Crossing rope bridge. 500fr, Hiking, horiz.

**1982, Apr. 13 Litho. *Perf. 13***

**631** A207 100fr multicolored 1.25 .25
**632** A207 150fr multicolored 1.50 .40
**633** A207 200fr multicolored 2.25 .55
**634** A207 300fr multicolored 3.25 .80
*Nos. 631-634 (4)* 8.25 2.00

**Souvenir Sheet**

**635** A207 500fr multicolored 5.00 1.75

For overprint see No. 726.

Franklin Roosevelt A208

**1982, June 12 Litho. *Perf. 13***

**636** A208 150fr shown 1.75 .60
**637** A208 250fr Washington 2.75 .85
**638** A208 350fr Goethe 3.75 1.10
*Nos. 636-638 (3)* 8.25 2.55

21st Birthday of Princess Diana, July 1 A209

**1982, June 12 *Perf. 14***

**639** A209 200fr Candles 2.00 .55
**640** A209 300fr "21" 2.75 .80

**Souvenir Sheet**

**641** A209 500fr Diana 5.00 1.40

5-Year Plan, 1982-1986 A210

60fr, Road construction. 100fr, Communications, vert. 125fr, Operating room equipment, vert. 150fr, Hydroelectric power, vert.

***Perf. 13x12½, 12½x13***

**1982, June 19**

**642** A210 60fr multicolored .80 .25
**643** A210 100fr multicolored 1.25 .30
**644** A210 125fr multicolored 1.60 .35
**645** A210 150fr multicolored 1.75 .40
*Nos. 642-645 (4)* 5.40 1.30

ITU Plenipotentiary Conference, Nairobi — A211

**1982, June 26 *Perf. 13***

**646** A211 300fr multicolored 3.00 .90

**Nos. 604-607 Overprinted in Blue**

**1982, July 30 *Perf. 14½***

**647** A196 100fr multicolored .90 .30
**648** A196 200fr multicolored 1.75 .60
**649** A196 300fr multicolored 2.75 1.00
*Nos. 647-649 (3)* 5.40 1.90

**Souvenir Sheet**

**650** A196 400fr multicolored 3.50 2.50

Birth of Prince William of Wales, June 21.

Nutrition Campaign — A212

**1982, July 24 Litho. *Perf. 12½***

**651** A212 100fr multicolored 1.40 .25

WHO African Headquarters, Brazzaville — A213

**1982, July 24 Litho. *Perf. 12½***

**652** A213 125fr multicolored 1.60 .45

TB Bacillus Centenary A214

**1982, Aug. 7 *Perf. 12½x12***

**653** A214 250fr Koch, bacillus 3.25 1.10

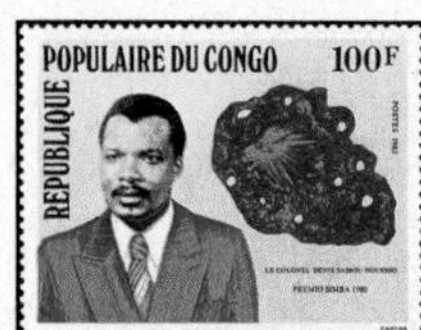

Pres. Sassou-Nguesso and 1980 Simba Prize — A215

**1982, Oct. 20 Litho. *Perf. 13***

**654** A215 100fr multicolored .90 .30

Turtles A216

Various turtles and tortoises.

**1982, Dec. 1**

**655** A216 30fr multicolored .90 .25
**656** A216 45fr multicolored 1.50 .30
**657** A216 55fr multicolored 1.60 .40
*Nos. 655-657 (3)* 4.00 .95

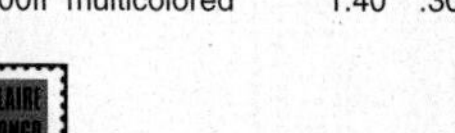

Boy Gathering Coconuts — A217

**1982, Dec. 11**

**658** A217 100fr multicolored 1.40 .30

Nest in Tree Trunk — A218

75fr, Nests in palm tree. 100fr, Woven nest on thorn branch.

**1982, Dec. 29 *Perf. 12½***

**659** A218 40fr shown 1.00 .25
**660** A218 75fr multicolored 1.60 .25
**661** A218 100fr multicolored 2.50 .40
*Nos. 659-661 (3)* 5.10 .90

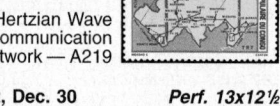

Hertzian Wave Communication Network — A219

**1982, Dec. 30 *Perf. 13x12½***

**662** A219 45fr multicolored .45 .25
**663** A219 60fr multicolored .50 .25
**664** A219 95fr multicolored .90 .30
*Nos. 662-664 (3)* 1.85 .80

30th Anniv. of Customs Cooperation Council — A220

**1983, Jan. 26 Litho. *Perf. 12½x13***

**665** A220 100fr Headquarters .90 .30

Mausoleum of Pres. Marien Ngouabi A221

**1983, Feb. 8 *Perf. 13***

**666** A221 60fr multicolored .50 .25
**667** A221 80fr multicolored .80 .25

Ironsmiths A222

**1983 *Perf. 12½***

**668** A222 45fr shown .80 .25
**669** A222 150fr Weaver, vert. 1.50 .50

Issue dates: 45fr, Mar. 5; 150fr, Feb. 24.

Carved Chess Pieces, by R. Engongonzo A223

Various pieces.

**1983, Feb. 26** *Perf. 13*

| | | | |
|---|---|---|---|
| **670** | A223 40fr multicolored | .40 | .25 |
| **671** | A223 60fr multicolored | 1.00 | .25 |
| **672** | A223 95fr multicolored | 2.00 | .50 |
| | *Nos. 670-672 (3)* | 3.40 | 1.00 |

Easter 1983 — A224

Raphael drawings: 200fr, Transfiguration study. 300fr, Deposition from Cross, horiz. 400fr, Christ in Glory.

**1983, Apr. 20** **Litho.** *Perf. 13*

| | | | |
|---|---|---|---|
| **673** | A224 200fr multicolored | 2.00 | .50 |
| **674** | A224 300fr multicolored | 3.25 | .65 |
| **675** | A224 400fr multicolored | 4.50 | .85 |
| | *Nos. 673-675 (3)* | 9.75 | 2.00 |

Seashells — A225

**1983** **Litho.** *Perf. 15x14*

| | | | |
|---|---|---|---|
| **675A** | A225 25fr multicolored | *150.00* | *65.00* |
| **676** | A225 35fr multicolored | 1.40 | .30 |
| **677** | A225 65fr multicolored | 1.75 | .35 |

Dated 1982.

A226

Various traditional combs.

**1983, May** *Perf. 14*

| | | | |
|---|---|---|---|
| **678** | A226 30fr multicolored | .35 | .25 |
| **679** | A226 70fr multicolored | .90 | .25 |
| **680** | A226 85fr multicolored | 1.00 | .25 |
| | *Nos. 678-680 (3)* | 2.25 | .75 |

A227

**Litho & Engr.**

**1983, Aug. 10** *Perf. 12½x13*

| | | | |
|---|---|---|---|
| **681** | A227 60fr multicolored | .65 | .25 |
| **682** | A227 100fr multicolored | .95 | .30 |

20th anniv. of revolution.

Centenary of the Arrival of Christian Missionaries A228

Churches and Clergymen: 150fr, A. Carrie, Church of the Sacred Heart, Loango, vert. 250fr, Msgr. Augouard; St. Louis, Liranga; St. Joseph, Linzolo.

**1983, Aug. 23** *Perf. 12½*

| | | | |
|---|---|---|---|
| **683** | A228 150fr multicolored | 1.60 | .40 |
| **684** | A228 250fr multicolored | 2.75 | .70 |

Local Flowers A229

5fr, Liana thunderaie, vert. 15fr, Bougainvillea. 20fr, Anthurium, vert. 45fr, Allamanda. 75fr, Hibiscus, vert.

**1984, Jan. 20** **Litho.** *Perf. 12½*

| | | | |
|---|---|---|---|
| **685** | A229 5fr multicolored | .25 | .25 |
| **686** | A229 15fr multicolored | .35 | .25 |
| **687** | A229 20fr multicolored | .50 | .25 |
| **688** | A229 45fr multicolored | 1.00 | .25 |
| **689** | A229 75fr multicolored | 1.40 | .30 |
| | *Nos. 685-689 (5)* | 3.50 | 1.30 |

35th Anniv. of World Peace Council — A230

**1984, Mar. 31** **Litho.** *Perf. 13x12½*

| | | | |
|---|---|---|---|
| **690** | A230 50fr multicolored | .45 | .25 |
| **691** | A230 100fr multicolored | .90 | .30 |

Anti-Nuclear Arms Campaign — A231

**1984, May 31** **Litho.** *Perf. 12x12½*

| | | | |
|---|---|---|---|
| **692** | A231 200fr Explosion, victims | 2.00 | .50 |

Agriculture Day — A232

10fr, Rice. 15fr, Pineapples. 60fr, Manioc, vert. 100fr, Palm tree, map, vert.

*Perf. 13x13½, 13½x13*

**1984, June 30** **Litho.**

| | | | |
|---|---|---|---|
| **693** | A232 10fr multicolored | .25 | .25 |
| **694** | A232 15fr multicolored | .25 | .25 |
| **695** | A232 60fr multicolored | .60 | .25 |
| **696** | A232 100fr multicolored | 1.10 | .35 |
| | *Nos. 693-696 (4)* | 2.20 | 1.10 |

Congress Palace A233

**1984, July 27** *Perf. 13*

| | | | |
|---|---|---|---|
| **697** | A233 60fr multicolored | .60 | .25 |
| **698** | A233 100fr multicolored | 1.00 | .30 |

Chinese-Congolese cooperation.

CFCO-Congo Railways, 50th Anniv. — A234

10fr, Loulombo Station. 25fr, Les Bandas Chinese Labor Camp. 125fr, "50". 200fr, Administration building.

**1984, July 30** *Perf. 13½*

| | | | |
|---|---|---|---|
| **699** | A234 10fr multicolored | .35 | .25 |
| **700** | A234 25fr multicolored | .60 | .25 |
| **701** | A234 125fr multicolored | 2.75 | .70 |
| **702** | A234 200fr multicolored | 6.25 | 1.00 |
| | *Nos. 699-702 (4)* | 9.95 | 2.20 |

Locomotives A235

Ships on the Congo River A236

No. 703, CC 203. No. 704, Tugboat. No. 705, BB 103. No. 706, Pusher tugboat. No. 707, BB-BB 301. No. 708, Dredger. No. 709, BB 420 L'Eclair. No. 710, Cargo ship.

**1984, Aug. 24** *Perf. 12½*

| | | | |
|---|---|---|---|
| **703** | A235 100fr multi | 1.10 | .35 |
| **704** | A236 100fr multi | 1.10 | .35 |
| **705** | A235 150fr multi | 1.60 | .50 |
| **706** | A236 150fr multi | 1.60 | .50 |
| **707** | A235 300fr multi | 3.25 | 1.10 |
| **708** | A236 300fr multi | 3.25 | 1.10 |
| **709** | A235 500fr multi | 5.25 | 1.75 |
| **710** | A236 500fr multi | 5.25 | 1.75 |
| | *Nos. 703-710 (8)* | 22.40 | 7.40 |

World Fisheries Year — A237

5fr, Basket of fish. 20fr, Net fishermen in boat. 25fr, School of fish. 40fr, Net fisherman. 55fr, Trawler

**1984, Oct. 16** *Perf. 13½*

| | | | |
|---|---|---|---|
| **711** | A237 5fr multicolored | .50 | .25 |
| **712** | A237 20fr multicolored | .80 | .25 |
| **713** | A237 25fr multicolored | .80 | .25 |
| **714** | A237 40fr multicolored | 1.25 | .30 |
| **715** | A237 55fr multicolored | 2.25 | .35 |
| | *Nos. 711-715 (5)* | 5.60 | 1.40 |

Anti-polio Campaign — A238

250fr, Disabled men, hand. 300fr, Target, disabled women, horiz.

**1984, Oct. 30**

| | | | |
|---|---|---|---|
| **716** | A238 250fr multicolored | 2.75 | .90 |
| **717** | A238 300fr multicolored | 3.25 | 1.00 |

M'Bamou Palace Hotel, Brazzaville — A239

**1984, Dec. 15** *Perf. 14½*

| | | | |
|---|---|---|---|
| **718** | A239 60fr multicolored | .50 | .25 |
| **719** | A239 100fr multicolored | 1.00 | .30 |

Fauna — A240

**1984, Dec.** *Perf. 15x14½*

| | | | |
|---|---|---|---|
| **720** | A240 30fr Pangolin | 5.00 | .75 |
| **721** | A240 70fr Bat | 6.25 | 1.50 |
| **722** | A240 85fr Civet cat | 8.00 | 2.00 |
| | *Nos. 720-722 (3)* | 19.25 | 4.25 |

Stamps are dated "1983".

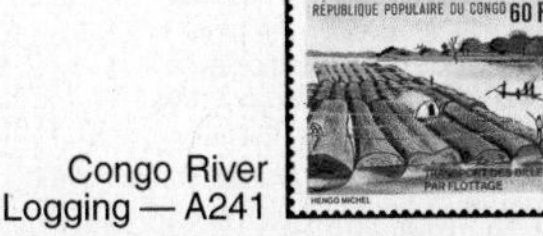


Congo River Logging — A241

60fr, Log raft, crew hut. 100fr, Tugboat pushing logs.

**1984, Dec.** *Perf. 13½x13*

| | | | |
|---|---|---|---|
| **723** | A241 60fr multicolored | .60 | .25 |
| **724** | A241 100fr multicolored | 1.25 | .35 |

**Nos. 584, 635 Ovptd. in Black or Green**

Souvenir Sheets

TSUKUBA EXPO '85

ITALIA '85 emblem, ROME

**1985, Mar. 8** *Perf. 14x13½, 13*

| | | | |
|---|---|---|---|
| **725** | A187 500fr multi | 5.75 | 4.50 |
| **726** | A207 500fr multi | 5.75 | 4.50 |

See Nos. C336-C337.

Zonocerus Variegatus — A242

**1985, Mar. 15** *Perf. 13*

| | | | |
|---|---|---|---|
| **727** | A242 125fr multicolored | 1.75 | .35 |

Burial of a Teke Chief A243

**1985, Apr. 30** *Perf. 12½*

| | | | |
|---|---|---|---|
| **728** | A243 225fr multicolored | 2.25 | .75 |

Edible Fruit — A244

5fr, Trichoscypha acuminata, vert. 10fr, Aframomum africanum. 125fr, Gambeya lacuurtiana. 150fr, Landolphia jumelei.

***Perf. 13½, 13 (#732A), 13½x13¼ (#732B)***

**1985, June 15**

| | | | |
|---|---|---|---|
| **729** | A244 5fr multicolored | .25 | .25 |
| **730** | A244 10fr multicolored | .25 | .25 |
| **730A** | A244 90fr like #730 | | |
| **731** | A244 125fr multicolored | 1.40 | .40 |
| **732** | A244 150fr multicolored | 1.75 | .55 |
| **732A** | A244 205fr like #731 | | |
| **732B** | A244 300fr Like #732 | — | — |

Sizes: No. 729, 22x36mm, Nos. 731, 732A, 36x22mm.

Nos. 730A, 732A, 732B inscribed "Congo" only.

For overprints, see Nos. 1155, 1170, 1183-1185.

Compare type A244 with type A352.

Lions Club Intl., 30th Anniv. — A245

250fr, Flag, District 403B.

**1985, June 25** *Perf. 12½*

**733** A245 250fr multicolored 2.75 .70

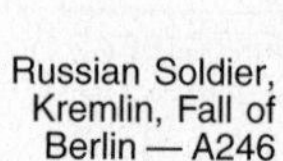

Russian Soldier, Kremlin, Fall of Berlin — A246

**1985, July 27** *Perf. 12*

**734** A246 60fr multicolored .80 .25

Defeat of Nazi Germany, end of World War II, 40th anniv.

Lady Olave Baden-Powell, Girl Guides Founder — A247

Anniversaries and events: 150fr, Girl Guides, 75th anniv. 250fr, Jacob Grimm, fabulist; Sleeping Beauty. 350fr, Johann Sebastian Bach, composer; European Music Year, St. Thomas Church organ, Leipzig. 450fr, Queen Mother, 85th birthday, vert. 500fr, Statue of Liberty, cent., vert.

**1985, Aug. 26** *Perf. 13*

**735** A247 150fr multicolored 1.60 .50
**736** A247 250fr multicolored 2.25 .90
**737** A247 350fr multicolored 3.00 1.25
**738** A247 450fr multicolored 3.75 1.60
**739** A247 500fr multicolored 5.00 2.00
*Nos. 735-739 (5)* 15.60 6.25

PHILEXAFRICA '85, Lome, Togo, Nov. 16-24 — A248

No. 741, Airport, postal van.

**1985, Oct. 10** *Perf. 13x12½*

**740** A248 250fr shown 2.75 1.00
**741** A248 250fr multicolored 2.75 1.00
*a.* Pair, #740-741 + label 6.50 6.50

Mushrooms A249

100fr, Coprinus, vert. 150fr, Cortinarius. 200fr, Armillariella mellea. 300fr, Dictyophora. 400fr, Crucibulum vulgare.

**1985, Dec. 14** **Litho.** *Perf. 13*

**742** A249 100fr multicolored 1.25 .35
**743** A249 150fr multicolored 2.00 .50
**744** A249 200fr multicolored 2.75 .85
**745** A249 300fr multicolored 3.50 1.25
**746** A249 400fr multicolored 5.50 1.50
*Nos. 742-746 (5)* 15.00 4.45

Arbor Day — A250

60fr, Planting sapling. 200fr, Map, lifecycle diagram.

**1986, Mar. 6** *Perf. 13½*

**747** A250 60fr multicolored .45 .25
**748** A250 200fr multicolored 1.90 .90

Children's Hoop Races — A251

**1986, Apr. 30** *Perf. 12½*

**749** A251 5fr Two boys .35 .25
**750** A251 10fr One boy .35 .25
**751** A251 60fr Three boys, horiz. .90 .25
*a.* Souvenir sheet of 3, #749-751 2.00 1.75
*Nos. 749-751 (3)* 1.60 .75

Intl. Environment Day — A252

60fr, Garbage disposal. 125fr, Dumping garbage.

**1986, June 5** **Litho.** *Perf. 13½*

**752** A252 60fr multicolored .70 .25
**753** A252 125fr multicolored 1.30 .45

A253

Traditional Modes of Transporting Goods: 5fr, Basket on head, child in sling carrier. 10fr, Child in carrier on hip, large basket strapped to forehead. 60fr, Man carrying load on shoulder.

**1986, July 15** **Litho.** *Perf. 13x12½*

**754** A253 5fr multicolored .30 .25
**755** A253 10fr multicolored .30 .25
**756** A253 60fr multicolored .80 .40
*Nos. 754-756 (3)* 1.40 .90

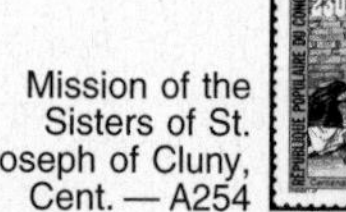

Mission of the Sisters of St. Joseph of Cluny, Cent. — A254

**1986, Aug. 19** **Litho.** *Perf. 12½x13*

**757** A254 230fr multicolored 2.75 1.25

A255

**1986, Aug. 30** **Litho.** *Perf. 13½*

**758** A255 40fr multicolored .45 .25
**759** A255 60fr multicolored .55 .25
**760** A255 100fr multicolored 1.00 .35
*Nos. 758-760 (3)* 2.00 .85

UNESCO intl. communications development program.

Intl. Peace Year — A256

**1986, Sept. 15** **Litho.** *Perf. 13½*

**761** A256 100fr multicolored 1.00 .30

World Food Day — A257

75fr, Food staples. 120fr, Mother feeding child.

**1986, Oct. 16**

**762** A257 75fr multicolored .80 .25
**763** A257 120fr multicolored 1.25 .40

UN Child Survival Campaign A258

Mothers, children and pinwheels in various designs.

**1986, Oct. 27**

**764** A258 15fr multi, vert. .25 .25
**765** A258 30fr multicolored .25 .25
**766** A258 70fr multi, vert. .70 .30
*Nos. 764-766 (3)* 1.20 .80

A258a

**1986, Dec. 5** **Litho.** *Perf. 12x12½*

**766A** A258a 100fr multicolored 1.50 .35

27th Soviet Communist Party congress.

A259

**1987, Feb. 10** **Litho.** *Perf. 13½*

**767** A259 30fr multicolored .25 .25
**768** A259 45fr multicolored .45 .25
**769** A259 75fr multicolored .70 .25
**770** A259 120fr multicolored 1.10 .35
*Nos. 767-770 (4)* 2.50 1.10

Election of President Sassou-Nguesso, head of the Organization of African States.

Traditional Wedding — A260

**1987, Feb. 18** **Litho.** *Perf. 12½x13*

**771** A260 5fr multicolored .25 .25
**772** A260 15fr multicolored .25 .25
**773** A260 20fr multicolored .25 .25
*Nos. 771-773 (3)* .75 .75

The Blue Lake A261

**1987, July 16** *Perf. 12½*

**774** A261 5fr multicolored .25 .25
**775** A261 15fr multicolored .25 .25
**776** A261 75fr multicolored 1.00 .30
**777** A261 120fr multicolored 1.25 .40
*Nos. 774-777 (4)* 2.75 1.20

Pres. Marien Ngouabi — A262

**1987, July 16** *Perf. 13*

**778** A262 75fr multicolored .75 .30
**779** A262 120fr multicolored 1.25 .40

Tenth death anniv.

Congress of African Scientists — A263

**1987, Sept. 10** *Perf. 13x12½*

**780** A263 15fr multicolored .25 .25
**781** A263 90fr multicolored .70 .30
**782** A263 230fr multicolored 2.00 .80
*Nos. 780-782 (3)* 2.95 1.35

4th African Games, Nairobi A264

**1987, Oct. 30** *Perf. 12½*

**783** A264 75fr multicolored .75 .40
**784** A264 120fr multicolored 1.25 .60

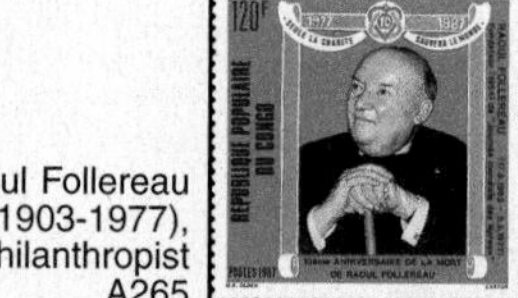

Raoul Follereau (1903-1977), Philanthropist A265

**1987, Oct. 20** *Perf. 13½*

**785** A265 120fr multicolored 1.50 .60

Cure leprosy.

FAO, 40th Anniv. A266

**1987, Nov. 17** *Perf. 12½*

**786** A266 300fr multicolored 2.75 1.10

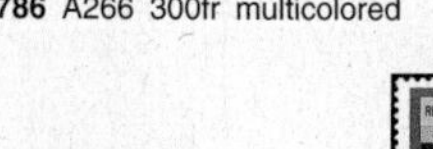

Anti-Apartheid Campaign A267

Nelson Mandela A268

*Perf. 13½x15, 14½x15*

**1987, Sept. 21** **Litho.**

**787** A267 60fr multicolored .60 .25
**788** A268 240fr multicolored 2.40 .75

Natl. UNICEF Vaccination Campaign — A269

30fr, Inoculating adults, horiz. 500fr, Inoculating children, horiz.

***Perf. 13½x14½, 14½x13½***

**1987, Sept. 28**

| | | | | |
|---|---|---|---|---|
| **789** | A269 | 30fr multicolored | .25 | .25 |
| **790** | A269 | 45fr shown | .50 | .25 |
| **791** | A269 | 500fr multicolored | 5.25 | 2.00 |
| | | *Nos. 789-791 (3)* | 6.00 | 2.50 |

No. 791 is airmail.

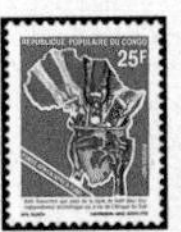

Africa Fund — A270

**1987, Sept. 28** ***Perf. 13½x15***

| | | | | |
|---|---|---|---|---|
| **792** | A270 | 25fr multicolored | .30 | .25 |
| **793** | A270 | 50fr multicolored | .65 | .25 |
| **794** | A270 | 70fr multicolored | .80 | .25 |
| | | *Nos. 792-794 (3)* | 1.75 | .75 |

Self-sufficiency in Food Production by the Year 2000 — A271

**1987, Nov. 20 Litho.** ***Perf. 13½***

| | | | | |
|---|---|---|---|---|
| **795** | A271 | 20fr multicolored | .30 | .25 |
| **796** | A271 | 55fr multicolored | .65 | .25 |
| **797** | A271 | 100fr multicolored | 1.20 | .35 |
| | | *Nos. 795-797 (3)* | 2.15 | .85 |

Simon Kimbangu (b. 1887), Founder of the Church of Christ on Earth A272

75fr, Kimbangu, vert. 120fr, Kimbangu, parrot, vert. 240fr, Kimbanguist Church, Nkamba.

**1987, Nov. 28** ***Perf. 12½***

| | | | | |
|---|---|---|---|---|
| **798** | A272 | 75fr multicolored | .70 | .30 |
| **799** | A272 | 120fr multicolored | 1.10 | .40 |
| **800** | A272 | 240fr multicolored | 2.75 | 1.00 |
| *a.* | | Souvenir sheet of 3, #798-800 | 5.75 | 5.00 |
| | | *Nos. 798-800 (3)* | 4.55 | 1.70 |

October Revolution, Russia, 70th Anniv. — A273

Lenin inspecting revolutionary troops, Red Square, from an unspecified painting.

**1988, Feb. 19 Litho.** ***Perf. 12½x12***

| | | | | |
|---|---|---|---|---|
| **801** | A273 | 75fr multicolored | 2.10 | .60 |
| **802** | A273 | 120fr multicolored | 3.00 | 1.00 |

African Writers Opposing Apartheid — A274

**1988, Apr. 6 Litho.** ***Perf. 13½***

| | | | | |
|---|---|---|---|---|
| **803** | A274 | 15fr multicolored | .30 | .25 |
| **804** | A274 | 60fr multicolored | .55 | .25 |
| **805** | A274 | 75fr multicolored | .90 | .30 |
| | | *Nos. 803-805 (3)* | 1.75 | .80 |

For overprint see No. 1157.

Intl. Fund for Agricultural Development (IFAD), 10th Anniv. — A275

**1988, Apr. 30**

| | | | | |
|---|---|---|---|---|
| **806** | A275 | 240fr multicolored | 2.25 | .85 |

Invention of the Telegraph by Samuel Morse, 150th Anniv. (in 1987) A276

**1988, Apr. 28**

| | | | | |
|---|---|---|---|---|
| **807** | A276 | 90fr Morse, vert. | .90 | .30 |
| **808** | A276 | 120fr shown | 1.10 | .40 |

A277

5fr, Eucalyptus trees, Brazzaville. 10fr, Stop cutting down trees.

**1988, Sept. 20 Litho.** ***Perf. 13½***

| | | | | |
|---|---|---|---|---|
| **809** | A277 | 5fr multicolored | .40 | .25 |
| **810** | A277 | 10fr multicolored | .60 | .25 |

Fight against desertification.

A278

Campaigns: No. 812, Return to the Land Campaign (farming). 120fr, Self-sufficiency in food production.

**1988, Aug. 12 Litho.** ***Perf. 13½***

| | | | | |
|---|---|---|---|---|
| **811** | A278 | 75fr shown | .80 | .30 |
| **812** | A278 | 75fr multicolored | .80 | .30 |
| **813** | A278 | 120fr multicolored | .95 | .40 |
| | | *Nos. 811-813 (3)* | 2.55 | 1.00 |

Congo Revolution, 25th anniv.

Yoro Fishing Village — A279

**1988, Sept. 1**

| | | | | |
|---|---|---|---|---|
| **814** | A279 | 35fr shown | .45 | .25 |
| **815** | A279 | 40fr Liberty Place | .45 | .25 |

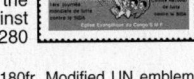

Intl. Day for the Fight Against AIDS — A280

75fr, Emblem. 180fr, Modified UN emblem, campaign emblem.

**1988, Dec. 1 Litho.** ***Perf. 13½***

| | | | | |
|---|---|---|---|---|
| **816** | A280 | 60fr shown | .45 | .25 |
| **817** | A280 | 75fr multicolored | .70 | .25 |
| **818** | A280 | 180fr multicolored | 1.75 | .60 |
| | | *Nos. 816-818 (3)* | 2.90 | 1.10 |

Natl. Committee for the Fight Against AIDS and Evangelical Anglican Church of Congo anti-AIDS campaign.

February 5 Movement, 10th Anniv. — A281

75fr, Rally. 120fr, Pres. Sassou-Nguesso, natl. achievements.

**1989, Apr. 21 Litho.** ***Perf. 13½***

| | | | | |
|---|---|---|---|---|
| **819** | A281 | 75fr multicolored | .75 | .30 |
| **820** | A281 | 120fr multicolored | 1.00 | .40 |

UN Declaration of Human Rights, 40th Anniv. (in 1988) — A282

**1989, May 19** ***Perf. 13***

| | | | | |
|---|---|---|---|---|
| **821** | A282 | 120fr multicolored | .90 | .40 |
| **822** | A282 | 350fr multicolored | 2.75 | 1.20 |

Marien Nguabi, Founder of Congo Labor Party — A282a

**1989, July 31 Litho.** ***Perf. 12½x13***

| | | | | |
|---|---|---|---|---|
| **822A** | A282a | 240fr red & yellow | 2.25 | .75 |

Red Cross and Red Crescent Societies, 125th Annivs. — A283

120fr, Dunant, emblem, Congo Red Cross.

**1989, Sept. 19 Litho.** ***Perf. 13***

| | | | | |
|---|---|---|---|---|
| **823** | A283 | 75fr shown | 1.20 | .40 |
| **824** | A283 | 120fr multicolored | 1.40 | .65 |

No. 824 is airmail.

Organization of African Unity, 25th Anniv. — A284

**1989, Oct. 19 Litho.** ***Perf. 12½***

| | | | | |
|---|---|---|---|---|
| **825** | A284 | 120fr multicolored | 1.10 | .40 |

African Development Bank, 25th Anniv. — A285

**1989, Dec. 22 Litho.** ***Perf. 12½x13***

| | | | | |
|---|---|---|---|---|
| **826** | A285 | 75fr multicolored | .80 | .35 |
| **827** | A285 | 120fr multicolored | 1.10 | .40 |

WHO, 40th Anniv. (in 1988) — A286

75fr, Blood donation, vert.

**1989, Dec. 28 Litho.** ***Perf. 12½***

| | | | | |
|---|---|---|---|---|
| **828** | A286 | 60fr shown | .75 | .35 |
| **829** | A286 | 75fr multicolored | .90 | .50 |

See Nos. 846-847 for overprints.

Congo Labor Party (PCT), 20th Anniv. — A287

**1989, Dec. 22 Litho.** ***Perf. 13x12½***

| | | | | |
|---|---|---|---|---|
| **830** | A287 | 75fr multicolored | .75 | .35 |
| **831** | A287 | 120fr multicolored | 1.10 | .40 |

Cacti — A288

35fr, Opuntia phaeacantha discata. 40fr, Opuntia ficus indica. 60fr, Opuntia erinacea. 75fr, Opuntia rufida. 120fr, Opuntia leptocaulis.
220fr, Opuntia compresa.

***Perf. 12½x13, 13x12½***

**1989, Nov. 22**

| | | | | |
|---|---|---|---|---|
| **832** | A288 | 35fr multicolored | .40 | .25 |
| **833** | A288 | 40fr multicolored | .55 | .25 |
| **834** | A288 | 60fr multicolored | 1.00 | .25 |
| **835** | A288 | 75fr multicolored | 1.40 | .30 |
| **836** | A288 | 120fr multicolored | 1.90 | .45 |
| | | *Nos. 832-836 (5)* | 5.25 | 1.50 |

**Souvenir Sheet**

***Perf. 12½***

| | | | | |
|---|---|---|---|---|
| **837** | A288 | 220fr multicolored | 5.00 | 2.10 |

Nos. 832-833, 835 and 837 vert. No. 837 contains one 32x40mm stamp.

1992 Winter Olympics, Albertville — A289

**1989, Dec. 22** ***Perf. 12½***

| | | | | |
|---|---|---|---|---|
| **838** | A289 | 75fr Ice dancing | .60 | .25 |
| **839** | A289 | 80fr Nordic skiing | .60 | .30 |
| **840** | A289 | 100fr Speed skating | .90 | .35 |
| **841** | A289 | 120fr Luge | 1.10 | .45 |
| **842** | A289 | 200fr Alpine skiing | 1.75 | .70 |
| **843** | A289 | 240fr Ice hockey | 2.25 | .85 |
| **844** | A289 | 400fr Ski jumping | 3.25 | 1.40 |
| | | *Nos. 838-844 (7)* | 10.45 | 4.30 |

**Souvenir Sheet**

***Perf. 13***

| | | | | |
|---|---|---|---|---|
| **845** | A289 | 500fr Bobsled | 4.50 | 2.40 |

No. 845 contains one 32x40mm stamp.

**Nos. 828-829 Ovptd. in 3 or 5 Lines**

**1989, Dec. 28** *Perf. 12½*

| | | | | |
|---|---|---|---|---|
| **846** | A286 | 60fr multicolored | .80 | .45 |
| **847** | A286 | 75fr multicolored | .95 | .60 |

Health care for everyone.

Intl. Literacy Year — A290

**1990, June 26** **Litho.** *Perf. 13½*

| | | | | |
|---|---|---|---|---|
| **848** | A290 | 75fr bl, blk & yel | .90 | .35 |

Birds — A291

Designs: 25fr, Tourterelle des bois. 50fr, Fauvette pitchou, vert. 70fr, Faucon crecerelle, vert. 150fr, Perroquet gris, vert.

**1990, July 10**

| | | | | |
|---|---|---|---|---|
| **849** | A291 | 25fr multicolored | .40 | .25 |
| **850** | A291 | 50fr multicolored | .75 | .30 |
| **851** | A291 | 70fr multicolored | 1.25 | .55 |
| **852** | A291 | 150fr multicolored | 2.50 | 1.25 |
| | | *Nos. 849-852 (4)* | 4.90 | 2.35 |

Dance Masks — A292

**1990, July 24** *Perf. 13*

| | | | | |
|---|---|---|---|---|
| **853** | A292 | 120fr Mondo | 1.10 | .40 |
| **854** | A292 | 360fr Bapunu | 3.50 | 1.25 |
| **855** | A292 | 400fr Kwele | 4.00 | 1.50 |
| | | *Nos. 853-855 (3)* | 8.60 | 3.15 |

For overprints see Nos. 1172, 1173.

Flowering Plants — A293

30fr, Tournesol (sunflower). 45fr, Cassia alata, horiz. 75fr, Oeillette (opium poppy). 90fr, Acalypha sanderil.

**1990, Sept. 15** **Litho.** *Perf. 12½*

| | | | | |
|---|---|---|---|---|
| **856** | A293 | 30fr multicolored | .30 | .25 |
| **857** | A293 | 45fr multicolored | .50 | .25 |
| **858** | A293 | 75fr multicolored | .75 | .25 |
| **859** | A293 | 90fr multicolored | 1.10 | .35 |
| | | *Nos. 856-859 (4)* | 2.65 | 1.10 |

1992 Summer Olympics, Barcelona A294

100fr, Street scene, vert. 200fr, Sailing, diff. 240fr, Marketplace. 350fr, Harbor. 500fr, Monument, vert.
750fr, Cathedral, vert.

**1990, June 28** **Litho.** *Perf. 13½*

| | | | | |
|---|---|---|---|---|
| **860** | A294 | 100fr multicolored | .70 | .30 |
| **861** | A294 | 150fr shown | .95 | .35 |
| **862** | A294 | 200fr multicolored | 1.20 | .40 |
| **863** | A294 | 240fr multicolored | 1.50 | .55 |
| **864** | A294 | 350fr multicolored | 2.40 | .75 |
| **865** | A294 | 500fr multicolored | 3.25 | .90 |
| | | *Nos. 860-865 (6)* | 10.00 | 3.25 |

**Souvenir Sheet**

| | | | | |
|---|---|---|---|---|
| **866** | A294 | 750fr multicolored | 5.50 | 3.50 |

Nos. 864-865 airmail. Nos. 860-865 exist in miniature sheets of 1.

Royal Necklaces A295

**1990, Aug. 18** **Litho.** *Perf. 13½*

| | | | | |
|---|---|---|---|---|
| **867** | A295 | 75fr shown | .75 | .35 |
| **868** | A295 | 100fr Necklace, diff. | 1.00 | .60 |

Boy Scouts Observing Nature — A296

Scout: 35fr, Photographing butterfly, Euphaedra eusimoides. 40fr, Picking mushrooms, Armillaria mellea. 75fr, Drawing butterfly, Palla decius. 80fr, Using magnifying glass, Kallima ansorgei. 500fr, Using microscope, Cortinarius speciocissimus. 600fr, Feeding butterfly, Graphium illyris. No. 874B, Photographing butterfly, Berberia plistonax, horiz. 750fr, Photographing mushrooms, Volvariella bombycina. No. 875A, Examining mushrooms, Coprinus domesticus.

**1991, June 8** **Litho.** *Perf. 13½*

| | | | | |
|---|---|---|---|---|
| **869** | A296 | 35fr multicolored | .50 | .25 |
| **870** | A296 | 40fr multicolored | .60 | .25 |
| **871** | A296 | 75fr multicolored | .80 | .25 |
| **872** | A296 | 80fr multicolored | 1.00 | .25 |
| **873** | A296 | 500fr multicolored | 4.50 | 1.25 |
| **874** | A296 | 600fr multicolored | 4.50 | 1.25 |
| *a.* | | Min. sheet of 4, #869, 871-872, 874 | 8.50 | 3.75 |
| | | *Nos. 869-874 (6)* | 11.90 | 3.50 |

**Litho. & Embossed**

| | | | | |
|---|---|---|---|---|
| **874B** | A296 | 1500fr gold & multi | *32.50* | — |

**Souvenir Sheets**

**Litho.**

| | | | | |
|---|---|---|---|---|
| **875** | A296 | 750fr multicolored | 5.25 | 2.25 |

**Litho. & Embossed**

| | | | | |
|---|---|---|---|---|
| **875A** | A296 | 1500fr gold & multi | 14.00 | — |

Nos. 869-874 exist in souvenir sheets of 1. Nos. 873-875 are airmail.

Medicinal Plants — A297

Designs: 15fr, Ocimum viride. 20fr, Kalanchoe pinnata, vert. 30fr, Euphorbia hirta. 60fr, Catharanthus roseus, vert. 75fr, Bidens pilosa, vert. 100fr, Brillantaisia patula, vert. 120fr, Cassia occidentalis, vert.

**1991, Jan. 30** **Litho.** *Perf. 11½*

| | | | | |
|---|---|---|---|---|
| **876** | A297 | 15fr multicolored | .30 | .25 |
| **877** | A297 | 20fr multicolored | .30 | .25 |
| **878** | A297 | 30fr multicolored | .30 | .25 |
| **879** | A297 | 60fr multicolored | .60 | .25 |
| **880** | A297 | 75fr multicolored | .80 | .35 |
| **881** | A297 | 100fr multicolored | 1.20 | .55 |
| **882** | A297 | 120fr multicolored | 1.25 | .75 |
| | | *Nos. 876-882 (7)* | 4.75 | 2.65 |

Mushrooms — A298

30fr, Amanita rubescens. 45fr, Catathelasma imperiale. 75fr, Amanita caesarea. 90fr, Boletus regius. 120fr, Pluteus cervinus. 150fr, Boletus chrysenteron. 200fr, Agaricus arvensis.
350fr, Boletus versipellis, horiz.

**1991, Mar. 25** **Litho.** *Perf. 13*

| | | | | |
|---|---|---|---|---|
| **883** | A298 | 30fr multi | .35 | .25 |
| **883A** | A298 | 45fr multi | .50 | .25 |
| **883B** | A298 | 75fr multi | .90 | .25 |
| **883C** | A298 | 90fr multi | 1.10 | .25 |
| **883D** | A298 | 120fr multi | 1.35 | .40 |
| **883E** | A298 | 150fr multi | 1.75 | .60 |
| **883F** | A298 | 200fr multi | 2.50 | .75 |
| | | *Nos. 883-883F (7)* | 8.45 | 2.75 |

**Souvenir Sheet**

*Perf. 12½*

| | | | | |
|---|---|---|---|---|
| **883G** | A298 | 350fr multi | 8.00 | 3.00 |

No. 883G contains one 40x32mm stamp.

Trains — A298a

Designs: 60fr, Dr-16, Finland. 75fr, TGV, France. 120fr, S350, Italy. 200fr, DE24000, Turkey. 250fr, DE1024, Germany
350fr, ETR450, Italy.

**1991, Apr. 10** **Litho.** *Perf. 12½x12¼*

| | | | | |
|---|---|---|---|---|
| **883H** | A298a | 60fr multi | .65 | .25 |
| **883I** | A298a | 75fr multi | .70 | .30 |
| **883J** | A298a | 120fr multi | 1.25 | .45 |
| **883K** | A298a | 200fr multi | 2.25 | .75 |
| **883L** | A298a | 250fr multi | 3.25 | 1.00 |
| | | *Nos. 883H-883L (5)* | 8.10 | 2.75 |

**Souvenir Sheet**

*Perf. 12½*

| | | | | |
|---|---|---|---|---|
| **883M** | A298a | 350fr multi | 6.00 | 1.50 |

Dated 1990.

African Tourism Year — A299

**1991, Apr. 15** **Litho.** *Perf. 13½*

| | | | | |
|---|---|---|---|---|
| **884** | A299 | 75fr shown | .80 | .35 |
| **885** | A299 | 120fr Zebra, map | 1.20 | .60 |

Allegory of New Republic — A300

**1991, May 13** **Litho.** *Perf. 13*

| | | | | |
|---|---|---|---|---|
| **888** | A300 | 15fr blue | .25 | .25 |
| **889** | A300 | 30fr brt grn | .25 | .25 |
| **890** | A300 | 60fr org yel | .40 | .25 |
| **891** | A300 | 75fr brt pink | .55 | .30 |
| **892** | A300 | 120fr dk brown | 1.00 | .45 |
| | | *Nos. 888-892 (5)* | 2.45 | 1.50 |

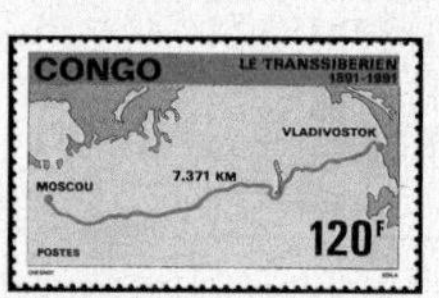

Trans-Siberian Railroad, Cent. — A301

**1991, June 6** **Litho.** *Perf. 13*

| | | | | |
|---|---|---|---|---|
| **899** | A301 | 120fr Map | 1.35 | .50 |
| **900** | A301 | 240fr Map, train | 2.75 | 1.20 |

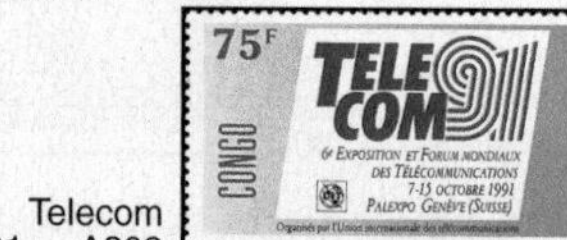

Telecom 91 — A302

**1991, June 29** **Litho.** *Perf. 13*

| | | | | |
|---|---|---|---|---|
| **901** | A302 | 75fr multicolored | .75 | .30 |
| **902** | A302 | 120fr multi, vert. | 1.25 | .60 |

6th World Forum and Exposition on Telecommunications, Geneva, Switzerland.

Insects — A303

**1991, July 2** *Perf. 12½*

| | | | | |
|---|---|---|---|---|
| **903** | A303 | 75fr Peanut beetle | 1.00 | .25 |
| **904** | A303 | 120fr Centaur, horiz. | 1.40 | .45 |
| **905** | A303 | 200fr Coffee beetle | 2.25 | .75 |
| **906** | A303 | 300fr Goliath beetle | 3.50 | 1.50 |
| | | *Nos. 903-906 (4)* | 8.15 | 2.95 |

Water conservation — A304

**1991, July 16** **Litho.** *Perf. 12½*

| | | | | |
|---|---|---|---|---|
| **907** | A304 | 75fr multicolored | .90 | .35 |

Amnesty Intl., 30th Anniv. — A305

Designs: 40fr, Candle, sun, vert. 75fr, "30," broken chains, vert.

**1991, Aug. 13** *Perf. 13½*

| | | | | |
|---|---|---|---|---|
| **908** | A305 | 40fr multicolored | .35 | .25 |
| **909** | A305 | 75fr multicolored | .60 | .25 |
| **910** | A305 | 80fr multicolored | .70 | .35 |
| | | *Nos. 908-910 (3)* | 1.65 | .85 |

Congo Postage Stamps, Cent. A306

75fr, Similar to French Congo #1. 120fr, Similar to French Congo #35. 240fr, Similar to Congo Republic #89. 500fr, Similar to French Congo #1, 35 and Congo Republic #89.

**Litho. & Engr.**

**1991, Aug.** *Perf. 13x13½*

| | | | | |
|---|---|---|---|---|
| **911** | A306 | 75fr beige & dk grn | .80 | .30 |
| **912** | A306 | 120fr beige, dk grn & brn | 1.10 | .45 |
| **913** | A306 | 240fr multicolored | 2.25 | 1.10 |
| **914** | A306 | 500fr multicolored | 4.50 | 2.00 |
| *a.* | | Strip of 4, #911-914 | 10.00 | 9.00 |
| | | *Nos. 911-914 (4)* | 8.65 | 3.85 |

Ducks — A307

75fr, Anas acuta. 120fr, Somateria mollissima, vert. 200fr, Anas clypeata, vert. 240fr, Anas platyrhynchos.

**1991, Aug. 8** **Litho.** *Perf. 12½*

| | | | | |
|---|---|---|---|---|
| **915** | A307 | 75fr multicolored | 1.25 | .30 |
| **916** | A307 | 120fr multicolored | 1.50 | .45 |
| **917** | A307 | 200fr multicolored | 2.00 | .75 |
| **918** | A307 | 240fr multicolored | 3.50 | 1.00 |
| | | *Nos. 915-918 (4)* | 8.25 | 2.50 |

Automobiles and Space — A308

Designs: 35fr, Ferrari 512S by Pininfarina. 40fr, Vincenzo Lancia, Lancia Stratos by Bertone. 75fr, Maybach Zeppelin type 12, Wilhelm Maybach. 80fr, Mars Observer, 1992. 500fr, Magellan probe surveying Venus. 600fr, Magnification of Sun, Ulysses probe. 750fr, Crew of Apollo 11.

**1991, Aug. 23 Litho. *Perf. 13½***

| | | | | |
|---|---|---|---|---|
| **919** | A308 | 35fr multicolored | .30 | .25 |
| **920** | A308 | 40fr multicolored | .30 | .25 |
| **921** | A308 | 75fr multicolored | .60 | .30 |
| **922** | A308 | 80fr multicolored | .65 | .30 |
| **923** | A308 | 500fr multicolored | 4.25 | 2.25 |
| **924** | A308 | 600fr multicolored | 5.00 | 2.50 |
| | | *Nos. 919-924 (6)* | 11.10 | 5.85 |

**Souvenir Sheet**

| | | | | |
|---|---|---|---|---|
| **925** | A308 | 750fr multicolored | 6.50 | 3.50 |

Nos. 923-925 are airmail. No. 925 contains one 60x42mm stamp. Nos. 919-921 exist in souvenir sheets of 1.

Butterflies — A309

75fr, Petit bleu. 120fr, Charaxe. 240fr, Papillon feuille, vert. 300fr, Papillon de l'oranger, vert.

**1991, Aug. 31 *Perf. 11½***

| | | | | |
|---|---|---|---|---|
| **926** | A309 | 75fr multi | 1.20 | .30 |
| **927** | A309 | 120fr multi | 1.50 | .50 |
| **928** | A309 | 240fr multi | 2.10 | .80 |
| **929** | A309 | 300fr multi | 3.75 | 1.00 |
| | | *Nos. 926-929 (4)* | 8.55 | 2.60 |

For overprints see Nos. 1156, 1165.

Celebrities and Organizations A310

Designs: 100fr, Bo Jackson, baseball and football player. 150fr, Nick Faldo, golfer. 200fr, Rickey Henderson, Barry Bonds, baseball players. 240fr, Garry Kasparov, World Chess Champion. 300fr, Starving child, Lions and Rotary Clubs emblems. 350fr, Wolfgang Amadeus Mozart. 400fr, De Gaulle, Churchill. 500fr, Jean-Henri Dunant, founder of Red Cross. 750fr, De Gaulle, vert.

**1991, Sept. 2 *Perf. 13½***

| | | | | |
|---|---|---|---|---|
| **930** | A310 | 100fr multicolored | 1.00 | .40 |
| **931** | A310 | 150fr multicolored | 1.40 | .60 |
| **932** | A310 | 200fr multicolored | 2.00 | .80 |
| **933** | A310 | 240fr multicolored | 2.75 | .95 |
| **934** | A310 | 300fr multicolored | 3.00 | 1.25 |
| **935** | A310 | 350fr multicolored | 3.75 | 1.40 |
| **936** | A310 | 400fr multicolored | 4.50 | 1.60 |
| **937** | A310 | 500fr multicolored | 5.00 | 2.00 |
| | | *Nos. 930-937 (8)* | 23.40 | 9.00 |

**Souvenir Sheet**

| | | | | |
|---|---|---|---|---|
| **938** | A310 | 750fr multicolored | 8.00 | 3.50 |

Nos. 936-938 are airmail. No. 938 contains one 35x50mm stamp.
For overprint, see No. 1199.

Gen. Charles de Gaulle in Africa A311

120fr, De Gaulle, Free French flag, vert. 240fr, De Gaulle, Appeal of Brazzaville, 1940.

**1991, Sept. 2 *Perf. 13½x13, 13x13½***

| | | | | |
|---|---|---|---|---|
| **939** | A311 | 75fr multicolored | .90 | .40 |
| **940** | A311 | 120fr multicolored | 1.25 | .60 |
| **941** | A311 | 240fr multicolored | 2.40 | 1.20 |
| | | *Nos. 939-941 (3)* | 4.55 | 2.20 |

A312

Paintings — A313

**1991, Oct. 12 *Perf. 11½***

| | | | | |
|---|---|---|---|---|
| **942** | A312 | 75fr multicolored | .75 | .35 |
| **943** | A313 | 120fr multicolored | 1.10 | .45 |

Discovery of America, 500th Anniv. (in 1992) — A314

20fr, Portrait of Christopher Columbus by Sebastian Del Pombo. 35fr, Portrait of Columbus. 40fr, Portrait of Columbus facing right. 55fr, Santa Maria. 75fr, Nina. 150fr, Pinta. 200fr, Arms & signature of Columbus.

**1991, May 30 *Perf. 13***

| | | | | |
|---|---|---|---|---|
| **944** | A314 | 20fr multicolored | .40 | .25 |
| **945** | A314 | 35fr multicolored | .40 | .25 |
| **946** | A314 | 40fr multicolored | .50 | .35 |
| **947** | A314 | 55fr multicolored | .65 | .35 |
| **948** | A314 | 75fr multicolored | .95 | .35 |
| **949** | A314 | 150fr multicolored | 1.75 | .85 |
| **950** | A314 | 200fr multicolored | 2.25 | 1.00 |
| | | *Nos. 944-950 (7)* | 6.90 | 3.40 |

Primates A315

30fr, Cercopithecus diana. 45fr, Pan troglodytes. 60fr, Theropithecus gelada. 75fr, Papio hamadryas. 90fr, Macaca nemestrina. 120fr, Gorilla gorilla. 240fr, Mandrillus sphinx.
250fr, Gorilla gorilla.

**1991, Dec. 13 Litho. *Perf. 13***

| | | | | |
|---|---|---|---|---|
| **951** | A315 | 30fr multicolored | .35 | .25 |
| **952** | A315 | 45fr multicolored | .45 | .25 |
| **953** | A315 | 60fr multicolored | .85 | .25 |
| **954** | A315 | 75fr multicolored | 1.00 | .35 |
| **955** | A315 | 90fr multicolored | 1.20 | .50 |
| **956** | A315 | 120fr multicolored | 1.60 | .50 |
| **957** | A315 | 240fr multicolored | 3.50 | .75 |
| | | *Nos. 951-957 (7)* | 8.95 | 2.85 |

**Souvenir Sheet**

| | | | | |
|---|---|---|---|---|
| **958** | A315 | 250fr multicolored | 4.25 | 1.50 |

Nos. 953-958 are vert.

Anniversaries and Events — A316

Designs: 50fr, Launching of Sputnik II with dog, Laika, 1957. 75fr, Mahatma Gandhi and Martin Luther King, Jr. 1964. 120fr, Launching of Meteosat and ERS-1 over Europe and Africa. 240fr, Maybach Zeppelin automobile and Ferdinand von Zeppelin, 75th death anniversary. 300fr, Konrad Adenauer, 25th death anniversary and opening of the Brandenburg Gate, 1989. 500fr, Pope John Paul II's visit to Africa. 600fr, Elvis Presley, American entertainer.

**1992, Feb. 4 Litho. *Perf. 13½***

| | | | | |
|---|---|---|---|---|
| **959** | A316 | 50fr multicolored | .75 | .25 |
| **960** | A316 | 75fr multicolored | .75 | .25 |
| **961** | A316 | 120fr multicolored | 1.25 | .45 |
| **962** | A316 | 240fr multicolored | 2.75 | .85 |
| **963** | A316 | 300fr multicolored | 2.50 | .80 |
| **964** | A316 | 500fr multicolored | 5.25 | 1.40 |
| *a.* | | Souvenir sheet of 3, #960, 963-964 | 11.50 | 5.75 |
| | | *Nos. 959-964 (6)* | 13.25 | 4.00 |

**Souvenir Sheet**

| | | | | |
|---|---|---|---|---|
| **965** | A316 | 600fr multicolored | 6.00 | 2.40 |

Nos. 959-964 exist in souvenir sheets of 1.
Nos. 962, 964-965 are airmail.
For Overprint, see No. 1166.

Explorers — A317

Genoa '92: 75fr, Juan de la Cosa, nautical chart. 95fr, Martin Alonso Pinzon, astrolabe. 120fr, Alonso de Ojeda, hour glass. 200fr, Vicente Yanez Pinzon, sun dial. 250fr, Bartholomew Columbus, quadrant.
400fr, Columbus, flag, horiz.

**1992, Oct. 21 Litho. *Perf. 13***

| | | | | |
|---|---|---|---|---|
| **966** | A317 | 75fr multicolored | .90 | .30 |
| **967** | A317 | 95fr multicolored | 1.10 | .30 |
| **968** | A317 | 120fr multicolored | 1.75 | .30 |
| **969** | A317 | 200fr multicolored | 2.50 | .40 |
| **970** | A317 | 250fr multicolored | 3.50 | .50 |
| | | *Nos. 966-970 (5)* | 9.75 | 1.80 |

**Souvenir Sheet**

| | | | | |
|---|---|---|---|---|
| **971** | A317 | 400fr multi | 12.50 | 12.50 |

Birds — A318

Designs: 60fr, Sagittarius serpentarius. 75fr, Ephippiorhynchus senegalensis. 120fr, Bugeranus carunculatus. 200fr, Ardea melanocephala. 250fr, Phoenicopterus ruber roseus.
400fr, Balearica regulorum.

**1992, Oct. 21**

| | | | | |
|---|---|---|---|---|
| **972** | A318 | 60fr multicolored | .70 | .25 |
| **973** | A318 | 75fr multicolored | .80 | .25 |
| **974** | A318 | 120fr multicolored | 1.10 | .30 |
| **975** | A318 | 200fr multicolored | 2.00 | .40 |
| **976** | A318 | 250fr multicolored | 2.75 | .50 |
| | | *Nos. 972-976 (5)* | 7.35 | 1.70 |

**Souvenir Sheet**

| | | | | |
|---|---|---|---|---|
| **977** | A318 | 400fr multicolored | 4.00 | 1.00 |

For overprint, see No. 1191.

Wild Cats — A319

45fr, Panthera leo. 60fr, Panthera tigris. 75fr, Lynx lynx. 95fr, Caracal caracal. 250fr, Leopardus pardalis.
500fr, Acinonyx jubatus.

**1992, Nov. 21 Litho. *Perf. 13***

| | | | | |
|---|---|---|---|---|
| **978** | A319 | 45fr multicolored | .50 | .50 |
| **979** | A319 | 60fr multicolored | .60 | .60 |
| **980** | A319 | 75fr multicolored | .70 | .70 |
| **981** | A319 | 95fr multicolored | .80 | .80 |
| **982** | A319 | 250fr multicolored | 2.25 | 2.25 |
| | | *Nos. 978-982 (5)* | 4.85 | 4.85 |

**Souvenir Sheet**

| | | | | |
|---|---|---|---|---|
| **983** | A319 | 400fr multicolored | 4.50 | 1.75 |

No. 983 contains one 32x40mm stamp.

1992 Winter Olympics, Albertville — A320

Gold medalists: 150fr, N. Mishkutyonok, A. Dmitriev, pairs figure skating, Unified team. 200fr, I. Appelt, H. Winkler, G. Haldacher, T. Schroll, 4-man bobsled, Austria. 500fr, Gunda Niemann, speed skating, Germany. 600fr, Bjorn Daehlie, cross-country skiing, Norway. 750fr, Alberto Tomba, giant slalom, Italy.

**1992, Dec. 21 Litho. *Perf. 13½***

| | | | | |
|---|---|---|---|---|
| **984** | A320 | 150fr multicolored | 1.25 | .40 |
| **985** | A320 | 200fr multicolored | 1.75 | .50 |
| **986** | A320 | 500fr multicolored | 4.00 | 1.10 |
| **987** | A320 | 600fr multicolored | 6.00 | 1.00 |
| | | *Nos. 984-987 (4)* | 13.00 | 3.00 |

**Souvenir Sheet**

| | | | | |
|---|---|---|---|---|
| **988** | A320 | 750fr multicolored | 7.00 | 2.00 |

Nos. 986-988 are airmail. No. 988 contains one 35x50mm stamp. Name on No. 987 spelled incorrectly.

1992 Summer Olympics, Barcelona — A321

Barcelona landmarks, Olympic event: 75fr, Steeple of La Sagrada Familia, baseball. 100fr, The Muse, Palace of Music, running. 150fr, Cupola interior, long jump. 200fr, St. Paul Hospital, pole vault. 400fr, Sculpture, by Miro, shot put. 500fr, Galley, Maritime Museum, table tennis. 750fr, La Sagrada Familia, tennis.

**1992, Dec. 21**

| | | | | |
|---|---|---|---|---|
| **989** | A321 | 75fr multicolored | .80 | .25 |
| **990** | A321 | 100fr multicolored | 1.00 | .30 |
| **991** | A321 | 150fr multicolored | 1.25 | .40 |
| **992** | A321 | 200fr multicolored | 2.00 | .65 |
| **993** | A321 | 400fr multicolored | 3.50 | .65 |
| **994** | A321 | 500fr multicolored | 4.50 | 1.00 |
| | | *Nos. 989-994 (6)* | 13.05 | 3.25 |

**Souvenir Sheet**

| | | | | |
|---|---|---|---|---|
| **995** | A321 | 750fr multicolored | 7.00 | 1.50 |

Nos. 993-995 are airmail.

Christmas — A321a

Paintings: 95fr, The Madonna of the Grand Duke, by Raphael. 120fr, Virgin and Child, by Francesco Mazzo. 200fr, The Madonna with a Book, by Botticelli. 250fr, The Madonna Carondelet, by Fra Bartolommeo. 400fr, Madonna and Child, by Raphael.

**1992, Dec. 20 Litho. *Perf. 12½***

| | | | | |
|---|---|---|---|---|
| **995A** | A321a | 95fr multicolored | 1.25 | .30 |
| **995B** | A321a | 120fr multicolored | — | — |
| **995C** | A321a | 200fr multicolored | 2.75 | .75 |
| **995D** | A321a | 250fr multicolored | 3.25 | 1.25 |
| | | *Nos. 995A-995D (4)* | 7.25 | 2.30 |

**Souvenir Sheet**

| | | | | |
|---|---|---|---|---|
| **995E** | A321a | 400fr multicolored | 4.50 | 1.90 |

Nos. 995A-995E were not available until late 1993.
For overprint, see No. 1192.

Birds of Prey — A322

**1993, Jan. 15 Litho. *Perf. 12½x13***

**996** A322 45fr Charognard .65 .25
**997** A322 75fr Vulture 2.00 .30
**998** A322 120fr Eagle 2.50 .65
*Nos. 996-998 (3)* 5.15 1.20

A323

Traditional ceramics: 45fr, Liloko. 75fr, Mbeya. 120fr, Jug with ladles, Mbeya.

**1993, Dec. 21 Litho. *Perf. 13½***

**999** A323 45fr multicolored .60 .30
**1000** A323 75fr multicolored 1.20 .50
**1001** A323 120fr multicolored 1.75 .85
*Nos. 999-1001 (3)* 3.55 1.65

1994 World Cup Soccer Championships, United States — A324

Design: 75fr, Player stretching to kick ball. 95fr, Goalie diving to stop ball. 120fr, Player stretching to kick ball. 200fr, Player kicking. 250fr, Goalie catching ball. 400fr, Players competing for ball.

**1993, Jan. 15 Litho. *Perf. 12¾***

**1002** A324 75fr multi 1.40 .80
**1003** A324 95fr multi 1.45 1.10
**1004** A324 120fr multi 2.40 1.40
**1005** A324 200fr multi 3.50 2.10
**1006** A324 250fr multi 4.00 2.75
*Nos. 1002-1006 (5)* 12.75 8.15

**Souvenir Sheet**

***Perf. 12½***

**1007** A324 400fr multi 6.00 4.00

No. 1007 contains one 40x32mm stamp.

Wild Animals — A325

Designs: 60fr, Damaliscus lunatus. 75fr, Gazella granti. 95fr, Equus quagga. 120fr, Panthera pardus. 200fr, Syncerus caffer. 250fr, Hippopotamus ampibius. 300fr, Necrosyrtes monachu. 350fr, Panthera leo.

**1993, Feb. 20 Litho. *Perf. 13***

**1008** A325 60fr multicolored .75 .25
**1009** A325 75fr multicolored 1.25 .25
**1010** A325 95fr multicolored 1.40 .30
**1011** A325 120fr multicolored 1.90 .30
**1012** A325 200fr multicolored 3.25 .40
**1013** A325 250fr multicolored 4.00 .40
**1014** A325 300fr multicolored 4.75 .40
**1015** A325 350fr multicolored 5.50 .75
*a.* Sheet of 8, #1008-1015 20.00 20.00
*Nos. 1008-1015 (8)* 22.80 3.05

No. 1015a is a continuous design.

Wild Flowers — A326

Designs: 75fr, Hibiscus schizopetalus. 95fr, Pentas lanceolata. 120fr, Ricinus communis. 200fr, Delonix regia. 250fr, Stapelia gigantea.

**1993, May 20 Litho. *Perf. 12½***

**1016** A326 75fr multicolored .85 .30
**1017** A326 95fr multicolored 1.10 .40
**1018** A326 120fr multicolored 2.25 .50
**1019** A326 200fr multicolored 3.75 1.00
**1020** A326 250fr multicolored 4.50 1.60
*Nos. 1016-1020 (5)* 12.45 3.80

Deep Sea Submersibles A327

75fr, Transport PC-1202. 95fr, J. Sea Link 1. 120fr, Nemo. 200fr, Robot. 250fr, Alvin. 400fr, Star III.

**1993, June 25**

**1021** A327 75fr multi 1.10 .50
**1022** A327 95fr multi 1.40 .75
**1023** A327 120fr multi 1.75 1.00
**1024** A327 200fr multi 2.75 1.50
**1025** A327 250fr multi 3.25 2.00
*Nos. 1021-1025 (5)* 10.25 5.75

**Souvenir Sheet**

**1026** A327 400fr multi 7.00 4.00

No. 1026 contains one 32x40mm stamp.

1996 Summer Olympic Games, Atlanta — A329

Designs: 50fr, Equestrian. 75fr, Cycling. 120fr, Sailing. 240fr, shown. 300fr, Hurdles. 500fr, Women's basketball. No. 1036, Running.

**1993, Apr. 26 Litho. *Perf. 13½***

**1030-1035** A329 Set of 6 15.00 4.00
*1035a* Sheet of 6, #1030-1035 17.50 6.00

**Souvenir Sheet**

**1036** A329 750fr multicolored 6.50 1.50

Nos. 1030-1036 exist imperf. Nos. 1030-1035 exist in souvenir sheets of 1.

Brasiliana '93 — A330

Birds: 75fr, Vidua whydah. 95fr, Vidua regia. 120fr, Steganura paradisea. 200fr, Vidua macroura. 250fr, Anthreptes platura. 400fr, Coliuspasser macrourus, horiz.

**1993, July 15 Litho. *Perf. 12x12½***

**1037-1041** A330 Set of 5 11.00 11.00

**Souvenir Sheet**

**1042** A330 400fr multicolored 10.00 10.00

Prehistoric Animals — A331

75fr, Ichthyostega. 95fr, Archaeopteryx. 120fr, Brachiosaurus. 200fr, Tyrannosaurus. 250fr, Pteranodon, vert. 400fr, Brontosaurus.

**1993, Aug. 20 Litho. *Perf. 13***

**1043** A331 75fr multicolored 1.00 1.00
**1044** A331 95fr multicolored 1.25 1.25
**1045** A331 120fr multicolored 1.60 1.60
**1046** A331 200fr multicolored 2.50 2.50
**1047** A331 250fr multicolored 3.50 3.50
*Nos. 1043-1047 (5)* 9.85 9.85

**Souvenir Sheet**

**1048** A331 400fr multicolored 6.50 6.50

No. 1048 contains one 32x40mm stamp.

Powered Flight, 90th Anniv. A332

Designs: 75fr, Wilbur Wright, Model B airplane, vert. 95fr, Orville Wright and Model B biplane, vert. 120fr, First flight by Orville Wright. 200fr, Flight at Kitty Hawk. 250fr, Wright Brothers and airplane.

***Perf. 12¼x12½, 12½x12¼***

**1993, Dec. 17 Litho.**

**1049** A332 75fr multi .65 .65
**1050** A332 95fr multi .85 .85
**1051** A332 120fr multi .95 .95
**1052** A332 200fr multi 1.75 1.75
**1053** A332 250fr multi 2.25 2.25
*Nos. 1049-1053 (5)* 6.45 6.45

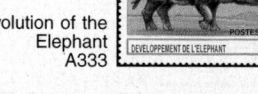

Evolution of the Elephant A333

25fr, Palaeomastodon. 45fr, Mammut. 50fr, Amebelodon. 75fr, Platybelodon. 120fr, Mammuthus.

**1994, June 20 Litho. *Perf. 12½***

**1054** A333 25fr multicolored .75 .30
**1055** A333 45fr multicolored 1.25 .50
**1056** A333 50fr multicolored 1.45 .50
**1057** A333 75fr multicolored 2.25 .80
**1058** A333 120fr multicolored 3.50 1.40
*Nos. 1054-1058 (5)* 9.20 3.50

Protection of Nature — A335

Designs: 50fr, Choeropsis liberiensis. 90fr, Hyemoschus aquaticus. 205fr, Taurotragus euryceros, vert. 300fr, Redunca redunca, vert.

**1994, Aug. 27 Litho. *Perf. 12½***

**1063** A335 50fr multicolored .50 .35
**1064** A335 90fr multicolored .80 .35
**1065** A335 205fr multicolored 1.90 1.10
**1066** A335 300fr multicolored 2.75 1.60
*Nos. 1063-1066 (4)* 5.95 3.40

For overprint see No. 1167.

Seaplanes A336

Designs: 30fr, Cant Z-505, Italy. 45fr, Martin Mariner PBM-3, US. No. 1069, E-59, Russia. No. 1070, Short Sunderland, Great Britain. No. 1071, Martin Mars XPB2M-1, US. 400fr, Boeing 314, US.

**1994, Sept. 2 Litho. *Perf. 12½***

**1067** A336 30fr multicolored .40 .25
**1068** A336 45fr multicolored .50 .25
**1069** A336 90fr multicolored 1.00 .40
**1070** A336 90fr multicolored 1.00 .40
**1071** A336 90fr multicolored 1.00 .40
*Nos. 1067-1071 (5)* 3.90 1.70

**Souvenir Sheet**

**1071A** A336 400fr multicolored 5.00 2.50

No. 1071A contains one 40x32mm stamp.

Intl. Year of the Family — A337

205fr, African map, child. 300fr, Family, native huts.

**1995, Jan. 28 Litho. *Perf. 12½***

**1072** A337 90fr shown .75 .40
**1073** A337 205fr multicolored 1.60 1.00
**1074** A337 300fr multicolored 2.50 1.50
*Nos. 1072-1074 (3)* 4.85 2.90

For overprint see No. 1168.

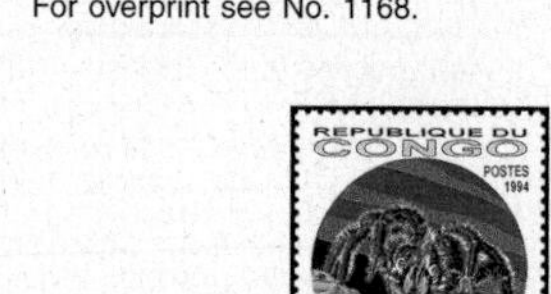

Insects — A338

**1994, July 24 Litho. *Perf. 12½***

**1075** A338 90fr Tarantula 1.90 .40
**1076** A338 205fr Spider 4.50 1.10
**1077** A338 240fr Ladybug 5.00 1.25
*Nos. 1075-1077 (3)* 11.40 2.75

**Souvenir Sheet**

**1078** A338 400fr Bee 4.75 2.00

Costumes — A338a

**1995 Litho. *Perf. 12¾x12½***

**1078A** A338a 90fr M'Bochi 1.00 .60
**1078B** A338a 205fr Téké 1.70 .90
**1078C** A338a 500fr Loango 3.75 1.50
*Nos. 1078A-1078C (3)* 6.45 3.00

Rotary Intl., 90th Anniv. — A339

Designs: 90fr, Polio victim. No. 1080, Playing ball with children. No. 1081, Children with food. 300fr, Delivering polio vaccine. 1500fr, Paul Harris, Rotary emblem.

**1996, Feb. 6 Litho. *Perf. 14***

**1079** A339 90fr multicolored .60 .25
**1080** A339 205fr multicolored 1.25 .50
**1081** A339 205fr multicolored 1.25 .50
**1082** A339 300fr multicolored 1.60 .60
*Nos. 1079-1082 (4)* 4.70 1.85

**Souvenir Sheet**

**1083** A339 1500fr multicolored 5.00 3.25

For overprint, see Mo. 1201.

18th World Scout Jamboree, The Netherlands — A340

Designs: No. 1084, Handshake. No. 1085, Scout helping another with arm sling. 205fr, Saving life in water. 300fr, Lord Baden-Powell. 1000fr, Scout salute.

**1996, Feb. 6 Litho. *Perf. 14***

**1084** A340 90fr multicolored .40 .25
**1085** A340 90fr multicolored .40 .25
**1086** A340 205fr multicolored 1.00 .40
**1087** A340 300fr multicolored 1.40 .50
*Nos. 1084-1087 (4)* 3.20 1.40

**Souvenir Sheet**

**1088** A340 1000fr multicolored 3.50 2.10

1998 World Cup Soccer Tournament A340a

Various players. Denominations: 90fr, 150fr, 205fr, 300fr, 400fr, 500fr.
No. 1088G, 100fr, Player's legs.

**1996 Litho. *Perf. 12¾***
**1088A-1088F** A340a Set of 6 5.00 5.00

**Souvenir Sheet**
***Perf. 13¼x13***
**1088G** A340a 1000fr multi 3.00 3.00

No. 1088G contains one 40x31mm stamp.

Antique Automobiles A341

90fr, 1936 Armstrong Siddeley Twelve. 150fr, 1935 Aston Martin Mark II. 205fr, 1938 Morris 8. 300fr, 1955-62 MG Series MGA. 400fr, 1932 SS1. 500fr, 1938 Alvis 25 SB.

**1996, Apr. 30 Litho. *Perf. 12½x12***
**1089** A341 90fr multicolored .40 .25
**1090** A341 150fr multicolored .65 .40
**1091** A341 205fr multicolored .85 .50
**1092** A341 300fr multicolored 1.25 .75
**1093** A341 400fr multicolored 1.75 1.00
**1094** A341 500fr multicolored 2.10 1.25
*Nos. 1089-1094 (6)* 7.00 4.15

Domestic Cats — A342

90fr, Persian. 150fr, Siamese. 205fr, Norwegian forest. 300fr, Exotic shorthair. 400fr, Maine coon. 500fr, Red abyssinian.
1000fr, Turkish Angora.

**1996, Mar. 10 *Perf. 13x12½***
**1095** A342 90fr multicolored .40 .25
**1096** A342 150fr multicolored .65 .40
**1097** A342 205fr multicolored .90 .50
**1098** A342 300fr multicolored 1.35 .75
**1099** A342 400fr multicolored 1.75 1.00
**1100** A342 500fr multicolored 2.25 1.25
*Nos. 1095-1100 (6)* 7.30 4.15

**Souvenir Sheet**
**1101** A342 1000fr multicolored 3.00 2.50

No. 1101 contains one 32x40mm stamp.

1996 Summer Olympic Games, Atlanta — A343

90fr, Fencing, vert. 150fr, Archery, vert. 205fr, Basketball, vert. 300fr, Baseball, vert. 400fr, Volleyball. 500fr, 2-man kayak.
1000fr, Judo, vert.

**1996 *Perf. 13x12½, 12½x13***
**1102** A343 90fr multi .40 .25
**1103** A343 150fr multi .65 .40
**1104** A343 205fr multi .95 .55
**1105** A343 300fr multi 1.40 .80
**1106** A343 400fr multi 2.00 1.10
**1107** A343 500fr multi 2.10 1.25
*Nos. 1102-1107 (6)* 7.50 4.35

**Souvenir Sheet**
**1108** A343 1000fr multi 4.75 2.50

No. 1108 contains one 32x40mm stamp.

Flowers — A344

Designs: 90fr, Nerium oleander. 150fr, Eucaliptus globulus. 205fr, Centaurea cyanus. 300fr, Coffea arabica. 400fr, Hibiscus sabdariffa. 500fr, Cassia angustifolia.

**1996, May 10 *Perf. 12½***
**1109** A344 90fr multicolored .35 .25
**1110** A344 150fr multicolored .60 .40
**1111** A344 205fr multicolored .80 .55
**1112** A344 300fr multicolored 1.10 .80
**1113** A344 400fr multicolored 1.50 1.10
**1114** A344 500fr multicolored 1.75 1.25
*Nos. 1109-1114 (6)* 6.10 4.35

Mother Carrying Baby — A345

**1996 Litho. *Perf. 13***
**1115** A345 40fr blue *4.00*
**1116** A345 50fr violet brown *5.00*
**1117** A345 90fr orange *9.00*
**1118** A345 100fr green blue *10.00*
**1119** A345 115fr gray *11.00*
**1120** A345 205fr brown *20.00*
*Nos. 1115-1120 (6)* *59.00*

It has been stated that this set was not issued.
See Nos. 1145-1150.
For overprints, see Nos. 1159, 1185A, 1236-1236A.

A346

**1996, Aug. 31 Litho. *Perf. 13½***
**1121** A346 90fr orange & multi .50 .30
**1122** A346 205fr green & multi 1.25 .75

Investiture of Pres. Pascal Lissouba, 4th anniv.

Owls — A347

**1996, Mar. 29 *Perf. 14½***
**1123** A347 90fr Tyto alba .70 .25
**1124** A347 205fr Bubo poensis 1.50 .50
**1125** A347 300fr Scotopelia peli 2.40 .90
**1126** A347 500fr Asio capensis 3.50 1.50
*Nos. 1123-1126 (4)* 8.10 3.15

Military Aircraft — A348

Designs: 90fr, Vought-Sikorsky Vindicator SB2U-1. 150fr, Grumman Wildcat F4F-3. 205fr, North American SNJ-2. 300fr, Brewster Bermuda. 400fr, Blackburn Skua 1. 500fr, Mitsubishi Type 98-1.
1000fr, P-40 Warhawk (Flying Tigers).

**1996, June 24 Litho. *Perf. 12½x12***
**1127** A348 90fr multicolored .35 .25
**1128** A348 150fr multicolored .60 .30
**1129** A348 205fr multicolored .80 .50
**1130** A348 300fr multicolored 1.20 .75
**1131** A348 400fr multicolored 1.60 1.00
**1132** A348 500fr multicolored 2.00 1.25
*Nos. 1127-1132 (6)* 6.55 4.05

**Souvenir Sheet**
***Perf. 13***
**1133** A348 1000fr multicolored 4.00 2.50

No. 1133 contains one 32x40mm stamp.

Aquatic Flowers — A348a

Design: 90fr, Cyrtosperma senegalense; 205fr, Pistia stratioque.

**1996, July 3 Litho. *Perf. 14x14¼***
**1133A** A348a 90fr multi .70 .50
**1133B** A348a 205fr multi 1.50 1.25

Crocodilians A348b

205fr, Nile crocodile. 255fr, Gavial. 300fr, Caiman.

**1996, July 16 Litho. *Perf. 14***
**1133C** A348b 205fr multi 1.25 .90
**1133D** A348b 255fr multi 1.60 1.00
**1133E** A348b 300fr multi 1.90 1.00
*Nos. 1133C-1133E (3)* 4.75 2.90

Volleyball, Cent. — A348c

Motion Pictures, Cent. — A348d

World Tourism Organization, 25th Anniv. — A348e

UNICEF, 50th Anniv. — A348f

Food and Agriculture Organization, 50th Anniv. — A348g

United Nations, 50th Anniv. — A348h

**1996 Litho. *Perf. 12½***
**1133F** A348c 90fr multi — —
**1133G** A348d 90fr multi — —
**1133H** A348e 205fr multi — —
**1133I** A348f 300fr multi — —
**1133J** A348g 300fr multi — —
**1133K** A348h 300fr multi — —

Arctocebus Calabarensis — A349

a, 90fr, With young. b, 205fr, Touching leaf. c, 300fr, Climbing to left. d, 255fr, Walking on branch.

**1998, June 3 Litho. *Perf. 14***
**1134** A349 Strip of 4, #a.-d. 5.00 5.00

No. 1134 issued in sheets of 12 stamps. World Wildlife Fund.

Endangered Species — A350

No. 1135, Kabus defassa, vert. No. 1136, Caphalophus sylvicutor. 205fr, Potamochoerus porcus. 300fr, Tragelaplus spekei.

**1996 Litho. *Perf. 14***
**1135** A350 90fr multi .55 .25
**1136** A350 90fr multi, vert. .55 .25
**1137** A350 205fr multi, vert. 1.10 .45
**1138** A350 300fr multi 1.60 .65
*Nos. 1135-1138 (4)* 3.80 1.60

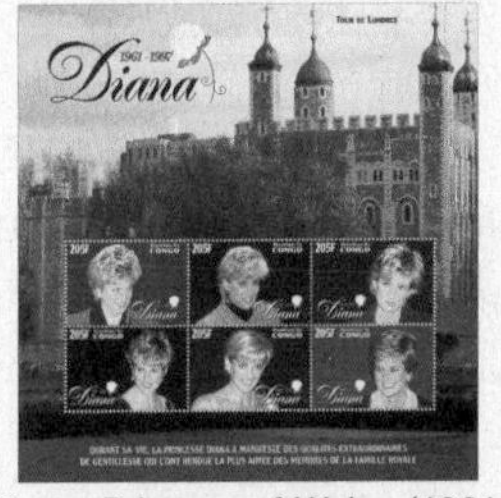

Diana, Princess of Wales (1961-97) — A351

Nos. 1139-1141: Various portraits with white rose.
Diana, rose, famous people in sheet margin: 750fr, Henry Kissinger, vert. No. 1143, Mother Teresa, vert. No. 1144, Hillary Clinton, vert.

**1998, Aug. 31 Litho. *Perf. 14***
**Sheets of 6**
**1139** A351 205fr #a.-f. 5.50 2.00
**1140** A351 255fr #a.-f., vert. 7.00 2.75
**1141** A351 300fr #a.-f., vert. 8.00 3.00

**Souvenir Sheets**
**1142** A351 750fr multicolored 3.00 3.00
**1143-1144** A351 1000fr each 5.00 5.00

Stamps of Type A345 inscribed only "Congo" ovptd.

**1998 Litho. *Perf. 13***
**1145** A345 40fr blue *12.50* *8.00*
**1146** A345 50fr violet brown *18.00* *8.00*
**1147** A345 90fr orange *18.00* *8.00*
**1148** A345 100fr green blue *18.00* *8.00*
**1149** A345 115fr gray *20.00* *8.00*
**1150** A345 205fr brown *25.00* *8.00*
*Nos. 1145-1150 (6)* *48.00*

A352

Designs: 90fr, Aframomum africanum. 205fr, Gambeya lacuurtiana (37x24mm). 300fr, Landolphia jumeli.

***Perf. 13½x13¼, 13 (#1152)***
**1998 Litho.**
**1151** A352 90fr multi *10.00*
**1152** A352 205fr multi — *10.00*
**1153** A352 300fr multi *10.00*
*Nos. 1151-1153 (3)* *30.00*

No. 1153 has denomination in yellow.

No. 732A Overprinted

No. 929 Overprinted

**1998 Litho. *Perf. 13***
**1155** A244 205fr multi — —
**1156** A309 300fr multi — —

An additional stamp was issued in this set. The editors would like to examine them.

**Nos. 732B, 804, 854, 855, 929, 963, 1066, 1074, 1118, 1133D and 1133J Overprinted Like**

***Perfs. as before, Perf. 14 (#1164), Perf. 13½x13¼ (#1170)***

**Methods as before, Litho. (#1164, 1170)**

**1998**

**1157** A274 60fr multi (#804)
**1159** A345 100fr green blue (#1118)
**1164** A348b 255fr multi (#1133D)
**1165** A309 300fr multi (#929)
**1166** A316 300fr multi (#963) —
**1167** A335 300fr multi (#1066)
*a.* Overprint reading horizontally
**1168** A337 300fr multi (#1074)
**1169** A348g 300fr multi (#1133J) — —
**1170** A244 300fr multi (#732B)
*a.* Overprint reading horizontally — —
**1172** A292 360fr multi (#854)
*a.* Inverted overprint — —
**1173** A292 400fr multi (#855) — —

Numbers have been reserved for additional overprinted stamps. Overprint reads horizontally on Nos. 1157, 1159, 1166, 1169, 1172 and 1173, vertically reading down on Nos. 1164, 1167, 1168 and 1170, and vertically reading up on No. 1165. No. 1170 has white denomination.

1998 World Cup Soccer Championships, France — A358

Designs: 90fr, Netherlands, 4th place. 205fr, Croatia, bronze medal. 300fr, Brazil, silver medal. 500fr, France, gold medal.

**1998, Nov. 16 Litho.** ***Perf. 13x13¼***
**1175-1178** A358 Set of 4 12.00 5.00

Masks — A359

90fr, Kwele wood mask. 150fr, Kwele wood mask. No. 1181, Teke/Tsangui wood mask. No. 1182, Kuyu wood mask.

***Perf. 13¼x13½***

**1998, Nov. 20 Litho.**
**1179** A359 90fr multicolored .90 .40
**1180** A359 150fr multicolored 1.20 .70
**1181** A359 205fr multicolored 1.20 1.00
**1182** A359 205fr multicolored 1.20 1.00
*Nos. 1179-1182 (4)* 4.50 3.10

**No. 732B Overprinted**

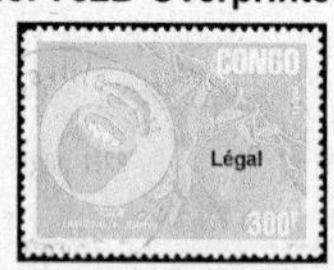


Type I — Unserifed Upper and Lower Case Letters, 7x3mm

Type II — Serifed Upper and Lower Case Letters, 12x3mm

Type III — Upper Case Letters, 9x2mm

**Methods and Perfs as Before**

**1999 ?**
**1183** A244 300fr multi (I) — —
**1184** A244 300fr multi (II) — —
**1185** A244 300fr multi (III) — —

**Nos. 1118, 1119 Overprinted Like No. 1149 But With Wider "G" In Overprint**

**Method and Perf. As Before**

**1999 ?**
**1185A** A345 100fr green blue —
**1185B** A345 115fr gray —

**Nos. 934, 975, 995B, 1082, 1133I, C342-C343 Overprinted Like No. 1157**

**Methods as Before, Litho. (#1204)**

**1999 ?** ***Perf. as Before, 12½ (#1204)***
**1187** AP120 200fr multi (#C342) — —
**1188** AP120 200fr multi (#C343) — —
*a.* Horiz. pair, #1187-1188, + central label — —
**1191** A318 200fr multi (#975) — —
**1192** A321a 200fr multi (#995C) — —
**1199** A310 300fr multi (#934) — —
**1201** A339 300fr multi (#1082) — —
**1204** A348f 300fr multi (#1133I) — —

Overprint reads horizontally on No. 1204, horizontally and inverted on Nos. 1187-1188, vertically reading down on Nos. 1191 and 1199, and vertically reading up on Nos. 1192 and 1201.

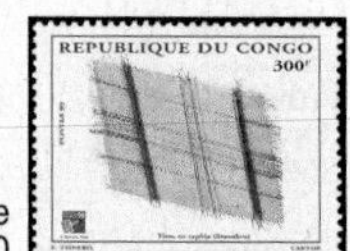


PhilexFrance 99 — A360

Design: 205fr, Raffia cloth with tassels. 300fr, Woven raffia cloth.

**1999, July 2 Litho.** ***Perf. 13x13¼***
**1211** A360 205fr multi 2.00 1.00
**1212** A360 300fr multi 2.50 1.50

First French Postage Stamp, 150th Anniv. — A361

**Litho. With Hologram**

**1999** ***Perf. 13x13¼***
**1213** A361 300fr multi 2.50 2.50

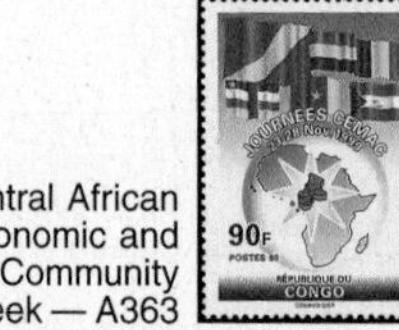


Central African Economic and Monetary Community Week — A363

Designs: 90fr, Map and flags. 205fr, Map and circle of flags.

**1999 Litho.** ***Perf. 14½***
**1227** A363 90fr multi — 5.00
**1228** A363 205fr multi — —

Additional stamps may exist in this set. The editors would like to examine any examples.

Third Pan-African Music Festival — A364

Designs: 120fr, Emblem. 270fr, Map of Africa with drummers.

**2001, Aug. 4 Litho.** ***Perf. 13½x13***
**1229-1230** A364 Set of 2 3.25 3.25

Independence, 40th Anniv. — A365

Designs: 90fr, Dove, vine, map, hands, people. 205fr, Tools, clasped and opened hands, map.

**2001, Nov. 15 Litho.** ***Perf. 13¼x13***
**1231-1232** A365 Set of 2 *30.00* —

Birds — A366

Designs: 90fr, Egretta garzetta. No. 1234, Ardea cenerea. No. 1234A, Egretta garzetta (white bird). 205fr, Ardea purpurea. No. 1235, Ciconia nigra. No. 1235A, Ciconia ciconia.

**2001** ***Perf. 13¼***
**1233** A366 90fr multi — —
**1234** A366 120fr multi — —
**1234A** A366 120fr multi — —
**1234B** A366 205fr multi —
**1235** A366 270fr multi — —
**1235A** A366 270fr multi — —

**Type of A345 Inscribed "REPUBLIQUE DU CONGO" Overprinted "LEGAL" Like No. 1145**

**2001 ? Litho.** ***Perf. 13***
**1236** A345 90fr blue — —
**1236A** A345 205fr green blue —

Fruit — A367

Designs: 40fr, Mbila esobe, horiz. 50fr, Ikami, horiz. 70fr, Tsiat. 80fr, Bamou, horiz. 120fr, Malombo, horiz. 270fr, Ntondolo. 380fr, Tsia. 1500fr, Ntondolo.

**2002, June 25 Litho.** ***Perf. 13½***
**1237** A367 40fr multi — —
**1238** A367 50fr multi — —
**1239** A367 70fr multi — —
**1240** A367 80fr multi — —
**1241** A367 120fr multi — —
**1242** A367 270fr multi — —
**1242A** A367 380fr multi — —
**1242B** A367 1500fr multi — —

Birds — A368

Designs: 40fr, Calao (hornbill). 80fr, Cigogne blanche (white stork). 120fr, Grue cendrée (gray crane). 270fr, Marabout.

**2002, July 23** ***Perf. 13½x13***
**1243-1246** A368 Set of 4 — —

Elephants — A369

Designs; 120fr, Mammoth. 270fr, Elephant on savannah, horiz. 350fr, Elephant, horiz. 500fr, Forest elephant near lake.

***Perf. 13¼x13, 13x13¼***

**2003, June 20**
**1247-1250** A369 Set of 4 — —

Flowers — A370

Designs: 120fr, Muflier (antirrhinum). 270fr, Pivoine (peony). 400fr, Petunia. 600fr, Mauve (mallow), horiz.

**2003, July 6**
**1251-1254** A370 Set of 4 8.00 8.00

Moringa Olifera — A371

Highlighted portion: 30fr, Bark. 70fr, Root. 90fr, Leaves. 115fr, Seeds and open pod. 120fr, Flowers. 360fr, Pod.

**2005, Feb. 3 Litho.** ***Perf. 13¼x13***
**1255-1260** A371 Set of 6 5.00 5.00

Dated 2004.

Fruits — A372

Designs: 120fr, Custard apple. 200fr, Tangerine. 270fr, Guava. 360fr, Grapefruit.

**2005, July 13 Litho.** ***Perf. 13½***
**1261-1264** A372 Set of 4 7.25 7.25

Albert Einstein (1879-1955), Physicist — A373

**2005, Aug. 17 Litho.** ***Perf. 13¼x13***
**1265** A373 400fr multi 4.25 4.25

A374

Brazzaville, 125th Anniv. — A375

**2005, Oct. 3** ***Perf. 13¼x13***
**1266** A374 120fr multi 1.10 1.10

***Perf. 13½x13¼***
**1267** A375 360fr multi 3.25 3.25

Pope Benedict XVI — A376

Pope Benedict XVI: 360fr, Waving. 500fr, Holding crucifix.

**2005, Nov. 28** ***Perf. 13¼x13½***
**1268-1269** A376 Set of 2 4.25 3.75

Coat of Arms — A377

Colors: 30fr, Dark brown. 40fr, Red. 50fr, Bister brown. 60fr, Dark green.

**2006, Jan. 4** **Litho.** ***Perf. 13½***
**1270-1273** A377 Set of 4 — —

Denis Sassou-Nguesso, President of African Union — A378

**2006, Mar. 14** **Litho.** ***Perf. 13x13¼***
**1274** A378 500fr multi 2.40 2.40

Léopold Sédar Senghor (1906-2001), First President of Senegal — A379

**2006, May 15**
**1275** A379 360fr multi 1.75 1.75

Animals — A380

Designs: 40fr, Crocodile. 50fr, Pangolin, horiz. 60fr, Lizard, horiz. 120fr, Cat, horiz.

**2006** **Litho.** ***Perf. 13¼x13, 13x13¼***
**1276-1279** A380 Set of 4 5.00 2.50

World Religion Day — A381

**2007** ***Perf. 13½x13***
**1280** A381 120fr multi 1.20 1.00

Opening of Pierre Savorgnan de Brazza Memorial, Brazzaville — A382

Memorial and: 120fr, Statue. 500fr, Photo of Savorgnan de Brazza. 1000fr, Statue, diff.

**2008** ***Perf. 13¼***
**1281-1283** A382 Set of 3 7.00 7.00

Centenary Emblem — A382a

Old Church — A382b

Vehicle on Dirt Road — A382c

**2009** **Litho.** ***Perf. 13x13¼***
**1283A** A382a 90fr multi — —
**1283B** A382b 360fr multi — —
**1283C** A382b 395fr multi — —
**1283D** A382c 1500fr multi — —

Protestant Evangelization in Congo, cent.

A383

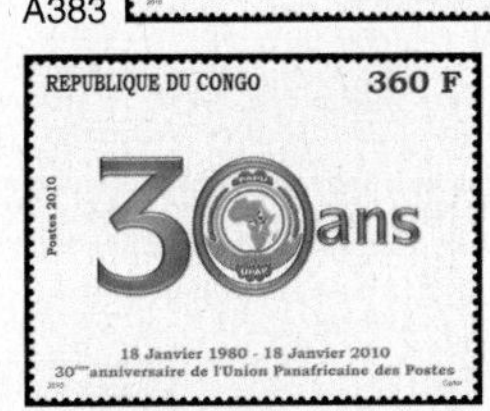


Pan-African Postal Union, 30th Anniv. — A384

**2010** **Litho.** ***Perf. 13½x13¼***
**1284** A383 120fr multi 1.00 1.00
**1285** A384 360fr multi 3.00 3.00

50th Anniv. Emblem — A385

President and Flag of Republic of Congo — A386

President and Flag of People's Republic of Congo — A387

President Denis Sassou-Nguesso and Flag of Republic of Congo — A388

President: No. 1287, Abbé Fulbert Youlou (1917-72). No. 1288, Alphonse Massamba-Débat (1921-77). No. 1288A, Marien Ngouabi (1938-77). No. 1289, Joachim Yhombi-Opango. No. 1290, Denis Sassou-Nguesso. No. 1291, Pascal Lissouba.

**2010** **Litho.** ***Perf. 13½***
**1286** A385 120fr multi — —
**1287** A386 270fr multi — —
**1288** A386 270fr multi — —
**1288A** A387 270fr multi — —
**1289** A387 270fr multi — —
**1290** A387 270fr multi — —
**1291** A386 270fr multi — —
**1292** A388 270fr multi — —
*a.* Souvenir sheet of 8, #1286-1288, 1288A, 1289-1292 — —

Republic of Congo, 50th anniv. Additional stamps may exist in this set. The editors would like to examine any examples.

15th Francophonie Summit, Dakar — A389

Designs: 120fr, Building, Pres. Denis Sassou-Nguesso. 360fr, Conferees on sofa.

**2014** **Litho.** ***Perf. 13¼x13***
**1293** A389 120fr multi — —
**1294** A389 360fr multi — —

Miniature Sheet

Diplomatic Relations Between Congo Republic and People's Republic of China, 50th Anniv. — A390

No. 1295: a, 120fr, Congolese and Chinese masks. b, 120fr, Gorilla and Giant panda. c, 240fr, Building, flags of Congo Republic and People's Republic of China. d, 240fr, Congo Republic #698, building, sculpture with Chinese inscription. e, 360fr, Meeting of Chinese Chairman Mao Zedong and Congo Republic President. f, 500fr, Meeting of Chinese President Xi Jinping and Congolese Pres. Denis Sassou-Nguesso, building, and flags of Congo Republic and People's Republic of China.

**2014, Feb. 22** **Litho.** ***Perf. 12***
**1295** A390 Sheet of 6, #a-f — —

11th African Games, Brazzaville — A391

**2015** **Litho.** ***Perf. 13¼x13***
**1296** A391 200fr multi — —

## SEMI-POSTAL STAMPS

### Anti-Malaria Issue
Common Design Type

**1962, Apr. 7** **Engr.** ***Perf. 12½x12***
**B3** CD108 25fr + 5fr bister 1.40 1.00

### Freedom from Hunger Issue
Common Design Type

**1963, Mar. 21** **Unwmk.** ***Perf. 13***
**B4** CD112 25fr + 5fr vio bl, bl grn & brn 1.40 1.00

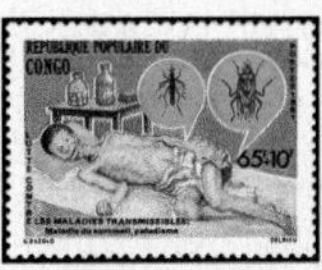


Boy Suffering from Sleeping Sickness — SP1

Fight Against Communicable Diseases; 40fr+5fr, Examination, treatment, vert.

**1981, June 6** **Litho.** ***Perf. 13***
**B5** SP1 40fr + 5fr multi .60 .25
**B6** SP1 65fr + 10fr multi 1.00 .30

### IYD Type of 1981

**1981, June 29** ***Perf. 12½***
**B7** A192 75fr + 5fr multi .90 .35

## AIR POST STAMPS

### Olympic Games Issue
French Equatorial Africa No. C37 Surcharged in Red Like Chad No. C1

**1960** **Unwmk.** **Engr.** ***Perf. 13***
**C1** AP8 250fr on 500fr grnsh blk, blk & sl 8.00 8.00

17th Olympic Games, Rome, 8/25-9/11.

Helicrysum Mechowiam AP1

Flowers: 200fr, Cogniauxia podolaena. 500fr, Thesium tencio.

**1961, Sept. 28** **Engr.** ***Perf. 13***
**C2** AP1 100fr grn, lil & yel 2.90 1.60
**C3** AP1 200fr bl grn, yel & brn 4.75 2.40
**C4** AP1 500fr brn red, yel & sl grn 14.50 6.00
*Nos. C2-C4 (3)* 22.15 10.00

### Air Afrique Issue
Common Design Type

**1961, Nov. 25** **Unwmk.** ***Perf. 13***
**C5** CD107 50fr lil rose, sl grn & grn 1.75 .90

Loading Timber, Pointe-Noire Harbor AP2

**1962, June 8** **Photo.** ***Perf. 12½x12***
**C6** AP2 50fr multicolored 1.50 .90

Opening of the Intl. Fair and Exhib., Pointe-Noire, June 8-11.

Abidjan Games — AP3

**1962, July 21** ***Perf. 12x12½***
**C7** AP3 100fr Basketball 2.50 1.25

Costus Spectabilis — AP4

Design: 250fr, Mountain acanthus.

**1963** **Unwmk.** ***Perf. 13***

**C8** AP4 100fr multicolored 4.00 1.75
**C9** AP4 250fr multicolored 8.00 3.25

Issued: 100fr, 8/9; 250fr, 11/4.

Brazzaville City Hall and Pres. Fulbert Youlou — AP4a

**1963, Aug.** **Photo.** ***Perf. 13x12***

**C10** AP4a 100fr multicolored 150.00 125.00

### African Postal Union Issue
Common Design Type

**1963, Sept. 8** ***Perf. 12½***

**C13** CD114 85fr pur, ocher & red 1.40 .75

### Air Afrique Issue, 1963
Common Design Type

***Perf. 13x12***

**1963, Nov. 19** **Unwmk.** **Photo.**

**C14** CD115 50fr multicolored 1.60 .60

Liberty Place, Brazzaville AP5

**1963, Nov. 28**

**C15** AP5 25fr multicolored 1.00 .40

See No. 118.

### Europafrica Issue
Common Design Type

**1963, Nov. 30** ***Perf. 12x13***

**C16** CD116 50fr gray, yel & dk brn 1.60 1.00

Timber Industry AP6

**1964, May 12** **Engr.** ***Perf. 13***

**C17** AP6 100fr grn, brn red & blk 2.50 1.10

### Chiefs of State Issue

Map and Presidents of Chad, Congo, Gabon and CAR — AP6a

**1964, June 23** **Photo.** ***Perf. 12½***

**C18** AP6a 100fr multicolored 1.60 1.00

See note after Central African Republic No. C19.

### Europafrica Issue

Sunburst, Wheat, Cogwheel and Globe — AP7

**1964, July 20** ***Perf. 12x13***

**C19** AP7 50fr yel, Prus bl & mar 1.60 .75

See note after Cameroun No. 402.

Hammer Thrower, Olympic Flame and Stadium AP8

50fr, 100fr, vert.

**1964, July 30** **Engr.** ***Perf. 13***

**C20** AP8 25fr shown .40 .30
**C21** AP8 50fr Weight lifter .75 .60
**C22** AP8 100fr Volleyball 1.60 1.10
**C23** AP8 200fr High jump 3.00 2.25
*a.* Min. sheet of 4, #C20-C23 7.25 7.25
*Nos. C20-C23 (4)* 5.75 4.25

18th Olympic Games, Tokyo, 10/10-25/64.

Communications Symbols — AP8a

**1964, Nov. 2** **Litho.** ***Perf. 12½x13***

**C24** AP8a 25fr dl rose & dk brn .90 .45

See note after Chad No. C19.

Town Hall, Brazzaville AP9

**1965, Jan. 30** **Photo.** ***Perf. 12½***

**C25** AP9 100fr multicolored 1.20 .75

Coupling Hooks AP10

**1965, Feb. 27** **Photo.** ***Perf. 13x12***

**C26** AP10 50fr multicolored 1.40 .75

Economic Europe-Africa Association.

Breguet Dial Telegraph, ITU Emblem and Telstar AP11

**1965, May 17** **Engr.** ***Perf. 13***

**C27** AP11 100fr dk bl, ocher & brn 2.25 .75

Cent. of the ITU.

Pope John XXIII (1881-1963), St. Peter's Cathedral AP12

***Perf. 12½x13***

**1965, June 26** **Photo.** **Unwmk.**

**C28** AP12 100fr gldn brn & multi 1.50 .75

Pres. John F. Kennedy — AP13

Portraits: 25fr on 50fr, Patrice Lumumba, premier of Congo Republic (ex-Belgian). 50fr, Sir Winston Churchill. 80fr, Barthélémy Boganda, premier of Central African Republic.

**1965, June** ***Perf. 12½***

**C29** AP13 25fr on 50fr dk brn & red .50 .40
*a.* Surcharge omitted 35.00 35.00
**C30** AP13 50fr dk brn & yel grn 1.00 1.00
**C31** AP13 80fr dk brn & bl 1.75 1.50
**C32** AP13 100fr dk brn & org yel 2.60 2.25
*a.* Min. sheet of 4, #C29-C32 6.25 6.25
*Nos. C29-C32 (4)* 5.85 5.15

A second miniature sheet contains one each of Nos. C29a, C30-C32. Value, $50.

Issued: 25fr, 80fr, 6/25; 50fr, 100fr, No. C32a, 6/26.

Log Rolling — AP14

**1965, Aug. 14** **Engr.** ***Perf. 13***

**C33** AP14 50fr grn, brn & red brn 1.60 .75

Issued to publicize national unity.

World Map and Symbols of Agriculture and Industry AP15

**1965, Oct. 18** **Engr.** ***Perf. 13***

**C34** AP15 50fr dk bl, blk, brn & org 1.40 .90

International Cooperation Year, 1965.

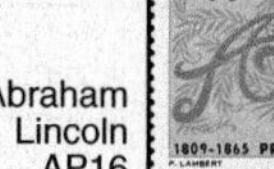

Abraham Lincoln AP16

**1965, Dec. 15** **Photo.** ***Perf. 13***

**C35** AP16 90fr pink & multi 1.40 .60

Centenary of death of Abraham Lincoln.

Charles de Gaulle, Torch and Map of Africa AP17

**1966, Feb. 28** **Engr.** ***Perf. 13***

**C36** AP17 500fr dk red, dk grn & dk red brn 30.00 26.00

22nd anniv. of the Brazzaville Conf.

D-1 Satellite over Brazzaville Space Tracking Station — AP18

**1966, May 15** **Engr.** ***Perf. 13***

**C37** AP18 150fr blk, dl red & bl grn 2.25 1.25

Grain, Atom Symbol and Map of Africa and Europe — AP19

**1966, July 20** **Photo.** ***Perf. 12x13***

**C38** AP19 50fr multicolored 1.10 .75

See note after Gabon No. C46.

Pres. Massamba-Debat and President's Palace — AP20

3rd anniv. of the Revolution: 30fr, Robespierre and storming of the Bastille. 50fr, Lenin and storming of the Winter Palace.

**1966, Aug. 15** **Photo.** ***Perf. 12x12½***

**C39** AP20 25fr multicolored .45 .30
**C40** AP20 30fr multicolored .65 .30
**C41** AP20 50fr multicolored 1.60 .50
*a.* Souv. sheet of 3, #C39-C41 2.25 2.25
*Nos. C39-C41 (3)* 2.70 1.10

### Air Afrique Issue, 1966
Common Design Type

**1966, Aug. 31** **Photo.** ***Perf. 13***

**C42** CD123 30fr lilac, lemon & blk 1.00 .25

Dr. Albert Schweitzer AP21

**1966, Sept. 4** **Photo.** ***Perf. 12½***

**C43** AP21 100fr red, blk, bl & lil 2.25 1.25

Issued to honor Dr. Albert Schweitzer (1875-1965), medical missionary.

Crab, Microscope and Pagoda — AP22

**1966, Dec. 26** **Photo.** ***Perf. 13***

**C44** AP22 100fr multicolored 1.75 1.00

9th Intl. Anticancer Cong., Tokyo. 10/23-29.

AP23

Birds: 50fr, Social Weaver. 75fr, European Bee-eater. 100fr, Lilac-breasted roller. 150fr, Regal sunbird. 200fr, Crowned cranes. 250fr, Secretary bird. 300fr, Knysna touraco.

**1967 Photo. *Perf. 13***

**C45** AP23 50fr multicolored 1.60 .75
**C46** AP23 75fr multicolored 3.25 1.00
**C47** AP23 100fr multicolored 3.25 1.00
**C48** AP23 150fr multicolored 4.25 2.25
**C49** AP23 200fr multicolored 7.50 2.50
**C50** AP23 250fr multicolored 9.50 3.00
**C51** AP23 300fr multicolored 13.50 5.00
*Nos. C45-C51 (7)* 42.85 15.50

Issued: Nos. C45-C47, 2/13; others, 6/20.

Shackled Hands — AP24

**1967, May 24 Photo. *Perf. 12½x13***

**C52** AP24 500fr multicolored 8.00 3.00

Issued for African Liberation Day.

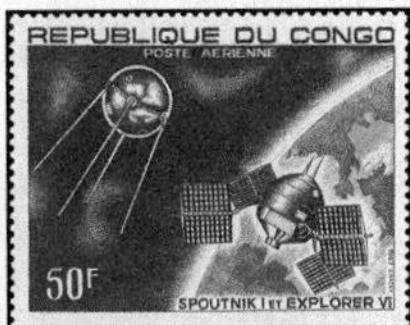


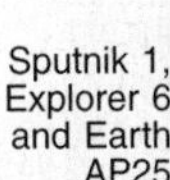

Sputnik 1, Explorer 6 and Earth AP25

Space Craft: 75fr, Ranger 6, Lunik 2 and moon. 100fr, Mars 1, Mariner 4 and Mars. 200fr, Gemini, Vostok and earth.

**1967, Aug. 1 Engr. *Perf. 13***

**C53** AP25 50fr multicolored .60 .30
**C54** AP25 75fr multicolored 1.10 .35
**C55** AP25 100fr multicolored 1.60 .60
**C56** AP25 200fr multicolored 2.75 1.50
*Nos. C53-C56 (4)* 6.05 2.75

Space explorations.

### African Postal Union Issue, 1967

Common Design Type

**1967, Sept. 9 Engr. *Perf. 13***

**C57** CD124 100fr ver, ol & emer 1.60 .60

Boy Scouts, Tents and Jamboree Emblem AP26

Design: 70c, Borah Peak, Idaho; tents, Scout sign and Jamboree emblem.

**1967, Sept. 29**

**C58** AP26 50fr multicolored .80 .30
**C59** AP26 70fr multicolored 1.20 .50

12th Boy Scout World Jamboree, Farragut State Park, ID, Aug. 1-9.

Sikorsky S-43 and Map of Africa AP27

**1967, Oct. 2 Photo. *Perf. 13***

**C60** AP27 30fr multicolored .90 .30

30th anniv. of the 1st airmail connection by Aeromaritime Lines from Casablanca to Pointe-Noire.

Men of Four Races Dancing on Globe AP28

**1968, Feb 8 Engr. *Perf. 13***

**C61** AP28 70fr dk brn, ultra & emer 1.50 .60

Friendship among peoples.

The Oath of the Horatii, by Jacques Louis David AP29

Paintings: 25fr, On the Barricades, by Delacroix. No. C63, Grandfather and Grandson, by Ghirlandajo, vert. No. C64, The Demolition of the Bastille, by Hubert Robert. 200fr, Negro Woman Arranging Peonies, by Jean F. Bazille.

**1968 Photo. *Perf. 12x12½, 12½x12***

**C62** AP29 25fr multicolored 1.75 .35
**C63** AP29 30fr multicolored .90 .30
**C64** AP29 30fr multicolored 1.75 .50
**C65** AP29 100fr multicolored 2.25 .90
**C66** AP29 200fr multicolored 5.00 1.75
*Nos. C62-C66 (5)* 11.65 3.80

Issue dates: Nos. C62, C64, Aug. 15. Nos. C63, C65-C66, Mar. 20.

See Nos. C78-C81, C111-C115.

### Early Automobile Type

**1968, July 29 Photo. *Perf. 13x12½***

**C67** A50 150fr Ford, 1915 3.50 1.75
**C68** A50 200fr Citroen, 1922 5.25 1.75

### Europafrica Issue

Square Knot AP30

**1968, July 20 Photo. *Perf. 13***

**C69** AP30 50fr multicolored 1.50 .50

5th anniv. of the economic agreement between the European Economic Community and the African and Malgache Union.

Martin Luther King, Jr. — AP31

**1968, Aug. 5 *Perf. 12½***

**C70** AP31 50fr lt grn, Prus grn & blk 1.60 .40

Robert F. Kennedy — AP32

**1968, Sept. 30 Photo. *Perf. 13x12½***

**C71** AP32 50fr dp car, ap grn & blk .85 .40

Running AP33

Olympic Rings and: 20fr, Soccer, vert. 60fr, Boxing, vert. 85fr, High jump.

**1968, Dec. 27 Engr. *Perf. 13***

**C72** AP33 5fr emer, brt bl & choc .25 .25
**C73** AP33 20fr dk bl, brn & dk grn .45 .25
**C74** AP33 60fr mar, brt grn & choc .90 .60
**C75** AP33 85fr blk, car rose & choc 1.75 .85
*Nos. C72-C75 (4)* 3.35 1.95

19th Olympic Games, Mexico City, 10/12-27.

### PHILEXAFRIQUE Issue

G. De Gueidan, by Nicolas de Largillière AP34

**1968, Dec. 30 Photo. *Perf. 12½***

**C76** AP34 100fr pink & multi 2.75 1.75

Issued to publicize PHILEXAFRIQUE, Philatelic Exhibition, in Abidjan, Feb. 14-23. Printed with alternating pink label.

See Nos. C89-C93.

### 2nd PHILEXAFRIQUE Issue

Common Design Type

Design: 50fr, Middle Congo No. 72 and Pointe-Noire harbor.

**1969, Feb. 14 Engr. *Perf. 13***

**C77** CD128 50fr car rose, sl grn & bis brn 2.00 1.75

### Painting Type of 1968

Paintings: 25fr, Battle of Rivoli, by Carle Vernet. 50fr, Battle of Marengo, by Jacques Augustin Pajou. 75fr, Battle of Friedland, by Horace Vernet. 100fr, Battle of Jena, by Charles Thevenin.

**1969, May 20 Photo. *Perf. 12x12½***

**C78** AP29 25fr vio bl & multi 1.25 .45
**C79** AP29 50fr cop red & multi 1.75 .80
**C80** AP29 75fr grn & multi 3.00 1.10
**C81** AP29 100fr brn & multi 5.00 1.40
*Nos. C78-C81 (4)* 11.00 3.75

Bicentenary of birth of Napoleon I.

Ernesto Ché Guevara — AP35

**1969, June 10 Photo. *Perf. 12½***

**C82** AP35 90fr brn, org & blk 1.30 .50

Issued in memory of Ernesto Ché Guevara (1928-1967), Cuban revolutionist.

Doll, Train and Space Toy — AP36

**1969, June 20 Engr. *Perf. 13***

**C83** AP36 100fr mag, org & gray 1.75 .75

International Toy Fair, Nuremberg, Germany.

### Europafrica Issue

Ribbon Tied Around Bar — AP37

**1969, Aug. 5 Photo. *Perf. 13x12***

**C84** AP37 50fr bl grn, lil & blk .90 .35

Souvenir Sheet

Armstrong, Aldrin and Collins — AP38

Design: No. C85b, Blast-off from Moon.

**Embossed on Gold Foil**

**1969, Sept. 15 *Imperf.***

**C85** AP38 1000fr #a-b 30.00 27.50

See note after Algeria No. 427. No. C85 contains one each of Nos. C85a and C85b with simulated perforations.

Painter, Poto-Poto School — AP39

150fr, Sculpture lesson (man, infant and sculpture). 200fr, Potter working on vase.

**1970, Feb. 20 Engr. *Perf. 13***

**C86** AP39 100fr multicolored 2.25 .60
**C87** AP39 150fr multicolored 3.00 .95
**C88** AP39 200fr multicolored 3.75 1.75
*Nos. C86-C88 (3)* 9.00 3.30

### Painting Type (Philexafrique)

Paintings: 150fr, Child with Cherries, by John Russell. 200fr, Erasmus, by Hans Holbein the Younger. 250fr, "Silence" (head), by Bernardino Luini. 300fr, Scene from the Massacre of Scio, by Delacroix. 500fr, The Capture of Constantinople by the Crusaders, by Delacroix.

**1970 Photo. *Perf. 12½***

**C89** AP34 150fr lil & multi 4.50 1.50
**C90** AP34 200fr multicolored 5.75 1.75
**C91** AP34 250fr brn & multi 6.25 2.25
**C92** AP34 300fr multicolored 8.00 3.25
**C93** AP34 500fr brn & multi 13.50 4.50
*Nos. C89-C93 (5)* 38.00 13.25

Aurichalcite AP40

**1970, Mar. 20**

**C94** AP40 100fr shown 5.25 1.75
**C95** AP40 150fr Dioptase 8.00 2.50

Lenin — AP41

**1970, June 25 Photo. *Perf. 12½***

| | | | | |
|---|---|---|---|---|
| C96 | AP41 | 45fr shown | 1.00 | .35 |
| C97 | AP41 | 75fr Lenin, seated | 1.75 | .50 |

Centenary of the birth of Lenin (1870-1924), Russian communist leader.

Karl Marx — AP42

Design: No. C99, Friedrich Engels.

**1970, July 10 Engr. *Perf. 13***

| | | | | |
|---|---|---|---|---|
| C98 | AP42 | 50fr emer, dk brn & dk red | 1.40 | .35 |
| C99 | AP42 | 50fr ultra, dk brn & dk red | 1.40 | .35 |

Karl Marx (1818-1883) and Friedrich Engels (1820-1895), German socialist writers.

Otto Lilienthal's Glider, 1891 AP43

Designs: 50fr, "Spirit of St. Louis," Lindbergh's first transatlantic solo flight, 1927. 70fr, Sputnik 1, first satellite in space. 90fr, First man on the moon, Apollo 11, 1969.

**1970, Sept. 5 Engr. *Perf. 13***

| | | | | |
|---|---|---|---|---|
| C100 | AP43 | 45fr dp car, bl & ol bis | 1.00 | .30 |
| C101 | AP43 | 50fr emer, sl grn & brn | 1.00 | .35 |
| C102 | AP43 | 70fr brt bl, ol bis & dp car | 1.25 | .50 |
| C103 | AP43 | 90fr brn, bl & ol gray | 1.90 | .75 |
| | | *Nos. C100-C103 (4)* | 5.15 | 1.90 |

Forerunners of space exploration.

Saint on Horseback — AP44

Designs from Stained Glass Windows, Brazzaville Cathedral: 150fr, Saint with staff. 250fr, The Elevation of the Host, from rose window.

**1970, Dec. 10 Photo. *Perf. 12½***

| | | | | |
|---|---|---|---|---|
| C104 | AP44 | 100fr multicolored | 1.25 | .50 |
| C105 | AP44 | 150fr multicolored | 1.75 | .85 |
| C106 | AP44 | 250fr multicolored | 3.00 | 1.75 |
| *a.* | | Souv. sheet of 3, #C104-C106 | 6.75 | 6.75 |
| | | *Nos. C104-C106 (3)* | 6.00 | 3.10 |

Christmas 1970.

Marilyn Monroe and NYC — AP45

Portraits: 150fr, Martine Carol and Paris. 200fr, Erich von Stroheim and Vienna. 250fr, Sergei Eisenstein and Moscow.

**1971, Mar. 16 Engr. *Perf. 13***

| | | | | |
|---|---|---|---|---|
| C107 | AP45 | 100fr brt grn, red brn & ultra | 7.00 | .50 |
| C108 | AP45 | 150fr brn, brt lil & ultra | 7.00 | .75 |
| C109 | AP45 | 200fr choc & ultra | 7.00 | 1.10 |
| C110 | AP45 | 250fr brt grn, brn vio & ultra | 7.00 | 1.25 |
| | | *Nos. C107-C110 (4)* | 28.00 | 3.60 |

History of motion pictures.

**Painting Type of 1968**

Paintings: 100fr, Christ Carrying Cross, by Paolo Veronese. 150fr, Christ on the Cross, Burgundian School, 1500, vert. 200fr, Descent from the Cross, by Rogier van der Weyden. 250fr, Christ Laid in the Tomb, Flemish School, 1500, vert. 500fr, Resurrection, by Hans Memling, vert.

**1971, Apr. 26 Photo. *Perf. 13***

| | | | | |
|---|---|---|---|---|
| C111 | AP29 | 100fr green & multi | 1.75 | .75 |
| C112 | AP29 | 150fr green & multi | 2.75 | .90 |
| C113 | AP29 | 200fr green & multi | 4.00 | 1.10 |
| C114 | AP29 | 250fr green & multi | 4.50 | 1.60 |
| C115 | AP29 | 500fr green & multi | 10.00 | 3.00 |
| | | *Nos. C111-C115 (5)* | 23.00 | 7.35 |

Easter 1971.

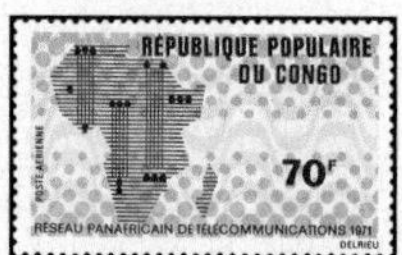
Map of Africa and Telecommunications System — AP46

**1971, June 18 Photo. *Perf. 12½***

| | | | | |
|---|---|---|---|---|
| C116 | AP46 | 70fr bl, gray & dk brn | .80 | .30 |
| C117 | AP46 | 85fr bl, lil rose & dk brn | 1.25 | .35 |
| C118 | AP46 | 90fr grn, yel & dk brn | 1.60 | .70 |
| | | *Nos. C116-C118 (3)* | 3.65 | 1.35 |

Pan-African telecommunications system.

Globe and Waves AP47

**1971, June 19**

| | | | | |
|---|---|---|---|---|
| C119 | AP47 | 65fr lt bl & multi | .80 | .30 |

3rd World Telecommunications Day.

Japanese Mask and Play — AP48

Design: 150fr, Japanese and African women, symbolic leaves.

**1971, June 28 Engr. *Perf. 13***

| | | | | |
|---|---|---|---|---|
| C120 | AP48 | 75fr lil, blk & mag | 1.00 | .70 |
| C121 | AP48 | 150fr dk brn, brn red & red lil | 1.60 | 1.10 |

PHILATOKYO '71 International Stamp Exhibition, Tokyo, Apr. 20-30.

Olympic Torch and Rings — AP49

350fr, Olympic rings and various sports.

**1971, July 20 Engr. *Perf. 13***

| | | | | |
|---|---|---|---|---|
| C122 | AP49 | 150fr multi | 1.90 | .95 |
| C123 | AP49 | 350fr multi, horiz. | 4.50 | 2.50 |

Pre-Olympic Year, 1971.

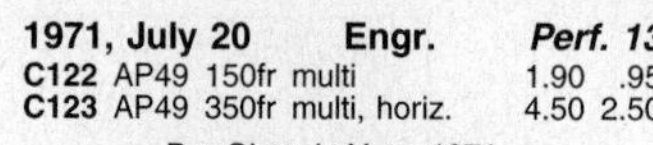

Scout Emblem, Japanese Dragon and African Carved Canoe AP50

Designs (Boy Scout Emblem and): 90fr, Japanese mask and African boy, vert. 100fr, Japanese woman and African drummer, vert. 250fr, Congolese mask.

**1971, Aug. 25**

| | | | | |
|---|---|---|---|---|
| C124 | AP50 | 85fr multicolored | 1.10 | .30 |
| C125 | AP50 | 90fr multicolored | 1.25 | .35 |
| C126 | AP50 | 100fr multicolored | 1.60 | .45 |
| C127 | AP50 | 250fr multicolored | 3.25 | .90 |
| | | *Nos. C124-C127 (4)* | 7.20 | 2.00 |

13th Boy Scout World Jamboree, Asagiri Plain, Japan, Aug. 2-10.

Olympic Rings and Running AP51

Designs (Olympic Rings and): 85fr, Hurdles. 90fr, Weight lifting, boxing, discus, running, javelin. 100fr, Wrestling. 150fr, Boxing.

**1971, Sept. 30**

| | | | | |
|---|---|---|---|---|
| C128 | AP51 | 75fr plum, bl & dk brn | .75 | .35 |
| C129 | AP51 | 85fr scar, sl & dk brn | .85 | .35 |
| C130 | AP51 | 90fr vio bl & dk brn | 1.10 | .60 |
| C131 | AP51 | 100fr brn & slate | 1.40 | .60 |
| C132 | AP51 | 150fr grn, red & dk brn | 2.40 | 1.00 |
| | | *Nos. C128-C132 (5)* | 6.50 | 2.90 |

75th anniv. of the 1st modern Olympic Games.

Congo No. C36 and de Gaulle AP52

Design: No. C135, Charles de Gaulle.

**1971, Nov. 9**

| | | | | |
|---|---|---|---|---|
| C133 | AP52 | 500fr slate grn & multi | 18.00 | 15.00 |

Pres. Marien Ngouabi's Tribute to de Gaulle — AP53

**Lithographed; Gold Embossed**
***Perf. 12½***

| | | | | |
|---|---|---|---|---|
| C134 | AP53 | 1000fr gold, grn & red | 27.50 | 20.00 |
| C135 | AP53 | 1000fr gold, grn & red | 27.50 | 20.00 |
| *a.* | | Pair, #C134-C135 | 55.00 | 55.00 |

Charles de Gaulle (1890-1970), president of France.

**African Postal Union Issue, 1971**
Common Design Type

Design: 100fr, Allegory of Congo Republic (woman) and UAMPT Building, Brazzaville.

**1971, Nov. 13 Photo. *Perf. 13x13½***

| | | | | |
|---|---|---|---|---|
| C136 | CD135 | 100fr bl & multi | 1.60 | .75 |

Flag of Congo Republic and "Revolution" AP54

**1971, Nov. 30**

| | | | | |
|---|---|---|---|---|
| C137 | AP54 | 100fr red & multi | 1.75 | .60 |

8th anniversary of revolution.

Workers and Flag AP55

40fr, Flag of Congo Republic and sun.

**1971, Dec. 31 Photo. *Perf. 13x12½***

| | | | | |
|---|---|---|---|---|
| C138 | AP55 | 30fr multicolored | .75 | .30 |
| C139 | AP55 | 40fr red & multi | 1.50 | .50 |

2nd anniv. of founding of Congolese Labor Party (No. C138), and adoption of red flag (No. C139).

Book Year Emblem — AP56

**1972, June 3 Litho. *Perf. 12½***

| | | | | |
|---|---|---|---|---|
| C140 | AP56 | 50fr red, grn & yel | 1.00 | .40 |

International Book Year 1972.

Congolese Soccer Team — AP57

No. C142, Captain of winning team and cup, vert.

**1973, Feb. 22 Photo. *Perf. 13***

| | | | | |
|---|---|---|---|---|
| C141 | AP57 | 100fr ultra, red & blk | 1.50 | .75 |
| C142 | AP57 | 100fr red, yel & blk | 1.50 | .75 |

Girl Holding Bird, Environment Emblem — AP58

**1973, Mar. 5 Engr.**

| | | | | |
|---|---|---|---|---|
| C143 | AP58 | 85fr org, slate grn & bl | 1.75 | .90 |

UN Conference on Human Environment, Stockholm, Sweden, June 5-16, 1972.

Miles Davis — AP59

Designs: 140fr, Ella Fitzgerald. 160fr, Count Basie. 175fr, John Coltrane.

**1973, Mar. 5 Photo. *Perf. 13x13½***

| | | | | |
|---|---|---|---|---|
| C144 | AP59 | 125fr multicolored | 3.50 | .95 |
| C145 | AP59 | 140fr multicolored | 3.50 | 1.00 |
| C146 | AP59 | 160fr multicolored | 4.50 | 1.50 |
| C147 | AP59 | 175fr multicolored | 4.50 | 1.50 |
| | | *Nos. C144-C147 (4)* | 16.00 | 4.95 |

Black American jazz musicians.

Olympic Rings, Hurdling AP60

150fr, Pole vault, vert. 250fr, Wrestling.

**1973, Mar. 15 Engr. *Perf. 13***
**C148** AP60 100fr shown 1.10 .60
**C149** AP60 150fr multi 1.75 .90
**C150** AP60 250fr multi 2.75 1.50
*Nos. C148-C150 (3)* 5.60 3.00

20th Olympic Games, Munich, 8/26-9/11/72.

Refinery and Storage Tanks, Djéno AP61

Designs: 230fr, Off-shore drilling platform, vert. 240fr, Workers assembling drill, vert. 260fr, Off-shore drilling installation.

**1973, Mar. 20**
**C151** AP61 180fr red, bl & indigo 3.25 1.50
**C152** AP61 230fr red, bl & blk 4.00 1.50
**C153** AP61 240fr red, ind & brn 4.50 1.60
**C154** AP61 260fr red, bl & blk 7.25 2.25
*Nos. C151-C154 (4)* 19.00 6.85

Oil installations, Pointe-Noire.

Astronauts, Landing Module and Lunar Rover on Moon AP62

**1973, Mar. 31**
**C155** AP62 250fr multicolored 4.00 1.75

Apollo 17 US moon mission, 12/7-19/72.

ITU Emblem, Symbols of Communications AP63

**1973, May 24 Engr. *Perf. 13***
**C156** AP63 120fr multicolored 2.25 .90

5th International Telecommunications Day.

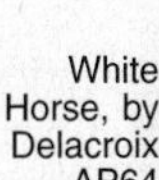

White Horse, by Delacroix AP64

Designs: Paintings by Eugene Delacroix.

**1973, June 30 Photo. *Perf. 13***
**C157** AP64 150fr shown 2.25 1.50
**C158** AP64 250fr Lion sleeping 5.00 2.40
**C159** AP64 300fr Lion and tiger 5.25 2.50
*Nos. C157-C159 (3)* 12.50 6.40

See Nos. C169-C171.

Copernicus and Heliocentric System AP65

**1973, June 30 Engr.**
**C160** AP65 50fr multicolored 1.00 .45

500th anniversary of the birth of Nicolaus Copernicus (1473-1543), Polish astronomer.

Plane, Ship, Rocket, Village, Sun and Clouds AP66

**1973, July**
**C161** AP66 50fr red & multi 1.60 .60

Cent. of intl. meteorological cooperation.

Pres. Marien Ngouabi — AP67

**1973, Aug. 12 Photo. *Perf. 13***
**C162** AP67 30fr multicolored .35 .25
**C163** AP67 40fr aqua & multi .45 .25
**C164** AP67 75fr red & multi 1.00 .35
*Nos. C162-C164 (3)* 1.80 .85

10th anniversary of independence.

Stamps, Album, African Woman — AP68

No. C167, Stamps in shape of map of Congo, album, globe. No. C168, Like 30fr.

**1973, Aug. 12**
**C165** AP68 30fr pur & multi 1.90 .30
**C166** AP68 40fr multicolored .25 .25
**C167** AP68 100fr dk brn & multi 3.75 .80
**C168** AP68 100fr ocher & multi .90 .40
*Nos. C165-C168 (4)* 6.80 1.75

Nos. C165, C168 for the 10th anniv. of the revolution, Nos. C166-C167 the Intl. Philatelic Exhib., Brazzaville.

**Painting Type of 1973 Inscribed "EUROPAFRIQUE"**

Details from "Earth and Paradise," by Jan Brueghel, the Elder: No. C169, Spotted hyena. No. C170, Leopard and lion. No. C171, Elephant and creatures.

**1973, Oct. 10 Photo. *Perf. 13***
**C169** AP64 100fr multi 3.00 1.50
**C170** AP64 100fr multi 3.00 1.50
**C171** AP64 100fr multi 3.00 1.50
*Nos. C169-C171 (3)* 9.00 4.50

US and Russian Spacecraft Docking AP69

Design: 80fr, US and USSR spacecraft docked in space and emblems of 1975 joint space mission.

**1973, Oct. 15 Engr. *Perf. 13***
**C172** AP69 40fr bl, red & brn .50 .35
**C173** AP69 80fr red, grn & bl 1.10 .50

Planned joint US and Soviet space missions.
For overprint see No. C251.

UPU Monument, Satellites, Big Dipper AP70

**1973, Nov. 20 Engr. *Perf. 13***
**C174** AP70 80fr vio bl & lt bl 1.60 .50

Universal Postal Union Day.

Astronauts Working in Space AP71

40fr, Spacecraft & Skylab docking in space.

**1973, Nov. 30**
**C175** AP71 30fr ultra, sl grn & choc .65 .25
**C176** AP71 40fr mag, org & sl grn .95 .25

Skylab, first space laboratory.

Goalkeeper, Soccer — AP72

Design: 100fr, Soccer player kicking ball.

**1973, Dec. 20**
**C177** AP72 40fr sl grn, sepia & brn .75 .25
**C178** AP72 100fr pur, red & slate grn 1.90 .75

World Soccer Cup, Munich, 1974.

John F. Kennedy (1917-1963) AP73

**1973, Dec. 20 Photo. *Perf. 12½***
**C179** AP73 150fr ultra, gold & blk 1.75 .90

Runners — AP74

**1973, Dec. 20 Engr. *Perf. 13***
**C180** AP74 40fr sl grn, red & brn .60 .25
**C181** AP74 100fr red, sl grn, & brn 1.75 .75

2nd African Games, Lagos, Nigeria.

Flag over Map of Congo — AP75

**1973, Dec. 31 Photo.**
**C182** AP75 40fr dp grn & multi .80 .25

4th anniversary of Congolese Labor Party and of the Congo Red Flag.

Soccer and Games Emblem — AP76

**1974, June 20 Photo. *Perf. 13***
**C183** AP76 250fr multicolored 3.75 1.90

World Cup Soccer Championship, Munich, June 13-July 7.

Astronauts Yuri A. Gagarin and Alan B. Shepard AP77

Designs: 30fr, Space, globe, Russian and American flags with names of astronauts who perished in space. 100fr, Alexei Leonov and Neil A. Armstrong in space and on moon.

**1974, June 30 Engr. *Perf. 13***
**C184** AP77 30fr red, ultra & brn .45 .25
**C185** AP77 40fr red, bl & brn .70 .25
**C186** AP77 100fr car, grn & brn 1.60 .90
*Nos. C184-C186 (3)* 2.75 1.40

For overprint see No. C254.

Soccer Game Superimposed on Ball — AP78

**1974, July 31 Photo. *Perf. 13***
**C187** AP78 250fr multicolored 3.50 1.75

Germany's victory in World Cup Soccer Championship.

Link-up Emblem, Stages of Link-up — AP79

300fr, Spacecraft docking over globe.

**1974, Aug. 8 Engr. *Perf. 13***
**C188** AP79 200fr pur, bl & red 2.25 1.10
**C189** AP79 300fr multi, horiz. 3.50 1.50

Russo-American space cooperation.
For overprint see No. C255.

Symbols of Communications, UPU Emblem — AP80

**1974, Aug. 10**
**C190** AP80 500fr blk & red 6.75 3.00

Centenary of Universal Postal Union.
For surcharge see No. C194.

Lenin and Pendulum Trace Pattern AP81

**1974, Sept. 16 Engr. *Perf. 13***
**C191** AP81 150fr multicolored 2.10 1.10

Lenin (1870-1924).

Churchill and Order of the Garter — AP82

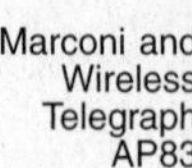

Marconi and Wireless Telegraph AP83

**1974, Oct. 1 Litho. *Perf. 13***

| | | | | |
|---|---|---|---|---|
| **C192** | AP82 | 200fr lt grn & multi | 2.50 | 1.25 |
| **C193** | AP83 | 200fr lt ultra & multi | 2.50 | 1.25 |

**No. C190 Srchd. in Violet Blue with New Value, 2 Bars and "9 OCTOBER 1974"**

**1974, Oct. 9**

| | | | | |
|---|---|---|---|---|
| **C194** | AP80 | 300fr on 500fr multi | 4.25 | 2.75 |

Universal Postal Union Day.

**UDEAC Issue**

Presidents and Flags of Cameroun, CAR, Gabon and Congo AP83a

**1974, Dec. 8 Photo. *Perf. 13***

| | | | | |
|---|---|---|---|---|
| **C195** | AP83a | 100fr gold & multi | 1.60 | .50 |

See note after Cameroun No. 595.

Regatta at Argenteuil, by Monet AP84

Impressionist Paintings: 40fr, Seated Dancer, by Degas. 50fr, Girl on Swing, by Renoir. 75fr, Girl with Straw Hat, by Renoir. All vertical.

**1974, Dec. 15**

| | | | | |
|---|---|---|---|---|
| **C196** | AP84 | 30fr gold & multi | 1.50 | .35 |
| **C197** | AP84 | 40fr gold & multi | 2.00 | .35 |
| **C198** | AP84 | 50fr gold & multi | 2.75 | .50 |
| **C199** | AP84 | 75fr gold & multi | 3.25 | .80 |
| | | *Nos. C196-C199 (4)* | 9.50 | 2.00 |

National Fair — AP85

**1974, Dec. 20**

| | | | | |
|---|---|---|---|---|
| **C200** | AP85 | 30fr multicolored | 1.05 | .35 |

National Fair, Aug. 24-Sept. 8.

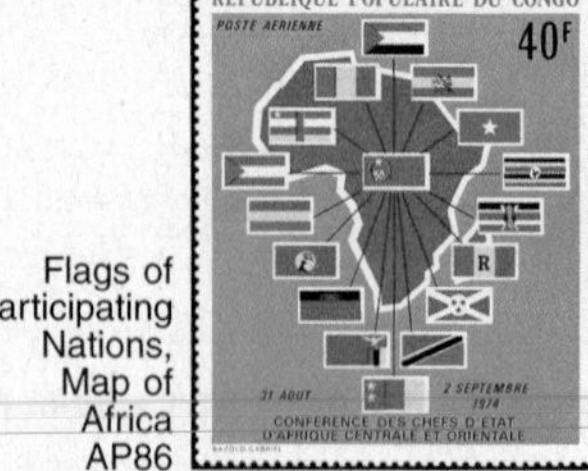

Flags of Participating Nations, Map of Africa AP86

**1974, Dec. 20 *Perf. 13***

| | | | | |
|---|---|---|---|---|
| **C201** | AP86 | 40fr ultra & multi | .80 | .45 |

Conference of Chiefs of State of Central and East Africa, Brazzaville, Aug. 31-Sept. 2.

"Five Weeks in a Balloon," by Jules Verne — AP87

Design: 50fr, "Around the World in 80 Days," by Jules Verne.

**1975, June 30 Litho. *Perf. 12½***

| | | | | |
|---|---|---|---|---|
| **C202** | AP87 | 40fr multicolored | 1.40 | .50 |
| **C203** | AP87 | 50fr multicolored | 1.75 | 1.00 |

Jules Verne (1828-1905), French science fiction writer, 70th death anniversary.

Paris-Brussels Train, 1890 — AP88

Design: 75fr, Santa Fe, 1880.

**1975, June 30**

| | | | | |
|---|---|---|---|---|
| **C204** | AP88 | 50fr ocher & multi | 2.00 | .75 |
| **C205** | AP88 | 75fr lt bl & multi | 4.25 | .90 |

Soyuz and Apollo-Soyuz Emblem — AP89

Design: 100fr, Apollo and emblem.

**1975, July 20 Litho. *Perf. 12½***

| | | | | |
|---|---|---|---|---|
| **C206** | AP89 | 95fr org, blk & mag | 1.25 | .50 |
| **C207** | AP89 | 100fr vio, bl & blk | 1.40 | .60 |

Apollo Soyuz space test project (Russo-American space cooperation), launching July 15; link-up, July 17.

For overprints see Nos. C252-C253.

Bicycling and Montreal Olympic Emblem AP90

Designs (Montreal Olympic Emblem and): 40fr, Boxing, vert. 50fr, Basketball, vert. 95fr, High jump. 100fr, Javelin. 150fr, Running.

***Perf. 12½x13, 13x12½***

**1975, Oct. 30 Photo.**

| | | | | |
|---|---|---|---|---|
| **C208** | AP90 | 40fr multicolored | .50 | .25 |
| **C209** | AP90 | 50fr red & multi | .60 | .25 |
| **C210** | AP90 | 85fr bl & multi | 1.00 | .35 |
| **C211** | AP90 | 95fr org & multi | 1.10 | .45 |
| **C212** | AP90 | 100fr multicolored | 1.40 | .50 |
| **C213** | AP90 | 150fr multicolored | 1.75 | .80 |
| | | *Nos. C208-C213 (6)* | 6.35 | 2.60 |

Pre-Olympic Year 1975.

Map of Africa, Sports and Flags — AP91

**1975, Dec. 20 Litho. *Perf. 12½***

| | | | | |
|---|---|---|---|---|
| **C214** | AP91 | 30fr multicolored | .80 | .35 |

1st African Games, Brazzaville, 10th anniv.

Workers and Flag — AP92

**1975, Dec. 31 Litho. *Perf. 12½***

| | | | | |
|---|---|---|---|---|
| **C215** | AP92 | 60fr multicolored | 1.10 | .25 |

Congolese Labor Party (P.C.T.), 6th anniv.

Alphonse Fondere AP93

Historic Ships: 5fr, like 30fr. 10fr, 40fr, Hamburg, 1839. 15fr, 50fr, Gomer, 1831. 20fr, 60fr, Great Eastern, 1858. 95fr, J.M. White II, 1878.

**1976 Engr. *Perf. 13***

| | | | | |
|---|---|---|---|---|
| **C216** | AP93 | 5fr multicolored | .25 | .25 |
| **C217** | AP93 | 10fr multicolored | .25 | .25 |
| **C218** | AP93 | 15fr multicolored | .30 | .25 |
| **C219** | AP93 | 20fr multicolored | .50 | .25 |
| **C220** | AP93 | 30fr multicolored | .75 | .25 |
| **C221** | AP93 | 40fr multicolored | 1.00 | .35 |
| **C222** | AP93 | 50fr multicolored | 1.25 | .50 |
| **C223** | AP93 | 60fr multicolored | 1.75 | .60 |
| **C224** | AP93 | 95fr multicolored | 2.50 | 1.00 |
| | | *Nos. C216-C224 (9)* | 8.55 | 3.70 |

Issued: Nos. C216-C219, May; Nos. C220-C224, Mar. 7.

**Europafrica Issue**

Peasant Family, by Louis Le Nain AP94

Paintings: 80fr, Boy with Top, by Jean B. Chardin. 95fr, Venus and Aeneas, by Nicolas Poussin. 100fr, The Rape of the Sabine Women, by Jacques Louis David.

**1976, Mar. 20 Litho. *Perf. 12½***

| | | | | |
|---|---|---|---|---|
| **C225** | AP94 | 60fr gold & multi | 1.25 | .45 |
| **C226** | AP94 | 80fr gold & multi | 1.40 | .70 |
| **C227** | AP94 | 95fr gold & multi | 1.90 | .70 |
| **C228** | AP94 | 100fr gold & multi | 2.10 | .85 |
| | | *Nos. C225-C228 (4)* | 6.65 | 2.70 |

Nos. C225-C228 printed in sheets of 8 stamps and horizontal gutter with commemorative inscription.

**Telephone Type of 1976**

**1976, Apr. 25 Litho. *Perf. 12½x13***

| | | | | |
|---|---|---|---|---|
| **C229** | A107 | 60fr pink, mar & crim | .90 | .30 |

**Sports Type of 1976**

Designs: 150fr, Runner and map of Central Africa. 200fr, Discus and map.

**1976, Oct. 25 *Perf. 12½***

| | | | | |
|---|---|---|---|---|
| **C230** | A110 | 150fr multicolored | 1.75 | .75 |
| **C231** | A110 | 200fr multicolored | 2.75 | 1.10 |

Map of Africa, Flag and OAU Headquarters — AP95

**1976, Dec. 16 Typo. *Perf. 13x14***

| | | | | |
|---|---|---|---|---|
| **C232** | AP95 | 60fr multicolored | .90 | .35 |

13th anniv. of the Organization for African Unity.

**Europafrica Issue**

Map of Europe and Africa AP96

**1977, June 28 Litho. *Perf. 13***

| | | | | |
|---|---|---|---|---|
| **C233** | AP96 | 75fr multicolored | 1.00 | .45 |

**Headdress Type of 1977**

**1977, June 30 *Perf. 12½***

250fr, Two straw caps. 300fr, Beaded cap.

| | | | | |
|---|---|---|---|---|
| **C234** | A118 | 250fr multicolored | 2.75 | 1.50 |
| **C235** | A118 | 300fr multicolored | 3.00 | 1.75 |

**Zeppelin Type of 1977**

Souvenir Sheet

Design: 500fr, LZ 127 over US Capitol.

**1977, Aug. 5 Litho. *Perf. 11***

| | | | | |
|---|---|---|---|---|
| **C236** | A120 | 500fr multicolored | 6.75 | 2.00 |

No. C236 exists imperf.

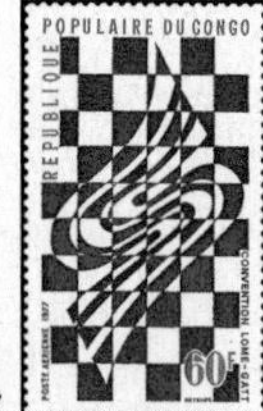

Checkerboard — AP97

**1977, Aug. 20 Engr. *Perf. 13***

| | | | | |
|---|---|---|---|---|
| **C237** | AP97 | 60fr red & blk | .90 | .35 |

Lomé Convention on General Agreement on Tariffs and Trade (GATT).

Newton, Intelsat Satellite and Classical "Planets" AP98

**1977, Aug. 25**

| | | | | |
|---|---|---|---|---|
| **C238** | AP98 | 140fr multicolored | 2.00 | .90 |

Isaac Newton (1642-1727), natural philosopher and mathematician.

**Elizabeth II Type of 1977**

Souvenir Sheet

Design: 500fr, Royal family on balcony.

**1977, Dec. 21 Litho. *Perf. 14***

| | | | | |
|---|---|---|---|---|
| **C239** | A128 | 500fr multicolored | 5.75 | 1.75 |

For overprint see No. C244.

Mallard — AP99

Birds: 75fr, Purple heron, vert. 150fr, Reed warbler, vert. 240fr, Hoopoe, vert.

**1978, May 22 *Perf. 13x12½, 12½x13***

| | | | | |
|---|---|---|---|---|
| **C240** | AP99 | 65fr multicolored | 1.40 | .50 |
| **C241** | AP99 | 75fr multicolored | 1.40 | .50 |
| **C242** | AP99 | 150fr multicolored | 3.50 | 1.00 |
| **C243** | AP99 | 240fr multicolored | 5.50 | 1.75 |
| | | *Nos. C240-C243 (4)* | 11.80 | 3.75 |

**No. C239 Overprinted in Silver: "ANNIVERSAIRE DU / COURONNEMENT / 1953-1978"**

**1978, Sept. Litho. *Perf. 14***

**Souvenir Sheet**

| | | | | |
|---|---|---|---|---|
| **C244** | A128 | 500fr multicolored | 4.50 | 3.00 |

25th anniv. of coronation of Elizabeth II.

**Philexafrique II-Essen Issue**

Common Design Types

No. C245, Leopard and Congo No. C243. No. C246, Eagle and Wurttemberg No. 1.

**1978, Nov. 1 Litho. *Perf. 12½***

**C245** CD138 100fr multicolored 2.00 1.10
**C246** CD139 100fr multicolored 2.00 1.10
*a.* Pair, #C245-C246 7.00 7.00

Map of Africa, Satellites — AP100

**1978, Nov. 25 Engr. *Perf. 13***

**C247** AP100 100fr multicolored 1.60 .50

Pan-African Telecommunications Network, PANAFTEL.

Map of Africa and People — AP101

**1979, Aug. 2 Litho. *Perf. 12½***

**C248** AP101 45fr multicolored .50 .25
**C249** AP101 75fr multicolored .85 .40

5th Conference of Panafrican Youth Movement, Brazzaville, Aug. 2-7.

Abala Peasant Woman — AP102

**1979, Aug. 20**

**C250** AP102 150fr multicolored 1.75 .90

**Nos. C173, C206-C207, C186, C189 Overprinted**

No. C251

No. C252

***Perf. 13, 12½***

**1979, Nov. 5 Engr., Litho.**

**C251** AP69 80fr multicolored 1.00 .90
**C252** AP89 95fr multicolored 1.10 1.00
**C253** AP89 100fr multicolored 1.10 1.00
**C254** AP77 100fr multicolored 1.10 1.00
**C255** AP79 300fr multicolored 3.00 2.75
*Nos. C251-C255 (5)* 7.30 6.65

Apollo 11 moon landing, 10th anniversary.

Runner, Olympic Rings AP103

Pre-Olympic Year: 100fr, Boxing. 200fr, Fencing. 300fr, Soccer. 500fr, Moscow '80 emblem.

**1979 Litho. *Perf. 13½***

**C256** AP103 65fr multi .60 .25
**C257** AP103 100fr multi .95 .25
**C258** AP103 200fr multi, vert. 1.90 .50

**C259** AP103 300fr multi 2.75 .75
**C260** AP103 500fr multi, vert. 4.75 1.25
*Nos. C256-C260 (5)* 10.95 3.00

Cross-Country Skiing — AP104

Lake Placid '80 Emblem and: 60fr, Slalom. 200fr, Ski jump, 350fr, Downhill skiing, horiz. 500fr, Woman skier.

**1979, Dec *Perf. 14½***

**Size: 24x42mm, 42x24mm**

**C261** AP104 40fr multicolored .45 .25
**C262** AP104 60fr multicolored .60 .25
**C263** AP104 200fr multicolored 1.90 .45
**C264** AP104 350fr multicolored 3.50 .90

**Size: 31½x46½mm**

***Perf. 14***

**C265** AP104 500fr multicolored 4.50 1.40
*Nos. C261-C265 (5)* 10.95 3.25

13th Winter Olympic Games, Lake Placid, NY, Feb. 12-24, 1980.

Nos. C261-C265 Overprinted in Black

40fr, Zimiatov. 60fr, Moser-Proell. 200fr, Tomanen. 350fr, Stock. 500fr, Stenmark-Wenzel.

**1980, Apr. 28**

**C266** AP104 40fr multi .45 .25
**C267** AP104 60fr multi .60 .25
**C268** AP104 200fr multi 1.90 .75
**C269** AP104 350fr multi 3.50 1.25
**C270** AP104 500fr multi 4.75 1.90
*Nos. C266-C270 (5)* 11.20 4.40

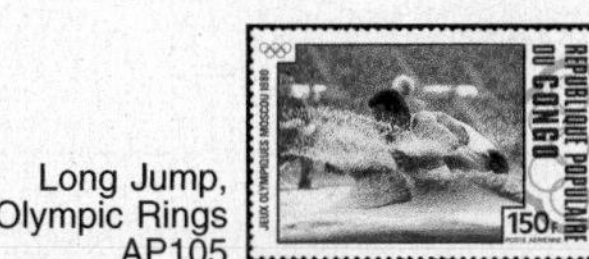

Long Jump, Olympic Rings AP105

**1980, May 2 Litho. *Perf. 14½***

**C271** AP105 75fr multi, vert. .90 .25
**C272** AP105 150fr multi 1.40 .30
**C273** AP105 250fr multi, vert. 2.25 .50
**C274** AP105 350fr multi, vert. 3.25 .70
*Nos. C271-C274 (4)* 7.80 1.75

**Souvenir Sheet**

**C275** AP105 500fr multi 5.00 1.60

22nd Summer Olympic Games, Moscow, July 19-Aug. 3.
For overprints see Nos. C292-C296.

Stadium, Mascot, Madrid Club Emblem AP106

Stadium, Mascot and Club Emblem: 75fr, Zaragoza. 100fr, Madrid Athletic Club. 150fr, Valencia. 175fr, Spain. 250fr, Barcelona.

**1980, June 23 Litho. *Perf. 14x13½***

**C276** AP106 60fr multicolored .60 .25
**C277** AP106 75fr multicolored .60 .25
**C278** AP106 100fr multicolored 1.00 .25
**C279** AP106 150fr multicolored 1.40 .35
**C280** AP106 175fr multicolored 1.60 .50
*Nos. C276-C280 (5)* 5.20 1.60

**Souvenir Sheet**

**C281** AP106 250fr multicolored 2.75 1.25

World Soccer Cup 1982.
For overprints see Nos. C298-C303.

Adoration of the Shepherds AP107

Rembrandt Paintings: 100fr, The Burial. 200fr, Christ at Emmaus. 300fr, Annunciation, vert. 500fr, Crucifixion, vert.

**1980, July 4 *Perf. 12½***

**C282** AP107 65fr multicolored .55 .30
**C283** AP107 100fr multicolored .85 .50
**C284** AP107 200fr multicolored 1.75 .60
**C285** AP107 300fr multicolored 2.50 .85
**C286** AP107 500fr multicolored 4.50 1.50
*Nos. C282-C286 (5)* 10.15 3.75

Albert Camus (1913-1960), Writer AP108

Design: 150fr, Jacques Offenbach (1819-1880), composer, vert.

**1980, July 5 Engr. *Perf. 13***

**C287** AP108 100fr multicolored 1.25 .50
**C288** AP108 150fr multicolored 2.25 1.25

Raffia Dancing Skirts AP109

Traditional Dancing Costumes: 300fr, Tam-tam dancers, vert. 350fr, Masks.

**1980, Aug. 6 Litho. *Perf. 13½***

**C289** AP109 250fr multicolored 2.75 .95
**C290** AP109 300fr multicolored 3.25 1.50
**C291** AP109 350fr multicolored 4.00 1.90
*Nos. C289-C291 (3)* 10.00 4.35

Nos. C271-C275 Overprinted

75fr, Dombrowki (RDA), 150fr, Saneiev (URSS), 250fr, Simeoni (IT), 350fr, Thompson (GB)

**1980, Nov. 14 Litho. *Perf. 14½***

**C292** AP105 75fr multicolored .70 .30
**C293** AP105 150fr multicolored 1.40 .60
**C294** AP105 250fr multicolored 2.25 .90
**C295** AP105 350fr multicolored 3.25 1.50
*Nos. C292-C295 (4)* 7.60 3.30

**Souvenir Sheet**

**C296** AP105 500fr multi 5.00 4.00

The Studio by Picasso AP109a

150fr, Landscape. 200fr, Cannes Studio. 300fr, Still Life. 500fr, Still Life, diff.

**1981, July 4 *Perf. 12½***

**C296A** AP109a 100fr shown 1.10 .50
**C296B** AP109a 150fr multi 1.60 .75
**C296C** AP109a 200fr multi 2.10 1.00
**C296D** AP109a 300fr multi 3.75 1.50
**C296E** AP109a 500fr multi 6.25 2.50
*Nos. C296A-C296E (5)* 14.80 6.25

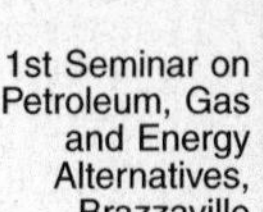

1st Seminar on Petroleum, Gas and Energy Alternatives, Brazzaville AP109b

45fr, Emblem, oil platform, other energy sources. 100fr, Emblem, map, oil platforms. 150fr, Map, other energy sources. 200fr, Maps of Africa, Congo, oil worker.

**1981 Litho. *Perf. 12½***

**C296F** AP109b 45fr multi 20.00 13.00
**C296G** AP109b 75fr multi 32.50 19.00
**C296H** AP109b 100fr multi 45.00 27.50
**C296I** AP109b 150fr multi 65.00 40.00
**C296J** AP109b 200fr multi 90.00 50.00
*Nos. C296F-C296J (5)* 252.50 149.50

1350th Anniv. of Mohamed's Death at Medina — AP110

400fr, Medina Mosque minaret.

**1982, July 17 Litho. *Perf. 13***

**C297** AP110 400fr multi 3.75 1.75

**Nos. C276-C281 Overprinted in Black on Silver**

No. C298

No. C299

No. C300

No. C301

No. C302

**1982, Oct. 7 Litho. *Perf. 14x13½***

**C298** AP106 60fr multicolored .55 .25
**C299** AP106 75fr multicolored .65 .30
**C300** AP106 100fr multicolored 1.00 .45
**C301** AP106 150fr multicolored 1.60 .60
**C302** AP106 175fr multicolored 1.75 .60
*Nos. C298-C302 (5)* 5.55 2.20

**Souvenir Sheet**

**C303** AP106 250fr multicolored 2.50 1.90

50th Anniv. of Amelia Earhart's Transatlantic Flight
AP111

**1982, Dec. 4 Engr. *Perf. 13***
**C304** AP111 150fr multicolored 1.75 .75

Wind Surfing — AP112

Various wind surfing scenes, 1984 Olympic Games, 100fr, 300fr, 400fr vert.

**1983, June 4 Litho. *Perf. 13***
**C305** AP112 100fr multicolored .90 .25
**C306** AP112 200fr multicolored 1.75 .50
**C307** AP112 300fr multicolored 2.75 .70
**C308** AP112 400fr multicolored 3.50 1.00
*Nos. C305-C308 (4)* 8.90 2.45

**Souvenir Sheet**

**C309** AP112 500fr multicolored 5.00 2.50

For overprint see No. C336.

Manned Flight Bicentenary
AP113

Various balloons: 100fr, Montgolfiere, 1783. 200fr, Flesselles, 1784. 300fr, Auguste Piccard, 1931. 400fr, Don Piccard.
500fr, Mail transport balloon, 1870.

**1983, June 7**
**C310** AP113 100fr multicolored 1.10 .25
**C311** AP113 200fr multicolored 2.10 .40
**C312** AP113 300fr multicolored 3.00 .60
**C313** AP113 400fr multicolored 4.50 .90
*Nos. C310-C313 (4)* 10.70 2.15

**Souvenir Sheet**

**C314** AP113 500fr multicolored 5.75 1.60

For overprint see No. C337.

Christmas 1983 — AP114

Various Virgin and Child Paintings by Botticelli.

**1984, Jan. 21 Litho. *Perf. 13***
**C315** AP114 150fr multicolored 1.25 .50
**C316** AP114 350fr multicolored 3.00 1.10
**C317** AP114 500fr multicolored 4.50 1.50
*Nos. C315-C317 (3)* 8.75 3.10

Vase of Flowers, by Manet (1832-83)
AP115

Paintings: 200fr, Small Holy Family, by Raphael. 300fr, La Belle Jardiniere, by Raphael. 400fr, Virgin of Loretto, by Raphael. 500fr, Portrait of Richard Wagner (1813-83), by Giuseppe Tivoli.

**1984, Feb. 24 Litho. *Perf. 13***
**C318** AP115 100fr multicolored .90 .30
**C319** AP115 200fr multicolored 1.90 .70
**C320** AP115 300fr multicolored 2.75 1.00
**C321** AP115 400fr multicolored 3.75 1.40
**C322** AP115 500fr multicolored 5.00 1.50
*Nos. C318-C322 (5)* 14.30 4.90

1984 Summer Olympics
AP116

**1984, Mar. 31 *Perf. 13***
**C323** AP116 45fr Judo, vert. .45 .25
**C324** AP116 75fr Judo, diff. .70 .25
**C325** AP116 150fr Wrestling 1.40 .50
**C326** AP116 175fr Fencing 1.60 .60
**C327** AP116 350fr Fencing, diff. 3.25 1.10
*Nos. C323-C327 (5)* 7.40 2.70

**Souvenir Sheet**

**C328** AP116 500fr Boxing 5.00 2.50

1984 Summer Olympic Gold Medalists
AP117

Sailing/yachting: 100fr, Stephan Van Den Berg, Netherlands, Windglider Class. 150fr, US, Soling Class. 200fr, Spain, 470 Class. 500fr, US, Flying Dutchman Class.

**1984, Dec. 18 Litho. *Perf. 13***
**C329** AP117 100fr multi, vert. 1.00 .45
**C330** AP117 150fr multi 1.40 .65
**C331** AP117 200fr multi 2.00 .90
**C332** AP117 500fr multi, vert. 4.50 2.25
*Nos. C329-C332 (4)* 8.90 4.25

Virgin and Child, by Giovanni Bellini (c. 1430-1516)
AP118

Religious paintings: 100fr, Holy Family, by Andrea del Sarto (1486-1530). 400fr, Virgin with Angels, by Cimabue (c. 1240-1302).

**1985, Feb. 12 Litho. *Perf. 13***
**C333** AP118 100fr multi, vert. .80 .45
**C334** AP118 200fr multi 1.60 .90
**C335** AP118 400fr multi, vert. 3.00 1.75
*Nos. C333-C335 (3)* 5.40 3.10

Christmas 1984.

**Nos. C309, C314 Ovptd. with Exhibition in Blue or Green**

Overprint's are: No. C336, OLYMPHILEX '85 / LAUSANNE (B). No. C337, MOPHILA '85 / HAM - BURG (G).

**1985, Mar. 8 *Perf. 13***

**Souvenir Sheets**

**C336** AP112 500fr multicolored 5.00 4.00
**C337** AP113 500fr multicolored 5.00 4.00

Audubon Birth Bicentenary
AP119

Illustrations of North American bird species by Audubon: 100fr, Passiformes fringillidae, vert. 150fr, Eudocimus ruber, vert. 200fr, Buteo jamaicensis. 350fr, Camptorhynchus labradorius.

**1985, Apr. 11 *Perf. 13½***
**C338** AP119 100fr multicolored 1.00 .45
**C339** AP119 150fr multicolored 1.50 .65
**C340** AP119 200fr multicolored 1.90 .90
**C341** AP119 350fr multicolored 3.75 1.50
*Nos. C338-C341 (4)* 8.15 3.50

PHILEXAFRICA '85, Lome — AP120

Youths in public service activities: No. C342, Community health care. No. C343, Agriculture.

**1985, May 20 *Perf. 13***
**C342** AP120 200fr multicolored 2.50 1.50
**C343** AP120 200fr multicolored 2.50 1.50
*a.* Pair, #C342-C343 + label 6.00 6.00

For overprints see Nos. 1187-1188.

Admission to UN, 25th Anniv.
AP121

**1985, Aug. 13**
**C344** AP121 190fr multicolored 1.75 .75

Rainbow, emblem — AP122

**1985, Oct. 25 *Perf. 12½***
**C345** AP122 180fr multicolored 1.60 .65

UN, 40th Anniv.

Christmas
AP123

Paintings: 100fr, The Virgin and the Infant Jesus, by David. 200fr, Adoration of the Magi, by Hieronymus Bosch (1450-1516). 400fr, Virgin and Child, by Van Dyck.

**1985, Dec. 20 Litho. *Perf. 13***
**C346** AP123 100fr multicolored .90 .35
**C347** AP123 200fr multicolored 1.90 .75
**C348** AP123 400fr multicolored 3.50 1.75
*Nos. C346-C348 (3)* 6.30 2.85

Nos. C346-C347 vert.

Halley's Comet
AP124

125fr, Halley, comet. 150fr, West's Comet, 1976. 225fr, Ikeya Seki's Comet, 1965. 300fr, Trajectory diagram. 350fr, Comet, Vega probe.

**1986, Feb. 17**
**C349** AP124 125fr multicolored 1.00 .50
**C350** AP124 150fr multicolored 1.25 .60
**C351** AP124 225fr multicolored 1.75 .90
**C352** AP124 300fr multicolored 2.25 1.25
**C353** AP124 350fr multicolored 2.75 1.50
*Nos. C349-C353 (5)* 9.00 4.75

Nos. C350-C351 vert.

Cosmos-Frantel Hotel — AP125

**1986, May 1 *Perf. 13½***
**C354** AP125 250fr multicolored 2.50 .90

1986 World Cup Soccer Championships, Mexico — AP126

Various soccer plays.

**1986, July 22 Litho. *Perf. 13***
**C355** AP126 150fr multicolored 1.25 .60
**C356** AP126 250fr multicolored 2.00 1.00
**C357** AP126 440fr multicolored 3.75 1.75
**C358** AP126 600fr multicolored 6.50 2.50
*Nos. C355-C358 (4)* 13.50 5.85

Air Africa, 25th Anniv. — AP127

**1986, Nov. 29 Litho. *Perf. 13½***
**C359** AP127 200fr multicolored 2.00 .75

1988 Winter Pre-Olympics, Calgary — AP128

150fr, Downhill skiing. 250fr, Bobsled. 440fr, Women's cross-country skiing. 600fr, Ski jumping.

**1986, Dec. 15 *Perf. 13***
**C360** AP128 150fr multicolored 1.25 .60
**C361** AP128 250fr multicolored 2.25 .95
**C362** AP128 440fr multicolored 4.00 1.50
**C363** AP128 600fr multicolored 5.75 2.40
*Nos. C360-C363 (4)* 13.25 5.45

Nos. C361-C362 vert.

Christmas — AP129

Paintings by Rogier van der Weyden (c.1399-1464): 250fr, Virgin and Child. 440fr, The Nativity. 500fr, Virgin with Carnation.

**1986, Dec. 23 *Perf. 13½***
**C364** AP129 250fr multicolored 2.25 1.00
**C365** AP129 440fr multicolored 4.25 1.75
**C366** AP129 500fr multicolored 4.50 2.10
*Nos. C364-C366 (3)* 11.00 4.85

Crocodiles, World Wildlife Fund
AP130

75fr, Osteolaemus tetraspis. 100fr, Crocodylus cataphractus. 125fr, Osteolaemus tetraspis, diff. 150fr, Crocodylus cataphractus, diff.

**1987, Jan. 22** *Perf. 13*

**C367** AP130 75fr multicolored 2.25 1.10
**C368** AP130 100fr multicolored 2.75 1.25
**C369** AP130 125fr multicolored 3.50 1.75
**C370** AP130 150fr multicolored 4.00 3.00
*Nos. C367-C370 (4)* 12.50 7.10

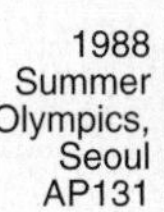
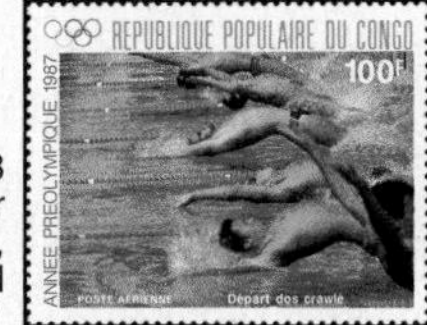


1988 Summer Olympics, Seoul AP131

**1987, July 11** **Litho.** *Perf. 13*

**C371** AP131 100fr Backstroke .90 .35
**C372** AP131 200fr Freestyle 1.75 .75
**C373** AP131 300fr Breaststroke 2.75 1.10
**C374** AP131 400fr Butterfly 3.50 1.40
*Nos. C371-C374 (4)* 8.90 3.60

**Souvenir Sheet**

**C375** AP131 750fr Start of event 6.75 3.50

Launch of Sputnik, First Artificial Satellite, 30th Anniv. AP132

**1987, June 5** *Perf. 12½x12*

**C376** AP132 60fr multicolored .50 .25
**C377** AP132 240fr multicolored 2.25 1.10

Butterflies AP133

75fr, Precis epicleli. 120fr, Deilephila nerii. 450fr, Euryphene senegalensis. 550fr, Precis almanta.

**1987, Sept. 4** *Perf. 12½*

**C378** AP133 75fr multicolored 1.20 .30
**C379** AP133 120fr multicolored 2.00 .45
**C380** AP133 450fr multicolored 6.00 1.75
**C381** AP133 550fr multicolored 8.00 2.40
*Nos. C378-C381 (4)* 17.20 4.90

Coubertin, Eternal Flame and Greece No. 125 AP134

Cameo portrait, athletes and stamps: 120fr, Runners, France No. 198. 350fr, Congo Republic No. C22, hurdler. 600fr, High jump, Congo Republic No. C75.

**1987, Nov. 4**

**C382** AP134 75fr shown .80 .30
**C383** AP134 120fr multicolored 1.10 .45
**C384** AP134 350fr multicolored 3.50 1.25
**C385** AP134 600fr multicolored 5.25 2.10
*Nos. C382-C385 (4)* 10.65 4.10

Pierre de Coubertin (1863-1937), promulgator of the modern Olympics.

Arrival of Schweitzer in Lambarene, 75th Anniv. AP135

**1988, Apr. 17** **Litho.** *Perf. 12½*

**C386** AP135 240fr multicolored 2.75 1.25

Dr. Albert Schweitzer (1875-1965), Nobel Peace Prize winner of 1952, founded Lambarene Hospital, Gabon, in 1913.

1988 Summer Olympics, Seoul AP136

Pentathlon: 75fr, Swimming. 170fr, Cross-country running, vert. 200fr, Shooting. 600fr, Equestrian. 700fr, Fencing.

**1988, June 10** **Litho.** *Perf. 13*

**C387** AP136 75fr multicolored .70 .25
**C388** AP136 170fr multicolored 1.60 .60
**C389** AP136 200fr multicolored 1.75 .70
**C390** AP136 600fr multicolored 5.00 2.00
*Nos. C387-C390 (4)* 9.05 3.55

**Souvenir Sheet**

**C391** AP136 750fr multicolored 7.00 3.75

Elimination Matches, 1990 World Cup Soccer Championships — AP137

Various athletes and cities in Italy.

**1989, June 15** **Litho.** *Perf. 13*

**C392** AP137 75fr Bari .60 .30
**C393** AP137 120fr Rome 1.00 .45
**C394** AP137 500fr Florence 4.75 1.90
**C395** AP137 550fr Naples 5.25 2.00
*Nos. C392-C395 (4)* 11.60 4.65

PHILEXFRANCE '89 — AP138

Paintings: 300fr, Storming of the Bastille, July 14, 1789, from a gouache by J.P. Houel. 400fr, Eiffel Tower, by G. Seurat.

**1989, June 22**

**C396** AP138 300fr multicolored 2.75 1.10
**C397** AP138 400fr multicolored 3.75 1.50

French revolution, bicent. (300fr); Eiffel Tower, cent. (400fr).

First Moon Landing, 20th Anniv. — AP139

Man's first step on the Moon: No. C398, Astronaut on ladder. No. C399, Conducting experiments on the Moon's surface.

**1989, June 22**

**C398** AP139 400fr multicolored 3.75 1.50
**C399** AP139 400fr multicolored 3.75 1.50

World Cup Soccer Championships, Italy — AP140

Various soccer plays and architecture.

**1990, June 8** **Litho.** *Perf. 13*

**C400** AP140 120fr multicolored 1.00 .50
**C401** AP140 240fr multicolored 2.10 .95
**C402** AP140 500fr multicolored 4.25 2.00
**C403** AP140 600fr multicolored 5.25 2.40
*Nos. C400-C403 (4)* 12.60 5.85

Pan African Postal Union, 10th Anniv. — AP141

**1991, Jan. 10** **Litho.** *Perf. 13½*

**C404** AP141 60fr shown .55 .25
**C405** AP141 120fr Emblem 1.00 .50

1992 Winter Olympics, Albertville — AP142

120fr, Ice hockey. 300fr, Speed skating. 1500fr, Slalom skiing.

**1991, June 8** **Litho.** *Perf. 13½*

**C406** AP142 120fr multi 1.40 .60
**C407** AP142 300fr multi 3.00 1.50

**Litho. & Embossed**

**C408** AP142 1500fr multi 7.50 7.50

Numbers have been reserved for souvenir sheets in this set.

1992 Summer Olympics, Barcelona AP143

No. C411, Equestrian. No. C412, Long jump.

**Litho. & Embossed**

**1992, Dec. 21** *Perf. 13½*

**C411** AP143 1500fr gold & multi 16.00 16.00

**Souvenir Sheet**

**C412** AP143 1500fr gold & multi 21.00 21.00

Anniversaries — AP144

Designs: 90fr, Victor Schoelcher, missionary, death cent. 205fr, Martin Luther King, civil rights reformer, 25th death anniv. 300fr, Claude Chappe (1763-1805), bicent. of visual telegraph.

**1993** **Litho.** *Perf. 14*

**C413** AP144 90fr multicolored *1.00 .50*
**C414** AP144 205fr multicolored *2.50 1.25*
**C415** AP144 300fr multicolored *3.50 1.75*
*Nos. C413-C415 (3) 7.00 3.50*

1994 Winter Olympics, Lillehammer AP145

400fr, Ice dancing. 600fr, Ice hockey. 750fr, Downhill skiing.

**1993, Apr. 26** **Litho.** *Perf. 13*

**C416** AP145 400fr multicolored *4.00 1.40*
**C417** AP145 600fr multicolored *7.50 1.75*

**Souvenir Sheet**

**C418** AP145 750fr multicolored *8.00 4.00*

Nos. C416-C417 exist in imperf. souvenir sheets of 1. Nos. C416-C418 exist imperf.

## AIR POST SEMI-POSTAL STAMPS

Hathor Pillar — SPAP1

**Unwmk.**

**1964, Mar. 9** **Engr.** *Perf. 13*

**CB1** SPAP1 10fr + 5fr vio & chnt .90 .50
**CB2** SPAP1 25fr + 5fr org brn & slate grn 1.10 .70
**CB3** SPAP1 50fr + 5fr slate grn & brn red 2.25 1.60
*Nos. CB1-CB3 (3)* 4.25 2.80

UNESCO world campaign to save historic monuments in Nubia.

## POSTAGE DUE STAMPS

Messenger — D6

MH. 1521 Broussard Plane — D7

Early Transportation: 1fr, Litter. 2fr, Canoe. 5fr, Bicyclist. 10fr, Steam locomotive. 25fr, Seaplane.

**Unwmk.**

**1961, Dec. 4** **Engr.** *Perf. 11*

**J34** D6 50c ultra, ol bis & red .25 .25
*a.* Pair, #J34, J40 .25
**J35** D6 1fr red brn, red & grn .25 .25
*a.* Pair, #J35, J41 .30
**J36** D6 2fr grn, ultra & brn .25 .25
*a.* Pair, #J36, J42 .40
**J37** D6 5fr pur & gray brn .25 .25
*a.* Pair, #J37, J43 .50
**J38** D6 10fr bl, grn & chocolate .70 .70
*a.* Pair, #J38, J44 1.40 1.40
**J39** D6 25fr bl, dk grn & dk brn 1.60 1.60
*a.* Pair, #J39, J45 3.25

Modern transportation: 1fr, Land Rover. 2fr, River boat transporting barge. 5fr, Trailer-truck. 10fr, Diesel locomotive. 25fr, Boeing 707 jet plane.

**J40** D7 50c ultra, olive bis & red .25 .25
**J41** D7 1fr red & grn .25 .25
**J42** D7 2fr ultra, grn & brn .25 .25
**J43** D7 5fr pur & gray brn .25 .25
**J44** D7 10fr dk grn & chocolate .70 .70
**J45** D7 25fr bl, dk grn & sepia 1.60 1.60
*Nos. J34-J45 (12)* 6.60 6.60

Pairs printed tête bêche, se-tenant at the base.

Flowers — D8

Flowers: 2fr, Phaeomeria magnifica. 5fr, Millettia laurentii. 10fr, Tuberose. 15fr, Pyrostegia venusta. 20fr, Hibiscus.

**1971, Mar. 25 Photo. *Perf. 12x12½***

| | | | | |
|---|---|---|---|---|
| **J46** | D8 | 1fr multi | .35 | .35 |
| **J47** | D8 | 2fr multi | .45 | .45 |
| **J48** | D8 | 5fr pink & multi | .55 | .55 |
| **J49** | D8 | 10fr dk grn & multi | .70 | .70 |
| **J50** | D8 | 15fr multi | 1.10 | 1.10 |
| **J51** | D8 | 20fr multi | 1.40 | 1.40 |
| | | *Nos. J46-J51 (6)* | 4.55 | 4.55 |

Flowers and Fruit — D9

5fr, Passiflora quadrangulares. 10fr, Cannaceae, vert. 15fr, Ananas comosus, vert.

**1986, June 5 Litho. *Perf. 13***

| | | | | |
|---|---|---|---|---|
| **J52** | D9 | 5fr multicolored | .25 | .25 |
| **J53** | D9 | 10fr multicolored | .45 | .45 |
| **J54** | D9 | 15fr multicolored | .55 | .55 |
| | | *Nos. J52-J54 (3)* | 1.25 | 1.25 |

### OFFICIAL STAMPS

Coat of Arms — O1

***Perf. 14x13***

**1968-70 Unwmk. Typo.**

| | | | | |
|---|---|---|---|---|
| **O1** | O1 | 1fr multi ('70) | .25 | .25 |
| **O2** | O1 | 2fr multi ('70) | .25 | .25 |
| **O3** | O1 | 5fr multi ('70) | .25 | .25 |
| **O4** | O1 | 10fr multi ('70) | .25 | .25 |
| **O5** | O1 | 25fr emer & multi | .45 | .25 |
| **O6** | O1 | 30fr red & multi | .60 | .25 |
| **O7** | O1 | 50fr multi ('70) | 1.10 | .50 |
| **O8** | O1 | 85fr multi ('70) | 2.25 | .90 |
| **O9** | O1 | 100fr multi ('70) | 2.75 | 1.10 |
| **O10** | O1 | 200fr multi ('70) | 3.75 | 2.00 |
| | | *Nos. O1-O10 (10)* | 11.90 | 6.00 |

## COOK ISLANDS

'kuk 'ī-ləndz

## (Rarotonga)

LOCATION — South Pacific Ocean, northeast of New Zealand
GOVT. — Internal self-government, linked to New Zealand
AREA — 91 sq. mi.
POP. — 19,103 (1996)
CAPITAL — Avarua

Fifteen islands in Northern and Southern groups extend over 850,000 square miles of ocean.

Separate stamp issues used by Aitutaki (1903-32 and 1972 onward) and Penrhyn Islands (1902-32 and 1973 onward). Niue is included geographically, but administered separately. It continues to issue separate stamps.

12 Pence = 1 Shilling
20 Shillings = 1 Pound
100 Cents = 1 Dollar (1967)

**Catalogue values for unused stamps in this country are for Never Hinged items, beginning with Scott 127 in the regular postage section, Scott B1 in the semi-postal section, Scott C1 in the air post section, Scott CB1 in the air post semi-postal section and Scott O16 in the official section.**

**For more detailed listings for classic issues of Cook Islands, see the Scott *Classic Specialized Catalogue of Stamps and Covers 1840-1940.***

### Watermarks

Wmk. 61 — Single-lined N Z and Star Close Together

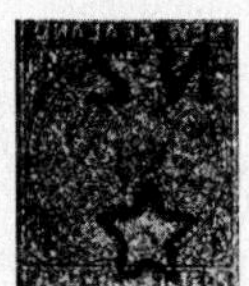
Wmk. 62 — Single-lined N Z and Star Wide Apart

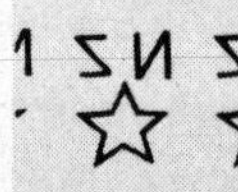
Wmk. 253 — Multiple N Z and Star

A1

**1892 Unwmk. Typo. *Perf. 12½***

**Toned Paper**

| | | | | |
|---|---|---|---|---|
| **1** | A1 | 1p black | 35.00 | 30.00 |
| **2** | A1 | 1½p violet | 50.00 | 45.00 |
| *a.* | | Imperf, pair | *19,000.* | |
| **3** | A1 | 2½p blue | 47.50 | 45.00 |
| **4** | A1 | 10p carmine | 160.00 | 150.00 |
| | | *Nos. 1-4 (4)* | 292.50 | 270.00 |

**White Paper**

| | | | | |
|---|---|---|---|---|
| **5** | A1 | 1p black | 35.00 | 30.00 |
| *a.* | | Vert. pair, imperf. between | *11,000.* | |
| **6** | A1 | 1½p violet | 50.00 | 45.00 |
| **7** | A1 | 2½p blue | 47.50 | 45.00 |
| **8** | A1 | 10p carmine | 160.00 | 150.00 |
| | | *Nos. 5-8 (4)* | 292.50 | 270.00 |

Nos. 1-8 were printed in sheets of 60 (6x10), from a setting of six slightly different cliches.

Queen Makea Takau — A2

**1893-94 Wmk. 62 *Perf. 12x11½***

| | | | | |
|---|---|---|---|---|
| **9** | A2 | 1p brown | 50.00 | *55.00* |
| **10** | A2 | 1p blue ('94) | 13.00 | 2.50 |
| **11** | A2 | 1½p brt violet | 19.00 | 8.50 |
| **12** | A2 | 2½p rose | 55.00 | 27.50 |
| **13** | A2 | 5p olive gray | 24.00 | 16.00 |
| **14** | A2 | 10p green | 85.00 | 57.50 |
| | | *Nos. 9-14 (6)* | 246.00 | *167.00* |

Torea — A3

**1898-1900 *Perf. 11***

| | | | | |
|---|---|---|---|---|
| **15** | A3 | ½p blue ('00) | 6.50 | *15.00* |
| *a.* | | "d" omitted at upper right | *1,750.* | |
| **16** | A2 | 1p brown | 32.50 | 21.00 |
| **17** | A2 | 1p blue | 6.00 | 5.50 |
| **18** | A2 | 1½p violet | 19.00 | 7.50 |
| **19** | A3 | 2p chocolate ('00) | 15.00 | 8.50 |
| **20** | A2 | 2½p car rose ('00) | 25.00 | 15.00 |
| **21** | A2 | 5p olive gray | 30.00 | 21.00 |
| **22** | A3 | 6p red violet ('00) | 24.00 | *29.00* |
| **23** | A2 | 10p green | 26.00 | *57.50* |
| **24** | A3 | 1sh car rose ('00) | 57.50 | 57.50 |
| | | *Nos. 15-24 (10)* | 241.50 | *237.50* |

No. 17 Surcharged in Black

**1899**

| | | | | |
|---|---|---|---|---|
| **25** | A2 | ½p on 1p blue | 40.00 | *50.00* |
| *a.* | | Double surcharge | 1,000. | *1,200.* |
| *b.* | | Inverted surcharge | 1,200. | 1,100. |

No. 16 Overprinted in Black

**1901**

| | | | | |
|---|---|---|---|---|
| **26** | A2 | 1p brown | 210.00 | 160.00 |
| *a.* | | Inverted overprint | 2,400. | 1,900. |
| *c.* | | Double overprint | 1,900. | 1,900. |

Some single stamps were overprinted by favor. Other varieties could exist.

Forgeries exist.

**Types of 1893-98**

**1902 Unwmk.**

| | | | | |
|---|---|---|---|---|
| **27** | A3 | ½p green | 10.00 | 10.00 |
| *a.* | | Vert. pair, imperf. horiz. | *1,400.* | |
| **28** | A2 | 1p rose | 16.00 | *11.00* |
| **29** | A2 | 2½p dull blue | 15.00 | *25.00* |
| | | *Nos. 27-29 (3)* | 41.00 | *46.00* |

**1902 Wmk. 61 *Perf. 11***

| | | | | |
|---|---|---|---|---|
| **30** | A3 | ½p green | 4.25 | *3.75* |
| **31** | A2 | 1p rose | 4.75 | *3.50* |
| **32** | A2 | 1½p brt violet | 4.75 | *10.00* |
| **33** | A3 | 2p chocolate | 11.00 | *12.00* |
| *a.* | | Figures of value omitted | *2,750.* | *3,600.* |
| *b.* | | Perf. 11x14 | *2,600.* | |
| **34** | A2 | 2½p dull blue | 4.50 | *8.25* |
| **35** | A2 | 5p olive gray | 42.50 | *57.50* |
| **36** | A3 | 6p purple | 37.50 | *32.50* |
| **37** | A2 | 10p blue green | 55.00 | *120.00* |
| **38** | A3 | 1sh car rose | 55.00 | *82.50* |
| *a.* | | Perf. 11x14 | *3,000.* | |
| | | *Nos. 30-38 (9)* | 219.25 | *330.00* |

**1909-19 *Perf. 14, 14x14½, 14½x14***

| | | | | |
|---|---|---|---|---|
| **39** | A3 | ½p green, perf 14½x14 ('11) | 13.00 | *9.50* |
| *a.* | | ½p dp grn, perf 14 ('15) | 42.50 | *17.50* |
| *b.* | | As "a," wmk upright | 14.00 | *22.50* |
| **40** | A2 | 1p red, wmk. sideways ('09) | 15.00 | 5.00 |
| **41** | A2 | 1½p purple, perf 14x15 ('16) | 21.00 | 4.75 |
| **42** | A3 | 2p dp brown ('19) | 6.00 | *57.50* |
| **43** | A2 | 10p dp green ('18) | 40.00 | *110.00* |
| **44** | A3 | 1sh car rose ('19) | 32.50 | *110.00* |
| | | *Nos. 39-44 (6)* | 127.50 | *296.75* |

Nos. 39-40 are on both ordinary and chalky paper; Nos. 41-44 on chalky paper.

New Zealand Stamps of 1909-19 Surcharged in Dark Blue or Red

**1919 Typo. *Perf. 14x15***

| | | | | |
|---|---|---|---|---|
| **48** | A43 | ½p yel green (R) | .45 | *1.25* |
| *a.* | | Pair, one without surcharge | | |
| **49** | A42 | 1p carmine | 1.25 | *5.00* |
| **50** | A47 | 1½p brown org (R) | .60 | *.90* |
| **51** | A43 | 2p yellow (R) | 1.75 | *2.00* |
| **52** | A43 | 3p chocolate | 3.25 | *15.00* |

**Engr. *Perf. 14x14½***

| | | | | |
|---|---|---|---|---|
| **53** | A44 | 2½p dull blue (R) | 2.75 | 2.50 |
| **54** | A45 | 3p violet brown | 3.50 | *4.00* |
| **55** | A45 | 4p purple | 2.25 | *4.25* |
| **56** | A44 | 4½p dark green | 2.25 | *9.50* |
| **57** | A45 | 6p car rose | 2.00 | *5.50* |
| **58** | A44 | 7½p red brown, perf 14x13½ | 2.10 | *6.50* |
| **59** | A45 | 9p ol green (R) | 3.00 | *17.50* |
| **60** | A45 | 1sh vermilion | 3.25 | *30.00* |
| | | *Nos. 48-60 (13)* | 28.40 | *103.90* |

The Polynesian surcharge restates the denomination of the basic stamp.

Landing of Capt. Cook A4

Avarua Waterfront A5

Capt. James Cook — A6

Palm — A7

Houses at Arorangi — A8

Avarua Harbor — A9

**1920 Unwmk. Engr. *Perf. 14***

| | | | | |
|---|---|---|---|---|
| **61** | A4 | ½p green & black | 4.75 | *30.00* |
| **62** | A5 | 1p car & black | 5.50 | *30.00* |
| *a.* | | Center inverted | *875.00* | |
| **63** | A6 | 1½p blue & black | 10.00 | 10.00 |
| **64** | A7 | 3p red brn & blk | 2.50 | *6.50* |
| **65** | A8 | 6p org & red brn | 4.75 | *10.00* |
| **66** | A9 | 1sh vio & black | 9.00 | *20.00* |
| *a.* | | Center inverted | *875.00* | |
| | | *Nos. 61-66 (6)* | 36.50 | *106.50* |

The stamps overprinted or inscribed "Rarotonga" were used throughout the Cook Islands.

For surcharges see Nos. 72, 73, 78, 79.

New Zealand Postal-Fiscal Stamps of 1906-13 Overprinted in Red or Dark Blue — a

***Perf. 14, 14½, 14x14½***

**1921 Typo. Wmk. 61**

| | | | | |
|---|---|---|---|---|
| **67** | PF1 | 2sh blue (R) | 32.50 | *65.00* |
| **68** | PF1 | 2sh6p brown | 22.50 | *60.00* |
| **69** | PF1 | 5sh green (R) | 32.50 | *77.50* |
| **70** | PF1 | 10sh claret | 90.00 | *140.00* |
| **71** | PF2 | £1 rose | 150.00 | *260.00* |
| | | *Nos. 67-71 (5)* | 327.50 | *602.50* |

**Types of 1920 Issue**

**1924-26 Engr. *Perf. 14***

| | | | | |
|---|---|---|---|---|
| **72** | A4 | ½p yel grn & black | 5.25 | 10.00 |
| **73** | A5 | 1p carmine & black | 7.00 | 2.50 |

Issued: ½p, May 13, 1926; 1p, Nov. 10, 1924.

New Zealand Stamps of 1926 Overprinted in Red

**1926-28 Typo. *Perf. 14, 14½x14***

| | | | | |
|---|---|---|---|---|
| **74** | A56 | 2sh blue ('27) | 19.00 | *47.50* |
| *a.* | | 2sh dark blue | 12.00 | *47.50* |
| **75** | A56 | 3sh violet ('28) | 19.00 | *50.00* |

Rarotongan Chief (Te Po) — A10

Avarua Harbor — A11

**1927, Oct. 15 Engr. *Perf. 14***

| | | | | |
|---|---|---|---|---|
| **76** | A10 | 2½p dk bl & red brn | 12.00 | *37.50* |
| **77** | A11 | 4p dull vio & bl grn | 19.00 | *17.50* |

No. 63 Surcharged in Red

**1931** **Unwmk.**

**78** A6 2p on 1½p blue & blk 11.00 4.75

### Same Surcharge on Type of 1920

**Wmk. 61**

**79** A6 2p on 1½p blue & blk 5.50 *13.00*

No. 79 was not issued without surcharge.

### New Zealand Postal-Fiscal Stamps of 1931-32 Overprinted Type "a" in Blue or Red

**1931, Nov. 12** **Typo.**

**80** PF5 2sh6p dp brown (Bl) 16.00 *26.00*
**81** PF5 5sh green (R) 27.50 *65.00*
**82** PF5 10sh dk car (Bl) 45.00 *110.00*
**83** PF5 £1 pink (Bl) ('32) 125.00 *200.00*
*Nos. 80-83 (4)* 213.50 *401.00*

See Nos. 103-108, 124A-126C.

Landing of Capt. Cook A12

Capt. James Cook A13

Double Canoe A14

Islanders Unloading Ship A15

View of Avarua Harbor A16

R.M.S. Monowai A17

King George V — A18

**Unwmk.**

**1932, Mar. 16** **Engr.** ***Perf. 13***

**Center in Black**

**84** A12 ½p deep green 4.00 *19.00*
  **a.** Perf. 14 32.50 *105.00*
**85** A13 1p brown lake 10.00 5.25
  **a.** Center inverted *9,500.* *9,500.*
  **b.** Perf. 14 17.50 *32.50*
**86** A14 2p brown 3.50 *8.75*
  **b.** Perf. 14 10.00 *24.00*
**87** A15 2½p dark ultra 27.50 *70.00*
  **b.** Perf. 14 20.00 *65.00*

***Perf. 14***

**88** A16 4p ultra 12.00 *65.00*
  **a.** Perf. 13 32.50 *75.00*
  **b.** Perf. 14x13 35.00 *130.00*
**89** A17 6p orange 5.00 *17.50*
  **a.** Perf. 13 30.00 *57.50*
**90** A18 1sh deep violet 24.00 *26.00*
*Nos. 84-90 (7)* 86.00 *211.50*

Nos. 84 to 90 were available for postage in Aitutaki, Penrhyn and Rarotonga and replaced the special issues for those islands.

Inverted centers of the ½p (value $1,000), 1p (value $550), and 2p (value $3,500) are from printers waste.

**1933-36** **Wmk. 61** ***Perf. 14***

**91** A12 ½p dp grn & blk 1.20 *5.25*
**92** A13 1p dk car & black ('35) 1.50 *2.40*
**93** A14 2p brn & blk ('36) 1.75 .60
**94** A15 2½p dk ultra & blk 1.75 *2.50*
**95** A16 4p blue & black 1.75 .60
**96** A17 6p org & blk ('36) 2.00 *2.50*
**97** A18 1sh dp vio & black ('36) 27.50 *42.50*
*Nos. 91-97 (7)* 37.45 *56.35*

See Nos. 116-121.

### Silver Jubilee Issue

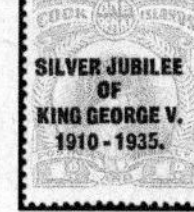


Types of 1932 Overprinted in Black or Red

**1935, May 7**

**98** A13 1p dk car & brn red .65 *1.50*
**99** A15 2½p dk ultra & bl (R) 2.00 *3.50*
**100** A17 6p dull org & green 7.00 *7.00*
*Nos. 98-100 (3)* 9.65 *12.00*
Set, never hinged 16.00

The vertical spacing of the overprint is wider on No. 100.

New Zealand Stamps of 1926 Overprinted in Black — b

**1936, July 15** **Typo.** ***Perf. 14***

**101** A56 2sh blue 15.00 *50.00*
**102** A56 3sh violet 16.00 *80.00*

1931-35 New Zealand Postal-Fiscal Stamps Ovptd. Type "b" in Black or Red

**1932-36**

**103** PF5 2sh6p brown ('36) 50.00 *110.00*
**104** PF5 5sh grn (R) ('36) 52.50 *130.00*
**105** PF5 10sh dk car ('36) 92.50 *250.00*
**106** PF5 £1 pink ('36) 125.00 *275.00*
**107** PF5 £3 lt grn (R) 500.00 *900.00*
**108** PF5 £5 dk blue (R) 250.00 *400.00*
*Nos. 103-108 (6)* 1,070. *2,065.*

Issue dates: Mar. 1932, July 15, 1936.

New Zealand Stamps of 1937 Overprinted in Black

***Perf. 14x13½***

**1937, June 1** **Engr.** **Wmk. 253**

**109** A78 1p rose carmine .25 .25
**110** A78 2½p dark blue .25 .25
**111** A78 6p vermilion .35 .30
*Nos. 109-111 (3)* .85 .80
Set, never hinged 2.25

King George VI A19

Village and Palms A20

Coastal Scene with Canoe — A21

**1938, May 2** **Wmk. 61** ***Perf. 14***

**112** A19 1sh dp violet & blk 6.00 *12.00*
**113** A20 2sh dk red brn & blk 13.50 15.00
**114** A21 3sh yel green & blue 37.50 *42.50*
*Nos. 112-114 (3)* 57.00 69.50
Set, never hinged 90.00

See Nos. 122-124.

Mt. Ikurangi behind Avarua — A22

***Perf. 13½x14***

**1940, Sept. 2** **Engr.** **Wmk. 253**

**115** A22 3p on 1½p violet & blk .80 .70

Issued only with surcharge. Stamps without surcharge are from the printer's archives. Value $275.

See Niue No. 76.

### Types of 1932-38

**1944-46** **Engr.** ***Perf. 14***

**116** A12 ½p dk ol grn & blk ('45) 1.00 *4.50*
**117** A13 1p dk car & blk ('45) 1.25 1.25
**118** A14 2p brn & blk ('46) 1.50 *7.00*
**119** A15 2½p dk bl & blk ('45) .60 *2.00*
**120** A16 4p blue & black 3.00 *15.00*
**121** A17 6p org & black 1.75 *2.50*
**122** A19 1sh dp vio & blk 2.00 *3.50*
**123** A20 2sh dk red brn & blk 25.00 *55.00*
**124** A21 3sh yel green & blue ('45) 26.00 *35.00*
*Nos. 116-124 (9)* 62.10 125.75
Set, never hinged 100.00

### New Zealand Nos. AR76, AR78, AR86 and Type of 1931 Postal-Fiscal Stamps Overprinted Type "b" in Black or Red

**1943-50** **Wmk. 253** **Typo.** ***Perf. 14***

**124A** PF5 2sh6p brn ('51) 30.00 *45.00*
**125** PF5 5sh green (R) 11.50 *37.50*
**126** PF5 10sh dp pink ('51) 50.00 *100.00*
**126A** PF5 £1 pink ('54) 45.00 *110.00*
**126B** PF5 £3 lt grn (R) ('53) 42.50 *175.00*
**126C** PF5 £5 dk bl (R) ('54) 200.00 *400.00*
*Nos. 124A-126C (6)* 379.00 *867.50*
Set, never hinged 575.00

Values for Nos. 124A-126C are for the second printing with watermarks inverted.

For surcharges see Nos. 192-194.

**Catalogue values for unused stamps in this section, from this point to the end of the section, are for Never Hinged items.**

### Peace Issue
### New Zealand Nos. 248, 250, 254 and 255 Overprinted in Black or Blue

c

d

***Perf. 13x13½, 13½x13***

**1946, June 1** **Engr.**

**127** A94 (c) 1p emerald .30 .25
**128** A96 (d) 2p rose vio (Bl) .35 .35
**129** A100(c) 6p org red & red brn .80 .70
**130** A101(c) 8p car & blk (Bl) .55 .55
*Nos. 127-130 (4)* 2.00 1.85

Ngatangiia Channel, Rarotonga A23

Capt. James Cook Statue and Map of Cook Islands A24

Designs: 1p, Cook and map of Hervey Isls. 2p, Rev. John Williams, his ship Messenger of Peace, and map of Rarotonga. 3p, Aitutaki map and palms. 5p, Mail plane landing at Rarotonga airport. 6p, Tongareva (Penrhyn) scene. 8p, Islander's house, Rarotonga. 2sh, Thatched house, mat weaver. 3sh, Steamer Matua offshore.

***Perf. 13½x13, 13x13½***

**1949, Aug.1** **Engr.** **Wmk. 253**

**131** A23 ½p brown & violet .25 *1.25*
**132** A23 1p green & orange 3.00 3.00
**133** A23 2p scar & red brn 1.75 3.00
**134** A23 3p ultra & green 4.50 *1.75*
**135** A23 5p purple & grn 5.00 1.25
**136** A23 6p car rose & blk 5.25 2.25
**137** A23 8p orange & olive .65 *2.25*
**138** A24 1sh chocolate & bl 3.50 3.00
**139** A24 2sh rose car & brn 5.00 *11.00*
**140** A24 3sh bl grn & lt ultra 17.50 *27.50*
*Nos. 131-140 (10)* 46.40 *56.25*

For surcharge see No. 147.

### Coronation Issue

Type of New Zealand

**1953, May 25** **Photo.** ***Perf. 14x14½***

**145** A113 3p brown 1.25 1.25
**146** A114 6p slate black 1.40 1.40

### No. 135 Surcharged in Black

**1960, Apr. 1** **Engr.** ***Perf. 13½x13***

**147** A23 1sh6p on 5p purple & grn .70 .55

Tiare Maori A25

Fishing God A26

Frangipani — A26a

Fairy Tern — A26b

Hibiscus — A26c

Bonito — A26d

Oranges — A26e

Queen Elizabeth II — A27

Island Scene — A28

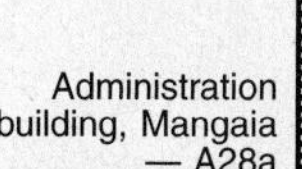

Administration building, Mangaia — A28a

Ship in Rarotonga Harbor — A28b

***Perf. 13½x13, 13x13½***

**Litho.; Engr.; (1sh6p)**

**1963, June 4**

**148** A25 1p multicolored .60 *.70*
**149** A26 2p multicolored .25 *.65*
**150** A26a 3p multicolored .55 *.55*
**151** A26b 5p multicolored 6.25 2.00
**152** A26c 6p multicolored .80 .60
**153** A26d 8p blue & dark blue 3.50 1.40
**154** A26e 1sh orange & green .80 .75
**155** A27 1sh6p violet 2.25 2.00
**156** A28 2sh gray & brown 1.60 1.25

| | | | | |
|---|---|---|---|---|
| **157** | A28a | 3sh emer & black | 1.60 | 1.90 |
| **158** | A28b | 5sh ultra & brown | 13.00 | 5.25 |
| | | *Nos. 148-158 (11)* | 31.20 | 17.05 |

For overprints and surcharges see Nos. 167-169, 179-181, 183-184, 186-190.

Solar Eclipse and Palm Tree — A29

**1965, May 31 Litho. *Perf. 13x13½***

| | | | | |
|---|---|---|---|---|
| **159** | A29 | 6p black, lt blue & yel | .30 | .30 |

Observation of the solar eclipse on Manuae Island, May 30, 1965. Exists imperf.

For surcharge see No. 185.

Flag of New Zealand and Map of Cook Islands — A30

Designs: 10p, London Missionary Society Church and graveyard. 1sh, Reading of Proclamation of Cession, Oct. 8, 1900, and Queen Elizabeth II. 1sh9p, Nikao School and flag of New Zealand.

***Perf. 13½x13***

**1965, Sept. 16 Litho. Wmk. 253**

| | | | | |
|---|---|---|---|---|
| **160** | A30 | 4p blue & red | .25 | .25 |
| **161** | A30 | 10p multicolored | .25 | .25 |
| **162** | A30 | 1sh multicolored | .25 | .25 |
| **163** | A30 | 1sh9p multicolored | .45 | .45 |
| | | *Nos. 160-163 (4)* | 1.20 | 1.20 |

Establishment of internal self-government.

For surcharges see Nos. 182, 191.

### Nos. 160-162 and 156-158 Overprinted in Red

**1966, Jan. 24 Litho. Wmk. 253**

| | | | | |
|---|---|---|---|---|
| **164** | A30 | 4p blue & red | 1.10 | .30 |
| **165** | A30 | 10p multicolored | 2.00 | .50 |
| *a.* | | Inverted overprint | *275.00* | |
| **166** | A30 | 1sh multicolored | 2.00 | .85 |
| *a.* | | Inverted overprint | *200.00* | |
| **167** | A28 | 2sh gray & brown | 2.00 | 1.25 |
| **168** | A28 | 3sh emer & black | 2.00 | 1.25 |
| **169** | A28 | 5sh ultra & brown | 2.25 | 1.75 |
| | | *Nos. 164-169 (6)* | 11.35 | 5.90 |

Statesman and WWII leader.

Lower case "l" instead of "1" in "1874" in overprint exists on all. Value set, $70.

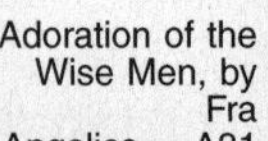

Adoration of the Wise Men, by Fra Angelico — A31

Paintings: 2p, Nativity, by Hans Memling, vert. 4p, Adoration of the Wise Men, by Velazquez. 10p, Adoration of the Wise Men, by Hieronymus Bosch. 1sh6p, Adoration of the Shepherds, by Jose Ribera, vert.

***Perf. 13x14½, 14½x13***

**1966, Nov. 28 Photo. Unwmk.**

| | | | | |
|---|---|---|---|---|
| **170** | A31 | 1p multicolored | .25 | .25 |
| **171** | A31 | 2p multicolored | .25 | .25 |
| **172** | A31 | 4p multicolored | .25 | .25 |
| **173** | A31 | 10p multicolored | .30 | .30 |
| **174** | A31 | 1sh6p multicolored | .40 | .40 |
| | | *Nos. 170-174 (5)* | 1.45 | 1.45 |

Christmas. Issued in sheets of 6 with ornamental gold border.

***Perf. 13x12, 12x13***

| | | | | |
|---|---|---|---|---|
| *170a* | A31 | 1p | .50 | *.85* |
| *171a* | A31 | 2p | 16.00 | *14.00* |
| *172a* | A31 | 4p | 1.25 | *1.25* |
| *173a* | A31 | 10p | 2.75 | *6.00* |
| *174a* | A31 | 1sh6p | 42.50 | 8.50 |
| | | *Nos. 170a-174a (5)* | 63.00 | *30.60* |

Tennis and Queen Elizabeth — A32

Sport: 1p, Women's basketball and Games' emblem. 4p, Boxing and team emblem. 7p, Soccer and Queen Elizabeth II.

**1967, Jan. 12 *Perf. 13½***

| | | | | |
|---|---|---|---|---|
| **175** | A32 | ½p brt olive & multi | .25 | .25 |
| **176** | A32 | 1p brt blue & multi | .25 | .25 |
| **177** | A32 | 4p purple & multi | .25 | .25 |
| **178** | A32 | 7p red & multi | .25 | .25 |
| | | *Nos. 175-178,C10-C11 (6)* | 1.50 | 1.50 |

Second South Pacific Games, Noumea, New Caledonia, Dec. 8-18, 1966.

### Nos. 148-155, 157-161 Surcharged with New Value or Black or Red

Pair (#181b), with Type I on left (#181) and Type II on right (#181a)

**1967**

| | | | | |
|---|---|---|---|---|
| **179** | A25 | 1c on 1p | .35 | *1.75* |
| **180** | A26 | 2c on 2p | .25 | .25 |
| **181** | A25 | 2½c on 3p (I) | .25 | .25 |
| *a.* | | Type II | .25 | .25 |
| *b.* | | Pair, #181 and #181a | .35 | .45 |
| **182** | A30 | 3c on 4p | .25 | .25 |
| **183** | A26 | 4c on 5p | 7.25 | .40 |
| **184** | A25 | 5c on 6p | .25 | .25 |
| **185** | A29 | 5c on 6p | 4.00 | 1.25 |
| **186** | A26 | 7c on 8p | .25 | .25 |
| **187** | A25 | 10c on 1sh | .25 | .25 |
| **188** | A27 | 15c on 1sh6p (R) | 1.60 | 1.10 |
| **189** | A28 | 30c on 3sh (R) | 22.50 | 7.00 |
| **190** | A28 | 50c on 5sh (R) | 3.25 | 2.00 |
| **191** | A30 | $1 on 10p (R) | 14.50 | 5.50 |
| | | *Nos. 179-191 (13)* | 54.95 | 20.50 |

Issued: 2c, 2½c, 3c, 5c, 7c, 10c, 4/3; others 5/4.

No. 191 is surcharged "10/ $1.00" and 3 bars over old value.

Numerous varieties of surcharge include wrong-font "c," thin numerals, etc.

### Nos. 126A, 126B and 126C Surcharged in Red

**Wmk. 253**

**1967, June 6 Typo. *Perf. 14***

| | | | | |
|---|---|---|---|---|
| **192** | PF5 | $2 on £1 pink | 70.00 | *100.00* |
| **193** | PF5 | $6 on £3 lt green | 175.00 | *200.00* |
| **194** | PF5 | $10 on £5 dk blue | 200.00 | *225.00* |
| | | *Nos. 192-194 (3)* | 445.00 | 525.00 |

Frequently found with stained gum.

Stamp of 1892, Village and Queen Victoria — A33

Designs: 3c (4p), PO, Rarotonga, and Elizabeth II. 8c (10p), View of Avarua, Rarotonga, and 10p stamp of 1892. 18c (1sh9p), Map of Cook Islands, DC-3, S.S. Moana Roa and Capt. Cook.

***Perf. 13½***

**1967, July 3 Photo. Unwmk.**

| | | | | |
|---|---|---|---|---|
| **195** | A33 | 1c (1p) multi | .25 | .25 |
| **196** | A33 | 3c (4p) multi | .25 | .25 |
| **197** | A33 | 8c (10p) multi | .30 | .30 |
| **198** | A33 | 18c (1sh9p) multi | 1.10 | .80 |
| *a.* | | Souvenir sheet of 4, #195-198 | 2.75 | 2.75 |
| | | *Nos. 195-198 (4)* | 1.90 | 1.60 |

75th anniv. of the 1st Cook Islands stamps. Issued in sheets of 8 stamps and 1 label with inscription in yellow margin.

Hibiscus A34

Elizabeth II A35

Elizabeth II and Flowers A36

Flowers: 1c, Rose of Sharon. 2c, 15c, Frangipani. 2½c, Butterfly pea. 3c, Suva queen and Queen Elizabeth II. 4c, Water lily. 5c, Bauhania. 6c, Yellow hibiscus. 8c, Alamanda and Queen Elizabeth II. 9c, Stephanotis. 10c, Flaymboyant poinciana. 20c, Thunbergia. 25c, Canna lily and Queen Elizabeth II. 30c, Poinsettia. 50c, Gardenia.

The $4 exists with "FOUR DOLLARS" in two widths: type 1, 32½mm; type 2, 33½mm.

**1967-69 Photo. *Perf. 14x13½***

| | | | | |
|---|---|---|---|---|
| **199** | A34 | ½c gold & multi | .30 | .25 |
| **200** | A34 | 1c gold & multi | .30 | .25 |
| **201** | A34 | 2c gold & multi | .30 | .25 |
| **202** | A34 | 2½c gold & multi | .55 | .25 |
| **203** | A34 | 3c gold & multi | .60 | .25 |
| **204** | A34 | 4c *Walter Lily* | .90 | *1.25* |
| **205** | A34 | 4c *Water Lily* | 2.25 | 2.00 |
| **206** | A34 | 5c gold & multi | .40 | .25 |
| **207** | A34 | 6c gold & multi | .45 | .25 |
| **208** | A34 | 8c gold & multi | .45 | .25 |
| **209** | A34 | 9c gold & multi | .45 | .25 |
| **210** | A34 | 10c gold & multi | .45 | .25 |
| **211** | A34 | 15c gold & multi | .45 | .25 |
| **212** | A34 | 20c gold & multi | 5.00 | 1.50 |
| **213** | A34 | 25c gold & multi | .90 | .45 |
| **214** | A34 | 30c gold & multi | .75 | .55 |
| **215** | A34 | 50c gold & multi | 1.10 | .55 |
| **216** | A35 | $1 gold & multi | 2.40 | .60 |
| **217** | A35 | $2 gold & multi | 5.50 | .90 |
| **218** | A36 | $4 multi, type 2 ('68) | 2.25 | *4.00* |
| *a.* | | Type 1 | 40.00 | *55.00* |
| **219** | A36 | $6 multi ('68) | 2.25 | *5.00* |
| **219A** | A36 | $8 multi ('69) | 6.25 | *12.00* |
| **220** | A36 | $10 multi ('68) | 4.25 | *11.00* |
| | | *Nos. 199-220 (23)* | 38.50 | 42.55 |

Nos. 199-220 (except No. 204) were reprinted in 1970/71 with the fluorescent printing described below. Value, set: unused $60; used $40.

For surcharges see Nos. 290-291, 305-309, B1-B13, B17-B18, B20. For overprints see Nos. 277-283, 302-304, 315, 351-356, O1-O15.

---

Fluorescence

Since 1968 a number of stamps have been issued with a "fluorescent security underprinting" in a multiple coat of arms pattern. Some issues have this underprint, some do not.

Stamps issued both with and without the underprint are Nos. 199-203, 205-220, 283, 290-291.

From Nos. 292-296 onward, all stamps have this underprint unless otherwise noted.

---

Ia Orana Maria, by Gauguin — A37

Gauguin Paintings: 3c, Riders on the Beach. 5c, Still Life with Flowers. 8c, Whispered Words. 15c, Maternity. 22c, Why Are You Angry?

**1967, Oct. 23 Photo. *Perf. 13½***

| | | | | |
|---|---|---|---|---|
| **221** | A37 | 1c gold & multi | .25 | .25 |
| **222** | A37 | 3c gold & multi | .25 | .25 |
| **223** | A37 | 5c gold & multi | .25 | .25 |
| **224** | A37 | 8c gold & multi | .25 | .25 |
| **225** | A37 | 15c gold & multi | .30 | .25 |
| **226** | A37 | 22c gold & multi | .40 | .40 |
| *a.* | | Souvenir sheet of 6, #221-226 | 2.75 | 2.75 |
| | | *Nos. 221-226 (6)* | 1.70 | 1.65 |

Nos. 221-226 are printed in sheets of 6 (3x2).

For surcharge see No. B3.

Holy Family by Rubens — A38

Paintings: 3c, Adoration of the Magi, by Albrecht Durer. 4c, The Lucca Madonna, by Jan Van Eyck. 8c, Adoration of the Shepherds, by Jacopo da Bassano. 15c, Nativity, by El Greco. 25c, Madonna and Child, by Antonio Allegri da Correggio.

**1967, Dec. 4 *Perf. 12x13***

| | | | | |
|---|---|---|---|---|
| **227** | A38 | 1c gold & multi | .25 | .25 |
| **228** | A38 | 3c gold & multi | .25 | .25 |
| **229** | A38 | 4c gold & multi | .25 | .25 |
| **230** | A38 | 8c gold & multi | .25 | .25 |
| **231** | A38 | 15c gold & multi | .25 | .25 |
| **232** | A38 | 25c gold & multi | .30 | .30 |
| | | *Nos. 227-232 (6)* | 1.55 | 1.55 |

Christmas.

Capt. Cook and Matavai Bay, Tahiti, by Sydney Parkinson — A39

1c, Ships off Huahine Island, Tahiti, by John & James Clevely. 2c, town & harbor of Kamchatka, by John Webber, & Queen Elizabeth II. 4c, "The Ice Islands" (Antarctica), by William Hodges.

**1968, Sept. 12 Photo. *Perf. 13***

| | | | | |
|---|---|---|---|---|
| **233** | A39 | ½c gold & multi | .25 | .25 |
| **234** | A39 | 1c gold & multi | .25 | .25 |
| **235** | A39 | 2c gold & multi | .25 | .25 |
| **236** | A39 | 4c gold & multi | .25 | .25 |
| | | *Nos. 233-236,C12-C15 (8)* | 3.20 | 3.20 |

Bicent. of Capt. Cook's 1st voyage of discovery. Printed in sheets of 10 stamps and 2 labels (3x4). Labels show portraits of Elizabeth II and Cook.

Gymnast — A40

**1968, Oct. 21**

| | | | | |
|---|---|---|---|---|
| **237** | A40 | 1c Sailing | .25 | .25 |
| **238** | A40 | 5c shown | .25 | .25 |
| **239** | A40 | 15c High jump | .25 | .25 |
| **240** | A40 | 20c Woman diver | .30 | .25 |
| **241** | A40 | 30c Bicyclist | .55 | .25 |
| **242** | A40 | 50c Woman hurdler | .45 | .30 |
| | | *Nos. 237-242 (6)* | 2.05 | 1.55 |

19th Olympic Games, Mexico City, Oct. 12-27. Printed in sheets of 10 stamps and 2 labels (3x4).

Virgin and Child, by Titian — A41

Paintings: 4c, Holy Family, by Raphael. 10c, Madonna of the Rosary, by Murillo. 20c, Adoration of the Magi, by Memling. 30c, Adoration of the Magi, by Ghirlandajo.

**1968, Dec. 2 Photo. *Perf. 13***

| | | | | |
|---|---|---|---|---|
| **243** | A41 | 1c gold & multi | .25 | .25 |
| **244** | A41 | 4c gold & multi | .25 | .25 |
| **245** | A41 | 10c gold & multi | .25 | .25 |
| **246** | A41 | 20c gold & multi | .25 | .25 |
| **247** | A41 | 30c gold & multi | .30 | .30 |
| *a.* | | Souv. sheet, #243-247 + label | 1.75 | 1.75 |
| | | *Nos. 243-247 (5)* | 1.30 | 1.30 |

Issued in sheets of 6 (2x3).

Training on Ropeway — A42

Designs: ½c, Boy Scouts cooking over campfire. 5c, Training with signal flags, and Queen Elizabeth II. 10c, Planting a tree. 20c, Erecting a hut. 30c, Lord Baden-Powell, lake and mountains (visit to Rarotonga in 1935).

**1969, Feb. 6 Photo. *Perf. 13½***

**248** A42 ½c multicolored .25 .25
**249** A42 1c multicolored .25 .25
**250** A42 5c multicolored .25 .25
**251** A42 10c multicolored .25 .25
**252** A42 20c multicolored .25 .25
**253** A42 30c multicolored .35 .35
*Nos. 248-253 (6)* 1.60 1.60

5th Natl. Boy Scout Jamboree, Christchurch, New Zealand, Jan. 2-12.
Issued in sheets of 10 stamps and 2 labels (4x3).

A43

No. 254a, Soccer. No. 254b, Pole vault. No. 255a, Weight lifting. No. 255b, Basketball, Elizabeth II. No. 256a, Long jump. No. 256b, Tennis. No. 257a, Running. No. 257b, Javelin, Elizabeth II. No. 258a, Boxing. No. 258b, Golf.

***Perf. 13½x13***

**1969, July 7 Photo. Unwmk.**

**254** A43 ½c Pair, #a.-b. .40 .40
**255** A43 1c Pair, #a.-b. .40 .40
**256** A43 4c Pair, #a.-b. 1.20 1.20
**257** A43 10c Pair, #a.-b. 1.60 1.60
**258** A43 15c Pair, #a.-b. 3.00 3.00
*c.* Souv. sheet, #254-258 + 2 labels 7.75 7.50
*Nos. 254-258 (5)* 6.60 6.60

3rd South Pacifc Games, Port Moresby, Papua and New Guinea, Aug. 13-23.
Issued in sheets of 10.

Map of Cook Islands and Capt. Cook A44

Map of Cook Islands and: 5c, Premier Albert Henry of Cook Islands. 25c, Coat of arms of New Zealand. 30c, Queen Elizabeth II.

**1969, Oct. 8 Photo. *Perf. 13***

**264** A44 5c red & multi .35 .35
**265** A44 10c lemon & multi 1.00 .50
**266** A44 25c green & multi .50 .50
**267** A44 30c blue & multi .50 .50
*Nos. 264-267 (4)* 2.35 1.85

South Pacific Conf., Noumea, Oct. 1969.

Madonna and Child, by Filippo Lippi — A45

Paintings: 4c, Holy Family, by Baccio della Porta. 10c, Madonna and Child, by Anton Raphael Mengs. 20c, Madonna and Child, by Le Maitre de Flemalle. 30c, Madonna and Child by Correggio.

**1969, Nov. 21 Photo. *Perf. 13½***

**268** A45 1c buff & multi .25 .25
**269** A45 4c buff & multi .25 .25
**270** A45 10c buff & multi .25 .25
**271** A45 20c buff & multi .25 .25
**272** A45 30c buff & multi .25 .25
*a.* Souv. sheet, #268-272 + label 1.50 1.50
*Nos. 268-272 (5)* 1.25 1.25

Issued in sheets of 8 stamps, one label with portrait of Queen Elizabeth II.

Resurrection of Christ, by Raphael — A46

The Resurrection of Christ by: 8c, Dirk Bouts. 20c, Albert Altdorfer. 25c, Murillo.

**1970, Mar. 12 Photo. *Perf. 13½***
**Size: 25½x56mm**

**273** A46 4c gold & multi .25 .25
**274** A46 8c gold & multi .25 .25
**275** A46 20c gold & multi .25 .25
**276** A46 25c gold & multi .25 .25
*a.* Souv. sheet, #273-276 + 2 labels 1.40 1.40
*Nos. 273-276 (4)* 1.00 1.00

Easter 1970.
Printed in sheets of 8 stamps and a label (3x3) showing portrait of Queen Elizabeth II and name of painting and painter.
See Nos. 316-318.

Nos. 205, 208, 211-212, 214, 217 Overprinted

**1970, Apr. *Perf. 14x13½***

**277** A34 4c gold & multi .30 .30
**278** A34 8c gold & multi .30 .30
**279** A34 15c gold & multi .30 .30
**280** A34 20c gold & multi .40 .40
**281** A34 30c gold & multi .30 .30
**282** A35 $2 gold & multi 1.25 1.25

**No. 218 Overprinted**



**283** A36 $4 gold & multi 2.50 2.50
*Nos. 277-283 (7)* 5.35 5.35

Splashdown of Apollo 13 west of Rarotonga, Apr. 17, 1970.
Issued: Nos. 277-282, 4/17; $4, 4/30.
Values for No. 283 is for stamps with fluorescence.
Stamps without fluorescence: Value, mint $32.50, used $50.

Queen Elizabeth II, Prince Philip, Princess Anne and Prince Charles A47

Design: 30c, Wedgwood bust of Capt. Cook and "Endeavour." $1, Royal visit commemorative coin, obverse and reverse.

**1970, June 12 Photo. *Perf. 13½***

**284** A47 5c gold & multi .90 .30
**285** A47 30c gold & multi 2.25 1.50
**286** A47 $1 gold & multi 3.00 3.00
*a.* Souv. sheet, #284-286 + label 9.75 9.75
*Nos. 284-286 (3)* 6.15 4.80

Visit of the British royal family.

**Nos. 284-286 Overprinted in Silver or Black: "Fifth Anniversary Self-Government August 1970"**

**1970, Aug. 27 Photo. *Perf. 13½***

**287** A47 5c gold & multi (S) .60 .25
**288** A47 30c gold & multi 1.10 .50
**289** A47 $1 gold & multi 1.50 1.25
*Nos. 287-289 (3)* 3.20 2.00

5th anniv. of self-government. The overprint on No. 287 is arranged in one line around 3 sides of the design; the overprint on Nos. 288-289 is in 3 horizontal lines.

**Nos. 219A-220 Surcharged**

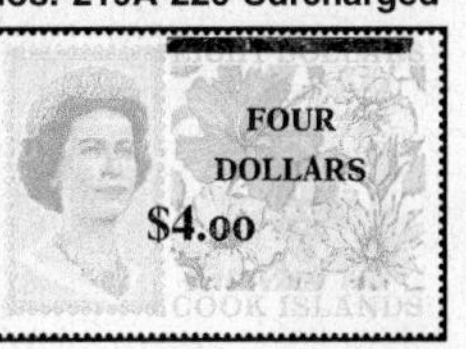


**1970, Nov. 11 Photo. *Perf. 14x13½***

**290** A36 $4 on $8 multi *3.50 3.50*
**291** A36 $4 on $10 multi *2.50 2.50*

In each sheet of 15, 3 stamps have 2 surcharged bars instead of one.
Nos. 290-291 without fluorescence: Value, mint $70, used $85.

Nativity — A48

Illuminations from 14th Century Robert de Lisle Psalter: 4c, Angel and shepherds. 10c, The Circumcision. 20c, The Adoration of the Kings. 30c, The Presentation at the Temple.

**1970, Nov. 30 Photo. *Perf. 13½***

**292** A48 1c gold & multi .25 .25
**293** A48 4c gold & multi .25 .25
**294** A48 10c gold & multi .25 .25
**295** A48 20c gold & multi .25 .25
**296** A48 30c gold & multi .25 .25
*a.* Souv. sheet, #292-296 + label 1.50 1.50
*Nos. 292-296 (5)* 1.25 1.25

Christmas.
Issued in sheets of 5 stamps and a label (3x2) showing portrait of Queen Elizabeth II and source of design.

Nos. 214-215 Overprinted

**1971**

**296B** A34 30c +20c multi .40 .60
**296C** A34 50c +20c multi 1.25 *2.00*

Issued: 30c, 2/25; 50c, 3/8.
Nos. 296B-296C were issued to prepay regular postage plus the fee of a private carrier who had contracted to deliver mail within the United Kingdom during a postal strike. The strike ended on March 8, and these stamps were withdrawn March 12.

Queen Elizabeth II and Prince Philip — A49

Designs: 4c, Royal family at Balmoral. 10c, Prince Philip sailing. 15c, Prince Philip as polo player. 25c, Prince Philip and royal yacht.

**1971, Mar. 11 Litho. *Perf. 13½***

**297** A49 1c brt blue & multi .25 .25
**298** A49 4c brt blue & multi .30 .30
**299** A49 10c brt blue & multi .85 .85
**300** A49 15c brt blue & multi 1.00 1.00
**301** A49 25c brt blue & multi 1.60 1.60
*a.* Souv. sheet, #297-301 + 2 labels 5.50 5.50
*Nos. 297-301 (5)* 4.00 4.00

Visit of Prince Philip, Duke of Edinburgh to Rarotonga, Feb. 27, 1971. Printed in sheets of 10 stamps and 2 labels showing Queen Elizabeth II commemorative coin and a portrait of Prince Philip.

Nos. 210, 213-214 Overprinted

**1971, Sept. 8 Photo. *Perf. 14x13½***

**302** A34 10c gold & multi .50 .50
**303** A34 25c gold & multi .50 .50
**304** A34 30c gold & multi .50 .50
*Nos. 302-304 (3)* 1.50 1.50

4th South Pacific Games, Papeete, French Polynesia, Sept. 8-19. See Nos. B8-B13

**Nos. 202, 205, 208-209 and 211 Surcharged with New Value and Three Bars**

**1971, Oct. 20**

**305** A34 10c on 2½c multi .25 .25
**306** A34 10c on 4c multi .25 .25
**307** A34 10c on 8c multi .25 .25
**308** A34 10c on 9c multi .25 .25
**309** A34 10c on 15c multi .25 .25
*Nos. 305-309 (5)* 1.25 1.25

Madonna and Child, by Bellini — A50

Christmas: Paintings of the Madonna and Child, by Giovanni Bellini.

**1971, Nov. 30 *Perf. 13½***

**310** A50 1c gold & multi .25 .25
**311** A50 4c gold & multi .25 .25
**312** A50 10c gold & multi .30 .30
**313** A50 20c gold & multi .40 .30
**314** A50 30c gold & multi .55 .40
*a.* Souv. sheet, #310-314 + label 2.25 2.25
*Nos. 310-314 (5)* 1.75 1.50

See No. B14.

**No. 216 Overprinted: "SOUTH PACIFIC / COMMISSION / FEB. 1947-1972"**

**1972, Feb. 17 Photo. *Perf. 14x13½***

**315** A35 $1 gold & multi .80 .80

South Pacific Commission, 25th anniv.

**Easter Type of 1970**

Illuminations from 14th century Robert de Lisle Psalter: 5c, St. John. 10c, Christ crucified. 30c, Virgin Mary.

**1972, Mar. 6 Photo. *Perf. 13½***
**Size: 21x68mm**

**316** A46 5c gold & multi .25 .25
**317** A46 10c gold & multi .25 .25
**318** A46 30c gold & multi .30 .30
*a.* Souvenir sheet of 3, #316-318 1.00 1.00
*Nos. 316-318 (3)* .80 .80

Printed in sheets of 12.
For surcharges see Nos. B15-B16, B19.

Rocket over Moon — A51

No. 319a, Shown. No. 319b, Earth over moon. No. 320a, Landing module and astronaut. No. 320b, Astronaut collecting moon rocks. No. 321a, Earth and rocket over moon. No. 321b, Lunar rover and astronaut. No. 322a, Helicopter over raft in Pacific. No. 322b, Capsule and parachutes.

**1972, Apr. 17**

**319** A51 5c Pair, #a.-b. .25 .25
**320** A51 10c Pair, #a.-b. .50 .50
**321** A51 25c Pair, #a.-b. 1.40 1.40
**322** A51 30c Pair, #a.-b. 1.60 1.60
*c.* Souvenir sheet of 8 6.00 6.00
*Nos. 319-322 (4)* 3.75 3.75

Apollo moon explorations.
No. 322c contains Nos. 319-322 arranged in 2 blocks of 4 divided by a map showing splashdown area of Apollo X, XII and XIII.
For surcharges see Nos. B21-B24.

High Jump, Olympic Rings — A52

**1972, June 26**

327 A52 10c shown .30 .30
328 A52 25c Running .55 .55
329 A52 30c Boxing .55 .55
 *a.* Souv. sheet, #327-329 + label 2.00 2.00
 *Nos. 327-329 (3)* 1.40 1.40

20th Olympic Games, Munich, Aug. 26-Sept. 10. Sheets of 8 stamps and label.
See No. B29.

Rest on Flight to Egypt, by Caravaggio — A53

Paintings: 5c, Virgin of the Swallows, by Guercino. 10c, Virgin with Green Cushion, by Andrea Solario. 20c, Virgin and Child, by Lorenzo di Credi. 30c, Virgin and Child, by Giovanni Bellini.

**1972, Oct. 11 Photo. *Perf. 13½***

330 A53 1c gold & multi .25 .25
331 A53 5c gold & multi .35 .25
332 A53 10c gold & multi .45 .25
333 A53 20c gold & multi .55 .30
334 A53 30c gold & multi .90 .40
 *a.* Souv. sheet, #330-334 + label 4.00 4.00
 *Nos. 330-334 (5)* 2.50 1.45

Christmas. See No. B30.

Princess Elizabeth and Prince Philip — A54

Designs: 5c, Wedding ceremony, Westminster Abbey. 15c, Bridal portrait. 30c, Official wedding picture of royal family.

**1972, Nov. 20 Size: 29x40mm**

335 A54 5c silver & multi .25 .25
336 A54 10c silver & multi .35 .35

**Size: 40x40mm**

337 A54 15c silver & multi .40 .40

**Size: 66x40mm**

338 A54 30c silver & multi .55 .55
 *Nos. 335-338 (4)* 1.55 1.55

25th anniversary of the marriage of Queen Elizabeth II and Prince Philip.
Nos. 335-337 printed in sheets of 8 stamps and one label; No. 338 in sheets of 6.

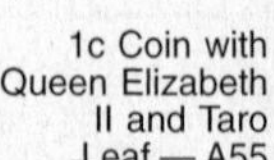

1c Coin with Queen Elizabeth II and Taro Leaf — A55

Queen Elizabeth II Coins: 2c, Pineapples. 5c, Hibiscus. 10c, Oranges. 20c, Fairy terns. 50c, Bonito. $1, Tangaroa, Polynesian god of creation, vert.

**1973, Mar. 15 Photo. *Perf. 13x13½***

**Size: 37x24mm**

339 A55 1c dp car, blk & gold .25 .25
340 A55 2c blue, blk & gold .25 .25
341 A55 5c green, blk & gold .25 .25

**Size: 46x30mm**

342 A55 10c vio, blue, blk & sil .25 .25
343 A55 20c dk green, blk & sil .35 .35
344 A55 50c dp car, black & sil .60 .60

**Size: 32x54½mm**

345 A55 $1 blue, blk & silver .80 .80
 *Nos. 339-345 (7)* 2.75 2.75

Coinage commemorating silver wedding anniversary of Queen Elizabeth II.
Printed in sheets of 20 stamps and label showing Westminster Abbey.

"Noli me Tangere," by Titian — A56

Paintings: 10c, Descent from the Cross, by Rubens. 30c, The Lamentation of Christ, by Dürer.

**1973, Apr. 9**

346 A56 5c gold & multi .25 .25
347 A56 10c gold & multi .30 .30
348 A56 30c gold & multi .35 .35
 *a.* Souvenir sheet of 3, #346-348 1.00 1.00
 *Nos. 346-348 (3)* .90 .90

Easter. Printed in sheets of 15 stamps and one label.
See Nos. 378-380, B31-B33, B39-B41.

Queen Elizabeth II in Coronation Regalia — A57

**1973, June 1 Photo. *Perf. 14x13½***

349 A57 10c gold & multi .75 .75

**Souvenir Sheet**

***Perf. 13½x14½***

350 A57 50c gold & multi 3.00 3.00

20th anniv. of the coronation of Queen Elizabeth II. No. 349 printed in sheets of 5 stamps and one label.

Nos. 206, 208, 210, 212-214 Overprinted

**1973, July 25 Photo. *Perf. 14x13½***

351 A34 5c gold & multi .25 .25
352 A34 8c gold & multi .25 .25
353 A34 10c gold & multi .25 .25
354 A34 20c gold & multi .25 .25
355 A34 25c gold & multi .25 .25
356 A34 30c gold & multi .25 .25
 *Nos. 351-356 (6)* 1.50 1.50

Nuclear Test Ban Treaty, 10th anniv. and as protest against French nuclear testing on Mururoa atoll.

Tipairua — A58

Historic South Pacific sailing vessels.

**1973, Sept. 17 Photo. *Perf. 13½x13***

357 A58 ½c shown .25 .25
358 A58 1c Wa'a Kaulua .25 .25
359 A58 1½c Tainui .25 .25
360 A58 5c War canoe .40 .25
361 A58 10c Pahi .50 .35
362 A58 15c Amatasi .85 .85
363 A58 25c Vaka 1.25 1.25
 *Nos. 357-363 (7)* 3.75 3.45

Annunciation — A59

Designs from 15th Century Prayer Book: 5c, The Visitation. 10c, Adoration of the Shepherds. 20c, Adoration of the Kings. 30c, Slaughter of the Innocents.

**1973, Oct. 30 Photo. *Perf. 13x13½***

364 A59 1c multicolored .25 .25
365 A59 5c multicolored .25 .25
366 A59 10c multicolored .25 .25
367 A59 20c multicolored .25 .25
368 A59 30c multicolored .25 .25
 *a.* Souv. sheet, #364-368 + label .90 .90
 *Nos. 364-368 (5)* 1.25 1.25

Christmas. See Nos. B34-B38.

Princess Anne — A60

30c, Mark Phillips. 50c, Princess and Mark Phillips.

**1973, Nov. 14 Photo. *Perf. 14***

369 A60 25c shown .25 .25
370 A60 30c multicolored .30 .25
371 A60 50c multicolored .35 .35
 *a.* Souv. sheet, #369-371 + label 1.00 1.00
 *Nos. 369-371 (3)* .90 .85

Wedding of Princess Anne and Capt. Mark Phillips.

Running and Games Emblem — A61

1c, Diving. 3c, Boxing. 10c, Weight lifting. 30c, Bicycling. 50c, Discobolus.

**1974, Jan. 24 Photo. *Perf. 14***

372 A61 1c multi, vert. .25 .25
373 A61 3c multi, vert. .25 .25
374 A61 5c multi .25 .25
375 A61 10c multi .25 .25
376 A61 30c multi .50 .50
 *Nos. 372-376 (5)* 1.50 1.50

**Souvenir Sheet**

377 A61 50c multi, vert. 1.25 1.25

10th British Commonwealth Games, Christchurch, New Zealand, Jan. 24-Feb. 2. No. 377 contains one stamp 35x45mm.

**Easter Type of 1973 Dated "1974"**

Paintings: 5c, Jesus Carrying Cross, by Raphael. 10c, Jesus in the Arms of God, by El Greco. 30c, Descent from the Cross, by Caravaggio.

**1974, Mar. 25 *Perf. 13½x13***

378 A56 5c gold & multi .25 .25
379 A56 10c gold & multi .25 .25
380 A56 30c gold & multi .30 .30
 *a.* Souvenir sheet of 3, #378-380 1.25 1.25
 *Nos. 378-380 (3)* .80 .80

Easter. See Nos. B39-B41.

Phallicium Glaucum A62

Queen Elizabeth II A63

Queen and Shells A64

Cook Islands sea shells: 1c, Vasum turbinellus. 1 ½c, Corculum cardissa. 2c, Terebellum terebellum. 3c, Aulica vespertilio. 4c, Strombus gibberulus. 5c, Cymatium pileare. 6c, Cyprae caputserpentis. 8c, Bursa granularis. 10c, Tenebra muscaria. 15c, Mitra mitra. 20c, Natica alapillonis roding. 25c, Gloripallium pallium. 30c, Conus miles. 50c, Conus textile. 60c, Oliva sericea roding.
The designs of the 2c, 5c, 10c, 30c include portrait of Queen Elizabeth II.

**1974-75 Photo. *Perf. 13½***

381 A62 ½c shown .30 .30
382 A62 1c multicolored .30 .30
383 A62 1½c multicolored .30 .30
384 A62 2c multicolored .30 .30
385 A62 3c multicolored .40 .30
386 A62 4c multicolored .45 .30
387 A62 5c multicolored .50 .30
388 A62 6c multicolored .50 .30
389 A62 8c multicolored .60 *1.50*
390 A62 10c multicolored .60 .40
391 A62 15c multicolored .65 .30
392 A62 20c multicolored .90 .30
393 A62 25c multicolored .95 *2.00*
394 A62 30c multicolored 1.00 .40
395 A62 50c multicolored 7.00 3.25
396 A62 60c multicolored 7.50 3.25
397 A63 $1 shown 2.50 *3.50*
398 A63 $2 multi ('75) 2.50 *2.75*

***Perf. 14x13½***

399 A64 $4 multi ('75) 3.50 5.50
400 A64 $6 multi ('75) 11.00 5.50
401 A64 $8 multi ('75) 12.50 9.00
402 A64 $10 multi ('75) 18.00 6.50
 *Nos. 381-402 (22)* 72.25 46.55

Issued: 50c, 60c, $1, 8/26; $2, 1/27; $4, 3/17; $6, 4/29; $8, 5/30; $10, 6/30; others, 5/17.
For surcharges & overprints see Nos. 488-498, 526-528, 991, O16-O26, O30-O31.

Soccer Player and Map of Oceania — A65

50c, Munich stadium & map of Oceania. $1, Soccer player, Munich stadium & World Cup.

**1974, July 5 Photo. *Perf. 13½***

**Size: 31x29mm**

403 A65 25c multicolored .30 .30
404 A65 50c multicolored .40 .40

**Size: 68x28½mm**

405 A65 $1 multicolored .75 .75
 *a.* Souvenir sheet of 3, #403-405 1.50 1.50
 *Nos. 403-405 (3)* 1.45 1.45

World Cup Soccer Championship, Munich, June 13-July 7. Nos. 403-405 printed in sheets of 8 and commemorative label.

$2.50 Capt. Cook Silver Coin — A66

Commemorative Silver Coins: $7.50, $7.50 coin with Queen Elizabeth II on obverse; Capt. Cook, map of Islands and "Resolution" on reverse. $2.50 coin shows "Resolution," "Adventure" and globe on reverse.

**1974, July 22 Photo. *Perf. 14***

406 A66 $2.50 sil, vio & blk 10.00 6.75
407 A66 $7.50 grn, sil & blk 20.00 15.00
 *a.* Souvenir sheet of 2, #406-407 37.50 37.50

Bicentenary of Capt. Cook's 2nd voyage of discovery. Nos. 406-407 printed in sheets of 5 and commemorative label.

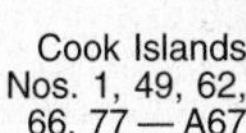

Cook Islands Nos. 1, 49, 62, 66, 77 — A67

Stamps of Cook Islands: 25c, DC-3 over old Rarotonga landing strip, and No. 19. 30c, Rarotonga Post Office, UPU emblem and No. 65. 50c, UPU emblem and Nos. 1, 19, 49, 62, 65-66 and 77.

**1974, Sept. 16 Photo. *Perf. 13½x14***

**408** A67 10c gold & multi .25 .25
**409** A67 25c gold & multi .35 .35
**410** A67 30c gold & multi .40 .40
**411** A67 50c gold & multi .75 .75
*a.* Souv. sheet, #408-411, perf. 13½ 1.60 1.60
*Nos. 408-411 (4)* 1.75 1.75

Cent. of UPU. Nos. 408-411 printed in sheets of 8 and commemorative label.

Virgin and Child, with St. John, by Raphael — A68

Paintings: 5c, Holy Family, by Andrea del Sarto. 10c, Nativity, by Correggio. 20c, Holy Family, by Rembrandt. 30c, Nativity, by Van der Weyden.

**1974, Oct. 15 Photo. *Perf. 13½***

**412** A68 1c multicolored .25 .25
**413** A68 5c multicolored .25 .25
**414** A68 10c multicolored .25 .25
**415** A68 20c multicolored .40 .40
**416** A68 30c multicolored .55 .55
*a.* Souv. sheet, #412-416 + label 1.75 1.75
*Nos. 412-416 (5)* 1.70 1.70

Christmas 1974. Nos. 412-416 printed in sheets of 15 and one label showing Queen Elizabeth II.
See Nos. B42-B46.

Churchill and Blenheim Palace — A69

Sir Winston Churchill (1874-1965) and: 10c, Parliament. 25c, Chartwell. 30c, Buckingham Palace. 50c, St. Paul's Cathedral.

**1974, Nov. 20 Photo. *Perf. 14***

**417** A69 5c violet & multi .25 .25
**418** A69 10c maroon & multi .25 .25
**419** A69 25c dk blue & multi .30 .30
**420** A69 30c brown & multi .40 .40
**421** A69 50c multicolored .75 .75
*a.* Souv. sheet, #417-421 + label 2.25 2.25
*Nos. 417-421 (5)* 1.95 1.95

Nos. 417-421 printed in sheets of 5 stamps and one label showing $100 commemorative gold coin.

Vasco Nunez de Balboa A70

5c, Ferdinand Magellan & route around South America. 10c, Juan Sebastian de Elcano & ship. 25c, Andres de Urdaneta & ship. 25c, Miguel Lopez de Legaspi & ship.

**1975, Feb. 3 *Perf. 13½***

**422** A70 1c multicolored .25 .25
**423** A70 5c multicolored .65 .25
**424** A70 10c multicolored 1.25 .30
**425** A70 25c multicolored 2.00 .90
**426** A70 30c multicolored 2.25 1.00
*Nos. 422-426 (5)* 6.40 2.70

16th century explorers of the Pacific Ocean.

Apollo and Apollo-Soyuz Emblem — A71

Apollo-Soyuz Emblem &: No. 427b, Soyuz. No. 428a, Aleksei A. Leonov & Valery N. Kubasov. No. 428b, Donald K. Slayton, Vance D. Brand & Thomas P. Stafford. No. 429a, Cosmonaut inside Soyuz capsule. No. 429b, American astronauts inside Apollo capsule.

**1975, July 15 Photo. *Perf. 13½***

**427** A71 25c Pair, #a.-b. .80 .80
**428** A71 30c Pair, #a.-b. .90 .90
**429** A71 50c Pair, #a.-b. 1.25 1.25
*c.* Souvenir sheet of 6, #427-429 2.75 2.75
*Nos. 427-429 (3)* 2.95 2.95

Apollo Soyuz space test project (Russo-American space cooperation), launching July 15; link-up, July 17. Printed sheets of 18 stamps and 2 labels showing flags.

$100 Gold Commemorative Coin — A72

**1975, Aug. 8 Photo. *Perf. 13½x13***

**433** A72 $2 gold & dp violet 3.50 3.25

Bicentenary of the completion of Capt. Cook's second voyage of discovery.

Cook Islands' Flag, Map of Islands and New Zealand — A73

Prime Minister Sir Albert Henry — A74

Design: 25c, View of Rarotonga and flag.

**1975, Aug. 8 *Perf. 13½x13, 13x13½***

**434** A73 5c gold & multi .40 .25
**435** A74 10c gold & multi .50 .25
**436** A73 25c gold & multi 1.25 .50
*Nos. 434-436 (3)* 2.15 1.00

Tenth anniversary of self-government.

Virgin and Child, 15th Century, Flemish — A75

Paintings: 10c, Madonna in the Field, by Raphael. 15c, Holy Family, by Raphael. 20c, Adoration of the Shepherds, by J. B. Mayno. 35c, Annunciation, by Murillo.

**1975, Dec. 1 Photo. *Perf. 13½***

**437** A75 6c gold & multi .25 .25
**438** A75 10c gold & multi .25 .25
**439** A75 15c gold & multi .30 .30
**440** A75 20c gold & multi .30 .30
**441** A75 35c gold & multi .45 .45
*a.* Souv. sheet, #437-441 + label 1.60 1.60
*Nos. 437-441 (5)* 1.55 1.55

Christmas. See Nos. B47-B51.

Descent from the Cross, by Raphael — A76

Paintings: 15c, Pieta, by Veronese. 35c, Pieta, by El Greco.

**1976, Mar. 29 Photo. *Perf. 13½***

**442** A76 7c gold & multi .25 .25
**443** A76 15c gold & multi .50 .50
**444** A76 35c gold & multi .80 .80
*a.* Souvenir sheet of 3, #442-444 1.75 1.75
*Nos. 442-444 (3)* 1.55 1.55

Easter. Nos. 442-444 printed in sheets of 20 with label showing Queen Elizabeth II.
See Nos. B52-B54.

Benjamin Franklin and "Resolution" A77

Designs: $2, Capt. James Cook and "Resolution." $3, Cook, "Resolution" and Franklin.

**1976, May 29 Photo. *Perf. 13½***

**445** A77 $1 gold & multi 3.75 2.50
**446** A77 $2 gold & multi 7.75 5.50

**Souvenir Sheet**

***Perf. 13***

**447** A77 $3 gold & multi 11.50 6.50

American Bicentennial. No. 447 contains one stamp 73x31mm. Nos. 445-446 printed in sheets of 5 and corner label with Franklin's request to assist Capt. Cook.
For overprint see No. O29.

**Nos. 445-447 Overprinted "Royal Visit July 1976"**

**1976, July 6 Photo. *Perf. 13½***

**448** A77 $1 gold & multi 2.25 1.75
**449** A77 $2 gold & multi 6.00 5.25

**Souvenir Sheet**

***Perf. 13***

**450** A77 $3 gold & multi 7.50 6.75

Visit of Queen Elizabeth II and Prince Philip to the United States.

High Hurdles A78

15c, Field hockey. 30c, Fencing. 35c, Soccer.

**1976, July 22 *Perf. 13½***

**451** A78 7c Pair, #a.-b. .40 .40
**452** A78 15c Pair, #a.-b. .50 .50
**453** A78 30c Pair, #a.-b. .90 .90
**454** A78 35c Pair, #a.-b. 1.10 1.10
*c.* Souvenir sheet of 8, #451-454 3.50 3.50
*Nos. 451-454 (4)* 2.90 2.90

21st Olympic Games, Montreal, Canada, 7/17-8/1. Printed in sheets of 10 stamps + 2 labels.

The Visitation — A80

Designs: 10c, Virgin and Child. 15c, Adoration of the Shepherds. 20c, Adoration of the Kings. 35c, Holy Family. After painted Renaissance altar sculptures.

**1976, Oct. 12 Photo. *Perf. 14x13½***

**459** A80 6c gold & multi .25 .25
**460** A80 10c gold & multi .25 .25
**461** A80 15c gold & multi .25 .25
**462** A80 20c gold & multi .25 .25
**463** A80 35c gold & multi .25 .25
*a.* Souv. sheet, #459-463 + label 1.25 1.25
*Nos. 459-463 (5)* 1.25 1.25

Christmas. Nos. 459-463 printed in sheets of 20 with label showing Queen Elizabeth II.
See Nos. B55-B59.

$5 Silver Coin, 1976 — A81

**1976, Nov. 15 Photo. *Perf. 13½***

**464** A81 $1 multicolored 2.00 1.50

National Wildlife and Conservation Day. Issued in sheets of 5 stamps and commemorative label.
See Nos. 502, 536.

A82

No. 465a, Crown. No. 465b, Elizabeth II in Coronation Vestments. No. 466a, Westminster Abbey. No. 466b, Coach in procession. No. 467a, Queen and Prince Philip after coronation. No. 467b, Investiture of Sir Albert Henry, Premier of Cook Islands, 1974.

**1977, Feb. 7 Photo. *Perf. 13½x13***

**465** A82 25c Pair, #a.-b. .40 .40
**466** A82 50c Pair, #a.-b. .75 .75
**467** A82 $1 Pair, #a.-b. 1.25 1.25
*c.* Souv. sheet, #465-467, perf. 13 2.75 2.75
*Nos. 465-467 (3)* 2.40 2.40

Reign of Queen Elizabeth II, 25th anniv. Printed in sheets of 8.
For overprints see No. O27.

Crucifixion, by Rubens — A83

Paintings by Rubens: 15c, Christ Between the Thieves. 35c, Descent from the Cross.

**1977, Mar. 28 Photo. *Perf. 14x13½***

**471** A83 7c gold & multi .40 .40
**472** A83 15c gold & multi .50 .50
**473** A83 35c gold & multi 1.00 1.00
*a.* Souv. sheet, #471-473, perf 13 2.00 2.00
*Nos. 471-473 (3)* 1.90 1.90

Easter 1977, and 400th birth anniv. of Peter Paul Rubens (1577-1640), Flemish painter. Nos. 471-473 printed in sheets of 24 stamps and corner label with portrait of Queen Elizabeth II and description.
See Nos. B60-B62.

Virgin and Child, by Memling — A84

Virgin and Child by: 10c, Hans Memling. 15c, Geertgen Tot Sin Jans. 20c, Carlo Crivelli. 35c, School of Henry Blex.

**1977, Oct. 3 Photo. *Perf. 13½***

**474** A84 6c gold & multi .25 .25
**475** A84 10c gold & multi .25 .25
**476** A84 15c gold & multi .25 .25
**477** A84 20c gold & multi .35 .35
**478** A84 35c gold & multi .55 .55
*a.* Souv. sheet, #474-478 + label 1.60 1.60
*Nos. 474-478 (5)* 1.65 1.65

Christmas. Nos. 474-478 printed in sheets of 24 and label. See Nos. B63-B67.

$5-silver Coin, 1977 — A85

**1977, Nov. 15 Photo. *Perf. 13½***

**479** A85 $1 silver & multi 2.00 .95

National Wildlife Conservation Day. No. 479 issued in sheets of 5 and one label.

Capt. Cook, by Nathaniel Dance and "Resolution" A86

$1, "Capt. Cook Landing at Owyhee" and Capt. Cook. $2, Cook Islands $200 commemorative coin, 1978, and Cook Monument, Hawaii, 1825.

**1978, Jan. 20 Litho. *Perf. 13½***

**480** A86 50c gold & multi .80 .80
**481** A86 $1 gold & multi 1.25 1.25
**482** A86 $2 gold & multi 2.50 2.50
*a.* Souvenir sheet of 3, #480-482 4.75 4.75
*Nos. 480-482 (3)* 4.55 4.55

Bicentennial of Capt. Cook's arrival in Hawaii.

Nos. 480-482 issued in sheets of 5 with corner label showing ship off Hawaiian coast.

For overprints see Nos. 499-501a.

Pieta, by Rogier van der Weyden — A87

Paintings, National Gallery, London: 35c, Burial of Jesus, by Michelangelo. 75c, Jesus at Emmaus, by Caravaggio.

**1978, Mar. 20 Photo. *Perf. 13½x13***

**483** A87 15c gold & multi .30 .30
**484** A87 35c gold & multi .50 .50
**485** A87 75c gold & multi .75 .75
*a.* Souv. sheet, #483-485 + label 1.25 1.25
*Nos. 483-485 (3)* 1.55 1.55

Easter. Nos. 483-485 printed in sheets of 5 and corner label showing National Gallery.

See Nos. B68-B70.

### Souvenir Sheets

Coronation of Queen Elizabeth II, 25th anniv. — A88

**1978, June 6 Photo. *Perf. 13***

**486** A88 Sheet of 4 + 2 labels 1.30 1.30
*a.* 50c Queen Elizabeth II .30 .30
*b.* 50c Lion of England .30 .30
*c.* 50c Imperial State Crown .30 .30
*d.* 50c Tangaroa figure .30 .30
**487** A88 Sheet of 4 + label 1.55 1.30
*a.* 70c like 486a .30 .30
*b.* 70c Scepter with Cross .30 .30
*c.* 70c St. Edward's Crown .30 .30
*d.* 70c Rarotongan staff god .30 .30
*e.* Souv. sheet of 8, #486a-487d + label 2.50 2.50

Coronation of Queen Elizabeth II, 25th anniv.

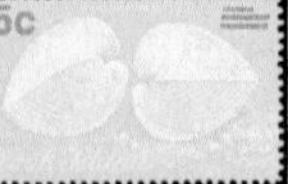


Nos. 381, 383, 388-389, 393-396 Srchd. in Silver, Black or Gold

**1978, Nov. 10 Photo. *Perf. 13½***

**488** A62 5c on 1½c multi (S) .25 .25
**489** A62 7c on ½c multi .25 .25
**490** A62 10c on 6c multi (G) .40 .40
**491** A62 10c on 8c multi (G) .40 .40
**492** A62 15c on ½c multi .65 .60
**493** A62 15c on 25c multi (S) .65 .60
**494** A62 15c on 30c multi .65 .60
**495** A62 15c on 50c multi (S) .65 .60
**496** A62 15c on 60c multi (G) .65 .60
**497** A62 17c on ½c multi .80 .80
**498** A62 17c on 50c multi (S) .80 .80
*Nos. 488-498 (11)* 6.15 5.90

See Nos. 526-528.

### Nos. 480-482a Overprinted in Black on Silver Panel

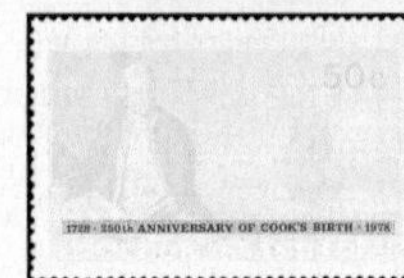

**1978, Nov. 13 Litho. *Perf. 13½***

**499** A86 50c gold & multi 1.00 1.00
**500** A86 $1 gold & multi 1.50 1.50
**501** A86 $2 gold & multi 2.25 2.25
*a.* Souvenir sheet of 3, #499-501 15.00 15.00
*Nos. 499-501 (3)* 4.75 4.75

250th anniv. of Capt. Cook's birth. Similar overprint in 4 lines was applied to labels. Label of No. 501a overprinted only with dates 1728, 1978.

### Coin Type of 1976

$1, $5 Silver coin, 1978 (Polynesian warbler).

**1978, Nov. 15 Photo. *Perf. 13½***

**502** A81 $1 multicolored 1.60 1.60

National Wildlife and Conservation Day. Sheets of 24 containing 4 panes of 6.

A89

Virgin and Child by: 15c, Rogier van der Weyden. 17c, Carlo Crivelli. 35c, Murillo.

**1978, Dec. 8 Photo. *Perf. 13***

**503** A89 15c multicolored .35 .35
**504** A89 17c multicolored .45 .45
**505** A89 35c multicolored .75 .75
*a.* Souvenir sheet of 3, #503-505 1.60 1.60
*Nos. 503-505 (3)* 1.55 1.55

Christmas. See Nos. B71-B73.

A90

Descent from the Cross, by Gaspar de Crayer (Details): 10c, Pieta. 12c, St. John. 15c, Mary Magdalene. 20c, Cherubs.

**1979, Apr. 5 Photo. *Perf. 13***

**506** A90 10c multicolored .25 .25
**507** A90 12c multicolored .25 .25
**508** A90 15c multicolored .25 .25
**509** A90 20c multicolored .50 .50
*Nos. 506-509 (4)* 1.25 1.25

Easter. See No. B74.

A91

20c, Capt. Cook, by John Weber. 30c, Resolution, by Henry Roberts. 35c, Endeavour. 50c, Death of Capt. Cook, by George Carter.

**1979, July 23 Photo. *Perf. 14x13½***

**510** A91 20c multicolored .40 .40
**511** A91 30c multicolored .55 .55
**512** A91 35c multicolored .65 .65
**513** A91 50c multicolored .80 .80
*a.* Souvenir sheet of 4 2.50 2.50
*Nos. 510-513 (4)* 2.40 2.40

Capt. Cook (1728-1779), explorer. No. 513a contains 4 stamps similar to Nos. 510-513 with black frames.

Sir Rowland Hill, Originator of Penny Postage A92

No. 514a, Postrider. No. 514b, Stagecoach. No. 514c, Automobile. No. 514d, Streamlined train. No. 515a, Cap-Horniers, sailing ship. No. 515b, River steamer. No. 515c, Liner Deutschland. No. 515d, Liner United States. No. 516a, Balloon Neptune. No. 516b, Junkers F13. No. 516c, Graf Zeppelin. No. 516d, Concorde.

**1979, Sept. 10 *Perf. 14½***

**514** A92 30c Block of 4, #a.-d. 1.00 1.00
**515** A92 35c Block of 4, #a.-d. 1.10 1.10
**516** A92 50c Block of 4, #a.-d. 1.60 1.60
*e.* Souv. sheet of 12, #514-516 4.00 4.00
*Nos. 514-516 (3)* 3.70 3.70

Nos. 381, 383, 396 Srchd. in Gold or Silver

**1979, Sept. 12 Photo. *Perf. 13½***

**526** A62 6c on ½c multi .25 .25
**527** A62 10c on 1½c multi (S) .25 .25
**528** A62 15c on 60c multi .25 .25
*Nos. 526-528 (3)* .75 .75

Nos. 526-528 have 3 thick bars of equal length over old value.

Girl and Baby, IYC Emblem — A93

IYC Emblem and: 50c, Boy playing tree drum. 65c, Children dancing.

**1979, Oct. 10 *Perf. 13***

**529** A93 30c multicolored .25 .25
**530** A93 50c multicolored .35 .35
**531** A93 65c multicolored .45 .45
*Nos. 529-531 (3)* 1.05 1.05

See No. B75.

Apollo 11 Emblem — A94

50c, Apollo 11 crew, lunar map. 60c, Astronaut walking on moon. 65c, Splashdown.

**1979, Nov. 7 *Perf. 14***

**532** A94 30c multicolored .30 .30
**533** A94 50c multicolored .50 .50
**534** A94 60c multicolored .60 .60
**535** A94 65c multicolored .70 .70
*a.* Souv. sheet, #532-535, perf. 13 2.50 2.50
*Nos. 532-535 (4)* 2.10 2.10

Apollo 11 moon landing, 10th anniv.

### Coin Type of 1976

$1, $5 Silver coin, 1979 (Rarotonga fruit dove).

***Perf. 13½x14½***

**1979, Nov. 15 Photo.**

**536** A81 $1 multicolored 1.75 1.75

National Wildlife and Conservation Day.

Christmas Tree Ornaments — A95

Christmas (Flowers and): 10c, Star. 12c, Bells and candle. 15c, Ancestral statue.

**1979, Dec. 14 *Perf. 14***

**537** A95 6c multicolored .25 .25
**538** A95 10c multicolored .25 .25
**539** A95 12c multicolored .25 .25
**540** A95 15c multicolored .25 .25
*Nos. 537-540,B76-B79 (8)* 2.00 2.00

See also Nos. C16-C19, CB1-CB4.

Easter — A96

Bible illustrations by Gustave Dore, 1833-1883: No. 541a, Flagellation. No. 541b, Jesus Wearing Crown of Thorns. No. 542a, Jesus Mocked. No. 542b, Jesus Falls. No. 543a, The Crucifixion. No. 543b, Descent from the Cross.

**1980, Mar. 31 Photo. *Perf. 13***

**541** A96 20c Pair, #a.-b. .50 .50
**542** A96 30c Pair, #a.-b. .70 .70
**543** A96 35c Pair, #a.-b. .80 .80
*Nos. 541-543 (3)* 2.00 2.00

See Nos. 553, B80-B83.

Doves with Olive Branch, Rotary Emblem — A97

**1980, May 27 Photo. *Perf. 14***

**547** A97 30c shown .35 .35
**548** A97 35c Flowers .40 .40
**549** A97 50c Flags, globe .55 .55
*Nos. 547-549 (3)* 1.30 1.30

Rotary Intl., 75th anniv. See No. B87

### Easter Type of 1980 and

New Zealand No. 1 — A98

No. 550a, Postrider. No. 550b, Coach. No. 550c, Automobile. No. 550d, Train.

New Zealand #2 and: No. 551a, Sailing ship. No. 551b, River steamer. No. 551c, Transatlantic liner (facing left). No. 551d, Transatlantic liner (facing right).

New Zealand #3 and: No. 552a, 1870-71 mail balloon. No. 552b, 1919 plane. No. 552c, Graf Zeppelin. No. 552d, Concorde.

**1980, Aug. 22 Photo. *Perf. 14***

**550** A98 30c Block of 4, #a.-d. 1.25 1.00
**551** A98 35c Block of 4, #a.-d. 1.60 1.25
**552** A98 50c Block of 4, #a.-d. 2.25 1.40
*e.* Souvenir sheet of 12 6.25 5.50
*Nos. 550-552 (3)* 5.10 3.65

### Souvenir Sheet
*Perf. 13*

**553** A96 Sheet of 6, #541-543 2.50 1.50

ZEAPEX '80, New Zealand Intl. Stamp Exhib., Auckland, Aug. 23-31. No. 552e contains four each of Nos. 550-552 arranged horizontally (4x3). No. 553 has black on gold overprint: "ZEAPEX / '80 / Auckland / +10c" in margin.

Queen Mother Elizabeth, 80th Birthday — A99

**1980, Sept. 22 Photo. *Perf. 13***
**554** A99 50c multicolored .75 .75

### Souvenir Sheet

**555** A99 $2 multicolored 1.50 1.50

No. 554 issued in sheets of 9 (3x3).

Johannes Kepler, Spacecraft — A100

Designs: Nos. 556a, 559a, Kepler, spacecraft (diff.). No. 556b, Kepler, Apollo Command Module, moon. No. 559b, Kepler, lunar rover, astronaut on moon. Nos. 557a-558b, Jules Verne, various scenes from From Earth to Moon, vert.

**1980, Nov. 7 Photo. *Perf. 13***
**556** A100 12c Pair, #a-b 1.00 1.00
**557** A100 20c Pair, #a-b 1.00 1.00
**558** A100 30c Pair, #a-b 1.10 1.10
*c.* Souvenir sheet, #557-558 2.25 2.25
**559** A100 50c Pair, #a-b 2.00 2.00
*c.* Souv. sheet, #556, 559 3.00 3.00
*Nos. 556-559 (4)* 5.10 5.10

Death anniversaries of Johannes Kepler, German astronomer and Jules Verne, French science fiction writer.

Burning Bush Coral A101

Daisy Coral A102

Nos. 564a, 570a, 576a, Siphonogorgia. Nos. 564b, 570b, 576b, Pavona practorta. Nos. 564c, 570c, 576c, Stylaster echinatus. Nos. 564d, 570d, 576d, Tubastraea. Nos. 565a, 571a, 577a, Millepora alcicornis. Nos. 565b, 571b, 577b, Junceella gemmaea. Nos. 565c, 571c, 577c, Fungia fungites. Nos. 565d, 571d, 577d, Heliofungia actiniformis. Nos. 566a, 572a, 578a, Distichopora violacea. Nos. 566b, 572b, 578b, Stylaster. Nos. 566c, 572c, 578c, Gonipora. Nos. 566d, 572d, 578d, Caulastraea echinulata. Nos. 567a, 573a, 579a, Ptilosarcus gurneyi. Nos. 567b, 573b, 579b, Stylophora pistillata. Nos. 567c, 573c, 579c, Melithaea squamata. Nos. 567d, 573d, 579d, Porites andrewsi. Nos. 568a, 574a, 580a, Lobophyllia bemprichii. Nos. 568b, 574b, 580b, Palauastrea ramosa. Nos. 568c, 574c, 580c, Bellonella indica. Nos. 568d, 574d, 580d, Pectinia alcicornis. Nos. 569a, 575a, 581a, Sarcophyton digitatum. Nos. 569b, 575b, 581b, Melithaea albitincta. Nos. 569c, 575c, 581c, Plerogyra sinuosa. Nos. 569d, 575d, 581d, Dendrophyllia gracilis.

**1980-82 *Perf. 13½x13***
**Strips of 4 (#564-575) or Blocks of 4 (#576-581)**

**564** A101 1c #a.-d. .60 .60
**565** A101 3c #a.-d. .65 .65
**566** A101 4c #a.-d. .70 .70
**567** A101 5c #a.-d. .75 .75
**568** A101 6c #a.-d. .80 .80
**569** A101 8c #a.-d. .85 .85
**570** A101 10c #a.-d. .90 .90
**571** A101 12c #a.-d. 1.00 1.00
**572** A101 15c #a.-d. 1.10 1.10
**573** A101 20c #a.-d. 1.25 1.25
**574** A101 25c #a.-d. 1.40 1.40
**575** A101 30c #a.-d. 1.75 1.75
**576** A101 35c #a.-d. 1.90 1.90
**577** A101 50c #a.-d. 2.50 2.50
**578** A101 60c #a.-d. 2.75 2.75
**579** A101 70c #a.-d. 7.00 7.00
**580** A101 80c #a.-d. 7.50 7.50
**581** A101 $1 #a.-d. 8.00 8.00

*Perf. 14x13½*

**582** A102 $2 like #566c 8.00 3.25
**583** A102 $3 like #565d 10.00 3.25
**584** A102 $4 like #567b 4.00 *10.00*
**585** A102 $6 like #564c 6.00 *15.00*
**586** A102 $10 like #569b 22.50 *27.50*
*Nos. 564-586 (23)* 91.90 100.40

Issued: 1-8c, 11/21/80; 10-30c, 12/19/80; 35-60c, 3/16/81; 70c, 80c, 4/13/81; $1, 5/20/81; $2, $3, 11/27/81; $4, $6, 1/11/82; $10, 3/5/82.

For surcharges see Nos. 710-714, 716, 738, 740, 811-815, 953-954, 956-957, 959, 961-962, 964, 978-979, 984-986, B109-B111, O50-O53. For overprints see Nos. 992, 1049.

Annunciation, 13th Century Prayerbook Illustration — A102a

**1980, Dec. 1 Photo. *Perf. 14***
**652** A102a 15c shown .25 .25
**653** A102a 30c Visitation .30 .30
**654** A102a 40c Nativity .40 .40
**655** A102a 50c Epiphany .50 .50
*a.* Souvenir sheet of 4, #652-655 1.35 1.35
*Nos. 652-655 (4)* 1.45 1.45

Christmas. See Nos. B88-B91.

Crucifixion, 12th Cent. Prayerbook Illustration A103

**1981, Apr. 10 *Perf. 14***
**656** A103 15c shown .25 .25
**657** A103 25c Placing in Tomb .35 .35
**658** A103 40c Marys at the Tomb .50 .50
*Nos. 656-658 (3)* 1.10 1.10

Easter. See Nos. B92-B95.

Prince Charles and Lady Diana — A104

**1981, July 29 Photo. *Perf. 14***
**659** A104 $1 Charles .50 .50
**660** A104 $2 shown 1.25 1.25
*a.* Souv. sheet of 2, #659-660 2.00 2.00

Royal Wedding. Issued in sheets of 4.

For overprints and surcharges see Nos. 679-680, 715, 835, 980-981, B97-B98.

Soccer Players A105

Designs: Various soccer players.

**1981, Oct 20 Photo. *Perf. 14***
**661** A105 20c Pair, #a.-b. .80 .80
**662** A105 30c Pair, #a.-b. 1.00 1.00
**663** A105 35c Pair, #a.-b. 1.40 1.40
**664** A105 50c Pair, #a.-b. 1.75 1.75
*Nos. 661-664 (4)* 4.95 4.95

ESPANA '82 World Cup Soccer Championships. See No. B96.

Virgin and Child, by Rubens — A107

Christmas: Rubens Paintings: 15c, Coronation of St. Catherine. 40c, Adoration of the Shepherds. 50c, Adoration of the Kings.

**1981, Dec. 14 Photo. *Perf. 14x13½***
**669** A107 8c shown .45 .25
**670** A107 15c multicolored .55 .25
**671** A107 40c multicolored 1.00 1.00
**672** A107 50c multicolored 1.25 1.25
*Nos. 669-672 (4)* 3.25 2.75

### Souvenir Sheets

**1982, Jan. 18**
**673** A107 75c +5c like #669 .85 .85
**674** A107 75c +5c like #670 .85 .85
**675** A107 75c +5c like #671 .85 .85
**676** A107 75c +5c like #672 .85 .85

Surtax was for school children. See No. B99.

21st Birthday of Princess Diana A108

No. 677a, 21st Birthday. No. 677b, 1 July 1982. No. 678a, Wedding portrait. No. 678b, 1 July 1982. No. 678cd, $1.25, No. 678ce, $2.50, both inscribed "21st Birthday / 1 July 1982."

**1982, June 21 Photo. *Perf. 14***
**677** A108 $1.25 Pair, #a.-b. 3.50 3.50
**678** A108 $2.50 Pair, #a.-b. 4.00 4.00
*c.* Souv. sheet of 2, #d.-e. 6.25 6.25

Issued in sheets of 4.

See Nos. 681-682. For surcharges and overprints see Nos. 739-740, 833-834, 982.

### Nos. 659-660a Overprinted

No. 680cd, $1; No. 680ce, $2, both inscribed "21 JUNE 1982 ROYAL BIRTH."

**1982, July 12**
**679** A104 $1 Pair, #a.-b. 1.75 1.75
**680** A104 $2 Pair, #a.-b. 4.00 4.00
*c.* Souv. sheet of 2, #d.-e. 4.25 4.25

Issued in sheets of 4.

For surcharges see Nos. 987-988.

### Design A108 Inscribed

No. 682cd, $1.25; No. 682ce, $2.50, both inscribed "Royal Birth / June 1982."

**1982, Aug. 3**
**681** A108 $1.25 Pair, #a.-b. 2.50 2.50
**682** A108 $2.50 Pair, #a.-b. 5.00 5.00
*c.* Souv. sheet of 2, #d.-e. 5.50 5.50

Issued in sheets of 4.

Serenade, by Norman Rockwell (1894-1978) A109

10c, The Hikers. 20c, The Doctor and the Doll. 30c, Home From Camp.

**1982, Sept. 10 Photo. *Perf. 14***
**683** A109 5c shown .25 .25
**684** A109 10c multicolored .25 .25
**685** A109 20c multicolored .25 .25
**686** A109 30c multicolored .25 .25
*Nos. 683-686 (4)* 1.00 1.00

Christmas A110

Princess Diana Holding Prince William. Various Details from Virgin with Garlands, by Rubens.

**1982, Nov. 30 Photo. *Perf. 14***
**687** A110 35c multicolored 1.40 .75
**688** A110 48c multicolored 2.00 1.50
**689** A110 60c multicolored 2.25 1.75
**690** A110 $1.70 multicolored 3.00 *5.00*
*Nos. 687-690 (4)* 8.65 9.00

### Souvenir Sheets
*Perf. 13½*

**691** Sheet of 4 6.50 6.50
*a.* A110 60c like 35c 1.50 1.50
*b.* A110 60c like 48c 1.50 1.50
*c.* A110 60c like #689 1.50 1.50
*d.* A110 60c like $1.70 1.50 1.50
**692** A110 75c + 5c like 35c 1.75 1.75
**693** A110 75c + 5c like 48c 1.75 1.75
**694** A110 75c + 5c like 60c 1.75 1.75
**695** A110 75c + 5c like $1.70 1.75 1.75

No. 691 contains 4 stamps (27x32mm, showing only painting details) plus 2 labels showing Diana and William. Nos. 692-695 show Diana and William (27x39mm), multicolored margins show painting details. Surtax was for child welfare.

Commonwealth Day — A111

No. 696a, Tangaroa statue. No. 696b, Rarotonga oranges. No. 696c, Rarotonga Airport. No. 696d, Prime Minister Thomas Davis.

**1983, Mar. 14 Photo. *Perf. 14***
**696** A111 60c Block of 4, #a.-d. 2.75 2.75

For overprints see No. O46.

Scouting Year A112

36c, Camping. 48c, Rope swing. 60c, Tree planting.

**1983, Apr. 5 Photo. *Perf. 13x13½***
**700** A112 12c Pair, #a.-b. .90 .90
**701** A112 36c Pair, #a.-b. 1.25 1.25
**702** A112 48c Pair, #a.-b. 1.75 1.75
**703** A112 60c Pair, #a.-b. 2.75 2.75
*Nos. 700-703 (4)* 6.65 6.65

### Souvenir Sheet of 8

**704** #a.-d. 7.00 7.00

No. 704 contains one each of Nos. 700-703 with 2c surtax.

### Nos. 700-704 Overprinted

**1983, July 4 Photo. *Perf. 13x13½***

**705** A112 12c Pair, #a.-b. 1.25 1.25
**706** A112 36c Pair, #a.-b. 1.75 1.75
**707** A112 48c Pair, #a.-b. 2.25 2.25
**708** A112 60c Pair, #a.-b. 3.00 3.00
*Nos. 705-708 (4)* 8.25 8.25

**Souvenir Sheet of 8**

**709** A112 #a.-d. 6.50 6.50

### Nos. 569, 572, 574-575, 579, 587, 660 Surcharged in Black or Gold

No. 710a

No. 712a

No. 715

No. 716

***Perf. 13½x13, 14x13½, 14***

**1983, Aug. 12 Photo.**

**Strips of 4, #a.-d. (#710-713) or Block of 4, #a.-d. (#714)**

**710** A101 18c on 8c #569 2.75 2.75
**711** A101 36c on 15c #572 4.25 4.25
**712** A101 36c on 30c #575 4.50 4.50
**713** A101 48c on 25c #574 6.00 6.00
**714** A101 72c on 70c #579 10.00 10.00
**715** A104 96c on $2 #660 (G) 7.50 5.00
**716** A102 $5.60 on $6 #585 (G) 20.00 18.00
*Nos. 710-716 (7)* 55.00 50.50

A114

A115

**1983, Sept. 9 *Perf. 14***

**732** Pair 1.00 1.00
*a.* A114 6c Gt. Britain .50 .50
*b.* A115 6c Cook Islds. Group Federal flag .50 .50
**733** Pair 1.25 1.25
*a.* A114 12c Raratonga ensign .60 .60
*b.* A115 12c New Zealand .60 .60
**734** Pair 1.50 1.50
*a.* A114 15c Cook Islds, 1973-79 .70 .70
*b.* A115 15c Cook Islds, 1983 .70 .70
*c.* Souvenir sheet of 6, #732-734 2.00 2.00
**735** Pair 1.50 1.50
*a.* A114 20c like #732a .70 .70
*b.* A115 20c like #732b .70 .70
**736** Pair 1.60 1.60
*a.* A114 30c like #733a .75 .75
*b.* A115 30c like #733b .75 .75
**737** Pair 1.75 1.75
*a.* A114 35c like #734a .85 .85
*b.* A115 35c like #734b .85 .85
*c.* Souvenir sheet of 6, #735-737 3.50 3.50
*Nos. 732-737 (6)* 8.60 8.60

Nos. 732-737 have different background landscapes; Nos. 735-737 airmail with silver background. Nos. 734c, 737c perf. 13½.

### Nos. 576, 586, 678 Surcharged in Black or Gold

***Perf. 13½x13, 14x13½, 14***

**1983, Aug. 30 Photo.**

**Block of 4, #a.-d.**

**738** A101 36c on 35c #576 4.25 4.25

**Pair, #a.-b. (#739)**

**739** A108 96c on $2.50 #678 (G) 5.50 5.50
**740** A102 $5.60 on $10 #586 (G) 20.00 18.00
*Nos. 738-740 (3)* 29.75 27.75

Satellite Earth Station — A116

Designs: Various satellites in orbit.

**1983, Oct. 10 Litho. *Perf. 13½***

**744** A116 36c multicolored .75 .75
**745** A116 48c multicolored 1.00 1.00
**746** A116 60c multicolored 1.25 1.25
**747** A116 96c multicolored 1.75 1.75
*Nos. 744-747 (4)* 4.75 4.75

**Souvenir Sheet**

**748** A116 $2 multicolored 3.50 3.50

World Communications Year.

Christmas — A117

Raphael Paintings: 12c, La Belle Jardiniere. 18c, Madonna and Child with Five Saints. 36c, Madonna and Child with Saint John. 48c, Madonna of the Fish. 60c, Madonna of the Baldacchino.

**1983 Photo. *Perf. 14***

**749** A117 12c multicolored .75 .75
**750** A117 18c multicolored 1.00 1.00
**751** A117 36c multicolored 1.50 1.50
**752** A117 48c multicolored 1.90 1.90
**753** A117 60c multicolored 2.50 2.50
*Nos. 749-753 (5)* 7.65 7.65

**Souvenir Sheets**

***Perf. 13½***

**754** Sheet of 5 3.00 3.00
*a.* A117 12c + 3c like #749 .25 .25
*b.* A117 18c + 3c like #750 .25 .25
*c.* A117 36c + 3c like #751 .50 .50
*d.* A117 48c + 3c like #752 .65 .65
*e.* A117 60c + 3c like #753 .85 .85
**755** A117 85c + 5c like #749 1.20 1.20
**756** A117 85c + 5c like #750 1.20 1.20
**757** A117 85c + 5c like #751 1.20 1.20
**758** A117 85c + 5c like #752 1.20 1.20
**759** A117 85c + 5c like #753 1.20 1.20

Nos. 749-753 issued in sheets of 5 + label. Surtax was for children's charities.

Issued: Nos. 749-754, Nov. 14; others, Dec. 9.

Manned Flight Bicent. — A118

Various balloons: 36c, 1st manned flight, 1783. 48c, Ascent of Adorne, Strasbourg, 1784. 60c, 1785. 72c, Man on horse, 1785. 96c, Godard's aerial acrobatics, 1850.
$2.50, Blanchard & Jefferies, 1785.

**1984, Jan. 16 Photo. *Perf. 13***

**760** A118 36c multicolored .70 .70
**761** A118 48c multicolored .85 .85
**762** A118 60c multicolored .95 .95
**763** A118 72c multicolored 1.10 1.10
**764** A118 96c multicolored 1.25 1.25
*Nos. 760-764 (5)* 4.85 4.85

**Souvenir Sheets**

**765** A118 $2.50 multicolored 3.25 3.25
**766** Sheet of 5 4.75 4.75
*a.* A118 36c + 5c like 36c .60 .60
*b.* A118 48c + 5c like 48c .70 .70
*c.* A118 60c + 5c like 60c 1.05 1.05
*d.* A118 72c + 5c like 72c 1.20 1.20
*e.* A118 96c + 5c like 96c 1.60 1.60

No. 765 contains 1 stamp 30x48mm, perf. 13½.

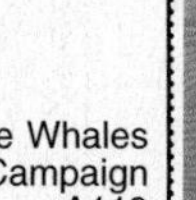


Save the Whales Campaign A119

10c, Cuvier's beaked whale. 18c, Risso's dolphin. 20c, True's beaked whale. 24c, Long-finned pilot whale. 30c, Narwhal. 36c, Beluga whale. 42c, Common dolphin. 48c, Commerson's dolphin. 60c, Bottle-nosed dolphin. 72c, Sowerby's whale. 96c, Common porpoise. $2, Boutu.

**1984, Feb. 10 Photo. *Perf. 13***

**767** A119 10c multicolored .55 .55
**768** A119 18c multicolored .75 .75
**769** A119 20c multicolored .85 .85
**770** A119 24c multicolored .90 .90
**771** A119 30c multicolored 1.00 1.00
**772** A119 36c multicolored 1.25 1.25
**773** A119 42c multicolored 1.50 1.50
**774** A119 48c multicolored 1.60 1.60
**775** A119 60c multicolored 1.75 1.75
**776** A119 72c multicolored 2.25 2.25
**777** A119 96c multicolored 2.50 2.50
**778** A119 $2 multicolored 3.50 3.50
*Nos. 767-778 (12)* 18.40 18.40

1984 Summer Olympics — A120

Posters of Various Summer Olympics: 18c, Athens, 1896. 24c, Paris, 1900. 36c, St. Louis, 1904. 48c, London, 1948. 60c, Tokyo, 1964. 72c, Berlin, 1936. 96c, Rome, 1960. $1.20, Los Angeles, 1932.
72c, 96c, $1.20 airmail.

**1984, Mar. 8 Photo. *Perf. 13½***

**779** A120 18c multicolored .45 .45
**780** A120 24c multicolored .50 .55
**781** A120 36c multicolored .60 .60
**782** A120 48c multicolored .70 .70
**783** A120 60c multicolored .80 .80
**784** A120 72c multicolored .90 .90
**785** A120 96c multicolored 1.00 1.00
**786** A120 $1.20 multicolored 1.25 1.25
*Nos. 779-786 (8)* 6.20 6.25

For overprints see Nos. 826-828.

Coral — A121

and

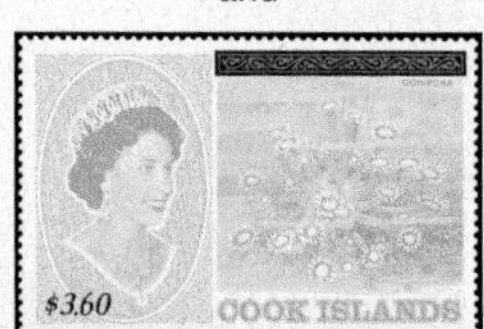


Nos. 582-586 Surcharged

1c, Siphonogorgia. 2c, Millepora alcicornis. 3c, Distichopora violacea. 5c, Ptilosarcus gurneyi. 10c, Lobophyllia bemprichii. 12c, Sarcophyton digitatum. 14c, Pavona praetorta. 18c, Junceela gemmacea. 20c, Stylaster. 24c, Stylophora pistillata. 30c, Palauastrea ramosa. 36c, Melithaea albitincta. 40c, Stylaster echinatus. 42c, Fungia fungites. 48c, Gonipora. 50c, Melithaea squamata. 52c, Bellonella indica. 55c, Plerogyra sinuosa. 60c, Tubastraea. 70c, Heliofungia actinformis. 85c, Caulastraea echinulata. 96c, Porites andrewsi. $1.10, Pectinia alcicornis. $1.20, Dendrophyllia gracilis.

**1984 *Perf. 13½x13***

**787** A121 1c multi .25 .50
**788** A121 2c multi .25 .25
**789** A121 3c multi .30 .30
**790** A121 5c multi .30 .30
**791** A121 10c multi .30 .30
**792** A121 12c multi .30 .30
**793** A121 14c multi .40 .30
**794** A121 18c multi .55 .35
**795** A121 20c multi .65 .35
**796** A121 24c multi .75 .35
**797** A121 30c multi .90 .35
**798** A121 36c multi 1.00 .40
**799** A121 40c multi 1.10 .40
**800** A121 42c multi 1.25 .40
**801** A121 48c multi 1.25 .40
**802** A121 50c multi 1.25 .40
**803** A121 52c multi 1.30 .40
**804** A121 55c multi 1.40 .60
**805** A121 60c multi 1.50 .60
**806** A121 70c multi 2.00 .60
**807** A121 85c multi 2.00 1.25
**808** A121 96c multi 2.00 1.50
**809** A121 $1.10 multi 2.00 1.75
**810** A121 $1.20 multi 2.50 2.50

***Perf. 14x13½***

**Size: 59½x38½mm**

**811** A102 $3.60 on $2 #582 5.75 5.75
**812** A102 $4.20 on $3 #583 6.25 6.25
**813** A102 $5 on $4 #584 6.50 6.50
**814** A102 $7.20 on $6 #585 9.00 9.00
**815** A102 $9.60 on $10 #586 11.00 11.00
*Nos. 787-815 (29)* 64.00 53.35

Issued: Nos. 787-801, 3/23; Nos. 802-810, 5/15; Nos. 811-813, 6/28; No. 814, 7/20; No. 815, 8/10.

For surcharges & overprints see Nos. 948-952, 955, 958, 960, 963, 965-967, B105-B108, O32-O45.

### Nos. 784-786 Overprinted With Winners

No. 826

No. 827

No. 828

**1984, Aug. 24 Photo. *Perf. 13½***

**826** A120 72c multicolored .75 .75
**827** A120 96c multicolored 1.10 1.10
**828** A120 $1.20 multicolored 1.75 1.75
*Nos. 826-828 (3)* 3.60 3.60

1984 Summer Olympics. Nos. 826-828 airmail.

AUSIPEX '84 A123

36c, Captain Cook's cottage. 48c, The Endeavour. 60c, Cook's landing. $2, Portrait, by John Webber.

**1984, Sept. 20**

**829** A123 36c multicolored 1.75 1.50
**830** A123 48c multicolored 2.50 2.50
**831** A123 60c multicolored 2.60 2.75

**832** A123 $2 multicolored 3.00 3.00
*a.* Souv. sheet, #829-832, 90c ea 8.50 8.50
*b.* Sheet of 4, STAMPEX '86 emblem 8.00 8.00
*Nos. 829-832 (4)* 9.85 9.75

No. 832b issued Aug. 4, 1986, for STAMPEX '86, Adelaide, Aug. 4-10; margin ovptd. with exhibition emblem, stamp picturing James Cook ovptd. with gold circle and black "Stampex 86 / Adelaide."

### Nos. 677-678 Ovptd. & Surcharged in Gold

No. 659 Ovptd. & Surcharged in Silver

**1984, Oct. 15 Photo. *Perf. 14***
**833** A108 $1.25 Pair, #a.-b. 1.75 1.75
**834** A108 $2.50 Pair, #a.-b. 4.50 4.50
**835** A104 $3 on $1 No. 659 3.25 3.25
*Nos. 833-835 (3)* 9.50 9.50

Nos. 833-835 printed in sheets of 4 stamps.

A124

Christmas (Paintings): 36c, Virgin on Throne with Child, by Giovanni Bellini (c. 1430-1516). 48c, Virgin and Child, 15th century, artistunknown. 60c, Virgin and Child with Saints, by Alvise Vivarini (c. 1446-1505). 96c, Virgin and Child with Angels, by Hans Memling (c. 1435-1494). $1.20, Adoration of the Magi, by Giovanni Tiepolo (1696-1770).

**1984**
**838** A124 36c multicolored 1.25 .85
**839** A124 48c multicolored 1.50 .95
**840** A124 60c multicolored 2.00 2.00
**841** A124 96c multicolored 2.50 2.50
**842** A124 $1.20 multicolored 3.00 3.00
*Nos. 838-842 (5)* 10.25 9.30

### Souvenir Sheets
***Perf. 13½***

**843** Sheet of 5 4.25 4.25
*a.* A124 36c +5c like #838 .50 .50
*b.* A124 48c +5c like #839 .65 .65
*c.* A124 60c +5c like #840 .75 .75
*d.* A124 96c +5c like #841 1.10 1.10
*e.* A124 $1.20 +5c like #842 1.25 1.25
**844** A124 95c + 5c like #838 1.25 1.25
**845** A124 95c + 5c like #839 1.25 1.25
**846** A124 95c + 5c like #840 1.25 1.25
**847** A124 95c + 5c like #841 1.25 1.25
**848** A124 95c + 5c like #842 1.25 1.25

Surtax of No. 843 for children's organizations, of Nos. 844-848 for youth education.
Issued: Nos. 838-843, 11/21; Nos. 844-848, 12/10.

A125

Illustrations of North American bird species by artist, naturalist John J. Audubon: 30c, Downy woodpecker. 55c, Black-throated blue warbler. 65c, Yellow-throated warbler. 75c, Chestnut-sided warbler. 95c, Dickcissel. $1.15, White-crowned sparrow.
$1.30, Red-cockaded woodpecker. $2.80, Seaside sparrow. $5.30, Zenaida dove.

**1985, Apr. 23 *Perf. 13x13½***
**849** A125 30c multicolored 1.25 1.25
**850** A125 55c multicolored 2.00 2.00
**851** A125 65c multicolored 2.25 2.25
**852** A125 75c multicolored 2.50 2.50
**853** A125 95c multicolored 2.75 2.75
**854** A125 $1.15 multicolored 3.00 3.00
*Nos. 849-854 (6)* 13.75 13.75

### Souvenir Sheets

**855** A125 $1.30 multicolored 2.00 2.00
**856** A125 $2.80 multicolored 3.50 3.50
**857** A125 $5.30 multicolored 7.50 7.50

Audubon birth bicentenary.

Locomotives A126

20c, Kingston Flyer, New Zealand. 55c, Class 640, Italy. 65c, Gotthard, Switzerland. 75c, Union Pacific 6900, US. 95c, Super Continental, Canada. $1.15, TGV, France. $2.20, Flying Scotsman, U.K. $3.40, Orient Express, Europe.

**1985, May 14 Litho. *Perf. 14x13½***
**858** A126 20c multicolored .25 .25
**859** A126 55c multicolored .35 .35
**860** A126 65c multicolored .45 .45
**861** A126 75c multicolored .50 .50
**862** A126 95c multicolored .60 .60
**863** A126 $1.15 multicolored .65 .65
**864** A126 $2.20 multicolored 1.00 1.00
**865** A126 $3.40 multicolored 1.25 1.25
*Nos. 858-865 (8)* 5.05 5.05

Intl. Youth Year — A127

Paintings: 55c, Helena Fourment, by Rubens. 65c, Vigee-Lebrun and Daughter, by Elizabeth Vigee-Lebrun (1755-1842). 75c, On the Terrace, by Renoir. $1.30, Young Mother Sewing, by Mary Cassatt (1845-1926).

**1985, June 6 Photo. *Perf. 13x13½***
**866** A127 55c multicolored 2.75 2.75
**867** A127 65c multicolored 3.25 3.25
**868** A127 75c multicolored 3.75 3.75
**869** A127 $1.30 multicolored 6.00 6.00
*Nos. 866-869 (4)* 15.75 15.75

### Souvenir Sheet

**870** Sheet of 4 8.75 8.75
*a.* A127 55c + 10c like #866 1.25 1.25
*b.* A127 65c + 10c like #867 1.50 1.50
*c.* A127 75c + 10c like #868 2.00 2.00
*d.* A127 $1.30 + 10c like #869 3.25 3.25

Surtax for youth organizations.

Queen Mother, 85th Birthday — A128

Portraits: 65c, Lady Elizabeth, 1908, by Mable Hankey. 75c, Duchess of York, 1923, by Savely Sorine. $1.15, Duchess of York, 1925, by Philip De Laszlo. $2.80, $5.30, Queen Elizabeth, 1938, by Sir Gerald Kelly.

**1985, June 28**
**871** A128 65c multi .55 .55
**872** A128 75c multi .65 .65
**873** A128 $1.15 multi 1.00 1.00
**874** A128 $2.80 multi 1.50 1.50
**874A** Sheet of 4 ('86) 6.00 6.00
*b.-e.* A128 55c, like #871-874 1.40 1.40
*Nos. 871-874A (5)* 9.70 9.70

### Souvenir Sheet

**875** A128 $5.30 multi 4.50 4.50

Nos. 871-874 printed in sheets of four.
No. 874A issued 8/4/86, for 86th birthday.
For surcharges see Nos. B114, B116, B122, B134, B140.

A129

Portraits of prime ministers: 30c, Albert Henry, 1965-78. 50c, Sir Thomas Davis, 1978-83. 65c, Geoffrey Henry, 1983.

**1985, July 29**
**876** A129 30c multicolored 1.00 1.00
**877** A129 50c multicolored 1.50 1.50
**878** A129 65c multicolored 2.00 2.00
*Nos. 876-878 (3)* 4.50 4.50

### Souvenir Sheet

**879** Sheet of 3 3.75 3.75
*a.* A129 55c like #876 1.20 1.20
*b.* A129 55c like #877 1.20 1.20
*c.* A129 55c like #878 1.20 1.20

Self-government, 20th anniv.

A130

**1985, July 29 *Perf. 14***
**880** A130 55c Golf 4.00 4.00
**881** A130 65c Rugby 4.25 4.25
**882** A130 75c Tennis 5.25 5.25
*Nos. 880-882 (3)* 13.50 13.50

### Souvenir Sheet

**883** Sheet of 3 11.50 11.50
*a.* A130 55c + 10c like #880 3.25 3.25
*b.* A130 65c + 10c like #881 3.25 3.25
*c.* A130 75c + 10c like #882 3.25 3.25

South Pacific Mini Games, Rarotonga, July 31-Aug. 10. Surtax for the benefit of the Mini Games.

A131

Seahorse & conf. emblems: 55c, South Pacific Bureau for Economic Cooperation. 65c, No. 887b, South Pacific Forum. 75c, No. 887c, Pacific Islands Conf.

**1985, July 29 *Perf. 14***
**884** A131 55c blk, scar & gold 1.25 1.25
**885** A131 65c blk, vio & gold 1.40 1.40
**886** A131 75c blk, brt grn & gold 1.50 1.50
*Nos. 884-886 (3)* 4.15 4.15

### Souvenir Sheet

**887** 50c Sheet of 3, #a.-c. 2.50 2.50

Pacific islands conf., Rarotonga, 7/30-8/10.

A132

Virgin and Child paintings by Botticelli: 55c, Madonna of the Magnificent. 65c, Madonna with Pomegranate. 75c, Madonna with Child & Six Angels. 95c, Madonna & Child with St. John.

**1985**
**888** A132 55c multicolored 1.60 1.60
**889** A132 65c multicolored 2.10 2.10
**890** A132 75c multicolored 2.50 2.60
**891** A132 95c multicolored 3.25 3.25
*Nos. 888-891 (4)* 9.45 9.55

### Souvenir Sheets
***Perf. 13½***

**892** A132 $2.75 Sheet of 4 6.00 6.00
*a.* A132 50c like #888 1.25 1.25
*b.* A132 50c like #889 1.25 1.25
*c.* A132 50c like #890 1.25 1.25
*d.* A132 50c like #891 1.25 1.25

### *Imperf*

**893** A132 $1.20 like #888 1.75 1.75
**894** A132 $1.45 like #889 2.00 2.00
**895** A132 $2.20 like #890 3.25 3.25
**896** A132 $2.75 like #891 3.50 3.50

Christmas. Issue dates: Nos. 888-892, Nov. 18; Nos. 893-896, Dec. 9.

Halley's Comet — A133

Paintings: 55c, No. 902a, The Eve of the Deluge, by John Martin (1789-1854). 65c, No. 902b, Lot and His Daughters, by Lucas van Leyden (1494-1533). 75c, No. 902c, Auspicious Comet, 1587, anonymous. $1.25, No. 902d, Events Following Charles I, by Herman Saftleven (1609-1658). $2, No. 902e, Ossian Receiving Napoleonic Officers, by Anne Louis Girodet-Trioson (1764-1824). $4, Halley's Comet over the Thames, 1759, by Samuel Scott (1702-1772).

**1986, Mar. 13 Photo. *Perf. 14***
**897** A133 55c multicolored 1.25 1.25
**898** A133 65c multicolored 1.50 1.50
**899** A133 75c multicolored 1.75 1.75
**900** A133 $1.25 multicolored 2.25 2.25
**901** A133 $2 multicolored 3.50 3.50
*Nos. 897-901 (5)* 10.25 10.25

### Souvenir Sheets
***Perf. 13½***

**902** Sheet of 5 + label 6.00 6.00
*a.-e.* A133 70c, each single 1.10 1.10
**903** A133 $4 multicolored 7.50 7.50

For surcharges see Nos. B113, B115, B117, B123, B129.

Elizabeth II, 60th Birthday — A134

Various portraits.

**1986, Apr. 21 *Perf. 13x13½***
**904** A134 95c multi 1.10 1.10
**905** A134 $1.25 multi 1.25 1.25
**906** A134 $1.50 multi 1.60 1.60
*Nos. 904-906 (3)* 3.95 3.95

### Souvenir Sheets

**907** A134 $1.10 like #904 2.00 2.00
**908** A134 $1.95 like #905 3.50 3.50
**909** A134 $2.45 like #906 4.75 5.75

For surcharges see Nos. 972-974, B118, B124, B127, B136-B137, B139.

AMERIPEX '86 A135

Designs: $1, US No. 1, The Resolution, Rarotonga. $1.50, Downtown Chicago. $2, No. 398, Benjamin Franklin, The Resolution.

**1986, May 21 Photo. *Perf. 14***
**910** A135 $1 multi 3.50 3.50
**911** A135 $1.50 multi 5.25 5.25
**912** A135 $2 multi 6.75 6.75
*Nos. 910-912 (3)* 15.50 15.50

For surcharges see Nos. B119, B128, B130.

Statue of Liberty, Cent. — A136

**1986, July 4**

**913** A136 $1 Head 1.00 1.00
**914** A136 $1.25 Torch 1.25 1.25
**915** A136 $2.75 Liberty Is. 2.75 2.75
*Nos. 913-915 (3)* 5.00 5.00

For surcharges see Nos. B120, B125, B132.

Wedding of Prince Andrew and Sarah Ferguson — A137

**1986, July 23**

**916** A137 $1 Sarah Ferguson .80 .80
**917** A137 $2 Prince Andrew 1.60 1.60

**Size: 60x33½mm**

***Perf. 13½x13***

**918** A137 $3 Couple 2.40 2.40
*Nos. 916-918 (3)* 4.80 4.80

Nos. 916-918 each printed in sheets of 4.
For surch. see Nos. 975-977, B121, B131, B135.

Christmas — A138

Paintings by Rubens: 55c, No. 922a, The Holy Family. $1.30, $6.40, No. 922b, Virgin with Garland. $2.75, No. 922c, Adoration of Magi.

**1986, Nov. 17 Litho. *Perf. 13½***

**919** A138 55c multi 1.40 1.40
**920** A138 $1.30 multi 3.25 3.25
**921** A138 $2.75 multi 6.50 6.50
*Nos. 919-921 (3)* 11.15 11.15

**Souvenir Sheets**

**922** Sheet of 3 14.00 14.00
***a.-c.*** A138 $2.40, any single 4.50 4.50
**923** A138 $6.40 multi 15.00 15.00

No. 922 contains 3 stamps 38½x49mm.
For surcharges see Nos. B100-B104, B112, B126, B133, B138, B141A.

Stamps of 1980-84 Surcharged in Black

**Strips of 4, #a.-d. (#953, 954, 956, 957) or Blocks of 4, #a.-d. (#959, 961, 962, 964)**

**1987, Feb. Litho. *Perfs. as before***

**948** A121 5c on 1c #787 .25 .25
**949** A121 5c on 2c #788 .25 .25
**950** A121 5c on 3c #789 .25 .25
**951** A121 5c on 12c #792 .25 .25
**952** A121 5c on 14c #793 .25 .25
**953** A101 10c on 15c #572 .55 .55
**954** A101 10c on 25c #574 .55 .55
**955** A121 18c on 24c #796 .25 .25
**956** A101 18c on 12c #571 1.10 1.10
**957** A101 18c on 20c #573 1.10 1.10
**958** A121 55c on 52c #803 .90 .90
**959** A101 55c on 35c #576 3.25 3.25
**960** A121 65c on 42c #800 1.00 1.00
**961** A101 65c on 50c #577 4.50 4.50
**962** A101 65c on 60c #578 4.50 4.50
**963** A121 75c on 48c #801 1.25 1.25
**964** A101 75c on 70c #579 4.50 4.50
**965** A121 95c on 96c #808 1.50 1.50
**966** A121 95c on $1.10 #809 1.50 1.50
**967** A121 95c on $1.20 #810 1.50 1.50

**Stamps of 1981-86 Surcharged in Black (A102), Black and Gold (#968-970, A137) or Gold (#971, A134, A104, A108)**

**968** A123 $1.30 on 36c #829 1.90 1.90
**969** A123 $1.30 on 48c #830 1.90 1.90
**970** A123 $1.30 on 60c #831 1.90 1.90
**971** A123 $1.30 on $2 #832 1.90 1.90
**972** A134 $2.80 on 95c #904 4.25 4.25
**973** A134 $2.80 on $1.25 #905 4.25 4.25
**974** A134 $2.80 on $1.50 #906 4.25 4.25
**975** A137 $2.80 on $1 #916 4.25 4.25
**976** A137 $2.80 on $2 #917 4.25 4.25
**977** A137 $2.80 on $3 #918 4.25 4.25
**978** A102 $6.40 on $4 #584 7.50 7.50
**979** A102 $7.20 on $6 #585 8.50 8.50
**980** A104 $9.40 on $1 #659 11.00 11.00
**981** A104 $9.40 on $2 #660 11.00 11.00

**Pair, #a.-b.**

**982** A108 $9.40 on $2.50 #678 22.00 22.00
*Nos. 948-982 (35)* 122.30 122.30

Issued: 5c, Nos. 955, 958, 960, 963, 95c, $6.40, $7.20, 2/10; 10c, Nos. 956-957, 959, 961-962, 964, 2/11; $12.30, $2.80, $9.40, 2/12.
For surcharge see No. B111.

**Stamps of 1980-82 Surcharged in Black (A102) or Gold (A104)**

No. 984

No. 989

***Perfs. as before***

**1987, June 17 Photo.**

**984** A102 $2.80 on $2 #582 2.75 2.75
**985** A102 $5 on $3 #583 4.75 4.75
**986** A102 $9.40 on $10 #586 8.50 8.50

**Pairs, #a.-b.**

**987** A104 $9.40 on $1 #679 17.00 17.00
**988** A104 $9.40 on $2 #680 17.00 17.00
*Nos. 984-988 (5)* 50.00 50.00

**Souvenir Sheet**

**989** A104 $9.20 on #680c 15.00 15.00

**Nos. 399 and 584 Ovptd. in Black on Gold Bar**

**1987, Nov. 20 Photo. *Perf. 14x13½***

**991** A64 $4 on #399 4.00 4.00
**992** A102 $4 on #584 4.00 4.00

Christmas A139

The Holy Family, religious paintings by Rembrandt in European museums: $1.25, No. 996a, The Louvre, Paris. $1.50, No. 996b, $6, The Holy Family with Angels, The Hermitage, Leningrad. $1.95, No. 996c, The Alte Pinakothek, Munich.

**1987, Dec. 7 Photo. *Perf. 13½***

**993** A139 $1.25 multi 2.50 2.50
**994** A139 $1.50 multi 3.50 3.50
**995** A139 $1.95 multi 4.50 4.50
*Nos. 993-995 (3)* 10.50 10.50

**Souvenir Sheets**

**996** Sheet of 3 8.50 8.50
***a.-c.*** A139 $1.15 any single 2.50 2.50

***Perf. 13x13½***

**997** A139 $6 multi 11.00 11.00

Size of Nos. 996a-996c: 49½x38½mm. No. 997 contains 1 stamp 39½x31½mm.

1988 Summer Olympics, Seoul — A140

Designs: a, Cook Islands commemorative silver coin (obverse and reverse) issued on Aug. 20, 1987, for the '88 Summer Games. b, Seoul Olympic Park, torch and emblem. c, Steffi Graf, women's tennis champion, and '88 gold medal.

**1988, Apr. 26 Photo. *Perf. 13½x14***

**998** Strip of 3 15.00 15.00
***a.-c.*** A140 $1.50 multicolored 5.00 5.00

**Souvenir Sheet**

***Perf. 13½***

**999** A140 $10 multi 15.00 15.00

Participation of national athletes in the Olympics for the first time, introduction of tennis as an Olympic gold-medal event.
No. 999 contains one stamp 114x47mm combining the designs of Nos. 998a-998c.

**Nos. 998-999 Overprinted**

a-c

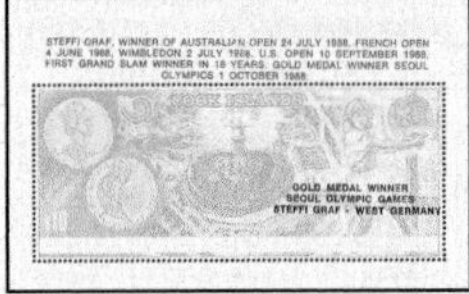

d

**1988, Oct. 12 Photo. *Perf. 13½x14***

**1000** Strip of 3 12.00 12.00
***a.-c.*** A140 $1.50 multicolored 4.00 4.00

**Souvenir Sheet**

***Perf. 13½***

**1001** A140(d) $10 on No. 999 16.00 16.00

Christmas — A141

Paintings by Albrecht Durer: 70c, Virgin and Child. 85c, Virgin and Child, diff. 95c, Virgin and Child, diff. $1.25, Virgin and Child, diff. $6.40, The Nativity.

**1988, Nov. 11 *Perf. 13½***

**1002** A141 70c multi 2.75 2.75
**1003** A141 85c multi 3.25 3.25
**1004** A141 95c multi 3.75 3.75
**1005** A141 $1.25 multi 5.00 5.00
*Nos. 1002-1005 (4)* 14.75 14.75

**Souvenir Sheet**

**1006** A141 $6.40 multi 12.00 12.00

No. 1006 contains one stamp 45x60mm.

Scene and Left Half of Mission Emblem — A142

1st Moon Landing, 20th Anniv. A144

No. 1007a, Launch vehicle in space. No. 1007b, *Eagle* landing on Moon. No. 1008a, Astronaut descending ladder. No. 1008b, Astronaut on Moon. No. 1009a, Seismic experiment. No. 1009b, Solar wind experiment. No. 1010a, Liftoff from Moon. No. 1010b, Splashdown and recovery.
The "b" stamps have the right half of the emblem.

**1989, July 14 Photo. *Perf. 13***

**1007** A142 40c Pair, #a.-b. 3.00 3.00
**1008** A142 55c Pair, #a.-b. 4.50 4.50
**1009** A142 65c Pair, #a.-b. 5.00 5.00
**1010** A142 75c Pair, #a.-b. 5.50 5.50
*Nos. 1007-1010 (4)* 18.00 18.00

**Souvenir Sheet**

**1011** A144 $4.20 Armstrong and Aldrin 8.75 8.75

Printed with continuous designs.

World Wildlife Fund — A145

Endangered bird species: 15c, $1, Pomarea dimidiata. 20c, $1.25, Pomarea dimidiata (two). 65c, $1.50, Ptilinopus rarotongensis (two). 70c, $1.75, Ptilinopus rarotongensis.

**1989, Oct. 4 Photo. *Perf. 13½x13***

**1016** A145 15c multicolored 1.40 1.40
**1017** A145 20c multicolored 2.00 2.00
**1018** A145 65c multicolored 5.50 5.50
**1019** A145 70c multicolored 6.25 6.25
*Nos. 1016-1019 (4)* 15.15 15.15

**Souvenir Sheets**

**Without WWF Emblem**

***Perf. 13½***

**1020** A145 $1 like 15c 2.75 2.75
**1021** A145 $1.25 like 20c 3.25 3.25
**1022** A145 $1.50 like 65c 3.75 3.75
**1023** A145 $1.75 like 70c 4.25 4.25

World Wildlife Fund. Nos. 1020-1023 are airmail and contain one 52x34mm stamp; decorative margins continue the designs.
For overprints see Nos. C24-C27.

Christmas A146

Details of *Adoration of the Magi,* by Rubens: 70c, Witnesses. 85c, Madonna. 95c, Christ child. $1.50, Attendant. $6.40, Entire painting.

**1989, Nov. 24 Photo. *Perf. 13½x13***

**1024** A146 70c multicolored 1.60 1.60
**1025** A146 85c multicolored 1.75 1.75
**1026** A146 95c multicolored 2.10 2.10
**1027** A146 $1.50 multicolored 3.25 3.25
*Nos. 1024-1027 (4)* 8.70 8.70

**Souvenir Sheet**

***Perf. 13½***

**1028** A146 $6.40 multicolored 15.00 15.00

No. 1028 contains one 45x60mm stamp.

Religious History — A147

70c, John Williams, LMS Mission Church. 85c, Bernardine Castanie, Roman Catholic Church. 95c, Osborne J.P. Widstoe, Church of Jesus Christ of Latter Day Saints. $1.60, J.E. Caldwell, Seventh Day Adventist Church.

**1990, Feb. 19 Photo. *Perf. 13½x13***

| | | | | |
|---|---|---|---|---|
| **1029** | A147 | 70c multicolored | 1.00 | 1.00 |
| **1030** | A147 | 85c multicolored | 1.20 | 1.20 |
| **1031** | A147 | 95c multicolored | 1.40 | 1.40 |
| **1032** | A147 | $1.60 multicolored | 2.40 | 2.40 |
| | | *Nos. 1029-1032 (4)* | 6.00 | 6.00 |

**Souvenir Sheet**

***Perf. 13½***

| | | | |
|---|---|---|---|
| **1033** | Sheet of 4 | 7.00 | 7.00 |
| ***a.*** | A147 90c like 70c | 1.50 | 1.50 |
| ***b.*** | A147 90c like 85c | 1.50 | 1.50 |
| ***c.*** | A147 90c like 95c | 1.50 | 1.50 |
| ***d.*** | A147 90c like $1.60 | 1.50 | 1.50 |

No. 1033 contains 4 36x36mm stamps.

Penny Black, 150th Anniv. — A148

Paintings: 85c, No. 1038a, *Woman Writing a Letter,* by Gerard Terborch (1617-1681). $1.15, No. 1038b, *Portrait of George Gisze,* by Hans Holbein the Younger. $1.55, No. 1038c, *Portrait of Mrs. John Douglas,* by Thomas Gainsborough. $1.85, No. 1038d, *Portrait of a Gentleman,* by Albrecht Durer.

**1990, May 2 Photo. *Perf. 13½***

| | | | | |
|---|---|---|---|---|
| **1034** | A148 | 85c multicolored | 1.40 | 1.40 |
| **1035** | A148 | $1.15 multicolored | 2.00 | 2.00 |
| **1036** | A148 | $1.55 multicolored | 2.60 | 2.60 |
| **1037** | A148 | $1.85 multicolored | 3.25 | 3.25 |
| | | *Nos. 1034-1037 (4)* | 9.25 | 9.25 |

**Souvenir Sheet**

| | | | |
|---|---|---|---|
| **1038** | Sheet of 4 | 13.00 | 13.00 |
| ***a.-d.*** | A148 $1.05 any single | 3.00 | 3.00 |

The margin of No. 1038 pictures the Stamp World '90 emblem and Great Britain #1-2.

1992 Olympics A149

Designs: a. Summer Games, Barcelona (runners). b. Eternal flame, commemorative coin obverse (Queen Elizabeth II) and reverse (athletes). c. Winter Games, Albertville (skier).

**1990, June 15 Photo. *Perf. 14***

| | | | |
|---|---|---|---|
| **1039** | Strip of 3 | 18.00 | 18.00 |
| ***a.-c.*** | A149 $1.85 any single | 6.00 | 6.00 |

Queen Mother, 90th Birthday — A150

**1990, July 20 Photo. *Perf. 13½***

| | | | | |
|---|---|---|---|---|
| **1040** | A150 | $1.85 multicolored | 6.50 | 6.50 |

**Souvenir Sheet**

| | | | | |
|---|---|---|---|---|
| **1041** | A150 | $6.40 multicolored | 13.00 | 13.00 |

Christmas A151

Paintings: 70c, Adoration of the Magi by Memling. 85c, The Holy Family by Lotto. 95c, Madonna and Child with Saints John and Catherine by Titian. $1.50, The Holy Family by Titian. $6.40, Madonna and Child Enthroned, Surrounded by Saints by Vivarini.

**1990, Nov. 29 Litho. *Perf. 14***

| | | | | |
|---|---|---|---|---|
| **1042** | A151 | 70c multicolored | 1.75 | 1.75 |
| **1043** | A151 | 85c multicolored | 2.40 | 2.40 |
| **1044** | A151 | 95c multicolored | 2.50 | 2.50 |
| **1045** | A151 | $1.50 multicolored | 3.75 | 3.75 |
| | | *Nos. 1042-1045 (4)* | 10.40 | 10.40 |

**Souvenir Sheet**

| | | | | |
|---|---|---|---|---|
| **1046** | A151 | $6.40 multicolored | 15.00 | 15.00 |

For overprints and surcharges see Nos. 1251, 1254, 1257-1258.

Souvenir Sheet

1992 Olympic Games — A152

**1991, Feb. 12 *Perf. 13½***

| | | | | |
|---|---|---|---|---|
| **1047** | A152 | $6.40 multicolored | 15.00 | 15.00 |

Discovery of America 500th Anniv. (in 1992) — A153

**1991, Feb. 14 Photo. *Perf. 13½x13***

| | | | | |
|---|---|---|---|---|
| **1048** | A153 | $1 multicolored | 4.25 | 4.25 |

**No. 586 Ovptd. "65th BIRTHDAY" in Gold**

**1991, Apr. 22 Litho. *Perf. 14x13½***

| | | | | |
|---|---|---|---|---|
| **1049** | A102 | $10 multicolored | 18.00 | 18.00 |

Christmas A154

Paintings: 70c, Adoration of the Child, by Delle Notti (Gerrit van Honthorst). 85c, Birth of the Virgin, by Murillo. $1.15, Adoration of the Shepherds, by Rembrandt. $1.50, Adoration of the Shepherds, by Le Nain. $6.40, Madonna and Child, by Fra Filippo Lippi, vert.

**1991, Nov. 12 Litho. *Perf. 14***

| | | | | |
|---|---|---|---|---|
| **1050** | A154 | 70c multicolored | 1.00 | 1.00 |
| **1051** | A154 | 85c multicolored | 3.00 | 3.00 |
| **1052** | A154 | $1.15 multicolored | 4.25 | 4.25 |
| **1053** | A154 | $1.50 multicolored | 5.75 | 5.75 |
| | | *Nos. 1050-1053 (4)* | 14.00 | 14.00 |

**Souvenir Sheet**

| | | | | |
|---|---|---|---|---|
| **1054** | A154 | $6.40 multicolored | 15.00 | 15.00 |

For overprints and surcharges see Nos. 1252-1253, 1255-1256.

Marine Life — A155

A155a

5c, Red-breasted maori wrasse. 10c, Blue sea star. 15c, Black & gold angelfish. 20c, Spotted pebble crab. 25c, Black-tipped cod. 30c, Spanish dancer. 50c, Royal angelfish. 80c, Squirrel fish. 85c, Red pencil sea urchin. 90c, Red-spot rainbow fish. $1, Black-lined maori wrasse. $2, Longnose butterflyfish. $3, Red-spot rainbow fish. $5, Blue sea star. $7, Royal angelfish. $10, Spotted pebble crab. $15, Red pencil sea urchin.

**1992-94 Litho. *Perf. 14½x13½***

| | | | | |
|---|---|---|---|---|
| **1058** | A155 | 5c multi | .40 | .40 |
| **1059** | A155 | 10c multi | .40 | .40 |
| **1062** | A155 | 15c multi | .40 | .40 |
| **1064** | A155 | 20c multi | .50 | .50 |
| **1065** | A155 | 25c multi | .55 | .55 |
| **1066** | A155 | 30c multi | .65 | .65 |
| **1071** | A155 | 50c multi | 1.10 | 1.10 |
| **1076** | A155 | 80c multi | 1.75 | 1.75 |
| **1077** | A155 | 85c multi | 1.75 | 1.75 |
| **1078** | A155 | 90c multi | 1.75 | 1.75 |
| **1080** | A155 | $1 multi | 2.00 | 2.00 |
| **1081** | A155 | $2 multi | 3.75 | 3.75 |
| **1082** | A155a | $3 multi | 4.50 | 4.50 |
| **1083** | A155a | $5 multi | 8.00 | 8.00 |
| **1085** | A155a | $7 multi | 12.00 | 12.00 |
| **1087** | A155a | $10 multi | 17.00 | 17.00 |
| **1089** | A155a | $15 multi | 25.00 | 25.00 |
| | | *Nos. 1058-1089 (17)* | 81.50 | 81.50 |

Issued: 85c, 90c, $1, $2, 3/23/92; $3, $5, 10/25/93; $7, 12/6/93; $10, 1/31/94; $15, 9/9/94; others, 1/22/92.

See Nos. 1154-1176 for stamps with buff border. For overprints see Nos. O54-O68.

Endangered Wildlife — A156

$1.15 each: No. 1095, Tiger. No. 1096, Asiatic elephant. No. 1097, Grizzly bear. No. 1098, Black rhinoceros. No. 1099, Chimpanzee. No. 1100, Asian bighorn. No. 1101, Heavisides dolphin. No. 1102, Eagle owl. No. 1103, Bee hummingbird. No. 1104, Feliscon-color cougar. No. 1105, European otter. No. 1106, Red kangaroo.

**1992 Litho. *Perf. 14***

| | | | | |
|---|---|---|---|---|
| **1095-1106** | A156 | Set of 12 | 20.00 | 20.00 |

Issued: No. 1095, 4/6; No. 1096, 4/7; No. 1097, 4/8; No. 1098, 4/9; No. 1099, 4/10; No. 1100, 4/11; No. 1101, 7/13; No. 1102, 7/14; No. 1103, 7/15; No. 1104, 7/16; No. 1105, 7/17; No. 1106, 7/18.

See Nos. 1119-1124, 1134-1138.

For surcharges see Nos. 1239-1250.

Discovery of America, 500th Anniv. — A157

**1992, May 22 Litho. *Perf. 14x14½***

| | | | | |
|---|---|---|---|---|
| **1107** | A157 | $6 multicolored | 9.00 | 9.00 |

**Souvenir Sheet**

***Perf. 15x14***

| | | | | |
|---|---|---|---|---|
| **1107A** | A157 | $10 Coming ashore | 10.50 | 10.50 |

Issued: No. 1107, 5/22. No. 1107A, 9/21.

No. 1107A contains one 40x30mm stamp.

1992 Summer Olympics, Barcelona A158

Designs: No. 1108a, $50 coin, soccer players. b, Flags of Spain, Cook Islands, Barcelona medal. c, $10 coin, basketball players. No. 1109a, Runners. b, $10, $50 coins. c, Cyclists. $6.40, Javelin.

**1992, July 24 Litho. *Perf. 13***

| | | | | |
|---|---|---|---|---|
| **1108** | A158 | $1.75 Strip of 3, #a.-c. | 9.00 | 9.00 |
| **1109** | A158 | $2.25 Strip of 3, #a.-c. | 11.00 | 11.00 |

**Souvenir Sheet**

| | | | | |
|---|---|---|---|---|
| **1110** | A158 | $6.40 multicolored | 19.00 | 19.00 |

6th Festival of Pacific Arts, Rarotonga — A159

80c, UNESCO poster. 85c, $1, $1.75, Different carvings of Rarotongan fertility god, Tangaroa.

**1992, Oct. 16 Litho. *Perf. 15x14***

| | | | | |
|---|---|---|---|---|
| **1111** | A159 | 80c multicolored | 1.75 | 1.75 |
| **1112** | A159 | 85c multicolored | 2.00 | 2.00 |
| **1113** | A159 | $1 multicolored | 2.40 | 2.40 |
| **1114** | A159 | $1.75 multicolored | 3.75 | 3.75 |
| | | *Nos. 1111-1114 (4)* | 9.90 | 9.90 |

For overprints see Nos. 1231-1234.

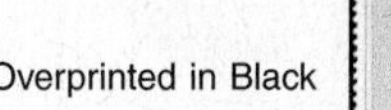

Overprinted in Black

**1992, Oct. 16**

| | | | | |
|---|---|---|---|---|
| **1115** | A159 | 80c on #1111 | 2.10 | 2.10 |
| **1116** | A159 | 85c on #1112 | 2.50 | 2.50 |
| **1117** | A159 | $1 on #1113 | 2.50 | 2.50 |
| **1118** | A159 | $1.75 on #1114 | 4.75 | 4.75 |
| | | *Nos. 1115-1118 (4)* | 11.85 | 11.85 |

**Endangered Wildlife Type of 1992**

No. 1119, Jackass penguin. No. 1120, Asian lion. No. 1121, Peregrine falcon. No. 1122, Persian fallow deer. No. 1123, Key deer. No. 1124, Alpine ibex.

**1992 Litho. *Perf. 14***

| | | | | |
|---|---|---|---|---|
| **1119** | A156 | $1.15 multicolored | 1.75 | 1.75 |
| **1120** | A156 | $1.15 multicolored | 1.75 | 1.75 |
| **1121** | A156 | $1.15 multicolored | 1.75 | 1.75 |
| **1122** | A156 | $1.15 multicolored | 1.75 | 1.75 |
| **1123** | A156 | $1.15 multicolored | 1.75 | 1.75 |
| **1124** | A156 | $1.15 multicolored | 1.75 | 1.75 |
| | | *Nos. 1119-1124 (6)* | 10.50 | 10.50 |

Issued: No. 1119, 11/2; No. 1120, 11/3; No. 1121, 11/4; No. 1122, 11/5; No. 1123, 11/6; No. 1124, 11/7.

Christmas — A160

Paintings by El Parmigianino: 70c, Worship of Shepherds. 85c, $6.40, Virgin with Long Neck. $1.15, Virgin with Rose. $1.90, St. Margaret's Virgin.

**1992, Nov. 20 Litho. *Perf. 13½***

| | | | | |
|---|---|---|---|---|
| **1125** | A160 | 70c multicolored | 1.00 | 1.00 |
| **1126** | A160 | 85c multicolored | 1.60 | 1.60 |
| **1127** | A160 | $1.15 multicolored | 2.10 | 2.10 |
| **1128** | A160 | $1.90 multicolored | 3.75 | 3.75 |
| | | *Nos. 1125-1128 (4)* | 8.45 | 8.45 |

**Souvenir Sheet**

| | | | | |
|---|---|---|---|---|
| **1129** | A160 | $6.40 multicolored | 12.50 | 12.50 |

No. 1129 contains one 36x47mm stamp.

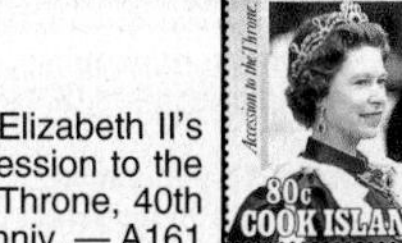

Queen Elizabeth II's Accession to the Throne, 40th Anniv. — A161

Various portraits of Queen Elizabeth II.

**1992, Dec. 10 Litho. *Perf. 14***

| | | | | | |
|---|---|---|---|---|---|
| **1130** | A161 | 80c | multicolored | 1.25 | 1.25 |
| **1131** | A161 | $1.15 | multicolored | 2.00 | 2.00 |
| **1132** | A161 | $1.50 | multicolored | 3.25 | 3.25 |
| **1133** | A161 | $1.95 | multicolored | 4.50 | 4.50 |
| | *Nos. 1130-1133 (4)* | | | 11.00 | 11.00 |

### Endangered Wildlife Type of 1992

No. 1134, English mandrill. No. 1135, Gorilla. No. 1136, Vanessa atlanta. No. 1137, Sichuan takin. No. 1138, Ring tailed lemur.

**1993 Litho. *Perf. 14***

| | | | | | |
|---|---|---|---|---|---|
| **1134** | A156 | $1.15 | multicolored | 2.00 | 2.00 |
| **1135** | A156 | $1.15 | multicolored | 2.00 | 2.00 |
| **1136** | A156 | $1.15 | multicolored | 2.00 | 2.00 |
| **1137** | A156 | $1.15 | multicolored | 2.00 | 2.00 |
| **1138** | A156 | $1.15 | multicolored | 2.00 | 2.00 |
| | *Nos. 1134-1138 (5)* | | | 10.00 | 10.00 |

Issued: No. 1134, 2/1; No. 1135, 2/2; No. 1136, 2/3; No. 1137, 2/4; No. 1138, 2/5.

Coronation of Queen Elizabeth II, 40th Anniv. — A162

Designs: $1, Coronation ceremony. $2, Coronation portrait. $3, Queen, family on balcony, Buckingham Palace.

**1993, June 2 Litho. *Perf. 14***

| | | | | | |
|---|---|---|---|---|---|
| **1139** | A162 | $1 | multicolored | 2.25 | 2.25 |
| **1140** | A162 | $2 | multicolored | 4.75 | 4.75 |
| **1141** | A162 | $3 | multicolored | 7.00 | 7.00 |
| | *Nos. 1139-1141 (3)* | | | 14.00 | 14.00 |

Christmas — A163

Paintings: 70c, Virgin with Child, by Filippo Lippi. 85c, Bargellini Madonna, by Lodovico Carracci. $1.15, Virgin of the Curtain, by Raphael. $2.50, Holy Family, by Il Bronzino. $4, Saint Zachary Virgin, by Il Parmigianino.

**1993, Nov. 8 Litho. *Perf. 14***

| | | | | | |
|---|---|---|---|---|---|
| **1142** | A163 | 70c | multicolored | 1.00 | 1.00 |
| **1143** | A163 | 85c | multicolored | 1.40 | 1.40 |
| **1144** | A163 | $1.15 | multicolored | 1.75 | 1.75 |
| **1145** | A163 | $2.50 | multicolored | 3.50 | 3.50 |

**Size: 32x47mm**

***Perf. 13½***

| | | | | | |
|---|---|---|---|---|---|
| **1146** | A163 | $4.00 | multicolored | 6.25 | 6.25 |
| | *Nos. 1142-1146 (5)* | | | 13.90 | 13.90 |

1994 Winter Olympics, Lillehammer — A164

**1994, Feb. 11 Litho. *Perf. 13½x14***

**1147** A164 $5 multicolored 10.00 10.00

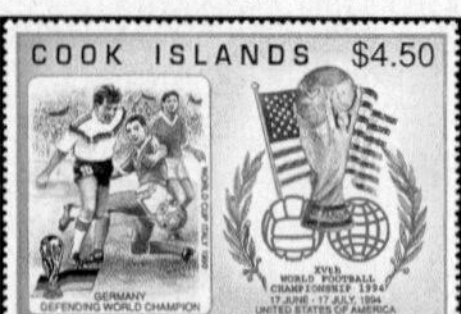

1994 World Cup Soccer Championships, US — A165

**1994, June 17 Litho. *Perf. 14***

**1148** A165 $4.50 multicolored 8.00 8.00

First Manned Moon Landing, 25th Anniv. A166

Apollo 11 emblem and: No. 1149a, First step onto Moon, US flag. No. 1149b, Astronaut carrying experiment packs on Moon. No. 1150a, Astronaut, US flag. No. 1150b, Flag, reflection shown in astronaut's visor.

**1994, July 20**

| | | | | | |
|---|---|---|---|---|---|
| **1149** | A166 | $2.25 | Pair, #a.-b. + label | 9.00 | 9.00 |
| **1150** | A166 | $2.25 | Pair, #a.-b. + label | 9.00 | 9.00 |

### Living Reef Type of 1992

**1994, Oct. 24 Litho. *Perf. 14½x13½***

**Size: 41x31mm**

**Buff & Multicolored**

| | | | | | |
|---|---|---|---|---|---|
| **1154** | A155 | 5c | like #1058 | .50 | .50 |
| **1158** | A155 | 15c | like #1062 | .50 | .50 |
| **1160** | A155 | 20c | like #1064 | .60 | .60 |
| **1161** | A155 | 25c | like #1065 | .65 | .65 |
| **1162** | A155 | 30c | like #1066 | .75 | .75 |
| **1167** | A155 | 50c | like #1071 | 1.40 | 1.40 |
| **1172** | A155 | 80c | like #1076 | 2.25 | 2.25 |
| **1173** | A155 | 85c | like #1077 | 2.40 | 2.40 |
| **1174** | A155 | 90c | like #1078 | 2.50 | 2.50 |
| **1176** | A155 | $1 | like #1080 | 2.75 | 2.75 |
| | *Nos. 1154-1176 (10)* | | | 14.30 | 14.30 |

### Nos. 1158 and 1161 Surcharged

### Method and Perf. As Before

**1998 ?**

| | | | | | |
|---|---|---|---|---|---|
| **1177** | A155 | 10c | on 15c #1158 | — | — |
| **1178** | A155 | 20c | on 25c #1161 | — | — |

The year of issue of Nos. 1177-1178 is unknown. A damaged example of No. 1178 exists uncanceled on cover.

Miniature Sheet

The Return of Tommy Tricker — A167

Scenes from film: a, Three people in canoe. b, Traditional dancers. c, Couple walking on beach. d, Aerial view of island. e, Girls performing hand gestures. f, Girls walking along sand bar.

**1994, Nov. 23 Litho. *Perf. 14***

**1191** A167 85c Sheet of 6, #a.-f. 9.50 9.50

See No. 1213.

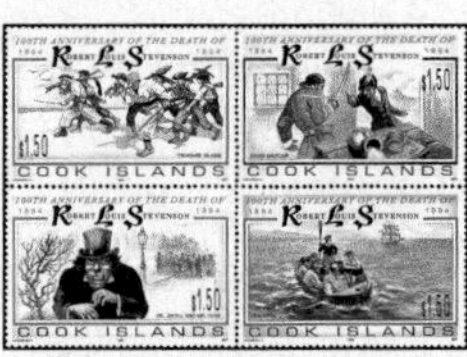

Christmas A168

Paintings: No. 1192a, The Virgin and Child, by Morales. b, Adoration of Kings, by Gerard David. c, Adoration of Kings, by Vinc Foppa. d, The Madonna & Child with St. Joseph & Infant Baptist, by Baroccio.

No. 1193a, Madonna with Iris, in style of Durer. b, Adoration of Shepherds, by Le Nain. c, The Virgin and Child, by follower of Leonardo. d, The Mystic Nativity, by Botticelli.

**1994, Nov. 30 Litho. *Perf. 14***

| | | | | | |
|---|---|---|---|---|---|
| **1192** | A168 | 85c | Block of 4, #a.-d. | 6.75 | 6.75 |
| **1193** | A168 | $1 | Block of 4, #a.-d. | 7.75 | 7.75 |

Robert Louis Stevenson (1850-94), Writer — A169

Adventure scenes from books: a, "Treasure Island." b, "David Balfour." c, "Dr. Jekyll and Mr. Hyde." d, "Kidnapped."

**1994, Dec. 12 *Perf. 14x15***

**1194** A169 $1.50 Block of 4, #a.-d. 14.00 14.00

UN, 50th Anniv. A170

$4.50, FAO, 50th anniv.

**1995 Litho. *Perf. 13x13½***

**1195** A170 $4.75 multicolored 6.25 6.25

***Perf. 13½***

**1196** A170 $4.50 multicolored 6.75 6.75

Each issued in sheets of 4.
Issued: $4.75, 7/17; $4.50, 10/12.

Queen Mother, 95th Birthday A172

**1995, Aug. 31**

**1197** A172 $5 multicolored 12.00 12.00

End of World War II, 50th Anniv. A173

Designs: a, German surrender, Rheims. b, Japanese surrender, Tokyo Bay.

**1995, Sept. 4 *Perf. 13***

**1198** A173 $3.50 Pair, #a.-b. 22.00 22.00

No. 1198 was issued in sheets of 4 stamps.

Year of the Sea Turtle — A174

Designs: 85c, Green turtle in water. $1, Hawksbill turtle in water. $1.75, Green turtle nesting. $2.25, Hawksbill turtle hatchlings leaving nest.

**1995, Nov. 20 Litho. *Perf. 14***

| | | | | | |
|---|---|---|---|---|---|
| **1199** | A174 | 85c | multicolored | 2.00 | 2.00 |
| **1200** | A174 | $1 | multicolored | 2.75 | 2.75 |
| **1201** | A174 | $1.75 | multicolored | 4.25 | 4.25 |
| **1202** | A174 | $2.25 | multicolored | 5.75 | 5.75 |
| | *Nos. 1199-1202 (4)* | | | 14.75 | 14.75 |

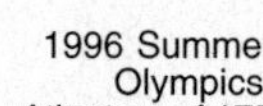

1996 Summer Olympics, Atlanta — A175

**1996, Jan. 12 Litho. *Perf. 14***

| | | | | | |
|---|---|---|---|---|---|
| **1203** | A175 | 85c | Discus | 1.40 | 1.40 |
| **1204** | A175 | $1 | Torch bearer | 1.75 | 1.75 |
| **1205** | A175 | $1.50 | Sprinting | 2.60 | 2.60 |
| **1206** | A175 | $1.85 | Gymnastics | 3.50 | 3.50 |
| **1207** | A175 | $2.10 | Archery | 4.00 | 4.00 |
| **1208** | A175 | $2.50 | Javelin | 4.50 | 4.50 |
| | *Nos. 1203-1208 (6)* | | | 17.75 | 17.75 |

Queen Elizabeth II, 70th Birthday — A176

Designs: $1.90, No. 1212a, In blue hat, coat. $2.25, No. 1212b, Wearing tiara. $2.75, No. 1212c, In robes of Order of the Garter.

**1996, June 21 Litho. *Perf. 14***

| | | | | | |
|---|---|---|---|---|---|
| **1209** | A176 | $1.90 | multicolored | 3.00 | 3.00 |
| **1210** | A176 | $2.25 | multicolored | 4.00 | 4.00 |
| **1211** | A176 | $2.75 | multicolored | 4.50 | 4.50 |
| | *Nos. 1209-1211 (3)* | | | 11.50 | 11.50 |

**Sheet of 3**

**1212** A176 $2.50 #a.-c. + label 14.00 14.00

Nos. 1209-1211 were issued in sheets of 4.

### "The Return of Tommy Tricker" Type of 1994

No. 1213a-1213f, like #1191a-1191f.

**1997, Aug. 28 Litho. *Perf. 14***

**1213** A167 90c Sheet of 6, #a.-f. 9.50 9.50

### Nos. 1213a-1213f Overprinted in Silver

a

b

**1997, Sept. 12 Litho. *Perf. 14***

**1214** A167 90c Sheet 6, #a.-f. 9.00 9.00

Nos. 1214a, 1214d-1214e are overprinted type "a"; Nos. 1214b-1214c, 1214f type "b."

Butterflies — A177

5c, Lampides boeticus (female). 10c, Vanessa atalanta. 15c, Lampides boeticus (male). 20c, Papilio godeffroyi. 25c, Danaus hamata. 30c, Xois sesara. 50c, Vagrans egista. 70c, Parthenos sylvia. 80c, Hyblaea sanguinea. 85c, Melanitis leda. 90c, Ascalapha odorata. $1, Precis villida. $1.50, Parthenos sylvia. $2, Lampides boeticus. $3, Precis villida. $4, Melanitis leda. $5, Vagrans egista. $7, Hyblaea sanguinea. $10, Vanessa atalanta. $15, Papilio godeffroyi.

**1997-98 Litho. *Perf. 13***

| | | | | | |
|---|---|---|---|---|---|
| **1215** | A177 | 5c | multi | .25 | .25 |
| **1216** | A177 | 10c | multi | .25 | .25 |
| **1217** | A177 | 15c | multi | .25 | .25 |
| **1218** | A177 | 20c | multi | .30 | .30 |
| **1219** | A177 | 25c | multi | .35 | .35 |
| **1220** | A177 | 30c | multi | .35 | .35 |
| **1221** | A177 | 50c | multi | .55 | .55 |
| **1222** | A177 | 70c | multi | .80 | .80 |
| **1223** | A177 | 80c | multi | .95 | .95 |
| **1224** | A177 | 85c | multi | .95 | .95 |
| **1225** | A177 | 90c | multi | 1.00 | 1.00 |

**1226** A177 $1 multi 1.10 1.10

***Perf. 13½***

**Size: 41x25mm**

**1226A** A177 $1.50 multi 1.60 1.60
**1226B** A177 $2 multi 2.25 2.25
**1226C** A177 $3 multi 3.25 3.25
**1226D** A177 $4 multi 4.75 4.75
**1226E** A177 $5 multi 5.50 5.50
**1226F** A177 $7 multi 8.50 8.50
**1226G** A177 $10 multi 11.50 11.50
**1226H** A177 $15 multi 15.00 15.00
*Nos. 1215-1226H (20)* 59.45 59.45

Issued: 5c, 10c, 15c, 20c, 25c, 30c, 50c, 70c, 10/22/97; 80c, 85c, 90c, $1, 11/12/97; $1.50, $2, $3, 3/11/98; $4, $5, 6/19/98; $7, $10, 9/18/98; $15, 11/13/98.

For surcharges, see Nos. 1259-1264.

Queen Elizabeth II and Prince Philip, 50th Wedding Anniv. — A178

**1997, Nov. 20** ***Perf. 14***

**1227** A178 $2 multicolored 3.00 3.00

**Souvenir Sheet**

**1228** A178 $5 like #1227, close-up 9.00 9.00

No. 1228 is a continuous design.

Diana, Princess of Wales (1961-97) — A179

**1998, Mar. 18** **Litho.** ***Perf. 14***

**1229** A179 $1.15 shown 1.50 1.50

**Souvenir Sheet**

**1230** A179 $3.50 like #1229 5.25 5.25

No. 1229 was issued in sheets of 5 + label. See No. B142.

Nos. 1111-1114 Ovptd.

**Printing Methods and Perfs as before**

**1999, Dec. 31**

**1231** A159 80c on #1111 1.25 1.25
**1232** A159 85c on #1112 1.25 1.25
**1233** A159 $1 on #1113 1.50 1.50
**1234** A159 $1.75 on #1114 2.50 2.50
*Nos. 1231-1234 (4)* 6.50 6.50

Queen Mother, 100th Birthday A180

No. 1235: a, As child. b, As young woman. c, Wearing green hat. d, Wearing tiara.

**2000, Oct. 20** **Litho.** ***Perf. 14***

**1235** A180 $4.50 Sheet of 4, #a-d 18.00 18.00

**Souvenir Sheet**

**1236** A180 $6 Wearing blue hat 5.50 5.50

2000 Summer Olympics, Sydney — A181

No. 1237: a, Ancient runner. b, Track and field. c, Ancient archery. d, Archery.

**2000, Nov. 14**

**1237** A181 $1.75 Sheet of 4, #a-d 9.00 9.00

**Souvenir Sheet**

**1238** A181 $3.90 Torch bearer 4.50 4.50

**Nos. 1095-1106 Surcharged in Gold**

**2001, Apr. 30** **Litho.** ***Perf. 14***

**1239** A156 80c on $1.15 #1101 1.25 1.25
**1240** A156 80c on $1.15 #1102 1.25 1.25
**1241** A156 80c on $1.15 #1103 1.25 1.25
**1242** A156 80c on $1.15 #1104 1.25 1.25
**1243** A156 80c on $1.15 #1105 1.25 1.25
**1244** A156 80c on $1.15 #1106 1.25 1.25
**1245** A156 90c on $1.15 #1095 1.25 1.25
**1246** A156 90c on $1.15 #1096 1.25 1.25
**1247** A156 90c on $1.15 #1097 1.25 1.25
**1248** A156 90c on $1.15 #1098 1.25 1.25
**1249** A156 90c on $1.15 #1099 1.25 1.25
**1250** A156 90c on $1.15 #1100 1.25 1.25
*Nos. 1239-1250 (12)* 15.00 15.00

**Nos. 1042-1045, 1050-1053 Surcharged or Overprinted in Black or Gold**

**2002, Nov. 11** **Litho.** ***Perf. 14***

**1251** A151 20c on 70c #1042 .25 .25
**1252** A154 20c on 70c #1050 .25 .25
**1253** A154 80c on $1.15 #1052 (G) 1.50 1.50
**1254** A151 85c #1043 1.60 1.60
**1255** A154 85c #1051 1.60 1.60
**1256** A154 90c on $1.50 #1053 1.75 1.75
**1257** A151 95c #1044 1.90 1.90
**1258** A151 $1 on $1.50 #1045 2.25 2.25
*Nos. 1251-1258 (8)* 11.10 11.10

**Nos. 1226A-1226F Surcharged**

Nos. 1260-1264

**Methods and Perfs As Before**

**2003, June 30**

**1259** A177 20c on $1.50 #1226A .30 .30
**1260** A177 80c on $2 #1226B 1.00 1.00
**1261** A177 85c on $3 #1226C 1.25 1.25
**1262** A177 85c on $4 #1226D 1.25 1.25
**1263** A177 90c on $5 #1226E 1.50 1.50
**1264** A177 90c on $7 #1226F 1.50 1.50
*Nos. 1259-1264 (6)* 6.80 6.80

Obliterator on Nos. 1260-1264 is a Moai head.

United We Stand — A182

**2003, Sept. 30** **Litho.** ***Perf. 14***

**1265** A182 90c multi 3.00 3.00

Printed in sheets of 4.

2004 Summer Olympics, Athens — A183

Designs: 40c, Poster for 1992 Barcelona Olympics. 60c, Pancration, horiz. $1, Cycling, horiz. $2, Gold medal, 1936 Berlin Olympics.

**2004, Sept. 29** **Litho.** ***Perf. 14¼***

**1266-1269** A183 Set of 4 6.50 6.50

For overprints, see Nos. 1275-1278.

Worldwide Fund for Nature (WWF) — A184

Birds of Suwarrow National Park: 80c, Cook Islands reed warblers. 90c, Mangaia kingfishers. $1.15, Rarotonga starlings. $1.95, Atiu swiftlets.

**2005, June 13** **Litho.** ***Perf. 14***

**1270-1273** A184 Set of 4 6.50 6.50

Each stamp printed in sheets of 4.

Pope John Paul II (1920-2005) — A185

**2005, Nov. 11**

**1274** A185 $1.35 multi 2.75 2.75

Printed in sheets of 5 + label.

**Sheets of Nos. 1266-1269 Overprinted in Gold**

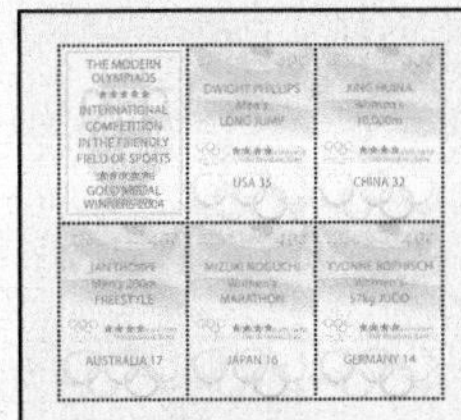

Overprints on Nos. 1276, 1277 and 1278: a, "DWIGHT PHILLIPS / Men's / LONG JUMP / **** / USA 35." b, "XING HUINA / Women's / 10,000m / **** / CHINA 32." c, "IAN THORPE / Men's 200m / FREESTYLE / **** / AUSTRALIA 17." d, "MIZUKI NOGUCHI / Women's / MARATHON / **** / JAPAN 16." e, "YVONNE BOENISCH / Women's / 57kg JUDO / **** / GERMANY 14."

**Methods and Perfs. As Before**

**2005, Nov. 29**

**1275** A183 40c Sheet of 5, #a-e, + label (#1266) — —
**1276** A183 60c Sheet of 5, #a-e, + label (#1267) — —
**1277** A183 $1 Sheet of 5, #a-e, + label (#1268) — —
**1278** A183 $2 Sheet of 5, #a-e, + label (#1269) — —

A186

A187

A188

Designs: 5c, Black-lined Maori wrasse. 10c, Blue lorikeets. 20c, Daisy coral. 30c, Ocean sunfish. 40c, Female Lampides boeticus butterfly. 50c, Rarotonga starlings.

No. 1285: a, Mangaia kingfishers. b, Cook Islands reef warblers. c, Rarotonga starlings, diff. d, Matiu swiftlets.

No. 1286: a, Male Lampides boeticus. b, Vagrans egista. c, Melantis leda. d, Female Lampides boeticus, diff.

No. 1287: a, Daisy coral, diff. b, Hydroid coral. c, Sea star. d, Smooth sea star.

No. 1288: a, Black-tipped cod. b, Red spot rainbow fish. c, Black-lined Maori wrasse, diff. d, Fish (incorrectly identified as Smooth sea star).

No. 1289: a, Three Ocean sunfish, Latin name at LL. b, Three Ocean sunfish, large clump of seaweed, Latin name at LR. c, Two Ocean sunfish, diver. d, Three Ocean sunfish, small clump of seaweed at top, Latin name at LR.

No. 1290: a, Blue lorikeets on palm branch. b, Blue lorikeets in tree hollow. c, Blue lorikeets and white flowers. d, Blue lorikeets and pink flowers.

No. 1291 — Queen Elizabeth II and: a, Hawksbill turtle. b, Leatherback turtle. c, Green turtle. d, Olive ridley turtle.

No. 1292 — Queen Elizabeth II and: a, Sowerby's whales. b, Cuvier's beaked whales. c, Bottle-nosed dolphin. d, Commerson's dolphins.

$7.50, Queen Elizabeth II, fish and marine life. $10, Queen Elizabeth II, butterflies and flowers. $15, Queen Elizabeth II and birds.

Illustrations A187 and A188 reduced.

**2007** **Litho.** ***Perf. 13¼***

**1279** A186 5c multi .25 .25
**1280** A186 10c multi .25 .25
**1281** A186 20c multi .30 .30
**1282** A186 30c multi .45 .45
**1283** A186 40c multi .60 .60
**1284** A186 50c multi .75 .75

**Size: 48x27mm**

***Perf. 14x14¾***

**1285** Block of 4 4.75 4.75
*a.-d.* A186 80c Any single 1.10 1.10
**1286** Block of 4 5.25 5.25
*a.-d.* A186 90c Any single 1.25 1.25
**1287** Block of 4 5.75 5.75
*a.-d.* A186 $1 Any single 1.40 1.40
**1288** Block of 4 6.50 6.50
*a.-d.* A186 $1.10 Any single 1.60 1.60
**1289** Block of 4 7.00 7.00
*a.-d.* A186 $1.20 Any single 1.75 1.75
**1290** Block of 4 11.50 11.50
*a.-d.* A186 $2 Any single 2.75 2.75

***Perf. 13¾***

**1291** Block of 4 19.00 19.00
*a.-d.* A187 $3 Any single 4.75 4.75

**1292** Block of 4 31.00 31.00
*a.-d.* A187 $5 Any single 7.75 7.75

***Perf. 13¼***

**1293** A188 $7.50 multi 12.00 12.00
**1294** A188 $10 multi 15.50 15.50
**1295** A188 $15 multi 24.00 24.00
*Nos. 1279-1295 (17)* 144.85 144.85

Issued: Nos. 1279-1290, 3/20; No. 1291, 10/10; No. 1292, 11/13; Nos. 1293-1295, 12/10.

Miniature Sheet

2008 Summer Olympics, Beijing — A189

No. 1296: a, 40c, Weight lifting. b, 60c, High jump. c, $1, Swimming. d, $1.50, Running.

**2008, July 28 Litho. *Perf. 14¾x14***
**1296** A189 Sheet of 4, #a-d 5.25 5.25

Pacific Mini-Games, Rarotonga — A190

Designs: 20c, Shot put and discus. 80c, High jump. 90c, Weight lifting. $3, Running.

**2009, Sept. 21 Litho. *Perf. 13¾***
**1297-1300** A190 Set of 4 7.25 7.25
*1300a* Souvenir sheet, #1297-1300 7.25 7.25

Nos. 1297-1300 Ovptd. in Gold with Names of Winners

Overprint text: 20c, Daniel Kilama / New Caledonia / Men's Discus Throw / 27th Sept. 2009. 80c, Johanna Sui / Tahiti / Women's High Jump / 24th Sept. 2009. 90c, Yukio Peter / Nauru / 84kg Clean & Jerk / 1st Oct. 2009. $3, Niko Verekauta / Fiji / Men's 100 metres / 24th Sept. 2009.

**2009, Oct. 21 Litho. *Perf. 13¾***
**1301-1304** A190 Set of 4 7.25 7.25
*1304a* Souvenir sheet, #1301-1304 7.25 7.25

Flowers A191

Designs: 10c, Catharanthus roseus. 20c, Ixora casei. 30c, Hibiscus rosa-sinensis cultivar. 40c, Heliconia psittacorum. 50c, Hibiscus schizopetalus, vert. 70c, Alpinia purpurata, vert. 80c, Bougainvillea spectabilis. 90c, Hibiscus rosa-sinensis. $1, Nymphaea capensis. $1.10, Euphorbia pulcherrima. $1.20, Impatiens walleriana. $2, Anthurium andraeanum. $3, Chrysanthemum cultivar. $4, Acalypha pendula, vert. $5, Heliconia rostrata, vert. $7.50, Tagetes patular cultivar. $10, Phalaenopsis cultivar. $20, Catharanthus roseus, diff.

**2010, Sept. 10 Litho. *Perf. 13¾***
**Sizes: 60x37mm, 37x60mm**

**1305** A191 10c multi .25 .25
**1306** A191 20c multi .30 .30
**1307** A191 30c multi .45 .45
**1308** A191 40c multi .60 .60
**1309** A191 50c multi .75 .75
**1310** A191 70c multi 1.00 1.00
**1311** A191 80c multi 1.25 1.25
**1312** A191 90c multi 1.40 1.40
**1313** A191 $1 multi 1.50 1.50
**1314** A191 $1.10 multi 1.60 1.60
**1315** A191 $1.20 multi 1.75 1.75
**1316** A191 $2 multi 3.00 3.00
**1317** A191 $3 multi 4.50 4.50
**1318** A191 $4 multi 5.75 5.75
**1319** A191 $5 multi 7.25 7.25
**1320** A191 $7.50 multi 11.00 11.00
**1321** A191 $10 multi 14.50 14.50
**1322** A191 $20 multi 29.00 29.00
*Nos. 1305-1322 (18)* 85.85 85.85

See Nos. 1328-1337, 1388-1389.
For overprints see Nos. O70-O117.

ANZAC Day — A192

Designs: 80c, Girl Guides in parade. 90c, Boy Scouts in parade. $1.10, Monument, vert. $1.20, Cook Islands flag, vert.
No. 1327: a, Church interior. b, Church exterior.

***Perf. 14¾x14¼, 14¼x14¾***
**2010, Sept. 14**
**1323-1326** A192 Set of 4 6.00 6.00

**Souvenir Sheet**

**1327** A192 $3 Sheet of 2, #a-b 9.00 9.00

For overprints, see Nos. 1391-1400.

**Flower Type of 2010 in Smaller Sizes**

Designs as before.

**2010, Oct. 27 Litho. *Perf. 14***
**Sizes: 42x28mm, 28x42mm**

**1328** A191 10c multi .25 .25
**1329** A191 20c multi .30 .30
**1330** A191 30c multi .50 .50
**1331** A191 50c multi .80 .80
**1332** A191 80c multi 1.25 1.25
**1333** A191 90c multi 1.50 1.50
**1334** A191 $1 multi 1.60 1.60
**1335** A191 $1.10 multi 1.75 1.75
**1336** A191 $1.20 multi 1.90 1.90
**1337** A191 $2 multi 3.25 3.25
*Nos. 1328-1337 (10)* 13.10 13.10

For surcharges, see Nos. 1437-1445.

Expo 2010, Shanghai — A193

Designs: 80c, Anthurium flower. 90c, Angelfish. $1.10, Fish near ocean floor. $1.20, Coconuts.
$6, Palm tree and ocean, vert.

**2010, Oct. 27 *Perf. 14¾x14¼***
**1338-1341** A193 Set of 4 6.50 6.50

**Souvenir Sheet**

***Perf. 14¼***

**1342** A193 $6 multi 9.75 9.75

No. 1342 contains one 38x50mm stamp.

Miniature Sheet

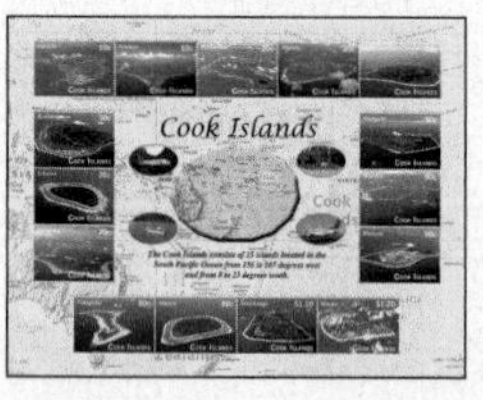


Aerial Views of Islands A194

No. 1343: a, 10c, Aitutaki. b, 10c, Penrhyn. c, 20c, Palmerston. d, 20c, Mitiaro. e, 30c, Rarotonga. f, 30c, Takutea. g, 50c, Atiu. h, 70c, Suwarrow. i, 80c, Pukapuka. j, 80c, Nassau. k, 90c, Manihiki. m, 90c, Manuae. n, $1.10, Rakahanga. o, $1.20, Mauke.

**2010, Nov. 8 *Perf. 14***
**1343** A194 Sheet of 15, #a-o 14.00 14.00

Service of Queen Elizabeth II and Prince Philip A195

Designs: 80c, Queen Elizabeth II. 90c, Queen and Prince Philip. $1, Queen and Prince Philip, diff. $1.10, Queen and Prince Philip, diff. $1.20, Queen and Prince Philip, diff. $1.50, Prince Philip.
$6.60, Queen and Prince Philip, diff.

**2010, Dec. 6 Litho. *Perf. 13¼***
**1344-1349** A195 Set of 6 9.75 9.75
*1349a* Sheet of 6, #1344-1349, + 3 labels 9.75 9.75

**Souvenir Sheet**

**1350** A195 $6.60 multi 10.00 10.00

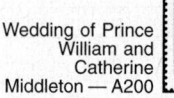

Worldwide Fund for Nature (WWF) — A196

Rimatara lorikeet: 80c, Pair on flower. 90c, In flight. $2.40, On branch. $3.60, Trio at nest.

**2010, Dec. 9 Litho. *Perf. 14***
**1351-1354** A196 Set of 4 11.50 11.50

A197

Engagement of Prince William and Catherine Middleton — A198

Designs: Nos. 1355, 1358a, 1360, Middleton. Nos. 1356, 1358b, 1361, Prince in military uniform.
No. 1357: a, Prince in military uniform. b, Prince playing polo. c, Middleton, fence. d, Prince, man and woman in background. e, Middleton, woman in background. f, Couple, Prince at left. g, Middleton with black hat. h, Prince. i, Couple, Middleton at left. j, Hands of couple, engagement ring.
$8.10, Couple, Prince in uniform at left.

**2011, Jan. 14 *Perf. 14***
**1355** A197 $2.40 multi 3.75 3.75
**1356** A197 $3.60 multi 5.50 5.50

**Miniature Sheets**

**1357** A198 10c Sheet of 10, #a-j 1.60 1.60

***Perf. 13¾x13½***

**1358** A197 Sheet of 2, #a-b 9.25 9.25

**Souvenir Sheets**

***Perf. 14¼***

**1359** A197 $8.10 multi 12.50 12.50
**1360** A197 $11 multi 17.00 17.00
**1361** A197 $11 multi 17.00 17.00
*Nos. 1359-1361 (3)* 46.50 46.50

No. 1358 contains two 28x44mm stamps. Nos. 1359-1361 each contain one 38x50mm stamp.

Peonies A199

No. 1362: a, 80c, Pink peonies (30x40mm). b, 90c, Purple peony (30x30mm). c, $1.10, Peach peonies (30x30mm). d, $1.20, Pink peony (30x30mm).
$8.10, Red peony.

**2011, Apr. 8 Litho. *Perf. 14¾***
**1362** A199 Sheet of 4, #a-d 6.25 6.25

**Souvenir Sheet**

**1363** A199 $8.10 multi 13.00 13.00

No. 1363 contains one 70x60mm stamp.

Wedding of Prince William and Catherine Middleton — A200

Designs: 20c, Couple, Prince at right. 30c, Westminster Abbey. 80c, Couple, Prince at left.

**2011, Apr. 29 *Perf. 13¼***
**1364-1366** A200 Set of 3 2.10 2.10
*1366a* Souvenir sheet of 3, #1364-1366 2.10 2.10

Rarotonga Tourism — A201

Designs: 10c, Whale breaching ocean's surface near boat. 20c, Palm trees, boat. 30c, Starfish. 50c, Palm trees near ocean. 70c, Crab. 80c, Cook Islands flag on boat. 90c, Airplane, windsurfer. $1, Trees near beach. $1.10, Cliffs, airplane. $1.20, Palm trees near beach. $1.50, Goat. $2, Chicken. $3, Island and beach. $4, Fish. $5, Aerial view of Rarotonga. cruise ship.

**2011, July 22 Litho. *Perf. 14***
**1367** A201 10c multi .25 .25
**1368** A201 20c multi .35 .35
**1369** A201 30c multi .50 .50
**1370** A201 50c multi .85 .85
**1371** A201 70c multi 1.25 1.25
**1372** A201 80c multi 1.40 1.40
**1373** A201 90c multi 1.50 1.50
**1374** A201 $1 multi 1.75 1.75
**1375** A201 $1.10 multi 1.90 1.90
**1376** A201 $1.20 multi 2.00 2.00
**1377** A201 $1.50 multi 2.50 2.50
**1378** A201 $2 multi 3.50 3.50
**1379** A201 $3 multi 5.00 5.00
**1380** A201 $4 multi 6.75 6.75
**1381** A201 $5 multi 8.50 8.50
*a.* Sheet of 15, #1367-1381 38.00 38.00
*Nos. 1367-1381 (15)* 38.00 38.00

National Environment Service — A202

Designs: 80c, Bristle-thighed curlew. 90c, Fiddler crab. $1.10, Taro plant and flower. $1.20, Wetlands flora.

**2011, Oct. 21 *Perf. 13¾***
**1382-1385** A202 Set of 4 6.50 6.50

Nos. 1382-1385 each were printed in sheets of 4.

Souvenir Sheets

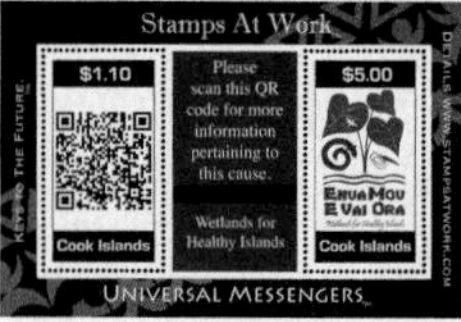


Stamps at Work A203

No. 1386: a, $1.10, Quick response code. b, $5, Emblem for Wetlands for Healthy Islands.
No. 1387: a, $1.10, Quick response code, text and website address. b, $5, Damage from 2011 Japan tsunami.

**2011, Oct. 21 *Perf. 15x14¼***
**Sheets of 2, #a-b**

**1386-1387** A203 Set of 2 19.50 19.50

Twenty percent of the sales of No. 1387 were donated to Japan tsunami relief efforts.

### Flowers Type of 2010 With Head of Queen Elizabeth II Added at Lower Right

Designs: $26.90, Plumeria rubra. $31.10, Hypolimnas bolina.

**2011, Oct. 25** ***Perf. 14¼x15***

**Size: 44x29mm**

**1388** A191 $26.90 multi 42.50 42.50
**1389** A191 $31.10 multi 50.00 50.00

Christmas — A204

No. 1390: a, Five gold rings. b, Six geese a laying. c, Seven swans a swimming. d, Eight maids a milking.

**2011, Dec. 23** **Litho.** ***Perf. 13¼***

**1390** Horiz. strip of 4 13.00 13.00
*a.* A204 $1.10 multi 1.75 1.75
*b.* A204 $1.20 multi 1.90 1.90
*c.* A204 $2.10 multi 3.50 3.50
*d.* A204 $3.60 multi 5.75 5.75
*e.* Souvenir sheet of 4, #1390a-1390d 13.00 13.00

### Nos. 1323-1327 Overprinted in Gold or Silver

### Methods and Perfs As Before

**2012, Jan. 10**

**1391** A192 80c On No. 1323 (G) 1.40 1.40
**1392** A192 80c On No. 1323 (S) 1.40 1.40
**1393** A192 90c On No. 1324 (G) 1.50 1.50
**1394** A192 90c On No. 1324 (S) 1.50 1.50
**1395** A192 $1.10 On No. 1325 (G) 1.90 1.90
**1396** A192 $1.10 On No. 1325 (S) 1.90 1.90
**1397** A192 $1.20 On No. 1326 (G) 2.00 2.00
**1398** A192 $1.20 On No. 1326 (S) 2.00 2.00
*Nos. 1391-1398 (8)* 13.60 13.60

### Souvenir Sheets of 2, #a-b

**1399** A192 $3 On No. 1327 (G) 10.00 10.00
**1400** A192 $3 On No. 1327 (S) 10.00 10.00

Overprint reads up on Nos. 1395-1398.

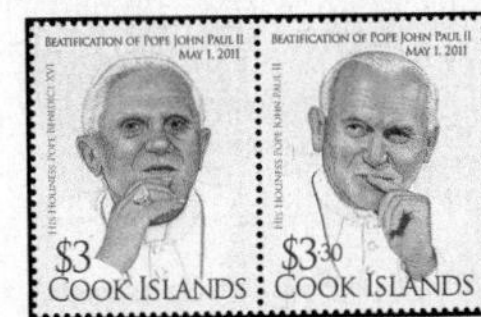

Beatification of Pope John Paul II — A205

No. 1401: a, $3, Pope Benedict XVI. b, $3.30, Pope John Paul II.

**2012, Jan. 10** **Litho.** ***Perf. 13¾***

**1401** A205 Horiz. pair, #a-b 10.50 10.50

No. 1401 was printed in sheets containing two pairs.

Reign of Queen Elizabeth II, 60th Anniv. A206

Queen Elizabeth II: 80c, Wearing tiara. 90c, Wearing red hat. $1, Wearing tiara, diff. $1.10, Wearing gray hat. $1.20, With dog. $1.50, Wearing aquamarine dress.
$6.60, Wearing aquamarine dress, diff.

**2012, Feb. 6** ***Perf. 13¼***

**1402-1407** A206 Set of 6 11.00 11.00
*1407a* Souvenir sheet of 6, #1402-1407, + 3 labels 11.00 11.00

### Souvenir Sheet

**1408** A206 $6.60 multi 11.00 11.00

Worldwide Fund for Nature (WWF) — A207

Designs: 90c, Partula assimilis. $1.20, Libera fratercula. $1.50, Lamprocystis globosa. $2.70, Sinployea peasei.

**2012, Apr. 11** ***Perf. 14***

**1409-1412** A207 Set of 4 10.00 10.00
*1412a* Sheet of 16, 4 each #1409-1412 40.00 40.00

2012 Summer Olympics, London — A208

Designs: 80c, Swimming. 90c, Map of South Pacific, Great Britain and Ireland. $2, Sailing.

**2012, June 22** ***Perf. 13¾***

**1413-1415** A208 Set of 3 6.00 6.00
*1415a* Souvenir sheet of 3, #1413-1415 6.00 6.00
*1415b* Souvenir sheet of 6, 2 each #1413-1415 12.00 12.00

### Miniature Sheets

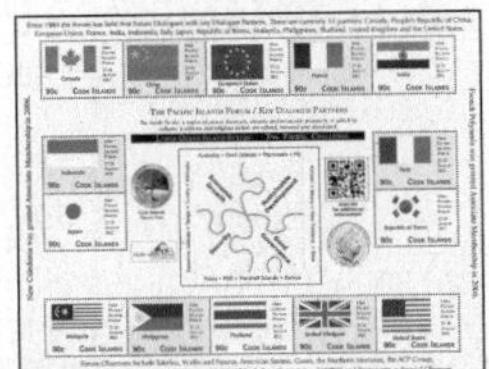

43rd Pacific Islands Forum, Rarotonga — A209

No. 1416 — Flag of: a, Canada. b, People's Republic of China. c, European Union. d, France. e, India. f, Indonesia. g, Italy. h, Japan. i, Republic of Korea. j, Malaysia. k, Philippines. l, Thailand. m, United Kingdom. n, United States.

No. 1417 — Flag of: a, Australia. b, Cook Islands. c, Fiji. d, Kiribati. e, Micronesia. f, Nauru. g, New Zealand. h, Niue. i, Palau. j, Papua New Guinea. k, Marshall Islands. l, Samoa. m, Solomon Islands. n, Tonga. o, Tuvalu. p, Vanuatu.

**2012, Aug. 22** ***Perf. 14***

**1416** A209 90c Sheet of 14, #a-n 21.00 21.00
**1417** A209 90c Sheet of 16, #a-p 24.00 24.00

Adoration of the Magi, by Giotto di Bondone — A210

Entry into Jerusalem, by Giotto — A211

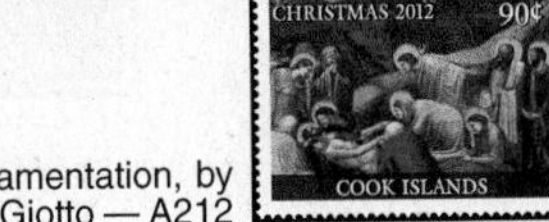

Lamentation, by Giotto — A212

Kiss of Judas, by Giotto — A213

Life of Mary Magdalene - Raising of Lazarus, by Giotto — A214

Death of Mary, by Giotto — A215

***Perf. 14¾x14¼***

**2012, Nov. 16** **Litho.**

### Stamps With White Frames

**1418** Horiz. pair 2.80 2.80
*a.* A210 80c multi 1.40 1.40
*b.* A211 80c multi 1.40 1.40
**1419** Horiz. pair 3.00 3.00
*a.* A212 90c multi 1.50 1.50
*b.* A213 90c multi 1.50 1.50
**1420** Horiz. pair 10.00 10.00
*a.* A214 $3 multi 5.00 5.00
*b.* A215 $3 multi 5.00 5.00
*Nos. 1418-1420 (3)* 15.80 15.80

### Miniature Sheet
### Stamps Without White Frame

**1421** Sheet of 6 16.00 16.00
*a.* A210 80c multi 1.40 1.40
*b.* A211 80c multi 1.40 1.40
*c.* A212 90c multi 1.50 1.50
*d.* A213 90c multi 1.50 1.50
*e.* A214 $3 multi 5.00 5.00
*f.* A215 $3 multi 5.00 5.00

Christmas.

### Miniature Sheets

A215a

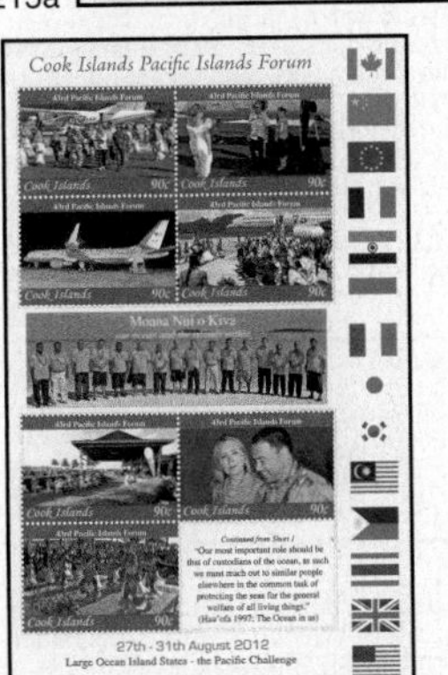

43rd Pacific Islands Forum, Rarotonga — A215b

No. 1422G: i, Woman with Cook Islands sash with Minister of Education Teina Bishop, New Zealand Prime Minister John Key and John Carter, New Zealand High Commissioner to the Cook Islands. j, Canoe with sails. k, Women from Aitutaki holding a quilted bedspread. l, Leaders of Pacific islands seated in row. m, President of French Polynesia Oscar Temaru and Cook Islands Prime Minister Henry Puna in front of airplane. n, Australian Prime Minister Julia Gillard. o, Canoe on shore.

No. 1422H: p, Pres. Temaru, Prime Minister Puna, Cook Islands Deputy Prime Minister Tom Marsters and entourage walking away from airplane. q, Prime Minister Puna departing airplane, two women. r, U.S. airplane. s, People leaving Royal New Zealand Air Force airplane. t, Crowds near entrance to Aitutaki Airport. u, U.S. Secretary of State Hillary Clinton with Cook Island Minister of Finance Mark Brown. v, Aitutaki dancers performing for leaders.

**2012, Nov. 30** **Litho.** ***Perf. 14***

**1421G** A215a 80c Sheet of 7, #i-o, + label 9.50 9.50
**1421H** A215b 90c Sheet of 7, #p-v, + label 10.50 10.50

A216

Personalizable Stamps — A217

A216a A216b

**2012, Dec. 21** **Litho.** ***Perf. 14x14¾***

**1422** A216 $4 multi 6.75 6.75
*a.* A216a 50c multi .70 .70
*b.* A216b $1 multi 1.40 1.40
**1423** A217 $4 multi 6.75 6.75

Christmas (#1422a, 1422b). Issued: Nos. 1422a, 1422b, 12/16/19. Nos. 1422a-1422b have the same frame as the personalizable stamp No. 1422, but have different denominations. The editors do not know if 50c and $1 stamps having these frames were made available to the public that may have different personalized images other than the images shown above placed in the vignette area. The editors also do not know if there are stamps of type A216 that are available in denominations other than 50c, $1, or $4.

Items Commemorating British Coronations A218

Coronation of Queen Elizabeth II, 60th Anniv. — A219

Various items commemorating the coronation of: 80c, Queen Victoria. 90c, King Edward VII. $1.10, King George V. $1.20, Seed packet for Coronation mixture of sweet pea seeds. $3.60, Illustration from *The Coronation Cut-Out Story Book.*
$3.90, Queen Elizabeth II.

**2013, Feb. 6** **Litho.** ***Perf. 14***

**1424-1428** A218 Set of 5 12.50 12.50

### Souvenir Sheet

***Perf. 15x14***

**1429** A219 $3.90 multi 6.50 6.50

Nos. 1424-1428 each were printed isn sheets of 8 + central label.

A220

A221

A222

A223

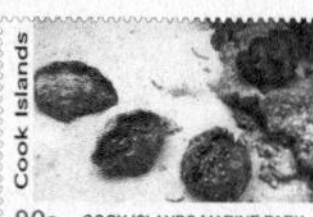

A224

Cook Islands Marine Park — A225

**2013, Feb. 20 Litho. *Perf. 14***

**1430** A220 80c multi 1.40 1.40
**1431** A221 80c multi 1.40 1.40
**1432** A222 80c multi 1.40 1.40
**1433** A223 90c multi 1.50 1.50
**1434** A224 90c multi 1.50 1.50
**1435** A225 90c multi 1.50 1.50
*Nos. 1430-1435 (6)* 8.70 8.70

New Year 2013 (Year of the Snake) — A226

No. 1436 — Snake with background color of: a, Green. b, Red.

***Perf. 14¾x14¼***
**2013, Feb. 21 Litho.**
**1436** A226 $1.20 pair, #a-b 4.00 4.00

Printed in sheets containing 2 each of Nos. 1436a-1436b.

**Nos. 1328, 1330-1337 Surcharged in Gold**

**Methods and Perfs. As Before**
**2013, Apr. 9**

**1437** A191 20c on 10c #1328 .35 .35
**1438** A191 20c on 30c #1330 .35 .35
**1439** A191 20c on 50c #1331 .35 .35
**1440** A191 20c on 80c #1332 .35 .35
**1441** A191 20c on 90c #1333 .35 .35
**1442** A191 20c on $1 #1334 .35 .35
**1443** A191 20c on $1.10 #1335 .35 .35
**1444** A191 20c on $1.20 #1336 .35 .35
**1445** A191 20c on $2 #1337 .35 .35
*Nos. 1437-1445 (9)* 3.15 3.15

Ships A227

No. 1446, 20c: a, Ndrua. b, Hamatafua.
No. 1447, 50c: a, Single-masted Vaa Kalua. b, Double-masted Vaa Kalua.
No. 1448, 60c: a, Vaka Motu. b, Toniaki.
No. 1449, 80c: a, Vaka. b, Pahi.
No. 1450, 90c: a, Vaka, diff. b, Pahi, diff.
No. 1451, $2.30: a, Vaka Motu, diff. b, Tipaerua.
No. 1452, $4.50: a, Pahi, diff. b, Waka Tou. c, Tipaerua, diff.

**2013, May 24 Litho. *Perf. 14¾x14¼***
**Horiz. Pairs, #a-b**
**1446-1451** A227 Set of 6 17.00 17.00

**Souvenir Sheet**
**1452** A227 $4.50 Sheet of 3, #a-c 22.00 22.00

Animals A228

Designs: No. 1453, $1.50, American bison. No. 1454, $1.50, Gazella dama. No. 1455, $1.50, Phascolarctos cinereus. No. 1456, $1.50, Eurasian lynx. No. 1457, $1.50, Loxodonta africana. No. 1458, $1.50, Grus americana.

**2013, May 31 Litho. *Perf. 14x14¾***
**1453-1458** A228 Set of 6 14.50 14.50

Miniature Sheet

Duchess of Cambridge — A229

No. 1459 — Duchess of Cambridge: a, Wearing pink dress (40x52mm). b, Wearing dark blue jacket and black hat (40x26mm). c, Wearing yellow jacket and hat, meeting with group of dignitaries (40x26mm). d, Wearing white dress and hat, reviewing Scout troop (40x26mm). e, Wearing light blue dress (40x52mm). f, Wearing polka dot dress (40x52mm). g, Wearing wedding gown, kissing Duke of Cambridge (40x26mm).

**2013, Aug. 1 Litho. *Perf. 13¼***
**1459** A229 $1 Sheet of 7, #a-g 11.50 11.50

Insects and Spiders — A230

Designs: 30c, Alphitobius diaperinus. 50c, Leptocoris rufomarginatus. 70c, Nabis capsiformis. $1, Polistes jokahamae. $1.30, Agrius convulvi. $1.50, Harmonia octomaculata. $1.70, Cosmopolites sordidus. $3.80, Graeffea crouanii. $4.10, Leptoglossus australis. $5.30, Nezara viridula. $6.50, Neoscona theisi. $8.50, Tholumis tillarga.

**2013, Sept. 2 Litho. *Perf. 14***
**Stamps With White Frames**

**1460** A230 30c multi .50 .50
**1461** A230 50c multi .85 .85
**1462** A230 70c multi 1.25 1.25
**1463** A230 $1 multi 1.60 1.60
**1464** A230 $1.30 multi 2.10 2.10
**1465** A230 $1.50 multi 2.50 2.50
**1466** A230 $1.70 multi 2.75 2.75
**1467** A230 $3.80 multi 6.25 6.25
**1468** A230 $4.10 multi 6.75 6.75
**1469** A230 $5.30 multi 8.75 8.75
**1470** A230 $6.50 multi 10.50 10.50
**1471** A230 $8.50 multi 14.00 14.00
*Nos. 1460-1471 (12)* 57.80 57.80

**Miniature Sheet**
**Stamp Without White Frame**

**1472** Sheet of 12 58.00 58.00
*a.* A230 30c multi .50 .50
*b.* A230 50c multi .85 .85
*c.* A230 70c multi 1.25 1.25
*d.* A230 $1 multi 1.60 1.60
*e.* A230 $1.30 multi 2.10 2.10
*f.* A230 $1.50 multi 2.50 2.50
*g.* A230 $1.70 multi 2.75 2.75
*h.* A230 $3.80 multi 6.25 6.25
*i.* A230 $4.10 multi 6.75 6.75
*j.* A230 $5.30 multi 8.75 8.75
*k.* A230 $6.50 multi 10.50 10.50
*l.* A230 $8.50 multi 14.00 14.00

See Nos. 1491-1503.

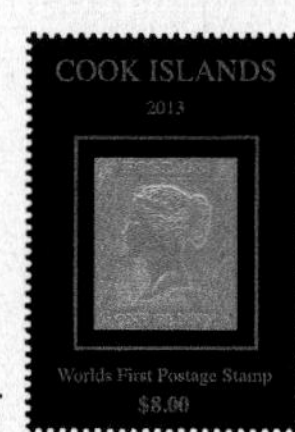

Great Britain No. 1 — A231

**Litho. & Embossed With Foil Application**
**2013, Sept. 18 *Perf. 13x13¼***
**1473** A231 $8 blk & gold 13.50 13.50

Souvenir Sheets

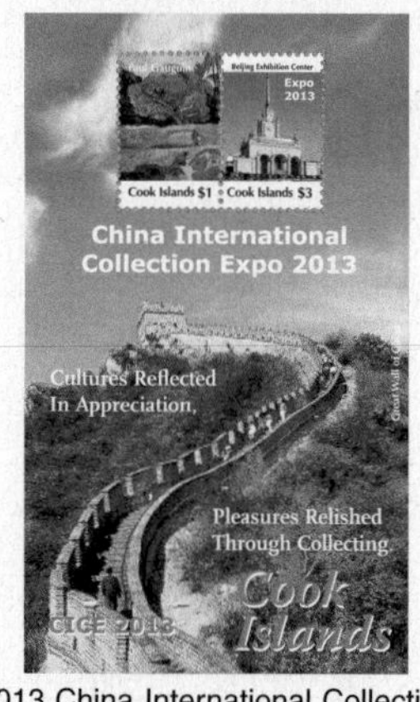

2013 China International Collection Exposition, Beijing — A232

No. 1474 — Stamps inscribed "Cook Islands": a, $1, Painting by Paul Gauguin. b, $3, Beijing Exhibition Center.
No. 1475 — Stamps inscribed "Rarotonga / Cook Islands": a, $1, Painting by Paul Gauguin, diff. b, $3, Beijing Exhibition Center.

**2013, Sept. 26 Litho. *Perf. 12***
**1474** A232 Sheet of 2, #a-b 6.75 6.75
**1475** A232 Sheet of 2, #a-b 6.75 6.75

Pres. John F. Kennedy (1917-63) — A233

Designs: $2.40, Pres. Kennedy. $3.10, Pres. Kennedy and quote,

**2013, Nov. 8 Litho. *Perf. 14¼***
**1476-1477** A233 Set of 2 9.00 9.00

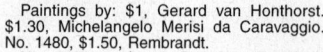

Christmas — A234

Paintings by: $1, Gerard van Honthorst. $1.30, Michelangelo Merisi da Caravaggio. No. 1480, $1.50, Rembrandt.
No. 1481: a, $1.50, Bernardo Daddi. b, $1.70, Pieter Aertsen. c, $4.50, Lorenzo Lotto.

**2013, Nov. 18 Litho. *Perf. 13¼***
**1478-1480** A234 Set of 3 6.25 6.25

**Souvenir Sheet**
**1481** A234 Sheet of 3, #a-c 13.00 13.00

Highland Paradise Scenes — A235

Various scenes from Highland Paradise tourist educational show.

**2014, Jan. 3 Litho. *Perf. 13¼***
**1482** A235 10c multi .25 .25
**1483** A235 20c multi .35 .35
**1484** A235 30c multi .50 .50
**1485** A235 50c multi .85 .85
**1486** A235 60c multi 1.00 1.00
**1487** A235 $1 multi 1.60 1.60
**1488** A235 $1.30 multi 2.10 2.10
**1489** A235 $1.50 multi 2.50 2.50
**1490** A235 $1.70 multi 2.75 2.75
*Nos. 1482-1490 (9)* 11.90 11.90

Dated "2013."

**Insects and Spiders Type of 2013**

Designs: 10c, Teleogryllus oceanicus. 40c, Euconocephalus roberti. $1, Apis mellifera. $2.10, Crocidolomia pavonana. $2.50, Junonia villida. $3, Aedes polynesiensis. $3.50, Homalodisca coagulata. $4.50, Lygus flavoscutellatus. $5.50, Euploea lewinii perryi. $6.70, Hypolimnas bolina. $7, Porcellio laevis. $10.10, Vagrans egista bodenia.

**2014, Jan. 6 Litho. *Perf. 14***
**Stamps With White Frames**

**1491** A230 10c multi .25 .25
**1492** A230 40c multi .65 .65
**1493** A230 $1 multi 1.60 1.60
**1494** A230 $2.10 multi 3.50 3.50
**1495** A230 $2.50 multi 4.00 4.00
**1496** A230 $3 multi 5.00 5.00
**1497** A230 $3.50 multi 5.75 5.75
**1498** A230 $4.50 multi 7.25 7.25
**1499** A230 $5.50 multi 9.00 9.00
**1500** A230 $6.70 multi 11.00 11.00
**1501** A230 $7 multi 11.50 11.50
**1502** A230 $10.10 multi 16.50 16.50
*Nos. 1491-1502 (12)* 76.00 76.00

**Miniature Sheet**
**Stamp Without White Frame**

**1503** Sheet of 12 76.00 76.00
*a.* A230 10c multi .25 .25
*b.* A230 40c multi .65 .65
*c.* A230 $1 multi 1.60 1.60
*d.* A230 $2.10 multi 3.50 3.50
*e.* A230 $2.50 multi 4.00 4.00
*f.* A230 $3 multi 5.00 5.00
*g.* A230 $3.50 multi 5.75 5.75
*h.* A230 $4.50 multi 7.25 7.25
*i.* A230 $5.50 multi 9.00 9.00
*j.* A230 $6.70 multi 11.00 11.00
*k.* A230 $7 multi 11.50 11.50
*l.* A230 $10.10 multi 16.50 16.50

Souvenir Sheet

New Year 2014 (Year of the Horse) A236

No. 1504 — Horse, with denomination color of: a, Red. b, White.

**2014, Jan. 8 Litho. *Perf. 13¼***
**1504** A236 $3 Sheet of 2, #a-b 9.75 9.75

Souvenir Sheet

Christening of Prince George of Cambridge — A237

No. 1505 — Prince George being held by: a, $4, Duchess of Cambridge. b, $5, Duke of Cambridge.

**2014, Jan. 14 Litho. *Perf. 14***

**1505** A237 Sheet of 2, #a-b 14.50 14.50

Easter A238

No. 1506 — Religious painting by: a, 50c, Il Moro. b, $1, Tintoretto. c, $1.30, Giovanni Bellini. d, $1.50, Raphael (Sanzio). e, $1.70, William Blake.

$9.50, Painting by Hans Memling.

**2014, Apr. 9 Litho. *Perf. 13¼***

**1506** A238 Sheet of 5, #a-e, + label 10.50 10.50

**Souvenir Sheet**

**1507** A238 $9.50 multi 16.50 16.50

Small Island Developing States — A239

No. 1508: a, Tropical cyclone. b. Rising sea levels at Rarotonga. c, Pacific Small Island Developing States emblem. d, Map of Cook Islands. e, "Island Voices Global Choices" emblem. f, Fishing boats. g, Sailboat. h, Cruise liner. i, Kayak. j, Wind surfing. k, Nurse shark. l, Barracuda. m, Triggerfish. n, Pilot whale. o, Manta ray. p, Flag of Cook Islands.

No. 1509: a, Like #1508a. b, Like #1508p. c, Like #1508b. d, Like #1508c. e, Like #1508d. f, Like #1508e.

No. 1510: a, Like #1508f. b, Like #1508p. c, Like #1508g. d, Like #1508h. e, Like #1508i. f, Like #1508j.

No. 1511: a, Like #1508k. b, Like #1508p. c, Like #1508l. d, Like #1508m. e, Like #1508n. f, Like #1508o.

**2014, May 9 Litho. *Perf. 13¼***

**1508** Block of 18, #1508a-1508o, 3 #1508p 15.50 15.50
*a.-p.* A239 50c Any single .85 .85

**Miniature Sheets**

**1509** Sheet of 6 21.00 21.00
*a.-f.* A239 $2 Any single 3.50 3.50
**1510** Sheet of 6 25.50 25.50
*a.-f.* A239 $2.40 Any single 4.25 4.25
**1511** Sheet of 6 27.00 27.00
*a.-f.* A239 $2.60 Any single 4.50 4.50
*Nos. 1509-1511 (3)* 73.50 73.50

No. 1508 was printed in sheets containing 3 blocks of 18. The frame on each stramp in the sheet, depicting a map of the Pacific Ocean, differs.

Souvenir Sheet

Nelson Mandela (1918-2013), President of South Africa — A240

No. 1512 — Mandela with: a, $2.50, Child. b, $4.50, U. S. Pres. Bill Clinton.

**2014, May 13 Litho. *Perf. 14***

**1512** A240 Sheet of 2, #a-b 12.00 12.00

Tourism A241

No. 1513, 30c: a, Relaxing. b, Shopping. c, Dancing. d, Dining.

No. 1514, 50c: a, Church service. b, Scootering. c, Hiking. d, Snorkeling.

No. 1515, $1: a, Kayaking. b, Swimming. c, Scuba diving. d, Fishing.

No. 1516, $1.70: a, Vaka sailing. b, Windsurfing. c, Kitesurfing. d, Paddleboarding.

No. 1517, $3.80: a, Whale watching, b, Sightseeing. c, Glass bottom boat. d, Birdwatching.

No. 1518, $4.10: a, Rugby. b, Beach volleyball. c, Golfing. d, Bike riding.

**2014, June 23 Litho. *Perf. 14¼x14***

**Blocks of 4, #a-d**

**1513-1518** A241 Set of 6 80.00 80.00

Insects A242

No. 1519: a, $4, Western honey bee. b, $11.50, Castor semi-looper moth. c, $13.60, Spotted ladybird.

**2014, Sept. 12 Litho. *Perf. 13¼***

**1519** A242 Horiz. strip of 3, #a-c, + 3 labels 46.00 46.00

Worldwide Fund for Nature (WWF) — A243

Various depictions of spotless crake: Nos. 1520, 1524a, $1. Nos. 1521, 1524b, $1.30. Nos. 1522, 1524c, $1.50. Nos. 1523, 1524d, $1.70

$7.50, Spotless crake, diff.

***Perf. 14¾x14¼***

**2014, Nov. 28 Litho.**

**Stamps With White Frame**

**1520-1523** A243 Set of 4 8.75 8.75

**Stamps Without White Frame**

**1524** A243 Strip of 4, #a-d 8.75 8.75

**Souvenir Sheet**

**1525** A243 $7.50 multi 12.00 12.00

For surcharges, see Nos. 1571-1576.

Souvenir Sheet

Christmas — A244

No. 1526 — Religious paintings by: a, Giotto di Bondone. b, Jan Gossaert. c, Caravaggio.

***Perf. 14¾x14¼***

**2014, Dec. 12 Litho.**

**1526** A244 $1.50 Sheet of 3, #a-c 7.00 7.00

Souvenir Sheet

New Year 2015 (Year of the Sheep) A245

No. 1527: a, $3.80, Red ram. b, $4.10, Blue ram.

**2015, Jan. 5 Litho. *Perf. 13¼***

**1527** A245 Sheet of 2, #a-b 11.50 11.50

Miniature Sheet

Easter A246

No. 1528 — Religious paintings by: a, Matthias Grünewald. b, Peter Paul Rubens. c, Jean Jouvenet. d, Giampietrino.

**2015, Mar. 31 Litho. *Perf. 14***

**1528** A246 $2 Sheet of 4, #a-d 12.50 12.50

Souvenir Sheet

Birth of Princess Charlotte of Cambridge — A247

No. 1529: a, Duchess of Cambridge holding Princess Charlotte. b, Duke of Cambridge holding Prince George.

***Perf. 14¾x14¼***

**2015, June 23 Litho.**

**1529** A247 $4.50 Sheet of 2, #a-b 12.00 12.00

Magna Carta, 800th Anniv. — A248

Quotations starting with: $1, "To no one will we deny or delay. . ." $1.30, "No free man shall be seized. . ." $1.50, "Given by our hand in the meadow. . ." $1.70, "To no one will we deny or delay. . .," diff.

**2015, July 15 Litho. *Perf. 14¼x14¾***

**1530-1533** A248 Set of 4 7.25 7.25

A249

Self-Government, 50th Anniv. — A250

No. 1535 — Cook Islands stamps: a, #162. b, #164. c, #195. d, #233. e, #253. f, #288. g, #301. h, #322. i, #357. j, #409.

No. 1536 — Cook Islands stamps: a, #435. b, #464. c, #479. d, #502. e, #531. f, #549. g, #660. h, #685. i, #696a. j, #760. k, #877. l, #B100. m, #B113. n, #998a. o, #1010b.

No. 1537 — Cook Islands stamps: a, #1029. b, #1048. c, #1111. d, #1140. e, #1191b. f, #1198b. g, #1204. h, #1214a. i, #O68. j, #1234. k, #1238. l, #1241. m, #1258. n, #1265. o, #1269.

No. 1538 — Cook Islands stamps: a, #1271. b, #1291a. c, #1296c. d, #1299. e, #1343a. f, #1383. g, #1422Hq. h, #1434. i, #1482. j, #1534.

**2015, Aug. 5 Litho. *Perf. 14***

**1534** A249 $1 multi 1.25 1.25

**Miniature Sheets**

***Perf. 13¾***

**1535** Sheet of 10 1.25 1.25
*a.-j.* A250 10c Any single .25 .25
**1536** Sheet of 15 6.00 6.00
*a.-o.* A250 30c Any single .40 .40
**1537** Sheet of 15 7.50 7.50
*a.-o.* A250 40c Any single .50 .50
**1538** Sheet of 10 6.50 6.50
*a.-j.* A250 50c Any single .65 .65
*Nos. 1535-1538 (4)* 21.25 21.25

New Year 2016 (Year of the Monkey) — A251

Designs: $2.60: Adult and juvenile monkeys, leaves. $3, Juvenile monkey on back of adult.

No. 1541: a, $3.80, Like $2.60. b, $4.10, Like $3.

**2015, Sept. 25 Litho. *Perf. 13¼***

**1539-1540** A251 Set of 2 7.25 7.25

**Self-Adhesive**

**1541** A251 Sheet of 2, #a-b 10.50 10.50

No. 1541 contains two 51x51mm diamond-shaped stamps.

Miniature Sheet

Queen Elizabeth II, Longest-Reigning British Monarch — A252

No. 1542 — Various photographs of Queen Elizabeth II: a, $1.30. b, $1.50. c, $1.70. d, $2.

**2015, Nov. 20 Litho. *Perf. 14***

**1542** A252 Sheet of 4, #a-d 8.75 8.75

Souvenir Sheet

Christmas — A253

No. 1543 — Details from Nativity, by Antoniazzo Romano: a, Joseph and saint. b, Infant Jesus and animals. c, Virgin Mary and saint.

**2015, Dec. 9 Litho. *Perf. 13¼***
**1543** A253 $1 Sheet of 3, #a-c 4.00 4.00

A254

A255

Night Skies A256

Various depictions of night sky, as shown.

***Perf. 14¾x14¼***
**2015, Dec. 29 Litho.**
**1544** A254 30c Block of 4, #a-d 1.60 1.60
**1545** A255 $1 Block of 4, #a-d 5.50 5.50
**1546** A256 $1.30 Block of 4, #a-d 7.00 7.00
*Nos. 1544-1546 (3)* 14.10 14.10

Worldwide Fund for Nature (WWF) — A257

Various depictions of Reef manta ray: Nos. 1547, 1551a, $1. Nos. 1548, 1551b, $1.50. Nos. 1549, 1551c, $1.70. Nos. 1550, 1551d, $2.

**2016, Feb. 15 Litho. *Perf. 14¾x14***
**Stamps With White Frames**
**1547-1550** A257 Set of 4 8.25 8.25
**Stamps Without White Frames**
**1551** A257 Horiz. strip of 4, #a-d 8.25 8.25

No. 1551 printed in sheets containing two strips.

Souvenir Sheet

Queen Elizabeth II, 90th Birthday A258

No. 1552 — Queen Elizabeth II: a, Holding parasol. b, Wearing coat.

**2016, May 10 Litho. *Perf. 13¼***
**1552** A258 $3 Sheet of 2, #a-b 8.25 8.25

Marae Moana Marine Park — A259

Designs: 30c, Sperm whales. 80c, Melon-headed whales. $1, Emblem of Marae Moana Marine Park. $1.10, Spinner dolphin. $1.30, Spotted dolphins. $1.50, Whale shark. $1.70, Tiger shark. $2, Staghorn coral. $2.40, Yellow scroll coral. $2.50, Black saddled coral groupers. $2.60, Green turtles. $3, Bristle-thighed curlews.

**2016, May 27 Litho. *Perf. 14¼x14¾***
**1553** A259 30c multi .40 .40
**1554** A259 80c multi 1.10 1.10
**1555** A259 $1 multi 1.40 1.40
**1556** A259 $1.10 multi 1.50 1.50
**1557** A259 $1.30 multi 1.75 1.75
**1558** A259 $1.50 multi 2.10 2.10
**1559** A259 $1.70 multi 2.40 2.40
**1560** A259 $2 multi 2.75 2.75
**1561** A259 $2.40 multi 3.25 3.25
**1562** A259 $2.50 multi 3.50 3.50
**1563** A259 $2.60 multi 3.50 3.50
**1564** A259 $3 multi 4.25 4.25
*Nos. 1553-1564 (12)* 27.90 27.90

New Year 2017 (Year of the Rooster) — A260

Designs: $2.30, Red rooster. $4.50, Turquoise blue rooster.

**2016, Aug. 10 Litho. *Perf. 13¼***
**1565-1566** A260 Set of 2 10.00 10.00
*1566a* Souvenir sheet of 2, #1565-1566 10.00 10.00

2016 Summer Olympics, Rio de Janeiro — A261

No. 1567: a, Sailing. b, Canoeing slalom. c, Weight lifting. d, Swimming. e, Track and field.

**2016, Sept. 6 Litho. *Perf. 13¾***
**1567** Horiz. strip of 5 15.00 15.00
***a.-e.*** A261 $2 Any single 3.00 3.00

A262

Christmas — A263

No. 1568: a, Stained-glass window depicting Holy Family. b, Five-sectioned stained-glass window.

No. 1569: a, Stained-glass window depicting Holy Family, diff. b, Two-sectioned stained-glass window.

**2016, Dec. 19 Litho. *Perf. 13¼***
**1568** A262 50c Vert. pair, #a-b 1.40 1.40
**1569** A263 $1 Vert. pair, #a-b 2.75 2.75

Miniature Sheet

Easter A264

No. 1570 — Paintings of the Resurrection of Jesus by: a, Giacomo Cavedone. b, Giovanni Battista Gaulli. c, Jan Alojzy Matejko. d, Tintoretto.

**2017, Apr. 12 Litho. *Perf. 13***
**1570** A264 $1Sheet of 4, #a-d 5.50 5.50

**Nos. 1521-1523 Surcharged**

**Methods and Perfs. As Before**
**2017, June 9**
**1571** A243 50c on $1.30 #1521 .75 .75
**1572** A243 50c on $1.50 #1522 .75 .75
**1573** A243 50c on $1.70 #1523 .75 .75
**1574** A243 $1 on $1.30 #1521 1.50 1.50
**1575** A243 $1 on $1.50 #1522 1.50 1.50
**1576** A243 $1 on $1.70 #1523 1.50 1.50
*Nos. 1571-1576 (6)* 6.75 6.75

Miniature Sheet

Pres. John F. Kennedy (1917-63) — A265

No. 1577: a, $1, Alan Shepard, Jr. (1923-98), astronaut, and Friedship 7 space capsule. b, $1, Pres. Kennedy looking in window of Friendship 7. c, $2.50, Pres. Kennedy signing Nuclear Test Ban Treaty. d, $2.50, Nuclear weapon test Bravo on Bikini Atoll.

**2017, July 3 Litho. *Perf. 13***
**1577** A265 Sheet of 4, #a-d 10.50 10.50

Miniature Sheet

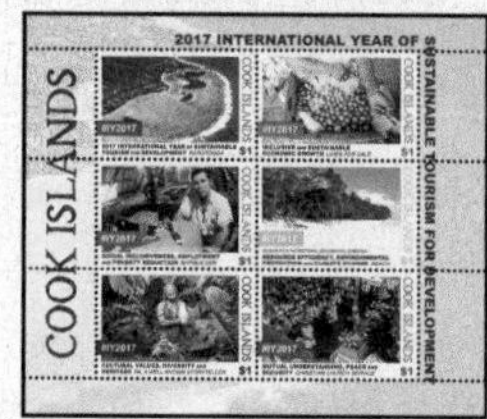

International Year of Sustainable Tourism for Development — A266

No. 1578: a, Aerial view of Rarotonga. b, Limes for sale. c, Shipbuilder. d, Beach. e, Pa, a well-known storyteller. f, Christian church service.

**2017, July 14 Litho. *Perf. 13***
**1578** A266 $1 Sheet of 6, #a-f 9.00 9.00

Miniature Sheet

Reign of Queen Elizabeth II, 65th Anniv. A267

No. 1579 — Queen Elizabeth II wearing: a, Turquoise blue hat. b, White hat with gray fringe and flower. c, White hat, Queen waving. d, Tiara.

**2017, July 17 Litho. *Perf. 13***
**1579** A267 $2.50 Sheet of 4, #a-d 15.00 15.00

Winning Photographs in Cook Islands News Memories of Summer Photography Contest — A268

Photograph: $1.60, Woman casting fishing net, by Pua Tua (third place). $2.40, Child splashing water, by Raita Rongo (second place). $4.80, Child in sprinkler stream, by Rongo (first place).

**2017, Aug. 28 Litho. *Perf. 13***
**1580-1582** A268 Set of 3 12.50 12.50

Worldwide Fund for Nature (WWF) — A269

Various depictions of bristle-thighed curlew: Nos. 1583, 1587a, $1. Nos. 1584, 1587b, $1.60. Nos. 1585, 1587c, $1.70. Nos. 1586, 1587d, $2.40.

**2017, Oct. 31 Litho. *Perf. 13x13¼***
**Stamps With White Frame**
**1583-1586** A269 Set of 4 9.25 9.25
**Stamps Without White Frame**
**1587** A269 Strip of 4, #a-d 9.25 9.25

No. 1587 was printed in sheets containing two strips. For surcharges, see Nos. 1690-1692.

New Year 2018 (Year of the Dog) — A270

Dog: $3, Standing. $3.80, Prone.

**2017, Nov. 1 Litho. *Perf. 13¼***
**1588-1589** A270 Set of 2 9.50 9.50
*1589a* Souvenir sheet of 2, #1588-1589 9.50 9.50

Christmas — A271

No. 1590, $1: a, Beach sandals. b, Star and bow.

No. 1591, $2.40: a, Christmas ornament on palm tree. b, Church.

**2017, Dec. 5 Litho. *Perf. 12½***
**Horiz. pairs, #a-b**
**1590-1591** A271 Set of 2 9.75 9.75

Miniature Sheet

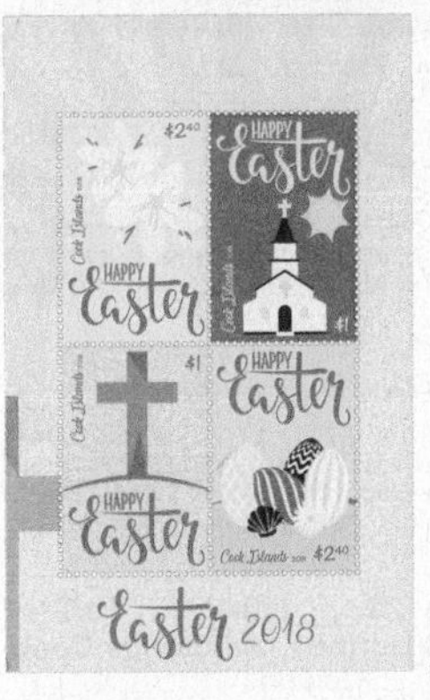

Easter A272

No. 1592: a, $1, Church. b. $1, Cross. c, $2.40, Flowers. d, $2.40, Easter eggs, shell and flower.

**2018, Mar. 19 Litho. *Perf. 13***

**1592** A272 Sheet of 4, #a-d 10.00 10.00

Souvenir Sheet

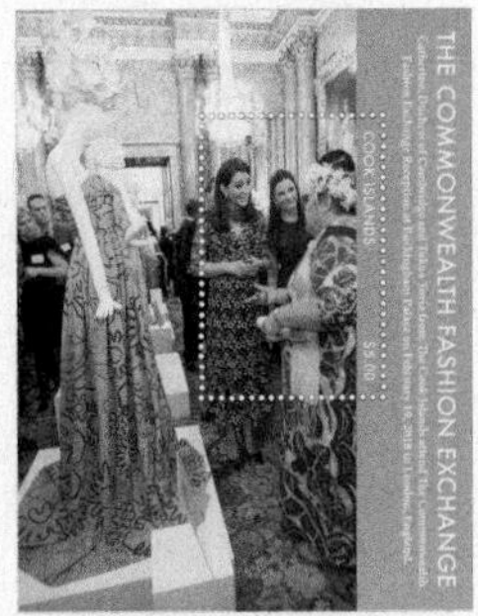

Dutchess of Cambridge at Commonwealth Fashion Exchange, London — A273

**2018, Apr. 10 Litho. *Perf. 13***

**1593** A273 $5 multi 7.00 7.00

2018 Birdpex Philatelic Exhibition, Mondorf-les-Bains, Luxembourg — A274

No. 1594: a, Short-tailed shearwater. b, Tropical shearwater.

**2018, May 4 Litho. *Perf. 13½x13***

**1594** A274 Horiz. pair 8.25 8.25
*a.* $1 multi 1.40 1.40
*b.* $4.80 multi 6.75 6.75

For surcharges, see No. 1632.

Souvenir Sheet

Birth of Prince Louis of Cambridge — A275

No. 1595: a, Prince George of Cambridge. b, Duke and Duchess of Cambridge holding Prince Louis. c, Princess Charlotte of Cambridge.

**2018, May 21 Litho. *Perf. 13***

**1595** A275 $2.40 Sheet of 3, #a-c 10.00 10.00

Wedding of Prince Harry and Meghan Markle A276

No. 1596 — Bride and groom: a, On church steps. b, Kissing.
$8, Bride and groom in carriage.

**2018, Aug. 2 Litho. *Perf. 13***

**1596** A276 $4.80 Sheet of 2, #a-b 12.50 12.50

Souvenir Sheet

**1597** A276 $8 multi 10.50 10.50

New Year 2019 (Year of the Pig) — A277

Pig facing: $3, Left. $3.80, Right.

**2018, Dec. 10 Litho. *Perf. 13½***

**1598-1599** A277 Set of 2 9.25 9.25

Miniature Sheets

Christmas — A278

No. 1600 — Details of religious paintings by: a, Raphael. b, Rogier van der Weyden. c, Bartolomeo Montagna. d, Carlo Crivelli. e, Guido Reni. f, Antonello da Messina.

No. 1601 — Details of religious paintings by: a, Raphael. b, Gerard David. c, Montagna. d, Peter Paul Rubens. e, Hans Memling. f, Sandro Botticelli.

**2018, Dec. 14 Litho. *Perf. 13***

**1600** A278 50c Sheet of 6, #a-f 4.00 4.00
**1601** A278 $1 Sheet of 6, #a-f 8.00 8.00

Birds — A279

Stamps inscribed "Cook Islands": Nos. 1602, 1614a, 20c, Swamp harrier. Nos. 1603, 1614b, 30c, Bateleur eagle. Nos. 1604, 1614c, 40c, Eurasian pygmy owls. Nos. 1605, 1614d, 50c, Madagascar harrier hawk. Nos. 1606, 1614e, $1, Barn owl. Nos. 1607, 1614f, $2, Japanese sparrowhawk. Nos. 1608, 1614g, $2.40, Hooded vultures. Nos. 1609, 1614h, $2.60, Booted eagle and chick. Nos. 1610, 1614i, $4.50, Whistling kite. Nos. 1611, 1614j, $5, Letter-winged kites. Nos. 1612, 1614k, $7.50, Egyptian vulture and eggs. Nos. 1613, 1614l, $10, Barking owls.

Stamps inscribed "Rarotonga Cook Islands": Nos. 1615, 1627a, 20c, Pale chanting goshawk. Nos. 1616, 1627b, 30c, Great horned owl. Nos. 1617, 1627c, 40c, Eurasian eagle owl. Nos. 1618, 1627d, 50c, Costa Rican pygmy owl. Nos. 1619, 1627e, $1, Jackal buzzard. Nos. 1620, 1627f, $2, Northern harrier. Nos. 1621, 1627g, $2.40, Eastern marsh harrier. Nos. 1622, 1627h, $2.60, Long-winged harrier. Nos. 1623, 1627i, $4.50, Asian barred owlet. Nos. 1624, 1627j, $5, Crested eagles. Nos. 1625, 1627k, $7.50, Lesser spotted eagle. Nos. 1626, 1627l, $10, White-browed hawk owl.

**2018, Dec. 20 Litho. *Perf. 13***

**Stamps Inscribed "Cook Islands"**

**Stamps With White Frames**

**1602** A279 20c multi .25 .25
**1603** A279 30c multi .40 .40
**1604** A279 40c multi .55 .55
**1605** A279 50c multi .65 .65
**1606** A279 $1 multi 1.40 1.40
**1607** A279 $2 multi 2.75 2.75
*a.* Souvenir sheet of 6, #1602-1607 6.00 6.00
**1608** A279 $2.40 multi 3.25 3.25
**1609** A279 $2.60 multi 3.50 3.50
**1610** A279 $4.50 multi 6.00 6.00
**1611** A279 $5 multi 6.75 6.75
**1612** A279 $7.50 multi 10.00 10.00
**1613** A279 $10 multi 13.50 13.50
*a.* Souvenir sheet of 6, #1608-1613 43.00 43.00
*Nos. 1602-1613 (12)* 49.00 49.00

**Stamps Without White Frames**

**1614** A279 Sheet of 12, #a-l 49.00 49.00

**Stamps Inscribed "Rarotonga Cook Islands"**

**Stamps With White Frames**

**1615** A279 20c multi .25 .25
**1616** A279 30c multi .40 .40
**1617** A279 40c multi .55 .55
**1618** A279 50c multi .65 .65
**1619** A279 $1 multi 1.40 1.40
**1620** A279 $2 multi 2.75 2.75
*a.* Souvenir sheet of 6, #1615-1620 6.00 6.00
**1621** A279 $2.40 multi 3.25 3.25
**1622** A279 $2.60 multi 3.50 3.50
**1623** A279 $4.50 multi 6.00 6.00
**1624** A279 $5 multi 6.75 6.75
**1625** A279 $7.50 multi 10.00 10.00
**1626** A279 $10 multi 13.50 13.50
*a.* Souvenir sheet of 6, #1621-1626 43.00 43.00
*Nos. 1615-1626 (12)* 49.00 49.00

**Stamps Without White Frames**

**1627** A279 Sheet of 12, #a-l 49.00 49.00

Nos. 1607a, 1613a, 1620a and 1626a have stamps with white frames on one or two sides.

See Nos. 1640-1649, 1650-1659, 1670-1674, 1675-1679, 1703-1707, 1708-1712.

Suwarrow Atoll National Park — A280

No. 1628: a, Frigatebird and Red-footed booby. b, Masked boobies. c, Two people conducting seabird survey. d, Four people conducting seabird study. e, Coconut crab. f, Brown booby juvenile.
$4.50, Frigatebird chick in nest.

**2019, May 30 Litho. *Perf. 13***

**1628** A280 50c Sheet of 6, #a-f 4.00 4.00

Souvenir Sheet

***Perf. 13¼x13***

**1629** A280 $4.50 multi 6.00 6.00

No. 1629 contains one 48x40mm stamp.

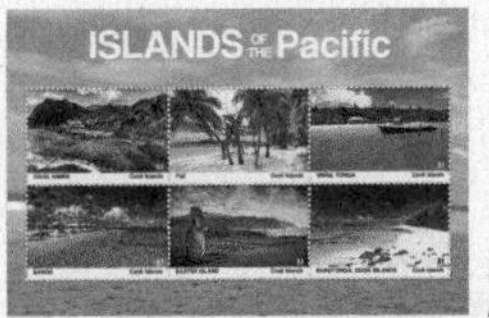


Islands A281

No. 1630: a, Oahu, Hawaii. b, Fiji. c, Vavau, Tonga. d, Samoa. e, Easter Island. f, Rarotonga, Cook Islands.
$10, Mitre Peak and Milford Sound, South Island, New Zealand.

**2019, June 11 Litho. *Perf. 13***

**1630** A281 $1 Sheet of 6, #a-f 8.00 8.00

Souvenir Sheet

***Perf. 13¼x13***

**1631** A281 $10 multi 13.50 13.50

No. 1631 contains one 48x40mm stamp.

**No. 1594 Surcharged**

**Methods and Perfs. As Before**

**2019, June 19**

**1632** A274 Horiz. pair 1.40 1.40
*a.* 50c on $1 #1594a .70 .70
*b.* 50c on $4.80 #1594b .70 .70

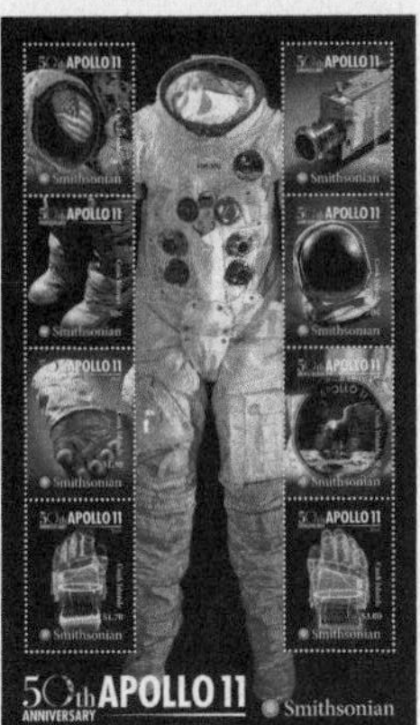


Flight of Apollo 11, 50th Anniv. A282

No. 1633: a, 30c, Reflections of U.S. flag in visors of astronaut's helmets. b, 40c, Video camera. c, 50c, Astronaut's boots. d, 70c, Astronaut's helmets. e, $1.30, Astronaut's glove. f, $1.50, Apollo 11 mission patch on space suit. g, $1.70, Wiring in left hand glove. h, $3, Wiring in right hand glove.

No. 1634, horiz.: a, $1.10, Camera. b, $2.60, Astronaut near Lunar Module on Moon, shadow of astronaut. c, $5, Astronaut's footprint on Moon.

No. 1635: a, $1, Lunar Module leaving Moon. b, $2, Astronaut in Command Module. c, $2.50, Soldiers in life raft approaching Command Module in ocean. d, $4, Astronaut's mobile quarantine facility.

**2019, June 19 Litho. *Perf. 13¼x13***

**1633** A282 Sheet of 8, #a-h 12.50 12.50

***Perf. 13x13¼***

**1634** A282 Sheet of 3, #a-c 12.00 12.00

***Perf. 13***

**1635** A282 Sheet of 4, #a-d 13.00 13.00
*Nos. 1633-1635 (3)* 37.50 37.50

No. 1635 contains four 40x40mm stamps.

New Year 2020 (Year of the Rat) — A283

Stamps inscribed "Cook Islands" — Rat with front legs at: $3, Left. $3.80. Right.

Stamps inscribed "Rarotonga": $3, Rats and jar. $3.80, Three rats.

**2019, Oct. 11 Litho. *Perf. 13¼***

**Stamps Inscribed "Cook Islands"**

**1636-1637** A283 Set of 2 8.75 8.75

**Stamps Inscribed "Rarotonga"**

**1638-1639** A283 Set of 2 8.75 8.75

**Birds Type of 2018**

Stamps inscribed "Cook Islands": Nos. 1640, 1644a, $2.50, White-backed vulture. Nos. 1641, 1644b, $20.60, Red-backed hawk. Nos. 1642, 1644c, $25, Galapagos hawk and juveniles. Nos. 1643, 1644d, $30, Wedge-tailed eagle.

Stamps inscribed "Rarotonga Cook Islands": Nos. 1645, 1649a, $2.50, Levant sparrowhawk. Nos. 1646, 1649b, $3, Zone-tailed hawk. Nos. 1647, 1649c, $4, Roadside hawk. Nos. 1648, 1649d, $6, Harris's hawk.

**2019, Nov. 15 Litho. *Perf. 13***

**Stamps Inscribed "Cook Islands"**

**Stamps With White Frames**

**1640** A279 $2.50 multi 3.25 3.25
**1641** A279 $20.60 multi 27.00 27.00
**1642** A279 $25 multi 32.50 32.50
**1643** A279 $30 multi 39.00 39.00
*Nos. 1640-1643 (4)* 101.75 101.75

**Stamps Without White Frames**

**Stamp Size: 48x40mm**

***Perf. 13¼x13***

**1644** A279 Block or vert. strip of 4, #a-d 102.00 102.00
*e.* Souvenir sheet of 4, #1644a-1644d 102.00 102.00

### Stamps Inscribed "Rarotonga Cook Islands"
### Stamps With White Frames

*Perf. 13*

**1645** A279 $2.50 multi 3.25 3.25
**1646** A279 $3 multi 4.00 4.00
**1647** A279 $4 multi 5.25 5.25
**1648** A279 $6 multi 8.00 8.00
*Nos. 1645-1648 (4)* 20.50 20.50

### Stamps Without White Frames
### Stamp Size: 48x40mm

*Perf. 13¼x13*

**1649** A279 Block or vert. strip of 4, #a-d 20.50 20.50
*e.* Souvenir sheet of 4, #1649a-1649d 20.50 20.50

Stamps from Nos. 1644e and 1649e have white frames on two sides.

### Birds Type of 2018

Stamps inscribed "Cook Islands": Nos. 1650, 1654a, $5.50, Military macaw. Nos. 1651, 1654b, $6.70, Blue-and-yellow macaw. Nos. 1652, 1654c, $22.40, Red-and-green macaw. Nos. 1653, 1654d, $29.90, Red-fronted macaw.

Stamps inscribed "Rarotonga Cook Islands": Nos. 1655, 1659a, $5.50, Long-tailed sylph, vert. Nos. 1656, 1659b, $6.70, Violet-crowned woodnymph, vert. Nos. 1657, 1659c, $22.40, Sword-billed hummingbird, vert. Nos. 1658, 1659d, $22.90, Green hermit, vert.

**2019, Nov. 20** **Litho.** ***Perf. 13***

### Stamps Inscribed "Cook Islands"
### Stamps With White Frames

**1650** A279 $5.50 multi 7.25 7.25
**1651** A279 $6.70 multi 8.75 8.75
**1652** A279 $22.40 multi 29.00 29.00
**1653** A279 $29.90 multi 39.00 39.00
*Nos. 1650-1653 (4)* 84.00 84.00

### Stamps Without White Frames
### Stamp Size: 48x40mm

*Perf. 13¼x13*

**1654** A279 Block or vert. strip of 4, #a-d 84.00 84.00
*e.* Souvenir sheet of 4, #1654a-1654d 84.00 84.00

### Stamps Inscribed "Rarotonga Cook Islands"
### Stamps With White Frames

*Perf. 13*

**1655** A279 $5.50 multi 7.25 7.25
**1656** A279 $6.70 multi 8.75 8.75
**1657** A279 $22.40 multi 29.00 29.00
**1658** A279 $22.90 multi 30.00 30.00
*Nos. 1655-1658 (4)* 75.00 75.00

### Stamps Without White Frames
### Stamp Size: 48x40mm

*Perf. 13x13¼*

**1659** A279 Block or vert. strip of 4, #a-d 75.00 75.00
*e.* Souvenir sheet of 4, #1659a-1659d 75.00 75.00

Stamps from Nos. 1654e and 1659e have white frames on two sides.

Butterflies A284

Designs: Nos. 1660, 1668a, 50c, Richmond birdwing butterfly. Nos. 1661, 1668b, $1, Purple emperor butterfly. Nos. 1662, 1668c, $5, Sapho longwing butterfly. Nos. 1663, 1668d, $7, Spicebush swallowtail butterfly. Nos. 1664, 1669a, $10, Silvery blue butterfly. Nos. 1665, 1669b, $20, Common Saturn butterfly. Nos 1666, 1669c, $30, Common banded peacock butterfly. Nos. 1667, 1669d, $34.70, Monarch butterfly.

**2020, Jan. 13** **Litho.** ***Perf. 13***

### Stamps Inscribed "Cook Islands"
### Stamps With White Frames

**1660** A284 50c multi .65 .65
**1661** A284 $1 multi 1.30 1.30
**1662** A284 $5 multi 6.50 6.50
**1663** A284 $7 multi 9.00 9.00
**1664** A284 $10 multi 13.00 13.00
**1665** A284 $20 multi 26.00 26.00
**1666** A284 $30 multi 39.00 39.00
**1667** A284 $34.70 multi 45.00 45.00
*Nos. 1660-1667 (8)* 140.45 140.45

### Stamps Without White Frames
### Stamp Size: 48x40mm

*Perf. 13¼x13*

**1668** A284 Block or vert. strip of 4, #a-d 17.50 17.50
*e.* Souvenir sheet of 4, #1668a-1668d 17.50 17.50
**1669** A284 Block or vert. strip of 4, #a-d 125.00 125.00
*e.* Souvenir sheet of 4, #1669a-1669d 125.00 125.00

Nos. 1668a-1668d and 1669a-1669d were printed in sheets of 8 containing two of each stamp. Stamps on Nos. 1668e and 1669e have white frames on two adjacent sides.

See Nos. 1713-1722.

### Birds Type of 2018

Kingfishers: Nos. 1670, 1674a, $2.50, Yellow-billed kingfisher. Nos. 1671, 1674b, $3, Common kingfisher. Nos. 1672, 1674c, $4, Blue-winged kookaburra. Nos. 1673, 1674d, $6, Collared kingfishers.

**2020, May 8** **Litho.** ***Perf. 13***

### Stamps Inscribed "Cook Islands"
### Stamps With White Frames

**1670** A279 $2.50 multi 3.25 3.25
**1671** A279 $3 multi 3.75 3.75
**1672** A279 $4 multi 5.00 5.00
**1673** A279 $6 multi 7.50 7.50
*Nos. 1670-1673 (4)* 19.50 19.50

### Stamps Without White Frames
### Stamp Size: 48x40mm

*Perf. 13¼x13*

**1674** A279 Block or vert. strip of 4, #a-d 19.50 19.50
*e.* Souvenir sheet of 4, #1674a-1674d 19.50 19.50

Nos. 1674a-1674d were printed in sheets of 8 containing two of each stamp. Stamps on No. 1674e have white frames on two adjacent sides.

### Birds Type of 2018

Ducks: Nos. 1675, 1679a, $5.50, Black-bellied whistling ducks. Nos. 1676, 1679b, $6.70, King eider. Nos. 1677, 1679c, $22.40, Common goldeneye. Nos. 1678, 1679d, $29.90, Mandarin duck.

**2020, May 20** **Litho.** ***Perf. 13***

### Stamps Inscribed "Cook Islands"
### Stamps With White Frames

**1675** A279 $5.50 multi 7.00 7.00
**1676** A279 $6.70 multi 8.50 8.50
**1677** A279 $22.40 multi 28.00 28.00
**1678** A279 $29.90 multi 37.50 37.50
*Nos. 1675-1678 (4)* 81.00 81.00

### Stamps Without White Frames
### Stamp Size: 48x40mm

*Perf. 13¼x13*

**1679** A279 Block or vert. strip of 4, #a-d 81.00 81.00
*e.* Souvenir sheet of 4, #1679a-1679d 81.00 81.00

Nos. 1679a-1679d were printed in sheets of 8 containing two of each stamp. Stamps on No. 1679e have white frames on two adjacent sides.

Dolphins and Whales — A285

Designs: Nos. 1680, 1688a, 50c, Spinner dolphin. Nos. 1681, 1688b, $1, Striped dolphin. Nos. 1682, 1688c, $5, Blue whale. Nos. 1683, 1688d, $7, Sperm whale. Nos. 1684, 1689a, $10, Short-beaked common dolphin. Nos. 1685, 1689b, $20, Killer whale. Nos 1686, 1689c, $30, Humpback whale. Nos. 1687, 1689d, $34.70, Atlantic spotted dolphin.

**2020, June 15** **Litho.** ***Perf. 13***

### Stamps Inscribed "Cook Islands"
### Stamps With White Frames

**1680** A285 50c multi .65 .65
**1681** A285 $1 multi 1.30 1.30
**1682** A285 $5 multi 6.50 6.50
**1683** A285 $7 multi 9.00 9.00
**1684** A285 $10 multi 13.00 13.00
**1685** A285 $20 multi 26.00 26.00
**1686** A285 $30 multi 39.00 39.00
**1687** A285 $34.70 multi 45.00 45.00
*Nos. 1680-1687 (8)* 140.45 140.45

### Stamps Without White Frames
### Stamp Size: 48x40mm

*Perf. 13¼x13*

**1688** A285 Block or vert. strip of 4, #a-d 17.50 17.50
*e.* Souvenir sheet of 4, #1688a-1688d 17.50 17.50
**1689** A285 Block or vert. strip of 4, #a-d 125.00 125.00
*e.* Souvenir sheet of 4, #1689a-1689d 125.00 125.00

Nos. 1688a-1688d and 1689a-1689d were printed in sheets of 8 containing two of each stamp. Stamps on Nos. 1688e and 1689e have white frames on two adjacent sides.

### Nos. 1584-1586 Surcharged

### Methods and Perfs. As Before

**2020, Dec. 29**

**1690** A269 70c on $1.70 #1585 1.00 1.00
**1691** A269 $5.30 on $1.60 #1584 7.75 7.75
**1692** A269 $8.50 on $2.40 #1586 12.50 12.50
*Nos. 1690-1692 (3)* 21.25 21.25

Turtles — A286

Designs: Nos. 1693, 1701a, 50c, Hawksbill sea turtle. Nos. 1694, 1701b, $1, Hawksbill sea turtle, diff. Nos. 1695, 1701c, $5, Hawksbill sea turtle, diff. Nos. 1696, 1701d, $7, Hawksbill sea turtle, diff. Nos. 1697, 1702a, $10, Green sea turtle. Nos. 1698, 1702b, $20, Green sea turtle, diff. Nos 1699, 1702c, $30, Green sea turtle, diff. Nos. 1700, 1702d, $34.70, Green sea turtle, diff.

**2020, Jan. 13** **Litho.** ***Perf. 13***

### Stamps Inscribed "Rarotonga Cook Islands"
### Stamps With White Frames

**1693** A286 50c multi .65 .65
**1694** A286 $1 multi 1.30 1.30
**1695** A286 $5 multi 6.50 6.50
**1696** A286 $7 multi 9.00 9.00
**1697** A286 $10 multi 13.00 13.00
**1698** A286 $20 multi 26.00 26.00
**1699** A286 $30 multi 39.00 39.00
**1700** A286 $34.70 multi 45.00 45.00
*Nos. 1693-1700 (8)* 140.45 140.45

### Stamps Without White Frames
### Stamp Size: 48x40mm

*Perf. 13¼x13*

**1701** A286 Block or vert. strip of 4, #a-d 17.50 17.50
*e.* Souvenir sheet of 4, #1701a-1701d 17.50 17.50
**1702** A286 Block or vert. strip of 4, #a-d 125.00 125.00
*e.* Souvenir sheet of 4, #1702a-1702d 125.00 125.00

Nos. 1701a-1701d and 1702a-1702d were printed in sheets of 8 containing two of each stamp. Stamps on Nos. 1701e and 1702e have white frames on two adjacent sides.

### Birds Type of 2018

Parrots: Nos. 1703, 1707a, $2.50, Lilac-crowned parrot. Nos. 1704, 1707b, $3, Sun conure. Nos. 1705, 1707c, $4, Hyacinth macaw. Nos. 1706, 1707d, $6, Sipix's macaw.

**2020, May 8** **Litho.** ***Perf. 13***

### Stamps Inscribed "Rarotonga Cook Islands"
### Stamps With White Frames

**1703** A279 $2.50 multi 3.25 3.25
**1704** A279 $3 multi 3.75 3.75
**1705** A279 $4 multi 5.00 5.00
**1706** A279 $6 multi 7.50 7.50
*Nos. 1703-1706 (4)* 19.50 19.50

### Stamps Without White Frames
### Stamp Size: 48x40mm

*Perf. 13¼x13*

**1707** A279 Block or vert. strip of 4, #a-d 19.50 19.50
*e.* Souvenir sheet of 4, #1707a-1707d 19.50 19.50

Nos. 1707a-1707d were printed in sheets of 8 containing two of each stamp. Stamps on No. 1707e have white frames on two adjacent sides.

### Birds Type of 2018

Herons: Nos. 1708, 1712a, $5.50, Great blue heron. Nos. 1709, 1712b, $6.70, Boat-billed heron. Nos. 1710, 1712c, $22.40, Black-crowned night heron. Nos. 1711, 1712d, $29.90, Goliath heron.

**2020, May 20** **Litho.** ***Perf. 13***

### Stamps Inscribed "Rarotonga Cook Islands"
### Stamps With White Frames

**1708** A279 $5.50 multi 7.00 7.00
**1709** A279 $6.70 multi 8.50 8.50
**1710** A279 $22.40 multi 28.00 28.00
**1711** A279 $29.90 multi 37.50 37.50
*Nos. 1708-1711 (4)* 81.00 81.00

### Stamps Without White Frames
### Stamp Size: 48x40mm

*Perf. 13¼x13*

**1712** A279 Block or vert. strip of 4, #a-d 81.00 81.00
*e.* Souvenir sheet of 4, #1712a-1712d 81.00 81.00

Nos. 1712a-1712d were printed in sheets of 8 containing two of each stamp. Stamps on No. 1712e have white frames on two adjacent sides.

### Butterflies Type of 2020

Designs: Nos. 1713, 1721a, 50c, Adonis blue butterfly. Nos. 1714, 1721b, $1, Black hairstreak butterfly. Nos. 1715, 1721c, $5, Essex skipper butterfly. Nos. 1716, 1721d, $7, Dingy skipper butterfly. Nos. 1717, 1722a, $10, Heath fritillary butterfly. Nos. 1718, 1722b, $20, Brown hairstreak butterfly. Nos 1719, 1722c, $30, Orange-tip butterfly. Nos. 1720, 1722d, $34.70, Large skipper butterfly.

**2020, June 15** **Litho.** ***Perf. 13***

### Stamps Inscribed "Rarotonga Cook Islands"
### Stamps With White Frames

**1713** A284 50c multi .65 .65
**1714** A284 $1 multi 1.30 1.30
**1715** A284 $5 multi 6.50 6.50
**1716** A284 $7 multi 9.00 9.00
**1717** A284 $10 multi 13.00 13.00
**1718** A284 $20 multi 26.00 26.00
**1719** A284 $30 multi 39.00 39.00
**1720** A284 $34.70 multi 45.00 45.00
*Nos. 1713-1720 (8)* 140.45 140.45

### Stamps Without White Frames
### Stamp Size: 48x40mm

*Perf. 13¼x13*

**1721** A284 Block or vert. strip of 4, #a-d 17.50 17.50
*e.* Souvenir sheet of 4, #1721a-1721d 17.50 17.50
**1722** A284 Block or vert. strip of 4, #a-d 125.00 125.00
*e.* Souvenir sheet of 4, #1722a-1722d 125.00 125.00

Nos. 1721a-1721d and 1722a-1722d were printed in sheets of 8 containing two of each stamp. Stamps on Nos. 1721e and 1722e have white frames on two adjacent sides.

Miniature Sheet

Easter A287

No. 1723 — Religious paintings by: a, Leonardo da Vinci. b, Pieter Bruegel the Elder. c, Caravaggio. d, Antonio Ciseri. e, José de Madrazo. f, Tiziano Vecellio (Titian).

**2021, Apr. 2** **Litho.** ***Perf. 13***

**1723** A287 $1 Sheet of 6, #a-f 8.75 8.75

Souvenir Sheet

New Year 2021 (Year of the Ox) A288

**2021, Apr. 7 Litho.** *Perf. 13¼x13*
**1724** A288 $5.50 multi 8.00 8.00

American Bison — A289

Various depictions of American bisons: 50c, $1, $1.30, $5.
$10, American bisons.

**2021, May 5 Litho.** *Perf. 13*
**1725-1728** A289 Set of 4 11.50 11.50

**Souvenir Sheet**

*Perf. 13¼x13*

**1729** A289 $10 multi 14.50 14.50

No. 1729 contains one 48x40mm stamp.

A290

1962 Spaceflight of Friendship 7 — A291

No. 1730: a, Space helmet used by astronaut John H. Glenn, Jr. (1921-2016) in Friendship 7 flight. b, Glenn in spacesuit, Friendship 7. c, Friendship 7. d, Spacesuit worn by Glenn.
$5.30, Pres. John F. Kennedy looking through hatch of Friendship 7, horiz.

**2021, May 5 Litho.** *Perf. 13*
**1730** A290 $1.50 Sheet of 4, #a-d 8.25 8.25

**Souvenir Sheet**

*Perf. 13¼x13*

**1731** A291 $5.30 multi 7.75 7.75

Souvenir Sheets

A292

Items in Smithsonian Institution Collections — A293

No. 1732: a, Flower, Smithsonian Gardens. b, Fish, National Fish Collection. c, Elephant, National Zoo. d, Grasshopper, O. Orkin Insect Zoo. e, Corals. f, Mineral crystal.
No. 1733: a, Electric guitar, Division of Cultural and Community Life. b, Quilt, National Quilt Collection. c, Austrian airline poster, Aviation Poster Collection. d, Machine, Division of Work and Industry. e, Cover of *From the Earth to the Moon,* by Jules Verne, Smithsonian Libraries and Archives. f, Hope Diamond, National Gem Collection.

**2021, May 5 Litho.** *Perf. 13*
**1732** A292 10c Sheet of 6, #a-f .90 .90
**1733** A293 70c Sheet of 6, #a-f 6.25 6.25

## SEMI-POSTAL STAMPS

**Catalogue values for unused stamps in this section are for Never Hinged items.**

### Nos. 203-204, 223, 210, 213, 215-216 Surcharged

No. B1

No. B3

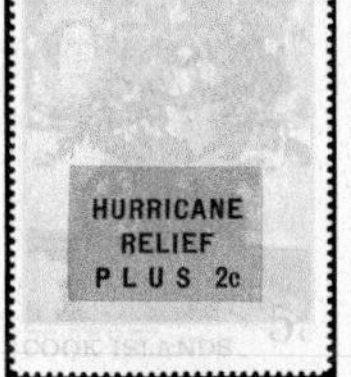


No. B7

*Perf. 14x13½, 13½*

**1968, Feb. 12** **Photo.**
**B1** A34 3c + 1c multi .25 .25
**B2** A34 4c + 1c multi .25 .25
**B3** A37 5c + 2c multi .25 .25
**B4** A34 10c + 2c multi .25 .25
**B5** A34 25c + 5c multi .30 .30
**B6** A34 50c + 10c multi .60 .60
**B7** A35 $1 + 10c multi 1.00 1.00
*Nos. B1-B7 (7)* 2.90 2.90

Surtax for the victims of hurricane of Dec. 15-18, 1967. The surcharge on No. B3 is printed on a silver rectangle. The surcharge on No. B7 is in smaller type with serifs, measuring 7½mm in depth.

Nos. 210, 213-214 Surcharged in Ultramarine

**1971, Sept. 8 Photo.** *Perf. 14x13½*
**B8** A34 10c + 1c multi .25 .25
**B9** A34 10c + 3c multi .25 .25
**B10** A34 25c + 1c multi .40 .40
**B11** A34 25c + 3c multi .40 .40
**B12** A34 30c + 1c multi .50 .50
**B13** A34 30c + 3c multi .50 .50
*Nos. B8-B13 (6)* 2.30 2.30

4th South Pacific Games, Papeete, French Polynesia, Sept. 8-19.

### Christmas Type of Regular Issue

Souvenir Sheet

50c+5c, Holy Family in a Garland of Flowers, by Jan Brueghel and Pieter van Avont.

**1971, Nov. 30 Photo.** *Perf. 13½*
**B14** A50 50c + 5c gold & multi 1.10 1.10

No. B14 contains one stamp 45x40mm.

### Nos. 316-318, 211, 213 and 215 Surcharged in Red or Black

a

b

**1972, Mar. 30 Photo.** *Perf. 13½*
**B15** A46(a) 5c + 2c multi (R) .25 .25
**B16** A46(a) 10c + 2c multi (R) .25 .25
**B17** A34(b) 15c + 5c multi .25 .25
**B18** A34(b) 25c + 5c multi .40 .40
**B19** A46(a) 30c + 5c multi (R) .50 .50
**B20** A34(b) 50c + 10c multi .60 .60
*Nos. B15-B20 (6)* 2.25 2.25

Surtax for victims of hurricane of Mar. 22-26.

### Nos. 319-322c with Surcharge Similar to Type "a"

**1972, May 24 Photo.** *Perf. 13½*
**B21** A51 5c + 2c, pair, #a.-b. .35 .35
**B22** A51 10c + 2c, pair, #a.-b. .45 .45
**B23** A51 25c + 2c, pair, #a.-b. .55 .55
**B24** A51 30c + 2c, pair, #a.-b. .65 .65
*c.* Souvenir sheet of 8 3.50 3.50
*Nos. B21-B24 (4)* 2.00 2.00

Surtax for victims of hurricane of Mar. 22-26. Stamps of No. B24c each surcharged 3c.

### Olympic Type of Regular Issue

Souvenir Sheet

50c+5c, Pierre de Coubertin, Olympic rings.

**1972, June 26**
**B29** A52 50c + 5c multi 2.00 2.00

### Christmas Type of Regular Issue

Souvenir Sheet

Design: 50c+5c, Nativity, by Correggio.

**1972, Oct. 11 Photo.** *Perf. 13½*
**B30** A53 50c + 5c multi 1.50 1.25

No. B30 contains one stamp 30x40mm.

### Easter Type of Regular Issue

Souvenir Sheets

**1973, Apr. 30 Photo.** *Perf. 13½x14*
**B31** A56 50c + 5c like #346 .50 .50
**B32** A56 50c + 5c like #347 .50 .50
**B33** A56 50c + 5c like #348 .50 .50
*Nos. B31-B33 (3)* 1.50 1.50

Surtax was for school children.

### Christmas Type of Regular Issue

Souvenir Sheets

**1973, Dec. 3 Photo.** *Perf. 13x13½*
**B34** A59 50c + 5c like #364 .35 .35
**B35** A59 50c + 5c like #365 .35 .35
**B36** A59 50c + 5c like #366 .35 .35
**B37** A59 50c + 5c like #367 .35 .35
**B38** A59 50c + 5c like #368 .35 .35
*Nos. B34-B38 (5)* 1.75 1.75

Surtax was for school children.

### Easter Type of 1973

Dated "1974"

Souvenir Sheets

**1974, Apr. 22** *Perf. 13½x14*
**B39** A56 50c + 5c like #378 .50 .50
**B40** A56 50c + 5c like #379 .50 .50
**B41** A56 50c + 5c like #380 .50 .50
*Nos. B39-B41 (3)* 1.50 1.50

### Christmas Type of 1974

Souvenir Sheets

**1974 Photo.** *Perf. 13½x13*
**B42** A68 50c + 5c like #412 .35 .35
**B43** A68 50c + 5c like #413 .35 .35
**B44** A68 50c + 5c like #414 .35 .35
**B45** A68 50c + 5c like #415 .35 .35
**B46** A68 50c + 5c like #416 .35 .35
*Nos. B42-B46 (5)* 1.75 1.75

### Christmas Type of 1975

Souvenir Sheets

**1975, Dec. 1** *Perf. 13½*
**B47** A75 75c + 5c like #437 .50 .50
**B48** A75 75c + 5c like #438 .50 .50
**B49** A75 75c + 5c like #439 .50 .50
**B50** A75 75c + 5c like #440 .50 .50
**B51** A75 75c + 5c like #441 .50 .50
*Nos. B47-B51 (5)* 2.50 2.50

Size of stamps: 23x40mm.

### Easter Type of 1976

Souvenir Sheets

**1976, May 3 Photo.** *Perf. 13½*
**B52** A76 60c + 5c like #442 .55 .55
**B53** A76 60c + 5c like #443 .55 .55
**B54** A76 60c + 5c like #444 .55 .55
*Nos. B52-B54 (3)* 1.65 1.65

Size of stamps: 36x36mm.

### Christmas Type of 1976

Souvenir Sheets

**1976, Nov. 2 Photo.** *Perf. 14x13½*
**B55** A80 75c + 5c like #459 .50 .50
**B56** A80 75c + 5c like #460 .50 .50
**B57** A80 75c + 5c like #461 .50 .50
**B58** A80 75c + 5c like #462 .50 .50
**B59** A80 75c + 5c like #463 .50 .50
*Nos. B55-B59 (5)* 2.50 2.50

### Easter Type of 1977

Souvenir Sheets

**1977, Apr. 18 Photo.** *Perf. 13½x14*
**B60** A83 60c + 5c like #471 .60 .60
**B61** A83 60c + 5c like #472 .60 .60
**B62** A83 60c + 5c like #473 .60 .60
*Nos. B60-B62 (3)* 1.80 1.80

Size of stamps: 30x42mm.

### Christmas Type of 1977

Souvenir Sheets

**1977, Oct. 31 Photo.** *Perf. 14x13½*
**B63** A84 75c + 5c like #474 .45 .45
**B64** A84 75c + 5c like #475 .45 .45
**B65** A84 75c + 5c like #476 .45 .45
**B66** A84 75c + 5c like #477 .45 .45
**B67** A84 75c + 5c like #478 .45 .45
*Nos. B63-B67 (5)* 2.25 2.25

### Easter Type of 1978

Souvenir Sheets

**1978, Apr. 10 Photo.** *Perf. 14x13½*
**B68** A87 60c + 5c like #483 .45 .45
**B69** A87 60c + 5c like #484 .45 .45
**B70** A87 60c + 5c like #485 .45 .45
*Nos. B68-B70 (3)* 1.35 1.35

### Christmas Type of 1978

Souvenir Sheets

**1979, Jan. 12 Photo.** *Perf. 13*
**B71** A89 75c + 5c like #503 .45 .45
**B72** A89 75c + 5c like #504 .45 .45
**B73** A89 75c + 5c like #505 .45 .45
*Nos. B71-B73 (3)* 1.35 1.35

### Easter Type of 1979

Souvenir Sheet

**1979, Apr. 5 Photo.** *Perf. 13*
**B74** Sheet of 4 1.00 1.00
*a.* A90 10c + 2c like #506 .25 .25
*b.* A90 12c + 2c like #507 .25 .25
*c.* A90 15c + 2c like #508 .25 .25
*d.* A90 20c + 2c like #509 .25 .25

### IYC Type of 1979

Souvenir Sheet

**1979, Oct. 10**
**B75** Sheet of 3 1.40 1.40
*a.* A93 30c + 5c like #529 .30 .30
*b.* A93 50c + 5c like #530 .40 .40
*c.* A93 65c + 5c like #531 .50 .50

### Christmas Type of 1979

**1980, Jan. 15 Photo. *Perf. 14***

| | | | | |
|---|---|---|---|---|
| **B76** | A95 | 6c + 2c like #537 | .25 | .25 |
| **B77** | A95 | 10c + 2c like #538 | .25 | .25 |
| **B78** | A95 | 12c + 2c like #539 | .25 | .25 |
| **B79** | A95 | 15c + 2c like #540 | .25 | .25 |
| | | *Nos. B76-B79 (4)* | 1.00 | 1.00 |

### Easter Type of 1980
Souvenir Sheets

**1980, Mar. 31 Photo. *Perf. 13***

| | | | | |
|---|---|---|---|---|
| **B80** | A96 | Sheet of 6, #a.-f. | 1.40 | 1.40 |

No. B80 contains Nos. 541-543, each stamp with 2c surcharge.

**1980, Apr. 23 Souvenir Sheets**

| | | | | |
|---|---|---|---|---|
| **B81** | A96 | 75c + 5c like #541a | .50 | .50 |
| **B82** | A96 | 75c + 5c like #541b | .50 | .50 |
| **B83** | A96 | 75c + 5c like #542a | .50 | .50 |
| **B84** | A96 | 75c + 5c like #542b | .50 | .50 |
| **B85** | A96 | 75c + 5c like #543a | .50 | .50 |
| **B86** | A96 | 75c + 5c like #543b | .50 | .50 |
| | | *Nos. B81-B86 (6)* | 3.00 | 3.00 |

Surtax was for school children.

### Rotary Type of 1980
Souvenir Sheet

**1980, May 27 Photo. *Perf. 14***

| | | | | |
|---|---|---|---|---|
| **B87** | | Sheet of 3 | 1.50 | 1.50 |
| *a.* | A97 | 30c + 3c like #547 | .35 | .35 |
| *b.* | A97 | 35c + 3c like #548 | .45 | .45 |
| *c.* | A97 | 50c + 3c like #549 | .60 | .60 |

### Christmas Type of 1980
Souvenir Sheets

**1981, Jan. 9 Photo. *Imperf.***

| | | | | |
|---|---|---|---|---|
| **B88** | A102a | 75c + 5c like #652 | .50 | .50 |
| **B89** | A102a | 75c + 5c like #653 | .50 | .50 |
| **B90** | A102a | 75c + 5c like #654 | .50 | .50 |
| **B91** | A102a | 75c + 5c like #655 | .50 | .50 |
| | | *Nos. B88-B91 (4)* | 2.00 | 2.00 |

### Easter Type of 1981
Souvenir Sheets

**1981, Apr. 10 Photo. *Perf. 13½***

| | | | | |
|---|---|---|---|---|
| **B92** | | Sheet of 3 | 1.20 | 1.20 |
| *a.* | A103 | 15c + 2c like #656 | .25 | .25 |
| *b.* | A103 | 25c + 2c like #657 | .30 | .30 |
| *c.* | A103 | 40c + 2c like #658 | .50 | .50 |

**1981, Apr. 28 *Imperf.***

| | | | | |
|---|---|---|---|---|
| **B93** | A103 | 75c + 5c like #656 | .65 | .65 |
| **B94** | A103 | 75c + 5c like #657 | .65 | .65 |
| **B95** | A103 | 75c + 5c like #658 | .65 | .65 |
| | | *Nos. B93-B95 (3)* | 1.95 | 1.95 |

Surtax was for school children.

### Espana '82 Soccer Type
Souvenir Sheet

**1981 Photo. *Perf. 13½***

| | | | | |
|---|---|---|---|---|
| **B96** | A105 | Sheet of 8, #a.-h. | 6.50 | 6.50 |

No. B96 contains Nos. 661-664, each stamp with 3c surcharge.

### Royal Wedding Type of 1981
Nos. 659-660a Surcharged in Black

**1981, Nov. 10 Photo. *Perf. 14***

| | | | | |
|---|---|---|---|---|
| **B97** | A104 | $1 + 5c multi | .75 | *1.50* |
| **B98** | A104 | $2 + 5c multi | 1.50 | *2.50* |
| *a.* | | Souvenir sheet of 2 | 3.50 | *4.00* |

Intl. Year of the Disabled. No. B98a contains Nos. B97-B98 each with 10c surtax, which was for benefit of the disabled; black overprint in margin.

### Christmas Type of 1981
Souvenir Sheet

**1981, Dec. 14 Photo. *Perf. 13½***

| | | | | |
|---|---|---|---|---|
| **B99** | | Sheet of 4 | 2.75 | 2.75 |
| *a.* | A107 | 8c + 3c like #669 | .25 | .25 |
| *b.* | A107 | 15c + 3c like #670 | .35 | .35 |
| *c.* | A107 | 40c + 3c like #671 | .75 | .75 |
| *d.* | A107 | 50c + 3c like #672 | 1.00 | 1.00 |

Surtax was for school children.

### Nos. 919-923 Surcharged in Silver

No. B100

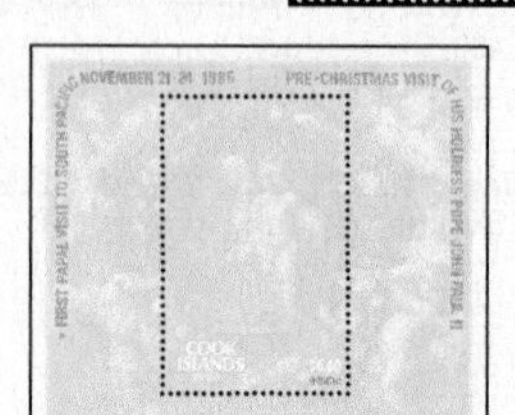


No. B104

**1986, Nov. 21 Litho. *Perf. 13½***

| | | | | |
|---|---|---|---|---|
| **B100** | A138 | 55c + 10c multi | 2.50 | 2.50 |
| **B101** | A138 | $1.30 + 10c multi | 5.25 | 5.25 |
| **B102** | A138 | $2.75 + 10c multi | 10.00 | 10.00 |
| | | *Nos. B100-B102 (3)* | 17.75 | 17.75 |

**Souvenir Sheets**

| | | | | |
|---|---|---|---|---|
| **B103** | | Sheet of 3 | 16.00 | 16.00 |
| *a.-c.* | A138 | $2.40 + 10c on Nos. 922a-922c, any single | 5.25 | 5.25 |
| **B104** | A138 | $6.40 + 50c multi | 16.00 | 16.00 |

No. B103 ovptd. in margin "VISIT TO SOUTH PACIFIC / OF POPE JOHN PAUL II" and "FIRST PAPAL VISIT / NOVEMBER 21-24 1986."

For surcharges see Nos. B112, B141.

Stamps of 1982 and 1987 Surcharged in Sans-serif Capitals

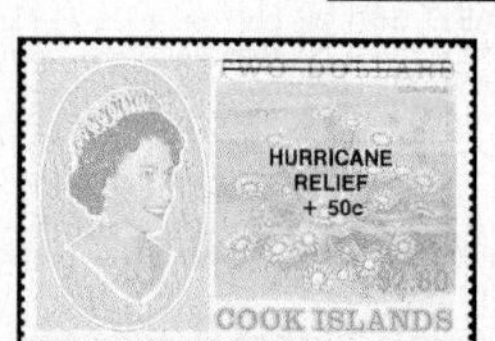


No. B109

***Perfs. as before***

**1987, June 30 Photo.**

**Surcharged +25c**

| | | | | |
|---|---|---|---|---|
| **B105** | A121 | 55c on #958 | 1.10 | 1.10 |
| **B106** | A121 | 65c on #960 | 1.25 | 1.25 |
| **B107** | A121 | 75c on #963 | 1.40 | 1.40 |
| **B108** | A121 | 95c on #965 | 1.60 | 1.60 |

**Surcharged +50c**

| | | | | |
|---|---|---|---|---|
| **B109** | A101 | $2.80 on #582 | 4.50 | 4.50 |
| **B110** | A101 | $5 on #583 | 7.75 | 7.75 |
| **B111** | A102 | $6.40 on #978 | 9.50 | 9.50 |
| | | *Nos. B105-B111 (7)* | 27.10 | 27.10 |

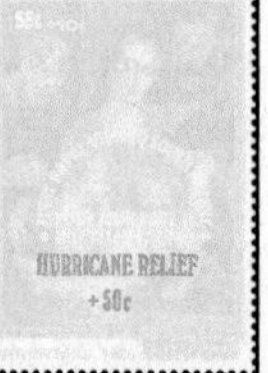


Stamps of 1985-86 Surcharged in Silver or Black

**1987, June 30 *Perfs. as before***

**Surcharged +50c**

| | | | | |
|---|---|---|---|---|
| **B112** | A138 | 55c on #B100 | 1.40 | 1.40 |
| **B113** | A133 | 55c on #897 (B) | 1.40 | 1.40 |
| **B114** | A128 | 65c on #871 | 1.50 | 1.50 |
| **B115** | A133 | 65c on #898 | 1.50 | 1.50 |
| **B116** | A128 | 75c on #872 | 1.60 | 1.60 |
| **B117** | A133 | 75c on #899 | 1.60 | 1.60 |
| **B118** | A134 | 95c on #908 (B) | 1.90 | 1.90 |
| **B119** | A135 | $1 on #910 | 2.10 | 2.10 |
| **B120** | A136 | $1 on #913 | 2.10 | 2.10 |
| **B121** | A137 | $1 on #916 | 2.10 | 2.10 |
| **B122** | A128 | $1.15 on #873 | 2.25 | 2.25 |
| **B123** | A133 | $1.25 on #900 | 2.25 | 2.25 |
| **B124** | A134 | $1.25 on #905 | 2.25 | 2.25 |
| **B125** | A136 | $1.25 on #914 (B) | 2.25 | 2.25 |
| **B126** | A138 | $1.30 on #920 | 2.50 | 2.50 |
| **B127** | A134 | $1.50 on #906 (B) | 2.50 | 2.50 |
| **B128** | A135 | $1.50 on #911 (B) | 2.50 | 2.50 |
| **B129** | A133 | $2 on #901 (B) | 3.25 | 3.25 |
| **B130** | A135 | $2 on #912 (B) | 3.25 | 3.25 |
| **B131** | A137 | $2 on #917 | 3.25 | 3.25 |
| **B132** | A136 | $2.75 on #915 | 4.50 | 4.50 |
| **B133** | A138 | $2.75 on #921 | 4.50 | 4.50 |
| **B134** | A128 | $2.80 on #874 | 4.50 | 4.50 |
| **B135** | A137 | $3 on #918 | 4.75 | 4.75 |
| | | *Nos. B112-B135 (24)* | 61.70 | 61.70 |

**Souvenir Sheets**

| | | | | |
|---|---|---|---|---|
| **B136** | A134 | $1.10 on #907 (B) | 2.00 | 2.00 |
| **B137** | A134 | $1.95 on #908 | 3.00 | 3.00 |
| **B138** | A138 | $2.40 on #922 | 11.00 | 11.00 |
| **B139** | A134 | $2.45 on #909 (B) | 3.75 | 3.75 |
| **B140** | A128 | $5.30 on #875 | 7.25 | 7.25 |
| **B141** | A138 | $6.40 on #B104 | 8.50 | 8.50 |
| **B141A** | A138 | $6.40 on #923 | — | |
| | | *Nos. B136-B141 (6)* | 35.50 | 35.50 |

Issued: Nos. B118, B121, B124, B127, B131, B135-B137, B139-B140, 7/31; others 6/30.

### No. 1230 Surcharged in Silver
Souvenir Sheet

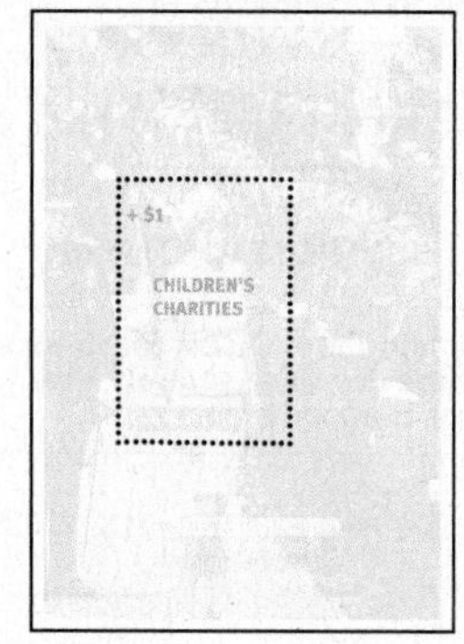


**1998, Nov. 20 Litho. *Perf. 14***

| | | | | |
|---|---|---|---|---|
| **B142** | A179 | $3.50 +$1 multi | 4.75 | 4.75 |

---

## AIR POST STAMPS

**Catalogue values for unused stamps in this section are for Never Hinged items.**

Stamps of 1936-63 Overprinted and Surcharged

***Perf. 13x13½, 13½x13***
**Litho., Engr.**

**1966, Apr. 22 Wmk. 253**

| | | | | |
|---|---|---|---|---|
| **C1** | A25 | 6p on #152 | .70 | .25 |
| **C2** | A26 | 7p on 8p #153 | 1.00 | .25 |
| **C3** | A25 | 10p on 3p #150 | .65 | .35 |
| **C4** | A25 | 1sh on #154 | .70 | .45 |
| **C5** | A27 | 1sh6p on #155 | 1.25 | 1.25 |
| **C6** | A28 | 2sh3p on 3sh #157 | 1.00 | 1.00 |
| **C7** | A28 | 5sh on #158 | 1.60 | 1.75 |
| **C8** | A28 | 10sh on 2sh #156 | 2.00 | *8.00* |

No. 106 Overprinted

***Perf. 14***
**Typo.**

| | | | | |
|---|---|---|---|---|
| **C9** | PF5 | £1 pink | 12.00 | *16.00* |
| *a.* | | Airplane missing | *37.50* | *50.00* |
| | | *Nos. C1-C9 (9)* | 20.90 | 29.30 |

No. C9a occurs on all stamps from the right vertical column of the sheet due to a lack of airplane symbols. The size and position of the airplane symbol varies in relation to "Airmail" on the other stamps. The surcharges are printed on silver ovals.

### 2nd South Pacific Games Type

Sport: 10p, Women runners and Games' emblem. 2sh3p, Runner and team emblem.

***Perf. 13½***

**1967, Jan. 12 Unwmk. Photo.**

| | | | | |
|---|---|---|---|---|
| **C10** | A32 | 10p org & multi | .25 | .25 |
| **C11** | A32 | 2sh3p multi | .25 | .25 |

### Capt. Cook Type of Regular Issue

6c, The "Resolution" and "Discovery" Beating Through the Ice, by Webber. 10c, The Island of Otaheite, by Hodges, and Queen Elizabeth II. 15c, View of Karakakooa (Kealakekua), Hawaii, by Webber. 25c, The Landing at Middleburg, Tonga, by Hodges, & Captain Cook. (All horiz.)

**1968, Sept. 12 Photo. *Perf. 13***

| | | | | |
|---|---|---|---|---|
| **C12** | A39 | 6c gold & multi | .35 | .35 |
| **C13** | A39 | 10c gold & multi | .40 | .40 |
| **C14** | A39 | 15c gold & multi | .45 | .45 |
| **C15** | A39 | 25c gold & multi | 1.00 | 1.00 |
| | | *Nos. C12-C15 (4)* | 2.20 | 2.20 |

See note after No. 236.

### Christmas Type of 1979

**1979, Dec. 14 Photo. *Perf. 14***

| | | | | |
|---|---|---|---|---|
| **C16** | A95 | 20c like #537 | .25 | .25 |
| **C17** | A95 | 25c like #538 | .25 | .25 |
| **C18** | A95 | 30c like #539 | .30 | .30 |
| **C19** | A95 | 35c like #540 | .40 | .40 |
| | | *Nos. C16-C19 (4)* | 1.20 | 1.20 |

Franklin D. Roosevelt — AP1

80c, Benjamin Franklin. $1.40, George Washington, by Gilbert Stuart.

**1982, Sept. 30 Photo. *Perf. 14***

| | | | | |
|---|---|---|---|---|
| **C20** | AP1 | 60c multicolored | .80 | .80 |
| **C21** | AP1 | 80c multicolored | 1.00 | 1.00 |
| **C22** | AP1 | $1.40 multicolored | 1.75 | 1.75 |
| *a.* | | Souvenir sheet of 3 | 4.00 | 4.00 |
| | | *Nos. C20-C22 (3)* | 3.55 | 3.55 |

No. C22a contains Nos. C20-C22, perf. 13½ with portraits in square frames.

No. C22 Overprinted in Gold and Black

**1983, Aug. 12 Photo. *Perf. 14***

| | | | | |
|---|---|---|---|---|
| **C23** | AP1 | 96c on $1.40 multi | 1.60 | 1.60 |

### Endangered Bird Species Type
Souvenir Sheets

Nos. 1020-1023 Overprinted

**1990, Dec. 5 Litho. *Perf. 13½***

| | | | | |
|---|---|---|---|---|
| **C24** | A145 | $1 Flycatcher | 3.50 | 3.50 |
| **C25** | A145 | $1.25 Flycatchers | 4.25 | 4.25 |
| **C26** | A145 | $1.50 Fruit dove | 5.50 | 5.50 |
| **C27** | A145 | $1.75 Fruit doves | 6.25 | 6.25 |
| | | *Nos. C24-C27 (4)* | 19.50 | 19.50 |

Birdpex '90, 20th Intl. Ornithological Cong., New Zealand.

---

## AIR POST SEMI-POSTAL STAMPS

**Catalogue values for unused stamps in this section are for Never Hinged items.**

**Christmas Type of 1979**

**1980, Jan. 15 Photo. *Perf. 14***

| | | | | |
|---|---|---|---|---|
| **CB1** | A95 | 20c + 4c like #C16 | .25 | .25 |
| **CB2** | A95 | 25c + 4c like #C17 | .30 | .30 |
| **CB3** | A95 | 30c + 4c like #C18 | .35 | .35 |
| **CB4** | A95 | 35c + 4c like #C19 | .40 | .40 |
| | | *Nos. CB1-CB4 (4)* | 1.30 | 1.30 |

## OFFICIAL STAMPS

Flower Issue of 1967-69 Overprinted or Surcharged in Black on Silver

**1975 Photo. Unwmk. *Perf. 14x13½***

| | | | |
|---|---|---|---|
| **O1** | A34 | 1c multi (#200) | .25 |
| **O2** | A34 | 2c multi (#201) | .25 |
| **O3** | A34 | 3c multi (#203) | .25 |
| **O4** | A34 | 4c multi (#205) | .25 |
| **O5** | A34 | 5c on 2½c multi (#202) | .25 |
| **O6** | A34 | 8c multi (#208) | .30 |
| **O7** | A34 | 10c on 6c multi (#207) | .30 |
| **O8** | A34 | 18c on 20c multi (#212) | .35 |
| **O9** | A34 | 25c on 9c multi (#209) | .55 |
| **O10** | A34 | 30c on 15c multi (#211) | .65 |
| **O11** | A34 | 50c multi (#215) | .70 |
| **O12** | A35 | $1 multi (#216) | 1.30 |
| **O13** | A35 | $2 multi (#217) | 2.00 |
| **O14** | A36 | $4 multi (#218) | 3.75 |
| **O15** | A36 | $6 multi (#219) | 4.50 |
| | | *Nos. O1-O15 (15)* | 15.65 |

No. O1-O15 were not sold to the public unused. Arrangement of surcharge varies on different denominations.

Silver panel on Nos. O14-O15 measures 26½x6mm and is rounded at both ends.

Issue dates: 1c-$2, Mar. 17, $4-$6, May 19.

**Catalogue values for unused stamps in this section, from this point to the end of the section, are for Never Hinged items.**

**Nos. 381-382, 389, 393-396, 467, 446 Ovptd. or Srchd. in Silver or Black**

No. O16

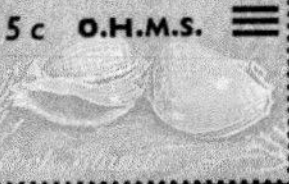



No. O18

No. O27

**Photo., Litho.**

**1978, Oct. 19 *Perf. 13½***

| | | | | |
|---|---|---|---|---|
| **O16** | A62 | 1c multi (S) | .85 | .25 |
| **O17** | A62 | 2c on ½c multi | .85 | .25 |
| **O18** | A62 | 5c on ½c multi | .95 | .25 |
| **O19** | A62 | 10c on 8c multi (S) | 1.10 | .25 |
| **O20** | A62 | 15c on 50c multi (S) | 1.25 | .25 |
| **O21** | A62 | 18c on 60c multi (S) | 1.25 | .25 |
| **O22** | A62 | 25c multicolored | 1.60 | .25 |
| **O23** | A62 | 30c multi (S) | 1.60 | .30 |
| **O24** | A62 | 35c on 60c multi (S) | 1.60 | .35 |
| **O25** | A62 | 50c multi (S) | 2.10 | .50 |
| **O26** | A62 | 60c multi (S) | 2.40 | .60 |
| **O27** | A82 | $1 Pair, #a.-b. (S) | 10.00 | 2.00 |
| **O29** | A77 | $2 multicolored | 7.25 | 2.25 |
| **O30** | A64 | $4 multi ('79) | 13.50 | 3.50 |
| **O31** | A64 | $6 multi ('79) | 13.50 | 5.50 |
| | | *Nos. O16-O31 (15)* | 59.80 | 16.75 |

Diagonal overprints on No. O27. Overprint on No. O29-O31: 19x4mm.

Nos. 790-791, 795, 797, 799, 805, 807, 809-810 Ovptd. or Srchd. in Silver

**1985, July 10 Photo. *Perf. 13½x13***

| | | | | |
|---|---|---|---|---|
| **O32** | A121 | 5c multi | .55 | .55 |
| **O33** | A121 | 10c multi | .55 | .55 |
| **O34** | A121 | 20c multi | .65 | .65 |
| **O35** | A121 | 30c multi | .65 | .65 |
| **O36** | A121 | 40c multi | .65 | .65 |
| **O37** | A121 | 55c on 85c multi | .80 | .80 |
| **O38** | A121 | 60c multi | .80 | .80 |
| **O39** | A121 | $1.10 multi | 1.60 | 1.25 |
| **O40** | A121 | $2 on $1.20 multi | 3.25 | 2.50 |
| | | *Nos. O32-O40 (9)* | 9.50 | 8.40 |

**Nos. 792-794, 802, 806, 696 and 583-586 Ovptd. or Srchd. in Silver, Gold (75c) or Black and Silver ($5, $18)**

No. O41

No. O53

**1986-90 Photo. *Perfs. as Before***

| | | | | |
|---|---|---|---|---|
| **O41** | A121 | 12c multi | 5.00 | 5.00 |
| **O42** | A121 | 14c multi | 5.00 | 5.00 |
| **O43** | A121 | 18c multi | 5.00 | 5.00 |
| **O44** | A121 | 50c multi | 6.25 | 6.25 |
| **O45** | A121 | 70c multi | 6.75 | 6.75 |
| **O46** | A111 | 75c on 60c, #a.-d. | 13.50 | 13.50 |
| **O50** | A102 | $5 on $3 multi | 17.00 | 17.00 |
| **O51** | A102 | $9 on $4 multi | 9.00 | 9.00 |
| **O52** | A102 | $14 on $6 multi | 14.00 | 14.00 |
| **O53** | A102 | $18 on $10 multi | 20.00 | 20.00 |
| | | *Nos. O41-O53 (10)* | 101.50 | 101.50 |

Issued: $9, 5/30/89; $14, 7/12/89; $18, 6/4/90; others 5/5/86.

Nos. 1058-1059, 1062, 1064-1066, 1071, 1076-1078, 1080-1083, 1085, 1087 Ovptd. in Silver

**1995-98 Litho. *Perf. 14½x13½***

| | | | | |
|---|---|---|---|---|
| **O54** | A155 | 5c multicolored | .40 | .40 |
| **O55** | A155 | 10c multicolored | .40 | .40 |
| **O56** | A155 | 15c multicolored | .50 | .50 |
| **O57** | A155 | 20c multicolored | .55 | .55 |
| **O58** | A155 | 25c multicolored | .60 | .60 |
| **O59** | A155 | 30c multicolored | .65 | .65 |
| **O60** | A155 | 50c multicolored | .80 | .80 |
| **O61** | A155 | 80c multicolored | 1.30 | 1.30 |
| **O62** | A155 | 85c multicolored | 1.30 | 1.30 |
| **O63** | A155 | 90c multicolored | 1.30 | 1.30 |
| **O64** | A155 | $1 multicolored | 1.50 | 1.50 |
| **O65** | A155 | $2 multicolored | 2.40 | 2.40 |
| **O66** | A155a | $3 multicolored | 3.75 | 3.75 |
| **O67** | A155a | $5 multicolored | 4.75 | 4.75 |
| **O68** | A155a | $7 multicolored | 6.75 | 6.75 |
| **O69** | A155a | $10 multi | 8.50 | 8.50 |
| | | *Nos. O54-O69 (16)* | 35.45 | 35.45 |

Overprint on Nos. O66-O69 has larger, sans serif letters.

Nos. O66-O69 were not sold unused to local customers.

Issued: 5c-90c, 2/24/95; $1-$2, 5/15/95; $3-$7, 7/17/98, $10, 11/12/98.

**Nos. 1305-1322 Overprinted in Gold**

**2010, Oct. 12 Litho. *Perf. 13¾***
**Sizes: 60x37mm, 37x60mm**

| | | | | |
|---|---|---|---|---|
| **O70** | A191 | 10c multi | .25 | .25 |
| **O71** | A191 | 20c multi | .30 | .30 |
| **O72** | A191 | 30c multi | .50 | .50 |
| **O73** | A191 | 40c multi | .65 | .65 |
| **O74** | A191 | 50c multi | .80 | .80 |
| **O75** | A191 | 70c multi | 1.10 | 1.10 |
| **O76** | A191 | 80c multi | 1.25 | 1.25 |
| **O77** | A191 | 90c multi | 1.50 | 1.50 |
| **O78** | A191 | $1 multi | 1.60 | 1.60 |
| **O79** | A191 | $1.10 multi | 1.75 | 1.75 |
| **O80** | A191 | $1.20 multi | 1.90 | 1.90 |
| **O81** | A191 | $2 multi | 3.25 | 3.25 |
| **O82** | A191 | $3 multi | 4.75 | 4.75 |
| **O83** | A191 | $4 multi | 6.50 | 6.50 |
| **O84** | A191 | $5 multi | 8.00 | 8.00 |

**Size: 60x37mm**

| | | | | |
|---|---|---|---|---|
| **O85** | A191 | $7.50 multi | 12.00 | 12.00 |
| **O86** | A191 | $10 multi | 16.00 | 16.00 |
| **O87** | A191 | $20 multi | 32.00 | 32.00 |
| | | *Nos. O70-O87 (18)* | 94.10 | 94.10 |

Overprint reads up on vertical stamps.

**Nos. 1305-1309 Overprinted in Metallic Green Like No. O70**

**2010, Oct. 12 Litho. *Perf. 13¾***
**Sizes: 60x37mm, 37x60mm**

| | | | | |
|---|---|---|---|---|
| **O88** | A191 | 10c multi | .25 | .25 |
| **O89** | A191 | 20c multi | .30 | .30 |
| **O90** | A191 | 30c multi | .50 | .50 |
| **O91** | A191 | 40c multi | .65 | .65 |
| **O92** | A191 | 50c multi | .80 | .80 |
| **O93** | A191 | 70c multi | 1.10 | 1.10 |
| **O94** | A191 | 80c multi | 1.25 | 1.25 |
| **O95** | A191 | 90c multi | 1.50 | 1.50 |
| **O96** | A191 | $1 multi | 1.60 | 1.60 |
| **O97** | A191 | $1.10 multi | 1.75 | 1.75 |
| **O98** | A191 | $1.20 multi | 1.90 | 1.90 |
| **O99** | A191 | $2 multi | 3.25 | 3.25 |
| **O100** | A191 | $3 multi | 4.75 | 4.75 |
| **O101** | A191 | $4 multi | 6.50 | 6.50 |
| **O102** | A191 | $5 multi | 8.00 | 8.00 |
| | | *Nos. O88-O102 (15)* | 34.10 | 34.10 |

Overprint reads up on vertical stamps.

**Nos. 1305-1309 Overprinted in Metallic Red Like No. O70**

**2010, Oct. 12 Litho. *Perf. 13¾***
**Sizes: 60x37mm, 37x60mm**

| | | | | |
|---|---|---|---|---|
| **O103** | A191 | 10c multi | .25 | .25 |
| **O104** | A191 | 20c multi | .30 | .30 |
| **O105** | A191 | 30c multi | .50 | .50 |
| **O106** | A191 | 40c multi | .65 | .65 |
| **O107** | A191 | 50c multi | .80 | .80 |
| **O108** | A191 | 70c multi | 1.10 | 1.10 |
| **O109** | A191 | 80c multi | 1.25 | 1.25 |
| **O110** | A191 | 90c multi | 1.50 | 1.50 |
| **O111** | A191 | $1 multi | 1.60 | 1.60 |
| **O112** | A191 | $1.10 multi | 1.75 | 1.75 |
| **O113** | A191 | $1.20 multi | 1.90 | 1.90 |
| **O114** | A191 | $2 multi | 3.25 | 3.25 |
| **O115** | A191 | $3 multi | 4.75 | 4.75 |
| **O116** | A191 | $4 multi | 6.50 | 6.50 |
| **O117** | A191 | $5 multi | 8.00 | 8.00 |
| | | *Nos. O103-O117 (15)* | 34.10 | 34.10 |

Overprint reads up on vertical stamps.

# CORFU

kor-'fü

LOCATION — An island in the Ionian Sea opposite the Greek-Albanian border

GOVT. — A department of Greece

AREA — 245 sq. mi.

POP. — 114,620 (1938)

CAPITAL — Corfu

In 1922 Italy occupied Corfu (Kerkyra) during a controversy with Greece over the assassination of an Italian official in Epirus. Italy again occupied Corfu in 1941-43.

100 Centesimi = 1 Lira
100 Lepta = 1 Drachma

**Watermarks**

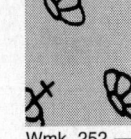

Wmk. 140 — Crown

Wmk. 252 — Crowns

## ISSUED UNDER ITALIAN OCCUPATION

Italian Stamps of 1901-23 Overprinted

**1923, Sept. 20 Wmk. 140 *Perf. 14***

| | | | | |
|---|---|---|---|---|
| **N1** | A48 | 5c green | 6.25 | *11.50* |
| **N2** | A48 | 10c claret | 6.25 | *11.50* |
| **N3** | A48 | 15c slate | 6.25 | *11.50* |
| **N4** | A50 | 20c brown orange | 6.25 | *11.50* |
| **N5** | A49 | 30c orange brown | 6.25 | *11.50* |
| **N6** | A49 | 50c violet | 6.25 | *11.50* |
| **N7** | A49 | 60c blue | 6.25 | *11.50* |
| *a.* | | Vert. pair, one without overprint | *1,500.* | |
| **N8** | A46 | 1 l brown & green | 6.25 | *11.50* |
| | | *Nos. N1-N8 (8)* | 50.00 | *92.00* |
| | | Set, never hinged | 115.00 | |

Italian Stamps of 1901-23 Surcharged

**1923, Sept. 24**

| | | | | |
|---|---|---|---|---|
| **N9** | A48 | 25 l on 10c claret | 60.00 | 45.00 |
| **N10** | A49 | 60 l on 25c blue | 10.00 | |
| **N11** | A49 | 70 l on 30c org brn | 10.00 | |
| **N12** | A49 | 1.20d on 50c violet | 25.00 | *45.00* |
| **N13** | A46 | 2.40d on 1 l brn & grn | 25.00 | *45.00* |
| **N14** | A46 | 4.75d on 2 l grn & org | 15.00 | |
| | | *Nos. N9-N14 (6)* | 145.00 | |
| | | Set, never hinged | 267.00 | |

Nos. N10, N11, N14 were not placed in use.

**Issue for Corfu and Paxos**

Nos. N15-N34, NC1-NC12, NJ1-NJ11 and NRA1-NRA3 have been extensively counterfeited, some with forged cancellations.

Stamps of Greece, 1937-38, Overprinted in Black

***Perf. 12x13½, 12½x12, 13½x12***

**1941, June 5 Wmk. 252**

| | | | | |
|---|---|---|---|---|
| **N15** | A69 | 5 l brn red & blue | 5.75 | 3.75 |
| *a.* | | Inverted overprint | *60.00* | *47.50* |
| *b.* | | Double overprint | *80.00* | *110.00* |
| **N16** | A70 | 10 l bl & brn red (On 397) | 1.90 | *2.75* |
| **N17** | A70 | 10 l bl & brn red (On 413) | 1,550. | 1,350. |
| **N18** | A71 | 20 l black & grn | 2.75 | *3.75* |
| *a.* | | Inverted overprint | *80.00* | *47.50* |
| **N19** | A72 | 40 l green & blk | 3.25 | *4.25* |
| *a.* | | Inverted overprint | *80.00* | *47.50* |
| *b.* | | Double overprint | *80.00* | *110.00* |
| **N20** | A73 | 50 l brown & blk | 1.90 | *2.75* |
| *a.* | | Inverted overprint | *55.00* | *47.50* |
| **N21** | A74 | 80 l ind & yel brn | 3.75 | *5.00* |
| **N22** | A67 | 1d green | 14.50 | 14.50 |
| **N23** | A84 | 1.50d green | 14.50 | 14.50 |
| **N24** | A75 | 2d ultra | 7.75 | *11.00* |
| **N25** | A67 | 3d red brown | 7.75 | 11.00 |
| **N26** | A76 | 5d red | 7.75 | *11.00* |
| **N27** | A77 | 6d olive brown | 7.75 | *11.00* |

| | | | | |
|---|---|---|---|---|
| **N28** | A78 | 7d dark brown | 12.00 | *12.00* |
| **N29** | A67 | 8d deep blue | 24.50 | 24.50 |
| **N30** | A79 | 10d red brown | 725.00 | 375.00 |
| **N31** | A80 | 15d green | 28.00 | 28.00 |
| **N32** | A81 | 25d dark blue | 28.00 | 28.00 |
| **N33** | A84 | 30d org brn | 115.00 | 100.00 |
| **N34** | A67 | 100d carmine lake | 375.00 | 350.00 |
| | | *Nos. N15-N34 (20)* | 2,937. | 2,363. |
| | | Set, never hinged | 3,900. | |

## AIR POST STAMPS

**Greece Nos. C37 and C26-C35, Overprinted Like Nos. N15-N34**

***Perf. 12½x13, 13x12½, 13½x12½***

**1941, June 5** **Unwmk.**

| | | | | |
|---|---|---|---|---|
| **NC1** | D3 | 50 l dk brown | 11.00 | 7.75 |
| **NC2** | AP16 | 1d red | 750.00 | 275.00 |
| **NC3** | AP17 | 2d gray blue | 11.00 | 7.75 |
| **NC4** | AP18 | 5d violet | 13.50 | 13.00 |
| **NC5** | AP19 | 7d deep ultra | 17.50 | 13.00 |
| **NC6** | AP20 | 10d bister brn (On C26) | 950.00 | 400.00 |
| **NC7** | AP20 | 10d brown org (On C35) | 62.50 | 50.00 |
| **NC8** | AP21 | 25d rose | 135.00 | 60.00 |
| **NC9** | AP22 | 30d dk grn | 145.00 | 90.00 |
| **NC10** | AP23 | 50d violet | 145.00 | 90.00 |
| *a.* | | Double overprint | | *550.00* |
| **NC11** | AP24 | 100d brown | *1,300.* | *650.00* |

**On No. C36**

***Serrate Roulette 13½***

| | | | | |
|---|---|---|---|---|
| **NC12** | D3 | 50 l vio brn | 90.00 | 23.00 |
| *a.* | | On No. C36a | *350.00* | |
| | | *Nos. NC1-NC12 (12)* | *3,631.* | *1,680.* |
| | | Set, never hinged | 5,500. | |

## POSTAGE DUE STAMPS

**Postage Due Stamps of Greece, 1913-35 Overprinted Like #N15-N34**

**1941, June 5** **Unwmk.**

***Serrate Roulette 13½***

| | | | | |
|---|---|---|---|---|
| **NJ1** | D3 | 10 l carmine | 4.50 | *5.00* |
| **NJ2** | D3 | 25 l ultra | 4.50 | *5.00* |
| **NJ3** | D3 | 80 l lilac brown | *1,150.* | *450.00* |

***Perf. 12½x13, 13½x12½***

| | | | | |
|---|---|---|---|---|
| **NJ4** | D3 | 1d lt bl (On J80) | *1,600.* | *900.00* |
| **NJ5** | D3 | 2d light red | 8.50 | *14.00* |
| **NJ6** | D3 | 5d gray | 22.50 | *24.00* |
| **NJ7** | D3 | 10d gray green | 22.50 | *24.00* |
| **NJ8** | D3 | 15d red brown | 22.50 | *24.00* |
| **NJ9** | D3 | 25d light red | 22.50 | *24.00* |
| **NJ10** | D3 | 50d orange | 22.50 | *24.00* |
| **NJ11** | D3 | 100d slate green | 600.00 | 450.00 |
| | | *Nos. NJ1-NJ11 (11)* | *3,480.* | *1,944.* |
| | | Set, never hinged | 5,000. | |

## POSTAL TAX STAMPS

**Greece Nos. RA61-RA63 Overprinted Like Nos. N15-N34 Wmk., Unwmk.**

**1941, June 5** ***Perf. 13½***

| | | | | |
|---|---|---|---|---|
| **NRA1** | PT7 | 10 l brt rose, *pale rose* | 3.25 | *4.50* |
| **NRA2** | PT7 | 50 l gray grn, *pale green* | 5.50 | *7.00* |
| **NRA3** | PT7 | 1d dull blue, *lt blue* | 37.50 | *45.00* |
| | | *Nos. NRA1-NRA3 (3)* | 46.25 | *56.50* |
| | | Set, never hinged | 67.50 | |

Stamps overprinted "CORFU" were replaced by Italian stamps overprinted "Isole Jonie." See Ionian Islands.

# COSTA RICA

ˌkōs-tə-ˈrē-kə

LOCATION — Central America between Nicaragua and Panama
GOVT. — Republic
AREA — 19,730 sq. mi.
POP. — 3,674,490 (1999 est.)
CAPITAL — San Jose

8 Reales = 100 Centavos = 1 Peso
100 Centimos = 1 Colon (1900)

**Catalogue values for unused stamps in this country are for Never Hinged items, beginning with Scott 238 in the regular postage section, Scott C117 in the air post section, Scott CE1 in the air post special delivery section, Scott E1 in the special delivery section, and Scott RA1 in the postal tax section.**

**Watermarks**

Wmk. 215 — Small Star in Shield, Multiple

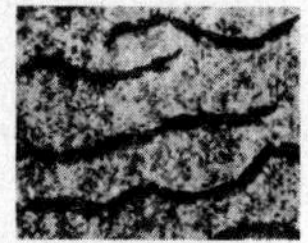

Wmk. 229 — Wavy Lines

Wmk. 334 — Rectangles

Values for unused stamps are for examples with original gum as defined in the catalogue introduction. Very fine examples of Nos. 1-22 will have perforations just clear of the design on one or more sides due to the placement of the stamps on the plates and to imperfect perforating methods.

Coat of Arms — A1

**1863** **Unwmk.** **Engr.** ***Perf. 12***

| | | | | |
|---|---|---|---|---|
| **1** | A1 | ½r blue | .50 | *1.10* |
| *a.* | | ½r light blue | .50 | *1.10* |
| *b.* | | Pair, imperf. horiz. | *6,000.* | |
| **2** | A1 | 2r scarlet | 2.25 | *2.25* |
| **3** | A1 | 4r green | 16.00 | *16.00* |
| **4** | A1 | 1p orange | 35.00 | *35.00* |
| | | *Nos. 1-4 (4)* | 53.75 | 54.35 |

The ½r was printed from two plates. The second is in light blue with little or no sky over the mountains.

Imperforate stamps of Nos. 1-2 are corner stamps from poorly perforated sheets.

**Nos. 1-3 Surcharged in Red or Black**

a

b

c

d

e

**1881-82** **Red or Black Surcharge**

| | | | | |
|---|---|---|---|---|
| **7** | A1(a) | 1c on ½r ('82) | 3.00 | *6.00* |
| *a.* | | On No. 1a | 15.00 | — |
| **8** | A1(b) | 1c on ½r ('82) | 18.00 | *30.00* |
| **9** | A1(c) | 2c on ½r, #1a | 3.00 | 2.75 |
| *a.* | | On No. 1 | 8.00 | — |
| **12** | A1(c) | 5c on ½r | 15.00 | |
| **13** | A1(d) | 5c on ½r ('82) | 35.00 | |
| **14** | A1(d) | 10c on 2r (Bk) ('82) | 72.50 | — |
| **15** | A1(e) | 20c on 4r ('82) | 300.00 | — |

Overprints with different fonts and "OFICIAL" were never placed in use, and are said to have been surcharged to a dealer's order. The ½r surcharged "DOS CTS" is not a postage stamp. It probably is an essay.

Postally used examples of Nos. 7-15 are rare. Nos. 13-15 exist with a favor cancel having a hyphen between "San" and "Jose." Values same as unused. Fake cancellations exist.

Counterfeits exist of surcharges on Nos. 7-15.

Gen. Prospero Fernández — A6

**1883, Jan. 1**

| | | | | |
|---|---|---|---|---|
| **16** | A6 | 1c green | 3.00 | 1.50 |
| **17** | A6 | 2c carmine | 3.25 | 1.50 |
| **18** | A6 | 5c blue violet | 32.50 | 2.00 |
| **19** | A6 | 10c orange | 150.00 | 12.00 |
| **20** | A6 | 40c blue | 3.00 | *3.00* |
| | | *Nos. 16-20 (5)* | 191.75 | 20.00 |

Unused examples of 40c usually lack gum.

For overprints see Nos. O1-O20, O24, Guanacaste 1-38, 44.

President Bernardo Soto Alfaro — A7

**1887**

| | | | | |
|---|---|---|---|---|
| **21** | A7 | 5c blue violet | 7.00 | .50 |
| **22** | A7 | 10c orange | 4.00 | 3.00 |

Unused examples of 5c usually lack gum.

For overprints see Nos. O22-O23, Guanacaste 42-43, 45.

A8

A9

**1889** **Black Overprint**

| | | | | |
|---|---|---|---|---|
| **23** | A8 | 1c rose | 5.00 | 3.00 |
| **24** | A9 | 5c brown | 7.00 | 3.00 |

Vertical and inverted overprints are fakes.

For overprints see Guanacaste Nos. 47-54.

President Soto Alfaro
A10 A11

A12

A13

A14

A15

A16

A17

A18

A19

**1889** ***Perf. 14-16 & Compound***

| | | | | |
|---|---|---|---|---|
| **25** | A10 | 1c brown | .35 | *.45* |
| *a.* | | Horiz. pair, imperf. vert | *150.00* | |
| *b.* | | Imperf. pair | *150.00* | |
| *c.* | | Horiz. or vert. pair, imperf. btwn. | *150.00* | |
| **26** | A11 | 2c dark green | .35 | *.45* |
| *a.* | | Imperf., pair | 50.00 | |
| *b.* | | Vert. pair, imperf. horiz. | 125.00 | |
| *c.* | | Horiz. pair, imperf. btwn. | 125.00 | |
| **27** | A12 | 5c orange | .45 | .35 |
| *a.* | | Imperf., pair | | *750.00* |
| *b.* | | Horiz. pair, imperf. btwn. | *350.00* | |
| **28** | A13 | 10c red brown | .40 | .35 |
| *a.* | | Vert. or horiz. pair, imperf. btwn. | *150.00* | *500.00* |
| **29** | A14 | 20c yellow green | .30 | *.35* |
| *a.* | | Vert. pair, imperf. horiz. | 200.00 | |
| *b.* | | Horizontal pair, imperf. btwn. | *150.00* | |
| **30** | A15 | 50c rose red | 1.00 | |
| | | Telegram cancel | | .75 |
| **31** | A16 | 1p blue | 1.25 | |
| | | Telegram cancel | | .75 |
| **32** | A17 | 2p dull violet | 6.00 | |
| *a.* | | 2p slate | 6.00 | 10.00 |
| | | Telegram cancel | | 4.00 |
| **33** | A18 | 5p olive green | 25.00 | |
| | | Telegram cancel | | 10.00 |
| **34** | A19 | 10p black | 100.00 | |
| | | Telegram cancel | | 45.00 |
| | | *Nos. 25-34 (10)* | 135.10 | 1.95 |

Nos. 30-34 normally were used on telegrams and most examples were removed from the forms and sold by the government.

Most unused examples of No. 34 have no gum or only part gum. These sell for somewhat less.

For overprints see Nos. O25-O30, Guanacaste 55-67.

Arms of Costa Rica
A20 A21

A22

A23

A24

A25

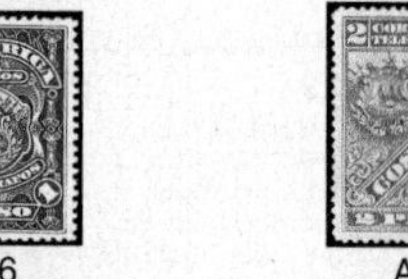

A26 A27

A28

A29

**1892** ***Perf. 12-15 & Compound***

| | | | | |
|---|---|---|---|---|
| **35** | A20 | 1c grnsh blue | .30 | *.40* |
| **36** | A21 | 2c yellow | .30 | *.40* |
| **37** | A22 | 5c red lilac | .30 | .25 |
| *a.* | | 5c violet | 60.00 | .40 |
| **38** | A23 | 10c lt green | .80 | .35 |
| *a.* | | Horiz. pair, imperf. btwn. | — | *100.00* |
| **39** | A24 | 20c scarlet | 12.00 | .25 |
| *a.* | | Horiz. pair, imperf. btwn. | — | *100.00* |

| | | | | |
|---|---|---|---|---|
| **40** | A25 | 50c gray blue | 4.00 | *4.25* |
| **41** | A26 | 1p green, *yel* | 1.25 | 1.00 |
| **42** | A27 | 2p brown red, *lilac* | 3.00 | 1.00 |
| *a.* | | 2p rose red, *pale lil* | 12.00 | 1.00 |
| **43** | A28 | 5p dk blue, *blue* | 2.00 | 1.00 |
| **44** | A29 | 10p brown, *pale buff* | 35.00 | 5.00 |
| *a.* | | 10p brown, *yellow* | 8.00 | |
| | | *Nos. 35-44 (10)* | 58.95 | 13.90 |

Imperfs. of Nos. 35-44 are proofs.
For overprints see Nos. O31-O36.

Statue of Juan Santamaría A30

Juan Mora Fernández A31

View of Port Limón A32

Braulio Carrillo ("Branlio" on stamp) A33

National Theater A34

José M. Castro A35

Birris Bridge A36

Juan Rafael Mora A37

Jesús Jiménez A38

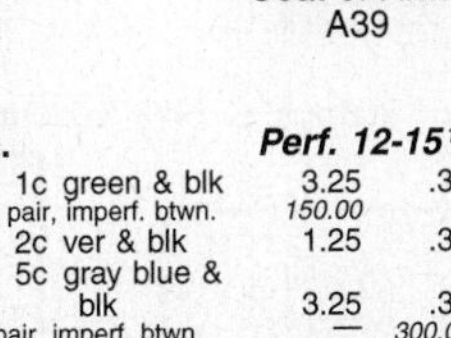

Coat of Arms A39

**1901, Jan.** ***Perf. 12-15½***

| | | | | |
|---|---|---|---|---|
| **45** | A30 | 1c green & blk | 3.25 | .30 |
| *a.* | | Horiz. pair, imperf. btwn. | *150.00* | |
| **46** | A31 | 2c ver & blk | 1.25 | .30 |
| **47** | A32 | 5c gray blue & blk | 3.25 | .30 |
| *a.* | | Vert. pair, imperf. btwn. | — | *300.00* |
| **48** | A33 | 10c ocher & blk | 3.25 | .35 |
| **49** | A34 | 20c lake & blk | 22.50 | .25 |
| *a.* | | Vert. pair, imperf. btwn. | *1,000.* | |
| **50** | A35 | 50c dull lil & dk bl | 5.50 | 1.00 |
| **51** | A36 | 1col ol bis & blk | 110.00 | 3.50 |
| **52** | A37 | 2col car rose & dk grn | 16.00 | 3.00 |
| **53** | A38 | 5col brown & blk | 75.00 | 3.50 |
| **54** | A39 | 10col yel grn & brn red | 29.00 | 3.00 |
| | | *Nos. 45-54 (10)* | 269.00 | 15.50 |

The 2c exists with center inverted. Value $77,500.

Nos. 45-57 in other colors are private reprints made in 1948. They have little value.

For surcharge and overprints see Nos. 58, 78, O37-O44.

### Remainders

In 1914 the government sold a large quantity of stamps at very much less than face value. The lot included most regular issues from 1901 to 1911 inclusive, postage due stamps of 1903 and Official stamps of 1901-03. These stamps were canceled with groups of thin parallel bars. The higher valued used stamps, such as Nos. 64, 65-68a, sell for much less than the values quoted, which are for stamps with regular postal cancellations. A few sell for much higher prices.

José M. Cañas A40

Julián Volio A41

Eusebio Figueroa Oreamuno — A42

**1903** ***Perf. 13½, 14, 15***

| | | | | |
|---|---|---|---|---|
| **55** | A40 | 4c red vio & blk | 2.00 | .70 |
| **56** | A41 | 6c olive grn & blk | 7.25 | 4.00 |
| **57** | A42 | 25c gray lil & brn | 16.00 | .30 |
| | | *Nos. 55-57 (3)* | 25.25 | 5.00 |

See note on private reprints following No. 54.
For overprints see Nos. 81, O45-O47.

No. 49 Surcharged in Black:

**1905**

| | | | | |
|---|---|---|---|---|
| **58** | A34 | 1c on 20c lake & blk | .60 | .60 |
| *a.* | | Inverted surcharge | 10.00 | 10.00 |
| *b.* | | Diagonal surcharge | .60 | .60 |

Examples surcharged in other colors are proofs.

Statue of Juan Santamaria A43

Juan Mora Fernández A44

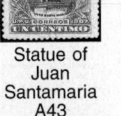

José M. Cañas A45

Mauro Fernández A46

Braulio Carrillo A47

Julián Volio A48

Eusebio Figueroa Oreamuno A49

José M. Castro A50

Jesús Jiménez A51

Juan Rafael Mora A52

***Perf. 11x14, 14 (1c, 5c, 10c, 25c)***

**1907** **Unwmk.**

| | | | | |
|---|---|---|---|---|
| **59** | A43 | 1c red brn & ind | 8.00 | .40 |
| *a.* | | Perf. 11x14 | 60.00 | 3.00 |
| *b.* | | Imperf pair | 20.00 | — |
| **60** | A44 | 2c yel grn & blk | 3.00 | .40 |
| *a.* | | Perf. 14 | 3.00 | .40 |
| *b.* | | Imperf pair | 15.00 | — |
| **61** | A45 | 4c car & indigo | 12.00 | 2.50 |
| *a.* | | Perf. 14 | 500.00 | 45.00 |
| *b.* | | Imperf pair | 15.00 | — |
| **62** | A46 | 5c yel & dull bl | 3.00 | .40 |
| *a.* | | Perf. 11x14 | 60.00 | 1.00 |
| *b.* | | Imperf pair | 15.00 | — |
| **63** | A47 | 10c blue & blk | 10.00 | .50 |
| *a.* | | Perf. 11x14 | 20.00 | 1.00 |
| *b.* | | Imperf pair | 30.00 | — |
| **64** | A48 | 20c olive grn & blk | 25.00 | 6.00 |
| *a.* | | Perf. 14 | 25.00 | 6.00 |
| | | Remainder cancel | | 2.00 |
| *b.* | | Imperf pair | — | |
| **65** | A49 | 25c gray lil & blk | 3.00 | 3.00 |
| | | Remainder cancel | | 1.00 |
| *a.* | | Perf. 11x14 | 150.00 | 50.00 |
| *b.* | | Imperf pair | | |
| **66** | A50 | 50c red lil & blue | 75.00 | 25.00 |
| | | Remainder cancel | | 2.00 |
| *a.* | | Perf. 14 | 175.00 | 50.00 |
| | | Remainder cancel | | 5.00 |
| *b.* | | Imperf pair | 100.00 | |
| **67** | A51 | 1col brown & blk | 25.00 | 20.00 |
| | | Remainder cancel | | 2.00 |
| *a.* | | Perf. 14 | 25.00 | 20.00 |
| | | Remainder cancel | | 2.00 |
| *b.* | | Imperf pair | — | |
| **68** | A52 | 2col claret & grn | 160.00 | 100.00 |
| | | Remainder cancel | | 3.00 |
| *a.* | | Perf. 14 | 300.00 | 150.00 |
| *b.* | | Imperf pair | 200.00 | |
| | | *Nos. 59-68 (10)* | 324.00 | 158.20 |

The remainder cancel value applies to both perforations.

The imperforate varieties of the above set are valued without gum. Ungummed stamps were probably placed on the market in London, while gummed stamps appear to have been sent to Costa Rica and accepted for postal use. There is a small premium for gummed stamps.

The 1c, 2c, 5c, 20c, 50c, 1 col and 2 col exist with center inverted. Value, set $62,500.

Nos. 59-68 exist with papermaker's watermark.

No. 65b with brown vignette is a proof. Value, pair $40. The actual No. 65b (black vignette) is worth much more.

For overprints see Nos. 77, 79-80, 82-84, O48-O55, O60-O64.

Statue of Juan Santamaria A53

Juan Mora Fernández A54

José M. Cañas A55

Mauro Fernández A56

Braulio Carrillo A57

Julián Volio A58

Eusebio Figueroa Oreamuno A59

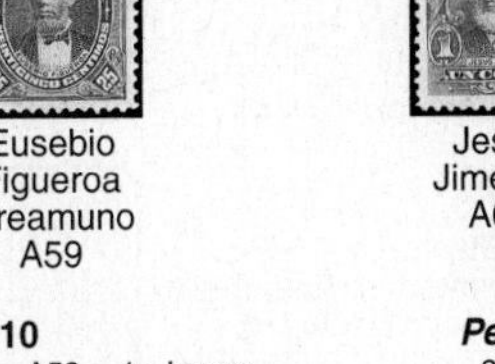

Jesús Jiménez A60

**1910** ***Perf. 12***

| | | | | |
|---|---|---|---|---|
| **69** | A53 | 1c brown | .25 | .25 |
| **70** | A54 | 2c dp green | .30 | .25 |
| **71** | A55 | 4c scarlet | .35 | .35 |
| **72** | A56 | 5c orange | 1.00 | .25 |
| **73** | A57 | 10c deep blue | .40 | .25 |
| **74** | A58 | 20c olive grn | .50 | .35 |
| **75** | A59 | 25c dp violet | 17.00 | 1.50 |
| **76** | A60 | 1col dk brown | .50 | .50 |
| | | *Nos. 69-76 (8)* | 20.30 | 3.70 |

For overprints and surcharge see Nos. 111C-111J, B1, C2, O56-O59.

No. 60a Overprinted in Red

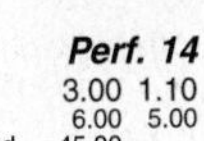

**1911** ***Perf. 14***

| | | | | |
|---|---|---|---|---|
| **77** | A44 | 2c yel grn & blk | 3.00 | 1.10 |
| *a.* | | Inverted overprint | 6.00 | 5.00 |
| *b.* | | Double overprint, both inverted | 45.00 | |

Stamps of 1901-07 Overprinted in Red or Black

78 A30 1c grn & blk (R) 4.00 1.00
a. Black overprint 35.00 18.00
b. Inverted overprint
79 A43 1c red brn & ind (Bk) 1.25 .40
a. Inverted overprint 4.50 3.50
b. Double overprint 5.50 5.00
80 A44 2c yel grn & blk (Bk) 1.00 .40
a. Inverted overprint 5.00 3.50
b. Dbl. ovpt., one as on No. 77 40.00 27.50
c. Double overprint, one inverted 15.00 15.00
d. Pair, one stamp No. 77 25.00 25.00
e. Perf. 11x14 30.00 *1.00*

No. 55 Overprinted in Black

81 A40 4c red vio & blk 1.50 .65

Stamps of 1907 Overprinted in Blue, Black or Rose

***Perf. 14, 11x14 (#83, 84)***

82 A46 5c yel & bl (Bl) 3.00 .40
a. "Habilitada" 3.25 2.50
b. "2911" 5.50 3.25
c. Roman "I" in "1911" 4.00 2.50
d. Double overprint 5.50 5.00
e. Inverted overprint 6.00 3.75
f. Black overprint *250.00* 2.00
g. Triple overprint 6.00
h. Vert. pair, imperf. horiz. *100.00*
83 A47 10c blue & blk (Bk) 5.00 1.40
a. As #83, Roman "I" in "1911" 7.00 5.00
c. As #83, double overprint 20.00 11.50
d. Perf. 14 45.00 5.25
84 A47 10c blue & blk (R) 15.00 13.50
a. Roman "I" in "1911" *100.00* *100.00*
c. Perf. 14 *100.00* *100.00*
*Nos. 77-84 (8)* 33.75 18.85

Many counterfeits of overprint exist.

**Telegraph Stamps Surcharged in Rose, Blue or Black**

A61

A62

A63

**1911** ***Perf. 12***

86 A61 1c on 10c bl (R) .50 .40
a. "Coereos" 7.75 6.00
b. Inverted surcharge
87 A61 1c on 10c bl (Bk) *210.00* *100.00*
88 A61 1c on 25c vio (Bk) .50 .40
a. "Coereos" 8.75 6.00
b. Pair, one without surcharge 20.00
c. Double surcharge 9.00
e. Double surch., one inverted 12.50
89 A61 1c on 50c red brn (Bl) .55 .40
a. Inverted surcharge 5.50 5.00
b. Double surcharge 4.50
90 A61 1c on 1col brn (R) .55 .40
91 A61 1c on 5col red (Bl) 1.00 .55
92 A61 1c on 10col dk brn (R) 1.50 .70

***Perf. 14***

93 A62 2c on 5c brn org (Bk) 3.50 1.90
a. Inverted surcharge *9.00* *3.75*
b. "Correos" inverted *17.50*
c. Double surcharge 9.00

***Perf. 14x11***

94 A62 2c on 10c bl (R) 100.00 100.00
a. Perf. 14 *350.00* *350.00*
b. "Correos" inverted 2,000.
c. As "b," perf. 14 3,500.
95 A62 2c on 50c cl (Bk) 1.00 .55
a. Inverted surcharge 4.50 3.25
b. Double surcharge 12.50
c. Perf. 14 45.00 20.00
96 A62 2c on 1col brn (Bk) 1.25 .70
a. Inverted surcharge 12.50
b. Double surcharge 16.00
c. Perf. 14 2.00 .80
97 A62 2c on 2col car (Bk) 1.25 .60
a. Inverted surcharge 8.00 5.00
b. "Correos" inverted 10.00 5.50
c. Double surcharge
d. Perf. 14 27.50 16.00
98 A62 2c on 5col grn (Bk) 1.00 .70
a. Inverted surcharge 10.00 7.00
b. "Correos" inverted *16.00* *4.25*
c. Perf. 14 6.00 3.00
99 A62 2c on 10col mar (Bk) 1.50 .70
a. "Correos" inverted *400.00*
b. Perf. 14 6.00 3.00

***Perf. 12***

100 A63 5c on 5c org (Bl) .40 .40
a. Double surcharge 27.50 16.00
b. Inverted surcharge 27.50 9.50
c. Pair, one without surcharge 16.00

Counterfeits exist of Nos. 87, 94 and all minor varieties. Genuine used examples of No. 94 are rare and have a cancel only used on registered mail. Genuine "Coereos" errors do not exist on No. 87. Used examples of No. 94 with target cancels are counterfeits. No. 94c is unique. All examples of Nos. 94b and 94c have stains and are valued thus.

Nos. 93-99 exist with papermaker's watermark.

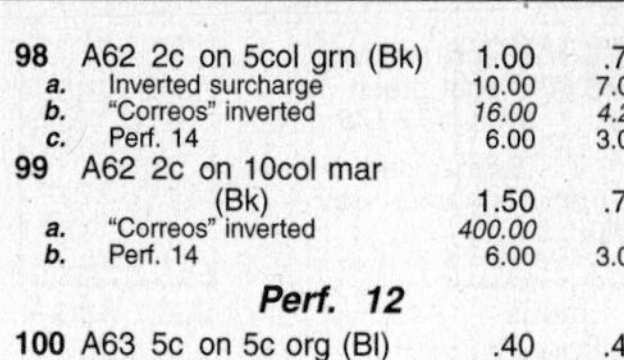

Coffee Plantation A64

**1921, June 17** **Litho.** ***Perf. 11½***

103 A64 5c bl & blk 3.00 3.00
a. Tête bêche pair 15.00 6.50
b. Imperf., pair *60.00*
c. As "a," imperf. *200.00*

Centenary of coffee raising in Costa Rica.

No. 103 exists on pink surfaced paper. Value: single, $200; tete-beche pair, $2,000.

Liberty with Torch of Freedom — A65

**1921** **Typo.** ***Perf. 11***

104 A65 5c violet 1.00 .40
a. Imperf, pair *100.00*

Cent. of Central American independence.

Beware of trimmed singles that look like No. 104a.

For overprint see No. 111.

Juan Mora and Julio Acosta — A66

**1921, Sept. 15** ***Perf. 11½***

105 A66 2c orange & blk 3.50 3.50
106 A66 3c green & blk 3.50 3.50
107 A66 6c scarlet & blk 7.00 7.00
108 A66 15c dk blue & blk 16.00 16.00
109 A66 30c orange brn & blk 20.00 20.00
*Nos. 105-109 (5)* 50.00 50.00

Centenary of Central American independence. Issue requested by Costa Rican Philatelic Society. Authorized by decree calling for 2,000 of 30c and 5,000 each of other values. Nos. 105-109 imperf were not regularly issued. Inverted centers exist of both perf and imperf. They are rare. Used values are for Independence commemorative cancel.

Each sheet of 20 (4x5) contains 5 tête-bêche pairs. Value, set of 5 pairs $75.

Simón Bolívar — A67

**1921** **Engr.** ***Perf. 12***

110 A67 15c deep violet .75 .30

For overprint see No. 111H. For surcharge see No. 148.

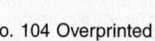

No. 104 Overprinted

**1922** ***Perf. 11***

111 A65 5c violet .75 .40
a. Inverted overprint 10.00
b. Double overprint 15.00

Stamps of 1910-1921 Overprinted in Blue, Red, Black or Gold

**1922** ***Perf. 12***

111C A53 1c brown (Bl) .30 .25
111D A54 2c deep green (R) .40 .25
111E A55 4c scarlet .30 .25
111F A56 5c orange 3.00 .40
111G A57 10c deep blue (R) .75 .40
111H A67 15c deep violet (G) 8.00 3.00
*Nos. 111C-111H (6)* 12.75 4.55

Inverted overprints occur on all values. Value, set $20. Counterfeits predominate.

No. 72 Overprinted

**1923**

111J A56 5c orange 3.00 .75
k. "VD." for "UD." *75.00* *75.00*

Jesús Jiménez — A68

**1923, June 18** **Litho.** ***Perf. 11½***

112 A68 2c brown .40 .40
113 A68 4c green .40 .40
114 A68 5c blue .60 .40
115 A68 20c carmine .85 .50
116 A68 1col violet 1.10 1.25
*Nos. 112-116 (5)* 3.35 2.95

Pres. Jesús Jiménez (1823-98).

Nos. 112-116, imperf, were not regularly issued. Value, set $4.

For overprints see Nos. O65-O69.

National Monument A70

Harvesting Coffee A71

Banana Growing A73

General Post Office A74

Columbus Soliciting Aid of Isabella — A75

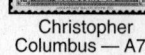

Christopher Columbus — A76

Columbus at Cariari — A77

Map of Costa Rica — A78

Manuel M. Gutiérrez — A79

**1923-26** **Engr.** ***Perf. 12***

117 A70 1c violet .25 .25
118 A71 2c yellow .50 .25
119 A73 4c deep green .75 .30
120 A74 5c light blue 1.50 .25
121 A74 5c yellow grn ('26) .50 .25
122 A75 10c red brown 3.00 .25
123 A75 10c car rose ('26) .50 .25
124 A76 12c carmine rose 10.00 6.00
125 A77 20c deep blue 10.00 .75
126 A78 40c orange 11.00 6.00
127 A79 1col olive green 2.40 1.00
*Nos. 117-127 (11)* 40.40 15.55

See Nos. 151-156. For surcharges & overprints see Nos. 136-140, 147, 189, 218, C2.

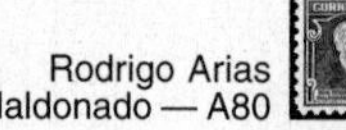

Rodrigo Arias Maldonado — A80

**1924** ***Perf. 12½***

128 A80 2c dark green .40 .40
a. Perf. 14 .50 .40

See No. 162.

Map of Guanacaste A81

Mission at Nicoya A82

**1924** **Litho.** ***Perf. 12***

129 A81 1c carmine rose .30 .25
130 A81 2c violet .40 .25
131 A81 5c green .40 .25
132 A81 10c orange 2.25 .50
133 A82 15c light blue 1.00 .50
134 A82 20c gray black 2.00 1.00
135 A82 25c light brown 3.00 1.50
*Nos. 129-135 (7)* 9.35 4.25

Centenary of annexation of Province of Guanacaste to Costa Rica.

Exist imperf. Value, set, $50.

**Stamps of 1923 Surcharged**

a

b

**1925**

136 A74(a) 3c on 5c lt blue .30 .30
137 A75(a) 6c on 10c red brn .40 .30
138 A78(a) 30c on 40c orange 1.50 .40
139 A79(b) 45c on 1col ol grn 1.75 .50
a. Double surcharge *250.00*
*Nos. 136-139 (4)* 3.95 1.50

No. 124 Surcharged

**1926**

140 A76 10c on 12c car rose 1.50 .40

College of San Luis, Cartago — A83

Chapui Asylum, San José — A84

Normal School, Heredia — A85

Ruins of Ujarrás — A86

**1926 Unwmk. Engr. *Perf. 12½***

143 A83 3c ultra .55 .25
144 A84 6c dark brown .55 .25
145 A85 30c deep orange 3.00 .40
146 A86 45c black violet 5.00 1.60
*Nos. 143-146 (4)* 9.10 2.50

For surcharges see Nos. 190-190D, 217.

No. 124 Surcharged in Black

**1928, Jan. 7 *Perf. 12***

147 A76 10c on 12c car rose 4.75 4.75

Issued in honor of Col. Charles A. Lindbergh during his Good Will Tour of Central America.

The surcharge was privately reprinted using an original die. Reprints can be distinguished by distinct dots under the "10s." All errors and inverted surcharges are reprints.

No. 110 Surcharged

**1928**

148 A67 5(c) on 15c dp violet .40 .40
*a.* Inverted surcharge 35.00

Type I — A88

Type II

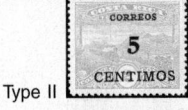

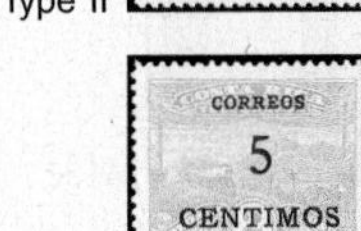
Type III

Type IV

Type V

**Surcharge Typo. (I-V) & Litho. (V)**

**1929 *Perf. 12½***

149 A88 5c on 2col car (I) 1.00 .40
*a.-d.* Types II-V 1.20 .40
*e.* Type V (litho.) 3.00 3.00

**Telegraph Stamp Surcharged for Postage as in 1929, Surcharge Lithographed**

**1929**

150 A88 13c on 40c deep grn .40 .40
*a.* Inverted surcharge 2.00 2.00

Excellent counterfeits exist of No. 150a.

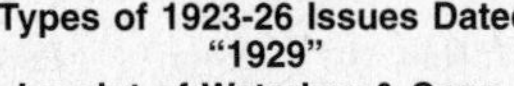

**Types of 1923-26 Issues Dated "1929"**

**Imprint of Waterlow & Sons**

**1930 Size: 26x21½mm *Perf. 12½***

151 A70 1c dark violet .70 .40
155 A74 5c green .70 .40
156 A75 10c carmine rose .70 .40
*Nos. 151-156 (3)* 2.10 1.20

Juan Rafael Mora — A89

**1931, Jan. 29**

157 A89 13c carmine rose 2.50 .40

For surcharge see No. 209.

Seal of Costa Rica Philatelic Society ("Octubre 12 de 1932") A90

**1932, Oct. 12 *Perf. 12***

158 A90 3c orange .25 .35
159 A90 5c dark green .40 .35
160 A90 10c carmine rose .50 .35
161 A90 20c dark blue .85 .55
*Nos. 158-161 (4)* 2.00 1.60

Phil. Exhib., Oct. 12, 1932. See Nos. 179-183.

**Maldonado Type of 1924**

**1934, Aug. 11 *Perf. 12½***

162 A80 3c dark green 1.00 .40

Red Cross Nurse — A91

**1935, May 31 *Perf. 12***

163 A91 10c rose carmine 7.50 .40

50th anniv. of the founding of the Costa Rican Red Cross Society.

Air View of Cartago — A92

Miraculous Statuette and View of Cathedral — A93

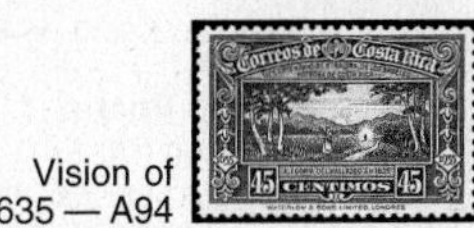
Vision of 1635 — A94

**1935, Aug. 1 *Perf. 12½***

164 A92 5c green .25 .25
165 A93 10c carmine .25 .25
166 A92 30c orange .25 .25
167 A94 45c dark violet 1.50 .55
168 A93 50c blue black 1.50 1.00
*Nos. 164-168 (5)* 3.75 2.30

Tercentenary of the Patron Saint, Our Lady of the Angels, of Costa Rica.

Map of Cocos Island — A95

**1936, Jan. 29 *Perf. 14, 11½ (25c)***

169 A95 4c ocher .50 .25
170 A95 8c dark violet .65 .25
171 A95 25c orange .80 .25
172 A95 35c brown vio .95 .25
173 A95 40c brown 1.25 .40
174 A95 50c yellow 1.50 .60
175 A95 2col yellow grn 11.00 10.00
176 A95 5col green 30.00 25.00
*Nos. 169-176 (8)* 46.65 37.00

Exist imperf. Value, set, $50.

For surcharges see Nos. 196-200, C55-C56.

Map of Cocos Island and Ships of Columbus — A96

**1936, Dec. 5 *Perf. 12***

177 A96 5c green .40 .40
178 A96 10c carmine rose .55 .40

For overprints see Nos. 247, O80-O81.

Seal of Costa Rica Philatelic Society ("Diciembre 1937") — A97

**1937, Dec. 15**

179 A97 2c dark brown .45 .40
180 A97 3c black .45 .40
181 A97 5c green .45 .40
182 A97 10c orange red .45 .40
*Nos. 179-182 (4)* 1.80 1.60

**Souvenir Sheet**

***Imperf***

183 Sheet of 4 6.50 4.00
*a.* A97 2c dark brown .40 .40
*b.* A97 3c black .40 .40
*c.* A97 5c green .40 .40
*d.* A97 10c orange red .40 .40

Phil. Exhib., Dec. 1937.

Purple Guaria Orchid, National Flower A98

Tuna A99

Native with Donkey Carrying Bananas — A101

3c, Cacao pod. 10c, Coffee harvesting.

**1937-38 Wmk. 229 *Perf. 12½***

184 A98 1c green & vio ('38) .90 .40
185 A98 3c chocolate ('38) .90 .40

**Unwmk. *Perf. 12***

186 A99 2c olive gray .65 .40
187 A101 5c dark green .90 .40
188 A101 10c carmine rose 1.50 .40
*Nos. 184-188 (5)* 4.85 2.00

National Exposition.

No. 125 Overprinted in Black

**1938, Sept. 23 Unwmk. *Perf. 12***

189 A77 20c deep blue 7.50 .40

**No. 146 Surcharged in Red**

a

b

c

d

e

**1940 *Perf. 12½***

190 A86(a) 15c on 45c blk vio 1.00 .40
190A A86(b) 15c on 45c blk vio 1.00 .40
190B A86(c) 15c on 45c blk vio 1.00 .40
190C A86(d) 15c on 45c blk vio 1.00 .40
190D A86(e) 15c on 45c blk vio 1.00 .40
*Nos. 190-190D (5)* 5.00 2.00

No. 190D exists with inverted surcharge. Value, $5.

Allegory — A103

**Black Overprint**

**1940, Dec. 2 Engr. *Perf. 12***

191 A103 5c green .35 .25
192 A103 10c rose carmine .75 .25
193 A103 20c deep blue 2.00 .75
194 A103 40c brown 8.00 2.25
195 A103 55c orange yellow 22.50 9.50
*Nos. 191-195 (5)* 33.60 13.00

Pan-American Health Day. See Nos. C46-C54.

Exist without overprint.

Stamps of 1936 Srchd. in Black

**1941 *Perf. 14, 11½***

196 A95 15c on 25c orange .75 .75
197 A95 15c on 35c brn vio .75 .75
198 A95 15c on 40c brown .75 .75
199 A95 15c on 2col yel grn .75 .75
200 A95 15c on 5col green 2.00 2.00
*Nos. 196-200 (5)* 5.00 5.00

Nos. 196-200 exist with surcharge inverted. Value, set of 5, $30.

National Stadium A104

**Engr.; Flags Typo. in Natl. Colors**

**1941, May 8 *Perf. 12½***

201 A104 5c green .70 .25
*a.* Flags omitted 250.00
202 A104 10c orange .55 .30
203 A104 15c car rose .80 .40
204 A104 25c dk blue .85 .55
205 A104 40c chestnut 3.25 1.40
206 A104 50c purple 4.25 2.00
207 A104 75c red orange 6.75 5.75
208 A104 1col dk carmine 13.00 10.50
*Nos. 201-208 (8)* 30.15 21.15

Caribbean and Central American Soccer Championship. See Nos. C57-C66, C121-C123.

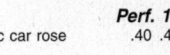

No. 157 Surcharged in Black

**1941, July 26 *Perf. 12***

209 A89 5c on 13c car rose .40 .40

Cleto González Viquez — A105

Design: 5c, José Rodriguez.

**1941-45 Engr. *Perf. 12½***

| | | | | |
|---|---|---|---|---|
| 210 | A105 | 3c dp orange | .40 | .40 |
| 210A | A105 | 3c dp plum ('43) | .40 | .40 |
| 210B | A105 | 3c carmine ('45) | .40 | .40 |
| 211 | A105 | 5c dp violet | .40 | .40 |
| 211A | A105 | 5c brown blk ('43) | .40 | .40 |
| | | *Nos. 210-211A (5)* | 2.00 | 2.00 |

See No. 256.

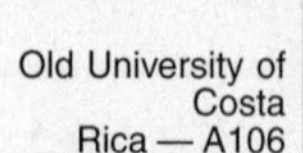

Old University of Costa Rica — A106

New National University — A107

**1941, Aug. 26 *Perf. 12***

| | | | | |
|---|---|---|---|---|
| 212 | A106 | 5c green | .40 | .25 |
| 213 | A107 | 10c yellow org | .40 | .25 |
| 214 | A106 | 15c lilac rose | .75 | .25 |
| 215 | A107 | 25c dull blue | 1.00 | .35 |
| 216 | A106 | 50c fawn | 7.50 | 2.25 |
| | | *Nos. 212-216 (5)* | 10.05 | 3.35 |

National University, founded in 1940. See Nos. C74-C80.

Nos. 144, 189 Srchd. in Black or Red

**1942, April *Perf. 12½, 12***

| | | | | |
|---|---|---|---|---|
| 217 | A84 | 5c on 6c dk brn | 2.00 | .40 |
| 218 | A77 | 15c on 20c dp bl (R) | 8.00 | .40 |

Nos. 217-218 exist with inverted surcharge. Value, each $10.

Torch of Freedom, "Victory" and Flags of American Nations — A108

**1942, Sept. 25 *Perf. 12***

| | | | | |
|---|---|---|---|---|
| 219 | A108 | 5c rose | .40 | .40 |
| 220 | A108 | 5c yellow grn | .40 | .40 |
| 221 | A108 | 5c purple | .40 | .40 |
| 222 | A108 | 5c dp blue | .40 | .40 |
| 223 | A108 | 5c red orange | .40 | .40 |
| | | *Nos. 219-223 (5)* | 2.00 | 2.00 |

For overprints see Nos. 238-241.

Juan Mora Fernández — A109

Designs: 2c, Bruno Carranza. 3c, Tomas Guardia. 5c, Manuel Aguilar. 15c, Francisco Morazan. 25c, Jose M. Alfaro. 50c, Francisco M. Oreamuno. 1col, Jose M. Castro. 2col, Juan Rafael Mora.

**1943-47 Engr.**

| | | | | |
|---|---|---|---|---|
| 224 | A109 | 1c red lilac | .40 | .40 |
| 225 | A109 | 2c black | .40 | .40 |
| 226 | A109 | 3c deep blue | .40 | .40 |
| 227 | A109 | 5c brt blue grn | .40 | .40 |
| *a.* | | 5c bright green ('47) | .40 | .40 |
| 228 | A109 | 15c scarlet | .40 | .40 |
| 229 | A109 | 25c brt ultra | 1.25 | .40 |
| 230 | A109 | 50c dp violet | 5.25 | .80 |
| 231 | A109 | 1col black brown | 7.00 | 3.75 |
| 232 | A109 | 2col deep orange | 8.75 | 5.50 |
| | | *Nos. 224-232 (9)* | 24.25 | 12.45 |

See Nos. 344-368, C81-C91A, C124-C127, C154-C158, C179-C181, C768-C772, C790-C794, C854-C858. For surcharges see Nos. C154-C158, C182, C184-C185.

View of San Ramón — A118

**1944, Jan. 19**

| | | | | |
|---|---|---|---|---|
| 233 | A118 | 5c dark green | .25 | .25 |
| 234 | A118 | 10c orange | .25 | .25 |
| 235 | A118 | 15c rose pink | .30 | .25 |
| 236 | A118 | 40c gray black | 1.25 | .80 |
| 237 | A118 | 50c deep blue | 2.40 | 1.60 |
| | | *Nos. 233-237 (5)* | 4.45 | 3.15 |

100th anniv. of the founding of the City of San Ramón. See Nos. C94-C102.

**Catalogue values for unused stamps in this section, from this point to the end of the section, are for Never Hinged items.**

Nos. 220-223 Overprinted in Red or Black

**1944, Sept. 18**

| | | | | |
|---|---|---|---|---|
| 238 | A108 | 5c yel green | .70 | .40 |
| 239 | A108 | 5c purple (R) | .70 | .40 |
| 240 | A108 | 5c dp blue (R) | .70 | .40 |
| 241 | A108 | 5c red orange | .70 | .40 |
| | | *Nos. 238-241 (4)* | 2.80 | 1.60 |

Amicable settlement of a boundary dispute with Panama. This overprint also exists on No. 219.

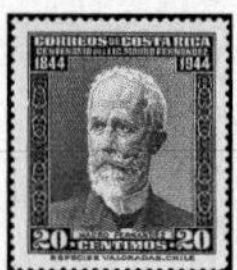

Mauro Fernández (1844-1905), Statesman — A119

**Unwmk.**

**1945, July 21 Engr. *Perf. 14***

| | | | | |
|---|---|---|---|---|
| 242 | A119 | 20c deep green | .80 | .40 |

For surcharge see No. 246.

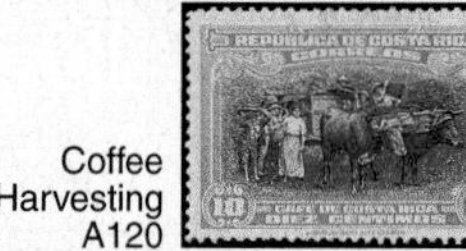

Coffee Harvesting A120

**1945, Oct. 9 *Perf. 12***

| | | | | |
|---|---|---|---|---|
| 243 | A120 | 5c dk green & blk | .60 | .40 |
| 244 | A120 | 10c orange & blk | .60 | .40 |
| 245 | A120 | 20c car rose & blk | 1.40 | .40 |
| | | *Nos. 243-245 (3)* | 2.60 | 1.20 |

**No. 242 Surcharged in Red Brown**

**1946 Unwmk. *Perf. 14***

| | | | | |
|---|---|---|---|---|
| 246 | A119 | 15c on 20c dp green | .80 | .40 |

Exists with inverted surcharge. Value, $6.

No. O80 Overprinted in Red

**1947, Mar. 19 *Perf. 12***

| | | | | |
|---|---|---|---|---|
| 247 | A96 | 5c green | .80 | .40 |

Exist with inverted overprint. Value, $10.

Cervantes — A121

**Wmk. 215**

**1947, Nov. 10 Engr. *Perf. 14***

| | | | | |
|---|---|---|---|---|
| 249 | A121 | 30c deep blue | .85 | .40 |
| 250 | A121 | 55c deep carmine | 1.40 | .40 |

Miguel de Cervantes Saavedra, novelist, playwright & poet, 400th birth anniv.

A122

**1947, Aug. 26 Unwmk. *Perf. 12***

| | | | | |
|---|---|---|---|---|
| 251 | A122 | 5c brt green | .45 | .25 |
| 252 | A122 | 10c car rose | .45 | .25 |
| 253 | A122 | 15c ultra | .45 | .25 |
| 254 | A122 | 25c orange red | .65 | .25 |
| 255 | A122 | 50c lilac | 1.00 | .30 |
| | | *Nos. 251-255,C160-C167 (13)* | 13.40 | 6.30 |

Franklin D. Roosevelt. For surcharges see Nos. C224-C226.

**Small Portrait Type of 1941**

Design: 3c, Bishop Bernardo A. Thiel.

**1948 *Perf. 12½***

| | | | | |
|---|---|---|---|---|
| 256 | A105 | 3c deep ultra | .65 | .40 |

Old University of Costa Rica — A123

**Black Surcharge**

**1953, June 25 Litho. *Perf. 12***

| | | | | |
|---|---|---|---|---|
| 257 | A123 | 5c on 10c green | .85 | .40 |

Inverted and double overprints exist. Exists without overprint. Value, $100.

Revenue Stamp Surcharged in Red or Blue — A124

**1955-56 Unwmk. Engr. *Perf. 12***

| | | | | |
|---|---|---|---|---|
| 258 | A124 | 5c on 2c emerald | .65 | .40 |
| 259 | A124 | 15c on 2c emer (Bl) | .65 | .40 |
| 260 | A124 | 15c on 2c emer ('56) | .65 | .40 |
| | | *Nos. 258-260,C341-C344 (7)* | 6.00 | 2.80 |

For surcharges see Nos. C341-C344, C431-C433.

Justo A. Facio — A125

**1960, Apr. 20 Photo. *Perf. 13½***

| | | | | |
|---|---|---|---|---|
| 261 | A125 | 10c brown red | .90 | .40 |

Centenary of the birth (in 1859) of Prof. Justo A. Facio. Exists imperf. Value, $35.

Nos. RA12-RA15 Surcharged in Red

**1963, Mar.**

| | | | | |
|---|---|---|---|---|
| 262 | PT3 | 10c on 5c dk car | .90 | .40 |
| 263 | PT3 | 10c on 5c sepia | .90 | .40 |
| 264 | PT3 | 10c on 5c dull grn | .90 | .40 |
| 265 | PT3 | 10c on 5c blue | .90 | .40 |
| | | *Nos. 262-265 (4)* | 3.60 | 1.60 |

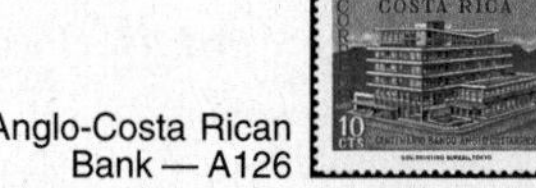

Anglo-Costa Rican Bank — A126

**1963 Unwmk. *Perf. 13½***

| | | | | |
|---|---|---|---|---|
| 266 | A126 | 10c gray | .85 | .40 |

Centenary of the Anglo-Costa Rican Bank.

Arms of San José — A127

Coats of Arms: 35c, Cartago. 50c, Heredia. 55c, Alajuela. 65c, Guanacaste. 1col, Puntarenas. 2col, Limon.

**1969, Sept. 14 Litho. *Perf. 14x13½***

| | | | | |
|---|---|---|---|---|
| 267 | A127 | 15c multicolored | .40 | .30 |
| 268 | A127 | 35c multicolored | .40 | .30 |
| 269 | A127 | 50c gray & multi | .40 | .30 |
| 270 | A127 | 55c buff & multi | .40 | .30 |
| 271 | A127 | 65c multicolored | 1.00 | .40 |
| 272 | A127 | 1col pink & multi | 3.75 | .45 |
| 273 | A127 | 2col multicolored | 5.25 | .70 |
| | | *Nos. 267-273 (7)* | 11.60 | 2.75 |

Alberto M. Brenes Mora — A128

**1976, Mar. 1 Litho. *Perf. 10½***

| | | | | |
|---|---|---|---|---|
| 274 | A128 | 1col violet blue | .85 | .40 |
| | | *Nos. 274,C653-C657 (6)* | 12.30 | 5.30 |

Prof. Alberto Manuel Brenes Mora, botanist, birth centenary.

Map of Costa Rica, Reader with Book — A129

**1978, July 17 Litho. *Perf. 13½***

| | | | | |
|---|---|---|---|---|
| 275 | A129 | 50c multicolored | .90 | .40 |

National five-year literacy plan.

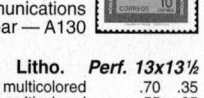

World Communications Year — A130

**1983, May 17 Litho. *Perf. 13x13½***

| | | | | |
|---|---|---|---|---|
| 276 | A130 | 10c multicolored | .70 | .35 |
| 277 | A130 | 50c multicolored | .55 | .35 |
| 278 | A130 | 10col multicolored | 2.40 | .50 |
| | | *Nos. 276-278 (3)* | 3.65 | 1.20 |

A131

**1983, May 30 Litho. *Perf. 10½***

| | | | | |
|---|---|---|---|---|
| 279 | A131 | 20col black | 2.75 | .55 |

1st World Cong. of Human Rights, 1982.

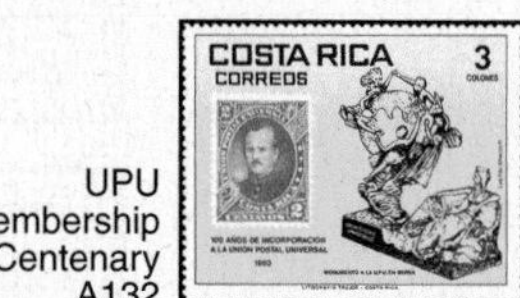

UPU Membership Centenary A132

3col, #17, UPU monument. 10col, #20, San Jose post office.

**1983, June 30 Litho. *Perf. 16***

| | | | | |
|---|---|---|---|---|
| 280 | A132 | 3col multi | 1.60 | .35 |
| 281 | A132 | 10col multi | 3.00 | .65 |

French Alliance Centenary — A133

Scene in San Jose, by Christina Fournier.

**1983, July 21 Litho. *Perf. 11***
**282** A133 12col multicolored 2.50 .55

Christmas 1983 — A134

Nativity tableau in continuous design.

**1983, Dec. 5 Litho. *Perf. 13½***
**283** 1.50col multi .60 .40
**284** 1.50col multi .60 .40
**285** 1.50col multi .60 .40
*a.* A134 Strip of 3, #283-285 3.25 2.50

Costa Rican Gardens Association.

Fishery Development Administration — A135

**1983, Dec. 19 Litho. *Perf. 13½***
**286** A135 8.50col multi 1.25 .40

Local Birds — A136

10c, Quetzal. 50c, Cyanerpes cyaneus. 1col, Turdus grayi. 1.50col, Momotus momota. 3col, Colibri thalassinus. 10col, Notiochelindon cyanoleuca.

**1984, Jan. 9 Litho. *Perf. 13½***
**287** A136 10c multicolored 1.10 .75
**288** A136 50c multicolored 1.30 .75
**289** A136 1col multicolored 1.30 .75
**290** A136 1.50col multicolored 1.30 .75
**291** A136 3col multicolored 2.75 .75
**292** A136 10col multicolored 9.25 1.25
*Nos. 287-292 (6)* 17.00 5.00

Dated 1983. 10c, 1.50col, 3col vert.

José Joaquin Mora, Hero of 1856 Independence Campaign — A137

Paintings, Juan Santamaria Museum, San José: 1.50col, Pancha Carrasco. 3 col, Death of Juan Santamaria, horiz. 8.50col, Juan Rafael Mora Porras.

**1984, Apr. 10 Litho. *Perf. 10½***
**293** A137 50c multi .55 .35
**294** A137 1.50col multi .55 .35
**295** A137 3col multi .55 .35
**296** A137 8.50col multi 3.00 .55
*Nos. 293-296 (4)* 4.65 1.60

For surcharge see No. 440.

Jesus Bonilla Chavarria, Composer — A138

Musicians and Composers: 5col, Benjamin Gutierrez (b. 1937). 12col, Pilar Jimenez (1835-1922). 13col, Jose Daniel Zuniga Zeledon (1889-1981).

**1984, May 30 Litho. *Perf. 13½***
**297** A138 3.50col black & lil .45 .25
**298** A138 5col black & pink .60 .25
**299** A138 12col black & grn 1.60 .80
**300** A138 13col black & yel 2.25 .90
*Nos. 297-300 (4)* 4.90 2.20

Figurines, Jade Museum — A139

**1984, June 27 Litho. *Perf. 13½***
**301** A139 4col Man (pendant) 1.50 .30
**302** A139 7col Seated man 3.00 .50
**303** A139 10col Dish, horiz. 4.00 .70
*Nos. 301-303 (3)* 8.50 1.50

1984 Summer Olympics — A140

**1984, July 27**
**304** A140 1col Basketball .30 .30
**305** A140 8col Swimming .90 .50
**306** A140 11col Bicycling 1.30 .80
**307** A140 14col Running 1.75 1.25
**308** A140 20col Boxing 2.25 2.00
**309** A140 30col Soccer 3.50 2.75
*Nos. 304-309 (6)* 10.00 7.60

Public Street Lighting Centenary — A141

6col, Street scene by Luis Chacon.

**1984, Aug. 9 Litho. *Perf. 10½***
**310** A141 6col multi 1.10 .40

10th Natl. Stamp Exhibition, Sept. 10-16 — A142

No. 311, Natl. monument. No. 312, Juan Mora Fernandez monument.

**1984, Sept. 10 Litho. *Perf. 10½***
**311** A142 10col multicolored 1.40 .75
**312** A142 10col multicolored 1.40 .75
*a.* Min. sheet, 2 each #311-312 17.00 10.00

Natl. Arms — A143

**1984, Oct. 29 Engr. *Perf. 14x13½***
**313** A143 100col dk green 9.00 3.75
**314** A143 100col yel org 9.00 3.75

Detail from Sistine Virgin by Raphael A144

**1984, Dec. 7 Litho. *Perf. 10½***
**315** 3col multicolored .25 .25
**316** 3col multicolored .25 .25
*a.* A144 Pair, #315-316 3.50 2.50

20th Intl. Bicycle Race, Costa Rica — A146

**1984, Dec. 19 Litho. *Perf. 13½***
**317** A146 6col multi 1.10 .90

Intl. Youth Year — A147

11col, IYY emblem, #C476.

**1985, Jan. 31 *Perf. 10½***
**322** A147 11col multi 2.00 .55

Scouting Movement, 75th anniv.

Labor Monument, San Jose — A148

Natl. values: 11col, Freedom of speech-wooden hand printing press. 13col, Neutrality-dove, natl. flag, outline map.

**1985, Feb. 28**
**323** A148 6col shown 1.00 .45
**324** A148 11col bl, blk & yel 1.50 .80
**325** A148 13col multi 1.75 .90

**Size: 68x38mm**

**326** A148 30col Nos. 323-325 5.00 1.75
*Nos. 323-326 (4)* 9.25 3.90

Natl. Red Cross Cent., UN 40th Anniv. A149

**1985, May 3 *Perf. 10½***
**327** A149 3col No. 163, horiz. 3.00 1.00
**328** A149 5col No. C120 3.00 1.50

Club Emblem — A150

1st Club Pres., Ricardo Saprissa Ayma — A151

Design: No. 330, Hands holding soccer ball.

**1985, July 16 *Perf. 10½***
**329** A150 3col multi 1.50 .30
**330** A150 3col multi 1.50 .30
*a.* Pair, #329-330 3.50 1.50
**331** A151 6col multi 2.75 .35
*Nos. 329-331 (3)* 5.75 .95

Saprissa Soccer Club, 50th Anniv.

Orchids — A152

No. 332, Brassia arcuigera. No. 333, Encyclia peraltensis. No. 334, Maxillaria especie. No. 335, Oncidium turialbae. No. 336, Trichopilia marginata. No. 337, Stanhopea ecornuta.

**1985, Dec. 3**
**332** A152 6col multicolored 8.25 1.20
**333** A152 6col multicolored 8.25 1.20
**334** A152 6col multicolored 8.25 1.20
*a.* Strip of 3, #332-334 25.00 15.00
**335** A152 13col multicolored 7.25 2.00
**336** A152 13col multicolored 7.25 2.00
**337** A152 13col multicolored 7.25 2.00
*a.* Strip of 3, #335-337 25.00 15.00
*Nos. 332-337 (6)* 46.50 9.60

11th Natl. Philatelic Exposition — A153

**1985, Dec. 3 Litho. *Perf. 13½***
**338** A153 20col No. C41 2.00 .75

Christmas 1985 — A153a

**1985, Dec. 12 Litho. *Perf. 10½***
**338A** A153a 3col multi .90 .40

Compulsory Education, Cent. — A154

Designs: 3col, Primary school, horiz. 30col, Mauro Fernandez Acuna, founder.

**1986, Feb. 28 *Perf. 13½***
**339** A154 3col pale yel & brn .45 .40
**340** A154 30col pale pink & brn 2.60 1.60

Agriculture Students — A155

No. 341, Students on farm. No. 342, IDB emblem. No. 343, Capo Bianco fisherman.

**1986, Mar. 21 *Perf. 10½***
**341** 10col multi 1.25 .40
**342** 10col multi 1.25 .40
**343** 10col multi 6.00 6.00
*a.* A155 Strip of 3, #341-343 5.50 5.50
*Nos. 341-343 (3)* 8.50 6.80

Inter-American Development Bank Annual Governors' Assembly, San Jose.

### Presidents Type of 1943

Designs: Nos. 344, 349, 354, 359, 364, Francisco J. Orlich Bolmarcich, 1962-66.

Nos. 345, 350, 355, 360, 365, Jose Joaquin Trejos Fernandez, 1966-70.

Nos. 346, 351, 356, 361, 366, Daniel Oduber Quiros, 1974-78.

Nos. 347, 352, 357, 362, 367, Rodrigo Carazo Odio, 1978-82.

Nos. 348, 353, 358, 363, 368, Luis Alberto Monge Alvarez, 1982-86.

**1986, May 12 Litho. *Perf. 10½***
**344** A109 3col turq blue .50 .25
**345** A109 3col turq blue .50 .25
**346** A109 3col turq blue .50 .25
**347** A109 3col turq blue .50 .25
**348** A109 3col turq blue .50 .25
*a.* Strip of 5, #344-348 *3.75 3.25*
**349** A109 6col yel brn .75 .25
**350** A109 6col yel brn .75 .25
**351** A109 6col yel brn .75 .25
**352** A109 6col yel brn .75 .25
**353** A109 6col yel brn .75 .25
*a.* Strip of 5, #349-353 8.50 8.50
**354** A109 10col brn org 1.20 .30
**355** A109 10col brn org 1.20 .30
**356** A109 10col brn org 1.20 .30
**357** A109 10col brn org 1.20 .30
**358** A109 10col brn org 1.20 .30
*a.* Strip of 5, #354-358 14.50 13.00
**359** A109 11col slate gray 1.50 .40
**360** A109 11col slate gray 1.50 .40
**361** A109 11col slate gray 1.50 .40
**362** A109 11col slate gray 1.50 .40

**363** A109 11col slate gray 1.50 .40
*a.* Strip of 5, #359-363 17.50 16.00
**364** A109 13col olive 1.75 .45
**365** A109 13col olive 1.75 .45
**366** A109 13col olive 1.75 .45
**367** A109 13col olive 1.75 .45
**368** A109 13col olive 1.75 .45
*a.* Strip of 5, #364-368 25.00 19.00
*Nos. 344-368 (25)* 28.50 8.25
*Nos. 348a-368a (5)* 70.00

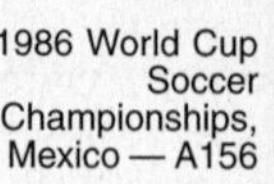

1986 World Cup Soccer Championships, Mexico — A156

No. 369, Players. No. 370, Character trademark, vert. No. 373, Players, diff.

**1986, May 30 Litho. *Perf. 13½***
**369** A156 1col multi .45 .40
**370** A156 1col multi .45 .40
**371** A156 4col as No. 370 2.25 .40
**372** A156 6col as No. 369 3.00 .40
**373** A156 11col multi 6.00 .90
*Nos. 369-373 (5)* 12.15 2.50

A second printing of No. 370 differs in paper and shade from the first printing, but the most obvious difference is in the absence of the initials "LIL" by the left foot of the soccer player. Unused stamps are rare. Value for used, $10.

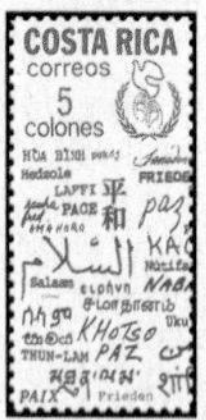

Intl. Peace Year — A157

Peace in many languages: a, "Hoa binh," etc. b, "Vrede," etc. c, "Pace," etc.

**1986, July 31 Litho. *Perf. 10½***
**374** Strip of 3 8.50 4.00
*a.-c.* A157 5col, any single 2.00 .40

A158

Gold Museum, Central Bank of Costa Rica — A158a

Designs: Various undescribed works of Pre-Columbian art.

**1986, Sept. 19 *Perf. 10½***
**375** A158 Strip of 5 22.00 10.00
*a.-e.* 6col any single 2.50 .75
**376** A158a Strip of 5 16.00 7.50
*a.-e.* 13col any single 1.25 1.25

Exist perf 13½, value $17.50 for the two strips of 5 unused

A159

Fauna and Flora — A160

2col, Centurio senex. 3col, Glossophaga soricina. 4col, Ectophylla alba. 5col, Ectophylla alba, diff. 6col, Agalychnis callidryas. 10col, Dendrobates pumilio. 11col, Hyla ebraccata. 20col, Phyllobates lugubris. 50col, Agalychnis callidryas, diff.

**1986, Dec. 16 Litho. *Perf. 13x13½***
**377** A159 2col multicolored .80 .80
**378** A159 3col multicolored 1.50 1.20
**379** A159 4col multicolored 1.90 1.20
**380** A159 5col multicolored 2.60 1.20
**381** A159 6col multicolored 3.25 1.20
**382** A159 10col multicolored 4.50 1.20
**383** A159 11col multicolored 5.00 2.10
**384** A159 20col multicolored 8.00 3.50
*Nos. 377-384 (8)* 27.55 12.40

**Souvenir Sheet**
***Perf. 12½x12***
**385** A160 50col multicolored *87.50 60.00*

Natl. Science and Technology Day — A161

Mural (detail), by Francisco Amighetti, Clorito Picado Social Security Clinic.

**1987, July 31 Litho. *Perf. 10½***
**386** A161 8col multi *6.50* .40

Natl. Museum, Cent. A162

Artifacts: No. 387a, Dowel-shaped figure of a man. No. 387b, Ape-like carved stone figurine. No. 387c, Polished stone ritual figure. No. 387d, Carved granite capital. No. 387e, Two-legged pot. No. 388a, Bowl. No. 388b, Sculpture. No. 388c, Water jar.

**1987, Aug. 7**
**387** Strip of 5 17.50 5.00
*a.-e.* A162 8col any single, vert. .75 .40
**388** Strip of 3 17.50 6.00
*a.-c.* A162 15col any single 1.00 .40
*Nos. 387-388 (2)* 35.00 11.00

Horse-drawn Wagon — A163

No. 390, Street in old San Jose. No. 391, Provincial coat of arms.

**1987, Oct. 26**
**389** A163 20col shown 1.25 .50
**390** A163 20col multicolored 1.25 .50
*a.* Pair, #389-390 2.75 2.00
**391** A163 20col multicolored 1.25 .50
*Nos. 389-391 (3)* 3.75 1.50

City of San Jose, 250th anniv. Rotary Club, 60th anniv.

Columbus Day — A164

**1987, Oct. 26 *Perf. 10½***
**392** A164 30col Map, 16th cent. 3.50 .65

Day of the Race; 495th anniv. of Columbus's departure from Palos, Spain, on first journey to the New World.

Discovery of America, 500th Anniv. (in 1992) — A165

Maps of Honduras, Nicaragua, Costa Rica and Panama, believed to be Asia by Columbus: No. 393, Costa Rica, 16th cent. No. 394, Map of "Asia" by Bartholomeu Columbus (1461-1514).

**1987, Nov. 20 Litho. *Perf. 13½***
**393** A165 4col yel & dk red brn .40 .40
**394** A165 4col yel & dk red brn .40 .40
*a.* Pair, #393-394 4.50 4.00

Pres. Oscar Arias, 1987 Nobel Peace Prize Winner — A166

**1987, Dec. 2 *Perf. 10½***
**395** A166 10col multi *3.50* .40

Two Houses, a Watercolor by Fausto Pacheco (1899-1966) A167

**1987, Dec. 22 Litho. *Perf. 10½***
**396** A167 1col multi 1.00 .40

Intl. Year of Shelter for the Homeless.

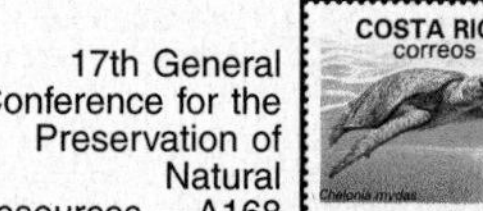

17th General Conference for the Preservation of Natural Resources — A168

No. 397, Green turtle. No. 398, Emblem, golden toad. No. 399, Blue butterfly.

**1988, Feb. 1 Litho. *Perf. 13½***
**397** A168 5col multi 1.00 .40
**398** A168 5col multi 1.00 .40
**399** A168 5col multi 1.00 .40
*a.* A168 Strip of 3, #397-399 4.00 3.25

Intl. Red Cross and Red Crescent Organizations, 125th Annivs. — A169

**1988, Apr. 18 Litho. *Perf. 10½***
**400** A169 30col lt blue & dark red 1.75 .65

North and South Campaign — A170

18col, Adult education. 20col, Cultural radio programs.

**1988, June 6 Photo. *Perf. 11½***
**Granite Paper**
**401** A170 18col multi 2.75 1.20
**402** A170 20col multi 2.75 1.20

Cultural cooperation with Liechtenstein. See Liechtenstein Nos. 886-887. For overprint see No. C921.

A171

**1988, June 27 Litho. *Perf. 10½***
**403** A171 3col dk blue, dark red & yel 1.50 .40

Anglo-Costa Rican Bank, 125th anniv.

A172

No. 404, Character trademark. No. 405, Games emblem.

**1988, Sept. 16 Litho. *Perf. 13½***
**404** A172 25col multicolored 1.25 .60
**405** A172 25col multicolored 1.25 .60
*a.* Pair, #404-405 7.00 5.50

1988 Summer Olympics, Seoul.

Girls' High School, Cent. — A173

10col, Student, courtyard.

**1988, Oct. 17 Litho. *Perf. 10½***
**406** A173 10col cream, brown 1.50 .40

A174

**1988, Nov. 18**
**407** A174 10col gray, greenish bl & red brn .90 .40

Educator Omar Dengo (1888-1928) and the Teachers' College, Heredia.

A175

Indian glass-bead and lion-tooth necklace.

**1988, Nov. 28 *Perf. 13½***
**408** A175 4col multi 1.50 .40

Discovery of America, 500th anniv. (in 1992).

A176

**1988, Dec. 26 Litho. *Perf. 10½***
**409** A176 2col Observation tower 1.10 .40

Natl. Meteorological Institute, cent. For surcharge see No. 439.

A177

Indigenous flora: 5col, Eschweilera costarricensis. 10col, Heliconia wagneriana. 15col, Heliconia lophocarpa. 20col, Aechmea magdalenae. 25col, Psammisia ramiflora. 30col, Passiflora vitifolia.

**1989, Feb. 28**
**410** A177 5col multicolored .70 .50
**411** A177 10col multicolored 1.25 .50
**412** A177 15col multicolored 1.75 1.00
**413** A177 20col multicolored 2.00 1.00
**414** A177 25col multicolored 2.25 1.00
**415** A177 30col multicolored 2.90 1.00
*Nos. 410-415 (6)* 10.85 5.00

Nation at Arms — A178

**1989, July 1 Litho. *Perf. 10½***
**416** A178 30col multi 1.75 .70

French Revolution, bicent.

Sugar Mill — A179

**1989, Aug. 28 Litho. *Perf. 13½***
**417** A179 10col multi 1.10 .90

Grecia County, 151st anniv.
For overprints see Nos. RA106-RA109.

America Issue — A180

UPAE emblem and pre-Columbian stone carvings: 50col, Three-footed bench for grinding corn. 100col, Sphere.

**Litho. & Engr.**
***Perf. 12½x12***
**1989, Oct. 12 Wmk. 334**
**418** A180 50col multi 2.75 1.75
**419** A180 100col multi 5.75 3.25

For overprint see No. C916.

Orchid — A181

***Perf. 10½***
**1989, Oct. 23 Litho. Unwmk.**
**420** A181 10col multi *6.50* 1.00

"100 Years of Democracy" summit of Presidents.

Map, H.F. Pittier, Emblem — A182

***Perf. 13½***
**1989, Nov. 27 Litho. Unwmk.**
**421** A182 18col multi 1.25 .40

Natl. Geographic Institute, cent.
For surcharge see No. 452.

America Issue — A183

Pre-Columbian gold frog figurine and facing portraits of Ferdinand V and Isabella I on gold coin struck by Spain from 1476 to 1516.

**1989, Dec. 4 *Perf. 10½***
**422** A183 4col multicolored 1.50 .40

Discovery of America, 500th anniv. (in 1992).

Natl. Theater, Cent. — A184

***Perf. 10½***
**1990, Feb. 27 Litho. Unwmk.**
**423** A184 5col *Coffee Allegory* 1.25 1.00

World Cup Soccer Championships, Italy — A185

**1990, June 1 Litho. *Perf. 10½***
**424** A185 5col multicolored .90 .40

Univ. of Costa Rica, 50th Anniv. — A187

**1990, Aug. 24 Litho. *Perf. 10½***
**426** A187 18col multicolored 1.50 .50

Education, Democracy, Peace — A188

**Litho. & Engr.**
**1990, Oct. 31 *Perf. 12½***
**427** A188 100col shown 4.75 2.25
**428** A188 200col Flag as map 10.00 4.00
**429** A188 500col National arms 24.00 9.00
*Nos. 427-429 (3)* 38.75 15.25

"Invisible" security printing is sometimes visible.
For overprints see Nos. 448, C920. For surcharges see Nos. 546-548, 553.

Hospitals — A190

No. 431, St. Vincent de Paul Hospital, Heredia. No. 432, Natl. Psychiatric hospital.

**1990, Dec. 18 Engr. *Perf. 13x12½***
**431** A190 50col multicolored 3.00 .75
**432** A190 100col multicolored 5.00 1.25

America Issue — A191

No. 433, Ara macao. No. 434, Ara ambigua. No. 435, Cassia grandis. No. 436, Tabebuia ochracea.

**1990, Dec. 21 Litho. *Perf. 10½***
**433** A191 18col multi 2.00 1.00
**434** A191 18col multi 2.00 1.00
*a.* Pair, #433-434 10.00 8.00
**435** A191 24col multi 3.00 2.00
**436** A191 24col multi 3.00 2.00
*a.* Pair, #435-436 10.00 8.00
*Nos. 433-436 (4)* 10.00 6.00

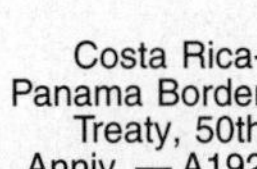

Costa Rica-Panama Border Treaty, 50th Anniv. — A192

Designs: a, Flags, national arms. b, Presidents. c, Map.

**1991, May 24 Litho. *Perf. 10½***
**437** Strip of 3 5.25 2.50
*a.-c.* A192 10col Any single 1.00 .60

No. 437 was issued in a sheet of five strips. Value $20.

Discovery of America, 500th Anniv. (in 1992) — A193

**1991, Oct. 11 Litho. *Perf. 13½***
**438** A193 4col multicolored 1.20 .95

No. 409 Surcharged

No. 296 Surcharged

**1991, Oct. 21 Litho. *Perf. 10½***
**439** A176 1col on 2col #409 .90 .65
**440** A137 3col on 8.50col #296 .90 .65

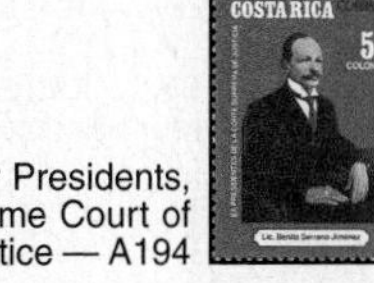


Former Presidents, Supreme Court of Justice — A194

Designs: a, Benito Serrano Jimenez. b, Luis Davila Solera. c, Fernando Baudrit Solera. d, Alejandro Alvarado Garcia.

***Perf. 14½x13½***
**1992, Feb. 28 Litho.**
**441** A194 5col Strip of 4, #a.-d. 5.50 2.50

A sheet exists containing an unissued 5th stamp. Value, sheet $500.

DINADECO, Natl. Directorate of Community Development, 25th Anniv. — A195

**1992, Apr. 28 Litho. *Perf. 10½***
**442** A195 15col multicolored 3.50 2.00

Compare with No. C505.

A196

**1992, May 26 Litho. *Perf. 13½***
**443** A196 15col lake & black 1.75 .75

Dr. Solon Nunez Frutos, public health pioneer.

Solar Eclipse — A197

a, Total eclipse. b, Post Office Bldg. during eclipse. c, Partial eclipse.

**1992, July 17 Litho. *Perf. 13***
**444** A197 45col Strip of 3, #a.-c. 12.00 7.00

A198

**1992, Aug. 14 Litho. *Perf. 13½***
**445** A198 35col multicolored 2.50 1.00

Interamerican Institute for Agricultural Cooperation, 50th anniv.

A199

**1992, Nov. 5 Litho. *Perf. 10½***
**446** A199 2col Waterfall 1.40 1.00
**447** A199 15col Coastline 1.75 1.75

Cocos Island, 450th anniv. of discovery.

No. 427 Overprinted

**Litho. & Engr.**
**1992, Nov. 27 *Perf. 12½***
**448** A188 100col black & blue 6.00 3.00

America Issue — A200

15col, Anolis townsendi. 35col, Pinaroloxias inornata.

**1992, Dec. 15 Litho. *Perf. 10½***
**449** A200 15col multi *3.75* 1.00
**450** A200 35col multi *5.75* 2.00

Natl. Theater — A201

Detail from painting "Allegory of Fine Arts," by Roberto Fontana.

**1993, Jan. 29 Litho. *Perf. 10½***
**451** A201 20col multicolored 1.25 .75

No. 421 Surcharged

**1993, Mar. 26 Litho. Perf. 13½**
**452** A182 5col on 18col multi 1.00 .75

50,000 stamps originally were overprinted with a tiny block and four thin bars over the value, but this was considered unacceptable. So these stamps plus 1,550,000 unoverprinted stamps were overprinted with the large black square and surcharge, as shown.

Protection of the Dolphin — A202

10col, Delphinus delphis. 20col, Stenella coeruleoalbus.

**1993, May 17 Litho. Perf. 10½**
**453** A202 10col multicolored 2.25 2.50
**454** A202 20col multicolored 4.75 2.50

Costa Rican Civil Service, 40th Anniv. — A203

**1993, May 28 Litho. Perf. 13½**
**455** A203 5col multicolored .95 .70

Costa Rican Chamber of Industries, 50th Anniv. — A204

**1993, July 15 Perf. 10½**
**456** A204 45col multicolored 2.25 1.60

School of Communication Sciences, University of Costa Rica, 25th Anniv. — A205

**1993, Aug. 19 Litho. Perf. 13½**
**457** A205 20col black, blue & red 1.50 1.25

Protection of the Tropical Rain Forest — A206

2col, Passiflora vitifolia. 35col, Gurania megistantha.

**1993, Aug. 27 Perf. 10½**
**458** A206 2col multi 2.00 1.75
**459** A206 35col multi 3.00 3.00

Social Guarantees and Labor Code, 50th Anniv. — A207

**1993, Sept. 14 Litho. Perf. 10½**
**460** A207 20col multicolored 1.00 .75

A208

**1993, Oct. 25 Litho. Perf. 13½**
**461** A208 45col multicolored 1.50 1.25

Intl. Assoc. of Professional Custom-House Agents, 15th Congress.

A209

**1993, Nov. 26 Perf. 10½**
**462** A209 20col multicolored 1.40 1.10

Miguel Angel Castro Carazo (1893-1960), educator and humanitarian.
For surcharge see No. 481.

Law School of Costa Rica, 150th Anniv. — A211

**1993, Dec. 23 Litho. Perf. 10½**
**464** A211 20col multicolored 1.10 .85

Natl. Theater — A212

**1994, Mar. 18 Litho. Perf. 13**
**465** A212 20col multi 1.10 .65

Marine Life — A213

5col, Cyphoma gibbosum. 10col, Ophioderma rubicundum. 15col, Myripristis jacobus. 20col, Holocanthus passer. 35col, Paranthias furcifer. 45col, Tubastraea coccinea. 50col, Acanthaster planci. 55col, Ocypode. 70col, Arothron meleagris. 100col, Thalassoma lucasanum.

**Litho. & Embossed**

**1994, Apr. 29 Perf. 12½x12**
**466** A213 5col multicolored .50 .45
**467** A213 10col multicolored .95 .85
**468** A213 15col multicolored 1.50 1.10
**469** A213 20col multicolored 1.90 .75
**470** A213 35col multicolored 3.25 3.00
**471** A213 45col multicolored 4.00 3.50
**472** A213 50col multicolored 5.00 4.50
**473** A213 55col multicolored 5.50 5.00
**474** A213 70col multicolored 6.50 6.00
*Nos. 466-474 (9)* 29.10 25.15

**Souvenir Sheet**

***Perf. 13***

**475** A213 100col multicolored 11.50 11.00

America Issue A214

Illustrations from 19th century Book of Figueroa: a, Man on horseback. b, Back of ox carrying bundles.

**1994, Dec. 19 Litho. Perf. 10½**
**476** A214 20col Pair, #a.-b. + label 10.00 6.00

No. 476 is a continuous design.

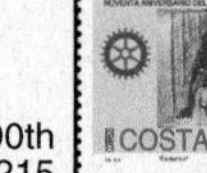

Rotary Intl., 90th Anniv. — A215

**1995, Mar. Litho. Perf. 13½**
**477** A215 20col multicolored 1.40 1.10

Antonio Jose de Sucre (1795-1830) — A216

Design: 30col, Jose Marti (1853-95).

**1995, June Litho. Perf. 10½**
**478** A216 10col multicolored .60 .40
**479** A216 30col multicolored 1.25 1.00

Guanacaste Institute, 50th Anniv. — A217

**1995, July 24 Perf. 13½**
**480** A217 50col ol grn, blk & cream 1.60 1.40

No. 462 Surcharged in Blue or Black

**1995, Sept. 11 Litho. Perf. 10½**
**481** A209 5col on 20col multi .85 .60

UN, 50th Anniv. — A218

**1995, Oct. 24 Litho. Perf. 10½**
**482** A218 5col multicolored .90 .65

13th Natl. Philatelic Expo — A219

Paintings by Lola Fernández: No. 483, Noviembre. No. 484, Enero.

**1995, Dec. 1**
**483** A219 50col multicolored 3.50 3.00
**484** A219 50col multicolored 3.50 3.00
*a.* Pair, Nos. 483-484 13.50 13.00

America Issue — A220

30col, Jabiru mycteria. No. 486, View of coast. No. 487, River, trees. 50col, Atta cephalotes.

**1995, Dec. 25 Litho. Rouletted 13½**
**485** A220 30col multicolored 1.50 .80
**486** A220 40col multicolored 1.50 1.25
**487** A220 40col multicolored 1.50 1.25
*a.* Pair, #486-487 7.00 6.00
**488** A220 50col multicolored 2.50 1.50
*a.* Souvenir sheet, #485-488 13.00 12.00
*Nos. 485-488 (4)* 7.00 4.80

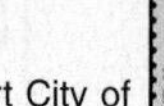

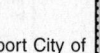

Seaport City of Limón — A221

Designs: a, Early picture of steam train. b, Photo of ship in port, 1922. c, Aerial view of seaport, 1995. d, Painting of fruit seller, by Diego Villalobos. e, Drawing of Calipso singers, by Jorge Esquivel.

**1996, Jan. 31 Litho. Perf. 10½**
**489** Strip of 5 8.25 7.00
*a.-e.* A221 30col Any single 1.50 1.00

Jerusalem, 3000th Anniv. — A222

**1996, May 17 Litho. Perf. 13½**
**490** A222 30col multicolored 1.25 1.00

1996 Summer Olympic Games, Atlanta — A223

Olympic swimmers, coaches from Costa Rica: a, F. Rivas, M.M. Paris. b, S. Poll, R. Yglesias. c, C. Poll, A. Cruz.

**1996, July 18 Litho. Perf. 10½**
**491** Strip of 3 5.00 4.00
*a.-c.* A223 5col Any single 1.50 1.00

No. 491 is a continuous design.

A224

First lady, presidents: a, Juana del Castillo. b, Juan Mora Fernández. c, J.M. Castro Madriz. d, Pacífica Fernández.

**1996, Sept. 13 Litho. Perf. 10½**
**492** Block of 4, #a.-d. 5.00 3.50
*a.-d.* A224 30col Any single 1.00 .75

Independence, 175th anniv. No. 492 was issued in sheets of 16 stamps.

A225

**1996, Oct. 4 Litho. Perf. 13½**
**493** A225 15col multicolored .90 .65

Aqueducts and sewage systems, 35th anniv.
Exists imperf.

A226

America issue (Paintings): No. 494, Black from Lemon, by Manuel da la Cruz González. No. 495, Peasant Women, by Gonzalo Morales Alvarado, vert.

**1996, Dec. 16 Perf. 10½**
**494** A226 45col multicolored 3.00 2.50
**495** A226 45col multicolored 3.00 2.50

A227

Entrance of the Saints at San Ramón, parade of people: a, Building with palm trees on top. b, Church on hill. c, Tree, holy family.

**1997, Aug. 14 Litho. *Perf. 13½***
**496** A227 30col Strip of 3 6.25 4.00
*a.-c.* A227 30col Any single 1.75 1.00

Costa Rican traditions.

School of Fine Arts, Cent. — A228

**1997, Sept. 24 *Perf. 10½***
**497** A228 50col multicolored 1.75 1.50

Radio Netherlands, 50th Anniv. — A229

**1997, Sept. 26 *Perf. 13½***
**498** A229 45col multicolored 1.50 1.25

Exists imperf.

14th Natl. Philatelic Exhibition A230

**1997, Oct. 9 *Perf. 10½***
**499** A230 30col Postmen 1.50 1.25

America Issue.

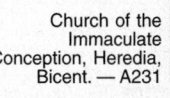

Church of the Immaculate Conception, Heredia, Bicent. — A231

**1997, Nov. 10 Litho. *Perf. 10½***
**502** A231 50col multicolored 1.75 1.50

Second Republic, 50th Anniv. — A232

Former Pres. José Figueres demolishing wall of Fort Bellavista: 10col, 45col, Complete photo. 30col, Detail of Figueres' head. 50col, Hammer head hitting wall.

**Litho. & Engr.**

**1998, Mar. 30 *Perf. 12½***
**503** A232 10col multicolored .80 .80
**504** A232 30col multicolored 1.20 1.10
**505** A232 45col multicolored 1.80 1.40
**506** A232 50col multicolored 2.00 1.60
*a.* Souvenir sheet of 2, #504, 506 8.00 5.00

Natl. University, 25th Anniv. — A233

**1998, July 27 Litho. *Perf. 10½***
**507** A233 50col multicolored 3.00 2.50

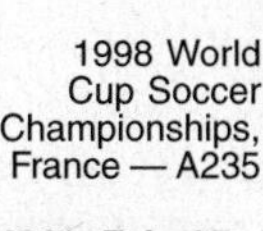

Butterflies A234

10col, Caligo memnon. 15col, Morpho peleides. 20col, Papilio thoas. 30col, Siproeta stelenes. 35col, Ascia monuste. 40col, Parides iphidamas. 45col, Smyrna blonfildia. 50col, Callicore pitheas. 55col, Historis odius. 60col, Danaus plexippus.

**1998, July 16**
**508** A234 10col multicolored .85 .80
**509** A234 15col multicolored 1.40 1.25
**510** A234 20col multicolored 1.90 1.75
**511** A234 30col multicolored 2.75 2.50
**512** A234 35col multicolored 3.25 3.00
**513** A234 40col multicolored 3.50 3.25
**514** A234 45col multicolored 3.25 3.50
**515** A234 50col multicolored 4.25 4.00
**516** A234 55col multicolored 4.90 4.50
**517** A234 60col multicolored 6.00 5.50
*Nos. 508-517 (10)* 32.05 30.05

1998 World Cup Soccer Championships, France — A235

**1998, Feb. 27 Litho. *Perf. 10½***
**518** A235 50col multicolored 1.75 1.50

A236

**1998, Nov. 30 Litho. *Perf. 13½***
**519** A236 50col brn, yel brn & lt yel 2.50 2.25

Carmen Lyra (1888-1949), author.

Gandhi (1869-1948) — A237

**1998, Dec. 11 Litho. *Perf. 13½***
**520** A237 50col multicolored 3.00 2.50

Intl. Union for the Conservation of Nature, 50th Anniv. — A238

Turtles: a, Rhinociemmys pulcherrima. b, Trachemys scripta. c, Chelydra serpentina.

**1998, Dec. 1**
**521** A238 Strip of 3 14.00 11.00
*a.* A238 70col multi 4.50 3.50
*b.* A238 60col multi 4.50 3.00
*c.* A238 70col multi 4.50 3.50

Mushrooms A239

No. 522: a, Morchella esculenta. b, Boletus edulis.

**1999, July 2 Litho. *Perf. 10½***
**522** Pair 5.50 5.00
*a.-b.* A239 50col Either single 2.25 2.25

SOS Children's Villages, 50th Anniv. — A240

**1999, June Litho. *Perf. 10½***
**523** A240 50col multicolored 3.00 2.50

Costa Rican Institute of Electricity, 50th Anniv. — A241

**1999, Sept. 21 Litho. *Perf. 13¼***
**524** A241 75col multi 1.25 .90

A242

**1999, Oct. 7 Engr. *Perf. 13¾x14***
**525** A242 300col violet 3.50 3.00

Archbishop Víctor M. Sanabria (1899-1952). See No. 538.

Intl. Year of Older Persons — A243

**1999, Oct. 29 Litho. *Perf. 13¼***
**526** A243 50col multi 1.25 .90

Supreme Election Tribunal, 50th Anniv. — A244

**1999, Nov. 5 *Perf. 10½***
**527** A244 70col multi 2.25 1.50

UPU, 125th Anniv. — A245

**1999, Dec. 1 *Perf. 13¼***
**528** A245 75col multi 1.25 1.00

Carmen Granados (1915-99), Humorist — A246

**1999, Dec. 1**
**529** A246 50col multi 1.25 .90

America Issue, A New Millennium Without Arms — A247

70col, Male face, both hands.

**1999, Dec. 1**
**530** A247 50col shown 1.25 .90
**531** A247 70col multicolored 1.50 1.00

PhilexFrance '99 — A248

No. 533, Flower, Eiffel Tower.

**1999, Dec. 1**
**532** A248 300col shown 5.25 3.50
**533** A248 300col multi 5.25 3.50

Natl. Bank, 50th Anniv. A249

No. 534 — Pre-Columbian artifacts: a, Jaguar. b, Scorpion. c, Bat. d, Crab. e, Beast with horns.

No. 535 — Obverse and reverse of coins: a, Gold, from 1825. b, Gold, from 1850. c, Silver one-eighth peso. d, Gold 20-peso. e, 1935 1-colon.

**2000, Jan. 28 Litho. *Perf. 13¼***
**534** Vert. strip of 5 10.00 7.00
*a.-e.* A249 60col Any single 1.25 1.00
**535** Vert. strip of 5 24.00 12.50
*a.-e.* A249 90col Any single 3.00 1.50

Nos. 534-535 were printed in sheets of three strips. Value, set of two sheets $100.

2000 Summer Olympics, Sydney — A250

No. 536, 60col: a, Taekwando. b, Cycling. c, Swimming. d, Soccer.

No. 537, 70col: a, Running. b, Boxing. c, Men's rings. d, Tennis.

**2000, Aug. 31 Blocks of 4, #a-d**
**536-537** A250 Set of 2 12.00 10.00

There were two printings of Nos. 536-537. In the first printing, colors are paler, and the green Olympic ring is misregistered on Nos. 536a-536d. In the second, colors are more intense, and the green ring is properly registered. Values the same.

**Famous Person Type of 1999**

Pres. Rafael A. Calderón Guardia (1900-70).

**2000, Sept. 14 Engr. *Perf. 12½***
**538** A242 100col deep blue 3.75 .75
*a.* Perf 13¾x14 5.25 2.50

Paintings by Max Jiménez A251

No. 539: a, Fishermen in Cojimar. b, Adamant.

**2000, Nov. Litho. *Perf. 10½***
**539** Horiz. pair 5.00 3.50
*a.-b.* A251 50col Either single 1.50 1.00

America Issue, Fight Against AIDS — A252

Designs: 60col, Stylized people. 90col, Stylized person.

**2000, Dec. *Perf. 13¼***
**540-541** A252 Set of 2 3.50 2.50

Christmas A253

**2000, Dec.**
**542** A253 100col multi 2.00 1.50

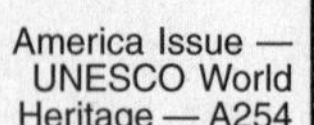

America Issue — UNESCO World Heritage — A254

Birds form Cocos Island Natl. Park: 95col, Coccyzus ferrugineus. 115col, Pinaroloxias inornata.

**2001, Apr. 5 Litho. *Perf. 10½***
**543-544** A254 Set of 2 7.00 4.00

Costa Rica — Netherlands Diplomatic Relations, 150th Anniv. — A255

**2001, July 20**
**545** A255 65col multi 2.25 1.50

No. 429 Surcharged

**2001 Method and Perf. As Before**
**546** A188 65col on 500col multi 1.50 1.00
**547** A188 80col on 500col multi 2.50 1.50
**548** A188 95col on 500col multi 3.50 2.50
*Nos. 546-548 (3)* 7.50 5.00

Issued: No. 546, 8/24. Nos. 547-548, 9/7.

Third Hispanic-Costa Rican Exposition — A256

Orchids: a, Guaria turrialba. b, Tricopilia.

**2001, Oct. 5 Litho. *Perf. 13¼***
**549** A256 65col Horiz. pair, #a-b 6.00 4.00

Campaign Against Child Labor A257

**2001, Nov. 15 *Perf. 13¼***
**550** A257 100col multi 2.25 1.50

Pres. Tomás Guardia (1832-82) and Locomotive A258

**2001, Nov. 21**
**551** A258 65col multi 3.50 1.25

A second printing of No. 551 was issued in 2002. It features a lighter beige and has yellow gum. This printing of 500 sheets of 15 stamps was made to complete the contract. Value, unused $25.

Costa Rican Team for 2002 World Cup Soccer Championships, Japan and Korea — A259

**2002, Mar. 15 *Perf. 10½***
**552** A259 65col multi 3.00 1.00

No. 428 Surcharged in Red

**Litho. & Engr.**

**2002, Jan. 24 *Perf. 12½***
**553** A188 65col on 200col multi 1.50 1.00

America Issue — Youth, Education and Literacy — A260

Designs: 65col, Children and globe. 100col, Blind person reading Braille.

**Litho. & Embossed**

**2002, Mar. *Perf. 10½***
**554-555** A260 Set of 2 3.75 3.00

Taiwan Friendship Bridge — A261

**2002, Apr. 3 Litho.**
**556** A261 95col multi 2.60 2.25

16th Rio Group Congress — A262

**2002, Apr. 10**
**557** A262 65col blue & green 1.50 1.00

Pan-American Health Organization, Cent. — A263

No. 558: a, People (red denomination at UR). b, Emblem. c, Mother and child (black denomination at LR). d, Child and man (red denomination at LR).
50col, Emblem.

**2002, July 5**
**558** A263 10col Block of 4, #a-d 3.25 2.25
**559** A263 50col multi 1.75 1.50

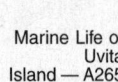

In Remembrance of Sept. 11, 2001 Terrorist Attacks — A264

**Litho. & Embossed**

**2002, Sept. 11**
**560** A264 110col multi 7.00 3.00

Marine Life of Uvita Island — A265

Designs: No. 561, 75col, Gorgona flabellum. No. 562, 75col, Ulva lactuca. No. 563, 75col, Cittarium pica. No. 564, 75col, Liriope tetraphyla.

**Litho & Embossed**

**2002, Sept. 25**
**561-564** A265 Set of 4 8.00 6.50

Space Exploration — A266

No. 565: a, Dr. Franklin Chang-Diaz, astronaut, and space shuttle. b, Phanaeus changdiazi and satellite.

**Litho. & Embossed**

**2003, June 15 *Perf. 10½***
**565** A266 115col Horiz. pair, #a-b 7.50 7.50

No. 565 was printed in sheets of 5 pairs. Value, $37.50.

Coco Island National Park A267

No. 566: a, Denomination at UR. b, Denomination at UL.

**2003, Aug. 1**
**566** A267 75col Horiz. pair, #a-b 4.50 4.00

No. 566 was printed in sheets of 5 pairs. Value, $27.50.

America Issue - Fish A268

No. 567: a, Archocentrus sajica. b, Astatheros diquis.

**2003**
**567** A268 110col Horiz. pair, #a-b 6.50 5.50

Scenes from Cocorí, by Joaquín Gutiérrez A269

No. 568: a, Boy, turtle, monkey and bird. b, Boy looking at reflection in water. c, Toucan in tree, boy and monkey on ground. d, Sailor, girl and boy. e, Boy, bird on branch. f, Jaguar, turtle armadillo, monkey, boy and father. g, Boy and monkey pushing turtle. h, Monkey with open arms, turtle, boy. i, Mother and boy. j, Mother, boy, rose bush. k, Boy, father playing musical instrument (80x150mm).

**Litho. & Embossed**

**2003, Sept. 3 *Perf. 10½***
**568** A269 Sheet of 11 20.00 20.00
*a.-j.* 25col Any single .80 .60
*k.* 225col multi 5.00 5.00

National Anthem, Cent. A270

No. 569: a, Lyricist José Maria Zeledón (24x35mm). b, Flag, text of anthem (49x35mm).

**2003, Sept. 10 Litho.**
**569** A270 75col Horiz. pair, #a-b 5.00 4.50

No. 569 was printed in sheets of 5 pairs. Value, $24.

Election of Pope John Paul II, 25th Anniv. — A271

**2003, Oct. 16 Litho. *Perf. 13¼x13½***
**570** A271 130col multi 3.50 3.00

Charles Lindbergh's Flight to Costa Rica, 75th Anniv. — A272

**Litho. & Embossed**

**2003, Dec. 16 *Perf. 13½x13¼***
**571** A272 110col multi 2.60 2.25

Guayabo de Turrialba Archaeological Monument A273

**2003, Dec. 18**
**572** A273 110col multi 2.60 2.25

America Issue — A274

Flora: No. 573, 75col, Ceiba pentandra. No. 574, 75col, Tetranema floribundum. 90col, Ceiba pentandra, diff. 110col, Tetranema gamboanum.

**2004, Mar. 23 Litho. *Perf. 10½***
**573-576** A274 Set of 4 8.00 7.00

Volcanoes A275

Designs: 85col, Arenal. 120col, Irazú. 140col, Poás.

**2004-05 *Perf. 10½***
**577-579** A275 Set of 3 7.75 7.00
*577a* Perf. 13¼ ('05) 2.00 2.00
*578a* Perf. 13¼ ('05) 3.50 3.50
*579a* Perf. 13¼ ('05) 3.75 3.75

Issued: Nos. 577-579, 6/24/04; 577a, 578a, 579a, 2005.
Nos. 577a, 578a and 579a have printer's inscription "LIL S.A."

2004 Summer Olympics, Athens — A276

No. 580 — Various athletes in: a, Blue. b, Yellow orange. c, Green. d, Red.

**2004, July 15**
**580** Horiz. strip of 4 12.00 12.00
*a.-d.* A276 120col Any single 2.50 2.50

A277

Design: Dr. Miguel Angel Rodríguez, Organization of American States President.

**2004, Sept. 15**
**581** A277 120col multi 3.00 3.00

FIFA (Fédération Internationale de Football Association), Cent. — A278

No. 582: a, Emblem (34x34mm). b, Soccer player and field (39x34mm).

**2004, Feb. 15 Litho. *Perf. 10½***
**582** A278 140col Horiz. pair, #a-b 10.00 9.50

No. 582 was printed in sheets of 5 pairs. Value, $54.

Rotary International, Cent. — A279

No. 583: a, Emblem and frog. b, Centenary emblem. c, Emblem and butterfly.

**2005, Feb. 23**

**583** Horiz. strip of 3 9.75 9.00
***a.-c.*** A279 140col Any single 2.50 2.50

### Souvenir Sheet

Popes A280

No. 584: a, Pope John Paul II (1920-2005). b, Pope Benedict XVI.

**2005, Aug. 22**

**584** A280 140col Sheet of 4, 2 each #a-b 12.00 12.00
***a.-b.*** A281 95col Either single 5.00 5.00

An imperf. sheet lacking postal validity exists. Value, $150.

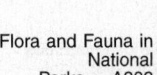

Intl. Year of Physics A281

No. 585: a, Albert Einstein (1879-1955). b, Max Planck (1858-1947).

**2005, June 7**

**585** Horiz. pair 5.00 4.50
***a.-b.*** A281 95col Either single 2.00 2.00

No. 585 was printed in sheets of five pairs. Value, $25.

Flora and Fauna in National Parks — A282

No. 586: a, Passiflora vitifolia. b, Dryas iulia moderata. c, Potos flavus.

**2005, Oct. 11 Litho. *Perf. 10½***

**586** Strip of 3 6.00 5.25
***a.-c.*** A282 85col Any single 1.50 1.50

America Issue, Fight Against Poverty — A283

No. 587: a, Child at computer. b, Man sawing wood. c, Medical worker.

**2005, Oct. 19**

**587** Strip of 3 8.50 7.50
***a.-c.*** A283 120col Any single 2.25 2.25

Intl. Year of Sports and Physical Education A284

**2005, Dec. 6**

**588** A284 85col multi 2.25 2.00

Cartago Sport Club, Cent. A285

**2006, Mar. 20**

**589** A285 85col multi 2.25 2.00

No. 589 was printed in sheets of 5. Value, $12.

### Miniature Sheet

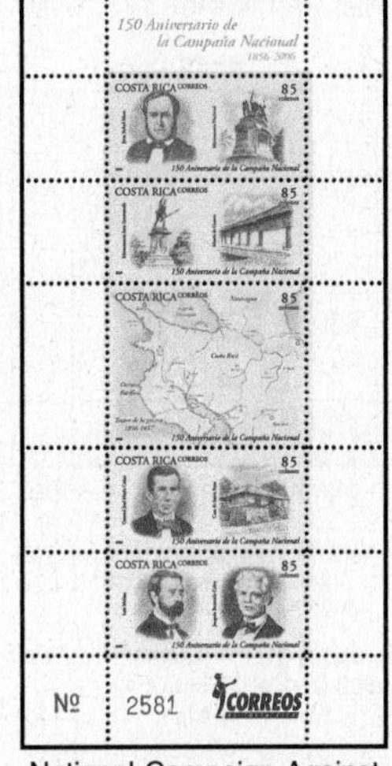


National Campaign Against Nicaraguan Pres. William Walker, 150th Anniv. — A286

No. 590: a, Juan Rafael Mora, National Monument. b, Juan Santamaría Monument, barracks. c, Map (50x40mm). d, Gen. José María Cañas, Santa Rosa House. e, Luis Molina, Joaquín Bernardo Calvo.

**2006, Apr. 7**

**590** A286 85col Sheet of 5, #a-e 10.75 9.50

2006 World Cup Soccer Championships, Germany — A287

**2006, May 15**

**591** A287 120col multi 3.25 2.75

No. 591 was printed in sheets of 9 + 6 tabs. Value, $27.50.

America Issue, Energy Conservation A288

**2006, July 31 Litho. *Perf. 10½***

**592** A288 155col multi + label 3.75 3.50

### Miniature Sheet

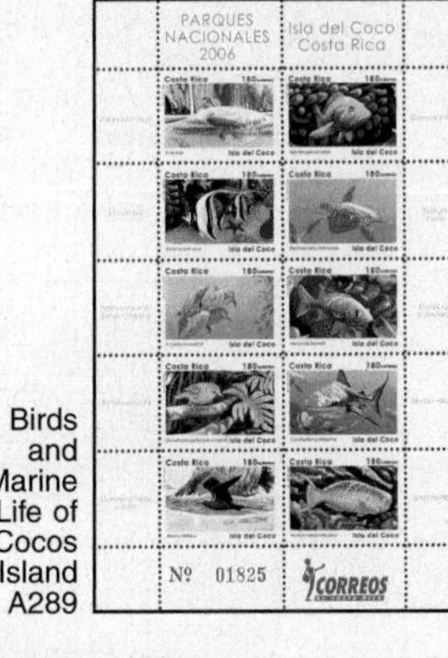


Birds and Marine Life of Cocos Island A289

No. 593: a, Sula sula. b, Mycteroperca olfax. c, Zanclus cornutis. d, Eretmochely imbricaas. e, Tursiops truncatus. f, Myripristis berndti. g, Dendroica petechia aureola. h, Carcharhinus limbatus. i, Anous stolidus. j, Acarus rubroviolaceus.

**2006, Aug. 25 Litho. *Perf. 10½***

**593** A289 180col Sheet of 10, #a-j 50.00 50.00

Pres. José Figueres Ferrer (1906-90) A290

**2006, Sept. 25 *Perf. 10½***

**594** A290 115col gray & multi 3.50 3.00

### Souvenir Sheet

### *Imperf*

**595** A290 1000col tan & multi 30.00 30.00

No. 594 was printed in sheets of 6 + 3 labels. Value, $20.

Fruits — A291

No. 596: a, Hymenaea courbaril. b, Bixa orellana. c, Garcinia intermedia.

**2006, Oct. 12 *Perf. 10½***

**596** Strip of 3 13.00 12.50
***a.-c.*** A291 155col Any single 4.00 4.00

National Symbols A292

No. 597: a, Flag. b, Coat of arms.

**2006, Nov. 27**

**597** A292 155col Pair, #a-b 7.00 6.50

Printed in sheets containing two pairs. Value, $14.

Pres. Francisco J. Orlich (1907-69) A293

**2007, Mar. 7**

**598** A293 115col multi 3.25 3.00

No. 598 was printed in sheets of 6 + central label. Value, $20.

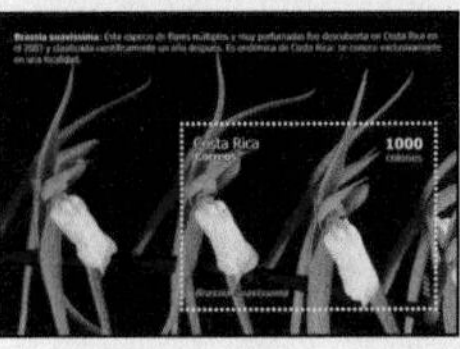


Orchids A294

No. 599: a, Guarianthe skinneri (pink flowers). b, Galeandra arundinis. c, Encyclia ossenbachiana. d, Dracula inexperata. e, Guarianthe skinneri (white flowers). f, Kefersteinia retanae. g, Coryanthes kaiseriana. h, Psychopsis krameriana. i, Chondroscaphe yamilethae. j, Cattleya dowiana.
1000col, Brassia suavissima.

**2007, Mar. 19 Litho. *Perf. 10½***

**599** A294 180col Sheet of 10, #a-j 32.50 30.00

### Souvenir Sheet

### *Imperf*

**600** A294 1000col multi 42.00 40.00

No. 599 contains ten 45x37mm stamps. No. 600 has simulated perforations.

Salesian Order in Costa Rica, Cent. — A295

**2007, Apr. 30 *Perf. 10½***

**601** A295 110col multi 3.50 3.25

### Miniature Sheet

Pre-Columbian Art — A296

No. 602: a, Frog-shaped gold pendant (25x45mm). b, Bird-shaped jadeite pendant (25x45mm). c, Stone metate, horiz. (50x30mm). d, Ceramic censer with alligator (25x45mm). e, Stone figure of warrior (25x45mm).

**2007, May 4**

**602** A296 155col Sheet of 5, #a-e 17.00 16.00

America Issue, Education For All — A297

No. 603: a, 115col, Teacher and students. b, 155col, Family around fire.

**2007, June 8**

**603** A297 Horiz. pair 8.00 7.50

Plasma Technology — A298

No. 604: a, Astronaut and spacecraft's robot arm. b, Plasma containment vessel.

**2007, July 6**
**604** A298 240col Horiz. pair, #a-b 10.50 9.50

Nos. 604a and 604b were printed in sheets of containing two of each stamp. Value, $20.

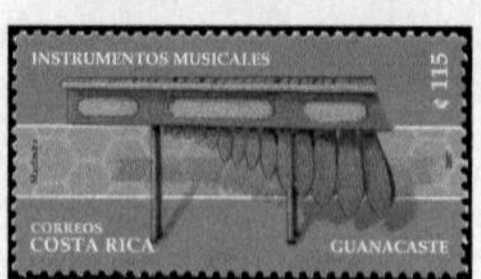


Guanacaste Musical Instruments — A299

Designs: No. 605, 115col, Marimba. No. 606, 115col, Quijongo, vert. (30x50mm).

**2007, July 25**
**605-606** A299 Set of 2 5.50 5.00

Nos. 605-606 were printed in sheets containing two of each stamp + label. Value, $10.

Virgin of the Angels Icon, 225th Anniv. as Patron of Cartago A300

No. 607 — Icon with denomination at: a, LR. b, LL.
1000col, Interior of Cartago Basilica, vert.

**2007, July 27**
**607** A300 115col Horiz. pair, #a-b 5.50 5.00

No. 607 was printed in sheets of 3 pairs + 1 label. Value, $17.

**Souvenir Sheet**

**608** A300 1000col multi 30.00 30.00

No. 608 contains one 75x115mm stamp.

Fauna of National Parks — A301

No. 609: a, Oxybelis fulgidus. b, Stagmomantis sp. c, Heliodoxa jacula. d, Pulsatrix perspicillata.

**2007, Aug. 17 Litho. *Perf. 10½***
**609** Horiz. strip of 4 20.00 19.00
***a.-d.*** A301 235col Any single 4.50 4.50

No. 609 was printed in sheets of two strips of 4. Value, $36.

2007 Special Olympics, Shanghai A302

No. 610: a, Cycling. b, Swimming. c, Running.

**2007, Sept. 10**
**610** Horiz. strip of 3 16.00 15.00
***a.-c.*** A302 240col Any single 3.50 3.50

Accounts of My Aunt Panchita, Children's Book by Carmen Lyra — A303

No. 611, vert. — Text: a, Por qué Tío Conejo tiene las orejas tan largas. b, La Mica. c, Uvieta. d, Tío Conejo y los caites de su abuela.
1000col, De como Tío Conejo salió de un apuro.

**2007, Oct. 18**
**611** A303 100col Sheet of 4, #a-d 10.00 9.00

**Souvenir Sheet**

**612** A303 1000col multi 30.00 30.00

No. 611 contains four 37x50mm stamps.

Ox Cart Heritage A304

No. 613: a, Man with oxen. b, Decorated wheel.

**2007, Nov. 23**
**613** A304 180col Vert. pair, #a-b, + central label 8.00 7.50

Nos. 613a and 613b were printed in sheets of containing two of each stamp. Value, $15.

Esquipulas II Central American Peace Accords, 20th Anniv. — A305

No. 614 — Nobel Peace medal of Pres. Oscar Arias Sánchez: a, Reverse (three men). b, Obverse (Alfred Nobel).

**2007, Dec. 10**
**614** A305 135col Horiz. pair, #a-b 6.50 6.00

No. 614 was printed in sheets of 4 pairs. Value, $26.

Dr. Fernando Centeno Güell (1907-93), Poet and Educator A306

**2008, Feb. 14**
**615** A306 115col multi 2.75 2.25

No. 615 was printed in sheets of 6. Value, $15.

Churches — A307

No. 616: a, Our Lord of Agony Chapel, Guanacaste. b, San Francisco Church, San José. c, Our Lady of Sorrow Church, San José. d, Santa Ana Church, San José. e, Our Lady of Carmel Cathedral, Puntarenas. f, San Bartolomé Apóstol Church, Heredia.
1000col, Our Lady of Mercy Parish Church, San José.

**2008, Mar. 17**
**616** A307 230col Sheet of 6, #a-f 29.00 27.50

**Souvenir Sheet**

**617** A307 1000col multi 72.50 50.00

No. 616 contains six 40x40mm stamps.

Souvenir Sheet

Women's Superior College, 120th Anniv. A308

**2008, Mar. 31**
**618** A308 1000col multi 30.00 30.00

Miniature Sheet

Marine Mammals — A309

No. 619: a, Megaptera novaeangliae, side view. b, Sotalia guianensis. c, Stenella attenuata. d, Megaptera novaeangliae flukes.

**2008, June 16 Litho. *Perf. 10½***
**619** A309 240col Sheet of 4, #a-d 21.00 20.00

Intl. Year of Planet Earth A310

No. 620: a, San Vicente Cataracts. b, Santa Elena Peninsula.

**2008, July 1**
**620** Pair 8.00 7.50
***a.-b.*** A310 175col Either single 3.50 3.50

Nos. 620a and 620b were printed in sheets of containing two of each stamp. Value, $15.

Miniature Sheet

Art A311

No. 621: a, La Ultima Escena, by Rudy Espinoza. b, Mujer que Avanza, sculpture by Crisanto Badilla. c, Transitoriedad del Hombre, by Miguel Hernández. d, Arquetipo, by Lola Fernández.

**2008, July 3**
**621** A311 240col Sheet of 4, #a-d 21.00 19.00

Miniature Sheet

Ministry of Labor and Social Security, 80th Anniv. A312

No. 622 — Details from mural "The Second Republic," by Luccio Ranucci: a, Man with hat, striped pole. b, Woman with basket of fruit. c, Man and woman embracing. d, Man carrying sack on head.

**2008, Aug. 28 Litho. *Perf. 10½***
**622** A312 240col Sheet of 4, #a-d 21.00 20.00

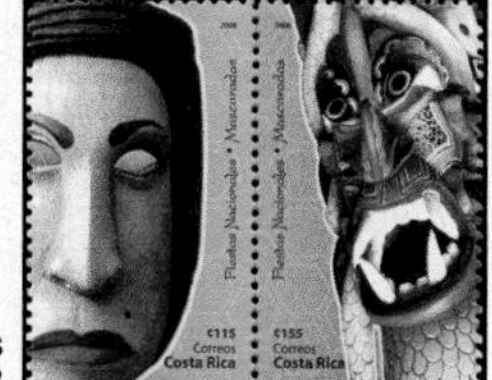


Masks A313

No. 623 — Masks with background colors of: a, 115col, Brown orange. b, 155col, Green.

**2008, Oct. 31**
**623** A313 Horiz. pair, #a-b 6.50 6.00

Nos. 623a and 623b were printed in sheets of containing two of each stamp. Value, $12.

Hogar Crea Drug Rehabilitation Centers in Costa Rica, 25th Anniv. — A314

**2009, Feb. 25 Litho. *Perf. 10½***
**624** A314 160col multi 3.50 3.25

No. 624 was issued in sheets of 6. Value, $16.

Carlos Luis Fallas (1906-66), Author — A315

**2009, Apr. 30 Litho. *Perf. 10½***
**625** A315 150col multi 2.50 2.25

No. 625 was issued in sheets of 6. Value, $13.

Miniature Sheet

Children's Literature — A316

No. 626: a, Tolo, the Giant North Wind (kite), by Adela Ferreto de Saénz. b, The Ship of the Stars (ship and boy), by Alfredo Cardona Peña. c, Old Stories (rabbit and gourds), by María Leal de Noguera. d, Paul's Music (boy holding box), by Lara Ríos.

**2009, May 27**
**626** A316 65col Sheet of 4, #a-d 7.00 6.00

Alberto Martén, Economist, Solidarity Movement Founder — A317

**2009, June 19**

**627** A317 135col multi 3.00 2.75

Miniature Sheet

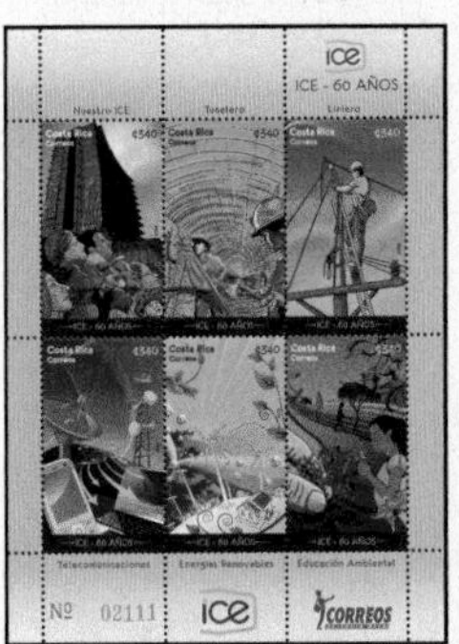

Costa Rican Electrical Institute (ICE), 60th Anniv. A318

No. 628: a, People and ICE building. b, Construction workers in tunnel. c, Lineman on ladder. d, Computers and satellite dishes. e, Houses and windmills. f, Hand planting seedling, girl.

**2009, June 30**

**628** A318 340col Sheet of 6, #a-f 34.00 32.50

Diplomatic Relations Between Costa Rica and Switzerland — A319

**2009, July 8**

**629** A319 225col multi 4.75 4.25

Miniature Sheet

National Parks A320

No. 630: a, Arenal Volcano. b, Celeste River. c, Cerro Chirripó. d, Cocos Island. e, Monteverde. f, Poás Volcano. g, Tortuguero.

**2009, Aug. 24**

**630** A320 240col Sheet of 7, #a-g 11.25 9.50

America Issue, Traditional Games — A321

No. 631: a, Marbles. b, Kite flying.

**2009, Sept. 9 Litho. *Perf. 10½***

**631** Horiz. pair 3.00 2.50
*a.-b.* A321 135col Either single .75 .75

Intl. Holocaust Remembrance Day — A322

**2010, Jan. 27 *Perf. 13¼***

**632** A322 500col gray & black 7.00 5.00

No. 632 was printed in sheets of four with labels at left, bottom and right. Value, $30.

Miniature Sheet

Locomotives — A323

No. 633: a, Steam locomotive, 1889. b, Electric Series AEG locomotive, 1926. c, Yellow and white Apolo Series Diesel-electric locomotive, 1990. d, Blue, white and red Diesel-electric locomotive, 1979-80.

**2010, May 4 Litho. *Perf. 10½***

**633** A323 200col Sheet of 4, #a-d 6.00 6.00

America Issue, National Symbols A324

**2010, June 24**

**634** Horiz. pair 7.00 6.50
*a.* A324 280col Turdus grayi 2.00 2.00
*b.* A324 340col Odocoileus virginianus 3.00 3.00

No. 634 was printed in sheets containing two pairs. Value, $15.

Miniature Sheet

Endangered Birds — A325

No. 635: a, 400col, Platalea ajaja. b, 400col, Icterus mesomelas. c, 1000col, Morphnus guianensis. d, 1000col, Harpia harpyja.

**2010, June 24 Litho. *Perf. 10½***

**635** A325 Sheet of 4, #a-d 17.00 16.00

University Anniversaries — A326

No. 636: a, Mural by Eduardo Torijano at University of Costa Rica. b, Monument to Disarmament, Work and Peace by Thelvia Marin at Univeristy for Peace.

**2010, Aug. 26**

**636** A326 500col Pair, #a-b 6.50 6.00

University of Costa Rica, 70th anniv., University for Peace, 30th anniv.

Miniature Sheet

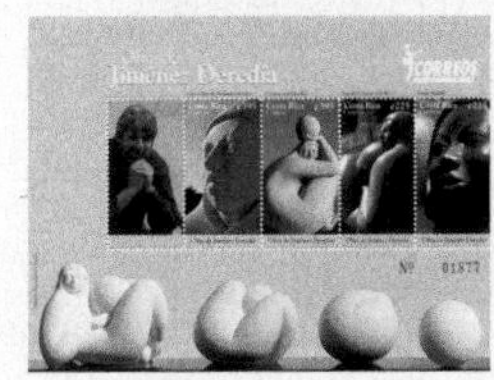

Details of Sculptures by Jiménez Deredia — A327

No. 637: a, 225col, Pareja. b, 225col, Ricordo Profondo. c, 395col, Continuación. d, 395col, Génesi Ricordo Profondo. Names of sculptures are in sheet margin above stamps.

***Perf. 10½ on 2 or 3 Sides***

**2011, Feb. 23**

**637** A327 Sheet of 4, #a-d, + label 8.50 7.50

Souvenir Sheet

Opening of New National Stadium A328

No. 638 — National Stadium built in: a, 1924. b, 2011.

**2011, Mar. 26 *Perf. 10½***

**638** A328 1000col Sheet of 2, #a-b 11.50 10.00

Pres. Laura Chinchilla — A329

**2011, May 9 *Perf. 10½ Vert.***

**639** A329 340col multi 2.50 2.25

No. 639 was printed in sheets of 2 + 2 labels. Value, $8.50.

Souvenir Sheet

Cartoons by Costa Rican Artists A330

No. 640 — Cartoons by: a, 500col, Francisco "Paco" Hernández (1885-1961) and Noé Solano (1889-1971). b, 1000col, Hugo Diaz "Lalo" (1930-2001) and Jorge Chavarria "Kokin" (1932-94).

**2011, June 15 *Perf. 10½***

**640** A330 Sheet of 2, #a-b 9.50 9.00

Miniature Sheet

Athletes A331

No. 641: a, 200col, Hanna Gabriel, boxer. b, 200col, Nery Brenes, sprinter. c, 330col, Bryan Ruiz, soccer player. d, 330col, Andrey Amador, cyclist.

**2011, July 14**

**641** A331 Sheet of 4, #a-d 8.00 7.00

Rights of the Child — A332

No. 642 — Banner inscribed: a, Participación. b, No Discriminación. c, Educación.

**2011, Aug. 12**

**642** Horiz. strip of 3 8.00 7.25
*a.* A332 225col multi 1.25 1.10
*b.* A332 340col multi 2.00 1.75
*c.* A332 600col multi 3.25 3.00

Miniature Sheet

Flora and Fauna of Monteverde Children's Forest — A333

No. 643: a, 500col, Forest and lake. b, 500col, Lithobates vibicarius. c, 1000col, Lepanthes ciliisepala. d, 1000col, Leopardus wiedii.

**2011, Aug. 24 *Perf. 10½ on 3 Sides***

**643** A333 Sheet of 4, #a-d, + 2 labels 18.00 17.00

Tricolín, Comic Strip by Carlos Figueroa — A334

No. 644: a, Tricolín, Tricolína and Costa Rican flag. b, Tricolín and Tricolína donating money for Red Cross. c, Tricolín and Pepín planting flower. d, Tricolín, Tricolína, and Pepín.

**2011, Sept. 9 *Die Cut Perf. 12x11½***

**Self-Adhesive**

**644** Block or horiz. strip of 4 17.00 16.00
*a.* A334 300col multi 3.50 3.50
*b.* A334 320col multi 3.50 3.50
*c.* A334 350col multi 3.75 3.75
*d.* A334 395col multi 4.00 4.00

Mailboxes A335

No. 645: a, Black mailbox. b, Blue mailbox.

**2011, Oct. 10 *Perf. 10½***

**645** A335 400col Pair, #a-b 6.00 5.50

America issue. No. 645 was printed in sheets containing two pairs. Value, $11.

Souvenir Sheet

Scouting in Costa Rica, Cent. A336

No. 646 — Boy Scouts and Girl Guides: a, Near tents. b, Around campfire.

**2011, Oct. 28**
**646** A336 340col Sheet of 2, #a-b 4.25 3.75

Souvenir Sheet

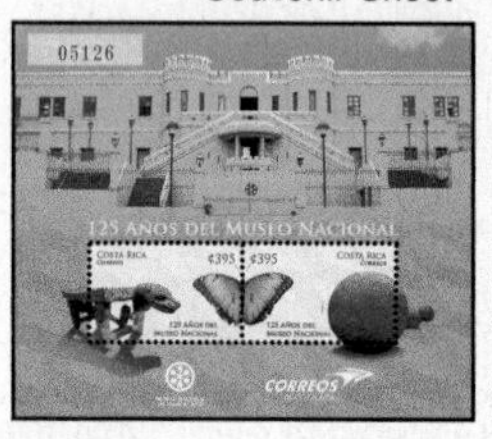

National Museum, 125th Anniv. A337

No. 647: a, Grinding stone, butterfly at right. b, Butterfly at left, Pre-Columbian stone sphere.

**2012, May 4**
**647** A337 395col Sheet of 2, #a-b 4.75 4.25

Bank of Costa Rica, 135th Anniv. — A338

**2012, June 7**
**648** A338 275col multi 2.00 1.75

No. 648 was printed in sheets of 2. Value, $4.

Souvenir Sheet

2012 Summer Olympics, London — A339

No. 649: a, 365col, Runner. b. 435col, Taekwondo.

**2012, June 25**
**649** A339 Sheet of 2, #a-b 5.00 4.50

Souvenir Sheet

Intl. Year of Cooperatives — A340

No. 650: a, 275col, People holding rainbow and trees. b, 395col, People wrapping ribbons around sphere.

**2012, July 6**
**650** A340 Sheet of 2, #a-b 4.25 4.00

Manuel Antonio National Park — A341

**2012, Aug. 24** ***Perf. 10½ Horiz.***

**Booklet Stamp**

**651** A341 545col multi 3.50 3.00
*a.* Booklet pane of 3 15.00 —
Complete booklet, #651a 21.00

Souvenir Sheet

America Issue A342

No. 652: a, 385col, Legend of La Segua. b, 485col, Legend of the Cart Without Oxen.

**2012, Oct. 9** ***Perf. 10½***
**652** A342 Sheet of 2, #a-b 5.25 5.00

Souvenir Sheet

First Costa Rican Postage Stamps, 150th Anniv. A343

No. 653: a, Costa Rica #1. b, Costa Rica #2.

**Litho. & Embossed With Foil Application**

**2013, Apr. 17**
**653** A343 1000col Sheet of 2, #a-b 16.50 10.00

Souvenir Sheet

Bancrédito Commercial Bank, 95th Anniv. — A344

**2013, May 15** **Litho.**
**654** A344 400col multi 2.50 2.25

"Costa Rica, Land of Immigrants" A345

**2013, June 20**
**655** A345 500col multi 3.00 2.75

No. 655 was printed in sheets of 2. Value, $6.

Souvenir Sheet

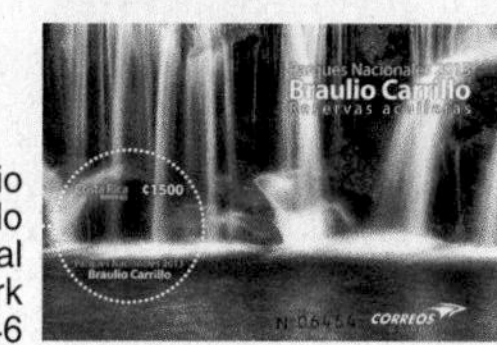

Braulio Carrillo National Park A346

**2013, Aug. 23** **Litho.** ***Perf.***
**656** A346 1500col multi 8.25 7.50

Jorge Manuel Dengo (1918-2012), Vice-President A347

**2013, Sept. 18** **Litho.** ***Perf. 10½***
**657** A347 500col multi 3.00 2.75

No. 657 was printed in sheets of 2. Value, $6.50.

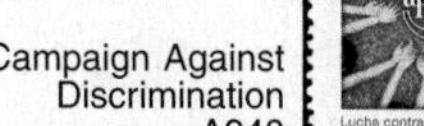

Campaign Against Discrimination A348

**2013, Oct. 9** **Litho.** ***Perf. 10½***
**658** A348 300col multi 2.00 1.75

America issue. No. 658 was printed in sheets of 2 + central label. Value, $4.50.

Souvenir Sheet

Pres. Juan Rafael Mora Porras (1814-60) — A349

**2014, Feb. 7** **Litho.** ***Perf. 10½***
**659** A349 360col multi 2.50 2.00

America issue.

Souvenir Sheet

Election of Pope Francis, 1st Anniv. A350

**2014, Mar. 19** **Litho.** ***Perf. 10½***
**660** A350 300col multi 2.50 2.25

Souvenir Sheet

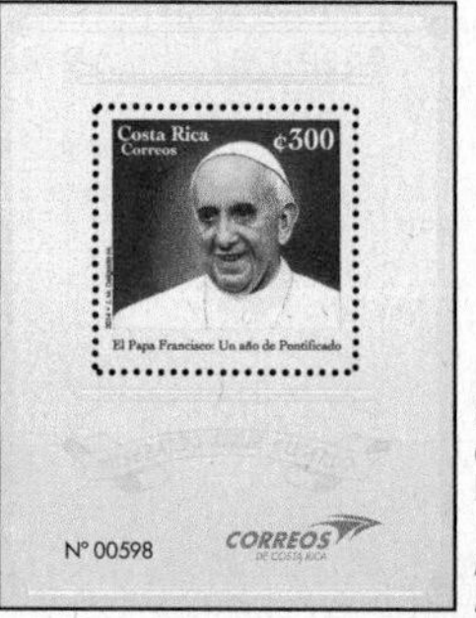

2014 World Cup Soccer Championships, Brazil — A351

No. 661: a, 500col, 2014 World Cup mascot. b, 710col, World Cup.

**2014, Apr. 24** **Litho.** ***Perf. 10½***
**661** A351 Sheet of 2, #a-b 7.00 6.00

Souvenir Sheet

Endangered Cats in Corcovado National Park — A352

No. 662: a, 690col, Puma yagouaroundi. 1220col, Panthera onca.

**2014, Aug. 22** **Litho.** ***Perf. 13***
**662** A352 Sheet of 2, #a-b 10.50 10.00

Souvenir Sheet

National Bank, Cent. A353

**2014, Nov. 3** **Litho.** ***Perf. 10½***
**663** A353 500col multi 3.00 2.75

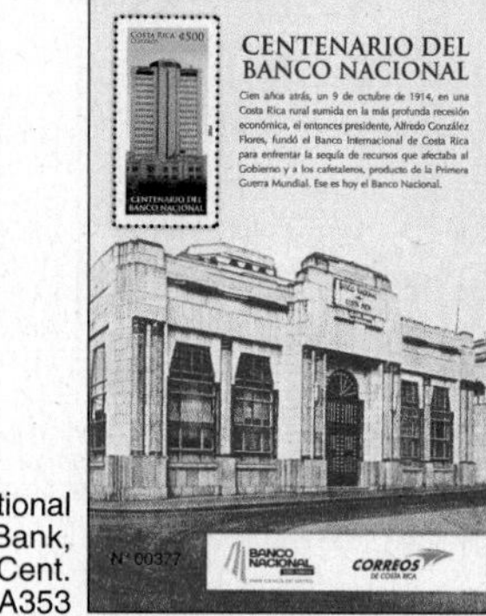

Vuelta de Costa Rica Bicycle Race, 50th Anniv. — A354

**2014, Dec. 11** **Litho.** ***Perf. 13¼***
**664** A354 500col multi 3.00 2.50

No. 664 was printed in sheets of 2. Value, $6.50.

Souvenir Sheet

Forensic Medicine in Costa Rica, 50th Anniv. A355

**2015, Jan. 30** **Litho.** ***Perf. 10½***
**665** A355 360col multi 2.50 2.00

Costa Rica Chamber of Commerce, Cent. — A356

**2015, Mar. 4** **Litho.** ***Perf. 10½***
**666** A356 500col multi 3.15 2.90

No. 666 was printed in sheets of 2. Value, $5.75.

Souvenir Sheet

El Buen Pastor Episcopal Church, San José, 150th Anniv. — A357

**2015, Apr. 23 Litho. *Imperf.***
**667** A357 1000col multi 5.50 5.25

No. 667 has simulated perforations.

Souvenir Sheet

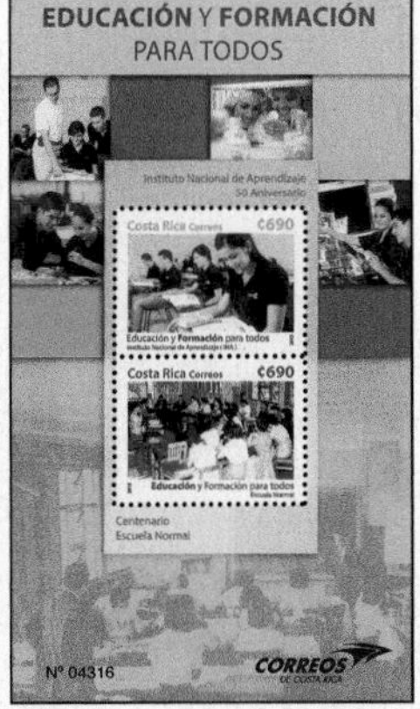


Education and Training For All — A358

No. 668 — Adult students with denomination in: a, Orange yellow. b, Blue.

**2015, May 7 Litho. *Perf. 10½***
**668** A358 690col Sheet of 2, #a-b 7.75 7.00

National Apprentice Institute, 50th anniv.; Normal School, cent.

Fire Departments in Costa Rica, 150th Anniv. — A359

No. 669: a, Fire fighters spraying water on fire. b, Fire fighters, truck and children.

**2015, July 16 Litho. *Perf. 14***
**669** A359 1500col Sheet of 2, #a-b 15.00 15.00

Nelson Mandela (1918-2013), President of South Africa — A360

**2015, July 18 Litho. *Perf. 10½***

**Booklet Stamp**

**670** A360 1220col multi 6.75 6.50
*a.* Booklet pane of 3 19.00 —
Complete booklet, #670a 20.00

Coral Reefs of Cahuita National Park A361

No. 671: a, Coral and sea urchin. b, Coral. 1000col, Coral, diff.

**2015, Aug. 24 Litho. *Perf. 13x13¼***
**671** A361 500col Sheet of 2, #a-b 4.00 3.50

**Souvenir Sheet**

**672** A361 1000col multi 7.25 6.50

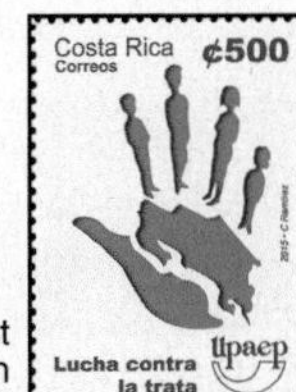


Campaign Against Human Trafficking — A362

**2015, Oct. 9 Litho. *Perf. 10½***
**673** A362 500col black & blue 3.00 2.50

America Issue. No. 673 was printed in sheets of 2. Value, $6.25.

Coope Ande Credit Union, 50th Anniv. — A363

**2015, Nov. 4 Litho. *Perf. 10½***
**674** A363 600col multi 3.50 3.50

No. 674 was printed in sheets of 2. Value, $7.50.

Souvenir Sheet

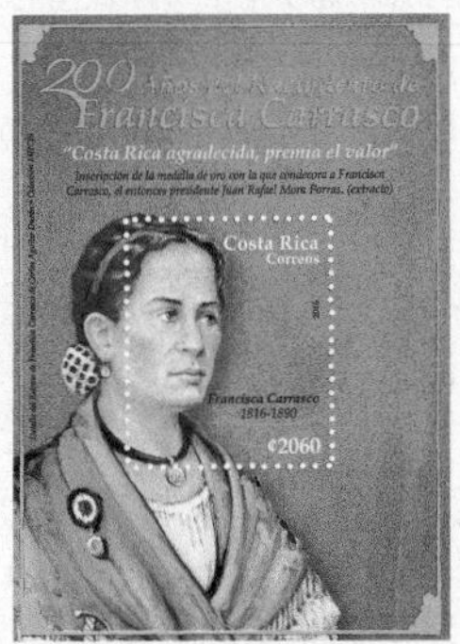

Francisca Carrasco (1816-90), First Woman in Costa Rican Military — A364

**Litho., Sheet Margin Litho. With Foil Application**

**2016, Apr. 4 *Perf. 10½***
**675** A364 2060col multi 10.75 10.00

Souvenir Sheet

Pres. José Joaquín Trejos Fernández (1916-2010) — A365

**2016, Apr. 18 Litho. *Perf. 10½***
**676** A365 1950col multi 10.00 9.50

Souvenir Sheet

Archaeological Sites — A366

Diquís Culture Stone Spheres: No. 677: a, Stone sphere. b, Stone sphere and triangular ramp of stones at archaeological dig site.

**Litho. & Thermography**

**2016, June 23 *Perf. 13¼x13½***
**677** A366 650col Sheet of 2, #a-b 8.00 7.00

Souvenir Sheet

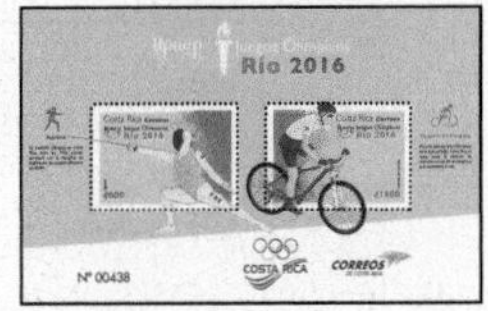

2016 Summer Olympics, Rio de Janeiro — A367

No. 678: a, 600col, Fencing. b, 1400col, Mountain biking.

**2016, July 15 Litho. *Perf. 10½***
**678** A367 Sheet of 2, #a-b 11.00 10.00

Dermochelys Coriacea — A368

No. 679 — Turtle facing: a, 1370col, Right. b, 2100col, Left.
1100col, Turtle facing forward.

**Litho. & Embossed**

**2016, Aug. 24 *Perf. 13½x13¼***
**679** A368 Sheet of 2, #a-b 10.00 6.00

**Souvenir Sheet**

**680** A368 1100col multi 40.00 40.00

Fauna of Marino Las Baulas National Park.

Souvenir Sheet

Writers A369

No. 681: a, 420col, Aquileo J. Echeverría (1866-1909). b, 650col, Yolanda Oreamuno (1916-56).

**2016, Oct. 10 Litho. *Perf. 10½***
**681** A369 Sheet of 2, #a-b 6.25 5.25

Maternity, Sculpture by Francisco Zuñiga — A370

**2016, Nov. 1 Litho. *Perf. 10½***
**682** A370 600col multi 3.50 3.00

Social Security Fund, 75th anniv. No. 682 was printed in sheets of 2. Value, $7.

Souvenir Sheet

University of Costa Rica Nursing School, Cent. — A371

**2017, Mar. 1 Litho. *Perf. 10½***
**683** A371 2100col multi 10.75 10.00

Souvenir Sheet

International Women's Day — A372

No. 684: a, 550col, Shirley Cruz, soccer player. b, 600col, Christiana Figueres, diplomat. c, 600col, Sandra Cauffman, electrical engineer, physicist and NASA official.

**2017, Mar. 8 Litho. *Perf. 10½***
**684** A372 Sheet of 3, #a-c 11.25 9.50

Souvenir Sheet

Panal, by Rafael "Felo" García A373

**2017, Apr. 7 Litho. *Perf. 10½***
**685** A373 2060col multi 11.00 10.00

National Directorate of Community Development, 50th anniv.

Souvenir Sheet

Guarianthe Skinneri and Great Wall of China — A374

**2017, June 30 Litho. *Perf. 10½***
**686** A374 1400col multi 5.50 5.00

Diplomatic relations between Costa Rica and People's Republic of China.

Miniature Sheet

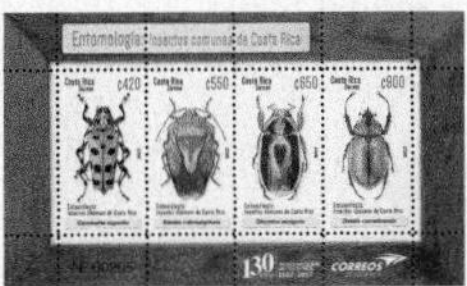

Insects A375

No. 687: a, 420col, Carneades superba. b, 550col, Edessa rufomarginata. c, 650col, Chrysina aurigans, d, 900col, Golofa costaricensis.

**2017, July 20 Litho. *Perf. 10½***
**687** A375 Sheet of 4, #a-d 10.75 8.75

National Museum of Costa Rica, 130th anniv.

Craugastor Escoces
A376

**2017, Aug. 24** **Litho.** ***Perf. 10½***
**688** A376 1100col multi 5.50 5.00

Juan Castro Blanco National Park. No. 688 was printed in sheets of 2. Value, $11.25.

Miniature Sheet

Independence, 200th Anniv. (in 2021) — A377

No. 689 — Costa Rican: a, 650col, Flag. b, 800col, Coat of arms. c, 900col, National anthem.

**2017, Sept. 14** **Litho.** ***Perf. 13¼***
**689** A377 Sheet of 6, 2 each #689a-689c, + 3 labels 24.00 24.00

See Nos. 701, 711, 722.

America Issue
A378

No. 690 — San Juan-La Selva Biological Corridor: a, 420col, Parrot (30x40mm). b, 650col, Pond and forest (50x40mm).

**2017, Sept. 27** **Litho.** ***Perf. 14***
**690** A378 Horiz. pair, #a-b 5.75 4.50

Main Post Office, San José, Cent.
A379

No. 691: a, 1100col, Entrance. b, 1400col, Corner of building.
2100col, Arch decoration.

**Litho. & Embossed**

**2017, Oct. 9** ***Perf. 10½***
**691** A379 Sheet of 2, #a-b 12.50 11.00

**Souvenir Sheet**

**692** A379 2100col multi 10.25 9.50

National Association of Educators, 75th Anniv. — A380

**2017, Oct. 24** **Litho.** ***Perf. 13¼***
**693** A380 600col multi 3.25 2.75

Souvenir Sheet

Fountain at University of Costa Rica — A381

**2018, Mar. 5** **Litho.** ***Perf. 10½***
**694** A381 2165col multi 10.75 10.00

Economic Sciences Faculty, 75th anniv., School of Collective Communication Sciences, 50th anniv.

Souvenir Sheet

Writers
A382

No. 695: a, 630col, Fabián Dobles (1918-97). b, 685col, Joaquín Gutiérrez (1918-2000).

**2018, Apr. 4** **Litho.** ***Perf. 10½***
**695** A382 Sheet of 2, #a-b 7.50 6.50

Miniature Sheet

Composers — A383

No. 696: a, 630col, Guadalupe Urbina. b, 630col, Fidel Gamboa (1961-2011). c, 685col, José Campany (1961-2001). d, 685col, Amelia Barquero.

**2018, May 31** **Litho.** ***Perf. 10½***
**696** A383 Sheet of 4, #a-d 14.50 13.50

Souvenir Sheet

2018 World Cup Soccer Championships, Russia — A384

No. 697: a, World Cup. b, Mascot Zabivaka.

**2018, June 12** **Litho.** ***Perf. 13¾***
**697** A384 1155col Sheet of 2, #a-b 11.50 10.50

Souvenir Sheet

Social Guarantees, 75th Anniv. — A385

**2018, July 2** **Litho.** ***Perf. 10½***
**698** A385 2890col multi 12.75 12.00

Nasua Narica
A386

**2018, Aug. 24** **Litho.** ***Perf. 10½***
**699** A386 580col multi 3.00 2.10

Carara National Park. No. 699 was printed in sheets of 2. Value, $6.

Souvenir Sheet

José María Castro Madriz (1818-92), First President of Costa Rica — A387

**2018, Aug. 31** **Litho.** ***Perf. 10½***
**700** A387 1155col multi 5.50 4.50

**Independence Type of 2017**

Miniature Sheet

No. 701: a, 580col, Turdus craye. b, 630col, Trichechus manatus. c, 685col, Odocoileus virginianus.

**Litho. & Embossed**

**2018, Sept. 13** ***Perf. 13¼***
**701** A377 Sheet of 6, 2 each #701a-701c, + 3 labels 19.00 17.00

America Issue
A389

No. 702: a, 445col, Chicken. b, 840col, Horse.

**2018, Oct. 9** **Litho.** ***Perf. 10½***
**702** A389 Horiz. pair, #a-b 6.50 5.50

Souvenir Sheet

Mauro Fernández Acuña (1843-1905), Politician — A390

**2018, Dec. 19** **Litho.** ***Perf. 10½***
**703** A390 2205col multi 9.75 9.00

Souvenir Sheet

Clean Energy
A391

**2019, Mar. 29** **Litho.** ***Perf. 10½***
**704** A391 1470col multi 6.75 6.00

Souvenir Sheet

Pres. Jesús Jiménez (1823-97), Valeriano Fernández (1831-1925), Philosopher, and Caridad Salazar (1869-1948), Children's Writer — A392

**2019, Apr. 22** **Litho.** ***Perf. 10½***
**705** A392 2165col multi 9.75 9.00

Declaration of free and compulsory primary education, 150th anniv.

Souvenir Sheet

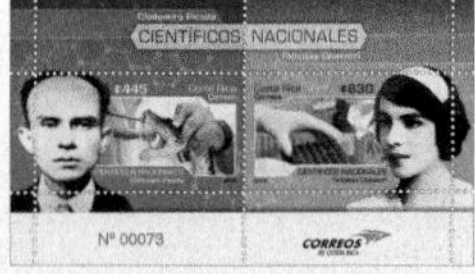


Scientists — A393

No. 706: a, 445col, Clodomiro Picado (1887-1944), developer of antivenins. b, 630col, Felícitas Chaverri (1886-1934), head of Department of Drugs and Narcotics.

**2019, May 16** **Litho.** ***Perf. 10½***
**706** A393 Sheet of 2, #a-b 6.25 5.25

Souvenir Sheet

Cities
A394

No. 707: a, 685col, Orosí. b, 845col, Santo Domingo.

**2019, May 24** **Litho.** ***Perf. 10½***
**707** A394 Sheet of 2, #a-b 8.25 7.50

Chirripó National Park
A395

No. 708: a, 580col, Slug. b, 685col, Stenostylus sp.
1440col, Crestones rock formation.

**2019, Aug. 23** **Litho.** ***Perf. 13x13¼***
**708** A395 Sheet of 2, #a-b 7.00 6.00

**Souvenir Sheet**

**709** A395 1440col multi 7.50 7.00

### Souvenir Sheet

Traditional Foods — A396

No. 710: a, 445col, Ceviche. b, 945col, Rice and beans.

**2019, Aug. 30 Litho. *Perf. 10½***
**710** A396 Sheet of 2, #a-b 8.00 7.00

America issue.

### Independence Type of 2017
### Miniature Sheet

No. 711: a, 630col, Diquis stone spheres. b, 685col, National Theater. c, 840col, Crestones of Cerro Chirripó.

**2019, Sept. 12 Litho. *Perf. 13¼***
**711** A377 Sheet of 6, 2 each #711a-711c, + 3 labels 24.00 20.00

### Souvenir Sheet

Writers A397

No. 712: a, 630col, Eunice Odio (1919-74), poet. b, 840col, Carmen Naranjo (1928-2012), writer.

**2019, Oct. 9 Litho. *Perf. 10½***
**712** A397 Sheet of 2, #a-b 8.00 7.00

### Souvenir Sheet

Presidents — A398

No. 713: a, 445col, Pres. José Figueres Ferrer (1906-90), abolisher of National Army. b, 580col, Pres. Tomás Guardia Gutiérrez (1831-82), abolisher of death penalty. c, 630col, Pres. Juan Rafael Mora Porres (1814-60), leader of national forces in 1856 Filibuster War.

**2019, Oct. 29 Litho. *Perf. 13¼***
**713** A398 Sheet of 3, #a-c 9.50 8.50

American Convention on Human Rights (Pact of San José), 50th Anniv. — A399

No. 714: a, 685col, Gavel (26x36mm). b, 945col, Inter-American Court of Human Rights, San José (51x36mm).

**2019, Nov. 22 Litho. *Perf. 10½***
**714** A399 Horiz. pair, #a-b 8.50 8.00

### Souvenir Sheet

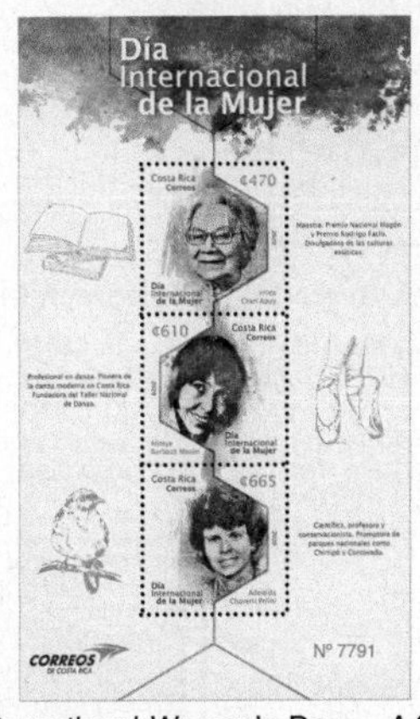

International Women's Day — A400

No. 715: a, 470col, Hilda Chen Apuy (1923-2017), co-founder of University of Costa Rica School of Anthropology. b, 610col, Mireya Barboza Mesén (1935-2000), ballerina and choreographer. c, 665col, Adelaida Chaverri Polini (1947-2003), ecologist.

**2020, Mar. 9 Litho. *Perf. 10½***
**715** A400 Sheet of 3, #a-c 8.25 8.25

### Souvenir Sheet

National Commission on Emergencies — A401

**2020, Apr. 24 Litho. *Perf. 10½***
**716** A401 1215col multi 5.50 4.50

### Souvenir Sheet

Musicians — A402

No. 717: a, 720col, María Mayela Padilla, singer and songwriter. b, 885col, Marta Fonseca and Bernal Villegas, rock musicians. c, 1215col, Walter "Gavitt" Ferguson, calypso singer and songwriter.

**2020, May 29 Litho. *Perf. 10½***
**717** A402 Sheet of 3, #a-c 12.75 11.00

Turrialba Volcano National Park — A404

**2020, Aug. 24 Litho. *Perf. 10½***
**719** A404 720col multi 7.50 5.00

### Souvenir Sheet

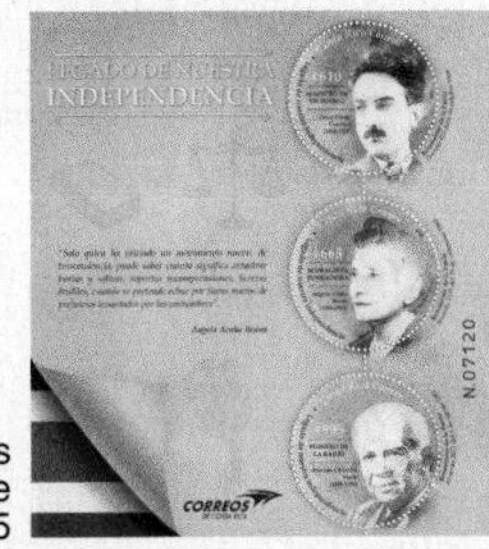

Famous People A405

No. 720: a, 610col, Omar Dengo Guerrero (1888-1928), educator and writer. b, 665col, Angela Acuña Braun (1888-1983), lawyer and suffragist. c, 995col, Amando Céspedes Marín (1888-1976), radio newscaster.

**2020, Nov. 16 Litho. *Perf.***
**720** A405 Sheet of 3, #a-c 10.50 9.00

### Souvenir Sheet

America Issue A406

No. 721: a, 470col, Buenaventura Corrales Elementary School, San José. b, 1515col, San Juan de Dios Hospital, San José.

**2020, Dec. Litho. *Perf. 10½***
**721** A406 Sheet of 2, #a-b 9.00 7.50

### Independence Type of 2017
### Miniature Sheet

No. 722 — National symbols: a, 470col, Marimba. b, 610col, Torch. c, 665col, Oxcart.

**2020, Sept. 24 Litho. *Perf. 13¼***
**722** A377 Sheet of 6, 2 each #722a-722c, + 3 labels 16.00 13.00

### Souvenir Sheet

International Women's Day — A407

No. 723: a, 470col, María Francisca Morales Matamoros, midwife and organic farmer. b, 995col, Rosa María Acosta Ramírez, President of Association of Domestic Workers. c, 1515col, Mercedes Chacón (1896-1963), obstetrical nurse.

**2021, Mar. 9 Litho. *Perf. 10½***
**723** A407 Sheet of 3, #a-c 13.00 11.00

Teacher's Life Insurance Society, Cent. — A408

**2021, Mar. 26 Litho. *Perf. 10½***
**724** A408 1545col multi 6.50 5.50

No. 724 was printed in sheets of 2. Value, $13.

### Independence Type of 2017
### Miniature Sheet

No. 725: a, 6100col, Guarianthe skinneri. b, 720col, Enterolobium cyclocarpum. c, 885col, Coffea arabica.

**2021, July 13 Litho. *Perf. 13¼***
**725** A377 Sheet of 6, 2 each #725a-725c, + 3 labels 19.50 17.50

### Souvenir Sheet

Tourism A409

No. 726: a, 470col, Drum sticks, musical notes, zipliner, kayaker, boater and parrot. b, 610col, Parachutist, family on beach, athlete, frog, gymnast, hiker, potter, tourist with binoculars and coffee beans.

**2021, Aug. 9 Litho. *Perf. 13x13¼***
**726** A409 Sheet of 2, #a-b 5.00 4.00

America issue.

### Souvenir Sheet

Santa Rosa National Park A410

**2021, Aug. 24 Litho. *Perf. 10½***
**727** A410 885col multi 8.00 6.50

Independence, 200th Anniv. — A411

**2021, Sept. 15 Litho. *Perf. 10½***
**728** A411 885col multi 4.25 3.50

### Souvenir Sheet

Political Leaders of Newly Independent Costa Rica — A412

No. 729: a, 720col, Pablo de Alvarado (1785-1851), writer of draft of constitution. b, 1215col, Gregorio José Ramírez (1796-1823), second general commander of arms. c, 1545col, Juan Mora Fernández (1784-1854), first elected head of state.

**2021, Nov. 29 Litho. *Perf.***
**729** A412 Sheet of 3, #a-c 11.00 11.00

Choloepus Hoffmanni and Bradypus Variegatus A413

**2021, Dec. 8 Litho. *Perf. 13¼***
**730** A413 995col multi 3.25 3.25

No. 730 was printed in sheets of 2 + 2 labels.

### Souvenir Sheet

International Women's Day — A414

No. 731: a, 445col, Olga Espinach Fernández (1918-2009), journalist, and founder of theaters. b, 665col, Emilia Prieto Tugores (1902-86), graphic artist and folklorist. c, 1215col, María Teresa Obregón Zamora (1888-1956), politician.

**2022, Mar. 8 Litho. *Perf. 10½***
**731** A414 Sheet of 3, #a-c 7.25 7.25

Souvenir Sheet

America Issue A415

No. 732: a, 610col, Ana Poltronieri (1929-2015), actress. b, 720col, Daniel Gallegos (1930-2018), playwright.

**2022, Apr. 27 Litho. *Perf. 10½***

| No. | Design | Description | Unused | Used |
|---|---|---|---|---|
| **732** | A415 | Sheet of 2, #a-b, + central label | 4.00 | 4.00 |

## POSTAL-FISCAL STAMPS

From April 1884 through September 1889 revenue stamps were permitted for postal use, when post offices exhausted supplies of regular postage stamps.

Used values are for stamps with postal cancels.

PF1

**1884 Engr. *Perf. 12***

| No. | Design | Description | Unused | Used |
|---|---|---|---|---|
| **AR1** | PF1 | 1c rose | .50 | *5.00* |
| **AR2** | PF1 | 2c light blue | *20.00* | 5.00 |

PF2

**1888**

| No. | Design | Description | Unused | Used |
|---|---|---|---|---|
| **AR3** | PF2 | 5c brown | .50 | *3.00* |
| **AR4** | PF2 | 10c blue | *.40* | 3.00 |

Nos. AR2-AR4 are normally found without gum.

## SEMI-POSTAL STAMPS

No. 72 Surcharged in Red

**1922 Unwmk. *Perf. 12***

| No. | Design | Description | Unused | Used |
|---|---|---|---|---|
| **B1** | A56 | 5c + 5c orange | 1.00 | .40 |

Issued for the benefit of the Costa Rican Red Cross Society. In 1928, owing to a temporary shortage of the ordinary 5c stamp, No. B1 was placed on sale as a regular 5c stamp, the surtax being disregarded.

Discus Thrower SP1

Trophy SP2

Parthenon — SP3

**1924 Litho. *Imperf.***

| No. | Design | Description | Unused | Used |
|---|---|---|---|---|
| **B2** | SP1 | 5c dark green | 1.60 | *2.00* |
| **B3** | SP2 | 10c carmine | 1.60 | *2.00* |
| **B4** | SP3 | 20c dark blue | 20.00 | *20.00* |
| *a.* | | Tête bêche pair | 60.00 | *60.00* |

***Perf. 12***

| No. | Design | Description | Unused | Used |
|---|---|---|---|---|
| **B5** | SP1 | 5c dark green | 1.60 | *2.25* |
| **B6** | SP2 | 10c carmine | 1.60 | *2.25* |
| **B7** | SP3 | 20c dark blue | 3.50 | *4.00* |
| *a.* | | Tête bêche pair | 16.00 | *20.00* |
| | | *Nos. B2-B7 (6)* | 29.90 | *32.50* |

These stamps were sold at a premium of 10c each, to help defray the expenses of athletic games held at San José in Dec. 1924.

## AIR POST STAMPS

Airplane — AP1

***Perf. 12½***

**1926, June 4 Unwmk. Engr.**

| No. | Design | Description | Unused | Used |
|---|---|---|---|---|
| **C1** | AP1 | 20c ultramarine | 3.00 | .65 |

No. 123 Overprinted

**1930, Mar. 14 *Perf. 12***

| No. | Design | Description | Unused | Used |
|---|---|---|---|---|
| **C2** | A75 | 10c carmine rose | 2.00 | .40 |

Inverted or double overprints are fakes.

AP3

**1930-32 *Perf. 12½***

| No. | Design | Description | Unused | Used |
|---|---|---|---|---|
| **C3** | AP3 | 5c on 10c dk brn ('32) | .40 | .40 |
| **C4** | AP3 | 20c on 50c ultra | .50 | .40 |
| **C5** | AP3 | 40c on 50c ultra | .60 | .40 |
| | | *Nos. C3-C5 (3)* | 1.50 | 1.20 |

Almost all inverted or double surcharges of Nos. C3-C5 are fakes.

Telegraph Stamp Overprinted

**1930, Mar. 19**

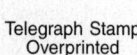

| No. | Design | Description | Unused | Used |
|---|---|---|---|---|
| **C6** | AP3 | 1col orange | 2.00 | .50 |

No. O79 Surcharged in Red

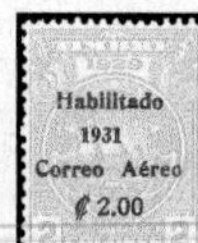

**1930, Mar. 11**

| No. | Design | Description | Unused | Used |
|---|---|---|---|---|
| **C7** | O7 | 8c on 1col lilac & blk | .80 | .65 |
| **C8** | O7 | 20c on 1col lilac & blk | 1.25 | .70 |
| **C9** | O7 | 40c on 1col lilac & blk | 2.40 | 1.50 |
| **C10** | O7 | 1col on 1col lilac & blk | 3.50 | 2.00 |
| | | *Nos. C7-C10 (4)* | 7.95 | 4.85 |

AP6

**Red Surcharge on Revenue Stamps**

**1931-32 *Perf. 12***

| No. | Design | Description | Unused | Used |
|---|---|---|---|---|
| **C11** | AP6 | 2col on 2col gray grn | 35.00 | 35.00 |
| **C12** | AP6 | 3col on 5col lil brn | 35.00 | 35.00 |
| **C13** | AP6 | 5col on 10col gray blk | 35.00 | 35.00 |
| | | *Nos. C11-C13 (3)* | 105.00 | 105.00 |

There were two printings of this issue which were practically identical in the colors of the stamps and the surcharges.

Nos. C11 and C13 have the date "1929" on the stamp, No. C12 has "1930."

AP7

**Black Overprint on Telegraph Stamp**

**1932, Mar. 8 *Perf. 12½***

| No. | Design | Description | Unused | Used |
|---|---|---|---|---|
| **C14** | AP7 | 40c green | 3.00 | .40 |
| *a.* | | Inverted overprint | 35.00 | 27.50 |

Unofficial "proofs," inverts and double overprints were made from a defaced plate.

Mail Plane about to Land — AP8

Allegory of Flight — AP9

**1934, Mar. 14 *Perf. 12***

| No. | Design | Description | Unused | Used |
|---|---|---|---|---|
| **C15** | AP8 | 5c green | .35 | .30 |
| **C16** | AP8 | 10c carmine rose | .35 | .30 |
| **C17** | AP8 | 15c chocolate | .55 | .30 |
| **C18** | AP8 | 20c deep blue | .55 | .30 |
| **C19** | AP8 | 25c deep orange | .75 | .30 |
| **C20** | AP8 | 40c olive blk | 2.40 | .30 |
| **C21** | AP8 | 50c gray blk | 1.20 | .30 |
| **C22** | AP8 | 60c orange yel | 2.10 | .30 |
| **C23** | AP8 | 75c dull violet | 3.75 | .60 |
| **C24** | AP9 | 1col deep rose | 2.10 | .30 |
| **C25** | AP9 | 2col lt blue | 10.50 | 1.25 |
| **C26** | AP9 | 5col black | 10.50 | 5.00 |
| **C27** | AP9 | 10col red brown | 14.00 | 4.50 |
| | | *Nos. C15-C27 (13)* | 49.10 | 14.05 |

Nos. C15-C27 with holes punched through were for use of government officials.

See Nos. C216-C219. For overprints see Nos. C67-C73, C92-C93, C103-C116, CO1-CO13.

Airplane over Poás Volcano AP10

**1937, Feb. 10**

| No. | Design | Description | Unused | Used |
|---|---|---|---|---|
| **C28** | AP10 | 1c black | .45 | .40 |
| **C29** | AP10 | 2c brown | .45 | .40 |
| **C30** | AP10 | 3c dk violet | .45 | .40 |
| | | *Nos. C28-C30 (3)* | 1.35 | 1.20 |

First Fair of Costa Rica.

Puntarenas AP11

***Perf. 12, 12½***

**1937, Dec. 15 Unwmk.**

| No. | Design | Description | Unused | Used |
|---|---|---|---|---|
| **C31** | AP11 | 2c black gray | .25 | .25 |
| **C32** | AP11 | 5c green | .30 | .25 |
| **C33** | AP11 | 20c deep blue | .30 | .25 |
| **C34** | AP11 | 1.40col olive brn | 2.50 | 2.50 |
| | | *Nos. C31-C34 (4)* | 3.35 | 3.25 |

National Bank — AP12

**1938, Jan. 11 Wmk. 229 *Perf. 12½***

| No. | Design | Description | Unused | Used |
|---|---|---|---|---|
| **C35** | AP12 | 1c purple | .25 | .25 |
| **C36** | AP12 | 3c red orange | .25 | .25 |
| **C37** | AP12 | 10c carmine rose | .30 | .25 |
| **C38** | AP12 | 75c brown | 2.50 | 2.00 |
| | | *Nos. C35-C38 (4)* | 3.30 | 2.75 |

Nos. C31-C38 for the Natl. Products Exposition held at San José, Dec. 1937.

Airport Administration Building, La Sabana — AP13

**1940, May 2 Engr. Unwmk.**

| No. | Design | Description | Unused | Used |
|---|---|---|---|---|
| **C39** | AP13 | 5c green | .65 | .40 |
| **C40** | AP13 | 10c rose pink | .65 | .40 |
| **C41** | AP13 | 25c lt blue | .85 | .40 |
| **C42** | AP13 | 35c red brown | .85 | .40 |
| **C43** | AP13 | 60c red org | 1.40 | .50 |
| **C44** | AP13 | 85c violet | 3.25 | 1.10 |
| **C45** | AP13 | 2.35col turq grn | 14.00 | 6.00 |
| | | *Nos. C39-C45 (7)* | 21.65 | 9.20 |

Opening of the Intl. Airport at La Sabana.

Duran Sanatorium AP14

**Overprinted in Black**

**1940, Dec. 2 *Perf. 12***

| No. | Design | Description | Unused | Used |
|---|---|---|---|---|
| **C46** | AP14 | 10c scarlet | .25 | .25 |
| **C47** | AP14 | 15c purple | .25 | .25 |
| **C48** | AP14 | 25c lt blue | .50 | .50 |
| **C49** | AP14 | 35c bister brn | .70 | .70 |
| **C50** | AP14 | 60c pck green | 1.00 | 1.00 |
| **C51** | AP14 | 75c olive | 2.75 | 2.75 |
| **C52** | AP14 | 1.35col red org | 8.75 | 8.75 |
| **C53** | AP14 | 5col sepia | 45.00 | 45.00 |
| **C54** | AP14 | 10col red lilac | 140.00 | 140.00 |
| | | *Nos. C46-C54 (9)* | 199.20 | 199.20 |

Pan-American Health Day. Nos. C46-C54 exist without overprint. Value, set $5,000.

No. 174 Surcharged in Black or Blue

**1940, Dec. 17 *Perf. 14***

| No. | Design | Description | Unused | Used |
|---|---|---|---|---|
| **C55** | A95 | 15c on 50c yel (Bk) | 1.00 | 1.00 |
| **C56** | A95 | 30c on 50c yel (Bl) | 1.00 | 1.00 |

Pan-American Aviation Day, proclaimed by President F. D. Roosevelt.

The 15c surcharge exists normal and inverted on No. 171, Value, normal $50. Inverted surcharge is worth more.

International Soccer Game at National Stadium — AP15

**1941, May 8 *Perf. 12***

| No. | Design | Description | Unused | Used |
|---|---|---|---|---|
| **C57** | AP15 | 15c red | .80 | .25 |
| **C58** | AP15 | 30c dp ultra | .90 | .25 |
| **C59** | AP15 | 40c red brn | .95 | .35 |
| **C60** | AP15 | 50c purple | 1.40 | .80 |
| **C61** | AP15 | 60c brt green | 1.60 | .90 |
| **C62** | AP15 | 75c yel org | 2.75 | 1.40 |
| **C63** | AP15 | 1col dull vio | 4.75 | 4.50 |
| **C64** | AP15 | 1.40col rose | 9.50 | 8.75 |
| **C65** | AP15 | 2col blue grn | 20.00 | 17.50 |
| **C66** | AP15 | 5col black | 52.50 | 37.50 |
| | | *Nos. C57-C66 (10)* | 95.15 | 72.20 |

Caribbean and Central American Soccer Championship. See Nos. C121-C123. For surcharges see Nos. C145-C147.

**Air Post Stamps of 1934 Overprinted or Surcharged in Black**

**1941, June 2**

| No. | Design | Description | Unused | Used |
|---|---|---|---|---|
| **C67** | AP8 | 5c on 20c dp bl | .25 | .25 |
| **C68** | AP8 | 15c on 20c dp bl | .25 | .25 |
| **C69** | AP8 | 40c on 75c dl vio | .35 | .25 |
| **C70** | AP9 | 65c on 1col dp rose | .65 | .50 |
| **C71** | AP9 | 1.40col on 2col lt bl | 3.25 | 3.25 |

**C72** AP9 5col black 12.00 12.00
**C73** AP9 10col red brn 14.50 12.50
*Nos. C67-C73 (7)* 31.25 29.00

Issued in commemoration of the settlement of the Costa Rica-Panama border dispute.

Nos. C67-C73 are found with hyphen omitted in overprint.

Nos. C67-C69 exist with inverted overprint. Value, each, $35.

### University Types of 1941

**1941, Aug. 26** *Perf. 12*

**C74** A107 15c salmon .25 .25
**C75** A106 30c lt blue .30 .25
**C76** A107 40c orange .40 .30
**C77** A106 60c turq green .50 .40
**C78** A107 1col violet 1.90 1.90
**C79** A106 2col black 4.75 4.75
**C80** A107 5col sepia 16.00 16.00
*Nos. C74-C80 (7)* 24.10 23.85

### Portrait Type of 1943-47

Designs: 40c, Manuel Aguilar. No. C83, Francisco Morazan. No. C83A, Jose R. De Gallegos. 50c, Jose M. Alfaro. 60c, Francisco M. Oreamuno. 65c, Jose M. Castro. 85c, Juan Rafael Mora. 1col, Jose M. Montealegre. 1.05col, Braulio Carrillo. 1.15col, Jesus Jimenez. 1.40col, Bruno Carranza. 2col, Tomas Guardia.

**1943-45** **Engr.**

**C81** A109 10c rose pink .25 .25
**C82** A109 40c blue .30 .25
**C82A** A109 40c car rose .30 .25
**C83** A109 45c magenta .50 .30
**C83A** A109 45c black .25 .25
**C84** A109 50c turq grn 1.75 .25
**C84A** A109 50c red org .40 .25
**C85** A109 60c brt ultra .65 .25
**C85A** A109 60c brt green .25 .25
**C86** A109 65c scarlet .95 .30
**C86A** A109 65c brt ultra .30 .25
**C87** A109 85c dp org 1.25 .50
**C87A** A109 85c dull pur 1.60 .65
**C88** A109 1col black 1.60 .50
**C88A** A109 1col scarlet .65 .40
**C88B** A109 1.05col bis brn .90 .55
**C89** A109 1.15col red brn 2.10 1.75
**C89A** A109 1.15col green 3.00 1.25
**C90** A109 1.40col dp vio 3.25 2.40
**C90A** A109 1.40col org yel 1.75 1.60
**C91** A109 2col black 5.25 1.25
**C91A** A109 2col olive grn 1.60 .50
*Nos. C81-C91A (22)* 28.85 14.20

Issued: Nos. C82A, C83A, C84A, C85A, C86A, C87A, C88A, C88B, C89A, C90A, C91A, 1945.

See Nos. C124-C127, C179-C181. For surcharges see Nos. C154-C158, C182, C184-C185.

Nos. C26-C27 Ovptd. in Red or Blue

**1943, Sept. 16**

**C92** AP9 5col black (R) 4.50 3.00
**C93** AP9 10col red brown (Bl) 5.25 3.25

Mercury and Plane — AP31

**1944, Jan. 19**

**C94** AP31 10c red org .25 .25
**C95** AP31 15c dk car .25 .25
**C96** AP31 40c brt ultra .40 .30
**C97** AP31 45c dp red lil .40 .35
**C98** AP31 60c turq grn .55 .45
**C99** AP31 1col dk red brn 1.60 .65
**C100** AP31 1.40col gray blk 8.75 5.75
**C101** AP31 5col violet 24.00 17.50
**C102** AP31 10col black 70.00 67.50
*Nos. C94-C102 (9)* 106.20 93.00

City of San Ramón founding, 100th anniv.

No. CO10 With Additional Overprint in Black

**1944, Nov. 22**

**C103** AP9 1col deep rose 2.00 .95
*a.* Blue overprint 150.00 100.00

Nos. CO1-CO13 Overprinted in Carmine or Black

**1945, Jan. 12** **Unwmk.** *Perf. 12*

**C104** AP8 5c green .60 .50
**C105** AP8 10c car rose (Bk) .60 .55
**C106** AP8 15c chocolate .60 .55
**C107** AP8 20c deep blue .50 .40
**C108** AP8 25c dp org (Bk) .60 .60
**C109** AP8 40c olive blk .35 .35
**C110** AP8 50c gray blk .60 .60
**C111** AP8 60c org yel (Bk) .90 .35
**C112** AP8 75c dull violet .75 .50
**C113** AP9 1col dp rose (Bk) .75 .35
**C114** AP9 2col light blue 8.00 4.50
**C115** AP9 5col black 8.00 5.50
**C116** AP9 10col red brn (Bk) 11.00 8.25
*Nos. C104-C116 (13)* 33.25 23.00

No. C104 exists with the overprint inverted. No. C104 with the overprint in black is probably a trial color. Value, $200.

**Catalogue values for unused stamps in this section, from this point to the end of the section, are for Never Hinged items.**

AP32

### Telegraph Stamps Overprinted in Black or Carmine

**1945, Feb. 28** **Unwmk.** *Perf. 12½*

**C117** AP32 40c green (C) .75 .25
**C118** AP32 50c ultra (C) .40 .25
**C119** AP32 1col orange (Bk) 1.90 .40
*Nos. C117-C119 (3)* 3.05 .90

No. C117 exists with inverted overprint. Value, $15.

Florence Nightingale and Edith Cavell — AP33

**1945** **Engr.**

**C120** AP33 1col black & car 1.50 .50

Costa Rican Red Cross Soc., 60th anniv

For surcharge see No. C183.

### Soccer Type of 1941 Inscribed: "Febrero 1946"

**1946, May 13** *Perf. 12*

**C121** AP15 25c green 1.75 .65
**C122** AP15 30c dull yellow 2.50 .65
**C123** AP15 55c deep blue 2.75 .65
*Nos. C121-C123 (3)* 7.00 1.95

### Portrait Type of 1943-47

Designs: 25c, Aniceto Esquivel. 30c, Vicente Herrera. 55c, Prospero Fernandez. 75c, Bernardo Soto.

**1946, May 12**

**C124** A109 25c blue .40 .40
**C125** A109 30c red brown .40 .40
**C126** A109 55c plum .75 .40
**C127** A109 75c blue green 1.60 .40
*Nos. C124-C127 (4)* 3.15 1.60

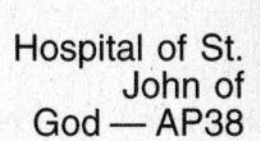

Hospital of St. John of God — AP38

**1946, June 24** **Unwmk.** *Perf. 12½*

**Center in Black**

**C128** AP38 5c yellow grn .45 .25
**C129** AP38 10c dk brown .55 .25
**C130** AP38 15c carmine .55 .25
**C131** AP38 25c dk blue .55 .25
**C132** AP38 30c dp orange 1.00 .25
**C133** AP38 40c olive grn .55 .25
**C134** AP38 50c violet 1.00 .25
**C135** AP38 60c dk sl grn 2.25 .55
**C136** AP38 75c brown 1.60 .40
*a.* Horiz. pair, imperf. btwn. 100.00
**C137** AP38 1col blue 2.25 .35
**C138** AP38 2col brn org 2.75 .80
**C139** AP38 3col dk vio brn 5.50 2.00
**C140** AP38 5col yellow 7.75 2.40
*Nos. C128-C140 (13)* 26.75 8.25

Nos. C128, C129, C131, C132, C134, C135 and C140 exist imperf.

Rafael Iglesias — AP39

3col, Ascensión Esquivel. 5col, Cleto González Víquez. 10col, Ricardo Jiménez Oreamuno.

**1947, Jan. 15** **Wmk. 215** *Perf. 14*

**Center in Black**

**C141** AP39 2col blue 2.25 1.25
**C142** AP39 3col dp car 3.00 1.60
**C143** AP39 5col dk green 5.00 2.00
**C144** AP39 10col orange 7.50 5.25
*Nos. C141-C144 (4)* 17.75 10.10

Nos. C141-C144 also exist in a souvenir sheet of 4. Value, $600. The sheet in sepia is a proof and worth less.

### Nos. C121-C123 Surcharged in Black

**1947, May 5** **Unwmk.** *Perf. 12*

**C145** AP15 15c on 25c green 1.35 .80
**C146** AP15 15c on 30c dull yel 1.35 .80
**C147** AP15 15c on 55c dp blue 1.35 .80
*Nos. C145-C147 (3)* 4.05 2.40

Nos. C145-C147 exist with inverted surcharge.

Columbus in Cariari — AP43

**1947, May 18** **Engr.** *Perf. 12½*

**Center in Black**

**C148** AP43 25c green .45 .30
**C149** AP43 30c dp ultra .55 .30
**C150** AP43 40c red orange .75 .30
**C151** AP43 45c violet .95 .30
**C152** AP43 50c brt carmine 1.10 .30
**C153** AP43 65c brown org 3.00 .95
*Nos. C148-C153 (6)* 6.80 2.45

For surcharges see Nos. C178, C220-C223.

Nos. C84A, C85A, C127, C88A-C88B Surcharged in Black or Red

**1947, June 3** *Perf. 12*

**C154** A109 15c on 50c red org .85 .35
**C155** A109 15c on 60c brt grn (R) .85 .35
**C156** A109 15c on 75c bl grn (R) .85 .35
**C157** A109 15c on 1col scar 1.10 .50
**C158** A109 15c on 1.05col bis brn .85 .35
*Nos. C154-C158 (5)* 4.50 1.90

No. C155 is known with black surcharge. Value, $10. No. C156 with inverted surcharge. Value, $10.

Early Steam Locomotive AP44

**1947, Nov. 10** *Perf. 12½*

**C159** AP44 35c bl grn & blk 2.50 .55

Electric railroad to the Pacific coast, 50th anniv.

### Roosevelt Type of Regular Issue

**1947, Aug. 26** *Perf. 12*

**C160** A122 15c green .45 .25
**C161** A122 30c car rose .45 .25
**C162** A122 45c red brown .45 .25
**C163** A122 65c orange yel .45 .25
**C164** A122 75c blue .60 .25
**C165** A122 1col olive grn 1.00 .35
**C166** A122 2col black 2.50 1.00
**C167** A122 5col scarlet 4.50 2.40
*Nos. C160-C167 (8)* 10.40 5.00

For surcharges see Nos. C224-C226.

National Theater AP46

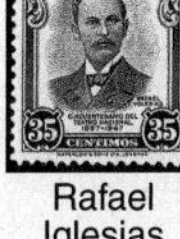


Rafael Iglesias AP47

**1948, Jan. 26** *Perf. 12½*

**Center in Black**

**C168** AP46 15c brt ultra .30 .25
**C169** AP46 20c red .30 .25
**C170** AP47 35c dk green .45 .25
**C171** AP46 45c purple .55 .25
**C172** AP46 50c carmine .55 .25
**C173** AP46 75c red violet 1.20 .80
**C174** AP46 1col olive 2.25 1.10
**C175** AP46 2col red brn 3.50 1.60
**C176** AP47 5col org yel 5.75 4.00
**C177** AP47 10col brt blue 13.00 8.00
*Nos. C168-C177 (10)* 27.85 16.75

50th anniversary of National Theater.

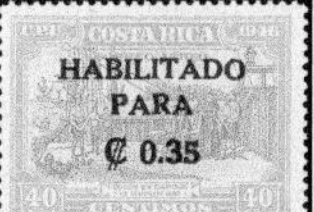


No. C150 Surcharged in Carmine

**1948, Apr. 21**

**C178** AP43 35c on 40c 1.50 .50

Exists with surcharge inverted.

### Portrait Type of 1943-47

5c, Salvador Lara. 15c, Carlos Duran.

**1948** **Engr.** *Perf. 12*

**C179** A109 5c sepia .65 .40
**C180** A109 10c olive brown .65 .40
**C181** A109 15c violet .65 .40
*Nos. C179-C181 (3)* 1.95 1.20

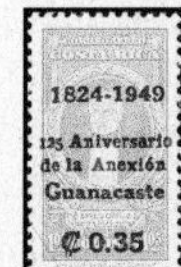


Nos. C88B, C120, C89A and C90A Surcharged in Carmine or Black

***Perf. 12½, 12***

**1949, Aug. 28** **Unwmk.**

**C182** A109 35c on 1.05col bis brn .50 .25
**C183** AP33 50c on 1col blk & car .90 .45
*a.* 2nd & 3rd lines both read "125 Aniversario" 7.50 3.00
**C184** A109 55c on 1.15col grn 1.50 .70
**C185** A109 55c on 1.40col org yel (Bk) 1.50 .60
*Nos. C182-C185 (4)* 4.40 2.00

125th anniv. of the annexation of the province of Guanacaste.

Overprint differs on No. C183, with "Guanacaste" in capitals, and lower case "a" in "Anexión."

The variety "I" for "i" in "Anexion" is found on Nos. C182, C184 and C185.

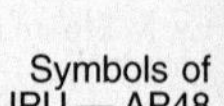

Symbols of UPU — AP48

**1950, Jan. 11 Photo. *Perf. 11½***

**C186** AP48 15c lilac rose .50 .25
**C187** AP48 25c chalky blue .75 .40
**C188** AP48 1col gray green 1.25 .55
*Nos. C186-C188 (3)* 2.50 1.20

75th anniv. of the UPU.

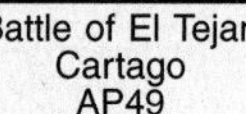

Battle of El Tejar, Cartago AP49

Occupation of Limón AP50

25c, Lucha ranch. 35c, Trenches of San Isidro Battalion. 55c, 75c, Observation post. 80c, 1col, Dr. Carlos Luis Valverde.

**Inscribed: "Guerra de Liberacion Nacional 1948"**

**Engraved; Center Photogravure**

**1950, July 20 *Perf. 12½***

**Center in Black**

**C189** AP49 15c brt car .40 .30
**C190** AP50 20c dull green .40 .30
**C191** AP49 25c dull blue .45 .30
**C192** AP49 35c chestnut .65 .30
**C193** AP49 55c lilac 1.10 .30
**C194** AP49 75c red org 1.90 .35
**C195** AP50 80c gray 1.90 .60
**C196** AP50 1col org yel 2.60 .65
*Nos. C189-C196 (8)* 9.40 3.10

2nd anniv. of the War for Natl. Liberation.

Bull (Cattle Raising) — AP51

1c, 10c, 2col, Bull. 2c, 30c, 3col, Tuna fishing. 3c, 65c, Pineapple. 5c, 50c, 5col, Bananas. 45c, 80c, 10col, Coffee picker.

**Inscribed: "Feria Nacional Agricola Ganadera e Industrial Cartago 1950"**

**1950, July 27 Center in Black**

**C197** AP51 1c brt green .75 .25
**C198** AP51 2c brt blue .75 .25
**C199** AP51 3c chocolate .85 .25
**C200** AP51 5c dp ultra .85 .25
**C201** AP51 10c green .85 .25
**C202** AP51 30c purple .85 .25
**C203** AP51 45c vermilion .95 .25
**C204** AP51 50c blue gray 1.10 .25
**C205** AP51 65c dk blue 1.10 .25
**C206** AP51 80c dp rose 2.90 .65
**C207** AP51 2col org yel 5.00 1.60
**C208** AP51 3col blue 9.00 4.00
**C209** AP51 5col carmine 12.75 6.50
**C210** AP51 10col dp claret 12.75 6.50
*Nos. C197-C210 (14)* 50.45 21.50

National Agricultural, Livestock and Industrial Fair, Cartago, 1950.
For surcharge see No. RA1.

Queen Isabella I and Caravels of Columbus AP52

**Unwmk.**

**1952, Mar. 4 Engr. *Perf. 13***

**C211** AP52 15c carmine .35 .30
**C212** AP52 20c orange .65 .35
**C213** AP52 25c ultra .95 .35
**C214** AP52 55c dp green 3.25 .35
**C215** AP52 2col violet 6.50 .60
*Nos. C211-C215 (5)* 11.70 1.95

Birth of Queen Isabella I of Spain, 500th anniv.

**Mail Plane Type of 1934**

**1952-53 *Perf. 12***

**C216** AP8 5c blue .65 .40
**C217** AP8 10c green .65 .40
**C218** AP8 15c car rose ('53) .95 .40
**C219** AP8 35c purple 2.25 .40
*Nos. C216-C219 (4)* 4.50 1.60

Nos. C216-C217 were reprinted in 1953 in different shades. Values the same. Value, set mint $1.50.

**Nos. C149-C151, C153 Surcharged in Red: "HABILITADO PARA CINCO CENTIMOS 1953"**

**1953, Apr. 24 *Perf. 12½***

**Center in Black**

**C220** AP43 5c on 30c dp ultra 3.00 1.50
**C221** AP43 5c on 40c red org .65 .30
**C222** AP43 5c on 45c vio .65 .30
**C223** AP43 5c on 65c brn org .65 .30
*Nos. C220-C223 (4)* 4.95 2.40

Nos. C161-C163 Surcharged in Black

**1953, Apr. 11 *Perf. 12***

**C224** A122 15c on 30c car rose .80 .40
**C225** A122 15c on 45c red brn .80 .40
**C226** A122 15c on 65c org yel .80 .40
*Nos. C224-C226 (3)* 2.40 1.20

Refinery of Vegetable Oils and Fats — AP53

Industries: 10c, Pottery. 15c, Sugar. 20c, Soap. 25c, Lumber. 30c, Matches. 35c, Textiles. 40c, Leather. 45c, Tobacco. 50c, Preserving. 55c, Canning. 60c, General. 65c, Metals. 75c, Pharmaceuticals. 80c, Pharmaceuticals. 1col, Paper. 2col, Rubber. 3col, Airplane maintenance. 5col, Marble. 10col, Beer.

**Engraved; Center Photogravure**

**1954-59 Unwmk. *Perf. 13x12½***

**Center in Black**

**C227** AP53 5c red .30 .25
**C228** AP53 10c dk blue .30 .25
**C229** AP53 15c green .30 .25
**C230** AP53 20c violet .30 .25
**C231** AP53 25c magenta .35 .25
**C232** AP53 30c purple .75 .40
**C233** AP53 35c red vio .50 .25
**C234** AP53 40c black .75 .30
**C235** AP53 45c dk green 1.60 .40
**C236** AP53 50c vio brown .95 .25
**C237** AP53 55c yellow .75 .25
**C238** AP53 60c brown 1.90 .65
**C239** AP53 65c carmine 2.25 .95
**C240** AP53 75c violet 3.00 .80
**C240A** AP53 80c pur & gray 1.60 .80
**C241** AP53 1col blue .95 .40
*a.* Imperf., pair 200.00
**C242** AP53 2col rose pink 3.00 1.25
**C243** AP53 3col ol grn 4.00 2.00
**C244** AP53 5col black 6.00 1.60
**C245** AP53 10col yellow 17.50 9.50
*Nos. C227-C245 (20)* 47.05 21.05

Issued: 30c, 35c, 60c, 65c, 75c, 2col, 3col, Oct. 20; 80c, Oct. 2, 1959; others, Sept. 1.
See Nos. C252-C255. For surcharges and overprint, see Nos. C314-C315, C334-C336, RA2, RA11.

Globe, Rotary Emblem — AP54

25c, Hand protecting boy. 40c, 2col, Hospital. 45c, Globe & palm leaves. 60c, Lighthouse.

**1956, Feb. 7 Engr. *Perf. 12***

**C246** AP54 10c green .40 .30
**C247** AP54 25c dk blue .40 .30
**C248** AP54 40c dk brown .95 .45
**C249** AP54 45c brt red .60 .30
**C250** AP54 60c dk red vio .95 .35
**C251** AP54 2col yel org 2.60 .70
*Nos. C246-C251 (6)* 5.90 2.40

50th anniv. of Rotary Intl. (in 1955).

**Industries Type of 1954**

Designs as in 1954.

**Engraved; Center Photogravure**

**1956, Feb. 17 *Perf. 12***

**Center in Black**

**C252** AP53 5c ultra .50 .40
**C253** AP53 10c violet blue .80 .40
**C254** AP53 15c orange yel .95 .40
**C255** AP53 75c red orange 1.60 .40
*Nos. C252-C255 (4)* 3.85 1.60

Map of Costa Rica — AP55

10c, Map of Guanacaste. 15c, Inn. 20c, House of Santa Rosa. 25c, Gen. Jose Manuel Quiros. 30c, Old Presidential Palace. 35c, Joaquin Bernardo Calvo. 40c, Luis Molina. 45c, Gen. Jose Joaquin Mora. 50c, Gen. Jose Maria Canas. 55c, Juan Santamaria monument. 60c, National monument. 65c, Antonio Vallerriestra. 70c, Ramon Castilla y Marquesado. 75c, San Carlos fortress. 80c, Francisco Maria Oreamuno. 1col, Pres. Juan Rafael Mora.

**1957, June 21 Engr. *Perf. 13½x13***

**C256** AP55 5c lt blue .35 .30
**C257** AP55 10c green .45 .35
**C258** AP55 15c dp orange .45 .35
**C259** AP55 20c lt brown .45 .35
**C260** AP55 25c vio blue .55 .35
**C261** AP55 30c violet .75 .35
**C262** AP55 35c car rose .80 .35
**C263** AP55 40c slate .80 .35
**C264** AP55 45c rose red .90 .35
**C265** AP55 50c ultra 1.00 .35
**C266** AP55 55c ocher 1.75 .35
**C267** AP55 60c brt car 1.60 .40
**C268** AP55 65c carmine 1.75 .40
**C269** AP55 70c orange yel 2.00 .40
**C270** AP55 75c emerald 2.00 .40
**C271** AP55 80c dk brown 2.60 .55
**C272** AP55 1col black 3.00 .55
*Nos. C256-C272 (17)* 21.20 6.50

Centenary of War of 1856-57.

Cleto Gonzalez Viquez AP56

Highway and Gonzalez Viquez AP57

Designs: 10c, Ricardo Jimenez Oreamuno. 20c, Puntarenas wharf and Jimenez. 35c, Post and Telegraph Bldg. and Jimenez. 55c, Pipeline and Gonzalez Viquez. 80c, National Library and Gonzalez Viquez. 1col, Electric train and Jimenez. 2col, Gonzales and Jimenez.

**1959, Nov. 23 Engr. *Perf. 13½***

**C274** AP56 5c car & ultra .40 .25
**C275** AP56 10c red & gray .40 .25

***Perf. 13½x13***

**C276** AP57 15c dk bl grn & blk .40 .25
**C277** AP57 20c car & brn .75 .25
**C278** AP57 35c rose lil & bl .40 .25
**C279** AP57 55c olive & vio .75 .25
**C280** AP57 80c ultra 1.00 .35
**C281** AP57 1col orange & mar 1.60 .50
**C282** AP57 2col gray & mar 3.50 1.60
*Nos. C274-C282 (9)* 9.20 3.95

For surcharge and overprint see Nos. C337, C339.

Soccer — AP58

Designs: Various soccer scenes.

***Perf. 13½***

**1960, Mar. 7 Unwmk. Photo.**

**C283** AP58 10c black .40 .30
**C284** AP58 25c ultra .40 .30
**C285** AP58 35c red orange .40 .30
**C286** AP58 50c red brown .60 .30
**C287** AP58 85c Prus green 1.75 .90
**C288** AP58 5col dp claret 4.25 2.50
*Nos. C283-C288 (6)* 7.80 4.60

**Souvenir Sheet**

***Imperf***

**C289** AP58 2col blue 7.00 6.50

3rd Pan-American Soccer Games, San José, Mar. 1960.
Nos. C283-C288 exist imperf. Value, pair $150.

WRY Uprooted Oak Emblem — AP59

**1960, Apr. 7 Unwmk. *Perf. 11½***

**Granite Paper**

**C290** AP59 35c vio bl, blk & yel .45 .25
**C291** AP59 85c black & brt pink 1.40 .55

Refugee Year, July 1, 1959-June 30, 1960.

Banner and "OEA" AP60

35c, "OEA" in oval. 55c, Clasped hands. 5col, Flags forming bird. 10col, Map of Costa Rica, flags & "OEA."
2col, "OEA" & map of Americas.

**1960, Aug. 15 Litho. *Perf. 10***

**C292** AP60 25c black & multi .30 .25
*a.* Multi, impression sideways 60.00
**C293** AP60 35c multicolored .40 .30
*a.* Pair, imperf. between 60.00
**C294** AP60 55c multicolored .60 .40
**C295** AP60 5col multicolored 3.75 2.75
**C296** AP60 10col black & multi 6.00 4.50
*Nos. C292-C296 (5)* 11.05 8.20

**Souvenir Sheet**

***Imperf***

**C297** AP60 2col multicolored 3.25 2.75

Pan-American Conf., San Jose, Aug. 15.

St. Louisa de Marillac and Orphanage — AP61

St. Vincent de Paul — AP62

25c, St. Vincent & old seminary. 50c, St. Louisa & sickroom. 1col, St. Vincent & new seminary.

**1960, Oct. 26 Engr. *Perf. 14x13½***

**C298** AP61 10c green .40 .25
**C299** AP61 25c carmine .40 .25
**C300** AP61 50c dk blue .40 .25
**C301** AP61 1col brown org .90 .30
**C302** AP62 5col brown 5.00 1.75
*Nos. C298-C302 (5)* 7.10 2.80

St. Vincent (1581?-1660) and St. Louisa (1591-1660). Nos. C298-C302 exist imperf.

Runner — AP63

Sports: 2c, Woman swimmer. 3c, Bicyclist. 4c, Weight lifter. 5c, Woman tennis player. 10c, Boxers. 25c, Soccer player. 85c, Basketball player. 1col, Baseball batter. 5col, Romulus and Remus statue. 10col, Pistol marksman.

*Perf. 13½x14*

**1960, Dec. 14 Photo. Unwmk.**

**Designs in Black**

| | | | | |
|---|---|---|---|---|
| **C303** | AP63 | 1c brt yellow | .35 | .25 |
| **C304** | AP63 | 2c lt ultra | .35 | .25 |
| **C305** | AP63 | 3c dp rose | .35 | .25 |
| **C306** | AP63 | 4c yellow | .35 | .25 |
| **C307** | AP63 | 5c brt yel grn | .35 | .25 |
| **C308** | AP63 | 10c pink | .35 | .25 |
| **C309** | AP63 | 25c lt bl grn | .35 | .25 |
| **C310** | AP63 | 85c lilac | 1.60 | .80 |
| **C311** | AP63 | 1col gray | 1.90 | 1.00 |
| **C312** | AP63 | 10col lt violet | 13.00 | 8.00 |
| | | *Nos. C303-C312 (10)* | 18.95 | 11.55 |

**Souvenir Sheets**

*Perf. 14x13½*

| | | | | |
|---|---|---|---|---|
| **C313** | AP63 | 5col multi | 6.50 | 6.00 |

17th Olympic Games, Rome, 8/25-9/11.
Nos. C303-C313 exist imperf.

No. C255 Srchd. and Ovptd. in Blue or Ultramarine

**Engraved and Photogravure**

**1961, Apr. 21** *Perf. 12*

**Center in Black**

| | | | | |
|---|---|---|---|---|
| **C314** | AP53 | 25c on 75c red org (Bl) | .65 | .40 |
| **C315** | AP53 | 75c red orange (U) | 1.10 | .40 |

15th Amateur Baseball Championships.

Alberto Brenes C. — AP64

No. C317, Manuel Aguilar. No. C318, Agustin Gutierrez L. No. C319, Vicente Herrera.

**1961, June 12 Photo.** *Perf. 12*

| | | | | |
|---|---|---|---|---|
| **C316** | AP64 | 10c deep claret | .80 | .40 |
| **C317** | AP64 | 10c blue | .80 | .40 |
| **C318** | AP64 | 25c bright violet | .80 | .40 |
| **C319** | AP64 | 25c gray | .80 | .40 |
| | | *Nos. C316-C319 (4)* | 3.20 | 1.60 |

First Continental Congress of Lawyers, San José, June 11-15. Exist imperf.
See Nos. C330-C333.

Miguel Obregon — AP65

**1961, July 19 Litho.** *Perf. 13½*

| | | | | |
|---|---|---|---|---|
| **C320** | AP65 | 10c Prussian green | .90 | .40 |

Birth centenary of Prof. Miguel Obregon L. Exists imperf. Value $50.

UN Food and Agriculture Organization — AP66

UN day (UN Organizations): 20c, WHO. 25c, ILO. 30, ITU. 35c, World Meteorological Organization. 45c, UNESCO. 85c, ICAO. 5col, "United Nations" holding the world. 10col, Int. Bank for Reconstruction and Development.

*Perf. 11½*

**1961, Oct. 24 Unwmk. Engr.**

| | | | | |
|---|---|---|---|---|
| **C321** | AP66 | 10c lt green | .30 | .25 |
| **C322** | AP66 | 20c orange | .30 | .25 |
| **C323** | AP66 | 25c Prus grn | .30 | .25 |
| **C324** | AP66 | 30c dk blue | .30 | .25 |
| **C325** | AP66 | 35c carmine rose | 1.25 | .25 |
| **C326** | AP66 | 45c violet | .45 | .25 |
| **C327** | AP66 | 85c blue | .95 | .55 |
| **C328** | AP66 | 10col dk sl grn | 7.50 | 4.50 |
| | | *Nos. C321-C328 (8)* | 11.35 | 6.55 |

**Souvenir Sheet**

*Imperf*

| | | | | |
|---|---|---|---|---|
| **C329** | AP66 | 5col ultra | 5.00 | 4.50 |

For overprint see No. C338.

**Portrait Type of 1961**

No. C330, Dr. José Maria Soto Alfaro. No. C331, Dr. Elias Rojas Roman. No. C332, Dr. Andres Saenz Llorente. No. C333, Dr. Juan José Ulloa Giralt.

**1961 Photo.** *Perf. 13½*

| | | | | |
|---|---|---|---|---|
| **C330** | AP64 | 10c blue green | .45 | .40 |
| **C331** | AP64 | 10c violet | .45 | .40 |
| **C332** | AP64 | 25c dark gray | .85 | .40 |
| **C333** | AP64 | 25c deep claret | .85 | .40 |
| | | *Nos. C330-C333 (4)* | 2.60 | 1.60 |

9th Congress of Physicians of Central America and Panama.

**Nos. C229, C236 and C280 Surcharged in Black, Orange or Red**

No. C334

No. C334A

**Engraved; Center Photogravure**

**1962** *Perf. 13x12½, 13½x13*

| | | | | |
|---|---|---|---|---|
| **C334** | AP53 | 10c ("10") on 15c | .50 | .30 |
| **C334A** | AP53 | 10c ("c0.10") on 15c (R) | .50 | .30 |
| **C335** | AP53 | 25c on 15c | .50 | .30 |
| **C336** | AP53 | 35c on 50c (O) | .70 | .30 |

**Engr.**

| | | | | |
|---|---|---|---|---|
| **C337** | AP57 | 85c on 80c (R) | 2.60 | .80 |
| | | *Nos. C334-C337 (5)* | 4.80 | 2.00 |

No. C336 exists with double surcharge. Value, $35.

Nos. C324 and C282 Overprinted in Red

**1962, Sept. 12** *Perf. 11½, 13½x13*

| | | | | |
|---|---|---|---|---|
| **C338** | AP66 | 30c dark blue | .90 | .40 |
| **C339** | AP57 | 2col gray & mar | 2.25 | 1.25 |

2nd Central American Phil. Convention.

Revenue Stamp Surcharged in Red

**1962 Engr.** *Perf. 12*

| | | | | |
|---|---|---|---|---|
| **C341** | A124 | 25c on 2c emer | .65 | .40 |
| **C342** | A124 | 35c on 2c emer | .65 | .40 |
| **C343** | A124 | 45c on 2c emer | 1.00 | .40 |
| **C344** | A124 | 85c on 2c emer | 1.75 | .40 |
| | | *Nos. C341-C344 (4)* | 4.05 | 1.60 |

Arms and Malaria Eradication Emblem — AP67

**1963, Feb. 14 Photo.** *Perf. 11½*

| | | | | |
|---|---|---|---|---|
| **C345** | AP67 | 25c brt rose | .40 | .25 |
| **C346** | AP67 | 35c brown org | .40 | .25 |
| **C347** | AP67 | 45c ultra | .55 | .25 |
| **C348** | AP67 | 85c blue grn | 1.25 | .50 |
| **C349** | AP67 | 1col dk blue | 2.00 | .65 |
| | | *Nos. C345-C349 (5)* | 4.60 | 1.90 |

WHO drive to eradicate malaria.

Central American Tapir — AP68

Designs: 5c, Paca. 25c, Jaguar. 30c, Ocelot. 35c, Whitetail deer. 40c, Manatee. 85c, White-throated capuchin monkey. 5col, White-lipped peccary.

*Perf. 13½*

**1963, May Unwmk. Photo.**

| | | | | |
|---|---|---|---|---|
| **C354** | AP68 | 5c yel ol & brn | .30 | .30 |
| **C355** | AP68 | 10c orange & sl | .35 | .30 |
| **C356** | AP68 | 25c blue & yel | .55 | .50 |
| **C357** | AP68 | 30c lt yel grn & brn | .75 | .60 |
| **C358** | AP68 | 35c bis & red brn | 1.40 | .60 |
| **C359** | AP68 | 40c emer & sl bl | 1.60 | 1.00 |
| **C360** | AP68 | 85c green & blk | 5.00 | 1.00 |
| **C361** | AP68 | 5col gray grn & choc | 14.00 | 10.00 |
| | | *Nos. C354-C361 (8)* | 23.95 | 14.30 |

See Nos. C367-C370.

Stamp of 1863 and Packet "Monarch" AP69

Issue of 1863 and: 2col, Recaredo Bonilla Carrillo, Postmaster, 1862-63. 3col, Burros, overland mail transport, 1839. 10col, Burro railway car.

**1963, June 26 Litho.**

| | | | | |
|---|---|---|---|---|
| **C362** | AP69 | 25c dl rose & chlky bl | .25 | .25 |
| **C363** | AP69 | 2col gray bl & org | 1.75 | 1.25 |
| **C364** | AP69 | 3col bister & emer | 3.25 | 2.00 |
| **C365** | AP69 | 10col dl grn & ocher | 12.00 | 6.00 |
| | | *Nos. C362-C365 (4)* | 17.25 | 9.50 |

Centenary of Costa Rica's stamps.
No. C362 is inscribed "William Le Lacheur," the builder and captain of the "Monarch."

**Souvenir Sheets**

Stamps of 1863 and San José Postmark AP70

*Perf. 13½, Imperf.*

**1963, June 26 Unwmk.**

| | | | | |
|---|---|---|---|---|
| **C366** | AP70 | 5col bl, red, grn & org | 5.50 | 5.50 |

Cent. of Costa Rica's stamps.
In 1968 examples of No. C366 were overprinted "2-4 Agosto 1968" and "III Exposicion Filatelica Nacional / 'Costa Rica 68'". Value, $10.50.

**Animal Type of 1963 Surcharged in Red**

No. C367, Little anteater. No. C368, Gray fox. No. C369, Armadillo. No. C370, Great anteater.

**1963, Sept. 14 Photo.** *Perf. 13½*

| | | | | |
|---|---|---|---|---|
| **C367** | AP68 | 10c on 1c brt grn & org brn | 1.40 | .30 |
| **C368** | AP68 | 25c on 2c org yel & ol grn | 1.40 | .30 |
| **C369** | AP68 | 35c on 3c bluish grn & brn | 1.75 | .30 |
| **C370** | AP68 | 85c on 4c dp rose & dk brn | 3.25 | .65 |
| | | *Nos. C367-C370 (4)* | 7.80 | 1.55 |

Examples of No. C370 exist without surcharge. Value, $1,000, less than 10 exist.

Pres. Kennedy — AP71

Portraits — Presidents: 25c, Francisco J. Orlich, Costa Rica. 30c, Julio A. Rivera, El Salvador. 35c, Miguel Ydigoras F., Guatemala. 85c, Dr. Ramon Villeda M., Honduras. 1col, Luis A. Somoza, Nicaragua. 3col, Roberto F. Chiari, Panama.

**1963, Dec. 7 Unwmk.** *Perf. 14*

**Portraits in Black Brown**

| | | | | |
|---|---|---|---|---|
| **C371** | AP71 | 25c violet brn | .40 | .30 |
| **C372** | AP71 | 30c brt lil rose | .40 | .30 |
| **C373** | AP71 | 35c ocher | .40 | .30 |
| **C374** | AP71 | 85c gray blue | .70 | .30 |
| **C375** | AP71 | 1col orange brn | .80 | .40 |
| **C376** | AP71 | 3col lt ol grn | 3.50 | 1.75 |
| **C377** | AP71 | 5col gray | 4.50 | 2.75 |
| | | *Nos. C371-C377 (7)* | 10.70 | 6.10 |

Meeting of Central American Presidents with Pres. John F. Kennedy, San José, Mar. 18-20, 1963.

Ancestral Figure — AP72

Ancient Art: 5c, Dog, horiz. 10c, Ornamental stool, horiz. 25c, Male figure. 30c, Ceremonial dancer. 35c, Ceramic vase. 50c, Frog. 55c, Bell. 75c, Six-limbed figure. 85c, Seated man. 90c, Bird-shaped jug. 1col, Twin human beaker, horiz. 2col, Alligator, horiz. 3col, Twin-tailed lizard. 5col, Figure under arch. 10col, Polished stone figure.

**1963-64 Photo.** *Perf. 12*

| | | | | |
|---|---|---|---|---|
| **C378** | AP72 | 5c lt yel grn & Prus grn | .30 | .25 |
| **C379** | AP72 | 10c buff & dk grn | .30 | .25 |
| **C380** | AP72 | 25c rose & dk brn | .30 | .25 |
| **C381** | AP72 | 30c ocher & Prus grn ('64) | .30 | .25 |
| **C382** | AP72 | 35c sal & sl grn | .30 | .25 |
| **C383** | AP72 | 45c lt bl & dk brn | .30 | .25 |
| **C384** | AP72 | 50c dl bl & dk brn | .50 | .25 |
| **C385** | AP72 | 55c yel grn & dk brn | .65 | .25 |
| **C386** | AP72 | 75c ocher & dk red brn | .65 | .25 |
| **C387** | AP72 | 85c yel & red brn | 1.60 | 1.40 |
| **C388** | AP72 | 90c cit & red brn ('64) | 2.10 | 1.75 |
| **C389** | AP72 | 1col lt bl & dk brn ('64) | 1.40 | .30 |
| **C390** | AP72 | 2col buff & dk grn ('64) | 2.25 | .65 |
| **C391** | AP72 | 3col yel grn & dk brn ('64) | 6.50 | .95 |
| **C392** | AP72 | 5col cit & sep ('64) | 6.50 | 5.25 |
| **C393** | AP72 | 10col rose lil & sl grn | 11.00 | 8.75 |
| | | *Nos. C378-C393 (16)* | 34.95 | 21.30 |

For surcharges and overprint see Nos. C395, C397-C398, C400, C426-C428.

Flags of Central American States — AP73

**1964, Mar. 11** *Perf. 14*

| | | | | |
|---|---|---|---|---|
| **C394** | AP73 | 30c bl, gray, red & blk | 1.50 | .40 |

Central American Independence issue. For surcharge see No. C396.

Nos. C381, C394 and C387 Surcharged

**1964, Oct.** *Perf. 12, 14*

**C395** AP72 5c on 30c 1.00 .40
**C396** AP73 15c on 30c 1.00 .40
**C397** AP72 15c on 85c 1.00 .40
*Nos. C395-C397 (3)* 3.00 1.20

No. C388 Surcharged in Black

**1964, Nov. 22** *Perf. 12*

**C398** AP72 15c on 90c cit & red brn 1.00 .40

Paris Postal Conference.

Alfredo Gonzalez F. — AP74

**1965, June** **Photo.** *Perf. 12*

**C399** AP74 35c dk blue green 3.75 .35

50th anniv. of the National Bank and honoring Alfredo Gonzalez Flores (1877-1962), 1st governor of the bank.

No. C390 Overprinted in Black

**1965, Aug. 14** **Unwmk.** *Perf. 12*

**C400** AP72 2col buff & dk grn 1.75 .80

75th anniv. of Chapui Asylum, San José.

Girl, FAO Emblem and Hands Holding Grain — AP75

FAO Emblem and: 15c, Map of Costa Rica and silos, horiz. 50c, World population chart and children. 1col, Plane over map of Costa Rica, horiz.

**1965, Oct. 25** **Litho.** *Perf. 14*

**C401** AP75 15c lt brn & blk .60 .40
**C402** AP75 35c black & yel .60 .40
**C403** AP75 50c ultra & dk grn .60 .40
**C404** AP75 1col grn, blk & sil 1.40 .40
*Nos. C401-C404 (4)* 3.20 1.60

FAO "Freedom from Hunger" campaign.

Church of Nicoya — AP76

5c, Leonidas Briceno B. 15c, Scroll dated "25 de Julio de 1964." 35c, Map of Guanacaste and Nicoya peninsula. 50c, Dancing couple. 1col, Map showing local products.

**1965, Dec. 20** *Perf. 13½x14*

**C405** AP76 5c red brn & blk .70 .40
**C406** AP76 10c blue & gray .70 .40
**C407** AP76 15c bis & slate .70 .40
**C408** AP76 35c blue & slate .70 .40
**C409** AP76 50c gray & vio bl 1.00 .40
**C410** AP76 1col buff & slate 2.00 .40
*Nos. C405-C410 (6)* 5.80 2.40

Acquisition of the Nicoya territory.

Runner and Olympic Rings — AP77

Olympic Rings and Emblem: 10c, Bicyclists. 40c, Judo. 65c, Basketball. 80c, Soccer. 1col, Hands holding torches, and Mt. Fuji.

**1965, Dec. 23** *Perf. 13x13½*

**C411** AP77 5c bister & multi .50 .40
**C412** AP77 10c lt lil & multi .50 .40
**C413** AP77 40c multicolored .50 .40
**C414** AP77 65c lemon & multi .50 .40
**C415** AP77 80c tan & multi 1.00 .40
**C416** AP77 1col multicolored 1.50 .40
*a.* Souvenir sheet of 2 7.00 6.50
*Nos. C411-C416 (6)* 4.50 2.40

18th Olympic Games, Tokyo, Oct. 10-25, 1964. No. C416a contains two 1col stamps, one like No. C416, the other with gray background replacing yellow orange.

No. C416a was issued both perf and imperf. Same values.

Nos. C411-C416 exist imperf.

Pres. Kennedy Speaking in San José Cathedral — AP78

Designs: 45c, Friendship 7 capsule circling globe, and Kennedy, horiz. 85c, Kennedy and John, Jr. 1col, Curtis-Lee Mansion and flame from Kennedy grave, Arlington, Va.

*Perf. 13½x13, 13x13½*

**1965, Dec. 23** **Litho.** **Unwmk.**

**C417** AP78 45c brt bl & lil .45 .40
**C418** AP78 55c org & brt bl .55 .40
**C419** AP78 85c gray, dk brn & red brn 1.10 .50
**C420** AP78 1col multicolored 1.40 .60
*a.* Souvenir sheet of 2 4.00 3.50
*Nos. C417-C420 (4)* 3.50 1.90

President John F. Kennedy (1917-63). No. C420a contains two 1col stamps, one like No. C420, the other with blue green background replacing dark blue. Exists with light blue background instead of green; value $150.

No. C420a was issued both perf and imperf. Same values.

Nos. C417-C420 exist imperf.

For surcharges see Nos. C429-C430.

Firemen with Hoses — AP79

Designs: 5c, Fire engine "Knox," horiz. 10c, 1866 fire pump. 35c, Fireman's badge. 50c, Emblem and flags of Confederation of Central American Fire Brigades.

**1966, Mar. 12** **Litho.** *Perf. 11*

**C421** AP79 5c black & red .65 .40
**C422** AP79 10c bister & red 1.00 .40
**C423** AP79 15c blk, red brn & red 1.30 .40
**C424** AP79 35c black & yel 2.60 .40
**C425** AP79 50c dk blue & red 5.00 .80
*Nos. C421-C425 (5)* 10.55 2.40

Centenary of San José Fire Brigade.

**Nos. C381, C383, C386 and C418-C419 Surcharged**

a

b

**1966, Dec.** **Photo.** *Perf. 12*

**C426** AP72(a) 15c on 30c .50 .40
**C427** AP72(a) 15c on 45c .50 .40
**C428** AP72(a) 35c on 75c .50 .40

**Litho.** *Perf. 13x13½*

**C429** AP78(a) 35c on 55c .50 .40
**C430** AP78(b) 50c on 85c 1.90 .40
*Nos. C426-C430 (5)* 3.90 2.00

Revenue Stamps (Basic Type of A124) Surcharged

**1967, Jan.** **Engr.** *Perf. 12*

**C431** A124 15c on 5c blue .50 .40
**C432** A124 35c on 10c claret .70 .40
**C433** A124 50c on 20c rose red 1.25 .40
*Nos. C431-C433 (3)* 2.45 1.20

Central Bank of Costa Rica — AP80

**1967, Mar. 1** **Litho.** *Perf. 11*

**C434** AP80 5c brt green .85 .40
**C435** AP80 15c brown .85 .40
**C436** AP80 35c scarlet .85 .40
*Nos. C434-C436 (3)* 2.55 1.20

Power Lines — AP81

Telecommunications Building, San Pedro — AP82

Electrification Program: 15c, Telephone Central. 25c, La Garita Dam. 35c, Rio Mache Reservoir. 50c, Cachi Dam.

**1967, Apr. 24** **Litho.** *Perf. 11*

**C437** AP81 5c dark gray .65 .40
**C438** AP82 10c brt rose .65 .40
**C439** AP81 15c brown org .65 .40
**C440** AP82 25c brt ultra .65 .40
**C441** AP82 35c brt green .75 .40
**C442** AP82 50c red brown .95 .40
*Nos. C437-C442 (6)* 4.30 2.40

Chondrorhyncha Aromatica — AP83

Orchids: 10c, Miltonia endresii. 15c, Stanhopea cirrhata. 25c, Trichopilia suavis. 35c, Odontoglossum schlieperianum. 50c, Cattleya skinneri. 1col, Cattleya dowiana. 2col, Odontoglossum chiriquense.

**1967, June 15** **Engr.** *Perf. 13x13½*

**Orchids in Natural Colors**

**C443** AP83 5c multicolored .40 .25
**C444** AP83 10c olive & multi .50 .30
**C445** AP83 15c multicolored .65 .30
**C446** AP83 25c multicolored 1.10 .30
**C447** AP83 35c dull vio & multi 1.40 .30
**C448** AP83 50c brown & multi 1.90 .30
**C449** AP83 1col vio & multi 4.00 .80
**C450** AP83 2col dk ol bis & multi 7.50 1.50
*Nos. C443-C450 (8)* 17.45 4.05

Issued for the University Library.

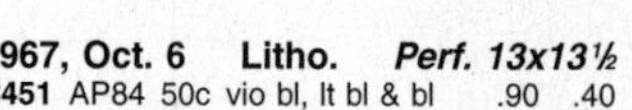

Institute Emblem — AP84

**1967, Oct. 6** **Litho.** *Perf. 13x13½*

**C451** AP84 50c vio bl, lt bl & bl .90 .40

Inter-American Agriculture Institute, 25th anniv.

Church of Solitude — AP85

Costa Rican Churches: 10c, Basilica of Santo Domingo, Heredia. 15c, Cathedral of Tilaran. 25c, Cathedral of Alajuela. 30c, Mercy Church. 35c, Basilica of Our Lady of Angels. 40c, Church of St. Raphael, Heredia. 45c, Ujarras ruins. 50c, Ruins of parish church, Cartago. 55c, Cathedral of San José. 65c, Parish church, Puntarenas. 75c, Church of Orosi. 80c, Cathedral of St. Isidro, the General. 85c, St. Ramon Church. 90c, Church of the Abandoned. 1col, Coronado Church. 2col, Church of St. Teresita. 3col, Parish Church, Heredia. 5col, Carmelite Church. 10col, Limon Cathedral.

**1967, Dec. 15** **Engr.** *Perf. 12½*

**C452** AP85 5c green .30 .25
**C453** AP85 10c blue .30 .25
**C454** AP85 15c lilac .30 .25
**C455** AP85 25c dull yel .30 .25
**C456** AP85 30c orange brn .30 .25
**C457** AP85 35c lt blue .30 .25
**C458** AP85 40c dp orange .35 .25
**C459** AP85 45c dl bl grn .35 .25
**C460** AP85 50c olive .45 .25
**C461** AP85 55c brown .45 .25
**C462** AP85 65c car rose .70 .25
**C463** AP85 75c sepia .75 .30
**C464** AP85 80c yellow 1.50 .45
**C465** AP85 85c violet blk 1.25 .45
**C466** AP85 90c emerald 1.75 .65
**C467** AP85 1col slate 1.40 .35
**C468** AP85 2col brt green 6.00 1.75
**C469** AP85 3col orange 8.00 3.00
**C470** AP85 5col vio blue 8.75 3.00
**C471** AP85 10col carmine 10.50 4.50
*Nos. C452-C471 (20)* 44.00 17.20

Nos. C452 and C454 exist imperf; Nos. C455 and C470 exist imperf horiz.

See Nos. C561-C576.

LACSA Emblem — AP86

45c, LACSA emblem, jet, horiz. 50c, Decorated wheel, anniversary emblem.

*Perf. 13x13½, 13½x13*

**1967, Dec. 12** **Litho. & Engr.**

**C472** AP86 40c ultra, grnsh bl & gold .60 .40
**C473** AP86 45c blk, pale grn, ultra & gold .75 .40
**C474** AP86 50c blue & multi 1.00 .40
*Nos. C472-C474 (3)* 2.35 1.20

20th anniv. (in 1966) of Lineas Aereas Costaricenses, LACSA, Costa Rican Airlines.

Scout Directing Traffic — AP87

Designs: 25c, Campfire under tree. 35c, Flag of Costa Rica, Scout flag and emblem. 50c, Encampment, horiz. 65c, Photograph of first Scout troop, horiz.

**1968, Mar. 15** *Perf. 13*

**C475** AP87 15c lt bl, blk & lt brn .45 .40
**C476** AP87 25c lt ultra, vio bl & org .45 .40
**C477** AP87 35c blue & multi .80 .40
**C478** AP87 50c multicolored 1.20 .40
**C479** AP87 65c sal, dk bl & brn 2.00 .40
*Nos. C475-C479 (5)* 4.90 2.00

Costa Rican Boy Scouts, 50th anniversary.

Runner — AP88

Sports: 40c, Women's running. 55c, Boxing. 65c, Bicycling. 75c, Weight lifting. 1col, High diving. 3col, Rifle shooting.

**1969, Jan. 17 Litho. *Perf. 10x11***

| | | | | |
|---|---|---|---|---|
| **C481** | AP88 | 30c multi | .40 | .30 |
| **C482** | AP88 | 40c multi | .40 | .30 |
| **C483** | AP88 | 55c multi | .40 | .30 |
| **C484** | AP88 | 65c lil & multi | .55 | .30 |
| **C485** | AP88 | 75c multi | .55 | .30 |
| **C486** | AP88 | 1col multi | .75 | .30 |
| **C487** | AP88 | 3col multi | 3.50 | 1.00 |
| | | *Nos. C481-C487 (7)* | 6.55 | 2.80 |

19th Olympic Games, Mexico City, 10/12-27.

Philatelic Exhibition Emblem — AP89

**1969, June 5 Litho. *Perf. 11x10***

| | | | | |
|---|---|---|---|---|
| **C488** | AP89 | 35c multicolored | 1.20 | .40 |
| **C489** | AP89 | 40c pink & multi | 1.20 | .40 |
| **C490** | AP89 | 50c lt blue & multi | 1.20 | .40 |
| **C491** | AP89 | 2col multicolored | 1.60 | .55 |
| | | *Nos. C488-C491 (4)* | 5.20 | 1.75 |

4th Natl. Philatelic Exhib., San José, 6/5-8.

ILO Emblem — AP90

**1969, Oct. 29 Litho. *Perf. 10***

| | | | | |
|---|---|---|---|---|
| **C492** | AP90 | 35c bl grn & blk | .80 | .40 |
| **C493** | AP90 | 50c scarlet & blk | .80 | .40 |

50th anniv. of the ILO.

Soccer — AP91

Designs: 65c, Soccer ball, map of North and Central America. 85c, Soccer player. 1col, Two players in action.

**1969, Nov. 23 Litho. *Perf. 11x10***

| | | | | |
|---|---|---|---|---|
| **C494** | AP91 | 65c gray & multi | .70 | .40 |
| **C495** | AP91 | 75c multicolored | .70 | .40 |
| **C496** | AP91 | 85c multicolored | .90 | .40 |
| **C497** | AP91 | 1col pink & multi | 1.25 | .40 |
| | | *Nos. C494-C497 (4)* | 3.55 | 1.60 |

Issued to publicize the 4th Soccer Championships (CONCACAF), Nov. 23-Dec. 7.

Stylized Crab — AP92

**1970, May 14 Litho. *Perf. 12½***

| | | | | |
|---|---|---|---|---|
| **C498** | AP92 | 10c blk & lil rose | .45 | .40 |
| **C499** | AP92 | 15c blk & yel | .45 | .40 |
| **C500** | AP92 | 50c blk & brn org | .45 | .40 |
| **C501** | AP92 | 1.10col blk & emer | 2.00 | .40 |
| | | *Nos. C498-C501 (4)* | 3.35 | 1.60 |

10th Inter-American Cancer Cong., 5/22-29.

Costa Rica No. 124, Magnifying Glass and Stamps — AP93

2col, Father, son with stamps, album.

**1970, Sept. 14 Litho. *Perf. 11***

| | | | | |
|---|---|---|---|---|
| **C502** | AP93 | 1col ultra, brn & car rose | 1.25 | .25 |
| **C503** | AP93 | 2col blk, pink & ultra | 1.75 | .55 |

The 5th National Philatelic Exhibition.

EXPO Emblem and Costa Rican Cart AP94

EXPO Emblem and: 10c, Japanese floral arrangement, vert. 35c, Pavilion and Tower of the Sun. 40c, Japanese tea ceremony. 45c, Woman picking coffee, vert. 55c, Earth seen from moon, vert.

**1970, Oct. 22 Litho. *Perf. 13x13½***

| | | | | |
|---|---|---|---|---|
| **C504** | AP94 | 10c multicolored | .40 | .40 |
| **C505** | AP94 | 15c green & multi | .40 | .40 |
| **C506** | AP94 | 35c blue & multi | .80 | .40 |
| **C507** | AP94 | 40c gray & multi | .95 | .40 |
| **C508** | AP94 | 45c multicolored | 1.20 | .40 |
| **C509** | AP94 | 55c black & multi | 3.00 | .40 |
| | | *Nos. C504-C509 (6)* | 6.75 | 2.40 |

EXPO '70 International Exhibition, Osaka, Japan, Mar. 15-Sept. 13.

Escazu Valley, by Margarita Bertheau AP95

Paintings: 25c, "Irazu," by Rafael A. Garcia, vert. 80c, Shore landscape, by Teodorico Quiros. 1col, "The Other Face," by Cesar Valverde. 2.50col, Mother and Child, by Luis Daell, vert.

**1970, Nov. 4 Litho. *Perf. 12½***

| | | | | |
|---|---|---|---|---|
| **C510** | AP95 | 25c multi | 1.00 | .30 |
| **C511** | AP95 | 45c multi | 1.00 | .30 |
| **C512** | AP95 | 80c multi | 1.60 | .55 |
| **C513** | AP95 | 1col multi | 1.60 | .65 |
| **C514** | AP95 | 2.50col multi | 3.25 | 2.00 |
| | | *Nos. C510-C514 (5)* | 8.45 | 3.80 |

Arms of Costa Rica, 1964 — AP96

Various Coats of Arms, dated: 10c, Nov. 27, 1906. 15c, Sept. 29, 1848. 25c, Apr. 21, 1840. 35c, Nov. 22, 1824. 50c, Nov. 2, 1824. 1col, Mar. 6, 1824. 2col, May 10, 1823.

**1971, Feb. 10 Litho. *Perf. 14x13½***

| | | | | |
|---|---|---|---|---|
| **C515** | AP96 | 5c buff & multi | .70 | .30 |
| **C516** | AP96 | 10c multi | .70 | .30 |
| **C517** | AP96 | 15c yel & multi | .85 | .30 |
| **C518** | AP96 | 25c pink & multi | .85 | .30 |
| **C519** | AP96 | 35c multi | 1.10 | .30 |
| **C520** | AP96 | 50c rose & multi | 1.20 | .30 |
| **C521** | AP96 | 1col beige & multi | 1.60 | .50 |
| **C522** | AP96 | 2col multi | 2.25 | .90 |
| | | *Nos. C515-C522 (8)* | 9.25 | 3.20 |

National Theater — AP97

**1971, Apr. 14 Litho. *Perf. 11***

| | | | | |
|---|---|---|---|---|
| **C523** | AP97 | 2col plum | .90 | .40 |

Organization of American States meeting.

José Matias Delgado, Manuel José Arce — AP98

Flag of Costa Rica — AP99

Independence Leaders: 10c, Miguel Larreinaga and Manuel Antonio de la Cerda, Nicaragua. 15c, José Cecilio del Valle, Dionisio de Herrera, Honduras. 35c, Pablo Alvarado and Florencio del Castillo, Costa Rica. 50c, Antonio Larrazabal and Pedro Molina, Guatemala. 2col, Costa Rica coat of arms.

**1971, Sept. 14 *Perf. 13***

| | | | | |
|---|---|---|---|---|
| **C524** | AP98 | 5c multi | .45 | .40 |
| **C525** | AP98 | 10c multi | .45 | .40 |
| **C526** | AP98 | 15c gray, brn & blk | .45 | .40 |
| **C527** | AP98 | 35c multi | .45 | .40 |
| **C528** | AP98 | 50c multi | .45 | .40 |
| **C529** | AP99 | 1col multi | .45 | .40 |
| **C530** | AP99 | 2col multi | 2.25 | .40 |
| | | *Nos. C524-C530 (7)* | 4.95 | 2.80 |

Central American independence, sesqui.

Soccer Federation Emblem — AP100

**1971, Dec. 6**

| | | | | |
|---|---|---|---|---|
| **C531** | AP100 | 50c multi | .80 | .40 |
| **C532** | AP100 | 60c multi | .80 | .40 |

50th anniv. of Soccer Federation of Costa Rica.

Children of the World — AP101

**1972, Jan. 11 *Perf. 12½***

| | | | | |
|---|---|---|---|---|
| **C533** | AP101 | 50c multi | .65 | .40 |
| **C534** | AP101 | 1.10col red & multi | .85 | .40 |

25th anniv. (in 1971) of UNICEF.

Tree of Guanacaste AP102

Designs: 40c, Hermitage, Liberia. 55c, Petroglyphs, Rincón Brujo. 60c, Painted head, sculpture from Curubandé, vert.

**1972, Feb. 28 *Perf. 11***

| | | | | |
|---|---|---|---|---|
| **C535** | AP102 | 20c brn, ol & brt grn | .90 | .40 |
| **C536** | AP102 | 40c brn & ol | .90 | .40 |
| **C537** | AP102 | 55c blk & brn | .90 | .40 |
| **C538** | AP102 | 60c blk, buff & ver | .90 | .40 |
| | | *Nos. C535-C538 (4)* | 3.60 | 1.60 |

Bicentenary of the founding of the city of Liberia, Guanacaste.

Farm and Family — AP103

Designs: 45c, Cattle, dairy products and meat, horiz. 50c, Kneeling figure with plant. 10col, Farmer and map of Americas.

**1972, June 30 Litho. *Perf. 12½***

| | | | | |
|---|---|---|---|---|
| **C539** | AP103 | 20c multi | .50 | .25 |
| **C540** | AP103 | 45c multi | .50 | .25 |
| **C541** | AP103 | 50c dp yel, grn & blk | .50 | .25 |
| **C542** | AP103 | 10col brn, org & blk | 4.00 | 1.75 |
| | | *Nos. C539-C542 (4)* | 5.50 | 2.50 |

30th anniversary of the Inter-American Institute of Agricultural Sciences.

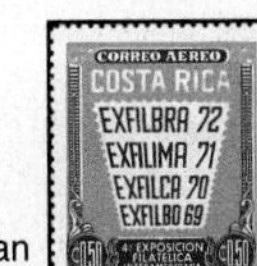

Inter-American Exhibitions — AP104

**1972, Aug. 26 Litho. *Perf. 13***

| | | | | |
|---|---|---|---|---|
| **C543** | AP104 | 50c orange & brn | .50 | .30 |
| **C544** | AP104 | 2col blue & vio | 1.00 | .40 |

4th Interamerican Philatelic Exhibition, EXFILBRA, Rio de Janeiro, Aug. 26-Sept. 2.

First Book Printed in Costa Rica — AP105

Intl. Book Year: 50c, 5col, Natl. Library, horiz.

**1972, Dec. 7 Litho. *Perf. 12½***

| | | | | |
|---|---|---|---|---|
| **C545** | AP105 | 20c brt blue | .65 | .25 |
| **C546** | AP105 | 50c gold & multi | .65 | .25 |
| **C547** | AP105 | 75c multicolored | .65 | .25 |
| **C548** | AP105 | 5col multicolored | 3.00 | .95 |
| | | *Nos. C545-C548 (4)* | 4.95 | 1.70 |

No. C545 exists on thin dull paper with shiny gum. Values: unused $20, used $10.

Road to Irazú Volcano — AP106

15c, Coco-Culebra Bay. 40c, Manuel Antonio Beach. 45c, Tourist Office emblem. 50c, Lindora Lake. 60c, San Jose P.O., vert.

**1972-73 *Perf. 11x11½, 11½x11***

| | | | | |
|---|---|---|---|---|
| **C549** | AP106 | 5c like 20c | .65 | .35 |
| **C550** | AP106 | 15c multi | .65 | .35 |
| **C551** | AP106 | 20c shown | .65 | .35 |
| **C552** | AP106 | 25c like 15c | .65 | .35 |
| **C553** | AP106 | 40c multi | .65 | .35 |
| **C554** | AP106 | 45c multi | .65 | .35 |
| **C555** | AP106 | 50c multi | .65 | .35 |
| **C556** | AP106 | 60c multi | .65 | .35 |
| **C557** | AP106 | 80c like 40c | .95 | .35 |
| **C558** | AP106 | 90c like 45c | .95 | .35 |
| **C559** | AP106 | 1col like 50c | .95 | .35 |
| **C560** | AP106 | 2col like 60c | 1.90 | .75 |
| | | *Nos. C549-C560 (12)* | 9.95 | 4.60 |

Tourism year of the Americas.

Issued: 20c, 25c, 80c, 90c, 1col, 2col, 12/26; others, 3/21/73.

No. C555 exists with inverted center, used only. Value $10,000.

### Church Type of 1967

Designs as before.

**1973, July 16 Engr. *Perf. 12½***

| | | | | |
|---|---|---|---|---|
| **C561** | AP85 | 5c slate grn | .50 | .35 |
| **C562** | AP85 | 10c olive | .50 | .35 |
| **C563** | AP85 | 15c orange | .50 | .35 |
| **C564** | AP85 | 25c brown | .50 | .35 |
| **C565** | AP85 | 30c rose claret | .50 | .35 |
| **C566** | AP85 | 35c violet | .50 | .35 |
| **C567** | AP85 | 40c brt green | .50 | .35 |
| **C568** | AP85 | 45c dull yellow | .50 | .35 |
| **C569** | AP85 | 50c rose magenta | .50 | .35 |
| **C570** | AP85 | 55c blue | .50 | .35 |
| **C571** | AP85 | 65c black | .75 | .35 |
| **C572** | AP85 | 75c rose red | .95 | .35 |
| **C573** | AP85 | 80c yellow grn | 1.10 | .35 |
| **C574** | AP85 | 85c lilac | 1.40 | .35 |
| **C575** | AP85 | 90c brt pink | 1.50 | .35 |
| **C576** | AP85 | 1col dark blue | 1.90 | .35 |
| | | *Nos. C561-C576 (16)* | 12.60 | 5.60 |

Human Rights Flame — AP107

**1973, Dec. 10 Photo. *Perf. 10½***

| | | | | |
|---|---|---|---|---|
| **C577** | AP107 | 50c black & red | .90 | .40 |

25th anniversary of the Universal Declaration of Human Rights.

OAS Emblem — AP108

**1973, Dec. 17 Litho. *Perf. 10½***

| | | | | |
|---|---|---|---|---|
| **C578** | AP108 | 20c dk bl & dp car | .90 | .40 |

25th anniv. of the OAS.

Joaquin Vargas Calvo — AP109

No. C580, Alejandro Monestel. No. C581, Julio Mata. No. C582, Julio Fonseca. No. C583, Rafael A. Chaves. No. C584, Manuel M. Gutierrez.

**1974, Jan. 14**

| | | | | | |
|---|---|---|---|---|---|
| **C579** | AP109 | 20c | shown | .60 | .35 |
| **C580** | AP109 | 20c | multicolored | .60 | .35 |
| **C581** | AP109 | 20c | multicolored | .60 | .35 |
| **C582** | AP109 | 60c | multicolored | .60 | .35 |
| **C583** | AP109 | 2col | multicolored | 1.50 | .40 |
| **C584** | AP109 | 5col | multicolored | 3.25 | 1.50 |
| | | | *Nos. C579-C584 (6)* | 7.15 | 3.30 |

Costa Rican composers honored by the National Symphony Orchestra.

Revenue Stamps Overprinted in Black — AP110

**1974, Apr. 5 Engr. *Perf. 12***

| | | | | | |
|---|---|---|---|---|---|
| **C585** | AP110 | 50c | brown | .45 | .35 |
| **C586** | AP110 | 1col | violet | .50 | .35 |
| **C587** | AP110 | 2col | orange | 1.25 | .45 |
| **C588** | AP110 | 5col | olive | 2.75 | 2.60 |
| | | | *Nos. C585-C588 (4)* | 4.95 | 3.75 |

Telephone Building, San Pedro — AP111

Designs: 65c, Rio Macho Control, horiz. 85c, Turbines, Rio Macho Center. 1.25col, Cachi Dam and reservoir, horiz. 2col, I.C.E. Headquarters.

**1974, July 30 Litho. *Perf. 10½***

| | | | | | |
|---|---|---|---|---|---|
| **C589** | AP111 | 50c | gold & multi | .40 | .35 |
| **C590** | AP111 | 65c | gold & multi | .40 | .25 |
| **C591** | AP111 | 85c | gold & multi | .55 | .35 |
| **C592** | AP111 | 1.25col | gold & multi | .90 | .35 |
| **C593** | AP111 | 2col | gold & multi | 1.75 | .55 |
| | | | *Nos. C589-C593 (5)* | 4.00 | 1.85 |

25th anniversary of Costa Rican Electrical Institute (I.C.E.).

EXFILMEX 74 Emblem — AP112

**1974, Aug. 22 *Perf. 13***

| | | | | | |
|---|---|---|---|---|---|
| **C594** | AP112 | 65c | green | .40 | .40 |
| **C595** | AP112 | 3col | lilac rose | 1.50 | .40 |

5th Inter-American Philatelic Exhibition, EXFILMEX-74 UPU, Mexico City, Oct. 26-Nov. 3.

Map of Costa Rica, 4-S Emblem — AP113

50c, Young harvesters and 4-S emblem.

**1974, Oct. 7 Litho. *Perf. 12x11***

| | | | | | |
|---|---|---|---|---|---|
| **C596** | AP113 | 20c | brt green | .90 | .40 |
| **C597** | AP113 | 50c | multicolored | .90 | .40 |

25th anniversary of 4-S Clubs of Costa Rica (similar to US 4-H Clubs).

Roberto Brenes Mesen — AP114

Designs: 85c, "Love and Death," manuscript. 5col, Hands of writer, horiz.

**1974, Oct. 14 Litho. *Perf. 10½***

| | | | | | |
|---|---|---|---|---|---|
| **C598** | AP114 | 20c | black & brn | .45 | .25 |
| **C599** | AP114 | 85c | black & red | .45 | .25 |
| **C600** | AP114 | 5col | black & red brn | 2.50 | .90 |
| | | | *Nos. C598-C600 (3)* | 3.40 | 1.40 |

Mesen, educator & writer, birth centenary.

"Life Insurance" — AP115

Designs: 20c, Ricardo Jiménez Oreamuno and Tomás Soley Güell, horiz. 50c, Harvest Insurance (hand holding shovel), horiz. 85c, Maritime insurance (hand holding paper boat). 1.25col, INS emblem. 2col, Workers rehabilitation (arm with crutch). 2.50col, Workers' Compensation (hand holding wrench). 20col, Fire insurance (hands protecting house).

**1974, Oct. 30 *Perf. 14***

| | | | | | |
|---|---|---|---|---|---|
| **C601** | AP115 | 20c | multi | .45 | .25 |
| **C602** | AP115 | 50c | multi | .45 | .25 |
| **C603** | AP115 | 65c | multi | .45 | .25 |
| **C604** | AP115 | 85c | multi | .45 | .25 |
| **C605** | AP115 | 1.25col | multi | .50 | .25 |
| **C606** | AP115 | 2col | multi | .85 | .25 |
| **C607** | AP115 | 2.50col | multi | 1.00 | .40 |
| **C608** | AP115 | 20col | multi | 6.75 | 4.50 |
| | | | *Nos. C601-C608 (8)* | 10.90 | 6.40 |

Costa Rican Insurance Institute (Instituto Nacional de Seguros, INS), 50th anniversary. For surcharges see Nos. C721-C722.

WPY Emblem — AP116

**1974, Nov. 13 Litho. *Perf. 11x11½***

| | | | | | |
|---|---|---|---|---|---|
| **C609** | AP116 | 2col | vio bl & red | 1.10 | .40 |

World Population Year.

Oscar J. Pinto F. — AP117

Designs: 50c, Alberto Montes de Oca D., champion sharpshooter. 1col, Eduardo Garnier, sports promoter. O. J. Pinto, introducer of soccer.

**1974, Dec. 2 *Perf. 13***

| | | | | | |
|---|---|---|---|---|---|
| **C610** | AP117 | 20c | gray & dk bl | .50 | .40 |
| **C611** | AP117 | 50c | gray & dk bl | .50 | .40 |
| **C612** | AP117 | 1col | gray & dk bl | 1.40 | .40 |
| | | | *Nos. C610-C612 (3)* | 2.40 | 1.20 |

First Central American Olympic Games, held in Guatemala, 1973.

Mormodes Buccinator AP118

Masdevallia Ephippium AP119

Orchids: No. C614, Gongora claviodora. No. C616, Encyclia spondiadum. No. C617, Lycaste skinneri alba. No. C618, Peristeria elata. No. C619, Miltonia roezelii. No. C620, Brassavola digbyana. No. C621, Epidendrum mirabile. No. C622, Barkeria lindleyana. No. C623, Cattleya skinneri. No. C624, Sobralia macrantha. No. C625, Lycaste cruenta. No. C626, Oncidium obryzatum. No. C627, Gongora armeniaca. No. C628, Sievekingia suavis. No. C629, Hexisea imbricata. No. C630, Warcewiczella discolor. No. C631, Oncidium kramerianum. No. C632, Cattleya dowiana.

**1975, Mar. 7 Litho. *Perf. 10½, 13½***

| | | | | | |
|---|---|---|---|---|---|
| **C613** | AP118 | 25c | shown | 1.50 | .40 |
| **C614** | AP118 | 25c | multi | 1.50 | .40 |
| **C615** | AP119 | 25c | shown | 1.50 | .40 |
| **C616** | AP119 | 25c | multi | 1.50 | .40 |
| *a.* | | | Block of 4, #C613-C616 | 7.25 | 4.00 |
| *b.* | | | As "a," perf. 10½ | 5.00 | 3.50 |
| **C617** | AP118 | 65c | multi | 3.50 | .40 |
| **C618** | AP118 | 65c | multi | 3.50 | .40 |
| **C619** | AP119 | 65c | multi | 3.50 | .40 |
| **C620** | AP119 | 65c | multi | 3.50 | .40 |
| *a.* | | | Block of 4, #C617-C620, perf. 13½ | 18.00 | 8.00 |
| *b.* | | | As "a," perf. 10½ | 28.00 | 9.00 |
| **C621** | AP118 | 80c | multi | 5.50 | .40 |
| **C622** | AP118 | 80c | multi | 5.50 | .40 |
| **C623** | AP119 | 80c | multi | 5.50 | .40 |
| **C624** | AP119 | 80c | multi | 5.50 | .40 |
| *a.* | | | Block of 4, #C621-C624 | 25.00 | 10.00 |
| *b.* | | | As "a," perf. 10½ | 45.00 | 10.00 |
| **C625** | AP118 | 1.40col | multi | 6.00 | .50 |
| **C626** | AP118 | 1.40col | multi | 6.00 | .50 |
| **C627** | AP119 | 1.40col | multi | 6.00 | .50 |
| **C628** | AP119 | 1.40col | multi | 6.00 | .50 |
| *a.* | | | Block of 4, #C625-C628 | 30.00 | 12.00 |
| *b.* | | | As "a," perf. 10½ | 25.00 | 7.00 |

***Perf. 13½***

| | | | | | |
|---|---|---|---|---|---|
| **C629** | AP118 | 1.75col | multi | 4.50 | .50 |
| **C630** | AP118 | 2.15col | multi | 4.50 | .75 |
| **C631** | AP119 | 2.50col | multi | 7.50 | 1.50 |
| **C632** | AP119 | 3.25col | multi | 9.00 | 1.75 |
| | | | *Nos. C613-C632 (20)* | 91.50 | 11.30 |

5th National Orchid Exhibition.

Nos. C613-C628 were printed in both perforations on two different papers: dull finish and shiny. Nos. C629-C632 were printed on shiny paper.

Most examples of Nos. C617-C620, perf 10½, were surcharged.

For overprints and surcharges see Nos. C715-C720, C723-C728.

Radio Club Emblem AP120

Members' Flags and Emblem AP121

Design: 2col, Federation emblem.

**1975, Apr. 16 Litho. *Perf. 13½***

| | | | | | |
|---|---|---|---|---|---|
| **C633** | AP120 | 1col | blk & red lil | 1.00 | .40 |
| **C634** | AP121 | 1.10col | multi | 1.20 | .40 |
| **C635** | AP120 | 2col | black & bl | 1.90 | .40 |
| | | | *Nos. C633-C635 (3)* | 4.10 | 1.20 |

16th Central American Radio Amateurs' Convention, San José, May 2-4.

Nicoya Beach — AP122

Designs: 75c, Driving cattle. 1col, Colonial Church, Nicoya. 3col, Savannah riders, vert.

**1975, Aug. 1 Litho. *Perf. 13½***

| | | | | | |
|---|---|---|---|---|---|
| **C636** | AP122 | 25c | gray & multi | .45 | .25 |
| **C637** | AP122 | 75c | gray & multi | .45 | .25 |
| **C638** | AP122 | 1col | gray & multi | .70 | .25 |
| **C639** | AP122 | 3col | gray & multi | 2.10 | .85 |
| | | | *Nos. C636-C639 (4)* | 3.70 | 1.60 |

Sesqui. of annexation of Nicoya District.

Costa Rica #158 — AP123

Designs (Type A90 of 1932): No. C641, #159. No. C642, #160. No. C643, #161.

**1975, Aug. 14 Litho. *Perf. 12***

| | | | | | |
|---|---|---|---|---|---|
| **C640** | AP123 | 2.20col | blk & org | 1.00 | .50 |
| **C641** | AP123 | 2.20col | blk & dk grn | 1.00 | .50 |
| **C642** | AP123 | 2.20col | blk & car rose | 1.00 | .50 |
| **C643** | AP123 | 2.20col | blk & dk bl | 1.00 | .50 |
| *a.* | | | Block of 4, #C640-C643 | 8.00 | 7.00 |

6th Natl. Phil. Exhib., San José, Aug. 14-17.

For surcharges see Nos. C885-C892.

IWY Emblem — AP124

**1975, Oct. 9 Litho. *Perf. 10½***

| | | | | | |
|---|---|---|---|---|---|
| **C644** | AP124 | 40c | vio bl & red | .55 | .40 |
| **C645** | AP124 | 1.25col | blk & ultra | 1.10 | .40 |

International Women's Year 1975.

UN Emblem — AP125

UN, 30th Anniv.: 60c, UN General Assembly, horiz. 1.20col, UN Headquarters, NY.

**1975, Oct. 24 *Perf. 12***

| | | | | | |
|---|---|---|---|---|---|
| **C646** | AP125 | 10c | bl & blk | .50 | .40 |
| **C647** | AP125 | 60c | multi | .50 | .40 |
| **C648** | AP125 | 1.20col | multi | 1.40 | .40 |
| | | | *Nos. C646-C648 (3)* | 2.40 | 1.20 |

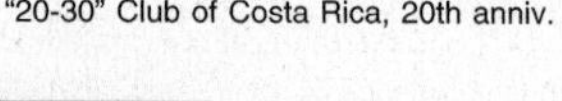


The Visitation, by Jorge Gallardo — AP126

Paintings by Jorge Gallardo: 1col, Nativity and Star. 5col, St. Joseph in his Workshop, Virgin and Child.

**1975, Nov. 3 *Perf. 10½***

| | | | | | |
|---|---|---|---|---|---|
| **C649** | AP126 | 50c | multi | .45 | .25 |
| **C650** | AP126 | 1col | multi | .75 | .25 |
| **C651** | AP126 | 5col | multi | 2.75 | .70 |
| | | | *Nos. C649-C651 (3)* | 3.95 | 1.20 |

Christmas 1975.

"20-30" Club Emblem — AP127

**1976, Jan. 16 Litho. *Perf. 12***

| | | | | | |
|---|---|---|---|---|---|
| **C652** | AP127 | 1col | multi | .85 | .40 |

"20-30" Club of Costa Rica, 20th anniv.

Quercus Brenessi Trel — AP128

Plants: 30c, Maxillaria albertii schecht. 55c, Calathea brenesii standl. 2col, Brenesia costaricensis schlecht. 10col, Philodendron brenesii standl.

**1976, Mar. 1 *Perf. 10½***

| | | | | | |
|---|---|---|---|---|---|
| **C653** | AP128 | 5c | multi | .70 | .40 |
| **C654** | AP128 | 30c | multi | .70 | .40 |
| **C655** | AP128 | 55c | multi | .95 | .40 |
| **C656** | AP128 | 2col | tan & multi | 1.60 | .45 |
| **C657** | AP128 | 10col | multi | 7.50 | 3.25 |
| | | | *Nos. C653-C657 (5)* | 11.45 | 4.90 |

Prof. Alberto Manuel Brenes Mora, botanist, birth centenary.

"Literary Development" AP129

Designs: 1.10col, Man holding book, stylized. 5col, Costa Rican flag emanating from book, horiz.

**1976, Apr. 9 Litho. *Perf. 16***

| | | | | |
|---|---|---|---|---|
| **C658** | AP129 | 15c multi | .45 | .25 |
| **C659** | AP129 | 1.10col multi | .45 | .25 |
| **C660** | AP129 | 5col multi | 2.00 | .80 |
| | | *Nos. C658-C660 (3)* | 2.90 | 1.30 |

Publishing in Costa Rica.

Nos. C658-C660 exist imperf.

Postrider, 1839 — AP130

Costa Rica No. 13, Post Office — AP131

Designs: 65c, Costa Rica No. 14 and Post Office. 85c, Costa Rica No. 15 and Post Office. 2col, UPU Monument, Bern, vert.

**1976, May 24 *Perf. 10½***

| | | | | |
|---|---|---|---|---|
| **C661** | AP130 | 20c apple grn & blk | .70 | .35 |
| **C662** | AP131 | 50c bister & multi | .70 | .35 |
| **C663** | AP131 | 65c multi | .70 | .35 |
| **C664** | AP131 | 85c multi | .70 | .35 |
| **C665** | AP130 | 2col blk & lt bl | 1.75 | .50 |
| | | *Nos. C661-C665 (5)* | 4.55 | 1.90 |

Cent. of UPU (in 1974).

Nos. C662-C664 exist without the surcharges on reproductions of Nos. 13-15.

Telephones, 1876 and 1976 — AP132

Designs: 2col, Wall telephone. 5col, Alexander Graham Bell.

**1976, June 28**

| | | | | |
|---|---|---|---|---|
| **C666** | AP132 | 1.60col lt bl & blk | .65 | .25 |
| **C667** | AP132 | 2col multicolored | .85 | .25 |
| **C668** | AP132 | 5col yellow & blk | 1.90 | .95 |
| | | *Nos. C666-C668 (3)* | 3.40 | 1.45 |

Centenary of first telephone call by Alexander Graham Bell, Mar. 10, 1876.

Inverted Center Stamp of 1901 and Association Emblems AP133

Design: 5col, 1901 stamp between Costa Rican Philatelic Society and Interamerican Philatelic Federation emblems.

**1976, Nov. 11 Litho. *Perf. 10½***

| | | | | |
|---|---|---|---|---|
| **C669** | AP133 | 50c multi | .50 | .40 |
| **C670** | AP133 | 1col multi | .50 | .40 |
| **C671** | AP133 | 2col multi | 1.75 | .40 |
| | | *Nos. C669-C671 (3)* | 2.75 | 1.20 |

**Souvenir Sheet**

***Perf. 12***

| | | | | |
|---|---|---|---|---|
| **C672** | AP133 | 5col multi | 5.75 | 5.50 |

7th Natl. Phil. Exhib. and 9th Plenary Assembly of the Interamerican Phil. Fed. (FIAF), San José, Nov. 1976.

No. C670 exists in colors of No. C671.

No. C671 exists on thin dull paper, with bright gum. Value, mint, $25.

No. C672 was issued both perf and imperf. Same values.

"Seeing Eye" and Map of Costa Rica AP134

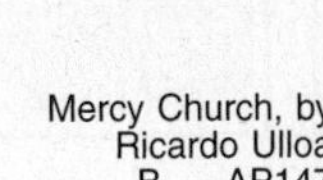

Amadeo Quiros Blanco AP135

**1976, Nov. 22 *Perf. 16***

| | | | | |
|---|---|---|---|---|
| **C673** | AP134 | 35c black & blue | .55 | .40 |
| **C674** | AP135 | 2col multicolored | 1.20 | .40 |

General Audit Office, 25th anniversary.

Nurse Attending Child — AP136

1.10col, National Children's Hospital, horiz.

**1976, Nov. 29**

| | | | | |
|---|---|---|---|---|
| **C675** | AP136 | 90c multi | .55 | .40 |
| **C676** | AP136 | 1.10col multi | 1.10 | .40 |

5th Panamerican Congress of Pediatric Surgery and 12th Congress of Pediatrics.

LACSA Circling Globe — AP137

Designs: 1.20col, Route map. 3col, LACSA emblem and Costa Rican flag.

**1976, Dec. 1 *Perf. 10½***

| | | | | |
|---|---|---|---|---|
| **C677** | AP137 | 1col multi | .45 | .25 |
| **C678** | AP137 | 1.20col multi | .70 | .25 |
| **C679** | AP137 | 3col multi | 2.00 | .70 |
| | | *Nos. C677-C679 (3)* | 3.15 | 1.20 |

Costa Rican Air Lines (LACSA), 30th anniversary.

Boston Tea Party — AP138

US Bicent.: 5col, Declaration of Independence. 10col, Ringing Liberty Bell to announce Independence, vert.

**1976, Dec. 24**

| | | | | |
|---|---|---|---|---|
| **C680** | AP138 | 2.20col multi | .55 | .30 |
| **C681** | AP138 | 5col multi | 1.50 | .70 |
| **C682** | AP138 | 10col multi | 2.00 | 1.40 |
| | | *Nos. C680-C682 (3)* | 4.05 | 2.40 |

Tree of Guanacaste AP139

Felipe J. Alvarado AP140

Designs (Rotary Emblem and): 60c, Dr. Paul Blanco Cervantes Hospital, horiz. 3col, Map of Costa Rica, horiz. 10col, Paul Harris.

**1977, Mar. 31 Litho. *Perf. 16***

| | | | | |
|---|---|---|---|---|
| **C683** | AP139 | 40c multi | .40 | .30 |
| **C684** | AP140 | 50c multi | .40 | .30 |
| **C685** | AP139 | 60c multi | .40 | .30 |
| **C686** | AP139 | 3col multi | 1.50 | .75 |
| **C687** | AP140 | 10col multi | 4.00 | 2.50 |
| | | *Nos. C683-C687 (5)* | 6.70 | 4.15 |

Rotary Club of San José, 50th anniversary.

Boruca Cloth — AP141

Design: 1.50col, Painted wood ornament.

**1977, Feb. 22**

| | | | | |
|---|---|---|---|---|
| **C688** | AP141 | 75c multi | .50 | .40 |
| **C689** | AP141 | 1.50col multi | 1.10 | .40 |

Natl. Artisan & Small Industry Program.

Juana Pereira — AP142

Designs: 1col, First Church of Our Lady of the Angels, horiz. 1.10col, Our Lady of the Angels (gold sculpture). 1.25col, Crown of Our Lady of the Angels.

**1977, June 6 Litho. *Perf. 10½***

| | | | | |
|---|---|---|---|---|
| **C690** | AP142 | 50c multi | .50 | .40 |
| **C691** | AP142 | 1col multi | .50 | .40 |
| **C692** | AP142 | 1.10col multi | .50 | .40 |
| **C693** | AP142 | 1.25col multi | 1.50 | .40 |
| | | *Nos. C690-C693 (4)* | 3.00 | 1.60 |

50th anniv. of the coronation of Our Lady of the Angels, patron saint of Costa Rica.

Alonso de Anguciana de Gamboa — AP143

Designs: 75c, Church of Esparza. 1col, Statue of Our Lady of Candlemas. 2col, Statue of Diego de Artieda y Chirino.

**1977, July 4 Litho. *Perf. 10½***

| | | | | |
|---|---|---|---|---|
| **C694** | AP143 | 35c multi | .50 | .40 |
| **C695** | AP143 | 75c multi | .50 | .40 |
| **C696** | AP143 | 1col multi | .70 | .40 |
| **C697** | AP143 | 2col multi | 1.75 | .40 |
| | | *Nos. C694-C697 (4)* | 3.45 | 1.60 |

400th anniv. of the founding of Esparza.

For surcharge see No. C883.

CARE Emblem and Child — AP144

1col, CARE emblem and soybeans, horiz.

**1977, Sept. 14 Litho. *Perf. 16***

| | | | | |
|---|---|---|---|---|
| **C698** | AP144 | 80c multi | .55 | .40 |
| **C699** | AP144 | 1col multi | 1.10 | .40 |

20th anniversary of CARE (relief organization) in Costa Rica.

Institute's Emblem AP145

First Map of Americas, 1540 AP146

**1977, Oct. 21 Litho. *Perf. 16***

| | | | | |
|---|---|---|---|---|
| **C700** | AP145 | 50c blk & multi | .80 | .30 |
| **C701** | AP146 | 1.40col blk & multi | 1.60 | .40 |

Hispanic Cultural Institute of Costa Rica, 25th anniversary.

Mercy Church, by Ricardo Ulloa B. — AP147

Paintings: 1col, Christ, by Floria Pinto de Herrero. 5col, St. Francis and the Birds, by Louisa Gonzalez Y Saenz.

**1977, Nov. 9 Litho. *Perf. 10½***

| | | | | |
|---|---|---|---|---|
| **C702** | AP147 | 50c multi | .80 | .25 |
| **C703** | AP147 | 1col multi | .80 | .25 |
| **C704** | AP147 | 5col multi | 2.60 | .70 |
| | | *Nos. C702-C704 (3)* | 4.20 | 1.20 |

Health Ministry Emblem — AP148

**1977, Nov. 16 *Perf. 16***

| | | | | |
|---|---|---|---|---|
| **C705** | AP148 | 1.40col multi | .90 | .40 |

Creation of Ministry of Health.

Picnic — AP149

Designs: 50c, Weaver. 2col, Beach scene. 5col, Fruit and vegetable market. 10col, Swans on lake.

**1978, Mar. 21 Litho. *Perf. 10½***

| | | | | |
|---|---|---|---|---|
| **C706** | AP149 | 50c blk & multi | .35 | .25 |
| **C707** | AP149 | 1col blk & multi | .50 | .25 |
| **C708** | AP149 | 2col blk & multi | 1.40 | .25 |
| **C709** | AP149 | 5col blk & multi | 2.60 | .85 |
| **C710** | AP149 | 10col blk & multi | 3.50 | 1.90 |
| | | *Nos. C706-C710 (5)* | 8.35 | 3.50 |

Conf. of Latin American Tourist Organizations.

San Martin — AP150

**1978, Aug. 7 Litho. *Perf. 10½***

| | | | | |
|---|---|---|---|---|
| **C711** | AP150 | 5col multi | 1.75 | .80 |

Gen. José de San Martin (1778-1850), soldier and statesman, fought for South American independence.

Geographical Institute Emblem — AP151

**1978, Aug. 28 Litho. *Perf. 12½***

| | | | | |
|---|---|---|---|---|
| **C712** | AP151 | 5col multi | 1.75 | .65 |

Pan-American Geography and History Institute, 50th anniversary. Exists imperf.

University Federation Emblem — AP152

**1978, Sept. 18 *Perf. 11***

| | | | | |
|---|---|---|---|---|
| **C713** | AP152 | 80c ultra | .90 | .40 |

Central American University Federation, 30th anniversary.

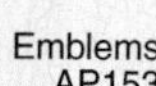

Emblems AP153

**1978, Oct. 24** *Perf. 16*

| | | | | |
|---|---|---|---|---|
| C714 | AP153 | 2col aqua, blk & gold | 1.00 | .40 |

6th Interamerican Philatelic Exhibition, Argentina 78, Buenos Aires, Oct. 1978.

Nos. C629-C631 Overprinted

**1978, Nov. 1** **Litho.** *Perf. 13½*

| | | | | |
|---|---|---|---|---|
| C715 | AP118 | 1.75col multi | .80 | .30 |
| C716 | AP118 | 2.15col multi | 1.00 | .40 |
| C717 | AP119 | 2.50col multi | 1.75 | .55 |
| | | *Nos. C715-C717 (3)* | 3.55 | 1.25 |

1st Pan Am flight in Costa Rica, 50th anniv.

### Nos. C629-C631 Overprinted: "50 Aniversario de la / visita de Lindbergh a / Costa Rica 1928-1978"

**1978, Nov. 1**

| | | | | |
|---|---|---|---|---|
| C718 | AP118 | 1.75col multi | 1.60 | .30 |
| C719 | AP118 | 2.15col multi | 1.90 | .40 |
| C720 | AP119 | 2.50col multi | 2.75 | .50 |
| | | *Nos. C718-C720 (3)* | 6.25 | 1.20 |

50th anniversary of Lindbergh's visit.

### Nos. C603 and C607 Surcharged

**1978, Nov. 8** *Perf. 14*

| | | | | |
|---|---|---|---|---|
| C721 | AP115 | 50c on 65c multi | .45 | .25 |
| C722 | AP115 | 2col on 2.50col multi | 1.25 | .25 |

Asilo Carlos Maria Ulloa, birth centenary.

No. C617-C620, C630-C631 Surcharged

*Perf. 10½, 13½*

**1978, Nov. 13** **Litho.**

| | | | | |
|---|---|---|---|---|
| C723 | AP118 | 50c on 65c | 1.00 | .60 |
| C724 | AP118 | 50c on 65c | 1.00 | .60 |
| C725 | AP119 | 50c on 65c | 1.00 | .60 |
| C726 | AP119 | 50c on 65c | 1.00 | .60 |
| *a.* | | Block of 4, #C723-C726 | 4.75 | 3.50 |
| C727 | AP118 | 1.20col on 2.15col | 1.90 | .55 |
| C728 | AP119 | 2col on 2.50col | 1.90 | .55 |
| | | *Nos. C723-C728 (6)* | 7.80 | 3.50 |

Nos. C723-C726, perf. 13½, value *$50*, unused, *$20*, used, each. No. C726a, unused, *$500*.

Star over Map of Costa Rica — AP154

**1978, Nov. 13** *Perf. 10½*

| | | | | |
|---|---|---|---|---|
| C729 | AP154 | 50c blue & blk | .50 | .35 |
| C730 | AP154 | 1col rose lil & blk | .50 | .35 |
| C731 | AP154 | 5col orange & blk | 1.75 | .65 |
| *a.* | | Strip of 3, #C729-C731 | 3.50 | 2.50 |

Christmas 1978. Nos. C729-C731 printed in sheets of 100 and se-tenant in sheet of 15 (3x5). Value, se-tenant sheet, $20.

"Flying Men," Chorotega — AP155

Designs: 1.20col, Oviedo giving his History of Indies to Duke of Calabria, horiz. 10col, Lord of Oviedo's coat of arms.

**1978, Nov. 20** *Perf. 11½*

| | | | | |
|---|---|---|---|---|
| C732 | AP155 | 85c multi | .45 | .25 |
| C733 | AP155 | 1.20col blk & lt bl | .45 | .25 |
| C734 | AP155 | 10col multi | 3.00 | 2.00 |
| | | *Nos. C732-C734 (3)* | 3.90 | 2.50 |

500th birth anniv. of Gonzalo Fernandez de Oviedo, 1st chronicler of Spanish Indies.

Msgr. Domingo Rivas AP156

San José Cathedral AP157

**1978, Dec. 6** *Perf. 16, 13½ (20col)*

| | | | | |
|---|---|---|---|---|
| C735 | AP156 | 1col black & indigo | .45 | .25 |
| C736 | AP157 | 20col multicolored | 4.50 | 3.50 |

Centenary of the Cathedral of San José.

View of Coco Island — AP158

Designs: 2.10, 3, 5 col, Various views of Coco Island. 10col, Installation of memorial plaque, people and flag. 5, 10col vert.

**1979, Apr. 30** **Litho.** *Perf. 10½*

| | | | | |
|---|---|---|---|---|
| C737 | AP158 | 90c multi | .50 | .45 |
| C738 | AP158 | 2.10col multi | 1.00 | .85 |
| C739 | AP158 | 3col multi | 1.60 | 1.40 |
| C740 | AP158 | 5col multi | 2.25 | 2.60 |
| C741 | AP158 | 10col multi | 4.50 | 4.00 |
| *a.* | | Souv. sheet, #C737-C741 | 14.00 | 13.00 |
| | | *Nos. C737-C741 (5)* | 9.85 | 9.30 |

Visit of Pres. Rodrigo Carazo Odio to Coco Island, June 24, 1978, in the interest of national defense.

No. C741a exists imperf. Value $750.

Shrimp — AP159

Designs: 85c, Mahogany snapper. 1.80col, Corvina. 3col, Crayfish. 10col, Tuna.

**1979, May 14** **Litho.** *Perf. 13½*

| | | | | |
|---|---|---|---|---|
| C742 | AP159 | 60c multi | .60 | .30 |
| C743 | AP159 | 85c multi | .60 | .30 |
| C744 | AP159 | 1.80col multi | 1.10 | .30 |
| C745 | AP159 | 3col multi | 1.60 | .60 |
| C746 | AP159 | 10col multi | 6.00 | 3.50 |
| | | *Nos. C742-C746 (5)* | 9.90 | 5.00 |

Marine life protection.

Hungry Nestlings, IYC Emblem — AP160

**1979, May 24** *Perf. 11*

| | | | | |
|---|---|---|---|---|
| C747 | AP160 | 1col multi | 1.10 | .50 |
| C748 | AP160 | 2col multi | 2.10 | 1.00 |
| C749 | AP160 | 20col multi | 14.00 | 8.00 |
| | | *Nos. C747-C749 (3)* | 17.20 | 9.50 |

International Year of the Child.

Microwave Transmitters, Mt. Irazu — AP161

Design: 1col, Arenal Dam, horiz.

**1979, June 28** **Litho.** *Perf. 14*

| | | | | |
|---|---|---|---|---|
| C750 | AP161 | 1col multi | .60 | .45 |
| C751 | AP161 | 5col multi | 1.75 | 1.10 |

Costa Rican Electricity Institute, 30th anniversary.

Costa Rica No. 1 and Rowland Hill — AP162

Design: 10col, Penny Black and Hill.

**1979, July 16** *Perf. 13*

| | | | | |
|---|---|---|---|---|
| C752 | AP162 | 5col lil rose & bl gray | 1.50 | 1.10 |
| C753 | AP162 | 10col dl bl & blk | 3.00 | 2.75 |

Sir Rowland Hill (1795-1879), originator of penny postage.

Poverty, by Juan Ramon Bonilla — AP163

National Sculpture Contest: 60c, Hope, by Hernan Gonzalez. 2.10col, Cattle, by Victor M. Bermudez, horiz. 5col, Bust of Clorito Picado, by Juan Rafael Chacon. 20col, Mother and Child, by Francisco Zuniga.

**1979, July 16** **Litho.** *Perf. 12*

| | | | | |
|---|---|---|---|---|
| C754 | AP163 | 60c multi | .35 | .25 |
| C755 | AP163 | 1col multi | .40 | .25 |
| C756 | AP163 | 2.10col multi | .75 | .25 |
| C757 | AP163 | 5col multi | 2.25 | 1.10 |
| C758 | AP163 | 20col multi | 6.50 | 2.50 |
| | | *Nos. C754-C758 (5)* | 10.25 | 4.35 |

Danaus Plexippus — AP164

Butterflies: 1col, Phoebis philea. 1.80col, Rothschildia. 2.10col, Prepona omphale. 2.60col, Marpesia marcella. 4.05col, Morpho cypris.

**1979, Aug. 31** **Litho.** *Perf. 13½*

| | | | | |
|---|---|---|---|---|
| C759 | AP164 | 60c multi | 3.00 | 1.10 |
| C760 | AP164 | 1col multi | 5.00 | 1.10 |
| C761 | AP164 | 1.80col multi | 7.00 | 1.75 |
| C762 | AP164 | 2.10col multi | 10.00 | 3.50 |
| C763 | AP164 | 2.60col multi | 10.00 | 7.00 |
| C764 | AP164 | 4.05col multi | 22.00 | 10.00 |
| | | *Nos. C759-C764 (6)* | 57.00 | 24.45 |

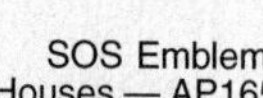

SOS Emblem, Houses — AP165

Children's Drawings: 5col, 5.50col, Landscapes, diff.

**1979, Sept. 18**

| | | | | |
|---|---|---|---|---|
| C765 | AP165 | 2.50col multi | 1.25 | 1.00 |
| C766 | AP165 | 5col multi | 2.50 | 1.75 |
| C767 | AP165 | 5.50col multi | 3.00 | 2.75 |
| | | *Nos. C765-C767 (3)* | 6.75 | 5.50 |

SOS Children's Villages, 30th anniversary.

### President Type of 1943

Presidents of Costa Rica: 60c, Rafael Yglesias C. 85c, Ascension Esquivel Ibarra. 1col, Cleto Gonzalez Viquez. 2col, Ricardo Jimenez Oreamuno.

**1979, Oct. 8** **Litho.** *Perf. 13½*

| | | | | |
|---|---|---|---|---|
| C768 | A109 | 10c dk blue | .45 | .40 |
| C769 | A109 | 60c dull purple | .45 | .40 |
| C770 | A109 | 85c red orange | .45 | .40 |
| C771 | A109 | 1col red orange | .55 | .40 |
| C772 | A109 | 2col brown | 1.25 | .65 |
| *a.* | | Strip of 5, #C768-C772 | 4.25 | 2.50 |
| | | *Nos. C768-C772 (5)* | 3.15 | 2.25 |

Printed in sheets of 100 and se-tenant in sheets of 25 (5x5).

See Nos. C790-C794.

Holy Family, Creche — AP167

**1979, Nov. 16** **Litho.** *Perf. 12½*

| | | | | |
|---|---|---|---|---|
| C773 | AP167 | 1col multi | .60 | .40 |
| C774 | AP167 | 1.60col multi | 1.25 | .75 |

Christmas 1979.

Reforestation — AP168

**1980, Jan. 14** **Litho.** *Perf. 11*

| | | | | |
|---|---|---|---|---|
| C775 | AP168 | 1col multi | .45 | .30 |
| C776 | AP168 | 3.40col multi | 1.40 | .85 |

Anatomy Lesson, by Rembrandt AP169

**1980, Feb. 7** **Litho.** *Perf. 10½*

| | | | | |
|---|---|---|---|---|
| C777 | AP169 | 10col multi | 6.00 | 2.00 |

Legal medicine teaching in Costa Rica, 50th anniversary.

Rotary Intl., 75th Anniv. — AP170

**1980, Feb. 26** *Perf. 16*

| | | | | |
|---|---|---|---|---|
| C778 | AP170 | 2.10col multi | .60 | .40 |
| C779 | AP170 | 5col multi | 1.75 | .85 |

14th Intl. Symposium on Remote Sensing of the Environment, San José, Apr. 23-30 — AP171

Designs: 2.10col, Puerto Limon. 5col, Gulf of Nicoya, satellite photo.

**1980, Mar. 10 Litho. *Perf. 12½***

**C780** AP171 2.10col multi .60 .40
**C781** AP171 5col multi 1.75 1.25

Exist imperf.

Soccer, Moscow '80 Emblem — AP172

3col, Bicycling. 4.05col, Baseball. 20col, Swimming.

**1980, Apr. 16 Litho. *Perf. 10½***

**C782** AP172 1col shown .65 .25
**C783** AP172 3col multi 8.50 .75
**C784** AP172 4.05col multi 8.50 1.00
**C785** AP172 20col multi 8.50 5.00
*Nos. C782-C785 (4)* 26.15 7.00

22nd Summer Olympic Games, Moscow, July 19-Aug. 3.

Poas Volcano — AP173

2.50col, Cahuita Beach.

**1980, May 14 Litho. *Perf. 10½***

**C786** AP173 1col shown .55 .40
**C787** AP173 2.50col multi 1.30 .75

National Parks Service, 10th anniversary.

José Maria Zeledon Brenes, Score — AP174

Design: 10col, Manuel Maria Gutierrez.

**1980, June 25 Litho. *Perf. 12½***

**C788** AP174 1col multi .45 .35
**C789** AP174 10col multi 2.40 1.75

National anthem composed by Brenes (words) and Gutierrez (music). Nos. C788-C789 exist imperf.

### President Type of 1943

1col, Alfredo Gonzalez F. 1.60col, Federico Tinoco G. 1.80col, Francisco Aguilar B. 2.10col, Julio Acosta G. 3col, Leon Cortes C.

**1980, Aug. 14 Litho. *Perf. 11***

**C790** A109 1col dk red .50 .35
**C791** A109 1.60col slate bl .75 .35
**C792** A109 1.80col brown .75 .35
**C793** A109 2.10col dull green 1.00 .35
**C794** A109 3col dark purple 1.75 .65
*Nos. C790-C794 (5)* 4.75 2.05

8th Natl. Phil. Exhib. — AP175

**1980, Sept. 11 *Perf. 13½***

**C795** AP175 5col multi .95 .60
**C796** AP175 20col multi 3.75 2.75

Fruits — AP176

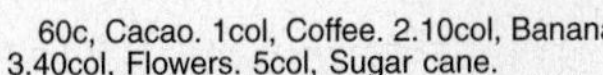

60c, Cacao. 1col, Coffee. 2.10col, Bananas. 3.40col, Flowers. 5col, Sugar cane.

**1980, Sept. 24 *Perf. 10½***

**C797** AP176 10c shown .40 .40
**C798** AP176 60c multi .65 .50
**C799** AP176 1col multi 1.00 .75
**C800** AP176 2.10col multi 2.00 1.50
**C801** AP176 3.40col multi 2.60 1.90
**C802** AP176 5col multi 3.25 3.00
*Nos. C797-C802 (6)* 9.90 8.05

Giant Tree, by Jorge Carvajal — AP177

Paintings: 2.10col, Secret Look, by Rolando Cubero. 2.45col, Consuelo, by Fernando Carballo. 3col, Volcano, by Lola Fernandez. 4.05col, attending Mass, by Francisco Amighetti.

**1980, Oct. 22 Litho. *Perf. 10½***

**C803** AP177 1col multi .60 .40
**C804** AP177 2.10col multi .85 .50

**Size: 28x30mm**

**C805** AP177 2.45col multi 1.00 .70

**Size: 22x36mm**

**C806** AP177 3col multi 1.20 1.00
**C807** AP177 4.05col multi 6.75 1.25
*Nos. C803-C807 (5)* 10.40 3.85

Virgin and Child, by Raphael — AP178

Christmas 1980: 10col, Virgin and Child and St. John, by Raphael.

**1980, Nov. 11 *Perf. 13½***

**C808** AP178 1col multi .60 .30
**C809** AP178 10col multi 2.90 1.75

Juan Santamaria International Airport — AP179

1col, Caldera Harbor. 2.10col, Rio Frio Railroad Bridge. 2.60col, Highway to Colon. 5col, Huetar post office.

**1980, Dec. 11 Litho. *Perf. 10½***

**Sizes: 30x30mm, 31x25mm (1.30col), 25x32mm (2.60col)**

**C810** AP179 1col multi .45 .30
**C811** AP179 1.30col shown .65 .35
**C812** AP179 2.10col multi 1.25 .50
**C813** AP179 2.60col multi 1.25 .50
**C814** AP179 5col multi 2.00 1.00
*Nos. C810-C814 (5)* 5.60 2.65

Paying your taxes means progress. For surcharge see No. C884.

Repertorio Americano Cover, J. Garcia Monge and Signature — AP180

**1981, Jan. 2 Litho. *Perf. 10½***

**C815** AP180 1.60col multi .65 .30
**C816** AP180 3col multi 1.25 .50

Birth centenary of J. Garcia Monge, founder of Repertorio Americano journal.

Arms of Aserri (Site of Cornea Bank) — AP181

**1981, Jan. 28 Litho. *Perf. 13½***

**C817** AP181 1col shown .45 .40
**C818** AP181 1.80col Eye 1.25 1.00
**C819** AP181 5col Rojas 3.75 2.60
*Nos. C817-C819 (3)* 5.45 4.00

Establishment of human cornea bank, founded by Abelardo Rojas.

Harpia Harpyja — AP182

2.50col, Ara macao. 3col, Felis concolor. 5.50col, Ateles geoffrovi.

**1980, Dec. 23 *Perf. 11***

**C820** AP182 2.10col shown 1.75 1.50
**C821** AP182 2.50col multi 2.25 1.90
**C822** AP182 3col multi 3.00 2.50
**C823** AP182 5.50col multi 7.00 6.00
*Nos. C820-C823 (4)* 14.00 11.90

Medical and Surgical Clinic — AP183

**1981, Apr. 8 Litho. *Perf. 10½***

**C824** AP183 5c multi .50 .35
**C825** AP183 10c multi .50 .35
**C826** AP183 50c multi .50 .35
**C827** AP183 1.30col multi .75 .35
**C828** AP183 3.40col multi 1.00 .75
**C829** AP183 4.05col multi, vert. 1.75 .85
*Nos. C824-C829 (6)* 5.00 3.00

University of Costa Rica, 40th anniversary.

Mail Transport by Horse — AP184

2.10col, Train, 1857. 10col, Mail carriers, 1858.

**1981, May 6 Litho. *Perf. 10½***

**C830** AP184 1col shown .40 .30
**C831** AP184 2.10col multi .75 .40
**C832** AP184 10col multi 3.75 2.00
*Nos. C830-C832 (3)* 4.90 2.70

Heinrich von Stephan (1831-97), UPU founder.

13th World Telecommunications Day — AP185

**1981, May 18 *Perf. 11***

**C833** AP185 5col multi 3.25 .60
**C834** AP185 25col multi 8.25 4.00

Bishop Bernardo Thiel — AP186

**1981, June 8 Litho. *Perf. 10½***

**C835** Strip of 5, stained glass windows 5.00 4.50
*a.* AP186 1col Sts. Peter & Paul .30 .30
*b.* AP186 1col St. Vincent de Paul .30 .30
*c.* AP186 1col Death of St. Joseph .30 .30
*d.* AP186 1col Archangel Michael .30 .30
*e.* AP186 1col Holy Family .30 .30
**C836** AP186 2col shown 1.75 .60

Consecration of Bernardo Augusto Thiel as Bishop of San Jose.

Juan Santamaria — AP187

2.40col, Alajuela Cathedral, horiz.

**1981, June 26 *Perf. 13½***

**C837** AP187 1col shown .50 .40
**C838** AP187 2.45col multi 1.25 .70

Alajuela province.

Potters — AP188

1.60col, Bricklayers. 1.80col, Farmers. 2.50col, Fishermen. 3col, Nurse, patient. 5col, Children, traffic policeman.

**1981, July 10 Litho. *Perf. 10½***

**C839** AP188 15c shown .50 .35
**C840** AP188 1.60col multi .50 .35
**C841** AP188 1.80col multi .50 .35
**C842** AP188 2.50col multi .50 .35
**C843** AP188 3col multi 1.20 .35
**C844** AP188 5col multi 1.75 .35
*Nos. C839-C844 (6)* 4.95 2.10

Model of New Natl. Archives — AP189

Natl. Archives Centenary: 1.40col, Leon Fernandez Bonilla, founder, vert. 2col, Arms, vert. 3col, St. Thomas University, former headquarters.

**1981, Aug. 24 Litho. *Perf. 13½***

**C845** AP189 1.40col multi .60 .50
**C846** AP189 2col multi 1.00 .50
**C847** AP189 3col multi 1.25 .75
**C848** AP189 3.50col multi 1.30 1.20
*Nos. C845-C848 (4)* 4.15 2.95

Men Reaching for Sun, Map — AP190

1col, Man in wheelchair, stairs, vert. 2.60col, Man reaching for scale, vert.

**1981, Sept. 9 Litho. *Perf. 11***

**C849** AP190 1col multi .40 .30
**C850** AP190 2.60col multi 1.60 .30
**C851** AP190 10col shown 4.50 1.00
*Nos. C849-C851 (3)* 6.50 1.60

Intl. Year of the Disabled.

World Food Day — AP191

**1981, Oct. 16 Litho. *Perf. 10½***

**C852** AP191 5col multi .80 .35
**C853** AP191 10col multi 1.40 .75

### President Type of 1943

1col, Rafael A. Calderon Guardia, 1940. 2col, Teodoro Picado Michalski, 1944. 3col, José Figueres Ferrer, 1953. 5col, Otilio Ulate Blanco, 1949. 10col, Mario Echandi Jimenez, 1958.

**1981, Dec. 7 Litho. *Perf. 13½***

**C854** A109 1col pink .70 .55
**C855** A109 2col orange .70 .55
**C856** A109 3col green .90 .55
**C857** A109 5col dk bl 1.75 .90
**C858** A109 10col blue 3.50 2.00
*Nos. C854-C858 (5)* 7.55 4.55

Bar Assoc. of Costa Rica Centenary (1981) — AP192

1col, Emblem, horiz. 2col, E. Figueroa, 1st president. 20col, Bar building, horiz.

**1982, Mar. 22 Litho. *Perf. 13½***

| | | | | |
|---|---|---|---|---|
| **C859** | AP192 | 1col multi | .50 | .30 |
| **C860** | AP192 | 2col multi | .50 | .30 |
| **C861** | AP192 | 20col multi | 3.50 | 1.40 |
| | | *Nos. C859-C861 (3)* | 4.50 | 2.00 |

National Progress — AP193

95c, Housing. 1.15col, Agricultural fair. 1.45col, Education. 1.65col, Drinkable water. 1.80col, Rural medical care. 2.10col, Recreational areas. 2.35col, Natl. Theater Square. 2.60col, Communications. 3col, Electric railroad. 4.05col, Irrigation.

**1982 *Perf. 10½***

| | | | | |
|---|---|---|---|---|
| **C862** | AP193 | 95c multi | .60 | .35 |
| **C863** | AP193 | 1.15col multi | .60 | .35 |
| **C864** | AP193 | 1.45col multi | .60 | .35 |
| **C865** | AP193 | 1.65col multi | .60 | .35 |
| **C866** | AP193 | 1.80col multi | .60 | .35 |
| **C867** | AP193 | 2.10col multi | .60 | .35 |
| **C868** | AP193 | 2.35col multi | .90 | .55 |
| **C869** | AP193 | 2.60col multi | 1.50 | .75 |
| **C870** | AP193 | 3col multi | 2.00 | 1.00 |
| **C871** | AP193 | 4.05col multi | 2.25 | 1.25 |
| | | *Nos. C862-C871 (10)* | 10.25 | 5.65 |

Issue dates: 1.80col, 2.10col, 2.60col, 3col, 4.05col, May 5; others, June 16.

City of Alajuela Bicentenary — AP194

Designs: 5col, Central Park Fountain. 10col, Juan Santamaria Historical and Cultural Museum, horiz. 15col, Church of Christ of Esquipulas. 20col, Monsignor Esteban Lorenzo de Tristan, 25col, Father Juan Manuel Lopez del Corral.

**1982, Aug. 9**

| | | | | |
|---|---|---|---|---|
| **C872** | AP194 | 5col multi | .65 | .35 |
| **C873** | AP194 | 10col multi | 1.40 | .55 |
| **C874** | AP194 | 15col multi | 2.10 | 1.25 |
| **C875** | AP194 | 20col multi | 2.75 | 1.25 |
| **C876** | AP194 | 25col multi | 3.75 | 1.60 |
| | | *Nos. C872-C876 (5)* | 10.65 | 5.00 |

Perez Zeledon County, 50th Anniv. (1981) — AP195

Designs: 10c, Saint's Stone. 50c, Monument to Mothers. 1col, Pedro Perez Zeledon. 1.25col, St. Isidore Labrador Church. 3.50col, Municipal Building, horiz. 4.25col, Arms.

**1982, Aug. 30**

| | | | | |
|---|---|---|---|---|
| **C877** | AP195 | 10c multi | .65 | .50 |
| **C878** | AP195 | 50c multi | .65 | .50 |
| **C879** | AP195 | 1col multi | .65 | .50 |
| **C880** | AP195 | 1.25col multi | .65 | .50 |
| **C881** | AP195 | 3.50col multi | 1.00 | .50 |
| **C882** | AP195 | 4.25col multi | 1.60 | .50 |
| | | *Nos. C877-C882 (6)* | 5.20 | 3.00 |

**Nos. C695 and C813 Surcharged**

No. C883

No. C884

**1982, Oct. 28 Litho. *Perf. 10½***

| | | | | |
|---|---|---|---|---|
| **C883** | AP143 | 3col on 75c multi | .70 | .45 |
| **C884** | AP179 | 5col on 2.60col multi | 1.25 | .75 |

**Nos. C640-C643 Surcharged and Overprinted**

**1982, Oct. 28 *Perf. 12***

| | | | | |
|---|---|---|---|---|
| **C885** | AP123 | 8.40col on #C640 | .90 | .65 |
| **C886** | AP123 | 8.40col on #C641 | .90 | .65 |
| **C887** | AP123 | 8.40col on #C642 | .90 | .65 |
| **C888** | AP123 | 8.40col on #C643 | .90 | .65 |
| **C889** | AP123 | 9.70col on #C640 | 1.20 | .75 |
| **C890** | AP123 | 9.70col on #C641 | 1.20 | .75 |
| **C891** | AP123 | 9.70col on #C642 | 1.20 | .75 |
| **C892** | AP123 | 9.70col on #C643 | 1.20 | .75 |
| | | *Nos. C885-C892 (8)* | 8.40 | 5.60 |

9th Natl. Stamp Exhibition.

TB Bacillus Centenary — AP196

1.50col, Koch. 3col, Koch, slide. 3.30col, Health Ministry.

**1982, Nov. 19 *Perf. 13½***

| | | | | |
|---|---|---|---|---|
| **C893** | AP196 | 1.50col multi | .50 | .45 |
| **C894** | AP196 | 3col multi | .95 | .45 |
| **C895** | AP196 | 3.30col multi | .95 | .45 |
| | | *Nos. C893-C895 (3)* | 2.40 | 1.35 |

Pan-American Blood Donors' Society, 7th Cong. — AP197

30col, Natl. Blood Assoc. emblem. 50col, Cong. emblem.

**1982, Nov. 25 *Perf. 11***

| | | | | |
|---|---|---|---|---|
| **C896** | AP197 | 30col multi | 2.50 | 2.10 |
| **C897** | AP197 | 50col multi | 3.75 | 3.00 |

AP198

8.40col, Emblem, horiz. 9.70col, Emblem, diff. 11.70col, Handshake, horiz. 13.05col, Emblem, diff., horiz.

**1982, Dec. 13 Litho. *Perf. 10½***

| | | | | |
|---|---|---|---|---|
| **C898** | AP198 | 8.40col multi | .90 | .50 |
| **C899** | AP198 | 9.70col multi | 1.25 | 1.00 |
| **C900** | AP198 | 11.70col multi | 1.25 | 1.00 |
| **C901** | AP198 | 13.05col multi | 1.60 | 1.20 |
| | | *Nos. C898-C901 (4)* | 5.00 | 3.70 |

Inter-Governmental Migration Committee, 30th anniv.

AP199

4.80col, St. Francis of Assisi, by El Greco. 7.40col, Portrait, diff.

**1983, Jan. 3 *Perf. 16***

| | | | | |
|---|---|---|---|---|
| **C902** | AP199 | 4.80col multi | .85 | .65 |
| **C903** | AP199 | 7.40col multi | 1.50 | 1.00 |

For surcharges see Nos. C908-C911.

Visit of Pope John Paul II — AP200

**1983, Mar. 1 Litho. *Perf. 10½***

| | | | | |
|---|---|---|---|---|
| **C904** | AP200 | 5col multi | 3.25 | 3.00 |
| **C905** | AP200 | 10col multi | 3.25 | 3.00 |
| **C906** | AP200 | 15col multi | 7.00 | 4.00 |
| | | *Nos. C904-C906 (3)* | 13.50 | 10.00 |

Bolivar, by Francisco Zuniga Chavarria — AP201

**1983, July 22 Litho. *Perf. 16***

| | | | | |
|---|---|---|---|---|
| **C907** | AP201 | 10col multi | 1.50 | 1.20 |

Nos. C902-C903 Surcharged

**1983, Sept. 23 Litho. *Perf. 16***

| | | | | |
|---|---|---|---|---|
| **C908** | AP199 | 10c on 4.80col | .80 | .40 |
| **C909** | AP199 | 50c on 4.80col | .80 | .40 |
| **C910** | AP199 | 1.50col on 7.40col | .80 | .40 |
| **C911** | AP199 | 3col on 7.40col | .80 | .40 |
| | | *Nos. C908-C911 (4)* | 3.20 | 1.60 |

LACSA Costa Rica Airlines, 40th Anniv. — AP202

Various childrens' drawings: 1col, Adriana E. Hidalgo. 7col, Osvaldo A.G. Vega. 16col, David V. Rodriguez.

**1986, Dec. 12 Litho. *Perf. 13½***

| | | | | |
|---|---|---|---|---|
| **C912** | AP202 | 1col multi | *.90* | .40 |
| **C913** | AP202 | 7col multi | *6.00* | 3.00 |
| **C914** | AP202 | 16col multi | *14.00* | 6.50 |
| | | *Nos. C912-C914 (3)* | *20.90* | 9.90 |

Nos. C912-C913 exist perf 11. Unused examples are rare. Value used, $5 each.

Roman Macaya Lahmann, Aviation Pioneer — AP203

**1988, Sept. 26 Litho. *Perf. 10½***

| | | | | |
|---|---|---|---|---|
| **C915** | AP203 | 10col multi | 1.00 | .65 |

No. 418 Overprinted

**1990, Nov. 5**

| | | | | |
|---|---|---|---|---|
| **C916** | A180 | 50col multicolored | 5.00 | 2.00 |

Bagging Coffee Beans — AP204

***Perf. 10½***

**1990, Nov. 16 Litho. Unwmk.**

| | | | | |
|---|---|---|---|---|
| **C917** | AP204 | 50col multicolored | 3.50 | 1.25 |

AP205

**1990, Dec. 6**

| | | | | |
|---|---|---|---|---|
| **C918** | AP205 | 50col blue & black | 4.00 | 2.00 |

First postage stamps, 150th anniv.

National Theater — AP206

Banana Picker, 1897, by Alleardo Villa.

**1991, Mar. 25 Litho. *Perf. 10½***

| | | | | |
|---|---|---|---|---|
| **C919** | AP206 | 30col multicolored | 3.00 | 1.00 |

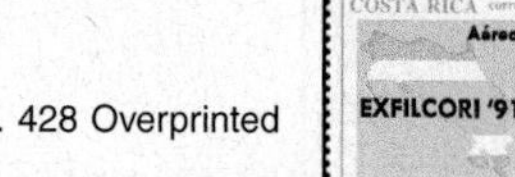

No. 428 Overprinted

**Litho. & Engr.**

**1991, Sept. 13 *Perf. 12½***

| | | | | |
|---|---|---|---|---|
| **C920** | A188 | 200col | 9.00 | 3.00 |

12th Natl. Philatelic Exposition.

No. 402 Overprinted

**1991, Oct. 11 Litho. *Perf. 11½***

**Granite Paper**

| | | | | |
|---|---|---|---|---|
| **C921** | A170 | 20col multicolored | 6.25 | 3.00 |

Basketball, cent.

Social Security Administration, 50th Anniv. — AP207

**1991, Nov. 1 Litho. *Perf. 13½***

| | | | | |
|---|---|---|---|---|
| **C922** | AP207 | 15col multicolored | 3.50 | 3.00 |

La Poesia by Vespasiano Bignami — AP208

**1992, Jan. 24 Litho. *Perf. 10½***

| | | | | |
|---|---|---|---|---|
| **C923** | AP208 | 35col multicolored | 6.00 | 4.00 |

National Theater.

Discovery of America, 500th Anniv. — AP209

No. C924 — Columbus' ships: a, Nina. b, Santa Maria. c, Pinta.

**1992, Oct. 8 Litho. *Perf. 13½***

| | | | | |
|---|---|---|---|---|
| **C924** | | Strip of 3 | 6.75 | 6.00 |
| ***a.-c.*** | A209 | 45col Any single | 1.50 | 1.50 |

Intl. Arts Festival — AP210

**1993, Mar. 15 Litho. *Perf. 13½***
**C925** AP210 45col multicolored 2.25 2.00

Telecommunications Institute, 30th Anniv. — AP211

**1993, Nov. 25 Litho. *Perf. 13½***
**C926** AP211 45col multicolored 1.75 1.40

Ministry of the Interior, 150th Anniv. — AP212

**1994, Mar. 8 Litho. *Perf. 10½***
**C927** AP212 45col multicolored 1.75 1.40

Intl. Year of the Family — AP213

**1994, May 5 Litho. *Perf. 10½***
**C928** AP213 45col multicolored 1.75 1.40

LACSA, 50th Anniv. — AP214

5col, Douglas DC-3. 10col, Curtiss C-46. 20col, Beechcraft. 30col, DC-6B. 35col, BAC 1-11. 40col, Convair CV 440. 45col, Electra L-188. 50col, Boeing 727-200. 55col, Douglas DC-8. 60col, Airbus A320.

**1996, Mar. 29 Litho. *Perf. 10½***

| | | | | |
|---|---|---|---|---|
| **C929** | AP214 | 5col multi | .35 | .30 |
| **C930** | AP214 | 10col multi | .35 | .30 |
| **C931** | AP214 | 20col multi | .55 | .45 |
| **C932** | AP214 | 30col multi | .95 | .80 |
| **C933** | AP214 | 35col multi | 1.00 | .85 |
| **C934** | AP214 | 40col multi | 1.30 | 1.10 |
| **C935** | AP214 | 45col multi | 1.30 | 1.10 |
| **C936** | AP214 | 50col multi | 1.50 | 1.20 |
| **C937** | AP214 | 55col multi | 1.75 | 1.50 |
| **C938** | AP214 | 60col multi | 1.90 | 1.60 |
| | | *Nos. C929-C938 (10)* | 10.95 | 9.20 |

No. C932 Surcharged

**2001, Oct. 5 Litho. *Perf. 10½***
**C939** AP214 5col on 30col multi 1.00 .75

10th Intl. Art Festival — AP215

**2006, Mar. 17 Litho. *Perf. 10½***
**C940** AP215 120col multi 2.50 2.00

## AIR POST SPECIAL DELIVERY STAMPS

**Catalogue values for unused stamps in this section are for Never Hinged items.**

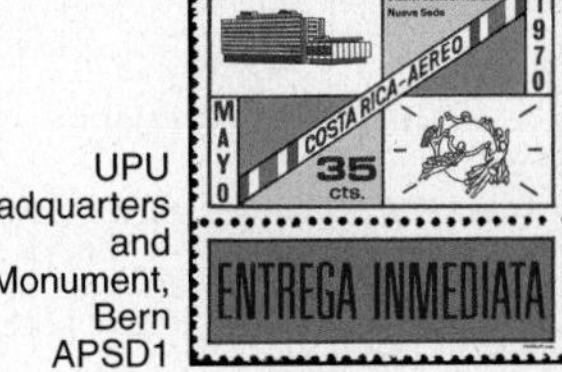


UPU Headquarters and Monument, Bern APSD1

***Perf. 10x11***
**1970, May 20 Litho. Unwmk.**
**CE1** APSD1 35c multi 1.25 .40
**CE2** APSD1 60c multi 1.25 .40

Opening of the UPU Headquarters in Bern. The red and black label attached to the 60c is inscribed "EXPRES." Values are for stamps with label attached.

Stamps with labels removed were used for regular airmail.

## AIR POST OFFICIAL STAMPS

Air Post Stamps of 1934 Ovptd. in Red

**1934 Unwmk. *Perf. 12***

| | | | | |
|---|---|---|---|---|
| **CO1** | AP8 | 5c green | .30 | .30 |
| **CO2** | AP8 | 10c car rose | .30 | .30 |
| **CO3** | AP8 | 15c chocolate | .60 | .60 |
| **CO4** | AP8 | 20c deep blue | .95 | .95 |
| **CO5** | AP8 | 25c deep org | .95 | .95 |
| **CO6** | AP8 | 40c olive blk | .95 | .95 |
| **CO7** | AP8 | 50c gray blk | .95 | .95 |
| **CO8** | AP8 | 60c org yel | 1.10 | 1.10 |
| **CO9** | AP8 | 75c dull vio | 1.10 | 1.10 |
| **CO10** | AP9 | 1col deep rose | 2.00 | 2.00 |
| **CO11** | AP9 | 2col light blue | 6.00 | 6.00 |
| **CO12** | AP9 | 5col black | 10.00 | 10.00 |
| **CO13** | AP9 | 10col red brown | 14.50 | 14.50 |
| | | *Nos. CO1-CO13 (13)* | 39.70 | 39.70 |

For overprints see Nos. C103-C116.

## SPECIAL DELIVERY STAMPS

**Catalogue values for unused stamps in this section are for Never Hinged items.**

Winged Letter — SD1

**Unwmk.**
**1972, Mar. 20 Litho. *Perf. 11***
**E1** SD1 75c brown & red .50 .40
**E2** SD1 1.50col blue & red 1.20 .40

**1973 *Perf. 11x12***
**E3** SD1 75c green & red .80 .40

**1973, Nov. 5 Litho. *Perf. 12***
**E4** SD1 75c lilac & orange 2.00 .75

Exists perf 11x11½.

Concorde — SD2

**1976, May 17 Litho. *Perf. 16***
**E5** SD2 1col vermilion & multi 1.25 .75

SD3

**1979, June 15 Litho. *Perf. 12½***
**E6** SD3 2col multi 1.40 .50

SD4

**1980, Dec. 18 Litho. *Perf. 12½***
**E7** SD4 2col multi 1.25 .50

**1982, Dec. 20 Litho. *Perf. 11***
**E8** SD4 4col multi 1.60 .50

## POSTAGE DUE STAMPS

D1

**1903 Unwmk. Engr. *Perf. 14***
**Numerals in Black**

| | | | | |
|---|---|---|---|---|
| **J1** | D1 | 5c slate blue | 8.50 | 1.25 |
| **J2** | D1 | 10c brown orange | 8.50 | 1.25 |
| **J3** | D1 | 15c yellow green | 4.25 | 1.75 |
| **J4** | D1 | 20c carmine | 6.00 | 1.75 |
| **J5** | D1 | 25c slate gray | 6.00 | 2.40 |
| **J6** | D1 | 30c brown | 6.25 | 2.50 |
| **J7** | D1 | 40c olive bister | 8.25 | 2.50 |
| **J8** | D1 | 50c red violet | 8.25 | 2.50 |
| | | *Nos. J1-J8 (8)* | 56.00 | 15.90 |

D2

**1915 Litho. *Perf. 12***

| | | | | |
|---|---|---|---|---|
| **J9** | D2 | 2c orange | 1.25 | .55 |
| **J10** | D2 | 4c dark blue | 1.25 | .55 |
| **J11** | D2 | 8c gray green | 1.25 | .55 |
| **J12** | D2 | 10c violet | 1.25 | .55 |
| **J13** | D2 | 20c brown | 1.25 | .55 |
| | | *Nos. J9-J13 (5)* | 6.25 | 2.75 |

## OFFICIAL STAMPS

Values for unused stamps are for examples with original gum as defined in the catalogue introduction. Examples without gum have probably been used and are so regarded.

Very fine examples of Nos. O1-O24 will have perforations just clear of the design on one or more sides.

Nos. O1-O55, to about 1915, normally were not canceled when affixed to official mail. Occasionally they were canceled in a foreign country of destination. Used values are for favor-canceled stamps or for stamps without gum.

### Regular Issues Overprinted

Overprinted in Red, Black, Blue or Green

**1883-85 Unwmk. *Perf. 12***

| | | | | |
|---|---|---|---|---|
| **O1** | A6 | 1c green (R) | 2.00 | 1.10 |
| **O2** | A6 | 1c green (Bk) | 4.00 | 1.10 |
| **O3** | A6 | 2c carmine (Bk) | 4.00 | 1.40 |
| **O4** | A6 | 2c carmine (Bl) | 2.40 | 1.60 |
| **O5** | A6 | 5c blue vio (R) | 7.00 | 3.00 |
| **O6** | A6 | 10c orange (G) | 10.00 | 4.00 |
| **O7** | A6 | 40c blue (R) | 10.00 | 4.00 |
| | | *Nos. O1-O7 (7)* | 39.40 | 16.20 |

Overprinted

**1886**

| | | | | |
|---|---|---|---|---|
| **O8** | A6 | 1c green (Bk) | 3.50 | 1.10 |
| **O9** | A6 | 2c carmine (Bk) | 3.50 | 1.60 |
| **O10** | A6 | 5c blue vio (R) | 24.00 | 11.00 |
| **O11** | A6 | 10c orange (Bk) | 24.00 | 11.00 |
| | | *Nos. O8-O11 (4)* | 55.00 | 24.70 |

Overprinted

| | | | | |
|---|---|---|---|---|
| **O12** | A6 | 1c green (Bk) | 3.50 | 1.00 |
| **O13** | A6 | 2c carmine (Bk) | 3.50 | 1.40 |
| **O14** | A6 | 5c blue vio (R) | 24.00 | 11.00 |
| **O15** | A6 | 10c orange (Bk) | 24.00 | 11.00 |
| | | *Nos. O12-O15 (4)* | 55.00 | 24.40 |

Nos. O8-O11 and O12-O15 exist se-tenant in vertical pairs.

Overprinted in Black

**O16** A6 5c blue vio 60.00 60.00
**O17** A6 10c orange — 275.00

Overprinted

**1887**

| | | | | |
|---|---|---|---|---|
| **O18** | A6 | 1c green | 1.25 | 1.25 |
| **O19** | A6 | 2c carmine | 1.25 | .50 |
| **O21** | A6 | 10c orange | 37.50 | 24.00 |
| | *c.* | Double overprint | 42.50 | |
| **O22** | A7 | 5c blue vio | 12.00 | 3.50 |
| **O23** | A7 | 10c orange | .90 | .50 |
| | *c.* | Double overprint | 27.50 | |
| **O24** | A6 | 40c blue | 1.25 | .50 |
| | | *Nos. O18-O24 (6)* | 54.15 | 30.25 |

**Overprinted "OFICAL"**

| | | | | |
|---|---|---|---|---|
| *O18a* | A6 | 1c green | *25.00* | *14.50* |
| *O19a* | A6 | 2c carmine | *25.00* | |
| *O22a* | A7 | 5c blue violet | *25.00* | |
| *O23a* | A7 | 10c orange | *25.00* | *3.50* |
| *O24a* | A6 | 40c blue | *25.00* | *17.00* |
| | | *Nos. O18a-O24a (5)* | *100.00* | |

Dangerous counterfeits exist of Nos. O18a-O24a.

**Without Period**

| | | | | |
|---|---|---|---|---|
| *O18b* | A6 | 1c green | 25.00 | 15.00 |
| *O19b* | A6 | 2c carmine | 25.00 | 15.00 |
| *O22b* | A7 | 5c blue violet | 25.00 | 15.00 |
| *O23b* | A7 | 10c orange | 25.00 | 15.00 |
| | | *Nos. O18b-O23b (4)* | 100.00 | 60.00 |

Nos. O18b-O23b are from a separate plate without periods. No. O23 exists without period (position 32). These must be collected in pairs.

Issues of 1889-1901 Overprinted

**1889** *Perf. 14, 15*

**O25** A10 1c brown .25 .25
**O26** A11 2c dk green .25 .25
**O27** A12 5c orange .25 .25
**O28** A13 10c red brown .25 .25
**O29** A14 20c yellow grn .40 .25
**O30** A15 50c rose red 1.40 1.40
*Nos. O25-O30 (6)* 2.80 2.65

**1892**

**O31** A20 1c grnsh blue .25 .25
**O32** A21 2c yellow .25 .25
**O33** A22 5c violet .25 .25
**O34** A23 10c lt green 4.00 1.60
**O35** A24 20c scarlet .25 .25
**O36** A25 50c gray blue 1.00 .55
*Nos. O31-O36 (6)* 6.00 3.15

**1901-02**

**O37** A30 1c green & blk .40 .40
**O38** A31 2c ver & blk .40 .40
**O39** A32 5c gray bl & blk .40 .40
**O40** A33 10c ocher & blk .80 .80
**O41** A34 20c lake & blk 1.25 1.25
**O42** A35 50c lilac & dk bl 10.00 4.00
**O43** A36 1col ol bis & blk 17.50 10.00
*Nos. O37-O43 (7)* 30.75 17.25

No. 46 Overprinted in Green

**1903**

**O44** A31 2c ver & blk 3.00 3.00
*b.* "PROVISIORO" 10.00 10.00
*d.* Inverted overprint 10.00 10.00
*f.* As "b," inverted 15.00 10.00

Counterfeit overprints exist.

**Regular Issue of 1903 Overprinted Like Nos. O25-O43**

**1903** *Perf. 14, 12½x14*

**O45** A40 4c red vio & blk 1.40 1.40
**O46** A41 6c ol grn & blk 1.75 1.75
**O47** A42 25c gray lil & brn 9.50 6.00
*Nos. O45-O47 (3)* 12.65 9.15

Counterfeit overprints exist.

Regular Issue of 1907 Overprinted

**1908** *Perf. 14*

**O48** A43 1c red brn & ind .25 .25
**O49** A44 2c yel grn & blk .25 .25
**O50** A45 4c car & ind .25 .25
**O51** A46 5c yel & dull bl .25 .25
**O52** A47 10c blue & blk .80 .80
**O53** A49 25c gray lil & blk .30 .25
**O54** A50 50c red lil & bl .55 .55
**O55** A51 1col brown & blk 1.25 1.25
*Nos. O48-O55 (8)* 3.90 3.85

Various varieties of the overprint and basic stamps exist.

Imperf examples of Nos. O48, O49, O53 were found in 1970.

Regular Issue of 1910 Overprinted in Black

**1917**

**O56** A56 5c orange .50 .50
*a.* Inverted overprint 6.00 3.50
**O57** A57 10c deep blue .30 .30
*a.* Inverted overprint 3.50 3.50

No. 74 Surcharged

**1920 Red Surcharge** *Perf. 12*

**O58** A58 15c on 20c olive grn .55 .55

**Nos. 72, 61, 59, 65-67 Surcharged or Overprinted**

**1921 Black Surcharge** *Perf. 12*

**O59** A56 10c on 5c orange .65 .65
*a.* "10 CTS." inverted 17.50

*Perf. 14*

**O60** A45 4c car & indigo .55 .55
*a.* "1291" for "1921" 12.00
**O61** A43 6c on 1c red brn & ind .70 .70
**O62** A49 20c on 25c gray lil & blk .70 .70

**Overprinted like No. O60**

**O63** A50 50c red lil & bl 5.00 2.00
**O64** A51 1col brown & blk 7.00 4.00
*Nos. O59-O64 (6)* 14.60 8.60

Nos. O60 to O64 exist with date and new values inverted. These may be printer's waste but probably were deliberately made.

Regular Issue of 1923 Overprinted

**1923** *Perf. 11½*

**O65** A68 2c brown .35 .35
**O66** A68 4c green .35 .35
**O67** A68 5c blue .40 .40
**O68** A68 20c carmine .35 .35
**O69** A68 1col violet .50 .50
*Nos. O65-O69 (5)* 1.95 1.95

Nos. O65 to O69 exist imperforate but were not regularly issued in that condition. Value, set: $5.

O7

**1926 Unwmk. Engr.** *Perf. 12½*

**O70** O7 2c ultra & blk .35 .35
**O71** O7 3c mag & blk .35 .35
**O72** O7 4c lt bl & blk .35 .35
**O73** O7 5c grn & blk .35 .35
**O74** O7 6c ocher & blk .35 .35
**O75** O7 10c rose red & blk .35 .35
**O76** O7 20c ol grn & blk .35 .35
**O77** O7 30c red org & blk .35 .35
**O78** O7 45c brown & blk .35 .35
**O79** O7 1col lilac & blk .50 .50
*Nos. O70-O79 (10)* 3.65 3.65

See Nos. O82-O94. For surcharges see Nos. C7-C10.

Regular Issue of 1936 Overprinted in Black

**1936 Unwmk.** *Perf. 12*

**O80** A96 5c green .25 .25
**O81** A96 10c carmine rose .25 .25

**Type of 1926**

**1937** *Perf. 12½*

**O82** O7 2c vio & blk .25 .25
**O83** O7 3c bis brn & blk .25 .25
**O84** O7 4c rose car & blk .25 .25
**O85** O7 5c ol grn & blk .25
**O86** O7 8c blk brn & blk .25
**O87** O7 10c rose lake & blk .25
**O88** O7 20c ind & blk .25 .25
**O89** O7 40c red org & blk .25 .25
**O90** O7 55c dk vio & blk .25
**O91** O7 1col brn vio & blk .30 .30
**O92** O7 2col gray bl & blk .70 .70
**O93** O7 5col dl yel & blk 3.00 3.00
**O94** O7 10col blue & blk 55.00 20.00
*Nos. O82-O94 (13)* 61.25 25.25

Nine stamps of this series exist with perforated star (2c, 3c, 4c, 20c, 40c, 1col, 2col, 5col, 10col). These were issued to officials for postal purposes. Unpunched stamps were sold to collectors but had no franking power. Values for unused are for unpunched. Value, punched set of 9: $25.

## POSTAL TAX STAMPS

The 1927 postal tax stamps covered the 10c per book charge for books sent by mail. The stamps were sold at the post office and applied to any package containing books.

Regular Stamps and Revenue Stamps Overprinted in Black

Nos. RA1B-RA1D Overprinted

**1927, Mar. 17**

**RA1A** A75 10c car rose *35.00* 5.00
**RA1B** 50c brown (overprinted on revenue stamp) *50.00* 10.00
**RA1C** A79 1col olive green *50.00* 10.00
**RA1D** 2col blue green (overprinted on revenue stamp) *1,000.* 500.00
*Nos. RA1A-RA1D (4)* *1,135.* 525.00

No. 124 Surcharged in Black

**1927, Dec. 23**

**RA1E** A76 10c on 12c carmine rose 25.00 5.00

**Catalogue values for unused stamps in this section, from this point to the end of the section, are for Never Hinged items.**

Most postal tax issues were to benefit the Children's Village and were obligatory on all mail during Dec.

No. C198 Surcharged in Red

**Engraved; Center Photogravure**

**1958 Unwmk.** *Perf. 12½*

**RA1** AP51 5c on 2c brt bl & blk .80 .40

Type of 1954 Surcharged in Green

Design: Like No. C228, pottery.

**RA2** AP53 5c on 10c dk bl & blk 1.00 .40
*a.* Inverted surcharge 8.50

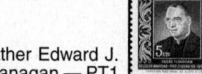

Father Edward J. Flanagan — PT1

Paintings: No. RA4, Boy by El Greco. No. RA5, Boy by Jose Ribera. No. RA6, Girl by Amadeo Modigliani.

*Perf. 13½*

**1959, Nov. 25 Unwmk. Photo.**

**RA3** PT1 5c green 1.10 .40
**RA4** PT1 5c dl gray vio 1.10 .40
**RA5** PT1 5c olive 1.10 .40
**RA6** PT1 5c lilac rose 1.10 .40
*Nos. RA3-RA6 (4)* 4.40 1.60

Nos. RA3-RA6 exist imperf.

Father Peralta — PT2

Designs: No. RA8, Girl by Renoir. No. RA9, Boys with cups by Velazquez. No. RA10, Singing children, sculpture by F. Zuñiga.

**1960 Litho.** *Perf. 14*

**RA7** PT2 5c chocolate 1.10 .40
**RA8** PT2 5c dp org 1.10 .40
**RA9** PT2 5c plum 1.10 .40
**RA10** PT2 5c grysh bl 1.10 .40
*Nos. RA7-RA10 (4)* 4.40 1.60

Nos. RA7-RA10 exist imperf.

No. C229 Surcharged in Black

**Engraved; Center Photogravure**

**1961** *Perf. 13x12½*

**RA11** AP53 5c on 15c grn & blk .90 .40

Nicolas, Son of Rubens — PT3

Designs: No. RA13, Madonna by Bellini. RA14, Angel playing stringed instrument by Melozzo. RA15, Msgr. Rubén Odio H.

**1962 Photo.** *Perf. 13½*

**RA12** PT3 5c dark carmine 1.10 .35
**RA13** PT3 5c sepia 1.10 .35
**RA14** PT3 5c dull green 1.10 .35
**RA15** PT3 5c blue 1.10 .35
*Nos. RA12-RA15 (4)* 4.40 1.40

For surcharges see Nos. 262-265.

**Type of 1962, Inscribed "1963"**

Designs as before.

**1963 Photo.** *Perf. 13½*

**RA16** PT3 5c sepia (RA12) .85 .35
**RA17** PT3 5c ultra (RA13) .85 .35
**RA18** PT3 5c dk car (RA14) .85 .35
**RA19** PT3 5c black (RA15) .85 .35
*Nos. RA16-RA19 (4)* 3.40 1.40

Boys in Workshop — PT4

Designs: No. RA21, Two playing boys. No. RA22, Teacher and children. No. RA23, Priest with boys.

**1964 Litho.** *Perf. 12½*

**RA20** PT4 5c bright green .90 .40
**RA21** PT4 5c rose lilac .90 .40
**RA22** PT4 5c blue .90 .40
**RA23** PT4 5c brown .90 .40
*Nos. RA20-RA23 (4)* 3.60 1.60

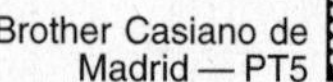
Brother Casiano de Madrid — PT5

Designs: No. RA25, National Children's Hospital. No. RA26, Poinsettia. No. RA27, Santa Claus with children (diamond).

**1965, Dec. 10 Litho. *Perf. 10***

| | | | | |
|---|---|---|---|---|
| **RA24** | PT5 | 5c red brown | .80 | .40 |
| **RA25** | PT5 | 5c green | .80 | .40 |
| **RA26** | PT5 | 5c red | .80 | .40 |
| **RA27** | PT5 | 5c ultra | .80 | .40 |
| | | *Nos. RA24-RA27 (4)* | 3.20 | 1.60 |

Christmas Ornaments — PT6

**1966 Litho. *Perf. 11***

| | | | | |
|---|---|---|---|---|
| **RA28** | PT6 | 5c shown | .80 | .40 |
| **RA29** | PT6 | 5c Angel | .80 | .40 |
| **RA30** | PT6 | 5c Church | .80 | .40 |
| **RA31** | PT6 | 5c Reindeer | .80 | .40 |
| | | *Nos. RA28-RA31 (4)* | 3.20 | 1.60 |

General Post Office, San José — PT7

**1967, Mar. Litho. *Perf. 11***

| | | | | |
|---|---|---|---|---|
| **RA32** | PT7 | 10c blue | .90 | .40 |

No. RA32 was issued as a postal tax stamp to be used by organizations normally allowed free postage. On Dec. 15, 1972, it was authorized for use as an ordinary postage stamp.

Madonna and Child — PT8

**1967 Litho. *Perf. 11***

| | | | | |
|---|---|---|---|---|
| **RA33** | PT8 | 5c olive green | .80 | .40 |
| **RA34** | PT8 | 5c dp lil rose | .80 | .40 |
| **RA35** | PT8 | 5c brt blue | .80 | .40 |
| **RA36** | PT8 | 5c grnsh blue | .80 | .40 |
| | | *Nos. RA33-RA36 (4)* | 3.20 | 1.60 |

Star of Bethlehem, Mother and Child — PT9

**1968, Dec. Litho. *Perf. 12½***

| | | | | |
|---|---|---|---|---|
| **RA37** | PT9 | 5c gray | .80 | .40 |
| **RA38** | PT9 | 5c rose red | .80 | .40 |
| **RA39** | PT9 | 5c dk rose brn | .80 | .40 |
| **RA40** | PT9 | 5c bister brn | .80 | .40 |
| | | *Nos. RA37-RA40 (4)* | 3.20 | 1.60 |

Madonna and Child — PT10

**1969, Dec. Litho. *Perf. 12½***

| | | | | |
|---|---|---|---|---|
| **RA41** | PT10 | 5c dk blue | .80 | .40 |
| **RA42** | PT10 | 5c orange | .80 | .40 |
| **RA43** | PT10 | 5c brown red | .80 | .40 |
| **RA44** | PT10 | 5c blue green | .80 | .40 |
| | | *Nos. RA41-RA44 (4)* | 3.20 | 1.60 |

Christ Child, Star — PT11

**1970, Dec. Litho. *Perf. 12½***

| | | | | |
|---|---|---|---|---|
| **RA45** | PT11 | 5c brt purple | .85 | .40 |
| **RA46** | PT11 | 5c lilac rose | .85 | .40 |
| **RA47** | PT11 | 5c olive | .85 | .40 |
| **RA48** | PT11 | 5c ocher | .85 | .40 |
| | | *Nos. RA45-RA48 (4)* | 3.40 | 1.60 |

Christ Child and "PAX" — PT12

**1971, Nov. 29**

| | | | | |
|---|---|---|---|---|
| **RA49** | PT12 | 10c dk blue | .80 | .40 |
| **RA50** | PT12 | 10c orange | .80 | .40 |
| **RA51** | PT12 | 10c brown | .80 | .40 |
| **RA52** | PT12 | 10c green | .80 | .40 |
| | | *Nos. RA49-RA52 (4)* | 3.20 | 1.60 |

Madonna and Child — PT13

**1972, Nov. 30 *Perf. 11x11½***

| | | | | |
|---|---|---|---|---|
| **RA53** | PT13 | 10c dk blue | .80 | .40 |
| **RA54** | PT13 | 10c brt red | .80 | .40 |
| **RA55** | PT13 | 10c lilac | .80 | .40 |
| **RA56** | PT13 | 10c green | .80 | .40 |
| | | *Nos. RA53-RA56 (4)* | 3.20 | 1.60 |

Madonna and Child — PT14

**1973, Nov. 30 Litho. *Perf. 12½***

| | | | | |
|---|---|---|---|---|
| **RA57** | PT14 | 10c purple | .80 | .40 |
| **RA58** | PT14 | 10c car rose | .80 | .40 |
| **RA59** | PT14 | 10c gray | .80 | .40 |
| **RA60** | PT14 | 10c orange brn | .80 | .40 |
| | | *Nos. RA57-RA60 (4)* | 3.20 | 1.60 |

Boys Eating Cake, by Murillo — PT15

Paintings: No. RA62, Virgin and Child, with St. John, by Raphael. No. RA63, Maternity, by Juan R. Bonilla. No. RA64, Praying Child, by Reynolds.

**1974, Nov. 25 *Perf. 13***

| | | | | |
|---|---|---|---|---|
| **RA61** | PT15 | 10c brt pink | .80 | .40 |
| **RA62** | PT15 | 10c rose lilac | .80 | .40 |
| **RA63** | PT15 | 10c dk gray | .80 | .40 |
| **RA64** | PT15 | 10c violet bl | .80 | .40 |
| | | *Nos. RA61-RA64 (4)* | 3.20 | 1.60 |

See No. RA110.

"Happy Dreams," by Sonia Romero — PT16

Paintings: No. RA66, Virgin with Carnation, by Leonardo da Vinci. No. RA67, Children with Tortoise, by Francisco Amighetti. No. RA68, Boy with Pigeon, by Picasso.

**1975, Nov. 25 Litho. *Perf. 10½***

| | | | | |
|---|---|---|---|---|
| **RA65** | PT16 | 10c gray | .95 | .40 |
| **RA66** | PT16 | 10c red lilac | .95 | .40 |
| **RA67** | PT16 | 10c orange brown | .95 | .40 |
| **RA68** | PT16 | 10c brt blue | .95 | .40 |
| | | *Nos. RA65-RA68 (4)* | 3.80 | 1.60 |

Virgin and Child, by Hans Memling — PT17

Paintings: No. RA70, Girl with Sombrero, by Auguste Renoir. No. RA71, Meditation (boy), by Floria Pinto de Herrero. No. RA72, Gaston de Mezerville (boy), by Lolita Zeller de Peralta.

**1976, Nov. 24 Litho. *Perf. 10½***

| | | | | |
|---|---|---|---|---|
| **RA69** | PT17 | 10c rose lilac | .80 | .35 |
| **RA70** | PT17 | 10c rose carmine | .80 | .35 |
| **RA71** | PT17 | 10c gray | .80 | .35 |
| **RA72** | PT17 | 10c violet blue | .80 | .35 |
| | | *Nos. RA69-RA72 (4)* | 3.20 | 1.40 |

Boy's Head, by Amparo Cruz — PT18

Paintings: No. RA74, Girl's head, by Rubens. No. RA75, Girl and infant, by Cristina Fournier. No. RA76, Mariano Goya, by Goya.

**1977, Nov. Litho. *Perf. 10½***

| | | | | |
|---|---|---|---|---|
| **RA73** | PT18 | 10c gray olive | .80 | .40 |
| **RA74** | PT18 | 10c rose red | .80 | .40 |
| **RA75** | PT18 | 10c brt ultra | .80 | .40 |
| **RA76** | PT18 | 10c brt rose lil | .80 | .40 |
| | | *Nos. RA73-RA76 (4)* | 3.20 | 1.60 |

Boy with Kite — PT19

Designs: Nos. RA78-RA79, Girl flying kite.

**1978, Nov. 20 Litho. *Perf. 12½***

| | | | | |
|---|---|---|---|---|
| **RA77** | PT19 | 10c magenta | .80 | .40 |
| **RA78** | PT19 | 10c slate | .80 | .40 |
| **RA79** | PT19 | 10c lilac | .80 | .40 |
| **RA80** | PT19 | 10c violet blue | .80 | .40 |
| | | *Nos. RA77-RA80 (4)* | 3.20 | 1.60 |

Boy Leaning on Tree — PT20

**1979, Nov. 19 Litho. *Perf. 12½***

| | | | | |
|---|---|---|---|---|
| **RA81** | PT20 | 10c blue | .80 | .40 |
| **RA82** | PT20 | 10c orange | .80 | .40 |
| **RA83** | PT20 | 10c magenta | .80 | .40 |
| **RA84** | PT20 | 10c green | .80 | .40 |
| | | *Nos. RA81-RA84 (4)* | 3.20 | 1.60 |

Boy on Swing — PT21

**1980, Nov. 18 Litho. *Perf. 12½***

| | | | | |
|---|---|---|---|---|
| **RA85** | PT21 | 10c brt blue | .80 | .40 |
| **RA86** | PT21 | 10c brt yellow | .80 | .40 |
| **RA87** | PT21 | 10c crimson rose | .80 | .40 |
| **RA88** | PT21 | 10c brt green | .80 | .40 |
| | | *Nos. RA85-RA88 (4)* | 3.20 | 1.60 |

Boy Riding Toy Car — PT22

**1981, Nov. 19 Litho. *Perf. 11***

| | | | | |
|---|---|---|---|---|
| **RA89** | PT22 | 10c blue | .80 | .40 |
| **RA90** | PT22 | 10c green | .80 | .40 |
| **RA91** | PT22 | 10c red | .80 | .40 |
| **RA92** | PT22 | 10c orange | .80 | .40 |
| | | *Nos. RA89-RA92 (4)* | 3.20 | 1.60 |

Youth Running Machine — PT23

**1982, Nov. 19 Litho. *Perf. 10½***

| | | | | |
|---|---|---|---|---|
| **RA93** | PT23 | 10c red | .80 | .40 |
| **RA94** | PT23 | 10c gray | .80 | .40 |
| **RA95** | PT23 | 10c purple | .80 | .40 |
| **RA96** | PT23 | 10c grnsh blue | .80 | .40 |
| | | *Nos. RA93-RA96 (4)* | 3.20 | 1.60 |

Youths Working on Wheelchair — PT24

**1983, Nov. 24 Litho. *Perf. 16***

| | | | | |
|---|---|---|---|---|
| **RA97** | PT24 | 10c red | .80 | .40 |
| **RA98** | PT24 | 10c orange | .80 | .40 |
| **RA99** | PT24 | 10c ultra | .80 | .40 |
| **RA100** | PT24 | 10c green | .80 | .40 |
| | | *Nos. RA97-RA100 (4)* | 3.20 | 1.60 |

Christmas 1983.

Girl on Bicycle — PT25

**1984, Nov. 20 Litho. *Perf. 10½***

| | | | | |
|---|---|---|---|---|
| **RA101** | PT25 | 10c violet | 1.25 | .40 |

Christmas 1984.

Taking a Child in Out of the Cold — PT26

**1985, Dec. 1 Litho. *Perf. 13***

| | | | | |
|---|---|---|---|---|
| **RA102** | PT26 | 10c dull brown | 1.20 | .40 |

Christmas 1985.

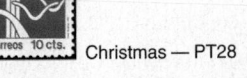

Depressed Child — PT27

**1986, Dec. 1 Litho. *Perf. 10½***

| | | | | |
|---|---|---|---|---|
| **RA103** | PT27 | 10c lemon | 1.20 | .40 |

Christmas stamps, 25th anniv.; Christmas 1986.

Christmas — PT28

**1987, Dec. 1 Litho. *Perf. 10½***

| | | | | |
|---|---|---|---|---|
| **RA104** | PT28 | 10c dk ol bis & brt bl | 1.10 | .40 |

No postal tax stamp was issued for 1988.

Teaching Children — PT29

**1989, Dec. 1 Litho. *Perf. 13½***

| | | | | |
|---|---|---|---|---|
| **RA105** | PT29 | 1col blue, blk & brt apple grn | 1.10 | .40 |

Christmas 1989.

No. 417 Ovptd. in Red, Blue, Green, or Orange

**1990, Nov. 16 Litho. *Perf. 13½***

**RA106** A179 10col multi (R) 5.25 .40
**RA107** A179 10col multi (Bl) 5.25 .40
**RA108** A179 10col multi (G) 5.25 .40
**RA109** A179 10col multi (O) 5.25 .40
*Nos. RA106-RA109 (4)* 21.00 1.60

No. RA109 exists with a silver overprint.

### Art Type of 1974

Design: 10col, Praying Child, by Reynolds.

**1991, Nov. 18 Litho. *Perf. 10½***

**RA110** PT15 10col dark ultra 1.75 .40

Christmas — PT30

Boy in workshop.

**1992, Dec. 1 Litho. *Perf. 10½***

**RA111** PT30 10col red 1.10 .40

Christmas — PT31

**1993, Nov. 17**

**RA112** PT31 10col multicolored 1.50 .40

Christmas — PT32

**1994, Nov. 23 Litho. *Perf. 10½***

**RA113** PT32 11col lilac & slate 1.50 .40

No. RA113 exists imperf.

Christmas — PT33

Painting of mother and child, by Claudio Carazo.

**1995, Dec. 1 *Perf. 13½***

**RA114** PT33 12col multicolored 1.20 .40
*a.* Miniature sheet, #RA114 + 5 labels 3.75 3.50

No. RA114a contains 4 progressive proofs of No. RA114 + one label of text and sold for 112col.

Sculpture — PT34

**1996, Dec. 1 Litho. *Perf. 10½***

**RA115** PT34 14col multi 1.10 .40

Christmas — PT35

Bust of Antonio Obando Chan, by Olger Villegas Cruz.

**1997, Dec. 1**

**RA116** PT35 15col multicolored 1.00 .50

Christmas — PT36

No. RA117: a, Flower. b, Flower up close, one in background. c, Berries on branch.

**1998 Litho. *Perf. 13½***

**RA117** Strip of 3 3.25 2.00
*a.-c.* PT36 16col Any single .85 .50

Children's Village — PT37

**1999, Dec. 1 Litho. *Perf. 13¼***

**RA118** PT37 17col multi 1.00 .40

Child — PT38

Color: a, Green. b, Red. c, Blue. d, Brown.

**2000, Dec. 1 Litho. *Perf. 10½***

**RA119** Horiz. strip of 4 10.50 6.50
*a.-d.* PT38 20col Any single 1.75 1.00

Child Examining Stamp — PT39

Panel color: a, Purple. b, Green. c, Red. d, Orange.

**2001, Dec. 1 Litho. *Perf. 10½***

**RA120** Horiz. strip of 4 4.25 3.00
*a.-d.* PT39 21col Any single .85 .50

Child — PT40

Panel color: a, Purple. b, Blue. c, Orange. d, Green.

**2002 Litho. *Perf. 10½***

**RA121** Horiz strip of 4 4.00 3.00
*a.-d.* PT40 22col Any single .75 .60

Child Pointing at Star — PT41

No. RA122 — Background color: a, Purple. b, Green. c, Red. d, Yellow orange.

**2003, Dec. 1 Litho. *Perf. 13½x13¼***

**RA122** Horiz. strip of 4 3.75 3.00
*a.-d.* PT41 23col Any single .75 .50

Three Magi — PT42

No. RA123 — Magi in: a, Lemon. b, Green. c, Purple. d, Red violet.

**2004 Litho. *Perf. 13¼***

**RA123** Horiz. strip of 4 4.50 3.50
*a.-d.* PT42 25col Any single .85 .65

Children — PT43

No. RA124 — Denomination color: a, White. b, Buff. c, Dull orange. d, Red.

**2005, Dec. 1 Litho. *Perf. 10½***

**RA124** Horiz. strip of 4 4.50 3.50
*a.-d.* PT43 28col Any single .65 .50

Surtax for Children's Village.

Child Reading — PT44

No. RA125 — Frame color: a, Yellow bister. b, Dull brown. c, Olive green. d, Orange brown.

**2006, Dec. 1 Litho. *Perf. 10½***

**RA125** Horiz. strip of 4 5.50 4.50
*a.-d.* PT44 32col Any single 1.00 .75

Children's Art — PT45

No. RA126: a, Family and hearts. b, Children at school. c, Children on playground equipment. d, Boy on skateboard.

**2007, Dec. 1 Litho. *Perf. 10½***

**RA126** Horiz. strip of 4 5.00 4.00
*a.-d.* PT45 35col Any single 1.00 .85

Surtax for Children's Village.

Children's Art — PT46

No. RA127: a, Child flying kite, by Luis Paulino Murillo Méndez. b, Boy and jaguar, by David Malavassi Zúñiga. c, Bird and sailboat, by Valeria Vargas Arias. d, Child in water, by Dannia María Berrocal Fonseca.

**2008, Dec. 1 Litho. *Perf. 13½***

**RA127** Horiz. strip of 4 6.75 6.00
*a.-d.* PT46 40col Any single 1.00 1.00

Surtax for Children's Village.

Miniature Sheet

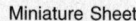

Masquerade Costumes — PT47

No. RA128: a, Devil and man in purple hat. b, Bull and clown. c, Grim reaper. d, Stilt walker and tall woman.

**2009, Dec. 1 Litho. *Perf. 10½***

**RA128** PT47 45col Sheet of 4, #a-d 4.50 3.50

Surtax for Children's Village.

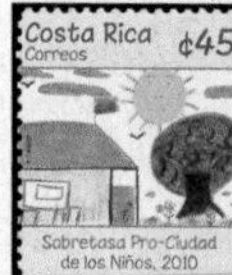

Children's Art — PT48

No. RA129: a, School, tree and sun (gray panels). b, Child in workshop (blue panels). c, Sun, hills, flora and fauna (pink panels). d, Sun, house on hill (yellow panels).

**2010, Dec. 1**

**RA129** Horiz. strip of 4 4.00 3.50
*a.-d.* PT48 45col Any single .80 .60

Surtax for Children's Village.

Children's Art — PT49

No. RA130: a, Head (orange yellow panel). b, Children with banner (blue panel). c, Children in playground (yellow green panel). d, Various children (bright rose panel).

**2011, Dec. 1**

**RA130** PT49 55col Block of 4, #a-d 5.25 4.25

Surtax for Children's Village.

Boy Holding Sun — PT50

No. RA131 — Background color: a, Light blue. b, Blue. c, Brown orange. d, Yellow bister.

**2012, Dec. 1 Litho. *Perf. 10½***

**RA131** Horiz. strip of 4 3.50 2.50
*a.-d.* PT50 60col Any single .65 .45

Surtax for Children's Village.

PT51

No. RA132: a, Forest (denomination in olive green). b, Arches in wall (denomination in orange). c, Rock formation (denomination in lilac). d, Toucan (denomination in blue).

**2013, Dec. 2 Litho. *Perf. 10½***

**RA132** PT51 60col Block of 4, #a-d 4.00 3.50

No. RA132 was printed in sheets of 20 (5 of each stamp) + 4 labels. Surtax for Children's Village.

Traditional Dishes — PT52

No. RA133: a, Gallo pinto. b, Olla de carne. c, Casado con pollo. d, Picadillo de Vainica.

**2014, Dec. 1 Litho. *Perf. 13½x13***

**RA133** Strip of 4 3.50 2.50
*a.-d.* PT52 65col Any single .65 .45

Surtax for Children's Village.

PT53

No. RA134: a, Our Lady of Consolation Church (pink panels). b, Welder (blue panels). c, Fountain and building, San Agustín Technical College (orange panels). d, Sculpure and building, San Agustín Technical College (green panels).

**2015, Dec. 1 Litho. *Perf. 14***

**RA134** PT53 65col Block or vert. strip of 4, #a-d 3.50 2.75

Surtax for Children's Village.

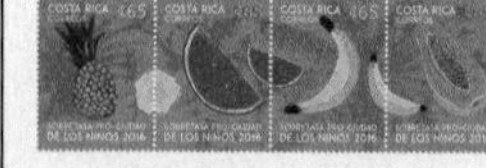

Fruit PT54

No. RA135: a, Whole and cut pineapple. b, Cut pineapple and watermelon slices. c, Watermelon slice and bananas. d, Banana and papaya.

**2016, Dec. 1 Litho. *Perf. 13¼***

| | | | |
|---|---|---|---|
| **RA135** | PT54 65col Horiz. strip of 4, #a-d | 3.25 | 2.50 |

Surtax for Children's Village.

Child's Drawing — PT55

No. RA136 — Frame color: a, Orange red. b, Bright yellow green. c, Blue. d, Purple.

**2017, Dec. 1 Litho. *Perf. 13***

| | | | |
|---|---|---|---|
| **RA136** | Horiz. strip of 4 | 3.50 | 2.50 |
| ***a.-d.*** | PT55 65col Any single | .65 | .45 |

Surtax for Children's Village.

Old Motor Vehicles — PT56

No. RA137: a, 1956 Willys Station Wagon. b, 1946 Chevrolet Pickup truck. c, 1933 Chrysler Convertible. d, 1927 Ford Model T.

**2018, Dec. 1 Litho. *Perf. 13***

| | | | |
|---|---|---|---|
| **RA137** | Horiz. strip of 4 | 3.50 | 2.50 |
| ***a.-d.*** | PT56 70col Any single | .65 | .40 |

Surtax for Children's Village.

Fish — PT57

No. RA138: a, Rhincodon typus. b, Sphyrna lewini. c, Mobula birostris. d, Pristis pristis.

**2019, Dec. 2 Litho. *Perf. 10½***

| | | | |
|---|---|---|---|
| **RA138** | Horiz. strip of 4 | 2.50 | 2.00 |
| ***a.-d.*** | PT57 70col Any single | .45 | .35 |

Surtax for Children's Village.

Fountains — PT58

No. RA139: a, Children's Fountain, Alajuela. b, Fountain of the Dolphins, Cartago. c, Centenary Fountain, Heredia. d, Moses Fountain, San José.

**2020, Dec. 1 Litho. *Perf. 10½***

| | | | |
|---|---|---|---|
| **RA139** | Horiz. strip of 4 | 2.50 | 2.00 |
| ***a.-d.*** | PT58 70col Any single | .45 | .35 |

Surtax for Children's Village.

## GUANACASTE

ˌgwä-nə-ˈkästā

(A province of Costa Rica)

LOCATION — Northwestern coast of Central America
AREA — 4,000 sq. mi. (approx.)
POP. — 69,531 (estimated)
CAPITAL — Liberia

Residents of Guanacaste were allowed to buy Costa Rican stamps, overprinted "Guanacaste," at a discount from face value because of the province's isolation and climate, which make it difficult to keep mint stamps. Use was restricted to the province.

Counterfeits of most Guanacaste overprints are plentiful.

For 5c stamps between Nos. 5-43, unused examples without gum sell for slightly more than the used value.

Very fine examples of Nos. 1-54 will have perforations just clear of the design on one or more sides.

Dangerous counterfeits exist of Nos. 1-63.

### On Issue of 1883

16mm

**1885 Unwmk. *Perf. 12***

**Overprinted Horizontally in Black**

| | | | | |
|---|---|---|---|---|
| **1** | A6 | 1c green | 4.00 | 3.25 |
| **2** | A6 | 2c carmine | 4.00 | 3.25 |
| *a.* | | "Gnanacaste" | *250.00* | |
| **3** | A6 | 10c orange | 35.00 | 21.00 |
| *a.* | | "Gnanacaste" | *1,500.* | |

**Same Overprint in Red**

| | | | | |
|---|---|---|---|---|
| **4** | A6 | 1c green | 4.00 | 4.00 |
| *a.* | | "Gnanacaste" | *200.00* | *200.00* |
| *b.* | | Overprinted in black & red | *300.00* | *350.00* |
| **5** | A6 | 5c blue violet | 30.00 | 4.00 |
| *a.* | | "Gnanacaste" | *350.00* | |
| **6** | A6 | 40c blue | 25.00 | 21.00 |

17½mm

**Overprinted Horizontally in Black**

| | | | | |
|---|---|---|---|---|
| **7** | A6 | 1c green | 10.00 | 7.00 |
| **8** | A6 | 2c carmine | 10.00 | 7.00 |
| **9** | A6 | 5c blue violet | 60.00 | 20.00 |
| **10** | A6 | 10c orange | 75.00 | 35.00 |
| **11** | A6 | 40c blue | 75.00 | 60.00 |

**Same Overprint in Red**

| | | | | |
|---|---|---|---|---|
| **12** | A6 | 5c blue violet | *2,000.* | 250.00 |
| **13** | A6 | 40c blue | *2,000.* | |

18½mm — c

**Overprinted Horizontally in Black**

| | | | | |
|---|---|---|---|---|
| **14** | A6 | 2c carmine | 10.00 | 7.00 |
| **15** | A6 | 10c orange | 100.00 | 75.00 |

**Same Overprint in Red**

| | | | | |
|---|---|---|---|---|
| **16** | A6 | 1c green | 7.00 | 7.00 |
| *a.* | | Double ovpt., one in blk | 250.00 | |
| **17** | A6 | 5c blue violet | 45.00 | 15.00 |
| **18** | A6 | 40c blue | 75.00 | 75.00 |

**Same Overprint, Vertically in Black**

| | | | | |
|---|---|---|---|---|
| **19** | A6 | 1c green | *7,000.* | |
| **20** | A6 | 2c carmine | *4,250.* | |
| **21** | A6 | 5c blue violet | 1,200. | 250.00 |
| **22** | A6 | 10c orange | 200.00 | 200.00 |

e

f

g

h

i

**Overprinted Type e, Vertically**

| | | | | |
|---|---|---|---|---|
| **23** | A6 | 1c green | 3,000. | 2,000. |
| **24** | A6 | 2c carmine | 2,000. | 300.00 |
| **25** | A6 | 5c blue violet | 500.00 | 75.00 |
| **26** | A6 | 10c orange | 75.00 | 75.00 |

**Overprinted Type f, Vertically**

| | | | | |
|---|---|---|---|---|
| **27** | A6 | 1c green | 3,000. | 2,000. |
| **28** | A6 | 2c carmine | 1,200. | 400.00 |
| **29** | A6 | 5c blue violet | 500.00 | 125.00 |
| **30** | A6 | 10c orange | 125.00 | 100.00 |

**Overprinted Type g, Vertically**

| | | | | |
|---|---|---|---|---|
| **31** | A6 | 1c green | 3,000. | 2,500. |
| **32** | A6 | 2c carmine | 2,000. | 1,000. |
| **33** | A6 | 5c blue violet | 1,600. | 250.00 |
| **34** | A6 | 10c orange | 200.00 | 150.00 |

**Overprinted Type h, Vertically**

| | | | | |
|---|---|---|---|---|
| **35** | A6 | 1c green | 3,000. | 1,500. |
| **36** | A6 | 2c carmine | 1,000. | 300.00 |
| **37** | A6 | 5c blue violet | 1,600. | 75.00 |
| **38** | A6 | 10c orange | 100.00 | 60.00 |

**Overprinted Type i, Vertically**

| | | | | |
|---|---|---|---|---|
| **39** | A6 | 1c green | *500.00* | |
| **39A** | A6 | 2c carmine | *300.00* | |
| **40** | A6 | 5c blue violet | 20.00 | |
| **41** | A6 | 10c orange | *250.00* | |

### On Issues of 1883-87

Overprinted Horizontally in Black

**1888-89**

| | | | | |
|---|---|---|---|---|
| **42** | A7 | 5c blue violet | 15.00 | 3.00 |

Overprinted Horizontally in Black

| | | | | |
|---|---|---|---|---|
| **43** | A7 | 5c blue violet | 15.00 | 3.00 |

Overprinted Horizontally in Black

| | | | | |
|---|---|---|---|---|
| **44** | A6 | 2c carmine | 4.00 | 4.00 |
| **45** | A7 | 10c orange | 4.00 | 4.00 |

Inverted overprints on Nos. 44-45 are fakes.

This overprint also exists on Costa Rica Nos. AR3 and AR4, which are normally found without gum. Value, $50 each. This overprint on Costa Rica No. AR1 is fake.

### On Issue of 1889

Overprinted Like Nos. 7-13

**1889 Horizontally**

| | | | |
|---|---|---|---|
| **47** | A8 | 2c blue | 25.00 |

**Vertically**

| | | | |
|---|---|---|---|
| **48** | A8 | 2c blue (c) | 250.00 |
| **49** | A8 | 2c blue (e) | 100.00 |
| **51** | A8 | 2c blue (f) | 100.00 |
| **52** | A8 | 2c blue (g) | 350.00 |
| **54** | A8 | 2c blue (h) | 100.00 |

Nos. 47-54 are overprinted "Correos." Stamps without "Correos" are known postally used. Unused examples are valued the same as Nos. 47-54, unused. The 1c without "Correos" is known postally used. The 1c with "Correos" is counterfeit.

On Nos. 25-33 Overprinted Horizontally in Black

**1889 *Perf. 14 and 15***

| | | | | |
|---|---|---|---|---|
| **55** | A10 | 1c brown | 10.00 | 3.50 |
| **56** | A11 | 2c dark green | 4.50 | 1.50 |
| **57** | A12 | 5c orange | 6.75 | 2.10 |
| **58** | A13 | 10c red brown | 6.75 | 2.10 |
| **59** | A14 | 20c yellow green | 1.00 | .70 |
| **60** | A15 | 50c rose red | 1.75 | 1.50 |
| **61** | A16 | 1p blue | 4.50 | 4.50 |
| **62** | A17 | 2p violet | 13.00 | 6.75 |
| **63** | A18 | 5p olive green | 60.00 | 37.50 |
| | | *Nos. 55-63 (9)* | 108.25 | 60.15 |

**Overprinted "GUAGACASTE"**

| | | | | |
|---|---|---|---|---|
| *60a* | A15 | 50c rose red | *500.00* | *325.00* |
| *61a* | A16 | 1p blue | *500.00* | *325.00* |
| *62a* | A17 | 2p violet | *750.00* | *500.00* |
| *63a* | A18 | 5p olive green | *3,000.* | *1,000.* |

Values for Nos. 60a-63a used are for examples with remainder cancels.

Overprinted Horizontally in Black

| | | | | |
|---|---|---|---|---|
| **64** | A10 | 1c brown | 2.25 | 1.50 |
| *a.* | | Vert. pair, imperf. between | | |
| **65** | A11 | 2c dark green | 2.25 | 1.50 |
| **66** | A12 | 5c orange | 2.25 | 1.50 |
| **67** | A13 | 10c red brown | 2.25 | 1.50 |
| | | *Nos. 64-67 (4)* | 9.00 | 6.00 |

# CRETE

'krēt

LOCATION — An island in the Mediterranean Sea south of Greece
GOVT. — A department of Greece
AREA — 3,235 sq. mi.
POP. — 336,150 (1913)
CAPITAL — Canea

Formerly Crete was a province of Turkey. After an extended period of civil wars, France, Great Britain, Italy and Russia intervened and declaring Crete an autonomy, placed it under the administration of Prince George of Greece as High Commissioner. In October, 1908, the Cretan Assembly voted for union with Greece and in 1913 the union was formally effected.

40 Paras = 1 Piaster
4 Metallik = 1 Grosion (1899)
100 Lepta = 1 Drachma (1900)

## Issued Under Joint Administration of France, Great Britain, Italy and Russia

### British Sphere of Administration District of Heraklion (Candia)

A1

**Handstamped**

**1898 Unwmk. *Imperf.***

| No. | Design | Description | Unused | Used |
|---|---|---|---|---|
| 1 | A1 | 20pa violet | 425.00 | 230.00 |

A2

Genuine

Forgery

Genuine: White paper, green color. The small circle with the dot centered above the denomination is complete at the bottom, the two smaller circles on either side of the straight line are not filled in.

Forgery: Yellow green color, on yellowish paper and very poor perfs. Has a dotted circle that is incomplete at the bottom, the two smaller circles on either side of the straight line are filled in.

**1898 Litho. *Perf. 11½***

| No. | Design | Description | Unused | Used |
|---|---|---|---|---|
| 2 | A2 | 10pa blue | 6.50 | 2.00 |
| a. | | Horiz. pair, imperf. btwn. | 210.00 | |
| b. | | Imperf., pair | 230.00 | |
| c. | | Horiz. pair, imperf. vert. | — | |
| 3 | A2 | 20pa green | 6.50 | 2.00 |
| a. | | Imperf., pair | 230.00 | |

**1899**

| No. | Design | Description | Unused | Used |
|---|---|---|---|---|
| 4 | A2 | 10pa brown | 6.50 | 2.00 |
| a. | | Horiz. pair, imperf. btwn. | 210.00 | |
| b. | | Imperf., pair | 230.00 | |
| 5 | A2 | 20pa rose | 6.50 | 2.00 |
| a. | | Imperf., pair | 230.00 | |

Used values for Nos. 2-5 are for stamps canceled by the straight-line "Heraklion" town postmark. Stamps canceled with any other postmark used for postal duty are scarce and worth much more. Other cancellations, values from: Ag. Thomas, $65; Ag. Myron, $70; Arkanais, $90; Episkopi, $170; Kastelli, $175; Moirais, $175; Xarakas, $190; Chersonissos, $235; and Moxos.

Counterfeits exist of Nos. 1-5.

### Russian Sphere of Administration District of Rethymnon

Coat of Arms
A3 A4

**1899 Handstamped *Imperf.***

**Laid paper**

**No Gum**

| No. | Design | Description | Unused | Used |
|---|---|---|---|---|
| 10 | A3 | 1m green | 13.50 | 5.75 |
| 11 | A3 | 2m black | 11.50 | 4.50 |
| 12 | A3 | 2m rose | 345.00 | 230.00 |
| 13 | A4 | 1m blue | 115.00 | 75.00 |

**Wove paper**

| No. | Design | Description | Unused | Used |
|---|---|---|---|---|
| 10E | A3 | 1m green | 13.00 | 5.00 |
| 11E | A3 | 2m black | 13.00 | 5.00 |
| 12E | A3 | 2m rose | 225.00 | 165.00 |
| 13E | A4 | 1m blue | 115.00 | 65.00 |

**Quadrille paper**

| No. | Design | Description | Unused | Used |
|---|---|---|---|---|
| 10J | A3 | 1m green | 375.00 | — |
| 11J | A3 | 2m black | 375.00 | 80.00 |
| 12J | A3 | 2m rose | 525.00 | |
| 13J | A4 | 1m violet | | 650.00 |

Nos. 10-13 normally have a circular control mark applied in violet or blue on blocks of four stamps. They also are known without this control mark (errors) and occasionally with the small round control marks of the next issue, in blue or violet (probably proofs). They are sometimes found with pin-perforations. Other varieties exist.

Counterfeits exist.

Poseidon's Trident — A5a
A5

**1899 Litho. *Perf. 11½***

**With Control Mark Overprinted in Violet**

**Without Stars at Sides**

| No. | Design | Description | Unused | Used |
|---|---|---|---|---|
| 14 | A5 | 1m orange | 175.00 | 115.00 |
| 15 | A5 | 2m orange | 175.00 | 115.00 |
| 16 | A5 | 1gr orange | 175.00 | 115.00 |
| 17 | A5 | 1m green | 175.00 | 115.00 |
| 18 | A5 | 2m green | 175.00 | 115.00 |
| 19 | A5 | 1gr green | 175.00 | 115.00 |
| 20 | A5 | 1m yellow | 175.00 | 115.00 |
| 21 | A5 | 2m yellow | 175.00 | 115.00 |
| 22 | A5 | 1gr yellow | 175.00 | 115.00 |
| 23 | A5 | 1m rose | 175.00 | 115.00 |
| 24 | A5 | 2m rose | 175.00 | 115.00 |
| 25 | A5 | 1gr rose | 175.00 | 115.00 |
| 26 | A5 | 1m violet | 175.00 | 115.00 |
| 27 | A5 | 2m violet | 175.00 | 115.00 |
| 28 | A5 | 1gr violet | 175.00 | 115.00 |
| 29 | A5 | 1m blue | 175.00 | 115.00 |
| 30 | A5 | 2m blue | 175.00 | 115.00 |
| 31 | A5 | 1gr blue | 175.00 | 115.00 |
| 32 | A5 | 1m black | 1,320. | 1,150. |
| 33 | A5 | 2m black | 1,320. | 1,150. |
| 34 | A5 | 1gr black | 1,320. | 1,150. |

**With Stars at Sides**

| No. | Design | Description | Unused | Used |
|---|---|---|---|---|
| 35 | A5a | 1m blue | 42.50 | 32.50 |
| 36 | A5a | 2m blue | 15.00 | 12.50 |
| 37 | A5a | 1gr blue | 13.50 | 9.00 |
| 38 | A5a | 1m rose | 165.00 | 75.00 |
| 39 | A5a | 2m rose | 15.00 | 12.50 |
| 40 | A5a | 1gr rose | 13.50 | 8.75 |
| 41 | A5a | 1m green | 42.50 | 32.50 |
| 42 | A5a | 2m green | 15.00 | 12.50 |
| 43 | A5a | 1gr green | 13.50 | 9.00 |
| 44 | A5a | 1m violet | 42.50 | 32.50 |
| 45 | A5a | 2m violet | 15.00 | 9.00 |
| 46 | A5a | 1gr violet | 13.50 | 8.75 |
| a. | | Horiz. pair, imperf. btwn. | 250.00 | |
| b. | | Vert. pair, imperf. horiz. | 190.00 | |
| | | *Nos. 35-46 (12)* | 406.50 | 254.50 |

Almost all of Nos. 14 to 46 may be found without control mark, with double control marks and in various colors.

Used values for Nos. 10-46 are for stamps with postmarks of Rethymnon. Thirteen other post offices existed, and stamps with postmarks other than Rethymnon are scarce and command significant premiums: Ag. Galini, $125; Amari, $90; Anogeia, $525; Garazo, $160; Damasta, $550; Kastelli, $125; Margaritais, $550; Melampes, $375; Pigi, $125; Roystika, $70; Xenia, $105; Spili, $105; Fodele, $550.

Counterfeits exist of Nos. 14-46.

Nos. 14-31 exist imperf. Value, unused pair each $1,150.

## Issued by the Cretan Government

Hermes
A6

Hera
A7

Prince George of Greece — A8

**1900, Mar. 1 Engr. *Perf. 14***

| No. | Design | Description | Unused | Used |
|---|---|---|---|---|
| 50 | A6 | 1 l violet brown | .45 | .45 |
| 51 | A7 | 5 l green | 1.80 | .45 |
| 52 | A8 | 10 l red | 1.35 | .45 |
| 53 | A7 | 20 l carmine rose | 5.00 | 2.25 |
| | | *Nos. 50-53 (4)* | 8.60 | 3.60 |

See #64-71. For overprints and surcharges see #54-63, 72-73, 85, 88, 93, 97-99, 108, 111.

Overprinted

**Red Overprint**

| No. | Design | Description | Unused | Used |
|---|---|---|---|---|
| 54 | A8 | 25 l blue | .80 | 1.25 |
| 55 | A6 | 50 l lilac | 2.00 | 1.35 |
| 56 | A9 | 1d gray violet | 11.50 | 13.50 |
| 57 | A10 | 2d brown | 35.00 | 35.00 |
| 58 | A11 | 5d green & blk | 185.00 | 200.00 |
| | | *Nos. 54-58 (5)* | 234.30 | 251.10 |

**Black Overprint**

| No. | Design | Description | Unused | Used |
|---|---|---|---|---|
| 59 | A8 | 25 l blue | 1.75 | .75 |
| 60 | A6 | 50 l lilac | 1.75 | 1.75 |
| 61 | A9 | 1d gray violet | 9.00 | 7.00 |
| a. | | Inverted overprint | *350.00* | *350.00* |
| 62 | A10 | 2d brown | 32.50 | 17.00 |
| 63 | A11 | 5d green & blk | 100.00 | 115.00 |
| | | *Nos. 59-63 (5)* | 145.00 | 141.50 |

Talos
A9

Minos
A10

St. George and the Dragon — A11

**1901 Without Overprint**

| No. | Design | Description | Unused | Used |
|---|---|---|---|---|
| 64 | A6 | 1 l bister | 1.00 | 1.15 |
| 65 | A7 | 20 l orange | 3.00 | 1.15 |
| 66 | A8 | 25 l blue | 8.75 | .90 |
| 67 | A6 | 50 l lilac | 37.50 | 27.50 |
| 68 | A6 | 50 l ultra | 13.50 | 13.00 |
| 69 | A9 | 1d gray violet | 40.00 | 28.00 |
| 70 | A10 | 2d brown | 13.00 | 11.50 |
| 71 | A11 | 5d green & blk | 17.50 | 13.00 |
| | | *Nos. 64-71 (8)* | 134.25 | 96.20 |

No. 64 is a revenue stamp that was used for postage for short periods in 1901 and 1904.

Types A6 to A8 in olive yellow, and types A9 to A11 in olive yellow and black are revenue stamps.

See note following No. 53.

Surcharges with the year "1922" on designs A6, A8, A9, A11, A13, A15-A23 and D1 are listed under Greece.

No. 66 Overprinted in Black

**1901**

| No. | Design | Description | Unused | Used |
|---|---|---|---|---|
| 72 | A8 | 25 l blue | 22.50 | .75 |
| a. | | First letter of ovpt. invtd. | 475.00 | 300.00 |
| b. | | Inverted overprint | 700.00 | 350.00 |
| c. | | "S" of "PROSORINON" omitted | 200.00 | 80.00 |

No. 65 Surcharged in Black

**1904, Dec.**

| No. | Design | Description | Unused | Used |
|---|---|---|---|---|
| 73 | A7 | 5 l on 20 l orange | 2.25 | .75 |
| a. | | Without "5" at right | *150.00* | *150.00* |

Mycenaean Seal
A12

Britomartis (Cortyna Coin)
A13

Prince George
A14

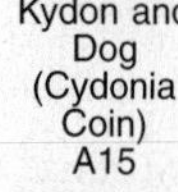

Kydon and Dog (Cydonia Coin)
A15

Triton (Itanos Coin)
A16

Ariadne (Knossos Coin)
A17

Zeus as Bull Abducting Europa (Cortyna Coin) — A18

Palace of Minos Ruins, Knossos — A19

Arkadi Monastery and Mt. Ida — A20

**1905, Feb. 15**

| No. | Design | Description | Unused | Used |
|---|---|---|---|---|
| 74 | A12 | 2 l dull violet | 1.25 | .35 |
| 75 | A13 | 5 l yellow grn | 1.50 | .35 |
| 76 | A14 | 10 l red | 1.50 | .75 |
| 77 | A15 | 20 l blue grn | 5.50 | 1.00 |
| 78 | A16 | 25 l ultra | 7.00 | 1.00 |
| 79 | A17 | 50 l yellow brn | 7.50 | 3.25 |
| 80 | A18 | 1d rose car & dp brn | 75.00 | 65.00 |
| 81 | A19 | 3d orange & blk | 50.00 | 40.00 |
| 82 | A20 | 5d ol grn & blk | 25.00 | 25.00 |
| | | *Nos. 74-82 (9)* | 174.25 | 136.70 |

For overprints see Nos. 86-87, 89, 91-92, 94-95, 104, 106, 109-110, 112-113, 115-120.

The so-called revolutionary stamps of 1905 were issued for sale to collectors and, so far as can be ascertained, were of no postal value.

A. T. A. Zaimis — A21

Prince George Landing at Suda — A22

**1907, Aug. 28**

**83** A21 25 l blue & blk 36.00 .90
**84** A22 1d green & blk 9.00 7.00

Administration under a High Commissioner.
For overprints see Nos. 90, 105, 107.

Stamps of 1900-1907 Overprinted in Black

**1908, Sept. 21**

**85** A6 1 l violet brn .60 .45
*a.* Inverted overprint —
**86** A12 2 l dull violet .60 .45
*a.* Pair, one without ovpt. —
**87** A13 5 l yellow grn .60 .45
**88** A8 10 l red 1.25 .90
*a.* Pair, one without ovpt. —
**89** A15 20 l blue grn 3.25 1.15
**90** A21 25 l blue & blk 9.00 2.75
**91** A17 50 l yellow brn 12.50 4.50
*a.* Inverted overprint
**92** A18 1d rose car & dp brn 97.50 70.00
**93** A10 2d brown 11.50 9.00
**94** A19 3d orange & blk 47.50 40.00
**95** A20 5d ol grn & blk 37.50 32.50
*Nos. 85-95 (11)* 221.80 162.15
Set, never hinged 400.00

This overprint exists inverted and double, as well as with incorrect, reversed, misplaced and omitted letters. Similar errors are found on the Postage Due and Official stamps with this overprint.

Hermes by Praxiteles — A23

**1908**

**96** A23 10 l brown red 2.75 .80
*a.* Pair, one without overprint 150.00 150.00

Nos. 96 and 114 were not regularly issued without overprint.
For overprints see Nos. 103, 114.
Genuine examples of No. 96 with overprint inverted or doubled are not known to exist.

No. 53 Surcharged

**1909**

**97** A7 5 l on 20 l car rose 230.00 *250.00*

Forgeries exist of No. 97.

**On No. 65**

**98** A7 5 l on 20 l orange 1.30 1.15
*a.* Inverted surcharge 150.00 150.00
*b.* Double surcharge 120.00 120.00

Overprinted on Nos. 64, J1

**99** A6 1 l bister 3.50 3.50
**100** D1 1 l red 1.30 1.30

No. J4 Surcharged

**101** D1 2 l on 20 l red 1.25 1.25
*b.* Inverted surcharge 75.00
*c.* Second letter of surcharge "D" instead of "P" 50.00 50.00

No. J4 Surcharged

**102** D1 2 l on 20 l red 1.25 1.25
*a.* Double overprint *125.00* *125.00*

**Overprinted in Black**

a

b

c

**103** A23(a) 10 l brown red 3.00 1.15
*a.* Inverted overprint 110.00
**104** A15(a) 20 l blue grn 4.00 1.15
**105** A21(c) 25 l blue & blk 5.50 2.00
**106** A17(a) 50 l yellow brn 7.75 4.25
**107** A22(b) 1d green & blk 12.50 7.25
**108** A10(a) 2d brown 12.50 10.50
**109** A19(b) 3d org & blk 127.50 115.00
**110** A20(b) 5d ol grn & blk 52.50 52.50
*Nos. 103-110 (8)* 225.25 193.80

Stamps of 1900-08 Overprinted in Red or Black

**1909-10**

**111** A6 1 l violet brown .35 .25
**112** A12 2 l dull violet .35 .25
**113** A13 5 l yellow green .35 .25
**114** A23 10 l brown red (Bk) .60 .60
**115** A15 20 l blue green 2.00 .75
**116** A16 25 l ultra 2.50 .80
**117** A17 50 l yellow brn 7.00 2.25
**118** A18 1d rose car & dp brn (Bk) 100.00 100.00
**119** A19 3d orange & blk 85.00 85.00
**120** A20 5d ol grn & blk 55.00 55.00
*Nos. 111-120 (10)* 253.15 245.15

**POSTAGE DUE STAMPS**

D1

**1901 Unwmk. Litho. *Perf. 14***

**J1** D1 1 l red .30 .30
**J2** D1 5 l red .50 .30
**J3** D1 10 l red .75 .45
**J4** D1 20 l red 1.00 *.50*
**J5** D1 40 l red 11.50 11.50
**J6** D1 50 l red 11.50 11.50
**J7** D1 1d red 22.50 22.50
**J8** D1 2d red 14.50 12.50
*Nos. J1-J8 (8)* 62.55 59.55
Set, never hinged 115.00

For overprints and surcharges see Nos. 100-102, J9-J26.

Surcharged in Black

**1901**

**J9** D1 1d on 1d red 11.50 10.00

Overprinted in Black

**1908**

**J10** D1 1 l red .35 .35
**J11** D1 5 l red .60 .60
**J12** D1 10 l red .60 .60
**J13** D1 20 l red 2.00 2.00
**J14** D1 40 l red 8.50 7.50
**J15** D1 50 l red 11.00 9.00
**J16** D1 1d red 475.00 475.00
*a.* Pair, one without ovpt. —
**J17** D1 1d on 1d red 11.50 10.00
**J18** D1 2d red 19.00 10.00
*Nos. J10-J18 (9)* 528.55 515.05

Nos. J10-J18 exist with inverted overprint. See note after No. 95.
Counterfeits of No. J16 exist.

Overprinted in Black

**1910**

**J19** D1 1 l red .45 .30
**J20** D1 5 l red 1.00 .35
**J21** D1 10 l red 1.00 .35
**J22** D1 20 l red 3.25 1.75
**J23** D1 40 l red 11.00 6.00
**J24** D1 50 l red 16.50 12.00
**J25** D1 1d red 27.50 27.50
**J26** D1 2d red 27.50 27.50
*Nos. J19-J26 (8)* 88.20 75.75

**OFFICIAL STAMPS**

O1

O2

**Unwmk.**

**1908, Jan. 14 Litho. *Perf. 14***

**O1** O1 10 l dull claret 18.00 1.50
**O2** O2 30 l blue 37.50 1.50

Nos. O1-O2 exist imperf.

Nos. O1-O2 Overprinted

**O3** O1 10 l dull claret 13.00 1.20
*a.* Inverted overprint 115.00 115.00
**O4** O2 30 l blue 27.50 1.30
*a.* Inverted overprint 200.00 200.00

See note after No. 95.

Nos. O1-O2 Overprinted

**1910**

**O5** O1 10 l dull claret 2.25 1.30
**O6** O2 30 l blue 2.25 1.30

Nos. O5-O6 remained in use until 1922, nine years after union with Greece.

# CROATIA

krō-ˈā-sh(ē-)ə

LOCATION — Southeastern Europe
GOVT. — Independent state
AREA — 44,453 sq. mi.
POP. — 7,000,000 (approx.)
CAPITAL — Zagreb

The Independent Croatian State of 1941-45 became part of the Yugoslav Federation in 1945.

Croatia declared its independence in 1991.

100 Paras = 1 Dinar
100 Banica = 1 Kuna

**Catalogue values for unused stamps in this country are for Never Hinged items, beginning with Scott 1 in the regular postage section, Scott B1 in the semi-postal section, Scott C1 in the airmail section and Scott RA1 in the postal tax section.**

**Watermark**

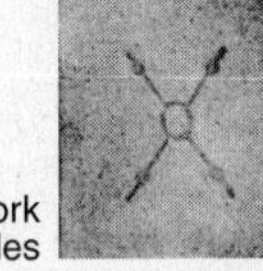

Wmk. 278 — Network Connecting Circles

Yugoslavia Nos. 143 to 148B Overprinted in Black

***Perf. 12½***

**1941, Apr. 12 Unwmk. Typo.**

**1** A16 50p orange 4.50 3.75
*a.* Inverted overprint 225.00
**2** A16 1d yellow grn 5.25 3.75
*a.* Double overprint 110.00
**3** A16 1.50d red 6.00 2.25
*a.* Double overprint 110.00
**4** A16 2d deep magenta 6.75 3.75
**5** A16 3d dull red brn 11.00 6.75
*a.* Double overprint 110.00
**6** A16 4d ultra 15.00 7.50
**7** A16 5d dark blue 18.50 8.25
**8** A16 5.50d dk violet brn 22.50 9.00
*a.* Double overprint 110.00
*Nos. 1-8 (8)* 89.50 45.00

Counterfeit overprints exist of Nos. 1-8, especially the inverted and double overprint varieties.

Yugoslavia Nos. 142 to 154 Overprinted in Black

**1941, Apr. 21**

**9** A16 25p black .75 .50
*a.* Inverted overprint 75.00
*b.* Double overprint 75.00
**10** A16 50p orange .75 .50
*a.* Inverted overprint 75.00
**11** A16 1d yellow grn .75 .50
*a.* Inverted overprint
**12** A16 1.50d red .80 .50
*a.* Double overprint 150.00
**13** A16 2d deep magenta .80 .50
**14** A16 3d dull red brn 1.10 .95
**15** A16 4d ultra 1.50 1.40
**16** A16 5d dark blue 1.90 1.40
*a.* Double overprint 200.00
**17** A16 5.50d dk violet brn 2.25 1.40
*a.* Inverted overprint 375.00
*b.* Double overprint 200.00
**18** A16 6d slate blue 3.00 2.25
**19** A16 8d sepia 3.75 2.25
**20** A16 12d brt violet 4.50 3.00
*a.* Inverted overprint 375.00
**21** A16 16d dull violet 5.25 4.50
*a.* Double overprint 200.00
**22** A16 20d blue 6.75 5.25
**23** A16 30d bright pink 12.00 10.00
*Nos. 9-23 (15)* 45.85 34.90

The overprint exists double, both inverted, on Nos. 16, 18 and 19.

Yugoslavia Nos. 147, 148 Surcharged in Black

**1941, May 16**

| No. | Type | Description | Unused | Used |
|---|---|---|---|---|
| 24 | A16 | 1d on 3d dull red brn | .40 | .40 |
| *a.* | | Inverted overprint | 75.00 | |
| *b.* | | Double overprint | 75.00 | |
| 25 | A16 | 2d on 4d ultra | .40 | .40 |
| *a.* | | Inverted overprint | 75.00 | |
| *b.* | | Double overprint | 75.00 | |

Postage Due Stamps of Yugoslavia, Nos. J28, J30 to J32, Overprinted in Black

**1941, May 17**

| No. | Type | Description | Unused | Used |
|---|---|---|---|---|
| 26 | D4 | 50p violet | .50 | .45 |
| 27 | D4 | 2d deep blue | 1.35 | 1.25 |
| 28 | D4 | 5d orange | 1.90 | 1.40 |
| 29 | D4 | 10d chocolate | 2.25 | 1.60 |
| | | *Nos. 26-29 (4)* | 6.00 | 4.70 |

Counterfeit cancellations exist for Nos. 1-29 on cover.

---

**Imperforates**

Nearly all Croatian stamps, from No. 30 through 80, B3 through B76, J6 through J25, O1 through O24 and RA1 through RA7 exist imperforate, imperforate vertically, and imperforate horizontally. These are primarily from the special Ministerial Albums issued by the State Printing Office.

---

Ozalj Castle — A1

Designs: 50b, City of Jajce. 75b, Old Warasdin. 1k, Velebit Mountains. 1.50k, Zelanjak. 2k, Zagreb Cathedral. 3k, Osjek Cathedral. 4k, Drina River. No. 38, Konjic. No. 39, Zemun. 6k, Dubrovnik. 7k, Save River. 8k, Sarajevo. 10k, Plitvice. 12k, Klis Fortress, Split. 20k, Hvar. 30k, Syrmia. 50k, Senj. 100k, Banjaluka (without "F.I.").

*Perf. 11¼.*

**1941-43 Unwmk. Photo.**

**Ordinary Paper**

| No. | Type | Description | Unused | Used |
|---|---|---|---|---|
| 30 | A1 | 25b henna | .25 | .25 |
| 31 | A1 | 50b slate blue | .25 | .25 |
| 32 | A1 | 75b dk olive grn | .25 | .25 |
| 33 | A1 | 1k Pruss grn | .25 | .25 |
| 34 | A1 | 1.50k deep green | .25 | .25 |
| 35 | A1 | 2k carmine lake | .25 | .25 |
| 36 | A1 | 3k brown red | .25 | .25 |
| 37 | A1 | 4k deep ultra | .25 | .25 |
| 38 | A1 | 5k black | 2.00 | 1.15 |
| 39 | A1 | 5k blue | .25 | .25 |
| 40 | A1 | 6k lt olive brn | .25 | .25 |
| 41 | A1 | 7k orange red | .30 | .25 |
| 42 | A1 | 8k chestnut | .40 | .30 |
| 43 | A1 | 10k dark plum | .90 | .45 |
| 44 | A1 | 12k olive brown | 1.50 | .50 |
| 45 | A1 | 20k golden brown | 1.10 | .40 |
| 46 | A1 | 30k black brown | 1.50 | .50 |
| 47 | A1 | 50k dk slate green | 3.75 | 1.50 |
| 48 | A1 | 100k violet | 5.25 | 3.50 |
| | | *Nos. 30-48 (19)* | 19.20 | *11.05* |

Nos. 30-48 exist with a variety of perforations, including 11¼x10¾ and 12. Examples of Nos. 30, 36 and 48 exist with a special printer's mark in the design. Two varieties of printer's mark are known for No. 30, one for the first printing, and one for the second. Usually one stamp per pane has the printer's mark.

Nos. 31, 35 and 43 exist on thin to pelure paper, as does No. 32, though the latter was not issued to the public. Shades of all values exist.

For overprints and surcharge see Nos. 49-51, 53.

**Tête bêche Pairs**

| No. | Type | Value | Unused | Used |
|---|---|---|---|---|
| *30a* | A1 | 25b | 1.75 | *2.75* |
| *31a* | A1 | 50b | 2.00 | *3.50* |
| *33a* | A1 | 1k | 2.50 | *4.00* |
| *34a* | A1 | 1.50k | 2.75 | *5.00* |
| *35a* | A1 | 2k | 3.00 | *6.00* |
| *37a* | A1 | 4k | 3.95 | *6.50* |
| *38a* | A1 | 5k | 7.00 | *7.50* |
| *40a* | A1 | 6k | 4.00 | *7.00* |
| *41a* | A1 | 7k | 4.50 | *7.25* |
| *42a* | A1 | 8k | 5.00 | *8.00* |
| *43a* | A1 | 10k | 5.50 | *9.50* |
| *45a* | A1 | 20k | 6.50 | *10.00* |
| *46a* | A1 | 30k | 7.25 | *11.00* |
| *47a* | A1 | 50k | 13.00 | *13.00* |
| | | *Nos. 30a-47a (14)* | 68.70 | *101.00* |

Types of 1941 Overprinted in Brown or Green

**1942, Apr. 9**

| No. | Type | Description | Unused | Used |
|---|---|---|---|---|
| 49 | A1 | 2k dark brown | .60 | .40 |
| 50 | A1 | 5k dark carmine | .90 | .85 |
| 51 | A1 | 10k dark blue green (G) | 1.50 | 1.25 |
| | | *Nos. 49-51 (3)* | 3.00 | *2.50* |

First anniversary of Croatian independence.

The overprint exists double on No. 50.

Tête bêche pairs of Nos. 49-51 are from Ministerial Albums.

Banjaluka ("F.I." at upper right) — A20

**1942, June 13**

| No. | Type | Description | Unused | Used |
|---|---|---|---|---|
| 52 | A20 | 100k violet | 4.25 | 4.25 |

Banjaluka Philatelic Exhibition.

No. 52 exists in se-tenant pair with No. 48. Value unused, $300.

No. 52 exists with a special printer's mark in the design. The mark typically appears on one stamp in a given pane.

**No. 35 Surcharged in Red Brown with New Value and Bar**

**1942, June 23**

| No. | Type | Description | Unused | Used |
|---|---|---|---|---|
| 53 | A1 | 25b on 2k carmine lake | .55 | .55 |
| *a.* | | Tête bêche pair | 3.25 | 3.25 |

No. 53 exists with double surcharge. It is not scarce.

Trakoscan Castle — A21

Design: 12.50k, Citadel of Veliki Tabor.

**1943, Mar. 28 Pelure Paper**

| No. | Type | Description | Unused | Used |
|---|---|---|---|---|
| 54 | A21 | 3.50k brown carmine | .75 | .55 |
| 55 | A21 | 12.50k violet black | 1.00 | .85 |

Nos. 54 was reissued in 1944 on ordinary paper, perf 12. Value the same for both varieties. No. 55 also exists on ordinary paper. It is scarce.

Catherine Zrinski — A23

2k, Fran Krsto Frankopan. 3.50k, Peter Zrinski.

**Various Frames**

**1943, June 7 Engr.** ***Perf. 12¼x12½***

| No. | Type | Description | Unused | Used |
|---|---|---|---|---|
| 56 | A23 | 1k dark blue | .40 | .40 |
| 57 | A23 | 2k dark olive green | .40 | .40 |
| 58 | A23 | 3.50k dark red | .50 | *.55* |
| | | *Nos. 56-58 (3)* | 1.30 | *1.35* |

Many perforation varieties of this issue exist, including 12x12½, 12½x13, 12½, 13, 12½x14, 13x12½, and 14x12½.

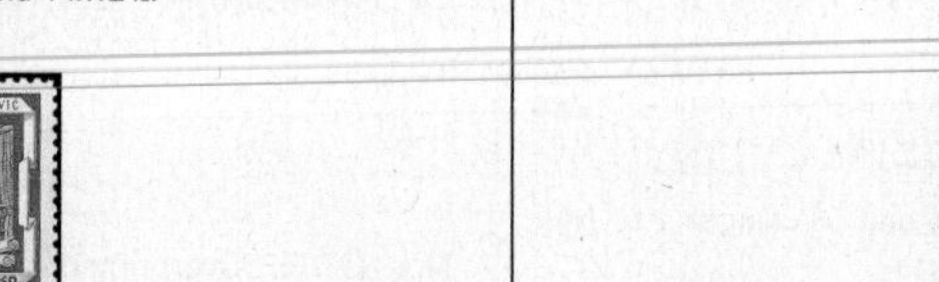


Rudjer Boscovich — A26

**1943, Dec. 13** ***Perf. 11***

| No. | Type | Description | Unused | Used |
|---|---|---|---|---|
| 59 | A26 | 3.50k copper red | .50 | .40 |
| 60 | A26 | 12.50k dk violet brn | .65 | .50 |

Rugjer Boscovich (1711-1787). Mathematician and physicist.

No. 60 exists with a special printer's mark in the design. The mark typically appears on one stamp in a given pane.

Ante Pavelich — A27

**1943-44 Litho.** ***Perf. 12½, 14***

| No. | Type | Description | Unused | Used |
|---|---|---|---|---|
| 61 | A27 | 25b orange ver | .30 | .25 |
| 62 | A27 | 50b Prus blue | .30 | .25 |
| 63 | A27 | 75b olive green | .30 | .25 |
| 64 | A27 | 1k lt green | .30 | .25 |
| 65 | A27 | 1.50k dull gray vio | .30 | .25 |
| 66 | A27 | 2k rose lake | .30 | .25 |
| 67 | A27 | 3k rose brown | .30 | .25 |
| 68 | A27 | 3.50k bright blue | .30 | .25 |
| *a.* | | 3.50k dark blue, perf. 11½ | 4.00 | *4.75* |
| 69 | A27 | 4k brt red violet | .30 | .25 |
| 70 | A27 | 5k ultra | .30 | .25 |
| 71 | A27 | 8k orange brn | .35 | .25 |
| 72 | A27 | 9k rose pink | .35 | .25 |
| 73 | A27 | 10k violet brn | .40 | .25 |
| 74 | A27 | 12k dk olive bis | .45 | .25 |
| 75 | A27 | 12.50k gray black | .55 | .25 |
| 76 | A27 | 18k dull brown | .70 | .30 |
| 77 | A27 | 32k dark brown | .75 | .30 |
| 78 | A27 | 50k grnsh blue | 1.50 | .50 |
| 79 | A27 | 70k orange | 1.90 | .90 |
| 80 | A27 | 100k violet | 3.00 | 1.50 |
| | | *Nos. 61-80 (20)* | 12.95 | 7.25 |

Nos. 61, 63, 70, and 77 measure 20½x26mm. Nos. 62, 64-69, 71-76, and 78-80 measure 22x27½mm.

Nos. 61, 63, 67, 70, 71 and 72 are perf 12½. Nos. 62, 64-66, 68, 69, 73 and 75-80 are perf 14. No. 74 exists either perf 12½ or 14.

No. 80 exists with a special printer's mark in the design. The mark typically appears on one stamp in a given pane.

Issue dates: 2k, 1943; No. 68a, June 13, 1943, Pavelich's Saint's Day; others, 1944.

"Labor Day 1945" — A28

**1945 Photo.** ***Perf. 11½***

| No. | Type | Description | Unused | Used |
|---|---|---|---|---|
| 81 | A28 | 3.50k red brown | .85 | *1.60* |

No. 81 exists imperforate. Value, never hinged $900.

**From 1951 to 1972 44 labels were circulated by a Croatian Government in Exile. These had no postal value.**

GOVT. — Independent state
AREA — 21,823 sq. mi.
POP. — 4,676,865 (1999 est.)
CAPITAL — Zagreb

Croatia declared its independence from Yugoslavia in 1991.

100 Paras = 1 Dinar (1991)
100 Lipa = 1 Kuna (1994)

Nos. RA20, RA20a Srchd. in Black and Gold

**1991, Nov. 21 Litho.** ***Perf. 14***

| No. | Type | Description | Unused | Used |
|---|---|---|---|---|
| 100 | PT10 | 4d on 1.20d #RA20 | .70 | .70 |
| *a.* | | Perf. 11x10½ | .50 | .50 |
| *b.* | | Perf. 11 | 7.50 | 7.50 |

A35

**1991, Dec. 10** ***Perf. 12***

| No. | Type | Description | Unused | Used |
|---|---|---|---|---|
| 101 | A35 | 30d multicolored | 2.00 | 2.00 |

Declaration of independence, 10/8/91.

Christmas — A36

Creche figures of the Holy Family from Kosljun Monastery.

**1991, Dec. 11** ***Perf. 12***

| No. | Type | Description | Unused | Used |
|---|---|---|---|---|
| 102 | A36 | 4d multicolored | .80 | .80 |

No. RA21 Surcharged in Black and Gold

**1992, Jan. 3** ***Perf. 10½x11***

| No. | Type | Description | Unused | Used |
|---|---|---|---|---|
| 103 | PT11 | 20d on 1.70d #RA21 | 5.75 | 5.75 |

Croatian Arms — A37

**1992, Jan. 15** ***Perf. 11x10½***

| No. | Type | Description | Unused | Used |
|---|---|---|---|---|
| 104 | A37 | 10d multicolored | .60 | .60 |
| *a.* | | Perf. 14 | .40 | .40 |

See No. RA22.

1992 Winter Olympics, Albertville — A38

**1992, Feb. 4** ***Perf. 11x10½***

| No. | Type | Description | Unused | Used |
|---|---|---|---|---|
| 105 | A38 | 30d multicolored | *1.50* | *1.50* |

Croatian Cities and Landmarks — A39

A39a

Designs: 6d, Knin. 7d, Eltz Castle, Vukovar. 20d, Church, Ilok. 30d, Starcevic Street, Gospic. 45d, Rector's Palace, Dubrovnik. 50d, St. Jakov's Cathedral, Sibenik. 100d, Vinkovci. 200d, Pazin, vert. No. 115, Beli Manastir. 500d, Slavonski Brod. 1000d, Varazdin. 2000d, Karlovac. 5000d, Zadar, vert. 10,000d, Vis.

**1992-94** ***Perf. 14***

| No. | Type | Description | Unused | Used |
|---|---|---|---|---|
| 107 | A39 | 6d multi | *.25* | *.25* |
| 108 | A39 | 7d multi | *.25* | *.25* |
| 109 | A39 | 20d multi | *.35* | *.35* |
| *a.* | | Perf. 11x10½ | *1.00* | *1.00* |
| 110 | A39 | 30d multi | *.90* | *.90* |
| 111 | A39 | 45d multi | *.90* | *.90* |
| 112 | A39 | 50d multi | *.90* | *.90* |
| 113 | A39a | 100d multi | *.65* | *.65* |
| 114 | A39a | 200d multi | *.35* | *.35* |
| 115 | A39 | 300d multi | *2.00* | *2.00* |
| 117 | A39a | 500d multi | *1.90* | *1.90* |
| 118 | A39a | 1000d multi | *1.00* | *.70* |
| 119 | A39a | 2000d multi | *2.00* | *1.50* |
| 120 | A39a | 5000d multi | *3.00* | *2.50* |
| 121 | A39a | 10,000d multi | *5.50* | *5.00* |
| | | *Nos. 107-121 (14)* | *19.95* | *18.15* |

Issued: 6d, 4/18; 7d, 4/8; No. 109, 2/28; No. 109a, 9/9; 30d, 5/21; 45d, 4/14; 50d, 4/28; 115, 6/26; 100d, 12/14; 500d, 2/9/93; 1000d, 3/16/93; 200d, 4/9/93; 2000d, 5/20/93; 5000d, 9/24/93; 10,000d, 2/22/94.

See Nos. 355-356, 437A, 456.

Statue of King Tomislav — A40

**1992, May 5 Engr. *Perf. 12½ Horiz.***
**Coil Stamp**

124 A40 10d dark green .40 .40

Railroad Station, Zagreb, Cent. — A41

**1992, June 30 Litho. *Perf. 14***

125 A41 30d multicolored .40 .30

Matica, Society of Knowledge and Literacy, 150th Anniv. — A42

**1992, July 8**

126 A42 20d red, gold & black .35 .30

Bishop Josip Juraj Strossmayer, Founder — A43

**1992, July 9**

127 A43 30d multicolored .40 .40

Croatian Academy of Arts and Sciences, 125th anniv., in 1991.

1992 Summer Olympics, Barcelona — A44

Design: 105d, Abstract design.

**1992, July 25**

128 A44 40d shown .30 .30
129 A44 105d multicolored 1.25 1.25

Flowers — A45

Designs: 30d, Edraianthus pumilio. 85d, Degenia velebitica, vert.

**1992, July 28**

130 A45 30d multicolored .35 .35
131 A45 85d multicolored .90 .90

Wildlife — A46

40d, Monticola solitarius. 75d, Elaphe situla.

**1992, July 31**

132 A46 40d multicolored .45 .45
133 A46 75d multicolored .85 .85

Discovery of America, 500th Anniv. — A47

Europa: 30d, 60d, Sailing ship. 75d, 130d, Indian in Chicago, by Ivan Mestrovic (1883-1962).

**1992, Sep. 4 Litho. *Perf. 14***

134 A47 30d multicolored *.55 .55*
135 A47 60d multicolored *1.15 1.15*
136 A47 75d red & black *1.30 1.30*
137 A47 130d red, blk & gold *2.00 2.00*
*Nos. 134-137 (4) 5.00 5.00*

Issued: 30d, 75d, July 31; others, Sept. 4.

A48

**1992, Oct. 2**

138 A48 40d reddish org & blue .35 .35
139 A48 130d pale blue & pur 1.00 1.00

Declaration of Croatian Literary Language, 25th Anniv. (No. 138). Spelling reform by Dr. Ivan Broz, cent. (No. 139).

City of Samobor, 750th Anniv. — A49

**1992, Oct. 16**

140 A49 90d multicolored .65 .40

Gift of the St. Juraj Church by Archbishop Mucimir, 1100th Anniv. — A50

**1992, Oct. 30**

141 A50 60d multicolored .40 .30

Reign of King Bela IV, 750th Anniv. — A51

**1992, Nov. 16 Litho. *Perf. 14***

142 A51 180d multicolored .85 .85

Christmas — A52

**1992, Dec. 7**

143 A52 80d multicolored .40 .35

Blaz Lorkovic (1839-1892), Scientist — A53

**1992, Dec. 21**

144 A53 250d multicolored .90 .90

Kolo Literature Review, 150th Anniv. — A54

**1992, Dec. 22**

145 A54 300d multicolored 1.10 1.10

Ivan Bunic-Vucic (1592-1658) — A55

**1992, Dec. 29**

146 A55 350d multicolored 1.10 1.10

800th Anniv. of Krapina — A55a

**1993, Jan. 15**

146A A55a 300d multicolored .70 .70

Nikola Tesla (1856-1943), Physicist — A56

**1993, Jan. 30**

147 A56 250d multicolored .70 .70

Self-Portrait, by Ferdo Quiquerez (1845-1893) — A57

**1993, Feb. 10**

148 A57 100d multicolored .40 .40

Wildlife — A58

500d, Cervus elaphus. 550d, Haliaeetus albicilla.

**1993, Feb. 23 Litho. *Perf. 14***

149 A58 500d multi 1.00 1.00
150 A58 550d multi 1.00 1.00

Self-Portrait, by Zlatko Sulentic (1893-1971) — A59

**1993, Mar. 17**

151 A59 350d multicolored .55 .55

Lipik Health and Convalescent Home, Cent. — A60

**1993, Apr. 22 Litho. *Perf. 14***

152 A60 400d multicolored .55 .55

Ivan Goran Kovacic (1913-1943), Author — A61

**1993, Apr. 24**

153 A61 200d multicolored .35 .35

59th PEN Congress, Dubrovnik — A62

**1993, Apr. 24**

154 A62 800d multicolored 1.25 1.25

Ivan Kukuljevic (1816-89), Politician, Historian, Writer — A63

**1993, May 2 Litho. *Perf. 14***

155 A63 500d multicolored .65 .65

Croatian Natl. Theatre, Split, Cent. — A64

**1993, May 6 Litho. *Perf. 14***

156 A64 600d multicolored .75 .75

Pag, 500th Anniv. — A65

**1993, May 18**

157 A65 800d multicolored .75 .75

Croatian Membership in United Nations, 1st Anniv. — A66

**1993, May 22**

158 A66 500d multicolored .60 .60

Europa — A67

Contemporary paintings by: 700d, Ivo Dulcic (1916-75). 1000d, Miljenko Stancic (1926-77). 1100d, Ljubo Ivancic (b. 1925).

**1993, June 5**

159 A67 700d multicolored *.75 .75*
160 A67 1000d multicolored *1.50 1.50*
161 A67 1100d multicolored *2.25 2.25*
*a.* Min. sheet, 2 each #159-161 *9.00 9.00*
*Nos. 159-161 (3) 4.50 4.50*

Intl. Art Biennial, Venice — A68

Works of art by: 250d, Milivoj Bijelic. 600d, Ivo Dekovic. 1000d, Zeljko Kipke.

**1993, June 10 Litho. *Perf. 14***

162 A68 250d multicolored .30 .30
*a.* Souvenir sheet of 4 1.00 1.00
163 A68 600d multicolored .85 .85
*a.* Souvenir sheet of 4 3.00 3.00
164 A68 1000d multicolored 1.20 1.20
*a.* Souvenir sheet of 4 4.00 4.00
*Nos. 162-164 (3)* 2.35 2.35

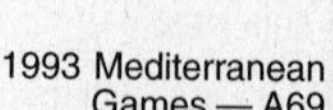

1993 Mediterranean Games — A69

**1993, June 15 Litho. *Perf. 14***

**165** A69 700d multicolored .65 .65

Adolf Waldinger (1843-1904), Painter — A70

**1993, June 16**

**166** A70 300d multicolored .35 .35

Famous Croatian Battles — A71

800d, Krbavskom, 1493. 1300d, Sisak, 1593.

**1993, July 6 Litho. *Perf. 14***

**167** A71 800d multi .65 .65
**168** A71 1300d multi 1.10 1.10

Miroslav Krleza (1893-1981), Writer — A72

**1993, July 7**

**169** A72 400d multicolored .40 .40

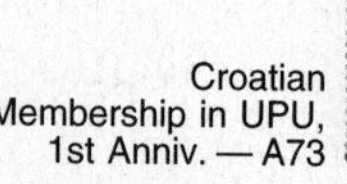

Croatian Membership in UPU, 1st Anniv. — A73

**1993, July 20 Litho. *Perf. 14***

**170** A73 1800d multicolored 1.25 .80

Vlaho Paljetak (1893-1944), Composer — A74

**1993, Aug. 7**

**171** A74 500d multicolored .45 .45

Stamp Day — A75

**1993, Sept. 9 Litho. *Perf. 14***

**172** A75 600d multicolored .50 .50

Map of Istria, 1620 — A76

**1993, Sept. 20**

**173** A76 2200d multicolored 1.20 1.20

Incorporation of Istria, Rijeka and Zadar into Croatia, 50th anniv.

Tadija Smiciklas (1843-1914), Historian — A77

**1993, Oct. 1**

**174** A77 800d black, gold & red .60 .60

Archaelogical Museum, Split, Cent. — A78

**1993, Oct. 27**

**175** A78 1000d multicolored .60 .60

A79

**1993, Nov. 17 Litho. *Perf. 14***

**176** A79 3000d multicolored 1.50 1.50

Uprising of 13th Pioneer Battalion, Villefranche-de-Rouergue, France, 50th anniv.

A80

Josip Eugen Tomic (1843-1906), writer.

**1993, Nov. 18**

**177** A80 900d multicolored .50 .50

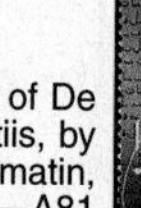

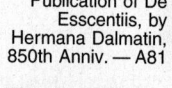

Publication of De Essentiis, by Hermana Dalmatin, 850th Anniv. — A81

**1993, Nov. 30**

**178** A81 1000d multicolored .50 .50

Christmas — A82

Paintings: 1000d, Christmas at the Front, by Miroslav Sutej. 4000d, Birth of Christ, 15th cent. fresco, Marienkirch of Dvigrad.

**1993, Dec. 3**

**179** A82 1000d multicolored 1.00 1.00
**180** A82 4000d multicolored 2.00 2.00

Nos. 179-180 are known with gold omitted. Values: No. 179, $90 mint; No. 180, $175 mint.

Organized Skiing in Croatia, Cent. — A83

**1993, Dec. 15**

**181** A83 1000d multicolored .80 .80

Croatian Natl. Guard, 125th Anniv. — A84

**1993, Dec. 22**

**182** A84 1100d multicolored .80 .80

Printers of Senj, 500th Anniv. — A85

**1994, Jan. 29**

**183** A85 2200d multicolored 1.10 .80

1994 Winter Olympics, Lillehammer — A86

**1994, Feb. 12**

**184** A86 4000d multicolored 1.90 1.60

Dinosaurs from Western Istria — A87

a, 2400d, Iguanodons. b, 4000d, Map, skeleton.

**1994, Mar. 7**

**185** A87 Pair, #a.-b. 3.25 3.25

Nos. 185a-185b are a continuous design.

Zora Dalmatinska Magazine, 150th Anniv. — A88

**1994, Mar. 15**

**186** A88 800d multicolored .50 .35

Croatian University, Zagreb, 325th Anniv. — A89

Design: 2200d, University building, Emperor Leopold I's seal, vice-chancellor's chain.

**1994, Apr. 19 Litho. *Perf. 14***

**187** A89 2200d multicolored 1.10 .75

Protect the Environment — A90

**1994, Apr. 22 Litho. *Perf. 14***

**188** A90 3800d Canis lupus 2.00 1.75

ILO, 75th Anniv. — A91

**1994, May 2**

**189** A91 1000d multicolored .60 .40

A92

Europa — A93

European inventions, discoveries: 3800d, Faust Vrancic (1551-1617), parachute. 4000d, Slavoljub Penkala (1871-1922), fountain pen.

**1994, May 16**

**190** A92 3800d multicolored *2.25 2.00*
**191** A93 4000d multicolored *2.75 2.00*

Flowers — A94

2.40k, Iris croatica. 4k, Colchicum visianii.

**1994, June 3**

**192** A94 2.40k multicolored 1.00 .60
**193** A94 4k multicolored 1.60 1.25

A95

Drazen Petrovic (1964-93), basketball player.

**1994, June 7**

**194** A95 1k multicolored .75 .75

Tourism in Croatia, 150th Anniv. — A96

Designs: 80 l, Plitvice Lakes Natl. Park. 1k, Waterfalls, Krka River. 1.10k, Kornati Islands Natl. Park. 2.20k, Kopacki Trscak nature reserve. 2.40k Sailboats, Opatijska Riviera resort. 3.80k, Brijuni islands. 4k, Trakoscan castle, Zagorje.

**1994, June 15 Litho. *Perf. 14***

**196** A96 80 l multicolored .45 .25
**197** A96 1k multicolored .50 .30
**198** A96 1.10k multicolored .55 .35
**199** A96 2.20k multicolored 1.25 .40
**200** A96 2.40k multicolored 1.40 .60
**201** A96 3.80k multicolored 2.10 .75
**202** A96 4k multicolored 2.40 1.00
*a.* Min. sheet of 7, #196-202 + 2 labels 8.50 8.00
*Nos. 196-202 (7)* 8.65 3.65

Croatian Musicians — A97

Designs: 1k, Kresimir Baranovic (1894-1975), composer, vert. 2.20k, Vatroslav Lisinski (1819-54), composer, vert. 2.40k, Pauline song-book (1644), harpist.

**1994, June 20**

**211** A97 1k multicolored .50 .35
**212** A97 2.20k multicolored 1.10 .75
**213** A97 2.40k multicolored 1.25 .85
*Nos. 211-213 (3)* 2.85 1.95

Croatian Fraternal Union, Cent. — A98

**1994, Aug. 15 Litho. *Perf. 14***

**214** A98 2.20k multicolored 1.25 1.25

Intl. Year of the Family — A99

**1994, Aug. 31**

**215** A99 80 l multicolored .50 .50

A100

**1994, Sept. 10**

**216** A100 1k multicolored .60 .60

Intl. Olympic Committee, cent.

Visit of Pope John Paul II — A101

**1994, Sept. 10**

**217** A101 1k multicolored .75 .75

No. 217 printed with se-tenant label.

Antoine de Saint-Exupery (1900-44), Aviator, Author — A102

**1994, Sept. 20**

**218** A102 3.80k multicolored 1.90 1.40

13th Intl. Congress on Early Christian Archeology — A103

**1994, Sept. 23**

**219** A103 4k multicolored 2.00 1.40

No. 219 printed with se-tenant label.

Modern Croatian Paintings A104

Designs: 2.40k, Still Life with Fruits and Basket, by Marino Tartaglia, 1926. 3.80k, In the Park, by Milan Steiner, c. 1918. 4k, Self-portrait, by Vilko Gecan, 1929.

**1994, Oct. 12**

**220** A104 2.40k multicolored 1.00 .75
**221** A104 3.80k multicolored 1.60 1.25
**222** A104 4k multicolored 1.75 1.25
*Nos. 220-222 (3)* 4.35 3.25

Ivan Belostenec (1594-1675), Writer & Lexicographer — A105

**1994, Nov. 9**

**223** A105 2.20k multicolored 1.10 .90

City of Zagreb, Zagreb Bishopric, 900th Anniv. — A106

Designs: No. 224a, 1k, Zagreb exchange building, designed by V. Kovacic, S. Penkala's airplane, Cibona office tower, designed by Hrzic, Pitesa and Serbetic. b, 1k, Maxi Cat, by Zlatko Grgic, Zagreb School of Animated Film. c, 1k, St. Mark's Church, Gradec; photo of gas lantern, by Toso Dabac. d, 4k, Late Gothic bishop's staff, Valvasor's view of Zagreb.

13.50k, Zagreb street scene, Penkala's airplane, vert.

**1994, Nov. 16**

**224** A106 Strip of 4, #a.-d. 3.00 3.00

**Souvenir Sheet**

**225** A106 13.50k multicolored 5.00 5.00

No. 224 is a continuous design. No. 225 contains one 24x48mm stamp.

Christmas — A107

Design: 1k, Epiphany, by unknown sculptor.

**1994, Dec. 1 Litho. *Perf. 14***

**226** A107 1k multicolored .60 .50

Virgin Mary's Sanctuary, Loreto, 700th Anniv. — A108

Design: 4k, The Moving of the Holy House, by Giovanni Battista Tiepolo.

**1994, Dec. 10**

**227** A108 4k multicolored 2.00 1.50

Necktie in Croatia — A109

Tie designs: 1.10k, Businessman's, 1995. 3.80k, English Dandy, 1810. 4k, Croatian soldier, 1630.

**1995, Jan. 19 Litho. *Perf. 14***

**228** A109 1.10k multicolored .60 .45
**229** A109 3.80k multicolored 1.90 1.50
**230** A109 4k multicolored 2.00 1.90
***a.*** Souvenir sheet of 3, #228-230 4.75 4.75
*Nos. 228-230 (3)* 4.50 3.85

Croatian Monasteries A110

1k, Jesuit Monastery, Zagreb, 350th anniv. 2.40k, Franciscan Monastery, Visovac, 550th anniv.

**1995, Feb. 16**

**231** A110 1k multicolored .50 .30
**232** A110 2.40k multicolored 1.25 .95

Hunting Dogs — A111

Designs: 2.20k, Istrian short-haired. 2.40k, Posavinian. 3.80k, Istrian wire-haired.

**1995, Mar. 9 Litho. *Perf. 14***

**233** A111 2.20k multicolored 1.00 .75
**234** A111 2.40k multicolored 1.25 .80
**235** A111 3.80k multicolored 1.75 1.40
*Nos. 233-235 (3)* 4.00 2.95

Town of Split, 1700th Anniv. A112

No. 236: a, 1k, Drawing of reconstruction of Diocletian's Palace. b, 2.20k, "Split Harbour," by Emanuel Vidovic, 1937. c, 4k, Modern view of town, bust of Marko Marulic by Ivan Mestrovic.

13.40k, Buildings, vert.

**1995, Apr. 20 Litho. *Perf. 14***

**236** A112 Strip of 3, #a.-c. 4.00 4.00

**Souvenir Sheet**

**237** A112 13.40k multicolored 6.25 6.25

No. 237 contains one 24x48mm stamp.

World Team Handball Championships, Iceland — A113

**1995, May 4**

**238** A113 4k multicolored 2.00 1.25

Peace & Freedom — A114

Europa: 2.40k, Clearing storm clouds. 4k, Hands of angel, by Francisco Robba.

**1995, May 9**

**239** A114 2.40k multicolored *1.75 1.25*
**240** A114 4k multicolored *2.25 1.60*

Anti-Austria Demonstrations, 150th Anniv. — A115

**1995, May 15**

**241** A115 1.10k multicolored .65 .45
**242** A115 3.80k multicolored 1.25 1.10

Croatian surrender to British forces at Bleiburg, 50th anniv. (No. 242).

Independence Day — A116

**1995, May 30 Litho. *Perf. 14***

**243** A116 1.10k multicolored .75 .40

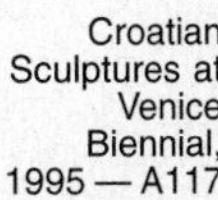

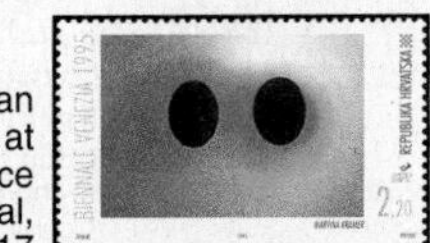

Croatian Sculptures at Venice Biennial, 1995 — A117

2.20k, Installation (a part), by Martina Kramer. 2.40k, Paracelsus Paraduchamps, by Mirko Zrinscak, vert. 4k, Shadows, by Goran Petercol.

**1995, June 8 Litho. *Perf. 14***

**244** A117 2.20k multicolored 1.00 .65
**245** A117 2.40k multicolored 1.10 .75
**246** A117 4k multicolored 1.90 1.75
*Nos. 244-246 (3)* 4.00 3.15

St. Anthony of Padua (1195-1231) A118

**1995, June 13**

**247** A118 1k multicolored .45 .30

Marine Life — A119

2.40k, Caretta caretta. 4k, Tursiops truncatus.

**1995, June 29 Litho. *Perf. 14***

**248** A119 2.40k multi 1.00 .90
**249** A119 4k multi 1.75 1.50

Liberation of the City of Knin — A120

**1995, Aug. 5 Litho. *Perf. 14***

**250** A120 1.30k multicolored .75 .60

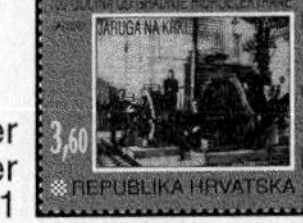

Krka River Hydroelectric Power Plant, Cent. — A121

**1995, Aug. 28**

**251** A121 3.60k multicolored 1.45 1.00

Stamp Day — A122

**1995, Sept. 9 Litho. *Perf. 14***

**252** A122 1.30k multicolored .70 .70

Franz von Suppe (1819-95), Composer — A123

**1995, Sept. 15**

**253** A123 6.50k multicolored 3.00 2.00

See Austria Nos. 1686-1687.

Liberation of Petrinja from Turkish Rule, 400th Anniv. — A124

**1995, Sept. 21**

**254** A124 2.20k multicolored 1.10 .90

Croatian Music — A125

Composers, conductors: 1.20k, Ivo Tijardovic (1895-1976). 1.40k, Lovro Von Matacic (1899-1985). 6.50k, Jakov Gotovac (1895-1982).

**1995, Sept. 23**

| No. | Type | Denom. | Color | Unused | Used |
|---|---|---|---|---|---|
| 255 | A125 | 1.20k | multicolored | .55 | .55 |
| 256 | A125 | 1.40k | multicolored | .65 | .60 |
| 257 | A125 | 6.50k | multicolored | 3.25 | 2.50 |
| | | | *Nos. 255-257 (3)* | 4.45 | 3.65 |

Herman Bollé (1845-1926), Architect A126

2.40k, Izidor Krsnjavi (1845-1927), painter. 3.60k, Croatian National Theatre, cent.

**1995, Oct. 14 Litho. *Perf. 14***

| No. | Type | Denom. | Color | Unused | Used |
|---|---|---|---|---|---|
| 258 | A126 | 1.80k | multicolored | .80 | .50 |
| 259 | A126 | 2.40k | multicolored | 1.00 | .70 |
| 260 | A126 | 3.60k | multicolored | 1.75 | 1.25 |
| | | | *Nos. 258-260 (3)* | 3.55 | 2.45 |

Croatian Towns — A127

**1995, Oct. 20**

| No. | Type | Denom. | Design | Unused | Used |
|---|---|---|---|---|---|
| 261 | A127 | 1k | Bjelovar | .45 | .45 |
| 262 | A127 | 1.30k | Osijek, vert. | .55 | .55 |
| 263 | A127 | 1.40k | Cakovec, vert. | .60 | .60 |
| 264 | A127 | 2.20k | Rovinj | 1.10 | 1.10 |
| 265 | A127 | 2.40k | Korcula | 1.25 | 1.25 |
| 266 | A127 | 3.60k | Zupanja | 1.60 | 1.60 |
| | | | *Nos. 261-266 (6)* | 5.55 | 5.55 |

See No. 448.

UN, FAO, 50th Anniv. — A128

No. 268, "5, 0" in form of cracker, FAO.

**1995, Oct. 24**

| No. | Type | Denom. | Color | Unused | Used |
|---|---|---|---|---|---|
| 267 | A128 | 3.60k | multicolored | 1.40 | 1.00 |
| 268 | A128 | 3.60k | multicolored | 1.60 | 1.00 |
| *a.* | | | Pair, #267-268 | 3.25 | 3.25 |

Croatian Scientists — A129

1k, Spiro Brusina (1845-1908). 2.20k, Bogoslav Sulek (1816-95). 6.50k, Front of European language dictionary, published by Faust Vrancic (1551-1617).

**1995, Oct. 30**

| No. | Type | Denom. | Color | Unused | Used |
|---|---|---|---|---|---|
| 269 | A129 | 1k | multicolored | .65 | .30 |
| 270 | A129 | 2.20k | multicolored | 1.00 | .65 |
| 271 | A129 | 6.50k | multicolored | 3.00 | 2.25 |
| | | | *Nos. 269-271 (3)* | 4.65 | 3.20 |

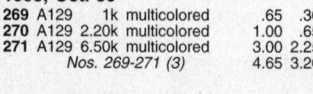

Institute for Blind Children, Cent. — A130

**1995, Nov. 23 Litho. *Perf. 14***

| No. | Type | Denom. | Color | Unused | Used |
|---|---|---|---|---|---|
| 272 | A130 | 1.20k | multicolored | 1.00 | 1.00 |

Christmas — A131

**1995, Dec. 1**

| No. | Type | Denom. | Color | Unused | Used |
|---|---|---|---|---|---|
| 273 | A131 | 1.30k | multicolored | .65 | .45 |

Maroc Polo's Return from China, 700th Anniv. — A132

**1995, Dec. 7**

| No. | Type | Denom. | Color | Unused | Used |
|---|---|---|---|---|---|
| 274 | A132 | 3.60k | multicolored | 1.75 | 1.50 |

Liberated Towns — A133

20 l, Hrvatska Kostajnica. 30 l, Slunj. 50 l, Gracac. 1.20k, Drnis, vert. 6.50k, Glina. 10k, Obrovac, vert.

**1995, Dec. 16**

| No. | Type | Denom. | Color | Unused | Used |
|---|---|---|---|---|---|
| 275 | A133 | 20 l | multi | .25 | .25 |
| 276 | A133 | 30 l | multi | .25 | .25 |
| 277 | A133 | 50 l | multi | .35 | .35 |
| 278 | A133 | 1.20k | multi | .70 | .70 |
| 279 | A133 | 6.50k | multi | 3.25 | 3.25 |
| 280 | A133 | 10k | multi | 4.50 | 4.50 |
| | | | *Nos. 275-280 (6)* | 9.30 | 9.30 |

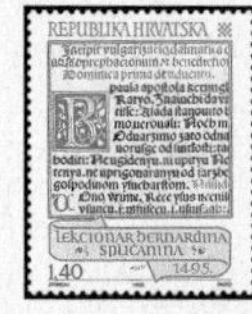

Incunabula — A134

Designs: 1.40k, Lectionary of Bernardin of Split. 3.60k, Spovid Opcena (General Confession).

**1995, Dec. 28**

| No. | Type | Denom. | Color | Unused | Used |
|---|---|---|---|---|---|
| 281 | A134 | 1.40k | multicolored | .75 | .40 |
| 282 | A134 | 3.60k | multicolored | 1.75 | 1.25 |

Spirituality of the Croats — A135

Designs: No. 283, Mosaic of St. Marko Krizevcanin (1589-1619), Catholic martyr. No. 284, Veneration of Miraculous Crucifix, St. Guido's Church, Rijeka, 700th anniv. No. 285, Ivan Merz (1896-1928), Catholic educator.

**1996, Jan. 18 Litho. *Perf. 14***

| No. | Type | Denom. | Color | Unused | Used |
|---|---|---|---|---|---|
| 283 | A135 | 1.30k | multicolored | .60 | .50 |
| 284 | A135 | 1.30k | multicolored | .60 | .50 |
| 285 | A135 | 1.30k | multicolored | .60 | .50 |
| *a.* | | | Strip of 3, Nos. 283-285 | 2.00 | 2.00 |

Political Anniversaries — A136

1.20k, Rakovica Uprising by Eugen Kvaternik, 125th anniv., horiz. 1.40k, Ante Starcevic (1823-96). 2.20k, Constitution of Neutral Peasant Republic of Croatia, 75th anniv., Stjepan Radic (1871-1928). 3.60k, Labin Republic, 75th anniv.

**1996, Feb. 28**

| No. | Type | Denom. | Color | Unused | Used |
|---|---|---|---|---|---|
| 286 | A136 | 1.20k | multicolored | .60 | .50 |
| 287 | A136 | 1.40k | multicolored | .70 | .60 |
| 288 | A136 | 2.20k | multicolored | .95 | .80 |
| 289 | A136 | 3.60k | multicolored | 1.75 | 1.40 |
| | | | *Nos. 286-289 (4)* | 4.00 | 3.30 |

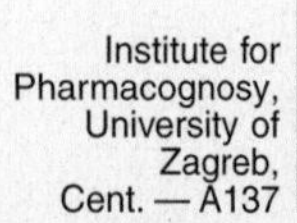

Institute for Pharmacognosy, University of Zagreb, Cent. — A137

**1996, Mar. 23 Litho. *Perf. 14***

| No. | Type | Denom. | Color | Unused | Used |
|---|---|---|---|---|---|
| 290 | A137 | 6.50k | multicolored | 3.00 | 2.00 |

Croatian Music — A138

a, Vinko Jelíc (1596-1636), composer. b, First performance of opera "Love and Music." c, Josip Stolcer Slavenski (1896-1955), composer. d, "Lijepa Nasa," Croatian national anthem, 150th anniv.

**1996, Mar. 28**

| No. | Type | Denom. | Description | Unused | Used |
|---|---|---|---|---|---|
| 291 | A138 | 2.20k | Strip of 4, #a.-d. | 3.75 | 3.75 |

Famous Women Writers — A139

(Europa): 2.20k, Cvijeta Zuzoric (b. 1551 or 1552). 3.60k, Ivana Brlic Mazuranic (1874-1938).

**1996, Apr. 11 Litho. *Perf. 14***

| No. | Type | Denom. | Color | Unused | Used |
|---|---|---|---|---|---|
| 292 | A139 | 2.20k | multicolored | 1.60 | 1.60 |
| 293 | A139 | 3.60k | multicolored | 2.25 | 2.25 |

A140

The Zrinskis and The Frankopans: 1.30k, Nikola Subic Zrinski of Sziget (1508-56). 1.40k, Nikola Zrinski (1620-64). 2.20k, Petar Zrinski (1621-71). 2.40k, Katarina Zrinski (1625-73). 3.60k, Fran Krsto Frankopan (1643-71).

**1996, Apr. 30**

| No. | Type | Denom. | Color | Unused | Used |
|---|---|---|---|---|---|
| 294 | A140 | 1.30k | multicolored | .55 | .55 |
| 295 | A140 | 1.40k | multicolored | .60 | .60 |
| 296 | A140 | 2.20k | multicolored | 1.00 | 1.00 |
| 297 | A140 | 2.40k | multicolored | 1.10 | 1.10 |
| 298 | A140 | 3.60k | multicolored | 1.40 | 1.40 |
| *a.* | | | Sheet of 5, #294-298 | 5.00 | 5.00 |
| | | | *Nos. 294-298 (5)* | 4.65 | 4.65 |

Natl. Guard, 5th Anniv. — A141

**1996, May 28 Litho. *Perf. 14***

| No. | Type | Denom. | Color | Unused | Used |
|---|---|---|---|---|---|
| 299 | A141 | 1.30k | multicolored | .65 | .65 |

Flowers — A142

Designs: 2.40k, Campanula istriaca. 3.60k, Centaurea ragusina.

**1996, June 5**

| No. | Type | Denom. | Color | Unused | Used |
|---|---|---|---|---|---|
| 300 | A142 | 2.40k | multicolored | 1.00 | 1.00 |
| 301 | A142 | 3.60k | multicolored | 1.60 | 1.60 |

England '96, European Soccer Championship A143

**1996, June 8**

| No. | Type | Denom. | Color | Unused | Used |
|---|---|---|---|---|---|
| 302 | A143 | 2.20k | red & black | 1.10 | .90 |

Father Ferdinand Konscak's Expedition to Lower California, 250th Anniv. — A144

**1996, June 10**

| No. | Type | Denom. | Color | Unused | Used |
|---|---|---|---|---|---|
| 303 | A144 | 2.40k | multicolored | 1.10 | 1.00 |

1996 Summer Olympics, Atlanta — A145

**1996, July 4**

| No. | Type | Denom. | Color | Unused | Used |
|---|---|---|---|---|---|
| 304 | A145 | 3.60k | multicolored | 1.75 | 1.25 |

A146

**1996, July 4**

| No. | Type | Denom. | Color | Unused | Used |
|---|---|---|---|---|---|
| 305 | A146 | 1.40k | multicolored | .65 | .60 |

Josip Fon, founder of Croatian Sokol Gymnastics Society, 150th birth anniv.

A147

**1996, Sept. 9 Litho. *Perf. 14***

| No. | Type | Denom. | Color | Unused | Used |
|---|---|---|---|---|---|
| 306 | A147 | 1.30k | multicolored | .65 | .40 |

Croatian postage stamps, 5th anniv.

1st Written Reference, Zumberak Region, 700th Anniv. — A148

**1996, Sept. 14**

| No. | Type | Denom. | Color | Unused | Used |
|---|---|---|---|---|---|
| 307 | A148 | 2.20k | multicolored | 1.00 | 1.00 |

A149

**1996, Sept. 19**

| No. | Type | Denom. | Color | Unused | Used |
|---|---|---|---|---|---|
| 308 | A149 | 1.30k | multicolored | .60 | .60 |

First written record of fishing in Croatia, 1000th anniv.

A150

Events of the early Middle Ages: 1.20k, Vekenega's Book of Gospels, 900th anniv. 1.40k, Visit by Saxon Benedictine abbot Gottschalk (805-870), to Duke Trpimir's court, 1150th anniv.

**1996, Sept. 19**

| No. | Type | Denom. | Color | Unused | Used |
|---|---|---|---|---|---|
| 309 | A150 | 1.20k | multicolored | .55 | .50 |
| 310 | A150 | 1.40k | multicolored | .65 | .55 |

Scientists — A151

Designs: a, Gjuro Pilar (1846-93), geologist. b, Frane Bulic (1846-1934), archeologist. c, Ante Sercer (1896-1968), otolaryngologist.

**1996, Oct. 4 Litho. *Perf. 14***

**311** A151 2.40k Strip of 3, #a.-c. 3.25 3.25

Beginning of Higher Education in Croatia, 600th Anniv. — A152

Oldest preserved Croatian text written in Latin script, "Order and Law" of Dominican nuns, Zadar.

**1996, Oct. 16 *Perf. 13½***

**312** A152 1.40k multicolored .70 .50

Paintings A153

Designs: 1.30k, Rain, by Menci Clement Crncic (1865-1930). 1.40k, The Peljesac-Korcula Channel, by Mato Celestin Medovic (1857-1919). 3.60k, Pink Dream, by Vlaho Bukovac (1855-1922).

**1996, Nov. 7 Litho. *Perf. 14***

| | | | | | |
|---|---|---|---|---|---|
| **313** | A153 | 1.30k | multicolored | .60 | .60 |
| **314** | A153 | 1.40k | multicolored | .70 | .70 |
| **315** | A153 | 3.60k | multicolored | 1.75 | 1.75 |
| | | | *Nos. 313-315 (3)* | 3.05 | 3.05 |

UNICEF, 50th Anniv. — A154

**1996, Nov. 15**

**316** A154 3.60k multicolored 1.60 1.25

City of Osijek, 800th Anniv. — A155

Views of city: No. 317, River bank, church, coat of arms. No. 318, Boats in water, view looking down covered walkway through building.

**1996, Dec. 2 Litho. *Perf. 14***

| | | | | | |
|---|---|---|---|---|---|
| **317** | A155 | 2.20k | multicolored | 1.00 | .75 |
| **318** | A155 | 2.20k | multicolored | 1.00 | .75 |
| ***a.*** | | | Pair, #317-318 | 2.25 | 2.25 |

Christmas — A156

**1996, Dec. 3**

**319** A156 1.30k multicolored .70 .50

First Croatian Savings Bank, Zagreb, 150th Anniv. — A157

Design: 3.60k, Publishing of "The Bases of Corn Trade," by Josip Sipus, bicent.

**1996, Dec. 14**

| | | | | | |
|---|---|---|---|---|---|
| **320** | A157 | 2.40k | multicolored | 1.00 | .80 |
| **321** | A157 | 3.60k | multicolored | 1.75 | 1.25 |

Motion Pictures, Cent. — A158

Designs: a, Shooting of film, "Vatroslav Lisinski," Oktavijan Miletic, cameraman, director. b, Characters from animated series, "Professor Baltazar." c, Mirjana Bohanec, Relja Basic in "Who Sings Means No Harm."

**1997, Jan. 16 Litho. *Perf. 14***

**322** A158 1.40k Strip of 3, #a.-c. 2.00 2.00

Great Europeans — A159

Designs: 2.20k, Miguel de Cervantes (1547-1676), author. 3.60k, Johannes Gutenberg (1397-1468), printer, horiz.

**1997, Feb. 7**

| | | | | | |
|---|---|---|---|---|---|
| **323** | A159 | 2.20k | multicolored | .90 | .65 |
| **324** | A159 | 3.60k | multicolored | 1.50 | 1.10 |

Legends — A160

Europa: 1.30k, Home Genies, from story, "Stribor's Forest." 3.60k, "Vili Joze," by Vladimir Nazor, vert.

**1997, Mar. 6 Litho. *Perf. 14***

| | | | | | |
|---|---|---|---|---|---|
| **325** | A160 | 1.30k | multicolored | *1.10* | *1.10* |
| **326** | A160 | 3.60k | multicolored | *2.75* | *2.75* |

Fauna of Croatia — A161

**1997, Apr. 22 Litho. *Perf. 14***

| | | | | | |
|---|---|---|---|---|---|
| **327** | A161 | 1.40k | Pinna nobilis | .60 | .60 |
| **328** | A161 | 2.40k | Radziella styx | 1.00 | 1.00 |
| **329** | A161 | 3.60k | Tonna galea | 1.60 | 1.60 |
| | | | *Nos. 327-329 (3)* | 3.20 | 3.20 |

Admission of Croatia to UN, 5th Anniv. — A162

6.50k, Pres. Franjo Tudjman.

**1997, May 22 Litho. *Perf. 14***

**330** A162 6.50k multi 3.00 3.00

First Croatian Esperantist Conference, 90th Anniv. — A163

Ludwig Lazarus Zamenhof, conf. logo.

**1997, May 31**

**331** A163 1.20k multicolored .70 .70

Congress of Intl. Amateur Rugby Federation, Dubrovnik — A164

**1997, June 6**

**332** A164 2.20k multicolored 1.10 .80

Siege of Vukovar, Serbo-Croatian War, 1991 — A165

Painting by Zlatko Kauzlaric Atac.

**1997, June 8 Litho. *Perf. 14***

**333** A165 6.50k multicolored 3.00 3.00

Croatian Kings — A166

1.30k, King Peter Svacic, 900th death anniv. 2.40k, King Stephen Drzislav, 1000th death anniv.

**1997, July 3**

| | | | | | |
|---|---|---|---|---|---|
| **334** | A166 | 1.30k | multicolored | .60 | .60 |
| **335** | A166 | 2.40k | multicolored | 1.25 | 1.25 |

16th Century Courier from Dubrovnik A167

**1997, Sept. 9 Litho. *Perf. 14***

**336** A167 2.30k multicolored 1.10 .90

Stamp Day.

Croatian Olympic Medals — A168

Designs: 1k, Tennis, bronze, Barcelona, 1992. 1.20k, Basketball, silver, Barcelona 1992. 1.40k, Water polo, silver, Atlanta, 1996. 2.20k, Handball, gold, Atlanta, 1996.

**1997, Sept. 10**

| | | | | | |
|---|---|---|---|---|---|
| **337** | A168 | 1k | multicolored | .40 | .40 |
| **338** | A168 | 1.20k | multicolored | .50 | .50 |

**Size: 27x31mm**

| | | | | | |
|---|---|---|---|---|---|
| **339** | A168 | 1.40k | multicolored | .75 | .75 |
| **340** | A168 | 2.20k | multicolored | 1.00 | 1.00 |
| | | | *Nos. 337-340 (4)* | 2.65 | 2.65 |

Defense of Sibenik A169

Designs: No. 341, Fort, airplanes. No. 342, Turkish cavalry, fort.

**1997, Sept. 18**

| | | | | | |
|---|---|---|---|---|---|
| **341** | A169 | 1.30k | multicolored | .50 | .50 |
| **342** | A169 | 1.30k | multicolored | .50 | .50 |
| ***a.*** | | | Pair, #341-342 | 1.25 | 1.25 |

Serbo-Croatian War, 1991 (No. 341). War with the Turks, 350th anniv. (No. 342).

Anniversaries A170

No. 343: a, Frane Petríc (1529-97), philosopher. b, Vicko Lovrin, 16th century painter. c, Frano Krsiníc (1897-1982), sculptor. d, Dubravko Dujsin (1894-1947), actor.

**1997, Oct. 17 Litho. *Perf. 14***

**343** A170 1.40k Strip of 4, #a.-d. 2.75 2.75

A171 A172

**1997, Oct. 23**

| | | | | | |
|---|---|---|---|---|---|
| **344** | A171 | 2.20k | multicolored | 1.00 | .70 |
| **345** | A172 | 3.60k | multicolored | 1.50 | 1.00 |

Use of Croatian language in parliament, 150th anniv. (No. 344).

Croatian Grammar School, Zadar, cent. (No. 345).

Palaeontological Finds in Croatia — A173

Designs: 1.40k, Gomphotherium angustidens. 2.40k, Viviparus novskaensis.

**1997, Nov. 6**

| | | | | | |
|---|---|---|---|---|---|
| **346** | A173 | 1.40k | multicolored | .60 | .60 |
| **347** | A173 | 2.40k | multicolored | 1.10 | 1.10 |

Modern Art — A174

Paintings: 1.30k, Painter in the Pond, by Nikola Masic (1852-1902). 2.20k, Angelus, by Emanuel Vidovic (1870-1953). 3.60k, Tree in the Snow, by Slava Raskaj (1877-1906).

**1997, Nov. 14**

| | | | | | |
|---|---|---|---|---|---|
| **348** | A174 | 1.30k | multicolored | .60 | .45 |
| **349** | A174 | 2.20k | multicolored | .90 | .55 |
| **350** | A174 | 3.60k | multicolored | 1.75 | 1.25 |
| | | | *Nos. 348-350 (3)* | 3.25 | 2.25 |

Contemporary Christmas Painting, by Ivan Antolcic A175

"Birth of Jesus," by Isidor Krsnjavi A176

**1997, Nov. 28 Litho. *Perf. 13½***
**351** A175 1.30k multicolored .50 .40

***Perf. 14***
**352** A176 3.60k multicolored 1.60 1.10

Croatian Literature — A177

**1997, Dec. 18 *Perf. 14***
**353** A177 1k shown .55 .40
**354** A177 1.20k Book, words .60 .40

Printing of the translation of "Electra," by Dominko Zlataric, 400th anniv. (No. 353). Publication of "The Best of Folk Speech and the Illyric or Croatian Language," by Filip Grabovac, 250th anniv. (No. 354).

**Cities and Landmarks Type of 1992**

**1997 Litho. *Perf. 14***
**355** A39 5 l Ilok .25 .25
**356** A39 10 l Dubrovnik .25 .25

Events and Festivals — A178

Europa: 1.45k, Varazdin Baroque Evenings, musical notes. 4k, Dubrovnik Summer Festival.

**1998, Jan. 23 *Perf. 13½***
**357** A178 1.45k multicolored *1.00 1.00*
**358** A178 4k multicolored *2.50 2.50*

1998 Winter Olympic Games, Nagano — A179

**1998, Feb. 7 *Perf. 14***
**359** A179 2.45k multicolored 1.10 .75

Croatian Events of 1848 — A180

a, 1.60k, Flag, battle near Moor. b, 4k, Portrait of Ban Josip Jelacic. c, 1.60k, Croatian Assembly.

**1998, Mar. 25 Litho. *Perf. 14***
**360** A180 Strip of 3, #a.-c. 3.25 3.25

No. 360b is 21x32mm.

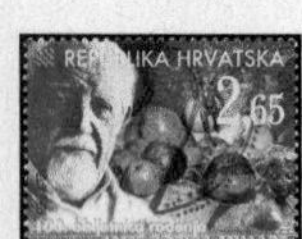
Ante Topic Mimara (1898-1987), Art Collector, Painter — A181

**1998, Apr. 7 Litho. *Perf. 14***
**361** A181 2.65k multicolored 1.25 .90

A182

Mushrooms: a, 1.30k, Amanita caesarea. b, 7.20k, Morchella conica. c, 1.30k, Lactarius deliciosus.

**1998, Apr. 22**
**362** A182 Strip of 3, #a.-c. 4.50 4.50

A183

**1998, May 8**
**363** A183 1.50k multicolored .65 .65

Archbishop Alojzije Stepinac (1898-1960).

27th European Regional Conference of Interpol, Dubrovnik — A184

**1998, May 13**
**364** A184 2.45k multicolored 1.10 .90

**Souvenir Sheet**

Expo '98, Lisbon A185

14.85k, Fishing boat, Falkusa.

**1998, June 3 Litho. *Perf. 14***
**365** A185 14.85k multi 6.25 6.25

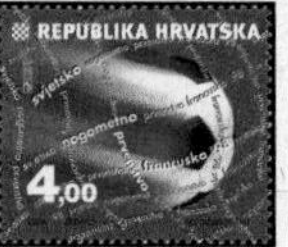
1998 World Cup Soccer Championships, France — A186

**1998, June 10**
**366** A186 4k multicolored 2.00 1.50

Writers — A187

1.20k, Juraj Barakovic (1548-1628). 1.50k, Milan Begovic (1876-1948). 1.60k, Mate Balota (Mijo Mirkovic, 1898-1963). 2.45k, Antun Gustav Matos (1873-1914). 2.65k, Matija Antun Relkovic (1732-98). 4.00k, Antun Branko Simic (1898-1925).

**1998, June 13 Litho. *Perf. 14***
**367** A187 1.20k multicolored .60 .50
**368** A187 1.50k multicolored .70 .60
**369** A187 1.60k multicolored .75 .70
**370** A187 2.45k multicolored 1.00 .90
**371** A187 2.65k multicolored 1.10 1.00
**372** A187 4k multicolored 1.75 1.60
*Nos. 367-372 (6)* 5.90 5.30

19th Conference of the Countries of the Danube Region, Osijek — A188

**1998, June 15**
**373** A188 1.80k multicolored .75 .65

Stjepan Betlheim (1898-1970), Psychiatrist — A189

**1998, July 22**
**374** A189 1.50k multicolored .65 .50

**Souvenir Sheet**

Croatian Soccer Team, Bronze Medalists at 1998 World Cup Soccer Championships, France — A190

Portions of team picture, denomination: a, red, LL. b, yellow, CR (player in yellow & blue shirt). c, yellow, CL. d, yellow, LR.

**1998, July 24**
**375** A190 4k Sheet of 4, #a.-d. 7.25 7.25

Croatian Ships — A191

1.20k, Serilia Liburnica. 1.50k, Condura Croatica. 1.60k, Dubrovnik carrack. 1.80k, Bracera. 2.45k, Ship from the Neretva. 2.65k, Bark. 4k, Training ship, "Villa Velebita." 7.20k, Passenger ship, "Amorella." 20k, Missile gun boat, "Kralj Petar Kresimir IV."

**1998, Aug. 27 Litho. *Perf. 14***
**376** A191 1.20k multi .70 .70
**376A** A191 1.50k multi .80 .80
**376B** A191 1.60k multi .85 .85
**376C** A191 1.80k multi .90 .90
**376D** A191 2.45k multi 1.30 1.30
**376E** A191 2.65k multi 1.50 1.50
**376F** A191 4k multi 2.00 2.00
**376G** A191 7.20k multi 3.50 3.50
**376H** A191 20k multi 9.25 9.25
*i.* Sheet of 9, #376-376H + 3 labels 20.00 20.00
*Nos. 376-376H (9)* 20.80 20.80

Stamp Day — A192

**1998, Sept. 9**
**377** A192 1.50k multicolored .65 .50

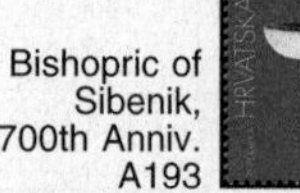

Bishopric of Sibenik, 700th Anniv. A193

**1998, Sept. 29 Litho. *Perf. 14***
**378** A193 4k multicolored 1.60 1.60

Pope John Paul II, Second Visit to Croatia — A194

**1998, Oct. 2**
**379** A194 1.50k multicolored .90 .90

History of Public Transportation A195

Designs: a, 1.50k, Horse tram. b, 1.50k, First automobile in Zagreb, 1901. c, 7.20k, Zagreb funicular. d, 1.50k, Karlovac-Rijeka Railway Line, 1873. e, 1.50k, New Highway, Zagreb-Rijeka.

**1998, Oct. 23 Litho. *Perf. 14***
**380** A195 Strip of 5, #a.-e. 6.00 6.00

No. 380c is 20x24mm.

Christmas — A196

Adoration of the Shepherds, by Juraj Julije Klovic (1498-1578).

**1998, Nov. 21 *Perf. 14x13***
**381** A196 1.50k multicolored .80 .75

See Vatican City No. 1088.

Father Luka Ibrisimovic (1620-98) — A197

**1998, Nov. 30 Litho. *Perf. 14***
**382** A197 1.90k multicolored .90 .75

Universal Declaration of Human Rights, 50th Anniv. — A198

**1998, Dec. 10**
**383** A198 5k multicolored 2.00 2.00

Modern Art — A199

Paintings: 1.90k, Paromlin Road, by Josip Vanista. 2.20k, Cypresses, by Frano Simunovic, vert. 5k, Koma, by Dalibor Martinis, vert.

**1998, Dec. 15**
**384** A199 1.90k multicolored .90 .90
**385** A199 2.20k multicolored 1.00 1.00
**386** A199 5k multicolored 2.10 2.10
*Nos. 384-386 (3)* 4.00 4.00

Zagreb Intl. Trade Fair — A200

**1999, Jan. 21 Litho. *Perf. 14***
**387** A200 1.80k multicolored .90 .80

Cardinal Juraj Haulik (1788-1869), Archbishop of Zagreb — A201

**Photo. & Engr.**

**1999, Jan. 28 *Perf. 11½***
**388** A201 5k multicolored 2.10 2.10

See Slovakia 321.

National Parks — A202

Europa: 1.80k, Mljet Island. 5k, Lonja Field.

**1999, Mar. 12 Litho. *Perf. 14***
**389** A202 1.80k multicolored *2.00 2.00*
**390** A202 5k multicolored *3.50 3.50*

Vipera Ursinii — A203

World Wildlife Fund: a, One coiled in grass and rock. b, Two. c, Head. d, One coiled on rock.

**1999, Apr. 27 Litho. *Perf. 14***
**391** A203 2.20k Strip of 4, #a.-d. 4.25 4.25

Council of Europe, 50th Anniv. — A204

**1999, May 5**
**392** A204 2.80k multicolored 1.25 1.25

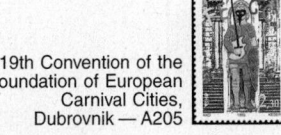

19th Convention of the Foundation of European Carnival Cities, Dubrovnik — A205

**1999, May 8**
**393** A205 2.30k multicolored 1.10 1.10

Croatian Coins — A206

Designs: a, 2.30k, Obv., rev. of 1849 kreutzer. b, 5k, One kuna.

**1999, May 30 Litho. *Perf. 14***
**394** A206 Pair, #a.-b. 3.25 3.25

Minting of Jelacic kreutzer, 150th anniv. (No. 394a). Croatian kuna, 5th anniv. (No. 394b).

Famous Croats — A207

1.80k, Vladimir Nazor (1876-1949), poet. 2.30k, Ferdo Livadic (1799-1879), composer. 2.50k, Ivan Rendic (1849-1932), sculptor. 2.80k, Milan Lenuci (1849-1924), architect. 3.50k, Vjekoslav Klaic (1849-1929), historian, muscician. 4k, Emilij Laszowski (1868-1949), historian. 5k, Antun Kanizlic (1699-1777), poet, missionary.

**1999, June 18**

| | | | | | |
|---|---|---|---|---|---|
| **395** | A207 | 1.80k | multicolored | .65 | .65 |
| **396** | A207 | 2.30k | multicolored | .95 | .90 |
| **397** | A207 | 2.50k | multicolored | 1.25 | 1.10 |
| **398** | A207 | 2.80k | multicolored | 1.30 | 1.30 |
| **399** | A207 | 3.50k | multicolored | 1.40 | 1.40 |
| **400** | A207 | 4k | multicolored | 1.60 | 1.60 |
| **401** | A207 | 5k | multicolored | 2.10 | 2.10 |
| | *Nos. 395-401 (7)* | | | 9.25 | 9.05 |

Euphrasian Basilica, Porec A208

**1999, June 25**
**402** A208 4k multicolored 1.75 1.75

2nd World Military Games, Zagreb — A209

**1999, Aug. 7 Litho. *Perf. 14***
**403** A209 2.30k multicolored 1.10 .90

Discovery of Early Krapina Man, Cent. — A210

Designs: a, 1.80k, Bones, rendition of Krapina man. b, 4k, Ancient bones, paleontologist Dragutin Gorjanovic-Kramberger.

**1999, Aug. 23**
**404** A210 Pair, #a.-b. 3.00 3.00

Stamp Day and UPU, 125th Anniv. — A211

**1999, Sept. 9 Litho. *Perf. 14***
**405** A211 2.30k multicolored 1.10 1.00

Paulist Order in Lepoglava, 600th Anniv. — A212

a, Lace, Jesus Expelling the Money Changers from Temple, by Ivan Ranger, altar angel from St. Mary's Church, Lepoglava. b, St. Mary's Church facade, altar angel. c, St. Elizabeth, lace.

**1999, Sept. 11 Litho.**
**406** A212 5k Strip of 3, #a.-c. 6.50 6.50

150th Anniv. of "Jelacic March" by Johann Strauss the Elder — A213

**1999, Sept. 16 Litho.**
**407** A213 3.50k multicolored 1.75 1.75

World Ozone Layer Protection Day — A214

**1999, Sept. 16 Litho.**
**408** A214 5k multicolored 2.10 2.10

Grammar School Anniversaries A215

2.30k, Pazin, cent. 3.50k, Pozega, 300th anniv.

**1999, Oct. 15 Litho. *Perf. 14***
**409** A215 2.30k multi 1.00 .90
**410** A215 3.50k multi 1.50 1.25

Andrija Hebrang (1899-1949), Politician — A216

**1999, Oct. 21**
**411** A216 1.80k multicolored .80 .80

Our Lady of the Rose Garden, by Blaz Jurjev Trogiranin — A217

**1999, Oct. 28**
**412** A217 5k multicolored 2.00 2.00

Christmas, opening of exhibition of Croatian religious art and artifacts, Vatican City.

Christmas — A218

**1999, Nov. 24 Litho. *Perf. 14***
**413** A218 2.30k multicolored 1.10 1.10

Modern Art — A219

Designs: 2.30k, Winter Landscape, by Gabrijel Jurkic (1886-1974). 3.50k, Klek, by Oton Postruznik (1900-78). 5k, Stone Table, by Ignjat Job (1895-1936), vert.

**1999, Dec. 15**

| | | | | | |
|---|---|---|---|---|---|
| **414** | A219 | 2.30k | multicolored | 1.10 | 1.10 |
| **415** | A219 | 3.50k | multicolored | 1.40 | 1.40 |
| **416** | A219 | 5k | multicolored | 2.00 | 2.00 |
| | *Nos. 414-416 (3)* | | | 4.50 | 4.50 |

Pres. Franjo Tudjman (1922-99) — A220

**1999, Dec. 16 Vignette Color**
**417** A220 2.30k black 1.10 1.00
**418** A220 5k blue 2.50 2.00

Millennium — A221

**2000, Jan. 1 Litho. *Perf. 14***
**419** A221 2.30k multi 2.75 2.25

Valentine's Day — A222

**2000, Feb. 1**
**420** A222 2.30k multi 2.00 1.60

Split Grammar School, 300th Anniv. — A223

**2000, Mar. 25 Litho. *Perf. 14***
**421** A223 2.80k multi 1.25 1.10

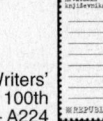

Croatian Writers' Assoc., 100th Anniv. — A224

**2000, Apr. 22 Litho. *Perf. 14***
**422** A224 2.30k black & red 2.75 2.75

A225

A226

A227

A228

A229

(1.80k) Lo Schiavone (Andrija Medulic, c. 1500-63), painter; (2.30k) Matija Petar Katancic (1750-1825), writer; (2.80k) Marija Ruzicka-Strozzi (1850-1937), actress; (3.50k) Marko Marulic (1450-1524), writer; (5k) Blaz Jurjev Trogiranin (c. 1390-1450), painter.

**2000, Apr. 22**

| | | | | | |
|---|---|---|---|---|---|
| **423** | A225 | 1.80k | multi | .65 | .65 |
| **424** | A226 | 2.30k | multi | .95 | .95 |
| **425** | A227 | 2.80k | multi | 1.10 | 1.10 |
| **426** | A228 | 3.50k | multi | 1.40 | 1.40 |
| **427** | A229 | 5k | multi | 1.90 | 1.90 |
| | *Nos. 423-427 (5)* | | | 6.00 | 6.00 |

**Europa, 2000**

Common Design Type and

A230

**2000, May 9**
**428** A230 2.30k multi *2.00 2.00*
**429** CD17 5k multi *4.25 4.25*

Independence Day — A231

**2000, May 30 Litho. *Perf. 14***
**430** A231 2.30k multi 1.50 1.50

Souvenir Sheet

Expo 2000, Hanover A232

**2000, June 1**
**431** A232 14.40k multi 6.25 6.25

Flora A233

No. 432: a, 3.50k, Micromeria croatica. b, 5k, Geranium dalmaticum.

**2000, June 5**

**432** A233 Pair, #a-b 4.00 4.00
*c.* Booklet pane of 10 #432a 15.00
Booklet, #432c 16.00
*d.* Booklet pane of 10 #432b 20.00
Booklet, #432d 21.00

Kastav Statute, 600th Anniv. — A234

**2000, June 6**

**433** A234 1.80k multi .85 .85

World Mathematics Year — A235

**2000, June 15**

**434** A235 3.50k multi 1.60 1.60

Ivan Ranger (1700-53), Artist — A236

**2000, June 19**

**435** A236 1.80k multi .85 .85

Souvenir Sheet

Baska Stone Tablet, 900th Anniv. A237

**2000, June 24**

**436** A237 16.70k multi 7.25 7.25

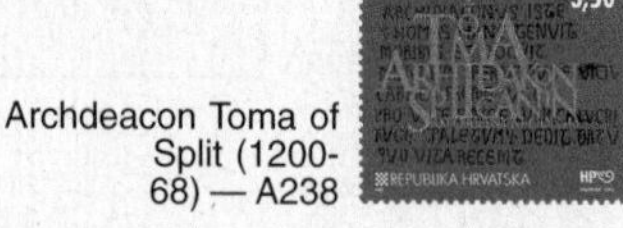

Archdeacon Toma of Split (1200-68) — A238

**2000, July 10**

**437** A238 3.50k multi 1.60 1.60

**Type of 1992-94 Redrawn**

**2000, Aug. 1 Litho. *Perf. 14***

**437A** A39a 3.50k Vis 1.60 1.60

No. 437A has "HP" and post horn in LR corner.

Stamp Day A239

No. 438: a, 2.30k, Austria #5. b, 2.30k, Automatic mail sorting equipment.

**2000, Sept. 9 Litho. *Perf. 14***

**438** A239 Pair, #a-b 2.25 2.25

First stamps used in Croatia, 150th anniv. (No. 438a).

2000 Summer Olympics, Sydney — A240

**2000, Sept. 15**

**439** A240 5k multicolored 3.00 3.00

Altarpiece, Church of the Blessed Virgin Mary, Ostarije — A241

**2000, Nov. 23**

**440** A241 2.30k multi 1.10 1.10
*a.* Booklet pane of 10 11.00
Booklet, #440a 11.50

Modern Art — A242

Designs: 1.80k, Korcula, by Vladimir Varlaj. 2.30k, Brusnik, by Duro Tiljak. 5k, Boats, by Ante Kastelacic.

**2000, Dec. 1**

**441-443** A242 Set of 3 4.00 4.00

See Nos. 471-473, 505-507.

Start of New Millennium — A243

**2001, Jan. 1 Litho. *Perf. 14***

**444** A243 2.30k multi 1.75 1.75

Souvenir Sheet

Equestrian Statue of Charlemagne — A244

**2001, Jan. 19**

**445** A244 14.40k multi 6.25 6.25

Crowning of Charlemagne as Emperor of the Romans, 1200th anniv. (in 2000).

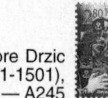

Dzore Drzic (1461-1501), Writer — A245

**2001, Mar. 15 Litho. *Perf. 14***

**446** A245 2.80k multi 1.40 1.40

Comic Strip "Black Rider," by Andrija Maurovic (1901-81) — A246

**2001, Mar. 29**

**447** A246 5k multi 2.25 2.25

Makarska — A247

**2001, Mar. 30**

**448** A247 2.30k multi 1.00 1.00
*a.* Perf. 14 syncopated 1.00 1.00

Issued: No. 448a, 6/2/06.

Janica Kostelic, Skier — A248

**2001, Apr. 19 Litho. *Perf. 14***

**449** A248 2.80k multi 2.40 2.00

Kastel Stafilic Olive Trees, 1500th Anniv. — A249

**2001, Apr. 20**

**450** A249 1.80k multi .85 .85

Europa A250

No. 451: a, 3.50k, Denomination at R. b, 5k, Denomination at L.

**2001, May 9**

**451** A250 Horiz. pair, #a-b 3.50 3.50

World No Smoking Day — A251

**2001, May 31**

**452** A251 2.50k multi 1.10 1.10

Butterflies — A252

Designs: 2.50k, Parnassius apollo. 2.80k, Maculinea teleius. 5k, Coenonympha oedippus.

**2001, June 5**

**453-455** A252 Set of 3 4.75 4.75

**Type of 1992 Redrawn**

2.80k, Eltz Castle, Vukovar.

**2001, June 21 Litho. *Perf. 14***

**456** A39 2.80k multi 1.25 1.25
*a.* Perf. 14 syncopated 1.10 1.10

No. 456 has "1991-2001" inscription, and "HP" and post horn at LL.
Issued: No. 456a, 6/19/06.

Souvenir Sheet

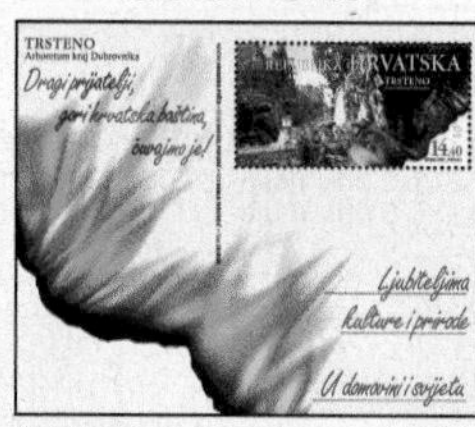

Trsteno Arboretum — A253

**2001, July 12 Litho. *Perf. 14***

**457** A253 14.40k multi 6.50 6.50

World Esperanto Congress, Zagreb — A254

**2001, July 21**

**458** A254 5k multi 2.40 2.40

Refugee Organizations, 50th Annivs. — A255

Designs: 1.80k, UN High Commissioner for Refugees. 5k, Intl. Organization for Migration.

**2001, July 28**

**459-460** A255 Set of 2 3.25 3.25

Victory of Goran Ivanisevic at Wimbledon — A256

**2001, Aug. 31**

**461** A256 2.50k multi 2.50 2.25

Printed in sheets of 9 + label.

Stamp Day — A257

**2001, Sept. 9**

**462** A257 2.50k multi .90 .90

Printed in sheets of 16 + 4 labels.

Native Dog Breeds — A258

Designs: 1.80k, Croatian sheepdog. 5k, Dalmatian.

**2001, Oct. 4**

**463-464** A258 Set of 2 3.25 3.25

Independence, 10th Anniv. — A259

**2001, Oct. 8**

**465** A259 2.30k multi 1.10 1.10

Printed in sheets of 25 + 5 labels.

Year of Dialogue Among Civilizations — A260

**2001, Oct. 9**

**466** A260 5k multi 4.00 4.00

Fortresses A261

Designs: 1.80k, Klis, 16th cent. 2.50k, Ston, 14th-15th cents. 3.50k, Sisak, 16th cent.

**2001, Oct. 26 Litho. *Perf. 14***

**467-469** A261 Set of 3 3.50 3.50

See Nos. 499-501, 525-527, 565-567, 594-596, 630-632.

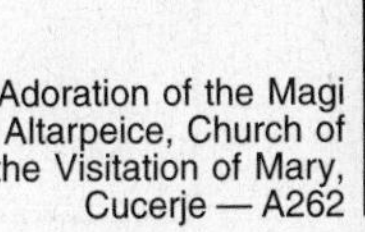

Adoration of the Magi Altarpeice, Church of the Visitation of Mary, Cucerje — A262

**2001, Nov. 22 Litho. *Perf. 14***

| | | | |
|---|---|---|---|
| **470** A262 2.30k multi | | 1.10 | 1.00 |
| *a.* | Booklet pane of 10 | 11.00 | 11.00 |
| | Complete booklet, #470a | 11.00 | |

**Modern Art Type of 2000**

Designs: No. 471, 2.50k, Maternité du Port-Royal, by Leo Junek. No. 472, 2.50k, Amphitheater Ruins, by Vjekoslav Parac. 5k, Nude with a Baroque Figure, by Slavko Sohaj, vert.

**2001, Dec. 1**
**471-473** A242 Set of 3 4.75 4.75

Croatian Nobel Laureates — A263

Laureates: 2.80k, Lavoslav (Leopold) Ruzicka, Chemistry, 1939. 3.50k, Vladimir Prelog, Chemistry, 1975. 5k, Ivo Andric, Literature, 1961.

**2001, Dec. 5**
**474-476** A263 Set of 3 5.50 5.50

Famous Croats and Events — A264

Designs: 1.80k, Ivan Gucetic (1451-1502), writer. 2.30k, Dobrisa Cesaric (1902-80), writer. 2.50k, Publishing of Juraj Rattkay's *History of Croatian Rulers,* 350th anniv. 2.80k, Franjo Vranjanin Laurana (c. 1420-1502), sculptor. 3.50k, Beatification of Bishop Augustin Kazotic (c. 1260-1323), 300th anniv. 5k, Matko Laginja (1852-1930), politician and writer.

**2002, Jan. 24 Litho. *Perf. 14***
**477-482** A264 Set of 6 8.00 8.00

2002 Winter Olympics, Salt Lake City — A265

**2002, Feb. 8**
**483** A265 5k multi 2.40 2.40

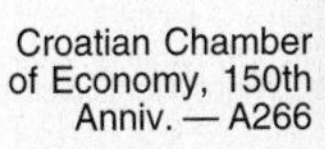

Croatian Chamber of Economy, 150th Anniv. — A266

**2002, Feb. 16**
**484** A266 2.50k multi 1.25 1.25

Souvenir Sheet

Trpimir's Deed of Gift, 1150th Anniv. A267

**2002, Mar. 4**
**485** A267 14.40k multi 6.50 6.50

Franjo Cardinal Kuharic (1919-2002) A268

**2002, Mar. 25**
**486** A268 2.30k multi .90 .90

Divan, by Vlaho Bukovac A269

**Litho. & Engr.**

**2002, Apr. 23 *Perf. 11¾***
**487** A269 5k multi 2.40 2.40

See Czech Republic No. 3169.

Royal Borough of Krizevci, 750th Anniv. — A270

**2002, Apr. 24 Litho. *Perf. 14***
**488** A270 1.80k multi .85 .85

Varazdin Post Office, Cent. — A271

**2002, Apr. 26**
**489** A271 2.30k multi 1.10 1.10

Europa A272

Clown color: a, 3.50k, Orange. b, 5k, Blue.

**2002, May 9 Litho. *Perf. 14***
**490** A272 Horiz. pair, #a-b *4.25 4.25*

2002 World Cup Soccer Championships, Japan and Korea — A273

Stylized players facing: a, 3.50k, Left. b, 5k, Right.

**2002, May 15**
**491** A273 Horiz. pair, #a-b 4.00 4.00

World Bowling Championships, Osijek — A274

**2002, May 18**
**492** A274 3.50k multi 1.60 1.60

Oak Trees — A275

Designs: 1.80k, Quercus rober. 2.50k, Quercus petraea. 2.80k, Quercus ilex.

**2002, June 5**

| | | | |
|---|---|---|---|
| **493-495** A275 Set of 3 | | 3.25 | 3.25 |
| *493a* | Booklet pane of 10 | 6.00 | — |
| | Complete booklet, #493a | 6.25 | |
| *494a* | Booklet pane of 10 | 12.00 | — |
| | Complete booklet, #494a | 12.50 | |
| *495a* | Booklet pane of 10 | 14.75 | — |
| | Complete booklet, #495a | 15.25 | |

15th World Animated Films Festival, Zagreb — A276

**2002, June 18**
**496** A276 5k multi 2.40 2.40

Lace — A277

Lace from: 3.50k, Pag Island, Croatia. 5k, Liedekerke, Belgium.

**2002, July 13 Photo. *Perf. 11½***
**497-498** A277 Set of 2 4.00 4.00

See Belgium Nos. 1927-1928.

**Fortresses Type of 2001**

Designs: No. 499, 2.50k, Nehaj, 16th cent. No. 500, 2.50k, Skocibuha, 16th cent. 5k, Veliki Tabor, 16th cent.

**2002, Sept. 20 Litho. *Perf. 14***
**499-501** A261 Set of 3 4.50 4.50

Old Slavonic Academy, Krk, Cent. — A278

**2002, Oct. 3 Litho. & Embossed**
**502** A278 4k red & black 1.75 1.75

Children's Help Line 48 26 051, 5th Anniv. — A279

**2002, Oct. 15 Litho.**
**503** A279 2.30k multi 1.10 1.10

Christmas — A280

**2002, Nov. 21**

| | | | |
|---|---|---|---|
| **504** A280 2.30k multi | | 1.25 | 1.25 |
| *a.* | Booklet pane of 10 | 12.50 | — |
| | Complete booklet, #504a | 13.00 | |

**Modern Art Type of 2002**

Designs: No. 505, 2.50k, Flowers on the Window, by Antun Motika (1902-92), vert. No. 506, 2.50k, The Girl in the Boat, by Milivoj Uzelac (1897-1977), vert. 5k, On the Drava River, by Krsto Hegedusic (1901-75).

**2002, Dec. 2 Litho. *Perf. 14***
**505-507** A242 Set of 3 4.75 4.75

Zagreb Bishopric, 150th Anniv. — A281

**2002, Dec. 11**
**508** A281 2.80k multi 1.40 1.40

Printed in sheets of 19 + label.

Pavao Ritter Vitezovic (1652-1713), Writer — A282

**2002, Dec. 13**
**509** A282 2.30k multi 1.10 1.10

Pacta Conventa, 900th Anniv. — A283

**2002, Dec. 14**
**510** A283 3.50k multi 1.60 1.60

Fairies From Stories by Ivana Brlic Mazuranic — A284

No. 511: a, 2.30k, Kosjenka, fairy character from *Regoc.* b, 2.80k, Tintilinic, fairy character from *Suma Striborova.*

**2003, Jan. 15**
**511** A284 Horiz. pair, #a-b 2.40 2.40

St. Valentine's Day — A285

**Litho. With Foil Application**

**2003, Feb. 1**
**512** A285 2.30k multi 1.10 1.10

Astronomy and Meteorology — A286

No. 513: a, 1.80k, Zagreb Astronomical Observatory, cent. b, 3.50k, Meteorological measurements in Zagreb, 150th anniv.; Meteorological station on Zavizan, 50th anniv.

**2003, Feb. 17 Litho.**
**513** A286 Pair, #a-b 2.25 2.25

Souvenir Sheet

Croatia, 2003 World Handball Champions — A287

No. 514: a, Five team members, one wearing red shirt. b, Eight team members, one with arm extended. c, Six team members. d, Four team members, one wearing blue shirt.

**2003, Feb. 20**
**514** A287 4k Sheet of 4, #a-d 7.00 7.00

Paulist High School, Lepoglava, 500th Anniv. — A288

**2003, Mar. 1**
**515** A288 5k multi 2.40 2.40

Missal of Hrvoje Vukcic Hrvatinic, 600th Anniv. — A289

**2003, Mar. 25**
**516** A289 5k multi 2.40 2.40

Land Mine Danger — A290

**2003, Apr. 8**
**517** A290 2.30k multi 1.10 1.10

Alpine Skiing World Cup Victories of Janica and Ivica Kostelic — A291

No. 518: a, Janica. b, Ivica.

**2003, Apr. 16**
**518** A291 3.50k Pair, #a-b 5.00 5.00

Printed in sheets containing 4 vertical pairs and 2 labels.

Christian Institutions in Rome Founded by Croatian Roman Brotherhood of St. Jerome, 550th Anniv. — A292

**2003, Apr. 22**
**519** A292 2.80k multi 1.25 1.25

Famous Croatians — A293

Designs: 1.80k, Antun Soljan (1932-93), writer. 2.30k, Hanibal Lucic (1485-1553), writer. 5k, Federiko Benkovic (1667-1753), painter.

**2003, Apr. 22**
**520-522** A293 Set of 3 4.25 4.25

Poster for Performance of Marya Delvard, by Tomislav Krizman, 1907 — A294

Poster for Performance of "The Firebird," by Boris Bucan, 1983 — A295

**2003, May 9** **Litho.** ***Perf. 14***
**523** A294 3.50k multi *1.50 1.50*
**524** A295 5k multi *2.25 2.25*

Europa.

**Fortresses Type of 2001**

Designs; 1.80k, Kostajnica, 15th-18th cent. 2.80k, Slavonski Brod, 18th cent. 5k, Minceta Tower, 15th cent., vert.

**2003, May 13**
**525-527** A261 Set of 3 4.25 4.25

Visit of Pope John Paul II — A296

**2003, June 2**
**528** A296 2.30k multi 1.75 1.75

Rodents — A297

Designs: 2.30k, Sciuris vulgaris. 2.80k, Glis glis. 3.50k, Castor fiber.

**2003, June 5**
**529-531** A297 Set of 3 4.00 4.00
*531a* Booklet pane, 6 #529, 2 each #530-531 13.00 —
Complete booklet, #531a 13.00

**Souvenir Sheet**

Robe of King Ladislaus, 11th Cent. — A298

**2003, June 13**
**532** A298 10k multi 4.25 4.25

Stamp Day — A299

**2003, Sept. 9** **Litho.** ***Perf. 14***
**533** A299 2.30k multi 1.10 1.10

**Souvenir Sheet**

Primosten Vineyards — A300

**Litho. with Foil Application**

**2003, Sept. 19**
**534** A300 10k multi 4.75 4.75

Ursuline Sisters in Croatia, 300th Anniv. — A301

**2003, Oct. 20** **Litho.**
**535** A301 2.50k multi 1.10 1.10

Christmas — A302

**2003, Nov. 20** **Litho.** ***Perf. 14***
**536** A302 2.30k multi 1.00 1.00

**Self-Adhesive**

***Serpentine Die Cut 5¼***

**537** A302 2.30k multi 1.00 1.00

Modern Art — A304

Designs: 1.80k, Flower Girl II, by Slavko Kopac, vert. No. 539, 3.50k, Dry Stone Wall 5-71, by Oton Gliha. No. 540, 3.50k, Pont des Arts, by Josip Racic.

**2003, Nov. 21** ***Perf. 14***
**538-540** A304 Set of 3 4.00 4.00

See Nos. 568-570, 604-606, 636-638, 668-670, 712-714, 749-751.

18th World Women's Handball Championships A305

**2003, Dec. 1**
**541** A305 5k multi 2.25 2.25

Musicians — A306

No. 542: a, Josip Hatze (1879-1959), composer. b, Zagreb Soloists, 50th anniv.

**2004, Jan. 5** **Litho.** ***Perf. 14***
**542** A306 5k Horiz. pair, #a-b 4.50 4.50

Hval's Manuscript, 600th Anniv. — A307

**2004, Jan. 22**
**543** A307 2.30k multi 1.40 1.40

European Boxing Championships, Pula — A308

**2004, Feb. 19** **Litho.** ***Perf. 14***
**544** A308 2.80k multi 1.25 1.25

Worldwide Fund for Nature (WWF) — A309

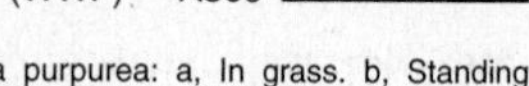

Ardea purpurea: a, In grass. b, Standing with head extended. c, With young. d, In flight.

**2004, Mar. 22**
**545** Strip or block of 4 8.50 8.50
*a.-d.* A309 5k Any single 1.75 1.75

Famous Croats — A310

Designs: 2.30k, Ivan Lucic (1604-79), historian. No. 547, 3.50k, Antun Vrancic (1504-75), archbishop, writer. No. 548, 3.50k, St. Jerome, sculpture by Andrija Alesi (c. 1425-1504). 10k, Printing of Croatian grammar book, by Bartol Kasic (1575-1650), 400th anniv.

**2004, Apr. 22**
**546-549** A310 Set of 4 8.25 8.25

**Souvenir Sheet**

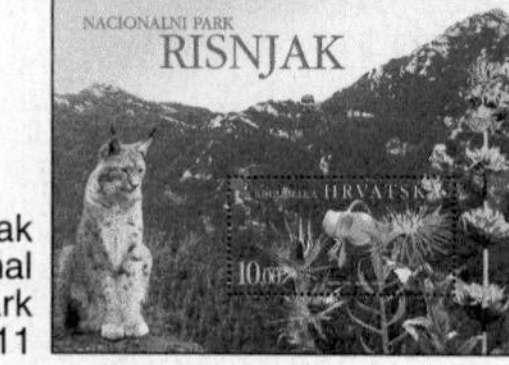


Risnjak National Park A311

**2004, Apr. 22**
**550** A311 10k multi 5.25 5.25

Martyrdom of St. Domnio, 1700th Anniv. — A312

**2004, May 7**
**551** A312 3.50k multi 1.75 1.75

Europa — A313

Designs: No. 552, 3.50k, Summer vacation items. No. 553, 3.50k, Winter vacation items.

**2004, May 9**
**552-553** A313 Set of 2 *3.00 3.00*

FIFA (Fédération Internationale de Football Association), Cent. — A314

**2004, May 21** **Litho.** ***Perf. 14***
**554** A314 2.50k multi 1.25 1.25

Medicinal Herbs — A315

Designs: 2.30k, Rosa canina. 2.80k, Viola odorata. 3.50k, Mentha piperita.

**2004, June 5**

| | | | | |
|---|---|---|---|---|
| **555-557** | A315 | Set of 3 | 4.00 | 4.00 |
| *555a* | | Booklet pane of 10 | 10.00 | — |
| | | Complete booklet, #555a | 10.50 | |
| *556a* | | Booklet pane of 10 | 12.50 | — |
| | | Complete booklet, #556a | 13.00 | |
| *557a* | | Booklet pane of 10 | 16.50 | — |
| | | Complete booklet, #557a | 17.50 | |

Nos. 555-557 are impregnated with a floral scent.

Intl. Marionette Union Congress, Intl. Puppetry Art Festival, Rijeka — A316

**2004, June 6**
**558** A316 3.50k multi 1.75 1.75

European Soccer Championships, Portugal — A317

**2004, June 12**
**559** A317 3.50k multi 1.75 1.75

Values are for stamps with surrounding selvage.

Restoration of Old Bridge, Mostar, Bosnia & Herzegovina A318

**2004, July 23** **Litho.** ***Perf. 14***
**560** A318 3.50k multi 1.75 1.75

2004 Summer Olympics, Athens — A319

**2004, Aug. 13**
**561** A319 3.50k multi 1.75 1.75

Virovitica — A320

**2004, Aug. 16**

| | | | | |
|---|---|---|---|---|
| **562** | A320 | 5k multi | 2.40 | 2.40 |
| *a.* | | Perf. 14 syncopated | — | — |

Issued: No. 562a, 12/7/07. For surcharge see No. 779.

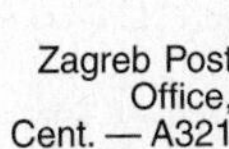

Zagreb Post Office, Cent. — A321

**2004, Sept. 9**
**563** A321 2.30k multi 1.00 1.00

Printed in sheets of 16 + 4 labels.

Father Andrija Kacic Miosic (1704-60), Poet — A322

**2004, Sept. 15**
**564** A322 2.80k multi 1.25 1.25

### Fortresses Type of 2001

Designs: No. 565, 3.50k, Dubovac, 15th-19th cent. No. 566, 3.50k, Gripe, 17th cent. No. 567, 3.50k, Valpovo, 15th-18th cent.

**2004, Sept. 29**
**565-567** A261 Set of 3 4.75 4.75

### Modern Art Type of 2003

Designs: No. 568, 2.30k, Self-portrait, by Miroslav Kraljevic, vert. No. 569, 2.30k, Noon in Supetar, by Jerolim Mise, vert. No. 570, 2.30k, Stari Grad, by Juraj Plancic, vert.

**2004, Nov. 15** **Litho.** ***Perf. 14***
**568-570** A304 Set of 3 3.25 3.25

Christmas — A323

**2004, Nov. 25**
**571** A323 2.30k multi 1.10 1.10

Antun and Stjepan Radic and Plowman A324

**2004, Dec. 22** **Litho.** ***Perf. 14***
**572** A324 7.20k multi 3.25 3.25

Croatian People's Peasant Party, Cent.

Fairy Tale Characters — A325

No. 573: a, Mermaid Halugica. b, Dwarf Pedalj Muza Lakat Brade.

**2005, Jan. 14**
**573** A325 5k Horiz. pair, #a-b 4.50 4.50

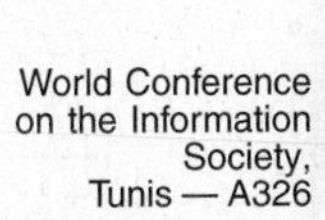

World Conference on the Information Society, Tunis — A326

**2005, Feb. 10**
**574** A326 2.80k multi 1.40 1.40

Values are for stamps with surrounding selvage.

Souvenir Sheet

Bust of Livia Drusilla A327

**2005, Feb. 24**
**575** A327 10k multi 5.00 5.00

Souvenir Sheet

Expo 2005, Aichi, Japan A328

**2005, Mar. 25** ***Perf.***
**576** A328 10k multi 5.00 5.00

Pope John Paul II (1920-2005) — A329

**2005, Apr. 8** ***Perf. 14***
**577** A329 2.30k multi 1.25 1.25

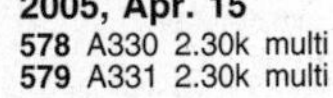

World Music Days, Zagreb A330

Stjepan Sulek (1914-86), Composer A331

**2005, Apr. 15**

| | | | | |
|---|---|---|---|---|
| **578** | A330 | 2.30k multi | 1.10 | 1.10 |
| **579** | A331 | 2.30k multi | 1.10 | 1.10 |

Insects — A332

Designs: 1.80k, Coccinella septempunctata. 2.30k, Rosalia alpina. 3.50k, Lucanus cervus.

**2005, Apr. 22**
**580-582** A332 Set of 3 3.75 3.75

Liberation of Western Slavonia, 10th Anniv. — A333

**2005, May 1**
**583** A333 1.80k multi .95 .95

Dr. Josip Buturac (1905-93), Historian — A334

**2005, May 6**
**584** A334 2.80k multi 1.25 1.25

Europa A335

No. 585: a, Loaf of bread. b, Glass of wine.

**2005, May 9**
**585** A335 3.50k Horiz. pair, #a-b *3.50* *3.50*

Coast of Hvar Island A336

No. 586: a, Rock at L, tree tops at bottom. b, Tree tops at LL. c, Rock at R. d, Canoe, rock at R. e, Small rock in center. f, Rocks at UL, trees. g, Rocks at R, trees. h, Tree tops at LL corner, rock at UR corner. i, Rocks at UL and LL corners. j, Rocks at LL.

**2005, May 24** **Litho.** ***Perf. 14***

| | | | | |
|---|---|---|---|---|
| **586** | A336 | Booklet pane of 10 | 13.00 | — |
| *a.-e.* | | 1.80k Any single | .90 | .90 |
| *f.-j.* | | 3.50k Any single | 1.40 | 1.40 |
| | | Complete booklet, #586 | 14.00 | |

Kresimir Cosic (1948-95), Basketball Player — A337

**2005, May 25**
**587** A337 3.50k multi 1.50 1.50

Printed in sheets of 9 + 1 label.

Krapanj Island Sponge and Coral Diving — A338

**2005, June 2** **Litho.**
**588** A338 3.50k multi 1.75 1.75

Portions of the design were applied by a thermographic process producing a shiny, raised effect.

Emperor Constantine's Bath, Varazdinske Toplice — A339

**2005, June 20** ***Perf. 14***
**589** A339 1.80k multi 1.00 1.00

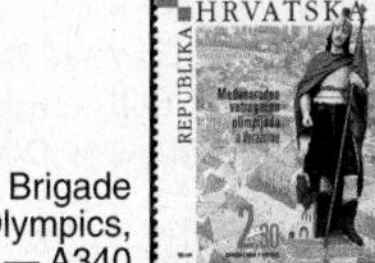


Intl. Fire Brigade Olympics, Varazdin — A340

**2005, July 15**
**590** A340 2.30k multi 1.25 1.25

Printed in sheets of 8 + 2 labels.

European Philatelic Cooperation, 50th Anniv. (in 2006) — A341

Designs: 7.20k, Vignette of #134. 8k, Stylized gull.

**2005, Sept. 8**

| | | | | |
|---|---|---|---|---|
| **591-592** | A341 | Set of 2 | *7.00* | *7.00* |
| *592a* | | Souvenir sheet, #591-592 | *60.00* | *60.00* |

Europa stamps, 50th anniv. (in 2006).

Telegraph — A342

**2005, Sept. 9**
**593** A342 2.30k multi 1.25 1.25

First overhead telegraph lines in Croatia, 155th anniv., Stamp Day.

### Fortresses Type of 2001

Designs: 1k, Ilok, 14th-15th cents. 2.30k, Motovun, 13th-15th cents., vert. 3.50k, St. Nicholas, 16th cent.

**2005, Sept. 15**
**594-596** A261 Set of 3 3.50 3.50

Famous People — A343

Designs: 1k, Adam Baltazar Krcelic (1715-78), historian. No. 598, 2.30k, Dragutin Tadijanovic (b. 1905), poet. No. 599, 2.30k, Tin Ujevic (1891-1955), poet. 2.80k, Madonna and Child, by Juraj Culinovic (c.1433-1504).

**2005, Nov. 4**

**597-600** A343 Set of 4 4.00 4.00

Clock Tower, Rijeka — A344

**2005, Nov. 10 Litho.** ***Perf. 14***

**601** A344 3.50k multi 1.75 1.75
*a.* Perf. 14 syncopated 1.75 1.75

Issued: No. 601a, 6/12/06. For surcharge see No. 778.

Christmas — A345

**2005, Nov. 22** ***Perf. 14***

**602** A345 2.30k multi 1.25 1.25

**Booklet Stamp**
**Self-Adhesive**
***Serpentine Die Cut 5¼***

**603** A345 2.30k multi 1.25 1.25
*a.* Booklet pane of 10 12.50 12.50
Complete booklet, #603a 12.50 12.50

**Modern Art Type of 2003**

Designs: 1.80k, Zadar, by Edo Murtic. 5k, Meander, by Julije Knifer. 10k, Drawing, by Miroslav Sutej, vert.

**2005, Dec. 1** ***Perf. 14***

**604-606** A304 Set of 3 8.75 8.75

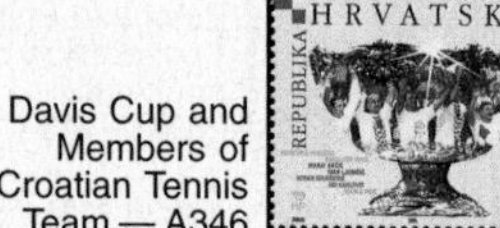
Davis Cup and Members of Croatian Tennis Team — A346

**2005, Dec. 22 Litho.** ***Perf. 14***

**607** A346 5k multi 2.75 2.75

Croatia, winners of 2005 Davis Cup. Printed in sheets of 9 + label.

Composers — A347

Designs: 1.80k, Boris Papandopulo (1906-91). 2.30k, Milo Cipra (1906-85). 2.80k, Ivan Brkanovic (1906-87).

**2006, Jan. 17**

**608-610** A347 Set of 3 3.50 3.50

2006 Winter Olympics, Turin — A348

**2006, Feb. 10**

**611** A348 3.50k multi 1.90 1.90

Rembrandt (1606-69), Painter — A349

**2006, Mar. 7**

**612** A349 5k multi 2.75 2.75

Famous Men — A350

Designs: No. 613, 1k, Andrija Ljudevit Adamic (1766-1828), merchant. No. 614, 1k, Josip Kozarac (1858-1906), writer. 5k, Vanja Radaus (1906-75), sculptor. 7.20k, Ljubo Karaman (1886-1971), art historian.

**2006, Mar. 21** ***Perf. 14 Syncopated***

**613-616** A350 Set of 4 7.25 7.25

European Track and Field Championships, Göteborg, Sweden — A351

**2006, Apr. 4**

**617** A351 2.30k multi 1.25 1.25

2006 World Cup Soccer Championships, Germany — A352

**2006, Apr. 4**

**618** A352 2.80k multi 1.25 1.25

Flag and Crowd A353

No. 619 — Location and placement of denomination: a, At left, with denomination above crowd. b, At right, with top of numerals over red in flag. c, At left, with top of "8" and "0" above white in flag. d, At left, with serif of "1" above red in flag. e, At left, with entire denomination above red in flag. f, At right, with parts of "5" and "0" above red in flag. g, At right, with entire denomination above red in flag. h, At right, with entire denomination above white in flag. i, At left, with entire denomination above red in flag. j, At right, with denomination above crowd.

**2006, Apr. 25**

**619** A353 Booklet pane of 10 16.00 —
*a.-e.* 1.80k Any single 1.00 1.00
*f.-j.* 3.50k Any single 2.10 2.10
Complete booklet, #619 17.00

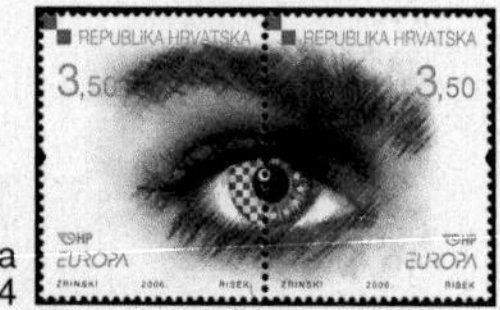
Europa A354

No. 620: a, Denomination at left. b, Denomination at right.

**2006, May 9**

**620** A354 3.50k Horiz. pair, #a-b 3.50 3.50

Worldwide Fund for Nature (WWF) — A355

No. 621 — Various views of Sterna albifrons with denomination in: a, Gray. b, Dull green. c, Yellow orange. d, Red.

**2006, May 23**

**621** Strip of 4 10.00 10.00
*a.-d.* A355 5k Any single 2.40 2.40

Croatian Automobile Club, Cent. — A356

***Perf. 13¾x14 Syncopated***

**2006, June 4**

**622** A356 5k multi 2.75 2.75

Aquatic Flowers — A357

Designs: 2.30k, Nymphaea alba. 2.80k, Nuphar lutea. 3.50k, Menyanthes trifoliata.

**2006, June 5** ***Perf. 14 Syncopated***

**623-625** A357 Set of 3 4.50 4.50
*623a* Booklet pane of 10 12.50 12.50
Complete booklet, #623a 12.50
*624a* Booklet pane of 10 14.00 14.00
Complete booklet, #624a 14.00
*625a* Booklet pane of 10 18.00 18.00
Complete booklet, #625a 18.00

Nikola Tesla (1856-1943), Inventor — A358

***Perf. 14x13½ Syncopated***

**2006, July 10 Litho.**

**626** A358 3.50k multi 1.75 1.75

Bjelovar, 250th Anniv. — A359

***Perf. 14 Syncopated***

**2006, Aug. 22 Litho.**

**627** A359 2.80k multi 1.50 1.50

Stamp Day — A360

**2006, Sept. 9 Litho. & Embossed**

**628** A360 2.30k multi 1.25 1.25

Jewish Community of Zagreb, 200th Anniv. — A361

***Perf. 14¼x13¾ Syncopated***

**2006, Sept. 15 Litho.**

**629** A361 5k multi 2.75 2.75

**Fortresses Type of 2001**

Designs: No. 630, 1k, St. Mary of Mercy Church, Vrboska, 16th cent. No. 631, 1k, Church of the Holy Spirit, Sudurad, Sipan, 16th cent. 7.20k, Frankapan Citadel, Ogulin, 16th cent.

***Perf. 13¾x14¼ Syncopated***

**2006, Sept. 21**

**630-632** A261 Set of 3 4.75 4.75

White Cane Safety Day — A362

***Perf. 14 Syncopated***

**2006, Oct. 15 Litho. & Embossed**

**633** A362 1.80k black & red 1.00 1.00

Christmas — A363

***Perf. 14¼ Syncopated***

**2006, Nov. 27 Litho.**

**634** A363 2.30k multi 1.25 1.25

**Booklet Stamp**
**Self-Adhesive**
***Serpentine Die Cut 5¼***

**635** A363 2.30k multi 1.25 1.25
*a.* Booklet pane of 10 12.50
Complete booklet, #635a 12.50

**Modern Art Type of 2003**

Designs: 1k, Still Life, by Vladimir Becic. 1.80k, Composition Tyma 3, by Ivan Picelj. 10k, Self-portrait as Hunter, by Nasta Rojc, vert.

**2006, Dec. 1** ***Perf. 14 Syncopated***

**636-638** A304 Set of 3 6.00 6.00

Classical Gymnasium, Zagreb, 400th Anniv. — A364

***Perf. 14 Syncopated***

**2007, Jan. 9 Litho.**

**639** A364 5k multi 2.40 2.40

Fairy Tale Characters — A365

No. 640: a, Monster Orko. b, Devil Macic.

**2007, Jan. 18**

**640** A365 2.30k Horiz. pair, #a-b 2.50 2.50

National and University Library, Zagreb, 400th Anniv. — A366

**2007, Feb. 22**

**641** A366 5k multi 2.50 2.50

Crustaceans A367

Designs: 1.80k, Palinurus elephas. 2.30k, Nephrops norvegicus. 2.80k, Astacus astacus.

**2007, Mar. 15**

| | | | |
|---|---|---|---|
| 642 A367 1.80k multi | | .85 | .85 |
| a. | Booklet pane of 10 | 8.50 | — |
| | Complete booklet, #642a | 8.50 | |
| 643 A367 2.30k multi | | 1.05 | 1.05 |
| a. | Booklet pane of 10 | 10.50 | — |
| | Complete booklet, #643a | 10.50 | |
| 644 A367 2.80k multi | | 1.35 | 1.35 |
| a. | Booklet pane of 10 | 13.50 | — |
| | Complete booklet, #644a | 13.50 | |
| | *Nos. 642-644 (3)* | 3.25 | 3.25 |

Native Breeds of Farm Animals — A368

Designs: 2.80k, Istrian ox. 3.50k, Posavina horse. 5k, Dalmatian donkey.

**2007, Mar. 20**

645-647 A368 Set of 3 5.75 5.75

Europa A369

No. 648: a, Scouting emblem and dove. b, Scout neckerchief.

**2007, Apr. 16**

648 A369 3.50k Horiz. pair, #a-b 3.25 3.25

Scouting, cent.

Scientists — A370

Designs: 5k, Andrija Mohorovicic (1857-1936), seismologist. 7.20k, Duro Baglivi (1668-1707), physician.

***Perf. 14x13½ Syncopated***

**2007, Apr. 23**

649-650 A370 Set of 2 6.00 6.00

Souvenir Sheet

World Championship Victory of Croatian Water Polo Team — A371

No. 651: a, Man with red shirt at right, denomination at UL. b, Man with red shirt at LR, denomination at UR. c, Man with red shirt at left, denomination at UR.

**Litho. With Foil Application**

**2007, May 3** ***Perf. 14¼ Syncopated***

651 A371 5k Sheet of 3, #a-c 7.75 7.75

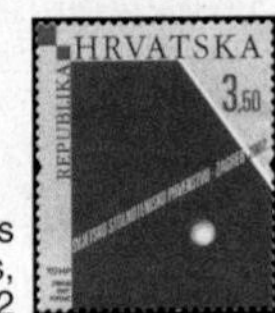


World Table Tennis Championships, Zagreb — A372

***Perf. 14 Syncopated***

**2007, May 21** **Litho. & Embossed**

652 A372 3.50k multi 1.75 1.75

Starting with No. 652 some stamps have an imprinted wing-shaped tagging design that looks like a watermark.

Diplomatic Relations Between Croatia and People's Republic of China, 15th Anniv. — A373

No. 653: a, "China" in Glagolithic letters. b, "Croatia" in Chinese characters.

**2007, May 30** **Litho.** ***Perf. 12***

653 A373 5k Horiz. pair, #a-b 5.00 5.00

Zagreb City Museum, Cent. — A374

**2007, May 31** ***Perf. 14 Syncopated***

654 A374 2.30k multi 1.10 1.10

Souvenir Sheet

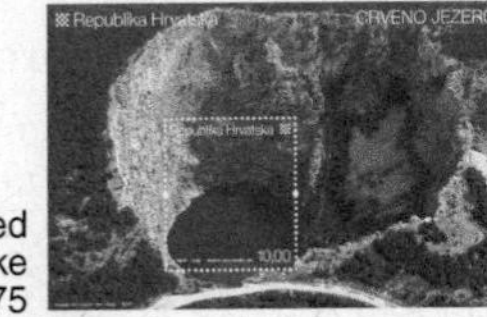


Red Lake A375

**2007, June 8**

655 A375 10k multi 4.50 4.50

First Croatian Philatelic Exhibition, Cent. — A376

***Perf. 14 Syncopated***

**2007, Sept. 9** **Litho. & Embossed**

656 A376 2.80k multi 1.25 1.25

Stamp Day.

Lighthouses A377

Designs: No. 657, 5k, St. John on the Sea Lighthouse. No. 658, 5k, Porer Lighthouse. No. 659, 5k, Savudrija Lighthouse.

***Perf. 13¾x14¼ Syncopated***

**2007, Sept. 14** **Litho.**

657-659 A377 Set of 3 7.00 7.00

Veprinac Statute, 500th Anniv. — A378

***Perf. 14¼x13¾ Syncopated***

**2007, Oct. 2**

660 A378 2.70k multi 1.25 1.25

City Views — A379

Designs: 1.80k, Omis. 2.30k, Koprivnica, horiz. 2.80k, Krk.

**2007, Oct. 30** ***Perf. 14 Syncopated***

| | | | |
|---|---|---|---|
| 661 A379 1.80k multi | | .85 | .85 |
| a. | Perf. 14 ('10) | .70 | .70 |
| 662 A379 2.30k multi | | 1.00 | 1.00 |
| 663 A379 2.80k multi | | 1.30 | 1.30 |
| | *Nos. 661-663 (3)* | 3.15 | 3.15 |

For surcharge see No. 777.

Blanka Vlasic, 2007 World Women's High Jump Champion — A380

**2007, Nov. 8**

664 A380 2.30k multi 1.25 1.25

Christmas — A381

***Perf. 14¼ Syncopated***

**2007, Nov. 15** **Litho.**

665 A381 2.30k multi 1.25 1.25

**Booklet Stamp**
**Self-Adhesive**
***Serpentine Die Cut 5¼***

| | | | |
|---|---|---|---|
| 666 A381 2.30k multi | | 1.25 | 1.25 |
| a. | Booklet pane of 10 | 12.50 | |
| | Complete booklet, #666a | 12.50 | |

Marija Juric Zagorka (1873-1957), Writer — A382

***Perf. 14¼x13¾ Syncopated***

**2007, Nov. 16**

667 A382 7.20k multi 3.25 3.25

**Modern Art Type of 2003**

Designs: 2.80k, Area by the Sava River, by Branko Senoa. No. 669, 5k, Pegasus's Garden, by Ferdinand Kulmer. No. 670, 5k, Bridgeport, by Ivan Benkovic.

***Perf. 14 Syncopated***

**2007, Dec. 1** **Litho.**

668-670 A304 Set of 3 5.75 5.75

New Year 2008 — A383

**2007, Dec. 5**

671 A383 1.80k multi .80 .80

Composers — A384

Designs: No. 672, 2.30k, Igor Kuljeric (1938-2006). No. 673, 2.30k, Krsto Odak (1888-1965).

**2008, Jan. 22**

672-673 A384 Set of 2 2.25 2.25

Publication of *Arithmetika Horvatszka*, by Mijo Silobod Bolsic, 250th Anniv. A385

***Perf. 13¾x14 Syncopated***

**2008, Jan. 25**

674 A385 3.50k multi 1.75 1.75

Steam Locomotives A386

Designs: No. 675, 5k, MAV 601/JZ 32. No. 676, 5k, MAV 651/JZ 31.

**2008, Feb. 15**

675-676 A386 Set of 2 4.50 4.50

Nos. 675-676 were printed in sheets of 6 containing three of each stamp.

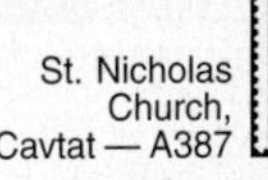

St. Nicholas Church, Cavtat — A387

***Perf. 14 Syncopated***

**2008, Mar. 8** **Litho.**

677 A387 7.20k multi 3.25 3.25

For surcharge see No. 780.

2008 Summer Olympics, Beijing — A388

**2008, Mar. 11**

678 A388 5k multi 2.00 2.00

Printed in sheets of 9 + label.

Flowers — A389

Designs: 1.80k, Helleborus niger. 2.80k, Onosma stellulata. 3.50k, Lonicera glutinosa.

**2008, Mar. 20**

| | | | |
|---|---|---|---|
| 679 A389 1.80k multi | | .95 | .95 |
| a. | Booklet pane of 10 | 9.50 | — |
| | Complete booklet, #679a | 9.50 | |
| 680 A389 2.80k multi | | 1.50 | 1.50 |
| a. | Booklet pane of 10 | 15.00 | — |
| | Complete booklet, #680a | 15.00 | |
| 681 A389 3.50k multi | | 1.75 | 1.75 |
| a. | Booklet pane of 10 | 17.50 | — |
| | Complete booklet, #681a | 17.50 | |
| | *Nos. 679-681 (3)* | 4.20 | 4.20 |

Famous Writers — A390

Designs: 2.30k, Petar Zoranic (1508-c. 1569), novelist. 2.80k, Silvije Strahimir Kranjcevic (1865-1908), poet. 7.20k, Marin Drzic (1508-67), dramatist.

***Perf. 14 Syncopated***

**2008, Apr. 22** **Litho.**

682-684 A390 Set of 3 5.75 5.75

Waterfall, Plitvice Lakes National Park — A391

No. 685 — Part of waterfall with: a, Country name in white, denomination at UL, "HP" symbol in white at LL. b, Country name in white, denomination at UR, "HP" symbol in white at LL, green foliage at UL. c, Country name in black, denomination at UR. d, Country name in white, denomination at UR, "HP" symbol in black at LL. e, Country name in white, denomination at UR, "HP" symbol in white at LL, green foliage at UR. f, Country name in white, denomination in black at LR, "HP" symbol in black at LL, rock with foliage in center. g, Country name in white, denomination in black at LR, "HP" symbol in black at LL, all rocks covered by spray. h, Country name in black, denomination at LR. i, Country name in white, denomination in white at LR. j, Country name in white, denomination in black at LR, "HP" symbol in white at LL.

***Perf. 14 Syncopated***

**2008, Apr. 25** **Litho.**

**685** Booklet pane of 10 17.50 —
*a.-j.* A391 3.50k Any single 1.75 1.75
Complete booklet, #685 17.50

2008 Volkswagen Beetle — A392

**2008, May 8**

**686** A392 2.30k multi + label 1.10 1.10

Europa — A393

Designs: 3.50k, Insured envelope with wax seal. 5k, Airmail envelope.

**2008, May 9** **Litho.**

**687** A393 3.50k multi 1.60 1.60

**Litho. & Embossed**

**688** A393 5k multi 2.40 2.40

Portions of the design of No. 687 were applied using a thermographic process producing a shiny raised effect.

UEFA Euro 2008 Soccer Championships, Austria and Switzerland — A394

**2008, May 14** **Litho.** ***Perf. 14x13½***

**689** A394 3.50k multi 1.50 1.50

Values are for stamps with surrounding selvage. Printed in sheets of 9 + label.

Adris Group A395

**2008, May 16** ***Perf. 14 Syncopated***

**690** A395 2.30k multi + label 1.10 1.10

**Souvenir Sheet**

Ivan Vucetic (1858-1925), Fingerprint Classifier — A396

**2008, Apr. 20**

**691** A396 10k multi 5.00 5.00

**Souvenir Sheet**

Expo Zaragoza 2008 A397

**Litho. With Foil Application**

**2008, June 16**

**692** A397 10k multi 4.50 4.50

**Souvenir Sheet**

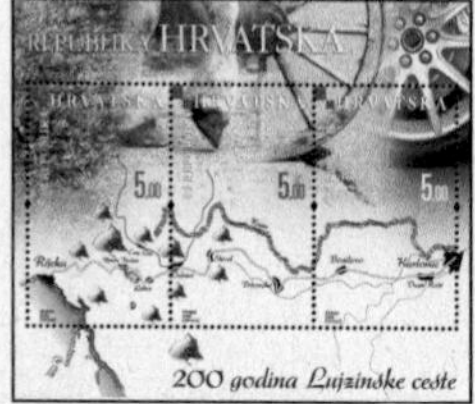

Lujzinske Road, 200th Anniv. A398

No. 693 — Parts of map of Lujzinske Road with denomination in: a, Red. b, Green. c, White.

***Perf. 14x13½ Syncopated***

**2008, June 17** **Litho.**

**693** A398 5k Sheet of 3, #a-c 7.00 7.00

Western Union A399

**2008, July 11** ***Perf. 14 Syncopated***

**694** A399 3.50k multi + label 1.50 1.50

Postal Workers' Games — A400

**Litho. With Foil Application**

**2008, Sept. 9** ***Perf. 14 Syncopated***

**695** A400 2.80k multi 1.30 1.30

Stamp Day.

Lighthouses — A401

Designs: No. 696, 5k, Pinida Lighthouse. No. 697, 5k, Vnetak Lighthouse. No. 698, 5k, Zaglav Lighthouse.

***Perf. 14¼x13¾ Syncopated***

**2008, Sept. 12** **Litho.**

**696-698** A401 Set of 3 7.00 7.00

Order of St. Clare, Split, 700th Anniv. — A402

**2008, Sept. 16**

**699** A402 2.80k multi 1.25 1.25

Details From Native Costumes — A403

Costume from: 10 l, Sunja. 20 l, Bistra. 50 l, Bizovac. 1k, Ravni Kotari. 10k, Pag.

**2008, Sept. 30** ***Perf. 14 Syncopated***

**700-704** A403 Set of 5 6.00 6.00
*701a* Perf. 14 ('10) .25 .25
*702a* Perf. 14 ('13) —
*703a* Perf. 14 ('10) .35 .35
*704a* Sheet of 5, #700-704 + label 6.00 6.00
*704b* Perf. 14 ('14) — —

European Healthy Cities Movement, 20th Anniv. — A404

**2008, Oct. 17** ***Perf. 14¼ Syncopated***

**705** A404 2.80k multi + label 1.25 1.25

Collegium Ragusinum, Dubrovnik, 350th Anniv. — A405

***Perf. 14¼x13¾ Syncopated***

**2008, Nov. 7** **Litho. & Embossed**

**706** A405 7.20k multi 3.00 3.00

Intl. Amateur Radio Union Region 1 Conference, Cavtat A406

***Perf. 13¾x14¼ Syncopated***

**2008, Nov. 14** **Litho.**

**707** A406 3.50k multi 1.50 1.50

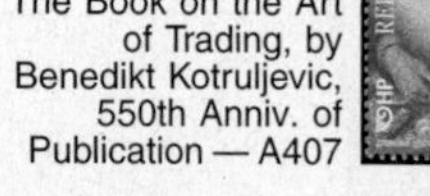

The Book on the Art of Trading, by Benedikt Kotruljevic, 550th Anniv. of Publication — A407

***Perf. 14¼x13¾ Syncopated***

**2008, Oct. 22** **Litho.**

**708** A407 2.80k multi 1.25 1.25

New Year's Day — A408

***Perf. 14 Syncopated***

**2008, Nov. 21** **Litho.**

**709** A408 1.80k multi .75 .75

Christmas — A409

**2008, Nov. 27** ***Perf. 14 Syncopated***

**710** A409 2.80k multi 1.50 1.50

**Booklet Stamp**
**Self-Adhesive**

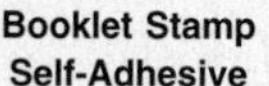

**711** A409 2.80k multi 1.00 1.00
*a.* Booklet pane of 10 10.00
Complete booklet, #711a 10.00

**Modern Art Type of 2003**

Designs: 1.65k, Two Trees at the Foot of a Hill, by Oskar Herman. 1.80k, Carousel, by Nevenka Djordjevic. 6.50k, Still Life, by Ivo Rezek.

***Perf. 14 Syncopated***

**2008, Dec. 1** **Litho.**

**712-714** A304 Set of 3 4.50 4.50

Zora Choral Society, 150th Anniv. — A410

***Perf. 14x13¾ Syncopated***

**2008, Dec. 5**

**715** A410 1.65k multi .75 .75

Ivan Mestrovic (1883-1962), Sculptor — A411

***Perf. 14 Syncopated***

**2008, Dec. 15** **Litho.**

**716** A411 5k multi 2.10 2.10

21st Men's World Handball Championships — A412

***Perf. 13¾x14¼ Syncopated***

**2009, Jan. 16** **Litho. & Embossed**

**717** A412 3.50k multi 1.50 1.50

Printed in sheets of 9 + label

Bruno Bjelinski (1909-92), Composer A413

Josip Andreis (1909-82), Musicologist A414

***Perf. 14¼x13¾ Syncopated***

**2009, Jan. 21** **Litho.**

**718** A413 1.80k multi .75 .75
**719** A414 3.50k multi 1.50 1.50

Street and Bridge, Sisak — A415

**2009, Jan. 22** ***Perf. 14 Syncopated***

**720** A415 8k multi 3.50 3.50

Remains of St. Tryphon in Kotor, 1200th Anniv. A416

No. 721 — St. Tryphon: a, Drawing. b, Sculpture from altarpiece, Kotor Cathedral.

**2009, Feb. 3** ***Perf. 14¼ Syncopated***
**721** A416 3.50k Horiz. pair, #a-b 2.75 2.75

Fairy Tale Characters — A417

No. 722: a, Svarozic. b, Bjesomar.

**2009, Feb. 27**
**722** A417 1.65k Horiz. pair, #a-b 1.50 1.50

Souvenir Sheet

Protection of Polar Regions and Glaciers — A418

No. 723: a, Sun over glacier. b, Intl. Polar Year emblem and glacier.

**2009, Mar. 27** **Litho. & Embossed**
**723** A418 5k Sheet of 2, #a-b 3.75 3.75

Easter — A419

***Perf. 14 Syncopated***

**2009, Mar. 30** **Litho.**
**724** A419 3.50k multi 1.60 1.60

Entry Into NATO — A420

**2009, Apr. 4**
**725** A420 8k multi 3.00 3.00

Juraj Sizgoric (1445-c. 1509), Poet — A421

Juraj Habdelic (1609-78), Writer — A422

Ljudevit Gaj (1809-72), Writer, Illyrian Movement Leader A423

Petar Segedin (1909-98), Writer A424

***Perf. 14¼x13¾ Syncopated***

**2009, Apr. 22**

| | | | | |
|---|---|---|---|---|
| **726** | A421 | 3.50k multi | 1.25 | 1.25 |
| **727** | A422 | 3.50k multi | 1.25 | 1.25 |
| **728** | A423 | 5k multi | 1.90 | 1.90 |
| **729** | A424 | 5k multi | 1.90 | 1.90 |
| | | *Nos. 726-729 (4)* | 6.30 | 6.30 |

Europa A425

No. 730 — Image of space from Hubble Space Telescope with red diamond at: a, Left. b, Right.

***Perf. 14x13½ Syncopated***

**2009, May 9** **Litho.**
**730** A425 8k Horiz. pair, #a-b 6.00 6.00

Intl. Year of Astronomy. Values are for stamps with surrounding selvage.

Franciscans in Cakovec, 350th Anniv. — A426

**2009, May 20** ***Perf. 14 Syncopated***
**731** A426 3.50k multi 1.40 1.40

Souvenir Sheet

King Andrew's Charter Proclaiming Varazdin as Free Royal Borough, 800th Anniv. — A427

***Perf. 14 Syncopated***

**2009, June 9** **Litho.**
**732** A427 15k multi 6.00 6.00

Souvenir Sheet

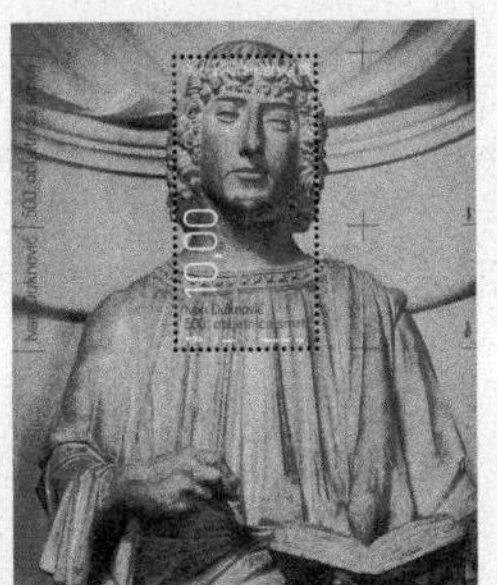
St. John, Sculpture by Ivan Duknovic (c. 1440-1509) — A428

**2009, June 23** ***Perf. 14***
**733** A428 10k multi 4.75 4.75

Zagreb Jazz Quartet, 50th Anniv. — A429

**2009, June 29**
**734** A429 10.70k multi 5.00 5.00

Fish — A430

Designs: 3.50k, Acipenser naccarii. No. 736, 5k, Knipowitschia mrakovcici. No. 737, 5k, Ballerus sapa.

**2009, Sept. 1** **Litho.** ***Perf. 14***

| | | | | |
|---|---|---|---|---|
| **735** | A430 | 3.50k multi | 1.75 | 1.75 |
| *a.* | | Booklet pane of 10 | 17.50 | — |
| | | Complete booklet, #735a | 17.50 | |
| **736** | A430 | 5k multi | 2.50 | 2.50 |
| *a.* | | Booklet pane of 10 | 25.00 | — |
| | | Complete booklet, #736a | 25.00 | |
| **737** | A430 | 5k multi | 2.50 | 2.50 |
| *a.* | | Booklet pane of 10 | 25.00 | — |
| | | Complete booklet, #737a | 25.00 | |
| | | *Nos. 735-737 (3)* | 6.75 | 6.75 |

Stamp Day — A431

**2009, Sept. 9**
**738** A431 3.50k multi 1.50 1.50

Croatian Post Inc., 10th Anniv.

Lighthouses — A432

Designs: No. 739, 3.50k, Gruica Lighthouse. No. 740, 3.50k, Strazica Lighthouse. 8k, Voscica Lighthouse.

**2009, Sept. 11**
**739-741** A432 Set of 3 5.75 5.75

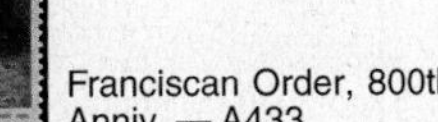
Franciscan Order, 800th Anniv. — A433

**2009, Sept. 17** **Litho.** ***Perf. 14***
**742** A433 3.50k multi 1.60 1.60

Souvenir Sheet

Stone Buildings A434

No. 743 — Stone building in: a, Pazin, Croatia. b, Kopriva na Krasu, Slovenia.

**2009, Sept. 25**
**743** A434 8k Sheet of 2, #a-b 7.50 7.50

See Slovenia No. 812.

St. Martin's Hermit Chapel, Podsused, 800th Anniv. — A435

**2009, Oct. 29**
**744** A435 3.50k multi 1.60 1.60

National Folk Dance Ensemble, 60th Anniv. — A436

**2009, Nov. 11**
**745** A436 3.50k multi 1.60 1.60

Rights of the Child — A437

**2009, Nov. 20**
**746** A437 3.50k multi 1.30 1.30

Declaration of the Rights of the Child, 50th anniv.; UN Convention on the Rights of the Child, 20th anniv.

New Year's Day — A438

**2009, Nov. 24** **Litho.** ***Perf. 14***
**747** A438 3.50k multi 1.50 1.50

***Serpentine Die Cut 5¼***
**Booklet Stamp**
**Self-Adhesive**

| | | | | |
|---|---|---|---|---|
| **748** | A438 | 3.50k multi | 1.50 | 1.50 |
| *a.* | | Booklet pane of 10 | 15.00 | |
| | | Complete booklet, #748a | 15.00 | |

**Modern Art Type of 2003**

Designs: No. 749, 1.80k, Gray Sail, by Zlatko Prica. No. 750, 1.80k, A Bosom Full of Wind, by Nives Kavuric Kurtovic, vert. No. 751, 1.80k, Flora, by Ordan Petlevski.

**2009, Dec. 1** **Litho.** ***Perf. 14***
**749-751** A304 Set of 3 2.00 2.00

A439

Christmas — A440

**2009, Dec. 4** **Litho.** ***Perf. 14***

| | | | | |
|---|---|---|---|---|
| **752** | A439 | 3.50k multi | 1.50 | 1.50 |
| **753** | A440 | 8k multi | 3.25 | 3.25 |

***Serpentine Die Cut 5¼***
**Booklet Stamp**
**Self-Adhesive**

| | | | | |
|---|---|---|---|---|
| **754** | A439 | 3.50k multi | 1.50 | 1.50 |
| *a.* | | Booklet pane of 10 | 15.00 | |
| | | Complete booklet, #754a | 15.00 | |

Statute of Lastovo, 700th Anniv. — A441

**2010, Jan. 8 Litho. *Perf. 14***
**755** A441 3.50k multi 1.60 1.60

2010 Winter Olympics, Vancouver — A442

**2010, Feb. 12 *Perf. 14¼x14***
**756** A442 3.50k multi 1.60 1.60

Souvenir Sheet

Peonies A443

No. 757: a, Paeonia mascula. b, Paeonia officinalis.

**2010, Mar. 8 Litho. *Perf. 14***
**757** A443 3k Sheet of 2, #a-b 3.00 3.00

Embroidery — A444

Embroidery from: 1.60k, Primorje. 3.10k, Medimurje. 4.60k, Posavina. 7.10k, Draganic.

**2010, Mar. 15**
**758-761** A444 Set of 4 7.75 7.75
*761a* Sheet of 4, #758-761 7.75 7.75

For surcharge, see No. 1140.

Fruit — A445

Designs: 1k, Fragaria vesca. No. 763, Vitis vinifera. No. 764, Ribes uva-crispa.

**2010, Mar. 16 Litho. & Embossed**
**762** A445 1k multi .45 .45
*a.* Booklet pane of 10 4.50 —
Complete booklet, #762a 4.50
**763** A445 4k multi 1.75 1.75
*a.* Booklet pane of 10 17.50 —
Complete booklet, #763a 17.50
**764** A445 4k multi 1.75 1.75
*a.* Booklet pane of 10 17.50 —
Complete booklet, #764a 17.50
*Nos. 762-764 (3)* 3.95 3.95

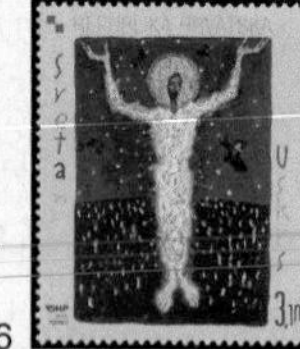
Easter — A446

**2010, Mar. 19 Litho. *Perf. 14***
**765** A446 3.10k multi 1.40 1.40

Establishment of Bjelovar-Krizevci Diocese — A447

**2010, Mar. 19**
**766** A447 6.50k multi 2.75 2.75

Printed in sheets of 8 + 2 labels.

Steam Locomotives A448

No. 767: a, Series MAV 326/JZ 125. b, Series SüdB 18.

**2010, Mar. 29**
**767** Vert. pair + central label 6.75 6.75
*a.-b.* A448 7.10k Either single 3.25 3.25

Capuchin Order in Croatia, 400th Anniv. — A449

**2010, Apr. 15**
**768** A449 6.10k multi 2.75 2.75

Famous Men — A450

Designs: 1.60k, Grgo Gamulin (1910-97), art historian. 3.10k, Janko Polic Kamov (1886-1910), writer. 4.50k, Ivan Matetic Ronjgov (1880-1960), composer. 6.10k, Marko Antun de Dominis (1560-1624), archbishop and physicist.

**2010, Apr. 22**
**769-772** A450 Set of 4 7.00 7.00

Souvenir Sheet

Expo 2010, Shanghai — A451

**2010, Apr. 29**
**773** A451 10k multi 4.50 4.50

Europa A452

No. 774 — Children's book and: a, Fairy on branch, fairy with horn. b, Fairy looking at butterfly, fairy on flower.

**Litho. With Foil Application**
**2010, May 7 *Perf. 14***
**774** A452 7.10k Horiz. pair, #a-b 6.25 6.25

Souvenir Sheet

Lubenice A453

**2010, May 21 Litho.**
**775** A453 10k multi 4.75 4.75

2010 World Cup Soccer Championships, South Africa — A454

**2010, June 11**
**776** A454 4.50k multi 2.25 2.25

Printed in sheets of 9 + label.

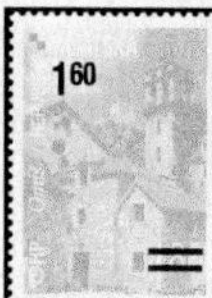
Nos. 562a, 601, 661a and 677 Surcharged

**Methods and Perfs. As Before**
**2010**
**777** A379 1.60k on 1.80k #661a .65 .65
**778** A344 3.10k on 3.50k #601 1.25 1.25
**779** A320 4.50k on 5k #562a 2.10 2.10
**780** A367 7.10k on 7.20k #677 3.25 3.25
*Nos. 777-780 (4)* 7.25 7.25

Issued: Nos. 777-778, 5/17; Nos. 779-780, 7/19.

Lighthouses — A455

Designs: No. 781, 3.10k, Vir Lighthouse. No. 782, 3.10k, Veli Rat Lighthouse. No. 783, 3.10k, Tajer Lighthouse.

**2010, Sept. 7 Litho. *Perf. 14***
**781-783** A455 Set of 3 4.50 4.50

Souvenir Sheet

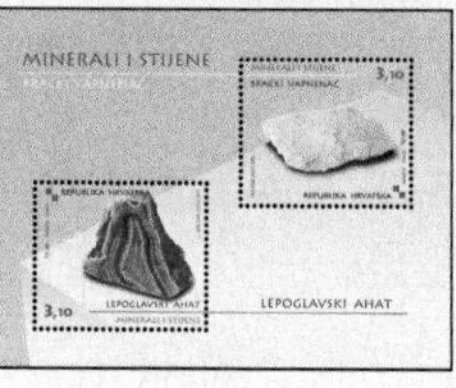
Minerals A456

No. 784: a, Calcite from Brac. b, Agate from Lepoglava.

**Litho. & Embossed (#784a), Litho.**
**2010, Oct. 15**
**784** A456 3.10k Sheet of 2, #a-b 3.00 3.00

Souvenir Sheet

Dubrovnik Tramway, Cent. — A457

**2010, Nov. 22 Litho. *Perf. 14***
**785** A457 15k multi 7.00 7.00

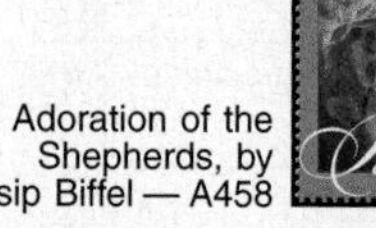
Adoration of the Shepherds, by Josip Biffel — A458

**2010, Nov. 25**
**786** A458 3.10k multi 1.50 1.50

**Booklet Stamp Self-Adhesive**
***Serpentine Die Cut 5¼***
**787** A458 3.10k multi 1.50 1.50
*a.* Booklet pane of 10 15.00
Complete booklet, #787a 15.00

Christmas.

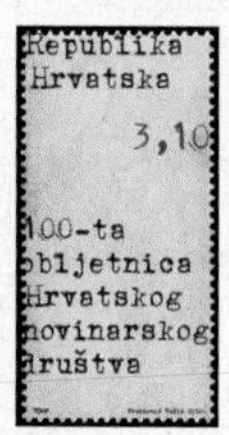

A459

**2010, Dec. 1 Litho. *Perf. 14***
**788** A459 3.10k multi 1.40 1.40

Croatian Journalist Society, cent.

New Year 2011 — A460

**2010, Dec. 6**
**789** A460 1.60k multi .75 .75

Intl. Children's Festival, Sibenik — A461

**2011, Feb. 14 Litho. *Perf. 14***
**790** A461 1.60k multi .85 .85

Fauna — A462

Designs: 1.60k, Ursus arctos. 3.10k, Falco eleonorae. 4.60k, Monachus monachus.

**2011, Mar. 15**
**791** A462 1.60k multi .80 .80
*a.* Booklet pane of 10 8.00 —
Complete booklet, #791a 8.00
**792** A462 3.10k multi 1.60 1.60
*a.* Booklet pane of 10 16.00 —
Complete booklet, #792a 16.00
**793** A462 4.60k multi 2.40 2.40
*a.* Booklet pane of 10 24.00 —
Complete booklet, #793a 24.00
*Nos. 791-793 (3)* 4.80 4.80

Stations of the Cross — A463

No. 794 — Station: a, 1. b, 2. c, 3. d, 4. e, 5. f, 6. g, 7. h, 8. i, 9. j, 10. k, 11. l, 12. m, 13. n, 14.

**2011, Mar. 23**

| | | | |
|---|---|---|---|
| **794** | Booklet pane of 14 | 24.50 | — |
| *a.-n.* | A463 3.10k Any single | 1.75 | 1.75 |
| | Complete booklet, #794 | 24.50 | |

Visit to Croatia of Pope Benedict XVI — A464

**2011, Apr. 4** **Litho.**

**795** A464 3.10k multi 1.75 1.75

Souvenir Sheet

Wreck of the Elhawi Star, Rijeka Harbor A465

**2011, Apr. 14** ***Perf. 14***

**796** A465 10k multi 5.00 5.00

Souvenir Sheet

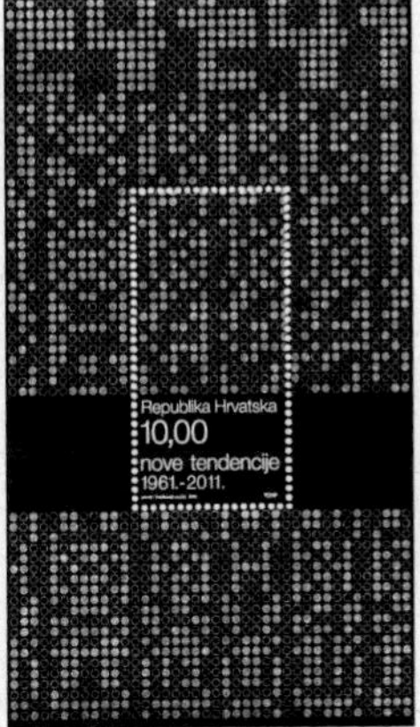

New Tendencies Art Exhibit, 50th Anniv. — A466

**2011, Apr. 15**

**797** A466 10k black & silver 5.00 5.00

Famous People — A467

Designs: No. 798, 1.60k, Jagoda Truhelka (1864-1957), writer. No. 799, 1.60k, August Harambasic (1861-1911), poet and politician. No. 800, 1.60k, Grigor Vitez (1911-66), writer.

**2011, Apr. 22**

**798-800** A467 Set of 3 2.25 2.25

Croatian Academy of Sciences and Arts, 150th Anniv. A468

**2011, Apr. 29**

**801** A468 9.50k multi 4.50 4.50

Europa A469

No. 802 — Paintings: a, Beech, by Josip Zanki. b, Forest Scene with Spider's Web, by Lovro Artukovic.

**2011, May 5**

**802** A469 7.10k Horiz. pair, #a-b 6.25 6.25

Intl. Year of Forests.

Castles and Palaces — A470

Arms and: No. 803, 3.10k, Pejacevic Castle, Nasice. No. 804, 3.10k, Hilleprand-Mailáth Castle, Donji Miholjac. No. 805, 4.60k, Hilleprand-Prandau Normann-Ehrenfels Castle, Valpovo. No. 806, 4.60k, Palace of Prince Eugene of Savoy, Bilje.

**2011, June 16** **Litho.** ***Perf. 14***

| | | | |
|---|---|---|---|
| **803-806** | A470 Set of 4 | 7.00 | 7.00 |
| *806a* | Sheet of 8, 2 each #803-806, + 8 labels | 15.00 | 15.00 |

Nos. 803-806 each were printed in sheets of 9 + label. See Nos. 876-879, 956-959.

Independence, 20th Anniv. — A471

**2011, June 24**

**807** A471 3.10k multi 1.50 1.50

Printed in sheets of 25 + 5 labels.

Eucharistic Miracle of Ludbreg, 600th Anniv. — A472

**2011, Sept. 1**

**808** A472 5k multi 2.50 2.50

Quick Response Code — A473

**2011, Sept. 9**

**809** A473 3.10k brown & black 1.60 1.60

Stamp Day.

Rudjer Boskovich (1711-87), Astronomer, and Dome of St. Peter's Basilica A474

**2011, Sept. 13**

**810** A474 7.10k multi 3.75 3.75

See Vatican City No. 1482.

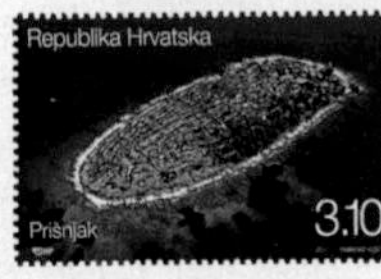

Lighthouses A475

Designs: No. 811, 3.10k, Prisnjak Lighthouse. No. 812, 3.10k, Mulo Lighthouse. 7.10k, Blitvenica Lighthouse.

**2011, Oct. 18**

**811-813** A475 Set of 3 6.50 6.50

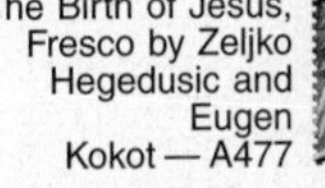

Institute of Art History, Zagreb, 50th Anniv. A476

**2011, Oct. 28**

**814** A476 4.60k multi 2.50 2.50

The Birth of Jesus, Fresco by Zeljko Hegedusic and Eugen Kokot — A477

**2011, Nov. 3**

**815** A477 3.10k multi 1.75 1.75

***Serpentine Die Cut 5¼***

**Booklet Stamp**
**Self-Adhesive**

| | | | |
|---|---|---|---|
| **816** | A477 3.10k multi | 1.75 | 1.75 |
| *a.* | Booklet pane of 10 | 17.50 | |
| | Complete booklet, #816a | 17.50 | |

Christmas.

Siege of Vukovar, 20th Anniv. — A478

**2011, Nov. 18** ***Perf. 14***

**817** A478 3.10k multi 1.75 1.75

Ivica Kostelic, 2011 World Cup Skiing Overall Champion — A479

**2011, Nov. 23**

**818** A479 7.10k multi 3.50 3.50

Printed in sheets of 9 + label.

New Year 2012 — A480

**Litho. With Foil Application**

**2011, Nov. 24**

**819** A480 3.10k multi 1.60 1.60

Art — A481

Designs: 3.10k, Space-B, by Ante Kuduz. 4.50k, Woman with Cat, by Marijan Trepse, vert. 9.50k, Lovers, by Anka Krizmanic.

**2011, Dec. 1** **Litho.** ***Perf. 14***

**820-822** A481 Set of 3 8.00 8.00

Vasa Posta Foundation — A482

**2011, Dec. 5**

**823** A482 3.10k multi 1.60 1.60

Printed in sheets of 8 + label.

New Year 2012 (Year of the Dragon) — A483

**2012, Jan. 4**

**824** A483 1.60k ol brn & blk .90 .90

St. Valentine's Day — A484

**2012, Feb. 1** ***Perf. 14x13¾***

| | | | |
|---|---|---|---|
| **825** | A484 3.10k multi + 2 labels | 2.25 | 2.25 |
| *a.* | Booklet pane of 4 + 8 labels | 9.00 | — |
| | Complete booklet, #825a | 9.00 | |

No. 825 was printed in sheets of 4 stamps + 8 labels. These sheets were affixed inside booklet covers, and booklet panes have folds along the left margin and throuch the center row of perforations.

Cats A485

No. 826: a, 1.60k, Ragdoll cat and bird. b, 1.60k, Domestic cat and ball. c, 3.10k, Siamese cat and sock. d, 3.10k, Persian cat and mouse.

**2012, Feb. 21** ***Perf. 14***

**826** A485 Block of 4, #a-d 4.50 4.50

Flowers — A486

Designs: 1.60k, Galanthus nivalis. 3.10k, Primula vulgaris. 4.60k, Crocus vernus.

**2012, Mar. 15**

| | | | |
|---|---|---|---|
| **827** | A486 1.60k multi | .80 | .80 |
| *a.* | Booklet pane of 10 | 8.00 | — |
| | Complete booklet, #827a | 8.00 | |
| **828** | A486 3.10k multi | 1.50 | 1.50 |
| *a.* | Booklet pane of 10 | 15.00 | — |
| | Complete booklet, #828a | 15.00 | |
| **829** | A486 4.60k multi | 2.25 | 2.25 |
| *a.* | Booklet pane of 10 | 22.50 | — |
| | Complete booklet, #829a | 22.50 | |
| | *Nos. 827-829 (3)* | 4.55 | 4.55 |

Easter — A487

**2012, Mar. 16**

830 A487 3.10k multi 1.50 1.50
*a.* Booklet pane of 4 6.00 —
Complete booklet, #830a 6.00

Famous People — A488

Designs: No. 831, 1.60k, Bishop Juraj Dobrila (1812-82). No. 832, 1.60k, Vesna Parun (1922-2010), poet. No. 833, 1.60k, Dragojla Jarnevic (1812-75), poet.

**2012, Apr. 19**

**831-833** A488 Set of 3 2.25 2.25

Statute of Split, 700th Anniv. — A489

**2012, Apr. 25**

**834** A489 3.10k multi 1.50 1.50

No. 834 was printed in sheets of 10 + 2 labels.

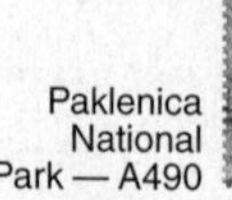
Paklenica National Park — A490

Apoxyomenos Statue Found in the Adriatic Sea — A491

**2012, May 9**

**835** A490 7.10k multi 3.50 3.50
**836** A491 7.10k multi 3.50 3.50

Europa.

Croatian Chess Federation, Cent. — A492

**2012, May 12**

**837** A492 4.60k multi 2.25 2.25

No. 837 was printed in sheets of 9 + label.

Lighthouses A493

Designs: 3.10k, St. Peter's Lighthouse. No. 839, 7.10k, St. Nicholas's Lighthouse. No. 840, 7.10k, Pokonji Dol Lighthouse.

**2012, May 31**

**838-840** A493 Set of 3 8.25 8.25

Croatian Soccer Team's Participation in 2012 European Soccer Championships A494

**2012, June 8**

**841** A494 4.60k multi 2.00 2.00

Printed in sheets of 9 + label.

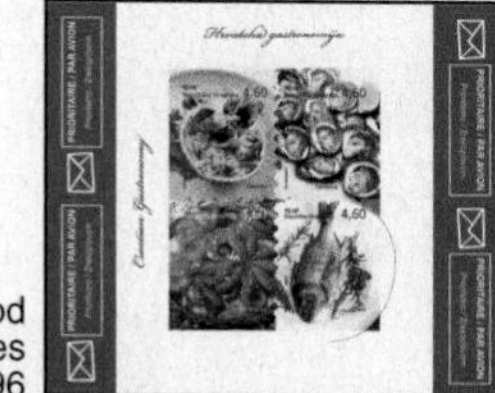
UNESCO Intangible Cultural Heritage of Croatia — A495

Designs: 1.60k, Festival of St. Blaise (Festa Sv. Vlaha). 3.10k, Lacemaking, Hvar. 4.60k, Gingerbread heart, butterfly and cross. 7.10k, Carved wooden bird toy.

**2012, June 12**

**842-845** A495 Set of 4 6.50 6.50
*845a* Souvenir sheet of 4, #842-845 + 5 labels 6.50 6.50

Miniature Sheet

Seafood Dishes A496

No. 846: a, Rakovica (spider crab). b, Kamenice (oysters). c, Hobotnica (octopi). d, Orada (gilthead sea bream).

**2012, July 2** ***Serpentine Die Cut 5¼***
**Self-Adhesive**

**846** A496 4.60k Sheet of 4, #a-d, + 4 etiquettes 7.50 7.50

2012 Summer Olympics, London — A497

**2012, July 23** ***Perf. 14***

**847** A497 3.10k multi 1.25 1.25

Printed in sheets of 9 + label.

A498

A499

A500

Hemaris Croatica — A501

**2012, Sept. 18**

**848** Strip of 4 7.00 7.00
*a.* A498 4.60k multi 1.75 1.75
*b.* A499 4.60k multi 1.75 1.75
*c.* A500 4.60k multi 1.75 1.75
*d.* A501 4.60k multi 1.75 1.75

Worldwide Fund for Nature (WWF).

Theater in Hvar, 400th Anniv. A502

**2012, Sept. 25**

**849** A502 1.60k multi .65 .65

Locomotives A503

No. 850: a, MAV 424/JDZ/JZ 11. b, SüdB 29/JDZ 124.

**2012, Oct. 1**

**850** Vert. pair + 2 central labels 5.50 5.50
*a.-b.* A503 7.10k Either single 2.75 2.75

First locomotives on Zidani Most-Sisak line, 150th anniv.

Souvenir Sheet

Diplomatic Relations Between Croatia and San Marino, 20th Anniv. — A504

No. 851 —Traditional costumes with denomination at: a, LR. b, LL.

**2012, Oct. 16**

**851** A504 7.10k Sheet of 2, #a-b 5.50 5.50

See San Marino No. 1874.

Euroherc Insurance Company, 20th Anniv. — A505

**2012, Oct. 19**

**852** A505 3.10k multi + label 1.25 1.25

Souvenir Sheet

Rocks and Minerals A506

No. 853: a, Roselite. b, Zebrato granite.

**Litho. & Embossed With Foil Application**

**2012, Oct. 24** ***Perf.***

**853** A506 5k Sheet of 2, #a-b 4.00 4.00

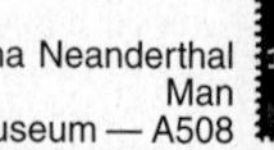
Intl. Day of the Romani Language — A507

**2012, Nov. 5** **Litho.** ***Perf. 14***

**854** A507 3.10k multi 1.25 1.25

Krapina Neanderthal Man Museum — A508

Designs: 1.60k. Timeline and statues of hominids. 3.10k, Diorama of Neanderthals in cave.

**2012, Nov. 7**

**855-856** A508 Set of 2 1.90 1.90

Christmas — A509

**Litho. With Foil Application**

**2012, Nov. 15** ***Perf. 14***

**857** A509 3.10k multi 1.25 1.25

**Booklet Stamp**
**Self-Adhesive**
***Serpentine Die Cut 5¼***

**858** A509 3.10k multi 1.25 1.25
*a.* Booklet pane of 10 12.50
Complete booklet, #858a 12.50

Greek Catholic Church in Croatia, 400th Anniv. — A510

**2012, Nov. 27** **Litho.** ***Perf. 14***

**859** A510 3.10k multi 1.25 1.25

New Year 2013 — A511

**Litho. With Foil Application**

**2012, Dec. 4**

**860** A511 3.10k multi 1.25 1.25

Dogs A512

No. 861: a, German shepherd with bone. b, Yorkshire terrier with sausages. c, Golden retriever with newspaper. d, Bichon frisé in basket.

**2013, Feb. 21** **Litho.**

**861** A512 3.10k Block or vert. strip of 4, #a-d 4.25 4.25

Easter — A513

**2013, Mar. 11**
**862** A513 3.10k multi 1.10 1.10

Amphibians — A514

Designs: 1.60k, Bombina bombina. 3.10k, Salamandra salamandra. 4.60k, Proteus anguinus.

**2013, Apr. 8**
**863** A514 1.60k multi .55 .55
*a.* Booklet pane of 10 5.50 —
Complete booklet, #863a 5.50
**864** A514 3.10k multi 1.10 1.10
*a.* Booklet pane of 10 11.00 —
Complete booklet, #864a 11.00
**865** A514 4.60k multi 1.60 1.60
*a.* Booklet pane of 10 16.00 —
Complete booklet, #865a 16.00
*Nos. 863-865 (3)* 3.25 3.25

Famous People — A515

Designs: No. 866, 1.20k, Stjepan Gradic (1613-83), diplomat. No. 867, 1.20k, Antonija Krasnik (1874-1956), decorative artist. No. 868, 5.80k, Ranko Marinkovic (1913-2001), writer. No. 869, 5.80k, Milka Trnina (1863-1941), opera singer.

**2013, Apr. 16**
**866-869** A515 Set of 4 5.00 5.00

Souvenir Sheet

Bridges A516

No. 870: a, Railway Bridge, Zagreb (49x24mm). b, Old Bridge, Tounj (36x30mm).

**2013, Apr. 29**
**870** A516 7.10k Sheet of 2, #a-b 5.00 5.00

Europa — A517

Postal vehicles: No. 871, 7.10k, Moped. No. 872, 7.10k, Van.

**2013, May 9**
**871-872** A517 Set of 2 5.25 5.25

A518

Admission of Croatia to European Union — A519

**2013, July 1**
**873** A518 3.10k multi 1.10 1.10

**Souvenir Sheet**

**874** A519 20k multi 7.00 7.00

No. 873 was printed in sheets of 25 stamps + 5 labels.

Pula Film Festival, 60th Anniv. — A520

**2013, July 2**
**875** A520 3.10k multi 1.10 1.10

**Castles and Palaces Type of 2011**

Arms and: No. 876, 1.60k, Odescalchi Castle, Ilok. No. 877, 1.60k, Eltz Castle, Vukovar. No. 878, 1.60k, Pejacevic Castle, Virovitica. No. 879, 1.60k, Turkovic Castle, Kutjevo.

**2013, July 18**
**876-879** A470 Set of 4 2.25 2.25
*879a* Souvenir sheet of 8, 2 each #876-879, + 8 labels 4.50 4.50

Mushrooms — A521

No. 880: a, Macrolepiota procera. b, Boletus regius. c, Tuber magnatum. Tuber melanosporum.

**2013, Sept. 3** ***Perf. 14***
**880** Horiz. strip of 3 5.25 5.25
*a.-c.* A521 4.60k Any single 1.75 1.75

Lapitch, the Little Shoemaker — A522

**2013, Sept. 4**
**881** A522 3.10k multi 1.10 1.10

Publishing of Lapitch, the Little Shoemaker, children's book by Ivana Brlic Mazuranic, cent.

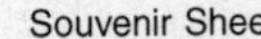

Souvenir Sheet

Portrait of Count Teodor Pejacevic (1855-1928), by Vlaho Bukovac — A523

**2013, Sept. 18**
**882** A523 11k multi 4.00 4.00

Diplomatic relations between Croatia and the Sovereign Military Order of Malta, 20th anniv.

Lighthouses A524

Designs: 4.60k, Plocica Lighthouse. 5.80k, Stoncica Lighthouse. 7.60k, Sucuraj Lighthouse.

**2013, Sept. 26** ***Perf. 14***
**883-885** A524 Set of 3 6.50 6.50

Salesians in Croatia, Cent. — A525

**2013, Oct. 1** **Litho.** ***Perf. 14***
**886** A525 1.20k multi .45 .45

Gas Lighting System in Zagreb, 150th Anniv. — A526

**2013, Oct. 3** **Litho.** ***Perf. 14***
**887** A526 7.60k multi 2.75 2.75

No. 887 was printed in sheets of 8 + label.

Souvenir Sheet

Peasant's Revolt, 440th Anniv. — A527

**2013, Oct. 11** **Litho.** ***Perf. 14***
**888** A527 11k multi 4.00 4.00

Mirko (1871-1913) and Stevo (1875-1936) Seljan, Explorers, Map of Guayra Falls, South America A528

**2013, Oct. 15** **Litho.** ***Perf. 14***
**889** A528 7.60k multi 2.75 2.75

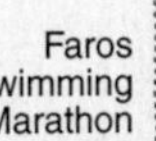

Faros Swimming Marathon A529

**2013, Nov. 5** **Litho.** ***Perf. 14***
**890** A529 7.60k multi 2.75 2.75

No. 890 was printed in sheets of 9 + label.

Christmas — A530

**Litho. With Foil Application**

**2013, Nov. 27** ***Perf. 14***
**891** A530 3.10k multi 1.10 1.10

**Litho.**
**Booklet Stamp**
**Self-Adhesive**

***Serpentine Die Cut 5¼***

**892** A530 3.10k multi 1.10 1.10
*a.* Booklet pane of 10 11.00
Complete booklet, #892a 11.00

Art — A531

Designs: 1.20k, Black Flag, by Ljubo Babic. 3.10k, Sappho, by Bela Cikos Sesija. 5.80k, PAFAMA, by Josip Seissel.

**2013, Dec. 3** **Litho.** ***Perf. 14***
**893-895** A531 Set of 3 3.75 3.75

New Year 2014 — A532

**Litho. With Foil Application**

**2013, Dec. 5** ***Perf. 14***
**896** A532 3.10k multi 1.10 1.10

2014 Winter Olympics, Sochi, Russia — A533

**2014, Feb. 7** **Litho.** ***Perf. 14***
**897** A533 3.10k multi 1.10 1.10

No. 897 was printed in sheets of 9 + label.

Pets A534

No. 898: a, Chinchilla eating apple slice. b, Guinea pig eating biscuit. c, Rabbit in top hat. d, Hamster with carrot.

**2014, Feb. 21** **Litho.** ***Perf. 14***
**898** A534 3.10k Block of 4, #a.-d. 4.50 4.50

Temple of Augustus, Pula — A535

**2014, Mar. 3 Litho. *Perf. 14***
**899** A535 2.80k multi 1.00 1.00

Souvenir Sheet

University of Zagreb Faculty of Science Botanical Garden, 125th Anniv. — A536

**2014, Apr. 1 Litho. *Perf. 14***
**900** A536 11k multi 4.00 4.00

Dalmatian Braided Bread — A537

**2014, Apr. 2 Litho. *Perf. 14***
**901** A537 3.10k multi 1.10 1.10

Easter.

Miniature Sheet

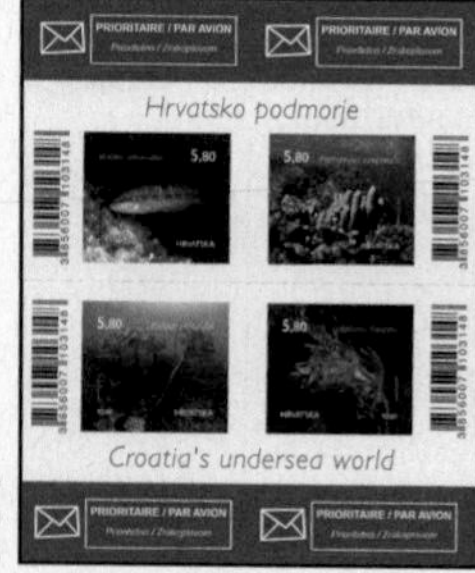

Marine Life A538

No. 902: a, Ornate wrasse (Vladika arbanaska). b, Golden sponge (Promjenjiva sumporaca). c, European fan worm (Kozasti perjanicar). d, mediterranean violet aeolid (Ljubicasta flabelina).

***Serpentine Die Cut 5¼***
**2014, Apr. 9 Litho.**
**Self-Adhesive**
**902** A538 Sheet of 4 + 4 etiquettes 8.50
*a.-d.* 5.80k Any single 2.10 2.10

Orchids — A539

Designs: No. 903, Ophrys dinarica. No. 904, Serapias istriaca. 3.10k, Ophrys libunica.

**2014, Apr. 11 Litho. *Perf. 14***
**903** A539 2.80k multi 1.00 1.00
*a.* Booklet pane of 10 10.00
Complete booklet, #903a 10.00
**904** A539 2.80k multi 1.00 1.00
*a.* Booklet pane of 10 10.00
Complete booklet, #904a 10.00
**905** A539 3.10 multi 1.10 1.10
*a.* Booklet pane of 10 11.00
Complete booklet, #905a 11.00

Famous People — A540

Designs: 1.20k, Ivan Bjelovucic (1889-1949), first man to fly over Alps. 2.80k, Ivan Gundulic (1589-1638), writer. 3.10k, Ivan Mazuranic (1814-90), poet. 7.60k, Dora Pejacevic (1885-1923), composer.

**2014, Apr. 18 Litho. *Perf. 14***
**906-909** A540 Set of 4 5.50 5.50

Canonization of Popes John Paul II and John XXIII — A541

No. 910—Arms and portrait of: a, Pope John Paul II. b, Pope John XXIII.

**2014, Apr. 25 Litho. *Perf. 14***
**910** A541 7.60k Pair, #a.-b. 5.75 5.75

Europa — A542

Musical instruments:3.10k, Lijerica. 7.60k, Sopile.

**2014, May 9 Litho. *Perf. 14***
**911-912** A542 Set of 2 4.00 4.00

Lighthouses A543

Designs: 2.80k, Palagruza Lighthouse. No. 914, 5.80k, Struga Lighthouse. No. 915, 5.80k, Susac Lighthouse.

**2014, May 30 Litho. *Perf. 14***
**913-915** A543 Set of 3 5.25 5.25

Villa Angiolina, Opatija, 170th Anniv. — A544

**2014, June 11 Litho. *Perf. 14***
**916** A544 2.80k multi 1.00 1.00

No. 916 was printed in sheets of 8 + central label.

2014 World Cup Soccer Championships, Brazil — A545

**2014, June 12 Litho. *Perf. 14***
**917** A545 7.60k multi 2.75 2.75

No. 917 was printed in sheets of 9 + label.

Volunteer Fire Departments in Croatia, 150th Anniv. — A546

**2014, June 17 Litho. *Perf. 14***
**918** A546 5k multi 1.90 1.90

No. 918 was printed in sheets of 8 + 2 labels.

Prelog, 750th Anniv. — A547

**2014, Sept. 23 Litho. *Perf. 14***
**919** A547 3.10k multi 1.10 1.10

Souvenir Sheet

Carved Wooden Doorway of Split Cathedral, 800th Anniv. — A548

**2014, Sept. 23 Litho. *Perf. 14***
**920** A548 11k multi 3.75 3.75

Statute of the Town and Island of Korcula, 800th Anniv. — A549

**2014, Sept. 26 Litho. *Perf. 14***
**921** A549 2.80k multi .95 .95

St. Nicholas Benedictine Monastery, Trogir, 950th Anniv. — A550

**2014, Sept. 30 Litho. *Perf. 14***
**922** A550 2.80k multi .95 .95

Locomotives A551

No. 923: a, KkStB 229/JDZ/JZ 116. b, MAV 375/JDZ/HDZ/JZ 51.

**2014, Oct. 1 Litho. *Perf. 14***
**923** Vert. pair + 2 central labels 3.50 3.50
*a.-b.* A551 5k Either single 1.75 1.75

Monument in Mirogoj Cemetery, Zagreb — A552

**2014, Oct. 14 Litho. *Perf. 14***
**924** A552 7.60k multi 2.50 2.50

World War I, cent.

Details from Traditional Costumes — A553

Detail from costume from: 3.10k, Slavonia. 5.80k, Vrlika. 7.60k, Gorski Kotar. 11k, Lovas.

**2014, Oct. 20 Litho. *Perf. 14***
**925** A553 3.10k multi 1.00 1.00
**926** A553 5.80k multi 1.90 1.90
**927** A553 7.60k multi 2.50 2.50
**928** A553 11k multi 3.75 3.75
*a.* Souvenir sheet of 4, #925-928 9.25 9.25
*Nos. 925-928 (4)* 9.15 9.15

See Nos. 1023-1026, 1076-1079.

Souvenir Sheet

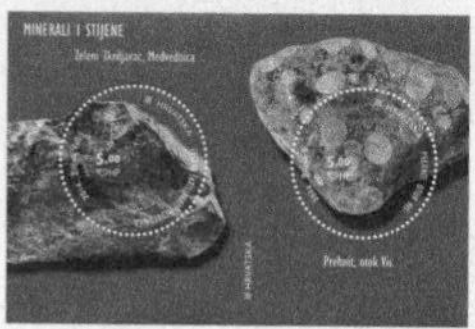

Rocks and Minerals A554

No. 929: a, Green schist (green background). b, Prehnite (blue background).

**Litho. & Embossed**
**2014, Oct. 24 *Perf.***
**929** A554 5k Sheet of 2, #a-b 3.25 3.25

Souvenir Sheet

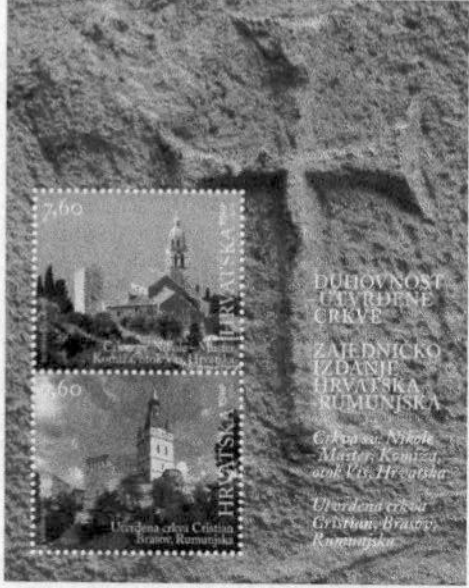

Fortified Churches — A555

No. 930: a, St. Nicholas Church, Komiza. b, Evangelical Church, Cristian, Romania.

**2014, Nov. 14 Litho. *Perf. 14***
**930** A555 7.60k Sheet of 2, #a-b 5.00 5.00

See Romania Nos. 5625-5626.

Requisition, by Ivan Generalic (1914-92) A556

**2014, Nov. 17 Litho. *Perf. 14***
**931** A556 3.10k multi 1.00 1.00

Christmas — A557

**Litho. With Foil Application**
**2014, Nov. 27 *Perf. 14***
**932** A557 3.10k multi 1.00 1.00

**Booklet Stamp**
**Self-Adhesive**
***Serpentine Die Cut 5¼***
**933** A557 3.10k multi 1.00 1.00
*a.* Booklet pane of 10 10.00
Complete booklet, #933a 10.00

Royal University Library and Land Archives — A558

Designs: No. 934, 4.60k, Building exterior. No. 935, 4.60k, Reading room. No. 936, 4.60k, Table lamps, vert.

**2014, Dec. 1 Litho. *Perf. 14***
**934-936** A558 Set of 3 4.50 4.50

New Year 2015 — A559

**2014, Dec. 4** **Litho.** ***Perf. 14***
**937** A559 3.10k multi 1.00 1.00

St. Valentine's Day — A560

**2015, Feb. 4** **Litho.** ***Perf. 14***
**938** A560 6.50k multi 1.90 1.90

Values are for stamps with surrounding selvage.

112 Emergency Services Day — A561

**2015, Feb. 11** **Litho.** ***Perf. 14***
**939** A561 6.50k brt orange & blk 1.90 1.90

Pet Birds A562

No. 940: a, Canary wearing horned helmet. b, Budgerigar wearing captain's hat. c, Zebra finch with didgeridoo. d, Sulphur-crested cockatoo wearing leather jacket.

**2015, Feb. 19** **Litho.** ***Perf. 14***
**940** A562 3.10k Block of 4, #a-d 3.75 3.75

Rotary International District 1913, 110th Anniv. A563

**2015, Feb. 23** **Litho.** ***Perf. 14***
**941** A563 3.10k multi .90 .90

Easter — A564

**Litho. With Foil Application**

**2015, Mar. 16** ***Perf. 14***
**942** A564 3.10k multi .90 .90

Croatian Paralympic Committee, 50th Anniv. — A565

**2015, Mar. 23** **Litho.** ***Perf. 14***
**943** A565 5k multi 1.50 1.50

No. 943 was printed in sheets of 9 + label.

Lace A566

No. 944: a, Colors of Croatian flag, lace from Lepoglav. b, Colors of Spanish flag, lace from Seville.

**2015, Mar. 31** **Litho.** ***Perf. 14***
**944** A566 7.60k Pair, #a-b 4.50 4.50

See Spain No. 4037.

Wildlife — A567

Designs: 2.80k, Capreolus capreolus. 4.60k, Vulpes vulpes. 6.50k, Sus scrofa.

**2015, Apr. 15** **Litho.** ***Perf. 14***
**945** A567 2.80k multi .85 .85
*a.* Booklet pane of 10 8.50 —
Complete booklet, #945a 8.50
**946** A567 4.60k multi 1.40 1.40
*a.* Booklet pane of 10 14.00 —
Complete booklet, #946a 14.00
**947** A567 6.50k multi 2.00 2.00
*a.* Booklet pane of 10 20.00 —
Complete booklet, #947a 20.00
*Nos. 945-947 (3)* 4.25 4.25

Famous People — A568

Designs: No. 948, 3.10k, Ivan Supek (1915-2007), scientist and writer. No. 949, 3.10k, Luka Sorkocevic (1734-89), composer. No. 950, 3.10k, Josip Juraj Strossmayer (1815-1905), bishop and politician.

**2015, Apr. 21** **Litho.** ***Perf. 14***
**948-950** A568 Set of 3 2.75 2.75

No. 949, a stamp that does not show an image of Sorkocevic, was designed, printed and sent to post offices after the original stamp, which showed a picture of Thomas Jefferson instead of Sorkocevic, was printed and distributed to post offices. The stamp with Jefferson's image was recalled from all post offices prior to the April 21 day of issue, but 22 examples of it were, nonetheless, sold at a post office before that day.

1000th Stamp Design of Croatia Post — A569

**2015, Apr. 27** **Litho.** ***Perf. 14***
**951** A569 3.10k multi .95 .95

Souvenir Sheet

Bridges A570

No. 952: a, Modrus 1 Bridge. b, Krka River Bridge.

**2015, Apr. 29** **Litho.** ***Perf. 14***
**952** A570 7.60k Sheet of 2, #a-b 4.50 4.50

Europa — A571

Toys: 4.60k, To Tak wood pieces and connectors. 7.60k, Porcelain doll.

**2015, May 7** **Litho.** ***Perf. 14***
**953-954** A571 Set of 2 3.75 3.75

International Telecommunications Union, 150th Anniv. — A572

**2015, May 15** **Litho.** ***Perf. 14***
**955** A572 10k multi 3.00 3.00

**Castles and Palaces Type of 2011**

Designs: No. 956, 4.60k, Jankovic Castle, Daruvar. No. 957, 4.60k, Markovic-Kulmer Castle, Cernik. No. 958, 4.60k, Erdödy-Rubido Castle, Gornja Rijeka. No. 959, 4.60k, Old Town, Durdevac.

**2015, May 20** **Litho.** ***Perf. 14***
**956-959** A470 Set of 4 5.50 5.50
*959a* Souvenir sheet of 8, 2 each #956-959, + 8 labels 11.00 11.00

Lighthouses A573

Designs: 2.80k, Daksa Lighthouse. 3.10k, Glavat Lighthouse. 4.60k, Grebeni Lighthouse. 6.50k, Sveti Andrija Lighthouse.

**2015, June 10** **Litho.** ***Perf. 14***
**960-963** A573 Set of 4 5.00 5.00

Bracera A574

**2015, July 9** **Litho.** ***Perf. 14***
**964** A574 5.80k multi 1.75 1.75

A575

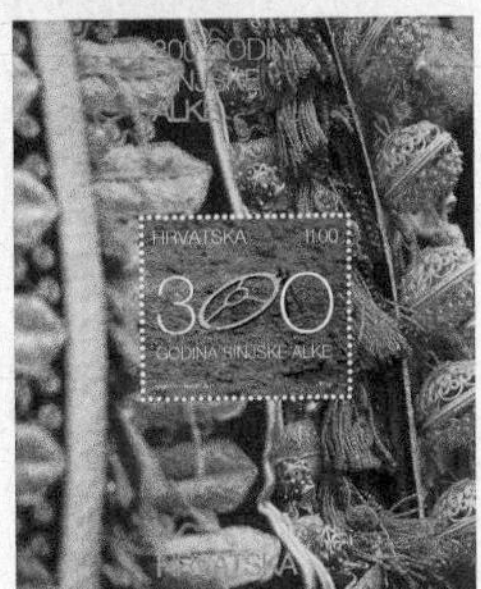
UNESCO Intangible Cultural Heritage — A576

Designs: No. 965, 3.10k, Zvoncari (carnival procession of bell ringers from Kastav). No. 966, 3.10k, Becarac (musician with stringed instrument). No. 967, 3.10k, Klapsko Pjevanje (a capella singers). No. 968, 3.10k, Sinjska Alka (horseman at Alka Chivalric Tournament, Sinj).

11k, Alka Chivalric Tournament, 300th anniv.

**2015, July 27** **Litho.** ***Perf. 14***
**965-968** A575 Set of 4 3.75 3.75
*968a* Souvenir sheet of 4, #965-968, + 5 labels 3.75 3.75

**Souvenir Sheet**

**Litho., Sheet Margin Litho. With Foil Application**

**969** A576 11k multi 3.25 3.25

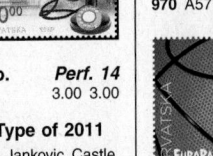

Victory and Homeland Thanksgiving Day — A577

**2015, Aug. 3** **Litho.** ***Perf. 14***
**970** A577 3.10k multi .90 .90

2015 Men's European Basketball Cahmpionships, Zagreb — A578

**2015, Sept. 4** **Litho.** ***Perf. 14***
**971** A578 5k multi 1.50 1.50

No. 971 was printed in sheets of 8 + label.

Traffic Safety — A579

**2015, Sept. 7** **Litho.** ***Perf. 14***
**972** A579 3.10k multi .95 .95

Christmas — A580

**2015, Nov. 25** **Litho.** ***Perf. 14***
**973** A580 3.10k multi .90 .90

**Booklet Stamp**
**Self-Adhesive**

***Serpentine Die Cut 5¼***

**974** A580 3.10k multi .90 .90
*a.* Booklet pane of 10 9.00
Complete booklet, #974a 9.00

Sculpture A581

Designs: 1.20k, Metal Sculpture XX, by Dusan Dzamonja. 3.10k, Dunja I, by Kosta Angeli Radovani. 4.60k, The Bull, by Vojin Bakic.

**2015, Dec. 1** **Litho.** ***Perf. 14***
**975-977** A581 Set of 3 2.50 2.50

Advertising Slogan for Mercedes-Benz Automobiles — A582

**2016, Feb. 2** **Litho.** ***Perf. 14***
**978** A582 4.60k lt bl + label 1.40 1.40

St. Blaise, by Carmelo Reggio — A583

**2016, Feb. 3** **Litho.** ***Perf. 14***
**979** A583 3.10k multi .90 .90

St. Blaise (d. 316), patron saint of Dubrovnik.

Pet Fish A584

No. 980: a, Angelfish and baby carriage. b, Goldfish, hat, gold and miner's pan. c, Guppy, rainbow, airplane. d, Siamese fighting fish, castle, shield and lance.

**2016, Feb. 22 Litho. *Perf. 14***
**980** A584 3.10k Block of 4, #a-d 3.50 3.50

Easter — A585

**2016, Mar. 8 Litho. *Perf. 14***
**981** A585 3.10k multi .95 .95

Herbs — A586

Designs: 2.80k, Rosmarinus officinalis. 3.10k, Lavandula angustifolia. 4.60k, Helichrysum italicum.

**2016, Mar. 21 Litho. *Perf. 14***
**982** A586 2.80k multi .85 .85
*a.* Booklet pane of 10 8.50 —
Complete booklet, #982a 8.50
**983** A586 3.10k multi .95 .95
*a.* Booklet pane of 10 9.50 —
Complete booklet, #983a 9.50
**984** A586 4.60k multi 1.40 1.40
*a.* Booklet pane of 10 14.00 —
Complete booklet, #984a 14.00
*Nos. 982-984 (3)* 3.20 3.20

Nos. 982-984 are impregnated with the scent of the depicted plant.

Famous People — A587

Designs: No. 985, 3.10k, Sidonija Erdödy Rubido (1819-84), opera singer. No. 986, 3.10k, Slavko Kolar (1891-1963), writer. No. 987, 3.10k, Mia Corak Slavenska (1916-2002), ballerina. No. 988, 3.10k, Mirko Bogovic (1816-93), poet.

**2016, Apr. 20 Litho. *Perf. 14***
**985-988** A587 Set of 4 3.75 3.75

Radio Announcer and Cameraman — A588

**2016, Apr. 26 Litho. *Perf. 14***
**989** A588 3.10k multi + label .95 .95

Croatian radio broadcasting 90th anniv.; Croatian television broadcasting, 60th anniv.

Islamic Center, Zagreb — A589

**2016, Apr. 27 Litho. *Perf. 14***
**990** A589 3.10k multi .95 .95

Islam in Croatia, cent.

Croatian Inventors and Their Inventions A590

Designs: 5k, Giovanni Biagio Luppis (1813-75) and torpedo. 6.50k, Eduard Slavoljub Penkala (1871-1922) and mechanical pencil, vert.

**2016, Apr. 27 Litho. *Perf. 14***
**991-992** A590 Set of 2 3.50 3.50

A591

Europa — A592

**2016, May 9 Litho. *Perf. 14***
**993** A591 4.60k multi 1.40 1.40
**994** A592 7.60k multi 2.25 2.25

Think Green Issue.

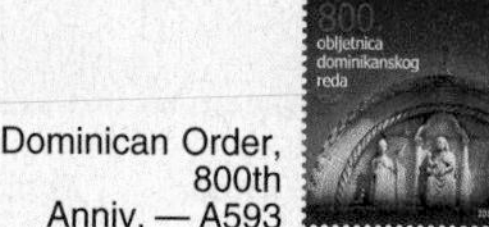

Dominican Order, 800th Anniv. — A593

**2016, May 24 Litho. *Perf. 14***
**995** A593 3.10k multi .95 .95

Greetings to the Sun, by Nikola Basic — A594

Sea Organ, by Basic — A595

**2016, June 1 Litho. *Perf. 14***
**996** A594 2.80k multi .85 .85
**997** A595 4.60k multi 1.40 1.40

Monuments in Zadar.

Declaration of Statehood, 25th Anniv. — A596

**2016, June 23 Litho. *Perf. 14***
**998** A596 3.10k multi .95 .95

No. 998 was printed in sheets of 26 + 4 labels.

2016 European University Games, Zagreb and Rijeka — A597

2016 European Junior Synchronized Swimming and Diving Championships, Rijeka — A598

**2016, June 28 Litho. *Perf. 14***
**999** A597 3.10k multi .95 .95
**1000** A598 3.10k multi .95 .95

Nos. 999-1000 were each printed in sheets of 9 + label.

Ocellated Wrasse A599

**2016, July 7 Litho. *Perf. 14***
**1001** A599 5.80k multi 1.75 1.75

Souvenir Sheet

Battle of Lissa (Vis), 150th Anniv. A600

**2016, July 18 Litho. *Perf. 14***
**1002** A600 7.60k multi 2.25 2.25

See Slovenia No. 1188.

2016 Summer Olympics, Rio de Janeiro — A601

**2016, Aug. 3 Litho. *Perf. 14***
**1003** A601 4.60k multi 1.40 1.40

No. 1003 was printed in sheets of 8 + label.

Souvenir Sheet

Battle of Szigetvár, 450th Anniv. — A602

No. 1004: a, 4.50k, Szigetvár coat of arms. b, 6.50k, Zrinski's Charge from the Szigetvár Fortress, by Bertalan Székely.

**2016, Sept. 5 Litho. *Perf. 14***
**1004** A602 Sheet of 2, #a-b 3.25 3.25

See Hungary No. 4402.

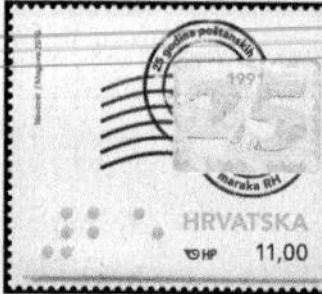

Resumption of Croatian Postage Stamps, 25th Anniv. — A603

**Litho. & Embossed With Hologram Affixed**

**2016, Sept. 9 *Perf. 14***
**1005** A603 11k multi 3.25 3.25

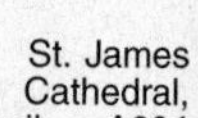

St. James Cathedral, Sibenik — A604

**2016, Sept. 15 Litho. *Perf. 14***
**1006** A604 3.10k multi .95 .95

Sibenik, 950th anniv.

Campaign Against Hate Speech — A605

**2016, Sept. 21 Litho. *Perf. 14***
**1007** A605 3.10k multi .95 .95

Locomotives A606

No. 1008: a, Steam locomotive model 207. b, Steam locomotive JDZ/HDZ/JZ 83-106.

**2016, Oct. 1 Litho. *Perf. 14***
**1008** Vert. pair + 2 central labels 6.00 6.00
*a.-b.* A606 9.50k Either single 3.00 3.00

Depictions of Fossilized Animals — A607

No. 1009: a, Panthera leo fossils (Lion of Dramalj). b, Mesocetus agrami (Whale of Zagreb).

**2016, Oct. 12 Litho. *Perf. 14***
**1009** A607 5k Pair, #a-b 3.00 3.00

Souvenir Sheet

Minerals A608

No. 1010: a, 4.50k, Sea salt crystals (35mm diameter). b, 6.50k, Rhyolite (30x36mm).

***Perf. (4.50k), Perf. 14 (6.50k)***
**2016, Oct. 24 Litho. & Embossed**
**1010** A608 Sheet of 2, #a-b 3.25 3.25

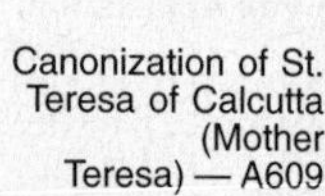

Canonization of St. Teresa of Calcutta (Mother Teresa) — A609

**2016, Nov. 15 Litho. *Perf. 14***
**1011** A609 7.60k multi 2.25 2.25

Adoration of the Magi, by an Italo-Cretan Master — A610

**2016, Nov. 24 Litho. *Perf. 14***
**1012** A610 3.10k multi .90 .90

### Booklet Stamp
### Self-Adhesive
### *Serpentine Die Cut 5¼*

**1013** A610 3.10k multi .90 .90
*a.* Booklet pane of 10 9.00
Complete booklet, #1013a 9.00

Christmas.

Adris Foundation — A611

**2016, Nov. 28 Litho. *Perf. 14***
**1014** A611 3.10k multi + label .90 .90

No. 1014 was printed in sheets of 10 + 10 labels.

Viktor Kovacic (1874-1924), Architect — A612

Designs: 2.80k, Furniture in room of Kovacic's apartment. 4.60k, Decorative detail by Kovacic, vert. 7.60k, Stock Exchange Palace (Croatian National Bank), Zagreb, vert.

**2016, Dec. 1 Litho. *Perf. 14***
**1015-1017** A612 Set of 3 4.25 4.25

### Souvenir Sheet

Statue of Ban Josip Jelacic, Zagreb, 150th Anniv. A613

**2016, Dec. 5 Litho. *Perf. 14***
**1018** A613 15k multi 4.25 4.25

Black Luca, Hrvatko and Emblem of Croatian National Bank A614

**2016, Dec. 9 Litho. *Perf. 14***
**1019** A614 3.10k multi + label .85 .85

No. 1019 was printed in sheets of 10 + 10 labels.

A615

A616

A617

Gyps Fulvus — A618

**2017, Jan. 23 Litho. *Perf. 14***
**1020** Strip of 4 5.75 5.75
*a.* A615 4.60k multi 1.40 1.40
*b.* A616 4.60k multi 1.40 1.40
*c.* A617 4.60k multi 1.40 1.40
*d.* A618 4.60k multi 1.40 1.40

Worldwide Fund for Nature (WWF).

St. Valentine's Day — A619

**2017, Feb. 3 Litho. *Perf. 14x13¾***
**1021** A619 3.10k multi .90 .90

Values are for stamps with surrounding selvage.

Reptiles A620

No. 1022: a, Iguana on hammock. b, Milk snake and striped socks. c, Veiled chameleon and package. d, Musk turtle and diving board.

**2017, Feb. 20 Litho. *Perf. 14***
**1022** A620 3.10k Block or vert. strip of 4, #a-d 3.75 3.75

### Details From Traditional Costumes Type of 2014

Designs: 3k, Pin on dress from Zlarin. 4.60k, Embroidery from Podravina. 5k, Embroidery from Konavle. 6.50k, Pleated skirt from Istria.

**2017, Mar. 14 Litho. *Perf. 14***
**1023** A553 3k multi .90 .90
**1024** A553 4.60k multi 1.40 1.40
**1025** A553 5k multi 1.50 1.50
**1026** A553 6.50k multi 1.90 1.90
*a.* Souvenir sheet of 4, #1023-1026 5.75 5.75
*Nos. 1023-1026 (4)* 5.70 5.70

World Poetry Day A622

**2017, Mar. 21 Litho. *Perf. 14***
**1027** A622 2.80k multi + label .80 .80

Bats — A623

Designs: 2.80k, Rhinolophus blasii. 3.10k, Plecotus kolombatovici. 6.50k, Myotis emarginatus.

**2017, Mar. 21 Litho. *Perf. 14***
**1028** A623 2.80k multi .80 .80
*a.* Booklet pane of 10 8.00 —
Complete booklet, #1028a 8.00
**1029** A623 3.10k multi .90 .90
*a.* Booklet pane of 10 9.00 —
Complete booklet, #1029a 9.00
**1030** A623 6.50k multi 1.90 1.90
*a.* Booklet pane of 10 19.00 —
Complete booklet, #1030a 19.00
*Nos. 1028-1030 (3)* 3.60 3.60

Easter Breakfast — A624

**2017, Apr. 3 Litho. *Perf. 14***
**1031** A624 3.10k multi .90 .90

Famous People — A625

Designs: No. 1032, 3.10k, Zinka Kunc Milanov (1906-89), opera singer. No. 1033, 3.10k, Frano Supilo (1870-1917), journalist and politician. No. 1034, 3.10k, Faust Vrancic (1551-1617), writer and lexicographer.

**2017, Apr. 18 Litho. *Perf. 14***
**1032-1034** A625 Set of 3 2.75 2.75

### Souvenir Sheet

Bridges A626

No. 1035: a, Kosinj Bridge over Lika River. b, Limska Draga Highway Viaduct.

**2017, Apr. 27 Litho. *Perf. 14***
**1035** A626 7.60k Sheet of 2, #a-b 4.50 4.50

Europa — A627

Designs: No. 1036, 7.60k, Veliki Tabor Castle. No. 1037, 7.60k, Trakoscan Castle.

**2017, May 9 Litho. *Perf. 14***
**1036-1037** A627 Set of 2 4.75 4.75

### Souvenir Sheet

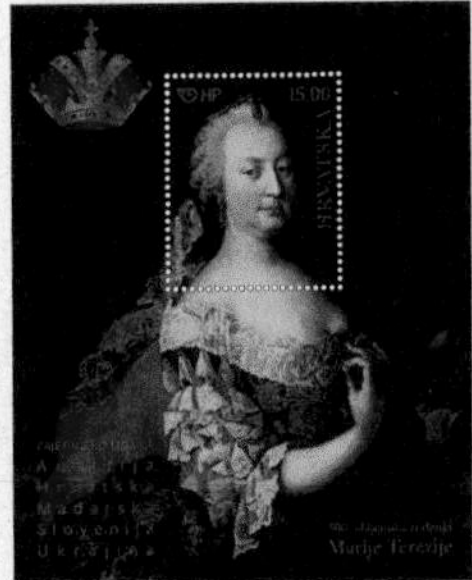

Holy Roman Empress Maria Theresa (1717-80) — A628

**2017, May 13 Litho. *Perf. 14***
**1038** A628 15k multi 4.50 4.50

See Austria No. 2677, Hungary No. 4433, Slovenia No. 1219, Ukraine No. 1093.

Admission of Croatia to United Nations, 25th Anniv. — A629

**2017, May 22 Litho. *Perf. 14***
**1039** A629 3.10k multi .95 .95

Lions Clubs International, Cent. — A630

**2017, June 7 Litho. *Perf. 14***
**1040** A630 3.10k multi .95 .95

Aerial Views of Zagreb Tourist Attractions — A631

Designs: 2.80k, Dolac Market. 5.80k, St. Mark's Church.

**2017, June 8 Litho. *Perf. 14***
**1041-1042** A631 Set of 2 2.75 2.75

Olive Grove, Lun — A632

**2017, July 10 Litho. *Perf. 14***
**1043** A632 5.80k multi 1.90 1.90

First Croatian Movie, *Brcko u Zagreb*, Cent. — A633

**2017, Aug. 28 Litho. *Perf. 14***
**1044** A633 7.60k multi 2.50 2.50

Anemone Coronaria and Iris Croatica Prodán — A634

**2017, Sept. 4 Litho. *Perf. 14***
**1045** A634 7.60k multi 2.40 2.40

Diplomatic relations between Croatia and Israel, 20th anniv. See Israel No. 2150.

Autism Awareness — A635

**2017, Sept. 18 Litho. *Perf. 14***
**1046** A635 3.10k multi 1.00 1.00

Matija Vlacic Ilirik (1520-75), Lutheran Theologian — A636

**2017, Oct. 4 Litho. *Perf. 14***
**1047** A636 3.10k multi 1.00 1.00

Protestant Reformation, 500th anniv.

7th Guards Brigade, 25th Anniv. — A637

**2017, Oct. 18 Litho. *Perf. 14***
**1048** A637 7.60k multi 2.40 2.40

Wax Figure of Jesus, Blessed Virgin Mary Church, Lepoglava — A638

**Litho. With Foil Application**

**2017, Nov. 23** Perf. 14
**1049** A638 3.10k gold & multi 1.00 1.00

**Booklet Stamp**
**Self-Adhesive**
*Serpentine Die Cut 5¼*

**1050** A638 3.10k gold & multi 1.00 1.00
*a.* Booklet pane of 10 10.00
Complete booklet, #1050a 10.00

Christmas.

Golden Spin of Zagreb International Ice Skating Competition, 50th Anniv. — A639

**2017, Nov. 27** Litho. *Perf. 14*
**1051** A639 3.10k multi 1.00 1.00

No. 1051 was printed in sheets of 9 + label.

Paintings A640

Designs: No. 1052, 3.10k, By the Red Light, by Robert Auer (1873-1952). No. 1053, 3.10k, Bora, by Ferdo Kovacevic (1870-1927). No. 1054, 3.10k, Astronomer, by Ivan Tisov (1870-1928).

**2017, Dec. 1** Litho. *Perf. 14*
**1052-1054** A640 Set of 3 3.00 3.00

University of Zagreb Faculty of Medicine, Cent. — A641

**2017, Dec. 4** Litho. *Perf. 14*
**1055** A641 3.10k multi 1.00 1.00

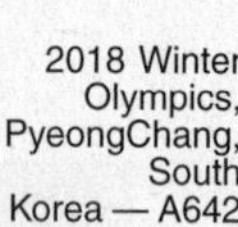
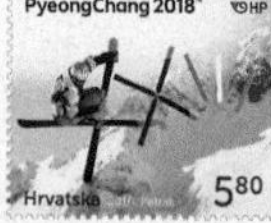

2018 Winter Olympics, PyeongChang, South Korea — A642

**2018, Feb. 7** Litho. *Perf. 14*
**1056** A642 5.80k multi 1.90 1.90

Cats A643

No. 1057 — Envelopes and: a, Russian Blue cat (Ruska Plava). b, Birman cat (Sveta Birma). c, Maine Coon cat. d, Himalayan cat (Himalajska).

**2018, Feb. 22** Litho. *Perf. 14*
**1057** A643 3.10k Block of 4, #a-d 4.00 4.00

Descent from the Cross, by Mile Skracic — A644

**2018, Mar. 15** Litho. *Perf. 14*
**1058** A644 3.10k multi 1.10 1.10

Easter.

Fruit and Nuts — A645

Designs: No. 1059, Cornus mas. No. 1060, Castanea sativa. No. 1061, Vaccinium myrtillus.

**2018, Mar. 21** Litho. *Perf. 14*
**1059** A645 3.10k multi 1.10 1.10
*a.* Booklet pane of 10 11.00 —
Complete booklet, #1059a 11.00
**1060** A645 3.10k multi 1.10 1.10
*a.* Booklet pane of 10 11.00 —
Complete booklet, #1060a 11.00
**1061** A645 3.10k multi 1.10 1.10
*a.* Booklet pane of 10 11.00 —
Complete booklet, #1061a 11.00
*Nos. 1059-1061 (3)* 3.30 3.30

International Landmine Awareness Day — A646

**2018, Apr. 4** Litho. *Perf. 14*
**1062** A646 3.10k multi 1.00 1.00

Protected Food Products — A647

Designs: No. 1063, 3.10k, Dalmatian prosciutto (Dalmatinski prsut). No. 1064, 3.10k, Cres extra virgin olive oil (Cres ekstra djevicansko maslinovo ulje). No. 1065, 3.10k, Neretva Valley tangerines (Neretvanska mandarina).

**2018, Apr. 12** Litho. *Perf. 14*
**1063-1065** A647 Set of 3 3.00 3.00

Famous People — A648

Designs: No. 1066, 3.10k, Marin Getaldic (1568-1626), mathematician. No. 1067, 3.10k, Nives Kavuric-Kurtovic (1938-2016), painter. No. 1068, 3.10k, Petar Preradovic (1818-72), poet.

**2018, Apr. 19** Litho. *Perf. 14*
**1066-1068** A648 Set of 3 3.00 3.00

Europa — A649

Designs: No. 1069, 3.10k, Stone bridge, Novigrad na Dobri. No. 1070, 3.10k, Dr. Franjo Tudman Bridge, Dubrovnik.

**2018, May 2** Litho. *Perf. 14*
**1069-1070** A649 Set of 2 2.00 2.00

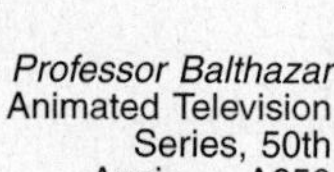

*Professor Balthazar* Animated Television Series, 50th Anniv. — A650

**2018, May 3** Litho. *Perf. 14*
**1071** A650 3.10k multi 1.00 1.00

Father Bernardin Sokol (1888-1944), Professor of Music — A651

**2018, May 15** Litho. *Perf. 14*
**1072** A651 3.10k multi 1.00 1.00

Church of St. Nicholas, Varazdin A652

Stilt Walker at Spancirfest, Varazdin — A653

**2018, June 4** Litho. *Perf. 14*
**1073** A652 3.10k multi 1.00 1.00
**1074** A653 3.10k multi 1.00 1.00

2018 World Cup Soccer Championships, Russia — A654

**2018, June 14** Litho. *Perf. 14*
**1075** A654 6.50k multi 2.10 2.10

No. 1075 was printed in sheets of 9 + label.

**Details From Traditional Costumes Type of 2014**

Designs: 1k, Embrodery from Sestine. 3.10k, Floral silk scarf designs from Slavonia. 8.60k, Woman's dress from Susak. 15k, Beaded headpiece from Bratina.

**2018, June 28** Litho. *Perf. 14*
**1076** A553 1k multi .30 .30
**1077** A553 3.10k multi .95 .95
**1078** A553 8.60k multi 2.75 2.75
**1079** A553 15k multi 4.75 4.75
*a.* Souvenir sheet of 4, #1076-1079 8.75 8.75
*Nos. 1076-1079 (4)* 8.75 8.75

Compare No. 1077 with No. 925.

*Arsen 2,* Record Album by Arsen Dedic (1938-2015) A655

*Jubilami Koncert,* Record Album by Ivo Robic (1923-2000) A656

*Mimo Teku Rijeke,* Record Album by Vice Vukov (1936-2008) — A657

*Serpentine Die Cut 11½*

**2018, July 4** Litho.

**Self-Adhesive**

**1080** A655 7.60k multi 2.40 2.40
**1081** A656 7.60k multi 2.40 2.40
**1082** A657 7.60k multi 2.40 2.40
*Nos. 1080-1082 (3)* 7.20 7.20

Stone House — A658

**2018, July 10** Litho. *Perf. 14*
**1083** A658 7.60k multi 2.40 2.40

**Souvenir Sheet**

Second-Place Finish of Croatian 2018 World Cup Soccer Team — A659

No. 1084 — Photograph of team wearing medals with 2018 World Cup emblem at: a, LL. b, LR.

**2018, Aug. 31** Litho. *Perf. 14*
**1084** A659 6k Sheet of 2, #a-b 3.75 3.75

Stamp Day — A660

**2018, Sept. 6** Litho. *Perf. 14*
**1085** A660 3.10k lilac & multi 1.00 1.00

**Souvenir Sheet**

**1086** Sheet of 4, #1085, 1086a-1086c 8.00 8.00
*a.* A660 1.50k red vio & multi .45 .45
*b.* A660 8.60k light blue & multi 2.75 2.75
*c.* A660 11.50k gray green & multi 3.75 3.75

First stamps of Croatia-Slavonia, cent.

Forest Protection — A661

**2018, Sept. 17** Litho. *Perf. 14*
**1087** A661 3.10k multi 1.00 1.00

Locomotives A662

No. 1088: a, Steam locomotive No. 7. b, DEV-1 Diesel-electric.

**2018, Oct. 5** Litho. *Perf. 14*
**1088** Vert. pair + 2 central labels 4.80 4.80
*a.-b.* A662 7.60k Either single 2.40 2.40

**Souvenir Sheet**

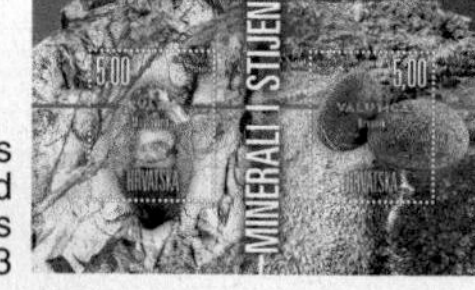

Minerals and Rocks A663

No. 1089: a, Quartz (red line). b, Augite diabase conglomerate rock (blue line).

**2018, Oct. 24 Litho. *Perf. 14***
**1089** A663 5k Sheet of 2, #a-b 3.25 3.25

Emblem of Tigers Brigade of 1st Guards — A664

**2018, Nov. 5 Litho. *Perf. 14***
**1090** A664 7.60k multi 2.40 2.40

No. 1090 was printed in sheets of 6 + label.

Souvenir Sheet

Lipizzan Horses A665

**2018, Nov. 7 Litho. *Perf. 14***
**1091** A665 15k multi 4.75 4.75

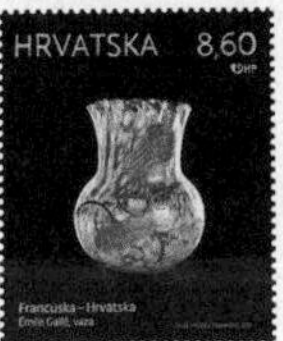

Vase by Emile Gallé (1846-1904) A666

Vase by Antonija Krasnik (1874-1956) A667

**Litho. With Foil Application**

**2018, Nov. 8 *Perf. 14***
**1092** A666 8.60k multi 2.75 2.75
**1093** A667 8.60k multi 2.75 2.75

See France Nos. 5544-5545.

Christmas — A668

**2018, Nov. 26 Litho. *Perf. 14***
**1094** A668 3.10k multi .95 .95

**Booklet Stamp Self-Adhesive**

***Serpentine Die Cut 5¼***

**1095** A668 3.10k multi .95 .95
*a.* Booklet pane of 10 9.50
Complete booklet, #1095a 9.50

Architecture and Designs by Vjenceslav Richter (1917-2002) A669

Designs: No. 1096, 3.10k, Yugoslavian Pavilion for 1958 World's Fair, Brussels. No. 1097, 3.10k, Sinusoids II sculpture, vert. No. 1098, 3.10k, Plywood and wrought iron chair, vert.

**2018, Nov. 29 Litho. *Perf. 14***
**1096-1098** A669 Set of 3 3.00 3.00

Souvenir Sheet

Forts A670

No. 1099: a, Fort Santiago, Manila, Philippines. b, St. Michael's Fortress, Sibenik, Croatia.

**2018, Dec. 5 Litho. *Perf. 14***
**1099** A670 6.50k Sheet of 2, #a-b 4.00 4.00

Diplomatic relations between Croatia and Philippines, 25th anniversary. See Philippines No. 3794.

20th Century Necklace — A671

**2019, Jan. 23 Litho. *Perf. 14***
**1100** A671 3.10k multi .95 .95

Ethnographic Museum, Zagreb, cent.

Dogs A672

No. 1101: a, St. Bernard. b, Pug. c, Siberian husky. d, Cavalier King Charles spaniel.

**2019, Feb. 20 Litho. *Perf. 14***
**1101** A672 3.10k Block or vert. strip of 4, #a-d 3.75 3.75

Rotary International in Croatia, 90th Anniv. A673

**2019, Mar. 6 Litho. *Perf. 14***
**1102** A673 3.10k multi .95 .95

Emblem of 1st Croatian Guards Brigade A674

Emblem of 2nd Croatian Guards Brigade "Thunders" A675

Emblem of 3rd Croatian Guards Brigade "Martens" A676

Emblem of 4th Croatian Guards Brigade "Spiders" A677

**2019, Mar. 11 Litho. *Perf. 14***
**1103** A674 8.60k multi 2.60 2.60
**1104** A675 8.60k multi 2.60 2.60
**1105** A676 8.60k multi 2.60 2.60
**1106** A677 8.60k multi 2.60 2.60
*Nos. 1103-1106 (4)* 10.40 10.40

Nos. 1103-1106 were each printed in sheets of 6 + central label.

Apis Mellifera Carnica — A678

Designs: No. 1107, Worker bee (radilica). No. 1108, Drone bee (trut). 6.50k, Queen bee (matica).

**2019, Mar. 21 Litho. *Perf. 14***
**1107** A678 3.10k multi .95 .95
*a.* Booklet pane of 10 9.50 —
Complete booklet, #1107a 9.50
**1108** A678 3.10k multi .95 .95
*a.* Booklet pane of 10 9.50 —
Complete booklet, #1108a 9.50
**1109** A678 6.50k multi 2.00 2.00
*a.* Booklet pane of 10 20.00 —
Complete booklet, #1109a 20.00
*Nos. 1107-1109 (3)* 3.90 3.90

Luka Modric, Soccer Player — A679

**2019, Mar. 25 Litho. *Perf. 14***
**1110** A679 10k multi 3.00 3.00

No. 1110 was printed in sheets of 9 + label.

Souvenir Sheet

2018 Davis Cup Championship of Croatian Tennis Team — A680

No. 1111 — Team members and Davis Cup with demomination at: a, UL. b, UR.

**2019, Mar. 28 Litho. *Perf. 14***
**1111** A680 Sheet of 2 4.00 4.00
*a.-b.* 6.50k Either single 2.00 2.00

Croatian Membership in North Atlantic Treaty Organization, 10th Anniv. — A681

**2019, Apr. 1 Litho. *Perf. 14***
**1112** A681 3.10k sil & multi .95 .95

Easter — A682

**2019, Apr. 4 Litho. *Perf. 14***
**1113** A682 3.10k multi .95 .95

Famous People — A683

Designs: No. 1114, 3.10k, Vatroslav Lisinski (1819-54), composer. No. 1115, 3.10k, Andela Horvat (1911-85), art historian. No. 1116, 3.10k, Jure Kastelan (1919-90), poet.

**2019, Apr. 16 Litho. *Perf. 14***
**1114-1116** A683 Set of 3 3.00 3.00

Souvenir Sheet

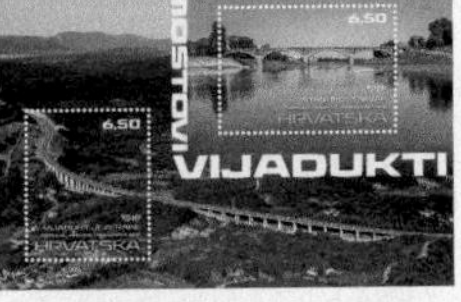

Bridges A684

No. 1117: a, Old Bridge, Sisak (43x30mm). b, Jezerane Viaduct (30x36mm).

**2019, Apr. 24 Litho. *Perf. 14***
**1117** A684 Sheet of 2 4.00 4.00
*a.-b.* 6.50k Either single 2.00 2.00

Europa — A685

Birds: No. 1118, 8.60k, Lastavica bregunica (sand martins). No. 1119, 8.60k, Galeb klaukavac (yellow-legged gulls).

**2019, May 9 Litho. *Perf. 14***
**1118-1119** A685 Set of 2 5.25 5.25

Castles — A686

Designs: No. 1120, 3.10k, Luznica Castle. No. 1121, 3.10k, Janusevec Castle. No. 1122, 3.10k, Orsic Castle. No. 1123, 3.10k, Lovrecina Castle.

**2019, May 20 Litho. *Perf. 14***
**1120-1123** A686 Set of 4 3.75 3.75
*1123a* Souvenir sheet of 8, 2 each #1120-1123, + 8 central labels 7.50 7.50

Kuna Currency, 25th Anniv. — A687

**2019, May 30 Litho. *Perf. 14***
**1124** A687 3.10k multi .95 .95

No. 1124 was printed in sheets of 25 + 5 labels.

Icons of the Virgin Mary A688

Marian Shrines A689

Designs: Nos. 1125, 1129, Statue of the Mother of God, Marian Bistrica. Nos. 1126, 1130, Painting of Our Lady of Vocin. Nos, 1127, 1131, Shrine, Marian Bistrica. Nos. 1128, 1132, Church of the Visitation of the Blessed Virgin Mary, Vocin.

**2019, June 4 Litho. *Perf. 14***

**1125** A688 3.10k multi .95 .95
**1126** A688 3.10k multi .95 .95
**1127** A689 8.60k multi 2.60 2.60
**1128** A689 8.60k multi 2.60 2.60
*Nos. 1125-1128 (4)* 7.10 7.10

**Booklet Stamps Self-Adhesive**

***Serpentine Die Cut 11***

**1129** A688 3.10k multi .95 .95
**1130** A688 3.10k multi .95 .95
**1131** A689 8.60k multi 2.60 2.60
*a.* Booklet pane of 10, 5 each #1129, 1131 18.00
**1132** A689 8.60k multi 2.60 2.60
*a.* Booklet pane of 10, 5 each #1130, 1132 18.00
*Nos. 1129-1132 (4)* 7.10 7.10

Nos. 1125-1128 were each printed in sheets of 8 + central label.

Small Waterfalls A690

Lake Kozjac Waterfall A691

Great Cascades A692

Great Waterfall in Winter A693

**2019, June 10 Litho. *Perf. 14***

**1133** A690 3.10k multi .95 .95
*a.* Booklet pane of 1 .95 —
**1134** A691 3.10k multi .95 .95
*a.* Booklet pane of 1 .95 —
**1135** A692 8.60k multi 2.60 2.60
*a.* Booklet pane of 1 2.60 —
**1136** A693 8.60k multi 2.60 2.60
*a.* Booklet pane of 1 2.60 —
Complete booklet, #1133a, 1134a, 1135a, 1136a 7.25
*b.* Souvenir sheet of 4, #1133-1136 7.25 7.25
*Nos. 1133-1136 (4)* 7.10 7.10

Plitvice Lakes waterfalls.

Children's Folk Costumes From Susak — A694

**2019, July 8 Litho. *Perf. 14***

**1137** A694 8.60k multi 2.60 2.60

National Parks and Flora — A695

Designs: No. 1138, 8.60k, Northern Velebit National Park, Croatia, and Dianthus velebiticus. No. 1139, 8.60k, Seoraksan National Park, South Korea, and Pinus pumila.

**2019, Aug. 29 Litho. *Perf. 14***

**1138-1139** A695 Set of 2 5.25 5.25

See South Korea No. 2558.

No. 758 Surcharged

**Methods and Perfs. As Before**

**2019, Sept. 2**

**1140** A444 3.60k on 1.60k #758 1.10 1.10

Health Through Sport — A696

**2019, Sept. 18 Litho. *Perf. 14***

**1141** A696 3.10k multi .95 .95

Miniature Sheet

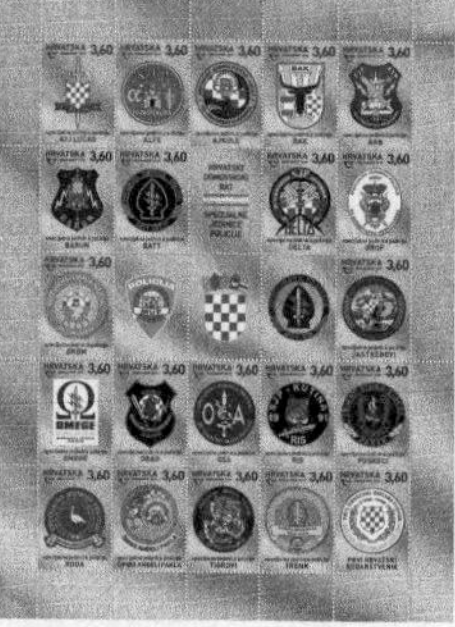
Emblems of Special Police Units A697

No. 1142: a, ATJ Lucko. b, Alfe. c, Ajkule. d, Bak. e, Ban. f, Barun. g, Batt. h, Delta. i, Grof. j, Grom. k, Jastrebovi. l, Omege. m, Orao. n, Osa. p, Ris. q, Poskoci. r, Roda. s, Simini Andeli Pakla. t, Tigrovi. u, Trenk. v, Prvi Hrvatski Redarstvenik.

**2019, Sept. 27 Litho. *Perf. 14***

**1142** A697 Sheet of 21 + 4 labels 23.50 23.50
*a.-u.* 3.60k Any single 1.10 1.10

Zagreb Fair, 110th Anniv. A698

**2019, Oct. 28 Litho. *Perf. 14***

**1143** A698 A multi + label .95 .95

No. 1143 sold for 3.10k on day of issue.

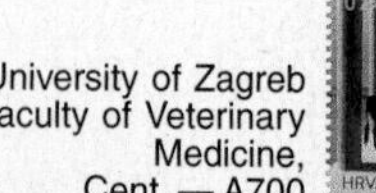

University of Zagreb, 350th Anniv. A699

**2019, Oct. 30 Litho. *Perf. 14***

**1144** A699 3.60k multi 1.10 1.10

University of Zagreb Faculty of Veterinary Medicine, Cent. — A700

**2019, Nov. 13 Litho. *Perf. 14***

**1145** A700 3.60k multi 1.10 1.10

Father Antun Cvek (1934-2019), Founder of Bishop Josip Lang Foundation — A701

**2019, Nov. 18 Litho. *Perf. 14***

**1146** A701 A multi .95 .95

No. 1146 sold for 3.10k on day of issue and was printed in sheets of 9 + label.

Christmas — A702

**Litho. With Foil Application**

**2019, Nov. 22 *Perf. 14***

**1147** A702 A multi .95 .95

**Booklet Stamp Self-Adhesive**

***Serpentine Die Cut 5¼***

**1148** A702 A multi .95 .95
*a.* Booklet pane of 10 9.50
Complete booklet, #1148a 9.50

Nos. 1147-1148 each sold for 3.10k on day of issue.

Paintings A703

Designs: No. 1149, 3.10k, Landscape, by Hugo Conrad von Hötzendorf (1807-69). No. 1150, 3.10k, Return of the Fishermen, by Jozo Kljakovic (1889-1969). No. 1151, 3.10k, Portrait of a Girl, by Vjekoslav Karas (1821-58), vert.

**2019, Nov. 25 Litho. *Perf. 14***

**1149-1151** A703 Set of 3 2.75 2.75

Zagreb Polytechnic School, Cent. — A704

**2019, Nov. 28 Litho. *Perf. 14***

**1152** A704 3.10k multi .95 .95

Sveti Duh Clinical Hospital, Zagreb, 215th Anniv. — A705

**2019, Dec. 23 Litho. *Perf. 14***

**1153** A705 3.10k multi .95 .95

Croatian Presidency of the Council of the European Union — A706

**2020, Jan. 2 Litho. *Perf. 14***

**1154** A706 8.60k multi 2.60 2.60

No. 1154 was printed in sheets of 25 + labels.

Rijeka, Croatia, 2020 European Capital of Culture — A707

Galway, Ireland, 2020 European Capital of Culture — A708

**2020, Jan. 23 Litho. *Perf. 14***

**1155** A707 8.60k multi 2.60 2.60
**1156** A708 8.60k multi 2.60 2.60

See Ireland Nos. 2265-2266.

Kopacki Rit Nature Park — A709

Blue Cave — A710

Lake Mir and Telascica Bay — A711

**2020, Jan. 28 Litho. *Perf. 14***

**1157** A709 A multi .95 .95
**1158** A710 B multi 2.60 2.60
**1159** A711 C multi 2.60 2.60
*Nos. 1157-1159 (3)* 6.15 6.15

**Coil Stamps Self-Adhesive**

***Serpentine Die Cut 11***

**1160** A709 A multi .95 .95
**1161** A710 B multi 2.60 2.60
**1162** A711 C multi 2.60 2.60
*Nos. 1160-1162 (3)* 6.15 6.15

Nos. 1159 and 1162 are airmail. On day of issue, Nos. 1157 and 1160 each sold for 3.10k, and Nos. 1158-1159, 1161-1162 each sold for 8.60k.

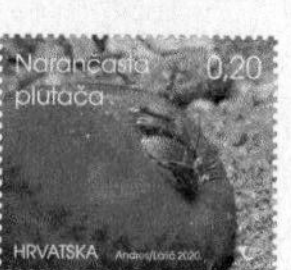

Suberites Domuncula A712

Eunicella Cavolini A713

Hacelia Attenuata — A714

**2020, Feb. 14 Litho. *Perf. 14***

**1163** A712 20 l multi .25 .25
**1164** A713 50 l multi .25 .25
**1165** A714 10k multi 3.00 3.00
*Nos. 1163-1165 (3)* 3.50 3.50

Small Animals A715

No. 1166: a, Shetland pony. b, Croatian dwarf chickens. c, African pygmy hedgehog. d, Vietnamese pot-bellied pig.

**2020, Feb. 20 Litho. *Perf. 14***

**1166** A715 3.10k Block or vert. strip of 4, #a-d 3.75 3.75

Emblem of 9th Croatian Guards Brigade "Wolves" A716

Emblem of 5th Croatian Guards Brigade "Falcons" A717

Emblem of 84th Croatian Guards Battalion "Termites" A718

Emblem of 81st Croatian Guards Battalion "Godfathers" A719

**2020, Mar. 11 Litho. *Perf. 14***

| | | | |
|---|---|---|---|
| **1167** A716 8.60k multi | 2.50 | 2.50 |
| **1168** A717 8.60k multi | 2.50 | 2.50 |
| **1169** A718 8.60k multi | 2.50 | 2.50 |
| **1170** A719 8.60k multi | 2.50 | 2.50 |
| *Nos. 1167-1170 (4)* | 10.00 | 10.00 |

Nos. 1167-1170 were each printed in sheets of 6 + central label.

Flowers — A720

Designs: No. 1171, Genista bolopetala. No. 1172, Moebringia tommasinii. 6.50k, Fritillaria meleagris.

**2020, Mar. 20 Litho. *Perf. 14***

| | | |
|---|---|---|
| **1171** A720 3.10k multi | .90 | .90 |
| *a.* Booklet pane of 10 | 9.00 | — |
| Complete booklet, #1171a | 9.00 | |
| **1172** A720 3.10k multi | .90 | .90 |
| *a.* Booklet pane of 10 | 9.00 | — |
| Complete booklet, #1172a | 9.00 | |
| **1173** A720 6.50k multi | 1.90 | 1.90 |
| *a.* Booklet pane of 10 | 19.00 | — |
| Complete booklet, #1173a | 19.00 | |
| *Nos. 1171-1173 (3)* | 3.70 | 3.70 |

Easter — A721

**2020, Mar. 26 Litho. *Perf. 14***

**1174** A721 3.10k multi .90 .90

Bicyclist A722

**2020, Mar. 27 Litho. *Perf. 14***

**1175** A722 A multi + label .90 .90

Campaign against global warming. No. 1175 sold for 3.10k on day of issue.

Protected Croatian Food Products — A723

Designs: No. 1176, 6.50k, Ogulinsko Kiselo Zelje (Ogulin sauerkraut). No. 1177, 6.50k, Licki Krumpir (Lika potatoes). No. 1178, 6.50k, Baranjski Kulen (Baranja sausage).

**2020, Apr. 14 Litho. *Perf. 14***

**1176-1178** A723 Set of 3 5.75 5.75

Famous People — A724

Designs: No. 1179, A, Ivan Krstitelj Rabjanin (1470-1540), cannon and bell founder. No. 1180, A, Count Janko Draskovic (1770-1856), politician and writer. No. 1181, A, Lelja Dobronic (1920-2006), art historian.

**2020, Apr. 22 Litho. *Perf. 14***

**1179-1181** A724 Set of 3 2.75 2.75

Nos. 1179-1181 each sold for 3.10k on day of issue.

Europa A725

No. 1182 — 19th century lithograph of St. Francis Chapel on Velebit Mountain: a, Mail coach. b, Chapel.

**2020, May 8 Litho. *Perf. 14***

**1182** A725 8.60k Horiz. pair, #a-b 5.00 5.00

Novigrad, 800th Anniv. — A726

**2020, May 20 Litho. *Perf. 14***

**1183** A726 3.10k multi .90 .90

St. Jerome (c. 347-420), Patron Saint of Dalmatia — A727

**2020, May 27 Litho. *Perf. 14***

**1184** A727 10k multi 3.00 3.00

30th Statehood Day — A728

**2020, May 28 Litho. *Perf. 14***

**1185** A728 3.10k multi .90 .90

No. 1185 was printed in sheets of 25 + 5 labels.

A729

Balbi's Arch, Rovinj — A730

A731

St. Euphemia's Church, Rovinj — A732

**2020 Litho. *Perf. 14***

| | | |
|---|---|---|
| **1186** A729 3.10k multi | .95 | .95 |
| **1187** A730 3.10k multi | .95 | .95 |
| **1188** A731 8.60k multi | 2.60 | 2.60 |
| **1189** A732 8.60k multi | 2.60 | 2.60 |
| *Nos. 1186-1189 (4)* | 7.10 | 7.10 |

Issued: Nos. 1186, 1188, 6/4; Nos. 1187, 1189, 6/25.

Canonization of St. Nicholas Tavelic (c. 1340-91), 50th Anniv. — A733

**2020, June 19 Litho. *Perf. 14***

**1190** A733 3.10k multi .95 .95

Rab Cake — A734

**2020, July 13 Litho. *Perf. 14***

**1191** A734 8.60k multi 2.75 2.75

Operations Lightning and Storm, 25th Anniv. — A735

**2020, Aug. 3 Litho. *Perf. 14***

**1192** A735 3.10k multi 1.00 1.00

No. 1192 was printed in sheets of 25 + 5 labels.

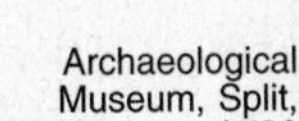

Archaeological Museum, Split, 200th Anniv. — A736

**2020, Aug. 17 Litho. *Perf. 14***

**1193** A736 A multi 1.00 1.00

No. 1193 sold for 3.10k on day of issue.

Drone, Airplane, Train, Ship, Van and QR Code A737

***Serpentine Die Cut 11½***

**2020, Sept. 9 Litho.**

**Self-Adhesive**

**1194** A737 50k multi 15.50 15.50

Cryptocurrency stamp for Stamp Day. No. 1194 is on a credit card-size piece of plastic and was sold in a protective cover.

Oliver Dragojevic (1947-2018), Singer — A738

Dino Dvornik (1964-2008), Singer — A739

Toma Bebic (1935-90), Singer — A740

***Serpentine Die Cut 11½***

**2020, Sept. 28 Litho.**

**Self-Adhesive**

| | | |
|---|---|---|
| **1195** A738 10k multi | 3.25 | 3.25 |
| **1196** A739 10k black | 3.25 | 3.25 |
| **1197** A740 10k multi | 3.25 | 3.25 |
| *Nos. 1195-1197 (3)* | 9.75 | 9.75 |

Locomotives — A741

No. 1198: a, Locomotive JZ 642. b, Locomotive JZ 661.

**2020, Oct. 5 Litho. *Perf. 14***

**1198** A741 6.50k Pair, #a-b 4.00 4.00

No. 1198 was printed in sheet containing 3 each of Nos. 1198a-1198b.

National Theater Building, Zagreb, 125th Anniv. — A742

**2020, Oct. 14 Litho. *Perf. 14***

**1199** A742 3.30k multi 1.00 1.00

Souvenir Sheet

Rocks A743

No. 1200: a, Hraschina meteorite, denomination at UL. b, Lithothamnium limestone, denomination at UR.

**2020, Oct. 22 Litho. *Perf. 14***
**1200** A743 5k Sheet of 2, #a-b 3.25 3.25

Ludwig van Beethoven (1770-1827), Composer A744

**2020, Nov. 11 Litho. *Perf. 14***
**1201** A744 13k multi 4.25 4.25

A745

Christmas — A746

**Litho. With Foil Application**

**2020, Nov. 26 *Perf. 14***
**1202** A745 3.30k gold & multi 1.10 1.10

**Litho.**

**1203** A746 3.30k multi 1.10 1.10

**Booklet Stamp**
**Self-Adhesive**

***Serpentine Die Cut 5¼***

**1204** A746 3.30k multi 1.10 1.10
*a.* Booklet pane of 10 11.00
Complete booklet, #1204a 11.00

Zagreb Buildings Designed by Stjepan Planic (1900-80) A747

Designs: No. 1205, 3.30k, Tomislavov Dom Hotel. No. 1206, 3.30k, Villa Cuvaj, vert. No. 1207, 3.30k, Napredak Cooperative Building, vert.

**2020, Nov. 30 Litho. *Perf. 14***
**1205-1207** A747 Set of 3 3.25 3.25

Methods of Postal Delivery and QR Code A748

***Serpentine Die Cut 11½***

**2020, Dec. 15 Litho.**

**Self-Adhesive**

**1208** A748 50k multi 16.50 16.50

Cryptocurrency stamp. No. 1208 is on a credit card-size piece of plastic and was sold in a protective cover.

Souvenir Sheet

Bridges A749

No. 1209: a, Kude's Bridge over Krupi River. b, Zeceve Drage Viaduct, horiz.

**2021, Jan. 22 Litho. *Perf. 14***
**1209** A749 5k Sheet of 2, #a-b 3.25 3.25

Zagreb Philharmonic Orchestra, 150th Anniv. — A750

**2021, Jan. 28 Litho. *Perf. 14***
**1210** A750 3.30k multi 1.10 1.10

Cats A751

No. 1211: a, Bengal cat (light green denomination. b, Bombay cat (white denomination). c, Egyptian Mau cat (beige denomination). d, Norwegian Forest cat (light blue denomination).

**2021, Feb. 22 Litho. *Perf. 14***
**1211** A751 3.30k Block or vert. strip of 4, #a-d 4.25 4.25

Easter — A752

**2021, Mar. 18 Litho. *Perf. 14***
**1212** A752 3.30k multi 1.10 1.10

Funeral Assistance Association, 90th Anniv. — A753

**2021, Mar. 19 Litho. *Perf. 14***
**1213** A753 3.30k multi + label 1.10 1.10

No. 1213 was printed in sheets of 10 + 10 labels.

Marine Life — A754

Designs No. 1214, Mobula mobular. No. 1215, Tursiops truncatus. 6.50k, Caretta caretta.

**2021, Mar. 22 Litho. *Perf. 14***
**1214** A754 3.30k multi 1.10 1.10
*a.* Booklet pane of 10 11.00
Complete booklet, #1214a 11.00
**1215** A754 3.30k multi 1.10 1.10
*a.* Booklet pane of 10 11.00
Complete booklet, #1215a 11.00
**1216** A754 6.50k multi 2.10 2.10
*a.* Booklet pane of 10 21.00
Complete booklet, #1216a 21.00

Famous People — A755

Designs: No. 1217, 3.30k, William Feller (1906-70), mathematician. No. 1218, 3.30k, Antun Mihanovic (1796-1861), Croatian national anthem lyricist. No. 1219, 3.30k, Ljiljana Molnar-Talajic (1938-2007), opera singer. No. 1220, 3.30k, Tonko Maroevic (1941-2020), writer.

**2021, Apr. 19 Litho. *Perf. 14***
**1217-1220** A755 Set of 4 4.25 4.25

University of Zagreb Computing Center, 50th Anniv. — A756

**2021, Apr. 29 Litho. *Perf. 14***
**1221** A756 14k multi 4.50 4.50

Souvenir Sheet

Beheaded Participants in the Zrinksi-Frankopan Conspiracy — A757

No. 1222: a, Petar IV Zrinski (1621-71), Ban of Croatia (30x43mm). b, Fran Krsto Frankopan (1643-71), poet (35x30mm).

**2021, Apr. 30 Litho. *Perf. 14***
**1222** A757 6.50k Sheet of 2, #a-b 4.25 4.25

Joint issue between Croatia and Bosnia & Herzegovina (Croat Administration). See Bosnia & Herzegovina (Croat Administration) No. 430.

Europa — A758

Endangered animals: 3.30k, Tetrao urogallus. 15k, Lynx lynx.

**2021, May 7 Litho. *Perf. 14***
**1223-1224** A758 Set of 2 6.00 6.00

Manor Houses and Castles — A759

Designs: No. 1225, 3.30k, Novi Dvori Manor, Zapresic. No. 1226, 3.30k, Laduc Manor, Dobrinovic. No. 1227, 3.30k, Brezovica Manor, Trakoscanski. No. 1228, 3.30k, Erdödy Castle, Jastrebarsko.

**2021, May 20 Litho. *Perf. 14***
**1225-1228** A759 Set of 4 4.25 4.25
*1228a* Souvenir sheet of 8, 2 each #1225-1228, + 8 labels 8.50 8.50

Shrine of Our Lady of Trsat A760

Church of the Assumption of the Blessed Virgin Mary, Remete A761

Mother of Mercy Icon, Shrine of Our Lady of Trsat A762

Statue of Mary, Church of the Assumption of the Blessed Virgin Mary, Remete A763

**2021, June 7 Litho. *Perf. 14***
**1229** A760 3.30k multi 1.10 1.10
**1230** A761 3.30k multi 1.10 1.10
**1231** A762 3.30k multi 1.10 1.10
**1232** A763 3.30k multi 1.10 1.10
*Nos. 1229-1232 (4)* 4.40 4.40

Marian shrines and icons in Croatia. Nos. 1229-1232 were each printed in sheets of 8 + central label.

Nin Tourism — A764

Designs: 3.30k, Church of the Holy Cross. 8.60k, Aerial view of Nin and harbor, horiz.

**2021, June 10 Litho. *Perf. 14***
**1233-1234** A764 Set of 2 3.75 3.75

Medimurska Popevka Folk Song — A765

Spring Procession of Queens from Gorjani — A766

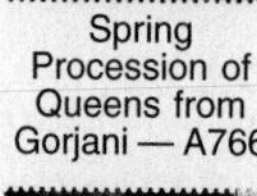

Dry Stone Wall Construction A767

Following the Cross Procession on Island of Hvar A768

**2021, July 1 Litho. *Perf. 14***
**1235** A765 3.30k black 1.10 1.10
**1236** A766 3.30k multi 1.10 1.10
**1237** A767 3.30k multi 1.10 1.10
**1238** A768 3.30k multi 1.10 1.10
*a.* Souvenir sheet of 4, #1235-1238, + 5 labels 4.50 4.50
*Nos. 1235-1238 (4)* 4.40 4.40

Croatian items on UNESCO's Intangible Cultural Heritage List.

Traditional Gold Earrings from Konavle — A769

**2021, July 12 Litho. *Perf. 14***
**1239** A769 12.30k multi 4.00 4.00

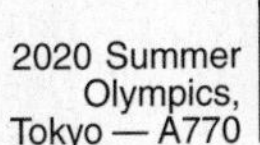

2020 Summer Olympics, Tokyo — A770

**2021, July 23** **Litho.** ***Perf. 14***
**1240** A770 8.60k multi 2.75 2.75

The 2020 Summer Olympics were postponed until 2021 because of the COVID-19 pandemic. No. 1240 was printed in sheets of 9 + label.

Statue in Split by Ivan Mestrovic Depicting Marko Marulic (1450-1524), Poet — A771

**2021, Aug. 2** **Litho.** ***Perf. 14***
**1241** A771 3.30k multi 1.10 1.10

Publication of Marulic's poem "Judith," 500th anniv.

Croatian Association of the Deaf and Hard of Hearing, Cent. — A772

**2021, Aug. 26** **Litho.** ***Perf. 14***
**1242** A772 3.30k multi 1.10 1.10

Rimac Nevera Sports Car and QR Code A773

***Serpentine Die Cut 11½***

**2021, Sept. 9** **Litho.**

**Self-Adhesive**

**1243** A773 50k multi 15.50 15.50

Cryptocurrency stamp for Stamp Day. No. 1243 is on a credit card-size piece of plastic and was sold in a protective cover.

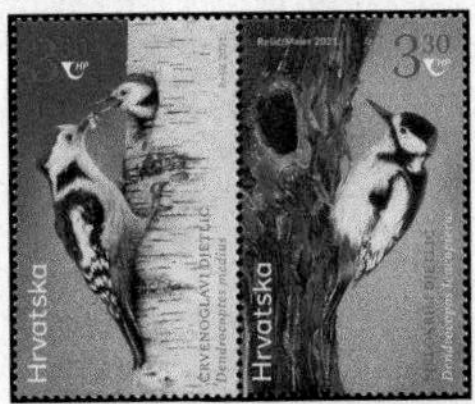

Woodpeckers — A774

No. 1244: a, Dendrocoptes medius. b, Dendrocopos leucopterus.

**2021, Sept. 22** **Litho.** ***Perf. 14***
**1244** A774 3.30k Horiz. pair, #a-b 2.10 2.10

See Kyrgyz Express Post Nos. 160-161.

Zagreb School of Medicine Otorhinolaryngology and Head and Neck Surgery Clinic, Cent. — A775

**2021, Sept. 24** **Litho.** ***Perf. 14***
**1245** A775 3.30k multi 1.10 1.10

UNICEF, 75th Anniv. — A776

**2021, Oct. 4** **Litho.** ***Perf. 14***
**1246** A776 3.30k multi 1.00 1.00

Croatian Membership in Council of Europe, 25th Anniv. — A777

**2021, Nov. 5** **Litho.** ***Perf. 14***
**1247** A777 3.30k multi 1.00 1.00

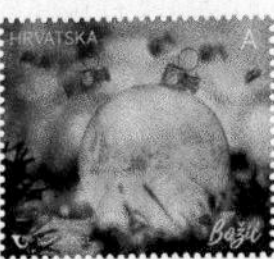

Christmas — A778

**2021, Nov. 22** **Litho.** ***Perf. 14***
**1248** A778 A multi 1.00 1.00

**Booklet Stamp**
**Self-Adhesive**

***Serpentine Die Cut 5¼***

**1249** A778 A multi 1.00 1.00
*a.* Booklet pane of 10 10.00 —
Complete booklet, #1249a 10.00

On day of issue, Nos. 1248-1249 each sold for 3.30k.

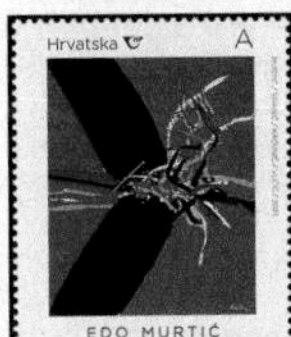

Good Day Red, Painting by Edo Murtic (1921-2005) A779

Grounded Sun, Sculpture by Ivan Kozaric (1921-2020) A780

**2021, Nov. 26** **Litho.** ***Perf. 14***
**1250** A779 A multi 1.00 1.00
**1251** A780 A multi 1.00 1.00

On day of issue, Nos. 1250-1251 each sold for 3.30k.

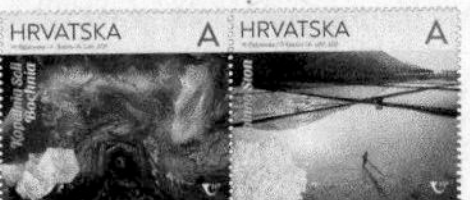

Salt Crystals and Their Sources A781

No. 1252: a, Bochnia Salt Mine, Poland. b, Ston Saltworks, Croatia.

**2021, Dec. 2** **Litho.** ***Perf. 14***
**1252** A781 A Pair, #a-b 2.00 2.00

Joint issue between Croatia and Poland. See Poland No. 4583. On day of issue, Nos. 1252a-1252b each sold for 3.30k.

International Recognition of Independent Croatia, 30th Anniv. — A782

**2022, Jan. 14** **Litho.** ***Perf. 14***
**1253** A782 A multi 1.00 1.00

No. 1253 sold for 3.30k on day of issue.

First Mention of Metkovic in Historic Documents, 600th Anniv. — A783

**2022, Jan. 17** **Litho.** ***Perf. 14***
**1254** A783 A multi 1.00 1.00

No. 1254 sold for 3.30k on day of issue.

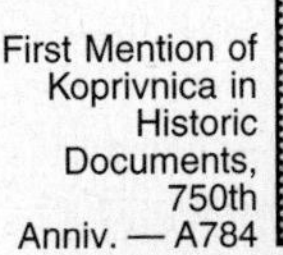

First Mention of Koprivnica in Historic Documents, 750th Anniv. — A784

**2022, Jan. 18** **Litho.** ***Perf. 14***
**1255** A784 A multi 1.00 1.00

No. 1255 sold for 3.30k on day of issue.

2022 Winter Olympics, Beijing — A785

**Litho. & Embossed**

**2022, Feb. 4** ***Perf. 14***
**1256** A785 B multi 2.60 2.60

No. 1256 sold for 8.60k on day of issue.

Dogs A786

No. 1257: a, Dalmatian in boat. b, Beagle wearing feathered hat. c, Pomeranian standing on chair. d, Scotch collie with sheep and shepherd's crook.

**2022, Feb. 21** **Litho.** ***Perf. 14***
**1257** A786 A Block of 4, #a-d 4.00 4.00

On day of issue, Nos. 1257a-1257d each sold for 3.30k.

Bistrica Roses A787

Slavoljub Penkala Roses A788

Christ Jubilee Roses — A789

**2022, Mar. 21** **Litho.** ***Perf. 14***
**1258** A787 A multi 1.00 1.00
*a.* Booklet pane of 10 10.00 —
Complete booklet, #1258a 10.00
**1259** A788 A multi 1.00 1.00
*a.* Booklet pane of 10 10.00 —
Complete booklet, #1259a 10.00
**1260** A789 A multi 1.00 1.00
*a.* Booklet pane of 10 10.00 —
Complete booklet, #1260a 10.00
*Nos. 1258-1260 (3)* 3.00 3.00

On day of issue, Nos. 1258-1260 each sold for 3.30k.

Matica Hrvatska Publishing House, 180th Anniv. — A790

**2022, Mar. 24** **Litho.** ***Perf. 14***
**1261** A790 A multi 1.00 1.00

No. 1261 sold for 3.30k on day of issue.

Easter — A791

**2022, Mar. 30** **Litho.** ***Perf. 14***
**1262** A791 A multi 1.00 1.00

No. 1262 sold for 3.30k on day of issue.

Field of Rapeseed Flowers — A792

**2022, Apr. 12** **Litho.** ***Perf. 14***
**1263** A792 B multi 2.40 2.40

Solidarity with Ukraine after its invasion by Russia. No. 1263 sold for 8.60k on day of issue.

Protected Agricultural and Food Products — A793

Designs: No. 1264, A, Pag cheese and sheep. No. 1265, A, Slavonian honey and field of sunflowers. No. 1266, A, Varadzin klipic (pastry) and buildings.

**2022, Apr. 14** **Litho.** ***Perf. 14***
**1264-1266** A793 Set of 3 2.75 2.75

On day of issue, Nos. 1264-1266 each sold for 3.30k.

Famous Men — A794

Designs: No. 1267, A, Grgo Martic (1822-1905), priest and poet. No. 1268, A, August Senoa (1838-81), newspaper editor, playwright and politician. No. 1269, A, Petar Hektorovi (1487-1582), poet.

**2022, Apr. 20** **Litho.** ***Perf. 14***
**1267-1269** A794 Set of 3 2.75 2.75

On day of issue, Nos. 1267-1269 each sold for 3.30k.

Family and Croatian Pension Insurance Institute, Zagreb — A795

**2022, Apr. 22** **Litho.** ***Perf. 14***
**1270** A795 A multi + label .95 .95

Croatian pension insurance, cent. No. 1270 sold for 3.30k on day of issue.

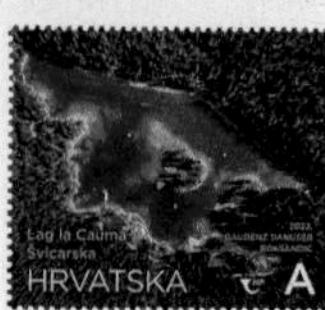

Lakes and Islands — A796

Designs: No. 1271, A, Island in Cauma Lake, Switzerland. No. 1272, A, Visovac Monastery on Visovac Island, Croatia.

**2022, May 5 Litho. *Perf. 14***
**1271-1272** A796 Set of 2 1.90 1.90

Joint issue between Croatia and Switzerland. See Switzerland Nos. 1865-1866. On day of issue, Nos. 1271-1272 each sold for 3.30k.

Europa A797

No. 1273 — Legend of the Tree of the World: a, Bear with antlers and man. b, Tree of the World, white hawk and ladybug.

**2022, May 9 Litho. *Perf. 14***
**1273** A797 B Horiz. pair, #a-b 5.00 5.00

On day of issue, Nos. 1273a-1273b each sold for 8.60k.

Franjo Tudjman (1922-99), First President of Croatia — A798

**2022, May 12 Litho. *Perf. 14***
**1274** A798 A multi .95 .95
*a.* Souvenir sheet of 1 .95 .95

No. 1274 sold for 3.30k on day of issue.

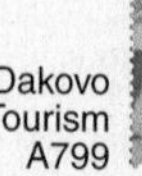

Dakovo Tourism A799

Designs: No. 1275, A, Dancers at Dakovo Embroidery Festival. No. 1276, A, St. Peter's Cathedral, vert.

**2022, June 2 Litho. *Perf. 14***
**1275-1276** A799 Set of 2 1.90 1.90

On day of issue, Nos. 1275-1276 each sold for 3.30k.

Pula Arena — A800

**2022, July 11 Litho. *Perf. 14***
**1277** A800 12.30k multi 3.50 3.50

Opening of Peljesac Bridge A801

**2022, July 26 Litho. *Perf. 14***
**1278** A801 A multi .90 .90

No. 1278 sold for 3.30k on day of issue.

Birdpex 2022, Gmunden, Austria — A802

No. 1279: a, Carduelis carduelis. b, Bubo bubo. c, Alcedo atthis. d, Calidris falcinellus.

**2022, July 27 Litho. *Perf. 14***
**1279** Strip of 4 3.75 3.75
*a.-d.* A802 A Any single .90 .90

On day of issue, Nos. 1279a-1279d each sold for 3.30k.

Souvenir Sheet

Wings of Storm Aerobatic Team — A803

No. 1280 — Airplanes with: a, Land in background. b, Water in background.

**2022, Aug. 3 Litho. *Perf. 14***
**1280** A803 B Sheet of 2, #a-b 2.40 2.40

On day of issue, Nos. 1280a-1280b each sold for 4.30k.

## SEMI-POSTAL STAMPS

**Catalogue values for unused stamps in this section are for Never Hinged items.**

**Types of Yugoslavia, 1941, Overprinted in Gold "NEZAVISNA / DRZAVA / HRVATSKA"**

***Perf. 11½***

**1941, May 10 Unwmk. Engr.**
**B1** SP80 1.50d + 1.50d bl blk 22.50 22.50
**B2** SP81 4d + 3d choc 22.50 22.50

Panes of 16 stamps and 9 labels.
This overprint exists on Yugoslavia No. B124. Value $2,500.

In 1941, 5,000 sets of Yugoslavia Nos. 142-154 were overprinted "NEZAVISNA DRZAVA HRVATSKA 10. IV. 1941" and with a small shield in red or blue. Sold for double face value. Value: set, $550.

Costume of Sinj, Dalmatia — SP1

Designs (Costumes): 2k+2k, Travnik, Bosnia. 4k+4k, Turopolje, Croatia.

**1941, Oct. 12 Photo. *Perf. 10½x10***
**B3** SP1 1.50k + 1.50k Prus bl & red 1.00 1.00
**B4** SP1 2k + 2k ol brn & red 1.25 1.25
**B5** SP1 4k + 4k brn lake & red 2.25 2.25
*Nos. B3-B5 (3)* 4.50 4.50

The surtax aided the Croatian Red Cross.
Nos. B3-B5 were issued in panes of 20 stamps and 5 labels.
Nos. B3-B5 exist with a special printer's mark in the design. The printer's mark appears on one stamp in one pane of the four in the printed sheet. Value, $35 each.

Soldiers with Arms of the Axis States — SP4

**1941, Dec. 3 *Perf. 11***
**B6** SP4 4k + 2k blue 3.75 *4.00*

The surtax was used for Croatian Volunteers in the East.
Issued in panes of 100 stamps.

Model Plane — SP5

Model Plane — SP6

Designs: 3k+3k, Boy with model plane. 4k+4k, Model seaplane in flight.

**1942, Mar. 25**
**B7** SP5 2k + 2k sepia 1.90 1.90
**B8** SP6 2.50k + 2.50k dl grn 1.90 1.90
**B9** SP5 3k + 3k brn car 1.90 1.90
**B10** SP6 4k + 4k dp bl 1.90 1.90
*Nos. B7-B10 (4)* 7.60 7.60

Nos. B7-B10 were issued both in panes of 25 and in panes of 24 plus label.
Nos. B7-B10 exist with a special printer's mark in the design. The mark appears on one stamp in every pane. Value, $10

Values for used souvenir sheets are for those with special philatelic cancels. Faked postal cancellations on souvenir sheets are common, especially using cancellers stolen after WWII. Genuine postal cancellations are the exception and sell for much more. Expertization is recommended.

**Souvenir Sheets**
***Perf. 11***

**B11** Sheet of 2 45.00 45.00
*a.* SP5 2k+8k brown carmine 15.00 15.00
*b.* SP5 3k+12k deep blue 15.00 15.00

***Imperf***

**B12** Sheet of 2 45.00 45.00
*a.* SP5 2k+8k deep blue 15.00 15.00
*b.* SP5 3k+12k brown carmine 15.00 15.00

The sheets measure 125x110mm.
Aviation Exposition of Zagreb. The surtax aided society of Croatian Wings (Hrvatska Krila).
Nos. B11-B12 exist with colors of stamps and inscriptions transposed, with missing colors and with one stamp missing.
Nos. B11-B12 exist with a special printer's mark in the design. The mark typically appears on one stamp in a given pane.

Boy Trumpeters SP10

Triumphal Arch SP11

Mother and Child — SP12

**1942, July 5 *Perf. 11½***
**B13** SP10 3k + 1k lake 1.50 1.50
**B14** SP11 4k + 2k dk brn 1.60 1.60
**B15** SP12 5k + 5k dp bl grn 2.40 2.40
*Nos. B13-B15 (3)* 5.50 5.50

The surtax was for national welfare.
Issued in panes of 25.
Nos. B13-B15 exist with a special printer's mark in the design. The printer's mark appears on one stamp in one pane of the four in the printed sheet. Value, $40 each.

Matthew Gubec SP13

Ante Starcevich SP14

SP15

**1942, Nov. 22 *Perf. 14½***
**B16** SP13 3k + 6k dark red 1.00 1.00
**B17** SP14 4k + 7k sepia 1.00 1.00

**Souvenir Sheets**
***Perf. 12, Imperf.***

**B18** SP15 5k + 20k dull blue 24.00 24.00

Heroes of Senj, May 9, 1937. Nos. B16-B17 were printed in panes of 16 + 9 labels, each bearing a hero's name. The surtax aided the Natl. Youth Soc.

Sestine Peasant — SP16

Designs: 3k+1k, Slavonian peasant. 4k+2k, Bosnian peasant. 10k+5k, Dalmatian peasant. 13k+6k, Sestine peasant.

**1942, Oct. 4 *Perf. 11½***
**B20** SP16 1.50k + 50b org brn & red 1.40 1.40
**B21** SP16 3k + 1k dl pur & red 1.40 1.40
**B22** SP16 4k + 2k dp bl & red 2.10 2.10
**B23** SP16 10k + 5k dk ol bis & red 3.00 3.00
**B24** SP16 13k + 6k rose lake & red 5.50 5.50
*Nos. B20-B24 (5)* 13.40 13.40

The surtax aided the Croatian Red Cross.
Issued in panes of 24 stamps plus label.

Croatian Labor Corpsman — SP20

Designs: 3k+3k, Corpsman with wheelbarrow. 7k+4k, Corpsman plowing.

**1943, Jan. 17 Wmk. 278 *Perf. 11***
**B25** SP20 2k + 1k ol gray & sepia 4.75 *5.00*
**B26** SP20 3k + 3k brn & sepia 4.75 *5.00*
**B27** SP20 7k + 4k gray bl & sepia 4.75 *5.00*
*Nos. B25-B27 (3)* 14.25 *15.00*

The surtax aided the State Labor Service (Drzavna Radna Sluzba). Issued in panes of 9.

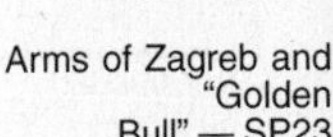

Arms of Zagreb and "Golden Bull" — SP23

**1943, Mar. 21** **Unwmk.**

**B28** SP23 3.50k (+ 6.50k) ultra 4.50 *4.75*

700th anniversary of Zagreb's "Golden Bull," a Magna Carta of civic rights and privileges granted to the city in 1242 by King Bela because the Croats annihilated Tartar hordes at Grobnik.

Issued in panes of 8 with marginal inscriptions.

Ante Pavelich — SP24

**1943, Apr. 10** ***Perf. 13¾14***

**B29** SP24 5k + 3k copper red .60 .60
*a.* Sheetlet of 16 #B29 + 9 labels 12.00 12.00
**B30** SP24 7k + 5k dark green .60 .60
*a.* Sheetlet of 16 #B30 + 9 labels 12.00 12.00

Surtax aided the National Youth Society.

Nos. B29-B30 were issued in panes of 100 stamps. Nos. B29a and B30a were issued Apr. 12 and are perf 14½.

**Souvenir Sheets**

**1943, May 17** ***Perf. 12, Imperf.***

**B31** SP24 12k + 8k dp ultra 30.00 30.00

Sailor at Sea of Azov — SP26

Designs: 2k+1k, Flier at Sevastopol and Rzhev. 3.50k+1.50k, Infantrymen at Stalingrad. 9k+4.50k, Panzer Division at Don River.

**1943, July 1** ***Perf. 11***

**B33** SP26 1k + 50b grn .40 .25
**B34** SP26 2k + 1k dk red .40 .25
**B35** SP26 3.50k + 1.50k dk bl .40 .25
**B36** SP26 9k + 4.50k chestnut .40 .25
*Nos. B33-B36 (4)* 1.60 1.00

**Souvenir Sheets**

***Perf. 11, Imperf.***

**B37** Sheet of 4 7.50 7.50
*a.* SP26 1k+50b dark blue 1.40 *1.40*
*b.* SP26 2k+1k green 1.40 *1.40*
*c.* SP26 3.50k+1.50k dk red brown 1.40 *1.40*
*d.* SP26 9k+4.50k bluish black 1.40 *1.40*

Surtax aided the National Youth Society. Issued to honor the Croatian Legion which fought with the Germans in Russia. The surtax aided the Legion.

Issued in panes of 100.

St. Mary's Church and Cistercian Cloister, Zagreb, in 1650 — SP31

**1943, Sept. 12** **Engr.** ***Perf. 14½***

**B39** SP31 18k + 9k dl gray vio 5.25 5.25

**Souvenir Sheet**

***Perf. 12½***

**B40** SP31 18k + 9k blk brn 13.00 13.00

Croatian Phil. Soc. Exhibition at Zagreb.

No. B39 issued in pane of 40.

Nos. B39-B40 exist with a special printer's mark in the design. The printer's mark appears on one stamp in the pane for No. 39, value $30; the mark appears on one souvenir sheet of the six in the printed sheet for No. B40, value $52.50.

No. B39 Ovptd. in Red

**1943, Sept. 12**

**B41** SP31 18k + 9k dl gray vio 12.00 *14.00*

Return to Croatia of the Dalmatian and Croatian coasts.

The overprint exists inverted, double, and double, one inverted.

No. B41 exists with a special printer's mark in the design. The mark typically appears on one stamp in a given pane.

Mother and Children SP33

Nurse and Patient SP34

**1943, Oct. 3** **Litho.** ***Perf. 11***

**Cross in Red**

**B42** SP33 1k + 50b bl grn .75 .75
**B43** SP33 2k + 1k bril car .75 .75
**B44** SP33 3.50k + 1.50k brt bl .75 .75
**B45** SP34 8k + 3k red brn .90 .90
**B46** SP34 9k + 4k yel grn 1.00 1.00
**B47** SP33 10k + 5k dp vio 1.00 1.00
**B48** SP34 12k + 6k brt ultra 1.25 1.25
**B49** SP33 12.50k + 6k dk brn 1.75 1.75
**B50** SP34 18k + 8k brn org 2.00 2.00
**B51** SP34 32k + 12k dk gray 3.25 3.25
*Nos. B42-B51 (10)* 13.40 13.40

The surtax aided the Croatian Red Cross. Issued in panes of 100.

Post Horn and Arms SP35

Carrier Pigeon and Plane SP36

Mercury SP37

Winged Wheel SP38

**1944, Feb. 3**

**B52** SP35 7k + 3.50k ol bis & red .90 .90
*a.* Double impression of red —
**B53** SP36 16k + 8k bl & dk bl .90 .90
**B54** SP37 24k + 12k red & rose red .90 .90
**B55** SP38 32k + 16k gray & red .90 .90
*Nos. B52-B55 (4)* 3.60 3.60

The surtax benefited communications and railway employees. Panes of 9.

St. Sebastian SP39

War Invalids SP40

Statue of Ancient Croatian King — SP41

Death of King Peter Svacic, 1097 — SP42

**1944, Feb. 15**

**B56** SP39 7k + 3.50k org red & rose car 1.00 1.00
**B57** SP40 16k + 8k yel grn & dk grn 1.00 1.00
**B58** SP41 24k + 12k yel brn & red 1.00 1.00
**B59** SP42 32k + 16k bl & dk bl 1.00 1.00
*Nos. B56-B59 (4)* 4.00 4.00

The surtax aided wounded war victims.

Issued in panes of eight stamps, with marginal inscriptions and a central label picturing St. Sebastian.

Black Legion in Combat SP43

Guarding the Drina SP44

Jure Francetic — SP45

**1944, May 22** **Photo.** ***Imperf.***

**B60** SP43 3.50k + 1.50k brn red .25 .25
**B61** SP44 12.50k + 6.50k slate bl .25 .25
**B62** SP45 18k + 9k olive brn .25 .25
*Nos. B60-B62 (3)* .75 .75

Third anniversary of Croatian independence.

The surtax aided the National Youth Society. Panes of 20.

***Perf. 14½***

**B63** SP45 12.50k + 287.50k int blk 12.00 *14.50*

Issued to commemorate Jure Francetic.

Issued in pane of 30.

Labor Corpsmen Marching SP46

Corpsman Digging SP47

Designs: 18k+9k, Officer instructing corpsman. 32k+16k, Pavelich reviewing Labor Corps. Panes of 8 plus label.

***Perf. 11½, 12½, 14½***

**1944, Aug. 20** **Engr.**

**B65** SP46 3.50k + 1k dk red .50 .50
**B66** SP47 12.50k + 6k sepia .50 .50
**B67** SP47 18k + 9k dk bl .50 .50
**B68** SP47 32k + 16k gray grn .50 .50
*Nos. B65-B68 (4)* 2.00 2.00

Nos. B68 exists only perf 12½, while B65-B67 exist perf 11½, 12½ or 14½. Values are for copies perf 11½ or 12½. Values Nos. B65-B67 perf 14½, $5 each unused or used.

**Souvenir Sheet**

***Perf. 12½***

**B69** SP47 32k + 16k dk brn, *cr* 4.50 *5.00*

The surtax aided the State Labor Service (Drzavna Radna Sluzba).

Palm Leaf — SP51

**1944, Nov. 12** **Litho.** ***Perf. 11***

**B70** SP51 2k + 1k dl grn & red .45 .45
**B71** SP51 3.50k + 1.50k car lake & red .45 .45
**B72** SP51 12.50k + 6k ind & red .45 .45
*Nos. B70-B72 (3)* 1.35 1.35

The surtax aided the Croatian Red Cross. Panes of 16.

Men of Storm Division SP52

70k+70k, Soldiers of Storm Division in action. 100k+100k, Storm Division emblem.

**1944** **Unwmk.** **Litho.** ***Perf. 11***

**B73** SP52 50k + 50k brick red 175.00 *190.00*
**B74** SP52 70k + 70k sepia 175.00 *190.00*
**B75** SP52 100k + 100k chlky, pale & dp bl 175.00 *190.00*
*Nos. B73-B75 (3)* 525.00 *570.00*

Nos. B73-B75 issued in panes of 20.

**Souvenir Sheet**

**B76** Sheet of 3 1,650. 1,650.
*a.* SP52 50k + 50k brick red 400. 400.
*b.* SP52 70k + 70k sepia 400. 400.
*c.* SP52 100k + 100k chalky, pale & deep blue 400. 400.

Nos. B76a to B76c are inscribed "O. A." in brick red at right below design. The sheet measures 216x132mm. The surtax aided the First Croatian Storm Division. Counterfeits are plentiful.

Postman SP55

Telephone Line Repairman SP56

24k+12k, Switchboard operator. 50k+25k, 100k+50k, Postman delivering parcel.

**1945** **Photo.**

**B77** SP55 3.50k + 1.50k sl gray .40 .40
**B78** SP56 12.50k + 6k brn car .40 .40
**B79** SP56 24k + 12k dk grn .40 .40
**B80** SP56 50k + 25k brn vio .40 .40
*Nos. B77-B80 (4)* 1.60 1.60

**Souvenir Sheet**

**B81** SP56 100k + 50k dp brn 11.00 11.00

The surtax on #B77-B81 aided employees of the P.T.T. Panes of 8.

Famous Croatians — SP60

No. B100, Ban Josip Jelacic (1801-59). No. B101, Dr. Ante Starcevic (1823-96). 7d + 3d, Stjepan Radic (1871-1928).

**1992** **Litho.** ***Perf. 11x10½***

**B100** SP60 4d +2d multi .65 .65
**B101** SP60 4d +2d multi .65 .65

*Perf. 14*

**B102** SP60 7d +3d multi .65 .65
*Nos. B100-B102 (3)* 1.95 1.95

Issued: No. B100, 2/1; No. B101, 3/4; No. B102, 4/2.

The surcharge on Nos. B100-B102 was initially an obligatory tax on all internal and overseas mail. From May 15, 1992, these stamps were valid for postage at their 6d or 10d face values.

## AIR POST STAMPS

**Catalogue values for unused stamps in this section are for Never Hinged items.**

Airplane, Zagreb Cathedral and Port of Dubrovnik
AP1

Airplane Over Ruins of Diocletian's Palace, Split
AP2

Coat of Arms, Airplane, Zagreb Cathedral and Pula Amphitheatre
AP3

Paper Airplane Made From Picture of Osijek Cathedral
AP4

**1991-92** **Litho.** ***Perf. 11x10½***

**C1** AP1 1d multicolored .50 .50
*a.* Perf. 14 .50 .50
**C2** AP2 2d multicolored 1.50 .50
*a.* Perf. 14 .50 .50
**C3** AP3 3d multicolored .50 .50
**C4** AP4 4d multicolored .50 .50
*Nos. C1-C4 (4)* 3.00 2.00

Issued: No. C1, 9/9/91; No. C1a, 6/24/92; No. C2, 10/9/91; No. C2a, 1992; No. C3, 11/20/91; No. C4, 2/14/92.

Miniature Sheet

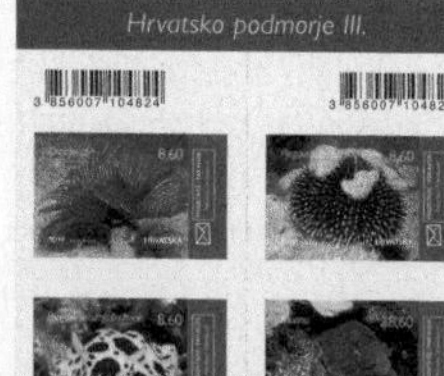


Marine Life
AP5

No. C5: a, Long-snouted seahorse (konjic dugokljunic). b, Violescent sea-whip (velika roznjaca). c, Cylinder anemone (opnena voskovica). d, Neptune's lace (neptunova cipka).

***Serpentine Die Cut 5½x5¼***

**2015, June 15** **Litho.**

**Self-Adhesive**

**C5** AP5 Sheet of 4 7.00
*a.-d.* 5.80k Any single 1.75 1.75

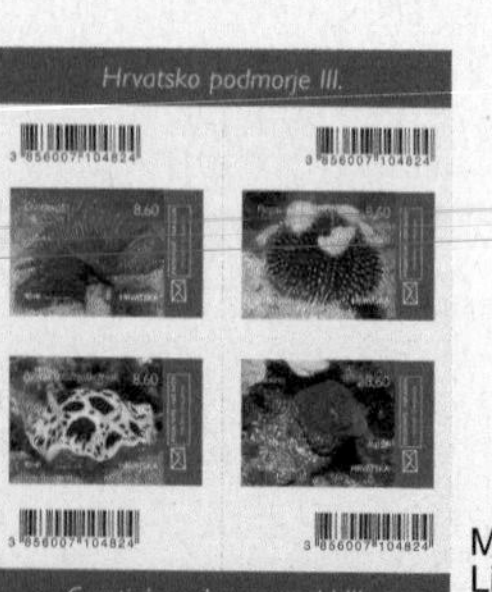


Marine Life
AP5

No.C6: a, Crv cjevas (Bispira volutacornis). b, Pjegavi jezinac (Sphaerechinus granularis). c, Pjegavi straznjoskrznjak (Peltodoris atromaculata). d, Murina (Muraena helena).

***Serpentine Die Cut 5½x5¼***

**2019, May 15** **Litho.**

**Self-Adhesive**

**C6** AP5 Sheet of 4 10.50
*a.-d.* 8.60k Any single 2.60 2.60

## POSTAGE DUE STAMPS

Yugoslavia Nos. J28-J32 Overprinted in Black

**1941, Apr. 26** **Unwmk.** ***Perf. 12½***

**J1** D4 50p violet .40 .65
*a.* Double overprint 150.00
*b.* 50p rose violet 9.00 18.00
*c.* As "b," double overprint 200.00
**J2** D4 1d deep magenta .40 .65
*a.* Inverted overprint 200.00
*b.* Double overprint 300.00
**J3** D4 2d deep blue 10.00 20.00
*a.* Double overprint 300.00
**J4** D4 5d orange 1.25 2.00
*a.* Double overprint 300.00
**J5** D4 10d chocolate 6.00 12.00
*Nos. J1-J5 (5)* 18.05 35.30
Set, never hinged 40.00

Counterfeit overprints exist, particularly of Nos. J3 and J5.

D1

**1941, Sept. 12** **Litho.** ***Perf. 11***

**J6** D1 50b carmine lake .25 .50
**J7** D1 1k carmine lake .25 .50
**J8** D1 2k carmine lake .30 .70
**J9** D1 5k carmine lake .50 1.00
**J10** D1 10k carmine lake .75 1.40
*Nos. J6-J10 (5)* 2.05 4.10
Set, never hinged 5.00

D2

**1943** ***Perf. 11½, 12x12½, 12½***

**Size: 24x24mm**

**J11** D2 50b lt blue & gray .25 .25
**J12** D2 1k lt blue & gray .25 .25
**J13** D2 2k lt blue & gray .25 .25
**J14** D2 4k lt blue & gray .25 .35
**J15** D2 5k lt blue & gray .25 .40
**J16** D2 6k lt blue & gray .25 .45
**J17** D2 10k blue & indigo .25 .40
**J18** D2 15k blue & indigo .25 1.10
**J19** D2 20k blue & indigo .65 1.60
*Nos. J11-J19 (9)* 2.65 5.05
Set, never hinged 5.00

**1942, July 30** ***Perf. 10½, 11½***

**Size: 25x24¼mm**

**J20** D2 50b lt blue & gray .25 .40
**J21** D2 1k lt blue & gray .25 .50
**J22** D2 2k lt blue & gray .25 .50
**J23** D2 5k lt blue & gray .25 .50
**J24** D2 10k lt blue & blue .65 1.10
**J25** D2 20k lt blue & blue .90 1.60
*Nos. J20-J25 (6)* 2.55 4.60
Set, never hinged 6.00

Nos. J21-J25 exist both perf 10½ and 11½. No. J20 exists only perf 11½.

## OFFICIAL STAMPS

Croatian Coat of Arms
O1 O2

**1942-43** **Unwmk.** **Litho.**

**Ordinary Paper**

***Perf. 11½***

**O1** O1 25b rose lake .25 .25
**O2** O1 50b slate blk .25 .25
**O3** O1 75b gray grn .25 .25
**O4** O1 1k orange brn .25 .25
**O5** O1 2k turq blue 1.10 1.10
**O6** O1 3k vermilion .25 .25
**O7** O1 4k brown vio .25 .25
**O8** O1 5k ultra, *thin paper* .25 .40
**O9** O1 6k brt violet .25 .25
**O10** O1 10k lt green .25 .30
**O11** O1 12k brown rose .25 .35
**O12** O1 20k dark blue .25 .40
**O13** O2 30k brn vio & gray .25 .40
**O14** O2 40k vio blk & gray .30 .50
**O15** O2 50k brn lake & gray .65 1.00
**O16** O2 100k black & pink .65 1.00
*Nos. O1-O16 (16)* 5.70 7.20
Set, never hinged 8.00

***Perf. 10½***

*O1a* O1 25b rose lake .25 .25
*O2a* O1 50b slate blk .25 .25
*O3a* O1 75b gray grn .25 .25
*O4a* O1 1k orange brn .25 .25
*O5a* O1 2k turq blue 1.10 2.00
*O6a* O1 3k vermilion .25 .25
*O7a* O1 4k brown vio .25 .25
*O8a* O1 5k ultra .95 1.75
*O9a* O1 6k brt violet 1.40 2.50
*O10a* O1 10k lt green .25 .25
*O11a* O1 12k brown rose 1.25 2.25
*O12a* O1 20k dark blue 1.25 2.25
*O13a* O2 30k brn vio & gray .25 .40
*O14a* O2 40k vio blk & gray .30 .50
*O15a* O2 50k brn lake & gray .65 1.00
*O16a* O2 100k black & pink .65 1.00
*Nos. O1a-O16a (16)* 9.55 15.40
Set, never hinged 15.00

**1943-44** **Thin Paper** ***Perf. 11½***

**O17** O1 25b claret .25 .25
**O18** O1 50b gray .25 .25
**O19** O1 75b dull green .25 .25
**O20** O1 1k orange brn .25 .25
**O21** O1 2k slate blue .25 .25
**O22** O1 3.50k car rose .25 .25
*a.* Ordinary paper 3.00 3.00
**O23** O1 6k brt red vio .25 .25
**O24** O1 12.50k deep orange .25 .25
*a.* Ordinary paper 2.00 2.00
Set, never hinged 1.50

## POSTAL TAX STAMPS

**Catalogue values for unused stamps in this section are for Never Hinged items.**

Nurse and Soldier — PT1

**Unwmk.**

**1942, Oct. 4** **Litho.** ***Perf. 11***

**RA1** PT1 1k olive grn & red .85 .80

The tax aided the Croatian Red Cross. Issued in sheets of 24 plus label.

No. RA1 can be found with a red cross printed on the nurse's hat. The original design included this element, but it was removed from the final approved design. Early printings of No. RA1, probably trial printings, included the red cross.

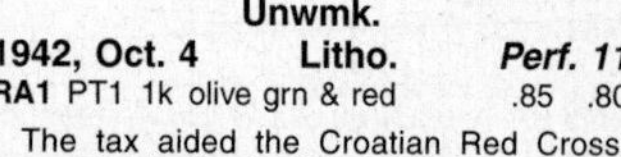

Wounded Soldier — PT2

**1943, Oct. 3**

**RA2** PT2 2k blue & red .70 .70

The tax aided the Croatian Red Cross.

Ruins — PT3

Wounded Soldier — PT4

**1944, Jan. 1** **Photo.** ***Perf. 12***

**RA3** PT3 1k dk slate green .25 .25
**RA4** PT4 2k carmine lake .30 .30
**RA5** PT4 5k black .35 .35
**RA6** PT4 10k deep blue .55 .40
**RA7** PT4 20k brown 1.10 .90
*Nos. RA3-RA7 (5)* 2.55 2.20

Interior of Zagreb Cathedral — PT10

**1991, Apr. 1** **Litho.** ***Perf. 14***

**RA20** PT10 1.20d black & gold .65 .55
*a.* Perf. 11x10½ .85 .80
*b.* Perf. 11 15.00 12.00
*c.* Imperf .90 .90

Worker's Fund. Required on mail during April 1991.

For surcharges see Nos. 100, 100a.

Shrine of the Virgin, 700th Anniv. — PT11

**1991, May 16** ***Perf. 10½x11***

**RA21** PT11 1.70d multicolored .80 .65
*a.* Imperf 1.25 1.10

Workers' Fund. Required on mail May 16-31.

**Croatian Arms Type of 1992**

**1991, July 1** ***Perf. 11x10½***

**RA22** A37 2.20d multicolored .80 .70
*a.* Imperf 1.25 1.00

Required on mail during July.

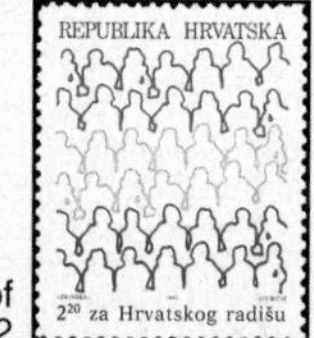


Members of Parliament — PT12

**1991, Aug. 1** ***Perf. 11x10½***

**RA23** PT12 2.20d multicolored .80 .70
*a.* Imperf 1.25 1.00

Worker's Fund. Required on mail during Aug.

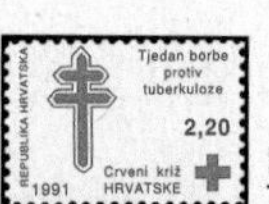


Red Cross and Tuberculosis — PT13

**1991, Sept 14** ***Perf. 11***

**RA24** PT13 2.20d blue & red .50 .45

Required on mail Sept. 14-21.

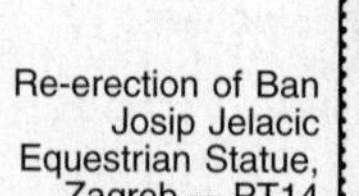

Re-erection of Ban Josip Jelacic Equestrian Statue, Zagreb — PT14

**1991, Nov. 1** ***Perf. 11x10½***

| | | | |
|---|---|---|---|
| **RA25** PT14 2.20d multicolored | .80 | .70 |
| *a.* Imperf. | 1.25 | 1.00 |

Worker's Fund. Required on mail during Nov.

New Constitution PT15

**1991, Dec. 2 Litho.** ***Perf. 10¾x10½***

**Language of Inscription**

| | | |
|---|---|---|
| **RA26** PT15 2.20d English | *3.25* | *3.00* |
| **RA27** PT15 2.20d Croatian | *1.15* | *1.00* |
| **RA28** PT15 2.20d French | *3.25* | *3.00* |
| **RA29** PT15 2.20d German | *3.25* | *3.00* |
| **RA30** PT15 2.20d Russian | *3.25* | *3.00* |
| **RA31** PT15 2.20d Spanish | *3.25* | *3.00* |
| *a.* Vert. strip, #RA26-RA31 | *35.00* | *35.00* |
| *Nos. RA26-RA31 (6)* | 17.40 | 16.00 |

Nos RA26-RA31 were printed in sheet containing 15 of No. RA27, 2 each of the other stamps and five labels. Obligatory on mail Dec. 2-31.

Sheet exists imperf. Value $225.

"VUKOVAR" with Barbed Wire — PT16

**1992, Jan. 1 Litho.** ***Perf. 11x10½***

| | | |
|---|---|---|
| **RA32** PT16 2.20d black & brown | 1.15 | .90 |
| *a.* Imperf. | 1.60 | 1.40 |

Vukovar Refugee's Fund. Required on mail during Jan.

Red Cross PT17

Red Cross and Solidarity PT18

**1992** ***Perf. 11***

| | | |
|---|---|---|
| **RA33** PT17 3d red & black | .50 | .50 |
| **RA34** PT18 3d red & black | .30 | .30 |

Issued: No. RA33, May 8. No. RA34, June 1.

No. RA33 was required on mail May 8-15; No. RA34, June 1-7.

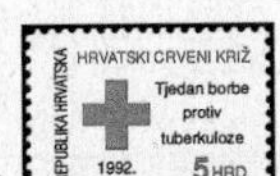

Madonna of Bistrica — PT19

**1992, Aug. 1 Litho.** ***Perf. 14***

| | | |
|---|---|---|
| **RA35** PT19 5d blue & gold | .45 | .40 |

Required on mail, Aug. 1-8.

Red Cross — PT20

**1992, Sept. 21 Litho.** ***Perf. 11***

| | | |
|---|---|---|
| **RA36** PT20 5d black & red | .50 | .30 |

Required on mail Sept. 14-21.

St. George Slaying Dragon — PT21

**1992, Nov. 4** ***Perf. 14***

| | | |
|---|---|---|
| **RA37** PT21 15d multicolored | .50 | .30 |

Cancer Research League. Required on mail Nov. 4-11.

See No. RA43.

Red Cross — PT22

**1993, May 8 Litho.** ***Rough Perf. 11***

| | | |
|---|---|---|
| **RA38** PT22 80d black & red | .50 | .30 |

Required on mail May 8-15.

Red Cross and Solidarity — PT23

**1993, June 1**

| | | |
|---|---|---|
| **RA39** PT23 100d black & red | .50 | .30 |

Required on mail June 1-7.

Cardinal Stepinac (1898-1960) — PT24

**1993, July 15 Litho.** ***Perf. 14***

| | | |
|---|---|---|
| **RA40** PT24 150d multicolored | .50 | .30 |

Required on mail July 15-22.

Zrinski-Frankopan Foundation — PT25

Design: 200d, Gen. Peter Zrinski (1621-1671), Politician and Fran Krsto Frankopan, Count of Tersat (1643-1671), Poet.

**1993, Aug. 12 Litho.** ***Perf. 14***

| | | |
|---|---|---|
| **RA41** PT25 200d gray & blue | .50 | .30 |

Required on mail Aug. 12-19.

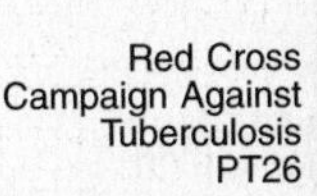

Red Cross Campaign Against Tuberculosis PT26

**1993, Sept. 14 Litho.** ***Perf. 11***

| | | |
|---|---|---|
| **RA42** PT26 300d gray, red & black | .50 | .45 |

Required on mail Sept. 14-21.

**St. George Slaying Dragon Type of 1992**

**1993, Oct. 11 Litho.** ***Perf. 14***

| | | |
|---|---|---|
| **RA43** PT21 400d multicolored | .45 | .40 |

Cancer Research League. Required on mail Oct. 11-31.

Save the Children of Croatia — PT27

**1993, Nov. 1** ***Perf. 13½x14***

| | | |
|---|---|---|
| **RA44** PT27 400d multicolored | .50 | .45 |

Required on mail Nov. 1-30.

Croatian Red Cross — PT28

**1994, May 5 Litho.** ***Perf. 11***

| | | |
|---|---|---|
| **RA45** PT28 500d multicolored | .50 | .45 |

Required on mail May 8-15.

Red Cross Solidarity — PT29

**1994, May 5 Litho.** ***Perf. 11***

| | | |
|---|---|---|
| **RA46** PT29 50 l multicolored | .50 | .45 |

Required on mail June 1-7.

Ludberg Church — PT30

**1994, July 15** ***Perf. 14***

| | | |
|---|---|---|
| **RA47** PT30 50 l multicolored | .50 | .30 |

Required on mail July 15-22.

Save the Children of Croatia — PT31

**1994, Aug. 16 Litho.** ***Perf. 14***

| | | |
|---|---|---|
| **RA48** PT31 50 l multicolored | .50 | .30 |

Required on mail Aug. 16-29.

St. George Slaying Dragon — PT32

**1994, Sept. 1**

| | | |
|---|---|---|
| **RA49** PT32 50 l multicolored | .50 | .30 |

Cancer Research League. Required on mail Sept. 1-8.

PT33

**1994, Sept. 14** ***Perf. 11***

| | | |
|---|---|---|
| **RA50** PT33 50 l blk, grn & red | .50 | .30 |

Red Cross Campaign against Tuberculosis. Required on mail Sept. 14-21.

PT34

**1994, Oct. 15 Litho.** ***Perf. 14***

| | | |
|---|---|---|
| **RA51** PT34 50 l multicolored | .50 | .35 |

Town of Slavonski Brod, 750th anniv.

Homage to Olympia, by Ivan Lackovic — PT35

Intl. Olympic Committee, Cent. — PT36

Designs: a, Tennis. b, Soccer. c, Basketball. d, Team handball. e, Canoeing, kayaking. f, Water polo. g, Track and field. h, Gymnastics.

**1994, Nov. 2 Litho.** ***Perf. 14***

| | | |
|---|---|---|
| **RA52** PT35 50 l Pair, #a.-b. | 1.40 | 1.25 |
| **RA53** PT36 50 l Sheet of 8, #a.-h. | 5.75 | 5.75 |
| **RA54** PT36 50 l Sheet of 8, #a.-h. | 5.75 | 5.75 |

Nos. RA52b, RA53a, RA53d-RA53e, RA53h, RA54b-RA54c, RA54f-RA54g have IOC centennial emblem. Others have emblem of Croatian Olympic Committee.

Required on mail Nov. 2-15.

Natl. Olympic Committee — PT37

Designs: a, Rowing. b, Pétanque. c, Monument to Drazen Petrovic, Olympic Park, Lausanne. d, Tennis. e, Basketball.

**1995, Apr. 17 Litho.** ***Perf. 14***

| | | |
|---|---|---|
| **RA55** PT37 50 l Strip of 5, #a.-e. | 2.00 | 2.00 |

Required on mail Apr. 17-30.

Red Cross Stamps — PT38

**1995, May 8** ***Perf. 11***

| | | |
|---|---|---|
| **RA56** PT38 50 l multicolored | .50 | .30 |

Required on mail May 8-15.

Red Cross Stamps — PT39

**1995, June 1**
**RA57** PT39 50 l multicolored .50 .30

Required on mail June 1-7.

Sts. Peter and Paul Cathedral, Osijek — PT40

**1995, July 17** ***Perf. 14***
**RA58** PT40 65 l multicolored .50 .40

Required on mail July 17-30.

Holy Mother of Freedom — PT41

Design: No. RA59, Like No. RA60, but with black surcharge on white panel. #RA60, Croatian Pieta, by Ivan Lackovic. #RA61, Gedenkstatte Church Project.

**1995, Aug. 14** **Litho.** ***Perf. 14***
**RA59** PT41 65 l on 50 l multi 2.50 2.50
**RA60** PT41 65 l multicolored .55 .50
**RA61** PT41 65 l multicolored .55 .50
*Nos. RA59-RA61 (3)* 3.60 3.50

No. RA59 not issued without surcharge. Examples without surcharge are printer's waste. Required on mail Aug. 14-27.

Red Cross and Tuberculosis — PT42

**1995, Sept. 14** **Litho.** ***Perf. 11***
**RA62** PT42 65 l multicolored .50 .40

Required on mail Sept. 14-21.

Save the Croatian Children — PT43

**1995, Oct. 16** ***Perf. 14***
**RA63** PT43 65 l multicolored .50 .40

Required on mail Oct. 16-29.

PT44

Performance scene: a, Woman seated at top of steps. b, Gathering of people. c, People, large statue in background.

**1995, Oct. 16**
**RA64** PT44 65 l Strip of 3, #a.-c. 1.50 1.50

Croatian Natl. Theater, Zagreb, cent. No. RA64 has continuous design. Required on mail 10/16-29.

Fight Against Drugs — PT45

**1995, Nov. 6** **Litho.** ***Perf. 14***
**RA65** PT45 65 l multicolored .50 .35

Required on mail Nov. 20-30.

PT46

**1995, Nov. 20** **Litho.** ***Perf. 14x13¾***
**RA66** PT46 65 l multicolored .50 .35

Croatian Anti-Cancer League. Required on mail Nov. 20-30.

PT47

**1996, Feb. 15** **Litho.** ***Perf. 14x13½***
**RA67** PT47 65 l multicolored .50 .35

Croatian Anti-Cancer League. Required on mail Feb. 15-28.

PT48

**1996, Mar. 18** **Litho.** ***Perf. 14***
**RA68** PT48 65 l multicolored .50 .35

Sanctuary of the Virgin Mary of Bistrica. Required on mail Mar. 18-31.

Croatian Olympic Committee — PT49

**1996, Apr. 17** **Litho.** ***Perf. 14***
**RA69** PT49 65 l multi .60 .35

No. RA69 exists imperf. and in booklets, which were not placed on sale. Required on mail Apr. 17-30.

Red Cross — PT50

**1996, May 8** **Litho.** ***Perf. 11***
**RA70** PT50 65 l multicolored .50 .35

Required on mail May 8-15.

Red Cross Solidarity Week — PT51

**1996, June 6** **Litho.** ***Perf. 11***
**RA71** PT51 65 l multicolored .50 .35

Required on mail June 1-7.

Croatian Children — PT52

**1996, June 14** **Litho.** ***Perf. 14x13½***
**RA72** PT52 65 l multicolored .50 .35

Required on mail 6/14-27.

PT53

**1996, July 3** **Litho.** ***Perf. 14***
**RA73** PT53 65 l multicolored .50 .35

Osijek, 800th anniv. Required on mail July 3-16.

PT54

**1996, July 17** **Litho.** ***Perf. 14***
**RA74** PT54 65 l multicolored .50 .35

Renovation of Dakovo Cathedral. Required on mail July 17-30.

Split, 1700th Anniv. — PT55

**1996, Aug. 1** **Litho.** ***Perf. 14***
**RA75** PT55 65 l multicolored .50 .35

Required on mail Aug. 1-14.

Aid to Vukovar — PT56

**1996, Aug. 16** **Litho.** ***Perf. 14x13½***
**RA76** PT56 65 l multicolored .50 .35

Required on mail 8/16-29.

Fight Against Drugs — PT57

**1996, Sept. 1** **Litho.** ***Perf. 14***
**RA77** PT57 65 l multicolored .55 .35

Required on mail Sept. 1-12.

PT58

**1996, Sept. 14** **Litho.** ***Perf. 11***
**RA78** PT58 65 l multicolored .50 .35

Red Cross Tuberculosis Week. Required on mail Sept. 14-21.

PT59

**1996, Oct. 10** **Litho.** ***Perf. 14***
**RA79** PT59 65 l multicolored .55 .35

Isolation of insulin, 75th anniv. Required on mail Oct. 10-17.

PT60

**1996, Nov. 11** **Litho.** ***Perf. 14***
**RA80** PT60 65 l multicolored .50 .35

Remete pilgrimage. Required on mail Nov. 11-24.

PT61

**1997, Jan. 6** **Litho.** ***Perf. 14***
**RA81** PT61 65 l multicolored .50 .35

Antun Mihanovic (1796-1861), natl. anthem lyricist. Required on mail Jan. 6-26.

House of Dr. Ante Starcevic — PT62

**1997, Jan. 27** **Litho.** ***Perf. 14***
**RA82** PT62 65 l multicolored .50 .35

Required on mail Jan. 27-Feb. 14.

PT63

**1997, Feb. 15** **Litho.** ***Perf. 14***
**RA83** PT63 65 l multicolored .50 .35

Croatian Anti-Cancer League. Required on mail Feb. 15-28.

Red Cross — PT64

**1997, May 8** **Litho.** ***Perf. 10½x11***
**RA84** PT64 65 l multicolored .50 .35
*a.* Perf 10½ .50 .35
*b.* Perf 11 *35.00*

Required on mail May 8-15.

Numerous charity stamps were issued between 1997 and 2001, but their use on mail was not obligatory.

Red Cross Solidarity Week — PT65

**2001, Dec. 8** **Litho.** ***Perf. 14***
**RA85** PT65 1.15k red & black 1.25 1.00
Obligatory on mail Dec. 8-15.

Red Cross Week — PT66

**2002, May 8**
**RA86** PT66 1.15k multi 1.25 1.10
Obligatory on mail May 8-15.

Red Cross Anti-Tuberculosis Week — PT67

**2002, Sept. 14**
**RA87** PT67 1.15k multi 1.25 1.00
Obligatory on mail Sept. 14-21.

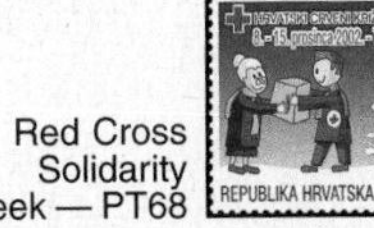

Red Cross Solidarity Week — PT68

**2002, Dec. 8**
**RA88** PT68 1.15k multi 1.25 1.00
Obligatory on mail Dec. 8-15.

Red Cross Week — PT69

**2003, May 8**
**RA89** PT69 1.15k multi 1.25 1.10
Obligatory on mail May 8-15.

Red Cross Anti-Tuberculosis Week — PT70

**2003, Sept. 14**
**RA90** PT70 1.15k multi 1.25 1.10
Obligatory on mail Sept. 14-21.

Red Cross Solidarity Week — PT71

**2003, Dec. 8**
**RA91** PT71 1.15k multi 1.25 1.10
Obligatory on mail Dec. 8-15.

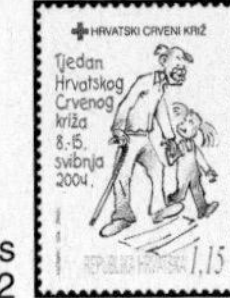

Red Cross Week — PT72

**2004, May 8**
**RA92** PT72 1.15k multi 1.25 1.10
Obligatory on mail May 8-15.

Red Cross Anti-Tuberculosis Week — PT73

**2004, Sept. 14**
**RA93** PT73 1.15k multi .50 .50
Obligatory on mail Sept. 14-21.

Red Cross Solidarity Week — PT74

**2004, Dec. 8**
**RA94** PT74 1.15k multi .50 .50
Obligatory on mail Dec. 8-15.

Red Cross Week — PT75

**2005, May 8** **Litho.** ***Perf. 14***
**RA95** PT75 1.15k multi .60 .60
Obligatory on mail May 8-15.

Red Cross Anti-Tuberculosis Week — PT76

**2005, Sept. 14**
**RA96** PT76 1.15k multi .50 .50
Obligatory on mail Sept. 14-21.

Red Cross Solidarity Week — PT77

**2005, Dec. 8**
**RA97** PT77 1.15k multi .50 .50
Obligatory on mail Dec. 8-15.

Red Cross Week — PT78

**2006, May 8** **Litho.** ***Perf. 14***
**RA98** PT78 1.15k multi 1.25 1.25
Obligatory on mail May 8-15.

Red Cross Anti-Tuberculosis Week — PT79

**2006, Sept. 14**
**RA99** PT79 1.15k multi 1.25 1.25
Obligatory on mail Sept. 14-21.

Red Cross Solidarity Week — PT80

**2006, Dec. 8**
**RA100** PT80 1.15k multi 1.25 1.25
Obligatory on mail Dec. 8-15.

Red Cross Week — PT81

**2007, May 8** **Litho.** ***Perf. 14¼***
**RA101** PT81 1.15k multi — —
Obligatory on mail May 8-15.

Red Cross Anti-Tuberculosis Week — PT82

**2007, Sept. 14** **Litho.** ***Perf. 14¼***
**RA102** PT82 1.15k multi — —
Obligatory on mail Sept. 14-21.

Red Cross Solidarity Week — PT83

**2007, Dec. 8** **Litho.** ***Perf. 14¼***
**RA103** PT83 1.15k multi — —
Obligatory on mail Dec. 8-15.

Red Cross Week — PT84

**2008, May 8** **Litho.** ***Perf. 14¼***
**RA104** PT84 1.15k multi — —
Obligatory on mail May 8-15.

Red Cross Anti-Tuberculosis Week — PT85

**2008, Sept. 14** **Litho.** ***Perf. 14¼***
**RA105** PT85 1.15k multi .45 .45
Obligatory on mail Sept. 14-21.

Red Cross Solidarity Week — PT86

**2008, Dec. 8** **Litho.** ***Perf. 14¼***
**RA106** PT86 1.15k multi — —
Obligatory on mail Dec. 8-15.

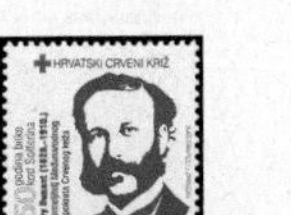

Red Cross Week — PT87

**2009, May 8** **Litho.** ***Perf. 14¼***
**RA107** PT87 1.75k multi — —
Obligatory on mail May 8-15.

Red Cross Anti-Tuberculosis Week — PT88

**2009, Sept. 14** **Litho.** ***Perf. 14¼***
**RA108** PT88 1.75k multi — —
Obligatory on mail Sept. 14-21.

Red Cross Solidarity Week — PT89

**2009, Dec. 8** **Litho.** ***Perf. 14¼***
**RA109** PT89 1.75k multi — —
Obligatory on mail Dec. 8-15.

Red Cross Week — PT90

**2010, May 8** **Litho.** ***Perf. 14¼***
**RA110** PT90 1.55k on 1.75k multi — —
Obligatory on mail May 8-15. No. RA110 was not issued without surcharge.

Red Cross Anti-Tuberculosis Week — PT91

**2010, Sept. 14** **Litho.** ***Perf. 14¼***
**RA111** PT91 1.55k multi — —
Obligatory on mail Sept. 14-21.

Red Cross Solidarity Week — PT92

**2010, Dec. 8** **Litho.** ***Perf. 14¼***
**RA112** PT92 1.55k multi — —
Obligatory on mail Dec. 8-15.

Red Cross Week — PT93

**2011, May 8** **Litho.** ***Perf. 14¼***
**RA113** PT93 1.55k multi — —

Obligatory on mail May 8-15.

Red Cross Anti-Tuberculosis Week — PT94

**2011, Sept. 14** **Litho.** ***Perf. 14¼***
**RA114** PT94 1.55k multi — —

Obligatory on mail Sept. 14-21.

Red Cross Solidarity Week — PT95

**2011, Dec. 8** **Litho.** ***Perf. 14¼***
**RA115** PT95 1.55k multi — —

Obligatory on mail Dec. 8-15.

Red Cross Week — PT96

**2012, May 8** **Litho.** ***Perf. 14¼***
**RA116** PT96 1.55k multi — —

Obligatory on mail May 8-15.

Red Cross Anti-Tuberculosis Week — PT97

**2012, Sept. 14** **Litho.** ***Perf. 14¼***
**RA117** PT97 1.55k multi — —

Obligatory on mail Sept. 14-21.

Red Cross Solidarity Week — PT98

**2012, Dec. 8** **Litho.** ***Perf. 14¼***
**RA118** PT98 1.55k multi — —

Obligatory on mail Dec. 8-15.

Red Cross Week — PT99

**2013, May 8** **Litho.** ***Perf. 14¼***
**RA119** PT99 1.55k multi — —

Obligatory on mail May 8-15.

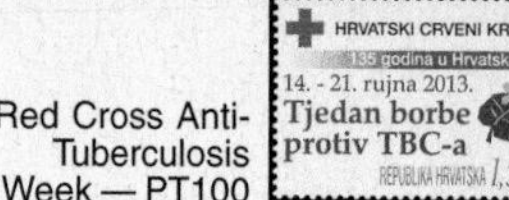


Red Cross Anti-Tuberculosis Week — PT100

**2013, Sept. 14** **Litho.** ***Perf. 14¼***
**RA120** PT100 1.55k multi — —

Obligatory on mail Sept. 14-21.

Red Cross Solidarity Week — PT101

**2013, Dec. 8** **Litho.** ***Perf. 14¼***
**RA121** PT101 1.55k multi — —

Obligatory on mail Dec. 8-15.

Red Cross Week — PT102

**2014, May 8** **Litho.** ***Perf. 14***
**RA122** PT102 1.55k multi — —

Obligatory on mail May 8-15.

Red Cross Anti-Tuberculosis Week — PT103

**2014, Sept. 14** **Litho.** ***Perf. 14***
**RA123** PT103 1.55k multi — —

Obligatory on mail Sept. 14-21.

Red Cross Anti-Tuberculosis Week — PT106

**2015, Sept. 14** **Litho.** ***Perf. 14***
**RA126** PT106 1.55k multi — —

Obligatory on mail Sept. 14-21.

Red Cross Solidarity Week — PT107

**2015, Dec. 8** **Litho.** ***Perf. 14***
**RA127** PT107 1.55k multi — —

Obligatory on mail Dec. 8-15.

Red Cross Week — PT108

**2016, May 8** **Litho.** ***Perf. 14***
**RA128** PT108 1.55k multi — —

20th National Youth Competition. Obligatory on mail May 8-15.

Red Cross Anti-Tuberculosis Week — PT109

**2016, Sept. 14** **Litho.** ***Perf. 14***
**RA129** PT109 1.55k multi — —

Obligatory on mail Sept. 14-21.

Red Cross Solidarity Week — PT110

**2016, Dec. 8** **Litho.** ***Perf. 14***
**RA130** PT110 1.55k multi — —

Obligatory on mail Dec. 8-15.

Red Cross Week — PT111

**2017, May 8** **Litho.** ***Perf. 14***
**RA131** PT111 1.55k multi — —

Obligatory on mail May 8-15.

Red Cross Anti-Tuberculosis Week — PT112

**2017, Aug. 1** **Litho.** ***Perf. 14***
**RA132** PT112 1.55k multi — —

Obligatory on mail Aug. 1-8.

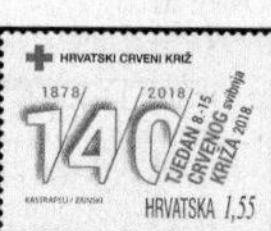


Red Cross Week — PT114

**2018, May 8** **Litho.** ***Perf. 14***
**RA134** PT114 1.55k multi — —

Croatian Red Cross, 140th anniv. Obligatory on mail May 8-15.

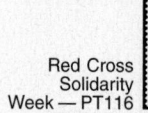

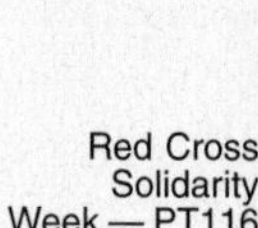

Red Cross Solidarity Week — PT116

**2018, Dec. 8** **Litho.** ***Perf. 14***
**RA136** PT116 1.55k multi — —

Obligatory on mail Dec. 8-15.

Red Cross Week — PT117

**2019, May 8** **Litho.** ***Perf. 14***
**RA137** PT117 1.55k multi — —

Obligatory on mail May 8-15.

Red Cross Anti-Tuberculosis Week — PT118

**2019, Sept. 14** **Litho.** ***Perf. 14¼***
**RA138** PT118 1.55k on 1.80k multi — —

Obligatory on mail Sept. 14-21. Not issued without surcharge.

Red Cross Solidarity Week — PT119

**2019, Dec. 8** **Litho.** ***Perf. 14¼***
**RA139** PT119 1.55k multi — —

Obligatory on mail Dec. 8-15.

## CUBA

'kyü-bə

LOCATION — The largest island of the West Indies; south of Florida
GOVT. — Former Spanish possession
AREA — 44,206 sq. mi.
POP. — 11,096,395 (1999 est.)
CAPITAL — Havana

Formerly a Spanish possession, Cuba made several unsuccessful attempts to gain her freedom, which finally led to the intervention of the US in 1898. In that year under the Treaty of Paris, Spain relinquished the island to the US in trust for its inhabitants.

In 1902 a republic was established and the Cuban Congress took over the government from the military authorities.

8 Reales Plata = 1 Peso
100 Centesimos = 1 Escudo or Peseta (1867)
1000 Milesimas = 100 Centavos = 1 Peso

**Catalogue values for unused stamps in this country are for Never Hinged items, beginning with Scott 402 in the regular postage section, Scott B3 in the semi-postal section, Scott C38 in the airpost section, Scott CB1 in the airpost semi-postal section, Scott E13 in the special delivery section, and Scott RA1 in the postal tax section.**

Pen cancellations are common on the earlier stamps of Cuba. Stamps so canceled sell for very much less than those with postmark cancellations.

**Watermarks**

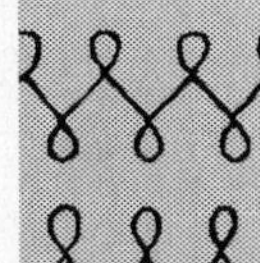

Wmk. 104 — Loops

Loops from different rows may or may not be directly opposite each other.

Wmk. 105 — Crossed Lines

Wmk. 106 — Star

Wmk. 229 — Wavy Lines

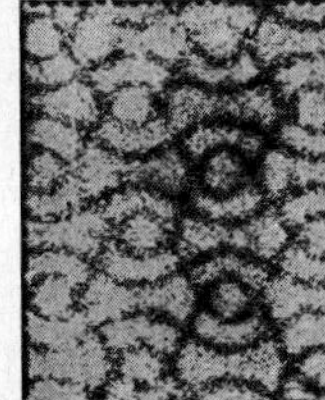

Wmk. 320

Wmk. 321 — "R de C"

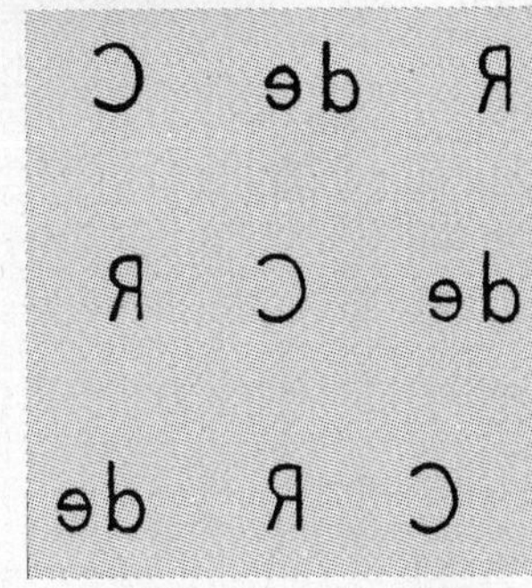

Wmk. 376 — "R de C"

### Issued under Spanish Dominion

Used also in Puerto Rico: Nos. 1-3, 9-14, 17-21, 32-34, 35A-37, 39-41, 43-45, 47-49, 51-53, 55-57.

Used also in the Philippines: Nos. 2-3.

Identifiable cancellations of those countries will increase the value of the stamps.

Queen Isabella II — A1

**Blue Paper**

**1855 Typo. Wmk. 104** ***Imperf.***

| No. | Type | Description | Unused | Used |
|---|---|---|---|---|
| 1 | A1 | ½r p blue green | 100.00 | 7.50 |
| a. | | ½r p blackish green | 150.00 | 30.00 |
| 2 | A1 | 1r p gray green | 100.00 | 6.50 |
| 3 | A1 | 2r p carmine | 750.00 | 15.00 |
| 4 | A1 | 2r p orange red | 1,500. | 20.00 |
| a. | | 2r p vermilion | 1,600. | 22.00 |
| | | *Nos. 1-4 (4)* | 2,450. | 49.00 |

See Nos. 9-14. For surcharges see Nos. 5-8, 15.

Counterfeit surcharges are plentiful.

Nos. 3-4 Surcharged

**1855-56**

| No. | Type | Description | Unused | Used |
|---|---|---|---|---|
| 5 | A1 | ¼r p on 2r p car | 1,200. | 300.00 |
| a. | | Without fraction bar | *3,000.* | 2,000. |
| 6 | A1 | ¼r p on 2r p org red | *4,000.* | 800.00 |
| a. | | Without fraction bar | — | *3,000.* |

Surcharged

| No. | Type | Description | Unused | Used |
|---|---|---|---|---|
| 7 | A1 | ¼r p on 2r p car | 1,000. | 250.00 |
| a. | | Without fraction bar | *2,500.* | 1,500 |
| 8 | A1 | ¼r p on 2r p org red | 1,600. | 500.00 |
| a. | | Without fraction bar | — | — |

The "Y ¼" surcharge met the "Ynterior" rate for delivery within the city of Havana.

**Rough Yellowish Paper**

**1856 Wmk. 105**

| No. | Type | Description | Unused | Used |
|---|---|---|---|---|
| 9 | A1 | ½r p yellow grn | 10.00 | 2.00 |
| 10 | A1 | 1r p green | 1,250. | 30.00 |
| a. | | 1r p emerald | *1,750.* | 100.00 |
| 11 | A1 | 2r p orange red | 700.00 | 40.00 |

**White Smooth Paper**

**1857 Unwmk.**

| No. | Type | Description | Unused | Used |
|---|---|---|---|---|
| 12 | A1 | ½r p blue | 5.00 | 1.00 |
| 13 | A1 | 1r p gray green | 5.00 | 1.00 |
| a. | | 1r p pale yellow green | 5.00 | 3.25 |
| 14 | A1 | 2r p dull rose | 25.00 | 5.00 |
| | | *Nos. 12-14 (3)* | 35.00 | 7.00 |

Surcharged

**1860**

| No. | Type | Description | Unused | Used |
|---|---|---|---|---|
| 15 | A1 | ¼r p on 2r p dl rose | 300.00 | 100.00 |
| a. | | 1 of ¼ inverted | 500.00 | 200.00 |
| | | On cover | | 1,500. |
| b. | | "Y ¹⁄₄" instead of "1 ¼" | | — |

Queen Isabella II
A2 A3

**1862-64** ***Imperf.***

| No. | Type | Description | Unused | Used |
|---|---|---|---|---|
| 16 | A2 | ¼r p black | 25.00 | *60.00* |
| 17 | A3 | ¼r p blk, *buff* ('64) | 250.00 | *60.00* |
| 18 | A3 | ½r p green ('64) | 5.00 | 1.00 |
| 19 | A3 | ½r p grn, *pale rose* ('64) | 15.00 | 3.00 |
| 20 | A3 | 1r p bl, *sal* ('64) | 6.00 | 2.00 |
| a. | | Diagonal half used as ½r p on cover | | 300.00 |
| 21 | A3 | 2r p ver, *buff* ('64) | 24.00 | 8.00 |
| a. | | 2r p red, *buff* | 35.00 | 15.00 |
| | | *Nos. 16-21 (6)* | 325.00 | 134.00 |

No. 17 Overprinted in Black

**1866**

| No. | Type | Description | Unused | Used |
|---|---|---|---|---|
| 22 | A3 | ¼r p black, *buff* | 85.00 | *120.00* |

Exists with handstamped "1866."

A5

**1866**

| No. | Type | Description | Unused | Used |
|---|---|---|---|---|
| 23 | A5 | 5c dull violet | 50.00 | 60.00 |
| 24 | A5 | 10c blue | 6.00 | 1.10 |
| 25 | A5 | 20c green | 4.00 | 1.10 |
| a. | | Diag. half used as 10c on cover | | — |
| 26 | A5 | 40c rose | 50.00 | 60.00 |
| | | *Nos. 23-26 (4)* | 110.00 | 122.20 |

For the Type A5 20c in dull lilac, see Spain No. 87.

**Stamps Dated "1867"**

**1867** ***Perf. 14***

| No. | Type | Description | Unused | Used |
|---|---|---|---|---|
| 27 | A5 | 5c dull violet | 40.00 | 35.00 |
| 28 | A5 | 10c blue | 35.00 | 4.00 |
| a. | | Imperf., pair | 110.00 | *6.50* |
| b. | | Diagonal half used as 5c on cover | | 300.00 |
| 29 | A5 | 20c green | 30.00 | 5.00 |
| a. | | Imperf., pair | 110.00 | 75.00 |
| b. | | Diag. half used as 10c on cover | | 325.00 |
| 30 | A5 | 40c rose | 20.00 | 30.00 |
| | | *Nos. 27-30 (4)* | 125.00 | 74.00 |

A6

**1868 Stamps Dated "1868"**

| No. | Type | Description | Unused | Used |
|---|---|---|---|---|
| 31 | A6 | 5c dull violet | 30.00 | 20.00 |
| 32 | A6 | 10c blue | 5.00 | 2.00 |
| a. | | Diagonal half used as 5c on cover | | 250.00 |
| 33 | A6 | 20c green | 10.00 | 4.00 |
| a. | | Diag. half used as 10c on cover | | 275.00 |
| 34 | A6 | 40c rose | 25.00 | 15.00 |
| a. | | Diag. half used as 20c on cover | | 175.00 |
| | | *Nos. 31-34 (4)* | 70.00 | 41.00 |

Nos. 31-34 Overprinted in Black

**1868**

| No. | Type | Description | Unused | Used |
|---|---|---|---|---|
| 35 | A6 | 5c dull violet | 75.00 | 32.50 |
| 35A | A6 | 10c blue | 75.00 | 32.50 |
| 36 | A6 | 20c green | 75.00 | 32.50 |
| 37 | A6 | 40c rose | 75.00 | 32.50 |
| | | *Nos. 35-37 (4)* | 300.00 | 130.00 |

**1869 Stamps Dated "1869"**

| No. | Type | Description | Unused | Used |
|---|---|---|---|---|
| 38 | A6 | 5c rose | 50.00 | 40.00 |
| 39 | A6 | 10c org brown | 5.00 | 2.00 |
| a. | | Diagonal half used as 5c on cover | | 140.00 |
| 40 | A6 | 20c orange | 10.00 | 3.00 |
| 41 | A6 | 40c dull violet | 40.00 | 30.00 |
| | | *Nos. 38-41 (4)* | 105.00 | 75.00 |

**Nos. 38-41 Ovptd. Like Nos. 35-37**

| No. | Type | Description | Unused | Used |
|---|---|---|---|---|
| 42 | A6 | 5c rose | 100.00 | 40.00 |
| 43 | A6 | 10c red brown | 100.00 | 40.00 |
| 44 | A6 | 20c orange | 100.00 | 40.00 |
| 45 | A6 | 40c dull violet | 100.00 | 40.00 |
| | | *Nos. 42-45 (4)* | 400.00 | 160.00 |

"Espana" — A8

**1870** ***Perf. 14***

| No. | Type | Description | Unused | Used |
|---|---|---|---|---|
| 46 | A8 | 5c blue | 250.00 | 125.00 |
| 47 | A8 | 10c green | 5.00 | 2.00 |
| a. | | Diagonal half used as 5c on cover | | 250.00 |
| 48 | A8 | 20c red brown | 4.00 | 3.00 |
| a. | | Diag. half used as 10c on cover | | 300.00 |
| 49 | A8 | 40c rose | 300.00 | 100.00 |

"Espana" — A9

**1871**

50 A9 12c red lilac 25.00 12.00
a. Imperf., pair 100.00 —
51 A9 25c ultra 3.00 1.00
a. Imperf., pair 50.00 —
b. Diagonal half used as 12c on cover 125.00
52 A9 50c gray green 4.00 2.00
a. Imperf., pair 75.00 —
b. Diagonal half used as 25c on cover 250.00
53 A9 1p yel brown 40.00 15.00
a. Imperf., pair 125.00 —
*Nos. 50-53 (4)* 72.00 30.00

King Amadeo — A10

**1873** ***Perf. 14***

54 A10 12½c dark green 40.00 30.00
55 A10 25c gray 3.00 1.00
a. Diagonal half used as 12½c on cover 120.00
b. 25c lilac 10.00 4.00
c. As "b," half used as 12½c on cover 150.00
d. As "b," imperf., pair 50.00 —
56 A10 50c brown 3.00 1.00
a. Imperf., pair 75.00 —
b. Half used as 25c on cover 200.00
57 A10 1p red brown 450.00 75.00
a. Diagonal half used as 50c on cover 750.00

"España" — A11

**1874**

58 A11 12½c brown 30.00 25.00
a. Half used as 5c on cover 500.00
59 A11 25c ultra 1.00 .60
a. Diagonal half used as 12½c on cover 100.00
60 A11 50c dp violet 2.00 5.00
a. Diagonal half used as 25c on cover 200.00
b. "1374" instead of "1874" — —
61 A11 50c gray 5.00 2.00
a. Diagonal half used as 25c on cover 175.00
62 A11 1p carmine 350.00 400.00
a. Imperf., pair 700.00 *250.00*
*Nos. 58-62 (5)* 388.00 432.60

Examples of Nos. 61, 63-65, 67-87 with fine impressions in slightly different colors are proofs.

Coat of Arms — A12

**1875**

63 A12 12½c lt violet 1.50 2.00
a. Imperf., pair 100.00
64 A12 25c ultra 1.25 1.60
a. Imperf., pair 100.00 —
b. Diagonal half used as 12½c on cover 100.00
65 A12 50c blue green 1.00 2.00
a. Imperf., pair 100.00
b. Diag. half used as 25c on cover *80.00*
66 A12 1p brown 15.00 10.00
b. Diag. half used as 50c on cover 135.00
*Nos. 63-66 (4)* 18.75 15.60

King Alfonso XII — A13

**1876**

67 A13 12½c green 3.00 6.00
a. 12½c emerald green 3.75 6.00
68 A13 25c gray 4.00 3.00
a. Diagonal half used as 12½c on cover 100.00
b. 25c pale violet 4.50 3.25
d. 25c bluish gray 4.50 3.25
69 A13 50c ultra 3.00 6.00
a. Imperf., pair 75.00 *16.00*
b. Diag. half used as 25c on cover 100.00
70 A13 1p black 15.00 25.00
a. Imperf., pair 40.00 *40.00*
b. Diag. half used as 50c on cover 125.00
*Nos. 67-70 (4)* 25.00 40.00

King Alfonso XII — A14

**1877**

71 A14 10c lt green 40.00 —
72 A14 12½c gray 10.00 10.00
a. Imperf., pair 100.00 —
b. Diagonal half used on cover 300.00
73 A14 25c dk green 1.00 .50
a. Imperf., pair 100.00 —
b. Diagonal half used as 12½c on cover 75.00
74 A14 50c black 1.00 1.50
a. Imperf., pair 100.00 —
b. Half used as 25c on cover 100.00
75 A14 1p brown 40.00 20.00
*Nos. 71-75 (5)* 92.00

No. 71 was not placed in use.

**1878** **Stamps Dated "1878"**

76 A14 5c blue 1.00 2.00
77 A14 10c black 100.00
78 A14 12½c brown bis 5.00 5.00
a. 12½c olive brown 6.00 10.00
c. Diagonal half used on cover 200.00
d. As "a," diagonal half used on cover 200.00
79 A14 25c yel green 1.00 1.00
b. No. 79, diagonal half used as 12½c on cover 100.00
c. 25c deep green 1.00 2.00
80 A14 50c dk blue grn 1.00 1.00
b. Diagonal half used as 25c on cover 100.00
81 A14 1p rose 20.00 10.00
b. 1p rose 16.00 *500.00*
c. Diagonal half used as 50c on cover *900.00*
*Nos. 76-81 (6)* 128.00 19.00

No. 77 was not placed in use.

**Imperf., Pairs**

*76a* A14 5c blue 100.00
*77a* A14 10c black 400.00
*78b* A14 12½c brown bister 100.00
*79a* A14 25c deep green 100.00
*80a* A14 50c dk blue green 200.00
*81a* A14 1p carmine 150.00

**1879** **Stamps Dated "1879"**

82 A14 5c slate black 1.00 3.00
83 A14 10c orange 200.00 *75.00*
84 A14 12½c rose 1.00 3.00
85 A14 25c ultra 1.00 2.00
a. Diagonal half used as 12½c on cover 100.00
b. Imperf., pair 75.00
86 A14 50c gray 1.00 1.00
a. Diag. half used as 25c on cover 100.00
87 A14 1p olive bister 25.00 30.00
*Nos. 82-87 (6)* 229.00 114.00

Forgeries exist of No. 83.

A15

**1880**

88 A15 5c green 1.00 1.00
89 A15 10c lake 125.00 —
a. Double impression of frame and lettering 200.00
90 A15 12½c gray 1.00 .50
91 A15 25c gray blue 1.00 .50
a. Diagonal half used as 12½c on cover 100.00
92 A15 50c brown 1.00 .50
a. Diagonal half used as 25c on cover 100.00
93 A15 1p yellow brn 5.00 5.00
a. Diagonal half used as 50c on cover 400.00
*Nos. 88-93 (6)* 134.00 7.50

No. 89 was not placed in use. Forged cancels exist.

A16

**1881**

94 A16 1c green 1.00 .50
95 A16 2c lake 50.00
96 A16 2½c olive bister 1.00 .50
97 A16 5c gray blue 1.00 .25
98 A16 10c yellow brown 1.00 .25
a. Diagonal half used as 5c on cover 100.00
99 A16 20c dark brown 6.00 10.00
*Nos. 94-99 (6)* 60.00 11.50

No. 95 was not placed in use.

A17

**1882**

100 A17 1c green 8.00 .50
a. Diag. half used as ½c on cover 150.00
101 A17 2c lake 3.00 3.00
a. Diag. half used as 1c on cover 100.00
102 A17 2½c dk brown 6.00 5.00
103 A17 5c gray blue 3.00 .50
a. Diag. half used as 2½c on cover 100.00
104 A17 10c olive bister .75 .50
a. Diag. half used as 5c on cover 100.00
105 A17 20c red brown 130.00 50.00
a. Diag. half used as 10c on cover 500.00
*Nos. 100-105 (6)* 150.75 59.50

See Nos. 121-131. For surcharges see Nos. 106-120.

**Issue of 1882 Surcharged or Overprinted in Black, Blue or Red**

a

b

c

d

e

**1883** **Type "a"**

106 A17 5 on 5c (R) 3.00 2.00
a. Triple surcharge
b. Double surcharge 25.00 25.00
c. Inverted surcharge 30.00 30.00
d. Without "5" in surcharge 20.00 20.00
e. Dbl. surch., types "a" & "d" 75.00 —
107 A17 10 on 10c (Bl) 3.50 2.50
a. Inverted surcharge 75.00
b. Double surcharge 30.00 30.00
108 A17 20 on 20c 45.00 75.00
a. "10" instead of "20" 75.00 *75.00*
b. Double surcharge 75.00
c. As "a," inverted surcharge *90.00* *90.00*

**Type "b"**

109 A17 5 on 5c (R) 3.00 2.00
a. Inverted surcharge 30.00 30.00
b. Double surcharge 25.00 25.00
110 A17 10 on 10c (Bl) 10.00 12.00
a. Inverted surcharge 35.00 35.00
b. Double surcharge 35.00 35.00
111 A17 20 on 20c 120.00 150.00
a. Double surcharge
b. Dbl. surch., types "b" & "c"

**Type "c"**

112 A17 5 on 5c (R) 2.50 2.00
a. Inverted surcharge 35.00 35.00
b. Dbl. surch., types "c" & "d" —
c. Dbl. surch., types "c" & "a"
113 A17 10 on 10c (Bl) 10.00 12.00
a. Inverted surcharge 40.00 40.00
b. Double surcharge 40.00 40.00
114 A17 20 on 20c 60.00 100.00
a. "10" instead of "20" 100.00 120.00
b. Double surcharge 100.00 120.00
c. Dbl. surch., types "a" & "c" 100.00 120.00

**Type "d"**

115 A17 5 on 5c (R) 3.00 2.00
a. Inverted surcharge 35.00 35.00
b. Double surcharge 30.00 30.00
116 A17 10 on 10c (Bl) 4.00 3.00
a. Inverted surcharge 40.00 40.00
b. Double surcharge 40.00 40.00
c. Dbl. surch., types "d" & "c" — —
117 A17 20 on 20c 85.00 100.00
a. Dbl. surch., types "a" & "d" — —

**Type "e"**

118 A17 5c gray blue (R) 4.00 3.00
a. Double overprint 40.00 40.00
119 A17 10c olive bis (Bl) 12.00 15.00
a. Double overprint 40.00 40.00
120 A17 20c red brown 250.00 300.00
a. Double overprint 300.00 300.00
*Nos. 106-120 (15)* 615.00 780.50

Handstamped overprints and surcharges are counterfeits.

Numerous other varieties exist.

**Type of 1882**

Original

1st retouch

2nd retouch

The differences between the stamps of 1882 and the various retouches are as follows:

Original state: The medallion is surrounded by a heavy line of color of nearly even thickness, touching the horizontal line below the word "Cuba" (or "Filipinas," "Puerto Rico," as the case may be); the opening in the hair above the temple is narrow and pointed.

1st retouch: The line around the medallion is thin, except at the upper right, and does not touch the horizontal line above it; the opening in the hair is slightly wider and a trifle rounded; the lock of hair above the forehead is shaped like a broad "V" and ends in a point; there is a faint white line below it, which is not found on the stamps in the original state. Owing to wear of the plate the shape of the lock of hair and the width of the white line below it vary.

2nd retouch: The opening in the hair forms a semi-circle; the lock above the forehead is nearly straight, having only a slight wave, and the white line is much broader than before.

**1883-86**

121 A17 1c grn, 2nd retouch 150.00 40.00
122 A17 2½c olive bister .50 .30
124 A17 2½c violet 1.00 .40
a. 2½c red lilac ('85) 1.00 .40
b. 2½c ultramarine 125.00 150.00
125 A17 5c gray bl, 1st retouch 100.00 .50
a. Diag. half used as 2½c on cover 75.00
126 A17 5c gray bl, 2nd retouch 120.00 2.00
a. Diag. half used as 2½c on cover 125.00
127 A17 10c brn, 1st retouch 3.00 1.00
a. Diagonal half used as 5c on cover 75.00
c. Imperf., pair 300.00 —
128 A17 20c olive bister 15.00 10.00
*Nos. 121-128 (7)* 389.50 54.20

**1888**

129 A17 2½c red brown 1.75 .85
130 A17 10c blue 1.50 1.00
a. Diagonal half used as 5c on cover 175.00
131 A17 20c brnsh gray 15.00 10.00
*Nos. 129-131 (3)* 18.25 11.85

King Alfonso XIII — A18

**1890-97**

132 A18 1c gray brown 20.00 6.50
133 A18 1c ol gray ('91) 10.00 4.00
134 A18 1c ultra ('94) 5.00 .50
135 A18 1c dk vio ('96) 1.50 .50
136 A18 2c slate blue 10.00 3.00
137 A18 2c lilac brn ('91) 2.00 .75
138 A18 2c rose ('94) 35.00 5.00
139 A18 2c claret ('96) 9.00 5.00
140 A18 2½c emerald 12.50 5.00
141 A18 2½c org ('91) 60.00 5.00
142 A18 2½c lilac ('94) 4.00 3.00
143 A18 2½c rose ('96) 4.00 6.00
144 A18 5c olive gray 1.00 .75
b. Diagonal half used as 2½c on cover 500.00
145 A18 5c emerald ('91) 1.00 .50
b. Diagonal half used as 2½c on cover 500.00
146 A18 5c sl blue ('96) .75 1.00
b. Diagonal half used as 2½c on cover 600.00
147 A18 10c brown violet 6.00 1.00
b. Diagonal half used as 5c on cover 500.00
148 A18 10c claret ('91) 2.50 .50
b. Diagonal half used as 5c on cover 400.00
149 A18 10c emerald ('96) 1.00 1.50
150 A18 20c lilac 2.00 1.00
151 A18 20c ultra ('91) 25.00 8.00
152 A18 20c red brn ('94) 20.00 30.00
153 A18 20c violet ('96) 15.00 10.00
b. Diagonal half used as 10c on cover 600.00
154 A18 40c orange brn ('97) 40.00 35.00
155 A18 80c lilac brn ('97) 80.00 70.00
*Nos. 132-155 (24)* 367.25 203.50

**Imperf., Pairs**

*134a* A18 1c ultramarine 100.00
*135a* A18 1c dark violet 100.00
*138a* A18 2c rose 100.00
*139a* A18 2c claret 100.00
*142a* A18 2½c lilac 100.00
*143a* A18 2½c rose 100.00
*145a* A18 5c emerald 100.00

*146a* A18 5c slate blue 100.00
*148a* A18 10c claret 100.00
*149a* A18 10c emerald 100.00
*152a* A18 20c red brown 135.00
*153a* A18 20c violet 125.00
*154a* A18 40c orange brown 115.00
*155a* A18 80c red brown 175.00

King Alfonso XIII — A19

**1898**

**156** A19 1m orange brn .70 .50
**157** A19 2m orange brn .30 .50
**158** A19 3m orange brn .30 .50
**159** A19 4m orange brn 5.75 6.00
**160** A19 5m orange brn .30 .50
**161** A19 1c black vio .30 .50
**162** A19 2c dk blue grn .30 .50
**163** A19 3c dk brown .30 .50
**164** A19 4c orange 15.00 6.00
**165** A19 5c car rose 1.15 .25
**166** A19 6c dk blue .50 .75
**167** A19 8c gray brown 1.90 1.90
**168** A19 10c vermilion 1.20 .40
**169** A19 15c slate green 5.50 4.75
**170** A19 20c maroon 3.75 .50
**171** A19 40c dark lilac 4.50 3.75
**172** A19 60c black 9.25 9.50
**173** A19 80c red brown 18.50 12.00
**174** A19 1p yel green 18.50 12.00
**175** A19 2p slate blue 32.00 19.00
*Nos. 156-175 (20)* 120.00 80.30

Nos. 156-160 were issued for use on newspapers.

Nos. 156-175 exist imperf. Value, unused pairs, $7,500. Only one set of pairs is currently known.

For surcharges see Nos. 176-189C, 196-200.

### Issued under Administration of the United States
### Puerto Principe Issue

Issues of Cuba of 1898 and 1896 Surcharged

a

b

### Black Surcharge on Nos. 156-158, 160

Types a, c, d, e, f, g and h are 17½mm high, the others are 19½mm high.

**1898-99**

**176** A19 (a) 1c on 1m org brn 100.00 60.00
**177** A19 (b) 1c on 1m org brn 600.00 115.00
*a.* Broken figure "1" *3,000.* 275.00
*b.* Inverted surcharge *500.00*
*d.* As "a," inverted *1,500.*

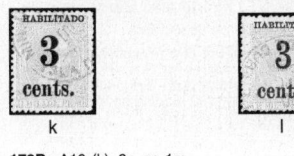
c d

**178** A19 (c) 2c on 2m org brn 65.00 62.50
*a.* Inverted surcharge 500.00 100.00
**179** A19 (d) 2c on 2m org brn 82.50 77.50
*a.* Inverted surcharge — *500.00*

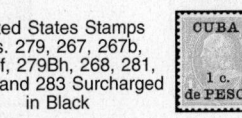
k l

**179B** A19 (k) 3c on 1m org brn 300. 175.
*c.* Double surcharge — *3,000.*

An unused example is known with "cents" omitted.

**179D** A19 (l) 3c on 1m org brn *1,350.* *675.00*

e

f

**179F** A19 (e) 3c on 2m org brn *1,500.*

Value is for examples with minor faults.

**179G** A19 (f) 3c on 2m org brn — *2,000.*

Value is for examples with minor faults.

**180** A19 (e) 3c on 3m org brn 150. *100.*
*a.* Inverted surcharge 375.
**181** A19 (f) 3c on 3m org brn 600. 400.
*a.* Inverted surcharge *750.*

g

h

i j

**182** A19 (g) 5c on 1m org brn 1,000. 165.
*a.* Inverted surcharge — *1,000.*
**183** A19 (h) 5c on 1m org brn *1,500.* *1,000.*
*a.* Inverted surcharge — *1,500.*
**184** A19 (g) 5c on 2m org brn 1,000. 275.
**185** A19 (h) 5c on 2m org brn 1,500. 600.
**186** A19 (g) 5c on 3m org brn 1,500. 350.
*a.* Inverted surcharge 1,200. 700.
**187** A19 (h) 5c on 3m org brn — 1,000.
*a.* Inverted surcharge — *1,000.*
**188** A19 (g) 5c on 5m org brn 145. 230.
*a.* Inverted surcharge — 750.
*b.* Double surcharge — —
**189** A19 (h) 5c on 5m org brn 3,000. 425.
*a.* Inverted surcharge *3,000.* *900.*
*b.* Double surcharge — —

The 2nd printing of Nos. 188-189 has shiny ink. Values are for the 1st printing.

**189C** A19 (i) 5c on 5m org brn *7,500.*

No. 191

### Black Surcharge on No. P25

**190** N2 (g) 5c on ½m bl grn 375. 115.
*a.* Inverted surcharge 1,000. 210.
*b.* Pair, one without surcharge 500.

Value for 190b is for pair with unsurcharged stamp at right. Also exists with unsurcharged stamp at left.

**191** N2 (h) 5c on ½m bl grn 1,000. 275.
*a.* Inverted surcharge *1,000.*
**192** N2 (i) 5c on ½m bl grn 3,000. 100.
*a.* Dbl. surch., one diagonal *3,500.* —
**193** N2 (j) 5c on ½m bl grn 900. 500.

### Red Surcharge on No. 161

**196** A19 (k) 3c on 1c blk vio 150. 125.
*a.* Inverted surcharge 500.
**197** A19 (l) 3c on 1c blk vio 250. 200.
*a.* Inverted surcharge *1,500.*
**198** A19 (i) 5c on 1c blk vio 92.50 72.50
*a.* Inverted surcharge 500.
*b.* Surcharge vert. reading up —
*c.* Double surcharge *600.* *2,750.*
*d.* Double invtd. surch. — —

Value for No. 198b is for surcharge reading up. One example is known with surcharge reading down.

**199** A19 (j) 5c on 1c blk vio 150. 115.
*a.* Inverted surcharge *3,000.*
*b.* Vertical surcharge — —
*c.* Double surcharge *3,000.* *3,000.*

m

**200** A19 (m) 10c on 1c blk vio 62.50 *92.50*
*a.* Broken figure "1" 160.00 *225.00*

### Black Surcharge on Nos. P26-P30

**201** N2 (k) 3c on 1m bl grn 350. 350.
*a.* Inverted surcharge 450.
*b.* "EENTS" 600. 450.
*c.* As "b", inverted 850.
**202** N2 (l) 3c on 1m bl grn 1,000. 400.
*a.* Inverted surcharge 850.
**203** N2 (k) 3c on 2m bl grn 1,650. 400.
*a.* "EENTS" 1,650. 500.
*b.* Inverted surcharge 1,500.
*c.* As "a," inverted *2,750.*
**204** N2 (l) 3c on 2m bl grn 2,750. 600.
*a.* Inverted surcharge *1,500.*
**205** N2 (k) 3c on 3m bl grn 900. 400.
*a.* Inverted surcharge 750.
*b.* "EENTS" 1,250. 450.
*c.* As "b," inverted *2,750.*
**206** N2 (l) 3c on 3m bl grn 1,500. 550.
*a.* Inverted surcharge *1,000.*
**211** N2 (i) 5c on 1m bl grn 1,800.
*a.* "EENTS" — 3,000.
**212** N2 (j) 5c on 1m bl grn — 2,250.
**213** N2 (i) 5c on 2m bl grn 3,000. 1,800.
*a.* "EENTS" 3,000. 3,000.
**214** N2 (j) 5c on 2m bl grn 3,250. 1,750.
**215** N2 (i) 5c on 3m bl grn 550.
*a.* "EENTS" 1,000.
**216** N2 (j) 5c on 3m bl grn 3,000. 1,000.
**217** N2 (i) 5c on 4m bl grn *3,000.* 900.
*a.* "EENTS" *3,000.* 1,500.
*b.* Inverted surcharge *2,000.*
*c.* As "a," inverted *3,000.*
**218** N2 (j) 5c on 4m bl grn 3,000. *1,500.*
*a.* Inverted surcharge *2,000.*
**219** N2 (i) 5c on 8m bl grn *2,500.* 1,250.
*a.* Inverted surcharge 1,500.
*b.* "EENTS" 3,000. 2,750.
*c.* As "b," inverted 2,500.
**220** N2 (j) 5c on 8m bl grn 2,000.
*a.* Inverted surcharge 2,500.

Beware of forgeries of the Puerto Principe issue. Obtaining expert opinions is recommended.

United States Stamps Nos. 279, 267, 267b, 279Bf, 279Bh, 268, 281, 282C and 283 Surcharged in Black

**1899 Wmk. 191 *Perf. 12***

**221** A87 1c on 1c yel grn 4.50 .40
Never hinged 11.50
**222** A88 2c on 2c reddish car, III 10.00 .75
Never hinged 25.00
*b.* 2c on 2c vermilion, type III 10.00 .75
**222A** A88 2c on 2c reddish car, IV 6.00 .40
Never hinged 15.00
*c.* 2c on 2c vermilion, IV 6.00 .40
*d.* As No. 222A, inverted surcharge *5,500.* *4,000.*
**223** A88 2½c on 2c reddish car, III 6.00 .80
Never hinged 15.00
*b.* 2½c on 2c vermilion, III 6.00 .80
**223A** A88 2½c on 2c reddish car, IV 3.50 .50
Never hinged 8.75
*c.* 2½c on 2c vermilion, IV 3.50 .50
**224** A89 3c on 3c purple 12.00 1.75
Never hinged 30.00
*a.* Period between "B" and "A" 40.00 35.00
**225** A91 5c on 5c blue 12.50 2.00
Never hinged 30.00
**226** A94 10c on 10c brn, I 25.00 6.00
Never hinged 70.00
*b.* "CUBA" omitted *7,000.* *4,000.*
**226A** A94 10c on 10c brn, II *6,000.*
*Nos. 221-226 (8)* 79.50 12.60

The 2½c was sold and used as a 2c stamp. Excellent counterfeits of this and the preceding issue exist, especially inverted and double surcharges.

### Issues of the Republic under US Military Rule

Statue of Columbus A20

Royal Palms A21

"Cuba" A22

Ocean Liner A23

Cane Field — A24

**1899 Wmk. US-C (191C) *Perf. 12***

**227** A20 1c yellow green 3.50 .25
Never hinged 8.75
**228** A21 2c carmine 3.50 .25
Never hinged 8.75
*a.* scarlet 3.50 .25
*b.* Booklet pane of 6 *5,500.*
**229** A22 3c purple 3.50 .30
Never hinged 8.75
**230** A23 5c blue 4.50 .30
Never hinged 11.00
**231** A24 10c brown 11.00 .80
Never hinged 27.50
*Nos. 227-231 (5)* 26.00 1.90

No. 228b was issued by the Republic.

See Nos. 233-237 in Scott Standard Catalogue Vol 2. For surcharge see No. 232.

### Issues of the Republic

No. 229 Surcharged in Carmine

**1902, Sept. 30**

**232** A22 1c on 3c purple 2.75 .75
Never hinged 4.00
*a.* Inverted surcharge 150.00 150.00
*b.* Surcharge sideways (numeral horizontal) 300.00 300.00
*c.* Double surcharge 200.00 200.00

No. 228b was issued by the Republic. Counterfeits of the errors are plentiful.

### Re-engraved

The re-engraved stamps of 1905-07 may be distinguished from the issue of 1899 as follows:

ORIGINAL RE-ENGRAVED

1c — The ends of the label inscribed "Centavo" are rounded instead of square.

2c — The foliate ornaments, inside the oval disks bearing the numerals of value, have been removed.

5c — Two lines forming a right angle have been added in the upper corners of the label bearing the word "Cuba."

10c — A small ball has been added to each of the square ends of the label bearing the word "Cuba."

**1905 Unwmk. *Perf. 12***

| | | | | |
|---|---|---|---|---|
| **233** | A20 1c green | | 2.00 | 1.50 |
| | Never hinged | | 4.00 | |
| **234** | A21 2c rose | | 1.75 | 1.10 |
| | Never hinged | | 3.75 | |
| *a.* | Booklet pane of 6 | | 175.00 | 75.00 |
| **236** | A23 5c blue | | 42.50 | 8.00 |
| | Never hinged | | 70.00 | |
| **237** | A24 10c brown | | 3.50 | .80 |
| | Never hinged | | 6.00 | |
| | *Nos. 233-237 (4)* | | 49.75 | 11.40 |

Maj. Gen. Antonio Maceo — A26

**1907**

| | | | |
|---|---|---|---|
| **238** | A26 50c gray bl & blk | 1.75 | .80 |
| | Never hinged | 3.25 | |

See No. 245.

Bartolomé Masó A27

Máximo Gómez A28

Julio Sanguily A29

Ignacio Agramonte A30

Calixto García A31

José M. Rodriquez y Rodriquez (Mayia) A32

Carlos Roloff — A33

**1910, Feb. 1**

| | | | |
|---|---|---|---|
| **239** | A27 1c grn & vio | 1.00 | .30 |
| *a.* | Center inverted | 350.00 | 200.00 |
| **240** | A28 2c car & grn | 2.50 | .30 |
| *a.* | Center inverted | 575.00 | 425.00 |
| *b.* | Center omitted | 1,500. | |
| **241** | A29 3c vio & bl | 2.50 | .30 |
| **242** | A30 5c bl & grn | 24.00 | 4.75 |
| **243** | A31 8c ol & vio | 2.00 | .30 |
| **244** | A32 10c brn & bl | 12.50 | 2.50 |
| *a.* | Center inverted | 925.00 | |
| **245** | A26 50c vio & blk | 2.50 | *3.00* |
| **246** | A33 1p slate & blk | 10.00 | 5.00 |
| | *Nos. 239-246 (8)* | 57.00 | 16.45 |
| | Set, never hinged | 72.50 | |

**1911-13**

| | | | |
|---|---|---|---|
| **247** | A27 1c green | 1.00 | .25 |
| **248** | A28 2c car rose | 1.35 | .25 |
| *a.* | Booklet pane of 6 ('13) | 200.00 | 100.00 |
| **250** | A30 5c ultra | 3.75 | .35 |
| **251** | A31 8c ol grn & blk | 2.40 | .90 |
| **252** | A33 1p black | 9.50 | 4.00 |
| | *Nos. 247-252 (5)* | 18.00 | 5.75 |
| | Set, never hinged | 25.00 | |

Map of Cuba — A34

**1914-15**

| | | | |
|---|---|---|---|
| **253** | A34 1c green | .80 | .25 |
| *a.* | Booklet pane of 6 | 150.00 | 75.00 |
| **254** | A34 2c car rose | .95 | .25 |
| *a.* | Booklet pane of 6 | 150.00 | 75.00 |
| **255** | A34 2c red ('15) | 1.50 | .25 |
| *a.* | Booklet pane of 6 | 150.00 | 75.00 |
| **256** | A34 3c violet | 4.75 | .35 |
| **257** | A34 5c blue | 6.50 | .35 |
| **258** | A34 8c ol grn | 5.25 | 3.00 |
| **259** | A34 10c brown | 9.50 | 3.00 |
| **260** | A34 10c ol grn ('15) | 11.50 | 3.00 |
| **261** | A34 50c orange | 70.00 | 20.00 |
| **262** | A34 1p gray | 100.00 | 24.00 |
| | *Nos. 253-262 (10)* | 210.75 | 54.45 |
| | Set, never hinged | 325.00 | |

Complete set of eight 1914 stamps, imperf. pairs, value $1,000.

Nos. 253, 254, 256 and E5 exist with "1917 GOB./CONSTITUCIONAL/CAMAGUEY" overprint. These were not authorized.

Gertrudis Gómez de Avellaneda, Cuban Poetess (1814-73) — A34a

**1914**

| | | | |
|---|---|---|---|
| **263** | A34a 5c blue | 18.00 | 7.00 |

José Martí A35

Máximo Gómez A36

José de la Luz Caballero A37

Calixto García A38

Ignacio Agramonte A39

Tomás Estrada Palma A40

José A. Saco A41

Antonio Maceo A42

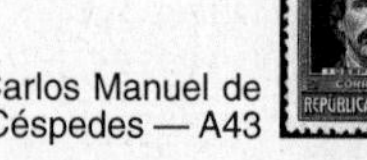

Carlos Manuel de Céspedes — A43

**1917-18 Unwmk. *Perf. 12***

| | | | |
|---|---|---|---|
| **264** | A35 1c bl grn | 1.00 | .25 |
| *a.* | Booklet pane of 6 | 75.00 | 50.00 |
| *b.* | Booklet pane of 30 | 350.00 | |
| **265** | A36 2c rose | 1.05 | .25 |
| *a.* | Booklet pane of 6 | 75.00 | 50.00 |
| *b.* | Booklet pane of 30 | 300.00 | |
| **266** | A36 2c lt red ('18) | .85 | .25 |
| *a.* | Booklet pane of 6 | 75.00 | 50.00 |
| **267** | A37 3c violet | 1.10 | .25 |
| *a.* | Imperf. pair | 275.00 | |
| *b.* | Booklet pane of 6 | 75.00 | 50.00 |
| **268** | A38 5c dp bl | 1.05 | .25 |
| **269** | A39 8c red brn | 5.50 | .25 |
| **270** | A40 10c yel brn | 3.25 | .25 |
| **271** | A41 20c gray grn | 18.50 | 1.60 |
| **272** | A42 50c dl rose | 18.50 | .70 |
| **273** | A43 1p black | 19.00 | .70 |
| | *Nos. 264-273 (10)* | 69.80 | 4.75 |
| | Set, never hinged | 110.00 | |

**1925-28 Wmk. 106 *Perf. 12***

| | | | |
|---|---|---|---|
| **274** | A35 1c bl grn | 1.10 | .25 |
| *a.* | Booklet pane of 6 | 350.00 | |
| *b.* | Booklet pane of 30 | *750.00* | |
| **275** | A36 2c brt rose | 1.20 | .25 |
| *a.* | Booklet pane of 6 | 125.00 | |
| *b.* | Booklet pane of 30 | 350.00 | |
| **276** | A38 5c dp bl | 2.50 | .25 |
| **277** | A39 8c red brn ('28) | 5.75 | .65 |
| **278** | A40 10c yel brn ('27) | 7.00 | .70 |
| **279** | A41 20c olive grn | 11.00 | 1.10 |
| | *Nos. 274-279 (6)* | 28.55 | 3.20 |
| | Set, never hinged | 50.00 | |

**1926 *Imperf.***

| | | | |
|---|---|---|---|
| **280** | A35 1c blue green | 2.50 | .80 |
| **281** | A36 2c brt rose | 1.60 | .70 |
| **282** | A38 5c deep blue | 2.50 | .80 |
| | *Nos. 280-282 (3)* | 6.60 | 2.30 |
| | Set, never hinged | 10.00 | |

See Nos. 304-310. For overprint and surcharge see Nos. 317-318, 644.

Arms of Republic — A44

**1927, May 20 Unwmk. *Perf. 12***

| | | | |
|---|---|---|---|
| **283** | A44 25c violet | 18.50 | 5.00 |
| | Never hinged | 30.00 | |

25th anniversary of the Republic.

For surcharges see Nos. 355, C3.

Tomás Estrada Palma — A45

Designs: 2c, Gen. Gerardo Machado. 5c, Morro Castle. 8c, Havana Railway Station. 10c, Presidential Palace. 13c, Tobacco Plantation. 20c, Treasury Building. 30c, Sugar Mill. 50c, Havana Cathedral. 1p, Galician Clubhouse, Havana.

**1928, Jan. 2 Wmk. 106**

| | | | |
|---|---|---|---|
| **284** | A45 1c deep green | 1.75 | .30 |
| **285** | A45 2c brt rose | 2.00 | .30 |
| **286** | A45 5c deep blue | 2.50 | .50 |
| **287** | A45 8c lt red brn | 3.75 | 1.75 |
| **288** | A45 10c bister brn | 2.50 | .80 |
| **289** | A45 13c orange | 3.50 | 1.50 |
| **290** | A45 20c olive grn | 2.50 | 1.00 |
| **291** | A45 30c dk violet | 6.50 | 1.75 |
| **292** | A45 50c carmine rose | 10.00 | 3.25 |
| **293** | A45 1p gray black | 16.00 | 6.25 |
| | *Nos. 284-293 (10)* | 51.00 | 17.40 |
| | Set, never hinged | 67.50 | |

Sixth Pan-American Conference.

Capitol, Havana — A55

**1929, May 18**

| | | | |
|---|---|---|---|
| **294** | A55 1c green | 1.75 | .35 |
| **295** | A55 2c carmine rose | 1.75 | .30 |
| **296** | A55 5c blue | 2.40 | .40 |
| **297** | A55 10c bister brn | 2.75 | .50 |
| **298** | A55 20c violet | 4.50 | 2.75 |
| | *Nos. 294-298 (5)* | 13.15 | 4.30 |
| | Set, never hinged | 21.00 | |

Opening of the Capitol, Havana.

Hurdler — A56

**1930, Mar. 15 Engr.**

| | | | |
|---|---|---|---|
| **299** | A56 1c green | 5.00 | 1.75 |
| **300** | A56 2c carmine | 3.50 | 1.50 |
| **301** | A56 5c deep blue | 3.50 | 2.00 |
| **302** | A56 10c bister brn | 5.50 | 2.50 |
| **303** | A56 20c violet | 18.00 | 3.25 |
| | *Nos. 299-303 (5)* | 35.50 | 11.00 |
| | Set, never hinged | 50.00 | |

2nd Central American Athletic Games.

**Types of 1917 Portrait Issue**
**Flat Plate Printing**

**1930-45 Wmk. 106 Engr. *Perf. 10***

| | | | |
|---|---|---|---|
| **304** | A35 1c blue green | .80 | .25 |
| *a.* | Booklet pane of 6 | 50.00 | |
| *b.* | Booklet pane of 30 | — | |
| **305** | A36 2c brt rose | 75.00 | — |
| *a.* | Booklet pane of 6 | 1,500. | |
| **305B** | A37 3c dk rose vio ('42) | 4.00 | .75 |
| *c.* | Booklet pane of 6 | 125.00 | — |
| **306** | A38 5c dk blue | 2.75 | .25 |
| **306A** | A39 8c red brn ('45) | 2.75 | .25 |
| **307** | A40 10c brown | 2.75 | .25 |
| *a.* | 10c yellow brown ('35) | 3.50 | .75 |
| **307B** | A41 20c olive grn ('41) | 4.75 | .75 |
| | *Nos. 304-307B (7)* | 92.80 | 2.50 |

Nos. 305 and 305B were printed for booklet panes and all examples have straight edges.

For surcharge see No. 644.

**Rotary Press Printing**

| | | | |
|---|---|---|---|
| **308** | A35 1c blue grn | 2.75 | .25 |
| *a.* | Booklet pane of 50 | *3,000.* | |
| **309** | A36 2c brt rose | 2.75 | .25 |
| *a.* | Booklet pane of 50 | *3,000.* | |
| **310** | A37 3c violet | 3.75 | .75 |
| *a.* | 3c dull violet ('38) | 3.75 | .75 |
| *b.* | 3c rose violet ('41) | 3.75 | .75 |
| *c.* | Booklet pane of 50 | 3,000. | |
| | *Nos. 308-310 (3)* | 9.25 | 1.25 |

Flat plate stamps measure 18½x21½mm; rotary press, 19x22mm.

The Mangos of Baragua A57

War Memorial A61

Battle of Mal Tiempo — A58

Battle of Coliseo — A59

Maceo, Gómez and Zayas — A60

**Wmk. 229**

**1933, Apr. 23 Photo. *Perf. 12½***

| | | | |
|---|---|---|---|
| **312** | A57 3c dk brown | 3.50 | 1.50 |
| **313** | A58 5c dk blue | 4.50 | 1.25 |
| **314** | A59 10c emerald | 5.50 | 1.50 |
| **315** | A60 13c red | 3.50 | 1.60 |
| **316** | A61 20c black | 7.75 | 2.00 |
| | *Nos. 312-316 (5)* | 24.75 | 7.85 |
| | Set, never hinged | 35.00 | |

War of Independence and dedication of the "Soldado Invasor" (the American Army that came to the aid of the revolution against Spain) monument.

Types of 1917 Issues with Carmine or Black Overprint Reading Up or Down

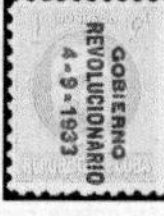


**Rotary Press Printing**

**Wmk. 106**

**1933, Dec. 23 Engr. *Perf. 10***

| | | | |
|---|---|---|---|
| **317** | A35 1c blue green (C) | 1.00 | .25 |

**With Additional Surcharge of New Value and Bars**

| | | | |
|---|---|---|---|
| **318** | A37 2c on 3c vio (Bk) | 1.60 | .30 |

Establishment of a revolutionary junta.

Catalogue values for Nos. 317-318 unused are for examples with overprint reading up. Values for overprint reading down: $4, unused; 75¢ used.

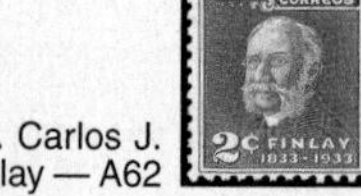

Dr. Carlos J. Finlay — A62

**1934, Dec. 3 Engr. *Perf. 10***

**319** A62 2c dark carmine 3.00 1.60
**320** A62 5c dark blue 3.50 2.00
Set, never hinged 9.50

Cent. of the birth of Dr. Carlos J. Finlay (1833-1915), physician-biologist who found that a mosquito transmitted yellow fever.

Pres. José Miguel Gómez — A63

Gómez Monument — A64

**1936, May *Perf. 10***

**322** A63 1c green 2.75 .40
**323** A64 2c carmine 4.50 .75
Set, never hinged 10.00

Unveiling of a monument to Gen. José Miguel Gómez, ex-president.

**Matanzas Issue**

Map of Cuba — A65

2c, Map of Free Zone. 4c, S. S. "Rex" in Matanzas Bay. 5c, Ships in Matanzas Bay. 8c, Caves of Bellamar. 10c, Valley of Yumuri. 20c, Yumuri River. 50c, Ships Leaving Port.

**Wmk. 229**

**1936, May 5 Photo. *Perf. 12½***

**324** A65 1c blue green .45 .25
**325** A65 2c red .70 .25
**326** A65 4c claret 1.20 .25
**327** A65 5c ultra 1.75 .25
**328** A65 8c orange brn 3.00 .70
**329** A65 10c emerald 3.25 .70
**330** A65 20c brown 6.25 2.50
**331** A65 50c slate 11.50 3.50
*Nos. 324-331,C18-C21,CE1,E8 (14)* 73.75 30.80
Set, never hinged 92.50

Exist imperf. Value 20% more.

"Peace and Work" A73

Máximo Gómez Monument A74

Torch A75

"Independence" A76

"Messenger of Peace" — A77

**1936, Nov. 18 *Perf. 12½***

**332** A73 1c emerald .75 .25
**333** A74 2c crimson 1.00 .30
**334** A75 4c maroon 1.20 .30
**335** A76 5c ultra 7.25 .55
**336** A77 8c dk green 9.00 2.00
*Nos. 332-336,C22-C23,E9 (8)* 36.45 7.75
Set, never hinged 52.50

Maj. Gen. Máximo Gómez, birth centenary.

Issued both perf and imperf. Values for imperfs are approx. 400% higher.

Sugar Cane — A78

Primitive Sugar Mill — A79

Modern Sugar Mill — A80

**Wmk. 106**

**1937, Oct. 2 Engr. *Perf. 10***

**337** A78 1c yellow green 1.50 .40
**338** A79 2c red 1.50 .25
**339** A80 5c bright blue 1.50 .40
*Nos. 337-339 (3)* 4.50 1.05
Set, never hinged 7.50

Cuban sugar cane industry, 400th anniv.

Argentine Emblem A81

Mountain Scene (Bolivia) A82

Arms of Brazil — A83

Canadian Scene — A84

Camilo Henriquez (Chile) A85

Gen, Francisco de Paula Santander (Colombia) A86

Natl. Monument (Costa Rica) A87

Autograph of José Marti (Cuba) A88

Columbus Lighthouse (Dominican Rep.) A89

Juan Montalvo (Ecuador) A90

Abraham Lincoln (US) A91

Quetzal and Scroll (Guatemala) A92

Arms of Haiti A93

Francisco Morazán (Honduras) A94

Fleet of Columbus — A95

**Wmk. 106**

**1937, Oct. 13 Engr. *Perf. 10***

**340** A81 1c deep green 2.50 2.50
**341** A82 1c green 2.00 2.00
**342** A83 2c carmine 1.50 1.50
**343** A84 2c carmine 1.50 1.50
**344** A85 3c violet 1.75 1.75
**345** A86 3c violet 1.75 1.75
**346** A87 4c bister brown 3.75 3.75
**347** A88 4c bister brown 3.75 3.75
**348** A89 5c blue 6.50 4.00
**349** A90 5c blue 6.50 3.75
**350** A91 8c citron 3.75 3.75
**351** A92 8c citron 3.25 3.25
**352** A93 10c maroon 2.50 2.50
**353** A94 10c maroon 2.50 2.50
**354** A95 25c rose lilac 26.00 8.00
*Nos. 340-354,C24-C29,E10-E11 (23)* 137.25 95.50
Set, never hinged 190.00

Nos. 340-354 were sold by the Cuban PO for 3 days, Oct. 13-15, during which no other stamps were sold. They were postally valid for the full face value. Proceeds from their three-day sale above 30,000 pesos were paid by the Cuban POD to the Assoc. of American Writers and Artists. Remainders were overprinted "SVP" (Without Postal Value).

No. 283 Surcharged in Green

**1937, Nov. 19 Unwmk. *Perf. 12***

**355** A44 10c on 25c violet 13.50 3.50
Never hinged 19.50

Centenary of Cuban railroads.

Ciboney Indian and Cigar A96

Cigar and Globe A97

Tobacco Plant and Cigars — A98

**1939, Aug. 28 Wmk. 106 *Perf. 10***

**356** A96 1c yellow green .75 .25
**357** A97 2c red 1.00 .25
**358** A98 5c brt ultra 1.25 .30
*Nos. 356-358 (3)* 3.00 .80
Set, never hinged 4.75

General Calixto García A99 A100

**1939, Nov. 6 *Perf. 10, Imperf.***

**359** A99 2c dark red 1.00 .25
**360** A100 5c deep blue 1.50 .40
Set, never hinged 3.75

Birth centenary of General Garcia.

Values are for perf examples. Value of imperfs approx. 20% higher.

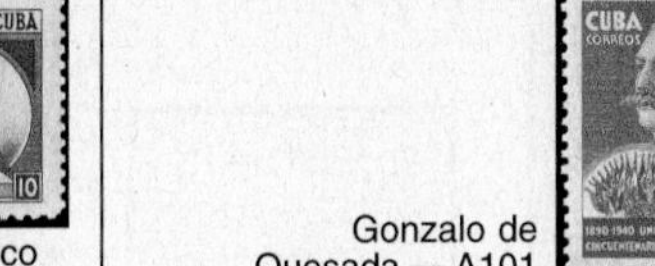


Gonzalo de Quesada — A101

**1940, Apr. 30 Engr. *Perf. 10***

**361** A101 2c rose red 2.40 .50
Never hinged 3.50

Pan American Union, 50th anniversary.

Rotary Club Emblem, Cuban Flag and Tobacco Plant — A102

**1940, May 18 Wmk. 106 *Perf. 10***

**362** A102 2c rose red 3.00 .75
Never hinged 4.50

Rotary Intl. Convention held at Havana.

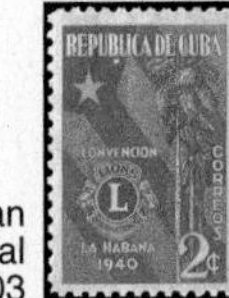


Lions Emblem, Cuban Flag and Royal Palms — A103

**1940, July 23**

**363** A103 2c orange vermilion 5.50 1.00
Never hinged 8.50

Lions International Convention, Havana.

Dr. Nicolás J. Gutiérrez A104

**1940, Oct. 28**

**364** A104 2c orange ver 1.90 .30
**365** A104 5c blue 2.00 .30
*a.* Sheet of four, imperf., unwmkd. 4.50 3.00
Never hinged 7.00
*b.* As "a," black overprint ('51) 11.00 4.75
Never hinged 17.00
Set, never hinged 5.50

100th anniv. of the publication of the 1st Cuban Medical Review, "El Repertorio Medico Habanero."

No. 365a contains 2 each of Nos. 364-365 imperf. and sold for 25c.

For overprint see No. C43A.

In 1951 No. 365a was overprinted in black: "50 Aniversario Descubrimiento Agente Transmisor de la Flebre Amarilla por el Dr. Carlos J. Finlay Honor a los Martires de la Ciencia 1901 1951." The overprint is illustrated over No. C43A, but does not include the plane and "Correo Aereo."

Major General Guillermo Moncada A105

Moncada Riding into Battle A106

**1941, June 25**

**366** A105 3c dk brown, *buff* 3.50 1.25
**367** A106 5c bright blue 3.50 1.25
Set, never hinged 10.00

Maj. Gen. Guillermo Moncada (1841-96).

Globe Showing Western Hemisphere A107

Maceo, Bolívar, Juárez, Lincoln and Arms of Cuba A108

"Labor: Wealth of America" A109

Tree of Fraternity, Havana A110

Statue of Liberty — A111

***Perf. 10, Imperf.***

**1942, Feb. 23** **Wmk. 106**

| | | | |
|---|---|---|---|
| **368** | A107 1c emerald | .75 | .25 |
| **369** | A108 3c orange brown | 1.00 | .25 |
| **370** | A109 5c blue | 2.00 | .75 |
| **371** | A110 10c red violet | 2.50 | .75 |
| **372** | A111 13c red | 2.50 | .65 |
| | *Nos. 368-372 (5)* | 8.75 | 2.65 |
| | Set, never hinged | 11.00 | |

Spirit of Democracy in the Americas.
The imperforate varieties are without gum. Value, set mint $10, used $5.

Ignacio Agramonte Loynaz A112

Rescue of Sanguily by Agramonte A113

**1942, Apr. 10** ***Perf. 10***

| | | | |
|---|---|---|---|
| **373** | A112 3c bister brn | 3.50 | 1.00 |
| **374** | A113 5c brt blue, *bluish* | 3.75 | 1.25 |
| | Set, never hinged | 11.00 | |

100th anniv. of the birth of Ignacio Agramonte Loynaz, patriot.

"Unmask the Fifth Columnists" A114

"Be Careful, The Fifth Column is Spying on You" — A115

"Destroy it. The Fifth Column is like a Serpent" A116

"Fulfill your Patriotic Duty by Destroying the Fifth Column" A117

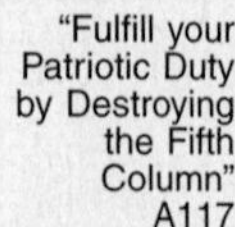

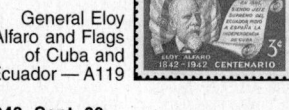

"Don't be Afraid of the Fifth Column. Attack it" — A118

**1943, July 5**

| | | | |
|---|---|---|---|
| **375** | A114 1c dk blue grn | 1.25 | .30 |
| **376** | A115 3c red | 1.75 | .30 |
| **377** | A116 5c brt blue | 1.90 | .45 |
| **378** | A117 10c brown | 4.25 | 1.90 |
| **379** | A118 13c dull rose vio | 4.00 | 1.75 |
| | *Nos. 375-379 (5)* | 13.15 | 4.70 |
| | Set, never hinged | 19.00 | |

General Eloy Alfaro and Flags of Cuba and Ecuador — A119

**1943, Sept. 20**

| | | | |
|---|---|---|---|
| **380** | A119 3c green | 2.50 | .30 |
| | Never hinged | 3.00 | |

General Eloy Alfaro of Ecuador, 100th birth anniv.

Retirement Security — A120

**1943, Nov. 8** **Wmk. 106** ***Perf. 10***

| | | | |
|---|---|---|---|
| **381** | A120 1c yellow green | 1.20 | .30 |
| **382** | A120 3c vermilion | 1.20 | .30 |
| **383** | A120 5c bright blue | 1.60 | .40 |

**1944, Mar. 18**

| | | | |
|---|---|---|---|
| **384** | A120 1c bright yel grn | 1.60 | .40 |
| **385** | A120 3c salmon | 2.00 | .40 |
| **386** | A120 5c light blue | 3.75 | 1.20 |
| | *Nos. 381-386 (6)* | 11.35 | 3.00 |
| | Set, never hinged | 17.00 | |

Half the proceeds from the sale of Nos. 381-386 were used for the Communications Ministry Employees' Retirement Fund.

Portrait of Columbus A121

Bartolomé de Las Casas A122

First Statue of Columbus at Cárdenas A123

Discovery of Tobacco A124

Columbus Sights Land — A125

**1944, May 19**

| | | | |
|---|---|---|---|
| **387** | A121 1c dk yellow grn | 2.75 | .40 |
| *a.* | Pair, imperf horiz. | | 175.00 |
| **388** | A122 3c brown | 2.50 | .25 |
| **389** | A123 5c brt blue | 3.00 | .75 |
| **390** | A124 10c dark violet | 3.75 | .75 |
| **391** | A125 13c dark red | 4.00 | 1.25 |
| | *Nos. 387-391,C36-C37 (7)* | 21.40 | 4.55 |
| | Set, never hinged | 32.50 | |

450th anniv. of the discovery of America.

Major General Carlos Roloff — A126

**1944, Aug. 21**

| | | | |
|---|---|---|---|
| **392** | A126 3c violet | 2.00 | .30 |
| | Never hinged | 3.00 | |

Maj. Gen. Carlos Roloff, 100th birth anniv.

Americas Map and 1st Brazilian Postage Stamps — A127

**1944, Dec. 20** **Engr.**

| | | | |
|---|---|---|---|
| **393** | A127 3c brown orange | 2.25 | .50 |
| | Never hinged | 3.25 | |

Cent. of the 1st postage stamps of the Americas, issued by Brazil in 1843.

Seal of the Society A128

Luis de las Casas and Luis Maria Penalyer A129

**1945, Oct. 5** **Wmk. 106** ***Perf. 10***

| | | | |
|---|---|---|---|
| **394** | A128 1c yellow green | 1.75 | .25 |
| **395** | A129 2c scarlet | 1.60 | .25 |
| | Set, never hinged | 5.00 | |

Sesquicentenary of the founding of the Economic Society of Friends of the Country.

Aged Couple — A130

**1945, Dec. 27**

| | | | |
|---|---|---|---|
| **396** | A130 1c dk yellow grn | .50 | .25 |
| **397** | A130 2c scarlet | .70 | .25 |
| **398** | A130 5c cobalt blue | 1.20 | .25 |

**1946, Mar. 26**

| | | | |
|---|---|---|---|
| **399** | A130 1c brt yellow grn | 1.00 | .25 |
| **400** | A130 2c salmon pink | .95 | .25 |
| **401** | A130 5c light blue | 2.25 | .25 |
| | *Nos. 396-401 (6)* | 6.60 | 1.50 |
| | Set, never hinged | 9.50 | |

See note after No. 386.

**Catalogue values for unused stamps in this section, from this point to the end of the section, are for Never Hinged items.**

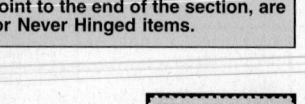

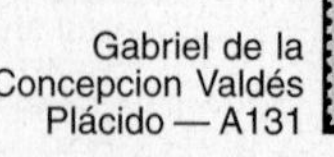

Gabriel de la Concepcion Valdés Plácido — A131

**1946, Feb. 5**

| | | | |
|---|---|---|---|
| **402** | A131 2c scarlet | 2.00 | .30 |

Cent. of the death of the poet Gabriel de la Concepcion Valdés.

Manuel Marquez Sterling — A132

**1946, Apr. 30**

| | | | |
|---|---|---|---|
| **403** | A132 2c scarlet | 4.00 | .50 |

Founding of the Manuel Marquez Sterling Professional School of Journalism, 3th anniv.

Globe and Cross — A133

**1946, July 4** **Engr.**

| | | | |
|---|---|---|---|
| **404** | A133 2c scarlet, *pink* | 2.40 | .25 |

80th anniv. of the Intl. Red Cross.

Cow and Milkmaid — A134

**1947, Feb. 20** **Wmk. 106** ***Perf. 10***

| | | | |
|---|---|---|---|
| **405** | A134 2c scarlet | 3.50 | .40 |

1947 National Livestock Exposition.

Franklin D. Roosevelt — A135

**1947, Apr. 12**

| | | | |
|---|---|---|---|
| **406** | A135 2c vermilion | 3.00 | .40 |

2nd anniv. of the death of Franklin D. Roosevelt.

Antonio Oms Sarret and Aged Couple — A136

**1947, Oct. 20**

| | | | |
|---|---|---|---|
| **407** | A136 1c dp yellow grn | 1.40 | .30 |
| **408** | A136 2c scarlet | 1.20 | .30 |
| **409** | A136 5c lt blue | 2.25 | .55 |
| | *Nos. 407-409 (3)* | 4.85 | 1.15 |

See note after No. 386.

Marta Abreu Arenabio de Estevez A137

"Charity" A138

Marta Abreu Monument, Santa Clara A139

"Patriotism" A140

**1947, Nov. 29**

| | | | | |
|---|---|---|---|---|
| **410** | A137 | 1c dp yellow grn | 2.25 | .40 |
| **411** | A138 | 2c scarlet | 2.00 | .30 |
| **412** | A139 | 5c brt blue | 2.50 | .40 |
| **413** | A140 | 10c dk violet | 4.25 | .90 |
| | | *Nos. 410-413 (4)* | 11.00 | 2.00 |

Birth cent. of Marta Abreu Arenabio de Estevez, philanthropist and humanitarian.

Armauer Hansen — A141

**1948, Apr. 9**

| | | | | |
|---|---|---|---|---|
| **414** | A141 | 2c rose carmine | 3.50 | .40 |

International Leprosy Congress, Havana.

Mother and Child — A142

**1948, Oct. 15** **Engr.**

| | | | | |
|---|---|---|---|---|
| **415** | A142 | 1c yellow grn | 1.40 | .25 |
| **416** | A142 | 2c scarlet | 1.25 | .25 |
| **417** | A142 | 5c brt blue | 2.40 | .40 |
| | | *Nos. 415-417 (3)* | 5.05 | .90 |

See note after No. 386.

Death of José Martí — A143

Martí Rowing to Shore — A144

**1948, Nov. 10** **Wmk. 106** ***Perf. 10***

| | | | | |
|---|---|---|---|---|
| **418** | A143 | 2c scarlet | 1.60 | .25 |
| **419** | A144 | 5c brt blue | 2.50 | .45 |

50th anniversary of the death of José Martí, patriot (in 1945).

Tobacco Picking A145

Liberty Carrying Flag and Cigars A146

Cigar and Arms of Cuba — A147

**1948, Dec. 6** **Size: 22½x26mm**

| | | | | |
|---|---|---|---|---|
| **420** | A145 | 1c green | 1.50 | .25 |
| **421** | A146 | 2c rose car | 1.40 | .30 |
| **422** | A147 | 5c brt blue | 2.75 | .30 |
| | | *Nos. 420-422 (3)* | 5.65 | .85 |

Cuba's tobacco industry. See Nos. 445-447. For overprints and surcharge see Nos. 448-451, 512.

Equestrian Statue of Gen. Antonio Maceo A148

Sword Salute to Maceo A149

Designs: 2c, Portrait of Maceo. 5c, Mausoleum, El Cacahual. 10c, East to West invasion. 20c, Battle of Peralejo. 50c, Declaration of Baragua. 1p, Death of Maceo at San Pedro.

**1948, Dec. 15** **Wmk. 229** ***Perf. 12½***

| | | | | |
|---|---|---|---|---|
| **423** | A148 | 1c blue green | 1.75 | .25 |
| **424** | A148 | 2c red | 1.60 | .25 |
| **425** | A148 | 5c blue | 2.40 | .25 |
| **426** | A149 | 8c black & brown | 1.60 | .45 |
| **427** | A149 | 10c brown & bl grn | 1.25 | .35 |
| **428** | A149 | 20c blue & car | 3.75 | 1.40 |
| **429** | A149 | 50c car & ultra | 6.00 | 4.00 |
| **430** | A149 | 1p black & violet | 12.00 | 6.00 |
| | | *Nos. 423-430 (8)* | 30.35 | 12.95 |

Birth cent. (in 1945) of Maceo.

Symbol of Pharmacy — A150

**1948, Dec. 28** ***Perf. 10***

| | | | | |
|---|---|---|---|---|
| **431** | A150 | 2c rose carmine | 3.50 | .40 |

1st Pan-American Congress of Pharmacy, Havana, Dec. 1948.

Morro Lighthouse — A151

**1949, Jan. 17** **Wmk. 229** ***Perf. 12½***

| | | | | |
|---|---|---|---|---|
| **432** | A151 | 2c carmine | 3.25 | .40 |

Centenary (in 1944) of the erection of the Morro Lighthouse.

Jagua Castle, Cienfuegos A152

**1949, Jan. 27** **Wmk. 106** ***Perf. 10***

| | | | | |
|---|---|---|---|---|
| **433** | A152 | 1c yellow green | 2.00 | .30 |
| **434** | A152 | 2c rose red | 3.00 | 1.00 |

200th anniv. of the construction of Jagua Castle and the cent. of the publication of the 1st newspaper in Cienfuegos.

Manuel Sanguily y Garritt — A153

**1949, Mar. 31**

| | | | | |
|---|---|---|---|---|
| **435** | A153 | 2c rose red | 1.40 | .30 |
| **436** | A153 | 5c blue | 2.00 | .30 |

Manuel Sanguily y Garritt (1848-1925), cabinet member, editor, author.

Map of Isle of Pines — A154

**1949, Apr. 26**

| | | | | |
|---|---|---|---|---|
| **437** | A154 | 5c blue | 4.00 | .70 |

20th anniv. of the recognition of Cuban ownership of the Isle of Pines.

Ismael Cespedes — A155

**1949, Sept. 28**

| | | | | |
|---|---|---|---|---|
| **438** | A155 | 1c yellow green | 1.75 | .30 |
| **439** | A155 | 2c scarlet | 1.25 | .30 |
| **440** | A155 | 5c brt blue | 1.75 | .30 |
| | | *Nos. 438-440 (3)* | 4.75 | .90 |

See note after No. 386.

Gen. Enrique Collazo — A156

**1950, Feb. 28** **Engr.** ***Perf. 10***

| | | | | |
|---|---|---|---|---|
| **441** | A156 | 2c scarlet | 1.60 | .25 |
| **442** | A156 | 5c brt blue | 2.00 | .45 |

Centenary (in 1948) of the birth of General Enrique Collazo.

Enrique José Varona — A157

**1950, Feb. 28**

| | | | | |
|---|---|---|---|---|
| **443** | A157 | 2c scarlet | 1.40 | .25 |
| **444** | A157 | 5c brt blue | 2.00 | .25 |

Centenary of the birth of Enrique José Varona, writer and patriot.

### Tobacco Types of 1948

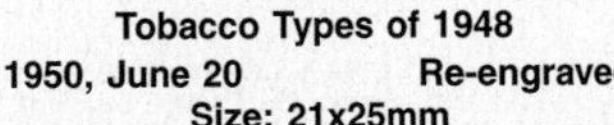

**1950, June 20** **Re-engraved**

**Size: 21x25mm**

| | | | | |
|---|---|---|---|---|
| **445** | A145 | 1c green | 1.25 | .30 |
| **446** | A146 | 2c rose red | 1.25 | .30 |
| **447** | A147 | 5c blue | 2.00 | .30 |
| | | *Nos. 445-447 (3)* | 4.50 | .90 |

The re-engraved stamps show slight differences in many minor details.

For overprints and surcharge see Nos. 448-451, 512.

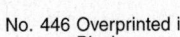

No. 446 Overprinted in Black

**1950, Apr. 27**

| | | | | |
|---|---|---|---|---|
| **448** | A146 | 2c rose red | 2.50 | .30 |

Natl. Bank of Cuba opening, Apr. 27, 1950.

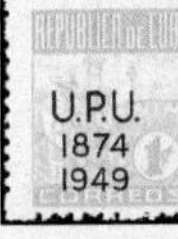


Re-engraved Tobacco Types of 1950 Overprinted in Carmine

**1950, May 18**

| | | | | |
|---|---|---|---|---|
| **449** | A145 | 1c yellow green | 1.00 | .30 |
| **450** | A146 | 2c lilac rose | 1.10 | .30 |
| **451** | A147 | 5c light blue | 1.30 | .30 |
| | | *Nos. 449-451 (3)* | 3.40 | .90 |

75th anniv. (in 1949) of the UPU.

No. 451 exists with surcharge inverted.

Manuel Balanzategui, Antonio L. Pausa and Train Wreck — A158

**1950, Sept. 21** **Engr.**

| | | | | |
|---|---|---|---|---|
| **452** | A158 | 1c yellow grn | 1.40 | .70 |
| **453** | A158 | 2c scarlet | 1.40 | .70 |
| **454** | A158 | 5c brt blue | 4.00 | .70 |
| | | *Nos. 452-454 (3)* | 6.80 | 2.10 |

Fernando Figueredo — A159

**1951, Mar. 17** **Wmk. 106** ***Perf. 10***

| | | | | |
|---|---|---|---|---|
| **455** | A159 | 1c green | 1.10 | .25 |
| **456** | A159 | 2c scarlet | 1.25 | .25 |
| **457** | A159 | 5c brt blue | 1.40 | .25 |
| | | *Nos. 455-457 (3)* | 3.75 | .75 |

Three-fourths of the proceeds from the sale of these stamps were used for the Communication Ministry Employees' Retirement Fund.

See Nos. 474, C51-C56, E15. For surcharges see Nos. 474, C51-C56, E15.

Miguel Teurbe Tolón and Flag A160

Narciso Lopez A161

Emilia Teurbe Tolón Sewing Flag A162

Cuban Flag A163

**Engraved and Lithographed**

**1951, July 3** **Wmk. 229** ***Perf. 13***

| | | | | |
|---|---|---|---|---|
| **458** | A160 | 1c Prus grn, ultra & red | 1.50 | .30 |
| **459** | A161 | 2c red & gray blk | 1.40 | .30 |
| **460** | A162 | 5c ultra & red | 1.60 | .65 |
| **461** | A163 | 10c rose vio, bl & red | 3.50 | 1.00 |
| | | *Nos. 458-461,C41-C43,E13 (8)* | 24.25 | 8.40 |

Centenary of adoption of Cuba's flag.

Clara Louise Maass and Hospitals — A164

Hospitals: Lutheran Memorial, Newark, N.J. and Las Animas, Havana.

**Wmk. 106**

**1951, Aug. 24** **Engr.** ***Perf. 10***

| | | | | |
|---|---|---|---|---|
| **462** | A164 | 2c scarlet | 2.00 | .50 |

75th anniv. of the birth of Clara Louise Maass, (1876-1901), American nurse and martyr in yellow fever fight.

**Airmail Type and**

José Raul Capablanca A165

Capablanca Club, Havana A166

**Wmk. 229**

**1951, Nov. 1 Photo. *Perf. 13***

| No. | Type | Description | Unused | Used |
|---|---|---|---|---|
| **463** | A165 | 1c blue grn & org | 3.75 | .65 |
| **464** | AP27 | 2c rose car & dk brn | 3.50 | .90 |
| **465** | A166 | 5c black & dp ultra | 12.00 | 1.90 |
| | | *Nos. 463-465,C44-C46,E14 (7)* | 75.25 | 18.10 |

Jose Raul Capablanca, World Chess titlist (1921). Value imperf., set of 7 pairs, $1,500.

Antonio Guiteras Holmes A167

Guiteras Preparing Social Legislation A168

Fort of the Morrillo — A169

**Wmk. 106**

**1951, Oct. 22 Engr. *Perf. 10***

| No. | Type | Description | Unused | Used |
|---|---|---|---|---|
| **466** | A167 | 1c yellow green | 1.50 | .25 |
| **467** | A168 | 2c rose carmine | 2.25 | .50 |
| **468** | A169 | 5c deep blue | 2.50 | .50 |
| | | *Nos. 466-468,C47-C49 (6)* | 18.25 | 4.95 |

16th anniv. of the Action of the Morrillo and to honor Antonio Guiteras Holmes, who was killed there.

Souvenir sheets containing stamps similar to Nos. 466-468, but in different colors, are listed as Nos. C49a-C49b.

Poinsettia — A170

**1951, Dec. 1 Engr. and Typo.**

| No. | Type | Description | Unused | Used |
|---|---|---|---|---|
| **469** | A170 | 1c green & car | 5.25 | 1.00 |
| **470** | A170 | 2c rose car & grn | 3.75 | .60 |

See Nos. 498-499.

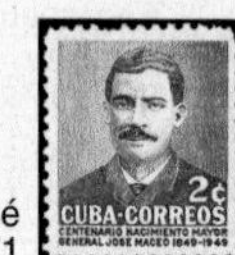

Maj. Gen. José Maceo — A171

**1952, Feb. 6 Engr.**

| No. | Type | Description | Unused | Used |
|---|---|---|---|---|
| **471** | A171 | 2c yellow brown | 2.50 | .25 |
| **472** | A171 | 5c indigo | 2.50 | .25 |

Birth centenary of Maceo.

Isabella I — A172

**1952, Feb. 22**

| No. | Type | Description | Unused | Used |
|---|---|---|---|---|
| **473** | A172 | 2c bright red | 2.75 | .50 |

500th anniv. of the birth of Queen Isabella I of Spain.

Souvenir sheets containing 2c stamps of type A172 are listed as Nos. C50a-C50b.

**Type of 1951 Surcharged in Green**

**1952, Mar. 18**

| No. | Type | Description | Unused | Used |
|---|---|---|---|---|
| **474** | A159 | 10c on 2c yel brn | 2.25 | 2.25 |

Receipt of Autonomy — A173

Designs: 2c, Tomas Estrada Palma and Luis Estevez Romero. 5c, Barnet, Finlay, Guiteras and Nuñez. 8c, Capitol. 20c, Map, Central Highway. 50c, Sugar Mill.

**Centers in Black**

**Wmk. 106**

**1952, May 27 Engr. *Perf. 12½***

| No. | Type | Description | Unused | Used |
|---|---|---|---|---|
| **475** | A173 | 1c dk green | 2.75 | .25 |
| **476** | A173 | 2c dk carmine | 1.60 | .25 |
| **477** | A173 | 5c dk blue | 1.25 | .25 |
| **478** | A173 | 8c dk brown car | 2.00 | .25 |
| **479** | A173 | 20c dk olive grn | 2.40 | .40 |
| **480** | A173 | 50c dp orange | 6.00 | 1.40 |
| | | *Nos. 475-480,C57-C60,E16 (11)* | 29.35 | 8.05 |

50th anniv. of the Republic of Cuba.

Hands Holding Coffee Beans — A174

Designs: 2c, Map and man picking coffee beans. 5c, Farmer with pan of beans.

**1952, Aug. 22 Wmk. 229 *Perf. 13½***

| No. | Type | Description | Unused | Used |
|---|---|---|---|---|
| **481** | A174 | 1c green | 2.00 | .25 |
| **482** | A174 | 2c rose red | 1.00 | .25 |
| **483** | A174 | 5c dk vio bl & aqua | 2.50 | .40 |
| | | *Nos. 481-483 (3)* | 5.50 | .90 |

Bicentenary of coffee cultivation.

Col. Charles Hernandez y Sandrino — A175

**1952, Oct. 7 Wmk. 106 *Perf. 10***

| No. | Type | Description | Unused | Used |
|---|---|---|---|---|
| **484** | A175 | 1c yellow grn | 3.50 | .30 |
| **485** | A175 | 2c scarlet | 5.00 | .30 |
| **486** | A175 | 5c blue | 4.50 | .30 |
| **487** | A175 | 8c black | 4.50 | .45 |
| **488** | A175 | 10c brown red | 5.50 | .45 |
| **489** | A175 | 20c brown | 9.00 | 3.75 |
| | | *Nos. 484-489,C63-C72,E17 (17)* | 85.35 | 25.20 |

See note after No. 457.

Alonso Alvarez de la Campa — A176

Portraits: 2c, Carlos A. Latorre. 3c, Anacleto Bermudez. 5c, Eladio G. Toledo. 8c, Angel Laborde. 10c, Jose M. Medina. 13c, Pascual Rodriguez. 20c, Carlos Verdugo.

**Frame Engraved; Center in Black**

**1952, Nov. 27**

| No. | Type | Description | Unused | Used |
|---|---|---|---|---|
| **490** | A176 | 1c green | 1.25 | .25 |
| **491** | A176 | 2c carmine | 2.50 | .25 |
| **492** | A176 | 3c purple | 1.75 | .25 |
| **493** | A176 | 5c blue | 1.75 | .60 |
| **494** | A176 | 8c bister brn | 2.25 | .50 |
| **495** | A176 | 10c orange brn | 2.10 | .50 |
| **496** | A176 | 13c lilac rose | 3.50 | .75 |
| **497** | A176 | 20c olive grn | 4.75 | 1.25 |
| | | *Nos. 490-497,C73-C74 (10)* | 26.85 | 6.15 |

Execution of 8 medical students, 81st anniv.

**Christmas Type of 1951**

Centers: Tree.

**Frame Engr.; Center Typo.**

**1952, Dec. 1 Dated "1952-1953"**

| No. | Type | Description | Unused | Used |
|---|---|---|---|---|
| **498** | A170 | 1c yel grn & car | 7.50 | 1.90 |
| **499** | A170 | 3c vio & dk grn | 7.50 | 1.50 |

Birthplace of José Martí A177

Marti at St. Lazarus Quarry A178

No. 501, Court martial. No. 502, Martiano house, Havana. No. 504, El Abra ranch, Isle of Pines. No. 505, Symbols, "Marti the Poet." No. 506, Marti and Bolivar statue, Caracas. No. 507, At desk in New York. No. 508, House where revolutionary party was formed. No. 509, 1st issue of "Patria."

**1953 Engr. *Perf. 10***

| No. | Type | Description | Unused | Used |
|---|---|---|---|---|
| **500** | A177 | 1c dk grn & red brn | 1.75 | .25 |
| **501** | A177 | 1c dk grn & red brn | 1.40 | .25 |
| **502** | A177 | 3c purple & brn | 2.00 | .25 |
| **503** | A178 | 3c purple & brn | 2.00 | .25 |
| **504** | A177 | 5c dp bl & dk brn | 1.25 | .25 |
| **505** | A178 | 5c ultra & brn | 1.75 | .25 |
| **506** | A178 | 10c red brn & blk | .80 | .40 |
| **507** | A178 | 10c dk brn & blk | 2.00 | .40 |
| **508** | A178 | 13c dk ol grn & dk brn | 2.00 | .80 |
| **509** | A177 | 13c dk ol grn & brn | 2.50 | 1.00 |
| | | *Nos. 500-509,C79-C89 (21)* | 28.55 | 12.90 |

Centenary of birth of José Martí.

Rafael Montoro Valdez — A179

**1953, Mar. 5**

| No. | Type | Description | Unused | Used |
|---|---|---|---|---|
| **510** | A179 | 3c dark violet | 3.00 | .40 |

Rafael Montoro Valdez, statesman, birth cent.

Francisco Carrera Justiz — A180

**1953, Mar. 9**

| No. | Type | Description | Unused | Used |
|---|---|---|---|---|
| **511** | A180 | 3c rose red | 3.25 | .50 |

Francisco Carrera Justiz, educator, statesman.

**No. 446 Surcharged with New Value**

**1953, June 16**

| No. | Type | Description | Unused | Used |
|---|---|---|---|---|
| **512** | A146 | 3c on 2c rose red | 1.50 | .25 |

Board of Accounts Bldg., Havana — A181

**1953, Nov. 3 Engr.**

| No. | Type | Description | Unused | Used |
|---|---|---|---|---|
| **513** | A181 | 3c blue | 1.35 | .45 |
| | | *Nos. 513,C90-C91 (3)* | 6.65 | 2.25 |

1st Intl. Cong. of Boards of Accounts, Havana, Nov. 2-9.

Miguel Coyula Llaguno — A182

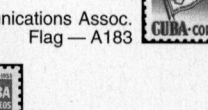

Communications Assoc. Flag — A183

Antonio Ginard Rojas — A183b

Designs: 3c, 8c, Enrique Calleja Hensell.

**1954 Dated 1953**

| No. | Type | Description | Unused | Used |
|---|---|---|---|---|
| **514** | A182 | 1c green | .30 | .25 |
| **515** | A182 | 3c rose red | .50 | .25 |
| **516** | A183 | 5c blue | 1.25 | .25 |
| **517** | A182 | 8c brn pur | 1.50 | .50 |
| **518** | A183b | 10c brown | 2.50 | 1.25 |
| | | *Nos. 514-518,C92-C95,E19 (10)* | 24.80 | 9.25 |

Nos. 515 and 517 show the same portrait, but inscriptions are arranged differently.

See note after No. 457.

Carlos J. Finlay — A184

Maximo Gomez — A184a

Portraits: 1c, José Marti. 3c, José de la Luz Caballero. 4c, Miguel Aldama. 5c, Calixto Garcia. 8c, Ignacio Agramonte. 10c, Tomas Estrada Palma. 14c, Serafin Sanchez. 20c, José Antonio Saco. 50c, Antonio Maceo. 1p, Carlos Manuel de Cespedes.

**1954-56 Wmk. 106 *Perf. 10***

| No. | Type | Description | Unused | Used |
|---|---|---|---|---|
| **519** | A184 | 1c green | .75 | .25 |
| **520** | A184a | 2c rose car | 1.00 | .25 |
| **521** | A184 | 3c violet | 1.00 | .25 |
| **521A** | A184 | 4c red lil ('56) | .75 | .25 |
| **522** | A184a | 5c slate bl | .75 | .25 |
| **523** | A184a | 8c car lake | 1.40 | .35 |
| **524** | A184 | 10c sepia | 1.40 | .35 |
| **525** | A184 | 13c org red | .75 | .35 |
| **525A** | A184a | 14c gray ('56) | 1.25 | .35 |
| **526** | A184 | 20c olive | 2.25 | .35 |
| **527** | A184a | 50c org yel | 2.40 | .45 |
| **528** | A184a | 1p orange | 2.75 | 1.00 |
| | | *Nos. 519-528 (12)* | 16.45 | 4.45 |

See Nos. 674-680. For surcharges see Nos. 636, 641-643.

Maj. Gen. José M. Rodriguez — A185

Design: 5c, Gen. Rodriguez on horseback.

**1954, June 8 Engr. *Perf. 12½***

**Center in Dark Brown**

| No. | Type | Description | Unused | Used |
|---|---|---|---|---|
| **529** | A185 | 2c dark carmine | 1.50 | .25 |
| **530** | A185 | 5c deep blue | 2.40 | .40 |

Cent. of the birth of Maj. Gen. José Maria Rodriguez (in 1851).

Gen. Batísta Sanatorium A186

**1954, Sept. 21 Wmk. 106 *Perf. 10***

| No. | Type | Description | Unused | Used |
|---|---|---|---|---|
| **531** | A186 | 3c deep blue | 3.00 | .25 |

See No. C107.

Santa Claus — A187

**1954, Dec. 15**

| No. | Type | Description | Unused | Used |
|---|---|---|---|---|
| **532** | A187 | 2c dk grn & car | 5.25 | 1.25 |
| **533** | A187 | 4c car & dk grn | 5.25 | 1.25 |

Christmas 1954.

Maria Luisa Dolz — A188

**1954, Dec. 23**

**534** A188 4c deep blue 2.75 .40

Cent. of the birth of Maria Luisa Dolz, educator and defender of women's rights. See No. C108.

Cuban Flag and Scouts Saluting — A189

**1954, Dec. 27** ***Perf. 12½***

**535** A189 4c dark green 3.25 .35

Issued to publicize the national patrol encampment of the Boy Scouts of Cuba.

Rotary Emblem and Paul P. Harris — A190

**1955, Feb. 23 Engr. Wmk. 106**

**536** A190 4c blue & dk blue 2.25 .25

Rotary International, 50th anniversary. See No. C109.

Maj. Gen. Francisco Carrillo — A191

Portrait: 5c, Gen. Carrillo standing.

**1955, Mar. 8** ***Perf. 10***

**537** A191 2c brt red & dk bl 1.25 .25
**538** A191 5c dk bl & dk brn 1.50 .30

Cent. of the birth of Maj. Gen. Francisco Carrillo (1851-1926).

Stamp of 1885 and Convent of San Francisco A192

Designs (including 1855 stamp): 4c, Volanta carriage. 10c, Havana, 19th century. 14c, Captain general's residence.

**1955, Apr.** ***Perf. 12½***

**539** A192 2c lil rose & dk grnsh bl 2.00 .25
**540** A192 4c ocher & dk grn 2.00 .30
**541** A192 10c ultra & dk red 2.00 .75
**542** A192 14c grn & dp org 3.00 .75
*Nos. 539-542,C110-C113 (8)* 21.50 4.40

Cent. of Cuba's 1st postage stamps.

Maj. Gen. Mario G. Menocal A193

Gen. Emilio Nuñez A194

Portraits: 10c, J. G. Gomez. 14c, A. Sanchez de Bustamente.

**1955, June 22**

**543** A193 2c dark green 1.25 .25
**544** A194 4c lilac rose 1.25 .25
**545** A193 10c deep blue 1.50 .40
**546** A194 14c gray violet 3.00 .90
*Nos. 543-546,C114-C116,E20 (8)* 25.75 7.40

See note after No. 457.

Turkey — A195

**1955, Dec. 15 Engr.**

**547** A195 2c slate grn & dk car 3.75 1.50
**548** A195 4c rose lake & brt grn 4.25 1.50

Christmas 1955.

Gen. Emilio Nuñez — A196

**1955, Dec. 27**

**549** A196 4c claret 1.60 .45
*Nos. 549,C127-C128 (3)* 6.20 1.75

Cent. of the birth of Gen. Emilio Nunez, Cuban revolutionary hero.

Francisco Cajigal de la Vega (1695-1777) — A197

**1956, Mar. 27** ***Perf. 12½***

**552** A197 4c rose brn & slate bl 3.75 .55

Cuban post bicent. See No. C129.

Julian del Casal — A198

Portraits: 4c, Luisa Perez de Zambrana. 10c, Juan Clemente Zenea. 14c, José Joaquin Palma.

**1956, May 2 Portraits in Black**

**553** A198 2c green .50 .25
**554** A198 4c rose lilac 1.50 .25
**555** A198 10c blue 1.90 .25
**556** A198 14c violet 3.25 .25
*Nos. 553-556,C131-C133,E21 (8)* 16.50 4.25

See note after No. 457.

Victor Muñoz — A199

**1956, May 13**

**557** A199 4c brown & green 1.50 .55

Victor Munoz (1873-1922), founder of Mother's Day in Cuba. See No. C134.

Masonic Temple, Havana — A200

**1956, June 5**

**558** A200 4c blue 2.25 .55

See No. C135.

Virgin of Charity, El Cobre — A201

**1956, Sept. 8** ***Perf. 12½***

**559** A201 4c brt blue & yel 3.00 .30

Issued in honor of Our Lady of Charity of Cobre, patroness of Cuba. See No. C149.

"The Cry of Yara" — A202

**1956, Oct. 10**

**560** A202 4c dk grn & brn 2.25 .30

Cuba's independence from Spain.

Raimundo G. Menocal — A203

**1956, Dec. 3 Wmk. 106** ***Perf. 12½***

**561** A203 4c dark brown 2.00 .30

Cent. of the birth of Prof. Raimundo G. Menocal, physician.

The Three Wise Men — A204

**1956, Dec. 1**

**562** A204 2c red & slate grn 5.00 1.10
**563** A204 4c slate grn & red 5.00 1.10

Christmas 1956.

Martin Morua Delgado — A205

**1957, Jan. 30**

**564** A205 4c dark green 2.00 .30

Delgado, patriot, birth cent.

Boy Scouts at Campfire — A206

**1957, Feb. 22 Wmk. 106** ***Perf. 12½***

**565** A206 4c slate grn & red 2.00 .40

Cent. of the birth of Lord Baden-Powell, founder of the Boy Scouts. See No. C152.

"The Blind," by M. Vega — A207

Paintings: 4c, "The Art Critics" by M. Melero. 10c, "Volanta in Storm" by A. Menocal. 14c, "The Convalescent" by L. Romañach.

**1957, Mar. Engr.** ***Perf. 12½***

**Side and Lower Inscriptions in Dark Brown**

**566** A207 2c olive green .50 .25
**567** A207 4c orange red 1.40 .30
**568** A207 10c olive green 1.60 .50
**569** A207 14c ultra 2.00 .55
*Nos. 566-569,C153-C155,E22 (8)* 14.60 4.30

See note after No. 457.

Emblem of Philatelic Club of Cuba — A208

**1957, Apr. 24**

**570** A208 4c ocher, blue & red 2.50 .30

Issued for Stamp Day, Apr. 24, and the National Philatelic Exhibition. See No. C156.

Juan F. Steegers — A209

**1957, Apr. 30**

**571** A209 4c blue 2.00 .30

Juan Francisco Steegers y Perera (1856-1921), dactyloscopy pioneer. See No. C157.

Victoria Bru Sanchez — A210

**1957, June 3 Wmk. 106** ***Perf. 12½***

**572** A210 4c indigo 3.25 .30

Joaquin de Aguero in Battle of Jucaral — A211

**1957, July 4**

**573** A211 4c dark green 2.50 .30

Issued to honor Joaquin de Aguero, Cuban freedom fighter and patriot. See No. C162.

Boy, Dogs and Cat — A212

**1957, July 17**

**574** A212 4c Prus green 1.75 .55

Mrs. Jeanette Ryder, founder of the Humane Society of Cuba. See Nos. C163-C163a.

Col. Rafael Manduley del Rio — A213

**1957, July 31**

**575** A213 4c Prus green 4.00 1.50

Issued to honor Col. Manduley del Rio, patriot, on the cent. of his birth (in 1856).

Palace of Justice — A214

**1957, Sept. 2 Engr.** ***Perf. 12½***

**576** A214 4c blue gray 2.00 .40

Opening of the new Palace of Justice in Havana. See No. C165.

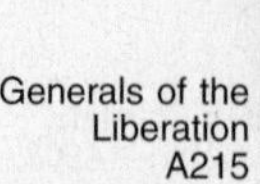

Generals of the Liberation A215

**1957, Sept. 26**

**577** A215 4c dl grn & red brn 1.25 .30
**578** A215 4c dl bl & red brn 1.25 .30
**579** A215 4c rose & brown 1.25 .30
**580** A215 4c org yel & brn 1.25 .30
**581** A215 4c lt violet & brn 1.25 .30
*Nos. 577-581 (5)* 6.25 1.50

Generals of the army of liberation.

1st Publication Printed in Cuba — A216

**1957, Oct. 18 Wmk. 106 *Perf. 12½***

**582** A216 4c slate blue 2.50 .40
*Nos. 582,C167-C168 (3)* 7.75 1.15

José Marti National Library.

Patio — A217

**1957, Nov. 19**

**583** A217 4c red brn & grn 1.50 .40
*Nos. 583,C173-C174 (3)* 6.50 1.40

Cent. of the 1st Cuban Normal School.

Trinidad, Founded 1514 — A218

Fortifications, Havana, 1611 — A219

Views: 10c, Padre Pico street, Santiago de Cuba. 14c, Church of Our Lady, Camaguey.

**1957, Dec. 17 Engr. *Perf. 12½***

**584** A218 2c brown & indigo .50 .25
**585** A219 4c slate grn & brn 1.10 .25
**586** A219 10c sepia & red 1.20 .30
**587** A219 14c green & dk red 1.00 .25
*Nos. 584-587,C175-C177,E23 (8)* 11.05 3.50

See note after No. 457.

Nativity — A220

**1957, Dec. 20**

**588** A220 2c multicolored 2.50 1.00
**589** A220 4c multicolored 3.50 1.00

Christmas 1957.

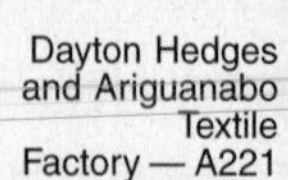

Dayton Hedges and Ariguanabo Textile Factory — A221

**1958, Jan. 30 Wmk. 106 *Perf. 12½***

**590** A221 4c blue 2.00 .70

Issued to honor Dayton Hedges, founder of Cuba's textile industry. See No. C178.

Dr. Francisco Dominguez Roldan — A222

**1958, Feb. 21**

**591** A222 4c green 2.75 .30

Roldan (1864-1942), who introduced radiotherapy and physiotherapy to Cuba.

José Ignacio Rivero y Alonso — A223

**1958, Apr. 1**

**592** A223 4c lt olive green 2.40 .70

José Ignacio Rivero y Alonso, editor of Diario de la Marina, 1919-44. See No. C179.

Map of Cuba and Mail Route, 1756 — A224

**1958, Apr. 24 *Perf. 12½***

**593** A224 4c dk grn, aqua & buff 2.50 .30

Issued for Stamp Day, Apr. 24 and the National Philatelic Exhibition. See No. C180.

Maj. Gen. José Miguel Gomez — A225

**1958, June 6 Wmk. 106 *Perf. 12½***

**594** A225 4c slate 1.90 .40

Maj. Gen. José Miguel Gomez, President of Cuba, 1909-13. See No. C181.

Nicolas Ruiz Espadero — A226

Musicians: 4c, Ignacio Cervantes. 10c, José White. 14c, Brindis de Salas.

**1958, June 27 *Perf. 12½***

**Indigo Emblem**

**595** A226 2c brown .60 .25
**596** A226 4c dark gray 1.20 .25
**597** A226 10c olive green 2.00 .25
**598** A226 14c red 2.00 .25

**Green Emblem**

Physicians: 2c, Tomas Romay Chacon. 4c, Angel Arturo Aballi. 10c, Fernando Gonzalez del Valle. 14c, Vicente Antonio de Castro.

**599** A226 2c brown 1.10 .25
**600** A226 4c gray 1.10 .25
**601** A226 10c dark carmine 1.40 .25
**602** A226 14c dark blue 2.00 .25

**Red Emblem**

Lawyers: 2c, Jose Maria Garcia Montes. 4c, Jose A. Gonzalez Lanuza. 10c, Juan B. Hernandez Barreiro. 14c, Pedro Gonzalez Llorente.

**603** A226 2c sepia .50 .25
**604** A226 4c gray .80 .25
**605** A226 10c olive grn 1.00 .25
**606** A226 14c slate blue 1.10 .25
*Nos. 595-606 (12)* 14.80 3.00

For surcharges see Nos. 629-631.

Carlos de la Torre — A227

**1958, Aug. 29 Engr. Wmk. 321**

**607** A227 4c violet blue 2.00 .40
*Nos. 607,C182-C184 (4)* 17.50 5.50

Dr. Carlos de la Torre y Huerta (1858-1950), naturalist. For surcharge see No. 632.

Poey's "Memorias" Title Page A228

Felipe Poey A229

**1958, Sept. 26 Wmk. 106**

**608** A228 2c black & lt violet 3.00 .25
**609** A229 4c brown black 3.25 .25
*Nos. 608-609,C185-C191,E26-E27 (11)* 87.50 18.80

Felipe Poey (1799-1891), naturalist.

Theodore Roosevelt — A230

**1958, Oct. 27 *Perf. 12½***

**610** A230 4c gray green 2.00 .40

Theodore Roosevelt, birth cent. See No. C192.

Cattleyopsis Lindenii Orchid — A231

4c, Oncidium Guibertianum Orchid.

**Engraved and Photogravure**

**1958, Dec. 16 Wmk. 321 *Perf. 12½***

**611** A231 2c multicolored 2.90 1.25
**612** A231 4c multicolored 3.75 1.25

Christmas. For surcharge see No. 633.

**Revolutionary Government**

Flag and Revolutionary — A232

**Engr. & Typo.**

**1959, Jan. 28 Wmk. 321**

**613** A232 2c car rose & gray .75 .30

Day of Liberation, Jan. 1, 1959.

Gen. Adolfo Flor Crombet (1848-95) — A233

**1959, Mar. 18 Engr. Wmk. 106**

**614** A233 4c slate green 2.00 .40

For surcharge see No. 634.

Maria Teresa Garcia Montes — A234

**1959, Nov. 11 *Perf. 12½***

**615** A234 4c brown 1.10 .40

Maria Teresa Garcia Montes (1880-1930), founder of the Musical Arts Society. See No. C198. For surcharge see No. 635.

Carlos Manuel de Cespedes — A235

Presidents: No. 617, Salvador Cisneros Betancourt. No. 618, Manuel de Jesus Calvar. No. 619, Bartolomé Maso. No. 620, Juan B. Spotorno. No. 621, Tomas Estrada Palma. No. 622, Francisco Javier de Céspedes. No. 623, Vicente Garcia.

**1959, Oct. 10 Wmk. 106 *Perf. 12½***

**616** A235 2c slate blue .55 .25
**617** A235 2c green .55 .25
**618** A235 2c deep violet .55 .25
**619** A235 2c orange brown .55 .25
**620** A235 4c dark carmine .70 .25
**621** A235 4c deep brown .70 .25
**622** A235 4c dark gray .70 .25
**623** A235 4c dark violet .70 .25
*Nos. 616-623 (8)* 5.00 2.00

Issued to honor former Cuban presidents.

No. B3 Surcharged in Red

**1960**

**624** SP2 2c on 2c + 1c car & ultra 1.25 .25

See No. C199.

Rebel Attack on Moncada Barracks — A236

Designs: 2c, Rebels disembarking from "Granma." 10c, Battle of the Uvero. 12c, Map of Cuba and rebel ("The Invasion").

**1960, Jan. 28 Wmk. 320**

**625** A236 1c gray ol, bl & ver .25 .25
**626** A236 2c bl, gray ol & brn .60 .25
**627** A236 10c bl, gray ol & red 1.75 .65
**628** A236 12c brt bl, brn & grn 2.40 .30
*Nos. 625-628,C200-C202 (7)* 12.10 3.80

First anniversary of revolution.

Stamps of 1956-59 Surcharged in Carmine or Silver

**1960, Feb. 3**

**629** A226 1c on 4c dk gray & ind .50 .25
**630** A226 1c on 4c gray & grn .50 .25
**631** A226 1c on 4c gray & red .50 .25
**632** A227 1c on 4c violet bl .50 .25
**633** A231 1c on 4c multi (S) 1.00 .50
**634** A233 1c on 4c slate grn .50 .25
**635** A234 1c on 4c brown .50 .25
**636** A184a 2c on 14c gray 1.25 .25
*Nos. 629-636,C203-C204 (10)* 9.60 3.55

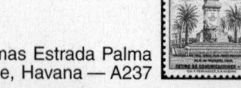

Tomas Estrada Palma Statue, Havana — A237

Statues: 2c, Mambi Victorioso (Battle of San Juan Hill), Santiago de Cuba. 10c, Marta Abreo de Estevez. 12c, Ignacio Agramonte, Camaguey.

**Wmk. 321**

**1960, Mar. 28 Engr. *Perf. 12½***

**637** A237 1c brn & dk bl .25 .25
**638** A237 2c green & red .30 .25
**639** A237 10c choc & red .90 .25
**640** A237 12c gray ol & vio 1.25 .45
*Nos. 637-640,C206-C208 (7)* 7.40 2.95

See note after No. 386.

Nos. 521A, 522 and 525 Surcharged in Violet Blue, Red or Black

**1960 Wmk. 106 *Perf. 10***

**641** A184 2c on 4c red lil (VB) .80 .40
**642** A184a 2c on 5c sl bl (R) 1.00 .40
**643** A184 2c on 13c org red 1.00 .40

No. 307B Surcharged in Black

**644** A41 10c on 20c ol grn 1.25 .50
*Nos. 641-644 (4)* 4.05 1.70

17th Olympic Games, Rome, Aug. 25-Sept. 11 — A238

**Wmk. 321**

**1960, Sept. 22 Engr. *Perf. 12½***

**645** A238 1c Sailboats .45 .25
**646** A238 2c Marksman .55 .25
*Nos. 645-646,C212-C213 (4)* 3.30 1.25

For souvenir sheet see No. C213a.

Camilo Cienfuegos and View of Escolar — A239

**1960, Oct. 27 Litho. Unwmk.**

**647** A239 2c brn, bl, grn & red 2.00 .25

1st anniv. of the death of Camilo Cienfuegos, revolutionary hero.

Morning Glory — A240

Tobacco and Christmas Hymn — A241

**1960 Litho. *Perf. 12½***

**648** A240 1c red .75 .75
**649** A241 1c Tobacco 1.50 1.50
**650** A241 1c Mariposa 1.50 1.50
**651** A241 1c Guaiacum 1.50 1.50
**652** A241 1c Coffee 1.50 1.50
 *a.* Block of 4, #649-652 7.00
**653** A240 2c ultra 1.00 1.00
**654** A241 2c Tobacco 3.00 3.00
**655** A241 2c Mariposa 3.00 3.00
**656** A241 2c Guaiacum 3.00 3.00
**657** A241 2c Coffee 3.00 3.00
 *a.* Block of 4, #654-657 14.00
**658** A240 10c ocher 4.00 2.50
**659** A241 10c Tobacco 6.00 6.00
**660** A241 10c Mariposa 6.00 6.00
**661** A241 10c Guaiacum 6.00 6.00
**662** A241 10c Coffee 6.00 6.00
 *a.* Block of 4, #659-662 30.00
*Nos. 648-662 (15)* 47.75 46.25

Issued for Christmas 1960.

Nos. 648-662 were printed in three sheets of 25. Nine stamps of type A240 form a center cross, stamps of type A241 form a block of four in each corner with the musical bars joined in an oval around the floral designs.

"Public Capital for Economic Benefit" A242

Designs: 2c, Chart and symbols of agriculture and industry. 6c, Cogwheels.

***Perf. 11½***

**1961, Jan. 10 Unwmk. Photo.**

**663** A242 1c yel, blk & org .40 .25
**664** A242 2c bl, blk & red .40 .25
**665** A242 6c yel, red org & blk 1.40 .25
*Nos. 663-665,C215-C218 (7)* 10.45 2.90

Issued to publicize the conference of underdeveloped countries, Havana.

Jesus Menéndez and Sugar Cane — A243

**1961, Jan. 22 Litho. *Perf. 12½***

**666** A243 2c dk grn & brn 1.50 .35

Jesus Menéndez, leader in sugar industry.

Overprinted in Red

**1961, May 2**

**667** A243 2c dk grn & brn 1.50 .35

Issued for May Day, 1961.

Dove and UN Emblem A244

**1961, Apr. 12 Litho. *Perf. 12½***

**668** A244 2c red brn & yel grn .40 .25
**669** A244 10c emer & rose lil 1.10 .45
 *a.* Souv. sheet, #668-669, imperf. 3.25 3.25
*Nos. 668-669,C222-C223 (4)* 3.50 1.45

15th anniv. (in 1960) of the UN.

Stamp Day — A245

Stamp Day: 1c, Revolutionary 10c stamp of 1874, 1868 "cancel." 2c, #238, 1902 "cancel." 10c, #613, 1959 "cancel."

**1961, Apr. 24 Unwmk.**

**670** A245 1c dull rose & dk grn .35 .25
**671** A245 2c salmon & dk grn .40 .25
**672** A245 10c pale grn, car rose & blk 1.50 .40
*Nos. 670-672 (3)* 2.25 .90

For overprint see No. 681.

Hand Releasing Dove — A246

**1961, July 26 *Perf. 12½***

**673** A246 2c blk, red, yel & gray 1.50 .25

26th of July (1953) movement, Castro's revolt against Fulgencio Batista.

Burelage on back consisting of wavy lines and diagonal rows of "CUBA CORREOS" in pale salmon.

**Portrait Type of 1954**

Designs: Same as before. On the 2c, "1833" is replaced by "?."

**Wmk. 321 (Nos. 674, 676); Unwmkd.**
***Perf. 12½ (Nos. 674, 676); Rouletted***

**1961-69 Engr.**

**674** A184 1c brown red .50 .25
**675** A184 1c lt blue ('69) .30 .25
**676** A184a 2c slate green .50 .25
**677** A184a 2c yel grn ('69) .30 .25
**678** A184 3c org ('64) 1.50 .25
**679** A184 13c brn ('64) 1.50 .30
**680** A184 20c lilac ('69) 1.75 .25
*Nos. 674-680 (7)* 6.35 1.80

Issued: Nos. 674, 676, 8/1; Nos. 678-679, 12/764; others, 9/69.

For Nos. 675, 677-680, see embargo note following No. 702.

No. 672 Ovptd. in Red

***Perf. 12½***

**1961, Oct. 7 Litho. Unwmk.**

**681** A245 10c pale grn, car rose & blk 2.00 .45

1st Official Phil. Exhib., Havana, Oct. 7-17.

Education Year — A247

Designs: One letter (per stamp) of "CUBA," book and various quotations by Jose Marti about the virtues of literacy.

**1961, Nov. 22**

**682** A247 1c pale grn, red & blk .25 .25
**683** A247 2c blue, red & blk .25 .25
**684** A247 10c vio, red & blk 1.00 .25
**685** A247 12c org, red & blk 2.00 .75
*Nos. 682-685 (4)* 3.50 1.50

A248

Christmas A249

No. 686, Polymita flammulata. No. 687, Polymita fulminata. No. 688, Polymita nigrofasciata. No. 689, Polymita fuscolimbata. No. 690, Polymita roseolimbata. No. 691, Tiaris canorus. No. 692, Ara tricolor. No. 693, Priotelus temnurus. No. 694, Mellisuga helenae. No. 695, Campephilus principalis. No. 696, Othreis toddi. No. 697, Uranidia boisduvalii. No. 698, Phoebis avellaneda. No. 699, Phaloe cubana. No. 700, Papilio gundlachianus.

1c, Snails. 2c, Birds, vert. 10c, Butterflies.

**1961, Dec. 1**

**686** A248 1c multicolored .50 .25
**687** A249 1c multicolored .50 .25
**688** A249 1c multicolored .50 .25
**689** A249 1c multicolored .50 .25
**690** A249 1c multicolored .50 .25
 *a.* Block of 5 + label, Nos. 686-690 2.50 1.50
**691** A248 2c multicolored 2.00 .50
**692** A249 2c multicolored 2.00 .50
**693** A249 2c multicolored 2.00 .50
**694** A249 2c multicolored 2.00 .50
**695** A249 2c multicolored 2.00 .50
 *a.* Block of 5 + label, Nos. 691-695 12.50 4.00
**696** A248 10c multicolored 3.00 1.00
**697** A249 10c multicolored 3.00 1.00
**698** A249 10c multicolored 3.00 1.00
**699** A249 10c multicolored 3.00 1.00
**700** A249 10c multicolored 3.00 1.00
 *a.* Block of 5 + label, Nos. 696-700 15.00 7.50
*Nos. 686-700 (15)* 27.50 8.75

Stamps of the same denomination printed se-tenant in sheets of 20 stamps plus 5 labels picturing bells and star. Stamps of Type A249 are arranged in blocks of 4; Type A248 stamps and labels form a cross in sheet.

See Nos. 760-774, 912-926, 1025-1039, 1179-1193, 1303-1317, 1464-1478, 1572-1586.

3rd Anniv. of the Revolution — A250

**1962, Jan. 3**

**701** A250 1c multi .85 .35
**702** A250 2c multi 1.75 .45

See Nos. C226-C228.

Cuban goods have been embargoed by the United States since a Feb. 7, 1962 proclamation by President Kennedy, but according to the Office of Foreign Assets Control of the Treasury Department, used Cuban stamps can be imported and sold without limitation, and unused stamps may be imported for personal use, but not resold.

Natl. Militia — A251

Silhouettes of militiamen and women and their peace-time occupations: 1c, Farmer. 2c, Welder. 3c, Seamstress.

**1962, Feb. 26**

**703** A251 1c blue grn & blk .40 .25
**704** A251 2c deep blue & blk .60 .35
**705** A251 10c brt org & blk 2.50 .55
*Nos. 703-705 (3)* 3.50 1.15

Bay of Pigs Invasion, 1st Anniv. — A252

**1962, Apr. 17**

**706** A252 2c multi .75 .25
**707** A252 3c multi .75 .25
**708** A252 10c multi 6.00 .50
*Nos. 706-708 (3)* 7.50 1.00

1st West Indies Packet A253

**1962, Apr. 24**

**709** A253 10c red & gray 3.25 .90

Stamp Day. See No. E32.

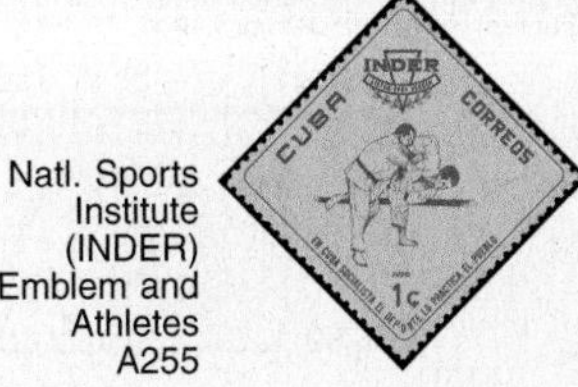


Intl. Labor Day — A254

**1962, May 1**

**710** A254 2c ocher & blk .35 .25
**711** A254 3c ver & blk .75 .25
**712** A254 10c greenish blue & blk 2.00 .70
*Nos. 710-712 (3)* 3.10 1.20

Natl. Sports Institute (INDER) Emblem and Athletes A255

No. 713, Judo. No. 714, Discus. No. 715, Gymnastics. No. 716, Wrestling. No. 717, Weight lifting. No. 718, Roller skating. No. 719, Equestrian. No. 720, Archery. No. 721, Bicycling. No. 722, Bowling. No. 723, Power boating. No. 724, One-man kayak. No. 725, Swimming. No. 726, Sculling. No. 727, Yachting. No. 728, Soccer. No. 729, Volleyball. No. 730, Baseball. No. 731, Basketball. No. 732, Tennis. No. 733, Boxing. No. 734, Underwater fishing. No. 735, Model-plane flying. No. 736, Pistol shooting. No. 737, Water polo. No. 738, Paddleball. No. 739, Fencing. No. 740, Sports Palace. No. 741, Chess. No. 742, Jai alai.

**1962, July 25** **Wmk. 321**

**713** A255 1c multi .35 .25
**714** A255 1c multi .35 .25
**715** A255 1c multi .35 .25
**716** A255 1c multi .35 .25
**717** A255 1c multi .35 .25
**718** A255 2c multi .35 .25
**719** A255 2c multi .35 .25
**720** A255 2c multi .35 .25
**721** A255 2c multi .35 .25
**722** A255 2c multi .35 .25
**723** A255 3c multi 1.00 .25
**724** A255 3c multi 1.00 .25
**725** A255 3c multi 1.00 .25
**726** A255 3c multi 1.00 .25
**727** A255 3c multi 1.00 .25
**728** A255 9c multi .90 .35
**729** A255 9c multi .90 .35
**730** A255 9c multi .90 .35
**731** A255 9c multi .90 .35
**732** A255 9c multi .90 .35
**733** A255 10c multi .90 .35
**734** A255 10c multi .90 .35
**735** A255 10c multi .90 .35
**736** A255 10c multi .90 .35
**737** A255 10c multi .90 .35
**738** A255 13c multi 1.00 .50
**739** A255 13c multi 1.00 .50
**740** A255 13c multi 1.00 .50
**741** A255 13c multi 1.00 .50
**742** A255 13c multi 1.00 .50
*Nos. 713-742 (30)* 22.50 9.75

Stamps of the same denomination printed se-tenant in sheets of 25. Various combinations possible.

9th Anniv. of the Revolution A256

Attack on Moncada Barracks: Abel Santamaria and: 2c, Barracks under siege. 3c, Children at Moncada School.

**1962, July 26**

**743** A256 2c brn car & dark ultra .75 .35
**744** A256 3c dark ultra & brn car 1.15 .55

8th World Youth Festival for Peace and Friendship, Helsinki, July 28-Aug. 6 — A257

**1962, July 28**

**745** A257 2c Dove, emblem 1.25 .25
**746** A257 3c Hand grip, emblem 1.75 .50
*a.* Min. sheet of 2, Nos. 745-746, imperf. 6.75 6.75

A258

**1962, Aug. 27**

**747** A258 1c Boxing .25 .25
**748** A258 2c Tennis .25 .25
**749** A258 3c Baseball .25 .25
**750** A258 13c Fencing 2.10 .90
*Nos. 747-750 (4)* 2.85 1.65

9th Central American and Caribbean Games, Kingston, Jamaica, Aug. 11-25.

A259

First Natl. Congress of the Federation of Cuban Women — A260

**1962, Oct. 1**

**751** A259 9c rose, blk & grn .75 .25
**752** A260 13c blk, grn & lt blue 1.90 .65

Latin American University Games A261

**1962, Oct. 13** **Wmk. 106**

**753** A261 1c Running .40 .25
**754** A261 2c Baseball .60 .25
**755** A261 3c Basketball .85 .25
**756** A261 13c World map 1.75 .55
*Nos. 753-756 (4)* 3.60 1.30

World Health Organization Campaign to Eradicate Malaria A262

Designs: 1c, Magnified specimen of the parasitic protozoa, microscope. 2c, Swamp and mosquito. 3c, Chemist's structural formulas for quinine, cinchona plant.

**1962, Dec. 14**

**757** A262 1c multi .35 .25
**758** A262 2c multi .35 .25
**759** A262 3c multi 1.25 .45
*Nos. 757-759 (3)* 1.95 .95

**Christmas Type of 1961**

No. 760, Epicrates angulifer. No. 761, Cricosaurus typica. No. 762, Anolis equestris. No. 763, Tropidophis wrighti. No. 764, Cyclura macleayi. No. 765, Cubispa turquino. No. 766, Chrysis superba. No. 767, Essostruta roberto. No. 768, Hortensia conciliata. No. 769, Lachnopus argus. No. 770, Monophyllus cubanus. No. 771, Capromys pilorides. No. 772, Capromys pre-hensilis. No. 773, Solenodon cubensis. No. 774, Capromys pilorides (Blanca).

2c, Reptiles. 3c, Insects, vert. 10c, Rodents.

**1962, Dec. 21** **Unwmk.**

**760** A248 2c multi .65 .25
**761** A249 2c multi .65 .25
**762** A249 2c multi .65 .25
**763** A249 2c multi .65 .25
**764** A249 2c multi .65 .25
*a.* Block of 5 + label, Nos. 760-764 3.50 1.50
**765** A248 3c multi 1.00 .60
**766** A249 3c multi 1.00 .60
**767** A249 3c multi 1.00 .60
**768** A249 3c multi 1.00 .60
**769** A249 3c multi 1.00 .60
*a.* Block of 5 + label, Nos. 765-769 5.50 4.50
**770** A248 10c multi 4.00 1.25
**771** A249 10c multi 4.00 1.25
**772** A249 10c multi 4.00 1.25
**773** A249 10c multi 4.00 1.25
**774** A249 10c multi 4.00 1.25
*a.* Block of 5 + label, Nos. 770-774 21.00 9.00
*Nos. 760-774 (15)* 28.25 10.50

Christmas 1962. See note after No. 700.

---

Around 1962 a 1ctv. label picturing Fidel Castro was used as a voluntary contribution stamp. It is not inscribed "Correos" and was not valid for postage.

---

Soviet Space Flights A263

Spacecraft and cosmonauts: 1c, Vostok 1, Yuri A. Gagarin, Apr. 12, 1961. 2c, Vostok 2, Gherman S. Titov, Aug. 6-7, 1961. 3c, Vostok 3, Andrian G. Nikolaev, Aug. 11-15, 1962, and Vostok 4, Pavel R. Popovich, Aug. 12-15, 1962. 9c, Vostok 5, Valery F. Bykovsky, June 14-19, 1963. 13c, Vostok 6, Valentina V. Tereshkova, June 16-19, 1963.

**1963-64** **Wmk. 321**

**775** A263 1c ultra, red & yel .35 .25
**776** A263 2c grn, yel & rose lake .65 .25
**777** A263 3c yel, vio & ver .65 .25
**778** A263 9c red, dark vio & yel 1.25 .45
**779** A263 13c dark blue green, dull red brown & yel 3.25 .70
*Nos. 775-779 (5)* 6.15 1.90

Issued: 1c, 2c, 3c, 2/26/63; others, 8/15/64.

Attack of the Presidential Palace, 6th Anniv. — A264

9c, Guerillas attacking palace. 13c, Four student leaders. 30c, Jose A. Echeverria, Menelao Mora.

**1963, Mar. 13**

**780** A264 9c dark red & blk 1.10 .25
**781** A264 13c chalky blue & sep 1.30 .45
**782** A264 30c org & grn 3.50 1.00
*Nos. 780-782 (3)* 5.90 1.70

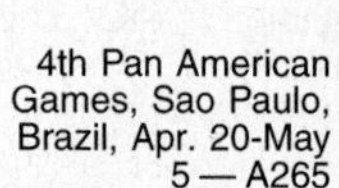

4th Pan American Games, Sao Paulo, Brazil, Apr. 20-May 5 — A265

**1963, Apr. 20**

**783** A265 1c Baseball 1.25 .35
**784** A265 13c Boxing 3.25 .65

Stamp Day — A266

3c, Mask mailbox, 19th cent. 10c, Mask mailbox at the Plaza de la Catedral, Havana.

**1963, Apr. 25**

**785** A266 3c black & dark org 1.00 .25
**786** A266 10c black & pur 2.50 .50

See Nos. 828-829, 956-957 and 1102-1103.

Labor Day — A267

**1963, May 1**

**787** A267 3c shown .50 .25
**788** A267 13c Four workers 1.75 .60

Intl. Children's Week, June 1-7 — A268

**1963, June 1**

**789** A268 3c blue blk & bister brn .50 .25
**790** A268 30c blue blk & red 2.75 .80

Ritual Effigy — A269

Taino Civilization artifacts: 3c, Wood-carved throne, horiz. 9c, Stone-carved figurine.

**1963, June 29**

**791** A269 2c org & red brn .75 .25
**792** A269 3c ultra & red brn .90 .25
**793** A269 9c rose & gray 1.60 .45
*Nos. 791-793 (3)* 3.25 .95

Montane Anthropology Museum, 60th anniv.

Broken Chains at Moncada — A270

2c, Attack on the Presidential Palace. 3c, The insurrection. 7c, Strike of April 9. 9c, Triumph of the revolution. 10c, Agricultural reform and nationalization of industry. 13c, Bay of Pigs victory.

**1963, July 26**

**794** A270 1c pink & blk .25 .25
**795** A270 2c lt blue & vio brn .30 .25
**796** A270 3c lt vio & brn .35 .25
**797** A270 7c apple green & rose .40 .25
**798** A270 9c olive bister & rose vio .95 .40
**799** A270 10c beige & sage grn 2.25 .60
**800** A270 13c pale org & slate blue 3.00 1.20
*Nos. 794-800 (7)* 7.50 3.20

Indigenous Fruit — A271

**1963, Aug. 19**

**801** A271 1c Star apple .25 .25
**802** A271 2c Cherimoya .25 .25
**803** A271 3c Cashew nut .45 .25
**804** A271 10c Custard apple 2.00 .60
**805** A271 13c Mangoes 2.25 1.50
*Nos. 801-805 (5)* 5.20 2.85

Geometric Shapes — A272 View of a Town — A273

Designs: No. 806, Circle, triangle, square, vert. No. 807, Roof, window, vert. No. 808, View of a town. No. 809, View of a town in blue. No. 810, View of a town in olive bister and red. No. 811, Circle, triangle, vert. No. 812, House, roof and doorway, vert. No. 813, House, girders.

**1963, Sept. 29** **Unwmk.**

**806** A272 3c multi .50 .25
**807** A272 3c multi .50 .25
**808** A273 3c multi .50 .25
**809** A273 3c multi .50 .25
**810** A273 13c multi 1.50 .55
**811** A272 13c multi 1.50 .55
**812** A272 13c multi 1.50 .55
**813** A272 13c multi 1.50 .55
*Nos. 806-813 (8)* 8.00 3.20

7th Intl. Congress of the Intl. Union of Architects.

Ernest Hemingway (1899-1961), American Author A274

Hemingway and: 3c, The Old Man and the Sea. 9c, For Whom the Bell Tolls. 13c, Hemingway Museum (former residence), San Francisco de Paula, near Havana.

**1963, Dec. 5** **Wmk. 321**

**814** A274 3c brn & lt blue .75 .25
**815** A274 9c sage grn & pink 1.75 .25
**816** A274 13c blk & yel grn 3.00 .60
*Nos. 814-816 (3)* 5.50 1.10

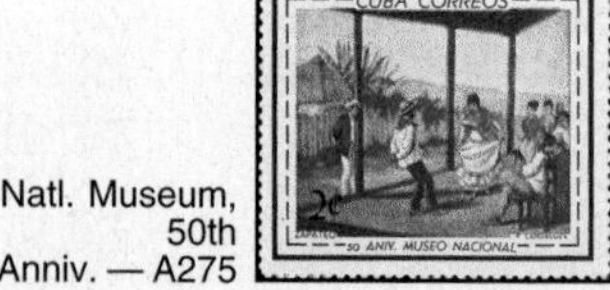


Natl. Museum, 50th Anniv. — A275

Works of art: 2c, El Zapateo (Dance), by Victor P. Landaluze. 3c, Abduction of the Mulatto Women, by Carlos Enriquez, vert. 9c, Greek Panathean amphora, vert. 13c, My

Beloved (bust of a young woman), by Jean Antoine Houdon, vert.

**1964, Mar. 19** **Unwmk.**

| No. | Type | Description | Unused | Used |
|---|---|---|---|---|
| **817** | A275 | 2c multi | .35 | .25 |
| **818** | A275 | 3c multi | .75 | .25 |
| **819** | A275 | 9c multi | 1.10 | .40 |
| **820** | A275 | 13c multi | 2.10 | .65 |
| | | *Nos. 817-820 (4)* | 4.30 | 1.55 |

General Strike on Apr. 9, 6th Anniv. — A276

Rebel leaders: 2c, Bernardo Juan Borrell. 3c, Marcelo Salado. 10c, Oscar Lucero. 13c, Sergio Gonzalez.

**1964, Apr. 9**

| No. | Type | Description | Unused | Used |
|---|---|---|---|---|
| **821** | A276 | 2c blk, yel grn & dull org | .40 | .25 |
| **822** | A276 | 3c blk, red & dull org | .70 | .25 |
| **823** | A276 | 10c blk, pur & beige | 1.25 | .30 |
| **824** | A276 | 13c blk, brt blue & beige | 2.50 | .60 |
| | | *Nos. 821-824 (4)* | 4.85 | 1.40 |

Bay of Pigs Invasion, 3rd Anniv. — A277

Designs: 3c, Fish in net. 10c, Victory Monument. 13c, Fallen eagle, vert.

**1964, Apr. 17**

| No. | Type | Description | Unused | Used |
|---|---|---|---|---|
| **825** | A277 | 3c multi | .35 | .25 |
| **826** | A277 | 10c multi | .70 | .35 |
| **827** | A277 | 13c multi | 2.25 | .70 |
| | | *Nos. 825-827 (3)* | 3.30 | 1.30 |

**Stamp Day Type of 1963**

3c, Vicente Mora Pera, 1st postal director. 13c, Unissued provisional stamp, 1871.

**1964, Apr. 24**

| No. | Type | Description | Unused | Used |
|---|---|---|---|---|
| **828** | A266 | 3c ocher & dull lil | .60 | .25 |
| **829** | A266 | 13c dull vio & lt olive grn | 2.75 | .50 |

Labor Day — A278

**1964, May 1**

| No. | Type | Description | Unused | Used |
|---|---|---|---|---|
| **830** | A278 | 3c Industry | .40 | .25 |
| **831** | A278 | 13c Agriculture | 1.60 | .55 |

Diplomatic Relations with China — A279

Designs: 1c, China Monument, Havana. 2c, Cuban and Chinese farmers. 3c, Natl. flags.

**1964, May 15**

| No. | Type | Description | Unused | Used |
|---|---|---|---|---|
| **832** | A279 | 1c multi | .35 | .25 |
| **833** | A279 | 2c org brn, blk & apple grn | .70 | .25 |
| **834** | A279 | 3c multi | 1.40 | .25 |
| | | *Nos. 832-834 (3)* | 2.45 | .75 |

15th UPU Congress, Vienna, May-June — A280

13c, Hemispheres on world map. 30c, Heinrich von Stephan. 50c, UPU Monument, Bern.

**1964, May 29**

| No. | Type | Description | Unused | Used |
|---|---|---|---|---|
| **835** | A280 | 13c multicolored | .85 | .30 |
| **836** | A280 | 30c multicolored | 1.90 | .80 |
| **837** | A280 | 50c multicolored | 4.00 | 1.40 |
| | | *Nos. 835-837 (3)* | 6.75 | 2.50 |

Development of Natl. Industry — A281

**1964, June 16**

| No. | Type | Description | Unused | Used |
|---|---|---|---|---|
| **838** | A281 | 1c Fish | .40 | .25 |
| **839** | A281 | 2c Cow | .60 | .25 |
| **840** | A281 | 13c Chickens | 2.75 | .50 |
| | | *Nos. 838-840 (3)* | 3.75 | 1.00 |

Merchant Fleet — A282

**1964, June 30**

| No. | Type | Description | Unused | Used |
|---|---|---|---|---|
| **841** | A282 | 1c Rio Jibacoa | .25 | .25 |
| **842** | A282 | 2c Camilo Cienfuegos | .50 | .25 |
| **843** | A282 | 3c Sierra Maestra | .75 | .25 |
| **844** | A282 | 9c Bahia de Siguanea | 1.50 | .50 |
| **845** | A282 | 10c Oriente | 4.00 | 1.00 |
| | | *Nos. 841-845 (5)* | 7.00 | 2.25 |

Unification of Viet Nam — A283

Designs: 2c, Vietnamese guerrilla, American soldier. 3c, Northerner and southerner shaking hands over map of united Viet Nam. 10c, Ox-drawn plow, machinised harvester. 13c, Natl. flags and profiles of Cuban and Vietnamese farmers.

**1964, July 20**

| No. | Type | Description | Unused | Used |
|---|---|---|---|---|
| **846** | A283 | 2c multi | .30 | .25 |
| **847** | A283 | 3c multi | .45 | .25 |
| **848** | A283 | 10c multi | 1.00 | .25 |
| **849** | A283 | 13c multi | 2.75 | .60 |
| | | *Nos. 846-849 (4)* | 4.50 | 1.35 |

11th Anniv. of the Revolution — A284

Designs: 3c, Raul Gomez Garcia and poem. 13c, Cover of La Historia Me Absolvera, by Fidel Castro.

**1964, July 25**

| No. | Type | Description | Unused | Used |
|---|---|---|---|---|
| **850** | A284 | 3c red, tan & blk | .75 | .25 |
| **851** | A284 | 13c multi | 3.00 | .60 |

1964 Summer Olympics, Tokyo, Oct. 10-25 — A285

1c, Gymnastics. 2c, Rowing. 3c, Boxing. 7c, Running, horiz. 10c, Fencing, horiz. 13c, Foil, cleats, oar, boxing glove, sun, horiz.

**1964, Oct. 10** **Wmk. 376** ***Perf. 10***

| No. | Type | Description | Unused | Used |
|---|---|---|---|---|
| **852** | A285 | 1c multi | .30 | .25 |
| **853** | A285 | 2c multi | .30 | .25 |
| **854** | A285 | 3c multi | .30 | .25 |
| **855** | A285 | 7c multi | .70 | .25 |
| **856** | A285 | 10c multi | 1.50 | .55 |
| **857** | A285 | 13c multi | 2.50 | .85 |
| | | *Nos. 852-857 (6)* | 5.60 | 2.40 |

Satellite and Globe — A286

Satellite and Partial Globe — A287

No. C31 and Partial Globe — A288

Various satellites and rockets.

**1964, Oct. 15**

| No. | Type | Description | Unused | Used |
|---|---|---|---|---|
| **858** | A286 | 1c shown | .25 | .25 |
| **859** | A287 | 1c shown | .25 | .25 |
| **860** | A287 | 1c Globe LL | .25 | .25 |
| **861** | A287 | 1c Globe UR | .25 | .25 |
| **862** | A287 | 1c Globe UL | .25 | .25 |
| *a.* | | Block of 5 + label, Nos. 858-862 | 1.00 | 1.00 |
| **863** | A286 | 2c Spacecraft and globe | .55 | .25 |
| **864** | A287 | 2c Globe LR | .55 | .25 |
| **865** | A287 | 2c Globe LL | .55 | .25 |
| **866** | A287 | 2c Globe UR | .55 | .25 |
| **867** | A287 | 2c Globe UL | .55 | .25 |
| *a.* | | Block of 5 + label, Nos. 863-867 | 3.00 | 1.50 |
| **868** | A286 | 3c Satellite and globe | .75 | .35 |
| **869** | A287 | 3c Globe LR | .75 | .35 |
| **870** | A287 | 3c Globe LL | .75 | .35 |
| **871** | A287 | 3c Globe UR | .75 | .35 |
| **872** | A287 | 3c Globe UL | .75 | .35 |
| *a.* | | Block of 5 + label, Nos. 868-872 | 4.00 | 2.50 |
| **873** | A286 | 9c Satellite and globe, diff | 1.75 | .70 |
| **874** | A287 | 9c Globe LR | 1.75 | .70 |
| **875** | A287 | 9c Globe LL | 1.75 | .70 |
| **876** | A287 | 9c Globe UR | 1.75 | .70 |
| **877** | A287 | 9c Globe UL | 1.75 | .70 |
| *a.* | | Block of 5 + label, Nos. 873-877 | 11.00 | 5.00 |
| **878** | A286 | 13c Satellite and globe, diff. | 2.40 | 1.75 |
| **879** | A287 | 13c Globe LR | 2.40 | 1.75 |
| **880** | A287 | 13c Globe LL | 2.40 | 1.75 |
| **881** | A287 | 13c Globe UR | 2.40 | 1.75 |
| **882** | A287 | 13c Globe UL | 2.40 | 1.75 |
| *a.* | | Block of 5 + label, Nos. 878-882 | 16.00 | 10.00 |
| **883** | A288 | 50c blk & lt grn | 4.00 | 2.50 |
| *a.* | | Souvenir sheet of one, Wmk. 321 | 15.00 | 12.50 |
| | | *Nos. 858-883 (26)* | 32.50 | 19.00 |

Experimental Cuban postal rocket flight, 25th anniv. Stamps of the same denomination printed se-tenant in sheets of 20 stamps and 5 inscribed labels. Stamps of Type A287 arranged in blocks of 4 with a complete globe in center of block; Type A286 stamps and labels form a cross in center of sheet. Inscribed "1939-Cohete Postal Cubano-1964."

No. 883a contains one 46x28mm stamp.

**Type of A288 Ovptd. in Silver**

**1964, Oct. 17** **Unwmk.**

| No. | Type | Description | Unused | Used |
|---|---|---|---|---|
| **884** | A288 | 50c dk red brn & lt grn | 5.00 | 1.50 |

No. 884 not issued without overprint.

40th Death Anniv. of Lenin — A289

Designs: 13c, Lenin Mausoleum, horiz. 30c, Lenin, star, hammer and sickle.

**1964, Nov. 7** **Wmk. 376**

| No. | Type | Description | Unused | Used |
|---|---|---|---|---|
| **885** | A289 | 3c org & blk | .65 | .25 |
| **886** | A289 | 13c pur, pink & blk | 1.10 | .35 |
| **887** | A289 | 30c blue & blk | 2.25 | .90 |
| | | *Nos. 885-887 (3)* | 4.00 | 1.50 |

Havana Zoo — A290

1c, Leopard, horiz. 2c, Elephant. 3c, Fallow deer. 4c, Kangaroo, horiz. 5c, Lions, horiz. 6c, Eland, horiz. 7c, Zebra, horiz. 8c, Hyena, horiz. 9c, Tiger, horiz. 10c, Guanaco, horiz. 13c, Chimpanzees, horiz. 20c, Peccary, horiz. 30c, Raccoon. 40c, Hippopotamus, horiz. 50c, Tapir, horiz. 60c, Dromedary. 70c, Bison, horiz. 80c, Black bear. 90c, Water buffalo, horiz. 1p, Deer in nature park, horiz.

**1964, Nov. 25**

| No. | Type | Description | Unused | Used |
|---|---|---|---|---|
| **888** | A290 | 1c multi | .30 | .25 |
| **889** | A290 | 2c multi | .30 | .25 |
| **890** | A290 | 3c multi | .30 | .25 |
| **891** | A290 | 4c multi | .30 | .25 |
| **892** | A290 | 5c multi | .40 | .25 |
| **893** | A290 | 6c multi | .50 | .25 |
| **894** | A290 | 7c multi | .50 | .25 |
| **895** | A290 | 8c multi | .75 | .25 |
| **896** | A290 | 9c multi | .75 | .25 |
| **897** | A290 | 10c multi | .80 | .25 |
| **898** | A290 | 13c multi | .90 | .25 |
| **899** | A290 | 20c multi | 1.10 | .25 |
| **900** | A290 | 30c multi | 1.60 | .60 |
| **901** | A290 | 40c multi | 2.75 | 1.00 |
| **902** | A290 | 50c multi | 3.00 | 1.40 |
| **903** | A290 | 60c multi | 4.50 | 1.90 |
| **904** | A290 | 70c multi | 4.75 | 1.90 |
| **905** | A290 | 80c multi | 5.00 | 2.40 |
| **906** | A290 | 90c multi | 5.50 | 3.00 |

**Size: 47x32mm**

| No. | Type | Description | Unused | Used |
|---|---|---|---|---|
| **907** | A290 | 1p multi | 9.25 | 3.00 |
| | | *Nos. 888-907 (20)* | 43.25 | 18.20 |

Heroes of the 1895 War of Independence A291

**1964, Dec. 7**

| No. | Type | Description | Unused | Used |
|---|---|---|---|---|
| **908** | A291 | 1c Jose Marti | .25 | .25 |
| **909** | A291 | 2c Antonio Maceo | .40 | .25 |
| **910** | A291 | 3c Maximo Gomez | .60 | .35 |
| **911** | A291 | 13c Calixto Garcia | 1.75 | .70 |
| | | *Nos. 908-911 (4)* | 3.00 | 1.55 |

**Christmas Type of 1961**

No. 912, Dwarf cup coral. No. 913, Eusmilia fastigiata. No. 914, Acropora palmata. No. 915, Acropora profilera. No. 916, Diploria labyrinthiformis. No. 917, Condylactis gigantea. No. 918, Physalia physalis. No. 919, Aurelia aurita. No. 920, Linuche unguiculata. No. 921, Cassiopea frondosa. No. 922, Neocrinus blakei. No. 923, Eucidaris tribuloidas. No. 924, Tripneutes. No. 925, Ophiocoma echinata. No. 926, Oreaster celiculatus.

2c, Coral. 3c, Jellyfish. 10c, Starfish, sea-urchins.

**1964, Dec. 18**

| No. | Type | Description | Unused | Used |
|---|---|---|---|---|
| **912** | A248 | 2c multi | .80 | .30 |
| **913** | A249 | 2c multi | .80 | .30 |
| **914** | A249 | 2c multi | .80 | .30 |
| **915** | A249 | 2c multi | .80 | .30 |
| **916** | A249 | 2c multi | .80 | .30 |
| *a.* | | Block of 5 + label, Nos. 912-916 | 4.50 | 2.00 |
| **917** | A248 | 3c multi | 1.25 | .50 |
| **918** | A249 | 3c multi | 1.25 | .50 |
| **919** | A249 | 3c multi | 1.25 | .50 |
| **920** | A249 | 3c multi | 1.25 | .50 |
| **921** | A249 | 3c multi | 1.25 | .50 |
| *a.* | | Block of 5 + label, Nos. 917-921 | 7.50 | 3.00 |
| **922** | A248 | 10c multi | 2.00 | 1.00 |
| **923** | A249 | 10c multi | 2.00 | 1.00 |
| **924** | A249 | 10c multi | 2.00 | 1.00 |
| **925** | A249 | 10c multi | 2.00 | 1.00 |
| **926** | A249 | 10c multi | 2.00 | 1.00 |
| *a.* | | Block of 5 + label, Nos. 922-926 | 12.50 | 7.00 |
| | | *Nos. 912-926 (15)* | 20.25 | 9.00 |

Christmas 1964. See note after No. 700.

Dr. Tomas Romay (1764-1849), Physician and Scientist — A292

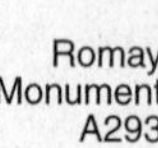

Romay Monument A293

Designs: 2c, First vaccination against small-pox. 3c, Portrait and treatise on vaccination.

**1964, Dec. 21**

| No. | Type | Description | Unused | Used |
|---|---|---|---|---|
| **927** | A292 | 1c blk & olive brn | .50 | .25 |
| **928** | A292 | 2c blk & tan | .50 | .25 |
| **929** | A293 | 3c olive & dk red brn | .75 | .25 |
| **930** | A293 | 10c bister & blk | 2.10 | .40 |
| | | *Nos. 927-930 (4)* | 3.85 | 1.15 |

Second Declaration of Havana — A294

Map of Latin America and ripples or map of Cuba and peasant breaking shackles under text from the Declaration of Havana: No. 931a, 932a "Visperas de su muerte..." No. 931b, 932b, "Un continente, que juntos suponen represestos..." No. 931c, 932c, "Y no se ocultaran ni el gobierna..." No. 931d, 932d, "Millones de mulatos latinamericanos que saben..." No. 931e, "A labran la tierra en condiciones..."

**1964, Dec. 23**

| No. | Type | Description | Unused | Used |
|---|---|---|---|---|
| **931** | | Strip of 5 | 5.00 | 3.50 |
| *a.-e.* | | A294 3c any single | .75 | .40 |
| **932** | | Strip of 5 | 15.00 | 12.50 |
| *a.-e.* | | A294 13c any single | 1.75 | 1.50 |

Nos. 931-932 printed in sheets of 25 (5x5).

Dioramas in New Cuban Postal Museum A295

**1965, Jan. 4**

**Yellow & Black Border**

| No. | Type | Description | Unused | Used |
|---|---|---|---|---|
| **933** | A295 | 13c Maritime Post | 2.50 | .85 |
| **934** | A295 | 30c Insurrection Post | 2.50 | 1.25 |

**Souvenir Sheet**

***Imperf***

| No. | Type | Description | Unused | Used |
|---|---|---|---|---|
| **935** | | Sheet of 2 | 8.50 | 7.50 |
| *a.* | | A295 13c like #933, blue & blk border | 1.00 | 1.00 |
| *b.* | | A295 30c like #934, blue & blk border | 3.00 | 3.00 |
| | | *Nos. 933-935 (3)* | 13.50 | 9.60 |

Stamps in No. 935 have simulated perforations; buff margin is inscribed "PRECIO 50c" LR.

Fishing Fleet — A296

**1965, May 1**

| No. | Type | Description | Unused | Used |
|---|---|---|---|---|
| **936** | A296 | 1c Schooner | .25 | .25 |
| **937** | A296 | 2c Omicron | .40 | .25 |
| **938** | A296 | 3c Victoria | .60 | .25 |
| **939** | A296 | 9c Cardenas | .90 | .60 |
| **940** | A296 | 10c Sigma | 2.10 | .40 |
| **941** | A296 | 13c Lambda | 3.25 | .90 |
| | | *Nos. 936-941 (6)* | 7.50 | 2.65 |

Intl. Women's Day — A297

**1965, Mar. 8**

| No. | Type | Description | Unused | Used |
|---|---|---|---|---|
| **942** | A297 | 3c Lidia Doce | 1.10 | .30 |
| **943** | A297 | 13c Clara Zetkin | 1.60 | .60 |

Technical Revolution A298

Designs: 3c, Jose Antonio Echeverria University School. 13c, Stylized symbols of science and research, molecular structure and satellite dish.

**1965, Mar. 31**

| No. | Type | Description | Unused | Used |
|---|---|---|---|---|
| **944** | A298 | 3c tan, blk & dark red brn | .50 | .25 |
| **945** | A298 | 13c multi | 2.50 | .75 |

Cosmonauts, Rocket A299

30c, Cosmonauts Pavel I. Balyayev, Aleksei A. Leonov taking first space walk.

**1965, Apr. 2**

| No. | Type | Description | Unused | Used |
|---|---|---|---|---|
| **946** | A299 | 30c dark blue, blk & brn | 2.50 | .70 |
| **947** | A299 | 50c brt pink & blue blk | 4.50 | 1.40 |

Flight of Voskhod 2, the first man to walk in space, Mar. 17.

Abstract Wood Carving by Eugenio Rodriguez — A300

Paintings in the Natl. Museum, Havana: 3c, Garden with Sunflowers, by Victor Manuel. 10c, Abstract, by Wilfredo Lam, horiz. 13c, Children, by Enrique Ponce, horiz.

**1965, Apr. 12**

| No. | Type | Description | Unused | Used |
|---|---|---|---|---|
| **948** | A300 | 2c multi | .35 | .25 |

**Size: 35x46mm**

| No. | Type | Description | Unused | Used |
|---|---|---|---|---|
| **949** | A300 | 3c multi | .55 | .25 |

**Size: 46x35mm**

| No. | Type | Description | Unused | Used |
|---|---|---|---|---|
| **950** | A300 | 10c multi | 1.50 | .45 |

**Size: 43x37mm**

| No. | Type | Description | Unused | Used |
|---|---|---|---|---|
| **951** | A300 | 13c multi | 2.50 | .80 |
| | | *Nos. 948-951 (4)* | 4.90 | 1.75 |

Abraham Lincoln — A301

Designs: 1c, Log cabin, birth site, horiz. 2c, Memorial, Washington, DC, horiz. 3c, Monument, Washington, DC. 13c, Portrait, quote.

**1965, Apr. 15**

| No. | Type | Description | Unused | Used |
|---|---|---|---|---|
| **952** | A301 | 1c yel bister, red brn & gray | .25 | .25 |
| **953** | A301 | 2c lt blue & dark blue | .45 | .25 |
| **954** | A301 | 3c red org, blk & blue blk | 1.25 | .35 |
| **955** | A301 | 13c org, blk & blue blk | 2.50 | .60 |
| | | *Nos. 952-955 (4)* | 4.45 | 1.45 |

**Stamp Day Type of 1963**

Stamp Day 1965: 3c, 18th Cent. postmarks and packet. 13c, No. C16 and airplanes over capital.

**1965, Apr. 24**

| No. | Type | Description | Unused | Used |
|---|---|---|---|---|
| **956** | A266 | 3c sep & dark org | 3.00 | .25 |
| **957** | A266 | 13c brt blue, sal rose & blk | 2.75 | .60 |

Intl. Quiet Sun Year — A302

1c, Sun, Earth's magnetic pole, horiz. 2c, Sun Year emblem. 3c, Earth's magnetic field, horiz. 6c, Atmospheric currents, horiz. 30c, Solar rays on planet surface. 50c, Effect on satellite orbits, horiz.

**1965, May 10**

| No. | Type | Description | Unused | Used |
|---|---|---|---|---|
| **958** | A302 | 1c multicolored | .30 | .25 |
| **959** | A302 | 2c multicolored | .35 | .25 |
| **960** | A302 | 3c multicolored | .60 | .25 |
| **961** | A302 | 6c multicolored | .70 | .25 |
| **962** | A302 | 30c multicolored | 2.25 | .55 |
| **963** | A302 | 50c multicolored | 3.00 | 1.25 |
| *a.* | | Souv. sheet of one, imperf. | 7.00 | 7.00 |
| *b.* | | As "a," changed colors | 10.00 | 10.00 |
| | | *Nos. 958-963 (6)* | 7.20 | 2.80 |

Stamps in Nos. 963a-963b have simulated perforations.

Stamp in No. 963b is blue blk, Prus blue, org yel & red. Issued Oct. 10 for the Philatelic Space Exhibition, Havana, Oct. 10-17.

Intl. Telecommunications Union, Cent. — A303

1c, Station, horiz. 2c, Satellite. 3c, Telstar, horiz. 10c, Telstar, receiving station. 30c, ITU emblem, horiz.

**1965, May 17**

| No. | Type | Description | Unused | Used |
|---|---|---|---|---|
| **964** | A303 | 1c gold & multi | .25 | .25 |
| **965** | A303 | 2c multi | .25 | .25 |
| **966** | A303 | 3c multi | .45 | .25 |
| **967** | A303 | 10c multi | 1.25 | .25 |
| **968** | A303 | 30c multi | 3.00 | .90 |
| | | *Nos. 964-968 (5)* | 5.20 | 1.90 |

9th Communist World Youth and Students Congress A304

13c, Flags of Cuba and Algeria, emblem. 30c, Flags, guerrillas.

**1965, June 10**

| No. | Type | Description | Unused | Used |
|---|---|---|---|---|
| **969** | A304 | 13c multi | 1.60 | .50 |
| **970** | A304 | 30c multi | 2.50 | .75 |

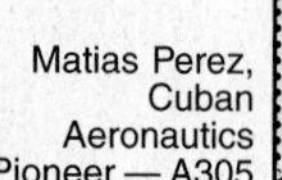

Matias Perez, Cuban Aeronautics Pioneer — A305

**1965, June 23**

| No. | Type | Description | Unused | Used |
|---|---|---|---|---|
| **971** | A305 | 3c pink & blk | 1.75 | .95 |
| **972** | A305 | 13c dull vio & blk, diff. | 2.75 | .95 |

Flowers and Maps of Their Locations — A306

1c, Rosa canina, Europe. 2c, Chrysanthemum hortorum, Asia. 3c, Strelitzia reginae, Africa. 4c, Dahlia pinnata, No. America. 5c, Cattleya labiata, So. America. 13c, Grevillea banksii, Oceania. 30c, Brunfelsia nitida, Cuba.

**1965, July 20**

| No. | Type | Description | Unused | Used |
|---|---|---|---|---|
| **973** | A306 | 1c multicolored | .25 | .25 |
| **974** | A306 | 2c multicolored | .30 | .25 |
| **975** | A306 | 3c multicolored | .30 | .30 |
| **976** | A306 | 4c multicolored | .30 | .25 |
| **977** | A306 | 5c multicolored | 1.60 | .25 |
| **978** | A306 | 13c multicolored | 3.25 | .95 |
| **979** | A306 | 30c multicolored | 4.75 | 1.60 |
| | | *Nos. 973-979 (7)* | 10.75 | 3.85 |

1st Natl. Games A307

**1965, July 25**

| No. | Type | Description | Unused | Used |
|---|---|---|---|---|
| **980** | A307 | 1c Swimming | .25 | .25 |
| **981** | A307 | 2c Basketball | .35 | .25 |
| **982** | A307 | 3c Gymnastics | .70 | .25 |
| **983** | A307 | 30c Hurdling | 2.50 | .70 |
| | | *Nos. 980-983 (4)* | 3.80 | 1.45 |

Revolution Museum Opening — A308

1c, Anti-tank guns. 2c, Tanks. 3c, Bazookas. 10c, Uniform, guerillas. 13c, Compass, yacht Granma.

**1965, July 26**

| No. | Type | Description | Unused | Used |
|---|---|---|---|---|
| **984** | A308 | 1c multi | .25 | .25 |
| **985** | A308 | 2c multi | .25 | .25 |
| **986** | A308 | 3c multi | .25 | .25 |
| **987** | A308 | 10c multi | .75 | .25 |
| **988** | A308 | 13c multi | 2.10 | .45 |
| | | *Nos. 984-988 (5)* | 3.60 | 1.45 |

A309

1c, Finlay's signature. 2c, Anopheles mosquito. 3c, Portrait. 7c, Microscope. 9c, Dr. Claudio Delgado. 10c, Monument. 13c, Discussing theory with doctors.

**1965, Aug. 20**

| No. | Type | Description | Unused | Used |
|---|---|---|---|---|
| **989** | A309 | 1c multicolored | .25 | .25 |
| **990** | A309 | 2c multicolored | .25 | .25 |
| **991** | A309 | 3c multicolored | .35 | .25 |
| **992** | A309 | 7c multicolored | .45 | .25 |
| **993** | A309 | 9c multicolored | .75 | .25 |
| **994** | A309 | 10c multicolored | 1.90 | .30 |
| **995** | A309 | 13c multicolored | 2.75 | .65 |
| | | *Nos. 989-995 (7)* | 6.70 | 2.20 |

Carlos J. Finlay (1833-1915), discovered transmission of yellow fever via aedes aegypti (not anopheles) mosquito. Nos. 990-995 vert.

Butterflies A310

No. 996, Dismorphia cubana. No. 997, Anetia numidia briarea. No. 998, Carathis gortynoides. No. 999, Hymenitis cubana. No. 1000, Eubaphe heros. No. 1001, Lycorea ceres demeter. No. 1002, Eubaphe disparitis. No. 1003, Siderone nemesis. No. 1004, Syntomidopsis variegata. No. 1005, Ctenuchidia virgo. No. 1006, Prepona antimache crossina. No. 1007, Sylepta reginalis. No. 1008, Chlosyne perezi perezi. No. 1009, Anaea clytemnestra iphigenia. No. 1010, Anetia cubana.

**1965, Sept. 22** **Unwmk.**

| No. | Type | Description | Unused | Used |
|---|---|---|---|---|
| **996** | A310 | 2c multicolored | .50 | .25 |
| **997** | A310 | 2c multicolored | .50 | .25 |
| **998** | A310 | 2c multicolored | .50 | .25 |
| **999** | A310 | 2c multicolored | .50 | .25 |
| **1000** | A310 | 2c multicolored | .50 | .25 |
| *a.* | | Strip of 5, Nos. 996-1000 | 3.75 | 2.50 |
| **1001** | A310 | 3c multicolored | .75 | .25 |
| **1002** | A310 | 3c multicolored | .75 | .25 |
| **1003** | A310 | 3c multicolored | .75 | .25 |
| **1004** | A310 | 3c multicolored | .75 | .25 |
| **1005** | A310 | 3c multicolored | .75 | .25 |
| *a.* | | Strip of 5, Nos. 1001-1005 | 5.00 | 3.25 |

1006 A310 13c multicolored 2.50 .80
1007 A310 13c multicolored 2.50 .80
1008 A310 13c multicolored 2.50 .80
1009 A310 13c multicolored 2.50 .80
1010 A310 13c multicolored 2.50 .80
*a.* Strip of 5, Nos. 1006-1010 15.00 7.50
*Nos. 996-1010 (15)* 18.75 6.50

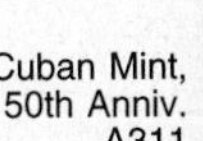

Cuban Mint, 50th Anniv. A311

Coins (obverse and reverse): No. 1011, 20 centavos, 1962. No. 1012, 1 peso, 1934. No. 1013, 40 centavos, 1962. No. 1014, 1 peso, 1915. No. 1015, Marti peso, 1953. No. 1016, 20 pesos, 1915.

**1965, Oct. 13**

**1011** A311 1c multicolored .30 .25
**1012** A311 2c multi .30 .25
**1013** A311 3c multi .30 .25
**1014** A311 8c multi .80 .25
**1015** A311 10c multi 1.90 .40
**1016** A311 13c multi 2.75 .50
*Nos. 1011-1016 (6)* 6.35 1.90

Tropical Fruit — A312

**1965, Nov. 15** ***Perf. 12½***

**1017** A312 1c Oranges .25 .25
**1018** A312 2c Custard apples .25 .25
**1019** A312 3c Papayas .25 .25
**1020** A312 4c Bananas .35 .25
**1021** A312 10c Avocado .60 .25
**1022** A312 13c Pineapple .95 .70
**1023** A312 20c Guavas 2.50 .70
**1024** A312 50c Marmalade plums 5.50 1.25
*Nos. 1017-1024 (8)* 10.65 3.90

**Christmas Type of 1961**

Birds: No. 1025, Icterus galbula. No. 1026, Passerina ciris. No. 1027, Setophaga ruticillar. No. 1028, Dendroica tusca. No. 1029, Pheucticus ludovicianus. No. 1030, Pyranga olivacea. No. 1031, Dendroica dominica. No. 1032, Vermivora pinus. No. 1033, Protonotaria citrea. No. 1034, Wilsonia citrina. No. 1035, Passerina cyanea. No. 1036, Anas discors. No. 1037, Aix sponsa. No. 1038, Spatula clypeata. No. 1039, Nycticorax hoactli.

**1965, Dec. 1**

**1025** A248 3c multicolored 1.50 1.25
**1026** A249 3c multicolored 1.50 1.25
**1027** A249 3c multicolored 1.50 1.25
**1028** A249 3c multicolored 1.50 1.25
**1029** A249 3c multicolored 1.50 1.25
*a.* Block of 5 + label, Nos. 1025-1029 9.00 7.25
**1030** A248 5c multicolored 1.60 1.60
**1031** A249 5c multicolored 1.60 1.60
**1032** A249 5c multicolored 1.60 1.60
**1033** A249 5c multicolored 1.60 1.60
**1034** A249 5c multicolored 1.60 1.60
*a.* Block of 5 + label, Nos. 1030-1034 10.00 10.00
**1035** A248 13c multicolored 3.50 2.75
**1036** A249 13c multicolored 3.50 2.75
**1037** A249 13c multicolored 3.50 2.75
**1038** A249 13c multicolored 3.50 2.75
**1039** A249 13c multicolored 3.50 2.75
*a.* Block of 5 + label, Nos. 1035-1039 21.00 20.00
*Nos. 1025-1039 (15)* 33.00 28.00

Christmas 1965. See note after No. 700.

Intl. Athletic Competition, Havana, 7th Anniv. — A313

**1965, Dec. 11** **Wmk. 376** ***Perf. 10***

**1040** A313 1c Hurdling .25 .25
**1041** A313 2c Discus .25 .25
**1042** A313 3c Shot put .55 .25
**1043** A313 7c Javelin .60 .25
**1044** A313 9c High jump .75 .35
**1045** A313 10c Hammer throw 1.60 .60
**1046** A313 13c Running 2.00 .90
*Nos. 1040-1046 (7)* 6.00 2.85

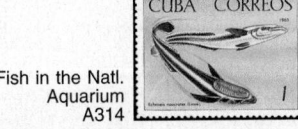

Fish in the Natl. Aquarium A314

1c, Echeneis naucrates. 2c, Katsuwonus pelamis. 3c, Abudefduf saxatilis. 4c, Istiophorus. 5c, Epinephelus striatus. 10c, Lutianus analis. 13c, Ocyurus chrysurus. 30c, Holocentrus ascensionis.

**1965, Dec. 5** **Unwmk.** ***Perf. 12½***

**1047** A314 1c multicolored .25 .25
**1048** A314 2c multicolored .25 .25
**1049** A314 3c multicolored .55 .25
**1050** A314 4c multicolored .75 .25
**1051** A314 5c multicolored .75 .25
**1052** A314 10c multicolored 1.00 .30
**1053** A314 13c multicolored 3.25 .80
**1054** A314 30c multicolored 5.00 1.25
*Nos. 1047-1054 (8)* 11.80 3.60

Andre Voisin (d. 1964), French Naturalist A315

13c, Portrait, flags, microscope, plant.

**1965, Dec. 21** **Wmk. 376**

**1055** A315 3c shown 1.00 .25
**1056** A315 13c multicolored 2.00 .55

Transportation A316

1c, Skoda bus, Czechoslovakia. 2c, Ikarus bus, Hungary. 3c, Leyland bus, G.B. 4c, TEM-4 locomotive, USSR. 7c, BB-69.000 locomotive, France. 10c, Remolcador tugboat, DDR. 13c, 15 de Marzo freighter, Spain. 20c, Ilyushin 18 jet, USSR.

**1965, Dec. 30**

**1057** A316 1c multicolored .25 .25
**1058** A316 2c multicolored .25 .25
**1059** A316 3c multicolored .25 .25
**1060** A316 4c multicolored 3.00 .70
**1061** A316 7c multicolored 3.00 .70
**1062** A316 10c multicolored 1.25 .35
**1063** A316 13c multicolored 2.00 .60
**1064** A316 20c multicolored 3.00 1.00
*Nos. 1057-1064 (8)* 13.00 4.10

A317

7th Anniv. of the Revolution — A318

1c, Guerrillas. 2c, Commander and tank. 3c, Sailor, patrol boat. 10c, Jet aircraft. 13c, Rocket.

**1966, Jan. 2**

**1065** A317 1c multi .40 .25
**1066** A317 2c multi .40 .25
**1067** A317 3c multi .90 .25
**1068** A318 10c multi 1.90 .45
**1069** A318 13c multi 2.40 .70
*Nos. 1065-1069 (5)* 6.00 1.90

Conference of Asian, African and South American Countries, Havana — A319

**1966, Jan. 3**

**1070** A319 2c Emblem at R .25 .25
**1071** A319 3c Emblem at L .40 .25
**1072** A319 13c Emblem at center 2.00 .50
*Nos. 1070-1072 (3)* 2.65 1.00

Guardalabarca Beach — A320

2c, Gran Piedra mountain. 3c, Guama Village. 13c, Soroa waterfall, vert.

**1966, Feb. 10**

**1073** A320 1c shown .30 .25
**1074** A320 2c multi .30 .25
**1075** A320 3c multi .90 .25
**1076** A320 13c multi 2.50 .60
*Nos. 1073-1076 (4)* 4.00 1.35

11th Medical and 7th Natl. Dental Congresses A321

**1966, Feb. 28** **Wmk. 376**

**1077** A321 3c multi .60 .25
**1078** A321 13c multi, diff. 2.50 .65

Folk Art — A322

1c, Afro-cuban ritual puppet. 2c, Sombreros. 3c, Ceramic vase. 7c, Lanterns, lamp. 9c, Table lamp. 10c, Shark, wood sculpture. 13c, Snail-shell necklace, earrings.

**1966, Feb. 28** **Unwmk.**

**1079** A322 1c multicolored .25 .25
**1080** A322 2c multicolored .25 .25
**1081** A322 3c multicolored .25 .25
**1082** A322 7c multicolored .25 .25
**1083** A322 9c multicolored .80 .25
**1084** A322 10c multicolored 1.20 .30
**1085** A322 13c multicolored 2.40 .60
*Nos. 1079-1085 (7)* 5.40 2.15

Nos. 1079-1083 vert.

Chelsea College, by Canaletto A323

Ceramics and paintings in the National Museum: 1c, Ming vase. 3c, Portrait of a Lady, by Goya. 13c, Portrait of Fayum, encaustic painting. Nos. 1086, 1088-1089 vert.

**1966, Mar. 31** **Wmk. 376**

**1086** A323 1c multi .25 .25
**1087** A323 2c multi .30 .25
**1088** A323 3c multi .75 .25
**1089** A323 13c multi 2.90 .70
*Nos. 1086-1089 (4)* 4.20 1.45

First Man in Space, 5th Anniv. — A324

Designs: 1c, Konstantin Eduardovich Tsiolkovsky (1857-1935), Soviet rocket and space sciences pioneer. 2c, Cosmonauts in training, vert. 3c, Yuri Gagarin, rocket, Earth. 7c, Cosmonauts Nikolaev and Popovich, vert. 9c, Tereshkova and Bykovsky. 10c, Komarov, Feoktistov and Yegorov. 13c, Leonov taking first space walk.

**1966, Apr. 12**

**1090** A324 1c multi .25 .25
**1091** A324 2c multi .25 .25
**1092** A324 3c multi .35 .25
**1093** A324 7c multi .60 .25
**1094** A324 9c multi .85 .25
**1095** A324 10c multi 1.10 .30
**1096** A324 13c multi 2.25 .55
*Nos. 1090-1096 (7)* 5.65 2.10

Bay of Pigs Invasion, 5th Anniv. — A325

2c, Tank. 3c, Burning ship, plane crash. 9c, Tank in ditch. 10c, Soldier, gunners. 13c, Operations map.

**1966, Apr. 17**

**1097** A325 2c multi .25 .25
**1098** A325 3c multi .95 .25
**1099** A325 9c multi .40 .25
**1100** A325 10c multi 1.50 .25
**1101** A325 13c multi 2.75 .50
*Nos. 1097-1101 (5)* 5.85 1.50

**Stamp Day Type of 1963**

Designs: 3c, Cuban Postal Museum interior. 13c, No. 613 and stamp collector.

**1966, Apr. 24**

**1102** A266 3c sage grn & sal rose 1.00 .25
**1103** A266 13c brn, sal rose & blk 3.00 .80

Stamp Day 1966. 1st Anniv. of the Cuban Postal Museum (No. 1102); 1st anniv. of the Cuban Philatelic Federation (No. 1103).

Flowers and Symbols of Industry — A326

2c, Anvil. 3c, Machete. 10c, Hammer. 13c, Hemisphere, gearwheel.

**1966, May 1**

**1104** A326 2c multi .25 .25
**1105** A326 3c multi .30 .25
**1106** A326 10c multi .70 .25
**1107** A326 13c multi 1.75 .90
*Nos. 1104-1107 (4)* 3.00 1.65

Labor Day.

Opening of the World Health Organization Headquarters, Geneva — A327

Views of WHO headquarters and emblem or emblem on flag.

**1966, May 3**

**1108** A327 2c blk & yel org .25 .25
**1109** A327 3c blk, lt blue & yel org .75 .25
**1110** A327 13c blk, lt blue & yel org 2.10 .55
*Nos. 1108-1110 (3)* 3.10 1.05

A328

**1966, June 11**

**1111** A328 1c Running, vert. .25 .25
**1112** A328 2c Rifle shooting .30 .25
**1113** A328 3c Baseball, vert. .40 .25
**1114** A328 7c Volleyball, vert. .45 .25
**1115** A328 9c Soccer, vert. .60 .25
**1116** A328 10c Boxing, vert. 1.20 .25
**1117** A328 13c Basketball, vert. 2.40 .55
*Nos. 1111-1117 (7)* 5.60 2.05

10th Central American and Caribbean Games, Puerto Rico, June 11-25.

Progress in Education — A329

Designs: 1c, Makarenko School, Playa de Tarara. 2c, Natl. Literacy Campaign Museum. 3c, Lantern, literacy campaign emblem for 1961. 10c, Frank Pais education team in the mountains. 13c, Farmer, factory worker.

**1966, June 15**

**1118** A329 1c grn & blk .25 .25
**1119** A329 2c yel, olive bister & blk .25 .25
**1120** A329 3c brt blue, lt blue & blk .30 .25
**1121** A329 10c golden brn, brn & blk .90 .25
**1122** A329 13c multi 2.40 .45
*Nos. 1118-1122 (5)* 4.10 1.45

1st Graduating class of Makarenko School (1c), 5th anniv. of the Natl. Literacy Campaign (3c), 4th anniv. of agricultural and industrial trade education (13c).

12th Congress of the Cuban Labor Organization — A330

**1966, Aug. 12**

**1123** A330 3c multi 1.00 .25

Sea Shells — A331

1c, Liguus flammellus. 2c, Cypraea zebra. 3c, Strombus pugilis. 7c, Aequipecten muscosu. 9c, Liguus fasciatus crenatus. 10c, Charonia variegata. 13c, Liguus fasciatus archeri.

**1966, Aug. 25** **Unwmk.**

**1124** A331 1c multicolored .35 .25
**1125** A331 2c multicolored .45 .25
**1126** A331 3c multicolored .70 .25
**1127** A331 7c multicolored .80 .25
**1128** A331 9c multicolored .90 .25
**1129** A331 10c multicolored 1.75 .40
**1130** A331 13c multicolored 3.50 .80
*Nos. 1124-1130 (7)* 8.45 2.45

Breeding Messenger Pigeons — A332

2c, Timer. 3c, Coops. 7c, Breeder tending coops. 9c, Pigeons in yard. 10c, Two men, message. 13c, Baracoa to Havana championship flight, July 26, 1959.

**1966, Sept. 18** **Wmk. 376**

**1131** A332 1c shown .40 .25
**1132** A332 2c multicolored .40 .25
**1133** A332 3c multicolored .40 .25
**1134** A332 7c multicolored .80 .25
**1135** A332 9c multicolored .80 .35
**1136** A332 10c multicolored 2.50 .50

**Size: 47x32mm**

**1137** A332 13c multicolored 3.75 .90
*Nos. 1131-1137 (7)* 9.05 2.75

Provincial and Natl. Coats of Arms, Map of Cuba — A333

**1966, Oct. 10**

**1138** A333 1c Pinar del Rio .25 .25
**1139** A333 2c Havana .30 .25
**1140** A333 3c Matanzas .30 .25
**1141** A333 4c Las Villas .40 .25
**1142** A333 5c Camaguey .60 .25
**1143** A333 9c Oriente 1.25 .50

**Size: 30x48mm**

**1144** A333 13c National arms 2.75 .75
*Nos. 1138-1144 (7)* 5.85 2.50

17th World Chess Olympiad, Havana — A334

1c, Pawn. 2c, Rook. 3c, Knight. 9c, Bishop. 10c, Queen, games, horiz. 13c, King and emblem, horiz.
30c, Capablanca Vs. Lasker, 1914, horiz.

**1966, Oct. 18**

**1145** A334 1c multicolored .30 .25
**1146** A334 2c multicolored .30 .25
**1147** A334 3c multicolored .50 .25
**1148** A334 9c multicolored 1.00 .25
**1149** A334 10c multicolored 2.40 .25
**1150** A334 13c multicolored 3.25 .60
*Nos. 1145-1150 (6)* 7.75 1.85

**Souvenir Sheet**

***Imperf***

**1151** A334 30c multicolored 12.00 12.00

No. 1151 contains one 49½x31mm stamp.

Cuban-Soviet Diplomatic Relations A335

2c, Lenin Hospital. 3c, Oil tanker, world map. 10c, Workers, gearwheels. 13c, Agriculture.

**1966, Nov. 7**

**1152** A335 2c multicolored .25 .25
**1153** A335 3c multicolored .35 .25
**1154** A335 10c multicolored 1.10 .25
**1155** A335 13c multicolored 2.25 .70
*Nos. 1152-1155 (4)* 3.95 1.45

2nd Song Festival — A336

Cuban composers and their compositions: 1c, Amadeo Roldan. 2c, Eduardo Sanchez de Fuentes. 3c, Moises Simons. 7c, Jorge Anckermann. 9c, Alejandro G. Caturla. 10c, Eliseo Grenet. 13c, Ernesto Lecuona.

**1966, Nov. 18**

**1156** A336 1c multicolored .25 .25
**1157** A336 2c multicolored .30 .25
**1158** A336 3c multicolored .30 .25
**1159** A336 7c multicolored .80 .25
**1160** A336 9c multicolored .80 .25
**1161** A336 10c multicolored 2.75 .50
**1162** A336 13c multicolored 3.50 1.00
*Nos. 1156-1162 (7)* 8.70 2.75

Viet Nam War — A337

Flag of Viet Nam and: 2c, US aircraft discharging bombs, dead cattle. 3c, Gas mask and victims. 13c, US bombs, women and children.

**1966, Nov. 23**

**1163** A337 2c multi .40 .25
**1164** A337 3c multi .60 .25
**1165** A337 13c multi 2.00 .60
*Nos. 1163-1165 (3)* 3.00 1.10

10th Anniv. of Successful Revolution Campaigns A338

Revolution leaders, scenes of the insurrection: 1c, Antonio Fernandez. 2c, Candido Gonzalez. 3c, Jose Tey. 7c, Tony Aloma. 9c, Otto Parellada. 10c, Juan Manuel Marquez. 13c, Frank Pais.

**1966, Nov. 30**

**1166** A338 1c multicolored .25 .25
**1167** A338 2c multicolored .25 .25
**1168** A338 3c multicolored .25 .25
**1169** A338 7c multicolored .30 .25
**1170** A338 9c multicolored .60 .25
**1171** A338 10c multicolored 2.00 .50
**1172** A338 13c multicolored 1.90 .80
*Nos. 1166-1172 (7)* 5.55 2.55

Intl. Leisure Time and Recreation Seminar A339

9c, World map, stopwatch, eye. 13c, Earth, clock, emblem.

**1966, Dec. 2**

**1173** A339 3c shown .25 .25
**1174** A339 9c multicolored 1.40 .25
**1175** A339 13c multicolored 2.00 .75
*Nos. 1173-1175 (3)* 3.65 1.25

1st Natl. Telecommunications Forum — A340

**1966, Dec. 12**

**1176** A340 3c shown .75 .25
**1177** A340 10c Satellite in orbit 3.50 .25
**1178** A340 13c Shell, satellite 4.75 .70
*a.* Souv. sheet of 3, #1176-1178, imperf 14.00 14.00
*Nos. 1176-1178 (3)* 9.00 1.20

No. 1178a sold for 30c.

**Christmas Type of 1961**

No. 1179, Cypripedium eurylochus. No. 1180, Cattleya speciosissima. No. 1181, Cattleya mendelii majestica. No. 1182, Cattleya trianae amesiana. No. 1183, Cattleya labiata macfarlanei. No. 1184, Cypripedium morganiae burfordense. No. 1185, Cattleya Countess of Derby. No. 1186, Cypripedium hookerae volunteanum. No. 1187, Cattleya warscewiczii reginae burfordense. No. 1188, Cypripedium stonei cannartae. No. 1189, Cattleya mendelii Duchess of Montrose. No. 1190, Oncidium macranthum. No. 1191, Cypripedium stonei platytoenium. No. 1192, Cattleya dowiana aurea. No. 1193, Laelia anceps.

**1966, Dec. 20** **Unwmk.**

**1179** A248 1c multicolored .75 .25
**1180** A249 1c multicolored .75 .25
**1181** A249 1c multicolored .75 .25
**1182** A249 1c multicolored .75 .25
**1183** A249 1c multicolored .75 .25
*a.* Block of 5 + label, #1179-1183 5.50 5.50
**1184** A248 3c multicolored 1.25 .25
**1185** A249 3c multicolored 1.25 .25
**1186** A249 3c multicolored 1.25 .25
**1187** A249 3c multicolored 1.25 .25
**1188** A249 3c multicolored 1.25 .25
*a.* Block of 5 + label, #1184-1188 9.00 9.00
**1189** A248 13c multicolored 4.00 .50
**1190** A249 13c multicolored 4.00 .50
**1191** A249 13c multicolored 4.00 .50
**1192** A249 13c multicolored 4.00 .50
**1193** A249 13c multicolored 4.00 .50
*a.* Block of 5 + label, #1189-1193 27.50 27.50
*Nos. 1179-1193 (15)* 30.00 5.00

Christmas 1966. See note after No. 700.

8th Anniv. of the Revolution A341

No. 1194, Liberation, 1959. No. 1195, Agrarian Reform, 1960. No. 1196, Education, 1961. No. 1197, Agriculture, 1965. No. 1198, Rodin's Thinker, Planning, 1962. No. 1199, Organization, 1963. No. 1200, Economy, 1964. No. 1201, Solidarity, 1966.

**1967, Jan. 2**

**1194** A341 3c multicolored .30 .25
**1195** A341 3c multicolored .30 .25
**1196** A341 3c multicolored .30 .25
**1197** A341 3c multicolored .30 .25
*a.* Strip of 4, Nos. 1194-1197 2.40 2.40
**1198** A341 13c multicolored 1.90 .45
**1199** A341 13c multicolored 1.90 .45
**1200** A341 13c multicolored 1.90 .45
**1201** A341 13c multicolored 1.90 .45
*a.* Strip of 4, Nos. 1198-1201 15.00 15.00
*Nos. 1194-1201 (8)* 8.80 2.80

Nos. 1198-1201 vert.

Spring, by Jorge Arche A342

Paintings in the Natl. Museum: 1c, Coffee Machine, by Angel Acosta Leon, vert. 2c, Country People, by Eduardo Abela, vert. 13c, Still-life, by Amelia Pelaez, vert. 30c, Landscape, by Gonzalo Escalante.

**1967, Feb. 27**

**1202** A342 1c multi .45 .25
**1203** A342 2c multi .75 .25
**1204** A342 3c multi 1.00 .30
**1205** A342 13c multi 2.25 1.00
**1206** A342 30c multi 6.00 2.00
*Nos. 1202-1206 (5)* 10.45 3.80

Natl. Events, Mar. 13, 1957 — A343

3c, Attack on Presidential Palace. 13c, Landing of Corynthia. 30c, Cienfuegos revolt.

**1967, Mar. 13** **Wmk. 376**

**1207** A343 3c multicolored .25 .25

**Size: 41x28mm**

**1208** A343 13c multicolored 2.50 .70
**1209** A343 30c multicolored 2.40 .80
*Nos. 1207-1209 (3)* 5.15 1.75

Evolution of Man — A344

Prehistoric men: 2c, Australopithecus. 3c, Pithecanthropus erectus. 4c, Sinanthropus pekinensis. 5c, Neanderthal man. 13c, Cro-magnon man carving tusk. 20c, Cro-magnon man painting petroglyph.

**1967, Mar. 31** **Unwmk.**

**1210** A344 1c multi .30 .25
**1211** A344 2c multi .50 .25
**1212** A344 3c multi .50 .25
**1213** A344 4c multi .75 .40
**1214** A344 5c multi 1.10 .50
**1215** A344 13c multi 3.75 .85
**1216** A344 20c multi 7.50 1.40
*Nos. 1210-1216 (7)* 14.40 3.90

Stamp Day — A345

Carriages.

**1967, Apr. 24**

**1217** A345 3c Victoria .35 .25
**1218** A345 9c Volante 2.00 .45
**1219** A345 13c Quitrin 3.00 .80
*Nos. 1217-1219 (3)* 5.35 1.50

EXPO '67, Montreal, Apr. 28-Oct. 27 — A346

1c, Cuban pavilion. 2c, Space exploration. 3c, Petroglyph, hieroglyph. 13c, Agriculture, computer technology. 20c, Athletes.

**1967, Apr. 28**

| | | | | |
|---|---|---|---|---|
| **1220** | A346 | 1c multicolored | .40 | .25 |
| **1221** | A346 | 2c multicolored | .40 | .25 |
| **1222** | A346 | 3c multicolored | .50 | .25 |
| **1223** | A346 | 13c multicolored | 2.90 | .70 |
| **1224** | A346 | 20c multicolored | 3.25 | .80 |
| | | *Nos. 1220-1224 (5)* | 7.45 | 2.25 |

Botanical Gardens, Sequicentennial A347

Flowering plants: 1c, Eugenia malaccencis. 2c, Jacaranda filicifolia. 3c, Coroupita guianensis. 4c, Spathodea campanulata. 5c, Cassia fistula. 13c, Plumieria alba. 20c, Erythrina poeppigiana.

**1967, May 30**

| | | | | |
|---|---|---|---|---|
| **1225** | A347 | 1c multicolored | .25 | .25 |
| **1226** | A347 | 2c multicolored | .25 | .25 |
| **1227** | A347 | 3c multicolored | .45 | .25 |
| **1228** | A347 | 4c multicolored | .45 | .25 |
| **1229** | A347 | 5c multicolored | .90 | .25 |
| **1230** | A347 | 13c multicolored | 2.25 | .55 |
| **1231** | A347 | 20c multicolored | 4.00 | .65 |
| | | *Nos. 1225-1231 (7)* | 8.55 | 2.45 |

Natl. Ballet — A348

**1967, June 15**

| | | | | |
|---|---|---|---|---|
| **1232** | A348 | 1c Giselle | .35 | .25 |
| **1233** | A348 | 2c Swan Lake | .35 | .25 |
| **1234** | A348 | 3c Don Quixote | .50 | .25 |
| **1235** | A348 | 4c Calaucan | 1.00 | .25 |
| **1236** | A348 | 13c Swan Lake | 2.75 | .70 |
| **1237** | A348 | 20c Nutcracker | 4.00 | 1.25 |
| | | *Nos. 1232-1237 (6)* | 8.95 | 2.95 |

Intl. Ballet Festival, Havana.

5th Pan American Games, Winnipeg, Canada, July 22-Aug. 7 — A349

1c, Baseball, horiz. 2c, Swimming, horiz. 3c, Basketball. 4c, Gymnastic rings. 5c, Water polo. 13c, Weight lifting, horiz. 20c, Javelin.

**1967, July 22**

| | | | | |
|---|---|---|---|---|
| **1238** | A349 | 1c multi | .25 | .25 |
| **1239** | A349 | 2c multi | .30 | .25 |
| **1240** | A349 | 3c multi | .45 | .25 |
| **1241** | A349 | 4c multi | .70 | .25 |
| **1242** | A349 | 5c multi | .80 | .25 |
| **1243** | A349 | 13c multi | 2.25 | .45 |
| **1244** | A349 | 20c multi | 3.25 | .80 |
| | | *Nos. 1238-1244 (7)* | 8.00 | 2.50 |

1st Conference of Latin American Solidarity Organization (OLAS) — A350

Portrait of representative, map of South American homeland: No. 1245, Camilo Torres, Colombia. No. 1246, Luis de la Puente Uceda, Peru. No. 1247, Luis A. Turcios Lima, Guatemala. No. 1248, Fabricio Ojeda, Venezuela.

**1967, July 28** **Wmk. 376**

| | | | | |
|---|---|---|---|---|
| **1245** | A350 | 13c pale grn, blk & red | 1.60 | .60 |
| **1246** | A350 | 13c lil, blk & red | 1.60 | .60 |
| **1247** | A350 | 13c dark chalky blue, blk & red | 1.60 | .60 |
| **1248** | A350 | 13c golden brn, blk & red | 1.60 | .60 |
| | | *Nos. 1245-1248 (4)* | 6.40 | 2.40 |

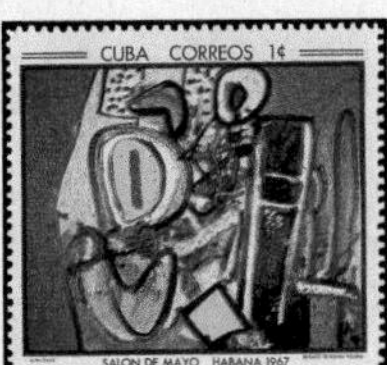

Portrait of Sonny Rollins, by Alan Davie — A351

Bathers, by Gustave Singier — A352

Modern Art: No. 1250, Twelve Selenites, by Felix Labisse. No. 1251, Night of the Drinker, by Friedensreich Hundertwasser. No. 1252, Figure, by Mariano. No. 1253, All-Souls, by Wilfredo Lam. No. 1254, Darkness and Cracks, by Antonio Tapies. No. 1256, Torso of a Muse, by Jean Arp. No. 1257, Figure, by M.W. Svanberg. No. 1258, Oppenheimer's Information, by Erro. No. 1259, Where Cardinals Are Born, by Max Ernst. No. 1260, Havana Landscape, by Portocarrero. No. 1261, EG 12, by Victor Vasarely. No. 1262, Frisco, by Alexander Calder. No. 1263, The Man with the Pipe, by Picasso. No. 1264, Abstract Composition, by Sergei Poliakoff. No. 1265, Painting, by Bram van Velde. No. 1266, Sower of Fires, by R. Matta. No. 1267, The Art of Living, by Rene Magritte. No. 1268, Poem, by Joan Miro. No. 1269, Young Tigers, by Jean Messagier. No. 1270, Painting, by M. Vieira da Silva. No. 1271, Live Cobra, by Pierre Alechinsky. No. 1272, Stalingrad, by Asger Jorn. 30c, Warriors, by Edouard Pignon. 50c, Cloister, a mural at the exhibition representing the Salon de Mayo pictures.

**1967, July 29** **Unwmk.**

| | | | | |
|---|---|---|---|---|
| **1249** | A351 | 1c shown | .75 | .25 |
| **1250** | A351 | 1c multi | .75 | .25 |
| **1251** | A351 | 1c multi | .75 | .25 |
| **1252** | A351 | 1c multi | .75 | .25 |
| **1253** | A351 | 1c multi | .75 | .25 |
| *a.* | | Strip of 5, Nos. 1249-1253 | 5.00 | 5.00 |

**Sizes: 36½x54mm, 36½x53mm, 36½x45mm, 36½x41mm**

| | | | | |
|---|---|---|---|---|
| **1254** | A352 | 2c multi | .75 | .25 |
| **1255** | A352 | 2c shown | .75 | .25 |
| **1256** | A352 | 2c multi | .75 | .25 |
| **1257** | A352 | 2c multi | .75 | .25 |
| **1258** | A352 | 2c multi | .75 | .25 |
| *a.* | | Strip of 5, Nos. 1254-1258 | 5.00 | 5.00 |

**Sizes: 36½x54mm, 36½x40mm, 36½x42mm, 36½x49mm**

| | | | | |
|---|---|---|---|---|
| **1259** | A352 | 3c multi | 1.40 | .30 |
| **1260** | A352 | 3c multi | 1.40 | .30 |
| **1261** | A352 | 3c multi | 1.40 | .30 |
| **1262** | A352 | 3c multi | 1.40 | .30 |
| **1263** | A352 | 3c multi | 1.40 | .30 |
| *a.* | | Strip of 5, Nos. 1259-1263 | 8.00 | 8.00 |

**Sizes: 35x15mm, 35x67mm, 35x46½mm, 35x55mm**

| | | | | |
|---|---|---|---|---|
| **1264** | A352 | 4c multi | 1.60 | 1.00 |
| **1265** | A352 | 4c multi | 1.60 | 1.00 |
| **1266** | A352 | 4c multi | 1.60 | 1.00 |
| **1267** | A352 | 4c multi | 1.60 | 1.00 |
| **1268** | A352 | 4c multi | 1.60 | 1.00 |
| *a.* | | Strip of 5, Nos. 1264-1268 | 10.00 | 10.00 |

**Sizes: 49x32mm, 49x35mm, 49x46mm**

| | | | | |
|---|---|---|---|---|
| **1269** | A351 | 13c multi | 4.25 | 3.00 |
| **1270** | A351 | 13c multi | 4.25 | 3.00 |
| **1271** | A351 | 13c multi | 4.25 | 3.00 |
| **1272** | A351 | 13c multi | 4.25 | 3.00 |
| *a.* | | Strip of 4, Nos. 1269-1272 | 20.00 | 20.00 |

**Size: 54x32mm**

| | | | | |
|---|---|---|---|---|
| **1273** | A351 | 30c multi | 17.50 | 11.00 |
| | | *Nos. 1249-1273 (25)* | 57.00 | 32.00 |

**Souvenir Sheet**

***Imperf***

| | | | | |
|---|---|---|---|---|
| **1274** | A351 | 50c multi | 18.00 | 12.50 |

Salon de Mayo Art Exhibition, Havana. No. 1274 contains one 88x45mm stamp with simulated perforations. Issued Oct. 7.

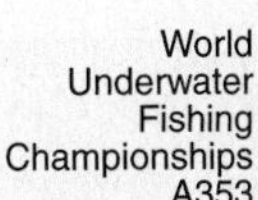

World Underwater Fishing Championships A353

**1967, Sept. 5**

| | | | | |
|---|---|---|---|---|
| **1275** | A353 | 1c Green moray | .25 | .25 |
| **1276** | A353 | 2c Octopus | .25 | .25 |
| **1277** | A353 | 3c Great barracuda | .25 | .25 |
| **1278** | A353 | 4c Blue shark | .75 | .25 |
| **1279** | A353 | 5c Spotted jewfish | 1.25 | .25 |
| **1280** | A353 | 13c Sting ray | 2.50 | .75 |
| **1281** | A353 | 20c Green turtle | 4.75 | 1.00 |
| | | *Nos. 1275-1281 (7)* | 10.00 | 3.00 |

Soviet Space Program — A354

**1967, Oct. 4** **Wmk. 376**

| | | | | |
|---|---|---|---|---|
| **1282** | A354 | 1c Sputnik 1 | .25 | .25 |
| **1283** | A354 | 2c Lunik 3 | .25 | .25 |
| **1284** | A354 | 3c Venusik | .25 | .25 |
| **1285** | A354 | 4c Cosmos | .40 | .25 |
| **1286** | A354 | 5c Mars 1 | .65 | .25 |
| **1287** | A354 | 9c Electron 1 & 2 | .75 | .25 |
| **1288** | A354 | 10c Luna 9 | 1.10 | .45 |
| **1289** | A354 | 13c Luna 10 | 2.25 | .60 |
| *a.* | | Souv. sheet of 8, #1282-1289, imperf. | 12.00 | 12.00 |
| | | *Nos. 1282-1289 (8)* | 5.90 | 2.55 |

Stamps in No. 1289a have simulated perfs.

50th Anniv. of the October Revolution, Russia — A355

Paintings: 1c, Storming the Winter Palace, by Sokolov-Skalia and Miasnikov. 2c, Lenin Addressing Congress, by W.A. Serov. 3c, Lenin, by H.D. Nalbandian. 4c, Lenin Explaining Electrification Map, by L.A. Schmatko. 5c, Dawn of the Five-Year Plan, by J.D. Romas. 13c, Kusnetzkroi Steel Furnace No. 1, by P. Kotov. 30c, Victory, by A. Krivonogov.

**1967, Nov. 7** **Unwmk.**

| | | | | |
|---|---|---|---|---|
| **1290** | A355 | 1c 64x36mm | .25 | .25 |
| **1291** | A355 | 2c 48x36mm | .25 | .25 |
| **1292** | A355 | 3c 35x37mm | .35 | .25 |
| **1293** | A355 | 4c 48x36mm | .40 | .25 |
| **1294** | A355 | 5c 50x36mm | 2.40 | .50 |
| **1295** | A355 | 13c 36x50mm | 2.25 | .50 |
| **1296** | A355 | 30c 50x36mm | 3.00 | .85 |
| | | *Nos. 1290-1296 (7)* | 8.90 | 2.85 |

Castle of the Royal Forces, Havana A356

Historic architecture: 2c, Iznaga Tower, Trinidad, vert. 3c, Castle of Our Lady of the Angels, Cienfuegos. 4c, St. Francis de Paula Church, Havana. 13c, St. Francis Convent, Havana. 30c, Castle del Morro, Santiago de Cuba.

**1967, Nov. 7** **Wmk. 376**

**Sizes: 26x47mm (1c), 41x29mm (3c, 4c), 38½x31mm (13c)**

| | | | | |
|---|---|---|---|---|
| **1297** | A356 | 1c multi | .25 | .25 |
| **1298** | A356 | 2c multi | .25 | .25 |
| **1299** | A356 | 3c multi | .65 | .25 |
| **1300** | A356 | 4c multi | .65 | .25 |
| **1301** | A356 | 13c multi | 3.25 | .50 |
| **1302** | A356 | 30c multi | 5.00 | 1.00 |
| | | *Nos. 1297-1302 (6)* | 10.05 | 2.50 |

**Christmas Type of 1961**

Birds: No. 1303, Struthia camelus australis. No. 1304, Chysolophus pictus. No. 1305, Ciconia ciconia ciconia. No. 1306, Balearica pavonina. No. 1307, Dromiceius novaeholandiae. No. 1308, Anodorhynchus hyacinthus. No. 1309, Psittacus erithacus. No. 1310, Domicella garrula. No. 1311, Ramphastos sulfuratus. No. 1312, Kakatoe galerita galerita. No. 1313, Phoenicopterus ruber. No. 1314, Pelecanus erythrorhynchos. No. 1315, Alopochen aegyptiacus. No. 1316, Dendronessa galericulata. No. 1317, Chenopsis atrata.

**1967, Dec. 20**

| | | | | |
|---|---|---|---|---|
| **1303** | A248 | 1c multicolored | 1.25 | .60 |
| **1304** | A249 | 1c multicolored | 1.25 | .60 |
| **1305** | A249 | 1c multicolored | 1.25 | .60 |
| **1306** | A249 | 1c multicolored | 1.25 | .60 |
| **1307** | A249 | 1c multicolored | 1.25 | .60 |
| *a.* | | Block of 5 + label, Nos. 1303-1307 | 9.00 | 9.00 |
| **1308** | A248 | 3c multicolored | 2.00 | 1.00 |
| **1309** | A249 | 3c multicolored | 2.00 | 1.00 |
| **1310** | A249 | 3c multicolored | 2.00 | 1.00 |
| **1311** | A249 | 3c multicolored | 2.00 | 1.00 |
| **1312** | A249 | 3c multicolored | 2.00 | 1.00 |
| *a.* | | Block of 5 + label, Nos. 1308-1312 | 14.00 | 14.00 |
| **1313** | A248 | 13c multicolored | 3.75 | 1.75 |
| **1314** | A249 | 13c multicolored | 3.75 | 1.75 |
| **1315** | A249 | 13c multicolored | 3.75 | 1.75 |
| **1316** | A249 | 13c multicolored | 3.75 | 1.75 |
| **1317** | A249 | 13c multicolored | 3.75 | 1.75 |
| *a.* | | Block of 5 + label, Nos. 1313-1317 | 25.00 | 25.00 |
| | | *Nos. 1303-1317 (15)* | 35.00 | 16.75 |

Christmas 1967. See note after No. 700.

Ernesto "Che" Guevara (1928-1967), Revolution Leader — A356a

**1968, Jan. 3**

| | | | | |
|---|---|---|---|---|
| **1318** | A356a | 13c blk, dark red & buff | 7.50 | 1.00 |

Cultural Congress, Havana A357

Abstract designs: No. 1319, Independence fostering culture. No. 1320, Integral formation of man. No. 1321, Responsibility of intellectuals. No. 1322, Relationship between culture and the mass media. No. 1323, The arts versus science and technology.

**1968, Jan. 4**

| | | | | |
|---|---|---|---|---|
| **1319** | A357 | 3c multi, vert. | .25 | .25 |
| **1320** | A357 | 3c multi, vert. | .25 | .25 |
| **1321** | A357 | 13c multi, vert. | 1.50 | .40 |
| **1322** | A357 | 13c multi, vert. | 1.60 | .50 |
| **1323** | A357 | 30c multi | 2.40 | 1.00 |
| | | *Nos. 1319-1323 (5)* | 6.00 | 2.40 |

Canaries and Breeding Cycles — A358

**1968, Apr. 13**

| | | | | |
|---|---|---|---|---|
| **1324** | A358 | 1c F.C.C. 4016 | .25 | .25 |
| **1325** | A358 | 2c A.C.C. 774 | .25 | .25 |
| **1326** | A358 | 3c A.C.C. 122 | .30 | .25 |
| **1327** | A358 | 4c F.C.C. 4477 | .30 | .25 |
| **1328** | A358 | 5c A.C.C 117 | .65 | .25 |

1329 A358 13c A.N.R. 1175 3.00 .55
1330 A358 20c A.C.C. 777 4.00 .70
*Nos. 1324-1330 (7)* 8.75 2.50

Stamp Day — A359

Paintings: 13c, The Village Postman, by J. Harris. 30c, The Philatelist, by G. Sciltian.

**1968, Apr. 24** **Unwmk.**
1331 A359 13c multi 1.75 .50
1332 A359 30c multi 2.75 .70

World Health Organization, 20th Anniv. — A360

13c, Nurse, mother, child. 30c, Surgeons.

**1968, May 10** **Wmk. 376**
1333 A360 13c multi 2.00 .75
1334 A360 30c multi 2.50 .90

Intl. Children's Day — A361

**1968, June 1**
1335 A361 3c multi 1.00 .25

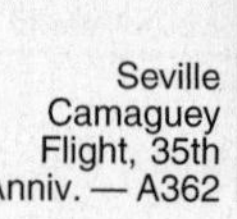
Seville Camaguey Flight, 35th Anniv. — A362

13c, Plane Four Winds. 30c, Capt. Barberan, Lt. Collar, pilots.

**1968, June 20**
1336 A362 13c multi 2.25 .45
1337 A362 30c multi 2.75 .60

Natl. Food Production A363

1c, Yellow tuna, can. 2c, Cow, dairy products. 3c, Rooster, eggs. 13c, Rum, sugar cane. 20c, Crayfish, box.

**1968, June 29**
1338 A363 1c multi .25 .25
1339 A363 2c multi .25 .25
1340 A363 3c multi .50 .25
1341 A363 13c multi 3.00 .50
1342 A363 20c multi 3.25 .70
*Nos. 1338-1342 (5)* 7.25 1.95

Attack of Moncada Barracks, 15th Anniv. — A364

3c, Siboney farmhouse. 13c, Assault route, Santiago de Cuba. 30c, Students, school.

**1968, July 26**
**Size: 43x29mm (13c)**
1343 A364 3c multi .50 .25
1344 A364 13c multi 2.50 .75
1345 A364 30c multi 4.00 1.00
*Nos. 1343-1345 (3)* 7.00 2.00

Committee for the Defense of the Revolution, 8th Anniv. — A365

**1968, Sept. 28**
1346 A365 3c multi 2.00 .25

Guerilla Day — A366

Che Guevara and: 1c, Rifleman and "En Cualquier Lugar..." 3c, Machine gunners and "Crear tres muchos Viet Nam." 9c, Silhouette of battalion and "Este Tipo De Lucha..." 10c, Guerillas cheering and "Hoy aquilatamos..." 13c, Map of Caribbean, So. America and "Hasta La Victoria Siempre."

**1968, Oct. 8**
1347 A366 1c gold, brt blue grn & blk .25 .25
1348 A366 3c gold, org brn blk .25 .25
1349 A366 9c multi .60 .25
1350 A366 10c gold, lt olive grn & blk 1.40 .25
1351 A366 13c gold, red org & blk 2.50 .70
*Nos. 1347-1351 (5)* 5.00 1.70

Cuban War of Independence, Cent. — A367

Independence fighters and scenes: No. 1352, C.M. de Cespedes, broken wheel. No. 1353, E. Betances, horsemen, flag. No. 1354, I. Agramonte, Clavellinas Monument. No. 1355, A. Maceo, Baragua Protest. No. 1356, J. Marti, horsemen. No. 1357, M. Gomez, The Invasion. No. 1358, J.A. Mella, declaration. No. 1359, A. Guiteras, El Morrillo monument. No. 1360, A. Santamaria, attack on Moncada Barracks. No. 1361, F. Pais memorial. No. 1362, J. Echeverria, student protest. No. 1363, C. Cienfuegos, insurrection. No. 1364, Che Guevara, 1st Declaration of Havana.

**1968, Oct. 10** **Unwmk.**
1352 A367 1c multicolored .30 .25
1353 A367 1c multicolored .30 .25
1354 A367 1c multicolored .30 .25
1355 A367 1c multicolored .30 .25
1356 A367 1c multicolored .30 .25
*a.* Strip of 5, Nos. 1352-1356 2.25 2.25
1357 A367 3c multicolored .30 .25
1358 A367 3c multicolored .30 .25
1359 A367 3c multicolored .30 .25
1360 A367 3c multicolored .30 .25
1361 A367 3c multicolored .30 .25
*a.* Strip of 5, Nos. 1357-1361 2.25 2.25
1362 A367 9c multicolored 1.50 .25
1363 A367 13c multicolored 3.25 .75
1364 A367 30c multicolored 3.75 1.25
*Nos. 1352-1364 (13)* 11.50 4.75

Souvenir Sheet

The Burning of Bayamo, by J.E. Hernandez Giro — A368

**1968, Oct. 18** ***Imperf.***
1365 A368 50c multi 12.50 12.50

Natl. Philatelic Exhibition, independence cent. Stamp in No. 1365 has simulated perforations.

19th Summer Olympics, Mexico City, Oct. 12-27 — A369

1c, Parade of athletes. 2c, Women's basketball, vert. 3c, Hammer throw, vert. 4c, Boxing. 5c, Water polo. 13c, Pistol shooting. 30c, Mexican flag, calendar stone.
50c, Running.

**1968, Oct. 21** ***Perf. 12½***
1366 A369 1c multicolored .25 .25
1367 A369 2c multicolored .25 .25
1368 A369 3c multicolored .25 .25
1369 A369 4c multicolored .25 .25
1370 A369 5c multicolored .45 .25
1371 A369 13c multicolored 2.50 .55

**Size: 32x50mm**
1372 A369 30c multicolored 3.75 .80
*Nos. 1366-1372 (7)* 7.70 2.60

**Souvenir Sheet**
***Imperf***
1373 A369 50c multicolored 10.00 4.00

Stamp in No. 1373 has simulated perforations.

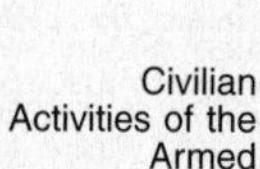
Civilian Activities of the Armed Forces — A370

3c, Crop dusting. 9c, Che Guevara's Brigade. 10c, Road building. 13c, Plowing, harvesting.

**1968, Dec. 2** **Wmk. 376** ***Perf. 12½***
1374 A370 3c multicolored .25 .25
1375 A370 9c multicolored .60 .25
1376 A370 10c multicolored 1.00 .25
1377 A370 13c multicolored 2.10 .70
*Nos. 1374-1377 (4)* 3.95 1.45

San Alejandro School of Painting, Sesquicentennial — A371

Paintings: 1c, Manrique de Lara's Family, by Jean Baptiste Vermay, vert. 2c, Seascape, by Leopoldo Romanach. 3c, Wild Cane, by Antonio Rodriguez, vert. 4c, Self-portrait, by Miguel Melero, vert. 5c, The Lottery List, by Jose Joaquin Tejada. 13c, Portrait of Nina, by Armando B. Menocal, vert. 30c, Landscape, by Esteban B. Chartrand. 50c, Siesta, by Guillermo Collazo.

**1968, Dec. 30** **Unwmk.**
**Sizes: 38x48mm (1c, 3c), 39x50mm (4c, 13c), 53x36mm (30c)**
1378 A371 1c multi .25 .25
1379 A371 2c multi .25 .25
1380 A371 3c multi .30 .25
1381 A371 4c multi .30 .25
1382 A371 5c multi 1.25 .40
1383 A371 13c multi 3.50 .70
1384 A371 30c multi 5.00 1.10
*Nos. 1378-1384 (7)* 10.85 3.20

**Souvenir Sheet**
***Imperf***
1385 A371 50c multi 9.00 3.50

No. 1385 contains one 52x41½mm stamp that has simulated perforations.

10th Anniv. of the Revolution — A372

**1969, Jan. 3** **Wmk. 376** ***Perf. 12½***
1386 A372 13c multi 2.00 .60

Villaclarenos Rebellion, Cent. — A373

3c, Gutierrez and Sanchez.

**1969, Feb. 6**
1387 A373 3c multi 1.10 .25

Women's Day — A374

Design: Mariana Grajales, rose and statue.

**1969, Mar. 8**
1388 A374 3c multi 1.00 .25

Cuban Pioneers and Young Communists Unions — A375

3c, Pioneers. 13c, Young Communists.

**1969, Apr. 4**
1389 A375 3c multi .40 .25
1390 A375 13c multi 2.00 .80

Guaimaro Assembly, Cent. — A376

**1969, Apr. 10**
1391 A376 3c dark brn 1.10 .25

The Postman, by Jean C. Cazin — A377

Paintings: 30c, Portrait of a Young Man, by George Romney.

**1969, Apr. 24** **Unwmk.**
1392 A377 13c multi 2.25 .75

**Size: 35½x43½mm**
1393 A377 30c multi 3.75 1.25

Stamp Day.

Agrarian Reform, 10th Anniv. — A378

**1969, May 17** **Wmk. 376**
**1394** A378 13c multi 2.50 .70

Marine Life — A379

1c, Petrochirus bahamensis. 2c, Stenopus hispidus. 3c, Panulirus argus. 4c, Callinectes sapidus. 5c, Gecarcinus ruricola. 13c, Macrobrachium carcinus. 30c, Carpilius coralinus.

**1969, May 20** **Unwmk.**
**1395** A379 1c multicolored .25 .25
**1396** A379 2c multicolored .40 .25
**1397** A379 3c multicolored .40 .25
**1398** A379 4c multicolored .50 .25
**1399** A379 5c multicolored .50 .25
**1400** A379 13c multicolored 3.25 .45
**1401** A379 30c multicolored 5.00 .80
*Nos. 1395-1401 (7)* 10.30 2.50

Intl. Labor Organization, 50th Anniv. — A380

13c, Blacksmith breaking chains.

**1969, June 6** **Wmk. 376**
**1402** A380 3c shown .40 .25
**1403** A380 13c multi 2.10 .70

Paintings in the Natl. Museum A381

Designs: 1c, Flowers, by Raul Milian, vert. 2c, Annunciation, by Antonia Eiriz. 3c, Factory, by Marcelo Pogolotti, vert. 4c, Territorial Waters, by Luis Martinez Pedro, vert. 5c, Miss Sarah Gale, by John Hoppner, vert. 13c, Two Women Wearing Mantilla, by Ignacio Zuloaga. 30c, Virgin and Child, by Francisco de Zurbaran.

**1969, June 15** **Unwmk.**
**1404** A381 1c 39x59mm .25 .25
**1405** A381 2c 49x40mm .25 .25
**1406** A381 3c 39½x49mm .45 .25
**1407** A381 4c 39½x43mm .30 .25
**1408** A381 5c 39½x45½mm .30 .25
**1409** A381 13c 38x41½mm 2.10 .70
**1410** A381 30c 39x45mm 3.25 .90
*Nos. 1404-1410 (7)* 6.90 2.85

Broadcasting Institute A382

13c, Hemispheres, tower. 1p, Waves on graph.

**1969, July 5** **Wmk. 376**
**1411** A382 3c shown .40 .25
**1412** A382 13c multicolored 2.00 .75
**1413** A382 1p multicolored 4.50 1.75
*Nos. 1411-1413 (3)* 6.90 2.75

Fish — A383

1c, Apogon maculatus. 2c, Bodianus rufus. 3c, Microspathodon chrysurus. 4c, Gramma loreto. 5c, Chromis marginatus. 13c, Myripristis jacobus. 30c, Nomeus gronovii, vert.

**1969, July 20** **Unwmk.**
**1414** A383 1c multicolored .25 .25
**1415** A383 2c multicolored .25 .25
**1416** A383 3c multicolored .35 .25
**1417** A383 4c multicolored .40 .25
**1418** A383 5c multicolored .50 .25
**1419** A383 13c multicolored 2.75 .55
**1420** A383 30c multicolored 4.50 .90
*Nos. 1414-1420 (7)* 9.00 2.70

Natl. Film Industry, 10th Anniv. — A384

**1969, Aug. 5** **Wmk. 376**
**1421** A384 1c Poster .25 .25
**1422** A384 3c Documentaries .25 .25
**1423** A384 13c Cartoons 2.50 .60
**1424** A384 30c Entertainers 3.50 .70
*Nos. 1421-1424 (4)* 6.50 1.80

Napoleon in Milan, by Andrea Appiani A385

Paintings in the Napoleon Museum, Havana: 2c, Hortensia de Beauharnais, by Francois Gerard. 3c, Napoleon as First Consul, by J.B. Regnault. 4c, Elisa Bonaparte, by Robert Lefevre. 5c, Napoleon Planning Coronation Ceremony, by J.G. Vibert, horiz. 13c, Napoleon as Cuirassier Corporal, by Jean Meissonier. 30c, Napoleon Bonaparte, by LeFevre.

**1969, Aug. 20** **Unwmk.**
**1425** A385 1c 46x56mm .25 .25
**1426** A385 2c 41½x55mm .25 .25
**1427** A385 3c 45½x56mm .25 .25
**1428** A385 4c 43x62½mm .45 .25
**1429** A385 5c 63x47½mm .70 .30
**1430** A385 13c 43x62½mm 3.25 .70
**1431** A385 30c 45x59½mm 4.25 .90
*Nos. 1425-1431 (7)* 9.40 2.90

See Nos. 2448-2453.

Cuba's Victory at the 17th World Amateur Baseball Championships, Santo Domingo — A386

**1969, Sept. 11**
**1432** A386 13c multi 2.50 .60

No. 1432 printed se-tenant with inscribed label listing finalists.

Alexander von Humboldt (1769-1859), German Naturalist — A387

**1969, Sept. 14**
**1433** A387 3c Surinam eel .25 .25
**1434** A387 13c Night ape 2.25 .75
**1435** A387 30c Condors 4.00 .85
*Nos. 1433-1435 (3)* 6.50 1.85

World Fencing Championships, Havana — A388

Designs: 1c, Ancient Egyptians in combat. 2c, Roman gladiators. 2c, Viking and Norman. 4c, Medieval tournament. 5c, French musketeers. 13c, Japanese samurai. 30c, Mounted Cubans, War of Independence. 50c, Modern fencers.

**1969, Oct. 2**
**1436** A388 1c multi .25 .25
**1437** A388 2c multi .25 .25
**1438** A388 3c multi .25 .25
**1439** A388 4c multi .40 .25
**1440** A388 5c multi .60 .25
**1441** A388 13c multi 2.75 .45
**1442** A388 30c multi 4.25 .80
*Nos. 1436-1442 (7)* 8.75 2.50

**Souvenir Sheet**

***Imperf***

**1443** A388 50c multi 12.00 12.00

Stamp in No. 1443 has simulated perforations.

Natl. Revolutionary Militia, 10th Anniv. — A389

**1969, Oct. 26** **Wmk. 376**
**1444** A389 3c multi 1.10 .25

Disappearance of Maj. Camilo Cienfuegos, 10th Anniv. — A390

**1969, Oct. 28**
**1445** A390 13c multi 2.00 .60

Agriculture A391

No. 1446, Strawberries, grapes. No. 1447, Onions, asparagus. No. 1448, Rice. No. 1449, Banana. No. 1450, Pineapple, vert. No. 1451, Tobacco, vert. No. 1452, Citrus fruits, vert. No. 1453, Coffee, vert. No. 1454, Rabbits, vert. No. 1455, Pigs, vert. No. 1456, Sugar cane. No. 1457, Bull.

**1969, Nov. 2** **Unwmk.**
**1446** A391 1c multicolored .25 .25
**1447** A391 1c multicolored .25 .25
**1448** A391 1c multicolored .25 .25
**1449** A391 1c multicolored .25 .25
*a.* Strip of 4, #1446-1449 1.25 1.25
**1450** A391 3c multicolored .50 .50
**1451** A391 3c multicolored .50 .50
**1452** A391 3c multicolored .50 .50
**1453** A391 3c multicolored .50 .50
**1454** A391 3c multicolored .50 .50
*a.* Strip of 5, #1450-1454 3.00 3.00
**1455** A391 10c multicolored .50 .25
**1456** A391 13c multicolored 2.75 .60
**1457** A391 30c multicolored 4.00 .85
*Nos. 1446-1457 (12)* 10.75 5.20

Sporting Events A392

1c, 2nd Natl. Games. 2c, 11th Anniv. Games. 3c, Barrientos Commemorative, vert. 10c, 2nd Olympic Trials, vert. 13c, 6th Socialist Bicycle Race, vert. 30c, 6th Capablanca Memorial Chess Championships, vert.

**1969, Nov. 15**
**1458** A392 1c multicolored .25 .25
**1459** A392 2c multicolored .25 .25
**1460** A392 3c multicolored .25 .25
**1461** A392 10c multicolored .30 .25
**1462** A392 13c multicolored 2.75 .80
**1463** A392 30c multicolored 3.75 1.25
*Nos. 1458-1463 (6)* 7.55 3.05

**Christmas Type of 1961**

Flowering plants: No. 1464, Plumbago capensis. No. 1465, Petrea volubilis. No. 1466, Clitoria ternatea. No. 1467, Duranta repens. No. 1468, Ruellia tuberosa. No. 1469, Turnera ulmifolia. No. 1470, Thevetia peruviana. No. 1471, Hibiscus elatus. No. 1472, Allamanda cathartica. No. 1473, Cosmos sulphureus. No. 1474, Delonix regia. No. 1475, Neriun oleander. No. 1476, Cordia sebestena. No. 1477, Lochnera rosea. No. 1478, Jatropha integerrima.

**1969, Dec. 1**
**1464** A248 1c multicolored .40 .25
**1465** A249 1c multicolored .40 .25
**1466** A249 1c multicolored .40 .25
**1467** A249 1c multicolored .40 .25
**1468** A249 1c multicolored .40 .25
*a.* Block of 5 + label, Nos. 1464-1468 3.00 3.00
**1469** A248 3c multicolored 1.00 .25
**1470** A249 3c multicolored 1.00 .25
**1471** A249 3c multicolored 1.00 .25
**1472** A249 3c multicolored 1.00 .25
**1473** A249 3c multicolored 1.00 .25
*a.* Block of 5 + label, Nos. 1469-1473 7.50 7.50
**1474** A248 13c multicolored 2.25 1.00
**1475** A249 13c multicolored 2.25 1.00
**1476** A249 13c multicolored 2.25 1.00
**1477** A249 13c multicolored 2.25 1.00
**1478** A249 13c multicolored 2.25 1.00
*a.* Block of 5 + label, Nos. 1474-1478 15.00 15.00
*Nos. 1464-1478 (15)* 18.25 7.50

Christmas 1969. See note after No. 700.

Zapata Swamp Fauna — A393

1c, Trelanorhynus variabilis. 2c, Hyla insulsa. 3c, Atractosteus tristoechus. 4c, Capromys nana. 5c, Crocodylus rhombifer. 13c, Amazona leucocephala. 30c, Agelaius phoeniceus assimilis.

**1969, Dec. 15**
**1479** A393 1c multicolored .25 .25
**1480** A393 2c multicolored .25 .25
**1481** A393 3c multicolored .25 .25
**1482** A393 4c multicolored .25 .25
**1483** A393 5c multicolored .25 .25
**1484** A393 13c multicolored 2.75 .55
**1485** A393 30c multicolored 4.25 1.00
*Nos. 1479-1485 (7)* 8.25 2.80

Nos. 1482, 1484-1485 vert.

Tourism — A394

1c, Jibacoa Beach. 3c, Trinidad City. 13c, Santiago de Cuba. 30c, Vinales Valley.

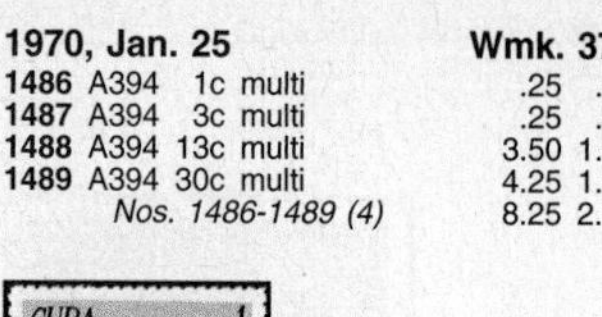

**1970, Jan. 25** **Wmk. 376**

**1486** A394 1c multi .25 .25
**1487** A394 3c multi .25 .25
**1488** A394 13c multi 3.50 1.00
**1489** A394 30c multi 4.25 1.25
*Nos. 1486-1489 (4)* 8.25 2.75

Medicinal Plants — A395

1c, Guarea guara. 3c, Ocimum sanctum. 10c, Canella winterana. 13c, Bidens pilosa. 30c, Turnera ulmifolia. 50c, Picramnia pentandra.

**1970, Feb. 10** **Unwmk.**

**1490** A395 1c multi .25 .25
**1491** A395 3c multi .25 .25
**1492** A395 10c multi .45 .25
**1493** A395 13c multi 2.25 .70
**1494** A395 30c multi 2.75 .85
**1495** A395 50c multi 4.00 1.00
*Nos. 1490-1495 (6)* 9.95 3.30

11th Central American and Caribbean Games, Panama, Feb. 28-Mar. 14 — A396

**1970, Feb. 28** **Wmk. 376**

**1496** A396 1c Weight lifting .25 .25
**1497** A396 3c Boxing .25 .25
**1498** A396 10c Gymnastics .25 .25
**1499** A396 13c Running 2.40 .65
**1500** A396 30c Fencing 3.25 .90
*Nos. 1496-1500 (5)* 6.40 2.30

**Souvenir Sheet**

***Imperf***

**1501** A396 50c Baseball 12.00 6.00

No. 1501 contains one 50x37mm stamp that has simulated perforations.

EXPO '70, Osaka, Japan, Mar. 15-Sept. 13 — A397

1c, Enjoying life. 2c, Improving on nature, vert. 3c, Better living standard. 13c, Intl. cooperation, vert. 30c, Cuban pavilion.

**1970, Mar. 15**

**1502** A397 1c multicolored .25 .25
**1503** A397 2c multicolored .40 .25
**1504** A397 3c multicolored .40 .25
**1505** A397 13c multicolored 2.75 .50
**1506** A397 30c multicolored 3.50 .75
*Nos. 1502-1506 (5)* 7.30 2.00

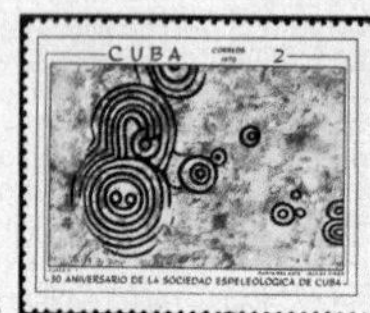


A398

Petroglyphs in Cuban caves: 1c, Ambrosio Cave, Varadero Matanzas. 2c, Cave No. 1, Punta del Este, Isle of Pines. 3c, Pichardo Cave, Cubitas Camaguey Mountains. 4c, Ambrosio Cave, diff. 5c, Cave No. 1, diff. 13c, Garcia Ribiou Cave, Havana. 30c, Cave No. 2, Punta del Este.

**1970, Mar. 28** **Unwmk.**

**Sizes: 29x45mm (1c, 3c, 4c, 13c)**

**1507** A398 1c multi .25 .25
**1508** A398 2c shown .25 .25
**1509** A398 3c multi .25 .25
**1510** A398 4c multi .25 .25
**1511** A398 5c multi .25 .25
**1512** A398 13c multi 2.25 .70
**1513** A398 30c multi 4.25 .80
*Nos. 1507-1513 (7)* 7.75 2.75

Speleological Society, 30th Anniv.

Aviation Pioneers A399

**1970, Apr. 10**

**1514** A399 3c Jose D. Blino 1.00 .25
**1515** A399 13c Adolfo Teodore 3.00 .65

Lenin Birth Centenary — A400

Paintings and quotes: 1c, Lenin in Kazan, by O. Vishniakov. 2c, Young Lenin, by V. Prager. 3c, Second Socialist Party Congress, by Y. Vinogradov. 4c, First Manifesto, by F. Golubkov. 5c, First Day of Soviet Power, by N. Babasiuk. 13c, Lenin in Smolny, by M. Sokolov. 30c, Autumn in Gorky, by A. Varlamov. 50c, Lenin at Gorky, by N. Baskakov.

**1970, Apr. 22**

**Sizes: 67½x46mm (1c, 4c, 5c)**

**1516** A400 1c multi .25 .25
**1517** A400 2c shown .25 .25
**1518** A400 3c multi .25 .25
**1519** A400 4c multi .25 .25
**1520** A400 5c multi .25 .25
**1521** A400 13c multi 2.75 .55
**1522** A400 30c multi 3.25 .70
*Nos. 1516-1522 (7)* 7.25 2.50

**Souvenir Sheet**

***Imperf***

**1523** A400 50c multi 13.00 6.50

No. 1523 contains one 48x46mm stamp that has simulated perforations.

Stamp Day — A401

13c, The Letter, by J. Arche. 30c, Portrait of A Cadet, Anonymous.

**1970, Apr. 24**

**1524** A401 13c multicolored 2.50 .60

**Size: 30x44mm**

**1525** A401 30c multicolored 3.00 .80

Da Vinci's Anatomical Drawing, Earth, Moon A402

**1970, May 17** **Wmk. 376**

**1526** A402 30c multi 3.25 .60

World Telecommunications Day.

Ho Chi Minh (1890-1969), President of North Viet Nam — A403

No. 1527, Vietnamese fisherman. No. 1528, Two women. No. 1529, Plowing field. No. 1530, Teacher, students in air-raid shelter. No. 1531, Nine women in paddy. No. 1532, Camouflaged machine shop.

**1970, May 19** **Unwmk.**

**1527** A403 1c multicolored .25 .25

**Size: 32x44mm**

**1528** A403 3c multicolored .50 .25
**1529** A403 3c multicolored .50 .25

**Size: 33x45mm**

**1530** A403 3c multicolored .50 .25
**1531** A403 3c multicolored .50 .25

**Size: 34x41½mm**

**1532** A403 3c multicolored .50 .25

**Size: 34x39mm**

**1533** A403 13c shown 2.25 .70
*Nos. 1527-1533 (7)* 5.00 2.20

Cuban Cigar Industry — A404

3c, Plantation, Eden cigar band. 13c, Factory, El Mambi band. 30c, Packing cigars, Lopez Hermanos band.

**1970, July 5**

**1534** A404 3c multicolored .25 .25
**1535** A404 13c multicolored 2.25 .70
**1536** A404 30c multicolored 3.25 1.00
*Nos. 1534-1536 (3)* 5.75 1.95

Projected Sugar Production: Over 10 Million Tons — A405

1c, Cane-crushing. 2c, Sowing and crop dusting. 3c, Cutting sugar cane. 10c, Transporting cane. 13c, Modern cutting machine. 30c, Intl. Brigade, cane cutters, vert. 1p, Sugar warehouse.

**1970, July 26**

**1537** A405 1c multicolored .25 .25
**1538** A405 2c multicolored .25 .25
**1539** A405 3c multicolored .25 .25
**1540** A405 10c multicolored 4.25 .45
**1541** A405 13c multicolored 1.50 .25
**1542** A405 30c multicolored 2.00 .75
**1543** A405 1p multicolored 4.00 2.00
*Nos. 1537-1543 (7)* 12.50 4.20

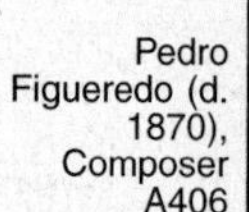

Pedro Figueredo (d. 1870), Composer A406

Versions of the Natl. Anthem.

**1970, Aug. 17**

**1544** A406 3c 1868 Version .30 .25
**1545** A406 20c 1898 Version 2.00 .60

Women's Federation, 10th Anniv. A407

**1970, Aug. 23**

**1546** A407 3c multi 1.00 .50

Militia, by Servando C. Moreno A408

Paintings in the Natl. Museum: 2c, Washerwomen, by Aristides Fernandez. 3c, Puerta del Sol, Madrid, by L. Paret Y Alcazar. 4c, Fishermen's Wives, by Joaquin Sorolla. 5c, Portrait of a Woman, by Thomas de Keyser. 13c, Mrs. Edward Foster, by Sir Thomas Lawrence. 30c, Tropical Gypsy, by Victor M. Garcia.

**1970, Aug. 31**

**1547** A408 1c shown .25 .25

**Size: 45x41mm**

**1548** A408 2c multi .25 .25
**1549** A408 3c multi .25 .25

**Size: 40x41mm**

**1550** A408 4c multi .25 .25

**Size: 38x45½mm**

**1551** A408 5c multi .25 .25
**1552** A408 13c multi 2.00 .50
**1553** A408 30c multi 3.00 .80
*Nos. 1547-1553 (7)* 6.25 2.55

See Nos. 1640-1646, 1669-1675, 1773-1779.

Havana Declaration, 10th Anniv. — A409

**1970, Sept. 2**

**1554** A409 3c Jose Marti Square .75 .25

Committee for the Defense of the Revolution, 10th Anniv. — A410

**1970, Sept. 28**

**1555** A410 3c multi .80 .25

39th Sugar Technician's Assoc. (ATAC) Conference — A411

**1970, Oct. 11**

**1556** A411 30c multi 3.00 .70

Wildlife A412

1c, Numida meleagris galeata. 2c, Dendrocygna arborea. 3c, Phasianus colchicus torquatus. 4c, Zenaida macroura macroura. 5c, Colinus virginianus cubanensis. 13c, Sus scrofa. 30c, Odocoileus virginianus.

**1970, Oct. 20**

**1557** A412 1c multicolored .75 .25
**1558** A412 2c multicolored 1.00 .25
**1559** A412 3c multicolored 1.00 .25
**1560** A412 4c multicolored 1.25 .25
**1561** A412 5c multicolored 1.50 .25
**1562** A412 13c multicolored 2.25 1.00
**1563** A412 30c multicolored 4.25 1.50
*Nos. 1557-1563 (7)* 12.00 3.75

Black-magic Feast, by M. Puente — A413

Afro-Cuban folk paintings: 3c, Hat Dance, by V.P. Landaluze. 10c, Los Hoyos Conga Dance, by Domingo Ravenet. 13c, Climax of the Rumba, by Eduardo Abela.

**1970, Nov. 5**

**Sizes: 36x48½mm (3c, 13c), 44½x44mm (10c)**

**1564** A413 1c shown .25 .25
**1565** A413 3c multi .35 .25
**1566** A413 10c multi .90 .45
**1567** A413 13c multi 2.50 .70
*Nos. 1564-1567 (4)* 4.00 1.65

Road Safety Week — A414

**1970, Nov. 15**

**1568** A414 3c Zebra, road signs .90 .25
**1569** A414 9c Prudence the Bear 1.30 .25

Intl. Education Year — A415

**1970, Nov. 20**

**1570** A415 13c Abacus, "a" 2.00 .30
**1571** A415 30c Cow, microscope 2.50 .70

### Christmas Type of 1961

Birds: No. 1572, Dives atroviolaceus. No. 1573, Glaucidium siju siju. No. 1574, Todus multicolor. No. 1575, Xiphidiopicus percussus percussus. No. 1576, Ferminia cerverai. No. 1577, Teretistris fornsi. No. 1578, Myadestes elisabeth elisabeth. No. 1579, Polioptila lembeyei. No. 1580, Vireo gundlachii gundlachii. No. 1581, Teretistris fernandinae. No. 1582, Torreornis inexpectata inexpectata. No. 1583, Chondrohierax wilsonii. No. 1584, Accipiter gundlachi. No. 1585, Starnoenas cyanocephala. No. 1586, Aratinga euops.

**1970, Dec. 1**

| | | | | |
|---|---|---|---|---|
| **1572** | A248 | 1c multicolored | .75 | .25 |
| **1573** | A249 | 1c multicolored | .75 | .25 |
| **1574** | A249 | 1c multicolored | .75 | .25 |
| **1575** | A249 | 1c multicolored | .75 | .25 |
| **1576** | A249 | 1c multicolored | .75 | .25 |
| *a.* | | Block of 5 + label, Nos. 1572-1576 | 5.00 | 5.00 |
| **1577** | A248 | 3c multicolored | 1.60 | .35 |
| **1578** | A249 | 3c multicolored | 1.60 | .35 |
| **1579** | A249 | 3c multicolored | 1.60 | .35 |
| **1580** | A249 | 3c multicolored | 1.60 | .35 |
| **1581** | A249 | 3c multicolored | 1.60 | .35 |
| *a.* | | Block of 5 + label, Nos. 1577-1581 | 10.00 | 10.00 |
| **1582** | A248 | 13c multicolored | 2.25 | .75 |
| **1583** | A249 | 13c multicolored | 2.25 | .75 |
| **1584** | A249 | 13c multicolored | 2.25 | .75 |
| **1585** | A249 | 13c multicolored | 2.25 | .75 |
| **1586** | A249 | 13c multicolored | 2.25 | .75 |
| *a.* | | Block of 5 + label, Nos. 1582-1586 | 15.00 | 15.00 |
| | | *Nos. 1572-1586 (15)* | 23.00 | 6.75 |

Christmas 1970. See note after No. 700.

Camilo Cienfuegos Military Academy A416

**1970, Dec. 2**

**1587** A416 3c multi .90 .25

7th Congress of the Intl. Organization of Journalists A417

**1971, Jan. 4**

**1588** A417 13c multi 2.10 .50

World Meteorology Day — A418

1c, Class, weather chart, computer, vert. 3c, Weather map. 8c, Equipment, vert.

**Size: 39½x35½mm (3c)**

**1971, Feb. 16**

| | | | | |
|---|---|---|---|---|
| **1589** | A418 | 1c multi | .25 | .25 |
| **1590** | A418 | 3c multi | .25 | .25 |
| **1591** | A418 | 8c multi | 1.00 | .25 |
| **1592** | A418 | 30c shown | 4.25 | 1.25 |
| | | *Nos. 1589-1592 (4)* | 5.75 | 2.00 |

6th Pan American Games, Cali, Colombia A419

1c, Emblem, vert. 2c, Women's running, vert. 3c, Rifle shooting. 4c, Gymnastics, vert. 5c, Boxing, vert. 13c, Water polo. 30c, Baseball.

**1971, Feb. 20**

| | | | | |
|---|---|---|---|---|
| **1593** | A419 | 1c multicolored | .25 | .25 |
| **1594** | A419 | 2c multicolored | .25 | .25 |
| **1595** | A419 | 3c multicolored | .25 | .25 |
| **1596** | A419 | 4c multicolored | .25 | .25 |
| **1597** | A419 | 5c multicolored | .25 | .25 |
| **1598** | A419 | 13c multicolored | 2.25 | .30 |
| **1599** | A419 | 30c multicolored | 2.75 | .55 |
| | | *Nos. 1593-1599 (7)* | 6.25 | 2.10 |

Porcelain and Mosaics in the Metropolitan Museum, Havana — A420

Designs: 1c, Parisian vase, 19th cent. 3c, Mexican bowl, 17th cent. 10c, Parisian vase, diff. 13c, Colosseum, Italian mosaic, 19th cent. 20c, Mexican bowl, 17th cent. 30c, St. Peter's Square, Italian mosaic, 19th cent.

**1971, Mar. 11**

**Sizes: 34½x53mm (1c, 10c), 46x53mm (3c), 42x48mm (20c)**

| | | | | |
|---|---|---|---|---|
| **1600** | A420 | 1c multi | .25 | .25 |
| **1601** | A420 | 3c multi | .25 | .25 |
| **1602** | A420 | 10c multi | .40 | .25 |
| **1603** | A420 | 13c shown | 2.25 | .25 |
| **1604** | A420 | 20c multi | 2.25 | .55 |
| **1605** | A420 | 30c multi | 2.75 | .65 |
| | | *Nos. 1600-1605 (6)* | 8.15 | 2.20 |

See Nos. 1699-1705.

Natl. Child Centers, 10th Anniv. — A421

**1971, Apr. 10**

**1606** A421 3c multicolored .85 .25

Manned Space Flight 10th Anniv. — A422

Cosmonauts in training.

**1971, Apr. 12**

| | | | | |
|---|---|---|---|---|
| **1607** | A422 | 1c multi | .25 | .25 |
| **1608** | A422 | 2c multi, diff. | .25 | .25 |
| **1609** | A422 | 3c multi, diff. | .25 | .25 |
| **1610** | A422 | 4c multi, diff. | .25 | .25 |
| **1611** | A422 | 5c multi, diff. | .25 | .25 |
| **1612** | A422 | 13c multi, diff. | 2.25 | .30 |
| **1613** | A422 | 30c multi, diff. | 3.00 | .65 |
| | | *Nos. 1607-1613 (7)* | 6.50 | 2.20 |

**Souvenir Sheet**

***Imperf***

**1614** A422 50c multi 8.00 8.00

Stamp in No. 1614 has simulated perf.

Bay of Pigs Invasion, 10th Anniv. — A423

**1971, Apr. 17**

**1615** A423 13c multi 3.00 .60

Stamp Day — A424

Packets: 13c, Jeune Richard attacking the Windsor Castle, 1807. 30c, Orinoco.

**1971, Apr. 24**

**1616** A424 13c multi 3.25 .90
**1617** A424 30c multi 4.50 1.00

Cuban Intl. Broadcast Service, 10th Anniv. A425

**1971, May 1** **Wmk. 376**

**1618** A425 3c multi .25 .25
**1619** A425 50c multi 4.00 .90

Orchids — A426

1c, Cattleya skinnerii. 2c, Vanda hibrida. 3c, Cypripedium collossum. 4c, Cypripedium gloucophyllum. 5c, Vanda tricolor. 13c, Cypripedium mowgh. 30c, Cypripedium solum.

**1971, May 15**

| | | | | |
|---|---|---|---|---|
| **1620** | A426 | 1c multicolored | .25 | .25 |
| **1621** | A426 | 2c multicolored | .25 | .25 |
| **1622** | A426 | 3c multicolored | .25 | .25 |
| **1623** | A426 | 4c multicolored | .25 | .25 |
| **1624** | A426 | 5c multicolored | .25 | .25 |
| **1625** | A426 | 13c multicolored | 2.25 | .45 |
| **1626** | A426 | 30c multicolored | 4.00 | .85 |
| | | *Nos. 1620-1626 (7)* | 7.50 | 2.55 |

See Nos. 1677-1683 and 1780-1786.

Enrique Loynaz del Castillo (b. 1861), Composer A427

3c, Portrait, Invasion Hymn.

**1971, June 5** **Wmk. 376**

**1627** A427 3c multicolored .90 .25

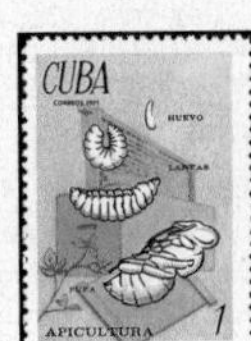
Bee Keeping — A428

**1971, June 20** **Unwmk.**

| | | | | |
|---|---|---|---|---|
| **1628** | A428 | 1c Egg, larvae, pupa | .25 | .25 |
| **1629** | A428 | 3c Worker | .25 | .25 |
| **1630** | A428 | 9c Drone | .50 | .25 |
| **1631** | A428 | 13c Defense of hive | 2.50 | .30 |
| **1632** | A428 | 30c Queen | 3.50 | .80 |
| | | *Nos. 1628-1632 (5)* | 7.00 | 1.85 |

Children's Drawings A429

1c, Sailboat. 3c, The Little Train. 9c, Sugar Cane Cutter. 10c, Return of the Fishermen. 13c, The Zoo. 20c, House and Garden. 30c, Landscape.

**1971, Aug. 30** **Size: 45x39mm**

**1633** A429 1c multi .25 .25
**1634** A429 3c multi .85 .25

**Sizes: 45½x35½mm (9c, 13c), 47x37½mm (10c)**

**1635** A429 9c multi .25 .25
**1636** A429 10c multi .40 .25
**1637** A429 13c multi 1.60 .30

**Size: 47x42mm**

**1638** A429 20c multi 2.50 .55

**Size: 31½x50mm**

**1639** A429 30c multi 2.75 .85
*Nos. 1633-1639 (7)* 8.60 2.70

### Art Type of 1970

Paintings in the Natl. Museum: 1c, St. Catherine of Alexandria, by F. Zurburan. 2c, The Cart, by Federico Americo. 3c, St. Christopher and Child, by J. Bassano. 4c, Little Devil, by Rene Portocarrero. 5c, Portrait of a Woman, by Nicolas Maes. 13c, Phoenix, by Raul Martinez. 30c, Sir William Pitt, by Thomas Gainsborough.

**1971, Sept. 20**

| | | | | |
|---|---|---|---|---|
| **1640** | A408 | 1c 31x55mm | .25 | .25 |
| **1641** | A408 | 2c 48x37mm | .25 | .25 |
| **1642** | A408 | 3c 31x55mm | .25 | .25 |
| **1643** | A408 | 4c 37x48mm | .25 | .25 |
| **1644** | A408 | 5c 37x48mm | .35 | .25 |
| **1645** | A408 | 13c 39x48½mm | 2.25 | .45 |
| **1646** | A408 | 30c 39x48½mm | 3.00 | .75 |
| | | *Nos. 1640-1646 (7)* | 6.60 | 2.45 |

Sport Fishing A431

1c, Albula vulpes. 2c, Seriola species. 3c, Micropterus salmoides. 4c, Coryphaena hippurus. 5c, Megalops atlantica. 13c, Acanthocybium solandri. 30c, Makaira ampla.

**1971, Oct. 30**

| | | | | |
|---|---|---|---|---|
| **1647** | A431 | 1c multicolored | .25 | .25 |
| **1648** | A431 | 2c multicolored | .25 | .25 |
| **1649** | A431 | 3c multicolored | .25 | .25 |
| **1650** | A431 | 4c multicolored | .25 | .25 |
| **1651** | A431 | 5c multicolored | .30 | .25 |
| **1652** | A431 | 13c multicolored | 2.00 | .55 |
| **1653** | A431 | 30c multicolored | 3.25 | .95 |
| | | *Nos. 1647-1653 (7)* | 6.55 | 2.75 |

19th World Amateur Baseball Championships — A432

**1971, Nov. 22** **Wmk. 376**

**1654** A432 3c shown .25 .25
**1655** A432 1p Globe as baseball 6.00 1.40

Execution of Medical Students, Cent. — A433

Paintings: 3c, Dr. Fermin Valdez Dominguez, anonymous. 13c, Execution of the Medical Students, by M. Mesa. 30c, Capt. Federico Capdevila, anonymous.

**1971, Nov. 27** **Unwmk.**

**Size: 61½x46mm (13c)**

**1656** A433 3c multi .35 .25
**1657** A433 13c multi 1.90 .40
**1658** A433 30c multi 2.75 .55
*Nos. 1656-1658 (3)* 5.00 1.20

Spindalis Zena Pretrei A434

Birds: 1c, Falco sparverius sparverioides vigors. 2c, Glaucidium siju siju. 3c, Priotelus temnurus temnurus. 4c, Saurothera merlini merlini. 5c, Nesoceleus fernandinae. 30c, Mimocichla plumbea rubripes. 50c, Chlorostilbon ricordii ricordii and Archilochus colubris. Nos. 1659-1663 vert.

**1971, Dec. 10**

**1659** A434 1c multi .40 .25
**1660** A434 2c multi .40 .25
**1661** A434 3c multi .50 .25
**1662** A434 4c multi .60 .25
**1663** A434 5c multi .75 .25
**1664** A434 13c shown 1.40 .55
**1665** A434 30c multi 2.75 1.00

**Size: 55½x29mm**

**1666** A434 50c multi 5.00 1.75
*Nos. 1659-1666 (8)* 11.80 4.55

Death centenary of Ramon de la Sagra, naturalist.

Cuba's Victory at the World Amateur Baseball Championships — A435

**1971, Dec. 8** **Wmk. 376**

**1667** A435 13c multi 1.50 .60

UNICEF, 25th Anniv. — A436

**1971, Dec. 11**

**1668** A436 13c multi 2.00 .70

**Art Type of 1970**

Paintings in the Natl. Museum: 1c, Arrival of an Ambassador, by Vittore Carpaccio. 2c, Senora Malpica, by G. Collazo. 3c, La Chorrera Tower, by Esteban Chartrand. 4c, Creole Landscape, by Carlos Enriquez. 5c, Sir William Lemon, by George Romney. 13c, Landscape, by Henry Cleenewerk. 30c, Valencia Beach, by Joaquin Sorolla y Bastida.

**1972, Jan. 25** **Unwmk.**

**1669** A408 1c 50x33mm .25 .25
**1670** A408 2c 27½x52mm .25 .25
**1671** A408 3c 50x33mm .25 .25
**1672** A408 4c 35x43mm .25 .25
**1673** A408 5c 35x43mm .25 .25
**1674** A408 13c 43x33mm 2.00 .40
**1675** A408 30c 43x33mm 3.50 .95
*Nos. 1669-1675 (7)* 6.75 2.60

Academy of Sciences, 10th Anniv. A437

13c, Capitol Type of 1929.

**1972, Feb. 20** **Wmk. 376**

**1676** A437 13c multi 1.90 .50

**Orchid Type of 1971**

1c, Brasso cattleya sindorossiana. 2c, Cypripedium doraeus. 3c, Cypripedium exul. 4c, Cypripedium rosy dawn. 5c, Cypripedium champolliom. 13c, Cypripedium bucolique. 30c, Cypripedium sullanum.

**1972, Feb. 25** **Unwmk.**

**1677** A426 1c multicolored .25 .25
**1678** A426 2c multicolored .25 .25
**1679** A426 3c multicolored .25 .25
**1680** A426 4c multicolored .25 .25
**1681** A426 5c multicolored .25 .25
**1682** A426 13c multicolored 2.25 .65
**1683** A426 30c multicolored 3.00 .80
*Nos. 1677-1683 (7)* 6.50 2.70

Eduardo Agramonte (1849-1872), Revolutionary, Physician — A438

3c, Portrait by F. Martinez.

**1972, Mar. 8**

**1684** A438 3c multi .75 .25

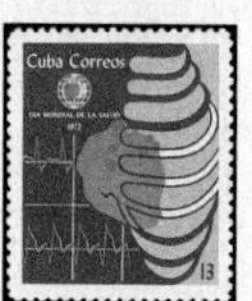

World Health Day — A439

**1972, Apr. 7** **Wmk. 376**

**1685** A439 13c multicolored 1.90 .50

Soviet Space Program A440

1c, Sputnik 1. 2c, Vostok 1. 3c, Valentina Tereshkova. 4c, Alexei Leonov. 5c, Lunokhod 1, moon vehicle. 13c, Linking Soyuz capsules. 30c, Victims of Soyuz 11 accident.

**1972, Apr. 12** **Unwmk.**

**1686** A440 1c multicolored .25 .25
**1687** A440 2c multicolored .25 .25
**1688** A440 3c multicolored .25 .25
**1689** A440 4c multicolored .25 .25
**1690** A440 5c multicolored .25 .25
**1691** A440 13c multicolored 2.10 .40
**1692** A440 30c multicolored 2.50 .70
*Nos. 1686-1692 (7)* 5.85 2.35

Stamp Day — A441

Designs: 13c, Postmaster-Gen. Vicente Mora Pera, by Ramon Loy. 30c, Soldier's Letter, Cuba to Venezuela, 1897.

**1972, Apr. 24**

**1693** A441 13c shown 1.50 .50

**Size: 48x39mm**

**1694** A441 30c multicolored 2.50 .55

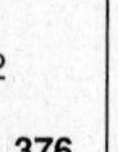

Labor Day — A442

**1972, May 1** **Wmk. 376**

**1695** A442 3c multicolored .90 .25

Jose Marti, Ho Chi Minh — A443

3rd Conference Against War in Indo-China, May 19 — A444

30c, Roses, conference emblem.

**1972, May 19**

**1696** A443 3c shown .40 .25
**1697** A444 13c shown 1.60 .40
**1698** A443 30c multicolored 2.00 .55
*Nos. 1696-1698 (3)* 4.00 1.20

**Metropolitan Museum Type of 1971**

Portraits: 1c, Salvador del Muro, by J. Del Rio. 2c, Luis de las Casas, by Del Rio. 3c, Cristopher Columbus, anonymous. 4c, Tomas Gamba, by V. Escobar. 5c, Maria Galarraga, by Escobar. 13c, Isabel II, by Federico Madrazo. 30c, Carlos III, by Miguel Melero.

**1972, May 25** **Unwmk.**

**Size: 34x43½mm**

**1699** A420 1c multi .25 .25
**1700** A420 2c multi .25 .25
**1701** A420 3c multi .25 .25
**1702** A420 4c multi .30 .25
**1703** A420 5c multi .30 .25

**Size: 34x51½mm**

**1704** A420 13c multi 1.75 .40
**1705** A420 30c multi 2.50 .70
*Nos. 1699-1705 (7)* 5.60 2.35

Children's Songs Competition, Natl. Library — A445

**1972, June 5** **Wmk. 376**

**1706** A445 3c multi .80 .25

Thoroughbred Horses — A446

**1972, June 30** **Unwmk.**

**1707** A446 1c Tarpan .25 .25
**1708** A446 2c Kertag .25 .25
**1709** A446 3c Creole .25 .25
**1710** A446 4c Andalusian .25 .25
**1711** A446 5c Arabian .25 .25
**1712** A446 13c Quarter horse 3.00 .55
**1713** A446 30c Pursang 3.50 .80
*Nos. 1707-1713 (7)* 7.75 2.60

Frank Pais (d. 1957), Educator, Revolutionary A447

**1972, July 26** **Wmk. 376**

**1714** A447 13c blk & red 1.50 .50

1972 Summer Olympics, Munich, Aug. 26-Sept. 10 — A448

1c, Athlete, emblems, vert. 2c, "M," boxing. 3c, "U," weight lifting. 4c, "N," fencing. 5c, "I," rifle shooting. 13c, "C," running. 30c, "H," basketball.
50c, Gymnastics.

**1972, Aug. 26** **Unwmk.**

**1715** A448 1c multicolored .25 .25
**1716** A448 2c multicolored .25 .25
**1717** A448 3c multicolored .25 .25
**1718** A448 4c multicolored .25 .25
**1719** A448 5c multicolored .25 .25
**1720** A448 13c multicolored 1.75 .35
**1721** A448 30c multicolored 2.25 .65
*Nos. 1715-1721 (7)* 5.25 2.25

**Souvenir Sheet**

***Imperf***

**1722** A448 50c multicolored 6.00 1.90

Stamp in No. 1722 has simulated perforations.

Intl. Hydrological Decade A449

Landscapes: 1c, Tree Trunks, by Domingo Ramos. 3c, Cyclone, by Tiburcio Lorenzo. 8c, Vinales, by Ramos. 30c, Forest and Brook, by Antonio R. Morey, vert.

**1972, Sept. 20**

**1723** A449 1c multi .25 .25
**1724** A449 3c multi .25 .25
**1725** A449 8c multi .80 .25
**1726** A449 30c multi 2.60 .50
*Nos. 1723-1726 (4)* 3.90 1.25

Butterflies from the Gundlach Collection A450

1c, Papilio thoas oviedo. 2c, Papilio devilliers. 3c, Papilio polixenes polixenes. 4c, Papilio androgeus epidaurus. 5c, Papilio cayguanabus. 13c, Papilio andraemon hernandezi. 30c, Papilio celadon.

**1972, Sept. 25**

**1727** A450 1c multicolored .25 .25
**1728** A450 2c multicolored .25 .25
**1729** A450 3c multicolored .25 .25
**1730** A450 4c multicolored .25 .25
**1731** A450 5c multicolored .30 .25
**1732** A450 13c multicolored 3.50 .85
**1733** A450 30c multicolored 4.75 1.10
*Nos. 1727-1733 (7)* 9.55 3.20

A451

Miguel de Cervantes Saavedra (1547-1616), Spanish Author — A452

Paintings by A. Fernandez: 3c, In La Mancha, vert. 13c, Battle with Wine Skins. 30c, Don Quixote de La Mancha, vert. 50c, Scene from Don Quixote, by Jose Moreno Carbonero.

**1972, Sept. 29**

**Size: 34½x46mm (3c, 30c)**

**1734** A451 3c multi .25 .25
**1735** A451 13c shown 2.10 .50
**1736** A451 30c multi 2.25 .55
*Nos. 1734-1736 (3)* 4.60 1.30

**Souvenir Sheet**

***Perf. 12½ on 3 Sides***

**1737** A452 50c shown 5.25 3.75

Guerrilla Day, 5th Anniv. A453

3c, Ernesto "Che" Guevara. 13c, Tamara "Tania" Bunke. 30c, Guido "Inti" Peredo.

**1972, Oct. 8**

| | | | | |
|---|---|---|---|---|
| **1738** | A453 | 3c multicolored | .25 | .25 |
| **1739** | A453 | 13c multicolored | 2.25 | .50 |
| **1740** | A453 | 30c multicolored | 2.40 | .60 |
| | | *Nos. 1738-1740 (3)* | 4.90 | 1.35 |

Traditional Musical Instruments A454

3c, Abwe (rattles). 13c, Bonko enchemiya (drum). 30c, Iya (drum).

**1972, Oct. 25**

| | | | | |
|---|---|---|---|---|
| **1741** | A454 | 3c multi | .25 | .25 |
| **1742** | A454 | 13c multi | 2.25 | .45 |
| **1743** | A454 | 30c multi | 2.25 | .55 |
| | | *Nos. 1741-1743 (3)* | 4.75 | 1.25 |

MATEX '72, 3rd Natl. Philatelic Exhibition, Matanzas — A455

**1972, Nov. 18** **Wmk. 376**

| | | | | |
|---|---|---|---|---|
| **1744** | A455 | 13c No. 467 | 2.50 | .45 |
| **1745** | A455 | 30c No. C49 | 3.25 | .55 |

Nos. 1744-1745 printed se-tenant with insribed labels picturing Type A232, emblem of the Cuban Philatelic Federation.

Historic Ships — A456

1c, Viking long boat, 6th-9th cent. 2c, Caravel, 15th cent., vert. 3c, Galleass, 16th cent. 4c, Galleon, 17th cent., vert. 5c, Clipper, 19th cent. 13c, Steam packet, 19th cent. 30c, Atomic icebreaker Lenin.

**1972, Nov. 30** **Unwmk.**

| | | | | |
|---|---|---|---|---|
| **1746** | A456 | 1c multicolored | .25 | .25 |
| **1747** | A456 | 2c multicolored | .25 | .25 |
| **1748** | A456 | 3c multicolored | .25 | .25 |
| **1749** | A456 | 4c multicolored | .30 | .25 |
| **1750** | A456 | 5c multicolored | .35 | .25 |
| **1751** | A456 | 13c multicolored | 2.10 | .75 |

**Size: 52½x29mm.**

| | | | | |
|---|---|---|---|---|
| **1752** | A456 | 30c multicolored | 4.25 | 1.25 |
| | | *Nos. 1746-1752 (7)* | 7.75 | 3.25 |

UNESCO Save Venice Campaign A457

3c, Lion of St. Mark. 13c, Bridge of Sighs, vert. 30c, St. Mark's Cathedral.

**1972, Dec. 8**

| | | | | |
|---|---|---|---|---|
| **1753** | A457 | 3c multicolored | .25 | .25 |
| **1754** | A457 | 13c multicolored | 1.75 | .45 |
| **1755** | A457 | 30c multicolored | 2.25 | .85 |
| | | *Nos. 1753-1755 (3)* | 4.25 | 1.55 |

Cuba, World Amateur Baseball Champion in 1972 — A458

**1972, Dec. 15**

| | | | | |
|---|---|---|---|---|
| **1756** | A458 | 3c Umpire | 1.25 | .30 |

Sport Events, 1972 — A459

**1972, Dec. 22**

| | | | | |
|---|---|---|---|---|
| **1757** | A459 | 1c shown | .25 | .25 |
| **1758** | A458 | 2c Pole vault | .25 | .25 |
| **1759** | A458 | 3c like No. 1756 | .25 | .25 |
| **1760** | A458 | 4c Wrestling | .25 | .25 |
| **1761** | A458 | 5c Fencing | .25 | .25 |
| **1762** | A458 | 13c Boxing | 1.60 | .55 |
| **1763** | A458 | 30c Marlin | 2.25 | .80 |
| | | *Nos. 1757-1763 (7)* | 5.10 | 2.60 |

Barrientos Memorial Athletics Championships, 11th Amateur Baseball Championships, Cerro Pelado Intl. Tournament, Central American and Caribbean Fencing Tournament, Giraldo Cordova Tournament, Ernest Hemingway Natl. Fishing Contest.

No. 1759 inscribed "XI serie nacional de beisbol aficionado."

Medals Won by Cubans at the 1972 Summer Olympics, Munich — A460

1c, Bronze, Women's 100-meter. 2c, Bronze, women's relay. 3c, Gold, 54kg boxing. 4c, Silver, 81kg boxing. 5c, Bronze, 51kg boxing. 13c, Gold, 87kg boxing. 30c, Gold, silver cup, heavyweight boxing. 50c, Bronze, basketball.

**1973, Jan. 28**

| | | | | |
|---|---|---|---|---|
| **1764** | A460 | 1c multi | .25 | .25 |
| **1765** | A460 | 2c multi | .25 | .25 |
| **1766** | A460 | 3c multi | .25 | .25 |
| **1767** | A460 | 4c multi | .25 | .25 |
| **1768** | A460 | 5c multi | .25 | .25 |
| **1769** | A460 | 13c multi | 1.75 | .60 |
| **1770** | A460 | 30c multi | 2.25 | .90 |
| | | *Nos. 1764-1770 (7)* | 5.25 | 2.75 |

**Souvenir Sheet**

***Imperf***

| | | | | |
|---|---|---|---|---|
| **1771** | A460 | 50c multi | 6.25 | 2.25 |

Stamp in No. 1771 has simulated perforations.

Portrait by A.M. Esquivel — A461

**1973, Feb. 10**

| | | | | |
|---|---|---|---|---|
| **1772** | A461 | 13c multi | 2.00 | .45 |

Gertrudis Gomez de Avellaneda (1814-1873), poet.

**Art Type of 1970**

Paintings in the Natl. Museum: 1c, Bathers in the Lagoon, by C. Enriquez. 2c, Still-life, by W.C. Heda. 3c, Gallantry, by P. Landaluze. 4c, Return in the Late Afternoon, by C. Troyon. 5c, Elizabetta Mascagni, by F.X. Fabre. 13c, The Picador, by De Lucas Padilla, horiz. 30c, In the Garden, by Arburu Morell.

**1973, Feb. 28**

**Sizes: 36x46mm, 46x36mm**

| | | | | |
|---|---|---|---|---|
| **1773** | A408 | 1c multi | .25 | .25 |
| **1774** | A408 | 2c multi | .25 | .25 |
| **1775** | A408 | 3c multi | .25 | .25 |
| **1776** | A408 | 4c multi | .25 | .25 |
| **1777** | A408 | 5c multi | .25 | .25 |
| **1778** | A408 | 13c multi | 1.75 | .55 |
| **1779** | A408 | 30c multi | 2.50 | .80 |
| | | *Nos. 1773-1779 (7)* | 5.50 | 2.60 |

**Orchid Type of 1971**

1c, Dendrobium hybrid. 2c, Cypripedium exul. 3c, Vanda miss. joaquin rose marie. 4c, Phalaenopsis schilleriana. 5c, Vanda gilbert tribulet. 13c, Dendrobium hybrid, diff. 30c, Arachnis catherine.

**1973, Mar. 26**

| | | | | |
|---|---|---|---|---|
| **1780** | A426 | 1c multicolored | .25 | .25 |
| **1781** | A426 | 2c multicolored | .25 | .25 |
| **1782** | A426 | 3c multicolored | .25 | .25 |
| **1783** | A426 | 4c multicolored | .30 | .25 |
| **1784** | A426 | 5c multicolored | .35 | .25 |
| **1785** | A426 | 13c multicolored | 2.50 | .55 |
| **1786** | A426 | 30c multicolored | 3.25 | .80 |
| | | *Nos. 1780-1786 (7)* | 7.15 | 2.60 |

A462

**1973, Apr. 7** **Wmk. 376**

| | | | | |
|---|---|---|---|---|
| **1787** | A462 | 10c multi, *buff* | 1.10 | .30 |

World Health Day. World Health Organization, 25th anniv.

Anti-Polio Campaign A463

**1973, Apr. 9** **Unwmk.**

| | | | | |
|---|---|---|---|---|
| **1788** | A463 | 3c multi | .75 | .25 |

Soviet Space Program A464

1c, Soyuz rocket launch, vert. 2c, Luna 1, Moon. 3c, Luna 16 taking-off from Moon, vert. 4c, Venera 7. 5c, Molniya 1, vert. 13c, Mars 3. 30c, Radar observation ship, Yuri Gagarin.

**1973, Apr. 12**

| | | | | |
|---|---|---|---|---|
| **1789** | A464 | 1c multicolored | .25 | .25 |
| **1790** | A464 | 2c multicolored | .25 | .25 |
| **1791** | A464 | 3c multicolored | .25 | .25 |
| **1792** | A464 | 4c multicolored | .25 | .25 |
| **1793** | A464 | 5c multicolored | .25 | .25 |
| **1794** | A464 | 13c multicolored | 1.25 | .70 |
| **1795** | A464 | 30c multicolored | 3.50 | .85 |
| | | *Nos. 1789-1795 (7)* | 6.00 | 2.80 |

Stamp Day — A465

Postmarks: 13c, Santiago de Cuba, 1760. 30c, Havana, 1760.

**1973, Apr. 24**

| | | | | |
|---|---|---|---|---|
| **1796** | A465 | 13c multi | 2.00 | .50 |
| **1797** | A465 | 30c multi | 2.10 | .60 |

See Nos. 1888-1891.

Portrait by A. Espinosa — A466

**1973, May 11**

| | | | | |
|---|---|---|---|---|
| **1798** | A466 | 13c multi | 1.50 | .45 |

Maj.-Gen. Ignacio Agramonte (1841-1873).

Birthplace, Torun, and Inventions A467

Copernicus Monument, Warsaw — A468

13c, Copernicus, spacecraft. 30c, Manuscript, Frombork Tower.

**1973, May 25**

| | | | | |
|---|---|---|---|---|
| **1799** | A467 | 3c shown | .25 | .25 |
| **1800** | A467 | 13c multicolored | 1.75 | .45 |
| **1801** | A467 | 30c multicolored | 3.00 | .60 |
| | | *Nos. 1799-1801 (3)* | 5.00 | 1.30 |

**Souvenir Sheet**

***Perf. 12½ on 3 Sides***

| | | | | |
|---|---|---|---|---|
| **1802** | A468 | 50c shown | 6.25 | 2.25 |

500th anniversary of the birth of Nicolaus Copernicus (1473-1543), Polish astronomer.

Improvement of School Education A469

**1973, June 12** **Wmk. 376**

| | | | | |
|---|---|---|---|---|
| **1803** | A469 | 13c multi | 1.25 | .25 |

Cattle — A470

**1973, June 28** **Unwmk.**

| | | | | |
|---|---|---|---|---|
| **1804** | A470 | 1c Jersey | .25 | .25 |
| **1805** | A470 | 2c Charolaise | .25 | .25 |
| **1806** | A470 | 3c Creole | .25 | .25 |
| **1807** | A470 | 4c Swiss | .25 | .25 |
| **1808** | A470 | 5c Holstein | .25 | .25 |
| **1809** | A470 | 13c Santa Gertrudis | 1.50 | .40 |
| **1810** | A470 | 30c Brahman | 3.00 | .75 |
| | | *Nos. 1804-1810 (7)* | 5.75 | 2.40 |

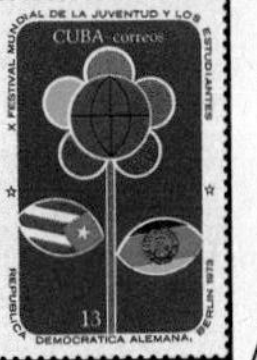


A471

**1973, July 10** **Wmk. 376**

| | | | | |
|---|---|---|---|---|
| **1811** | A471 | 13c multi | 1.40 | .30 |

10th Communist Festival of Youths and Students, East Berlin.

A472

3c, Siboney Farm, Santiago de Cuba. 13c, Moncada Barracks. 30c, Revolution Plaza, Havana.

**1973, July 26** **Unwmk.**
**1812** A472 3c multicolored .35 .25
**1813** A472 13c multicolored 1.40 .30
**1814** A472 30c multicolored 2.25 .45
*Nos. 1812-1814 (3)* 4.00 1.00

20th anniv. of the Revolution.

10th Anniv. of the Revolutionary Navy — A473

3c, Midshipman, missile frigate.

**1973, Aug. 3** **Wmk. 376**
**1815** A473 3c multicolored 1.00 .30

Interior, by Manuel Vicens — A474

Paintings in the Natl. Museum: 1c, Amalia of Saxony, by J.K. Rossler. 3c, Margarita of Austria, by J. Pantoja de la Cruz. 4c, City Hall Official, anonymous. 5c, View of Santiago de Cuba, by Hernandez Giro. 13c, The Catalan, by J.J. Tejada. 30c, Alley in Guayo, by Tejada.

**1973, Aug. 30** **Unwmk.**
**Sizes: 26½x41mm (1c, 3c), 28½x39mm (4c, 13c, 30c)**
**1816** A474 1c multi .25 .25
**1817** A474 2c multi .25 .25
**1818** A474 3c multi .25 .25
**1819** A474 4c multi .25 .25
**1820** A474 5c multi .25 .25
**1821** A474 13c multi 1.90 .60
**1822** A474 30c multi 2.25 .70
*Nos. 1816-1822 (7)* 5.40 2.55

WMO Emblem, Paintings by J. Madrazo A475

**1973, Sept. 4**
**1823** A475 8c Spring 1.00 .25
**1824** A475 8c Summer 1.00 .25
**1825** A475 8c Fall 1.00 .25
**1826** A475 8c Winter 1.00 .25
*Nos. 1823-1826 (4)* 4.00 1.00

World Meteorogical Organization, cent. Nos. 1823-1826 printed se-tenant in strips of 4; frame reversed on 2nd and 4th stamp in strip.

A476

27th World and 1st Pan American Weight Lifting Championships: Various weightlifting positions.

**1973, Sept. 12**
**1827** A476 1c multi, diff. .25 .25
**1828** A476 2c shown .25 .25
**1829** A476 3c multi, diff. .25 .25
**1830** A476 4c multi, diff. .25 .25
**1831** A476 5c multi, diff. .25 .25
**1832** A476 13c multi, diff. 1.25 .45
**1833** A476 30c multi, diff. 2.25 .75
*Nos. 1827-1833 (7)* 4.75 2.45

A477

Flowering plants: 1c, Erythrina standleyana. 2c, Lantana camara. 3c, Canavalia maritima. 4c, Dichromena colorata. 5c, Borrichia arborescens. 13c, Anguria pedata. 30c, Cordia sebestena.

**1973, Sept. 28**
**1834** A477 1c multicolored .25 .25
**1835** A477 2c multicolored .25 .25
**1836** A477 3c multicolored .25 .25
**1837** A477 4c multicolored .25 .25
**1838** A477 5c multicolored .25 .25
**1839** A477 13c multicolored 2.10 .65
**1840** A477 30c multicolored 3.00 .90
*Nos. 1835-1840 (6)* 6.10 2.55

8th World Trade Union Congress, Varna, Bulgaria A478

**1973, Oct. 5** **Wmk. 376**
**1841** A478 13c multi 1.40 .35

Cuban Natl. Ballet, 25th Anniv. — A479

**1973, Oct. 28** **Unwmk.**
**1842** A479 13c gold & brt ultra 2.00 .40

Sea Shells — A480

1c, Liguus fasciatus fasciatus. 2c, Liguus fasciatus guitarti. 3c, Liguus fasciatus whartoni. 4c, Liguus fasciatus angelae. 5c, Liguus fasciatus trinidadense. 13c, Liguus blainianus. 30c, Liguus vittatus.

**1973, Oct. 29**
**1843** A480 1c multicolored .25 .25
**1844** A480 2c multicolored .25 .25
**1845** A480 3c multicolored .25 .25
**1846** A480 4c multicolored .25 .25
**1847** A480 5c multicolored .25 .25
**1848** A480 13c multicolored 2.60 .70
**1849** A480 30c multicolored 3.50 .85
*Nos. 1843-1849 (7)* 7.35 2.80

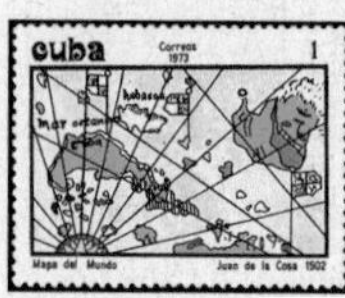

Maps of Cuba — A481

1c, Juan de la Cosa, 1502. 3c, Ortelius, 1572. 13c, Bellini, 1762. 40c, 1973.

**1973, Oct. 29**
**1850** A481 1c multi .25 .25
**1851** A481 3c multi .25 .25
**1852** A481 13c multi 2.00 .25
**1853** A481 40c multi 2.25 .80
*Nos. 1850-1853 (4)* 4.75 1.55

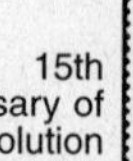

15th Anniversary of the Revolution A482

**1974, Jan. 2**
**1854** A482 1c No. 625 .25 .25
**1855** A482 3c No. 626 .25 .25
**1856** A482 13c No. C200 1.75 .55
**1857** A482 40c No. C201 3.50 .80
*Nos. 1854-1857 (4)* 5.75 1.85

Woman, by F. Ponce de Leon — A483

Portraits in the Camaguey Museum: 3c, Mexican Girls, by J. Arche. 8c, Young Woman, by A. Menocal. 10c, Mulatto Woman Drinking from Coconut, by L. Romanach. 13c, Head of an Old Man, by J. Arburu.

**1974, Jan. 10**
**1858** A483 1c multi .25 .25
**1859** A483 3c multi .25 .25
**1860** A483 8c multi .35 .25
**1861** A483 10c multi 1.25 .25
**1862** A483 13c multi 1.75 .40
*Nos. 1858-1862 (5)* 3.85 1.40

Amilcar Cabral — A484

**1974, Jan. 20**
**1863** A484 13c multi 1.30 .25

Amilcar Cabral, Guinea-Bissau freedom fighter, 1st death anniv.

Lenin, by I.V. Kosmin — A485

**1974, Jan. 21**
**1864** A485 30c multi 2.75 .55

50th death anniv. of Lenin.

12th Central American and Caribbean Games, Santo Domingo — A486

**1974, Feb. 8**
**1865** A486 1c Emblem .25 .25
**1866** A486 2c Javelin .25 .25
**1867** A486 3c Boxing .25 .25
**1868** A486 4c Baseball, horiz. .25 .25
**1869** A486 13c Basketball, horiz. 1.50 .25
**1870** A486 30c Volleyball, horiz. 2.00 .70
*Nos. 1865-1870 (6)* 4.50 1.95

Portrait by F. Martinez — A487

**1974, Feb. 27**
**1871** A487 13c multi 1.25 .25

Carlos M. de Cespedes (d. 1874), patriot.

Portrait of a Man, by J.B. Vermay — A488

Paintings in the Natl. Museum: 2c, The Wet Nurse, by C.A. Van Loo. 3c, Cattle in River, by R. Morey. 4c, Village, by Morey. 13c, Faun and Bacchus, by Rubens. 30c, Young Woman Playing Cards, by R. Madrazo.

**1974, Mar. 7**
**1872** A488 1c shown .25 .25
**1873** A488 2c multi .25 .25
**1874** A488 3c multi .25 .25
**1875** A488 4c multi .25 .25
**1876** A488 13c multi 1.25 .25
**1877** A488 30c multi 2.00 .55
*Nos. 1872-1877 (6)* 4.25 1.80

Council for Mutual Economic Assistance (COMECON), 25th Anniv. — A489

30c, Comecon building, Moscow.

**1974, Mar. 15**
**1878** A489 30c multicolored 2.00 .70

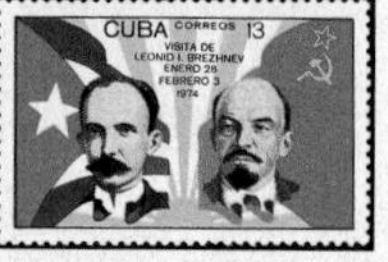

Visit of Leonid I. Brezhnev to Cuba, Jan. 28-Feb. 3 — A490

13c, Jose Marti, Lenin, flags. 30c, Brezhnev, Fidel Castro.

**1974, Mar. 28**
**1879** A490 13c multicolored 2.00 .30
**1880** A490 30c multicolored 2.10 .55
*Nos. 1879-1880 (2)* 4.10 .85

Science Fiction — A491

Paintings by A. Sokolov: 1c, Martian Crater. 2c, Fiery Labyrinth. 3c, Amber Wave. 4c, Flight Through Space. 13c, Planet in Nebula. 30c, World of Two Suns.

**1974, Apr. 12**
**1881** A491 1c multi .25 .25
**1882** A491 2c multi .25 .25
**1883** A491 3c multi .25 .25
**1884** A491 4c multi .25 .25
**1885** A491 13c multi 1.60 .25
**1886** A491 30c multi 2.75 .60
*Nos. 1881-1886 (6)* 5.35 1.85

Cosmonauts Day.

UPU, Cent. — A492

**1974, Apr. 15**
**1887** A492 30c Letter, 1874 2.50 .60

**Stamp Day Type of 1973**

Postmarks.

**1974, Apr. 24**

| | | | | |
|---|---|---|---|---|
| **1888** | A465 | 1c Havana | .25 | .25 |
| **1889** | A465 | 3c Matanzas | .30 | .25 |
| **1890** | A465 | 13c Trinidad | 1.40 | .25 |
| **1891** | A465 | 20c Guana Vacoa | 2.00 | .35 |
| | | *Nos. 1888-1891 (4)* | 3.95 | 1.10 |

18th Sports Congress of Friendly Armies — A493

**1974, May 5** **Wmk. 376**
**1892** A493 3c multi .80 .25

Felipe Poey (1799-1891), Naturalist A494

1c, Eumaeus atala atala. 2c, Pineria terebra. 3c, Chaetodon sedentarius. 4c, Eurema dina dina. 13c, Hemitrochus fuscolabiata. 30c, Eupomacentrus partitus. 50c, Apogon binotatus.

1c, 4c, Butterflies. 2c, 13c, Sea shells. 3c, 30c, 50c, Fish.

**1974, May 26** ***Perf. 12½x12***

| | | | | |
|---|---|---|---|---|
| **1893** | A494 | 1c multicolored | .25 | .25 |
| **1894** | A494 | 2c multicolored | .25 | .25 |
| **1895** | A494 | 3c multicolored | .25 | .25 |
| **1896** | A494 | 4c multicolored | .60 | .25 |
| **1897** | A494 | 13c multicolored | 2.25 | .45 |
| **1898** | A494 | 30c multicolored | 3.00 | .55 |
| | | *Nos. 1893-1898 (6)* | 6.60 | 2.00 |

**Souvenir Sheet**

***Imperf***

**1899** A494 50c multicolored 7.00 2.50

Stamp in No. 1899 has simulated perforations.

Havana Philharmonic Orchestra, 50th Anniv. — A495

1c, Antonio Mompo, cello. 3c, Cesar Perez Sentenat, piano. 5c, Pedro Mercado, trumpet. 10c, Pedro Sanjuan, Havana Philharmonic emblem. 13c, Roberto Ondina, flute.

**1974, June 8** ***Perf. 12½***

| | | | | |
|---|---|---|---|---|
| **1900** | A495 | 1c multi | .25 | .25 |
| **1901** | A495 | 3c multi | .25 | .25 |
| **1902** | A495 | 5c multi | .25 | .25 |
| **1903** | A495 | 10c multi | 1.40 | .25 |
| **1904** | A495 | 13c multi | 1.60 | .25 |
| | | *Nos. 1900-1904 (5)* | 3.75 | 1.25 |

Garden Flowers — A496

1c, Heliconia humilis. 2c, Anthurium andraeanum. 3c, Canna generalis. 4c, Alpinia purpurata. 13c, Gladiolus grandiflorus. 30c, Amomum capitatum.

**1974, June 12**

| | | | | |
|---|---|---|---|---|
| **1905** | A496 | 1c multicolored | .25 | .25 |
| **1906** | A496 | 2c multicolored | .25 | .25 |
| **1907** | A496 | 3c multicolored | .25 | .25 |
| **1908** | A496 | 4c multicolored | .25 | .25 |
| **1909** | A496 | 13c multicolored | 1.50 | .25 |
| **1910** | A496 | 30c multicolored | 4.25 | .60 |
| | | *Nos. 1905-1910 (6)* | 6.75 | 1.85 |

A497

World Amateur Boxing Championships: Emblem and various boxers.

***Perf. 12x12½***

**1974, Aug. 24** **Litho.** **Unwmk.**

| | | | | |
|---|---|---|---|---|
| **1911** | A497 | 1c multi | .25 | .25 |
| **1912** | A497 | 3c multi | .35 | .25 |
| **1913** | A497 | 13c multi | 1.50 | .25 |
| | | *Nos. 1911-1913 (3)* | 2.10 | .75 |

Extinct Birds — A498

1c, Dodo. 3c, Ara de Cuba (parrot). 8c, Passenger pigeon. 10c, Moa. 13c, Great auk.

**1974, Aug. 28** ***Perf. 13***

| | | | | |
|---|---|---|---|---|
| **1914** | A498 | 1c multi | .40 | .25 |
| **1915** | A498 | 3c multi | .40 | .25 |
| **1916** | A498 | 8c multi | .85 | .25 |
| **1917** | A498 | 10c multi | 2.75 | .55 |
| **1918** | A498 | 13c multi | 3.50 | .80 |
| | | *Nos. 1914-1918 (5)* | 7.90 | 2.10 |

Pres. Salvador Allende of Chile (d. 1973) — A499

**1974, Sept. 11**
**1919** A499 13c multi 1.60 .45

Wildflowers — A500

1c, Suriana maritima. 3c, Cassia ligustrina. 8c, Flaveria linearis. 10c, Stachytarpheta jamaicensis. 13c, Bacopa monnieri.

**1974, Sept. 14** ***Perf. 13x12½***

| | | | | |
|---|---|---|---|---|
| **1920** | A500 | 1c multi | .25 | .25 |
| **1921** | A500 | 3c multi | .25 | .25 |
| **1922** | A500 | 8c multi | .30 | .25 |
| **1923** | A500 | 10c multi | 2.10 | .25 |
| **1924** | A500 | 13c multi | 3.25 | .85 |
| | | *Nos. 1920-1924 (5)* | 6.15 | 1.85 |

Model Aircraft — A501

3c, Sky diving. 8c, Glider. 10c, Crop dusting. 13c, Commercial aviation.

**1974, Sept. 22** ***Perf. 12½***

| | | | | |
|---|---|---|---|---|
| **1925** | A501 | 1c shown | .25 | .25 |
| **1926** | A501 | 3c multi | .25 | .25 |
| **1927** | A501 | 8c multi | .45 | .25 |
| **1928** | A501 | 10c multi | 1.10 | .25 |
| **1929** | A501 | 13c multi | 2.00 | .25 |
| | | *Nos. 1925-1929 (5)* | 4.05 | 1.25 |

Civil Aeronautic Institute, 10th anniv. Nos. 1927-1929 horiz.

History of Cuban Baseball A502

1c, Indians playing ball. 3c, 1st Official game, 1874. 8c, Emilio Sabourin. 10c, Umpire, players, 1974. 13c, Latin-American Stadium, Havana.

**1974, Oct. 3** ***Perf. 13***

| | | | | |
|---|---|---|---|---|
| **1930** | A502 | 1c multicolored | .25 | .25 |
| **1931** | A502 | 3c multicolored | .25 | .25 |
| **1932** | A502 | 8c multicolored | .40 | .25 |
| **1933** | A502 | 10c multicolored | 1.20 | .25 |
| **1934** | A502 | 13c multicolored | 1.90 | .25 |
| | | *Nos. 1930-1934 (5)* | 4.00 | 1.25 |

Nos. 1930-1932 vert.

Mambi 10c Stamp (Revolutionary Junta Issue), Cent. — A503

**1974, Oct. 10**
**1935** A503 13c multi 1.25 .25

16th Conference of Customs Organizations of Socialist Countries A504

30c, Comecon Building, Moscow.

**1974, Oct. 15**
**1936** A504 30c multicolored 1.90 .55

Disappearance of Major Camilo Cienfuegos, 15th Anniv. — A505

**Wmk. 376**

**1974, Oct. 28** **Litho.** ***Perf. 13***
**1937** A505 3c multi 1.00 .25

8th World Mining Conference A506

**1974, Nov. 3**
**1938** A506 13c multi 2.00 .25

Petroleum Institute, 15th Anniv. — A507

**1974, Nov. 20**
**1939** A507 3c multi .70 .25

Intersputnik Earth Station Opening A508

13c, Satellite, satellite dish. 1p, Satellite, flags.

**1974, Nov. 30** **Unwmk.**

| | | | | |
|---|---|---|---|---|
| **1940** | A508 | 3c shown | .25 | .25 |
| **1941** | A508 | 13c multicolored | 1.25 | .25 |
| **1942** | A508 | 1p multicolored | 2.75 | 1.10 |
| | | *Nos. 1940-1942 (3)* | 4.25 | 1.60 |

Philatelic Federation, 10th Anniv. — A509

**1974, Nov. 30** ***Perf. 12½x13***
**1943** A509 30c multi 2.40 .45

**Souvenir Sheet**

Mercury — A510

**1974, Dec. 6** ***Imperf.***
**1944** A510 50c multi 6.00 1.25

4th Natl. Phil. Exhib., Havana.

1st World Peace Congress, 25th Anniv. — A511

30c, *F. Joliot-Curie,* by Picasso.

**1974, Dec. 16** **Wmk. 376** ***Perf. 13***
**1945** A511 30c red, blk & buff 3.00 .45

Ruben Martinez Villena (b. 1899), Revolutionary A512

**1974, Dec. 20** **Unwmk.**
**1946** A512 3c red org & yel 1.25 .25

**Souvenir Sheet**

Cuban Victories, 1st Amateur Boxing Championships — A513

**1975, Jan. 6** **Litho.** ***Imperf.***
**1947** A513 50c Trophy 6.25 1.25

*The Word,* by Marcelo Pogolotti A514

Paintings in the Natl. Museum: 2c, *The Silk-Cotton Tree,* by Henry Cleenewerk. 3c, *Landscape,* by Guillermo Collazo. 5c, *Still-life,* by Francisco Peralta. 13c, *Maria Wilson,* by Federico Martinez, vert. 30c, *The Couple,* by Mariano Fortuny.

**1975, Jan. 20** ***Perf. 13***

| | | | | |
|---|---|---|---|---|
| **1948** | A514 | 1c multi | .25 | .25 |
| **1949** | A514 | 2c multi | .25 | .25 |
| **1950** | A514 | 3c multi | .25 | .25 |
| **1951** | A514 | 5c multi | .25 | .25 |

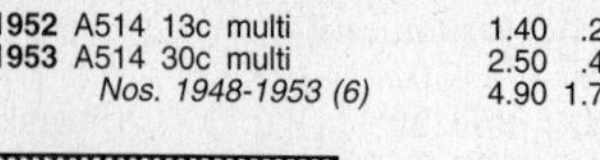

**1952** A514 13c multi 1.40 .25
**1953** A514 30c multi 2.50 .45
*Nos. 1948-1953 (6)* 4.90 1.70

Intl. Women's Year — A515

**1975, Feb. 6**
**1954** A515 13c multi 1.10 .25

Fishing Industry — A516

Various fish and fishing vessels: 1c, Long-finned tuna. 2c, Tuna. 3c, Mediterranean grouper. 8c, Hake. 13c, Prawn. 30c, Lobster.

**1975, Feb. 22**
**1955** A516 1c multicolored .25 .25
**1956** A516 2c multicolored .25 .25
**1957** A516 3c multicolored .25 .25
**1958** A516 8c multicolored .25 .25
**1959** A516 13c multicolored .85 .70
**1960** A516 30c multicolored 3.00 .70
*Nos. 1955-1960 (6)* 4.85 2.40

Minerals A517

**1975, Mar. 15 Litho. *Perf. 13x12½***
**1961** A517 3c Nickel .40 .25
**1962** A517 13c Copper 1.60 .25
**1963** A517 30c Chromium 3.00 .45
*Nos. 1961-1963 (3)* 5.00 .95

Cosmonaut's Day — A518

1c, Cosmodrome. 2c, Probe, vert. 3c, Eclipse. 5c, Threshold to Space. 13c, Midday on Mars. 30c, Cosmonaut's view of Earth.

**1975, Apr. 12 *Perf. 13x12½, 12½x13***
**1964** A518 1c multicolored .25 .25
**1965** A518 2c multicolored .25 .25
**1966** A518 3c multicolored .25 .25
**1967** A518 5c multicolored .30 .25
**1968** A518 13c multicolored 1.40 .25
**1969** A518 30c multicolored 2.25 .45
*Nos. 1964-1969 (6)* 4.70 1.70

The future of space.

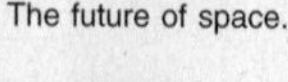

Stamp Day — A519

Various covers.

**1975, Apr. 24 *Perf. 13***
**1970** A519 3c multi .25 .25
**1971** A519 13c multi 1.40 .25
**1972** A519 30c multi 2.10 .40
*Nos. 1970-1972 (3)* 3.75 .90

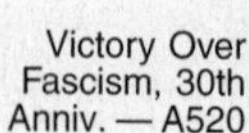

Victory Over Fascism, 30th Anniv. — A520

Design: Raising red flag over Reichstag, Berlin.

**1975, May 9 *Perf. 13x12½***
**1973** A520 30c multi 2.00 .40

A521

Works in the Decorative Art Museum — A522

1c, Sevres porcelain vase, vert. 2c, Meissen porcelain statue *Shepherdess and Dancers,* vert. 3c, Chinese porcelain dish *Lady with Parasol.* 5c, Chinese screen detail *The Phoenix,* vert. 13c, *Allegory of Music,* by Francois Boucher (1703-70), vert. 30c, *Portrait of a Lady,* by L. Tocque, vert. 50c, *The Swing,* by Hubert Robert (1733-1808).

**1975, May 10 *Perf. 12½x13, 13x12½***
**1974** A521 1c multi .25 .25
**1975** A521 2c multi .25 .25
**1976** A521 3c shown .25 .25
**1977** A521 5c multi .45 .25
**1978** A521 13c multi 1.40 .25
**1979** A521 30c multi 1.90 .40
*Nos. 1974-1979 (6)* 4.50 1.65

**Souvenir Sheet**
***Perf. 13x12½ on 3 Sides***
**1980** A522 50c shown 5.25 1.25

No. 1980 contains one 25x39mm stamp.

Intl. Children's Day — A523

**Wmk. 376**
**1975, May 31 Litho. *Perf. 13***
**1981** A523 3c multi .50 .25

Indigenous Birds — A524

Designs: 1c, Vireo gundlachi. 2c, Gymnoglaux lawrenci. 3c, Aratingo eoups. 5c, Staroenas cyanocephala. 13c, Chondrohierax wilsoni. 30c, Cyanolimnas cerverai.

**1975, June 18 Unwmk.**
**1982** A524 1c multicolored .25 .25
**1983** A524 2c multicolored .25 .25
**1984** A524 3c multicolored .25 .25
**1985** A524 5c multicolored .40 .25
**1986** A524 13c multicolored 1.75 .40
**1987** A524 30c multicolored 2.50 .70
*Nos. 1982-1987 (6)* 5.40 2.10

See Nos. 2121-2125, 2180-2182, C276-C276.

Scientific Investigation Center, 10th Anniv. A525

**1975, July 1 *Perf. 12½***
**1988** A525 13c multi 1.40 .25

Irrigation and Drainage Commission, 25th Anniv. — A526

**1975, Aug. 2 *Perf. 13***
**1989** A526 13c multi 1.40 .25

Afforestation — A527

Designs: 1c, Cedrela mexicana. 3c, Swietenia mahagoni. 5c, Calophyllum brasiliense. 13c, Hibiscus tiliaceus. 30c, Pinus caribaea.

**1975, Aug. 20**
**1990** A527 1c multicolored .25 .25
**1991** A527 3c multicolored .40 .25
**1992** A527 5c multicolored .40 .25
**1993** A527 13c multicolored 1.25 .25
**1994** A527 30c multicolored 1.90 .40
*Nos. 1990-1994 (5)* 4.20 1.40

Cuban Women's Federation, 15th Anniv. — A528

**1975, Aug. 23**
**1995** A528 3c multi .75 .25

Intl. Conference on the Independence of Puerto Rico — A529

**1975, Sept. 5 Litho.**
**1996** A529 13c multi 1.10 .25

A530

7th Pan American Games, Mexico: Aztec calendar stone and various athletes.

**1975, Sept. 20 *Perf. 12½x13***
**1997** A530 1c Baseball .25 .25
**1998** A530 3c Boxing .25 .25
**1999** A530 5c Basketball .25 .25
**2000** A530 13c High jump 1.50 .30
**2001** A530 30c Weight lifting 2.00 .30
*Nos. 1997-2001 (5)* 4.25 1.35

**Souvenir Sheet**
***Imperf***
**2002** A530 50c Stone, emblem 5.00 1.25

A531

**1975, Sept. 28 *Perf. 12½x13***
**2003** A531 3c multi .75 .25

Revolutionary Defense Committees (CDR), 15th anniv.

Friendship Among the Peoples Institute, 15th Anniv. — A532

**1975, Oct. 8 *Perf. 12½x13***
**2004** A532 3c multi .50 .25

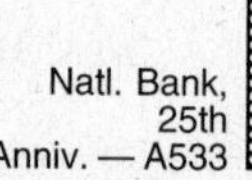

Natl. Bank, 25th Anniv. — A533

Designs: 1-peso coins and banknotes identified by serial numbers.

**1975, Oct. 13 *Perf. 13x12½***
**2005** A533 13c Coin, 1915 1.10 .25
**2006** A533 13c C882736A, 1934 1.10 .25
**2007** A533 13c A000387A, 1946 1.10 .25
**2008** A533 13c 933906, 1964 1.10 .25
**2009** A533 13c K000000, 1976 1.10 .25
*a.* Strip of 5, Nos. 2005-2009 6.75 6.75
*Nos. 2005-2009 (5)* 5.50 1.25

Locomotives A534

1c, La Junta, 1837. 3c, Steam engine 2-8-0 No. 12. 5c, Diesel TEM 4 No. 51010. 13c, Diesel DVM 9I-7 55. 30c, Diesel M 62K No. 61601.

**1975, Oct. 28 Unwmk. *Perf. 12½***
**2010** A534 1c multicolored .25 .25
**2011** A534 3c multicolored .30 .25
**2012** A534 5c multicolored .30 .25
**2013** A534 13c multicolored 3.00 .25
**2014** A534 30c multicolored 3.50 .45
*Nos. 2010-2014 (5)* 7.35 1.45

Railway history.

Development of the Textile Industry A535

13c, Bobbins, flag, loom operator.

**1975, Nov. 10 *Perf. 13x12½***
**2015** A535 13c multi 1.20 .25

Veterinary Medicine A536

Parasites and host species: 1c, Haemonchus, lamb. 2c, Ancylostoma caninum, dog. 3c, Disphatynx nasuta, rooster. 5c, Gasterophilus intestinalis, horse. 13c, Ascaris lumbricoides, pig. 30c, Boophilus microplus, bull.

**1975, Nov. 25 Litho. *Perf. 13***
**2016** A536 1c multicolored .25 .25
**2017** A536 2c multicolored .25 .25
**2018** A536 3c multicolored .25 .25
**2019** A536 5c multicolored .25 .25

**2020** A536 13c multicolored 1.40 .25
**2021** A536 30c multicolored 2.50 .40
*Nos. 2016-2021 (6)* 4.90 1.65

Manuel Ascunce Domenech Educational Detachment — A537

**1975, Nov. 27** **Litho.**
**2022** A537 3c multi .40 .25

Development of Agriculture and Irrigation A538

**1975, Dec. 15 Litho.** ***Perf. 13x12½***
**2023** A538 13c Irrigation 1.25 .25

1st Communist Party Congress A539

3c, "1," revolutionaries, vert. 30c, Party leaders.

**1975, Dec. 17** ***Perf. 12½x13, 13x12½***
**2024** A539 3c multi .25 .25
**2025** A539 13c shown 1.10 .25
**2026** A539 30c multi 1.50 .30
*Nos. 2024-2026 (3)* 2.85 .80

8th Latin-American Obstetrics and Gynecology Congress A540

**1976, Jan. 24** ***Perf. 13***
**2027** A540 3c multi .60 .25

Paintings in Natl. Museums A541

Designs: 1c, *Seated Woman,* by Victor Manuel, vert. 2c, *Garden,* by Santiago Rusinol. 3c, *Guadalquivir River,* by Manuel Barron y Carrillo. 5c, *Self-portrait,* by Jan Havicksz Steen, vert. 13c, *Portrait of a Woman,* by Louis Michel Van Loo, vert. 30c, *La Chula,* by Jose Arburu Morell, vert.

**Sizes: 29x40mm (1c, 5c, 13c), 40x29mm (2c), 44x27mm (3c), 27x44mm (30c)**

***Perf. 13, 12½ (3c, 30c)***

**1976, Jan. 30**
**2028** A541 1c multi .25 .25
**2029** A541 2c multi .25 .25
**2030** A541 3c multi .25 .25
**2031** A541 5c multi .25 .25
**2032** A541 13c multi 1.40 .25
**2033** A541 30c multi 2.25 .50
*Nos. 2028-2033 (6)* 4.65 1.75

10th Cong. of Ministers from Socialist Communications Organizations, Feb. 12, Havana — A542

**1976, Feb. 12** **Litho.** ***Perf. 13***
**2034** A542 13c multi 1.40 .25

Hunting Dogs — A543

1c, American foxhound. 2c, Labrador retriever. 3c, Borzoi. 5c, Irish setter. 13c, Pointer. 30c, Cocker spaniel.

**1976, Feb. 20**
**2035** A543 1c multi .25 .25
**2036** A543 2c multi .25 .25
**2037** A543 3c multi .25 .25
**2038** A543 5c multi .25 .25
**2039** A543 13c multi 1.50 .30
**2040** A543 30c multi 2.50 .40
*Nos. 2035-2040 (6)* 5.00 1.70

Socialist Constitution A544

13c, Natl. flag, arms, anthem.

**1976, Feb. 24** ***Perf. 12½***
**2041** A544 13c multi 1.40 .25

Chess Champions A545

Designs: 1c, Ruy Lopez Segura and chessboard. 2c, Francois Philidor and frontispiece of his book, *Analysis of the Game of Chess.* 3c, Wilhelm Steinitz and knight. 13c, Emanuel Lasker and king. 30c, Jose Raul Capablanca learning to play chess as a small boy.

**1976, Mar. 15** ***Perf. 13x12½***
**2042** A545 1c multi .25 .25
**2043** A545 2c multi .25 .25
**2044** A545 3c multi .25 .25
**2045** A545 13c multi 1.75 .25
**2046** A545 30c multi 1.90 .55
*Nos. 2042-2046 (5)* 4.40 1.55

Havana Radio Intl. Broadcasts, 15th Anniv. — A546

**1976, Mar. 26**
**2047** A546 50c multi 2.00 .70

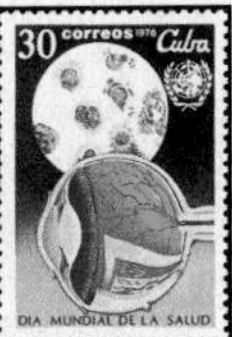

World Health Day — A547

**1976, Apr. 7**
**2048** A547 30c multi 1.50 .45

Child Care Centers, 15th Anniv. — A548

**1976, Apr. 10** ***Perf. 12½x13***
**2049** A548 3c multi .60 .25

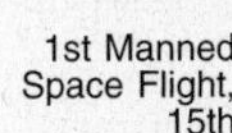

1st Manned Space Flight, 15th Anniv. — A549

1c, Gagarin, lift-off. 2c, V. Tesreshkova, rockets. 3c, A. Leonov's space walk, vert. 5c, Spacecraft, vert. 13c, Spacecraft, diff., vert. 30c, Space link-up.

**1976, Apr. 12** ***Perf. 13***
**2050** A549 1c multicolored .25 .25
**2051** A549 2c multicolored .25 .25
**2052** A549 3c multicolored .25 .25
**2053** A549 5c multicolored .40 .25
**2054** A549 13c multicolored 1.10 .25
**2055** A549 30c multicolored 1.75 .35
*Nos. 2050-2055 (6)* 4.00 1.60

Bay of Pigs Invasion, 15th Anniv. — A550

13c, Bomber, pilot. 30c, Soldiers exulting, vert.

**1976, Apr. 17** ***Perf. 13x12½, 12½x13***
**2056** A550 3c shown .25 .25
**2057** A550 13c multi .95 .25
**2058** A550 30c multi 1.75 .45
*Nos. 2056-2058 (3)* 2.95 .95

Natl. Militia, 17th anniv. (3c); Air Force, 15th anniv. (13c); proclamation of the socialist revolution, 15th anniv. (30c).

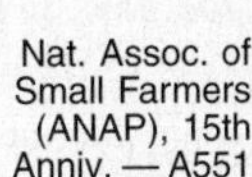

Nat. Assoc. of Small Farmers (ANAP), 15th Anniv. — A551

**1976, May 17** ***Perf. 13x12½***
**2059** A551 3c multi .55 .25

1976 Summer Olympics, Montreal — A552

1c, Volleyball. 2c, Basketball. 3c, Long jump. 4c, Boxing. 5c, Weight lifting. 13c, Judo. 30c, Swimming.
50c, Character trademark (beaver).

**1976, May 25** ***Perf. 12½x13***
**2060** A552 1c multi .25 .25
**2061** A552 2c multi .25 .25
**2062** A552 3c multi .25 .25
**2063** A552 4c multi .25 .25
**2064** A552 5c multi .25 .25
**2065** A552 13c multi 1.10 .25
**2066** A552 30c multi 1.50 .45
*Nos. 2060-2066 (7)* 3.85 1.95

**Souvenir Sheet**

***Imperf***

**2067** A552 50c multi 4.25 1.25

See Nos. 2106, 2112.

Modern Secondary Schools A553

**1976, June 12** **Litho.** ***Perf. 13***
**2068** A553 3c red, pale grn & blk .55 .25

Indigenous Birds — A554

Designs: 1c, Teretistris fornsi. 2c, Glaucidium siju. 3c, Nesoceleus fernandinae. 5c, Todus multicolor. 13c, Accipiter gundlachi. 30c, Priotelus temnurus.

**1976, June 15** ***Perf. 13x12½***
**2069** A554 1c multicolored .30 .25
**2070** A554 2c multicolored .30 .25
**2071** A554 3c multicolored .40 .25
**2072** A554 5c multicolored .70 .25
**2073** A554 13c multicolored 1.40 .25
**2074** A554 30c multicolored 3.25 .80
*Nos. 2069-2074 (6)* 6.35 2.05

EXPO '76, USSR — A555

Designs: 1c, Anatomical scanning device. 3c, Child, doe. 10c, Cosmonauts. 30c, Tupolev supersonic jet.

**1976, July 5** ***Perf. 12½x13, 13x12½***
**2075** A555 1c multicolored .25 .25
**2076** A555 3c multicolored .25 .25
**2077** A555 10c multicolored .45 .25
**2078** A555 30c multicolored 2.40 .55
*Nos. 2075-2078 (4)* 3.35 1.30

Public health and industrial safety (1c), environmental protection (3c), space exploration (10c) and modern transportation (30c). Nos. 2075-2077 vert.

Death Cent. of "El Inglesito" — A556

**1976, Aug. 4** ***Perf. 13***
**2079** A556 13c Henry M. Reeve .70 .25

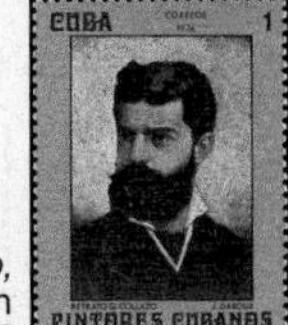

*Portrait of G. Collazo,* by Jean Dabour — A557

Paintings by Collazo: 2c, *The Art Lovers,* horiz. 3c, *The Patio.* 5c, *Coconut Tree.* 13c, *New York Studio,* horiz. 30c, *R. Emelina Collazo.*

**Sizes: 33x44mm, 44x33mm (2c), 31x46mm (5c, 30c), 46x31mm (13c)**

***Perf. 13, 12½x13 (5c, 30c), 13x12½ (13c)***

**1976, Sept. 2**
**2080** A557 1c multi .25 .25
**2081** A557 2c multi .25 .25
**2082** A557 3c multi .25 .25
**2083** A557 5c multi .25 .25
**2084** A557 13c multi .60 .25
**2085** A557 30c multi 1.90 .50
*Nos. 2080-2085 (6)* 3.50 1.75

Camilo Cienfuegos Military Schools, 10th Anniv. — A558

**1976, Sept. 23** ***Perf. 13***
**2086** A558 3c multi .40 .25

Development of the Merchant Marine A559

Various cargo and passenger ships.

**1976, Oct. 2** *Perf. 12½*

2087 A559 1c multi .30 .25
2088 A559 2c multi .30 .25
2089 A559 3c multi .30 .25
2090 A559 5c multi .40 .25
2091 A559 13c multi 1.25 .45
2092 A559 30c multi 2.60 .80
*Nos. 2087-2092 (6)* 5.15 2.25

8th Intl. Health Film Festival of Socialist Countries, Havana A560

**1976, Oct. 4** *Perf. 13x12½*

2093 A560 3c multi .40 .25

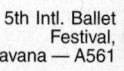

5th Intl. Ballet Festival, Havana — A561

Scenes from ballets: 1c, *Apollo.* 2c, *The River and the Forest,* vert. 3c, *Giselle.* 5c, *Oedipus Rex,* vert. 13c, *Carmen,* vert. 30c, *Vital Song,* vert.

**1976, Nov. 6** *Perf. 13*

2094 A561 1c multicolored .25 .25
2095 A561 2c multicolored .25 .25
2096 A561 3c multicolored .25 .25
2097 A561 5c multicolored .25 .25
2098 A561 13c multicolored 1.00 .25
2099 A561 30c multicolored 2.00 .35
*Nos. 2094-2099 (6)* 4.00 1.60

3rd Military Games — A562

**1976, Nov. 25** *Perf. 13*

2100 A562 3c multi .50 .25

*Granma* Landings, 20th Anniv. — A563

**1976, Dec. 2** *Perf. 13x12½*

2101 A563 1c Landing craft .25 .25
2102 A563 3c Landing force .25 .25
2103 A563 13c Castro, soldiers 1.00 .25
2104 A563 30c Globe, rifles 1.50 .55
*Nos. 2101-2104 (4)* 3.00 1.30

Souvenir Sheet

*Cuban Landscape,* by F. Cadava — A564

**1976, Dec. 8** *Perf. 13x13½*

2105 A564 50c multi 5.25 3.50

CIENFUEGOS '76, 5th natl. phil. exhib.

**Summer Olympics Type of 1976 and**

Victory of Cuban Athletes at the Montreal Games — A565

1c, Volleyball. 2c, Hurdles. 3c, Running (starting blocks). 8c, Boxing. 13c, Running (finish line). 30c, Judo.

**1976, Dec. 10** *Perf. 12½x13*

2106 A565 1c multicolored .25 .25
2107 A565 2c multicolored .25 .25
2108 A565 3c multicolored .25 .25
2109 A565 8c multicolored .25 .25
2110 A565 13c multicolored .85 .25
2111 A565 30c multicolored 1.50 .45
*Nos. 2106-2111 (6)* 3.35 1.70

**Souvenir Sheet**

***Imperf***

2112 A552 50c like No. 2063 5.25 4.00

Paintings in the Natl. Museum A566

1c, *Golden Cross Inn,* by S. Scott. 3c, *Portrait of a Man,* by J.C. Verspronck, vert. 5c, *Venetian Landscape,* by Francesco Guardi. 10c, *Valley Corner,* by H. Cleenewerck, vert. 13c, *F. Xaviera Paula,* anonymous, vert. 30c, *F. de Medici,* by C. Allori, vert.

***Perf. 13, 12½x13 (3c, 10c, 30c), 12½ (13c)***

**1977, Jan. 18**

**Sizes: 40x29mm, 27x42mm (3c, 10c, 30c), 27x43½mm (13c)**

2113 A566 1c multi .25 .25
2114 A566 3c multi .25 .25
2115 A566 5c multi .25 .25
2116 A566 10c multi .55 .25
2117 A566 13c multi .80 .25
2118 A566 30c multi 1.90 .40
*Nos. 2113-2118 (6)* 4.00 1.65

Rural Transport A567

**1977, Feb. 15** *Perf. 13*

2119 A567 3c multi .80 .25

Constitution of Popular Government A568

**1976, Dec. 1** *Perf. 13x12½*

2120 A568 13c multi .70 .25

**Bird Type of 1975**

Designs: 1c, Xiphidiopicus percussus. 4c, Tiaris canora. 10c, Dives atroviolaceus. 13c, Ferminia cerverai. 30c, Mellisuga helenae.

**1977, Feb. 25** *Perf. 13*

2121 A524 1c multicolored .40 .25
2122 A524 4c multicolored .45 .25
2123 A524 10c multicolored 1.00 .25
2124 A524 13c multicolored 1.50 .30
2125 A524 30c multicolored 3.00 .75
*Nos. 2121-2125 (5)* 6.35 1.80

Lenin Park Aquarium, Havana — A569

Designs: 1c, Chichlasoma meeki. 3c, Barbus tetrazona tetrazona. 5c, Cyprinus carpio. 10c, Betta splendens. 13c, Pterophyllum scalare, vert. 30c, Hemigrammus caudovittatus.

**1977, Mar. 15**

2126 A569 1c multicolored .25 .25
2127 A569 3c multicolored .25 .25
2128 A569 5c multicolored .25 .25
2129 A569 10c multicolored .30 .25
2130 A569 13c multicolored 1.10 .25
2131 A569 30c multicolored 2.40 .50
*Nos. 2126-2131 (6)* 4.55 1.75

*Sputnik* (1st Artificial Satellite), 20th Anniv. A570

1c, DDR #370, *Sputnik.* 3c, Hungary #1216, *Luna 16.* 5c, North Korea #134, *Cosmos.* 10c, Poland #822, *Sputnik 3.* 13c, Yugoslavia #870, Earth, Moon. 30c, Cuba #866, Earth, Moon. 50c, Russia #2021, *Sputnik.*

**1977, Apr. 12** *Perf. 13x12½*

2132 A570 1c multi .25 .25
2133 A570 3c multi .25 .25
2134 A570 5c multi .25 .25
2135 A570 10c multi .35 .25
2136 A570 13c multi 1.00 .25
2137 A570 30c multi 1.90 .40
*Nos. 2132-2137 (6)* 4.00 1.65

**Souvenir Sheet**

***Imperf***

2138 A570 50c multi 4.25 1.25

No. 2138 has simulated perfs.

Antonio Maria Romeu (1876-1955), Composer A571

**1977, May 10** **Litho.** *Perf. 13*

2139 A571 3c multi .40 .25

See No. C251.

Flowering Plants — A572

Designs: 1c, Hibiscus rosa sinensis. 2c, Nerium oleander. 5c, Allamanda cathartica. 10c, Pelargonium zonale.

**1977, May 31**

2140 A572 1c multicolored .25 .25
2141 A572 2c multicolored .25 .25
2142 A572 5c multicolored .25 .25
2143 A572 10c multicolored .40 .25
*Nos. 2140-2143 (4)* 1.15 1.00

Dr. Juan Tomas Roig (b. 1877), botanist. See Nos. C252-C254.

Fire Prevention Week — A573

2c, Horse-drawn fire pump, diff. 6c, Early motorized vehicle. 10c, Modern truck. 13c, Turntable-ladder truck. 30c, Crane vehicle.

**1977, June 20**

2144 A573 1c shown .25 .25
2145 A573 2c multicolored .25 .25
2146 A573 6c multicolored .25 .25
2147 A573 10c multicolored .50 .25
2148 A573 13c multicolored .90 .25
2149 A573 30c multicolored 1.90 .40
*Nos. 2144-2149 (6)* 4.05 1.65

Natl. Decorations (Ribbons and Medals of Honor) — A574

**1977, July 26** *Perf. 12x12½*

2150 A574 1c shown .25 .25
2151 A574 3c multi, diff. .25 .25

See Nos. C255-C256.

Paintings by Jorge Arche — A575

1c, *Portrait of Mary.* 3c, *Jose Marti.* 5c, *Portrait of Aristides.* 10c, *Bathers.*

***Perf. 13x12½, 12½x13 (10c), 13 (5c)***

**1977, Aug. 25**

**Sizes: 26x38mm, 29x40mm (5c), 38x26mm (10c)**

2152 A575 1c multicolored .25 .25
2153 A575 3c multicolored .25 .25
2154 A575 5c multicolored .25 .25
2155 A575 10c multicolored .50 .25
*Nos. 2152-2155 (4)* 1.25 1.00

Nos. 2152-2154 vert. See Nos. C257-C259.

4th Military Spartakiad (Summer Sports) — A576

**1977, Sept. 10** *Perf. 13*

2156 A576 1c Boxing .25 .25
2157 A576 3c Volleyball .25 .25
2158 A576 5c Parachuting .25 .25
2159 A576 10c Running .35 .25
*Nos. 2156-2159 (4)* 1.10 1.00

See Nos. C260-C261.

Intl. Airmail Service, 50th Anniv. — A577

Designs: 1c, Biplane and No. C62. 2c, Three-engine plane and Cuba-Key West 1st flight cancel, Oct. 28, 1927. 5c, Flying boat and intl. airmail service 1st flight cachet. 10c, DC-3 aircraft and Havana-Madrid cachet, Apr. 26, 1948.

**1977, Oct. 27** **Litho.** *Perf. 12x12½*

2160 A577 1c multi .25 .25
2161 A577 2c multi .25 .25
2162 A577 5c multi .25 .25
2163 A577 10c multi .50 .25
*Nos. 2160-2163 (4)* 1.25 1.00

See Nos. C263-C264.

October Revolution, Russia, 60th Anniv. — A578

3c, Cruiser *Aurora.* 13c, Lenin, Flags. 30c, Hammer, sickle, symbols of agriculture, technology.

**1977, Nov. 7** *Perf. 13x12½*

2164 A578 3c multicolored .25 .25
2165 A578 13c multicolored .40 .25
2166 A578 30c multicolored 1.40 .40
*Nos. 2164-2166 (3)* 2.05 .90

Felines, Havana Zoo — A579

**1977, Nov. 24 Litho. *Perf. 13***

| | | | | |
|---|---|---|---|---|
| **2167** | A579 | 1c Cat | .25 | .25 |
| **2168** | A579 | 2c Black panther | .25 | .25 |
| **2169** | A579 | 8c Puma | .25 | .25 |
| **2170** | A579 | 10c Leopard | 1.00 | .25 |
| | | *Nos. 2167-2170 (4)* | 1.75 | 1.00 |

See Nos. C266-C267.

Martyrs of the Revolution, 20th Death Annivs. A580

3c, Cienfuegos Uprising. 20c, Siege on the Presidential Palace.

**1977, Dec. 2 *Perf. 12½x12***

| | | | | |
|---|---|---|---|---|
| **2171** | A580 | 3c multicolored | .25 | .25 |
| **2172** | A580 | 20c multicolored | 1.00 | .25 |

See No. C268.

Intl. Measurement System A581

**1977, Dec. 9**

| | | | | |
|---|---|---|---|---|
| **2173** | A581 | 3c multicolored | .40 | .25 |

Havana University, 250th Anniv. A582

**1978, Jan. 5 *Perf. 13x12½***

| | | | | |
|---|---|---|---|---|
| **2174** | A582 | 3c multicolored | .25 | .25 |

See Nos. C270-C271.

*Landscape with Figures,* by J. Pilliment — A583

Paintings in the Natl. Museum of Art: 1c, *Seated Woman,* by R. Madrazo, vert. 4c, *Girl,* by J. Sorolla, vert. 10c, *The Cow,* by E. Abela.

***Perf. 12x12½, 13 (4c, 6c, 10c)***

**1978, Feb. 20**

**Sizes: 27x42mm, 29x40mm (4c), 40x29mm (6c, 10c)**

| | | | | |
|---|---|---|---|---|
| **2175** | A583 | 1c multi | .25 | .25 |
| **2176** | A583 | 4c multi | .25 | .25 |
| **2177** | A583 | 6c shown | .25 | .25 |
| **2178** | A583 | 10c multi | .55 | .25 |
| | | *Nos. 2175-2178 (4)* | 1.30 | 1.00 |

See Nos. C273-C274.

Frontier Troops, 15th Anniv. — A584

**1978, Mar. 5 *Perf. 13***

| | | | | |
|---|---|---|---|---|
| **2179** | A584 | 13c multi | 1.40 | .25 |

**Bird Type of 1975**

Birds: 1c, Myadestes elisabeth. 4c, Paloptila lembeyei. 10c, Teretistris fernandinae.

***Perf. 13, 12½x12 (4c)***

**1978, Mar. 10 Size: 42x27mm**

| | | | | |
|---|---|---|---|---|
| **2180** | A524 | 1c multicolored | .40 | .25 |
| **2181** | A524 | 4c multicolored | .50 | .25 |
| **2182** | A524 | 10c multicolored | 1.25 | .25 |
| | | *Nos. 2180-2182 (3)* | 2.15 | .75 |

Name of bird inscribed below vignette. See Nos. C275-C276.

Cosmonaut's Day — A585

**1978, Apr. 12 *Perf. 13***

| | | | | |
|---|---|---|---|---|
| **2183** | A585 | 1c Intercosmos, vert. | .25 | .25 |
| **2184** | A585 | 2c Luna 24 | .25 | .25 |
| **2185** | A585 | 5c Venera 9, vert. | .35 | .25 |
| **2186** | A585 | 10c Cosmos | .35 | .25 |
| | | *Nos. 2183-2186 (4)* | 1.20 | 1.00 |

See Nos. C278-C279.

9th World Trade Unions Congress, Prague — A586

**1978, Apr. 16**

| | | | | |
|---|---|---|---|---|
| **2187** | A586 | 30c ver, deep brn & blk | 1.00 | .45 |

Cactus Flowers — A587

Designs: 1c, Melocactus guitarti. 4c, Leptocereus wrightii. 6c, Opuntia militaris. 10c, Cylindropuntia hystrix.

**1978, May 15 *Perf. 12½x13 (1c), 13***

| | | | | |
|---|---|---|---|---|
| **2188** | A587 | 1c multicolored | .25 | .25 |
| **2189** | A587 | 4c multicolored | .25 | .25 |
| **2190** | A587 | 6c multicolored | .25 | .25 |
| **2191** | A587 | 10c multicolored | .65 | .25 |
| | | *Nos. 2188-2191 (4)* | 1.40 | 1.00 |

Natl. Botanical Gardens. See Nos. C281-C282.

Lenin Park Aquarium, Havana — A588

Designs: 1c, Barbus arulios. 4c, Hiphesobrycon flammeus. 6c, Poecilia reticulata. 10c, Colis lalia.

**1978, June 15 *Perf. 13***

| | | | | |
|---|---|---|---|---|
| **2192** | A588 | 1c multicolored | .25 | .25 |
| **2193** | A588 | 4c multicolored | .25 | .25 |
| **2194** | A588 | 6c multicolored | .25 | .25 |
| **2195** | A588 | 10c multicolored | .55 | .25 |
| | | *Nos. 2192-2195 (4)* | 1.30 | 1.00 |

See Nos. C286-C287.

MEDELLIN '78, 13th Central American and Caribbean Games — A589

**1978, July 1**

| | | | | |
|---|---|---|---|---|
| **2196** | A589 | 1c Basketball | .25 | .25 |
| **2197** | A589 | 3c Boxing | .25 | .25 |
| **2198** | A589 | 5c Weight lifting | .25 | .25 |
| **2199** | A589 | 10c Fencing, horiz. | .45 | .25 |
| | | *Nos. 2196-2199 (4)* | 1.20 | 1.00 |

See Nos. C288-C289.

Attack on Moncada Barracks, 25th Anniv. — A590

**1978, July 26**

| | | | | |
|---|---|---|---|---|
| **2200** | A590 | 3c multi | .30 | .25 |

See Nos. C290-C291.

World Youth and Students Festival, Havana — A591

Natl. flags and views of host cities.

**1978, July 28**

| | | | | |
|---|---|---|---|---|
| **2201** | A591 | 3c Prague, 1947 | .30 | .25 |
| **2202** | A591 | 3c Budapest, 1949 | .30 | .25 |
| **2203** | A591 | 3c Berlin, 1951 | .30 | .25 |
| **2204** | A591 | 3c Bucharest, 1953 | .30 | .25 |
| **2205** | A591 | 3c Warsaw, 1955 | .30 | .25 |
| *a.* | | Strip of 5, Nos. 2201-2205 | 1.60 | 1.60 |
| | | *Nos. 2201-2205 (5)* | 1.50 | 1.25 |

See Nos. C292-C297.

Young Workers' Army, 5th Anniv. — A592

**1978, Aug. 3**

| | | | | |
|---|---|---|---|---|
| **2206** | A592 | 3c multi | .30 | .25 |

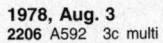

Tuna Industry A593

1c, Tuna boat. 2c, Processing ship. 5c, Shrimp boat. 10c, Inshore stern trawler.

**1978, Aug. 30 *Perf. 12½x12***

| | | | | |
|---|---|---|---|---|
| **2207** | A593 | 1c multicolored | .25 | .25 |
| **2208** | A593 | 2c multicolored | .25 | .25 |
| **2209** | A593 | 5c multicolored | .25 | .25 |
| **2210** | A593 | 10c multicolored | .35 | .25 |
| | | *Nos. 2207-2210 (4)* | 1.10 | 1.00 |

See Nos. C298-C299.

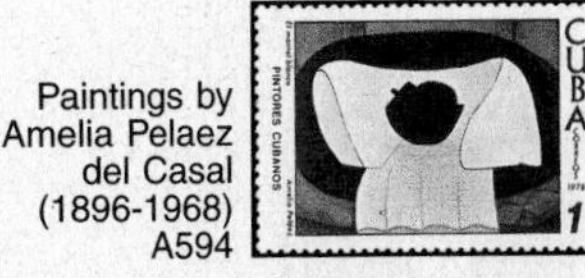


Paintings by Amelia Pelaez del Casal (1896-1968) A594

1c, *The White Mantle.* 3c, *Still-life with Flowers,* vert. 6c, *Women,* vert. 10c, *Fish,* vert.

***Perf. 13x12½, 13 (3c, 6c), 12½x13***

**1978, Sept. 15**

| | | | | |
|---|---|---|---|---|
| **2211** | A594 | 1c multicolored | .25 | .25 |
| **2212** | A594 | 3c multicolored | .25 | .25 |
| **2213** | A594 | 6c multicolored | .25 | .25 |
| **2214** | A594 | 10c multicolored | .45 | .25 |
| | | *Nos. 2211-2214 (4)* | 1.20 | 1.00 |

See Nos. C301-C303.

African Fauna, Havana Zoo — A595

**1978, Oct. 20 *Perf. 13***

| | | | | |
|---|---|---|---|---|
| **2215** | A595 | 1c Rhinoceros | .25 | .25 |
| **2216** | A595 | 4c Okapi, vert. | .25 | .25 |
| **2217** | A595 | 6c Mandrill | .25 | .25 |
| **2218** | A595 | 10c Giraffe, vert. | .65 | .25 |
| | | *Nos. 2215-2218 (4)* | 1.40 | 1.00 |

See Nos. C307-C308.

Natl. Ballet, 30th Anniv. A596

3c, *Grande Pas de Quatre.*

**1978, Oct. 28 *Perf. 13x12½***

| | | | | |
|---|---|---|---|---|
| **2219** | A596 | 3c multicolored | .35 | .25 |

See Nos. C309-C310.

A597

Flowers of the Pacific: Various species.

**1978, Nov. 30 Litho. *Perf. 13***

| | | | | |
|---|---|---|---|---|
| **2220** | A597 | 1c multi | .25 | .25 |
| **2221** | A597 | 4c multi | .25 | .25 |
| **2222** | A597 | 6c multi | .25 | .25 |
| **2223** | A597 | 10c multi | .50 | .25 |
| | | *Nos. 2220-2223 (4)* | 1.25 | 1.00 |

See Nos. C311-C312.

A598

3c, Castro, soldier. 13c, Industry. 1p, Flag, globe, flame.

**1979, Jan. 1 *Perf. 12½x13 (3c), 13***

| | | | | |
|---|---|---|---|---|
| **2224** | A598 | 3c multicolored | .25 | .25 |
| **2225** | A598 | 13c multicolored | .50 | .25 |
| **2226** | A598 | 1p multicolored | 3.00 | 1.50 |
| | | *Nos. 2224-2226 (3)* | 3.75 | 2.00 |

Triumph of the Revolution, 20th anniv.

Doves and Pigeons — A599

Designs: 1c, Starnoenas cyanocephala. 3c, Geotrygon chysia. 7c, Geotrygon caniceps. 8c, Geotrygon montana. 13c, Columba leucocephala. 30c, Columba inornata.

**1979, Jan. 30 *Perf. 13***

| | | | | |
|---|---|---|---|---|
| **2227** | A599 | 1c multicolored | .35 | .25 |
| **2228** | A599 | 3c multicolored | .45 | .25 |
| **2229** | A599 | 7c multicolored | .50 | .25 |
| **2230** | A599 | 8c multicolored | .60 | .25 |
| **2231** | A599 | 13c multicolored | 1.00 | .25 |
| **2232** | A599 | 30c multicolored | 2.10 | .80 |
| | | *Nos. 2227-2232 (6)* | 5.00 | 2.05 |

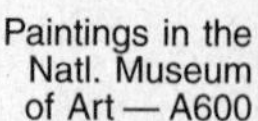

Paintings in the Natl. Museum of Art — A600

Designs: 1c, *Genre Scene,* by David Teniers. 3c, *Arrival of Spanish Troops,* by J. Louis Meissonier. 6c, *A Joyful Gathering,* by Sir David Wilkie. 10c, *A Robbery,* by E. De Lucas Padilla. 13c, *Tea Time,* by R. Madrazo, vert. 30c, *Peasants in Front of a Tavern,* by Adriaen van Ostade.

**1979, Feb. 20**

| | | | | |
|---|---|---|---|---|
| **2233** | A600 | 1c multi | .25 | .25 |
| **2234** | A600 | 3c multi | .25 | .25 |
| **2235** | A600 | 6c multi | .35 | .25 |
| **2236** | A600 | 10c multi | .50 | .25 |
| **2237** | A600 | 13c multi | .90 | .25 |
| **2238** | A600 | 30c multi | 1.75 | .30 |
| | | *Nos. 2233-2238 (6)* | 4.00 | 1.55 |

See Nos. 2262-2267, C317.

Marine Flora — A601

Designs: 3c, Nymphaea capensis. 10c, Nymphaea ampla. 13c, Nymphaea coerulea. 30c, Nymphaea rubra.

**1979, Mar. 20**

| | | | | |
|---|---|---|---|---|
| **2239** | A601 | 3c multicolored | .25 | .25 |
| **2240** | A601 | 10c multicolored | .40 | .25 |
| **2241** | A601 | 13c multicolored | .65 | .25 |
| **2242** | A601 | 30c multicolored | 1.50 | .40 |
| | | *Nos. 2239-2242 (4)* | 2.80 | 1.15 |

All are incorrectly inscribed "Nymphaca."

Cuban Film Industry, 20th Anniv. — A602

**1979, Mar. 24**

**2243** A602 3c multicolored .25 .25

Cosmonaut's Day — A603

**1979, Apr. 12**

| | | | | |
|---|---|---|---|---|
| **2244** | A603 | 1c Rocket launch | .25 | .25 |
| **2245** | A603 | 4c Soyuz | .25 | .25 |
| **2246** | A603 | 6c Salyut | .25 | .25 |
| **2247** | A603 | 10c Link-up | .40 | .25 |
| **2248** | A603 | 13c Soyuz, Salyut | .75 | .25 |
| **2249** | A603 | 30c Parachute landing | 1.40 | .25 |
| | | *Nos. 2244-2249 (6)* | 3.30 | 1.50 |

See No. C315.

6th Summit Meeting of Non-Aligned Countries A604

3c, Understanding, cooperation. 13c, Fight colonialism. 30c, New world economic order.

**1979, Apr. 17**

| | | | | |
|---|---|---|---|---|
| **2250** | A604 | 3c multicolored | .25 | .25 |
| **2251** | A604 | 13c multicolored | .50 | .25 |
| **2252** | A604 | 30c multicolored | 1.40 | .40 |
| | | *Nos. 2250-2252 (3)* | 2.15 | .90 |

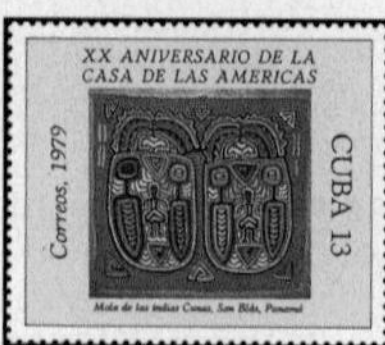

House of the Americas Museum, 20th Anniv. A605

13c, Cuna Indian tapestry.

**1979, Apr. 28** ***Perf. 13x12½***

**2253** A605 13c multicolored .50 .25

Agrarian Reform, 20th Anniv. — A606

**1979, May 17** ***Perf. 12½x12***

**2254** A606 3c multicolored .40 .25

**Souvenir Sheet**

*The Party,* by Jules Pascin A607

**1979, May 18** ***Perf. 13***

**2255** A607 50c multi 3.50 1.25

PHILASERDICA '79 phil. exhib., Sofia.

Nocturnal Butterflies A608

Designs: 1c, Eulepidotis rectimargo. 4c, Othreis materna. 6c, Noropsis hieroglyphica. 10c, Heterochroma. 13c, Melanchroia regnatrix. 30c, Attera gemmata.

**1979, May 25**

| | | | | |
|---|---|---|---|---|
| **2256** | A608 | 1c multicolored | .25 | .25 |
| **2257** | A608 | 4c multicolored | .25 | .25 |
| **2258** | A608 | 6c multicolored | .40 | .25 |
| **2259** | A608 | 10c multicolored | .40 | .25 |
| **2260** | A608 | 13c multicolored | .80 | .25 |
| **2261** | A608 | 30c multicolored | 2.00 | .45 |
| | | *Nos. 2256-2261 (6)* | 4.10 | 1.70 |

**Art Type of 1979**

Paintings by Victor Manuel Garcia (d. 1969): 1c, *Main Avenue, Paris.* 3c, *Portrait of Enmita.* 6c, *San Juan River, Matanzas.* 10c, *Woman Carrying Hay.* 13c, *Still-life with Vase.* 30c, *Street at Night.* Nos. 2262-2267 vert.

**1979, June 15**

| | | | | |
|---|---|---|---|---|
| **2262** | A600 | 1c multi | .25 | .25 |
| **2263** | A600 | 3c multi | .25 | .25 |
| **2264** | A600 | 6c multi | .25 | .25 |
| **2265** | A600 | 10c multi | .30 | .25 |
| **2266** | A600 | 13c multi | .40 | .25 |
| **2267** | A600 | 30c multi | 1.50 | .45 |
| | | *Nos. 2262-2267 (6)* | 2.95 | 1.70 |

See No. C317.

World Peace Council, 30th Anniv. — A609

**1979, June 29** ***Perf. 12½x13***

**2268** A609 30c multi 1.10 .35

1980 Summer Olympics, Moscow A610

1c, Wrestling. 4c, Boxing. 6c, Women's volleyball. 10c, Shooting. 13c, Weight lifting. 30c, High jump.

**1979, July 30** ***Perf. 13x12½***

| | | | | |
|---|---|---|---|---|
| **2269** | A610 | 1c multicolored | .25 | .25 |
| **2270** | A610 | 4c multicolored | .25 | .25 |
| **2271** | A610 | 6c multicolored | .25 | .25 |
| **2272** | A610 | 10c multicolored | .30 | .25 |
| **2273** | A610 | 13c multicolored | .50 | .25 |
| **2274** | A610 | 30c multicolored | 1.25 | .30 |
| | | *Nos. 2269-2274 (6)* | 2.80 | 1.55 |

Roses — A611

Designs: 1c, Rosa eglanteria. 2c, Rosa centifolia anemonoides. 3c, Rosa indica vulgaris. 5c, Rosa eglanteria punicea. 10c, Rosa sulfurea. 13c, Rosa muscosa alba. 20c, Rosa gallica purpurea velutina.

**1979, Aug. 20** ***Perf. 13***

| | | | | |
|---|---|---|---|---|
| **2275** | A611 | 1c multicolored | .25 | .25 |
| **2276** | A611 | 2c multicolored | .25 | .25 |
| **2277** | A611 | 3c multicolored | .25 | .25 |
| **2278** | A611 | 5c multicolored | .25 | .25 |
| **2279** | A611 | 10c multicolored | .30 | .25 |
| **2280** | A611 | 13c multicolored | .50 | .25 |
| **2281** | A611 | 20c multicolored | 1.00 | .25 |
| | | *Nos. 2275-2281 (7)* | 2.80 | 1.75 |

A612

**1979, Aug. 30**

**2282** A612 13c multicolored .50 .25

Council for Mutual Economic Assistance, 30th anniv.

Cubana Airlines, 50th Anniv. — A613

Various aircraft.

**1979, Oct. 8**

| | | | | |
|---|---|---|---|---|
| **2283** | A613 | 1c Ford trimotor | .25 | .25 |
| **2284** | A613 | 2c Sikorsky S-38 | .25 | .25 |
| **2285** | A613 | 3c Douglas DC-3 | .25 | .25 |
| **2286** | A613 | 4c Brittania | .25 | .25 |
| **2287** | A613 | 13c Ilyushin IL-14 | .75 | .25 |
| **2288** | A613 | 40c Tupolev TU-104 | 2.10 | .40 |
| | | *Nos. 2283-2288 (6)* | 3.85 | 1.65 |

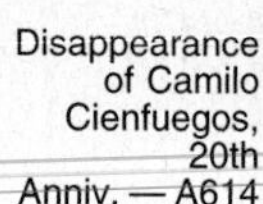

Disappearance of Camilo Cienfuegos, 20th Anniv. — A614

**1979, Oct. 28**

**2289** A614 3c multi .30 .25

Reinoso, Sugar Cane and Blossom A615

**1979, Nov. 12**

**2290** A615 13c multi .65 .25

Sugar Cane Research Institute, 15th anniv., and sesquicentennial of the birth of Alvaro Reinoso.

Zoo Animals — A616

**1979, Nov. 15**

| | | | | |
|---|---|---|---|---|
| **2291** | A616 | 1c Chimpanzees | .25 | .25 |
| **2292** | A616 | 2c Leopards | .25 | .25 |
| **2293** | A616 | 3c Deer | .25 | .25 |
| **2294** | A616 | 4c Lion cubs | .25 | .25 |
| **2295** | A616 | 5c Bear cubs | .25 | .25 |
| **2296** | A616 | 13c Squirrels | .50 | .25 |
| **2297** | A616 | 30c Pandas | 1.25 | .30 |
| **2298** | A616 | 50c Tiger cubs | 1.75 | .50 |
| | | *Nos. 2291-2298 (8)* | 4.75 | 2.30 |

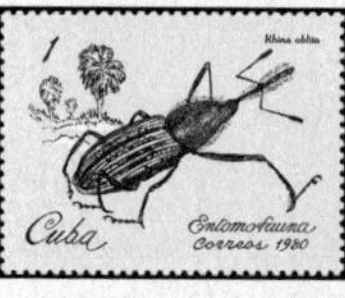

Insects — A617

Designs: 1c, Rhina oblita. 5c, Odontocera josemartii, vert. 6c, Pinthocoelium columbinum. 10c, Calasoma splendida, vert. 13c, Homophileurus cubanus, vert. 30c, Heterops dimidiata, vert.

**1980, Jan. 25**

| | | | | |
|---|---|---|---|---|
| **2299** | A617 | 1c multicolored | .25 | .25 |
| **2300** | A617 | 5c multicolored | .25 | .25 |
| **2301** | A617 | 6c multicolored | .25 | .25 |
| **2302** | A617 | 10c multicolored | .40 | .25 |
| **2303** | A617 | 13c multicolored | .70 | .25 |
| **2304** | A617 | 30c multicolored | 1.50 | .70 |
| | | *Nos. 2299-2304 (6)* | 3.35 | 1.95 |

1980 Summer Olympics, Moscow A618

**1980, Feb. 20** ***Perf. 12½***

| | | | | |
|---|---|---|---|---|
| **2305** | A618 | 1c Weight lifting | .25 | .25 |
| **2306** | A618 | 2c Shooting | .25 | .25 |
| **2307** | A618 | 5c Javelin | .30 | .25 |
| **2308** | A618 | 6c Wrestling | .30 | .25 |
| **2309** | A618 | 8c Judo | .30 | .25 |
| **2310** | A618 | 10c Running | .45 | .25 |
| **2311** | A618 | 13c Boxing | .75 | .25 |
| **2312** | A618 | 30c Women's volleyball | 1.60 | .60 |
| | | *Nos. 2305-2312 (8)* | 4.20 | 2.35 |

**Souvenir Sheet**

***Imperf***

**2313** A618 50c Mischa character 3.00 2.25

No. 2313 contains one 32x40mm stamp.

Paintings in the Natl. Museum A619

Designs: 1c, *The Oak Trees,* by Henry Joseph Harpignies, vert. 4c, *Family Reunion,* by Willem van Mieris. 6c, *Domestic Fowl,* by Melchior De Hondecoeter, vert. 9c, *Innocence,* by William A. Bougereau, vert. 13c, *Venetian Scene II,* by Michele Marieschi. 30c, *Spanish Peasant Woman,* by Joaquin Dominguez Bequer, vert.

**Sizes: 29x40mm, 40x29mm (4c), 28x42mm (9c, 30c), 38x26mm (13c)**

*Perf. 12½, 13 (9c, 30c), 12½x13 (13c)*

**1980, Mar. 11**

| | | | | |
|---|---|---|---|---|
| **2314** | A619 | 1c multi | .25 | .25 |
| **2315** | A619 | 4c multi | .25 | .25 |
| **2316** | A619 | 6c multi | .25 | .25 |
| **2317** | A619 | 9c multi | .50 | .25 |
| **2318** | A619 | 13c multi | .75 | .25 |
| **2319** | A619 | 30c multi | 1.50 | .65 |
| | | *Nos. 2314-2319 (6)* | 3.50 | 1.90 |

Souvenir Sheet

LONDON '80 — A620

50c, *Malvern Hall*, by John Constable.

**1980, Apr. 1** *Perf. 13*

**2320** A620 50c multi 3.00 2.25

Intercosmos Program A621

1c, Emblem, flags. 4c, Astrophysics. 6c, Satellite communications. 10c, Meteorology. 13c, Biology and medicine. 30c, Surveying satellite.

**1980, Apr. 12**

| | | | | |
|---|---|---|---|---|
| **2321** | A621 | 1c multicolored | .25 | .25 |
| **2322** | A621 | 4c multicolored | .25 | .25 |
| **2323** | A621 | 6c multicolored | .25 | .25 |
| **2324** | A621 | 10c multicolored | .45 | .25 |
| **2325** | A621 | 13c multicolored | .60 | .25 |
| **2326** | A621 | 30c multicolored | 1.90 | .65 |
| | | *Nos. 2321-2326 (6)* | 3.70 | 1.90 |

Cuban Postage Stamps, 125th Anniv. A622

30c, Nos. 1, 7 and 613.

**1980, Apr. 24** *Perf. 12½*

**2327** A622 30c multi 1.25 .45

Orchids — A623

Designs: 1c, Bletia purpurea. 4c, Oncidium leiboldii. 6c, Epidendrum cochieatum. 10c, Cattleyopsis lindenii. 13c, Encyclia fucata. 30c, Encyclia phoenicea.

**1980, May 20** *Perf. 13*

| | | | | |
|---|---|---|---|---|
| **2328** | A623 | 1c multicolored | .25 | .25 |
| **2329** | A623 | 4c multicolored | .25 | .25 |
| **2330** | A623 | 6c multicolored | .25 | .25 |
| **2331** | A623 | 10c multicolored | .50 | .25 |
| **2332** | A623 | 13c multicolored | .90 | .25 |
| **2333** | A623 | 30c multicolored | 1.90 | .60 |
| | | *Nos. 2328-2333 (6)* | 4.05 | 1.85 |

Marine Mammals A624

Designs: 1c, Tursiops truncatus. 3c, Megaptera novaeangliae, vert. 13c, Ziphius cavirostris. 30c, Monachus tropicalis.

**1980, June 20**

| | | | | |
|---|---|---|---|---|
| **2334** | A624 | 1c multicolored | .30 | .25 |
| **2335** | A624 | 3c multicolored | .30 | .25 |
| **2336** | A624 | 13c multicolored | 1.00 | .25 |
| **2337** | A624 | 30c multicolored | 2.50 | .50 |
| | | *Nos. 2334-2337 (4)* | 4.10 | 1.25 |

Urban Reform Campaign, 20th Anniv. — A625

Nationalization of Foreign Industry, 20th Anniv. — A626

**1980, July 26** *Perf. 13x12½, 12½x13*

| | | | | |
|---|---|---|---|---|
| **2338** | A625 | 3c multi | .25 | .25 |
| **2339** | A626 | 13c multi | .35 | .25 |

Moncada Program.

Colonial Copperware — A627

3c, Wine pitcher, 19th cent. 13c, Oil jar, 18th cent. 30c, Lidded pitcher, 19th cent.

*Perf. 12½, 12½x13 (13c)*

**1980, July 29**

**Sizes: 27x43½mm, 38x26mm (13c)**

| | | | | |
|---|---|---|---|---|
| **2340** | A627 | 3c multicolored | .25 | .25 |
| **2341** | A627 | 13c multicolored | .65 | .25 |
| **2342** | A627 | 30c multicolored | 1.25 | .30 |
| | | *Nos. 2340-2342 (3)* | 2.15 | .80 |

Cuban Women's Federation, 20th Anniv. — A628

**1980, Aug. 23** *Perf. 13*

**2343** A628 3c multi .40 .25

Souvenir Sheet

ESPAMER '80, Madrid — A629

Design: *Clotilde Passing Through the Country Garden*, by Joaquin Sorolla y Bastida.

**1980, Aug. 29**

**2344** A629 50c multi 3.00 2.25

Postage stamps of Spain, 130th anniv.

1st Havana Declaration, 20th Anniv. — A630

**1980, Sept. 2**

**2345** A630 13c multi .50 .25

Construction of Naval Vessels in Cuba, 360th Anniv. — A631

Ships under construction: 1c, *Our Lady of Atocha*, galleon, 1620. 3c, *El Rayo*, warship, 1749. 7c, *Santisima Trinidad*, 1769. 10c, *Santisima Trinidad*, diff., 1805, vert. 13c, Steamships *Congreso* and *Colon*, 1851. 30c, Cardenas and Chullima shipyards.

**1980, Sept. 15**

| | | | | |
|---|---|---|---|---|
| **2346** | A631 | 1c multi | .25 | .25 |
| **2347** | A631 | 3c multi | .25 | .25 |
| **2348** | A631 | 7c multi | .25 | .25 |
| **2349** | A631 | 10c multi | .50 | .25 |
| **2350** | A631 | 13c multi | .90 | .25 |
| **2351** | A631 | 30c multi | 1.50 | .60 |
| | | *Nos. 2346-2351 (6)* | 3.65 | 1.85 |

A633

**1980, Sept. 26** *Perf. 13*

**2354** A633 13c multi .60 .25

Fidel Castro's 1st speech before the UN General Assembly, 20th anniv.

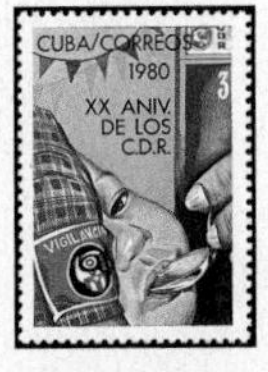

A634

**1980, Sept. 28** *Perf. 13x12½*

**2355** A634 3c multi .30 .25

Revolutionary defense committees, 20th anniv.

Souvenir Sheet

ESSEN '80, 49th Intl. Philatelic Federation Congress — A635

Painting: *Portrait of a Lady*, by Ludger Tom Ring The Younger.

**1980, Oct. 2** **Litho.** *Perf. 13*

**2356** A635 50c multi 3.00 2.25

Early Locomotives A636

1c, Josefa. 2c, Chaparra Sugar Co. No. 22. 7c, Steam storage locomotive. 10c, 2-4-2 locomotive. 13c, 2-4-0 locomotive. 30c, Oil combustion engine, 1909.

**1980, Oct. 15**

| | | | | |
|---|---|---|---|---|
| **2357** | A636 | 1c multicolored | .25 | .25 |
| **2358** | A636 | 2c multicolored | .25 | .25 |
| **2359** | A636 | 7c multicolored | .25 | .25 |
| **2360** | A636 | 10c multicolored | .60 | .25 |
| **2361** | A636 | 13c multicolored | 1.25 | .25 |
| **2362** | A636 | 30c multicolored | 2.40 | .60 |
| | | *Nos. 2357-2362 (6)* | 5.00 | 1.85 |

Lighthouses — A637

3c, Roncali, San Antonio. 13c, Jagua, Cienfuegos. 30c, Maisi Point, Guantanamo.

**1980, Oct. 30**

| | | | | |
|---|---|---|---|---|
| **2363** | A637 | 3c multicolored | .25 | .45 |
| **2364** | A637 | 13c multicolored | .70 | .45 |
| **2365** | A637 | 30c multicolored | 1.60 | .45 |
| | | *Nos. 2363-2365 (3)* | 2.55 | 1.35 |

See Nos. 2440-2442, 2553-2555, 2614-2616.

Victory of Cuban Athletes at the 1980 Summer Olympics, Moscow — A638

**1980, Nov. 10** **Litho.** *Perf. 12½x12*

| | | | | |
|---|---|---|---|---|
| **2366** | A638 | 13c Bronze medals | .50 | .25 |
| **2367** | A638 | 30c Silver medals | 1.10 | .25 |
| **2368** | A638 | 50c Gold medals | 2.25 | .55 |
| | | *Nos. 2366-2368 (3)* | 3.85 | 1.05 |

Nos. 2366-2368 each printed se-tenant with label containing statistical data.

Wildflowers — A639

Designs: 1c, Pancratium arenicolum. 4c, Urechites lutea. 6c, Solanum elaegnifolium. 10c, Hamelia patens. 13c, Morinda royoc. 30c, Centrosema virginianum.

**1980, Nov. 20** *Perf. 13*

| | | | | |
|---|---|---|---|---|
| **2369** | A639 | 1c multicolored | .25 | .25 |
| **2370** | A639 | 4c multicolored | .25 | .25 |
| **2371** | A639 | 6c multicolored | .30 | .25 |
| **2372** | A639 | 10c multicolored | .50 | .25 |
| **2373** | A639 | 13c multicolored | .95 | .25 |
| **2374** | A639 | 30c multicolored | 2.25 | .40 |
| | | *Nos. 2369-2374 (6)* | 4.50 | 1.65 |

Souvenir Sheet

7th Natl. Stamp Exhibition — A640

**1980, Nov. 22**

**2375** A640 50c Mail train 3.50 2.25

2nd Communist Party Congress — A641

13c, Industry, communication. 30c, Athletics, elderly, education.

**1980, Dec. 17**

| | | | | |
|---|---|---|---|---|
| **2376** | A641 | 3c shown | .25 | .25 |
| **2377** | A641 | 13c multicolored | .40 | .25 |
| **2378** | A641 | 30c multicolored | 1.00 | .25 |
| | | *Nos. 2376-2378 (3)* | 1.65 | .75 |

Paintings in the Natl. Museum of Art — A642

Designs: 1c, *Lady Mayo*, by Anton Van Dyck, vert. 6c, *The Spinner*, by Giovanni Battista Piazzetta, vert. 10c, *Daniel Collyer*, by Francis Cotes, vert. 13c, *Gardens, Palma de Mallorca*, by Santiago Rusinol Prats. 20c, *Landscape with Roadway and Houses*, by Frederick Waters Watts. 50c, *Landscape with Sheep*, by Jean-Francois Millet.

**1981, Jan. 20**

| | | | | |
|---|---|---|---|---|
| **2379** | A642 | 1c multi | .25 | .25 |
| **2380** | A642 | 6c multi | .25 | .25 |
| **2381** | A642 | 10c multi | .50 | .25 |

2382 A642 13c multi .55 .25
2383 A642 20c multi .90 .30
2384 A642 50c multi 1.90 .60
*Nos. 2379-2384 (6)* 4.35 1.90

See Nos. 2510-2515.

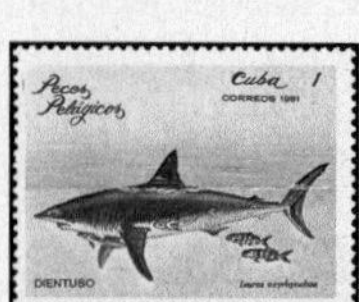

Pelagic Fish — A643

Designs: 1c, Isurus oxyrhynchus. 3c, Lampris regius. 10c, Istiophorus platypterus. 13c, Mola mola, vert. 30c, Coruphaena hippurus. 50c, Tetrapturus albidus.

**1981, Feb. 25**
2385 A643 1c multicolored .25 .25
2386 A643 3c multicolored .25 .25
2387 A643 10c multicolored .45 .25
2388 A643 13c multicolored 1.60 .25
2389 A643 30c multicolored 1.00 .40
2390 A643 50c multicolored 1.75 .95
*Nos. 2385-2390 (6)* 5.30 2.35

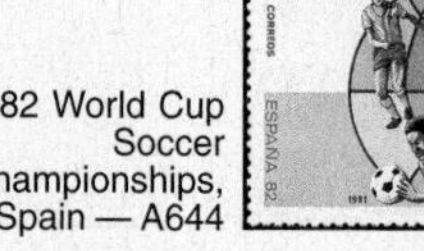

1982 World Cup Soccer Championships, Spain — A644

Globe and various soccer players.

**1981, Mar. 20** ***Perf. 12½***
2391 A644 1c multi .25 .25
2392 A644 2c multi .25 .25
2393 A644 3c multi .25 .25
2394 A644 10c multi, vert. .45 .25
2395 A644 13c multi, vert. .50 .25
2396 A644 50c multi 2.00 .65
*Nos. 2391-2396 (6)* 3.70 1.90

**Souvenir Sheet**
***Perf. 13***
2397 A644 1p Soccer ball, flag 4.50 2.00

No. 2397 contains one 40x32mm stamp.

Opening of the 1st Kindergarten, 20th Anniv. — A645

**1981, Apr. 10** ***Perf. 13***
2398 A645 3c multi .50 .25

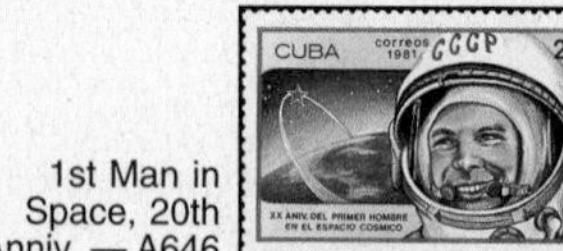

1st Man in Space, 20th Anniv. — A646

Designs: 1c, Jules Verne, Russian scientist Konstantin E. Tsiolkovski, and Sergei P. Korolev, designer of the 1st Soviet spacecraft, vert. 2c, Yuri Gagarin, 1st man in space. 3c, Valentina Tereshkova, 1st woman in space, and *Vostok 6*. 5c, Aleksei A. Leonov, 1st man to walk in space. 13c, Konstantin Feoktistov, Boris Yegorov and Vladimir Komarov, *Voskhod 1* crew, 1st 3-man orbital flight. 30c, Valeri Ryumin and Leonid Popov, set a space endurance record. 50c, Arnaldo Tamayo Mendez, 1st Cuban cosmonaut, and Soviet cosmonaut Yuri Romanenko on joint space flight, vert.

**1981, Apr. 12** ***Perf. 12½***
2399 A646 1c multi .25 .25
2400 A646 2c multi .25 .25
2401 A646 3c multi .25 .25
2402 A646 5c multi .25 .25
2403 A646 13c multi .45 .25
2404 A646 30c multi .90 .35
2405 A646 50c multi 2.00 .60
*Nos. 2399-2405 (7)* 4.35 2.20

A647

Designs: 3c, Rocket, aircraft. 13c, Hand raising gun.

**1981, Apr. 19** **Litho.** ***Perf. 13***
2406 A647 3c multi, vert. .25 .25
2407 A647 13c multi, vert. .40 .25
2408 A647 30c multi .85 .60
*Nos. 2406-2408 (3)* 1.50 1.10

Creation of armed forces (DAAFAR) (3c), Bay of Pigs Invasion, 20th Anniv. (13c), Proclamation of the socialist revolution (30c).

Attack on Goicuria Barracks, 25th Anniv. — A648

**1981, Apr. 29**
2409 A648 3c multi .30 .25

Natl. Assoc. of Small Farmers (ANAP), 20th Anniv. — A649

**1981, May 17**
2410 A649 3c multi .45 .25

**Souvenir Sheet**

WIPA '81 A650

**1981, May 22** **Litho.**
2411 A650 50c Austria No. 643 3.00 1.50

Fighting Cocks — A651

**1981, May 25** ***Perf. 12½x13, 13x12½***
2412 A651 1c Canelo, vert. .25 .25
2413 A651 3c Cenizo .25 .25
2414 A651 7c Blanco, vert. .25 .25
2415 A651 13c Pinto, vert. .50 .25
2416 A651 30c Giro 1.40 .35
2417 A651 50c Jabao, vert. 2.25 .60
*Nos. 2412-2417 (6)* 4.90 1.95

Ministry of the Interior, 20th Anniv. — A652

**1981, June 6** ***Perf. 13***
2418 A652 13c multi .40 .25

**Souvenir Sheet**

*Mother and Child*, by Zlatka Dabova A653

**1981, June 14**
2419 A653 50c gold, sil & blk 2.25 1.10

Bulgaria, 1300th anniv. BULGARIA '81 phil. exhib.

Horse-drawn Carriages A654

**1981, June 25**
2420 A654 1c Streetcar .25 .25
2421 A654 4c Bus .25 .25
2422 A654 9c Breake .25 .25
2423 A654 13c Landau .40 .25
2424 A654 30c Phaeton 1.25 .45
2425 A654 50c Funeral coach 2.25 .75
*Nos. 2420-2425 (6)* 4.65 2.20

*House in the Country*, by Mario Caridad — A655

**1981, July 15** ***Perf. 12½***
2426 A655 30c multi 1.25 .30

Intl. Year of the Disabled.

Sandinistas, 25th Anniv. — A656

**1981, July 23** ***Perf. 13***
2427 A656 13c multi .75 .25

State Institutions, 20th Annivs. — A657

**1981, July 26** ***Perf. 12½***
2428 A657 3c multi .25 .25
2429 A657 13c multi, diff. .45 .25
2430 A657 30c multi, diff. 1.25 .25
*Nos. 2428-2430 (3)* 1.95 .75

Institute for Sports, Physical Education and Recreation (3c); Radio Havana (13c); and Ministry of Foreign Trade (MINCEX) (30c).

Carlos J. Finlay and Cent. of His Theory of Biological Vectors — A658

**1981, Aug. 14** ***Perf. 13***
2431 A658 13c multi 1.00 .25

Nonaligned Countries Movement, 20th Anniv. — A659

**1981, Sept. 1**
2432 A659 50c multi 1.75 .80

Horses A660

Nos. 2433-2437 vert.

**1981, Sept. 15** ***Perf. 13***
**Size: 29x40mm**
2433 A660 1c multi .25 .25
2434 A660 3c multi, diff. .25 .25
2435 A660 8c multi, diff. .25 .25
2436 A660 13c multi, diff. .35 .25
2437 A660 30c multi, diff. 1.10 .45
**Size: 68x27mm**
***Perf. 12½***
2438 A660 50c Herd 2.00 .75
*Nos. 2433-2438 (6)* 4.20 2.20

**Souvenir Sheet**

*Idyll in a Tea House*, by Kitagawa Utamaro A661

**1981, Oct. 9** ***Perf. 13***
2439 A661 50c multi 2.75 1.25

PHILATOKYO '81.

**Lighthouse Type of 1980**

**1981, Oct. 15** **Litho.**
2440 A637 3c North Rock .25 .25
2441 A637 13c Lucrecia Point .50 .25
2442 A637 40c East Guano 2.10 .50
*Nos. 2440-2442 (3)* 2.85 1.00

Jose Marti Natl. Library, 80th Anniv. A662

Sugar mills, lithographs from *Los Ingenios*, by Eduardo Laplante (b. 1818): 3c, Flor de Cuba, 1838. 13c, El Progreso, 1845. 30c, Santa Teresa, 1847.

**1981, Oct. 18** ***Perf. 12½x12***
2443 A662 3c multi .25 .25
2444 A662 13c multi .30 .25
2445 A662 30c multi 1.10 .55
*Nos. 2443-2445 (3)* 1.65 1.05

Pablo Picasso (b. 1881) and No. 1263 — A663

**1981, Oct. 25** ***Perf. 12½x13***
2446 A663 30c multi 1.25 .40

Souvenir Sheet

ESPAMER '81, Buenos Aires — A664

**1981, Nov. 13** *Perf. 13*
**2447** A664 1p Packet 5.00 4.50

**Art Type of 1969**

Paintings in the Napoleon Museum: 1c, *Napoleon in Coronation Costume,* anonymous. 3c, *Napoleon with Landscape in the Background,* by Jean Horace Vernet. 10c, *Bonaparte in Egypt,* by Edouard Detaille. 13c, *Napoleon on Horseback,* by Hippolyte Bellange. 30c, *Napoleon in Normandy,* by Bellange. 50c, *Death of Napoleon,* anonymous.

**1981, Dec. 1** *Perf. 12½*
**Sizes: 42x58mm, 58x42mm (3c, 13c, 30c, 50c)**
**2448** A385 1c multi .25 .25
**2449** A385 3c multi, horiz. .25 .25
**2450** A385 10c multi .40 .25
**2451** A385 13c multi, horiz. .40 .25
**2452** A385 30c multi, horiz. 1.25 .40
**2453** A385 50c multi, horiz. 2.10 .70
*Nos. 2448-2453 (6)* 4.65 2.10

Napoleon Museum, 20th anniv.

25th Annivs. A665

3c, Revolutionaries, vert. 20c, Marksman. 1p, Yacht *Granma.*

**1981, Dec. 2** *Perf. 13*
**2454** A665 3c multi .25 .25
**2455** A665 20c multi .45 .25
**2456** A665 1p multi 4.75 1.40
*Nos. 2454-2456 (3)* 5.45 1.90

November 30th insurrection (3c); creation of the revolutionary armed forces (20c); and disembarking of revolutionary forces (1p).

Fauna — A666

**1981, Dec. 14 Litho.** *Perf. 12½x12*
**2457** A666 1c Hummingbird .60 .25
**2458** A666 2c Parakeet .95 .25
**2459** A666 5c Hutia .25 .25
**2460** A666 20c Almiqui .65 .25
**2461** A666 35c Manatee 1.00 .25
**2462** A666 40c Crocodile 1.00 .55
*Nos. 2457-2462 (6)* 4.45 1.80

Fernando Ortiz, Folklorist, Birth Cent. — A667

3c, Portrait by Jorge Arche y Silva. 10c, Hanging idol. 30c, Arara drum. 50c, Chango statue.

**1981, Dec. 20** *Perf. 12½x13*
**2463** A667 3c multi .25 .25
**2464** A667 10c multi .40 .25
**2465** A667 30c multi 1.40 .45
**2466** A667 50c multi 2.10 .70
*Nos. 2463-2466 (4)* 4.15 1.65

Literacy Campaign, 20th Anniv. — A668

No. 2467, Conrado Benitez. No. 2468, Manuel Asunce.

**1981, Dec. 25** *Perf. 12½x12*
**2467** A668 5c multi .30 .25
**2468** A668 5c multi .30 .25
*a.* Pair, #2467-2468 .75 .25
*Nos. 2467-2468 (2)* .60 .50

A669

1982 World Cup Soccer Championships, Spain — A670

Various athletes.

**1982, Jan. 15** *Perf. 13*
**2469** A669 1c multi, vert. .25 .25
**2470** A669 2c multi, vert. .25 .25
**2471** A669 5c multi, vert. .25 .25
**2472** A669 10c multi, vert. .30 .25
**2473** A669 20c shown .75 .25
**2474** A669 40c multi 1.40 .50
**2475** A669 50c multi, vert. 1.75 .70
*Nos. 2469-2475 (7)* 4.95 2.45

**Souvenir Sheet**

**2476** A670 1p shown 5.00 2.50

No. 2476 contains one 32x40mm stamp.

10th World Trade Unions Congress, Havana — A671

30c, Lazaro Pena, delegate.

**1982, Feb. 10** **Litho.**
**2477** A671 30c multi 1.00 .40

Butterflies A672

Designs: 1c, Euptoieta hegesia. 4c, Metamorpha stelenes insularis. 5c, Heliconius charithonius ramsdeni. 20c, Phoebis avellaneda. 30c, Hamadryas ferox diasia. 60c, Marpesia eleuchea.

**1982, Feb. 25** *Perf. 12½*
**2478** A672 1c multicolored .25 .25
**2479** A672 4c multicolored .25 .25
**2480** A672 5c multicolored .25 .25
**2481** A672 20c multicolored 1.40 .30
**2482** A672 30c multicolored 2.25 .55
**2483** A672 50c multicolored 4.00 .95
*Nos. 2478-2483 (6)* 8.40 2.55

Exports — A673

3c, Sugar (processing plant). 4c, Lobster (fishing boat). 6c, Canned fruits. 7c, Agricultural machinery. 8c, Nickel (passenger jet, industrial complex, car). 9c, Rum. 10c, Coffee. 30c, Fresh fruit. 50c, Tobacco. 1p, Cement. Nos. 2489-2493 vert.

**1982, Feb. 26** *Perf. 12x12½, 12½x12*
**2484** A673 3c lt grn .25 .25
**2485** A673 4c car rose .25 .25
**2486** A673 6c dull blue .25 .25
**2487** A673 7c brt org .40 .25
**2488** A673 8c brt vio .40 .25
**2489** A673 9c slate .40 .25
**2490** A673 10c dull red brn .50 .25
**2491** A673 30c bister .75 .25
**2492** A673 50c orange 2.10 .40
**2493** A673 1p olive bister 4.00 1.25
*Nos. 2484-2493 (10)* 9.30 3.65

Tulips — A674

**1982, Mar. 30** *Perf. 12½x13*
**2494** A674 1c Greenland .25 .25
**2495** A674 3c Mariette .25 .25
**2496** A674 8c Ringo .25 .25
**2497** A674 20c La Tulipe Noire .80 .25
**2498** A674 30c Jewel of Spring 1.40 .25
**2499** A674 50c Orange Parrot 1.90 .60
*Nos. 2494-2499 (6)* 4.85 1.85

Communist Youth Organization, 20th Anniv. — A675

**1982, Apr. 4** *Perf. 13*
**2500** A675 5c multi 2.75 1.00

2nd UN Congress on the Peaceful Use of Outer Space — A676

1c, Gorizont. 3c, Meteor. 6c, Salyut-Soyuz link-up. 20c, Lunokhod moon vehicle. 30c, Venera with heat shield. 50c, Intelsat-4a.

**1982, Apr. 12**
**2501** A676 1c multicolored .25 .25
**2502** A676 3c multicolored .25 .25
**2503** A676 6c multicolored .25 .25
**2504** A676 20c multicolored .50 .25
**2505** A676 30c multicolored 1.35 .30
**2506** A676 50c multicolored 1.90 .60
*Nos. 2501-2506 (6)* 4.50 1.90

Cover — A677

**1982, Apr. 24** *Perf. 12½x12*
**2507** A677 20c Havana-Veracruz .75 .25
**2508** A677 30c Havana-Tampico 1.25 .25

Stamp Day. English post office, 1842-1877 (20c); and French post office, 1862-1877 (30c).

Broadcasting and Television Institute (ICRT), 20th Anniv. — A678

**1982, May 24** *Perf. 12x12½*
**2509** A678 30c multi 1.00 .25

**Art Type of 1981 With Larger Type**

Paintings in the Natl. Museum of Art: 1c, *Portrait of a Youth* (girl), by Jean B. Greuze, vert. 3c, *Procession in Brittany,* by Jules Breton. 9c, *Landscape,* by Jean Piliment. 20c, *Late Afternoon,* by William A. Bouguereau, vert. 30c, *Tiger,* by Ferdinand V.E. Delacroix. 40c, *The Chair,* by Wilfredo Lam, vert.

***Perf. 13, 13x12½ (3c), 12x12½ (20c, 40c), 12½x12 (30c)***

**1982, May 31** **Litho.**
**2510** A642 1c 29x40mm .25 .25
**2511** A642 3c 46x36mm .25 .25
**2512** A642 9c 40x29mm .25 .25
**2513** A642 20c 27x42mm .65 .25
**2514** A642 30c 42x27mm 1.10 .40
**2515** A642 40c 27x42mm 1.75 .40
*Nos. 2510-2515 (6)* 4.25 1.80

Souvenir Sheet

PHILEXFRANCE '82 — A679

1p, Steamship Louisiana at St. Nazaire.

**1982, June 7** *Perf. 13*
**2516** A679 1p multicolored 5.00 2.50

DEPORFILEX '82 — A680

**1982, June 10** *Perf. 13x12½*
**2517** A680 20c Hurdler, No. 300 1.50 .25

Reptiles A681

Designs: 1c, Pseudemys decussata. 2c, Tropidophis pardalis. 3c, Crocodylus rhombifer. 20c, Cyclura nubila. 30c, Anolis allisonis. 50c, Alsophis cantherigerus.

**1982, June 15** *Perf. 13*
**2518** A681 1c multicolored .25 .25
**2519** A681 2c multicolored .25 .25
**2520** A681 3c multicolored .25 .25
**2521** A681 20c multicolored .85 .25
**2522** A681 30c multicolored 1.25 .30
**2523** A681 50c multicolored 2.40 .50
*Nos. 2518-2523 (6)* 5.25 1.80

George Dimitrov (1882-1949), Bulgarian Prime Minister — A682

**1982, June 18**
**2524** A682 30c multi 1.00 .25

Koch, Bacillus — A683

**1982, July 18**

| | | | | |
|---|---|---|---|---|
| **2525** | A683 | 20c multi | 1.25 | .25 |

Discovery of the tubercle bacillus by Dr. Robert Koch, cent.

14th Central American and Caribbean Games — A684

**1982, Aug. 1**

| | | | | |
|---|---|---|---|---|
| **2526** | A684 | 1c Baseball | .25 | .25 |
| **2527** | A684 | 2c Boxing | .25 | .25 |
| **2528** | A684 | 10c Water polo | .35 | .25 |
| **2529** | A684 | 20c Javelin | .80 | .30 |
| **2530** | A684 | 35c Weight lifting | 1.25 | .50 |
| **2531** | A684 | 50c Volleyball | 2.00 | .55 |
| | | *Nos. 2526-2531 (6)* | 4.90 | 2.10 |

Hydraulic Development Plan, 20th Anniv. — A685

5c, Fruit, *Eichornia crassipes,* ship. 20c, Arid soil, *Nymphaea alba,* irrigation & reservoir systems.

**1982, Aug. 9**

| | | | | |
|---|---|---|---|---|
| **2532** | A685 | 5c multi | .40 | .25 |
| **2533** | A685 | 20c multi | 1.00 | .25 |

Souvenir Sheet

DEPORFILEX '82, Intl. Stamp and Coin Exhibition — A686

1p, Cuco, character trademark.

**1982, Aug. 10** **Litho.**

| | | | | |
|---|---|---|---|---|
| **2534** | A686 | 1p multi | 4.75 | 2.25 |

14th Central American and Caribbean Games.

Namibia Day — A687

**1982, Aug. 26**

| | | | | |
|---|---|---|---|---|
| **2535** | A687 | 50c multi | 1.75 | .75 |

1982 World Cup Soccer Championships, Spain — A688

Various athletes.

**1982, Aug. 30**

| | | | | |
|---|---|---|---|---|
| **2536** | A688 | 5c multi | .25 | .25 |
| **2537** | A688 | 20c multi | .75 | .30 |
| **2538** | A688 | 30c multi | 1.10 | .40 |
| **2539** | A688 | 50c multi | 1.90 | .80 |
| | | *Nos. 2536-2539 (4)* | 4.00 | 1.75 |

Also exist in miniature sheets of 16 + 9 labels containing 4 each Nos. 2536-2539 in blocks of 4. Value $30.

Natl. Folklore Ensemble, 20th Anniv. — A689

Paintings by V.P. Landaluze.

**1982, Sept. 10**

| | | | | |
|---|---|---|---|---|
| **2540** | A689 | 20c *Little Devil,* vert. | .90 | .25 |
| **2541** | A689 | 30c *Day of Kings* | 1.10 | .45 |

Prehistoric Fauna — A690

Designs: 1c, Ornimegalonyx oteroi, vert. 5c, Crocodylus rhombifer. 7c, Aquila borrasi, vert. 20c, Geocapromys colombianus. 35c, Megalocnus rodens, vert. 50c, Nesophontes micrus.

**1982, Sept. 15** **Litho.**

| | | | | |
|---|---|---|---|---|
| **2542** | A690 | 1c multicolored | .65 | .25 |
| **2543** | A690 | 5c multicolored | .25 | .25 |
| **2544** | A690 | 7c multicolored | 2.50 | .40 |
| **2545** | A690 | 20c multicolored | .65 | .25 |
| **2546** | A690 | 35c multicolored | 1.00 | .50 |
| **2547** | A690 | 50c multicolored | 1.40 | .75 |
| | | *Nos. 2542-2547 (6)* | 6.45 | 2.40 |

15th Death Anniv. of Che Guevara A691

**1982, Oct. 8** ***Perf. 13x12½***

| | | | | |
|---|---|---|---|---|
| **2548** | A691 | 20c multi | 1.25 | .40 |

Discovery of America, 490th Anniv. — A692

**1982, Oct. 12** ***Perf. 13***

| | | | | |
|---|---|---|---|---|
| **2549** | A692 | 5c shown | 1.10 | .25 |
| **2550** | A692 | 20c *Santa Maria,* vert. | 1.25 | .40 |
| **2551** | A692 | 35c *Pinta,* vert. | 1.90 | .90 |
| **2552** | A692 | 50c *Nina,* vert. | 2.40 | 1.10 |
| | | *Nos. 2549-2552 (4)* | 6.65 | 2.65 |

**Lighthouse Type of 1980**

5c, Jutias Caye. 20c, Paredon Grande Caye. 30c, Morro Santiago de Cuba.

**1982, Oct. 25**

| | | | | |
|---|---|---|---|---|
| **2553** | A637 | 5c multicolored | 1.00 | .25 |
| **2554** | A637 | 20c multicolored | 2.75 | .25 |
| **2555** | A637 | 30c multicolored | 3.75 | .45 |
| | | *Nos. 2553-2555 (3)* | 7.50 | .95 |

George Washington, 250th Birth Anniv. — A693

Designs: Quotations and anonymous oil paintings, 18th-19th cent.

**1982, Oct. 29** ***Perf. 12x12½***

| | | | | |
|---|---|---|---|---|
| **2556** | A693 | 5c multi | .25 | .25 |
| **2557** | A693 | 20c multi, diff. | .75 | .25 |

Souvenir Sheet

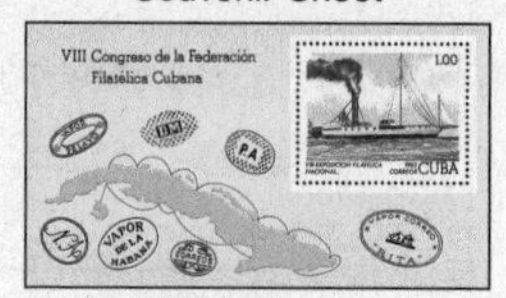

8th Natl. Philatelic Exposition, Ciego de Avila — A694

1p, Paddle steamer *Almendares.*

**1982, Nov. 13**

| | | | | |
|---|---|---|---|---|
| **2558** | A694 | 1p multi | 5.00 | 2.50 |

8th Congress of the Cuban Philatelic Federation, Nov. 13-22.

Lenin Park, 10th Anniv. — A695

**1982, Dec. 28**

| | | | | |
|---|---|---|---|---|
| **2559** | A695 | 5c multi | *16.00* | *16.00* |

Chess Champion Jose Raul Capablanca and King — A696

**1982, Dec. 29**

| | | | | |
|---|---|---|---|---|
| **2560** | A696 | 5c shown | .25 | .25 |
| **2561** | A696 | 20c Rook | 1.10 | .25 |
| **2562** | A696 | 30c Knight | 1.40 | .50 |
| **2563** | A696 | 50c Queen | 2.25 | .80 |
| *a.* | | Bklt. pane of 4, Nos. 2560-2563 | 25.00 | 25.00 |
| | | *Nos. 2560-2563 (4)* | 5.00 | 1.80 |

Exist in sheets of 4+2 labels picturing chessmen.

USSR, 60th Anniv. A697

**1982, Dec. 30** ***Perf. 13x12½***

| | | | | |
|---|---|---|---|---|
| **2564** | A697 | 30c multi | 1.25 | .25 |

World Communications Year — A698

**1983, Jan. 24** **Litho.** ***Perf. 13***

| | | | | |
|---|---|---|---|---|
| **2565** | A698 | 20c multi | .75 | .25 |

No. 507 and Birthplace A699

**1983, Jan. 28** ***Perf. 13x12½***

| | | | | |
|---|---|---|---|---|
| **2566** | A699 | 5c multi | .30 | .25 |

Jose Marti (b. 1853), writer, revolution leader.

1984 Summer Olympics, Los Angeles — A700

**1983, Jan. 31** ***Perf. 13***

| | | | | |
|---|---|---|---|---|
| **2567** | A700 | 1c Javelin | .25 | .25 |
| **2568** | A700 | 5c Volleyball | .25 | .25 |
| **2569** | A700 | 6c Basketball | .25 | .25 |
| **2570** | A700 | 20c Weight lifting | .80 | .25 |
| **2571** | A700 | 30c Wrestling | 1.10 | .40 |
| **2572** | A700 | 50c Boxing | 1.75 | .60 |
| *a.* | | Block of 6, #2567-2572 | 17.50 | 17.50 |
| | | With tabs | 23.00 | 23.00 |
| | | *Nos. 2567-2572 (6)* | 4.40 | 2.00 |

**Souvenir Sheet**

***Perf. 13½x13***

| | | | | |
|---|---|---|---|---|
| **2573** | A700 | 1p Judo | 5.25 | 4.50 |

No. 2573 contains one 32x40mm stamp.

Radio Rebelde, 25th Anniv. — A701

**1983, Feb. 24** ***Perf. 13***

| | | | | |
|---|---|---|---|---|
| **2574** | A701 | 20c multi | .70 | .25 |

Karl Marx, Death Cent. — A702

**1983, Mar. 14**

| | | | | |
|---|---|---|---|---|
| **2575** | A702 | 30c multi | 1.00 | .40 |

1st Manned Balloon Flight, Bicent. — A703

Various balloons.

**1983, Mar. 30**

| | | | | |
|---|---|---|---|---|
| **2576** | A703 | 1c multi | .25 | .25 |
| **2577** | A703 | 3c multi | .25 | .25 |
| **2578** | A703 | 5c multi | .25 | .25 |
| **2579** | A703 | 7c multi | .35 | .25 |
| **2580** | A703 | 30c multi | 2.10 | .70 |
| **2581** | A703 | 50c multi | 2.10 | .70 |
| *a.* | | Strip of 6 | 10.00 | 10.00 |
| | | With tabs | 14.00 | 14.00 |
| | | *Nos. 2576-2581 (6)* | 5.30 | 2.40 |

**Souvenir Sheet**

| | | | | |
|---|---|---|---|---|
| **2582** | A703 | 1p Jose D. Blino | 4.50 | 2.00 |

No. 2582 contains one 32x40mm stamp.

Cosmonauts' Day — A704

1c, *Vostok 1.* 4c, Satellite *Frances D1.* 5c, *Mars 2.* 20c, *Soyuz.* 30c, Meteorological satellite. 50c, Intercosmos satellite.

**1983, Apr. 12** **Litho.**

| | | | | |
|---|---|---|---|---|
| **2583** | A704 | 1c multicolored | .25 | .25 |
| **2584** | A704 | 4c multicolored | .25 | .25 |
| **2585** | A704 | 5c multicolored | .25 | .25 |
| **2586** | A704 | 20c multicolored | .75 | .25 |
| **2587** | A704 | 30c multicolored | 1.10 | .50 |
| **2588** | A704 | 50c multicolored | 1.75 | .70 |
| | | *Nos. 2583-2588 (6)* | 4.35 | 2.20 |

Stamp Day — A705

20c, Havana-Key West cover. 30c, Spain-Havana cover.

**1983, Apr. 24**

| | | | | |
|---|---|---|---|---|
| **2589** | A705 | 20c multicolored | .75 | .30 |
| **2590** | A705 | 30c multicolored | 1.25 | .30 |

1st Intl. airmail services.

Souvenir Sheet

TEMBAL '83, Basel A706

**1983, May 21** *Perf. 13½x13*

| | | | | |
|---|---|---|---|---|
| **2591** | A706 | 1p Weasel | 5.25 | 4.50 |

Simon Bolivar, Liberator of South America — A707

5c, Jose Rafael de las Heras. 20c, Bolivar.

**1983, July 24** *Perf. 12½x13*

| | | | | |
|---|---|---|---|---|
| **2592** | A707 | 5c multicolored | .25 | .25 |
| **2593** | A707 | 20c multicolored | .60 | .25 |

Attack of Moncada Barracks, 30th Anniv. — A708

Designs: 5c, Jose Marti, Moncada barracks. 20c, Abel Santamaria, Jose Luis Tasende and Boris Luis Santa Coloma, martyrs, vert. 30c, *History Will Absolve Me,* declaration of Fidel Castro, vert.

**1983, July 26** *Perf. 13*

| | | | | |
|---|---|---|---|---|
| **2594** | A708 | 5c multi | .25 | .25 |
| **2595** | A708 | 20c multi | .65 | .25 |
| **2596** | A708 | 30c multi | .85 | .50 |
| | | *Nos. 2594-2596 (3)* | 1.75 | 1.00 |

Souvenir Sheet

Alberto Santos-Dumont (1873-1932) — A709

**1983, July 29** *Perf. 13x13½*

| | | | | |
|---|---|---|---|---|
| **2597** | A709 | 1p Dumont's aircraft | 5.25 | 4.50 |

BRASILIANA '83, Rio; 140th anniv. of 1st stamp issued in the Americas.

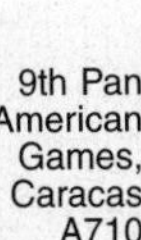

9th Pan American Games, Caracas A710

**1983, Aug. 14** *Perf. 13x12½*

| | | | | |
|---|---|---|---|---|
| **2598** | A710 | 1c Weight lifting | .25 | .25 |
| **2599** | A710 | 2c Volleyball | .25 | .25 |
| **2600** | A710 | 3c Baseball | .25 | .25 |
| **2601** | A710 | 20c High jump | .75 | .25 |
| **2602** | A710 | 30c Basketball | 1.00 | .50 |
| **2603** | A710 | 50c Boxing | 1.75 | .70 |
| | | *Nos. 2598-2603 (6)* | 4.25 | 2.20 |

*Port,* by Claude Joseph Vernet A711

**1983, Sept. 5**

| | | | | |
|---|---|---|---|---|
| **2604** | A711 | 30c multi | 1.50 | .55 |

French alliance, cent.

Pres. Salvador Allende of Chile (d. 1973) A712

**1983, Sept. 12**

| | | | | |
|---|---|---|---|---|
| **2605** | A712 | 20c multi | .70 | .25 |

1st Congress of Farmers at Arms, 25th Anniv. A713

**1983, Sept. 21** *Perf. 12½x12*

| | | | | |
|---|---|---|---|---|
| **2606** | A713 | 5c multi | .25 | .25 |

Raphael, 500th Birth Anniv. — A714

1c, *Girl with Veil.* 2c, *The Cardinal.* 5c, *Francesco M. Della Rovere.* 20c, *Portrait of a Youth.* 30c, *Magdalena Doni.* 50c, *La Fornarina.*

**1983, Sept. 30** **Litho.** *Perf. 13*

| | | | | |
|---|---|---|---|---|
| **2607** | A714 | 1c multi | .25 | .25 |
| **2608** | A714 | 2c multi | .25 | .25 |
| **2609** | A714 | 5c multi | .25 | .25 |
| **2610** | A714 | 20c multi | .75 | .25 |
| **2611** | A714 | 30c multi | 1.10 | .40 |
| **2612** | A714 | 50c multi | 1.75 | .65 |
| | | *Nos. 2607-2612 (6)* | 4.35 | 2.05 |

State Quality Seal — A715

**1983, Oct. 14**

| | | | | |
|---|---|---|---|---|
| **2613** | A715 | 5c multi | .60 | .25 |

**Lighthouse Type of 1980**

**1983, Oct. 20**

| | | | | |
|---|---|---|---|---|
| **2614** | A637 | 5c Carapachibey | .25 | .25 |
| **2615** | A637 | 20c Cadiz Bay | .80 | .30 |
| **2616** | A637 | 30c Gobernadora Point | 2.00 | .80 |
| | | *Nos. 2614-2616 (3)* | 3.05 | 1.35 |

Turtles — A716

Designs: 1c, Eretmochelys imbricata. 2c, Lepidochelys kempi. 5c, Chrysemys decussata. 20c, Caretta caretta. 30c, Chelonia mydas. 50c, Dermochelys coriacea.

**1983, Nov. 15**

| | | | | |
|---|---|---|---|---|
| **2617** | A716 | 1c multicolored | .25 | .25 |
| **2618** | A716 | 2c multicolored | .25 | .25 |
| **2619** | A716 | 5c multicolored | .25 | .25 |
| **2620** | A716 | 20c multicolored | .80 | .25 |
| **2621** | A716 | 30c multicolored | 1.40 | .25 |
| **2622** | A716 | 50c multicolored | 2.75 | .75 |
| | | *Nos. 2617-2622 (6)* | 5.70 | 2.00 |

World Communications Year — A717

1c, Bell's Gallow Frame, telephone. 5c, Telegram, airmail. 10c, Satellite, satellite dish. 20c, Television, radio. 30c, 24th Communications conference.

**1983, Nov. 23**

| | | | | |
|---|---|---|---|---|
| **2623** | A717 | 1c multicolored | .25 | .25 |
| **2624** | A717 | 5c multicolored | .25 | .25 |
| **2625** | A717 | 10c multicolored | .45 | .25 |
| **2626** | A717 | 20c multicolored | .75 | .25 |
| **2627** | A717 | 30c multicolored | 1.10 | .40 |
| | | *Nos. 2623-2627 (5)* | 2.80 | 1.40 |

Nos. 319 and 990 — A718

**1983, Dec. 3** *Perf. 13x12½*

| | | | | |
|---|---|---|---|---|
| **2628** | A718 | 20c multi | .70 | .25 |

See note after No. 320.

Flowers, Birds — A719

Designs: No. 2629, Opuntia dillenii. No. 2630, Euphorbia podocarpifolia. No. 2631, Dinema cubincola. No. 2632, Guaiacum officinale. No. 2633, Magnolia cubensis. No. 2634, Jatropha angustifolia. No. 2635, Cochlospermum vitifolium. No. 2636, Tabebuia lepidota. No. 2637, Kalmiella ericoides. No. 2638, Jatropha integerrima. No. 2639, Melocactus actinacanthus. No. 2640, Cordia sebestana. No. 2641, Tabernae - montana apoda. No. 2642, Lantana camara. No. 2643, Cordia gerascanthus. No. 2644, Tiaris canora. No. 2645, Phaethon lepturus. No. 2646, Myadestes elisabeth. No. 2647, Saurothera merlini. No. 2648, Polioptila lembeyei. No. 2649, Mellisuga helenae. No. 2650, Mimus polyglottos. No. 2651, Todus multicolor. No. 2652, Amazona leucocephala. No. 2653, Ferminia cerverai. No. 2654, Pelecanus occidentalis. No. 2655, Melanerpes superciliaris. No. 2656, Mimocichla plumbea. No. 2657, Aratinga euops. No. 2658, Sturnella magna.

No. 2658B, Hedychium coronarium. No. 2658C, Priotelus temnurus.

**1983, Dec. 20** *Perf. 13*

| | | | | |
|---|---|---|---|---|
| **2629** | A719 | 5c multicolored | .55 | .25 |
| **2630** | A719 | 5c multicolored | .55 | .25 |
| **2631** | A719 | 5c multicolored | .55 | .25 |
| **2632** | A719 | 5c multicolored | .55 | .25 |
| **2633** | A719 | 5c multicolored | .55 | .25 |
| *a.* | | Strip of 5, Nos. 2629-2633 | 4.50 | 4.50 |
| **2634** | A719 | 5c multicolored | .55 | .25 |
| **2635** | A719 | 5c multicolored | .55 | .25 |
| **2636** | A719 | 5c multicolored | .55 | .25 |
| **2637** | A719 | 5c multicolored | .55 | .25 |
| **2638** | A719 | 5c multicolored | .55 | .25 |
| **2639** | A719 | 5c multicolored | .55 | .25 |
| **2640** | A719 | 5c multicolored | .55 | .25 |
| **2641** | A719 | 5c multicolored | .55 | .25 |
| **2642** | A719 | 5c multicolored | .55 | .25 |
| **2643** | A719 | 5c multicolored | .55 | .25 |
| *a.* | | Block of 10, Nos. 2634-2643 | 9.00 | 9.00 |
| **2644** | A719 | 5c multicolored | .55 | .25 |
| **2645** | A719 | 5c multicolored | .55 | .25 |
| **2646** | A719 | 5c multicolored | .55 | .25 |
| **2647** | A719 | 5c multicolored | .55 | .25 |
| **2648** | A719 | 5c multicolored | .55 | .25 |
| *a.* | | Strip of 5, Nos. 2644-2648 | 4.50 | 4.50 |
| **2649** | A719 | 5c multicolored | .55 | .25 |
| **2650** | A719 | 5c multicolored | .55 | .25 |
| **2651** | A719 | 5c multicolored | .55 | .25 |
| **2652** | A719 | 5c multicolored | .55 | .25 |
| **2653** | A719 | 5c multicolored | .55 | .25 |
| **2654** | A719 | 5c multicolored | .55 | .25 |
| **2655** | A719 | 5c multicolored | .55 | .25 |
| **2656** | A719 | 5c multicolored | .55 | .25 |
| **2657** | A719 | 5c multicolored | .55 | .25 |
| **2658** | A719 | 5c multicolored | .55 | .25 |
| *a.* | | Block of 10, Nos. 2649-2658 | 9.00 | 9.00 |
| | | *Nos. 2629-2658 (30)* | 16.50 | 7.50 |

**Souvenir Sheets**

| | | | | |
|---|---|---|---|---|
| **2658B** | A719 | 100c multicolored | 5.25 | 4.50 |
| **2658C** | A719 | 100c multicolored | 5.25 | 4.50 |

Flowers — A720

**1983, Dec. 30** *Perf. 12½*

| | | | | |
|---|---|---|---|---|
| **2659** | A720 | 60c Tobacco | 1.75 | .55 |
| **2660** | A720 | 70c Lily | 2.25 | .60 |
| **2661** | A720 | 80c Mariposa | 2.50 | .70 |
| **2662** | A720 | 90c Orchid | 3.50 | 1.00 |
| | | *Nos. 2659-2662 (4)* | 10.00 | 2.85 |

25th Anniv. of the Revolution A721

20c, Flags, Santa Clara Railway tracks.

**1983, Dec. 31** **Litho.** *Perf. 13*

| | | | | |
|---|---|---|---|---|
| **2663** | A721 | 5c shown | .25 | .25 |
| **2664** | A721 | 20c multicolored | 2.25 | 1.00 |

25th Anniv. of the Revolution A722

No. 2665, Guevara, Castro. No. 2666, Star. No. 2667, PCC emblem, workers.

**1984, Jan. 8**

| | | | | |
|---|---|---|---|---|
| **2665** | A722 | 20c multi | .55 | .25 |
| **2666** | A722 | 20c multi | .55 | .25 |
| **2667** | A722 | 20c multi | 1.35 | .80 |
| *a.* | | Strip of 3, #2665-2667 | 2.60 | 1.50 |
| | | *Nos. 2665-2667 (3)* | 2.45 | 1.30 |

Lenin, 60th Death Anniv. A723

30p, Spasski Tower, Russia Nos. 295, 265.

**1984, Jan. 21** *Perf. 12½x12*

| | | | | |
|---|---|---|---|---|
| **2668** | A723 | 30p multi | 1.25 | .25 |

Cuban Labor Union, 45th Anniv. — A724

**1984, Jan. 28** *Perf. 13*

| | | | | |
|---|---|---|---|---|
| **2669** | A724 | 5c multi | .25 | .25 |

Butterflies A725

Designs: 1c, Ixias balice. 2c, Phoebis avellaneda. 3c, Anthocaris sara. 5c, Victorina. 20c, Heliconius cydno cydnides. 30c, Parides gundlachianus calzadillae. 50c, Catagramma sorana.

**1984, Jan. 31** *Perf. 13x12½*

| | | | | |
|---|---|---|---|---|
| **2670** | A725 | 1c multicolored | .25 | .25 |
| **2671** | A725 | 2c multicolored | .25 | .25 |
| **2672** | A725 | 3c multicolored | .25 | .25 |
| **2673** | A725 | 5c multicolored | .25 | .25 |
| **2674** | A725 | 20c multicolored | .80 | .25 |
| **2675** | A725 | 30c multicolored | 1.40 | .65 |
| **2676** | A725 | 50c multicolored | 2.40 | .95 |
| | | *Nos. 2670-2676 (7)* | 5.60 | 2.85 |

Marine Mammals A726

Designs: 1c, Grampus griseus, vert. 2c, Delphinus delphis, vert. 5c, Physeter catodon. 6c, Stenella plagiodon, vert. 10c, Pseudorca crassidens. 30c, Tursiops truncatus, vert. 50, Megaptera novaeangliae.

**1984, Feb. 15** *Perf. 12x12½, 12½x12*

| | | | | |
|---|---|---|---|---|
| **2677** | A726 | 1c multicolored | .25 | .25 |
| **2678** | A726 | 2c multicolored | .25 | .25 |
| **2679** | A726 | 5c multicolored | .25 | .25 |
| **2680** | A726 | 6c multicolored | .25 | .25 |
| **2681** | A726 | 10c multicolored | .70 | .25 |
| **2682** | A726 | 30c multicolored | 1.60 | .40 |
| **2683** | A726 | 50c multicolored | 2.75 | .70 |
| | | *Nos. 2677-2683 (7)* | 6.05 | 2.35 |

Augusto C. Sandino (1893-1934), Nicaraguan Revolutionary A727

**1984, Feb. 21** *Perf. 13*

| | | | | |
|---|---|---|---|---|
| **2684** | A727 | 20c multicolored | .70 | .25 |

Red Cross in Cuba, 75th Anniv. — A728

**1984, Mar. 10**

| | | | | |
|---|---|---|---|---|
| **2685** | A728 | 30c Flag, No. 404 | 1.25 | .35 |

Cuban Film Industry, 25th Anniv. — A729

**1984, Mar. 24**

| | | | | |
|---|---|---|---|---|
| **2686** | A729 | 20c multi | .85 | .30 |

Caribbean Flowers — A730

Designs: 1c, Brownea grandiceps. 2c, Couroupita guianensis. 5c, Triplaris surinamensis. 20c, Amherstia nobilis. 30c, Plumieria alba. 50c, Delonix regia.

**1984, Mar. 29**

| | | | | |
|---|---|---|---|---|
| **2687** | A730 | 1c multicolored | .25 | .25 |
| **2688** | A730 | 2c multicolored | .25 | .25 |
| **2689** | A730 | 5c multicolored | .25 | .25 |
| **2690** | A730 | 20c multicolored | .80 | .30 |
| **2691** | A730 | 30c multicolored | 1.10 | .50 |
| **2692** | A730 | 50c multicolored | 2.00 | .90 |
| | | *Nos. 2687-2692 (6)* | 4.65 | 2.45 |

Cosmonauts' Day — A731

2c, *Electron 1*, 1964. 3c, *Electron 2*, 1964. 5c, *Intercosmos 1*, 1969. 10c, *Mars 5*, 1974. 30c, *Soyuz*, 1969. 50c, USSR-Bulgaria space flight, 1979.
1p, *Luna 1*, 1959.

**1984, Apr. 12**

| | | | | |
|---|---|---|---|---|
| **2693** | A731 | 2c multi | .25 | .25 |
| **2694** | A731 | 3c multi | .25 | .25 |
| **2695** | A731 | 5c multi | .25 | .25 |
| **2696** | A731 | 10c multi | .30 | .25 |
| **2697** | A731 | 30c multi | .90 | .50 |
| **2698** | A731 | 50c multi | 1.90 | .90 |
| | | *Nos. 2693-2698 (6)* | 3.85 | 2.40 |

**Souvenir Sheet**

*Perf. 12½*

| | | | | |
|---|---|---|---|---|
| **2699** | A731 | 1p multi | 4.00 | 2.00 |

No. 2699 contains one 32x40mm stamp.

Mothers' Day — A732

**1984, Apr. 19** *Perf. 13*

| | | | | |
|---|---|---|---|---|
| **2700** | A732 | 20c Red roses | .85 | .30 |
| **2701** | A732 | 20c Pink roses | .85 | .30 |

Stamp Day — A733

Designs: Mural, by R. Rodriguez Radillo (details): 20c, Mexican runner. 30c, Egyptian boatman.

**1984, Apr. 24** *Perf. 13x12½*

| | | | | |
|---|---|---|---|---|
| **2702** | A733 | 20c multicolored | .90 | .30 |
| **2703** | A733 | 30c multicolored | 1.10 | .50 |

See Nos. 2787-2788, 2860-2861, 3025-3026, 3122-3123, 3213-3214.

**Souvenir Sheet**

ESPANA '84, Madrid A734

**1984, Apr. 27** *Perf. 13x13½*

| | | | | |
|---|---|---|---|---|
| **2704** | A734 | 1p Clipper ship | 5.00 | 4.00 |

Women's Basketball, 1984 Summer Olympics — A735

**1984, May 5** *Perf. 13*

| | | | | |
|---|---|---|---|---|
| **2705** | A735 | 20c multi | 1.25 | .35 |

Agrarian Reform Act, 25th Anniv. — A736

**1984, May 17** *Perf. 13½x13*

| | | | | |
|---|---|---|---|---|
| **2706** | A736 | 5c multi | .40 | .25 |

Banco Popular de Ahorro, 1st Anniv. — A737

**1984, May 18** *Perf. 13*

| | | | | |
|---|---|---|---|---|
| **2707** | A737 | 5c multi | .40 | .25 |

Early Locomotives A738

**1984, June 11** *Perf. 12½x12*

| | | | | |
|---|---|---|---|---|
| **2708** | A738 | 1c multi | .25 | .25 |
| **2709** | A738 | 4c multi, diff. | .25 | .25 |
| **2710** | A738 | 5c multi, diff. | .25 | .25 |
| **2711** | A738 | 10c multi, diff. | .50 | .25 |
| **2712** | A738 | 30c multi, diff. | 1.50 | .40 |
| **2713** | A738 | 50c multi, diff. | 2.25 | .80 |
| | | *Nos. 2708-2713 (6)* | 5.00 | 2.20 |

**Souvenir Sheet**

19th UPU Congress, HAMBURG '84 — A739

**1984, June 19** *Perf. 13x13½*

| | | | | |
|---|---|---|---|---|
| **2714** | A739 | 1p Nos. 73, 232 | 5.25 | 4.25 |

Intl. Olympic Committee, 90th Anniv. — A740

30c, Coubertin, torch-bearer.

**1984, June 23** *Perf. 13*

| | | | | |
|---|---|---|---|---|
| **2715** | A740 | 30c multi | 1.40 | .50 |

Children's Day — A741

**1984, July 15** *Perf. 12½x13*

| | | | | |
|---|---|---|---|---|
| **2716** | A741 | 5c multi | .25 | .25 |

1984 Summer Olympics, Los Angeles — A742

**1984, July 28** *Perf. 13*

| | | | | |
|---|---|---|---|---|
| **2717** | A742 | 1c Wrestling | .25 | .25 |
| **2718** | A742 | 3c Discus | .25 | .25 |
| **2719** | A742 | 5c Volleyball | .25 | .25 |
| **2720** | A742 | 20c Boxing | .80 | .30 |
| **2721** | A742 | 30c Basketball | 1.10 | .50 |
| **2722** | A742 | 50c Weight lifting | 2.00 | .90 |
| | | *Nos. 2717-2722 (6)* | 4.65 | 2.45 |

**Souvenir Sheet**

*Perf. 12½*

| | | | | |
|---|---|---|---|---|
| **2723** | A742 | 1p Baseball | 5.00 | 4.00 |

No. 2723 contains one 32x40mm stamp.

Emilio Roig de Leuchsenring (1889-1964), Historian — A743

**1984, Aug. 8** *Perf. 13*

| | | | | |
|---|---|---|---|---|
| **2724** | A743 | 5c multi | .25 | .25 |

Friendship Games, Aug. 18-26, Havana — A744

3c, Volleyball. 5c, Women's volleyball. 8c, Water polo. 30c, Boxing.

**1984, Aug. 18**

| | | | | |
|---|---|---|---|---|
| **2725** | A744 | 3c multicolored | .25 | .25 |
| **2726** | A744 | 5c multicolored | .35 | .25 |
| **2727** | A744 | 8c multicolored | .35 | .25 |
| **2728** | A744 | 30c multicolored | 1.00 | .35 |
| | | *Nos. 2725-2728 (4)* | 1.95 | 1.10 |

Cattle Breeding A745

**1984, Sept. 20**

| | | | | |
|---|---|---|---|---|
| **2729** | A745 | 2c Artificial pastures | .25 | .25 |
| **2730** | A745 | 3c Cuban carib | .25 | .25 |
| **2731** | A745 | 5c Charolaise, vert. | .25 | .25 |
| **2732** | A745 | 30c Cuban cebu, vert. | 1.25 | .40 |
| **2733** | A745 | 50c White-udder | 2.25 | .75 |
| | | *Nos. 2729-2733 (5)* | 4.25 | 1.90 |

**Souvenir Sheet**

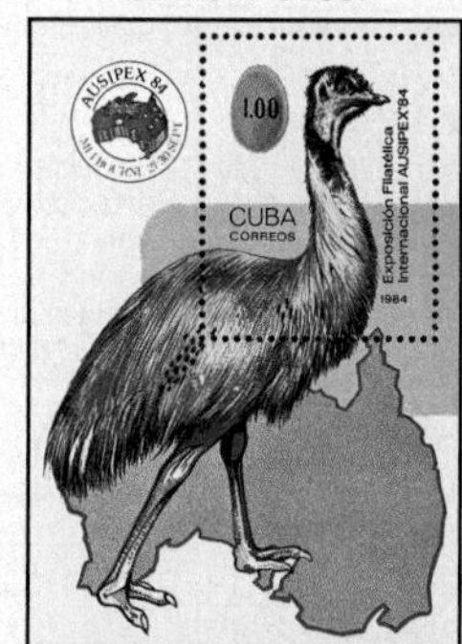


AUSIPEX '84, Sept. 21-30, Melbourne — A746

**1984, Sept. 21** *Perf. 12½*

| | | | | |
|---|---|---|---|---|
| **2734** | A746 | 1p Emu | 5.25 | 5.00 |

Fauna — A747

Designs: 1c, Polymita. 2c, Solenodon cubanus. 3c, Alsophis cantherigerus. 4c, Osteopilus septentrionalis. 5c, Mellisuga helenae. 10c, Capromys melanurus. 30c, Todus multicolor. 50c, Parrots (cotorra).

**1984, Oct. 10** *Perf. 13*

| | | | | |
|---|---|---|---|---|
| **2735** | A747 | 1c multicolored | .25 | .25 |
| **2736** | A747 | 2c multicolored | .25 | .25 |
| **2737** | A747 | 3c multicolored | .25 | .25 |
| **2738** | A747 | 4c multicolored | .25 | .25 |
| **2739** | A747 | 5c multicolored | .35 | .25 |
| **2740** | A747 | 10c multicolored | .25 | .25 |
| **2741** | A747 | 30c multicolored | 1.75 | .95 |
| **2742** | A747 | 50c multicolored | 2.75 | 1.25 |
| | | *Nos. 2735-2742 (8)* | 6.10 | 3.70 |

ESPAMER '85, Havana — A748

Columbus Day: a, Ferdinand, Isabella. b, Departure from Palos. c, *Nina, Pinta, Santa Maria.* d, Landing in America.

**1984, Oct. 12**

| | | | |
|---|---|---|---|
| **2743** | Sheet of 4 + 2 labels | 5.00 | 2.50 |
| *a.* | A748 5c multicolored | .25 | .25 |
| *b.* | A748 20c multicolored | 1.50 | .70 |
| *c.* | A748 30c multicolored | 2.25 | 1.10 |
| *d.* | A748 50c multicolored | 1.00 | .50 |

Souvenir Sheet

9th Natl. Phil. Exhibition, Oct. 20-28, Santiago de Cuba — A749

**1984, Oct. 20** ***Perf. 12½***

**2744** A749 1p multicolored 5.25 4.00

Natl. Revolutionary Militia, 25th Anniv. — A750

**1984, Oct. 26** ***Perf. 12½x13***

**2745** A750 5c multi .30 .25

Disappearance of Camilo Cienfuegos, 25th Anniv. — A751

**1984, Oct. 28** ***Perf. 13x12½***

**2746** A751 5c multi .40 .25

UN Child Survival Campaign — A752

**1984, Nov. 11** ***Perf. 13***

**2747** A752 5c Breast-feeding .45 .25

Classic Automobiles A753

1c, 1909 Morgan. 2c, 1922 Austin. 5c, 1903 De Dion-Bouton. 20c, 1908 Ford Model T. 30c, 1885 Benz. 50c, 1910 Benz.

**1984, Nov. 25**

| | | | | |
|---|---|---|---|---|
| **2748** | A753 | 1c multi | .25 | .25 |
| **2749** | A753 | 2c multi | .25 | .25 |
| **2750** | A753 | 5c multi | .25 | .25 |
| **2751** | A753 | 20c multi | .90 | .25 |
| **2752** | A753 | 30c multi | 1.40 | .35 |
| **2753** | A753 | 50c multi | 2.50 | .70 |
| | | *Nos. 2748-2753 (6)* | 5.55 | 2.05 |

Postal Museum, 20th Anniv. A754

**1985, Jan. 2** ***Perf. 13x12½***

**2754** A754 20c multi .75 .25

*Portrait of Celia Sanchez,* by E. Escobedo — A755

**1985, Jan. 11** ***Perf. 13***

**2755** A755 5c multi .40 .25

Celia Sanchez (1920-1980), party leader.

PORTO '85, Intl. Pigeon Exhibition A756

**1985, Jan. 23**

**2756** A756 20c multi .85 .25

1986 World Cup Soccer Championships, Mexico — A757

Athletes and Flags of previous host nations: 1c, Chile, 1962. 2c, Great Britain, 1966. 3c, Mexico, 1970. 4c, Federal Republic of Germany, 1974. 5c, Argentina, 1978. 30c, Spain, 1982. 50c, Sweden, 1958.
1p, Mexico, 1986.

**1985, Jan. 25**

| | | | | |
|---|---|---|---|---|
| **2757** | A757 | 1c multi | .25 | .25 |
| **2758** | A757 | 2c multi | .25 | .25 |
| **2759** | A757 | 3c multi | .25 | .25 |
| **2760** | A757 | 4c multi | .25 | .25 |
| **2761** | A757 | 5c multi | .25 | .25 |
| **2762** | A757 | 30c multi | 1.40 | .50 |
| **2763** | A757 | 50c multi | 2.10 | .65 |
| | | *Nos. 2757-2763 (7)* | 4.75 | 2.40 |

**Souvenir Sheet**

***Perf. 12½***

**2764** A757 1p multi 4.25 3.75

No. 2764 contains one 40x32mm stamp.

Baconao Natl. Park — A758

Dinosaurs.

**1985, Feb. 14** ***Perf. 13x12½***

| | | | | |
|---|---|---|---|---|
| **2765** | A758 | 1c Pteranodon | .30 | .25 |
| **2766** | A758 | 2c Brontosaurus | .30 | .25 |
| **2767** | A758 | 4c Iguanodontus | .30 | .25 |
| **2768** | A758 | 5c Estegosaurus | .30 | .25 |
| **2769** | A758 | 8c Monoclonius | .50 | .25 |
| **2770** | A758 | 30c Corythosaurus | 1.50 | .50 |
| **2771** | A758 | 50c Tyrannosaurus | 2.75 | .70 |
| | | *Nos. 2765-2771 (7)* | 5.95 | 2.45 |

13th Congress of the Postal Unions of the Americas, Havana — A759

Design: Uruguay #196, congress emblem and Argentina #287.

**1985, Mar. 11** ***Perf. 12½x12***

**2772** A759 20c multi 2.00 .70

ESPAMER '85 — A760

Indian activities: 1c, Playing ball. 2c, Medicine man preparing calumet and other ritual items. 5c, Net and spear fishing. 20c, Potter. 30c, Hunting. 50c, Hollowing-out canoe, decorating paddle. 1p, Cooking.

**1985, Mar. 19** ***Perf. 12½x13***

| | | | | |
|---|---|---|---|---|
| **2773** | A760 | 1c multi | .25 | .25 |
| **2774** | A760 | 2c multi | .25 | .25 |
| **2775** | A760 | 5c multi | .40 | .25 |
| **2776** | A760 | 20c multi | .40 | .25 |
| **2777** | A760 | 30c multi | .65 | .40 |
| **2778** | A760 | 50c multi | 2.75 | .80 |
| | | *Nos. 2773-2778 (6)* | 4.70 | 2.20 |

**Souvenir Sheet**

***Perf. 12½***

**2779** A760 1p multi 5.25 5.00

No. 2779 contains one 32x40mm stamp.
An imperf. souvenir sheet exists containing Nos. 2773-2779. Value $40.

Cosmonauts' Day — A761

Designs: 2c, Spacecraft orbiting Moon. 3c, Two spacecraft. 10c, Space walkers linked. 13c, Space walkers welding. 20c, *Vostok 2.* 50c, *Lunokhod 1* moon vehicle.

**1985, Apr. 12** ***Perf. 13x12½***

| | | | | |
|---|---|---|---|---|
| **2780** | A761 | 2c multi | .25 | .25 |
| **2781** | A761 | 3c multi | .25 | .25 |
| **2782** | A761 | 10c multi | .45 | .25 |
| **2783** | A761 | 13c multi | .60 | .25 |
| **2784** | A761 | 20c multi | .70 | .25 |
| **2785** | A761 | 50c multi | 2.25 | .70 |
| | | *Nos. 2780-2785 (6)* | 4.50 | 1.95 |

12th Youth and Students Festival, Moscow — A762

**1985, Apr. 19** ***Perf. 13***

**2786** A762 30c Lenin Mausoleum 1.00 .50

**Stamp Day Type of 1984**

Mural, by R. Rodriguez Radillo (1967), details: 20c, Roman charioteer (courier of *Cursus Publicus*). 30c, Medieval nobleman, monks (monastic messenger mail).

**1985, Apr. 24** ***Perf. 13x12½***

| | | | | |
|---|---|---|---|---|
| **2787** | A733 | 20c multi | .80 | .25 |
| **2788** | A733 | 30c multi | 1.10 | .40 |

Mothers' Day — A763

**1985, May 2** ***Perf. 13***

| | | | | |
|---|---|---|---|---|
| **2789** | A763 | 1c Peonies | .25 | .25 |
| **2790** | A763 | 4c Carnations | .25 | .25 |
| **2791** | A763 | 5c Dahlias | .25 | .25 |
| **2792** | A763 | 13c Roses | .45 | .25 |
| **2793** | A763 | 20c Roses, diff. | .75 | .25 |
| **2794** | A763 | 50c Tulips | 2.00 | .55 |
| | | *Nos. 2789-2794 (6)* | 3.95 | 1.80 |

50th Death Anniv. of Antonio Guiteras and Carlos Aponte, Revolutionaries — A764

**1985, May 9** ***Perf. 12½x12***

**2795** A764 5c multi .25 .25



End of WWII, 40th Anniv. A765

20c, Soviet memorial, Berlin-Treptow. 30c, Dove.

**1985, May 10**

| | | | | |
|---|---|---|---|---|
| **2796** | A765 | 5c shown | .25 | .25 |
| **2797** | A765 | 20c multicolored | .65 | .30 |
| **2798** | A765 | 30c multicolored | 1.10 | .55 |
| | | *Nos. 2796-2798 (3)* | 2.00 | 1.10 |

Souvenir Sheet

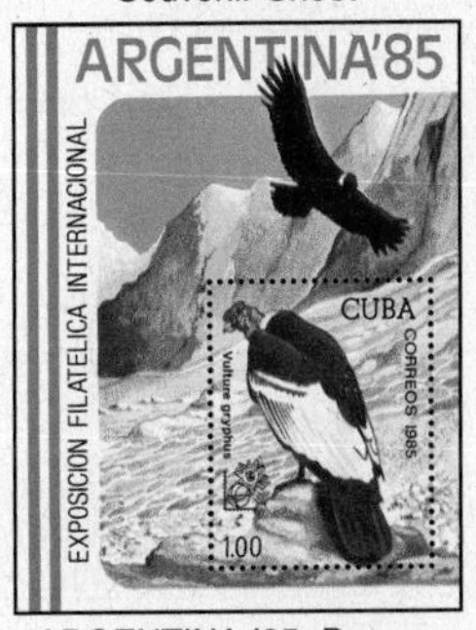


ARGENTINA '85, Buenos Aires — A766

**1985, June 5** ***Perf. 13½x13***

**2799** A766 1p *Vulture gryphus* 5.25 5.00

Motorcycle, Cent. — A767

2c, 1885 Daimler. 5c, 1910 Kaiser Tricycle. 10c, 1925 Fanomobile. 30c, 1926 Mars A20. 50c, 1936 Simson BSW.

**1985, June 28** ***Perf. 13***

| | | | | |
|---|---|---|---|---|
| **2800** | A767 | 2c multi | .25 | .25 |
| **2801** | A767 | 5c multi | .25 | .25 |
| **2802** | A767 | 10c multi | .50 | .25 |
| **2803** | A767 | 30c multi | 1.25 | .30 |
| **2804** | A767 | 50c multi | 2.25 | .70 |
| | | *Nos. 2800-2804 (5)* | 4.50 | 1.75 |

Development of Health Care Since the Revolution A768

**1985, July 18** ***Perf. 12½x12***

**2805** A768 5c Hospitals .25 .25

Federation of Cuban Women (FMC), 25th Anniv. — A769

**1985, Aug. 23**

**2806** A769 5c multi .25 .25

No. 2806 printed se-tenant with label picturing federation emblem.

Universiade Games, Japan — A770

**1985, Aug. 27** ***Perf. 13***

**2807** A770 50c multi 1.75 .55

1st Havana Declaration, 25th Anniv. — A771

5c, Jose Marti statue, revolutionaries.

**1985, Sept. 2**

**2808** A771 5c multicolored .50 .25

Souvenir Sheet

ITALIA '85 A772

**1985, Sept. 25** ***Perf. 12½***

**2809** A772 1p Roman galley 5.25 4.25

Revolutionary Defense Committees (CDR), 25th Anniv. — A773

**1985, Sept. 28** ***Perf. 13***

**2810** A773 5c multicolored .25 .25

Aquarium Fish — A774

Designs: 1c, Centropyge argi. 3c, Holacanthus tricolor. 5c, Chaetodon capistratus. 10c, Chaetodon sedentarius. 20c, Chaetodon ocellatus. 50c, Holacanthus ciliaris.

**1985, Sept. 30** **Litho.**

**2811** A774 1c multicolored .25 .25
**2812** A774 3c multicolored .25 .25
**2813** A774 5c multicolored .25 .25
**2814** A774 10c multicolored .35 .25
**2815** A774 20c multicolored .80 .50
**2816** A774 50c multicolored 2.10 1.60
*Nos. 2811-2816 (6)* 4.00 3.10

Communist Party Central Committee, 20th Anniv. — A775

**1985, Oct. 1**

**2817** A775 5c multicolored .40 .25

Souvenir Sheet

EXFILNA '85 A776

1p, Spain No. C45, Cuba No. 387.

**1985, Oct. 18**

**2818** A776 1p multicolored 5.25 4.25

UN, 40th Anniv. — A777

**1985, Oct. 24**

**2819** A777 20c multicolored .65 .25

Sites on the UNESCO World Heritage List — A778

Designs: 2c, Plaza Vieja, 16th cent. 5c, Royal Army Castle, c. 1558. 20c, Havana Cathedral, c. 1748. 30c, Captains-General Palace (Havana City Museum), 1776. 50c, The Temple, 1827.

**1985, Nov. 25**

**2820** A778 2c multi .25 .25
**2821** A778 5c multi .25 .25
**2822** A778 20c multi .70 .25
**2823** A778 30c multi 1.10 .45
**2824** A778 50c multi 1.90 .60
*Nos. 2820-2824 (5)* 4.20 1.80

1986 World Cup Soccer Championships, Mexico — A779

Various athletes.

**1986, Jan. 20**

**2825** A779 1c multi .25 .25
**2826** A779 4c multi .25 .25
**2827** A779 5c multi .25 .25
**2828** A779 10c multi .30 .25
**2829** A779 30c multi 1.00 .30
**2830** A779 50c multi 1.50 .55
*Nos. 2825-2830 (6)* 3.55 1.85

**Souvenir Sheet**

***Perf. 13½x13***

**2831** A779 1p multi 4.50 4.25

No. 2831 contains one 32x40mm stamp. No. 2831 exists imperf. Value $125.

3rd Communist Party Congress, Havana A780

20c, Party and natl. flags, emblem.

**1986, Feb. 4** ***Perf. 13***

**2832** A780 5c shown .25 .25
**2833** A780 20c multicolored 1.25 .25

Natl. Sports Institute (INDER), 25th Anniv. — A781

**1986, Feb. 23**

**2834** A781 5c multicolored .30 .25

A782

**1986, Feb. 23**

**2835** A782 5c multicolored .30 .25

Ministry of Domestic Trade, 25th anniv.

A783

Exotic flowers in the Botanical Gardens: 1c, Tecomaria capensis. 3c, Michelia champaca. 5c, Thunbergia grandiflora. 8c, Dendrobium phalaenopsis. 30c, Allamanda violacea. 50c, Rhodactus bleo.

**1986, Feb. 25** ***Perf. 12½x12***

**2836** A783 1c multicolored .25 .25
**2837** A783 3c multicolored .25 .25
**2838** A783 5c multicolored .25 .25
**2839** A783 8c multicolored .30 .25
**2840** A783 30c multicolored 1.00 .25
**2841** A783 50c multicolored 1.60 .40
*Nos. 2836-2841 (6)* 3.65 1.65

Gundlach and Birds — A784

Designs: 1c, Agelaius assimilis. 3c, Dendroica pityophila. 7c, Myiarchus sagrae. 9c, Dendroica petechia gundlachi. 30c, Geotrygon caniceps. 50c, Colaptes auratus chrysocaulosus.

**1986, Mar. 14** **Litho.** ***Perf. 13½x13***

**2842** A784 1c multicolored .25 .25
**2843** A784 3c multicolored .25 .25
**2844** A784 7c multicolored .30 .25
**2845** A784 9c multicolored .50 .30
**2846** A784 30c multicolored 2.00 1.00
**2847** A784 50c multicolored 3.25 1.60
*Nos. 2842-2847 (6)* 6.55 3.65

Juan Cristobal Gundlach (d. 1896), ornithologist.

Pioneers Youth Organization, 25th Anniv. — A785

**1986, Apr. 3** ***Perf. 13***

**2848** A785 5c Induction .30 .25

150th Birth Anniv. of Maximo Gomez — A786

**1986, Apr. 4**

**2849** A786 20c multicolored .70 .25

A787

**1986, Apr. 10** ***Perf. 12½***

**2850** A787 5c multicolored .40 .25

Kindergartens, 25th anniv.

A788

1st Man in Space, 25th Anniv.: 1c, *Vostok* and rocket designer Sergei Korolev. 2c, Yuri Gagarin, *Vostok 1.* 5c, Valentina Tereshkova, *Vostok 6.* 20c, *Salyut-Soyuz* space link. 30c, Capsule landing. 50c, *Soyuz* rocket launch. 1p, Konstantin Tsiolkovski (1857-1935), rocket scientist.

**1986, Apr. 12** ***Perf. 13x13½***

**2851** A788 1c multi .25 .25
**2852** A788 2c multi .25 .25
**2853** A788 5c multi .25 .25
**2854** A788 20c multi .60 .25
**2855** A788 30c multi .75 .25
**2856** A788 50c multi 1.50 .55
*Nos. 2851-2856 (6)* 3.60 1.80

**Souvenir Sheet**

***Perf. 12½***

**2857** A788 1p multi 4.50 4.00

No. 2857 contains one 32x40mm stamp.

Natl. Flag and No. 2407 — A789

20c, Banners, natl. crest.

**1986, Apr. 19** ***Perf. 13***

**2858** A789 5c shown .25 .25
**2859** A789 20c multicolored .75 .25

Bay of Pigs invasion, 25th anniv. (5c); Proclamation of Socialist Revolution, 25th anniv. (20c).

**Stamp Day Type of 1984**

Mural, by R. Rodriguez Radillo (1967), details: 20c, Mail coach, 18th-19th cent. 30c, Pony Express.

**1986, Apr. 24** ***Perf. 13x12½***

**2860** A733 20c multi .75 .25
**2861** A733 30c multi 1.00 .25

Radio Havana, 25th Anniv. — A790

**1986, May 1**

**2862** A790 5c multicolored .40 .25

EXPO '86, Vancouver A791

Locomotives: 1c, *Stourbridge Lion*, 1829, US. 4c, Stephenson's *Rocket*, 1829, GB. 5c, 1st Russian locomotive, 1845. 8c, Seguin's locomotive, 1830, France. 30c, 1st Canadian locomotive, 1836. 50c, Urban locomotive, Belgian Grand Central Rlwy., 1872. 1p, US locomotive pulling Cuban sugar train, 1837.

**1986, May 2 Litho.** ***Perf. 12½x12***

**2863** A791 1c multi .25 .25
**2864** A791 4c multi .25 .25
**2865** A791 5c multi .25 .25
**2866** A791 8c multi .25 .25
**2867** A791 30c multi .80 .30
**2868** A791 50c multi 2.10 .55
*Nos. 2863-2868 (6)* 3.90 1.85

**Souvenir Sheet**

***Perf. 13x13½***

**2869** A791 1p multi 5.25 5.00

No. 2869 contains one 40x32mm stamp.

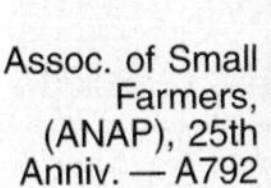

Assoc. of Small Farmers, (ANAP), 25th Anniv. — A792

**1986, May 17** ***Perf. 13***

**2870** A792 5c multicolored .40 .25

Intl. Peace Year — A793

**1986, June 2**

**2871** A793 30c multicolored 1.00 .25

Ministry of the Interior (MININT), 25th Anniv. — A794

**1986, June 6**

**2872** A794 5c multicolored .40 .25

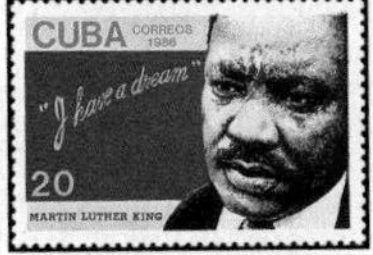

Martin Luther King, Jr. — A795

**1986, June 27** ***Perf. 13½x13***

**2873** A795 20c multicolored .90 .25

Bonifacio Byrne (d. 1936), Poet — A796

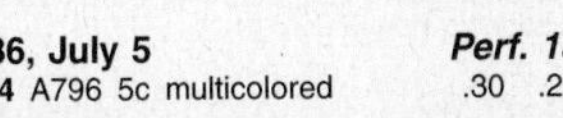

**1986, July 5** ***Perf. 13***

**2874** A796 5c multicolored .30 .25

Cuban Union of Writers and Artists (UNEAC), 25th Anniv. — A797

**1986, July 10** ***Perf. 13x12½***

**2875** A797 5c multi .45 .25

Sandinista Movement in Nicaragua (FSLN), 25th Anniv. — A798

Augusto Cesar Sandino and Carlos Fonseca.

**1986, July 23** ***Perf. 13x12***

**2876** A798 20c multi .65 .25

Ministry of Transportation, 25th Anniv. — A799

**1986, Aug. 1** ***Perf. 13***

**2877** A799 5c multicolored .40 .25

7th University Games of Central America and the Caribbean — A800

**1986, Aug. 9**

**2878** A800 20c multicolored .80 .25

**Souvenir Sheet**

STOCKHOLMIA '86 — A801

Designs: a, 2c Mambi Revolutionary stamp of 1897. b, Sweden Type A7, cancellation.

**1986, Aug. 28** ***Perf. 12½***

**2879** A801 Sheet of 2 4.50 3.75
*a.-b.* 50c multi

Nonaligned Countries Movement, 25th Anniv. — A802

**1986, Sept. 1** ***Perf. 13½x13***

**2880** A802 50c multi 1.75 .45

Orchids — A803

Designs: 1c, Cattleya hardyana. 4c, Brassolaelio cattleya. 5c, Phalaenopsis marget moses. 10c, Laelio cattleya prism palette. 30c, Phalaenopsis violacea. 50c, Disa uniflora.

**1986, Sept. 15** ***Perf. 12½***

**2881** A803 1c multicolored .25 .25
**2882** A803 4c multicolored .25 .25
**2883** A803 5c multicolored .25 .25
**2884** A803 10c multicolored .30 .25
**2885** A803 30c multicolored 1.25 .30
**2886** A803 50c multicolored 1.75 .50
*Nos. 2881-2886 (6)* 4.05 1.80

Latin American History — A804

Pre-Columbian artifacts: No. 2887, Mayan dwelling and votive jade sculpture. No. 2888, Inca vase and Tiahuanacu sun gate (Bolivia). No. 2889, Spain No. C47, discovery of America 500th anniv. emblem, scroll. No. 2890, Diaguitan duck-shaped pitcher and Pucara de Quitor ruins (Chile). No. 2891, San Agustin Archaeological Park megaliths and Quimbayan sculpture (Colombia). No. 2892, Moler grinding stone and Chorotega ceramic figurine. No. 2893, Tabaco idol and Indian dwelling (Cuba). No. 2894, Spain No. C38. No. 2895, Taino dwelling and chair (Dominica). No. 2896, Tolita statue and Ingapirca Castle ruins. No. 2897, Maya vase and Tikal Temple (Guatemala). No. 2898, Copan ruins and Maya idol. No. 2899, Spain No. C37. No. 2900, Chichen Itza Temple and Zapotecan urn (Mexico). No. 2901, Punta de Zapote megaliths and Ometepe ceramic figurine. No. 2902, Tonosi lidded ceramic bowl and Barriles monoliths. No. 2903, Ruins at Machu-Picchu and Inca statue (Peru). No. 2904, Spain No. C49. No. 2905, Teepees and triangular sculpture (Puerto Rico). No. 2906, Fertility statue from Santa Ana and Santo Domingo Cave.

**1986, Oct. 12** ***Perf. 13***

**2887** A804 1c multi .25 .25
**2888** A804 1c multi .25 .25
**2889** A804 1c multi .25 .25
**2890** A804 1c multi .25 .25
**2891** A804 1c multi .25 .25
*a.* Strip of 5, Nos. 2887-2891 3.50 3.50
**2892** A804 5c multi .25 .25
**2893** A804 5c multi .25 .25
**2894** A804 5c multi .25 .25
**2895** A804 5c multi .25 .25
**2896** A804 5c multi .25 .25
*a.* Strip of 5, Nos. 2892-2896 3.50 3.50
**2897** A804 10c multi .25 .25
**2898** A804 10c multi .25 .25
**2899** A804 10c multi .25 .25
**2900** A804 10c multi .25 .25
**2901** A804 10c multi .25 .25
*a.* Strip of 5, Nos. 2897-2901 4.00 4.00
**2902** A804 20c multi .65 .30
**2903** A804 20c multi .65 .30
**2904** A804 20c multi .65 .30
**2905** A804 20c multi .65 .30
**2906** A804 20c multi .65 .30
*a.* Strip of 5, Nos. 2902-2906 9.75 9.75
*Nos. 2887-2906 (20)* 7.00 5.25

Discovery of America, 500th anniv. (in 1992). See Nos. 2966-2985, 3065-3084, 3253-3272, 3463-3466.

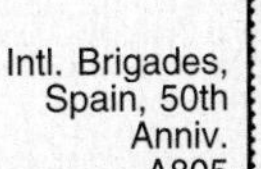

Intl. Brigades, Spain, 50th Anniv. A805

**1986, Oct. 14** ***Perf. 12½x12***

**2907** A805 30c multicolored .85 .35

Paintings in the Natl. Museum A806

Designs: 2c, *Two Children*, by Gutierrez de la Vega, vert. 4c, *Sed*, by Jean-Georges Vibert. 6c, *Virgin and Child*, by Niccolo Abbate, vert. 10c, *Bullfight*, by Eugenio de Lucas Velazquez. 30c, *The Five Senses*, anonymous. 50c, *Arrival at Thomops Castle*, by Jean Louis Ernest.

**1986, Nov. 5** ***Perf. 13***

**2908** A806 2c multi .25 .25
**2909** A806 4c multi .25 .25
**2910** A806 6c multi .25 .25
**2911** A806 10c multi .30 .25
**2912** A806 30c multi .60 .30
**2913** A806 50c multi 1.25 .55
*Nos. 2908-2913 (6)* 2.90 1.85

Anniversaries A807

**1986, Dec. 2 Litho.** ***Perf. 12½***

**2914** A807 5c *Granma* .40 .25

**Size: 26x38mm**

**2915** A807 20c Soldier, rifle, flag 1.00 .25

Granma Landings, 30th anniv. (5c); Revolutionary Armed Forces, 30th anniv. (20c).

Scholarship Program, 25th Anniv. — A808

**1986, Dec. 22** ***Perf. 13***

**2916** A808 5c Guevara, students .30 .25

Natl. Literacy Campaign, 25th Anniv. — A809

5c, Marti, man learning to write.

**1986, Dec. 25** ***Perf. 13x12½***

**2917** A809 5c multicolored .40 .25

Siege of La Plata, 30th Anniv. A810

5c, Map, revolutionaries.

**1987, Jan. 17** ***Perf. 12½x12***

**2918** A810 5c multicolored .30 .25

Paintings in the Natl. Museum A811

3c, *Gypsy*, by Joaquin Sorolla. 5c, *Sir Walter Scott*, by Sir John W. Gordon. 10c, *Farm Meadows*, by Alfred de Breanski. 20c, *Still-life*, by Isaac van Duynen. 30c, *Landscape with Figures*, by Francesco Zuccarelli. 40c, *The Failure* (defeated bullfighter), by Ignacio Zuloaga.

**1987, Feb. 5** ***Perf. 13***

**2919** A811 3c multi, vert. .25 .25
**2920** A811 5c multi, vert. .25 .25
**2921** A811 10c multi .30 .25
**2922** A811 20c multi .75 .25
**2923** A811 30c multi .80 .30
**2924** A811 40c multi, vert. 1.25 .50
*Nos. 2919-2924 (6)* 3.60 1.80

Siege of the Presidential Palace, 30th Anniv. A812

5c, Palace, van, Echeverra.

**1987, Mar. 13** ***Perf. 12½x12***

**2925** A812 5c multicolored .30 .25

Lazarus Ludwig Zamenhof and Russia Type A77 — A813

**1987, Mar. 16** ***Perf. 13½x13***

**2926** A813 30c multicolored 3.50 .60

Esperanto, cent.

**Souvenir Sheet**

EXFILNA '87, 10th Natl. Stamp Exposition, Holguin — A814

**1987, Mar. 28** ***Perf. 13x13½***

**2927** A814 1p Nos. 552, C129 4.50 3.75

25th Anniv. and 5th Cong. of the Youth Communist League (U.J.C.) — A815

**1987, Apr. 4** ***Perf. 13***

**2928** A815 5c multicolored .75 .25

Intercosmos, 20th Anniv. — A816

3c, Intercosmos 1. 5c, Intercosmos 2. 10c, TD. 20c, Cosmos 93. 30c, Prognoz. 50c, Vostok 3.
1p, Rocket, Vostok 3.

**1987, Apr. 12** **Litho.** ***Perf. 12½x12***

| | | | | |
|---|---|---|---|---|
| **2929** | A816 | 3c multicolored | .25 | .25 |
| **2930** | A816 | 5c multicolored | .25 | .25 |
| **2931** | A816 | 10c multicolored | .30 | .25 |
| **2932** | A816 | 20c multicolored | .65 | .25 |
| **2933** | A816 | 30c multicolored | 1.00 | .30 |
| **2934** | A816 | 50c multicolored | 1.50 | .55 |
| | | *Nos. 2929-2934 (6)* | 3.95 | 1.85 |

**Souvenir Sheet**

***Perf. 13½x13***

**2935** A816 1p multi 4.50 2.25

No. 2935 contains one 32x40mm stamp.

Stamp Day — A817

Stamped covers and canceled stamps: 30c, Havana, 1890. 50c, Santiago de Cuba, 1869.

**1987, Apr. 24** ***Perf. 13***

| | | | | |
|---|---|---|---|---|
| **2936** | A817 | 30c multi | 1.10 | .30 |
| **2937** | A817 | 50c multi | 1.90 | .60 |

Mothers' Day — A818

Various dahlias and roses.

**1987, May 2**

| | | | | |
|---|---|---|---|---|
| **2938** | A818 | 3c multi | .25 | .25 |
| **2939** | A818 | 5c multi | .25 | .25 |
| **2940** | A818 | 10c multi | .25 | .25 |
| **2941** | A818 | 13c multi | .30 | .25 |
| **2942** | A818 | 30c multi | .70 | .25 |
| **2943** | A818 | 50c multi | 1.25 | .50 |
| | | *Nos. 2938-2943 (6)* | 3.00 | 1.75 |

Bone-lengthening Procedure (Femur in Frame) — A819

**1987, May 4**

**2944** A819 5c multi .30 .25

ORTOPEDIA '87, medical congress for orthopedists from Spanish and Portuguese-speaking countries, Havana.

Cuban Broadcasting and Television Institute, 25th Anniv. — A820

**1987, May 24** ***Perf. 13***

**2945** A820 5c multi .30 .25

Battle of Uvero, 30th Anniv. — A821

Views of monument, Sierra Maestra Mts.

**1987, May 28** ***Perf. 13½x13***

**2946** A821 5c multicolored .30 .25

CAPEX '87 — A822

Natl. flags, stamps and 19th cent. mail carriers pictured on cigarette cards: 3c, Messenger, llamas and Bolivia Type A9. 5c, Early p.o., automobile and France Type A17. 10c, Messengers riding elephants and Thailand Type A2. 20c, Messenger riding camel and stamp of Egypt, 1879. 30c, Mail troika and stamp of Russia. 50c, Post rider and stamp of Indo-China. 1p, Post rider and Mambi Revolutionary stamp.

**1987, June 6** ***Perf. 12½x13***

| | | | | |
|---|---|---|---|---|
| **2947** | A822 | 3c multi | .25 | .25 |
| **2948** | A822 | 5c multi | .25 | .25 |
| **2949** | A822 | 10c multi | .25 | .25 |
| **2950** | A822 | 20c multi | .50 | .25 |
| **2951** | A822 | 30c multi | .70 | .25 |
| **2952** | A822 | 50c multi | 1.25 | .50 |
| | | *Nos. 2947-2952 (6)* | 3.20 | 1.75 |

**Souvenir Sheet**

***Perf. 13½x13***

**2953** A822 1p multi 4.50 2.25

No. 2953 contains one 32x40mm stamp.

Dinosaur Exhibits, Bacanao Natl. Park — A823

**1987, June 25** ***Perf. 13***

| | | | | |
|---|---|---|---|---|
| **2954** | A823 | 3c multi | .25 | .25 |
| **2955** | A823 | 5c multi | .25 | .25 |
| **2956** | A823 | 10c multi | .30 | .25 |
| **2957** | A823 | 20c multi | .80 | .25 |
| **2958** | A823 | 35c multi | 1.00 | .30 |
| **2959** | A823 | 40c multi | 1.10 | .40 |
| | | *Nos. 2954-2959 (6)* | 3.70 | 1.70 |

Frank Pais (d. 1957), Teacher and Student Leader A824

5c, Pais, Rafael Maria Mendive University.

**1987, July 30** ***Perf. 12½x12***

**2960** A824 5c multicolored .30 .25

10th Pan American Games, Indianapolis — A825

**1987, Aug. 8**

**2961** A825 50c multicolored 1.75 .45

Printed se-tenant with inscribed label picturing the 1991 Havana Games character trademark.

Siege of Cienfuegos, 30th Anniv. — A826

**1987, Sept. 5** ***Perf. 13***

**2962** A826 5c Memorial .30 .25

**Souvenir Sheet**

HAFNIA '87, Denmark A827

1p, Danish mailman, 1887, Type A6.

**1987, Sept. 16** ***Perf. 13½x13***

**2963** A827 1p multi 4.50 3.50

**Souvenir Sheet**

ESPAMER '87, La Coruna, Oct. 2-12 — A828

1p, La Coruna Port, 1525.

**1987, Oct. 2**

**2964** A828 1p multi 4.50 4.00

20th Heroic Guerrillas Day — A829

**1987, Oct. 8** ***Perf. 12½x12***

**2965** A829 50c Coins, #1364 1.25 .55

**Latin American History Type of 1986**

Indians and birds: No. 2966, Tehuelche Indian of Argentina, *Habia rubica*. No. 2967, *Ramphastos cuvieri*, Tibirica Indian of Brazil. No. 2968, Spain #C31 & discovery of America 500th anniv. emblem. No. 2969, *Vultur gryphus*, Lautaro Indian of Chile. No. 2970, Calarca Indian of Colombia, *Opisthocomus hoazin*. No. 2971, *Priotelus temnurus*, Hatuey Indian of Cuba. No. 2972, *Columbigallina passerina*, Enriquillo Indian of the Dominican Republic. No. 2973, Spain #427. #2974, *Semnornis ramphastinus*, Ruminahui Indian of Ecuador. No. 2975, *Pharomachrus mocinno*, Tecum Uman Indian of Guatemala. No. 2976, Anacaona Indian of Haiti, *Aramus guarauna*. No. 2977, Lempira Indian of Honduras, *Diglossa baritula*. #2978, Spain #C42. No. 2979, *Onychorhinchus mexicanus*, Cuauhtemoc Indian of Mexico. No. 2980, *Setofaga picta*, Nicarao Indian of Nicaragua. No. 2981, *Rupicola peruviana*, Atahualpa Indian of Peru. No. 2982, Atlacatl Indian of El Salvador, *Bluteo jamaicensis*. #2983, Spain #432. No. 2984, Abayuba Indian of Uruguay, *Phytotoma rutila*. No. 2985, Guaycaypuro Indian of Venezuela, *Ara arauna*.

**1987, Oct. 12** ***Perf. 13***

| | | | | |
|---|---|---|---|---|
| **2966** | A804 | 1c multi | .25 | .25 |
| **2967** | A804 | 1c multi | .25 | .25 |
| **2968** | A804 | 1c multi | .25 | .25 |
| **2969** | A804 | 1c multi | .25 | .25 |
| **2970** | A804 | 1c multi | .25 | .25 |
| *a.* | | Strip of 5, Nos. 2966-2970 | 1.00 | 1.00 |
| **2971** | A804 | 5c multi | .25 | .25 |
| **2972** | A804 | 5c multi | .25 | .25 |
| **2973** | A804 | 5c multi | .25 | .25 |
| **2974** | A804 | 5c multi | .25 | .25 |
| **2975** | A804 | 5c multi | .25 | .25 |
| *a.* | | Strip of 5, Nos. 2971-2975 | 1.25 | 1.25 |
| **2976** | A804 | 10c multi | .35 | .25 |
| **2977** | A804 | 10c multi | .35 | .25 |
| **2978** | A804 | 10c multi | .35 | .25 |
| **2979** | A804 | 10c multi | .35 | .25 |
| **2980** | A804 | 10c multi | .35 | .25 |
| *a.* | | Strip of 5, Nos. 2976-2980 | 1.90 | 1.90 |
| **2981** | A804 | 20c multi | .50 | .40 |
| **2982** | A804 | 20c multi | .50 | .40 |
| **2983** | A804 | 20c multi | .50 | .40 |
| **2984** | A804 | 20c multi | .50 | .40 |
| **2985** | A804 | 20c multi | .50 | .40 |
| *a.* | | Strip of 5, Nos. 2981-2985 | 2.75 | 2.75 |
| | | *Nos. 2966-2985 (20)* | 6.75 | 5.75 |

Discovery of America, 500th anniv. (in 1992).

October Revolution, Russia, 70th Anniv. A830

30c, Soviet spacecraft, Russia No. 379.

**1987, Nov. 7** ***Perf. 12½x12***

**2986** A830 30c multi 1.00 .25

Cuban Railway, 150th Anniv. A831

Stamps on stamps.

**1987, Nov. 19** ***Perf. 13x12½***

| | | | | |
|---|---|---|---|---|
| **2987** | A831 | 3c No. 453 | .25 | .25 |
| **2988** | A831 | 5c No. 1061 | .25 | .25 |
| **2989** | A831 | 10c No. 2010 | .25 | .25 |
| **2990** | A831 | 20c No. 2011 | .45 | .25 |
| **2991** | A831 | 35c No. 2360 | .85 | .30 |
| **2992** | A831 | 40c No. 2361 | .90 | .40 |
| | | *Nos. 2987-2992 (6)* | 2.95 | 1.70 |

**Souvenir Sheet**

***Perf. 13x13½***

**2993** A831 1p No. 355 4.75 2.25

No. 2993 contains 40x32mm one stamp.
An imperf. sheet containing Nos. 2987-2992 exists, inscribed to promote the 17th Pan American Railway Congress. Value, $7.

San Alejandro Art School, 170th Anniv. A832

Paintings: 1c, *Landscape,* by Domingo Ramos. 2c, *Portrait of Rodriguez Morey,* by Eugenio Gonzalez Olivera. 3c, *Landscape with Malangas and Palm Trees,* by Valentin Sanz Carta. 5c, *Wagons,* by Eduardo Morales. 10c, *Portrait of Elena Herrera,* by Armando Menocal, vert. 30c, *Rape of Dejanira,* by Miguel Melero, vert. 50c, *The Card Player,* by Leopoldo Romanach.

**1988, Jan. 12** *Perf. 13x12½, 12½x13*

| | | | | | |
|---|---|---|---|---|---|
| **2994** | A832 | 1c multi | | .25 | .25 |
| **2995** | A832 | 2c multi | | .25 | .25 |
| **2995A** | A832 | 3c multi | | .25 | .25 |
| **2996** | A832 | 5c multi | | .25 | .25 |
| **2997** | A832 | 10c multi | | .30 | .25 |
| **2998** | A832 | 30c multi | | .85 | .25 |
| **2999** | A832 | 50c multi | | 1.50 | .50 |
| | | *Nos. 2994-2999 (7)* | | 3.65 | 2.00 |

Poisonous Mushrooms — A833

Designs: 1c, Boletus satanas. 2c, Amanita citrina. 3c, Tylopilus felleus. 5c, Paxillus involutus. 10c, Inocybe patouillardii. 30c, Amanita muscaria. 50c, Hypholoma fasciculare.

**1988, Feb. 15** *Perf. 13*

| | | | | |
|---|---|---|---|---|
| **3000** | A833 | 1c multicolored | .25 | .25 |
| **3001** | A833 | 2c multicolored | .25 | .25 |
| **3002** | A833 | 3c multicolored | .25 | .25 |
| **3003** | A833 | 5c multicolored | .25 | .25 |
| **3004** | A833 | 10c multicolored | .55 | .25 |
| **3005** | A833 | 30c multicolored | 1.50 | .55 |
| **3006** | A833 | 50c multicolored | 2.40 | 1.00 |
| | | *Nos. 3000-3006 (7)* | 5.45 | 2.80 |

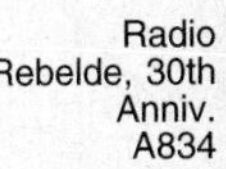

Radio Rebelde, 30th Anniv. A834

**1988, Feb. 24** *Perf. 12½x12*

**3007** A834 5c multi .30 .25

Monuments — A835

No. 3008, Mario Munoz, Santiago de Cuba. No. 3009, Frank Pais Memorial, eternal flame.

**1988** **Litho.** *Perf. 13*

| | | | | |
|---|---|---|---|---|
| **3008** | A835 | 5c multi | .45 | .25 |
| **3009** | A835 | 5c multi | .45 | .25 |

Battle fronts, 30th annivs. Issue dates: No. 3008, Mar. 5. No. 3009, Mar. 11.

Mothers' Day — A836

**1988, Mar. 30**

| | | | | |
|---|---|---|---|---|
| **3010** | A836 | 1c Red roses | .25 | .25 |
| **3011** | A836 | 2c Pale pink peonies | .25 | .25 |
| **3012** | A836 | 3c Daisies | .25 | .25 |
| **3013** | A836 | 5c Dahlias | .25 | .25 |
| **3014** | A836 | 13c White roses | .30 | .25 |
| **3015** | A836 | 35c Carnations | .90 | .25 |
| **3016** | A836 | 40c Pink roses | 1.10 | .30 |
| | | *Nos. 3010-3016 (7)* | 3.30 | 1.80 |

Cosmonauts' Day — A837

2c, Gorizont. 3c, Mir-Kvant space link. 4c, Signo 3. 5c, Mars, space probe. 10c, Phobos. 30c, Vega. 50c, Spacecraft.

1p, Spacecraft, diff.

**1988, Apr. 12**

| | | | | |
|---|---|---|---|---|
| **3017** | A837 | 2c multicolored | .25 | .25 |
| **3018** | A837 | 3c multicolored | .25 | .25 |
| **3019** | A837 | 4c multicolored | .25 | .25 |
| **3020** | A837 | 5c multicolored | .25 | .25 |
| **3021** | A837 | 10c multicolored | .25 | .25 |
| **3022** | A837 | 30c multicolored | .50 | .25 |
| **3023** | A837 | 50c multicolored | 1.10 | .50 |
| | | *Nos. 3017-3023 (7)* | 2.85 | 2.00 |

### Souvenir Sheet

*Perf. 13½x13*

**3024** A837 1p multicolored 4.50 2.00

No. 3024 contains one 32x40mm stamp.

### Stamp Day Type of 1984

Mural, by R. Rodriguez Radillo (1967) details: 30c, Mail coach, telegraph operator. 50c, Passenger pigeon.

**1988, Apr. 24** *Perf. 13x12½*

| | | | | |
|---|---|---|---|---|
| **3025** | A733 | 30c multi | 1.10 | .40 |
| **3026** | A733 | 50c multi | 1.90 | .50 |

Institute for Research on Sugar Cane and Byproducts (ICIDCA), 25th Anniv. A838

**1988, May 23** *Perf. 12½x12*

**3027** A838 5c multi .40 .25

Cubana Airlines Transatlantic Flights A839

**1988, May 25**

| | | | | |
|---|---|---|---|---|
| **3028** | A839 | 2c Madrid, 1948 | .25 | .25 |
| **3029** | A839 | 4c Prague, 1961 | .25 | .25 |
| **3030** | A839 | 5c Berlin, 1972 | .25 | .25 |
| **3031** | A839 | 10c Luanda, 1975 | .25 | .25 |
| **3032** | A839 | 30c Paris, 1983 | .90 | .25 |
| **3033** | A839 | 50c Moscow, 1987 | 1.60 | .50 |
| | | *Nos. 3028-3033 (6)* | 3.50 | 1.75 |

### Souvenir Sheet

FINLANDIA '88 — A840

1p, Steam packet Furst Menschikoff.

**1988, June 1** *Perf. 12½*

**3034** A840 1p multicolored 4.50 2.00

Postal Union of the Americas and Spain (UPAE) Conference on Stamps of the Americas, Havana — A841

**1988, June 20** *Perf. 12½x12*

**3035** A841 20c multi .75 .35

Beetles — A842

Designs: 1c, Megasoma elephas fabricus. 3c, Platycoelia flavoscutellata ohaus, vert.. 4c, Plusiotis argenteola bates. 5c, Heterosternus oberthuri ohaus. 10c, Odontotaenius zodiacus truqui. 35c, Chrysophora chrysochlora latreille, vert.. 40c, Phanaeus leander waterhouse.

**1988, June 30** *Perf. 13*

| | | | | |
|---|---|---|---|---|
| **3036** | A842 | 1c multicolored | .25 | .25 |
| **3037** | A842 | 3c multicolored | .25 | .25 |
| **3038** | A842 | 4c multicolored | .25 | .25 |
| **3039** | A842 | 5c multicolored | .25 | .25 |
| **3040** | A842 | 10c multicolored | .30 | .25 |
| **3041** | A842 | 35c multicolored | 1.00 | .30 |
| **3042** | A842 | 40c multicolored | 1.25 | .50 |
| | | *Nos. 3036-3042 (7)* | 3.55 | 2.05 |

Jose Raul Capablanca (1888-1942), Chess Champion A843

30c, Chessmen, vert. 40c, J. Corzo, Capablanca. 50c, Lasker, Capablanca. 1p, Winning configuration, 1921, vert. 3p, Portrait by E. Valderrama, vert. 5p, Chessmen, Capablanca.

**1988, July 15** *Perf. 12½x13, 13x12½*

| | | | | |
|---|---|---|---|---|
| **3043** | A843 | 30c multicolored | .80 | .35 |
| **3044** | A843 | 40c multicolored | 1.00 | .35 |
| **3045** | A843 | 50c multicolored | 1.25 | .45 |
| **3046** | A843 | 1p multicolored | 3.00 | 1.10 |
| **3047** | A843 | 3p multicolored | 8.50 | 3.00 |
| **3048** | A843 | 5p multicolored | 16.00 | 5.25 |
| | | *Nos. 3043-3048 (6)* | 30.55 | 10.50 |

### Souvenir Sheets

| | | | |
|---|---|---|---|
| **3049** | Sheet of 2 | 2.50 | 1.25 |
| *a.* | A843 30c No. 464, vert. | 1.00 | .60 |
| *b.* | like No. 3043, size: 32x40mm | 1.00 | .60 |
| **3050** | Sheet of 2 | 3.00 | 1.50 |
| *a.* | A843 40c No. 465 | 1.25 | .60 |
| *b.* | like No. 3044, size: 40x32mm | 1.25 | .60 |
| **3051** | Sheet of 2 | 4.25 | 2.10 |
| *a.* | A843 50c No. C44 | 1.75 | 1.00 |
| *b.* | like No. 3045, size: 40x32mm | 1.75 | 1.00 |
| **3052** | Sheet of 2 | 7.75 | 4.00 |
| *a.* | A843 1p No. 464, vert. | 3.25 | 1.75 |
| *b.* | like No. 3046, size: 32x40mm | 3.25 | 1.75 |
| **3053** | Sheet of 2 | 22.50 | 11.50 |
| *a.* | A843 3p No. C46, vert. | 9.50 | 4.75 |
| *b.* | like No. 3047, size: 32x40mm | 9.50 | 4.75 |
| **3054** | Sheet of 2 | 40.00 | 20.00 |
| *a.* | A843 5p No. C45, vert. | 18.00 | 9.00 |
| *b.* | like No. 3048, size: 32x40mm | 18.00 | 9.00 |
| | *Nos. 3049-3054 (6)* | 80.00 | 40.35 |

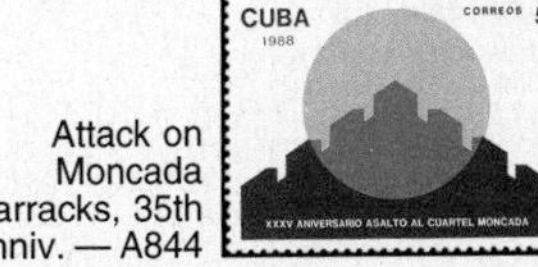


Attack on Moncada Barracks, 35th Anniv. — A844

**1988, July 26** *Perf. 13*

**3055** A844 5c blk, yel ocher & red .30 .25

### Souvenir Sheet

PRAGA '88 A845

1p, Czechoslovakia #45.

**1988, Aug. 26** *Perf. 12½*

**3056** A845 1p multicolored 4.50 2.00

Czechoslovakian postage stamps, 70th anniv.

Revolutionary Invasion Force, 30th Anniv. A846

**1988, Aug. 31** *Perf. 12½x12*

**3057** A846 5c multicolored .45 .25

World Marxist Review, 30th Anniv. — A847

**1988, Sept. 1** *Perf. 13*

**3058** A847 30c multi 1.25 .35

Locomotives A848

20c, Stephenson's Rocket, 1837. 30c, Miller, US, 1839. 50c, La Junta. 1p, J.G. Brill trolley, US, 1922. 2p, TEM 4K, USSR, c. 1960. 5p, CAP 9 electric, c. 1988.

**1988, Sept. 19** *Perf. 12½x13*

| | | | | |
|---|---|---|---|---|
| **3059** | A848 | 20c multicolored | .50 | .25 |
| **3060** | A848 | 30c multicolored | .95 | .45 |
| **3061** | A848 | 50c multicolored | 2.00 | .90 |
| **3062** | A848 | 1p multicolored | 3.75 | 1.25 |
| **3063** | A848 | 2p multicolored | 7.50 | 3.00 |
| **3064** | A848 | 5p multicolored | 16.00 | 8.25 |
| | | *Nos. 3059-3064 (6)* | 30.70 | 14.10 |

### Latin American History Type of 1986

Natl. arms & patriots: No. 3065, San Martin, Argentina. No. 3066, M.A. Padilla, Bolivia. No. 3067, #390 & discovery of America 500th anniv. emblem. No. 3068, Tiradentes, Brazil. No. 3069, O'Higgins, Chile. No. 3070, A. Narino, Colombia. No. 3071, Marti, Cuba. No. 3072, #391 & emblem. No. 3073, Duarte, Dominican Republic. No. 3074, Sucre, Ecuador. No. 3075, M.J. Arce, El Salvador. No. 3076, Dessalines, Haiti. No. 3077, #C36 & emblem. No. 3078, Hidalgo, Mexico. No. 3079, J.D. Estrada, Nicaragua. No. 3080, Diaz, Paraguay. No. 3081, F. Bolognesi, Peru. No. 3082, #C37 & emblem. No. 3083, Artigas, Uruguay. No. 3084, Bolivar, Venezuela.

**1988, Oct. 12** *Perf. 13*

| | | | | |
|---|---|---|---|---|
| **3065** | A804 | 1c multi | .25 | .25 |
| **3066** | A804 | 1c multi | .25 | .25 |
| **3067** | A804 | 1c multi | .25 | .25 |
| **3068** | A804 | 1c multi | .25 | .25 |
| **3069** | A804 | 1c multi | .25 | .25 |
| *a.* | | Strip of 5, Nos. 3065-3069 | 1.00 | 1.00 |
| **3070** | A804 | 5c multi | .25 | .25 |
| **3071** | A804 | 5c multi | .25 | .25 |
| **3072** | A804 | 5c multi | .25 | .25 |
| **3073** | A804 | 5c multi | .25 | .25 |
| **3074** | A804 | 5c multi | .25 | .25 |
| *a.* | | Strip of 5, Nos. 3070-3074 | 1.00 | 1.00 |
| **3075** | A804 | 10c multi | .25 | .25 |
| **3076** | A804 | 10c multi | .25 | .25 |
| **3077** | A804 | 10c multi | .25 | .25 |
| **3078** | A804 | 10c multi | .25 | .25 |
| **3079** | A804 | 10c multi | .25 | .25 |
| *a.* | | Strip of 5, Nos. 3075-3079 | 1.50 | 1.50 |
| **3080** | A804 | 20c multi | .40 | .25 |
| **3081** | A804 | 20c multi | .40 | .25 |
| **3082** | A804 | 20c multi | .40 | .25 |
| **3083** | A804 | 20c multi | .40 | .25 |
| **3084** | A804 | 20c multi | .40 | .25 |
| *a.* | | Strip of 5, Nos. 3080-3084 | 2.50 | 2.50 |
| *b.* | | Sheet of 20, Nos. 3065-3084 | 7.50 | 7.50 |
| | | *Nos. 3065-3084 (20)* | 5.75 | 5.00 |

Discovery of America, 500th anniv. (in 1992).

Havana Museum, 20th Anniv. A849

Design: Captain-General's Palace and Maces of Municipal Havana.

**1988, Oct. 16** **Litho.** *Perf. 12½x12*

**3085** A849 5c multi + label .50 .25

Anniversaries A850

No. 3086, Swan Lake. No. 3087, Theater in 1838 and 1988.

**1988, Oct. 28** *Perf. 13*

| | | | | |
|---|---|---|---|---|
| **3086** | A850 | 5c multicolored | .45 | .25 |
| **3087** | A850 | 5c multicolored | .45 | .25 |
| *a.* | | Pair, Nos. 3086-3087 | 1.00 | .85 |

Natl. Ballet, 40th anniv. (No. 3086); Grand Theater of Havana, 150th anniv. (No. 3087).

Intl. Literacy Year — A851

**1988, Dec. 5**

**3088** A851 5c multicolored .30 .25

UN Declaration of Human Rights, 40th Anniv. — A851a

**1988, Dec. 10**

**3088A** A851a 30c multi 1.25 .35

Battle of Santa Clara, 30th Anniv. A852

30c, Monument, Che Guevara Plaza.

**1988, Dec. 28** ***Perf. 13x12½***

**3089** A852 30c multicolored 1.25 .35

30th Anniv. of the Revolution A853

**1989, Jan. 1** ***Perf. 13***

| | | | | |
|---|---|---|---|---|
| **3090** | A853 | 5c multi | .25 | .25 |
| **3091** | A853 | 20c multi | .65 | .25 |
| **3092** | A853 | 30c multi | .85 | .25 |
| **3093** | A853 | 50c multi | 1.75 | .50 |
| | | *Nos. 3090-3093 (4)* | 3.50 | 1.25 |

Edible Mushrooms A854

Designs: 2c, Pleurotus levis. 3c, Pleurotus floridanus. 5c, Amanita caesarea. 10c, Lentinus cubensis. 40c,Pleurotus ostreatus (brown) . 50c, Pleurotus ostreatus (yellow)

**1989, Jan. 10**

| | | | | |
|---|---|---|---|---|
| **3094** | A854 | 2c multicolored | .25 | .25 |
| **3095** | A854 | 3c multicolored | .25 | .25 |
| **3096** | A854 | 5c multicolored | .25 | .25 |
| **3097** | A854 | 10c multicolored | .50 | .25 |
| **3098** | A854 | 40c multicolored | 2.00 | .40 |
| **3099** | A854 | 50c multicolored | 2.25 | .50 |
| | | *Nos. 3094-3099 (6)* | 5.50 | 1.90 |

2c, 3c, 5c, 40c, 50c, vert.

Souvenir Sheet

INDIA '89 A855

1p, Indian River Post, 1858.

**1989, Jan. 20**

**3100** A855 1p multicolored 4.50 2.00

Central Organization of Cuban Trade Unions (CTC), 50th Anniv. A856

5c, No. 2477, CTC emblem.

**1989, Jan. 28** ***Perf. 12½***

**3101** A856 5c multicolored .30 .25

Butterflies A857

Designs: 1c, Metamorpho dido. 3c, Callithea saphhira. 5c, Papilio zagreus. 10c, Mynes sestia. 30c, Papilio dardanus. 50c, Catagranma sorana.

**1989, Feb. 15**

| | | | | |
|---|---|---|---|---|
| **3102** | A857 | 1c multicolored | .25 | .25 |
| **3103** | A857 | 3c multicolored | .25 | .25 |
| **3104** | A857 | 5c multicolored | .25 | .25 |
| **3105** | A857 | 10c multicolored | .30 | .25 |
| **3106** | A857 | 30c multicolored | 1.40 | .30 |
| **3107** | A857 | 50c multicolored | 2.50 | .65 |
| | | *Nos. 3102-3107 (6)* | 4.95 | 1.95 |

1990 World Cup Soccer Championships, Italy — A858

Various athletes.

**1989, Mar. 15** ***Perf. 13***

| | | | | |
|---|---|---|---|---|
| **3108** | A858 | 1c multi | .25 | .25 |
| **3109** | A858 | 3c multi, diff. | .25 | .25 |
| **3110** | A858 | 5c multi, diff. | .25 | .25 |
| **3111** | A858 | 10c multi, diff. | .25 | .25 |
| **3112** | A858 | 30c multi, diff. | 1.00 | .25 |
| **3113** | A858 | 50c multi, diff. | 1.40 | .40 |
| | | *Nos. 3108-3113 (6)* | 3.40 | 1.65 |

**Souvenir Sheet**

***Perf. 12½***

**3114** A858 1p multi, diff., horiz. 4.50 2.00

No. 3114 contains one 40x32mm stamp.

Natl. Revolutionary Police (PNR), 30th Anniv. — A859

**1989, Mar. 23** ***Perf. 13***

**3115** A859 5c multicolored .30 .25

Cosmonauts' Day — A860

Spacecraft and rocket mail covers: 1c, *Zodiac* and cover, Australia 1934. 3c, Lighthouse and cover, India, 1934. 5c, Cover, England, 1934. 10c, *Icarus* and cover, The Netherlands, 1935. 40c, *La Douce France* and cover, France, 1935. 50c, Rocket mail cover, Cuba, 1939.

**1989, Apr. 12**

| | | | | |
|---|---|---|---|---|
| **3116** | A860 | 1c multi | .25 | .25 |
| **3117** | A860 | 3c multi | .25 | .25 |
| **3118** | A860 | 5c multi | .25 | .25 |
| **3119** | A860 | 10c multi | .25 | .25 |
| **3120** | A860 | 40c multi | 1.10 | .40 |
| **3121** | A860 | 50c multi | 1.40 | .55 |
| | | *Nos. 3116-3121 (6)* | 3.50 | 1.95 |

**Stamp Day Type of 1984**

Details of mural by R. Rodriguez Radillo (1967): 30c, Mail coach, Satellite dish. 50c, Galleon, longboats, train, passenger pigeon, horses.

**1989, Apr. 24 Litho.** ***Perf. 13x12½***

| | | | | |
|---|---|---|---|---|
| **3122** | A733 | 30c multi | .65 | .30 |
| **3123** | A733 | 50c multi | 3.00 | 2.00 |

Casa de Las Americas, 30th Anniv. — A861

**1989, Apr. 28** ***Perf. 12½x13***

**3124** A861 5c multi .30 .25

Souvenir Sheet

BULGARIA '89 — A862

**1989, May 1** ***Perf. 12½***

**3125** A862 1p Bulgaria No. 346 4.50 2.25

58th FIP Congress and 101st anniv. of Bulgarian Railways.

Cuban Postal Code — A863

**1989, May 5** ***Perf. 13***

**3126** A863 5c multi .30 .25

Mothers' Day — A864

Perfume bottles and flowers: 1c, Habano, tobacco. 3c, Violeta, violets. 5c, Mariposa, mariposa. 13c, Coral Negro, roses. 30c, Ala Alonso, jasmine. 50c, D'Man, lemon blossoms.

**1989, May 10**

| | | | | |
|---|---|---|---|---|
| **3127** | A864 | 1c multi | .25 | .25 |
| **3128** | A864 | 3c multi | .25 | .25 |
| **3129** | A864 | 5c multi | .25 | .25 |
| **3130** | A864 | 13c multi | .35 | .25 |
| **3131** | A864 | 30c multi | .90 | .30 |
| **3132** | A864 | 50c multi | 1.60 | .70 |
| | | *Nos. 3127-3132 (6)* | 3.60 | 2.00 |

Agrarian Reform Law, 30th Anniv. — A865

**1989, May 17** ***Perf. 12x12½***

**3133** A865 5c multi .30 .25

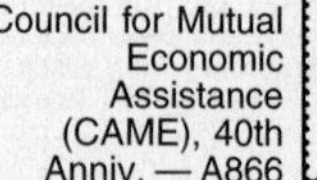

Council for Mutual Economic Assistance (CAME), 40th Anniv. — A866

**1989, June 1 Litho.** ***Perf. 12½x13***

**3134** A866 30c multi 1.25 .25

13th World Communist Youth and Student Festival, Pyongyang A867

**1989, July 1 Litho.** ***Perf. 12½***

**3135** A867 30c multi 1.25 .25

Souvenir Sheet

*Rouget de Lisle Singing La Marseillaise,* by Pils — A868

**1989, July 7** ***Perf. 13***

**3136** A868 1p multi 4.50 2.00

PHILEXFRANCE '89, French revolution bicent. and Cuban revolution 30th anniv.

BRASILIANA '89 — A869

Exotic birds: 1c, Ramphastos toco. 3c, Agamia agami. 5c, Eudocimus ruber. 10c, Psophia leucoptera. 35c, Harpia harpyja. 50c, Cephalopterus ornatus.

**1989, July 28 Litho.** ***Perf. 12½***

| | | | | |
|---|---|---|---|---|
| **3137** | A869 | 1c multicolored | .25 | .25 |
| **3138** | A869 | 3c multicolored | .25 | .25 |
| **3139** | A869 | 5c multicolored | .25 | .25 |
| **3140** | A869 | 10c multicolored | .30 | .25 |
| **3141** | A869 | 35c multicolored | 1.25 | .50 |
| **3142** | A869 | 50c multicolored | 1.75 | .70 |
| | | *Nos. 3137-3142 (6)* | 4.05 | 2.20 |

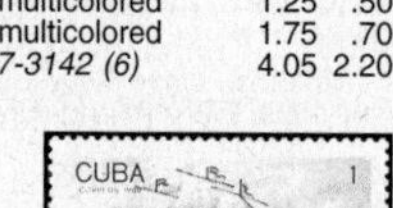

Warships A870

**1989, Sept. 29 Litho.** ***Perf. 12½***

| | | | | |
|---|---|---|---|---|
| **3143** | A870 | 1c *El Fenix* | .25 | .25 |
| **3144** | A870 | 3c *Triunfo* | .25 | .25 |
| **3145** | A870 | 5c *El Rayo* | .25 | .25 |
| **3146** | A870 | 10c *San Carlos* | .25 | .25 |
| **3147** | A870 | 30c *San Jose* | 1.00 | .40 |
| **3148** | A870 | 50c *San Genaro* | 1.50 | .70 |
| | | *Nos. 3143-3148 (6)* | 3.50 | 2.10 |

America Issue — A871

UPAE emblem and pre-Columbian art: 5p, Stone carving, Indians in dugout canoe. 20p, Petroglyph, Indian drawing on stone wall.

**1989, Oct. 12** ***Perf. 12½x12***

| | | | | |
|---|---|---|---|---|
| **3149** | A871 | 5c multi | .35 | .25 |
| **3150** | A871 | 20c multi | .85 | .40 |

Latin American History — A872

Writers and orchids: No. 3151, Domingo Sarmiento (1811-1888), Argentine educator, and *Govenia utriculata.* No. 3152, Joaquim

Maria Machado de Assis (1839-1908), Brazilian novelist, and *Laelia grandis.* No. 3153, Salvador No. 69 and discovery of America anniv. emblem. No. 3154, Jorge Isaacs (1837-1895), Colombian novelist, and *Cattleya trianae.* No. 3155, Alejo Carpentier, Cuban writer, and *Cochleanthes discolor.* No. 3156, Pablo Neruda (1904-1973), Chilean poet, and *Oxalis adenophylla.* No. 3157, Pedro Urena, Dominican writer, and *Epidendrum fragrans.* No. 3158, Salvador No. 86 and anniv. emblem. No. 3159, Juan Montalvo (1832-1889), Ecuadorian satirist, and *Miltonia vexillaria.* No. 3160, Miguel Asturias (1899-1974), Guatemalan writer awarded the 1966 Lenin Peace Prize and 1967 Nobel Prize for literature, and *Odontoglossum rossii.* No. 3161, Jose C. del Valle, Honduran writer, and *Laelia anceps.* No. 3162, Alfonso Reyes (1889-1959), Mexican poet, and *Laelia anceps alba.* No. 3163, Salvador No. 87 and anniv. emblem. No. 3164, Ruben Dario (1867-1917), Nicaraguan poet, and *Brassavola acaulis.* No. 3165, Belisario Porras (1856-1942), president of Panama, and *Pescatorea celina.* No. 3166, Ricardo Palma (1833-1919), Peruvian writer, and *Coryanthes leucocorys.* No. 3167, Eugenio Maria de Hostos (1839-1903), Puerto Rican writer, and *Guzmania berteroniana.* No. 3168, Salvador No. 88 and anniv. emblem. No. 3169, Jose E. Rodo (1872-1917), Uruguayan philosopher, essayist, and *Cypella hebertii.* No. 3170, Romulo Gallegos, Venezuelan writer, and *Cattleya mossiae.*

**1989, Oct. 27 Litho. *Perf. 13***

**3151** A872 1c multicolored .25 .25
**3152** A872 1c multicolored .25 .25
**3153** A872 1c multicolored .25 .25
**3154** A872 1c multicolored .25 .25
**3155** A872 1c multicolored .25 .25
*a.* Strip of 5, Nos. 3151-3155 1.00 1.00
**3156** A872 5c multicolored .25 .25
**3157** A872 5c multicolored .25 .25
**3158** A872 5c multicolored .25 .25
**3159** A872 5c multicolored .25 .25
**3160** A872 5c multicolored .25 .25
*a.* Strip of 5, Nos. 3156-3160 1.00 1.00
**3161** A872 10c multicolored .35 .25
**3162** A872 10c multicolored .35 .25
**3163** A872 10c multicolored .35 .25
**3164** A872 10c multicolored .35 .25
**3165** A872 10c multicolored .35 .25
*a.* Strip of 5, Nos. 3161-3165 2.00 2.00
**3166** A872 20c multicolored .55 .25
**3167** A872 20c multicolored .55 .25
**3168** A872 20c multicolored .55 .25
**3169** A872 20c multicolored .55 .25
**3170** A872 20c multicolored .55 .25
*a.* Strip of 5, Nos. 3166-3170 3.00 3.00
*b.* Sheet of 20, #3151-3170 8.00 8.00
*Nos. 3151-3170 (20)* 7.00 5.00

Discovery of America 500th anniv. (in 1992).

Disappearance of Camilo Cienfuegos, 30th Anniv. — A873

**1989, Oct. 28**

**3171** A873 5c multicolored .40 .25

Founding of the City of Trinidad, 475th Anniv. — A874

**1989, Nov. 6 *Perf. 12½x13***

**3172** A874 5c multicolored .40 .25

Paintings in the Natl. Museum A875

Designs: 1c, *Familiar Scene,* by Antoine Faivre. 2c, *Flowers,* by Emile Jean Horace Vernet (1789-1863). 5c, *The Judgement of Paris,* by Charles Le Brun (1619-1690). 20c, *Outskirts of Nice,* by Eugene Louis Boudin (1824-1898). 30c, *Portrait of Sarah Bernhardt,* by G.J.V. Clairin. 50c, *Fishermen in Port,* by C.J. Vernet.

***Perf. 12½, 12½x13 (30p)***

**1989, Nov. 20 Litho.**

**Size of 30p: 36x46mm**

**3173** A875 1c multicolored .25 .25
**3174** A875 2c multicolored .25 .25
**3175** A875 5c multicolored .25 .25
**3176** A875 20c multicolored .75 .25
**3177** A875 30c multicolored 1.00 .25
**3178** A875 50c multicolored 2.00 .55
*Nos. 3173-3178 (6)* 4.50 1.80

11th Pan-American Games, Havana, 1991 — A876

**1989, Dec. 15 Litho. *Perf. 12½***

**3179** A876 5c Cycling .25 .25
**3180** A876 5c Fencing .25 .25
**3181** A876 5c Water polo .25 .25
**3182** A876 5c Shooting .25 .25
**3183** A876 5c Archery .25 .25
**3184** A876 20c Tennis, vert. .65 .25
**3185** A876 30c Swimming, vert. 1.00 .25
**3186** A876 35c Diving, vert. 1.35 .30
**3187** A876 40c Field hockey 1.40 .30
**3188** A876 50c Basketball, vert. 2.10 .65
*Nos. 3179-3188 (10)* 7.75 3.00

Jose Marti's *Golden Age,* Cent. — A877

**1989, Dec. 20 *Perf. 13***

**3189** A877 5c scar, lt blue & blk .45 .25

Cuban Postal Museum, 25th Anniv. A878

**1990, Jan. 2 *Perf. 13x12½***

**3190** A878 5c *Almendares* .25 .25
**3191** A878 30c Mail train 1.50 .75

Speleological Soc., 50th Anniv. — A879

**1990, Jan. 15 *Perf. 12½***

**3192** A879 30c multicolored 1.50 .35

1990 World Cup Soccer Championships, Italy — A880

Various Italian architecture and athletes: No. 3193a, Dribbling (in red and blue). No. 3193b, Heading (in red and green). No. 3193c, Kicking (in green). 10c, Goalie catching ball. 30c, Dribbling, diff. 50c, Kicking, diff. 1p, Goalie catching ball, diff.

**1990, Jan. 30 Litho. *Perf. 12½***

**3193** Strip of 3 .50 .25
*a.-c.* A880 5c any single .25 .25
**3194** A880 10c multicolored .25 .25
**3195** A880 30c multicolored 1.25 .30
**3196** A880 50c multicolored 2.00 .55
*a.* Sheet of 6, #3193a-3193c, 3194-3196 + 3 labels 4.25 2.10
*Nos. 3193-3196 (4)* 4.00 1.35

**Souvenir Sheet**

**3197** A880 1p multicolored 4.50 1.75

No. 3193 has a continuous design picturing The Colosseum.

1992 Summer Olympics, Barcelona A881

1c, Baseball. 4c, Running. 5c, Basketball. 10c, Women's volleyball. 30c, Wrestling. 50c, Boxing.

1p, High jump.

**1990, Feb. 20 Litho. *Perf. 12½***

**3198** A881 1c multicolored .25 .25
**3199** A881 4c multicolored .25 .25
**3200** A881 5c multicolored .25 .25
**3201** A881 10c multicolored .45 .25
**3202** A881 30c multicolored 1.20 .30
**3203** A881 50c multicolored 2.10 .65
*Nos. 3198-3203 (6)* 4.50 1.95

**Souvenir Sheet**

**3204** A881 1p multicolored 4.50 2.00

Nos. 3198-3201 and 3203 are vert. No. 3204 contains one 40x32mm stamp.

75th Universal Esperanto Congress — A882

**1990, Mar. 7**

**3205** A882 30c Tower of Babel 1.25 .35

No. 3205 printed se-tenant with inscribed label publicizing the congress.

**Souvenir Sheet**

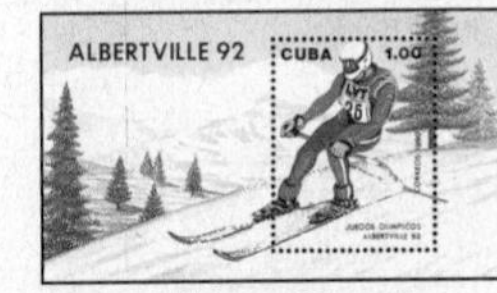


1992 Winter Olympics, Albertville — A883

**1990, Mar. 30 Litho. *Perf. 13***

**3206** A883 1p multicolored 4.50 2.25

Cosmonauts' Day — A884

Spacecraft and rocket mail covers: 1c, Austria, 1932. 2c, Germany, 1933. 3c, Netherlands, 1934. 10c, Belgium, 1935. 30c, Yugoslavia, 1935. 50c, United States, 1936.

**1990, Apr. 12 *Perf. 12½***

**3207** A884 1c multicolored .25 .25
**3208** A884 2c multicolored .25 .25
**3209** A884 3c multicolored .25 .25
**3210** A884 10c multicolored .25 .25
**3211** A884 30c multicolored 1.10 .25
**3212** A884 50c multicolored 2.00 .55
*Nos. 3207-3212 (6)* 4.10 1.80

**Stamp Day Type of 1984**

Details of mural by R. Rodriguez Radillo (1967): 30c, Train station. 50c, Jet aircraft in flight.

**1990, Apr. 24 *Perf. 13x12½***

**3213** A733 30c multicolored 2.25 .75
**3214** A733 50c multicolored 1.25 .45

Labor Day, Cent. — A885

**1990, Apr. 30 *Perf. 13***

**3215** A885 5c multicolored .45 .25

**Souvenir Sheet**

Great Britain No. 1 on Cover A886

**1990, May 3**

**3216** A886 1p multicolored 4.50 2.00

Stamp World London '90, Penny Black 150th anniv.

Penny Black, 150th Anniv. A887

Portraits of Sir Rowland Hill and stamps of Great Britain: 2c, No. 1. 3c, No. 2. 5c, Type A5. 10c, No. 5. 30c, First day postmark. 50c, 5 #1 on Mulready envelope.

**1990, May 6 Litho. *Perf. 12½x12***

**3217** A887 2c multicolored .25 .25
**3218** A887 3c multicolored .25 .25
**3219** A887 5c multicolored .25 .25
**3220** A887 10c multicolored .25 .25
**3221** A887 30c multicolored 1.25 .25
**3222** A887 50c multicolored 2.25 .60
*Nos. 3217-3222 (6)* 4.50 1.85

Celia Sanchez Manduley (1920-1980) A888

**1990, May 9 *Perf. 12½x13***

**3223** A888 5c multicolored .50 .25

Ho Chi Minh (1890-1969), Vietnamese Communist Party Leader — A889

**1990, May 19 *Perf. 12½***

**3224** A889 50c multicolored 1.90 .45

Oceanography Institute, 25th Anniv. — A890

Designs: 5c, Specimen analysis and *Lachnolaimus maximus.* 30c, Research ship, fish, coral reef. 50c, Specimen collection and *Panullrus argus.*

**1990, June 18 Litho. *Perf. 12½***

**3225** A890 5c multicolored .25 .25
**3226** A890 30c multicolored 1.10 .30
**3227** A890 50c multicolored 1.75 .50
*Nos. 3225-3227 (3)* 3.10 1.05

5th Latin American Botanical Conference — A891

Designs: 3c, Banara minutiflora. 5c, Oplonia nannophylla. 10c, Jacquinia brunnescens. 30c, Rondeletia brachycarpa. 50c, Rondeletia odorata.

**1990, June 25 Litho. *Perf. 12½***

**3228** A891 3c multicolored .25 .25
**3229** A891 5c multicolored .25 .25
**3230** A891 10c multicolored .30 .25
**3231** A891 30c multicolored 1.00 .25
**3232** A891 50c multicolored 1.50 .60
*Nos. 3228-3232 (5)* 3.30 1.60

Tourism — A892

**1990, June 30**

**3233** A892 5c Wind surfing .25 .25
**3234** A892 10c Spear fishing .35 .25
**3235** A892 30c Deep sea fishing 1.00 .25
**3236** A892 40c Hunting 1.60 .55
*Nos. 3233-3236 (4)* 3.20 1.30

Nos. 3233, 3236 vert.

Art Treasures — A893

5c, "La Flauta Del Dios Pan." 20c, "Un Pastor." 50c, "Ganimedes." 1p, "Venus Anadiomena."

**1990, July 20**

**3237** A893 5c multicolored .25 .25
**3238** A893 20c multicolored .60 .25
**3239** A893 50c multicolored 1.60 .40
**3240** A893 1p multicolored 2.75 .85
*a.* Sheet of 4, #3237-3240 6.50 6.50
*Nos. 3237-3240 (4)* 5.20 1.75

Birds — A894

Designs: 2c, Podiceps cristatus. 3c, Gallirallus australis. 5c, Nestor notabilis. 10c, Xenicus longipes. 30c, Cracticus torquatus. 50c, Prosthemadera novaeseelandiae.
1p, Kiwi.

**1990, Aug. 24 Litho. *Perf. 13***

**3241** A894 2c multicolored .25 .25
**3242** A894 3c multicolored .25 .25
**3243** A894 5c multicolored .25 .25
**3244** A894 10c multicolored .50 .25
**3245** A894 30c multicolored 1.10 .35
**3246** A894 50c multicolored 1.90 .65
*Nos. 3241-3246 (6)* 4.25 2.00

**Souvenir Sheet**

**3247** A894 1p multicolored 4.50 2.25

New Zealand '90. No. 3247 contains one 39x31mm stamp.

8th UN Congress on Crime Prevention — A895

**1990, Aug. 27 Litho. *Perf. 12½***

**3248** A895 50c blue, silver & red 2.25 .45

Discovery of America, 500th Anniv. (in 1992) — A896

**1990, Oct. 12 Litho. *Perf. 12½***

**3249** A896 5c Ship, shore .40 .25
**3250** A896 20c Columbus, village 1.00 .35

Cuban Television, 40th Anniv. — A897

**1990, Oct. 12 Litho. *Perf. 13***

**3251** A897 5c multicolored .45 .25

Nationalization of Railroads, 30th Anniv. — A898

**1990, Oct. 13 *Perf. 13x12½***

**3252** A898 50c multicolored 2.50 .75

**Latin American History Type of 1986**

Latin American stamps or flags and costumes: No. 3253, Argentina. No. 3254, Bolivia. No. 3255, Argentina No. 91. No. 3256, Colombia. No. 3257, Costa Rica. No. 3258, Cuba. No. 3259, Chile. No. 3260, Dominican Republic No. 110. No. 3261, Ecuador. No. 3262, El Salvador. No. 3263, Guatemala. No. 3264, Mexico. No. 3265, Puerto Rico No. 133. No. 3266, Nicaragua. No. 3267, Panama. No. 3268, Paraguay. No. 3269, Peru. No. 3270, El Salvador No. 103. No. 3271, Puerto Rico. No. 3272, Venezuela.

**1990, Oct. 27 *Perf. 12½***

**3253** A804 1c multicolored .25 .25
**3254** A804 1c multicolored .25 .25
**3255** A804 1c multicolored .25 .25
**3256** A804 1c multicolored .25 .25
**3257** A804 1c multicolored .25 .25
*a.* Strip of 5, Nos. 3253-3257 1.00 1.00
**3258** A804 5c multicolored .25 .25
**3259** A804 5c multicolored .25 .25
**3260** A804 5c multicolored .25 .25
**3261** A804 5c multicolored .25 .25
**3262** A804 5c multicolored .25 .25
*a.* Strip of 5, Nos. 3258-3262 1.00 1.00
**3263** A804 10c multicolored .30 .25
**3264** A804 10c multicolored .30 .25
**3265** A804 10c multicolored .30 .25
**3266** A804 10c multicolored .30 .25
**3267** A804 10c multicolored .30 .25
*a.* Strip of 5, Nos. 3263-3267 1.50 1.50
**3268** A804 20c multicolored .75 .25
**3269** A804 20c multicolored .75 .25
**3270** A804 20c multicolored .75 .25
**3271** A804 20c multicolored .75 .25
**3272** A804 20c multicolored .75 .25
*a.* Strip of 5, Nos. 3268-3272 4.50 4.50
*b.* Sheet of 20, #3253-3272 5.00 5.00
*Nos. 3253-3272 (20)* 7.75 5.00

Discovery of America, 500th anniv. (in 1992).

11th Jai Alai World Championships A899

**1990, Nov. 14 Litho. *Perf. 12½***

**3273** A899 30c multicolored 1.40 .40

No. 3273 printed with se-tenant label.

11th Pan American Games, Havana A900

No. 3274, Judo. No. 3275, Sailing. No. 3276, Kayak. No. 3277, Rowing. No. 3278, Equestrian. No. 3279, Table tennis. No. 3280, Men's gymnastics, vert. No. 3281, Baseball, vert. No. 3282, Team handball, vert. No. 3283, Soccer, vert.

**1990, Nov. 15 Litho. *Perf. 12½***

**3274** A900 5c multicolored .25 .25
**3275** A900 5c multicolored .25 .25
**3276** A900 5c multicolored .25 .25
**3277** A900 5c multicolored .25 .25
**3278** A900 5c multicolored .25 .25
**3279** A900 10c multicolored .30 .25
**3280** A900 20c multicolored .60 .25
**3281** A900 30c multicolored .90 .25
**3282** A900 35c multicolored 1.10 .35
**3283** A900 50c multicolored 1.60 .70
*Nos. 3274-3283 (10)* 5.75 3.05

See Nos. 3311-3320.

A901

**1990, Nov. 20 Litho. *Perf. 13***

**3284** A901 5c Boxing .25 .25
**3285** A901 30c Baseball 1.10 .25
**3286** A901 50c Volleyball 1.90 .50
*Nos. 3284-3286 (3)* 3.25 1.00

16th Central American and Caribbean Games, Mexico.

Butterflies — A902

Designs: 2c, Chioides marmorosa. 3c, Composia fidelissima. 5c, Danaus plexippus. 10c, Hypolimnas misippus. 30c, Hypna iphigenia. 50c, Hemiargus ammon

**1991, Jan. 25 Litho. *Perf. 12½***

**3287** A902 2c multicolored .25 .25
**3288** A902 3c multicolored .25 .25
**3289** A902 5c multicolored .35 .25
**3290** A902 10c multicolored .45 .25
**3291** A902 30c multicolored 1.25 .25
**3292** A902 50c multicolored 2.10 .50
*Nos. 3287-3292 (6)* 4.65 1.75

Jose Luis Guerra Aguiar (1914-1990), Director of Postal Museum A903

**1991, Feb. 17 Litho. *Perf. 12½***

**3293** A903 5c multicolored .45 .25

A904

**1991, Feb. 20**

**3294** A904 1c Long jump .25 .25
**3295** A904 2c Javelin .25 .25
**3296** A904 3c Field hockey .25 .25
**3297** A904 5c Weight lifting .25 .25
**3298** A904 40c Cycling 1.25 .35
**3299** A904 50c Gymnastics 1.75 .50
*Nos. 3294-3299 (6)* 4.00 1.85

**Souvenir Sheet**

**3300** A904 1p Torchbearer 3.50 1.75

1992 Summer Olympics, Barcelona.

A905

1st Man in Space, 30th anniv.: 5c, Yuri Gagarin. No. 3302, Cosmonaut Y. Romanenko. No. 3303, Cosmonaut A. Tamayo Mendez. No. 3304, Mir space station. No. 3305, Mir space station, docked Soyuz, earth. 50c, Soviet space shuttle Buran.

**1991, Apr. 12 Litho. *Perf. 13***

**3301** A905 5c multicolored .25 .25
**3302** A905 10c multicolored .25 .25
**3303** A905 10c multicolored .25 .25
*a.* Pair, #3302-3303 .40 .25
**3304** A905 30c multicolored 1.00 .25
**3305** A905 30c multicolored 1.00 .25
*a.* Pair, #3304-3305 2.00 1.00
**3306** A905 50c multicolored 1.60 .50
*a.* Sheet of 6, #3301-3306 4.50 —
*Nos. 3301-3306 (6)* 4.35 1.75

Proclamation of the Socialist Revolution, 30th Anniv. — A906

Design: 50c, Ship, jet on fire.

**1991, Apr. 19 *Perf. 12½***

**3307** A906 5c multicolored .25 .25
**3308** A906 50c multicolored 1.90 .80

Bay of Pigs invasion, 30th anniv., No. 3308.

Stamp Day — A907

Details from mural by R. Rodriguez Radillo: 30c, Rocket lift-off. 50c, Dish antenna, horiz.

**1991, Apr. 24 *Perf. 12½x13, 13x12½***

**3309** A907 30c multicolored 1.25 .30
**3310** A907 50c multicolored 1.90 .40

**11th Pan American Games Type of 1990**

**1991, May 15 Litho. *Perf. 12½***

**3311** A900 5c Volleyball .25 .25
**3312** A900 5c Rhythmic gymnastics .25 .25
**3313** A900 5c Synchronized swimming .25 .25
**3314** A900 5c Weight lifting .25 .25
**3315** A900 5c Baseball .25 .25
**3316** A900 10c Bowling .25 .25
**3317** A900 20c Boxing .55 .25
**3318** A900 30c Running .85 .25
**3319** A900 35c Wrestling 1.10 .30
**3320** A900 50c Karate 1.50 .50
*Nos. 3311-3320 (10)* 5.50 2.80

Nos. 3311-3315 & 3317 are vert.

Airships A908

Designs: 5c, First ellipsoidal, 1784, J.B.M. Meusnier. 10c, First with steam engine, 1852, H. Giffard. 20c, First with gas engine, 1872, P.

Haenlein. 30c, First with gasoline engine, 1896, H. Wolfert. 50c, First rigid aluminum, 1897, D. Schwarz. 1p, LZ-129 Hindenburg, 1936, F. von Zeppelin.

**1991, July 1 Litho. *Perf. 13***

**3321** A908 5c multicolored .25 .25
**3322** A908 10c multicolored .35 .25
**3323** A908 20c multicolored .70 .30
**3324** A908 30c multicolored .90 .50
**3325** A908 50c multicolored 1.60 .95
**3326** A908 1p multicolored 3.25 1.60
*Nos. 3321-3326 (6)* 7.05 3.85

Espamer '91, Buenos Aires, Argentina.

Simon Bolivar — A909

**1991, June 22 Litho. *Perf. 12½x13***

**3327** A909 50c multicolored 2.00 .60

Amphictyonic Cong. of Panama, 165th anniv.

Birds — A910

Designs: 45c, Melanerpes superciliaris. 50c, Myadestes elisabeth. 2p, Priotelus temnurus. 4p, Tiaris canora. 5p, Campephilus principalis. 10p, Amazona leucocephala, horiz. 16.45p, Mellisuga helenae, horiz.

**1991, July 15 *Perf. 12½x13, 13x12½***

**3328** A910 45c multicolored 1.25 .40
**3329** A910 50c multicolored 1.50 .50
**3330** A910 2p multicolored 5.25 2.00
**3331** A910 4p multicolored 10.00 3.50
**3332** A910 5p multicolored 12.50 4.25
**3333** A910 10p multicolored 25.00 6.50
**3334** A910 16.45p multicolored 40.00 13.00
*Nos. 3328-3334 (7)* 95.50 30.15

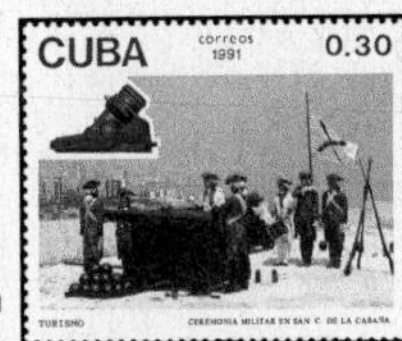


Tourism A911

Designs: No. 3335, Varadero Beach, vert. No. 3336, Cayo Largo, vert. No. 3337, Artillerymen at fortress San Carlos de la Cabana. No. 3338, Tres Reyes del Morro Castle.

**1991, July 30**

**3335** A911 20c multicolored .60 .25
**3336** A911 20c multicolored .60 .25
**3337** A911 30c multicolored 1.00 .30
**3338** A911 30c multicolored 1.00 .30
*Nos. 3335-3338 (4)* 3.20 1.10

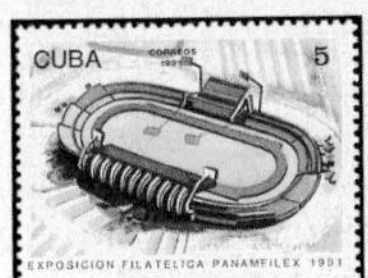


Panamfilex '91 — A912

11th Pan American Games venues: 5c, Pan American Stadium. 20c, Swimming venue. 30c, Multisports center. 50c, Velodrome. 1p, Havana City Coliseum and Sports Center.

**1991, Aug. 4 Litho. *Perf. 12½***

**3339** A912 5c multicolored .25 .25
**3340** A912 20c multicolored .60 .30
**3341** A912 30c multicolored .80 .50
**3342** A912 50c multicolored 1.50 .90
*Nos. 3339-3342 (4)* 3.15 1.95

**Souvenir Sheet**

**3343** A912 1p multicolored 3.50 1.75

No. 3343 contains one 40x32mm stamp.

Paintings — A913

5c, Kataoka Dengoemon Takafusa, by Utagawa Kuniyoshi. 10c, Evening Walk, by Hosoda Eishi. 20c, Courtesans, by Torii Kiyonaga. 30c, Conversation, by Utamaro. 50c, Bridge at Inari-bashi, by Hiroshige. 1p, On the Terrace, by Kiyonaga.

**1991, Sept. 9 Litho. *Perf. 12½x13***

**3344** A913 5c multicolored .25 .25
**3345** A913 10c multicolored .35 .25
**3346** A913 20c multicolored .70 .30
**3347** A913 30c multicolored .90 .40
**3348** A913 50c multicolored 1.60 .75
**3349** A913 1p multicolored 3.25 1.75
*Nos. 3344-3349 (6)* 7.05 3.70

Phila Nippon '91, Tokyo.

Souvenir Sheet

1992 Winter Olympics, Albertville — A914

**1991, Sept. 25 Litho. *Perf. 12½***

**3350** A914 1p multicolored 3.50 1.75

Cuban Communist Party, 4th Congress — A915

**1991, Oct. 10**

**3351** A915 5c shown .25 .25
**3352** A915 50c Congress symbol 1.75 .50

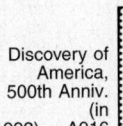

Discovery of America, 500th Anniv. (in 1992) — A916

Designs: 5c, Columbus, Vicente and Martin Pinzon. 20c, Santa Maria, Nina and Pinta.

**1991, Oct. 12**

**3353** A916 5c multicolored .25 .25
**3354** A916 20c multicolored 1.25 .25

Jose Marti — A917

**1991, Oct. 15 *Perf. 13x12½***

**3355** A917 50c multicolored 2.00 .40

Publication of "Simple Verses," cent.

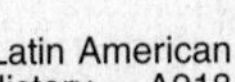

Latin American History — A918

Stamps or musicians and instruments: No. 3356, Julian Aguirre, Argentina, charango. No. 3357, Eduardo Caba, Bolivia, antara. No. 3358, Chile #2. No. 3359, Heitor Villalobos, Brazil, resonator trumpet. No. 3360, Guillermo Uribe-Holguin, Colombia, drum. No. 3361, Miguel Failde, Cuba, claves. No. 3362, Enrique Soro, Chile, drum. No. 3363, Chile #57. No. 3364, Segundo L. Moreno, Ecuador, xylophone. No. 3365, Ricardo Castillo, Guatemala, marimba. No. 3366, Carlos Chavez, Mexico, guitar. No. 3367, Luis A. Delgadillo, Nicaragua, maracas. No. 3368, Chile #69. No. 3369, Alfredo De Saint-Malo, Panama, mejorana. No. 3370, Jose Asuncion Flores, Paraguay, harp. No. 3371, Daniel Alomia, Peru, flute. No. 3372, Juan Morell y Campos, Puerto Rico, cuatro. No. 3373, Chile #72. No. 3374, Eduardo Farini, Uruguay, drums. No. 3375, Juan V. Lecuna, Venezuela, cuatro, diff.

**1991, Oct. 27 *Perf. 13***

**3356** A918 1c multicolored .25 .25
**3357** A918 1c multicolored .25 .25
**3358** A918 1c multicolored .25 .25
**3359** A918 1c multicolored .25 .25
**3360** A918 1c multicolored .25 .25
*a.* Strip of 5, #3356-3360 1.00 1.00
**3361** A918 5c multicolored .25 .25
**3362** A918 5c multicolored .25 .25
**3363** A918 5c multicolored .25 .25
**3364** A918 5c multicolored .25 .25
**3365** A918 5c multicolored .25 .25
*a.* Strip of 5, #3361-3365 1.00 1.00
**3366** A918 10c multicolored .40 .25
**3367** A918 10c multicolored .40 .25
**3368** A918 10c multicolored .40 .25
**3369** A918 10c multicolored .40 .25
**3370** A918 10c multicolored .40 .25
*a.* Strip of 5, #3366-3370 2.00 2.00
**3371** A918 20c multicolored .70 .25
**3372** A918 20c multicolored .70 .25
**3373** A918 20c multicolored .70 .25
**3374** A918 20c multicolored .70 .25
**3375** A918 20c multicolored .70 .25
*a.* Strip of 5, #3371-3375 4.00 4.00
*b.* Sheet of 20, #3356-3375 8.00 —
*Nos. 3356-3375 (20)* 8.00 5.00

Discovery of America, 500th anniv. in 1992 (Nos. 3358, 3363, 3368, 3373).

Jose Marti Pioneers Organization, 1st Congress — A919

**1991, Oct. 29**

**3376** A919 5c multicolored .40 .25

Toussaint L'Ouverture (1743-1803) A920

**1991, Nov. 20 *Perf. 12½x13***

**3377** A920 50c multicolored 2.00 .40

Haitian Revolution, Bicent.

Cuban Revolutionary Armed Forces, 35th Anniv. A921

Design: 50c, Landing of the Granma expedition, 35th anniv., vert.

***Perf. 12½x12, 12x12½***

**1991, Dec. 2 Litho.**

**3378** A921 5c multicolored .25 .25
**3379** A921 50c multicolored 1.40 .40

Gen. Ignacio Agramonte (1841-1873), Revolutionary Hero — A922

**1991, Dec. 23 Litho. *Perf. 12½x13***

**3380** A922 5c multicolored .40 .25

Souvenir Sheet

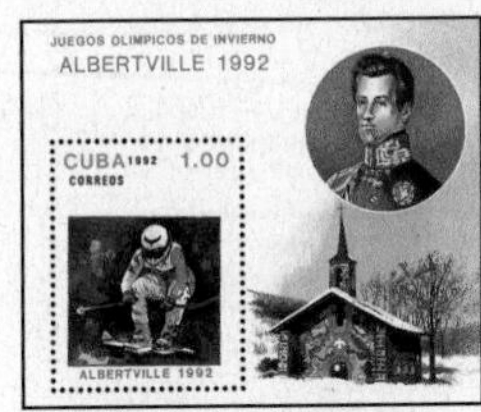


1992 Winter Olympics, Albertville — A923

**1992, Jan. 15 *Perf. 13***

**3381** A923 1p multicolored 3.00 1.75

1992 Summer Olympics, Barcelona A924

**1992, Jan. 20 Litho. *Perf. 13x12½***

**3382** A924 3c Table tennis .25 .25
**3383** A924 5c Handball .25 .25
**3384** A924 10c Shooting .30 .25
**3385** A924 20c Long jump, vert. .45 .25
**3386** A924 35c Judo 1.00 .40
**3387** A924 50c Fencing 1.40 .40
*Nos. 3382-3387 (6)* 3.65 1.80

**Souvenir Sheet**

***Perf. 12½***

**3388** A924 100c Rhythmic gymnastics, vert. 2.90 1.75

No. 3388 contains one 32x40mm stamp.

Environmental Protection — A925

5c, Terraced hillsides. 20c, Save the whales. 35c, Ozone hole over Antarctica. 40c, Nuclear disarmament.

**1992, Feb. 10 *Perf. 13***

**3389** A925 5c multicolored .25 .25
**3390** A925 20c multicolored .50 .25
**3391** A925 35c multicolored 1.00 .40
**3392** A925 40c multicolored 1.10 .40
*Nos. 3389-3392 (4)* 2.85 1.30

Dogs — A926

5c, Boxer. 10c, Great dane. 20c, German shepherd. 30c, Various breeds. 35c, Doberman pinscher. 40c, Fox terrier. 50c, Poodle.
1p, Bichon frise, vert.

**1992, Mar. 10 Litho. *Perf. 13x12½***

**3393** A926 5c multi .25 .25
**3394** A926 10c multi .25 .25
**3395** A926 20c multi .50 .25
**3396** A926 30c multi .95 .25
**3397** A926 35c multi .95 .30
**3398** A926 40c multi 1.20 .40
**3399** A926 50c multi 1.50 .50
*Nos. 3393-3399 (7)* 5.60 2.20

### Souvenir Sheet

*Perf. 12½*

**3400** A926 1p multi 3.00 2.00

No. 3400 contains one 32x40mm stamp. Nos. 3401-3404 will not be assigned.

Union of Young Communists, 30th Anniv. — A928

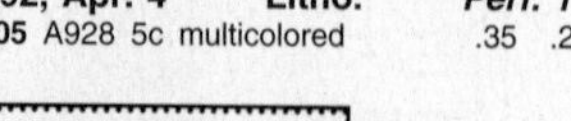

**1992, Apr. 4 Litho.** *Perf. 13*

**3405** A928 5c multicolored .35 .25

Cuban Revolutionary Party, Cent. A929

**1992, Apr. 10** *Perf. 13x12½*

**3406** A929 5c multicolored .25 .25
**3407** A929 50c multicolored 1.40 .50

Discovery of America, 500th Anniv. A930

5c, Landing at Bariay. 20c, Landing at San Salvador.

**1992, Apr. 14** *Perf. 12½*

**3408** A930 5c multi .25 .25
**3409** A930 20c multi .60 .25

Granada '92 Philatelic Exhibition A931

Views of the Alhambra, Granada: 5c, With Sierra Nevada mountains beyond. 10c, Arches at sunset. 20c, Interior architecture. 30c, Patio, fountain of lions. 35c, Bedroom. 50c, View of Albaicin.

**1992, Apr. 17** *Perf. 13*

**3410** A931 5c multicolored .25 .25
**3411** A931 10c multicolored .25 .25
**3412** A931 20c multicolored .60 .25
**3413** A931 30c multicolored 1.00 .25
**3414** A931 35c multicolored 1.10 .40
**3415** A931 50c multicolored 1.60 .50
*Nos. 3410-3415 (6)* 4.80 1.90

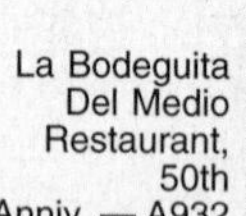

La Bodeguita Del Medio Restaurant, 50th Anniv. — A932

**1992, Apr. 26**

**3416** A932 50c multicolored 1.50 .50

Fish — A933

Designs: 5c, Holacanthus isabelita. 10c, Equetus lanceolatus. 20c, Acanthurus coeruleus. 30c, Abudefduf saxatilis. 50c, Microspathodon chrysurus.

**1992, May 15 Litho.** *Perf. 12½*

**3417** A933 5c multicolored .25 .25
**3418** A933 10c multicolored .25 .25
**3419** A933 20c multicolored .60 .25
**3420** A933 30c multicolored 1.00 .25
**3421** A933 50c multicolored 1.60 .50
*Nos. 3417-3421 (5)* 3.70 1.50

Orchids — A934

**1992, June 20 Litho.** *Perf. 12½*

**3422** A934 3c Cattleya hibrida .25 .25
**3423** A934 5c Phalaenopsis .25 .25
**3424** A934 10c Cattleyopsis lindenii .25 .25
**3425** A934 30c Bletia purpurea .90 .25
**3426** A934 35c Oncidium luridum 1.00 .30
**3427** A934 40c Vanda hibrida 1.25 .40
*Nos. 3422-3427 (6)* 3.90 1.70

Soroa Orchid Garden, 40th anniv.

Mellisuga Helenae A935

**1992, July 7** *Perf. 13*

**3428** A935 5c Sitting on nest .40 .25
**3429** A935 10c Wings extended .50 .30
**3430** A935 20c Sitting on branch 1.10 .40
**3431** A935 30c In flight 1.75 .60
*Nos. 3428-3431 (4)* 3.75 1.55

World Wildlife Fund.
Nos. 3428-3431 exist imperf.

Tourism — A936

10c, Guardalavaca Beach. 20c, Bucanero Hotel. 30c, Sailing ship, Havana. 50c, Varadero Beach.

**1992, July 15 Litho.** *Perf. 12½*

**3432** A936 10c multicolored .35 .25
**3433** A936 20c multicolored .60 .25
**3434** A936 30c multicolored 1.10 .40
**3435** A936 50c multicolored 1.40 .50
*Nos. 3432-3435 (4)* 3.45 1.40

### Souvenir Sheet

Expo '92, Seville A937

**1992, July 27 Litho.** *Perf. 13*

**3436** A937 1.50p multicolored 4.50 2.25

1992 Summer Olympics, Barcelona A938

Athlete, sport: 5c, Eligio (Kid Chocolate) Sardinas, boxing. 35c, Ramon Fonst, fencing. 40c, Sergio Martinez, cycling. 50c, Martin Dihigo, baseball.

**1992, July 20 Litho.** *Perf. 12½x13*

**3437** A938 5c multicolored .25 .25
**3438** A938 35c multicolored 1.00 .30
**3439** A938 40c multicolored 1.10 .40
**3440** A938 50c multicolored 1.50 .60
*Nos. 3437-3440 (4)* 3.85 1.55

Olymphilex '92.

Discovery of America, 500th Anniv. — A939

5c, Alvarez Cabral. 10c, Alonso Pinzon. 20c, Alonso de Ojeda. 30c, Amerigo Vespucci. 35c, Prince Henry the Navigator. 40c, Bartolomeu Dias. 1p, Columbus' fleet.

**1992, Sept. 18 Litho.** *Perf. 12½*

**3441** A939 5c multicolored .25 .25
**3442** A939 10c multicolored .30 .25
**3443** A939 20c multicolored .60 .25
**3444** A939 30c multicolored 1.00 .30
**3445** A939 35c multicolored 1.10 .30
**3446** A939 40c multicolored 1.25 .40
*Nos. 3441-3446 (6)* 4.50 1.75

### Souvenir Sheet

*Perf. 13*

**3447** A939 1p multi, vert. 3.00 1.60

Genoa '92. No. 3447 contains one 32x40mm stamp.

Nos. 3442 and 3444 exist imperf. Value, each $12.

1992 Summer Olympics Medal Winners, Barcelona A940

Medals and participants in events: No. 3448, Bronze, 4x100-meter relay, women's high jump, and women's 800-meter. No. 3449, Gold, high jump, women's discus. No. 3450, Silver, 4x400-meter relay, bronze, discus. No. 3451, Gold and silver, boxing. No. 3452, Gold, baseball. No. 3453, Gold, women's volleyball. No. 3454, Gold, silver, and bronze, judo. No. 3455, Gold and bronze, Greco-Roman and freestyle wrestling. No. 3456, Silver and bronze, fencing, silver, weight lifting.

**1992, Sept. 24 Litho.** *Perf. 13*

**3448** A940 5c multicolored .25 .25
**3449** A940 5c multicolored .25 .25
**3450** A940 5c multicolored .25 .25
**3451** A940 20c multicolored .55 .25
**3452** A940 20c multicolored .55 .25
**3453** A940 20c multicolored .55 .25
**3454** A940 50c multicolored 1.50 .50
**3455** A940 50c multicolored 1.50 .50
**3456** A940 50c multicolored 1.50 .50
*Nos. 3448-3456 (9)* 6.90 3.00

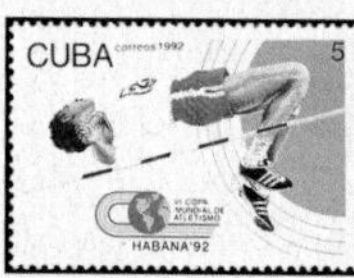

6th World Track and Field Cup, Havana A941

**1992, Sept. 24 Litho.** *Perf. 13*

**3457** A941 5c High jump .25 .25
**3458** A941 20c Javelin .60 .25
**3459** A941 30c Hammer throw .90 .25
**3460** A941 40c Long jump, vert. 1.25 .40
**3461** A941 50c Hurdles, vert. 1.50 .50
*Nos. 3457-3461 (5)* 4.50 1.65

### Souvenir Sheet

**3462** A941 1p Women's relay 3.00 1.75

No. 3462 contains one 40x32mm stamp.

### Latin American History Type of 1986

Discovery of America: No. 3463a, Columbus, Queen Isabella. b, Columbus at Rabida Monastery. c, Columbus, pointing up, outlining his plan. d, Columbus, with scroll, before Salamanca Council. e, Departure of Columbus' fleet from Palos.

No. 3464a, Three ships stopping at Canary Islands. b, Columbus speaking to crew. c, Land sighted, Oct. 12, 1492. d, Columbus landing in New World. e, Meeting natives.

No. 3465a, Grounding of Santa Maria at Hispanola. b, Arrival of Nina at Palos. c, Columbus welcomed in Barcelona. d, Columbus describes his voyage to Ferdinand and Isabella. e, Departure of fleet from Cadiz on second voyage.

No. 3466a, King and Queen welcome Columbus. b, Fleet on Columbus' third voyage. c, Columbus deported from Hispanola to Spain as prisoner. d, Columbus on ship, fourth voyage. e, Death of Columbus, May 20, 1506 in Valladolid.

**1992, Oct. 3** *Perf. 13*

**3463** A804 1c Strip of 5, #a.-e. .65 .30
**3464** A804 5c Strip of 5, #a.-e. .65 .30
**3465** A804 10c Strip of 5, #a.-e. 1.25 .75
**3466** A804 20c Strip of 5, #a.-e. 4.00 1.50
*a.* Sheet of 20, #3463-3466 20.00 20.00
*Nos. 3463-3466 (4)* 6.55 2.85

Jose Maria Chacon y Calvo (1892-1969), Historian — A942

**1992, Oct. 29** *Perf. 13*

**3467** A942 30c multicolored .90 .40

Churches — A943

Designs: 5c, Basilica of Nuestra Senora de la Caridad del Cobre. 20c, Santa Maria del Rosario Church. 30c, Espiritu Santo Church. 50c, Santo Angel Custodio Church.

**1992, Nov. 10 Litho.** *Perf. 12½*

**3468** A943 5c multicolored .25 .25
**3469** A943 20c multicolored .60 .25
**3470** A943 30c multicolored .90 .25
**3471** A943 50c multicolored 1.50 .30
*Nos. 3468-3471 (4)* 3.25 1.05

Development of the Diesel Engine A944

**1993, Jan. 20 Litho.** *Perf. 12½*

**3472** A944 5c Truck .25 .25
**3473** A944 10c Automobile .25 .25
**3474** A944 30c Tugboat .55 .40
**3475** A944 40c Locomotive 2.00 1.00
**3476** A944 50c Tractor 1.00 .65
*Nos. 3472-3476 (5)* 4.05 2.55

### Souvenir Sheet

**3477** A944 1p Rudolf Diesel 3.00 1.75

No. 3477 contains one 40x32mm stamp. Rudolf Diesel, 80th anniv. of death (No. 3477).

Davis Cup Tennis Competition A945

Various tennis players in action.

*Perf. 12x12½, 12½x12*

**1993, Feb. 10 Litho.**

**3478** A945 5c multi, vert. .25 .25
**3479** A945 20c multi, vert. .60 .25
**3480** A945 30c multi, vert. .90 .40
**3481** A945 35c multicolored 1.00 .50
**3482** A945 40c multicolored 1.25 .60
*Nos. 3478-3482 (5)* 4.00 2.00

### Souvenir Sheet

*Perf. 12½*

**3483** A945 1p multicolored 2.75 1.25

No. 3483 contains one 40x32mm stamp.

Scientists — A946

Designs: 3c, Pierre-Paul-Emile Roux (1853-1933), bacteriologist. 5c, Carlos J. Finlay

(1833-1915), suggested mosquito as carrier of yellow fever. 10c, Ivan Petrovich Pavlov (1849-1936), physiologist, investigated conditioned reflexes. 20c, Louis Pasteur, chemist, developer of pasteurization. 30c, Santiago Ramon y Cajal (1852-1934), histologist, isolated the neuron. 35c, Sigmund Freud, psychoanalyst. 40c, Wilhelm Conrad Roentgen, physicist, discoverer of x-ray. 50c, Joseph Lister, surgeon, introduced principle of antisepsis. 1p, Robert Koch, bacteriologist, developer of tuberculin, vert.

**1993, Mar. 3 Litho. *Perf. 12½***

**3484** A946 3c multicolored .25 .25
**3485** A946 5c multicolored .25 .25
**3486** A946 10c multicolored .25 .25
**3487** A946 20c multicolored .55 .25
**3488** A946 30c multicolored .80 .40
**3489** A946 35c multicolored .90 .50
**3490** A946 40c multicolored 1.10 .60
**3491** A946 50c multicolored 1.25 .65
*Nos. 3484-3491 (8)* 5.35 3.15

**Souvenir Sheet**

**3492** A946 1p multicolored 2.75 1.40

Most issues between Nos. 3493-3650 exist imperforate.

Bicycles A947

Bicycles designed by: 3c, Leonardo da Vinci, 15th cent. 5c, Karl Von Drais de Sauerbrun, 1813. 10c, Ernest Michaux, 1856. 20c, James Starley, 1869. 30c, Harry Lawson, 1879. 35c, Guaso (Cuba), 1992.

**1993, Apr. 14 *Perf. 13***

**3493** A947 3c multicolored .25 .25
**3494** A947 5c multicolored .25 .25
**3495** A947 10c multicolored .30 .25
**3496** A947 20c multicolored .60 .25
**3497** A947 30c multicolored .90 .40
**3498** A947 35c multicolored 1.00 .50
*Nos. 3493-3498 (6)* 3.30 1.90

Cuban Natl. Museum, 80th Anniv. — A948

Paintings by Joaquin Sorolla y Bastida (1863-1923): 3c, Child Eating Watermelon, 1920, vert. 5c, Valencian Fisherwomen, 1909. 10c, Regattas. 20c, Contadina, 1889. 40c, Summer, 1904. 50c, Boats on the Ocean, 1908.

**1993, May 29 Litho. *Perf. 13x12½***

**3499** A948 3c multicolored .25 .25

***Perf. 12½x13***

**3500** A948 5c multicolored .30 .25
**3501** A948 10c multicolored .35 .25
**3502** A948 20c multicolored .65 .25
**3503** A948 40c multicolored 1.25 .60
**3504** A948 50c multicolored 1.75 .65
*Nos. 3499-3504 (6)* 4.55 2.25

Water Birds — A949

Designs: 3c, Jacana spinosa. 5c, Ardea herodias, vert. 10c, Himantopus mexicanus. 20c, Nycticorax nycticorax. 30c, Grus canadensis, vert. 50c, Aramus guarauna.

***Perf. 12½, 13x12½ (5, 30c)***

**1993, June 15**

**3505** A949 3c multicolored .25 .25
**3506** A949 5c multicolored .25 .25
**3507** A949 10c multicolored .40 .25
**3508** A949 20c multicolored .80 .25
**3509** A949 30c multicolored 1.10 .40
**3510** A949 50c multicolored 2.25 .65
*Nos. 3505-3510 (6)* 5.05 2.05

Brasiliana '93. Nos. 3506, 3510 are 27x44mm.

Anniversaries A950

No. 3511, Jose Marti, Moncada Barracks. No. 3512, "History Will Absolve Me," declaration of Fidel Castro, Marti. No. 3513, Jose Marti, Rafael M. Mendive, vert. No. 3514, Carlos Manuel de Cespedes, gear wheels.

**1993, July 26 Litho. *Perf. 13***

**3511** A950 5c multicolored .25 .25
**3512** A950 5c multicolored .25 .25
**3513** A950 5c multicolored .25 .25
**3514** A950 5c multicolored .25 .25
*Nos. 3511-3514 (4)* 1.00 1.00

Attack on Moncada Barracks, 40th anniv. (No. 3511). Declaration of Fidel Castro, 40th anniv. (No. 3512). Birth of Jose Marti, 140th anniv. (No. 3513). Declaration of the Ten Years' War, 125th anniv. (No. 3514).

Flowers from Cienfuegos Botanical Gardens — A951

Designs: 3c, Sedum allantoides. 5c, Heliconia caribaea. 10c, Anthurium andraeanum. 20c, Pseudobombax ellipticum. 35c, Ixora coccinea. 50c, Callistemon specious.

**1993, Aug. 20**

**3515** A951 3c multicolored .25 .25
**3516** A951 5c multicolored .25 .25
**3517** A951 10c multicolored .35 .25
**3518** A951 20c multicolored .70 .25
**3519** A951 35c multicolored 1.10 .50
**3520** A951 50c multicolored 1.90 .65
*Nos. 3515-3520 (6)* 4.55 2.15

Bangkok '93, Intl. Philatelic Exhibition — A952

Butterflies: 3c, Battus devillievs. 5c, Anteos maerula. 20c, Ascia monuste evonima. 30c, Junonia coenia. 35c, Anartia jatrophae guantanamo. 50c, Hypolimnas misippus.

**1993, Sept. 10 Litho. *Perf. 13***

**3521** A952 3c multicolored .25 .25
**3522** A952 5c multicolored .25 .25
**3523** A952 20c multicolored .70 .25
**3524** A952 30c multicolored 1.00 .40
**3525** A952 35c multicolored 1.10 .40
**3526** A952 50c multicolored 1.60 .65
*Nos. 3521-3526 (6)* 4.90 2.20

Endangered Species — A953

5c, Phoenicopterus ruber. 50c, Ajaia ajaja.

**1993, Oct. 12 Litho. *Perf. 13***

**3527** A953 5c multicolored .25 .25
**3528** A953 50c multicolored 1.75 .65

Latin American Revolutionaries A954

Flags, map and: No. 3529, Simon Bolivar. No. 3530, Jose Marti. No. 3531, Benito Juarez, Mexican President. No. 3532, Ernesto "Che" Guevara.

**1993, Oct. 27 Litho. *Perf. 13***

**3529** A954 50c multicolored 1.40 .65
**3530** A954 50c multicolored 1.40 .65
**3531** A954 50c multicolored 1.40 .65
**3532** A954 50c multicolored 1.40 .65
*a.* Block of 4, #3529-3532 7.25 3.50
*Nos. 3529-3532 (4)* 5.60 2.60

17th Central American and Caribbean Games, Ponce, Puerto Rico — A955

**1993, Nov. 10 Litho. *Perf. 12½***

**3533** A955 5c Swimming .25 .25
**3534** A955 10c Pole vault .25 .25
**3535** A955 20c Boxing .70 .25
**3536** A955 35c Gymnastics, vert. 1.10 .40
**3537** A955 50c Baseball, vert. 1.60 .65
*Nos. 3533-3537 (5)* 3.90 1.80

**Souvenir Sheet**

**3538** A955 1p Basketball 3.75 1.75

No. 3538 contains one 40x32mm stamp.

Mariana Grajales (1808-93), Patriot — A956

**1993, Nov. 27 *Perf. 13***

**3539** A956 5p multicolored .50 .25

Peter I. Tchaikovsky (1840-93), Composer — A957

**1993, Nov. 30**

**3540** A957 5c Portrait .25 .25
**3541** A957 20c Swan Lake Ballet .65 .25
**3542** A957 30c Statue .90 .40
**3543** A957 50c Museum, horiz. 1.25 .65
*Nos. 3540-3543 (4)* 3.05 1.55

A958

**1994, Jan. 1 Litho. *Perf. 13***

**3544** A958 5c multicolored .30 .25

35th anniv. of the Revolution.

A959

Various soccer players.

**1994, Jan. 1**

**3545** A959 5c multicolored .25 .25
**3546** A959 20c multicolored .60 .25
**3547** A959 30c multicolored .85 .40
**3548** A959 35c multicolored .95 .40
**3549** A959 40c multicolored 1.25 .50
**3550** A959 50c multicolored 1.40 .65
*Nos. 3545-3550 (6)* 5.30 2.45

**Souvenir Sheet**

**3551** A959 1p multicolored 3.00 1.50

1994 World Cup Soccer Championships, US. No. 3551 contains one 40x31mm stamp.

Cats — A960

**1994, Feb. 15 Litho. *Perf. 12½***

**3552** A960 5c Blue Persian .25 .25
**3553** A960 10c Havana .25 .25
**3554** A960 20c Maine coon .70 .25
**3555** A960 30c Blue British shorthair 1.00 .40
**3556** A960 35c Bicolor Persian 1.10 .40
**3557** A960 50c Gold chinchilla 1.60 .65
*Nos. 3552-3557 (6)* 4.90 2.20

**Souvenir Sheet**

***Perf. 13***

**3558** A960 1p Abyssinian, vert. 3.50 2.00

No. 3558 contains one 30x38mm stamp.

Medicinal Plants — A961

Designs: 5c, Salvia officinalis. 10c, Aloe barbadensis. 20c, Helianthus annuus. 30c, Matricaria chamomilla. 40c, Calendula officinalis. 50c, Tilia platyphyllos.

**1994, Mar. 30 Litho. *Perf. 12½***

**3559** A961 5c multicolored .25 .25
**3560** A961 10c multicolored .25 .25
**3561** A961 20c multicolored .65 .25
**3562** A961 30c multicolored .90 .40
**3563** A961 40c multicolored 1.25 .50
**3564** A961 50c multicolored 1.50 .65
*Nos. 3559-3564 (6)* 4.80 2.30

Carriages A962

Designs: 5c, Public coach, 1860. 10c, Coach of Ferdinand VII, Maria Louisa. 30c, Louis XV-style coach. 35c, Elizabeth II gala day's coach. 40c, Catalina II's summer coach. 50c, Volanta habanera.

**1994, Apr. 20 *Perf. 12½x12***

**3565** A962 5c multicolored .25 .25
**3566** A962 10c multicolored .25 .25
**3567** A962 30c multicolored 1.00 .40
**3568** A962 35c multicolored 1.10 .40
**3569** A962 40c multicolored 1.25 .50
**3570** A962 50c multicolored 1.50 .65
*Nos. 3565-3570 (6)* 5.35 2.45

No. 3570 is 68x37mm.

Aquaculture A963

Designs: 5c, Crassostrea rhizophorae. 20c, Cardisoma guanhumi. 30c, Tilapia melanopleura. 35c, Hippospongia lachne. 40c, Panulirus argus. 50c, Cyprinus carpio.

**1994, May 10 Litho. *Perf. 12½***

**3571** A963 5c multicolored .35 .25
**3572** A963 20c multicolored .60 .25
**3573** A963 30c multicolored .85 .40
**3574** A963 35c multicolored 1.00 .40
**3575** A963 40c multicolored 1.25 .50
**3576** A963 50c multicolored 1.50 .65
*Nos. 3571-3576 (6)* 5.55 2.45

Intl. Olympic Committee, Cent. — A964

**1994, June 23 Litho. *Perf. 12½***

| | | | | |
|---|---|---|---|---|
| **3577** | A964 | 5c Flag, runners | .25 | .25 |
| **3578** | A964 | 30c Flag, world map | 1.10 | .40 |
| **3579** | A964 | 50c Flag, Olympic flame | 1.90 | .65 |
| | | *Nos. 3577-3579 (3)* | 3.25 | 1.30 |

Scientists — A965

Designs: 5c, Michael Faraday (1791-1867), physicist. 10c, Marie Curie (1867-1934), physical chemist. 20c, Pierre Curie (1859-1906), chemist. 30c, Albert Einstein (1879-1955), physicist, mathematician. 40c, Max Planck (1858-1947), theoretical physicist. 50c, Otto Hahn (1879-1968), physical chemist.

**1994, July 20 Litho. *Perf. 12½***

| | | | | |
|---|---|---|---|---|
| **3580** | A965 | 5c multicolored | .25 | .25 |
| **3581** | A965 | 10c multicolored | .25 | .25 |
| **3582** | A965 | 20c multicolored | .45 | .25 |
| **3583** | A965 | 30c multicolored | .75 | .40 |
| **3584** | A965 | 40c multicolored | 1.00 | .50 |
| **3585** | A965 | 50c multicolored | 1.25 | .65 |
| | | *Nos. 3580-3585 (6)* | 3.95 | 2.30 |

Cactus Flowers — A966

Designs: 5c, Opuntia dillenii. 10c, Opuntia millspaughii, vert. 30c, Leptocereus santamarinae. 35c, Pereskia marcanoi. 40c, Dendrocereus nudiflorus, vert. 50c, Pilocereus robinii.

**1994, Aug. 15 Litho. *Perf. 12½***

| | | | | |
|---|---|---|---|---|
| **3586** | A966 | 5c multicolored | .25 | .25 |
| **3587** | A966 | 10c multicolored | .25 | .25 |
| **3588** | A966 | 30c multicolored | .75 | .40 |
| **3589** | A966 | 35c multicolored | .80 | .40 |
| **3590** | A966 | 40c multicolored | 1.00 | .50 |
| **3591** | A966 | 50c multicolored | 1.25 | .65 |
| | | *Nos. 3586-3591 (6)* | 4.30 | 2.45 |

Souvenir Sheet

2nd Spanish-Cuban Philatelic Exhibition, Havana — A967

Design: 1p, Cuban postal rocket, #C31.

**1994, Sept. 18**

| | | | | |
|---|---|---|---|---|
| **3592** | A967 | 1p multicolored | 2.50 | 1.50 |

Experimental postal rocket flight, 55th anniv.

Dogs — A968

5c, Rough collie. 20c, American cocker spaniel. 30c, Dalmatian. 40c, Afghan hound. 50c, English cocker spaniel.

**1994, Sept. 20**

| | | | | |
|---|---|---|---|---|
| **3593** | A968 | 5c multicolored | .25 | .25 |
| **3594** | A968 | 20c multicolored | .50 | .25 |
| **3595** | A968 | 30c multicolored | .75 | .40 |
| **3596** | A968 | 40c multicolored | 1.00 | .50 |
| **3597** | A968 | 50c multicolored | 1.25 | .65 |
| | | *Nos. 3593-3597 (5)* | 3.75 | 2.05 |

Cayo Largo Island — A969

Fauna: 15c, Carpilius corallinus. 65c, Cyclura nubila, vert. 75c, Pelecanus occidentalis. 1p, Chelonia mydas.

**1994, Sept. 30 Litho. *Perf. 12½***

| | | | | |
|---|---|---|---|---|
| **3598** | A969 | 15c multicolored | .30 | .25 |
| **3599** | A969 | 65c multicolored | 1.50 | .90 |
| **3600** | A969 | 75c multicolored | 1.75 | 1.00 |
| **3601** | A969 | 1p multicolored | 2.50 | 1.25 |
| | | *Nos. 3598-3601 (4)* | 6.05 | 3.40 |

A970

**1994, Oct. 28**

| | | | | |
|---|---|---|---|---|
| **3602** | A970 | 15c multicolored | .50 | .25 |

Camilo Cienfuegos Gorriaran, revolutionary, 35th anniv. of disappearance.

A971

Fauna of the Caribbean: 10c, Epinephelus flavolimbatus, horiz. No. 3604, Phoenicopterus ruber. No. 3605, Aetobatus narinari. No. 3606, Istiophorus platypterus, horiz. No. 3607, Tursiops truncatus, horiz. No. 3608, Pelecanus occidentalis.

**1994, Oct. 30**

| | | | | |
|---|---|---|---|---|
| **3603** | A971 | 10c multicolored | .30 | .25 |
| **3604** | A971 | 15c multicolored | .30 | .25 |
| **3605** | A971 | 15c multicolored | .30 | .25 |
| **3606** | A971 | 15c multicolored | .30 | .25 |
| **3607** | A971 | 65c multicolored | 1.60 | .90 |
| **3608** | A971 | 65c multicolored | 1.60 | .90 |
| | | *Nos. 3603-3608 (6)* | 4.40 | 2.80 |

ICAO, 50th Anniv. — A972

**1994, Nov. 9**

| | | | | |
|---|---|---|---|---|
| **3609** | A972 | 65c multicolored | 1.50 | .90 |

Zoological Garden, Havana, 55th Anniv. — A973

15c, Bronze monument. 65c, Ara chloroptera. 75c, Carduelis carduelis.

**1994, Nov. 14 Litho. *Perf. 13***

| | | | | |
|---|---|---|---|---|
| **3610** | A973 | 15c multicolored | .25 | .25 |
| **3611** | A973 | 65c multicolored | 1.60 | .90 |
| **3612** | A973 | 75c multicolored | 1.90 | 1.00 |
| | | *Nos. 3610-3612 (3)* | 3.75 | 2.15 |

Cuban Philatelic Federation, 30th Anniv. — A974

**1994, Nov. 20**

| | | | | |
|---|---|---|---|---|
| **3613** | A974 | 15c multicolored | .50 | .25 |

America Issue — A975

Postal transportation: 15c, 18th Cent. Spanish galleon, maritime postal service, vert. 65c, 19th Cent. postal rider, insurgent postal service.

**1994, Dec. 12**

| | | | | |
|---|---|---|---|---|
| **3614** | A975 | 15c multicolored | .25 | .25 |
| **3615** | A975 | 65c multicolored | 1.75 | .90 |

Postal Museum, 30th Anniv. — A976

**1995, Jan. 2**

| | | | | |
|---|---|---|---|---|
| **3616** | A976 | 15c multicolored | .50 | .25 |

Lizards A977

Designs: 15c, Anolis baracoae. 65c, Sphaerodactylus ramsdeni. 75c, Leiocephalus raviceps. 85c, Sphaerodactylus ruibali. 90c, Anolis ophiolepis. 1p, Sphaerodactylus armasi.

**1994, Nov. 30 Litho. *Perf. 12½***

| | | | | |
|---|---|---|---|---|
| **3617** | A977 | 15c multicolored | .30 | .25 |
| **3618** | A977 | 65c multicolored | 1.60 | .90 |
| **3619** | A977 | 75c multicolored | 1.75 | 1.00 |
| **3620** | A977 | 85c multicolored | 2.00 | 1.25 |
| **3621** | A977 | 90c multicolored | 2.25 | 1.25 |
| **3622** | A977 | 1p multicolored | 2.50 | 1.40 |
| | | *Nos. 3617-3622 (6)* | 10.40 | 6.05 |

Cuban War of Independence, Cent. — A978

**1995, Feb. 24 Litho. *Perf. 12½***

| | | | | |
|---|---|---|---|---|
| **3623** | A978 | 15c Jose Marti, flag | .50 | .25 |

Pan American Games, Mar del Plata, Argentina A979

**1995, Mar. 11 Litho. *Perf. 13***

| | | | | |
|---|---|---|---|---|
| **3624** | A979 | 10c Boxing, vert. | .25 | .25 |
| **3625** | A979 | 15c Weight lifting, vert. | .25 | .25 |
| **3626** | A979 | 65c Volleyball, vert. | 1.25 | .80 |
| **3627** | A979 | 75c Wrestling | 1.40 | 1.00 |
| **3628** | A979 | 85c Baseball | 1.60 | 1.00 |
| **3629** | A979 | 90c High jump | 1.75 | 1.10 |
| | | *Nos. 3624-3629 (6)* | 6.50 | 4.40 |

National Aquarium, 35th Anniv. — A980

Fish: 10c, Holacanthus cillaris. 15c, Hypoplectrus guttavarius. 65c, Anisotremus virginicus. 75c, Amblycirrhitus pinos. 85c, Pomaacanthus paru. 90c, Acanthurus coeruleus.

**1995, Apr. 28 Litho. *Perf. 13***

| | | | | |
|---|---|---|---|---|
| **3630** | A980 | 10c multicolored | .25 | .25 |
| **3631** | A980 | 15c multicolored | .30 | .25 |
| **3632** | A980 | 65c multicolored | 1.25 | .70 |
| **3633** | A980 | 75c multicolored | 1.50 | .80 |
| **3634** | A980 | 85c multicolored | 1.75 | 1.10 |
| **3635** | A980 | 90c multicolored | 2.00 | 1.10 |
| | | *Nos. 3630-3635 (6)* | 7.05 | 4.20 |

FAO, 50th Anniv. — A981

**1995, Apr. 7 Litho. *Perf. 13***

| | | | | |
|---|---|---|---|---|
| **3636** | A981 | 75c multicolored | 1.40 | 1.00 |

First Cuban Postage Stamp, 140th Anniv. — A982

65c, Ornamental letter drop, envelope.

**1995. Apr. 24 Litho. *Perf. 12½***

| | | | | |
|---|---|---|---|---|
| **3637** | A982 | 15c blk & blue grn | .30 | .25 |
| **3638** | A982 | 65c multicolored | 1.40 | .75 |

Jose Marti, Death Cent. — A983

Designs: 15c, Marti killed in combat, signature, portrait. 65c, Landing of Marti, Cuban patriots on Playitas beach. 75c, Montecristi Manifesto signed in Dominican Republic, Marti. 85c, Meeting of Marti, Maceo, Gomez at La Mejorana Farm. 90c, Marti's mausoleum, Santiago, Cuba, vert.

**1995, May 19 *Perf. 12½x13, 13x12½***

| | | | | |
|---|---|---|---|---|
| **3639** | A983 | 15c multicolored | .25 | .25 |
| **3640** | A983 | 65c multicolored | 1.25 | .80 |
| **3641** | A983 | 75c multicolored | 1.40 | 1.00 |
| **3642** | A983 | 85c multicolored | 1.75 | 1.00 |
| **3643** | A983 | 90c multicolored | 1.75 | 1.10 |
| | | *Nos. 3639-3643 (5)* | 6.40 | 4.15 |

Antonio Maceo (1845-96), Revolutionary A984

**1995, June 14 Litho. *Perf. 12½***

| | | | | |
|---|---|---|---|---|
| **3644** | A984 | 15c multicolored | .90 | .25 |

Butterflies A985

Designs: 10c, Dione vanillae. 15c, Eunica tatila. 65c, Melete salacia. 75c, Greta cubana. 85c, Eurema daira. 90c, Phoebis sennae.

**1995, June 20 *Perf. 12½x13***

| | | | | |
|---|---|---|---|---|
| **3645** | A985 | 10c multicolored | .25 | .25 |
| **3646** | A985 | 15c multicolored | .25 | .25 |
| **3647** | A985 | 65c multicolored | 1.25 | .80 |
| **3648** | A985 | 75c multicolored | 1.40 | 1.00 |
| **3649** | A985 | 85c multicolored | 1.75 | 1.00 |
| **3650** | A985 | 90c multicolored | 1.75 | 1.10 |
| | | *Nos. 3645-3650 (6)* | 6.65 | 4.40 |

World War II Combat Planes A986

Designs: 10c, Supermarine "Spitfire," Great Britain. 15c, IL-2, Russia. 65c, Curtiss P-40, US. 75c, Messerschmitt Bf-109, Germany. 85c, Morane-Saunier 406, France.

**1995, July 30 Litho. *Perf. 12½***

| | | | | |
|---|---|---|---|---|
| **3651** | A986 | 10c multicolored | .30 | .25 |
| **3652** | A986 | 15c multicolored | .30 | .25 |
| **3653** | A986 | 65c multicolored | 1.40 | .80 |
| **3654** | A986 | 75c multicolored | 1.60 | 1.00 |
| **3655** | A986 | 85c multicolored | 1.90 | 1.00 |
| | | *Nos. 3651-3655 (5)* | 5.50 | 3.30 |

A987

**1995, Aug. 6 Litho. *Perf. 12½***

| | | | | |
|---|---|---|---|---|
| **3656** | A987 | 15c multicolored | .40 | .25 |

Ernesto Lecuona, composer, pianist, birth cent.

A988

**Color of Horse or Horses**

**1995, Aug. 10**

| | | | | |
|---|---|---|---|---|
| **3657** | A988 | 10c golden brn, white | .25 | .25 |
| **3658** | A988 | 15c white, horiz. | .25 | .25 |
| **3659** | A988 | 65c dk brn, white | 1.40 | .80 |
| **3660** | A988 | 75c red brown | 1.60 | 1.00 |
| **3661** | A988 | 85c tan | 1.75 | 1.00 |
| **3662** | A988 | 90c white | 2.00 | 1.10 |
| | | *Nos. 3657-3662 (6)* | 7.25 | 4.40 |

Singapore '95.

Souvenir Sheet

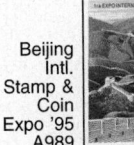

Beijing Intl. Stamp & Coin Expo '95 A989

**1995, Aug. 28 *Perf. 13***

| | | | | |
|---|---|---|---|---|
| **3663** | A989 | 50c multicolored | 1.25 | .75 |

1996 Summer Olympics, Atlanta — A990

10c, Wrestling. 15c, Weight lifting. 65c, Women's volleyball. 75c, Women's athletics. 85c, Baseball. 90c, Women's judo.
1p, Boxing.

**1995, Sept. 25 Litho. *Perf. 13***

| | | | | |
|---|---|---|---|---|
| **3664** | A990 | 10c multicolored | .25 | .25 |
| **3665** | A990 | 15c multicolored | .25 | .25 |
| **3666** | A990 | 65c multicolored | 1.25 | .80 |
| **3667** | A990 | 75c multicolored | 1.50 | 1.00 |
| **3668** | A990 | 85c multicolored | 1.60 | 1.00 |
| **3669** | A990 | 90c multicolored | 1.75 | 1.10 |
| | | *Nos. 3664-3669 (6)* | 6.60 | 4.40 |

**Souvenir Sheet**

| | | | | |
|---|---|---|---|---|
| **3670** | A990 | 1p multicolored | 2.50 | 1.50 |

No. 3670 contains one 30x36mm stamp.

Cuban Sugar Industry, 400th Anniv. — A991

Paintings from "Los Ingenios," by Edouard Laplante, 1852: 15c, Steam train, sugar factory. 65c, Sugar factory, tower, bridge.

**1995, Oct. 3**

| | | | | |
|---|---|---|---|---|
| **3671** | A991 | 15c multicolored | 1.00 | .35 |
| **3672** | A991 | 65c multicolored | .60 | .70 |

UN, 50th Anniv. — A992

**1995, Oct. 24 Litho. *Perf. 13***

| | | | | |
|---|---|---|---|---|
| **3673** | A992 | 65c multicolored | 1.25 | .80 |

Zoological Gardens, Havana — A993

Designs: 10c, Panthera leo, vert. 15c, Equus grevyi. 65c, Pongo pygmaeus, vert. 75c, Elephas maximus. 85c, Sciurus vulgaris. 90c, Procyon lotor.

**1995, Oct. 30 Litho. *Perf. 13***

| | | | | |
|---|---|---|---|---|
| **3674** | A993 | 10c multicolored | .25 | .25 |
| **3675** | A993 | 15c multicolored | .30 | .25 |
| **3676** | A993 | 65c multicolored | 1.25 | .80 |
| **3677** | A993 | 75c multicolored | 1.50 | 1.00 |
| **3678** | A993 | 85c multicolored | 1.75 | 1.00 |
| **3679** | A993 | 90c multicolored | 2.00 | 1.10 |
| | | *Nos. 3674-3679 (6)* | 7.05 | 4.40 |

UNESCO, 50th Anniv. — A994

UNESCO World Culture and National Heritage sites: 65c, Santa Clara de Asis Convent. 75c, San Francisco de Asis Minor Basilica.

**1995, Nov. 4**

| | | | | |
|---|---|---|---|---|
| **3680** | A994 | 65c multicolored | 1.20 | .80 |
| **3681** | A994 | 75c multicolored | 1.40 | 1.00 |

Orchids — A995

Designs: 5c, Epidendrum porpax. 10c, Cyrtopodium punctatum. 15c, Polyrrhiza lindeni. 40c, Bletia patula. 45c, Galeandra beyrichii. 50c, Vanilla dilloniana. 65c, Macradenia lutescens. 75c, Oncidium luridum. 85c, Ionopsis utricularioides.

**1995, Nov. 10 *Perf. 12½***

| | | | | |
|---|---|---|---|---|
| **3681A** | A995 | 5c multicolored | .25 | .25 |
| **3681B** | A995 | 10c multicolored | .30 | .25 |
| **3681C** | A995 | 15c multicolored | .40 | .25 |
| **3682** | A995 | 40c multicolored | .80 | .55 |
| **3683** | A995 | 45c multicolored | .90 | .55 |
| **3684** | A995 | 50c multicolored | 1.00 | .65 |
| **3685** | A995 | 65c multicolored | 1.25 | .80 |
| **3686** | A995 | 75c multicolored | 1.40 | 1.00 |
| **3687** | A995 | 85c multicolored | 1.60 | 1.00 |
| | | *Nos. 3681A-3687 (9)* | 7.90 | 5.30 |

Issued: 40c-85c, 11/10/95; 5c-15c, 6/28/96.

Motion Pictures, Cent. — A996

**1995, Dec. 7 *Perf. 13***

| | | | | |
|---|---|---|---|---|
| **3688** | A996 | 15c Lumiere Brothers | .30 | .25 |
| **3689** | A996 | 15c Marilyn Monroe | .30 | .25 |
| **3690** | A996 | 15c Marlene Dietrich | .30 | .25 |
| **3691** | A996 | 15c Vittorio DeSica | .30 | .25 |
| **3692** | A996 | 15c Charlie Chaplin | .30 | .25 |
| **3693** | A996 | 15c Greta Garbo | .30 | .25 |
| **3694** | A996 | 65c Humphrey Bogart | 1.40 | .80 |
| **3695** | A996 | 75c Montaner | 1.60 | 1.00 |
| **3696** | A996 | 85c Cantinflas | 1.90 | 1.00 |
| *a.* | | Sheet of 9, #3688-3696 | 17.50 | — |
| | | *Nos. 3688-3696 (9)* | 6.70 | 4.30 |

Souvenir Sheet

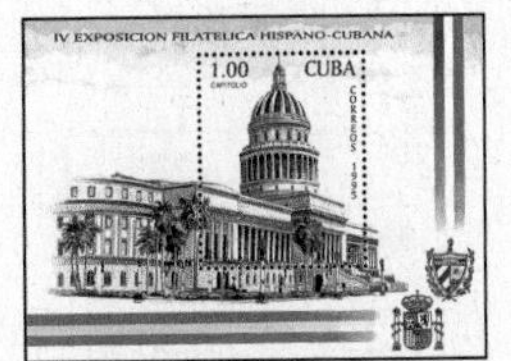

4th Cuban-Spanish Philatelic Exhibition, Havana — A997

**1995, Dec. 11 Litho. *Perf. 13***

| | | | | |
|---|---|---|---|---|
| **3697** | A997 | 1p multicolored | 2.50 | 1.50 |

America Issue — A998

15c, Centurus superciliaris. 65c, Todus multicolor.

**1995, Dec. 12**

| | | | | |
|---|---|---|---|---|
| **3698** | A998 | 15c multicolored | .35 | .25 |
| **3699** | A998 | 65c multicolored | 1.40 | .80 |

Generals Who Died in 1895 War — A999

Designs: No. 3700, Alfonso Goulet Goulet, Francisco Adolfo Crombet Ballon. No. 3701, Jesus Calvar O, Jose Guillermo Moncada, Tomas Jordan. No. 3702, Francisco Borrero Lavadi, Francisco Inchaustegui Cabrera.

**1995, Dec. 20 *Perf. 12½***

| | | | | |
|---|---|---|---|---|
| **3700** | A999 | 15c multicolored | .50 | .25 |
| **3701** | A999 | 15c multicolored | .50 | .25 |
| **3702** | A999 | 15c multicolored | .50 | .25 |
| *a.* | | Strip of 3, #3700-3702 | 1.75 | 1.50 |
| | | *Nos. 3700-3702 (3)* | 1.50 | .75 |

See Nos. 3758-3760.

Island of Coco Cay, Jardines del Rey — A1000

Bird, scenic view: 10c, Sterna antillarum, aerial view of island. 15c, Eudocimus albus, people on beach. 45c, Spindalis zena, couple on steps of resort complex. 50c, Turdus plumbeus, resort. 65c, Mimus polyglottos, resort. 75c, Phoenicopterus ruber, couple in pool at resort.

**1995, Dec. 23**

| | | | | |
|---|---|---|---|---|
| **3703** | A1000 | 10c multicolored | .25 | .25 |
| **3704** | A1000 | 15c multicolored | .30 | .25 |
| **3705** | A1000 | 45c multicolored | 1.00 | .55 |
| **3706** | A1000 | 50c multicolored | 1.10 | .60 |
| **3707** | A1000 | 65c multicolored | 1.40 | .80 |
| **3708** | A1000 | 75c multicolored | 1.60 | 1.00 |
| | | *Nos. 3703-3708 (6)* | 5.65 | 3.45 |

Patriots — A1001

Designs: 15c, Carlos M. de Céspedes (1819-74). 65c, José Martí (1853-95). 75c, Antonio Maceo (1845-96). 1.05p, Ignacio Agramonte (1841-73). 2.05p, Máximo Gómez (1836-1905). 3p, Calixto Garcia (1839-98).

**1996, Jan. 10**

| | | | | |
|---|---|---|---|---|
| **3709** | A1001 | 15c green | .25 | .25 |
| **3710** | A1001 | 65c blue | 1.10 | .80 |
| **3711** | A1001 | 75c carmine | 1.25 | 1.00 |
| **3712** | A1001 | 1.05p lilac | 1.90 | 1.40 |
| **3713** | A1001 | 2.05p brown | 4.00 | 2.50 |
| **3714** | A1001 | 3p light brown | 5.50 | 3.75 |
| | | *Nos. 3709-3714 (6)* | 14.00 | 9.70 |

See Nos. 3755-3757.

Organization of Solidarity of the Peoples of Africa, Asia and Latin America (OSPAAAL), 30th Anniv. — A1002

**1996, Jan. 14**

| | | | | |
|---|---|---|---|---|
| **3715** | A1002 | 65c multicolored | 1.40 | .75 |

Scientists A1003

10c, Leonardo da Vinci (1452-1519). 15c, Mikhail V. Lomonosov (1711-65), atmospheric scientist. 65c, James Watt (1736-1819), engineer, inventor. 75c, Guglielmo Marconi (1874-1937), physicist. 85c, Charles R. Darwin (1809-82), naturalist.

**1996, Jan. 30 Litho. *Perf. 12½***

| | | | | |
|---|---|---|---|---|
| **3716** | A1003 | 10c multicolored | .25 | .25 |
| **3717** | A1003 | 15c multicolored | .30 | .25 |
| **3718** | A1003 | 65c multicolored | 1.25 | .80 |
| **3719** | A1003 | 75c multicolored | 1.50 | 1.00 |
| **3720** | A1003 | 85c multicolored | 1.75 | 1.00 |
| | | *Nos. 3716-3720 (5)* | 5.05 | 3.30 |

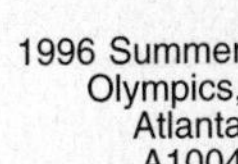

1996 Summer Olympics, Atlanta A1004

**1996, Feb. 15 Litho. *Perf. 12½***

| | | | | |
|---|---|---|---|---|
| **3721** | A1004 | 10c Athletics, vert. | .25 | .25 |
| **3722** | A1004 | 15c Weight lifting, vert. | .30 | .25 |
| **3723** | A1004 | 65c Judo, vert. | 1.25 | .80 |
| **3724** | A1004 | 75c Wrestling | 1.50 | 1.00 |
| **3725** | A1004 | 85c Boxing | 1.75 | 1.00 |
| | | *Nos. 3721-3725 (5)* | 5.05 | 3.30 |

**Souvenir Sheet**

| | | | | |
|---|---|---|---|---|
| **3726** | A1004 | 1p Baseball, vert. | 2.00 | 1.50 |

No. 3726 contains one 40x32mm stamp.

Espamer '96, Aviation and Space, Philatelic Exhibition, Seville A1005

**1996, Mar. 4**

**3727** A1005 15c C-4 Autogiro .25 .25
**3728** A1005 65c CASA C-352 1.25 .80
**3729** A1005 75c Alcotan C-201 1.60 1.00
**3730** A1005 85c CASA C-212 1.75 1.00
*Nos. 3727-3730 (4)* 4.85 3.05

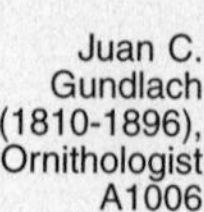

Juan C. Gundlach (1810-1896), Ornithologist A1006

Birds: 10c, Ceryle alcyon. 15c, Setophaga ruticilla. 65c, Geothlypis trichas. 75c, Passerina ciris. 85c, Bombycilla cedrorum.
1p, Vireo gundlachi.

**1996, Mar. 15** ***Perf. 12½***

**3731** A1006 10c multicolored .30 .25
**3732** A1006 15c multicolored .30 .25
**3733** A1006 65c multicolored 1.40 .80
**3734** A1006 75c multicolored 1.60 1.00
**3735** A1006 85c multicolored 1.90 1.00
*Nos. 3731-3735 (5)* 5.50 3.30

**Souvenir Sheet**

**3736** A1006 1p multicolored 3.00 1.90

No. 3736 contains one 40x32mm stamp.

Souvenir Sheet

ESPAMER '96, Stamp Exhibition of America and Europe, Seville — A1007

**1996, Mar. 14** **Litho.** ***Perf. 12½***

**3737** A1007 1p multicolored 3.00 1.50

First Man in Space, 35th Anniv. — A1008

Designs: 15c, Yuri A. Gagarin (1934-68). 65c, Spaceship, map showing orbital route.

**1996, Apr. 12** **Litho.** ***Perf. 12½***

**3738** A1008 15c multi .35 .25
**3739** A1008 65c multi, horiz. 1.25 .80

Bay of Pigs Invasion, 35th Anniv. — A1009

**1996, Apr. 19**

**3740** A1009 15c shown .35 .25
**3741** A1009 65c Natl. flags 1.25 .80

Cuban Sailing Ships — A1010

Designs: 10c, Bahama. 15c, Santísima Trinidad. 65c, Principe de Asturias. 75c, San Pedro de Alcántara. 85c, Santa Ana.
1p, San Genaro.

**1996, May 8** **Litho.** ***Perf. 12½***

**3742** A1010 10c multicolored .25 .25
**3743** A1010 15c multicolored .30 .25
**3744** A1010 65c multicolored 1.40 .80
**3745** A1010 75c multicolored 1.60 1.00
**3746** A1010 85c multicolored 1.75 1.00
*Nos. 3742-3746 (5)* 5.30 3.30

**Souvenir Sheet**

**3747** A1010 1p multicolored 2.00 1.00

CAPEX '96. No. 3747 contains one 40x32mm stamp.

Fauna of the Caribbean A1011

Designs: 10c, Todus multicolor. No. 3749, Eulampis jugularis. No. 3750, Aix sponsa. No. 3751, Chaetodon ocellatus. No. 3752, Papilio cresphontes. No. 3753, Hypoplectrus indigo.

**1996, June 18** **Litho.** ***Perf. 12½***

**3748** A1011 10c multicolored .30 .25
**3749** A1011 15c multicolored .30 .25
**3750** A1011 15c multicolored .30 .25
**3751** A1011 15c multicolored .30 .25
**3752** A1011 65c multicolored 1.40 .80
**3753** A1011 65c multicolored 1.40 .80
*Nos. 3748-3753 (6)* 4.00 2.60

Jose M. Maceo Grajales (1849-96), Revolutionary War Leader A1012

**1996, July 5**

**3754** A1012 15c multicolored .50 .25

**Patriot Type of 1996**

Designs: 10c. Serafin Sánchez. 85c, Juan Gualberto Gomez. 90c, Quintin Bandera.

**1996, July 10**

**3755** A1001 10c orange .25 .25
**3756** A1001 85c olive 1.75 1.00
**3757** A1001 90c olive brown 2.00 1.10
*Nos. 3755-3757 (3)* 4.00 2.35

**Generals Who Died in 1895 War Type of 1995**

No. 3758, Esteban Tamayo (1843-96), Angel Guerra (1842-96). No. 3759, Juan Fernández Ruz (1821-96), José Maria Aguirre (1843-96), Serafin Sánchez (1846-96). No. 3760, Juan Bruno Zayas (1867-96), Pedro Vargas Sotomayor (1868-96).

**1996, July 30**

**3758** A999 15c multicolored .35 .25
**3759** A999 15c multicolored .35 .25
**3760** A999 15c multicolored .35 .25
*a.* Strip of 3, #3758-3760 1.70 .90
*Nos. 3758-3760 (3)* 1.05 .75

Santiago de Cuba A1013

Flower, scenic view: 15c, Jacaranda arborea, beach. 65c, Begonia bissei, Fort San Pedro de la Roca. 75c, Byrsonima crassifolia, palm trees, mountains, vert. 85c, Pereskia zinniiflora, church, vert.

***Perf. 13x12½, 12½x13***

**1996, Sept. 27** **Litho.**

**3761** A1013 15c multicolored .30 .25
**3762** A1013 65c multicolored 1.25 .65
**3763** A1013 75c multicolored 1.50 .75
**3764** A1013 85c multicolored 1.60 .85
*Nos. 3761-3764 (4)* 4.65 2.50

Steam Locomotives A1014

Designs: 10c, Baldwin 0-4-2, 1878. 15c, American 2-6-0, 1904. 65c, Baldwin 4-6-0, 1906. 75c, Rogers 2-4-4, 1914. 90c, Baldwin 2-8-0, 1920.

**1996, Sept. 30** ***Perf. 12½***

**3765** A1014 10c multicolored .30 .25
**3766** A1014 15c multicolored .30 .25
**3767** A1014 65c multicolored 1.40 .80
**3768** A1014 75c multicolored 1.60 .90
**3769** A1014 90c multicolored 1.75 1.00
*Nos. 3765-3769 (5)* 5.35 3.20

Traditional Costumes — A1015

America Issue: 15c, Free black couple, 19th cent. 65c, Guayabera couple, 20th cent.

**1996, Oct. 12** **Litho.** ***Perf. 12½***

**3770** A1015 15c multicolored .35 .25
**3771** A1015 65c multicolored 1.25 .80

UNICEF, 50th Anniv. — A1016

**1996, Nov. 8** **Litho.** ***Perf. 12½***

**3772** A1016 15c multicolored .50 .25

World Chess Championship Won by José Raúl Capablanca, 75th Anniv. A1017

Designs: 15c, Portrait, chess board. 65c, Portrait, seated at chess board. 75c, Rook with top shaped as world, portrait. 85c, Playing chess as a child. 90c, In championship match, 1921.

**1996, Nov. 30** **Litho.** ***Perf. 12½***

**3773** A1017 15c multicolored .30 .25
**3774** A1017 65c multicolored 1.25 .80
**3775** A1017 75c multicolored 1.50 1.00
**3776** A1017 85c multicolored 1.75 1.00
**3777** A1017 90c multicolored 1.90 1.10
*Nos. 3773-3777 (5)* 6.70 4.15

Revolutionary Armed Forces and Return of Castro from Mexico, 40th Anniv. — A1018

**1996, Dec. 2**

**3778** A1018 15c Yacht Granma .25 .25
**3779** A1018 65c Armed forces 1.25 1.00

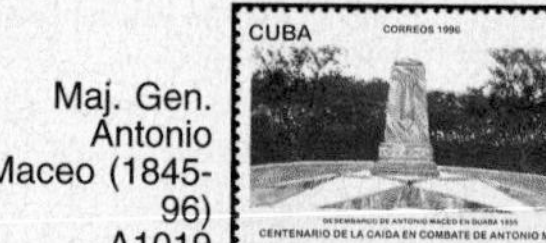

Maj. Gen. Antonio Maceo (1845-96) A1019

Designs: 10c, Monument, Santiago, vert. No. 3781, Portrait, vert. No. 3782, Monument, Duaba. 65c, Detail of painting showing Maceo dying from combat wounds. 75c, Maceo, young man and monument, San Pedro.

**1996, Dec. 7**

**3780** A1019 10c multicolored .25 .25
**3781** A1019 15c multicolored .30 .25
**3782** A1019 15c multicolored .30 .25
**3783** A1019 65c multicolored 1.40 1.10
**3784** A1019 75c multicolored 1.60 1.40
*Nos. 3780-3784 (5)* 3.85 3.25

Medals Won at 1996 Summer Olympic Games, Atlanta A1020

Medal, sport: No. 3785a, Gold, judo. b, Bronze, wrestling.
No. 3786: a, Gold, weight lifting. b, Gold, wrestling. c, Silver, fencing. d, Silver, swimming.
No. 3787: a, Gold, women's volleyball. b, Gold, boxing. c, Silver, women's running. d, Gold, baseball.

**1996, Dec. 10**

**3785** A1020 10c Pair, #a-b + 4 labels .50 .25
**3786** A1020 15c Block, #a-d + 2 labels 1.25 .65
**3787** A1020 65c Block, #a-d + 2 labels 5.00 2.50
*Nos. 3785-3787 (3)* 6.75 3.40

New Year 1996 (Year of the Rat) A1021

**1996, Dec. 28** **Litho.** ***Perf. 12½***

**3788** A1021 15c multicolored .50 .25

Espamer '98 — A1022

Locomotives: 15c, Minho Douro 0-6-0, Portugal. No. 3790, Vulcan Iron Works 0-4-0, Brazil. No. 3791, Baldwin 2-6-0, Dominican Republic. No. 3792, American Locomotive Co. 2-6-4, Panama. No. 3793, Baldwin 0-4-0, Puerto Rico. No. 3794, Slaughter, Gruning Co. 0-4-0, Spain. No. 3795, Yorkshire Engine Co. 4-4-0, Argentina. No. 3796, 2-6-0 Paraguay. No. 3797, H.K. Porter Co. 2-8-2, Chile. No. 3798, 2-6-0, Mexico.
1p, Baldwin 0-4-2 (1884), Cuba.

**1996, Dec. 30**

**3789** A1022 15c multicolored .30 .25
**3790** A1022 65c multicolored 1.40 .70
**3791** A1022 65c multicolored 1.40 .70
**3792** A1022 65c multicolored 1.40 .70
**3793** A1022 65c multicolored 1.40 .70
**3794** A1022 65c multicolored 1.40 .70
**3795** A1022 75c multicolored 1.50 .80
**3796** A1022 75c multicolored 1.50 .80
**3797** A1022 75c multicolored 1.50 .80
**3798** A1022 75c multicolored 1.50 .80
*Nos. 3789-3798 (10)* 13.30 6.95

**Souvenir Sheet**

**3799** A1022 1p multicolored 3.00 1.75

No. 3799 contains one 36x28mm.

Hong Kong '97, Intl. Philatelic Exhibition A1023

Cats: 10c, Brown-point Siamese, vert. No. 3801, Japanese bobtail. No. 3802, Burmese, vert. No. 3803, Singapore. No. 3804, Korat.
1p, Blue-point Siamese.

**1997, Jan. 15** **Litho.** ***Perf. 12½***

**3800** A1023 10c multicolored .25 .25
**3801** A1023 15c multicolored .30 .25
**3802** A1023 15c multicolored .30 .25
**3803** A1023 65c multicolored 1.50 1.00
**3804** A1023 75c multicolored 1.90 1.10
*Nos. 3800-3804 (5)* 4.25 2.85

**Souvenir Sheet**

**3805** A1023 1p multicolored 3.00 2.00

No. 3805 contains one 40x31mm stamp.

Motion Pictures, Cent. — A1024

Film scenes from: 15c, "El Romance del Palmar," directed by Ramón Peón. 65c, "Memorias del Subdesarrollo," directed by Tomás Gutiérrez Alea, vert.

**1997, Jan. 24 Litho. *Perf. 13***

**3806** A1024 15c multicolored .30 .25
**3807** A1024 65c multicolored 1.60 1.00

Zoo Animals — A1025

Designs: 10c, Camelus dromedarius. No. 3809, Ailuropada melanoleuca. No. 3810, Cerothoterium simun. 75c, Pongo pygmaeus. 90c, Bison bonasus.

**1997, Feb. 20 Litho. *Perf. 12½***

**3808** A1025 10c multicolored .25 .25
**3809** A1025 15c multicolored .30 .25
**3810** A1025 15c multicolored .30 .25
**3811** A1025 75c multicolored 1.75 1.00
**3812** A1025 90c multicolored 2.00 1.10
*Nos. 3808-3812 (5)* 4.60 2.85

New Year 1997 (Year of the Ox) A1026

**1997, Feb. 22**

**3813** A1026 15c multicolored .50 .25

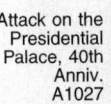

Attack on the Presidential Palace, 40th Anniv. A1027

15c, Menelao Mora Morales.

**1997, Mar. 13 Litho. *Perf. 12½***

**3814** A1027 15c multicolored .60 .25

1998 World Cup Soccer Championships, France A1028

Action scenes: 10c, Three players. No. 3816, Player in green, player in blue & yellow. No. 3817, Player in yellow & black, player in green. 65c, Player in yellow & blue, player in blue and red. 75c, Player in red & blue, player in yellow & black.

1p, Player down.

**1997, Mar. 25**

**3815** A1028 10c multicolored .25 .25
**3816** A1028 15c multicolored .30 .25
**3817** A1028 15c multicolored .30 .25
**3818** A1028 65c multicolored 1.25 1.00
**3819** A1028 75c multicolored 1.75 1.25
*Nos. 3815-3819 (5)* 3.85 3.00

**Souvenir Sheet**

**3820** A1028 1p multicolored 2.40 1.25

No. 3820 contains one 40x31mm stamp.

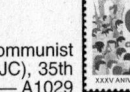

Young Communist League (UJC), 35th Anniv. — A1029

**1997, Apr. 4**

**3821** A1029 15c multicolored .75 .25

Paddle Steamer Caledonia A1030

Stamp Day: 15c, Maritime Postal Service, 170th anniv. 65c, Air Postal Service, 70th anniv.

**1997, Apr. 24 Litho. *Perf. 12½***

**3822** A1030 15c multicolored .40 .25
**3823** A1030 65c multicolored 1.60 .95

Death of Generals in War of 1895, 102nd Anniv. — A1031

No. 3824, Adolfo de Castillo, Enrique del Junco Cruz-Muñoz. No. 3825, Alberto Rodríguez Acosta, Mariano Sánchez Vaillant.

**1997, May 18 Litho. *Perf. 12½***

**3824** 15c multicolored .30 .25
**3825** 15c multicolored .30 .25
***a.*** A1031 Pair, #3824-3825 .65 .30

Gen. Gregorio Luperon, Death Cent. — A1032

**1997, May 20**

**3826** A1032 65c multicolored 1.50 1.00

Butterflies A1033

Designs: 10c, Eurema nicippe. No. 3828, Eurema dina. No. 3829, Colobura dirce clementi. 65c, Vanesa atalanta. 85c, Kricogonia castalia.

**1997, May 20**

**3827** A1033 10c multicolored .25 .25
**3828** A1033 15c multicolored .30 .25
**3829** A1033 15c multicolored .30 .25
**3830** A1033 65c multicolored 1.50 .90
**3831** A1033 85c multicolored 1.75 1.00
*Nos. 3827-3831 (5)* 4.10 2.65

Cuban Assoc. of the UN, 50th Anniv. — A1034

**1997, May 31**

**3832** A1034 65c multicolored 1.60 .95

Chinese In Cuba, 150th Anniv. — A1035

**1997, May 29 *Perf. 13***

**3833** A1035 15c multicolored 1.40 .50

14th World Festival of Youth and Students A1036

Designs: 10c, Dove holding olive twig, rainbow. No. 3835, Children playing on playground equipment, vert. No. 3836, Monument with arms extended. 65c, Maj. Ernesto "Che" Guevara, revolutionary hero. 75c, Monument, diff.

**1997, July 28 Litho. *Perf. 12½***

**3834** A1036 10c multicolored .25 .25
**3835** A1036 15c multicolored .30 .25
**3836** A1036 15c multicolored .30 .25
**3837** A1036 65c multicolored 1.50 .95
**3838** A1036 75c multicolored 1.75 1.00
*Nos. 3834-3838 (5)* 4.10 2.70

Frank País (1934-57), Revolutionary Hero — A1037

**1997, July 30**

**3839** A1037 15c multicolored .50 .25

Seven Wonders of the Ancient World — A1038

Designs: 10c, Lighthouse of Alexandria. No. 3841, Pyramids of Egypt. No. 3842, Gardens of Semiramis at Babylon. No. 3843, Colossus at Rhodes. No. 3844, Mausoleum of Halicarnassus. No. 3845, Statue of Zeus at Olympia. 75c, Temple of Artemis at Ephesus.

**1997, July 30**

**3840** A1038 10c multicolored .25 .25
**3841** A1038 15c multicolored .30 .25
**3842** A1038 15c multicolored .30 .25
**3843** A1038 15c multicolored .30 .25
**3844** A1038 65c multicolored 1.25 .95
**3845** A1038 65c multicolored 1.25 .95
**3846** A1038 75c multicolored 1.50 1.00
*Nos. 3840-3846 (7)* 5.15 3.90

Independence of India, 50th Anniv. — A1039

15c, Mahatma Gandhi.

**1997, Aug. 15**

**3847** A1039 15c multicolored .50 .25

Caribbean Birds — A1040

No. 3848, Sicalis flaveola. No. 3849, Eubucco bourcierii. No. 3850, Trogon curucui. No. 3851, Amazona leucocephala. No. 3852, Amazona ochrocephala. No. 3853, Hylocharis eliciae. No. 3854, Carduelis carduelis.

**1997, Aug. 15**

**3848** A1040 15c multicolored .30 .25
**3849** A1040 15c multicolored .30 .25
**3850** A1040 15c multicolored .30 .25
**3851** A1040 15c multicolored .30 .25
**3852** A1040 65c multicolored 1.40 1.00
**3853** A1040 65c multicolored 1.40 1.00
**3854** A1040 75c multicolored 1.60 1.10
*Nos. 3848-3854 (7)* 5.60 4.10

Famous Composers A1041

10c, Liszt. No. 3856, Chopin. No. 3857, Bach. No. 3858, Beethoven. 65c, Ignacio Cervantes (1847-1905). 75c, Mozart.

**1997, Sept. 15 Litho. *Perf. 12½***

**3855** A1041 10c multicolored .30 .25
**3856** A1041 15c multicolored .30 .25
**3857** A1041 15c multicolored .30 .25
**3858** A1041 15c multicolored .30 .25
**3859** A1041 65c multicolored 1.40 .95
**3860** A1041 75c multicolored 1.60 1.00
*Nos. 3855-3860 (6)* 4.20 2.95

Tourism in Pinar del Rio — A1042

Bird, scene: 10c, Myadestes elisabeth, Viñales Valley. 15c, Corvus nasicus, Jutia Key. 65c, Dendroica pityophila, Soroa Falls. 75c, Tyrannus cubensis, San Juan River.

**1997, Sept. 27 Litho.**

**3861** A1042 10c multi .40 .25
**3862** A1042 15c multi .40 .25
**3863** A1042 65c multi, vert. 1.60 .95
**3864** A1042 75c multi, vert. 1.75 1.00
*Nos. 3861-3864 (4)* 4.15 2.45

Caribbean Flowers A1043

Designs: No. 3865, Hibiscus elatus (majagua). No. 3866, Cordia sebestena (vomitel). No. 3867, Bidens pilosa (romerillo). No. 3868, Catharanthus roseus (vicaria). 65c, Reullia tuberosa (salta perico). 75c, Turnera ulmifolia (marilope).

**1997, Sept. 30**

**3865** A1043 15c multicolored .40 .25
**3866** A1043 15c multicolored .40 .25
**3867** A1043 15c multicolored .40 .25
**3868** A1043 15c multicolored .40 .25
**3869** A1043 65c multicolored 1.60 .95
**3870** A1043 75c multicolored 1.75 .95
*Nos. 3865-3870 (6)* 4.95 2.90

Eastern University, 50th Anniv. — A1044

**1997, Oct. 1 *Perf. 13***

**3871** A1044 15c multicolored .70 .25

Che Guevara (1928-67), 5th Cuban Communist Party Congress — A1045

No. 3872, Flags. No. 3873, Text, Guevara. No. 3874, Portrait of Guevara.

**1997, Oct. 8**

| | | | | |
|---|---|---|---|---|
| **3872** | A1045 | 15c multi | .40 | .25 |
| **3873** | A1045 | 15c multi | 1.60 | .95 |
| **3874** | A1045 | 75c multi | 1.75 | .95 |
| | | *Nos. 3872-3874 (3)* | 3.75 | 2.15 |

America Issue — A1046

15c, 19th cent. postman. 65c, 20th cent. postman.

**1997, Oct. 12 Litho. *Perf. 13***

| | | | | |
|---|---|---|---|---|
| **3875** | A1046 | 15c multi | .50 | .25 |
| **3876** | A1046 | 65c multi | 1.40 | .85 |

Hominids A1047

Designs: 10c, Australopithecus. No. 3878, Pithecanthropus (Java man). No. 3879, Sinanthropus (Peking man). No. 3880, Neanderthal. 65c, Cro-magnon man. 75c, Oberkassel man.

**1997, Oct. 30 *Perf. 12½***

| | | | | |
|---|---|---|---|---|
| **3877** | A1047 | 10c multicolored | .30 | .25 |
| **3878** | A1047 | 15c multicolored | .30 | .25 |
| **3879** | A1047 | 15c multicolored | .30 | .25 |
| **3880** | A1047 | 15c multicolored | .30 | .25 |
| **3881** | A1047 | 65c multicolored | 1.25 | .95 |
| **3882** | A1047 | 75c multicolored | 1.50 | .95 |
| | | *Nos. 3877-3882 (6)* | 3.95 | 2.90 |

October Revolution, 80th Anniv. — A1048

**1997, Nov. 7 *Perf. 12½***

| | | | | |
|---|---|---|---|---|
| **3884** | A1048 | 75c multicolored | 1.50 | 1.00 |

Cuban Railroad, 160th Anniv. A1049

10c, John Bull, 1830, UK. No. 3886, Old Ironsides, Baldwin, 1832, US. No. 3887, Baldwin Pacific Type 4-6-2, 1910-13, US. 65c, TE.M4:1 diesel electric, 1970, USSR. 75c, TE.114-K, diesel electric, 1975, USSR.

**1997, Nov. 19 Litho. *Perf. 12½***

| | | | | |
|---|---|---|---|---|
| **3885** | A1049 | 10c multicolored | .25 | .25 |
| **3886** | A1049 | 15c multicolored | .30 | .25 |
| **3887** | A1049 | 15c multicolored | .30 | .25 |
| **3888** | A1049 | 65c multicolored | 1.60 | .95 |
| **3889** | A1049 | 75c multicolored | 1.75 | .95 |
| | | *Nos. 3885-3889 (5)* | 4.20 | 2.65 |

UN Conference on Commerce and Employment, Havana, 50th Anniv. — A1050

**1997, Nov. 21**

| | | | | |
|---|---|---|---|---|
| **3890** | A1050 | 65c multicolored | 1.40 | .95 |

Victor Manuel Garcia, Painter, Birth Cent. — A1051

**1997, Dec. 29 Litho. *Perf. 12½***

| | | | | |
|---|---|---|---|---|
| **3891** | A1051 | 15c #1553, Garcia | .55 | .25 |

Visit of Pope John Paul II — A1052

Pope John Paul II, different coats of arms, and: 65c, Havana Cathedral. 75c, Basilica of Our Lady of Charity, Cobre, vert.

No. 3894, vert: a, Pope John Paul II greeting Fidel Castro. b, Pope waving.

**1998, Jan. 18 Litho. *Perf. 12½***

| | | | | |
|---|---|---|---|---|
| **3892** | A1052 | 65c multicolored | 1.40 | .95 |
| **3893** | A1052 | 75c multicolored | 1.60 | .95 |

**Souvenir Sheet of 2**

| | | | | |
|---|---|---|---|---|
| **3894** | A1052 | 50c #a.-b. | 2.00 | 1.50 |

Nos. 3894a-3894b are 32x40mm.

Assassination of Jesus Menendez, 50th Anniv. — A1053

**1998, Jan. 22**

| | | | | |
|---|---|---|---|---|
| **3895** | A1053 | 15c multicolored | .55 | .25 |

1998 World Cup Soccer Championships, France A1054

Various soccer plays: 10c, 2 players. No. 3897, Player in black & yellow. No. 3898, Player on ground, 1 in striped shirt. No. 3899, 3 players, 2 in striped shirts. No. 3900, 3 players, 2 in blue shirts.

1p, Player with #11 on sleeve.

**1998, Feb. 10 Litho. *Perf. 12½***

| | | | | |
|---|---|---|---|---|
| **3896** | A1054 | 10c multi, vert. | .30 | .25 |
| **3897** | A1054 | 15c multi, vert. | .40 | .25 |
| **3898** | A1054 | 15c multi, vert. | .40 | .25 |
| **3899** | A1054 | 65c multi | 1.50 | 1.00 |
| **3900** | A1054 | 65c multi | 1.50 | 1.00 |
| | | *Nos. 3896-3900 (5)* | 4.10 | 2.75 |

**Souvenir Sheet**

***Perf. 13***

| | | | | |
|---|---|---|---|---|
| **3901** | A1054 | 1p multicolored | 2.25 | 1.50 |

No. 3901 contains one 40x32mm stamp.

Capt. Isabel Rubio Diaz, Medical Aide During Revolution, Death Cent. — A1055

**1998, Feb. 15 *Perf. 13***

| | | | | |
|---|---|---|---|---|
| **3902** | A1055 | 15c multicolored | .65 | .25 |

Brig. Gen. Vidal Ducasse Reeve (1852-98) — A1056

**1998, Feb. 19 *Perf. 12½***

| | | | | |
|---|---|---|---|---|
| **3903** | A1056 | 15c multicolored | .65 | .25 |

No. 3903 inscribed "Revee."

"Radio Rebelde," 40th Anniv. A1057

**1998, Feb. 23**

| | | | | |
|---|---|---|---|---|
| **3904** | A1057 | 15c multicolored | .65 | .25 |

Fire Engines A1058

Designs: 10c, 1901 Shand Mason & Co., London. No. 3906, 1905 Horse-drawn municipal fire wagon, Havana. No. 3907, 1921 American-La France Fire Engine Co. 65c, 1952 Chevrolet 6400, US. 75c, 1956 American-La France Foamite Co., US.

**1998, Mar. 10**

| | | | | |
|---|---|---|---|---|
| **3905** | A1058 | 10c multicolored | .30 | .25 |
| **3906** | A1058 | 15c multicolored | .35 | .25 |
| **3907** | A1058 | 15c multicolored | .35 | .25 |
| **3908** | A1058 | 65c multicolored | 1.40 | .90 |
| **3909** | A1058 | 75c multicolored | 1.60 | .90 |
| | | *Nos. 3905-3909 (5)* | 4.00 | 2.55 |

Protest of Baragua, 120th Anniv. A1059

**1998, Mar. 15**

| | | | | |
|---|---|---|---|---|
| **3910** | A1059 | 15c multicolored | .65 | .25 |

Victory at Cuito Cuanavale, Angola, 10th Anniv. — A1060

**1998, Mar. 23 Litho. *Perf. 12½***

| | | | | |
|---|---|---|---|---|
| **3911** | A1060 | 15c multicolored | .65 | .25 |

New Year 1998 (Year of the Tiger) — A1061

**1998, Mar. 30**

| | | | | |
|---|---|---|---|---|
| **3912** | A1061 | 15c multicolored | .65 | .25 |

Dogs — A1062

**1998, Apr. 15 Litho. *Perf. 12½***

| | | | | |
|---|---|---|---|---|
| **3913** | A1062 | 10c Chihuahua | .40 | .25 |
| **3914** | A1062 | 15c Beagle | .45 | .25 |
| **3915** | A1062 | 15c Xoloitzcuintle | .45 | .25 |
| **3916** | A1062 | 65c German pointer | 1.50 | 1.00 |
| **3917** | A1062 | 75c Chow chow | 1.75 | 1.25 |
| | | *Nos. 3913-3917 (5)* | 4.55 | 3.00 |

Evolution of the Chimpanzee A1063

Pan troglodytes and: 10c, Proconsul. No. 3919, Cranium. No. 3920, Right hand and foot. 65c, New-born chimpanzee. 75c, Map of Africa showing chimpanzee's range.

**1998, May 15 Litho. *Perf. 12½***

| | | | | |
|---|---|---|---|---|
| **3918** | A1063 | 10c multicolored | .35 | .25 |
| **3919** | A1063 | 15c multicolored | .35 | .25 |
| **3920** | A1063 | 15c multicolored | .35 | .25 |
| **3921** | A1063 | 65c multicolored | 1.50 | 1.25 |
| **3922** | A1063 | 75c multicolored | 1.60 | 1.25 |
| | | *Nos. 3918-3922 (5)* | 4.15 | 3.25 |

Lisbon '98, World Stamp Exhibition A1064

Deep sea fish: No. 3923, Raja batis. No. 3924, Eurypharynx pelecanoides. 65c, Caulophryne. 75c, Chauliodus sloani.

**1998, May 22 Litho. *Perf. 12½***

| | | | | |
|---|---|---|---|---|
| **3923** | A1064 | 15c multicolored | .30 | .25 |
| **3924** | A1064 | 15c multicolored | .30 | .25 |
| **3925** | A1064 | 65c multicolored | 1.25 | 1.10 |
| **3926** | A1064 | 75c multicolored | 1.50 | 1.25 |
| | | *Nos. 3923-3926 (4)* | 3.35 | 2.85 |

**Souvenir Sheet**

Juvalux '98, World Stamp Exhibition for Youth Philately and Postal History, Luxembourg — A1065

1p, Postman on bicycle.

**1998, May 20 Litho. *Perf. 12½***

| | | | | |
|---|---|---|---|---|
| **3927** | A1065 | 1p multi | 2.00 | 1.50 |

Federico Garcia Lorca (1898-1936), Poet — A1066

**1998, June 2**

| | | | | |
|---|---|---|---|---|
| **3928** | A1066 | 75c multicolored | 2.00 | 1.25 |

Intl. Year of the Oceans — A1067

No. 3929, Canarreos flower coral, coral crab, small fish. No. 3030, French angel fish, brain coral, gorgonia.

**1998, June 5**

| | | | | |
|---|---|---|---|---|
| **3929** | A1067 | 65c multicolored | 1.50 | 1.00 |
| **3930** | A1067 | 65c multicolored | 1.50 | 1.00 |
| *a.* | | Pair, #3929-3930 | 3.50 | 1.75 |

Diana, Princess of Wales (1961-97) — A1068

Various portraits, color of clothes: No. 3931, Pale yellow and pink. No. 3932, Black and white. No. 3933, Multicolored print. No. 3934, Red. No. 3935, Pink and black plaid. 65c, White. 75c, Blue.

**1998, June 30** **Litho.** ***Perf. 13***

| | | | | |
|---|---|---|---|---|
| **3931** | A1068 10c multicolored | .30 | .25 |
| **3932** | A1068 10c multicolored | .30 | .25 |
| **3933** | A1068 10c multicolored | .30 | .25 |
| **3934** | A1068 15c multicolored | .40 | .25 |
| **3935** | A1068 15c multicolored | .40 | .25 |
| **3936** | A1068 65c multicolored | 1.90 | 1.10 |
| **3937** | A1068 75c multicolored | 2.10 | 1.25 |
| *a.* | Sheet of 7, #3931-3937 + tabs | 12.50 | — |
| | *Nos. 3931-3937 (7)* | 5.70 | 3.60 |

Expo 2000, Hanover A1069

No. 3938, Mascot, "Twipsy." No. 3939, Mascot in London, 1851. No. 3940, Mascot in Brussels, 1958. No. 3941, German flag, map of Germany. 65c, Mascot in Paris, 1889. 75c, Mascot on top of world, fireworks.

**1998, July 31** ***Perf. 12½***

| | | | |
|---|---|---|---|
| **3938** | A1069 15c multi, vert. | .40 | .25 |
| **3939** | A1069 15c multi | .40 | .25 |
| **3940** | A1069 15c multi | .40 | .25 |
| **3941** | A1069 15c multi | .40 | .25 |
| **3942** | A1069 65c multi, vert. | 1.40 | 1.00 |
| **3943** | A1069 75c multi | 1.60 | 1.25 |
| | *Nos. 3938-3943 (6)* | 4.60 | 3.25 |

Maracaibo '98, 18th Central America and Caribbean Games A1070

**1998, Aug. 8**

**3944** A1070 15c multicolored .50 .25

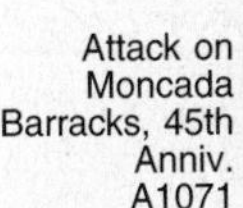

Attack on Moncada Barracks, 45th Anniv. A1071

Designs: 15c, Siboney farmhouse, Abel Santamaría. 65c, Barracks, José Marti.

**1998, July 26** **Litho.** ***Perf. 13***

**3945** A1071 15c multicolored .40 .25
**3946** A1071 65c multicolored 1.60 .95

Democratic Republic of Korea, 50th Anniv. — A1072

75c, Kim Il Sung (1912-94).

**1998, Sept. 8** **Litho.** ***Perf. 13***

**3947** A1072 75c multi 1.75 1.10

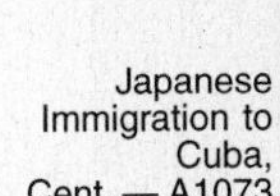

Japanese Immigration to Cuba, Cent. — A1073

**1998, Sept. 9** **Litho.** ***Perf. 13***

**3948** A1073 75c multicolored 1.75 1.10

Orchids — A1074

10c, Coelogyne flaccida. No. 3950, Dendrobium fimbriatum. No. 3951, Arunding graminifolia. No. 3952, Bletia patula. No. 3953, Phaius tankervilliaea.

**1998, Sept. 10**

| | | | |
|---|---|---|---|
| **3949** | A1074 10c multicolored | .30 | .25 |
| **3950** | A1074 15c multicolored | .40 | .25 |
| **3951** | A1074 15c multicolored | .40 | .25 |
| **3952** | A1074 65c multicolored | 1.50 | .75 |
| **3953** | A1074 65c multicolored | 1.50 | .75 |
| | *Nos. 3949-3953 (5)* | 4.10 | 2.25 |

5th Congress of the Revolution Defense Committees — A1075

**1998, Sept. 25** **Litho.** ***Perf. 13***

**3954** A1075 15c multicolored .45 .25

World Tourism Day — A1076

Holguin Province, reptiles: 10c, Looking through gateway, city of Gibara, anolis equestris, vert. 15c, Mayabe Valley, anolis vermiculatus, vert. 65c, Guardalavaca Beach, anolis allisoni. 75c, Mayari pine forest, anolis mestrei.

**1998, Sept. 27**

| | | | |
|---|---|---|---|
| **3955** | A1076 10c multicolored | .30 | .25 |
| **3956** | A1076 15c multicolored | .50 | .25 |
| **3957** | A1076 65c multicolored | 1.50 | .75 |
| **3958** | A1076 75c multicolored | 1.75 | 1.00 |
| | *Nos. 3955-3958 (4)* | 4.05 | 2.25 |

Women Who Aided Cuban Revolutionary Movements — A1077

America Issue: 65c, Bernarda Toro Pelegrin (1852-1911). 75c, Maria Magdalena Cabrales Isaac (1842-1905).

**1998, Oct. 12**

**3959** A1077 65c multicolored 1.40 .75
**3960** A1077 75c multicolored 1.60 .85

World Wildlife Fund Protected Fauna — A1078

Arantinga Euops: 10c, Two on tree branch. 15c, One looking out of nest. 65c, One on tree branch. 75c, One up close.

**1998, Oct. 21**

| | | | |
|---|---|---|---|
| **3961** | A1078 10c multicolored | .40 | .25 |
| **3962** | A1078 15c multicolored | .55 | .25 |
| **3963** | A1078 65c multicolored | 2.50 | .90 |
| **3964** | A1078 75c multicolored | 2.90 | 1.00 |
| *a.* | Strip of 4, #3961-3964 | 9.00 | — |
| | *Nos. 3961-3964 (4)* | 6.35 | 2.40 |

Cuban Natl. Ballet, 50th Anniv. — A1079

**1998, Oct. 28**

**3965** A1079 15c Swan Lake .50 .25
**3966** A1079 65c Giselle 1.40 .95

Massacre of O'Farrill and Goicuria, 40th Anniv. A1080

Rogelio Perea, Angel Ameijeiras, Pedro Gutiérrez.

**1998, Nov. 8**

**3967** A1080 15c multicolored .45 .25

Battle of Guisa, 40th Anniv. — A1081

Design: Capt. Braulio Coroneaux, tank.

**1998, Nov. 30** **Litho.** ***Perf. 12½***

**3968** A1081 15c multicolored .45 .25

A1082

**1998, Dec. 10** **Litho.** ***Perf. 12½***

**3969** A1082 65c multicolored 1.50 .95

Universal Declaration of Human Rights, 50th anniv.

A1083

Calixto Garcia Iñiguez (1839-98), revolutionary Major General.

**1998, Dec. 11** ***Perf. 13***

**3970** A1083 65c multicolored 1.50 .95

Padre Félix Varela (1788-1853) A1084

**1998, Dec. 16**

**3971** A1084 75c multicolored 1.90 1.10

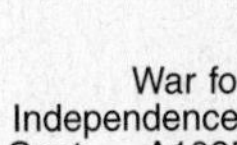

War for Independence, Cent. — A1085

War heroes, historical scene: No. 3972, Carlos Manuel de Céspedes. No. 3973, Ignacio Agramonte. No. 3974, Máximo Gómez. No. 3975, José Maceo. No. 3976, Salvador Cisneros. No. 3977, Calixto Garcia. No. 3978, Adolfo Flor. No. 3979, Serafin Sánchez. 65c, José Martí. 75c, Antonio Maceo.

**1998, Dec. 25** **Litho.** ***Perf. 12½***

| | | | |
|---|---|---|---|
| **3972** | A1085 15c multicolored | .30 | .25 |
| **3973** | A1085 15c multicolored | .30 | .25 |
| **3974** | A1085 15c multicolored | .30 | .25 |
| **3975** | A1085 15c multicolored | .30 | .25 |
| **3976** | A1085 15c multicolored | .30 | .25 |
| **3977** | A1085 15c multicolored | .30 | .25 |
| **3978** | A1085 15c multicolored | .30 | .25 |
| **3979** | A1085 15c multicolored | .30 | .25 |
| **3980** | A1085 65c multicolored | 1.40 | .75 |
| **3981** | A1085 75c multicolored | 1.75 | 1.00 |
| *a.* | Sheet of 10, #3972-3981 + 3 labels | 10.00 | 10.00 |
| | *Nos. 3972-3981 (10)* | 5.55 | 3.75 |

No. 3981a was initially issued with "como ellos" in the label inscription instead of "como nosotros." The error was caught quickly, and the sheet was reissued Jan. 5, 1999. Very few error sheets exist in collector hands. Value $1,100.

Battle for Palma Soriano, 40th Anniv. — A1086

**1998, Dec. 27** **Litho.** ***Perf. 13***

**3982** A1086 15c multicolored .45 .25

Cuban Revolution, 40th Anniv. — A1087

a, Boat, soldiers in water. b, Fidel Castro with soldier. c, Castro giving speech, pigeons.

**1999, Jan. 1**

**3983** A1087 65c Strip of 3, #a.-c. 4.00 2.40

Natl. Revolutionary Police, 40th Anniv. A1088

**1999, Jan. 5**

**3984** A1088 15c multicolored .60 .25

Cuban Workers' Trade Union Organization, 60th Anniv. — A1089

**1999, Jan. 28** **Litho.** ***Perf. 12½***

**3985** A1089 15c multicolored .45 .25

New Year 1999 (Year of the Rabbit) — A1090

**1999, Feb. 5** ***Perf. 13***

**3986** A1090 75c multicolored 2.60 1.25

Lenin (1870-1924)
A1091

**1999, Feb. 21 Litho. *Perf. 12½***

| | | | | |
|---|---|---|---|---|
| **3987** | A1091 75c multicolored | | 1.75 | 1.10 |

Dinosaurs
A1092

**1999, Mar. 10**

| | | | | |
|---|---|---|---|---|
| **3988** | A1092 10c Ornithosuchus | | .30 | .25 |
| **3989** | A1092 15c Saltopus | | .50 | .25 |
| **3990** | A1092 15c Bactrosaurus | | .50 | .25 |
| **3991** | A1092 65c Protosuchus | | 1.50 | .95 |
| **3992** | A1092 75c Mussaurus | | 1.75 | 1.10 |
| | *Nos. 3988-3992 (5)* | | 4.55 | 2.80 |

Cuban Musicians
A1093

No. 3993, Dámaso Pérez Prado. No. 3994, Benny Moré. No. 3995, Chano Pozo. No. 3996, Miguelito Valdés. No. 3997, Bola de Nieve. No. 3998, Rita Montaner.

**1999, Mar. 22 *Perf. 13***

| | | | |
|---|---|---|---|
| **3993** | A1093 5c multi | .25 | .25 |
| **3994** | A1093 15c multi | .40 | .25 |
| **3995** | A1093 15c multi | .40 | .25 |
| **3996** | A1093 35c multi | .90 | .50 |
| **3997** | A1093 65c multi | 1.50 | .95 |
| **3998** | A1093 75c multi | 1.75 | 1.10 |
| | *Nos. 3993-3998 (6)* | 5.20 | 3.30 |

Simón Bolivar's Visit to Cuba, Bicent. — A1094

**1999, Mar. 25**

| | | | |
|---|---|---|---|
| **3999** | A1094 65c Portrait | 1.50 | .95 |
| **4000** | A1094 65c Monument | 1.50 | .95 |
| *a.* | Pair, #3999-4000 | 3.50 | 2.00 |

State Security Organization, 40th Anniv. — A1095

**1999, Mar. 26 Litho. *Perf. 12½***

| | | | |
|---|---|---|---|
| **4001** | A1095 65c multicolored | 1.90 | .95 |

Souvenir Sheet

China '99 World Philatelic Exhibition — A1096

**1999, Apr. 10 Litho. *Perf. 12½***

| | | | |
|---|---|---|---|
| **4002** | A1096 1p Giant panda | 2.75 | 1.50 |

Stamp Day — A1097

**1999, Apr. 24**

| | | | |
|---|---|---|---|
| **4003** | A1097 15c Postal rocket | .50 | .25 |
| **4004** | A1097 65c Post rider | 1.50 | .80 |

Test of Cuban Postal Rocket, 60th anniv. Insurgent Postal Service, 130th anniv.

Casa de las Américas, 40th Anniv.
A1098

**1999, Apr. 24**

| | | | |
|---|---|---|---|
| **4005** | A1098 65c multicolored | 2.00 | .80 |

Souvenir Sheet

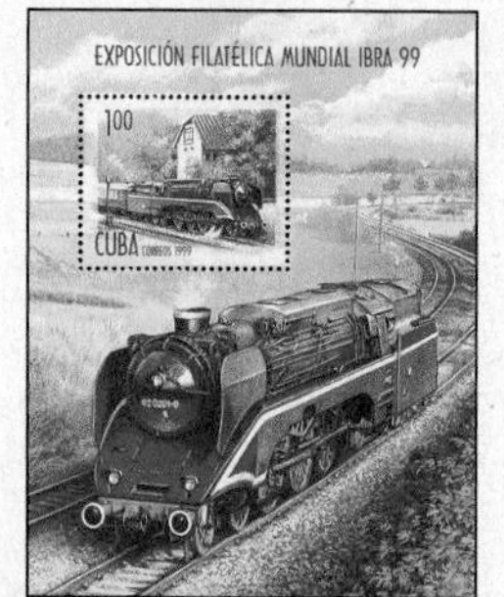

IBRA '99, World Philatelic Exhibition, Nuremberg — A1099

**1999, Apr. 27**

| | | | |
|---|---|---|---|
| **4006** | A1099 1p Train | 3.00 | 1.50 |

Agrarian Reform Law, 40th Anniv. — A1100

**1999, May 17**

| | | | |
|---|---|---|---|
| **4007** | A1100 65c multicolored | 1.50 | .80 |

Felipe Poey, Scientist, Birth Bicent.
A1101

Fish: 5c, Gramma loreto Poey. 15c, Liopropoma rubre Poey. No. 4010, Hypoplectrus gummigutta. No. 4011, Stegastes dorsopunicans.

1p, Portrait of Poey, hypoplectrus guttavarius.

**1999, May 26 Litho. *Perf. 12½***

| | | | |
|---|---|---|---|
| **4008** | A1101 5c multicolored | .25 | .25 |
| **4009** | A1101 15c multicolored | .40 | .25 |
| **4010** | A1101 65c multicolored | 1.90 | .80 |
| **4011** | A1101 65c multicolored | 1.90 | .80 |
| | *Nos. 4008-4011 (4)* | 4.45 | 2.10 |

**Souvenir Sheet**

***Perf. 13¼x13***

| | | | |
|---|---|---|---|
| **4012** | A1101 1p multicolored | 3.00 | 1.00 |

No. 4012 contains one 32x40mm stamp.

Souvenir Sheet

Philexfrance '99, World Philatelic Exhibition — A1102

Sculpture in sheet margin: "1814," by Jean Louis Meissonier (1815-1891).

**1999, June 2 *Perf. 13***

| | | | |
|---|---|---|---|
| **4013** | A1102 1p multicolored | 3.00 | 1.50 |

1999 Pan-American Games, Winnipeg
A1103

**1999, June 25 Litho. *Perf. 13***

| | | | |
|---|---|---|---|
| **4014** | A1103 15c Baseball | .40 | .25 |
| **4015** | A1103 65c Volleyball, vert | 1.50 | .80 |
| **4016** | A1103 75c Boxing | 1.75 | .90 |
| | *Nos. 4014-4016 (3)* | 3.65 | 1.95 |

People's Republic of China, 50th Anniv. — A1104

5c, Victory at Wioming, by Gao Hong. 15c, Nanchang Insurrection, by Cai Lang. 40c, Red Army Crossing a Swamp, by Gao Quan. 65c, Occupation of the Presidential Palace, by Cheng Yifei and Wei Jingshan. 75c, Proclamation of the People's Republic of China, by Dong Xiwen.

**1999, Aug. 21 Litho. *Perf. 12¾***

| | | | |
|---|---|---|---|
| **4017** | A1104 5c multicolored | .25 | .25 |
| **4018** | A1104 15c multicolored | .40 | .25 |
| **4019** | A1104 40c multicolored | 1.00 | .70 |
| **4020** | A1104 65c multicolored | 1.40 | 1.00 |
| **4021** | A1104 75c multicolored | 1.60 | 1.25 |
| | *Nos. 4017-4021 (5)* | 4.65 | 3.45 |

China 1999 World Philatelic Exhibition, Beijing
A1105

No. 4022, Morning Glories, by Qi Baishi. No. 4023, Three Galloping Horses, by Xu Beihong. No. 4024, Hunan Woman, by Fu Baoshi. No. 4025, Birthplace of Luxun, by Wu Guanzhong. No. 4026, Horse Riders, by Huangzhou. 40c, Pine Tree, by He Xiangning. 65c, Sleep, by Jin Shangyi. 75c, Poetic Scene in Xun Yang, by Chen Yifei.

**1999, Aug. 22 Litho. *Perf. 13***

| | | | |
|---|---|---|---|
| **4022** | A1105 5c multicolored | .25 | .25 |
| **4023** | A1105 5c multicolored | .25 | .25 |
| **4024** | A1105 15c multicolored | .35 | .25 |
| **4025** | A1105 15c multicolored | .35 | .25 |
| **4026** | A1105 15c multicolored | .35 | .25 |
| **4027** | A1105 40c multicolored | 1.00 | .70 |
| **4028** | A1105 65c multicolored | 1.40 | 1.10 |
| **4029** | A1105 75c multicolored | 1.60 | 1.25 |
| *a.* | Sheet of 8, #4022-4029 + label | 8.50 | 8.50 |
| | *Nos. 4022-4029 (8)* | 5.55 | 4.30 |

UPU, 125th Anniv. — A1106

**1999, Sept. 16 Litho. *Perf. 12¾***

| | | | |
|---|---|---|---|
| **4030** | A1106 75c multicolored | 1.00 | .75 |

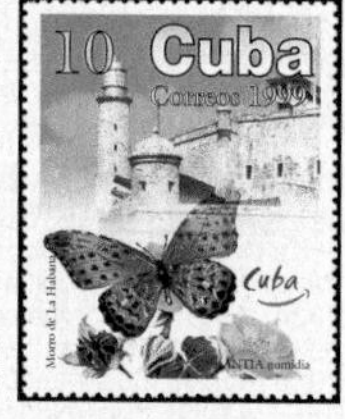

World Tourism Day — A1107

Butterflies and Havana tourist sites: 10c, Antia numidia, Morro Castle. 15c, Papilio polyxenes, Havana Cathedral. 65c, Dryas julia, Convent of San Francisco. 75c, Eueides cleobaea, Capitol.

**1999, Sept. 27 *Perf. 12½x12¾***

| | | | |
|---|---|---|---|
| **4031** | A1107 10c multicolored | .25 | .25 |
| **4032** | A1107 15c multicolored | .60 | .25 |
| **4033** | A1107 65c multicolored | 2.00 | 1.00 |
| **4034** | A1107 75c multicolored | 2.50 | 1.10 |
| | *Nos. 4031-4034 (4)* | 5.35 | 2.60 |

Expo 2000, Hanover, Germany
A1108

5c, World map, Expo 2000 emblem. No. 4036, "Twipsy" mascot, vert. No. 4037, "Twipsy" and 1876 Philadelphia Exposition. No. 4038, "Twipsy" and 1970 Osaka Exposition. 65c, "Twipsy" and 2000 Exposition. 75c, "Twipsy" and 1967 Montreal Exposition.

**1999, Oct. 1 *Perf. 12¾***

| | | | |
|---|---|---|---|
| **4035** | A1108 5c multicolored | .25 | .25 |
| **4036** | A1108 15c multicolored | .35 | .25 |
| **4037** | A1108 15c multicolored | .35 | .25 |
| **4038** | A1108 15c multicolored | .35 | .25 |
| **4039** | A1108 65c multicolored | 1.60 | 1.00 |
| **4040** | A1108 75c multicolored | 2.00 | 1.10 |
| | *Nos. 4035-4040 (6)* | 4.90 | 3.10 |

Cubana Airlines, 70th Anniv.
A1109

**1999, Oct. 8 *Perf. 12½x12¼***

| | | | |
|---|---|---|---|
| **4041** | A1109 15c Fokker | .35 | .25 |
| **4042** | A1109 15c DC-10 | .35 | .25 |
| **4043** | A1109 65c A-320 | 1.60 | 1.00 |
| **4044** | A1109 75c DC-3 | 2.00 | 1.10 |
| | *Nos. 4041-4044 (4)* | 4.30 | 2.60 |

America Issue, A New Millennium Without Arms — A1110

15c, Pigeon, mushroom cloud. 65c, Dove, globe.

**1999, Oct. 12 *Perf. 12¾***

| | | | |
|---|---|---|---|
| **4045** | A1110 15c multi | .40 | .25 |
| **4046** | A1110 65c multi | 1.25 | 1.10 |

National Instiutions, 40th Anniv. — A1111

15c, MINFAR. 65c, Natl. Revolutionary Militia.

**1999, Oct. 16** *Perf. 12¾*
**4047** A1111 15c multi .35 .25
**4048** A1111 65c multi 1.00 .75

Disappearance of Camilo Cienfuegos, 40th Anniv. — A1112

**1999, Oct. 28** **Litho.** *Perf. 12¾*
**4049** A1112 15c multicolored 1.00 .25

Souvenir Sheet

12th Congress of Cuban Philatelic Federation — A1113

**1999, Dec. 11** *Perf. 13*
**4050** A1113 1p multicolored 2.00 1.25

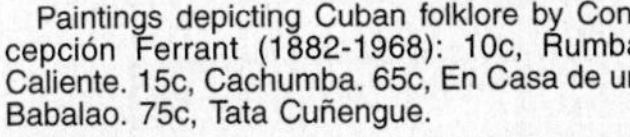
Ernest Hemingway (1899-1961), Writer A1114

**1999, Dec. 15** *Perf. 12½x12¼*
**4051** A1114 65c multicolored 1.75 1.00

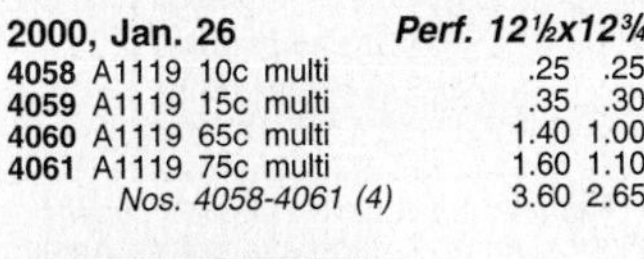
9th Summit of Ibero-American Heads of State and Government, Havana — A1115

Designs: 65c, Plaza Vieja. 75c, Plaza of St. Francis of Assisi.
1p, Plaza de Armas.

**1999, Nov. 5** **Litho.** *Perf. 12¾x12½*
**4052** A1115 65c multi .90 .75
**4053** A1115 75c multi 1.10 1.00

**Souvenir Sheet**
*Perf. 13*
**4054** A1115 1p multi 1.50 1.25
No. 4054 contains one 40x31mm stamp.

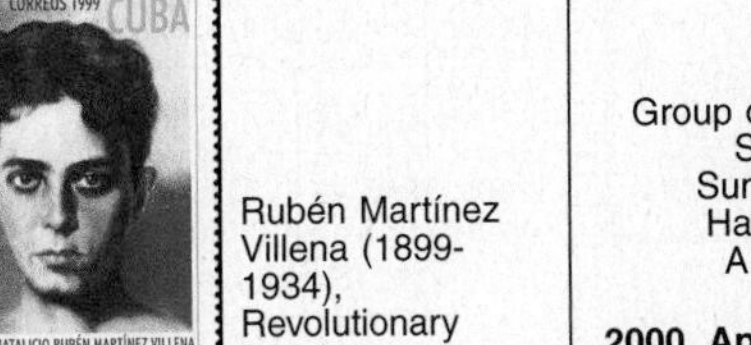
Rubén Martínez Villena (1899-1934), Revolutionary A1116

**1999, Dec. 20** *Perf. 12½x12¾*
**4055** A1116 15c multi .40 .25

Dr. Tomás Romay Chacón (1764-1849) — A1117

**1999, Dec. 21** *Perf. 13*
**4056** A1117 65c multi 1.00 .90

New Year 2000 (Year of the Dragon) A1118

**2000, Jan. 10** *Perf. 12½*
**4057** A1118 15c multi .75 .25

Folklore — A1119

Paintings depicting Cuban folklore by Concepción Ferrant (1882-1968): 10c, Rumba Caliente. 15c, Cachumba. 65c, En Casa de un Babalao. 75c, Tata Cuñengue.

**2000, Jan. 26** *Perf. 12½x12¾*
**4058** A1119 10c multi .25 .25
**4059** A1119 15c multi .35 .30
**4060** A1119 65c multi 1.40 1.00
**4061** A1119 75c multi 1.60 1.10
*Nos. 4058-4061 (4)* 3.60 2.65

Butterflies A1120

10c, Helcyra superba. No. 4063, Pantaporia punctata. No. 4064, Neptis themis. 65c, Curetis acuta. 75c, Chrysozephyrus ataxus.

**2000, Feb. 25** *Perf. 12¾*
**4062** A1120 10c multi .30 .25
**4063** A1120 15c multi .40 .30
**4064** A1120 15c multi .40 .30
**4065** A1120 65c multi 1.40 1.25
**4066** A1120 75c multi 1.60 1.40
*Nos. 4062-4066 (5)* 4.10 3.50
Bangkok 2000 Stamp Exhibition.

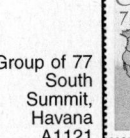

Group of 77 South Summit, Havana A1121

**2000, Apr. 7** **Litho.** *Perf. 13x12½*
**4067** A1121 75c multi 2.00 1.25

Lenin, 130th Anniv. of Birth — A1122

**2000, Apr. 22** *Perf. 12¾*
**4068** A1122 75c multi 1.90 1.25

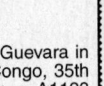

Che Guevara in Congo, 35th Anniv. — A1123

**2000, Apr. 24**
**4069** A1123 65c multi 1.75 1.10

Stamp Day — A1124

Designs: 65c, Cuba #2, building. 90c, Airplane, cover, Jaime González, pilot of first experimental airmail flight in Cuba.

**2000, Apr. 24**
**4070** A1124 65c multi 1.50 1.10
**4071** A1124 90c multi 2.00 1.50

Capt. San Luis (Eliseo Reyes), Military Hero (1940-67) — A1125

**2000, Apr. 27**
**4072** A1125 65c multi 1.60 1.00

The Stamp Show 2000, London A1126

Locomotives: 5c, 1882 Baldwin 0-6-0. 10c, 1895 Baldwin 2-8-0. 15c, 1912 Baldwin 2-8-0. 65c, 1919 Alco 2-8-0. 75c, 1925 Alco 2-8-2.
1p, 1920 Henschel 2-6-0.

**2000, May 5** *Perf. 12¾*
**4073** A1126 5c multi .25 .25
**4074** A1126 10c multi .30 .25
**4075** A1126 15c multi .40 .30
**4076** A1126 65c multi 1.60 1.10
**4077** A1126 75c multi 1.90 1.25
*Nos. 4073-4077 (5)* 4.45 3.15

**Souvenir Sheet**
*Perf. 13*
**4078** A1126 1p multi 3.00 1.50
No. 4078 contains one 40x32mm stamp.

WIPA 2000 Philatelic Exhibition, Vienna A1127

Airships of: 10c, Henri Giffard, 1852. 15c, Albert and Gaston Tissandier, 1883, vert. 50c, Charles Renard and Arthur Krebs, 1884. 65c, Pierre and Paul Lebaudy, 1903. 75c, August von Perseval, 1906.
1p, Ferdinand von Zeppelin.

*Perf. 12½x12¼, 12¼x12½*
**2000, May 18**
**4079** A1127 10c multi .35 .25
**4080** A1127 15c multi .50 .30
**4081** A1127 50c multi 1.40 .90
**4082** A1127 65c multi 1.90 1.10
**4083** A1127 75c multi 2.10 1.25
*Nos. 4079-4083 (5)* 6.25 3.80

**Souvenir Sheet**
*Perf. 12½*
**4084** A1127 1p multi 3.00 1.50
No. 4084 contains one 40x32mm stamp.

Second World Meeting of Friendship and Solidarity With Cuba — A1128

**2000, June 23** **Litho.** *Perf. 12¾*
**4085** A1128 65c multi 1.50 1.10

José de la Luz y Caballero (1800-62), Educator A1129

**2000, July 11** *Perf. 12½x12¼*
**4086** A1129 65c multi 1.50 1.10

Amadeo Roldan (1900-39), Violinist A1130

**2000, July 12** *Perf. 12¾*
**4087** A1130 65c multi 1.50 1.10

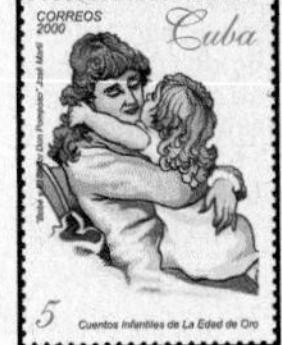
La Edad de Oro, by José Marti — A1131

5c, Bebé y El Señor Don Pomposo. 10c, La Muñeca Negra. 15c, Nene Traviesa. 50c, Los Dos Ruiseñores. 65c, Frontispiece of La Edad de Oro. 75c, El Camarón Encantado.

**2000, July 20**
**4088-4093** A1131 Set of 6 5.00 4.25
*4093a* Sheet of 6, #4088-4093 7.00 7.00

Latin American Association for Integration A1132

**2000, Aug. 12**
**4094** A1132 65c multi 1.50 1.25

Souvenir Sheet

Olymphilex 2000, Sydney — A1133

**2000, Aug. 17** *Perf. 13*
**4095** A1133 1p multi 2.25 1.10

2000 Summer Olympics, Sydney — A1134

Designs: 5c, Runners. 15c, Soccer. 65c, Baseball. 75c, Cycling.

**2000, Aug. 20** *Perf. 12¾*
**4096-4099** A1134 Set of 4 4.00 4.00

Dr. Pedro Kouri Esmeja (1900-64) — A1135

**2000, Aug. 21** **Litho.**
**4100** A1135 65c multi 1.50 1.25

Federation of Cuban Women, 40th Anniv. — A1136

**2000, Aug. 23**
**4101** A1136 15c multi .40 .30

España 2000 Intl. Philatelic Exhibition A1137

Designs: 10c, 1851 Havana-Bilbao stampless cover, ship. No. 4103, 15c, Spain #1, Cibeles Fountain, Madrid. No. 4104, 15c, 1850 Zaragoza-Cadiz cover, Palacio de Cristal, Madrid. 65c, Spain #1-5, Palacio de Comunicaciones, Madrid. 75c, Cuba #1, Centro Gallego, Havana.

**2000, Sept. 7** ***Perf. 12¾x12½***
**4102-4106** A1137 Set of 5 4.00 3.00
*4106a* Sheet of 5, #4102-4106 + label 4.75 4.75

**Souvenir Sheet**

***Perf. 12½***

**4107** A1137 100c Queen Isabella II, vert. 3.00 2.25

No. 4107 contains one 32x40mm stamp.

Beaches A1138

No. 4108, Coconuts Bay, PRC. No. 4109, Varadero Beach, Cuba.

**2000, Sept. 26** ***Perf. 12½x12¼***
**4108-4109** A1138 15c Set of 2 .60 .60
*4109a* Pair, #4108-4109 .80 .80

See People's Republic of China No. 3052.

World Tourism Day — A1139

Marine Life: 10c, Eretmochelys imbricata, vert. 15c, Epinephelus striatus, vert. 65c, Pomacanthus paru. 75c, Anisotremus surinamensis.

***Perf. 12½x12¾, 12¾x12½***

**2000, Sept. 27**
**4110-4113** A1139 Set of 4 3.50 2.00

Committees of Defense of the Revolution, 40th Anniv. — A1140

**2000, Sept. 28** ***Perf. 12¾***
**4114** A1140 15c multi .60 .30

America Issue — AIDS Prevention — A1141

Ribbon, heart-shaped map and: 15c, Family. 65c, Couple.

**2000, Oct. 12**
**4115-4116** A1141 Set of 2 2.00 1.25

Cuban Military in Angola, 25th Anniv. — A1142

**2000, Nov. 7**
**4117** A1142 75c multi 1.90 1.40

Visit by Alexander von Humboldt, Bicent. A1143

Humboldt and: 15c, House in Trinidad. 65c, House in Havana, Political Essay on the Island of Cuba.

**2000, Dec. 19** **Litho.** ***Perf. 12¾***
**4118-4119** A1143 Set of 2 2.00 1.25

20th Pan-American Railway Congress — A1144

**2000, Sept. 18** **Litho.** ***Perf. 12¾***
**4120** A1144 65c multi 1.50 1.25

Millennium — A1145

Snails: a, Polymita versicolor. b, Polymita picta iolimbata. c, Polymita picta roseolimbata. d, Polymita picta picta. e, Polymita picta nigrolimbata.

**2000, Dec. 20**
**4121** A1145 65c Block of 5, #a-e, + label 7.00 4.00

New Year 2001 (Year of the Snake) A1146

**2001, Jan. 10**
**4122** A1146 15c multi .75 .25

Hong Kong 2001 Stamp Exhibition A1147

Birds: 5c, Aix galericulata. 10c, Chrysolophus pictus. 15c, Ardea cinerea. 65c, Gallus gallus. 75c, Streptotelia decaocto.
1p, Grus grus.

**2001, Jan. 25** ***Perf. 12¾***
**4123-4127** A1147 Set of 5 4.25 3.25

**Souvenir Sheet**

***Perf. 12½***

**4128** A1147 1p multi 3.00 1.25

No. 4128 contains one 32x40mm stamp.

National Institute for Sport Physical Education and Recreation, 40th Anniv. A1148

**2001, Feb. 23** ***Perf. 12½x12¼***
**4129** A1148 65c multi 1.60 .80

UN High Commissioner for Refugees, 50th Anniv. — A1149

**2001, Mar. 15** ***Perf. 12¾x12½***
**4130** A1149 65c multi 1.50 .75

Antique Locomotives A1150

Locomotives from, 10c, 1863. 15c, 1876. 40c, 1885. 65c, 1914. 75c, 1932.

**2001, Mar. 20** ***Perf. 12½x12¼***
**4131-4135** A1150 Set of 5 4.75 2.40

105th Interparliamentary Union Congress, Havana — A1151

**2001, Mar. 30** ***Perf. 12¾***
**4136** A1151 65c multi 1.75 .80

Bay of Pigs Invasion, 40th Anniv. A1152

**2001, Apr. 19** ***Perf. 12¾x12½***
**4137** A1152 65c multi 1.50 .75

Cats and Dogs — A1153

Designs: 10c, Cats, emblem of Cat Aficionados Association. No. 4139, 15c, Dogs, Cats, emblem of Aniplant. No. 4140, 15c, Dogs, emblem of Cynological Federation of Cuba. 65c, Dogs, emblem of Sporting Dog Federation of Cuba. 75c, Dogs, cats.

**2001, Apr. 25** ***Perf. 12½x12¾***
**4138-4142** A1153 Set of 5 4.00 2.00

Radio Havana, 40th Anniv. A1154

**2001, May 1** ***Perf. 12½x12¼***
**4143** A1154 65c multi 1.50 .75

Tourism Convention A1155

**2001, May 7** ***Perf. 12¾x12½***
**4144** A1155 65c multi 1.50 .75

Belgica 2001 Intl. Stamp Exhibition, Brussels — A1156

Designs: 5c, St. Michel Cathedral. 10c, Sablon Church, horiz. 15c, Royal Residence, horiz. 65c, Sacred Heart Basilica, horiz. 75c, Atomium.
1p, Royal Palace.

**2001, May 10** ***Perf. 12¾***
**4145-4149** A1156 Set of 5 4.00 2.00

**Souvenir Sheet**

***Perf. 12½***

**4150** A1156 100c multi 2.40 1.25

No. 4150 contains one 32x40mm stamp.

Interior Ministry, 40th Anniv. — A1157

**2001, June 6** ***Perf. 12¾***
**4151** A1157 65c multi 1.75 .80

Phila Nippon '01, Japan — A1158

Japanese trains: 5c., JR 500. 10c, JR 700. 15c, MAX 1. 65c, MAX 2. 75c, 300.

**2001, June 20** **Litho.** ***Perf. 12¾***
**4152-4156** A1158 Set of 5 3.75 1.50

**Souvenir Sheet**

***Perf. 12½***

**4157** A1158 100c Zero 2.40 1.25

No. 4157 contains one 40x32mm stamp.

Republic of San Marino, 1700th Anniv. A1159

**2001, July 20** **Litho.** ***Perf. 12½x12¼***
**4158** A1159 75c multi 1.75 .75

Aquaculture A1160

Designs: 5c, Tinca tinca. 10c, Rana temporaria. 15c, Cardisoma guanhumi. 65c, Mytilus edulis. 75c, Tilapia mariae.
1p, Potamobius pallipes.

**2001, Sept. 17** ***Perf. 12¾***
**4159-4163** A1160 Set of 5 3.75 1.50

**Souvenir Sheet**

***Perf. 12½***

**4164** A1160 1p multi 2.40 1.25

No. 4164 contains one 40x32mm stamp.

Recovery of Raw Materials, 40th Anniv. A1161

**2001, Sept. 21** ***Perf. 12¾x12½***
**4165** A1161 65c multi 1.60 .75

Tourism A1162

Designs: 10c, Valle de Viñales. 15c, Trinidad. 65c, Sirena Beach, Cayo Largo del Sur. 75c, Morro Castle, Havana.

**2001, Sept. 27**
**4166-4169** A1162 Set of 4 3.75 1.75

Year of Dialogue Among Civilizations — A1163

**2001, Oct. 9** ***Perf. 12¾***
**4170** A1163 65c multi 2.00 .75

America Issue — UNESCO World Heritage — A1164

Flora and fauna from Desembarco del Granma Natl. Park: 15c, Tetramicra malpighiarum. 65c, Liggus vittatus.

**2001, Oct. 12** ***Perf. 12½x12¾***
**4171-4172** A1164 Set of 2 1.75 .85

José Marti National Library, Cent. — A1165

**2001, Oct. 18** ***Perf. 12¾***
**4173** A1165 15c multi .45 .25

Cuban Airliner Explosion Near Barbados, 25th Anniv. — A1166

Various details of painting.

**2001, Oct. 22**
**4174** Horiz. strip of 5 3.25 1.60
*a.* A1166 5c shown .25 .25
*b.* A1166 10c multi .25 .25
*c.* A1166 15c multi .35 .25
*d.* A1166 50c multi 1.10 .55
*e.* A1166 65c multi 1.40 .90

Eduardo R. Chibas, Communist Leader, Cent. of Birth — A1167

**2001, Nov. 27** **Litho.** ***Perf. 13***
**4175** A1167 65c multi 1.60 .80

Napoleonic Museum, 40th Anniv. A1168

Equestrian statues of Napoleon and map of battle of: No. 4176, 10c, Eylau. No. 4177, 10c, Marengo. 65c, Waterloo. 75c, Aboukir.

**2001, Dec. 1** ***Perf. 12¾x12½***
**4176-4179** A1168 Set of 4 3.75 1.75

Pablo de la Torriente Brau (1901-36), Writer — A1169

**2001, Dec. 12** ***Perf. 12¾***
**4180** A1169 75c multi 1.75 .80

Cuban Federation of Pigeon Fanciers, 4th Congress A1170

Pigeons: No. 4181, 65c, Empedrado oscura 2021-61-ME. No. 4182, 65c, Empedrado claro 2241-55-ME. No. 4183, 65c, Mosaico 1561-66-HM. No. 4184, 65c, Mosaico, 3013-67-HM. No. 4185, 65c Bronceado, 338-59-HE.

**2001, Dec. 14** ***Perf. 12½***
**4181-4185** A1170 Set of 5 7.00 3.50

Film Stars Who Never Won Academy Awards — A1171

Designs: 5c, Tyrone Power. No. 4187, 10c, Ava Gardner. No. 4188, 10c, Steve McQueen. No. 4189, 15c, Rita Hayworth. No. 4190, 15c, Marilyn Monroe. No. 4191, 15c, James Dean. No. 4192, 65c, Rock Hudson. No. 4193, 65c, Natalie Wood. 75c, Richard Burton.

**2001, Dec. 20**
**4186-4194** A1171 Set of 9 6.75 3.50
*a.* Sheet of 9, #4186-4194 8.00 8.00

New Year 2002 (Year of the Horse) — A1172

**2002, Jan. 21** **Litho.** ***Perf. 12½x12¾***
**4195** A1172 15c multi .75 .30

Cigar Production A1173

Cigars and: 5c, Hat, Cuba No. 358, tobacco leaf. 10c, Clock, cigar cylinder. 15c, Map of Cuba, Simon Bolivar. 65c, Cuba Nos. 356, 357, map, cigar smoker. 75c, Flag, tobacco field, man.
1p, Fidel Castro, map, star.

**2002, Feb. 15** ***Perf. 12¾***
**4196-4200** A1173 Set of 5 3.75 2.00

**Souvenir Sheet**

***Perf. 1313¼***

**4201** A1173 1p multi 2.50 1.25

Fourth Havana Festival, Cohiba brand, 36th anniv. No. 4201 contains one 40x32mm stamp.

Second UPAEP Information Workshop — A1174

**2002, Feb. 21** ***Perf. 12½x12¼***
**4202** A1174 65c multi 1.50 .75

Explorers — A1175

Explorers: 5c, Reading map. 15c, Tying knots. 50c, Starting campfire for cooking. 65c, Starting fire. 75c, Using orientation techniques.

**2002, Mar. 20** ***Perf. 12½***
**4203-4207** A1175 Set of 5 5.00 2.50
*a.* Sheet of 5, #4203-4207, + label 7.00 7.00

Union of Young Communists, 40th Anniv. A1176

**2002, Apr. 4** ***Perf. 12½x12¼***
**4208** A1176 15c multi .45 .25

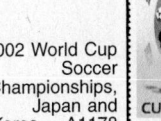

ExpoVid 2002 Wine Event A1177

Designs: 15c, Cigar smokers, wine bottles and glasses, map of wine producing areas. 65c, Wine glass and barrels. 75c, Wine glass and vineyard.

**2002, June 5** ***Perf. 12¾x12½***
**4209-4211** A1177 Set of 3 3.50 1.75

2002 World Cup Soccer Championships, Japan and Korea — A1178

Player and flag from: No. 4212, 15c, South Korea. No. 4213, 15c, France. No. 4214, 15c, Germany. No. 4215, 15c, Brazil. No. 4216, 15c, Spain. 65c, Argentina. 75c, Italy. 85c, Japan.

**2002, Apr. 21** **Litho.** ***Perf. 12½***
**4212-4219** A1178 Set of 8 6.50 3.25
*4219a* Sheet, #4212-4219 9.50 9.50

**Souvenir Sheet**

Hispano-Cubano Philatelic Exposition — A1179

**2002, Apr. 27** ***Perf. 13***
**4220** A1179 1p multi 2.25 1.10

Juan Tomas Roig, Botanist, 125th Anniv. of Birth — A1180

Designs: 5c, Bust of Roig, experimental agronomic station, Santiago de las Vegas. 10c, Bust and house of Roig. 15c, Roig, laboratory glassware and Nicotiana tabacum. 50c, Building, Allophyllum roiggi, and sculpture of Roig. 65c, Roig, laboratory glassware and botanical dictionary.

**2002, May 10** ***Perf. 12½x12¾***
**4221-4225** A1180 Set of 5 3.25 1.50
*4225a* Sheet, #4221-4225, + label 5.25 5.25

Medi Cuba Suiza — A1181

**2002, June 18** *Perf. 12¾x12½*
**4226** A1181 75c multi 1.60 .80

Mushrooms — A1182

Designs: 5c, Amanita junquillea. 15c, Lepiota puellaris. 45c, Cortinarius cumatilis. 65c, Pholliota adiposa. 75c, Coprinus comatus.

**2002, June 20** *Perf. 12¾*
**4227-4231** A1182 Set of 5 4.50 2.25
*4231a* Sheet, #4227-4231, + label 8.00 8.00

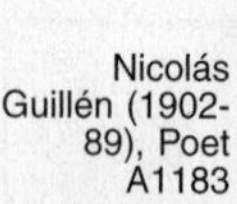

Nicolás Guillén (1902-89), Poet A1183

**2002, July 10** *Perf. 12¾x12½*
**4232** A1183 65c multi 1.75 .90

Dockers, By Marcelo Pogolotti (1902-88) — A1184

**2002, July 12** *Perf. 12¾*
**4233** A1184 15c multi .50 .30

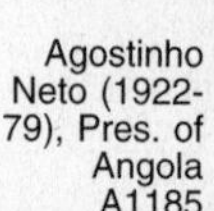

Agostinho Neto (1922-79), Pres. of Angola A1185

**2002, Sept. 17** *Perf. 12¾x12½*
**4234** A1185 65c multi 1.75 .90

España 2002 Youth Philatelic Exposition, Salamanca A1186

Birds: 5c, Calidris minutilla. 10c, Tringa melanoleucas. 15c, Charadius semipalmatus. 65c, Plurialis squatarola. 75c, Arenaria interpres.
1p, Porzana carolina.

**2002, Sept. 20** *Perf. 12½x12¼*
**4235-4239** A1186 Set of 5 4.50 2.25
*4239a* Sheet, #4235-4239, + label 6.00 6.00

**Souvenir Sheet**
*Perf. 13*

**4240** A1186 1p multi 2.50 1.25

No. 4240 contains one 40x31mm stamp.

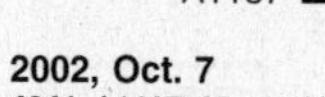

Third Intl. Meeting of War Correspondents A1187

**2002, Oct. 7** *Perf. 12¾*
**4241** A1187 65c multi 1.75 .90

Ernesto "Che" Guevara (1928-67), Revolutionary Leader — A1188

Various depictions of Guevara: 5c, 10c, 15c, 50c, 65c, 75c.

**2002, Oct. 8** **Litho.**
**4242-4247** A1188 Set of 6 5.25 2.75
*4247a* Sheet, #4242-4247 45.00 45.00

America Issue — Youth, Education and Literacy A1189

Designs: 15c, Emblem of Literacy Army, man with book, teacher with student. 65c, Building, flag, children at computer.

**2002, Oct. 12** *Perf. 12½x12¼*
**4248-4249** A1189 Set of 2 2.00 1.00

Old Automobiles A1190

Designs: No. 4250, 5c, 1956 Pontiac Catalina. No. 4251, 5c, 1957 Mercury Monterrey. 15c, 1959 Cadillac Fleetwood. 65c, Hudson Hornet. 75c, 1957 Chevrolet Bel Air. 85c, 1957 Mercedes-Benz 190SL.

**2002, Oct. 19** *Perf. 12¾*
**4250-4255** A1190 Set of 6 6.00 3.50
*a.* Sheet, #4250-4255, + 6 labels 17.00 17.00

15th Intercontinental Baseball Cup — A1191

Baseball players: 5c, G. Mesa. 15c, A. Pacheco. 50c, O. Linares. 65c, O. Kindelan. 75c, L. Ulacia.

**2002, Nov. 1**
**4256-4260** A1191 Set of 5 5.00 3.00
*4260a* Sheet of 5, #4256-4260 + 4 labels 17.00 17.00

20th Havana Intl. Fair — A1192

**2002, Nov. 3**
**4261** A1192 65c multi 1.75 .90

Railroads, 165th Anniv. A1193

Designs: 5c, Rocket. 15c, Miller. 50c, Vulcan. 65c, Consolidation. 75c, Mikado.

**2002, Nov. 12** *Perf. 12½x12¼*
**4262-4266** A1193 Set of 5 6.50 3.00
*4266a* Sheet, #4262-4266, + label 17.00 17.00

Camagüey Ballet, 35th Anniv. — A1194

Designs: 65c, Twelve dancers. 75c, Two dancers.

**2002, Dec. 1** *Perf. 12¾*
**4267-4268** A1194 Set of 2 3.25 2.00

Pan-American Health Organization, Cent. — A1195

**2002, Dec. 2**
**4269** A1195 65c multi 1.50 .90

Paintings of Wilfredo Lam (1902-82) — A1196

Designs: 15c, Emi Cosinca, 1950. 45c, Yo Soy, 1949. 65c, Retrado de H.H., 1941-42. 75c, Mujer Sentada, 1951.

**2002, Dec. 8** *Perf. 12¾*
**4270-4273** A1196 Set of 4 4.50 3.00
*4273a* Sheet, #4270-4273, + 4 labels 16.00 16.00

Dulce M. Loynaz (1902-97), Writer — A1197

*Perf. 12½x12¾*

**2002, Dec. 19** **Litho.**
**4274** A1197 65c multi 1.50 .90

**Souvenir Sheet**

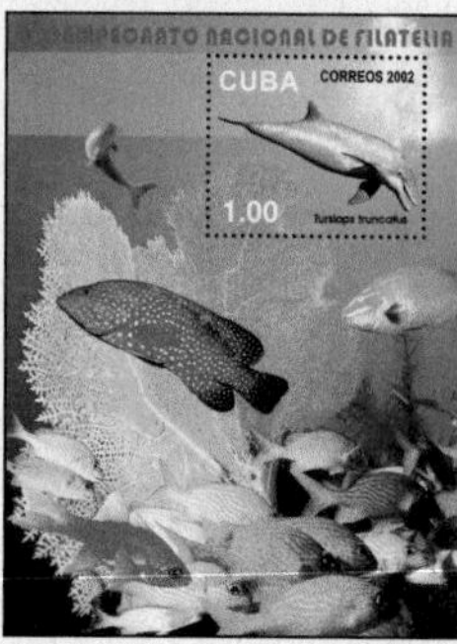


Tursiops Truncatus — A1198

**2002, Dec. 20** *Perf. 12½*
**4275** A1198 1p multi 3.00 1.50

Fifth National Philatelic Competition.

Prehistoric and Modern-Day Animals — A1199

Designs: 5c, Megaloceros, Cervus elaphus. 10c, Theropithecus, Papio anubis. 15c, Coelodonta, Diceros bicornis. 45c, Canis dirus, Canis lupus. 65c, Ursus spelaeus, Ursus arctos. 75c, Smilodon, Panthera leo.
1p, Mammuthus primigenius.

**2002, Dec. 27** *Perf. 12½x12¼*
**4276-4281** A1199 Set of 6 5.00 2.00

**Souvenir Sheet**
*Perf. 13*

**4282** A1199 1p multi 2.75 1.10

No. 4282 contains one 40x32mm stamp.

New Year 2003 (Year of the Ram) — A1200

Ram with background in: No. 4283, 15c, Green. No. 4284, 15c, Red.

**2003, Jan. 6** *Perf. 12½*
**4283-4284** A1200 Set of 2 1.75 .80

San Alejandro Academy for Arts, 185th Anniv. — A1201

Paintings by: 5c, Amelia Pelaez. 15c, René Portocarrero. 65c, Mario Carreña, horiz. 75c, Servando Cabrera.

**2003, Jan. 12** *Perf. 12¾*
**4285-4288** A1201 Set of 4 3.75 2.00

José Martí (1853-95), Patriot — A1202

Designs: 15c, Birthplace. No. 4290, 65c, Martí and text. No. 4291, 65c, Martí, sky and text, horiz. 75c, Portrait.
1p, Martí, horiz.

**2003, Jan. 28** *Perf. 12¾*
**4289-4292** A1202 Set of 4 4.25 2.50

**Souvenir Sheet**
*Perf. 12½*

**4293** A1202 1p multi 2.50 1.40

No. 4293 contains one 40x32mm stamp.

Arrival of Europeans at Havana, 510th Anniv. — A1203

Various Cuban stamps and: No. 4294, 15c, Woman with Cigar boxes, map of Cuba (diamond-shaped). No. 4295, 15c, Men at table holding cigars and drinks (diamond-shaped). 50c, Tobacco farmer, field, hands rolling cigar. 65c, Building, Trinidad. 75c, Cigar, building, palm tree, people in room.
1p, Indian lighting cigar, vert.

**2003, Feb. 6** *Perf. 12½*
**4294-4298** A1203 Set of 5 4.50 2.50

**Souvenir Sheet**

**4299** A1203 1p multi 2.50 1.40

No. 4299 contains one 32x40mm stamp.

Radio Rebelde, 45th Anniv. — A1204

**2003, Feb. 13** *Perf. 12¾*
**4300** A1204 65c multi 1.50 .85

Félix Varela (1788-1853), Priest — A1205

**2003, Feb. 25** *Perf. 12½*
**4301** A1205 65c multi 1.50 .85

Military Units, 45th Anniv. — A1206

Designs: No. 4302, 15c, 2nd Frank Pais Front. No. 4303, 15c, 3rd Mario Muñoz Front.

**2003** *Perf. 12¾*
**4302-4303** A1206 Set of 2 1.10 .55

Issued: No. 4302, 3/5; No. 4303, 3/11.

16th World Sexology Congress — A1207

**2003, Mar. 11**
**4304** A1207 65c multi 1.50 .85

Transportation and Shipping — A1208

Designs: 5c, Container ship. 10c, Truck. 15c, Train. 65c, Airplane and delivery van. 75c, Airplane and delivery van, diff.

**2003, Apr. 10** *Perf. 12½*
**4305-4309** A1208 Set of 5 3.75 2.00

Flora & Fauna — A1209

Designs: 5c, Nymphaea ampla, Lepisosteus tristoechus. 10c, Magnolia grandiflora, Spindalis zena pretrei. 15c, Lillium candidum, Polymita picta. 65c, Strelitzia regiae, Solenodon cubanus. 75c, Hibiscus rosasinensis, Mellisuga helenae.

**2003, May 15**
**4310-4314** A1209 Set of 5 4.00 2.00

Pan American Games, Santo Domingo, Dominican Republic — A1210

Designs: 5c, Kayaking. 15c, Judo. 50c, Track. 65c, Volleyball.

**2003, June 27** *Perf. 12½x12¾*
**4315-4318** A1210 Set of 4 3.00 1.50

Attack on Moncada Barracks, 50th Anniv. — A1211

Designs: 15c, Men and barracks. 65c, Fidel Castro, text.

**2003, July 26** *Perf. 12¾*
**4319-4320** A1211 Set of 2 1.75 .75

Railroads A1212

Designs: 5c, Three-wheeled handcar, 1930-35. 10c, Crane, 1920. 15c, B-B 120/120 E locomotive, 1925. 65c, DVM-9 Ganz Mavag locomotive, 1969. 75c, 2-6-0 locomotive, 1905.

**2003, Aug. 7**
**4321-4325** A1212 Set of 5 4.00 2.00

UN Conference to Combat Desertification — A1213

**2003, Aug. 25** *Perf. 12½x12¼*
**4326** A1213 65c multi 2.75 .85

Expo Bangkok — A1214

Wildlife: 5c, Nyctea scandiaca. 10c, Fratercula arctica. 15c, Sula bassana. 65c, Ursus maritimus. 75c, Alopex lagopus.
1p, Pagolphilus groenlandicus.

**2003, Aug. 28** *Perf. 12¾*
**4327-4331** A1214 Set of 5 4.00 2.00

**Souvenir Sheet**

*Perf. 12½*

**4332** A1214 1p multi 2.75 1.40

No. 4332 contains one 32x40mm stamp.

Butterflies and Flowers A1215

Designs: 5c, Dione juno, Gardenia jasminoides. 15c, Apatura ilia, Chrysanthemus sinence. 65c, Inachis io, Hibiscus rosasinensis. 75c, Marpesia iole, Althaea rosea.
1p, Danaus plexippus, Zantedeschia aethiopica, vert.

**2003, Sept. 11** **Litho.** *Perf. 12½*
**4333-4336** A1215 Set of 4 3.75 2.00

**Souvenir Sheet**

**4337** A1215 1p multi 2.75 1.40

No. 4337 contains one 32x40mm stamp.

Ecotourism A1216

Bird and location: 10c, Aratinga eops, Baracoa. 15c, Xiphidiopicus percussus, Valle de los Ingenios. 65c, Tiaris canora, Sierra Maestra. 75c, Priotelus temnurus, Granma.

**2003, Sept. 27** *Perf. 12¾x12½*
**4338-4341** A1216 Set of 4 2.75 1.75

Worldwide Fund for Nature (WWF) — A1217

Crocodylus rhombifer: No. 4342, 15c, Eggs and hatchling. No. 4343, 15c, Adult at water's edge. 65c, Capturing prey. 75c, With open mouth.

**2003, Sept. 30** **Litho.** *Perf. 12¾*
**4342-4345** A1217 Set of 4 4.00 2.00
*4345a* Sheet, 4 each #4342-4345 27.50 27.50

America Issue — Flora and Fauna — A1218

Designs: 15c, Xiphidiopicus percussus. 65c, Encyclia phoenicea.

**2003, Oct. 12**
**4346-4347** A1218 Set of 2 1.75 .85

35th Baseball World Cup — A1219

Cuban players: 5c, Antonio Muñoz. 10c, Lourdes Gourriel. No. 4350, 15c, Jorge L. Valdes. No. 4351, 15c, Lazaro Vargas. 65c, Lazaro Valle. 75c, Javier Mendez.
1p, Players celebrating, vert.

**2003, Oct. 17** *Perf. 12½x12¼*
**4348-4353** A1219 Set of 6 4.50 2.25

**Souvenir Sheet**

*Perf. 12½*

**4354** A1219 1p multi 2.75 1.40

No. 4354 contains one 32x40mm stamp.

Ballet A1220

Designs: No. 4355, 65c, National Ballet of Cuba, 55th anniv. No. 4356, 65c, Alicia Alonso as Giselle, 60th anniv., vert.

*Perf. 12¾x12½, 12½x12¾*

**2003, Oct. 28**
**4355-4356** A1220 Set of 2 3.00 1.50

Powered Flight, Cent. — A1221

Emblem and: 5c, Wright Brothers. 15c, Pitcairn PA-5. 65c, Stearman C-3MB. 75c, Douglas M-2.

**2003, Dec. 17** *Perf. 12½x12¼*
**4357-4360** A1221 Set of 4 4.00 2.00

Cuban Revolution, 45th Anniv. — A1222

**2004, Jan. 1** *Perf. 12¾*
**4361** A1222 65c multi 2.00 1.00

Expocuba, 15th Anniv. — A1223

**2004, Jan. 4** *Perf. 12½x12¼*
**4362** A1223 65c multi 1.50 .85

2004 Summer Olympics, Athens — A1224

Sports: 10c, Baseball. 15c (No. 4363A), Track. 65c, Boxing. 75c, Equestrian.

**2004, Jan. 6** **Litho.**
**4363-4365** A1224 Set of 4 3.75 1.90

New Year 2004 (Year of the Monkey) — A1225

Monkey with denomination in: No. 4366, 15c, Blue. No. 4367, 15c, Orange.

**2004, Jan. 9** *Perf. 12¾*
**4366-4367** A1225 Set of 2 1.00 .50

Julio A. Mella (1903-29), Communist Leader — A1226

**2004, Jan. 10**
**4368** A1226 65c multi 1.50 1.10

José Martí (1853-95) A1227

Designs: No. 4369, 5c, Martí in 1862, Colegio San Pablo, Prado No. 88. No. 4370, 5c, Martí's father, Mariano, Tapineria No. 16, Valencia. No. 4371, 5c, Martí's mother, Leonor Pérez, birthplace, Paula No. 41. No. 4372, 10c, Martí's high school, 1862, Martí, Fermín Valdés Domínguez, 1869. No. 4373, 10c, Martí in 1869, Havana Royal Jail. No. 4374,

15c, Martí in 1870, El Abra farm, Isle of Pines. No. 4375, 15c, Martí in 1870, Martí Forge. No. 4376, 15c, Martí and son, José Francisco, 1879, Guanabacoa Lyceum. 65c, Martí and son, 1879, Mercaderes Law Offices. 75c, Martí in 1895, La Jatía farm, Oriente.

**2004, Jan. 28** ***Perf. 12½x12¼***
**4369-4378** A1227 Set of 10 4.75 2.75

See Nos. 4525-4535, 4570-4578, 4691-4700, 4800-4807.

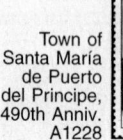

Town of Santa María de Puerto del Principe, 490th Anniv. A1228

**2004, Feb. 2** ***Perf. 12¾x12½***
**4379** A1228 15c multi .50 .25

Trolleys A1229

Designs: 5c, Santiago. 10c, Havana. 15c, Camagüey. 65c, Matanzas. 75c, Camagüey, diff.
1p, Havana, diff.

**2004, Feb. 20** ***Perf. 12¾***
**4380-4384** A1229 Set of 5 3.75 1.90

**Souvenir Sheet**
***Perf. 12½***
**4385** A1229 1p multi 2.50 1.25

No. 4385 contains one 40x32mm stamp.

Souvenir Sheet

Cuba — Mexico Binational Philatelic Exhibition — A1230

**2004, Feb. 25** ***Perf. 12½***
**4386** A1230 1p multi 2.50 1.25

EGREM Recording Co., 40th Anniv. — A1231

Recording artists: 10c, Cascarita, Julio Cuevas. 15c, Carlos Puebla. 65c, Benny Moré. 75c, Compay Segundo.

**2004, Mar. 24** ***Perf. 12¾***
**4387-4390** A1231 Set of 4 3.50 1.75

España 2004 Intl. Philatelic Exhibition A1232

Dogs: 5c, Spanish pointer. 10c, Spanish hound. 15c, Mallorquin bulldog. 65c, Catalan sheepdog. 75c, Pyrenean mastiff.
1p, Spanish mastiff.

**2004, Mar. 24** ***Perf. 12½x12¼***
**4391-4395** A1232 Set of 5 4.75 2.25

**Souvenir Sheet**
***Perf. 12½***
**4396** A1232 1p multi 3.25 1.50

No. 4396 contains one 40x32mm stamp.

National Police, 45th Anniv. A1233

**2004, Mar. 26** ***Perf. 12½x12¼***
**4397** A1233 15c multi + label .60 .25

Souvenir Sheet

Second Cuban Sports Olympiad — A1234

**2004, Apr. 18** ***Perf. 12½***
**4398** A1234 1p multi 2.50 1.25

Nature and Man Foundation, 10th Anniv. — A1235

**2004, May 16 Litho.** ***Perf. 12¼x12½***
**4399** A1235 65c multi 1.50 .75

FIFA (Fédération Internationale de Football Association), Cent. — A1236

FIFA emblem and various players: 10c, 15c, 65c, 75c.

**2004, May 21** ***Perf. 12¾***
**4400-4403** A1236 Set of 4 3.50 1.75

Pets — A1237

Designs: 5c, Parakeets. 10c, Fish. 15c, Dogs. 65c, Cats. 75c, Finches.
1p, Horse, horiz.

**2004, June 25** ***Perf. 12½x12¾***
**4404-4408** A1237 Set of 5 3.75 1.90

**Souvenir Sheet**
***Perf. 12½***
**4409** A1237 1p multi 2.50 1.25

No. 4409 contains one 40x32mm stamp.

Intl. Chess Federation, 80th Anniv. — A1238

Chess players: 15c, Maria Teresa Mora. 65c, José Raúl Capablanca, horiz. 75c, Ernesto "Che" Guevara.

**2004, July 20** ***Perf. 12¾***
**4410-4412** A1238 Set of 3 3.50 1.75

Minerals A1239

Designs: 5c, Corundum. 10c, Thenardite. 15c, Uraninite. 65c, Realgar. 75c, Fluorite.
1p, Copper.

**2004, July 30** ***Perf. 13***
**4413-4417** A1239 Set of 5 3.50 1.75

**Souvenir Sheet**
***Perf. 12½***
**4418** A1239 1p multi 2.50 1.25

No. 4418 contains one 40x32mm stamp.

Convention Hall, 25th Anniv. — A1240

**2004, Sept. 3** ***Perf. 12¾***
**4419** A1240 65c multi 1.50 1.25

Cuban Aviation, 75th Anniv. A1241

Designs: 15c, Lockheed Constellation. 65c, IL-62M. 75c, Airbus 330.

**2004, Oct. 8** ***Perf. 12½x12¼***
**4420-4422** A1241 Set of 3 3.50 1.75

America Issue A1242

Map of Cuba and: 15c, Bird over islands. 65c, Fish and marine life.

**2004, Oct. 12**
**4423-4424** A1242 Set of 2 1.75 .90

Marine Mammals A1243

Designs: 5c, Delphinus delphis. 10c, Lagenorhynchus obliquidens. 15c, Stenella attenuata. 65c, Grampus griseus. 75c, Tursiops truncatus.
1p, Orcinus orca.

**2004, Oct. 20** ***Perf. 12½x12¼***
**4425-4429** A1243 Set of 5 3.50 1.75

**Souvenir Sheet**
***Perf. 13***
**4430** A1243 1p multi 2.50 1.25

No. 4430 contains one 40x32mm stamp.

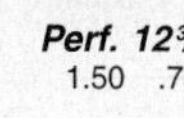

Disappearance of Camilo Cienfuegos, 45th Anniv. — A1244

**2004, Oct. 28** ***Perf. 12¾***
**4431** A1244 65c multi 1.50 .75

Railroad Stations, Cent. — A1245

Designs: 15c, Agramonte Station, 1906 ALCO No. 48 4-6-0. 65c, Aguacate Station, 1907 BLW No. 57 4-6-0. 75c, Guira de Melina Station, 1903 ALCO No. 7 4-4-0.

**2004, Nov. 10** ***Perf. 13***
**4432-4434** A1245 Set of 3 3.50 1.75

Souvenir Sheet

13th Philatelic Congress, Havana — A1245a

**2004, Nov. 20 Litho.** ***Perf. 12½***
**4434A** A1245a 1p multi 2.25 2.25

Founding of San Cristóbal de la Habana, 485th Anniv. — A1246

Designs: 15c, Temple. 65c, Painting showing priest in red vestments at base of tree. 75c, Paintig showing group of men at base of tree.

***Perf. 12½x12¾***
**2004, Nov. 30** **Litho.**
**4435-4437** A1246 Set of 3 3.00 1.50

Latin American Parliament Foundation, 40th Anniv. — A1246a

**2004, Nov. 30 Litho.** ***Perf. 12¾***
**4437A** A1246a 65c multi 1.40 .70

Ministry of Foreign Affairs, 45th Anniv. A1247

**2004, Dec. 23** ***Perf. 12½x12¼***
**4438** A1247 65c multi 1.40 .70

Alejo Carpentier (1904-80), Writer — A1248

**2004, Dec. 26** *Perf. 12¾*
**4439** A1248 65c multi 1.40 .70

First Baseball Game in Cuba, 130th Anniv. A1249

Baseball players: 5c, Rey Vicente Anglada. 10c, Braudilio Vinent. 15c, Rogelio Garcia. 65c, Luis G. Casanova. 75c, Victor Mesa.
1p, Martin Dihigo, vert.

**2004, Dec. 27** *Perf. 12½x12¼*
**4440-4444** A1249 Set of 5 4.00 2.00

**Souvenir Sheet**

*Perf. 12½*

**4445** A1249 1p multi 2.25 1.10

No. 4445 contains one 32x40mm stamp.

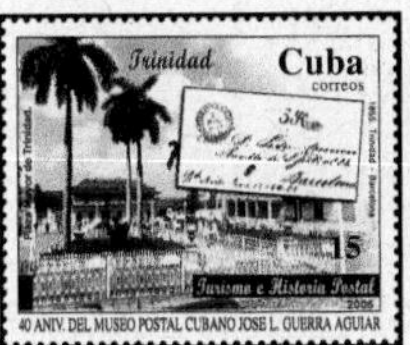


Jose L. Guerra Aguiar Cuban Postal Museum, 40th Anniv. A1250

Designs: 15c, Plaza Mayor, Trinidad and 1855 Trinidad to Barcelona cover. 65c, Charity Sanctuary, El Cobre and 1861 El Cobre to Santiago de Cuba cover. 85c, Matanzas Cathedral, Matanzas and 1848 Mantanzas to Havana cover.

**2005, Jan. 2** *Perf. 12¾x12½*
**4446-4448** A1250 Set of 3 3.50 1.75

New Year 2005 (Year of the Rooster) — A1251

Designs: No. 4449, 15c, Rooster in air. No. 4450, 15c, Rooster on ground.

**2005, Jan. 4** *Perf. 12¼x12½*
**4449-4450** A1251 Set of 2 .60 .30

Ministry of Information Technology and Communications, 5th Anniv. — A1252

**2005, Jan. 12** *Perf. 12½x12¼*
**4451** A1252 65c multi 1.40 .70

Dinosaurs A1253

Designs: 5c, Carnotaurus. 10c, Oviraptor. 30c, Parasaurolophus. 65c, Sauropelta. 90c, Iguanodon.
1p, Velociraptor.

**2005, Jan. 20 Litho.** *Perf. 12½x12¼*
**4452-4456** A1253 Set of 5 4.25 2.10

**Souvenir Sheet**

*Perf. 13*

**4457** A1253 1p multi 2.25 1.10

No. 4457 contains one 40x32mm stamp.

Miguel de Cervantes and Title Page of *Don Quixote* A1254

**2005, Jan. 24** *Perf. 12¾x12½*
**4458** A1254 65c multi 1.40 .70

Publication of *Don Quixote*, 400th anniv.

Bridges A1255

Designs: 10c, Bacunayagua Bridge. 15c, La Concordia Bridge. 50c, El Triunfo Bridge. 65c, Yayabo Bridge. 75c, Canimar Bridge.
1p, Plaza Bridge.

**2005, Feb. 5** *Perf. 13x12¾*
**4459-4463** A1255 Set of 5 4.75 2.40

**Souvenir Sheet**

*Perf. 13*

**4464** A1255 1p multi 2.25 1.10

No. 4464 contains one 40x32mm stamp.

Cuban Telecommunications Enterprise, 10th Anniv. — A1256

**2005, Feb. 24** *Perf. 12½x12¾*
**4465** A1256 90c multi 1.90 .95

Parrots A1257

Designs: 5c, Amazona ochrocephala, Amazona leucocephala. 10c, Agapornis personata, Agapornis fischeri. 15c, Cacatua galerita, Cacatua leadbeateri. 65c, Psittacula krameri, Psittacula himalayana, vert. 1.05p, Aratinga guarouba, Aratinga euops.
1p, Ara macao, Ara araruana, Anodorhynchus hyacythus.

*Perf. 12½x12¼, 12¼x12½*

**2005, Feb. 23** **Litho.**
**4466-4470** A1257 Set of 5 4.25 2.10

**Souvenir Sheet**

*Perf. 13*

**4471** A1257 1p multi 2.25 1.10

No. 4471 contain one 32x40mm stamp.

Cats — A1258

Various cats: 5c, 10c, 40c, 65c, 75c. 10c is vert.

**2005, Mar. 15** *Perf. 12¾*
**4472-4476** A1258 Set of 5 4.25 2.10

*Perf. 13*

**4477** A1258 1p Two cats, vert. 2.25 1.10

No. 4477 contains one 32x40mm stamp.

Cuba — Canada Diplomatic Relations, 60th Anniv. A1259

**2005, Mar. 20** *Perf. 12¾x12½*
**4478** A1259 65c multi 1.75 .70

Wildlife — A1260

**2005, Mar. 21** *Perf. 12½x12¼*

| | | | | |
|---|---|---|---|---|
| **4479** | A1260 15c Manatee | | .30 | .25 |
| **4480** | A1260 65c Parrot | | 1.40 | .70 |
| **4481** | A1260 75c Crocodile | | 1.50 | .75 |
| **4482** | A1260 90c Hummingbird | | 1.75 | .90 |
| | *Nos. 4479-4482 (4)* | | 4.95 | 2.60 |

World Water Day — A1261

**2005, Mar. 22** *Perf. 13*
**4483** A1261 90c multi 1.90 .95

Boats — A1262

Designs: 10c, Fishing boat, fish. 20c, Schooner, fish. 30c, Bonito boat, bonito. 45c, Shrimp boat, shrimp. 90c, Lobster boat, lobster.
1p, Cargo ship, horiz.

**2005, Apr. 15** *Perf. 12½*
**4484-4488** A1262 Set of 5 4.25 2.10

**Souvenir Sheet**

**4489** A1262 1p multi 2.25 1.10

First Cuban Postage Stamps, 150th Anniv. A1263

Designs: 15c, St. Francis of Assisi Convent, Cuba #1. 65c, Morro Lighthouse, Cuba #2. 75c, Colonial Post Office, Cuba #3.

**2005, Apr. 24** *Perf. 12¾x12½*
**4490-4492** A1263 Set of 3 3.50 1.75

Social Security For All — A1264

**2005, May 5** **Litho.**
**4493** A1264 65c multi 1.40 .70

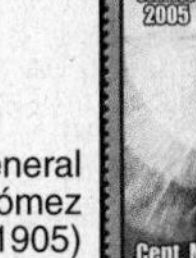


Major General Máximo Gómez (1836-1905) A1265

**2005, June 17** *Perf. 12½*
**4494** A1265 1.05p multi 2.25 1.10

**Souvenir Sheet**

Santiago de Cuba, 490th Anniv. A1266

**2005, July 4** *Perf. 13*
**4495** A1266 1p multi 2.25 1.10

16th World Youth and Student Festival, Venezuela A1267

**2005, July 29** *Perf. 12¾x12½*
**4496** A1267 65c multi 1.40 .70

Dances — A1268

Parrot and: No. 4497, 65c, Samba dancers and Brazilian flag. No. 4498, 65c, Son dancers, Cuban flag.

**2005, Aug. 15** *Perf. 12¾*
**4497-4498** A1268 Set of 2 2.75 1.50

See Brazil Nos. 2967-2968.

Cuban — Soviet Space Flight, 25th Anniv. A1269

No. 4499: a, Cosmonaut Arnaldo Tamayo Mendez. b, Cosmonaut Yuri Romanenko.

**2005, Sept. 18** *Perf. 12½*
**4499** A1269 90c Horiz. pair, #a-b 4.00 2.00

Albert Einstein's Visit to Cuba, 75th Anniv. — A1270

Designs: 65c, Caricature of Einstein. 75c, Equation for energy, Einstein writing.

**2005, Sept. 21**
**4500-4501** A1270 Set of 2 4.50 2.00

Locomotives A1271

Designs: 5c, DSB B40, 1869. 10c, Great Northern, 1902. No. 4504, 15c, Minaret, 1929. No. 4505, 15c, C. F. White, 1885. 2.05p, Western Pacific FP7A 805D.
1p, 14th No. 4 Krauss & Co., 1884.

**2005, May 10 Litho. *Perf. 12¾***
**4502-4506** A1271 Set of 5 5.50 2.75

**Souvenir Sheet**
***Perf. 13***

**4507** A1271 1p multi 2.25 1.10

No. 4507 contains one 40x32mm stamp.

Zoo Animals — A1272

Designs: 10c, Loxodonta africana. 15c, Acunonyx jubatus, horiz. 50c, Synceros caffer, horiz. 65c, Giraffa camelopardalis. 75c, Panthera leo.
1p, Equus burchelli, horiz.

**2005, July 21 *Perf. 12¾***
**4508-4512** A1272 Set of 5 4.75 2.40

**Souvenir Sheet**
***Perf. 13***

**4513** A1272 1p multi 2.25 1.10

No. 4513 contains one 40x32mm stamp.

Santiago de Cuba, 490th Anniv. A1273

**2005, Sept. 22 *Perf. 12¾x12½***
**4514** A1273 75c multi 2.00 1.00

Revolutionary Defense Committees, 45th Anniv. — A1274

**2005, Sept. 28 *Perf. 12½x12¼***
**4515** A1274 50c multi 1.10 .55

Diplomatic Relations Between Cuba and People's Republic of China, 45th Anniv. — A1275

No. 4516: a, Chinese General Secretary Hu Jintao and Cuban Pres. Fidel Castro. b, Great Wall of China and Morro Castle, Havana.

**2005, Sept. 28 *Perf. 13x13¼***
**4516** A1275 15c Horiz. pair, #a-b 1.00 .50

America Issue, Fight Against Poverty — A1276

Designs: 50c, Starving children, map of Africa. 75c, Woman and child, map of South America.

**2005, Oct. 12 *Perf. 12¾***
**4517-4518** A1276 Set of 2 2.75 1.40

Horses A1277

Breeds: 10c, Gelderlander. 20c, Arabian. 30c, Quarterhorse. 65c, Wild horses. 75c, Lipizzaner.
100c, Holsteiner, vert.

**2005, Oct. 21 *Perf. 12¾***
**4519-4523** A1277 Set of 5 4.25 2.10

**Souvenir Sheet**
***Perf. 12¾x12½***

**4524** A1277 100c multi 2.25 1.10

No. 4524 contains one 32x40mm stamp.

**José Martí Type of 2004**

Martí and: No. 4525, 5c, Central University, Madrid, 1871. No. 4526, 5c, Zaragoza University, 1871. No. 4527, 5c, F. Valdés Dominguez, Teatro Principal, Zaragoza, 1872. No. 4528, 10c, Victor Hugo House, Paris, 1872. No. 4529, 10c, Moneda No. 12, Mexico City, 1875. No. 4530, 15c, Normal School, Guatemala City, 1876. No. 4531, 15c, San Ildefonso No. 40, Mexico City, 1894. No. 4532, 15c, Plaza de Guardiola, Mexico City, 1894. 65c, Plaza Bolívar, Caracas, 1885. 75c, Santa María College, Caracas, 1893.
1p, Martínez Ibor Tobacco Factory, Tampa, 1892.

**2005, Oct. 20 *Perf. 12½x12¼***
**4525-4534** A1227 Set of 10 4.75 2.40

**Souvenir Sheet**
***Perf. 13***

**4535** A1227 1p multi 2.25 1.10

No. 4535 contains one 40x32mm stamp.

World Summit on the Information Society, Tunis A1278

**2005, Nov. 16 *Perf. 12½x12¼***
**4536** A1278 75c multi 1.60 .80

Establishment of Local Delivery of Mail in Havana, 150th Anniv. — A1279

Designs 15c, Cuba #7, cover to Havana. 65c, Cuba #16, Colonial Havana mailbox.

**2005, Nov. 19 *Perf. 12¾x12½***
**4537-4538** A1279 Set of 2 1.60 .80

Cuban Men Convicted of Terrorism Imprisoned In the United States — A1280

**2005, Nov. 25 *Perf. 12½x12¾***
**4539** A1280 65c multi 2.50 1.00

Europa Stamps, 50th Anniv. (in 2006) — A1281

Designs: 1.30p, Spain #1126, Castilla de la Fuerza, Havana. 2.05p, Spain #1010, Santisima Church, Trinidad, Cuba. 2.55p, Spain #1526, Morro Castle, Santiago de Cuba. 3.90p, Spain #1263, San Cristóbal Cathedral, Havana.

**2005, Nov. 30 *Perf. 12½***
**4540-4543** A1281 Set of 4 20.00 10.00
*4543a* Souvenir sheet, #4540-4543 20.00 20.00

Nos. 4540-4543, 4543a exist imperf. Values, same.

Jewelry — A1282

Jewelry by: 5c, Antonio Barcala. 10c, Raúl Valladares. 45c, Carlos de la Torre. 65c, J. Carlo Rafart. 75c, Osvaldo Castilla.
1p, 19th cent. jewelry in Gold Museum.

**2005, Dec. 1 *Perf. 12¾***
**4544-4548** A1282 Set of 5 4.25 2.10

**Souvenir Sheet**
***Perf. 12½***

**4549** A1282 1p multi 2.25 1.10

No. 4549 contains one 32x40mm stamp.

Friendship Among the Peoples Institute, 45th Anniv. A1283

**2005, Dec. 14 *Perf. 12¾x12½***
**4550** A1283 1.05p multi 2.25 1.10

Snails and Mushrooms — A1284

Designs: 10c, Clathrus cancellatus. 20c, Polymita genus picta. 30c, Lepiota puellaris. 65c, Polymita genus muscarum. 75c, Clitocybe infundibuliformis.
1p, Polymita genus versicolor, horiz.

**2005, Dec. 15 *Perf. 12¾***
**4551-4555** A1284 Set of 5 4.25 2.10

**Souvenir Sheet**
***Perf. 13***

**4556** A1284 1p multi 2.25 1.10

No. 4556 contains one 40x32mm stamp.

Hotel Inglaterra, 130th Anniv. A1285

**2005, Dec. 23 *Perf. 12¾x12½***
**4557** A1285 65c multi 1.25 .70

New Year 2006 (Year of the Dog) — A1286

Designs: No. 4558, 15c, Shih tzu. No. 4559, 15c, Pug.

**2006, Jan. 4 *Perf. 12¼x12½***
**4558-4559** A1286 Set of 2 1.00 .30

Organization of Solidarity of the People of Asia, Africa and Latin America, 40th Anniv. — A1287

**2006, Jan. 16 *Perf. 12¾***
**4560** A1287 65c multi 1.40 .70

Establishment of Cuban Postal Service, 250th Anniv. A1288

Stampless cover and: 75c, Horse and rider. 2.05p, Ship.

**2006, Mar. 1 *Perf. 12½x12¼***
**4561-4562** A1288 Set of 2 6.00 3.00

OPEC Intl. Development Fund, 30th Anniv. A1289

**2006, Mar. 23 Litho.**
**4563** A1289 75c multi 1.60 .80

**Souvenir Sheet**

Havana '06 Intl. Philatelic Exhibition — A1290

**2006, Mar. 25 *Perf. 12½***
**4564** A1290 1p multi 2.25 1.10

Pope John Paul II (1920-2005) — A1291

Designs: 65c, Pope, Mass in Santa Clara. 75c, Mass in Camagüey (44x27mm). 90c, Mass in Santiago de Cuba (44x27mm). 1.05p, Pope, Mass in Havana.

**2006, Apr. 2 *Perf. 12½x12¼***
**4565-4568** A1291 Set of 4 7.25 3.75

Bay of Pigs Invasion, 45th Anniv. — A1292

**2006, Apr. 17 *Perf. 12¼x12½***
**4569** A1292 65c multi 1.40 .70

### José Martí Type of 2004

Martí and: No. 4570, Madame Griffou's Hotel, New York, 1890. No. 4571, Gonzalo de Quesada, 116 West 64th Street, New York, 1893. No. 4572, Son, José Francisco, 324 Classon Ave., New York, 1885. No. 4573, Masonic Temple, New York, 1888.

No. 4574: a, Cajobabo beach, Gomez monument. b, Martí monument, monument at Dos Ríos.

Martí and: 75c, Hardman Hall, New York, 1891. 85c, Office, 120 Front Street, New York, 1891. 90c, María Mantilla, Bath Beach, Long Island.

1p, Home of Teodoro Pérez, Cayo Hueso, 1893.

**2006, May 19 Litho.** ***Perf. 12½x12¼***

| | | | | |
|---|---|---|---|---|
| **4570** | A1227 | 5c multi | .25 | .25 |
| **4571** | A1227 | 5c multi | .25 | .25 |
| **4572** | A1227 | 10c multi | .25 | .25 |
| **4573** | A1227 | 10c multi | .25 | .25 |
| **4574** | A1227 | 15c Horiz. pair, #a-b | .65 | .65 |
| **4575** | A1227 | 75c multi | 1.60 | 1.60 |
| **4576** | A1227 | 85c multi | 1.90 | 1.90 |
| **4577** | A1227 | 90c multi | 1.90 | 1.90 |
| | | *Nos. 4570-4577 (8)* | 7.05 | 7.05 |

**Souvenir Sheet**

***Perf. 13***

**4578** A1227 1p multi 2.25 2.25

No. 4578 contains one 40x32mm stamp.

Prehistoric Animals A1293

Designs: 5c, Dsungaripetrus, Yangchuanosaurus. 10c, Pterodactylus, Sprinosaurus. 30c, Pteranodon, Pachycephalosaurus. 35c, Scaphognathus, Muttaburrasaurus. 65c, Quetzalcoatlus, Stegosaurus. 1.05p, Sordes, Saichania.

1p, Stenonychosaurus, vert.

**2006, May 24** ***Perf. 12½x12¼***

**4579-4584** A1293 Set of 6 5.50 5.50

**Souvenir Sheet**

***Perf. 12½***

**4585** A1293 1p multi 2.25 2.25

No. 4585 contains one 32x40mm stamp.

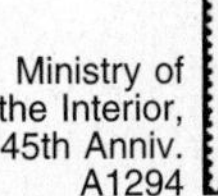

Ministry of the Interior, 45th Anniv. A1294

**2006, June 6** ***Perf. 12½x12¼***

**4586** A1294 75c multi 1.60 1.60

Fowl A1295

Designs: 5c, Chickens. No. 4588, 15c, Turkeys. No. 4589, 15c, Guinea fowl. 45c, Geese. 50c, Pheasants. 75c, Peafowl.

1p, Ducks.

**2006, June 15** ***Perf. 12½x12¼***

**4587-4592** A1295 Set of 6 4.50 4.50

**Souvenir Sheet**

***Perf. 13***

**4593** A1295 1p multi 2.25 2.25

No. 4593 contains one 40x32mm stamp.

Cerro Pelado Declaration, 40th Anniv. — A1296

Designs: 65c, Ship, man and crowd. 75c, People in cargo hoist. 85c, Men assisting woman down ship's stairs, flags of Cuba and Puerto Rico.

**2006, June 25** ***Perf. 12½x12¾***

**4594-4596** A1296 Set of 3 4.75 4.75

2006 World Cup Soccer Championships, Germany — A1296a

Various Cuban soccer players: 15c, 45c, 65c, 75c.

**2006, June Litho.** ***Perf. 12¾***

**4596A-4596D** A1296a Set of 4 4.00 4.00

Genetic Engineering and Biotechnology Center, 20th Anniv. A1297

**2006, July 1** ***Perf. 12½x12¼***

**4597** A1297 65c multi 1.40 1.40

Comic Strips by Virgilio Martinez A1298

Designs: 15c, Pucho y Sus Perrerias. 65c, Cucho.

**2006, July 16** ***Perf. 12¾x12¼***

**4598-4599** A1298 Set of 2 1.75 1.75

Airplanes A1299

Designs: 10c, Granville GeeBee R2. No. 4601, 15c, Bücker Jungmann. No. 4602, 15c, Comte AC-4 Gentleman. 50c, Mustang TF-51. 75c, Supermarine Spitfire. 85c, Lavochkin La-9.

1p, Bücker Jungmeister.

**2006, July 20** ***Perf. 12¾***

**4600-4605** A1299 Set of 6 5.50 5.50

**Souvenir Sheet**

***Imperf***

**4606** A1299 1p multi 2.25 2.25

No. 4606 contains one 36x28mm stamp.

Dogs A1300

Designs: 5c, Bulldog. 10c, American cocker spaniel. 15c, Shar-pei. 20c, Airedale terrier. 35c, Pomeranian. 2.05p, Dalmatian.

1p, Whippet, vert.

**2006, Aug. 18** ***Perf. 12½x12¼***

**4607-4612** A1300 Set of 6 6.25 6.25

**Souvenir Sheet**

***Perf. 13***

**4613** A1300 1p multi 2.25 2.25

Recovery of Raw Materials, 45th Anniv. — A1301

Designs: 15c, Ernesto "Che" Guevara. 65c, Cuban and recovery program flags.

**2006, Aug. 24** ***Perf. 12¾***

**4614-4615** A1301 Set of 2 1.75 1.75

14th Congress of Non-Aligned Countries, Havana — A1302

**2006, Sept. 10**

**4616** A1302 65c multi 1.40 1.40

Pedro Santacilia, Benito Juárez and Mexico House, Havana — A1303

**2006, Sept. 15** ***Perf. 12½x12¼***

**4617** A1303 65c multi 1.40 1.40

Benito Juárez (1806-72), President of Mexico.

Souvenir Sheet

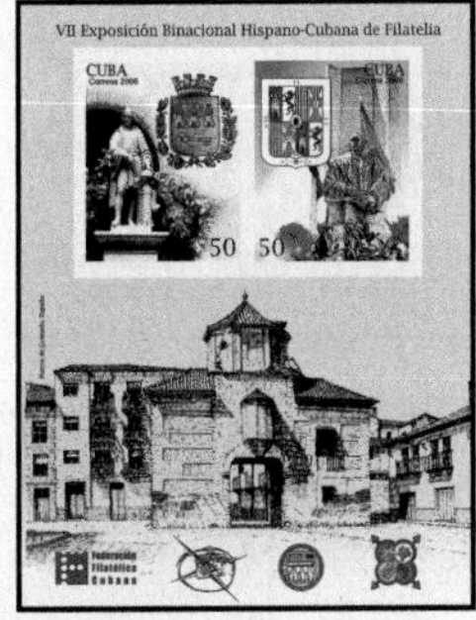

7th Hispano-Cuban Philatelic Exposition — A1304

No. 4618: a, Statue, arms of Cuba, denomination at LR. b, Statue, arms of Spain, denomination at LL.

**2006, Sept. 20** ***Imperf.***

**4618** A1304 50c Sheet of 2, #a-b 2.25 2.25

España 06 World Philatelic Exposition, Malaga, Spain — A1305

Designs: 5c, Rio Hanabanilla. 10c, Laguna Bacanao. 15c, Sierra de la Gran Piedra. 20c, Valle de los Ingenios. 50c, Laguna del Tesoro. 75c, Sierra Maestra.

1p, Valle de Viñales.

**2006, Sept. 20** ***Perf. 12¾***

**4619-4624** A1305 Set of 6 3.75 3.75

**Souvenir Sheet**

***Perf. 13***

**4625** A1305 1p multi 2.25 2.25

No. 4625 contains one 40x32mm stamp.

America Issue, Energy Conservation A1306

Equipment for harnessing energy source: No. 4626, 65c, Petroleum. No. 4627, 65c, Water. No. 4628, 65c, Solar. No. 4629, 65c, Wind.

**2006, Oct. 12** ***Perf. 12¾***

**4626-4629** A1306 Set of 4 5.50 5.50

Saiz Brothers Association, 20th Anniv. — A1307

**2006, Oct. 18**

**4630** A1307 75c multi 1.60 1.60

20th Intl. Ballet Festival, Havana — A1308

Dancers: 75c, Alicia Alonso and Igor Yousкévitch. 85c, Alonso.

**2006, Oct. 28** ***Perf. 12¼x12½***

**4631-4632** A1308 Set of 2 3.50 3.50

A1309

Belgica '06 Intl. Youth Philately Exposition, Belgium — A1310

Trains: 5c, Rocket and Intercity Diesel-electric. 10c, Turbine locomotive, Diesel-electric locomotive. 15c, Shinkasen and City of Los Angeles. 65c, Steam locomotive, Diesel locomotive. 75c, TEE Diesel-electric, TGV electric. 85c, Brisbane electric monorail, Wuppertal monorail.

No. 4639: a, Steam locomotive. b, Diesel locomotive.

**2006, Nov. 2** ***Perf. 12¾***

**4633-4638** A1309 Set of 6 5.50 5.50

**Souvenir Sheet**

***Perf. 12½***

**4639** A1310 50c Sheet of 2, #a-b 2.25 2.25

TeleFood Emblem A1311

**2006, Nov. 11** ***Perf. 12¾***

**4640** A1311 75c multi 1.60 1.60

Animals Serving Man — A1312

Designs: 5c, Equus caballus, Greek horse-drawn chariot. 15c, Camelus dromedarius, Ibn Battuta on camel. 30c, Capra aegagrus, Roman musician. 40c, Lama lama, Peruvian pre-Columbian ceramic llama. 50c, Felis catus, painting by Kuniyoshi Utagawa. 1.05p, Elephas maximus, elephant with Indian caparison.

1p, Canis familiaris, Grecian with dog.

**2006, Oct. 1 Litho.** ***Perf. 12½x12¼***

**4641-4646** A1312 Set of 6 5.50 5.50

**Souvenir Sheet**

***Perf. 12½***

**4647** A1312 1p multi 2.25 2.25

No. 4647 contains one 40x32mm stamp.

Fire Fighting and Rescue Equipment A1313

Designs: 5c, 1899 Horse-drawn ambulance, Brazil, and megaphone. 10c, Fireman's hat, and 1898 Merryweather fire truck, England. 20c, 1910 Laurin & Klement fire truck, Bohemia, and fire hydrant. 30c, 1939 American La France ladder truck, US, and badge. 45c, 1925 Leyland Motors pumper motorcycle, United Kingdom, and portable hose and tank. 90c, Brussels fire badge and 1930 Magirus ladder truck, Germany.
1p, Fireman spraying water, vert.

**2006, Nov. 13** ***Perf. 12¾***

**4648-4653** A1313 Set of 6 4.50 4.50

**Souvenir Sheet**

***Perf. 12½***

**4654** A1313 1p multi 2.25 2.25

No. 4654 contains one 32x40mm stamp.

Santiago Rebellion, 50th Anniv. A1314

**2006, Nov. 30** ***Perf. 12½x12¼***

**4655** A1314 65c multi 1.40 1.40

Governmental Reorganization, 30th Anniv. — A1315

**2006, Dec. 2**

**4656** A1315 75c multi 1.60 1.60

Granma Landings, 50th Anniv. A1316

Revolutionary Armed Forces, 50th Anniv. A1317

**2006, Dec. 2** ***Perf. 13***

**4657** A1316 65c multi 1.40 1.40
**4658** A1317 65c multi 1.40 1.40

General Antonio Maceo Grajales (1845-96) — A1317a

**2006, Dec. 7** **Litho.** ***Perf. 12½x12¼***

**4658A** A1317a 1.05p multi 2.10 2.10

Intl. Film and Television School, 20th Anniv. — A1318

**2006, Dec. 15** ***Perf. 12¾***

**4659** A1318 75c multi 1.60 1.60

Martí Forge Museum, 55th Anniv. A1319

**2006, Dec. 15** ***Perf. 12½x12¼***

**4660** A1319 90c multi 1.90 1.90

Literacy Campaign, 45th Anniv. — A1320

**2006, Dec. 19** ***Perf. 12¾***

**4661** A1320 65c multi 1.40 1.40

Major General Ignacio Agramonte y Loinaz (1841-73) A1321

**2006, Dec. 23** ***Perf. 12½x12¼***

**4662** A1321 65c multi 1.40 1.40

Special Education, 45th Anniv. — A1322

**2007, Jan. 4** ***Perf. 12¾***

**4663** A1322 85c multi 1.75 1.75

Francesa Pharmacy, 125th Anniv. — A1323

**2007, Jan. 18** **Litho.**

**4664** A1323 65c multi 1.40 1.40

Electric Trains — A1324

Designs: 5c, First American electric locomotive, 1895. 10c, Locomotive, Netherlands. 15c, Interurban train, Australia. 65c, High-speed train, Italy. 85c, Helensburgh-Bridgeton train, Great Britain. 1.05p, Lyon-St. Etienne interurban train, France.
1p, High-speed train, Germany.

**2007, Jan. 18** ***Perf. 12¾***

**4665-4670** A1324 Set of 6 6.00 6.00

**Souvenir Sheet**

***Imperf***

**4671** A1324 1p multi 2.25 2.25

No. 4671 contains one 40x32mm stamp with simulated perforations.

12th Intl. Information Fair and Convention — A1325

**2007, Feb. 12** ***Perf. 12½x12¼***

**4672** A1325 75c multi 1.60 1.60

Cats — A1326

Designs: 10c, Two cats. No. 4674, 15c, Kitten with paw raised. No. 4675, 15c, Cat. 50c, Cat and telephone. 75c, Cat with ball. 90c, Cat, diff.
1p, Cat, diff.

**2007, Feb. 14** ***Perf. 12¾***

**4673-4678** A1326 Set of 6 5.50 5.50

**Souvenir Sheet**

***Imperf***

**4679** A1326 1p multi 2.25 2.25

No. 4679 contains one 40x32mm stamp with simulated perforations.

Fifth Congress of Cuban Pigeon Fanciers Federation A1327

**2007, Feb. 24** ***Perf. 12¾***

**4680** A1327 75c multi 1.60 1.60

Souvenir Sheet

Patria Newspaper, 115th Anniv. — A1328

***Imperf. With Simulated Perforations***

**2007, Mar. 14**

**4681** A1328 1p multi 2.25 2.25

Animals in National Zoo — A1329

Designs: 5c, Ara ararauana. 10c, Tsetudo elephantopus. 15c, Balearica regulorum. 20c, Procyon lotor. 45c, Panthera pardus. 2.05p, Pongo pygmaeus.
1p, Giraffa camelopardalis, vert.

**2007, Mar. 31** ***Perf. 12½x12¼***

**4682-4687** A1329 Set of 6 6.50 6.50

**Souvenir Sheet**

***Imperf***

**4688** A1329 1p multi 2.25 2.25

No. 4688 contains one 32x40mm stamp with simulated perforations.

Raúl Roa García (1907-82), Foreign Minister — A1330

**2007, Apr. 18** ***Perf. 12¾***

**4689** A1330 65c multi 1.40 1.40

Union of Young Communists, 45th Anniv. A1331

**2007, Apr. 4** ***Perf. 12½x12¼***

**4690** A1331 75c multi 1.60 1.60

**José Martí Type of 2004**

Martí and: No. 4691, 5c, Cuban High School, Tampa, 1892. No. 4692, 5c, Casa de los Pedrosa, Tampa, 1892. No. 4693, 10c, Hotel Duval, Cayo Hueso, 1891. No. 4694, 10c, Hotel Cherokee, Tampa, 1891. No. 4695, 15c, Cayo Hueso Committee, 1891 (68x28mm). No. 4696, 15c, F. Valdés Domínguez, Gato Brothers Cigar Factory, Cayo Hueso, 1894. 35c, Club San Carlos, Cayo Hueso, 1893. 40c, Hotel Myrtle Bank, Kingston, 1892. 50c, Gen. Francisco Gómez Toro, Friends of the Country Society Building, Santo Domingo, 1894. 65c, Máximo Gómez, Gómez's house, Montecristi.

**2007, Apr. 10** ***Perf. 12½x12¼***

**4691-4700** A1227 Set of 10 5.50 5.50

World Food Program Children's Art Exhibition, 10th Anniv. — A1332

**2007, May 3** **Litho.** ***Perf. 12¾***

**4701** A1332 65c multi 1.40 1.40

Folklore Union — A1333

**2007, May 7** ***Perf. 12¼x12½***

**4702** A1333 75c multi 1.60 1.60

Islands and Wildlife A1334

Designs: 5c, Cayo Guillermo, pelican. No. 4704, 15c, Cayo Las Brujas, sea gull. No. 4705, 15c, Cayo Levisa, conches. 20c, Cayo Santa Maria, iguana. 50c, Cayo Ensenachos, plover. 85c, Cayo Largo, Carey turtle.
1p, Cayo Coco, flamingos.

**2007, May 8** ***Perf. 12½x12¼***

**4703-4708** A1334 Set of 6 4.25 4.25

**Souvenir Sheet**

***Imperf***

**4709** A1334 1p multi 2.25 2.25

No. 4709 contains one 40x32mm stamp.

Singers and Songwriters A1335

Designs: 5c, Benny Moré. 10c, Ignacio Piñeiro. 30c, Arsenio Rodríguez. 35c, Miguelito Cuní. 65c, Pio Leyva. 75c, Ibrahim Ferrer. 1p, Miguel Matamoros.

**2007, May 10** ***Perf. 12¾***
**4710-4715** A1335 Set of 6 4.75 4.75

**Souvenir Sheet**
***Imperf***

**4716** A1335 1p multi 2.25 2.25

No. 4716 contains one 32x40mm stamp with simulated perforations.

Souvenir Sheet

Martí Studies Youth Seminary, 35th Anniv. — A1336

**2007, May 19** ***Imperf.***
**4717** A1336 1p multi 2.25 2.25

Cuban Radio and Television Institute, 45th Anniv. A1337

**2007, May 24** ***Perf. 12½x12¼***
**4718** A1337 3p multi 6.50 6.50

Integral Development Group of the Capital, 20th Anniv. A1338

**2007, May 25** **Litho.**
**4719** A1338 65c multi 1.40 1.40

Cuban Admission to the United Nations, 60th Anniv. — A1339

**2007, May 29** ***Perf. 12¾***
**4720** A1339 65c multi 1.40 1.40

2007 Pan American Games, Rio de Janeiro A1340

Designs: No. 4721, 15c, Fencing. No. 4722, 15c, Boxing. 20c, Wrestling. 45c, Running. 65c, Gymnastics. 75c, Cycling. 1p, Games emblem, vert.

**2007, June 20** ***Perf. 12¾***
**4721-4726** A1340 Set of 6 5.00 5.00

**Souvenir Sheet**
***Imperf***

**4727** A1340 1p multi 2.25 2.25

No. 4727 contains one 32x40mm stamp.

Third Technological Transfer and Intl. Trade Workshop A1341

**2007, July 3** ***Perf. 12½x12¼***
**4728** A1341 65c multi 1.40 1.40

Frank País (1934-57), Revolutionary Hero — A1342

**2007, July 30** ***Perf. 12¾***
**4729** A1342 65c multi 1.40 1.40

Radio Cubana, 85th Anniv. — A1343

**2007, Aug. 22** ***Perf. 12¾***
**4730** A1343 65c multi 1.40 1.40

Seven Wonders of the Modern World — A1344

Designs: 10c, Great Wall of China. 15c, Petra, Jordan. 20c, Christ the Redeemer Statue, Brazil. 40c, Machu Picchu, Peru. 65c, Chichén Itzá Pyramids, Mexico. 75c, Roman Colosseum. 85c, Taj Mahal, India.

**2007, Aug. 16** **Litho.** ***Perf. 12¾***
**4731-4737** A1344 Set of 7 6.25 6.25

Transportation A1345

Designs: 10c, Cocotaxis (40x29mm). 15c, Lada 2105 taxi (40x29mm). 30c, Girón VI bus (40x29mm). 40c, Bus trailer on truck (44x27mm). 75c, DAF articulated bus (44x27mm). 85c, Yutong bus (44x27mm). 1p, La Gaviota train.

***Perf. 12¾, 12½x12¼ (#4741-4743)***
**2007, Sept. 3**
**4738-4743** A1345 Set of 6 5.25 5.25

**Souvenir Sheet**
***Imperf***

**4744** A1345 1p multi 2.00 2.00

No. 4744 contains one 40x32mm stamp with simulated perforations.

Central Youth Club, 20th Anniv. — A1346

**2007, Sept. 8** ***Perf. 12¼x12½***
**4745** A1346 65c multi 1.40 1.40

Cubans Convicted of Espionage by United States — A1347

Designs: No. 4746, 65c, Raised hand with "Cuban Five" emblem. No. 4747, 65c, Fernando González Liort. No. 4748, 65c, Gerardo Hernández Nordelo. No. 4749, 65c, Antonio Guerrero Rodriguez. No. 4750, 65c, Ramón Labañino Salazar. No. 4751, 65c, René González Schwerert.

**2007, Sept. 12** ***Perf. 12¾***
**4746-4751** A1347 Set of 6 8.00 8.00

Tree Planting Campaign A1348

**2007, Oct. 24** ***Perf. 12½x12¼***
**4752** A1348 65c multi 1.40 1.40

Rose Varieties A1349

Designs: 5c, Pink Parfait. No. 4754, 15c, Alison Wheatcroft. No. 4755, 15c, Prima Ballerina. 45c, Fragrant Cloud. 50c, Blue Moon. 75c, Grandmère Jenny. 1p, Rosa highdownensis.

**2007, Oct. 25** ***Perf. 12¾***
**4753-4758** A1349 Set of 6 4.25 4.25

**Souvenir Sheet**
***Imperf***

**4759** A1349 1p multi 2.00 2.00

No. 4759 contains one 40x32mm stamp with simulated perforations.

International Design Conference A1350

Designs: 75c, Electronic machine. 85c, Caricatures.

**2007, Oct. 26** ***Perf. 12½x12¼***
**4760-4761** A1350 Set of 2 3.25 3.25

Souvenir Sheet

International Air Mail Service From Cuba, 80th Anniv. — A1351

**2007, Oct. 27** ***Imperf.***
**4762** A1351 1p multi 2.00 2.00

Seventh Natl. Philatelic Championship. No. 4762 has simulated perforations.

Protected Animals A1352

Designs: 5c, Eretmochelys imbricata. 10c, Trichechus manatus. 20c, Mesocapromys sanfelipensis. 30c, Mesocapromys nanus. 45c, Epinephelus itajara. 85c, Balistes vetula. 1p, Chelonia mydas.

**2007, Nov. 15** ***Perf. 12½x12¼***
**4763-4768** A1352 Set of 6 4.00 4.00

**Souvenir Sheet**
***Imperf***

**4769** A1352 1p multi 2.00 2.00

No. 4769 contains one 40x32mm stamp with simulated perforations.

Cuban UNESCO Commission, 60th Anniv. A1353

**2007, Nov. 17** ***Perf. 12½x12¼***
**4770** A1353 65c multi 1.40 1.40

Cuban Railroads, 170th Anniv. — A1354

**2007, Nov. 19** ***Perf. 12¾***
**4771** A1354 3p multi 6.00 6.00

Camagüey Ballet, 40th Anniv. — A1355

**2007, Dec. 1** **Litho.**
**4772** A1355 75c multi 1.50 1.50

Infomed Health Network, 15th Anniv. — A1356

**2007, Dec. 15**
**4773** A1356 65c green & black 1.40 1.40

Federation of University Students, 85th Anniv. — A1357

**2007, Dec. 20**
**4774** A1357 65c multi 1.40 1.40

Seven Marvels of Cuban Civil Engineering A1358

Designs: 5c, White Aqueduct, Havana. 10c, Sewer system, Havana. 20c, Central Highway, Santiago. 30c La Bahia Tunnel, Havana. 85c, Bacunayagua Bridge, Matanzas. 90c, La Farola Viaduct, Guantánamo. 1p, FOSCA Building, Havana.

**2007, Dec. 31** ***Perf. 12¾***
**4775-4780** A1358 Set of 6 5.00 5.00

**Souvenir Sheet**
***Imperf***

**4781** A1358 1p multi 2.00 2.00

No. 4781 contains one 40x32mm stamp with simulated perforations.

World Ozone Layer Protection Day, 20th Anniv. — A1359

**2007** ***Perf. 12¾***
**4782** A1359 65c multi 1.40 1.40

Tourism A1360

No. 4783, 75c — El Yunque, Baracoa and: a, Atlantea perezi. b, Polymita picta.
No. 4784, 75c — Alexander von Humboldt National Park and: a, Eleutherodactylus iberia. b, Solenodon cubanus.

**2007** **Litho.** **Horiz. Pairs, #a-b**
**4783-4784** A1360 Set of 2 6.00 6.00

Miniature Sheet

America Issue, Education For All — A1361

No. 4785: a, Teacher and children, children in uniforms, girl at computer. b, Students at table. c, Students, flag, marchers. d, Artist, people sitting in front of building, man at computer.

**2007**
**4785** A1361 75c Sheet of 4, #a-d 6.00 6.00

Ernesto "Che" Guevara (1928-67) A1362

Designs: 65c, Guevara sitting with other men. 75c, Monument to Guevara, La Higuera, Bolivia. 85c, Guevara and text. 90c, Guevara and marchers.

**2007** ***Perf. 12½x12¼***
**4786-4789** A1362 Set of 4 6.50 6.50
*4789a* Miniature sheet, #4786-4789 6.50 6.50

Historic Central City of Cienfuegos A1363

Buildings: 15c, City Hall. 65c, San Lorenzo and Santo Tomás College. 75c, Tomás Terry Theater. 85c, Ferrer Palace.
1p, Gazebo, José Martí Park.

**2007** **Litho.** ***Perf. 12¾***
**4790-4793** A1363 Set of 4 5.00 5.00

**Souvenir Sheet**

***Imperf***

**4794** A1363 1p multi 2.00 2.00

No. 4794 contains one 40x32mm stamp with simulated perforations.

University of Havana, 280th Anniv. A1364

**2008, Jan. 5** **Litho.** ***Perf. 12½x12¼***
**4795** A1364 65c multi 1.40 1.40

2008 Summer Olympics, Beijing A1365

Designs: 15c, Baseball. 45c, Swimming. 65c, Discus. 75c, Volleyball.

**2008, Jan. 18** ***Perf. 12¾***
**4796-4799** A1365 Set of 4 4.00 4.00

**José Martí Type of 2004**

Designs: No. 4800, 15c, Martí at Twilight Park, New York, 1892, vert. No. 4801, 15c, Martí with members of Cuban Revolutionary Party, 1892, vert. 30c, Martí, and family of Carmen Miyares, Sandy Hill, New York, 1893, vert. 40c, Mausoleum, Santa Ifigenia, vert. 45c, Martí, tomb of Félix Varela, San Agustín. 50c, Martí, Dellundé House, Cabo Haitiano. 65c, Hanábana Memorial, Matanzas. 85c, Cover from 1889 in Postal Museum.

**2008, Jan. 28**
**4800-4807** A1227 Set of 8 7.00 7.00

Subway Trains and Stations A1366

Trains and stations in: No. 4808, 15c, New York. No. 4809, 15c, Paris. 30c, Caracas. 65c, Madrid. 75c, Mexico City. 1.05p, Tokyo.
No. 4814: a, 1866 London Underground train. b, Modern London Underground train, Westminster station emblem.

**2008, Feb. 15** ***Perf. 12½x12¼***
**4808-4813** A1366 Set of 6 6.25 6.25

**Souvenir Sheet**

***Imperf***

**4814** A1366 50c Sheet of 2, #a-b 2.00 2.00

No. 4814 contains two 39x24mm stamps with simulated perforations.

Radio Rebelde, 50th Anniv. — A1367

**2008, Feb. 24** ***Perf. 12¾***
**4815** A1367 75c multi 1.50 1.50

Frontier Guards, 45th Anniv. — A1368

**2008, Mar. 3**
**4816** A1368 65c multi 1.40 1.40

Dr. Mario Muñoz Monroy Third Guerrilla Front, 50th Anniv. — A1369

**2008, Mar. 6** **Litho.** ***Perf. 12¾***
**4817** A1369 75c multi 1.50 1.50

Aquaculture A1370

Designs: No. 4817A, Cyprinus carpio. No. 4817B, Hypophthalmicthys molitrix. 45c, Aristychthys nobilis. 65c, Penaeus vannamei. 75c, Ctenopharyngodon idella. 85c, Clarias gariepinus.
1p, Oreochromis aurea.

**2008, Apr. 8** ***Perf. 12½x12¼***
**4817A** A1370 15c multi .30 .30
**4817B** A1370 15c multi .30 .30
**4817C** A1370 45c multi .90 .90
**4818** A1370 65c multi 1.30 1.30
**4819** A1370 75c multi 1.50 1.50
**4820** A1370 85c multi 1.75 1.75
*Nos. 4817A-4820 (6)* 6.05 6.05

**Souvenir Sheet**

***Imperf***

**4821** A1370 1p multi 2.00 2.00

No. 4821 contains one 31x28mm stamp.

Souvenir Sheet

Cuban Postal Stationery, 130th Anniv. — A1371

**2008, Apr. 24** ***Imperf.***
**4822** A1371 1p multi 2.00 2.00

Bohemia Magazine, Cent. — A1372

**2008, May 10** ***Perf. 12¾***
**4823** A1372 65c multi 1.40 1.40

Second Frank Pais Front, 50th Anniv. — A1373

**2008, Mar. 11** **Litho.** ***Perf. 12¾***
**4824** A1373 65c multi 1.40 1.40

Birds — A1374

Designs: 5c, Cartacuba (Cuban tody). 10c, Ruiseñor (nightingale). 15c, Carpintero verde (green woodpecker). 50c, Tocororo (Cuban trogon). 65c, Catey (parakeet), horiz. 75c, Cabrerito de la Ciénaga (Zapata sparrow), horiz. 90c, Zunzuncito (hummingbird), horiz. 1.05p, Juan Chiví (Cuban vireo), horiz.

**2008, May 22**
**4825-4832** A1374 Set of 8 8.50 8.50

"Wings of Liberty" Symposium, Cuban National Museum of Natural History.

Visit of Indonesian Pres. Sukarno, 48th Anniv. A1375

Sukarno and: No. 4833, 65c, Fidel Castro (shown). No. 4834, 65c, Ernesto "Che" Guevara.

**2008** **Litho.** ***Perf. 12½x12¼***
**4833-4834** A1375 Set of 2 2.60 2.60

Flora and Fauna at Ramsar Sites in Cuba and Iran A1376

No. 4835: a, Cyanolimnas cerverai and Nymphaea ampla, Ciénaga de Zapata, Cuba. b, Nelumbo nucifera and Porphyrio porphyrio, Anzali, Iran.

**2008, Oct. 16** **Litho.** ***Perf. 12½x12¼***
**4835** Horiz. pair with central label 3.00 3.00
*a.-b.* A1376 75c Either single 1.50 1.50

See Iran No. 3003.

Cuban Literature, 400th Anniv. — A1377

Designs: 15c, Emblem written backward on torn page. 75c, Snails. 2.05p, White star in red triangle.

**2008, Oct. 20** ***Perf. 12¼x12½***
**4836-4838** A1377 Set of 3 6.00 6.00

National Ballet, 60th Anniv. — A1378

Designs: 10c, Dancers in Swan Lake (El Lago de los Cisnes). 15c, Dancers in Giselle. 50c, Dancers in Coppélia, horiz. 65c, Dancer in Romeo and Juliet, horiz. 75c, Dancers in The Nutcracker (Cascanueces), horiz. 85c, Scenery for Sleeping Beauty (La Bella Durmiente del Bosque), horiz.
1p, Ballerina at Intl. Ballet Festival, Havana.

**2008, Oct. 28** ***Perf. 12¾***
**4839-4844** A1378 Set of 6 6.00 6.00

**Souvenir Sheet**

***Imperf***

**4845** A1378 1p multi 2.00 2.00

No. 4845 has simulated perforations.

Vilma Espín Guillois (1930-2007), Wife of Pres. Raúl Castro A1379

**2008** ***Perf. 12¾***
**4846** A1379 65c multi 1.40 1.40

Joséito Fernández (1908-79), Singer — A1380

**2008**
**4847** A1380 65c multi 1.40 1.40

Dr. Carlos J. Finlay (1833-1915), Yellow Fever Researcher — A1381

**2008**
**4848** A1381 65c multi 1.40 1.40

José Raúl Capablanca (1888-1942), World Chess Champion A1382

Designs: 1.05p, Capablanca playing chess. 2.05p, Capablanca seated, vert.

**2008** ***Perf. 12½x12¼, 12¼x12½***
**4849-4850** A1382 Set of 2 6.25 6.25

Dogs — A1383

Designs: 10c, Neapolitan mastiff. 15c, Golden retriever. 40c, Rottweiler. 65c, Shetland sheepdog. 85c, Chow chow. 90c, Boxer.
1p, Chihuahua.

**2008** ***Perf. 12¾***
**4851-4856** A1383 Set of 6 6.25 6.25

**Souvenir Sheet**

***Imperf***

**4857** A1383 1p multi 2.00 2.00

Owls and Butterflies — A1384

Designs: No. 4858, 15c, Tyto alba, Lycaena dispar. No. 4859, 15c, Bubo bubo, Lolana iolas. 45c, Strix nebulosa, Vanessa cardui. 65c, Strix aluco, Colias erate. 75c, Asio otus, Aporia crataegi. 85c, Strix uralensis, Colias hecla.
1p, Anthocharis damone butterfly, horiz.

**2008** ***Perf. 12¾***
**4858-4863** A1384 Set of 6 6.00 6.00

**Souvenir Sheet**

***Imperf***

**4864** A1384 1p multi 2.00 2.00

No. 4864 contains one 40x32mm stamp. EFIRO 2008 Intl. Philatelic Exhibition, Romania (No. 4864).

Animals in National Zoo — A1385

Designs: 5c, Panthera leo. 10c, Ailurus fulgens. 15c, Cacatua galerita. 30c, Crocodylus rhombifer. 40c, Phoenicopterus ruber. 2.05p, Equus burchelli.
1p, Loxodonta africana.

**2008** ***Perf. 12½x12¼***
**4865-4870** A1385 Set of 6 6.25 6.25

**Souvenir Sheet**

***Imperf***

**4871** A1385 1p multi 2.00 2.00

No. 4871 contains one 40x32mm stamp with simulated perforations.

Ernesto "Che" Guevara (1928-67), Revolutionary Leader A1386

Designs: 65c, Guevara as infant with mother, birthplace in Rosario, Argentina. 75c, Guevara as boy, childhood home, Villa Nydia. 85c, Guevara as young man, Guevara on bicycle. 1.05p, Guevara on raft, Guevara with cigar.

**2008** ***Perf. 12¾***
**4872-4875** A1386 Set of 4 6.75 6.75
*4875a* Souvenir sheet, #4872-4875 6.75 6.75

America Issue, National Holidays A1387

Designs: 15c, Starting Day of the War of Independence. 65c, Liberation Day. 75c, Labor Day. 2.05p, National Rebellion Day.

**2008** **Litho.** ***Perf. 12½x12¼***
**4876-4879** A1387 Set of 4 7.25 7.25
*4879a* Souvenir sheet of 4, #4876-4879 7.25 7.25

Tourism — A1388

Buildings in: No. 4880, 15c, Havana. No. 4881, 15c, Trinidad. 30c, Sancti Spiritus. 65c, Camagüey. 75c, Bayamo. 85c, Santiago de Cuba.
1p, Baracoa.

**2008** ***Perf. 12¼x12½***
**4880-4885** A1388 Set of 6 5.75 5.75

**Souvenir Sheet**

***Imperf***

**4886** A1388 1p multi 2.00 2.00

No. 4886 contains one 32x40mm stamp with simulated perforations.

Gran Caribe Hotels, 50th Anniv. — A1389

Designs: 5c, Hotel Habana Riviera. 10c, Hotel Habana Libre, vert. 15c, Hotel Deauville, vert. 50c, Hotel Victoria, vert. 65c, Hotel Presidente.
1p, Hotel Sevilla, vert.

**2008** ***Perf. 12¾***
**4887-4891** A1389 Set of 5 3.00 3.00

**Souvenir Sheet**

***Imperf***

**4892** A1389 1p multi 2.00 2.00

No. 4892 contains one 32x40mm stamp with simulated perforations.

Carlos de la Torre y la Huerta (1858-1950), Naturalist A1390

De la Torre y la Huerta and: 5c, Hand holding shells. 15c, Polymita picta nigrolimbata, light blue background. 50c, Polymita picta nigrolimbata, pink background. 65c, Polymita picta iolimbata. 75c, Polymita picta nigrolimbata, light green background. 90c, Polymita picta fuscolimbata.
1p, Liguus fasciatus.

**2008** ***Perf. 12½x12¼***
**4893-4898** A1390 Set of 6 6.00 6.00

**Souvenir Sheet**

***Imperf***

**4899** A1390 1p multi 2.00 2.00

No. 4899 contains one 40x32mm stamp with simulated perforations.

Paleolithic Man and Animals A1391

Designs: 10c, Australopithecus afarensis and Megatherium. 15c, Australopithecus africanus and Toxodon. 50c, Australopithecus robustus and Bison. 65c, Homo habilis and Hippidion. 75c, Homo erectus and Meganteron. 90c, Neanderthal man and Mammoths.
1p, Coelodonts.

**2008** ***Perf. 12¾***
**4900-4905** A1391 Set of 6 6.25 6.25

**Souvenir Sheet**

***Imperf***

**4906** A1391 1p multi 2.00 2.00

No. 4906 contains one 45x34mm stamp with simulated perforations.

A1392

Transportation — A1392a

Designs: 15c, 1802 steam carriage of Richard Trevithick. 30c, 1829 steam carriage of Sir Goldsworthy Gurney. 40c, 1832 steam carriage of William Church. 65c, 1858 steam carriage of Thomas Rickett. 75c, 1890 Motorwagen of Karl Benz. 85c, 1836 steam omnibus of Walter Hancock.
1p, 1958 Panhard-Levassor automobile.

**2008** ***Perf. 12½x12¼***
**4907-4912** A1392 Set of 6 6.25 6.25

**Souvenir Sheet**

***Imperf***

**4913** A1392a 1p multi 2.00 2.00

No. 4913 has simulated perforations.

Matanzas, 315th Anniv. A1393

Designs: 15c, Building arches, Plaza de la Vigía. 40c, Palacio Junco Provincial Museum. 50c, Fire house. 75c, Palace of Justice. 85c, Sauto Theater. 90c, Palace of Government.
1p, Unknown Soldier's Monument, vert.

**2008** ***Perf. 12½x12¼***
**4914-4919** A1393 Set of 6 7.25 7.25

**Souvenir Sheet**

***Imperf***

**4920** A1393 1p multi 2.00 2.00

No. 4920 has simulated perforations.

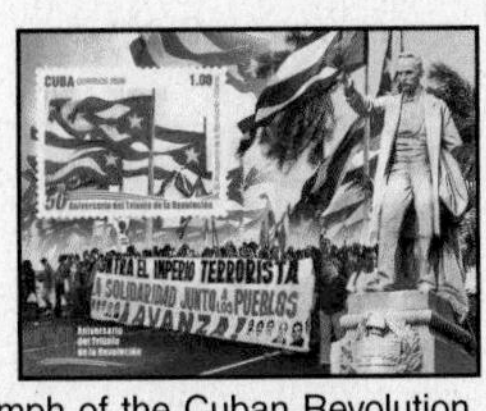

Triumph of the Cuban Revolution, 50th Anniv. — A1394

No. 4921, 15c: a, Liberation Day (man with wide-brimmed hat at left). b, Liberation Day (tank at left). c, Arrival of Fidel Castro in Havana. d, First march. e, Fidel Castro, Revolutionary Government Prime Minister, addressing crowd. f, Camilo Cienfuegos dissolves Bureau for the Repression of Communist Activities. g, Granting of Cuban citizenship to Ernesto "Che" Guevara. h, Fidel Castro's first visit to Venezuela. i, Creation of the P.N.R. (National Revolutionary Police). j, Creation of State Security organizations. k, Creation of T.G.F. (Border Guard). l, Agrarian Reform Law. m, Takeover of Cuban telephone system. n, Creation of the F.M.C. (Federation of Cuban Women). o, Creation of the C.D.R. (Committees for the Defense of the Revolution). p, Start of literacy campaign. q, Creation of I.N.D.E.R. (Institute of Sports, Physical Education and Recreation). r, Radio across Cuba. s, Designation of Guevara as Industry Minister. t, Creation of Union of Young Communists. u, Creation of the Civil Defense. v, Creation of the National Civil Defense Committee. w, First sugar harvest. x, Guevara speaks at the United Nations.

No. 4922, 15c: a, Constitution of the Central Committee of the Cuban Communist Party. b, Day of the Heroic Guerrilla. c, Free distribution of Guevara's diary. d, First National Education and Cultural Congress. e, First Congress of the P.C.C. (Cuban Communist Party). f, First Rural Education Congress. g, Establishment in Cuba of Intl. Children's Day. h, Vaccinations in Cuba, 205th anniv. i, Creation of M.I.N.A.Z. (Cuban Ministry of Sugar). j, Creation of I.N.P. (National Fishing Institute). k, Development of fishing industry. l, 11th World Youth and Student Festival. m, Cuban cosmonaut. n, Day of Cuban Science (building at right). o, Day of Cuban Science (building at left). p, Family doctors and nurses. q, Elimination of apartheid, 15th anniv. r, Beginning of Battle of Ideas. s, Social security. t, Creation of the E.I.E.D. u, National culture (ballet dancer at left). v, National culture (guitarists at right). w, Battle of Ideas program (classroom at right). x, Battle of Ideas program (people waving flags at right).

No. 4923, 1p, Cuban flags. No. 4924, 1p, Revolution Plaza, Havana.

**2009, Jan. 1** **Litho.** ***Perf. 12¾***

**Sheets of 24, #a-x**

**4921-4922** A1394 Set of 2 14.50 14.50

**Souvenir Sheets**

***Imperf***

**4923-4924** A1394 Set of 2 4.00 4.00

Nos. 4923-4924 have simulated perforations.

Ernesto "Che" Guevara and Cuban Flag — A1394a

**2009** **Litho.** ***Perf. 12¾***
**4924A** A1394a 75c multi 1.50 1.50

Cuban Revolution, 50th anniv. See Russia No. 7124.

Second World Baseball Classic A1395

Designs: 5c, Batter swinging at ball. 10c, Play at home plate. 15c, Fielder stretching to

catch ball. 45c, Pitcher in wind-up. 65c, Runner sliding into base. 75c, Runner and fielder watching ball.
1p, Cuban team.

**2009, Jan. 27** ***Perf. 12¾***
**4925-4930** A1395 Set of 6 4.50 4.50

**Souvenir Sheet**
***Imperf***

**4931** A1395 1p multi 2.00 2.00

No. 4931 has simulated perforations.

Souvenir Sheet

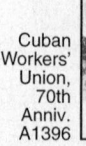

Cuban Workers' Union, 70th Anniv. A1396

**2009, Jan. 29** ***Imperf.***
**4932** A1396 1p multi 2.00 2.00

No. 4932 has simulated perforations.

Santa María del Puerto de Príncipe, 495th Anniv. — A1397

**2009, Feb. 2** ***Perf. 12¾***
**4933** A1397 90c multi 1.90 1.90

Souvenir Sheet

13th Intl. Information Fair and Convention, Havana — A1398

**2009, Feb. 9** ***Imperf.***
**4934** A1398 1p multi 2.00 2.00

No. 4934 has simulated perforations.

Charles Darwin (1809-92), Naturalist A1398a

Designs: 10c, Darwin and his birthplace, Shrewsbury, England. 65c, HMS Beagle and map of its expedition. 75c, Publication of *On the Origin of Species.* 85c, Darwin and his notes.

***Perf. 12½x12¼***
**2009, Feb. 12** **Litho.**
**4934A-4934D** A1398a Set of 4 4.75 4.75

Art — A1399

Designs: 15c, Coloritmo, by Alejandro Otero. 30c, Atmósfera Cromoplástica IV, by Luis Tomasello. 40c, Autopista del Sur, by León Ferrari. 65c, Tridim-L, by Victor Vasarely. 75c, Untitled work, by Jesús Soto. 85c, Untitled work, by Julio Le Parc.
1p, Physicromie 105, by Carlos Cruz Diez, horiz.

**2009, Feb. 25** ***Perf. 12¾***
**4935-4940** A1399 Set of 6 6.25 6.25

**Souvenir Sheet**
***Imperf***

**4941** A1399 1p multi 2.00 2.00

No. 4941 has simulated perforations.

High Speed Trains A1400

Designs: No. 4942, 15c, Acela Express, US. No. 4943, 15c, AVE, Spain. 30c, ATP Eurostar, Great Britain. 65c, ICE, Germany. 75c, ICN, Switzerland. 1.05p, TGV, France.
No. 4948: a, Shinkansen Model 500, Japan. b, Shinkansen Model 700, Japan.

**2009, Feb. 27** ***Perf. 12½x12¼***
**4942-4947** A1400 Set of 6 6.25 6.25

**Souvenir Sheet**
***Imperf***

**4948** A1400 50c Sheet of 2, #a-b 2.00 2.00

No. 4948 has simulated perforations.

Cuban Arts and Cinematographic Industry Institute, 50th Anniv. — A1401

Designs: No. 4949, 10c, Actress from *La Bella del Alhambra.* No. 4950, 10c, Actress from *Reina y Rey.* No. 4951, 15c, Character from animated film *Elpidio Valdés.* No. 4952, 15c, Actresses from *Lucía.* 45c, Actor from *Primera Carga al Machete.* 65c, Actor from *El Hombre de Maisinicú.* 75c, Actor and actress from *Clandestinos.* 90c, Actress from *Retrato de Teresa.* 1.05p, Santiago Alvarez, ICAIC reporter.
1p, Scene from *Fresa y Chocolate.*

**2009, Mar. 24** ***Perf. 12½x12¼***
**4949-4957** A1401 Set of 9 8.75 8.75

**Souvenir Sheet**
***Imperf***

**4958** A1401 1p multi 2.00 2.00

No. 4958 has simulated perforations.

State Security Organizations, 50th Anniv. — A1402

**2009, Mar. 26** ***Perf. 12¼x12½***
**4959** A1402 65c multi 1.40 1.40

Motorcycles A1403

Designs: 10c, Cagiva Mito N1. 15c, Honda CBR 900. 50c, Hyosung-GT 8. 65c, Kawasaki ZX-7R 750cc. 75c, Gussi MGS. 90c, Ducati Monster 900.
1p, Hyosung-GT 125-R-LD, vert.

**2009, Apr. 8** ***Perf. 12¾***
**4960-4965** A1403 Set of 6 6.25 6.25

**Souvenir Sheet**
***Imperf***

**4966** A1403 1p multi 2.00 2.00

China 2009 World Philatelic Exhibition, Luoyang. No. 4966 has simulated perforations.

Cats — A1404

Designs: 10c, Cat and kittens. 15c, Kittens and baseball. 40c, Two cats clawing fabric. 65c, Two cats on tile floor. 75c, Cat. 1.05p, Cat eating food.
1p, Two cats on roof, vert.

**2009, Apr. 12** ***Perf. 12¾***
**4967-4972** A1404 Set of 6 6.25 6.25

**Souvenir Sheet**
***Imperf***

**4973** A1404 1p multi 2.00 2.00

No. 4973 has simulated perforations.

Tourism — A1405

Art from hotels and restaurants: No. 4974, 10c, Stained-glass window, by René Portocarrero, Bodeguita del Medio Restaurant. No. 4975, Detail from mural, by Amelia Peláez, Hotel Habana Libre Tryp. 45c, Painting by Domingo Ramos, Hotel Nacional de Cuba, horiz. 65c, Detail from mural, by Mariano Rodríguez, Hotel Bello Caribe, horiz. 75c, Detail from mural, by Raúl Martínez, Hotel Bella Caribe, horiz. 85c, Mural, by Manuel A. Sosabravo, Hotel Habana Libre Tryp, horiz.
1p, Mural by various artists, Hotel Inglaterra, horiz.

**2009, Apr. 21** ***Perf. 12¾***
**4974-4979** A1405 Set of 6 6.00 6.00

**Souvenir Sheet**
***Imperf***

**4980** A1405 1p multi 2.00 2.00

No. 4980 has simulated perforations.

Haydee Santamaría Cuadrado (1922-80), Founder of Casa de las Americas A1406

**2009, Apr. 28** ***Perf. 12¾***
**4981** A1406 3p multi 6.00 6.00

World Heritage Sites — A1407

Designs: 15c, Havana. 45c, Cienfuegos. 50c, Trinidad. 1.05p, Camagüey.

**2009, May 8** **Litho.**
**4982-4985** A1407 Set of 4 4.50 4.50
*4985a* Souvenir sheet, #4982-4985 4.50 4.50

Parrots A1408

Designs: 5c, Guacamayo sereno. 10c, Guacamayo azul-dorado. 15c, Guacamayo de hombro rojo. No. 4989, 20c, Guacamayo cuellodorado. No. 4990, Guacamayo de Jacinto. 65c, Guacamayo escarlata. 75c, Guacamayo frente rojo. 90c, Guacamayo militar.

**2009, May 16**
**4986-4993** A1408 Set of 8 6.00 6.00

Institute of Design, 25th Anniv. A1409

**2009, May 28** ***Perf. 12½x12¼***
**4994** A1409 65c multi 1.40 1.40

Souvenir Sheet

Ernesto Guevara Central Palace of Pioneers, 30th Anniv. — A1410

**2009, June 1** ***Imperf.***
**4995** A1410 1p multi 2.00 2.00

No. 4995 has simulated perforations.

National Revolutionary Police, 50th Anniv. A1411

**2009, June 6** ***Perf. 12½x12¼***
**4996** A1411 1.05p multi 2.10 2.10

FORDES Gallery, 5th Anniv. A1412

**2009, June 14**
**4997** A1412 75c multi 1.50 1.50

Zoo Animals A1413

Designs: 5c, Ceratotherium simum. 10c, Syncerus caffer caffer. 15c, Acinonyx jubatus, vert. 30c, Papio hamadryas, vert. 40c, Struthio camelus, vert. 2.05p, Lycaon pictus, vert.
1p, Hippopotamus amphibius.

**2009, June 20** ***Perf. 12¾***
**4998-5003** A1413 Set of 6 6.25 6.25

**Souvenir Sheet**
***Imperf***

**5004** A1413 1p multi 2.00 2.00

No. 5004 contains one 47x30mm stamp with simulated perforations.

Cuban Cuisine A1414

Designs: 40c, Arroz con pollo a la chorrera (chicken with rice). 45c, Plátano maduro frito (fried plantains). 50c, Frijoles negros dormidos (black beans with onion).

**2009, June 29** ***Perf. 12½x12¼***
**5005-5007** A1414 Set of 3 2.75 2.75

Diplomatic Relations Between Cuba and Sri Lanka, 50th Anniv. — A1415

**2009, July 29** ***Perf. 12¼x12½***
**5008** A1415 1.05p multi 2.10 2.10

Peace and National Sovereignty Movement, 60th Anniv. — A1416

**2009, Aug. 4** ***Perf. 12¾***
**5009** A1416 65c multi 1.40 1.40

Los Malagones Peasant Militia, 50th Anniv. — A1417

**2009, Aug. 31** ***Perf. 12¼x12½***
**5010** A1417 90c multi 1.90 1.90

Havana Convention Center, 30th Anniv. — A1418

**2009, Sept. 3** ***Perf. 12¾***
**5011** A1418 50c multi 1.00 1.00

Tourism — A1419

Birds: 15c, Coloptes fernandinae. 40c, Toreonis inexpectata. 50c, Ferminia cerverai. 65c, Agelaius assimilis. 75c, Mellisuga helenae. 90c, todus multicolor.
1p, Aratinga euops.

**2009, Sept. 14** ***Perf. 12¾***
**5012-5017** A1419 Set of 6 6.75 6.75

**Souvenir Sheet**

***Imperf***

**5018** A1419 1p multi 2.00 2.00

No. 5018 has simulated perforations.

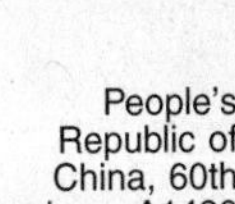

People's Republic of China, 60th Anniv. — A1420

**2009, Sept. 28** **Litho.** ***Perf. 12¾***
**5019** A1420 85c multi 1.75 1.75

Cubana Airlines, 80th Anniv. A1421

Designs: 5c, Ford Trimotor. 15c, Sikorsky S-38B. 45c, DC-3. 50c, DC-4. 65c, IL-62M. 75c, IL-96 300.
1p, Tu-204.

**2009, Oct. 8** ***Perf. 12½x12¼***
**5020-5025** A1421 Set of 6 5.25 5.25

**Souvenir Sheet**

***Imperf***

**5026** A1421 1p multi 2.00 2.00

No. 5026 has simulated perforations.

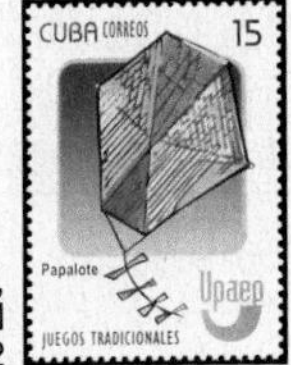


America Issue, Traditional Games — A1422

Designs: 15c, Kite. 65c, Top. 75c, Dominos. 2.05p, Jacks.

**2009, Oct. 12** ***Perf. 12¾***
**5027-5030** A1422 Set of 4 7.25 7.25
*5030a* Souvenir sheet, #5027-5030 7.25 7.25

Souvenir Sheet

First Rocket Mail Flight in Cuba, 70th Anniv. A1423

**2009, Oct. 15** ***Imperf.***
**5031** A1423 1p multi 2.00 2.00

Ministry of the Revolutionary Armed Forces, 50th Anniv. — A1424

**2009, Oct. 16** ***Perf. 12¾***
**5032** A1424 75c multi 1.50 1.50

Disappearance of Camilo Cienfuegos, 50th Anniv. — A1425

**2009, Oct. 28** ***Perf. 12½x12¼***
**5033** A1425 65c multi 1.40 1.40

Rights of the Child Convention, 20th Anniv. — A1426

**2009, Nov. 20** ***Perf. 12¾***
**5034** A1426 1.05p multi 2.10 2.10

Cuban Federation of Sport Fishing, 30th Anniv. — A1427

Designs: 15c, Fisherman pulling fish into boat. 30c, Fisherman in water holding rod and fish. 45c, Sailfish and boat. No. 5038, 65c, Fisherman in water holding rod and fish, horiz. 75c, Fish on line, two fishermen in boat, horiz. 85c, Fishermen on sea wall, horiz.
No,. 5041, 65c, Tilapia, horiz

***Perf. 12¼x12½, 12½x12¼***

**2009, Nov. 21**
**5035-5040** A1427 Set of 6 6.50 6.50

**Souvenir Sheet**

***Imperf***

**5041** A1427 65c multi 1.40 1.40

No. 5041 has simulated perforations.

Ministry of Foreign Relations, 50th Anniv. A1428

**2009, Dec. 23** ***Perf. 12½x12¼***
**5042** A1428 1.05p multi 2.10 2.10

Peony — A1429

**2009** ***Perf. 13¼x13½***
**5043** A1429 30c multi .60 .60

Printed in sheets of 4.

José L. Guerra Aguiar Cuban Postal Museum, 45th Anniv. A1430

**2010, Jan. 2** ***Perf. 12½x12¼***
**5044** A1430 65c multi 1.40 1.40

A1431

A1432

A1433

New Year 2010 (Year of the Tiger) — A1434

**2010, Jan. 5** ***Perf. 12¾***
**5045** A1431 15c multi .30 .30
**5046** A1432 15c multi .30 .30
**5047** A1433 15c multi .30 .30
**5048** A1434 15c multi .30 .30
***a.*** Souvenir sheet, #5045-5048 1.25 1.25
*Nos. 5045-5048 (4)* 1.20 1.20

January 1960 Speech of Fidel Castro, 50th Anniv. A1435

**2010, Jan. 15** ***Perf. 12½x12¼***
**5049** A1435 65c multi 1.40 1.40

Diplomatic Relations Between Cuba and Indonesia, 50th Anniv. A1436

**2010, Jan. 22**
**5050** A1436 85c multi 1.75 1.75

Association of Rebel Youth, 50th Anniv. A1437

**2010, Jan. 28**
**5051** A1437 3p multi 6.00 6.00

Trains — A1438

Designs: 5c, Fidel Castro leaving train. 10c, DF7G-C locomotive. 15c, Tank car. 65c, Flat car carrying shipping containers. 75c, Box cars. 1.05p, DF7K-C locomotive.
1p, Locomotive at end of track, vert.

**2010, Jan. 29** ***Perf. 12¾***
**5052-5057** A1438 Set of 6 5.50 5.50

**Souvenir Sheet**

***Imperf***

**5058** A1438 1p multi 2.00 2.00

Diplomatic Relations Between Cuba and India, 50th Anniv. — A1439

**2010, Feb. 10** ***Perf. 12¾***
**5059** A1439 85c multi 1.75 1.75

National Aquarium, 50th Anniv. — A1440

Designs: 10c, Bispira brunnea. No. 5061, 15c, Hypoplectrus gummigutta. No. 5062, 15c, Holocanthus ciliaris. 50c, Seal. 75c, Epinephelus guttatus. 85c, Tursiops truncatus.
1p, Acanthurus coeruleus.

**2010, Feb. 12** ***Perf. 12¾***
**5060-5065** A1440 Set of 6 5.00 5.00

**Souvenir Sheet**

***Imperf***

**5066** A1440 1p multi 2.00 2.00

No. 5066 has simulated perforations.

A1441

La Colmenita Youth Theater Company, 20th Anniv. — A1442

**2010, Feb. 14** ***Perf. 12¾***
**5067** A1441 50c multi 1.00 1.00
**5068** A1442 50c multi 1.00 1.00

Underwater Photography A1443

Designs: 10c, Fish and coral. 15c, Coral and starfish. 45c, Crab and sea anemone. 50c, Sponges and feather duster worms. 75c, Sea cucumber and coral. 85c, Sea horse and diver photographing tube worm.
1p, Fish and diver.

**2010, Feb. 20** ***Perf. 12½x12¼***
**5069-5074** A1443 Set of 6 5.75 5.75

**Souvenir Sheet**

***Imperf***

**5075** A1443 1p multi 2.00 2.00

Central Planning, 50th Anniv. A1444

**2010, Mar. 11** ***Perf. 12½x12¼***
**5076** A1444 75c multi 1.50 1.50

Dogs and Art — A1445

Designs: 10c, Peruvian hairless dog, Mochica figurine of dog, Peru. 15c, Bichon Frise, pitcher depicting hunter and dogs. 40c, Neapolitan mastiff, Roman mosaic of hunter and dog. 65c, Chihuahua, figurine of dog, map of Colima, Mexico. 75c, Pug, Chinese painting of hunters and dog. 90c, King Charles spaniel, The Birth of Louis XIII, by Peter Paul Rubens.
1p, Pharaoh hound, Egyptian painting from tomb of Ipy.

**2010, Mar. 12** ***Perf. 12¾***
**5077-5082** A1445 Set of 6 6.00 6.00

**Souvenir Sheet**

***Imperf***

**5083** A1445 1p multi 2.00 2.00

No. 5083 has simulated perforations.

Diplomatic Relations Between Cuba and Canada, 65th Anniv. — A1446

**2010, Mar. 16** ***Perf. 12¾***
**5084** A1446 65c multi 1.40 1.40

Bilateral Relations Between Cuba and Namibia, 20th Anniv. — A1447

**2010, Mar. 24** **Litho.**
**5085** A1447 85c multi 1.75 1.75

2010 World Cup Soccer Championships, South Africa — A1448

Flags of competing nations, various soccer players and list of teams in: 15c, Groups A and B. 45c, Groups C and D. 65c, Groups E and F. 75c, Groups G and H.

**2010, Mar. 24**
**5086-5089** A1448 Set of 4 4.00 4.00

Congress of the Young Communist's League A1449

**2010, Apr. 2**
**5090** A1449 65c multi 1.40 1.40

National Symphonic Orchestra, 50th Anniv. A1450

Designs: 15c, Amadeo Roldán (1900-39), composer. 30c, Gonzalo Roig (1890-1970), composer. 40c, Enrique González Mántici (1912-74), composer. 75c, Manuel Duchesne Cuzán, General director of National Symphonic Orchestra.

**2010, Apr. 11** ***Perf. 12½x12¼***
**5091-5094** A1450 Set of 4 3.25 3.25

Diplomatic Relations Between Cuba and Cambodia, 50th Anniv. A1451

**2010, Apr. 15**
**5095** A1451 85c multi 1.75 1.75

Cuban National Chorus, 50th Anniv. A1452

**2010, Apr. 17** **Litho.**
**5096** A1452 90c multi 1.90 1.90

First Cuban Computer, 40th Anniv. — A1453

**2010, Apr. 18** ***Perf. 12¾***
**5097** A1453 75c multi 1.50 1.50

First Cuban Stamps, 155th Anniv. A1454

Designs: 75c, Matanzas mail box, 1859, bicyclist in front of building. 85c, Cuba #147, account book of first postal administrator, 1765.

**2010, Apr. 24** ***Perf. 12½x12¼***
**5098-5099** A1454 Set of 2 3.25 3.25

Tourism — A1455

Designs: 15c, Santiago de Cuba. 20c, Guantánamo. 35c, Holguín. 65c, Camagüey. 75c, Granma. 90c, Las Tunas.
1p, Santiago de Cuba, diff.

**2010, May 4** ***Perf. 12¼x12½***
**5100-5105** A1455 Set of 6 6.00 6.00

**Souvenir Sheet**

***Imperf***

**5106** A1455 1p multi 2.00 2.00

ICAIC Latin American Newsreels, 50th Anniv. — A1456

**2010, June 1** ***Perf. 12¾***
**5107** A1456 75c multi 1.50 1.50

Flora and Fauna A1457

Designs: 15c, Dellia sp. 35c, Bietia purpurea. 40c, Anolis equestris. 65c, Broughtonia orgiesiana. 75c, Priotrochatella stellata. 85c, Todus multicolor, vert.
1p, Pinus caribaea.

***Perf. 12½x12¼, 12¼x12½***

**2010, June 11**
**5108-5113** A1457 Set of 6 6.50 6.50

**Souvenir Sheet**

***Imperf***

**5114** A1457 1p multi 2.00 2.00

Expo 2010, Shanghai A1458

Map of China, aviation posters and aircraft: 5c, Savoia-Marchetti 55X. 10c, Farman 60 Goliath. 15c, Fokker VII. 45c, Koolhoven F.K. 50. 65c, Junkers 52/3M. 85c, Latécoère 28.
1p, Handley Page 42E.

**2010, Apr. 26 Litho.** ***Perf. 12½x12¼***
**5115-5120** A1458 Set of 6 4.50 4.50

**Souvenir Sheet**

***Imperf***

**5121** A1458 1p multi 2.00 2.00

No. 5121 has simulated perforations.

Writings of José Martí A1459

Designs: No. 5122, 15c, *La Patria Libre,* white warbler, flag similar to Chile's. No. 5123, 15c, *La Nacion,* great antshrike, flag of Argentina. No. 5124, 15c, *Revista Universal,* king vulture, flag of Mexico. No. 5125, 15c, Proclamation of President of Paraguay, plantcutter, flag of Paraguay. No. 5126, 15c, *Patria,* hummingbird, flag of Cuba. No. 5127, 15c, Montecristi Manifesto, woodpecker, flag similar to Dominican Republic's. No. 5128, 15c, *La República Española y la Revolucion Cubana,* house sparrow and flag similar to Spain's, vert. No. 5129, 15c, *Mis Hijos* (translation of Victor Hugo's *Mes Fils*), long-tailed tit, flag of France, vert. No. 5130, 15c, *Guatemala,* quetzal, flag of Guatemala, vert. 65c, Pamphlet for International Monetary Conference, crested gallito, flag of Uruguay, vert. 75c, *Revista Venezolana,* troupial, flag of Venezuela, vert. 90c, Books of poetry, quill pen and inkwell, vert.

***Perf. 12½x12¼, 12¼x12½***

**2010, May 19**
**5122-5133** A1459 Set of 12 7.50 7.50

Birds Endemic to Various Countries A1460

Designs: 5c, Eumomota superciliosa, Nicaragua. 10c, Priotelus temnurus, Cuba. 15c, Amazona imperialis, Dominica. No. 5137, 20c, Amazona guildingii, St. Vincent and the Grenadines. No. 5138, 20c, Fregata magnificens, Antigua and Barbuda. 65c, Vultur gryphus, Bolivia. 75c, Icterus icterus, Venezuela, vert. 90c, Turdus rufiventris, Brazil, vert.

**2010, May 26** ***Perf. 12¾***
**5134-5141** A1460 Set of 8 6.00 6.00

Ernest Hemingway Intl. Fishing Tournament, 60th Anniv. — A1461

Emblem and: No. 5142, 65c, Fishing boat, rod and reel. No. 5143, 65c, Ernest Hemingway. No. 5144, 65c, Swordfish. No. 5145, 65c Trophy.

**2010, May 29** ***Perf. 12¼x12½***
**5142-5145** A1461 Set of 4 5.25 5.25

Dr. Enrique Hart Ramírez (1900-89), Judge — A1462

**2010, June 1** ***Perf. 12¾***
**5146** A1462 65c multi 1.40 1.40

Diplomatic Relations Between Cuba and North Korea, 50th Anniv. — A1463

**2010, Aug. 29** **Litho.**
**5147** A1463 85c multi 1.75 1.75

La Caridad Theater, Santa Clara, 125th Anniv. — A1464

Designs: 15c, Theater in 1885. 30c, Theater in 2010. 75c, Theater interior. 90c, Marta Abreu de Estévez (1845-1909), philanthropist, vert.

**2010, Sept. 8**
**5148-5151** A1464 Set of 4 4.25 4.25

Architectural Arches of Havana A1465

Designs: 15c, Elliptical arch. 65c, Mixtilinear arch. 75c, Polylobular arch.

**2010, Sept. 9** ***Perf. 12½x12¼***
**5152-5154** A1465 Set of 3 3.25 3.25

Lighthouses — A1466

Maps and: No. 5155, 15c, Cayo Jutía Lighthouse, Pinar del Rio. No. 5156, 15c, Cayo Cruz del Padre Lighthouse, Matanzas. No. 5157, 15c, Cayo Lucrecia Lighthouse, Holguin. 2.05p, Morro Lighthouse, Santiago de Cuba.

**2010, Sept. 15** *Perf. 12¼x12½*
**5155-5158** A1466 Set of 4 5.00 5.00
*5158a* Souvenir sheet, #5155-5158 5.00 5.00

Electric Automobiles A1467

Designs: 5c, 1893 Jeantaud and Raffard. 10c, 1903 American Pope-Tribune. 15c, 1903 STAE. 20c, Matra Zoom. 45c, Zilent. 75c, Jeep Treo.
1p, Aptera, vert.

**2010, Sept. 20** *Perf. 12¾*
**5159-5164** A1467 Set of 6 3.50 3.50

**Souvenir Sheet**

***Imperf***

**5165** A1467 1p multi 2.00 2.00

Portugal 2010 Intl. Philatelic Exhibition. No. 5165 has simulated perforations.

Tourism A1468

Designs: 20c, Papilio androgeus epidaurus, Viñales National Park. 50c, Mesocapromys nanus, Ciénaga de Zapata National Park. 75c, Trichechus manatus manatus, Alejandro de Humboldt National Park. 90c, Amazona leucocephala, Desembarco del Granma National Park.

**2010, Sept. 27** *Perf. 12½x12¼*
**5166-5169** A1468 Set of 4 4.75 4.75

Diplomatic Relations Between Cuba and People's Republic of China, 50th Anniv. A1469

Designs: No. 5170, 15c, Chinese Army, flag of People's Republic of China. No. 5171, 15c, Chinese landscape, arms of People's Republic of China. No. 5172, 85c, Cuban soldiers, horses and boat, flag of Cuba. No. 5173, 85c, Cuban landscape, arms of Cuba.

**2010, Sept. 28**
**5170-5173** A1469 Set of 4 4.00 4.00

America Issue, National Symbols — A1470

Designs: No. 5174, 65c, School children, Cuban flag and coat of arms, bust of José Marti. No. 5175, 65c, Cuban coat of arms. No. 5176, 65c, Cuban flag. No. 5177, 65c, Cuban national anthem.

**2010, Oct. 12** **Litho.** *Perf. 12¾*
**5174-5177** A1470 Set of 4 5.25 5.25

World Statistics Day — A1471

**2010** *Perf. 12½x12¼*
**5178** A1471 65c multi 1.40 1.40

Cuban Television, 60th Anniv. — A1472

**2010, Oct. 24** *Perf. 12¾*
**5179** A1472 1.05p multi 2.10 2.10

22nd Intl. Ballet Festival, Havana — A1473

**2010, Oct. 28** *Perf. 12¼x12½*
**5180** A1473 65c multi 1.40 1.40

Souvenir Sheet

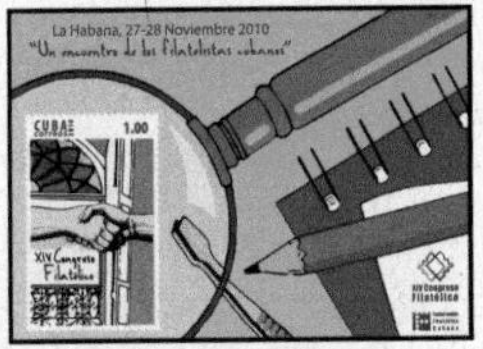

14th Philatelic Congress, Havana — A1474

**2010** ***Imperf.***
**5181** A1474 1p multi 2.00 2.00

Diplomatic Relations Between Cuba and Viet Nam. 50th Anniv. — A1475

**2010, Dec. 2** *Perf. 12¼x12½*
**5182** A1475 85c multi 1.75 1.75

Diplomatic Relations Between Cuba and Russia, 50th Anniv. — A1476

**2010, Dec. 2** *Perf. 12¾*
**5183** A1476 75c multi 1.50 1.50

Diplomatic Relations Between Cuba and Bulgaria, 50th Anniv. — A1477

No. 5184: a, Alexander Nevsky Cathedral, Sofia, Bulgaria, flag of Bulgaria. b, Flag of Cuba, Havana Cathedral.

**2010, Dec. 10** *Perf. 12½x12¼*
**5184** A1477 75c Horiz. pair, #a-b 3.00 3.00

Dora Alonso (1910-2001), Writer — A1478

**2010, Dec. 22** *Perf. 12¾*
**5185** A1478 75c multi 1.50 1.50

Diplomatic Relations Between Cuba and Mongolia, 50th Anniv. — A1479

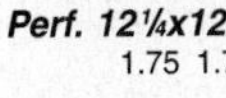

**2010** *Perf. 12¼x12½*
**5186** A1479 85c multi 1.75 1.75

José Lezama Lima (1910-76), Writer — A1480

**2010, Dec. 19** **Litho.** *Perf. 12¾*
**5187** A1480 65c multi 1.40 1.40

Souvenir Sheet

14th Intl. Information Convention and Fair, Havana — A1481

**2011, Feb. 7** **Litho.** ***Imperf.***
**5188** A1481 1p multi 2.00 2.00

Airplanes and Female Aviators A1482

Designs: 10c, Bleriot, Matilde Moisant (1878-1964). 15c, Stinson "American Girl," Ruth Elder (1902-77). 20c, Lockheed Vega, Ruth Rowland (1901-60). 50c, Golden Eagle, Bobbi Trout (1906-2003). 65c, Seversky Executive, Jacqueline Cochran (1906-80). 90c, Lockheed Electra, Amelia Earhart (1897-1937).
1p, Curtiss Robin, Berta Moraleda, first Cuban aviatrix.

**2011, Feb. 12** *Perf. 12½x12¼*
**5189-5194** A1482 Set of 6 5.00 5.00

**Souvenir Sheet**

***Imperf***

**5195** A1482 1p multi 2.00 2.00

Indipex 2011 Intl. Philatelic Exhibition, New Delhi.

New Year 2011 (Year of the Rabbit) A1483

Rabbit and background color of: No. 5196, 15c, Green. No. 5197, 15c, Red.

**2011, Feb. 15** *Perf. 12¾*
**5196-5197** A1483 Set of 2 .60 .60

Postal Union of the Americas, Spain and Portugal (UPAEP), Cent. — A1484

**2011, Feb. 17**
**5198** A1484 65c multi 1.40 1.40

Central Army, 50th Anniv. A1485

**2011, Apr. 4** **Litho.** *Perf. 12½x12¼*
**5199** A1485 65c multi 1.40 1.40

Eastern Army, 50th Anniv. A1486

**2011, Apr. 21** **Litho.** *Perf. 12½x12¼*
**5200** A1486 65c multi 1.40 1.40

Earth Day — A1487

Designs: 65c, Cart. 90c, Fountain.

**2011, Apr. 22** *Perf. 12¾*
**5201-5202** A1487 Set of 2 3.25 3.25

Radio Havana, 50th Anniv. A1488

**2011, May 1** *Perf. 12½x12¼*
**5203** A1488 2.05p multi 4.25 4.25

Flora and Fauna — A1489

Designs: 15c, Anolis vermiculata, Nymphaea. 35c, Apis mellifera, Bidens alba. 40c, Lycorea ceres demeter, Euphorbia helenae. 65c, Osteopilus septentrionalis, Plumeria obtusa. 75c, Ardea alba, Avicennia germinanas. 85c, Liguus fasciatus, Catopsis sp.
1p, Crocodylus rhombifer, Coccoloba uvifera, vert.

**2011, June 6** *Perf. 12¾*
**5204-5209** A1489 Set of 6 6.50 6.50

**Souvenir Sheet**

***Imperf***

**5210** A1489 1p multi 2.00 2.00

Ministry of the Interior, 50th Anniv. A1490

**2011, June 8** *Perf. 12½x12¼*
**5211** A1490 90c multi 1.90 1.90

Western Army, 50th Anniv. — A1491

**2011, June 14** *Perf. 12¾*
**5212** A1491 75c multi 1.50 1.50

Dances — A1492

Designs: No. 5213, 10c, Danzón. No. 5214, 10c, Mambo. 45c, Son. 65c, Rumba. 75c, Cha cha cha. 85c, Salsa.
No. 5219: a, Female Carnaval dancer. b, Male Carnaval dancer.

**2011, June 29** *Perf. 12¼x12½*
**5213-5218** A1492 Set of 6 6.00 6.00

**Souvenir Sheet**

***Imperf***

**5219** A1492 50c Sheet of 2, #a-b 2.00 2.00

Diplomatic Relations Between Cuba and the Philippines, 65th Anniv. — A1493

**2011, July 1** *Perf. 12¾*
**5220** A1493 85c multi 1.75 1.75

Locomotives A1494

Designs: 5c, Best Friend of Charleston, 1830. 10c, Lafayette, 1837. 15c, Robert Stephenson Patentee, 1830. 65c, Thomas Ellis St. David, 1848. 75c, Stephenson long-boiler, 1848. 90c, 4-2-2 Stirling single-wheeler No. 1, 1870.
1p, Shinkansen, 1964.

**2011, July 28** *Perf. 12½x12¼*
**5221-5226** A1494 Set of 6 5.25 5.25

**Souvenir Sheet**

***Imperf***

**5227** A1494 1p multi 2.00 2.00

Japan 2011 Intl. Philatelic Exhibition, Yokohama.

Baracoa, 500th Anniv. A1495

**2011, Aug. 15** *Perf. 12½x12¼*
**5228** A1495 3p multi 6.00 6.00

Non-Aligned Countries Movement, 50th Anniv. — A1496

**2011, Sept. 6** *Perf. 12¾*
**5229** A1496 65c multi 1.40 1.40

Birds Endemic to Various Countries A1497

Designs: 5c, Ramphastos sulfuratus, Belize. 10c, Melanerpes portoricensis, Puerto Rico. 15c, Icterus nigrogularis, Curaçao. 30c, Eumomota superciliosa, El Salvador. 50c, Vanellus chilensis lampronotus, Uruguay, vert. 65c, Pharomachrus mocinno, Guatemala, vert. 75c, Pelecanus occidentalis, St. Kitts and Nevis, vert. 85c, Orthorhycus cristatus, St. Eustatius, Caribbenan Netherlands, vert.

***Perf. 12½x12¼, 12¼x12½***

**2011, Sept. 19**
**5230-5237** A1497 Set of 8 6.75 6.75

America Issue — A1498

Designs: No. 5238, 65c, Blue mailbox, denomination in pale orange. No. 5239, 65c, Blue green mailbox, denomination in pale rose. No. 5240, 65c, Three mailboxes, denomination in light blue. No. 5241, 65c, Blue green mailbox, denomination in lilac.

**2011, Oct. 12** *Perf. 12¾*
**5238-5241** A1498 Set of 4 5.25 5.25

Animals A1499

Designs: 5c, Ursus maritimus, map of Arctic region. 10c, Cervus elaphus canadensis, map of North America. 15c, Lama glama, map of South America. 50c, Canis lupus, map of Europe. 65c, Pongo pygmaeus, map of East Asia. 85c, Phascolarctos cinereus, map of Australia.
1p, Panthera leo, map of Africa.

**2011, Oct. 18** *Perf. 12½x12¼*
**5242-5247** A1499 Set of 6 4.75 4.75

**Souvenir Sheet**

***Imperf***

**5248** A1499 1p multi 2.00 2.00

Coral and Fish — A1500

Corals: 10c, Scolymia cubensis. 15c, Mussa angulosa. 20c, Manicina areolata. 30c, Mycetophyllia lamarckiana. 50c, Acropora prolifera. 65c, Tubastraea coccinea.
1p, Stylaster roseus.

**2011, Oct. 18** *Perf. 12½x12¼*
**5249-5254** A1500 Set of 6 4.00 4.00

**Souvenir Sheet**

***Imperf***

**5255** A1500 1p multi 2.00 2.00

Revista Pionero, 50th Anniv. A1501

**2011, Nov. 25** *Perf. 12½x12¼*
**5256** A1501 1.05p multi 2.10 2.10

Havana Tourist Attractions — A1502

Designs: 5c, La Giraldilla, Castillo de la Fuerza. 10c, El Templete Monument. 15c, Plaza de la Catedra. 20c, Bacardi Building. 65c, Grand Theater of Havana. 75c, National Capitol (now Cuban Academy of Sciences).
1p, Morro Castle.

**2011, Dec. 12** *Perf. 12¼x12½*
**5257-5262** A1502 Set of 6 4.00 4.00

**Souvenir Sheet**

***Imperf***

**5263** A1502 1p multi 2.00 2.00

Birds and Protected Habitats — A1503

Designs: 5c, Contopus caribaeus, Hanabanilla Nature Preserve. 10c, Saurothera merlini, Caguanes National Park. 20c, Spindalis zena, Topes de Collantes Nature Preserve. 45c, Otus lawrencii, Jobo Rosado Protected Area. 65c, Teretistris fernandinae, Alturas de Banao Ecological Reserve. 85c, Priotelus temnurus, El Nicho Nature Preserve.
1p, Grus canadensis, Caguanes National Park.

**2011, Dec. 13** *Perf. 12¼x12½*
**5264-5269** A1503 Set of 6 4.75 4.75

**Souvenir Sheet**

***Imperf***

**5270** A1503 1p multi 2.00 2.00

Stage Debut of Ballerina Alicia Alonso, 80th Anniv. A1504

No. 5271 — Alonso with feet: a, Not visible. b, Visible.

**2011, Dec. 29** *Perf. 12¼x12½*
**5271** A1504 65c Horiz. pair, #a-b 2.60 2.60

African National Congress, Cent. — A1505

**2012, Jan. 8** *Perf. 12¾*
**5272** A1505 85c multi 1.75 1.75

Artemisa Province, 1st Anniv. — A1506

**2012, Jan. 9**
**5273** A1506 65c multi 1.40 1.40

Electrical Workers Day — A1507

**2012, Jan. 14**
**5274** A1507 75c multi 1.50 1.50

Communication Workers Day — A1508

**2012, Feb. 24** *Perf. 12½x12¼*
**5275** A1508 65c multi 1.40 1.40

Woman at a Window, by René Portocarrero (1912-85) — A1509

**2012, Feb. 24** *Perf. 12¾*
**5276** A1509 1.05p multi 2.10 2.10

Diplomatic Relations Between Ukraine and Cuba, 20th Anniv. A1510

**2012, Mar. 12** *Perf. 12½x12¼*
**5277** A1510 75c multi 1.50 1.50

Alejandro Robaina and His Automobile — A1511

No. 5278 — Tobacco field and: a, Robaina (1919-2010), farmer of cigar tobacco. b, Automobile.

**2012, Mar. 20** *Perf. 12¾*
**5278** A1511 65c Horiz. pair, #a-b 2.60 2.60

Diplomatic Relations Between Azerbaijan and Cuba, 20th Anniv. — A1512

**2012, Apr. 16** **Litho.**
**5279** A1512 75c multi 1.50 1.50

Diplomatic Relations Between Belarus and Cuba, 20th Anniv. A1513

**2012, Apr. 16** *Perf. 12½x12¼*
**5280** A1513 75c multi 1.50 1.50



A1514

Design: Capt. Orlando Pantoja Tamayo (1933-67), Capt. Eliseo Reyes Rodriguez (1940-67), First Lt. Antonio Briones Montoto (1939-67), Guerrillas in Intl. Conflicts.

**2012, Apr. 25 Litho. *Perf. 12½x12¼***
**5281** A1514 65c multi 1.40 1.40

Afro-Cuban Dances — A1515

Designs: 15c, Elegbá. 20c, Ogún. 30c, Shangó. 50c, Oyá. 65c, Yemayá. 75c, Obatalá.
1p, Oghún.

**2012, May 7 Litho. *Perf. 12¼x12½***
**5282-5287** A1515 Set of 6 5.25 5.25

**Souvenir Sheet**

***Imperf***

**5288** A1515 1p multi 2.00 2.00

No. 5288 has simulated perforations.

Butterflies A1516

Designs: 5c, Phoebis avellaneda. 10c, Parides gundiachianus. 15c, Greta cubana. 35c, Eurytides celadon. 40c, Anartia chrysopelea. 65c, Dismorphia cubana. 75c, Calisto israel. 85c, Libytheana motya.

**2012, May 22 Litho. *Perf. 12¾***
**5289-5296** A1516 Set of 8 6.75 6.75

Cuban Institute of Radio and Television, 50th Anniv. — A1517

**2012, May 24 Litho. *Perf. 12¾***
**5297** A1517 90c multi 1.90 1.90

Visit of Pope Benedict XVI to Cuba — A1518

**2012, June 6 Litho. *Perf. 12¼x12½***
**5298** A1518 75c multi 1.50 1.50

Shells — A1519

Designs: 10c, Cypraea auratum. 30c, Strombus pugilis. 45c, Voluta fulgetrum. 65c, Architectonica maximum. 75c, Murex beaui. 85c, Spondylus aurantium.
1p, Epitonium pretiosum, vert.

**2012, June 6 Litho. *Perf. 12¾***
**5299-5304** A1519 Set of 6 6.25 6.25

**Souvenir Sheet**

***Imperf***

**5305** A1519 1p multi 2.00 2.00

No. 5305 has simulated perforations.

Paulina Alvarez (1912-65), Singer — A1520

**2012, June 13 Litho. *Perf. 12¾***
**5306** A1520 1.05p multi 2.10 2.10

2012 Summer Olympics, London — A1521

Cuban Olympic gold medal winning athletes: 10c, Orlando Martinez. 15c, Téofilo Stevenson. 20c, Alberto Juantorena. 50c, María Caridad Colón. 65c, Driulys González. 90c, Mireya Luis.
1p, Javier Sotomayor, horiz.

**2012, July 5 Litho. *Perf. 12¾***
**5307-5312** A1521 Set of 6 5.00 5.00

**Souvenir Sheet**

***Imperf***

**5313** A1521 1p multi 2.00 2.00

No. 5313 has simulated perforations.

Diplomatic Relations Between Cuba and Timor, 10th Anniv. A1522

**2012, July 18 Litho. *Perf. 12½x12¼***
**5314** A1522 75c multi 1.50 1.50

Civil Defense, 50th Anniv. A1523

**2012, July 20 Litho. *Perf. 12½x12¼***
**5315** A1523 65c multi 1.40 1.40

Cienfuegos Military Insurrection, 55th Anniv. — A1524

**2012, Sept. 5 Litho. *Perf. 12¼x12½***
**5316** A1524 65c multi 1.40 1.40

2012 National Census A1525

**2012, Sept. 6 Litho. *Perf. 12½x12¼***
**5317** A1525 65c multi 1.40 1.40

National Lyric Theater, 50th Anniv. — A1526

***Perf. 12¼x12½***

**2012, Sept. 14 Litho.**
**5318** A1526 65c multi 1.40 1.40

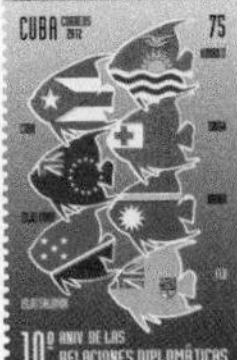

Diplomatic Relations Between Cuba and Kiribati, Tonga, Cook Islands, Nauru, Solomon Islands and Fiji, 10th Anniv. — A1527

***Perf. 12¼x12½***

**2012, Sept. 26 Litho.**
**5319** A1527 75c multi 1.50 1.50

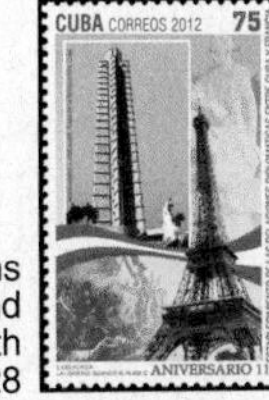

Diplomatic Relations Between Cuba and France, 110th Anniv. — A1528

**2012, Oct. 3 Litho. *Perf. 12¼x12½***
**5320** A1528 75c multi 1.50 1.50

Diplomatic Relations Between Cuba and Switzerland, 110th Anniv. — A1529

**2012, Oct. 3 Litho. *Perf. 12¼x12½***
**5321** A1529 75c multi 1.50 1.50

Myths and Legends A1530

Designs: No. 5322, 65c, La Gaviota del Rio San Juan (The Gull of San Juan River). No. 5323, 65c, El Güije. No. 5324, 65c, La Giraldilla statue, La Macorina driving car. No. 5325, 65c, La Tatagua y las Matas de Guao.

**2012, Oct. 12 Litho. *Perf. 12¾***
**5322-5325** A1530 Set of 4 5.25 5.25

America Issue.

Miner's Day — A1531

**2012, Oct. 24 Litho. *Perf. 12½x12¼***
**5326** A1531 65c multi 1.40 1.40

Cirilo Villaverde (1812-94), Writer A1532

**2012, Oct. 27 Litho. *Perf. 12½x12¼***
**5327** A1532 75c multi 1.50 1.50

First Cuban Expedition to Antarctica, 30th Anniv. — A1533

**2012, Nov. 7 Litho. *Perf. 12¾***
**5328** A1533 75c multi 1.50 1.50

Road Safety Campaign A1534

Designs: 65c, Children's drawing of girl and traffic light. 90c, Children, car, traffic signs.

**2012, Nov. 20 Litho. *Perf. 12¾***
**5329-5330** A1534 Set of 2 3.25 3.25

Ameijeiras Brothers Hospital, Havana, 30th Anniv. — A1535

**2012, Nov. 26 Litho. *Perf. 12¾***
**5331** A1535 65c multi 1.40 1.40

Flora and Fauna A1536

Designs: 5c, Ardilla (squirrel). 10c, Bala de Cañón (cannonball tree flower). 15c, Flor de loto (lotus flower). 65c, Pavo real (peacock), vert. 75c, Polimita (snail), vert. 90c, Orquídea (orchid), vert.
1p, Zorzal real (red-legged thrush), vert.

***Perf. 12½x12¼, 12¼x12½***

**2012, Nov. 29 Litho.**
**5332-5337** A1536 Set of 6 5.25 5.25

**Souvenir Sheet**

***Imperf***

**5338** A1536 1p multi 2.00 2.00

Second Cuban Philatelic Cup.

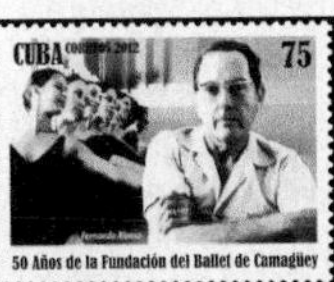

Camagüey Ballet, 50th Anniv. — A1537

Designs: 75c, Fernando Alonso (1914-2013), ballet director, and dancers. 85c, Dancers in *Don Quixote*.

**2012, Dec. 1 Litho. *Perf. 12¾***
**5339-5340** A1537 Set of 2 3.25 3.25

Diplomatic Relations Between Cuba and Jamaica, Trinidad & Tobago, Barbados and Guyana, 40th Anniv. — A1538

**2012, Dec. 6 Litho. *Perf. 12¾***
**5341** A1538 65c multi 1.40 1.40

Program For Combatting Diabetic Foot Ulcers, 5th Anniv. — A1539

Designs: 65c, Person's feet. 75c, Boxes and vial of Heberprot-P.

**2012, Dec. 14 Litho. *Perf. 12¾***
**5342-5343** A1539 Set of 2 3.00 3.00

Orchids — A1540

Various orchids: 5c, 10c, 15c, 65c, 75c, 90c. 1p, Orchid, diff.

**2013, Jan. 15 Litho. *Perf. 12¾***
**5344-5349** A1540 Set of 6 5.25 5.25

**Souvenir Sheet**

***Imperf***

**5350** A1540 1p multi 2.00 2.00

No. 5350 has simulated perforations.

Finland-Cuba Friendship Association, 50th Anniv. — A1541

**2013, Jan. 17 Litho. *Perf. 12¾***
**5351** A1541 75c multi 1.50 1.50

Bust of José Martí, by Alberto Lescay Menencio — A1542

**2013, Jan. 19 Litho. *Perf. 12¾***
**5352** A1542 3p multi 6.00 6.00

Martí (1853-95), national hero.

National Museum, Cent. — A1543

Paintings: 5c, Torre de Babel (Tower of Babel), by School of Marten van Valckenborgh. 10c, Paisaje (Landscape), by Thomas Creswick. 50c, Saludos al Mar Caribe (Salute to the Caribbean Sea), by Mario Carreño. 65c, Jarrón con Flores (Vase with Flowers), by Amelia Pelaéz. 75c, Gallo Amarillo (Yellow Rooster), by Mariano Rodríguez. 85c, La Alicantina (Woman from Alicante), by Hermenegildo Anglada.

1p, Homenaje a la Soledad (Homage to Solitude), by Servando Cabrera Moreno.

**2013, Jan. 25 Litho. *Perf. 12¾***
**5353-5358** A1543 Set of 6 6.00 6.00

**Souvenir Sheet**

***Imperf***

**5359** A1543 1p multi 2.00 2.00

No. 5359 has simulated perforations.

Items Connected to José Martí (1853-95), National Hero — A1544

Designs: 10c, Braid of Martí's hair from childhood, drawing of woman sewing. 15c, Shackle, drawing of men trying to remove leg shackles. 20c, Rostrum from San Carlos Club, Tampa, Florida. 30c, Mambisa badge with flag design. 35c, Colt revolvers. 40c, Pen, drawing of Martí writing.

**2013, Jan. 28 Litho. *Perf. 12¾***
**5360-5365** A1544 Set of 6 3.00 3.00

Chamber of Commerce, 50th Anniv. — A1545

**2013, Feb. 1 Litho. *Perf. 12¾***
**5366** A1545 90c multi 1.90 1.90

Customs Department, 50th Anniv. — A1546

**2013, Feb. 5 Litho. *Perf. 12¾***
**5367** A1546 1.05p multi 2.10 2.10

Third World Baseball Classic A1547

No. 5368, 15c — Baseball and: a, Cuban uniform shirt., flags of Japan, People's Republic of China, Cuba and Brazil. b, Pitcher for Cuban team, trophy.

No. 5369, 65c — Baseball and: a, Player with glove, trophy. b, Flags of United States, Mexico, Italy and Canada, baseball glove.

No. 5370, 75c — Baseball and: a, Batter, trophy. b, Flags of Venezuela, Puerto Rico, Dominican Republic and Spain, batting helmet.

No. 5371, 85c — Baseball and: a, Catcher's mask, flags of South Korea, Netherlands, Australia and Republic of China. b, Catcher, trophy.

**2013, Mar. 2 Litho. *Perf. 12½x12¼***

**Horiz. Pairs, #a-b**

**5368-5371** A1547 Set of 4 9.75 9.75

José Raúl Capablanca (1888-1942), World Chess Champion A1548

Capablanca and chess position in match between Capablanca and: 15c, Ossip Bernstein, 1911. 65c, Rudolf Spielmann, 1927. 75c, Mikhail Botvinnik, 1936. 85c, Jens Enevoldsen, 1939.

**2013, Mar. 8 Litho. *Perf. 12½x12¼***
**5372-5375** A1548 Set of 4 5.00 5.00

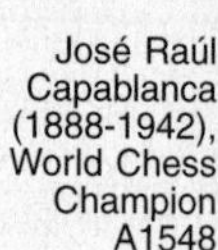

Pets — A1549

Designs: 5c, Pigeon. 15c, Parrot, vert. 50c, Dog. 65c, Turtle. 75c, Cat. 85c, Rabbit.

1p, Horse.

***Perf. 12½x12¼, 12¼x12½***

**2013, Mar. 12 Litho.**
**5376-5381** A1549 Set of 6 6.00 6.00

**Souvenir Sheet**

***Imperf***

**5382** A1549 1p multi 2.00 2.00

No. 5382 has simulated perforations.

Souvenir Sheet

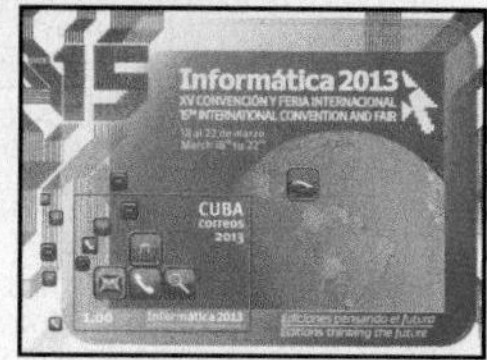

Informática 2013 International Convention and Fair — A1550

**2013, Mar. 18 Litho. *Imperf.***
**5383** A1550 1p multi 2.00 2.00

Prehistoric Animals A1551

Designs: 5c, Cricosaurus. 15c, Pterosaurus, vert. 50c, Caribemys. 65c, Gallardosaurus. 75c, Camarasaurus. 85c, Ichthyosaurus.

1p, Vinialesaurus.

***Perf. 12½x12¼, 12¼x12½***

**2013, Apr. 3 Litho.**
**5384-5389** A1551 Set of 6 6.00 6.00

**Souvenir Sheet**

***Imperf***

**5390** A1551 1p multi 2.00 2.00

No. 5390 has simulated perforations.

Sauto Theater, 150th Anniv. — A1552

**2013, Apr. 6 Litho. *Perf. 12¾***
**5391** A1552 65c multi 1.40 1.40

Australia 2013 Intl. Philatelic Exhibition, Melbourne — A1553

No. 5392, 15c: a, Parrot. b, Lyrebird.
No. 5393, 45c: a, Garfish. b, Platypus.
No. 5394, 85c: a, Hutia. b, Koala.
1p, Kangaroo and crocodile, horiz.

**2013, Apr. 10 Litho. *Perf. 12¼x12½***

**Horiz. Pairs, #a-b**

**5392-5394** A1553 Set of 3 6.00 6.00

**Souvenir Sheet**

***Imperf***

**5395** A1553 1p multi 2.00 2.00

No. 5392 has simulated perforations.

Labor Day — A1554

**2013, May 1 Litho. *Perf. 12¾***
**5396** A1554 65c multi 1.40 1.40

Visit of Dr. Alexander Fleming to Cuba, 60th Anniv. A1555

**2013, May 12 Litho. *Perf. 12½x12¼***
**5397** A1555 65c multi 1.40 1.40

First Flight From Key West to Havana, by Domingo Rosillo del Toro, Cent. A1556

**2013, May 17 Litho. *Perf. 12½x12¼***
**5398** A1556 2.05p multi 4.25 4.25

Souvenir Sheet

National Ballet of Cubaa, 65th Anniv. A1557

**2013, May 20 Litho. *Imperf.***
**5399** A1557 1p multi 2.00 2.00

No. 5399 has simulated perforations.

Butterflies A1558

Designs: 5c, Papilio caiguanabus. 10c, Proteides maysi. 15c, Allosmaitia coelebs. 40c, Anetia cubana. 65c, Kricogonia cabrerai. 75c, Papilio oxynius. 85c, Atlantea perezi. 90c, Eurema lucina.

**2013, May 22 Litho. *Perf. 12¾***
**5400-5407** A1558 Set of 8 7.75 7.75

Compare with Type A1608.

Ministry of Construction, 50th Anniv. — A1559

**2013, May 23 Litho. *Perf. 12¾***
**5408** A1559 90c multi 1.90 1.90

Debut of Alicia Alonso in Ballet *Giselle*, 70th Anniv. — A1560

Paintings of Alonso by: 5c, Servando Cabrera Moreno. 15c, Lorenzo Homar. 20c, Carlos Guzmán. 65c, Alicia Leal. 75c, Francisco Rodón (48x31mm). 90c, Agostino Brotto (48x31mm).

1p, Photograph of Alonso and other dancers, vert.

***Perf. 12¾, 12½x12¾ (75p, 90p)***

**2013, June 5 Litho.**
**5409-5414** A1560 Set of 6 5.50 5.50

**Souvenir Sheet**

***Imperf***

**5415** A1560 1p multi 2.00 2.00

No. 5415 contains one 31x48mm stamp with simulated perforations.

Eighth Federation of University Students Congress A1561

**2013, June 12 Litho. *Perf. 12¾***
5416 A1561 65c multi 1.40 1.40

**Souvenir Sheet**

Seventh International Forum on Industrial Design, Havana — A1562

**2013, June 18 Litho. *Imperf.***
5417 A1562 1p multi 2.00 2.00

No. 5417 has simulated perforations.

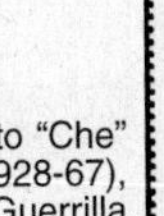

Ernesto "Che" Guevara (1928-67), Guerrilla Leader — A1563

**2013, June 28 Litho. *Perf. 12¾***
5418 A1563 65c multi 1.40 1.40

Birds A1564

Designs: 10c, Lophura diardi. 35c, Polyplectron bicalcaratum. 40c, Grus japonensis, vert. 50c, Pica sericea. 65c, Phasianus versicolor. 75c, Falco cherrug, vert.
1p, Pavo cristatus, vert.

***Perf. 12½x12¼, 12¼x12½***
**2013, July 17 Litho.**
5419-5424 A1564 Set of 6 5.50 5.50

**Souvenir Sheet**
***Imperf***
5425 A1564 1p multi 2.00 2.00

Thailand 2013 International Philatelic Exhibition, Bangkok. No. 5425 has simulated perforations.

Simón Bolívar (1783-1830), Liberator of South America A1565

Designs: No. 5426, 65c, Paintings of Bolívar. No. 5427, 65c, Bolívar House, Havana, vert.

***Perf. 12½x12¼, 12¼x12½***
**2013, July 24 Litho.**
5426-5427 A1565 Set of 2 2.60 2.60

Bolívar House, 20th anniv. as museum.

Dr. Mario Muñoz Monroy (1912-53), Revolutionist A1566

**2013, July 26 Litho. *Perf. 12¾***
5428 A1566 75c multi 1.50 1.50

Assault on the Moncada and Carlos M. De Céspedes Barracks, 60th Anniv. — A1567

Designs: 45c, Moncada Barracks. 75c, Barracks, diff.

**2013, July 26 Litho. *Perf. 12¾***
5429-5430 A1567 Set of 2 2.40 2.40

Angerona Coffee Plantation, 200th Anniv. — A1568

**2013, Aug. 12 Litho. *Perf. 12¾***
5431 A1568 1.05p multi 2.10 2.10

El Brinco Cave A1569

**2013, Sept. 6 Litho. *Perf. 12½x12¼***
5432 A1569 75c multi 1.50 1.50

22nd Congress of the Postal Union of Spain, Portugal and the Americas, Havana A1570

Designs: 65p, Quill pen writing on computer screen. 1p, UPAEP emblem.

**2013, Sept. 9 Litho. *Perf. 12¾***
5433 A1570 65c multi 1.40 1.40

**Souvenir Sheet**
***Imperf***
5434 A1570 1p multi 2.00 2.00

No. 5434 contains one 40x32mm stamp.

Armed Peasants Congress, 55th Anniv. — A1571

**2013, Sept. 21 Litho. *Perf. 12¾***
5435 A1571 85c multi 1.75 1.75

8th Congress of the Committee for the Defense of the Revolution A1572

**2013, Sept. 28 Litho. *Perf. 12¾***
5436 A1572 65c multi 1.40 1.40

Matanzas, 320th Anniv. — A1573

**2013, Oct. 12 Litho. *Perf. 12¾***
5437 A1573 65c multi 1.40 1.40

Campaign Against Discrimination A1574

Campaign against: No. 5438, 65c, Child abuse. No. 5439, 65c, Homophobia. No. 5440, 65c, Racial discrimination. No. 5441, 65c, Disability discrimination.

**2013, Oct. 12 Litho. *Perf. 12¾***
5438-5441 A1574 Set of 4 5.25 5.25

America Issue.

North Korean National Holiday, 65th Anniv. — A1575

**2013, Oct. 16 Litho. *Perf. 12¼x12½***
5442 A1575 85c multi 1.75 1.75

Brasiliana 2013 International Philatelic Exhibition, Rio de Janeiro — A1576

No. 5443, 15c: a, Cuica player. b, Tres player.
No. 5444, 40c: a, Woman of Candomblé religion. b, Woman of Cuban Santería religion.
No. 5445, 90c: a, Samba dancer. b, Rumba dancer.
1p, Statue of Jesus Christ, Havana.

**2013, Oct. 16 Litho. *Perf. 12¼x12½***
**Horiz. Pairs, #a-b**
5443-5445 A1576 Set of 3 6.00 6.00

**Souvenir Sheet**
***Imperf***
5446 A1576 1p multi 2.00 2.00

No. 5446 has simulated perforations.

Tenth National Championship of Philately A1577

Famous people: 15c, Mario Benedetti (1920-2009), writer. 20c, Alexander von Humboldt (1769-1859), geographer and naturalist. 45c, Nat King Cole (1919-65), singer. 65c, Juan Manuel Fangio (1911-95), race car driver. 75c, Antonio Gades (1936-2004), flamenco dancer. 85c, María Félix (1914-2002), actress.
1p, Ernest Hemingway (1899-1961), writer.

**2013, Oct. 22 Litho. *Perf. 12½x12¼***
5447-5452 A1577 Set of 6 6.25 6.25

**Souvenir Sheet**
***Imperf***
5453 A1577 1p multi 2.00 2.00

No. 5453 has simulated perforations.

Bayamo, 500th Anniv. — A1578

Designs: 50c, Church steeple. 65c, Carlos M. Céspedes Barracks and flagpole, horiz.

**2013, Nov. 5 Litho. *Perf. 12¾***
5454-5455 A1578 Set of 2 2.40 2.40

Arab House, Havana, 30th Anniv. — A1579

Designs: 75c, Bottle from Syria, 19th cent. 85c, Doorway.

**2013, Nov. 13 Litho. *Perf. 12¾***
5456-5457 A1579 Set of 2 3.25 3.25

National Museum of Dance, Havana — A1580

***Perf. 12¼x12½***
**2013, Nov. 25 Litho.**
5458 A1580 75c multi 1.50 1.50

Cuban Revolutionary Fighters Association, 20th Anniv. — A1581

**2013, Dec. 6 Litho. *Perf. 12¾***
5459 A1581 1.05p multi 2.10 2.10

General Prosecutor's Office, 40th Anniv. — A1582

**2013, Dec. 23 Litho. *Perf. 12¾***
5460 A1582 65c multi 1.40 1.40

Colonel Juan Delgado González (1868-98) A1583

***Perf. 12½x12¼***
**2013, Dec. 27 Litho.**
5461 A1583 90c multi 1.90 1.90

Triumph of Cuban Revolutionists, 55th Anniv. — A1584

**2013, Dec. 30 Litho. *Perf. 12¾***
5462 A1584 65c multi 1.40 1.40

Santísima Trinidad, 500th Anniv. — A1585

Designs: 40c, Trinidad Church. 85c, Manaca-Iznaga Tower, locomotive.

**2014, Jan. 12 Litho. *Perf. 12¼x12½***
**5463-5464** A1585 Set of 2 2.50 2.50

Consecration of the Greek Orthodox Cathedral of St. Nicholas, 10th Anniv. A1586

Designs: 90c, Cathedral, Archbishop Bartholomew of Constantinople, Fidel Castro. 1p, St. Nicholas, vert.

**2014, Jan. 25 Litho. *Perf. 12½x12¼***
**5465** A1586 90c multi 1.90 1.90

**Souvenir Sheet**

***Imperf***

**5466** A1586 1p multi 2.00 2.00

No. 5466 has simulated perforations.

2014 World Cup Soccer Championships, Brazil — A1587

Designs: 35c, Soccer player. 65c, Maracana Stadium, Rio de Janeiro. 75c, Mascot. 85c, Player making bicycle kick.

**2014, Feb. 1 Litho. *Perf. 12¼x12½***
**5467-5470** A1587 Set of 4 5.25 5.25

Santa María del Puerto Príncipe (Camagüey), 500th Anniv. — A1588

Famous people from Camagüey: 5c, Enrique José Varona (1848-1933), writer. 10c, Gertrudis Gómez de Avellaneda (1814-73), writer. 15c, Vicentina de la Torre (1926-95), dancer. 65c, Fidelio Ponce de León (1895-1949), painter. 75c, Rafael Fortún (1919-82), sprinter. 85c, Jorge González Allué (1910-2001), composer.
1p, Plaza del Carmen, vert.

**2014, Feb. 2 Litho. *Perf. 12¾***
**5471-5476** A1588 Set of 6 5.25 5.25

**Souvenir Sheet**

***Imperf***

**5477** A1588 1p multi 2.00 2.00

No. 5477 has simulated perforations.

Diplomatic Relations Between Cuba and Haiti, 110th Anniv. — A1589

**2014, Feb. 3 Litho. *Perf. 12¾***
**5478** A1589 3p multi 6.00 6.00

Fans A1590

Woman holding fan and fan from: 5c, 1860. 10c, 1860, diff. 15c, 1920. 45c, 1795-1800. 65c, 1850. 75c, 1717.

***Perf. 12½x12¼***

**2014, Feb. 14 Litho.**
**5479-5484** A1590 Set of 6 4.50 4.50

20th Congress of Worker's Central Union A1591

***Perf. 12½x12¼***

**2014, Feb. 21 Litho.**
**5485** A1591 75c multi 1.50 1.50

Community of Latin American States Summit, Havana — A1592

***Perf. 12¼x12½***

**2014, Feb. 24 Litho.**
**5486** A1592 75c multi 1.50 1.50

9th Congress of Federation of Cuban Women — A1593

**2014, Mar. 5 Litho. *Perf. 12¼x12½***
**5487** A1593 65c multi 1.40 1.40

Hugo Chávez (1954-2013), President of Venezuela A1594

Chávez: 65c, Saluting. 75c, With hand over heart. 85c, With arm raised.

**2014, Mar. 5 Litho. *Perf. 12½x12¼***
**5488-5490** A1594 Set of 3 4.50 4.50

Alejandro Robaina Pereda (1919-2010), Tobacco Grower A1595

Cigar box and: 10c, Hand holding tobacco seedling, classification of tobacco leaves. 15c, Tobacco growers in field. 30c, Tobacco leaves and equipment for cigar making. 65c, Cigars with Robaina band. 75c, Cigar humidor, lit match. 85c, Cigar box art for Vegas Robaina cigars.
1p, Robaina, vert.

***Perf. 12½x12¼***

**2014, Mar. 20 Litho.**
**5491-5496** A1595 Set of 6 5.75 5.75

**Souvenir Sheet**

***Imperf***

**5497** A1595 1p multi 2.00 2.00

No. 5497 has simulated perforations.

Gertrudis Gomez de Avellaneda (1814-73), Writer — A1596

***Perf. 12¼x12½***

**2014, Mar. 22 Litho.**
**5498** A1596 1.05p multi 2.10 2.10

Operation Transbordo, 50th Anniv. — A1597

Designs: 45c, Alberto Delgado Delgado (1932-64), undercover agent. 65c, Boat.

**2014, Mar. 26 Litho. *Perf. 12¾***
**5499-5500** A1597 Set of 2 2.25 2.25

Diplomatic Relations Between Antigua and Barbuda and Cuba, 20th Anniv. — A1598

**2014, Apr. 4 Litho. *Perf. 12¾***
**5501** A1598 65c multi 1.40 1.40

National Revolutionary Police, 55th Anniv. — A1599

**2014, Apr. 19 Litho. *Perf. 12¾***
**5502** A1599 90c multi 1.90 1.90

Ministry of Science, Technology and the Environment, 20th Anniv. A1600

**2014, Apr. 21 Litho. *Perf. 12½x12¼***
**5503** A1600 90c multi 1.90 1.90

Flags of South Africa and Cuba, Nelson Mandela (1918-2013), President of South Africa — A1601

**2014, Apr. 28 Litho. *Perf. 12¾***
**5504** A1601 85c multi 1.75 1.75

Diplomatic relations between South Africa and Cuba, end of apartheid in South Africa, 20th anniv.

Labor Day — A1602

**2014, May 1 Litho. *Perf. 12¼x12½***
**5505** A1602 65c multi 1.40 1.40

Ernesto "Che" Guevara (1928-67), Minister of Industry, and Metallurgical Industries A1603

Guevara, photographs of industry, plants or finished products and emblem of: 10c, Planta Mecanica. 45c, Profix. 75c, CIME. 85c, Inpud. 90c, Taino.

**2014, May 2 Litho. *Perf. 12½x12¼***
**5506-5510** A1603 Set of 5 6.25 6.25

State Council Historical Affairs Office, 50th Anniv. A1604

**2014, May 9 Litho. *Perf. 12½x12¼***
**5511** A1604 75c multi 1.50 1.50

Bejucal, 300th Anniv. — A1605

**2014, May 10 Litho. *Perf. 12¼x12½***
**5512** A1605 65c multi 1.40 1.40

St. Francis of Assisi Basilica and Convent Museum, 20th Anniv. A1606

**2014, May 16 Litho. *Perf. 12½x12¼***
**5513** A1606 90c multi 1.90 1.90

First Agrarian Reform Law, 55th Anniv. A1607

**2014, May 17 Litho. *Perf. 12½x12¼***
**5514** A1607 65c multi 1.40 1.40

Butterflies A1608

Designs: 5c, Eurema amelia. 10c, Astraptes cassander. 15c, Panoquina corrupta. 20c, Chioides marmorosa. 40c, Eunica heraclitus. 50c, Parachoranthus magdalia. 65c, Holguinia holguin. 75c, Eantis munroei. 90c, Oarisma nanus.

**2014, May 22 Litho. *Perf. 12¾***
**5515-5523** A1608 Set of 9 7.50 7.50

Compare with Type A1558.

Diplomatic Relations Between Cuba and Congo Republic, 50th Anniv. — A1609

**2014, May 23 Litho. *Perf. 12¼x12½***
**5524** A1609 85c multi 1.75 1.75

National Museum of Natural History, 50th Anniv. A1610

**2014, May 26 Litho. *Perf. 12½x12¼***
**5525** A1610 75c multi 1.50 1.50

Souvenir Sheet

Hotel Cubanacan Comodoro — A1611

**2014, May 31 Litho. *Imperf.***
5526 A1611 1p multi 2.00 2.00

Third Cuba Philately Cup.

Sancti Spiritus, 500th Anniv. A1612

Designs: 65c, Rio Yayabo Bridge. 75c, Parroquial Mayor Church, vert.

***Perf. 12½x12¼, 12¼x12½***
**2014, June 4 Litho.**
5527-5528 A1612 Set of 2 3.00 3.00

Diplomatic Relations Between Nigeria and Cuba, 40th Anniv. — A1613

**2014, July 1 Litho. *Perf. 12¼x12½***
5529 A1613 85c multi 1.75 1.75

Office of the Comptroller General, 5th Anniv. A1614

**2014, Aug. 1 Litho. *Perf. 12½x12¼***
5530 A1614 90c multi 1.90 1.90

Spanish Heritage Festival, 25th Anniv. A1615

**2014, Aug. 5 Litho. *Perf. 12½x12¼***
5531 A1615 65c multi 1.40 1.40

Show Jumping Horses A1616

Designs: 15c, Golden Horse. 20c, Captain VZ. 30c, Fairmont R.E. 65c, Gigaa VDP. 75c, Google. 85c, Goldmann Jr.
1p, Fumuto and rider.

***Perf. 12½x12¼***
**2014, Aug. 16 Litho.**
5532-5537 A1616 Set of 6 6.00 6.00

**Size: 83x83mm**

***Imperf***
5538 A1616 1p multi 2.00 2.00

No. 5538 has simulated perforations.

African Animals and Map of Africa A1617

**2014, Sept. 2 Litho. *Perf. 12½x12¼***
5539 A1617 85c multi 1.75 1.75

Diplomatic relations between Cuba and Burundi, Cameroun, Gabon, Senegal, Uganda, Liberia and Madagascar, 40th anniv.

Latin American Parliament, 50th Anniv. A1618

**2014, Sept. 5 Litho. *Perf. 12½x12¼***
5540 A1618 65c multi 1.40 1.40

Diplomatic Relations Between Benin and Cuba, 40th Anniv. — A1619

**2014, Sept. 12 Litho. *Perf. 12¾***
5541 A1619 85c multi 1.75 1.75

Guitars — A1620

***Perf. 12¼x12½***
**2014, Sept. 25 Litho.**
5542 A1620 65c multi 1.40 1.40

75th birthday of Leo Brouwer, guitarist and composer.

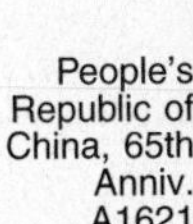

People's Republic of China, 65th Anniv. A1621

***Perf. 12½x12¼***
**2014, Sept. 29 Litho.**
5543 A1621 85c multi 1.75 1.75

Lighthouses — A1622

Designs: 15c, Morro Castle Lighthouse, Havana. 35c, Cayo Jutías Lighthouse, Pinar del Rio. 75c, Cayo Cruz del Padre Lighthouse, Matanzas. 85c, Morro Lighthouse, Santiago.

**2014, Oct. 5 Litho. *Perf. 12¼x12½***
5544-5547 A1622 Set of 4 4.25 4.25

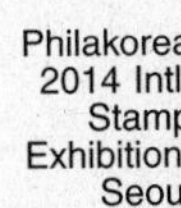

Philakorea 2014 Intl. Stamp Exhibition, Seoul A1623

Dogs: 10c, Poodle (caniche). 20c, Yorkshire terrier. 30c, Schnauzer. 40c, Beagle. 65c, German shepherd (pastor aleman). 75c, Golden retriever.
1p, Collie (pastor escocés de pelo largo).

***Perf. 12½x12¼***
**2014, June 15 Litho.**
5548-5553 A1623 Set of 6 5.00 5.00

**Souvenir Sheet**

***Imperf***
5554 A1623 1p multi 2.00 2.00

No. 5554 contains one 43x33mm stamp with simulated perforations.

Malaysia 2014 Intl. Stamp Exhibition, Kuala Lumpur — A1624

Cats: 10c, Shorthaired cat (pelos cortos). 20c, Persian cat (Persas). 40c, Balinese cat (Balineses). 65c. Bengal cat (Bengalies). 75c, Siamese cat (Siameses), horiz. 85c, Semi-longhaired cat (pelos semi-largos).
1p, Cuban blue cat (azules cubanos).

***Perf. 12¼x12½, 12½x12¼***
**2014, July 30 Litho.**
5555-5560 A1624 Set of 6 6.00 6.00

**Souvenir Sheet**

***Imperf***
5561 A1624 1p multi 2.00 2.00

No. 5554 has simulated perforations.

Trains A1625

Designs: 5c, Talgo AVE series 100. 15c, Alstom FGC series 113. 50c, Siemens AVE series 103. 65c, Talgo AVE series 130. 75c, CRH380A. 85c, JR-Maglev MLX01.
1p, Cabina AVE series 102.

***Perf. 12½x12¼***
**2014, Sept. 15 Litho.**
5562-5567 A1625 Set of 6 6.00 6.00

**Souvenir Sheet**

***Imperf***
5568 A1625 1p multi 2.00 2.00

No. 5568 contains one 61x26mm trapezoidal stamp with simulated perforations.

Marine Life — A1626

Designs: 5c, Volvarina moresi. 10c, Sepia officinalis. 30c, Amblyrhynchus cristatus. 65c, Physeter macrocephalus, vert. 75c, Aptenodytes patagonicus, vert. 85c, Eretmochelys imbricata, vert.
1p, Pomacanthus arcuatus, vert.

**2014, Oct. 4 Litho. *Perf. 12¾***
5569-5574 A1626 Set of 6 5.50 5.50

**Souvenir Sheet**

***Imperf***
5575 A1626 1p multi 2.00 2.00

No. 5575 has simulated perforations.

Famous Men — A1626a

Designs: No. 5575A, 65c, José Martí (1853-95), writer. No. 5575B, 65c, Antonio Maceo Grajales (1845-96), military leader. No. 5575C, 65c, Ignacio Agramonte y Loynaz (1841-73), revolutionist. No. 5575D, 65c, Carlos Manuel de Céspedes (1819-74), declarer of Cuban independence.

**2014, Oct. 12 Litho. *Perf. 12¾***
5575A-5575D A1626a Set of 4 5.25 5.25

America Issue.

Airplanes of Cubana Arilines A1627

Designs: 15c, Curtiss Robin. 20c, Bristol Britannia. 45c, Lockheed 10 Electra. 75c, Antonov 158.

**2014, Oct. 22 Litho. *Perf. 12½x12¼***
5576-5579 A1627 Set of 4 3.25 3.25

Independence of Malawi, Tanzania and Zambia, 50th Anniv. — A1628

**2014, Oct. 24 Litho. *Perf. 12¼x12½***
5580 A1628 85c multi 1.75 1.75

National Road Safety Day — A1629

Children's drawings: 15c, Taxi and signs. 20c, Children in crosswalk. 40c, Tractor and cow on road. 50c, Car, sign and traffic light. 65c, Child chasing ball in street. 75c, Railroad crossing.
1p, Policeman, crosswalk, traffic light.

**2014, Nov. 17 Litho. *Perf. 12¾***
5581-5586 A1629 Set of 6 5.50 5.50

**Souvenir Sheet**

***Imperf***
5587 A1629 1p multi 2.00 2.00

No. 5587 has simulated perforations.

Cuban Philatelic Treasures — A1630

Designs: 10c, Stampless cover, ship. 20c, Cover with three stamps, mask. 30c, Havana local post cover with two stamps, watchtower, horiz. 65c, Cover with Mambí insurrection stamps, mounted soldier with Cuban flag. 75c, Cover with Puerto Principe surcharges, tower. 85c, Experimental rocket mail cover, rocket.
1p, Statue and birds, horiz.

***Perf. 12¼x12½, 12½x12¼***
**2014, Nov. 20 Litho.**
5588-5593 A1630 Set of 6 5.75 5.75

**Souvenir Sheet**

***Imperf***
5594 A1630 1p multi 2.00 2.00

No. 5554 contains one 44x31mm stamp with simulated perforations.

Diplomatic Relations Between Cuba and the Bahamas, 40th Anniv. — A1631

*Perf. 12½x12¼*

**2014, Nov. 28** **Litho.**
**5595** A1631 3p multi 6.00 6.00

José Antonio Echeverria City University, 50th Anniv. A1632

**2014, Dec. 2** **Litho.** ***Perf. 12½x12¼***
**5596** A1632 65c multi 1.40 1.40

2014 Diabetes Congress, Varadero Beach A1633

Designs: 65c, Infected foot, bottle of medicine and surgeon's saw. 75c, People pulling on fabric covering over feet.

*Perf. 12½x12¼*

**2014, Dec. 10** **Litho.**
**5597-5598** A1633 Set of 2 3.00 3.00

Protected Flora and Fauna — A1634

Designs: 5c, Todus multicolor. 10c, Peireskia cubensis. 15c, Eretmochelys imbricata. 75c, Tetramicra eulophiae. 85c, Starnoenas cyanocephala. 90c, Bonnetia cubensis.
1p, Colaptes fernandinae, vert.

**2014, Dec. 15** **Litho.** ***Perf. 12¾***
**5599-5604** A1634 Set of 6 5.75 5.75

**Souvenir Sheet**

***Imperf***

**5605** A1634 1p multi 2.00 2.00

No. 5605 has simulated perforations.

Tomás Romay Chacón (1764-1849), Physician A1635

*Perf. 12½x12¼*

**2014, Dec. 21** **Litho.**
**5606** A1635 65c multi 1.40 1.40

José Luis Guerra Aguiar Postal Museum, 50th Anniv. A1636

Designs: 5c, 1826 stampless cover from Santiago de Cuba to Puerto Principe. 10c, 1883 cover with stamps depicting King Alfonso XII. 15c, Handstamp and free frank covers of General Máximo Gómez Báez. 20c, Cuba #238, printing stone for stamp similar to #238. 65c, Handstamp, cover with Cuba #C324-C325. 75c, Children looking at museum exhibit, magnifying glass and album pages.
1p, Cover with Cuba #935a-935b.

**2015 Jan. 9** **Litho.** ***Perf. 12½x12¼***
**5607-5612** A1636 Set of 6 4.00 4.00

**Souvenir Sheet**

***Imperf***

**5613** A1636 1p multi 2.00 2.00

No. 5613 contains one 44x33mm stamp with simulated perforations.

National Organization of Collective Law Offices, 50th Anniv. A1637

**2015, Jan. 22** **Litho.** ***Perf. 12½x12¼***
**5614** A1637 65c multi 1.40 1.40

Fish — A1638

Inscriptions: 5c, Siamese fighting fish (Luchador de Siam). 15c, Clown loach (Locha payaso), horiz. 45c, Pearl gourami (Gurami perla), horiz. 65c, Butterfly cichlid (Ciclido mariposa), horiz. 75c, Mollies (Pez molly), horiz. 90c, Goldfish, horiz.
1p, Angelfish (Escalar).

*Perf. 12¼x12½, 12½x12¼*

**2015, Jan. 20** **Litho.**
**5615-5620** A1638 Set of 6 6.00 6.00

**Souvenir Sheet**

***Imperf***

**5621** A1638 1p multi 2.00 2.00

No. 5621 contains one 29x45mm stamp with simulated perforations.

Dogs A1639

Designs: 15c, Cocker spaniels. 30c, Golden retrievers. 40c, Border collies. 65c, Alaskan malamutes. 75c, Labrador retrievers. 85c, St. Bernards.
1p, German shepherds, vert.

**2015, Jan. 20** **Litho.** ***Perf. 12½x12¼***
**5622-5627** A1639 Set of 6 6.25 6.25

**Souvenir Sheet**

***Imperf***

**5628** A1639 1p multi 2.00 2.00

No. 5628 has simulated perforations.

Faustino Pérez Hernández (1920-92), Central Committee Member, Zaza Dam — A1640

*Perf. 12½x12¼*

**2015, Feb. 15** **Litho.**
**5629** A1640 1.05p multi 2.10 2.10

Ballet "Dioné," 75th Anniv. A1641

Designs: 75c, Composer Eduardo Sánchez de Fuentes (1874-1944) and scene from ballet. 90c, Dancers Alicia and Fernando Alonso.

**2015, Mar. 4** **Litho.** ***Perf. 12½x12¼***
**5630-5631** A1641 Set of 2 3.50 3.50

Ballet Performances of Anna Pavlova in Cuba, Cent. — A1642

*Perf. 12¼x12½*

**2015, Mar. 18** **Litho.**
**5632** A1642 65c multi 1.40 1.40

Manuel López Portilla (1940-60), State Security Agent — A1643

*Perf. 12¼x12½*

**2015, Mar. 26** **Litho.**
**5633** A1643 65c multi 1.40 1.40

Explosion of Ship "La Coubre" in Havana Harbor, 55th Anniv. A1644

**2015, Apr. 1** **Litho.** ***Perf. 12½x12¼***
**5634** A1644 3p multi 6.00 6.00

Railway Cars — A1645

Designs: 10c, Tanker cars. 20c, Flat cars. 50c, Lumber cars. 65c, Cars carrying intermodal containers. 75c, Coal cars. 85c, Automobile carrier.
1p, Poultry car.

**2015, Mar. 4** **Litho.** ***Perf. 12½x12¼***
**5635-5640** A1645 Set of 6 6.25 6.25

**Souvenir Sheet**

***Imperf***

**5641** A1645 1p multi 2.00 2.00

No. 5641 contains one 45x30mm stamp with simulated perforations.

Endangered Birds A1646

Birds and maps of their range: 5c, Passerina ciris. 15c, Chiroxiphia caudata, vert. 20c, Amadina fasciata. 75c, Carduelis carduelis, vert. 85c, Chloebia gouldiae, vert. 90c, Leiothrix argentauris.
1p, Ferminia cerverai, vert.

*Perf. 12½x12¼, 12¼x12½*

**2015, Apr. 10** **Litho.**
**5642-5647** A1646 Set of 6 6.00 6.00

**Souvenir Sheet**

***Imperf***

**5648** A1646 1p multi 2.00 2.00

No. 5648 has simulated perforations.

Landing of José Martí and General Máximo Gómez Báez at Playita, 120th Anniv. A1647

No. 5649 — Playita and: a, 65c, Martí. b, 75c, Gómez.

**2015, Apr. 11** **Litho.** ***Perf. 12¼x12½***
**5649** A1647 Horiz. pair, #a-b 3.00 3.00

Raúl Ferrer (1915-93), Poet and Educator A1648

**2015, Apr. 17** **Litho.** ***Perf. 12¾***
**5650** A1648 75c multi 1.50 1.50

Use of First Stamps in Cuba, 160th Anniv. A1649

No. 5651: a, 10c, Havana postal badge, mailman and mailboxes. b, 30c, Padlock and key, horse-drawn postal wagons. c, 65c, Post office scale, postal workers sorting mail. d, 75c, Title of Postal Administration, post office.

**2015, Apr. 24** **Litho.** ***Perf. 12½x12¼***
**5651** A1649 Block of 4, #a-d 3.75 3.75

Labor Day — A1650

**2015, May 1** **Litho.** ***Perf. 12¼x12½***
**5652** A1650 75c multi 1.50 1.50



Diplomatic Relations Between Cuba and Russia, 55th Anniv. — A1651

**2015, May 8** **Litho.** ***Perf. 12¼x12½***
**5653** A1651 85c multi 1.75 1.75



Havana Explosion and Fire of 1890, 125th Anniv. — A1652

Firefighter killed in explosion and horse-drawn: 5c, Cervantes pumper. 10c, Colón pumper. 15c, Fire wagon. 40c, Ambulance. 65c, Gámiz pumper. 75c, Cuba pumper.
1p, Megaphone and monument plaque listing the victims, vert.

**2015, May 15 Litho. *Perf. 12¾***
**5654-5659** A1652 Set of 6 4.25 4.25

**Souvenir Sheet**

***Imperf***

**5660** A1652 1p multi 2.00 2.00

No. 5660 has simulated perforations.

Ferry "Pinero" A1653

**2015, May 16 Litho. *Perf. 12½x12¼***
**5661** A1653 75c multi 1.50 1.50

Arrival of Fidel Castro and other Moncada Barracks attackers at Batabanó, 60th anniv.

International Telecommunication Union, 150th Anniv. — A1654

**2015, May 17 Litho. *Perf. 12¼x12½***
**5662** A1654 65c multi 1.40 1.40

Elisio Reyes (1940-67), Guerrilla Fighter A1655

**2015, May 23 Litho. *Perf. 12½x12¼***
**5663** A1655 65c multi 1.40 1.40

Wild Cats — A1656

Designs: 15c, Panthera onca, Olmec ceremonial hatchet. 35c, Puma concolor, gorget. 50c, Panthera tigris, carving of tiger. 65c, Panthera leo, Thracian grave decoration. 75c, Acinonyx jubatus, decorated Egyptian knife. 85c, Panthera pardus, Nigerian bronze plaque.
1p, Felis silvestris catus, Japanese drawing of cat.

**2015, Apr. 15 Litho. *Perf. 12½x12¼***
**5664-5669** A1656 Set of 6 6.50 6.50

**Souvenir Sheet**

***Imperf***

**5670** A1656 1p multi 2.00 2.00

No. 5670 has simulated perforations.

Prehistoric Fauna A1657

Designs: 10c, Carcharodon megalodon. 35c, Metaxytherium. 50c, Ptychodus. 65c, Aetomylaeus cubensis. 75c, Physetérid. 85c, Orycterocetus.
1p, Aspidorhynchus.

**2015, May 6 Litho. *Perf. 12½x12¼***
**5671-5676** A1657 Set of 6 6.50 6.50

**Souvenir Sheet**

***Imperf***

**5677** A1657 1p multi 2.00 2.00

No. 5677 has simulated perforations.

Santiago de Cuba, 500th Anniv. — A1658

Designs: 5c, Lieutenant General Maceo Grajales, painting by Luis Desangles. 10c, Monument to Frank Pais. 15c, Fidel Castro at Mausoleum of José Martí. 30c, San Pedro de la Roca Castle. 75c, La Isabelica coffee plantation building, horiz. 85c, Tumba Francesa dancers and musicians, horiz.
1p, City Hall.

**2015, May 20 Litho. *Perf. 12¾***
**5678-5683** A1658 Set of 6 4.50 4.50

**Souvenir Sheet**

***Imperf***

**5684** A1658 1p multi 2.00 2.00

No. 5684 has simulated perforations.

National Flowers of Central and South American Countries — A1659

Flowers: 5c, Dahlia (Mexico). 15c, Golden trumpet (Brazil). 20c, Mayflower orchid (Venezuela). 30c, Ceibo (Argentina, Uruguay). 40c, Virgin orchid (Honduras). 65c, Rose (Ecuador). 75c, Copihue (Chile). 90c, White ginger (Cuba).

**2015, May 26 Litho. *Perf. 12¼x12½***
**5685-5692** A1659 Set of 8 7.00 7.00

Watercraft A1660

Designs: 5c, SC CL Globe, China. 20c, Paraw, Philippines. 50c, Paddlewheeler Junco, Viet Nam. 65c, Kettuvallam, India. 75c, Dhoni, Maldive Islands, vert. 85c, Junk, China, vert.
1p, Turtle ship, Korea, vert.

***Perf. 12½x12¼, 12¼x12½***

**2015, June 1 Litho.**
**5693-5698** A1660 Set of 6 6.00 6.00

**Souvenir Sheet**

***Imperf***

**5699** A1660 1p multi 2.00 2.00

Singapore 2015 Intl. Philatelic Exhibition. No. 5699 contains one 32x48mm stamp with simulated perforations.

San Juan de los Remedios, 500th Anniv. A1661

Designs: 65c, Buildings of San Juan de los Remedios. 75c, Alejandro García Caturla (1906-40), composer.

***Perf. 12½x12¼***

**2015, June 24 Litho.**
**5700-5701** A1661 Set of 2 3.00 3.00

National Office of Tax Administration, 20th Anniv. — A1662

***Perf. 12¼x12½***

**2015, June 28 Litho.**
**5702** A1662 65c multi 1.40 1.40

History of the Telephone — A1663

Designs: 10c, 19th cent. desk telephone. 20c, 20th cent. wall telephone. 30c, 19th cent. desk telephone, diff. 50c, 20th cent. desk telephone. 65c, 20th cent. desk telephones, diff. 75c, 20th cent. two desk telphones.
1p, 20th cent. public pay telephone.

**2015, July 14 Litho. *Perf. 12¾***
**5703-5708** A1663 Set of 6 5.00 5.00

**Souvenir Sheet**

***Imperf***

**5709** A1663 1p multi 2.00 2.00

No. 5709 has simulated perforations.

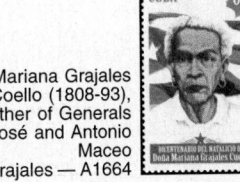

Mariana Grajales Coello (1808-93), Mother of Generals José and Antonio Maceo Grajales — A1664

Designs: 65c, Mariana Grajales Coello and Cuban flag. 75c, Monument.

**2015, July 24 Litho. *Perf. 12¼x12½***
**5710-5711** A1664 Set of 2 3.00 3.00

Alicia Alonso National School of Ballet, 65th Anniv. A1665

**2015, Aug. 5 Litho. *Perf. 12½x12¼***
**5712** A1665 65c multi 1.40 1.40

Cuban Court of International Commercial Arbitration, 50th Anniv. — A1666

***Perf. 12¼x12½***

**2015, Sept. 16 Litho.**
**5713** A1666 3p multi 6.00 6.00

Committee for the Defense of the Revolution, 55th Anniv. A1667

***Perf. 12½x12¼***

**2015, Sept. 21 Litho.**
**5714** A1667 65c multi 1.40 1.40

Campaign Against Human Trafficking — A1668

Campaign against: No. 5715, 65c, Sexual exploitation (Explotación sexual). No. 5716, 65c, Forced labor (Trabajo forzado). No. 5717, 65c, Organ extraction (Extracción de órganos). No. 5718, 65c, Servitude (Servidumbre).

**2015, Oct. 12 Litho. *Perf. 12¼x12½***
**5715-5718** A1668 Set of 4 5.25 5.25

America Issue.

Paintings and Artifacts Connected to José Martí — A1669

Designs: 5c, Martí on horseback, spurs from Battle of Dos Ríos. 10c, House of General Máximo Gómez, Montecristi, and inkstand. 15c, Martí leading cavalrymen, Winchester rifle. 20c, Martí in rowboat, oarlocks. 30c, Martí reading *Patria* newspaper, plaque from Patria building. 40c, Martí addressing crowd, pulpit. 75c, María García Granados (1860-78), love interest of Martí and subject of Martí poem, cushion. 85c, Martí writing, desk and chair.

**2015, Oct. 15 Litho. *Perf. 12¼x12½***
**5719-5726** A1669 Set of 8 5.75 5.75

Cuban Television, 65th Anniv. — A1670

**2015, Oct. 24 Litho. *Perf. 12¾***
**5727** A1670 75c multi 1.50 1.50
*a.* Dated "2015" — —

No. 5727 has "201" date at lower right.

Cuban Wushu and Qigong School, 20th Anniv. A1671

**2015, Oct. 26 Litho. *Perf. 12½x12¼***
**5728** A1671 85c multi 1.75 1.75

Visit of Pope Francis A1672

***Perf. 12½x12¼***

**2015, Nov. 11 Litho.**
**5729** A1672 75c multi 1.50 1.50

11th National Stamp Championships — A1673

Designs: 10c, Marlon Brando (1924-2004), actor, Academy Award. 15c, Mother Teresa (St. Teresa of Calcutta) (1910-97), crucifix. 20c, Babe Ruth (1895-1948), baseball player, baseball. 65c, Charles A. Lindbergh (1902-74), aviator, Spirit of St. Louis. 75c, Gabriel García Márquez (1927-2014), writer, book, eyeglasses and butterflies. 85c, Diego Rivera (1886-1957), painter, detail of "The Uprising."
1p, Diego A. Maradona, soccer player, World Cup trophy.

***Perf. 12½x12¼***

**2015, Nov. 20 Litho.**
**5730-5735** A1673 Set of 6 5.50 5.50

**Souvenir Sheet**

***Imperf***

**5736** A1673 1p multi 2.00 2.00

No. 5736 has simulated perforations.

Nico López (1932-56), Revolutionary A1674

**2015, Dec. 2 Litho. *Perf. 12½x12¼***
**5737** A1674 65c multi 1.40 1.40

Communist Party Schools, 55th anniv.

Souvenir Sheet

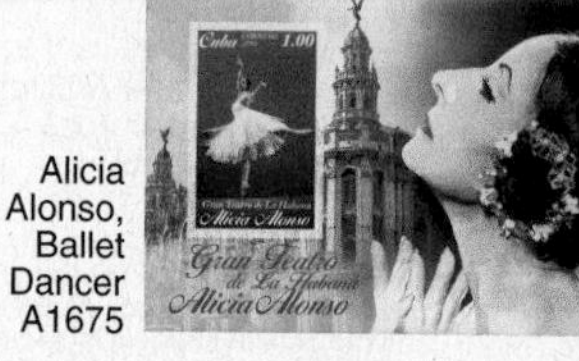

Alicia Alonso, Ballet Dancer A1675

**2016, Jan. 1 Litho. *Imperf.***
**5738** A1675 1p multi 2.00 2.00

Reopening of Alicia Alonso Grand Theater, Havana.

Conrado Benítez (1942-61), Revolutionary Martyr — A1676

**2016, Jan. 5 Litho. *Perf. 12¾***
**5739** A1676 90c multi 1.90 1.90

Research Center for Animal Breeding of Tropical Livestock, 45th Anniv. A1677

Designs: 65c, Research center, livestock. 75c, Researchers and livestock.

**2016, Jan. 8 Litho. *Perf. 12½x12¼***
**5740-5741** A1677 Set of 2 3.00 3.00

Mayabeque Province, 5th Anniv. — A1678

**2016, Jan. 9 Litho. *Perf. 12¼x12½***
**5742** A1678 90c multi 1.90 1.90

Francisco de Albear Fernández y de Lara (1816-87), Civil Engineer A1679

**2016, Jan. 11 Litho. *Perf. 12½x12¼***
**5743** A1679 1.05p multi 2.10 2.10

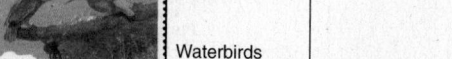

Waterbirds A1680

Designs: 10c, Alcedo atthis. 15c, Phaethon rubricauda. 45c, Branta canadensis. 75c, Threskiornis aethiopicus. 85c, Anas platyrhynchos. 90c, Branta canadensis, vert.

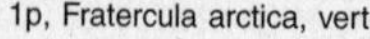

1p, Fratercula arctica, vert.

***Perf. 12½x12¼, 12¼x12½***
**2016, Jan. 15 Litho.**
**5744-5749** A1680 Set of 6 6.50 6.50

**Souvenir Sheet**
***Imperf***

**5750** A1680 1p multi 2.00 2.00

No. 5750 contains one 30x36mm stamp with simulated perforations. Bird name inscription on No. 5749 is incorrect.

General Calixto García University Hospital, Havana, 120th Anniv. — A1681

**2016, Jan. 23 Litho. *Perf. 12¼x12½***
**5751** A1681 65c multi 1.40 1.40

Second "Con Todos y Para el Bien de Todos" International Conference on Works of José Martí, Havana — A1682

**2016, Jan. 25 Litho. *Perf. 12¼x12½***
**5752** A1682 2.05p multi 4.25 4.25

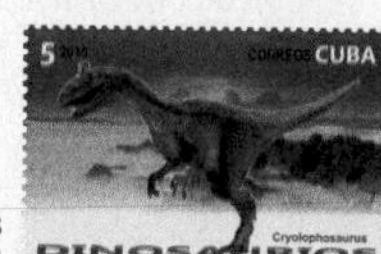

Dinosaurs A1683

Designs: 5c, Cryolophosaurus. 20c, Amargasaurus. 65c, Camarasaurus. 75c, Pachyrhinosaurus. 85c, Baryonyx. 90c, Allosaurus.
1p, Gorgosaurus.

**2016, Jan. 31 Litho. *Perf. 12½x12¼***
**5753-5758** A1683 Set of 6 7.00 7.00

**Souvenir Sheet**
***Imperf***

**5759** A1683 1p multi 2.00 2.00

No. 5759 has simulated perforations.

Classic Automobiles A1684

Designs: 5c, 1932 Duesenberg SJ Dual-cowl Phaeton. 15c, 1936 Bugatti Type 57SC Atlantic. 50c, 1931 Lincoln Model K. 65c, 1936 Mercedes-Benz 540 K. 75c, 1934 Chevrolet Master Sport Coupe. 85c, 1934 Ford Deluxe Roadster.
1p, 1938 Volkswagen Type 1.

***Perf. 12½x12¼***
**2016, Feb. 20 Litho.**
**5760-5765** A1684 Set of 6 6.00 6.00

**Souvenir Sheet**
***Imperf***

**5766** A1684 1p multi 2.00 2.00

No. 5766 has simulated perforations.

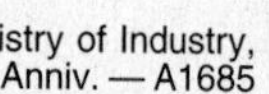

Ministry of Industry, 55th Anniv. — A1685

***Perf. 12¼x12½***
**2016, Feb. 22 Litho.**
**5767** A1685 3p multi 6.00 6.00

Restoration of Teatro Martí, Havana A1686

Designs: 45c, Building exterior. 50c, Stage. 65c, Seats and ceiling.

**2016, Feb. 24 Litho. *Perf. 12¾***
**5768-5770** A1686 Set of 3 3.25 3.25

Establishment of Cuban Postal Service, 260th Anniv. — A1687

Designs: 10c, Mail ship and captain, 1777. 40c, Postman, horse and carriage, 1902. 65c, Special delivery postman on motorcycle, 1950. 85c, Postman on bicycle, 2013.
1p, Postman on horse.

**2016, Mar. 1 Litho. *Perf. 12¾***
**5771-5774** A1687 Set of 4 4.00 4.00

**Souvenir Sheet**
***Imperf***

**5775** A1687 1p multi 2.00 2.00

No. 5775 has simulated perforations.

Fe del Valle Ramos (1917-61), Department Store Worker Killed in Arson Fire — A1688

**2016, Mar. 8 Litho. *Perf. 12¾***
**5776** A1688 65c multi 1.40 1.40

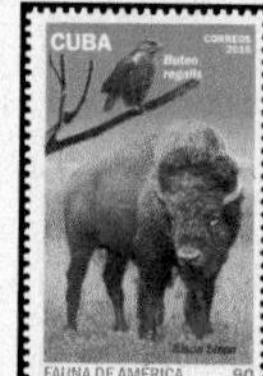

Fauna — A1689

Designs: No. 5777, 90c, Buteo regalis, Bison bison. No. 5778, 90c, Ramphastos toco, Leopardus pardalis. No. 5779, 90c, Oncorhynchus mykiss. No. 5780, 90c, Trichechus manatus, Atractosteus tristoechus.

***Perf. 12¼x12½***
**2016, Mar. 10 Litho.**
**5777-5780** A1689 Set of 4 7.25 7.25

Souvenir Sheet

16th Informática Intl. Convention and Fair — A1690

**2016, Mar. 14 Litho. *Imperf.***
**5781** A1690 1p multi 2.00 2.00

Central Army, 55th Anniv. — A1691

**2016, Apr. 4 Litho. *Perf. 12¼x12½***
**5782** A1691 65c multi 1.40 1.40

Sculptures by José Villa Soberón A1692

Designs: 10c, Caballero de Paris. 35c, Tin Tan. 40c, Gabriel García Márquez. 75c, John Lennon. 85c, Benny Moré. 90c, Antonio Gades.
1p, Ernest Hemingway, vert.

**2016, Apr. 5 Litho. *Perf. 12½x12¼***
**5783-5788** A1692 Set of 6 6.75 6.75

**Souvenir Sheet**
***Imperf***

**5789** A1692 1p multi 2.00 2.00

2016 Copa Cuba National Stamp Exhibition. No. 5789 has simulated perforations.

Trains A1693

Designs: 10c, Liverpool & Manchester Railway train, 1830. 20c, American express train, 1885. 35c, Orient Express, 1883. 75c, Trans-Siberian train, 1883. 85c, Blue Train, 1903. 90c, Union Pacific train.
1p, Shinkansen Sereis 700 train.

**2016, Apr. 5 Litho. *Perf. 12½x12¼***
**5790-5795** A1693 Set of 6 6.50 6.50

**Souvenir Sheet**
***Imperf***

**5796** A1693 1p multi 2.00 2.00

No. 5796 has simulated perforations.

Eastern Army, 55th Anniv. A1694

**2016, Apr. 21 Litho. *Perf. 12½x12¼***
**5797** A1694 65c multi 1.40 1.40

Labor Day — A1695

**2016, Apr. 29 Litho. *Perf. 12¼x12½***
**5798** A1695 75c multi 1.50 1.50

National Association of Small Farmers, 55th Anniv. — A1696

**2016, May 17 Litho. *Perf. 12¼x12½***
**5799** A1696 85c multi 1.75 1.75

Musical Instruments A1697

Designs: 5c, Laúd. 15c, Corneta China. 35c, Catá. 75c, Chequeré. 85c, Iyá.

**2016, May 18 Litho.** ***Perf. 12½x12¼***
**5800-5804** A1697 Set of 5 4.50 4.50

Enrique José Varona (1848-1933), Writer A1698

**2016, May 19 Litho.** ***Perf. 12½x12¼***
**5805** A1698 75c multi 1.50 1.50

Cuban Academy of Language, 90th anniv.

Extinct and Endangered Hutias — A1699

Designs: 5c, Mesocapromys sanfelipensis. 15c, Mesocapromys nanus. 35c, Mesocapromys angelcabrerai. 45c, Mesocapromys auritus. 75c, Mysateles melanurus. 85c, Mysateles prehensilis.
1p, Capromys pilorides.

**2016, May 23 Litho.** ***Perf. 12¼x12½***
**5806-5811** A1699 Set of 6 5.25 5.25

**Souvenir Sheet**

***Imperf***

**5812** A1699 1p multi 2.00 2.00

No. 5812 has simulated perforations.

National Flowers of North and South American Countries A1700

Designs: 5c, Maga, Puerto Rico. 15c, Bougainvillea (bugambilia), Canada. 20c, Romerillo, St. Lucia. 30c, Plumeria (sacuanjoche), Nicaragua. 40c, Soufriere tree flower, St. Vincent and the Grenadines. 65c, Poinciana (framboyán), Haiti and St. Kitts and Nevis, vert. 75c, Dagger's log, Antigua and Barbuda, vert. 90c, Kantuta, Bolivia, vert.

**2016, May 26 Litho.** ***Perf. 12¾***
**5813-5820** A1700 Set of 8 7.00 7.00

Victims of Terrorism A1701

Designs: 65c, Airplane, boat, people walking on street. 75c, Newspaper headline, people looking at wall of photographs.

**2016, June 3 Litho.** ***Perf. 12½x12¼***
**5821-5822** A1701 Set of 2 3.00 3.00

Ministry of the Interior, 55th Anniv. — A1702

**2016, June 5 Litho.** ***Perf. 12¾***
**5823** A1702 90c multi 1.90 1.90

Western Army, 55th Anniv. A1703

***Perf. 12½x12¼***

**2016, June 14 Litho.**
**5824** A1703 65c multi 1.40 1.40

Center for Genetic Engineering and Biotechnology, 30th Anniv. — A1704

**2016, July 1 Litho.** ***Perf. 12¾***
**5825** A1704 90c multi 1.90 1.90

Cuban Amateur Radio Federation, 50th Anniv. — A1705

**2016, July 15 Litho.** ***Perf. 12¼x12½***
**5826** A1705 1.05p multi 2.10 2.10

Miguel de Cervantes (c. 1547-1616), Writer — A1706

William Shakespeare (1564-1616), Writer — A1707

No. 5827: a, Don Quixote and windmill. b, Cervantes and quotation.
No. 5828: a, Roses and dagger. b, Shakespeare and quotation.

**2016, Apr. 23 Litho.** ***Perf. 12½x12¼***
**5827** A1706 65c Horiz. pair, #a-b 2.60 2.60
**5828** A1707 75c Horiz. pair, #a-b 3.00 3.00

Ships A1708

Designs: 15c, López Mena, Argentina and Uruguay. 30c, Beringov Proliv, Russia. 50c, Tûranor PlanetSolar, Switzerland. 65c, Horizon Ferry, Singapore. 75c, Adastra, Hong Kong. 85c, Madame Gu, Netherlands.
1p, Siem Moxie, Norway, vert.

**2016, May 28 Litho.** ***Perf. 12½x12¼***
**5829-5834** A1708 Set of 6 6.50 6.50

**Souvenir Sheet**

***Imperf***

**5835** A1708 1p multi 2.00 2.00

No. 5835 contains one 33x49mm stamp with simulated perforations.

Ministry of Transportation, 55th Anniv. — A1709

**2016, Aug. 3 Litho.** ***Perf. 12½x12¼***
**5836** A1709 3p multi 6.00 6.00

Desembarco del Granma National Park — A1710

Designs: 65c, Cabo Cruz Lighthouse, Thalasseus maximus. 75c, Terrace system, Plumeria sp. 85c, Coccothrinax saxicola, Polymita venusta. 90c, Hoyo de Morlotte, Liguus vittatus.

**2016, Aug. 13 Litho.** ***Perf. 12¾***
**5837-5840** A1710 Set of 4 6.50 6.50

2016 Summer Olympics, Rio de Janeiro A1711

Designs: 10c, Boxing. 20c, Rowing. 30c, Volleyball, vert. 65c, Wrestling, vert. 75c, Judo. 85c, Taekwondo.
1p, Running, vert.

***Perf. 12½x12¼, 12¼x12½***

**2016, Aug. 21 Litho.**
**5841-5846** A1711 Set of 6 5.75 5.75

**Souvenir Sheet**

***Imperf***

**5847** A1711 1p multi 2.00 2.00

No. 5835 has simulated perforations.

Mella Theater, Havana, 55th Anniv. — A1712

***Perf. 12¼x12½***

**2016, Sept. 10 Litho.**
**5848** A1712 1.05p multi 2.10 2.10

University Student Federation's Relief Performance for Alicia Alonso, 60th Anniv. — A1713

**2016, Sept. 15 Litho.** ***Perf. 12¾***
**5849** A1713 90c multi 1.90 1.90

Caricatos Talent Agency, 16th Anniv. — A1714

Designs: 65c, Enrique Almirante (1930-2007), actor. 90c, Raúl Pomares (1934-2015), actor and director.

**2016, Sept. 24 Litho.** ***Perf. 12¾***
**5850-5851** A1714 Set of 2 3.25 3.25

Copextel, 25th Anniv. — A1715

**2016, Oct. 6 Litho.** ***Perf. 12¾***
**5852** A1715 75c multi 1.50 1.50

2016 Summer Olympics, Rio de Janeiro — A1716

Designs: No. 5853, 65c, 90-day journey of Olympic torch from Mt. Olympus to Rio de Janeiro. No. 5854, 65c, Rio de Janeiro, first South American host city of Olympics. No. 5855, 65c, Golf returns as Olympic sport. No. 5856, 65c, Rugby returns as an Olympic sport.

**2016, Oct. 12 Litho.** ***Perf. 12¼x12½***
**5853-5856** A1716 Set of 4 5.25 5.25

Asociación Hermanos Saíz (Hip-Hop and Rap Music Promotional Organization), 30th Anniv. — A1717

**2016, Oct. 18 Litho.** ***Perf. 12¼x12½***
**5857** A1717 75c multi 1.50 1.50

Alicia Alonso International Festival of Ballet, Havana, 25th Anniv. — A1718

Designs: 15c, Dido Abandonada. 35c, Ad Libitum. 40c, La Diva. 65c, Elegía por un Joven. 75c, Tula, horiz. 85c, Cascanueces, horiz.
1p, Carmen, horiz.

***Perf. 12¼x12½, 12½x12¼***

**2016, Oct. 28 Litho.**
**5858-5863** A1718 Set of 6 6.50 6.50

**Souvenir Sheet**

***Imperf***

**5864** A1718 1p multi 2.00 2.00

No. 5864 has simulated perforations.

Fire Brigades in Cuba, 320th Anniv. A1719

Designs: 5c, Fire fighters and horse-drawn wagon, 1898. 10c, Havana fire fighters, 1920. 15c, DGPCI fire fighters, 1985. 40c, Fire fighters with hose, 2016. 65c, Fire fighter on rope, 2016. 85c, Fire fighter with rescue dog, 2016.
1p, Fire fighter Enriqueta Reyes, 1957, vert.

***Perf. 12½x12¼***

**2016, Nov. 13 Litho.**
**5865-5870** A1719 Set of 6 4.50 4.50

**Souvenir Sheet**

***Imperf***

**5871** A1719 1p multi 2.00 2.00

No. 5871 contains one 33x44mm stamp with simulated perforations.

Road Safety Day — A1720

Designs: 10c, Surveyors. 15c, Bus at bus stop. 45c, Car testing. 75c, Motorcyclist and bicylist. 85c, Person being put in ambulance.

***Perf. 12½x12¼***

**2016, Nov. 16 Litho.**
**5872-5876** A1720 Set of 5 4.75 4.75

Return of Fidel Castro to Cuba on the Granma, 60th Anniv. A1721

Designs: 65c, Granma and map of voyage. 75c, Cuban revolutionary soldier.

***Perf. 12½x12¼***

**2016, Nov. 25** **Litho.**

**5877-5878** A1721 Set of 2 3.00 3.00

Lt. General José Antonio de la Caridad Maceo y Grajales (1845-96) — A1722

Maceo: 50c, On horse. 65c, On rearing horse.

**2016, Dec. 7** **Litho.** ***Perf. 12¾***

**5879-5880** A1722 Set of 2 3.00 3.00

Flora and Fauna of Pico Turquino National Park — A1723

Designs: 40c, Anetia briarea numidia. 65c, Lepanthes turquinoensis. 75c, Spindalis zena. 85c, Cysticopsis.

***Perf. 12¼x12½***

**2016, Dec. 15** **Litho.**

**5881-5884** A1723 Set of 4 5.50 5.50

Declaration of Melena del Sur as First Cuban Municipality Free of Illiteracy, 55th Anniv. — A1724

***Perf. 12¼x12½***

**2016, Dec. 22** **Litho.**

**5885** A1724 65c multi 1.40 1.40

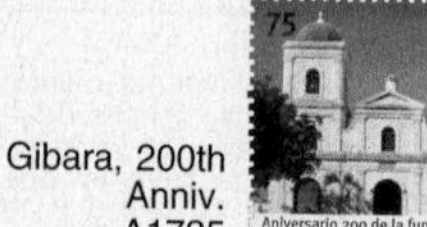

Gibara, 200th Anniv. A1725

Designs: 75c, Calixto García Park. 85c, Gibara Bay.

**2017, Jan. 17** **Litho.** ***Perf. 12½x12¼***

**5886-5887** A1725 Set of 2 3.25 3.25

Special Education in Cuba, 55th Anniv. A1726

**2017, Jan. 18** **Litho.** ***Perf. 12½x12¼***

**5888** A1726 1.05p multi 2.10 2.10

Cuban Theater Day — A1727

Designs: 10c, *Aire Frío,* play by Virgilio Piñera. 15c, National Folklore Group. 35c, Raquel Revuelta in *Madre Coraje.* 40c, National Lyrical Theater production of *The Magic Flute.* 50c, Roberto Blanco, vert. 75c, Vicente Revuelta in *Galileo Galilei,* vert. 1p, Villanueva Theater events

***Perf. 12½x12¼, 12¼x12½***

**2017, Jan. 22** **Litho.**

**5889-5894** A1727 Set of 6 4.50 4.50

**Souvenir Sheet**

***Imperf***

**5895** A1727 1p multi 2.00 2.00

No. 5895 contains one 49x33mm stamp with simulated perforations.

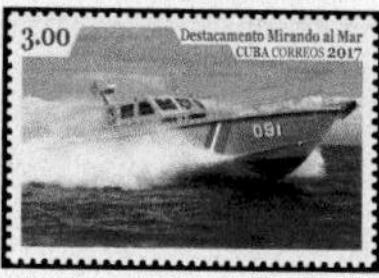

Cuban Coast Guard Boat — A1728

**2017, Feb. 8** **Litho.** ***Perf. 12½x12¼***

**5896** A1728 3p multi 6.00 6.00

Shipbuilding Slips at Boca de Jaruco, 500th Anniv. A1729

**2017, Mar. 8** **Litho.** ***Perf. 12½x12¼***

**5897** A1729 65c multi 1.40 1.40

Birds of Guanahacabibes Peninsula Reserve, 30th Anniv. — A1730

Designs: 65c, Elanoides forficatus, Roncali Lighthouse, map. 75c, Ictinia mississippiensis. 85c, Pandion haliaetus. 90c, Falco peregrinus.

**2017, Mar. 16** **Litho.** ***Perf. 12¾***

**5898-5901** A1730 Set of 4 6.50 6.50

Cuban Oil Union, 25th Anniv. A1731

***Perf. 12½x12¼***

**2017, Mar. 25** **Litho.**

**5902** A1731 85c multi 1.75 1.75

Birds and Lighthouses — A1732

Designs: No. 5903, 90c, Buteogallus gundlachii, Columbus Lighthouse, Cayo Sabinal, Cuba. No. 5904, 90c, Athene cunicularia arubensis, California Lighthouse, Aruba. No. 5905, 90c, Calliphlox evelynae, Hope Town Lighthouse, Elbow Cay, Bahamas. No. 5906, 90c, Aratinga acuticaudata neoxena, Punta Zaragoza Lighthouse, Isla Margarita, Venezuela.

**2017, Apr. 1** **Litho.** ***Perf. 12¼x12½***

**5903-5906** A1732 Set of 4 7.25 7.25

Young Communist League, 55th Anniv. A1733

**2017, Apr. 3** **Litho.** ***Perf. 12½x12¼***

**5907** A1733 65c multi 1.40 1.40

José Martí Program, 20th Anniv. — A1734

**2017, Apr. 6** **Litho.** ***Perf. 12¾***

**5908** A1734 90c multi 1.90 1.90

*Antes del Alba* Ballet, 70th Anniv. — A1735

Various sketches for costumes for ballet by Carlos Enríquez: 10c, 15c, 30c, 50c, 75c, 90c. 1p, Ballerina in costume.

**2017, Apr. 20** **Litho.** ***Perf. 12¾***

**5909-5914** A1735 Set of 6 5.50 5.50

**Souvenir Sheet**

***Imperf***

**5915** A1735 1p multi 2.00 2.00

No. 5915 has simulated perforations.

Gran Teatro de La Habana Alicia Alonso, 180th Anniv. — A1736

Designs: 10c, Illustration of theater in 19th century. 15c, Stage, 1856. 40c, Theater, 1953. 65c, García Lorca Hall, 2016. 75c, Stage, 2016. 85c, Ceiling, lamp and balconies, 2016. 1p, Illustration of coach outside of theater.

**2017, Apr. 22** **Litho.** ***Perf. 12¾***

**5916-5921** A1736 Set of 6 6.00 6.00

**Souvenir Sheet**

***Imperf***

**5922** A1736 1p multi 2.00 2.00

No. 5922 has simulated perforations.

Birds of Prey — A1737

Designs: 10c, Falco sparverius. 35c, Falco columbarius. 65c, Buteogallus anthracinus. 75c, Rostrhamus sociabilis. 85c, Buteo platypterus. 90c, Glaucidium siju. 1p, Athene cunicularia.

**2017, Jan. 16** **Litho.** ***Perf. 12¾***

**5923-5928** A1737 Set of 6 7.25 7.25

**Souvenir Sheet**

***Imperf***

**5929** A1737 1p multi 2.00 2.00

No. 5929 has simulated perforations.

Bees — A1738

Designs: 5c, Apis mellifera sentellata. 20c, Apis cerana. 65c, Apis mellifera ligustica. 75c, Apis mellifera carnica. 85c, Apis mellifera lamarckii. 90c, Megachile centuncularis. 1p, Apis mellifera mellifera.

**2017, Feb. 11** **Litho.** ***Perf. 12¾***

**5930-5935** A1738 Set of 6 7.00 7.00

**Souvenir Sheet**

***Imperf***

**5936** A1738 1p multi 2.00 2.00

No. 5936 has simulated perforations.

Technology A1739

Designs: 40c, Software and video games. 45c, Digital television. 65c, Wi-fi. 75c, Internet.

***Perf. 12½x12¼***

**2017, Mar. 15** **Litho.**

**5937-5940** A1739 Set of 4 4.50 4.50

National Flowers A1740

Flower and map of: 5c, Peristeria elata, Panama. 15c, Guarianthe skinneri, Costa Rica. 20c, Rose, United States. 30c, Guaiacum officinale, Jamaica, vert. 40c, Pereskia quisqueyana, Dominican Republic. 65c, Warszewiczia coccinea, Trinidad & Tobago. 75c, Ixora coccinea, Surinam. 90c, Prosthechea cochleata, Belize, vert.

***Perf. 12½x12¼, 12¼x12½***

**2017, May 26** **Litho.**

**5941-5948** A1740 Set of 8 7.00 7.00

Admission of Cuba to the United Nations, 70th Anniv. — A1741

**2017, May 29** **Litho.** ***Perf. 12¼x12½***

**5949** A1741 85c multi 1.75 1.75

Ministry of the Interior Fighters Who Died in Bolivia With Ernesto "Che" Guevara in 1968 — A1742

**2017, June 5** **Litho.** ***Perf. 12¾***

**5950** A1742 75c multi 1.50 1.50

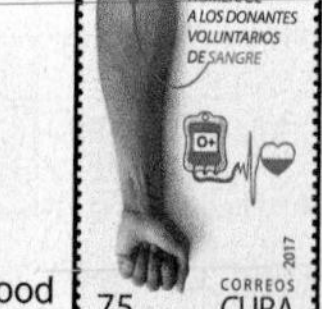

Blood Donation — A1743

**2017, June 8** **Litho.** ***Perf. 12¼x12½***

**5951** A1743 75c multi 1.50 1.50

Artistic Agency of Performing Arts (ACTUAR), 38th Anniv. — A1744

Designs: 65c, Alden Knight, actor. 85c, Rosita Fornes, actress.

**2017, July 3 Litho. *Perf. 12¾***
**5952-5953** A1744 Set of 2 3.00 3.00

World Environment Day — A1745

Designs: 10c, Sea turtles on beach, Guanahacabibes Peninsula Biosphere Reserve. 15c, Hutia, Sierra del Rosario Biosphere Reserve, horiz. 20c, Cuban crocodile, Ciénaga de Zapata Biosphere Reserve, horiz. 35c, Flamingos, Buenavista Biosphere Reserve, horiz. 85c, Cuban tody, Baconao Biosphere Reserve. 90c, Cuban land snail, Cuchillas del Toa Biosphere Reserve, horiz.
1p, Coral reef, Guanahacabibes Peninsula Biosphere Reserve.

***Perf. 12¼x12½, 12½x12¼***
**2017, July 5 Litho.**
**5954-5959** A1745 Set of 6 5.25 5.25

**Souvenir Sheet**

***Imperf***

**5960** A1745 1p multi 2.00 2.00

No. 5960 has simulated perforations.

Helicopters A1746

Designs: 10c, Eurocopter HH-65 Dolphin. 15c, Westland WS-61 Sea King. 30c, MBB/Kawasaki BK117. 75c, Sikorsky S-92. 85c, Kamov Ka-32A11BC. 90c, Agusta Westland CH-149 Cormorant.
1p, Mil Mi-17.

**2017, July 15 Litho. *Perf. 12½x12¼***
**5961-5966** A1746 Set of 6 6.25 6.25

**Souvenir Sheet**

***Imperf***

**5967** A1746 1p multi 2.00 2.00

No. 5967 has simulated perforations.

Cintio Vitier (1921-2009), Poet — A1747

**2017, July 19 Litho. *Perf. 12¾***
**5968** A1747 65c multi 1.40 1.40

Center for José Martí Studies, 40th anniv.

Course of Study for Childhood Nursing, 130th Anniv. A1748

Designs: 50c, Nurse examining woman. 75c, Nurse treating child.

**2017, July 28 Litho. *Perf. 12½x12¼***
**5969-5970** A1748 Set of 2 2.50 2.50

Civil Defense, 55th Anniv. A1749

**2017, July 31 Litho. *Perf. 12½x12¼***
**5971** A1749 75c multi 1.50 1.50

Continuous Broadcasting of Radio Cubana, 95th Anniv. A1750

***Perf. 12½x12¼***
**2017, Aug. 15 Litho.**
**5972** A1750 75c multi 1.50 1.50

Cuban National Commission of UNESCO, 70th Anniv. — A1751

No. 5973 — Buildings and: a, Woman. b, Man playing drum.

***Perf. 12¼x12½***
**2017, Aug. 29 Litho.**
**5973** A1751 75c Vert. pair, #a-b 3.00 3.00

September 5, 1957 Cienfuegos Uprising, 60th Anniv. A1752

Buildings and: 65c, Man waving flag. 75c, Men with rifles.

**2017, Sept. 5 Litho. *Perf. 12½x12¼***
**5974-5975** A1752 Set of 2 3.00 3.00

Youth Electronics and Computing Club, 30th Anniv. A1753

**2017, Sept. 7 Litho. *Perf. 12½x12¼***
**5976** A1753 75c multi 1.50 1.50

First Protest Song Festival, 50th Anniv. — A1754

**2017, Sept. 8 Litho. *Perf. 12¼x12½***
**5977** A1754 65c multi 1.40 1.40

Miniature Sheet

Capture and Execution of Ernesto "Che" Guevara (1928-67), 50th Anniv. — A1755

No. 5978: a, Guevara and cover of his Bolivian Diary. b, Map and Guevara holding rifle. c, Guevara and other guerrilla fighters. d, Monument to Guevara, La Higuera, Bolivia.

**2017, Oct. 8 Litho. *Perf. 12½x12¼***
**5978** A1755 85c Sheet of 4, #a-d 7.00 7.00

University of Oriente, 70th Anniv. A1756

**2017, Oct. 10 Litho. *Perf. 12½x12¼***
**5979** A1756 65c multi 1.40 1.40

National Pharmaceutical Association, 110th Anniv. — A1757

**2017, Oct. 10 Litho. *Perf. 12¼x12½***
**5980** A1757 90c multi 1.90 1.90

America Issue A1758

Tourist attractions: No. 5981, 65c, Valle de Viñales. No. 5982, 65c, Ciudad Trinidad. No. 5983, 65c, Ciénaga de Zapata. No. 5984, 65c, Playa Santa Lucía.

**2017, Oct. 12 Litho. *Perf. 12½x12¼***
**5981-5984** A1758 Set of 4 5.25 5.25

Beaches — A1759

Designs: 5c, Playa Sirena. 20c, Playa Santa Lucía, horiz. 40c, Playa Pilar, horiz. 45c, Playa Varadero, horiz. 75c, Playa Ensenachos. 85c, Playa Ancón, horiz.
1p, Playa Guardalavaca.

***Perf. 12¼x12½, 12½x12¼***
**2017, Oct. 24 Litho.**
**5985-5990** A1759 Set of 6 5.50 5.50

**Souvenir Sheet**

***Imperf***

**5991** A1759 1p multi 2.00 2.00

No. 5991 contains one 42x29mm stamp that has simulated perforations.

Tropical Food Research Institute, 50th Anniv. A1760

**2017, Oct. 27 Litho. *Perf. 12½x12¼***
**5992** A1760 65c multi 1.40 1.40

Brasiliana 2017 International Philatelic Exhibition, Brasilia, Brazil A1761

Birds: 5c, Cardenilla dominica (red-cowled cardinal). 15c, Guaruba guarouba, vert. 45c, Tangara cyanoventris. 75c, Ramphodon naevius. 85c, Cotinga maculata, vert. 90c, Antilophia bokermanni.
1p, Anodorhynchus leari.

***Perf. 12½x12¼, 12¼x12½***
**2017, Nov. 1 Litho.**
**5993-5998** A1761 Set of 6 6.50 6.50

**Souvenir Sheet**

***Imperf***

**5999** A1761 1p multi 2.00 2.00

No. 5999 has simulated perforations.

Ignacio Agramonte Loynaz University of Camagüey, 50th Anniv. — A1762

**2017, Nov. 6 Litho. *Perf. 12¼x12½***
**6000** A1762 90c multi 1.90 1.90

October Revolution, Cent. — A1763

Designs: 75c, Lenin Memorial, Lenin Hill, Havana. 85c, Sculpture of Worker and Kolkhoz Woman, Moscow.

**2017, Nov. 7 Litho. *Perf. 12¼x12½***
**6001-6002** A1763 Set of 2 3.25 3.25

Endangered Animals A1764

Designs: 15c, Polar bear. 30c, Orangutan. 50c, Sperm whale. 75c, Bengal tiger. 85c, African elephants. 90c, Kangaroos.
1p, Cuban solenodon.

***Perf. 12½x12¼***
**2017, Nov. 15 Litho.**
**6003-6008** A1764 Set of 6 7.00 7.00

**Souvenir Sheet**

***Imperf***

**6009** A1764 1p multi 2.00 2.00

No. 6009 contains one 45x29mm stamp that has simulated perforations.

José María Pérez Capote (1911-57), Executed Labor Leader A1765

***Perf. 12½x12¼***
**2017, Nov. 20 Litho.**
**6010** A1765 85c multi 1.75 1.75

First Railway In Cuba, 180th Anniv. A1766

*Perf. 12½x12¼*

**2017, Nov. 20** **Litho.**
**6011** A1766 90c multi 1.90 1.90

Marta Abreu Central University, Las Villas, 65th Anniv. A1767

*Perf. 12½x12¼*

**2017, Nov. 30** **Litho.**
**6012** A1767 65c multi 1.40 1.40

National Union of Culture Workers, 40th Anniv. A1768

*Perf. 12½x12¼*

**2017, Dec. 14** **Litho.**
**6013** A1768 75c multi 1.50 1.50

Reactivation of Camilo Cienfuegos Oil Refinery, 10th Anniv. — A1769

Cienfuegos and various oil tankers and smokestacks: 15c, 35c, 50c, 85c.

*Perf. 12¼x12½*

**2017, Dec. 21** **Litho.**
**6014-6017** A1769 Set of 4 3.75 3.75

Life of José Martí (1853-95), National Hero A1770

Martí: 10c, With his sisters, 1864. 15c, With teacher at school, 1868. 20c, Holding manuscript, 1875. 45c, With his family, 1879. 65c, At home, 1890. 75c, As delegate of Cuban Revolutionary Party, 1892.

**2018, Jan. 27** **Litho.** ***Perf. 12½x12¼***
**6018-6023** A1770 Set of 6 4.75 4/75

Cuban Chamber of Commerce, 55th Anniv. A1771

**2018, Feb. 1** **Litho.** ***Perf. 12½x12¼***
**6024** A1771 65c multi 1.40 1.40

Pedro Felipe Figueredo Cisneros (1818-70), composer of Cuban National Anthem A1772

*Perf. 12½x12¼*

**2018, Feb. 18** **Litho.**
**6025** A1772 75c multi 1.50 1.50

Endangered Birds A1773

Designs: 10c, Branta ruficollis. 30c, Amazona oratrix. 65c, Porphyrio martello. 75c, Harpyhailaetus coronatus. 85c, Rhynochetos jubatus. 90c, Crax rubra.
1p, Tyrannus cubensis.

*Perf. 12½x12¼*

**2018, Feb. 20** **Litho.**
**6026-6031** A1773 Set of 6 7.25 7.25

**Souvenir Sheet**

***Imperf***

**6032** A1773 1p multi 2.00 2.00

No. 6032 has simulated perforations.

Specialized Communications of the Revolutionary Armed Forces, 60th Anniv — A1774

**2018, Feb. 21** **Litho.** ***Perf. 12¾***
**6033** A1774 65c multi 1.40 1.40

2018 World Cup Soccer Championships, Russia — A1775

Soccer player and flags of competing countries in: 10c, Group A. 15c, Group E. 35c, Group B. 50c, Group F. 65c, Group C. 75c, Group G. 85c, Group D. 90c, Group H.
1p, Mascot of 2018 World Cup.

**2018, Mar. 5** **Litho.** ***Perf. 12½x12¼***
**6034-6041** A1775 Set of 8 8.50 8.50

**Souvenir Sheet**

***Imperf***

**6042** A1775 1p multi 2.00 2.00

No. 6042 contains one 48x32mm stamp with simulated perforations.

Che Guevara International Pedagogical Detachment, 40th Anniv. A1776

**2018, Mar. 8** **Litho.** ***Perf. 12½x12¼***
**6043** A1776 90c multi 1.90 1.90

Cuban Military Mission to Ethiopia, 40th Anniv. — A1777

**2018, Mar. 9** **Litho.** ***Perf. 12¼x12½***
**6044** A1777 85c multi 1.75 1.75

Marius Petipa (1818-1910), Ballet Dancer and Choreographer A1778

Designs: 85c, Petipa. 90c, Alicia Alonso in *Don Quixote.*

*Perf. 12¼x12½*

**2018, Mar. 11** **Litho.**
**6045-6046** A1778 Set of 2 3.50 3.50

Baraguá Protest, 140th Anniv. — A1779

*Perf. 12¼x12½*

**2018, Mar. 15** **Litho.**
**6047** A1779 65c multi 1.40 1.40

Labor Day — A1780

**2018, Apr. 20** **Litho.** ***Perf. 12¼x12½***
**6048** A1780 65c multi 1.40 1.40

Transportation for Tourists A1781

Designs: 10c, Motorcycle. 15c, 1950's convertible. 40c, Bicycle. 65c, Double-decker bus. 75c, Catamaran. 85c, Recreational vehicle.

**2018, Apr. 30** **Litho.** ***Perf. 12½x12¼***
**6049-6054** A1781 Set of 6 6.00 6.00

Segundo Cabo Palace, Havana — A1782

**2018, May 9** **Litho.** ***Perf. 12¼x12½***
**6055** A1782 75c multi 1.50 1.50

Cuban Day Against Homophobia and Transphobia A1783

**2018, May 10** **Litho.** ***Perf. 12½x12¼***
**6056** A1783 75c multi 1.50 1.50

Marine Life — A1784

Designs: 10c, Abyssobrotula galatheae. 20c, Anoplogaster cornuta. 45c, Oxynotus caribbaeus. 75c, Mithrax spinosissimus. 90c, Scarus coeruleus. 1.05p, Megalops atlanticus.
1p, Mulloidichthys martinicus.

**2018, May 15** **Litho.** ***Perf. 12½x12¼***
**6057-6062** A1784 Set of 6 7.00 7.00

**Souvenir Sheet**

***Imperf***

**6063** A1784 1p multi 2.00 2.00

No. 6063 has simulated perforations.

Flora of Western Hemisphere Nations A1785

Designs: 10c, Passiflora edulis, Paraguay. 15c, Tabebuia chrysotricha, Brazil, vert. 20c, Yucca elephantipes, El Salvador. 30c, Cantua buxifolia, Peru, vert. 40c, Victoria amazonica, Guyana. 65c, Acer saccharum leaf, Canada, vert. 75c, Lycaste skinneri, Guatemala. 90c, Cattleya trianae, Colombia, vert.

*Perf. 12½x12¼, 12¼x12½*

**2018, May 26** **Litho.**
**6064-6071** A1785 Set of 8 7.00 7.00

**Miniature Sheet**

Ernesto "Che" Guevara (1928-67), Guerilla Leader and Finance Minister — A1786

No. 6072 — Guevara: a, With cinder block and handcart. b, With podium. c, Playing chess. d, With cameras.

*Perf. 12½x12¼*

**2018, June 14** **Litho.**
**6072** A1786 90c Sheet of 4, #a-d 7.25 7.25

Health and Medicine Achievements A1787

Designs: 40c, Dr. Carlos M. Ramírez Corría (1903-77), neurosurgeon. 50c, Cuban Institute of Ocular Microsurgery, 30th anniv. 65c, First international medical mission by Cubans, 55th anniv. 75c, Cuban Pediatrics Society, 90th anniv.

**2018, July 4** **Litho.** ***Perf. 12½x12¼***
**6073-6076** A1787 Set of 4 4.75 4.75

23rd Central American and Caribbean Games, Barranquilla, Colombia — A1788

Cuban athletes: 65c, Raúl Cascaret (1962-95), wrestler. 75c, Baseball players in 1982 Cuba vs. Puerto Rico game. 85c, Player on National baseball team. 90c, Teofilo Stevenson (1952-2012), boxer.

**2018, July 13** **Litho.** ***Perf. 12¼x12½***
**6077-6080** A1788 Set of 4 6.50 6.50

Latin American Integration Association — A1789

**2018, July 23** **Litho.** ***Perf. 12¼x12½***
**6081** A1789 65c multi 1.40 1.40

Horses A1790

Designs: 10c, Percheron horse. 40c, Argentine polo ponies. 45c, Appaloosa horse. 75c, Trakehner horse. 85c, Lippizaner horses. 90c, Mustangs.
1p, Przewalski's horse.

*Perf. 12½x12¼*

**2018, Aug. 30** **Litho.**
**6082-6087** A1790 Set of 6 7.00 7.00

**Souvenir Sheet**

***Imperf***

**6088** A1790 1p multi 2.00 2.00

2018 Thailand World Stamp Exhibition, Bangkok. No. 6088 has simulated perforations.

First World Championship of Cuban Women's Volleyball Team, 40th Anniv. — A1791

No. 6089: a, Team photograph. b, Player hitting ball over net.

**2018, Sept. 6 Litho.** ***Perf. 12½x12¼***
**6089** A1791 65c Horiz. pair, #a-b 2.60 2.60

Cuban Criminal Forensics, 55th Anniv. A1792

**2018, Sept. 7 Litho.** ***Perf. 12½x12¼***
**6090** A1792 65c multi 1.40 1.40

Cuban War of Independence, 150th Anniv. — A1793

Flag of Cuba and: 10c, Carlos Manuel de Céspedes (1819-74), Ignacio Agramonte (1841-73), revolution heroes, La Demajagua National Park. 15c, Mariana Grajales (1808-93), mother of Lieutenant General Antonio Maceo (1845-96) and Major General José Maceo (1849-96), Mangos de Baraguá Monument. 30c, José Martí (1853-95), national hero, Major General Máximo Gómez (1836-1905), General Calixto García (1839-98), Monument to the Invading Soldier, Mantua. 45c, Julio Antonio Mella (1903-29), founder of Cuban Communist Party, Rubén Martínez Villena (1899-1934), revolutionary leader, Antonio Guiteras (1906-35), politician, University of Havana. 65c, Aracelio Iglesias (1901-48), union leader, Jesús Menéndez (1911-48), union leader, Lázaro Peña (1911-74), labor leader, Society of Cigar Rollers Building, Havana. 75c, Abel Santamaría (1927-53), Frank País (1934-57), and José A. Echeverría (1932-57), leaders of revolution against Fulgencio Batista, Moncada Barracks, Santiago de Cuba. 85c, Ernesto "Che" Guevara (1928-67), guerilla leader, Celia Sánchez (1920-80), revolution leader, Camilo Cienfuegos (1932-59), revolution leader, Rebel Army General Command Headquarters, La Plata. 90c, Pres. Fidel Castro (1926-2016), José Martí Monument, Revolution Square, Havana.

**2018, Oct. 10 Litho.** ***Perf. 12¼x12½***
**6091-6098** A1793 Set of 8 8.50 8.50

Domesticated Animals — A1794

No. 6099, 65c: a, Horses and donkey. b, Cows,
No. 6100, 65c: a, Chickens. b, Bee.

**2018, Oct. 12 Litho.** ***Perf. 12½x12¼***
**Horiz. pairs, #a-b**
**6099-6100** A1794 Set of 2 5.25 5.25

America issue.

Cuban National Ballet, 70th Anniv. — A1795

Designs: 30c, Alicia Alonso and Igor Youskevitch in *The Nutcracker.* 35c, Dancers in *Tribute to José White.* 50c, Dancers in *Rítmicas.* 65c, Dancers in *Despertar (The Awakening).* 75c, Dancers in *Tarde in la Siesta (Late in the Afternoon).* 90c, Dancers in *Swan Lake.*
1p, Dancer in *La Avanzada.*

**2018, Oct. 28 Litho.** ***Perf. 12¼x12½***
**6101-6106** A1795 Set of 6 7.00 7.00

**Souvenir Sheet**

***Imperf***

**6107** A1795 1p multi 2.00 2.00

No. 6107 has simulated perforations.

Birds — A1796

Designs: 10c, Colaptes fernandinae. 30c, Teretistris fernandinae, horiz. 65c, Icterus melanopsis, horiz. 75c, Caprimulgus cubanensis. 85c, Dives atroviolaceus. 90c, Gymnolgaux lawrencii, horiz.
1p, Buteogallus gundlachii.

**2018, Nov. 3 Litho.** ***Perf. 12¾***
**6108-6113** A1796 Set of 6 7.25 7.25

**Souvenir Sheet**

***Imperf***

**6114** A1796 1p multi 2.00 2.00

15th Philatelic Congress. No. 6114 has simulated perforations.

Restoration of Arango y Parreño House, Havana — A1797

**2018, Nov. 8 Litho.** ***Perf. 12¼x12½***
**6115** A1797 65c multi 1.40 1.40

Palacio de Marqués de Arcos, Havana — A1798

**2018, Nov. 8 Litho.** ***Perf. 12¼x12½***
**6116** A1798 75c multi 1.50 1.50

José Raúl Capablanca (1888-1942), World Chess Champion A1799

Capablanca: No. 6117, 1.05p, With chessboard and clock. No. 6118, 1.05p, Playing many opponents simultaneously. No. 6119, 1.05p, Playing chess, vert.

**2018, Nov. 19 Litho.** ***Perf. 12¾***
**6117-6119** A1799 Set of 3 6.50 6.50

Association of Combatants of the Cuban Revolution, 25th Anniv. A1800

**2018, Dec. 7 Litho.** ***Perf. 12½x12¼***
**6120** A1800 65c multi 1.40 1.40

Major General Ignacio Agramonte (1841-73) — A1801

*Perf. 12¼x12½*

**2018, Dec. 23** **Litho.**
**6121** A1801 65c multi 1.40 1.40

Office of the Attorney General, 45th anniv.

Battle of Santa Clara, 60th Anniv. A1802

*Perf. 12½x12¼*

**2018, Dec. 30** **Litho.**
**6122** A1802 75c multi 1.50 1.50

National Revolutionary Police Force, 60th Anniv. — A1803

**2019, Jan. 5 Litho.** ***Perf. 12¼x12½***
**6123** A1803 2.05p multi 4.25 4.25

Worker's Central Union of Cuba, 60th Anniv. — A1804

**2019, Jan. 28 Litho.** ***Perf. 12¼x12½***
**6124** A1804 75c multi 1.50 1.50

**Souvenir Sheet**

Statue of José Martí, by Anna Hyatt Huntington — A1805

**2019, Jan. 28** **Litho.** ***Imperf.***
**6125** A1805 1p multi 2.00 2.00

Fourth International Congress for World Equilibrium, Havana. No. 6125 has simulated perforations.

Tenth Congress of the Federation of Cuban Women, Havana A1806

Flag of Cuba, sword and: 5c, Ana Betancourt (1832-1901), Candelario Figueredo (1852-1914), patriots. 10c, Bernarda del Toro (1852-1911), wife of Major General Máximo Gómez, María Cabrales (1842-1905), wife of Lieutenant General Antonio Maceo. 20c, Rosa Castellanos (1834-1907), nurse, Adela Azcuy (1861-1914), nurse and poet. 30c, Lidia Doce (1916-58), Clodomira Acosta (1936-58), members of Cuban Rebel Army. 75c, Haydée Santamaría (1922-80), Melba Hernández (1921-2014), politicians. 85c, Celia Sánchez (1920-80), politician, Vilma Espín (1930-2007), Federation founder.

**2019, Mar. 4 Litho.** ***Perf. 12½x12¼***
**6126-6131** A1806 Set of 6 4.50 4.50

**Souvenir Sheet**

Santiago Alvarez (1919-98), Documentary Filmmaker — A1807

**2019, Mar. 18** **Litho.** ***Imperf.***
**6132** A1807 1p multi 2.00 2.00

No. 6132 has simulated perforations.

**Souvenir Sheet**

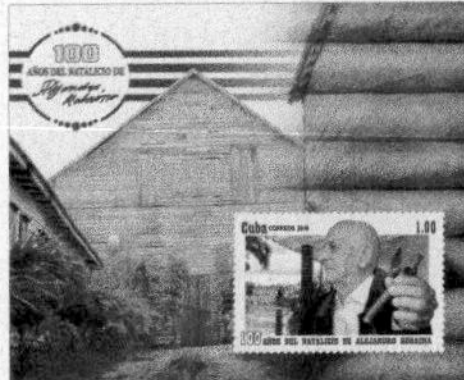

Alejandro Robaina (1919-2010), Tobacco Grower — A1808

**2019, Mar. 20** **Litho.** ***Imperf.***
**6133** A1808 1p multi 2.00 2.00

No. 6133 has simulated perforations.

Cuban Institute of Cinematographic Art and Industry, 60th Anniv. — A1809

Movie posters and scenes: 5c, *The Adventures of Juan Quin Quin,* directed by Julio García Espinosa (1926-2016). 10c, *Historias de la Revolución,* directed by Tomás Gutiérrez Alea (1928-96). 20c, *The Last Supper,* directed by Gutiérrez Alea. 75c, *Vampires in Havana,* directed by Juan Padrón. 85c, *José Martí: el Ojo de Canario,* directed by Fernando Pérez. 90c, *Conducta,* directed by Ernesto Daranas Serrano.

*Perf. 12½x12¼*

**2019, Mar. 24** **Litho.**
**6134-6139** A1809 Set of 6 5.75 5.75

State Security and Intelligence Organizations, 60th Anniv. — A1810

*Perf. 12¼x12½*

**2019, Mar. 26** **Litho.**
**6140** A1810 65c multi 1.40 1.40

Recording Artists A1811

Designs: 30c, Rafael Somavilla (1927-80), orchestra leader. 35c, César Portillo de la Luz (1922-2013), musician. 65c, Celina González (1929-2015), singer. 75c, Juan Formell (1942-2014), musician.

***Perf. 12½x12¼***

**2019, Mar. 31 Litho.**
**6141-6144** A1811 Set of 4 4.25 4.25

EGREM (national recording label), 55th anniv.

Verde Olivo Magazine, 60th Anniv. — A1812

**2019, Apr. 9 Litho. *Perf. 12¼x12½***
**6145** A1812 85c multi 1.75 1.75

Forest Rangers, 60th Anniv. — A1813

**2019, Apr. 10 Litho. *Perf. 12¼x12½***
**6146** A1813 75c multi 1.50 1.50

Cienfuegos, 200th Anniv. — A1814

No. 6147: a, 40c, La India Guanaroca, sculpture by Rita Longa, flamingos on Guanaroca Lake. b, 45c, Fortress of Nuestra Señora de los Angeles de Jagua, flag of Cienfuegos. c, 65c, Turnera ulmifolia, Old Town Hall. d, 75c, Founding of Fernandina de Jagua Colony, Now Cienfuegos, by Juan Roldán and Eduardo Carbonell.
1p, Coat of arms of Cienfuegos, Statue of José Martí.

**2019, Apr. 22 Litho. *Perf. 12½x12¼***
**6147** A1814 Block of 4, #a-d 4.50 4.50

**Souvenir Sheet**

***Imperf***

**6148** A1814 1p multi 2.00 2.00

No. 6148 has simulated perforations.

Carlos Manuel de Céspedes del Castillo (1819-74), National Hero, and Birthplace Museum, Bayamo A1815

**2019, Apr. 18 Litho. *Perf. 12½x12¼***
**6149** A1815 85c multi 1.75 1.75

Aboriginal Cultural Heritage A1816

Designs: 5c, Yagua fiber sieve, woman making basket. 10c, Stone sculpture, traditional houses. 20c, Sandstone sculpture, traditional medicine. 30c, Fertility idol, farmers. 85c, Cassava tuber, food preparation. 90c, Tobacco implements, aborigines and modern people smoking.
1p, Dancers and musicians.

**2019, Apr. 24 Litho. *Perf. 12½x12¼***
**6150-6155** A1816 Set of 6 5.00 5.00

**Souvenir Sheet**

***Imperf***

**6156** A1816 1p multi 2.00 2.00

No. 6156 has simulated perforations.

Labor Day — A1817

**2019, Apr. 26 Litho. *Perf. 12¼x12½***
**6157** A1817 65c red & black 1.40 1.40

Expocuba, 30th Anniv. A1818

**2019, Apr. 29 Litho. *Perf. 12½x12¼***
**6158** A1818 85c multi 1.75 1.75

Martí Forest, Ariguanabo, 25th Anniv. A1819

Quotations by José Martí and: 10c, Ceiba pentandra. 15c, Mangifera indica. 30c, Guibourtia hymenifolia. 35c, Pinus cubensis. 75c, Talipariti elatum. 85c, Calycophyllum candidissimum.
1p, Monument to Simón Bolívar and José Martí.

**2019, May 19 Litho. *Perf. 12½x12¼***
**6159-6164** A1819 Set of 6 5.00 5.00

**Souvenir Sheet**

***Imperf***

**6165** A1819 1p multi 2.00 2.00

No. 6165 has simulated perforations.

Campaign for Road Safety A1820

**2019, May 20 Litho. *Perf. 12½x12¼***
**6166** A1820 75c multi 1.50 1.50

Animals and Landmarks in Their Habitats — A1821

Designs: 65c, Leiocephalus cubensis, Peñón del Fraile. 75c, Tiaris olivaceus, Natural Bridge over Río Bitirí. 2.05p, Eleutherodactylus simulans, Río Yumurí Canyon.

**2019, June 5 Litho. *Perf. 12¼x12½***
**6167-6169** A1821 Set of 3 7.00 7.00

China 2019 World Stamp Exhibition, Wuhan — A1822

Designs: 15c, Tea pot, cups and leaves. 40c, Dragon. 65c, Giant panda. 75c, Stylized flower. 85c, Chinese junk, horiz. 95c, Torii, horiz.
1p, Pig, flowers, Chinese lanterns, horiz.

***Perf. 12¼x12½, 12½x12¼***

**2019, June 10 Litho.**
**6170-6175** A1822 Set of 6 7.50 7.50

**Souvenir Sheet**

***Imperf***

**6176** A1822 1p multi 2.00 2.00

No. 6176 has simulated perforations.

Havana Psychiatric Hospital and Statue of Dr. Eduardo Bernabé Ordaz (1921-2006) A1823

***Perf. 12½x12¼***

**2019, June 14 Litho.**
**6177** A1823 75c multi 1.50 1.50

Selection of Dr. Bernabé Ordaz as director of Havana Psychiatric Hospital, 60th anniv.

National Association of Economists and Accountants of Cuba, 40th Anniv. A1824

***Perf. 12½x12¼***

**2019, June 16 Litho.**
**6178** A1824 85c multi 1.75 1.75

Owls — A1825

Designs: 20c, Tyto alba. 40c, Asio stygius, vert. 50c, Asio flammeus. 75c, Asio otus, vert. 85c, Athene cunicularia, vert. 90c, Margarobyas lawrencii, vert.
1p, Glaucidium siju, vert.

***Perf. 12½x12¾, 12¾x12½***

**2019, June 16 Litho.**
**6179-6184** A1825 Set of 6 7.25 7.25

**Souvenir Sheet**

***Imperf***

**6185** A1825 1p multi 2.00 2.00

No. 6185 has simulated perforations.

22nd Caribbean Postal Union Conference, Guadeloupe A1826

***Perf. 12½x12¼***

**2019, June 26 Litho.**
**6186** A1826 65c multi 1.30 1.30

Comptroller General, 10th Anniv. — A1827

**2019, July 18 Litho. *Perf. 12¼x12½***
**6187** A1827 65c multi 1.30 1.30

Extreme Sports A1828

Designs: 45c, Rock climbing. 75c, Surfing. 85c, Skateboarding. 90c, Mountain biking, vert.

***Perf. 12½x12¼, 12¼x12½***

**2019, July 20 Litho.**
**6188-6191** A1828 Set of 4 6.00 6.00

**Souvenir Sheet**

Ernesto Guevara Central Palace of Pioneers, Havana, 40th Anniv. — A1829

**2019, Aug. 13 Litho. *Imperf.***
**6192** A1829 1p multi 2.00 .00

No. 6192 has simulated perforations.

Diplomatic Relations Between Cuba and Iran, 40th Anniv. — A1830

**2019, Sept. 3 Litho. *Perf. 12¼x12½***
**6193** A1830 85c multi 1.75 1.75

Mohandas K. Gandhi (1869-1948), Indian Nationalist Leader A1831

**2019, Sept. 5 Litho. *Perf. 12½x12¼***
**6194** A1831 75c multi 1.50 1.50

Farm Animals A1832

Designs: 15c, Anas platyrhynchos domesticus. 35c, Gallus gallus domesticus. 65c, Capra aegagrus hircus. 75c, Anser anser domesticus. 85c, Oryctolagus cuniculus. 90c, Sus scrofa domesticus.
1p, Bos taurus.

**2019, Oct. 9 Litho. *Perf. 12½x12¼***
**6195-6200** A1832 Set of 6 7.50 7.50

**Souvenir Sheet**

***Imperf***

**6201** A1832 1p multi 2.00 2.00

No. 6201 has simulated perforations.

Traditional Foods A1833

Designs: No. 6202, 65c, Buñuelos en almíbar (fritters with syrup). Nos. 6203, 65c, Masas de cerdo asado (pork dumplings). No. 6204, 65c, Ajiaco cubano (Cuban stew). No. 6205, 65c, Frituras de malanga (malanga fritters).

**2019, Oct. 12 Litho. *Perf. 12½x12¼***
**6202-6205** A1833 Set of 4 5.25 5.25
America issue.

Ministry of the Revolutionary Armed Forces, 60th Anniv. — A1834

**2019, Oct. 16 Litho. *Perf. 12¼x12½***
**6206** A1834 65c multi 1.30 1.30

Miniature Sheet

Camilo Cienfuegos (1932-59), Head of Cuban Armed Forces — A1835

No. 6207: a, Monument to Ciengfuegos. b, Cienfuegos playing baseball. c, Cienfuegos and soldiers on horseback. d, Cienfuegos holding sledgehammer.

**2019, Oct. 28 Litho. *Perf. 12½x12¼***
**6207** A1835 65c Sheet of 4, #a-d 5.25 5.25

Havana, 500th Anniv. — A1836

Various Havana coats of arms from 1666 Book 13 of the Acts of the City Council: 5c, 10c, 15c, 20c, 30c, 35c, 40c, 45c, 50c, 65c, 75c, 85c.

***Perf. 12¼x12½***
**2019, Nov. 16 Litho.**
**6208-6219** A1836 Set of 12 9.50 9.50

Bats — A1837

Designs: 5c, Natalus primus. 20c, Chilonatalus macer. 30c, Mormopterus minutus. 85c, Dasypterus insularis. 90c, Nycticeius cubanus. 1.05p, Phyllonycteris poeyi.
1p, Antrozous koopmani.

***Perf. 12¼x12½***
**2019, Nov. 22 Litho.**
**6220-6225** A1837 Set of 6 6.75 6.75

**Souvenir Sheet**
***Imperf***
**6226** A1837 1p multi 2.00 2.00
No. 6226 has simulated perforations.

2019 Pan American Games, Lima, Peru — A1838

Designs: 50c, Fencing. 65c, Pole vaulting, vert. 75c, Wrestling. 85c, Shooting, vert.

***Perf. 12½x12¼, 12¼x12½***
**2019, Aug. 19 Litho.**
**6227-6230** A1838 Set of 4 5.50 5.50

Wildlife A1839

Designs: 20c, Cryptoprocta ferox. 30c, Bradypus pygmaeus. 65c, Gorilla berengei. 75c, Pantholops hodgsonii. 85c, Canis simensis. 90c, Orycteropus afer.
1p, Canis lupus.

**2019, Oct. 21 Litho. *Perf. 12½x12¼***
**6231-6236** A1839 Set of 6 7.50 7.50

**Souvenir Sheet**
***Imperf***
**6237** A1839 1p multi 2.00 2.00
No. 6237 contains one 36x27mm stamp with simulated perforations.

Steam Locomotives A1840

Designs: 10c, American 4-6-0. 20c, Rogers 2-6-0. 45c, Baldwin 2-8-0. 50c, Henschel 2-4-0T. 85c, Vulcan 2-6-0. 90c, Davenport 0-4-0ST.
1p, Manning 0-6-0ST, vert.

***Perf. 12½x12¼***
**2019, Nov. 26 Litho.**
**6238-6243** A1840 Set of 6 6.00 6.00

**Souvenir Sheet**
***Imperf***
**6244** A1840 1p multi 2.00 2.00
No. 6244 contains one 31x48mm stamp with simulated perforations.

15th National Philatelic Championship A1841

Famous people: 15c, Igor Stravinsky (1882-1971), composer. 30c, Jorge Negrete (1911-53), singer and actor. 40c, Jesse Owens (1913-80), Olympic gold medalist. 75c, Yuri Gagarin (1934-68), first man in space. 85c, Gabriela Mistral (1889-1957), 1945 Nobel Literature laureate. 90c, Albert Einstein (1879-1955), physicist.
No. 6251: a, Mikhail Chigorin (1850-1908), chess player. b, Wilhelm Steinitz (1836-1900), chess player.

***Perf. 12½x12¼***
**2019, Nov. 29 Litho.**
**6245-6250** A1841 Set of 6 6.75 6.75

**Souvenir Sheet**
***Imperf***
**6251** A1841 50c Sheet of 2, #a-b 2.00 2.00
No. 6251 contains two 41x26mm stamps with simulated perforations.

Diplomatic Relations Between Cuba and Qatar, 30th Anniv. A1842

***Perf. 12½x12¼***
**2019, Dec. 13 Litho.**
**6252** A1842 85c multi 1.75 1.75

Diplomatic Relations Between Cuba and Japan, 90th Anniv. — A1843

***Perf. 12¼x12½***
**2019, Dec. 19 Litho.**
**6253** A1843 85c multi 1.75 1.75

University of Guantánamo, 40th Anniv. A1844

**2020, Jan. 23 Litho. *Perf. 12½x12¼***
**6254** A1844 1.05p multi 2.10 2.10

Miniature Sheet

Primates A1845

No. 6255: a, Loris tardigradus, Lemur catta. b, Saimiri boliviensis, Alouatta seniculus. c, Pongo abelii, Nasalis larvatus. d, Hylobates lar, Mandrillus sphinx.

***Perf. 12½x12¼***
**2020, Feb. 28 Litho.**
**6255** A1845 75c Sheet of 4, #a-d 6.00 6.00

Celia Sánchez Manduley (1920-80), Secretary to the Presidency of the Council of Ministers A1846

**2020, May 9 Litho. *Perf. 12½x12¼***
**6256** A1846 75c multi 1.50 1.50

1895 Cuban War of Independence A1847

Designs: 15c, José Martí (1853-95), national hero, Máximo Gómez (1836-1905), Generalissimo in Cuban War of Independence, House of Salustiano Leyva, Cajobabo. 20c, Paquito Borrero (1846-95), Angel Guerra (1842-96), military leaders in Cuban War of Independence, Cave of Juan Ramírez. 45c, César Salas (1867-97), Marcos del Rosario (1859-1944), military leaders in Cuban War of Independence, Alto de Pavano. 65c, May 5, 1895 meeting of revolution leaders at La Mejorana, tree and monument. 75c, Map of encampments of rebels.

**2020, May 13 Litho. *Perf. 12½x12¼***
**6257-6261** A1847 Set of 5 4.50 4.50

Fruits — A1848

Designs: 15c, Pouteria campechiana. 30c, Cocos nucifera. 75c, Mammea americana. 85c, Melicoccus bijugatus. 90c, Tamarindus indica.

**2020, Aug. 1 Litho. *Perf. 12¼x12½***
**6262-6266** A1848 Set of 5 6.00 6.00

Special National Brigade, 40th Anniv. — A1849

**2020, Aug. 9 Litho. *Perf. 12¼x12½***
**6267** A1849 75c multi 1.50 1.50

Diplomatic Relations Between Cuba and People's Republic of China, 60th Anniv. — A1850

***Perf. 12¼x12½***
**2020, Sept. 28 Litho.**
**6268** A1850 85c multi 1.75 1.75

RadioCuba, 25th Anniv. A1851

**2020, Oct. 1 Litho. *Perf. 12½x12¼***
**6269** A1851 75c multi 1.50 1.50

Universal Postal Union, 145th Anniv. — A1852

**2020, Oct. 9 Litho. *Perf. 12¾***
**6270** A1852 85c multi 1.75 1.75

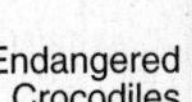
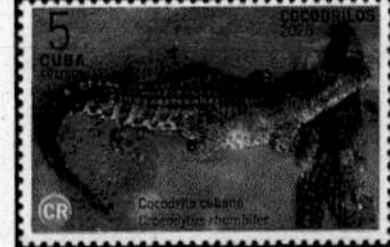
Endangered Crocodiles A1853

Designs: 5c, Crocodylus rhombifer. 10c, Crocodylus acutus. 15c, Crocodylus moreletii. 20c, Crocodylus niloticus. 35c, Crocodylus intermedius. 3p, Crocodylus johnstoni.
1p, Crocodylus rhombifer, diff.

**2020, Oct. 9 Litho. *Perf. 12½x12¼***
**6271-6276** A1853 Set of 6 7.75 7.75

**Souvenir Sheet**
***Imperf***
**6277** A1853 1p multi 2.00 2.00
No. 6277 contains one 37x29mm stamp with simulated perforations.

Pigeons A1854

Birds and map of habitat: 10c, Columba leuconota. 35c, Columba larvata. 50c, Columba elphinstonii. 75c, Columba hodgsonii. 85c, Columba eversmanni. 90c, Columba arquatrix.
1p, Columba oenas.

**2020, Oct. 11 Litho. *Perf. 12½x12¼***
**6278-6283** A1854 Set of 6 7.00 7.00

**Souvenir Sheet**
***Imperf***

**6284** A1854 1p multi 2.00 2.00

No. 6284 contains one 45x29mm stamp with simulated perforations.

America Issue — A1855

Columns from: No. 6285, 65c, University of Havana. No. 6286, 65c, Calle Reino, Havana. No. 6287, 65c, Palacio de las Ursulinas, Havana. No. 6288, 65c, Palacio de las Cariátides, Havana.

**2020, Oct. 12 Litho. *Perf. 12¼x12½***
**6285-6288** A1855 Set of 4 5.25 5.25

First Commercial Airline Flight in Cuba, Cent. — A1856

**2020, Oct. 30 Litho. *Perf. 12¼x12½***
**6289** A1856 90c multi 1.90 1.90

First Cuban Military Mission in Angola, 45th Anniv. A1857

**2020, Nov. 5 Litho. *Perf. 12½x12¼***
**6290** A1857 85c multi 1.75 1.75

Restoration of the Capitol Building — A1858

Designs: 40c, Building façade and dome. 45c, Hall of the Lost Steps. 65c, Chamber. 75c, Library.

***Perf. 12¼x12½***
**2020, Nov. 16 Litho.**
**6291-6294** A1858 Set of 4 4.50 4.50

Famous Chess Players A1859

Designs: 20c, Paul Keres (1916-75). 30c, David Bronstein (1924-2006). 40c, Miguel Najdorf (1910-97). 65c, Aron Nimzowitsch (1886-1935). 85c, Akiba Rubinstein (1880-1961). 90c, Viktor Korchnoi (1931-2016).

***Perf. 12½x12¼***
**2020, Nov. 19 Litho.**
**6295-6300** A1859 Set of 6 6.75 6.75

Miniature Sheet

Endangered Sea Turtles — A1860

No. 6301: a, Chelonia mydas. b, Dermochelys coriacea. c, Caretta caretta. d, Eretmochelys imbricata.

***Perf. 12½x12¼***
**2020, Nov. 19 Litho.**
**6301** A1860 90c Sheet of 4, #a-d 7.25 7.25

Guantànamo, 150th Anniv. A1861

Designs: 45c, Mariana Grajales Memorial, Plaza de la Revolucion. 65c, Mausoleum of the Mambisado Guantanmero, vert. 90c, Statue of Fame, vert.

***Perf. 12½x12¼, 12¼x12½***
**2020, Nov. 27 Litho.**
**6302-6304** A1861 Set of 3 4.00 4.00

Castle of Atarés, Havana A1862

Imperial Citadel of Thang Long, Hanoi A1863

**2020, Dec. 2 Litho. *Perf. 12½x12¼***
**6305** A1862 85c multi 1.75 1.75
**6306** A1863 85c multi 1.75 1.75

Diplomatic relations between Cuba and Viet Nam, 60th anniv. See Viet Nam Nos. 3700-3701.

Snakes — A1864

Designs: 15c, Arrhyton vittatum. 40c, Arrhyton dolichura. 50c, Arrhyton taeniatum. 65c, Caraiba andreae. 75c, Tropidophis feicki. 85c, Tropidophis melanurus.
1p, Chilabothrus angulifer.

**2020, Dec. 11 Litho. *Perf. 12¾***
**6307-6312** A1864 Set of 6 6.75 6.75

**Souvenir Sheet**
***Imperf***

**6313** A1864 1p multi 2.00 2.00

No. 6313 contains one 30x40mm stamp with simulated perforations.

Birds A1865

No. 6314: a, 10c, Nyctanassa violacea. b, 20c, Egretta thula. c, 40c, Egretta tricolor. d, 75c, Egretta rufescens. e, 85c, Phoenicopterus ruber.

***Perf. 12¼x12½***
**2020, Dec. 15 Litho.**
**6314** A1865 Block of 5, #a-e, + label 4.75 4.75

Alicia Alonso (1920-2019), Prima Ballerina and Choreographer A1866

Alonso in: 5c, Undertow. 15c, Theme and Variations. 35c, Fall River Legend. 45c, La Corona Sangrienta. 85c, Medea. 90c, Diario Perdido.
1p, Yagruma.

***Perf. 12¼x12½***
**2020, Dec. 21 Litho.**
**6315-6320** A1866 Set of 6 5.50 5.50

**Souvenir Sheet**
***Imperf***

**6321** A1866 1p multi 2.00 2.00

No. 6321 has simulated perforations.

Campaign Against Violence Toward Women and Children — A1867

***Perf. 12¼x12½***
**2020, Dec. 28 Litho.**
**6322** A1867 65c multi 1.30 1.30

Hotel Nacional de Cuba, 90th Anniv. A1868

***Perf. 12½x12¼***
**2020, Dec. 30 Litho.**
**6323** A1868 75c multi 1.50 1.50

New Year 2021 (Year of the Ox) — A1869

***Perf. 12½x12¼***
**2021, Feb. 12 Litho.**
**6331** A1869 9p multi .75 .75

Cuban Postal Service, 265th Anniv. — A1870

Various mailboxes: 2.20p, 2.65p, 4p.

**2021, Mar. 1 Litho. *Perf. 12¼x12½***
**6332-6334** A1870 Set of 3 .70 .70

Central Palace of Computers and Electronics, 30th Anniv. A1871

**2021, Mar. 7 Litho. *Perf. 12½x12¼***
**6335** A1871 4p multi .35 .35

Campaign Against COVID-19 — A1872

No. 6336: a, Structure of SARS CoV-2 virus. b, Methods to prevent contagion. c, Health care workers with Cuban flags, people receiving vaccinations. d, Health care workers, vaccine vials and hypodermic needle.

**2021, Mar. 11 Litho. *Perf. 12¾***
**6336** A1872 1.90p Sheet of 4, #a-d .60 .60

National Atlas, 60th Anniv. A1873

Maps of Cuba by: 1p, Girolamo Benzoni, 1594. 1.75p, Willem Janszoon Blaeu, 1638. 1.90p, Pieter van der Aa, 1728. 2p, Esteban Pichardo, 1855.

**2021, Apr. 20 Litho. *Perf. 12½x12¼***
**6337-6340** A1873 Set of 4 .55 .55

Labor Day — A1874

**2021, Apr. 26 Litho. *Perf. 12¼x12½***
**6341** A1874 1p multi .30 .30

Napoleon Bonaparte (1769-1821), Emperor of France — A1875

No. 6342: a, Laureated image of Napoleon Bonaparte, Tuileries Palace. b, Star of the Legion d'Honneur. c, Napoleon Bonaparte and Civil Code. d, Napoleon Bonaparte, his wife, Josephine (1763-1814), Fontainebleau Palace.

**2021, May 5 Litho. *Perf. 12½x12¼***
**6342** A1875 3p Sheet of 4, #a-d 1.00 1.00

Ministry of the Interior, 60th Anniv. — A1876

**2021, June 6 Litho. *Perf. 12¼x12½***
**6343** A1876 3p multi .30 .30

Francisco Vicente Aguilera Tamayo (1822-77), Vice-President of Cuba — A1877

***Perf. 12¼x12½***

**2021, June 23 Litho.**
**6344** A1877 3p multi .30 .30

Center for Genetic Engineering and Biotechnology, 35th Anniv. — A1878

**2021, July 1 Litho. *Perf. 12¼x12½***
**6345** A1878 7p multi .60 .60

2020 Summer Olympics, Tokyo A1879

Designs: 50c, Boxing. 60c, Long jump. 1.65p, Taekwondo. 1.75p, Shooting. 1.85p, Greco-Roman wrestling. 1.90p, Rowing. 3p, Discus, vert.

**2021, July 19 Litho. *Perf. 12½x12¼***
**6346-6351** A1879 Set of 6 .70 .70

**Souvenir Sheet**
***Imperf***

**6352** A1879 3p multi .30 .30

The 2020 Summer Olympics were postponed until 2021 because of the COVID-19 pandemic. No. 6352 contains one 29x42mm stamp with simulated perforations.

Ministry of Transportation, 60th Anniv. — A1880

**2021, Aug. 1 Litho. *Perf. 12½x12¼***
**6353** A1880 9p multi .75 .75

Arachnids A1881

Designs: 50c, Heteroctenus junceus. 60c, Paraphrynus robustus. 1.35p, Pseudocellus silvai. 1.75p, Trinimontius darlingtoni. 1.85p, Antillobisium tomasi. 1.90p, Micrathena cubana.
3p, Cubanana cristinae, vert.

**2021, Oct. 4 Litho. *Perf. 12½x12¼***
**6354-6359** A1881 Set of 6 .65 .65

**Souvenir Sheet**
***Imperf***

**6360** A1881 3p multi .30 .30

No. 6360 contains one 30x40mm stamp with simulated perforations.

America Issue — A1882

Designs: No. 6361, 3p, Sunbather and boaters. No. 6362, 3p, Horseback riding. No. 6363, 3p, Cuban Capitol, Chevrolet from 1950s. No. 6364, 3p, Scuba diver and fish.

**2021, Oct. 12 Litho. *Perf. 12¼x12½***
**6361-6364** A1882 Set of 4 1.00 1.00

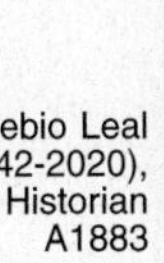

Eusebio Leal (1942-2020), Historian A1883

Leal and: 1p, Casa Arango y Parreño. 1.65p, Casa Pedroso. 1.75p, Palacio de Lombillo. 1.90p, Museo de la Ciudad. 2.20p, Capitol Building. 3p, Statue of Carlos Manuel de Cespedes.

**2021, Nov. 16 Litho. *Perf. 12¾***
**6365-6370** A1883 Set of 6 .95 .95

José Raúl Capablanca (1888-1942), World Chess Champion — A1884

No. 6371 — Part of chess board and: a, Capablanca. b, Medal depicting chess pieces. c, Capablanca on cover of *Time.* d, Chess clock.

***Perf. 12½x12¼***

**2021, Nov. 19 Litho.**
**6371** A1884 3p Sheet of 4, #a-d 1.00 1.00

Capablanca's victory in World Chess Championship, cent.

Central Institute of Pedagogical Sciences, 45th Anniv. — A1885

***Perf. 12¼x12½***

**2021, Nov. 30 Litho.**
**6372** A1885 3p multi .30 .30

Literacy Campaign, 60th Anniv. A1887

***Perf. 12½x12¼***

**2021, Dec. 22 Litho.**
**6374** A1887 1p multi .30 .30

---

## SEMI-POSTAL STAMPS

---

Common Design Types pictured following the introduction.

---

**Curie Issue**
Common Design Type

**Wmk. 106**

**1938, Nov. 23 Engr. *Perf. 10***
**B1** CD80 2c + 1c salmon 6.00 1.60
**B2** CD80 5c + 1c deep ultra 6.00 1.75
Set, never hinged 18.00

40th anniv. of the discovery of radium by Pierre and Marie Curie. Surtax for the benefit of the Intl. Union for the Control of Cancer.

**Catalogue values for unused stamps in this section, from this point to the end of the section, are for Never Hinged items.**

**Revolutionary Government**

"Agriculture" Supporting "Industry" — SP2

**Engr., Center Typo.**

**1959, May 7 Wmk. 321 *Perf. 12½***
**B3** SP2 2c + 1c car & ultra 1.50 .30

Agricultural reforms. See No. CB1. For surcharges see Nos. 624, C199.

Nurse SP3

**Wmk. 229**

**1959, Sept. 22 Photo. *Perf. 12½***
**B4** SP3 2c + 1c crimson rose 1.40 .75

Exists imperf, value about double.

---

## AIR POST STAMPS

Seaplane over Havana Harbor — AP1

**Wmk. 106**

**1927, Nov. 1 Engr. *Perf. 12***
**C1** AP1 5c dark blue 7.75 .75
Never hinged 12.50

For overprint see No. C30.

Type of 1927 Issue Overprinted

**1928, Feb. 8**
**C2** AP1 5c carmine rose 6.00 1.60
Never hinged 8.75

No. 283 Surcharged in Red

**1930, Oct. 27 Unwmk.**
**C3** A44 10c on 25c violet 5.75 1.60
Never hinged 8.50

Airplane and Coast of Cuba — AP3

**For Foreign Postage**

**1931, Feb. 26 Wmk. 106 *Perf. 10***
**C4** AP3 5c green .50 .25
**C5** AP3 10c dk blue 1.25 .25
**C6** AP3 15c rose 5.00 .75
**C7** AP3 20c brown 1.90 .25
**C8** AP3 30c dk violet 4.00 .50
**C9** AP3 40c dp orange 4.75 .50
**C10** AP3 50c olive grn 6.50 .75
**C11** AP3 1p black 13.00 2.00
*Nos. C4-C11 (8)* 36.90 5.25
Set, never hinged 55.00

See No. C40. For surcharges see Nos. C16-C17, C203, C225.

Airplane — AP4

**For Domestic Postage**

**1931-46**
**C12** AP4 5c rose vio ('32) 1.00 .25
*a.* 5c brown violet ('36) 1.00 .25
**C13** AP4 10c gray blk 2.00 .25
**C14** AP4 20c car rose 5.00 1.00
**C14A** AP4 20c rose pink ('46) 4.00 .25
**C15** AP4 50c dark blue 5.50 1.00
*Nos. C12-C15 (5)* 17.50 2.75
Set, never hinged 27.50

See #C130. For overprints see #C31, E29-E30.

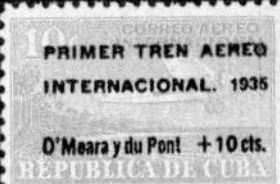

Type of 1931 Surcharged in Black

**1935, Apr. 24 *Perf. 10***
**C16** AP3 10c + 10c red 15.00 14.00
Never hinged 20.00
*a.* Double surcharge 160.00

***Imperf***

**C17** AP3 10c + 10c red 40.00 40.00
Never hinged 55.00 55.00

**Matanzas Issue**

Air View of Matanzas — AP5

10c, Airship "Macon." 20c, Airplane "The Four Winds." 50c, Air View of Fort San Severino.

**Wmk. 229**

**1936, May 5 Photo. *Perf. 12½***
**C18** AP5 5c violet 2.90 1.00
**C19** AP5 10c yellow orange 3.00 1.40
**C20** AP5 20c green 7.75 3.00
**C21** AP5 50c greenish slate 19.00 10.00
*Nos. C18-C21 (4)* 32.65 15.40
Set, never hinged 42.50

Exist imperf. Value 20% more.

"Lightning" AP9

Allegory of Flight — AP10

**1936, Nov. 18**
**C22** AP9 5c violet 3.00 1.10
*a.* Imperf., pair 100.00
**C23** AP10 10c orange brown 5.25 1.25
*a.* Imperf., pair 100.00
Set, never hinged 12.00

Major Gen. Maximo Gomez, birth cent.

Flat Arch (Panama) AP11

Carlos Antonio López (Paraguay) AP12

Inca Gate, Cuzco (Peru) AP13

Atlacatl (Salvador) AP14

José Enrique Rodó (Uruguay) AP15

Simón Bolívar (Venezuela) AP16

**Wmk. 106**

**1937, Oct. 13 Engr. *Perf. 10***

| | | | | |
|---|---|---|---|---|
| **C24** | AP11 | 5c red | 7.75 | 6.00 |
| **C25** | AP12 | 5c red | 8.50 | 6.00 |
| **C26** | AP13 | 10c blue | 9.50 | 6.75 |
| **C27** | AP14 | 10c blue | 9.50 | 6.75 |
| **C28** | AP15 | 20c green | 8.00 | 5.00 |
| **C29** | AP16 | 20c green | 8.00 | 5.00 |
| | | *Nos. C24-C29 (6)* | 51.25 | 35.50 |
| | | Set, never hinged | 70.00 | |

See note after No. 354.

Type of 1927 Ovptd. in Black

**1938, May Wmk. 106**

| | | | | |
|---|---|---|---|---|
| **C30** | AP1 | 5c dark orange | 7.25 | 3.75 |
| | | Never hinged | 9.50 | |

1st airplane flight from Key West to Havana, made by Domingo Rosillo, 1913.

Type of 1931-32 Overprinted

**1939, Oct. 15**

| | | | | |
|---|---|---|---|---|
| **C31** | AP4 | 10c emerald | 13.50 | 7.75 |
| | | Never hinged | 26.00 | |

Issued in connection with an experimental postal rocket flight held at Havana.

Sir Rowland Hill, Map of Cuba and First Stamps of Britain, Spanish Cuba and Republic of Cuba — AP17

**1940, Nov. 28 Engr. Wmk. 106**

| | | | | |
|---|---|---|---|---|
| **C32** | AP17 | 10c brown | 5.50 | 1.50 |
| | | Never hinged | 8.00 | |

**Souvenir Sheet**

**Unwmk. *Imperf.***

| | | | | |
|---|---|---|---|---|
| **C33** | | Sheet of 4 | 27.50 | 20.00 |
| | | Never hinged | 37.50 | |
| *a.* | AP17 | 10c light brown | 5.50 | 4.50 |
| | | Never hinged | 8.00 | |

Cent. of the 1st postage stamp. Sheet sold for 60c.

No. C33 exists with each of the four stamps overprinted in black: "Exposicion de la ACNU/24 de Octubre de 1951/Dia de las Naciones" and "Historia de la Aviacion" in lower margin. Value, $80.

For overprints see Nos. C39, C211.

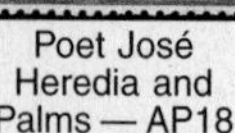


Poet José Heredia and Palms — AP18

Heredia and Niagara Falls — AP19

**1940, Dec. 30 Wmk. 106**

| | | | | |
|---|---|---|---|---|
| **C34** | AP18 | 5c emerald | 3.25 | 1.00 |
| **C35** | AP19 | 10c greenish slate | 4.75 | 1.60 |
| | | Set, never hinged | 11.00 | |

Death cent. of José Maria Heredia y Campuzano (1803-39), poet and patriot.

First Cuban Land Sighted by Columbus AP20

Columbus Lighthouse AP21

**1944, May 19**

| | | | | |
|---|---|---|---|---|
| **C36** | AP20 | 5c olive green | 2.40 | .40 |
| **C37** | AP21 | 10c slate black | 3.00 | .75 |

450th anniv. of the discovery of America.

**Catalogue values for unused stamps in this section, from this point to the end of the section, are for Never Hinged items.**

Conference of La Mejorana (Maceo, Gomez and Marti) — AP22

**1948, May 21 Wmk. 229 *Perf. 12½***

| | | | | |
|---|---|---|---|---|
| **C38** | AP22 | 8c org yel & blk | 3.75 | .80 |

50th anniv. of the start of the War of 1895.

**Souvenir Sheet**

No. C33 Overprinted in Ultramarine

**1948, May 21 Unwmk. *Imperf.***

| | | | | |
|---|---|---|---|---|
| **C39** | AP17 | Sheet of 4 | 25.00 | 9.50 |

The overprint is applied in the center of the sheet, so that a part of the overprint falls on each stamp.

American Air Mail Soc. Convention, Havana, May 21 to 23, 1948. The sheets sold for 60c each.

**Type of 1931**

**1948, June 15 Wmk. 106 *Perf. 10***

| | | | | |
|---|---|---|---|---|
| **C40** | AP3 | 8c orange brown | 2.75 | .80 |

Narciso Lopez Landing at Cárdenas AP23

Flag on Cuban Fort AP24

Flag on Morro Castle, Havana — AP25

**Engraved and Lithographed**

**1951, July 3 Wmk. 229 *Perf. 13***

| | | | | |
|---|---|---|---|---|
| **C41** | AP23 | 5c ol grn, ultra & red | 2.75 | 1.25 |
| **C42** | AP24 | 8c red brn, bl & red | 2.75 | 1.25 |
| **C43** | AP25 | 25c gray blk, bl & red | 5.00 | 1.40 |
| | | *Nos. C41-C43 (3)* | 10.50 | 3.90 |

Centenary of adoption of Cuba's flag.

**Souvenir Sheet**

No. 365a Overprinted in Green

**1951, Aug. 24 Unwmk. *Imperf.***

| | | | | |
|---|---|---|---|---|
| **C43A** | A104 | 5c Sheet of 4 | 19.00 | 9.00 |

50th anniv. of the discovery of the cause of yellow fever by Dr. Carlos J. Finlay, and to honor the martyrs of science.

**Postage Type and**

Resignation Play of Dr. Lasker AP26

Capablanca Making "The Exact Play" AP27

**Wmk. 229**

**1951, Nov. 1 Photo. *Perf. 13***

| | | | | |
|---|---|---|---|---|
| **C44** | AP26 | 5c shown | 8.00 | 2.90 |
| **C45** | AP27 | 8c shown | 12.00 | 2.75 |
| **C46** | A165 | 25c Capablanca | 18.00 | 3.25 |
| | | *Nos. C44-C46 (3)* | 38.00 | 8.90 |

30th anniv. of the winning of the World Chess title by José Raul Capablanca.

**Morrillo Types of Regular Issue**

**Wmk. 106**

**1951, Nov. 22 Engr. *Perf. 10***

| | | | | |
|---|---|---|---|---|
| **C47** | A167 | 5c violet | 2.50 | .70 |
| **C48** | A168 | 8c deep green | 2.50 | 1.00 |
| **C49** | A169 | 25c dark brown | 7.00 | 2.00 |
| *a.* | | Souv. sheet of 6, black brown, perf. 13 | 72.50 | 35.00 |
| *b.* | | Souv. sheet of 6, green, imperf. | 225.00 | 125.00 |
| | | *Nos. C47-C49 (3)* | 12.00 | 3.70 |

Nos. C49a and C49b contain one each of the 1c, 2c and 5c of types A167-A169 and of the 5c, 8c and 25c airmail stamps of types A167-A169. Sheets are unwatermarked and measure 124x133mm.

**Isabella Type of Regular Issue, 1952**

**1952, Feb. 22**

| | | | | |
|---|---|---|---|---|
| **C50** | A172 | 25c purple | 4.50 | .75 |
| *a.* | | Souv. sheet of 2, perf. 11 | 35.00 | 35.00 |
| *b.* | | Souv. sheet of 2, imperf. | 25.00 | 25.00 |

Nos. C50a and C50b contain one each of a 2c of type A172 and a 25c air-mail stamp of type A172. In No. C50a, the 2c and marginal inscriptions are brown carmine; the 25c, dark blue. In No. C50b, the 2c and marginal inscriptions are dark blue; the 25c, brown carmine. Sheets measure 108x18mm.

Type of Regular Issue of 1951 Surcharged in Various Colors

**1952, Mar. 18**

**Color: Yellow Brown**

| | | | | |
|---|---|---|---|---|
| **C51** | A159 | 5c on 2c | 3.50 | .30 |
| **C52** | A159 | 8c on 2c (C) | 2.60 | .30 |
| **C53** | A159 | 10c on 2c (Bl) | 2.00 | .30 |
| **C54** | A159 | 25c on 2c (V) | 3.75 | 1.10 |
| **C55** | A159 | 50c on 2c (C) | 8.00 | 5.00 |
| **C56** | A159 | 1p on 2c (Bl) | 10.00 | 7.50 |
| | | *Nos. C51-C56 (6)* | 29.85 | 14.50 |

Country School AP32

Entrance, University of Havana AP33

10c, Presidential Mansion. 25c, Banknote.

**Wmk. 106**

**1952, May 27 Engr. *Perf. 12½***

**Centers Various Shades of Green**

| | | | | |
|---|---|---|---|---|
| **C57** | AP32 | 5c dark purple | 2.10 | .25 |
| **C58** | AP33 | 8c dark red | 2.00 | .50 |
| **C59** | AP32 | 10c deep blue | 2.50 | .75 |
| **C60** | AP32 | 25c dark violet brn | 2.75 | 1.25 |
| | | *Nos. C57-C60 (4)* | 9.35 | 2.75 |

Foundation of the Republic of Cuba, 50th anniv.

Plane and Map AP34

Agustín Parlá AP35

**1952, July 22 Engr. *Perf. 10***

| | | | | |
|---|---|---|---|---|
| **C61** | AP34 | 8c black | 2.50 | .55 |
| *a.* | | Souv. sheet, 8c deep blue | 18.00 | 10.00 |
| *b.* | | Souv. sheet, 8c deep green | 18.00 | 10.00 |
| **C62** | AP35 | 25c ultra | 3.25 | .75 |
| *a.* | | Souv. sheet, 25c deep blue | 18.00 | 10.00 |
| *b.* | | Souv. sheet, 25c deep green | 18.00 | 10.00 |

30th anniv. of the Key West-Mariel flight of Agustin Parla.

The four souvenir sheets are perf. 11.

Col. Charles Hernandez y Sandrino — AP36

**1952, Oct. 7**

| | | | | |
|---|---|---|---|---|
| **C63** | AP36 | 5c orange | 1.00 | .30 |
| **C64** | AP36 | 8c brt yel grn | 1.00 | .30 |
| **C65** | AP36 | 10c dk brown | 1.60 | .75 |
| **C66** | AP36 | 15c dk Prus grn | 1.90 | .80 |
| **C67** | AP36 | 20c aqua | 2.50 | 1.00 |
| **C68** | AP36 | 25c crimson | 2.10 | 1.00 |
| **C69** | AP36 | 30c dk vio bl | 5.25 | 2.50 |
| **C70** | AP36 | 45c rose lilac | 9.25 | 3.50 |
| **C71** | AP36 | 50c indigo | 5.75 | 2.50 |
| **C72** | AP36 | 1p bister | 18.00 | 5.00 |
| | | *Nos. C63-C72 (10)* | 48.35 | 17.65 |

Three-fourths of the proceeds from the sale were used for the Communications Ministry Employees' Retirement Fund.

Entrance, University of Havana AP37

F. V. Dominguez, M. Estebanez and F. Capdevila AP38

**Engr.; Center Typo.**

**1952, Nov. 27**

| | | | | |
|---|---|---|---|---|
| **C73** | AP37 | 5c indigo & dk blue | 2.25 | .40 |
| **C74** | AP38 | 25c org & dk grn | 4.75 | 1.40 |

Execution of 8 medical students, 81st anniv.

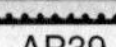

AP39

Lockheed Constellation Airliners — AP40

**1953, May 22** **Engr.**

| | | | | |
|---|---|---|---|---|
| **C75** | AP39 | 8c orange brn | 1.75 | .25 |
| **C76** | AP39 | 15c scarlet | 3.25 | .70 |

**Typographed and Engraved**

| | | | | |
|---|---|---|---|---|
| **C77** | AP40 | 2p dp green & dk brn | 42.50 | 10.00 |
| **C78** | AP40 | 5p blue & dk brn | 82.50 | 17.50 |
| | | *Nos. C75-C78 (4)* | 130.00 | 28.45 |

See Nos. C120-C121. For surcharge, see No. C224.

Page of Manifesto of Montecristi AP42

House of Maximo Gomez AP43

No. C79, Marti in Kingston, Jamaica, No. C80, With Workers in Tampa, Florida. No. C83, Marti addressing liberating army. No. C84, Portrait. No. C85, Dos Rios obelisk. No. C86, Marti's first tomb. No. C87, Present tomb. No. C88, Monument in Havana. No. C89, Martian forge.

**1953** **Engr.** ***Perf. 10***

| | | | | |
|---|---|---|---|---|
| **C79** | AP42 | 5c dk car & blk | .30 | .25 |
| **C80** | AP42 | 5c dk car & blk | .30 | .25 |
| **C81** | AP43 | 8c dk green & blk | .75 | .25 |
| **C82** | AP42 | 8c dk green & blk | .75 | .25 |
| **C83** | AP43 | 10c dk blue & dk car | 1.00 | .75 |
| **C84** | AP42 | 10c dk blue & dk car | .75 | .75 |
| **C85** | AP42 | 15c violet & gray | 1.25 | .90 |
| **C86** | AP42 | 15c violet & gray | .90 | .90 |
| **C87** | AP42 | 25c brown & car | 1.50 | 1.25 |
| **C88** | AP42 | 25c brown & car | 1.60 | 1.25 |
| **C89** | AP43 | 50c yellow & bl | 2.00 | 2.00 |
| | | *Nos. C79-C89 (11)* | 11.10 | 8.80 |

Cent. of the birth of José Marti.

Board of Accounts Building — AP44

25c, Plane above Board of Accounts Bldg.

**1953, Nov. 3**

| | | | | |
|---|---|---|---|---|
| **C90** | AP44 | 8c rose carmine | 2.40 | .70 |
| **C91** | AP44 | 25c dk gray grn | 2.90 | 1.10 |

1st Intl. Cong. of Boards of Account, Havana, Nov. 2-9, 1953.

Miguel Coyula Llaguno AP45

Antonio Ginard Rojas AP46

Communications Association Flag — AP46a

Designs: 10c, Gregorio Hernandez Saez.

**1954**

| | | | | |
|---|---|---|---|---|
| **C92** | AP45 | 5c dark blue | .65 | .25 |
| **C93** | AP46 | 8c red violet | 1.60 | .40 |
| **C94** | AP46 | 10c orange | 2.00 | .50 |
| **C95** | AP46a | 1p black | 9.50 | 4.50 |
| | | *Nos. C92-C95 (4)* | 13.75 | 5.65 |

See note after No. C72.

Alvaro Reinoso AP47

Plane and Harvesters Cutting Cane AP48

Designs in Lower Triangle: 5c, Four-engine Plane and Cane Field. 10c, Tractor pulling loaded wagons. 15c, Train of sugar cane. 20c, Modern mill. 25c, Evaporators. 30, Sacks of sugar. 40c, Loading sugar on ship. 45c, Ox cart. 50c, Primitive sugar mill.

**1954, Apr. 27** **Engr.**

| | | | | |
|---|---|---|---|---|
| **C96** | AP47 | 5c yellow green | 1.50 | .30 |
| **C97** | AP48 | 8c brown | 1.50 | .50 |
| **C98** | AP48 | 10c dark green | 1.50 | .50 |
| **C99** | AP48 | 15c henna brn | 3.00 | .50 |
| **C100** | AP48 | 20c blue | 1.50 | .30 |
| **C101** | AP48 | 25c scarlet | 1.15 | .30 |
| **C102** | AP48 | 30c lilac rose | 2.75 | .95 |
| **C103** | AP48 | 40c deep blue | 6.25 | 1.25 |
| **C104** | AP48 | 45c violet | 5.00 | 2.50 |
| **C105** | AP48 | 50c brt blue | 5.00 | 1.60 |
| **C106** | AP47 | 1p dk gray blue | 13.50 | 3.25 |
| | | *Nos. C96-C106 (11)* | 42.65 | 11.95 |

For surcharges see Nos. C204.

**Sanatorium Type of Regular Issue**

**1954, Sept. 21** **Wmk. 106** ***Perf. 10***

| | | | | |
|---|---|---|---|---|
| **C107** | A186 | 9c deep green | 2.75 | .65 |

**Dolz Type of Regular Issue, 1954**

**1954, Dec. 23**

| | | | | |
|---|---|---|---|---|
| **C108** | A188 | 12c carmine | 4.50 | .70 |

**Rotary Type of Regular Issue, 1955**

**1955, Feb. 23**

| | | | | |
|---|---|---|---|---|
| **C109** | A190 | 12c carmine | 2.25 | .65 |

Stamps of 1855 and 1905, Palace of Fine Arts — AP52

Designs (including 2 stamps): 12c, Plaza de la Fraternidad. 24c, View of Havana. 30c, Plaza de la Republica.

**1955, Apr. 24** ***Perf. 12½***

| | | | | |
|---|---|---|---|---|
| **C110** | AP52 | 8c dk grnsh bl & grn | 2.00 | .35 |
| **C111** | AP52 | 12c dk ol grn & red | 2.75 | .35 |
| **C112** | AP52 | 24c dk red & ultra | 3.50 | .75 |
| **C113** | AP52 | 30c dp org & brn | 4.25 | .90 |
| | | *Nos. C110-C113 (4)* | 12.50 | 2.35 |

Cent. of Cuba's 1st postage stamps.

Mariel Bay — AP53

Views: 12c, Varadero beach. 1p, Vinales valley.

**1955, June 22** **Wmk. 106**

| | | | | |
|---|---|---|---|---|
| **C114** | AP53 | 8c dk car & dk grn | 1.25 | 1.25 |
| **C115** | AP53 | 12c dk ocher & brt bl | 7.00 | 1.60 |
| **C116** | AP53 | 1p dk grn & ocher | 7.50 | 2.00 |
| | | *Nos. C114-C116 (3)* | 15.75 | 4.85 |

See note after No. C72.

Map of Crocier's 1914 Flight — AP54

Design: 30c, Crocier in plane.

**1955, July 4** ***Perf. 10***

| | | | | |
|---|---|---|---|---|
| **C117** | AP54 | 12c red & dk grn | 2.50 | .25 |
| **C118** | AP54 | 30c dk grn & mag | 2.75 | .65 |

35th anniv. of the death of Jaime Gonzalez Crocier, aviation pioneer.

Cuban Museum, Tampa, Fla. — AP55

**1955, July 1** **Engr.** ***Perf. 12½***

| | | | | |
|---|---|---|---|---|
| **C119** | AP55 | 12c red & dk brn | 3.25 | .65 |

Cent. of Tampa's incorporation as a town.

**Lockheed Type of 1953**

**Typographed and Engraved**

**1955, Sept. 21** **Wmk. 106**

| | | | | |
|---|---|---|---|---|
| **C120** | AP40 | 2p bl & ol grn | 40.00 | 6.50 |
| **C121** | AP40 | 5p dp rose & ol grn | 70.00 | 15.00 |

Wright Brothers' Plane and Stamps — AP56

Designs: 12c, Spirit of St. Louis. 24c, Graf Zeppelin. 30c, Constellation passenger plane. 50c, Convair jet fighter.

**Engraved and Photogravure**

**1955, Nov. 12** **Wmk. 106** ***Perf. 12½***

**Inscription and Plane in Black**

| | | | | |
|---|---|---|---|---|
| **C122** | AP56 | 8c car & bl | 3.00 | .50 |
| **C123** | AP56 | 12c yel grn & car | 3.00 | .90 |
| **C124** | AP56 | 24c vio & car | 3.75 | 1.50 |
| **C125** | AP56 | 30c bl & red org | 3.50 | 1.50 |
| **C126** | AP56 | 50c ol grn & red org | 5.00 | 2.50 |
| *a.* | | Souvenir sheet of 5 | 60.00 | 26.00 |
| | | *Nos. C122-C126 (5)* | 18.25 | 6.90 |

International Centenary Philatelic Exhibition in Havana, Nov. 12-19, 1955.

No. C126a is printed on thick paper and measures 140x178mm. It contains one each of Nos. C122-C126 with the background of each stamp printed in a different color from the perforated stamps.

"Three Friends" and Gen. Emilio Nuñez — AP57

Design: 12c, Landing on the Cuban Coast.

**1955, Dec. 27** **Engr.** **Unwmk.**

| | | | | |
|---|---|---|---|---|
| **C127** | AP57 | 8c ultra & dk car | 2.10 | .55 |
| **C128** | AP57 | 12c grn & dk red brn | 2.50 | .75 |

Gen. Emilio Nuñez, Cuban revolutionary hero, birth cent.

**Post Type of Regular Issue, 1956**

Bishop P. A. Morell de Santa Cruz (1694-1768).

**1956, Mar. 27** **Wmk. 106**

| | | | | |
|---|---|---|---|---|
| **C129** | A197 | 12c dk brn & grn | 3.25 | .55 |

**Plane Type of 1931-46**

**1956** **Engr.** ***Perf. 10***

| | | | | |
|---|---|---|---|---|
| **C130** | AP4 | 50c greenish blue | 5.00 | 1.00 |

**Portrait Type of Regular Issue, 1956**

Portraits: 8c, Gen. Julio Sanguily. 12c, Gen. José Maria Aguirre. 30c, Col. Ernesto Fonts Sterling.

**1956, May 2** ***Perf. 12½***

**Portraits in Black**

| | | | | |
|---|---|---|---|---|
| **C131** | A198 | 8c brown | 1.25 | .25 |
| **C132** | A198 | 12c dull yellow | 1.60 | .75 |
| **C133** | A198 | 30c indigo | 3.00 | 1.25 |
| | | *Nos. C131-C133 (3)* | 5.85 | 2.25 |

See note after No. C72.

Mother and Child — AP60

**1956, May 13** **Wmk. 106** ***Perf. 12½***

| | | | | |
|---|---|---|---|---|
| **C134** | AP60 | 12c ultra & red | 2.00 | .40 |

Issued in honor of Mother's Day 1956.

Masonic Temple Havana — AP61

**1956, June 5**

| | | | | |
|---|---|---|---|---|
| **C135** | AP61 | 12c olive green | 1.75 | .55 |

Pigeon AP62

Gundlach Hawk AP63

Birds: 8c, Wood duck. 19c, Herring gulls. 24c, White pelicans. 29c, Common merganser. 30c, Quail. 50c, Herons (great white, great blue and Wurdemann's). 1p, Northern caracara. 2p, Middle American jacana. 5p, Ivory-billed woodpecker.

**1956**

| | | | | |
|---|---|---|---|---|
| **C136** | AP62 | 8c blue | 8.50 | .25 |
| **C137** | AP62 | 12c gray blue | 5.25 | .25 |
| **C138** | AP63 | 14c green | 2.25 | .25 |
| **C139** | AP63 | 19c redsh brn | 2.75 | .55 |
| **C140** | AP63 | 24c lilac rose | 2.25 | .55 |
| **C141** | AP62 | 29c green | 2.25 | .55 |
| **C142** | AP62 | 30c dk olive bis | 1.90 | .80 |
| **C143** | AP63 | 50c slate blk | 3.25 | 1.10 |
| **C144** | AP63 | 1p dk car rose | 11.00 | 3.00 |
| **C145** | AP62 | 2p rose violet | 10.00 | 4.25 |
| **C146** | AP63 | 5p brt red | 23.50 | 8.75 |
| | | *Nos. C136-C146 (11)* | 72.90 | 20.30 |

See Nos. C205, C235-C237. For surcharges and overprints, see Nos. C147, C151, C197, C209-C210

Type of 1956 Surcharged

Design: 24c, White pelicans.

**1956, July 13**

| | | | | |
|---|---|---|---|---|
| **C147** | AP63 | 8c on 24c deep org | 2.00 | .70 |

Opening of the new building of the Cuba Philatelic Club, Havana, July 14, 1956.

Hubert de Blanck — AP64

**1956, July 6**

| | | | | |
|---|---|---|---|---|
| **C148** | AP64 | 12c ultra | 2.60 | .40 |

Hubert de Blanck (1856-1932), composer.

Church of Our Lady of Charity — AP65

**1956, Sept. 8**

| | | | | |
|---|---|---|---|---|
| **C149** | AP65 | 12c grn & car | 2.75 | .55 |
| *a.* | | Souvenir sheet of 2, imperf. | 18.00 | 9.50 |

Issued in honor of Our Lady of Charity of Cobre, patroness of Cuba.

No. C149a contains one each of Nos. 559 and C149. No. C149a exists with yellow of No. 559 omitted.

Benjamin Franklin — AP66

**1956, Oct. 5 Engr. *Perf. 12½***
**C150** AP66 12c red brown 3.25 .55

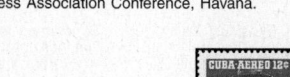

Type of 1956 Surcharged in Blue

Design: 2p, Middle American jacana.

**1956, Oct. 26 Wmk. 106**
**C151** AP62 12c on 2p dark gray 1.60 .95

Issued in honor of the 12th Inter-American Press Association Conference, Havana.

Lord Baden-Powell — AP67

**1957, Feb. 22**
**C152** AP67 12c slate 2.75 .70

Centenary of the birth of Lord Baden-Powell, founder of the Boy Scouts.

Hanabanilla Waterfall — AP68

12c, Sierra de Cubitas. 30c, Puerto Boniato.

**1957, Mar. 29**
**C153** AP68 8c blue & red 1.10 .25
**C154** AP68 12c green & red 2.00 .50
**C155** AP68 30c ol grn & dk pur 3.00 .70
*Nos. C153-C155 (3)* 6.10 1.45

See note after No. 457.

Philatelic Club, Havana — AP69

**1957, Apr. 24 Wmk. 106 *Perf. 12½***
**C156** AP69 12c yel, grn & brn 3.00 .40

Stamp Day, and the Natl. Phil. Exhib.

Fingerprint — AP70

**1957, Apr. 30**
**C157** AP70 12c claret brown 3.00 .40

Birth cent. (in 1856) of Juan Francisco Steegers y Perera, dactyloscopy pioneer.

Baseball Player — AP71

**1957, May 17 Wmk. 106 *Perf. 12½***
**C158** AP71 8c shown 2.50 .40
**C159** AP71 12c Ballerina 2.75 .50
**C160** AP71 24c Girl diver 3.50 .75
**C161** AP71 30c Boxers 3.75 .75
*Nos. C158-C161 (4)* 12.50 2.40

Issued to honor young Cuban athletes.

Joaquin de Aguero — AP72

**1957, July 4**
**C162** AP72 12c indigo 3.00 .40

Issued to honor Joaquin de Aguero, Cuban freedom fighter and patriot.

Jeanette Ryder — AP73

**1957, July 17**
**C163** AP73 12c dk red brn 1.50 .55
*a.* Pair, #574, C163 4.80 2.00

Mrs. Jeanette Ryder, founder of the Humane Society of Cuba.

José M. de Heredia y Girard — AP74

**1957, Aug. 16 Engr. Wmk. 106**
**C164** AP74 8c dk blue vio 3.00 .30

José Maria de Heredia y Girard (1842-1905), Cuban born French poet.

**Justice Type of Regular Issue, 1957**

**1957, Sept. 2 *Perf. 12½***
**C165** A214 12c green 2.75 .50

John Robert Gregg — AP75

**1957, Oct. 1**
**C166** AP75 12c dark green 2.50 .70

90th anniv. of the birth of John Robert Gregg, inventor of the Gregg shorthand system.

D. Figarola Caneda AP76

José Marti National Library AP77

**1957, Oct. 18 Wmk. 106 *Perf. 12½***
**C167** AP76 8c ultra 3.00 .25
**C168** AP77 12c chocolate 2.25 .50

José Marti National Library.

Map of Cuba and UN Emblem — AP78

**1957, Oct. 24**
**C169** AP78 8c dk green & brn 2.00 .25
**C170** AP78 12c car rose & bl grn 1.60 .55
**C171** AP78 30c dk bl & brt pink 2.50 1.25
*Nos. C169-C171 (3)* 6.10 2.05

Issued for United Nations Day, 1957.

Map of Cuba and Florida — AP79

**1957, Oct. 28**
**C172** AP79 12c dk red brn & bl 3.50 .80

30th anniv. of airmail service from Key West to Havana.

**Type of Regular Issue, 1957 and**

Stairway and Bell Tower — AP80

Design: 12c, Facade of Normal School.

**1957, Nov. 19 Engr. *Perf. 12½***
**C173** A217 12c indigo & ocher 1.75 .40
**C174** AP80 30c dk car & gray 3.25 .60

**View Types of Regular Issue, 1957**

Views: 8c, El Viso Fort, El Caney. 12c, Sancti Spiritus Church. 30c, Concordia Bridge, Matanzas.

**1957, Dec. 17 *Perf. 12½***
**C175** A218 8c dk gray & red 1.00 .30
**C176** A219 12c brown & gray 1.75 .40
**C177** A218 30c red brn & bl gray 2.00 .75
*Nos. C175-C177 (3)* 4.75 1.45

See note after No. C72.

**Hedges Types of Regular Issue, 1958**

8c, Dayton Hedges & Matanzas rayon factory.

**1958, Jan. 30 Wmk. 106 *Perf. 12½***
**C178** A221 8c green 2.25 .80

Diario de la Marina Building — AP81

**1958, Apr. 1**
**C179** AP81 29c black 4.25 1.10

Jose Ignacio Rivero y Alonso, editor of the newspaper, Diario de la Marina.

Map Showing Sea Mail Route, 1765 — AP82

**1958, Apr. 24 Wmk. 106 *Perf. 12½***
**C180** AP82 29c dk bl aqua & buff 3.50 1.25

Issued for Stamp Day, Apr. 24, and the National Philatelic Exhibition.

Gen. Gomez in Battle — AP83

**1958, June 6 Engr.**
**C181** AP83 12c slate green 2.00 .55

Issued in honor of Maj. Gen. José Miguel Gomez, President of Cuba, 1909-13.

Snail (Polymita Picta) — AP84

12c, Megalocnus Rodens. 30c, Ammonite.

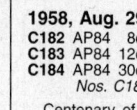

**1958, Aug. 29 Wmk. 321 *Perf. 12½***
**C182** AP84 8c gray, red & yel 4.00 1.25
**C183** AP84 12c brn, *yel grn* 5.50 1.75
**C184** AP84 30c grn, *pink* 6.00 2.10
*Nos. C182-C184 (3)* 15.50 5.10

Centenary of the birth of Dr. Carlos de la Torre, naturalist.

Papilio Caiguanabus AP85

Cuban Sea Bass AP86

12c, Teria gundlachia. 14c, Teria ebriola. 19c, Nathalis felicia. 29c, Butter Hamlet. 30c, Tattler.

**1958, Sept. 26 Wmk. 106 *Perf. 12½***
**C185** AP85 8c multicolored 3.75 .65
**C186** AP85 12c emer, blk & org 4.00 .65
**C187** AP85 14c multicolored 5.25 .90
**C188** AP85 19c bl, blk & yel 4.75 1.25
**C189** AP86 24c multicolored 5.50 1.25
**C190** AP86 29c blk, brn & ultra 16.00 1.60
**C191** AP86 30c blk, yel grn & sep 16.00 2.25
*Nos. C185-C191 (7)* 55.25 8.55

Felipe Poey (1799-1891), naturalist.

Battle of San Juan Hill, 1898 — AP87

**Wmk. 106**

**1958, Oct. 27 Engr. *Perf. 12½***
**C192** AP87 12c black brown 2.75 .50

Birth centenary of Theodore Roosevelt.

UNESCO Building, Paris — AP88

Design: 30c, "UNESCO" and map of Cuba.

**1958, Nov. 7**
**C193** AP88 12c dk slate grn 2.00 .50
**C194** AP88 30c dp ultra 2.00 1.00

UNESCO Headquarters in Paris opening, Nov. 3.

**Revolutionary Government**

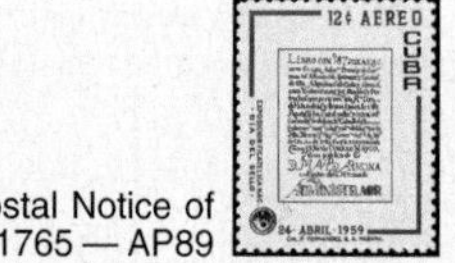


Postal Notice of 1765 — AP89

Design: 30c, Administrative postal book of St. Cristobal, Havana, 1765.

**1959, Apr. 24 Wmk. 321 *Perf. 12½***
**C195** AP89 12c Prus blue & sep 1.50 .40
**C196** AP89 30c sepia & Prus bl 2.50 1.40

Issued for Stamp Day, Apr. 24, and the National Philatelic Exhibition.

Type of 1956 Surcharged in Dark Blue

**1959, Oct. 17 Wmk. 321 *Perf. 12½***
**C197** AP63 12c on 1p emerald 2.75 1.50

Issued to publicize the meeting of the American Soc. of Travel Agents, Oct. 17-23.

Musical Arts Building — AP90

**Wmk. 106**

**1959, Nov. 11 Engr. *Perf. 12½***
**C198** AP90 12c yellow green 3.00 .90

40th anniversary of the Musical Arts Society.

**No. CB1 Surcharged in Red**

**Engr. & Typo.**

**1960 Wmk. 321 *Perf. 12½***
**C199** SPAP1 12c on 12 + 3c car & grn 2.25 .75

**Type of Regular Issue, 1960**

8c, Battle of Santa Clara. 12c, Rebel forces entering Havana. 29c, Bank-note changing hands ("Clandestine activities in the cities").

**Wmk. 320**

**1960, Jan. 28 Engr. *Perf. 12½***
**C200** A236 8c bl, gray ol & sal 1.60 .50
**C201** A236 12c gray ol & ocher 2.50 .60
**C202** A236 29c gray & car 3.00 1.25
*Nos. C200-C202 (3)* 7.10 2.35

Nos. C9 and C104 Srchd. in Red

**1960, Feb. 3 Wmk. 106**
**C203** AP3 12c on 40c dp org 2.10 .65
**C204** AP48 12c on 45c vio 2.25 .65

**Pigeon Type of 1956**

**1960, Feb. 12 Wmk. 321**
**C205** AP62 12c brt blue grn 2.00 .55

**Statue Type of Regular Issue, 1960.**

Statues: 8c, José Marti, Matanzas. 12c, Heroes of the Cacarajicara, Pinar del Rio. 30c, Cosme de la Torriente, Isle of Pines, horiz.

**1960, Mar. 28 *Perf. 12½***
**C206** A237 8c gray & car .70 .25
**C207** A237 12c blue & car 1.25 .25
**C208** A237 30c violet & brn 2.75 1.25
*Nos. C206-C208 (3)* 4.70 1.75

See note after No. 386.

Type of 1956 and No. C33 Overprinted in Dark Blue

**1960, Apr. 24 Wmk. 321 *Perf. 12½***
**C209** AP62 8c orange yel .65 .40
**C210** AP62 12c cerise 1.75 .65

**Souvenir Sheet**

**C211** AP17 Sheet of 4 35.00 35.00

Stamp Day, 4/24/60, and Natl. Phil. Exhib.
No. C211 has added marginal inscription in dark blue for cent. of the ¼r on 2r (No. 15).

**Type of Olympic Games Issue, 1960**

**Wmk. 321**

**1960, Sept. 22 Engr. *Perf. 12½***
**C212** A238 8c Boxer .80 .25
**C213** A238 12c Runner 1.50 .50
*a.* Souvenir sheet of 4 5.50 5.50

17th Olympic Games, Rome, Aug. 25-Sept. 11. No. C213a contains one each imperf. of types of Nos. 645-646 and Nos. C212-C213 in dark blue.

No. C3 and Flight Symbols of 1930, 1960 — AP91

**1960, Oct. 30 Litho. Unwmk.**
**C214** AP91 8c multicolored 3.00 2.00

30th anniv. of national air mail service.

Sword of Sheaf of Wheat — AP92

12c, Two workers, horiz. 30c, Three maps, horiz. 50c, Hand inscribed "Peace" in 5 languages.

**1961, Jan. 10 Photo. *Perf. 11½***

**Granite Paper**

**C215** AP92 8c multicolored .75 .25
**C216** AP92 12c multicolored 2.00 .25
**C217** AP92 30c black & red 2.50 .65
**C218** AP92 50c blk, bl & red 3.00 1.00
*Nos. C215-C218 (4)* 8.25 2.15

Conf. of Underdeveloped Countries, Havana.

José Marti and "Declaration of Havana" — AP93

Background in Spanish, English or French.

**1961, Jan. 28 Litho. *Perf. 12½***
**C219** AP93 8c pale grn, blk & red 1.25 .85
**C220** AP93 12c org yel, blk & pale vio 1.75 1.00
**C221** AP93 30c pale bl, blk & pale brn 4.00 3.50
*a.* Souvenir sheet of 3 15.00 15.00
*Nos. C219-C221 (3)* 7.00 5.35

Declaration of Havana, Sept. 1, 1960.
Sheets of 25 are imprinted in margin "E" for Spanish, "I" for English or "F" for French.
No. C221a contains one each of Nos. C219-C221, imperf. The 8c has background in Spanish, the 12c in English and the 30e in French.

**UN Type of 1961**

**1961, Apr. 12 Unwmk. *Perf. 12½***
**C222** A244 8c dp car & yel .60 .25
**C223** A244 12c brt ultra & org 1.40 .50
*a.* Souv. sheet of 2, #C222-C223, imperf. 4.00 4.00

Nos. C76 and C7 Surcharged

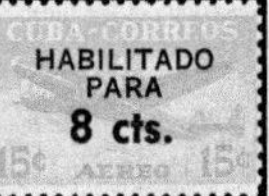


**Wmk. 106**

**1961, Oct. 1 Engr. *Perf. 10***
**C224** AP39 8c on 15c No. C76 1.00 .40
**C225** AP3 8c on 20c No. C7 1.00 .40

**Revolution Anniv. Type of 1962**

***Perf. 12½***

**1962, Jan. 3 Litho. Unwmk.**
**C226** A250 8c multi 1.00 .30
**C227** A250 12c multi 1.90 .55
**C228** A250 30c multi 2.50 .90
*Nos. C226-C228 (3)* 5.40 1.75

1st Sugarcane Harvest in Socialist Cuba, 1st Anniv. — AP94

**1962, Jan. 16**
**C229** AP94 8c salmon pink & dark brn 1.00 .25
**C230** AP94 12c bluish lil & blk 2.50 .45

Cuban goods have been embargoed by the United States since a Feb. 7, 1962 proclamation by President Kennedy, but according to the Office of Foreign Assets Control of the Treasury Department, used Cuban stamps can be imported and sold without limitation, and unused stamps may be imported for personal use, but not resold.

Intl. Radio Service — AP95

**1962, Mar. 26 Wmk. 321**
**C231** AP95 8c multi 1.10 .25
**C232** AP95 12c multi 2.10 .55
**C233** AP95 30c multi 3.00 1.25
**C234** AP95 1p multi 6.00 3.25
*Nos. C231-C234 (4)* 12.20 5.30

**Bird Type of 1956**

**1962, July 20 Engr. Wmk. 321**
**C235** AP63 1p like #C144, royal blue 9.50 7.50
**C236** AP62 2p like #C145, dark red 17.00 14.00
**C237** AP63 5p like #C146, rose lake 22.50 17.50
*Nos. C235-C237 (3)* 49.00 39.00

PRAGA '62 — AP96

No. C238, Czechoslovakia No. 1080.

**1962, Aug. 18 Litho.**
**C238** AP96 31c multi 3.50 1.50

**Souvenir Sheet**

***Imperf***

**C239** AP96 31c like No. C238 17.50 12.00

No. C239 contains one 60x35½mm stamp.

Achievements of the Revolution AP97

1c, Agrarian reform. 2c, Industrialization. 3c, Urban reform. 7c, Eradication of unemployment. 9c, Education. 10c, Public health. 13c, Excerpt from *La Historia Me Absolvera*, by Castro.

**1966, July 26 Wmk. 376 *Perf. 12½***
**C240** AP97 1c multi .25 .25
**C241** AP97 2c multi .25 .25
**C242** AP97 3c multi .50 .25
**C243** AP97 7c multi .50 .25
**C244** AP97 9c multi .95 .25
**C245** AP97 10c multi 2.10 .25
**C246** AP97 13c multi 2.75 .45
*Nos. C240-C246 (7)* 7.30 1.95

Camaguey-Seville Flight, 35th Anniv. — AP98

13c, Aircraft. 30c, Map, Lieut. Menendez Palaez.

**1971, Jan. 12 Unwmk.**
**C247** AP98 13c multi 2.25 .25
**C248** AP98 30c multi 3.25 .70

Havana-Santiago de Chile Direct Air Service, 1st Anniv. — AP99

**1972, June 26 Wmk. 376**
**C249** AP99 25c multi 1.50 .75

6th Congress of Latin American and Caribbean Exporters of Sugar, Havana AP100

***Perf. 12½x12***

**1977, Feb. 28 Unwmk.**
**C250** AP100 13c multi .75 .25

**Composer Type of 1977**

13c, Jorge Ankerman and score.

**1977, May 10 *Perf. 13***
**C251** A571 13c multi 1.00 .25

**Flower Type of 1977**

Designs: 13c, Caesalpinia pulcherrima. 30c, .Catharanthus roseus.

**1977, May 31**
**C252** A572 13c multicolored .80 .25
**C253** A572 30c multicolored 1.60 .50

**Souvenir Sheet**

***Perf. 13½x13***

**C254** A572 50c Juan Tomas Roig 4.00 .90

No. C254 contains one 32x40mm stamp.

**Natl. Decorations Type of 1977**

**1977, July 26 *Perf. 12x12½***
**C255** A574 13c multi, diff. .80 .25
**C256** A574 30c multi, diff. 1.50 .45

**Art Type of 1977**

Paintings by Jorge Arche: 13c, *My Wife and I*, vert. 30c, *Domino Players*. 50c, *Self-portrait*, vert.

**1977, Aug. 25 *Perf. 13x12½***

**Size: 26x38mm**

**C257** A575 13c multi .60 .25

**Size: 40x29mm**

***Perf. 13***

**C258** A575 30c multi 1.50 .40

**Souvenir Sheet**

***Perf. 13½x13***

**C259** A575 50c multi 4.00 4.00

No. C259 contains one 32x40mm stamp.

**Spartakiad Type of 1977**

13c, Grenade-throwing. 30c, Rifle-shooting, horiz.

**1977, Sept. 10 *Perf. 13***
**C260** A576 13c multi .60 .25
**C261** A576 30c multi 1.25 .40

10th Heroic Guerrilla's Day — AP101

13c, Guerrilla fighters.

**1977, Oct. 8 *Perf. 12½x13***
**C262** AP101 13c multi 2.75 .25

**Airmail Service Type of 1977**

13c, Havana-Mexico cachet. 30c, Havana-Prague cachet.

**1977, Oct. 27** *Perf. 12x12½*

**C263** A577 13c multi .85 .25
**C264** A577 30c multi 1.50 .55

Souvenir Sheet

*Adoration of the Magi,* by Rubens — AP102

**1977, Nov. 18** *Perf. 13*

**C265** AP102 50c multi 4.00 4.00

Rubens' 400th birth anniv.

### Havana Zoo Type of 1977

**1977, Nov. 24**

**C266** A579 13c Tiger 1.25 .25
**C267** A579 30c Lion 1.60 .55

### Revolution Martyrs Type of 1977

**1977, Dec. 2** *Perf. 12½x12*

**C268** A580 13c *Corynthia* landing .75 .25

Pan American Health Organization (OPS), 75th Anniv. AP103

**1977, Dec. 2**

**C269** AP103 13c multi .75 .25

### Havana University Type of 1978

13c, Crossed sabres, university. 30c, University, statue, crowd.

**1978, Jan. 5** *Perf. 13x12½*

**C270** A582 13c multi .75 .25
**C271** A582 30c multi 1.10 .50

Portrait of Jose Marti (b. 1853), by A. Menocal — AP104

**1978, Jan. 28**

**C272** AP104 13c multi .80 .25

### Art Type of 1978

Paintings in the Nat. Museum of Art: 13c, *El Guadalquivir,* by M. Barron. 30c, *Portrait of H.E. Ridley,* by J.J. Masqueries, vert.

**1978, Feb. 20** *Perf. 12½x12, 13*

**Sizes: 42x27mm, 29x40mm**

**C273** A583 13c multi .90 .25
**C274** A583 30c multi 1.10 .40

### Bird Type of 1975

Designs: 13c, Torreornis inexpectata, horiz. 30c, Ara tricolor.

**1978, Mar. 10** *Perf. 12½x12, 13*

**Size: 42x27mm, 27x42mm**

**C275** A524 13c multicolored 1.40 .50
**C276** A524 30c multicolored 2.10 1.10

Baragua Protest, Cent. — AP105

13c, *Antonio Maceo,* by A. Melero.

**1978, Mar. 15** *Perf. 13x13½*

**C277** AP105 13c multi .70 .25

### Cosmonaut's Day Type of 1978

**1978, Apr. 12** *Perf. 13*

**C278** A585 13c Venera 10 .70 .25

**Size: 36x46mm**

***Perf. 12½x13***

**C279** A585 30c Lunokhod 2, vert. 1.25 .50

SOCFILEX '78, Budapest AP106

30c, Parliament, Hungary No. 217.

**1978, May 7** *Perf. 13x12½*

**C280** AP106 30c multi 1.60 .55

### Cactus Type of 1978

Designs: 13c, Rhodocactus cubensis. 30c, Harrisia taetra.

**1978, May 15** *Perf. 13*

**C281** A587 13c multicolored .80 .25
**C282** A587 30c multicolored 1.75 .35

World Telecommunications Day — AP107

**1978, May 17**

**C283** AP107 30c multi 2.00 .45

Organization of African Unity, 15th Anniv. — AP108

**1978, May 25** *Perf. 13x12½*

**C284** AP108 30c multi 1.20 .45

Souvenir Sheet

CAPEX '78, Toronto — AP109

50c, *Niven, Wales,* by G.H. Russell.

**1978, June 9** *Perf. 13x13½*

**C285** AP109 50c multi 3.50 2.25

### Aquarium Type of 1978

Designs: 13c, Carassias auratus, vert. 30c, Symphysodon aequifasciata axelrodi.

**1978, June 15** *Perf. 13*

**C286** A588 13c multicolored 1.00 .25
**C287** A588 30c multicolored 1.50 .50

### MEDELLIN Games Type of 1978

**1978, July 1**

**C288** A589 13c Volleyball .60 .25
**C289** A589 30c Running 1.25 .45

### Attack on Moncada Type of 1978

13c, Soldiers bearing rifles. 30c, Stylized dove, banners.

**1978, July 26**

**C290** A590 13c multi .50 .25
**C291** A590 30c multi 1.10 .35

### Youth Festival Type of 1978

Natl. flags and views of host cities.

**1978, July 28**

**C292** A591 13c Moscow, 1957 .70 .25
**C293** A591 13c Vienna, 1959 .70 .25
**C294** A591 13c Helsinki, 1962 .70 .25
**C295** A591 13c Sofia, 1968 .70 .25
**C296** A591 13c Berlin, 1973 .70 .25
*a.* Strip of 5, Nos. C292-C296 3.75 1.75
*Nos. C292-C296 (5)* 3.50 1.25

**Size: 46x36mm**

***Perf. 13x12½***

**C297** A591 30c Havana, 1978 1.50 .35

### Tuna Industry Type of 1978

**1978, Aug. 30** *Perf. 12½x12*

**C298** A593 13c Stern trawler .85 .25
**C299** A593 30c Refrigerator ship 1.50 .60

Souvenir Sheet

PRAGA '78 — AP110

50c, *Marina,* by A. Brandeis.

**1978, Sept. 8** *Perf. 13*

**C300** AP110 50c multi 3.50 2.00

### Art Type of 1978

Paintings by Amelia Pelaez del Casal (1896-1968): 13c, *Yellow Flowers,* vert. 30c, *Still-life in Blue,* vert. 50c, *Portrait of Amelia,* by L. Romanach, vert.

**1978, Sept. 15** *Perf. 12x12½, 13*

**C301** A594 13c multi .50 .25
**C302** A594 30c multi 1.20 .45

**Souvenir Sheet**

***Perf. 13½x13***

**C303** A594 50c multi 3.00 .90

No. C303 contains one 32x40mm stamp.

Socialist Communication Organizations Congress (OSS), 20th Anniv. AP111

**1978, Sept. 25** *Perf. 13*

**C304** AP111 30c multi 2.50 .50

Souvenir Sheet

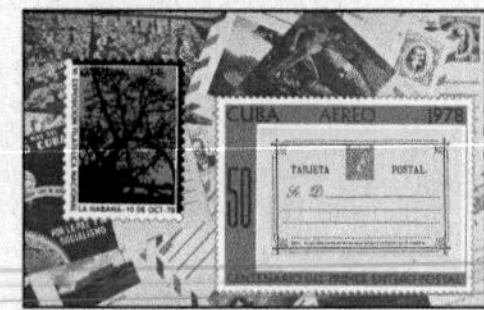


EXFILNA '78, 6th Natl. Philatelic Exposition — AP112

50c, 1st Postal Card, issued in 1878.

**1978, Oct. 10** *Imperf.*

**C305** AP112 50c multi 3.50 2.75

No. C305 has simulated perfs.

Intl. Anti-Apartheid Year — AP113

**1978, Oct. 16** *Perf. 12½*

**C306** AP113 13c multi 1.00 .75

### Zoo Type of 1978

Designs: 13c, Acinonyx jubatos. 30c, Loxodonta africana, vert.

**1978, Oct. 20** *Perf. 13*

**C307** A595 13c multicolored .85 .25
**C308** A595 30c multicolored 1.75 .65

### Natl. Ballet Type of 1978

**1978, Oct. 28** *Perf. 12½x13*

**C309** A596 13c *Giselle,* vert. .85 .25
**C310** A596 30c *Genesis,* vert. 1.60 .30

### Pacific Flora Type of 1978

**1978, Nov. 30** *Perf. 13*

**C311** A597 13c multi, diff. .80 .25
**C312** A597 30c multi, diff. 1.60 .30

25th Death Anniv. of Julius and Ethel Rosenberg, American Communists Executed for Espionage AP114

**1978, Dec. 20**

**C313** AP114 13c multi .65 .25

Julio A. Mella (d. 1929) AP115

**1979, Jan. 10**

**C314** AP115 13c multi .65 .25

### Cosmonaut's Day Type of 1979

**1979, Apr. 12** *Perf. 13½x13*

**Souvenir Sheet**

**C315** A603 50c Orbital complex 3.50 2.75

No. C315 contains one 32x40mm stamp.

Intl. Year of the Child AP116

**1979, June 1** *Perf. 13x12½*

**C316** AP116 13c multi .90 .25

### Art Type of 1979

50c, Portrait of Victor Emmanuel Garcia, by J. Arche, vert.

**1979, June 15** *Perf. 13½x13*

**C317** A600 50c multicolored 3.25 1.75

No. C317 contains one 32x40mm stamp.

CARIFESTA '79, Festival of Caribbean Peoples, Havana — AP117

**1979, July 16** *Perf. 12½x13*

**C318** AP117 13c multi 1.50 .25

10th World Universiade Games, Mexico City AP118

**1979, Sept. 1** ***Perf. 13x12½***
**C319** AP118 13c grn, pale grn & gold .65 .25

6th Conference of Nonaligned Countries AP119

50c, Convention Palace.

**1979, Sept. 3**
**C320** AP119 50c multi 1.75 .90

Sir Rowland Hill (d. 1879), Originator of Penny Postage AP120

**1979, Sept. 4** ***Perf. 13½x13***
**C321** AP120 30c Hill, casket 1.40 .25

SOCFILEX '79, Bucharest — AP121

30c, Romania No. 683, flags.

**1979, Oct. 25** ***Perf. 12½***
**C322** AP121 30c multi 1.40 .40

Intl. Radio Consultative Committee (CCIR), 50th Anniv. AP122

30c, Ground receiving station.

**1979, Nov. 30** ***Perf. 12½x12***
**C323** AP122 30c multi 1.50 .40

1st Soviet-Cuban Joint Space Flight AP123

**1980, Sept. 23** ***Perf. 12½***
**C324** AP123 13c multi .75 .25
**C325** AP123 30c multi 1.75 .35

Capt. Mariano Barberan, Lt. Joaquin Collar, and Their Airplane Cuatro Vientos. AP124

**1993, June 11** **Litho.** ***Perf. 13***
**C326** AP124 30c multicolored 1.10 .45

1st Flight Seville-Camaguey, 60th anniv.

---

## AIR POST SEMI-POSTAL STAMP

**Catalogue values for unused stamps in this section are for Never Hinged items.**

Farm Couple and Factory SPAP1

**Engr. & Typo.**
**1959, May 7** **Wmk. 321** ***Perf. 12½***
**CB1** SPAP1 12c + 3c car & grn 2.00 .80

Agricultural reforms. See No. C199.

---

## AIR POST SPECIAL DELIVERY STAMPS

### Matanzas Issue

Matanzas Harbor APSD1

**Wmk. 229**
**1936, May 5** **Photo.** ***Perf. 12½***
**CE1** ASPD1 15c light blue 5.00 3.50
Never hinged 8.00

Exists imperf. Value $6.50 unused, $4.50 used.

---

## SPECIAL DELIVERY STAMPS

### Issued under Administration of the United States

US No. E5 Surcharged in Red

**1899** **Wmk. 191** ***Perf. 12***
**E1** SD3 10c blue 130. 100.
Never hinged 300.
*a.* No period after "CUBA" 575. 400.

### Issue of the Republic under US Military Rule

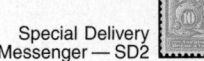

Special Delivery Messenger — SD2

Printed by the US Bureau of Engraving and Printing

**1899** **Wmk. US-C (191C)**
**Inscribed: "Immediata"**
**E2** SD2 10c orange 52.50 15.00
Never hinged 120.00

### Issues of the Republic Inscribed: "Inmediata"

**1902** ***Perf. 12***
**E3** SD2 10c orange 7.50 3.00

J. B. Zayas — SD3

**1910** **Unwmk.**
**E4** SD3 10c orange & blue 30.00 10.00
Never hinged 50.00
*a.* Center inverted 1,250.

Airplane and Morro Castle — SD4

**1914, Feb. 24** ***Perf. 12***
**E5** SD4 10c dark blue 15.00 1.25

Exists imperf. Value, pair $500.

**1927** **Wmk. Star (106)**
**E6** SD4 10c deep blue 12.00 .50
Never hinged 18.00

**1935** ***Perf. 10***
**E7** SD4 10c blue 12.00 .40
Never hinged 15.00

### Matanzas Issue

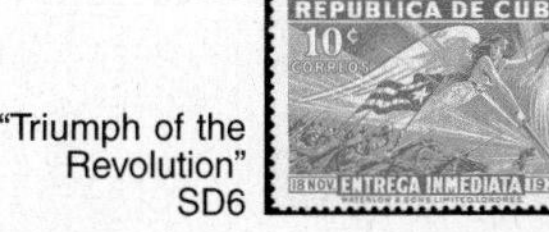


Mercury — SD5

**Wmk. Wavy Lines (229)**
**1936, May 5** **Photo.** ***Perf. 12½***
**E8** SD5 10c deep claret 8.00 3.50
Never hinged 9.50

Exists imperf. Value $7.50 unused, $5 used.

"Triumph of the Revolution" SD6

**1936, Nov. 18**
**E9** SD6 10c red orange 9.00 2.00
Never hinged 12.00

Maj. Gen. Máximo Gómez (1836-1905).

Temple of Quetzalcoatl (Mexico) SD7

Ruben Dario (Nicaragua) SD8

**Wmk. 106**
**1937, Oct. 13** **Engr.** ***Perf. 10***
**E10** SD7 10c deep orange 8.00 6.50
**E11** SD8 10c deep orange 8.50 7.25
Set, never hinged 23.50

Issued for the benefit of the Association of American Writers and Artists. See note after No. 354.

Letter and Symbols of Transportation SD9

**1945, Oct. 30**
**E12** SD9 10c olive brown 2.75 .40
Never hinged 4.00

**Catalogue values for unused stamps in this section, from this point to the end of the section, are for Never Hinged items.**

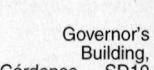

Governor's Building, Cárdenas — SD10

**Engraved and Lithographed**
**1951, July 3** **Wmk. 229** ***Perf. 13***
**E13** SD10 10c henna brn, ultra & red 5.75 2.25

Cent. of the adoption of Cuba's flag.

### Chess Type of Regular Issue, 1951

**1951, Nov. 1** **Photo.**
**E14** A166 10c dk grn & rose brn 18.00 5.75

Type of Regular Issue of 1951 Surcharged in Red Violet

**Wmk. 106**
**1952, Mar. 18** **Engr.** ***Perf. 10***
**E15** A159 10c on 2c yel brn 6.00 2.00

Arms and Bars from National Hymn — SD12

**1952, May 27** ***Perf. 12½***
**E16** SD12 10c dp org & bl 4.00 2.50

Republic of Cuba founding, 50th anniv.

### Type of Air Post Stamps of 1952 Inscribed: "Entrega Especial"

**1952, Oct. 7** ***Perf. 10***
**E17** AP36 10c pale olive grn 5.00 2.00

Three-fourths of the proceeds from the sale of No. E17 were used for the Communications Ministry Employees' Retirement Fund.

Roseate Tern — SD13

**1953, July 28**
**E18** SD13 10c blue 4.00 1.10

Gregorio Hernandez Saez — SD14

**1954, Feb. 23**
**E19** SD14 10c olive green 5.00 1.10

Felix Varela — SD15

**1955, June 22** ***Perf. 12½***
**E20** SD15 10c brown car 3.00 .75

See note after No. E17.

### Portrait Type of Regular Issue, 1956 Inscribed: "Entrega Especial"

Portrait: 10c, Jose Jacinto Milanes.

**1956, May 2** **Wmk. 106**
**E21** A198 10c dk car rose & blk 3.50 1.00

See note after No. E17.

### Painting Type of Regular Issue, 1957 Inscribed: "Entrega Especial"

10c, "Yesterday" by E. Garcia Cabrera.

**1957, Mar. 15 Engr. *Perf. 12½***

| | | | | |
|---|---|---|---|---|
| **E22** | A207 | 10c dk brn & turq bl | 3.00 | 1.25 |

See note after No. E17.

### View Type of Regular Issue, 1957 Inscribed: "Entrega Especial"

10c, Independence square, Pino del Rio.

**1957, Dec. 17**

| | | | | |
|---|---|---|---|---|
| **E23** | A218 | 10c dk pur & brn | 2.50 | 1.00 |

See note after No. E17.

View in Havana and Messenger SD16

**1958, Jan. 10 Engr.**

| | | | | |
|---|---|---|---|---|
| **E24** | SD16 | 10c blue | 2.75 | .70 |
| **E25** | SD16 | 20c green | 3.25 | .70 |

See Nos. E28, E31.

### Fish Type of Regular Issue, 1958 Inscribed: "Entrega Especial"

Fish: 10c, Blackfish snapper. 20c, Mosquitofish.

**1958, Sept. 26 Wmk. 106 *Perf. 12½***

| | | | | |
|---|---|---|---|---|
| **E26** | AP86 | 10c blk, bl, pink & yel | 9.00 | 1.75 |
| **E27** | AP86 | 20c blk, ultra & pink | 17.00 | 8.00 |

See note after No. C191.

### Revolutionary Government Messenger Type of 1958

**1960 Wmk. 321 *Perf. 12½***

| | | | | |
|---|---|---|---|---|
| **E28** | SD16 | 10c brt vio | 3.50 | .80 |

Plane Type of Air Post Issue, of 1931-46, Srchd. in Black or Red

**1960 Wmk. 106 *Perf. 10***

| | | | | |
|---|---|---|---|---|
| **E29** | AP4 | 10c on 20c car rose | 3.00 | .50 |
| **E30** | AP4 | 10c on 50c grnsh bl (R) | 3.00 | .50 |

### Messenger Type of 1958

**1961, June 28 Wmk. 321 *Perf. 12½***

| | | | | |
|---|---|---|---|---|
| **E31** | SD16 | 10c orange | 3.50 | .80 |

### West Indies Packet Type of 1962

***Perf. 12½***

**1962, Apr. 24 Litho. Unwmk.**

| | | | | |
|---|---|---|---|---|
| **E32** | A253 | 10c buff, dull ultra & brn | 7.00 | 1.50 |

## POSTAGE DUE STAMPS

### Issued under Administration of the United States

Postage Due Stamps of the United States Nos. J38, J39, J41 and J42 Srchd. in Black Like Nos. 221-226A

**1899 Wmk. 191 *Perf. 12***

| | | | | |
|---|---|---|---|---|
| **J1** | D2 | 1c dp claret | 45.00 | 5.25 |
| | | Never hinged | 110.00 | |
| **J2** | D2 | 2c dp claret | 45.00 | 5.25 |
| | | Never hinged | 110.00 | |
| | *a.* | Inverted surcharge | | *4,000.* |
| **J3** | D2 | 5c dp claret | 42.50 | 5.25 |
| | | Never hinged | 105.00 | |
| **J4** | D2 | 10c dp claret | 25.00 | 2.50 |
| | | Never hinged | 60.00 | |
| | | *Nos. J1-J4 (4)* | 157.50 | 18.25 |

### Issues of the Republic

D1

**1914 Unwmk. Engr. *Perf. 12***

| | | | | |
|---|---|---|---|---|
| **J5** | D1 | 1c carmine rose | 8.00 | 1.25 |
| **J6** | D1 | 2c carmine rose | 9.00 | 1.25 |
| **J7** | D1 | 5c carmine rose | 10.00 | 2.50 |
| | | *Nos. J5-J7 (3)* | 27.00 | 5.00 |

**1927-28**

| | | | | |
|---|---|---|---|---|
| **J8** | D1 | 1c rose red | 5.50 | .90 |
| **J9** | D1 | 2c rose red | 8.50 | .90 |
| **J10** | D1 | 5c rose red | 10.00 | 1.25 |
| | | *Nos. J8-J10 (3)* | 24.00 | 3.05 |

## NEWSPAPER STAMPS

### Issued under Spanish Dominion

N1

**1888 Unwmk. Typo. *Perf. 14***

| | | | | |
|---|---|---|---|---|
| **P1** | N1 | ½m black | .25 | *.25* |
| **P2** | N1 | 1m black | .25 | *.30* |
| **P3** | N1 | 2m black | .25 | *.30* |
| **P4** | N1 | 3m black | 1.60 | 1.00 |
| **P5** | N1 | 4m black | 2.10 | *2.00* |
| **P6** | N1 | 8m black | 8.00 | *8.50* |
| | | *Nos. P1-P6 (6)* | 12.45 | 12.35 |

N2

**1890**

| | | | | |
|---|---|---|---|---|
| **P7** | N2 | ½m red brown | .55 | *.65* |
| **P8** | N2 | 1m red brown | .55 | *.65* |
| **P9** | N2 | 2m red brown | .90 | *.95* |
| **P10** | N2 | 3m red brown | 1.10 | *1.10* |
| **P11** | N2 | 4m red brown | 8.25 | 5.50 |
| **P12** | N2 | 8m red brown | 8.25 | 5.50 |
| | | *Nos. P7-P12 (6)* | 19.60 | 14.35 |

**1892**

| | | | | |
|---|---|---|---|---|
| **P13** | N2 | ½m violet | .25 | *.30* |
| **P14** | N2 | 1m violet | .25 | *.30* |
| **P15** | N2 | 2m violet | .25 | *.30* |
| **P16** | N2 | 3m violet | 1.10 | .35 |
| **P17** | N2 | 4m violet | 4.25 | 1.90 |
| **P18** | N2 | 8m violet | 8.75 | 3.00 |
| | | *Nos. P13-P18 (6)* | 14.85 | 6.15 |

**1894**

| | | | | |
|---|---|---|---|---|
| **P19** | N2 | ½m rose | .25 | *.30* |
| | *a.* | Imperf. pair | 40.00 | 40.00 |
| **P20** | N2 | 1m rose | .50 | .35 |
| **P21** | N2 | 2m rose | .55 | .35 |
| **P22** | N2 | 3m rose | 2.10 | 1.40 |
| **P23** | N2 | 4m rose | 3.50 | 1.60 |
| **P24** | N2 | 8m rose | 6.00 | 4.00 |
| | | *Nos. P19-P24 (6)* | 12.90 | 8.00 |

**1896**

| | | | | |
|---|---|---|---|---|
| **P25** | N2 | ½m blue green | .25 | *.30* |
| **P26** | N2 | 1m blue green | .25 | *.30* |
| **P27** | N2 | 2m blue green | .25 | *.30* |
| **P28** | N2 | 3m blue green | 2.75 | 1.50 |
| **P29** | N2 | 4m blue green | 5.75 | *7.00* |
| **P30** | N2 | 8m blue green | 10.50 | *10.00* |
| | | *Nos. P25-P30 (6)* | 19.75 | 19.40 |

For surcharges see Nos. 190-193, 201-220.

## POSTAL TAX STAMPS

**Catalogue values for unused stamps in this section are for Never Hinged items.**

Mother and Child — PT1

**Wmk. Star. (106)**

**1938, Dec. 1 Engr. *Perf. 10***

| | | | | |
|---|---|---|---|---|
| **RA1** | PT1 | 1c bright green | 2.50 | .25 |

The tax benefited the National Council of Tuberculosis fund for children's hospitals. Obligatory on all mail during December and January. This note applies also to Nos. RA2-RA4, RA7-RA10, RA12-RA15, RA17-RA21.

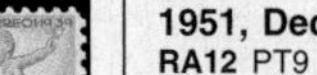

Nurse with Child — PT2

**1939, Dec. 1**

| | | | | |
|---|---|---|---|---|
| **RA2** | PT2 | 1c orange vermilion | 2.75 | .25 |

"Health" Protecting Children — PT3

**1940, Dec. 1**

| | | | | |
|---|---|---|---|---|
| **RA3** | PT3 | 1c deep blue | 2.50 | .25 |

Mother and Child — PT4

**1941, Dec. 1**

| | | | | |
|---|---|---|---|---|
| **RA4** | PT4 | 1c olive bister | 2.75 | .25 |

Victory — PT5

**1942-44**

| | | | | |
|---|---|---|---|---|
| **RA5** | PT5 | ½c orange | 3.00 | .25 |
| **RA6** | PT5 | ½c gray ('44) | 2.75 | .25 |

Issued: No. RA5, 7/1/42; No. RA6, 10/3/44.

Type of 1941 Overprinted in Black

**1942, Dec. 1**

| | | | | |
|---|---|---|---|---|
| **RA7** | PT4 | 1c salmon | 2.25 | .30 |
| | *a.* | Inverted overprint | 100.00 | 75.00 |

As PT3 — PT6

**1943, Dec. 1**

| | | | | |
|---|---|---|---|---|
| **RA8** | PT6 | 1c brown | 2.25 | .25 |

As PT4 — PT7

**1949, Dec. 9**

| | | | | |
|---|---|---|---|---|
| **RA9** | PT7 | 1c blue | 1.50 | .25 |

### Type of 1949 Inscribed: "1950"

**1950, Dec. 1 Engr.**

| | | | | |
|---|---|---|---|---|
| **RA10** | PT7 | 1c rose red | 2.50 | .25 |

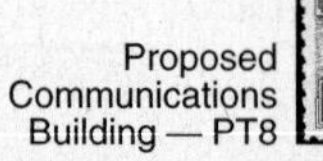

Proposed Communications Building — PT8

**1951, June 5 Wmk. 106 *Perf. 10***

| | | | | |
|---|---|---|---|---|
| **RA11** | PT8 | 1c violet | 1.75 | .25 |

The tax was to help build a new Communications Building. This note applies also to Nos. RA16, RA34, RA43.

Woman Holding Child Aloft — PT9

**1951, Dec. 1**

| | | | | |
|---|---|---|---|---|
| **RA12** | PT9 | 1c violet blue | 1.10 | .25 |
| **RA13** | PT9 | 1c brown carmine | 1.10 | .25 |
| **RA14** | PT9 | 1c olive bister | 1.10 | .25 |
| **RA15** | PT9 | 1c deep green | 1.10 | .25 |
| | | *Nos. RA12-RA15 (4)* | 4.40 | 1.00 |

Proposed Communications Building — PT10

**1952, Feb. 8**

| | | | | |
|---|---|---|---|---|
| **RA16** | PT10 | 1c slate blue | 2.00 | .25 |

See Nos. RA34, RA43.

Child — PT11

**1952, Dec. 1**

| | | | | |
|---|---|---|---|---|
| **RA17** | PT11 | 1c rose carmine | 1.00 | .25 |
| **RA18** | PT11 | 1c yellow green | 1.00 | .25 |
| **RA19** | PT11 | 1c blue | 1.00 | .25 |
| **RA20** | PT11 | 1c orange | 1.00 | .25 |
| | | *Nos. RA17-RA20 (4)* | 4.00 | 1.00 |

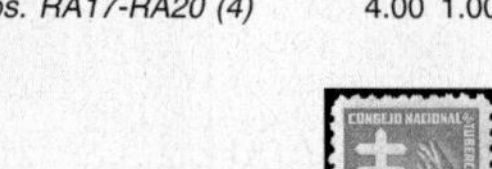

Hands Reaching for Lorraine Cross — PT12

**1953, Dec. 1 *Perf. 9½***

| | | | | |
|---|---|---|---|---|
| **RA21** | PT12 | 1c rose carmine | 1.75 | .30 |

Child's Head, Lorraine Cross — PT13

**1954, Nov. 1 *Perf. 9½x10***

| | | | | |
|---|---|---|---|---|
| **RA22** | PT13 | 1c rose red | .75 | .30 |
| **RA23** | PT13 | 1c violet | .75 | .30 |
| **RA24** | PT13 | 1c bright blue | .75 | .30 |
| **RA25** | PT13 | 1c emerald | .75 | .30 |
| | | *Nos. RA22-RA25 (4)* | 3.00 | 1.20 |

The tax benefited the Natl. Council of Tuberculosis fund for children's hospitals. Obligatory on all mail during Nov., Dec., Jan. & Feb. This note also applies to Nos. RA26-RA33, RA35-RA42.

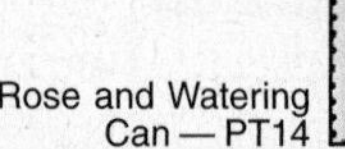

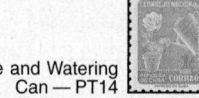

Rose and Watering Can — PT14

**1955, Nov. 1**

| | | | | |
|---|---|---|---|---|
| **RA26** | PT14 | 1c red orange | 2.00 | .30 |
| **RA27** | PT14 | 1c red lilac | 2.00 | .30 |
| **RA28** | PT14 | 1c bright blue | 2.00 | .30 |
| **RA29** | PT14 | 1c orange yellow | 2.00 | .30 |
| | | *Nos. RA26-RA29 (4)* | 8.00 | 1.20 |

Child and Protective Hands — PT15

**1956, Nov. 1**

| | | | | |
|---|---|---|---|---|
| **RA30** | PT15 | 1c rose red | 1.50 | .30 |
| **RA31** | PT15 | 1c yellow brown | 1.50 | .30 |
| **RA32** | PT15 | 1c bright blue | 1.50 | .30 |
| **RA33** | PT15 | 1c emerald | 1.50 | .30 |
| | | *Nos. RA30-RA33 (4)* | 6.00 | 1.20 |

### Building Type of 1952

**1957, Jan. 18 *Perf. 10***

| | | | | |
|---|---|---|---|---|
| **RA34** | PT10 | 1c rose red | 1.75 | .30 |

Mother and Child by Silvia Arrojo Fernandez — PT16

**Wmk. 321**

**1957, Nov. 1 Engr. *Perf. 10***

| | | | | |
|---|---|---|---|---|
| **RA35** | PT16 | 1c dull rose | 1.75 | .30 |
| **RA36** | PT16 | 1c bright blue | 1.75 | .30 |
| **RA37** | PT16 | 1c gray | 1.75 | .30 |
| **RA38** | PT16 | 1c emerald | 1.75 | .30 |
| | | *Nos. RA35-RA38 (4)* | 7.00 | 1.20 |

National Council of Tuberculosis — PT17

**1958**

| | | | | |
|---|---|---|---|---|
| **RA39** | PT17 | 1c rose red | 1.50 | .30 |
| **RA40** | PT17 | 1c red brown | 1.50 | .30 |
| **RA41** | PT17 | 1c gray | 1.50 | .30 |
| **RA42** | PT17 | 1c emerald | 1.50 | .30 |
| | | *Nos. RA39-RA42 (4)* | 6.00 | 1.20 |

**Building Type of 1952**

**1958 Wmk. 321**

| | | | | |
|---|---|---|---|---|
| **RA43** | PT10 | 1c rose red | 1.25 | .30 |

## CURACAO

ˈcər-ə-sau

LOCATION — North of Venezuela, east of Aruba in Caribbean Sea
AREA — 171 sq. mi.
POP. — 135,822 (2005)
CAPITAL — Willemstad

On Oct. 10, 2010, Curaçao, formerly part of Netherlands Antilles, became a constituent state within the Kingdom of the Netherlands. Stamps issued from 1873 to 1949 inscribed "Curaçao" were valid in all islands that comprised the Netherlands Antilles. These stamps are listed under "Netherlands Antilles."

100 Cents = 1 Gulden

**Catalogue values for all unused stamps in this country are for Never Hinged items.**

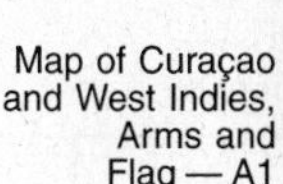

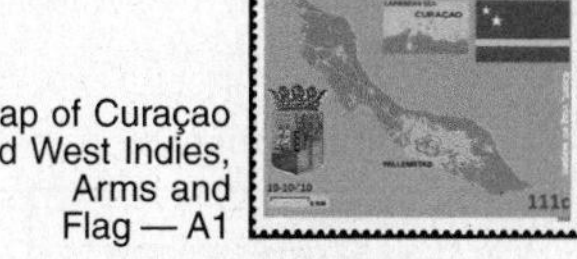

Map of Curaçao and West Indies, Arms and Flag — A1

***Perf. 13¾***

**2010, Oct. 10 Litho. Unwmk.**

| | | | | |
|---|---|---|---|---|
| **1** | A1 | 111c multi | 1.25 | 1.25 |

Souvenir Sheet

Touit Purpurata — A2

**2010, Oct. 25 Litho. *Perf. 13¾***

| | | | | |
|---|---|---|---|---|
| **2** | A2 | 1500c multi | 17.00 | 17.00 |

New Constitutional Status — A3

Designs: 1c, Sphere with colors of Curaçao flag, Diploria labyrinthiformis. 3c, Yellowtail snapper. 5c, Yellow goatfish. 30c, Blue hamlet. 63c, Rock beauty angelfish. 81c, Palometa jack. 112c, Spotfin butterflyfish. 166c, Cherubfish. 285c, Cocoa damselfish. 405c, Jewel damselfish. 630c, Schoolmaster snapper. Fish have colors of Curaçao flag.

**2011, Jan. 11 *Perf. 13¼x12¾***

| | | | | |
|---|---|---|---|---|
| **3** | A3 | 1c multi | .25 | .25 |
| **4** | A3 | 3c multi | .25 | .25 |
| **5** | A3 | 5c multi | .25 | .25 |
| **6** | A3 | 30c multi | .35 | .35 |
| **7** | A3 | 63c multi | .70 | .70 |
| **8** | A3 | 81c multi | .90 | .90 |
| **9** | A3 | 112c multi | 1.25 | 1.25 |
| **10** | A3 | 166c multi | 1.90 | 1.90 |
| **11** | A3 | 285c multi | 3.25 | 3.25 |
| **12** | A3 | 405c multi | 4.50 | 4.50 |
| **13** | A3 | 630c multi | 7.00 | 7.00 |
| | | *Nos. 3-13 (11)* | 20.60 | 20.60 |

See Nos. 13A-13C, 215-216.

**New Constitutional Status Type of 2011**

Designs: 8c, Schoolmaster snapper. 115c, Spotfin butterflyfish. 171c, Cherubfish.

**2012 Litho. *Perf. 13¼x12¾***

| | | | | |
|---|---|---|---|---|
| **13A** | A3 | 8c multi | *20.00* | *20.00* |
| **13B** | A3 | 115c multi | *20.00* | *20.00* |
| **13C** | A3 | 171c multi | *20.00* | *20.00* |

A4

Rabbit and: 112c, Big Wild Goose Pagoda, Xian, China. 145c, Great Wall of China, horiz. 166c, Temple of Heaven. 285c, Mountains near Li River, horiz. 405c, Paper lanterns.

***Perf. 12¾x13¼, 13¼x12¾***

**2011, Feb. 11 Litho.**

| | | | | |
|---|---|---|---|---|
| **14-18** | A4 | Set of 5 | 12.50 | 12.50 |

New Year 2011 (Year of the Rabbit).

A5

Musical instruments: 49c, Double bass. 63c, Steel pan drums. 82c, Accordion. 145c, Saxophone. 166c, Djembe. 236c, Piano. 285c, Trombone. 405c, Pan flute. 700c, Cymbals.

**2011, Mar. 11 *Perf. 12¾x13¼***

| | | | | |
|---|---|---|---|---|
| **19-27** | A5 | Set of 9 | 24.00 | 24.00 |

Banknotes — A6

Designs: 63c, 1947 Curaçao 1-gulden note. 75c, 1970 Netherlands Antilles 2½-gulden note. 112c, 1958 Curaçao 5-gulden note. 175c, 1948 Curaçao 10-gulden note. 200c, 1970 Netherlands Antilles 1-gulden note. 250c, 1967 Netherlands Antilles 5-gulden note. 300c, 1979 Netherlands Antilles 25-gulden note. 350c, 1972 Netherlands Antilles 50-gulden note. 475c, 1967 Netherlands Antilles 250-gulden note. 500c, 1962 Netherlands Antilles 500-gulden note.

**2011, Apr. 11 *Perf. 14***

| | | | | |
|---|---|---|---|---|
| **28-37** | A6 | Set of 10 | 28.00 | 28.00 |

2011 Paper Money Fair, Maastricht, Netherlands.

Souvenir Sheet

Prehistoric Animals — A7

No. 38: a, 700c, Ankylosaurus. b, 800c, Spinosaurus. c, 1000c, Saurolophus.

**2011, June 11 *Perf. 13¼x12¾***

| | | | | |
|---|---|---|---|---|
| **38** | A7 | Sheet of 3, #a-c | 27.00 | 27.00 |

New Technologies — A8

Designs: 275c, Social media. 375c, Fiber optics. 475c Blackberry PIN messaging. 625c, Cloud computing.

**2011, July 11**

| | | | | |
|---|---|---|---|---|
| **39-42** | A8 | Set of 4 | 19.50 | 19.50 |

Souvenir Sheet

Preservation of Polar Regions and Glaciers — A9

No. 43 — Iceberg and: a, 112c, Emblem. b, 405c, Map of Antarctica.

**2011, Aug. 11 *Perf. 13½***

| | | | | |
|---|---|---|---|---|
| **43** | A9 | Sheet of 2, #a-b | 5.50 | 5.50 |

Foods — A10

Designs: 63c, Almond cake. 81c, Apple pie. 112c, Blueberry pancakes. 145c, Broken glass cake. 166c, Lemon cake. 172c, Funchi (polenta cake). 195c, Chocolate cake. 285c, Fruit cake. 405c, Cherry cheesecake. 630c, Pumpkin cake

**2011, Sept. 11 *Perf. 13¼x12¾***

| | | | | |
|---|---|---|---|---|
| **44-53** | A10 | Set of 10 | 22.50 | 22.50 |

Christmas — A11

Evergreen branches, candle and: 63c, Christmas cake (Bolo di Pasku), candy cane and hard candies. 112c, Ayaka. 145c, New Year's cake (Pan dushi) and hard candies. 166c, Christmas ham (Ham di Pasku). 172c, Salmon (Salmou di bari). 250c, Nuts (Nechi). 405c, Pickled pork (Sult).

**2011, Nov. 11 *Perf. 12¾x13¼***

| | | | | |
|---|---|---|---|---|
| **54-60** | A11 | Set of 7 | 13.50 | 13.50 |

Miniature Sheet

Vegetables — A12

No. 61: a, 150c, Pumpkin and squashes. b, 200c, Okra. c, 225c, Onions. d, 325c, Bell peppers. e, 500c, Corn. f, 750c, Tomatoes.

**2011, Dec. 11**

| | | | | |
|---|---|---|---|---|
| **61** | A12 | Sheet of 6, #a-f | 22.00 | 22.00 |

Fish — A13

Designs: 25c, Myripristis botche. 150c, Neoniphon opercularis. 225c, Sargocentron spiniferum. 325c, Anyperodon leucogrammicus. 475c, Cephalopholis sonnerati. 500c, Epinephelus caeruleopunctatus. 700c, Abudefduf vaigiensis.

**2012, Jan. 12 *Perf. 14***

| | | | | |
|---|---|---|---|---|
| **62-68** | A13 | Set of 7 | 27.00 | 27.00 |

Nos. 62-68 were printed in sheets of 14 containing two of each stamp and a central label.

New Year 2012 (Year of the Dragon) — A14

Designs: No. 69, 500c, Dragon. No. 70, 500c, Dragon facing left, horiz.
No. 71, 500c, Yin-yang, dragon, Chinese character.

***Perf. 13½x14, 14x13½***

**2012, Feb. 13 Litho. & Embossed**

| | | | | |
|---|---|---|---|---|
| **69-70** | A14 | Set of 2 | 10.00 | 10.00 |

**Souvenir Sheet**

| | | | | |
|---|---|---|---|---|
| **71** | A14 | 500c multi | 5.00 | 5.00 |

Miniature Sheet

Birds — A15

No. 72: a, 75c, Laughing gulls (24x27mm). b, 150c, Dunlins (36x27mm). c, 200c, Gannets (24x27mm). d, 225c, Frigatebirds (36x27mm). e, 300c, Snowy egret (24x27mm). f, 350c,

Flamingos (36x27mm). g, 500c, Great blue heron (24x27mm). h, 700c, Pelican (36x27mm).

*Perf. 13¼x13¾*

**2012, Mar. 12** **Litho.**
**72** A15 Sheet of 8, #a-h 26.00 26.00

Miniature Sheet

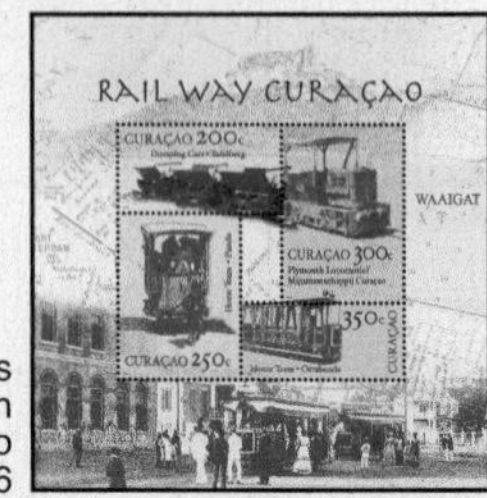


Railways in Curacao A16

No. 73: a, 200c, Dumping cars (40x21mm). b, 250c, Horse tram (30x39mm). c, 300c, Plymouth locomotive (30x42mm). d, 350c, Motor tram (40x18mm).

**2012, Apr. 12** ***Perf. 14x13½***
**73** A16 Sheet of 4, #a-d, + central label 12.50 12.50

Souvenir Sheet

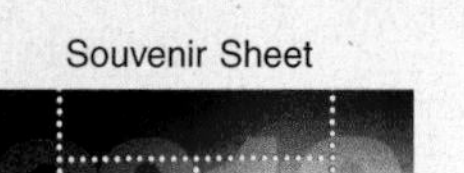
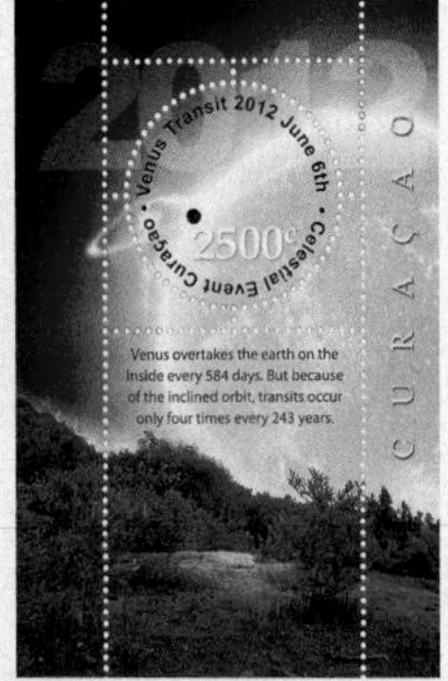


June 6, 2012 Transit of Venus — A17

**2012, May 21** ***Perf. 13¼***
**74** A17 2500c multi 25.00 25.00

A18

Indonesia 2012 World Stamp Exhibition, Jakarta — A19

**2012, June 18** ***Perf. 13½x13***
**75** A18 10c multi .25 .25

**Souvenir Sheet**

***Perf.***

**76** A19 200c multi 2.25 2.25

Fruit — A20

Designs: 275c, Watermelons. 375c, Pineapples. 475c, Bananas. 625c, Mangos.

**2012, June 12** ***Perf. 13x13½***
**77-80** A20 Set of 4 19.50 19.50

Miniature Sheet

Sports — A21

No. 81: a, 25c, Cycling. b, 50c, Swimming. c, 75c, Sailboarding. d, 100c, Soccer. e, 125c, Handball. f, 150c, Judo. g, 175c, Track. h, 200c, Baseball.

**2012, July 12** ***Perf. 13¾***
**81** A21 Sheet of 8, #a-h 10.00 10.00

Flora — A22

Designs: 75c, Datura metel. 100c, Opuntia wentiana. 150c, Caesalpina pulcherrima. 200c, Melocactus macracanthus. 250c, Crescentia cujete, horiz. 300c, Ritterocereus griseus, horiz. 350c, Calutropis procera, horiz. 450c, Zizyphus spina-cristi, horiz.

***Perf. 13x13½, 13½x13***

**2012, Aug. 13**
**82-89** A22 Set of 8 21.00 21.00

Miniature Sheet

Tourist Attractions — A23

No. 90: a, Tafelberg. b, Penha. c, Brug di Ponton Koningin Emmabrug (Queen Emma Pontoon Bridge), Willemstad. d, Bark'i Fruta (fruit market). e, Kenepa Grandi Beach. f, Landhuis Zeelandia. g, Koningin Julianabrug (Queen Juliana Bridge). h, Houses along Berg Altena. i, Handelskade, Willemstad. j, Statuut-monument (Statute of Autonomy Monument).

**2012, Sept. 27** ***Perf. 13½x13***
**90** A23 171c Sheet of 10, #a-j 19.50 19.50

Christmas — A24

Designs: 64c, Angel. 115c, Madonna and Child. 171c, Shepherd and donkey. 190c, Star of Bethlehem. 293c, Three Kings.

**2012, Nov. 12** ***Perf. 13x13¼***
**91-95** A24 Set of 5 9.50 9.50

Souvenir Sheet

End of Mayan Calendar Cycle A25

No. 96: a, 200c, Pyramid at Chichen Itza, Mexico. b, 400c, Mayan Calendar. c, 600c, Date of end of Mayan Calendar cycle (Dec. 21, 2012).

**2012, Dec. 21** ***Perf.***
**96** A25 Sheet of 3, #a-c 13.50 13.50

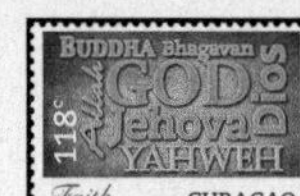


Faith — A26

Designs: 118c, Names of various deities. 175c, Words for "faith" in various languages. 200c, Candles. 250c, Statue of Buddha and prayer wheel. 300c, Cross and stained-glass window depicting saint. 350c, Star of David and Torah.

**2013, Jan. 21** ***Perf. 13¼x12¾***

| | | | |
|---|---|---|---|
| **97** | A26 118c multi | 1.40 | 1.40 |
| *a.* | Tete-beche pair | 2.80 | 2.80 |
| **98** | A26 175c multi | 2.00 | 2.00 |
| *a.* | Tete-beche pair | 4.00 | 4.00 |
| **99** | A26 200c multi | 2.25 | 2.25 |
| *a.* | Tete-beche pair | 4.50 | 4.50 |
| **100** | A26 250c multi | 2.75 | 2.75 |
| *a.* | Tete-beche pair | 5.50 | 5.50 |
| **101** | A26 300c multi | 3.50 | 3.50 |
| *a.* | Tete-beche pair | 7.00 | 7.00 |
| **102** | A26 350c multi | 4.00 | 4.00 |
| *a.* | Tete-beche pair | 8.00 | 8.00 |
| | *Nos. 97-102 (6)* | 15.90 | 15.90 |

New Year 2013 (Year of the Snake) — A27

Various snakes and flowers: 175c, 301c, 428c.
500c, Snake in tree.

**2013, Feb. 22** ***Perf. 13¼x12¾***
**103-105** A27 Set of 3 10.50 10.50

**Souvenir Sheet**

***Perf. 14x13¼***

**106** A27 500c multi 5.00 5.00

No. 106 contains one 50x40mm stamp.

Abstract Art — A28

Various works of abstract art and silhouettes of people: 118c, 175c, 200c, 250c, 301c, 450c.
250c, 301c, 450c are vert.

***Perf. 13¼x12¾, 12¾x13¼***

**2013, Mar. 13**
**107-112** A28 Set of 6 17.00 17.00

Suggestions for Environmentally Friendly Living — A29

Inscriptions: 65c, Saving energy using LED lights. 118c, Drive Green. 175c, Solar energy. 181c, Recycle. 301c, Wind energy. 350c, Rainwater. 428c, Plant trees and protect wetlands.

**2013, Apr. 15** ***Perf. 13¼x12¾***
**113-119** A29 Set of 7 18.00 18.00

Souvenir Sheet

Royal Transition in the Netherlands — A30

No. 120 — Silhouette of: a, New King Willem-Alexander. b, Abdicating Queen Beatrix.

**Litho. with Foil Application**

**2013, Apr. 30** ***Perf. 13¾***
**120** A30 1000c Sheet of 2, #a-b 22.50 22.50

Baseball — A31

Designs: 65c, Batter hitting ball. 118c, Catcher. 175c, Pitcher. 181c, Team celebrating victory. 301c, Outfielder. 350c, Fielder tagging runner out at base. 428c, Baseball field.

**2013, May 13** **Litho.** ***Perf. 13¼x12¾***
**121-127** A31 Set of 7 16.00 16.00

Ocean Liner Freewinds — A32

Freewinds and: 118c, Palm fronds. 175c, Birds.
250c, Bow of Freewinds, vert.

**2013, June 1** **Litho.** ***Perf. 13½x13***
**128-129** A32 Set of 2 3.25 3.25

**Souvenir Sheet**

***Perf. 13x13½***

**130** A32 250c multi 3.00 3.00

Virtues — A33

Designs: 118c, Respect. 175c, Love. 250c, Hope. 301c, Forgiveness. 350c, Mercy. 428c, Peace.

**2013, July 22** **Litho.** ***Perf. 12¾x13¼***
**131-136** A33 Set of 6 18.00 18.00

Souvenir Sheet

Schottegat, Curaçao — A34

**2013, Aug. 20** **Litho.** ***Perf. 13¾***
**137** A34 1000c multi 11.50 11.50

See Malta No. 1491.

Miniature Sheet

Tourist Attractions — A35

No. 138: a, Den Dunki Bridge. b, Spaanse (Spanish) Water. c, Blue Room. d, Veeris Hill. e, Boca Tabla Natural Bridge. f, Playa Kanoa. g, Noordkant. h, Blow hole near Watamula. i, Hato Caves. j, Natural Swimming Pool.

***Perf. 13¼x12¾***

**2013, Sept. 27** **Litho.**
**138** A35 175c Sheet of 10, #a-j 19.50 19.50

Fairy Tales — A36

Designs: 100c, The Wolf and the Seven Goats. 145c, The Frog Prince. 190c, Little Red Riding Hood. 293c, Pinocchio, vert. 301c, Puss in Boots, vert. 428c, Jack and the Beanstalk, vert.

*Perf. 13¼x12¾, 12¾x13¼*

**2013, Oct. 21** **Litho.**

**139-144** A36 Set of 6 16.50 16.50

Christmas — A37

Fireworks and: 65c, Building with wreath and decorations in fence. 118c, Building with wreaths on gate. 175c, Shop, other buildings, street lights, Christmas tree. 190c, Church tower, vert. 301c, Clock tower with bells, street light, vert.

*Perf. 13¼x12¾, 12¾x13¼*

**2013, Nov. 13** **Litho.**

**145-149** A37 Set of 5 9.50 9.50

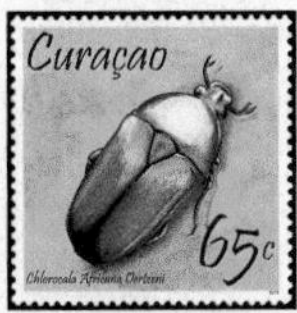

Beetles — A38

Designs: 65c, Chlorocala africana oertzeni. 118c, Stephanorrhina julia. 175c, Amaurodes passerinii nyanzanus. 181c, Cetonischema speciosa jouselini protaetia. 250c, Goliathus orientalis. 301c, Eudicella aethiopica. 428c, Ranzania bertoloni. 500c, Dicronorrhina layardi.

*Perf. 13¾x12¾*

**2013, Dec. 13** **Litho.**

**150-157** A38 Set of 8 22.50 22.50

A39

A40

A41

Emancipation of Slaves in Kingdom of the Netherlands, 150th Anniv. — A42

**2013** **Litho.**

**158** Souvenir booklet 28.50
- *a.* A39 500c multi, perf. 13¼ 5.75 5.75
- *b.* A40 500c multi, perf. 5.75 5.75
- *c.* A41 750c multi, perf. 13¼ 8.50 8.50
- *d.* A42 750c multi, perf. 13¼x14 8.50 8.50

Nos. 158a-158d were each printed in booklet panes of 1.

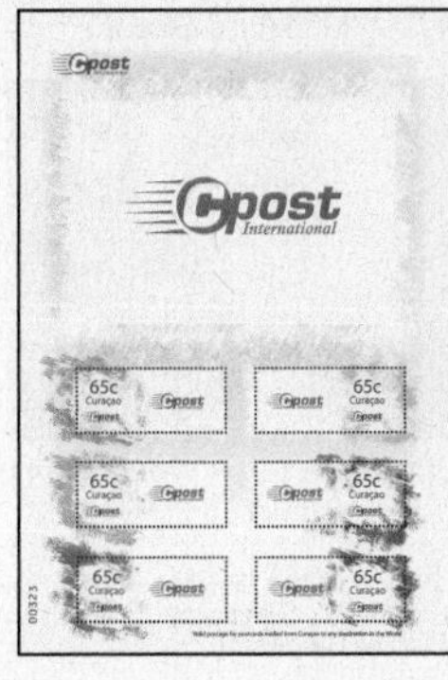

In 2014 Curacao began issuing personalizable stamps. Stamps were made available in sheets of 6 stamps. Numerous different frame designs, inscriptions, emblems and denominations have been reported.

Kingdom of the Netherlands, 200th Anniv. — A43

Designs: 150c, Crown and heraldic lion. 200c, Crown. 250c, Coat of arms. 300c, Post horn and motto, horiz. 350c, Heraldic lion and motto, horiz.

*Perf. 12¾x13¼, 13¼x12¼*

**2014, Jan. 14** **Litho.**

**159-163** A43 Set of 5 14.00 14.00

Miniature Sheet

New Year 2014 (Year of the Horse) A44

No. 164 — Horse and: a, Men on boat (40x21mm). b, Building (30x42mm). c, Lanterns (30x39mm). d, Man carrying buckets (40x18mm).

**2014, Jan. 31** **Litho.** ***Perf. 14x13¼***

**164** A44 300c Sheet of 4, #a-d, + central label 13.50 13.50

Friendship — A45

Quote and heart with: 65c, Cake. 119c, Roses. 177c, Chocolate candies. 183c, Tedddy bear. 305c, Gemstone. 434c, Drink with fruit garnishes.

*Perf. 12¾x13¼*

**2014, Feb. 14** **Litho.**

**165-170** A45 Set of 6 14.50 14.50

Birds of Prey — A46

Designs: 100c, Haliaeetus leucocephalus. 200c, Spizaetus ornatus. 250c, Aquila chrysaetos. 300c, Geranoaetus melanoleucus. 350c, Falconidae polyborinae. 400c, Pandion haliaetus.

**2014, Mar. 14** **Litho.** ***Perf. 13¼***

**171-176** A46 Set of 6 18.00 18.00

Miniature Sheet

William Shakespeare (1564-1616), Writer — A47

No. 177 — Shakespeare, with denomination at: a, Lower right. b, Upper right. c, Bottom center above name. d, Lower left, next to country name.

**2014, Apr. 23** **Litho.** ***Perf. 12¾x13¼***

**177** A47 400c Sheet of 4, #a-d 18.00 18.00

Automobiles — A48

Designs: 65c, 1964 Ford Mustang. 119c, 1965 Ford Mustang Fastback. 177c, 2014 Ford Mustang. 183c, 1958 Porsche 356A Speedster. 430c, 1964 Porsche 356C. 676c, 2014 Porsche 911 Targa.

**2014, May 14** **Litho.** ***Perf. 13¼x12¾***

**178-183** A48 Set of 6 18.50 18.50

Miniature Sheet

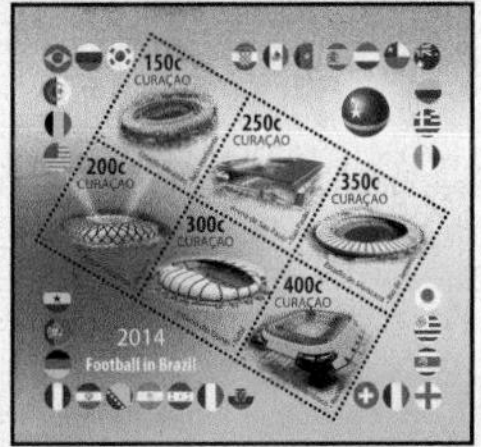

Stadiums of the 2014 World Cup Soccer Championships, Brazil — A49

No. 184: a, 150c, Estadio Mineirao, Belo Horizonte. b, 200c, Arena Amazonia, Manaus. c, 250c, Arena de Sao Paulo, Sao Paulo. d, 300c, Estadio das Dunas, Natal. e, 350c, Estadio do Maracana, Rio de Janeiro. f, 400c, Arena Pernambuco, Recife.

**2014, June 12** **Litho.** ***Perf. 14x13¼***

**184** A49 Sheet of 6, #a-f 18.50 18.50

Peace — A50

Designs: 65c, Dove and "Peace." 119c, Hebrew, Dutch, French and Latin words for "peace." 177c, Hindi, German, Danish and Italian words for "peace." 183c, Family, Papiamento word for "peace," Papiamento, English, Spanish and French words for "family." 305c, Arabic, Farsi, Russian and Spanish words for "peace." 434c, Chinese, Icelandic, Greek and Finnish words for "peace."

**2014, July 28** **Litho.** ***Perf. 13¼x12¾***

**185-190** A50 Set of 6 14.50 14.50

Miniature Sheet

PhilaKorea 2014 World Stamp Exhibition, Seoul — A51

No. 191 — Pinwheel and: a, Girl facing left. b, Dove. c, Rainbow. d, Boy facing right.

**2014, Aug. 7** **Litho.** ***Perf. 12¾x13¼***

**191** A51 400c Sheet of 4, #a-d 18.00 18.00

Fight Against Cancer — A52

Ribbons and various silhouettes of people: 86c, 119c, 177c, 183c, 285c, 750c.

*Perf. 12¾x13¼*

**2014, Aug. 22** **Litho.**

**192-197** A52 Set of 6 18.00 18.00

World Orchid Conference, South Africa — A53

Orchids: 119c, Angraecum stella-africae. 177c, Disa longicornu. 183c, Stenoglottis fimbriata. 305c, Ansellia africana. 382c, Calanthe sylvatica. 434c, Disa uniflora.

*Perf. 12¾x13¼*

**2014, Sept. 10** **Litho.**

**198-203** A53 Set of 6 18.00 18.00

Miniature Sheet

XCOR Space Expeditions — A54

No. 204: a, Space plane at space port. b, Space plane control panel. c, Space port. d, Stars, wing of space plane. e, Nose of space plane. f, XCOR Space Expeditions emblem. g, Earth's horizon as seen from space. h, Burning exhaust of test engine. i, Burning exhaust of space plane in flight. j, Earth, wing of space plane.

**2014, Sept. 26** **Litho.** ***Perf. 14***

**204** A54 177c Sheet of 10, #a-j 20.00 20.00

Caricatures of Marine Life — A55

Designs: 100c, Turtle, starfish, shell. 119c, Fish, oyster with pearl. 177c, Octopus, snail. 305c, Dolphin. 500c, Crab, sea urchin, shells, starfish.

**2014, Oct. 14** **Litho.** ***Perf. 13x13½***

**205-209** A55 Set of 5 13.50 13.50

Christmas — A56

Christmas gifts and various children: 65c, 119c, 117c, 183c, 305c.

**2014, Nov. 14 Litho. *Perf. 13¼***
**210-214** A56 Set of 5 9.50 9.50

**New Constitutional Status Type of 2011**

Designs: 2c, Cocoa damselfish. 4c, Jewel damselfish.

**2014 Litho. *Perf. 13¼x12¾***
**215** A3 2c multi .25 .25
**216** A3 4c multi .25 .25

Miniature Sheet

Fish A57

No. 217: a, Bladefin bass. b, Yellowbar basslet. c, Spanish flag. d, Spottail golden bass. e, Rough-tongue bass. f, Dragonette. g, Saber goby. h, Longfin-scorpionfish. i, Deep sea toad. j, Banded basslet.

**2014, Nov. 30 Litho. *Perf. 14x13¾***
**217** A57 177c Sheet of 10, #a-j 20.00 20.00

Curaçao Carnaval, 45th Anniv. — A58

Various costumed participants: 65c, 119c, 177c, 183c, 305c, 434c.

**2015, Jan. 19 Litho. *Perf. 13¼x13¾***
**218-223** A58 Set of 6 14.50 14.50

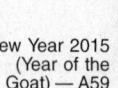

New Year 2015 (Year of the Goat) — A59

Various goats: 177c, 183c, 305c, 535c.

**2015, Feb. 19 Litho. *Perf. 13½x14***
**224-227** A59 Set of 4 13.50 13.50

Miniature Sheet

Zeppelins — A60

No. 228 — Various zeppelins with color of: a, 343c, Purple. b, 350c, Red. c, 425c, Green. d, 500c, Yellow.

**2015, Mar. 19 Litho. *Perf. 13x12¾***
**228** A60 Sheet of 4, #a-d 18.00 18.00

Miniature Sheet

Travels of Pope Francis A61

No. 229: a, Pope Francis, two women. b, Dove, Pope Francis, hands and camera. c, Back of head of Pope Francis. d, Pope Francis kissing child.

**2015, Apr. 20 Litho. *Perf. 13¼***
**229** A61 400c Sheet of 4, #a-d 18.00 18.00

Mammals — A62

Designs: 65c, Solenodontidae. 119c, Hutias. 177c, Odocoileus virginianus curassavicus. 183c, Sylvilagus floridanus. 430c, Tursiops truncatus. 676c, Leptonycteris curasoae.

**2015, May 19 Litho. *Perf. 13¾***
**230-235** A62 Set of 6 18.50 18.50

Miniature Sheet

Space A63

No. 236: a, 200c, Pluto and Charon. b, 250c, First man on the Moon, 1969. c, 400c, Mars Lander. d, 750c, Mars Rover Curiosity.

**2015, June 29 Litho. *Perf. 13¼***
**236** A63 Sheet of 4, #a-d 18.00 18.00

Miniature Sheet

World War I, Cent. A64

No. 237 — Poppy and: a, 250c, Soldiers. b, 350c, Soldier's helmet and gas mask. c, 450c, Airplane, airship and tank. d, 550c, Medal and cemetery.

**2015, July 15 Litho. *Perf. 13¾x13½***
**237** A64 Sheet of 4, #a-d 18.00 18.00

A65 A66

A67 A68

A69

Self-Portraits of Vincent van Gogh (1853-90) and Places in Curaçao — A70

***Perf. 13¼x12¾, 12¾x13¼***
**2015, July 29 Litho.**
**238** A65 119c multi 1.40 1.40
**239** A66 177c multi 2.00 2.00
**240** A67 183c multi 2.10 2.10
**241** A68 285c multi 3.25 3.25
**242** A69 305c multi 3.50 3.50
**243** A70 434c multi 5.00 5.00
*Nos. 238-243 (6)* 17.25 17.25

Miniature Sheet

Singapore 2015 World Stamp Exhibition — A71

No. 244: a, 325c, Merlion statue. b, 400c, Orchid. c, 425c, Singapore coat of arms. d, 500c, Flag of Singapore.

**2015, Aug. 14 Litho. *Perf. 12¾x13***
**244** A71 Sheet of 4, #a-d 18.50 18.50

Miniature Sheet

Elvis Presley (1935-77) — A72

No. 245: a, 300c, Presley and RCA Victor emblem. b, 400c, Presley. c, 400c, Presley holding microphone and guitar, horiz. d, 500c, Presley playing guitar, horiz.

***Perf. 13½x14, 14x13½***
**2015, Aug. 28 Litho.**
**245** A72 Sheet of 4, #a-d 18.00 18.00

Dogs — A73

Dogs of various breeds: 86c, 119c, 177c, 183c, 305c, 434c.

**2015, Sept. 24 Litho. *Perf. 13¾***
**246-251** A73 Set of 6 14.50 14.50

Face and "Algemeen Kiesrecht" (1948 Universal Suffrage) — A74

Face and "Eilandenregeling" (1951 Islands Regulation of the Netherlands Antilles) — A75

Face and "Statuut" (1954 Charter for the Kingdom of the Netherlands) A76

Face and "Van Eiland Naar Land" (2010 Dissolution of the Netherlands Antilles) A77

**2015, Oct. 8 Litho. *Perf. 13¼***
**252** A74 1.19g multi 1.40 1.40
**253** A75 1.77g multi 2.00 2.00
**254** A76 3.05g multi 3.50 3.50
**255** A77 3.05g multi 3.50 3.50
*Nos. 252-255 (4)* 10.40 10.40

Curaçao as constituent state within the Kingdom of the Netherlands, 5th anniv.

Youth Health — A78

Designs: 65c, Girl brushing teeth. 119c, Boy washing hands. 177c, Girl sitting on toilet. 305c, Child showering. 434c, Girl brushing hair.

**2015, Oct. 29 Litho. *Perf. 13¼x13***
**256-260** A78 Set of 5 12.50 12.50

Cactus A79

Ship A80

Klein Curaçao Lighthouse A81

Santa Claus, Sleigh and Reindeer A82

Crane — A83

Queen Juliana Bridge — A84

**2015, Nov. 26 Litho. *Perf. 14x13½***
**261** A79 65c multi .75 .75
**262** A80 86c multi 1.00 1.00
**263** A81 119c multi 1.40 1.40
**264** A82 177c multi 2.00 2.00
**265** A83 183c multi 2.10 2.10
**266** A84 305c multi 3.50 3.50
*Nos. 261-266 (6)* 10.75 10.75

Christmas.

Repeating Numerals — A85

Denomination color: 66c, Orange. 86c, Red. 121c, Purple. 179c, Deep green. 308c, Royal blue. 440c, Carmine red.

**2016, Jan. 28 Litho. *Perf. 13¾***
**267-272** A85 Set of 6 13.50 13.50

Miniature Sheet

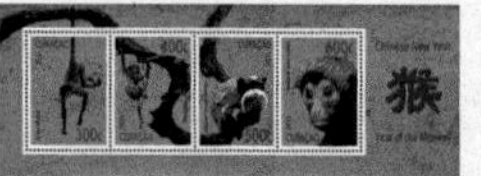

New Year 2016 (Year of the Monkey) A86

No. 273: a, 300c, Spider monkey. b, 400c, Orangutan. c, 500c, Emperor tamarin monkey. d, 600c, Red-faced spider monkey.

**2016, Feb. 8 Litho. *Perf. 14x13½***
**273** A86 Sheet of 4, #a-d 20.00 20.00

Native Indian Drawings — A87

Various drawings: 93c, 121c, 156c, 185c, 285c, 684c.

*Perf. 12¾x13¼*

**2016, Mar. 24** **Litho.**

**274-279** A87 Set of 6 17.00 17.00

Ship Hulls — A88

Various details of ship hulls: 300c, 350c, 400c, 450c, 500c, 550c.

**2016, Apr. 28** **Litho.** ***Perf. 13¼x12¾***

**280-285** A88 Set of 6 28.50 28.50

Bays — A89

Designs: 66c, Jan Kok Bay. 121c, Santa Martha Bay. 179c, Piscadera Bay. 308c, San Juan Bay. 440c, Spanish Water Bay, vert. 684c, Sint Joris Bay.

*Perf. 14x13½, 13½x14*

**2016, Aug. 8** **Litho.**

**286-291** A89 Set of 6 20.00 20.00

Parts of Nos. 286-291 are coated with a thick varnish containing grit.

Christmas A90

Designs: 66c, Christmas tree. 121c, Candy canes. 179c, Bells. 308c, Christmas ornaments. 440c, Holly. 684c, Stars.

**2016, Nov. 17** **Litho.** ***Perf. 13½***

**292-297** A90 Set of 6 20.00 20.00

Nerw Year 2017 (Year of the Rooster) — A91

Head of rooster with: 66c, Brown ochre feathers. 121c, Orange brown feathers. 179c, Black feathers.

No. 301: a, Head of rooster facing right. b, Entire rooster. c, Head of rooster facing left.

**2017, Feb. 28** **Litho.** ***Perf. 13¼***

**298-300** A91 Set of 3 4.25 4.25

**Souvenir Sheet**

**301** A91 500c Sheet of 3, #a-c 17.00 17.00

Miniature Sheet

King Willem-Alexander, 50th Birthday — A92

No. 302: a, 121c, King Willem-Alexander, Queen Máxima and daughters (42x32mm). b, 179c, King Willem-Alexander (42x49mm). c, 308c, King Willem-Alexander (86x30mm). d, 440c, Wedding photograph of King Willem-Alexander and Queen Máxima (58x62mm). e, 684c, King Willem-Alexander and Queen Máxima, diff. (60mm diameter)

**2017, Apr. 27** **Litho.** ***Perf. 14¼x14½***

**302** A92 Sheet of 5, #a-e 19.50 19.50

Butterflies — A93

Designs: 121c, Dryas iulia. 145c, Tropical checkered skipper. 179c, Junonia evarete. 211c, Danaus plexippus. 308c, Heliconius erato. 684c, Danaus eresimus.

**2017, May 3** **Litho.** ***Perf. 13¼x12¾***

**303-308** A93 Set of 6 18.50 18.50

Curaçao in the 1950s — A94

Designs: 121c, Sailboat and buildings. 179c, Airport. 211c, Car, bridge and buildings. 308c, Ship and buildings. 440c, City street. 684c, Marketplace.

*Perf. 13¼x12¾*

**2017, June 19** **Litho.**

**309-314** A94 Set of 6 22.00 22.00

Writers — A95

Designs: 66c, Elis Juliana (1927-2013). 121c, Boeli van Leeuwen (1922-2007). 179c, May Henriquez (1915-99). 308c, Tip Marrug (1923-2006). 440c, Luis Daal (1919-97). 684c, Frank Martinus Arion (1936-2015).

**2017, Sept. 22** **Litho.** ***Perf. 13¼***

**315-320** A95 Set of 6 20.00 20.00

Christmas — A96

Various Nativity scenes: 121c, 179c, 308c, 440c, 684c.

*Perf. 13¼x12¾*

**2017, Nov. 17** **Litho.**

**321-325** A96 Set of 5 19.50 19.50

New Year 2018 (Year of the Dog) — A97

Dog and: 66c, Waterfront buildings. 122c, Bridge and ship, horiz. 180c, Cactus, horiz. 310c, House and windmill, horiz. 443c, Bone, tree and hills, horiz. 690c, Building.

*Perf. 12¾x13¼, 13¼x12¾*

**2018, Feb. 16** **Litho.**

**326-331** A97 Set of 6 20.50 20.50

Flowers — A98

Designs: 86c, West Indian jasmine. 122c, Passion flower. 180c, Rubber vine. 190c, Orange Geiger tree. 285c, Peacock flowers. 425c, White and yellow frangipani. 443c, Giant milkweed. 690c, Prickly pear.

**2018, Apr. 18** **Litho.** ***Perf. 14***

**332-339** A98 Set of 8 27.00 27.00

Lighthouses — A99

Designs: 66c, Feu de Marigot Lighthouse, St. Martin. 122c, Klein Curaçao Lighthouse, Curaçao. 180c, Noordpunt Lighthouse, Curaçao. 310c, Fort Orange Lighthouse, Bonaire. 443c, California Lighthouse, Aruba. 690c, Ceru Bentana Lighthouse, Bonaire, horiz.

*Perf. 13¼x13¾, 13¾x13¼*

**2018, July 18** **Litho.**

**340-345** A99 Set of 6 20.50 20.50

Cruise Ship Freewinds — A100

Designs: 122c, Ship at dock. 180c, Ship at sea, vert.

300c, Bow of ship, vert.

*Perf. 13¼x12¾, 12¾x13¼*

**2018, July 26** **Litho.**

**346-347** A100 Set of 2 3.50 3.50

**Souvenir Sheet**

**348** A100 300c multi 3.50 3.50

Christmas — A101

Designs: 66c, Christmas tree in house. 122c, Houses with Christmas decorations. 180c, House with Christmas decorations, bright star in sky. 310c, Family watching fireworks display. 443c, Man playing guitar to woman and child, Christmas tree in house. 690c, Goats and cacti, bright star in sky.

**Litho. With Glitter Affixed**

**2018, Nov. 1** ***Perf. 13¼***

**349-354** A101 Set of 6 20.50 20.50

Aspects of Life in Curaçao — A102

Designs: 68c, House and iguana. 1, Woman in traditional costume. 160c, Goat and dog. 2, Buildings. 319c, Chair and lamp in room. 456c, Sandals on beach and catamaran.

**2019, Jan. 21** **Litho.** ***Perf. 13¼***

**355-360** A102 Set of 6 15.00 15.00

On day of issue, No. 356 sold for 124c and No. 358 sold for 186c.

Miniature Sheet

New Year 2019 (Year of the Pig) A103

No. 361 — Various depictions of pigs: a, 350c. b, 400c. c, 450c. d, 500c. e, 550c. f, 600c.

**2019, Feb. 5** **Litho.** ***Perf. 14x13¼***

**361** A103 Sheet of 6, #a-f 32.00 32.00

Marine Life — A104

Designs: 68c, Pylopagurus discoidalis. 1, Linckia nodosa. 2, Entemnotrochus adansonianus. 319c, Ophiarachnella petersi. 456c, Mantellina translucens. 711c, Calliostoma rosewateri.

No. 368: a, Acanthodromia erinacea. b, Allodardanus bredini. c, Stenocionops spinosissimus. d, Myropsis quinquespinosa.

*Perf. 13½x12¾*

**2019, Mar. 19** **Litho.**

**362-367** A104 Set of 6 21.00 21.00

**Souvenir Sheet**

**368** A104 300c Sheet of 4, #a-d 13.50 13.50

No. 363 sold for 124c and No. 364 sold for 186c on day of issue.

Musicians — A105

Designs: 68c, Janchi Bosklajon (1863-1936). 1, Nicolaas "Shon Cola" Susana (1916-2003). 160c, Edgar Palm (1905-98). 2, Wim Statius Muller (1930-2019). 319c, Clara Henriquez (1939-63). 711c, Julián B. Coco (1924-2013).

**2019, Apr. 26** **Litho.** ***Perf. 12¾x13¼***

**369-374** A105 Set of 6 17.50 17.50

On day of issue, No. 370 sold for 124c, and No. 372 sold for 186c.

Souvenir Sheet

Worker's Revolt, 50th Anniv. A106

**2019, May 30** **Litho.** ***Perf. 13¼x14***

**375** A106 1000c multi 11.50 11.50

Souvenir Sheet

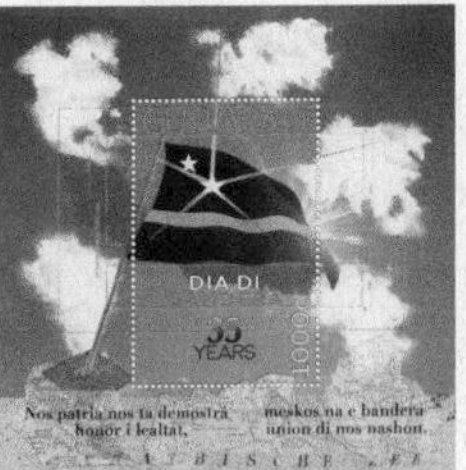

Flag Day, 35th Anniv. A107

**2019, July 2** **Litho.** ***Perf. 14x13¼***

**376** A107 1000c multi 11.50 11.50

Miniature Sheet

Modern Architecture — A108

No. 377 — Various buildings: a, 450c. b, 550c. c, 650c. d, 750c.

**2019, July 26** **Litho.** ***Perf. 13½***

**377** A108 Sheet of 4, #a-d 27.00 27.00

Miniature Sheet

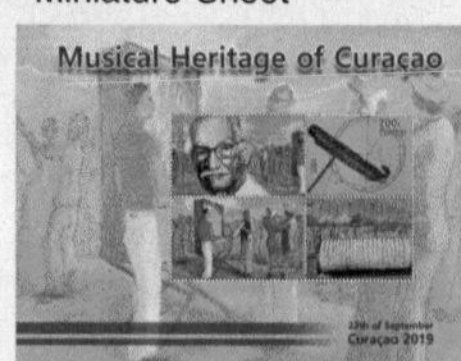

Musical Heritage A109

No. 378: a, 200c, Wiri (40x30mm). b, 300c, Cylinder (40x30mm), c, 500c, Ka'i orgel at dance party (50x30mm). d, 800c, Horace J. Sprock (1866-1949), importer of ka'i orgel to Curaçao (50x30mm).

**2019, Sept. 23 Litho. *Perf. 14x13¼***
**378** A109 Sheet of 4, #a-d 20.00 20.00

Children — A110

Designs: 68c, Girl walking. 124c, Girl sitting. 186c, Boy crouching, horiz. 315c, Boy sitting. 319c, Girl on knees, horiz. 456c, Girl sitting, horiz.

***Perf. 13¼x14, 14x13¼***
**2019, Oct. 19 Litho.**
**379-384** A110 Set of 6 16.50 16.50

Souvenir Sheet

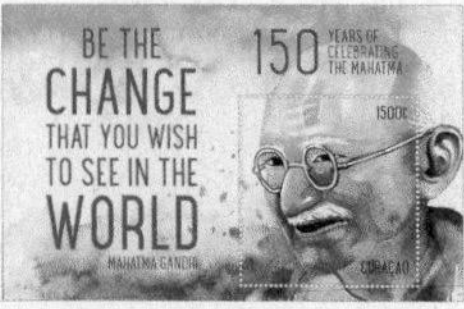

Mohandas K. Gandhi (1869-1948), Indian Nationalist Leader — A111

**2019, Nov. 19 Litho. *Perf. 14x13¼***
**385** A111 1500c multi 17.00 17.00

Biblical Figures — A112

Designs: 68c, Samson. 1, Moses, horiz. 2, Jesus, Simon and Andrew on boat, horiz. 315c, Daniel and lion. 319c, Jonah and whale. 711c, David and Goliath.

***Perf. 12¾x13¼, 13¼x12¾***
**2019, Dec. 1 Litho.**
**386-391** A112 Set of 6 19.50 19.50

Christmas. On day of issue, No. 387 sold for 124c and No. 388 sold for 186c.

Miniature Sheet

KLM Royal Dutch Airlines, Cent. A113

No. 392: a, 124c, DC-4 "Flying Dutchman" (30x21mm). b, 186c, Fokker F.XVIII "Snip and map" (40x21mm). c, 315c, DC-10 and flight map (30x42mm). d, 319c, Dr. Albert Plesman Airport, Curaçao (30x39mm). e, 456c, Lockheed-14 Super Electra (30x39mm). f, 747c, Boeing 747-400 (40x18mm).

**2019, Dec. 19 Litho. *Perf. 14x13¼***
**392** A113 Sheet of 6, #a-f, + label 24.00 24.00

New Year 2020 (Year of the Rat) — A114

Various rats: 70c, 1, 2, 331c, 474c, 739c.

**Litho. With Foil Application**
**2020, Jan. 25 *Perf. 12¾x13¼***
**393-398** A114 Set of 6 21.50 21.50

On day of issue, No. 394 sold for 127c and No. 395 sold for 192c,

50th Curaçao Carnival — A115

Designs: 70c, Dancers. 1, Tumba Festival announcer. 2, Text and masks. 331c, Woman in costume. 474c, Woman wearing sash. 739c, Drummers.

**2020, Feb. 20 Litho. *Perf. 13¼***
**399-404** A115 Set of 6 21.50 21.50

On day of issue, No. 400 sold for 127c and No. 401 sold for 192c,

Souvenir Sheet

Margareth Abraham (1945-70), Flight Attendant Killed in Crash of ALM Flight 980 — A116

No. 405: a, 474c, Abraham seated in airplane. b, 739c, Abraham on stairway.

**2020, May 2 Litho. *Perf. 14x13¼***
**405** A116 Sheet of 2, #a-b 13.50 13.50

Souvenir Sheet

Front Line Workers in Coronavirus Pandemic — A117

No. 406 — Various front line workers with: a, Denomination in white. b, Country name in white. c, "Thank you" in white.

**2020, June 18 Litho. *Perf. 13¼x14***
**406** A117 600c Sheet of 3, #a-c 20.00 20.00

All proceeds of the sale of No. 406 were donated to Voedselbank Curaçao charity.

Sports — A118

Designs: 1, Soccer. 2, Baseball, 331c, Basketball. 335c, Cycling, horiz. 474c, Tennis. 739c, Sailing, horiz.

***Perf. 13¼x14, 14x13¼***
**2020, Aug. 19 Litho.**
**407-412** A118 Set of 6 24.50 24.50

On day of issue, No. 407 sold for 127c and No. 408 sold for 192c,

Birds — A119

Designs: 70c, Blue-and-yellow macaw. 1, Green-headed tanager. 2, Masked trogon. 331c, Guianan toucan. 474c, Blue-crowned motmot. 739c, Toucan barbet.

**2020, Sept. 20 Litho. *Perf. 11¼x12***
**413-418** A119 Set of 6 21.50 21.50

On day of issue, No. 4140 sold for 128c and No. 415 sold for 193c.

Miniature Sheet

Presidents of the United States — A120

No. 419: a, 100c, George Washington (1732-99). b, 160c, Abraham Lincoln (1809-65). c, 320c, Franklin D. Roosevelt (1882-1945). d, 350c, John F. Kennedy (1917-63). e, Ronald Reagan (1911-2004). f, 440c, Barack Obama. g, 450c, Donald Trump.

**2020, Oct. 6 Litho. *Perf. 13¾x13½***
**419** A120 Sheet of 7, #a-g 25.00 25.00

Antique Automobiles A121

Designs: 70c, 1956 Ford Fairlane Sunliner. No. 421, 1, 1936 Buick Victoria Special. No. 422, 1, 1949 Packard Clipper. No. 423, 2, 1923 Ford Model T Touring Car. No. 424, 2, 1937 Ford Deluxe Convertible. 331c, 1956 Packard 400. 335c, 1948 Chevrolet Stylemaster. 474c, 1952 Dodge Coronet Gyromatic. 739c, 1953 Chevrolet Bel Air.

**2020, Oct. 31 Litho. *Perf. 13¼x12¾***
**420-428** A121 Set of 9 29.00 29.00

On day of issue, Nos. 421 and 422 each sold for 128c and Nos. 423 and 424 each sold for 193c.

Christmas Traditions of Various Countries — A122

Designs: 70c, Paskong Pinoy, Philippines. 1, Krampus, Austria. 2, Yule Lad, Iceland. 331c, Pohutukawa, New Zealand. 474c, Gävle Goat, Sweden. 739c, Hallacas, Venezuela.

**2020, Dec. 1 Litho. *Perf. 13¼x13***
**429-434** A122 Set of 6 22.00 22.00

On day of issue, No. 430 sold for 128c and No. 431 sold for 193c.

New Year 2021 (Year of the Ox) — A123

Various depictions of ox: 70c, 1, 2, 334c, 478c, 746c. 1 and 746c are horiz.

***Perf. 13¼x13, 13x13¼***
**2021, Jan. 12 Litho.**
**435-440** A123 Set of 6 22.00 22.00

On day of issue, No. 436 sold for 129c and No. 437 sold for 194c.

## SEMI-POSTAL STAMPS

Youth Care — SP1

Rabbit: 63c+26c, Writing molecular diagram on blackboard, molecular model. 112c+45c, With chemicals in test tubes and flasks. 166c+75c, Conducting experiment with plants and chemicals. 285c+125c, In rocket ship.

**2011, Oct. 11 Litho. *Perf. 12¾x13¼***
**B1-B4** SP1 Set of 4 10.00 10.00

Intl. Year of Chemistry.

Intl. Year of Cooperatives SP2

Stylized people and: 64c+26c, Construction tools, bird. 190c+75c, Rowboat, fish. 293c+125c, Rowboat, house, flower, bird, fish.

**2012, Oct. 9 *Perf. 13¼x12¾***
**B5-B7** SP2 Set of 3 8.75 8.75

SP3 SP4

SP5 Abolition of Slavery, 150th Anniv. — SP6

**2013, July 1 Litho. *Perf. 13¼x12¾***

| | | | | |
|---|---|---|---|---|
| **B8** | SP3 | 65c +25c multi | 1.00 | 1.00 |
| **B9** | SP4 | 118c +45c multi | 1.90 | 1.90 |
| **B10** | SP5 | 175c +75c multi | 2.75 | 2.75 |
| **B11** | SP6 | 301c +125c multi | 4.75 | 4.75 |
| | | *Nos. B8-B11 (4)* | 10.40 | 10.40 |

Wladimir "Coco" Balantien, Holder of New Record for Home Runs in a Japanese Baseball Season — SP7

**2013, Dec. 2 Litho. *Perf. 12¾x13¼***
**B12** SP7 118c +100c multi 2.50 2.50

# Pronunciation Symbols

ə .... banana, collide, abut

ˈə, ˌə .... humdrum, abut

ə .... immediately preceding \l\, \n\, \m\, \ŋ\, as in battle, mitten, eaten, and sometimes open \ˈō-pᵊm\, lock and key \-ᵊŋ-\; immediately following \l\, \m\, \r\, as often in French table, prisme, titre

ər .... further, merger, bird

ˈər-, ˈə-r .... as in two different pronunciations of hurry \ˈhər-ē, ˈhə-rē\

a .... mat, map, mad, gag, snap, patch

ā .... day, fade, date, aorta, drape, cape

ä .... bother, cot, and, with most American speakers, father, cart

ȧ .... father as pronounced by speakers who do not rhyme it with *bother*; French patte

au̇ .... now, loud, out

b .... baby, rib

ch .... chin, nature \ˈnā-chər\

d .... did, adder

e .... bet, bed, peck

ˈē, ˌē .... beat, nosebleed, evenly, easy

ē .... easy, mealy

f .... fifty, cuff

g .... go, big, gift

h .... hat, ahead

hw .... whale as pronounced by those who do not have the same pronunciation for both *whale* and *wail*

i .... tip, banish, active

ī .... site, side, buy, tripe

j .... job, gem, edge, join, judge

k .... kin, cook, ache

k̲ .... German ich, Buch; one pronunciation of loch

l .... lily, pool

m .... murmur, dim, nymph

n .... no, own

ⁿ .... indicates that a preceding vowel or diphthong is pronounced with the nasal passages open, as in French *un bon vin blanc* \œⁿ -bōⁿ -vaⁿ -bläⁿ\

ŋ .... sing \ˈsiŋ\, singer \ˈsiŋ-ər\, finger \ˈfiŋ-gər\, ink \ˈiŋk \

ō .... bone, know, beau

ȯ .... saw, all, gnaw, caught

œ .... French boeuf, German Hölle

œ̄ .... French feu, German Höhle

ȯi .... coin, destroy

p .... pepper, lip

r .... red, car, rarity

s .... source, less

sh .... as in shy, mission, machine, special (actually, this is a single sound, not two); with a hyphen between, two sounds as in *grasshopper* \ˈgras-ˌhä-pər\

t .... tie, attack, late, later, latter

th .... as in thin, ether (actually, this is a single sound, not two); with a hyphen between, two sounds as in *knighthood* \ˈnīt-ˌhu̇d\

t̲h̲ .... then, either, this (actually, this is a single sound, not two)

ü .... rule, youth, union \ˈyün-yən\, few \ˈfyü\

u̇ .... pull, wood, book, curable \ˈkyu̇r-ə-bəl\, fury \ˈfyu̇r-ē\

ue .... German füllen, hübsch

u̅e̅ .... French rue, German fühlen

v .... vivid, give

w .... we, away

y .... yard, young, cue \ˈkyü\, mute \ˈmyüt\, union \ˈyün-yən\

ʸ .... indicates that during the articulation of the sound represented by the preceding character the front of the tongue has substantially the position it has for the articulation of the first sound of *yard*, as in French *digne* \dēnʸ\

z .... zone, raise

zh .... as in vision, azure \ˈa-zhər\ (actually, this is a single sound, not two); with a hyphen between, two sounds as in *hogshead* \ˈhȯgz-ˌhed, ˈhägz-\

\ .... slant line used in pairs to mark the beginning and end of a transcription: \ˈpen\

ˈ .... mark preceding a syllable with primary (strongest) stress: \ˈpen-mən-ˌship\

ˌ .... mark preceding a syllable with secondary (medium) stress: \ˈpen-mən-ˌship\

- .... mark of syllable division

( ) .... indicate that what is symbolized between is present in some utterances but not in others: *factory* \ˈfak-t(ə-)rē\

÷ .... indicates that many regard as unacceptable the pronunciation variant immediately following: *cupola* \ˈkyü-pə-lə, ÷-ˌlō\

# INDEX AND IDENTIFIER

All page numbers shown are those in this Volume 2A.

Postage stamps that do not have English words on them are shown in the Illustrated Identifier.

# INDEX TO ADVERTISERS
# 2024 VOLUME 2A

# 2024
# VOLUME 2A
# DEALER DIRECTORY
# YELLOW PAGE LISTINGS

**This section of your Scott Catalogue contains advertisements to help you conveniently find what you need, when you need it...!**

## Aerophilately

**HENRY GITNER PHILATELISTS, INC.**
PO Box 3077-S
Middletown, NY 10940
PH: 845-343-5151
PH: 800-947-8267
FAX: 845-343-0068
hgitner@hgitner.com
www.hgitner.com

## Appraisals

**DR. ROBERT FRIEDMAN & SONS STAMP & COIN BUYING CENTER**
2029 W. 75th St.
Woodridge, IL 60517
PH: 800-588-8100
FAX: 630-985-1588
stampcollections@drbobstamps.com
www.drbobfriedmanstamps.com

## Asia

**KELLEHER & ROGERS LTD.**
22 Shelter Rock Lane, Unit #53
Danbury, CT 06810
PH: 203-830-2500
Toll Free: 800-212-2830
info@kelleherauctions.com
www.kelleherauctions.com

## Auctions

**DUTCH COUNTRY AUCTIONS**
The Stamp Center
4115 Concord Pike
Wilmington, DE 19803
PH: 302-478-8740
FAX: 302-478-8779
auctions@dutchcountryauctions.com
www.dutchcountryauctions.com

**KELLEHER & ROGERS LTD.**
22 Shelter Rock Lane, Unit #53
Danbury, CT 06810
PH: 203-830-2500
Toll Free: 800-212-2830
info@kelleherauctions.com
www.kelleherauctions.com

## British Commonwealth

**ARON R. HALBERSTAM PHILATELISTS, LTD.**
PO Box 150168
Van Brunt Station
Brooklyn, NY 11215-0168
PH: 718-788-3978
arh@arhstamps.com
www.arhstamps.com

**ROY'S STAMPS**
PO Box 28001
600 Ontario Street
St. Catharines, ON
CANADA L2N 7P8
Phone: 905-934-8377
Email: roystamp@cogeco.ca
www.roysstamps.com

**THE STAMP ACT**
PO Box 1136
Belmont, CA 94002
PH: 650-703-2342
thestampact@sbcglobal.net

## Buying

**DR. ROBERT FRIEDMAN & SONS STAMP & COIN BUYING CENTER**
2029 W. 75th St.
Woodridge, IL 60517
PH: 800-588-8100
FAX: 630-985-1588
stampcollections@drbobstamps.com
www.drbobfriedmanstamps.com

## Canada

**CANADA STAMP FINDER LLC**
2800 N 6th Street, Unit 1-708
St. Augustine, FL 32084
PH: 904-217-2166
Canadian Address:
PO Box 92591
Brampton, ON L6W 4R1
PH: 514-238-5751
Toll Free in North America:
877-412-3106
FAX: 323-315-2635
canadastampfinder@gmail.com
www.canadastampfinder.com

**ROY'S STAMPS**
PO Box 28001
600 Ontario Street
St. Catharines, ON
CANADA L2N 7P8
Phone: 905-934-8377
Email: roystamp@cogeco.ca
www.roysstamps.com

## China

**ASIA PHILATELICS**
3276 Andora Drive
San Jose, CA 95148
PH: 408-238-0893
Richard@asiaphilatelics.com

**KELLEHER & ROGERS LTD.**
22 Shelter Rock Lane, Unit #53
Danbury, CT 06810
PH: 203-830-2500
Toll Free: 800-212-2830
info@kelleherauctions.com
www.kelleherauctions.com

**THE STAMP ACT**
PO Box 1136
Belmont, CA 94002
PH: 650-703-2342
thestampact@sbcglobal.net

## Collections

**DR. ROBERT FRIEDMAN & SONS STAMP & COIN BUYING CENTER**
2029 W. 75th St.
Woodridge, IL 60517
PH: 800-588-8100
FAX: 630-985-1588
stampcollections@drbobstamps.com
www.drbobfriedmanstamps.com

## Ducks

**MICHAEL JAFFE**
PO Box 61484
Vancouver, WA 98666
PH: 360-695-6161
PH: 800-782-6770
FAX: 360-695-1616
mjaffe@brookmanstamps.com
www.brookmanstamps.com

## France & Colonies

**E. JOSEPH MCCONNELL, INC.**
PO Box 683
Monroe, NY 10949
PH: 845-783-9791
ejstamps@gmail.com
www.EJMcConnell.com

## French S. Antarctic

**E. JOSEPH MCCONNELL, INC.**
PO Box 683
Monroe, NY 10949
PH: 845-783-9791
ejstamps@gmail.com
www.EJMcConnell.com

## Japan

**KELLEHER & ROGERS LTD.**
22 Shelter Rock Lane, Unit #53
Danbury, CT 06810
PH: 203-830-2500
Toll Free: 800-212-2830
info@kelleherauctions.com
www.kelleherauctions.com

## Korea

**KELLEHER & ROGERS LTD.**
22 Shelter Rock Lane, Unit #53
Danbury, CT 06810
PH: 203-830-2500
Toll Free: 800-212-2830
info@kelleherauctions.com
www.kelleherauctions.com

## Manchukuo

**KELLEHER & ROGERS LTD.**
22 Shelter Rock Lane, Unit #53
Danbury, CT 06810
PH: 203-830-2500
Toll Free: 800-212-2830
info@kelleherauctions.com
www.kelleherauctions.com

## Middle East - Arab

**KELLEHER & ROGERS LTD.**
22 Shelter Rock Lane, Unit #53
Danbury, CT 06810
PH: 203-830-2500
Toll Free: 800-212-2830
info@kelleherauctions.com
www.kelleherauctions.com

## New Issues

**DAVIDSON'S STAMP SERVICE**
Personalized Service since 1970
PO Box 36355
Indianapolis, IN 46236-0355
PH: 317-826-2620
ed-davidson@earthlink.net
www.newstampissues.com

## Proofs & Essays

**HENRY GITNER PHILATELISTS, INC.**
PO Box 3077-S
Middletown, NY 10940
PH: 845-343-5151
PH: 800-947-8267
FAX: 845-343-0068
hgitner@hgitner.com
www.hgitner.com

## Stamp Stores

### Delaware

**DUTCH COUNTRY AUCTIONS**
The Stamp Center
4115 Concord Pike
Wilmington, DE 19803
PH: 302-478-8740
FAX: 302-478-8779
auctions@dutchcountryauctions.com
www.dutchcountryauctions.com

## British Commonwealth

## Stamp Stores

### Florida

**DR. ROBERT FRIEDMAN & SONS STAMP & COIN BUYING CENTER**
PH: 800-588-8100
FAX: 630-985-1588
stampcollections@drbobstamps.com
www.drbobfriedmanstamps.com

### Illinois

**DR. ROBERT FRIEDMAN & SONS STAMP & COIN BUYING CENTER**
2029 W. 75th St.
Woodridge, IL 60517
PH: 800-588-8100
FAX: 630-985-1588
stampcollections@drbobstamps.com
www.drbobfriedmanstamps.com

### Indiana

**KNIGHT STAMP & COIN CO.**
237 Main St.
Hobart, IN 46342
PH: 219-942-4341
PH: 800-634-2646
knight@knightcoin.com
www.knightcoin.com

### New Jersey

**BERGEN STAMPS & COLLECTIBLES**
306 Queen Anne Rd.
Teaneck, NJ 07666
PH: 201-836-8987
bergenstamps@gmail.com

**TRENTON STAMP & COIN**
Thomas DeLuca
Store: Forest Glen Plaza
1800 Highway #33, Suite 103
Hamilton Square, NJ 08690
Mail: PO Box 8574
Trenton, NJ 08650
PH: 609-584-8100
FAX: 609-587-8664
TOMD4TSC@aol.com
www.trentonstampandcoin.com

### New York

**CHAMPION STAMP CO., INC.**
432 West 54th St.
New York, NY 10019
PH: 212-489-8130
FAX: 212-581-8130
championstamp@aol.com
www.championstamp.com

### Ohio

**HILLTOP STAMP SERVICE**
Richard A. Peterson
PO Box 626
Wooster, OH 44691
PH: 330-262-8907 (0)
PH: 330-201-1377 (H)
hilltop@bright.net
hilltopstamps@sssnet.com
www.hilltopstamps.com

## Supplies

**BROOKLYN GALLERY COIN & STAMP, INC.**
8725 4th Ave.
Brooklyn, NY 11209
PH: 718-745-5701
FAX: 718-745-2775
info@brooklyngallery.com
www.brooklyngallery.com

## Topicals

**E. JOSEPH MCCONNELL, INC.**
PO Box 683
Monroe, NY 10949
PH: 845-783-9791
ejstamps@gmail.com
www.EJMcConnell.com

## Topicals - Columbus

**MR. COLUMBUS**
PO Box 1492
Fennville, MI 49408
PH: 269-543-4755
David@MrColumbus1492.com
www.MrColumbus1492.com

## United States

**ACS STAMP COMPANY**
2914 W 135th Ave
Broomfield, Colorado 80020
303-841-8666
www.ACSStamp.com

**BROOKMAN STAMP CO.**
PO Box 90
Vancouver, WA 98666
PH: 360-695-1391
PH: 800-545-4871
FAX: 360-695-1616
info@brookmanstamps.com
www.brookmanstamps.com

## U.S. Classics/Moderns

**BARDO STAMPS**
PO Box 7437
Buffalo Grove, IL 60089
PH: 847-634-2676
jfb7437@aol.com
www.bardostamps.com

## U.S.-Collections Wanted

**DUTCH COUNTRY AUCTIONS**
The Stamp Center
4115 Concord Pike
Wilmington, DE 19803
PH: 302-478-8740
FAX: 302-478-8779
auctions@dutchcountryauctions.com
www.dutchcountryauctions.com

**DR. ROBERT FRIEDMAN & SONS STAMP & COIN BUYING CENTER**
2029 W. 75th St.
Woodridge, IL 60517
PH: 800-588-8100
FAX: 630-985-1588
stampcollections@drbobstamps.com
www.drbobfriedmanstamps.com

## Wanted - Worldwide Collections

**DUTCH COUNTRY AUCTIONS**
The Stamp Center
4115 Concord Pike
Wilmington, DE 19803
PH: 302-478-8740
FAX: 302-478-8779
auctions@dutchcountryauctions.com
www.dutchcountryauctions.com

## Websites

**ACS STAMP COMPANY**
2914 W 135th Ave
Broomfield, Colorado 80020
303-841-8666
www.ACSStamp.com

## Wholesale

**HENRY GITNER PHILATELISTS, INC.**
PO Box 3077-S
Middletown, NY 10940
PH: 845-343-5151
PH: 800-947-8267
FAX: 845-343-0068
hgitner@hgitner.com
www.hgitner.com

## Worldwide

**KELLEHER & ROGERS LTD.**
22 Shelter Rock Lane, Unit #53
Danbury, CT 06810
PH: 203-830-2500
Toll Free: 800-212-2830
info@kelleherauctions.com
www.kelleherauctions.com

**GUILLERMO JALIL**
Maipu 466, local 4
1006 Buenos Aires
Argentina
guillermo@jalilstamps.com
philatino@philatino.com
www.philatino.com (worldwide stamp auctions)
www.jalilstamps.com (direct sale, worldwide stamps)

## Worldwide-Collections

**DR. ROBERT FRIEDMAN & SONS STAMP & COIN BUYING CENTER**
2029 W. 75th St.
Woodridge, IL 60517
PH: 800-588-8100
FAX: 630-985-1588
stampcollections@drbobstamps.com
www.drbobfriedmanstamps.com